EUROPEAN RAIL TIMETAB

SUMMER 2022

GENERAL INFORMATION

EXTRA FEATURES

TIMETABLES

CONTACT DETAILS

Director and Editor-in-chief	John Potter
Editor	Chris Woodcock
Editorial Team	Graham Benbow Andrea Collins Richard Stirk Reuben Turner Peter Weller
Commercial Manager	Gemma Donaldson
Subscriptions Manager	Peter Weller

Cover created by Andrea Collins website: www.millstonecreative.co.uk
Printed and bound by CPI Group (UK) Ltd, Croydon, CR0 4YY

Front cover: *RailJet* **656**, the 1326 from Graz to Wien passes over the Krauselklause Viaduct on the Semmeringbahn between Semmering and Breitenstein on September 30, 2018 (Table **980**). © Peter Hürzeler.

ISBN 978-1-8384080-3-9

European Rail Timetable Limited (formerly *Thomas Cook European Rail Timetable*)
28 Monson Way
Oundle
Northamptonshire PE8 4QG, United Kingdom
website: www.europeanrailtimetable.eu
e-mail: editorial@europeanrailtimetable.eu
sales: sales@europeanrailtimetable.eu
telephone: + 44 (0)1832 270198 Mondays to Fridays 1000 - 1600

CALENDAR

CALENDRIER CALENDARIO KALENDER CALENDARIO

2022

JANUARY

M	T	W	T	F	S	S
①	②	③	④	⑤	⑥	⑦
31	–	–	–	–	1	2
3	4	5	6	7	8	9
10	11	12	13	14	15	16
17	18	19	20	21	22	23
24	25	26	27	28	29	30

FEBRUARY

M	T	W	T	F	S	S
①	②	③	④	⑤	⑥	⑦
–	1	2	3	4	5	6
7	8	9	10	11	12	13
14	15	16	17	18	19	20
21	22	23	24	25	26	27
28	–	–	–	–	–	–

MARCH

M	T	W	T	F	S	S
①	②	③	④	⑤	⑥	⑦
–	1	2	3	4	5	6
7	8	9	10	11	12	13
14	15	16	17	18	19	20
21	22	23	24	25	26	27
28	29	30	31	–	–	–

APRIL

M	T	W	T	F	S	S
①	②	③	④	⑤	⑥	⑦
–	–	–	–	1	2	3
4	5	6	7	8	9	10
11	12	13	14	15	16	17
18	19	20	21	22	23	24
25	26	27	28	29	30	–

MAY

M	T	W	T	F	S	S
①	②	③	④	⑤	⑥	⑦
30	31	–	–	–	–	1
2	3	4	5	6	7	8
9	10	11	12	13	14	15
16	17	18	19	20	21	22
23	24	25	26	27	28	29

JUNE

M	T	W	T	F	S	S
①	②	③	④	⑤	⑥	⑦
–	–	1	2	3	4	5
6	7	8	9	10	11	12
13	14	15	16	17	18	19
20	21	22	23	24	25	26
27	28	29	30	–	–	–

JULY

M	T	W	T	F	S	S
①	②	③	④	⑤	⑥	⑦
–	–	–	–	1	2	3
4	5	6	7	8	9	10
11	12	13	14	15	16	17
18	19	20	21	22	23	24
25	26	27	28	29	30	31

AUGUST

M	T	W	T	F	S	S
①	②	③	④	⑤	⑥	⑦
1	2	3	4	5	6	7
8	9	10	11	12	13	14
15	16	17	18	19	20	21
22	23	24	25	26	27	28
29	30	31	–	–	–	–

SEPTEMBER

M	T	W	T	F	S	S
①	②	③	④	⑤	⑥	⑦
–	–	–	1	2	3	4
5	6	7	8	9	10	11
12	13	14	15	16	17	18
19	20	21	22	23	24	25
26	27	28	29	30	–	–

OCTOBER

M	T	W	T	F	S	S
①	②	③	④	⑤	⑥	⑦
31	–	–	–	–	1	2
3	4	5	6	7	8	9
10	11	12	13	14	15	16
17	18	19	20	21	22	23
24	25	26	27	28	29	30

NOVEMBER

M	T	W	T	F	S	S
①	②	③	④	⑤	⑥	⑦
–	1	2	3	4	5	6
7	8	9	10	11	12	13
14	15	16	17	18	19	20
21	22	23	24	25	26	27
28	29	30	–	–	–	–

DECEMBER

M	T	W	T	F	S	S
①	②	③	④	⑤	⑥	⑦
–	–	–	1	2	3	4
5	6	7	8	9	10	11
12	13	14	15	16	17	18
19	20	21	22	23	24	25
26	27	28	29	30	31	–

2023

JANUARY

M	T	W	T	F	S	S
①	②	③	④	⑤	⑥	⑦
30	31	–	–	–	–	1
2	3	4	5	6	7	8
9	10	11	12	13	14	15
16	17	18	19	20	21	22
23	24	25	26	27	28	29

FEBRUARY

M	T	W	T	F	S	S
①	②	③	④	⑤	⑥	⑦
–	–	1	2	3	4	5
6	7	8	9	10	11	12
13	14	15	16	17	18	19
20	21	22	23	24	25	26
27	28	–	–	–	–	–

MARCH

M	T	W	T	F	S	S
①	②	③	④	⑤	⑥	⑦
–	–	1	2	3	4	5
6	7	8	9	10	11	12
13	14	15	16	17	18	19
20	21	22	23	24	25	26
27	28	29	30	31	–	–

APRIL

M	T	W	T	F	S	S
①	②	③	④	⑤	⑥	⑦
–	–	–	–	–	1	2
3	4	5	6	7	8	9
10	11	12	13	14	15	16
17	18	19	20	21	22	23
24	25	26	27	28	29	30

MAY

M	T	W	T	F	S	S
①	②	③	④	⑤	⑥	⑦
1	2	3	4	5	6	7
8	9	10	11	12	13	14
15	16	17	18	19	20	21
22	23	24	25	26	27	28
29	30	31	–	–	–	–

JUNE

M	T	W	T	F	S	S
①	②	③	④	⑤	⑥	⑦
–	–	–	1	2	3	4
5	6	7	8	9	10	11
12	13	14	15	16	17	18
19	20	21	22	23	24	25
26	27	28	29	30	–	–

PUBLIC HOLIDAYS 2022

JOURS FÉRIÉS GIORNI FESTIVI FEIERTAGE DÍAS FESTIVOS

The dates given below are those of national public holidays. They do not include regional, half-day or unofficial holidays. Passengers intending to travel on public holidays, or on days immediately preceding or following them, are strongly recommended to reserve seats and to confirm timings locally. Further information regarding special transport conditions applying on holiday dates may be found in the introduction to each country.

Austria: Jan. 1, 6, Apr. 18, May 1, 26, June 6, 16, Aug. 15, Oct. 26, Nov. 1, Dec. 8, 25, 26.

Belarus: Jan. 1, 2, 7, Mar. 7, 8, May 1–3, 9, July 3, Nov. 7, Dec. 25.

Belgium: Jan. 1, Apr. 17, 18, May 1, 26, June 5, 6, July 21, Aug. 15, Nov. 1, 11, Dec. 25.

Bosnia-Herzegovina: Jan. 1–3, May 1–3. *Other religious holidays are observed in certain areas.*

Bulgaria: Jan. 1, 3, Mar. 3, Apr. 22–25, May 1, 2, 6, 24, Sept. 6, 22, Dec. 24–28.

Croatia: Jan. 1, 6, Apr. 17, 18, May 1, 30, June 16, 22, Aug. 5, 15, Nov. 1, 18, Dec. 25, 26.

Czech Republic: Jan. 1, Apr. 15, 18, May 1, 8, July 5, 6, Sept. 28, Oct. 28, Nov. 17, Dec. 24, 25, 26.

Denmark: Jan. 1, Apr. 14, 15, 17, 18, May 1, 13, 26, June 5, 6, Dec. 25, 26.

Estonia: Jan. 1, Feb. 24, Apr. 15, 17, May 1, June 5, 23, 24, Aug. 20, Dec. 24, 25, 26.

Finland: Jan. 1, 6, Apr. 15, 18, May 1, 26, June 24, 25, Nov. 5, Dec. 6, 24, 25, 26.

France: Jan. 1, Apr. 18, May 1, 8, 26, June 6, July 14, Aug. 15, Nov. 1, 11, Dec. 25.

Germany: Jan. 1, 6*, Apr. 15, 18, May 1, 26, June 6, 16*, Aug. 15*, Oct. 3, 31*, Nov. 1*, 16*, Dec. 25, 26.
* *Observed in certain regions: see also page 366.*

Great Britain: *England & Wales*: Jan. 1, 3, Apr. 15, 18, May 2, June 2, 3, Aug. 29, Dec. 25–27.
Scotland: Jan. 1, 3, 4, Apr. 15, May 2, June 2, 3, Aug. 1, Nov. 30, Dec. 25–27.

Greece: Jan. 1, 6, Mar. 7, 25, Apr. 22, 25, May 2, June 13, Aug. 15, Oct. 28, Dec. 25, 26.

Hungary: Jan. 1, Mar. 14, 15, Apr. 15, 18, May 1, June 6, Aug. 20, Oct. 23, 31, Nov. 1, Dec. 25, 26.

Iceland: Jan. 1, Apr. 14, 15, 17, 18, 21, May 1, 26, June 5, 6, 17, Aug. 1, Dec. 25, 26.

Ireland (Northern): Jan. 1, 3, Mar. 17, Apr. 15, 18, May 2, June 2, 3, July 12, Aug. 29, Dec. 25–27.

Ireland (Republic): Jan. 1, Mar. 17, Apr. 18, May 2, June 6, Aug. 1, Oct. 31, Dec. 25, 26.

Italy: Jan. 1, 6, Apr. 17, 18, 25, May 1, June 2, Aug. 15, Nov. 1, Dec. 8, 25, 26.

Kosovo: Jan. 1, 3, 7, Feb. 17, Apr. 11, 17, 18, 24, 25, May 2, 3, 9, July 10, Dec. 26.

Latvia: Jan. 1, Apr. 15, 17, 18, May 1, 4, 8, June 5, 23, 24, Nov. 18, Dec. 24, 25, 26, 31.

Lithuania: Jan. 1, Feb. 16, Mar. 11, Apr. 17, 18, May 1, June 24, July 6, Aug. 15, Nov. 1, 2, Dec. 24, 25, 26.

Luxembourg: Jan. 1, Apr. 18, May 1, 9, 26, June 6, 23, Aug. 15, Nov. 1, Dec. 25, 26.

North Macedonia: Jan. 1, 7, Apr. 25, May 1–3, 24, Aug. 2, Sept. 8, Oct. 11, 23, 24, Dec. 8. *Other religious holidays are observed in certain areas.*

Moldova: Jan. 1, 7, 8, Mar. 8, Apr. 24, 25, May 1, 2, 9, June 1, Aug. 27, 31, Dec. 25.

Netherlands: Jan. 1, Apr. 15, 17, 18, 27, May 5, 26, June 5, 6, Dec. 25, 26.

Norway: Jan. 1, Apr. 14, 15, 17, 18, May 1, 17, 26, June 5, 6, Dec. 25, 26.

Poland: Jan. 1, 6, Apr. 17, 18, May 1, 3, June 5, 16, Aug. 15, Nov. 1, 11, Dec. 25, 26.

Portugal: Jan. 1, Apr. 15, 17, 25, May 1, June 10, 16, Aug. 15, Oct. 5, Nov. 1, Dec. 1, 8, 25.

Romania: Jan. 1, 2, 24, Apr. 22, 24, 25, May 1, June 1, 12, 13, Aug. 15, Nov. 30, Dec. 1, 25, 26.

Russia: Jan. 1–9, Feb. 23, Mar. 7, 8, May 2, 3, 9, 10, June 13, Nov. 4.

Serbia: Jan. 1, 3, 7, Feb. 15, 16, Apr. 22–25, May 2, 3, Nov. 11.

Slovakia: Jan. 1, 6, Apr. 15, 18, May 1, 8, July 5, Aug. 29, Sept. 1, 15, Nov. 1, 17, Dec. 24, 25, 26.

Slovenia: Jan. 1, 2, Feb. 8, Apr. 17, 18, 27, May 1, 2, June 5, 25, Aug. 15, Oct. 31, Nov. 1, Dec. 25, 26.

Spain: Jan. 1, 6, Apr. 15, Aug. 15, Oct. 12, Nov. 1, Dec. 6, 8, 25. *Also many regional and local holidays.*

Sweden: Jan. 1, 6, Apr. 15, 17, 18, May 1, 26, June 5, 6, 25, Nov. 5, Dec. 25, 26.

Switzerland: Jan. 1, 2*, 6*, Mar. 19*, Apr. 15*, 18*, May 1*, 26, June 6*, 16*, Aug. 1, 15*, Nov. 1*, Dec. 8*, 25, 26*. *Also some local holidays.*
* *Observed in certain regions.*

Turkey: Jan. 1, Apr. 23, May 1, 19, July 15, Aug. 30, Oct. 29 (also 2022 feast holiday periods May 3–5, July 10–13).

Ukraine: Jan. 1, 3, 7, Mar. 8, Apr. 24, 25, May 1, 2, 9, June 12, 13, 28, Aug. 24, Oct. 14, Dec. 25, 26.

MOVABLE HOLIDAYS

Fêtes mobiles – Feste mobile
Bewegliche Feste – Fiestas movibles

	2022	2023
Good Friday	Apr. 15 •	Apr. 7 •
Easter Monday	Apr. 18 •	Apr. 10 •
Ascension Day	May 26 •	May 18 •
Whit Monday (Pentecost)	June 6 •	May 29 •
Corpus Christi	June 16	June 3

• *One week later in the Orthodox calendar*

TIME COMPARISON

COMPARAISON DES HEURES COMPARAZIONE DELLE ORE ZEITVERGLEICH COMPARACIÓN DE LAS HORAS

West European Time	*WINTER: UTC* *SUMMER: UTC + 1*	Ireland, Portugal, United Kingdom Iceland *(UTC all year)*
Central European Time	*WINTER: UTC + 1* *SUMMER: UTC + 2*	Albania, Austria, Belgium, Bosnia, Croatia, Czech Rep., Denmark, France, Germany, Hungary, Italy, Luxembourg, North Macedonia, Malta, Montenegro, Netherlands, Norway, Poland, Serbia, Slovakia, Slovenia, Spain, Sweden, Switzerland
East European Time	*WINTER: UTC + 2* *SUMMER: UTC + 3*	Bulgaria, Estonia, Finland, Greece, Latvia, Lithuania, Moldova, Romania, Ukraine Belarus and Western Russia *(UTC + 3 all year)* Kaliningrad *(UTC + 2 all year)* Turkey *(UTC + 3 all year)*

Daylight Saving Time ('Summer Time') applies in 2022 between 0100 GMT on March 27 and 0100 GMT on October 30 *(GMT = Greenwich Mean Time = UT*

NEWSLINES

Tables in this Summer seasonal edition are generally valid from June 12 to December 11 although, as is usual in our first summer edition, we have only been able to make limited updates in our Italian section. The latest versions of all eight Beyond Europe sections are included this month together with an expanded rail passes section which, in addition to pricing for the popular Interrail and Eurail passes, contains details of many domestic rail passes that are currently available. A fully updated *Rail Extra* feature will be found on pages 653 to 665 which is packed full of useful transport-based information presented on a country by country basis (including details of many popular tourist railways).

Selected news items that appeared in the April and May digital editions have been reproduced on pages 564 and 565.

CAR CARRYING TRAINS

Optima Tours has resumed its car-carrying service between Villach (Austria) and Edirne (Turkey).

INTERNATIONAL

Summer Eurostar Table **10** has been split into four date periods spread over three pages with timings now confirmed until December 10. Each subsequent date period sees additional services being reinstated. Please note that international tables that include Eurostar connections have not been updated as yet, but include warnings to advise readers to cross-check with the relevant version of Table **10**.

Thalys will run its Amsterdam – Brussels – Marseille *Thalys Soleil* on nine summer Saturdays this year (Tables **11** and **18**). This service last ran in the summer of 2019. All tables that feature Thalys services have been updated with schedules valid until December 10.

The high-speed, low-cost service between Paris and Brussels, branded *izy*, will cease running from July 10 (Table **18a**).

Swedish Railways (SJ) will introduce a new overnight service between Stockholm and Hamburg from September 1 which will convey sleeping cars, couchettes and seated accommodation (Table **50**).

A daytime journey is now possible from Sofia to Beograd but the segment between Dimitrovgrad (Serbia) and Niš is by bus (Table **61**). Unfortunately, a similar journey is not possible in the opposite direction.

Recent media reports indicate that the Brussels – Amsterdam – Berlin – Praha overnight service proposed by *European Sleeper* will not now commence running until this Autumn (Table **78**).

Schedules obtained from early versions of the 2023 timetable indicate that the four hour gap in the Zürich to München timetable will be filled, with seven daily services in each direction departing every two hours. In addition, the first services of the day from both cities will be an hour earlier (Table **75**).

GREAT BRITAIN

Great Western is running its usual summer Saturday through trains between London and Newquay, but Cross Country is not running services to the Cornish resort this year (Tables **110** and **112**). Note that the Saturday service in Table **110** is only valid until September 10. Services between Exeter and Okehampton now run on an hourly basis (Table **113**). Great Western has withdrawn all of its remaining services between Fareham and Brighton (Table **140**).

Cross Country has reinstated three further services between Bristol and Manchester and several of its Newcastle services are extended to run to and from Edinburgh (Tables **116** and **124**). An hourly service continues to run between Birmingham and Cambridge, but now only extends to serve Stansted Airport every other hour on Mondays to Saturdays (Table **208**). Note that Greater Anglia continue to operate hourly services between Cambridge and Stansted Airport.

Transport for Wales has increased the number of trains between Swansea and Fishguard to six daily and extended most Pembroke – Carmarthen services through to Swansea (Table **136**). Four additional trains have been added in each direction between Shrewsbury and Aberystwyth on Mondays to Saturdays (Table **147**). The next phase of work to upgrade the historic Barmouth Bridge will see the Machynlleth to Pwllheli route temporarily closed from September 11 with all services operated by bus (timings for which have been included in Table **148**). Most Manchester Airport to Chester trains have been extended along the North Wales coast to Llandudno (Table **160**).

Northern Trains has removed a number of services from its schedules resulting in some long service gaps on some routes. The Saturdays only service between Sheffield and Cleethorpes has been discontinued for the time being. In Table **211** the early morning Whitby to Middlesbrough service is withdrawn, as is the last train in the opposite direction (although the evening service does have a bus replacement).

Hull Trains has added an additional Sunday service in each direction between London and Hull (Table **181**). Grand Central is running an extra daily service in each direction between London and Sunderland (Table **182a**). Lumo's full service of five trains a day in each direction between London and Edinburgh is now operating (Table **183**).

TransPennine Express will implement some major changes from September 10 so we are currently only showing its service until September 9 (Table **188**). Note that, due to engineering work affecting current weekend schedules, we have had to show the Saturday service in a separate location, on page 571.

Greater Anglia has reinstated most of its services between London and Norwich, although the two faster 90 minute journeys in each direction continue to be omitted from the schedules (Table **200**).

In Scotland, all through trains between Edinburgh and Inverness now operate via Stirling (Table **223**). From May 24 ScotRail introduced a temporary reduced timetable on all of its routes on Mondays to Fridays owing to driver shortages. However, it is hoped that this will only be a short-term measure. Our tables show the full planned service so it is advisable to check any journey plans when travelling around Scotland.

FRANCE

Tables in our French section are mostly valid until December 11. However, high-summer schedules in western France always vary considerably to schedules during the rest of the year, so most of our tables radiating from Paris Montparnasse and Austerlitz stations are only valid from July 2 to August 28 (the service from August 29 will be included in the Autumn seasonal edition). Regional trains in northern France are also only valid during the the summer period.

Due to the large number of variations to trains in Table **250** we have had to include two versions of the table. Services until July 17 will be found on pages 163 and 166, whilst the service from July 18 to August 28 can be found on pages 559 and 560.

TER Normandie services shown in Tables **270**, **275** and **276** are only valid from July 11 to August 12. Outside of this period the number of variations has made it impossible to compile coherant long-term tables and so will be updated on a short-term basis.

Trains in Table **290** are affected by engineering work during the summer. *Intercités* services will run via Les Aubrais-Orléans rather than Chenonceaux adding approximately 80 minutes to the journey (trains leave Nantes earlier and arrive later). The single daily TER service between Tours and Lyon starts from / terminates at Vierzon. Various rail replacement bus services are provided to and from Vierzon.

The overnight train to Lourdes is extended to Pau, Bayonne, Biarritz and Hendaye during July and August (Table **319**).

Readers should note the timetables in France are often extremely complex and timings of both long-distance and regional trains may vary by a few minutes compared to what is shown in our tables. It is simply not possible for us to show all minor variations so it is always advisable to check timings before travelling.

ITALY

Owing to the late availability of summer schedules, we have only been able to check timings for selected long-distance services in Italy (mainly high-speed services operated by Trenitalia). Other services, including all regional timings, have not been checked and are valid until June 11. However, major alterations are not expected from June 12. We will endeavour to check the Italian section in time for the July digital edition.

CONTINUED ON PAGE 36

EXPLANATION OF STANDARD SYMBOLS

	EXPLANATION OF SYMBOLS	EXPLICATION DES SIGNES	DELUCIDAZIONE DEI SEGNI	ZEICHENERKLÄRUNG	EXPLICACIÓN DE LOS SIGNOS
	SERVICES	**SERVICES**	**SERVIZI**	**DIENSTE**	**SERVICIOS**
12	Through service (1st and 2nd class seats)	Relation directe (places assises 1re et 2e classe)	Relazione diretta (con posti di 1a e 2a classe)	Direkte Verbindung (Sitzplätze 1. und 2. Klasse)	Relación directa (con asientos de 1a y 2a clase)
	Sleeping car	Voiture-lits	Carrozza letti	Schlafwagen	Coche-camas
	Couchette car	Voiture-couchettes	Carrozza cuccette	Liegewagen	Coche-literas
✕	Restaurant car	Voiture-restaurant	Carrozza ristorante	Speisewagen	Coche-restaurante
	Snacks and drinks available *(see page 10)*	Voiture-bar ou vente ambulante *(voir page 10)*	Carrozza bar o servizio di buffet *(vedere pagina 10)*	Imbiss und Getränke im Zug *(siehe Seite 10)*	Servicio de cafetería o bar móvil *(véase pág. 10)*
2	Second class only	Uniquement deuxième classe	Sola seconda classe	Nur zweite Klasse	Sólo segunda clase
	Bus or coach service	Service routier	Servizio automobilistico	Buslinie	Servicio de autobuses
	Ferry service	Service maritime	Servizio marittimo	Schifffahrtslinie	Servicio marítimo
	DAYS OF RUNNING	**JOURS DE CIRCULATION**	**GIORNI DI EFFETTUAZIONE**	**VERKEHRSTAGE**	**DÍAS DE CIRCULACIÓN**
⚒	Mondays to Saturdays except holidays*	Du lundi au samedi, sauf les fêtes*	Dal lunedì al sabato, salvo i giorni festivi*	Montag bis Samstag außer Feiertage*	De lunes a sábado, excepto festivos*
Ⓐ	Mondays to Fridays except holidays*	Du lundi au vendredi, sauf les fêtes*	Dal lunedì al venerdì, salvo i giorni festivi*	Montag bis Freitag außer Feiertage*	De lunes a viernes, excepto festivos*
Ⓑ	Daily except Saturdays	Tous les jours sauf les samedis	Giornalmente, salvo il sabato	Täglich außer Samstag	Diario excepto sábados
Ⓒ	Saturdays, Sundays and holidays*	Les samedis, dimanches et fêtes*	Sabato, domenica e giorni festivi*	Samstage, Sonn- und Feiertage*	Sábados, domingos y festivos*
†	Sundays and holidays*	Les dimanches et fêtes*	Domenica e giorni festivi*	Sonn- und Feiertage*	Domingos y festivos*
①②	Mondays, Tuesdays	Les lundis, mardis	Lunedì, martedì	Montag, Dienstag	Lunes, martes
③④	Wednesdays, Thurdays	Les mercredis, jeudis	Mercoledì, giovedì	Mittwoch, Donnerstag	Miércoles, jueves
⑤⑥	Fridays, Saturdays	Les vendredis, samedis	Venerdì, sabato	Freitag, Samstag	Viernes, sábados
⑦	Sundays	Les dimanches	Domenica	Sonntag	Domingos
①–④	Mondays to Thursdays	Des lundis aux jeudis	Dal lunedì al giovedì	Montag bis Donnerstag	De lunes a jueves
	OTHER SYMBOLS	**AUTRES SIGNES**	**ALTRI SIMBOLI**	**SONSTIGE SYMBOLE**	**OTROS SÍMBOLOS**
IC **29**	Train number (**bold figures** above train times)	Numéro du train (en **caractères gras** au-dessus de l'horaire du train)	Numero del treno (in **neretto** sopra gli orari del treno)	Zugnummer (über den Fahrplanzeiten in **fetter Schrift** gesetzt)	Número del tren (figura en **negrita** encima del horario del tren)
♦	See footnotes (listed by train number)	Renvoi aux notes données en bas de page (dans l'ordre numérique des trains)	Vedi in calce alla pagina l'annotazione corrispondente al numero del treno	Siehe die nach Zugnummern geordneten Fußnoten	Véase al pie de la página la nota correspondiente al número del tren
[R]	Reservation compulsory	Réservation obligatoire	Prenotazione obbligatoria	Reservierung erforderlich	Reserva obligatoria
	Frontier station	Gare frontalière	Stazione di frontiera	Grenzbahnhof	Estación fronteriza
✈	Airport	Aéroport	Aeroporto	Flughafen	Aeropuerto
|	Train does not stop	Sans arrêt	Il treno non ferma qui	Zug hält nicht	El tren no para aquí
▬	Separates two trains in the same column between which no connection is possible	Sépare deux trains de la même colonne qui ne sont pas en correspondance	Separa due treni della stessa colonna che non sono in coincidenza	Trennt zwei in derselben Spalte angegebene Züge, zwischen denen kein Anschluß besteht	Separa dos trenes de la misma columna entre los cuales no hay enlace
→	Continued in later column	Suite dans une colonne à droite	Continuazione più avanti a destra	Fortsetzung weiter rechts	Continuación a la derecha
←	Continued from earlier column	Suite d'une colonne à gauche	Seguito di una colonna a sinistra	Fortsetzung von links	Continuación desde la izquierda
v.v.	Vice versa	Vice versa	Viceversa	Umgekehrt	A la inversa
	** Public holiday dates for each country are given on page 4.* *Other, special symbols are explained in table footnotes or in the introduction to each country.*	** Les dates des fêtes légales nationales sont données en page 4.* *D'autres signes particuliers sont expliqués dans les notes ou bien dans l'avant-propos relatif à chaque pays.*	** Per le date dei giorni festivi civili nei diversi paesi vedere pagina 4.* *Altri segni particolari vengono spiegati nelle note in calce ai quadri o nella introduzione attinente a ogni paese.*	** Gesetzlichen Feiertage der jeweiligen Länder finden Sie auf Seite 4.* *Besondere Symbole sind in den Fußnoten bzw. in der Einleitung zu den einzelnen Ländern erklärt.*	** Las fechas de los días festivos en cada país figuran en la página 4.* *La explicación de otros signos particulares se da en las notas o en el preámbulo correspondiente a cada país.*

For explanation of train types (AP, IC, TGV etc) see the introduction to each country section

What is the European Rail Timetable?

The European Rail Timetable is a concise guide to rail and ferry schedules throughout Europe, and also includes selected areas of the world outside Europe. Needless to say, it cannot be comprehensive (it would run into thousands of pages), but through our knowledge and experience, together with valuable feedback from our readers, we can select those services which we believe will satisfy the needs of most travellers.

When do the services change?

There is a major annual timetable change in mid-December affecting almost all European countries, with many countries having a second change in mid-June. There are, of course, exceptions. For example, the British summer timetable starts in late May, Sweden changes again in mid-August, whilst there are changes in Ukraine from late March (coinciding with the clock change). Many holiday areas also have separate timetables for the high-summer period, particularly areas of France, Italy and Hungary. In fact, changes can happen at any time of year, and railways issue amendments either on set dates or as and when necessary. Engineering work also causes frequent changes, and shipping schedules can change at any time.

How are the trains selected for inclusion?

People travel for many reasons, whether for leisure, business, sightseeing, visiting friends or relations, or just for the fun of it, and there are no hard and fast rules for selecting the services that we show. Naturally, major towns and inter-city services are shown as a matter of course, but the level of smaller places and local trains shown will depend on the country and even the area. It's surprising just how many minor lines we manage to squeeze in! Generally we will show a greater number of local trains in areas which are popular tourist destinations or where other services are sparse.

It is not possible to show suburban trains within cities or conurbations, or most outer-suburban routes to places close to large cities. However, where there are places of particular interest or importance in this category we do try to show brief details of frequency and journey time.

When should I use the International section?

The rail tables are divided into two sections - International (Tables **9** to **99**) and Country by Country (Tables **100** upwards). For some international services between adjacent countries (for example Stockholm - Oslo or Hamburg - Århus) it is necessary to use the relevant Country tables - the index or maps will guide you. Local trains which cross international frontiers will usually only be found in the Country sections.

Some international trains also carry passengers internally within each country and will therefore be found in the Country tables as well as the International section. Some services are primarily for international travel and will therefore only be found in the International section - this includes *Eurostar* trains (London - Paris / Brussels / Amsterdam) and *Thalys* services (Paris - Brussels - Amsterdam / Köln), as well as certain long-distance night trains.

What about places outside Europe?

The European Rail Timetable includes the whole of Turkey and Russia. Furthermore, our **Beyond Europe** section at the back of each edition features timetables from different areas of the world each month. Eight areas are featured, each appearing at least twice a year. The areas covered are **India**, **South East Asia, Australia, New Zealand, China, Japan, South America, North America, South Korea, Africa and the Middle East**. Details of when each region appears will be found in the introduction of the Beyond Europe section. Please note that we include **all** of the latest Beyond Europe sections in our expanded Winter and Summer editions.

What else does it contain?

A summary of international sleeper services will be found on page 35, listing types of accommodation, operators and facilities on board.

We also include a summary of European rail passes (see the list of contents on page 3 for its current location) with a more detailed version appearing in our expanded seasonal Summer and Winter editions. The seasonal editions also include a *Rail Extra* feature containing useful transport based information on a country by country basis (including details of many popular tourist railways).

Our timetables and other products may be purchased from our website **www.europeanrailtimetable.eu**.

HOW TO USE THE TIMETABLE

Using the index

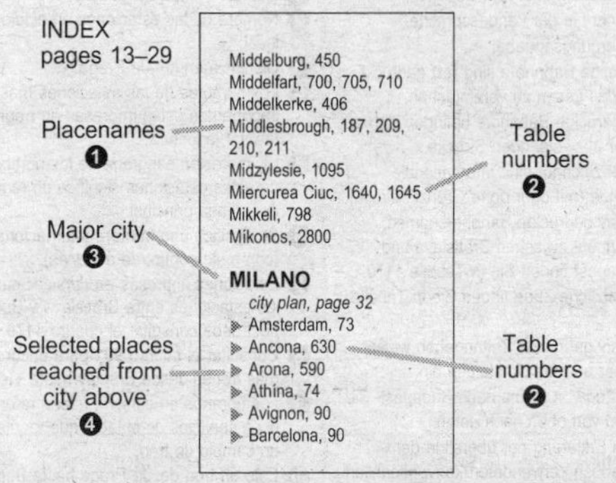

Look up the two places between which you are travelling. It can often be helpful to start your search from the *smaller* of the two locations. ❺

Using the maps

The maps can be the quickest way of finding the required table number, if you already know the geographical location of the places required. ❿

COMMENT TROUVER VOTRE TRAIN

❶ Localité.
❷ Numéros des tableaux.
❸ Grande ville.
❹ Localités sélectionnées à gagner de la grande ville en haut.
❺ Cherchez les deux bouts du parcours désiré sur la liste des villes. Commencer par la ville de moindre importance peut faciliter la recherche.
❻ Ligne principale.
❼ Ligne secondaire.
❽ Ligne à grande vitesse.
❾ Liaison en autocar.
❿ La consultation des cartes – si vous savez déjà la location géographique de vos points de départ et d'arrivée – est le moyen le plus rapide de repérer les numéros des tableaux relatifs à votre parcours.

COME TROVARE IL VOSTRO TRENO

❶ Località.
❷ Numeri dei quadri-orario.
❸ Grandi città.
❹ Principali destinazione raggiungibili dalla località in neretto sopra.
❺ Cercate le localita' tra le quali dovrete viaggiare; spesso può essere di aiuto iniziare la ricerca dalla località più piccola.
❻ Principale linea ferroviaria.
❼ Linea ferroviaria secondaria.
❽ Linea ad alta velocità.
❾ Autobus.
❿ Le mappe sono il metodo più rapido per trovare i numeri dei quadri-orario di cui avete bisogno, quando gia' siete a conoscenza della collocazione geografica delle localita' di partenza e arrivo del vostro viaggio.

WIE FINDE ICH MEINEN ZUG?

❶ Ortsname.
❷ Tabellennummer.
❸ Großstadt.
❹ Knotenpunkte erreichbar von der Großstadt oben.
❺ Suchen Sie Ihre Start- und Endbahnhof im Ortsverzeichnis. Dazu empfehlen wir, Ihre Suche aus der Richtung des *kleineren* Ortes aufzunehmen.
❻ Hauptstrecke.
❼ Nebenstrecke.
❽ Hochgeschwindigkeitsstrecke.
❾ Busverbindung.
❿ Kennen Sie die geographische Lage der Ausgangs- und Bestimmungsorte Ihrer Reise, dann empfehlen wir einen Blick in die im Kursbuch enthaltene Übersichtskarte.

COMO BUSCAR SU TREN

❶ Localidad.
❷ Números de los cuadros horarios.
❸ Gran ciudad.
❹ Principales destinos accesibles a través de esta localidad.
❺ Busque los dos lugares a través de los cuales viaja. Normalmente facilita la búsqueda empezar por la localidad más pequeña.
❻ Línea principal.
❼ Línea secundaria.
❽ Línea de alta velocidad.
❾ Línea de autobuses.
❿ Los mapas pueden ser la forma más rápida de encontrar los cuadros que debe consultar, si ya conoce el punto de inicio y conclusión de su viaje.

Numbers in circles refer to translations below

Reading the tables

Trains run daily unless otherwise shown by symbol or footnote (15)

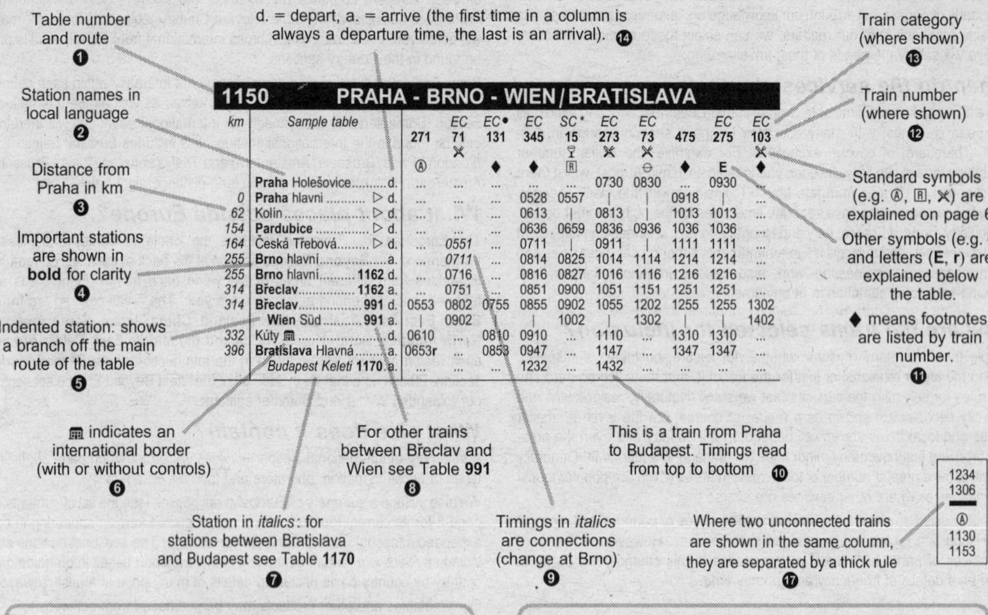
d. = depart, a. = arrive (the first time in a column is always a departure time, the last is an arrival). (14)
Table number and route (1)
Station names in local language (2)
Distance from Praha in km (3)
Important stations are shown in **bold** for clarity (4)
Indented station: shows a branch off the main route of the table (5)
Train category (where shown) (13)
Train number (where shown) (12)
Standard symbols (e.g. Ⓐ, 🅁, ✕) are explained on page 6.
Other symbols (e.g. ⊖) and letters (**E**, **r**) are explained below the table.
♦ means footnotes are listed by train number. (11)
⛩ indicates an international border (with or without controls) (6)
For other trains between Břeclav and Wien see Table **991** (8)
This is a train from Praha to Budapest. Timings read from top to bottom (10)
Station in *italics*: for stations between Bratislava and Budapest see Table **1170** (7)
Timings in *italics* are connections (change at Brno) (9)
Where two unconnected trains are shown in the same column, they are separated by a thick rule (17)
1234
1306
Ⓐ
1130
1153

1150 PRAHA - BRNO - WIEN / BRATISLAVA

km	Sample table		*EC*	*EC*•	*EC*	*SC**	*EC*	*EC*		*EC*	*EC*
		271	**71**	**131**	**345**	**15**	**273**	**73**	**475**	**275**	**103**
			✕			🍷	✕	✕			✕
		Ⓐ		♦	♦	🅁		⊖	♦	**E**	♦
	Praha Holešovice.........d.	...	...	...	...	...	0730	0830	...	0930	...
0	**Praha** hlavni .... ▷ d.	...	...	...	0528	0557	|	|	0918	|	...
62	Kolín .... ▷ d.	...	...	...	0613	|	0813	|	1013	1013	...
154	**Pardubice** .... ▷ d.	...	...	...	0636	0659	0836	0936	1036	1036	...
164	Česká Třebová......... ▷ d.	...	*0551*	...	0711	|	0911	|	1111	1111	...
255	**Brno** hlavní..................a.	...	*0711*	...	0814	0825	1014	1114	1214	1214	...
255	**Brno** hlavní.......... **1162** d.	...	0716	...	0816	0827	1016	1116	1216	1216	...
314	**Břeclav**............... **1162** a.	...	0751	...	0851	0900	1051	1151	1251	1251	...
314	**Břeclav**................. **991** d.	0553	0802	0755	0855	0902	1055	1202	1255	1255	1302
	Wien Süd .... **991** a.	|	0902	|	|	1002	|	1302	|	|	1402
332	Kúty ⛩ ....d.	0610	...	0810	0910	...	1110	...	1310	1310	...
396	**Bratislava** Hlavná.........a.	0653r	...	0853	0947	...	1147	...	1347	1347	...
	Budapest Keleti **1170**.a.	...	...	...	1232	...	1432	...	...	...	...

CLASSES OF TRAVEL:
Trains have 1st and 2nd class seats unless otherwise shown. However, local trains may only have 2nd class seats. (15)

TIME ZONES:
Times are in local time (Russian times are in Moscow time). For time zones see page 4. Timings are given in 24 hour clock (see page 11). (16)

COMMENT LIRE LES TABLEAUX

(1) Numéro et parcours du tableau.
(2) Nom de la gare en langue locale.
(3) La distance en km de Praha.
(4) Les noms de gares importantes sont imprimés en **gras** pour faciliter la lecture.
(5) La mise en retrait des noms de gares indique une ligne d'embranchement.
(6) ⛩ indique une frontière internationale (avec ou sans le contrôle).
(7) Les noms de gares imprimés en *italique*: vous trouverez des gares sur le trajet Bratislava - Budapest en consultant le tableau **1170**.
(8) Consultez le tableau **991** pour trouver des trains supplémentaires de Břeclav à Wien.
(9) Les heures en *italique* indiquent une *correspondance* et supposent dans tous les cas un changement de train.
(10) Ici un train de Praha à Budapest. Lire de haut en bas.
(11) Les signes conventionnels sont expliqués à la page 6. Les autres signes et lettres sont expliqués en bas du tableau. Le symbole ♦ à l'en-tête d'une colonne signifie qu'il faut consulter le note qui porte le numéro du train concerné.
(12) Le numéro du train (en cas échéant).
(13) Indication de catégorie (en cas échéant).
(14) d. = départ, a. = arrivée. Pour chaque train la *première* mention est toujours une heure de *départ*, la *dernière* toujours une heure d'*arrivée*.
(15) Sauf indication contraire, les trains circulent *tous les jours* et y compris des places assises de 1ère et 2ème classe.
(16) Toutes les indications horaires sont données en heures locales (voir page 4). En Russie c'est à l'heure Moskva.
(17) Deux trains de la même colonne qui ne sont pas en correspondance sont separés par une règle épaisse.

COME SI CONSULTA UN QUADRO ORARIO

(1) Numero del quadro e percorso.
(2) Nome della stazione nella lingua locale.
(3) Distanze in km da Praha.
(4) I nomi delle stazioni piu' importante sono stampati in **neretto** per renderne più facile la lettura.
(5) I nomi delle stazioni rientrati rispetto alla colonna principale indicano una diramazione dal percorso principale del quadro-orario in questione.
(6) ⛩ indica una stazione di confine (con o senza controllo).
(7) Stazioni in *corsivo*: per gli orari tra le stazione di Bratislava e Budapest bisogna consultare il quadro **1170**.
(8) Consultare il quadro **991** per ulteriori treni da Břeclav a Wien.
(9) Gli orari *in corsivo* si riferiscono a servizi *in coincidenza* che implicano un cambio di treno.
(10) Questo e' un treno da Praha a Budapest. La lettura viene fatta dall'alto verso il basso.
(11) I simboli convenzionali sono spiegate a pagina 6. Altri simboli e lettere sono spiegati sotto il quadro-orario in questione. Il simbolo ♦ all'inizio di una colonna-orario significa che bisogna fare riferimento alla nota corrispondente al numero del treno in questione.
(12) Numero del treno (quando indicato).
(13) Classificazione del treno (quando indicato).
(14) d. = partenza, a. = arrivo. Notare che l'orario che compare per *primo* nel quadro-orario è sempre un l'orario di *partenza*, mentre quello che compare per *ultimo* è sempre l'orario di *arrivo*.
(15) Se non ci sono altre indicazioni i treni si intendono giornalieri, con prima e seconda classe di viaggio.
(16) Gli orari sono sempre espressi in ora locale (in Russia e' utilizzati l'ora di Mosca). Per informazioni sui fusi orari vedere a pagina 4.
(17) Quando nella colonna-orario ci sono due treni che non sono in coincidenza tra loro, questo e' indicato dalla linea in grassetto che li separa.

WIE LESE ICH DIE FAHRPLÄNE

(1) Tabellennummer und Strecke.
(2) Bahnhof in der Landessprache.
(3) Entfernungsangabe.
(4) Wichtige Bahnhöfe sind **fett** gedruckt um das Lesen zu vereinfachen.
(5) Eingerückte Bahnhöfe befinden sich auf einer abzweigenden Strecke.
(6) ⛩ Bezeichnet eine internationale Grenze (mit oder ohne Grenzkontrolle).
(7) *Kursiv* gedruckte Bahnhofsnamen: Bahnhöfe zwischen Bratislava und Budapest finden Sie in Tabelle **1170**.
(8) Zusätzliche Züge finden Sie in Tabelle **991**.
(9) *Kursiv* gedruckte Zeitangaben weisen immer auf das Umsteigen hin.
(10) Ein Zug von Praha nach Budapest. Sie lesen von oben nach unten.
(11) Eine Erklärung der überall in dem Kursbuch verwendeten konventionellen Zeichen finden Sie auf Seite 6. Anderen Zeichen und Buchstaben finden Sie unter der Fahrplantabelle. Das Zeichen ♦ im Kopf der Zugspalte bedeutet: Sehen Sie bei der Fußnote des Zuges mit der betreffenden Zugnummer nach.
(12) Zugnummer (wo zutreffend).
(13) Zuggattung (wo zutreffend).
(14) d. = Abfahrt, a. = Ankunft. Es handelt sich stets bei der ersten für einen Zug angegebenen Zeit um eine Abfahrtzeit, bei der letzten um eine Ankunftzeit.
(15) Sofern nicht anders angemeldet, verkehren die Züge *täglich*. Im Allgemeinen führen die Züge die 1. und 2. Wagenklasse.
(16) Fahrzeiten sind immer in der jeweiligen Landeszeit angegeben (Seite 4). Russische Fahrzeiten sind auf Moskauer Zeit.
(17) Im Falle von zwei Züge in der gleichen Spalte ohne Anschlussmöglichkeit, liegt das Zeichen ▬ zwischen den Zügen.

COMO LEER LOS CUADROS

(1) Número y línea del cuadro.
(2) Nombre de las estaciones en el idioma local.
(3) Distancia en km de Praga.
(4) Los nombres de las estaciones más importantes están impresas en **negrita** facilitar la lectura.
(5) La impresión sangrada de los nombres de estas estaciones significa un ramal de la línea principal.
(6) ⛩ significa una frontera internacional (con o sin control de aduanas).
(7) Estaciones impresas en *cursiva*: para las estaciones entre Bratislava y Budapest debe consultar el cuadro **1170**.
(8) Consultar el cuadro **991** para encontrar más trenes desde Břeclav hasta Viena.
(9) Los horarios en cursiva, hacen referencia a servicios de enlace, que requieren un cambio de tren.
(10) Esto un tren desde Praga hasta Budapest. Leer de arriba a abajo.
(11) La explicación de los signos convencionales se da en la página 6. Ostros símbolos y letras se explican al pie del cuadro. El símbolo ♦ en el encabezamiento de la columna quiere decir: consulte la nota que lleva el número del tren interesado.
(12) Número de tren (si se indica).
(13) Tipo de tren (si se indica).
(14) d. = salida, a. = llegada. Nótese que el primer horario indicado en las columnas es siempre un horario de salida, y el último un horario de llegada.
(15) Salvo indicación contraria, los trenes circulan a *diario* y llevan plazas sentadas de primera y segunda clases.
(16) Todas las indicaciones horarias son en horario local (Para Rusia se utiliza la hora local de Moscú). Para comprobar las franjas horarias mirar la página 4. Los horarios utilizan el sistema horario de 24h (ver página 11).
(17) Cuando dos trenes que no tienen conexión aparecen en la misma columna, estos se encuentran separados por el símbolo ▬.

Reading the footnotes

These footnotes relate to the sample table on page 8 ❶

In certain tables, footnotes are listed by train number, shown by ♦ on relevant trains ❷

♦ –	**NOTES** (LISTED BY TRAIN NUMBERS)
102/3 –	POLONIA – 🛏12 ✕ Warszawa - Ostrava - Břeclav - Wien and v.v.
131 –	MORAVIA – 🛏12 Bohumin - Ostrava - Břeclav - Bratislava.
345 –	AVALA – 🛏12 ✕ Praha - Bratislava - Budapest - Beograd. Conveys on ⑤ June 12 - Sept. 18 ▬ 2 cl. Praha - Beograd (**335**) - Thessaloniki.
475 –	JADRAN – June 19 - Sept. 4. 🛏 1, 2 cl., ▬ 2 cl., 🛏2 Praha - Bratislava - Zagreb - Split (Table **92**); 🛏12 Praha - Bratislava.
E –	SLOVAN, not June 19 - Sept. 4.
r –	0659 on ⑥.
▷ –	See also Table **1160**.
⊖ –	Runs 10 mins later on Aug. 15.
• –	*Ex* in Slovakia.
* –	Pendolino tilting train. Classified *EC* in Austria.

OTHER TRAIN NAMES:

71 –	GUSTAV MAHLER
73 –	FRANZ SCHUBERT

Letters and symbols may be found above the timings (e.g. **E**) or against individual times (e.g. **r**). Symbols may also appear in the station column (e.g. ▷). ❻

Train names are sometimes listed separately. ❺

Train **345** is named 'AVALA' and runs daily from Praha to Beograd with 1st and 2nd class seats and a restaurant car. On Fridays June 12 to September 18, a through couchette car runs from Praha to Thessaloniki, attached to train **335** between Beograd and Thessaloniki. ❸

Train **475** is named 'JADRAN' and runs only from June 19 to September 4. It has a sleeper, couchettes and second class seats from Praha to Split via Bratislava and Zagreb, as well as first and second class seats only going as far as Bratislava. Further details will be found in Table **92**. ❹

Always read the footnotes; they may contain important information. Standard symbols are explained on page 6. ❼

Dates shown are where a train **starts** its journey (unless otherwise noted). Some notes show both directions of the train (e.g. **102/3**) with "and v.v." ❽

FURTHER HINTS ON READING THE TIMETABLE

- Refer to the introduction to each country for important information such as train types, supplements, compulsory reservation, and the dates of validity of the timings. Exceptions are noted in individual tables.
- For dates of public holidays see page 4.
- Please allow adequate time for changing trains, especially at large stations. Connections are not guaranteed, especially when late running occurs (connecting trains are sometimes held for late running trains).
- A Glossary of common terms appears on page 12.

LES NOTES EN BAS DU TABLEAU

❶ Ces notes se rapportent au example de tableau à la page 8.
❷ Dans certains tableaux, le symbole ♦ à l'en-tête d'une colonne signifie qu'il faut consulter le note qui porte le numéro du train concerné.
❸ Le train **345** s'appelle AVALA et circule tous les jours de Praha à Beograd avec des places assises de 1ère et 2ème classe et une voiture-restaurant. Tous les vendredis du 12 juin jusqu'au 18 sept il y a aussi une voiture-couchettes de Praha à Thessaloniki, qui se joint au train **335** entre Beograd et Thessaloniki.
❹ Le train **475** s'appelle JADRAN et circule seulement entre le 19 juin et le 4 septembre. Il compris des voitures-lits, couchettes et places assises de 2ème classe à Split via Zagreb, et des places assises de 1ère et 2ème classe jusqu'à Bratislava. Voir le tableau **92**.
❺ Les noms des trains sont parfois indiqués séparément.
❻ Les lettres et signes sont situés à l'en-tête d'une colonne ou à côté d'une heure dans la colonne. Une signe peut sortir également a côté d'un nom de gare.
❼ Les notes peuvent vous donner des informations importantes. Les signes conventionnels sont expliqués à la page 6.
❽ Sauf indication contraire, les jours et dates de circulation mentionnés sont ceux applicables à la *gare d'origine* du train (mentionnée si elle ne figure pas sur le tableau même dans les notes). Les notes peuvent expliquer les deux sens d'un train (e.g. **102/3**) utilisant "and v.v." (et vice versa).

PLUS DE CONSEILS

- Il vous est fortement recommandé de consulter aussi l'introduction à chaque section nationale: vous y trouverez des précisions concernant la classification des trains, les prestations offertes à bord des trains, les suppléments, la réservation des places, etc.
- Jours fériés - voir page 4.
- Aucune correspondance n'est garantie pourtant. N'oubliez pas non plus que dans les grandes gares les changements peuvent entraîner une longue marche et l'emprunt d'escaliers.
- Lexique - voir page 12.

NOTE ALLA FINE DEL QUADRO-ORARIO

❶ Queste note si riferiscono all' esempio a pagina 8.
❷ In certi quadri-orario, il simbolo ♦ nelle note di testa significa che bisogna fare riferimento alla nota con il numero di treno corrispondente.
❸ Il treno **345** si chiama AVALA ed e' giornaliero tra Praha a Beograd con posti di 1ª e 2ª classe e carrozza ristorante. Il venerdì dal 12 giugno fino al 18 settembre e' aggiunta a Beograd una carrozza cuccette diretta a Thessaloniki, combinandosi con il treno **335** tra Beograd e Thessaloniki.
❹ Il treno **475** si chiama JADRAN ed e' operativo solo dal 19 giugno al 4 settembre. Il treno si compone di carrozze letti, carrozze cuccette, e posti di 2ª classe tra Praha e Split, via Bratislava e Zagrabria; inoltre ci sono anche posti di 1ª e 2ª classe fino a Bratislava. Consultare anche il quadro-orario **92** al riguardo
❺ I nomi dei treni sono talvolta indicati separatamente.
❻ Lettere e simboli possono essere sia alla testa di una colonna-orario, che accanto all'orario del treno stesso. Un simbolo potrebbe anche essere accanto al nome di una stazione.
❼ E' importante leggere sempre le note a le informazioni a fine quadro. I segni convenzionali sono elencati e spiegati a pagina 6.
❽ Salvo casi in cui sia diversamente indicato, le date di circolazione dei treni si riferiscono sempre alla stazione dove il treno inizia il suo viaggio (come viene riportato nelle note a fine quadro, e Inoltre nel quadro stesso).

ALTRI CONSIGLI UTILI

- Vi consigliamo vivamente di consultare anche l'introduzione dedicata ad ogni nazione. Troverete importanti informazioni riguardanti i servizi di trasporto di ciascun paese, così come le categorie dei treni, la ristorazione, il pagamento di supplementi, le necessità di prenotazione, ecc.
- I giorni festivi suddivisi per paese sono elencati a pagina 4.
- Le coincidenze indicate non sono garantite. Tenete presente che che nelle grandi stazioni il trasferimento tra due binari potrebbe significare un lungo tratto da percorrere a piedi e con l'uso di scale.
- Il glossario si trova a pagina 12.

FUSSNOTEN

❶ Fußnoten beziehen sich auf die Beispieltabelle auf Seite 8.
❷ ♦: Sehen Sie bei der Fußnote des Zuges mit der betreffenden Zugnummer nach.
❸ Zug **345** heißt AVALA und fährt täglich zwischen Praha und Beograd mit Sitzplätzen 1. und 2. Klasse. An Freitagen vom 12. Juni bis 18. September führt dieser Zug durchgehende Liegewagen von Praha nach Thessaloniki (mit Zug **335** vereinigt von Beograd nach Thessaloniki).
❹ Zug **475** heißt JADRAN und fährt nur von 19. Juni bis 4. September. Er führt Schlaf-, Liege und Sitzwagen 2. Klasse von Praha nach Split über Zagreb, auch Sitzwagen 1. und 2. Klasse, die nur bis Bratislava fahren. Auf Tabelle **92** finden Sie weitere Informationen.
❺ Zugnamen können besonders aufgeführt sein.
❻ Zeichen und Buchstaben finden sich im Kopf der Zugspalte oder neben einer bestimmten Zeitangabe. Zeichen sind auch in der Bahnhofsspalte möglich.
❼ In Fußnoten findet man wichtige Informationen. Standardzeichen sind auf Seite 6 erklärt.
❽ Die erwähnten Tage und Zeitabschnitte für Züge, die nicht täglich verkehren, gelten für den Ausgangsbahnhof des Zuges (wenn dieser nicht in der Tabelle steht, ist er in einer Fußnote erwähnt). Fußnoten dürfen beide Richtungen erklären (z.B. **102/3**), mit "and v.v." (und umgekehrt).

WEITERE HINWEISE

- Es ist zu empfehlen, die Einleitungen zu jedem einzelnen Land zu lesen. Darin werden Sie wichtige Informationen über die Besonderheiten jedes Landes finden: Zugcharakterisierung, Services an Bord der Züge, Zuschlagpflicht, Reservierungsbedingungen usw.
- Feiertage - siehe Seite 4.
- Anschlussversäumnisse durch Verspätung oder Ausfall von Zügen sind immer möglich. Bitte beachten Sie, dass auf Großstadtbahnhöfen häufig längere Fußwege zurückgelegt bzw. Treppen benutzen werden müssen.
- Glossar - siehe Seite 12.

LAS NOTAS AL PIE DEL CUADRO

❶ Estas notas hacen referencia al ejemplo de la página 8.
❷ El símbolo ♦ ciertas tablas horarias significa: que hay que consultar la nota a pie de página con el número correspondiente.
❸ El Tren **345** se llama AVALA y circula a diario entre Praga y Belgrado con plazas sentadas de 1ra y 2da clase, además de con coche-restaurante. Los Viernes del 12 de junio al 18 de septiembre el tren lleva coches litera desde Praga hasta Tesalónica que se combinan con el tren **335** entre Belgrado y Tesalónica.
❹ El Tren **475** se llama JADRAN y circula solamente del 19 de junio al 4 de septiembre. El Tren **475** se llama JADRAN y circula solamente del 19 de junio al 4 de sept. El tren dispone de lleva vagones de coches cama, litera, y plazas sentadas de 2da clase entre Praga y Split a través de Zagreb, también plazas sentadas de 1ra y 2da clase hasta Bratislava. Consulte el cuadro **92**.
❺ Los nombres de los Trenes a veces son enumerados por separado.
❻ Las letras y signos se encuentran en el encabezamiento de las distintas columnas horarias o adyacentes a horas de salida individuales. Los símbolos también pueden aparecer en la columna de la estación.
❼ Lea siempre las notas a pie de cuadro ya que pueden contener información importante. La explicación de los signos convencionales se da en la página 6.
❽ Salvo indicación contraria los días y fechas de circulación de los trenes son aquéllos mencionados en la estación de *origen* del tren. Algunas notas muestran ambas direcciones del tren mediante la nota "and v.v." (y viceversa).

INFORMACIÓN ADICIONAL

- Se recomienda vivamente que consulte también los preámbulos al comienzo de cada sección nacional: le proporcionarán datos importantes sobre las particularidades de cada país: tipos de trenes, restauración, pago de suplementos, y necesidades de reservación anticipada.
- Días festivos - cunsulte la página 4.
- Los trasbordos no se pueden garantizar, sobretodo en el caso de retrasos. Hay que ser consciente también que el trasbordo en las estaciones de grandes ciudades puede suponer un desplazamiento bastante largo a pie y el uso de escaleras.
- Glosario - cunsulte la página 12.

The following is designed to be an outline guide to travelling around Europe by train. For further details of types of accommodation available, catering, supplements etc., see the introduction to each country.

BUYING YOUR TICKET

Train tickets must be purchased before travelling, either from travel agents or at the station ticket office (or machine). Where a station has neither a ticket office nor a ticket machine, the ticket may usually be purchased on the train.

Tickets which are not dated when purchased (for example in France and Italy) must be validated before travel in one of the machines at the entrance to the platform.

In certain Eastern European countries foreign nationals may have to buy international rail tickets at the office of the state tourist board concerned and not at the railway station. The tickets can sometimes only be purchased in western currency and buying tickets can take a long time.

Most countries in Europe offer two classes of rail accommodation, usually 1st and 2nd class. 1st class is more comfortable and therefore more expensive than 2nd class. Local trains are often 2nd class only. In Southern and Eastern Europe, 1st class travel is advisable for visitors as fares are reasonable and 2nd class can be very overcrowded.

RESERVATIONS

Many express trains in Europe are restricted to passengers holding advance seat reservations, particularly in France, Italy, Sweden and Spain. This is indicated by the symbol Ⓡ in the tables, or by notes in the introduction to each country. All *TGV*, *Eurostar* and *Thalys* trains require advance reservation, as do all long-distance trains in Spain.

Reservations can usually be made up to two months in advance. A small fee is charged, but where a supplement is payable the reservation fee is often included. Reservations can often be made on other long-distance services and this is recommended at busy times.

SUPPLEMENTS

Many countries have faster train services for which an extra charge is made. This supplement is payable when the ticket is purchased and often includes the price of a seat reservation. The supplement can sometimes be paid on the train, but usually at extra cost. The introduction to each country gives further information. On certain high-speed services, the first class fare includes the provision of a meal.

RAIL PASSES

Passes are available which give unlimited travel on most trains in a given area. These range from Interrail and Eurail passes which cover most of Europe for up to one month, to local passes which cover limited areas for one day. Further details of Interrail and Eurail passes appear elsewhere in this edition, and a special feature on rail passes appears in the twice-yearly Independent Travellers Edition.

FINDING YOUR TRAIN

At most stations departures are listed on large paper sheets (often yellow), and/or on electronic departure indicators. These list trains by departure, giving principal stops, and indicate from which platform they leave.

On each platform of principal European stations, a display board can be found giving details of the main trains calling at that platform. This includes the location of individual coaches, together with their destinations and the type of accommodation provided.

A sign may be carried on the side of the carriage indicating the train name, principal stops and destination and a label or sign near the door will indicate the number allocated to the carriage, which is shown on reservation tickets. 1st class accommodation is usually indicated by a yellow band above the windows and doors and/or a figure '1' near the door or on the windows

A sign above the compartment door will indicate seat numbers and which seats are reserved. In non-compartment trains, reserved seats have labels on their headrests. In some countries reserved seats are not marked and occupants will be asked to move when the passenger who has reserved the seat boards the train.

LUGGAGE & BICYCLES

Luggage may be registered at many larger stations and sent separately by rail to your destination. In some countries, bicycles may also be registered in advance and certain local and some express trains will convey bicycles (there may be a charge). The relevant railways will advise exact details on request.

✕ CATERING 🍸

Many high-quality and long-distance trains in Europe have restaurant cars serving full meals, usually with waiter service. An at-seat service may also be provided to passengers in first class accommodation. Such trains are identified with the symbol ✕ in the tables. Full meals may only be available at set times, sometimes with separate sittings, and may only be available to passengers holding first class tickets. However, the restaurant car is often supplemented by a counter or trolley service offering light snacks and drinks.

Other types of catering are shown with the symbol 🍸. This varies from a self-service buffet car serving light meals (sometimes called bistro or café) to a trolley which is wheeled through the train, serving drinks and light refreshments. Where possible, the introduction to each country gives further information on the level of catering to be expected on particular types of train.

Please note that the catering shown may not be available throughout the journey and may be suspended or altered at weekends or on holidays.

SLEEPING CARS 🛏

Sleeping cars are indicated by the symobol 🛏 in the tables. Standard sleeping car types have bedroom style compartments with limited washing facilities and full bedding. Toilets are located at one or both ends of the coach. An attendant travels with each car or pair of cars and will serve drinks, snacks and breakfast at an extra charge. Traditionally, 1st class sleeping compartments have one or two berths (in Britain and Norway two berth compartments require only 2nd class tickets) and 2nd class compartments have three berths. Some trains convey special T2 cabins, shown as 🛏 (T2) in the tables, with one berth in 1st class and two berths in 2nd class. On certain routes it is now possible to reserve a single compartment with a 2nd class ticket.

Compartments are allocated for occupation exclusively by men or by women except when married couples or families occupy all berths. Children travelling alone, or who cannot be accommodated in the same compartment as their family, are placed in women's compartments. In Russia and other countries of the CIS, however, berths are allocated in strict order of booking and men and women often share the same compartments.

Some trains have communicating doors between sleeping compartments which can be opened to create a larger room if both compartments are occupied by the same family group. Berths can be reserved up to 2 months (3 months on certain trains) before the date of travel and early reservation is recommended as space is often limited. Berths should be claimed within 15 minutes of boarding the train or they may be resold.

HOTEL TRAINS

High quality overnight trains, often referred to as Hotel trains, run on a selection of national and international routes. The facilities are of a higher standard than those offered in conventional sleeping cars, and special fares are payable. The trains fall into the following categories:

ÖBB nightjet: Many night trains radiating from Germany and Austria, are operated by Austrian Railways and are branded *ÖBB nightjet*. They operate on 17 routes serving four countries and all convey sleeping-car, couchette and seating accommodation. Standard sleeping-car compartments can be configured with one, two or three berths and have a washbasin (with toiletries provided). *Deluxe* sleeping-car compartments can also be configured with one, two or three berths and have an en-suite washroom with WC, washbasin and shower (shower gel and towels are provided). The sleeping-car fare includes a welcome drink, a bottle of water, a newspaper and a full breakfast served in the morning (including free hot drink refills). Four and six berth couchettes are available, the price of which includes a bottle of water and a small breakfast. Women only, family and wheelchair couchette compartments are provided. 2nd class seating cars (with six seat compartments) are also conveyed. Reservation is compulsory in all categories of accommodation and special all-inclusive fares are available. Please note that Interrail and Eurail pass holders must pay a special pass holders fare.

Trenhotel (Spain). These *Talgo*-type trains run on the international routes from Madrid to Lisboa and from Irún / Hendaye to Lisboa. They also operate on internal routes within Spain, from Barcelona to A Coruña, Granada and Vigo, and from Madrid to A Coruña, Ferrol and Pontevedra. The highest class of accommodation is *Gran Clase*, which has shower and toilet facilities in each compartment and can be used for single or double occupancy.

Compartments with showers are also available on some domestic overnight services in Sweden and Italy, and on certain other international routes as indicated on our international overnight services summary on page 35.

COUCHETTES ━

Couchettes (━) are a more basic form of overnight accommodation consisting of simple bunk beds with a sheet, blanket and pillow. The couchettes are converted from ordinary seating cars for the night, and there are usually 4 berths per compartment in 1st class, 6 berths in 2nd class. On certain trains (e.g. in Austria and Italy), 4 berth compartments are available to 2nd class passengers, at a higher supplement. Washing and toilet facilities are provided at the ends of each coach. Men and women are booked into the same compartments and are expected to sleep in daytime clothes. A small number of trains in Germany, however, have women-only couchette compartments.

INTERNATIONAL OVERNIGHT SERVICES

A summary of international overnight services will be found on page 35 which specifies the various types of accommodation and catering provided on each individual service (including details of the operator).

CAR-SLEEPERS

Trains which convey motor cars operate throughout much of Europe and are shown in Table **1** for international services and Table **2** for other services. The motor cars are conveyed in special wagons while passengers travel in sleeping cars or couchettes, usually (but not always) in the same train.

WHEELCHAIR ACCESS ♿

Most main-line domestic and international trains, together with an increasing number of local trains, are specially equipped to accommodate passengers in wheelchairs. Access ramps are available at many stations and some trains are fitted with special lifts. These trains have at least one wheelchair space, and are equipped with accessible toilets.

Most railways publish guides to accessibility, and many countries provide dedicated staff to assist disabled travellers. Wheelchair users normally need to reserve in advance, stating their requirements.

HEALTH REQUIREMENTS

It is not mandatory for visitors to Europe to be vaccinated against infectious diseases unless they are travelling from areas where these are endemic. For travellers' peace of mind, however, protection against the following diseases should be considered:

COVID-19	Measles / Rubella
Hepatitis A / B	Polio
HIV	Tetanus
Influenza	Tuberculosis

Full information is available from the manual published by the World Health Organisation, and travellers should seek advice from their Travel Agent.

DRINKING WATER

Tap water is usually safe to drink in most parts of Europe. The water in washrooms or toilets on trains is, however, not suitable for drinking. Those who doubt the purity of the tap water are recommended to boil it, to use sterilisation tablets, or to drink bottled water.

CLIMATE

Most of Europe lies within the temperate zone but there can be considerable differences between North and South, East and West, as illustrated in the table below. Local temperatures are also affected by altitude and the difference between summer and winter temperatures tends to be less marked in coastal regions than in areas far removed from the sea.

	Bucureşti	Dublin	Madrid	Moskva
JANUARY				
Highest	3°	8°	10°	− 6°
Lowest	− 5°	2°	3°	− 12°
Rain days	9	13	8	11
APRIL				
Highest	18°	12°	18°	10°
Lowest	5°	5°	8°	2°
Rain days	10	11	10	9
JULY				
Highest	30°	20°	32°	23°
Lowest	15°	12°	19°	14°
Rain days	10	11	3	12
OCTOBER				
Highest	18°	14°	19°	8°
Lowest	5°	7°	11°	2°
Rain days	8	12	10	10

Highest = Average highest daily temperature in °C
Lowest = Average lowest daily temperature in °C
Rain days = Average number of days with recorded precipitation

Source : World Weather Information Service

FIND US ON FACEBOOK!

www.facebook.com/EuropeanRailTimetable

and on **Twitter** @EuropeanRailTT

CURRENCY CONVERSION

The information shown below is intended to be indicative only. Rates fluctuate from day to day and commercial exchange rates normally include a commission element.

Country	unit	code	1 GBP =	1 USD =	1 EUR =	100 JPY =
Euro zone (‡)	**euro**	**EUR**	**1.17**	**0.93**	**1.00**	**0.73**
Albania	lek	ALL	142.61	112.92	121.21	88.77
Belarus	rubl	BYN	4.26	3.37	3.62	2.65
Bosnia	marka	BAM	2.30	1.82	1.95	1.43
Bulgaria	lev	BGN	2.30	1.82	1.95	1.43
Croatia	kuna	HRK	8.86	7.02	7.53	5.51
Czech Republic	koruna	CZK	29.05	23.00	24.69	18.08
Denmark	krone	DKK	8.75	6.92	7.43	5.44
Georgia	lari	GEL	3.61	2.86	3.07	2.25
Hungary	forint	HUF	463.77	367.20	394.15	288.67
Iceland	krona	ISK	162.34	128.54	137.97	101.05
Macedonia	denar	MKD	72.67	57.54	61.76	45.23
Moldova	leu	MDL	23.99	19.00	20.39	14.93
Norway	krone	NOK	11.95	9.46	10.15	7.43
Poland	złoty	PLN	5.37	4.25	4.57	3.34
Romania	leu	RON	5.81	4.60	4.94	3.62
Russia	ruble	RUB	83.98	66.49	71.37	59.27
Serbia	dinar	RSD	138.25	109.46	117.50	86.05
Sweden	krona	SEK	12.35	9.77	10.49	7.68
Switzerland	franc	CHF	1.20	0.95	1.02	0.75
Turkey	lira	TRY	20.51	16.23	17.43	12.76
Ukraine	hryvnya	UAH	37.47	29.67	31.85	23.32
United Kingdom	pound	GBP	1.00	0.79	0.84	0.62
United States	dollar	USD	1.26	1.00	1.07	0.78

‡ – Austria, Belgium, Cyprus, Estonia, Finland, France, Germany, Greece, Ireland, Italy, Latvia, Lithuania, Luxembourg, Malta, the Netherlands, Portugal, Slovakia, Slovenia and Spain.

The euro is also legal tender in Andorra, Kosovo, Monaco, Montenegro, San Marino, and the Vatican City.

PASSPORTS AND VISAS

Nationals of one country intending to travel to or pass through another country normally require a valid passport and will also require a visa unless a special visa-abolition agreement has been made between the countries concerned. The limit of stay permitted in each country is usually 3 months.

Applications for visas should be made well in advance of the date of travel to the local consulate of the country concerned. Consuls usually make a charge for issuing a visa. Before issuing a transit visa, a consul normally requires to see the visa of the country of destination.

The possession of a valid passport or visa does not necessarily grant the holder automatic access to all areas of the country to be visited. Certain countries have zones which are restricted or prohibited to foreign nationals.

All border controls have been abolished, however, between those countries which have signed the **Schengen Agreement** (see list below), and a visa allowing entry to any of these countries is valid in all of them.

LIST OF SCHENGEN AREA COUNTRIES

Austria, Belgium, Czech Republic, Denmark, Estonia, Finland, France, Germany, Greece, Hungary, Iceland, Italy, Latvia, Lithuania, Luxembourg, Malta, Netherlands, Norway, Poland, Portugal, Slovakia, Slovenia, Spain, Sweden, Switzerland.

METRIC CONVERSION TABLES

The Celsius system of temperature measurement, the metric system of distance measurement and the twenty-four hour clock are used throughout this book. The tables below give Fahrenheit, mile and twelve-hour clock equivalents.

TEMPERATURE

°C	°F
−20	−4
−15	5
−10	14
−5	23
0	32
5	41
10	50
15	59
20	68
25	77
30	86
35	95
40	104

Conversion formulae :
°C = (°F − 32) x 5 / 9
°F = (°C x 9 / 5) + 32

DISTANCE

km	miles	km	miles	km	miles
1	0.62	45	27.96	300	186.41
2	1.24	50	31.07	400	248.55
3	1.86	55	34.18	500	310.69
4	2.49	60	37.28	600	372.82
5	3.11	65	40.39	700	434.96
6	3.73	70	43.50	800	497.10
7	4.35	75	46.60	900	559.23
8	4.97	80	49.71	1000	621.37
9	5.59	85	52.82	1100	683.51
10	6.21	90	55.92	1200	745.65
15	9.32	95	59.03	1300	807.78
20	12.43	100	62.14	1400	869.92
25	15.53	125	77.67	1500	932.06
30	18.64	150	93.21	2000	1242.74
35	21.75	175	108.74	3000	1864.11
40	24.85	200	124.27	4000	2485.48

TIME

Midnight departure	= 0000
1 am	= 0100
5 am	= 0500
5.30 am	= 0530
11 am	= 1100
12 noon	= 1200
1 pm	= 1300
3.45 pm	= 1545
Midnight arrival	= 2400

GLOSSARY

O┳	FRANCAIS	ITALIANO	DEUTSCH	ESPAÑOL
additional trains	d'autres trains	ulteriori treni	weitere Züge	otros trenes
also	[circule] aussi	[si effettua] anche	[verkehrt] auch	[circula] también
alteration	modification	variazione	Änderung	modificación
approximately	environ	circa	ungefähr	aproximadamente
arrival, arrives (a.)	arrivée, arrive	arrivo, arriva	Ankunft, kommt an	llegada, llega
and at the same minutes past each hour until	puis toutes les heures aux mêmes minutes jusqu'à	poi ai stessi minuti di ogni ora fino a	und so weiter im Takt bis	luego a los mismos minutos de cada hora hasta
calls at	s'arrête à	ferma a	hält in	efectúa parada en
certain	déterminé	certo	bestimmt	determinado
change at	changer à	cambiare a	umsteigen in	cambiar en
composition	composition	composizione	Zugbildung	composición
confirmation	confirmation	conferma	Bestätigung	confirmación
connection	correspondance, relation	coincidenza, relazione	Anschluss, Verbindung	correspondencia, enlace
conveys	comporte, achemine	ha in composizione	befördert, führt	lleva
daily	tous les jours	giornalmente	täglich	diariamente
delay	retard	ritardo	Verspätung	retraso
departure, departs (d.)	départ, part	partenza, parte	Abfahrt, fährt ab	salida, sale
earlier	plus tôt	più presto	früher	más temprano
engineering work	travaux de voie	lavori sul binario	Bauarbeiten	obras de vía
even / uneven dates	jours pairs / impairs	giorni pari / dispari	gerade / ungerade Daten	fechas pares / impares
every 30 minutes	toutes les 30 minutes	ogni 30 minuti	alle 30 Minuten	cada 30 minutos
except	sauf	escluso	außer	excepto
fast(er)	(plus) rapide	(più) rapido	schnell(er)	(más) rápido
for	pour	per	für	para
from Rennes	(en provenance) de Rennes	(proviene) da Rennes	von Rennes	(procede) de Rennes
from Jan. 15	à partir du 15 janvier	dal 15 di gennaio	vom 15. Januar (an)	desde el 15 de enero
hourly	toutes les heures	ogni ora	stündlich	cada hora
hours (hrs)	heures	ore	Stunden	horas
journey	voyage, trajet	viaggio, percorso	Reise	viaje, trayecto
journey time	temps de parcours	tempo di tragitto	Reisezeit	duración del recorrido
later	plus tard	più tardi	später	más tarde
may	peut, peuvent	può, possono	kann, können	puede(n)
minutes (mins)	minutes	minuti	Minuten	minutos
not	ne [circule] pas	non [si effettua]	[verkehrt] nicht	no [circula]
not available	pas disponible	non disponibile	nicht erhältlich	no disponible
on the dates shown in Table **81**	les jours indiqués dans le tableau **81**	nei giorni indicati nel quadro **81**	an den in der Tabelle **81** angegebene Daten	los días indicados en el cuadro **81**
only	seulement	esclusivamente	nur	sólo
operator	entreprise de transports	azienda di trasporto	Verkehrsunternehmen	empresa de transportes
other	autre	altro	andere	otros
runs	circule	circola, si effettua	verkehrt	circula
sailing	traversée	traversata	Überfahrt	travesía
ship	bateau, navire	nave, battello	Schiff	barco
stopping trains	trains omnibus	treni regionali	Nahverkehrszüge	trenes regionales
stops	s'arrête	ferma	hält	efectúa parada
subject to	sous réserve de	soggetto a	vorbehaltlich	sujeto a
summer	été	estate	Sommer	verano
supplement payable	avec supplément	con pagamento di supplemento	zuschlagpflichtig	con pago de suplemento
then	puis	poi	dann	luego
through train	train direct	treno diretto	durchgehender Zug	tren directo
timings	horaires	orari	Zeitangaben	horarios
to York	vers, à destination de York	(diretto) a York	nach York	(continúa) a York
to / until July 23	jusqu'au 23 juillet	fino al 23 di luglio	bis zum 23. Juli	hasta el día 23 de julio
to pick up	pour laisser monter	per viaggiatori in partenza	zum Zusteigen	para recoger viajeros
to set down	pour laisser descendre	per viaggiatori in arrivo	zum Aussteigen	para dejar viajeros
unless otherwise shown	sauf indication contraire	salvo indicazione contraria	sofern nicht anders angezeigt	salvo indicación contraria
valid	valable	valido	gültig	válido
when train **44** runs	lors de la circulation du train **44**	quando circola il treno **44**	beim Verkehren des Zuges **44**	cuando circula el tren **44**
winter	hiver	inverno	Winter	invierno

INDEX OF PLACES by table number

The BEYOND EUROPE section is indexed separately - see the back of each edition

🚌 Connection by train from the nearest station shown in this timetable.
⛴ Connection by boat from the nearest station shown in this timetable.
🚌 Connection by bus from the nearest station shown in this timetable.
10/355 Consult both indicated tables to find the best connecting services.

CRUISE TRAINS

The services shown in the European Rail Timetable are the regular scheduled services of the railway companies concerned. However, a number of specialised operators also run luxurious cruise trains taking several days to complete their journey. Overnight accommodation is provided either on the train or in hotels. Cruise trains are bookable only through the operating company or its appointed agents and normal rail tickets are not valid on these trains. A selection of operators is shown below.

The Danube Express : Fully escorted holidays in central and eastern Europe by luxury private train based in Budapest. Operator: Danube Express, Offley Holes Farm, Charlton Road, Preston, Hitchin, SG4 7TD, UK; ✆ +44 (0)1462 441400. Website: www.danube-express.com

Belmond Royal Scotsman : Luxury tours of Scotland starting from Edinburgh. Operator: Belmond Royal Scotsman, Shackleton House, 4 Battle Bridge Lane, London, SE1 2HP, UK; ✆ 0845 217 0799 (UK only) or +44 (0) 20 3117 1300. Website: www.royalscotsman.com

El Transcantábrico and **El Expreso de La Robla** : Rail cruises along Spain's northern coast. Operator: Trenes Turísticos de Lujo, Plaza de los Ferroviarios s/n., 33012 Oviedo, Asturias, Spain; ✆ +34 902 555 902, fax +34 985 981 711. Website: www.trenesturisticosdelujo.com

Trans-Siberian Express : Tours by private hotel train along the Trans-Siberian Railway. Operator: Golden Eagle Luxury Trains, Denzell House, Denzell Gardens, Dunham Road, Altrincham, WA14 4QF, UK; ✆ +44 (0)16 1 928 9410, fax +44 (0)161 941 6101. Website: www.goldeneagleluxurytrains.com.

Venice Simplon-Orient-Express : This well-known luxury train runs once or twice weekly from late March to early November, mostly on its established London - Paris - Venezia route. Operator: Belmond VSOE, Shackleton House, 4 Battle Bridge Lane, London, SE1 2HP, UK; ✆ 0845 217 0799 (UK only) or +44 (0) 20 3117 1300. Website: www.vsoe.com

LIST OF ADVERTISERS

Advertiser	Pages
AERA	79, 112, 155, 159, 327, 403
BAHNREISEN SUTTER	52, 561
COOL CULINARIA	59, 76
ECONEX	inside front cover
EUROPE BY RAIL	563, 674
EUROPEAN RAIL TIMETABLE	12, 521, back cover
HIDDEN EUROPE	100, 313, inside back cover
LOCOMOTIVES INTERNATIONAL	58, 77, 105, 328
MIDDLETON PRESS	560
MILLSTONE CREATIVE	47, 56, 80, 316, 560
RAILBOOKERS	65, 67, 106, 282
ROVOS RAIL	57, 73

LIST OF RETAILERS

The European Rail Timetable is available for purchase direct from the retailers listed below. Some also stock the Rail Map Europe.

Great Britain

Blackwell's Bookshop	Oxford
Daunt Books	Six stores in London
Foyles	London and Birmingham
Magazine Heaven	Rushden Lakes, Northamptonshire
Stanfords	London and Bristol
Tornado Books & Hobbies	Birmingham

Austria

Buchhandlung und Antiquariat	Wien
Freytag & Berndt	Wien

Belgium

Press Shop / Relay	Brugge railway station

France

La Librairie du Voyage	Rennes
Smith&Son (formerly WHSmith)	Paris, 248 Rue de Rivoli

Germany

FachBuchZentrum & Antiquariat Stiletto	München Neuhausen
Freytag & Berndt	Regensburg and Nürnberg
Gleisnost Reisebuero	Freiburg railway station
GVE-Verlag / BahnBuchShop	Berlin Lichtenberg railway station info@gve-verlag.de
Dussmann das Kulturkaufhaus	Berlin, Friedrichstraße 90
Schropp Maps	Berlin, Hardenbergstraße 9a

Italy

Anglo-American Bookshop	Roma

Netherlands

Stanley & Livingstone	Den Haag
The American Book Center	Amsterdam
Treinreiswinkel	Amsterdam and Leiden

Switzerland

Fahrplancenter	Winterthur, Switzerland

CITY STATION LOCATION PLANS

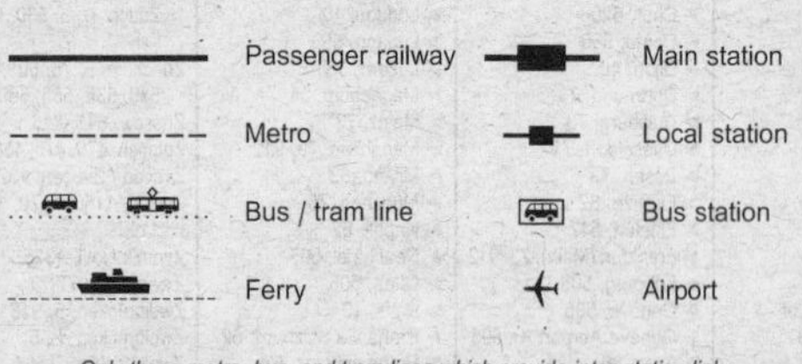

Only those metro, bus, and tram lines which provide inter-station links or connect outlying main stations to the city centre are shown.

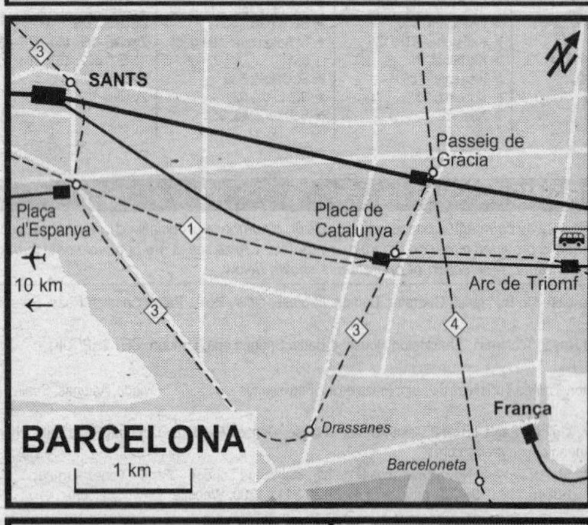

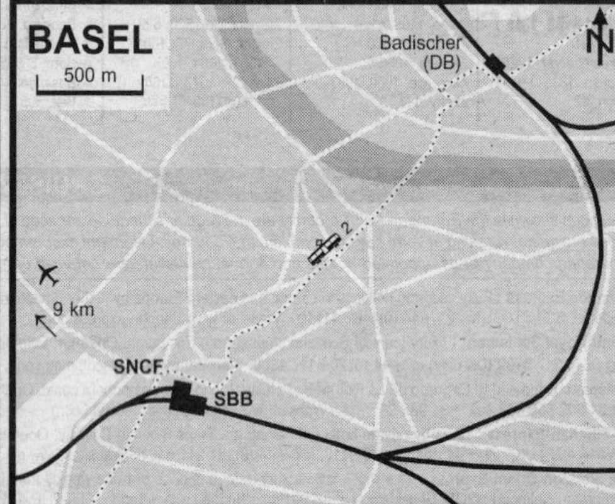

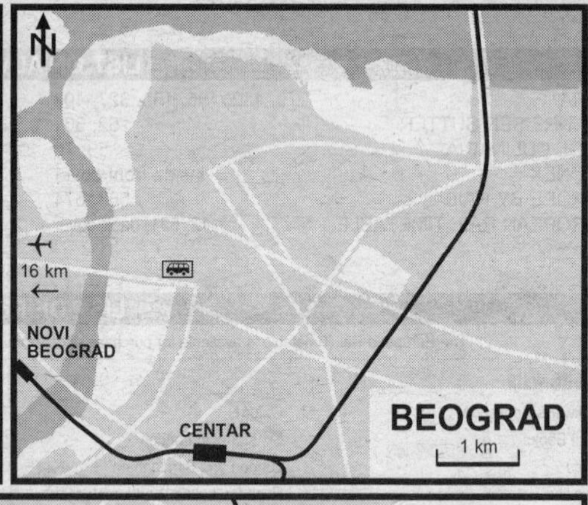

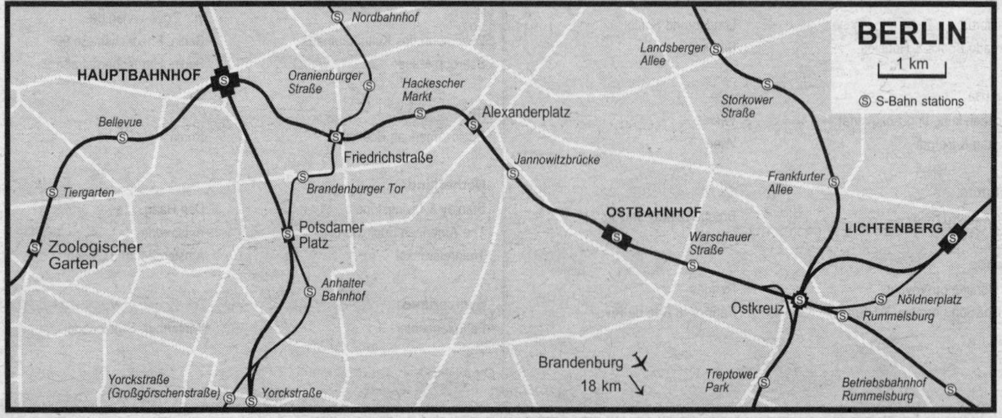

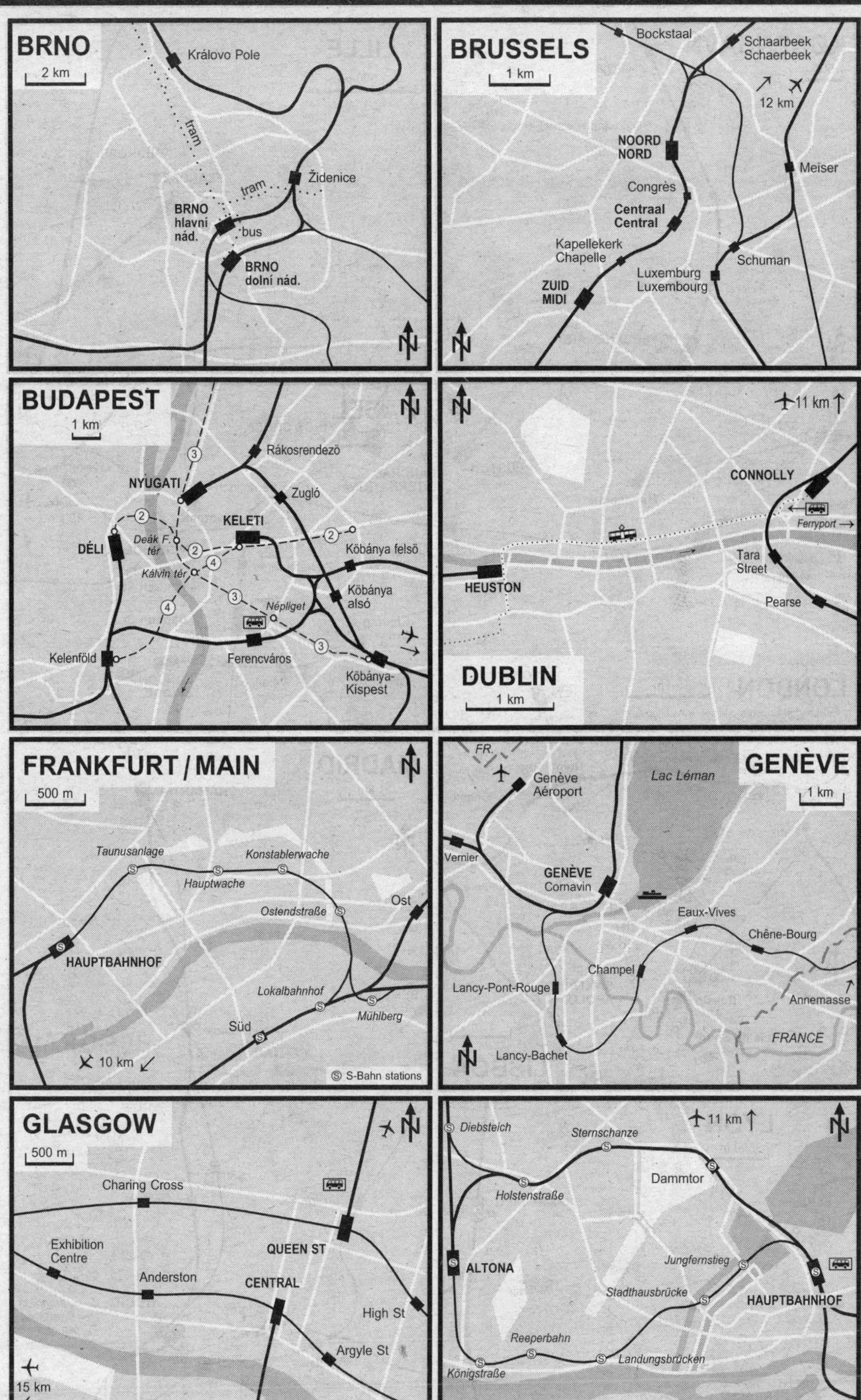
BRNO
2 km
Královo Pole
tram
Židenice
tram
BRNO hlavní nád.
bus
BRNO dolní nád.
BRUSSELS
1 km
Bockstaal
Schaarbeek Schaerbeek
12 km
NOORD NORD
Meiser
Congrès
Centraal Central
Kapellekerk Chapelle
Schuman
Luxemburg Luxembourg
ZUID MIDI
BUDAPEST
1 km
Rákosrendező
NYUGATI
Zugló
KELETI
DÉLI
Deák F. tér
Kálvin tér
Kőbánya felső
Kőbánya alsó
Népliget
Kelenföld
Ferencváros
Kőbánya-Kispest
11 km
CONNOLLY
Ferryport
HEUSTON
Tara Street
Pearse
DUBLIN
1 km
FRANKFURT / MAIN
500 m
Taunusanlage
Konstablerwache
Hauptwache
Ostendstraße
Ost
HAUPTBAHNHOF
Lokalbahnhof
Mühlberg
Süd
10 km
S-Bahn stations
FR.
Genève Aéroport
Lac Léman
GENÈVE
1 km
Vernier
GENÈVE Cornavin
Eaux-Vives
Chêne-Bourg
Champel
Lancy-Pont-Rouge
Annemasse
FRANCE
Lancy-Bachet
GLASGOW
500 m
Charing Cross
Exhibition Centre
QUEEN ST
Anderston
CENTRAL
High St
Argyle St
15 km
Diebsteich
11 km
Sternschanze
Dammtor
Holstenstraße
ALTONA
Jungfernstieg
Stadthausbrücke
HAUPTBAHNHOF
Reeperbahn
Landungsbrücken
Königstraße
HAMBURG
1 km
S-Bahn stations

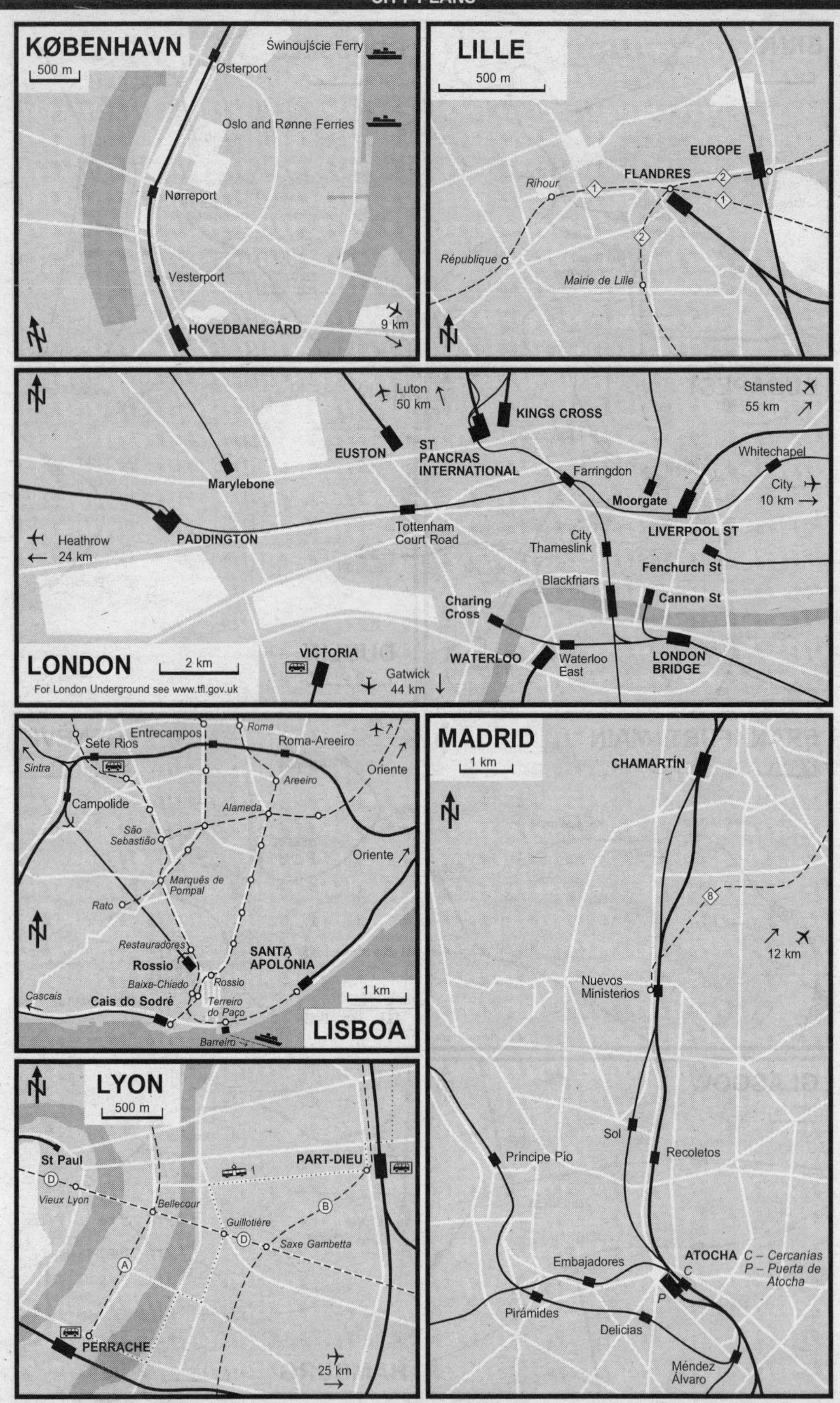
KØBENHAVN
500 m
Świnoujście Ferry
Østerport
Oslo and Rønne Ferries
Nørreport
Vesterport
HOVEDBANEGÅRD
9 km
LILLE
500 m
EUROPE
FLANDRES
Rihour
République
Mairie de Lille
LONDON
2 km
For London Underground see www.tfl.gov.uk
Luton
50 km
Stansted
55 km
KINGS CROSS
EUSTON
ST PANCRAS INTERNATIONAL
Marylebone
Farringdon
Whitechapel
City
10 km
Moorgate
LIVERPOOL ST
Heathrow
24 km
PADDINGTON
Tottenham Court Road
City Thameslink
Fenchurch St
Blackfriars
Cannon St
Charing Cross
VICTORIA
WATERLOO
Waterloo East
LONDON BRIDGE
Gatwick
44 km
Entrecampos
Roma
Sete Rios
Roma-Areeiro
Sintra
Oriente
Areeiro
Campolide
Alameda
São Sebastião
Oriente
Marquês de Pombal
Rato
Restauradores
Rossio
SANTA APOLÓNIA
Baixa-Chiado
Rossio
Cascais
Cais do Sodré
Terreiro do Paço
1 km
LISBOA
Barreiro
LYON
500 m
St Paul
PART-DIEU
Vieux Lyon
Bellecour
Guillotière
Saxe Gambetta
PERRACHE
25 km
MADRID
1 km
CHAMARTÍN
12 km
Nuevos Ministerios
Sol
Recoletos
Príncipe Pío
ATOCHA
C – Cercanías
P – Puerta de Atocha
Embajadores
Pirámides
Delicias
Méndez Álvaro

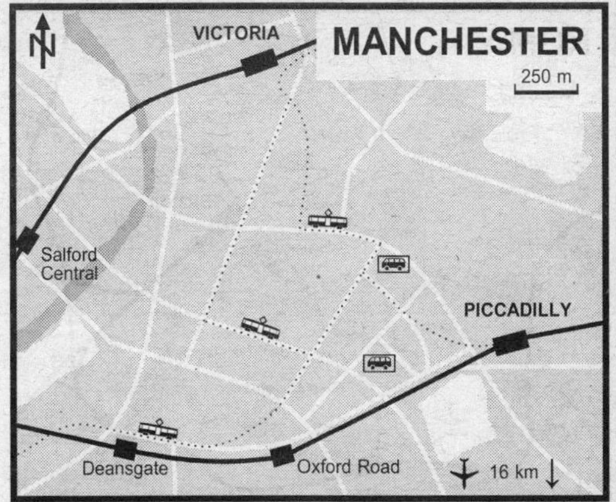
MANCHESTER
250 m
VICTORIA
Salford Central
PICCADILLY
Deansgate
Oxford Road
16 km

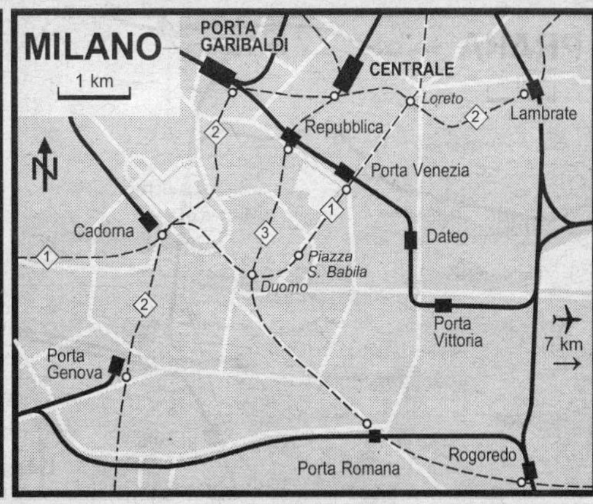
MILANO
1 km
PORTA GARIBALDI
CENTRALE
Loreto
Lambrate
Repubblica
Porta Venezia
Cadorna
Dateo
Piazza S. Babila
Duomo
Porta Vittoria
7 km
Porta Genova
Porta Romana
Rogoredo

27 km
Savyolovsky
Rizhskaya
Yaroslavskaya
BELORUSSKAYA
(Smolenskaya)
OKTYABRSKAYA
(Leningradski vokzal)
Komsomolskaya
Kazanskaya
Kurskaya
KIYEVSKAYA
Paveletskaya
MOSKVA
1 km

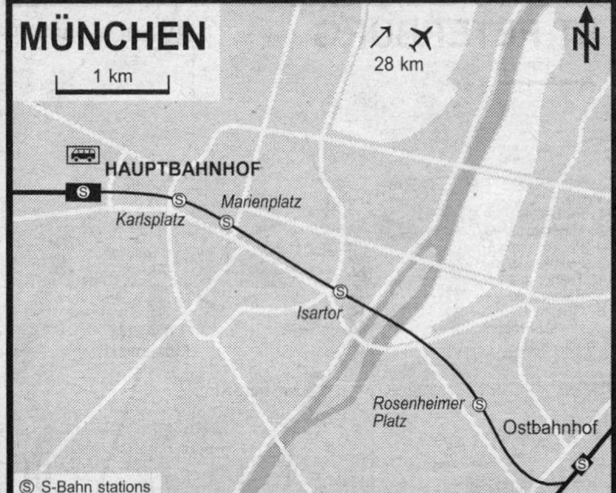
MÜNCHEN
1 km
28 km
HAUPTBAHNHOF
Marienplatz
Karlsplatz
Isartor
Rosenheimer Platz
Ostbahnhof
S-Bahn stations

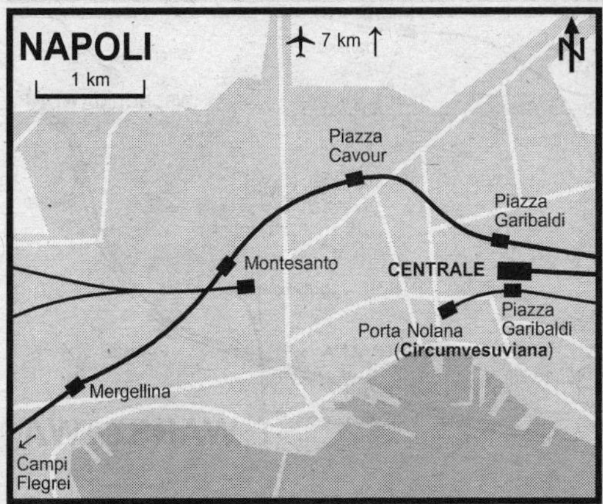
NAPOLI
1 km
7 km
Piazza Cavour
Piazza Garibaldi
Montesanto
CENTRALE
Porta Nolana
(Circumvesuviana)
Piazza Garibaldi
Mergellina
Campi Flegrei

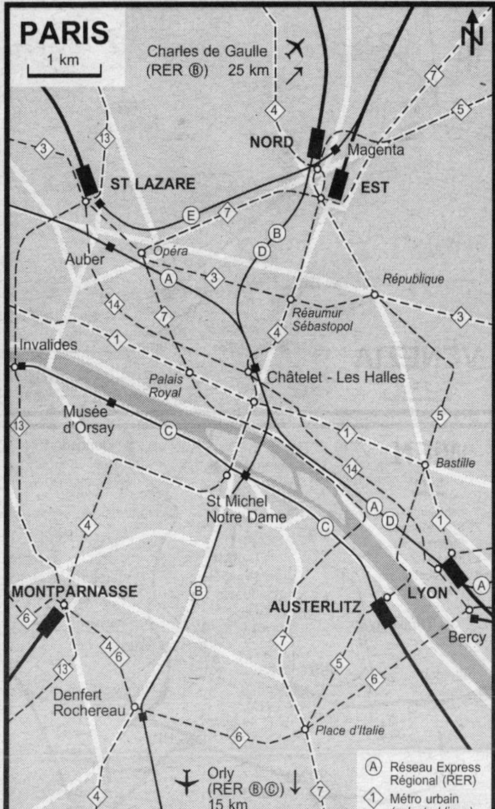
PARIS
1 km
Charles de Gaulle
(RER B) 25 km
NORD
Magenta
ST LAZARE
EST
Opéra
Auber
République
Réaumur Sébastopol
Invalides
Châtelet - Les Halles
Palais Royal
Musée d'Orsay
Bastille
St Michel Notre Dame
MONTPARNASSE
AUSTERLITZ
LYON
Bercy
Denfert Rochereau
Place d'Italie
Orly
(RER B C)
15 km
Réseau Express Régional (RER)
Métro urbain (selected lines)

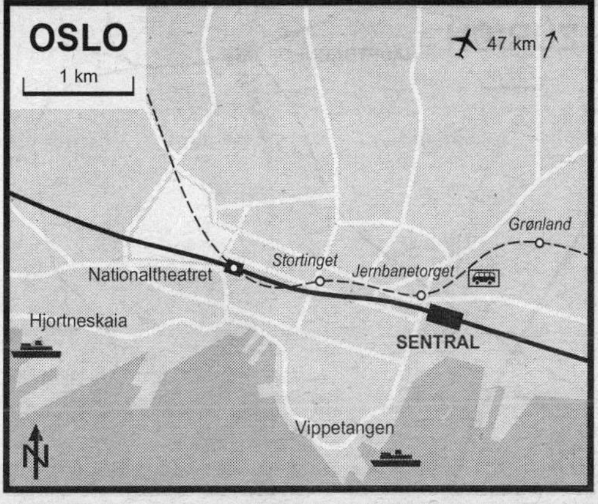
OSLO
1 km
47 km
Grønland
Stortinget
Jernbanetorget
Nationaltheatret
Hjortneskaia
SENTRAL
Vippetangen

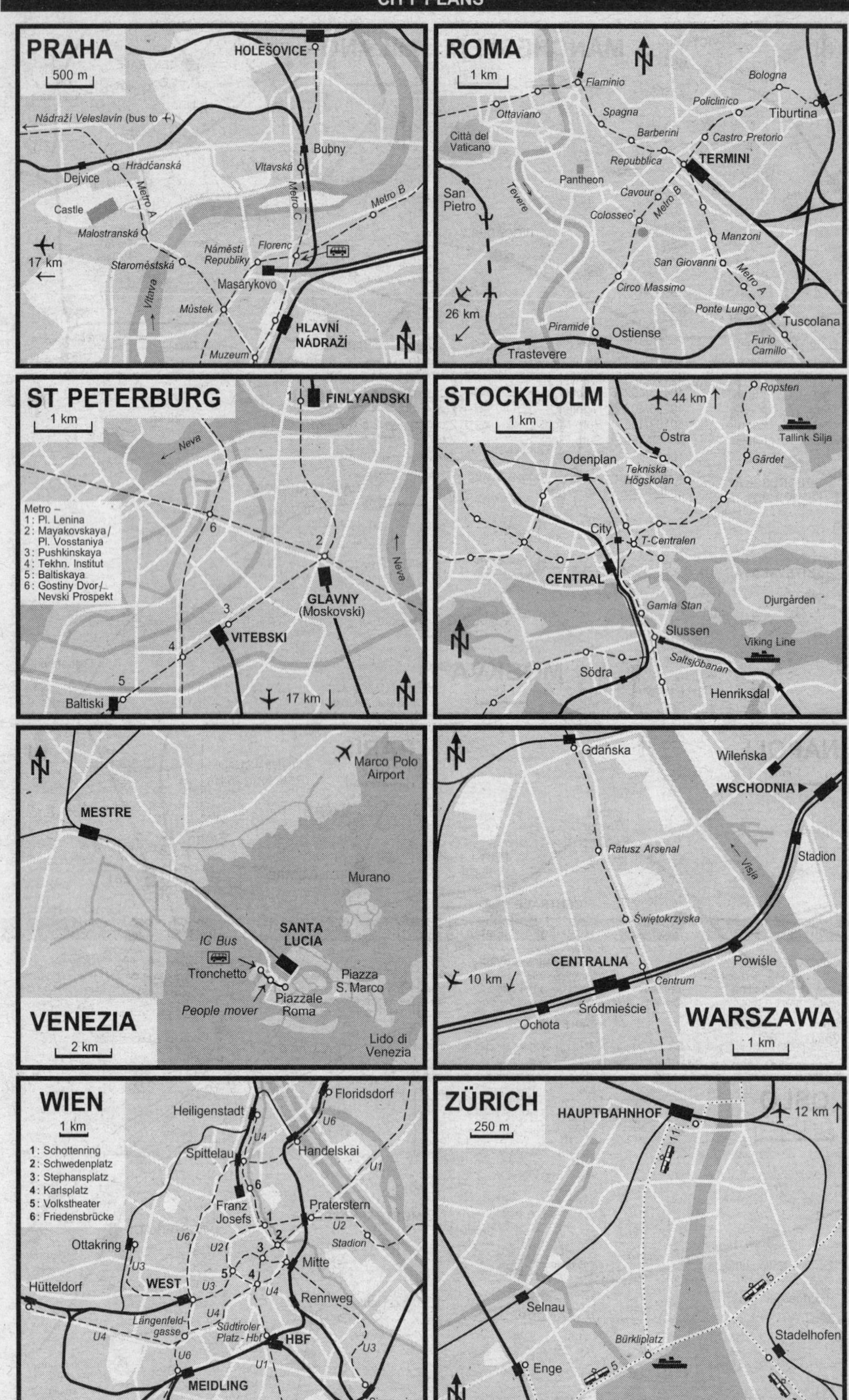
PRAHA
500 m
HOLEŠOVICE
Nádraží Veleslavín (bus to ✈)
Bubny
Dejvice
Hradčanská
Vltavská
Metro A
Metro C
Metro B
Castle
Malostranská
17 km
Staroměstská
Náměstí Republiky
Florenc
Vltava
Masarykovo
Můstek
HLAVNÍ NÁDRAŽÍ
Muzeum
ROMA
1 km
Flaminio
Bologna
Policlinico
Ottaviano
Spagna
Tiburtina
Città del Vaticano
Barberini
Castro Pretorio
Repubblica
TERMINI
Pantheon
San Pietro
Tevere
Cavour
Metro B
Colosseo
Manzoni
San Giovanni
Metro A
Circo Massimo
26 km
Ponte Lungo
Tuscolana
Piramide
Ostiense
Furio Camillo
Trastevere
ST PETERBURG
1 km
FINLYANDSKI
Neva
Metro –
1: Pl. Lenina
2: Mayakovskaya / Pl. Vosstaniya
3: Pushkinskaya
4: Tekhn. Institut
5: Baltiskaya
6: Gostiny Dvor / Nevski Prospekt
GLAVNY (Moskovski)
VITEBSKI
Baltiski
17 km
STOCKHOLM
1 km
44 km
Ropsten
Östra
Tallink Silja
Odenplan
Tekniska Högskolan
Gärdet
City
T-Centralen
CENTRAL
Gamla Stan
Djurgården
Slussen
Viking Line
Saltsjöbanan
Södra
Henriksdal
MESTRE
Marco Polo Airport
Murano
IC Bus
SANTA LUCIA
Tronchetto
Piazza S. Marco
Piazzale Roma
People mover
VENEZIA
2 km
Lido di Venezia
Gdańska
Wileńska
WSCHODNIA ▶
Ratusz Arsenal
Stadion
Wisła
Świętokrzyska
CENTRALNA
Powiśle
10 km
Centrum
Śródmieście
Ochota
WARSZAWA
1 km
WIEN
1 km
Floridsdorf
Heiligenstadt
U6
U4
Handelskai
Spittelau
U1
1: Schottenring
2: Schwedenplatz
3: Stephansplatz
4: Karlsplatz
5: Volkstheater
6: Friedensbrücke
Franz Josefs
Praterstern
U2
Stadion
Ottakring
Mitte
U3
WEST
Hütteldorf
Rennweg
Längenfeld-gasse
Südtiroler Platz - Hbf
HBF
U1
MEIDLING
Simmering
ZÜRICH
250 m
HAUPTBAHNHOF
12 km
Selnau
Bürkliplatz
Stadelhofen
Enge

SELECTED DAILY INTERNATIONAL SLEEPER SERVICES

From	To	Train no.	Brand	Facilities and owner	Train Name	International table no.
Amsterdam	Zürich	403/402	Nightjet	🛏 1, 2 cl.(öbb), ▬ 2 cl.(öbb)		73
Amsterdam	Wien	40421/40490	Nightjet	🛏 1, 2 cl. 🚿(öbb), ▬ 2 cl.(öbb)		73
München	Budapest	463/462	Euro Night	🛏 1, 2 cl.(mav), ▬ 2 cl.(mav)	Kálmán Imre	32, 65
Wien	Bucureşti	347/346	Euro Night	🛏 1, 2 cl.(cfr), ▬ 2 cl.(cfr), ✕(cfr)	Dacia	32, 61
Wien	Bucureşti	50347/349	Euro Night	🛏 1, 2 cl.(cfr)		61
Budapest	Bucureşti	473/472	Euro Night	🛏 1, 2 cl.(cfr), ▬ 1, 2 cl.(cfr)	Ister	32, 61
Irún / Hendaye	Lisboa	312/310	Trenhotel talgo	🛏 1, 2 cl. 🚿(renfe), ✕(renfe)	Surex / Sud Expresso	45
Lisboa	Madrid	335/332	Trenhotel talgo	🛏 1, 2 cl. 🚿(renfe), ✕(renfe)	Lusitania	45
Zürich	Praha	50467/50466	Euro Night	🛏 1, 2 cl. 🚿(čd)		52
Berlin	Zürich	471/470	Nightjet	🛏 1, 2 cl. 🚿(öbb), ▬ 2 cl.(öbb)		54, 73
Berlin	Wien	457/456	Nightjet	🛏 1, 2 cl. 🚿(öbb), ▬ 2 cl.(öbb)	Metropol	77
Berlin	Budapest	40457 / 40476	Nightjet	🛏 1, 2 cl. (mav), ▬ 2 cl.(mav)	Metropol	77
Berlin	Przemyśl	60457/60456		🛏 1, 2 cl.(pkp)		77
Warszawa	Kyiv	68/67		🛏 1, 2 cl.(uz)	Kyiv Ekspres	56
Praha	Budapest	573-477/476-572	Euro Night	🛏 1, 2 cl. 🚿(čd), ▬ 2 cl.(čd)	Metropol	60
Budapest	Beograd	341/340		🛏 1, 2 cl.(žs), ▬ 2 cl.(žs)		61
Beograd	Thessaloníki	335/334		▬ 2 cl.(mz)	Hellas Express	61
Bucuresti	istanbul	461/492		▬ 2 cl. 4-berth (tcdd)	Bosphor	61
Hamburg	Wien	491/490	Nightjet	🛏 1, 2 cl. 🚿(öbb), ▬ 2 cl.(öbb)		53, 64
Hamburg	Zürich	401/40470	Nightjet	🛏 1, 2 cl. 🚿(öbb), ▬ 2 cl.(öbb)		54, 73
Hamburg	Innsbruck	40491/40420	Nightjet	🛏 1, 2 cl. 🚿(öbb), ▬ 2 cl.(öbb)		53, 64
München	Roma	295/294	Nightjet	🛏 1, 2 cl. 🚿(db), ▬ 2 cl.(db)		70
München	Venezia	40463/40236	Nightjet	🛏 1, 2 cl. 🚿(db), ▬ 2 cl.(db)		70
München	Milano	40295/40235	Nightjet	🛏 1, 2 cl. 🚿(db), ▬ 2 cl.(db)		70
München	Zagreb	50463/498	Euro Night	🛏 1, 2 cl.(hz), ▬ 2 cl.(hz)		86
München	Rijeka	60463/469	Euro Night	🛏 1, 2 cl.(hz)		62
Zürich	Zagreb	40465/40414	Euro Night	🛏 1, 2 cl.(hz), ▬ 2 cl.(hz)		86
Zürich	Budapest	40467/40462	Euro Night	🛏 1, 2 cl.(mav), ▬ 2 cl.(mav)		86
Zürich	Graz	465/464	Nightjet	🛏 1, 2 cl. 🚿(öbb), ▬ 2 cl.(öbb)		86
Zürich	Wien	467/466	Nightjet	🛏 1, 2 cl. 🚿(öbb), ▬ 2 cl.(öbb)		86
Wien	Roma	40233/40294	Nightjet	🛏 1, 2 cl. 🚿(öbb), ▬ 2 cl.(öbb)		88
Wien	Venezia	40466/236	Nightjet	🛏 1, 2 cl. 🚿(öbb), ▬ 2 cl.(öbb)		88
Wien	Milano	233/235	Nightjet	🛏 1, 2 cl.(ti), ▬ 2 cl.(ti)		88
Košice	Kyiv	8813-29/81-8812		🛏 1, 2 cl.(uz)		96
Wien	Kyiv	40147/40749		🛏 1, 2 cl.(uz)	Hortobágy	96
Warszawa	Budapest	407-457-477 / 476-456-406		🛏 1, 2 cl.(pkp), ▬ 2 cl.(pkp)		99
Warszawa	Wien	407/40456		🛏 1, 2 cl. 🚿(pkp)	Chopin	99
Warszawa	Praha	407-442 / 443-406		🛏 1, 2 cl.(pkp), ▬ 2 cl.(pkp)		99
Helsinki	Moskva	31/32	Firménny	🛏 1, 2 cl. 🚿(rzd), ✕	Lev Tolstoi	1910
Non daily sleepers (other seasonal services operate):						
Düsseldorf	Wien	40421/40490	Nightjet	🛏 1, 2 cl. 🚿(öbb), ▬ 2 cl.(öbb)		28, 53, 66
Düsseldorf	Innsbruck	421/420	Nightjet	🛏 1, 2 cl. 🚿(öbb), ▬ 2 cl.(öbb)		28, 53
Brussels	Wien	425/50490	Nightjet	🛏 1, 2 cl. 🚿(öbb), ▬ 2 cl.(öbb)		21, 53
Paris	Wien	469/468	Nightjet	🛏 1, 2 cl. 🚿(öbb), ▬ 2 cl.(öbb)		32
Amsterdam	Innsbruck	421/420	Nightjet	🛏 1, 2 cl. 🚿(öbb), ▬ 2 cl.(öbb)		28, 53
Berlin	Malmö	301/300	Euro Night	▬ 2 cl.(bne)	Berlin Night Express	50
Paris	Moskva	24/23	Euro Night	🛏 1, 2 cl. 🚿(rzd), ✕(pkp, rzd)	Trans European Express	24
Nice	Moskva	18/17		🛏 1, 2 cl. 🚿(rzd), ✕(pkp, rzd)		25
Praha	Moskva	22/21		🛏 1, 2 cl.(rzd)	Vltavà	95
Warszawa	Moskva	10/9		🛏 1, 2 cl.(rzd)	Polonez	56
Berlin	Moskva	14/13		🛏 1, 2 cl.(rzd)		56

Note: This list excludes trains not shown in our International section (e.g. Czech Republic to Slovakia, Ukraine to Russia).

Key to ownership of sleeping cars: bdz - Bulgarian; bc - Belarussian; bne - Berlin Night Express; cd - Czech; cfr - Romanian; db - German; hz - Croatian; mav - Hungarian; mz - Macedonian; öbb - Austrian; pkp - Polish; renfe - Spanish; rzd - Russian; sbb - Swiss; ti - Italian; uz - Ukrainian; zs - Serbian.

🚿 – Shower.

Shaded services are suspended until further notice.

Steam trains in the European Rail Timetable

There are numerous tourist and heritage lines operating around Europe, most of which operate a seasonal service using steam or heritage diesel traction. Unfortunately, space limitations mean that we are unable to show timings for most of these lines. However, there are a number of routes that offer a daily service throughout the year and for these we do include timings, together with a few services hauled by steam traction on main-line rail routes. The panel below lists tourist railway **steam** train schedules that are included in our regular timetable pages.

Readers should note that our expanded seasonal editions (published in March, June, September and December) provide details of many other tourist railways in our special ***Rail Extra*** feature, including a brief description of selected routes and an overview of the service provided. The feature also includes other useful rail travel information on a country by country basis.

COUNTRY	RAILWAY	TABLE	NOTES
GREAT BRITAIN	The Shakespeare Express	**127**	Regular summer Sunday main-line steam excursions between Stratford upon Avon and Birmingham
	Ffestiniog / Welsh Highland Railways	**160**	Two narrow gauge railways linked at Porthmadog running through spectacular Welsh mountain landscapes
	North Yorkshire Moors Railway	**211**	Regular services run from spring to autumn, many steam-hauled through to Whitby via a link to the main line at Grosmont
	The Jacobite	**218**	A regular main-line steam excursion operating from spring to autumn over the spectacular West Highland line
FRANCE	Train des Pignes	**359**	A summer Sunday steam-hauled service running over part of the scenic Nice to Digne route
SWITZERLAND	Brienz Rothorn Bahn	**553**	A swiss mountain rack railway operating regular steam services from June to October
PORTUGAL	Comboio Historico	**694**	Enjoy a steam-hauled journey along the scenic Douro Valley between Régua and Tua at weekends from June to October
SWEDEN	Arvidsjaur Järnvägsförening	**766**	Operates twice a week from mid-July to early August over a section of the Inlandsbanan (Arvidsjaur - Slagnäs)
GERMANY	Rügensche Bäderbahn	**844a**	Daily steam services on the island of Rügen
	Lößnitzgrundbahn	**853**	Daily steam services between Radebeul Ost and Radeburg (near Dresden)
	Weißeritztalbahn	**853**	Daily steam services between Freital-Hainsberg and Kurort Kipsdorf (near Dresden)
	Zittauer Schmalspurbahn	**853**	Daily steam services between Zittau and Kurort Jonsdorf / Kurort Oybin
	Harzer Schmalspurbahnen	**867**	A famous narrow gauge network in central Germany with some services steam-hauled on a daily basis
	Fichtelbergbahn	**882**	Daily steam services between Cranzahl and Kurort Oberwiesenthal
AUSTRIA	Zillertalbahn	**955**	A single return steam service runs on selected days from May to October
	Achenseebahn	**956**	A narrow gauge steam rack railway with daily services running May to October
	Pinzgauer Lokalbahn	**957**	A single return steam service runs once or twice a week at certain times of the year
	Schneebergbahn	**984**	Most service are operated by modern diesel trains but a steam service also runs on Sundays during the summer
	Mariazellerbahn	**994**	An occasional steam service runs along this world famous mountain route (also a service hauled by heritage electric traction)
	Murtalbahn	**998**	Steam trains run between Murau and Tamsweg once or twice a week during the summer
POLAND	Koleje Wielkopolskie	**1099**	The popular scheduled steam services operating on the Wolsztyn to Poznań and Wolsztyn to Leszno routes
CZECH REPUBLIC	Jindřichohradecké Místní Dráhy	**1169**	A steam train runs on Saturdays from April to September (daily during July and August)

NEWSLINES *(continued from page 5)*

SPAIN

A new early morning *Media Distancia* service in each direction between Jaén and Córdoba has been introduced (Table **661**).

All *Avant* services between Madrid and Toledo have been reinstated (Table **679**). A number of *Avant* services have also returned on the Madrid – Ciudad Real – Puertollano route (Table **660**). An additional *AVE* service was introduced between Madrid and Sevilla from June 1 with a further addition planned from July 15. An extra *AVE* between Madrid and Málaga will also be provided from July 15 (Table **660**).

During the summer period a pair of InterCity services will run between Madrid and Huelva (Table **671**).

Certain services on the Bilbao – Santander, Santander – Oviedo and Oviedo – Ferrol routes have been retimed (Table **687**).

We understand the high-speed line between Plasencia and Mérida could open this month (Table **677**) and the high-speed line between Venta de Baños and Burgos (Table **689**) could open in July. However, we also understand that the Aranjuez to Cuenca section of the Aranjuez to València line could formally close this month (Table **669**).

PORTUGAL

On the *Linha do Douro* an additional pair of Porto São Bento – Pocinho *IR* trains will operate this summer (Table **694**). We have also been able to include operating dates for the *Comboio Historico* steam-hauled tourist train.

GERMANY

Timings in our German section are currently valid until September 22 as engineering work on various routes has resulted in some significant alterations (see further details below). Updated timings valid from September 23 will be shown in the Autumn seasonal edition.

Over the past few years Deutsche Bahn has been gradually upgrading sections of its high-speed network which has resulted in temporary changes to long-distance services whilst the work is undertaken. The latest section of line to be affected is that between Würzburg and Fulda which will be closed to rail traffic from June 11 to December 10 (although a 25 kilometre section at the southern end of the line will reopen from October 17). Until October 16 all services between Würzburg and Frankfurt (Table **920**) / Fulda (Table **900**) are diverted via the sinuous classic route through Gemünden resulting in considerably extended journey times. Fewer trains will be able to run meaning a number of services are suspended. From October 17 journey times between Würzburg and Frankfurt will return to normal as these trains will once again be able to utilise the high-speed infrastructure.

Further north, the main line between Hannover and Hamburg will also see various alterations until September 22 with some services diverted whilst others are retimed with extra stops being made (Table **900**). During this period services on the Karlsruhe – Frankfurt – Gießen – Hannover – Hamburg – Stralsund route are rerouted north of Hannover to run to and from Bremen while certain services between München and Hamburg are extended to run to and from Stralsund. Combined with the diversion between Würzburg and Fulda, a typical journey time between München and Hamburg via Hannover has temporarily increased from around 5½ hours to over seven hours. The fastest journeys between München and Hamburg during this period will actually be via Erfurt and Berlin (Table **850**).

From June 25 to August 4 part of the line between Osnabrück and Rheine will be closed to rail traffic meaning InterCity services on the Berlin – Amsterdam route will be diverted via Münster resulting in extended journey times. A special table with amended timings of these services will be found on page 566.

The important international corridor between München and Salzburg will see a much reduced long-distance service until August 1 (see also the Austrian news item below). Services at the München end of the route are affected by further amendments until July 13 with many services not running between München Hbf and Ost stations. A special version of Table **890** will be found on page 567 with full details of amended timings during this period.

The *Eifelstrecke* between Köln and Trier via Gerolstein was severely damaged by extreme weather conditions in July 2021 meaning that rail replacement bus services have been operating along most of the route while work to repair the line continues. However, from June 12 two further sections of the line will reopen to rail traffic: Euskirchen to Kall at the northern end of the route and Kyllburg to Auw an der Kyll further south. Table **915a** has been updated with the latest schedules.

Independent operator FlixTrain continues to expand its network with new routes added during May and June. Since May 19 a service between Hamburg and Stuttgart has been operating five times a week and a thrice weekly service started running between Berlin and Wiesbaden from June 2. From June 23 a direct service, running five times a week in each direction, will be introduced between Berlin and Basel Badischer Bahnhof. The Hamburg – Köln – Frankfurt – München service now runs daily with a second service running on the Köln – Frankfurt section four days a week. Full details of the latest FlixTrain timings will be found in Table **927**.

AUSTRIA

Certain domestic services operating via the Salzburg – Kufstein route (operating non-stop through Germany) are affected by engineering work taking place in Germany until August 1. Most international services to and from München are also affected and further information will be found in special versions of Tables **951** and **970** on pages 561 and 562 (also German Table **890** on page 567).

POLAND

Train **141/142** *Balti* is expected to commence running from July 1 between Suwałki and Kaunas. An extension of the service to and from Białystok may also be implemented (Table **1042**).

CZECH REPUBLIC

News reports suggest that Regiojet will extend some of its Wien services to and from Wien Flughafen from June, however details were not available as we closed for press.

Leo Express has decided to restrict its domestic operations to the Praha to Bohumín route with the withdrawal of its services between Praha and Staré Město u Uherské Hradiště. Its thrice-weekly service from Praha to Kraków still runs but is retimed in the Kraków direction (Tables **1160** and **1162**).

SLOVAKIA

Until October 10 the line between Šurany and Levice is closed for engineering work. Replacement bus services will operate between Šal'a and Nová Baňa resulting in significantly extended journey times (Table **1170**).

HUNGARY

As is usual at this time of year there is a significant uplift of services serving the lake Balaton area. Special versions of Tables **1220** and **1225**, valid June 18 - August 28, will be found on pages 569 and 570.

Long term engineering work continues to result in changes to long-distance trains between Hungary and Romania shown in Table **1275**. From June 18 to November 6 the line between Püspökladány and Biharkeresztes will be closed with trains replaced by buses and long-distance trains diverted. Train **367/366** *Hargita* is replaced between Budapest and Oradea by a domestic *IC* train / bus connection. Trains **143/146** *Transilvania* and **407/406** *Corona* are diverted via Debrecen, Nyirábrány and Valea lui Mihai. Train **347/346** *Dacia* returns to its previous route via Békéscsaba, Lökösháza and Curtici (Table **1280**). Local trains **364**, **365**, **368** and **369** are suspended. The diversion of trains via Debrecen, Nyirábrány and Valea lui Mihai impacts on services in Table **1277** where trains **6812/6811** are cut back to run within Hungary only.

FERRIES

A new ferry service between Greece and Cyprus, operated by Scandro Holding Ltd, commences on June 19 for the summer period until September 16. It sails twice a week in each direction, from Pireas on Tuesdays and Fridays, returning from Lemesos on Sundays and Wednesdays (Table **2846**).

CONTINUED ON PAGE 37

NEWSLINES *(continued from page 36)*

BEYOND EUROPE

TANZANIA

In the Spring edition we reported that the new standard gauge railway between Dar es Salaam and Morogoro was due to open in April. However, due to delays to the completion of a hydro-electric scheme that will provide power for the new railway, this opening date was not met. Conflicting news reports suggest it could now be between three months and two years before the railway can open!

Other news reports suggest that services on the *Tazara* route between Dar es Salaam and Kapiri Mposhi (Zambia) could resume in July.

ISRAEL

Israel Railways has opened a new section of railway that has allowed the introduction of direct trains between Jerusalem and Modi'in. Timings will be found in new Table **4515**. We have also checked and updated the other tables for Israel as necessary.

INDIA

In April the railway from Jaynagar to Kurtha (Nepal) reopened after several years, during which the track was converted to Indian broad gauge (1.676m). We have added a new Table **5325** to show this service and connections from Delhi and Kolkata.

As is usual at this time of year the monsoon season will affect services in Table **5220** – a different timetable to the one we show will operate so please check locally for changes.

All other tables in India have been checked and updated which has resulted in a number of table number changes.

NEW ZEALAND

Kiwirail has announced that the Auckland – Wellington *Northern Explorer* and Picton – Christchurch *Coastal Pacific* trains will return to service at the end of September.

CHINA

We had hoped to be able to update the China section for this edition but, owing to the continued lockdown of major cities, information has become very difficult to obtain, so we have not been able to do so.

CANADA

Via Rail increased the frequency of the *Canadian* (Table **9050**) to twice-weekly from April 29 and of the *Ocean* (Table **9000**) to thrice-weekly from June 3. Other routes that will see an increase in frequencies during June are the Québec City – Windsor corridor (Tables **9010**, **9015** and **9020**), Jasper – Prince Rupert (Table **9060**), Sudbury – White River (Table **9035**) and Montréal – Jonquière / Senneterre (Table **9005**). The additional frequencies for the *Canadian* and *Ocean* are included in this edition; the other routes will be updated in time for our Autumn edition. We have updated all other tables in Canada with the latest available information.

UNITED STATES

We have updated most of our tables for the United States of America. Please be aware that most of them show the service level in mid-April. As Covid restrictions ease more trains are reintroduced so there may be more trains running than are shown.

The New York – Philadelphia – Harrisburg *Keystone* service, formerly shown in Table **9230**, has been moved to the foot of Table **9215**.

Table **9235** has been split with Washington – Cleveland – Chicago trains shown in a new Table **9230** while Boston / New York – Albany – Chicago trains remain in Table **9235**.

Trains between Chicago and St Louis, shown in Table **9260**, have been accelerated by up to 15 minutes due to the completion of infrastructure upgrades. However, one return pair of St Louis – Kansas City *River Runner* trains has been suspended indefinitely due to the withdrawal of state funding.

LONDON - LILLE - PARIS and BRUSSELS *by Eurostar* — 10

TABLE TEMPORARILY LOCATED FROM PAGE 48

Minimum check-in time is 30 minutes, but passengers are advised to allow longer due to immigration procedures. Not available for London - Ebbsfleet - Ashford or v.v. Special fares payable that include three classes of service: business premier, standard premier and standard. All times shown are local times (France and Belgium are one hour ahead of Great Britain).
All Eurostar services are 🄡, non-smoking and convey ✕ in Business Premier and Standard Premier, 🍸 in Standard.

Service November 5 - December 10. For service June 12 - November 4 see pages 47 - 48.

km	*km*	*train number*	**9004**	**9008**	**9114**	**9116**	**9014**	**9018**	**9126**	**9024**	**9132**	**9028**	
		notes	①–⑤	①–⑥								Ⓑ	
		notes	**K**		**A**				**A**				
0	*0*	**London** St Pancras ..... d.	0701	0801	0816	0901	0931	1022	1104	1231	1301	1331	...
35	*35*	Ebbsfleet International ..... d.	│	│	│	│	│	│	│	│	│	│	...
90	*90*	Ashford International ..... d.	│	│	│	│	│	│	│	│	│	│	...
166	*166*	Calais Fréthun ..... a.	│	│	│	│	│	│	│	│	│	│	...
267	*267*	Lille Europe ..... a.	│	│	│	1127	│	│	1326	│	1526	│	...
	373	**Brussels** Midi / Zuid ..... a.	│	│	1112	1205	│	│	1405	│	1606	│	...
492		**Paris** Nord ..... a.	1017	1117	...	...	1247	1347	...	1547	...	1647	...

train number	**9032**	**9142**	**9036**	**9040**	**9046**	**9152**	**9050**	**9054**					
notes						Ⓑ		⑥⑦					
notes						**A**							
London St Pancras ..... d.	1431	1504	1531	1631	1801	1804	1901	2001	...	...	...	...	...
Ebbsfleet International ..... d.	│	│	│	│	│	│	│	│	...	...	...	...	...
Ashford International ..... d.	│	│	│	│	│	│	│	│	...	...	...	...	...
Calais Fréthun ..... a.	│	│	│	│	│	│	│	│	...	...	...	...	...
Lille Europe ..... a.	│	1726	│	│	│	2026	│	│	...	...	...	...	...
Brussels Midi / Zuid ..... a.	│	1805	│	│	│	2105	│	│	...	...	...	...	...
Paris Nord ..... a.	1747	...	1847	1947	2117	...	2217	2317	...	...	...	...	...

train number	**9007**	**9009**	**9117**	**9015**	**9023**	**9135**	**9031**	**9035**	**9039**	**9145**	**9043**		
notes	①–⑥	①–⑤						⑦					
notes	**K**									**A**			
Paris Nord ..... d.	0713	0743	...	0913	1113	...	1313	1413	1513	...	1613	...	...
Brussels Midi / Zuid ..... d.	│	│	0852	│	│	1256	│	│	│	1552	│	...	...
Lille Europe ..... d.	│	│	0930	│	│	1335	│	│	│	1635	│	...	...
Calais Fréthun ..... d.	│	│	│	│	│	│	│	│	│	│	│	...	...
Ashford International ..... a.	│	│	│	│	│	│	│	│	│	│	│	...	...
Ebbsfleet International ..... a.	│	│	│	│	│	│	│	│	│	│	│	...	...
London St Pancras ..... a.	0832	0900	0957	1030	1230	1400	1430	1530	1637	1700	1739	...	...

train number	**9047**	**9153**	**9051**	**9157**	**9055**	**9059**	**9167**	**9063**					
notes			⑦				Ⓑ	Ⓑ					
notes				**A**			**A**						
Paris Nord ..... d.	1713	...	1813	...	1913	2013	...	2113	...	...	...	...	...
Brussels Midi / Zuid ..... d.	│	1756	│	1856	│	│	2056	│	...	...	...	...	...
Lille Europe ..... d.	│	1835	│	1935	│	│	2135	│	...	...	...	...	...
Calais Fréthun ..... d.	│	│	│	│	│	│	│	│	...	...	...	...	...
Ashford International ..... a.	│	│	│	│	│	│	│	│	...	...	...	...	...
Ebbsfleet International ..... a.	│	│	│	│	│	│	│	│	...	...	...	...	...
London St Pancras ..... a.	1840	1900	1930	1957	2030	2130	2157	2230	...	...	...	...	...

A – To / from Amsterdam, see Table **18**.

K – Not Nov. 11.

AUTO-TRAIN, AUTOREISEZÜGE, MOTORAIL

Car-carrying trains are composed of special wagons or vans for the conveyance of motorcars usually with sleeping cars and couchettes enabling the driver and passengers to travel overnight in comfort in the same train. Some services convey vehicles separately allowing passengers a choice of trains for their own journey. Some shorter distance services run by day and convey seating coaches.

Cars are often loaded on the trains at separate stations from the passenger station and may be loaded some time before the passenger train departs. International car-carrying trains are shown in Table **1**, Domestic car-carrying trains in Table **2**. Some services also carry passengers without cars.

Details of Channel Tunnel shuttle services may be found on page 46. Details of domestic car-carrying shuttle trains may be found as follows: Austria (Table **969**), Germany (Table **821**), Italy (Table **590**), Slovenia (Table **1302**) and Switzerland (Tables **545** and **562**).

Readers should be careful to check that dates refer to current schedules, as old dates may be left in the table until such time as current information is received. Loading and train times may vary on some dates, but will be confirmed by the agent when booking.

Contact details:

BahnTouristikExpress: ✆ +49 (0)91 12 403 822. www.rdc-deutschland.de
ÖBB Nightjet: ✆ +43 (0) 5 1717. www.nightjet.com
Optima Tours: ✆ +49 (0)89 54 880 111. www.optimatours.de
Urlaubs-Express: ✆ +49 (0)22 18 002 0820. www.urlaubs-express.de
For the contact details of national operators please see the relevant country headings.

1 INTERNATIONAL CAR-CARRYING TRAINS

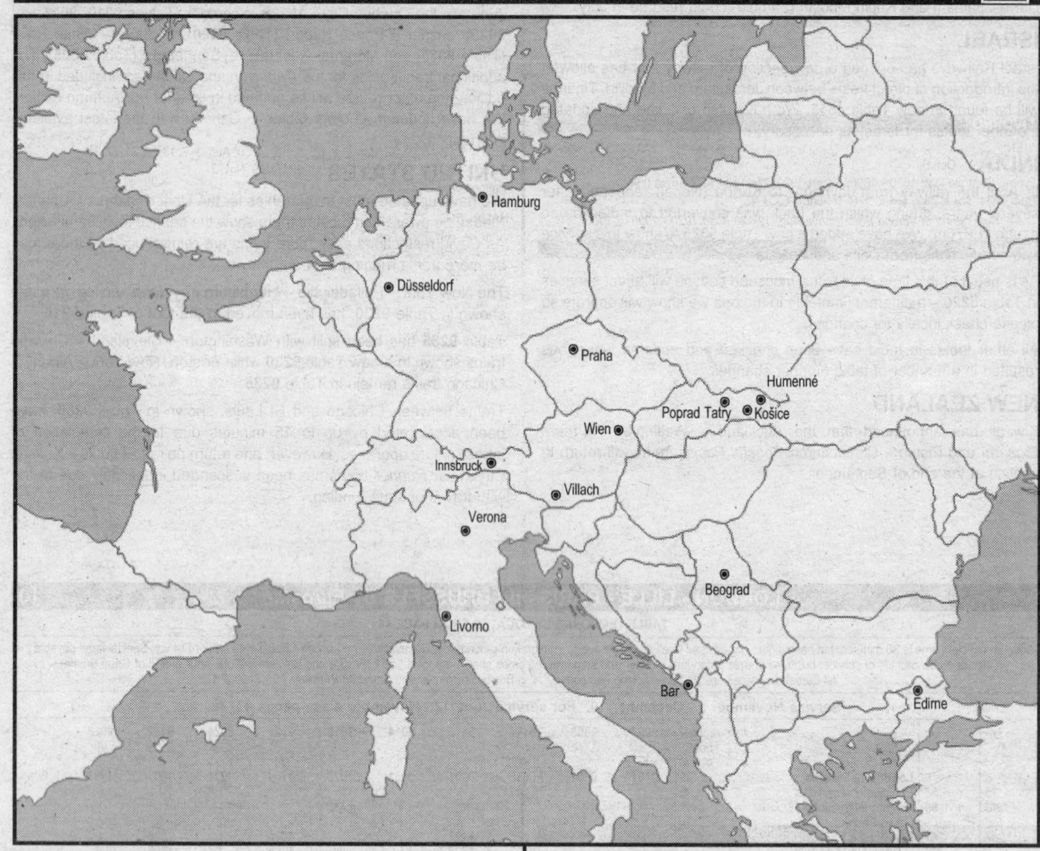

BAR

BEOGRAD:
Bar load time not advised, depart 1900, Beograd arrive 0615.
Train **432**: 🛏 1, 2 cl., ▬ 2 cl., (2).

BEOGRAD

BAR:
Beograd load time not advised, depart 2110, Bar arrive 0812.
Train **433**: 🛏 1, 2 cl., ▬ 2 cl., (2).

DÜSSELDORF

INNSBRUCK: *Urlaubs-Express*
July 4, Aug. 6, 25, Sept. 12, 22, Oct. 1.
Düsseldorf Hbf load time not advised, depart 2136, Innsbruck Hbf arrive 0829.
Train **1389**: 🛏, ▬ ✕.

VERONA: *Urlaubs-Express*
⑤ July 2 - Sept. 24 (not Aug. 6).
Düsseldorf Hbfload time not advised, depart 1844, Verona Porta Nuova arrive 0955.
Train **1385**: 🛏, ▬ ✕.

VILLACH: *Urlaubs-Express*
July 7, 21, Aug. 1, 15, 22, Sept. 5.
Düsseldorf Hbf load time not advised, depart 1934, Villach Autoverladung arrive 0846.
Train **1387**: 🛏, ▬ ✕.

WIEN: *Urlaubs-Express*
Sept. 19, Oct. 3, 8, 15.
Düsseldorf Hbf load time not advised, depart 2136, Wien Hbf ARZ arrive 0852.
Train **1851**: 🛏, ▬ ✕.

EDIRNE

VILLACH: *Optima Tours*
June 2, 6, 10, 16, 20, 24, 30, July 4, 8, 14, 18, 22, 28, Aug. 1, 5, 11, 15, 19, 25, 29, Sept. 2, 8, 15, 19, 23, 29, Oct. 3, 7, 13, 17, 21, 27, Nov. 2, 9.
Timings vary. ▬ ✕.

HAMBURG

INNSBRUCK: *ÖBB Nightjet*
Daily.
Hamburg Altona load 1900 - 1945, depart 2029, Innsbruck Hbf arrive 0914.
Train **40491**: 🛏 1, 2 cl., ▬ 2 cl. (4, 6 berth), (2).

VERONA: *Urlaubs-Express*
June 25, July 2, 9, 16, 23, 30, Aug. 13, 20, 27, Sept. 3, 10, 17, 24.
Hamburg Altona load time not advised, depart 1800, Verona Porta Nuova arrive 0955.
Train **1395**: 🛏, ▬ ✕.

VILLACH: *Urlaubs-Express*
June 23, July 7, 21, Aug. 1, 15, 22, Sept. 5.
Hamburg Altona load time not advised, depart 1851, Villach Autoverladung arrive 0846.
Train **1397**: 🛏, ▬ ✕.

WIEN: *Urlaubs-Express*
Sept. 19, Oct. 3, 8, 15.
Hamburg Altona load time not advised, depart 2035, Wien Hbf ARZ arrive 0852.
Train **1371**: 🛏, ▬ ✕.

HELSINKI

MOSKVA: *SERVICE SUSPENDED*
Helsinki load time not advised, depart 1844, Moskva Oktyabrskaya arrive 0919.
Train **31**: 🛏 1, 2 cl., ✕.

INTERNATIONAL CAR-CARRYING TRAINS 1

HUMENNÉ

PRAHA:
Daily (not Dec. 24, 31).
Humenné load 1835 - 1845, depart 1930, Praha hlavní nádraží arrive 0755.
Train *EN* **442**: 🛏 1, 2 cl., ▬ 2 cl. 🚗.

INNSBRUCK

DÜSSELDORF: *Urlaubs-Express*
July 15, Aug. 7, 26, Sept. 13, 23, Oct. 2.
Innsbruck Hbf load time not advised, depart 2012, Düsseldorf Hbf arrive 0708.
Train **1388**: 🛏, ▬ ✕.

HAMBURG: *ÖBB Nightjet*
Daily.
Innsbruck Hbf load 1945 - 2005, depart 2044, Hamburg Altona arrive 0847.
Train **40420**: 🛏 1, 2 cl., ▬ 2 cl. (4, 6 berth), 🚗.

KOŠICE

PRAHA:
Daily.
Košice load 2005 - 2015, depart 2157, Praha hlavní nádraží arrive 0732.
Train *EN* **444**: 🛏 1, 2 cl., ▬ 2 cl. 🚗.

LIVORNO

WIEN: *ÖBB Nightjet*
④⑥ May 27 - Oct. 9.
Livorno Centrale load 1630 - 1800, depart 1920, Wien Hbf ARZ arrive 0842.
Train **1234**: 🛏 1, 2 cl., ▬ 2 cl. (4, 6 berth), 🚗 🍸.
Note: starts at Verona Porta Nuova Aug. 12 – 28 (load 1920 - 2020, d. 2153).

MOSKVA

HELSINKI: *SERVICE SUSPENDED*
Moskva Oktyabrskaya load time not advised, depart 2310, Helsinki arrive 1330.
Train **32**: 🛏 1, 2 cl., ✕.
*Note: Helsinki arrival time is 1 hour earlier in Winter (see Table **1910**).*

POPRAD TATRY

PRAHA:
⑥ until Oct. 30.
Poprad Tatry load 2205 - 2215, depart 2332, Praha hlavní nádraží arrive 0732.
Train *EN* **442**: 🛏 1, 2 cl., ▬ 2 cl. 🚗.

PRAHA

HUMENNÉ:
Daily (not Dec. 24, 31).
Praha hlavní nádraží load 1945 - 2000, depart 2205, Humenné arrive 1033.
Train *EN* **443**: 🛏 1, 2 cl., ▬ 2 cl. 🚗.

KOŠICE:
Daily.
Praha hlavní nádraží load 2000 - 1030, depart 2218, Košice arrive 0829.
Train *EN* **443**: 🛏 1, 2 cl., ▬ 2 cl. 🚗.

POPRAD TATRY:
⑤ until Oct. 29.
Praha hlavní nádraží load 2015 - 2045 (until Oct. 5), depart 2218, Poprad Tatry arrive 0641.
Train *EN* **443**: 🛏 1, 2 cl., ▬ 2 cl. 🚗.

SPLIT

WIEN: *ÖBB Nightjet*
③⑥ June 19 - Sept. 11.
Split load 1500 - 1545, depart 1648, Wien Hbf ARZ arrive 0858.
Train **1252**: 🛏, 🚗.

VERONA

DÜSSELDORF: *Urlaubs-Express*
⑥ June 26 - Sept. 25 (not Aug. 7).
Verona Porta Nuova load time not advised, depart 1805, Düsseldorf Hbf arrive 0843.
Train **1384**: 🛏, ▬ ✕.

HAMBURG: *Urlaubs-Express*
June 26, July 3, 10, 17, 24, 31, Aug. 14, 21, 28, Sept. 4, 11, 18, 25.
Verona Porta Nuova load time not advised, depart 1805, Hamburg Altona arrive 0955.
Train **1394**: 🛏, ▬ ✕.

VILLACH

DÜSSELDORF: *Urlaubs-Express*
July 8, 22, Aug. 2, 16, 23, Sept. 6.
Villach Autoverladung load time not advised, depart 1800, Düsseldorf arrive 0757.
Train **1386**: 🛏, ▬ ✕.

EDIRNE: *Optima Tours*
June 4, 8, 12, 18, 22, 26, July 2, 6, 10, 16, 20, 24, 30, Aug. 3, 7, 13, 17, 21, 27, 31, Sept. 4, 11, 17, 21, 25, Oct. 1, 5, 9, 15, 19, 23, 29 Nov. 7.
Timings vary. ▬ ✕.

HAMBURG: *Urlaubs-Express*
June 24, July 8, 22, Aug. 2, 16, 23, Sept. 6.
Villach Autoverladung load time not advised, depart 1800, Hamburg Altona arrive 0826.
Train **1396**: 🛏, ▬ ✕.

WIEN

DÜSSELDORF: *Urlaubs-Express*
Sept. 20, Oct. 4, 9, 16.
Wien Hbf ARZ load time not advised, depart 1954, Düsseldorf arrive 0725.
Train **1850**: 🛏, ▬ ✕.

HAMBURG: *Urlaubs-Express*
Sept. 20, Oct. 4, 9, 16.
Wien Hbf ARZ load time not advised, depart 1954, Hamburg Altona arrive 0852.
Train **1370**: 🛏, ▬ ✕.

LIVORNO: *ÖBB Nightjet*
③⑤ May 26 - Oct. 8.
Wien Hbf ARZ load 1905 - 1930, depart 2001, Livorno Centrale arrive 0900.
Train **1237**: 🛏 1, 2 cl., ▬ 2 cl. (4, 6 berth), 🚗 🍸.
Note: terminates at Verona Porta Nuova Aug. 11 – 27 (a. 0638).

SPLIT: *ÖBB Nightjet*
②⑤ June 18 - Sept. 10.
Wien Hbf ARZ load 1600 - 1645, depart 1801, Split arrive 0950.
Train **1253**: 🛏, 🚗.

DOMESTIC LONG-DISTANCE CAR-CARRYING TRAINS 2

AUSTRIA

Daily return services operate from Feldkirch to Graz, Villach and Wien Hbf ARZ.

CROATIA

Split - Zagreb and v.v.:
Split load times not advised, depart 2140, Zagreb a. 0547 (not July 28, 29, 31, Aug. 17, 21).
Zagreb load times not advised, depart 2305, Split a. 0705 (not July 28, 30, Aug. 16, 20, Sept. 4).
Summer only (until Sept. 4). Trains **820 / 821**: 🛏 1, 2 cl., ▬ 2 cl., 🚗.

FINLAND

Services operate on the following routes - contact operator for schedules:
Helsinki - Kemijärvi and v.v.
Helsinki - Oulu and v.v.
Kolari - Tampere and v.v.
Rovaniemi - Turku and v.v.
Helsinki - Kolari and v.v.
Helsinki - Rovaniemi and v.v.
Rovaniemi - Tampere and v.v.
Note: Helsinki trains load and unload at Pasila station (3 km north of Helsinki station)

GERMANY

Düsseldorf Hbf - **München** Ost and v.v. (operator: Urlaubs-Express):
From Düsseldorf July 4, 28, Aug. 11, Sept. 19, Oct. 3, 8, 15.
From München July 15, 29, Aug. 12, Sept. 20, Oct. 4, 9, 16.

Hamburg Altona - **Lörrach** and v.v. (operator: BahnTouristikExpress):
From Hamburg: June 4, 18, 23, 25, 27, July 1, 3, 6, 8, 10, 15 – 17, 21 – 24, 28 – 31, Aug. 1, 4 – 8, 11 – 15, 20, 27, Sept. 3, 5, 10, 12, 17, 19, 24, 26, Oct. 1, 3, 8, 15.
From Basel: June 5, 19, 24, 26, 28, July 2, 4, 7, 9, 11, 16 – 18, 22 – 25, 29 – 31, Aug. 1, 2, 12 – 16, 21, 28, Sept. 4, 6, 11, 13, 18, 20, 25, 27, Oct. 2, 4, 9, 16.

Hamburg Altona - **Lörrach** and v.v. (operator: Urlaubs-Express):
From Hamburg June 4, 18, 23, 25, 27, July 1, 3, 8, 10, 15 – 17, 21 – 24, 28 – 31, Aug. 1, 4 – 8, 11 – 15, 20, 27, Sept. 3, 5, 10, 12, 17, 19, 24, 26, Oct. 1, 3, 8, 15.
From Lörrach June 5, 19, 24, 26, 28, July 2, 4, 9, 11, 16 – 18, 22 – 25, 29 – 31, Aug. 1, 2, 5 – 9, 12 – 16, 21, 28, Sept. 4, 6, 11, 13, 18, 20, 25, 27, Oct. 2, 4, 9, 16.

GERMANY (continued)

Hamburg Altona - **München** Ost and v.v. (operator: Urlaubs-Express):
From Hamburg July 4, 14, 28, Aug. 6, 11, 25, Sept. 12, 19, 22, Oct. 1, 3, 8, 15.
From München July 5, 15, 29, Aug. 7, 12, 26, Sept. 13, 20, 23, Oct. 2, 4, 9, 16.

GREECE

Athína - Thessaloníki and v.v.: *SERVICE SUSPENDED*
Athína load by 2150, depart 2350, Thessaloníki arrive 0520.
Thessaloníki load by 2150, depart 2350, Athína arrive 0506.
Daily. Trains **600 / 601**.

RUSSIA

Services operate on the following routes - contact operator for schedules:
Kazan - Adler and v.v.
Moskva - Adler and v.v.
Moskva - Rostov na Donu and v.v.
St. Peterburg - Adler and v.v.
Kazan - Rostov na Donu and v.v.
Moskva - Kazan and v.v.
Moskva - St. Peterburg and v.v.
St. Peterburg - Vorkuta and v.v.

SLOVAKIA

Bratislava - Humenne and v.v.:
Bratislava load 2125 - 2135, depart 2253, Humenné arrive 0633.
Humenné load 2040 - 2050, depart 2145, Bratislava arrive 0549.
Daily (not Dec. 24, 31). Trains **615 / 614**: 🛏 1, 2 cl., ▬ 2 cl., 🚗.

Bratislava - Košice and v.v.:
Bratislava load 2110 - 2120, depart 2253, Košice arrive 0444.
Košice load 2210 - 2220, depart 2345, Bratislava arrive 0549.
Daily. Trains **615 / 614**: 🛏 1, 2 cl., ▬ 2 cl., 🚗.

Scenic Rail Routes of Europe

The following is a list of some of the most scenic rail routes of Europe, timings for most of which can be found within the timetable (the relevant table number has been specified in bold). Routes marked * are some of the editorial team's favourite journeys. Please note that this list does not include specialised mountain and tourist railways.

Types of scenery: C - Coastline, F - Forest, G - Gorge, L - Lake, M - Mountain, R - River

AUSTRIA

Route	Scenery	Table
Bruck an der Mur - Villach	M R	**980**
Gmunden - Stainach Irdning*	ML	**961**
Innsbruck - Brennero	M	**595**
Innsbruck - Garmisch*	M	**895**
Innsbruck - Schwarzach-St Veit	M G	**960**
Krems - Emmersdorf	R	**991**
Landeck - Bludenz*	M	**951**
St Pölten - Mariazell*	M	**994**
Salzburg - Villach*	M G	**970**
Selzthal - Kleinreifling - Steyr	M G R	**976/977**
Wiener Neustadt - Graz	M	**980**

BELGIUM and LUXEMBOURG

Route	Scenery	Table
Liège - Luxembourg*	R	**446**
Liège - Marloie	R	**447**
Namur - Dinant	R	**440**

BULGARIA

Route	Scenery	Table
Septemvri - Dobrinishte	M	**1510**
Sofia - Burgas	M	**1500**
Tulovo - Gorna Oryakhovitsa	M	**1525**

CROATIA and BOSNIA

Route	Scenery	Table
Novi Grad - Sarajevo	M G R	**1350**
Ogulin - Split	M	**1330**
Rijeka - Ogulin	M	**1310**
Sarajevo - Ploče	M G R	**1355**

CZECH REPUBLIC

Route	Scenery	Table
Karlovy Vary - Mariánské Lázně	R F	**1123**
Karlovy Vary - Chomutov	R	**1110**
Praha - Děčín	R	**1100**

DENMARK

Route	Scenery	Table
Struer - Thisted	C	**716**

FINLAND

Route	Scenery	Table
Kouvola - Joensuu	L F	**797**

FRANCE

Route	Scenery	Table
Aurillac - Neussargues	M G	**331**
Bastia - Ajaccio	M	**369**
Bourg-en-Bresse - Bellegarde	M	**341**
Chambéry - Bourg St Maurice	M	**366**
Chambéry - Modane	ML	**367**
Chamonix - Martigny*	M G	**572**
Clermont Ferrand - Béziers	M G	**332**
Clermont Ferrand - Nîmes*	M G R	**333**
Gap - Briançon	ML	**358**
Genève - Aix les Bains	M R	**364**
Grenoble - Veynes - Marseille	M	**358**
Marseille - Ventimiglia	C	**360/361**
Mouchard - Montbéliard	R	**378**
Nice - Digne	M	**359**
Nice - Cuneo*	M G	**581**
Perpignan - Latour de Carol*	M G	**354**
Portbou - Perpignan	C	**355**
Sarlat - Bergerac	R	**318**
Toulouse - Latour de Carol	M	**312**
Valence - Veynes	M	**358**

GERMANY

Route	Scenery	Table
Arnstadt - Meiningen	M	**870**
Dresden - Děčín	G R	**1100**
Freiburg - Donaueschingen	G F	**938**
Garmisch - Reutte - Kempten	M	**888**
Heidelberg - Neckarelz	R	**923/924**
Koblenz - Mainz*	G R	**911/914**
München - Lindau	M	**935**
Murnau - Oberammergau	ML	**897**
Naumburg - Saalfeld	R	**849**
Niebüll - Westerland	C	**821**

GERMANY - continued

Route	Scenery	Table
Nürnberg - Pegnitz	G R	**880**
Offenburg - Konstanz	M F	**916**
Pforzheim - Nagold / Wildbad	F	**941**
Plattling - Bayerisch Eisenstein	F	**929**
Rosenheim - Berchtesgaden	ML	**890/891**
Rosenheim - Wörgl	M	**951**
Siegburg/Bonn - Siegen	R	**807**
Stuttgart - Singen	F	**940**
Titisee - Seebrugg	L F	**938**
Trier - Koblenz - Giessen	R	**906/915**
Ulm - Göppingen	M	**930**
Ulm - Tuttlingen	R	**938**

GREAT BRITAIN and IRELAND

Route	Scenery	Table
Alnmouth - Dunbar	C	**180**
Barrow in Furness - Maryport	C	**159**
Coleraine - Londonderry	C	**231**
Dun Laoghaire - Wicklow	C	**237**
Edinburgh - Aberdeen	C	**222**
Exeter - Newton Abbot	C	**110/111**
Glasgow - Oban / Mallaig*	ML	**218**
Inverness - Kyle of Lochalsh*	M C	**226**
Lancaster - Carlisle - Carstairs	M G R	**154**
Liskeard - Looe	R	**113**
Llanelli - Craven Arms	M	**146**
Machynlleth - Pwllheli	M C	**148**
Perth - Inverness	M	**223**
Plymouth - Gunnislake	R	**113**
St Erth - St Ives	C	**113**
Sheffield - Chinley	M	**193/206**
Shrewsbury - Aberystwyth	M R	**147**
Skipton - Settle - Carlisle	M R	**173**

GREECE

Route	Scenery	Table
Diakoftó - Kalávrita	M G	**1455**

HUNGARY

Route	Scenery	Table
Budapest - Szob	R	**1255**
Eger - Szilvásvárad	M	**1299**
Székesfehérvár - Balatonszentgyörgy	L	**1220**
Székesfehérvár - Tapolca	L	**1225**

ITALY

Route	Scenery	Table
Bologna - Pistoia	M	**583**
Bolzano - Merano	M	**595**
Brennero - Verona*	M	**595**
Brig - Arona	ML	**590**
Domodossola - Locarno*	M G	**551**
Firenze - Viareggio	M	**614**
Fortezza - San Candido	M	**597**
Genova - Pisa	C	**610**
Genova - Ventimiglia	C	**580**
Lecco - Tirano	ML	**593**
Messina - Palermo	C	**641**
Napoli - Sorrento	C	**639**
Roma - Pescara	M	**624**
Salerno - Reggio Calabria	C	**640**
Taranto - Reggio Calabria	C	**637**
Torino - Aosta	M	**586**
Ventimiglia - Cuneo*	M G	**581**

NORWAY

Route	Scenery	Table
Bergen - Oslo*	ML	**780/781**
Bodø - Trondheim	ML	**787**
Dombås - Åndalsnes	M	**785**
Drammen - Larvik	C	**783**
Myrdal - Flåm*	M C	**781**
Oslo - Kongsvinger	R	**750**
Oslo / Røros - Trondheim	ML	**784/785**
Stavanger - Kristiansand	M	**775**

POLAND

Route	Scenery	Table
Jelenia Góra - Walbrzych	M	**1084**
Kraków - Zakopane	M	**1066**
Olsztyn - Elk	L	**1035**
Olsztyn - Morag	L	**1035**
Tarnów - Krynica	M	**1078**

PORTUGAL

Route	Scenery	Table
Covilhã - Entroncamento	M R	**691**
Pampilhosa - Guarda	M	**692**
Porto - Coimbra	C R	**690**
Porto - Pocinho*	R	**694**
Porto - Valença	M C	**696**

ROMANIA

Route	Scenery	Table
Braşov - Ploeşti	M	**1600**
Caransebeş - Craiova	M G R	**1630**
Feteşti - Constanţa	R	**1680**
Oradea - Cluj Napoca	R	**1625**
Salva - Sighetu Marmaţiei	M R F	**1660**
Salva - Suceava	M F	**1660**

SERBIA and MONTENEGRO

Route	Scenery	Table
Kraljevo - Mitrovica / Mitrovicë	M R	**1375**
Priboj - Bar	ML	**1370**

SLOVAKIA

Route	Scenery	Table
Banská Bystrica - Brezno - Košice	M	**1188**
Žilina - Poprad Tatry	M	**1180**

SLOVENIA

Route	Scenery	Table
Jesenice - Sežana	M G R	**1302**
Maribor - Zidani Most	M	**1315**
Maribor - Bleiburg	M G R	**1315**
Villa Opicina - Ljubljana - Zagreb	G R	**1305**

SPAIN

Route	Scenery	Table
Algeciras - Ronda	M R	**673**
Barcelona - Latour de Carol	M	**656**
Bilbao - San Sebastián	M	**686**
Bilbao - Santander	M	**687**
Ferrol - Gijón*	C	**681**
Granada - Almería	M	**673**
Huesca - Canfranc	M G R	**670**
León - Monforte de Lemos	M	**682**
León - Oviedo	M	**685**
Lleida - La Pobla de Segur	ML	**653**
Málaga - Bobadilla	G	**673**
Santander - Oviedo	M C	**687**
Zaragoza - València	M R	**670**

SWEDEN

Route	Scenery	Table
Bollnäs - Ånge - Sundsvall	ML	**761**
Borlänge - Mora	ML F	**758**
Borlänge - Ludvika - Frövi	ML F	**755**
Narvik - Kiruna	M F	**765**
Östersund - Storlien	L F	**761**

SWITZERLAND

Route	Scenery	Table
Andermatt - Göschenen	G	**576**
Basel - Delémont - Moutier	M R	**505a**
Basel / Luzern / Zurich - Chiasso	ML	**547/548**
Chur - Arosa	M G	**545**
Chur - Brig - Zermatt*	M	**575/576**
Chur - St Moritz*	M G	**545**
Davos - Filisur	M G	**545**
Davos - Landquart	M	**545**
Interlaken Ost - Jungfraujoch*	M	**564**
Interlaken Ost - Luzern	ML	**561**
Interlaken West - Spiez	L	**560**
Lausanne - Brig	ML R	**570**
Lausanne - Neuchâtel - Biel	ML	**505**
Montreux - Zweisimmen - Lenk	ML G	**566**
Rorschach - Kreuzlingen	L	**538**
St Moritz - Scuol Tarasp	M	**545**
St Moritz - Tirano*	M	**545**
Spiez - Zweisimmen	G	**563**
Thun - Kandersteg - Brig*	ML	**562**
Zürich - Chur	ML	**520**

City Plans are on pages 30–34

Airport code and name	City	Distance	Journey	Transport ‡	City terminal	Table
AAR Aarhus	Aarhus	37 km	40 mins	🚌 flybus: connects with flights	Banegårdspladsen, Central rail station	
ABZ Aberdeen, Dyce	Aberdeen	11 km	40 mins	🚌 **727**: ①–⑤ ± 6 per hour; ⑥⑦ ± 3 per hour	Union Square bus station.	
ALC Alacant	Alacant	12 km	30 mins	🚌 **C6**: every 20 mins 0705 - 2000	Plaza Puerta del Mar	
AMS Amsterdam, Schiphol	Amsterdam	17 km	17 mins	Train: every 10 mins	Centraal rail station	**451, 452, 454, 460**
	Rotterdam	65 km	45 mins	Train: every 30 mins	Centraal rail station	**450, 454, 460**
	Den Haag	43 km	35 mins	Train: every 30 mins	Centraal rail station	**454, 460**
AOI Ancona (also known as Marche)	Ancona	16 km	30 mins	1) 🚌 *Aerobus* 2) Train: hourly at peak times: 17 mins	Main rail station	
ATH Athína, Eleftherios Venizélos	Athína	27 km	39 mins	Metro line **3**: 2 per hour	Syntagma	**1440**
	Pireás	41 km	90 mins	🚌 **X96**: 3 - 4 per hour	Platía Karaiskáki	
BCN Barcelona, Aeroport del Prat	Barcelona	14 km	19 mins	Train: 2 per hour	Sants. Also calls at Passeig de Gràcia rail station (26 mins)	**659**
BSL Basel - Mulhouse - Freiburg	Basel	9 km	20 mins	🚌 **50**: ①–⑤ 8 per hour; ⑥⑦ 6 per hour	SBB rail station / Kannenfeldplatz	
	Freiburg	60 km	55 mins	🚌: ①–⑤ every 1 - 2 hours; ⑥⑦ every 2 hours	Rail station	
BHD Belfast, City, George Best	Belfast	2 km	15 mins	🚌 *Airlink* **600**: ①–⑥ every 20 mins; ⑦ every 40 mins	Europa Buscentre. Also train from Sydenham rail station	
BFS Belfast, International	Belfast	26 km	40 mins	🚌 *Airbus* **300**: Ⓐ every 15 mins; ⑥ every 20; ⑦ every 30	Europa Buscentre (adjacent to Great Victoria St rail station)	
BEG Beograd, Nikola Tesla	Beograd	18 km	35 mins	🚌 **72**: every 30 minutes	Rail station	
BER Berlin, Brandenburg	Berlin	24 km	30 mins	Train *Regional* **RE7 / RB14 / FEX**: 4 per hour	Hbf, also Sudkreuz, Ostkreuz rail stations	**847**
BER Berlin, Brandenburg T5	Berlin	24 km	28 mins	Train **S9**: 3 per hour	Hbf, also Ost, Alexanderplatz and Zoo rail stations	**847**
BIQ Biarritz - Anglet - Bayonne	Biarritz	3 km	15 mins	🚌 *Chronoplus* **36**: every hour approx.	Town centre	
	Bayonne	7 km	23 mins	🚌 *Chronoplus* **4**: every hour approx.	Rail station	
BIO Bilbao, Sondika	Bilbao	10 km	45 mins	🚌 Bizkaibus **A-3247**: every 20 mins 0620 - 0000	Plaza Moyúa (Metro station Moyúa)	
BLL Billund	Vejle	25 km	34 mins	🚌 *Sydtrafik* **43**	Town centre	
BHX Birmingham, International	Birmingham	12 km	11 mins	Train: ①–⑥ ± 9 per hour, ⑦ 6 per hour	New Street rail station from International	**114, 141, 145, 150**
BLQ Bologna, Guglielmo Marconi	Bologna	8 km	7 mins	Train *Marconi Express*: daily every 7 mins 0540 - 1810	Centrale rail station	
BOD Bordeaux, Mérignac	Bordeaux	12 km	30 mins	🚌 *30'Direct*: every 45 mins 0825 - 2245	St Jean rail station	
	Bordeaux	12 km	45 mins	🚌 **1**: every 10 mins 0500 - 2400	St Jean rail station	
BOH Bournemouth, Hurn	Bournemouth	10 km	38 mins	🚌 **737** *Yellow Buses*: hourly 0600 - 1900	Rail station, Bus station (Travel Interchange)	
BTS Bratislava, Milan Rastislav Štefánika	Bratislava	10 km	25 mins	🚌 **61**: 3 - 4 per hour	Main rail station (Hlavná stanica)	
BRE Bremen	Bremen	3 km	20 mins	Tram **6**: ①–⑥ every 10 mins, ⑦ every 20 mins	Main rail station	
VBS Brescia, Montichiari, Verona	Verona	50 km	45 mins	🚌 connects with Ryanair flights	Main rail station	
	Brescia	18 km	20 mins	🚌 connects with Ryanair flights	Main rail station	
BRS Bristol, International	Bristol	13 km	30 mins	🚌 *Airport Flyer Exp*: ①–⑥ 3 - 6 per hour; ⑦ 2 - 6 per hour	Temple Meads rail station, also bus station	
BRQ Brno	Brno	8 km	20 mins	🚌 **76**: 2 per hour	Main rail station, also bus station	
BRU Brussels, Zaventem	Brussels	12 km	25 mins	Train: 6 per hour	Midi / Zuid rail station (also calls at Central and Nord)	**401**
	Antwerpen	38 km	34 mins	Train: Ⓐ 2 per hour, Ⓒ hourly.	Centraal	**420, 432**
OTP București, Henri Coandă, Otopeni	București	16 km	45 mins	🚌 **783**; ①–⑤ every 15 - 30 mins; ⑥⑦ every 30 mins	Piața Victoriei (800m from Nord station or 1 stop on subway)	
	București	23 km	25 mins	Train: every 40 mins	Main rail station	
BUD Budapest, Ferihegy	Budapest	16 km	40 mins	🚌 **200E**: every 10 - 20 mins	Nagyvárad-tér metro station (metro connection to city centre)	
	Budapest	18 km	25 mins	Train: 2 - 6 per hour	🚌 **200E**, to Ferihegy station then train to Nyugati rail station.	
BZG Bydgoszcz	Bydgoszcz	4 km	30 mins	🚌 **80**: 2 per hour	Main rail station	
CCF Carcassonne, Salvaza	Carcassonne	5 km	10 mins	🚌: connects with Ryanair flights	Place Davilla and Carcassonne rail station	
CWL Cardiff	Cardiff	19 km	40 mins	🚌 *Airbus Xpress* **T9**: ①–⑥ hourly, ⑦ every 2 hours	Central rail station, city centre	
	Cardiff	19 km	50 mins	🚌 to Rhoose then train: ①–⑥ hourly, ⑦ every 2 hours	Central rail station	
CTA Catania Fontanarossa	Catania	5 km	9 mins	Train: hourly ± 2 per hour, 🚌 shuttle to station	Main rail station Catania Centrale, also Messina and Syracuse	
CRL Charleroi, Brussels South	Brussels	55 km	60 mins	🚌 *Brussels City Shuttle*: every 30 mins	Brussels Midi (corner of Rue de France / Rue de l'Instruction)	
	Charleroi	11 km	18 mins	🚌 *Line A*: ①–⑤ 2 per hour, ⑥⑦ hourly	Main rail station	
ORK Cork	Cork	8 km	25 mins	🚌 **226**: ①–⑥ 2 per hour, ⑦ hourly	Rail station, also Parnell Place bus station	
LDY Derry (Londonderry)	Londonderry	11 km	30 mins	🚌 connects with flights	Foyle Street bus station	
DNR Dinard - Pleurtuit - St-Malo	St Malo	14 km	20 mins	Taxis only. Dinard 6 km 10 mins		
DSA Doncaster - Sheffield	Doncaster	10 km	25 mins	🚌 **57a, 57c**: ①–⑥ 2 per hour; ⑦ hourly	Frenchgate Interchange (bus station)	
DTM Dortmund, Wickede	Dortmund	10 km	25 mins;	🚌 AirportExpress: every hour	Main rail station (Hbf). Also 🚌 to Holzwickede rail station	
DRS Dresden	Dresden	15 km	21 mins	Train (S-Bahn **S2**): every 30 mins	Main rail stations (Hbf and Neustadt)	**857a**
DUB Dublin	Dublin	11 km	60 mins	🚌 **16**: every 10 mins (15 mins on ⑦)	Bus station (Busáras) 30min, O'Connell St.	
	Belfast	157 km	130 mins	🚌 **705X**: 15 per day (0155 - 2255)	Glengall Street (City Centre) also serves Dublin city centre.	
DBV Dubrovnik, Čilipi	Dubrovnik	21 km	30 mins	🚌 *Atlas Bus*: connects with flights	Bus station	
DUS Düsseldorf, International	Düsseldorf	7 km	12 mins	Train (S-Bahn **S11**): Ⓐ every 20 mins, Ⓒ every 30 mins	Main rail station (Hauptbahnhof)	**800, 802**
EMA East Midlands, Nottingham - - Leicester - Derby	East Midlands	10 km	10 mins	Taxi shuttle	East Midlands Parkway rail station	
	Nottingham	21 km	55 mins	🚌 *Skylink*: 24/7, every 20 mins peak times	Greyfriar Gate (pending re-opening of Broadmarsh bus station)	
	Derby	19 km	45 mins	🚌 *Skylink*: 24/7, every 20 mins peak times	Bus station	
	Loughborough	8 km	25 mins	🚌 *Skylink*: 24/7, every 20 mins peak times	Lemyngton Street / High Street	
	Leicester	23 km	55 mins	🚌 *Skylink*: 24/7, every 20 mins peak times	St Margaret's bus station	
EDI Edinburgh, Turnhouse	Edinburgh	11 km	25 mins	🚌 *Airlink* **100**: every 20 mins. 0430 - 0030.	Haymarket rail station; St Andrew Square (for Waverley station)	
	Edinburgh	11 km	35 mins	Tram: every 3 - 8 mins 0618 - 1853, every 10 mins until 2248	Haymarket rail station; St Andrew Square (for Waverley station)	
ERF Erfurt	Erfurt	6 km	25 mins	Tram Line 4: Ⓐ 3 - 6 per hour, Ⓒ 2 per hour	Main rail station (Hauptbahnhof)	
EBJ Esbjerg	Esbjerg	12 km	21 mins	🚌 **7c / 944X**: hourly	*Bybusterminal*	
EXT Exeter	Exeter	8 km	35 mins	🚌 **56**: 1 per hour	St Davids rail station	
FAO Faro	Faro	6 km	20 mins	🚌 *Proxima* **16**: hourly	Rail station, Bus station	
FLR Firenze, Amerigo Vespucci	Firenze	7 km	20 mins	🚌 BusItalia *Vola in bus* **62**: every 30 mins	Santa Maria Novella rail station	
HHN Frankfurt, Hahn	Frankfurt	120 km	105 mins	🚌 connects with Ryanair flights	Mannheimer Straße, adjacent to main rail station (Hauptbahnhof)	
Also 🚌 to; Bingen, 60 mins; Heidelberg hbf, 140 mins; Koblenz, 70 mins; Köln hbf, 135 mins; Luxembourg, 110 mins; Mainz, 70 mins; Mannheim, 110 mins						
FRA Frankfurt	Frankfurt	10 km	15 mins	Train (S-Bahn **S8** or **S9**): 4 - 6 times hourly	Main rail station (Hauptbahnhof)	**917a**
FDH Friedrichshafen	Friedrichshafen	4 km	7 mins	Train: 1 - 2 trains per hour	Main rail station (Stadt) or Harbour (Hafen)	
GDN Gdańsk, Lech Walesa	Gdańsk	10 km	22 mins	Train *PKM*: Port Lotniczy, 3 - 4 per hour	Wrzeszcz rail station, then 3 stops (every 15 mins) to Główny	
GVA Genève	Genève	6 km	6 mins	Train: 5 times hourly	Cornavin rail station	**505, 570**
GOA Genova, Cristoforo Colombo	Genova	7 km	30 mins	🚌 *Volabus*: 1 - 2 per hour	Principe rail station	

‡ – The frequencies shown apply during daytime on weekdays and are from the airport to the city centre. There may be fewer journeys in the evenings, at weekends and during the winter months. Extended 🚌 journey times could apply during peak hours.

WARNING! Services are subject to alteration during coronavirus pandemic.

5 AIRPORT → CITY CENTRE LINKS

City Plans are on pages 30 – 34

Airport code and name	City	Distance	Journey	Transport ‡	City terminal	Table
GRO Girona	Girona	12 km	25 mins	🚌: hourly	Rail / Bus station (Estación autobuses)	
	Barcelona	102 km	70 mins	🚌 connects with Ryanair flights	Estacio del Nord, corner of carrer Ali Bei 80 / Sicilia	
GLA Glasgow, International	Glasgow	15 km	25 mins	🚌 **500**: ①–⑥ every 10 mins, ⑦ every 15 mins.	Central rail station	
PIK Glasgow, Prestwick	Glasgow	61 km	50 mins	Train: ①–⑥ 4 per hour, ⑦ 2 per hour	Central rail station	**216**
GOT Göteborg, Landvetter	Göteborg	25 km	30 mins	🚌: ①–⑤ 3 per hour, ⑥⑦ 2 - 3 per hour	Nils Ericson Terminalen (bus station) / Central rail station	
GRZ Graz	Graz	9 km	9 mins	Train **S5**: ①–⑥ 1 - 2 per hour, ⑦ every hour ¶	Main rail station (Hauptbahnhof)	**980**
GNB Grenoble, St Geoirs	Grenoble	37 km	45 mins	🚌 connects with flights	Main rail station, also bus station	
HAM Hamburg, Fuhlsbüttel	Hamburg	11 km	25 mins	Train (S-Bahn **S1**): every 10 mins	Main rail station (Hauptbahnhof)	
HAJ Hannover, Langenhagen	Hannover	15 km	18 mins	Train (S-Bahn **S5**): every 30 mins	Main rail station (Hauptbahnhof)	**809**
HEL Helsinki, Vantaa	Helsinki	19 km	35 mins	Train: ①–⑥ 4 - 6 per hour, ⑦ 3 - 4 per hour	Main rail station	
NOC Ireland West Airport Knock	Ballyhaunis	22 km	30 mins	🚌 **64**: 0855, 1255. 🚌 **440**: 1058, 1758.	Rail station **64** Ballyhaunis, **440** Claremorris	**235**
IOM Isle of Man, Ronaldsway	Douglas	16 km	30 mins	🚌 **1**: hourly (every 30 mins during peak periods)	Lord street	
IST İstanbul, Havalimani	istanbul	43 km	60 mins	🚌 *HAVAIST* **5** Airport Shuttle	Esenler Intercity Bus Terminal (city centre)	
SAW İstanbul, Sabiha Gökçen	İstanbul	32 km	60 mins	🚌: 1 – 2 per hour, 0540 - 2040	Bus station. Also Pendik rail station is 4km from airport	
XRY Jerez	Jerez	10 km	9 mins	Train: 11 trains per day	Jerez de la Frontera, then to Cadiz	**671**
FKB Karlsruhe - Baden-Baden	Baden-Baden	8 km	15 mins	🚌 **285** 1 an hour to Baden-Baden	Rail station; also **234, X34** to Rastatt rail station	
KTW Katowice, Pyrzowice	Katowice	34 km	50 mins	🚌 *ZTM*: **AP3** 1 per hour approx	Katowice Dworzec (main rail station)	
KUN Kaunas	Kaunas	13 km	40 mins	🚌 **29**	City centre	
	Vilnius	102 km	90 mins	🚌 connects with Ryanair flights	Hotel Panorama, close to bus and rail stations	
KLU Klagenfurt	Klagenfurt	5 km	25 mins	🚌 **45** (or walk to Annabichl rail station, then train or 🚌 **40**)	Main rail station and bus station	
CPH København, Kastrup	København	12 km	15 mins	Train: every 10 mins	Main rail station (Hovedbanegård)	**703**
	Malmö	36 km	22 mins	Train: every 20 mins	Central rail station	**703**
CGN Köln / Bonn, Konrad Adenauer	Bonn	25 km	32 mins	🚌 **SB60**: ①–⑤ 2 per hour; ⑥⑦ 1 - 2 per hour	Main rail station (Hauptbahnhof)	
	Köln	15 km	16 mins	Train **S13**: ①–⑤ every 20 mins, ⑥⑦ every 30 mins	Main rail station (Hbf). Also to Mönchengladbach, Koblenz	**802**
KRK Kraków John Paul II Airport (Balice)	Kraków	12 km	17 mins	Train: 2 per hour, from Lotnisko station	Kraków Główny	**1099**
KBP Kyiv, Boryspil	Kyiv	34 km	40 mins	Train: 1 - 2 per hour	Main rail station **Airport Temporarily Closed**	
LBA Leeds - Bradford	Leeds	16 km	45 mins	🚌 *Flyer* **A1**: 2 per hour	Main rail station and bus station	
	Bradford	11 km	40 mins	🚌 *Flyer* **A2, A3**: 2 per hour	Interchange rail station	
AOC Leipzig, Altenburg - Nobitz	Leipzig	75 km	70 mins	🚌 **250** *ThüSac*: connects with Ryanair flights	Main rail station. Also stops at Altenburg rail station after 15 mins	
LEJ Leipzig - Halle	Leipzig	20 km	14 mins	Train: 2 - 3 per hour	Main rail station (Hauptbahnhof)	**866, 881**
	Halle	18 km	12 mins	Train: 2 per hour	Main rail station (Hauptbahnhof)	**866, 881**
LNZ Linz, Blue Danube	Linz	12 km	19 mins	🚌 **601** connects with Ryanair flights	Main rail station. Also free 🚌 to Hörsching rail station, 3 mins	
LIS Lisboa, Portela	Lisboa	3 km	9 mins	Train, Red (Vermelho) line: every 5 - 9 mins	Oriente rail station. For Santa Apolónia change at São Sebastião	
LPL Liverpool, John Lennon	Liverpool	11 km	37 mins	🚌 **500**: every 30 mins 0400 - 2400	Lime Street rail station, Liverpool One bus station	
LJU Ljubljana, Jože Pučnik, Brnik	Ljubljana	26 km	45 mins	🚌: Ⓐ hourly 0500 - 2000, © 0700, every 2 hours 1000 - 2000	Bus station (Avtobusna postaja)	
LCJ Łódź, Lublinek	Łódź	6 km	20 mins	🚌 **65A, 65B**	Kaliska rail station	
LCY London, City	London	12 km	25 mins	Train (Docklands Light Railway): every 8 - 10 mins	Bank underground (tube) station	**100**
LGW London, Gatwick	London	44 km	30 mins	Train *Gatwick Express*: every 15 minutes	Victoria rail station	**102, 100, 185**
LHR London, Heathrow	London	24 km	15 mins	Train *Heathrow Express*: every 15 minutes	Paddington rail station	**100**
	London	24 km	58 mins	Underground train (tube): every 6 - 12 mins	King's Cross St Pancras rail station	**100**
LTN London, Luton	London	50 km	35 mins	🚌 to Parkway rail station, then train: 6 - 7 per hour	St Pancras International rail station	**103, 100, 170**
SEN London, Southend	London	64 km	55 mins	Train: 3 per hour	Liverpool Street rail station	
STN London, Stansted	London	55 km	46 mins	Train *Stansted Express*: every 15 minutes	Liverpool Street rail station	**100**
LBC Lübeck, Blankensee	Lübeck	8 km	30 mins	🚌 **6**: 2 per hour.	Bus station (bus stop 5). Also train from Flughafen 300m walk	**827**
LUZ Lublin	Lublin	10 km	15 mins	Train: ①–⑥ 2 - 3 per day, ⑦ 1 per day, connects with flights	Main rail station	
LUX Luxembourg, Findel	Luxembourg	7 km	25 mins	🚌 **16**: ①–⑥ every 15 mins ⑦, every 30 mins	Central rail station	
LWO Lviv, Skniliv	Lvov	10 km	25 mins	Trolleybus **29**: every 9 - 16 minutes 0600 - 2215	City Centre	
LYS Lyon, St Exupéry	Lyon	23 km	30 mins	Tram *RhôneExpress*: 4 per hour	Part Dieu rail station	
	Chambéry	87 km	60 mins	🚌 Flixbus: 2 per day	Bus station (gare routière)	
	Grenoble	91 km	65 mins	🚌 Flixbus: hourly 0830 - 2000	Bus station (gare routière); Place de la Grenoble	
MAD Madrid, Barajas T4	Madrid	12 km	16 mins	Train Cercanías from T4: every 15/20 mins 0602 - 2225.	Chamartín, also Atocha 29 mins. 🚌 from T4 to T1, T2 and T3.	
AGP Málaga	Málaga	8 km	12 mins	Train: every 30 mins	María Zambrano (Renfe) and Centro-Alameda rail stations	**662**
MMX Malmö, Sturup	Malmö	30 km	40 mins	🚌 *flygbussarna*: 1 - 2 per hour	Central rail station	
MAN Manchester	Manchester	16 km	20 mins	Train: every 10 minutes 0419 - 0038	Piccadilly rail station	
MRS Marseille, Provence	Marseille	28 km	25 mins	🚌 L91: every 30 mins. See also rail / bus on Table **351**	St Charles rail station; also 🚌 to Aix TGV rail stn. every 30 mins	
FMM Memmingen	Memmingen	5 km	10 mins	🚌 **2, 810**	Bus station and rail station; also 🚌 to München, 80 mins	
LIN Milano, Linate	Milano	9 km	20 mins	1) 🚌 **73**: every 10 mins; 2) 🚌 *Starfly*: every 30 mins	1) Piazza S. Babila, Metro line 1; 2) Centrale rail station	
MXP Milano, Malpensa	Milano	45 km	40 mins	Train: 1) Malpensa Express: every 30 mins; 2) 1 - 2 per hour	1) Cadorna and Bovisa rail stations; 2) Centrale rail station	**606**
		45 km	50 mins	🚌 *Bus Express*: 2 per hour. 🚌 *Shuttle Air*: 3 per hour	Centrale rail station. Also 🚌 to Gallarate (Table **590**)	
BGY Milano, Orio al Serio, Bergamo	Milano	45 km	60 mins	🚌: 1 - 2 per hour	Centrale rail station (Air Terminal)	
	Bergamo	4 km	10 mins	🚌 **ATB 1**: 2 per hour	Rail station	
MSQ Minsk	Minsk	42 km	60 mins	🚌 **173, 300**	Vostochniy and Moskovskiy bus stations	
DME Moskva, Domodedovo	Moskva	35 km	47 mins	Train, *Aeroexpress*: 1 - 2 per hour approx	Paveletskaya rail station	**1901**
SVO Moskva, Sheremetyevo	Moskva	35 km	35 mins	Train, *Aeroexpress*: 1 - 2 per hour approx	Belorusskaya rail station	**1901**
VKO Moskva, Vnukovo	Moskva	28 km	40 mins	Train, *Aeroexpress*: 1 per hour approx	Kiyevskaya rail station	**1901**
MUC München, International	München	37 km	40 mins	Train: **S1, S8** for Hbf, every 10 mins; **S8** for Ost, every 20 mins	Main rail stations (Hauptbahnhof, Ostbahnhof)	**892**
	Freising	6 km	10 mins	Train: hourly 0828 - 0028	Rail station for Regensburg and connections to Passau	**892, 878**
RMU Murcia, Corvera	Murcia	25km	30 mins	🚌 connects with flights	City centre	
NTE Nantes, Atlantique	Nantes	9 km	20 mins	🚌 *Tan Air*: ⚒ 0615 - 2315, † 0700 - 2315; every 20/30 mins	Main rail station	
NAP Napoli, Capodichino	Napoli	7 km	15 mins	🚌 *Alibus*: 2 per hour	Piazza Garibaldi (Centrale rail station)	
NCL Newcastle, International	Newcastle	9 km	25 mins	Metro train: every 12 mins	Main rail station	

‡ – The frequencies shown apply during daytime on weekdays and are from the airport to the city centre. There may be fewer journeys in the evenings, at weekends and during the winter months. Extended 🚌 journey times could apply during peak hours.

¶ – Graz Airport - Feldkirchen rail station is located about 300 metres away from the airport.

City Plans are on pages 30 – 34

AIRPORT → CITY CENTRE LINKS

5

Airport code and name	City	Distance	Journey	Transport ‡	City terminal	Table
NCE Nice, Côte d'Azur	Nice	5 km	7 mins	Train from Nice St Augustin (see note ◧)	SNCF station	**361**
		7 km	24 mins	Tram **2**: ①–⑤ every 9 mins, ⑥ 6 per hour, ⑦ 5 per hour	Magnan (Central Nice), Durandy (Nice Ville)	
FNI Nîmes - Arles - Camargue	Nîmes	12 km	20 mins	🚌 connects with Ryanair flights	Rail station	
NWI Norwich	Norwich	8 km	24 mins	🚌 **501**: ①–⑥ 4 per hour 0805 - 1735	Bus station	
NUE Nürnberg	Nürnberg	6 km	12 mins	Train U-bahn **U2**: 4 - 6 per hour	Main rail station (Hauptbahnhof)	
ODS Odesa	Odesa	9 km	30 mins	🚌 **117**: Trolleybus **14**	Rail station	
OSL Oslo, Gardermoen	Oslo	49 km	19 mins	Train *Flytoget*: 3 - 6 per hour	Central rail station	**771**
TRF Oslo, Sandefjord Torp	Oslo	123 km	116 mins	🚌 to Torp rail station (4 mins), then train to Oslo	Also 🚌 to Oslo Bus terminal	**783**
RYG Oslo, Rygge	Oslo	69 km	51 mins	🚌 connects with Ryanair flights to Rygge rail station (4 km).	Sentral rail station (51 mins from Rygge to Oslo Sentral)	**770**
OSR Ostrava, Leoš Janáček	Ostrava	31km	31 mins	Train **S4**: 10 per day	Ostrava hlavní	
PMO Palermo, Falcone-Borsellino	Palermo	24 km	45 mins	Train *Trinacria express*: ①–⑥ 2 per hour, ⑦ hourly	Centrale rail station	
PMI Palma, Mallorca	Palma	11 km	30 mins	🚌 **A1**: every 30 mins	Paseo de Mallorca, Plaça d'Espanya (for rail stations), the Port	
BVA Paris, Beauvais	Paris	80 km	75 mins	🚌 connects with Ryanair and WizzAir flights	Porte Maillot, Metro (Line 1) for Châtelet Les Halles, Gare de Lyon	
CDG Paris, Charles de Gaulle	Paris	25 km	35 mins	RER train (Line B): every 7 - 15 mins	Nord, Châtelet Les Halles, and St Michel rail stations	**398**
	Disneyland	23 km	45 mins	🚌 **VEA** Magical Navette / Shuttle: every 20 minutes	Disneyland Resort, Disneyland hotels	
ORY Paris, Orly	Paris	15 km	35 mins	🚌 to Pont de Rungis, then RER train (Line C): 4 per hr.	Austerlitz, St Michel, Musée d'Orsay, and Invalides rail stns.	**398**
	Paris	15 km	35 mins	ORLYVAL shuttle to Antony then RER train, (Line B): 4 per hr.	Châlet-Les-Halles, Nord rail stations	**398**
PGF Perpignan, Rivesaltes	Perpignan	5 km	15 mins	🚌 connects with flights	Rail station, bus station (gare routière)	
PSA Pisa, Galileo Galilei	Pisa	2 km	5 mins	People Mover: every 5 - 8 minutes 0600 - 2400	Centrale rail station	
OPO Porto	Porto	17 km	35 mins	Metro Train: Line E, 3 per hour	Campanhã rail station	
POZ Poznań, Ławica	Poznań	6 km	21 mins	🚌 **159** *MPK*: 2 - 3 per hour	Rail station (Główny)	
PRG Praha, Václav Havel	Praha	24 km	25 mins	🚌 **AE** *Airport Express*: every 20 - 30 mins 0530 - 2100	Hlavní rail station	
	Praha	17 km	60 mins	🚌 **119**: every 10 mins	Nádraží Veleslavín metro station, then Metro line A to muzeum	
PUY Pula	Pula	6 km	15 mins	🚌 connects with flights	Main bus station.	
REU Reus	Reus	6 km	11 mins	🚌 **50** *Hispano Igualadina*: hourly 0800, 0905 - 2005	Rail station	**652**
	Barcelona	90 km	90 mins	🚌 *Hispano Igualadina* connects with Ryanair flights	Sants rail station	
KEF Reykjavík, Keflavík	Reykjavík	50 km	45 mins	🚌 *flybus* connects with all flights	BSÍ bus terminal	
RIX Riga	Riga	13 km	30 mins	🚌 **22**: every 10 - 30 mins	Abrenes iela (street) next to rail station	
RJK Rijeka	Rijeka	30 km	45 mins	🚌 *Autotrans*: connects with flights	Bus station, Jelačić Square	
CIA Roma, Ciampino	Roma	15 km	35 mins	🚌 *Airlink*: 1 - 3 per hour, to Ciampino, then train	Termini rail station	**622**
FCO Roma, Fiumicino	Roma	26 km	42 mins	Train: ①–⑥ 4 per hour, ⑦ 2 per hour	Ostiense and Tiburtina rail stations	**622**
(also known as Leonardo da Vinci)		26 km	32 mins	Train *Leonardo Express*: every 30 mins	Termini rail station	**622**
RTM Rotterdam	Rotterdam	5 km	20 mins	*Airport Shuttle* **33**: ①–⑤ every 10 mins, ⑥⑦ every 15 mins	Groot Handelsgebouw (adjacent to Centraal rail station)	
RZE Rzeszów, Jasionka	Rzeszów	15 km	20 mins	🚌 **51**: connects with flights	Main rail station and bus station	
LED St Peterburg, Pulkovo II	St Peterburg	17 km	60 mins	🚌 **39, 39Ex, K39** (Minivan Taxi)	Moskovskaya Metro station, Line 2 for Nevski Pr. (see City Plans)	
SZG Salzburg, W. A. Mozart	Salzburg	5 km	22 mins	🚌 **2**: ①–⑥ every 10 - 20 mins, ⑦ every 20 mins	Main rail station	
SIP Simferopol	Simferopol	12 km	28 mins	🚌 **49a, 20** (trolleybus): every 10–15 mins	Main rail station	
SKP Skopje, Alexander the Great	Skopje	14 km	25 mins	🚌 Airport Shuttle Service: connects with flights	Bus station	
SOF Sofia, International	Sofia	10 km	26 mins	Train Line **1**: from Terminal 2, every 10 mins	City centre. Change at Serdika for Line **2**, for Central rail station	
SOU Southampton	Southampton	8 km	8 mins	Train: 50 metres from terminal, 4 - 5 trains per hour	Central rail station	**106, 114**
SPU Split, Kaštela	Split	16 km	50 mins	🚌: connects with flights	Bus station. Departs 200m from Airport terminal	
SVG Stavanger, Sola	Stavanger	14 km	30 mins	🚌: ①–⑤ every 20 mins, ⑥ 2 per hour, ⑦ hourly	Atlantic Hotel / Fiskepiren	
ARN Stockholm, Arlanda	Stockholm	44 km	20 mins	*Arlanda Express* train: every 15 mins	Central rail station	**747, 760**
NYO Stockholm, Skavsta	Stockholm	103 km	80 mins	🚌: connects with flights	Cityterminal (bus station), also 🚌 to Nyköping rail station	
VST Stockholm, Västerås	Stockholm	107 km	75 mins	🚌: connects with Ryanair flights	Cityterminal (bus station), also 🚌 **941** to Västerås rail station	
SXB Strasbourg, Entzheim	Strasbourg	10 km	8 mins	Train: from Entzheim Aéroport (300m walk) 1 - 5 per hour	Gare Centrale (Central rail station)	**382**
STR Stuttgart, Echterdingen	Stuttgart	20 km	27 mins	Train (S-Bahn **S2, S3**): 2 - 4 times hourly	Main rail station (Hauptbahnhof)	**936a**
SZZ Szczecin, Goleniów	Szczecin	35 km	40 mins	Train: 14 - 20 per day.	Szczecin Główny.	
TLL Tallinn, Ülemiste	Tallinn	5 km	27 mins	🚌: various frequent services 0600 - 0000	Balti jaam (rail station)	
TMP Tampere, Pirkkala	Tampere	18 km	25 mins	🚌 connects with Ryanair flights	Main rail station	
TBS Tbilisi	Tbilisi	19 km	35 mins	Train	Rail station	**1995**
TIA Tirana (Tiranë), Nënë Tereza	Tirana	12 km	45 mins	🚌 *1. Rinas Express, 2. LU-NA shpk*: every hour 0600 - 1800	1. National Museum city centre 2. National Theatre of Opera	
TRN Torino, Caselle	Torino	16 km	20 mins	*GTT* train: every 30 mins	Torino Porta Susa rail station. Change at Venaria for 🚌 **SF2**	
	Torino	16 km	30 mins	🚌: ①–⑤ half hourly, ⑥⑦ hourly	Torino Porta Nuova and Porta Susa rail stations	
TLS Toulouse, Blagnac	Toulouse	8 km	38 mins	Tram **T2**: every 15 minutes for Arènes then Metro line **A**	for Marengo-SNCF, then 300m to Matabiau rail station	
	Toulouse	8 km	20 mins	🚌 *Aero*: every 20 minutes	Place Jeanne d'Arc / Matabiau rail / bus station (gare routière)	
TRS Trieste, Ronchi dei Legionari	Trieste	33 km	29 mins	Train: hourly	Rail station	**601**
	Monfalcone	5 km	6 mins	Train: hourly	Rail station	**601**
TRD Trondheim, Værnes	Trondheim	33 km	37 mins	Train: ①–⑤ hourly, ⑥⑦ every two hours	Rail station. Værnes rail station is 220m from Airport terminal	**787**
VLC València	València	9 km	22 mins	Train Lines **3, 5**: Ⓐ every 15 mins; Ⓒ every 20 mins	Xátiva for Nord rail station	
VCE Venezia, Marco Polo	Venezia	12 km	25 mins	🚌 **5, 35**: 2 per hour	Piazzale Roma (see city plans p32)	
	Venezia		80 mins	Waterbus *Alilaguna*: ± every 30 mins	Lido 53 - 63 mins / Piazza S. Marco, 72 - 80 mins	
TSF Venezia, Treviso	Venezia	30 km	70 mins	🚌: connects with flights	Mestre rail station, Piazzale Roma (see city plans p32)	
VRN Verona, Villafranca	Verona	12 km	20 mins	🚌: every 20 mins 0635 - 2335	Rail station	
VNO Vilnius	Vilnius	4 km	7 mins	Train: every ± 40 minutes	Rail station	**1816**
WAW Warszawa, Frederic Chopin, Okęcie,	Warszawa	13 km	23 mins	SKM / KM train: 3 - 5 per hour	Śródmieście (2 - 3 per hr) or Centralna (1 - 2 per hr) rail stations	
WMI Warszawa, Modlin	Warszawa	40 km	59 mins	🚌 to Modlin rail stn, then train: approx 1 - 2 per hour	Centralna or Gdánska rail stations	**1099**
NRN Weeze, Niederhein	Düsseldorf	70 km	75 mins	🚌: connects with Ryanair flights	Main rail station (Hauptbahnhof) Worringer Street	
	Düsseldorf	74 km	82 mins	🚌 **SW1**: to Weeze rail station, then train	Main rail station (Hauptbahnhof)	**802**
VIE Wien, Schwechat	Wien	21 km	16 mins	*City Airport Train (CAT)*: every 30 mins (special fares)	Mitte rail station	**985**
	Wien	21 km	25 mins	S-bahn: every 30 mins	Mitte rail station	**985**
	Bratislava	54 km	60 mins	🚌 *ÖBB - Postbus / Slovak Lines*: hourly	AS Mlynské nivy (bus station) / Einsteinnova/Petrzalka	**985**
WRO Wrocław, Copernicus	Wrocław	10 km	40 mins	🚌 **106**: every 15 minutes	Rail station, bus station	
ZAG Zagreb	Zagreb	17 km	40 mins	🚌: 1 - 2 per hour connects with flights	Bus station (Autobusni kolodvor), Avenija Marina Drzica	
ZAZ Zaragoza	Zaragoza	10 km	30 mins	🚌: ①–⑥ 1 - 2 per hour 0615 - 2315, ⑦ hourly 0645 - 2245	Paseo María Agustín, 150m from Portillo rail station	
ZRH Zürich	Zürich	10 km	13 mins	Train: 7 - 8 per hour	Main rail station (HB)	**505, 510, 530, 535, 555, 560**
ZQW Zweibrücken	Zweibrucken	4 km	10 mins	Taxi	Rail station. Also 🚌 **199** to Saarbrücken	**918**

‡ – The frequencies shown apply during daytime on weekdays and are from the airport to the city centre. There may be fewer journeys in the evenings, at weekends and during the winter months. Extended 🚌 journey times could apply during peak hours.

◧ – Nice St Augustin station is approximately 800m from Terminal 1.

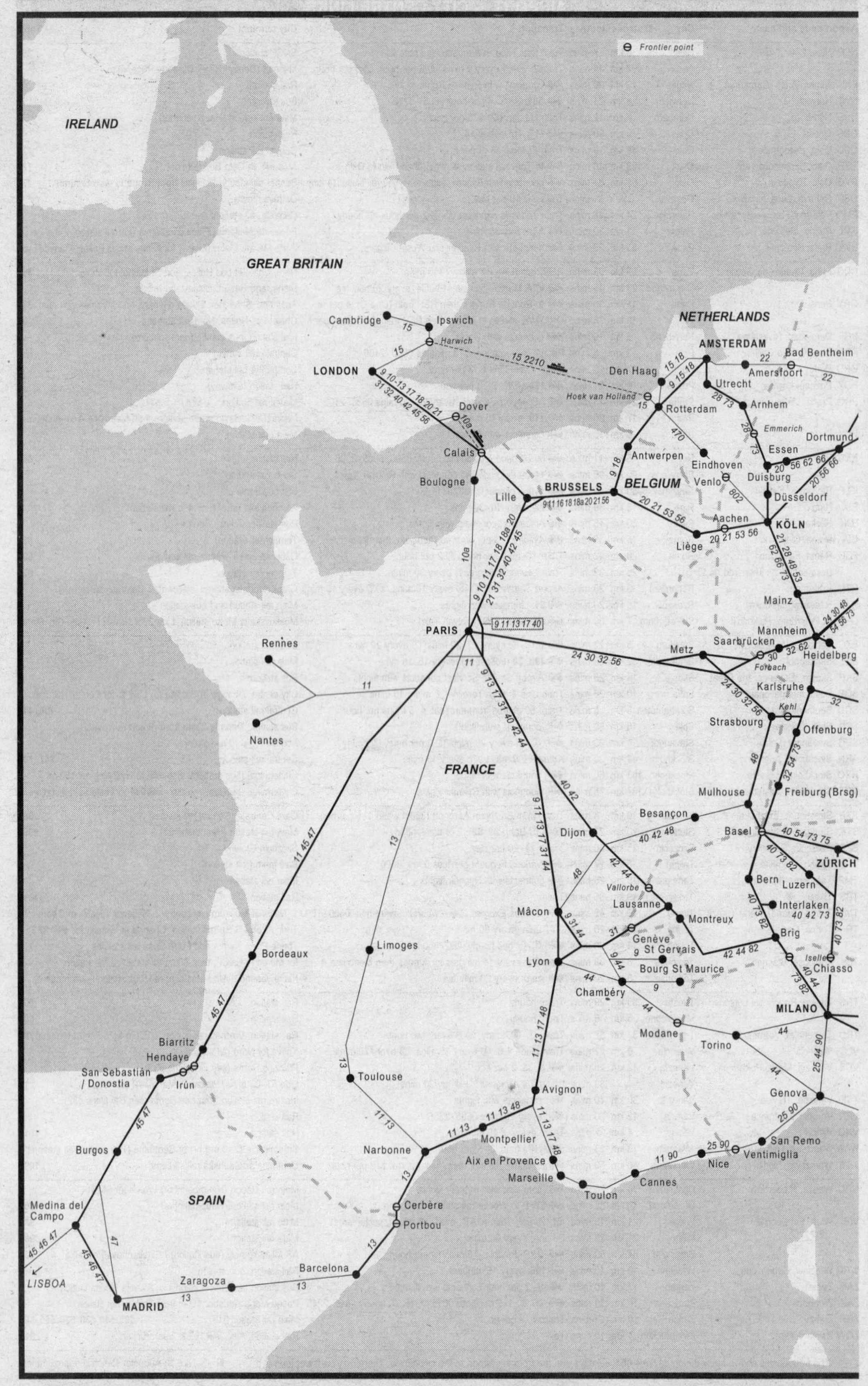
Frontier point
IRELAND
GREAT BRITAIN
NETHERLANDS
BELGIUM
FRANCE
SPAIN
Cambridge
Ipswich
Harwich
LONDON
Dover
Calais
Boulogne
Lille
BRUSSELS
PARIS
Rennes
Nantes
AMSTERDAM
Den Haag
Hoek van Holland
Rotterdam
Utrecht
Amersfoort
Bad Bentheim
Arnhem
Emmerich
Antwerpen
Eindhoven
Venlo
Essen
Dortmund
Duisburg
Düsseldorf
Aachen
Liège
KÖLN
Mainz
Mannheim
Heidelberg
Saarbrücken
Forbach
Metz
Karlsruhe
Kehl
Strasbourg
Offenburg
Freiburg (Brsg)
Mulhouse
Besançon
Basel
ZÜRICH
Dijon
Bern
Luzern
Interlaken
Vallorbe
Lausanne
Montreux
Brig
Mâcon
Genève
St Gervais
Iselle
Chiasso
Lyon
Bourg St Maurice
Chambéry
Modane
MILANO
Torino
Genova
Limoges
Bordeaux
Biarritz
Hendaye
Irún
San Sebastián / Donostia
Toulouse
Avignon
Montpellier
Narbonne
Aix en Provence
Marseille
Toulon
Cannes
Nice
Ventimiglia
San Remo
Cerbère
Portbou
Barcelona
Burgos
Medina del Campo
LISBOA
Zaragoza
MADRID

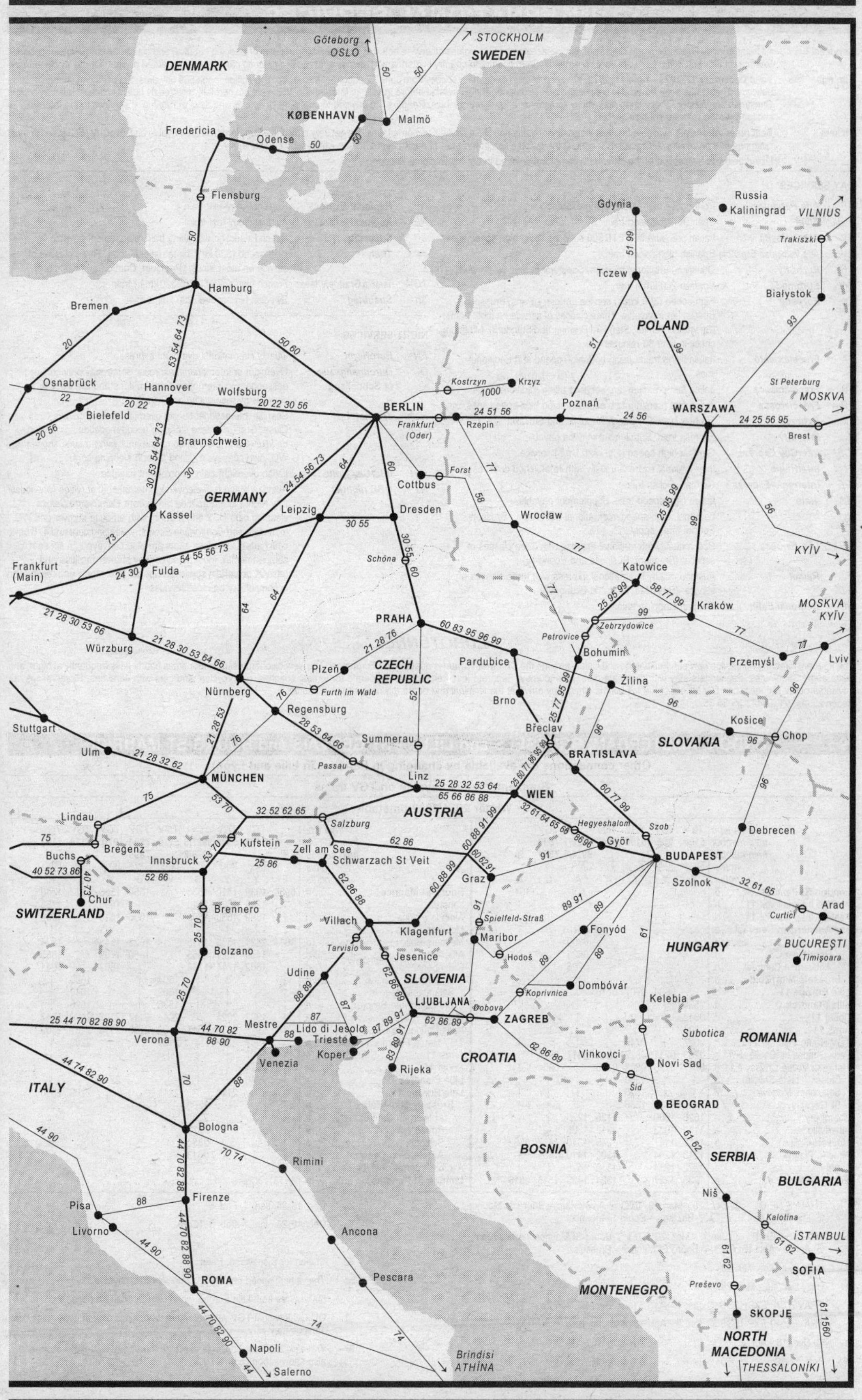
Göteborg
OSLO
STOCKHOLM
SWEDEN
DENMARK
KØBENHAVN
Malmö
Fredericia
Odense
Flensburg
Hamburg
Bremen
Osnabrück
Hannover
Wolfsburg
Bielefeld
Braunschweig
BERLIN
Kostrzyn
Krzyz
Frankfurt (Oder)
Rzepin
Poznań
Gdynia
Tczew
POLAND
Russia
Kaliningrad
VILNIUS
Trakiszki
Białystok
WARSZAWA
St Peterburg
MOSKVA
Brest
KYĪV
Cottbus
Forst
Dresden
Leipzig
Kassel
GERMANY
Frankfurt (Main)
Fulda
Würzburg
Schöna
Wrocław
Katowice
Kraków
MOSKVA
KYĪV
PRAHA
CZECH REPUBLIC
Plzeň
Furth im Wald
Pardubice
Brno
Petrovice
Zebrzydowice
Bohumin
Žilina
Przemyśl
Lviv
Nürnberg
Regensburg
Stuttgart
Ulm
MÜNCHEN
Passau
Summerau
Linz
Břeclav
BRATISLAVA
SLOVAKIA
Košice
Chop
WIEN
AUSTRIA
Salzburg
Lindau
Bregenz
Buchs
Chur
SWITZERLAND
Innsbruck
Kufstein
Zell am See
Schwarzach St Veit
Hegyeshalom
Györ
Szob
BUDAPEST
Debrecen
Szolnok
Curtici
Arad
BUCUREŞTI
Timişoara
Graz
Spielfeld-Straß
Maribor
Hodoš
Brennero
Villach
Tarvisio
Klagenfurt
Jesenice
SLOVENIA
Fonyód
Dombóvár
Koprivnica
HUNGARY
Bolzano
Udine
LJUBLJANA
Dobova
ZAGREB
Kelebia
Subotica
ROMANIA
Verona
Mestre
Lido di Jesolo
Trieste
Koper
Venezia
Rijeka
CROATIA
Vinkovci
Šid
Novi Sad
BEOGRAD
ITALY
Bologna
Rimini
BOSNIA
SERBIA
BULGARIA
Niš
Kalotina
İSTANBUL
SOFIA
Pisa
Livorno
Firenze
Ancona
Pescara
ROMA
Preševo
MONTENEGRO
SKOPJE
NORTH MACEDONIA
THESSALONÍKI
Napoli
Salerno
Brindisi
ATHÍNA

INTERNATIONAL SERVICES

Services All trains convey first and second classes of seating accommodation unless otherwise noted. For information on types of sleeping car (🛏) and couchette car (▬) see page 10. Restaurant (✕) and buffet (🍷) cars vary considerably from country to country in standard of service offered. The catering car may not be carried or open for the whole journey.

Timings **Valid December 12, 2021 - June 11, 2022.** Advance details of summer services from June 12 appear at the back of this edition, page 569 onwards. Services can change at short notice and passengers are advised to consult the latest European Rail Timetable before travelling. International trains are not normally affected by public holidays, but may alter at Christmas and Easter - these changes (where known) are shown in the tables. Readers are advised to cross-check timings and days of running of services in the International section with the relevant country section.

Tickets **Seat reservations** are available for most international trains and are advisable as some trains can get very crowded. **Supplements** are payable on **EuroCity** (*EC*) trains in most countries and on most InterCity trains – consult the introduction at the start of each country to see which supplements apply.

Listed below is a selection of the different types of trains found in the International Section.

DAY SERVICES:

AP	***Alfa Pendular***	Portuguese high-quality tilting express train.
Alvia	***Alvia***	Spanish high-speed train.
AV	***Alta Velocità***	Italian premium fare **ETR 500** services using high-speed lines.
AVE	***Alta Velocidad Española***	Spanish high-speed train.
EC	***EuroCity***	Quality international express. Supplement may be payable.
Em	***Euromed***	Spanish 200 km/h train.
☆	***Eurostar***	High-speed (300 km/h) service London - Paris / Brussels. Special fares payable. Three classes of service on most trains: (Business Premier, Standard Premier and Standard). Minimum check-in time 30 minutes.
FA	***Frecciargento***	Italian tilting trains using both high-speed and traditional lines.
FB	***Frecciabianca***	Italian fast premium fare services using traditional lines.
FR	***Frecciarossa***	Italian fast premium fare services using high-speed lines.
Ex	***Express***	Express between Czech Republic and Slovakia.
IC	***InterCity***	Express train. Supplement may be payable.
ICE	***InterCity Express***	German high-speed (230 - 320 km/h) service.
IR	***InterRegio***	Inter-regional express usually with refurbished coaches.
IRE	***Interregio-Express***	German / Polish train.
ITA	***.italo***	Italian high-speed train. Supplement payable.
izy	***izy***	Low cost, high-speed international train Paris - Brussels. Special fares apply.
LE	***Leo Express***	Czech quality international express with three classes of service: (Premium, Business and Economy).
RJ *RJX*	***Railjet***	Austrian quality international express with three classes of service: (Business, First and Economy).
RB	***Regional Bahn***	German stopping train.
RE	***Regional Express***	Regional semi-fast train.
REX	***Regional Express***	Austrian semi-fast train.
SC	***SuperCity***	Czech Pendolino **680** tilting train, supplement payable.
⇌	***Thalys***	High-speed (300 km/h) international train. Three classes of service on most trains: (Premium, Comfort and Standard).
TGV	**Train à Grande Vitesse**	French high-speed (270 - 320 km/h) train.
Sn	***Snabbtåg***	Swedish high-speed (200 km/h) train.

NIGHT SERVICES:

EN	***EuroNight***	Quality international overnight express.
D	***Durchgangszug*** or **Schnellzug**	Overnight or international express. Some may only convey passengers to international destinations and are likely to be compulsory reservation, marked 🅁.
Hotel	***Trenhotel***	Spanish international quality overnight train. Conveys Gran Clase / Grande Classe sleeping accommodation comprising *de luxe* (1 and 2 berth) compartments with en-suite shower and WC. Also conveys 1, 2 and 4 berth sleeping cars.
ICN	***InterCity Notte***	Italian overnight train, supplement payable.
NJ	***ÖBB nightjet***	Austrian brand name covering international services (previously City Night Line). Facilities range from *Comfortline Deluxe* sleeping cars (1, 2 and 3 berth) with en-suite shower and WC, to modernised *Comfortline Economy* sleeping cars and 4 / 6 berth couchettes. 2nd class seats are also conveyed (in six seat compartments). Most trains convey shower facilities and 🍷 (also ✕ on certain services). Special fares apply and reservation is compulsory on most services.

EUROTUNNEL

The frequent car-carrying service between Folkestone and Calais through the **Channel Tunnel** is operated by Eurotunnel. The service operates up to four times hourly (less frequently at night) and takes about 35 minutes. Passengers stay with their cars during the journey. Separate less-frequent trains operate for lorries, coaches, motorcycles, and cars with caravans. Reservations are advisable but passengers can buy tickets at the toll booths when they arrive at the terminal and board the next available shuttle.

Reservations: ✆ 08443 35 35 35.

9 LONDON, AMSTERDAM, BRUSSELS and LILLE - ST GERVAIS and BOURG ST MAURICE

Other connections are available by changing in Paris (or in Lille and Lyon)

Supplements are payable on TGV trains

Winter 2021/2022 timetable.

train type	*TGV*	*TGV*	*TGV*	*TGV*	⇌	*TGV*		
train number	**5190**	**964**	**5108**	**5146**	**9920/1**	**7890**		
train number					**9924/5**	**7891**	❦	
notes	R 🍷	R 🍷	R 🍷	R 🍷	R 🍷	⊠		
notes	**Y**	**Y**	**Y**	**Y**	**A**	**C**	**E**	
London St Pancras d.	...	...	...	...	...	...	1945	...
Ashford International **11** a.	...	...	...	...	...	...	|	...
Ashford International **11** d.	...	...	...	...	...	...	|	...
Amsterdam Centraal d.	...	...	...	...	0540	...	|	...
Schiphol d.	...	...	...	...	0600	...	|	...
Rotterdam CS d.	...	...	...	...	0625	...	|	...
Antwerpen Centraal d.	...	...	...	...	0706	...	|	...
Brussels Midi / Zuid d.	...	...	...	...	0800	...	|	...
Lille Europe 11 d.	...	0604	0707	0718	|	...	|	...
Lille Flandres ◇ d.	0530	|	|	|	|	...	|	...
Douai **11** d.	0549	|	|	|	|	...	|	...
Arras **11** d.	0607	|	|	|	|	...	|	...
TGV Haute Picardie **11** d.	0627	|	0746	|	|	...	|	...
Paris Charles de Gaulle ✈ **11** d.	0703	0711	0822	0819	0917	0934	|	...
Marne la Valleé Chessy § **11** d.	0717	0725	0838	0835	|	0954	|	...
Cluses (Haute Savoie) a.	|	|	1300	|	|	|	|	...
Salanches Megève a.	|	|	1325	|	|	|	|	...
St Gervais a.	|	|	1336	|	|	|	|	...
Chambéry a.	1026	1000	...	1125	1225	|	|	...
Albertville a.	1110	1053	...	1213	1305	1401	|	...
Moûtiers-Salins a.	1157	1147	...	1246	1340	1437	0532	...
Aime la Plagne a.	1213	1204	...	1302	1410	1455	|	...
Landry a.	1222	1214	...	1312	1420	|	|	...
Bourg St Maurice a.	1235	1227	...	1324	1435	1516	0616	...

train type		*TGV*	*TGV*	⇌	*TGV*	*TGV*	*TGV*	*TGV*	*TGV*	
train number		**5174**	**5188**	**9987/6**	**5178**	**7894**	**970**	**5178**	**5198**	
train number	❦			**9979/8**		**7895**				
notes		R 🍷	R 🍷	R 🍷	R 🍷	⊠	R 🍷	R 🍷	R 🍷	
notes	**F**	**Y**	**Y**	**B**	**W**	**D**	**Y**	**X**	**P**	
Bourg St Maurice d.	0934	1339	1510	1535	...	1550	1558	...	1748	...
Landry d.	|	1349	1520	1540	...	|	1608	...	1758	...
Aime la Plagne d.	|	1359	1530	1600	...	1606	1618	...	1808	...
Moûtiers-Salins a.	|	|	|	|	...	|	|	...	|	...
Moûtiers-Salins d.	1014	1424	1555	1615	...	1623	1643	...	1824	...
Albertville d.	|	1450	1621	1655	...	1659	1709	...	1855	...
Chambéry d.	|	1602	1714	1740	...	|	1802	...	1941	...
St Gervais d.	|	|	|	|	1504	|	|	1600	|	...
Salanches Megève d.	|	|	|	|	1509	|	|	1610	|	...
Cluses (Haute Savoie) d.	|	|	|	|	1535	|	|	1626	|	...
Marne la Vallée Chessy § **11** a.	|	1902	2024	|	2044	2117	2102	2120	2247	...
Paris Charles de Gaulle ✈ **11** a.	|	1916	2038	2047	2106	2133	2116	2137	2302	...
TGV Haute Picardie **11** a.	|	1947	|	|	2139	...	|	2209	|	...
Arras **11** a.	|	2007	|	|	|	...	|	|	|	...
Douai **11** a.	|	2024	|	|	|	...	|	|	|	...
Lille Flandres ◇ a.	|	2046	|	|	|	...	2214	|	|	...
Lille Europe 11 a.	|	...	2133	|	2211	...	...	2239	2356	...
Brussels Midi / Zuid a.	|	...	...	2205	...	...	...	...	...	...
Antwerpen Centraal a.	|	...	...	2257	...	...	...	...	...	...
Rotterdam CS a.	|	...	...	2333	...	...	...	...	...	...
Schiphol a.	|	...	...	2354	...	...	...	...	...	...
Amsterdam Centraal a.	|	...	...	0013	...	...	...	...	...	...
Ashford International **11** a.	|	...	...	...	...	...	...	...	...	...
London St Pancras a.	1613	...	...	...	...	...	...	...	...	...

A – THALYS NEIGE – ⑥ Dec. 25 - Mar. 19: (12) 🍷 Amsterdam - Bourg St Maurice; ⑥ Mar. 26. - Apr. 9: (12) 🍷 Brussels - Bourg St Maurice.

B – THALYS NEIGE – ⑥ Jan. 1 - Mar. 26: (12) 🍷 Bourg St Maurice - Amsterdam; ⑥ Apr. 2 - Apr. 16: (12) 🍷 Bourg St Maurice - Brussels.

C – Daily Dec. 12 - Mar. 28.

D – Daily Dec. 16 - Mar. 28.

E – TRAVELSKI EXPRESS ⑤ Jan. 7 - Apr. 8 (also Dec. 26, Jan 2).

F – TRAVELSKI EXPRESS ⑥ Jan. 8 - Apr. 16 (also Jan. 3).

P – ⑥ Dec. 18 - Apr. 2.

W – Feb. 12, 19.

X – Dec. 18, 25, Jan. 1, Feb. 5.

Y – Dec. 18, 25, Jan. 1, Feb. 5, 12, 19.

§ – Station for Disneyland, Paris.

⇌ – *Thalys* high-speed train R 🍷. Special fares payable.

◇ – 500 metres from Lille Europe (see Lille City Plan on page 32).

⊠ – OUIGO low-cost TGV service. Internet bookings only at www.ouigo.com. Timings may vary.

❦ – *Travelski Express*, bookings available through www.travelski.com and also snowcarbon.co.uk

LONDON - LILLE - PARIS and BRUSSELS *by Eurostar* — 10

Minimum check-in time is 30 minutes, but passengers are advised to allow longer due to immigration procedures. Not available for London - Ebbsfleet - Ashford or v.v. Special fares payable that include three classes of service: business premier, standard premier and standard. All times shown are local times (France and Belgium are one hour ahead of Great Britain). All Eurostar services are Ⓡ, non-smoking and convey ✕ in Business Premier and Standard Premier, 🍸 in Standard.

Service June 12 - July 30. For service July 31 - November 5 see page 48. For service November 6 - December 10 see page 37.

km	km	*train number*	**9080**	**9004**	**9110**	**9008**	**9114**	**9116**	**9014**	**9018**	**9126**	**9024**	**9132**
		notes	①–⑤	①–⑤	⑥		①–⑥						
		notes					A				A		
0	*0*	**London** St Pancras d.	0559	0701	0704	0801	0816	0901	0931	1022	1104	1231	1304
35	*35*	Ebbsfleet International d.	|	|	|	|	|	|	|	|	|	|	|
90	*90*	Ashford International d.	|	|	|	|	|	|	|	|	|	|	|
166	*166*	Calais Fréthun a.	|	|	|	|	|	|	|	|	|	|	|
267	*267*	Lille Europe a.	|	|	0926	|	|	1127	|	|	1326	|	1526
	373	**Brussels** Midi / Zuid a.	|	|	1005	|	1112	1205	|	|	1405	|	1605
492		**Paris** Nord a.	0927	1020	...	1123	...	...	1253	1350	...	1550	...

train number	**9028**	**9032**	**9142**	**9036**	**9040**	**9148**	**9046**	**9152**	**9050**	**9158**	**9054**	
notes						①–⑤	①–⑤	Ⓑ				
notes								A				
London St Pancras d.	1331	1431	1504	1531	1631	1704	1801	1804	1901	1904	2001	...
Ebbsfleet International d.	|	|	|	|	|	|	|	|	|	|	|	...
Ashford International d.	|	|	|	|	|	|	|	|	|	|	|	...
Calais Fréthun a.	|	|	|	|	|	|	|	|	|	|	|	...
Lille Europe a.	|	|	1726	|	|	1926	|	2026	|	2130	|	...
Brussels Midi / Zuid a.	|	|	1805	|	|	2005	|	2105	|	2205	|	...
Paris Nord a.	1653	1750	...	1849	1950	...	2120	...	2223	...	2320	...

train number	**9007**	**9009**	**9117**	**9015**	**9121**	**9019**	**9023**	**9135**	**9031**	**9035**	**9141**	**9039**	
notes	①–⑥	①–⑤			①–⑤					⑥⑦			
notes													
Paris Nord d.	0713	0743	...	0912	...	1013	1113	...	1313	1413	...	1513	...
Brussels Midi / Zuid d.	|	|	0852	|	0938	|	|	1256	|	|	1452	|	...
Lille Europe d.	|	|	0930	|	1035	|	|	1335	|	|	1530	|	...
Calais Fréthun d.	|	|	|	|	|	|	|	|	|	|	|	|	...
Ashford International a.	|	|	|	|	|	|	|	|	|	|	|	|	...
Ebbsfleet International a.	|	|	|	|	|	|	|	|	|	|	|	|	...
London St Pancras a.	0832	0900	0957	1030	1100	1130	1230	1400	1430	1530	1605	1630	...

train number	**9145**	**9043**	**9047**	**9051**	**9153**	**9157**	**9055**	**9059**	**9167**	**9063**			
notes				Ⓑ		①–⑥			Ⓑ	Ⓑ			
notes	A					A			A				
Paris Nord d.	...	1613	1713	1813	...	...	1913	2013	...	2113	...	...	...
Brussels Midi / Zuid d.	1556	|	|	|	1756	1856	|	|	2056	|	...	...	...
Lille Europe d.	1635	|	|	|	1835	1935	|	|	2135	|	...	...	...
Calais Fréthun d.	|	|	|	|	|	|	|	|	|	|	...	...	...
Ashford International a.	|	|	|	|	|	|	|	|	|	|	...	...	...
Ebbsfleet International a.	|	|	|	|	|	|	|	|	|	|	...	...	...
London St Pancras a.	1700	1730	1830	1930	1900	1957	2039	2130	2157	2244	...	...	...

A – To / from Amsterdam, see Table **18**.

LONDON – PARIS *by rail – sea – rail* — 10a

Other services are available by taking normal service trains between London and Dover (Tables **100**, **101**), sailings between Dover and Calais (Table **2110**) and normal service trains between Calais and Paris, by changing at Boulogne (Table **261**), passengers making their own way between stations and docks at Dover and Calais, allowing at least 1 hour for connections.

French train number		⚡	⛴					⚡	⛴					⚡	⛴					⚡	⛴			
sea crossing (see below)	Ⓐ	Ⓐ		Ⓐ	⑦	⑦	Ⓒ	⑥	⑥	⑥	⑥	Ⓐ	⑦	Ⓑ	Ⓑ	Ⓐ	Ⓐ	⑦	Ⓐ	Ⓐ	Ⓐ	Ⓐ	Ⓐ	
notes																								
London St Pancras d.	...	0725	...	...	...	...	...	0934	...	...	...	...	...	0937	...	...	...	...	...	1037	...	...	...	...
London Charing Cross d.	0709	|	...	...	...	...	0840	|	...	...	...	0834	0840	|	...	...	...	...	0940	|	...	...	...	...
Dover Priory ❦ a.	0911	0837	...	...	...	...	1033	1041	...	...	...	1038	1033	1041	...	...	...	...	1133	1141	...	...	...	...
Dover Eastern Docks 🚌 ❦ d.	...	...	1000	...	...	...	...	...	1130	...	...	...	...	...	1305	...	...	...	...	...	1430	...	...	...
Calais Port 🚌 ❖ a.	...	...	1230	...	...	...	...	...	1400	...	...	...	...	...	1535	...	...	...	...	...	1700	...	...	...
Calais Ville ❖ d.	...	...	...	1436	1436	...	...	...	...	1611	...	...	...	...	...	1636	...	1636	...	...	...	1820	...	...
Boulogne Ville d.	...	...	...	1504	1504	...	...	...	...	1647	...	...	...	...	...	1704	...	1704	...	...	...	1850	...	...
Amiens a.	...	...	...	1620	1623	1921	...	...	...	1811	1921	...	...	...	...	1820	1921	1820	...	...	...	2011	1921	...
Paris Nord a.	...	...	...	1729	...	2056	...	...	...	...	2056	...	...	...	...	...	2056	1929	...	...	...	...	2056	...

French train number		⛴	⚡			⛴	⚡			⛴	⚡		⛴	⚡			⛴	⚡					⛴	⚡
sea crossing (see below)	Ⓐ	Ⓐ	Ⓐ	Ⓐ	Ⓐ	Ⓐ	Ⓐ	Ⓐ	⑦	⑦	⑦	Ⓐ	Ⓐ	Ⓐ	Ⓐ	⑥	⑥	⑥	⑥	⑥	Ⓐ	Ⓐ	①–⑥	①–⑥
notes																								
Paris Nord d.	0731	...	...	...	...	...	...	...	...	...	...	...	...	...	...	...	...	...	...	1431	1431	...	...	...
Amiens d.	0840	...	...	...	1048	...	...	...	1137	...	...	1249	...	...	...	1337	...	...	...	1540	1540	1549	...	...
Boulogne Ville d.	0958	...	...	...	1210	...	...	...	1304	...	...	1410	...	...	...	1503	...	...	...	1659	...	1710	...	...
Calais Ville ❖ a.	1024	...	...	...	1240	...	...	...	1338	...	...	1440	...	...	...	1538	...	...	...	1724	...	1740	...	...
Calais Port 🚌 ❖ d.	...	1235	...	...	...	1420	...	...	...	1520	...	...	1520	...	...	...	1850	...	...	...	...	...	1955	...
Dover Eastern Docks 🚌 ❦ a.	...	1255	...	...	...	1450	...	...	...	1550	...	...	1550	...	...	...	1920	...	...	...	...	...	2025	...
Dover Priory ❦ d.	...	...	1349	1358	...	...	1549	1558	...	...	1649	...	...	1649	1658	...	...	2049	2058	...	...	...	...	2149
London Charing Cross a.	...	...	|	1552	...	...	|	1752	...	...	|	...	...	|	1857	...	...	|	2252	...	...	...	...	|
London St Pancras a.	...	...	1454	...	...	...	1654	...	...	...	1754	...	...	1754	...	...	...	2154	...	...	...	...	...	2254

⚡ – Supplement payable.

⛴ – Ship service, operated by P & O Ferries. ✕ on ship. One class only on ship. For additional ferry services see Table **2110**. Check in will close 60 minutes before departure. 60 minutes allowed between rail station and port.

❦ – Passengers make their own way between Dover Priory and Dover Eastern Docks.

❖ – 🚌 service (not a guaranteed connection): From Calais Port to Calais Ville station 1120, 1220, 1305, 1405, 1500, 1640, 1740, 1835. From Calais Ville station to Calais Port 1040, 1135, 1235, 1320, 1420, 1515, 1655, 1755.

10 LONDON - LILLE - PARIS and BRUSSELS *by Eurostar*

Minimum check-in time is 30 minutes, but passengers are advised to allow longer due to immigration procedures. Not available for London - Ebbsfleet - Ashford or v.v. Special fares payable that include three classes of service: business premier, standard premier and standard. All times shown are local times (France and Belgium are one hour ahead of Great Britain).
All Eurostar services are Ⓡ, non-smoking and convey ✕ in Business Premier and Standard Premier, 🍸 in Standard.

Service July 31 - Sept. 3.

For service June 12 - July 30 see page 47. For service September 4 - November 5 see below. For service November 6 - December 10 see page 37.

km	km	train number	9004	9008	9114	9116	9014	9018	9126	9024	9132	9028	
		notes	①–⑤	①–⑥								Ⓑ	
		notes	K	K	A				A				
0	0	**London** St Pancras d.	0701	0801	0816	0901	0931	1022	1104	1231	1304	1331	...
35	35	Ebbsfleet International d.	│	│	│	│	│	│	│	│	│	│	...
90	90	Ashford International d.	│	│	│	│	│	│	│	│	│	│	...
166	166	Calais Fréthun a.	│	│	│	│	│	│	│	│	│	│	...
267	267	Lille Europe a.	│	│	│	1127	│	│	1326	│	1526	│	...
	373	**Brussels** Midi / Zuid a.	│	│	1112	1205	│	│	1405	│	1607	│	...
492		**Paris** Nord a.	1017	1117	...	...	1247	1347	...	1547	...	1647	...

train number	9032	9142	9036	9040	9046	9152	9050	9054				
notes						Ⓑ		⑥⑦				
notes						A		C				
London St Pancras d.	1431	1504	1531	1631	1801	1804	1901	2001	...	...	...	...
Ebbsfleet International d.	│	│	│	│	│	│	│	│	...	...	...	...
Ashford International d.	│	│	│	│	│	│	│	│	...	...	...	...
Calais Fréthun a.	│	│	│	│	│	│	│	│	...	...	...	...
Lille Europe a.	│	1726	│	│	│	2026	│	│	...	...	...	...
Brussels Midi / Zuid a.	│	1805	│	│	│	2105	│	│	...	...	...	...
Paris Nord a.	1747	...	1847	1947	2117	...	2217	2317	...	...	...	...

train number	9007	9009	9117	9015	9023	9135	9031	9035	9039	9145	9043	9047
notes	①–⑥	①–⑤						⑦				
notes	K	K								A		
Paris Nord d.	0713	0743	...	0913	1113	...	1313	1413	1513	...	1613	1713
Brussels Midi / Zuid d.	│	│	0852	│	│	1256	│	│	│	1556	│	│
Lille Europe d.	│	│	0930	│	│	1335	│	│	│	1635	│	│
Calais Fréthun d.	│	│	│	│	│	│	│	│	│	│	│
Ashford International a.	│	│	│	│	│	│	│	│	│	│	│
Ebbsfleet International a.	│	│	│	│	│	│	│	│	│	│	│
London St Pancras a.	0832	0900	0957	1039	1230	1400	1430	1530	1637	1700	1739	1840

train number	9153	9051	9157	9055	9059	9167	9063					
notes		⑦				Ⓑ	Ⓑ					
notes			A			A						
Paris Nord d.	...	1813	...	1913	2013	...	2113	...	...	...	...	...
Brussels Midi / Zuid d.	1756	│	1856	│	│	2056	│	...	...	...	...	...
Lille Europe d.	1835	│	1935	│	│	2135	│	...	...	...	...	...
Calais Fréthun d.	│	│	│	│	│	│	│	...	...	...	...	...
Ashford International a.	│	│	│	│	│	│	│	...	...	...	...	...
Ebbsfleet International a.	│	│	│	│	│	│	│	...	...	...	...	...
London St Pancras a.	1900	1930	1957	2030	2130	2157	2230	...	...	...	...	...

A – To / from Amsterdam, see Table **18**. C – Also Aug. 29. K – Not Aug. 29.

10 LONDON - LILLE - PARIS and BRUSSELS *by Eurostar*

Minimum check-in time is 30 minutes, but passengers are advised to allow longer due to immigration procedures. Not available for London - Ebbsfleet - Ashford or v.v. Special fares payable that include three classes of service: business premier, standard premier and standard. All times shown are local times (France and Belgium are one hour ahead of Great Britain).
All Eurostar services are Ⓡ, non-smoking and convey ✕ in Business Premier and Standard Premier, 🍸 in Standard.

Service September 4 - November 5.

For service June 12 - July 30 see page 47. For service July 31 - September 3 see above. For service November 6 - December 10 see page 37.

km	km	train number	9004	9008	9114	9116	9014	9018	9126	9024	9132	9028	
		notes	①–⑤	①–⑥								Ⓑ	
		notes	K		A				A				
0	0	**London** St Pancras d.	0701	0801	0816	0901	0931	1022	1104	1231	1301	1331	...
35	35	Ebbsfleet International d.	│	│	│	│	│	│	│	│	│	│	...
90	90	Ashford International d.	│	│	│	│	│	│	│	│	│	│	...
166	166	Calais Fréthun a.	│	│	│	│	│	│	│	│	│	│	...
267	267	Lille Europe a.	│	│	│	1127	│	│	1326	│	1526	│	...
	373	**Brussels** Midi / Zuid a.	│	│	1112	1205	│	│	1405	│	1606	│	...
492		**Paris** Nord a.	1017	1117	...	...	1247	1347	...	1547	...	1647	...

train number	9032	9142	9036	9040	9046	9152	9050	9054				
notes						Ⓑ		⑥⑦				
notes						A						
London St Pancras d.	1431	1504	1531	1631	1801	1804	1901	2001	...	...	...	...
Ebbsfleet International d.	│	│	│	│	│	│	│	│	...	...	...	...
Ashford International d.	│	│	│	│	│	│	│	│	...	...	...	...
Calais Fréthun a.	│	│	│	│	│	│	│	│	...	...	...	...
Lille Europe a.	│	1726	│	│	│	2026	│	│	...	...	...	...
Brussels Midi / Zuid a.	│	1805	│	│	│	2105	│	│	...	...	...	...
Paris Nord a.	1747	...	1847	1947	2117	...	2217	2317	...	...	...	...

train number	9007	9009	9117	9015	9023	9135	9031	9035	9039	9145	9043	9047
notes	①–⑥	①–⑤						⑦				
notes	K									A		
Paris Nord d.	0713	0743	...	0913	1113	...	1313	1413	1513	...	1613	1713
Brussels Midi / Zuid d.	│	│	0852	│	│	1256	│	│	│	1552	│	│
Lille Europe d.	│	│	0930	│	│	1335	│	│	│	1635	│	│
Calais Fréthun d.	│	│	│	│	│	│	│	│	│	│	│
Ashford International a.	│	│	│	│	│	│	│	│	│	│	│
Ebbsfleet International a.	│	│	│	│	│	│	│	│	│	│	│
London St Pancras a.	0832	0900	0957	1030	1230	1400	1430	1530	1637	1700	1739	1840

train number	9153	9051	9157	9055	9059	9167	9063					
notes		⑦				Ⓑ	Ⓑ					
notes			A			A						
Paris Nord d.	...	1813	...	1913	2013	...	2113	...	...	...	...	...
Brussels Midi / Zuid d.	1756	│	1856	│	│	2056	│	...	...	...	...	...
Lille Europe d.	1835	│	1935	│	│	2135	│	...	...	...	...	...
Calais Fréthun d.	│	│	│	│	│	│	│	...	...	...	...	...
Ashford International a.	│	│	│	│	│	│	│	...	...	...	...	...
Ebbsfleet International a.	│	│	│	│	│	│	│	...	...	...	...	...
London St Pancras a.	1900	1930	1957	2030	2130	2157	2230	...	...	...	...	...

A – To / from Amsterdam, see Table **18**. K – Not Nov. 1.

LONDON / BRUSSELS - LILLE - CHARLES DE GAULLE ✈ - WESTERN / SOUTHERN FRANCE 11

DAY TRAINS (FOR NIGHT TRAINS SEE TABLE 13). Supplements are payable on *TGV* trains. Connections at Lille are not guaranteed. Other connections available via Paris.

km	*train type*	*TGV*	*TGV*	*TGV*	*TGV*	*TGV*	*TGV*	*TGV*	*TGV*	*TGV*	*TGV*	*TGV*	*TGV*	*TGV*	*TGV*	*TGV*	*TGV*	*TGV*		⇌	*TGV*		
	train number	**5210**	**5102**	**7831**	**7669**	**9802**	**5110**	**9810**	**9810**	**5214**	**5214**	**7867**	**6823**	**9870**	**7667**	**9812**	**5113**	**6823**		**9926**	**5224**		
	train number			**7830**	**7668**			**9811**	**9811**	**5215**	**5215**	**7866**	**6822**	**9871**		**9813**		**6822**		**9927**			
	notes	R 🍸	R 🍸	R	R	R 🍸	R 🍸	R 🍸	R 🍸	R 🍸	R 🍸	R	R 🍸	R 🍸	R	R 🍸	R 🍸	R 🍸		R 🍸	R 🍸		
			⚒	⊠	⊠		⚒	†	⚒	⑥	⑧	⊠			⊠ △		⑥	①–⑤		B			
	London St Pancras d.	...	...	...	...	...	...	...	...	...	...	...	...	...	...	...	...	...	...	...	...	...	...
	Brussels Midi / Zuid d.	...	...	...	...	0617	...	0637	0702	...	...	...	...	0717	...	0817	...	...	...	0925	...	...	...
	Tourcoing d.	...	...	...	0602	|	...	|	|	...	...	0747	...	|	...	|	...	...	...	|	...	...	...
	Lille Europe a.	...	...	...	|	0652	...	0713	|	...	...	|	...	0752	...	0852	...	...	...	|	...	...	...
0	**Lille** Europe d.	0539	0539	...	|	0703	...	0725	|	0752	...	|	...	0802	...	0902	0902	...	...	|	...	...	...
	Lille Flandres ◇ d.	|	|	...	|	|	0645	|	|	|	...	|	...	|	...	|	|	...	...	|	0932	...	...
	Douai d.	|	|	...	|	|	0713	|	|	|	...	|	...	|	...	|	|	...	...	|	1000	...	...
	Arras d.	|	|	...	|	|	0729	|	|	|	...	|	...	|	...	|	|	...	...	|	1021	...	...
99	TGV Haute Picardie d.	0609	0609	...	0643	|	0748	0754	|	|	...	|	...	|	...	|	|	...	...	|	|	...	...
203	Paris Charles de Gaulle ✈ a.	0639	0639	...	0712	0754	0817	0822	0822	0843	...	0846	...	0853	...	0954	0954	...	...	1039	1106	...	...
203	Paris Charles de Gaulle ✈ d.	0644	0644	0659	0717	0810	0828	0828	0828	0848	0848	0852	...	0859	0936	1000	1000	...	...	1046	1116	...	...
227	Marne la Vallée § d.	0702	0713	0715	0732	0832	0843	0843	0843	0902	0902	0910	...	|	0951	1013	1013	...	...	|	1132	...	...
	Strasbourg a.	|	|	|	|	|	|	|	|	|	|	|	...	1105x	|	|	|	...	...	|	|	...	...
289	Massy TGV d.	0742	|	|	0814	0914	|	|	|	0942	0942	|	...	...	1026	|	|	...	...	|	1212	...	...
	Le Mans a.	0829	|	|	|	|	|	|	|	1029	1029	|	...	...	|	|	|	...	...	|	|	...	...
	Rennes a.	0917	|	|	|	|	|	|	|	|	|	|	...	...	1149	|	|	...	...	|	|	...	...
	Angers St Laud a.	...	|	|	|	|	|	|	|	1109	1109	|	...	...	...	|	|	...	...	|	1400	...	...
	Nantes a.	...	|	|	|	|	|	|	|	1150	1150	|	...	...	...	|	|	...	...	|	1442	...	...
	St Pierre des Corps a.	...	|	|	0906	1006	|	|	|	...	...	|	...	...	...	|	|	...	...	|	...	...	...
	Poitiers a.	...	|	|	0940	1040	|	|	|	...	...	|	...	...	...	|	|	...	...	|	...	...	...
	Angoulême a.	...	|	|	1022	1123	|	|	|	...	...	|	...	...	...	|	|	...	...	|	...	...	...
	Bordeaux a.	...	|	|	1101	1202	|	|	|	...	...	|	...	...	...	|	|	...	...	|	...	...	...
	Le Creusot TGV a.	...	|	|	...	...	|	|	|	...	...	|	...	...	...	|	|	...	...	|	...	...	...
521	**Lyon** Part Dieu a.	...	0900	|	...	...	1030	1030	1030	...	...	1100	1126	...	...	1200	1200	1210	...	|	...	...	...
	Lyon St Exupéry ✈ a.	...	|	|	...	...	|	|	|	...	...	|	|	...	...	|	|	|	...	|	...	...	...
	Valence TGV a.	...	|	|	...	...	1114	1114	1114	...	...	1146	1159	...	...	1246	1246	1247	...	1301	...	...	...
	Avignon TGV a.	...	1009	0947	...	...	1150	1150	1150	...	...	|	|	...	...	|	1328	|	...	1337	...	...	...
	Nîmes a.	...	|	|	...	...	|	|	|	...	...	|	1245	...	...	1335	|	1335	...	|	...	...	...
	Nîmes Pont-du-Gard a.	...	|	|	...	...	|	|	|	...	...	1229	|	...	...	|	|	|	...	|	...	...	...
	Montpellier Sud de France a.	...	|	|	...	...	|	|	|	...	...	1253	|	...	...	|	|	|	...	|	...	...	...
	Montpellier Saint-Roch a.	...	|	|	...	...	|	|	|	...	...	...	1316	...	...	1406	|	1405	...	|	...	...	...
	Béziers a.	...	|	|	...	...	|	|	|	...	...	...	1353	...	...	...	|	1446	...	|	...	...	...
	Narbonne a.	...	|	|	...	...	|	|	|	...	...	...	1409	...	...	...	|	1502	...	|	...	...	...
	Toulouse Matabiau a.	...	|	|	...	...	|	|	|	...	...	...	1524	...	...	...	|	1618	...	|	...	...	...
	Perpignan a.	...	|	|	...	...	|	|	|	...	...	...	...	...	...	...	|	...	...	|	...	...	...
	Aix en Provence TGV a.	...	1031	1009	...	...	|	|	|	...	...	...	...	...	...	...	|	...	...	1404	...	...	...
	Marseille St Charles a.	...	1046	1024	...	...	1223	1223	1223	...	...	...	...	...	...	...	1401	...	...	1419	...	...	...
	Toulon a.	...	...	...	...	...	...	...	...	...	...	...	...	...	...	...	...	...	...	...	...	...	...
	St Raphaël - Valescure a.	...	...	...	...	...	...	...	...	...	...	...	...	...	...	...	...	...	...	...	...	...	...
	Cannes a.	...	...	...	...	...	...	...	...	...	...	...	...	...	...	...	...	...	...	...	...	...	...
	Nice a.	...	...	...	...	...	...	...	...	...	...	...	...	...	...	...	...	...	...	...	...	...	...

train type	☆	☆	*TGV*	*TGV*	*TGV*	*AVE*	*TGV*	*TGV*	*TGV*		☆	*TGV*		☆	☆	*TGV*	*TGV*	*TGV*	*TGV*				
train number	**9110**	**9110**	**9826**	**5026**	**5026**	**9743**	**7841**	**5226**	**5400**		**9116**	**7835**		**9074**	**9126**	**9830**	**5030**	**6825**	**7845**				
train number			**9827**				**7840**	**5227**				**7834**				**9831**		**6824**	**7844**				
notes	R ✕	R ✕	R 🍸	R 🍸	R 🍸		R	R 🍸	R 🍸		R ✕	R		R ✕	R ✕	R 🍸	R 🍸	R 🍸	R				
	②③④	⑥		⑧	⑥		⊠					⊠					⑤⑥		⊠				
						b								C									
London St Pancras d.	0647	0657	...	...	...	...	...	...	...	...	0901	...	...	1014	1104	...	...	...	...	...	...	...	...
Brussels Midi / Zuid d.	|	|	1017	...	...	...	...	...	...	...	|	...	...	|	|	1317	...	...	...	...	...	...	...
Tourcoing d.	|	|	|	...	...	...	...	...	...	...	|	...	...	|	|	|	...	...	...	...	...	...	...
Lille Europe a.	0926	0926	1052	...	...	...	...	...	...	...	1127	...	...	1254	1326	1353	...	...	...	...	...	...	...
Lille Europe d.	...	...	1103	1103	1103	...	...	...	1125	...	...	...	...	|	...	1403	1403	...	...	...	...	...	...
Lille Flandres ◇ d.	...	...	|	|	|	...	1138	1126	|	...	...	1259	...	|	...	|	|	...	1541	...	...	...	...
Douai d.	...	...	|	|	|	...	|	|	|	...	...	|	...	|	...	|	|	...	|	...	...	...	...
Arras d.	...	...	|	|	|	...	|	|	|	...	...	|	...	|	...	|	|	...	|	...	...	...	...
TGV Haute Picardie d.	...	...	|	|	|	...	|	1156	1154	...	...	|	...	|	...	|	|	...	1618	...	...	...	...
Paris Charles de Gaulle ✈ a.	...	...	1153	1153	1153	...	|	1224	1224	...	...	1357	...	|	...	1453	1453	...	1648	...	...	...	...
Paris Charles de Gaulle ✈ d.	...	...	1159	1159	1159	...	|	1238	1243	...	...	1358	...	|	...	1458	1458	...	1706	...	...	...	...
Marne la Vallée § d.	...	...	1213	1213	1213	...	1246	1302	|	...	...	1412	...	1403	...	1513	1513	...	1722	...	...	...	...
Strasbourg a.	...	...	|	|	|	...	|	|	1435	...	...	|	...	...	...	|	|	...	|	...	...	...	...
Massy TGV d.	...	...	|	|	|	...	|	1342	...	...	...	|	...	...	...	|	|	...	|	...	...	...	...
Le Mans a.	...	...	|	|	|	...	|	1429	...	...	...	|	...	...	...	|	|	...	|	...	...	...	...
Rennes a.	...	...	|	|	|	...	|	1529	...	...	...	|	...	...	...	|	|	...	|	...	...	...	...
Angers St Laud a.	...	...	|	|	|	...	|	...	...	...	...	|	...	...	...	|	|	...	|	...	...	...	...
Nantes a.	...	...	|	|	|	...	|	...	...	...	...	|	...	...	...	|	|	...	|	...	...	...	...
St Pierre des Corps a.	...	...	|	|	|	...	|	...	...	...	...	|	...	...	...	|	|	...	|	...	...	...	...
Poitiers a.	...	...	|	|	|	...	|	...	...	...	...	|	...	...	...	|	|	...	|	...	...	...	...
Angoulême a.	...	...	|	|	|	...	|	...	...	...	...	|	...	...	...	|	|	...	|	...	...	...	...
Bordeaux a.	...	...	|	|	|	...	|	...	...	...	...	|	...	...	...	|	|	...	|	...	...	...	...
Le Creusot TGV a.	...	...	|	|	|	...	|	...	...	...	...	|	...	...	...	|	|	...	|	...	...	...	...
Lyon Part Dieu a.	...	...	1400	1400	1400	1435	|	...	...	...	...	1600	...	...	...	1700	1700	1810	|	...	...	...	...
Lyon St Exupéry ✈ a.	...	...	|	...	|	|	1432	...	...	...	...	|	...	...	...	|	|	|	1909	...	...	...	...
Valence TGV a.	...	...	1446	...	1446	1508	|	...	...	...	...	|	...	...	...	|	|	1846	|	...	...	...	...
Avignon TGV a.	...	...	|	...	|	|	1528	...	...	...	...	1710	...	...	...	1808	1808	|	2004	...	...	...	...
Nîmes a.	...	...	|	...	|	1554	|	...	...	...	...	|	...	...	...	|	|	1935	|	...	...	...	...
Nîmes Pont-du-Gard a.	...	...	1529	...	1529	|	|	...	...	...	...	|	...	...	...	|	|	|	|	...	...	...	...
Montpellier Sud de France a.	...	...	1553	...	1553	|	|	...	...	...	...	|	...	...	...	|	|	|	|	...	...	...	...
Montpellier Saint-Roch a.	...	...	...	...	...	1624	|	...	...	...	...	|	...	...	...	|	|	2006	|	...	...	...	...
Béziers a.	...	...	...	...	...	1712	|	...	...	...	...	|	...	...	...	|	|	2050	|	...	...	...	...
Narbonne a.	...	...	...	...	...	1728	|	...	...	...	...	|	...	...	...	|	|	2106	|	...	...	...	...
Toulouse Matabiau a.	...	...	...	...	...	|	|	...	...	...	...	|	...	...	...	|	|	2222	|	...	...	...	...
Perpignan a.	...	...	...	...	...	1806	|	...	...	...	...	|	...	...	...	|	|	...	|	...	...	...	...
Aix en Provence TGV a.	...	...	...	...	...	...	1550	...	...	...	...	|	...	...	...	1831	1831	...	2026	...	...	...	...
Marseille St Charles a.	...	...	...	...	...	...	1605	...	...	...	...	1741	...	...	...	1846	1846	...	2041	...	...	...	...
Toulon a.	...	...	...	...	...	...	...	...	...	...	...	...	...	...	...	...	...	...	...	...	...	...	...
St Raphaël - Valescure a.	...	...	...	...	...	...	...	...	...	...	...	...	...	...	...	...	...	...	...	...	...	...	...
Cannes a.	...	...	...	...	...	...	...	...	...	...	...	...	...	...	...	...	...	...	...	...	...	...	...
Nice a.	...	...	...	...	...	...	...	...	...	...	...	...	...	...	...	...	...	...	...	...	...	...	...

B – THALYS SOLEIL – ⑥ July 2 - Aug. 27: 12 🍸 Brussels - Marseille. ⑥ July 9 - Aug. 27: 12 🍸 Amsterdam (depart 0715; see Table **18**) - Brussels - Marseille.

C – ①③⑤⑦ June 12 - Dec. 9 (daily Oct. 21 – 31) also Jul 23, Aug. 27. See Table **17**.

b – To Barcelona (Table **13**).

x – Arrive 1049 on ⑤⑥⑦.

AVE – Alta Velocidad Española R 🍸 ✗.

§ – Marne la Vallée - Chessy (station for Disneyland).

◇ – 500 metres from Lille Europe (see Lille City Plan on page 32).

△ – To / from Lorient or Quimper on dates in Table **285**.

☆ – Eurostar train. Special fares payable. ✕ in Business Premier and Standard Premier, 🍸 in Standard. Business Premier not available to Marne la Vallée - Chessy and Marseille. Minimum check-in time 30 minutes. Valid June 12 - Sept. 3. **Additional services are available, see Table 10, pages 47 – 48.**

⊠ – OUIGO low-cost TGV service. Internet bookings only at www.ouigo.com. Timings may vary.

☛ **Shaded services are temporarily suspended.**

11 LONDON / BRUSSELS - LILLE - CHARLES DE GAULLE ✈ - WESTERN / SOUTHERN FRANCE

DAY TRAINS (FOR NIGHT TRAINS SEE TABLE 13). Supplements payable on all *TGV* services. Connections at Lille are not guaranteed. Other connections available via Paris.

train type		☆	*TGV*	*TGV*	*TGV*	*TGV*	*TGV*	*TGV*	*TGV*	*TGV*			☆	*TGV*	*TGV*	*TGV*	*TGV*			☆	*TGV*			
train number		**9132**	**5120**	**9836**	**9836**	**9835**	**5036**	**5240**	**9838**	**9833**			**9142**	**5124**	**5130**	**9872**	**7814**			**9148**	**9846**			
train number				**9837**	**9837**			**5241**	**9839**						**5131**	**9873**	**7815**							
notes		🅁✕	🅁 ④⑤⑦	🅁🍷 ①②③④	🅁🍷 ⑤⑥⑦	🅁🍷 ⑥	🅁🍷 Ⓑ	🅁🍷	🅁🍷 △	🅁🍷			🅁✕	🅁🍷 Ⓑ	🅁🍷 ▷	🅁🍷	🅁🍷 ⊠			🅁✕ ⑥	🅁🍷 Ⓑ			
London St Pancras d.	...	1258	...	...	...	...	...	...	...	...	...	...	1504	...	...	...	...	...	...	1704	...	...	...	...
Brussels Midi / Zuid d.	...	│	...	1617	1617	1617	...	...	1655	1655	...	...	│	...	...	1817	...	...	...	│	1917	...	...	...
Tourcoing d.	...	│	...	│	│	│	...	...	│	│	...	...	│	...	...	│	...	...	...	│	│	...	...	...
Lille Europe a.	...	1530	...	1653	1653	1653	...	...	1727	1727	...	...	1726	...	...	1852	...	...	...	1926	1951	...	...	...
Lille Europe d.	...	...	1602	1703	1703	1703	1703	...	1739	1739	...	...	...	1826	...	1903	...	...	...	...	2001	...	...	...
Lille Flandres ◇ d.	...	...	│	│	│	│	│	1716	│	│	...	...	...	│	1857	│	1938	...	...	...	│	...	...	...
Douai d.	...	...	│	│	│	│	│	│	│	│	...	...	...	│	│	│	│	...	...	...	│	...	...	...
Arras d.	...	...	│	│	│	│	│	│	│	│	...	...	...	│	│	│	│	...	...	...	2035	...	...	...
TGV Haute Picardie d.	...	...	│	│	│	│	│	│	1815	1815	...	...	...	1855	│	│	│	...	...	...	│	...	...	...
Paris Charles de Gaulle ✈ a.	...	...	1653	1753	1753	1753	1753	1810	1842	1842	...	...	...	1923	1949	1954	│	...	...	...	2016	...	...	...
Paris Charles de Gaulle ✈ d.	...	...	1658	1758	1758	1758	1758	1818	1847	1847	...	...	...	1928	1954	2002	│	...	...	...	2121	...	...	...
Marne la Vallée § d.	...	...	1713	1813	1813	1813	1813	1832	1900	1900	...	...	...	1954	2004	│	2052	...	...	...	2137	...	...	...
Strasbourg a.	...	...	│	│	│	│	│	│	│	│	...	...	...	│	...	2159	│	...	...	...	│	...	...	...
Massy TGV d.	...	...	│	│	│	│	│	1912	1942	1942	...	...	...	│	...	...	│	...	...	...	│	...	...	...
Le Mans a.	...	...	│	│	│	│	│	│	2029	2029	...	...	...	│	...	...	│	...	...	...	│	...	...	...
Rennes a.	...	...	│	│	│	│	│	│	2119	│	...	...	...	│	...	...	│	...	...	...	│	...	...	...
Angers St Laud a.	...	...	│	│	│	│	│	│	...	2110	...	...	...	│	...	...	│	...	...	...	│	...	...	...
Nantes a.	...	...	│	│	│	│	│	│	...	2151	...	...	...	│	...	...	│	...	...	...	│	...	...	...
St Pierre des Corps a.	...	...	│	│	│	│	│	2006	...	...	...	...	...	│	...	...	│	...	...	...	│	...	...	...
Poitiers a.	...	...	│	│	│	│	│	2040	...	...	...	...	...	│	...	...	│	...	...	...	│	...	...	...
Angoulême a.	...	...	│	│	│	│	│	2123	...	...	...	...	...	│	...	...	│	...	...	...	│	...	...	...
Bordeaux a.	...	...	│	│	│	│	│	2202	...	...	...	...	...	│	...	...	│	...	...	...	│	...	...	...
Le Creusot TGV a.	...	...	│	│	│	│	│	...	...	...	...	...	...	│	...	...	│	...	...	...	2249	...	...	...
Lyon Part Dieu a.	...	...	1900	2000	2000	2000	2000	...	...	...	...	...	...	2140	...	...	2248**p**	...	...	...	2329	...	...	...
Lyon St Exupéry ✈ a.	...	...	│	│	│	│	│	...	...	...	...	...	...	│	...	...	...	...	...	...	...	...	...	...
Valence TGV a.	...	...	1946	2047	2047	2047	2047	...	...	...	...	...	...	│	...	...	...	...	...	...	...	...	...	...
Avignon TGV a.	...	...	│	│	│	2128	│	...	...	...	...	...	...	2302	...	...	...	...	...	...	...	...	...	...
Nîmes a.	...	...	│	2134	2134	│	2134	...	...	...	...	...	...	│	...	...	...	...	...	...	...	...	...	...
Nîmes Pont-du-Gard a.	...	...	2029	│	│	│	│	...	...	...	...	...	...	│	...	...	...	...	...	...	...	...	...	...
Montpellier Sud de France a.	...	...	2053	│	│	│	│	...	...	...	...	...	...	│	...	...	...	...	...	...	...	...	...	...
Montpellier Saint-Roch a.	...	...	...	2205	2205	│	2205	...	...	...	...	...	...	│	...	...	...	...	...	...	...	...	...	...
Béziers a.	...	...	...	...	2256	│	...	...	...	...	...	...	...	│	...	...	...	...	...	...	...	...	...	...
Narbonne a.	...	...	...	...	2312	│	...	...	...	...	...	...	...	│	...	...	...	...	...	...	...	...	...	...
Toulouse Matabiau a.	...	...	...	...	│	│	...	...	...	...	...	...	...	│	...	...	...	...	...	...	...	...	...	...
Perpignan a.	...	...	...	...	2359	│	...	...	...	...	...	...	...	│	...	...	...	...	...	...	...	...	...	...
Aix en Provence TGV a.	...	...	...	...	...	2150	...	...	...	...	...	...	...	2326	...	...	...	...	...	...	...	...	...	...
Marseille St Charles a.	...	...	...	...	...	2207	...	...	...	...	...	...	...	2341	...	...	...	...	...	...	...	...	...	...
Toulon a.	...	...	...	...	...	...	...	...	...	...	...	...	...	...	...	...	...	...	...	...	...	...	...	...
St Raphaël - Valescure a.	...	...	...	...	...	...	...	...	...	...	...	...	...	...	...	...	...	...	...	...	...	...	...	...
Cannes a.	...	...	...	...	...	...	...	...	...	...	...	...	...	...	...	...	...	...	...	...	...	...	...	...
Nice a.	...	...	...	...	...	...	...	...	...	...	...	...	...	...	...	...	...	...	...	...	...	...	...	...

train type		*TGV*	*TGV*	*TGV*	*TGV*	☆		*TGV*	*TGV*	*TGV*	*TGV*	*TGV*	*TGV*	*TGV*	*TGV*	*TGV*	☆	☆		*TGV*	☆			
train number		**9809**	**9852**	**9890**	**5420**	**9117**		**5152**	**9886**	**9884**	**5260**	**5156**	**7838**	**9854**	**5054**	**5054**	**9125**	**9129**		**7818**	**9133**			
train number			**9853**	**9891**	**5421**			**5153**		**9885**	**5261**		**7839**	**9855**						**7819**				
notes		🅁🍷 Ⓐ	🅁🍷 ①–⑥	🅁🍷 ⑦	🅁🍷 ①–⑥	🅁✕		🅁🍷 ▷	🅁🍷	🅁🍷	🅁🍷	🅁 ①⑤	🅁 ⊠	🅁🍷	🅁🍷 ①②③④⑥	🅁🍷 ⑤	🅁✕ ⑤	🅁✕ ⑦		🅁 ⊠	🅁✕ ①–⑥			
Nice d.	...	...	...	...	...	...	...	...	...	...	...	...	...	...	...	...	...	...	...	...	...	...	...	...
Cannes d.	...	...	...	...	...	...	...	...	...	...	...	...	...	...	...	...	...	...	...	...	...	...	...	...
St Raphaël - Valescure d.	...	...	...	...	...	...	...	...	...	...	...	...	...	...	...	...	...	...	...	...	...	...	...	...
Toulon d.	...	...	...	...	...	...	...	...	...	...	...	...	...	...	...	...	...	...	...	...	...	...	...	...
Marseille St Charles d.	...	...	...	...	...	...	...	...	...	...	...	...	0613	0636	0636	0636	...	...	...	...	...	...	...	...
Aix en Provence TGV d.	...	...	...	...	...	...	...	...	...	...	...	...	0628	0651	0651	0651	...	...	...	...	...	...	...	...
Perpignan d.	...	...	...	...	...	...	...	...	...	...	...	...	│	│	│	│	...	...	...	...	...	...	...	...
Toulouse Matabiau d.	...	...	...	...	...	...	...	...	...	...	...	...	│	│	│	│	...	...	...	...	...	...	...	...
Narbonne d.	...	...	...	...	...	...	...	...	...	...	...	...	│	│	│	│	...	...	...	...	...	...	...	...
Béziers d.	...	...	...	...	...	...	...	...	...	...	...	...	│	│	│	│	...	...	...	...	...	...	...	...
Montpellier Saint-Roch d.	...	...	...	...	...	...	...	...	...	...	...	0524	│	│	│	│	...	...	...	...	...	...	...	...
Montpellier Sud de France d.	...	...	...	...	...	...	...	...	...	...	...	│	│	│	│	│	...	...	...	...	...	...	...	...
Nîmes Pont-du-Gard d.	...	...	...	...	...	...	...	...	...	...	...	│	│	│	│	│	...	...	...	...	...	...	...	...
Nîmes d.	...	...	...	...	...	...	...	...	...	...	...	0555	│	│	│	│	...	...	...	...	...	...	...	...
Avignon TGV d.	...	...	...	...	...	...	...	...	...	...	...	│	0650	0716	0717	0716	...	...	...	...	...	...	...	...
Valence TGV d.	...	...	...	...	...	...	...	...	...	...	...	0645	│	│	│	│	...	...	...	...	...	...	...	...
Lyon St Exupéry ✈ d.	...	...	...	...	...	...	...	...	...	...	...	│	0744	│	│	│	...	...	...	...	...	...	...	...
Lyon Part Dieu d.	...	...	0550	...	...	...	...	...	...	...	...	0730	│	0830	0830	0830	...	...	...	0904**p**	...	...	...	...
Le Creusot TGV d.	...	...	0632	...	...	...	...	...	...	...	...	│	│	│	│	│	...	...	...	│	...	...	...	...
Bordeaux d.	...	...	│	...	...	...	...	...	...	...	0558	│	│	│	│	│	...	...	...	│	...	...	...	...
Angoulême d.	...	...	│	...	...	...	...	...	...	...	0636	│	│	│	│	│	...	...	...	│	...	...	...	...
Poitiers d.	...	...	│	...	...	...	...	...	...	...	0719	│	│	│	│	│	...	...	...	│	...	...	...	...
St Pierre des Corps d.	...	...	│	...	...	...	...	...	...	...	0754	│	│	│	│	│	...	...	...	│	...	...	...	...
Nantes d.	...	...	│	...	...	...	...	...	0601	...	│	│	│	│	│	│	...	...	...	│	...	...	...	...
Angers St Laud d.	...	...	│	...	...	...	...	...	0640	...	│	│	│	│	│	│	...	...	...	│	...	...	...	...
Rennes d.	...	...	│	...	...	...	...	...	│	0625	│	│	│	│	│	│	...	...	...	│	...	...	...	...
Le Mans d.	...	...	│	...	...	...	...	...	0730	0730	│	│	│	│	│	│	...	...	...	│	...	...	...	...
Massy TGV d.	...	...	│	...	...	...	...	...	0826	0826	0855	│	│	│	│	│	...	...	...	│	...	...	...	...
Strasbourg d.	...	...	│	0607	0607	...	...	...	│	│	│	│	│	│	│	│	...	...	...	│	...	...	...	...
Marne la Vallée § d.	...	...	0752	│	│	...	...	0851	0901	0901	0930	0921	0946	1021	1021	1021	...	...	...	1112	...	...	...	...
Paris Charles de Gaulle ✈ a.	...	...	0802	0757	0758	...	...	0902	0911	0911	0941	0933	│	1032	1032	1032	...	...	...	1121	...	...	...	...
Paris Charles de Gaulle ✈ d.	...	...	0807	0806	0811	...	...	0907	0916	0916	0946	0946	│	1037	...	1037	...	...	...	1127	...	...	...	...
TGV Haute Picardie d.	...	...	│	│	0840	...	...	│	0950	0950	│	│	│	│	...	│	...	...	...	│	...	...	...	...
Arras a.	...	...	│	│	│	...	...	│	│	│	│	│	│	│	...	│	...	...	...	│	...	...	...	...
Douai a.	...	...	│	│	│	...	...	│	│	│	│	│	│	│	...	│	...	...	...	│	...	...	...	...
Lille Flandres ◇ a.	...	...	│	│	│	...	...	│	│	│	1040	1040	1044	│	...	│	...	...	...	1221	...	...	...	...
Lille Europe a.	...	...	0858	0858	0907	...	...	0957	1017	1017	...	...	...	1127	...	1127	...	...	...	...	...	...	...	...
Lille Europe d.	...	0720	0909	0908	...	0930	...	...	1027	1027	...	...	...	1137	...	...	1135	1235	...	...	1330	...	...	...
Tourcoing a.	...	│	│	│	...	│	...	...	│	│	...	...	...	│	...	...	│	│	...	...	│	...	...	...
Brussels Midi / Zuid a.	...	0755	0943	0943	...	│	...	...	1101	1101	...	...	...	1217	...	...	│	│	...	...	│	...	...	...
London St Pancras a.	...	...	...	...	...	0957	...	...	...	...	...	...	...	...	...	...	1157	1257	...	...	1405	...	...	...

p – Lyon **Perrache**.

▽ – To / from Le Croisic on dates in Table **288**.

△ – To / from Lorient or Quimper on dates in Table **285**.

▷ – To / from Dijon, Besancon and Mulhouse (Table **370**).

§ – Marne la Vallée - Chessy. Station for Disneyland Paris.

◇ – 500 metres from Lille Europe (see Lille City Plan on page 32).

☆ – Eurostar train. Special fares payable. ✕ in Business Premier and Standard Premier, 🍷 in Standard. Minimum check-in time 30 minutes. Valid June 12 - Sept. 3. **Additional services are available, see Table 10, pages 47 – 48.**

⊠ – OUIGO low-cost TGV service. Internet bookings only at www.ouigo.com. Timings may vary.

☛ **Shaded services are temporarily suspended.**

SOUTHERN / WESTERN FRANCE - CHARLES DE GAULLE ✈ - LILLE - BRUSSELS / LONDON 11

DAY TRAINS (FOR NIGHT TRAINS SEE TABLE 13). Supplements payable on all *TGV* services. Connections at Lille are not guaranteed. Other connections available via Paris.

train type	*TGV*	*TGV*	*TGV*	*TGV*	*TGV*	*TGV*	*TGV*	☆		*TGV*	*AVE*	*TGV*	*TGV*	*TGV*	*TGV*	*TGV*	☆	*TGV*	*TGV*			
train number	**5062**	**5062**	**9862**	**9862**	**7842**	**9892**	**5280**	**9145**		**6870**	**9736**	**9866**	**5166**	**5158**	**9894**	**9820**	**9153**	**5276**	**5278**			
train number			**9863**	**9863**	**7842**	**9893**	**5281**			**6871**		**9867**			**9895**	**9821**			**5279**			
notes	R 🍷	R 🍷	R 🍷	R 🍷	R	R 🍷	R 🍷	R 🍴		R 🍷		R 🍷	R 🍷	R 🍷	R 🍷	R 🍷	R 🍴	R 🍷	R 🍷			
					⊠		△					⑥⑦	Ⓑ	⑥					①②③			
	①–⑤	⑥⑦	①–⑤	⑥⑦							b							⑤	④⑥			
Nice d.	...	...	...	...	...	...	...	...	...	...	...	...	...	...	...	...	...	...	...	...	...	...
Cannes d.	...	...	...	...	...	...	...	...	...	...	...	...	...	...	...	...	...	...	...	...	...	...
St Raphaël - Valescure d.	...	...	...	...	...	...	...	...	...	...	...	...	...	...	...	...	...	...	...	...	...	...
Toulon d.	...	...	...	...	...	...	...	...	...	...	...	...	...	...	...	...	...	...	...	...	...	...
Marseille St Charles d.	...	...	...	...	1002	...	...	...	...	...	...	1210	1210	...	...	...	...	...	...	...	...	...
Aix en Provence TGV d.	...	...	...	...	1017	...	...	...	...	...	...	1226	1226	...	...	...	...	...	...	...	...	...
Perpignan d.	...	...	...	0703	|	...	...	...	...	...	0941	|	|	...	...	...	...	...	...	...	...	...
Toulouse Matabiau d.	...	...	...	|	|	...	...	...	...	0744	|	|	|	...	...	...	...	...	...	...	...	...
Narbonne d.	...	...	...	0745	|	...	...	...	...	0859	1019	|	|	...	...	...	...	...	...	...	...	...
Béziers d.	...	...	...	0804	|	...	...	...	...	0915	|	|	|	...	...	...	...	...	...	...	...	...
Montpellier Saint-Roch d.	...	0857	...	0857	|	...	...	...	...	|	1125	|	|	1157	...	...	...	...	...	...	...	...
Montpellier Sud de France d.	0910	|	0910	|	|	...	...	...	...	1007	|	|	|	|	...	...	...	...	...	...	...	...
Nîmes Pont-du-Gard d.	0932	|	0932	|	|	...	...	...	...	1030	|	|	|	|	...	...	...	...	...	...	...	...
Nîmes d.	|	0925	|	0925	|	...	...	...	...	|	1200	|	|	1225	...	...	...	...	...	...	...	...
Avignon TGV d.	|	|	|	|	1040	...	...	...	...	|	|	1248	1248	|	...	...	...	...	...	...	...	...
Valence TGV d.	1015	1015	1015	1015	|	...	...	...	...	1115	1246	|	|	1315	...	...	...	...	...	...	...	...
Lyon St Exupéry ✈ d.	|	|	|	|	1135	...	...	...	...	|	|	|	|	|	...	...	...	...	...	...	...	...
Lyon Part Dieu d.	1100	1100	1100	1100	|	...	...	...	...	1150	1320	1400	1400	1400	...	...	...	...	...	...	...	...
Le Creusot TGV d.	|	|	|	|	|	...	...	...	...	...	...	|	|	|	...	...	...	...	...	...	...	...
Bordeaux d.	|	|	|	|	|	...	...	...	...	...	...	|	|	|	...	1258	...	...	...	...	...	...
Angoulême d.	|	|	|	|	|	...	...	...	...	...	...	|	|	|	...	1336	...	...	...	...	...	...
Poitiers d.	|	|	|	|	|	...	...	...	...	...	...	|	|	|	...	1419	...	...	...	...	...	...
St Pierre des Corps d.	|	|	|	|	|	...	...	...	...	...	...	|	|	|	...	1454	...	...	...	...	...	...
Nantes d.	|	|	|	|	|	...	...	...	...	...	...	|	|	|	...	|	...	1353	1354	...	...	...
Angers St Laud d.	|	|	|	|	|	...	...	...	...	...	...	|	|	|	...	|	...	1432	1439	...	...	...
Rennes d.	|	|	|	|	|	...	1153	...	...	...	...	|	|	|	...	|	...	|	|	...	...	...
Le Mans d.	|	|	|	|	|	...	1257	...	...	...	...	|	|	|	...	|	...	1529	1530	...	...	...
Massy TGV d.	|	|	|	|	|	...	1355	...	...	...	...	|	|	|	...	1555	...	1626	1626	...	...	...
Strasbourg d.	|	|	|	|	|	1241	|	...	...	...	...	|	|	|	1459	|	...	|	|	...	...	...
Marne la Vallée § d.	1251	1251	1251	1251	1321	|	1431	...	...	...	...	1552	1552	1552	|	1631	...	1657	1703	...	...	...
Paris Charles de Gaulle ✈ a.	1302	1302	1302	1302	1331	1437	1442	...	...	...	...	1602	1602	1602	1702	1642	...	...	1713	...	...	...
Paris Charles de Gaulle ✈ d.	1307	1307	1307	1307	1336	1449	1458	...	...	...	...	1607	1607	1607	1707	1707	...	...	1737	...	...	...
TGV Haute Picardie d.	1338	1338	1338	1338	|	|	|	...	...	...	...	|	|	|	|	|	...	...	|	...	...	...
Arras a.	1355	1355	1355	1355	|	|	|	...	...	...	...	|	|	|	|	|	...	...	|	...	...	...
Douai a.	|	|	|	|	|	|	|	...	...	...	...	|	|	|	|	|	...	...	|	...	...	...
Lille Flandres ◇ a.	|	|	|	|	1430	|	|	...	...	...	...	|	|	|	|	|	...	...	1830	...	...	...
Lille Europe a.	1424	1424	1424	1424	...	1538	1549	...	...	...	...	1657	1657	1657	1757	1757	...	...	...	...	...	...
Lille Europe d.	...	...	1459	1459	...	1555	...	1635	...	...	...	1708	...	...	1808	1808	1835	...	...	...	...	...
Tourcoing a.	...	...	|	|	...	|	...	|	...	...	...	|	...	...	|	|	|	...	...	...	...	...
Brussels Midi / Zuid a.	...	...	1533	1533	...	1633	...	|	...	...	...	1743	...	...	1843	1843	|	...	...	...	...	...
London St Pancras a.	...	...	...	...	...	...	...	1700	...	...	...	...	...	...	...	...	1900	...	...	...	...	...

train type		*TGV*	☆	*TGV*	*TGV*		*TGV*	*TGV*	*TGV*	*TGV*	☆	⇌		*TGV*	*TGV*	*TGV*	*TGV*	*TGV*		*TGV*		
train number		**7860**	**9057**	**5192**	**5192**		**5288**	**9868**	**9864**	**5291**	**9167**	**9954**		**7832**	**7662**	**7660**	**5182**	**9882**		**7836**		
train number				**5193**	**5193**			**9869**	**9865**	**5290**		**9955**		**7833**		**7661**		**9883**		**7837**		
notes		R	R 🍴	R 🍷	R 🍷		R 🍷	R 🍷	R 🍷	R 🍷	R 🍴	R 🍷		R	R	R	R 🍷	R 🍷		R		
		⊠		Ⓑ	⑥						Ⓑ			⊠	⊠	⊠				⊠		
			D									**B**			**C** △							
Nice d.	...	...	...	...	...	...	...	...	...	...	...	...	...	...	...	...	...	...	...	...	...	...
Cannes d.	...	...	...	...	...	...	...	...	...	...	...	...	...	...	...	...	...	...	...	...	...	...
St Raphaël - Valescure d.	...	...	...	...	...	...	...	...	...	...	...	...	...	...	...	...	...	...	...	...	...	...
Toulon d.	...	...	...	...	...	...	...	...	...	...	...	...	...	...	...	...	...	...	...	...	...	...
Marseille St Charles d.	...	...	...	...	1410	...	...	1510	...	...	...	1610	...	1644	...	...	...	1710	...	1815	...	...
Aix en Provence TGV d.	...	...	...	...	1426	...	...	1526	...	...	...	1624	...	|	...	...	...	1726	...	1829	...	...
Perpignan d.	...	...	...	...	|	...	...	|	...	...	...	|	...	|	...	...	...	|	...	|	...	...
Toulouse Matabiau d.	...	...	...	...	|	...	...	|	...	...	...	|	...	|	...	...	...	|	...	|	...	...
Narbonne d.	...	...	...	...	|	...	...	|	...	...	...	|	...	|	...	...	...	|	...	|	...	...
Béziers d.	...	...	...	...	|	...	...	|	...	...	...	|	...	|	...	...	...	|	...	|	...	...
Montpellier Saint-Roch d.	...	...	...	...	|	...	...	|	1450	...	...	|	...	|	...	...	...	|	...	|	...	...
Montpellier Sud de France d.	...	1407	...	...	|	...	...	|	|	...	...	|	...	|	...	...	1710	|	...	|	...	...
Nîmes Pont-du-Gard d.	...	1429	...	...	|	...	...	|	|	...	...	|	...	|	...	...	1732	|	...	|	...	...
Nîmes d.	...	|	...	...	|	...	...	|	1519	...	...	|	...	|	...	...	|	|	...	|	...	...
Avignon TGV d.	...	|	...	...	1448	...	...	1548	|	...	...	1647	...	1719	...	...	|	1748	...	1851	...	...
Valence TGV d.	...	|	...	...	|	...	...	|	1615	...	...	1727	...	|	...	...	1815	|	...	|	...	...
Lyon St Exupéry ✈ d.	...	1536	...	...	|	...	...	|	|	...	...	|	...	1815	...	...	|	|	...	|	...	...
Lyon Part Dieu d.	...	|	...	1600	1600	...	...	1700	1700	...	...	|	...	|	...	...	1900	1900	...	2000	...	...
Le Creusot TGV d.	...	|	...	|	|	...	...	|	|	...	...	|	...	|	...	...	|	|	...	|	...	...
Bordeaux d.	...	|	...	|	|	...	...	|	|	...	...	|	...	|	...	1659	|	|	...	|	...	...
Angoulême d.	...	|	...	|	|	...	...	|	|	...	...	|	...	|	...	1737	|	|	...	|	...	...
Poitiers d.	...	|	...	|	|	...	...	|	|	...	...	|	...	|	...	1820	|	|	...	|	...	...
St Pierre des Corps d.	...	|	...	|	|	...	...	|	|	...	...	|	...	|	...	1854	|	|	...	|	...	...
Nantes d.	...	|	...	|	|	...	1535	|	|	...	...	|	...	|	...	|	|	|	...	|	...	...
Angers St Laud d.	...	|	...	|	|	...	1616	|	|	...	...	|	...	|	...	|	|	|	...	|	...	...
Rennes d.	...	|	...	|	|	...	|	|	|	1653	...	|	...	|	1810	|	|	|	...	|	...	...
Le Mans d.	...	|	...	|	|	...	1657	|	|	|	...	|	...	|	|	|	|	|	...	|	...	...
Massy TGV d.	...	|	...	|	|	...	1755	|	|	1826	...	|	...	|	1946	1955	|	|	...	|	...	...
Strasbourg d.	...	|	...	|	|	...	|	|	|	|	...	|	...	|	|	|	|	|	...	|	...	...
Marne la Vallée § d.	...	1730	1803	1751	1751	...	1831	1851	1851	1905	...	|	...	2012	2030	2031	2051	2051	...	2152	...	...
Paris Charles de Gaulle ✈ a.	...	1740	|	1802	1802	...	1841	1902	1902	1916	...	1954	...	2022	2040	2042	2102	2102	...	2202	...	...
Paris Charles de Gaulle ✈ d.	...	1746	|	1807	1807	...	...	1907	1907	1938	...	1959	...	...	...	2058	2107	2107	...	2207	...	...
TGV Haute Picardie d.	...	1831	|	1839	1839	...	...	|	|	2009	...	|	...	...	...	2135	|	|	...	|	...	...
Arras a.	...	|	|	1856	1856	...	...	|	|	|	...	|	...	...	...	|	|	|	...	|	...	...
Douai a.	...	|	|	1914	1914	...	...	|	|	|	...	|	...	...	...	|	|	|	...	|	...	...
Lille Flandres ◇ a.	...	1903	|	1944	1944	...	...	|	|	2036	...	|	...	...	...	|	|	|	...	|	...	...
Lille Europe a.	...	...	|	...	...	...	...	1956	1956	...	...	|	...	...	...	|	2159	2159	...	|	...	...
Lille Europe d.	...	...	|	...	...	...	...	2008	2008	...	2135	|	...	...	...	|	...	2209	...	|	...	...
Tourcoing a.	...	...	|	...	...	...	...	|	|	...	|	|	...	...	...	2214	...	|	...	2309	...	...
Brussels Midi / Zuid a.	...	...	|	...	...	...	...	2043	2043	...	|	2110	...	...	...	...	...	2243	...	...	...	...
London St Pancras a.	...	...	1946	...	...	...	...	...	...	...	2157	...	...	...	...	...	...	...	...	...	...	...

B – THALYS SOLEIL – ⑥ July 2 - Aug. 27: 12 🍷 Marseille – Brussels.
⑥ July 9 - Aug. 27: 12 🍷 Marseille – Brussels – Amsterdam (arrive 2324; see Table **18**).

C – ①⑤⑥⑦ Apr. 2 – July 2.

D – ①③⑤⑦ June 12 - Dec. 9 (daily Oct. 21 – 31) also Jul 23, Aug. 27. See Table **17**.

b – From Barcelona (Table **13**).

AVE – Alta Velocidad Española R 🍷 ✓.

§ – Marne la Vallée - Chessy, station for Disneyland Paris.

△ – To / from Lorient or Quimper on dates in Table **285**.

◇ – 500 metres from Lille Europe (see Lille City Plan on page 32).

⊠ – OUIGO low-cost TGV service. Internet bookings only at www.ouigo.com. Timings may vary.

☆ – Eurostar train. Special fares payable. 🍴 in Business Premier and Standard Premier, 🍷 in Standard. Business Premier not available from Marne la Vallée - Chessy and Marseille. Minimum check-in time 30 mins. Valid June 12 - Sept. 3. **Additional services are available, see Table 10, pages 47 – 48.**

13 LONDON - PARIS - BARCELONA - MADRID

train type		AVE		TGV	AVE		TGV	AVE	AVE		☆	TGV		☆									
train number		9731		9713	3170		9826	9743	3202		9018	9715		9040	3971	3971			3737	3737			
train number / notes					Ⓑ										[R] F	[R] F	Ⓐ	Ⓒ	[R] L	[R] L			
notes												A			①-⑤	⑥⑦	2	2	⑤	⑦	2		
London St Pancras d.	...	...	...	...	...	...	...	...	...	...	1022	...	...	1622	...	...	...	...	...	...	...	...	...
Lille Europe d.	...	...	...	...	...	...	1103	...	...	...	│	...	...	│	...	...	...	...	...	...	...	...	...
Paris Nord a.	...	...	...	...	...	...	│	...	...	...	1347	...	...	1947	...	...	...	...	...	...	...	...	...
Paris Gare de Lyon d.	...	...	...	1014	...	...	│	...	...	...	...	1512	...	...	...	...	...	...	...	...	...	...	...
Paris Austerlitz d.	...	...	...	│	...	...	│	...	...	...	...	│	...	...	2114	2151	...	...	2214	2151	...	...	...
Les Aubrais-Orléans d.	...	...	...	│	...	...	│	...	...	...	...	│	...	...	2217	2254	...	...	2217	2254	...	...	...
Lyon Part Dieu d.	...	...	...	│	...	...	1400	1435	...	...	...	│	...	...	│	│	...	...	│	│	...	...	...
Valence TGV d.	...	...	...	1227	...	...	...	1511	...	...	...	1727	...	...	│	│	...	...	│	│	...	...	...
Marseille St Charles d.	...	0802	...	│	...	...	...	│	...	...	...	│	...	...	│	│	...	...	│	│	...	...	...
Aix en Provence TGV d.	...	0818	...	│	...	...	...	│	...	...	...	│	...	...	│	│	...	...	│	│	...	...	...
Avignon TGV d.	...	0840	...	│	...	...	...	│	...	...	...	│	...	...	│	│	...	...	│	│	...	...	...
Nîmes Centre d.	...	0908	...	1314	...	...	...	1557	...	...	...	1815	...	...	│	│	...	...	│	│	...	...	...
Montpellier Saint-Roch d.	...	0939	...	1347	...	...	...	1628	...	...	...	1846	...	...	│	│	...	...	│	│	...	...	...
Béziers d.	...	1017	...	1435	...	...	...	1715	...	...	...	1935	...	...	│	│	...	...	│	│	...	...	...
Toulouse Matabiau d.	...	│	...	│	...	...	...	│	...	...	...	│	...	...	│	│	...	...	│	│	...	...	...
Carcassonne d.	...	│	...	│	...	...	...	│	...	...	...	│	...	...	│	│	...	...	0633a	0633a	...	...	...
Narbonne d.	...	1033	...	1452	...	...	...	1731	...	...	...	1952	...	...	│	│	...	...	0745a	0745a	...	...	...
Perpignan d.	...	1112	...	1533	...	...	...	1810	...	...	...	2033	...	...	│	│	...	...	0834a	0834a	...	...	...
Latour de Carol 🏛 a.	...	│	...	│	...	...	...	│	...	...	...	│	...	...	0912	0912	1044	1110	│	│	...	...	...
Cerbère 🏛 a.	...	│	...	│	...	...	...	│	...	...	...	│	...	...	...	...	│	│	0922	0922	...	...	...
Portbou 🏛 a.	...	│	...	│	...	...	...	│	...	...	...	│	...	...	...	...	│	│	0926	0926	1035	...	...
Figueres Vilafant ◇ a.	...	1139	...	1556	...	...	...	1834	...	...	...	2056	...	...	...	...	│	│	...	...	1058x	...	...
Girona a.	...	1153	...	1613	...	...	...	1851	...	...	...	2113	...	...	...	...	│	│	...	...	1138	...	...
Barcelona Sants a.	...	1234	...	1654	...	...	...	1932	...	...	...	2154	...	...	...	...	1354	1411	...	...	1310	...	...
Barcelona Sants d.	...	1250	...	...	1725	...	...	...	2000	...	...	...	...	...	...	...	...	...	...	...	...	...	...
Zaragoza Delicias a.	...	1422	...	...	│	...	...	...	2142	...	...	...	...	...	...	...	...	...	...	...	...	...	...
Madrid Puerta de Atocha a	...	1545	...	...	1955	...	...	...	2317	...	...	...	...	...	...	...	...	...	...	...	...	...	...

train type	AVE	TGV	☆	TGV	AVE	AVE	TGV	☆	AVE	AVLO	TGV		AVE										
train number	9736	9866	9153	9708	3063	3071	9702	9055	3093	6303	9704		9724				3970	3970		3738	3738	9015	
train number / notes		9867			①-⑤	①-④				①-⑤					Ⓐ	Ⓒ	[R] H	[R] H		[R] G	[R] G		
notes				C			D				B				2	2	⑥⑦	①-⑤	2	⑦	⑤		
Madrid Puerta de Atocha d.	...	...	...	...	0630	0700	...	...	0930	1030	...	...	1325	...	...	...	...	...	...	...	...	...	...
Zaragoza Delicias d.	...	...	...	...	0752	│	...	...	1046	1146	...	...	1450	...	...	...	...	...	...	...	...	...	...
Barcelona Sants a.	...	...	...	...	0920	0930	...	...	1237	1315	...	...	1622	...	...	...	...	...	...	...	...	...	...
Barcelona Sants d.	0815	...	...	0910	...	...	1000	...	...	...	1400	...	1636	...	1501	1510	...	...	1516	...	...	...	...
Girona d.	0856	...	...	0951	...	...	1041	...	...	...	1441	...	1717	...	│	│	...	...	1648	...	...	...	...
Figueres Vilafant ◇ d.	0913	...	...	1008	...	...	1058	...	...	...	1458	...	1734	...	│	│	...	...	1727x	...	...	...	...
Portbou 🏛 d.	│	...	...	│	...	...	│	...	...	...	│	...	│	...	│	│	...	...	1751	...	...	...	...
Cerbère 🏛 d.	│	...	...	│	...	...	│	...	...	...	│	...	│	...	│	│	...	...	1756	1907	1907	...	...
Latour de Carol 🏛 d.	│	...	...	│	...	...	│	...	...	...	│	...	│	...	1805	1817	1918	1925	...	│	│	...	...
Perpignan a.	0937	...	...	1034	...	...	1123	...	...	...	1523	...	1758	...	...	...	│	│	...	1957	1957	...	...
Narbonne a.	1015	...	...	1119	...	...	1207	...	...	...	1607	...	1840	...	...	...	│	│	...	│	│	...	...
Carcassonne d.	│	...	...	│	...	...	│	...	...	...	│	...	│	...	...	...	│	│	...	2148	2148	...	...
Toulouse Matabiau d.	│	...	...	│	...	...	│	...	...	...	│	...	│	...	...	...	│	│	...	│	│	...	...
Béziers a.	│	...	...	1136	...	...	1223	...	...	...	1624	...	1856	...	...	...	│	│	...	│	│	...	...
Montpellier Saint-Roch a.	1121	...	...	1226f	...	...	1313	...	...	...	1713	...	1945	...	...	...	│	│	...	│	│	...	...
Nîmes Centre a.	1155	...	...	1252z	...	...	1345	...	...	...	1745	...	2022	...	...	...	│	│	...	│	│	...	...
Avignon TGV a.	│	...	...	│	...	...	│	...	...	...	│	...	2047	...	...	...	│	│	...	│	│	...	...
Aix en Provence TGV a.	│	...	...	│	...	...	│	...	...	...	│	...	2111	...	...	...	│	│	...	│	│	...	...
Marseille St Charles a.	│	...	...	│	...	...	│	...	...	...	│	...	2126	...	...	...	│	│	...	│	│	...	...
Valence TGV a.	1243	...	...	1332	...	...	1432	...	...	...	1832	...	...	...	...	...	│	│	...	│	│	...	...
Lyon Part Dieu a.	1320	1400	...	│	...	...	│	...	...	...	│	...	...	...	...	...	│	│	...	│	│	...	...
Les Aubrais-Orléans a.	...	│	...	│	...	...	│	...	...	...	│	...	...	...	...	...	0525	0603	...	0525	0603	...	...
Paris Austerlitz a.	...	│	...	│	...	...	│	...	...	...	│	...	...	...	...	...	0635	0709	...	0635	0709	...	...
Paris Gare de Lyon a.	...	│	...	1546	...	...	1647	...	...	...	2048	...	...	...	...	...	...	...	...	...	...	...	...
Paris Nord d.	...	│	...	...	...	...	...	1903	...	...	...	...	...	...	...	...	...	...	...	...	...	0903	...
Lille Europe a.	...	1657	1835	...	...	...	...	│	...	...	...	...	...	...	...	...	...	...	...	...	...	│	...
London St Pancras a.	...	...	1857	...	...	...	...	2030	...	...	...	...	...	...	...	...	...	...	...	...	...	1039	...

A – June 14 - Sept. 30.
B – June 15 - Oct. 1.
C – Dec. 12 - July 1, Aug. 29 - Dec. 10.
D – July 2 - Aug. 28.
F – 🛏 1, 2 cl., 🛋 Paris - Toulouse - Latour de Carol.
G – 🛏 1, 2 cl., 🛋 Cerbère - Toulouse - Paris.
H – 🛏 1, 2 cl., 🛋 Latour de Carol - Toulouse - Paris.
L – 🛏 1, 2 cl., 🛋 Paris - Toulouse - Portbou.

a – Arrival time.
f – Montpellier **Sud de France**.
x – Figueres.
z – Nîmes **Pont-du-Gard.**

TGV – *Train à Grande Vitesse* [R] 🍸 ⁄.
AVE – Alta Velocidad Española [R] 🍸 ⁄.
AVLO – Low-cost AVE.

⁄ – Supplement payable.
◇ – 🚌 connections available to Figueres bus station. (Table **657**).
☆ – Eurostar train. [R], 🍴 in Business Premier and Standard Premier, 🍸 in Standard. Special fares payable. Minimum check-in time 30 minutes. Valid June 12 - Sept. 3. **Additional services are available, see Table 10, pages 47 – 48.**

LONDON - AMSTERDAM *by rail–sea–rail via Harwich - Hoek van Holland* 15

notes	①–⑥	⑥	①–⑤	①–⑥ 🚢	①–⑥ 🚋	①–⑥	①–⑥	⑦	⑦	⑦ 🚢	⑦ 🚋	⑦	⑦	①–⑤	⑥	①–⑥	①–⑥ 🚢	⑥⑦ 🚋	②–⑤ 🚋	②–⑥	⑦	②–⑦
London Liverpool Street d.	...	0638	0638	...	...	...	...	...	0757	...	...	...	...	1932	1932	...	...	...	...	...	...	...
Colchester d.	...	0740	0743	...	...	...	...	...	0905	...	...	...	...	2025	2032	...	...	...	...	...	...	...
Manningtree d.	...	0748	0751	...	...	...	...	...	0914	...	...	...	...	2034	2040	...	...	...	...	...	...	...
Cambridge d.	...	|	|	...	...	...	...	...	|	...	...	...	...	|	|	1947	...	...	...	...	...	...
Ipswich d.	0659	|	|	...	...	...	...	0801	|	...	...	...	...	|	|	2101	...	...	...	...	...	...
Harwich International 🏛 d.	0726	0809	0810	0900	...	...	...	0826	0930	1000	...	...	...	2054	2056	2129	2300	...	...	...	...	...
Hoek van Holland Haven 🏛 a.	...	...	...	1715	1751	...	...	...	...	1800	1847	...	...	...	...	...	0800	0847	0851	...	...	...
Schiedam Centrum a.	...	...	...	...	1816	1843	1846	...	...	...	1910	1928	1946	...	...	...	...	0910	0915	0928	0943	0946
Rotterdam Centraal a.	...	...	...	...	...	1848	|	...	...	...	...	1933	|	...	...	...	...	...	...	0933	0948	|
Den Haag HS a.	...	...	...	...	...	...	1901	...	...	...	...	...	2001	...	...	...	...	...	...	...	...	1001
Schiphol ✈ a.	...	...	...	...	...	...	|	...	...	...	...	...	|	...	...	...	...	...	...	...	...	|
Amsterdam Centraal a.	...	...	...	...	...	...	1955	...	...	...	...	...	2055	...	...	...	...	...	...	...	...	1055

notes	⑦	⑦	⑦ 🚢	① 🚋	①	①
London Liverpool Street d.	2000	...	...	...	...	...
Colchester d.	2056	...	...	...	...	...
Manningtree d.	2104	...	...	...	...	...
Cambridge d.	|	1946	...	...	...	...
Ipswich d.	|	2103	...	...	...	...
Harwich International 🏛 d.	2124	2129	2300	...	...	...
Hoek van Holland Haven 🏛 a.	...	...	0800	0851	...	...
Schiedam Centrum a.	...	...	...	0914	0928	0946
Rotterdam Centraal a.	...	...	...	...	0933	|
Den Haag HS a.	...	...	...	...	...	1001
Schiphol ✈ a.	...	...	...	...	...	|
Amsterdam Centraal a.	...	...	...	...	...	1055

notes	⑦	⑦	⑦ 🚋	⑦ 🚢	⑦	⑦
Amsterdam Centraal d.	...	1104	...	...	...	...
Schiphol ✈ d.	...	|	...	...	...	...
Den Haag HS d.	...	1159	...	...	...	...
Rotterdam Centraal d.	1206	|	...	...	...	...
Schiedam Centrum d.	1211	1213	1219	...	...	...
Hoek van Holland Haven 🏛 d.	...	...	1242	1345	...	...
Harwich International 🏛 a.	...	...	...	1945	2030	2138
Ipswich a.	...	...	...	...	|	2204
Cambridge a.	...	...	...	...	|	...
Manningtree a.	...	...	...	...	2043	...
Colchester a.	...	...	...	...	2052	...
London Liverpool Street a.	...	...	...	...	2146	...

notes	①–⑥	①–⑥	①–⑥ 🚋	①–⑥ 🚢	①–⑥	①–⑥			🚋	🚢	①–⑤	⑥	⑦	①–⑤	⑥	⑦
Amsterdam Centraal d.	1134	...	...	...	...	...	...	1904	...	...	...	...	...	...	...	...
Schiphol ✈ d.	|	...	...	...	...	...	...	|	...	...	...	...	...	...	...	...
Den Haag HS d.	1229	...	...	...	...	...	...	1959	...	...	...	...	...	...	...	...
Rotterdam Centraal d.	|	1227	...	...	...	...	2006	|	...	...	...	...	...	...	...	...
Schiedam Centrum d.	1243	1231	1256	...	...	...	2011	2013	2018	...	...	...	...	...	...	...
Hoek van Holland Haven 🏛 d.	...	...	1320	1415	...	...	...	...	2042	2200	...	...	...	...	...	...
Harwich International 🏛 a.	...	...	...	1945	2045	2138	...	...	...	0630	0715	0720	0720	0750	0750	0850
Ipswich a.	...	...	...	...	|	2204	...	...	...	...	|	|	|	0818	0818	0914
Cambridge a.	...	...	...	...	|	...	...	...	...	...	|	|	|	0942	0940	1040
Manningtree a.	...	...	...	...	2058	...	...	...	...	...	0731	0733	0733	...	...	...
Colchester a.	...	...	...	...	2107	...	...	...	...	...	0741	0742	0742	...	...	...
London Liverpool Street a.	...	...	...	...	2214	...	...	...	...	...	0854	0846	0858	...	...	...

🚋 – Tram, Rotterdam Metro line **B**.

SEA CROSSING (for rail / sea / rail journeys): 🚢 – Ship operated by Stena Line. Ⓡ. Stena Plus lounge (supplement payable) and ✕ on ship. A cabin must be booked on night sailings.

LILLE - BRUSSELS (Summary Table) 16

train type	*TGV*	*TGV*	☆	*TGV*	*TGV*	☆	☆	*TGV*	☆	*TGV*	*TGV*	☆	*TGV*	☆	*TGV*	☆	☆	*TGV*
train number	**9809**	**9852**	**9110**	**9886**	**9854**	**9116**	**9126**	**9862**	**9132**	**9892**	**9866**	**9142**	**9894**	**9148**	**9868**	**9152**	**9158**	**9882**
notes	Ⓐ	**9890**	①–⑥	**9884**										⑥		Ⓑ		
notes							**A**											
Lille Europe d.	0720	0907	0930	1027	1137	1130	1330	1455	1533	1554	1708	1730	1808	1930	2009	2030	2203	2208
Brussels Midi / Zuid a.	0755	0943	1005	1102	1217	1205	1405	1533	1608	1629	1743	1805	1843	2005	2043	2105	2238	2243

train type	*TGV*	☆	*TGV*	☆	*TGV*	☆	*TGV*	☆	☆	☆	*TGV*	☆	*TGV*	*TGV*	☆	☆	*TGV*	☆	*TGV*	☆
train number	**9810**	**9109**	**9870**	**9113**	**9812**	**9117**	**9826**	**9125**	**9129**	**9133**	**9830**	**9145**	**9836**	**9832**	**9149**	**9153**	**9872**	**9157**	**9846**	**9167**
notes		①		①–⑥				⑤	⑦	①–⑥					⑥⑦			①–⑥		Ⓑ
notes												**A**								**A**
Brussels Midi / Zuid d.	0624	0656	0717	0756	0817	0852	1017	1052	1156	1252	1259	1556	1617	1655	1700	1756	1817	1856	1917	2056
Lille Europe a.	0712	0730	0752	0830	0852	0926	1052	1130	1230	1326	13350	1632	1653	1728	1730	1830	1856	1930	1952	2130

A – To / from Amsterdam, see Table **18**.

TGV – High-speed train. Ⓡ 🍷.

☆ – Eurostar train. Ⓡ, ✕ in Business Premier and Standard Premier, 🍷 in Standard. Special fares payable. Minimun check-in time 30 minutes departure from Brussels. Valid June 12 - Sept. 3. **Additional services are available, see Table 10, pages 47 – 48.**

☛ **Shaded services are temporarily suspended.**

LONDON - MARSEILLE and MARNE LA VALLÉE 17

train type	☆	☆
train number	**9084**	**9074**
train number	**9085**	
notes		**A**
London St Pancras d.	0715	1014
Ebbsfleet International d.	|	|
Ashford International d.	|	|
Lille Europe a.	|	1254
Marne la Vallée § a.	|	1403
Lyon Part Dieu a.	1300	...
Avignon TGV a.	1408	...
Marseille St Charles a.	1447	...

train type	☆	☆	☆
train number	**9057**	**9087**	**9087**
train number		**9086**	**9086**
notes	**A**		
Marseille St Charles d.	...	1522	...
Avignon TGV d.	...	1559	...
Lyon Part Dieu d.	...	1725	...
Marne la Vallée § d.	1803	|	...
Lille Europe d.	|	2021	2136
Ashford International a.	|	...	2134
Ebbsfleet International a.	|	...	|
London St Pancras a.	1946	...	2212

A – ①③⑤⑦ June 12 - Dec. 9 (daily Oct. 21 – 31) also July 23, Aug. 27.

§ – Marne la Vallée - Chessy (station for Disneyland).

☆ – Eurostar train. Ⓡ, ✕ in Standard Premier, 🍷 in Standard. Special fares payable. Minimum check-in time 30 minutes. Eurostar will not serve Ebbsfleet International or Ashford International in 2022.

☛ **Shaded services are suspended until further notice.**

18 LONDON / PARIS - BRUSSELS - AMSTERDAM

Services subject to alteration November 10–13

train type	ICd	⇌	IC	⇌	⇌	ICd	ICd	⇌	⇌	⇌	⇌	ICd	⇌	☆	☆	⇌	IC	⇌		
train number	**9211**	**9397**	**9691**	**9303**	**9303**	**9219**	**9223**	**9309**	**9309**	**9411**	**9315**	**9227**	**9315**	**9110**	**9110**	**9317**	**9693**	**9321**		
notes		①–⑤		⑥	①–⑤			⑥	①–⑤	①–⑥	⑦		①–⑥	①–⑤	⑥	⑥		①–⑤		
notes		**D**		**S**	**D**			**S**	**D**	**K**	**B**		**K**			**F**		**D**		
London St Pancras d.	...	...	...	...	...	...	...	...	...	...	...	...	...	0647	0657	...	...	...	...	...
Marne la Vallée - Chessy § d.	...	...	...	...	...	...	...	...	...	...	...	...	...	|	|	...	...	...	...	...
Paris Charles de Gaulle ✈ d.	...	...	...	...	...	...	...	...	...	...	...	...	...	|	|	...	...	...	...	...
Paris Nord d.	...	...	...	...	0613	...	...	0704	0725	0755	0755j	...	0825	|	|	0855	...	0922	...	...
Lille Europe d.	...	...	...	...	|	...	...	|	|	|	|	...	|	0930	0930	|	...	|	...	...
Brussels Midi / Zuid ◧ a.	...	...	...	...	0745	...	...	0841	0847	0917	0934	...	0947	1007	1005	1017	...	1044	...	...
Brussels Midi / Zuid ◧ △ d.	0544	0652	0644	0752	0752	0744	0844	0852	0852	...	0952	0944	0952	...	...	...	1044	1052	...	...
Brussels Airport ✈ d.	0611	|	0711	|	|	0811	0911	|	|	...	|	1011	|	...	...	...	1111	|	...	...
Mechelen d.	0624	|	0724	|	|	0824	0924	|	|	...	|	1024	|	...	...	...	1124	|	...	...
Antwerpen Centraal a.	0644	0727	0744	0827	0827	0844	0944	0927	0927	...	1027	1044	1027	...	...	...	1144	1127	...	...
Breda a.	0718	|	0818	|	|	0918	1018	|	|	...	|	1118	|	...	...	...	1218	|	...	...
Breda d.	0726	|	0826	|	|	0926	1026	|	|	...	|	1126	|	...	...	...	1226	|	...	...
Rotterdam Centraal a.	0749	0802	0849	0902	0902	0949	1049	1002	1002	...	1102	1149	1102	...	...	...	1249	1202	...	...
Den Haag HS a.	|	|	0920	|	|	|	|	|	|	...	|	|	|	...	...	...	1320	|	...	...
Schiphol ✈ a.	0822	0825	...	0925	0925	1022	1122	1025	1025	...	1125	1222	1125	...	...	...	...	1225	...	...
Amsterdam Centraal a.	0838	0844	...	0944	0944	1038	1138	1044	1044	...	1144	1238	1144	...	...	...	...	1244	...	...

train type	☆	⇌	ICd		⇌	☆	ICd	⇌	⇌	⇌	ICd	⇌	⇌	⇌	☆	⇌	IC	⇌	ICd	⇌
train number	**9114**	**9423**	**9235**		**9327**	**9116**	**9239**	**9333**	**9333**	**9435**	**9243**	**9939**	**9339**	**9339**	**9128**	**9341**	**9695**	**9345**	**9251**	**9351**
notes	①–⑥							①	②–⑤			⑤	①–⑤					⑤		
notes								**E**	**V**	**G**			**N**	**U**		**L**				
London St Pancras d.	0816	...	...	...	...	0901	...	...	...	...	...	...	...	...	1104	...	...	...	...	...
Marne la Vallée - Chessy § d.	|	...	...	...	...	|	...	...	...	...	...	1204	...	...	|	...	...	...	...	...
Paris Charles de Gaulle ✈ d.	|	...	...	...	...	|	...	...	...	...	...	1218	...	...	|	...	...	...	...	...
Paris Nord d.	|	0955	...	...	1025	|	...	1122	...	1155	...	|	1219	1225	|	1255	...	...	...	1425
Lille Europe d.	|	|	...	...	|	1130	...	|	...	|	...	|	|	|	1330	|	...	...	...	|
Brussels Midi / Zuid ◧ a.	1112	1117	...	...	1147	1205	...	1244	...	1317	...	1334	1341	1347	1405	1417	...	...	...	1547
Brussels Midi / Zuid ◧ △ d.	1122	...	1144	...	1152	...	1244	1252	1252	...	1344	...	1352	1352	1422	...	1444	1452	1544	1552
Brussels Airport ✈ d.	|	...	1211	...	|	...	1311	|	|	...	1411	...	|	|	|	...	1511	|	1611	|
Mechelen d.	|	...	1224	...	|	...	1324	|	|	...	1424	...	|	|	|	...	1524	|	1624	|
Antwerpen Centraal a.	|	...	1244	...	1227	...	1344	1327	1327	...	1444	...	1427	1427	|	...	1544	1527	1644	1627
Breda a.	|	...	1318	...	|	...	1418	|	|	...	1518	...	|	|	|	...	1618	|	1718	|
Breda d.	|	...	1326	...	|	...	1426	|	|	...	1526	...	|	|	|	...	1626	|	1726	|
Rotterdam Centraal a.	1232	...	1349	...	1302	...	1449	1402	1402	...	1549	...	1502	1502	1532	...	1649	1602	1749	1702
Den Haag HS a.	|	...	|	...	|	...	|	|	|	...	|	...	|	|	|	...	1722	|	|	|
Schiphol ✈ a.	|	...	1422	...	1325	...	1522	1425	1425	...	1622	...	1525	1525	|	...	...	1625	1822	1725
Amsterdam Centraal a.	1311	...	1438	...	1344	...	1538	1444	1444	...	1638	...	1544	1544	1611	...	...	1644	1838	1744

train type	☆	ICd	⇌	⇌	⇌	ICd	⇌	⇌	⇌	⇌	☆	IC	⇌		⇌	ICd		⇌		
train number	**9132**	**9255**	**9357**	**9357**	**9459**	**9259**	**9963**	**9363**	**9363**	**9365**	**9140**	**9697**	**9369**		**9471**	**9267**		**9375**		
notes			⑤⑦	①–④			⑦	①–⑤	⑦	①–⑤								Ⓑ		
notes			**X**	**D**			**B**	**D**	**R**	**C**					**M**					
London St Pancras d.	1304	...	...	...	...	...	...	...	...	...	1504	...	...	...	...	...	...	...	...	...
Marne la Vallée - Chessy § d.	|	...	...	...	...	...	1604	...	...	...	|	...	...	...	...	...	...	...	...	...
Paris Charles de Gaulle ✈ d.	|	...	...	...	...	...	1619	...	...	...	|	...	...	...	...	...	...	...	...	...
Paris Nord d.	|	...	1522	...	1555	...	|	1625	1625	1655	|	...	1725	...	1755	...	...	1825	...	...
Lille Europe d.	1530	...	|	...	|	...	|	|	|	|	1730	...	|	...	|	...	...	|	...	...
Brussels Midi / Zuid ◧ a.	1607	...	1644	...	1717	...	1733	1747	1747	1817	1805	...	1847	...	1917	...	...	1947	...	...
Brussels Midi / Zuid ◧ △ d.	...	1644	1652	1652	...	1744	1752	1752	...	...	...	1844	1852	...	...	1944	...	1952	...	...
Brussels Airport ✈ d.	...	1711	|	|	...	1811	|	|	...	...	...	1911	|	...	...	2011	...	|	...	...
Mechelen d.	...	1724	|	|	...	1824	|	|	...	...	...	1925	|	...	...	2024	...	|	...	...
Antwerpen Centraal a.	...	1744	1727	1727	...	1844	1827	1827	...	...	...	1944	1927	...	...	2044	...	2027	...	...
Breda a.	...	1818	|	|	...	1918	|	|	...	...	...	2018	|	...	...	2118	...	|	...	...
Breda d.	...	1826	|	|	...	1926	|	|	...	...	...	2026	|	...	...	2126	...	|	...	...
Rotterdam Centraal a.	...	1849	1802	1802	...	1949	1902	1902	...	...	...	2049	2002	...	...	2149	...	2102	...	...
Den Haag HS a.	...	|	|	|	...	|	|	|	...	...	...	2122	|	...	...	|	...	|	...	...
Schiphol ✈ a.	...	1922	1825	1825	...	2022	1925	1925	...	...	...	2149	2025	...	...	2222	...	2125	...	...
Amsterdam Centraal a.	...	1938	1844	1844	...	2038	1944	1944	...	...	...	2205	2044	...	...	2238	...	2144	...	...

train type	☆	☆	ICd		⇌		☆	⇌	⇌	⇌	⇌	⇌	⇌	⇌	⇌	⇌				
train number	**9148**	**9148**	**9271**		**9381**		**9152**	**9955/4**	**9387**	**9387**	**9387**	**9387**	**9389**	**9393**	**9393**	**9395**				
notes notes	⑦	⑤					Ⓑ	⊗	⑥	⑤				⑤	⑤	⑦				
notes								**Z**	**S**	**W**	**A**	**J**	**Q**	**W**	**Y**	**H**				
London St Pancras d.	1655	1704	...	...	...	...	1804	...	...	...	...	...	...	...	...	...	...	...	...	...
Marne la Vallée - Chessy § d.	|	|	...	...	...	...	|	...	2004	...	...	...	...	...	...	...	...	...	...	...
Paris Charles de Gaulle ✈ d.	|	|	...	...	...	...	|	...	2018	...	...	...	...	...	...	...	...	...	...	...
Paris Nord d.	|	|	...	...	1925	...	|	...	|	2019	2025	2025	2055	2125	2135	2155	...	...	...	...
Lille Europe d.	1930	1930	...	...	|	...	2030	...	|	|	|	|	|	|	|	|	...	...	...	...
Brussels Midi / Zuid ◧ a.	2005	2005	...	...	2047	...	2105	2110	2134	2142	2147	2147	2217	2247	2257	2317	...	...	...	...
Brussels Midi / Zuid ◧ △ d.	...	...	2044	...	2052	...	2122	|	2152	2152	2152	...	...	...	...	...	...	...	...	...
Brussels Airport ✈ d.	...	...	2111	...	|	...	|	|	|	|	|	...	...	...	...	...	...	...	...	...
Mechelen d.	...	...	2124	...	|	...	|	|	|	|	|	...	...	...	...	...	...	...	...	...
Antwerpen Centraal a.	...	...	2144	...	2127	...	|	2203	2227	2227	2227	...	...	...	...	...	...	...	...	...
Breda a.	...	...	2218	...	|	...	|	|	|	|	|	...	...	...	...	...	...	...	...	...
Breda d.	...	...	2226	...	|	...	|	|	|	|	|	...	...	...	...	...	...	...	...	...
Rotterdam Centraal a.	...	...	2249	...	2202	...	2232	2242	2302	2302	2302	...	...	...	...	...	...	...	...	...
Den Haag HS a.	...	...	|	...	|	...	|	|	|	|	|	...	...	...	...	...	...	...	...	...
Schiphol ✈ a.	...	...	2322	...	2225	...	|	2308	2325	2325	2325	...	...	...	...	...	...	...	...	...
Amsterdam Centraal a.	...	...	2338	...	2244	...	2311	2324	2344	2344	2344	...	...	...	...	...	...	...	...	...

A – ⑦ June 12 - Sept. 3. ⑤⑦ Sept. 4 - Dec. 10 (also Nov. 1).

B – Also Aug. 15, Nov. 1.

C – Not Nov. 1.

D – Not July 21, Aug. 15, Nov. 1.

E – Also Aug. 16, Nov. 2.

F – ⑥ June 12 - Sept. 3 (also July 21). ①⑥ Sept. 4 - Dec. 10 (also Nov. 2).

G – ⑤⑥⑦ June 12 - July 16. ①⑤⑥⑦ July 17 - Sept. 3 (also July 21, Aug. 16). Daily Sept. 4 - Dec. 10.

H – Also Nov. 1.

J – ①–④ Sept. 4 - Dec. 10 (not Nov. 11).

K – Not Aug. 15, Nov. 1.

L – ⑦ July 17 - Sept. 3 (also Aug. 15; not Aug. 14). Ⓑ Sept. 4 - Dec. 10.

M – Ⓑ June 12 - July 16. Daily July 17 - Dec. 10.

N – ①–⑤ June 12 - Sept. 3 (not July 21, Aug. 15).

Q – ①②③④⑥ June 12 - Sept. 3 (not Aug. 15). ⑥ Sept. 4 - Dec. 10.

R – ⑦ July 17 - Dec. 10 (also Aug. 15, Nov. 1; not Aug. 14).

S – Also July 21.

U – ⑥⑦ June 12 - Sept. 3 (also July 14, 21, Aug. 15). Daily Sept. 4 - Dec. 10.

V – Not July 21, Aug. 16, Nov. 1, 2.

W – ⑤ June 12 - Sept. 3.

X – Also Aug. 15, Nov. 1.

Y – ①–⑤ Sept. 4 - Dec. 10 (not Nov. 1).

Z – ⑥ July 9 - Aug. 27: *THALYS* SOLEIL – 12 🍸 Marseille - Brussels - Amsterdam (Table **11**).

j – 0801 July 17 - Dec. 10.

⊗ – Calls to set down only.

§ – Station for Disneyland.

◧ – Connections at Brussels are not guaranteed.

⇌ – *Thalys* high-speed train. Ⓡ 🍸. Special fares payable. Three classes of service: (Premium, Comfort and Standard). Valid June 12 - Dec. 10.

△ – All *IC* and *ICd* services call at Brussels Central 5 minutes, and at Brussels Nord 12 minutes, after Brussels Midi / Zuid.

☆ – Eurostar train. Ⓡ, ✕ in Business Premier and Standard Premier, 🍸 in Standard. Special fares payable. Minimum check-in time 30 minutes. Valid June 12 - Sept. 3. **Additional services are available, see Table 10, pages 47–48.**

☛ **Shaded services are temporarily suspended.**

Brussels - Disneyland: see Table 11

AMSTERDAM - BRUSSELS - PARIS / LONDON — 18

Services subject to alteration November 10–13

km	km	train type	⇌	⇌	⇌	⇌	⇌	☆		⇌	⇌	⇌	⇌	IC	☆	⇌	ICd	⇌	☆	
		train number	9302	9304	9308	9310	9412 9312	9117		9914	9316	9926/7	9916	9692	9119	9322	9216	9424	9125	
		notes	C	① U	①–⑥ V	①–⑤ W				⑥	①–⑤ W	⊕ B	⑤		①–⑥					
0	0	**Amsterdam** Centraal d.	...	...	...	0615	...	...	...	0645	0715	0715	0715	0555	0747	0815	0725	...	...	...
17	17	Schiphol ✈ ⊕ d.	...	...	...	0634	...	...	...	0704	0734	0734	0734	0611	|	0834	0740	...	...	...
60		Den Haag HS d.	...	...	...	|	...	...	...	|	|	|	|	0640	|	|	|	...	...	...
82	70	**Rotterdam** Centraal d.	...	...	...	0658	...	...	...	0728	0758	0758	0758	0710	0828	0858	0810	...	...	...
140	117	Breda a.	...	...	...	|	...	...	...	|	|	|	|	0734	|	|	0834	...	...	...
140	117	Breda d.	...	...	...	|	...	...	...	|	|	|	|	0742	|	|	0842	...	...	...
181	•165	**Antwerpen** Centraal d.	...	...	...	0734	...	...	...	0804	0833	0833	0833	0816	|	0933	0916	...	...	...
		Mechelen d.	...	...	...	|	...	...	...	|	|	|	|	0837	|	|	0937	...	...	...
		Brussels Airport ✈ d.	...	...	...	|	...	...	...	|	|	|	|	0850	|	|	0950	...	...	...
229	212	**Brussels** Midi / Zuid ◧ △ a.	...	...	...	0808	...	...	...	0838	0908	|	0908	0917	0938	1008	1017	...	...	...
229	212	**Brussels** Midi / Zuid ◧ d.	0642	0713	0743	0813	0843	0852	...	0900	0916	0925	0922	...	1005	1013	...	1043	1056	...
		Lille Europe a.	|	|	|	|	|	0926	...	|	|	...	|	...	|	|	...	|	1130	...
541	524	**Paris** Nord a.	0805	0835	0905	0935	1005	|	...	|	1038	...	|	...	|	1135	...	1205	|	...
		Paris Charles de Gaulle ✈ a.	...	...	...	...	...	|	...	1012	...	...	1040	...	|	...	...	...	|	...
		Marne la Vallée - Chessy § a.	...	...	...	...	...	|	...	1027	...	...	1059	...	|	...	...	...	|	...
		London St Pancras a.	...	...	...	...	...	0957	...	...	...	...	...	...	1057	...	...	...	1157	...

train type	⇌	ICd		⇌	⇌	ICd	⇌	☆		⇌	IC		ICd	⇌	⇌	☆	⇌			
train number	9328	9220		9334	9334	9224	9336	9135		9340	9694		9232	9346	9448	9141	9352			
notes	①–⑥ X			①–⑤ W	⑥⑦ Y		P							①–⑤ W		①–⑤				
Amsterdam Centraal d.	0915	0825	...	1015	1015	0925	...	...	...	1115	...	...	1125	1215	...	...	1315	...	...	...
Schiphol ✈ ⊕ d.	0934	0840	...	1034	1034	0940	...	...	...	1134	...	...	1140	1234	...	...	1334	...	...	...
Den Haag HS d.	|	|	...	|	|	|	...	...	...	|	1040	...	|	|	...	...	|	...	...	...
Rotterdam Centraal d.	0958	0910	...	1058	1058	1010	...	...	...	1158	1110	...	1210	1258	...	...	1358	...	...	...
Breda a.	|	0934	...	|	|	1034	...	...	...	|	1134	...	1234	|	...	...	|	...	...	...
Breda d.	|	0942	...	|	|	1042	...	...	...	|	1142	...	1242	|	...	...	|	...	...	...
Antwerpen Centraal d.	1033	1016	...	1133	1133	1116	...	...	...	1233	1216	...	1316	1333	...	...	1433	...	...	...
Mechelen d.	|	1037	...	|	|	1137	...	...	...	|	1237	...	1337	|	...	...	|	...	...	...
Brussels Airport ✈ d.	|	1050	...	|	|	1150	...	...	...	|	1250	...	1350	|	...	...	|	...	...	...
Brussels Midi / Zuid ◧ △ a.	1108	1117	...	1208	1208	1217	...	...	...	1308	1317	...	1417	1408	...	...	1508	...	...	...
Brussels Midi / Zuid ◧ d.	1113	...	...	...	1216	...	1243	1252	...	1313	...	...	...	...	1443	1452	1516	...	...	...
Lille Europe a.	|	...	...	...	|	...	|	1326	...	|	...	...	...	...	|	1530	|	...	...	...
Paris Nord a.	1235	...	...	...	1338	...	1405	|	...	1435	...	...	...	...	1605	|	1638	...	...	...
Paris Charles de Gaulle ✈ a.	...	...	...	...	...	...	...	|	...	...	...	...	...	...	...	|	...	...	...	...
Marne la Vallée - Chessy § a.	...	...	...	...	...	...	...	|	...	...	...	...	...	...	...	|	...	...	...	...
London St Pancras a.	...	...	...	...	...	...	...	1405	...	...	...	...	...	...	...	1603	...	...	...	...

train type	ICd	☆	⇌	⇌	⇌		ICd	⇌	IC	⇌	☆		⇌	ICd	⇌	☆		ICd	⇌	
train number	9236	9145	9354	9358	9358		9240	9364	9696	9358	9153		9370	9248	9472	9157		9252	9376	
notes			D	⑤	A					F			Ⓑ			①–⑥			Ⓑ	
Amsterdam Centraal d.	1225	1347	...	1415	...	...	1325	1515	...	...	...	...	1615	1525	...	1647	...	1625	1715	...
Schiphol ✈ ⊕ d.	1240	|	...	1434	...	...	1340	1534	...	...	...	...	1634	1540	...	|	...	1640	1734	...
Den Haag HS d.	|	|	...	|	...	...	|	|	1440	...	...	...	|	|	...	|	...	|	|	...
Rotterdam Centraal d.	1310	1428	...	1458	...	...	1410	1558	1510	...	...	...	1658	1610	...	1728	...	1710	1758	...
Breda a.	1334	|	...	|	...	...	1434	|	1534	...	...	...	|	1634	...	|	...	1734	|	...
Breda d.	1342	|	...	|	...	...	1442	|	1542	...	...	...	|	1642	...	|	...	1742	|	...
Antwerpen Centraal d.	1416	|	...	1533	...	...	1516	1633	1616	...	...	...	1733	1716	...	|	...	1816	1833	...
Mechelen d.	1437	|	...	|	...	...	1537	|	1637	...	...	...	|	1737	...	|	...	1837	|	...
Brussels Airport ✈ d.	1450	|	...	|	...	...	1550	|	1650	...	...	...	|	1750	...	|	...	1850	|	...
Brussels Midi / Zuid ◧ △ a.	1517	1538	...	1608	...	...	1617	1708	1717	...	...	...	1808	1817	...	1838	...	1917	1908	...
Brussels Midi / Zuid ◧ d.	...	1556	1543	1613	1613	...	...	1713	...	1743	1756	...	1813	...	1842	1856	...	...	1913f	...
Lille Europe a.	...	1630	|	|	|	...	...	|	...	|	1830	...	|	...	|	1930	...	...	|	...
Paris Nord a.	...	|	1705	1735	1735	...	...	1835	...	1905	|	...	1935	...	2005	|	...	...	2035f	...
Paris Charles de Gaulle ✈ a.	...	|	...	...	...	...	...	...	...	...	|	...	...	...	...	|	...	...	...	...
Marne la Vallée - Chessy § a.	...	|	...	...	...	...	...	...	...	...	|	...	...	...	...	|	...	...	...	...
London St Pancras a.	...	1700	...	...	...	...	...	...	...	...	1900	...	...	...	...	1957	...	...	...	...

train type	⇌		ICd	⇌	☆	⇌		IC	⇌	⇌		ICd		ICd	⇌	ICd				
train number	9382		9256	9484	9167	9388		9698	9394	9394		9264		9268	9398	9272				
notes				R	①–⑥	Ⓑ			①–⑤ W	⑦ Z					⑦ Z					
Amsterdam Centraal d.	1815	...	1725	...	1847	1915	...	...	2015	2015	...	1925	...	2025	2115	2125	...	...	...	...
Schiphol ✈ ⊕ d.	1834	...	1740	...	|	1934	...	...	2034	2034	...	1940	...	2040	2134	2140	...	...	...	...
Den Haag HS d.	|	...	|	...	|	|	...	1840	|	|	...	|	...	|	|	|	...	...	...	...
Rotterdam Centraal d.	1858	...	1810	...	1928	1958	...	1910	2058	2058	...	2010	...	2110	2158	2210	...	...	...	...
Breda a.	|	...	1834	...	|	|	...	1934	|	|	...	2034	...	2134	|	2234	...	...	...	...
Breda d.	|	...	1842	...	|	|	...	1942	|	|	...	2042	...	2142	|	2242	...	...	...	...
Antwerpen Centraal d.	1933	...	1916	...	|	2033	...	2016	2133	2133	...	2116	...	2216	2233	2316	...	...	...	...
Mechelen d.	|	...	1937	...	|	|	...	2037	|	|	...	2137	...	2237	|	2337	...	...	...	...
Brussels Airport ✈ d.	|	...	1950	...	|	|	...	2050	|	|	...	2150	...	2250	|	2350	...	...	...	...
Brussels Midi / Zuid ◧ △ a.	2008	...	2017	...	2038	2108	...	2117	2208	2208	...	2217	...	2317	2308	0017	...	...	...	...
Brussels Midi / Zuid ◧ d.	2016	...	...	2043	2056	2116	...	...	...	2216	...	...	...	...	...	...	...	...	...	...
Lille Europe a.	|	...	...	|	2130	|	...	...	...	|	...	...	...	...	...	...	...	...	...	...
Paris Nord a.	2138	...	...	2205	|	2238	...	...	...	2338	...	...	...	...	...	...	...	...	...	...
Paris Charles de Gaulle ✈ a.	...	...	...	...	|	...	...	...	...	...	...	...	...	...	...	...	...	...	...	...
Marne la Vallée - Chessy § a.	...	...	...	...	|	...	...	...	...	...	...	...	...	...	...	...	...	...	...	...
London St Pancras a.	...	...	...	...	2157	...	...	...	...	...	...	...	...	...	...	...	...	...	...	...

A – ①②③④⑦ June 12 - July 16.
⑦ July 17 - Sept. 3.
①②③④⑦ Sept. 4 - Dec. 10.
B – ⑥ July 9 - Aug. 27: *THALYS* SOLEIL – [12] 🍷 Amsterdam - Brussels - Marseille (Table **11**).
C – ①-⑤ June 12 - July 16, Sept. 4 - Dec. 10 (not July 14, Nov. 1).
D – ⑤ Sept. 4 - Dec. 10.
F – ①-⑤ Sept. 4 - Dec. 10 (not Sept. 15, Oct. 6, 20, Nov. 1, 24.
P – ⑤ June 12 - July 16.
①-⑤ Sept. 4 - Dec. 10.
R – ⑤⑦ June 12 - July 16.
⑤⑥⑦ July 17 - Sept. 3.
Daily Sept. 4 - Dec. 10.

U – Also Nov. 2.
V – Not Nov. 1.
W – Not July 21, Aug. 15, Nov. 1.
X – Not Aug. 15, Nov. 1.
Y – Also July 21, Aug. 15, Nov. 1.
Z – Also Aug. 15, Nov. 1.

f – 10 mins later Sept. 4 - Dec. 10.

⊕ – Calls to pick up only.
§ – Station for Disneyland.
• – Distance via Breda is 174km.

◧ – Connections at Brussels are not guaranteed.
△ – All *IC* and *ICd* services call at Brussels Nord 12 minutes, and at Brussels Central 5 minutes, before Brussels Midi / Zuid.
⇌ – *Thalys* high-speed train. Ⓡ 🍷. Special fares payable. Three classes of service: (Premium, Comfort and Standard). Valid June 12 - Dec. 10.
☆ – Eurostar train. Ⓡ, ✕ in Business Premier and Standard Premier, 🍷 in Standard. Special fares payable. Minimum check-in time 30 minutes. Valid June 12 - Sept. 3. **Additional services are available, see Table 10, pages 47 – 48.**

☛ **Shaded services are temporarily suspended.**

PARIS - BRUSSELS — 18a

izy Timings may vary

Service until July 10

train type / number		izy		izy		izy		izy	
train number		9600		9600		9606		9606	
notes		⑥		①		⑤		⑦	
Brussels Midi / Zuid d.	...	0813	...	0828	...	1528	...	1552	...
Paris Nord a.	...	1040	...	1120	...	1756	...	1832	...

train type / number		izy		izy		izy			
train number		9603		9605		9615			
notes		⑥		①		⑤⑦			
Paris Nord d.	...	1131	...	1346	...	1949	...	...	...
Brussels Midi / Zuid a.	...	1343	...	1600	...	2213	...	...	...

Low-cost *TGV* services branded **izy**, internet booking only through www.izy.com. Timings may vary. Subject to alteration.

20 LONDON, PARIS and BRUSSELS - KÖLN, HAMBURG and BERLIN

For the full service London - Brussels see Table **10**. For Paris - Brussels see Table **18**. Connections at Brussels are not guaranteed.

train type	*ICE*	*ICE*	*IC*		⇌	*ICE*	*ICE*	*ICE*	*IC*		⇌	*ICE*	*ICE*		⇌	⇌	⇌	*ICE*	*ICE*	*ICE*				
train number	**11**	**555**	**2310**		**9303**	**13**	**13**	**557**	**2216**		**9411**	**859**	**612**		**9315**	**9315**	**9315**	**15**	**559**	**714**				
notes					①–⑤ D	Ⓐ	Ⓒ				①–⑥ K				⑦ P	⑦ Q	①–⑥ K							
London St Pancras d.	...	...	...	...	...	...	...	...	...	...	...	...	...	...	...	...	...	...	...	...	...	...	...	...
Paris Nord d.	...	...	...	...	0613	...	...	...	...	...	0755	...	...	...	0755	0801	0825	...	...	...	...	...	...	...
Brussels Midi/Zuid a.	...	...	...	...	0745	...	...	...	...	...	0917	...	...	...	0934	0939	0947	...	...	...	...	...	...	...
Brussels Midi/Zuid d.	0625	...	...	...	...	0823	0825	...	...	...	0925	...	...	...	...	...	...	1025	...	...	...	...	...	...
Brussels Nord d.	0632	...	...	...	...	0832	0834	...	...	...	|	...	...	...	...	...	...	1034	...	...	...	...	...	...
Liège Guillemins d.	0712	...	...	...	...	0914	0914	...	...	...	1013	...	...	...	...	...	...	1114	...	...	...	...	...	...
Aachen 🏛 a.	0736	...	...	...	...	0936	0936	...	...	...	1034	...	...	...	...	...	...	1136	...	...	...	...	...	...
Köln Hbf a.	0816	...	...	...	...	1015	1015	...	...	...	1115	...	...	...	...	...	...	1215	...	...	...	...	...	...
Köln Hbf d.	...	0848	0909	...	...	...	...	1048	1109	...	...	1148	1211	...	...	...	...	...	1248	1309	...	...	...	...
Wuppertal Hbf a.	...	0914	|	...	...	...	...	1114	|	...	...	1214	1241	...	...	...	...	...	1314	|	...	...	...	...
Hagen Hbf a.	...	0933	|	...	...	...	...	1133	|	...	...	1233	1259	...	...	...	...	...	1333	|	...	...	...	...
Düsseldorf Hbf a.	...	|	0931	...	...	...	...	|	1131	...	...	|	|	...	...	...	...	...	|	1331	...	...	...	...
Duisburg Hbf a.	...	|	0945	...	...	...	...	|	1145	...	...	|	|	...	...	...	...	...	|	1345	...	...	...	...
Essen Hbf a.	...	|	0958	...	...	...	...	|	1158	...	...	|	|	...	...	...	...	...	|	1358	...	...	...	...
Bochum Hbf a.	...	|	|	...	...	...	...	|	|	...	...	|	|	...	...	...	...	...	|	|	...	...	...	...
Dortmund Hbf a.	...	|	|	...	...	...	...	|	|	...	...	|	1321	...	...	...	...	...	|	|	...	...	...	...
Hamm (Westf) a.	...	1002	|	...	...	...	...	1202	|	...	...	1302	|	...	...	...	...	...	1402	|	...	...	...	...
Bielefeld Hbf a.	...	1036	|	...	...	...	...	1236	|	...	...	1336	|	...	...	...	...	...	1436	|	...	...	...	...
Münster a.	...	|	1054	...	...	...	...	|	1254	...	...	|	1354	...	...	...	...	...	|	1454	...	...	...	...
Osnabrück Hbf a.	...	|	1121	...	...	...	...	|	1321	...	...	|	1421	...	...	...	...	...	|	1521	...	...	...	...
Bremen Hbf a.	...	|	1215	...	...	...	...	|	1415	...	...	|	1515	...	...	...	...	...	|	1616	...	...	...	...
Hannover Hbf a.	...	1128	|	...	...	...	...	1328	|	...	...	1428	|	...	...	...	...	...	1528	|	...	...	...	...
Hamburg Hbf a.	...	|	1314	...	...	...	...	|	1512	...	...	|	1614	...	...	...	...	...	|	1714	...	...	...	...
Berlin Hbf a.	...	1310	...	...	...	...	...	1510	...	...	...	1614	...	...	...	...	...	...	1710	...	...	...	...	...

train type	⇌	*ICE*	*ICE*	⇌	☆	*ICE*	*ICE*	*IC*		⇌	⇌	*ICE*	*ICE*	⇌	⇌	☆	*ICE*	*ICE*	*EC*	⇌	*ICE*	*ICE*	*ICE*	*EC*
train number	**9423**	**951**	**610**	**9327**	**9116**	**315**	**651**	**2312**		**9435**	**9435**	**953**	**518**	**9339**	**9339**	**9126**	**17**	**653**	**8**	**9351**	**317**	**317**	**655**	**6**
notes										⑤⑥⑦ P	A			N	U						Ⓐ	Ⓒ		
London St Pancras d.	...	...	...	...	0901	...	...	...	...	...	...	...	...	...	...	1104	...	...	...	...	...	...	...	...
Paris Nord d.	0955	...	...	1025	|	...	...	...	...	1155	1155	...	...	1219	1225	|	...	...	...	1425	...	...	...	...
Brussels Midi/Zuid a.	1117	...	...	1147	1205	...	...	...	...	1317	1317	...	...	1341	1347	1405	...	...	...	1547	...	...	...	...
Brussels Midi/Zuid d.	1125	...	...	...	...	1225	...	...	...	1325	1325	...	...	...	...	...	1425	...	...	...	1622	1625	...	...
Brussels Nord d.	|	...	...	...	...	1234	...	...	...	|	|	...	...	...	...	...	1434	...	...	...	1632	1634	...	...
Liège Guillemins d.	1213	...	...	...	...	1314	...	...	...	1413	1413	...	...	...	...	...	1514	...	...	...	1714	1714	...	...
Aachen 🏛 a.	1235	...	...	...	...	1336	...	...	...	1435	1435	...	...	...	...	...	1536	...	...	...	1736	1736	...	...
Köln Hbf a.	1316	...	...	...	...	1415	...	...	...	1515	1515	...	...	...	...	...	1615	...	...	...	1816	1816	...	...
Köln Hbf d.	1323	1348	1411	...	...	...	1448	1509	...	1525	1525	1548	1611	...	...	...	...	1648	1709	...	...	...	1848	1909
Wuppertal Hbf a.	|	1414	|	...	...	...	1514	|	...	|	|	1614	|	...	...	...	...	1714	|	...	...	...	1914	|
Hagen a.	|	1433	|	...	...	...	1533	|	...	|	|	1633	|	...	...	...	...	1733	|	...	...	...	1933	|
Düsseldorf Hbf a.	1345	|	1432	...	...	...	|	1531	...	1552	1552	|	1632	...	...	...	...	|	1731	...	...	...	|	1931
Duisburg Hbf a.	1400	|	1446	...	...	...	|	1545	...	1613	...	|	1646	...	...	...	...	|	1745	...	...	...	|	1945
Essen Hbf a.	1415	|	1458	...	...	...	|	1558	...	1631	...	|	1659	...	...	...	...	|	1758	...	...	...	|	1958
Bochum Hbf a.	...	|	1509	...	...	...	|	|	...	...	...	|	1709	...	...	...	...	|	|	...	...	...	|	|
Dortmund Hbf a.	...	|	1521	...	...	...	|	|	...	...	...	|	1722	...	...	...	...	|	|	...	...	...	|	|
Hamm (Westf) a.	...	1502	|	...	...	...	1602	|	...	...	...	1702	|	...	...	...	...	1802	|	...	...	...	2002	|
Bielefeld a.	...	1536	|	...	...	...	1636	|	...	...	...	1736	|	...	...	...	...	1836	|	...	...	...	2036	|
Münster a.	...	|	1554	...	...	...	|	1654	...	...	...	|	1755	...	...	...	...	|	1854	...	...	...	|	2054
Osnabrück a.	...	|	1621	...	...	...	|	1721	...	...	...	|	1821	...	...	...	...	|	1921	...	...	...	|	2121
Bremen Hbf a.	...	|	1715	...	...	...	|	1815	...	...	...	|	1915	...	...	...	...	|	2015	...	...	...	|	2217
Hannover Hbf a.	...	1628	|	...	...	...	1728	|	...	...	...	1828	|	...	...	...	...	1928	|	...	...	...	2128	|
Hamburg Hbf a.	...	|	1814	...	...	...	|	1914	...	...	...	|	2014	...	...	...	...	|	2114	...	...	...	|	2316
Berlin Hbf a.	...	1810	...	...	...	...	1908	...	...	...	...	2014	...	...	...	...	...	2109	...	...	...	...	2310	...

train type	⇌	*ICE*	*ICE*	*ICE*	*ICE*		⇌	☆	*ICE*	*ICE*	*IC*		⇌	*ICE*		⇌	*ICE*							
train number	**9459**	**947**	**957**	**26**	**514**		**9363**	**9142**	**19**	**657**	**2318**		**9471**	**512**		**9375**	**319**							
notes		T	⑤⑦				C			⑤⑦			BG			Ⓑ	⑦							
London St Pancras d.	...	...	...	...	...	...	...	1504	...	...	...	...	...	...	...	...	...	...	...	...	...	...	...	...
Paris Nord d.	1555	...	...	...	...	...	1625	|	...	...	...	...	1755	...	...	1825	...	...	...	...	...	...	...	...
Brussels Midi/Zuid a.	1717	...	...	...	...	...	1747	1805	...	...	...	...	1917	...	...	1947	...	...	...	...	...	...	...	...
Brussels Midi/Zuid d.	1727	...	...	...	...	...	...	...	1825	...	...	...	1925	...	...	...	2025	...	...	...	...	...	...	...
Brussels Nord d.	|	...	...	...	...	...	...	...	1834	...	...	...	|	...	...	...	2034	...	...	...	...	...	...	...
Liège Guillemins d.	1814	...	...	...	...	...	...	...	1914	...	...	...	2013	...	...	...	2114	...	...	...	...	...	...	...
Aachen 🏛 a.	1834	...	...	...	...	...	...	...	1936	1959	...	...	2034	...	...	...	2136	...	...	...	...	...	...	...
Köln Hbf a.	1915	...	...	...	...	...	...	...	2015	2045	...	...	2115	...	...	...	2213	...	...	...	...	...	...	...
Köln Hbf d.	1918	1927	1948	2009	2011	...	...	...	...	2048	2113	...	2118	2211	...	...	...	...	...	...	...	...	...	...
Wuppertal Hbf a.	|	|	2014	2041	|	...	...	...	...	2114	2142	...	|	|	...	...	...	...	...	...	...	...	...	...
Hagen Hbf a.	|	|	2033	2059	|	...	...	...	...	2133	2200	...	|	|	...	...	...	...	...	...	...	...	...	...
Düsseldorf Hbf a.	1940	1949	|	|	2032	...	...	...	...	|	|	...	2141	2232	...	...	...	...	...	...	...	...	...	...
Duisburg Hbf a.	1953	2008	|	|	2046	...	...	...	...	|	|	...	2202	2246	...	...	...	...	...	...	...	...	...	...
Essen Hbf a.	2007	2021	|	|	2058	...	...	...	...	|	|	...	2215	2259	...	...	...	...	...	...	...	...	...	...
Bochum Hbf a.	|	2033	|	|	2109	...	...	...	...	|	|	...	|	|	...	...	...	...	...	...	...	...	...	...
Dortmund Hbf a.	2039	2046	|	2121	2121	...	...	...	...	|	2221	...	2243	|	...	...	...	...	...	...	...	...	...	...
Hamm (Westf) a.	...	2107	2102	...	|	...	...	...	...	2202	2244	...	...	|	...	...	...	...	...	...	...	...	...	...
Bielefeld Hbf a.	...	2136	2136	...	|	...	...	...	...	2236	2319	...	...	|	...	...	...	...	...	...	...	...	...	...
Münster a.	...	|	|	...	2154	...	...	...	...	|	|	...	...	0001	...	...	...	...	...	...	...	...	...	...
Osnabrück Hbf a.	...	|	|	...	2221	...	...	...	...	|	|	...	...	...	...	...	...	...	...	...	...	...	...	...
Bremen Hbf a.	...	|	|	...	2315	...	...	...	...	|	|	...	...	...	...	...	...	...	...	...	...	...	...	...
Hannover Hbf a.	...	2228	2228	...	|	...	...	...	...	2328	0018	...	...	...	...	...	...	...	...	...	...	...	...	...
Hamburg Hbf a.	...	|	|	...	0014	...	...	...	...	|	...	...	...	...	...	...	...	...	...	...	...	...	...	...
Berlin Hbf a.	...	0013	0013	...	...	...	...	...	...	0114	...	...	...	...	...	...	...	...	...	...	...	...	...	...

A – ①⑤⑥⑦ July 17 - Sept. 3 (also July 21, Aug. 16). Daily Sept. 4 - Dec. 10.
B – Ⓑ June 12 - July 16. Daily July 17 - Dec. 10.
C – ①–⑤ (Ⓑ July 17 - Dec. 10, not July 21, Aug. 14).
D – Not July 21, Aug. 15, Nov. 1.
G – Calls at Düsseldorf Flughafen ✈ arrives 2149.
K – Not Aug. 15, Nov. 1.
N – ①–⑤ June 12 - Sept. 3 (not July 21, Aug. 15).
P – June 12 - July 16.
Q – July 17 - Dec. 10.
T – ①②③④⑥.
U – ⑥⑦ June 12 - Sept. 3 (also July 14, 21, Aug. 15). Daily Sept. 4 - Dec. 10.
f – ⑦.
⇌ – *Thalys* high-speed train. 🅁 🍷. Special fares payable. Three classes of service: Premium, Comfort and Standard. Valid June 12 - Dec. 10.
☆ – Eurostar train. 🅁, ✕ in Business Premier and Standard Premier, 🍷 in Standard. Special fares payable. Minimum check-in time 30 minutes. Valid June 12 - Sept. 3. **Additional services are available, see Table 10, pages 47 – 48.**

BERLIN, HAMBURG and KÖLN - BRUSSELS, PARIS and LONDON — 20

For the full service Brussels - London see Table **10**. For Brussels - Paris see Table **18**. Connections at Brussels are not guaranteed.

train type	⇌	*ICE*	*IC*	*ICE*	⇌		*ICE*	*EC*	⇌		*EC*	*IC*	*ICE*	*ICE*	⇌	⇌	⇌		*EC*	*ICE*	*ICE*		
train number	**9412**	**101**	**2319**	**18**	**9322**		**513**	**115**	**9424**		**7**	**119**	**656**	**316**	**9334**	**9336**	**9340**		**9**	**654**	**16**		
notes	J	⚒	⚒				🍷	🍷				🍷	⚒		⑥⑦ Y	P							
Berlin Hbf d.	...	...	...	...	...	...	...	...	...	...	...	...	0430	...	...	...	...	...	...	0646	...	...	...
Hamburg Hbf d.	...	...	...	...	...	...	...	...	...	...	0437	...	|	...	...	...	...	...	0646	|	...	...	...
Hannover Hbf d.	...	...	...	...	...	...	...	...	...	...	|	...	0621	...	...	...	...	...	|	0831	...	...	...
Bremen Hbf d.	...	...	...	...	...	...	...	...	...	...	0540	...	|	...	...	...	...	...	0744	|	...	...	...
Osnabrück Hbf d.	...	...	...	...	...	...	...	...	...	...	0636	...	|	...	...	...	...	...	0836	|	...	...	...
Münster d.	...	...	0503	...	...	...	0603	0631	...	...	0703	...	|	...	...	...	...	...	0903	|	...	...	...
Bielefeld Hbf d.	...	...	|	...	...	...	|	|	...	...	|	...	0721	...	...	...	...	...	|	0922	...	...	...
Hamm (Westf) d.	...	...	|	...	...	...	|	|	...	...	|	...	0754	...	...	...	...	...	|	0954	...	...	...
Dortmund Hbf d.	0458	0528	0536	...	...	...	0636	|	0651	...	|	0750	|	...	...	...	...	...	|	|	...	...	...
Bochum Hbf d.	|	|	0548	...	...	...	0648	|	|	...	|	|	|	...	...	...	...	...	|	|	...	...	...
Essen Hbf d.	0542	|	0600	...	...	...	0700	|	0740	...	0757	|	|	...	...	...	...	...	0957	|	...	...	...
Duisburg Hbf d.	0556	|	0613	...	...	...	0713	0734	|	...	0810	|	|	...	...	...	...	...	1010	|	...	...	...
Düsseldorf Hbf d.	0617	|	0627	...	...	...	0727	0750	0813	...	0824	|	|	...	...	...	...	...	1024	|	...	...	...
Hagen Hbf d.	|	0557	|	...	...	...	|	|	|	...	|	0816	0823	...	...	...	...	...	|	1023	...	...	...
Wuppertal Hbf d.	|	0615	|	...	...	...	|	|	|	...	|	0834	0840	...	...	...	...	...	|	1040	...	...	...
Köln Hbf a.	0641	0646	0650	...	...	...	0749	0815	0835	...	0850	0912	0909	...	...	...	...	...	1050	1109	...	...	...
Köln Hbf d.	0645	...	...	0742	...	...	...	...	0844	...	...	...	...	0942	...	...	...	...	...	...	1143	...	...
Aachen 🏢 d.	0723	...	...	0821	...	...	...	...	0924	...	...	...	...	1021	...	...	...	...	...	...	1221	...	...
Liège Guillemins d.	0753	...	...	0846	...	...	...	...	0951	...	...	...	...	1046	...	...	...	...	...	...	1246	...	...
Brussels Nord a.	|	...	...	0926	...	...	...	...	|	...	...	...	...	1126	...	...	...	...	...	...	1326	...	...
Brussels Midi/Zuid a.	0836	...	...	0935	...	...	...	...	1035	...	...	...	...	1135	...	...	...	...	...	...	1335	...	...
Brussels Midi/Zuid d.	0843	...	...	...	1013	...	...	...	1043	...	...	...	...	...	1216	1243	1313	...	...	...	...	...	...
Paris Nord a.	1005	...	...	...	1135	...	...	...	1205	...	...	...	...	...	1338	1405	1435	...	...	...	...	...	...
London St Pancras a.	...	...	...	...	...	...	...	...	...	...	...	...	...	...	...	...	...	...	...	...	...	...	...

train type	*ICE*	*ICE*	⇌	⇌		*ICE*	*ICE*	*ICE*	☆	⇌	⇌		*IC*	*ICE*	*ICE*	⇌	☆		*ICE*	*ICE*	⇌		
train number	**517**	**954**	**9448**	**9448**		**713**	**652**	**314**	**9145**	**9358**	**9364**		**2217**	**650**	**14**	**9370**	**9157**		**611**	**950**	**9472**		
notes			⑦	①–⑥						C						Ⓑ	①–⑥						
Berlin Hauptbahnhof d.	...	0746	...	...	...	...	0846	...	...	...	...	...	...	1046	...	...	...	...	...	1146	...	...	...
Hamburg Hbf d.	0746	|	...	...	...	0846	|	...	...	...	...	...	1046	|	...	...	...	...	1146	|	...	...	...
Hannover Hbf d.	|	0931	...	...	...	|	1031	...	...	...	...	...	|	1231	...	...	...	...	|	1331	...	...	...
Bremen Hbf d.	0844	|	...	...	...	0944	|	...	...	...	...	...	1144	|	...	...	...	...	1244	|	...	...	...
Osnabrück Hbf d.	0937	|	...	...	...	1037	|	...	...	...	...	...	1237	|	...	...	...	...	1337	|	...	...	...
Münster d.	1003	|	...	...	...	1103	|	...	...	...	...	...	1303	|	...	...	...	...	1403	|	...	...	...
Bielefeld Hbf d.	|	1022	...	...	...	|	1122	...	...	...	...	...	|	1322	...	...	...	...	|	1422	...	...	...
Hamm (Westf) d.	|	1054	...	...	...	|	1154	...	...	...	...	...	|	1354	...	...	...	...	|	1454	...	...	...
Dortmund Hbf d.	1036	|	1051	...	...	|	|	...	...	...	...	...	|	|	...	...	...	...	1435	|	...	...	...
Bochum Hbf d.	1047	|	|	...	...	|	|	...	...	...	...	...	|	|	...	...	...	...	|	|	...	...	...
Essen Hbf d.	1100	|	1126	...	...	1157	|	...	...	...	...	...	1400	|	...	...	...	...	|	|	1544	...	...
Duisburg Hbf d.	|	|	|	...	...	1210	|	...	...	...	...	...	1413	|	...	...	...	...	|	|	1557	...	...
Düsseldorf Hbf d.	1124	|	1154	...	...	1224	|	...	...	...	...	...	1427	|	...	...	...	...	|	|	1612	...	...
Hagen Hbf d.	|	1123	|	...	...	|	1223	...	...	...	...	...	|	1423	...	...	...	...	1457	1523	|	...	...
Wuppertal Hbf d.	|	1140	|	...	...	|	1240	...	...	...	...	...	|	1440	...	...	...	...	1514	1540	|	...	...
Köln Hbf a.	1149	1209	1226	...	...	1250	1309	...	...	...	...	...	1450	1509	...	...	...	...	1546	1609	1640	...	...
Köln Hbf d.	...	...	1243	1243	...	...	...	1342	...	...	...	...	...	...	1540	...	...	...	...	...	1644	...	...
Aachen 🏢 d.	...	...	1324	1324	...	...	...	1421	...	...	...	...	...	...	1621	...	...	...	...	...	1724	...	...
Liège Guillemins d.	...	...	1351	1351	...	...	...	1446	...	...	...	...	...	...	1646	...	...	...	...	...	1751	...	...
Brussels Nord a.	...	...	|	|	...	...	...	1526	...	...	...	...	...	...	1726	...	...	...	...	...	|	...	...
Brussels Midi/Zuid a.	...	...	1435	1435	...	...	...	1535	...	...	...	...	...	...	1735	...	...	...	...	...	1835	...	...
Brussels Midi/Zuid d.	...	...	1443	1443	...	...	...	...	1556	1613	1713	...	...	...	...	1813	1856	...	...	...	1842	...	...
Paris Nord a.	...	...	1605	1605	...	...	...	...	|	1735	1835	...	...	...	...	1935	|	...	...	...	2005	...	...
London St Pancras a.	...	...	...	...	...	...	...	...	1700	...	...	...	...	...	...	...	1957	...	...	...	...	...	...

train type	*IC*	*ICE*	*ICE*	⇌	☆		*ICE*	*ICE*	⇌	⇌	⇌	⇌	*IC*	*ICE*	*ICE*	⇌		*IC*	*ICE*	*ICE*			
train number	**2311**	**558**	**12**	**9382**	**9167**		**613**	**1050**	**9484**	**9484**	**9484**	**9484**	**2213**	**556**	**10**	**9394**		**2215**	**544**	**318**			
notes					Ⓑ				D	G	H	A				⑦ Z				⑦			
Berlin Hauptbahnhof d.	...	1246	...	...	...	...	...	1306	...	...	...	...	...	1446	...	...	...	...	1647	...	...	...	...
Hamburg Hbf d.	1246	|	...	...	...	...	1346	|	...	...	...	...	1446	|	...	...	...	1646	|	...	...	...	...
Hannover Hbf d.	|	1431	...	...	...	...	|	1456	...	...	...	...	|	1631	...	...	...	|	1831	...	...	...	...
Bremen Hbf d.	1344	|	...	...	...	...	1444	|	...	...	...	...	1544	|	...	...	...	1744	|	...	...	...	...
Osnabrück Hbf d.	1437	|	...	...	...	...	1537	|	...	...	...	...	1637	|	...	...	...	1837	|	...	...	...	...
Münster d.	1503	|	...	...	...	...	1603	|	...	...	...	...	1703	|	...	...	...	1903	|	...	...	...	...
Bielefeld Hbf d.	|	1522	...	...	...	...	|	1553	...	...	...	...	|	1722	...	...	...	|	1922	...	...	...	...
Hamm (Westf) d.	|	1554	...	...	...	...	|	1626	...	...	...	...	|	1754	...	...	...	|	1954	...	...	...	...
Dortmund Hbf d.	|	|	...	...	...	...	1636	1651	...	...	...	...	|	|	...	...	...	|	|	...	...	...	...
Bochum Hbf d.	|	|	...	...	...	...	1648	1703	...	...	...	...	|	|	...	...	...	|	|	...	...	...	...
Essen Hbf d.	1600	|	...	...	...	...	1700	1715	1749	...	...	...	1759	|	...	...	...	2000	|	...	...	...	...
Duisburg Hbf d.	1613	|	...	...	...	...	|	1731	1803	1747	1747	...	1813	|	...	...	...	2013	|	...	...	...	...
Düsseldorf Hbf d.	1627	|	...	...	...	...	1724	1745	1818	1803	1803	1803	1827	|	...	...	...	2027	|	...	...	...	...
Hagen Hbf d.	|	1623	...	...	...	...	|	|	|	|	|	|	|	1823	...	...	...	|	2023	...	...	...	...
Wuppertal Hbf d.	|	1640	...	...	...	...	|	|	|	|	|	|	|	1840	...	...	...	|	2040	...	...	...	...
Köln Hbf a.	1650	1709	...	...	...	...	1749	1816	1841	1841	1841	1841	1850	1909	...	...	...	2050	2111	...	...	...	...
Köln Hbf d.	...	...	1741	...	...	...	...	...	1844	1844	1844	1844	...	...	1940	...	...	...	...	2142	...	...	...
Aachen 🏢 d.	...	...	1821	...	...	...	...	...	1924	1924	1924	1924	...	...	2021	...	...	...	...	2221	...	...	...
Liège Guillemins d.	...	...	1846	...	...	...	...	...	1951	1951	1951	1951	...	...	2046	...	...	...	...	2246	...	...	...
Brussels Nord a.	...	...	1926	...	...	...	...	...	|	|	|	|	...	...	2126	...	...	...	...	2326	...	...	...
Brussels Midi/Zuid a.	...	...	1935	...	...	...	...	...	2035	2035	2035	2035	...	...	2135	...	...	...	...	2335	...	...	...
Brussels Midi/Zuid d.	...	...	...	2016	2056	...	...	...	2043	2043	...	2043	...	...	...	2216	...	...	...	...	...	...	...
Paris Nord a.	...	...	...	2138	|	...	...	...	2205	2205	...	2205	...	...	...	2338	...	...	...	...	...	...	...
London St Pancras a.	...	...	...	...	2157	...	...	...	...	...	...	...	...	...	...	...	...	...	...	...	...	...	...

A – Daily Sept. 4 - Dec. 10.

C – Ⓑ June 12 - July 16.
⑤⑦ July 17 - Sept. 3.
Ⓑ Sept. 4 - Dec. 10.

D – ⑤⑦ June 12 - July 16.

G – ⑤⑥⑦ July 17 - Sept. 3.

H – ① July 17 - Sept. 3.

J – Calls at Düsseldorf Flughafen ✈ departs 0605.

P – ⑤ June 12 - July 16.
①-⑤ Sept. 4 - Dec. 10.

Y – Also July 21, Aug. 15, Nov. 1.

Z – Also Aug. 15, Nov. 1.

☆ – Eurostar train. Ⓡ, ✕ in Business Premier and Standard Premier, 🍷 in Standard. Special fares payable. Minimum check-in time 30 minutes. Valid June 12 - Sept. 3. **Additional services are available, see Table 10, pages 47 – 48.**

⇌ – *Thalys* high-speed train. Ⓡ 🍷. Special fares payable. Three classes of service: (Premium, Comfort and Standard). Valid June 12 - Dec. 10.

21 LONDON, PARIS and BRUSSELS - FRANKFURT - MÜNCHEN

For the full service London - Brussels see Table 10. For Paris - Brussels see Table 18. Connections at Brussels are not guaranteed.

train type	ICE	ICE	ICE	ICE	EC	⇌	ICE	ICE	ICE	ICE	ICE	EC	ICE	⇌	ICE	ICE	ICE	⇌	⇌	⇌	ICE	ICE	ICE	ICE	ICE
train number	11	571	593	529	7	9303	13	13	573	595	623	9	27	9411	625	517	29	9315	9315	9315	15	575	597	627	29
notes						①-⑤ G	Ⓐ	Ⓒ						①-⑥ K				⑦ P	⑦ Q	①-⑥ K					
London St Pancras d.	...	...	...	...	...	...	...	...	...	...	...	...	...	...	...	...	...	...	...	...	...	...	...	...	...
Paris Nord d.	...	...	...	...	...	0613	...	...	...	...	...	...	...	0755	...	...	...	0755	0801	0825	...	...	...	...	...
Brussels Midi/Zuid a.	...	...	...	...	...	0745	...	...	...	...	...	...	...	0917	...	...	...	0934	0939	0947	...	...	...	...	...
Brussels Midi/Zuid d.	0625	...	...	...	...	...	0823	0825	...	...	...	...	...	0925	...	...	...	...	...	...	1025	...	...	...	...
Brussels Nord d.	0632	...	...	...	...	...	0832	0834	...	...	...	...	...	|	...	...	...	...	...	...	1034	...	...	...	...
Liège Guillemins d.	0712	...	...	...	...	...	0914	0914	...	...	...	...	...	1013	...	...	...	...	...	...	1114	...	...	...	...
Aachen Hbf a.	0736	...	...	...	...	...	0936	0936	...	...	...	...	...	1034	...	...	...	...	...	...	1136	...	...	...	...
Köln Hbf a.	0816	...	...	...	...	...	1015	1015	...	...	...	...	...	1115	...	...	...	...	...	...	1215	...	...	...	...
Köln Hbf d.	0823	...	...	...	0853	...	1018	1018	...	...	...	1053	...	...	1130x	1155	1153	...	...	...	1218	...	...	...	...
Bonn Hbf a.	|	...	...	...	0912	...	|	|	...	...	...	1112	...	...	|	|	1212	...	...	...	|	...	...	...	...
Koblenz Hbf a.	|	...	...	...	0946	...	|	|	...	...	...	1146	...	...	|	|	1246	...	...	...	|	...	...	...	...
Mainz Hbf a.	|	...	...	...	1039	...	|	|	...	...	...	1239	...	...	|	|	1339	...	...	...	|	...	...	...	←
Frankfurt Flughafen ✈ a.	0917	0924	...	...	|	...	1117	1117	1124	...	...	|	1201	...	1235	1250	1359	...	...	...	1317	1324	...	...	1401
Frankfurt (Main) Hbf a.	0931	|	0950	0953	|	...	1131	1131	|	1150	1153	|	|	...	1248	|	→	...	...	...	1331	|	1350	1353	|
Würzburg Hbf a.	...	|	|	1124	|	...	...	...	|	|	1324	|	1332	...	1424	|	...	...	...	...	...	|	|	1524	1532
Nürnberg Hbf a.	...	|	|	1220	|	...	...	...	|	|	1420	|	1427	...	1520	|	...	...	...	...	...	|	|	1621	1629
Wien Hbf a.	...	|	|	...	|	...	...	...	|	|	...	|	1845	...	...	|	...	...	...	...	...	|	|	...	2045
Mannheim Hbf a.	...	0956	1027	...	1121	...	...	...	1156	1229	...	1321	...	...	...	1323	...	...	...	...	...	1356	1427	...	...
Stuttgart Hbf a.	...	1039	1108	...	...	...	...	...	1238	1308	...	...	...	...	...	1408	...	...	...	...	...	1438	1508	...	...
Ulm Hbf a.	...	...	1210	...	...	...	...	...	...	1410	...	...	...	...	...	1510	...	...	...	...	...	...	1610	...	...
Augsburg Hbf a.	...	...	1253	...	...	...	...	...	...	1453	...	...	...	...	...	1553	...	...	...	...	...	...	1653	...	...
München Hbf a.	...	...	1327	...	...	...	...	...	...	1528	...	...	...	...	...	1628	...	...	...	...	...	...	1727	...	...

train type/number	⇌	ICE	⇌	☆	ICE	ICE	ICE	ICE	ICE	⇌	ICE	ICE	⇌	⇌	☆	ICE	ICE	ICE	⇌	ICE	ICE	ICE	ICE	ICE	ICE
train number	9423	229	9327	9116	315	577	599	721	229	9435	723	611	9339	9339	9126	17	691	725	9351	317	317	771	693	693	729
notes										C			N	H						Ⓐ	Ⓒ		Ⓑ	⑥	
London St Pancras d.	...	...	...	0901	...	...	...	...	...	...	...	...	...	...	1104	...	...	...	...	...	...	...	...	...	...
Paris Nord d.	0955	...	1025	|	...	...	...	...	...	1155	...	...	1219	1225	|	...	...	...	1425	...	...	...	...	...	...
Brussels Midi/Zuid a.	1117	...	1147	1205	...	...	...	...	...	1317	...	...	1341	1347	1405	...	...	...	1547	...	...	...	...	...	...
Brussels Midi/Zuid d.	1125	...	...	...	1225	...	...	...	...	1325	...	...	▬	...	...	1425	...	...	...	1622	1625	...	...	...	...
Brussels Nord d.	|	...	...	...	1234	...	...	...	...	|	...	...	...	...	...	1434	...	...	...	1632	1634	...	...	...	...
Liège Guillemins d.	1213	...	...	...	1314	...	...	...	...	1413	...	...	...	...	...	1514	...	...	...	1714	1714	...	...	...	...
Aachen Hbf a.	1235	...	...	...	1336	...	...	...	...	1435	...	...	*ICE*	...	...	1536	...	...	...	1736	1736	...	...	...	...
Köln Hbf a.	1316	...	...	...	1415	...	...	...	...	1515	...	...	**927**	...	...	1615	...	...	...	1816	1816	...	...	...	...
Köln Hbf d.	...	1353	...	...	1427	...	...	...	...	...	1536x	1555	1553	...	...	1620	...	...	...	1819	1819	...	...	...	...
Bonn Hbf a.	...	1412	...	...	|	...	...	...	...	...	|	|	1612	...	...	|	...	...	...	|	|	...	...	...	...
Koblenz Hbf a.	...	1446	...	...	|	...	...	...	...	...	|	|	1646	...	...	|	...	...	...	|	|	...	...	...	...
Mainz Hbf a.	...	1539	...	...	|	...	...	...	←	...	|	|	1739	...	...	|	...	...	...	|	|	...	...	...	...
Frankfurt Flughafen ✈ a.	...	1559	...	...	1517	1524	...	...	1601	...	1633	1650	1759	...	...	1724t	...	...	...	1917	1917	1924	...	...	...
Frankfurt (Main) Hbf a.	...	→	...	...	1531	|	1550	1553	|	...	1648	|	|	...	...	1740t	1750	1753	...	1931	1931	|	1950	1950	1953
Würzburg Hbf a.	...	...	...	...	...	|	|	1724	1732	...	1824	|	1932	...	...	...	|	1923	...	...	...	|	|	|	2124
Nürnberg Hbf a.	...	...	...	...	...	|	|	1820	1828	...	1920	|	2028	...	...	...	|	2020	...	...	...	|	|	|	2220
Wien Hbf a.	...	...	...	...	...	|	|	...	2305	...	...	|	...	...	...	...	|	...	...	...	...	|	|	|	...
Mannheim Hbf a.	...	...	...	...	...	1556	1627	...	...	...	...	1723	...	...	...	...	1827	...	...	...	...	1955	2027	2027	...
Stuttgart Hbf a.	...	...	...	...	...	1639	1708	...	...	...	...	1808	...	...	...	...	1908	...	...	...	...	2038	2108	2108	...
Ulm Hbf a.	...	...	...	...	...	...	1810	...	...	...	...	1910	...	...	...	...	2010	...	...	...	...	2158j	2210	...	...
Augsburg Hbf a.	...	...	...	...	...	...	1853	...	...	...	...	1953	...	...	...	...	2053	...	...	...	...	2245j	2253	...	...
München Hbf a.	...	...	...	...	...	...	1927	...	...	...	...	2028	...	...	...	...	2127	...	...	...	...	2319j	2329	...	...

train type	⇌	ICE	ICE	⇌	☆	ICE	ICE	ICE	IC	⇌	ICE	ICE	NJ	NJ	⇌	ICE	ICE
train number	9459	1021	615	9363	9142	19	773	1021	2215	9473	1627	617	421	425	9375	319	619
notes				D						F			♣ A	①③⑤ B♣	Ⓑ	⑦	
London St Pancras d.	...	...	...	...	1504	...	...	...	...	...	...	...	...	...	...	...	...
Paris Nord d.	1555	...	...	1625	|	...	...	...	...	1755	...	...	...	...	1825	...	...
Brussels Midi/Zuid a.	1717	...	...	1747	1805	...	...	...	...	1917	...	...	...	...	1947	...	...
Brussels Midi/Zuid d.	1727	...	...	...	...	1825	...	...	...	1925	...	...	...	1932	...	2025	...
Brussels Nord d.	|	...	...	...	...	1834	...	...	...	|	...	...	...	1943	...	2034	...
Liège Guillemins d.	1814	...	...	...	...	1914	...	...	...	2013	...	...	...	2033	...	2114	...
Aachen Hbf a.	1834	...	...	...	...	1936	...	...	...	2034	...	...	...	2119	...	2136	...
Köln Hbf a.	1915	...	...	...	...	2015	...	...	...	2115	...	...	...	|	...	2213	...
Köln Hbf d.	...	1953	1955	...	...	2017	...	...	2053	...	2153	2155	2226	|	...	...	2355
Bonn Hbf a.	...	2012	|	...	...	|	...	...	2112	...	2212	|	2309	2309	...	...	|
Koblenz Hbf a.	...	2046	|	...	...	|	...	...	2146	...	2246	|	2344	2344	...	...	|
Mainz Hbf a.	...	2142	|	...	...	|	...	...	2239	...	2355	|	0054	0054	...	...	|
Frankfurt Flughafen ✈ a.	...	2159	2050	...	...	2117	2124	←	2259	...	0016	2254	0115	0115	...	...	0054
Frankfurt (Main) Hbf a.	...	2213	|	...	...	2131	|	2234	2312	...	0030	|	0129f	0129f	...	...	0110
Würzburg Hbf a.	...	→	|	...	...	...	|	2356	...	...	...	|	0240	0240	...	...	|
Nürnberg Hbf a.	...	...	|	...	...	...	|	0053	...	...	...	|	0336	0336	...	...	|
Wien Hbf a.	...	...	|	...	...	...	|	...	...	...	...	|	|	0919	...	...	|
Mannheim Hbf a.	...	...	2123	...	...	...	2155	...	...	...	...	2327	|	...	...	...	0202
Stuttgart Hbf a.	...	...	2208	...	...	...	2251	...	...	...	...	0008	|	...	...	...	0334
Ulm Hbf a.	...	...	2310	...	...	...	...	...	...	...	...	...	|	...	...	...	0440
Augsburg Hbf a.	...	...	2353	...	...	...	...	...	...	...	...	...	0623	...	...	...	0530
München Hbf a.	...	...	0027	...	...	...	...	...	...	...	...	...	0711	...	...	...	0603

A – *ÖBB nightjet* sleeper 1, 2 cl., couchette 2 cl. (4, 6 berth), seats (2) Amsterdam - Köln - München - Innsbruck ♣ (Table **53**).

B – ①③⑤: *ÖBB nightjet* sleeper 1, 2 cl., couchette 2 cl. (4, 6 berth), seats (2) Brussels - Wien ♣ (Table **53**).

C – ⑤⑥⑦ June 12 - July 16. ①⑤⑥⑦ July 17 - Sept. 3 (also July 21, Aug. 16). Daily Sept. 4 - Dec. 10.

D – ①-⑤ (Ⓑ July 17 - Dec. 10, not July 21, Aug. 14).

F – Ⓑ June 12 - July 16. Daily July 17 - Dec. 10.

G – Not July 21, Aug. 15, Nov. 1.

H – ⑥⑦ June 12 - Sept. 3 (also July 14, 21, Aug. 15). Daily Sept. 4 - Dec. 10.

K – Not Aug. 15, Nov. 1.

N – ①-⑤ June 12 - Sept. 3 (not July 21, Aug. 15).

P – June 12 - July 16.

Q – July 17 - Dec. 10.

f – Frankfurt (Main) **Süd**.

j – ④⑤.

t – On ⑥ arrive Frankfurt Flughafen 1717, Frankfurt (Main) Hbf 1731.

x – Köln **Messe / Deutz** (Table **910**). Connections from Köln Hbf depart every 2 - 5 minutes, journey time 2 - 3 minutes.

⇌ – *Thalys* high-speed train. Ⓡ 🍸. Special fares payable. Three classes of service: (Premium, Comfort and Standard). Valid June 12 - Dec. 10.

¶ – For connections to Praha by train, via Nürnberg and Regensburg, see Table **76**.

☆ – Eurostar train. Ⓡ, ✕ in Business Premier and Standard Premier, 🍸 in Standard. Special fares payable. Minimum check-in time 30 minutes. Valid June 12 - Sept. 3. **Additional services are available, see Table 10, pages 47 – 48.**

♣ – Special fares apply.

MÜNCHEN - FRANKFURT - BRUSSELS, PARIS and LONDON 21

For the full service London - Brussels see Table 10. For Paris - Brussels see Table 18. Connections at Brussels are not guaranteed.

train type	*ICE*	⇌		*NJ*	*IC*	*ICE*	*ICE*	*NJ*	⇌		*ICE*	*ICE*	⇌		*ICE*	*ICE*	*IC*	*ICE*	⇌	⇌	⇌				
train number	**618**	**9412**		**420**	**2212**	**774**	**18**	**50490**	**9322**		**1626**	**616**	**9424**		**822**	**1014**	**2310**	**316**	**9334**	**9336**	**9340**				
notes				♣		①–⑥		②④⑦							①–⑥	⚒			⑥⑦						
notes				**B**				**C**♣											**Y**	**P**					
München Hbf....d.	0001	...	...	2250	...	...	...	...	...	...	...	0324	...	...	0427	...	...	...	...	...	...	...	...	...	...
Augsburg Hbf....d.	0032	...	...	2323	...	...	...	...	...	...	...	0357	...	...	|	...	...	...	...	...	...	...	...	...	...
Ulm Hbf....d.	0116	...	...	|	...	...	...	...	...	...	...	0439	...	...	|	...	...	...	...	...	...	...	...	...	...
Stuttgart Hbf....d.	0222	...	...	|	...	0502	...	...	...	...	...	0551	...	...	|	0637	...	...	...	...	...	...	...	...	...
Mannheim Hbf....d.	0401	...	...	|	...	0605	...	...	...	...	...	0633	...	...	|	0721	...	...	...	...	...	...	...	...	...
Wien Hbf....d.	|	...	...	|	...	|	...	2013	...	...	...	|	...	...	|	|	...	...	...	...	...	...	...	...	...
Nürnberg Hbf....d.	|	...	...	0141	...	|	...	0141	...	...	...	|	...	...	0536	|	...	...	...	...	...	...	...	...	...
Würzburg Hbf....d.	|	...	...	|	...	|	...	|	...	...	...	|	...	...	0632	|	...	...	...	...	...	...	...	...	...
Frankfurt (Main) Hbf...d.	0446	...	...	0347f	...	|	0628	0347f	...	...	...	|	...	...	0804	|	...	0816	...	...	...	...	...	...	...
Frankfurt Flughafen ✈..d.	0500	...	...	0359	...	0635	0642	0359	...	...	...	0708	...	...	...	0753	...	0830	...	...	...	...	...	...	...
Mainz Hbf....d.	|	...	...	0418	...	...	|	0418	...	...	0617	|	...	...	...	|	0717	|	...	...	...	...	...	...	...
Koblenz Hbf....d.	|	...	...	0513	0605	...	|	0513	...	...	0713	|	...	...	...	|	0813	|	...	...	...	...	...	...	...
Bonn Hbf....d.	|	...	...	0601	0645	...	|	0601	...	...	0745	|	...	...	...	|	0845	|	...	...	...	...	...	...	...
Köln Hbf....a.	0603	...	...	0651	0705	...	0732	|	...	...	0805	0805	...	...	...	0842z	0905	0933	...	...	...	...	...	...	...
Köln Hbf....d.	...	0645	...	...	...	...	0742	|	...	...	...	...	0844	...	...	...	...	0942	...	...	...	...	...	...	...
Aachen Hbf 🏛....d.	...	0723	...	...	...	...	0821	0747	...	...	...	...	0924	...	...	...	...	1021	...	...	...	...	...	...	...
Liège Guillemins....d.	...	0753	...	...	...	...	0846	0850	...	...	...	...	0951	...	...	...	...	1046	...	...	...	...	...	...	...
Brussels Nord....a.	...	|	...	...	...	...	0926	0942	...	...	...	...	|	...	...	...	...	1126	...	...	...	...	...	...	...
Brussels Midi / Zuid....a.	...	0836	...	...	...	...	0935	0952	...	...	...	...	1035	...	...	...	...	1135	...	...	...	...	...	...	...
Brussels Midi / Zuid....d.	...	0843	...	...	...	...	...	...	1013	...	...	...	1043	...	...	...	...	...	1216	1243	1313	...	...	...	...
Paris Nord....d.	...	1005	...	...	...	...	...	...	1135	...	...	...	1205	...	...	...	...	...	1338	1405	1435	...	...	...	...
London St Pancras....a.	...	...	...	...	...	...	...	...	...	...	...	...	...	...	...	...	...	...	...	...	...	...	...	...	...

train type	*IC*	*ICE*	*ICE*	*ICE*	*ICE*	*ICE*	*ICE*	⇌		*ICE*	*ICE*	*ICE*	*ICE*	*ICE*	☆	⇌	⇌	*IC*	*ICE*	*ICE*	*ICE*	*ICE*	*ICE*	⇌	☆
train number	**2216**	**728**	**692**	**770**	**16**	**1020**	**612**	**9448**		**714**	**724**	**690**	**578**	**314**	**9145**	**9358**	**9364**	**2312**	**228**	**598**	**720**	**576**	**14**	**9370**	**9157**
notes			⚒																					Ⓑ	①–⑥
notes																**E**									
München Hbf....d.	...	...	0629	...	...	...	0728	...	...	...	...	0827	...	...	...	...	...	...	...	1028	1051	...	...	...	...
Augsburg Hbf....d.	...	...	0704	...	...	...	0803	...	...	...	...	0903	...	...	...	...	...	...	...	1103	|	...	...	...	...
Ulm Hbf....d.	...	...	0749	...	...	...	0848	...	...	...	...	0948	...	...	...	...	...	...	...	1148	|	...	...	...	...
Stuttgart Hbf....d.	...	...	0851	0923	...	...	0951	...	...	...	...	1051	1123	...	...	...	...	...	...	1251	|	1323	...	...	...
Mannheim Hbf....d.	...	...	0932	1005	...	...	1036	...	...	...	...	1132	1205	...	...	...	...	...	...	1332	|	1405	...	...	...
Wien Hbf....d.	...	...	|	|	...	...	|	...	...	...	...	|	|	...	...	...	...	...	0651	|	|	|	...	...	...
Nürnberg Hbf....d.	...	0735	|	|	...	0727	|	...	...	...	0926	|	|	...	...	...	...	...	1130	|	1200	|	...	...	...
Würzburg Hbf....d.	...	0832	|	|	...	0824	|	...	...	...	1032	|	|	...	...	...	...	...	1224	|	1256	|	...	...	...
Frankfurt (Main) Hbf...d.	...	1004	1008	|	1026	|	|	...	...	...	1204	1208	|	1229	...	...	...	...	|	1408	1404	|	1426	...	...
Frankfurt Flughafen ✈..d.	...	...	...	1035	1042	0958	1109	...	...	...	...	...	1235	1242	...	...	...	...	1356	...	...	1435	1442	...	...
Mainz Hbf....d.	0920	...	...	...	|	1020	|	...	...	1120	...	...	...	|	...	...	...	1320	...	...	...	...	|	...	...
Koblenz Hbf....d.	1013	...	...	...	|	1113	|	...	...	1213	...	...	...	|	...	...	...	1413	...	...	...	...	|	...	...
Bonn Hbf....d.	1045	...	...	...	|	1145	|	...	...	1245	...	...	...	|	...	...	...	1445	...	...	...	...	|	...	...
Köln Hbf....a.	1105	...	...	...	1133	1205	1205	...	...	1305	...	...	...	1333	...	...	...	1505	...	...	...	...	1533	...	...
Köln Hbf....d.	...	...	...	...	1143	...	...	1243	...	...	...	...	...	1342	...	...	...	...	...	...	...	...	1540	...	...
Aachen Hbf 🏛....d.	...	...	...	...	1221	...	...	1324	...	...	...	...	...	1421	...	...	...	...	...	...	...	...	1621	...	...
Liège Guillemins....d.	...	...	...	...	1246	...	...	1351	...	...	...	...	...	1446	...	...	...	...	...	...	...	...	1646	...	...
Brussels Nord....a.	...	...	...	...	1326	...	...	|	...	...	...	...	...	1526	...	...	...	...	...	...	...	...	1726	...	...
Brussels Midi / Zuid....a.	...	...	...	...	1335	...	...	1435	...	...	...	...	...	1535	...	...	...	...	...	...	...	...	1735	...	...
Brussels Midi / Zuid....d.	...	...	...	...	...	...	...	1443	...	...	...	...	...	...	1556	1613	1713	...	...	...	...	...	...	1813	1856
Paris Nord....a.	...	...	...	...	...	...	...	1605	...	...	...	...	...	...	|	1735	1835	...	...	...	...	...	...	1935	|
London St Pancras....a.	...	...	...	...	...	...	...	...	...	...	...	...	...	...	1700	...	...	...	...	...	...	...	...	...	1957

train type	*ICE*	*ICE*	*ICE*	⇌	*ICE*	*ICE*	*ICE*	*EC*	*ICE*	*ICE*	⇌	☆	*ICE*	*ICE*	*ICE*	⇌	⇌	*ICE*	*ICE*	*ICE*	*ICE*	*EC*	*ICE*	⇌	*ICE*
train number	**228**	**518**	**628**	**9472**	**28**	**596**	**626**	**8**	**574**	**12**	**9382**	**9167**	**28**	**516**	**624**	**9484**	**9484**	**26**	**594**	**622**	**572**	**6**	**10**	**9394**	**318**
notes												Ⓑ												⑦	⑦
notes																**L**	**H**							**Z**	
München Hbf....d.	...	1128	...	...	...	1228	...	...	...	...	...	...	...	1328	...	...	...	...	1428	...	...	...	...	...	...
Augsburg Hbf....d.	...	1203	...	...	...	1302	...	...	...	...	...	...	...	1403	...	...	...	...	1503	...	...	...	...	...	...
Ulm Hbf....d.	...	1248	...	...	...	1348	...	...	...	...	...	...	...	1448	...	...	...	...	1548	...	...	...	...	...	...
Stuttgart Hbf....d.	...	1351	...	...	...	1451	...	...	1523	...	...	...	...	1551	...	...	...	...	1651	...	1723	...	...	...	...
Mannheim Hbf....d.	...	1436	...	...	...	1532	...	...	1605	...	...	...	...	1636	...	...	...	...	1732	...	1805	...	...	...	...
Wien Hbf....d.	0651	|	...	...	0915	|	...	...	|	...	...	...	...	|	...	...	...	1115	|	...	|	...	...	...	...
Nürnberg Hbf....d.	1130	|	1235	...	1330	|	1326	...	|	...	...	...	...	|	1434	...	...	1531	|	1526	|	...	...	...	...
Würzburg Hbf....d.	1224	|	1332	...	1424	|	1432	...	|	...	...	...	...	|	1532	...	...	1624	|	1632	|	...	...	...	...
Frankfurt (Main) Hbf...d.	|	|	1509	...	|	1608	1604	...	|	1628	...	...	...	|	1709	...	...	|	1808	1804	|	...	1828	...	2016
Frankfurt Flughafen ✈..d.	1358	1509	1524	...	1556	...	...	...	1635	1642	...	...	...	1709	1724	...	...	1756	...	...	1835	...	1842	...	2029
Mainz Hbf....d.	1420	|	|	...	...	...	...	1520	...	|	...	...	1620	|	|	...	...	...	...	...	...	1720	|	...	|
Koblenz Hbf....d.	1513	|	|	...	...	...	...	1613	...	|	...	...	1713	|	|	...	...	...	...	...	...	1813	|	...	|
Bonn Hbf....d.	1545	|	|	...	...	...	...	1645	...	|	...	...	1745	|	|	...	...	...	...	...	...	1845	|	...	|
Köln Hbf....a.	1605	1605	1615z	...	...	...	...	1705	...	1736	...	...	1805	1805	1813z	...	...	...	...	...	...	1905	1933	...	2140
Köln Hbf....d.	...	...	...	1644	...	...	...	...	...	1741	...	...	...	...	...	1844	1844	...	...	...	...	...	1940	...	2142
Aachen Hbf 🏛....d.	...	...	...	1724	...	...	...	...	...	1821	...	...	...	...	...	1924	1924	...	...	...	...	...	2021	...	2221
Liège Guillemins....d.	...	...	...	1751	...	...	...	...	...	1846	...	...	...	...	...	1951	1951	...	...	...	...	...	2046	...	2246
Brussels Nord....a.	...	...	...	|	...	...	...	...	...	1926	...	...	...	...	...	|	|	...	...	...	...	...	2126	...	2326
Brussels Midi / Zuid....a.	...	...	...	1835	...	...	...	...	...	1935	...	...	...	...	...	2035	2035	...	...	...	...	...	2135	...	2335
Brussels Midi / Zuid....d.	...	...	...	1842	...	...	...	...	...	...	2016	2056	...	...	...	2043	...	...	...	...	...	...	...	2216	...
Paris Nord....d.	...	...	...	2005	...	...	...	...	...	...	2138	|	...	...	...	2205	...	...	...	...	...	...	...	2338	...
London St Pancras....a.	...	...	...	...	...	...	...	...	...	...	...	2157	...	...	...	...	...	...	...	...	...	...	...	...	...

B – *ÖBB nightjet* 🛏 1, 2 cl., 🛏 2 cl. (4, 6 berth), (2) Innsbruck - München - Köln - Amsterdam ♣ (Table **53**).

C – ②④⑦: *ÖBB nightjet* 🛏 1, 2 cl., 🛏 2 cl. (4, 6 berth), (2) Wien - Brussels ♣ (Table **53**).

E – Ⓑ June 12 - July 16. ⑤⑦ July 17 - Sept. 3. Ⓑ Sept. 4 - Dec. 10.

L – ⑤⑦ June 12 - July 16. ⑤⑥⑦ July 17 - Sept. 3. Daily Sept. 4 - Dec. 10.

H – ① July 17 - Sept. 3.

P – ⑤ June 12 - July 16. ①–⑤ Sept. 4 - Dec. 10.

Y – Also July 21, Aug. 15, Nov. 1.

Z – Also Aug. 15, Nov. 1.

c – ①–⑥.

f – Frankfurt (Main) **Süd**.

z – Köln **Messe / Deutz** (Table **910**). Connections to Köln Hbf depart every 2 - 5 minutes, journey time 2 - 3 minutes.

¶ – For connections from Praha by train, via Regensburg and Nürnberg, see Table **76**.

⇌ – *Thalys* high-speed train. Ⓡ 🍸. Special fares payable. Three classes of service: (Premium, Comfort and Standard). Valid June 12 - Dec. 10.

☆ – Eurostar train. Ⓡ, ✕ in Business Premier and Standard Premier, 🍸 in Standard. Special fares payable. Minimum check-in time 30 minutes. Valid June 12 - Sept. 3. **Additional services are available, see Table 10, pages 47 – 48.**

♣ – Special fares apply.

22 AMSTERDAM - BERLIN

Services between Amsterdam and Berlin are affected by engineering work from June 25 until August 4. See special Table 810 on page 566.

train type	IC	IC		IC		IC		IC		IC		IC		IC	IC	IC	ICE		RE	IC	IC		
train number	**245**	**245**		**141**		**143**		**145**		**147**		**149**		**241**	**241**	**241**	**645**			**243**	**243**		
notes	①–⑥	①–⑥												⑥	⑧	⑦		⑥	⑥	⑦	①–⑤	①–⑤	
	J	**K**													**H**						**E**		
Amsterdam Centraal d.	...	0502	...	0700	...	0910	...	1100	...	1300	...	1500	...	1710	1710	1710	...	...	...	1900	1900	...	...
Hilversum d.	...	0525	...	0722	...	0932	...	1122	...	1322	...	1523	...	1732	1732	1732	...	...	...	1922	1922	...	...
Amersfoort d.	...	0540	...	0736	...	0945	...	1136	...	1336	...	1536	...	1745	1745	1745	...	...	...	1936	1936	...	...
Apeldoorn d.	...	0605	...	0801	...	1010	...	1201	...	1401	...	1601	...	|	|	|	...	...	...	2001	2001	...	...
Deventer d.	...	0617	...	0818	...	1022	...	1218	...	1418	...	1618	...	1821	1821	1821	...	...	...	2018	2018	...	...
Almelo d.	...	0642	...	0845	...	1047	...	1245	...	1445	...	1645	...	1847	1847	1847	...	...	...	2045	2045	...	...
Hengelo ▲ d.	...	0655	...	0858	...	1059	...	1258	...	1458	...	1658	...	1859	1859	1859	...	1934	...	2058	2058	2134	...
Bad Bentheim 🛃 ▲ a.	0721	0711	...	0916	...	1116	...	1316	...	1516	...	1716	...	1916	1916	1916	...	1952	...	2116	2116	2152	...
Rheine ▲ a.	0733	0733	...	0940	...	1140	...	1340	...	1540	...	1740	...	...	1940	1940	...	2012	2038	2140	...	2212	...
Osnabrück Hbf ▲ a.	0803	0803	...	1006	...	1206	...	1406	...	1606	...	1806	...	...	2006	2006	...	2045	2113	2206	...	2245	...
Minden a.	0847	0847	...	1046	...	1246	...	1446	...	1646	...	1846	...	...	2046	2046	...	...	2207	2246	...	...	...
Hannover Hbf a.	0918	0918	...	1118	...	1318	...	1518	...	1718	...	1918	...	...	2118	2118	2131	...	2250	2321	...	...	...
Wolfsburg a.	0953	0953	...	1153	...	1353	...	1553	...	1753	...	1953	...	...	...	2153	|	...	...	...	...	...	...
Stendal a.	1025	1025	...	1225	...	1425	...	1625	...	1825	...	2025	...	...	...	2225	|	...	...	...	...	...	...
Berlin Hauptbahnhof a.	1122	1122	...	1322	...	1522	...	1722	...	1922	...	2123	...	...	...	2322	2305	...	...	...	...	...	...
Berlin Ostbahnhof a.	1134	1134	...	1334	...	1534	...	1734	...	1934	...	2135	...	...	...	2334	...	...	...	...	...	...	...

train type			IC		ICE	IC		RE		IC	IC	IC		IC		IC		IC		IC		IC	
train number			**244**		**646**	**242**				**240**	**240**	**240**		**148**		**146**		**144**		**142**		**140**	
notes		①	①		①–⑤	①–⑥		⑦	⑦		①–⑥												
			D									**B**											
Berlin Ostbahnhof d.	...	...	...	...	...	...	...	...	...	...	0622	...	...	0822	...	1022	...	1222	...	1422	...	1622	...
Berlin Hauptbahnhof d.	...	...	...	...	0430	...	...	...	...	...	0634	...	...	0834	...	1034	...	1234	...	1434	...	1634	...
Stendal d.	...	...	...	...	0514	...	...	...	...	...	0731	...	...	0931	...	1131	...	1331	...	1531	...	1731	...
Wolfsburg d.	...	...	...	...	0548	...	...	...	...	...	0801	...	...	1001	...	1201	...	1401	...	1601	...	1801	...
Hannover Hbf d.	...	...	...	...	0618	0640	...	0709	...	...	0840	0840	...	1040	...	1240	...	1440	...	1640	...	1840	...
Minden d.	...	...	...	...	...	0712	...	0752	...	...	0911	0911	...	1111	...	1311	...	1511	...	1711	...	1911	...
Osnabrück Hbf ▲ d.	...	0614	...	...	...	0753	...	0841	0914	...	0953	0953	...	1153	...	1353	...	1553	...	1753	...	1953	...
Rheine ▲ d.	...	0648	...	...	...	0820	...	0921	0948	...	1021	1020	...	1221	...	1420	...	1621	...	1821	...	2021	...
Bad Bentheim 🛃 ▲ d.	...	0709	0744	...	...	0844	...	...	1009	1044	1044	1044	...	1244	...	1444	...	1644	...	1844	...	2044	...
Hengelo ▲ a.	...	0726	0801	...	...	0901	...	...	1026	1101	1101	1101	...	1301	...	1501	...	1701	...	1901	...	2101	...
Almelo a.	...	...	0813	...	...	0913	...	...	...	1113	1113	1113	...	1313	...	1512	...	1713	...	1913	...	2113	...
Deventer a.	...	...	0841	...	...	0941	...	...	...	1141	1141	1141	...	1341	...	1537	...	1741	...	1941	...	2141	...
Apeldoorn a.	...	...	0858	...	...	0958	...	...	...	1158	1158	1158	...	1358	...	|	...	1758	...	1958	...	2158	...
Amersfoort a.	...	...	0924	...	...	1024	...	...	...	1224	1224	1224	...	1424	...	1614	...	1824	...	2024	...	2224	...
Hilversum a.	...	...	0938	...	...	1038	...	...	...	1238	1238	1238	...	1438	...	1627	...	1838	...	2038	...	2238	...
Amsterdam Centraal a.	...	...	1000	...	...	1100	...	...	...	1300	1300	1300	...	1500	...	1650	...	1900	...	2100	...	2300	...

B – Daily Apr. 11 - Sept. 4.
D – ① Apr. 11 - Aug. 29.
E – ①–⑤ Dec. 13 - Apr. 8, Sept. 5 - Dec. 9.
H – ⑧ (daily Apr. 11 - Sept. 4).
J – ①–⑥ Sept. 5 - Dec. 10.
K – ①–⑥ Apr. 11 - Sept. 3.

▲ – For other regional trains Hengelo – Osnabrück and v.v. see Table **811** on page 381.

24 PARIS - MOSKVA

train number	24 *JI*	24 *JI*
train number	**453**	**453**
notes	**AP** ④	**AQ** ④
Paris Est d.	1858	1858
Saarbrücken d.	|	|
Frankfurt (Main) Süd d.	0158	0158
Ertfurt Hbf d.	0443	0443
Berlin Hbf a.	0721	0721
Berlin Hbf d.	0726	0726
Berlin Lichtenberg a.	0740	0740
Berlin Lichtenberg d.	0801	0759
Frankfurt (Oder) 🛃 d.	0855	0855
Rzepin d.	0919	0919
Poznań Gł. d.	1043	1043
Warszawa Centralna d.	|	|
Warszawa Wschodnia a.	1511	1508
Warszawa Wschodnia d.	1542	1542
Terespol a.	1755	1746
Terespol 🛃 d.	1824	1824
Brest Tsentralny 🛃 a.	2010	2115
Brest Tsentralny d.	2323	2323
Baranavichy a.	0127	0127
Minsk a.	0305	0305
Orsha Tsentralnaya § a.	0536	0536
Smolensk Tsentralny § a.	0709	0709
Vyazma a.	0856	0856
Moskva Belorusskaya a.	1144	1144

train number	23 *JI*	23 *JI*
train number	**452**	**452**
notes	**BP** ②	**BQ** ②
Moskva Belorusskaya d.	1817	1817
Vyazma d.	2132	2132
Smolensk Tsentralny § d.	2315	2315
Orsha Tsentralnaya § d.	0044	0044
Minsk d.	0313	0313
Baranavichy d.	0451	0451
Brest Tsentralny a.	0641	0641
Brest Tsentralny 🛃 d.	0943	1043
Terespol 🛃 a.	0901	0901
Terespol d.	0946	0946
Warszawa Wschodnia a.	1149	1148
Warszawa Wschodnia d.	1225	1223
Warszawa Centralna d.	|	|
Poznań Gł. d.	1658	1653
Rzepin d.	1820	1820
Frankfurt (Oder) 🛃 a.	1842	1842
Berlin Lichtenberg a.	1946	1946
Berlin Lichtenberg d.	2034	2034
Berlin Hbf a.	2053	2053
Berlin Hbf d.	2102	2102
Ertfurt Hbf d.	2327	2327
Frankfurt (Main) Süd a.	0138	0138
Saarbrücken a.	|	|
Paris Est a.	0940	0940

25 NICE - MOSKVA

train number	18 *BJ*	18 *BJ*	
notes	⑦	⑦	
notes	**DP**	**DQ**	
Nice d.	0929	0929	⑦
Monaco-Monte Carlo d.	0944	0944	:
Menton d.	0954	0954	:
Ventimiglia 🛃 d.	1040	1040	:
Bordighera d.	1049	1049	:
San Remo d.	1059	1059	:
Genova Piazza Principe d.	1250	1250	:
Milano Rogoredo d.	1517	1517	:
Verona d.	1735	1735	:
Bolzano / Bozen d.	2008	2008	:
Brennero / Brenner 🛃 d.	2158	2158	:
Innsbruck Hbf d.	2314	2314	:
Jenbach d.	2343	2343	:
Kirchberg in Tirol d.	0030	0030	:
Zell am See d.	0131	0131	①
Bischofshofen d.	0221	0221	:
Linz Hbf d.	0421	0421	:
Wien Hbf d.	0547	0547	:
Břeclav 🛃 d.	0728	0728	:
Bohumín 🛃 d.	0951	0951	:
Chałupki 🛃 d.	0958	0958	:
Katowice d.	|	|	:
Warszawa Centralna d.	1430	1445	:
Warszawa Wschodnia a.	1436	1451	:
Warszawa Wschodnia d.	1546	1542	:
Terespol a.	1755	1746	:
Terespol 🛃 d.	1837	1824	:
Brest Tsentralny 🛃 a.	2010	2110	:
Brest Tsentralny d.	2323	2323	:
Baranavichy a.	0127	0127	②
Minsk a.	0305	0305	:
Orsha Tsentralnaya § a.	0536	0536	:
Smolensk Tsentralny § a.	0709	0709	:
Vyazma a.	0856	0856	:
Moskva Belorusskaya a.	1144	1144	:

train number	17 *BJ*	17 *BJ*	
notes	④	④	
notes	**CP**	**CQ**	
Moskva Belorusskaya d.	1817	1817	④
Vyazma d.	2132	2132	:
Smolensk Tsentralny § d.	2315	2315	⑤
Orsha Tsentralnaya § d.	0044	0044	:
Minsk d.	0313	0313	:
Baranavichy d.	0451	0451	:
Brest Tsentralny a.	0641	0641	:
Brest Tsentralny 🛃 d.	0943	1043	:
Terespol 🛃 a.	0901	0901	:
Terespol d.	0946	0946	:
Warszawa Wschodnia a.	1149	1148	:
Warszawa Wschodnia d.	1224	1224	:
Warszawa Centralna d.	1238	1235	:
Katowice d.	|	|	:
Chałupki 🛃 d.	1717	1717	:
Bohumín 🛃 d.	1758	1758	:
Břeclav 🛃 d.	2014	2014	:
Wien Hbf d.	2120	2120	:
Linz Hbf d.	2328	2328	:
Bischofshofen d.	0131	0131	⑥
Zell am See d.	0220	0220	:
Kirchberg in Tirol d.	0313	0313	:
Jenbach d.	0411	0411	:
Innsbruck Hbf d.	0457	0457	:
Brennero / Brenner 🛃 d.	0707	0707	:
Bolzano / Bozen d.	0814	0814	:
Verona d.	1040	1040	:
Milano Rogoredo d.	1212	1212	:
Genova Piazza Principe d.	1419	1419	:
San Remo d.	1653	1653	:
Bordighera d.	1705	1705	:
Ventimiglia 🛃 d.	1743	1743	:
Menton a.	1757	1757	:
Monaco-Monte Carlo a.	1807	1807	:
Nice a.	1830	1830	:

Notes for tables 24 and 25

A – TRANSEUROPEAN EXPRESS ④: 🛏 1, 2 cl. Paris (**453**) - Berlin - Brest (**24** *JI*) - Moskva (arrive ⑥). ✕ (PKP) Paris - Warszawa. ✕ (RZD) Brest - Moskva.
B – TRANSEUROPEAN EXPRESS ②: 🛏 1, 2 cl. Moskva (**23** *JI*) - Brest (**452**) - Berlin - Paris (arrive ④). ✕ (RZD) Moskva - Brest. ✕ (PKP) Warszawa - Paris.
C – ④: 🛏 1 cl. (lux), 🛏 1, 2 cl. Moskva - Nice. ✕ (RZD) Moskva - Brest and ✕ (PKP) Warszawa - Nice (journey two nights).
D – ⑦: 🛏 1 cl. (lux), 🛏 1, 2 cl. Nice - Moskva. ✕ (PKP) Nice - Warszawa and ✕ (RZD) Brest - Moskva (journey two nights).
P – Mar. 28, 2021 - Oct. 30, 2021. Timings subject to confirmation.
Q – Oct. 31, 2021 - Dec. 11, 2021. Timings subject to confirmation.

✕ (PKP) – Polish railways restaurant car.
✕ (RZD) – Russian railways restaurant car.
§ – 🛃: Osinovka (BY) / Krasnoye (RU).

☛ **Shaded services are suspended until further notice.**

AMSTERDAM - FRANKFURT, WIEN and MÜNCHEN 28

train type		ICE	ICE	ICE		ICE	ICE	ICE	🚌		ICE	ICE	ICE	ICE		ICE	ICE	ICE		ICE	ICE	ICE				
train number		121	621	515		105	595	27	42012		123	629	519	229		125	723	611		127	727	613				
notes	Ⓐ	①–⑥							[R] 🍷																	
						C			2																	
Amsterdam Centraal d.	...	0638	...	...	...	0808	...	...	...	...	1038	...	...	...	...	1238	...	...	...	1438	...	...	...	...	...	...
Rotterdam Centraal d.	0605	|	...	...	0735	|	...	...	...	1005	|	...	...	...	1205	|	...	...	1405	|	...	...	...	...	...	...
Utrecht Centraal d.	0642	0706	...	...	0812	0834	...	...	...	1042	1104	...	...	...	1242	1304	...	...	1442	1504	...	...	...	...	...	...
Arnhem ◐ ▲ d.	...	0737	...	...	...	0907	...	...	...	...	1137	...	...	...	...	1337	...	...	...	1537	...	...	...	...	...	...
Oberhausen Hbf ◐ ▲ d.	...	0826	...	...	...	0958	...	...	...	...	1226	...	...	...	...	1426	...	...	...	1626	...	...	...	...	...	...
Duisburg Hbf ▲ d.	...	0834	...	...	...	|	...	...	...	...	1234	...	...	...	...	1438	...	...	...	1634	...	...	...	...	...	...
Düsseldorf Hbf ▲ d.	...	0848	...	...	...	1019	...	...	...	...	1248	...	...	...	...	1454	...	...	...	1651	...	...	...	...	...	...
Köln Messe / Deutz d.	...	0928	...	...	...	|	...	...	...	...	1319	...	...	...	...	1521	...	...	...	1721	...	...	...	...	...	...
Köln Hbf a.	...	|	...	...	...	1045	...	...	...	...	|	...	...	...	...	|	...	...	...	|	...	...	...	...	...	...
Köln Hbf d.	...	|	...	...	...	1054	...	...	...	...	|	...	...	1353	...	|	...	...	...	|	...	...	...	...	...	...
Frankfurt Flughafen ✈ a.	...	1017	...	1052	...	1149	...	1201	...	...	1412	...	1452	1559	...	1617	...	1652	...	1817	...	1852	...	...	...	...
Frankfurt (Main) Hbf a.	...	1031	1053	|	...	|	...	|	...	...	1426	1453	|	|	...	1631	1654	|	...	1831	1853	|	...	...	...	...
Würzburg a.	...	...	1224	|	...	|	...	1332	...	...	...	1624	|	1732	...	...	1824	|	...	...	2024	|	...	...	...	...
Nürnberg a.	...	...	1320	|	...	|	...	1427	1450	...	...	1720	|	1828	...	...	1920	|	...	...	2120	|	...	...	...	...
Regensburg a.	...	...	...	|	...	|	...	1524	|	...	...	...	|	1924	...	...	...	|	...	...	...	|	...	...	...	...
Praha hl. n. a.	...	...	...	|	...	|	...	|	1825	...	...	...	|	|	...	...	...	|	...	...	...	|	...	...	...	...
Mannheim a.	...	...	...	1123	...	1223	1230	|	...	...	...	...	1523	|	...	...	...	1723	...	...	...	1923	...	...	...	...
Stuttgart a.	...	...	...	1208	...	...	1308	|	...	...	...	...	1608	|	...	...	...	1808	...	...	...	2008	...	...	...	...
Ulm a.	...	...	...	1310	...	...	1410	|	...	...	...	...	1710	|	...	...	...	1910	...	...	...	2110	...	...	...	...
Augsburg a.	...	...	...	1353	...	...	1453	|	...	...	...	...	1753	|	...	...	...	1953	...	...	...	2153	...	...	...	...
München Hbf a.	...	...	...	1427	...	...	1528	|	...	...	...	...	1827	|	...	...	...	2028	...	...	...	2226	...	...	...	...
Passau 🏛 a.	...	...	...	...	...	...	...	1625	...	...	...	...	...	2026	...	...	...	...	...	...	...	...	...	...	...	...
Linz Hbf a.	...	...	...	...	...	...	...	1725	...	...	...	...	...	2133	...	...	...	...	...	...	...	...	...	...	...	...
Wien Hbf a.	...	...	...	...	...	...	...	1845	...	...	...	...	...	2305	...	...	...	...	...	...	...	...	...	...	...	...

train type		ICE	ICE	ICE		ICE	NJ	NJ	
train number		129	821	615		221	40421	421	
notes							A	B	
Amsterdam Centraal d.	...	1638	...	...	...	1838	1930	1930	...
Rotterdam Centraal d.	1605	|	...	...	1805	|	|	|	...
Utrecht Centraal d.	1642	1704	...	...	1842	1904	2002	2002	...
Arnhem ◐ ▲ d.	...	1737	...	...	...	1937	2037	2037	...
Oberhausen Hbf ◐ ▲ d.	...	1826	...	...	...	2026	|	|	...
Duisburg Hbf ▲ d.	...	1834	...	...	...	2034	|	|	...
Düsseldorf Hbf ▲ d.	...	1848	...	...	...	2049	2144	2144	...
Köln Messe / Deutz d.	...	1916	...	...	...	2128	|	|	...
Köln Hbf a.	...	|	...	...	...	|	2214	2214	...
Köln Hbf d.	...	|	...	...	...	|	2216	2216	...
Bonn Hbf d.	...	|	...	...	...	|	2311	2311	...
Koblenz d.	...	|	...	...	...	|	2346	2346	...
Mainz d.	...	|	...	...	...	|	0041	0041	...
Frankfurt Flughafen ✈ a.	...	2015	...	2052	...	2217	0103**d**	0103**d**	...
Frankfurt (Main) Hbf a.	...	2030	2053	|	...	2231	|	|	...
Frankfurt (Main) Süd a.	...	...	|	|	...	...	0117**d**	0117**d**	...
Würzburg a.	...	...	2223	|	...	...	0239	0239	...
Nürnberg a.	...	...	2320	|	...	...	0336	0336	...
Regensburg a.	...	...	...	|	...	...	0511	|	...
Praha hl. n. a.	...	...	...	|	...	...	|	|	...
Mannheim a.	...	...	...	2123	...	...	|	|	...
Stuttgart a.	...	...	...	2208	...	...	|	|	...
Ulm a.	...	...	...	2310	...	...	|	|	...
Augsburg a.	...	...	...	2353	...	...	|	0624	...
München Hbf a.	...	...	...	0027	...	...	|	0711	...
Innsbruck Hbf a.	...	...	...	...	...	...	|	0914	...
Passau 🏛 a.	...	...	...	...	...	...	0616	...	...
Linz Hbf a.	...	...	...	...	...	...	0747	...	...
Wien Hbf a.	...	...	...	...	...	...	0919	...	...

train type	ICE		NJ	NJ	ICE	ICE		ICE	ICE	ICE		
train number	222		420	40490	616	220		614	820	128		
notes									①–⑥			
			B	A								
Wien Hbf d.	...	...	...	2013	...	...	...	...	...	...	...	...
Linz Hbf d.	...	...	...	2136	...	...	...	...	...	...	...	...
Passau 🏛 d.	...	...	...	2253	...	...	...	...	...	...	...	...
Innsbruck Hbf d.	...	...	2044	|	...	...	...	...	...	...	...	...
München Hbf d.	...	...	2250	|	0324	...	...	0533	...	...	...	...
Augsburg d.	...	...	2324	|	0357	...	...	0605	...	...	...	...
Ulm d.	...	...	|	|	0439	...	...	0648	...	...	...	...
Stuttgart d.	...	...	|	|	0551	...	...	0751	...	...	...	...
Mannheim d.	...	...	|	|	0636	...	...	0836	...	...	...	...
Praha hl. n. d.	...	...	|	|	|	...	...	|	...	...	...	...
Regensburg d.	...	...	|	2356	|	...	...	|	...	...	...	...
Nürnberg d.	...	...	0141	0141	|	...	...	|	0634	...	...	...
Würzburg d.	...	...	|	|	|	...	...	|	0732	...	...	...
Frankfurt (Main) Süd d.	...	...	0345**a**	0345**a**	|	...	...	|	|	...	...	...
Frankfurt (Main) Hbf d.	0528	...	|	|	|	0728	...	|	0904	0926	...	...
Frankfurt Flughafen ✈ d.	0542	...	0356**a**	0356**a**	0706	0742	...	0906	...	0942	...	...
Mainz a.	|	...	0416	0416	...	|	...	...	...	|	...	...
Koblenz a.	|	...	0511	0511	...	|	...	...	...	|	...	...
Bonn Hbf a.	|	...	0559	0559	...	|	...	...	...	|	...	...
Köln Hbf a.	|	...	0651	0651	...	|	...	...	...	|	...	...
Köln Hbf d.	|	...	0658	0658	...	|	...	...	...	|	...	...
Köln Messe / Deutz a.	0636	...	|	|	...	0830	...	...	...	1030	...	...
Düsseldorf Hbf ▲ a.	0708	...	0725	0725	...	0906	...	...	...	1104	...	...
Duisburg Hbf ▲ a.	0725	...	0740	0740	...	0923	...	...	...	1123	...	...
Oberhausen Hbf ◐ ▲ a.	0733	...	|	|	...	0932	...	...	...	1132	...	...
Arnhem ◐ ▲ a.	0827	...	0844	0844	...	1027	...	...	...	1227	...	...
Utrecht Centraal a.	0859	0918	0952	0925	...	1059	1118	...	...	1259	1318	...
Rotterdam Centraal a.	|	0955	|	|	...	|	1155	...	...	|	1355	...
Amsterdam Centraal a.	0929	...	0958	0958	...	1129	...	...	...	1329	...	...

train type	ICE	ICE	ICE		ICE	ICE	ICE			🚌	ICE	ICE	ICE	ICE			🚌	ICE	ICE	ICE		ICE	ICE	ICE		
train number	612	726	126		610	722	124			42007	28	626	596	122			42011	26	594	104		514	620	120		
notes										[R] 🍷							[R] 🍷							Ⓑ		
										2							2			C						
Wien Hbf d.	...	...	...	...	...	...	...	...	...	...	0915	...	...	...	...	...	...	1115	...	...	...	...	...	...	...	...
Linz Hbf d.	...	...	...	...	...	...	...	...	...	...	1035	...	...	...	...	...	...	1235	...	...	...	...	...	...	...	...
Passau 🏛 d.	...	...	...	...	...	...	...	...	...	...	1134	...	...	...	...	...	...	1337	...	...	...	...	...	...	...	...
München Hbf d.	0728	...	...	...	0928	...	...	...	...	...	|	...	1227	...	...	...	...	|	1427	...	...	1528	...	...	...	...
Augsburg d.	0803	...	...	...	1003	...	...	...	...	...	|	...	1302	...	...	...	...	|	1503	...	...	1603	...	...	...	...
Ulm d.	0848	...	...	...	1048	...	...	...	...	...	|	...	1348	...	...	...	...	|	1548	...	...	1648	...	...	...	...
Stuttgart d.	0951	...	...	...	1151	...	...	...	...	...	|	...	1451	...	...	...	...	|	1651	...	...	1751	...	...	...	...
Mannheim d.	1036	...	...	...	1233	...	...	...	...	...	|	...	1532	...	...	...	...	|	1729	1736	...	1836	...	...	...	...
Praha hl. n. d.	|	...	...	...	|	...	...	...	...	0935	|	...	|	...	...	...	1135	|	...	|	...	|	...	...	...	...
Regensburg d.	|	...	...	...	|	...	...	...	...	|	1232	...	|	...	...	...	|	1435	...	|	...	|	...	...	...	...
Nürnberg d.	|	0835	...	...	|	1035	...	...	...	1310	1330	1326	|	...	...	...	1510	1531	...	|	...	|	1636	...	...	...
Würzburg d.	|	0932	...	...	|	1132	...	...	...	...	1424	1432	|	...	...	...	...	1624	...	|	...	|	1732	...	...	...
Frankfurt (Main) Hbf d.	|	1104	1128	...	|	1304	1326	...	...	...	|	1604	1608	1628	...	...	...	|	...	|	...	|	1904	1928	...	...
Frankfurt Flughafen ✈ d.	1106	...	1142	...	1306	...	1342	...	...	...	1556	...	...	1642	...	...	...	1756	...	1809	...	1906	...	1942	...	...
Köln Hbf a.	...	...	|	...	...	...	|	...	...	...	...	...	...	1736	...	...	...	...	...	1904	...	...	...	|	...	...
Köln Hbf d.	...	...	|	...	...	...	|	...	...	...	...	...	...	1746	...	...	...	...	...	1914	...	...	...	|	...	...
Köln Messe / Deutz a.	...	...	1230	...	...	...	1430	...	...	...	...	...	...	|	...	...	...	...	...	|	...	...	...	2030	...	...
Düsseldorf Hbf ▲ a.	...	...	1256	...	...	...	1456	...	...	...	...	...	...	1810	...	...	...	...	...	1935	...	...	...	2056	...	...
Duisburg Hbf ▲ a.	...	...	1323	...	...	...	1525	...	...	...	...	...	...	1823	...	...	...	...	...	1949	...	...	...	2123	...	...
Oberhausen Hbf ◐ ▲ a.	...	...	1332	...	...	...	1533	...	...	...	...	...	...	1832	...	...	...	...	...	1957	...	...	...	2132	...	...
Arnhem ◐ ▲ a.	...	...	1427	...	...	...	1627	...	...	...	...	...	...	1927	...	...	...	...	...	2057	...	...	...	2227	...	...
Utrecht Centraal a.	...	...	1459	1518	...	...	1659	1718	...	...	...	...	...	1959	2018	...	...	...	...	2129	2148	...	...	2259	2318	...
Rotterdam Centraal a.	...	...	|	1555	...	...	|	1755	...	...	...	...	...	|	2055	...	...	...	...	|	2225	...	...	|	2355	...
Amsterdam Centraal a.	...	...	1529	...	...	...	1729	...	...	...	...	...	...	2029	...	...	...	...	...	2159	...	...	...	2329	...	...

A – *ÖBB nightjet* 🛏 1, 2 cl., 🛌 2 cl. (4, 6 berth), 🚃2 Amsterdam - Wien and v.v. ♣ (Table **53**).

B – *ÖBB nightjet* 🛏 1, 2 cl., 🛌 2 cl. (4, 6 berth), 🚃2 Amsterdam - Innsbruck and v.v. ♣ (Table **53**).

C – 🚃12 🍷 Amsterdam - Mannheim - Basel and v.v. (Table **73**).

a – Arrival time.

d – Departure time.

▲ – For other regional trains Düsseldorf – Arnhem and v.v. See Table **802** on page 374 (service *RE19*).

🚌 – **DB / ČD** *ExpressBus*. [R] 🍷. Rail tickets valid. 2nd class only. See Table **76**.

◐ – 🏛 between Arnhem and Oberhausen is Emmerich.

⊖ – Via Köln - Frankfurt high speed line.

♣ – Special fares apply.

☛ – Köln **Messe / Deutz** (Table **910**). Connections from Köln Hbf depart every 2 – 5 mins., journey time 2 – 3 mins.

30 PARIS - FRANKFURT - BERLIN, LEIPZIG, DRESDEN and PRAHA

Alternative services Paris - Frankfurt are available via Brussels (Table **21**). Alternative services Paris - Berlin are available via Brussels (Table **20**).

train type	*TGV*	*ICE*	*ICE*	*EC*	*ICE*	*TGV*	*ICE*	*ICE*	*EC*	*ICE*		*ICE*	*ICE*	*ICE*	*ICE*		*ICE*	*ICE*	*ICE*	*ICE*	*ICE*	*ICE*	*ICE*		*ICE*	*TGV*	*NJ*	
train number	**9561**	**372**	**1559**	**177**	**623**	**9551**	**370**	**1651**	**179**	**627**		**9553**	**276**	**1655**	**725**		**9563**	**274**	**1657**	**729**	**9555**	**1659**	**1021**		**9557**	**9559**	**470**	
notes	R★					R★						R★					R★				R★				R★	R★		
notes	①–⑥																				Ⓑ	Ⓑ			Ⓑ	⑥		
		J		**A**					**A**																		**C**	
Paris Est ... d.	0720	...	...	...	...	0906	...	...	...	...	...	1310	...	...	...	...	1520	...	...	...	1710	...	...	...	1906	1906	...	...
Strasbourg ... d.	0912	...	...	...	...	|	...	...	...	...	...	|	...	...	...	...	1713	...	...	...	|	...	...	...	|	|	...	...
Forbach 🚌 ... d.	◧	...	...	...	...	1047	...	...	...	...	...	|	...	...	...	...	◧	...	...	...	|	...	...	...	2049	2049	...	...
Saarbrücken ... d.	|	...	...	...	...	1058	...	...	...	...	...	1459	...	...	...	...	|	...	...	...	1859	...	...	...	2059	2059	...	...
Kaiserlautern ... d.	|	...	...	...	...	1136	...	...	...	...	...	1537	...	...	...	...	|	...	...	...	1937	...	...	...	2137	2136	...	...
Karlsruhe Hbf ... d.	0955	...	...	...	...	|	...	...	...	...	...	|	...	...	...	...	1755	...	...	...	|	...	...	...	|	|	...	...
Mannheim ... d.	1021	...	...	...	...	1219	...	...	...	...	...	1619	...	...	...	...	1821	...	...	...	2019	...	...	...	2219	2219	2342	...
Frankfurt (Main) Hbf ... d.	1059	1114	1119	...	1153	1259	1314	1319	...	1353	...	1659	1714	1719	1753	...	1859	1914	1919	1953	2059	2119	2234	...	2259	2259	0052	...
Würzburg ... a.	...	|	|	...	1324	...	|	|	...	1524	...	...	|	|	1923	...	...	|	|	2124	...	|	2356	...	...	...	|	...
Nürnberg ... a.	...	|	|	...	1420	...	|	|	...	1621	...	...	|	|	2020	...	...	|	|	2220	...	|	0053	...	...	...	|	...
Fulda ... a.	...	1210	1212	...	...	...	1410	1412	...	...	...	...	1810	1812	...	...	...	2010	2012	...	...	2212	...	...	...	...	0147	...
Erfurt ... a.	...	|	1338	...	...	...	|	1538	...	...	...	...	|	1938	...	...	...	|	2138	...	...	2338	...	...	...	...	|	...
Leipzig Hbf ... a.	...	|	1424	...	...	...	|	1624	...	...	...	...	|	2024	...	...	...	|	2224	...	...	0028j	...	...	...	...	|	...
Dresden Hbf ... a.	...	|	1537	1710	...	...	|	1737	1910	...	...	...	|	2137	...	...	...	|	2337	...	...	...	...	...	...	...	|	...
Děčín (🚌 = Schöna) ... a.	...	|	...	1754	...	...	|	...	1954	...	...	...	|	...	...	...	...	|	...	...	...	...	...	...	...	...	|	...
Praha Holešovice ... a.	...	|	...	1926	...	...	|	...	2126	...	...	...	|	...	...	...	...	|	...	...	...	...	...	...	...	...	|	...
Praha hl. n. ... a.	...	|	...	1935	...	...	|	...	2135	...	...	...	|	...	...	...	...	|	...	...	...	...	...	...	...	...	|	...
Kassel Wilhelmshöhe ... a.	...	1243	...	...	...	...	1443	...	...	...	...	...	1843	...	...	...	...	2043	...	...	...	...	...	...	...	...	|	...
Göttingen ... a.	...	1303	...	...	...	...	1503	...	...	...	...	...	1903	...	...	...	...	2103	...	...	...	...	...	...	...	...	0314	...
Braunschweig ... a.	...	1359	...	...	...	...	1559	...	...	...	...	...	1959	...	...	...	...	2159	...	...	...	...	...	...	...	...	0457	...
Wolfsburg ... a.	...	1417	...	...	...	...	1617	...	...	...	...	...	2017	...	...	...	...	2217	...	...	...	...	...	...	...	...	|	...
Berlin Hauptbahnhof ... a.	...	1527	...	...	...	...	1727	...	...	...	...	...	2127	...	...	...	...	2327	...	...	...	...	...	...	...	...	0738	...

train type	*NJ*	*ICE*	*ICE*	*ICE*	*ICE*	*ICE*	*ICE*	*ICE*	*ICE*	*ICE*	*ICE*	*ICE*	*ICE*	*ICE*	*ICE*	*ICE*	*TGV*	*ICE*	*ICE*	*EC*	*ICE*	*TGV*	*EC*	*ICE*	*ICE*	*ICE*	*ICE*	
train number	**471**	**9558**	**9568**	**9586**	**822**	**1656**	**275**	**9556**	**9566**	**728**	**1654**	**277**	**9554**	**724**	**1652**	**279**	**9552**	**626**	**373**	**176**	**1558**	**9560**	**174**	**622**	**1556**	**375**	**9550**	
notes		R★	R★	R★				R★	R★			🍷	R★				R★					R★					R★	
notes		①–⑤	Ⓑ	⑥	①–⑥	①–⑥	①–⑤	①–⑤	⑥				⑥⑦														Ⓑ	
	C						**J**												**J**	**A**			**A**					
Berlin Hauptbahnhof ... d.	2054	...	...	...	...	...	0430	...	...	...	...	0630	...	...	...	0830	...	...	1230	...	...	...	...	...	...	1430	...	...
Wolfsburg ... d.	|	...	...	...	...	...	0538	...	...	...	...	0738	...	...	...	0938	...	...	1338	...	...	...	...	...	...	1538	...	...
Braunschweig ... d.	2328	...	...	...	...	...	0557	...	...	...	...	0757	...	...	...	0957	...	...	1357	...	...	...	...	...	...	1557	...	...
Göttingen ... d.	0116	...	...	...	...	...	0652	...	...	...	...	0852	...	...	...	1052	...	...	1452	...	...	...	...	...	...	1652	...	...
Kassel Wilhelmshöhe ... d.	|	...	...	...	...	...	0714	...	...	...	...	0914	...	...	...	1114	...	...	1514	...	...	...	...	...	...	1714	...	...
Praha hl. n. ... d.	|	...	...	...	...	...	|	...	...	...	...	|	...	...	...	|	...	...	|	0825	...	...	1025	...	...	|	...	...
Praha Holešovice ... d.	|	...	...	...	...	...	|	...	...	...	...	|	...	...	...	|	...	...	|	0834	...	...	1034	...	...	|	...	...
Děčín (🚌 = Schöna) ... d.	|	...	...	...	...	...	|	...	...	...	...	|	...	...	...	|	...	...	|	1007	...	...	1207	...	...	|	...	...
Dresden Hbf ... d.	|	...	...	...	...	...	|	...	...	...	0612	|	...	...	0812	|	...	...	|	1051	1212	...	1251	...	1412	|	...	...
Leipzig Hbf ... d.	|	...	...	...	...	0533	|	...	...	...	0733	|	...	...	0933	|	...	...	|	...	1333	...	...	...	1533	|	...	...
Erfurt ... d.	|	...	...	...	...	0617	|	...	...	...	0817	|	...	...	1017	|	...	...	|	...	1417	...	...	...	1617	|	...	...
Fulda ... d.	0245	...	...	...	...	0743	0747	...	...	...	0943	0947	...	...	1143	1147	...	...	1547	...	1543	...	...	...	1743	1747	...	...
Nürnberg ... d.	|	...	...	...	0536	|	|	...	...	0735	|	|	...	0926	|	|	...	1326	|	...	|	...	...	1526	|	|	...	...
Würzburg ... d.	|	...	...	...	0632	|	|	...	...	0832	|	|	...	1032	|	|	...	1432	|	...	|	...	...	1632	|	|	...	...
Frankfurt (Main) Hbf ... d.	0400	0556	0656	0656	0804	0836	0844	0856	0856	1004	1036	1044	1056	1204	1236	1244	1256	1604	1644	...	1636	1656	...	1804	1836	1844	1856	...
Mannheim ... d.	0440	0640	0738	0740	...	...	...	0940	0939	...	...	...	1142	...	...	...	1342	...	...	...	...	1738	...	...	...	...	1940	...
Karlsruhe Hbf ... d.	...	|	0806	|	...	...	...	|	1006	...	...	...	|	...	...	...	|	...	...	...	...	1805	...	...	...	...	|	...
Kaiserlautern ... d.	...	0722	|	0823	...	...	...	1022	|	...	...	...	1224	...	...	...	1424	...	...	...	...	|	...	...	...	...	2022	...
Saarbrücken ... d.	...	0800	|	0903	...	...	...	1101	|	...	...	...	1303	...	...	...	1503	...	...	...	...	|	...	...	...	...	2101	...
Forbach 🚌 ... a.	...	0809	◧	0912	...	...	...	|	◧	...	...	...	1312	...	...	...	|	...	...	...	...	◧	...	...	...	...	2110	...
Strasbourg ... a.	...	|	0847	|	...	...	...	|	1047	...	...	...	|	...	...	...	|	...	...	...	...	1848	...	...	...	...	|	...
Paris Est ... a.	...	0951	1038	1053	...	...	...	1252	1238	...	...	...	1454	...	...	...	1654	...	...	...	...	2041	...	...	...	...	2252	...

A – (12) ✕ Praha - Dresden - Hamburg and v.v.

C – *ÖBB nightjet* – 🛏 1, 2 cl., 🛏 2 cl. (4, 6 berth), (2) Zürich - Mannheim - Berlin and v.v. Special fares apply.

J – (12) 🍷 Interlaken Ost - Mannheim - Berlin and v.v.

j – ①⑥.

◧ – 🚌 is at Kehl.

★ – *Alleo* ICE / TGV service. A DB / SNCF joint enterprise.

31 LONDON - GENÈVE

For the full service Paris - Genève, see Table **341**. 90 minutes (including Eurostar check-in time of 30 minutes) has been allowed from Paris Gare de Lyon to Paris Nord. 60 minutes has been allowed from Paris Nord to Paris Gare de Lyon. Additional Eurostar services are available, see Table **10**.

train type		☆	*TGV*		*TGV*			☆	*TGV*		☆	*TGV*										
train number		**9008**	**9773**		**9826**	**96565**		**9014**	**9775**		**9024**	**9781**										
notes		①–⑥			**5026**				**L**													
notes		**A**	♥		R				♥			♥										
London St Pancras **10** ... d.	...	0801	...	...	...	...	...	0931	...	...	1224	...	...	...	...	...	...	...	...	...	...	...
Lille Europe ... d.	...	|	...	...	1103	...	...	|	...	...	|	...	...	...	...	...	...	...	...	...	...	...
Paris Nord **10** ... a.	...	1127	...	...	|	...	...	1257	...	...	1557	...	...	...	...	...	...	...	...	...	...	...
Paris Gare de Lyon ... d.	...	...	1218	...	|	...	...	...	1418	...	...	1818	...	...	...	...	...	...	...	...	...	...
Lyon Part Dieu ... a.	...	...	|	...	1400	1438	...	...	|	...	...	|	...	...	...	...	...	...	...	...	...	...
Bellegarde ... a.	...	...	1500	...	...	1607	...	...	1700	...	...	2100	...	...	...	...	...	...	...	...	...	...
Genève ... a.	...	...	1529	...	...	1635	...	...	1729	...	...	2129	...	...	...	...	...	...	...	...	...	...

train type		*TGV*	☆		*TGV*	☆		*TGV*	☆		*TGV*	☆		*TGV*	☆	*TGV*	☆	☆				
train number		**9760**	**9031**		**9764**	**9039**		**9768**	**9047**		**9770**	**9055**	**96566**	**5192**	**9167**	**9774**	**9059**	**9063**				
notes		①–⑥						**L**							Ⓑ	**L**	⑦	Ⓑ				
notes		♥			♥			♥			♥					♥	**B**					
Genève ... d.	...	0629	...	...	0829	...	...	1029	...	...	1229	...	1330	...	...	1429	...	...	...	...	...	...
Bellegarde ... d.	...	0702	...	...	0900	...	...	1102	...	...	1302	...	1400	...	...	1502	...	...	...	...	...	...
Lyon Part Dieu ... d.	...	|	...	...	|	...	...	|	...	...	|	...	1525	1600	...	|	...	...	...	...	...	...
Paris Gare de Lyon ... a.	...	0942	...	...	1142	...	...	1342	...	...	1542	...	...	|	...	1742	...	...	...	...	...	...
Paris Nord **10** ... d.	...	...	1303	...	...	1503	...	...	1703	...	...	1903	...	|	...	...	2003	2103	...	...	...	...
Lille Europe ... d.	...	...	|	...	...	|	...	...	|	...	...	|	...	1944f	2135	...	|	|	...	...	...	...
London St Pancras **10** ... a.	...	...	1430	...	...	1637	...	...	1840	...	...	2030	...	...	2157	...	2130	2230	...	...	...	...

A – Not Aug. 29.

B – Also Aug. 29.

L – To / from Lausanne (Table **42**).

f – Lille **Flandres** (◇).

◇ – 500 metres from Lille Europe (see Lille City Plan on page 30).

♥ – *TGV Lyria* service. R 🍷. Special fares payable, three classes of service: Business 1ère, Standard 1ère and Standard. At-seat meal service in Business 1ère. Valid June 12 - July 1.

☆ – Eurostar train. R, ✕ in Business Premier and Standard Premier, 🍷 in Standard. Special fares payable. Minimum check-in time 30 minutes. Connections across Paris between *TGV* and Eurostar services are not guaranteed. Valid June 12 - Sept. 3. **Additional services are available, see Table 10, pages 47 – 48.**

LONDON - PARIS - MÜNCHEN - WIEN - BUDAPEST - BUCURESTI 32

Alternative services London - München are available via Brussels (Table **21**)

Engineering work is affecting services between München and Salzburg until August 1

train type	RJX	IC	ICE	RJX	IC	EC	RJX	EC	ICE	ICE	RJX	EN	TGV	ICE	EC	RJX	ICE	TGV	ICE	RJX	☆	TGV	ICE	NJ	RJX
train number	**61**	**79**	**511**	**65**	**473**	**113**	**563**	**149**	**9571**	**513**	**67**	**347**	**9551**	**595**	**219**	**167**	**9573**	**9593**	**517**	**261**	**9008**	**9575**	**599**	**295**	**367**
train number/notes		❖			❖				★			✕	★			✕	★	★				★		Ⓡ	
notes		**J**			**B**			**A**				**M** ❖			x	**H**	Ⓑ	⑥			①–⑥ **G**				
London St Pancras **10** d.	...	...	...	...	...	...	...	...	...	...	...	...	...	...	...	...	...	...	...	...	0801	...	...	...	...
Paris Nord **10** a.	...	...	...	...	...	...	...	...	...	...	...	...	...	...	...	...	...	...	...	...	1127	...	...	...	...
Paris Est d.	...	...	...	...	...	...	...	...	0655	...	...	...	0906	...	...	...	1055	1055	...	...	...	1355	...	...	...
Strasbourg d.	...	...	...	...	...	...	...	...	0846	...	...	...	|	...	...	...	1246	1246	...	...	...	1546	...	...	...
Kehl 🏛 d.	...	...	...	...	...	...	...	...	|	...	...	...	◧	...	...	...	|	|	...	...	...	|	...	...	...
Karlsruhe Hbf d.	...	...	...	...	...	...	...	...	0928	...	...	...	|	...	...	...	1328	1328	...	...	...	1628	...	...	...
Mannheim Hbf d.	...	...	0731	...	...	...	...	...	|	...	...	...	1217	1230	...	...	|	|	...	...	...	|	...	...	...
Stuttgart Hbf d.	...	...	0814	...	...	0958	...	...	1005	1014	...	...	...	1314	...	...	1404	1405	1414	...	...	1704	1714	...	...
Ulm Hbf d.	...	...	0912	...	...	1056	...	...	...	1112	...	...	...	1412	...	...	...	...	1512	...	...	...	1812	...	...
Augsburg Hbf d.	...	...	0955	...	...	1141	...	...	...	1155	...	...	...	1455	...	...	...	...	1555	...	...	...	1855	...	...
München Pasing a.	...	...	1018	...	...	|	...	...	...	1217	...	...	...	1518	...	...	...	...	1618	...	...	...	1918	...	...
München Hbf a.	...	...	1027	...	...	1210	...	...	...	1227	...	...	...	1528	...	...	...	...	1627	...	...	...	1927	...	...
München Hbf d.	0723	...	...	1130	...	1217	...	...	...	...	1329	...	...	...	1617	...	...	...	...	1730	...	...	...	2010	...
Salzburg Hbf 🏛 a.	0858	...	...	1258	...	1359	1408	...	...	...	1458	...	...	...	1759	1808	...	...	...	1858	...	...	...	2152	2208
Linz Hbf a.	1014	...	...	1414	...	...	1514	...	...	...	1614	...	...	...	...	1914	...	...	...	2014	...	...	...	...	2317
St Pölten Hbf a.	1100	...	...	1500	...	...	1600	...	...	...	1700	...	...	...	...	2000	...	...	...	2100	...	...	...	...	0003
Wien Hbf a.	1130	...	...	1530	...	...	1630	1642	...	...	1730	1942	...	...	...	2030	...	...	...	2130	...	...	...	...	0033
Hegyeshalom 🏛 a.	1225	...	...	1625	...	...	...	1725	...	...	1825	2025	...	...	...	...	...	...	...	2225	...	...	...	...	...
Györ a.	1253	...	...	1653	...	...	...	1753	...	...	1853	2053	...	...	...	...	...	...	...	2253	...	...	...	...	...
Budapest Keleti a.	1419	1510	...	1819	1910	...	...	1919	...	...	2019	2220	...	...	...	...	...	...	...	0019	...	...	...	...	...
Bucuresti Nord a.	...	0830	...	...	1233	...	...	...	...	...	...	1600	...	...	...	...	...	...	...	...	...	...	...	...	...

train type	☆	TGV	☆	TGV	TGV	TGV	ICE	☆	ICE	TGV	ICE	NJ
train number	**9018**	**9577**	**9024**	**9591**	**9579**	**9579**	**693**	**9032**	**9557**	**9559**	**695**	**469**
train number/notes		★			★	★			★	★		
notes		Ⓑ			⑥	Ⓑ	Ⓑ		Ⓑ	⑥		②⑤⑦ **E**
London St Pancras **10** d.	1022	...	1224	...	...	...	...	1431	...	...	...	...
Paris Nord **10** a.	1357	...	1557	...	...	...	...	1757	...	...	...	...
Paris Est d.	...	1555	▬	1725	1755	1755	...	...	1906	1906	...	1958
Strasbourg d.	...	1746	...	1918	1946	1946	...	...	|	|	...	0036
Kehl 🏛 d.	...	|	...	|	|	|	...	...	◧	◧	...	|
Offenburg a.	...	|	...	1939	|	|	...	...	|	|	...	|
Freiburg (Brsg) Hbf a.	...	|	...	2026	|	|	...	...	|	|	...	|
Karlsruhe Hbf d.	...	1827	...	...	2028	2028	...	...	|	|	...	0215
Mannheim Hbf d.	...	|	...	...	|	|	...	...	2217	2217	2230	|
Stuttgart Hbf d.	...	1922	...	...	2114	2104	2114	...	...	...	2308	|
Ulm Hbf d.	...	2020	...	...	2212	...	2212	...	...	...	...	|
Augsburg Hbf d.	...	2106	*EN*	...	2258	...	2255	...	...	...	...	|
München Pasing a.	...	|	**463**	...	|	...	2320	...	...	...	...	|
München Hbf a.	...	2136	**K**	...	2329	...	2329	...	...	...	...	0543o
München Hbf d.	...	...	2320	...	...	...	...	...	...	...	...	|
Salzburg Hbf 🏛 a.	...	...	0106	...	...	...	...	...	...	...	...	0726
Linz Hbf a.	...	...	0452	...	...	...	...	...	...	...	...	0844
St Pölten Hbf a.	...	...	0600	...	...	...	...	...	...	...	...	0936
Wien Hbf a.	...	...	0634	...	...	...	...	...	...	...	...	1012
Hegyeshalom 🏛 a.	...	...	0723	...	...	...	...	...	...	...	...	...
Györ a.	...	...	0753	...	...	...	...	...	...	...	...	...
Budapest Keleti a.	...	...	0919	...	...	...	...	...	...	...	...	...
Bucuresti Nord a.	...	...	...	...	...	...	...	...	...	...	...	...

train type	TGV	ICE	ICE	☆		TGV	TGV	☆	
train number	**9590**	**616**	**9558**	**9023**		**9578**	**9588**	**9031**	
train number/notes			★			★			
notes	①–⑤		①–⑤			①–⑥	⑥⑦		
Bucuresti Nord d.	...	...	...	...	...	...	...	...	...
Budapest Keleti d.	...	...	...	...	...	...	...	...	...
Györ d.	...	...	...	...	...	...	...	...	...
Hegyeshalom 🏛 d.	...	...	...	...	...	...	...	...	...
Wien Hbf d.	...	...	...	...	...	...	...	...	...
St Pölten Hbf d.	...	...	...	...	...	...	...	...	...
Linz Hbf d.	...	...	...	...	...	...	...	...	...
Salzburg Hbf 🏛 d.	...	...	...	...	...	...	...	...	...
München Hbf a.	...	...	...	...	...	...	...	...	...
München Hbf d.	...	0324	...	...	...	...	...	...	...
München Pasing d.	...	0332	...	...	...	...	...	...	...
Augsburg Hbf d.	...	0357	...	...	...	...	...	...	...
Ulm Hbf d.	...	0439	...	...	...	...	...	...	...
Stuttgart Hbf d.	...	0551	...	...	...	0652	...	...	...
Mannheim Hbf d.	...	0628	0640	...	...	|	...	...	...
Karlsruhe Hbf d.	...	...	|	...	...	0732	...	...	...
Freiburg (Brsg) Hbf d.	0634	...	|	...	...	|	0708	...	...
Offenburg d.	0713	...	|	...	...	|	0746	...	...
Kehl 🏛 d.	|	...	◧	...	...	|	|	...	...
Strasbourg a.	0740	...	|	...	...	0812	0813	...	...
Paris Est a.	0935	...	0951	...	...	1005	1005	...	...
Paris Nord **10** d.	...	...	...	1103	...	...	...	1303	...
London St Pancras **10** a.	...	...	...	1230	...	...	...	1430	...

train type	EN	TGV	☆	IC	ICE	ICE	☆	RJX	EC	ICE	ICE	TGV	☆	☆	ICE	TGV	EN	RJX	EC	TGV	IC	RJX	IC	NJ	
train number	**462**	**9576**	**9039**	**1296**	**690**	**9574**	**9047**	**260**	**218**	**596**	**9572**	**9592**	**9059**	**9063**	**594**	**9560**	**346**	**60**	**112**	**9570**	**472**	**62**	**266**	**468**	
train number/notes		★				★					★	★				★	❖	✕		★	❖	✕			
notes	**K**			①–⑥					z		Ⓑ	⑥	⑦ **F**	Ⓑ			**M**				**B**			①④⑥ **D**	
Bucuresti Nord d.	...	...	...	...	...	...	...	...	...	...	...	...	...	...	...	...	1400	...	...	...	1745	...	...	...	...
Budapest Keleti d.	2040	...	...	...	...	...	...	...	...	...	...	...	...	...	...	...	0540	0740	...	...	0850	0940	...	...	...
Györ d.	2202	...	...	...	...	...	...	...	...	...	...	...	...	...	...	...	0702	0902	...	...	...	1102	...	...	...
Hegyeshalom 🏛 d.	2232	...	...	...	...	...	...	...	...	...	...	...	...	...	...	...	0732	0932	...	...	...	1132	...	...	...
Wien Hbf d.	2327	...	...	...	...	...	...	0630	...	...	...	...	...	...	...	...	0821	1030	...	...	...	1230	...	1940	...
St Pölten Hbf d.	0001	...	...	...	...	...	...	0700	...	...	...	...	...	...	...	...	...	1100	...	...	...	1300	...	2015	...
Linz Hbf d.	0059	...	...	...	...	...	...	0746	...	...	...	...	...	...	...	...	...	1146	...	...	...	1346	...	2102	...
Salzburg Hbf 🏛 d.	0427	...	...	0543	...	...	...	0900	1000	...	...	...	...	...	...	...	...	1300	1400	...	...	1500	...	2218	...
München Hbf a.	0629	...	...	0730	...	...	...	1030	1141	...	...	...	...	...	...	...	...	1432	1541	...	...	1633	...	|	...
München Hbf d.	...	0646	...	...	0827	...	...	...	...	1227	...	...	...	...	1427	...	...	...	1547	...	...	...	1646	0003o	...
München Pasing d.	...	|	...	...	0837	...	...	...	...	1237	...	...	...	...	1437	...	...	...	|	...	...	...	1655	|	...
Augsburg Hbf d.	...	0716	...	...	0903	...	...	...	...	1302	...	...	...	...	1503	...	...	...	1616	...	...	...	1721	|	...
Ulm Hbf d.	...	0802	...	...	0948	...	...	...	...	1348	...	...	...	...	1548	...	...	...	1703	...	...	...	1803	|	...
Stuttgart Hbf d.	...	0910	...	...	1045	1052	...	...	...	1445	1452	1455	...	...	1651	...	...	...	1759	1852	...	...	1910	|	...
Mannheim Hbf d.	...	|	...	...	...	|	...	...	...	...	|	|	...	...	1729	1738	...	...	...	|	...	...	|	|	...
Karlsruhe Hbf d.	...	0953	...	...	...	1131	...	...	...	...	1532	1532	...	...	...	1805	...	...	...	1932	...	...	1953	0412	...
Kehl 🏛 d.	...	|	...	...	...	|	...	...	...	...	|	|	...	...	...	◧	...	...	...	|	...	...	...	|	...
Strasbourg a.	...	1037	...	...	...	1213	...	...	...	...	1612	1612	...	...	...	1848	...	...	...	2013	...	...	...	0506	...
Paris Est a.	...	1231	...	...	...	1405	...	...	...	...	1805	1805	...	...	...	2041	...	...	...	2205	...	...	...	0942	...
Paris Nord **10** d.	...	...	1503	...	...	...	1703	...	...	...	...	...	2003	2103	...	...	...	...	...	...	...	...	...	...	...
London St Pancras **10** a.	...	...	1637	...	...	...	1840	...	...	...	...	...	2130	2230	...	...	...	...	...	...	...	...	...	...	...

A – [12] HORTOBÁGY – Wien - Budapest - Szolnok (arrive 2102) - Debrecen (2235) - Zahony (0010). Conveys 🛏 1, 2 cl. Wien - Zahony - Lviv - Kyïv (Table **96**).

B – *EuroNight* ISTER – 🛏 1, 2 cl., ▬ 1, 2 cl., [2] Budapest - Bucuresti and v.v.

D – ①④⑥: *ÖBB nightjet* – 🛏 1, 2 cl., ▬ 2 cl. (4, 6 berth), [2] Wien - Salzburg - Paris. Special fares apply.

E – ②⑤⑦: *ÖBB nightjet* – 🛏 1, 2 cl., ▬ 2 cl. (4, 6 berth), [2] Paris - Salzburg - Wien. Special fares apply.

F – Also Aug. 29.

G – Not Aug. 29.

H – To Bratislava, arrive 2152.

J – MUNTENIA – [2] Budapest - Timişoara - Bucureşti and v.v.

K – KÁLMÁN IMRE – 🛏 1, 2 cl., ▬ 2 cl. (4, 6 berth) [2] München - Budapest and v.v.

M – DACIA – 🛏 1, 2 cl., ▬ 2 cl., [2] Wien - Budapest - Bucuresti and v.v.

o – München **Ost**.

x – To Graz (arrive 2214; Table **62**).

z – From Graz (depart 0545; Table **62**).

◧ – 🏛 is at Forbach.

RJ – ÖBB *Railjet* service. ✕, [1] (business class), [1] (first class), [2] (economy class).

★ – *Alleo* ICE / TGV service. A DB / SNCF joint enterprise.

TGV – Ⓡ, supplement payable, 🍸.

❖ – Compulsory reservation for international journeys between Hungary and Romania.

☆ – Eurostar train. Ⓡ, ✕ in Business Premier and Standard Premier, 🍸 in Standard. Special fares payable. Minimum check-in time 30 minutes. Valid June 12 - Sept. 3. **Additional services are available, see Table 10, pages 47 – 48.**

‡ – Train number **9596** on ⑦.

40 LONDON - PARIS - BASEL - ZÜRICH, INTERLAKEN, BRIG and MILANO

train type/number	TGV	IC	IC	EC	IC	TGV	EC	IC	IR	IC	EC	☆	TGV	IC	IC	IR	IC	EC
train number	9203	967	814	151	567	9211	7	820	2327	573	321	9004	9213	977	824	2331	577	323
notes	♥ ①–⑥			Ⓡ 🍷 ⊗		♥					Ⓡ 🍷 ⊗	①–⑤ H	♥					Ⓡ 🍷 ⊗
London St Pancras d.												0701						
Paris Nord a.												1027						
Paris Gare de Lyon d.	0722					1022							1222					
Dijon d.						1200							1401					
Besançon TGV ⊖ d.																		
Belfort TGV ⊡ d.	0941																	
Mulhouse d.	1006					1306							1506					
Basel SBB a.	1026					1326							1526					
Basel SBB d.	1033x	1056		1103		1333x	1356		1403				1533x	1556		1603		
Zürich HB a.	1126x				1138	1426x				1438	1533		1626x				1638	1733
Landquart a.					1242					1542							1742	
Chur a.					1252					1552							1752	
Luzern a.				1205					1505							1705		
Arth Goldau a.				1245					1545		1616					1745		1816
Arth Goldau d.				1249							1618							1818
Bellinzona a.				1342							1712							1912
Lugano a.				1358							1732							1932
Chiasso 🏛 a.				1456							1802							2002
Bern a.		1156	1207				1456	1507						1656	1707			
Thun a.		1223	1225				1523	1525						1723	1725			
Spiez a.		1233	1236				1533	1536						1733	1736			
Interlaken West a.		1251					1551							1751				
Interlaken Ost a.		1258					1558							1758				
Brig a.			1311					1611							1811			
Como San Giovanni a.				1501							1810							2010
Milano Centrale a.				1550							1850							2050

train type/number	☆	TGV	ICE	IC	IR	IC	EC	☆	TGV	ICE	IR	IC	IC	IC	IR	IC	☆	TGV	IR	IC	IC	
train number	9014	9215	371	828	2335	583	325	9018	9219	373	2339	1087	585	889	2441	691	9024	9223	2343	989	589	4293
notes		♥	Ⓡ 🍷 ⊗				Ⓡ 🍷 ⊗		♥			1089		①–⑤				♥				
London St Pancras d.	0931							1022									1224					
Paris Nord a.	1257							1357									1557					
Paris Gare de Lyon d.		1422							1622									1822				
Dijon d.																		2001				
Besançon TGV ⊖ d.																						
Belfort TGV ⊡ d.		1640							1841													
Mulhouse d.		1706							1906									2107				
Basel SBB a.		1726							1926									2126				
Basel SBB d.			1756		1803	1833			1933x	1956	2003	2028				2103		2133x	2203	2156		
Zürich HB a.						1926	1933		2026x				2038	2105	2205			2226x			2238	
Landquart a.						2042							2142								2349	
Chur a.						2052							2152								2357	
Luzern a.					1905						2105					2205			2305			
Arth Goldau a.					1945		2016				2145			2145	2245	2245			2338			
Arth Goldau d.							2018							2149		2249						
Bellinzona a.							2112							2242		2342						
Lugano a.							2132							2302		0002						
Chiasso 🏛 a.							2202							2330		0030						
Bern a.			1856	1907						2056		2126								2256		
Thun a.			1923	1925						2125		2152								2226		
Spiez a.			1933	1936						2136		2202								2337		0013
Interlaken West a.			1952							2154										2355		
Interlaken Ost a.			1958							2159										2400		
Brig a.				2011								2241f										0123
Como San Giovanni a.							2210															
Milano Centrale a.							2250															

train type	IC	IC	IR	ICE	TGV	☆	IC	IC	IC	IR	IC	TGV	☆	EC	IC	EC	IR	ICE	TGV	☆
train number	862	558	2308	372	9206	9039	866	562	1060	2312	962	9210	9047	312	566	50	2316	278	9218	9055
notes					♥							♥		Ⓡ 🍷 ⊗		Ⓡ 🍷 ⊗			♥	
Milano Centrale d.														0710		0720				
Como San Giovanni d.														0754		◧				
Brig d.									0718							0918				
Interlaken Ost d.				0558							0800							1000		
Interlaken West d.				0603							0805							1005		
Spiez d.				0622					0754		0822					0954		1022		
Thun d.				0633					0804		0833					1004		1033		
Bern d.				0704					0836		0904					1036		1104		
Chiasso 🏛 d.														0805						
Lugano d.							0701							0830						
Bellinzona d.	0507						0718							0847						
Arth Goldau a.	0611						0811							0942						
Arth Goldau d.	0615		0603				0815			0803				0945			1003			
Luzern d.			0654							0854							1054			
Chur d.		0608						0808							1008					
Landquart d.		0618						0818							1018					
Zürich HB d.	0655	0722			0734x		0855	0922				0934x		1027	1122				1134x	
Basel SBB a.			0756	0801	0828x				0932	0956	1001	1028x				1132	1156	1201	1228x	
Basel SBB d.					0834							1034							1234	
Mulhouse a.					0853							1052							1253	
Belfort TGV ⊡ a.					0917														1317	
Besançon TGV ⊖ a.																				
Dijon a.												1157								
Paris Gare de Lyon a.					1138							1338							1538	
Paris Nord d.						1503							1703							1903
London St Pancras a.						1637							1840							2030

H – Not Aug. 29.

f – 2303 on ⑦.

x – Not June 7 - July 24.

⊡ – Full name: Belfort Montbéliard TGV.

⊖ – Full name: Besancon Franche-Comté TGV.

◧ – 🏛 between Brig and Milano is Domodossola. Ticket point is **Iselle**.

♥ – *TGV Lyria* service. Ⓡ ✕. Special fares payable, three classes of service: Business 1ère, Standard 1ère and Standard. At-seat meal service in Business 1ère. Valid June 12 - July 1.

⊗ – Compulsory reservation for international journeys. Supplement payable for international journeys and for internal journeys within Italy.

☆ – Eurostar train. Ⓡ, ✕ in Business Premier and Standard Premier, 🍷 in Standard. Special fares payable. Minimum check-in time 30 minutes. Valid June 12 - Sept. 3. **Additional services are available, see Table 10, pages 47 – 48.**

MILANO, BRIG, INTERLAKEN and ZÜRICH - BASEL - PARIS - LONDON 40

train type	*EC*	*IC*	*IC*	*IR*	*EC*	*TGV*	☆	☆		*EC*	*IC*	*EC*	*IR*	*IC*	*TGV*		*EC*	*IC*	*IR*	*IC*	*IC*	*TGV*	
train number	**314**	**570**	**1068**	**2320**	**6**	**9222**	**9059**	**9063**		**316**	**574**	**52**	**2324**	**974**	**9226**		**318**	**1076**	**2328**	**978**	**578**	**9230**	
notes	🅁 🍸 ⊗					♥	⑦ C	Ⓑ		🅁 🍸 ⊗		🅁 🍸 ⊗			♥		🅁 🍸 ⊗					♥	
Milano Centrale d.	0910	...	...	...	...	...	...	...	...	1110	...	1120	...	...	...	...	1310	...	...	...	...	...	...
Como San Giovanni d.	0950	...	...	...	...	...	...	...	...	1150	...	◧	...	...	...	...	1350	...	...	...	...	...	...
Brig d.	|	...	1118	...	...	...	...	...	...	|	...	1318	...	...	...	...	|	1518	...	...	...	...	...
Interlaken Ost d.	|	...	|	...	1200	...	...	...	...	|	...	|	...	1400	...	...	|	|	...	1600	...	...	...
Interlaken West d.	|	...	|	...	1205	...	...	...	...	|	...	|	...	1405	...	...	|	|	...	1605	...	...	...
Spiez d.	|	...	1154	...	1222	...	...	...	...	|	...	1354	...	1422	...	...	|	1554	...	1622	...	...	...
Thun d.	|	...	1204	...	1233	...	...	...	...	|	...	1404	...	1433	...	...	|	1604	...	1633	...	...	...
Bern d.	|	...	1236	...	1304	...	...	...	...	|	...	1436	...	1504	...	...	|	1636	...	1704	...	...	...
Chiasso ▦ d.	1005	...	|	...	|	...	...	...	...	1205	...	|	...	|	...	...	1405	|	...	|	...	...	...
Lugano d.	1030	...	|	...	|	...	...	...	...	1230	...	|	...	|	...	...	1430	|	...	|	...	...	...
Bellinzona d.	1047	...	|	...	|	...	...	...	...	1247	...	|	...	|	...	...	1447	|	...	|	...	...	...
Arth Goldau a.	1142	...	|	...	|	...	...	...	...	1342	...	|	...	|	...	...	1542	|	...	|	...	...	...
Arth Goldau d.	1145	...	|	1203	|	...	...	...	...	1345	...	|	1403	|	...	...	1545	|	1603	|	...	...	...
Luzern d.	|	...	|	1254	|	...	...	...	...	|	...	|	1454	|	...	...	|	|	1654	|	...	...	...
Chur d.	|	1208	|	|	|	...	...	...	...	|	1408	|	|	|	...	...	|	|	|	|	1608	...	...
Landquart d.	|	1218	|	|	|	...	...	...	...	|	1418	|	|	|	...	...	|	|	|	|	1618	...	...
Zürich HB d.	1227	1322	|	|	|	1334**x**	...	...	...	1427	1522	|	|	|	1534**x**	...	1627	|	|	|	1722	1734**x**	...
Basel SBB a.	...	...	1332	1356	1401	1428**x**	...	...	...	...	...	1532	1556	1601	1628**x**	...	...	1732	1756	1801	...	1828**x**	...
Basel SBB d.	...	...	...	...	...	1434	...	...	...	...	...	...	...	...	1634	...	...	...	...	...	...	1834	...
Mulhouse a.	...	...	...	...	...	1453	...	...	...	...	...	...	...	...	1653	...	...	...	...	...	...	1854	...
Belfort TGV ⊡ a.	...	...	...	...	...	|	...	...	...	...	...	...	...	...	|	...	...	...	...	...	...	1919	...
Besançon TGV ⊖ a.	...	...	...	...	...	|	...	...	...	...	...	...	...	...	|	...	...	...	...	...	...	|	...
Dijon a.	...	...	...	...	...	1558	...	...	...	...	...	...	...	...	1758	...	...	...	...	...	...	|	...
Paris Gare de Lyon a.	...	...	...	...	...	1738	...	...	...	...	...	...	...	...	1939	...	...	...	...	...	...	2140	...
Paris Nord d.	...	...	...	...	...	...	2003	2103	...	...	...	...	...	...	...	...	...	...	...	...	...	...	...
London St Pancras a.	...	...	...	...	...	...	2130	2230	...	...	...	...	...	...	...	...	...	...	...	...	...	...	...

C – Also Aug. 29.

⊖ – Full name:-Besancon Franche-Comté TGV.

⊡ – Full name: Belfort Montbéliard TGV.

◧ – ▦ between Brig and Milano is Domodossola. Ticket point is **Iselle**.

☆ – Eurostar train. 🅁, ✕ in Business Premier and Standard Premier, 🍸 in Standard. Special fares payable. Minimum check-in time 30 minutes. Valid June 12 - Sept. 3. **Additional services are available, see Table 10, pages 47 – 48.**

♥ – *TGV Lyria* service. 🅁 🍸. Special fares payable, three classes of service: Business 1ère, Standard 1ère and Standard. At-seat meal service in Business 1ère. Valid June 12 - July 1.

⊗ – Compulsory reservation for international journeys. Supplement payable for international journeys and for internal journeys within Italy.

LONDON - PARIS - LAUSANNE - BRIG 42

train type	*TGV*	*IR*	*TGV*	*IR*		☆	*TGV*	*IR*	☆	*TGV*	*IR*	☆	*TGV*	*IR*	☆	*TGV*	*IR*			
train number	**9761**	**1715**	**9261**	**1817**		**9004**	**9269**	**1825**	**9014**	**9775**	**1731**	**9018**	**9777**	**1735**	**9024**	**9277**	**1837**			
notes	♥ ①–⑥		♥			①–⑤ B	♥			♥			♥			♥				
London St Pancras **10** d.	...	...	...	...	...	0701	...	...	0931	...	...	1022	...	...	1224	...	...	...	...	...
Paris Nord **10** a.	...	...	...	...	...	1027	...	...	1257	...	...	1357	...	...	1557	...	...	...	...	...
Paris Gare de Lyon d.	0618	...	0756	...	...	...	1156	...	...	1418	...	...	1618	...	...	1756	...	...	...	...
Dijon d.	|	...	0934	...	...	...	1334	...	...	|	...	...	|	...	...	1933	...	...	...	...
Frasne a.	◧	...	1042	...	...	...	1442	...	...	◧	...	...	◧	...	...	2042	...	...	...	...
Vallorbe ▦ a.	|	...	1057	...	...	...	1457	...	...	|	...	...	|	...	...	2057	...	...	...	...
Lausanne a.	1015	...	1137	...	...	...	1537	...	...	1815	...	...	2015	...	...	2137	...	...	...	...
Lausanne d.	...	1021	...	1150	...	...	...	1550	...	...	1821	...	...	2021	...	...	2150	...	...	...
Montreux a.	...	1043	...	1211	...	...	...	1611	...	...	1843	...	...	2043	...	...	2211	...	...	...
Aigle a.	...	1053	...	1222	...	...	...	1622	...	...	1853	...	...	2053	...	...	2222	...	...	...
Martigny a.	...	1111	...	1243	...	...	...	1643	...	...	1911	...	...	2111	...	...	2243	...	...	...
Sion a.	...	1125	...	1257	...	...	...	1657	...	...	1925	...	...	2125	...	...	2257	...	...	...
Sierre a.	...	1135	...	1308	...	...	...	1708	...	...	1935	...	...	2135	...	...	2308	...	...	...
Visp a.	...	1153	...	1323	...	...	...	1723	...	...	1953	...	...	2153	...	...	2326	...	...	...
Brig a.	...	1202	...	1332	...	...	...	1732	...	...	2002	...	...	2202	...	...	2332	...	...	...

train type	*IR*	*TGV*	☆		*IR*	*TGV*	☆	*EC*	*IR*	*TGV*	☆	*IR*	*TGV*	☆	☆		*IR*	*TGV*	*IR*	*TGV*
train number	**1806**	**9264**	**9031**		**1810**	**9768**	**9039**	**32**	**1816**	**9268**	**9055**	**1818**	**9774**	**9059**	**9063**		**1824**	**9270**	**1828**	**9784**
notes		♥				♥		🅁 🍸 ⊗		♥			♥	⑦ A	Ⓑ			♥		♥ ⑤⑦
Brig d.	0524	...	...	...	0726	...	...	1016	1026	...	...	1126	...	...	...	...	1426	...	1626	...
Visp d.	0532	...	...	...	0735	...	...	|	1035	...	...	1135	...	...	...	...	1435	...	1635	...
Sierre d.	0550	...	...	...	0750	...	...	|	1050	...	...	1150	...	...	...	...	1450	...	1650	...
Sion d.	0601	...	...	...	0801	...	...	1047	1101	...	...	1201	...	...	...	...	1501	...	1701	...
Martigny d.	0616	...	...	...	0816	...	...	|	1116	...	...	1216	...	...	...	...	1516	...	1716	...
Aigle d.	0638	...	...	...	0837	...	...	|	1137	...	...	1237	...	...	...	...	1537	...	1737	...
Montreux d.	0648	...	...	...	0848	...	...	1123	1148	...	...	1248	...	...	...	...	1548	...	1748	...
Lausanne a.	0710	...	...	...	0910	...	...	1142	1210	...	...	1310	...	...	...	...	1610	...	1810	...
Lausanne d.	...	0723	...	...	...	0945	...	...	...	1223	...	...	1345	...	...	...	...	1623	...	1945
Vallorbe ▦ d.	...	0800	...	...	...	|	...	...	...	1300	...	...	|	...	...	...	...	1700	...	|
Frasne a.	...	0813	...	...	...	◧	...	...	...	1313	...	...	◧	...	...	...	...	1713	...	◧
Dijon a.	...	0926	...	...	...	|	...	...	...	1424	...	...	|	...	...	...	...	1824	...	|
Paris Gare de Lyon a.	...	1104	...	...	...	1342	...	...	...	1604	...	...	1742	...	...	...	...	2004	...	2345
Paris Nord **10** d.	...	...	1303	...	...	...	1503	...	...	...	1903	...	...	2003	2103	...	...	...	...	...
London St Pancras **10** a.	...	...	1430	...	...	...	1637	...	...	...	2030	...	...	2130	2230	...	...	...	...	...

A – Also Aug. 29.

B – Not Aug. 29.

◧ – Via Genève.

◇ – Stopping train. 2nd class only.

♥ – *TGV Lyria* service. 🅁 🍸. Special fares payable, three classes of service: business 1ère, standard 1ère and standard. At-seat meal service in first class. Valid June 12 - July 1.

⊗ – Compulsory reservation for international journeys. Supplement payable for international journeys and for internal journeys within Italy.

☆ – Eurostar train. 🅁, ✕ in Business Premier and Standard Premier, 🍸 in Standard. Minimum check-in time 30 minutes. Special fares payable. Valid June 12 - Sept. 3. **Additional services are available, see Table 10, pages 47 – 48.**

44 PARIS - TORINO - MILANO - VENEZIA and ROMA

train type	TGV	FR	ITA	FR	ITA	FR	FR	FR	ITA	TGV	FR	FR	FR	ITA	TGV	ICN	FR
train number	9241	9543	8153	9281	8987	9735	9641	9547	9947	9251	9759	9567	9559	9963	9249	797	9287
train number					[R]												
notes	[R] ✕	[R]	[R]	[R]	⚡	[R]	[R]	[R]	[R]	[R] ✕	[R]	[R]	[R]	[R]	[R] ✕	[R]	[R]
notes	♣	⚡	⚡	A	①④⑤⑥⑦	⚡	⚡ ⑧	⚡	⚡	♣	⚡	⚡ ①–⑤	⚡ ⑥⑦	⚡	♣	H ⚡	A
Paris Gare de Lyon d.	0647	...	...	0726	...	...	...	...	...	1247	...	...	...	...	1443	...	1518
Lyon Part Dieu d.	|	...	...	0926	...	...	...	...	...	|	...	...	...	...	|	...	1722
Lyon St Exupéry TGV ✈ d.	|	...	...	|	...	...	...	...	...	|	...	...	...	...	1638	...	|
Chambéry d.	0944	...	...	1055	...	...	...	...	...	1544	...	...	...	...	1744	...	1844
Modane 🛃 d.	1055	...	...	1210	...	...	...	...	...	1655	...	...	...	...	1855	...	2010
Oulx ▲ a.	1123	...	...	|	...	...	...	...	...	1728	...	...	...	...	1923	...	|
Torino Porta Susa a.	1224	1310	1330	1320	...	...	1400	...	1440	1820	1850	1910	1910	1935	2018	2040	2120
Novara a.	|	|	|	|	...	...	|	...	|	|	|	|	|	|	|	2137	|
Milano Porta Garibaldi ✣ a.	1350	|	|	|	...	...	|	...	|	1955	|	|	|	|	2150	2213	|
Milano Centrale a.	...	1402	1430	1407	...	...	1450	...	1530	...	|	2002	2002	2030	...	|	2207
Milano Centrale d.	...	1410	1440	...	1435	1445	1500	1510	1540	...	|	2010	2010	2040	...	|	...
Verona Porta Nuova a.	...	|	|	...	1547	1558	|	|	|	...	2053	|	|	|	...	|	...
Venezia Mestre a.	...	|	|	...	1652	1700	|	|	|	...	2155	|	|	|	...	|	...
Venezia Santa Lucia a.	...	|	|	...	1703	1712	|	|	|	...	...	|	|	|	...	|	...
Reggio Emilia AV a.	...	1456	1528	...	...	...	|	1556	1628	...	...	2056	2056	2128	...	|	...
Bologna Centrale a.	...	1524	1554	...	...	...	1604	1624	1654	...	...	2124	2124	2154	...	|	...
Firenze SMN a.	...	1604	1635	...	...	...	|	1704	1735	...	...	2204	2204	2235	...	|	...
Roma Termini a.	...	1749	1819	...	...	...	1810	1849	1919	...	...	2349	0025	0019	...	0553t	...
Napoli Centrale a.	...	1913	1928f	...	...	...	...	2010	2043	...	...	...	...	...	...	0846	...
Salerno a.	...	2005	2011	...	...	...	...	2057	2132	...	...	...	...	...	...	0945	...

train type	FR	TGV	ICN	FR	ITA	TGV	ITA	FR	TGV	FA	FR	ITA	FR	FR	TGV
train number	9292	9240	798	9516	9916	9244	9920	9310	9252	9728	9415	9928	9296	9532	9248
train number															
notes	[R]	[R] ✕	[R]	[R]	[R]	[R] ✕	[R]	[R]	[R] ✕	[R]	[R]	[R]	[R]	[R]	[R] ✕
notes	A	♣	H ⚡	⚡	⚡	♣ ⑥⑦	⚡	⚡	♣ ①–⑤	⚡	⚡	⚡	A	⚡	♣
Salerno d.	...	...	2038	0550	0620	...	0720	...	...	...	0846	...	...	...	...
Napoli Centrale d.	...	...	2135	0640	0720	...	0820	0855	...	...	0940	...	...	1040	...
Roma Termini d.	...	...	2355t	0810	0840	...	0940	1025	...	...	1110	1140	...	1210	...
Firenze SMN d.	...	...	|	0955	1025	...	1125	1210	...	...	1255	1325	...	1355	...
Bologna Centrale d.	...	...	|	1036	1106	...	1206	1251	...	...	1336	1406	...	1436	...
Reggio Emilia AV d.	...	...	|	1100	1130	...	1230	1313	...	...	1400	1435	...	1500	...
Venezia Santa Lucia d.	...	...	|	|	|	...	|	|	...	1148	|	|	...	|	...
Venezia Mestre d.	...	...	|	|	|	...	|	|	...	1200	|	|	...	|	...
Verona Porta Nuova d.	...	...	|	|	|	...	|	|	...	1302	|	|	...	|	...
Milano Centrale a.	...	...	|	1150	1220	...	1320	1358	...	1415	1450	1520	...	1550	...
Milano Centrale d.	0553	...	|	1202	1230	...	1330	1410	...	...	1502	1530	1607	1602	...
Milano Porta Garibaldi d.	|	0600	0655a	|	|	1212	|	|	1412	...	|	|	|	|	1612
Novara d.	|	0631	0802a	|	|	|	|	|	|	...	|	|	|	|	|
Torino Porta Susa d.	0639	0739	0905	1249	1318	1338	1418	1459	1525	...	1549	1629	1659	1649	1743
Oulx ▲ d.	|	0836	...	...	...	1440	...	...	1627	...	...	...	1809	...	1848
Modane 🛃 a.	0750	0905	...	...	...	1505	...	...	1705	...	...	...	1843	...	1900
Chambéry a.	0913	1015	...	...	...	1615	...	...	1815	...	...	...	|	...	2015
Lyon St Exupéry TGV ✈ a.	|	|	...	...	...	|	...	...	|	...	...	...	|	...	|
Lyon Part Dieu a.	1028	|	...	...	...	|	...	...	|	...	...	...	2118	...	|
Paris Gare de Lyon a.	1231	1312	...	...	...	1912	...	...	2112	...	...	...	2317	...	2312

A – *Frecciarossa* ETR1000 high-speed service.

H – 🛏 1, 2 cl., ▬ 2 cl. (4 berth) Torino - Milano - Salerno and v.v.

a – Arrival time.

d – Departure time.

f – Napoli **Afragola**.

t – Roma **Tiburtina**.

y – Calls at Aix les Bains at 1303, Mâcon Loché TGV 1433.

⚡ – Supplement payable.

♣ – *TGV* France-Italy service. [R] ✕ Special fares payable.

▲ – Station for the resorts of Cesana, Claviere and Sestriere.

✣ – Change at Torino Porta Susa for stations beyond Milano.

83 PRAHA - BRATISLAVA - ZAGREB - RIJEKA / SPLIT

Temporarily relocated from page 80

	EN	RJ	RJ
	1153	1221	1221
	C	A	A
Praha hl. n. d.	...	1638	1638
Kolín d.	...	1722	1722
Brno hl. n. d.	...	1948	1948
Břeclav d.	...	2020	2020
Bratislava hl. st. d.	1551	2132	2132
Györ d.	|	|	|
Budapest Kelenföld d.	|	|	|
Wien Hbf d.	1801	|	|
Wien Meidling d.	1808	|	|
Wiener Neustadt Hbf d.	1850	|	|
Graz Hbf d.	2102	|	|
Spielfeld-Straß 🛃 d.	2148	|	|
Maribor d.	2205	|	|
Dobova 🛃 d.	0023	|	|
Zagreb a.	0048	0517	0517
Ogulin a.	0248	0751	0751
Rijeka a.	|	1013	|
Gračac a.	|	...	1030
Knin a.	0709	...	|
Perković a.	0818	...	|
Split a.	0950	...	1344

	RJ	RJ	EN
	1046	1046	1152
	B	B	D
Split d.	1551	...	1728
Perković d.	|	...	1844
Knin d.	|	...	1949
Gračac d.	1900	...	|
Rijeka d.	|	1955	|
Ogulin d.	2222	2222	2340
Zagreb d.	0113	0113	0200
Dobova 🛃 a.	|	|	0225
Maribor a.	|	|	0436
Spielfeld-Straß 🛃 a.	|	|	0502
Graz Hbf a.	|	|	0553
Wiener Neustadt Hbf a.	|	|	0808
Wien Meidling a.	|	|	0851
Wien Hbf a.	|	|	0858
Budapest Kelenföld a.	|	|	|
Györ a.	|	|	|
Bratislava hl. st. a.	0828	0828	1049
Břeclav a.	0936	0936	...
Brno hl. n. a.	1007	1007	...
Kolín a.	1230	1230	...
Praha hl. n. a.	1314	1314	...

A – ①③⑥ May 28 - Sept. 26 (daily July 1 - Aug. 31): ▬ 2 cl. (4 berth), [2] Praha - Rijeka / Split.

B – ②④⑦ May 29 - Sept. 27 (daily July 2 - Sept. 1): ▬ 2 cl. (4 berth), [2] Rijeka / Split - Praha.

C – ②⑤ June 3 - Sept. 23: 🛏 1, 2 cl., [2] Bratislava - Split.

D – ③⑥ June 4 - Sept. 24: 🛏 1, 2 cl., [2] Split - Bratislava.

LONDON - PARIS / MADRID - LISBOA and PORTO 45

train type / number		☆	TGV	Hotel	Hotel	IR
train number		9008	8541	313	332	823
notes		①–⑥	🅡 ⁄	🅡 🍷	🅡 🍷	🅡 🍷
				A	L	
London St Pancras 10	d.	0755	...	...	...	...
Paris Nord 10	a.	1117	...	...	...	...
Paris Montparnasse	d.	...	1252	...	...	...
Bordeaux St Jean	d.	...	1502	...	...	...
Biarritz	d.	...	1703	...	...	...
Hendaye	a.	...	1733	1835	...	...
Irún 🏛	a.	...	...	1845	...	...
San Sebastián / Donostia	a.	...	...	1908	...	...
Vitoria / Gasteiz	a.	...	...	2045	...	...
Miranda de Ebro	a.	...	...	2107	...	...
Burgos Rosa Manzano	a.	...	...	2158	...	...
Valladolid Campo Grande	a.	...	...	2308	...	...
Madrid Chamartín	d.	...	...	|	2143	...
Ávila	d.	...	...	|	2311	...
Medina del Campo	a.	...	...	2351	2355	...
Salamanca	a.	...	...	0057	0057	...
Ciudad Rodrigo	a.	...	...	0206	0206	...
Fuentes d'Oñoro 🏛 ES	d.	...	...	0230	0230	...
Vilar Formoso 🏛 PT	d.	...	...	0150	0150	...
Guarda	a.	...	...	0221	0221	...
Mangualde	a.	...	...	0323	0323	...
Coimbra-B	a.	...	...	0445	0445	0510
Pombal	a.	...	...	0521	0521	|
Entroncamento	a.	...	...	0605	0605	|
Lisboa Oriente	a.	...	...	0720	0720	|
Lisboa Santa Apolónia	a.	...	...	0730	0730	|
Aveiro	a.	...	...	...	...	0553
Porto Campanhã	a.	...	...	...	...	0646

train type / number		IR	Hotel	Hotel	TGV	☆
train number		822	335	310	8540	9059
notes		🅡 🍷	🅡 🍷	🅡 🍷	🅡 ⁄	
			L	A		M
Porto Campanhã	d.	2150	...	...	...	...
Aveiro	d.	2242	...	...	...	...
Lisboa Santa Apolónia	d.	|	2125	2125	...	...
Lisboa Oriente	d.	|	2134	2134	...	...
Entroncamento	d.	|	2229	2229	...	...
Pombal	d.	|	2306	2306	...	...
Coimbra-B	d.	2326	2333	2333	...	...
Mangualde	d.	...	0043	0043	...	...
Guarda	d.	...	0141	0141	...	...
Vilar Formoso 🏛 PT	d.	...	0235	0235	...	...
Fuentes d'Oñoro 🏛 ES	d.	...	0340	0340	...	...
Ciudad Rodrigo	d.	...	0359	0359	...	...
Salamanca	d.	...	0456	0456	...	...
Medina del Campo	d.	...	0618	0600	...	...
Ávila	a.	...	0705	|	...	...
Madrid Chamartín	a.	...	0840	|	...	...
Valladolid Campo Grande	d.	...	...	0635	...	...
Burgos Rosa Manzano	d.	...	...	0748	...	...
Miranda de Ebro	d.	...	...	0848	...	...
Vitoria / Gasteiz	d.	...	...	0912	...	...
San Sebastián / Donostia	d.	...	...	1055	...	...
Irún	a.	...	...	1123	...	...
Hendaye 🏛	a.	...	...	1133	1329	...
Biarritz	a.	...	...	...	1353	...
Bordeaux St Jean	a.	...	...	...	1558	...
Paris Montparnasse	a.	...	...	...	1808	...
Paris Nord 10	d.	...	...	...	...	2003
London St Pancras 10	a.	...	...	...	...	2139

MADRID - LISBOA 46

For train services see Table 45		🚌 E	🚌 C ⑤⑦	🚌 E
Madrid Estación Sur ✥	d.	0930	1430	2230
Cáceres	d.	|	1845	0200
Badajoz ⊠ 🏛 ES	d.	1445	2000	0400
Elvas 🏛 PT	d.	|	|	|
Lisboa Oriente	a.	1630	2200	0545

For train services see Table 45		🚌 E	🚌 C ⑤⑦	🚌 E
Lisboa Oriente	d.	1000	1245	2145
Elvas 🏛 PT	d.	|	|	|
Badajoz ⊠ 🏛 ES	d.	1345	1700	0125
Cáceres	a.	|	1830	|
Madrid Estación Sur ✥	a.	1910	2220	0640

bookers
BOOK
European Rail Holidays
up to 2 years in advance
CALL 020 3697 6878 TODAY

NOTES FOR TABLES 45 AND 46

A – SUREX / SUD EXPRESSO *Trenhotel* – 🛏 *Gran Clase / Gran Classe* (1, 2 berths), 🛏 *Preferente* (1, 2 berths), 🛏 *Turista* (4 berths), ▭ 🍷 Hendaye (**312**) - Vilar Formoso (**313**) - Lisboa and Lisboa (**310**) - Vilar Formoso (**311**) - Hendaye.
C – 🚌 operated by Avanza, rail tickets not valid; www.avanzabus.com
E – 🚌 operated by Alsa, rail tickets not valid; www.alsa.es
L – LUSITANIA *Hotel Train* – 🛏 *Gran Clase / Gran Classe* (1, 2 berths), 🛏 *Preferente* (1, 2 berths), 🛏 *Turista* (4 berths), ▭ 🍷 🅡 Madrid (**332/3**) - Medina del Campo (**312**) - Lisboa and Lisboa (**310**) - Medina del Campo (**330/5**) - Madrid. Special fares apply.
M – ①②③④⑥.

ES – Spain (Central European Time).
PT – Portugal (West European Time).

⁄ – Supplement payable.
✥ – Madrid south bus station close to Méndez Álvaro metro (see Madrid city plan on page 32).
⊠ – Badajoz railway station is 1 km north of Badajoz city centre and Badajoz bus station is 2.5 km south of Badajoz city centre.
☆ – Eurostar train. 🅡, ✕ in Business Premier and Standard Premier, 🍷 in Standard. Special fares payable. Minimum check-in time 30 minutes. Additional Eurostar services are available, see Table **10**.

☛ **Shaded services are suspended until further notice.**

PARIS - HENDAYE / IRÚN - MADRID 47

train type / number		TGV	MD	RE	Alvia
train number		8531	18014	18318	4166
notes		🅡 ⁄ ①–⑥	2	2	
Paris Montparnasse	d.	0752	...	...	...
Paris Austerlitz	d.	|	...	...	...
Les Aubrais-Orléans	d.	|	...	...	...
Bordeaux St Jean	d.	1002	...	...	...
Biarritz	d.	1159	...	...	...
Hendaye	a.	1228	...	...	...
Irún 🏛	a.	...	1258	...	1535
San Sebastián / Donostia	a.	...	1323	...	1631
Vitoria / Gasteiz	a.	...	1555	...	1807
Miranda de Ebro	a.	...	1616	...	1829
Burgos Rosa Manzano	a.	...	1715	...	1931
Valladolid Campo Grande	a.	...	1844	1856	2048
Medina del Campo	a.	...	1915	1933	|
Salamanca	a.	...	|	2027	|
Ávila	a.	...	2001	...	|
Madrid Chamartín	d.	...	2142p	...	2206

train type / number		RE	Alvia	TGV	TGV
train number		18302	4087	8544	8550
notes		2		🅡 ⁄ ⑧	🅡 ⁄
Madrid Chamartín	d.	...	0810	...	...
Ávila	d.	...	|	...	...
Salamanca	d.	0712	|	...	...
Medina del Campo	d.	0800	|	...	...
Valladolid Campo Grande	d.	0828	0928	...	...
Burgos Rosa Manzano	d.	...	1038	...	...
Miranda de Ebro	d.	...	1138	...	...
Vitoria / Gasteiz	d.	...	1201	...	...
San Sebastián / Donostia	d.	...	1351	...	...
Irún	a.	...	1418	...	...
Hendaye 🏛	a.	...	...	1528	1828
Biarritz	a.	...	...	1552	1852
Bordeaux St Jean	a.	...	...	1758	2058
Les Aubrais-Orléans	a.	...	...	|	|
Paris Austerlitz	a.	...	...	|	|
Paris Montparnasse	a.	...	...	2008	2308

p – Madrid **Principe Pio**. ⁄ – Supplement payable. *Alvia* – 🅡 🍷⁄.

FRANKFURT - STRASBOURG - LYON - MARSEILLE 48

train type		ICE	ICE	TGV	TGV	ICE	TGV	TGV
train number		511	9568	9877	9826	107	9580 9581	9836
notes			🅡★ ⑧	🅡	🅡		🅡★	🅡
Köln Hbf	d.	0548	...	...	...	1254	...	...
Frankfurt (Main) Hbf	d.	|	0656	...	...	|	1356	...
Mannheim	d.	0723	0738	...	...	1423	1439	...
Karlsruhe	d.	...	0806	...	...	...	1512	...
Baden-Baden	d.	...	|	...	...	...	1535	...
Strasbourg	a.	...	0847	...	...	...	1601	...
Strasbourg	d.	...	...	0905	...	...	1614	...
Mulhouse	a.	...	...	0950	...	...	1705	...
Belfort Montbéliard TGV	a.	...	...	1021	...	...	1731	...
Besançon TGV ⊖	a.	...	...	1044	...	...	1755	...
Chalon sur Saône	a.	...	...	|	...	...	1853	...
Lyon Part Dieu	a.	...	...	1304	1410	...	1956	2010
Avignon TGV	a.	...	...	1419	|	...	2111	|
Aix en Provence TGV	a.	...	...	1442	|	...	2133	|
Marseille St Charles	a.	...	...	1457	|	...	2149	|
Nîmes	a.	...	...	...	1523p	...	...	2135
Montpellier	a.	...	...	...	1547q	...	...	2204

train type		TGV	TGV	ICE	TGV	TGV	ICE	ICE
train number		9898	9583 9582	106	5062	5516	9563	514
notes		🅡	🅡★		🅡	🅡		
Montpellier	d.	0630	...	...	0910q	...	...	...
Nîmes	d.	0700	...	...	0932p	...	...	...
Marseille St Charles	d.	|	0810	...	|	0946	...	...
Aix en Provence TGV	d.	|	0826	...	|	1004	...	...
Avignon TGV	d.	|	0848	...	|	1027	...	...
Lyon Part Dieu	d.	0824	1004	...	1050	1134	...	...
Chalon sur Saône	d.	...	1106	...	...	1244	...	...
Besançon TGV ⊖	d.	...	1203	...	...	1413	...	...
Belfort Montbéliard TGV	d.	...	1227	...	...	1436	...	...
Mulhouse	d.	...	1255	...	...	1501	...	...
Strasbourg	a.	...	1343	...	...	1554	...	...
Strasbourg	d.	...	1355	...	...	...	1713	...
Baden-Baden	a.	...	1422	...	...	...	|	...
Karlsruhe	a.	...	1446	...	...	...	1752	...
Mannheim	a.	...	1518	1536	...	...	1819	1835
Frankfurt (Main) Hbf	a.	...	1559	|	...	...	1859	|
Köln Hbf	a.	...	...	1704	...	...	...	2005

p – Nîmes **Pont-du-Gard**. q – Montpellier **Sud de France**. ★ – *Alleo* TGV service. A DB / SNCF joint enterprise. ⊖ – Full name: Besançon Franche-Comté TGV.

50 OSLO, STOCKHOLM and KØBENHAVN - HAMBURG and BERLIN

train type/train number	IC	ICE		IC	ICE		IC	ICE				Sn		IC	ICE	Sn	Sn		IC	ICE			
train number	1191	509		393	1601		1193	603	1/3		1039	519		395	1605	521	523		1197	1607			
notes	🅁	Ⓑ		🅁			🅁		🅁			①–⑤		🅁		①–⑥	Ⓑ		🅁				
notes	P			Q			P		A			S											
Oslo Sentral d.	...	...	...	...	...	...	...	...	...	...	...	...	...	...	...	...	...	...	...	...	...	...	...
Stockholm Central d.	...	...	...	...	...	...	...	...	2309	...	...	0519	...	...	...	0617	0720	...	...	...	...	...	...
Göteborg d.	...	...	...	...	...	...	...	...	|	...	0640	|	...	...	...	|	|	...	...	...	...	...	...
Malmö C ⊡ d.	...	...	0613	...	...	0813	...	...	0602f	0633	0953	0948	1013	...	...	1050	1150	1213	...	...	...	...	...
København H. ⊡ d.	0517	...	0649	0717	...	0849	0917	...	...	0709	1029	...	1049	1117	...	1124	1224	1249	1317	...	...	...	...
Odense d.	0640	...	...	0840	...	...	1040	...	...	...	...	...	...	1240	...	...	...	...	1440	...	...	...	...
Kolding d.	0718	...	...	0918	...	...	1118	...	...	...	...	...	...	1318	...	...	...	...	1518	...	...	...	...
Padborg 🏛 d.	0802	...	...	1002	...	...	1202	...	...	...	...	...	...	1402	...	...	...	...	1602	...	...	...	...
Hamburg Hbf a.	1005	1034	...	1204	1234	...	1407	1435	...	...	...	...	...	1602	1634	...	...	...	1802	1835	...	...	...
Berlin Hbf a.	...	1220	...	...	1420	...	...	1622	...	...	...	...	...	...	1820	...	...	...	...	2020	...	...	...

train type/train number	Sn	103		Sn		IC	ICE	ICE	Sn		IC	ICE	107	111			EN	119			IC	EN	
train number	525	391	1063	527		397	609	905	529		1199	907	393	395	477	1105	301/3	397	1111		399	497	
notes		①–⑤		10527		🅁	Ⓑ				🅁	⑤⑦	⑥	Ⓑ			309				🅁		
notes						Q					P						D				R	G	
Oslo Sentral d.	...	0601	...	...	...	...	...	...	...	...	...	...	0801	1001	...	...	...	1401	...	...	...	...	...
Stockholm Central d.	0821	|	...	0922	...	...	...	...	1022	...	...	...	|	|	...	...	1615	|	...	...	...	1734	...
Göteborg d.	|	0945	1040	|	...	...	...	...	|	...	...	...	1145	1345	1424	1740	|	1740	1840	...	...	|	...
København H. ⊡ d.	|	...	|	|	...	...	...	...	|	...	...	...	...	...	|	|	|	...	|	...	...	|	...
Malmö C ⊡ d.	1250	...	1353	1357	1413	...	...	...	1450	1613	...	...	...	...	1700	2053	2210z	...	2153	2233	...	2333	...
København H. ⊡ d.	1325	...	1429	...	1449	1526	...	...	1524	1649	1717	...	...	...	...	2129	2306h	...	2229	2309	2354	0004k	...
Odense d.	...	...	...	...	...	1640	...	...	...	...	1840	...	...	...	...	...	|	...	...	...	0137	0202	...
Kolding d.	...	...	...	...	...	1718	...	...	...	...	1918	...	...	...	...	...	|	...	...	...	|	|	...
Padborg 🏛 d.	...	...	...	...	...	1802	...	...	...	...	2002	...	...	...	...	...	|	...	...	...	0328	|	...
Hamburg Hbf a.	...	...	...	...	...	2002	2034	2151	...	...	2158	2251	...	...	...	...	0531	...	...	...	0615j	0635j	...
Berlin Hbf a.	...	...	...	...	...	...	2223	2354	...	...	...	0054	...	...	...	...	0858	...	...	...	...	...	...

train type	IC		Sn		ICE	IC		Sn			ICE	IC		Sn									
train number	1198		538		808	396		542	1062		806	1196		546									
notes	🅁				①–⑥	🅁						🅁											
notes	P					Q						P											
Berlin Hbf d.	...	...	...	...	0638	...	...	...	...	...	0838	...	...	...	...	...	...	...	...	...	...	...	...
Hamburg Hbf d.	0652j	...	...	...	0825	0856	...	...	...	...	1021	1053	...	...	...	...	...	...	...	...	...	...	...
Padborg 🏛 a.	0859	...	...	...	...	1053	...	...	...	...	...	1253	...	...	...	...	...	...	...	...	...	...	...
Kolding a.	0940	...	...	...	...	1140	...	...	...	...	...	1340	...	...	...	...	...	...	...	...	...	...	...
Odense a.	1019	...	...	...	...	1219	...	...	...	...	...	1419	...	...	...	...	...	...	...	...	...	...	...
København H. ⊡ d.	1136	1147	1219	...	...	1336	1347	1419	1427	...	...	1536	1547	1619	...	...	...	...	...	...	...	...	...
Malmö C ⊡ d.	...	1226	1304	...	...	...	1426	1504	1508	...	...	...	1626	1704	...	...	...	...	...	...	...	...	...
København H. ⊡ d.	...	...	|	...	...	...	...	|	|	...	...	...	...	|	...	...	...	...	...	...	...	...	...
Göteborg a.	...	...	|	...	...	...	...	|	1820	...	...	...	...	|	...	...	...	...	...	...	...	...	...
Stockholm Central a.	...	...	1737	...	...	...	...	1937	...	...	...	...	...	2138	...	...	...	...	...	...	...	...	...
Oslo Sentral a.	...	...	...	...	...	...	...	...	...	...	...	...	...	...	...	...	...	...	...	...	...	...	...

train type/train number	ICE	IC		Sn			ICE	IC		ICE	IC		ICE	IC		EN	ICE	IC		EN		396	
train number	804	394		542	1086	2	802	1192		800	392		708	1190		496	502	390/8		300/2	1020	126	
notes		🅁		Ⓑ		🅁		🅁			🅁			🅁				🅁		334			
notes						F		P			Q			P		G		R		C			
Berlin Hbf d.	1038	...	...	...	...	...	1238	...	...	1438	...	...	1638	...	...	...	2138	...	...	2058	...	...	...
Hamburg Hbf d.	1221	1253	...	...	...	...	1421	1453	...	1621	1654	...	1822	1853	...	2155j	2333	2356	...	2359	...	...	...
Padborg 🏛 a.	...	1453	...	...	...	...	...	1653	...	...	1853	...	...	2053	...	|	...	0302	...	|	...	...	...
Kolding a.	...	1540	...	...	...	...	...	1740	...	...	1940	...	...	2140	...	|	...	|	...	|	...	...	...
Odense a.	...	1619	...	...	...	...	...	1819	...	...	2019	...	...	2219	...	0154	...	0516	...	|	...	...	...
København H. ⊡ d.	...	1736	1747	1819	1827	...	...	1936	1947	...	2136	2147	...	2333	2347	0347k	...	0655	0707	0620h	...	...	...
Malmö C ⊡ d.	...	...	1826	1904	1908	2232	...	...	2026	...	...	2226	...	...	0026	0424	...	...	0746	0919x	0808	...	...
Göteborg a.	...	...	...	|	2220	|	...	...	...	...	...	...	...	...	...	|	...	...	...	|	1120	...	...
Stockholm Central a.	...	...	...	2341	...	0555	...	...	...	...	...	...	...	...	...	0955	...	...	...	1415	...	1415	...
Oslo Sentral a.	...	...	...	...	...	...	...	...	...	...	...	...	...	...	...	...	...	...	...	...	...	1751	...

A – Daily June 14 - Aug. 5. Ⓑ Aug. 7 - Dec. 9: 🛏 1, 2 cl., ▬ 2 cl., (2) 🍷 🅁 Stockholm - Malmö.

C – Daily until Sept. 24. From Sept. 25 to be advised. BERLIN NIGHT EXPRESS – 🅁 Special fares apply. ▬ 2 cl., 🍷 (Dresden depart 1744 Sept. 5, 9, 12, 16 -) Berlin - Hamburg - Høje Taastrup - Malmö - Stockholm. ✕ Malmö - Stockholm.

D – Daily until Sept. 23. From Sept. 24 to be advised. BERLIN NIGHT EXPRESS – 🅁 Special fares apply. ▬ 2 cl., 🍷 Stockholm - Malmö - Høje Taastrup - Hamburg - Berlin (- Dresden arrive 1231 Sept. 5, 9, 12, 16). ✕ Stockholm - Malmö.

F – Ⓑ: 🛏 1, 2 cl., ▬ 2 cl., (2) 🍷 🅁 Malmö - Stockholm.

G – From Sept 1: 🛏 1, 2 cl., ▬ 2 cl., (2) 🍷 🅁 Stockholm - Hamburg and v.v.

H – HUNGARIA – (12) ✕ Hamburg - Berlin - Praha.

P – June 18 - Aug. 21.

Q – Not June 18 - Aug. 21.

R – June 17 - Sept. 11.

S – Not July 2 - Aug. 14.

f – On certain dates arrive 0538. Connection to København depart Malmö C 0613, arrive København 0649.

h – Høje Taastrup (20km from København).

j – Hamburg **Altona**.

k – København Lufthavn ✈.

x – Arrive 0725.

z – Arrive 2115.

Sn – *Snabbtåg* high speed train. 🅁 ✕.

⊡ – Additional services Malmö - København and v.v. are available, see Table **703**.

51 BERLIN - GDYNIA

train type	EC/IC	
train number	59	
notes	75000	
notes	🅁	
	G	
Berlin Hbf d.	1237	...
Berlin Ost d.	1252	...
Frankfurt (Oder) 🏛 d.	1345	...
Rzepin a.	1404	...
Poznań Gł. a.	1531	...
Gniezno a.	1604	...
Inowrocław a.	1633	...
Bydgoszcz Gł. a.	1700	...
Tczew a.	1807	...
Gdańsk Gł. a.	1827	...
Sopot a.	1845	...
Gdynia Gł. a.	1853	...

train type	IC/EC	
train number	58	
notes	57000	
	🅁	
	G	
Gdynia Gł. d.	0858	...
Sopot d.	0907	...
Gdańsk Gł. d.	0923	...
Tczew d.	0940	...
Bydgoszcz Gł. d.	1051	...
Inowrocław d.	1118	...
Gniezno d.	1151	...
Poznań Gł. d.	1225	...
Rzepin d.	1352	...
Frankfurt (Oder) 🏛 a.	1412	...
Berlin Ost a.	1506	...
Berlin Hbf a.	1516	...

G – BERLIN GDANSK EXPRESS/GEDANIA (12) ✕ 🅁 Berlin - Poznań - Gdynia and v.v.

52 PRAHA - LINZ - ZÜRICH

Engineering work between Praha and Linz is affecting services until August 22.

train type	EC	EC	EC	EC337
train number	331	333	335	50466
notes				B
Praha Holešovice d.	...	0950f	1350	1750
Praha hl. n. d.	0604	1004	1404	1804
Tábor d.	0719	1119	1519	1919
Veselí nad Lužnicí d.	|	|	|	|
České Budějovice d.	0806	1206	1606	2006
Summerau 🏛 d.	0908	1308	1708	2108
Linz Hbf a.	1006	1406	1807	2206
				|
	RJX	RJX	RJX	|
	162	166	760	|
	✕	✕	✕	|
Linz Hbf d.	1046	1446	1846	0100
Salzburg a.	1152	1552	1952	0210
Innsbruck Hbf a.	1344	1744	2144	0423
Zürich HB a.	1720	2120	...	0820

train type	RJX	EC	RJX	RJX	RJX	50467
train number	765	163	563	165	869	EC330
notes	✕	🍷	✕	🍷	✕	A
Zürich HB d.	...	0840	...	1040	...	2140
Innsbruck Hbf d.	0817	1211	1217	1411	1514	0128
Salzburg d.	1008	...	1408	...	1708	0345
Linz Hbf a.	1114	...	1514	...	1814	0452
						|
						|
	EC		EC		EC	|
	332		334		336	|
Linz Hbf d.	1154	...	1554	...	1854	0652
Summerau 🏛 a.	1250	...	1652	...	1952	0752
České Budějovice a.	1352	...	1752	...	2052	0852
Veselí nad Lužnicí a.	|	...	|	...	2123	|
Tábor a.	1438	...	1838	...	2146	0938
Praha hl. n. a.	1557	...	1957	...	2303	1057
Praha Holešovice a.	1611	...	...	...	...	1111

A – From Aug. 23: 🛏 1, 2 cl. Zürich (*EN* **50467**) - Linz (**330**) - Praha. (12) Linz - Praha. 🍷 České Budějovice - Praha.

B – From Aug. 22: 🛏 1, 2 cl. Praha (**337**) - Linz (*EN* **50466**) - Zürich. (12) Praha - Linz. 🍷 Praha - České Budějovice.

f – ⚒.

RJX – ÖBB *Railjet* service. (1) (premium class), (1) (first class), (2) (economy class), ✕.

HAMBURG / DÜSSELDORF / BRUSSELS - NÜRNBERG - INNSBRUCK / WIEN 53

	NJ 491	NJ 40491	NJ 425	NJ 40421	NJ 421	
			①③⑤			
	C	D	G	A	B	
Hamburg Altona d.	2011	2011	...	...	...	...
Hamburg Hbf d.	2029	2029	...	...	...	...
Hannover Hbf d.	2157	2157	...	...	...	...
Göttingen d.	2259	2259	...	...	...	...
Amsterdam Centraal d.	|	|	...	1930	1930	...
Utrecht Centraal d.	|	|	...	2003	2003	...
Arnhem d.	|	|	...	2037	2037	...
Duisburg Hbf d.	|	|	...	|	|	...
Düsseldorf Hbf d.	|	|	...	2143	2143	...
Brussels Midi/Zuid d.	|	|	1932	|	|	...
Liège Guillemins d.	|	|	2033	|	|	...
Aachen ⊞ d.	|	|	2139	|	|	...
Köln Hbf d.	|	|	|	2216	2216	...
Bonn Hbf d.	|	|	2311	2311	2311	...
Koblenz Hbf d.	|	|	2346	2346	2346	...
Mainz Hbf d.	|	|	0056	0056	0056	...
Frankfurt Flughafen ✈ d.	|	|	0120	0120	0120	...
Frankfurt (Main) Süd d.	|	|	0131	0131	0131	...
Würzburg Hbf d.	0135	0135	0242	0242	0242	...
Nürnberg Hbf a.	0253	0253	0336	0336	0336	...
Nürnberg Hbf d.	0408	0435	0408	0408	0435	...
Regensburg Hbf a.	0505	|	0505	0505	|	...
Augsburg Hbf a.	|	0623	|	|	0623	...
München Hbf a.	|	0711	|	|	0711	...
Kufstein ⊞ a.	|	0826	|	|	0826	...
Wörgl Hbf a.	|	0837	|	|	0837	...
Jenbach a.	|	0853	|	|	0853	...
Innsbruck Hbf a.	|	0914	|	|	0914	...
Passau ⊞ a.	0613	...	0613	0613	...	...
Wels Hbf a.	0714	...	0714	0714	...	...
Linz Hbf a.	0746	...	0746	0746	...	...
St Pölten Hbf a.	0842	...	0842	0842	...	...
Wien Meidling a.	0911	...	0911	0911	...	...
Wien Hbf a.	0919	...	0919	0919	...	...

	NJ 40490	NJ 490	NJ 50490	NJ 420	NJ 40420	
			②④⑦			
	Q	C	K	P	D	
Wien Hbf d.	2013	2013	2013	...	...	...
Wien Meidling d.	2021	2021	2021	...	...	...
St Pölten Hbf d.	2047	2047	2047	...	...	...
Linz Hbf d.	2136	2136	2136	...	...	...
Wels Hbf d.	2150	2150	2150	...	...	...
Passau ⊞ d.	2253	2253	2253	...	...	...
Innsbruck Hbf d.	|	|	|	2044	2044	...
Jenbach d.	|	|	|	2106	2106	...
Wörgl Hbf d.	|	|	|	2123	2123	...
Kufstein ⊞ d.	|	|	|	2135	2135	...
München Hbf d.	|	|	|	2250	2250	...
Augsburg Hbf d.	|	|	|	2323	2323	...
Regensburg Hbf d.	2356	2356	2356	|	|	...
Nürnberg Hbf a.	0056	0056	0056	0052	0052	...
Nürnberg Hbf d.	0141	0151	0141	0141	0151	...
Würzburg Hbf a.	|	0247	|	|	0247	...
Frankfurt (Main) Süd a.	0345	|	0345	0345	|	...
Frankfurt Flughafen ✈ a.	0356	|	0356	0356	|	...
Mainz Hbf a.	0416	|	0416	0416	|	...
Koblenz Hbf a.	0511	|	0511	0511	|	...
Bonn Hbf a.	0558	|	0558	0558	|	...
Köln Hbf a.	0651	|	|	0651	|	...
Aachen ⊞ a.	|	|	0722	|	|	...
Liège Guillemins a.	|	|	0848	|	|	...
Brussels Midi/Zuid a.	|	|	0952	|	|	...
Düsseldorf Hbf a.	0723	|	...	0723	|	...
Duisburg Hbf a.	0740	|	...	0740	|	...
Arnhem a.	0851	|	...	0851	|	...
Utrecht Centraal a.	0929	|	...	0929	|	...
Amsterdam Centraal a.	0959	|	...	0959	|	...
Göttingen a.	...	0551	...	...	0551	...
Hannover Hbf a.	...	0649	...	...	0649	...
Hamburg Hbf a.	...	0847	...	...	0847	...
Hamburg Altona a.	...	0904	...	...	0904	...

NOTES FOR TABLES 53 AND 54

- A – *ÖBB nightjet* 🛏 1, 2 cl., ▬ 2 cl. (4, 6 berth), (2) Amsterdam - Wien. ♣.
- B – *ÖBB nightjet* 🛏 1, 2 cl., ▬ 2 cl. (4, 6 berth), (2) Amsterdam - Innsbruck. ♣.
- C – *ÖBB nightjet* 🛏 1, 2 cl., ▬ 2 cl. (4, 6 berth), (2) Hamburg - Wien and v.v. ♣.
- D – *ÖBB nightjet* 🛏 1, 2 cl., ▬ 2 cl. (4, 6 berth), (2) Hamburg - Innsbruck and v.v. ♣.
- G – ①③⑤: *ÖBB nightjet* 🛏 1, 2 cl., ▬ 2 cl. (4, 6 berth), (2) Brussels - Wien. ♣.
- K – ②④⑦: *ÖBB nightjet* 🛏 1, 2 cl., ▬ 2 cl. (4, 6 berth), (2) Wien - Brussels. ♣.
- P – *ÖBB nightjet* 🛏 1, 2 cl., ▬ 2 cl. (4, 6 berth), (2) Innsbruck - Amsterdam. ♣.
- Q – *ÖBB nightjet* 🛏 1, 2 cl., ▬ 2 cl. (4, 6 berth), (2) Wien - Amsterdam. ♣.
- R – *ÖBB nightjet* 🛏 1, 2 cl., ▬ 2 cl. (4, 6 berth), (2) Hamburg -Zürich and v.v. ♣.
- S – *ÖBB nightjet* 🛏 1, 2 cl., ▬ 2 cl. (4, 6 berth), (2) Berlin - Zürich and v.v. ♣.

♣ – Special fares apply.

HAMBURG - BERLIN - BASEL - ZÜRICH 54

	NJ 401	NJ 471	
	R	S	
Hamburg Altona d.	2035	...	...
Hamburg Hbf d.	2050	...	...
Berlin Hbf d.	|	2054	...
Berlin Südkreuz d.	|	2103	...
Brandenburg d.	|	2159	...
Magdeburg Hbf d.	|	2241	...
Braunschweig d.	|	2328	...
Hannover Hbf d.	2319	|	...
Fulda d.	0245	0245	...
Frankfurt (Main) Hbf a.	0346	0346	...
Mannheim Hbf a.	0440	0440	...
Karlsruhe Hbf a.	0508	0508	...
Baden-Baden a.	0527	0527	...
Offenburg a.	0546	0546	...
Freiburg (Brsg) Hbf a.	0618	0618	...
Basel Bad Bf ⊞ a.	0658	0658	...
Basel SBB a.	0720	0720	...
Zürich HB a.	0905	0905	...

	NJ 470	NJ 40470	
	S	R	
Zürich HB d.	1959	1959	...
Basel SBB d.	2113	2113	...
Basel Bad Bf ⊞ d.	2122	2122	...
Freiburg (Brsg) Hbf d.	2158	2158	...
Offenburg d.	2231	2231	...
Baden-Baden d.	|	|	...
Karlsruhe Hbf d.	2306	2306	...
Mannheim Hbf d.	2342	2342	...
Frankfurt (Main) Hbf d.	0052	0052	...
Fulda a.	0147	0147	...
Hannover Hbf a.	|	0601	...
Braunschweig a.	0457	|	...
Magdeburg Hbf a.	0555	|	...
Brandenburg a.	0640	|	...
Berlin Südkreuz a.	0718	|	...
Berlin Hbf a.	0738	|	...
Hamburg Hbf a.	...	0754	...
Hamburg Altona a.	...	0810	...

FRANKFURT - LEIPZIG - DRESDEN - PRAHA 55

train type			*EC*			*EC*	*ICE*		*EC*	*ICE*		*EC*	*ICE*		*EC*	*ICE*		*EC*			
train number			**171**			**173**	**1555**		**379**	**1557**		**175**	**1559**		**177**	**1651**		**179**			
notes			X D			X H	X		X A	X		X D	X		X H	X		X H			
Frankfurt (Main) Hbf d.	...	...	...	...	...	...	0716	...	...	0919	...	...	1119	...	...	1319	...	...	...	...	...
Fulda d.	...	...	...	...	...	...	0814	...	...	1014	...	...	1214	...	...	1414	...	...	...	...	...
Erfurt Hbf d.	...	...	...	...	...	...	0940	...	...	1140	...	...	1340	...	...	1540	...	...	...	...	...
Leipzig Hbf d.	...	0700	...	...	0900	...	1031	1100	...	1231	1300	...	1431	1500	...	1631	1700	...	...	...	...
Dresden Hbf d.	...	0841	0910	...	1041	1110	1137	1241	1310	1337	1441	1510	1537	1641	1710	1737	1841	1910	...	...	...
Bad Schandau ⊞ ◧ d.	...	...	0937	...	...	1137	...	...	1337	...	...	1537	...	...	1737	...	...	1937	...	...	...
Děčín ⊞ ◧ d.	...	...	1002	...	...	1202	...	...	1402	...	...	1602	...	...	1802	...	...	2002	...	...	...
Praha Holešovice a.	...	...	1126	...	...	1326	...	...	1526	...	...	1726	...	...	1926	...	...	2126	...	...	...
Praha hl. n. a.	...	...	1135	...	...	1335	...	...	1535	...	...	1735	...	...	1935	...	...	2135	...	...	...

train type		*EC*		*ICE*	*EC*		*ICE*	*EC*		*ICE*	*EC*		*ICE*	*EC*		*ICE*	*EC*		*ICE*		
train number		**178**		**1650**	**176**		**1558**	**174**		**1556**	**378**		**1554**	**172**		**1552**	**170**		**1550**		
notes		X D		X	X H		X	X H		X	X A		X	X H		X	X D		X Ⓑ		
Praha hl. n. d.	...	0625	...	...	0825	...	...	1025	...	...	1225	...	...	1425	...	...	1625	...	...	...	...
Praha Holešovice d.	...	0634	...	...	0834	...	...	1034	...	...	1234	...	...	1434	...	...	1634	...	...	...	...
Děčín ⊞ ◧ d.	...	0807	...	...	1007	...	...	1207	...	...	1407	...	...	1607	...	...	1807	...	...	...	...
Bad Schandau ⊞ ◧ a.	...	0823	...	...	1023	...	...	1223	...	...	1423	...	...	1623	...	...	1823	...	...	...	...
Dresden Hbf a.	...	0851	0906	1012	1051	1106	1212	1251	1306	1412	1451	1506	1612	1651	1706	1812	1851	1906	...	...	...
Leipzig Hbf a.	...	...	1050	1133	...	1250	1333	...	1450	1533	...	1650	1733	...	1850	1933	...	2050	2133	...	...
Erfurt Hbf a.	...	...	...	1215	...	...	1415	...	...	1615	...	...	1815	...	...	2015	...	...	2215	...	...
Fulda a.	...	...	...	1343	...	...	1543	...	...	1743	...	...	1943	...	...	2143	...	...	2343	...	...
Frankfurt (Main) Hbf a.	...	...	...	1436	...	...	1636	...	...	1836	...	...	2036	...	...	2236	...	...	0040	...	...

- A – (12) X Kiel - Berlin - Dresden - Praha and v.v.
- D – (12) X Berlin - Dresden - Praha and v.v.
- H – (12) X Hamburg - Berlin - Dresden - Praha and v.v.
- ◧ – Ticketing point is Schöna.

56 LONDON / PARIS - KÖLN - BERLIN - WARSZAWA - KYIV / MOSKVA

train type	EC			ICE				ICE	ICE	ICE	ICE	ICE	ICE	☆	⇌	☆	☆	ICE	ICE	EC	⇌	☆	ICE	ICE	441
train number	41	24JI	24JI	541	68LJ	96BJ	96BJ	843	855	11	555	13	557	9108	9315	9110	9110	15	559	249	9423	9116	315	651	14MJ
notes	⚒	453	453	①-⑥	12011									①⑤		②③④	⑥			⑧					①⑥
	T	MY	MZ		C	PY	PZ													T					JY
London St Pancras d.	...	...	...	...	...	...	...	...	...	...	...	...	...	0613	...	0647	0657	...	...	...	...	0901	...	...	...
Paris Nord d.	...	...	...	...	...	...	...	...	...	...	...	...	...	|	0825j	|	|	...	...	...	0955	|	...	...	...
Paris Est d.	...	1858	1858	...	...	...	...	...	...	...	...	...	...	|	|	|	|	...	...	...	|	|	...	...	...
Brussels Midi/Zuid d.	...	|	|	...	...	...	...	...	...	0625	...	0823	...	0922	0947	1007	1005	1025	...	...	1117	1205	1225	...	...
Liège Guillemins d.	...	|	|	...	...	...	...	...	...	0712	...	0914	...	...	...	...	...	1114	...	...	...	...	1314	...	...
Aachen 🏛 d.	...	|	|	...	...	...	...	...	...	0739	...	0939	...	...	...	...	...	1139	...	...	...	...	1339	...	...
Köln Hbf a.	...	|	|	...	...	...	...	...	...	0816	...	1015	...	...	...	...	...	1215	...	...	...	...	1415	...	...
Köln Hbf d.	...	|	|	0426	...	...	...	0525	0748	...	0848	...	1048	...	...	...	...	...	1248	...	...	...	...	1448	...
Köln Messe/Deutz ♣ d.	...	|	|	|	...	...	...	|	|	...	|	...	|	...	...	...	...	...	|	...	...	...	...	|	...
Bielefeld Hbf d.	...	|	|	0640	...	...	...	0738	0938	...	1038	...	1238	...	...	...	...	...	1438	...	...	...	...	1638	...
Hannover Hbf d.	...	|	|	0731	...	...	...	0831	1031	...	1131	...	1331	...	...	...	...	...	1531	...	...	...	...	1731	...
Berlin Hbf a.	...	0721	0721	0910	...	...	...	1014	1214	...	1310	...	1510	...	...	...	...	...	1710	...	...	...	...	1908	...
		|	|	EC 45 T				EC 57 W	EC 59 N		EC 49 T		EC 247 T											441 14MJ ①⑥ JZ	
Berlin Hbf d.	0543f	0726	0726	0938	...	...	...	1039	1238	...	1341	...	1541	...	...	...	...	...	...	1741	...	...	...	2008	2008
Berlin Ostbahnhof d.	0555o	0759k	0759k	0952	...	...	...	1052	1252	...	1353	...	1555	...	...	...	...	...	...	1753	...	...	...	2018	2018
Frankfurt (Oder) 🏛 d.	0645	0855	0855	1045	...	...	...	1145	1345	...	1445	...	1645	...	...	...	...	...	...	1845	...	...	...	2134	2134
Rzepin d.	0707	0919	0919	1107	...	...	...	1206	1407	...	1507	...	1707	...	...	...	...	...	...	1907	...	...	...	2156	2156
Poznań Gł. d.	0841	1043	1038	1236	...	...	...	...	1531	...	1642	...	1836	...	...	...	...	...	...	2036	...	...	...	2322	2319
Warszawa Centralna a.	1146	|	|	1539	...	1915	1915	...	...	...	1941	...	2132	...	...	...	...	...	...	2335	...	...	...	|	|
Warszawa Wschodnia d.	1156	1542	1542	1553	1749	1924	1924	...	...	...	1952	...	2143	...	...	...	...	...	...	2346	...	...	...	0450	0445
Terespol a.	...	1755	1746	...	|	2129	2117	...	...	...	...	...	...	...	...	...	...	...	...	...	...	...	...	0632	0632
Brest Tsentralny 🏛 a.	...	2010	2115	...	|	2358	0100	...	...	...	...	...	...	...	...	...	...	...	...	...	...	...	...	1000	0900
Lublin a.	...	|	|	...	1948	|	|	...	...	...	...	...	...	...	...	...	...	...	...	...	...	...	...	|	|
Kyiv a.	...	|	|	...	1100	|	|	...	...	...	...	...	...	...	...	...	...	...	...	...	...	...	...	|	|
Minsk a.	...	0305	0305	...	...	0619	0608	...	...	...	...	...	...	...	...	...	...	...	...	...	...	...	...	1328	1328
Orsha Tsentralnaya § a.	...	0536	0536	...	...	0925	0925	...	...	...	...	...	...	...	...	...	...	...	...	...	...	...	...	1555	1555
Smolensk Tsentralny 🏛 § a.	...	0709	0709	...	...	1057	1057	...	...	...	...	...	...	...	...	...	...	...	...	...	...	...	...	1719	1719
Moskva Belorusskaya ‡ a.	...	1144	1144	...	...	1658	1658	...	...	...	...	...	...	...	...	...	...	...	...	...	...	...	...	2124	2124

train type/number	440	440	ICE	⇌	☆	EC	ICE	⇌	☆	EC	ICE	⇌	☆	EC	ICE	EC	ICE	EC				EC			EC
train number	13MJ	13MJ	954	9448	9145	248	14	9370	9157	246	12	9382	9167	48	10	58	318	56	27BJ	27BJ	67KJ	44	23JI	23JI	40
notes	⑤⑦	⑤⑦				⚒		⑧	①-⑥				⑧				⑦				21010		452	452	⑧
	KY	KZ				T				T				T		N		W	QY	QZ	C	T	FY	FZ	T
Moskva Belorusskaya ‡ d.	0956	0956	...	...	...	...	...	...	...	...	...	...	...	...	...	...	...	...	1415	1415	...	...	1817	1817	...
Smolensk Tsentralny 🏛 § d.	1344	1344	...	...	...	...	...	...	...	...	...	...	...	...	...	...	...	...	1917	1917	...	...	2315	2315	...
Orsha Tsentralnaya § d.	1507	1507	...	...	...	...	...	...	...	...	...	...	...	...	...	...	...	...	2055	2055	...	...	0044	0044	...
Minsk d.	1720	1720	...	...	...	...	...	...	...	...	...	...	...	...	...	...	...	...	0030	0010	...	...	0313	0313	...
Kyiv d.	|	|	...	...	...	...	...	...	...	...	...	...	...	...	...	...	...	...	|	|	1913z	...	|	|	...
Lublin d.	|	|	...	...	...	...	...	...	...	...	...	...	...	...	...	...	...	...	|	|	0802	...	|	|	...
Brest Tsentralny 🏛 d.	2040	2140	...	...	...	...	...	...	...	...	...	...	...	...	...	...	...	...	0550	0711	|	...	0943t	1043t	...
Terespol d.	2105	2105	...	...	...	...	...	...	...	...	...	...	...	...	...	...	...	...	0637	0637	|	...	0946	0946	...
Warszawa Wschodnia a.	2248	2241	...	...	...	0404	...	...	...	0604	...	...	...	0753	...	...	...	...	0840	0836	1004	1155	1149	1148	1554
Warszawa Centralna d.	|	|	...	...	...	0415	...	...	...	0614	...	...	...	0812	...	...	...	...	0850	0845	...	1215	|	|	1615
Poznań Gł. d.	0343	0324	...	...	...	0728	...	...	...	0925	...	...	...	1128	...	1225	...	...	...	...	...	1528	1658	1653	1928
Rzepin d.	0503	0448	...	...	...	0852	...	...	...	1052	...	...	...	1252	...	1352	...	1550	...	...	...	1652	1820	1820	2052
Frankfurt (Oder) 🏛 a.	0512	0512	...	...	...	0912	...	...	...	1112	...	...	...	1312	...	1412	...	1612	...	...	...	1712	1842	1842	2112
Berlin Ostbahnhof a.	0606	0606	...	...	...	1006	...	...	...	1206	...	...	...	1406	...	1506	...	1706	...	...	...	1806	1946k	1946k	2208
Berlin Hbf a.	0646	0646	...	...	...	1016	...	...	...	1216	...	...	...	1416	...	1516	...	1716	...	...	...	1816	2053	2053	2216
						ICE 650				ICE 558				ICE 556		ICE 856		ICE 844				ICE 552	|	|	
Berlin Hbf d.	...	...	0746	...	...	1046	...	...	...	1246	...	...	...	1446	...	1546	...	1746	...	...	...	1846	2102	2102	...
Hannover Hbf a.	...	...	0928	...	...	1228	...	...	...	1428	...	...	...	1628	...	1728	...	1928	...	...	...	2028	|	|	...
Bielefeld Hbf a.	...	...	1020	...	...	1320	...	...	...	1520	...	...	...	1720	...	1820	...	2020	...	...	...	2120	|	|	...
Köln Messe/Deutz ♣ a.	...	...	|	...	...	|	...	...	...	|	...	...	...	|	...	|	...	|	...	...	...	|	|	|	...
Köln Hbf a.	...	...	1209	...	...	1509	...	...	...	1709	...	...	...	1909	...	2009	...	2232	...	...	...	2313	|	|	...
Köln Hbf d.	...	...	...	1243	...	...	1540	...	...	...	1741	...	...	...	1940	...	2142	...	...	...	...	...	|	|	...
Aachen 🏛 a.	...	...	...	1316	...	...	1616	...	...	...	1816	...	...	...	2016	...	2215	...	...	...	...	...	|	|	...
Liège Guillemins a.	...	...	...	1344	...	...	1644	...	...	...	1844	...	...	...	2044	...	2244	...	...	...	...	...	|	|	...
Brussels Midi/Zuid a.	...	...	...	1435	1556	...	1735	1813	1856	...	1935	2016	2056	...	2135	...	2335	...	...	...	...	...	|	|	...
Paris Est a.	...	...	...	...	|	...	...	|	|	...	...	...	|	...	...	...	...	...	...	...	...	...	0940	0940	...
Paris Nord a.	...	...	...	1605	|	...	...	1935	|	...	...	2138	|	...	...	...	...	...	...	...	...	...	...	...	...
London St Pancras a.	...	...	...	...	1700	...	...	...	1957	...	...	...	2157	...	...	...	...	...	...	...	...	...	...	...	...

C – KYIV EKSPRES / KIEV EXPRESS – 🛏 1, 2 cl. Warszawa - Kyiv and v.v.
F – TRANSEUROPEAN EXPRESS ②: 🛏 1, 2 cl. Moskva (**23JI**) - Brest (**452**) - Berlin - Paris. ✕ (RZD) Moskva - Brest. ✕ (PKP) Warszawa - Paris.
J – ①⑥: 🛏 1 cl. (lux), 🛏 1, 2 cl., 🚃 ✕ 🄱 Berlin - Moskva, Strizh (Swift) Talgo train.
K – ⑤⑦: 🛏 1 cl. (lux), 🛏 1, 2 cl., 🚃 ✕ 🄱 Moskva - Berlin, Strizh (Swift) Talgo train.
M – TRANSEUROPEAN EXPRESS ④: 🛏 1, 2 cl. Paris (**453**) - Berlin - Brest (**24JI**) - Moskva. ✕ (PKP) Paris - Warszawa. ✕ (RZD) Brest - Moskva.
N – BERLIN GDANSK EXPRESS / GEDANIA 🚃 ✕ 🄱 Berlin - Poznań - Gdynia and v.v.
P – 🛏 1, 2 cl. Praha (**115**) - Bohumín (**130**) - Terespol (**136**) - Brest (**656**) - Minsk (**96BJ**) - Moskva.
Q – 🛏 1, 2 cl. Moskva (**27BJ**) - Minsk (**655**) - Brest (**137**) - Terespol (**131**) - Bohumín (**114**) - Praha.
T – BERLIN WARSZAWA EXPRESS – 🚃 ✕ 🄱 Berlin - Warszawa and v.v.
W – WAWEL – 🚃 ✕ 🄱 Berlin - Wrocław - Krakow - Przemyśl and v.v.
Y – Mar. 28, 2021 - Oct. 30, 2021. Timings subject to confirmation.
Z – Oct. 31, 2021 - Dec. 11, 2021. Timings subject to confirmation.

f – 0515 June 13 - July 8.
j – 0801 on ⑦.
k – Berlin **Lichtenberg**.
o – Berlin **Ostkreuz**.
t – Arrive 0641.
z – Passengers to be on board by 1848 for customs and passport control.

§ – 🏛: Osinovka (BY) / Krasnoye (RU).
‡ – Also known as Moskva **Smolenskaya** station.

☆ – Eurostar train. Special fares payable. ✕ in Business Premier and Standard Premier, 🍸 in Standard. Minimum check-in time 30 minutes. Valid June 12 - Sept. 3. **Additional services are available, see Table 10, pages 47 – 48.**
♣ – Köln **Messe / Deutz**. Connections from Köln Hbf depart every 2 - 5 minutes, journey time 2 - 3 minutes.
⇌ – *Thalys* high-speed train. 🄱 🍸. Three classes of service: Premium, Comfort and Standard. Special fares payable. Valid June 12 - Dec. 10.
☛ – **Shaded services are suspended until further notice.**

58 BERLIN - WROCLAW

	IRE	EC/IC	IRE	NJ
	5837	57	5839	457
	⑥	73000	⑤	14010
	K	W	K	M
Berlin Hbf. d.	...	1039	...	1843
Berlin Ostkreuz d.	...	|	...	|
Berlin Lichtenberg d.	0826	|	1346	|
Berlin Ostkreuz d.	0832	|	1352	|
Cottbus d.	0952	|	1526	|
Forst 🏛 a.	|	|	|	|
Forst 🏛 d.	1020	|	1556	|
Tuplice d.	|	|	|	|
Žary a.	1052	|	1627	|
Zagań a.	1104	|	1638	|
Legnica a.	1207	1415	1755	2208
Wrocław Gł. a.	1242	1452	1836	2243

	IC/EC	IRE	IRE	NJ
	56	5836	5838	456
	37000	⑦	⑤	47010
	W	K	K	M
Wrocław Gł. d.	1307	1732	2011	0538
Legnica d.	1345	1814	2054	0616
Zagań d.	|	1915	2153	|
Žary d.	|	1928	2206	|
Tuplice d.	|	|	|	|
Forst 🏛 a.	|	2001	2240	|
Forst 🏛 d.	|	|	|	|
Cottbus a.	|	2028	2305	|
Berlin Ostkreuz a.	|	2203	0039	|
Berlin Lichtenberg a.	|	2212	0045	|
Berlin Ostkreuz a.	|	|	...	|
Berlin Hbf a.	1716	...	...	0951

K – KULTURZUG / POCIAG DO KULTURY - 🚃 Berlin - Wrocław and v.v. For International journeys only. Special fares apply.
M – *ÖBB nightjet* METROPOL – 🛏 1, 2 cl., 🛌 2 cl., 🚃 Berlin - Wrocław - Wien and v.v. (Table **77**).
W – WAWEL – 🚃 ✕ 🄱 Berlin - Wrocław - Krakow - Przemyśl and v.v.

HAMBURG - BERLIN - PRAHA - WIEN / BUDAPEST 60

train type	EC	RJ	EC		RJ	EC	RJ	EC	RJ	EC	EC	RJ	EC		EC	EC	EC	RJ	EC	EC	RJ	EC	
train number	271	71	273	1031	73	275	75	277	257	279	171	79	131	1035	287	173	173	371	281	379	373	283	
notes	✕	✕ ⚒	✕	🍷 ♥	✕	✕	✕	✕	✕	✕	✕	✕	✕ V	🍷 ♥	✕ K	✕ L	✕ J	✕	✕	✕ H	✕	✕	
Hamburg Altona d.	...	...	...	...	...	...	...	...	...	...	...	...	...	...	...	0636	0636	...	...	...	...	...	...
Hamburg Hbf d.	...	...	...	...	...	...	...	...	...	...	...	...	...	...	...	0648	0648	...	...	0851	...	...	...
Berlin Hbf d.	...	...	...	...	...	...	...	...	0457	...	0716	...	...	...	...	0916	0916	...	...	1116	...	...	...
Berlin Südkreuz d.	...	...	...	...	...	...	...	...	0503	...	0723	...	...	...	...	0923	0923	...	...	1123	...	...	...
Dresden Hbf d.	...	...	...	...	...	...	...	...	0727	...	0910	...	...	...	...	1110	1110	...	...	1310	...	...	...
Bad Schandau ▣ ⊖ d.	...	...	...	...	...	...	...	...	0803	...	0937	...	...	...	..	1137	1137	...	...	1337	...	...	...
Děčín d.	...	...	...	...	...	...	...	...	0831	...	1002	...	...	...	...	1202	1202	...	...	1402	...	...	...
Ústí nad Labem hl. n. d.	...	...	...	...	...	...	...	...	0848	...	1021	...	...	...	...	1221	1221	...	...	1421	...	...	...
Praha Holešovice a.	...	...	...	...	...	...	...	...	1011	...	1126	...	...	...	...	1326	1326	...	...	1526	...	...	...
Praha hl. n. a.	...	...	...	...	...	...	...	...	|	...	1135	...	...	...	...	|	1335	...	...	1535	...	...	...
Praha hl. n. d.	...	0412	0512	0538	0612	0712	0812	0912	|	1112	...	1212	...	1238	1312	|	...	1412	1512	...	1612	1712	...
Pardubice d.	...	|	|	|	|	|	|	|	|	|	...	|	...	|	|	|	...	|	|	...	|	|	...
Brno hl. n. d.	0622	0722	0822	0848	0922	1022	1122	1222	1322	1422	...	1522	...	1548	1622	1622	...	1722	1822	...	1922	2022	...
Břeclav a.	0652	0752	0852	0918	0952	1052	1152	1252	1352	1452	...	1552	...	1618	1652	1652	...	1752	1852	...	1952	2052	...
Břeclav d.	0655	0755	0855	0920	0955	1055	1155	1255	1355	1455	...	1555	1555	1620	1655	1655	...	1755	1855	...	1955	2055	...
Wien Hbf a.	|	0849	|	1021	1049	|	1249	|	1449	|	...	1649	|	1721	|	|	...	1849	|	...	2049	|	...
Wien Meidling a.	|	0903	|	1032	1103	|	1303	|	1503	|	...	1703	|	1732	|	|	...	1903	|	...	2103	|	...
Wiener Neustadt Hbf a.	|	0928	|	|	1128	|	1328	|	1528	|	...	1728	|	|	|	|	...	1928	|	...	2128	|	...
Graz Hbf a.	|	1133	|	|	1333	|	1533	|	1733	|	...	1933	|	|	|	|	...	2133	|	...	2333	|	...
Kúty ▣ a.	0711	...	0911	|	...	1111	...	1311	...	1511	...	...	1611	|	1711	1711	...	...	1911	...	...	2111	...
Bratislava hl. st. a.	0754	...	0954	|	...	1154	...	1354	...	1554	...	...	1702	|	1754	1754	...	...	1954	...	...	2154	...
Štúrovo ▣ △ a.	0916	...	1116	◐	...	1316	...	1516	...	1716	...	...	1826	◐	1916	1916	...	...	2119	...	...	...	...
Budapest Nyugati a.	1020	...	1220	|	...	1420	...	1620	...	1820	...	...	1934	|	2020	2020	...	...	2223	...	...	...	...
Budapest Déli a.	...	...	...	1314	...	...	...	...	...	...	...	...	...	2014	...	...	...	...	...	...	...	...	...

train type	EC	RJ	EC	EC	EC	EN	NJ	NJ
train number	175	375	285	177	179	575 477	40457 477	457
notes	✕	✕	✕	✕	✕	B	S	R
Hamburg Altona d.	...	...	...	1237	...	...	...	...
Hamburg Hbf d.	1021	...	...	1251	...	...	...	...
Berlin Hbf d.	1316	...	...	1516	1716	...	1843	1843
Berlin Südkreuz d.	1323	...	...	1523	1723	...	|	|
Dresden Hbf d.	1510	...	...	1710	1910	...	|	|
Bad Schandau ▣ ⊖ d.	1537	...	...	1737	1937	...	|	|
Děčín d.	1602	...	...	1802	2002	...	◧	◧
Ústí nad Labem hl. n. d.	1621	...	...	1821	2021	...	|	|
Praha Holešovice a.	1726	...	...	1926	2126	...	|	|
Praha hl. n. a.	1735	...	...	1935	2135	...	|	|
Praha hl. n. d.	...	1812	1912	...	...	2234	|	|
Pardubice d.	...	|	|	...	...	|	|	|
Brno hl. n. d.	...	2122	2222	...	...	0141	|	|
Břeclav a.	...	2152	2252	...	...	0211	0410	0410
Břeclav d.	...	2155	2255	...	...	0455	0455	0549
Wien Hbf a.	...	2249	|	...	...	|	|	0700
Wien Meidling a.	...	...	|	...	...	|	|	|
Wiener Neustadt Hbf a.	...	...	|	...	...	|	|	0751
Graz Hbf a.	...	...	|	...	...	|	|	1002
Kúty ▣ a.	...	...	|	...	...	0511	0511	...
Bratislava hl. st. a.	...	...	2354	...	...	0554	0554	...
Štúrovo ▣ △ a.	...	...	...	...	...	0716	0716	...
Budapest Nyugati a.	...	...	...	...	...	0820	0820	...

train type/number	EC	EC	RJ	EC	EC	RJ	EC	EC	EC
train number	178	176	284	174	282	70	104	378	280
notes	✕	✕	✕	✕	✕	✕	✕	✕ G	✕
Budapest Nyugati d.	...	...	...	...	...	...	...	...	0540
Štúrovo ▣ △ d.	...	...	...	...	...	...	...	...	0644
Bratislava hl. st. d.	...	...	0457	...	0606	...	...	...	0806
Kúty ▣ d.	...	...	0545	...	0649	...	...	...	0849
Graz Hbf d.	...	...	|	...	|	...	0528	...	|
Wiener Neustadt Hbf d.	...	...	|	...	|	...	0730	...	|
Wien Meidling d.	...	...	|	...	|	...	0757	...	|
Wien Hbf d.	...	...	|	...	|	0710	0810	...	|
Břeclav a.	...	...	0600	...	0704	0804	0904	...	0904
Břeclav d.	...	...	0607	...	0707	0807	...	...	0907
Brno hl. n. d.	...	...	0638	...	0738	0838	...	...	0938
Pardubice d.	...	...	|	...	|	|	...	...	|
Praha hl. n. a.	...	...	0942	...	1042	1142	...	...	1242
Praha hl. n. d.	0625	0825	...	1025	...	...	...	1225	...
Praha Holešovice d.	0634	0834	...	1034	...	...	...	1234	...
Ústí nad Labem hl. n. d.	0739	0939	...	1139	...	...	...	1339	...
Děčín d.	0807	1007	...	1207	...	...	...	1407	...
Bad Schandau ▣ ⊖ a.	0823	1023	...	1223	...	...	...	1423	...
Dresden Hbf a.	0851	1051	...	1251	...	...	...	1451	...
Berlin Südkreuz a.	1035	1235	...	1435	...	...	...	1635	...
Berlin Hbf a.	1042	1242	...	1442	...	...	...	1642	...
Hamburg Hbf a.	...	1512	...	1711	...	...	...	1912	...
Hamburg Altona a.	...	1527	...	...	...	...	...	...	...

train type/number	RJ	EC	EC	EC		EC	RJ	EC	EC	RJ	EC	RJ	EC	RJ		EC	RJ	EC	RJ	EN	NJ	NJ	
train number	72	172	286	172	1032	130	74	170	278	256	276	78	274	370	1036	272	372	270	374	476 574	40476 456	456	
notes	✕	✕ J	✕ K	✕ L	🍷 ♥	✕ V	✕	✕	✕	✕	✕	✕	✕	✕	🍷 ♥	✕	✕	✕	✕	C	T	R	
Budapest Déli d.	...	...	...	...	0745	...	...	...	...	...	...	...	...	...	1445	...	...	...	...	...	...	...	...
Budapest Nyugati d.	...	...	0740	0740	|	0828	...	...	0940	...	1140	...	1340	...	|	1540	...	1740	...	1940	1940	...	...
Štúrovo ▣ △ d.	...	...	0844	0844	◐	0935	...	...	1044	...	1244	...	1444	...	◐	1644	...	1844	...	2044	2044	...	...
Bratislava hl. st. d.	...	...	1006	1006	|	1057	...	...	1206	...	1406	...	1606	...	|	1806	...	2006	...	2206	2206	...	...
Kúty ▣ d.	...	...	1049	1049	|	1148	...	...	1249	...	1449	...	1649	...	|	1849	...	2049	...	2249	2249	...	...
Graz Hbf d.	0626	...	|	|	|	|	0826	...	|	1026	|	1226	|	1426	|	|	1626	|	1826	|	|	1921	...
Wiener Neustadt Hbf d.	0832	...	|	|	|	|	1032	...	|	1232	|	1432	|	1632	|	|	1832	|	2032	|	|	2135	...
Wien Meidling d.	0857	...	|	|	1027	|	1057	...	|	1257	|	1457	|	1657	1727	|	1857	|	2057	|	|	|	...
Wien Hbf d.	0910	...	|	|	1039	|	1110	...	|	1310	|	1510	|	1710	1736	|	1910	|	2110	|	|	2210	...
Břeclav a.	1004	...	1104	1104	1136	1204	1204	...	1304	1404	1504	1604	1704	1804	1836	1904	2004	2104	2204	2304	2304	2307	...
Břeclav d.	1007	...	1107	1107	1138	...	1207	...	1307	1407	1507	1607	1707	1807	1838	1907	2007	2107	2207	0507	2350	2350	...
Brno hl. n. d.	1038	...	1138	1138	1209	...	1238	...	1338	1438	1538	1638	1738	1838	1909	1938	2038	2136	2236	0538	|	|	...
Pardubice d.	|	...	|	|	|	...	|	...	|	|	|	|	|	|	|	|	|	...	...	|	|	|	...
Praha hl. n. a.	1342	...	1442	|	1519	...	1542	...	1642	|	1842	1942	2042	2141	2214	2241	2343	...	...	0842	|	|	...
Praha hl. n. d.	...	1425	...	|	...	...	...	1625	...	|	...	...	...	...	...	...	...	...	...	...	|	|	...
Praha Holešovice d.	...	1434	...	1434	...	...	...	1634	...	1742	...	...	...	...	...	...	...	...	...	...	|	|	...
Ústí nad Labem hl. n. d.	...	1539	...	1539	...	...	...	1739	...	1914	...	...	...	...	...	...	...	...	...	...	|	|	...
Děčín d.	...	1607	...	1607	...	...	...	1807	...	1937	...	...	...	...	...	...	...	...	...	...	◧	◧	...
Bad Schandau ▣ ⊖ a.	...	1623	...	1623	...	...	...	1823	...	1953	...	...	...	...	...	...	...	...	...	...	|	|	...
Dresden Hbf a.	...	1651	...	1651	...	...	...	1851	...	2020	...	...	...	...	...	...	...	...	...	...	|	|	...
Berlin Südkreuz a.	...	1835	...	1835	...	...	...	2035	...	2235	...	...	...	...	...	...	...	...	...	...	|	|	...
Berlin Hbf a.	...	1842	...	1842	...	...	...	2042	...	2242	...	...	...	...	...	...	...	...	...	...	0951	0951	...
Hamburg Hbf a.	...	2119	...	2119	...	...	...	...	...	...	...	...	...	...	...	...	...	...	...	...	...	...	...
Hamburg Altona a.	...	2135	...	2135	...	...	...	...	...	...	...	...	...	...	...	...	...	...	...	...	...	...	...

B – METROPOL – 🛏 1, 2 cl., (━ 2 cl. June 12 - Dec. 10) Praha (**575**) - Břeclav (**477**) - Budapest. (12) ✕ Praha - Břeclav. (12) Břeclav - Budapest.

C – METROPOL – 🛏 1, 2 cl., (━ 2 cl. June 13 - Dec. 10) Budapest (**476**) - Břeclav (**574**) - Praha. (12) Budapest - Břeclav. (12) ✕ Břeclav - Praha.

G – (12) ✕ Praha - Berlin - Hamburg - Kiel (arrive 2020).

H – (12) ✕ Kiel (depart 0742) - Hamburg - Berlin - Praha.

J – Dec. 12 - Aug. 31: HUNGARIA – (12) ✕ Hamburg - Berlin - Praha and v.v.

K – Dec. 12 - Aug. 31: HUNGARIA – (12) ✕ Praha - Břeclav - Budapest and v.v.

L – Sept. 1 - Dec. 10: HUNGARIA – (12) ✕ Hamburg - Berlin - Praha Holešovice - Břeclav - Budapest and v.v.

R – *ÖBB nightjet* METROPOL – 🛏 1, 2 cl., ━ 2 cl., (2) Berlin - Wrocław - Bohumín - Břeclav - Wien - Graz and v.v.

S – *ÖBB nightjet* METROPOL – 🛏 1, 2 cl., ━ 2 cl., (2) Berlin (**40457**) - Wrocław - Bohumín - Břeclav (**477**) - Budapest.

T – *ÖBB nightjet* METROPOL – 🛏 1, 2 cl., ━ 2 cl., (2) Budapest (**40476**) - Břeclav (**456**) - Bohumín - Wrocław - Berlin.

V – BATHORY – (12) ✕ Terespol - Warszawa - Katowice - Břeclav - Budapest and v.v. (Table **99**).

♥ – Operated by REGIOJET. Separate fare tariff applies.

△ – Routeing point for international tickets : Szob.

⊖ – Routeing point for international tickets : Schöna.

RJ – ÖBB *Railjet* service. (1) (business class), (1) (first class), (2) (economy class), ✕.

◐ – ▣ at Hegyeshalom.

◧ – Via Wrocław and Bohumín (Table **77**).

☛ – Additional services Praha - Wien and Praha - Bratislava are operated by REGIOJET. For timings see Table **1150**.

61 WIEN - BUDAPEST - BEOGRAD / BUCUREŞTI and İSTANBUL / THESSALONÍKI

train type	IC		IC	RJX	IC										IC				463		EN	EN	EN
train number	73	1335	75	41	714	343	343				🚌	7991	493	493	79	1095	463	465	465	463	473	347	50347
notes	Ⓡ		Ⓡ		Ⓡ	🚌		🚌			①–⑥	2			Ⓡ	463	2	2	493	Ⓡ	Ⓡ	Ⓡ	348
	H	K	P			C	✣	✣			≋		A	C	G	J	J	J	ⓇU	W T	R	S	ⓇE
Wien Hbf d.	...	...	...	0740	...	...	...	...	...	...	...	...	...	...	...	...	...	...	...	...	...	1942	1942
Budapest Keleti d.	0710	...	0910	1019	1153n	...	...	...	...	...	...	...	...	...	1510	...	...	...	...	...	1910	2245	2245
Lököshaza a.	1010	...	1210	...	|	...	...	...	...	...	...	...	...	...	1810	...	...	...	...	...	2210	0159	0159
Curtici 🛃 a.	1155	...	1355	...	|	...	...	...	...	...	...	...	...	...	1955	...	...	...	...	...	2355	0349	0349
Arad a.	1237	...	1543	...	|	...	...	...	...	...	...	...	...	...	2046	...	...	...	...	...	0038	0428	0428
Timişoara a.	1327	...	|	...	|	...	...	...	...	...	...	...	...	...	2139	...	...	...	...	...	|	|	0552
Braşov a.	|	...	0055	...	|	...	...	...	...	...	...	...	...	...	|	...	...	...	...	...	0954	1326	|
Bucureşti Nord d.	2359	...	...	...	|	...	...	...	...	...	...	...	...	...	0830	1055	...	...	1055	1055	1233	1547	1600
Videle a.	...	...	...	...	|	...	...	...	...	...	...	...	...	...	...	1145	...	...	1145	1145	...	...	...
Giurgiu Nord 🛃 a.	...	...	...	...	|	...	...	...	...	...	...	...	...	...	...	1301	...	...	1301	1301	...	...	...
Giurgiu Nord 🛃 d.	...	...	...	...	|	...	...	...	...	...	...	...	...	...	...	1320	...	...	1320	1320	...	...	...
Ruse 🛃 a.	...	...	...	...	|	...	...	...	...	...	...	...	...	...	...	1345	...	...	1345	1345	...	...	...
Ruse 🛃 d.	...	...	...	...	|	...	...	...	...	...	...	...	...	...	...	1404	...	...	1410	1410	...	...	...
Gorna Orjahovica d.	...	...	...	...	...	...	...	...	...	...	...	...	...	...	...	1610	1615	1725	1725	1615	...	...	...
Szeged d.	...	...	...	...	1415	1422	...	...	...	...	...	...	...	...	...	...	|	|	|	|	...	...	...
Kelebia 🛃 d.	...	...	...	...	...	1517	1541	...	...	...	...	...	...	...	...	...	|	|	|	|	...	...	...
Subotica 🛃 a.	...	...	...	...	...	...	1555	1800	...	...	...	...	...	...	...	...	|	|	|	|	...	...	...
Novi Sad a.	...	...	...	...	...	...	...	2000	2101	...	...	...	...	...	...	...	|	|	|	|	...	...	...
Beograd Centar a.	...	1825	...	...	...	...	...	...	2158	...	...	...	...	...	...	...	|	|	|	|	...	...	...
Niš a.	...	2308	...	...	...	...	...	...	...	...	0620	...	...	...	...	...	|	|	|	|	...	...	...
Tabanovci 🛃 a.	...	0320	...	...	...	...	...	...	...	...	|	...	...	...	...	...	|	|	|	|	...	...	...
Skopje a.	...	0425	...	...	...	...	...	...	...	...	|	...	...	...	...	...	|	|	|	|	...	...	...
Gevgelija 🛃 a.	...	0650	...	...	...	...	...	...	...	...	|	...	...	...	...	...	|	|	|	|	...	...	...
Dimitrovgrad (Serbia) 🛃 a.	...	|	...	...	...	...	...	...	...	...	0802	...	...	...	...	...	|	|	|	|	...	...	...
Dragoman 🛃 a.	...	|	...	...	...	...	...	...	...	...	...	1400	...	...	...	...	|	|	|	|	...	...	...
Pleven a.	...	|	...	...	...	...	...	...	...	...	...	|	...	...	...	...	1725	|	|	1725	...	...	...
Mezdra a.	...	|	...	...	...	...	...	...	...	...	...	|	...	...	...	...	1840	|	|	1840	...	...	...
Vidin 🛃 a.	...	|	...	...	...	...	...	...	...	...	...	|	...	...	...	...	|	|	|	|	...	...	...
Sofia a.	...	|	...	...	...	...	...	...	...	...	...	1500	...	...	...	...	2010	|	|	2010	...	...	...
Sofia d.	...	|	...	...	...	...	...	...	...	...	...	...	1830	1830	...	...	...	|	|	...	...	...	...
Dimitrovgrad (Bulgaria) a.	...	|	...	...	...	...	...	...	...	...	...	...	2228	2228	...	...	...	2216	2216	...	...	...	...
Svilengrad a.	...	|	...	...	...	...	...	...	...	...	...	...	2332	2332	...	...	...	...	2332	...	...	...	...
Kapikule 🛃 a.	...	|	...	...	...	...	...	...	...	...	...	...	0037	0137	...	...	...	...	0037	...	...	...	...
Çerkezköy a.	...	|	...	...	...	...	...	...	...	...	...	...	0408	0453	...	...	...	...	0408	...	...	...	...
Halkalı ◇ a.	...	|	...	...	...	...	...	...	...	...	...	...	0534	0600	...	...	...	...	0534	...	...	...	...
İstanbul Sirkeci ◇ a.	...	|	...	...	...	...	...	...	...	...	...	...	◇	◇	...	...	...	...	◇	...	...	...	...
İstanbul Söğütlüçesme ◇ a.	...	|	...	...	...	...	...	...	...	...	...	...	◇	◇	...	...	...	...	◇	...	...	...	...
Ankara a.	...	|	...	...	...	...	...	...	...	...	...	...	...	...	...	...	...	...	...	...	...	...	...
Kulata 🛃 a.	...	|	...	...	...	...	...	...	...	...	...	...	...	...	...	...	...	...	...	...	...	...	...
Thessaloníki a.	...	1033	...	...	...	...	...	...	...	...	...	...	...	...	...	...	...	...	...	...	...	...	...

train type/number		EN	EN	EN	492										IC	IC	IC				IC	RJX	IC
train number	1334	349	346	472	464	462	492	492	7990		2906	464	462	1094	78	74	570		342	342	713	264	72
notes		2Ⓡ	Ⓡ	Ⓡ	462	Ⓡ			2	🚌	2	2	2		Ⓡ	Ⓡ	Ⓡ	🚌		🚌	Ⓡ		Ⓡ
	L	E	S	R	ⓇF	W T	B	D		≋		J	J	J	G	P		✣	✣				H
Thessaloníki d.	1851	...	...	...	...	...	...	...	...	...	...	...	...	...	...	...	...	...	...	...	...	...	...
Kulata 🛃 d.	|	...	...	...	...	...	...	...	...	...	...	...	...	...	...	...	...	...	...	...	...	...	...
Ankara d.	|	...	...	...	...	...	...	...	...	...	...	...	...	...	...	...	...	...	...	...	...	...	...
İstanbul Söğütlüçesme ◇ d.	|	...	...	...	◇	...	◇	◇	...	...	...	...	...	...	...	...	...	...	...	...	...	...	...
İstanbul Sirkeci ◇ d.	|	...	...	...	◇	...	◇	◇	...	...	...	...	...	...	...	...	...	...	...	...	...	...	...
Halkalı ◇ d.	|	...	...	...	2140	...	2140	2240	...	...	...	...	...	...	...	...	...	...	...	...	...	...	...
Çerkezköy d.	|	...	...	...	2307	...	2307	0007	...	...	...	...	...	...	...	...	...	...	...	...	...	...	...
Kapikule 🛃 d.	|	...	...	...	0220	...	0220	0320	...	...	...	...	...	...	...	...	...	...	...	...	...	...	...
Svilengrad d.	|	...	...	...	0325	...	0325	0325	...	...	...	...	...	...	...	...	...	...	...	...	...	...	...
Dimitrovgrad (Bulgaria) d.	|	...	...	...	0600	...	0424	0424	...	...	...	0600	...	...	...	...	...	...	...	...	...	...	...
Sofia a.	|	...	...	...	|	...	0935	0935	...	...	...	|	...	...	...	...	...	...	...	...	...	...	...
Sofia d.	|	...	...	...	|	0715	...	...	0920	...	...	|	0715	...	...	...	...	...	...	...	...	...	...
Vidin 🛃 d.	|	...	...	...	|	|	...	...	|	...	...	|	|	...	...	...	...	...	...	...	...	...	...
Mezdra d.	|	...	...	...	|	0844	...	...	|	...	...	|	0844	...	...	...	...	...	...	...	...	...	...
Pleven d.	|	...	...	...	|	1001	...	...	|	...	...	|	1001	...	...	...	...	...	...	...	...	...	...
Dragoman 🛃 d.	|	...	...	...	|	|	...	...	1019	...	...	|	|	...	...	...	...	...	...	...	...	...	...
Dimitrovgrad (Serbia) 🛃 d.	|	...	...	...	|	|	...	...	...	1200	...	|	|	...	...	...	...	...	...	...	...	...	...
Gevgelija 🛃 d.	1948	...	...	...	|	|	...	...	...	|	...	|	|	...	...	...	...	...	...	...	...	...	...
Skopje d.	2219	...	...	...	|	|	...	...	...	|	...	|	|	...	...	...	...	...	...	...	...	...	...
Tabanovci 🛃 d.	2329	...	...	...	|	|	...	...	...	|	...	|	|	...	...	...	...	...	...	...	...	...	...
Niš d.	0337	...	...	...	|	|	...	...	...	1400	1552	|	|	...	...	...	...	...	...	...	...	...	...
Beograd Centar d.	0813	...	...	...	|	|	...	...	...	...	2110	|	|	...	...	...	0935	...	...	...	...	...	...
Novi Sad d.	...	...	...	...	|	|	...	...	...	...	...	|	|	...	...	...	1011	1040	...	...	...	...	...
Subotica 🛃 d.	...	...	...	...	|	|	...	...	...	...	...	|	|	...	...	...	...	1230	1402	...	...	...	...
Kelebia 🛃 d.	...	...	...	...	|	|	...	...	...	...	...	|	|	...	...	...	...	...	1416	1440	...	...	...
Szeged d.	...	...	...	...	|	|	...	...	...	...	...	|	|	...	...	...	...	...	...	1535	1545	...	...
Gorna Orjahovica d.	...	...	...	...	1130	1130	...	...	...	...	...	1036	1130	...	...	...	...	...	...	...	|	...	...
Ruse 🛃 a.	...	...	...	...	1324	1324	...	...	...	...	...	...	1324	...	...	...	...	...	...	...	|	...	...
Ruse 🛃 d.	...	...	...	...	1415	1415	...	...	...	...	...	...	...	1415	...	...	...	...	...	...	|	...	...
Giurgiu Nord 🛃 a.	...	...	...	...	1440	1440	...	...	...	...	...	...	...	1440	...	...	...	...	...	...	|	...	...
Giurgiu Nord 🛃 d.	...	...	...	...	1500	1500	...	...	...	...	...	...	...	1500	...	...	...	...	...	...	|	...	...
Videle d.	...	...	...	...	1619	1619	...	...	...	...	...	...	...	1619	...	...	...	...	...	...	|	...	...
Bucureşti Nord d.	...	1345	1400	1745	1705	1705	...	...	...	...	...	...	...	1705	2205	...	...	...	...	...	|	...	0546
Braşov d.	...	|	1621	2022	...	...	...	...	...	...	...	...	...	...	|	0523	...	...	...	...	|	...	|
Timişoara d.	...	2356	|	|	...	...	...	...	...	...	...	...	...	...	0826	|	...	...	...	...	|	...	1538
Arad d.	...	0120	0120	0452	...	...	...	...	...	...	...	...	...	...	0921	1417	...	...	...	...	|	...	1629
Curtici 🛃 d.	...	0210	0210	0534	...	...	...	...	...	...	...	...	...	...	0934	1534	...	...	...	...	|	...	1734
Lököshaza d.	...	0200	0200	0540	...	...	...	...	...	...	...	...	...	...	0940	1540	...	...	...	...	|	...	1740
Budapest Keleti a.	...	0520	0520	0850	...	...	...	...	...	...	...	...	...	...	1250	1850	...	...	...	...	1807n	1940	2050
Wien Hbf a.	...	0821	0821	...	...	...	...	...	...	...	...	...	...	...	...	...	...	...	...	...	...	2221	...

A – Apr. 26 - Oct. 30: SOFIA EXPRESS – 🛋 1, 2 cl., 🛏 2 cl. (4-berth) Sofia - Halkalı.

B – Apr. 25 - Oct. 29: SOFIA EXPRESS – 🛋 1, 2 cl., 🛏 2 cl. (4-berth) Halkalı - Sofia.

C – Oct. 31 - Dec. 10: SOFIA EXPRESS – 🛋 1, 2 cl., 🛏 2 cl. (4-berth) Sofia - Halkalı.

D – Oct. 30 - Dec. 10: SOFIA EXPRESS – 🛋 1, 2 cl., 🛏 2 cl. (4-berth) Halkalı - Sofia.

E – 🛋 1, 2 cl. Wien - Timişoara - Bucureşti and v.v.

F – June 2 - Oct. 1: BOSPHOR EXPRESS – 🛏 2 cl. (4-berth) İstanbul (**12502/492/1622**) - Dimitrovgrad (**464**) - Gorna Orjahovica (**462/1094**) - Ruse - Bucureşti.

G – MUNTENIA – 🚃2 Budapest - Timişoara - Bucureşti and v.v.

H – TRAIANUS – 🚃2 Budapest - Timişoara - Bucureşti and v.v.

J – Oct. 4 - Dec. 10.

K – June 3 - Sept. 20: HELLAS – 🛏 2 cl., 🚃2 Beograd - Thessaloníki.

L – June 2 - Sept. 19: HELLAS – 🛏 2 cl., 🚃2 Thessaloníki - Beograd.

P – FOGARAS – 🚃12 Budapest - Braşov and v.v.

R – *EuroNight* ISTER – 🛋 1, 2 cl., 🛏 1, 2 cl., 🚃2 Budapest - Bucureşti and v.v.

S – DACIA - 🛋 1, 2 cl., 🛏 2 cl., 🚃2 Wien - Braşov - Bucureşti and v.v.

T – June 3 - Oct. 3.

U – June 4 - Oct. 3: BOSPHOR EXPRESS – 🛏 2 cl. (4-berth) Bucureşti (**463/1095**) - Ruse - Gorna Orjahovica (**465**) - Dimitrovgrad (**493/12501**) - istanbul.

W – 🚃2 ROMANIA – Bucureşti - Ruse - Sofia and v.v.

n – Budapest **Nyugati**.

✣ – Engineering work is affecting services between Budapest and Kelebia until 2024. For through journeys between Budapest and Subotica see Tables **1290** & **1295**. **Rail tickets are not valid on bus services Subotica - Novi Sad.**

≋ Rail tickets are not valid on bus services Dimitrovgrad (Serbia) - Niš.

◇ – Frequent surburban services operate from Halkalı to istanbul Sirkeci (journey time 38 mins.) and istanbul Söğütlüçesme (51 mins). See Table **1570**.

☛ **Shaded services are suspended until further notice.**

FRANKFURT - MÜNCHEN - LJUBLJANA - ZAGREB - BEOGRAD - THESSALONÍKI 62

Engineering work is affecting services between München and Salzburg until August 1

train type/number	RJ	D	EC	EC	EC	EC	D	D	EC	EC	EN	EN	D	D	🚌	
train number	111	211	217	113	113	115	315	315	219	117	60463	50463	415	415		7991
notes		T			213			411				499		413	①–⑥	2
					◧	W		P			R	L	B	B	✣	
Dortmund Hbf d.	...	...	...	...	...	...	...	...	...	...	...	...	...	...	...	...
Münster Hbf d.	...	...	...	...	...	0631	...	...	...	...	...	...	...	...	...	...
Köln Hbf d.	...	...	...	...	...	0818	...	...	...	...	...	...	...	...	...	...
Frankfurt (Main) Hbf d.	...	...	...	0820	0820	|	...	...	1220	1420	...	...	...	...	...	...
Saarbrücken d.	...	...	0537	|	|	|	...	...	|	|	...	...	...	...	...	...
Mannheim d.	...	...	0711	|	|	1102	...	...	|	|	...	...	...	...	...	...
Heidelberg d.	...	...	|	0913	0913	|	...	...	1313	1513	...	...	...	...	...	...
Stuttgart Hbf d.	...	...	0758	0958	0958	1158	...	...	1358	1558	...	...	...	...	...	...
Ulm d.	...	...	0856	1056	1056	1256	...	...	1456	1656	...	...	...	...	...	...
Augsburg d.	...	...	0941	1141	1141	1341	...	...	1541	1741	...	...	...	...	...	...
München Hbf d.	0817	...	1017	1217	1217	1417	...	...	1617	1817	2320	2320	...	...	...	...
Salzburg Hbf 🛃 d.	1012	...	1216	1412	1412	1612	...	...	1816	2012	0140	0140	...	...	...	...
Bischofshofen d.	1054	...	1312	1454	1454	1654	...	...	1912	2054	|	|	...	...	...	...
Selzthal a.	|	...	1439	|	|	|	...	...	2039	|	|	|	...	...	...	...
Graz a.	|	...	1614	|	|	|	...	...	2214	|	|	|	...	...	...	...
Schwarzach St Veit d.	1111	...	...	1511	1511	1711	...	...	...	2111	|	|	0425	0425	...	...
Bad Gastein d.	1142	...	...	1542	1542	1742	...	...	...	2142	|	|	0500	0500	...	...
Villach Hbf a.	1243	1253	...	1643	1643	1843	1853	...	...	2243	0357	0357	0604	0604	...	...
Klagenfurt a.	1316	|	...	1717	|	1916	|	...	...	2316	|	|	|	|	...	...
Jesenice 🛃 a.	...	1329	...	...	1729	...	1929	...	...	...	0451	0451	0704	0704	...	...
Ljubljana a.	...	1432	...	...	1831	...	2033	2105	...	...	0600	0600	0809	0809	...	...
Rijeka a.	...	|	...	...	|	...	|	|	...	...	0927	|	|	|	...	...
Dobova 🛃 a.	...	1622	...	...	2006	...	2241	2242	...	...	...	0749	1000	1000	...	...
Zagreb a.	...	1710	...	...	2047	...	...	2337	...	...	...	0835	1041	1041	...	...
Zagreb d.	...	1732	...	...	...	...	...	2341	...	...	...	...	...	1107	...	...
Vinkovci a.	...	2119	...	...	...	...	...	0303	...	...	...	...	...	1432	...	...
Šid 🛃 a.	...	...	...	...	...	...	...	0341	...	...	...	...	...	1517	...	...
Beograd Centar a.	...	...	...	...	...	...	...	0605	...	...	...	...	...	1812	...	...
Beograd Topčider d.	...	...	...	...	...	...	...	...	...	...	...	...	...	...	...	...
Niš a.	...	...	...	...	...	...	...	...	...	...	...	...	...	...	0620	...
Dimitrovgrad (Serbia) 🛃 a.	...	...	...	...	...	...	...	...	...	...	...	...	...	...	0802	...
Dragoman 🛃 a.	...	...	...	...	...	...	...	...	...	...	...	...	...	...	...	1400
Sofia a.	...	...	...	...	...	...	...	...	...	...	...	...	...	...	...	1500
Tabanovci 🛃 a.	...	...	...	...	...	...	...	...	...	...	...	...	...	...	...	...
Skopje a.	...	...	...	...	...	...	...	...	...	...	...	...	...	...	...	...
Gevgelija 🛃 a.	...	...	...	...	...	...	...	...	...	...	...	...	...	...	...	...
Thessaloníki a.	...	...	...	...	...	...	...	...	...	...	...	...	...	...	...	...

train type		🚌		D	D	EN	EN	EC	D	D	EC	EC	EC	EC	D	RJ
train number	7990		2906	412	414	498	480	218	410	314	114	112	212	216	210	110
notes	2		2	414					314				112		T	
		✣		C	C	L	R		Q		W		◧			
Thessaloníki d.	...	...	...	...	...	...	...	...	...	...	...	...	...	...	...	...
Gevgelija 🛃 d.	...	...	...	...	...	...	...	...	...	...	...	...	...	...	...	...
Skopje d.	...	...	...	...	...	...	...	...	...	...	...	...	...	...	...	...
Tabanovci 🛃 d.	...	...	...	...	...	...	...	...	...	...	...	...	...	...	...	...
Sofia d.	0920	...	...	...	...	...	...	...	...	...	...	...	...	...	...	...
Dragoman 🛃 d.	1019	...	...	...	...	...	...	...	...	...	...	...	...	...	...	...
Dimitrovgrad (Serbia) 🛃 d.	...	1200	...	...	...	...	...	...	...	...	...	...	...	...	...	...
Niš d.	...	1400	1552	...	...	...	...	...	...	...	...	...	...	...	...	...
Beograd Topčider a.	...	...	|	...	...	...	...	...	...	...	...	...	...	...	...	...
Beograd Centar d.	...	...	2110	1005	...	...	...	...	2058	...	...	...	...	...	...	...
Šid 🛃 d.	...	...	...	1333	...	...	...	...	0022	...	...	...	...	...	...	...
Vinkovci d.	...	...	...	1443	...	...	...	...	0103	...	...	...	...	...	0853	...
Zagreb a.	...	...	...	1804	...	...	...	...	0428	...	...	...	...	...	1210	...
Zagreb d.	...	...	...	1839	1839	2127	...	...	0440	...	...	...	0702	...	1247	...
Dobova 🛃 d.	...	...	...	1925	1925	2207	...	...	0540	0540	...	...	0745	...	1332	...
Rijeka d.	...	...	...	|	|	|	2040	...	|	|	...	...	|	...	|	...
Ljubljana d.	...	...	...	2110	2110	2351	2351	...	0717	0726	...	...	0923	...	1527	...
Jesenice 🛃 d.	...	...	...	2213	2213	0057	0057	...	...	0832	...	...	1022	...	1632	...
Klagenfurt d.	...	...	...	|	|	|	|	...	...	|	0842	1027	|	...	|	1642
Villach Hbf d.	...	...	...	2326	2326	0150	0150	...	...	0908	0916	1116	1116	...	1708	1716
Bad Gastein a.	...	...	...	0027	0027	|	|	...	...	...	1016	1216	1216	...	...	1816
Schwarzach St Veit a.	...	...	...	0058	0058	0313	0313	...	...	...	1048	1248	1248	...	...	1848
Graz d.	...	...	...	...	...	|	|	0545	...	...	|	|	|	1145	...	|
Selzthal d.	...	...	...	...	...	|	|	0719	...	...	|	|	|	1319	...	|
Bischofshofen a.	...	...	...	...	...	|	|	0848	...	...	1105	1305	1305	1448	...	1905
Salzburg Hbf 🛃 a.	...	...	...	...	...	0404	0404	0944	...	...	1148	1348	1348	1544	...	1948
München Hbf a.	...	...	...	...	...	0629	0629	1141	...	...	1341	1541	1541	1741	...	2141
Augsburg a.	...	...	...	...	...	...	...	1215	...	...	1415	1615	1615	1815	...	...
Ulm a.	...	...	...	...	...	...	...	1301	...	...	1501	1701	1701	1901	...	...
Stuttgart Hbf a.	...	...	...	...	...	...	...	1359	...	...	1559	1759	1759	1959	...	...
Heidelberg a.	...	...	...	...	...	...	...	1444	...	...	|	1844	1844	|	...	...
Mannheim a.	...	...	...	...	...	...	...	|	...	...	1655	|	|	2048	...	...
Saarbrücken a.	...	...	...	...	...	...	...	|	...	...	|	|	|	2218	...	...
Frankfurt (Main) Hbf a.	...	...	...	...	...	...	...	1555	...	...	|	1940	1940	...	...	...
Köln Hbf a.	...	...	...	...	...	...	...	...	...	...	1943	...	...	...	...	...
Münster Hbf a.	...	...	...	...	...	...	...	...	...	...	|	...	...	...	...	...
Dortmund Hbf a.	...	...	...	...	...	...	...	...	...	...	2108	...	...	...	...	...

B – (2) Zürich (**465**) - Schwarzach St Veit (**415**) - Zagreb - Beograd. (2) Villach - Beograd. Conveys *EN* **40465** 🛏 1, 2 cl., ▬ 2 cl. (4, 6 berth) Zürich - Zagreb (Table **86**).

C – (2) Beograd (**414**) - Zagreb - Schwarzach St Veit (**464**) - Zürich. (2) Beograd - Villach. Conveys *EN* **414** 🛏 1, 2 cl., ▬ 2 cl. (4, 6 berth) Zagreb - Zürich (Table **86**).

F – (2) Zürich (**465**) - Schwarzach St Veit (**415**) - Zagreb - Beograd and Beograd (**414**) - Zagreb - Schwarzach St Veit (**464**) - Zürich. (12) Villach - Beograd and v.v. Conveys 🛏 1, 2 cl., ▬ 2 cl. Zürich - Zagreb and v.v. (Table **86**).

L – LISINSKI – 🛏 1, 2 cl., ▬ 2 cl. (4, 6 berth), (2) München - Salzburg - Zagreb and v.v.

P – June 20 - Sept. 13: ▬ 2 cl., (12) Ljubljana - Zagreb - Beograd.

Q – June 21 - Sept. 14: ▬ 2 cl., (12) Beograd - Zagreb - Ljubljana.

R – (2) (also 🛏 1, 2 cl., Aug. 1 - Sept. 30) München - Salzburg - Ljubljana - Rijeka and v.v.

T – SAVA – (2) Villach - Jesenice 🛃 - Ljubljana - Zagreb - Vinkovci and v.v. ✕ Jesenice 🛃 - Zagreb and v.v.

W – WÖRTHERSEE – (12) ✕ Münster - Klagenfurt and Klagenfurt - Dortmund.

✣ Rail tickets are not valid on bus services Dimitrovgrad (Serbia) - Niš.

◧ – Supplement payable: Jesenice 🛃 - Zagreb and v.v.

☛ **Shaded services are suspended until further notice.**

64 HAMBURG and BERLIN - WIEN - BUDAPEST

For alternative services via Břeclav see Table **60**

train type	ICE	ICE	ICE	ICE	ICE	RJX	ICE	ICE	ICE	RJX	ICE	RJX	ICE	ICE	ICE	EN	ICE	ICE	ICE	ICE	ICE	ICE	NJ	IC	
train number	**501**	**21**	**503**	**581**	**23**	**65**	**505**	**583**	**91**	**67**	**93**	**165**	**507**	**585**	**27**	**347**	**509**	**587**	**29**	**1601**	**639**	**229**	**491**	**95**	
notes	⚒			⚒										**535**		🅁				**1711**					
						C				**C**						**D**							**A**		
Hamburg Hbf d.		...	...	0454	...	...	...	0626	...	...	0804	...	...	0828	...	...	...	1028	...	...	1228	...	2029	...	...
Hannover Hbf d.	...	...	...	0626	...	...	...	0826	...	...	|	...	...	1026	...	...	...	1226	...	...	1426	...	2157	...	...
Berlin Hbf d.	0430	...	0630	|	...	...	0830	|	...	...	1004	...	1030	|	...	...	1230	|	...	1430	|	...	|	2229	...
Leipzig Hbf d.	0548	...	0748	|	...	...	0948	|	...	...	|	...	1148	|	...	...	1348	|	...	1548	|	...	|	0035	...
Nürnberg Hbf d.	0808	0831	0953	1024	1031	...	1153	1224	1231	...	1332	...	1353	1424	1431	...	1553	1628	1631	1753	1824	1831	0408	0600	...
Passau 🏛 d.	...	1026	...	...	1229	...	...	...	1429	...	1529	...	...	...	1629	...	...	...	1829	...	...	2031	0615	0824	...
Linz Hbf a.	...	1124	...	...	1325	...	...	...	1525	...	1625	...	...	...	1725	...	...	...	1925	...	...	2133	0746	0923	...
Wien Hbf a.	...	1245	...	...	1445	1542	...	...	1645	1740	1745	1842	...	...	1845	1942	...	...	2045	...	...	2305	0919	1045	...
Budapest Keleti § a.	...	...	...	...	...	1819	...	...	...	2019	...	2119	...	...	...	2220	...	...	...	...	...	...	...	...	...

train type	ICE	ICE	ICE	EN	ICE	ICE	ICE	RJX	ICE	ICE	RJX	ICE	ICE	ICE	RJX	ICE	ICE	ICE	RJX	ICE	ICE	ICE	IC	EC	NJ
train number	**228**	**538**	**508**	**346**	**28**	**586**	**506**	**162**	**92**	**786**	**60**	**26**	**584**	**504**	**62**	**90**	**582**	**502**	**64**	**22**	**580**	**500**	**94**	**148**	**490**
notes				🅁																					
				D							**C**				**C**				**C**		⑦			**J**	**A**
Budapest Keleti § d.	...	...	...	0540	...	...	...	0640	...	...	0740	...	...	...	0940	...	...	...	1140	...	...	...	...	1640	...
Wien Hbf d.	0651	...	...	0821	0915	...	...	0921	1015	...	1021	1115	...	...	1221	1315	...	...	1421	1515	...	...	1915	1921	2013
Linz Hbf d.	0817	...	...	...	1035	...	...	...	1135	...	...	1235	...	...	...	1435	...	...	...	1635	...	...	2037	...	2136
Passau 🏛 a.	0924	...	...	...	1131	...	...	...	1231	...	...	1331	...	...	...	1531	...	...	...	1731	...	...	2137	...	2235
Nürnberg Hbf a.	1127	1133	1204	...	1327	1333	1404	...	1428	1429	...	1528	1534	1604	...	1729	1735	1804	...	1928	1934	2004	2400	...	0056
Leipzig Hbf a.	...	|	1410	...	...	|	1610	...	|	|	...	...	|	1810	...	...	|	2010	...	...	|	2210	0450	...	|
Berlin Hbf a.	...	|	1529	...	...	|	1729	...	1758	|	...	...	|	1930	...	...	|	2129	...	...	|	2335	0631	...	|
Hannover Hbf a.	...	1532	...	...	...	1732	...	...	...	1832	...	...	1932	...	...	...	2132	...	...	...	2341	...	...	...	0649
Hamburg Hbf a.	...	1729	...	...	...	1929	...	...	...	2029	...	...	2129	...	...	...	2329	...	...	...	0117	...	...	...	0847

A – *ÖBB nightjet* – 🛏 1, 2 cl., ▬ 2 cl. (4, 6 berth), (2) Hamburg - Wien and v.v. Special fares apply. See Table **53**.

C – ÖBB *Railjet* service: München - Wien - Budapest and v.v.

D – DACIA – 🛏 1, 2 cl., ▬ 2 cl., (2) Wien - Budapest - Bucuresti and v.v.

J – SEMMELWEIS – (12) Budapest - Wien.

§ – 🏛 is at Hegyeshalom.

RJ / RJX – ÖBB *Railjet* service, ✕, (1) (business class), (1) (first class), (2) (economy class).

65 MÜNCHEN - SALZBURG - WIEN - BUDAPEST - BUCUREŞTI

Engineering work is affecting services between München and Salzburg until August 1

train type	RJX	EN	RJX	EC	RJX	RJX	EC	RJX	RJ	RJX	EC	RJX	EC	RJX	EC	RJX	EN	EC	RJX	EC	RJX	RJX	EN	EC	RJX	RJX
train number	**41**	**467**	**761**	**141**	**269**	**265**	**143**	**61**	**111**	**765**	**145**	**63**	**217**	**161**	**147**	**65**	**473**	**113**	**563**	**149**	**67**	**165**	**347**	**115**	**165**	**69**
notes		**B**					**L**					**F**					🅁			**G**			🅁			
																	C						**D**			
München Hbf d.	...	...	...	...	...	0622	...	0723	0817	...	...	0929	1017	...	...	1129	...	1217	...	...	1329	...	...	1417	...	1529
Salzburg Hbf 🏛 a.	...	...	...	...	...	0758	...	0858	0959	...	...	1058	1159	...	...	1258	...	1359	...	...	1458	...	...	1559	...	1658
Salzburg Hbf 🏛 d.	...	0436	0605	...	0708	0808	...	0908	...	1008	...	1108	...	1208	...	1308	...	...	1408	...	1508	...	...	...	1608	1708
Linz Hbf d.	...	0558	0716	...	0816	0916	...	1016	...	1116	...	1216	...	1316	...	1416	...	...	1516	...	1616	...	...	...	1716	1816
St Pölten Hbf d.	...	0710	0802	...	0902	1002	...	1102	...	1202	...	1302	...	1402	...	1502	...	...	1602	...	1702	...	...	...	1802	1902
Wien Meidling d.	...	0744	0825	...	0925	1025	...	1125	...	1225	...	1325	...	1425	...	1525	...	...	1625	...	1725	...	...	...	1825	1925
Wien Hbf d.	0740	0755	0830	0840	0940	1030	1040	1140	...	1230	1240	1340	...	1430	1437	1542	...	...	1630	1642	1740	1842	1942	...	1830	1930
Hegyeshalom 🏛 a.	0825	...	...	0925	1025	...	1125	1225	...	...	1325	1425	...	...	1521	1625	...	...	...	1725	1825	1925	2025	...	...	...
Györ a.	0853	...	...	0953	1053	...	1153	1253	...	...	1353	1453	...	...	1553	1653	...	...	...	1753	1853	1953	2053	...	...	...
Budapest Keleti a.	1019	...	...	1119	1219	...	1319	1419	...	...	1519	1619	...	...	1719	1819	1910	...	...	1919	2019	2119	2220	...	...	...
Bucureşti Nord a.	...	...	...	...	...	...	...	...	...	...	...	...	...	...	...	...	1233	...	...	...	...	...	1600	...	...	...

train type	EC	RJX	EC	RJX	EC	RJX	IC	RJX	IC	RJ	EN
train number	**219**	**167**	**341**	**261**	**117**	**169**	**1299**	**663**	**1291**	**367**	**463**
notes		**Q**									**A**
							Ⓑ		Ⓑ		
München Hbf d.	1617	...	...	1730	1817	...	1917	...	2017	...	2320
Salzburg Hbf 🏛 a.	1759	...	...	1858	1959	...	2100	...	2202	...	0106
Salzburg Hbf 🏛 d.	...	1808	...	1908	...	2008	...	2108	...	2208	0345
Linz Hbf d.	...	1916	...	2016	...	2116	...	2216	...	2319	0510
St Pölten Hbf d.	...	2002	...	2102	...	2202	...	2302	...	0005	0602
Wien Meidling d.	...	2025	...	2125	...	2225	...	2325	...	0026	0629
Wien Hbf d.	...	2030	2042	2140	...	2230	...	2330	...	0033	0640
Hegyeshalom 🏛 a.	...	...	2125	2225	...	...	...	...	...	...	0723
Györ a.	...	...	2153	2253	...	...	...	...	...	...	0753
Budapest Keleti a.	...	...	2319	0019	...	...	...	...	...	...	0919
Bucureşti Nord a.	...	...	...	...	...	...	...	...	...	...	...

train type	RJX	IC	RJX	RJX	EC	RJX	EN	RJX	EC	RJX
train number	**368**	**1290**	**260**	**160**	**218**	**262**	**346**	**162**	**114**	**60**
notes				**P**			🅁			
							D			
Bucureşti Nord d.	...	...	...	...	...	...	1400	...	...	...
Budapest Keleti d.	...	...	...	...	...	...	0540	0640	...	0740
Györ d.	...	...	...	...	...	...	0702	0802	...	0902
Hegyeshalom 🏛 d.	...	...	...	...	...	...	0732	0832	...	0932
Wien Hbf d.	0530	...	0630	0730	...	0830	0821	0930	...	1030
Wien Meidling d.	0537	...	0637	0737	...	0837	...	0937	...	1037
St Pölten Hbf d.	0600	...	0700	0800	...	0900	...	1000	...	1100
Linz Hbf d.	0646	...	0746	0846	...	0946	...	1046	...	1146
Salzburg Hbf 🏛 a.	0754	...	0852	0952	...	1052	...	1152	...	1252
Salzburg Hbf 🏛 d.	...	0800	0900	...	1000	1100	...	...	1200	1300
München Hbf a.	...	0941	1030	...	1141	1230	...	...	1341	1432

train type	EC	RJX	EC	EN	RJX	EC	RJX	EC	RJX	EC	RJX		RJX	EC	RJX	RJ	RJX	EC	RJX	RJX		EC	NJ	RJX	EN	
train number	**140**	**564**	**112**	**472**	**62**	**142**	**166**	**216**	**64**	**144**	**168**		**66**	**146**	**760**	**110**	**68**	**148**	**762**	**42**		**340**	**466**	**264**	**462**	
notes	**J**			🅁								2	**866**	**N**							2		**B**		**A**	
				C									**F**													
Bucureşti Nord d.	...	...	...	1745	...	...	...	...	...	...	...	...	...	...	...	...	...	...	...	...	...	...	...	...	...	...
Budapest Keleti d.	0840	...	...	0850	0940	1040	...	...	1140	1240	...	...	1340	1440	...	...	1540	1640	...	1740	...	1840	...	1940	2040	...
Györ d.	1002	...	...	...	1102	1202	...	...	1302	1402	...	...	1502	1602	...	...	1702	1802	...	1902	...	2002	...	2102	2202	...
Hegyeshalom 🏛 d.	1032	...	...	...	1132	1232	...	...	1332	1432	...	...	1532	1632	...	...	1732	1832	...	1932	...	2032	...	2132	2232	...
Wien Hbf d.	1121	1130	...	...	1230	1321	1330	...	1430	1521	1530	...	1630	1721	1730	...	1830	1921	1930	2030	...	2118	2127	2221	2327	...
Wien Meidling d.	...	1137	...	...	1237	...	1337	...	1437	...	1537	...	1637	...	1737	...	1837	...	1937	2037	...	...	2135	...	2335	...
St Pölten Hbf d.	...	1200	...	...	1300	...	1400	...	1500	...	1600	...	1700	...	1800	...	1900	...	2000	2100	...	...	2202	...	0001	...
Linz Hbf d.	...	1246	...	...	1346	...	1446	...	1546	...	1646	...	1746	...	1846	...	1946	...	2046	2146	...	...	2258	...	0059	...
Salzburg Hbf 🏛 a.	...	1352	...	...	1452	...	1552	...	1652	...	1752	...	1852	...	1952	...	2052	...	2152	2251	...	...	0024	...	0210	...
Salzburg Hbf 🏛 d.	...	...	1400	...	1500	...	...	1600	1700	...	...	1815	1900	...	...	2000	2100	...	...	...	2300	...	...	...	0427	...
München Hbf a.	...	...	1541	...	1633	...	...	1741	1831	...	...	2006	2032	...	...	2141	2231	...	...	...	0058	...	...	...	0629	...

A – KÁLMÁN IMRE – 🛏 1, 2 cl., ▬ 2 cl. (4, 6 berth) (2) München - Wien - Budapest and v.v.

B – *ÖBB nightjet*. WIENER WALZER - 🛏 1, 2 cl., ▬ 2 cl. (4, 6 berth), (2) Wien - Salzburg - Zürich and v.v.

C – *EuroNight* ISTER – 🛏 1, 2 cl., ▬ 1, 2 cl., (2) Budapest - Bucureşti and v.v.

D – DACIA – 🛏 1, 2 cl., ▬ 2 cl., (2) ✕ Wien - Budapest - Bucureşti and v.v.

F – From / to Frankfurt (Main) Hbf / Stuttgart on dates shown in Table **930**.

G – (12) Wien - Budapest - Szolnok (arrive 2102) - Debrecen (2235) - Zahony (0010). Conveys 🛏 1, 2 cl. Wien - Zahony - Lviv - Kyïv; see Table **96**.

J – (12) Zahony (depart 0405) - Debrecen (0531) - Szolnok (0657) - Budapest - Wien. Conveys 🛏 1, 2 cl. Kyïv - Lviv - Zahony - Wien; see Table **96**.

L – TRANSILVANIA – (12) ✕ Wien - Budapest - Szolnok (arrive 1502) - Cluj Napoca (2225).

N – TRANSILVANIA – (12) ✕ Cluj Napoca (depart 0740) - Szolnok (1257) - Budapest - Wien.

P – From Bratislava, depart 0608.

Q – To Bratislava, arrive 2152.

r – ①–⑥.

RJ / RJX – ÖBB *Railjet* service, ✕, (1) (business class), (1) (first class), (2) (economy class).

♥ – Operated by REGIOJET. Separate fare tariff applies.

DORTMUND - KÖLN - FRANKFURT - WIEN - BUDAPEST 66

Engineering work is affecting services Frankfurt - Würzburg and v.v.; please refer to Table 920 for amended timings

train type	*ICE*	*ICE*	*ICE*	*ICE*	*EN*	*ICE*	*ICE*	*NJ*	*RJX*
train number	**21**	**23**	**91**	**27**	**347**	**29**	**229**	**40421**	**269**
notes					D Ⓡ			A	
Dortmund Hbf ..... d.	...	0431	0627	0827	...	1027	1227	...	...
Düsseldorf Hbf ..... d.	...	0527	⊙	⊙	...	⊙	⊙	2143	...
Köln Hbf ..... d.	...	0553	0753	0953	...	1153	1353	2216	...
Bonn Hbf ..... d.	...	0614	0814	1014	...	1214	1414	2311	...
Koblenz Hbf ..... d.	...	0648	0848	1048	...	1248	1448	2346	...
Mainz Hbf ..... d.	...	0740	0742	1142	...	1342	1542	0056	...
Frankfurt Flug. ✈ ..... d.	...	0802	1001	1202	...	1402	1602	0120	...
Frankfurt (M) Hbf ..... d.	0621	0822	1011f	1222	...	1422	1621	0131f	...
Würzburg Hbf ..... d.	0735	0934	1134	1334	...	1534	1735	0242	...
Nürnberg Hbf ..... d.	0831	1031	1231	1431	...	1631	1831	0408	...
Regensburg Hbf ..... d.	0926	1126	1326	1526	...	1726	1926	0505	...
Passau Hbf 🏛 ..... d.	1026	1229	1429	1629	...	1829	2031	0613	...
Linz ..... a.	1124	1325	1525	1725	...	1925	2133	0746	...
Wien Hbf ..... a.	1245	1445	1645	1845	...	2045	2305	0919	...
	RJX	*RJX*	*RJX*			*RJX*			
	63	**65**	**67**			**261**			
Wien Hbf ..... d.	1340	1542	1740	...	1942	2140	...	...	0942
Hegyeshalom 🏛 ..... a.	1425	1625	1825	...	2025	2225	...	...	1025
Budapest Keleti ..... a.	1619	1819	2019	...	2220	0019	...	...	1219

train type	*ICE*	*EN*	*RJX*	*RJX*	*RJX*	*RJX*	*EC*	*NJ*	
train number	**228**	**346**	**60**	**62**	**64**	**66**	**148**	**40490**	
notes		D Ⓡ					S	A	
Budapest Keleti ..... d.	...	0540	0740	0940	1140	1340	1640	...	...
Hegyeshalom 🏛 ..... d.	...	0732	0932	1132	1332	1532	1832	...	...
Wien Hbf ..... a.	...	0821	1021	1221	1421	1621	1921	...	...
		ICE	*ICE*	*ICE*	*ICE*	*ICE*			
		28	**26**	**90**	**22**	**20**			
Wien Hbf ..... d.	0651	0915	1115	1315	1515	1715	...	2013	...
Linz ..... d.	0817	1035	1235	1435	1635	1835	...	2136	...
Passau Hbf 🏛 ..... a.	0925	1131	1331	1531	1731	1934	...	2235	...
Regensburg Hbf ..... a.	1030	1230	1433	1633	1833	2033	...	2354	...
Nürnberg Hbf ..... a.	1127	1327	1528	1729	1928	2128	...	0056	...
Würzburg Hbf ..... a.	1222	1422	1622	1821	2022	2222	...	|	...
Frankfurt (M) Hbf ..... a.	1336	1536	1736	1945f	2136	2339	...	0345f	...
Frankfurt Flug. ✈ ..... a.	1356	1556	1756	1956	2157	...	...	0356	...
Mainz Hbf ..... a.	1418	1618	1818	2018	2218	...	...	0416	...
Koblenz Hbf ..... a.	1511	1711	1911	2111	2311	...	...	0511	...
Bonn Hbf ..... a.	1543	1743	1942	2143	2343	...	...	0558	...
Köln Hbf ..... a.	1605	1805	2005	2205	0005	...	...	0651	...
Düsseldorf Hbf ..... a.	⊙	1832	⊙	⊙	0031	...	...	0723	...
Dortmund Hbf ..... a.	1721	2016	2129	2321	0121	...	...	...	...

A – *ÖBB nightjet* 🛏 1, 2 cl., 🛌 2 cl. (4, 6 berth), 🚃2 Amsterdam - Düsseldorf - Wien and v.v. ♣ (Table **53**).

D – DACIA – 🛏 1, 2 cl., 🛌 2 cl., 🚃2 ✗ Wien - Budapest - Bucureşti and v.v.

S – SEMMELWEIS – 🚃12 Budapest - Wien.

f – Frankfurt (Main) **Süd**.

⊙ – Via Hagen, Wuppertal (Table **800**).

♣ – Special fares apply.

RJ – ÖBB *Railjet* service. 🚃1 (business class), 🚃1 (first class), 🚃2 (economy class), ✗.

MÜNCHEN - INNSBRUCK - VENEZIA and MILANO 70

Engineering work is affecting services between München and Innsbruck until August 1

	EC	*EC*	*EC*	*FR*	*EC*		*FR*	*FR*	*EC*	*EC*	*FA*	*EC*	*FR*	*FR*	*EC*	*FR*	*EC*	*EC*		*NJ*	*NJ*		*NJ*		
	1281	**81**	**37**	**9732**	**83**		**9738**	**9439**	**85**	**42**	**8525**	**87**	**9751**	**9756**	**89**	**9759**	**287**	**289**		**295**	**40295**		**40463**		
	♥	♥	Ⓡ	Ⓡ	♥		Ⓡ	**9441**	♥	Ⓡ	Ⓡ	♥	Ⓡ	Ⓡ	♥	Ⓡ	♥	♥							
	⑥⑦	①–⑤	⊗	↯	P	2	↯	Ⓡ↯		⊗	↯		↯	↯		↯				B	D		C		
	✗	✗	🍷	🍷	✗		🍷	🍷	✗	🍷	🍷	✗	🍷	🍷	✗	🍷	🍷	🍷		🍷	🍷		🍷		
München Hbf ..... d.	0734	0734	...	...	0934	...	...	...	1134	...	...	1334	...	...	1534	...	1734	1934	...	2010	2010	...	2320	...	...
München Ost ..... d.	0744	0744	...	...	0944	...	...	...	1144	...	...	1344	...	...	1544	...	1744	1944	...	2020	2020	...	2331	...	...
Kufstein 🏛 ..... a.	0834	0834	...	...	1034	...	...	...	1234	...	...	1434	...	...	1634	...	1834	2034	...	|	|	...	|	...	...
Wörgl ..... a.	0844	0844	...	...	1044	...	...	...	1244	...	...	1444	...	...	1644	...	1844	2044	...	|	|	...	|	...	...
Jenbach ..... a.	0859	0859	...	...	1059	...	...	...	1259	...	...	1459	...	...	1659	...	1859	2059	...	|	|	...	|	...	...
Innsbruck Hbf ..... a.	0918	0918	...	...	1118	...	...	...	1318	...	...	1518	...	...	1718	...	1918	2118	...	|	|	...	|	...	...
Innsbruck Hbf ..... d.	0924	0924	...	...	1124	...	...	...	1324	...	...	1524	...	...	1724	...	...	...	...	|	|	...	|	...	...
Brennero / Brenner 🏛 ..... a.	1000	1000	...	...	1200	...	...	...	1400	...	...	1600	...	...	1800	...	...	...	...	◧	◧	...	◧	...	...
Bolzano / Bozen ..... a.	1127	1127	...	...	1327	...	...	...	1527	...	...	1727	...	...	1927	...	...	...	...	|	|	...	|	...	...
Trento ..... a.	1202	1202	...	...	1402	...	...	...	1602	...	...	1802	...	...	2002	...	...	...	...	|	|	...	|	...	...
Padova ..... a.	|	|	...	...	|	...	...	...	|	...	...	|	...	...	|	...	...	...	...	|	0457	...	|	...	...
Verona ..... a.	1256	1256	1330	1402	1458	1521	1532	...	1658	1732	1752	1858	1930	1932	2056	2130	...	...	...	|	0551	...	|	...	...
Padova ..... a.	1358	|	1412	|	|	1619	|	...	1756	|	|	|	2012	|	...	2212	...	...	...	0409	|	...	|	...	...
Venezia Mestre ..... a.	1414	|	1428	|	|	1636	|	...	1812	|	|	|	2028	|	...	2228	...	...	...	|	|	...	0822	...	...
Venezia Santa Lucia ..... a.	1428	|	1440	|	|	1648	|	...	1825	|	|	|	2040	|	...	2240	...	...	...	|	|	...	0834	...	...
Milano Centrale ..... a.	...	|	...	1515	|	...	1645	...	...	1855	|	|	...	2045	...	...	...	...	...	|	0810j	...	...	...	...
Bologna Centrale ..... a.	...	1410	...	...	1619	...	...	1655	...	...	1842	2016	...	...	...	...	...	...	...	0515	...	...	...	...	...
Rimini ..... a.	...	...	...	...	1733t	...	...	|	...	...	|	...	...	...	...	...	...	...	...	|	...	...	...	...	...
Firenze SMN ..... a.	...	...	...	...	...	...	...	1730	...	...	1925¶	...	...	...	...	...	...	...	...	0618	...	...	...	...	...
Roma Termini ..... a.	...	...	...	...	...	...	...	1910	...	...	2045	...	...	...	...	...	...	...	...	0910	...	...	...	...	...

	EC	*EC*	*FR*	*FR*	*EC*	*FR*	*FR*	*FR*	*EC*	*FB*	*FR*	*FR*	*FR*	*EC*	*FA*	*EC*	*EC*		*FR*	*EC*	*EC*	*EC*	*NJ*	*NJ*	*NJ*
	288	**286**	**9708**	**9705**	**88**	**8504**	**9716**	**8709**	**86**	**9715**	**9717**	**9724**	**9518**	**84**	**8512**	**15**	**82**		**9737**	**10**	**80**	**1280**	**40236**	**294**	**40235**
	♥	♥	Ⓡ	Ⓡ	♥	Ⓡ	Ⓡ	Ⓡ	♥	Ⓡ	Ⓡ↯	Ⓡ	Ⓡ	♥	Ⓡ	Ⓡ	♥		Ⓡ	Ⓡ	♥	♥			
			↯	↯		↯	↯	↯		↯	⑥⑦	↯	↯	R	↯	↯			↯	⊗	①–⑤	⑥⑦	F	B	G
	🍷	🍷	🍷	🍷	✗	🍷	🍷	🍷	✗	🍷	🍷	🍷	🍷	✗	🍷	🍷	✗		🍷	🍷	✗	✗	🍷	🍷	🍷
Roma Termini ..... d.	...	...	...	...	...	0645	...	...	...	...	...	...	0920	...	1045	...	...	...	...	...	...	...	...	2017	...
Firenze SMN ..... d.	...	...	...	...	...	0803¶	...	...	...	...	...	...	1100	...	1203¶	...	...	...	...	...	...	...	...	2231	...
Rimini ..... d.	...	...	...	...	...	|	...	...	...	...	...	...	|	1034f	|	...	...	...	...	...	...	...	...	|	...
Bologna Centrale ..... d.	...	...	...	...	0745	0845	...	...	...	...	...	...	1135	1152	1245	...	...	1410	...	...	1550	...	...	2345	...
Milano Centrale ..... d.	...	...	...	0715	|	|	...	0915	...	0945	1015	...	...	|	|	1305	...	|	1515	...	|	...	...	|	2110j
Venezia Santa Lucia ..... d.	...	...	0720	|	|	|	...	|	...	|	|	1050	...	|	|	|	1335	|	|	1520	|	1535	2105	|	|
Venezia Mestre ..... d.	...	...	0732	|	|	|	0902	|	...	|	|	1102	...	|	|	|	1347	|	|	1532	|	1547	2117	|	|
Padova ..... d.	...	...	0748	|	|	|	0918	|	...	|	|	1118	...	|	|	|	1403	|	|	1548	|	1603	|	0049	|
Verona ..... d.	...	...	0830	0828	0901	0937	1000	1028	1101	1058	1128	1200	...	1301	1337	1428	1501	1540	1628	1630	1701	1701	|	|	2258
Padova ..... d.	...	...	...	...	|	...	...	...	|	...	...	...	...	|	...	...	...	...	...	...	|	|	|	|	2343
Trento ..... d.	...	...	...	...	0959	...	...	...	1159	...	...	...	...	1359	...	...	1559	...	...	...	1759	1759	|	|	|
Bolzano / Bozen ..... d.	...	...	...	...	1034	...	...	...	1234	...	...	...	...	1434	...	...	1634	...	...	...	1834	1834	|	|	|
Brennero / Brenner 🏛 ..... d.	...	...	...	...	1200	...	...	...	1400	...	...	...	...	1600	...	...	1800	...	...	...	2000	2000	◧	◧	◧
Innsbruck Hbf ..... a.	...	...	...	...	1236	...	...	...	1436	...	...	...	...	1636	...	...	1836	...	...	...	2036	2036	|	|	|
Innsbruck Hbf ..... d.	0717	1040	...	...	1240	...	...	...	1440	...	...	...	...	1640	...	...	1840	...	...	...	2040	2040	|	|	|
Jenbach ..... d.	0735	1101	...	...	1301	...	...	...	1501	...	...	...	...	1701	...	...	1901	...	...	...	2101	2101	|	|	|
Wörgl ..... d.	0749	1116	...	...	1316	...	...	...	1516	...	...	...	...	1716	...	...	1916	...	...	...	2116	2116	|	|	|
Kufstein 🏛 ..... a.	0757	1124	...	...	1324	...	...	...	1524	...	...	...	...	1724	...	...	1924	...	...	...	2124	2124	|	|	|
München Ost ..... a.	0849	1215	...	...	1416	...	...	...	1616	...	...	...	...	1816	...	...	2014	...	...	...	2216	2216	0615	|	|
München Hbf ..... a.	0902	1226	...	...	1427	...	...	...	1627	...	...	...	...	1827	...	...	2026	...	...	...	2227	2227	0629	0920	0920

B – *ÖBB nightjet* – 🛏 1, 2 cl., 🛌 2 cl. (4, 6 berth), 🚃2 München - Villach - Tarvisio 🏛 - Roma and v.v. Special fares apply.

C – *ÖBB nightjet* – 🛏 1, 2 cl., 🛌 2 cl. (4, 6 berth), 🚃2 München (**463**) - Villach (**237**) - Tarvisio 🏛 - Venezia. Special fares apply.

D – *ÖBB nightjet* – 🛏 1, 2 cl., 🛌 2 cl. (4, 6 berth), 🚃2 München (**295**) - Villach (**233**) - Tarvisio 🏛 - Verona - Milano. Special fares apply.

F – *ÖBB nightjet* – 🛏 1, 2 cl., 🛌 2 cl. (4, 6 berth), 🚃2 Venezia (**236**) - Tarvisio 🏛 - Villach (**498**) - München. Special fares apply.

G – *ÖBB nightjet* – 🛏 1, 2 cl., 🛌 2 cl. (4, 6 berth), 🚃2 Milano (**234**) - Verona - Tarvisio 🏛 - Villach (**294**) - München. Special fares apply.

P – 🚃12 ✗ München - Bologna - (Rimini May 26 - Sept. 10).

R – 🚃12 ✗ (Rimini May 27 - Sept. 11) - Bologna - München.

f – May 27 - Sept. 11.

j – Milano **Porta Garibaldi**.

t – May 26 - Sept. 10.

⊗ – Compulsory reservation for international journeys. Supplement payable for international journeys and for internal journeys within Italy.

◧ – 🏛 is Tarvisio (Table **88**).

↯ – Supplement payable.

♥ – DB-ÖBB EuroCity service.

¶ – Firenze **Campo di Marte**.

73 AMSTERDAM, BERLIN, DORTMUND and KÖLN - BASEL - ZÜRICH and MILANO

train type	ICE	EC	ICE	ICE	EC	ICE	EC	ICE	EC	ICE	EC	ICE	ICE	IR	EC	ICE	ICE	EC	ICE	EC	EC
train number	3	315	271	5	327	101	151	275	57	71	7	121	277	2327	321	105	73	9	279	9	323
notes	Ⓐ	🄁 ⊗	1271 M	⚒	🄁 ⊗		🄁 ⊗		🄁 ⊗			⚒			🄁 ⊗						🄁 ⊗
Hamburg Hbf d.	...	...	0045e	...	...	...	...	...	...	0554	0437	...	...	...	...	...	0802	0646	...	...	...
Bremen Hbf d.	...	...	|	...	...	...	...	...	...	|	0540	...	...	...	...	...	|	0744	...	...	...
Berlin Hbf d.	...	...	|	...	...	...	...	0430p	...	|	|	...	0630	...	...	...	|	|	0830	...	...
Hannover Hbf d.	...	...	0210e	...	...	...	...	|	...	0741	|	...	|	...	...	...	0941	|	|	...	...
Dortmund Hbf d.	...	...	|	...	...	0536v	...	|	...	|	|	...	|	...	...	...	|	|	|	...	...
Essen Hbf d.	...	...	|	...	...	|	...	|	...	|	0800	...	|	...	...	...	|	1000	|	...	...
Amsterdam Centraal d.	...	...	|	...	...	|	...	|	...	|	|	0638	|	...	...	0808	|	|	|	...	...
Utrecht Centraal d.	...	...	|	...	...	|	...	|	...	|	|	0706	|	...	...	0834	|	|	|	...	...
Arnhem ⊙ d.	...	...	|	...	...	|	...	|	...	|	|	0737	|	...	...	0907	|	|	|	...	...
Duisburg Hbf d.	...	...	|	...	...	h	...	|	...	|	0813	0834	|	...	...	1007	|	1013	|	...	...
Düsseldorf Hbf d.	...	...	|	...	...	|	...	|	...	|	0827	0848	|	...	...	1022	|	1027	|	...	...
Köln Hbf d.	...	...	|	...	...	0654	...	|	...	|	0853	0928x	|	...	...	1054	|	1053	|	...	...
Bonn Hbf d.	...	...	|	...	...	|	...	|	...	|	0914	|	|	...	...	|	|	1114	|	...	...
Koblenz Hbf d.	...	...	|	...	...	⊖	...	|	...	|	0948	⊖	|	...	...	⊖	|	1148	|	...	...
Mainz Hbf d.	...	...	|	...	...	|	...	|	...	|	1042	|	|	...	...	|	|	1242	|	...	...
Frankfurt Flughafen ✈ d.	...	...	|	...	...	0752	...	|	...	|	|	1018	|	...	...	1152	|	|	|	...	...
Frankfurt (Main) Hbf d.	...	...	0550	0648	...	|	0804	0850	...	1006	|	1031	1050	...	...	|	1206	|	1250	...	...
Mannheim Hbf d.	...	...	0633	0735	...	0835	0849	0935	...	1046	1123	...	1134	...	...	1235	1246	1323	1335	...	...
Karlsruhe Hbf d.	0556	...	0658	0800	...	0900	0913	1000	...	1111	1149	...	1200	...	...	1300	1311	1349	1400	...	...
Freiburg (Brsg) Hbf d.	0702	...	0803	0901	...	1005	1016	1102	...	1213	1250	...	1302	...	...	1401	1413	1455	1501	...	...
Basel Bad Bf 🏛 a.	0736	...	0836	0935	...	1038	1046	1135	...	1246	1324	...	1337	...	...	1435	1446	1528	1535	←	...
Basel SBB a.	0747	...	0847	0947	...	1047	1055	1147	...	1255	1333	...	1347	...	...	1447	1455	1536	1547	1536	...
Basel SBB ★ d.	0806	...	0906	...	...	...	1103	1156	1228	1306	1356	...	...	1403	...	...	1506	1606	...	1606	...
Bern a.	|	...	|	...	...	...	|	1256	1326	|	1456	...	...	|	...	...	|	→	...	|	...
Interlaken Ost a.	|	...	|	...	...	...	|	1358	|	|	1558	...	...	|	...	...	|	...	...	|	...
Zürich HB a.	0900	0933	1000	...	1033	...	|	...	|	1400	...	...	...	|	1533	...	1600	...	...	1700	1733
Chur a.	...	|	1123	...	|	...	|	...	|	1523	...	...	...	|	|	...	...	...	...	...	|
Arth-Goldau a.	...	1016	...	...	1116	...	1245	...	|	...	...	...	...	1545	1616	...	...	...	...	...	1816
Bellinzona a.	...	1112	...	...	1212	...	1342	...	|	...	...	...	...	...	1712	...	...	...	...	...	1912
Lugano a.	...	1132	...	...	1230	...	1358	...	|	...	...	...	...	...	1732	...	...	...	...	...	1932
Chiasso 🏛 a.	...	1202	...	...	1255	...	1446	...	◧	...	...	...	...	...	1802	...	...	...	...	...	2002
Como San Giovanni a.	...	1210	...	...	1308	...	1501	...	|	...	...	...	...	...	1810	...	...	...	...	...	2038
Milano Centrale a.	...	1250	...	...	1409f	...	1555g	...	1640	...	...	...	...	...	1850	...	...	...	...	...	2050

train type	ICE	ICE	EC	EC	ICE	ICE	ICE	ICE	ICE	ICE	ICE		NJ	NJ	NJ	IC	EC
train number	107	75	59	325	123	371	109	77	125	373	79		403	401	471	2315	315
notes			🄁 ⊗	🄁 ⊗									E	471 A	B		🄁 ⊗
Hamburg Hbf d.	...	1001	...	...	...	...	...	1201	...	...	1401	...	...	2050	...	...	...
Bremen Hbf d.	...	|	...	...	...	...	...	|	...	...	|	...	...	2153	...	...	...
Berlin Hbf d.	...	|	...	...	...	1030	...	|	...	1230	|	...	...	|	2054	...	...
Hannover Hbf d.	...	1141	...	...	...	|	...	1341	...	|	1541	...	...	0040	|	...	...
Dortmund Hbf d.	...	|	...	...	...	|	...	|	...	|	|	...	...	|	|	...	...
Essen Hbf d.	...	|	...	...	...	|	...	|	...	|	|	...	...	|	|	...	...
Amsterdam Centraal d.	...	|	...	...	1038	|	...	|	1238	|	|	...	2045	|	|	...	...
Utrecht Centraal d.	...	|	...	...	1104	|	...	|	1304	|	|	...	2126	|	|	...	...
Arnhem ⊙ d.	...	|	...	...	1137	|	...	|	1337	|	|	...	|	|	|	...	...
Duisburg Hbf d.	...	|	...	...	1234	|	...	|	1438	|	|	...	2301	|	|	...	...
Düsseldorf Hbf d.	...	|	...	...	1248	|	...	|	1454	|	|	...	2316	|	|	...	...
Köln Hbf d.	1254	|	...	...	1328x	|	1454	|	1521x	|	|	...	2353	|	|	...	...
Bonn Hbf d.	|	|	...	...	|	|	|	|	|	|	|	...	0014	|	|	...	...
Koblenz Hbf d.	⊖	|	...	...	⊖	|	⊖	|	⊖	|	|	...	0049	|	|	...	...
Mainz Hbf d.	|	|	...	...	|	|	|	|	|	|	|	...	0142	|	|	...	...
Frankfurt Flughafen ✈ d.	1352	|	...	...	1413	|	1552	|	1618	|	|	...	0211	|	|	...	...
Frankfurt (Main) Hbf d.	|	1406	...	...	1426	1450	|	1606	1631	1650	1806	...	0245	0400	0400	...	...
Mannheim Hbf d.	1435	1446	...	...	...	1535	1635	1646	...	1735	1846	...	0333	0440	0440	...	...
Karlsruhe Hbf d.	1500	1511	...	...	...	1600	1700	1711	...	1800	1911	...	0403	0509	0509	...	...
Freiburg (Brsg) Hbf d.	1601	1613	...	...	...	1701	1801	1813	...	1901	2013	...	0529	0620	0620	...	...
Basel Bad Bf 🏛 a.	1635	1646	...	...	...	1735	1835	1846	...	1935	2046	...	0611	0657	0657	...	...
Basel SBB a.	1647	1655	...	...	...	1747	1847	1855	...	1947	2055	...	0620	0720	0720	...	...
Basel SBB ★ d.	...	1706	1728	...	...	1756	...	1906	...	1956	2106	...	|	|	|	0803	...
Bern a.	...	|	1826	...	...	1856	...	|	...	2056	|	...	|	|	|	|	...
Interlaken Ost a.	...	|	|	...	...	1958	...	|	...	2159	|	...	|	|	|	|	...
Zürich HB a.	...	1800	|	1933	...	...	...	2000	...	...	2200	...	0805	0905	0905	|	0933
Chur a.	...	1923	|	|	...	...	...	...	...	...	...	...	...	...	...	|	|
Arth-Goldau a.	...	...	|	2016	...	...	...	...	...	...	...	...	...	...	...	0945	1016
Bellinzona a.	...	...	|	2112	...	...	...	...	...	...	...	...	...	...	...	...	1112
Lugano a.	...	...	|	2132	...	...	...	...	...	...	...	...	...	...	...	...	1132
Chiasso 🏛 a.	...	...	◧	2202	...	...	...	...	...	...	...	...	...	...	...	...	1202
Como San Giovanni a.	...	...	|	2210	...	...	...	...	...	...	...	...	...	...	...	...	1210
Milano Centrale a.	...	...	2140	2250	...	...	...	...	...	...	...	...	...	...	...	...	1250

A – *ÖBB nightjet* – 🛏 1, 2 cl., 🛏 2 cl. (4, 6 berth), (2.) Hamburg - Frankfurt - Zürich. Special fares apply. (Table **53**).

B – *ÖBB nightjet* – 🛏 1, 2 cl., 🛏 2 cl. (4, 6 berth), (2.) Berlin - Frankfurt - Zürich. Special fares apply. (Table **53**).

E – *ÖBB nightjet* – 🛏 1, 2 cl., 🛏 2 cl. (4, 6 berth), (2.) Amsterdam - Frankfurt - Zürich. Special fares apply.

M – (12.) 🍷 (Hamburg ①) - (Frankfurt ⚒) - Basel - Chur.

e – ①.

f – Milano **Lambrate**.

g – Milano **Porta Garibaldi**.

h – Via Hagen and Wuppertal.

p – Ⓐ.

v – ⚒.

x – Köln **Messe / Deutz**.

⊙ – 🏛 is at Emmerich.

◧ – Via Brig. 🏛 is at Domodossola; ticket point is **Iselle**.

⊖ – Via Köln - Frankfurt high speed line.

★ – Connections at Basel are not guaranteed.

⊗ – Compulsory reservation for international journeys. Supplement payable for international journeys and for internal journeys within Italy.

CONNECTING SERVICES

Basel - Luzern - Chiasso: Table **550**, Basel - Bern - Interlaken and Brig: Table **560**.

Zürich - Landquart - Chur: Table **520**, Chur - St Moritz: Table **540**, Zürich - Bellinzona - Chiasso: Table **550**.

MILANO and ZÜRICH - KÖLN, DORTMUND, BERLIN and AMSTERDAM 73

train type	ICE	ICE	ICE	ICE	ICE	ICE		ICE		EC	EC	EC	ICE	EC	ICE	ICE	ICE	EC	EC	ICE	EC	ICE	
train number	**78**	**372**	**126**	**76**	**370**	**124**		**74**		**312**	**8**	**50**	**278**	**8**	**72**	**122**	**276**	**6**	**314**	**70**	**158**	**104**	
notes										🅁 ⊗		🅁 ⊗							🅁 ⊗		🅁 ⊗		
Milano Centrale d.	...	...	...	...	...	...	...	...	...	0710	...	0720	...	...	...	...	...	...	0910	...	1005g	...	...
Como San Giovanni d.	...	...	...	...	...	...	...	...	...	0754	...	|	...	...	...	...	...	...	0950	...	1059	...	...
Chiasso 🏛 d.	...	...	...	...	...	...	...	...	...	0805	...	◧	...	...	...	...	...	...	1005	...	1130	...	...
Lugano d.	...	...	...	...	...	...	...	...	...	0830	...	|	...	...	...	...	...	...	1030	...	1201	...	...
Bellinzona d.	...	...	...	...	...	...	...	...	...	0847	...	|	...	...	...	...	...	...	1047	...	1218	...	...
Arth-Goldau d.	...	...	...	...	...	...	...	...	...	0945	...	|	...	...	...	...	...	...	1145	...	1315	...	...
Chur d.	...	...	...	...	...	...	...	...	...	|	...	|	...	...	1037	...	...	...	|	1237	|	...	...
Zürich HB d.	0559	...	...	0759	...	...	...	0959	...	1027	1059	|	...	...	1159	...	...	...	1227	1359	|	...	...
Interlaken Ost d.	|	0558	...	|	...	...	...	|	...	...	|	|	1000	...	|	...	...	1200	...	|	|	...	...
Bern d.	|	0704	...	|	...	...	...	|	...	...	|	1036	1104	←	|	...	...	1304	...	|	|	...	...
Basel SBB ★ a.	0653	0801	...	0853	...	...	...	1053	...	...	1153	1132	1201	1153	1253	...	...	1401	...	1453	1456	...	...
Basel SBB d.	0706	0813	...	0906	1013	...	...	1106	...	...	1220	...	1213	1220	1306	...	1413	1427	...	1506	...	1513	...
Basel Bad Bf 🏛 d.	0714	0823	...	0914	1023	...	...	1114	...	...	→	...	1223	1228	1314	...	1423	1435	...	1514	...	1523	...
Freiburg (Brsg) Hbf d.	0748	0856	...	0948	1056	...	...	1148	...	...	...	...	1256	1304	1348	...	1454	1507	...	1548	...	1556	...
Karlsruhe Hbf d.	0851	1000	...	1051	1200	...	...	1251	...	...	...	...	1400	1412	1451	...	1601	1613	...	1651	...	1700	...
Mannheim Hbf a.	0914	1024	...	1114	1224	...	...	1314	...	...	...	...	1424	1437	1514	...	1625	1637	...	1715	...	1724	...
Frankfurt (Main) Hbf a.	0952	1108	1129	1152	1308	1326	...	1352	...	...	...	...	1508	|	1552	1628	1708	|	...	1752	...	|	...
Frankfurt Flughafen ✈ a.	|	|	1139	|	|	1342	...	|	...	...	...	...	|	|	|	1639	|	|	...	|	...	1806	...
Mainz Hbf a.	|	|	|	|	|	|	...	|	...	...	...	...	|	1518	|	|	|	1718	...	|	...	|	...
Koblenz Hbf a.	|	|	⊖	|	|	⊖	...	|	...	...	...	...	|	1611	|	⊖	|	1811	...	|	...	⊖	...
Bonn Hbf a.	|	|	|	|	|	|	...	|	...	...	...	...	|	1643	|	|	|	1843	...	|	...	|	...
Köln Hbf a.	|	|	1230**x**	|	|	1430**x**	...	|	...	...	...	...	|	1705	|	1736	|	1905	...	|	...	1904	...
Düsseldorf Hbf a.	|	|	1256	|	|	1456	...	|	...	...	...	...	|	1731	|	1810	|	1931	...	|	...	1935	...
Duisburg Hbf a.	|	|	1323	|	|	1525	...	|	...	...	...	...	|	1745	|	1823	|	1945	...	|	...	1949	...
Arnhem ⊙ a.	|	|	1424	|	|	1627	...	|	...	...	...	...	|	|	|	1927	|	|	...	|	...	2057	...
Utrecht Centraal a.	|	|	1459	|	|	1659	...	|	...	...	...	...	|	|	|	1959	|	|	...	|	...	2129	...
Amsterdam Centraal a.	|	|	1529	|	|	1729	...	|	...	...	...	...	|	|	|	2029	|	|	...	|	...	2159	...
Essen Hbf a.	|	|	...	|	|	...	...	|	...	...	...	...	|	1758	|	...	|	1958	...	|	...	...	...
Dortmund Hbf a.	|	|	...	|	|	...	...	|	...	...	...	...	|	|	|	...	|	|	...	|	...	...	...
Hannover Hbf a.	1217	|	...	1417	|	...	...	1617	...	...	...	...	|	|	1817	...	|	|	...	2017	...	...	...
Berlin Hbf a.	|	1527	...	|	1727	...	...	|	...	...	...	...	1927	|	|	...	2127	|	...	|	...	...	...
Bremen Hbf a.	|	...	...	|	...	...	...	|	...	...	...	...	...	2015	|	...	...	2217	...	|	...	...	...
Hamburg Hbf a.	1354	...	...	1555	...	...	...	1754	...	...	...	...	...	2114	1954	...	...	2316	...	2154	...	...	...

train type	EC	EC	IC	ICE	ICE	ICE	ICE		EC	ICE	ICE		EC	ICE	EC	NJ	NJ		NJ				
train number	**52**	**316**	**776**	**274**	**120**	**376**	**102**		**318**	**272** **292**	**100**		**320**	**4**	**308**	**470**	**40470**		**402**				
notes	🅁 ⊗	🅁 ⊗			Ⓑ				🅁 ⊗				🅁 ⊗		🅁 ⊗	**A**	**B**		**C**				
Milano Centrale d.	1120	1110	...	...	...	...	...	...	1310	...	...	...	1510	...	1610	...	...	...	...	...	...	...	...
Como San Giovanni d.	|	1150	...	...	...	...	...	...	1350	...	...	...	1550	...	1650	...	...	...	...	...	...	...	...
Chiasso 🏛 d.	◧	1205	...	...	...	...	...	...	1405	...	...	...	1605	...	1705	...	...	...	...	...	...	...	...
Lugano d.	|	1230	...	...	...	...	...	...	1430	...	...	...	1630	...	1730	...	...	...	...	...	...	...	...
Bellinzona d.	|	1247	...	...	...	...	...	...	1447	...	...	...	1647	...	1747	...	...	...	...	...	...	...	...
Arth-Goldau d.	|	1345	...	...	...	...	...	...	1545	...	...	...	1745	...	1845	...	...	...	...	...	...	...	...
Chur d.	|	|	...	...	...	...	...	...	|	...	...	...	|	...	|	...	...	...	...	...	...	...	...
Zürich HB d.	|	1427	1459	...	...	...	...	...	1627	1659	...	...	1827	1859	1927	1959	1959	...	2159	...	...	...	...
Interlaken Ost d.	|	...	|	...	...	1500	...	...	...	|	...	...	...	|	...	|	|	...	|	...	...	...	...
Bern d.	1436	...	|	...	...	1604	...	...	...	|	...	...	...	|	...	|	|	...	|	...	...	...	...
Basel SBB ★ a.	1532	...	1553	...	...	1701	...	...	...	1753	...	...	...	1953	...	2053	2053	...	|	...	...	...	...
Basel SBB d.	1538	...	...	1613	...	1707	1713	...	...	1813	1913	...	...	2009	...	2113	2113	...	2313	...	...	...	...
Basel Bad Bf 🏛 d.	1552	...	...	1623	...	1715	1722	...	...	1823	1922	...	...	2018	...	2122	2122	...	2323	...	...	...	...
Freiburg (Brsg) Hbf d.	1622	...	...	1654	...	1748	1754	...	...	1856	1955	...	...	2054	...	2158	2158	...	0005	...	...	...	...
Karlsruhe Hbf d.	1730	...	...	1801	...	1851	1900	...	...	2000	2101	...	...	2201	...	2306	2306	...	0120	...	...	...	...
Mannheim Hbf a.	1758	...	...	1825	...	1914	1924	...	...	2024	2125	...	...	2224	...	2340	2340	...	0149	...	...	...	...
Frankfurt (Main) Hbf a.	1844	...	...	1908	1928	1952	|	...	...	2108	|	...	...	2308	...	0027	0027	...	0245	...	...	...	...
Frankfurt Flughafen ✈ a.	...	...	...	|	1939	|	2006	...	...	...	2206	...	...	...	...	|	|	...	0326	...	...	...	...
Mainz Hbf a.	...	...	...	|	|	|	|	...	...	...	|	...	...	...	...	|	|	...	0346	...	...	...	...
Koblenz Hbf a.	...	...	...	|	⊖	|	⊖	...	...	...	⊖	...	...	...	...	|	|	...	0441	...	...	...	...
Bonn Hbf a.	...	...	...	|	|	|	|	...	...	...	|	...	...	...	...	|	|	...	0524	...	...	...	...
Köln Hbf a.	...	...	...	|	2030**x**	|	2105	...	...	...	2304	...	...	...	...	|	|	...	0553	...	...	...	...
Düsseldorf Hbf a.	...	...	...	|	2056	|	...	...	...	...	2332	...	...	...	...	|	|	...	0623	...	...	...	...
Duisburg Hbf a.	...	...	...	|	2123	|	...	...	...	...	2346	...	...	...	...	|	|	...	0640	...	...	...	...
Arnhem ⊙ a.	...	...	...	|	2227	|	...	...	...	...	|	...	...	...	...	|	|	...	|	...	...	...	...
Utrecht Centraal a.	...	...	...	|	2259	|	...	...	...	...	|	...	...	...	...	|	|	...	0833	...	...	...	...
Amsterdam Centraal a.	...	...	...	|	2329	|	...	...	...	...	|	...	...	...	...	|	|	...	0914	...	...	...	...
Essen Hbf a.	...	...	...	|	...	|	...	...	...	...	2358	...	...	...	...	|	|	...	...	...	...	...	...
Dortmund Hbf a.	...	...	...	|	...	|	...	...	...	...	0021	...	...	...	...	|	|	...	...	...	...	...	...
Hannover Hbf a.	...	...	...	|	...	2217**f**	...	...	...	...	...	...	...	...	...	|	0558	...	...	...	...	...	...
Berlin Hbf a.	...	...	...	2327	...	|	...	...	...	...	...	...	...	...	...	0738	|	...	...	...	...	...	...
Bremen Hbf a.	...	...	...	...	...	|	...	...	...	...	...	...	...	...	...	...	|	...	...	...	...	...	...
Hamburg Hbf a.	...	...	...	...	...	2358**f**	...	...	...	...	...	...	...	...	...	...	0754	...	...	...	...	...	...

A – *ÖBB nightjet* – 🛏 1, 2 cl., 🛏 2 cl. (4, 6 berth), (2) Zürich - Frankfurt - Berlin. Special fares apply. (Table **53**).

B – *ÖBB nightjet* – 🛏 1, 2 cl., 🛏 2 cl. (4, 6 berth), (2) Zürich - Frankfurt - Hamburg. Special fares apply. (Table **53**).

C – *ÖBB nightjet* – 🛏 1, 2 cl., (12) Zürich - Frankfurt - Amsterdam. Special fares apply.

f – Not ⑥.

g – Milano **Porta Garibaldi**.

x – Köln **Messe / Deutz**.

⊙ – 🏛 is at Emmerich.

◧ – Via Brig. 🏛 is at Domodossola; ticket point is **Iselle**.

★ – Connections at Basel are not guaranteed.

⊖ – Via Köln - Frankfurt high speed line.

⊗ – Compulsory reservation for international journeys. Supplement payable for international journeys and for internal journeys within Italy.

CONNECTING SERVICES

Basel - Luzern - Chiasso: Table **550**, Basel - Bern - Interlaken and Brig: Table **560**.

Zürich - Landquart - Chur: Table **520**, Chur - St Moritz: Table **540**, Zürich - Bellinzona - Chiasso: Table **550**.

74 MILANO - PÁTRA - ATHÍNAI

train type	FB			IC	FB			
train number	8803			605	8809			
notes	Ⓡ ✕	⛴		Ⓡ ✕	Ⓡ ✕	⛴	⛴	
	⚡	SF		⚡	⚡	SF	SF	
Milano Centrale d.	0735	...	...	0705	1035	...	...	...
Bologna d.	0945	...	...	0958	1245	...	...	...
Ancona d.	1130	...	...	1228	1436	...	...	...
Ancona Marittima d.	...	1330	...	|	|	1630	...	...
Pescara Centrale d.	...	|	...	1401	1547	|	...	...
Foggia d.	...	|	...	1551	1722	|	...	...
Bari Centrale a.	...	|	...	1705	1825	|	...	...
Bari Marittima d.	...	|	...	...	...	|	1930	...
Pátra a.	...	1430	...	...	...	1500	1300	...
Athína Lárisa a.	...	✣	...	...	...	✣	✣	...

train type			FB				FB	IC		
train number			8820				8820	612		
notes		⛴	Ⓡ ✕	⛴		⛴	Ⓡ ✕	Ⓡ ✕		
		SF	⚡	SF		SF	⚡	⚡		
Athína Lárisa d.	...	✣	...	✣	...	✣	...	...	...	...
Pátra d.	...	1730	...	1730	...	1800	...	...	...	...
Bari Marittima a.	...	|	...	|	...	0930	...	...	...	...
Bari Centrale d.	...	|	...	|	...	...	1132	1155	...	...
Foggia d.	...	|	...	|	...	...	1239	1313	...	...
Pescara Centrale d.	...	|	...	|	...	...	1414	1502	...	...
Ancona Marittima a.	...	1400	...	1630	...	...	|	|	...	...
Ancona d.	...	...	1525	...	...	...	1525	1638	...	...
Bologna a.	...	...	1715	...	...	...	1718	1901	...	...
Milano Centrale a.	...	...	1925	...	...	...	1925	2145	...	...

⚡ – Supplement payable.

✣ – For 🚌/rail connections Pátra - Athína and v.v. see Tables **1440**, **1450**.

SF – **Superfast Ferries**, for days of running see Tables **2715**, **2755**.

75 MÜNCHEN - ZÜRICH

train type		EC	EC		EC	EC	EC	EC		
train number		198	196		192	190	98	96		
notes		✕	✕		✕	✕	✕	✕		
München Hbf d.	...	0655	0855	...	1255	1455	1652	1852	...	...
Buchloe d.	...	0736	0936	...	1336	1536	1736	1936	...	...
Memmingen d.	...	0801	1001	...	1401	1601	1801	2001	...	...
Lindau Reutin ▦ d.	...	0852	1052	...	1452	1652	1852	2052	...	...
Bregenz ▦ d.	...	0900	1100	...	1500	1700	1900	2100	...	...
St Margrethen ▦ a.	...	0909	1109	...	1509	1709	1909	2109	...	...
St Gallen a.	...	0928	1128	...	1528	1728	1928	2128	...	...
Winterthur a.	...	1001	1201	...	1601	1801	2001	2201	...	...
Zürich Flughafen ✈ a.	...	1016	1216	...	1616	1816	2016	2216	...	...
Zürich HB a.	...	1027	1227	...	1627	1827	2027	2227	...	...

train type		EC	EC	EC	EC		EC	EC		
train number		97	99	191	193		197	199		
notes		✕	✕	✕	✕		✕	✕		
Zürich HB d.	...	0733	0933	1133	1333	...	1733	1933	...	...
Zürich Flughafen ✈ d.	...	0743	0943	1143	1343	...	1743	1943	...	...
Winterthur d.	...	0758	0958	1158	1358	...	1758	1958	...	...
St Gallen d.	...	0832	1032	1232	1432	...	1832	2032	...	...
St Margrethen ▦ d.	...	0851	1051	1251	1451	...	1849	2051	...	...
Bregenz ▦ d.	...	0902	1102	1302	1502	...	1902	2102	...	...
Lindau Reutin ▦ d.	...	0910	1110	1310	1510	...	1910	2110	...	...
Memmingen a.	...	0959	1159	1359	1558	...	2001	2159	...	...
Buchloe a.	...	1022	1222	1423	1622	...	2022	2222	...	...
München Hbf a.	...	1104	1304	1504	1704	...	2104	2304	...	...

76 MÜNCHEN and NÜRNBERG - PRAHA

train type	RE	RE	ALX	ALX	🚌	🚌	RE	ALX	ALX	ALX	RE	ALX	🚌	🚌	RE	ALX	🚌	RE	ALX	🚌	🚌	RE	ALX	RE	ALX
train number			351	351	P	P		79853	353	353		355	P	P		357	P		359	P	P		361		363
notes	①-⑥	⑥⑦	⚒	†	Ⓡ	Ⓡ		†	⚒	†			Ⓡ	Ⓡ		¶	Ⓡ		¶	Ⓡ	Ⓡ		¶		¶
notes			¶	¶					¶	¶		¶													
München Hbf d.	...	...	0444	...	...	...	...	0644	0644	...	...	0843	...	...	...	1043	...	...	1243	...	...	...	1443	...	1643
Nürnberg Hbf d.	0434	0535	|	...	0720	0850	0738	|	|	...	0943	|	1035	1120	1143	|	1250	1343	|	1450	1650	1543	|	1743	|
Regensburg d.	|	|	0615	0615	|	|	|	0815	0815	...	|	1014	|	|	|	1214	|	|	1414	|	|	|	1615	|	1814
Schwandorf d.	0542	0643	0654	0654	|	|	0846	0842	0852	0852	1046	1052	|	|	1246	1252	|	1446	1452	|	|	1647	1652	1846	1852
Furth im Wald ▦ d.	...	...	0740	0740	◐	◐	...	...	0940	0940	...	1140	◐	◐	...	1340	◐	...	1540	◐	◐	...	1740	...	1940
Plzeň hl. n. a.	...	...	0847	0847	|	|	...	...	1047	1047	...	1247	|	|	...	1447	|	...	1647	|	|	...	1847	...	2047
Praha hl. n. a.	...	...	1021	1021	1055	1225	...	...	1221	1221	...	1421	1410	1455	...	1621	1625	...	1821	1825	2025	...	2021	...	2221

train type	ALX	RE	ALX	RE	🚌	ALX	RE	🚌	ALX	RE	🚌		ALX	RE	🚌	ALX	RE	🚌	🚌	ALX	ALX	RE	🚌		
train number	362		360		P	358		P	356		P		354		P	352		P	P	350	350		P		
notes	¶		¶		Ⓡ	¶		Ⓡ	¶		Ⓡ		¶		Ⓡ	¶		Ⓡ	Ⓡ	¶	¶		Ⓡ		
notes																					Ⓑ				
Praha hl. n. d.	0538	...	0738	...	0805	0938	...	0935	1138	...	1135	...	1338	...	1335	1538	...	1535	1605	1738	1738	...	1735	...	...
Plzeň hl. n. d.	0711	...	0911	...	|	1111	...	|	1311	...	|	...	1511	...	|	1711	...	|	|	1911	1911	...	|	...	...
Furth im Wald ▦ a.	0820	...	1020	...	◐	1220	...	◐	1420	...	◐	...	1620	...	◐	1820	...	◐	◐	2020	2020	...	◐	...	...
Schwandorf a.	0904	0907	1104	1107	|	1304	1307	|	1504	1507	|	...	1704	1707	|	1904	1908	|	|	2105	2105	2110	|	...	...
Regensburg a.	0945	|	1145	|	|	1345	|	|	1545	|	|	...	1745	|	|	1945	|	|	|	...	2149	|	|	...	...
Nürnberg Hbf a.	|	1014	|	1214	1140	|	1414	1310	|	1615	1510	...	|	1814	1710	|	2014	1910	1940	...	|	2222	2110	...	...
München Hbf a.	1118	...	1318	...	...	1518	...	...	1718	...	...	...	1918	...	...	2118	...	...	...	...	2321	...	...	...	...

P – 🚌 **DB / ČD** *IC Bus*. Rail tickets valid. Ⓡ 🍸. Supplement payable. 2nd class only. At Praha hl. n. railway station the bus stop is located outside the old building on the upper level (access from platform one); street name is Wilsonova. At Nürnberg Hbf the bus stop is at Bahnhofvorplatz Hauptausgang (main entrance). At Plzeň the bus stop is located at Plzeň Autobusove nadrazi (Husova).

¶ – *Ex* in the Czech Republic.

◐ – ▦ is Waidhaus (Germany).

ALX – Arriva Länderbahn Express.

77 BERLIN - WROCŁAW - WIEN / BUDAPEST / PRZEMYŚL

train type / number	EC/IC	NJ	NJ
train number	57	457	457
notes	73000		477
	W	A	S
Berlin Hbf d.	1039	1843	1843
Berlin Ost d.	1052	1853	1853
Frankfurt / Oder d.	1145	1945	1945
Rzepin d.	1210	2010	2010
Zielona Góra d.	1256	2056	2056
Glogów d.	1334	2132	2132
Wrocław Gł a.	1457	2252	2252
Wrocław Gł d.	1502	2307	2307
Opole Gł d.	1554	2355	2355
Kedzierzyn-Koźle d.	|	0031	0031
Racibórz d.	|	0056	0056
Bohumín d.	|	0215	0215
Ostrava hlavní d.	|	0224	0224
Břeclav a.	|	0410	0410
Wien Hbf a.	|	0700	|
Graz Hbf a.	|	1002	|
Bratislava hl. st. a.	|	...	0554
Budapest Nyugati a.	|	...	0820
Gliwice a.	1643	...	...
Katowice a.	1706	...	...
Kraków Gł a.	1801	...	...
Rzeszów a.	1958	...	...
Przemyśl a.	2105	...	...

train type / number	IC/EC	NJ	NJ
train number	37000	476	456
notes	56	456	
	W	T	A
Przemyśl d.	0718	...	...
Rzeszów d.	0823	...	...
Kraków Gł d.	1012	...	...
Katowice d.	1109	...	...
Gliwice d.	1130	...	...
Budapest Nyugati d.	|	1940	...
Bratislava hl. st. d.	|	2206	...
Graz Hbf d.	|	|	1921
Wien Hbf d.	|	|	2210
Břeclav d.	|	2350	2350
Ostrava hlavní a.	|	0131	0131
Bohumín a.	|	0140	0140
Racibórz a.	|	0307	0307
Kedzierzyn-Koźle a.	|	0342	0342
Opole Gł a.	1217	0416	0416
Wrocław Gł a.	1301	0505	0505
Wrocław Gł d.	1306	0532	0532
Glogów a.	1420	0655	0655
Zielona Góra a.	1502	0733	0733
Rzepin a.	1547	0820	0820
Frankfurt / Oder a.	1612	0844	0844
Berlin Ost a.	1706	0940	0940
Berlin Hbf a.	1716	0951	0951

A – Berlin - Wien: *ÖBB nightjet* METROPOL – 🛏 1, 2 cl., ▬ 2 cl., (2.) Berlin - Graz and v.v.

S – *ÖBB nightjet* METROPOL – 🛏 1, 2 cl., ▬ 2 cl., (2.) Berlin (**457**) - Břeclav (**477**) - Budapest.

T – *ÖBB nightjet* METROPOL – 🛏 1, 2 cl., ▬ 2 cl., (2.) Budapest (**476**) - Břeclav (**456**) - Berlin.

W – WAWEL – (12) ✕ Berlin - Wrocław - Krakow - Przemyśl and v.v.

⊖ – ▦ = Medyka / Mostiska II.

PL – Poland (UTC + 1 winter, UTC + 2 summer).

UA – Ukraine (UTC + 2 winter, UTC + 3 summer).

78 BRUSSELS - AMSTERDAM - BERLIN - PRAHA

train type	EN	
train number	xxxx	
notes	①③⑤	
	Z	
Brussels Midi / Zuid d.	1922	...
Antwerpen Centraal d.	2001	...
Roosendaal d.	2045	...
Rotterdam Centraal d.	2122	...
Den Haag HS d.	2142	...
Amsterdam Centraal d.	2234	...
Bad Bentheim ▦ d.	0100	...
Hannover Hbf d.	0256	...
Berlin Hbf a.	0552	...
Dresden Neustadt a.	0743	...
Dresden Hbf a.	0749	...
Bad Schandau ▦ a.	0816	...
Děčín a.	0841	...
Ústí nad Labem hl. n. a.	0900	...
Praha Holešovice a.	1014	...
Praha hl. n. a.	1024	...

train type	EN	
train number	zzzz	
notes	②④⑦	
	Z	
Praha hl. n. d.	1831	...
Praha Holešovice d.	1841	...
Ústí nad Labem hl. n. d.	1945	...
Děčín d.	2011	...
Bad Schandau ▦ d.	2029	...
Dresden Hbf d.	2102	...
Dresden Neustadt d.	2108	...
Berlin Hbf d.	2305	...
Hannover Hbf a.	0221	...
Bad Bentheim ▦ a.	0419	...
Amsterdam Centraal a.	0626	...
Den Haag HS a.	|	...
Rotterdam Centraal a.	0727	...
Roosendaal a.	0810	...
Antwerpen Centraal a.	0847	...
Brussels Midi / Zuid a.	0954	...

Z – European Sleeper, from a date to be announced, possibly Autumn 2022: 🛏 1, 2 cl. Brussels - Praha and v.v.

GENÈVE, BASEL and ZÜRICH - MILANO, VENEZIA and ROMA 82

train type	IC	EC	IC	EC	IR	EC	IR	EC	FR	IC	EC	FR	IC	EC	IR	EC	IC	EC	FR	IR	IR	EC	EC	FR	
train number	802	35	659	311	2311	313	1807	51	9531	806	37 47	9529	663	307	2315	315	667	327	9543	1815	2319	53	317	9541	
notes		R 🍸 ⊗		R 🍸 ⊗		R 🍸 ⊗		R 🍸 ⊗	R ✕ ↗		R 🍸 ⊗	R ✕ ↗		R 🍸 ⊗		R 🍸 ⊗		R 🍸 ⊗	R ✕ ↗			R 🍸 ⊗	R 🍸 ⊗	R ✕ ↗	
Genève Aéroport ✈ d.	...	...	...	...	...	...	...	...	...	...	...	...	...	...	...	...	...	...	...	1001	...	...	...	...	...
Genève d.	...	0539	...	...	...	...	0609	...	...	...	0739	...	...	...	...	...	...	...	...	1011	...	...	...	...	...
Lausanne d.	...	0618	...	...	...	...	0650	...	...	...	0818	...	...	...	...	...	...	...	...	1050	...	...	...	...	...
Montreux d.	...	0637	...	...	...	...	0711	...	...	...	0837	...	...	...	...	...	...	...	...	1111	...	...	...	...	...
Aigle d.	...	│	...	...	...	...	0722	...	...	...	│	...	...	...	...	...	...	...	...	1122	...	...	...	...	...
Martigny d.	...	│	...	...	...	...	0743	...	...	...	│	...	...	...	...	...	...	...	...	1143	...	...	...	...	...
Sion d.	...	0712	...	...	...	...	0757	...	...	...	0912	...	...	...	...	...	...	...	...	1157	...	...	...	...	...
Zürich HB d.	...	│	...	0633	...	0733	│	...	...	...	│	...	...	0833	...	0933	...	1033	...	│	...	...	1133	...	...
Basel SBB d.	...	│	0503	│	0603	│	│	0628	...	...	│	...	0703	│	0803	│	0903	│	...	│	1003	1028	│	...	...
Olten d.	...	│	0530	│	0630	│	│	0658	...	...	│	...	0830	│	0830	│	0930	│	...	│	1030	1058	│	...	...
Bern d.	0607	│	│	│	│	│	│	0734	...	0807	│	...	│	│	│	│	│	│	...	│	│	1134	│	...	...
Spiez d.	0636	│	│	│	│	│	│	0805	...	0836	│	...	│	│	│	│	│	│	...	│	│	1205	│	...	...
Luzern d.	│	│	0618	│	0718	│	│	│	...	│	│	...	0818	│	0918	│	1018	│	...	│	1118	│	│	...	...
Arth-Goldau d.	│	│	0645	0718	0745	0818	│	│	...	│	│	...	0845	0918	0945	1018	1045	1118	...	│	1145	│	1218	...	...
Bellinzona d.	│	│	...	0814	▬	0914	│	│	...	│	│	...	...	1014	...	1114	...	1214	...	│	...	│	1314	...	...
Lugano d.	│	│	...	0832	...	0932	│	│	...	│	│	...	...	1032	...	1132	...	1232	...	│	...	│	1332	...	...
Chiasso 🏛 d.	│	│	...	0902	...	1002	│	│	...	│	│	...	...	1102	...	1202	...	1302	...	│	...	│	1402	...	...
Como San Giovanni a.	│	│	...	0908	...	1010	│	│	...	│	│	...	...	1108	...	1210	...	1308	...	│	...	│	1410	...	...
Visp d.	0703	│	...	│	...	│	0825	0833	...	0903	│	...	...	│	...	│	...	│	...	1225	...	1233	│	...	...
Brig d.	0711	0744	...	│	...	│	0832	0844	...	0911	0944	...	...	│	...	│	...	│	...	1232	...	1244	│	...	...
Domodossola 🏛 ¶ a.	...	0812	...	│	...	│	...	0912	...	▬	1012	...	...	│	...	│	...	│	...	...	...	1312	│	...	...
Stresa a.	...	0838	...	│	...	│	...	0938	...	...	│	...	...	│	...	│	...	│	...	...	...	1338	│	...	...
Gallarate a.	...	│	...	│	...	│	...	│	...	...	1105	...	...	│	...	│	...	│	...	...	...	│	│	...	...
Milano Centrale a.	...	0940	...	0950	...	1050	...	1040	...	...	1140	...	...	1209f	...	1250	...	1409f	...	...	...	1440	1450	...	...
				│	ITA					FR	│			│		FR		│					FR		
				│	9927					9723	│			│		9533		│					9737		
				│	R ✕ ↗					R ✕ ↗	│			│		R ✕ ↗		│					R ✕ ↗		
Milano Centrale d.	...	...	...	1005	1040	...	...	...	1110	1145	1205	1220	...	1211f	...	1320	...	1411f	1410	...	...	...	1515	1520	...
Verona Porta Nuova a.	...	...	...	1128	│	...	...	...	│	1258	1328	│	...	│	...	│	...	│	│	...	...	...	1628	│	...
Venezia Mestre a.	...	...	...	1230	│	...	...	...	│	1358	1428	│	...	│	...	│	...	│	│	...	...	...	1728	│	...
Venezia Santa Lucia a.	...	...	...	1242	│	...	...	...	│	1410	1440	│	...	│	...	│	...	│	│	...	...	...	...	│	...
Genova a.	...	...	...	...	│	...	...	...	│	...	...	│	...	│	...	│	...	1552	│	...	...	...	...	│	...
Bologna Centrale a.	...	...	...	...	1152	...	...	...	1222	...	...	1322	...	1435	...	1422	...	...	1522	...	...	...	...	1622	...
Firenze SMN a.	...	...	...	...	1235	...	...	...	1259	...	...	1359	...	...	...	1459	...	...	1604	...	...	...	...	1659	...
Roma Termini a.	...	...	...	...	1419	...	...	...	1440	...	...	1540	...	...	...	1640	...	...	1749	...	...	...	...	1840	...
Napoli Centrale a.	...	...	...	...	1543	...	...	...	1602	...	...	1700	...	...	...	1800	...	...	1912	...	...	...	...	2000	...

train type	IR	EC	FR	IR	EC	IR	EC	FR	IC	IC	EC	FR	IR	EC	FR	EC	IR	EC	IR	EC	ICN	IC	EC	IR	EC
train number	2421	151	9545	2323	319	1819	57	9549	971	818	39	9553	2327	321	9557	153	2331	323	1829	59	797	828	41	2335	325
notes		R ⊗ F	R ✕ ↗		R 🍸 ⊗		R 🍸 ⊗	R ✕ ↗			R 🍸 ⊗	R ✕ ↗		R 🍸 ⊗	R ✕ ↗	R 🍸 ⊗		R 🍸 ⊗		R 🍸 ⊗	R ↗ A		R 🍸 ⊗		R 🍸 ⊗
Genève Aéroport ✈ d.	...	...	...	...	...	1201	...	...	...	...	...	...	...	...	...	...	...	...	1701	...	...	...	...	...	...
Genève d.	...	...	...	...	...	1211	...	...	...	...	1339	...	...	...	...	...	...	...	1711	...	...	...	1839	...	...
Lausanne d.	...	...	...	...	...	1250	...	...	...	...	1418	...	...	...	...	...	...	...	1750	...	...	...	1918	...	...
Montreux d.	...	...	...	...	...	1311	...	...	...	...	1437	...	...	...	...	...	...	...	1811	...	...	...	1937	...	...
Aigle d.	...	...	...	...	...	1322	...	...	...	...	│	...	...	...	...	...	...	...	1822	...	...	...	│	...	...
Martigny d.	...	...	...	...	...	1343	...	...	...	...	│	...	...	...	...	...	...	...	1843	...	...	...	│	...	...
Sion d.	...	...	...	...	...	1357	...	...	...	...	1512	...	...	...	...	...	...	...	1857	...	...	...	2012	...	...
Zürich HB d.	1205	...	...	...	1333	│	...	...	...	...	│	...	...	1533	...	...	...	1733	│	...	...	...	│	...	1933
Basel SBB d.	│	1103	...	1203	│	│	1228	...	1256	...	│	...	1403	│	...	1503	1603	│	│	1728	...	...	│	1803	│
Oltern d.	│	1130	...	1230	│	│	1258	...	1329	...	│	...	1430	│	...	1530	1630	│	│	1758	...	...	│	1830	│
Bern d.	│	│	...	│	│	│	1334	...	1356	1407	│	...	│	│	...	│	│	│	│	1834	...	1907	│	│	│
Spiez d.	│	│	...	│	│	│	1405	...	...	1436	│	...	│	│	...	│	│	│	│	1905	...	1936	│	│	│
Luzern d.	│	1218	...	1318	│	│	│	...	...	│	│	...	1518	│	...	1618	1718	│	│	│	...	│	│	1918	│
Arth-Goldau d.	1245	1249	...	1345	1418	│	│	...	...	│	│	...	1545	1618	...	1649	1745	1818	│	│	...	│	│	1945	2018
Bellinzona d.	...	1344	...	...	1514	│	│	...	...	│	│	...	...	1714	...	1744	...	1914	│	│	...	│	│	...	2114
Lugano d.	...	1410	...	...	1532	│	│	...	...	│	│	...	...	1732	...	1810	...	1932	│	│	...	│	│	...	2132
Chiasso 🏛 d.	...	1455	...	...	1602	│	│	...	...	│	│	...	...	1802	...	1846	...	2002	│	│	...	│	│	...	2202
Como San Giovanni a.	...	1501	...	...	1610	│	│	...	...	│	│	...	...	1810	...	...	...	2010	│	│	...	│	│	...	2210
Visp d.	...	│	...	...	│	1425	1433	...	...	1503	│	...	...	│	...	...	...	│	1925	1933	...	2003	│	...	│
Brig d.	...	│	...	...	│	1432	1444	...	...	1511	1544	...	...	│	...	...	...	│	1932	1944	...	2011	2044	...	│
Domodossola 🏛 ¶ a.	...	│	...	...	│	...	1512	...	...	...	1612	...	...	│	...	...	...	│	...	2012	...	...	2112	...	│
Stresa a.	...	│	...	...	│	...	1539	...	...	...	1639	...	...	│	...	...	...	│	...	│	...	...	2138	...	│
Gallarate a.	...	│	...	...	│	...	│	...	...	...	│	...	...	│	...	...	...	│	...	2103	...	...	│	...	│
Milano Centrale a.	...	1555g	...	...	1650	...	1640	...	...	...	1740	...	...	1850	...	...	...	2050	...	2140	...	...	2240	...	2250
		FR					FR				FR			FR											
		9743					9747				9751			9755				2085		2087					2051
		R ✕ ↗					R ✕ ↗				R ✕ ↗			R ✕ ↗				2		2					2
Milano Centrale d.	...	1615	1615	...	...	...	1715	1720	...	...	1815	1820	...	1915	1920	...	...	2125	...	2225	2317g	...	...	...	0015
Verona Porta Nuova a.	...	1728	│	...	...	...	1828	│	...	...	1928	│	...	2028	│	...	...	2315	...	0015	│	...	...	...	0215
Venezia Mestre a.	...	1828	│	...	...	...	1928	│	...	...	2028	│	...	2128	│	...	...	...	...	...	│	...	...	...	...
Venezia Santa Lucia a.	...	1840	│	...	...	...	...	│	...	...	2040	│	...	2140	│	...	...	...	...	...	│	...	...	...	...
Genova a.	...	...	│	...	...	...	...	│	...	...	...	│	...	...	│	...	...	...	...	...	│	...	...	...	...
Bologna Centrale a.	...	...	1722	...	...	...	...	1822	...	...	...	1922	...	...	2022	...	...	...	...	...	0215	...	...	...	...
Firenze SMN a.	...	...	1759	...	...	...	...	1859	...	...	...	1959	...	...	2059	...	...	...	...	...	0407y	...	...	...	...
Roma Termini a.	...	...	1940	...	...	...	...	2040	...	...	...	2140	...	...	2240	...	...	...	...	...	0717t	...	...	...	...
Napoli Centrale a.	...	...	2100	...	...	...	...	2200	...	...	...	2300	...	...	...	...	...	...	...	...	0938	...	...	...	...

A – 🛏 1, 2 cl., ▬ 2 cl. (4 berth), [2] Milano - Napoli - Salerno.
F – From Frankfurt (depart 0804) (Table **73**).

f – Milano **Lambrate**.
g – Milano **Porta Garibaldi**.
t – Roma **Tiburtina**.
y – Firenze **Campo di Marte**.

↗ – Supplement payable.
¶ – Ticketing point is **Iselle**.

⊗ – Compulsory reservation for international journeys. Supplement payable for international journeys and for internal journeys within Italy.

82 ROMA, VENEZIA and MILANO - ZÜRICH, BASEL and GENÈVE

train type	EC	IR	EC	IR	ICN			IC	IC	FR	EC	IR	FR	FR	FR	FR	IR	EC	IR	FR	IR	EC	IC	IR	
train number	**312**	**2316**	**50**	**1814**	**798**	**2051**	**2122**	**817**	**968**	**9702**	**314**	**2320**	**9606**	**9708**	**9508**	**9714**	**1822**	**316**	**2324**	**9518**	**2328**	**34**	**1076**	**1826**	
notes	R 🍷 ⊗		R 🍷 ⊗		A	2				R ✕ ↯	R 🍷 ⊗		R ✕ ↯ ①–⑤	R ✕ ↯	R ✕ ↯	R ✕ ↯		R 🍷 ⊗		R ✕ ↯		R 🍷 ⊗			
Napoli Centrale d.	...	...	...	...	2131	...	...	...	...	...	...	...	0500	...	...	...	...	...	...	0800	...	...	...	...	...
Roma Termini d.	...	...	...	...	2353t	...	...	...	...	...	...	...	0625	...	0720	...	...	...	...	0920	...	...	...	...	...
Firenze SMN d.	...	...	...	...	0315y	...	...	...	...	...	...	...	|	...	0900	...	...	...	...	1100	...	...	...	...	...
Bologna Centrale d.	...	...	...	...	|	...	0528	...	...	...	...	...	|	...	0938	...	...	...	...	1138	...	...	...	...	...
Genova d.	...	...	...	...	|	...	|	...	...	...	...	...	|	...	|	...	...	...	...	|	...	...	...	...	...
Venezia Santa Lucia d.	...	...	...	...	|	...	|	...	...	0620	...	...	|	0720	|	0820	...	...	...	|	...	...	...	...	...
Venezia Mestre d.	...	...	...	...	|	...	|	...	...	0632	...	...	|	0732	|	0832	...	...	...	|	...	...	...	...	...
Verona Porta Nuova d.	...	...	...	...	|	0545	|	...	...	0732	...	...	|	0832	|	0932	...	...	...	|	...	...	...	...	...
Milano Centrale a.	...	...	...	...	0711g	0735	0800	...	...	0845	...	...	0924	0945	1040	1045	...	...	...	1240	...	...	...	...	...
							EC **32** R 🍷 **Q** ⊗						*EC* **158** R 🍷 ⊗			*EC* **52** R **F** ⊗				*EC* **318** R 🍷 ⊗					
Milano Centrale d.	0710	...	0720	...	...	...	0820	...	...	...	0910	...	1005g	...	...	1120	...	1110	...	1310	...	1320	...	...	...
Gallarate d.	|	...	0754	...	...	...	|	...	...	...	|	...	|	...	...	|	...	|	...	|	...	|	...	...	...
Stresa d.	|	...	|	...	...	...	0921	...	...	...	|	...	|	...	...	1220	...	|	...	|	...	1412	...	...	...
Domodossola 🏛 ¶ d.	|	...	0848	...	...	*EC*	0948	...	...	...	|	...	|	...	...	1248	...	|	...	|	...	1448	...	...	...
Brig a.	|	...	0916	0926	...	**156**	1014	1048	...	...	|	...	|	...	...	1316	1326	|	...	|	...	1514	1518	1526	...
Visp a.	|	...	0925	0932	...	R 🍷	|	1055	...	...	|	...	|	...	...	1325	1332	|	...	|	...	|	1525	1532	...
Como San Giovanni d.	0754	...	|	|	...	⊗	|	|	...	...	0950	...	1059	...	...	|	|	1150	...	1350	...	|	|	|	...
Chiasso 🏛 a.	0758	...	|	|	...	0924	|	|	...	...	1005	...	1110	...	...	|	|	1205	...	1405	...	|	|	|	...
Lugano a.	0830	...	|	|	...	0950	|	|	...	...	1030	...	1150	...	...	|	|	1230	...	1430	...	|	|	|	...
Bellinzona a.	0845	...	|	|	...	1016	|	|	...	...	1045	...	1216	...	...	|	|	1245	...	1445	...	|	|	|	...
Arth-Goldau a.	0942	1015	|	|	...	1111	|	|	...	...	1142	1215	1311	...	...	|	|	1342	1415	1542	1615	|	|	|	...
Luzern a.	|	1041	|	|	...	1141	|	|	...	...	|	1241	1341	...	...	|	|	|	1441	|	1641	|	|	|	...
Spiez a.	|	|	0953	|	...	|	|	1123	...	...	|	|	|	...	...	1353	|	|	|	|	|	|	1553	|	...
Bern a.	|	|	1024	|	...	|	|	1154	1204	...	|	|	|	...	...	1424	|	|	|	|	|	|	1624	|	...
Olten a.	|	1128	1103	|	...	1228	|	...	1230	...	|	1328	1428	...	...	1503	|	|	1528	|	1728	|	1703	|	...
Basel SBB a.	|	1156	1132	|	...	1256	|	...	1301	...	|	1356	1456	...	...	1532	|	|	1556	|	1756	|	1732	|	...
Zürich HB a.	1027	...	...	|	...	...	|	...	...	...	1227	...	...	...	...	...	|	1427	...	1627	...	|	...	|	...
Sion a.	...	...	...	1001	...	...	1047	...	...	...	...	...	...	...	...	...	1401	...	...	...	...	1547	...	1601	...
Martigny a.	...	...	...	1016	...	...	|	...	...	...	...	...	...	...	...	...	1416	...	...	...	...	|	...	1616	...
Aigle a.	...	...	...	1037	...	...	|	...	...	...	...	...	...	...	...	...	1437	...	...	...	...	|	...	1637	...
Montreux a.	...	...	...	1048	...	...	1123	...	...	...	...	...	...	...	...	...	1448	...	...	...	...	1623	...	1648	...
Lausanne a.	...	...	...	1110	...	...	1142	...	...	...	...	...	...	...	...	...	1510	...	...	...	...	1642	...	1710	...
Genève a.	...	...	...	1152	...	...	1221	...	...	...	...	...	...	...	...	...	1552	...	...	...	...	1721	...	1752	...
Genève Aéroport ✈ a.	...	...	...	1159	...	...	...	...	...	...	...	...	...	...	...	...	1559	...	...	...	...	...	...	1759	...

train type/number	FR	FR	EC	EC	IR	EC	FR	EC	IR	EC	IC	EC	IC	FR	EC	IR	FR	EC	EC	IC	IC	EC	IR	EC	
train number	**9728**	**9526**	**320**	**54**	**1830**	**308**	**9532**	**322**	**2336**	**36 46**	**1084**	**310**	**692**	**9536**	**56**	**1836**	**9540**	**42**	**44**	**1088**	**338**	**324**	**2340**	**326**	
notes	R ✕ ↯	R ✕ ↯	R 🍷 ⊗	R 🍷 ⊗		R 🍷 ⊗	R ✕ ↯	R 🍷 ⊗		R 🍷 ⊗		R 🍷 ⊗		R ✕ ↯	R 🍷 ⊗		R ✕ ↯	R 🍷 ⊗ ⑤⑥	R 🍷 ⊗ ⑦–④			R ✕ ⊗		R 🍷 ⊗	
Napoli Centrale d.	...	1000	...	...	...	...	1200	...	...	...	...	...	...	1300	...	...	1400	...	...	...	...	...	...	...	...
Roma Termini d.	...	1120	...	...	...	...	1320	...	...	...	...	...	...	1420	...	...	1522	...	...	...	...	...	...	...	...
Firenze SMN d.	...	1300	...	...	...	...	1500	...	...	...	...	...	...	1600	...	...	1700	...	...	...	...	...	...	...	...
Bologna Centrale d.	...	1338	...	...	...	...	1538	...	...	...	...	...	...	1638	...	...	1738	...	...	...	...	...	...	1726	...
Genova d.	...	|	...	...	...	...	|	...	...	...	...	1612	...	|	...	...	|	...	...	...	...	...	...	|	...
Venezia Santa Lucia d.	1150	|	...	...	...	1318	|	...	...	...	...	|	...	|	...	...	|	1618	1618	...	...	...	...	|	...
Venezia Mestre d.	1202	|	...	...	...	1330	|	...	...	...	...	|	...	|	...	...	|	1630	1630	...	...	...	...	|	...
Verona Porta Nuova d.	1302	|	...	...	...	1432	|	...	...	...	...	|	...	|	...	...	|	1732	1732	...	...	...	...	|	...
Milano Centrale a.	1415	1440	...	...	...	1555	1645	...	...	...	...	1750f	...	1742	...	...	1842	1855	1855	...	...	...	...	1949f	...
Milano Centrale d.	...	...	1510	1520	...	1610	...	1710	...	1720	...	1752f	...	...	1820	...	...	1920	1920	...	...	1910	...	1951f	...
Gallarate d.	...	...	|	|	...	|	...	|	...	|	...	|	...	...	|	...	...	1954	1954	...	...	|	...	|	...
Stresa d.	...	...	|	1620	...	|	...	|	...	1821	...	|	...	...	1920	...	...	|	|	...	...	|	...	|	...
Domodossola 🏛 ¶ d.	...	...	|	1648	...	|	...	|	...	1848	...	|	...	...	1948	...	...	2048	2048	...	...	|	...	|	...
Brig a.	...	...	|	1716	1726	|	...	|	...	1914	1918	|	...	...	2016	2026	...	2114	2114	2118	...	|	...	|	...
Visp a.	...	...	|	1725	1732	|	...	|	...	|	1925	|	...	...	2026	2032	...	|	2132	2125	...	|	...	|	...
Como San Giovanni d.	...	...	1550	|	|	1650	...	1750	...	|	|	1850	...	...	|	|	...	|	|	|	...	1950	...	2050	...
Chiasso 🏛 a.	...	...	1605	|	|	1658	*IC*	1805	...	|	|	1858	...	...	|	|	...	|	|	|	...	2005	...	2058	...
Lugano a.	...	...	1630	|	|	1728	**688**	1830	...	|	|	1928	...	...	|	|	...	|	|	|	...	2030	...	2128	...
Bellinzona a.	...	...	1645	|	|	1745		1845	...	|	|	1945	...	...	|	|	...	|	|	|	...	2045	...	2145	...
Arth-Goldau a.	...	...	1742	|	|	1842	1915	1942	2015	|	|	2042	2115	...	|	|	...	|	|	|	...	2142	2215	2242	...
Luzern a.	...	...	|	|	|	|	1941	|	2041	|	|	|	2141	...	|	|	...	|	|	|	...	|	2241	|	...
Spiez a.	...	...	|	1753	|	|	|	|	|	|	1953	|	|	...	2053	|	...	|	|	2153	...	|	|	|	...
Bern a.	...	...	|	1824	|	|	|	|	|	|	2024	|	|	...	2124	|	...	|	|	2224	2236	|	|	|	...
Olten a.	...	...	|	1903	|	|	2028	|	2128	|	2103	|	2228	...	2203	|	...	|	|	...	2303	|	2328	|	...
Basel SBB a.	...	...	|	1932	|	|	2056	|	2156	|	2132	|	2300	...	2232	|	...	|	|	...	2337	|	2400	|	...
Zürich HB a.	...	...	1827	...	|	1927	...	2027	...	|	...	2127	...	...	...	|	...	|	|	...	...	2227	...	2327	...
Sion a.	...	...	...	...	1801	...	...	...	...	1947	...	...	...	...	...	2101	...	2147	2159	...	...	...	...	...	...
Martigny a.	...	...	...	...	1816	...	...	...	...	|	...	...	...	...	...	2116	...	|	2215	...	...	...	...	...	...
Aigle a.	...	...	...	...	1837	...	...	...	...	|	...	...	...	...	...	2137	...	|	2237	...	...	...	...	...	...
Montreux a.	...	...	...	...	1848	...	...	...	...	2023	...	...	...	...	...	2148	...	2223	2248	...	...	...	...	...	...
Lausanne a.	...	...	...	...	1910	...	...	...	...	2042	...	...	...	...	...	2210	...	2242	2310	...	...	...	...	...	...
Genève a.	...	...	...	...	1952	...	...	...	...	2121	...	...	...	...	...	2252	...	2321	2355	...	...	...	...	...	...
Genève Aéroport ✈ a.	...	...	...	...	1959	...	...	...	...	...	...	...	...	...	...	2259	...	...	0003	...	...	...	...	...	...

A – 🛏 1, 2 cl., 🛏 2 cl. (4 berth), (2) Salerno - Milano.

F – To Frankfurt (arrive 1844).

f – Milano **Lambrate**.

g – Milano **Porta Garibaldi**.

t – Roma **Tiburtina**.

y – Firenze **Campo di Marte**.

↯ – Supplement payable.

¶ – Ticketing point is **Iselle**.

⊗ – Compulsory reservation for international journeys. Supplement payable for international journeys and for internal journeys within Italy.

83 PRAHA - BRATISLAVA - ZAGREB - RIJEKA / SPLIT

Temporarily relocated to page 66

ZÜRICH - INNSBRUCK - WIEN, GRAZ, ZAGREB and BUDAPEST 86

train type/number	RJX	RJX	IC	RJ	D	RJX	RJ	EC	EC	RJX	EC	RJX	EC	D	IC	RJX	EC	RJX	EC	RJX	RJX	NJ	EN	D	EN	NJ	
train number	269	765	515	111	211	161	596	217	163	563	113	165	115	315	611	167	219	169	117	367	369	465	40465	413	40467	467	
notes	✕	✕	🍷	✕	2	✕	✕	🍷	🍷	✕	213	✕	🍷		🍷	✕	🍷	✕	1217	✕	✕			2			
						G			B		H								🍷			Z	A		C	W	
Zürich HB ... d.	...	...	...	...	...	0640	...	...	0840	...	...	1040	...	...	...	1240	...	1440	...	1640	1840	2040	2040	...	2140	2140	...
Sargans ... d.	...	...	...	...	...	0736	...	...	0936	...	...	1136	...	...	...	1336	...	1536	...	1736	1936	2137	2137	...	2237	2237	...
Buchs ▦ ... d.	...	...	...	...	...	0754	...	...	1000	...	...	1154	...	...	...	1354	...	1554	...	1800	1954	2205	2205	...	2305	2305	...
Feldkirch ... d.	...	0613	...	...	...	0817	...	...	1017	...	...	1217	...	...	...	1417	...	1617	...	1817	2017	2245	2245	...	2324	2324	...
Bludenz ... d.	...	0626	...	...	...	0830	...	...	1030	...	...	1230	...	...	...	1430	...	1630	...	1830	2030	2301	2301	...	2340	2340	...
St Anton am Arlberg . d.	...	0703	...	...	...	0903	...	...	1103	...	...	1303	...	...	...	1503	...	1703	...	1903	2103	2345	2345	...	|	|	...
Landeck-Zams ... d.	...	0727	...	...	...	0927	...	...	1127	...	...	1327	...	...	...	1527	...	1727	...	1927	2127	0009	0009	...	0036	0036	...
Ötztal ... d.	...	0751	...	...	...	0948	...	...	1148	...	...	1348	...	...	...	1548	...	1748	...	1951	2151	|	|	...	|	|	...
Innsbruck Hbf ... d.	0510	0817	0821	...	...	1017	...	...	1221e	1217	...	1417	...	...	...	1617	...	1817	...	2017	2217	0056	0056	...	0128	0128	...
Jenbach ... d.	0527	|	0844	...	...	|	...	...	1244	|	...	|	...	...	...	|	...	|	...	|	|	|	|	...	|	|	...
Wörgl ... d.	0541	0843	0859	...	...	1043	...	...	1259	1243	...	1443	...	...	...	1643	...	1843	...	2043	2243	|	|	...	|	|	...
Kitzbühel ... d.	|	|	0929	...	...	|	...	...	1329	|	...	|	...	...	...	|	...	|	...	|	|	|	|	...	|	|	...
St Johann in Tirol ... d.	|	|	0937	...	...	|	...	...	1337	|	...	|	...	...	...	|	...	|	...	|	|	|	|	...	|	|	...
Saalfelden ... d.	|	|	1005	...	...	|	...	...	1405	|	...	|	...	...	...	|	...	|	...	|	|	|	|	...	|	|	...
Zell am See ... d.	|	|	1015	...	...	|	...	...	1416	|	...	|	...	...	...	|	...	|	...	|	|	|	|	...	|	|	...
Schwarzach St Veit ... a.	|	|	|	...	...	|	...	...	|	|	...	|	...	...	...	|	...	|	...	|	|	0317	0317	...	|	|	...
Salzburg Hbf ... d.	0708	1008	|	1012	...	1208	1212	1215	|	1408	...	1608	1612	...	1615	1808	1815	2008	2012	2206	0012	|	|	...	0350	0436	...
Bischofshofen ... a.	|	|	|	1052	...	|	1252	1302	|	|	...	|	1652	...	1702	|	1902	|	2052	...	...	0336	|	...	|	|	...
Schwarzach St Veit ... a.	|	|	1046	1109	...	|	1309	|	1446	|	1511	|	1709	...	|	|	|	|	2109	...	...	|	|	...	|	|	...
Selzthal ... a.	|	|	1239	|	...	|	|	1439	1639	|	|	|	|	...	1839	|	2039	|	|	...	...	0504	|	...	|	|	...
Graz Hbf ... a.	|	|	1414	|	...	|	|	1614	1814	|	|	|	|	...	2014	|	2214	|	|	...	...	0700	|	...	|	|	...
Villach Hbf ... a.	|	|	▬	1243	1253	|	1443	...	...	|	1643	|	1843	1853	▬	|	...	|	2243	...	...	...	0604	...	|	|	...
Klagenfurt ... a.	|	|	...	1316	|	|	1513	...	...	|	1718	|	1916	|	**411**	|	...	|	2316	...	...	...	|	...	|	|	...
Jesenice ▦ ... a.	|	|	...	...	1329	|	▬	...	...	|	1729	|	▬	1926	**P**	|	...	|	...	...	...	...	0704	...	|	|	...
Ljubljana ⊙ ... a.	|	|	...	...	1432	|	...	...	...	|	1831	|	...	2033	2105	|	...	|	...	...	...	...	0809	...	|	|	...
Zagreb ⊙ ... a.	|	|	...	...	1710	|	...	...	...	|	2047	|	...	...	2337	|	...	|	...	...	...	...	1041	1107	|	|	...
Vinkovci ⊕ ... a.	|	|	...	...	2119	|	...	...	...	|	▬	|	...	...	0303	|	...	|	...	...	...	...	...	1432	|	|	...
Beograd Centar ⊕ . a.	|	|	...	...	...	|	...	...	...	|	...	|	...	...	0605	|	...	|	...	...	...	...	...	1812	|	|	...
Linz Hbf ... a.	0814	1114	...	...	...	1314	...	...	...	1514	...	1714	...	...	...	1914	...	2114	...	...	...	...	...	...	0452	0558	...
St Pölten ... a.	0900	1200	...	...	...	1400	...	...	...	1600	*EC*	1800	*EN*	...	...	2000	...	2200	...	...	...	...	...	...	0600	0710	...
Wien Meidling ... a.	0923	1223	*EC*	...	...	1423	*EC*	...	...	1623	**149**	1823	**347**	...	...	2023	...	2223	...	...	...	...	...	...	0626	0744	...
Wien Hbf. ... a.	0930	1230	**145**	...	...	1430	**147**	...	...	1630	**D**	1830	**K**	...	...	2030	...	2230	...	...	...	...	...	...	0634	0755	...
Wien Hbf. ... d.	0940	...	1240	...	...	...	1437	...	...	...	1642	1842	1942	...	...	2042	...	...	...	...	...	...	...	...	0658	...	...
Bratislava hl. st. a.	|	...	|	...	...	...	|	...	...	...	|	|	|	...	...	2151	...	...	...	...	...	...	...	...	|	...	...
Hegyeshalom ▦ ... a.	1025	...	1325	...	...	...	1521	...	...	...	1725	1925	2025	...	...	...	...	...	...	...	...	...	...	...	0723	...	...
Győr ... a.	1053	...	1353	...	...	...	1553	...	...	...	1753	1953	2053	...	...	...	...	...	...	...	...	...	...	...	0753	...	...
Budapest Keleti ... a.	1219	...	1519	...	...	...	1719	...	...	...	1919	2119	2220	...	...	...	...	...	...	...	...	...	...	...	0919	...	...

train type/number	RJX	RJX	EC	RJ	RJX	D	D	EC	RJX	RJX	RJX	EC	EC	EC	RJX	RJX	RJX	RJX	IC	D	RJX	RJX	NJ	EN	NJ	D	EN
train number	366	368	218	691	160	410	314	114	162	60	564	212	164	216	62	166	64	168	610	210	66	760	466	40462	464	412	40414
notes	✕	✕	🍷	✕	✕	314		🍷	✕	✕	✕	112	🍷	🍷	✕	✕	✕	✕	🍷	2	✕	✕				414	
						Q						H	B					G					W	E	Z	2	A
Budapest Keleti ... d.	...	...	...	...	...	...	...	...	0640	0740	...	...	...	...	0940	...	1140	...	...	...	1340	...	...	2040	...	...	...
Győr ... d.	...	...	...	...	...	...	...	...	0802	0902	...	...	...	...	1102	...	1302	...	...	...	1502	...	...	2202	...	...	...
Hegyeshalom ▦ ... d.	...	...	...	...	...	...	...	...	0832	0932	...	...	...	...	1132	...	1332	...	...	...	1532	...	...	2232	...	...	...
Bratislava hl. st. d.	...	...	...	...	0610	...	...	...	|	|	...	...	...	...	|	...	|	...	...	...	|	...	...	|	...	...	...
Wien Hbf ... a.	...	...	...	...	0718	...	...	...	0918	1021	...	...	...	...	1221	...	1421	...	...	...	1621	...	...	2321	...	...	...
Wien Hbf ... d.	...	...	...	...	0730	...	...	...	0930	1030	1130	...	...	...	▬	1330	▬	1530	...	...	▬	1730	2127	2327	...	...	...
Wien Meidling ... d.	...	...	...	...	0737	...	...	...	0937	1037	1137	...	...	...	...	1337	...	1537	...	...	...	1737	2135	2335	...	...	...
St Pölten ... d.	...	...	...	...	0800	...	...	...	1000	1100	1200	...	...	...	...	1400	...	1600	...	...	...	1800	2201	0001	...	...	...
Linz Hbf ... d.	...	...	...	...	0846	...	...	...	1046	1146	1246	...	...	...	...	1446	...	1646	...	...	...	1846	2256	0100	...	...	...
Beograd Centar ⊕ . d.	...	...	...	...	|	2058	...	...	|	|	|	...	...	...	...	|	...	|	...	...	...	|	|	|	...	1005	...
Vinkovci ⊕ ... d.	...	...	...	...	|	0103	...	...	|	|	|	...	...	...	...	|	...	|	...	0853	...	|	|	|	...	1443	...
Zagreb ⊙ ... d.	...	...	...	...	|	0440	...	...	|	|	|	0702	...	...	...	|	...	|	...	1247	*RJ*	|	|	|	...	1804	1839
Ljubljana ⊙ ... d.	...	...	...	...	|	0717	0726	...	|	|	|	0923	...	...	*IC*	|	...	|	...	1527	**110**	|	|	|	...	...	2110
Jesenice ▦ ... d.	...	...	...	...	|	▬	0832	...	|	|	|	1022	...	...	**793**	|	*IC*	|	...	1632	✕	|	|	|	...	...	2213
Klagenfurt ... d.	...	...	...	0645	|	*IC*	|	0842	|	|	|	1027	...	...	1245	|	**518**	|	...	|	1642	|	|	|	...	...	|
Villach Hbf ... d.	...	...	...	0716	|	**512**	0908	0916	|	|	|	1058	...	...	1316	|	🍷	|	...	1708	1716	|	|	|	...	...	2326
Graz Hbf ... d.	...	...	0545	|	|	0745	...	|	|	|	|	|	0945	1145	|	|	1345	|	1545	...	|	|	|	|	2226	...	|
Selzthal ... d.	...	...	0719	|	|	0919	...	|	|	|	|	|	1119	1319	|	|	1519	|	1719	...	|	|	|	|	0028	...	|
Schwarzach St Veit ... d.	...	...	|	0852	|	|	...	1052	|	|	|	1248	1313	|	1452	|	|	|	|	...	1852	|	|	|	|	...	|
Bischofshofen ... d.	...	...	0857	0907	|	1057	...	1107	|	|	|	...	|	1457	1507	|	1650	|	1857	...	1907	|	|	|	0158	...	|
Salzburg Hbf ... d.	0554	0756	0944	0948	0956	1144	...	1148	1156	1252	1356	...	|	1544	1548	1556	|	1756	1944	...	1948	1956	0230	0230	|	...	|
Schwarzach St Veit ... d.	|	|	...	...	|	...	...	...	|	...	|	...	|	...	...	|	1713	|	...	...	...	|	|	|	0232	...	0232
Zell am See ... d.	|	|	...	...	|	...	...	...	|	...	|	...	1344	...	...	|	1744	|	...	...	...	|	|	|	|	...	|
Saalfelden ... d.	|	|	...	...	|	...	...	...	|	...	|	...	1354	...	...	|	1754	|	...	...	...	|	|	|	|	...	|
St Johann in Tirol ... d.	|	|	...	...	|	...	...	...	|	...	|	...	1422	...	...	|	1822	|	...	...	...	|	|	|	|	...	|
Kitzbühel ... d.	|	|	...	...	|	...	...	...	|	...	|	...	1430	...	...	|	1830	|	...	...	...	|	|	|	|	...	|
Wörgl ... d.	0719	0919	...	...	1119	...	...	...	1319	...	1519	...	1502	...	...	1719	1902	1919	...	...	...	2119	|	|	|	...	|
Jenbach ... d.	|	|	...	...	|	...	...	...	|	...	|	...	1518	...	...	|	1918	|	...	...	...	|	|	|	|	...	|
Innsbruck Hbf ... d.	0748	0948	...	...	1148	...	...	...	1348	...	1544	...	1548	...	...	1748	1940	1948	...	...	...	2148	0431	0431	0453	...	0453
Ötztal ... d.	0812	1012	...	...	1212	...	...	...	1412	...	...	...	1612	...	...	1812	...	2012	...	...	...	2212	|	|	|	...	|
Landeck-Zams ... d.	0833	1033	...	...	1233	...	...	...	1433	...	...	...	1633	...	...	1833	...	2036	...	...	...	2236	0520	0520	0545	...	0545
St Anton am Arlberg . d.	0857	1057	...	...	1257	...	...	...	1457	...	...	...	1657	...	...	1857	...	2100	...	...	...	2300	|	|	0616	...	0616
Bludenz ... d.	0931	1131	...	...	1331	...	...	...	1531	...	...	...	1731	...	...	1931	...	2134	...	...	...	2337	0625	0625	0706	...	0706
Feldkirch ... d.	0944	1148	...	...	1348	...	...	...	1548	...	...	...	1744	...	...	1948	...	2148	...	...	...	2348	0640	0640	0738	...	0738
Buchs ▦ ... a.	0959	1206	...	...	1406	...	...	...	1606	...	...	...	1759	...	...	2006	...	2203	...	...	...	...	0656	0656	0753	...	0753
Sargans ... a.	1023	1223	...	...	1423	...	...	...	1623	...	...	...	1823	...	...	2023	...	2223	...	...	...	...	0724	0724	0824	...	0824
Zürich HB ... a.	1120	1320	...	...	1520	...	...	...	1720	...	...	...	1920	...	...	2120	...	2320	...	...	...	...	0820	0820	0920	...	0920

A – *ÖBB nightjet* ALPINE PEARLS – 🛏 1, 2 cl., ▬ 2 cl. (4, 6 berth), (2) Zürich - Graz and v.v.

B – TRANSALPIN (1) (observation car), (12) 🍷 Zürich - Innsbruck - Graz and v.v.

C – 🛏 1, 2 cl., ▬ 2 cl., (2) Zürich - Wien - Budapest. From Aug. 23 conveys 🛏 1, 2 cl. (**50467**) Zürich - Linz - Praha. Special fares payable.

D – HORTOBÁGY (12) Wien - Budapest - Szolnok (arrive 2102) - Debrecen (2235) - Záhony (0010). Conveys 🛏 1, 2 cl. Wien (**40147**) - Budapest - Záhony - Lviv - Kyïv (Table **96**).

E – 🛏 1, 2 cl., ▬ 2 cl., (2) Budapest - Wien - Zürich. From Aug. 22 conveys 🛏 1, 2 cl. (**50466**) Praha - Linz - Zürich. Special fares payable.

G – (12) 🍷 Zürich - Innsbruck - Wien and v.v. Conveys (12) 🍷 Bolzano (depart 0745; arrive 2220, *RJX* **185**/**184**) - Innsbruck - Wien and v.v.

H – (12) Schwarzach St Veit - Villach - Klagenfurt and Schwarzach St Veit - Villach - Ljubljana - Zagreb and v.v.

K – DACIA – 🛏 1, 2 cl., ▬ 2 cl., (2) ✕ Wien - Budapest - București.

P – June 20 - Sept. 13: ▬ 2 cl., (12) Ljubljana - Zagreb - Beograd.

Q – June 21 - Sept. 14: ▬ 2 cl., (12) Beograd - Zagreb - Ljubljana.

W – *ÖBB nightjet* WIENER WALZER – 🛏 1, 2 cl., ▬ 2 cl. (4, 6 berth), (2) Zürich - Wien and v.v. Special fares payable.

Z – Zürich - Graz: *ÖBB nightjet* ZÜRICHSEE – 🛏 1, 2 cl., ▬ 2 cl. (4, 6 berth), (2) Zürich - Graz and v.v.

e – Arrive 1211.

j – Change at Villach.

RJ – ÖBB *Railjet* service. ✕, (1) (business class), (1) (first class), (2) (economy class).

⊙ – ▦ between Ljubljana and Zagreb is Dobova.

⊕ – ▦ between Vinkovci and Beograd is Šid.

☛ **Shaded services are suspended until further notice.**

87 LJUBLJANA - TRIESTE - UDINE / VENEZIA

					EC	*FR*			
	1824				**134**	**9758**	**1810**	**1896**	
	2	2			**E**		Ⓑ 2	2	
Ljubljana	d. 0552	...	...	...	1409	...	1606	...	...
Postojna	d. 0654	...	...	...	1513	...	1717	...	...
Pivka	d. 0707	...	...	...	1526	...	1731	...	...
Divača	d. 0727	...	...	...	1549	...	1755	...	...
Sežana 🏛	d. 0739	...	...	...	1559	...	1807	...	...
Villa Opicina 🏛	a. 0750	...	...	...	1610	...	1818	...	...
Villa Opicina 🏛	d. ...	0805	...	...	1625	...	...	1823	...
Trieste Centrale	a. ...	0838	...	...	1652	...	...	1853	...
Trieste Centrale	d. ...	0850	0915	...	...	1705	...	...	1915
Monfalcone	d. ...	0914	0939	...	...	1730	...	...	1939
Trieste Airport	d. ...	0919	0944	...	...	1736	...	...	1944
Cervignano-Aquileia-Grado	d. ...	0927	0952	...	...	1743	...	...	1952
Udine	a. ...	0952	|	...	...	|	...	...	|
Venezia Mestre	a. ...	...	1108	...	...	1850	...	...	2108
Venezia Santa Lucia	a. ...	...	1120	...	...	|	...	...	2124
Milano Centrale	a. ...	...	...	...	...	2200	...	...	...

E – [12] Wien (**151**) - Ljubljana (**134**) - Trieste.

					FR	*EC*				
				1825	**9707**	**135**			**1897**	**1897**
			2	2		**F**			2	2
Milano Centrale	d.	...	...	...	0745	...	...	...	...	...
Venezia Santa Lucia	d.	0641	...	...	|	...	...	1641	...	...
Venezia Mestre	d.	0653	...	...	1011	...	...	1653	...	...
Udine	d.	|	...	...	|	...	...	|	1754	...
Cervignano-Aquileia-Grado	d.	0809	...	...	1126	...	...	1809	1823	...
Trieste Airport	d.	0817	...	...	1135	...	...	1817	1830	...
Monfalcone	d.	0823	...	...	1142	...	...	1823	1835	...
Trieste Centrale	a.	0848	...	...	1205	...	...	1846	1858	...
Trieste Centrale	d.	...	0902	...	...	1303	...	...	1907	...
Villa Opicina 🏛	a.	...	0930	...	...	1330	...	...	1936	...
Villa Opicina 🏛	d.	...	...	0945	...	1345	...	...	...	1945
Sežana 🏛	d.	...	...	0958	...	1358	...	...	...	1958
Divača	d.	...	...	1008	...	1410	...	...	...	2009
Pivka	d.	...	...	1029	...	1431	...	...	...	2030
Postojna	d.	...	...	1041	...	1443	...	...	...	2042
Ljubljana	a.	...	...	1146	...	1547	...	...	...	2145

F – [12] Trieste (**135**) - Ljubljana (**150**) - Wien.

88 WIEN - KLAGENFURT - VENEZIA, MILANO and ROMA

train type / number	🚌	*REX*			*IC*	🚌		*RJ*	*RJ*	*EC*	*RJ*	*RJ*	🚌	*REX*		*NJ*	*NJ*		*NJ*	*NJ*		*NJ*
train number	**831**	**1821**	**131**		**533**	**835**		**535**	**73**	**140**	**133**	**539**	**837**	**1823**		**40233**	**233**		**1237**	**1237**		**237**
notes	Ⓡ	**1817**	✕		✕	Ⓡ		✕	✕	**J**	✕	✕	Ⓡ	**1819**		**A**	**B**		**G**	**H**		**C**
	Y	2				**Y**							**Y**	2								
Praha hlavní d.	...	...	...	...	...	...	...	...	0612	...	...	...	...	...	...	...	...	...	...	...	...	...
Břeclav d.	...	...	...	...	...	...	...	...	0955	...	...	...	...	...	...	...	...	...	...	...	...	...
Budapest Keleti d.	...	...	...	...	...	...	...	...	|	0840	...	...	...	...	...	...	...	...	...	...	...	...
Györ d.	...	...	...	...	...	...	...	...	|	1002	...	...	...	...	...	...	...	...	...	...	...	...
Wien Hbf d.	...	...	0625	...	0825	...	...	1025	1049	1121	1225	1425	...	...	...	1923	1923	...	2001	2001	...	2127
Wien Meidling d.	...	...	0632	...	0832	...	...	1032	...	...	1232	1432	...	...	...	1931	1931	...	2008	2008	...	2135
Bruck an der Mur d.	...	...	0815	...	1015	...	...	1215	...	...	1415	1615	...	...	...	2127	2127	...	2222	2222	...	|
Klagenfurt Hbf d.	...	...	1022	...	1222	...	...	1422	...	...	1622	1822	...	...	...	2337	2337	...	0021	0021	...	|
Linz Hbf d.	...	...	|	...	|	...	...	|	...	...	|	|	...	...	...	|	|	...	|	|	...	2258
Salzburg Hbf d.	...	...	|	...	|	...	...	|	...	...	|	|	...	...	...	|	|	...	|	|	...	0140
Villach Hbf d.	0650	0945	1050	...	1246	1256	...	1446	...	...	1649	1846	1856	1929	...	0055	0134	...	0045	0045	...	0445
Tarvisio 🏛 a.	|	1013	1112	...	...	|	...	...	...	...	1712	...	|	1957	...	0119	0157	...	0108	0108	...	0508
Udine a.	0825	1130	1216	...	...	1430	...	...	...	...	1816	...	2030	2113	...	|	|	...	|	|	...	0623
Trieste Centrale a.	|	1259x	|	...	...	|	...	...	...	...	|	...	2150	2239x	...	|	|	...	|	|	...	|
Venezia Mestre a.	1000	...	1402	...	...	1605	...	...	...	...	1952	...	...	...	...	|	|	...	|	|	...	0823
Venezia Tronchetto ★ a.	1020	...	|	...	...	1625	...	...	...	...	|	...	...	...	...	|	|	...	|	|	...	|
Venezia Santa Lucia a.	...	...	1414	...	...	...	...	...	...	...	2004	...	...	...	...	|	|	...	|	|	...	0834
Padova a.	...	...								...	...	...	...	...	...	|	0457	...	0415	0423	...	...
Verona Porta Nuova a.	...	...								...	...	...	...	...	...	|	0551	...	|	|	...	...
Milano Porta Garibaldi a.	...	...								...	...	...	...	...	...	|	0810	...	|	|	...	...
Bologna Centrale a.	...	...								...	...	...	...	...	...	0520	...	...	0541	0541	...	...
Firenze SMN a.	...	...								...	...	...	...	...	...	0632	...	...	0653	0713	...	...
Pisa Centrale a.	...	...								...	...	...	...	...	...	|	...	...	0831	0840	...	...
Livorno Centrale a.	...	...								...	...	...	...	...	...	|	...	...	0850	0900	...	...
Roma Termini a.	...	...								...	...	...	...	...	...	0910	...	...	...	...	...	...

OTHER CONNECTING SERVICES

Praha - Wien: Table **1150**
Budapest - Wien: Table **1250**
Venezia - Roma: Table **600**
Venezia - Milano: Table **605**

train type / number	*REX*	*RJ*	🚌	*RJ*	*RJ*	*EC*	*EC*	*RJX*	*RJ*	🚌	*IC*	*REX*	*RJ*	🚌		*NJ*	*NJ*	*NJ*	*NJ*	*NJ*	*NJ*	
train number	**1816**	**534**	**830**	**536**	**132**	**100**	**272**	**165**	**372**	**832**	**632**	**1818**	**130**	**838**		**236**	**1234**	**1234**	**1234**	**235**	**40294**	
notes	**1820**	✕	Ⓡ	✕	✕		✕		✕	Ⓡ	🍸	**1822**	✕	Ⓡ		**C**	**K**	**E**	**D**	**B**	**A**	
	2		**Y**							**Y**		2		**Y**								
Roma Termini d.	...	...	...	...	...	...	...	...	...	...	...	...	...	...	...	...	...	...	...	...	2017	...
Livorno Centrale d.	...	...	...	...	...	...	...	...	...	...	...	...	...	...	...	...	1532	1920	1920	...	|	...
Pisa Centrale d.	...	...	...	...	...	...	...	...	...	...	...	...	...	...	...	...	1550	1945	1946	...	|	...
Firenze SMN d.	...	...	...	...	...	...	...	...	...	...	...	...	...	...	...	...	|	2105	2105	...	2231	...
Bologna Centrale d.	...	...	...	...	...	...	...	...	...	...	...	...	...	...	...	...	|	2223	2223	...	2345	...
Milano Porta Garibaldi d.	...	...	...	...	...	...	...	...	...	...	...	...	...	...	...	...	|	|	|	2110	|	...
Verona Porta Nuova d.	...	...	...	...	...	...	...	...	...	...	...	...	...	...	...	...	|	|	|	2258	|	...
Padova d.	...	...	...	...	...	...	...	...	...	...	...	...	...	...	...	...	2336	2349	2349	2343	|	...
Venezia Santa Lucia d.	...	...	...	...	0956	...	...	...	...	...	...	...	1552	...	...	2105	|	|	|	|	|	...
Venezia Tronchetto ★ d.	...	...	...	...	|	...	...	...	...	1320	...	...	|	1720	...	|	|	|	|	|	|	...
Venezia Mestre d.	...	...	...	...	1008	...	...	...	...	1340	...	...	1604	1740	...	2117	0017	|	|	|	|	...
Trieste Centrale d.	0545x	...	0755	...	|	...	...	...	...	|	...	1550x	|	|	...	|	|	|	|	|	|	...
Udine d.	0714	...	0915	...	1146	...	...	...	...	1515	...	1722	1746	1915	...	2301	|	|	|	|	|	...
Tarvisio 🏛 d.	0827	...	|	...	1249	...	...	...	...	|	...	1840	1849	|	...	|	0319	0319	0319	0245	0325	...
Villach Hbf a.	0854	0914	1050	1114	1311	...	...	...	...	1650	1714	1907	1911	2050	...	0042	0341	0341	0341	0307	0347	...
Salzburg Hbf a.	...	|	...	|	|	...	...	...	...	...	|	...	|	...	...	0404	|	|	|	|	|	...
Linz Hbf a.	...	|	...	|	|	...	...	...	...	...	|	...	|	...	...	0558	|	|	|	|	|	...
Klagenfurt Hbf a.	...	0937	...	1137	1337	...	...	...	...	...	1737	...	1937	...	...	|	0407	0407	0407	0439	0439	...
Bruck an der Mur a.	...	1144	...	1344	1544	...	...	...	...	...	1944	...	2144	...	...	|	0620	0620	0620	0639	0639	...
Wien Meidling a.	...	1328	...	1528	1728	...	...	...	...	...	2128	...	2328	...	...	0744	0836	0836	0836	0845	0845	...
Wien Hbf a.	...	1335	...	1535	1735	1810	...	1842	1910	...	2135	...	2335	...	...	0755	0842	0842	0842	0852	0852	...
Györ a.	...	...	...	...	...	|	...	1953	|	...	...	...	...	...	...	...	...	...	...	...	...	...
Budapest Keleti a.	...	...	...	...	...	|	...	2119	|	...	...	...	...	...	...	...	...	...	...	...	...	...
Břeclav a.	...	...	...	...	...	1904	1907	...	2004	...	...	...	...	...	...	...	...	...	...	...	...	...
Praha hlavní a.	...	...	...	...	...	...	2241	...	2343	...	...	...	...	...	...	...	...	...	...	...	...	...

A – *ÖBB nightjet* 🛏 1, 2 cl., couchette 2 cl. (4, 6 berth), [2] 🍸 Wien - Roma and v.v.

B – *ÖBB nightjet* 🛏 1, 2 cl., couchette 2 cl. (4, 6 berth), [2] 🍸 Wien - Milano and v.v.

C – *ÖBB nightjet* 🛏 1, 2 cl., couchette 2 cl. (4, 6 berth), [2] Wien - Venezia and v.v.

D – ④⑥ May 27 - June 10: *ÖBB nightjet* 🛏 1, 2 cl., couchette 2 cl. (4, 6 berth), [2] 🍸 Livorno - Firenze - Wien.

E – ④⑥ July 1 - Sept. 30 (also Oct. 7; not July 10, 17, 24, Aug. 7, Sept. 25): *ÖBB nightjet* 🛏 1, 2 cl., couchette 2 cl. (4, 6 berth), [2] 🍸 Livorno - Firenze - Wien.

G – ③⑤ May 26 - June 11, Sept. 8 - Oct. 8: *ÖBB nightjet* 🛏 1, 2 cl., couchette 2 cl. (4, 6 berth), [2] 🍸 Wien - Firenze - Livorno.

H – ③⑤ June 16 - Sept. 3: *ÖBB nightjet* 🛏 1, 2 cl., couchette 2 cl. (4, 6 berth), [2] 🍸 Wien - Firenze - Livorno.

J – [12] Zahony (depart 0405) - Debrecen (0531) - Szolnok (0657) - Budapest - Wien. Conveys 🛏 1, 2 cl. Kyïv - Lviv - Zahony - Wien; see Table **96**.

K – July 10, 17, 24, Aug. 7, Sept. 25, Oct. 2, 9: *ÖBB nightjet* 🛏 1, 2 cl., couchette 2 cl. (4, 6 berth), [2] 🍸 Livorno - Wien.

Y – June 2 - Sept. 26.

x – Ⓒ.

⁄ – Supplement payable.

★ – See Venezia City Plan on page 32.

RJ – ÖBB *Railjet* service. [1] (business class), [1] (first class), [2] (economy class), ✕.

🚌 – **ÖBB** *IC Bus*. Rail tickets valid. Ⓡ. Supplement payable. 2nd class only. Connections to / from Wien are made at Villach.

VILLACH - LJUBLJANA - ZAGREB - BUDAPEST and BEOGRAD 89

train type	D	D	D	D		EC	D	D	1604	480	D
train number	703	415	247	581		213	315	315	1247	1247	1205
notes	205	413		201				411	959	959	
notes	A		H	R				P	K	E	C
Villach Hbf d.	...	0625	...	...	...	1653	1853	...	...	...	...
Koper a.	...	|	...	...	...	|	|	...	2015	...	...
Rijeka d.	...	|	...	...	...	|	|	...	|	2045	...
Ljubljana d.	...	0830	0935	...	...	1838	2105	2105	0030	0030	...
Dobova 🏛 d.	...	1015	|	...	...	2021	2241	2306	|	|	...
Split d.	...	|	|	...	...	|	...	|	|	|	1828
Zagreb a.	...	1041	|	...	...	2047	...	2337	|	|	0243
Zagreb d.	1005	1107	|	1635	...	...	...	2341	|	|	0317
Vinkovci a.	|	1432	|	|	...	...	...	0303	|	|	|
Šid 🏛 a.	|	1517	|	|	...	...	...	0341	|	|	|
Beograd Centar a.	|	1812	|	|	...	...	...	0605	|	|	|
Koprivnica 🏛 d.	1135	...	|	1758	...	...	...	...	|	|	0449
Gyékényes 🏛 a.	1133	...	|	1808	...	...	...	...	|	|	0549
Nagykanizsa a.	1241	...	|	1902	...	...	...	...	|	|	0616
Hodoš 🏛 a.	|	...	1248	|	...	...	...	...	0338	0338	|
Zalaegerszeg a.	|	...	1337	|	...	...	...	...	0431	0431	|
Fonyód a.	1422	...	|	2022	...	...	...	...	|	|	0718
Siófok a.	1501	...	|	2101	...	...	...	...	|	|	0749
Székesfehérvár a.	1536	...	1611	2136	...	...	...	...	0811	0811	0825
Budapest Déli a.	1624	...	1659	2224	...	...	...	...	0859	0859	|
Budapest Keleti a.	...	...	...	...	...	...	...	...	...	...	0935

train type	D	D		EC	D	D	D	D	D	9008	9008
train number	410	314		212	200	412	246	204	1204	1246	1246
notes	314					414		782		1605	481
notes	Q				A		H	R	D	J	G
Budapest Keleti d.	...	...	...	...	...	...	...	...	1845	...	...
Budapest Déli d.	...	...	...	...	0635	...	0900	1535	|	2035	2035
Székesfehérvár d.	...	...	...	...	0721	...	0946	1621	1943	2116	2121
Siófok d.	...	...	...	...	0757	...	|	1657	2027	|	|
Fonyód d.	...	...	...	...	0837	...	|	1737	2100	|	|
Zalaegerszeg d.	...	...	...	...	|	...	1222	|	|	0012	0012
Hodoš 🏛 d.	...	...	...	...	|	...	1315	|	|	0103	0103
Nagykanizsa d.	...	...	...	...	0956	...	|	1841	2159	|	|
Gyékényes 🏛 d.	...	...	...	...	1044	...	|	1927	2255	|	|
Koprivnica 🏛 a.	...	...	...	...	1055	...	|	1938	2306	|	|
Beograd Centar d.	2058	...	...	...	|	1005	|	|	|	|	|
Šid 🏛 d.	0022	...	...	...	|	1333	|	|	|	|	|
Vinkovci d.	0103	...	...	...	|	1443	|	|	|	|	|
Zagreb a.	0428	...	...	...	1255	1804	|	2103	0022	|	|
Zagreb d.	0440	...	...	0702	...	1839	|	...	0038	|	|
Split a.	|	...	...	|	...	|	|	...	0846	|	|
Dobova 🏛 d.	0540	0540	...	0745	...	1925	|	...	...	|	|
Ljubljana d.	0717	0726	...	0923	...	2110	1635	...	...	0603	0630
Rijeka a.	...	|	...	|	...	|	...	...	...	|	0927
Koper a.	...	|	...	|	...	|	...	...	...	0833	...
Villach Hbf a.	...	0908	...	1058	...	2247	...	...	...	...	...

A – GRADEC June 6 - Sept. 11: (12) Budapest - Zagreb and v.v.

C – ADRIA ①③⑥ June 19 - Aug. 29; : 🛏 1, 2 cl., ▬ 2 cl., (2) Split - Zagreb - Budapest.

D – ADRIA ②⑤⑦ June 18 - Aug. 28: 🛏 1, 2 cl., ▬ 2 cl., (2) Budapest - Zagreb - Split.

E – ISTRA June 18 - Aug. 30: 🛏 1, 2 cl., ▬ 2 cl., (2) Rijeka - Hodoš 🏛 - Budapest (Table **91**).

G – ISTRA June 17 - Aug. 29: 🛏 1, 2 cl., ▬ 2 cl., (2) Budapest - Hodoš 🏛 - Rijeka (Table **91**).

H – CITADELLA (2) Budapest - Hodoš - Ljubljana and v.v. (Table **91**).

J – ISTRA June 17 - Aug. 29: ▬ 2 cl. (2) Budapest - Hodoš 🏛 - Koper (Table **91**).

K – ISTRA June 18 - Aug. 30: ▬ 2 cl. (2) Koper - Hodoš 🏛 - Budapest (Table **91**).

P – June 20 - Sept. 13: ▬ 2 cl., (12) Ljubljana - Zagreb - Beograd.

Q – June 21 - Sept. 14: ▬ 2 cl., (12) Beograd - Zagreb - Ljubljana.

R – AGRAM-TOPART (12) Zagreb - Budapest and v.v.

RJ – ÖBB *Railjet* service. (1) (business class), (1) (first class), (2) (economy class), ✕.

☛ Shaded services are suspended until further notice.

MARSEILLE - NICE - MILANO, ROMA and VENEZIA 90

train type			FB			IC	IC	FB	FR	FA			FB	IC	ITA	FR			IC	IC		FB	ICN	ICN	ICN
train number			8613			745	665	8619	9547	9741			8655	673	8997	9663			681	679		8659	1963	799	799
train number																									
notes		2	🅁🍷		2	🅁	🅁	🅁🍷	🅁🍷	🅁🍷			🅁🍷	🅁	🅁🍷	🅁🍷			🅁	🅁		🅁🍷	🅁	🅁	🅁
notes			⚡			⚡	⚡	⚡	⚡	⚡			⚡	⚡	⚡	⚡			⚡	⚡		⚡	⚡	⚡	⚡
notes																Ⓑ							C	AP	AQ
Marseille St Charles d.	...	...	...	0548	...	...	...	...	...	...	0957	...	...	...	...	...	1157	...	...	...	...	...	...	...	...
Toulon d.	...	...	...	0644	...	...	...	...	...	...	1044	...	...	...	...	...	1244	...	...	...	...	...	...	...	...
Cannes d.	0521x	...	...	0812	0822	...	...	...	...	...	1211	1222	...	...	...	...	1411	...	...	...	1752	...	...	...	...
Nice d.	0604	...	...	0848	0906	...	...	...	...	...	1241	1309	...	...	...	...	1441	1543	...	...	1836	...	...	...	...
Monaco - Monte Carlo d.	0629	...	...	▬	0932	...	...	...	...	...	...	1334	...	...	...	...	▬	1609	...	...	1902	...	...	...	...
Ventimiglia 🏛 d.	0701	0757	...	*IC* **511**	1001	1103	...	...	...	...	...	1401	1510	...	...	...	*FR*	1635	1703	...	1931	1943	...	...	...
San Remo d.	...	0812	...	🅁⚡	...	1120	...	...	...	...	...	...	1523	...	...	...	**9567**	...	1720	...	...	1956	...	...	...
Genova Piazza Principe a.	...	1021	1210	1224	...	1305	1347	1502	...	...	...	...	1705	1747	...	...	🅁⚡	...	1908	1947	...	2142	2156	2207	2353
Milano Centrale a.	...	...	|	|	...	1455	|	|	1510	1545	...	...	1855	|	1935	1925	2010	...	2057	|	...	2340	|	|	|
Verona a.	...	...	|	|	...	...	|	|	|	1658	...	...	...	|	2047	|	|	...	...	|	...	...	|	|	|
Venezia Santa Lucia a.	...	...	|	|	...	...	|	|	|	1812	...	...	...	|	2203	|	|	...	...	|	...	...	|	|	|
La Spezia a.	...	...	1315	1350	...	...	1521	1615	|	...	...	...	...	1921	...	|	|	...	...	2121	...	...	2306	2352	0125
Pisa Centrale a.	...	...	1404	1447	...	...	...	1704	|	...	...	...	...	2017	...	|	|	...	...	2217	...	...	2356	0048	0216
Firenze SMN a.	...	...	|	|	...	...	...	|	1704	...	...	...	...	...	...	|	2204	...	...	...	...	...	...	|	|
Roma Termini a.	...	...	1703	1803	...	...	...	2003	1849	...	...	...	...	...	...	2240	2349	...	...	...	...	...	...	0543o	0543o
Napoli Centrale a.	...	...	...	2029	...	...	...	...	2010	...	...	...	...	...	...	0005	...	...	...	...	...	...	...	0817	0817

train type	ICN			ICN	IC	ICN	FB		IC	ICN		IC			IC	IC	FR	FR	FB		ITA	FR	IC	IC	
train number	796			796	658	1962	8639		662	1962		659			510	674	9728	9415	8643		8984	9584	680	675	
train number																									
notes	🅁⚡	2		🅁⚡	🅁	🅁⚡	🅁🍷		🅁	🅁⚡	2	🅁			🅁	🅁	🅁🍷	🅁🍷	🅁🍷		🅁🍷	🅁🍷	🅁	🅁	
notes	A			A	⚡	C	⚡		⚡	C		⚡			⚡	⚡	⚡	⚡	⚡		⚡	⚡	⚡	⚡	
notes	⑥⑦	⚒		①–⑤		⑥⑦				①–⑤	Ⓐ									⑤⑥⑦					⑥
Napoli Centrale d.	2146	...	...	2146	...	...	...	...	...	...	...	...	...	...	0731	...	...	0940	...	...	...	1140	...	...	...
Roma Termini d.	0011o	...	...	0011o	...	...	...	...	...	...	...	...	...	...	0957	...	...	1110	...	...	...	1310	...	...	...
Firenze SMN d.	|	...	...	|	...	...	...	...	...	...	...	...	...	...	|	...	...	1255	...	...	...	1455	...	...	...
Pisa Centrale d.	0326	...	...	0500	0542	0557	...	...	0642	0647	...	...	...	...	1302	1342	...	|	...	...	...	|	...	...	...
La Spezia d.	0425	...	...	0552	0638	0654	...	...	0738	0758	...	...	...	...	1405	1438	...	|	...	...	...	|	1638	...	...
Venezia Santa Lucia d.	|	...	...	|	|	|	...	...	|	|	...	...	...	...	|	|	1148	|	...	...	1357	|	|	...	...
Verona d.	|	...	...	|	|	|	...	...	|	|	...	...	...	...	|	|	1302	|	...	...	1512	|	|	...	...
Milano Centrale d.	|	...	...	|	|	|	0710	...	|	|	...	0910	...	...	|	|	1415	1450	1510	...	1625	1650	|	1705	...
Genova Piazza Principe d.	0601	0646	...	0757	0816	0839	0858	...	0915	0936	0943	1058	...	...	1535	1614	...	...	1658	...	...	...	1815	1858	...
San Remo d.	...	0906	...	...	...	...	1042	...	▬	...	1145	1241f	...	...	...	...	...	...	1842	...	...	...	...	2041	...
Ventimiglia 🏛 a.	...	0922	1022	...	...	...	1054	1206	...	...	1203	1258f	1315	...	...	...	...	...	1854	1952	...	...	...	2058	2325
Monaco - Monte Carlo a.	...	...	1057	...	...	...	...	1241	...	...	...	...	1350	...	...	...	...	...	...	2027	...	...	...	...	2358
Nice a.	...	...	1123	...	...	...	...	1305	1320	...	...	...	1415	1420	...	...	...	...	...	2051	...	...	...	...	0023
Cannes a.	...	...	1210	...	...	...	...	1410	1353	...	...	...	1508	1453	...	...	...	...	...	2138	...	...	...	...	...
Toulon a.	...	...	...	...	...	...	...	...	1515	...	...	...	...	1615	...	...	...	...	...	...	...	...	...	...	...
Marseille St Charles a.	...	...	...	...	...	...	...	...	1602	...	...	...	...	1703	...	...	...	...	...	...	...	...	...	...	...

A – 🛏 1, 2 cl., ▬ 2 cl. (4 berth), (2) Torino - Genova - Napoli - Salerno and v.v.

C – 🛏 1, 2 cl., ▬ 2 cl. (4 berth) Milano - Genova - Pisa - Siracusa and v.v.
🛏 1, 2 cl., ▬ 2 cl. (4 berth) Milano - Genova - Pisa - Palermo and v.v.

P – ①–⑤ Dec. 12 - Mar. 15.

Q – ⑥⑦ (daily Mar. 16 - Dec. 10).

f – On Ⓒ depart San Remo 1257, arrive Ventimiglia 1312.

o – Roma **Ostiense**.

x – Not ⑥.

⚡ – Supplement payable.

91 WIEN - LJUBLJANA and ZAGREB

train type	EC			D	EC	IC	IC	9008	9008
train number	151	483	2752	246	159¶	523	310	1246	1246
notes	134		2		✕⚡	2	🍷	1605	481
	✕E		🚌	G	C			P	J
Wien Hbf ... d.	0758	...	...	...	1558	...	...	...	...
Wien Meidling ... d.	0805	...	...	...	1605	...	...	...	...
Wiener Neustadt Hbf ... d.	0832	...	...	...	1632	...	...	...	...
Budapest Keleti ... d.	|	...	...	...	|	...	1615	...	...
Budapest Déli ... d.	|	...	...	0900	|	...	|	2035	2035
Szombathely ... d.	|	...	...	|	|	...	1906	|	|
Hodoš ⊞ ... d.	|	...	...	1315	|	...	|	0103	0103
Graz Hbf ... d.	1037	...	...	|	1837	...	2137	|	|
Spielfeld-Straß ⊞ ... d.	1125	...	...	|	1926	...	2225	|	|
Maribor ... a.	1140	...	...	|	1941	2005	2240	0225	0225
Pragersko ... a.	1145	...	...	1432	2004	2018	2259	0337	0337
Zidani Most ... a.	1303	...	...	1536	|	2118	0002	0446	0446
Dobova ⊞ ... a.	|	...	...	|	2146	|	|	|	|
Zagreb ... a.	|	...	...	|	2227	|	|	|	|
Ljubljana ... a.	1400	1511	1550	1635	...	2208	0056	0547	0547
Koper ... a.	|	|	1817	...	...	...	...	0833	|
Rijeka ... a.	|	1814	...	...	...	...	...	...	0927
Villa Opicina ⊞ ... a.	1610	...	...	...	...	...	...	...	...
Trieste ... a.	1652	...	...	...	...	...	...	...	...

train type / number	IC	IC	ICS	EC	D			EC	480	1604
train number	311	508	14	158	247	2751	482	135	1247	1247
notes	🍷		2	✕⚡		2		150	959	959
				C	H	🚌		✕F	K	Q
Trieste ... d.	...	...	...	...	...	...	...	1303	...	...
Villa Opicina ⊞ ... d.	...	...	...	...	...	...	...	1345	...	...
Rijeka ... d.	...	...	...	...	...	...	1150	|	2045	...
Koper ... d.	...	0525	...	...	...	1004	|	|	|	2015
Ljubljana ... d.	0505	0753	0805	...	0935	1245	1459	1555	0030	0030
Zagreb ... d.	|	...	|	0727	|	...	...	|	|	|
Dobova ⊞ ... d.	|	...	|	0812	|	...	...	|	|	|
Zidani Most ... d.	0559	...	0850	|	1030	...	...	1701	0122	0122
Pragersko ... d.	0700	...	0943	0959	1133	...	...	1800	0226	0226
Maribor ... d.	0719	...	0955	1019	|	...	...	1821	|	|
Spielfeld-Straß ⊞ ... a.	0734	...	...	1034	|	...	...	1836	|	|
Graz Hbf ... a.	0823	...	...	1120	|	...	...	1922	|	|
Hodoš ⊞ ... a.	|	...	...	|	1248	...	...	|	0338	0338
Szombathely ... a.	1053	...	...	|	|	...	...	|	|	|
Budapest Déli ... a.	|	...	...	|	1659	...	...	|	0859	0859
Budapest Keleti ... a.	1344	...	...	|	...	...	...	|	...	...
Wiener Neustadt Hbf ... a.	...	...	...	1328	...	...	...	2128	...	...
Wien Meidling ... a.	...	...	...	1355	...	...	...	2155	...	...
Wien Hbf ... a.	...	...	...	1402	...	...	...	2202	...	...

C – CROATIA [12] ✕ Wien - Zagreb and v.v.

E – EMONA [12] ✕ Wien - Ljubljana. Conveys [12] Wien (**151**) - Ljubljana (**134**) - Trieste.

F – EMONA [12] ✕ Ljubljana - Wien. Conveys [12] Trieste (**135**) - Ljubljana (**150**) - Wien.

G – CITADELLA [2] Budapest - Hodoš - Ljubljana and v.v. (Table **89**).

J – ISTRA June 17 - Aug. 29: 🛏 1, 2 cl., ▬ 2 cl., [2] Budapest - Hodoš ⊞ - Rijeka (Table **89**).

K – ISTRA June 18 - Aug. 30: 🛏 1, 2 cl., ▬ 2 cl., [2] Rijeka - Hodoš ⊞ - Budapest (Table **89**).

P – ISTRA June 17 - Aug. 29: ▬ 2 cl., [2] Budapest - Hodoš ⊞ - Koper (Table **89**).

Q – ISTRA June 18 - Aug. 30: ▬ 2 cl., [2] Koper - Hodoš ⊞ - Budapest (Table **89**).

⚡ – Supplement payable.

◇ – Stopping train.

¶ – Train number **1259** on ⓒ.

93 WARSZAWA - VILNIUS

train type				TLK				IC	
train number	143			31103		142		81103	
notes	⑥⑦			H		B		🅁	
	2			🅁					
Warszawa Centralna ... d.	...	...	...	0750	...	...	...	1621	...
Warszawa Wschodnia ... d.	...	...	...	0759	...	...	...	1633	...
Małkinia ... d.	...	...	...	0904	...	...	...	1729	...
Białystok ... d.	0755	...	...	1100	1458	...	...	1920	...
Suwałki ... d.	1008	...	...	1247	1708	1743	...	2105	...
Mockava ⊞ ◐ ... a.	|	...	...	...	...	|	...	...	...
Šeštokai ... a.	|	...	...	...	...	2054	...	...	...
Kaunas ... a.	1357	1430	...	...	...	2220	...	...	...
Vilnius ... a.	...	1549	...	...	...	...	...	...	...

train type					TLK				
train number		141			13102			146	
notes		C			H			⑥⑦	
					🅁			2	
Vilnius ... d.	0533	...	...	...	...	...	1548	...	...
Kaunas ... d.	0708	0910	...	...	...	...	1704	1730	...
Šeštokai ... d.	...	1034	...	...	...	...	...	|	...
Mockava ⊞ ◐ ... d.	...	|	...	...	...	...	...	|	...
Suwałki ... d.	...	1037	1145	...	1521	...	...	1907	...
Białystok ... d.	...	...	1410	...	1740	...	...	2048	...
Małkinia ... d.	...	...	...	...	1911	...	...	...	...
Warszawa Wschodnia ... a.	...	...	...	...	2012	...	...	...	...
Warszawa Centralna ... a.	...	...	...	...	2020	...	...	...	...

B – ⑤⑥ July 1 - Sept. 2: BALTI - [2] Suwałki - Kaunas. Lithuanian times to be confirmed.

C – ⑥⑦ July 2 - Sept. 3: BALTI - [2] Kaunas - Suwałki. Lithuanian times to be confirmed.

H – HAŃCZA – [12] 🅁 Kraków - Warszawa - Białystok - Suwałki and v.v.

g – Warszawa **Gdańska**.

◐ – ⊞ = Trakiszki (Poland) / Mockava (Lithuania); ticketing point is Mockava.

☛ – **Shaded services are suspended until further notice.**

95 MOSKVA - WARSZAWA - PRAHA and WIEN

train number							23*JI*	23*JI*	
train number	13*MJ*	13*MJ*	27*BJ*	27*BJ*	17*BJ*	17*BJ*	452	452	
notes									
notes	KW	KX	PW	PX	HW	HX	BW	BX	
	⑤⑦	⑤⑦			④	④	②	②	
Moskva Belorusskaya ... d.	0956	0956	1415	1415	1817	1817	1817	1817	...
Smolensk Tsentralny ⊞ ... § d.	1344	1344	1917	1917	2315	2315	2315	2315	...
Orsha Tsentralnaya ... § d.	1507	1507	2055	2055	0044	0044	0044	0044	...
Minsk ... d.	1720	1720	0010	0010	0313	0313	0313	0313	...
Brest Tsentralny ⊞ ... a.	2027	2027	0348	0348	0641	0641	0641	0641	...
Brest Tsentralny ⊞ ... d.	2040	2140	0553	0711	0943	1043	1043	1043	...
Terespol ⊞ ... a.	2022	2022	0529	0539	0901	0901	0901	0901	...
Terespol ⊞ ... d.	2105	2105	0637	0637	0946	0946	0946	0946	...
Warszawa Wschodnia ... a.	2248	2241	0840	0836	1149	1148	1149	1148	...
Warszawa Centralna ... a.	...	...	0850	0845	1230	1230	...	...	...
Katowice ... a.	...	...	1143	1141	|	|	...	...	...
Bohumín ⊞ ... a.	...	...	1320	1320	1723	1723	...	...	...
Ostrava hlavní ... a.	...	...	1407	1407	|	|	...	...	...
Břeclav ... a.	...	...	|	|	1945	1945	...	...	...
Wien Hbf ... a.	...	...	|	|	2117	2117	...	...	...
Olomouc ... a.	...	...	1512	1512	...	...	...	...	...
Pardubice ... a.	...	...	1643	1643	...	...	...	...	...
Praha hlavní ... a.	...	...	1752	1752	...	...	...	...	...

train number									
train number	18*BJ*	18*BJ*	96*BJ*	96*BJ*	24*JI*	24*JI*	14*MJ*	14*MJ*	
notes					453	453			
notes	TW	TX	QW	QX	AW	AX	JW	JX	
	①	①			⑤	⑤	②⑦	②⑦	
Praha hlavní ... d.	...	...	1002	1002	...	...	...	...	...
Pardubice ... d.	...	...	1113	1113	...	...	...	...	...
Olomouc ... d.	...	...	1245	1245	...	...	...	...	...
Wien Hbf ... d.	0547	0547	|	|	...	...	...	...	...
Břeclav ... d.	0728	0728	|	|	...	...	...	...	...
Ostrava hlavní ... d.	|	|	1350	1350	...	...	...	...	...
Bohumín ⊞ ... d.	0951	0951	1440	1440	...	...	...	...	...
Katowice ... d.	|	|	1619	1621	...	...	...	...	...
Warszawa Centralna ... d.	1430	1445	1915	1915	...	...	...	...	...
Warszawa Wschodnia ... d.	1546	1542	1924	1924	1546	1534	0445	0450	...
Terespol ⊞ ... a.	1755	1746	2129	2117	1755	1744	0632	0632	...
Terespol ⊞ ... d.	1837	1824	2214	2202	1837	1829	0717	0717	...
Brest Tsentralny ⊞ ... a.	2010	2110	0100	0038	2010	2115	0900	1000	...
Brest Tsentralny ⊞ ... d.	2323	2323	0235	0235	2323	2323	0950	1010	...
Minsk ... a.	0305	0305	0619	0608	0305	0305	1328	1328	...
Orsha Tsentralnaya ... § a.	0536	0536	0925	0925	0536	0536	1555	1555	...
Smolensk Tsentralny ⊞ ... § a.	0709	0709	1057	1057	0709	0709	1719	1719	...
Moskva Beloruśskaya ... a.	1144	1144	1658	1658	1144	1144	2124	2124	...

A – TRANSEUROPEAN EXPRESS ④: 🛏 1, 2 cl. Paris (**453**) - Berlin - Warszawa - Brest (**24** *JI*) - Moskva. ✕ (RZD) Brest - Moskva.

B – TRANSEUROPEAN EXPRESS ②: 🛏 1, 2 cl. Moskva (**23** *JI*) - Brest (**452**) - Warszawa - Berlin - Paris. ✕ (RZD) Moskva - Brest.

H – ④: 🛏 1 cl. (lux), 🛏 1, 2 cl. Moskva ④ - Wien ⑤ - Nice ⑥. ✕ (RZD) Moskva - Brest and ✕ (PKP) Warszawa - Nice (journey two nights).

J – ①⑥: 🛏 1 cl. (lux), 🛏 1, 2 cl., [1] ✕ 🅁 Berlin - Warszawa - Moskva, Talgo train.

K – ⑤⑦: 🛏 1 cl. (lux), 🛏 1, 2 cl., [1] ✕ 🅁 Moskva - Warszawa - Berlin, Talgo train.

P – 🛏 1, 2 cl. Moskva (27*BJ*) - Minsk (655) - Brest (137) - Terespol (131) - Bohumín (114) - Praha.

Q – 🛏 1, 2 cl. Praha (115) - Bohumín (130) - Terespol (136) - Brest (656) - Minsk (96*BJ*) - Moskva.

T – ⑦: 🛏 1 cl. (lux), 🛏 1, 2 cl. Nice ⑦ - Wien ① - Moskva ②. ✕ (PKP) Nice - Warszawa and ✕ (RZD) Brest - Moskva (journey two nights).

W – Mar. 28, 2021 - Oct. 30, 2021. Timings subject to confirmation.

X – Oct. 31, 2021 - Dec. 11, 2021. Timings subject to confirmation.

§ – ⊞: Osinovka (BY) / Krasnoye (RU).

☛ – **Shaded services are suspended until further notice.**

WIEN / BUDAPEST / PRAHA / BRATISLAVA - LVIV - KYIV 96

train number		IC			SC	8862		40149	
train number		34		603	241	29		EC 149	
notes		[R]		✕	🍷 [R]			749	
notes		C				P		B	
Wien Hbf d.	...	...	...	...	...	...	...	1642	...
Budapest Nyugati d.	...	0723	...	...	...	...	...	|	...
Budapest Keleti d.	...	|	...	...	...	...	...	1940	...
Szolnok d.	...	0838	...	...	...	...	...	2104	...
Debrecen d.	...	0953	...	...	...	...	...	2237	...
Záhony ⊞ d.	...	1223	...	...	...	...	...	0110	...
Praha hl. n. d.	...	|	...	...	0625	...	...	|	...
Bratislava hl. st. d.	...	|	...	0813	|	...	...	|	...
Žilina d.	...	|	...	1042	1119	...	...	|	...
Košice a.	...	|	...	1403	1418	1513	...	|	...
Čierna nad Tisou ⊞ a.	...	|	...	...	...	1651	...	|	...
Chop ⊞ a.	...	1340	...	...	...	1847	...	0228	...
Mukachevo a.	...	1530	...	...	...	2155	...	0622	...
Lviv a.	...	...	...	...	...	0220	...	1014	...
Khmelnytsky a.	...	...	...	...	...	|	...	|	...
Vinnytsya a.	...	...	...	...	...	|	...	|	...
Kyiv a.	...	...	...	...	...	1011	...	1722	...

train number		749		81	SC			IC	
train number		40749		8861	240	612		33	
notes		EC 140			🍷 [R]	✕		[R]	
notes		A		Q				C	
Kyiv d.	...	1407	...	1830	...	...	...	...	...
Vinnytsya d.	...	|	...	2149	...	...	...	...	...
Khmelnytsky d.	...	|	...	2356	...	...	...	...	...
Lviv d.	...	2100	...	0409	...	...	...	...	...
Mukachevo d.	...	0054	...	0852	...	...	...	1230	...
Chop ⊞ d.	...	0328	...	1135	...	...	...	1410	...
Čierna nad Tisou ⊞ d.	...	|	...	1204	...	...	...	|	...
Košice d.	...	|	...	1349	1459	1557	...	|	...
Žilina a.	...	|	...	...	1751	1918	...	|	...
Bratislava hl. st. a.	...	|	...	...	|	2147	...	|	...
Praha hl. n. a.	...	|	...	...	2233	...	...	|	...
Záhony ⊞ a.	...	0246	...	...	...	...	...	1327	...
Debrecen a.	...	0529	...	...	...	...	...	1605	...
Szolnok a.	...	0652	...	...	...	...	...	1720	...
Budapest Keleti a.	...	0820	...	...	...	...	...	|	...
Budapest Nyugati a.	...	|	...	...	...	...	...	1837	...
Wien Hbf a.	...	1121	...	...	...	...	...	...	...

A – HORTOBÁGY – 🛏 1, 2 cl. Kyiv (**749**) - Lviv (**145**) - Chop (**140**) - Záhony - Budapest - Wien. [12] Záhony - Wien.

B – HORTOBÁGY – 🛏 1, 2 cl. Wien (**149**) - Budapest - Záhony - Chop (**146**) - Lviv (**749**) - Kyiv. [12] Wien - Záhony.

C – LATORCA – [12] Budapest - Záhony - Chop - Mukachevo and v.v.

P – 🛏 1, 2 cl. Košice (**8862**) - Čierna nad Tisou - Chop (**29**) - Lviv - Kyiv.

Q – 🛏 1, 2 cl. Kyiv (**81**) - Lviv - Chop (**8861**) - Čierna nad Tisou (**8802**) - Košice.

☛ **Shaded services are suspended until further notice.**

WARSZAWA and KRAKÓW - PRAHA, WIEN and BUDAPEST 99

train type/train number	IC¶	EC	LE	IC¶	EC¶	EC	IC¶	IC	IC¶	RJ	IC¶	IC¶	EC	IC*	TLK	EC¶	EC	IC*	TLK	EN	EN	EN
train number	101	273	412	116	103	277	114	114	131	79	114	105	281	112	300	107	283	110	310	407	407	407
notes/train number	✕	✕	🍷	✕	✕	✕	🍷	131	✕	✕	🍷	✕	✕	🍷		✕	✕	🍷		457	457	442
notes			①⑤⑥	⊡	⊡		⊡	⊡	⊡		⊡	⊡		⊡		⊡		⊡	2	477		
notes	H		N	Z	X		L	2	V		L	E			J	W			R	B	C	P
Gdynia Główny d.	...	...	...	...	...	...	...	...	...	...	...	...	...	...	...	1054	...	...	...	...	...	...
Gdańsk Główny d.	...	...	...	...	...	...	...	...	...	...	...	...	...	...	...	1120	...	...	...	...	...	...
Warszawa Wschodnia d.	...	...	...	0443	0552	...	...	...	0817	...	...	...	...	1254	...	1353	...	1710	...	1939	1939	1939*
Warszawa Centralna d.	...	...	...	0454	0602	...	...	...	0828	...	...	...	...	1305	...	1405	...	1721	...	1949	1949	1949
Przemyśl d.	...	...	...	|	|	...	0710	0710	|	...	...	1021	...	|	...	|	...	|	...	|	|	|
Rzeszów d.	...	...	...	|	|	...	0819	0819	|	...	...	1132	...	|	...	|	...	|	1700	|	|	|
Kraków Główny d.	...	...	0401	|	|	...	1047	1047	|	...	...	1353	...	|	1506	|	...	|	1910	2257	2257	2257
Katowice d.	0455	...	0512	0813	0905	...	1144	1144	1124	...	...	1451	...	1614	1618	1703	...	2024	2016	0002	0002	0002
Chałupki ⊞ d.	0622	...	0711	0937	1024	...	1310	1310	1258	...	←	1615	...	1737	1745	1824	...	2143	2152	0122	0122	0122
Bohumín ⊞ a.	0630	...	0717	0943	1030	...	1316	1316	1308	...	1316	1621	...	1743	|	1830	...	|	2158	0128	0128	0128
Bohumín ⊞ d.	0642	...	0736	1000	1042	...	1400	1342	1342	...	1400	1642	...	1800	|	1842	...	|	...	0215	0215	0328
Ostrava hl. n. a.	0649	...	0742	1007	1049	...	→	1349	1349	...	1407	1649	...	1807	1758	1849	...	2156	...	0222	0222	0335
Přerov a.	0744	...	0843	|	1144	...	...	1444	1444	...	|	1744	...	|	...	1944	...	...	...	|	|	|
Olomouc a.	|	...	0858	1112	|	...	...	|	|	...	1512	|	...	1912	...	|	...	...	...	|	|	0443
Pardubice a.	|	...	1031	1243	|	...	...	|	|	...	1643	|	...	2043	...	|	...	...	...	|	|	0621
Praha hl. n. a.	|	...	1137	1352	|	...	...	|	|	...	1752	|	...	2152	...	|	...	...	...	|	|	0755
Břeclav a.	0845	0855	...	...	1245	1255	...	1545	1545	1555	...	1845	1855	...	...	2045	2055	...	...	0410	0410	...
Wien Hbf a.	0949	|	...	...	1349	|	...	|	|	1649	...	1949	|	...	...	2149	|	...	...	|	0700	...
Kúty ⊞ a.	...	0911	...	...	...	1311	...	1611	1611	...	...	...	1911	...	...	...	2111	...	...	0511	...	...
Bratislava hl. st. a.	...	0954	...	...	...	1354	...	1702	1702	...	...	...	1954	...	...	...	2154	...	...	0554	...	...
Štúrovo ⊞ △ a.	...	1116	...	...	...	1516	...	1826	1826	...	...	...	2119	...	...	...	...	...	...	0716	...	...
Budapest Nyugati a.	...	1220	...	...	...	1620	...	1934	1934	...	...	...	2223	...	...	...	...	...	...	0820	...	...

train type/train number	TLK	IC*	EC	EC	IC*	TLK	EC	EC	IC¶	RJ	IC	IC¶	EC	EC	EC	IC¶	LE	EC	EC	EN	EN	EN
train number	311	111	282	106	113	301	280	104	115	74	130	115	130	276	102	117	411	272	100	456	476	443
notes/train number		🍷	✕	✕	🍷		✕	✕	🍷	✕	115	🍷	✕	✕	✕	🍷	🍷	✕	✕	406	456	406
notes	R	⊡		⊡	⊡			⊡	⊡		⊡	⊡	⊡		⊡	⊡	④⑤⑦				406	
notes				W		J		G	L		2	L	V		X	Z	M		H	D	A	Q
Budapest Nyugati d.	...	...	...	...	...	...	0540	...	...	...	0828	...	0828	1140	...	...	...	1540	...	...	1940	...
Štúrovo ⊞ △ d.	...	...	...	...	...	...	0644	...	...	...	0935	...	0935	1244	...	...	...	1644	...	...	2044	...
Bratislava hl. st. d.	...	...	0606	...	...	...	0806	...	...	...	1057	...	1057	1406	...	...	...	1806	...	...	2206	...
Kúty ⊞ d.	...	...	0649	...	...	...	0849	...	...	...	1148	...	1148	1449	...	...	...	1849	...	...	2249	...
Wien Hbf d.	...	...	|	0610	...	...	|	0810	...	1110	|	...	|	|	1410	...	...	|	1810	2210	|	...
Břeclav d.	...	...	0704	0710	...	...	0904	0910	...	1204	1210	...	1210	1504	1510	...	...	1904	1910	2350	2350	...
Praha hl. n. d.	...	...	...	|	0602	...	...	|	1002	...	|	...	|	...	|	1402	1528	...	|	|	|	2205
Pardubice d.	...	...	...	|	0713	...	...	|	1113	...	|	...	|	...	|	1513	1633	...	|	|	|	2321
Olomouc d.	...	...	...	|	0845	...	...	|	1245	...	|	...	|	...	|	1645	1800	...	|	|	|	0108
Přerov d.	...	...	...	0813	|	...	...	1013	|	...	1313	...	1313	...	1613	|	1820	...	2013	|	|	|
Ostrava hl. n. d.	...	0604	...	0909	0950	1000	...	1109	1350	...	1409	←	1409	...	1709	1750	1917	...	2109	0133	0133	0221
Bohumín ⊞ a.	...	|	...	0916	0957	|	...	1116	1357	...	1416	1357	1416	...	1716	1757	1924	...	2116	0140	0140	0228
Bohumín ⊞ d.	0426	|	...	0926	1009	|	...	1128	1446	...	1446	1446	1454	...	1728	1809	1936	...	2128	0318	0318	0318
Chałupki ⊞ a.	0432	0618	...	0932	1015	1014	...	1134	→	...	1453	1453	1500	...	1734	1815	1941	...	2134	0324	0324	0324
Katowice a.	0605	0739	...	1050	1139	1143	...	1254	...	...	1609	1609	1630	...	1850	1949	2112	...	2303	0442	0442	0442
Kraków Główny a.	0707	|	...	|	|	1248	...	1356	...	...	1704	1704	|	...	|	|	2223	...	...	0546	0546	0546
Rzeszów a.	0933	|	...	|	|	...	...	1549	...	...	1905	1905	|	...	|	|	...	...	...	|	|	|
Przemyśl a.	...	|	...	|	|	...	...	1703	...	...	2017	2017	|	...	|	|	...	...	...	|	|	|
Warszawa Centralna a.	...	1035	...	1333	1431	...	...	...	...	...	...	...	1929	...	2123	2305	...	...	...	|	|	|
Warszawa Wschodnia a.	...	1046	...	1406	1441	...	...	...	...	...	...	...	1942	...	2134	2316	...	...	...	0904	0904	0904
Gdańsk Główny a.	...	...	...	1646	...	...	...	...	...	...	...	...	...	...	...	...	...	...	...	...	...	...
Gdynia Główny a.	...	...	...	1711	...	...	...	...	...	...	...	...	...	...	...	...	...	...	...	...	...	...

A – 🛏 1, 2 cl., ▬ 2 cl., [2] Budapest (**476**) - Břeclav (**456**) - Bohumín (**406**) - Kraków - Warszawa. Conveys 🛏 1, 2 cl., ▬ 2 cl., [2] Budapest (**476**) - Břeclav (**456**) - Bohumín - Wrocław - Berlin.

B – 🛏 1, 2 cl., ▬ 2 cl., [2] Warszawa (**407**) - Kraków - Bohumín (**457**) - Břeclav (**477**) - Budapest. Conveys 🛏 1, 2 cl., ▬ 2 cl., [2] Berlin (**457**) - Wrocław - Břeclav (**477**) - Budapest.

C – CHOPIN – 🛏 1, 2 cl., ▬ 2 cl. [2] Warszawa (**407**) - Kraków - Bohumín (**457**) - Wien. Conveys 🛏 1, 2 cl., ▬ 2 cl., [2] Berlin (**457**) - Wrocław - Bohumín - Wien.

D – CHOPIN – 🛏 1, 2 cl., ▬ 2 cl. [2] Wien (**456**) - Bohumín (**406**) - Kraków - Warszawa. Conveys 🛏 1, 2 cl., ▬ 2 cl., [2] Wien (**456**) - Bohumín - Wrocław - Berlin.

E – PORTA MORAVIA / PORTA MORAVICA – [12] ✕ Przemyśl - Kraków - Katowice - Wien - Graz (a. 2222).

G – PORTA MORAVIA / PORTA MORAVICA – [12] ✕ Graz (d. 0526) - Wien - Katowice - Kraków - Przemyśl.

H – MORAVIA – [12] ✕ Katowice - Bohumín - Ostrava - Břeclav - Wien and v.v.

J – GALICJA – [12] Kraków - Katowice - Ostrava and v.v.

L – CRACOVIA – [12] 🍷 Przemyśl - Kraków - Bohumín - Praha and v.v.

M – ④⑤⑦: LEO EXPRESS – [12] 🍷 Praha - Bohumín - Kraków.

N – ①⑤⑥: LEO EXPRESS – [12] 🍷 Kraków - Bohumín - Praha.

P – 🛏 1, 2 cl., ▬ 2 cl., [2] Warszawa (**407**) - Kraków - Bohumín (**442**) - Praha.

Q – 🛏 1, 2 cl., ▬ 2 cl., [2] Praha (**443**) - Bohumín (**406**) - Kraków - Warszawa.

R – To / from Lublin.

V – BÁTHORY – [12] ✕ Terespol (depart 0616; arrive 2136) - Warszawa - Bohumín - Budapest and v.v.

W – SOBIESKI – [12] ✕ Gdynia - Warszawa - Katowice - Wien and v.v.

X – POLONIA – [12] ✕ Warszawa - Katowice - Wien and v.v.

Z – SILESIA – [12] ✕ Warszawa - Praha and v.v.

△ – Routeing point for international tickets: Szob.

⊡ – Supplement payable in Poland; Reservation compulsory in Poland.

* – Classified *Ex* in Czech Republic.

¶ – Classified *EC* in Czech Republic.

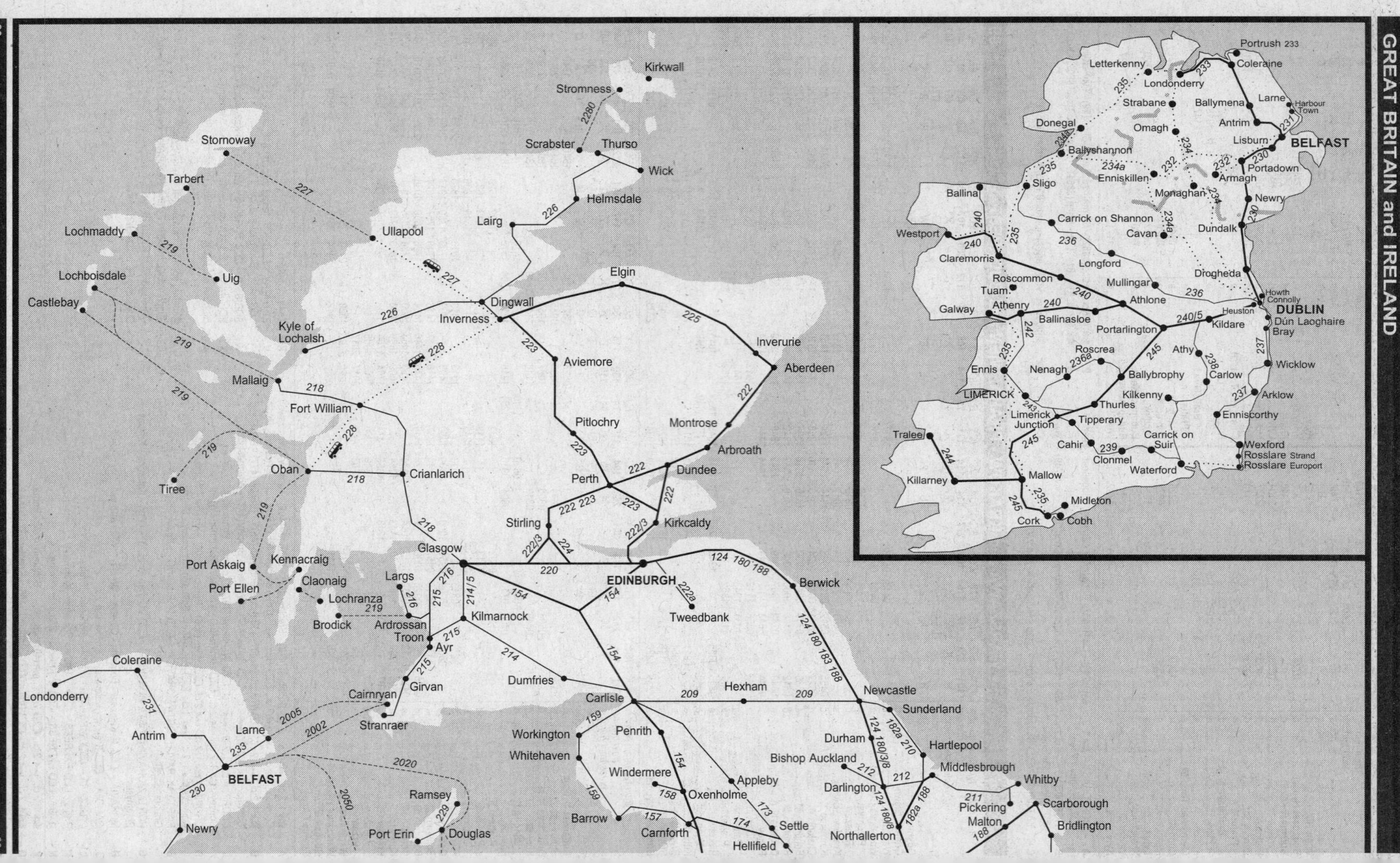
Kirkwall
Stromness
Stornoway
Scrabster
Thurso
Wick
Tarbert
Helmsdale
Lairg
Ullapool
Lochmaddy
Uig
Lochboisdale
Castlebay
Elgin
Dingwall
Inverness
Kyle of Lochalsh
Inverurie
Aberdeen
Aviemore
Mallaig
Fort William
Pitlochry
Montrose
Arbroath
Oban
Crianlarich
Tiree
Perth
Dundee
Stirling
Kirkcaldy
Glasgow
EDINBURGH
Berwick
Port Askaig
Kennacraig
Port Ellen
Claonaig
Lochranza
Largs
Brodick
Ardrossan
Troon
Ayr
Kilmarnock
Tweedbank
Dumfries
Girvan
Cairnryan
Stranraer
Carlisle
Hexham
Newcastle
Sunderland
Coleraine
Londonderry
Antrim
Larne
BELFAST
Newry
Workington
Whitehaven
Penrith
Durham
Hartlepool
Bishop Auckland
Middlesbrough
Windermere
Appleby
Oxenholme
Darlington
Whitby
Ramsey
Pickering
Scarborough
Malton
Bridlington
Barrow
Settle
Carnforth
Northallerton
Port Erin
Douglas
Hellifield
Letterkenny
Portrush 233
Coleraine
Londonderry
Strabane
Ballymena
Larne
Harbour
Town
Donegal
Omagh
Antrim
Lisburn
BELFAST
Ballyshannon
Enniskillen
Portadown
Armagh
Sligo
Monaghan
Newry
Ballina
Carrick on Shannon
Westport
Cavan
Dundalk
Claremorris
Longford
Drogheda
Roscommon
Mullingar
Howth
Connolly
Tuam
DUBLIN
Galway
Athenry
Athlone
Heuston
Ballinasloe
Kildare
Dún Laoghaire
Portarlington
Bray
Roscrea
Athy
Ennis
Nenagh
Ballybrophy
Carlow
Wicklow
LIMERICK
Kilkenny
Arklow
Thurles
Limerick Junction
Tipperary
Enniscorthy
Tralee
Carrick on Suir
Cahir
Wexford
Clonmel
Rosslare Strand
Waterford
Rosslare Europort
Mallow
Killarney
Midleton
Cork
Cobh

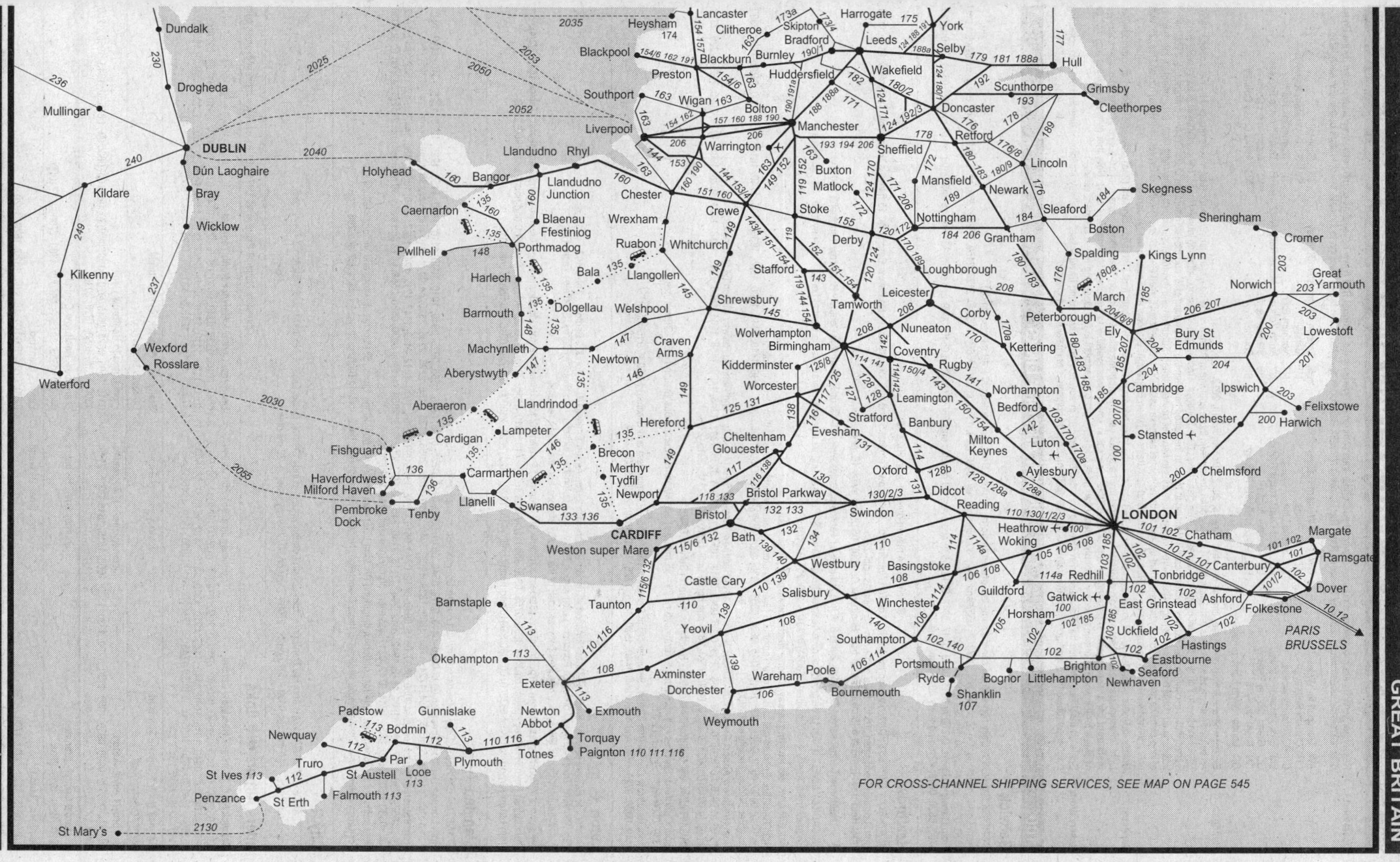
FOR CROSS-CHANNEL SHIPPING SERVICES, SEE MAP ON PAGE 545
PARIS
BRUSSELS
LONDON
CARDIFF
DUBLIN
Dundalk
Drogheda
Mullingar
Dún Laoghaire
Bray
Wicklow
Kildare
Kilkenny
Wexford
Rosslare
Waterford
Lancaster
Heysham
Clitheroe
Skipton
Harrogate
York
Bradford
Leeds
Selby
Hull
Blackpool
Blackburn
Burnley
Preston
Huddersfield
Wakefield
Scunthorpe
Grimsby
Cleethorpes
Southport
Wigan
Bolton
Doncaster
Liverpool
Manchester
Warrington
Sheffield
Retford
Lincoln
Holyhead
Bangor
Llandudno
Rhyl
Llandudno Junction
Chester
Crewe
Buxton
Matlock
Mansfield
Newark
Skegness
Caernarfon
Blaenau Ffestiniog
Wrexham
Stoke
Nottingham
Sleaford
Boston
Sheringham
Cromer
Pwllheli
Porthmadog
Ruabon
Whitchurch
Derby
Grantham
Harlech
Bala
Llangollen
Stafford
Loughborough
Spalding
Kings Lynn
Great Yarmouth
Norwich
Barmouth
Dolgellau
Welshpool
Shrewsbury
Tamworth
Leicester
March
Machynlleth
Wolverhampton
Birmingham
Nuneaton
Corby
Peterborough
Ely
Bury St Edmunds
Lowestoft
Craven Arms
Newtown
Coventry
Kettering
Aberystwyth
Kidderminster
Rugby
Worcester
Northampton
Cambridge
Ipswich
Felixstowe
Llandrindod
Leamington
Aberaeron
Stratford
Bedford
Harwich
Colchester
Cardigan
Lampeter
Hereford
Evesham
Banbury
Milton Keynes
Stansted
Cheltenham
Gloucester
Luton
Fishguard
Brecon
Haverfordwest
Milford Haven
Carmarthen
Merthyr Tydfil
Oxford
Aylesbury
Chelmsford
Newport
Bristol Parkway
Didcot
Pembroke Dock
Tenby
Llanelli
Swansea
Swindon
Reading
Bristol
Heathrow
Woking
Chatham
Margate
Bath
Weston super Mare
Westbury
Basingstoke
Redhill
Canterbury
Ramsgate
Tonbridge
Dover
Castle Cary
Guildford
Gatwick
East Grinstead
Ashford
Folkestone
Barnstaple
Taunton
Salisbury
Winchester
Horsham
Uckfield
Yeovil
Southampton
Hastings
Okehampton
Portsmouth
Brighton
Seaford
Eastbourne
Exeter
Axminster
Ryde
Bognor
Littlehampton
Newhaven
Dorchester
Wareham
Poole
Bournemouth
Shanklin
Exmouth
Weymouth
Padstow
Gunnislake
Newton Abbot
Bodmin
Torquay
Paignton
Newquay
Plymouth
Totnes
Truro
Par
Looe
St Ives
St Austell
Penzance
St Erth
Falmouth
St Mary's

GREAT BRITAIN

Operators: Passenger services are provided by a number of private passenger train companies operating the **National Rail** (www.nationalrail.co.uk) network on lines owned by the British national railway infrastructure company **Network Rail**. The following Network Rail codes are used in the table headings to indicate the operators of trains in each table:

AW	Transport for Wales	GW	Great Western Railway	LM	London Northwestern Railway	SR	ScotRail
CH	Chiltern Railways	HT	Hull Trains	ME	Merseyrail	SW	South Western Railway
CS	Caledonian Sleeper	IL	Island Line	NT	Northern Rail	TL	Thameslink Railway
EM	East Midlands Railway	LD	East Coast Trains (Lumo)	NY	North Yorkshire Moors Railway	TP	TransPennine Express
GC	Grand Central Railway	LE	Greater Anglia	SE	Southeastern	VT	Avanti West Coast
GN	Great Northern	LM	West Midlands Railway	SN	Southern	XC	Arriva Cross Country
GR	London North Eastern Railway						

Timings: Except where indicated otherwise, timings are valid **May 15, 2022 - December 10, 2022**
As service patterns at weekends (especially on ⑦) usually differ greatly from those applying on Mondays to Fridays, the timings in most tables are grouped by days of operation: Ⓐ = Mondays to Fridays; ⚒ = Mondays to Saturdays; ⑥ = Saturdays; ⑦ = Sundays. Track engineering work, affecting journey times, frequently takes place at weekends, so it is advisable to confirm your journey details locally if planning to travel in the period between the late evening of ⑥ and the late afternoon of ⑦. Confirm timings, too, if you intend travelling on public holidays (see page 4) as there may be alterations to services at these times. Suburban and commuter services are the most likely to be affected; the majority of long-distance and cross-country trains marked Ⓐ and ⚒ run as normal on these dates. No trains (except limited Gatwick and Heathrow Express services) run on **Dec. 25**, with only a limited service on certain routes on **Dec. 26**. In Scotland only trains between Edinburgh / Glasgow and England run on **Jan. 1**.

Services: Unless indicated otherwise (by '2' in the train column or '2nd class' in the table heading), trains convey both **first** (1st) and **standard** (2nd) classes of seated accommodation. Light refreshments (snacks, hot and cold drinks) are available from a **buffet car** or a **mobile trolley service** on board those trains marked 🍸 and ✕: the latter also convey a **restaurant car** or serve meals to passengers at their seats (this service is in some cases available to first-class ticket holders only). Note that catering facilities may not be available for the whole of a train's journey. **Sleeping-cars** (🛏) have one berth per compartment in first class and two in standard class.

Reservations: Seats on most long-distance trains and berths in sleeping-cars can be reserved in advance when purchasing travel tickets at railway stations or directly from train operating companies (quote the departure time of the train and your destination). Seat reservation is normally free of charge.

100 LONDON AIRPORT LINKS

Gatwick ✈

GATWICK EXPRESS: Daily non-stop rail service from / to **London Victoria**. Journey time: 30 minutes (30 – 40 minutes on ⑦).

From **London** Victoria: On ⚒ at 0514Ⓐ, 0529⑥, 0559 and every 30 minutes until 1859, 1928, 1958, 2029, 2056Ⓐ, 2059⑥, 2129, 2159, 2229, 2259; on ⑦ at 0500 and every 30 minutes until 0830, 0859 and every 30 minutes until 2159, 2229.

From **Gatwick Airport**: On Ⓐ at 0611, 0643, 0717, 0847, 0918, 0939 and every 30 minutes until 2309; On ⑥ at 0540, 0609 and every 30 minutes until 2309; on ⑦ at 0550, 0620, 0650, 0720, 0750, 0820, 0845, 0915 and every 30 minutes until 2315.

Heathrow ✈

❢ Terminal 4 may re-open in June 2022. ❢

HEATHROW EXPRESS: Daily non-stop rail service **London** Paddington - **Heathrow** Terminal 5 and v.v. Journey times: **Heathrow** Central ♣, 15 minutes, **Heathrow** Terminal 5, 21 minutes.
From **London** Paddington: 0510, 0525 and every 15 minutes until 2325.
From **Heathrow** Terminal 5 (5 minutes later from **Heathrow** Central): 0512 and every 15 minutes until 2342, 2357.

♣ – **Heathrow** Central serves Terminals 2 and 3. A free rail transfer service operates every 15 minutes **Heathrow** Central - **Heathrow** Terminal 5 and v.v.

PICCADILLY LINE: London Underground service between **Kings Cross St Pancras** and all **Heathrow** terminals via Central London. Journey time: 50 – 58 minutes.
Frequent trains (every 4 – 10 minutes) 0530⚒ / 0730⑦ - 2300⚒ / 2330⑦.

RAILAIR LINK 🚌 **Reading** railway station - **Heathrow Airport** (Service **RA1**).
From **Reading**: Services call at Heathrow Terminal 5 (± 46 minutes), Heathrow Central Bus Station (± 60 minutes):
On Ⓐ at 0400, 0500, 0600, 0635, 0710, 0745, 0820, 0855, 0930, 1005, 1040, 1115, 1150, 1225, 1300, 1335, 1410, 1445, 1520, 1555, 1630, 1705, 1740, 1815, 1900, 2000, 2100, 2200, 2300.
On Ⓒ at 0400 and hourly until 2300.
From **Heathrow Airport** Central Bus Station: Services call at Heathrow Terminal 5 (± 14 minutes) and Reading Railway Station (± 54 minutes).
On Ⓐ at 0025, 0518, 0618, 0718, 0758, 0833, 0908, 0943, 1018, 1053, 1128, 1203, 1238, 1313, 1348, 1423, 1458, 1533, 1608, 1643, 1718, 1753, 1828, 1903, 1938, 2020, 2120, 2225, 2325.
On Ⓒ at 0015⑦, 0025⑥, 0520, 0620, 0720, 0830 and hourly until 1930, 2025, 2115, 2215, 2315.

RAILAIR LINK 🚌 **Guildford** rail station - **Heathrow Airport** (Service **RA2**).
From **Guildford**: Services call at Heathrow Terminal 5 (± 25 - 35 minutes) and Heathrow Central Bus Station (± 63 - 79 minutes).
0330, 0500 and hourly until 2100.
From **Heathrow** Central Bus Station: Services call at Heathrow Terminal 5 (± 15 minutes) and Guidford (± 60 - 79 minutes).
0440, 0620, 0720, 0840 and hourly until 1440, 1530, 1625, 1725, 1830, 1930, 2040, 2140, 2240.

Luton ✈

Thameslink Railway services Brighton - Gatwick Airport - London St Pancras - Luton Airport Parkway ◧ - Luton ◧ - Bedford: Table **103**.
East Midlands Trains services London St Pancras - Luton Airport Parkway ◧ - Luton ◧ - Leicester - Nottingham / Derby / Sheffield: Table **170**.
◧ – A frequent shuttle 🚌 service operates between each of the railway stations and the airport terminal.

🚌 service **Milton Keynes** - **Luton Airport** and v.v. (Stagecoach route **99**. Journey 55 minutes); for connections from / to **Birmingham**, **Liverpool** and **Manchester** (Tables **150/1/2/3/4**).
From **Milton Keynes** railway station: on ⚒ at 0635, 0755, 0900 and hourly until 1600, 1710, 1810, 1910, 2010, 2110, 2210Ⓐ; on ⑦ at 0900 and hourly until 1900, 2100.
From **Luton Airport**: on ⚒ at 0530, 0700, 0800, 0915 and hourly until 1715, 1820, 1920, 2020, 2120Ⓐ; on ⑦ at 0815 and hourly until 2015.

Stansted ✈

STANSTED EXPRESS: Daily rail service from / to **London** Liverpool St. Journey time ± 45 minutes.
From **London** Liverpool Street: on Ⓐ at 0410, 0440, 0510, 0540, 0610, 0640, 0710, 0725, 0755, 0825, 0855, 0925, 0940, 1010, 1040, 1110, 1140, 1155, 1225, 1255, 1325, 1340, 1410, 1440, 1510, 1540, 1555, 1625, 1654, 1724, 1754, 1809, 1839, 1909, 1940, 2010, 2025, 2055, 2125, 2155, 2225, 2255, 2325; on Ⓒ at 0410 and every 30 minutes until 2240, 2325.
From **Stansted Airport**: on Ⓐ at 0030, 0600, 0615, 0640, 0712, 0740, 0813, 0827, 0857, 0927, 0957, 1030, 1042, 1112, 1142, 1212, 1243, 1257, 1330, 1357, 1430, 1442, 1512, 1542, 1612, 1642, 1657, 1730, 1757, 1827, 1900, 1912, 1942, 2012, 2042, 2115, 2130, 2157, 2230, 2300, 2328, 2359; on ⑥ at 0030, 0530, 0558, 0612 and every 30 minutes until 2312, 2342; on ⑦ at 0030, 0530, 0600, 0630, 0655, 0714, 0742, 0812 and every 30 minutes until 2242, 2315, 2345.
Most trains call at **Tottenham Hale** for London Underground (Victoria Line) connections to / from Kings Cross, St Pancras, Euston, and Victoria stations.
For *Cross Country* and *Greater Anglia* services to / from Cambridge, Norwich, Peterborough, Leicester and Birmingham see Tables **207** and **208**.

City ✈

DOCKLANDS LIGHT RAILWAY from / to **Bank** (interchange with London Underground: Central, Circle, District, Northern, and Waterloo & City Lines).
Trains run every 7 - 10 minutes 0530 - 0030 on ⚒, 0700 - 2330 on ⑦. Journey time: ± 22 minutes.

Inter - Airport 🚌 links

Operator: National Express ✆ 08717 81 81 81. www.nationalexpress.com

Gatwick North Terminal - **Heathrow** Central. Journey time: 65 - 85 minutes
0350, 0505Ⓐ, 0520Ⓒ, 0535Ⓐ, 0605Ⓒ, 0710, 0720Ⓐ, 0740Ⓒ, 0755Ⓐ, 0810Ⓒ, 0815, 0835Ⓐ, 0840Ⓒ, 0940, 1010, 1040, 1140, 1145, 1210, 1240, 1310, 1410, 1510Ⓐ, 1515Ⓒ, 1525Ⓐ, 1540Ⓒ, 1610, 1655Ⓐ, 1710Ⓒ, 1745Ⓐ, 1755Ⓒ, 1810, 1900, 1910, 1945, 2045, 2110, 2215, 2230, 2310, 2350.

Heathrow Central - **Gatwick** North Terminal.
0040, 0305, 0325, 0340, 0510, 0545, 0710, 0740, 0745, 0800Ⓐ, 0910, 0915Ⓒ, 0920Ⓐ, 1020, 1100, 1110, 1150, 1230, 1250, 1310, 1355, 1450Ⓒ, 1500, 1510, 1550Ⓒ, 1605Ⓐ, 1725Ⓒ, 1745Ⓐ, 1810Ⓒ, 1815Ⓒ, 1825, 1835, 1955, 2115, 2240

Gatwick North Terminal - **Stansted**. Journey time: ± 3 hours
Currently suspended

Stansted - **Gatwick** North Terminal.
Currently suspended

Heathrow Central - **Luton**. Journey time: 50 - 70 minutes
0640Ⓐ, 0655Ⓒ, 0900, 0930, 1000, 1130, 1200, 1330, 1400, 1600, 1615, 1815, 2015, 2115, 2300

From **Luton** to **Heathrow** Central.
0315, 0505, 0625, 0645 Ⓐ, 0700 Ⓒ, 0810Ⓐ, 0825 Ⓒ, 0835 Ⓐ, 0845 Ⓒ, 1045, 1050, 1250, 1300, 1515, 1650, 1820, 2035

Heathrow Central - **Stansted**. Journey time: 1½ hours
0920, 1250, 1635, 2035

Stansted - **Heathrow** Central.
0410Ⓒ, 0555, 0910Ⓐ, 0920Ⓒ, 1300, 1700Ⓒ, 1710Ⓐ

Stansted - **Luton**. Journey time: 1½ hours
0030, 0915, 1130, 1400, 1700, 2000

Luton - **Stansted**.
0250, 0720, 1000 Ⓐ, 1020 Ⓒ, 1320, 1620, 1920

SE 2nd class — High-speed services LONDON - MARGATE and RAMSGATE/DOVER — 101

High-speed supplement payable. For slower services see Table **102**.

Via Faversham

km			Ⓐ	Ⓐ	Ⓐ	Ⓐ	Ⓐ	Ⓐ	Ⓐ		Ⓐ	Ⓐ	Ⓐ	Ⓐ	Ⓐ	Ⓐ	Ⓐ	Ⓐ	Ⓐ	Ⓐ	Ⓐ	Ⓐ		Ⓐ	Ⓐ	Ⓐ	Ⓐ
0	**London** St Pancras d.	Ⓐ	...	0625	0722	0755	0825	0855	0925	...	1025	1125	1225	1325	1425	1455	1525	1555	1625	1655	1725	1755	...	1825	1855	1925	1955
9	Stratford International d.		...	0632	0729	0802	0832	0902	0932	...	1032	1132	1332	1332	1432	1502	1532	1602	1632	1702	1732	1802	...	1832	1902	1932	2002
35	Ebbsfleet International d.		...	0643	0740	0813	0843	0913	0943	...	1043	1143	1243	1343	1443	1513	1543	1613	1643	1713	1743	1813	...	1843	1913	1943	2013
52	Rochester d.		...	0702	0758	0834	0902	0932	1002	...	1102	1202	1302	1402	1502	1532	1602	1632	1702	1732	1802	1832	...	1902	1932	2002	2032
54	Chatham d.		...	0706	0801	0838	0906	0936	1006	...	1106	1206	1306	1406	1506	1536	1606	1636	1706	1736	1806	1836	...	1906	1936	2006	2036
70	Sittingbourne d.		...	0723	0819	0856	0923	0953	1023	...	1123	1223	1323	1423	1523	1553	1623	1653	1723	1753	1824	1854	...	1923	1953	2023	2053
83	Faversham d.		0622	0731	0831	0904	0931	1001	1031	...	1131	1231	1331	1431	1531	1601	1631	1701	1731	1805	1835	1905	...	1933	2001	2031	2101
100	Herne Bay d.		0638	...	0845	...	0945	...	1045	...	1145	1245	1345	1445	*1551*	...	*1651*	...	*1751*	...	1849	1919	...	1947	...	2045	...
118	**Margate** d.		0655	...	0859	...	0959	...	1059	...	1159	1259	1359	1459	*1607*	...	*1707*	...	*1808*	...	1907	1935	...	2002	...	2059	...
126	**Ramsgate** a.		0709	...	0911	...	1011	...	1111	...	1211	1311	1411	1511	*1620*	...	*1719*	...	*1825*	...	...	1951	...	2021z	...	2114	...

	Ⓐ	Ⓐ	Ⓐ A	Ⓐ	Ⓐ B		⑥	⑥	⑥	⑥	⑥		⑥	⑥	⑥		⑦	⑦	⑦	⑦		⑦	⑦		⑦
London St Pancras d.	2025	2125	2225	2325	2355	⑥	...	...	...	0725	0825		2225	2325	2355	⑦	...	...	0825	0925		2125	2225	...	2325
Stratford International d.	2032	2132	2232	2332	0002		...	...	...	0732	0832		2232	2332	0002		...	...	0832	0932		2132	2232	...	2332
Ebbsfleet International d.	2043	2143	2243	2343	0013		...	...	...	0743	0843	and at	2243	2343	0013		...	...	0843	0943	and at	2143	2243	...	2343
Rochester d.	2102	2202	2302	0002	0032		...	*0640*	0721	0802	0902	the same	2302	0002	0032		...	0821	0902	1002	the same	2202	2302	...	0002
Chatham d.	2106	2206	2306	0006	0036		...	*0643*	0724	0806	0906	minutes	2306	0006	0036		...	0824	0906	1006	minutes	2206	2306	...	0006
Sittingbourne d.	2123	2223	2323	0023	0052s		*0611*	*0711*	0741	0823	0923	past each	2323	0023	0053		0739	0842	0923	1023	past each	2223	2323	...	0023
Faversham d.	2131	2231	2331	0031	0101		0630	0730	0752	0831	0931	hour until	2332	0031	0101		0752	0852	0931	1031	hour until	2231	2331	...	0031
Herne Bay d.	2145	2245	*0007*	...	*0124*s		0645	0745	0807	0845	0945		2345	*0107*s	*0138*s		0807	0907	0945	1045		2245	*0009*	...	...
Margate d.	2159	2259	*0024*	...	*0140*s		0702	0802	0824	0859	0959		2359	*0123*s	*0155*s		0824	0924	0959	1059		2259	*0025*	...	...
Ramsgate a.	2211	2311	*0038*	...	*0153*		0714	0814	0838	0911	1011		0011	*0138*	*0208*		0838	0938	1011	1111		2311	*0039*	...	...

		Ⓐ	Ⓐ	Ⓐ	Ⓐ	Ⓐ	Ⓐ	Ⓐ	Ⓐ	Ⓐ	Ⓐ	Ⓐ	Ⓐ	Ⓐ	Ⓐ	Ⓐ	Ⓐ	Ⓐ	Ⓐ	Ⓐ	Ⓐ	Ⓐ	Ⓐ	Ⓐ	Ⓐ	Ⓐ	Ⓐ
Ramsgate d.	Ⓐ	...	*0422*	...	...	...	...	...	*0740*	*0812*	...	0920	1020	1120	1220	1320	1420	...	1520	...	1620	...	*1716*	1920	2020	2120	2153
Margate d.		...	*0433*	0522	...	0628	0657	...	*0751*	*0823*	...	0930	1030	1130	1230	1330	1430	...	1530	...	1630	...	*1727*	1930	2030	2130	2204
Herne Bay d.		...	*0449*	0539	...	0642	0711	...	*0807*	*0839*	...	0944	1044	1144	1244	1344	1444	...	1544	...	1644	...	*1743*	1944	2044	2144	2220
Faversham d.		0457	0527	0557	0627	0656	0728	0800	0828	0900	0928	1000	1058	1158	1258	1358	1458	1528	1558	1628	1700	1728	1828	1958	2058	2158	2248t
Sittingbourne d.		0505	0535	0606	0635	0706	0738	0808	0838	0908	0938	1008	1108	1208	1308	1408	1508	1538	1608	1638	1708	1738	1838	2008	2108	2208	2259
Chatham d.		0522	0554	0623	0654	0723	0755	0825	0855	0925	0955	1025	1125	1225	1325	1425	1525	1555	1625	1655	1725	1755	1855	2025	2125	2225	2319
Rochester d.		0526	0558	0627	0658	0727	0759	0829	0859	0929	0959	1029	1129	1229	1329	1429	1529	1559	1629	1659	1729	1759	1859	2029	2129	2229	2322
Ebbsfleet International a.		0546	0616	0646	0716	0746	0816	0846	0916	0946	1016	1046	1146	1246	1346	1446	1546	1616	1646	1716	1746	1816	1916	2046	2146	2246	...
Stratford International a.		0558	0628	0658	0728	0758	0829	0858	0928	0958	1029	1058	1158	1258	1358	1458	1558	1629	1658	1728	1758	1829	1928	2058	2158	2258	...
London St Pancras a.		0606	0636	0706	0736	0806	0837	0906	0936	1006	1037	1106	1206	1306	1406	1506	1606	1637	1706	1736	1810	1837	1936	2106	2206	2306	...

	Ⓐ		⑥	⑥	⑥	⑥	⑥		⑥	⑥	⑥	⑥	⑥	⑥		⑦	⑦	⑦	⑦	⑦		⑦	⑦	⑦	⑦
Ramsgate d.	2253	⑥	*0439*	...	0617	0717	0820		1820	1920	2020	2120	2153	b2320	⑦	...	*0653*	0817	0920	1020		2020	2120	*2153*	2253
Margate d.	2304		*0450*	...	0627	0727	0830	and at	1830	1930	2030	2130	2204	2332		...	*0704*	0827	0930	1030	and at	2030	2130	*2204*	2304
Herne Bay d.	2320		*0506*	...	0641	0741	0844	the same	1844	1944	2044	2144	2220	2348		...	*0720*	0841	0944	1044	the same	2044	2144	*2220*	2320
Faversham d.	2337		0527	0557	0657	0757	0900	minutes	1900	2000	2100	2200	2237	0007		0657	0757	0857	1000	1100	minutes	2100	2200	2245	2337
Sittingbourne d.	2347		0535	0605	0705	0805	0908	past each	1908	2008	2108	2208	2245	0017		0705	0805	0905	1008	1108	past each	2108	2208	2256	2347
Chatham d.	...		0584	0622	0723	0823	0925	hour	1925	2025	2125	2225	2302	...		0722	0823	0923	1025	1125	hour	2125	2225	2315	...
Rochester d.	...		0559	0626	0727	0827	0929	until	1929	2029	2129	2229	2305	...		0729	0827	0927	1029	1129	until	2129	2229	2318	...
Ebbsfleet International a.	...		0616	0646	0746	0846	0946		1946	2046	2146	2246	...	...		0746	0846	0946	1046	1146		2146	2246	...	...
Stratford International a.	...		0628	0658	0758	0858	0958		1958	2058	2158	2258	...	...		0758	0858	0958	1058	1158		2158	2258	...	...
London St Pancras a.	...		0636	0706	0806	0906	1006		2006	2106	2206	2306	...	...		0806	0906	1006	1106	1206		2206	2306	...	...

Via Ashford and Dover

km			Ⓐ	Ⓐ	Ⓐ	Ⓐ	Ⓐ	Ⓐ	✣	Ⓐ	Ⓐ	Ⓐ	Ⓐ	Ⓐ	Ⓐ	Ⓐ	Ⓐ	Ⓐ	Ⓐ	Ⓐ	Ⓐ	Ⓐ	Ⓐ	Ⓐ	
0	**London** St Pancras d.	Ⓐ	0637	0712	0734	0810	0834	0912		1437	1512	1537	1610	1634	1650	1707	1720	1737	1807	1820	1834	1912	1937	2012	
9	Stratford International d.		0644	0719	0741	0817	0841	0919	and at	1444	1519	1544	1617	1641	1657	1714	1727	1744	1814	1827	1841	1919	1944	2019	and at
35	Ebbsfleet International d.		0655	0730	0752	0830	0852	0930	the same	1455	1530	1555	1628	1652	|	1725	|	1755	1825	|	1852	1930	1955	2030	the same
90	Ashford International d.		0715	0752	0815	0852	0915	0952	minutes	1515	1552	1615	1652	1715	1726	1746	1756	1815	1845	1856	1915	1952	2015	2052	minutes
112	**Folkestone** Central d.		0730	|	0830	|	0930	|	past each	1530	|	1630	|	1730	|	1802	|	1833	1903	|	1930	|	2030	|	past each
124	**Dover** Priory a.		0740	|	0840	|	0942	|	hour until	1540	|	1640	|	1740	|	1816	|	1844	1913	|	1942	|	2040	|	hour until
112	Canterbury West d.		...	0808	...	0908	|	1008		...	1608	...	1708	...	1742	...	1811	|	...	1911	...	2008	...	2108	
140	Ramsgate a.		...	0827	...	0929	1023	1027		...	1627	...	1730	...	1803	...	1832	1925	...	1931	...	2032	...	2127	
149	**Margate** a.		...	0838	...	0940	...	1038		...	1638	...	1741	...	1817	...	1846	...	...	1946	...	2045	...	2138	

	Ⓐ	Ⓐ	③–⑤	②	①	Ⓐ		⑥	⑥	⑥	⑥	⑥	⑥	⑥	⑥	⑥	⑥	⑥	✣	⑥	⑥		⑦	⑦	⑦	⑦
London St Pancras d.	2212	2237	2312	2312	2312	2337	⑥	...	...	...	...	0637	0712	0737	0810	0837	0912	0934		2312	2337	⑦	...	...	...	0837
Stratford International d.	2219	2244	2319	2319	2319	2344		...	...	...	...	0644	0719	0744	0817	0844	0919	0941	and at	2319	2344		...	...	...	0844
Ebbsfleet International d.	2230	2255	2330	2330	2330	2355		...	...	...	...	0655	0730	0755	0830	0855	0930	0952	the same	2330	2355		...	...	...	0855
Ashford International d.	2252	2315	2352	2352	2352	0015		0559	0602	0659	0705	0715	0752	0815	0852	0915	0952	1012	minutes	2352	0015		0801	0804	0852	0915
Folkestone Central d.	|	2330	|	|	|	0029s		0619	|	0719	|	0730	|	0830	|	0930	|	1030	past each	|	0030		0820	|	|	0930
Dover Priory a.	|	2340	|	|	|	0040		0631	|	0731	|	0740	|	0840	|	0940	|	1040	hour until	|	0040		0832	|	|	0940
Canterbury West d.	2308	...	0008	0008	*0031*j	...		|	0624	|	0727	...	0808	...	0908	...	1008	...		0008	...		|	0826	0908	...
Ramsgate a.	2329	...	0026	0032	0045	...		0710	0649	0810	0749	...	0827	...	0927	...	1027	...		0027	...		0911	0851	0926	...
Margate a.	2340f	...	0039	*0055*r	0058	...		...	...	...	...	...	0838	...	0938	...	1038	...		0038	...		...	...	0938	...

	⑦	⑦	⑦	⑦	⑦	⑦	✣	⑦	⑦	⑦
London St Pancras d.	0912	0937	1012	1037	1110	1134		2237	2312	2337
Stratford International d.	0919	0944	1019	1044	1117	1141	and at	2244	2319	2344
Ebbsfleet International d.	0930	0955	1030	1055	1130	1152	the same	2255	2330	2355
Ashford International d.	0952	1015	1052	1115	1152	1215	minutes	2315	2352	0014
Folkestone Central d.	|	1030	|	1130	|	1230	past each	2330	|	...
Dover Priory d.	|	1040	|	1140	|	1240	hour until	2340	|	...
Canterbury West d.	1008	...	1108	...	1208	...		...	0008	...
Ramsgate a.	1026	...	1126	...	1226	...		...	0026	...
Margate a.	1038	...	1138	...	1238	...		...	0038	...

		Ⓐ	Ⓐ	Ⓐ	Ⓐ	Ⓐ	Ⓐ	Ⓐ	Ⓐ	Ⓐ	Ⓐ
Margate d.	Ⓐ	...	...	...	0545	...	...	0645	...	0715	...
Ramsgate d.		...	0455	...	0557	...	0605	0657	...	0727	...
Canterbury West d.		...	0518	...	0616	...	|	0716	...	0746	...
Dover Priory d.		*0417*	|	0546	|	0615	0644	|	0713	|	0749
Folkestone Cent. d.		*0438*	|	0557	|	0626	0655	|	0724	|	0800
Ashford International d.		0513	0543	0616	0632	0646	0716	0736	0743	0806	0816
Ebbsfleet International a.		0532	0602	0635	0654	0705	0735	|	0802	|	0835
Stratford International a.		0544	0614	0647	0706	0717	0747	0804	0814	0834	0847
London St Pancras a.		0551	0621	0654	0713	0725	0754	0812	0821	0842	0854

	Ⓐ	Ⓐ	Ⓐ	Ⓐ		Ⓐ	Ⓐ	Ⓐ	Ⓐ	Ⓐ	Ⓐ	Ⓐ		Ⓐ	Ⓐ	Ⓐ	Ⓐ	Ⓐ	Ⓐ		⑥	⑥	⑥	⑥	⑥
Margate d.	0755	...	0853	...		...	1455	...	1555	...	1655	...		2155	...	...	...	2255	...	⑥	...	...	0552	...	0652
Ramsgate d.	0807	...	0905	0912	and at	1412	1507	...	1607	...	1707	...		2207	...	2240	2225	2307	2325		0504	...	0604	...	0704
Canterbury West d.	0826	...	0924	|	the same	|	1526	...	1626	...	1726	...	and at	2226	...	2303	|	2326	|		0523	...	0623	...	0723
Dover Priory d.	|	0849	|	0949	minutes	1449	|	1549	|	1649	|	1749	the same	|	2249	|	2300	|	0001		|	0549	|	0649	|
Folkestone Central d.	|	0900	|	1000	past each	1500	|	1600	|	1700	|	1800	minutes	|	2300	|	2311	|	0012		|	0600	|	0700	|
Ashford International d.	0843	0916	0943	1019	hour until	1519	1543	1616	1643	1722	1743	1816	past each	2243	2316	2325	2330	2341	0028		0543	0616	0643	0716	0743
Ebbsfleet International a.	0902	0935	1002	1038		1538	1602	1635	1702	1741	1802	1835	hour until	2302	2335	...	...	...	...		0602	0635	0702	0735	0802
Stratford International a.	0914	0947	1014	1050		1550	1614	1647	1714	1753	1814	1847		2314	2347	...	...	...	...		0614	0647	0714	0747	0814
London St Pancras a.	0921	0954	1021	1057		1558	1621	1654	1721	1800	1821	1854		2321	2354	...	...	...	...		0621	0654	0721	0754	0821

	⑥	⑥	⑥	⊠	⑥	⑥	⑥	⑥	⑥	⑥		⑦	⑦	⑦	⑦	⑦	⑦	⑦	⊠	⑦	⑦	⑦	⑦	⑦	⑦
Margate d.	...	0755	...		2155	...	...	...	2255	...	⑦	...	...	0752	...	0852	...	0955		2055	...	...	2155	...	2255
Ramsgate d.	...	0807	...	and at	2207	...	2225	2242	2307	2325		0704	...	0804	...	0904	...	1007	and at	2107	...	2125	2207	2225	2307
Canterbury West d.	...	0826	...	the same	2226	...	|	2305	2326	|		0724	...	0823	...	0923	...	1026	the same	2126	...	|	2226	|	2326
Dover Priory d.	0749	|	0849	minutes	|	2249	2300	|	|	2359		|	0749	|	0849	|	0949	|	minutes	|	2149	2200	|	2300	|
Folkestone Central d.	0800	|	0900	past each	|	2300	2311	|	|	0011		|	0800	|	0900	|	1000	|	past each	|	2200	2211	|	2311	|
Ashford International d.	0816	0843	0916	hour until	2243	2316	2330	2326	2341	0027		0743	0816	0843	0916	0943	1016	1043	hour until	2143	2216	2230	2243	2330	2341
Ebbsfleet International a.	0835	0902	0938		2302	2335	...	...	...	...		0802	0835	0902	0935	1002	1038	1102		2202	2235	...	2302	...	...
Stratford International a.	0847	0914	0950		2314	2347	...	...	...	...		0814	0847	0914	0947	1014	1050	1114		2214	2247	...	2314	...	...
London St Pancras a.	0854	0921	0958		2321	2354	...	...	...	...		0821	0854	0921	0954	1021	1057	1121		2221	2254	...	2321	...	...

A – On ② service is operated by 🚌 from Faversham (Faversham d. 2356, Herne Bay a. 0033**s**, Margate a. 0041, Ramsgate a. 0102).

B – On ③ mornings service is operated by 🚌 from Faversham (Faversham d. 0108, Herne Bay a. 0145**s**, Margate a. 0153, Ramsgate a. 0214).

f – *2355* on ② (by 🚌 from Ramsgate).

j – Arrival time. Connection by 🚌 from Ashford.

r – Connection by 🚌.

s – Calls to set down only.

t – Arrives 2236.

z – Until Oct. 7 arrives 2015.

✣ – xx34 departures may be up to 3 minutes later.

⊠ – Arrival times of xx49 from Dover may be up to 4 minutes earlier.

102 LONDON - THE SOUTH and SOUTH EAST — SE, SN

Typical off-peak journey time in hours and minutes
READ DOWN ↓ READ UP ↑

During peak hours on Ⓐ (0600 - 0900 and 1600 - 1900) services generally run more frequently (particularly to and from London) and journey times may vary.

LONDON VICTORIA - RAMSGATE — SE

km					
0	0h00	↓	d. **London** Victoria....a.	↑	1h57
18	0h17		d. Bromley South.......d.		1h40
53	0h47	↓	d. Rochester..............d.	↑	1h12
72	1h09		d. Sittingbourne.........d.		0h50
84	1h21	↓	d. Faversham.............d.	↑	0h42
101	1h36		d. Herne Bay..............d.		0h26
119	1h49	↓	d. Margate.................d.	↑	0h10
128	1h59		a. **Ramsgate**............d.		0h00

Frequency: Twice an hour.
Usual off-peak departures:
From London Victoria at xx25 and xx40 (not 1440, 1540 on Ⓐ).
From Ramsgate at xx40 and xx53 (not 1553 on Ⓐ).

LONDON VICTORIA - DOVER — SE

km					
0	0h00	↓	d. **London** Victoria....a.	↑	2h02
18	0h17		d. Bromley South.......d.		1h43
53	0h47	↓	d. Rochester..............d.	↑	1h17
72	1h09		d. Sittingbourne.........d.		0h58
84	1h21	↓	d. Faversham.............d.	↑	0h47
99	1h37		d. Canterbury East....d.		0h27
124	1h58	↓	a. **Dover** Priory ....d.	↑	0h00

Frequency: Hourly.
Usual off-peak departures:
From London Victoria at xx10 except ⑥ until Sept. 3 when 0710, 0810, 0842, 0942, 1042, 1142, 1310, then xx10. From Dover at xx18 on Ⓐ until 1518 then xx48; xx18 on ⑥ until Sept. 3 until 1518, then xx50; xx18 on ⑥ from Sept. 10; xx50 on ⑦.

LONDON CHARING CROSS - CANTERBURY WEST — SE

km					
0	0h00	↓	d. **London** Ch Cross.a.	↑	1h46
1	0h03		d. **London** W'loo(E)..a.		1h42
3	0h08	↓	d. **London** Bridge......a.	↑	1h36
36	0h32		d. Sevenoaks..............d.		1h13
48	0h40	↓	d. Tonbridge...............d.	↑	1h04
90	1h20		a. Ashford Int'l...........d.		0h27
113	1h38	↓	a. **Canterbury** West..d.	↑	0h00

Frequency: Hourly.
Usual off-peak departures:
From London Charing Cross at xx40 with a change at Ashford International.
Direct trains on Ⓐ at 0710, 1510 - 1910.
From Canterbury West at xx03 with a change at Ashford International.
Direct trains on Ⓐ at 0603, 0634 - 0839.

LONDON CHARING CROSS - DOVER — SE

km					
0	0h00	↓	d. **London** Ch Cross.a.	↑	1h58
1	0h03		d. **London** W'loo(E)..a.		1h53
3	0h08	↓	d. **London** Bridge......a.	↑	1h42
36	0h32		d. Sevenoaks..............d.		1h18
48	0h40	↓	d. Tonbridge...............d.	↑	1h06
90	1h20		d. Ashford Int'l...........d.		0h29
113	1h40	↓	d. Folkstone Central..d.	↑	0h12
124	1h52		a. **Dover** Priory ....d.		0h00

Frequency: Hourly.
Usual off-peak departures:
From London Charing Cross at xx40.
From Dover at xx00.

LONDON VICTORIA - ASHFORD INTERNATIONAL — SE

km					
0	0h00	↓	d. **London** Victoria....a.	↑	1h29
18	0h17		d. Bromley South.......d.		1h14
28	0h28	↓	d. Swanley.................d.	↑	1h03
56	0h52		d. West Malling.........d.		0h42
64	1h03	↓	d. Maidstone East.....d.	↑	0h30
68	1h09		d. Bearsted...............d.		0h25
95	1h31	↓	a. **Ashford** Int'l..........d.	↑	0h00

Frequency: Hourly.
Usual off-peak departures:
From London Victoria at xx25, xx55 on Ⓐ (not 0955,1155, 1255, 1355); xx25, xx55 on ⑥; xx25 on ⑦.
From Ashford at xx26 on Ⓐ; xx03, xx31 on ⑥; xx27 on ⑦.

LONDON CHARING CROSS - HASTINGS — SE

km					
0	0h00	↓	d. **London** Ch Cross.a.	↑	1h43
1	0h03		d. **London** W'loo(E)..a.		1h39
3	0h08	↓	d. **London** Bridge ....a.	↑	1h35
36	0h34		d. Sevenoaks..............d.		1h09
48	0h43	↓	d. Tonbridge...............d.	↑	1h00
55	0h55		d. Tunbridge Wells △ d.		0h49
89	1h33	↓	d. Battle....................d.	↑	0h16
100	1h45		a. **Hastings**..............d.		0h00

Frequency: Every 30 minutes.
Usual off-peak departures:
From London Charing Cross at xx15, xx45 on ⚒; xx25, xx55 on ⑦.
From Hastings at xx31, xx50 on ⚒; xx30, xx50 on ⑦.
Timings from Hastings vary after the 1550 departure on Ⓐ.

LONDON VICTORIA - EASTBOURNE — SN

km					
0	0h00	↓	d. **London** Victoria....a.	↑	1h26
17	0h16		d. East Croydon........d.		1h09
43	0h33	↓	d. Gatwick Airport......d.	↑	0h53
61	0h50		d. Haywards Heath....d.		0h34
81	1h06	↓	d. Lewes...................d.	↑	0h19
106	1h27		a. **Eastbourne**...........d.		0h00

Frequency: Every 30 minutes on ⚒; hourly on ⑦.
Usual off-peak departures:
From London Victoria at xx24, xx54 on ⚒‡; xx46 on ⑦.
From Eastbourne at xx06, xx35 on ⚒; xx00 on ⑦. Not 1035, 1135, 1235 on Ⓐ.

ASHFORD - HASTINGS - EASTBOURNE - (BRIGHTON) — SN

km					
0	0h00	↓	d. **Ashford** Int'l..........a.	↑	1h20
14	0h12		d. Appledore...............d.		1h07
25	0h23	↓	d. Rye........................d.	↑	0h56
41	0h42		d. Ore........................d.		0h40
42	0h45	↓	d. **Hastings**..............d.	↑	0h36
50	0h57		d. Bexhill...................d.		0h25
67	1h14	↓	a. **Eastbourne**..........d.	↑	0h00

Frequency: Hourly.
Usual off-peak departures:
From Ashford at xx25.
From Eastbourne at xx49 on ⚒; xx56 on ⑦.
☛ Local services are available Brighton / Lewes - Eastbourne - Hastings v.v.

LONDON BRIDGE - UCKFIELD — SN

km					
0	0h00	↓	d. **London** Bridge......a.	↑	1h15
16	0h16		d. East Croydon........d.		0h59
32	0h29	↓	d. Oxted....................d.	↑	0h44
57	0h55		d. Eridge △...............d.		0h17
70	1h01	↓	d. Crowborough.........d.	↑	0h12
74	1h15		a. **Uckfield**.............d.		0h00

Frequency: Hourly ¶.
Usual off-peak departures:
From London Bridge at xx07 on ⚒.
From Uckfield at xx33 on ⚒.
On ⑦ use East Grinstead services from / to London Victoria and change trains at Oxted (Uckfield d. xx34).

LONDON VICTORIA - EAST GRINSTEAD — SN

km					
0	0h00	↓	d. **London** Victoria....a.	↑	0h56
17	0h17		d. East Croydon........d.		0h37
33	0h37	↓	d. Oxted....................d.	↑	0h16
42	0h43		d. Lingfield...............d.		0h12
48	0h54	↓	a. **East Grinstead** ▽ d.	↑	0h00

Frequency: Every 30 minutes.
Usual off-peak departures:
From London Victoria at xx20, xx50 on ⚒; xx21, xx51 on ⑦.
From East Grinstead at xx06, xx36 on ⚒; xx12, xx42 on ⑦.

LONDON VICTORIA - LITTLEHAMPTON — SN

km					
0	0h00	↓	d. **London** Victoria....a.	↑	1h42
17	0h16		d. East Croydon........a.		1h25
43	0h33	↓	d. Gatwick Airport......a.	↑	1h09
61	0h50		d. Haywards Heath....a.		0h54
82	1h06	↓	d. Hove.....................a.	↑	0h35
96	1h21		d. Worthing...............d.		0h21
114	1h41	↓	a. **Littlehampton**......d.	↑	0h00

Frequency: Every 30 minutes on ⚒; hourly on ⑦.
Usual off-peak departures:
From London Victoria at xx15, xx45 on ⚒✣; xx16 on ⑦.
From Littlehampton at xx13, xx43 on ⚒✣; xx13 on ⑦.

LONDON VICTORIA - BOGNOR REGIS — SN

km					
0	0h00	↓	d. **London** Victoria....a.	↑	1h50
17	0h16		d. East Croydon........d.		1h30
43	0h37	↓	d. Gatwick Airport......d.	↑	1h08
61	1h03		d. Horsham...............d.		0h50
94	1h30	↓	d. Arundel.................d.	↑	0h16
110	1h40		d. Barnham...............d.		0h07
116	1h46	↓	a. **Bognor Regis**......d.	↑	0h00

Frequency: Every 30 minutes on ⚒; hourly on ⑦.
Usual off-peak departures:
From London Victoria at xx05, xx35 on ⚒; xx35 on ⑦.
From Bognor Regis at xx29, xx56 on ⚒; xx31 on ⑦.

BRIGHTON - PORTSMOUTH HARBOUR — SN

km	◧				◧
0	0h00	↓	d. **Brighton**..............d.	↑	1h19
2	0h04		d. Hove.....................d.		1h15
16	0h22	↓	d. Worthing...............d.	↑	0h57
35	0h42		d. Barnham...............d.		0h39
45	0h49	↓	d. Chichester.............d.	↑	0h31
59	1h04		d. Havant..................d.		0h17
71	1h16	↓	a. **Portsmouth** & SS.d.	↑	0h04
72	1h20		a. **Portsmouth** Hbr...d.		0h00

Frequency: Hourly.
Usual off-peak departures:
From Brighton at xx00 on ⚒; xx30 on ⑦.
From Portsmouth & Southsea at xx33 on ⚒; xx18 on ⑦.
See note ◧.

BRIGHTON - SOUTHAMPTON CENTRAL — SN

km	◐				◐
0	0h00	↓	d. **Brighton**..............d.	↑	1h45
2	0h04		d. Hove.....................d.		1h41
16	0h23	↓	d. Worthing...............d.	↑	1h23
35	0h46		d. Barnham...............d.		1h00
45	0h54	↓	d. Chichester.............d.	↑	0h52
59	1h06		d. Havant..................d.		0h38
75	1h22	↓	d. Fareham...............d.	↑	0h23
98	1h48		a. **Southampton** C....d.		0h00

Frequency: Hourly.
Usual off-peak departures:
From Brighton at xx30 on Ⓐ; xx32 on ⑥; xx00 on ⑦.
From Southampton at xx26 on ⚒; xx30 on ⑦.
See note ◐.

LONDON WATERLOO - READING — SW

km					
0	0h00	↓	d. **London** Waterloo. a.	↑	1h22
16	0h16		d. Richmond.............. d.		1h03
18	0h20	↓	d. Twickenham........... d.	↑	0h58
30	0h33		d. Staines.................. d.		0h36
46	0h53	↓	d. Ascot..................... d.	↑	0h28
70	1h20		a. **Reading**................ d.		0h00

Frequency: Every 30 minutes.
Usual off-peak departures:
From London Waterloo at xx20, xx50 on ⚒; xx09, xx39 on ⑦.
From Reading at xx12, xx42 on ⚒; xx24, xx54 on ⑦.

LONDON WATERLOO - WINDSOR — SW

km					
0	0h00	↓	d. **London** Waterloo. a.	↑	0h56
16	0h20		d. Richmond.............. d.		0h34
18	0h24	↓	d. Twickenham........... d.	↑	0h30
30	0h39		d. Staines.................. d.		0h15
41	0h53	↓	a. **Windsor** ▷.......... d.	↑	0h00

Frequency: Every 30 minutes.
Usual off-peak departures:
From London Waterloo at xx28, xx58 on ⚒; xx25, xx44 on ⑦.
From Windsor at xx23, xx53 on ⚒; xx01, xx34 on ⑦.

SEAFORD - BRIGHTON — SN

km					
0	0h00	↓	d. **Seaford**...............a.	↑	0h36
4	0h05		d. Newhaven Harbour.d.		0h30
5	0h07	↓	d. Newhaven Town....d.	↑	0h28
15	0h19		d. Lewes...................d.		0h18
22	0h26	↓	d. Falmer..................d.	↑	0h09
28	0h35		a. **Brighton**..............d.		0h00

Frequency: Every 30 minutes.
Usual off-peak departures:
From Seaford at xx25, xx53 on ⚒; xx29, xx59 on ⑦. Not 1253 on Ⓐ.
From Brighton at xx11, xx41 on ⚒; xx17, xx47 on ⑦. Not 1211 on Ⓐ.

TONBRIDGE - REDHILL — SN

km					
0	0h00	↓	d. **Tonbridge**............a.	↑	0h31
7	0h08		d. Penshurst..............d.		0h22
15	0h15	↓	d. Edenbridge............d.	↑	0h16
22	0h21		d. Godstone...............d.		0h10
32	0h35	↓	a. **Redhill**.................d.	↑	0h00

Frequency: Hourly.
Usual off-peak departures:
From Tonbridge at xx01 on ⚒§; xx26 on ⑦.
From Redhill at xx00 on ⚒; xx09 on ⑦.

◧ – Journey time on ⑦ extended by up to 17 minutes.
◐ – Journey time on ⑦ extended by up to 10 minutes.
▷ – Windsor and Eton Riverside.
§ – Timings vary after 1501 departure on Ⓐ.

‡ – Not 1224, 1324, 1424 on Ⓐ.
¶ – On Ⓐ not 1007, 1207, 1407 from London Bridge; not 1133, 1333, 1533 from Uckfield.
✣ – On Ⓐ not 1145, 1245 from London Victoria; not 0943, 1043, 1443 from Littlehampton.

△ – **Spa Valley Railway** (🚂 Eridge - Tunbridge Wells West: *8 km*). ✆ 01892 537715. www.spavalleyrailway.co.uk
▽ – **Bluebell Railway** (🚂 East Grinstead - Sheffield Park: *18 km*). ✆ 01825 720800. www.bluebell-railway.com

SN, TL — BEDFORD - LONDON - GATWICK ✈ - BRIGHTON — 103

km			⚒	⚒	⚒	⚒	⚒	Ⓐ	⑥	⚒	⚒	⚒	⚒	⚒	⚒	♠	⚒	⚒	⚒	⚒	⚒	⑥	Ⓐ		⑦	⑦
0	**Bedford** 170 d.	⚒	0015	0115	0153	0215	0253	0253	0343	0413	0443	0515	0547	0619		2119	2149	2217	2243	2307	2337	2343	⑦	0555	0625
31	Luton 170 d.		0040	0140	0218	0240	0318	0318	0409	0438	0508	0540	0611	0642		2143	2213	2241	2308	2332	0002	0010		0620	0650
33	Luton Airport P ✈ ◇ 170 d.		0043	0143	0221	0243	0321	0321	0412	0441	0511	0543	0614	0645	and	2146	2216	2244	2311	2335	0005	0013		0623	0653
48	St. Albans d.		0055	0155	0233	0255	0333	0333	0424	0453	0523	0555	0625	0657	at the	2157	2227	2255	2323	2347	0017	0025		0635	0705
80	**London** St Pancras 170 d.		0132	0232	0302	0332	0402	0402	0452	0520	0550	0620	0650	0720	same	2220	2250	2322	2352	0022	0052	0052		0710	0740
82	Farringdon 185 d.		|	|	|	|	|	|	0457	0524	0554	0624	0654	0724	minutes	2224	2254	2327	2356	0027	|	|		▬	▬
83	**London** Blackfriars 185 d.		0140	0240	0310	0340	0410	0410	0501	0529	0559	0629	0659	0729	past	2229	2259	2331	0002	0031	0102	0102		⑦	⑦
84	**London** Bridge 185 d.		|	|	|	|	|	|	|	0535	0605	0635	0705	0735	each	2235	2305	2336	|	|	|	|		0709	0739
99	East Croydon 185 d.		0207	0307	0337	0407	0437	0437	0528	0549	0619	0649	0719	0749	hour	2249	2319	2351	0028	0058	0128	0128		0723	0753
124	Gatwick Airport ✈ 185 d.		0230	0330	0358	0430	0458	0504	0548	0606	0636	0705	0735	0805	until	2306	2336	0018	0049	0120	0158	0158		0743	0815
142	Haywards Heath 185 d.		...	...	...	...	0514	0520	0606	0623	0651	0721	0751	0821		2323	2351	0036	0104	...	0214	0214		0758	0832
163	**Brighton** 185 a.		...	...	...	...	0532	0538	0626	0643	0713	0743	0813	0843		2345	0013	0056	0124	...	0228	0228		0818	0852

	⑦	⑦	⑦	⑦	⑦	♠	⑦	⑦	⑦	⑦	⑦	⑦
Bedford 170 d.	0655	0733	0805	0817	0847		2119	2149	2209	2243	2305	2343
Luton 170 d.	0720	0758	0830	0842	0912		2143	2213	2233	2308	2330	0010
Luton Airport P ✈ ◇ 170 d.	0723	0801	0833	0845	0915	and	2146	2216	2236	2311	2333	0013
St. Albans d.	0735	0813	0845	0857	0927	at the	2157	2227	2248	2323	2345	0025
London St Pancras 170 d.	0810	0838	0910	0924	0954	same	2224	2254	2324	2352	0021	0052
Farringdon 185 d.	▬	▬	▬	0928	0958	minutes	2228	2258	2328	2356	0026	|
London Blackfriars 185 d.	⑦	⑦	⑦	0933	1003	past	2233	2303	2333	0002	0031	0102
London Bridge 185 d.	0809	0839	0909	0939	1009	each	2239	2309	2339	|	|	|
East Croydon 185 d.	0823	0853	0923	0953	1023	hour	2253	2323	2353	0028	0058	0128
Gatwick Airport ✈ 185 d.	0843	0909	0939	1009	1039	until	2309	2339	0017	0049	0120	0158
Haywards Heath 185 d.	0858	0926	0954	1024	1054		2326	2358	0034	0104	...	0214
Brighton 185 a.	0918	0946	1014	1044	1114		2346	0018	0054	0124	...	0228

		⚒	⚒	⚒	⚒	⑥	Ⓐ	⚒
Brighton 185 d.	⚒	0004	...	...	...	0412	0412	0525
Haywards Heath 185 d.		0025	...	...	...	0426	0426	0546
Gatwick Airport ✈ 185 d.		0042	0146	0246	0346	0441	0441	0606
East Croydon 185 d.		0110	0210	0310	0410	0510	0510	0621
London Bridge 185 d.		|	|	|	|	0525	0525	0635
London Blackfriars 185 d.		0136	0236	0336	0436	0531	0531	0642
Farringdon 185 d.		|	|	|	|	0536	0536	0646
London St Pancras 170 d.		0144	0244	0344	0444	0540	0540	0651
St Albans City d.		0219	0317	0417	0517	0601	0605	0711
Luton Airport P ◇ 170 d.		0230	0330	0430	0530	0612	0618	0723
Luton 170 d.		0235	0334	0434	0534	0617	0622	0727
Bedford 170 a.		0259	0359	0459	0559	0641	0647	0751

	Ⓐ	⑥	Ⓐ	⑥	Ⓐ	⑥	⚒	⚒	⚒	⚒	⚒		⚒	⚒	⑥	Ⓐ	⚒	⚒		⚒	⚒	⚒	⚒	⚒
Brighton 185 d.	0601	0555	0620	0625	0653	0655	0723	0755f	0825f	0855	0925		1525	1555	1625	1625	1655	1725		2125	2155	2225	2255	2325
Haywards Heath 185 d.	0620	0616	0641	0646	0716	0716	0746	0816	0846	0916	0946		1546	1616	1646	1647	1716	1746		2146	2216	2246	2316	2346
Gatwick Airport ✈ 185 d.	0636	0636	0655	0706	0732	0736	0802f	0836	0906	0936	1006	and	1606	1636	1706	1706	1736	1806	and	2206	2236	2306	2334	0004
East Croydon 185 d.	0651	0651	0710	0721	0751	0751	0821	0851	0921	0951	1021	at the	1621	1651	1721	1721	1751	1821	at the	2221	2251	2321	2353	0023
London Bridge 185 d.	0706	0705	0724	0735	0806	0805	0835	0905	0935	1005	1035	same	1635	1705	1735	1735	1805	1835	same	2235	2305	2335	|	|
London Blackfriars 185 d.	0712	0712	0732	0742	0812	0812	0842	0912	0942	1012	1042	minutes	1642	1712	1742	1742	1812	1842	minutes	2242	2312	2342	0022	0050
Farringdon 185 d.	0716	0716	0736	0746	0816	0816	0846	0916	0946	1016	1046	past	1646	1716	1746	1746	1816	1846	past	2246	2316	2346	0026	|
London St Pancras 170 d.	0721	0721	0741	0751	0821	0821	0851	0921	0951	1021	1051	each	1651	1721	1751	1751	1821	1851	each	2251	2321	2351	0031	0059
St Albans City d.	0741	0741	0759	0811	|	0841	0911	0941	1011	1041	1111	hour	1711	1741	1811	1809	1841	1910	hour	2316	2346	0016	0056	0134
Luton Airport P ◇ 170 d.	0753	0753	0811	0823	0846	0853	0923	0953	1023	1053	1123	until	1723	1753	1823	|	1853	1922	until	2327	2358	0028	0108	0145
Luton 170 d.	0757	0757	0815	0827	0850	0857	0927	0957	1027	1057	1127		1727	1757	1827	1822	1857	1926		2331	0002	0032	0112	0150
Bedford 170 a.	0821	0821	0835	0851	0918	0921	0951	1021	1051	1121	1151		1751	1822	1851	1843	1922	1952		2356	0026	0056	0136	0214

	⚒		⑦	⑦	⑦	⑦	⑦	⑦	⑦	⑦	⑦	⑦	⑦	⑦	⑦	⑦	⑦		⑦	⑦	⑦	⑦	⑦	⑦	⑦
Brighton 185 d.	2337	⑦	0004	0542	0557	0628	0657	0728	0757	...	0829	0859	0929	0959	1029	1059	1129		2059	2129	2157	2229	2242	2318	2342
Haywards Heath 185 d.	2358		0025	0604	0618	0650	0718	0750	0818	...	0851	0921	0951	1021	1051	1121	1151	and	2121	2151	2218	2251	2304	2334	0004
Gatwick Airport ✈ 185 d.	0017		0042	0622	0636	0705	0736	0805	0836	0830	0906	0936	1006	1036	1106	1136	1216	at the	2136	2206	2236	2306	2321	2351	0021
East Croydon 185 d.	0040		0110	0640	0656	0726	0756	0826	0853	0903	0921	0951	1021	1051	1121	1151	1221	same	2151	2221	2251	2321	2340	0012	0040
London Bridge 185 d.	|		|	0656	0712	0742	0812	0842	0908	0919	0936	1006	1036	1106	1136	1206	1236	minutes	2206	2236	2306	2336	|	|	|
London Blackfriars 185 d.	0106		0136	▬	▬	▬	▬	▬	▬	0926	0942	1012	1042	1112	1142	1212	1242	past	2212	2242	2312	2347	0006	0038	0106
Farringdon 185 d.	|		|	⑦	⑦	⑦	⑦	⑦	⑦	0930	0946	1016	1046	1116	1146	1216	1246	each	2216	2246	2316	2351	0011	|	|
London St Pancras 170 d.	0114		0144	0621	0721	0751	0821	0851	0921	0935	0951	1021	1051	1121	1151	1221	1251	hour	2221	2251	2321	2356	0016	0046	0116
St Albans City d.	0141		0219	0656	0756	0826	0856	0915	0945	0959	1015	1045	1115	1145	1215	1241	1311	until	2241	2313	2347	0022	0051	0121	0141
Luton Airport P ◇ 170 d.	0152		0230	0708	0808	0838	0908	0928	0958	1011	1028	1058	1127	1157	1227	1252	1322		2252	2324	2359	0034	0102	0132	0152
Luton 170 d.	0157		0235	0712	0812	0842	0912	0931	1001	1015	1031	1101	1131	1201	1232	1257	1327		2257	2329	0003	0038	0107	0137	0157
Bedford 170 a.	0221		0259	0736	0836	0906	0936	0955	1025	1039	1055	1125	1155	1225	1256	1322	1352		2322	2353	0027	0102	0131	0201	0221

f – Departs 4–5 minutes later on ⑥.

◇ – Luton Airport Parkway.

♠ – Timings may vary by ± 3 minutes.

☛ Additional trains run Bedford - Gatwick Airport and v.v. Frequent services (operated by SN/GX) also run **London Victoria - Gatwick ✈ - Brighton** and v.v. (4 trains per hour on ⚒, 2 trains per hour on ✝). For other services London Victoria - Gatwick Airport and v.v. see Table **100**.

SW — 🍸 on most trains — LONDON - GUILDFORD - PORTSMOUTH — 105

km			Ⓐ	Ⓐ	Ⓐ	Ⓐ	Ⓐ	Ⓐ	Ⓐ	Ⓐ	Ⓐ	Ⓐ		Ⓐ	Ⓐ	Ⓐ	Ⓐ	Ⓐ	Ⓐ	Ⓐ	Ⓐ	Ⓐ	Ⓐ	Ⓐ	Ⓐ
0	**London** Waterloo 108 d.	Ⓐ	...	0508	0520	0615	0700	0730	0800	0830	0900	0930		1430	1500	1530	1600	1630	1700	1730	1800	1830	1900	1930	2000
39	Woking 108 d.		...	0552	0613	0643	0725	0755	0826	0855	0925	0955	and at	1455	1525	1555	1625	1655	1725	1755	1824	1856	|	1955	2025
49	Guildford d.		0509	0603	0630a	0653	0733	0804	0833	0903	0933	1003	the same	1503	1533	1603	1634	1703	1734	1810	1833	1906	1934	2004	2034
69	Haslemere d.		0524	0628	0655	0720	0753	0824	0854	0924	0952	1021	minutes	1521	1552	1628	1653	1724	1754	1828	1851	1925	1952	2024	2054
88	Petersfield d.		0545	0645	0711	0736	0805	0835	0905	0935	*1013*	1032	past each	1532	1604	1645	1704	1736	1806	1840	1903	1937	2004	2036	*2115*
107	Havant a.		0600	0659	0726	0753	0819	0851	0918	0951	*1027*	1045	hour until	1545	1617	1659	1717	1749	1818	1853	1917	1953	2017	2051	*2129*
118	**Portsmouth** & Southsea a.		0616	0716	0747	0809	0831	0904	0931	1003	*1045*	1057		1557	1629	1719	1730	1803	1831	1906	1929	2006	2030	2104	*2148*
120	**Portsmouth** Harbour a.		0620	0721	0751	0813	0836	0908	0936	1008	...	1102		1602	1636	1725	1736	1809	1838	1912	1938	2012	2034	2108	...

	Ⓐ	Ⓐ	Ⓐ	Ⓐ	Ⓐ	Ⓐ	Ⓐ		⑥	⑥	⑥	⑥	⑥		⑥	⑥	⑥	⑥	⑥	⑥	⑥		⑦	⑦	⑦
London Waterloo 108 d.	2030	2100	2130	2200	2230	2300	2332	⑥	...	0520	0645	0730	0800		2100	2130	2200	2230	2300	2315	2345	⑦	...	0800	0830
Woking 108 d.	2055	2125	2155	2225	2255	2327	0001		...	0613	0713	0755	0825	and at	2125	2155	2225	2255	2327	2344	0014		0732	0835	0904
Guildford d.	2104	2134	2204	2234	2304	2334	0009		0515	0625	0725	0803	0833	the same	2132	2203	2233	2304	2336	2353	0026		0742	0845	0917
Haslemere d.	2122	2154	2224	2254	2323	0005	0034		0530	0650	0749	0821	0853	minutes	2154	2221	2254	2324	2354	0013	0051		0807	0912	0934
Petersfield d.	2133	*2215*	2234	*2315*	2334	0021	0050		0546	0706	0806	0832	0904	past each	2205	2232	2305	2335	0005	0024	0107		0823	0928	0945
Havant a.	2146	*2231*	2246	*2329*	2349	0036	0105		0601	0722	0824	0845	0917	hour until	2218	2245	2318	2348	0018	0036	0122		0838	0943	0958
Portsmouth & Southsea a.	2158	*2247*	2303	*2347*	0002	0052	0120		0617	0738	0848	0857	0930		2231	2257	2330	0001	0030	0049	0138		0853	0958	1010
Portsmouth Harbour a.	2203	*2251*	2307	...	0006	...	0124		0622	0743	0852	0902	0934		2236	2302	2336	0005	0035	0054	...		0857	1004	1014

	⑦	⑦	⑦	⑦		⑦	⑦	⑦	⑦	⑦
London Waterloo 108 d.	0900	0930	1000	1030		2130	2200	2230	2300	2330
Woking 108 d.	0935	1004	1033	1102	and at	2202	2232	2302	2332	0002
Guildford d.	0945	1017	1042	1112	the same	2212	2242	2312	2342	0012
Haslemere d.	1012	1034	1107	1130	minutes	2230	2307	2330	0007	0029
Petersfield d.	1028	1045	1123	1141	past each	2241	2323	2341	0023	0040
Havant a.	1043	1058	1140	1153	hour until	2253	2342	2353	0038	0053
Portsmouth & Southsea a.	1058	1110	1156	1207		2307	2357	0006	0053	0105
Portsmouth Harbour a.	1104	1114	1200	1213		2311	0001	0010	0058	0109

		Ⓐ	Ⓐ	Ⓐ	Ⓐ	Ⓐ	Ⓐ	Ⓐ	Ⓐ	Ⓐ
Portsmouth Harbour d.	Ⓐ	0425	0511	0550	0615	0640	0713	0745	0815	0845
Portsmouth & Southsea d.		0430	0516	0555	0620	0645	0718	0750	0820	0850
Havant d.		0446	0529	0611	0634	0659	0732	0804	0834	0904
Petersfield d.		0503	0543	0628	0648	0714	0747	0818	0848	0918
Haslemere d.		0521	0558	0648	0702	0734	0801	0832	0902	0932
Guildford d.		0550	0624	0709	0718	0753	0819	0853	0919	0951
Woking 108 a.		0600	0635	0717	0725	|	0826	|	0927	0959
London Waterloo 108 a.		0630	0709	0746	0753	0831	0854	0930	0955	1029

	Ⓐ	Ⓐ	Ⓐ	Ⓐ	Ⓐ	✣	Ⓐ	Ⓐ	Ⓐ	Ⓐ	Ⓐ	Ⓐ	Ⓐ	Ⓐ	Ⓐ	Ⓐ	Ⓐ	Ⓐ	Ⓐ	Ⓐ	Ⓐ	Ⓐ	Ⓐ	Ⓐ		⑥
Portsmouth Harbour d.	...	0919	0945	...	...		...	...	1445	1515	1545	1615	1645	1715	1745	1815	1845	1915	1945	2019	2119	2219	2319	⑥	0436f
Portsmouth & Southsea d.	...	0924	0950	...	1024		...	1424	1450	1520	1550	1619	1650	1719	1750	1820	1849	1919	1950	2024	2124	2224	2324		0440f
Havant d.	...	0940	1003	...	1040	and at	...	1440	1503	1533	1604	1634	1704	1734	1804	1835	1903	1934	2003	2040	2140	2240	2340		0456f
Petersfield d.	...	0956	1017	...	1056	the same	...	1456	1517	1547	1618	1648	1718	1748	1818	1849	1917	1948	2017	2056	2156	2257	2357		0513f
Haslemere d.	1002	1014	1030	1102	1114	minutes	1502	1514	1530	1600	1637	1702	1737	1802	1832	1902	1930	2002	2031	2114	2214	2315	0015		0536
Guildford d.	1019	1035	1049	1119	1135	past each	1519	1535	1549	1621	1701	1719	1801	1822	1853	1923t	1949	2018	2049	2139	2237	2339	0037		0601
Woking 108 a.	1026	1045	1057	1126	1145	hour until	1526	1545	1556	1629	1711	1726	1811	1833	1904	|	1956	2026	2057	2157	2247	2351	...		0611
London Waterloo 108 a.	1052	1114	1124	1153	1216		1555	1616	1624	1701	1744	1759	1843	1859	1929	1959	2027	2051	2129	2227	2316	0032	...		0640

	⑥	⑥	⑥	⑥	⊠	⑥	⑥	⑥	⑥	⑥		⑦	⑦	⑦	⑦	⑦	⑦	⑦	⑦	⑦	⊠	⑦	⑦	⑦
Portsmouth Harbour d.	0515f	0615	0645	0715		2015	2045	2119	2219	2319	⑦	0643r	0728r	0743r	0828r	0848	0932	0948	1032	1048		2148	2232	2248
Portsmouth & Southsea d.	0520f	0620	0650	0720		2020	2050	2124	2224	2324		0648r	0733r	0747r	0833r	0852	0937	0952	1037	1052		2152	2237	2252
Havant d.	0536f	0634	0703	0734	and at	2034	2103	2140	2240	2340		0702r	0746r	0802r	0846r	0907	0950	1007	1050	1107	and at	2207	2250	2307
Petersfield d.	0552f	0648	0717	0748	the same	2048	2117	2156	2257	2357		0719r	0800r	0819r	0900r	0924	1004	1024	1104	1124	the same	2224	2304	2324
Haslemere d.	0613	0702	0730	0802	minutes	2102	2130	2214	2315	0015		0739	0814	0839	0915	0942	1017	1042	1117	1142	minutes	2242	2317	2342
Guildford d.	0639	0719	0749	0819	past each	2119	2149	2237	2340	0037		0803	0835	0903	0933	1005	1035	1105	1135	1205	past each	2305	2335	0005
Woking 108 a.	0649	|	0756	0826	hour until	2126	2158	2247	2351	...		0813	0842	0915	0942	1015	1042	1114	1144	1214	hour until	2314	2342	0013
London Waterloo 108 a.	0718	0804	0824	0854		2152	2228	2316	0030	...		0851	0923	0953	1019	1050	1122	1150	1217	1244		2344	0021	...

a – Arrives 0623.

f – Departs 4–5 minutes later until Oct. 8.

r – Departs 4–5 minutes later until Oct. 2.

t – Arrives 1918.

✣ – The 1402 from Haslemere arrives London Waterloo at 1457.

⊠ – Arrivals at London Waterloo may vary ± 4 minutes.

106 LONDON - SOUTHAMPTON - BOURNEMOUTH - WEYMOUTH

🍸 on most trains. SW

km	Ⓐ	①	①🚌	Ⓐ	Ⓐ	Ⓐ	Ⓐ	Ⓐ	Ⓐ	Ⓐ	Ⓐ	Ⓐ	Ⓐ	Ⓐ	Ⓐ		Ⓐ	Ⓐ	Ⓐ	Ⓐ	Ⓐ	Ⓐ	Ⓐ	Ⓐ	Ⓐ
0	**London** Waterloo .. 108 d.	0010	0105	...	...	...	0530	...	...	0630	0703	0735	0805	0835	0905		1505	1535	1605	1635	1705	1735	1805	1835	1905
39	Woking .... 108 d.	0042	|	...	...	...	0601	...	...	0657	0730	0800	|	0900	|	and	|	1600	|	1659u	|	|	|	|	|
77	Basingstoke .... 108 114 d.	0101	0317s	...	...	...	0621	...	...	0718	0750	0820	0849	|	0948	at	1549	|	1648	|	1746	1817	1846	1917	1948
107	Winchester .... 114 d.	0118	0352s	...	...	...	0638	...	...	0735	0807	0837	0906	0932	1005	the	1605	1633	1706	1733	1803	1833	1903	1934	2005
120	**Southampton** ✈ ... 114 d.	0132	0416s	...	...	...	0653	...	...	0750	0818	0851	0914	0941	1014	same	1614	1642	1715	1742	1811	1842	1911	1943	2014
128	**Southampton** Cen 114 d.	0140	0435	...	...	0622	0702	...	0730	0759	0827	0900	0925	0951	1024	minutes	1626	1653	1725	1753	1822	1853	1922	1953	2025
149	Brockenhurst .... 114 d.	...	...	...	0610*	0641	0718	...	0757	0820	0844	0914	0939	1005	1038	past	1640	1709	1740	1808	|	|	|	|	2041
174	**Bournemouth** .... 114 d.	...	...	0606*	0639*	0709	0746	0811	0817	0847	0911	0933f	1004	1024	1104	each	1702	1725	1757	1826	1850	1922	1950	2022	2101
183	Poole .... d.	...	...	0620*	0652*	0721*	0758	0824	0828	0900	0923	0945	1014	1037	1114	hour	1717	1738	1807	1838	1903	1935	2003	2038	2113
193	Wareham .... d.	...	...	0635	0706*	0735*	0812	0838	...	0912	0937	0957	1028	1049	1128	until	1730	1750	1821	1850	1917	1947	2017	2049	2126
219	Dorchester South .... d.	...	...	0656	0730	0757	0833	0858	...	0933	0957	1013	1054f	1105	1149		1751	1809	1849	1909	1937	2004	2037	2107	2147
230	**Weymouth** .... a.	...	...	0709	0742	0810	0844	0909	...	0944	1008	1023	1106	1116	1202		1802	1818	1900	1923	1950	2015	2050	2117	2159

	Ⓐ	Ⓐ	Ⓐ	Ⓐ	Ⓐ	Ⓐ	⑥	⑥	⑥	⑥	⑥	⑥	⑥	⑥	⑥	⑥	⑥	⑥	⑥		⑥	⑥	⑥	⑥	⑥
London Waterloo .. 108 d.	1935	2005	2035	2135	2235	2335	0105	...	...	...	...	0530	...	0630	...	0735	0805	0835	0905		1835	1905	1935	2005	2035
Woking .... 108 d.	2000	|	2100	2200	2300	0004	0142	...	...	...	...	0603	...	0657	...	0800	|	0900	|	and	1900	|	2000	|	2100
Basingstoke ..... 108 114 d.	|	2049	|	|	|	0035	0209s	0510	...	...	...	0624	...	0718	...	0821	0849	|	0948	at	|	1949	|	2049	|
Winchester .... 114 d.	2032	2105	2133	2233	2333	0051	0226s	0526	...	...	...	0643	...	0734	...	0838	0905	0933	1005	the	1933	2006	2033	2105	2133
Southampton ✈ ... 114 d.	2041	2114	2142	2242	2342	0105	0239s	0540	...	...	...	0656	...	0748	...	0851	0914	0942	1014	same	1942	2014	2042	2114	2142
Southampton Cen 114 d.	2051	2125	2151	2251	2353	0113	0249	0549	...	...	0621	0705	0721	0800	0817	0900	0924	0951	1024	minutes	1951	2024	2051	2124	2151
Brockenhurst .... 114 d.	2108	2142	2205	2310	0007	0129s	...	...	...	0615	0640	0722	0740	0817	0838	0917	0938	1005	1038	past	2005	2038	2105	2143	2205
Bournemouth .... 114 d.	2127	2208	2224	2328	0023	0152	...	...	0606*	0644	0711f	0749	0811f	0844	0909f	0944	1004	1024	1104	each	2024	2104	2124	2212	2224
Poole .... d.	2139	...	2237	2341	0035	...	...	...	0619*	0657	0724	0802	0824	0857	0922	0957	1014	1037	1114	hour	2037	2114	2137	2226	2237
Wareham .... d.	2151	...	2249	2353	...	...	...	...	0633*	0711	0738	0813	0838	0909	0935	1009	1028	1049	1128	until	2049	2126	2149	...	2249
Dorchester South .... d.	2212	...	2309	0013	...	...	...	...	0656	0731	0758	0834	0858	0929	0956	1027	1051	1105	1149		2105	2151	2209	...	2309
Weymouth .... a.	2223	...	2320	0024	...	...	...	...	0709	0744	0811	0845	0909	0940	1007	1035	1102	1115	1201		2113	2202	2220	...	2320

	⑥	⑥	⑥	⑥	⑥	⑦	⑦	⑦	⑦	⑦	⑦	⑦	⑦	♥	⑦	⑦	⑦	⑦		⑦	⑦	⑦	⑦	⑦
London Waterloo .. 108 d.	2105	2135	2205	2235	2305	0010	0105	...	...	...	0753	0835	0853		1435	1454	1535	1605		2035	2105	2135	2205	2305
Woking .... 108 d.	2132	2200	2232	2300	2332	0040	0149	...	...	...	0828	0907	0928	and	1507	1528	1607	1637	and	2107	2137	2207	2237	2337
Basingstoke ..... 108 114 d.	2151	|	2252	|	2352	0100	0216s	...	0748	...	0848	0927	0947	at	1527	1547	1627	1657	at	2127	2157	2227	2257	2357
Winchester .... 114 d.	2208	2233	2308	2333	0011	0116	0233s	...	0807	...	0908	0944	1007	the	1544	1607	1644	1714	the	2144	2214	2244	2314	0014
Southampton ✈ ... 114 d.	2220	2242	2323	2342	0026	0129	0246s	...	0825	...	0927	0953	1025	same	1553	1625	1653	1727	same	2153	2227	2253	2327	0028
Southampton Cen 114 d.	2229	2251	2332	2351	0037	0138	0256	...	0834	0903	0935	1003	1033	minutes	1603	1634	1703	1736	minutes	2203	2236	2303	2336	0040
Brockenhurst .... 114 d.	2248	2305	2351	0005	0053s	0154s	...	...	0855	0917	0957	1017	1055	past	1617	1655	1717	1757	past	2217	2257	2317	2355	0056s
Bournemouth .... 114 d.	2317	2327	0018	0023	0117	0219	...	0839	0924	0939f	1024	1039f	1122	each	1639f	1723	1739f	1824	each	2239f	2324	2339f	0022	0120
Poole .... d.	2330	2340	0030	0036	0128	...	...	0851	0933	0951	1033	1051	1133	hour	1651	1732	1751	1833	hour	2251	2333	2351	0034	0132
Wareham .... d.	...	2351	...	...	...	...	...	0903	...	1003	...	1103	...	until	1703	...	1803	...	until	2303	...	0003	...	...
Dorchester South .... d.	...	0012	...	...	...	...	...	0924	...	1024	...	1124	...		1724	...	1824	...		2324	...	0024	...	...
Weymouth .... a.	...	0023	...	...	...	...	...	0935	...	1035	...	1135	...		1735	...	1837	...		2336	...	0035	...	...

Ⓐ	Ⓐ	Ⓐ	Ⓐ	Ⓐ	Ⓐ	Ⓐ	Ⓐ	Ⓐ	Ⓐ	Ⓐ	Ⓐ	Ⓐ	Ⓐ	♠	Ⓐ	Ⓐ	Ⓐ	Ⓐ	Ⓐ	Ⓐ	Ⓐ	Ⓐ	Ⓐ	Ⓐ	Ⓐ
Weymouth .... a.	...	...	...	0550*	0620*	0651*	...	0725	0755	0820	0903	0920	1003		1503	1520	1603	1620	1703	1720	1803	1820	1903	1920	1959
Dorchester South .... d.	...	...	...	0602*	0632*	0703*	...	0737	0807	0833	0913	0933	1013	and	1513	1533	1613	1633	1713	1733	1813	1833	1913	1937f	2011
Wareham .... d.	...	...	...	0622*	0652*	0723*	...	0757	0827	0853	0928	0953	1028	at	1528	1553	1628	1653	1728	1753	1828	1853	1928	1957	2028
Poole .... d.	0457	0539	...	0638	0708	0738	0755	0811	0841	0907	0940	1007	1040	the	1540	1607	1640	1707	1740	1807	1840	1907	1940	2009	2040
Bournemouth .... 114 d.	0512	0554	0601	0653	0723	0756f	0810	0825	0859f	0922f	0959f	1022f	1059f	same	1559f	1622f	1659f	1722	1759	1822f	1859f	1922f	1959f	2022	2059f
Brockenhurst .... 114 d.	0534	0611	0630	|	|	0811	0840	0852	0914	0944	1014	1044	1114	minutes	1614	1644	1714	1744	1814	1844	1914	1944	2014	2044	2114
Southampton Cen 114 d.	0555	0630	0700t	0730f	0800	0830	0900	...	0930	1000	1030	1100	1130	past	1630	1700	1730	1800	1830	1900	1930	2000	2030	2100	2130
Southampton ✈ ... 114 d.	0603	0638	0708	0738	0808	0838	0908	...	0938	1008	1038	1108	1138	each	1638	1708	1738	1808	1838	1908	1938	2008	2038	2108	2138
Winchester .... 114 d.	0618	0648	0718	0748	0818	0848	0918	...	0948	1018	1048	1118	1148	hour	1648	1718	1748	1818	1848	1918	1948	2018	2048	2118	2148
Basingstoke ..... 108 114 a.	0635	|	|	|	0834	|	0936	...	|	1034	|	1135	|	until	|	1734	|	1834	|	1934	|	2034	|	2134	|
Woking .... 108 a.	0654	|	|	|	0853	0922	0955	...	1021	|	1120	|	1220		1720	|	1820	|	1925	|	2021	|	2122	2153	2223
London Waterloo .. 108 a.	0725	0748	0817	0851	0926	0953	1024	...	1049	1120	1149	1220	1249		1750	1820	1849	1920	1951	2020	2049	2127	2151	2222	2249

	Ⓐ	Ⓐ	Ⓐ	Ⓐ	⑥	⑥	⑥	⑥	⑥	⑥	⑥	⑥	⑥	⑥	⑥	♠	⑥	⑥	⑥	⑥	⑥	⑥	⑥	⑥	⑥	⑥
Weymouth .... a.	2007	2100	2210	2310		...	...	...	...	0538*	0615*	0650*	0720	0803	0820		1803	1820	1903	1920	...	2010	2058	...	2210	2310
Dorchester South .... d.	2021	2112	2223	2322		...	...	...	...	0548*	0628*	0707	0733	0813	0833	and	1813	1833	1913	1933	...	2022	2110	...	2222	2322
Wareham .... d.	2042	2132	2242	2342		...	...	...	...	0606*	0648*	0727	0753	0828	0853	at	1828	1853	1928	1953	...	2042	2130	...	2242	2342
Poole .... d.	2054	2144	2354	2354		...	...	...	0524	0621	0704	0741	0807	0840	0907	the	1840	1907	1940	2007	...	2054	2142	...	2254	2354
Bournemouth .... 114 d.	2112f	2212c	2307	0003		...	...	...	0540	0640f	0719f	0759f	0822f	0858f	0922f	same	1859f	1922f	1959f	2022f	2059	2112f	2159f	2212	2312f	0003
Brockenhurst .... 114 d.	2139	2239	...	...		...	...	...	0608	0708	0741	0814	0844	0914	0944	minutes	1914	1944	2014	2044	2114	2139	2214	2239	2339	...
Southampton Cen 114 d.	2200	2300	...	...		0509	0527	0600	0630	0730	0800	0830	0900	0929	1000	past	1930	2000	2030	2100	2130	2200	2230	2300	2359	...
Southampton ✈ ... 114 d.	2208	2308	...	...		0517	0539	0608	0638	0738	0808	0838	0908	0938	1008	each	1938	2008	2038	2108	2138	2208	2238	2308	0010	...
Winchester .... 114 d.	2224	2324	...	...		0531	0558	0623	0651	0748	0818	0848	0918	0948	1018	hour	1948	2018	2048	2118	2148	2223	2256	2325	...	...
Basingstoke ..... 108 114 a.	2240	2324	...	...		0550	0618	0639	0707	|	0834	|	0935	|	1034	until	|	2034	|	2134	|	2239	2312	2343	...	...
Woking .... 108 a.	2259	0018	...	...		0628	0658	0659	0726	0821	|	0920	|	1020	|		2020	|	2120	2154	2219	2259	2332	0018	...	...
London Waterloo .. 108 a.	2331	...	...	...		0706	0734	0732	0752	0849	0920	0949	1020	1049	1120		2051	2120	2149	2223	2249	2331	0011	0104	...	...

⑦	⑦	⑦	⑦	⑦	⑦		⑦	⑦	⑦	⑦		⑦	⑦	⑦	⑦		⑦	⑦	⑦	⑦	⑦	⑦	⑦	⑦
Weymouth .... a.	...	...	...	...	0743*	...	...	0843*	...	0948		1248	...	1348	...		1745	...	1848	...	1958	2058	2158	2258
Dorchester South .... d.	...	...	...	...	0757	...	...	0857	...	1000	and	1300	...	1400	...	and	1800f	...	1900	...	2010	2110	2210	2310
Wareham .... d.	...	...	...	...	0817	...	...	0917	...	1020	at	1320	...	1420	...	at	1820	...	1920	...	2030	2130	2230	2330
Poole .... d.	...	...	0718	0747	0829	...	0852	0929	0955	1032	the	1332	1355	1432	1455	the	1832	1855	1932	1955	2050j	2150j	2250j	2350j
Bournemouth .... 114 d.	...	...	0733	0803	0847f	...	0903	0951	1006	1050	same	1350	1406	1450	1506	same	1850	1906	1950	2006	2106	2208f	2308f	0003
Brockenhurst .... 114 d.	...	...	0800	0830	0906	...	0930	1009	1033	1109	minutes	1409	1433	1509	1533	minutes	1909	1933	2009	2033	2133	2235	2336	...
Southampton Cen 114 d.	0655	0755	0826	0855	0925	...	0955	1025	1055	1125	past	1425	1455	1525	1555	past	1925	1955	2025	2055	2155	2255	2355	...
Southampton ✈ ... 114 d.	0703	0803	0834	0903	0933	...	1003	1033	1103	1133	each	1433	1503	1533	1603	each	1933	2003	2033	2103	2203	2303	...	...
Winchester .... 114 d.	0723	0823	0843	0923	0942	...	1023	1042	1123	1142	hour	1442	1523	1542	1617	hour	1942	2017	2042	2117	2217	2323	...	...
Basingstoke ..... 108 114 a.	0742	0844	0901	0942	0958	...	1042	1058	1142	1158	until	1458	1542	1558	1633	until	1958	2033	2058	2133	2234	2342	...	...
Woking .... 108 a.	0802	0903	0928	1002	1019	...	1102	1118	1203	1218		1518	1602	1618	1653		2018	2053	2118	2153	2254	0002	...	...
London Waterloo .. 108 a.	0846	0943	1015	1043	1053	...	1141	1154	1237	1249		1549	1637	1649	1725		2049	2124	2149	2224	2324	0033	...	...

Brockenhurst - Lymington Pier (for ⛴ to Isle of Wight).
Journey 11 minutes. Trains call at Lymington Town 6 minutes later:
Ⓐ: 0559 and every 30 minutes until 0929, 1012 and every 30 minutes until 1612, 1644, 1714, 1744, 1814, 1848 and every 30 minutes until 2218.
⑥: 0612, 0642 and every 30 minutes until 2112, 2148, 2218.
⑦: 0859, 0929 and every 30 minutes until 2059, 2129, 2159.

Lymington Pier - Brockenhurst.
Journey 11 minutes. Trains call at Lymington Town 2 minutes later:
Ⓐ: 0614 and every 30 minutes until 0944, 1027 and every 30 minutes until 1627, 1659, 1729, 1759, 1829, 1903 and every 30 minutes until 2203, 2236.
⑥: 0627, 0657 and every 30 minutes until 2127, 2203, 2236.
⑦: 0914, 0944 and every 30 minutes until 2114, 2144, 2214.

c – Arrives 2157.
f – Arrives 4–6 minutes earlier.
j – Arrives 8 minutes earlier.
s – Calls to set down only.
t – Arrives 0651.
u – Calls to pick up only.
♠ – Arrivals into London Waterloo may be up to 4 minutes later than shown.
♥ – Some departures may by up to 3 minutes later.
* – Departs 4–5 minutes later until Oct. 8.

☛ For ⛴ services Portsmouth / Poole – Jersey / Guernsey / St Malo and v.v., see Table **2100**.

107 PORTSMOUTH - RYDE - SHANKLIN

2nd class IL

Through fares including ferry are available. Allow 10 minutes for connections between trains and ferries. Operator: Wightlink ✆ 0333 999 7333. www.wightlink.co.uk

Portsmouth Harbour - Ryde Pierhead: ⛴
0515Ⓐ, 0615Ⓐ, 0715 and hourly until 1815, 1920, 2020 (not 1115 and 1415 on Ⓐ).

Ryde Pierhead - Portsmouth Harbour: Journey: ± 22 minutes
0545Ⓐ, 0645Ⓐ, 0745 and hourly until 1845, 1947, 2052 (not 1145 and 1445 on Ⓐ).

Additional services may operate on Ⓐ and on public holidays.

Ryde Pierhead - Shanklin (trains call at Ryde Esplanade 2 minutes later and Sandown 18 minutes later): *14 km*
0545⚒, 0645, 0745, 0845, 0945*, 1045*, 1145* **a**, 1245*, 1345*, 1445* **a**, 1545*, 1645, 1745, 1845, 1949, 2049, 2149.
Additional services operate from Ryde Esplanade - Shanklin on ⚒ at: 0614Ⓐ, 0714Ⓐ, 0814Ⓐ, 1014⑥, 1114⑥, 1214⑥, 1145* **b**, 1445* **b**, 1615, 1714, 1814.

Shanklin - Ryde Pierhead (trains call at Sandown ± 5 minutes later and Ryde Esplanade ± 22 minutes later): Journey: ± 24 minutes
0615⚒, 0715, 0815, 0915, 1015*, 1115* **a**, 1215*, 1315*, 1415* **a**, 1515*, 1615*, 1715, 1815, 1915, 2019, 2119, 2242.
Additional services operate from Shanklin - Ryde Esplanade on ⚒ at: 0648Ⓐ, 0748Ⓐ, 0848Ⓐ, 1048⑥, 1117* **b**, 1148⑥, 1417* **b**, 1548* Ⓐ, 1648, 1748, 1848.

a – Ⓒ (daily from Nov. 5).
b – Ⓐ until Nov. 4.
* – Also calls at Smallbrook Junction (connection with **Isle of Wight Steam Railway**, see note △) 9 minutes from Ryde / 15 minutes from Shanklin, when Steam Railway is operating.
△ – **Isle of Wight Steam Railway** (🚂 Smallbrook Junction - Haven Street - Wootton: *9 km*). ✆ 01983 882204. www.iwsteamrailway.co.uk

SW 🍷 on most services London - Axminster and v.v. LONDON - SALISBURY - EXETER 108

km			⚒	Ⓐ	⑥	Ⓐ	⑥	Ⓐ	⑥	⑥	Ⓐ	⑥	Ⓐ	Ⓐ	⚒	⑥F	⚒	Ⓐ	⚒	⑥	Ⓐ	⚒	⚒	⚒	⚒	⚒
0	**London** Waterloo 106 d.	⚒	...	...	...	...	...	...	...	0635	0635	0710	0710	0750	0820	0850	0920	...	1020	1050	...	1120	1150j	1220	1250j	1320
39	Woking 106 d.		...	...	...	...	...	...	...	0701	0702	0736	0736	0817	0846	0916	0946	...	1046	1116	...	1146	1216j	1246	1316j	1346
77	Basingstoke 106 d.		...	...	...	...	...	...	...	0723	0724	0759	0800	0838	0906	0938	1007	1038	1107	1138	1137	1207	1238	1307	1338	1407
107	Andover d.		...	...	...	...	...	...	...	0745	0747	0821	0822	0900	0924	1000	1024	1100	1124	1200	1159	1224	1300	1324	1400	1424
134	**Salisbury** a.		...	...	...	...	...	...	...	0805	0806	0842	0843	0920	0943	1020	1043	1119	1144	1220	1218	1243	1320	1344	1420	1443
134	**Salisbury** 140 d.		...	...	...	0610	0615	0738	0747	0813	0808	0847	0847	0924	0947	...	1047	1124	1147	▬	1222	1247	...	1347	▬	1447
169	Gillingham d.		...	0551	...	0642	0642	0811	0814	0900b	0837	0917	0917	|	1017	...	1117	|	1217	...	|	1317	...	1417	...	1517
190	Sherborne d.		...	0606	...	0657	0657	0826	0829	0915	...	0932	0932	◧	1032	...	1132	◧	1232	...	◧	1332	...	1432	...	1532
197	**Yeovil** Junction a.		...	0612	...	0703	0703	0832	0835	0920	...	0938	0938	|	1038	...	1138	1300g	1238	Ⓐ	1400g	1338	...	1438	Ⓐ	1538
197	**Yeovil** Junction 139 d.		...	0615	0615	0707	0707	0839	0839	...	...	0939	0942	|	1039	...	1139	|	1239	1317	|	1339	...	1439	1451	1539
200	**Yeovil** Pen Mill 139 a.		...	|	|	|	|	|	|	...	...	|	|	1038	|	...	|	1253	|	1322	1352	|	...	|	1456	|
211	Crewkerne d.		...	0624	0624	0716	0716	0849	0849	...	...	0949	0951	...	1049	...	1149	...	1249	...	...	1349	...	1449	...	1549
233	Axminster d.		0550	0657a	0657a	0737	0738	0903	0903	...	...	1003	1006	...	1103	...	1203	...	1303	...	...	1403	...	1503	...	1603
249	Honiton d.		0604	0712	0712	0752	0754t	0916	0916	...	...	1016	1018	...	1116	...	1216	...	1316	...	...	1416	...	1515	...	1616
277	**Exeter** St Davids △ a.		0632	0742	0742	0822	0823	0944	0944	...	...	1042	1043	...	1144	...	1243	...	1343	...	...	1443	...	1543	...	1643

	Ⓐ	⚒	⚒	Ⓐ	⑥	Ⓐ	⑥	Ⓐ	ⒶW	Ⓐ	⑥	Ⓐ	⑥	⑥	Ⓐ	Ⓐ	⑥	Ⓐ	⑥	Ⓐ	Ⓐ	⑥	Ⓐ	Ⓐ	⑥	⑥
London Waterloo 106 d.	...	1420	1450j	1520	1520	...	1620	1621	1650	1720	1720	1750	1750	1820	1820	...	1920	1920	2020	2020	2120	2120	...	2220	2220	2339
Woking 106 d.	...	1446	1516j	1546	1546	...	1646	1647u	1716u	1746u	1746	|	1816	1846	1846u	...	1946	1946u	2046	2046	2146	2146	...	2246	2246	0008
Basingstoke 106 d.	1438	1507	1538	1607	1607	1638	1707	1707	1738	1807	1807	1838	1838	1907	1907	1939	2007	2007	2107	2107	2207	2207	2237	2308	2308	0029
Andover d.	1500	1524	1600	1624	1624	1700	1724	1730	1800	1830	1824	1900	1900	1924	1930	2001	2024	2030	2124	2129	2229	2229	2300	2330	2330	0051
Salisbury a.	1520	1545	1620	1644	1642	1721	1742	1750	1821	1850	1843	1920	1920	1943	1950	2021	2045	2050	2144	2148	2249	2248	2322	2349	2350	0111
Salisbury 140 d.	1525	1547	...	1647	1647	1723	1747	1754	1823	1854	1847	1924	1927	1947	1954	2024	2047	2054	2148	2150	...	2255	...	2349	...	...
Gillingham d.	1548	1617	...	1717	1717	1752t	1817	1819	1852t	1920	1919	1954t	|	2017	2020	2051	2117	2119	2217	2218	...	2319s	...	0015s	...	...
Sherborne d.	...	1632	...	1732	1732	1807	1832	1834	1907	1935	1934	2009	◧	2032	2035	2106	2132	2134	2232	2233	...	2334s	...	0030s	...	...
Yeovil Junction a.	...	1638	...	1738	1738	1813	1838	1840	1912	1940	1939	2014	2045g	2038	2040	2112	2138	2139	2238	2239	...	2340	...	0036	...	...
Yeovil Junction 139 d.	...	1639	...	1739	1739	...	1839	1841	1917	1941	1941	2019	|	2039	2041	2117	2139	2142	2239	2240	...	...	...	...	...	...
Yeovil Pen Mill 139 a.	...	|	...	|	|	...	|	|	1924	|	|	2026	2037	|	|	2124	|	|	|	|	...	...	...	...	...	...
Crewkerne d.	...	1649	...	1749	1749	...	1849	1850	...	1951	1950	...	...	2049	2051	...	2149	2152	2249	2250	...	...	...	...	...	...
Axminster d.	...	1703	...	1804	1803	...	1903	1905	...	2005	2005	...	...	2103	2105	...	2203	2206	2303	2305	...	...	...	...	...	...
Honiton d.	...	1716	...	1816	1816	...	1916	1918	...	2017	2016	...	...	2117	2117	...	2217	2218	2315	2338r	...	...	...	...	...	...
Exeter St Davids △ a.	...	1743	...	1844	1842	...	1942	1944	...	2044	2045	...	...	2142	2143	...	2245	2244	...	0005	...	...	...	...	...	...

	①–④	⑤		⑦	⑦	⑦	⑦	⑦	⑦	⑦	⑦	⑦	⑦	⑦	⑦	⑦	⑦	⑦	⑦	⑦	⑦	⑦	⑦	⑦e	⑦	⑦
London Waterloo 106 d.	2340	2340	⑦	...	...	...	0815	0915	1015	1115	1215	...	1315	1415	...	1520	1620	1720	1745	1820	1845	1920	2020	2120	2220	2335
Woking 106 d.	0009	0009		...	...	...	0847	0948	1046	1146	1246	...	1345	1446	...	1546	1646	1746	1813	1846	1913	1946	2046	2146	2246	0008
Basingstoke 106 d.	0029	0029		...	0804	...	0908	1009	1107	1207	1307	1331	1407	1507	1531	1607	1707	1807	1834	1907	1934	2007	2107	2207	2307	0040
Andover d.	0051	0051		...	0826	...	0925	1026	1124	1224	1324	1354	1424	1524	1553	1624	1724	1824	1856	1924	1956	2024	2124	2224	2329	0103
Salisbury a.	0111	0111		...	0846	...	0942	1042	1142	1242	1343	1414	1442	1540	1613	1646	1742	1842	1917	1943	2017	2042	2143	2242	2348	0122
Salisbury 140 d.	...	0114		0654	0847	...	0947	1047	1147	1247	1347	1419	1447	1547	1614	1647	1747	1847	...	1947	...	2047	2147	2247	...	...
Gillingham d.	...	0137s		0717	0917	...	1018	1117	1217	1317	1417	1451c	1517	1617	1643	1717	1817	1917	...	2017	...	2117	2218	2318	...	...
Sherborne d.	...	0153s		0732	0932	...	1033	1132	1232	1332	1432	1506	1532	1632	...	1732	1832	1932	...	2032	...	2132	2233	2333	...	...
Yeovil Junction a.	...	0159		0738	0938	...	1038	1138	1238	1338	1438	1511	1538	1638	...	1738	1838	1938	...	2038	...	2138	2238	2338	...	...
Yeovil Junction 139 d.	...	...		0739	0939	0945	1039	1139	1239	1339	1439	1516	1539	1639	...	1739	1839	1940	...	2039	...	2139	...	2339	...	...
Yeovil Pen Mill 139 a.	...	...		|	|	0950	|	|	|	|	|	1521	|	|	...	|	|	|	...	|	...	|	...	|	...	...
Crewkerne d.	...	...		0749	0949	...	1049	1149	1249	1349	1449	...	1549	1649	...	1749	1849	1950	...	2049	...	2149	...	2349	...	...
Axminster d.	...	...		0804	1003	...	1103	1203	1303	1403	1503	...	1603	1703	...	1803	1903	2004	...	2103	...	2204	...	0009	...	...
Honiton d.	...	...		0817	1016	...	1116	1216	1316	1416	1516	...	1616	1716	...	1816	1916	2017	...	2117	...	2217	...	0020s	...	...
Exeter St Davids △ a.	...	...		0845	1044	...	1142	1242	1342	1442	1542	...	1642	1741	...	1842	1942	2043	...	2143	...	2244	...	0047	...	...

		Ⓐ	Ⓐ	Ⓐ	⑥	⑥	Ⓐ	Ⓐ	Ⓐ	⑥	Ⓐ	⑥C	Ⓐ	⑥	Ⓐ	⚒	⑥	⚒	⚒	Ⓐ	⚒E	⚒	⚒	Ⓐ	⚒	Ⓐ
Exeter St Davids ▽ d.	⚒	...	...	0510	0510	...	...	...	...	...	0640	0640	0725	0725	...	0823	...	0925	...	...	1025	...	1125	...	1225	...
Honiton d.		...	...	0541	0541	0620	0620	...	...	...	0712	0713	0752	0755	...	0855	...	0955	...	...	1055	...	1155	...	1255	...
Axminster d.		...	...	0553	0552	0631	0631	...	...	...	0724	0724	0804	0806	...	0906	...	1006	...	...	1106	...	1206	...	1306	...
Crewkerne d.		...	...	0606	0605	0644	0644	...	...	...	0737	0737	0817	0819	...	0919	...	1019	...	...	1119	...	1219	...	1319	...
Yeovil Pen Mill 139 d.		...	0541	|	|	|	|	0655	0711	...	|	|	|	|	...	|	...	|	...	1044	|	...	|	1255	|	1324
Yeovil Junction 139 a.		..	0546	0615	0614	0653	0653	|	0716	...	0745	0746	0825	0828	...	0929	...	1028	...	|	1128	...	1228	1300	1328	|
Yeovil Junction d.		0511v	0550	0620	0620	0654	0654	|	0720	...	0750	0753	0829	0829	...	0929	0953	1029	...	|	1129	...	1229	▬	1329	1317f
Sherborne d.		0517v	0556	0626	0626	0700	0700	◧	0726	...	0756	0759	0835	0835	...	0935	0959	1035	...	◧	1135	...	1235	...	1335	◧
Gillingham d.		0533v	0612	0642	0642	0717	0716	|	0742	...	0812	0817	0851	0851	0918	0951	1017	1051	...	|	1151	...	1251	...	1351	|
Salisbury 140 a.		0601	0639	0707	0707	0742	0741	0812	0806	...	0837	0842	0917	0916	0943	1017	1042	1116	...	1209	1217	...	1317	⚒	1417	1443
Salisbury d.		0606	0645	0715	0721	0746	0745	0815	0815	0821	0846	0847	0921	0921	0947	1021	1047	1121	1147	1221	1221	1247	1321	1347	1421	1447
Andover d.		0626	0705	0735	0738	0806	0805	0835	0835	0838	0906	0906	0938	0938	1006	1038	1106	1138	1206	1238	1238	1306	1338	1406	1438	1506
Basingstoke 106 d.		0651	0730	0759	0758	0830	0828	0859	0859	0857	0928	0930	0957	0957	1029	1057	1130	1157	1230	1257	1257	1330	1357	1429	1457	1530
Woking 106 d.		|	|	0819	0818	0850	...	0919	0919	0916	...	0950	1017	1016	...	1116	1150	1216	1250j	1316	1316	1350j	1416	1450j	1516	1550
London Waterloo 106 a.		0737	0814	0846	0849	0919	...	0953	0953	0949	...	1019	1049	1049	...	1149	1219	1249	1319j	1349	1349	1419j	1449	1519j	1549	1618

	Ⓐ	⚒	⚒	Ⓐ	⚒	⑥	Ⓐ	⚒	⚒	⑥	Ⓐ	⚒	⑥	Ⓐ	Ⓐ	Ⓐ	⑥	Ⓐ	⑥	Ⓐ	⑥	Ⓐ	⑥	Ⓐ	⑥	Ⓐ
Exeter St Davids ▽ d.	...	1325	...	...	1425	...	...	1525	...	1625	1625	...	1725	1725	1748	1825	1825	...	...	1925	1925	...	...	2025	2025	...
Honiton d.	...	1355	...	...	1455	...	...	1555	...	1655	1656	...	1756	1756	1818	1856	1855	...	...	1955	1955	...	...	2055	2056	...
Axminster d.	...	1406	...	...	1506	...	...	1606	...	1706	1707	...	1808	1808	1828	1908	1906	...	...	2006	2006	...	...	2106	2108	...
Crewkerne d.	...	1419	...	...	1519	...	...	1619	...	1719	1720	...	1821	1821	▬	1921	1919	...	...	2019	2019	...	...	2119	2121	...
Yeovil Pen Mill 139 d.	1354	|	...	1500	|	...	...	|	...	|	|	...	|	|	...	|	|	...	...	|	|	2030	2039	|	|	2130
Yeovil Junction 139 a.	1400	1428	...	|	1528	...	...	1628	...	1728	1729	...	1829	1829	...	1929	1928	...	...	2028	2028	2035	2045	2128	2129	2135
Yeovil Junction d.	▬	1429	...	1451f	1529	...	...	1629	...	1729	1730	...	1830	1830	...	1930	1929	...	...	2029	2029	▬	...	2129	2130	...
Sherborne d.	...	1435	...	◧	1535	...	...	1635	...	1735	1736	...	1837	1837	...	1937	1935	...	...	2035	2035	...	...	2135	2137	...
Gillingham d.	...	1451	...	|	1551	...	1618	1651	...	1751	1752	...	1852	1852	...	1952	1951	...	...	2051	2051	...	...	2151	2152	...
Salisbury 140 a.	⑥	1516	...	1612	1616	...	1643	1716	...	1816	1822	...	1918	1922	Ⓐ	2022	2016	...	...	2121	2116	Ⓐ	...	2221	2218	...
Salisbury d.	1447	1521	1547	1621	1621	1647	1647	1720	1747	1821	1826	1847	1921	1924	1947	2023	2026	2047	2052	2125	2126	2149	...	2225	2226	...
Andover d.	1506	1538	1606	1638	1638	1706	1706	1737	1806	1838	1843	1906	1942	1947c	2006	2041	2045	2106	2112	2142	2145	2208	...	2244	2245	...
Basingstoke 106 d.	1530	1557	1630	1657	1657	1730	1728	1757	1829	1857	1901	1929	2010	2011	2029	2059	2111	2129	2130	2200	2209	2231	...	2307	2309	...
Woking 106 d.	1550	1616	1650	1717	1716	1750	...	1816	1850j	1916	1921	1950j	2036t	2032	...	2118	2136t	...	2150	2219	2228	...	...	2327	2329	...
London Waterloo 106 a.	1619	1649	1719	1751	1751	1819	...	1849	1919j	1949	1949	2019j	2104	2102	...	2149	2204	...	2219	2249	2258	...	...	2356	0001	...

	Ⓐ	Ⓐ	⑥	Ⓐ	⑥	Ⓐ		⑦	⑦	⑦	⑦	⑦		⑦	⑦	⑦	⑦	⑦	⑦	⑦	⑦	⑦	⑦	⑦	⑦
Exeter St Davids ▽ d.	...	2125	2125	2225	2300	2306	⑦	...	...	0824	...	0925		1425	...	1525	...	1625	1725	1825	1925	2025	2125	2225	2313
Honiton d.	...	2156	2156	2257	2332	2337		...	...	0856	...	0955	and	1455	...	1555	...	1655	1755	1855	1955	2056	2156	2258	2340s
Axminster d.	...	2208	2208	2308	2343	2348		...	...	0907	...	1006	at	1506	...	1606	...	1706	1806	1906	2006	2108	2208	2309	2352s
Crewkerne d.	...	2221	2221	2321	2356	0002		...	...	0920	...	1019	the	1519	...	1619	...	1719	1819	1919	2019	2121	2221	2322	0008s
Yeovil Pen Mill 139 d.	2152	|	|	|	|	|		...	...	|	0953	|	same	|	1543	|	...	|	|	|	|	|	|	|	|
Yeovil Junction 139 a.	|	2229	2229	2330	0005	0009		...	...	0929	|	1028	minutes	1528	1548	1628	...	1728	1828	1928	2028	2129	2229	2331	0017
Yeovil Junction d.	2145f	2230	2230	2331	0006	...		0729	0829	0930	0945f	1029	past	1529	1553	1629	...	1729	1829	1929	2029	2130	2230	2333	...
Sherborne d.	◧	2236	2237	|	|	...		0735	0835	0936	◧	1035	each	1535	1559	1635	...	1735	1835	1935	2035	2137	2237	|	...
Gillingham d.	|	2252	2252	|	|	...		0751	0851	0952	|	1051	hour	1551	1618	1651	1717	1751	1851	1951	2051	2152	2252	|	...
Salisbury 140 a.	2342	2319	2323	0017	0041	...		0816	0916	1016	1112	1116	until	1616	1643	1716	1742	1816	1916	2016	2116	2217	2317	0020	...
Salisbury d.	...	...	...	...	...	...		0827	0927	1027	1127	1127		1627	1644	1727	1744	1827	1927	2021	2121	2227	...	...	...
Andover d.	...	...	...	...	...	...		0845	0945	1045	1145	1145		1645	1704	1745	1803	1845	1945	2040	2140	2246	...	...	...
Basingstoke 106 d.	...	...	...	...	...	...		0904	1004	1104	1204	1204		1704	1728	1804	1827	1904	2004	2104	2204	2310	...	...	...
Woking 106 d.	...	...	...	...	...	...		0924	1025	1124	1224	1224		1724	|	1824	|	1924	2024	2124	2224	2330	...	...	...
London Waterloo 106 a.	...	...	...	...	...	...		1000	1057	1157	1254	1254		1754	1819	1854	1917	1954	2054	2154	2254	2358	...	...	...

☛ Additional services **London** Waterloo - **Salisbury** and v.v.:
From **London** Waterloo: on Ⓐ at 0850; on ⑥ at 0750, 0950, 1350, 1550, 1650, 1850, 1950, 2050, 2250; on ⑦ at 1945, 2045.
From **Salisbury**: on Ⓐ at 0510, 0543; on ⑥ at 0512 **v**, 0544 **v**, 0620, 0646, 0947; on ⑦ at 0642 **v**, 0724 **v**, 1844.

C – Conveys (12) Castle Cary - London (Tables **139**/**140**).
E – On ⑥ conveys (12) Frome - Salisbury - London (Tables **139** and **140**).
F – To Frome (Tables **139** and **140**).
W – To Westbury (Table **139**).

a – Arrives 13 minutes earlier.
b – Arrives 0842.
c – Arrives 7–8 minutes earlier.
e – Does not call at Exeter Central.
f – Calls at Yeovil Junction before Yeovil Pen Mill.
g – Calls at Yeovil Pen Mill before Yeovil Junction.
j – ⑥ only.
r – Arrives 2316.
s – Calls to set down only.

t – Arrives 5 minutes earlier.
v – Departs 3 minutes later until Oct. 9.
u – Calls to pick up only.

◧ – Via Westbury (Tables **139** and **140**).
△ – Trains to Exeter St Davids also call at **Exeter Central** 5–6 minutes earlier.
▽ – Trains from Exeter St Davids also call at **Exeter Central** 4–5 minutes later.

110 LONDON - EXETER - PAIGNTON and PLYMOUTH — GW

km	Ⓐ	Ⓐ 2★	Ⓐ 2★	Ⓐ 🍷★	Ⓐ 2	Ⓐ 🍷	Ⓐ2 ★B	Ⓐ 2★	Ⓐ 🍷★	Ⓐ 🍷	Ⓐ2 🍷D	Ⓐ 🍷	Ⓐ2 ★D	Ⓐ 🍷★	Ⓐ 🍷	Ⓐ 🍷	Ⓐ 🍷	Ⓐ2 ★D	Ⓐ 🍷	Ⓐ 🍷	Ⓐ 🍴	Ⓐ 2D	Ⓐ 🍷	Ⓐ2 ★D	Ⓐ 🍷★	Ⓐ 🍷	Ⓐ 🍷
0	**London** Padd **130/1/2/3/4** d.	...	...	...	...	0637	...	...	0704	0804	★	0904	...	0937	1004	1035	1104	...	1204	1233	1304	...	1404	...	1436	1504	1604
58	**Reading** **130/1/2/3/4** d.	...	...	...	...	0703	...	...	0730	0829	...	0929	...	1002	1029t	1101	1129	...	1229t	1301	1329t	...	1429t	...	1502	1529t	1629t
85	Newbury d.	...	...	...	...	|	...	...	0745	|	...	|	...	1017	|	1116	|	...	|	1316	|	...	|	...	1517	|	|
154	Westbury **140** d.	...	...	...	...	|	...	...	0822	|	...	|	...	1055	|	1156	|	...	|	1356	|	...	|	...	1554	|	|
186	Castle Cary **140** d.	...	...	...	...	|	...	...	0842	|	...	1029c	...	1115	|	1216	|	...	|	1416	|	...	|	...	1614	|	1727
	Bristol T M **115/6 132** d.	...	0540	...	0650	|	0749	0752	|	|	0856	|	0956	|	|	|	|	1155	|	|	|	1355	|	1455	|	|	|
230	Taunton **115 116** d.	...	0622	...	0737	0818	0826	0857	0903	0945	0957	1048	1056	1137	1146	1238	1247	1255	1346	1438	1445	1456	1547	1555	1635	1649	1749
253	Tiverton Parkway **116** d.	...	0635	...	0749	|	0838	|	0916	|	1009	1100	1108	1149	1158	|	1259	1307	|	|	1458	1508	1559	1606	|	1702	1802
279	**Exeter** St Davids **116** a.	...	0650	...	0804	0841	0852	0923	0929	1007	1023	1114	1123	1204	1211	1307	1313	1322	1409	1507	1512	1523	1612	1621	1659	1715	1815
279	**Exeter** St Davids **111 116** d.	0625	0655	0727	0809	0845	0855	0925	0931	1011	1025	1116	1125	1207	1214	...	1315	1325	1412	...	1513	1525	1615	1628	1701	1717	1820
311	Newton Abbot **111 116** d.	0652	0723	0751	0829	|	0920	0951	0958	1031	1051	1136	1150	1232	1236	...	1335	1350	1432	...	1534	1546	1635	1653	1726	1738	1841
321	Torquay **111 116** d.	|	|	|	|	|	|	|	1011	|	|	|	|	1245	|	...	|	|	|	...	|	|	|	|	1739	|	|
324	**Paignton** **111 116** a.	|	|	|	|	|	|	|	1016	|	|	|	|	1250	|	...	|	|	|	...	|	|	|	|	1744	|	|
325	Totnes **116** d.	0705	0735	0802	0841	|	0933	1004	...	1043	1104	1148	1203	...	1248	...	1347	1403	1444	...	1545	1559	1647	1706	...	1749	1852
363	**Plymouth** **116** a.	0736	0804	0831	0910	0936	1002	1033	...	1108	1133	1214	1232	...	1312	...	1413	1432	1508	...	1612	1629	1712	1735	...	1816	1920
	Newquay **112** a.	|	|	...	|	|	|	|	...	|	|	1417v	|	...	|	...	...	|	|	...	...	|	|	|	...	|	|
	Penzance **112** a.	0940	1010	...	1114a	1140	1212	1240	...	1307	1340	...	1440	...	1507	...	...	1640	1708	...	...	1841	1923	1940	...	2010	2120

	Ⓐ 🍷	Ⓐ 🍷	Ⓐ 🍷★	Ⓐ 🍷	Ⓐ 2D	Ⓐ 🍷	①–④ 🍴	⑤ 🍴	Ⓐ2 ★D	Ⓐ 🍷★	Ⓐ 🍷	Ⓐ 2	Ⓐ 2	Ⓐ 🍷	Ⓐ A
London Padd **130/1/2/3/4** d.	1636	1704	1736	1804	...	1836	1904	1904	...	2003	2104	...	...	2202	2345
Reading **130/1/2/3/4** d.	1702	1729t	1803	1829t	...	1901	1931	1931t	...	2029	2129	...	...	2227	0049u
Newbury d.	1717	|	1819	1844	...	1916	|	|	...	2044	2144	...	...	|	|
Westbury **140** d.	1757	|	1856	|	...	1959	|	|	...	2121	2222	...	...	|	|
Castle Cary **140** d.	1817	|	1916	|	...	2019	|	|	...	2141	2242	...	...	|	|
Bristol T M **115/6 132** d.	|	|	|	|	1855	|	|	|	1953	|	|	2200	2305	2348	|
Taunton **115 116** d.	1838	1848	1938	1949	2001	2041	2049	2049	2058	2202	2303	2314	0009s	0044s	0237
Tiverton Parkway **116** d.	|	1901	1950	|	2013	2053	2101	2101	2110	2214	2316	2329	0024s	0057s	|
Exeter St Davids **116** a.	1902	1915	2004	2012	2029	2109	2115	2115	2124	2228	2330	2346	0040	0112s	0307
Exeter St Davids **111 116** d.	1911	1920	2006	2014	2041	2111	2118	2118	2138	2230	2335	...	...	|	0411
Newton Abbot **111 116** d.	1933	1943	2044	2034	2101	2131	2139	2139	2203	2255	2355	...	...	0133s	0433
Torquay **111 116** d.	|	|	2111	|	|	|	|	|	|	|	|	...	...	|	|
Paignton **111 116** a.	|	|	2125	|	|	|	|	|	|	|	|	...	...	|	|
Totnes **116** d.	1944	1954	...	2046	2113	2143	2151	2151	2216	2307	0006	...	...	|	|
Plymouth **116** a.	2013	2020	...	2112	2143	2209	2217	2217	2246	2336	0033	...	...	0210	0511
Newquay **112** a.	...	|	...	|	|	...	|	|	...	...	...	...	...	...	|
Penzance **112** a.	...	2225	...	2259	2340	...	0035	0035	...	...	...	...	...	...	0754

⑥ ❖ ♠	⑥ 2★	⑥ 2★	⑥ 2★	⑥ 🍷	⑥ 🍷	⑥ 🍷	⑥ 2★	⑥ 🍷	⑥2 ★D	⑥ 🍷★	⑥ 🍷	⑥2 ★D
London Padd **130/1/2/3/4** d.	...	...	...	...	...	0700	...	0804	...	0835	0904	...
Reading **130/1/2/3/4** d.	...	...	...	...	...	0728	...	0829	...	0902	0930	...
Newbury d.	...	...	...	...	...	|	...	|	...	0917	|	...
Westbury **140** d.	...	...	...	...	...	0815	...	|	...	0955	|	...
Castle Cary **140** d.	...	...	...	...	...	|	...	|	...	1017	1027	...
Bristol T M **115/6 132** d.	...	0540	...	0640	0742	|	0755	|	0855	|	|	0955
Taunton **115 116** d.	...	0627	...	0730	0814	0853	0859	0945	0952	1039	1048	1055
Tiverton Parkway **116** d.	...	0639	...	0742	|	|	|	|	1004	1052	|	1107
Exeter St Davids **116** a.	...	0653	...	0756	0837	0917	0924	1009	1018	1107	1110	1122
Exeter St Davids **111 116** d.	0628	0655	0722	0800	0845	0920	0926	1011	1025	1110	1114	1125
Newton Abbot **111 116** d.	0654	0723	0748	0822	0905	0940	0951	1032	1050	1146	1135	1150
Torquay **111 116** d.	|	|	|	|	|	|	|	|	|	1159	|	|
Paignton **111 116** a.	|	|	|	|	|	|	|	|	|	1205	|	|
Totnes **116** d.	0707	0735	0800	|	0917	|	1004	1044	1103	...	1147	1202
Plymouth **116** a.	0737	0805	0831	0857	0943	1015	1032	1110	1132	...	1213	1231
Newquay **112** a.	|	|	...	1036	|	|	|	|	|	...	|	|
Penzance **112** a.	0935	1011	...	...	1141	1217	1240	1308	1340	...	1416	1440

SEE NOTE ❖	⑥ 🍷	⑥ 🍷★	⑥ 🍷	⑥2 ★D	⑥ 🍷	⑥ 🍷	⑥ 🍷★	⑥ 🍷	⑥2 ★D	⑥ 🍷	⑥2 ★D	⑥ 🍷★	⑥ 🍷	⑥2 ★D	⑥ 🍷	⑥ 🍷★	⑥ 🍷	⑥ 🍷	⑥2 ★D	⑥ 🍷★	⑥ 🍷★	⑥ 2D	⑥ 🍷
London Padd **130/1/2/3/4** d.	1004	1035	1104	...	1137	1204	1235	1304	...	1404	...	1436	1504	...	1604	1636	1704	1804	...	1904	2004	...	2032
Reading **130/1/2/3/4** d.	1030	1101	1130	...	1205	1230	1301	1330	...	1429	...	1501	1529	...	1629	1701	1730	1829	...	1929	2029	...	2057
Newbury d.	|	1116	|	...	|	|	1316	|	...	|	...	1516	|	...	|	1716	|	|	...	1944	2044	...	|
Westbury **140** d.	|	1153	|	...	1250	|	1356	|	...	|	...	1553	|	...	|	1753	|	|	...	2024	2121	...	|
Castle Cary **140** d.	|	1213	|	...	|	|	1419	|	...	|	...	1613	|	...	1728	1813	|	|	...	2044	2141	...	|
Bristol T M **115/6 132** d.	|	|	|	1155	|	|	|	|	1355	|	1455	|	|	1555	|	|	|	|	1853	|	|	2152	2208
Taunton **115 116** d.	1147	1235	1245	1300	1328	1347	1441	1449	1456	1547	1555	1635	1647	1655	1750	1834	1847	1945	1953	2106	2203	2257	2307
Tiverton Parkway **116** d.	1159	|	1257	1313	1340	|	|	1501	1508	1559	1607	|	1659	1707	1802	1847	1859	1957	2005	2118	2215	2311	2320
Exeter St Davids **116** a.	1213	1258	1311	1330	1354	1410	1506	1514	1523	1613	1623	1657	1713	1723	1816	1900	1914	2010	2019	2132	2229	2326	2335
Exeter St Davids **111 116** d.	1216	1301	1314	1332	1358	1413	1507	1517	1526	1615	1625	1700	1715	1725	1820	1902	1917	2013	2027	2136	2232	...	...
Newton Abbot **111 116** d.	1236	1331	1334	1359	1421	1433	1535	1537	1551	1635	1650	1726	1736	1752	1841	1928	1938	2034	2053	2201	2257	...	...
Torquay **111 116** d.	|	1342	|	|	|	|	1548	|	|	|	|	|	|	|	|	1941	|	|	|	|	|	...	...
Paignton **111 116** a.	|	1347	|	|	|	|	1553	|	|	|	|	|	|	|	|	1946	|	|	|	|	|	...	...
Totnes **116** d.	1248	...	1346	1411	|	1445	...	1549	1604	1647	1703	|	1748	1804	1853	...	1949	2046	2105	2213	2309	...	...
Plymouth **116** a.	1315	...	1412	1440	1456	1511	...	1615	1632	1713	1731	1801	1814	1833	1922	...	2016	2112	2134	2239	2338	...	...
Newquay **112** a.	|	...	|	|	1641	|	...	|	|	|	|	...	|	|	...	...	|	|	...	...	...	...	...
Penzance **112** a.	1509	...	1509	1640	...	1709	...	1811	1841	1909	1940	...	2010	2041	...	...	2217	2315	...	...	...	...	...

⑦	⑦ 2★	⑦ 2★	⑦ 🍷	⑦ 🍷
London Padd **130/1/2/3/4** d.	...	...	0752	0813
Reading **130/1/2/3/4** d.	...	...	0822	0837
Newbury d.	...	...	0839	|
Westbury **140** d.	...	...	0917	|
Castle Cary **140** d.	...	...	0937	|
Bristol T M **115/6 132** d.	...	0800	|	0950
Taunton **115 116** d.	...	0856	0958	1027
Tiverton Parkway **116** d.	...	0908	1010	1040
Exeter St Davids **116** a.	...	0922	1024	1056
Exeter St Davids **111 116** d.	0851	0925	1026	...
Newton Abbot **111 116** d.	0916	0951	1046	...
Torquay **111 116** d.	|	|	|	...
Paignton **111 116** a.	|	|	|	...
Totnes **116** d.	0928	1003	1058	...
Plymouth **116** a.	0959	1032	1125	...
Newquay **112** a.	...	|	|	...
Penzance **112** a.	...	1240	1340	...

	⑦ 🍷	⑦ 2	⑦ 🍷	⑦ 🍷★	⑦ 🍷	⑦2 ★D	⑦ 🍷	⑦ 2D	⑦ 🍷★	⑦ 🍷	⑦2 ★D	⑦ 🍷	⑦2 ★D	⑦ 🍷	⑦ 🍷	⑦2 ★D	⑦ 🍷	⑦ 2★	⑦ 🍷	⑦ 🍷	⑦ 🍷★	⑦ 🍷	⑦ 🍷	⑦ 🍷★	⑦ 🍷	⑦ 🍷★	⑦ 🍷	⑦ A
London Padd **130/1/2/3/4** d.	0851	...	1003	1036	1103	...	1203	...	1236	1303	...	1403	...	1436	1503	...	1603	...	1637	1703	1630	1803	1800	1836	1903	2003	2103	2350
Reading **130/1/2/3/4** d.	0918	...	1028	1101	1128	...	1228	...	1301	1328	...	1428	...	1501	1528	...	1628	...	1702	1728	1655	1828	1825	1901	1928	2028	2128	0049u
Newbury d.	|	...	|	1116	|	...	|	...	1316	|	...	|	...	1516	|	...	|	...	1717	|	|	|	|	1916	|	2044	|	|
Westbury **140** d.	1004	...	|	1153	|	...	|	...	1353	|	...	|	...	1553	|	...	|	...	1754	|	|	|	|	1953	|	2122	|	|
Castle Cary **140** d.	1024	...	|	1213	|	...	|	...	1413	|	...	|	...	1613	|	...	|	...	1814	|	|	|	|	2013	|	2142	|	|
Bristol T M **115/6 132** d.	|	0955	|	|	|	1145	|	1254	|	|	1354	|	1454	|	|	1554	|	...	|	|	1810	|	1935	|	|	|	|	|
Taunton **115 116** d.	1045	1105	1144	1234	1243	1249	1343	1354	1434	1443	1449	1544	1552	1634	1644	1656	1744	...	1835	1843	1906	1943	2009	2034	2043	2203	2242s	|
Tiverton Parkway **116** d.	|	1117	1156	|	1255	1301	1355	|	|	1455	1501	1556	|	|	1656	1708	1756	...	|	1856	|	1956	|	|	2056	2216	2255s	|
Exeter St Davids **116** a.	1109	1132	1210	1259	1309	1315	1409	1423	1457	1508	1517	1610	1616	1659	1710	1722	1810	...	1859	1912	1929	2011	2032	2058	2111	2230	2311	0323
Exeter St Davids **111 116** d.	1110	1138	1212	1302	1311	1320	1412	...	1459	1514	1524	1613	1618	...	1713	1724	1812	1820	1900	1913	1931	2013	2034	2059	2113	2232	...	0436
Newton Abbot **111 116** d.	1131	1158	1235	1327	1331	1346	1432	...	1528	1535	1549	1634	1646	...	1733	1753	1833	1846	1921	1933	1956	2033	2054	2125	2133	2257	...	0457
Torquay **111 116** a.	|	|	|	1338	|	|	|	...	1541	|	|	|	|	...	|	|	|	|	|	|	|	|	|	|	|	|	...	|
Paignton **111 116** a.	|	|	|	1344	|	|	|	...	1546	|	|	|	|	...	|	|	|	|	|	|	|	|	|	|	|	|	...	|
Totnes **116** a.	1142	1210	1246	...	1343	1358	1444	...	...	1547	1600	1645	1658	...	1745	1805	1844	1858	1932	1945	2008	2045	2106	2136	2145	2309	...	|
Plymouth **116** a.	1210	1239	1313	...	1409	1430	1510	...	...	1613	1629	1712	1726	...	1811	1833	1911	1926	2002	2012	2034	2111	2132	2205	2212	2335	...	0536
Newquay **112** a.	|	|	|	...	1551v	|	|	...	...	...	|	|	|	...	...	|	|	|	...	|	...	|	...	...	...	...	...	|
Penzance **112** a.	1406	1438	1506	...	...	1636	1705	...	...	...	1829	1906	1930	...	...	2030	2106	2130	...	2205	...	2312	...	...	...	...	...	0754

A – THE NIGHT RIVIERA – Conveys 🛏 1, 2. cl and (2). See also note ‡ on next page.
B – From Gloucester (Table **138**).
D – From Cardiff (Table **115**).
a – Arrives 1110 from Sept. 12.
c – ⑤ until Sept. 9. Calls to pick-up only.
f – Arrives 1046.
s – Stops to set down only.
t – Stops to pick up only on ⑤.
u – Stops to pick up only.
v – Until Sept. 11.
♠ – Service valid until Sept. 10.
★ – Also calls at Dawlish (10 – 15 minutes after Exeter) and Teignmouth (15 – 18 minutes after Exeter).
❖ – On ⑥ all trains until 1804 from London Paddington call at Reading to pick-up only.

111 EXETER - PAIGNTON

*See also Tables **110** and **116*** — 2nd class — GW

km	⚒	Ⓐ	⑥		⚒	⑥	Ⓐ	Ⓐ	⑥	Ⓐ	⑥	⚒	Ⓐ	⑥	⚒	⚒	⑥	Ⓐ	Ⓐ	⑥	⚒	Ⓐ	⑥	⚒	⑥	Ⓐ
0	**Exeter** St Davids d.	0458	0500	...	0530	0555	0558	0630	0635	0659	0659	0730	0800	0808	0832	0900	0930	0935	0959	1005	1028	1100	1100	1129	1201	1202
20	Dawlish d.	0519	0521	...	0546	0618	0621	0653	0658	0722	0722	0758	0825	0829	0900	0913	1004	1004	1014	1027	1052	1113	1116	1152	1217	1230
24	Teignmouth d.	0524	0526	...	0551	0623	0626	0658	0703	0727	0727	0803	0830	0834	0905	0918	1009	1009	1019	1032	1057	1118	1121	1157	1222	1235
32	Newton Abbot d.	0533	0534	...	0559	0632	0635	0706	0712	0737	0735	0812	0838	0843	0913	0925	1017	1017	1035c	1042	1105	1126	1138r	1205	1230	1243
42	Torquay d.	0544	0545	...	0610	0643	0646	0719	0723	0748	0747	0823	0849	0854	0925	0937	1029	1028	1046	1054	1118	1137	1150	1218	1243	1254
45	**Paignton** 🚂 a.	0550	0552	...	0616	0650	0652	0726	0729	0754	0755	0830	0855	0900	0931	0945	1035	1034	1052	1100	1125	1143	1158	1225	1250	1300

	⑥	Ⓐ	Ⓐ	⑥	Ⓐ	⑥	Ⓐ	⑥	⚒	Ⓐ	⑥d	⑥e	Ⓐ	⑥	Ⓐ	⑥	Ⓐ	⑥	⚒	⚒	Ⓐ	⑥	Ⓐ	⑥	Ⓐ	⑥	Ⓐ
Exeter St Davids d.	1229	1231	1300	1306	1329	1336	1400	1406	1429	1500	1459	1505	1529	1530	1558	1605	1631	1631	1703	1732	1800	1801	1831	1835	1901	1906	1930
Dawlish d.	1252	1254	1313	1329	1352	1403	1413	1428	1452	1513	1515	1521	1552	1553	1619	1629	1702	1703	1730	1802	1835	1835	1851	1902	1935	1932	1950
Teignmouth d.	1257	1259	1318	1335	1357	1408	1418	1434	1457	1518	1520	1526	1557	1558	1624	1635	1707	1708	1736	1807	1840	1840	1856	1907	1940	1937	1955
Newton Abbot d.	1306	1311t	1326	1343	1405	1417	1426	1443	1505	1526	1528	1541j	1609t	1606	1631	1644	1715	1716	1744	1815	1848	1848	1904	1915	1948	1945	2010j
Torquay a.	1318	1322	1337	1355	1417	1428	1437	1454	1517	1537	1540	1552	1620	1618	1643	1655	1726	1728	1756	1826	1900	1900	1917	1928	1959	1956	2021
Paignton 🚂 a.	1325	1328	1343	1402	1424	1435	1443	1500	1525	1543	1546	1558	1626	1625	1649	1702	1731	1735	1802	1835	1909	1906	1924	1934	2005	2003	2027

	Ⓐ	⑥	Ⓐ	Ⓐ	⑥	Ⓐ	⑥	Ⓐ	
Exeter St Davids d.	2000	2016	2030	2100	2136	2201	2232	2302	...
Dawlish d.	2013	2045	2105	2133	2148	2224	2244	2325	...
Teignmouth d.	2018	2050	2110	2138	2153	2229	2249	2330	...
Newton Abbot d.	2025	2059	2117	2146	2200	2237	2256	2337	...
Torquay a.	2038	2110	2129	2158	...	2249	...	2349	...
Paignton 🚂 a.	2044	2116	2135	2204	...	2255	...	2355	...

⑦	⑦	⑦	⑦	⑦	⑦	⑦	⑦	⑦	⑦	⑦	⑦	⑦	⑦	⑦	⑦	⑦	⑦
Exeter St Davids d.	0830	0930	1030	1126	1230	1306	1329	1427	1503	1530	1627	1700	1728	1828	1935	2038	2132
Dawlish d.	0853	0958	1053	1153	1253	1326	1352	1450	1530	1553	1650	1715	1751	1851	1958	2105	2152
Teignmouth d.	0858	1003	1058	1158	1258	1331	1357	1455	1535	1558	1655	1720	1756	1856	2003	2110	2157
Newton Abbot d.	0906	1011	1105	1205	1305	1339	1404	1503	1542	1605	1703	1728	1803	1904	2011	2118	2205
Torquay a.	0918	1023	1117	1217	1317	1350	1416	1514	1554	1618	1715	1739	1815	1915	2022	2129	2217
Paignton 🚂 a.	0924	1029	1123	1223	1323	1357	1422	1520	1600	1624	1721	1745	1821	1921	2028	2135	2223

c – Arrives 1026.
d – Until Sept. 10.
e – From Sept. 17.
j – Arrives 8 minutes earlier.
r – Arrives 1128.
t – Arrives 5 minutes earlier.
🚂 – Dartmouth Steam Railway (Paignton - Kingswear). ✆ 01803 555 872. www.dartmouthrailriver.co.uk

GW — PLYMOUTH and PAIGNTON - EXETER - LONDON — 110

km		Ⓐ 🍷v	Ⓐ 🍷	Ⓐ 2D	Ⓐ 🍷	Ⓐ 🍷☆	Ⓐ 🍷	Ⓐ 🍷☆	Ⓐ2 D☆	Ⓐ 🍷	Ⓐ 🍷☆	Ⓐ2 D☆	Ⓐ 🍷	Ⓐ 2D	Ⓐ 🍷	Ⓐ 🍷☆	Ⓐ 2D	Ⓐ 🍷	Ⓐ 🍷	Ⓐ 🍷	Ⓐ 2D	Ⓐ ✕	Ⓐ 🍷☆	Ⓐ 🍷	Ⓐ 🍷	Ⓐ2 D☆	Ⓐ 🍷	Ⓐ 🍷
	Penzance 112 d.	...	...	...	...	...	0503	...	0540	0605	...	0640	0710	0740	0815	...	0850	0910	1015	...	1050	...	...	1215	...	1250	...	1415
	Newquay 112 d.	...	...	...	...	...	|	...	|	|	...	|	|	|	|	...	|	|	|	...	|	1118t	...	|	...	|	...	|
0	**Plymouth** 116 d.	...	0454	...	0549	0534	0655	0640	0746	0815	0835	0850	0915	0937	1015	...	1050	1115	1215	...	1250	1315	...	1414	...	1448	1515	1615
38	Totnes 116 d.	...	|	...	|	0602	|	0709	0814	0842	0903	0916	0942	1005	1042	...	1121	1142	1242	...	1319	1342	...	1441	...	1516	1542	1642
	Paignton 111 116 d.	...	|	...	|	|	|	|	|	|	|	|	|	|	|	1055	|	|	|	...	|	|	1410	|	...	|	|	|
	Torquay 111 116 d.	...	|	...	|	|	|	|	|	|	|	|	|	|	|	1101	|	|	|	...	|	|	1416	|	...	|	|	|
52	Newton Abbot 111 116 d.	...	0530	...	0625	0615	0731	0721	0826	0854	0916	0929	0954	1018	1054	1113	1133	1154	1255	...	1331	1354	1427	1454	...	1528	1554	1654
84	**Exeter** St Davids 111 116 a.	...	0548	...	0643	0639	0750	0746	0851	0913	0939	0953	1012	1038	1113	1136	1153	1212	1313	...	1351	1412	1450	1512	...	1552	1612	1712
84	**Exeter** St Davids 116 d.	...	0552	0636	0646	0652	0752	0800	0852	0915	0941	0955	1015	1044	1115	1142	1154	1215	1315	1343	1353	1416	1454	1514	1540	1553	1615	1715
110	Tiverton Parkway 116 d.	...	0606	0650	|	0706	|	0814	0906	0929	|	|	1029	1058	1129	|	|	1229	1330	1358	|	1430	|	1529	|	|	1629	1729
133	Taunton 115 116 d.	...	0620	0704	0709	0719	0815	0827	0920	0942	1004	1019	1042	1111	1142	1205	1218	1242	1343	1411	1419	1443	1517	1541	1605	1617	1642	1742
205	**Bristol** T M. 115/6 132 a.	0510	|	0816	|	|	|	|	1020	|	|	1117	|	1217	|	|	1316	|	|	|	1516	|	|	|	|	1719	|	|
	Castle Cary 140 a.	|	0639	...	|	0738	|	0846	...	|	1024	...	|	...	|	1225	...	|	|	1430	...	|	|	|	1624	...	|	|
	Westbury 140 a.	0549y	0700	...	|	0759	|	0911	...	|	1044	...	|	...	|	1247	...	|	|	1450	...	|	1553	|	1644	...	|	|
	Newbury a.	0644	0744	...	0813	0837	|	|	...	|	1121	...	|	...	|	1326	...	|	|	1531	...	|	|	|	1724	...	|	|
337	**Reading** 130/1/2/3/4 a.	0708	0801	...	0830	0853	0930	1002	...	1058	1138	...	1201	...	1258	1342	...	1402	1458	1547	...	1557	1643	1701	1742	...	1757	1857
395	**London** Padd 130/1/2/3/4 a.	0736	0835	...	0901	0924	0955	1029	...	1129	1206	...	1229	...	1329	1407	...	1427	1529	1614	...	1629	1710	1729	1807	...	1824	1924

	Ⓐ 🍷	Ⓐ 2☆	Ⓐ ✕	Ⓐ 🍷	Ⓐ 2D	Ⓐ 🍷☆	Ⓐ 🍷	Ⓐ 2D	Ⓐ 2☆	Ⓐ 2☆	Ⓐ 2☆	Ⓐ 2☆	Ⓐ 2	Ⓐ A	⑥ ♠ 2D	⑥ 🍷	⑥ 🍷	⑥ 🍷	⑥ 🍷☆	⑥2 D☆	⑥ 🍷	⑥ 🍷☆	⑥2 D☆	⑥ 🍷	⑥ 2D	⑥ 2☆	⑥ 🍷	⑥ 🍷☆
Penzance 112 d.	...	1550	1615	...	1650	...	1750	...	1815	...	1915	...	...	2145	...	...	...	...	...	0540	0612	...	0640	0710	...	0740	0815	...
Newquay 112 d.	1455t	|	|	...	|	...	|	...	|	...	|	...	...	|	...	...	...	...	...	|	|	...	|	|	...	|	|	...
Plymouth 116 d.	1650	1750	1816	...	1848	...	1950	...	2024	...	2125	2225	2315	2354	...	0558	...	0655	0640	0747	0814	...	0848	0914	...	0950	1014	...
Totnes 116 d.	1718	1819	1843	...	1917	...	2017	...	2052	...	2154	2255	2344	0022	...	0625	...	|	0710	0815	0841	...	0917	0941	...	1019	1041	...
Paignton 111 116 d.	|	|	|	...	|	1905	|	...	|	2108	|	|	|	|	...	|	...	|	|	|	|	0855	|	|	...	|	|	1056
Torquay 111 116 d.	|	|	|	...	|	1911	|	...	|	2113	|	|	|	|	...	|	...	|	|	|	|	0901	|	|	...	|	|	1102
Newton Abbot 111 116 d.	1731	1832	1855	...	1929	1921	2029	...	2106	2125	2207	2308	2357	0036	...	0637	...	0732	0723	0828	0854	0914	0929	0954	...	1031	1054	1112
Exeter St Davids 111 116 a.	1749	1859	1915	...	1948	1953	2048	...	2133	2202	2237	2333	0020	0058	...	0656	...	0751	0756	0852	0913	0943	0953	1013	...	1100	1113	1142
Exeter St Davids 116 d.	1751	1903	1917	1935	1950	1955	2050	2106	...	2203	2242	...	...	0107	0548	0700	0733	0752	0758	0855	0916	0945	0955	1016	1043	...	1116	1145
Tiverton Parkway 116 d.	1806	|	1932	1950	|	2010	2104	|	...	2220	2256	...	...	|	0602	0715	|	|	0812	|	0931	|	|	1031	|	...	1131	|
Taunton 115 116 d.	1818	1927	1944	2003	2016	2023	2117	2132	...	2236	2310	...	...	0140	0615	0728	0758	0815	0825	0919	0944	1009	1019	1044	1108	...	1144	1207
Bristol T M. 115/6 132 a.	|	2002	|	2057	2118	|	2149	2230	...	2317	0004	...	...	|	0720	|	0855	|	|	1015	|	|	1116	|	1218	...	|	|
Castle Cary 140 a.	1838	...	|	|	...	2042	|	...	...	...	...	...	...	|	...	0747	|	|	0844	...	|	1028	...	|	...	...	|	1226
Westbury 140 a.	1858	...	|	|	...	2101	|	...	...	...	...	...	...	|	...	0808	|	|	0909	...	|	1048	...	|	...	...	|	1248
Newbury a.	1935	...	|	|	...	2139	|	...	...	...	...	...	...	|	...	0847	|	0925	|	...	|	1127	...	|	...	...	|	1326
Reading 130/1/2/3/4 a.	1954	...	2100	2208	...	2200	2310	...	...	...	...	...	...	0400s	...	0903	1010	0943	1000	...	1101	1143	...	1200	...	...	1259	1343
London Padd 130/1/2/3/4 a.	2019	...	2129	2236	...	2229	2356	...	...	...	...	...	...	0507	...	0929	1036	1009	1029	...	1129	1209	...	1229	...	...	1329	1409

	⑥2 D☆	⑥ 🍷	⑥ 🍷	⑥ 🍷☆	⑥ 2☆	⑥ 🍷	⑥ 🍷	⑥ 🍷	⑥ 🍷☆	⑥2 D☆	⑥ 🍷	⑥2 D☆	⑥ 🍷	⑥ 🍷	⑥ 🍷☆	⑥ 2☆	⑥ 🍷	⑥2 D☆	⑥ 🍷☆	⑥ 🍷☆	⑥ 🍷	⑥ 2☆	⑥ 2☆	⑦ 2	⑦ 🍷	⑦ 🍷☆	⑦ 2D	⑦ 🍷
Penzance 112 d.	0852	0912	1015	...	1045	...	1112	1218	...	1250	1310	1350	1420	1445	...	1550	1620	...	1645	...	1750	1815	...	...	...	...	...	...
Newquay 112 d.	|	|	|	...	|	1115	|	|	...	|	|	|	|	|	...	|	|	...	|	1730	|	|	...	...	...	...	...	...
Plymouth 116 d.	1049	1114	1214	...	1243	1256	1315	1415	...	1448	1514	1548	1615	1650	...	1748	1816	...	1850	1930	1950	2020	2150	...	...	0827	...	0912
Totnes 116 d.	1118	1141	1241	...	1311	|	1342	1442	...	1517	1541	1615	1642	1719	...	1817	1843	...	1917	1957	2017	2048	2219	...	...	0854	...	0939
Paignton 111 116 d.	|	|	|	1256	|	|	|	|	1456	|	|	|	|	|	1705	|	|	1837	|	|	|	|	|	...	...	|	...	|
Torquay 111 116 d.	|	|	|	1302	|	|	|	|	1502	|	|	|	|	|	1711	|	|	1852	|	|	|	|	|	...	...	|	...	|
Newton Abbot 111 116 d.	1130	1154	1254	1312	1324	1332	1354	1454	1513	1530	1554	1628	1655	1731	1723	1830	1856	1920	1930	2009	2029	2102	2232	...	...	0907	...	0952
Exeter St Davids 111 116 a.	1154	1214	1313	1336	1358	1351	1413	1513	1541	1554	1613	1653	1715	1751	1758	1854	1916	1946	1954	2033	2048	2130	2307	...	...	0931	...	1011
Exeter St Davids 116 d.	1155	1216	1316	1343	...	1354	1416	1516	1543	1556	1615	1655	1717	1755	1802	1904	1918	1948	1956	2035	2051	...	...	0759	0835	0933	0944	1012
Tiverton Parkway 116 d.	|	1231	1331	|	...	|	1431	1531	|	|	1630	|	1731	1811	1817	1918	1932	2002	|	|	2105	...	...	0814	0850	0947	0957	|
Taunton 115 116 d.	1220	1244	1344	1406	...	|	1444	1544	1607	1620	1643	1720	1744	1825	1830	1932	1945	2024c	2019	2058	2119	...	...	0828	0904	100	1011	1034
Bristol T M. 115/6 132 a.	1316	|	|	|	...	|	|	|	|	1720	|	1816	|	|	1926	2016	|	2125	|	2143	2149	...	...	0932	|	|	1106	|
Castle Cary 140 a.	...	|	|	1426	...	|	|	|	1626	...	|	...	|	1844	...	...	2004	...	|	...	|	...	...	...	0923	1020	...	|
Westbury 140 a.	...	|	|	1446	...	|	|	|	1646	...	|	...	|	1907	...	...	2024	...	|	...	|	...	...	...	0943	1039	...	1111
Newbury a.	...	|	|	1532	...	|	|	|	1728	...	|	...	|	1945	...	...	|	...	2123	...	|	...	...	...	1025	1118	...	|
Reading 130/1/2/3/4 a.	...	1359	1500	1552	...	1531	1600	1659	1744	...	1800	...	1859	2002	...	...	2115	...	2143	...	2311	...	...	...	1041	1135	...	1158
London Padd 130/1/2/3/4 a.	...	1429	1529	1622	...	1556	1629	1729	1809	...	1829	...	1929	2026	...	...	2139	...	2209	...	2342	...	...	...	1110	1159	...	1224

	⑦2 D☆	⑦ 🍷	⑦ 🍷☆	⑦2 D☆	⑦ 🍷	⑦ 🍷	⑦ 🍷	⑦2 D☆	⑦ 🍷	⑦2 D☆	⑦ 🍷	⑦ 🍷☆	⑦ 2D	⑦ 🍷	⑦ 🍷	⑦2 D☆	⑦ 🍷	⑦ 🍷	⑦ 🍷☆	⑦ 2☆	⑦ 🍷	⑦ 🍷☆	⑦ 🍷	⑦ 🍷☆	⑦ 2	⑦ 🍷	⑦ 🍷	⑦ 2☆	⑦ A
Penzance 112 d.	...	0814	...	0850	0918	1018	...	1050	...	1150	1218	...	...	...	...	1350	1418	...	...	1450	1518	...	1618	...	...	1750	...	...	2115
Newquay 112 d.	...	|	...	|	|	|	...	|	...	|	|	...	...	...	1330t	|	|	...	...	|	|	...	|	1718t	...	|	...	...	|
Plymouth 116 d.	0947	1011	...	1048	1115	1215	...	1245	...	1345	1415	...	...	1456	1515	1547	1615	...	...	1647	1715	1745	1815	1915	...	1945	2015	2126	2320
Totnes 116 d.	1015	1038	...	1116	1141	1241	...	1313	...	1413	1441	...	...	|	1541	1616	1641	...	...	1715	1741	1814	1841	1943	...	2015	2042	2154	2348
Paignton 111 116 d.	|	|	1036	|	|	|	...	|	...	|	|	1453	...	|	|	|	|	...	1652	|	|	|	|	|	...	|	|	|	|
Torquay 111 116 d.	|	|	1042	|	|	|	...	|	...	|	|	1459	...	|	|	|	|	...	1658	|	|	|	|	|	...	|	|	|	|
Newton Abbot 111 116 d.	1027	1050	1055	1128	1154	1254	...	1325	...	1426	1454	1509	...	1532	1554	1628	1654	...	1710	1728	1754	1826	1854	1956	...	2027	2054	2207	0001
Exeter St Davids 111 116 a.	1051	1109	1119	1154	1213	1313	...	1352	...	1451	1512	1533	...	1551	1613	1652	1711	...	1735	1800	1813	1850	1913	2020	...	2046	2113	2232	0023
Exeter St Davids 116 d.	1052	1113	1122	1156	1215	1315	1341	1353	1413	1453	1515	1534	1542	1555	1615	1654	1715	1732	1737	...	1815	1852	1915	2023	2030	2048	2115	...	0059
Tiverton Parkway 116 d.	1106	1127	|	|	1229	1329	|	|	1429	|	1529	|	1558	|	1629	1707	1729	|	|	...	1830	|	1929	2037	2045	2103	2129	...	|
Taunton 115 116 d.	1119	1140	1149f	1220	1243	1342	1405	1417	1442	1517	1542	1600	1612	1620	1642	1720	1742	1757	1802	...	1842	1915	1942	2050	2107r	2116	2142	...	|
Bristol T M. 115/6 132 a.	1212	|	|	1315	|	|	|	1511	|	1612	|	|	1712	1658	|	1814	|	1854	|	...	|	|	|	|	2210	|	2223	...	|
Castle Cary 140 a.	...	|	1208	...	|	|	1424	...	|	...	|	1619	...	|	|	...	|	|	1821	...	|	|	|	|	...	2135	|	...	|
Westbury 140 a.	...	|	1230	...	|	|	1446	...	|	...	|	1639	...	|	|	...	|	|	1842	...	|	1954	|	|	...	2155	|	...	|
Newbury a.	...	|	1310	...	|	|	1525	...	|	...	|	1720	...	|	|	...	|	|	1922	...	|	|	|	|	...	2234	|	...	|
Reading 130/1/2/3/4 a.	...	1255	1326	...	1358	1457	1541	...	1558	...	1658	1736	...	1806	1757	...	1858	2012	1938	...	1957	2042	2058	2205	...	2250	2335	...	0405s
London Padd 130/1/2/3/4 a.	...	1324	1352	...	1424	1524	1607	...	1624	...	1724	1805	...	1836	1824	...	1924	2039	2005	...	2024	2107	2123	2241	...	2335	0009	...	0503

A – THE NIGHT RIVIERA – Conveys 🛏 1, 2. cl and (2). See also note ‡.
D – To Cardiff (Table **115**).
c – Arrives 2014.
f – Arrives 1144.
r – Arrives 2058.
s – Calls to set down only.
t – Until Sept. 11.
v – Via Trowbridge (Table **140**).
y – Departs 0559.
♠ – Service valid until Sept. 10.
☆ – Also calls at Teignmouth (7–10 minutes after Newton Abbot) and Dawlish (12–15 minutes after Newton Abbot).
‡ – Passengers may occupy cabins at London Paddington from 2230 and at Penzance from 2045⑦/2115Ⓐ.

GW 2nd class — PAIGNTON - EXETER — 111

*See also Tables **110** and **116***

	⚒	②–⑥	Ⓐ	⑥	⑥	Ⓐ	⑥	Ⓐ	Ⓐ	⑥	⚒	⑥	Ⓐ	⑥	Ⓐ	⑥	Ⓐ	⑥	⑥	Ⓐ	Ⓐ	⑥d	⑥e	⑥	Ⓐ	⚒	⚒
Paignton 🚂 d.		0001	0604	0610	0637	0639	0710	0719	0739	0750	0815	0840	0853	0855	0917	0916	0945	0948	1017	1024	1042	1045	1055	1118	1120	1153	1218
Torquay d.		0006	0609	0615	0642	0644	0715	0724	0744	0755	0820	0846	0858	0901	0922	0922	0950	0956	1023	1029	1047	1050	1100	1124	1125	1159	1224
Newton Abbot d.		0018	0634a	0628	0655	0656	0735c	0736	0756	0807	0832	0900	0910	0914	0934	0934	1009t	1011	1036	1041	1105t	1103	1113	1137	1138	1212	1236
Teignmouth d.		0025	0641	0635	0702	0703	0742	0743	0803	0814	0839	0907	0917	0922	0941	0942	1016	1018	1044	1048	1112	1111	1120	1144	1145	1219	1244
Dawlish d.		0030	0646	0640	0707	0708	0747	0748	0808	0819	0844	0912	0922	0927	0946	0947	1021	1024	1049	1053	1117	1116	1125	1150	1150	1224	1249
Exeter St Davids a.		0047	0711	0710	0736	0741	0812	0814	0841	0841	0910	0934	0949	0943	1009	1009	1047	1047	1110	1110	1147	1139	1147	1210	1210	1248	1309

	⑥d	⑥e	Ⓐ	⚒	⚒	⚒	⑥	Ⓐ	⑥	Ⓐ	⑥	Ⓐ	Ⓐ	⑥	Ⓐ	⑥	⑥	Ⓐ	⑥	Ⓐ	⑥	Ⓐ	⚒	⑥	Ⓐ	⑥	Ⓐ
Paignton 🚂 d.	1240	1253	1255	1318	1353	1418	1441	1452	1518	1524	1539	1551	1608	1615	1640	1652	1714	1719	1739	1748	1818	1818	1850	1918	1920	1938	1947
Torquay d.	1245	1259	1300	1324	1358	1424	1446	1458	1524	1529	1544	1556	1613	1621	1645	1657	1720	1724	1744	1753	1824	1824	1855	1923	1925	1943	1952
Newton Abbot d.	1258	1312	1312	1337	1411	1437	1458	1512	1537	1541	1557	1610	1625	1634	1657	1710	1734	1736	1757	1805	1837	1840t	1909	1936	1937	1955	2004
Teignmouth d.	1305	1319	1319	1344	1418	1444	1505	1519	1544	1548	1604	1617	1632	1641	1704	1717	1741	1743	1804	1812	1844	1847	1916	1943	1944	2002	2011
Dawlish d.	1310	1324	1324	1349	1424	1449	1510	1524	1550	1553	1609	1622	1637	1647	1709	1723	1746	1748	1809	1817	1849	1852	1921	1948	1949	2007	2016
Exeter St Davids a.	1347	1347	1347	1409	1447	1510	1537	1547	1609	1610	1640	1646	1709	1711	1735	1748	1813	1813	1838	1842	1909	1909	1944	2012	2009	2029	2038

	Ⓐ	⑥	Ⓐ	⑥	Ⓐ	Ⓐ	Ⓐ	Ⓐ	⑦	⑦	⑦	⑦	⑦	⑦	⑦	⑦	⑦	⑦	⑦	⑦	⑦	⑦	⑦	⑦	⑦	⑦
Paignton 🚂 d.	2028	2016	2055	2120	2108	2139	2220	2320	0930	1036	1057	1154	1253	1353	1415	1440	1551	1614	1640	1730	1751	1853	1943	2054	2155	2235
Torquay d.	2033	2022	2100	2125	2113	2144	2225	2325	0936	1042	1102	1159	1259	1358	1420	1445	1557	1620	1645	1736	1757	1859	1948	2100	2200	2240
Newton Abbot d.	2045	2035	2112	2137	2125	2156	2237	2337	0956f	1055	1114	1211	1311	1410	1432	1457	1610	1633	1657	1748	1809	1912	2000	2112	2212	2253
Teignmouth d.	2052	2042	2119	2144	2132	2203	2244	2344	1003	1102	1121	1218	1318	1417	1439	1504	1617	1640	1704	...	1816	1919	2007	2119	2219	2300
Dawlish d.	2057	2047	2124	2149	2137	2208	2249	2349	1008	1107	1126	1223	1323	1422	1444	1509	1622	1645	1709	...	1821	1924	2012	2124	2224	2305
Exeter St Davids a.	2114	2113	2149	2211	2202	2233	2314	0014	1038	1119	1151	1249	1348	1447	1509	1547	1648	1710	1747	...	1846	1949	2037	2148	2249	2319

a – Arrives 0620.
c – Arrives 0726.
d – Until Sept. 10.
e – From Sept. 17.
f – Arrives 10–12 minutes earlier.
t – Arrives 5–6 minutes earlier.
🚂 – Dartmouth Steam Railway (Paignton - Kingswear). ✆ 01803 555 872. www.dartmouthrailriver.co.uk

GREAT BRITAIN

112 PLYMOUTH - NEWQUAY and PENZANCE — GW, XC

km	Ⓐ	Ⓐ	Ⓐ	Ⓐ	Ⓐ	Ⓐ	Ⓐ	Ⓐ	Ⓐ	Ⓐ	Ⓐ	Ⓐ	Ⓐ	Ⓐ	Ⓐ	Ⓐ	Ⓐ	Ⓐ	Ⓐ	Ⓐ	Ⓐ	Ⓐ	Ⓐ	Ⓐ	Ⓐ	Ⓐ
			A	🍷	2	🍷	2	2E	2	2	🍷b	2a	2b	🍷	2G	2	🍷	2B	🍷b	2	2B	🍷	2	2	2B	🍷
	London Padd **110** d.	...	2345p	...	...	...	...	...	...	...	...	...	...	0637	...	...	0804	...	0904	*0904*b	...	1004	...	...	...	1204
	Bristol T M **110 116** d.	...	|	...	...	...	...	...	0540	...	...	0650	0650	|	0749	0752	|	0856	|	|	0956	|	...	...	1155	|
0	**Plymouth** d.	0535	|	0618	0639	0712	...	0743	0808	0847	0910	0913	0918	0945	1015	1044	1120	1144	1225	1219	1246	1317	1343	1418	1446	1515
7	Saltash d.	0544	|	|	0648	0723	...	0752	0825	0857	0920	0924	0929	0954	1026	1055	|	1153	1236	1228	1255	|	1356	1427	1455	|
29	Liskeard d.	0604	0612	0641	0707	0747	...	0811	0843	0917	0940	0944	0948	1014	1045	1114	1144	1214	1255	1246	1314	1341	1415	1445	1514	1539
43	Bodmin Parkway 🚌 d.	0616	0626	0654	0719	0759	...	0823	0855	0929	0952	0956	1001	1026	1057	1125	1156	1226	1308	1257	1326	1354	1427	1457	1526	1552
49	Lostwithiel d.	0621	0633	|	0724	0804	...	0829	0900	0934	|	1001	1006	1031	1102	1130	|	1231	|	1302	1331	|	1432	1502	1531	|
56	Par ❖♡ d.	0629	0641	0707	0731	0811	0818	0836	0907	0941	1004	1008	1013	|	1109	1138	1206	1237	1325	1309	1337	1404	1438	1509	1537	1602
89	**Newquay** ❖♡ a.	|	|	|	|	|	0910	|	|	|	1049	|	|	|	|	|	|	|	1417	|	|	|	|	|	|	|
63	St Austell d.	0636	0649	0714	0738	0819	...	0843	0914	0948	...	1014	1019	1043	1116	1145	1213	1245	...	1317	1345	1411	1446	1517	1545	1609
86	Truro d.	0659	0707	0731	0755	0836	...	0901	0931	1004	...	1031	1036	1100	1133	1202	1230	1301	...	1334	1401	1429	1502	1533	1601	1627
101	Redruth d.	0710	0720	0743	0807	0848	...	0914	0943	1016	...	1043	1048	1112	1145	1214	1242	1313	...	1346	1413	1441	1514	1545	1613	1639
107	Camborne d.	0717	0728	|	0813	0855	...	0920	0949	1023	...	1049	1054	1119	1151	1220	1248	1319	...	1352	1419	1448	1520	1551	1619	1646
119	St Erth d.	0729	0742	0803	0826	0908	...	0931	1001	1034	...	1101	1105	1131	1203	1231	1258	1331	...	1403	1431	1458	1531	1603	1631	1659
128	**Penzance** a.	0738	0754	0812	0835	0919	...	0940	1010	1043	...	1110	1114	1140	1212	1240	1307	1340	...	1412	1440	1507	1540	1612	1640	1708

	Ⓐ	Ⓐ	Ⓐ	Ⓐ	Ⓐ	Ⓐ	Ⓐ	Ⓐ	Ⓐ	Ⓐ	Ⓐ	Ⓐ	Ⓐ
	2	2	2B	🍷	2B	🍷	2	C	🍷	🍷	🍷	2B	2N
London Padd **110** d.	...	...	...	1404	...	1504	...	...	1604	1704	1804	...	1904c
Bristol T M **110 116** d.	...	...	1355	|	1455	|	...	1645	|	|	|	1855	|
Plymouth d.	1547	1555	1647	1720	1746	1821	1830	1853	1925	2028	2117	2146	2238
Saltash d.	1556	1616	1656	1730	1755	|	1848	|	1934	2037	|	2155	2247
Liskeard d.	1614	1639	1714	1749	1814	1845	1910	1918	1954	2057	2141	2214	2306
Bodmin Parkway 🚌 d.	1626	1651	1725	1802	1826	1857	1922	1931	2006	2109	2153	2226	2318
Lostwithiel d.	1631	1657	1730	1808	1831	|	1927	|	|	2115	|	2231	2323
Par ❖♡ d.	1638	1704	1738	1815	1838	1908	1933	|	2016	2122	2204	2238	2330
Newquay ❖♡ a.	|	|	|	|	|	|	|	|	|	|	|	|	|
St Austell d.	1645	1712	1746	1822	1845	1915	1940	1949	2023	2129	2211	2245	2338
Truro d.	1702	1731	1802	1839	1901	1932	1956	2009	2040	2147	2228	2302	2355
Redruth d.	1714	1743	1814	1851	1913	1944	2009	2021	2052	2200	2239	2313	0007
Camborne d.	1720	1749	1820	1858	1919	1951	2015	|	2059	2206	|	2319	0013
St Erth d.	1731	1801	1832	1913	1931	2001	2026	2037	2111	2216	|	2331	0026
Penzance a.	1740	1810	1841	1923	1940	2010	2035	2047	2120	2225	2259	2340	0035

	⑥	⑥	⑥	⑥	⑥	⑥	⑥2	⑥2	⑥	⑥	⑥	⑥	⑥
	2	A	2	2E	2	2n	En	Ek	🍷k	2	🍷	2n	🍷k
London Padd **110** d.	...	2345p	...	...	...	...	...	...	...	...	...	...	0700
Bristol T M **110 116** d.	...	|	...	...	0540	...	...	...	0640	0642n	0742	...	|
Plymouth d.	0518	|	...	0740	0808	...	0846	0844	0900	0911	0946	1017	1018
Saltash d.	|	|	...	0749	0826	...	0855	0854	|	0922	0955	1026	1027
Liskeard d.	0541	0605	...	0809	0845	...	0914	0913	0925	0944	1012	1114	1047
Bodmin Parkway 🚌 d.	0552	0619	...	0821	0856	...	0925	0926	0937	0956	1025	1126	1059
Lostwithiel d.	0557	0626	...	0826	0901	...	0930	0931	|	1001	|	1131	1105
Par ❖♡ d.	0605	0634	0652	0833	0909	0925	0938	0938	0950	1008	1035	1138	1112
Newquay ❖♡ a.	|	|	0743	|	|	1016	|	|	1036	|	|	|	|
St Austell d.	0611	0643	...	0840	0915	...	0944	0946	...	1015	1043	1145	1120
Truro d.	0627	0703	...	0856	0932	...	1001	1003	...	1032	1100	1202	1137
Redruth d.	0639	0717	...	0908	0944	...	1013	1015	...	1044	1112	1214	1148
Camborne d.	0645	0724	...	0914	0950	...	1019	1022	...	1050	1119	1220	1155
St Erth d.	0658	0739	...	0926	1002	...	1031	1035	...	1102	1132	1231	1208
Penzance a.	0707	0750	...	0935	1011	...	1040	1044	...	1111	1141	1240	1217

	⑥	⑥	⑥	⑥	⑥	⑥	⑥	⑥	⑥	⑥	⑥	⑥	⑥	⑥	⑥	⑥	⑥	⑥	⑥	⑥	⑥	⑥	⑥	⑥	⑥	⑥	⑥
	2	🍷	2	2B	2n	🍷k	2B	🍷	2	2E	2n	🍷k	2B	🍷k	🍷	2n	2	🍷	2B	🍷	2	2B	🍷	2B	C	2	2
London Padd **110** d.	...	0804	...	...	...	0904	...	1004	...	...	...	1104	...	1137	1204	...	...	1304	...	1404	...	...	1504	...	...	...	...
Bristol T M **110 116** d.	0755	|	...	0855	...	|	0955	|	...	...	...	|	1155	|	|	...	...	|	1355	|	...	1455	|	1555	1645	...	...
Plymouth d.	1043	1115	...	1144	1220	1218	1245	1318	...	1345	1418	1415	1445	1503	1518	...	1542	1618	1645	1718	...	1746	1820	1836	1902	1927	...
Saltash d.	1055	|	...	1153	1229	1227	1254	|	...	1354	1427	1424	1454	|	|	...	1552	|	1654	|	...	1755	|	1854	|	1936	...
Liskeard d.	1114	1140	...	1213	1244	1244	1313	1343	...	1414	1446	1444	1513	|	1543	...	1614	1643	1714	1743	...	1814	1845	1914	1925	1955	...
Bodmin Parkway 🚌 d.	1126	1152	...	1225	1256	1257	1325	1355	...	1425	1458	1456	1525	|	1555	...	1625	1655	1726	1755	...	1826	1857	1926	1938	2006	...
Lostwithiel d.	1131	|	...	1230	1301	1302	1330	|	...	1430	1503	1502	1530	|	|	...	1630	|	1731	|	...	1831	|	1931	|	2011	...
Par ♡ d.	1138	1203	1212	1237	1308	1310	1337	1406	1412	1438	1510	1509	1537	1548	1606	1612	1638	1706	1739	1806	1813	1838	1908	1939	|	2019	2025
Newquay ♡ a.	|	|	1303	|	|	|	|	|	1503	|	|	|	|	1641	|	1703	|	|	|	|	1904	|	|	|	|	|	2116
St Austell d.	1145	1211	...	1244	1315	1317	1344	1414	...	1444	1517	1517	1544	...	1614	...	1645	1714	1745	1813	...	1845	1915	1945	1956	2025	...
Truro d.	1202	1229	...	1301	1332	1335	1401	1431	...	1501	1534	1534	1601	...	1631	...	1702	1730	1802	1830	...	1901	1932	2002	2015	2042	...
Redruth d.	1214	1241	...	1313	1344	1347	1413	1443	...	1513	1543	1546	1613	...	1643	...	1714	1742	1814	1842	...	1913	1944	2014	2027	2053	...
Camborne d.	1220	1248	...	1319	1350	1354	1419	1450	...	1519	1552	1553	1619	...	1650	...	1720	1749	1820	1849	...	1919	1950	2020	|	2059	...
St Erth d.	1231	1259	...	1331	1401	1407	1431	1500	...	1531	1604	1606	1631	...	1700	...	1731	1802	1832	1900	...	1931	2001	2032	2043	2112	...
Penzance a.	1240	1308	...	1340	1410	1416	1440	1509	...	1540	1613	1615	1640	...	1709	...	1740	1811	1841	1909	...	1940	2010	2041	2053	2121	...

	⑥	⑥	⑥
	D	🍷	🍷
London Padd **110** d.	...	1704	1804
Bristol T M **110 116** d.	1745	|	|
Plymouth d.	1951	2023	2123
Saltash d.	|	2033	|
Liskeard d.	2014	2053	2147
Bodmin Parkway 🚌 d.	2026	2105	2159
Lostwithiel d.	|	|	2205
Par ❖♡ d.	|	2115	2212
Newquay ❖♡ a.	|	|	|
St Austell d.	2044	2122	2219
Truro d.	2100	2139	2236
Redruth d.	2111	2151	2247
Camborne d.	|	2157	2254
St Erth d.	2130	2208	2306
Penzance a.	2139	2217	2315

	⑦	⑦	⑦	⑦	⑦	⑦	⑦	⑦	⑦	⑦	⑦	⑦	⑦	⑦	⑦	⑦	⑦	⑦	⑦	⑦	⑦	⑦	⑦
	2	🍷	2E	2d	2	🍷d	🍷	🍷	2	🍷	2	🍷d	2B	🍷	2	2B	🍷	2B	2B	🍷	2E	🍷	🍷
London Padd **110** d.	...	...	...	...	...	...	0752	0851	...	1003	...	1103	...	1203	...	...	1403	...	...	1603	...	1703	1803
Bristol T M **110 116** d.	...	...	...	...	0800	...	|	|	0955	|	...	|	1145	|	...	1354	|	1454	1554	|	...	|	|
Plymouth d.	0849	0914	1001	...	1040	1123	1140	1215	1245	1315	1340	1415	1440	1515	1540	1635	1715	1735	1835	1915	1935	2015	2115
Saltash d.	0905	|	1009	...	1054	|	1149	|	1254	|	1349	|	1449	|	1549	1645	|	1744	1846	|	1945	|	2124
Liskeard d.	0924	0938	1029	...	1113	1147	1209	1239	1313	1339	1409	1439	1508	1539	1609	1705	1739	1805	1903	1939	2004	2039	2144
Bodmin Parkway 🚌 d.	0936	0950	1040	...	1125	1200	1221	1252	1325	1352	1421	1452	1520	1552	1620	1716	1752	1817	1915	1952	2016	2052	2156
Lostwithiel d.	0941	|	1044	...	1130	|	1227	|	1330	|	1426	|	1525	|	1625	1721	|	1822	1920	|	2021	|	2201
Par ❖♡ d.	0948	1000	1054	1057	1138	1212	1234	1303	1338	1403	1433	1505	1533	1602	1632	1728	1803	1829	1928	2003	2029	2102	2208
Newquay ❖♡ a.	|	|	|	1143	|	1256	|	|	|	|	|	1551	|	|	|	|	|	|	|	|	|	|	|
St Austell d.	0954	1008	1102	...	1145	...	1242	1310	1345	1410	1440	...	1540	1610	1639	1735	1810	1835	1934	2010	2035	2110	2216
Truro d.	1010	1025	1119	...	1201	...	1259	1327	1400	1427	1456	...	1556	1627	1656	1751	1827	1851	1951	2027	2051	2127	2233
Redruth d.	1022	1036	1132	...	1213	...	1311	1339	1412	1439	1508	...	1608	1639	1708	1803	1839	1903	2003	2039	2103	2139	2244
Camborne d.	1028	1043	1138	...	1219	...	1318	1346	1418	1446	1515	...	1615	1646	1715	1809	1846	1910	2009	2046	2109	2146	2251
St Erth d.	1039	1053	1150	...	1231	...	1331	1357	1429	1457	1527	...	1627	1656	1727	1820	1857	1921	2021	2057	2121	2156	2303
Penzance a.	1048	1102	1159	...	1240	...	1340	1406	1438	1506	1536	...	1636	1705	1736	1829	1906	1930	2030	2106	2130	2205	2312

A – THE NIGHT RIVIERA – Conveys 🛏 1, 2. cl and (2). See also note ‡ on page 95. **For overnight journeys only**.
B – From/to Cardiff Central (Tables **110** and **115**).
C – From/to Edinburgh (Table **116**).
D – From Aberdeen (Tables **222** and **116**).
E – From/to Exeter St Davids (Table **110**).
G – From/to Gloucester (Tables **138** and **110**).
N – On ⑤ conveys (12) and 🍷.
P – Until Sept. 10 to Exeter St Davids (Table **110**).
a – From Sept. 12.
b – Until Sept. 9.
c – ⑤ only.
d – Until Sept. 11.
h – From Sept. 18.
k – Until Sept. 10.
n – From Sept. 17.
p – Previous night.

NOTES CONTINUE ON NEXT PAGE ▶ ▶ ▶

113 BRANCH LINES and BUS CONNECTIONS IN DEVON and CORNWALL — 2nd class GW

EXETER - EXMOUTH *'The Avocet Line'* *18 km*

From Exeter St Davids: on Ⓐ at 0520, 0544, 0607, 0648, 0716, 0744, 0817, 0846, 0916, 0952, 1015, 1051, 1115, 1151, 1215, 1250, 1313, 1351, 1415, 1450, 1515, 1550, 1615, 1649, 1715, 1739, 1817, 1846, 1913, 1948, 2015, 2042, 2118, 2153, 2240, 2340; on ⑥ at 0608, 0648, 0717, 0746, 0817, 0845, 0915, 0945, 1017, 1052, 1116, 1145**f**, 1152**g**, 1217, 1252, 1317, 1352, 1417, 1453, 1516, 1545, 1617, 1646, 1716, 1751 1816, 1846, 1916, 2017, 2117, 2217, 2313; on ⑦ at 0817, 0915, 0950, 1012, 1041, 1115, 1155, 1216, 1252, 1315, 1350, 1415, 1451, 1516, 1551, 1616, 1651, 1717, 1750, 1816, 1850, 1953, 2049, 2153, 2253.

From Exmouth: on Ⓐ at 0019②–⑤, 0551, 0615, 0655, 0724, 0754, 0824, 0854, 0923, 0957 and at the same minutes past each hour until 1523, 1555, 1623, 1657, 1726, 1756, 1826, 1856, 1924, 1956, 2024, 2054, 2126, 2156, 2224, 2319; on ⑥ at 0019, 0655, 0725, 0755, 0825, 0855, 0925, 0955, 1024, 1057, 1124, 1157, 1224, 1257, 1324, 1357, 1424, 1457, 1525, 1555, 1626, 1656, 1726, 1756, 1828, 1857, 1925, 1958, 2058, 2154, 2254, 2349; on ⑦ at 0855, 0955, 1021, 1054, 1157, 1226, 1257, 1324, 1357, 1424, 1457, 1524, 1554, 1624, 1656, 1723, 1757, 1824, 1856, 1959, 2056, 2127, 2230, 2330.

Journey: 37–40 minutes. Trains call at Exeter Central 3–4 minutes from Exeter St Davids.

f – Until Sept. 10. **g** – From Sept. 17.

EXETER - BARNSTAPLE *'The Tarka Line'* *63 km*

From Exeter St Davids: on Ⓐ at 0522, 0612, 0708, 0810, 0919 and hourly until 1519, 1618, 1720, 1821, 1922, 2023, 2127, 2255⑤; on ⑥ at 0524, 0616, 0710, 0818, 0920, 1019 and hourly until 1419, 1520, 1619, 1720, 1822, 1922, 2025, 2125; on ⑦ at 0828, 0918, 1020, 1118, 1219, 1319, 1419, 1519, 1618, 1719, 1819, 1919, 2017.

From Barnstaple: on Ⓐ at 0625, 0722, 0835 and hourly until 1535, 1631, 1733, 1838, 1942, 2041, 2141, 2241①–④, 2311⑤; on ⑥ at 0007, 0631, 0726, 0834, 0935, 1035, 1135, 1232, 1335, 1435, 1535, 1639, 1736, 1843, 1942, 2040, 2140, 2240; on ⑦ at 0937, 1037, 1132, 1236, 1336, 1431, 1532, 1630, 1737, 1832, 1935, 2036, 2136.

*Journey: 65 minutes. Trains call at **Crediton** (11 minutes from Exeter/54 minutes from Barnstaple) and **Eggesford** (40 minutes from Exeter/25 minutes from Barnstaple).*

PLYMOUTH - GUNNISLAKE *'The Tamar Valley Line'* *24 km*

From Plymouth:
on Ⓐ at 0457, 0630, 0824, 1028, 1228, 1428, 1638, 1838, 2130; on ⑥ at 0627, 0822, 1024, 1224, 1424, 1636, 1826, 2130; on ⑦ at 0903, 1110, 1320, 1520, 1744, 2001**a**.

From Gunnislake:
on Ⓐ at 0542, 0725, 0919, 1119, 1319, 1519, 1733, 1933, 2222; on ⑥ at 0716, 0914, 1114, 1314, 1514, 1734, 1918, 2220; on ⑦ at 1011, 1211, 1411, 1611, 1835, 2052**a**.

Journey: 45–60 minutes. **a** – Until Sept. 11.

LISKEARD - LOOE *'The Looe Valley Line'* *14 km*

From Liskeard:
on Ⓐ at 0557, 0713, 0830, 0936, 1036, 1136, 1236, 1346, 1446, 1550, 1654, 1757, 1900, 2005, 2105; on ⑥ at 0600, 0722, 0827, 0936, 1036, 1136, 1236, 1350, 1450, 1554, 1656, 1758, 1858, 2000, 2102; on ⑦ until Oct. 23 at 0936, 1040, 1220, 1350, 1511, 1633, 1755, 2015.

From Looe:
on Ⓐ at 0630, 0754, 0905, 1008, 1106, 1208, 1306, 1418, 1516, 1625, 1725, 1830, 1930, 2037, 2137; on ⑥ at 0632, 0755, 0902, 1008, 1105, 1208, 1305, 1422, 1519, 1629, 1726, 1830, 1928, 2032, 2136; on ⑦ until Oct. 23 at 1008, 1112, 1255, 1422, 1543, 1705, 1829, 2050.

Journey: 28–33 minutes.

EXETER - OKEHAMPTON *40 km*

From Exeter St. Davids:
0630⚒, 0738⚒, 0839⚒, 0842⑦, 0937, 1037, 1136, 1237, 1337, 1437, 1537, 1637, 1738⚒, 1742⑦, 1845, 1933⑥, 1942Ⓑ, 2110⑥, 2115Ⓐ, 2118⑦.

From Okehampton:
0725⚒, 0825⚒, 0925, 1025⚒, 1030⑦, 1125, 1225, 1325, 1425, 1525, 1623, 1725, 1830⚒, 1833⑦, 1929, 2025⑦, 2030⚒, 2201⑦, 2219Ⓐ, 2224⑥.

*Journey: 40–42 minutes. Trains call at **Crediton** (approx. 10 minutes from Exeter).*

GW, XC — PENZANCE and NEWQUAY - PLYMOUTH — 112

Ⓐ	Ⓐ	Ⓐ	Ⓐ	Ⓐ	Ⓐ	Ⓐ	Ⓐ	Ⓐ	Ⓐ	Ⓐ	Ⓐ	Ⓐ	Ⓐ	Ⓐ	Ⓐ	Ⓐ	Ⓐ	Ⓐ	Ⓐ	Ⓐ	Ⓐ	Ⓐ	Ⓐ	Ⓐ	Ⓐ	Ⓐ
	🍷	2	2B	🍷	2B	🍷	2B	🍷	2B	🍷	🍷C	2	🍷	2B	🍷b	2	2	🍷	2B	2	2	🍷	🍷b	2	2	2G
Penzance d.	0503	0520	0540	0605	0640	0710	0740	0815	0850	0910	0925	0950	1015	1050	...	1115	1150	1215	1250	1315	1350	1415	...	1450	1515	1550
St Erth d.	|	|	0548	|	0648	0719	0748	0824	0858	0920	0934	0958	1024	1058	...	1123	1158	1224	1258	1323	1358	1424	...	1458	1523	1558
Camborne d.	|	0540	0600	0622	0701	0730	0801	0835	0911	0934	|	1011	1035	1111	...	1136	1211	1235	1311	1336	1411	1435	...	1511	1536	1611
Redruth d.	0524	|	0606	0629	0707	0737	0807	0842	0917	0941	0954	1017	1042	1117	...	1142	1217	1242	1317	1342	1417	1442	...	1517	1542	1617
Truro d.	0536	0555	0618	0641	0720	0749	0820	0854	0930	0955	1007	1030	1055	1130	...	1155	1229	1255	1330	1354	1430	1454	...	1529	1554	1630
St Austell d.	0553	...	0633	0658	0736	0805	0835	0910	0946	1011	1023	1046	1111	1146	...	1211	1246	1311	1346	1410	1446	1511	...	1545	1610	1646
Newquay ★♡ d.	|	...	|	|	|	|	|	|	|	|	|	|	|	|	1118	|	|	|	|	|	|	|	1455	|	|	|
Par ★♡ d.	|	...	0639	0705	0743	0812	0842	0918	0953	1019	|	1053	1119	1153	1205	1217	1253	1319	1353	1417	1453	1519	1543	1553	1617	1653
Lostwithiel d.	|	...	0647	0712	0750	0819	0849	|	0959	|	|	1102	|	1159	1213	1224	1259	|	1359	1424	1500	|	|	1600	1624	1700
Bodmin Parkway 🚂 d.	0609	...	0652	0719	0755	0826	0855	0930	1005	1031	1041	1108	1131	1205	1220	1229	1305	1331	1405	1429	1505	1531	1556	1605	1629	1705
Liskeard d.	0622	...	0705	0732	0808	0839	0908	0944	1017	1044	1053	1122	1144	1217	1233	1242	1317	1344	1417	1442	1517	1544	1610	1618	1641	1718
Saltash d.	0637	...	0726	0753	0828	0857	0925	|	1037	|	|	1139	|	1236	1255r	1302	1339	|	1435	1500	1535	|	|	1636	1704	1735
Plymouth a.	0648	...	0743	0805	0846	0908	0934	1008	1046	1107	1116	1149	1208	1245	1306	1312	1352	1409	1445	1509	1544	1608	1635	1645	1720	1744
Bristol T M **110 116** a.	|	...	1020	|	1117	|	1217	|	1316	|	1326	...	|	1516	|	...	...	|	1719	...	...	|	|	w	...	2002
London Padd **110** a.	0955	...	...	1129	...	1229	...	1329	...	1427	...	...	1529	...	1629	...	...	1729	...	...	...	1924	2019	...	...	...

	Ⓐ	Ⓐ	Ⓐ	Ⓐ	Ⓐ	Ⓐ	Ⓐ	Ⓐ	Ⓐ	Ⓐ	Ⓐ	⑥	⑥	⑥	⑥	⑥	⑥	⑥	⑥	⑥	⑥	⑥	⑥	⑥	⑥2	⑥2
	🍷	2B	2	🍷	2E	2	2	2	2	A		2	2B	🍷	2B	🍷	2	2P	🍷	2B	🍷	2	2n	🍷	Ek	Bn
Penzance d.	1615	1650	1715	1750	1815	1850	1915	2015	2100	2145	2208	0515	0540	0612	0640	0710	...	0740	0815	0852	0912	0950	...	1015	1045	1050
St Erth d.	1624	1658	1723	1759	1823	1858	1923	2023	2109	2155	2217	|	0549	|	0649	0719	...	0749	0825	0900	0922	0958	...	1025	1054	1059
Camborne d.	1635	1711	1736	1812	1836	1911	1936	2036	2122	2208	2231	0532	0602	0629	0702	0733	...	0802	0836	0913	0936	1011	...	1036	1107	1112
Redruth d.	1642	1717	1742	1818	1842	1917	1942	2043	2129	2216	2237	0538	0608	0636	0708	0740	...	0808	0843	0919	0943	1017	...	1043	1113	1118
Truro d.	1655	1730	1754	1830	1854	1930	1953	2055	2141	2229	2250	0550	0620	0648	0720	0752	...	0820	0856	0931	0956	1030	...	1056	1125	1130
St Austell d.	1711	1746	1811	1846	1910	1946	2011	2111	2157	2247	2306	...	0636	0705	0736	0808	...	0836	0913	0947	1013	1046	...	1113	1141	1146
Newquay ★♡ d.	|	|	|	|	|	|	|	|	|	|	|	...	|	|	|	|	0748	|	|	|	|	|	1020	|	|	|
Par ★♡ d.	1719	1753	1817	1853	1917	1953	2018	2118	2205	2256	2313	...	0643	0712	0743	0815	0838	0843	0920	0954	1020	1053	1110	1120	1148	1153
Lostwithiel d.	|	1759	1824	1900	1924	2000	2025	2125	2212	|	2320	...	0649	|	0749	|	...	0850	|	1000	|	1059	...	|	1154	1159
Bodmin Parkway 🚂 d.	1731	1805	1829	1907	1929	2005	2031	2131	2218	2308	2326	...	0655	0724	0755	0827	...	0856	0932	1006	1032	1105	...	1132	1200	1205
Liskeard d.	1744	1817	1842	1921	1942	2018	2044	2144	2231	2324	2338	...	0708	0737	0808	0840	...	0910	0946	1018	1046	1118	...	1146	1213	1218
Saltash d.	|	1835	1903	|	2000	2039	2104	2201	2249	|	|	...	0727	0755	0828	0858	...	0928	|	1038	|	1136	...	|	1232	1236
Plymouth a.	1807	1844	1914	1946	2009	2048	2121	2213	2259	|	0002	...	0745	0806	0846	0909	...	0937	1009	1048	1109	1145	...	1209	1241	1245
Bristol T M **110 116** a.	|	2118	...	2149	...	...	0004	...	...	|	...	...	1015	|	1116	|	...	...	|	1316	|	...	...	|	...	1516
London Padd **110** a.	2129	...	...	2356	...	...	...	...	...	0507	...	...	...	1129	...	1229	...	...	1329	...	1429	...	...	1529	...	...

	⑥	⑥	⑥	⑥	⑥	⑥	⑥	⑥	⑥	⑥	⑥	⑥	⑥	⑥	⑥	⑥	⑥	⑥	⑥2	⑥	⑥	⑥	⑥	⑥	⑥	⑥	⑥
	🍷k	🍷k	2n	2	🍷	2B	2	🍷k	2n	2B	🍷	🍷k	2n	2	2	2	🍷	🍷k	Bn	2n	2	🍷k	🍷	2E	2	2	
Penzance d.	...	1112	1115	1150	1218	1250	...	1310	1315	1350	1420	1445	1450	...	1515	1550	1620	1645	1650	...	1715	...	1750	1815	...	1930	2043
St Erth d.	...	1122	1123	1159	1228	1259	...	1319	1323	1359	1429	1454	1458	...	1523	1559	1629	1654	1659	...	1724	...	1759	1823	...	1939	2051
Camborne d.	...	1136	1136	1212	1239	1312	...	1333	1336	1412	1440	1508	1511	...	1536	1612	1640	1708	1712	...	1737	...	1813	1836	...	1952	2104
Redruth d.	...	1143	1142	1218	1246	1318	...	1340	1342	1418	1447	1515	1517	...	1542	1618	1647	1715	1718	...	1743	...	1820	1843	...	1958	2111
Truro d.	...	1156	1154	1230	1259	1330	...	1352	1354	1430	1500	1528	1530	...	1554	1630	1700	1727	1730	...	1755	...	1832	1855	...	2010	2123
St Austell d.	...	1212	1210	1246	1315	1346	...	1408	1410	1446	1516	1544	1546	...	1610	1646	1716	1743	1746	...	1811	...	1848	1911	...	2026	2139
Newquay ♡ d.	1115	|	|	|	|	|	1310	|	|	|	|	|	|	1510	|	|	|	|	|	1710	|	1730	|	|	1908	|	|
Par ♡ d.	1203	1220	1217	1253	1323	1353	1400	1416	1417	1453	1523	1552	1553	1600	1617	1653	1723	1750	1753	1800	1818	1828r	1855	1918	1958	2033	2146
Lostwithiel d.	|	1227	1223	1259	|	1359	...	1423	1423	1459	|	1559	1559	...	1623	1659	|	1757	1759	...	1824	|	1902	1925	...	2039	2153
Bodmin Parkway 🚂 d.	1216	1234	1229	1305	1335	1405	...	1430	1429	1505	1535	1606	1605	...	1629	1705	1735	1804	1805	...	1830	1841	1909	1931	...	2045	2159
Liskeard d.	1229	1247	1241	1318	1348	1418	...	1443	1442	1518	1548	1619	1618	...	1642	1718	1748	1817	1818	...	1843	1900t	1923	1945	...	2102r	2212
Saltash d.	|	1302	1259	1337	|	1436	...	1501	1500	1536	|	1637	1636	...	1702	1736	|	1835	1836	...	1901	|	|	2003	...	2122	2230
Plymouth a.	1253	1312	1308	1350	1411	1445	...	1511	1509	1546	1611	1647	1645	...	1721	1745	1811	1845	1845	...	1910	1923	1947	2012	...	2140	2240
Bristol T M **110 116** a.	|	|	...	...	|	1720	...	|	...	1816	|	|	...	...	...	2016	|	|	2125	...	...	2143	2149	...	...	...	...
London Padd **110** a.	1556	1629	...	...	1729	...	...	1829	...	...	1929	2026	...	...	...	...	2139	2209	...	...	...	...	2342	...	...	...	...

	⑥	⑥	⑦	⑦	⑦	⑦	⑦	⑦	⑦	⑦	⑦	⑦	⑦	⑦	⑦	⑦•	⑦	⑦	⑦	⑦	⑦	⑦	⑦	⑦	⑦	⑦
	2		🍷	2B	🍷	C	🍷	2B	2B	🍷	2	🍷d	2B	🍷	2E	🍷	2	🍷	2	🍷d	🍷	2	2	2	A	
Penzance d.	...	2130	0814	0850	0918	0930	1018	1050	1150	1218	1250	...	1350	1418	1450	1518	1550	1618	1650	...	1750	1815	1915	2040	2115	2132
St Erth d.	...	2139	0822	0858	0927	0938	1028	1058	1158	1227	1258	...	1358	1427	1458	1527	1558	1627	1658	...	1759	1823	1923	2048	2125	2140
Camborne d.	...	|	0833	0911	0938	|	1039	1111	1211	1238	1311	...	1411	1438	1511	1540	1610	1638	1710	...	1812	1836	1935	2101	2137	2153
Redruth d.	...	2156	0839	0917	0945	0955	1046	1117	1217	1245	1317	...	1417	1445	1517	1547	1615	1645	1715	...	1819	1842	1940	2108	2146	2200
Truro d.	...	2208	0851	0929	0957	1008	1058	1129	1229	1257	1329	...	1429	1457	1532r	1559	1627	1657	1727	...	1831	1853	1952	2120	2201	2212
St Austell d.	...	2225	0908	0945	1013	1024	1114	1145	1245	1313	1345	...	1445	1513	1548	1616	1642	1713	1742	...	1848	1910	2008	2136	2219	2228
Newquay ★♡ d.	2120	|	|	|	|	|	|	|	|	|	|	1330	|	|	|	|	|	|	|	1718	|	|	|	|	|	|
Par ★♡ d.	2212	|	0915	0951	1021	|	1122	1152	1251	1321	1352	1417	1451	1521	1554	1623	1649	1721	1749	1811	1855	1916	2014	2143	|	2235
Lostwithiel d.	2219	|	|	0957	|	|	|	1158	1257	|	1359	|	1457	|	1600	|	1655	|	1756	1820	|	1923	2020	2150	|	2242
Bodmin Parkway 🚂 d.	2225	2242	0927	1003	1033	1041	1134	1204	1303	1333	1404	|	1503	1533	1605	1635	1700	1733	1801	1827	1907	1929	2025	2156	2235	2248
Liskeard d.	2238	2254	0941	1015	1046	1055	1147	1216	1315	1346	1418	|	1515	1546	1617	1648	1712	1746	1813	1840	1920	1942	2037	2209	2250	2301
Saltash d.	2258	|	0958	1035	|	|	|	1234	1333	|	1438	|	1533	|	1634	|	1730	|	1833	|	|	2000	2056	2226	|	2318
Plymouth a.	2314	2318	1008	1044	1110	1120	1211	1243	1342	1409	1447	1501	1542	1609	1644	1711	1739	1809	1846	1903	1943	2009	2113	2238	|	2328
Bristol T M **110 116** a.	...	...	|	1315	|	1324	|	1511	1612	|	...	|	1814	|	...	|	...	|	...	|	|	...	...	...	|	...
London Padd **110** a.	...	...	1324	...	1424	...	1524	...	...	1724	...	1824	...	1924	...	2024	...	2123	...	2241	2335	...	...	...	0503	...

◄◄◄ **NOTES** (Continued from previous page).

r – Arrives 5–6 minutes earlier.
t – Arrives 1852.
w – Connects with train in previous column.

♡ – Par - Newquay: *'The Atlantic Coast Line'*.

🚂 –Bodmin & Wenford Railway (Bodmin Parkway - Bodmin General - Boscarne Junction *10 km*). ✆ 01208 73555. www.bodminrailway.co.uk

❖ – Additional trains **Par - Newquay**: On Ⓐ at 0600, 1013 **a**, 1213, 1413 **a**, 1613, 1823, 2029; on ⑦ at 0900 **d**, 1004 **h** 1315 **h**, 1735 **d**, 1615 **h**, 1931 **d**.

★ – Additional trains **Newquay - Par**: On Ⓐ at 0712, 0915, 1109 **a**, 1310, 1510 **a**, 1719, 1922, 2126; on ⑦ at 0955 **d**, 1156 **d**, 1058 **h**, 1425 **h**, 1755 **h**, 1834 **d**, 2027 **d**.

GW 2nd class — BRANCH LINES and BUS CONNECTIONS IN DEVON and CORNWALL — 113

Rail tickets are generally not valid on 🚌 services shown in this table.

BODMIN PARKWAY - PADSTOW — *Go Cornwall Bus 🚌 service 10*

From Bodmin Parkway station:
on ⚒ at 0652, 0740 **n**, 0810 **p**, 0910 and hourly until 1810, 1912, 2022, 2122;
on ⑦ at 0800, 1000, 1200, 1400, 1600, 1800.

From Padstow Station Road:
on ⚒ at 0610, 0730, 0800, 0930 and hourly until 1530, 1640, 1730, 1820, 1920, 2020, 2130;
on ⑦ at 0900, 1100, 1300, 1500, 1700, 1900.

Journey: 68 minutes. Buses also make calls in Bodmin town centre and at Bodmin General station, and call at ***Wadebridge*** *(35 minutes after Bodmin / 25 minutes after Padstow).*

TRURO - FALMOUTH DOCKS — *'The Maritime Line'* — *20 km*

From Truro:
on Ⓐ at 0600, 0627, 0712, 0742, 0815 and every 30 minutes until 1615, 1646, 1718, 1749, 1820, 1906, 1941 **P**, 2050, 2156, 2256; on ⑥ at 0604, 0630, 0715 and every 30 minutes until 1645, 1718, 1748, 1838, 1912, 1942, 2046, 2148, 2244; on ⑦ at 0855, 0950, 1050, 1150, 1247, 1341, 1445, 1550, 1650, 1755, 1855, 1955, 2100, 2205.

From Falmouth Docks:
on Ⓐ at 0627, 0712, 0742, 0815 and every 30 minutes until 1615, 1646, 1718, 1749, 1820, 1906, 1941, 2017, 2122, 2226, 2322; on ⑥ at 0631, 0715, 0745, 0815 and every 30 minutes untill 1645, 1718, 1748, 1838, 1912, 1942, 2008, 2120, 2215, 2310; on ⑦ at 0922, 1017, 1117, 1217, 1313, 1407, 1517, 1617, 1717, 1821, 1921, 2021, 2127, 2233.

Trains call at ***Falmouth Town*** *22 minutes after Truro and 3 minutes after Falmouth Docks.*
Journey: 25 minutes.

h – Until Sept. 11.
k – Until Oct. 23.
n – Schooldays - check locally for details.
p – School holidays (check locally for details) and ⑥.

ST AUSTELL - EDEN PROJECT — *First Kernow 🚌 service 27*

From St Austell bus station:
On Ⓐ at 0905, 0935 and hourly until 1635.
On ⑥ at 0835 and hourly until 1635.

From Eden Project:
⚒ at 0947 and hourly until 1647, 1717.
Journey: 20 minutes.

ST ERTH - ST IVES — *'The St Ives Bay Line'* — *7 km*

From St Erth:
on Ⓐ at 0706, 0750, 0838, 0938, 1018 and every 30 minutes until 1848, 1920, 1950, 2020, 2050, 2120, 2220;
on ⑥ at 0701, 0750, 0850, 0924, 0952, 1022, 1051, 1122 and every 30 minutes until 1652, 1726, 1808, 1907, 2005, 2036, 2117, 2147;
on ⑦ at 0851**h**, 0928**h**, 0959**h**, 1048**k**, 1118**k**, 1148 and every 30 minutes until 1748, 1833, 1933.

From St Ives:
on Ⓐ at 0732, 0807, 0902, 1003 and every 30 minutes until 1703, 1732, 1803, 1833, 1905, 1934, 2005, 2034, 2105, 2137, 2248;
on ⑥ at 0730, 0806, 0904, 0937, 1001036, 1105, 1136 and every 30 minutes until 1706, 1740, 1828, 1922, 2020, 2052, 2131, 2205;
on ⑦ at 0941**h**, 1012**h**, 1103**k**, 1133**k**, 1203 and every 30 minutes until 1803, 1903, 1948.

Journey: 15 minutes.

114 BIRMINGHAM - READING - SOUTHAMPTON - BOURNEMOUTH

Most services convey 🍷 XC

km		⚒	Ⓐ	⑥	⑥	Ⓐ	⚒A	Ⓐ	⑥	⚒	Ⓐ	⑥	Ⓐ	⚒	Ⓐ	⑥	Ⓐ	⑥	Ⓐ	⑥	Ⓐ	⑥	Ⓐ	⑥	Ⓐ
	Manchester Piccadilly **119** d.		...	...	0511	0511	...	0727	0727	0827	0927	0927	...	1027	1127	1127	...	1227	1227	1327	1327	1427	1427	1527	1527
	Newcastle **124** d.		...	...	|	|	...	|	|	|	|	|	0835	|	|	|	1035	|	|	|	|	|	|	|	|
	York **124** d.		...	...	|	|	...	|	|	|	|	|	0938	|	|	|	1137	|	|	|	|	|	|	|	|
	Leeds **124** d.		...	...	|	|	...	|	|	|	|	|	|	|	|	|	|	|	|	|	|	|	|	|	|
	Sheffield **124** d.		...	...	|	|	...	|	|	|	|	|	1024	|	|	|	1224	|	|	|	|	|	|	|	|
0	**Birmingham** New Street. **142 150** d.		0604	0604	0704	0704	0804	0904	0904	1004	1104	1104	1133	1204	1304	1304	1333	1404	1404	1504	1504	1604	1604	1704	1704
13	Birmingham Int'l ✈ **142 150** d.		0614	0614	0714	0714	0814	0914	0914	1014	1114	1114	|	1214	1314	1314	|	1414	1414	1514	1514	1614	1614	1714	1714
30	Coventry **141 142 150** d.		0625	0625	0725	0727	0825	0925	0925	1025	1125	1125	|	1225	1325	1325	|	1425	1425	1525	1525	1625	1625	1725	1725
45	Leamington Spa **128 141** d.		0637	0637	0737	0739	0837	0937	0937	1037	1137	1137	1202	1237	1337	1337	1403	1437	1440**a**	1537	1537	1637	1637	1737	1737
77	Banbury **128** d.		0655	0655	0755	0756	0855	0955	0955	1055	1155	1155	1218	1255	1355	1355	1419	1456	1456	1555	1555	1655	1655	1755	1755
114	Oxford a.		0714	0714	0813	0815	0914	1013	1013	1114	1213	1213	...	1313	1413	1415	...	1514	1515	1613	1613	1713	1713	1813	1814
114	Oxford **131** d.		0716	0716	0816	0816	0916	1016	1016	1116	1216	1216	...	1316	1416	1416	...	1516	1516	1616	1616	1716	1716	1816	1816
158	**Reading** **131** a.		0743	0742	0839	0846	0940	1044	1041	1141	1242	1239	...	1341	1441	1440	...	1540	1541	1639	1641	1740	1741	1841	1843
158	**Reading** d.		0752	...	0852	0852	...	1052	1051	...	1252	1252	...	...	1452	1453	...	...	...	1652	1652	...	1752	1852	...
183	Basingstoke **106** a.		0808	...	0909	0910	...	1110	1110	...	1308	1309	...	...	1510	1509	...	...	...	1709	1710	...	1810	1909	...
213	Winchester **106** a.		0826	...	0926	0926	...	1126	1126	...	1326	1326	...	...	1526	1526	...	...	...	1726	1726	...	1826	|	...
226	**Southampton** Airport ✈ **106** a.		0835	...	0934	0934	...	1135	1134	...	1334	1334	...	...	1534	1534	...	...	...	1734	1734	...	1834	1934	...
234	**Southampton** Central **106** a.		0843	...	0942	0942	...	1143	1142	...	1342	1342	...	...	1542	1542	...	...	...	1742	1742	...	1843	1942	...
255	Brockenhurst **106** a.		|	...	0958	0958	...	|	|	...	|	|	...	...	|	|	...	...	...	|	|	...	1858	1958	...
280	**Bournemouth** **106** a.		0914	...	1013	1013	...	1213	1213	...	1413	1413	...	...	1613	1613	...	...	...	1813	1817	...	1914	2013	...

	⑥	Ⓐ	⑥	Ⓐ	Ⓐ	⑥		Ⓐ	⑥	Ⓐ	⑦	⑦	⑦	⑦	⑦	⑦	⑦	⑦	⑦	⑦	⑦	⑦	⑦	⑦	⑦
Manchester Piccadilly **119** d.	1627	1627	1727	1727	1827	1827	...	1927	1927	2027		...	...	0827	0927	1027	1127	1227	1327	1427	1527	1627	1727	1827	1927
Newcastle **124** d.	|	|	|	|	|	|	...	|	|	|		...	...	|	|	|	|	|	|	|	|	|	|	|	|
York **124** d.	|	|	|	|	|	|	...	|	|	|		...	...	|	|	|	|	|	|	|	|	|	|	|	|
Leeds **124** d.	|	|	|	|	|	|	...	|	|	|		...	...	|	|	|	|	|	|	|	|	|	|	|	|
Sheffield **124** d.	|	|	|	|	|	|	...	|	|	|		...	...	|	|	|	|	|	|	|	|	|	|	|	|
Birmingham New Street. **142 150** d.	1804	1804	1904	1904	2004	2004	...	2104	2104	2204		...	0904	1004	1104	1204	1304	1404	1504	1604	1704	1804	1904	2004	2104
Birmingham Int'l ✈ **142 150** d.	1814	1814	1914	1914	2014	2014	...	2114	2114	2214		...	0914	1014	1114	1214	1314	1414	1514	1614	1714	1814	1914	2014	2114
Coventry **141 142 150** d.	1825	1825	1926	1925	2025	2027	...	2125	2125	2225		...	0925	1025	1125	1225	1325	1425	1525	1625	1725	1825	1926	2025	2125
Leamington Spa **128 141** d.	1837	1837	1938	1937	2037	2039	...	2137	2137	2237		...	0937	1037	1137	1237	1337	1437	1537	1637	1737	1837	1938	2038	2137
Banbury **128** d.	1855	1855	1955	1955	2054	2055	...	2155	2155	2255		...	0955	1055	1155	1255	1355	1455	1555	1655	1755	1855	1955	2055	2155
Oxford a.	1913	1913	2014	2014	2112	2114	...	2214	2213	2313		...	1013	1113	1213	1313	1413	1513	1613	1713	1813	1913	2013	2113	2213
Oxford **131** d.	1916	1916	2016	2018	2116	2116	...	2216	2216	2316		...	1016	1116	1216	1316	1416	1516	1616	1716	1816	1916	2016	2116	2216
Reading **131** a.	1940	1941	2039	2043	2141	2139	...	2241	2241	2350		...	1039	1139	1239	1339	1441	1539	1639	1739	1839	1939	2039	2139	2239
Reading d.	...	1950	2052	...	2152	2152	...	2249	2252	...		0952	...	1152	...	1352	...	1552	...	1752	...	1952	2052	2152	...
Basingstoke **106** a.	...	2010	2110	...	2210	2209	...	2307	2308	...		1011	...	1210	...	1410	...	1609	...	1810	...	2008	2110	2209	...
Winchester **106** a.	...	|	|	...	|	|	...	|	|	...		1026	...	1226	...	1426	...	1626	...	1826	...	|	|	|	...
Southampton Airport ✈ **106** a.	...	2034	2134	...	2234	2234	...	2334	2334	...		1034	...	1234	...	1434	...	1634	...	1834	...	2032	2134	2234	...
Southampton Central **106** a.	...	2043	2144	...	2244	2242	...	2344	2342	...		1042**b**	...	1242**b**	...	1442**b**	...	1642**b**	...	1842**b**	...	2043**c**	2142**b**	2242	...
Brockenhurst **106** a.	...	|	|	...	|	|	...	...	...	...		1103**c**	...	|	...	|	...	|	...	1903**c**	...	|	|	...	...
Bournemouth **106** a.	...	2115	2215	...	2314	2319	...	...	...	...		1126	...	1326	...	1525	...	1725	...	1926	...	2126	2226	...	...

	⚒	⑥	Ⓐ	Ⓐ	⑥	Ⓐ	⑥	Ⓐ	⑥	⚒		⚒	Ⓐ	Ⓐ	⑥	Ⓐ	⑥		Ⓐ	⚒	Ⓐ	⑥	⑥	Ⓐ	⚒
Bournemouth **106** d.		...	...	...	...	0630	...	0730	0745	...	...	0945	...	...	...	1145	1145	...	...	...	1345	1345	...	...	1545
Brockenhurst **106** d.		...	...	...	...	|	...	|	|	...	...	1000	...	...	...	|	|	...	...	...	|	|	...	...	|
Southampton Central **106** d.		...	0515	...	0615	0715**j**	...	0815**j**	0815	...	...	1015	...	...	...	1215	1215	...	...	...	1415	1415	...	...	1615
Southampton Airport ✈ **106** d.		...	0523	...	0623	0723	...	0823	0823	...	...	1023	...	...	...	1223	1223	...	...	...	1423	1423	...	...	1623
Winchester **106** d.		...	|	...	0631	0731	...	0831	0831	...	...	1031	...	...	...	1231	1231	...	...	...	1431	1431	...	...	1631
Basingstoke **106** d.		...	0548	...	0648	0748	...	0848	0848	...	...	1048	...	...	...	1248	1248	...	...	...	1448	1448	...	...	1648
Reading a.		...	0605	...	0705	0809	...	0905	0907	...	...	1105	...	...	...	1305	1305	...	...	...	1505	1505	...	...	1706
Reading **131** d.		0615	0615	0714	0715	0815	0815	0913	0915	1015	...	1115	...	1213	1215	1315	1315	...	...	1415	1515	1515	1615	1616	1715
Oxford **131** a.		0638	0637	0737	0738	0838	0838	0936	0938	1038	...	1138	...	1238	1238	1338	1338	...	...	1438	1538	1538	1638	1638	1738
Oxford d.		0639	0639	0739	0739	0839	0839	0939	0939	1039	...	1139	...	1239	1239	1339	1339	...	...	1439	1539	1539	1639	1639	1739
Banbury **128** d.		0657	0657	0757	0757	0857	0857	0957	0957	1057	...	1157	1228	1257	1257	1357	1357	...	1430	1457	1557	1557	1657	1658	1757
Leamington Spa **128 141** d.		0715	0715	0815	0815	0915	0915	1015	1015	1115	...	1215	1249	1315	1315	1415	1415	...	1449	1515	1615	1615	1715	1715	1815
Coventry **141 142 150** d.		0727	0727	0827	0827	0927	0927	1027	1027	1127	...	1227	|	1327	1327	1427	1427	...	|	1527	1627	1627	1727	1728	1827
Birmingham Int'l ✈ **142 150** d.		0738	0739	0838	0838	0938	0938	1038	1038	1138	...	1238	|	1338	1338	1438	1438	...	|	1538	1638	1638	1738	1738	1838
Birmingham New Street. **142 150** a.		0748	0749	0849	0849	0949	0948	1048	1048	1149	...	1248	1318	1349	1348	1449	1448	...	1518	1549	1648	1649	1748	1748	1848
Sheffield **124** a.		|	|	|	|	|	|	|	|	|	...	|	1447	|	|	|	|	...	...	|	|	|	|	|	|
Leeds **124** a.		|	|	|	|	|	|	|	|	|	...	|	|	|	|	|	|	...	...	|	|	|	|	|	|
York **124** a.		|	|	|	|	|	|	|	|	|	...	|	1542	|	|	|	|	...	...	|	|	|	|	|	|
Newcastle **124** a.		|	|	|	|	|	|	|	|	|	...	|	1644	|	|	|	|	...	...	|	|	|	|	|	|
Manchester Piccadilly **119** a.		0923	0923	1023	1023	1123	1123	1223	1223	1323	...	1423	...	1523	1523	1623	1623	...	...	1723	1823	1823	1923	1923	2023

	Ⓐ	⑥	Ⓐ	⑥		Ⓐ	⑥	Ⓐ	⑥	⑦	⑦	⑦	⑦	⑦	⑦		⑦	⑦	⑦	⑦		⑦	⑦	⑦	⑦
Bournemouth **106** d.	1645	...	...	1745	...	1845	...	1945	1945		...	...	0940	...	1140	...	...	1340	...	1540	...	...	1740	...	1940
Brockenhurst **106** d.	|	...	...	|	...	1900	...	|	2000		...	...	0955	...	|	...	...	|	...	|	...	...	1755	...	|
Southampton Central **106** d.	1715	...	...	1815	...	1915	...	2015	2015		...	0915	1015**r**	...	1215**r**	...	...	1415**r**	...	1615**r**	...	...	1815**c**	...	2015**r**
Southampton Airport ✈ **106** d.	1723	...	...	1823	...	1923	...	2023	2023		...	0923	1023	...	1223	...	...	1423	...	1623	...	...	1823	...	2023
Winchester **106** d.	1731	...	...	1831	...	|	...	|	|		...	0931	1031	...	1231	...	...	1431	...	1631	...	...	|	...	|
Basingstoke **106** d.	1748	...	...	1848	...	1948	...	2049	2048		...	0948	1048	...	1248	...	...	1448	...	1648	...	...	1848	...	2048
Reading a.	1805	...	...	1906	...	2007	...	2107	2105		...	1005	1105	...	1305	...	...	1505	...	1705	...	...	1905	...	2105
Reading **131** d.	1815	1815	1915	1915	...	2015	2015	2113	2115		0915	1015	1115	1215	1315	...	1415	1515	1615	1715	...	1815	1915	2015	2112
Oxford **131** a.	1839	1838	1938	1938	...	2038	2038	2136	2138		0938	1038	1138	1238	1338	...	1438	1538	1638	1738	...	1838	1938	2038	2133
Oxford d.	1840	1839	1939	1939	...	2039	2039	2137	2139		0939	1039	1139	1239	1339	...	1439	1539	1639	1739	...	1839	1939	2039	2136
Banbury **128** d.	1858	1857	1957	1957	...	2057	2057	2157	2157		0957	1057	1157	1257	1357	...	1457	1557	1657	1757	...	1857	1957	2057	2154
Leamington Spa **128 141** d.	1916	1915	2015	2015	...	2115	2115	2215	2215		1015	1115	1215	1315	1415	...	1515	1615	1715	1815	...	1915	2015	2115	2212
Coventry **141 142 150** d.	1928	1927	2027	2027	...	2127	2127	2227	2228		1027	1127	1227	1327	1427	...	1527	1627	1727	1827	...	1927	2027	2127	2224
Birmingham Int'l ✈ **142 150** d.	1938	1938	2038	2038	...	2138	2139	2238	2239		1038	1138	1238	1338	1438	...	1538	1638	1738	1838	...	1938	2038	2138	2234
Birmingham New Street. **142 150** a.	1949	1948	2049	2048	...	2150	2149	2248	2249		1049	1149	1249	1348	1448	...	1548	1648	1748	1848	...	1948	2048	2148	2244
Sheffield **124** a.	|	|	|	|	...	|	|	...	...		|	|	|	|	|	...	|	|	|	|	...	|	|	|	...
Leeds **124** a.	|	|	|	|	...	|	|	...	...		|	|	|	|	|	...	|	|	|	|	...	|	|	|	...
York **124** a.	|	|	|	|	...	|	|	...	...		|	|	|	|	|	...	|	|	|	|	...	|	|	|	...
Newcastle **124** a.	|	|	|	|	...	|	|	...	...		|	|	|	|	|	...	|	|	|	|	...	|	|	|	...
Manchester Piccadilly **119** a.	2123	2123	2223	2233	...	2323	2328	...	...		1239	1325	1424	1523	1626	...	1726	1826	1924	2025	...	2125	2224	2323	...

A – From Nottingham (Table **120**).

a – Arrives 1436.

b – Departs 8 – 10 minutes later.

c – Departs 5 – 7 minutes later.

j – Arrives 13 minutes earlier.

r – Arrives 7 – 9 minutes earlier.

GW — GATWICK AIRPORT ✈ - READING — 114a

km			Ⓐ	Ⓐ		Ⓐ	Ⓐ		Ⓐ	Ⓐ	Ⓐ	Ⓐ	Ⓐ	Ⓐ	Ⓐ	Ⓐ	Ⓐ	Ⓐ	Ⓐ	Ⓐ	Ⓐ	Ⓐ	Ⓐ
0	**Gatwick Airport** ✈ .... 185 d.	Ⓐ	0510	0600	...	0702	0802	...	0929	1029	1129	1229	1329	1429	1529	1629	1729	1829	1929	2029	2129	2229	2320
10	Redhill.................. 185 ⊡ d.		0530	0618	0642	0716	0816	...	0943	1043	1143	1243	1343	1443	1543	1645	1745	1845	1945	2043	2144	2243	2334
43	Guildford .... ⊡ d.		0603	0649	0728	0750	0848	...	1015	1114	1214	1314	1414	1514	1618	1716	1819	1916	2016	2114	2228	2326	0006
84	**Reading**.................... ⊡ a.		0651	0734	0816	0834	0925	...	1053	1151	1251	1351	1451	1551	1703	1802	1905	2004	2053	2156	2316	0017	0044

		⑥	⑥	⑥		⑥	⑥	⑥	⑥	⑥		⑦	⑦	⑦		⑦	⑦	⑦	⑦
Gatwick Airport ✈ .... 185 d.	⑥	0524	0629	0729	and at the same	1929	2029	2059	2217	2320	⑦	0611	0815	0915	and at the same	2015	2103	2218	2304
Redhill .... 185 ⊡ d.		0542	0643	0743	minutes past	1943	2043	2113	2231	2334		0623	0828	0928	minutes past	2028	2115	2231	2316
Guildford........................ ⊡ d.		0615	0714	0814	each hour until	2016	2114	2146	2313	0006		0656	0901	1001	each hour until	2101	2159	2304	0001
Reading........................ ⊡ a.		0704	0751	0851		2058	2158	2226	0003	0044		0741	0940	1038		2141	2245	2344	0049

		Ⓐ	Ⓐ	Ⓐ	Ⓐ	Ⓐ	Ⓐ	Ⓐ	Ⓐ		Ⓐ	Ⓐ	Ⓐ	Ⓐ	Ⓐ	Ⓐ	Ⓐ	Ⓐ		⑥	⑥
Reading........................ ⊡ d.	Ⓐ	0432	0531	0626	0650	0750	0901	1004	1101	and at the same	1601	1650	1750	1901	2001	2101	2134	2333	⑥	0426	0600
Guildford........................ ⊡ d.		0512	0612	0705	0748	0837	0940	1042	1140	minutes past	1640	1739	1837	1940	2040	2139	2221	0023		0510	0640
Redhill .... 185 ⊡ a.		0544	0646	0737	0837	0908	1012	1114	1212	each hour until	1714	1812	1909	2012	2112	2213	2303	0055		0541	0712
Gatwick Airport ✈ .... 185 a.		0555	0658	0753	0853	0925	1025	1125	1225		1725	1824	1920	2025	2125	2225	2315	0107		0555	0725

	⑥	⑥	⊙	⑥	⑥	⑥	⑥	⑥	⑥		⑦	⑦	⑦	❖	⑦	⑦	⑦	⑦	⑦
Reading........................ ⊡ d.	0701	0801	and at the same	1801	1901	1920	2032	2133	2334	⑦	0603	0657	0818f	and at the same	1818f	1918f	2012	2113	2303
Guildford........................ ⊡ d.	0741	0840	minutes past	1840	1940	2007	2112	2220	0022		0641	0735	0900	minutes past	1900	1958	2058	2200	2349
Redhill .... 185 ⊡ a.	0812	0912	each hour until	1912	2014	2043	2143	2303	0053		0713	0807	0934	each hour until	1934	2031	2141	2234	0030
Gatwick Airport ✈ .... 185 a.	0826	0925		1925	2025	2055	2156	2316	0104		0726	0823	0945		1945	2046	2154	2247	0041

f – Departs 2 minutes later until Oct. 2.

⊙ – Additional train: Reading d. 1320, Guildford d. 1407, Redhill a. 1442, Gatwick a. 1455. The 1401 from Reading does not run.

⊡ – Additional trains run Redhill - Reading and v.v.

❖ – The 1520 from Reading arrives Redhill 1637 and Gatwick 1648.

GW 2nd class — BRISTOL - TAUNTON — 115

km			Ⓐ	ⒶH	ⒶB	ⒶB	Ⓐ	ⒶA	ⒶB	ⒶB	ⒶB	Ⓐ	ⒶB	Ⓐ	ⒶB	ⒶB	Ⓐ	Ⓐ	Ⓐ	ⒶF	ⒶB	ⒶF	ⒶR	Ⓐ
	Cardiff Central 119 ....d.	Ⓐ	...	...	...	...	...	B	...	0800	0900	1000	1100	1200	1300	1400	1500	1600	1700	...	1800	...	1900	2000
0	**Bristol** Temple M.... 116 132 d.		0500	0525	0540	0650	0703	0749	0752	0856	0956	1055	1155	1256	1355	1455	1551	1652	1753	1815	1855	1910	1953	2058
31	Weston-super-Mare .... 132 d.		0534	0545	|	0709	0737	|	0827	0929r	1026	1126	1224	1325	1428r	1525	1627	1730	1829	1843	1932	1945r	2029	2137r
43	Highbridge and Burnham ....d.		0544	0556	|	0719	0748	|	0838	0939	1036	1136	1234	1335	1438	1535	1637	1740	1839	1854	1942	1956	2039	2147
53	Bridgwater ....d.		0551	0604	0611	0726	0755	0815	0845	0946	1043	1144	1242	1342	1445	1542	1645	1748	1846	1901	1950	2003	2046	2154
72	**Taunton**.................. 116 132 a.		0604	0616	0620	0735	0806	0824	0856	0956	1055	1155	1251	1352	1455	1552	1655	1758	1856	1912	1959	2014	2056	2205

	ⒶH	ⒶH	ⒶC		⑥H	⑥B	⑥	⑥K	⑥		⑥B	⑥B	⑥B	⑥F	⑥	⑥B	⑥	⑥B	⑥B	⑥B	⑥	⑥	⑥F	⑥R
Cardiff Central 119 ....d.	...	...	...	⑥	...	...	...	...	...	...	...	0800	0900	...	1000	1100	1200	1300	1400	1500	1600	1700	...	1800
Bristol Temple M ... 116 132 d.	2200	2305	2348		0520	0540	0619	0640	0725	...	0755	0855	0955	1010	1055	1155	1255	1355	1455	1555	1655	1755	1808	1853
Weston-super-Mare .... 132 d.	2239r	2340	0015s		0543	0559	0649	0700	0759	...	0827r	0924	1025	1035	1125	1225	1325	1426	1525	1625	1725	1825	1836	1926
Highbridge and Burnham ....d.	2250	2351	0026s		0554	0609	0659	0711	0809	...	0838	0934	1035	1046	1135	1235	1335	1436	1535	1636	1735	1835	1847	1935
Bridgwater ....d.	2257	2358	0033s		0602	0616	0706	0718	0816	...	0846	0941	1042	1054	1142	1242	1342	1443	1542	1643	1742	1842	1855	1942
Taunton.................. 116 132 a.	2314	0009	0044		0614	0625	0717	0729	0826	...	0858	0950	1052	1105	1152	1253	1352	1453	1551	1653	1753	1852	1906	1951

	⑥	⑥F	⑥F	⑥H	⑥J		⑦B	⑦J	⑦B	⑦	⑦B	⑦H	⑦B	⑦B	⑦B	⑦		⑦F	⑦	⑦C	⑦H	⑦	⑦	⑦
Cardiff Central 119 ....d.	1900	...	...	2100	...	⑦	...	...	...	...	1055	1200	1300	1400	1500	1555	...	...	1700	...	...	1759	1900	2000
Bristol Temple M ... 116 132 d.	1955	2011	2108	2152	2208		0800	0950	0955	1102	1145	1254	1354	1454	1554	1653	...	1705	1754	1810	1825	1851	1954	2053
Weston-super-Mare .... 132 d.	2028	2040	2139	2226	2235s		0828	|	1025	1129	1223	1323	1421	1524	1628r	1722	...	1735	1825	1839	1900	1927	2028	2126
Highbridge and Burnham ....d.	2038	2052	2150	2237	2247s		0838	|	1035	1138	1232	1334	1431	1534	1637	1732	...	1746	1835	|	1912	1937	2039	2135
Bridgwater ....d.	2045	2100	2157	2244	2254s		0845	1016	1042	1145	1239	1341	1437	1541	1644	1739	...	1753	1842	1854	1920	1944	2046	2142
Taunton.................. 116 132 a.	2055	2112	2208	2255	2306		0854	1026	1051	1155	1248	1352	1447	1551	1655	1749	...	1804	1853	1904	1932	1955	2058	2152

		Ⓐ	Ⓐ	Ⓐ	ⒶF	ⒶH	ⒶF	Ⓐ	ⒶB	ⒶB	ⒶB	ⒶB		Ⓐ	ⒶB	Ⓐ	ⒶB	Ⓐ	Ⓐ	Ⓐ	ⒶA	ⒶJ	ⒶB	ⒶH
Taunton.................. 116 132 d.	Ⓐ	0514	0611	0637	0655	0704	0723	0819	0920	1019	1111	1218	...	1309	1419	1513	1617	1711	1810	1914	1927	2003	2016	2132
Bridgwater ....d.		0525	0621	0648	0706	0715	0734	0829	0930	1029	1121	1228	...	1319	1429	1525	1627	1722	1821	1924	1937	2014	2026	2143
Highbridge and Burnham ....d.		0532	0629	0655	0713	0723	0742	0837	0937	1036	1128	1236	...	1327	1436	1533	1634	1730	1829	1932	|	|	2034	2150
Weston-super-Mare .... 132 d.		0545	0640	0710r	0724	0739r	0754	0847	0948	1047	1147f	1247	...	1347f	1447	1547r	1645	1745r	1845r	1947r	|	2029	2047	2201
Bristol Temple M ... 116 132 a.		0618	0716	0744	0752	0816	0824	0920	1020	1117	1217	1316	...	1415	1516	1616	1719	1819	1919	2016	2002	2057	2118	2230
Cardiff Central 119 ....a.		...	0822	...	...	0919	...	1019	1123	1221	1326	1420	...	1521	1622	1719	1821	1927	2023	2124	...	...	2218	2333j

	Ⓐ	ⒶB		⑥	⑥H	⑥F	⑥	⑥J	⑥	⑥B	⑥B	⑥J	⑥B	⑥	⑥L	⑥N	⑥B	⑥B	⑥	⑥P	⑥A	⑥B	⑥F	⑥M
Taunton.................. 116 132 d.	2244	2310	⑥	0513	0615	0657	0738	0758	0820	0919	1019	1108	1220	1320	1420	1520	1620	1720	1820	1830	1909	1932	1958	2024
Bridgwater ....d.	2254	2320		0524	0625	0707	0749	0808	0830	0929	1029	1118	1230	1330	1430	1530	1630	1730	1830	1840	1919	1942	2009	2034
Highbridge and Burnham ....d.	2301	2327		0531	0633	0715	0757	0815	0837	0937	1037	1125	1237	1337	1437	1537	1637	1737	1837	1848	1927	|	2016	2041
Weston-super-Mare .... 132 d.	2313	2341		0542	0646	0727	0810	0827	0848	0947	1047	1147f	1248	1347	1448	1547	1648	1747	1848	1902	1940	1956	2029	2051
Bristol Temple M ... 116 132 a.	2347	0004		0618	0720	0754	0844	0855	0916	1015	1116	1218	1316	1416	1516	1616	1720	1816	1916	1926	2007	2016	2056	2125
Cardiff Central 119 ....a.	...	...		...	0813	...	...	...	1021	1122	1222	1321	1412	1527	1621	1720	1821	1921	2028	...	...	...	...	2227

	⑥Q	⑥	⑥F	⑥H		⑦H	⑦H	⑦R	⑦B	⑦	⑦B		⑦B	⑦H	⑦C	⑦F	⑦B	⑦J	⑦	⑦F	⑦	⑦	⑦H	⑦
Taunton.................. 116 132 d.	2058	2128	2140	2150	⑦	0828	1011	1119	1220	1318	1417	...	1517	1612	1620	1704	1720	1757	1811	1858	1927	2017	2107	2210
Bridgwater ....d.	2109	2138	2151	2201		0839	1020	1128	1230	1328	1427	...	1527	1623	1631	1714	1730	1808	1821	1909	1936	2026	2118	2220
Highbridge and Burnham ....d.	|	2145	2158	2208		0846	1027	1135	1237	1336	1434	...	1534	1630	|	1721	1737	1815	1828	1916	1943	2033	2125	2227
Weston-super-Mare .... 132 d.	2124	2155	2210	2225r		0858	1040	1146	1247	1347	1444	...	1544	1643	|	1731	1747	1826	1840	1927	1953	2044	2136	2240
Bristol Temple M ... 116 132 a.	2143	2229	2237	2250		0932	1106	1212	1315	1415	1511	...	1612	1711	1658	1758	1814	1854	1913	1955	2026	2117	2210	2313
Cardiff Central 119 ....a.	...	...	...	...		...	1203	1259	1406	1505	1608	...	1702	1805	...	...	1905	...	...	...	...	...	...	...

A – To/from Gloucester (Table **138**).
B – To/from Penzance (Tables **110** and **112**).
C – [12] 🍷 London Paddington - Plymouth and v.v. (Table **110**).
F – [12] 🍷 London Paddington - Taunton and v.v. (Table **132**).
H – To/from Exeter St. Davids (Table **110**).
J – [12] 🍷 London Paddington - Exeter St Davids and v.v. (Table **132**).
K – Until Sept. 10 [12] 🍷 to Newquay (Tables **110** and **112**); from Sept. 17 [2] to Penzance (Tables **110** and **112**).
L – Until Sept. 10 from Taunton; From Sept. 17 from Penzance (Tables **110** and **112**).
M – Until Sept. 10 from Plymouth (Table **110**); from Sept. 17 from Penzance (Tables **110** and **112**).
N – Until Sept. 10 from Exeter St Davids (Table **110**); from Sept. 17 from Taunton.
P – Until Sept. 10 [12] 🍷 Paignton - London Paddington (Table **110**).
Q – Until Sept. 10 [12] 🍷 from Newquay.
R – To/from Plymouth (Table **110**).

f – Arrives 9–12 minutes earlier.
j – 2320 on ⑤.
r – Arrives 5–8 minutes earlier.
s – Calls to set down only.

116 BIRMINGHAM - BRISTOL - PAIGNTON and PLYMOUTH

Most services convey 🍷 XC

km		Ⓐ	Ⓐ	Ⓐ	Ⓐ	Ⓐ	Ⓐ	Ⓐ	Ⓐ	Ⓐ	Ⓐ	Ⓐ	Ⓐ	Ⓐ	Ⓐ	Ⓐ	Ⓐ	Ⓐ	Ⓐ	Ⓐ	Ⓐ
				D												★	B		⊠	b	
	Glasgow Central **124 220** d.	...	...	...	...	...	...	...	...	...	...	...	...	0748	...	...	...	...	...	...	...
	Edinburgh Waverley **124 220** d.	...	...	...	...	...	...	...	...	0606	0701	0806	...	0905	1003	...	1106	...	1203	1305	...
	Newcastle **124** d.	...	...	...	...	...	...	0640	...	0740	0840	0941	...	1041	1139	...	1241	...	1337	1440	...
	York **124** d.	...	...	...	...	...	0645	0744	...	0844	0944	1044	...	1144	1243	...	1344	...	1444	1544	...
	Leeds **124** d.	...	...	...	0611	...	0710	0811	...	0911	1011	1111	...	1211	1311	...	1411	...	1511	1611	...
	Sheffield **124** d.	...	...	...	0653	...	0753	0856	...	0956	1056	1155	...	1256	1355	...	1456	...	1556	1656	...
	Manchester Picc **119** d.	...	...	...	|	0705	|	|	0905	|	|	|	...	|	|	...	|	...	|	|	1705
0	**Birmingham** New Street **117** d.	...	...	0712	0812	0842	0912	1012	1042	1112	1212	1312	1342	1412	1512	1542	1612	1642	1712	1812	1842
73	Cheltenham Spa **117 138** d.	...	...	0752	0852	0932	0952	1052	1131	1152	1252	1352	1430	1452	1552	1630	1652	1730	1752	1852	1929
135	**Bristol** Parkway **138** d.	...	...	0827	0929g	1003	1022	1121	1210	1222	1321	1423	1501	1521	1622	1701	1722	1759	1824	1937	1958
145	**Bristol** Temple Meads **138** a.	...	...	0839	0938	1012	1032	1131	1219	1233	1332	1433	1514	1534	1632	1700	1732	1808	1833	1946	2008
145	**Bristol** Temple Meads **115 110** d.	0640	0812	0845	0945	...	1045	...	...	1245	1345	1445	...	1545	1645	1712	1745	1847	...	1949	...
217	Taunton **115 110** d.	0711	0843	0918	1017	...	1130	...	...	1317	1417	1518	...	1617	1718	1743	1817	1920	...	2021	...
240	Tiverton Parkway **110** d.	0723	0855	0931	1030	...	1142	...	...	1330	1430	1531	...	1630	1730	1755	1829	1932	...	2033	...
266	**Exeter** St Davids **110 111** d.	0743f	0912	0948	1049f	...	1158	...	...	1349f	1448	1548	...	1648	1748	1811	1847	1948	...	2050	...
298	Newton Abbot **110 111** d.	0802	0937f	1008	1109	...	1218	...	...	1409	1508	1609	...	1707	1808	1835	1908	2008	...	2110	...
308	Torquay **110 111** a.	|	0946	|	|	...	|	...	...	|	|	|	...	|	|	1845	|	|	...	|	...
311	**Paignton** **110 111** a.	|	0954	|	|	...	|	...	...	|	|	|	...	|	|	1852	|	|	...	|	...
312	Totnes **110** d.	0814	...	1020	1121	...	1231	...	...	1421	1521	1622	...	1719	1820	...	1920	2020	...	2123	...
350	**Plymouth** **110** a.	0840	...	1046	1148	...	1257	...	...	1448	1547	1648	...	1745	1847	...	1946	2046	...	2151	...
	Newquay **112** a.	...	...	...	...	...	...	...	...	...	...	...	...	...	|	...	...	...	...	...	...
	Penzance **112** a.	...	...	...	...	...	...	...	...	...	...	...	...	...	2047	...	...	...	...	...	...

	Ⓐ	Ⓐ	Ⓐ	Ⓐ	⑥	⑥	⑥	⑥	⑥	⑥	⑥	⑥	⑥	⑥	⑥	⑥	⑥	⑥	⑥	⑥	⑥
			c				D												★	B	
Glasgow Central **124 220** d.	...	...	...	...	...	...	...	...	...	...	...	...	...	...	...	...	0748	...	...	...	...
Edinburgh Waverley **124 220** d.	...	1508	1607	1707	...	...	...	...	...	...	...	...	0606	0658	0807	...	0908	1005	...	1108	1205
Newcastle **124** d.	1539	1639	1738	1840	...	...	...	...	...	...	...	...	0739	0839	0940	...	1043	1139	...	1242	1339
York **124** d.	1643	1744	1844	1944	...	...	...	...	...	0611	0744	...	0844	0944	1044	...	1143	1244	...	1344	1444
Leeds **124** d.	1711	1811	1911	2011	...	...	...	0609	...	0711	0811	...	0911	1011	1111	...	1211	1311	...	1411	1511
Sheffield **124** d.	1756	1856	1956	2056	...	...	...	0653	...	0755	0856	...	0956	1055	1155	...	1256	1356	...	1456	1556
Manchester Picc **119** d.	|	|	|	|	...	...	...	|	0705	|	|	0906	|	|	|	...	|	|	...	|	|
Birmingham New Street **117** d.	1912	2012	2112	2212	...	...	0712	0812	0842	0912	1012	1042	1112	1212	1312	1342	1412	1512	...	1612	1712
Cheltenham Spa **117 138** d.	1952	2053	2152	2252	...	...	0752	0852	0929	0952	1052	1129	1152	1252	1352	1429	1452	1552	...	1652	1752
Bristol Parkway **138** d.	2022	2127f	2234	2321	...	...	0825f	0925	0959	1025f	1125	1158	1227	1325	1425	1458	1525	1625	...	1725	1825f
Bristol Temple Meads **138** a.	2032	2136	2244	2331	...	...	0836	0934	1008	1036	1135	1210	1238	1336	1434	1507	1536	1634	...	1735	1834
Bristol Temple Meads **115 110** d.	...	2144	...	...	0607	0810	0845	0945	...	1045	...	...	1245	1345	...	...	1545	1645	1710	1745	...
Taunton **115 110** d.	...	2215	...	...	0714	0842	0917	1017	...	1117	...	...	1317	1417	...	...	1617	1717	1741	1817	...
Tiverton Parkway **110** d.	...	2228	...	...	0726	0854	0932	1030	...	1130	...	...	1330	1430	...	...	1630	1730	1753	1830	...
Exeter St Davids **110 111** d.	...	2243	...	...	0743	0912	0949	1049f	...	1149	...	...	1347	1449	...	...	1649	1749	1810	1847	...
Newton Abbot **110 111** d.	...	2303	...	...	0802	0933	1009	1109	...	1209	...	...	1409	1509	...	...	1709	1809	1838	1906	...
Torquay **110 111** a.	...	|	...	...	|	0945	|	|	...	|	...	...	|	|	...	...	|	|	1847	|	...
Paignton **110 111** a.	...	|	...	...	|	0952	|	|	...	|	...	...	|	|	...	...	|	|	1854	|	...
Totnes **110** d.	...	2315	...	...	0814	...	1021	1121	...	1221	...	...	1421	1521	...	...	1721	1821	...	1918	...
Plymouth **110** a.	...	2343	...	...	0840	...	1047	1148	...	1247	...	...	1448	1549	...	...	1747	1848	...	1944	...
Newquay **112** a.	...	...	...	...	...	...	...	...	...	...	...	...	...	...	...	...	...	|	...	|	...
Penzance **112** a.	...	...	...	...	...	...	...	...	...	...	...	...	...	...	...	...	...	2053	...	2139	...

	⑥	⑥	⑥	⑥	⑥	⑦	⑦	⑦	⑦	⑦	⑦	⑦	⑦	⑦	⑦	⑦	⑦	⑦	⑦	⑦	⑦
					c								★					B		c	
Glasgow Central **124 220** d.	...	...	...	...	...	...	...	...	...	...	...	...	...	...	...	...	...	...	...	...	...
Edinburgh Waverley **124 220** d.	1309	...	1404	1505	1606	...	...	...	...	...	...	0908	...	1005	1105	1205	1309	1408	1508	1608	1708
Newcastle **124** d.	1443	...	1539	1638	1739	...	...	...	...	...	0935	1039	...	1140	1240	1339	1441	1540	1640	1739	1839
York **124** d.	1544	...	1644	1742	1844	...	...	...	...	0935	1034	1144	...	1244	1344	1443	1544	1644	1744	1844	1944
Leeds **124** d.	1611	...	1711	1811	1911	...	...	0811	0900	1000	1100	1211	...	1311	1411	1511	1611	1711	1811	1911	2011
Sheffield **124** d.	1656	...	1756	1856	1956	...	...	0856	0958	1056	1156	1256	...	1356	1456	1556	1656	1756	1856	1956	2056
Manchester Picc **119** d.	|	1705	|	|	|	...	...	|	|	|	|	|	...	|	|	|	|	|	|	|	|
Birmingham New Street **117** d.	1812	1842	1912	2012	2112	...	0930	1030	1130	1212	1312	1412	1442	1512	1612	1712	1812	1912	2012	2112	2212
Cheltenham Spa **117 138** d.	1852	1931	1952	2052	2152	...	1010	1110	1210	1252	1352	1452	1526	1552	1652	1752	1852	1952	2052	2152	2252
Bristol Parkway **138** d.	1925	2000	2025	2125f	2231	...	1040	1142	1243	1324	1425	1524	1557	1625f	1725f	1825	1925	2025f	2125f	2231	2321
Bristol Temple Meads **138** a.	1936	2009	2036	2134	2240	...	1049	1151	1253	1333	1436	1536	1608	1636	1734	1836	1936	2035	2135	2240	2330
Bristol Temple Meads **115 110** d.	1945	...	...	2145	...	0844	1055	1156	...	1345	...	1545	1614	...	1745	...	1945	...	2145	...	...
Taunton **115 110** d.	2017	...	...	2217	...	0915	1126	1228	...	1418	...	1617	1650	...	1819	...	2017	...	2217	...	...
Tiverton Parkway **110** d.	2030	...	...	2230	...	0927	1138	1240	...	1431	...	1629	1702	...	1831	...	2030	...	2230	...	...
Exeter St Davids **110 111** d.	2046	...	...	2249f	...	0942	1153	1258	...	1447	...	1645	1719	...	1848	...	2046	...	2246	...	...
Newton Abbot **110 111** d.	2105	...	...	2309	...	1002	1213	1318	...	1507	...	1705	1743	...	1908	...	2109	...	2306	...	...
Torquay **110 111** a.	|	...	...	|	...	|	|	|	...	|	...	|	1754	...	|	...	|	...	|	...	...
Paignton **110 111** a.	|	...	...	|	...	|	|	|	...	|	...	|	1800	...	|	...	|	...	|	...	...
Totnes **110** d.	2117	...	...	2321	...	1014	1225	1331	...	1519	...	1718	...	...	1920	...	2122	...	2318	...	...
Plymouth **110** a.	2143	...	...	2347	...	1040	1251	1357	...	1546	...	1744	...	...	1946	...	2148	...	2344	...	...
Newquay **112** a.	...	...	...	...	...	...	...	...	...	...	...	...	...	...	...	...	...	...	...	...	...
Penzance **112** a.	...	...	...	...	...	...	...	...	...	...	...	...	...	...	...	...	...	...	...	...	...

B – From Aberdeen (Table **222**).
D – From Derby (Table **124**).

b – Also calls at Gloucester (a. 1902 / d. 1908).
c – Also calls at Gloucester (a. 2200 / d. 2205).
f – Arrives 5 – 7 minutes earlier.
g – Arrives 0921.

★ – Also calls at Dawlish (10 – 15 minutes after Exeter) and Teignmouth (15 – 18 minutes after Exeter).
⊠ – Connects at Bristol Temple Meads with train in previous column.

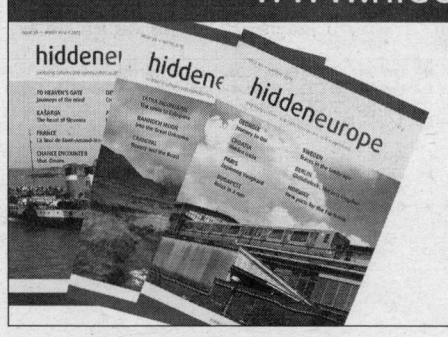

XC Most services convey 🍷 PLYMOUTH and PAIGNTON - BRISTOL - BIRMINGHAM 116

		Ⓐ	Ⓐ	Ⓐ	Ⓐ	Ⓐ	Ⓐ	Ⓐ	Ⓐ	Ⓐ	Ⓐ		Ⓐ	Ⓐ	Ⓐ	Ⓐ	Ⓐ	Ⓐ	Ⓐ	Ⓐ
		S c						B	☆											
Penzance **112** d.	Ⓐ	...	...	...	...	...	...	...	...	...	...	...	0925	...	...	...	...	...	...	...
Newquay **112** d.		...	...	...	...	...	...	...	...	...	...	...	|	...	...	...	...	...	...	...
Plymouth 110 d.		...	...	0525	0627	0725	...	0927	...	...	...	...	1127	1153	1227	...	1327	...	1427	1527
Totnes 110 d.		...	...	0551	0653	0751	...	0953	...	...	...	...	1153	1219	1253	...	1353	...	1453	1553
Paignton 110 d.		...	...	|	|	|	...	|	1014	...	...	...	|	|	|	...	|	...	|	|
Torquay 110 d.		...	...	|	|	|	...	|	1020	...	...	...	|	|	|	...	|	...	|	|
Newton Abbot 110 d.		...	...	0603	0706	0804	...	1005	1029	...	...	...	1206	1231	1306	...	1406	...	1506	1606
Exeter St Davids 110 d.		...	...	0625	0727	0827	...	1027	1055	...	...	...	1227	1252	1327	...	1427	...	1527	1627
Tiverton Parkway 110 d.		...	...	0638	0741	0841	...	1041	1109	...	...	...	1241	1306	1341	...	1441	...	1541	1641
Taunton 115 110 d.		...	...	0651	0753	0853	...	1053	1122	...	...	...	1253	1320	1353	...	1453	...	1553	1653
Bristol Temple Meads 115 110 a.		...	...	0725	0827	0924	...	1124	1154	...	...	...	1326	1357	1426	...	1526	...	1624	1727
Bristol Temple Meads 138 d.		0624	0634	0735	0835	0932	1035	1134	1200	1235	1300	...	1335	1400	1435	1500	1535	1600	1635	1735
Bristol Parkway 138 d.		0634	0643	0744	0844	0944	1044	1144	1209	1244	1309	...	1344	1409	1444	1510	1544	1609	1644	1744
Cheltenham Spa 117 138 d.		0718	0713	0815	0915	1015	1115	1215	1240	1315	1340	...	1415	1439	1515	1540	1615	1640	1715	1815
Birmingham New Street 117 a.		0816	0756	0856	0958	1056	1158	1256	1325	1356	1425	...	1456	1526	1556	1626	1656	1723	1756	1856
Manchester Piccadilly **119** a.		...	|	|	|	|	|	|	...	|	|	...	|	1711	|	...	|	1902	|	|
Sheffield **124** a.		...	0918	1018	1118	1218	1318	1418	...	1518	1549	...	1618	...	1718	...	1818	...	1918	2018
Leeds **124** a.		...	1001	1101	1201	1301	1401	1501	...	1601	|	...	1702	...	1802	...	1905	...	2002	2102
York **124** a.		...	1030	1130	1230	1330	1430	1530	...	1630	1639	...	1730	...	1831	...	1931	...	2030	...
Newcastle **124** a.		...	1129	1229	1329	1432	1529	1632	...	1729	1744	...	1831	...	1932	...	2036	...	2128	...
Edinburgh Waverley **124 220** a.		...	1300	1406	1501	...	1705	1807	...	1904	...	...	2011	...	2108	...	2213	...	2303	...
Glasgow Central **124 220** a.		...	...	...	...	...	1812	...	...	2016	...	...	...	...	...	...	...	...	...	...

	Ⓐ	Ⓐ	Ⓐ	Ⓐ		⑥	⑥	⑥	⑥	⑥	⑥	⑥	⑥	⑥	⑥	⑥	⑥	⑥	⑥	⑥
						c					B	☆								
Penzance **112** d.	...	...	...	...	⑥	...	...	...	...	...	...	...	...	...	...	...	...	...	...	...
Newquay **112** d.	...	...	...	...		...	...	...	...	...	...	...	...	...	...	...	...	...	...	...
Plymouth 110 d.	1627	...	1827	...		...	0527	0624	0725	...	0927	...	...	1127	...	1227	...	...	1427	1527
Totnes 110 d.	1653	...	1853	...		...	0553	0650	0751	...	0953	...	...	1153	...	1253	...	...	1453	1553
Paignton 110 d.	|	...	|	2019		...	|	|	|	...	|	1010	...	|	...	|	...	...	|	|
Torquay 110 d.	|	...	|	2025		...	|	|	|	...	|	1016	...	|	...	|	...	...	|	|
Newton Abbot 110 d.	1706	...	1906	2035		...	0606	0703	0803	...	1006	1026	...	1206	...	1306	...	...	1506	1606
Exeter St Davids 110 d.	1727	...	1927	2056		...	0627	0727f	0827f	...	1027	1055f	...	1227	...	1327	...	...	1527	1627
Tiverton Parkway 110 d.	1741	...	1941	2109		...	0641	0741	0841	...	1041	1109	...	1241	...	1341	...	...	1541	1641
Taunton 115 110 d.	1753	...	1953	2122		...	0653	0753	0853	...	1053	1122	...	1253	...	1353	...	...	1553	1653
Bristol Temple Meads 115 110 a.	1824	...	2024	2156		...	0724	0824	0924	...	1124	1153	...	1324	...	1426	...	...	1624	1726
Bristol Temple Meads 138 d.	1835	1935	2035	2200		0615	0735	0835	0935	1035	1135	1200	1235	1335	1400	1435	1535	1600	1635	1735
Bristol Parkway 138 d.	1844	1944	2044	2209		0624	0744	0844	0944	1044	1144	1209	1244	1344	1409	1444	1544	1609	1644	1744
Cheltenham Spa 117 138 d.	1915	2015	2115	2242		0710	0815	0915	1015	1115	1215	1240	1315	1415	1440	1515	1615	1640	1715	1815
Birmingham New Street 117 a.	1956	2056	2201	2341		0756	0856	0956	1056	1156	1256	1325	1356	1456	1525	1556	1656	1725	1756	1856
Manchester Piccadilly **119** a.	|	|	...	...		|	|	|	|	|	|	...	|	|	1702	|	|	1902	|	|
Sheffield **124** a.	2120	2224	...	...		0919	1019	1118	1218	1318	1418	...	1519	1618	...	1718	1818	...	1918	2019
Leeds **124** a.	2203	2334	...	...		1001	1101	1201	1301	1401	1501	...	1601	1701	...	1802	1903	...	2005	2102
York **124** a.	...	...	...	...		1030	1130	1230	1330	1430	1530	...	1630	1730	...	1831	1930	...	2030	2146
Newcastle **124** a.	...	...	...	...		1129	1230	1329	1432	1529	1629	...	1730	1833	...	1932	2035	...	2129	...
Edinburgh Waverley **124 220** a.	...	...	...	...		1305	1402	1502	1606	1703	1803	...	1903	2007	...	2108	2212	...	2301	...
Glasgow Central **124 220** a.	...	...	...	...		...	...	...	...	1814	...	...	2017	...	...	...	...	...	...	...

	⑥	⑥	⑥	⑥		⑦	⑦	⑦	⑦	⑦	⑦	⑦	⑦	⑦	⑦	⑦	⑦	⑦	⑦	⑦
			D			c		B		☆										
Penzance **112** d.	...	...	...	...	⑦	...	...	...	...	...	0930	...	...	...	...	...	...	...	...	...
Newquay **112** d.	...	...	...	...		...	...	...	...	...	|	...	...	...	...	...	...	...	...	...
Plymouth 110 d.	1627	...	1827	...		...	...	0927	1027	...	1127	1227	...	1427	...	1627	...	...	1827	...
Totnes 110 d.	1653	...	1853	...		...	...	0953	1053	...	1153	1253	...	1453	...	1653	...	...	1853	...
Paignton 110 d.	|	...	|	1928		...	...	|	|	1049	|	|	...	|	...	|	...	1820	|	...
Torquay 110 d.	|	...	|	1934		...	...	|	|	1055	|	|	...	|	...	|	...	1826	|	...
Newton Abbot 110 d.	1706	...	1906	1944		...	...	1005	1106	1109f	1206	1306	...	1506	...	1706	...	1835	1906	...
Exeter St Davids 110 d.	1727	...	1927	2008f		...	...	1027	1127	1135	1227	1327	...	1527	...	1727	...	1857	1927	...
Tiverton Parkway 110 d.	1741	...	1941	2021		...	...	1041	1141	1148	1241	1341	...	1541	...	1741	...	1910	1941	...
Taunton 115 110 d.	1753	...	1953	2034		...	...	1053	1153	1201	1253	1353	...	1553	...	1753	...	1923	1953	...
Bristol Temple Meads 115 110 a.	1826	...	2024	2105		...	...	1124	1224	1245	1324	1426	...	1626	...	1826	...	1957	2026	...
Bristol Temple Meads 138 d.	1835	1931	2031	...		0915	1031	1131	1231	1300	1331	1431	1531	1631	1731	1831	1931	...	2031	2210
Bristol Parkway 138 d.	1844	1940	2040	...		0924	1040	1140	1240	1309	1340	1440	1540	1640	1740	1840	1940	...	2040	2219
Cheltenham Spa 117 138 d.	1915	2011	2111	...		1011	1111	1211	1311	1341	1411	1511	1611	1711	1811	1911	2011	...	2111	2250
Birmingham New Street 117 a.	1956	2053	2154	...		1049	1149	1249	1349	1419	1449	1550	1649	1750	1850	1950	2055	...	2150	2341
Manchester Piccadilly **119** a.	|	|	...	...		|	|	|	|	...	|	|	|	|	|	|	|	...	|	...
Sheffield **124** a.	2119	2223	...	...		1218	1318	1419	1518	...	1618	1718	1819	1919	2021	2119	2217	...	2318	...
Leeds **124** a.	2202	2327	...	...		1302	1402	1502	1602	...	1702	1802	1902	2002	2103	2202	2303	...	0012	...
York **124** a.	...	...	...	...		1329	1429	1529	1629	...	1729	1830	1930	2030	2130	...	...	...	...	...
Newcastle **124** a.	...	...	...	...		1427	1528	1628	1728	...	1827	1931	2028	2131	...	...	...	...	...	...
Edinburgh Waverley **124 220** a.	...	...	...	...		1559	1700	1759	1901	...	2005	2105	2208	2303	...	...	...	...	...	...
Glasgow Central **124 220** a.	...	...	...	...		...	1813	...	2015	...	...	...	...	...	...	...	...	...	...	...

B – To Aberdeen (Table **222**).
D – To Derby (Table **124**).
S – To Stansted Airport (Tables **117** and **208**).

c – Also calls at Gloucester (a. 0704 / d. 0708 on Ⓐ, a. 0650 / d. 0659 on ⑥, a. 0950 / d. 1002 on ⑦).
f – Arrives 5 – 6 minutes earlier.

☆ – Also calls at Teignmouth (7 – 10 minutes after Newton Abbot) and Dawlish (12 – 15 minutes after Newton Abbot).

117 BIRMINGHAM - CARDIFF

AW, XC

km		Ⓐ	Ⓐ2	Ⓐ	Ⓐ	Ⓐ2	Ⓐ	Ⓐ	Ⓐ2	Ⓐ	Ⓐ	Ⓐ2	Ⓐ🍷	Ⓐ2	Ⓐ🍷	Ⓐ🍷	Ⓐ2	Ⓐ🍷	Ⓐ2	Ⓐ🍷	Ⓐ🍷	Ⓐ2
	Nottingham **120** d.		...	...	...	...	...	0600	...	0704	0808	...	0907	...	1007	1107	...	1207	...	1307	1407	...
	Derby **116 120** d.		...	...	...	...	0610	0638	...	0738	0841	...	0940	...	1041	1140	...	1238	...	1338	1438	...
0	**Birmingham** New Street **116** d.		...	0500	0537	...	0712	0730	...	0830	0930	...	1030	...	1130	1230	...	1330	...	1430	1530	...
43	Worcestershire Parkway d.		...	|	|	...	|	0758	...	0858	0958	...	1058	...	1158	1258	...	1358	...	1458	1558	...
73	Cheltenham Spa **116 135 138** d.		0537	0606	0640	0746	0750	0815	0846	0915	1015	1045	1115	1145	1215	1315	1346	1415	...	1515	1615	1646
83	**Gloucester** **135 138** d.		0549	0616	0651	0758	...	0827	0858	0927	1027	1100	1127	1159	1227	1328	1359	1427	1457	1527	1626	1700
115	Lydney 🚂 d.		0609	0635	0710	0817	...	|	0917	|	1046	1119	|	1218	|	1347	1418	|	1516	|	1646	1719
127	Chepstow d.		0618	0645	0720	0826	...	0853	0926	0953	|	1129	1153	1227	1253	|	1427	1453	1525	1553	1656	1729
138	Caldicot d.		0627	0653	0728	0835	...	|	0935	|	|	1137	|	1236	|	|	1436	|	1534	|	|	1737
155	Newport **118 134 149** a.		0642	0709	0742	0850	...	0911	0950	1011	1111	1152	1211	1251	1311	1412	1451	1511	1549	1611	1713	1753
174	**Cardiff** Central **118 134 149** a.		0657	0722	0800	0905	...	0925	1007	1025	1125	1209	1225	1305	1325	1425	1505	1525	1602	1625	1727	1811

	Ⓐ	Ⓐ2	Ⓐ	Ⓐ2	Ⓐ🍷	Ⓐ	Ⓐ2	Ⓐ	Ⓐ	Ⓐ	ⒶL	Ⓐ	⑤2	①–④	⑥	⑥2	⑥	⑥	⑥2	⑥	⑥	⑥2
Nottingham **120** d.	1507	...	1607	...	...	1707	...	1805	1908	*1935*	...	*2041*	...	2		...	...	...	...	...	0600	...
Derby **116 120** d.	1538	...	1638	...	1731	1738	...	1838	1941	2031	...	2131	...	...		...	...	...	...	0610	0638	...
Birmingham New Street **116** d.	1630	...	1730	...	1812	1830	...	1930	2030	2112	2130	2212	...	...		...	0500	0542	...	0712	0730	...
Worcestershire Parkway d.	1658	...	1758	...	|	1858	...	1958	2058	|	2158	|	...	...		...	|	|	...	|	0758	...
Cheltenham Spa **116 135 138** d.	1719	1745	1819	1846	1852	1915	1946	2015	2115	2152	2221	2250	2258	2258		...	0603	0644	0746	0750	0815	0846
Gloucester **135 138** d.	1730	1800	1830	1903**d**	1902	1927	2000	2027	2125	2200	2230	...	2310	2310		0548	0615	0657	0757	...	0827	0901**c**
Lydney 🚂 d.	1749	1819	|	1922	...	|	2019	|	2144	...	...	...	2330	2330		0607	0635	0716	0816	...	|	0920
Chepstow d.	|	1829	|	1932	...	|	2028	|	2153	...	...	...	2339	2339		0617	0644	0726	0825	...	0853	0929
Caldicot d.	|	1837	|	1940	...	|	2037	|	2202	...	...	...	2348	2348		0625	0653	0734	0834	...	|	0938
Newport **118 134 149** a.	1815	1853	1915	1955	...	2012	2052	2109	2216	...	...	...	0007	0014		0640	0707	0750	0851	...	0912	0953
Cardiff Central **118 134 149** a.	1828	1909	1928	2011	...	2026	2107	2124	2236**f**	...	...	...	0022	0037		0653	0720	0805	0905	...	0926	1008

	⑥	⑥	⑥2	⑥🍷	⑥2	⑥🍷	⑥🍷	⑥2	⑥🍷		⑥B	⑥🍷	⑥🍷	⑥2	⑥	⑥2	⑥	⑥2	⑥	⑥2	⑥	⑥
Nottingham **120** d.	0703	0807	...	0907	...	1007	1107	...	1207	...	...	1307	1407	...	1507	...	1607	...	1707	...	1807	1907
Derby **116 120** d.	0736	0842	...	0938	...	1038	1138	...	1238	...	...	1338	1438	...	1539	...	1638	...	1739	...	1838	1938
Birmingham New Street **116** d.	0830	0930	...	1030	...	1130	1230	...	1330	...	...	1430	1530	...	1630	...	1730	...	1830	...	1930	2030
Worcestershire Parkway d.	0858	0958	...	1058	...	1158	1258	...	1358	...	...	1458	1558	...	1658	...	1758	...	1858	...	1958	2058
Cheltenham Spa **116 135 138** d.	0915	1015	1041	1115	1146	1215	1315	1346	1415	...	...	1515	1615	1646	1715	1735	1819	1846	1915	1942	2015	2115
Gloucester **135 138** d.	0927	1027	1052	1127	1158	1227	1330**d**	1358	1427	...	1442	1527	1627	1658	1727	1746	1830	1858	1927	1958**c**	2027	2127
Lydney 🚂 d.	|	1046	1111	|	1217	|	1349	1417	|	...	1501	|	1646	1717	1746	1805	|	1917	|	2017	|	2146
Chepstow d.	0953	|	1120	1153	1227	1253	|	1426	1453	...	1511	1553	1656	1726	|	1815	|	1927	|	2027	|	2156
Caldicot d.	|	|	1129	|	1235	|	|	1435	|	...	1519	|	|	1735	|	1823	|	1935	|	2035	|	2204
Newport **118 134 149** a.	1012	1111	1145	1212	1252	1312	1414	1450	1511	...	1537	1611	1713	1750	1811	1838	1912	1950	2009	2052	2109	2224
Cardiff Central **118 134 149** a.	1027	1125	1200	1226	1306	1325	1429	1507	1525	...	1553	1625	1727	1807	1827	1852	1925	2007	2022	2107	2122	2245

	⑥🍷	⑥2	⑦	⑦2	⑦2	⑦🍷	⑦	⑦2	⑦	⑦	⑦2	⑦🍷	⑦🍷	⑦2	⑦🍷	⑦🍷	⑦2	⑦🍷	⑦🍷	⑦2	⑦🍷	⑦2
Nottingham **120** d.	*1932*	...		...	...	...	0955	...	1116	1216	...	1316	1416	...	1512	1616	...	1716	1816	...	*1923*	...
Derby **116 120** d.	2031	...		...	...	...	1020	...	1140	1240	...	1340	1440	...	1537	1640	...	1742	1840	...	2031	...
Birmingham New Street **116** d.	2112	...		...	*0930*	1012	1112	...	1230	1330	...	1430	1530	...	1630	1730	...	1830	1930	...	2112	...
Worcestershire Parkway d.	|	...		...	|	1040	1140	...	1258	1358	...	1458	1558	...	1658	1758	...	1858	1958	...	|	...
Cheltenham Spa **116 135 138** d.	2152	...		...	1038	1100	1200	1235	1318	1415	1409	1515	1615	1610	1715	1815	1835	1915	2015	2010	2152	...
Gloucester **135 138** d.	2200	2309		0845	1048	1111	1211	1246	1330	1425	1429**a**	1530**c**	1625	1629**c**	1725	1828	1848	1925	2025	2033**e**	2200	2240
Lydney 🚂 d.	...	2328		0904	1107	|	|	1305	|	|	1448	|	|	1648	|	|	1907	|	|	2052	...	2259
Chepstow d.	...	2338		0914	1116	|	|	1314	|	|	1458	|	|	1658	|	|	1916	|	|	2102	...	2308
Caldicot d.	...	2346		0922	1125	|	|	1323	|	|	1506	|	|	1706	|	|	1925	|	|	2111	...	2317
Newport **118 134 149** a.	...	0009		0944	1140	1153	1253	1338	1412	1507	1521	1612	1708	1721	1807	1911	1946	2007	2107	2133	...	2332
Cardiff Central **118 134 149** a.	...	0030		1004	1155	1207	1306	1353	1425	1525	1536	1625	1721	1735	1820	1925	2000	2020	2120	2148	...	2347

	Ⓐ	Ⓐ	ⒶC	Ⓐ2	Ⓐ	Ⓐ2	Ⓐ	Ⓐ	Ⓐ2	Ⓐ🍷	Ⓐ2	Ⓐ	Ⓐ🍷	Ⓐ2	Ⓐ🍷	Ⓐ2	Ⓐ🍷	Ⓐ🍷	Ⓐ2	Ⓐ🍷	Ⓐ2	Ⓐ🍷
Cardiff Central **118 134 149** d.		...	...	0610	0640	0705	0745	0845	0906	0945	1009	1045	1145	1210	1245	1307	1345	1445	1508	1545	1608	1645
Newport **118 134 149** d.		...	...	0624	0654	0720	0801	0900	0922	0959	1024	1100	1159	1225	1259	1322	1359	1459	1523	1559	1623	1659
Caldicot d.		...	...	0637	0707	0733	|	|	0936	|	1037	|	|	1238	|	1335	|	|	1536	|	1636	|
Chepstow d.		...	...	0645	0715	0741	|	0919	0945	1016	1045	|	1216	1247	1316	1343	|	1519	1544	1616	1644	|
Lydney 🚂 d.		...	...	0654	0724	0750	0827	|	0954	|	1054	1125	|	1255	|	1352	1423	|	1553	|	1653	1725
Gloucester **135 138** d.		...	0708	0717	0745	0811	0849	0949	1016	1049**c**	1116	1149	1245	1317	1349**c**	1412	1449**c**	1549	1616	1645	1717	1749
Cheltenham Spa **116 135 138** d.		0713	0718	0727	0755	0821	0859	1000	1027	1059	1126	1159	1255	1326	1359	...	1459	1559	1626	1655	1724	1759
Worcestershire Parkway d.		|	0736	...	0814	...	0914	1015	...	1114	...	1214	1314	...	1414	...	1514	1614	...	1714	...	1814
Birmingham New Street **116** a.		0756	0816	...	0845	...	0945	1046	...	1145	...	1245	1345	...	1445	...	1545	1645	...	1745	...	1845
Derby **116 120** a.		0840	...	...	0932	...	1032	1132	...	1232	...	1331	1431	...	1536	...	1631	1731	...	1838	...	1931
Nottingham **120** a.		*0933*	...	...	1003	...	1103	1204	...	1303	...	1403	1503	...	1603	...	1703	1803	...	1906	...	2004

	Ⓐ2	Ⓐ🍷	Ⓐ2	Ⓐ	Ⓐ	Ⓐ	Ⓐ2	Ⓐ	⑤	①–④	⑥	⑥🍷	⑥E	⑥2	⑥	⑥2	⑥	⑥	⑥2	⑥🍷	⑥2	⑥
Cardiff Central **118 134 149** d.	1708	1745	1807	1845	1950	2106	2110	2145	2320	2312		...	...	0610	0640	0707	0745	0845	0904	0945	1008	1045
Newport **118 134 149** d.	1723	1759	1823	1859	2004	2120	2125	2159	2334	2330		...	...	0626	0654	0722	0800	0859	0921	0959	1023	1100
Caldicot d.	1736	|	1837	|	2017	|	2138	|	2348	2351		...	...	0640	0707	0736	|	|	0935	|	1036	|
Chepstow d.	1745	1816	1846	1918	2025	|	2146	|	2357	0001		...	...	0649	0715	0745	|	0916	0944	1016	1044	|
Lydney 🚂 d.	1753	|	1856	|	2034	|	2155	|	0005	0009		...	...	0657	0724	0753	0825	|	0953	|	1053	1124
Gloucester **135 138** d.	1818**c**	1845	1918	1949	2056	2203	2218	2249	0026	0033		0659	0705	0718	0745	0822	0849	0949**c**	1015	1049**c**	1114	1149**c**
Cheltenham Spa **116 135 138** d.	1826	1855	1928	1959	2106	2213	2228	2259	*0043*	...		0710	0714	0729	0755	0834	0859	0959	1026	1059	1124	1159
Worcestershire Parkway d.	...	1914	...	2014	2120	2232	...	|	...	...		|	0733	...	0814	...	0914	1014	...	1114	...	1214
Birmingham New Street **116** a.	...	1945	...	2045	2154	2305	...	2358	...	...		0756	0806	...	0845	...	0945	1045	...	1145	...	1245
Derby **116 120** a.	...	2031	...	2137	2250	...	...	...	...	...		0840	...	...	0931	...	1032	1131	...	1232	...	1331
Nottingham **120** a.	...	2105	...	2217	2326	...	...	...	...	...		*0921*	...	...	1003	...	1103	1204	...	1303	...	1403

	⑥2	⑥🍷	⑥2	⑥🍷	⑥🍷	⑥2	⑥🍷	⑥2	⑥🍷	⑥2	⑥🍷	⑥2		⑥	⑥	⑥	⑥2	⑥2	⑦	⑦2	⑦	⑦2
Cardiff Central **118 134 149** d.	1208	1245	1307	1345	1445	1507	1545	1607	1645	1707	1745	1809	...	1845	2000	2048	2110	2314		0823	...	1030
Newport **118 134 149** d.	1222	1259	1327	1359	1459	1522	1559	1622	1659	1722	1759	1824	...	1859	2014	2102	2125	2332		0841	...	1044
Caldicot d.	1235	|	1341	|	|	1535	|	1635	|	1735	|	1838	...	|	2027	|	2138	2354		0905	...	1059
Chepstow d.	1244	1316	1350	|	1518	1544	1616	1643	|	1743	1817	1846	...	1916	2036	|	2147	0003		0914	...	1107
Lydney 🚂 d.	1252	|	1359	1423	|	1552	|	1652	1724	1752	|	1855	...	|	2044	|	2155	0012		0922	...	1116
Gloucester **135 138** d.	1313	1349**c**	1420	1449**c**	1549**c**	1613	1645	1713	1749**c**	1813	1845	1917	...	1949**c**	2107	2149**c**	2216	0034		0944	1002	1138
Cheltenham Spa **116 135 138** d.	1323	1359	...	1459	1559	1624	1655	1722	1759	1823	1855	1926	...	1959	2118	2159	...	...		0956	1011	1148
Worcestershire Parkway d.	...	1414	...	1514	1614	...	1714	...	1814	...	1914	...	...	2014	|	2214	...	...		...	|	...
Birmingham New Street **116** a.	...	1445	...	1545	1645	...	1745	...	1845	...	1945	...	...	2045	2207	2245	...	...		...	1049	...
Derby **116 120** a.	...	1536	...	1631	1731	...	1836	...	1931	...	2031	...	...	2131	2255	2331	...	...		...	1136	...
Nottingham **120** a.	...	1603	...	1703	1803	...	1903	...	2003	...	2103	...	...	2215	2327	...	...	...		...	*1253*	...

	⑦		⑦	⑦2	⑦🍷	⑦🍷	⑦2	⑦🍷		⑦🍷	⑦2	⑦🍷	⑦🍷	⑦2		⑦🍷	⑦🍷	⑦D	⑦🍷	⑦2	⑦	⑦2
Cardiff Central **118 134 149** d.	1045	...	1145	1229	1245	1345	1429	1445	...	1545	1625	1645	1745	1829	...	1845	...	1945	...	2025	2045	2226
Newport **118 134 149** d.	1059	...	1159	1243	1258	1401	1443	1459	...	1559	1643	1659	1759	1844	...	1859	...	1959	...	2039	2059	2240
Caldicot d.	|	...	|	1256	|	|	1457	|	...	|	1657	|	|	1858	...	|	...	|	...	2052	|	2258
Chepstow d.	|	...	|	1305	|	|	1505	|	...	|	1706	|	|	1906	...	|	...	|	...	2100	|	2306
Lydney 🚂 d.	|	...	|	1313	|	|	1514	|	...	|	1714	|	|	1915	...	|	...	|	...	2109	|	2315
Gloucester **135 138** d.	1149**d**	...	1249**d**	1335	1349**d**	1449	1535	1549**d**	...	1649**d**	1736	1749**d**	1849**d**	1936	...	1949**d**	...	2049	...	2131	2149**d**	2338
Cheltenham Spa **116 135 138** d.	1159	...	1259	1345	1359	1459	1545	1559	...	1659	1746	1759	1859	1946	...	1959	2011	2059	2111	...	2159	*0011*
Worcestershire Parkway d.	1214	...	1314	...	1414	1514	...	1614	...	1714	...	1814	1914	...	...	2014	|	2114	|	...	2214	...
Birmingham New Street **116** a.	1245	...	1345	...	1445	1545	...	1645	...	1745	...	1845	1945	...	...	2045	2055	2145	2150	...	2245	...
Derby **116 120** a.	1329	...	1429	...	1531	1629	...	1729	...	1829	...	1931	2029	...	...	2129	2140	...	2239	...	...	...
Nottingham **120** a.	1353	...	1453	...	1555	1653	...	1754	...	1854	...	1957	2054	...	...	2154	*2245*	...	...	...	...	...

B – (2) Gloucester - Fishguard Harbour (Table **136**).
C – (12) and 🍷 Bristol Temple Meads - Stansted Airport (Tables **116** and **208**).
D – (12) Cardiff - Leicester (Table **208**).
E – (12) to Stansted Airport (Table **208**).
L – (12) Leicester - Gloucester (Table **208**).

a – Arrives 10 minutes earlier.
c – Arrives 5–6 minutes earlier.
d – Arrives 7–8 minutes earlier.
e – Arrives 2022.
f – 2229 on ⑤.

🚂 – DEAN FOREST RAILWAY (Lydney Junction - Parkend. *7 km*). ✆ 01594 845840. www.deanforestrailway.co.uk
Lydney Junction station is 10 minutes walk from the National Rail station.

GW 2nd class CARDIFF - BRISTOL 118

km		Ⓐ	Ⓐ A	Ⓐ	Ⓐ A	Ⓐ B	Ⓐ A	Ⓐ B	Ⓐ A		Ⓐ H	Ⓐ A	Ⓐ B	Ⓐ A	Ⓐ H	Ⓐ A	Ⓐ B	Ⓐ A	Ⓐ B	Ⓐ A	Ⓐ H	Ⓐ A	Ⓐ H	Ⓐ A	Ⓐ H	Ⓐ A
0	**Cardiff** Central ‡d.		0628	0657	0728	0800	0828	0900	0928	...	1000	1030	1100	1130	1200	1230	1300	1330	1400	1430	1500	1530	1600	1627	1700	1727
19	Newport ‡d.		0642	0710	0742	0814	0842	0914	0942	...	1014	1044	1114	1144	1214	1244	1314	1344	1415	1444	1514	1544	1614	1641	1714	1741
61	**Bristol** Temple Meads a.		0718	0749	0816	0852	0920	0953	1016	...	1050	1117	1150	1215	1250	1319	1350	1417	1450	1515	1549	1617	1650	1715	1749	1815

	Ⓐ B	Ⓐ A	Ⓐ P	Ⓐ A	Ⓐ H		Ⓐ A	Ⓐ	Ⓐ C	Ⓐ	⑤	①–④	⑤	①–④	⑥	⑥ A	⑥ A	⑥ B	⑥ A	⑥ B		⑥ A	⑥ H	⑥ A	⑥ B	⑥ A
Cardiff Central ‡d.	1800	1830	1900	1930	2000	...	2030	2100	2130	2200	2230	2230	2330	2330		0629	0727	0800	0827	0900	...	0927	1000	1030	1100	1130
Newport ‡d.	1814	1844	1914	1944	2014	...	2044	2114	2144	2216	2244	2248	2344	2350		0644	0741	0814	0841	0914	...	0941	1014	1044	1114	1144
Bristol Temple Meads a.	1850	1919	1951	2016	2055	...	2121	2150	2220	2303	2320	2335	0025	0039		0719	0817	0852	0917	0950	...	1018	1050	1117	1149	1216

	⑥ H	⑥ A	⑥ B	⑥ A	⑥ B	⑥ A	⑥ B	⑥ A	⑥ H	⑥ A	⑥ H		⑥ A	⑥ P	⑥ A	⑥ H	⑥ A	⑥	⑥ A	⑥ E	⑥	⑥	⑦	⑦ A	⑦	⑦ A
Cardiff Central ‡d.	1200	1227	1300	1330	1400	1430	1500	1530	1600	1627	1700	...	1727	1800	1827	1900	1929	1954	2029	2100	2200	2247		0918	1000	1025
Newport ‡d.	1214	1241	1314	1344	1414	1444	1514	1544	1614	1641	1714	...	1741	1814	1841	1914	1943	2008	2043	2114	2215	2302		0936	1013	1039
Bristol Temple Meads a.	1249	1313	1349	1417	1450	1517	1550	1617	1649	1717	1750	...	1817	1850	1917	1950	2016	2047	2115	2150	2301	2341		1015	1052	1112

	⑦ B	⑦ A	⑦ E	⑦ A	⑦ B	⑦ A	⑦ B	⑦ A	⑦ B		⑦ A	⑦ H	⑦ A	⑦	⑦ H	⑦ A	⑦ A	⑦ H	⑦ A	⑦ H	⑦ A	⑦ H	⑦ A	⑦ A	⑦ A	⑦
Cardiff Central ‡d.	1055	1125	1200	1225	1300	1325	1400	1425	1500	...	1525	1555	1625	1636	1700	1725	1740	1759	1825	1900	1925	2000	2030	2125	2215	2311
Newport ‡d.	1109	1139	1214	1239	1314	1339	1414	1439	1516	...	1539	1610	1639	1651	1714	1739	1754	1814	1840	1914	1940	2014	2044	2139	2228	2325
Bristol Temple Meads a.	1143	1210	1249	1310	1349	1410	1449	1510	1550	...	1613	1644	1710	1725	1749	1810	1831	1850	1911	1950	2011	2049	2121	2219	2305	2356

	Ⓐ	①	②–⑥	Ⓐ	Ⓐ	Ⓐ A	Ⓐ R	Ⓐ H	Ⓐ C	Ⓐ E	Ⓐ A	Ⓐ H	Ⓐ A		Ⓐ B	Ⓐ A	Ⓐ B	Ⓐ A	Ⓐ B	Ⓐ A	Ⓐ B	Ⓐ A	Ⓐ H	Ⓐ A	Ⓐ B	Ⓐ A
Bristol Temple Meads d.		0520	0520	0553	0628	0653	0706	0724	0755	0821	0858	0927	1000	...	1027	1058	1127	1158	1227	1259	1327	1358	1427	1458	1527	1557
Newport ‡a.		0600	0606	0628	0704	0729	0749	0807	0833	0903	0932	1002	1037	...	1105	1131	1203	1231	1306	1332	1401	1434	1506	1533	1604	1630
Cardiff Central ‡a.		0621	0621	0642	0718	0750	0803	0822	0847	0919	0948	1019	1051	...	1123	1146	1221	1245	1326	1346	1420	1448	1521	1547	1622	1644

	Ⓐ H	Ⓐ A	Ⓐ B	Ⓐ A	Ⓐ H	Ⓐ A	Ⓐ H	Ⓐ A	Ⓐ H	Ⓐ A	Ⓐ B	⑤ A	①–④ A	⑤ E	①–④ E	⑤ A	①–④ A	⑥	⑥	⑥	⑥ S	⑥ E	⑥	⑥	⑥ A	⑥ H
Bristol Temple Meads d.	1627	1657	1724	1757	1824	1858	1923	1957	2020	2057	2131	2157	2157	2234	2234	2258	2258		0628	0654	0703	0723	0757	0823	0857	0929
Newport ‡a.	1704	1733	1756	1832	1910	1935	2007	2032	2101	2133	2204	2232	2238	2306	2313	2332	2338		0701	0729	0744	0756	0830	0858	0931	1006
Cardiff Central ‡a.	1719	1747	1821	1846	1927	1949	2023	2046	2124	2147	2218	2246	2258	2320	2333	2346	2358		0715	0746	0758	0813	0845	0913	0945	1021

	⑥ A	⑥ B	⑥ A	⑥ B	⑥ A	⑥ E	⑥ A	⑥ B	⑥ A	⑥ H	⑥ A	⑥ T	⑥ A	⑥ V		⑥ A	⑥ B	⑥ A	⑥ B	⑥ A	⑥ H	⑥ A	⑥ A	⑥ W	⑥ A	⑥ A
Bristol Temple Meads d.	0957	1030	1057	1132	1157	1232	1257	1323	1357	1432	1457	1532	1557	1622	...	1657	1732	1757	1832	1857	1928	1957	2057	2127	2200	2254
Newport ‡a.	1031	1106	1131	1207	1231	1307	1330	1356	1430	1507	1531	1607	1631	1700	...	1732	1806	1832	1906	1932	2013	2031	2131	2208	2241	2336
Cardiff Central ‡a.	1045	1122	1145	1222	1245	1321	1345	1412	1445	1527	1545	1621	1645	1720	...	1746	1821	1846	1921	1947	2028	2045	2145	2227	2301	2356

	⑦	⑦	⑦ A	⑦	⑦ K	⑦ E	⑦ A	⑦ P	⑦ A	⑦ B	⑦ A	⑦ H		⑦ A	⑦ B	⑦ A	⑦ B	⑦ A	⑦ E	⑦ A	⑦ B	⑦ A	⑦ A	⑦ A	⑦ A	⑦ A
Bristol Temple Meads d.		0918	0954	1010	1042	1110	1156	1214	1256	1318	1356	1418	...	1456	1513	1556	1615	1656	1715	1756	1816	1855	1945	2045	2145	2247
Newport ‡a.		0955	1024	1044	1110	1143	1227	1243	1326	1350	1425	1450	...	1530	1543	1627	1647	1730	1749	1826	1848	1930	2016	2118	2219	2319
Cardiff Central ‡a.		1015	1038	1102	1126	1203	1241	1259	1340	1406	1440	1505	...	1545	1608	1641	1702	1744	1805	1841	1905	1944	2030	2131	2233	2333

A – To/from Portsmouth Harbour, Westbury or Warminster (Table **140**).
B – To/from Penzance (Tables **110** and **112**).
C – From Frome (Table **139**).
E – To/from Exeter St Davids (Table **110**).
H – To/from Taunton (Table **115**).
K – From Weymouth (Table **139**).
P – To/from Plymouth (Table **110**).
Q – 12 and 🍸 London Paddington - Cardiff (Table **134**).
R – 12 and 🍸 London Paddington - Swansea (Table **134**).
S – 12 and 🍸 to Swansea (Table **136**).
T – Until Sept. 10 from Penzance (Tables **110** and **112**); from Sept. 17 from Taunton (Table **115**).
V – Until Sept. 10 from Exeter St Davids (Table **110**); from Sept. 17 from Taunton (Table **115**).
W – Until Sept. 10 from Plymouth (Table **110**); From Sept. 17 from Penzance (Tables **110** and **112**).
s – Calls to set down only.
‡ – For additional services see Tables **117**, **133** and **149**.

XC Most services convey 🍸 BIRMINGHAM - MANCHESTER 119

km		Ⓐ	Ⓐ	Ⓐ	Ⓐ	Ⓐ S	Ⓐ	Ⓐ	Ⓐ	Ⓐ	Ⓐ	Ⓐ	Ⓐ	Ⓐ P	Ⓐ	Ⓐ	Ⓐ	Ⓐ	Ⓐ	Ⓐ	Ⓐ	Ⓐ
	Bournemouth **114** d.		...	...	...	...	...	0630	0730	...	0945	...	1145	...	...	1345	...	...	1545	1645	...	1845
	Reading **114** d.		...	...	...	0615	0714	0815	0913	1015	1115	1213	1315	...	1415	1515	...	1616	1715	1815	1915	2015
	Paignton **116** d.		...	...	...	|	|	|	|	|	|	|	|	...	|	|	...	|	|	|	|	|
	Exeter St Davids **116** d.		...	...	...	|	|	|	|	|	|	|	|	1227	|	|	...	|	|	|	|	|
	Bristol Temple Meads **116** d.		...	...	...	|	|	|	|	|	|	|	|	1335	|	|	1600	|	|	|	|	|
0	**Birmingham** New St **144 150** d.		0557	0653	0731	0757	0857	0957	1057	1157	1257	1357	1457	1531	1557	1657	1731	1757	1857	1957	2057	2157
20	Wolverhampton **144 150** d.		0614	0710	0750	0814	0914	1014	1114	1214	1314	1414	1514	1548	1614	1714	1748	1814	1914	2014	2114	2214
46	Stafford **144** d.		0628	0724	0804	0828	0928	1028	1128	1228	1328	1428	1528	1616a	1628	1728	1804	1828	1928	2028	2129	2228
72	Stoke on Trent **144 152** d.		0644	|	0820	0844	0944	1044	1144	1244	1344	1444	1544	1632	1644	1744	1820	1844	1944	2044	2145	2244
104	Macclesfield **152** d.		0705	|	0836	0901	1001	1101	1201	1301	1401	1501	1601	1649	1701	1801	1836	1901	2001	2101	2201	2301
123	Stockport **152** a.		0719	0809j	0849	0913	1013	1113	1213	1313	1414	1513	1613	1702	1713	1813	1849	1913	2013	2113	2214	2313
132	**Manchester** Piccadilly **152** a.		0730	0823	0902	0923	1023	1123	1223	1323	1423	1523	1623	1711	1723	1823	1902	1923	2023	2123	2223	2323

	⑥	⑥	⑥	⑥	⑥	⑥ S	⑥	⑥	⑥	⑥	⑥		⑥	⑥	⑥	⑥	⑥	⑥	⑥	⑥	⑥	⑥
Bournemouth **114** d.		...	...	...	...	...	...	0745	...	0945	...	...	1145	...	...	1345	...	...	1545	...	1745	...
Reading **114** d.		...	...	...	0615	0715	0815	0915	1015	1115	1215	...	1315	...	1415	1515	...	1615	1715	1815	1915	2015
Paignton **116** d.		...	...	...	|	|	|	|	|	|	|	...	|	...	|	|	...	|	|	|	|	|
Exeter St Davids **116** d.		...	...	...	|	|	|	|	|	|	|	...	|	...	|	|	...	|	|	|	|	|
Bristol Temple Meads **116** d.		...	...	...	|	|	|	|	|	|	|	...	|	1400	|	|	1600	|	|	|	|	|
Birmingham New St **144 150** d.		0557	0657	0731	0757	0857	0957	1057	1157	1257	1357	...	1457	1531	1557	1657	1731	1757	1857	1957	2057	2157
Wolverhampton **144 150** d.		0616	0714	0751	0814	0914	1014	1114	1214	1314	1414	...	1514	1548	1614	1714	1748	1814	1914	2014	2116	2214
Stafford **144** d.		0631	0728	0806	0828	0928	1028	1128	1228	1328	1428	...	1528	1602	1628	1728	1804	1828	1928	2028	2130	2228
Stoke on Trent **144 152** d.		0647	|	0823	0844	0944	1044	1144	1244	1344	1444	...	1544	1619	1644	1744	1820	1844	1944	2044	2148	2244
Macclesfield **152** d.		0705	|	0840	0901	1001	1101	1201	1301	1401	1501	...	1601	1636	1701	1801	1836	1901	2001	2101	2204	2301
Stockport **152** a.		0719	0814	0853	0913	1013	1113	1213	1313	1413	1513	...	1613	1649	1713	1813	1949	1913	2013	2113	2217r	2313
Manchester Piccadilly **152** a.		0730	0823	0905	0923	1023	1123	1223	1323	1423	1523	...	1623	1702	1723	1823	1902	1923	2023	2123	2233	2328

	⑦	⑦		⑦	⑦		⑦ S	⑦		⑦	⑦		⑦	⑦	⑦		⑦	⑦		⑦		⑦
Bournemouth **114** d.		...	...	...	...	...	...	0940	...	...	1140	...	...	1340	...	...	1540	...	...	1740	...	...
Reading **114** d.		...	...	...	0915	...	1015	1115	...	1215	1315	...	1415	1515	1615	...	1715	1815	...	1915	...	2015
Paignton **116** d.		...	...	...	|	...	|	|	...	|	|	...	|	|	|	...	|	|	...	|	...	|
Exeter St Davids **116** d.		...	...	...	|	...	|	|	...	|	|	...	|	|	|	...	|	|	...	|	...	|
Bristol Temple Meads **116** d.		...	...	...	|	...	|	|	...	|	|	...	|	|	|	...	|	|	...	|	...	|
Birmingham New St **144 150** d.		0901	...	1001	1101	...	1157	1257	...	1357	1457	...	1557	1657	1757	...	1857	1957	...	2057	...	2157
Wolverhampton **144 150** d.		0918	...	1018	1118	...	1214	1314	...	1414	1514	...	1614	1714	1814	...	1914	2014	...	2114	...	2214
Stafford **144** d.		0932	...	1032	1132	...	1228	1328	...	1428	1528	...	1628	1728	1828	...	1928	2028	...	2128	...	2228
Stoke on Trent **144 152** d.		0953	...	1053f	1152	...	1244	1344	...	1444	1547	...	1648	1748	1846	...	1947	2046	...	2146	...	2244
Macclesfield **152** d.		1009	...	1109	1208	...	1301	1401	...	1501	1604	...	1704	1804	1902	...	2003	2103	...	2202	...	2301
Stockport **152** a.		1022r	...	1122	1221t	...	1315	1414	...	1514	1616	...	1717	1817	1915	...	2016	2115	...	2215	...	2313
Manchester Piccadilly **152** a.		1038	...	1133	1241	...	1325	1424	...	1523	1626	...	1726	1826	1924	...	2025	2125	...	2224	...	2323

P – From Plymouth (Table **116**).
S – From Southampton Central (Table **114**).
a – Arrives 1602.
f – Arrives 5–6 minutes earlier.
j – Departs 0814.
r – Departs 7 minutes later.
t – Departs 1231.

119 MANCHESTER - BIRMINGHAM

Most services convey 🍷 XC

		Ⓐ	Ⓐ	Ⓐ	Ⓐ	Ⓐ	Ⓐ	Ⓐ	Ⓐ	Ⓐ	Ⓐ	Ⓐ		Ⓐ	Ⓐ	Ⓐ	Ⓐ	Ⓐ	Ⓐ	Ⓐ	ⒶS	Ⓐ
Manchester Piccadilly 152 d.		0511	0627	0705	0727	0827	0905	0927	1027	1127	1227	1327	...	1427	1527	1627	1705	1727	1827	1905	1927	2027
Stockport 152 d.	Ⓐ	|	0636	0713	0736	0836	0913	0936	1036	1136	1236	1336	...	1436	1536	1636	1713	1736	1836	1913	1936	2036
Macclesfield 152 d.		|	0649	0726	0749	0849	0926	0949	1049	1149	1249	1349	...	1449	1549	1649	1726	|	1849	1926	1949	2049
Stoke on Trent 144 152 d.		0608	0706	0745	0808	0908	0944	1007	1108	1208	1308	1408	...	1508	1608	1708	1744	|	1908	1944	2008	2108
Stafford 144 d.		0625	0724	0804	0826	0926	1003	1023	1128f	1228f	1327	1428f	...	1528f	1625	1726	1802	1827	1928f	2002	2027	2128f
Wolverhampton 144 150 d.		0639	0745f	0818	0842	0940	1017	1042	1142	1242	1342	1442	...	1542	1642	1742	1817	1842	1942	2017	2042	2142
Birmingham New St 144 150 a.		0655	0804	0835	0858	0958	1034	1058	1158	1258	1358	1459	...	1559	1658	1758	1836	1858	1958	2034	2100	2200
Bristol Temple Meads 116 a.		|	...	1012	|	|	1219	|	|	|	|	|	...	|	|	|	2008	|	|	...	|	|
Exeter St Davids 116 a.		|	...	...	|	|	...	|	|	|	|	|	...	|	|	|	...	|	|	...	|	|
Paignton 116 a.		|	...	...	|	|	...	|	|	|	|	|	...	|	|	|	...	|	|	...	|	|
Reading 114 a.		0846	...	...	1044	1141	...	1242	1341	1441	1541	1641	...	1741	1843	1941	...	2043	2141	...	2241	2350
Bournemouth 114 a.		1013	...	...	1213	...	...	1413	...	1613	...	1817	...	1914	...	2115	...	...	2314	...	...	...

	Ⓐ	Ⓐ		⑥	⑥	⑥	⑥	⑥	⑥		⑥	⑥	⑥		⑥	⑥	⑥	⑥	⑥	⑥	⑥	⑥S
Manchester Piccadilly 152 d.	2127	2207		0511	0705	0727	0827	0906	0927	...	1027	1127	1227	...	1327	1427	1527	1627	1705	1727	1827	1927
Stockport 152 d.	2136	2217	⑥	|	0713	0736	0836	0914	0936	...	1036	1136	1236	...	1336	1436	1536	1636	1713	1736	1836	1936
Macclesfield 152 d.	2149	2230		|	0726	0749	0849	0927	0949	...	1049	1149	1249	...	1349	1449	1549	1649	1726	1749	1849	1949
Stoke on Trent 144 152 d.	2208	2249		0608	0745	0808	0908	0945	1008	...	1108	1208	1308	...	1408	1508	1608	1708	1744	1808	1908	2008
Stafford 144 d.	2228f	2306		0628f	0803	0828	0928f	1001	1028f	...	1128	1228f	1328f	...	1428f	1528	1628f	1725	1803	1828f	1928f	2028
Wolverhampton 144 150 d.	2242	2320		0642	0817	0842	0942	1015	1042	...	1142	1242	1342	...	1442	1542	1642	1742	1817	1842	1942	2042
Birmingham New St 144 150 a.	2300	2337		0658	0833	0859	0958	1034	1059	...	1159	1259	1359	...	1459	1559	1659	1759	1834	1858	1958	2100
Bristol Temple Meads 116 a.	...	...		|	1008	|	|	1210	|	...	|	|	|	...	|	|	|	|	2009	|	|	|
Exeter St Davids 116 a.	...	...		|	...	|	|	...	|	...	|	|	|	...	|	|	|	|	...	|	|	|
Paignton 116 a.	...	...		|	...	|	|	...	|	...	|	|	|	...	|	|	|	|	...	|	|	|
Reading 114 a.	...	...		0839	...	1041	1139	...	1239	...	1339	1440	1540	...	1639	1740	1841	1940	...	2039	2139	2241
Bournemouth 114 a.	...	...		1013	...	1213	...	...	1413	...	...	1613	...	...	1813	...	2013	...	...	2215	2319	...

	⑥	⑥		⑦	⑦	⑦	⑦		⑦	⑦	⑦		⑦	⑦		⑦	⑦S		⑦	⑦		⑦
Manchester Piccadilly 152 d.	2027	2127		0827	0927	1027	1127	...	1227	1327	1427	...	1527	1627	...	1727	1827	...	1927	2105	...	2205
Stockport 152 d.	2036	2137	⑦	0835	0936	1036	1136	...	1236	1336	1436	...	1536	1636	...	1736	1836	...	1936	2113	...	2213
Macclesfield 152 d.	2049	2150		|	0949	1049	1149	...	1249	1349	1449	...	1549	1649	...	1749	1849	...	1949	2126	...	2226
Stoke on Trent 144 152 d.	2108	2210		|	1008	1108	1208	...	1308	1408	1508	...	1608	1708	...	1808	1908	...	2008	2149	...	2249f
Stafford 144 d.	2128f	2230f		0927	1026	1128	1228	...	1328	1428	1528f	...	1628f	1728f	...	1828	1928f	...	2028	2205	...	2305
Wolverhampton 144 150 d.	2146	2245		0942	1042	1142	1242	...	1342	1442	1542	...	1642	1742	...	1842	1942	...	2042	2220	...	2320
Birmingham New St 144 150 a.	2202	2302		0958	1058	1158	1258	...	1358	1458	1558	...	1658	1758	...	1858	1958	...	2059	2236	...	2336
Bristol Temple Meads 116 a.	...	...		|	|	|	|	...	|	|	|	...	|	|	...	|	|	...	|	...	...	...
Exeter St Davids 116 a.	...	...		|	|	|	|	...	|	|	|	...	|	|	...	|	|	...	|	...	...	...
Paignton 116 a.	...	...		|	|	|	|	...	|	|	|	...	|	|	...	|	|	...	|	...	...	...
Reading 114 a.	...	...		1139	1239	1339	1441	...	1539	1639	1739	...	1839	1939	...	2039	2139	...	2239	...	...	...
Bournemouth 114 a.	...	...		1326	...	1525	...	...	1725	...	1926	...	...	2126	...	2226	...	...	...	...	...	...

S – To Southampton Central (Table 114).

f – Arrives 5–6 minutes earlier.

120 BIRMINGHAM - NOTTINGHAM

XC

km			Ⓐ	Ⓐ	Ⓐ🍷	Ⓐ	Ⓐ🍷	Ⓐ	Ⓐ🍷	Ⓐ	Ⓐ🍷	Ⓐ	Ⓐ🍷	Ⓐ🍷	Ⓐ🍷	Ⓐ	Ⓐ	Ⓐ🍷	Ⓐ	Ⓐ🍷	Ⓐ	Ⓐ🍷	Ⓐ	Ⓐ🍷	Ⓐ	Ⓐ🍷
	Cardiff Central 117 d.		...	...	...	...	...	0640	...	0745	...	0845	...	0945	...	1045	...	1145	...	1245	...	1345	...	1445	...	1545
0	**Birmingham** New Street 124 d.	Ⓐ	0619	0649	0719	0749	0818	0849	0912	0949	1012	1049	1118	1149	1219	1249	1319	1349	1418	1449	1512	1549	1618	1649	1712	1749
28	Tamworth 124 d.		0638	0706	0738	0806	0835	0908	0929	1006	1029	1109	1135	1206	1236	1308	1336	1408	1435	1508	1529	1608	1635	1708	1730	1812
48	Burton-on-Trent 124 d.		0650	0718	0750	0818	0846	0920	0941	1018	1041	1120	1147	1218	1250	1320	1347	1420	1446	1520	1542	1620	1646	1720	1742	1823
67	**Derby** 124 a.		0701	0733	0804	0833	0900	0932	0953	1032	1053	1132	1200	1232	1304	1331	1400	1431	1459	1536	1553	1631	1658	1731	1754	1838
67	**Derby** 155 172 d.		0708	0742	0809	0840	0912	0940	0959	1039	1059	1140	1213	1240	1313	1340	1413	1440	1513	1540	1600	1640	1712	1740	1759	1843
93	**Nottingham** 155 172 a.		0736	0808	0834	0906	0933	1003	1023	1103	1122	1204	1235	1303	1336	1403	1436	1503	1535	1603	1623	1703	1736	1803	1823	1906

	Ⓐ	Ⓐ🍷	Ⓐ	Ⓐ🍷	Ⓐ	Ⓐ	Ⓐ		⑥	⑥	⑥🍷	⑥	⑥🍷	⑥	⑥🍷	⑥	⑥🍷	⑥	⑥🍷	⑥🍷	⑥🍷	⑥	⑥	⑥🍷	⑥	⑥🍷
Cardiff Central 117 d.	...	1645	...	1745	1845	1950	...		...	...	...	...	...	0640	...	0745	...	0845	...	0945	...	1045	...	1145	...	1245
Birmingham New Street 124 d.	1818	1849	1912	1949	2049	2203	2309	⑥	0619	0649	0719	0749	0812	0849	0918	0949	1012	1049	1112	1149	1212	1249	1312	1349	1412	1449
Tamworth 124 d.	1835	1908	1929	2008	2108	2227	2328		0638	0706	0738	0806	0829	0908	0935	1006	1029	1108	1129	1206	1229	1308	1329	1408	1429	1508
Burton-on-Trent 124 d.	1847	1920	1941	2020	2120	2239	2340		0650	0718	0750	0818	0841	0920	0946	1018	1041	1120	1141	1218	1241	1320	1341	1420	1441	1520
Derby 124 a.	1901	1931	1952	2031	2137	2250	2354		0701	0734	0804	0835	0852	0931	0959	1032	1053	1131	1155	1232	1252	1331	1353	1431	1453	1536
Derby 155 172 d.	1913	1940	1956	2040	2146	2258	2358		0710	0742	0808	0840	0859	0940	1008	1040	1101	1140	1201	1240	1301	1340	1401	1440	1501	1540
Nottingham 155 172 a.	1936	2004	2018	2105	2217	2326	0018		0738	0806	0831	0905	0921	1003	1029	1103	1122	1204	1223	1303	1324	1403	1424	1503	1523	1603

	⑥	⑥🍷	⑥	⑥🍷	⑥	⑥🍷	⑥	⑥🍷	⑥	⑥🍷	⑥	⑥	⑥		⑦🍷	⑦🍷	⑦	⑦	⑦🍷	⑦🍷	⑦🍷	⑦🍷	⑦🍷	⑦🍷	⑦🍷	⑦🍷
Cardiff Central 117 d.	...	1345	...	1445	...	1545	...	1645	...	1745	1845	2000	2048		...	...	1045	1145	1245	1345	1445	1545	1645	1745	1845	*1945*
Birmingham New Street 124 d.	1512	1549	1612	1649	1712	1749	1812	1849	1912	1949	2049	2210	2249	⑦	1003	1149	1249	1349	1449	1549	1649	1749	1849	1949	2049	2203
Tamworth 124 d.	1529	1608	1629	1708	1730	1808	1829	1908	1929	2008	2108	2228	2308		1019	1206	1306	1406	1508	1606	1706	1806	1908	2006	2106	2220
Burton-on-Trent 124 d.	1541	1620	1641	1720	1744	1820	1841	1920	1941	2020	2120	2240	2320		1030	1218	1318	1418	1520	1618	1718	1818	1920	2017	2117	|
Derby 124 a.	1553	1631	1653	1731	1755	1836	1852	1931	1952	2031	2131	2255	2331		1040	1229	1329	1429	1531	1629	1729	1829	1931	2029	2129	2239
Derby 155 172 d.	1601	1640	1701	1740	1759	1840	1856	1940	1959	2040	2146	2259	...		...	1233	1333	1433	1535	1633	1733	1833	1937	2034	2134	...
Nottingham 155 172 a.	1624	1703	1724	1803	1824	1903	1924	2003	2019	2103	2215	2327	...		...	1253	1353	1453	1555	1653	1754	1854	1957	2054	2154	...

		Ⓐ	ⒶA	Ⓐ	Ⓐ	Ⓐ	Ⓐ	Ⓐ🍷	Ⓐ	Ⓐ🍷	Ⓐ	Ⓐ🍷	Ⓐ	Ⓐ🍷	Ⓐ	Ⓐ🍷	Ⓐ🍷	Ⓐ🍷	Ⓐ	Ⓐ	Ⓐ🍷	Ⓐ	Ⓐ🍷	Ⓐ	Ⓐ🍷	Ⓐ
Nottingham 155 172 d.		0600	0639	0704	0737	0808	0839	0907	0941	1007	1041	1107	1141	1207	1241	1307	1341	1407	1441	1507	1541	1607	1641	1707	1741	1805
Derby 155 172 a.	Ⓐ	0633	0701	0734	0802	0838	0907	0937	1001	1038	1101	1136	1202	1235	1301	1335	1402	1435	1501	1535	1601	1635	1702	1734	1806	1831
Derby 124 d.		0638	0713	0738	0806	0841	0910	0940	1010	1041	1110	1140	1210	1238	1310	1338	1410	1438	1510	1538	1610	1638	1710	1738	1810	1838
Burton-on-Trent 124 d.		0650	0723	0752	0818	0852	0921	0954	1021	1052	1121	1151	1221	1250	1324	1350	1421	1450	1524	1550	1621	1650	1724	1750	1824	1850
Tamworth 124 d.		0703	0734	0803	0830	0903	0933	1006	1033	1103	1133	1203	1233	1303	1336	1403	1433	1503	1536	1603	1632	1703	1736	1803	1836	1903
Birmingham New Street 124 a.		0724	0752	0825	0855	0924	0955	1024	1055	1124	1155	1224	1255	1324	1355	1424	1456	1524	1555	1624	1655	1724	1755	1824	1855	1924
Cardiff Central 117 a.		0925	...	1025	...	1125	...	1225	...	1325	...	1425	...	1525	...	1625	...	1727	...	1828	...	1928	...	2026	...	2124

	Ⓐ	Ⓐ	Ⓐ	Ⓐ	Ⓐ	Ⓐ🍷		⑥	⑥A	⑥	⑥	⑥	⑥	⑥🍷	⑥	⑥🍷	⑥	⑥🍷	⑥	⑥🍷	⑥	⑥🍷	⑥🍷	⑥🍷	⑥	⑥
Nottingham 155 172 d.	1845	1908	1935	2041	2136	...		0600	0642	0703	0737	0807	0841	0907	0941	1007	1041	1107	1141	1207	1241	1307	1341	1407	1441	1507
Derby 155 172 a.	1907	1938	2004	2106	2206	...	⑥	0631	0704	0731	0802	0837	0904	0935	1001	1034	1101	1135	1201	1235	1301	1335	1401	1435	1501	1535
Derby 124 d.	1912	1941	2010	2110	2210	2250		0638	0713	0736	0806	0842	0910	0938	1010	1038	1110	1138	1210	1238	1310	1338	1410	1438	1510	1539
Burton-on-Trent 124 d.	1923	1953	2021	2124	2221	2300		0650	0723	0750	0818	0853	0921	0952	1021	1050	1121	1150	1221	1250	1324	1350	1421	1450	1524	1550
Tamworth 124 d.	1935	2005	2033	2136	2232	2310		0703	0734	0803	0830	0904	0933	1003	1033	1103	1133	1203	1233	1303	1336	1403	1433	1503	1536	1603
Birmingham New Street 124 a.	1956	2024	2055	2158	2301	2327		0724	0754	0824	0855	0924	0955	1024	1055	1124	1155	1224	1255	1324	1355	1425	1456	1524	1555	1624
Cardiff Central 117 a.	...	2236a	...	...	...	...		0926	...	1027	...	1125	...	1226	...	1325	...	1429	...	1525	...	1625	...	1727	...	1827

	⑥🍷	⑥	⑥🍷	⑥	⑥🍷	⑥	⑥	⑥	⑥	⑥	⑥	⑥🍷		⑦	⑦	⑦	⑦🍷	⑦🍷	⑦🍷	⑦🍷	⑦🍷	⑦🍷	⑦	⑦	⑦	⑦🍷
Nottingham 155 172 d.	1541	1607	1641	1707	1741	1807	1845	1907	1932	2039	2137	...		0955	1116	1216	1316	1416	1512	1616	1716	1816	1915	2016	2117	...
Derby 155 172 a.	1601	1635	1701	1735	1801	1834	1905	1935	2003	2104	2207	...	⑦	1015	1136	1236	1337	1436	1533	1636	1738	1836	1937	2036	2139	...
Derby 124 d.	1610	1638	1710	1739	1810	1838	1910	1938	2010	2110	2213	2229		1020	1140	1240	1340	1440	1537	1640	1742	1840	1941	2040	2142	2231
Burton-on-Trent 124 d.	1621	1650	1724	1750	1824	1850	1921	1950	2021	2124	2224	2239		1031	1151	1251	1351	1451	1548	1651	1753	1851	1952	2051	2153	2241
Tamworth 124 d.	1633	1703	1736	1803	1836	1903	1933	2003	2033	2136	2235	2249		1043	1203	1303	1403	1503	1600	1703	1804	1903	2003	2103	2205	2251
Birmingham New Street 124 a.	1655	1724	1755	1824	1855	1924	1955	2024	2055	2158	2304	2308		1101	1221	1321	1421	1521	1621	1721	1823	1921	2025	2121	2226	2309
Cardiff Central 117 a.	...	1925	...	2022	...	2122	...	2245	...	...	...	...		1306	1425	1525	1625	1721	1820	1925	2020	2120	...	...	...	...

A – To Reading (Table 114).

a – Arrives 2229 on ⑤.

XC BIRMINGHAM - SHEFFIELD - LEEDS - YORK - NEWCASTLE - EDINBURGH 124

km	Ⓐ	Ⓐ	Ⓐ	Ⓐ	Ⓐ	Ⓐ	Ⓐ	Ⓐ	Ⓐ	Ⓐ		ⒶC	ⒶH	Ⓐ	Ⓐ	ⒶB	Ⓐ	Ⓐ	Ⓐ	Ⓐ	Ⓐ	Ⓐ
	Plymouth 116 d.	...	...	...	...	...	0525	0627	0725	...	...	0927	...	...	...	1127	1227	1327	1427	1527	1627	...
	Bristol Temple Meads 116 d.	...	...	...	...	0634	0735	0835	0932	1035	...	1134	...	1235	1300	1335	1435	1535	1635	1735	1835	1935
	Southampton Central 114 d.	...	...	...	...	|	|	|	|	|	...	|	...	|	|	|	|	|	|	|	|	|
	Reading 114 d.	...	...	...	...	|	|	|	|	|	...	|	...	|	|	|	|	|	|	|	|	|
0	**Birmingham** New Street 120 d.	...	0603	0630	0703	0803	0903	1003	1103	1203	...	1303	1330	1403	1430	1503	1603	1703	1803	1903	2003	2103
28	Tamworth 120 d.	...	|	|	0719	0819	|	1019	|	1219	...	|	|	1419	|	|	1620	|	1819	|	2019	2129
48	Burton on Trent 120 d.	...	|	|	0730	0830	0926	|	1126	|	...	1326	|	|	|	1526	|	1727	|	1926	|	2140
67	**Derby** 120 a.	...	0635	0706	0740	0840	0936	1038	1136	1237	...	1336	1405	1438	1504	1538	1640	1737	1842	1937	2037	2150
	Derby 170 d.	...	0645	0717	0750	0845	0945	1045	1145	1245	...	1345	1416	1445	1521	1545	1645	1745	1845	1945	2048	2152
105	Chesterfield 170 d.	...	0703	|	0808	0905	|	1105	|	1305	...	|	|	1505	|	1605	1705	1805	|	|	2106	|
125	**Sheffield** 170 d.	...	0721b	0749	0822	0921	1021	1121	1221	1321	...	1421	1452b	1521	1551	1621	1721	1821	1921	2021	2123	2228
154	Doncaster 180 d.	...	|	0819b	|	|	|	|	|	|	...	|	1519	|	1617	|	|	|	|	|	|	2301
171	Wakefield Westgate 180 d.	...	0747	|	0848	0947	1047	1147	1247	1347	...	1447	|	1547	|	1647	1747	1850	1947	2047	2147	2319
187	**Leeds** 180 a.	...	0803	|	0903	1001	1101	1201	1301	1401	...	1501	|	1601	|	1702	1802	1905	2002	2102	2203	2334
	Leeds 188 191 d.	0543	0808	|	0908	1008	1108	1208	1308	1408	...	1508	|	1608	|	1707	1808	1908	2008	...	...	...
199	**York** 180 188 191 a.	0605	0830	0842	0930	1030	1130	1230	1330	1430	...	1530	1542	1630	1639	1730	1831	1931	2030	...	...	...
	York 180 188 d.	0627	0832	0844	0932	1032	1132	1232	1332	1432	...	1532	1546	1632	1645	1731	1832	1934	2032	...	...	...
270	Darlington 180 188 d.	0655	0900	0915	1000	1100	1200	1300	1403	1500	...	1600	1614	1700	1713	1800	1901	2005	2059	...	...	...
305	Durham 180 188 d.	0713	0917	0932	1017	1117	1217	1317	1420	1517	...	1617	1631	1717	1730	1818	1919	2023	2116	...	...	...
328	**Newcastle** 180 188 a.	0729	0929	0945	1029	1129	1229	1329	1432	1529	...	1632	1644	1729	1744	1831	1932	2036	2128	...	...	...
	Newcastle 180 188 d.	0735	0933	...	1035	1132	1236	1332	...	1537	...	1635	...	1736	...	1837	1935	2038	2135	...	...	...
384	Alnmouth 180 a.	|	0957	...	|	|	|	1358	...	1601	...	1702	...	1800	...	|	2000	|	2200	...	...	...
436	Berwick upon Tweed 180 a.	0820	1019	...	|	1218	|	1419	...	1623	...	|	...	1822	...	1924	2023	2125	|	...	...	...
528	**Edinburgh** Waverley 180 188 a.	0903	1106	...	1204	1300	1406	1501	...	1705	...	1807	...	1904	...	2011	2108	2213	2303	...	...	...
620	*Glasgow Central 220* a.	...	...	...	...	...	...	...	...	1812	...	...	...	2016	...	...	...	...	...	...	...	...

⑥	⑥	⑥	⑥	⑥		⑥	⑥	⑥	⑥	⑥	⑥C	⑥		⑥	⑥	⑥	⑥		⑥	⑥	⑥	⑥
Plymouth 116 d.	...	...	...	...	...	...	0527	0624	0725	...	0927	...	...	...	1127	1227	...	...	1427	1527	1627	...
Bristol Temple Meads 116 d.	...	...	...	...	...	0615	0735	0835	0935	1035	1135	1235	...	...	1335	1435	1535	...	1635	1735	1835	1931
Southampton Central 114 d.	...	...	...	...	...	|	|	|	|	|	|	|	...	...	|	|	|	...	|	|	|	|
Reading 114 d.	...	...	...	...	...	|	|	|	|	|	|	|	...	...	|	|	|	...	|	|	|	|
Birmingham New Street 120 d.	...	0603	0630	0703	...	0803	0903	1003	1103	1203	1303	1403	...	1428	1503	1603	1703	...	1803	1903	2003	2103
Tamworth 120 d.	...	0619	0646	0719	...	0819	|	1019	|	1219	|	1419	...	|	|	1620	|	...	1819	|	2020	2120
Burton on Trent 120 d.	...	0630	0657	0730	...	0830	0926	|	1126	|	1326	|	...	|	1526	|	1726	...	|	1926	|	2131
Derby 120 a.	...	0640	0707	0740	...	0840	0936	1037	1136	1237	1336	1437	...	1458	1538	1639	1736	...	1837	1937	2039	2142
Derby 170 d.	...	0645	0717	0750	...	0845	0945	1045	1145	1245	1345	1445	...	1500	1545	1645	1745	...	1845	1945	2045	2145
Chesterfield 170 d.	...	0703	|	0808	...	0905	|	1105	1205	|	1405	|	...	|	1605	1705	1805	...	|	2005	|	2208
Sheffield 170 d.	...	0721	0750	0822	...	0921	1021	1121	1221	1321	1421	1521	...	1529	1621	1721	1821	...	1921	2021	2121	2225
Doncaster 180 d.	...	|	0819b	|	...	|	|	|	|	|	|	|	...	1558	|	|	|	...	|	|	|	2255b
Wakefield Westgate 180 d.	...	0747	|	0848	...	0947	1047	1147	1247	1347	1447	1547	...	|	1647	1747	1847	...	1948	2047	2147	2313
Leeds 180 a.	...	0803	|	0903	...	1001	1101	1201	1301	1401	1501	1601	...	|	1701	1802	1903	...	2005	2102	2202	2327
Leeds 188 191 d.	...	0808	|	0908	...	1008	1108	1208	1308	1408	1508	1608	...	|	1708	1808	1908	...	2008	2108	...	...
York 180 188 191 a.	...	0830	0840	0930	...	1030	1130	1230	1330	1430	1530	1630	...	1618	1730	1831	1930	...	2030	2146	...	...
York 180 188 d.	...	0832	0844	0932	...	1032	1132	1232	1332	1432	1532	1632	...	1620	1732	1832	1934	...	2031	...	...	...
Darlington 180 188 d.	...	0900	0916	1000	...	1100	1201	1300	1403	1500	1600	1700	...	1647	1800	1901	2005	...	2100	...	...	...
Durham 180 188 d.	...	0917	0933	1017	...	1117	1217	1317	1420	1517	1617	1717	...	1704	1817	1919	2022	...	2116	...	...	...
Newcastle 180 188 a.	...	0929	0946	1030	...	1129	1230	1329	1432	1529	1629	1730	...	1717	1833	1932	2035	...	2129	...	...	...
Newcastle 180 188 d.	0738	0933	...	1035	...	1133	1234	1334	1435	1535	1633	1734	...	...	1839	1936	2042	...	2135	...	...	...
Alnmouth 180 a.	|	0957	...	|	...	|	|	1358	|	1559	1700	1759	...	...	|	2001	|	...	2200	...	...	...
Berwick upon Tweed 180 a.	0823	1019	...	|	...	1218	|	1420	|	1621	|	1821	...	...	1922	2024	2127	...	|	...	...	...
Edinburgh Waverley 180 188 a.	0908	1103	...	1201	...	1305	1402	1502	1606	1703	1803	1903	...	...	2007	2108	2212	...	2301	...	...	...
Glasgow Central 220 a.	...	...	...	...	...	...	...	...	...	1814	...	2017	...	...	...	...	...	...	...	...	...	...

⑦	⑦	⑦	⑦		⑦	⑦	⑦		⑦C	⑦		⑦B	⑦		⑦	⑦	⑦		⑦	⑦		⑦
Plymouth 116 d.	...	...	...	...	...	...	...	...	0927	1027	...	1127	1227	...	...	1427	...	...	1627	...	...	1827
Bristol Temple Meads 116 d.	...	...	...	...	...	0915	1031	...	1131	1231	...	1331	1431	...	1531	1631	1731	...	1831	1931	...	2031
Southampton Central 114 d.	...	...	...	...	...	|	|	...	|	|	...	|	|	...	|	|	|	...	|	|	...	|
Reading 114 d.	...	...	...	...	...	|	|	...	|	|	...	|	|	...	|	|	|	...	|	|	...	|
Birmingham New Street 120 d.	...	...	0903	...	1003	1103	1203	...	1303	1403	...	1503	1603	...	1703	1803	1903	...	2003	2103	...	2203
Tamworth 120 d.	...	...	0919	...	1019	|	1219	...	|	1419	...	|	1620	...	|	1820	|	...	2020	2119	...	2220
Burton on Trent 120 d.	...	...	0930	...	1030	1126	|	...	1326	|	...	1526	|	...	1726	|	1926	...	|	2130	...	|
Derby 120 a.	...	...	0940	...	1040	1136	1237	...	1336	1437	...	1536	1639	...	1736	1839	1937	...	2039	2140	...	2239
Derby 170 d.	...	...	0945	...	1045	1145	1245	...	1345	1445	...	1545	1645	...	1745	1845	1945	...	2045	2145	...	2245
Chesterfield 170 d.	...	...	1005	...	1105	1205	|	...	1405	|	...	1605	1705	...	1805	1905	|	...	|	|	...	2305
Sheffield 170 d.	...	0921	1021	...	1121	1221	1321	...	1421	1521	...	1621	1721	...	1821	1921	2023	...	2120	2221	...	2321
Doncaster 180 d.	...	|	|	...	|	|	|	...	|	|	...	|	|	...	|	|	|	...	|	|	...	|
Wakefield Westgate 180 d.	...	0947	1047	...	1147	1247	1347	...	1447	1547	...	1647	1747	...	1847	1947	2049	...	2147	2249	...	|
Leeds 180 a.	...	1001	1102	...	1202	1302	1402	...	1502	1602	...	1702	1802	...	1902	2002	2103	...	2202	2303	...	0012
Leeds 188 191 d.	0918	1007	1107	...	1207	1307	1407	...	1507	1607	...	1707	1807	...	1907	2007	2107	...	...	...	...	...
York 180 188 191 a.	0940	1029	1129	...	1229	1329	1429	...	1529	1629	...	1729	1830	...	1930	2030	2130	...	...	...	...	...
York 180 188 d.	0943	1031	1131	...	1231	1331	1431	...	1531	1631	...	1731	1831	...	1931	2031	...	...	...	...	...	...
Darlington 180 188 d.	1011	1059	1159	...	1259	1358	1459	...	1559	1659	...	1758	1900	...	1959	2100	...	...	...	...	...	...
Durham 180 188 d.	1028	1116	1216	...	1316	1415	1516	...	1616	1716	...	1815	1918	...	2016	2118	...	...	...	...	...	...
Newcastle 180 188 a.	1040	1128	1228	...	1328	1427	1528	...	1628	1728	...	1827	1931	...	2028	2131	...	...	...	...	...	...
Newcastle 180 188 d.	1042	1131	1230	...	1331	1431	1530	...	1631	1730	...	1834	1932	...	2036	2134	...	...	...	...	...	...
Alnmouth 180 a.	|	|	|	...	1355	|	1554	...	1655	1757	...	|	1958	...	|	2159	...	...	...	...	...	...
Berwick upon Tweed 180 a.	1124	1216	|	...	1416	|	1615	...	|	1818	...	1916	2020	...	2123	|	...	...	...	...	...	...
Edinburgh Waverley 180 188 a.	1210	1259	1357	...	1459	1559	1700	...	1759	1901	...	2005	2105	...	2208	2303	...	...	...	...	...	...
Glasgow Central 220 a.	...	...	...	...	...	...	1813	...	...	2015	...	...	...	...	...	...	...	...	...	...	...	...

B – From Penzance (Tables 112/116). C – To Aberdeen (Table 222). H – From Banbury (Table 114). b – Arrives 5–6 minutes earlier.

Most trains convey 🍸

124 EDINBURGH - NEWCASTLE - YORK - LEEDS - SHEFFIELD - BIRMINGHAM XC

Ⓐ		Ⓐ	Ⓐ	Ⓐ	Ⓐ	Ⓐ	ⒶH	Ⓐ	Ⓐ	ⒶH	Ⓐ	ⒶB	ⒶC	Ⓐ	Ⓐ	Ⓐ	Ⓐ	Ⓐ	Ⓐ	Ⓐ	Ⓐ	Ⓐ
Glasgow Central **220**	d.	...	...	...	...	...	...	...	...	...	0748	...	...	...	...	...	...	...	...	...	...	1900
Edinburgh Waverley **180 188**	d.	...	...	...	...	0606	...	0701	0806	...	0905	1003	1106	1203	1305	...	1508	1607	...	1707	1808	2003
Berwick upon Tweed **180**	d.	...	...	...	...	0648	...	0746	0848	...	0948	1047	1150	1245	|	...	|	|	...	1751	1852	2047
Alnmouth **180**	d.	...	...	...	...	0710	...	0807	|	...	1009	|	1211	|	1410	...	|	1705	...	|	1913	2108
Newcastle **180 188**	a.	...	...	...	...	0737	...	0836	0939	...	1036	1136	1237	1334	1437	...	1633	1734	...	1838	1939	2135
Newcastle **180 188**	d.	...	...	...	0640	0740	0835	0840	0941	1035	1041	1139	1241	1337	1440	1539	1639	1738	1835	1840	1942	2137
Durham **180 188**	d.	...	...	...	0653	0753	0848	0854	0955	1048	1053	1153	1254	1351	1453	1552	1653	1752	1849	1854	1955	2150
Darlington **180 188**	d.	...	...	...	0711	0811	0906	0912	1012	1106	1111	1212	1311	1411	1512	1610	1711	1810	1907	1912	2013	2209
York **180 188**	a.	...	...	...	0738	0838	0934	0939	1039	1134	1138	1239	1338	1438	1539	1636	1738	1838	1933	1938	2041	2235
York **180 188 191**	d.	...	...	0645	0744	0844	0938	0944	1044	1137	1144	1243	1344	1444	1544	1643	1744	1844	1936	1944	2044	...
Leeds **188 191**	a.	...	...	0708	0808	0908	|	1007	1107	|	1208	1308	1407	1507	1607	1707	1807	1907	|	2008	2107	...
Leeds **180**	d.	...	0611	0710	0811	0911	|	1011	1111	|	1211	1311	1411	1511	1611	1711	1811	1911	|	2011	2111	...
Wakefield Westgate **180**	d.	...	0623	0723	0823	0923	|	1023	1123	|	1223	1323	1423	1523	1623	1723	1823	1923	|	2023	2123	...
Doncaster **180**	d.	...	|	|	|	|	1000	|	|	1159	|	|	|	|	|	|	|	|	1959	|	|	...
Sheffield **170**	d.	...	0653	0753	0856	0956	1024	1056	1155	1224	1256	1355	1456	1556	1656	1756	1856	1956	2024	2056	2202b	...
Chesterfield **170**	d.	...	0706	0806	0908	|	|	1108	|	|	1308	|	|	1608	1708	1808	|	2008	|	|	2225	...
Derby **170**	a.	...	0724	0824	0926	1027	1051	1126	1226	1251	1326	1426	1526	1626	1727	1826	1926	2026	2051	2126	2243	...
Derby **120**	d.	0610	0727	0827	0931	1031	1053	1131	1231	1253	1331	1431	1528	1631	1731	1831	1931	2031	2053	2131	2250	...
Burton on Trent **120**	d.	0620	0738	0838	0941	|	|	|	|	|	1341	|	1539	|	1742	|	1941	|	|	2141	2300	...
Tamworth **120**	d.	0632	0750	0850	|	1050	|	|	1250	|	|	1450	|	1649	|	1849	|	2049	|	2151	2310	...
Birmingham New Street **120**	a.	0652	0808	0908	1004	1108	1127	1204	1308	1327	1404	1508	1604	1706	1806	1906	2005	2106	2129	2208	2327	...
Reading **114**	a.	|	|	|	|	|	...	|	|	...	|	|	|	|	|	|	|	|	...	|	...	...
Southampton Central **114**	a.	|	|	|	|	|	...	|	|	...	|	|	|	|	|	|	|	|	...	|	...	...
Bristol Temple Meads **116**	a.	0839	0938	1032	1131	1233	...	1332	1433	...	1534	1632	1732	1833	1946	2032	2136	2244	...	2331	...	...
Plymouth **116**	a.	1046	1148	1257	...	1448	...	1547	1648	...	1745	1847	1946	...	2151	...	2343	...	...	...	...	...
⑥		⑥	⑥	⑥	⑥	⑥		⑥	⑥	⑥	⑥	⑥B	⑥ CB	⑥	⑥	⑥		⑥	⑥	⑥	⑥	⑥
Glasgow Central **220**	d.	...	...	...	...	...	...	...	...	...	0748	...		...	...	...	...	...	...	...	...	...
Edinburgh Waverley **180 188**	d.	...	...	...	...	0606	...	0658	0807	...	0908	1005	1108	1205	1309	1404	...	1505	1606	...	1709	1807
Berwick upon Tweed **180**	d.	...	...	...	...	0648	...	0745	0849	...	0948	1047	1152	1245	|	1445	...	|	|	...	1753	1851
Alnmouth **180**	d.	...	...	...	...	0710	...	0807	0911	...	|	|	1213	|	1411	|	...	|	1704	...	|	1912
Newcastle **180 188**	a.	...	...	...	...	0737	...	0837	0938	...	1036	1136	1240	1334	1438	1534	...	1631	1733	...	1837	1938
Newcastle **180 188**	d.	...	...	...	...	0739	...	0839	0940	1035	1043	1139	1242	1339	1443	1539	...	1638	1739	1835	1839	1943
Durham **180 188**	d.	...	...	...	...	0752	...	0853	0954	1048	1055	1154	1255	1352	1455	1552	...	1651	1753	1848	1853	1955
Darlington **180 188**	d.	...	...	...	...	0811	...	0911	1012	1106	1113	1212	1312	1412	1513	1610	...	1711	1811	1906	1912	2013
York **180 188**	a.	...	...	...	...	0838	...	0938	1039	1134	1139	1239	1340	1440	1541	1636	...	1738	1838	1933	1938	2039
York **180 188 191**	d.	...	...	0611	0744	0844	...	0944	1044	1137	1143	1244	1344	1444	1544	1644	...	1742	1844	1936	1944	2043
Leeds **188 191**	a.	...	...	0658	0808	0908	...	1007	1107	|	1207	1308	1407	1507	1607	1707	...	1807	1907	|	2007	2107
Leeds **180**	d.	...	0609	0711	0811	0911	...	1011	1111	|	1211	1311	1411	1511	1611	1711	...	1811	1911	|	2011	2111
Wakefield Westgate **180**	d.	...	0623	0723	0823	0923	...	1023	1123	|	1223	1323	1423	1523	1623	1723	...	1823	1923	|	2023	2123
Doncaster **180**	d.	...	|	|	|	|	...	|	|	1159	|	|	|	|	|	|	...	|	|	1959	|	|
Sheffield **170**	d.	...	0653	0755	0856	0956	...	1055	1155	1224	1256	1356	1456	1556	1656	1756	...	1856	1956	2024	2056	2157
Chesterfield **170**	d.	...	0706	0808	0908	|	...	1108	|	|	1308	|	1508	1608	1708	1808	...	|	2008	|	2108	2209
Derby **170**	a.	...	0724	0826	0926	1027	...	1126	1226	1251	1326	1427	1526	1626	1726	1826	...	1926	2026	2051	2126	2227
Derby **120**	d.	0610	0727	0828	0931	1031	...	1131	1231	1253	1331	1431	1528	1631	1731	1828	...	1931	2031	2053	2131	2229
Burton on Trent **120**	d.	0620	0738	0838	0941	|	...	1142	|	|	1341	|	1539	|	1741	|	...	1941	|	|	2141	2239
Tamworth **120**	d.	0631	0750	0851	|	1050	...	|	1250	|	|	1450	|	1649	|	1847	...	|	2049	|	2151	2249
Birmingham New Street **120**	a.	0648	0808	0908	1004	1108	...	1206	1308	1328	1404	1508	1603	1706	1804	1904	...	2004	2107	2124	2208	2308
Reading **114**	a.	|	|	|	|	|	...	|	|	...	|	|	|	|	|	|	...	|	|	...	...	...
Southampton Central **114**	a.	|	|	|	|	|	...	|	|	...	|	|	|	|	|	|	...	|	|	...	...	...
Bristol Temple Meads **116**	a.	0836	0934	1036	1135	1238	...	1336	1434	...	1536	1634	1735	1834	1936	2036	...	2134	2240	...	...	...
Plymouth **116**	a.	1047	1148	1247	...	1448	...	1549	...	...	1747	1848	1944	...	2143	...	...	2347	...	...	...	...
⑦		⑦	⑦	⑦		⑦	⑦		⑦	⑦		⑦	⑦		⑦C	⑦	⑦		⑦	⑦		⑦
Glasgow Central **220**	d.	...	...	...	...	...	...	...	...	...	...	...	...	...	...	...	...	...	...	...	...	1900
Edinburgh Waverley **180 188**	d.	...	...	...	...	...	0908	...	1005	1105	...	1205	1309	...	1408	1508	1608	...	1708	1806	...	2018
Berwick upon Tweed **180**	d.	...	...	...	...	...	0950	...	|	1149	...	1245	|	...	1448	|	|	...	1748	1850	...	2102
Alnmouth **180**	d.	...	...	...	...	...	|	...	1106	1210	...	|	1411	...	|	|	1706	...	|	|	...	|
Newcastle **180 188**	a.	...	...	...	...	...	1035	...	1136	1236	...	1331	1438	...	1535	1636	1735	...	1832	1936	...	2148
Newcastle **180 188**	d.	...	...	...	...	0935	1039	...	1140	1240	...	1339	1441	...	1540	1640	1739	...	1839	1941	...	...
Durham **180 188**	d.	...	...	...	...	0948	1052	...	1153	1252	...	1353	1454	...	1553	1653	1753	...	1851	1953	...	...
Darlington **180 188**	d.	...	...	...	...	1006	1110	...	1211	1310	...	1411	1512	...	1611	1711	1811	...	1908	2011	...	...
York **180 188**	a.	...	...	...	...	1032	1138	...	1237	1336	...	1437	1541	...	1637	1740	1840	...	1936	2037	...	...
York **180 188 191**	d.	...	...	0935	...	1034	1144	...	1244	1344	...	1443	1544	...	1644	1744	1844	...	1944	2044	...	...
Leeds **188 191**	a.	...	...	0958	...	1059	1207	...	1307	1407	...	1507	1607	...	1709	1807	1907	...	2007	2107	...	...
Leeds **180**	d.	0811	0900	1000	...	1100	1211	...	1311	1411	...	1511	1611	...	1711	1811	1911	...	2011	2111	...	...
Wakefield Westgate **180**	d.	0823	0912	1012	...	1112	1223	...	1323	1423	...	1523	1623	...	1723	1823	1923	...	2023	2123	...	...
Doncaster **180**	d.	|	0931	1031	...	1131	|	...	|	|	...	|	|	...	|	|	|	...	|	|	...	...
Sheffield **170**	d.	0856	0958	1056	...	1156	1256	...	1356	1456	...	1556	1656	...	1756	1856	1956	...	2056	2156	...	...
Chesterfield **170**	d.	0908	1011	1108	...	|	1308	...	|	1508	...	1608	1708	...	1808	|	|	...	|	2208	...	...
Derby **170**	a.	0927	1029	1128	...	1227	1327	...	1426	1526	...	1626	1726	...	1826	1926	2026	...	2126	2226	...	...
Derby **120**	d.	0931	1031	1131	...	1231	1331	...	1431	1531	...	1631	1731	...	1831	1931	2031	...	2130	2231	...	...
Burton on Trent **120**	d.	|	|	1142	...	|	1342	...	|	1541	...	|	1741	...	|	1941	|	...	2140	2241	...	...
Tamworth **120**	d.	|	1053	|	...	1249	|	...	1449	|	...	1649	|	...	1849	|	2049	...	2150	2251	...	...
Birmingham New Street **120**	a.	1020	1119	1206	...	1306	1406	...	1506	1604	...	1706	1804	...	1906	2004	2105	...	2207	2309	...	...
Reading **114**	a.	|	|	|	...	|	|	...	|	|	...	|	|	...	|	|	|	...	|	...	...	...
Southampton Central **114**	a.	|	|	|	...	|	|	...	|	|	...	|	|	...	|	|	|	...	|	...	...	...
Bristol Temple Meads **116**	a.	1151	1253	1333	...	1436	1536	...	1636	1734	...	1836	1936	...	2035	2135	2240	...	2330	...	...	...
Plymouth **116**	a.	1357	...	1546	...	...	1744	...	...	1946	...	...	2148	...	...	2344	...	...	...	...	...	...

B – To Penzance (Tables **112**/**116**). **C** – From Aberdeen (Table **222**). **H** – To Banbury (Table **114**). **b** – Arrives 2155.

LM 2nd class BIRMINGHAM - WORCESTER - HEREFORD 125

km			Ⓐ	Ⓐ	Ⓐ	Ⓐ	Ⓐ		Ⓐ	Ⓐ	Ⓐ	Ⓐ	Ⓐ	Ⓐ	Ⓐ	Ⓐ	Ⓐ	Ⓐ		⑥	⑥	⑥	⑥	
0	**Birmingham** New Street ★ d.	Ⓐ	...	0659	0720	0800	0850		1550	1650	1720	1750	1820	1920	2000	2100	2200	2300	⑥	...	0650	0750	0850	
21	Bromsgrove d.		...	0721	0744	0822	0912		1612	1712	1744	1812	1842	1942	2021	2121	2223	2321		...	0713	0810	0912	
32	Droitwich Spa ★ d.		...	0731	0756	0832	0922	and	1621	1722	1756	1822	1852	1953	2031	2131	2233	2331		...	0723	0820	0922	and
40	**Worcester** Shrub Hill ★ a.		...	|	0803	0839	|		|	1729	|	1833	|	2007	2039	|	2241	2338		...	|	|	|	
	Worcester Shrub Hill.. 138 130 d.		0625	|	0808	0844	|	hourly	|	1733	|	...	|	2016	2106	|	2257	...		0630	|	|	|	hourly
41	**Worcester** Foregate St.. 130 ★ d.		0631	0742	0811	0847	0932		1631	1736	1806	...	1901	2019	2109	2141	2300	...		0632	0732	0830	0931	
54	Great Malvern 130 138 d.		0643	0800f	0822	0904f	0945	until	1645	1748	1819	...	1914	2031	2124	2200f	2311	...		0645	0745	0845	0945	until
65	Ledbury 130 d.		0659	0813	...	0917	0958		1659	1801	1831	...	1927	2045	2147r	2219f	...	...		0659	0759	0859	0959	
87	**Hereford** 130 a.		0714	0829	...	0932	1016		1715	1817	1846	...	1942	2101	2204	2234	...	...		0717	0815	0914	1014	

	⑥	⑥	⑥	⑥	⑥	⑥	⑥	⑥		⑦	⑦	⑦	⑦	⑦	⑦	⑦	⑦	⑦	⑦	⑦	⑦	⑦	⑦	⑦
Birmingham New Street ★ d.	1650	1720	1750	1850	1950	2050	2123	2221	⑦	...	1000	1100	1200	1300	1400	1500	1600	1700	1800	1900	2000	2100	2200	2230
Bromsgrove d.	1712	1744	1812	1912	2012	2111	2143	2241		...	1020	1120	1220	1320	1420	1520	1621	1721	1820	1920	2020	2120	2220	2250
Droitwich Spa ★ d.	1722	1756	1822	1922	2022	2121	2154	2251		...	1030	1129	1232	1329	1430	1531	1631	1731	1832	1931	2030	2130	2237	2300
Worcester Shrub Hill ★ a.	|	|	1829	|	|	|	|	|		...	1038	|	1240	|	|	1537	1638	|	1841	1939	2044	2138	2246	2307
Worcester Shrub Hill.. 138 130 d.	|	|	1833	|	|	|	|	|		0859	1042	|	1247	|	|	1552	1648	|	1848	1948	2103	2142	2251	...
Worcester Foregate St.. 130 ★ d.	1731	1805	1836	1931	2034	2135f	2203	2301		0902	1045	1139	1250	1339	1442	1555	165[illegible]	1739	1851	1951	2109	2145	2254	...
Great Malvern 130 138 d.	1745	1817	1848	1944	2048	2147	2215	2315		0914	1101	...	1302	...	1454	1607	1703	...	1903	2003	2125	2157	2305	...
Ledbury 130 d.	1759	...	1901	1959	2101	...	2228	...		0926	1113	...	1315	...	1506	1619	1716	...	1915	2015	2139	2210	...	...
Hereford 130 a.	1814	...	1916	2014	2117	...	2243	...		0944	1129	...	1332	...	1522	1635	1734	...	1932	2031	2155	2229	...	...

		Ⓐ	Ⓐ	Ⓐ	Ⓐ	Ⓐ	Ⓐ	Ⓐ	Ⓐ		Ⓐ	Ⓐ	Ⓐ	Ⓐ	Ⓐ	Ⓐ	Ⓐ	Ⓐ		⑥	⑥	⑥	⑥	⑥
Hereford 130 d.	Ⓐ	0449	0523	...	0713	0732	...	0837	0939		1739	...	1848	1951	2058	2128	2200	2259	⑥	...	...	0639	0737	0839
Ledbury 130 d.		0506	0540	...	0729	0750	...	0855	0958		1759	...	1904	2007	2114	2145	2217	2315		...	...	0659	0759f	0858
Great Malvern 130 138 d.		0543	0553	0646	0740	0807f	0836	0908	1010	and	1811	...	1915	2019	2126	2157	2229	2327		...	0617	0711	0810	0910
Worcester Foregate St.. 130 ★ d.		0602f	0606	0658	0753	0824f	0849	0924	1024		1825	...	1928	2033	2138	2210	2242	2340		...	0628	0723	0822	0924
Worcester Shrub Hill.. 138 130 a.		|	0609	0700	|	|	|	|	|	hourly	|	...	|	|	2140	|	2245	2350		...	|	0725	|	|
Worcester Shrub Hill ★ d.		|	0625	0705	|	|	|	|	|		|	1850	|	|	2150	|	...	...		0607	|	0731	|	|
Droitwich Spa ★ d.		0611	0633	0713	0803	0833	0858	0932	1033	until	1834	1858	1937	2042	2158	2219	...	...		0615	0637	0739	0833	0933
Bromsgrove d.		0621	0643	0723	|	0842	0908	0943	1042		1843	1908	1947	2052	|	2229	...	...		|	0647	0747	0843	0943
Birmingham New Street ★ a.		0648	0709	0746	0838	0909	0937	1008	1110		1909	1934	2019	2120	2239	2255	...	...		0645	0719	0816	0909	1009

	⑥	⑥		⑥	⑥	⑥	⑥	⑥		⑦	⑦	⑦	⑦	⑦	⑦	⑦	⑦	⑦	⑦	⑦	⑦	⑦	⑦	⑦
Hereford 130 d.	...	0938		1842	1940	2035	2131	2250	⑦	...	...	1005	...	1202	1227	1402	...	1558	1656	1803	...	1956	2100	2239
Ledbury 130 d.	...	0958		1901	1959	2101t	2155f	2306		...	...	1022	...	1218	1246	1419	...	1619f	1717	1819	...	2017	2117	2258
Great Malvern 130 138 d.	...	1010	and	1911	2010	2113	2207	2317		...	0858	1034	1050	1230	1300	1431	1458	1631	1731	1831	1857	2029	2128	2310
Worcester Foregate St.. 130 ★ d.	...	1024		1924	2024	2125	2218	2329		0854	0911	1051	1155	1242	1349	1443	1510	1643	1743	1843	1911	2041	2140	2323
Worcester Shrub Hill.. 138 130 a.	...	|	hourly	|	|	2127	2222	2336		0856	0914	1054	|	1244	|	1445	1513	1645	1745	1845	1914	2043	|	2327
Worcester Shrub Hill ★ d.	0949	|		|	|	2131	...	...		0905	1005	1058	|	1250	|	1450	1539	1651	1750	1850	1952	2050	|	...
Droitwich Spa ★ d.	0957	1033	until	1933	2033	2139	...	...		0913	1013	1106	1204	1258	1358	1458	1547	1659	1758	1858	2004	2058	2149	...
Bromsgrove d.	1007	1043		1943	2043	2149	...	...		0922	1023	1116	1214	1308	1408	1508	1557	1709	1808	1908	2013	2108	2158	...
Birmingham New Street ★ a.	1035	1111		2009	2110	2217	...	...		0945	1046	1139	1237	1337	1437	1537	1620	1737	1837	1937	2036	2137	2221	...

f – Arrives 5–7 minutes earlier.
r – Arrives 2138.
t – Arrives 2052.

★ – Regular trains also operate Birmingham **Moor Street** - Birmingham **Snow Hill** - Kidderminster - Droitwich Spa - Worcester Shrub Hill / Worcester Foregate St (2 trains per hour on ⚒, hourly on ⑦). Journey times from Birmingham Moor Street: to Kidderminster ± 40 minutes, Droitwich Spa ± 50 minutes, Worcester Shrub Hill or Foregate St ± 65 minutes.
Kidderminster is the station for the **Severn Valley Railway** (🚂 Kidderminster - Bridgnorth: *26 km*). ✆ 01299 403816. www.svr.co.uk

LM 2nd class STRATFORD UPON AVON - BIRMINGHAM 127

km			Ⓐ	Ⓐ	Ⓐ	Ⓐ		Ⓐ	Ⓐ	Ⓐ	Ⓐ	Ⓐ	and at	Ⓐ	Ⓐ	Ⓐ	Ⓐ		Ⓐ	Ⓐ	Ⓐ	Ⓐ	Ⓐ	Ⓐ
0	**Stratford upon Avon** d.	Ⓐ	0623	0700	0723	0826	...	0852	0926	1001	1026	1103	the same	1703	1726	1803	1827	...	1903	1927	2027	2127	2230	2330
13	Henley in Arden d.		0637	0712	0739	0841	...	|	0941	|	1041	|	minutes	|	1741	|	1842	...	|	1942	2042	2142	2243	|
40	**Birmingham** Moor St a.		0720	0745	0821	0920	...	0934	1021	1051	1121	1150	past each	1751	1821	1850	1922	...	1952	2023	2122	2225	2319	0006
41	**Birmingham** Snow Hill a.		...	0747	0824	0922	...	0936	1023	1053	1123	1154	hour until	1753	1823	1852	1924	...	1954	2025	2124	2227	2321	0012

		⑥	⑥	⑥	⑥	and at	⑥	⑥	⑥	⑥	⑥	⑥	⑥	⑥	⑥		⑦	⑦	⑦	⑦		⑦	⑦	⑦
Stratford upon Avon d.	⑥	0700	0726	0826	0902	the same	1726	1802	1826	1908	1926	2026	2126	2231	2330	⑦	0927	1027	1126	1227	and	1727	1827	1927
Henley in Arden d.		0716	0741	0841	|	minutes	1741	|	1841	|	1941	2041	2140	2245	|		0942	1042	1141	1242	hourly	1743	1843	1943
Birmingham Moor St a.		0754	0820	0920	0950	past each	1820	1849	1920	1950	2020	2117	2217	2319	0007		1015	1116	1215	1316	until	1814	1914	2014
Birmingham Snow Hill a.		0802	0823	0923	0953	hour until	1823	1852	1923	1953	2023	2120	2223	2321	0010		1019	1119	1218	1319		1817	1917	2017

		Ⓐ	Ⓐ	Ⓐ	Ⓐ	Ⓐ	Ⓐ	Ⓐ	Ⓐ	and at	Ⓐ	Ⓐ	Ⓐ	Ⓐ	Ⓐ	Ⓐ	Ⓐ	Ⓐ	Ⓐ	Ⓐ		⑥	⑥	⑥
Birmingham Snow Hill d.	Ⓐ	0611	0622	0725	0759	0828	0859	0928	0958	the same	1559	1628	1658	1728	1758	1828	1926	2028	2128	2228	⑥	0625	0725	0758
Birmingham Moor St d.		0614	0625	0728	0802	0831	0902	0931	1001	minutes	1602	1631	1701	1731	1801	1831	1929	2031	2131	2231		0628	0728	0801
Henley in Arden d.		|	0703	0806	|	0906	|	1006	|	past each	|	1706	|	1807	|	1907	2007	2107	2209	2307		0706	0806	|
Stratford upon Avon a.		0655	0720	0823	0848	0921	0943	1023	1044	hour until	1650	1723	1750	1824	1858	1923	2024	2123	2226	2323		0721	0823	0841

	⑥	⑥	⑥	⑥	⑥	⑥	and at	⑥	⑥	⑥	⑥	⑥	⑥	⑥	⑥	⑥	⑥		⑦	⑦	⑦	⑦		⑦
Birmingham Snow Hill d.	0827	0857	0928	0958	1027	1058	the same	1558	1627	1658	1728	1758	1827	1927	2027	2128	2227	⑦	0836	0927	1027	1127	and	1827
Birmingham Moor St d.	0830	0902	0931	1001	1030	1101	minutes	1601	1630	1701	1731	1801	1830	1930	2030	2131	2230		0839	0930	1030	1130	hourly	1830
Henley in Arden d.	0905	|	1005	|	1105	|	past each	|	1705	|	1806	|	1905	2006	2106	2207	2306		|	1003	1103	1201	until	1901
Stratford upon Avon a.	0923	0944	1023	1043	1123	1141	hour until	1644	1723	1744	1821	1851	1923	2023	2123	2224	2326		0910	1017	1121	1217		1915

🚂 – **THE SHAKESPEARE EXPRESS** – (12), ✕ (1st class only) and 🍷 Birmingham Snow Hill - Stratford upon Avon and v.v. on ⑦ July 17 - Sept. 4 2022. National Rail tickets NOT valid. From Birmingham Snow Hill 1000 and 1356 (Birmingham Moor Street 5 minutes later); from Stratford upon Avon at 1236 and 1613. Journey time: 59–68 minutes. To book and confirm timings contact **Vintage Trains Ltd.** ✆ 0121 708 4960. www.vintagetrains.co.uk/the-shakespeare-express

CH 2nd class LONDON - BANBURY - BIRMINGHAM and STRATFORD UPON AVON 128

km			①	②–⑤	Ⓐ	Ⓐ	Ⓐ	Ⓐ	Ⓐ	Ⓐ	Ⓐ	Ⓐ	Ⓐ	Ⓐ	Ⓐ	Ⓐ	Ⓐ	Ⓐ	Ⓐ	Ⓐ	Ⓐ	Ⓐ	Ⓐ	Ⓐ	Ⓐ	Ⓐ
0	**London** Marylebone 128a ◇ d.	Ⓐ	0003	0005	...	...	0605	0616	0710	...	0735	0811	...	0910	...	1010	...	1037	1110	...	1137	1210	...	1234	...	1337
45	High Wycombe 128a ◇ d.		0037	0036	...	...	0629	0701	|	...	0805	|	...	0936	...	1036	...	1101	1135	...	1200	1235	...	1258	...	1400
88	Bicester North ◇ d.		0108	0106	0548	...	0655	0733	0754	...	0836t	0855	...	|	...	|	...	1128	|	...	1227	|	...	1324	...	1427
111	Banbury 114 ◇ d.		0127	0124	0604	...	0708	0749	0807	...	0850	0908	...	1009	...	1107	...	1142	1208	...	1240	1308	...	1340	...	1440
143	Leamington Spa 114 d.		...	...	0625	0651	0725	0808	0825	0832	0908	0926	0941	1026	1032	1126	1132	1200	1227	1232	1258	1326	1332	1358	1432	1458
146	Warwick d.		...	...	0630	0656	0729	0813	0829	0838	0912	0930	0946	|	1038	|	1137	1204	|	1238	1302	|	1337	1402	1438	1502
147	Warwick Parkway d.		...	...	0633	|	0733	|	0833	|	0916	0934	|	1033	|	1133	|	1208	1233	|	1306	1333	|	1406	|	1506
168	**Stratford-upon-Avon** a.		...	...	|	0728	|	0843	|	|	|	|	1014	|	|	|	1204	|	|	|	|	|	1404	|	|	|
169	Solihull d.		...	...	0650	...	0753	...	0845	0901	0933	0946	...	1045	1101	1145	...	1223	1245	1301	1322	1345	...	1422	1501	1522
180	**Birmingham** Moor Street a.		...	...	0700	...	0803	...	0853	0914	0945	0954	...	1056	1114	1156	...	1234	1256	1314	1334	1356	...	1434	1514	1534
181	**Birmingham** Snow Hill a.		...	...	0705	...	0809	...	0859	...	...	0959	...	...	...	...	...	1240	...	...	1340	...	...	1440	...	1540

	Ⓐ	Ⓐ	Ⓐ	Ⓐ	Ⓐ	Ⓐ	Ⓐ	Ⓐ	Ⓐ	Ⓐ	Ⓐ	Ⓐ	Ⓐ	Ⓐ	Ⓐ	Ⓐ	Ⓐ	Ⓐ	Ⓐ	Ⓐ	Ⓐ	Ⓐ		Ⓐ	Ⓐ	Ⓐ
London Marylebone 128a ◇ d.	1410	...	1437	1510	...	1537	1618	1647	...	1714	1747	...	1815	1821	1847	1915	1946	2010	2036	...	2110	2208	...	2233	2307	2311
High Wycombe 128a ◇ d.	1434	...	1501	1535	...	1600	1646	|	...	|	|	...	|	1854	|	|	|	2035	|	...	2134	2234	...	2303	|	2346
Bicester North ◇ d.	|	...	1528	|	...	1627	1711	1734	...	|	1834	...	|	1926	1933	2002	2033	2059	2125	...	2156	2259	...	2330	2350	b
Banbury 114 ◇ d.	1507	...	1544	1608	...	1640	1724	1747	...	1809	1848	...	1909	1942	1951	2016	2047	2112	2139	...	2213	2313	...	2343	0004	0111
Leamington Spa 114 d.	1525	1532	1601	1625	1632	1658	1741	1804	1811	1827	1905	1932	1928	...	2009	2034	2105	2130	2157	2226	2231	2331	...	0002	0024	...
Warwick d.	|	1537	1605	1630	1638	1702	|	1808	1816	|	1909	1937	|	...	2013	|	2108	|	2201	2231	2235	|	...	0007	0028	...
Warwick Parkway d.	1530	|	1609	1633	|	1707	1747	1812	|	1834	1913	|	1935	...	2017	2040	2112	2136	2205	|	2239	2337	...	0011	0031	...
Stratford-upon-Avon a.	|	1608	|	|	1710f	|	|	|	1852	|	|	2005	|	...	|	|	|	|	|	2258	|	|	...	|	|	...
Solihull d.	1545	...	1625	1645	1701	1723	1802	1827	...	1849	1928	...	1951	...	2033	2055	2134	2149	2221	...	2301	2349	...	0027	0043	...
Birmingham Moor Street a.	1556	...	1635	1655	1714	1736	1812	1838	...	1859	1938	...	2000	...	2042	2107	2143	2200	2232	...	2309	0001	...	0039	0055	...
Birmingham Snow Hill a.	...	...	1640	1700	...	1741	1818	...	...	1902	1945	...	2004	...	2047	...	2148	...	2238	...	2312	...	...	...	...	...
Kidderminster ▲ a.	...	...	...	...	...	...	...	...	...	1940	...	...	2045	...	...	...	...	...	...	...	2349r	...	...	...	...	...

b – Via Oxford (Table **128a**).
f – Change at Hatton (a. 1644 / d. 1648).
r – Stourbridge Junction.
t – Arrives 0831.

◇ – Additional services operate between these stations.
▲ – Only through services are shown to Kidderminster. Regular local trains also operate Birmingham **Moor Street** - Birmingham **Snow Hill** - Kidderminster (2 trains per hour on ⚒, hourly on ⑦). Kidderminster is the station for the **Severn Valley Railway** (🚂 Kidderminster - Bridgnorth: *26 km*). ✆ 01299 403816. www.svr.co.uk

128 LONDON - BANBURY - BIRMINGHAM and STRATFORD UPON AVON 2nd class CH

		⑥	⑥	⑥		⑥	⑥	⑥	⑥		⑥	⑥	⑥		⑥	⑥	⑥	⑥		⑥	⑥		⑥	⑥	⑥
London Marylebone **128a** ◇ d.		0005	...	...	...	0700	...	0800	0900	...	1000	...	1100	...	1200	...	1237	1300	...	1400	...	...	1500	1600	...
High Wycombe .... **128a** ◇ d.		0036	...	0615	...	0725	...	0824	0926	...	1024	...	1126	...	1224	...	|	1326	...	1424	...	...	1526	1624	...
Bicester North .... ◇ d.	⑥	0106	...	0646	...	0754	...	0856	0957	...	1051	...	1155	...	1251	...	1326	1357	...	1452	...	...	1557	1651	...
Banbury .... **114** ◇ d.		0124	0600	0703	...	0807	...	0913	1012	...	1109	...	1210	...	1309	...	1339	1410	...	1509	...	...	1612	1709	...
Leamington Spa .... **114** d.		...	0621	0721	...	0825	0840	0932	1031	...	1127	1132	1229	...	1327	1332	1357	1431	...	1527	1532	...	1631	1727	1732
Warwick ....d.		...	0625	0725	...	0829	0845	0936	1037	...	1131	1137	1234	...	1331	1337	1402	1437	...	1531	1537	...	1637	1731	1737
Warwick Parkway ....d.		...	0629	0729	...	0833	|	0940	1043	...	1135	|	1238	...	1335	|	1406	1443	...	1535	|	...	1643	1735	|
Stratford-upon-Avon ....a.		...	|	|	...	|	0914	|	|	...	|	1208	|	...	|	1408	|	|	...	|	1608	...	|	|	1808
Solihull ....d.		...	0647	0750	...	0849	...	1001	1101	...	1158	...	1255	...	1358	...	1421	1501	...	1558	...	...	1701	1758	...
Birmingham Moor Street ......a.		...	0658	0802	...	0900	...	1012	1112	...	1209	...	1306	...	1409	...	1436	1512	...	1609	...	...	1712	1809	...
Birmingham Snow Hill ....a.		...	...	...	...	...	...	...	...	...	...	...	...	...	...	...	...	...	...	...	...	...	...	...	...

	⑥	⑥		⑥	⑥		⑥	⑥		⑥		⑥	⑥	⑥	⑥	⑥		⑦	⑦	⑦	⑦		⑦		⑦
London Marylebone **128a** ◇ d.	1700	1800	...	1837	1900	...	1937	2000	...	2037	...	2100	2208	2240	2315	2345		0800	0900	...	1000	...	1100	...	1200
High Wycombe .... **128a** ◇ d.	1724	1824	...	|	1925	...	|	2024	...	|	...	2126	2232	2314	2349	0021		0824	0925	...	1024	...	1126	...	1224
Bicester North .... ◇ d.	1753	1851	...	1926	1953	...	2023	2052	...	2126	...	2157	2257	2345	0019	0051	⑦	0853	0954	...	1052	...	1157	...	1252
Banbury .... **114** ◇ d.	1807	1905	...	1943	2007	...	2037	2109	...	2139	...	2212	2310	0001	0033	0109		0910	1012t	...	1109	...	1212	...	1309
Leamington Spa .... **114** d.	1825	1924	1932	2001	2025	...	2055	2127	2132	2157	...	2231	2328	...	...	...		0928	1031	1040	1127	...	1231	...	1327
Warwick ....d.	1830	1928	1937	2006	2030	...	2059	2131	2137	2202	...	2237	2332	...	...	...		0933	1037	1045	1131	...	1237	...	1331
Warwick Parkway ....d.	1835	1932	|	2010	2033	...	2103	2135	|	2206	...	2243	2337	...	...	...		0938	1043	|	1135	...	1243	...	1335
Stratford-upon-Avon ....a.	|	|	2008	|	|	...	|	|	2208	|	...	|	|	...	...	...		|	|	1115	|	...	|	...	|
Solihull ....d.	1851	1948	...	2033	2049	...	2119	2200	...	2221	...	2301	2353	...	...	...		1001	1101	...	1158	...	1301	...	1358
Birmingham Moor Street ......a.	1859	2000	...	2045	2102	...	2127	2212	...	2232	...	2312	0004	...	...	...		1012	1112	...	1209	...	1312	...	1409
Birmingham Snow Hill ....a.	1902	...	...	...	...	...	2131	...	...	...	...	...	...	...	...	...		...	...	...	...	...	...	...	...
Kidderminster .... ▲ a.	1941	...	...	...	...	...	2209	...	...	...	...	...	...	...	...	...		...	...	...	...	...	...	...	...

	⑦	⑦	⑦		⑦	⑦		⑦	⑦	⑦	⑦		⑦		⑦		⑦	⑦		⑦	⑦	⑦		⑦	⑦
London Marylebone **128a** ◇ d.	...	1237	1300	...	1400	...	...	1500	1600	...	1700	...	1800	...	1837	...	1900	1937	...	2000	2100	2208	...	2240	2315
High Wycombe .... **128a** ◇ d.	...	|	1326	...	1424	...	...	1526	1624	...	1725	...	1824	...	|	...	1925	|	...	2025	2125	2231	...	2314	2349
Bicester North .... ◇ d.	...	1326	1357	...	1452	...	...	1557	1652	...	1754	...	1852	...	1926	...	1954	2026	...	2055	2153	2256	...	2343	0018
Banbury .... **114** ◇ d.	...	1339	1412	...	1509	...	...	1612	1709	...	1808	...	1909	...	1940	...	2009	2040	...	2113	2207	2309	...	2357	0032
Leamington Spa .... **114** d.	1340	1357	1431	...	1527	1540	...	1631	1727	1740	1827	...	1927	1940	1958	...	2028	2058	...	2132	2225	2327	...	...	...
Warwick ....d.	1345	1401	1437	...	1531	1545	...	1637	1731	1745	1832	...	1931	1945	2003	...	2034	2103	...	2136	2231	2332	...	...	...
Warwick Parkway ....d.	|	1405	1443	...	1535	|	...	1643	1735	|	1838	...	1935	|	2007	...	2040	2107	...	2140	2237	2337	...	...	...
Stratford-upon-Avon ....a.	1411	|	|	...	|	1611	...	|	|	1811	|	...	|	2011	|	...	|	|	...	|	|	|	...	...	...
Solihull ....d.	...	1421	1501	...	1558	...	...	1701	1758	...	1856	...	1958	...	2023	...	2058	2123	...	2203	2255	2353	...	...	...
Birmingham Moor Street ......a.	...	1432	1512	...	1609	...	...	1712	1809	...	1904	...	2009	...	2034	...	2109	2131	...	2214	2306	0004	...	...	...
Birmingham Snow Hill ....a.	...	...	...	...	...	...	...	...	...	...	1908	...	...	...	...	...	...	2135	...	...	...	...	...	...	...
Kidderminster .... ▲ a.	...	...	...	...	...	...	...	...	...	...	1945	...	...	...	...	...	...	2210	...	...	...	...	...	...	...

		Ⓐ	Ⓐ	Ⓐ	Ⓐ	Ⓐ	Ⓐ	Ⓐ	Ⓐ	Ⓐ	Ⓐ	Ⓐ	Ⓐ	Ⓐ	Ⓐ	Ⓐ	Ⓐ	Ⓐ	Ⓐ	Ⓐ	Ⓐ	Ⓐ	Ⓐ	Ⓐ	Ⓐ
Kidderminster .... ▲ d.		...	...	...	...	...	...	0624r	0641r	...	...	0716r	...	0807	...	...	...	...	...	...	...	...	...	...	...
Birmingham Snow Hill ....d.	Ⓐ	...	...	...	...	...	...	0656	0707	...	0719	0749	0822	0851	...	0912	...	...	1012	...	...	...	...	...	...
Birmingham Moor Street ......d.		...	0515	0542	0610	...	0633	0700	0711	...	0722	0753	0825	0855	...	0915	0934	0955	1015	...	1055	1115	1134	1155	...
Solihull ....d.		...	0523	0551	0619	...	0642	0714	0722	...	0736	0802	0837	0907	...	0925	0943	1004	1024	...	1104	1124	1143	1203	...
Stratford upon Avon ....d.		...	|	|	|	0606	|	0734	|	0733	|	|	|	|	0900	|	|	|	|	1040	|	|	|	|	1242
Warwick Parkway ....d.		...	0535	0605	0634	|	0657	0737	0740	0800	|	0815	0902	0919	|	0940	|	1016	1039	|	1117	1139	|	1215	|
Warwick ....d.		...	|	0608	|	0640	0700	0742	|	0804	0809	|	0905	|	0928	0943	1006	|	1043	1108	|	1142	1207	1218	1308
Leamington Spa .... **114** d.		...	0541	0613	0641	0646	0706	...	0747	0811	0816	0821	0910	0925	0934	0947	1016	1023	1048	1116	1123	1146	1216	1222	1316
Banbury .... **114** ◇ d.		0517	0559	0631	0659	...	0725	...	0806	0830	...	0841	0933	0942	...	1005	...	1041	1106	...	1141	1204	...	1243	...
Bicester North .... ◇ d.		0533	0611	0647	0712	...	0740	...	0819	0845	...	0855	0945	|	...	1018	...	|	1119	...	|	1217	...	1256	...
High Wycombe .... **128a** ◇ d.		0559	0635	|	|	...	|	...	0841	0911	...	|	1009	|	...	|	...	1115	|	...	1214	|	...	1324	...
London Marylebone **128a** ◇ a.		0632	0703	0736	0803	...	0836	...	0910	0955	...	0943	1036	1042	...	1112	...	1145	1210	...	1245	1311	...	1405	...

	Ⓐ	Ⓐ	Ⓐ	Ⓐ	Ⓐ	Ⓐ	Ⓐ	Ⓐ	Ⓐ	Ⓐ	Ⓐ	Ⓐ	Ⓐ	Ⓐ	Ⓐ	Ⓐ	Ⓐ	Ⓐ	Ⓐ	Ⓐ	Ⓐ	Ⓐ	Ⓐ	Ⓐ	Ⓐ
Birmingham Snow Hill ....d.	...	1312	...	...	1412	...	...	1512	...	1612	1651	1707	...	...	1752	1832	...	...	2015	2110	...	...	2211	...	2330
Birmingham Moor Street ......d.	1255	1315	1335	1355	1415	...	1455	1515	1535	1615	1654	1710	1721	...	1755	1835	...	1917	2018	2118	...	...	2214	...	2333
Solihull ....d.	1304	1324	1344	1404	1424	...	1504	1524	1544	1624	1703	1719	1731	...	1804	1849	...	1929	2028	2127	...	...	2229	...	2348
Stratford upon Avon ....d.	|	|	|	|	|	1441	|	|	|	*1618f*	|	|	|	1738	|	|	1912	|	|	|	2135	...	|	2314	|
Warwick Parkway ....d.	1316	1340	|	1415	1439	|	1516	1539	|	1642	1714	1736	|	|	1824	1907	|	1949	2043	2146	|	...	2251	|	0010
Warwick ....d.	|	1343	1409	|	1442	1508	|	1543	1609	1645	1717	1739	1752	1805	1827	|	1943	1953	2046	2149	2200	...	2254	2333	0013
Leamington Spa .... **114** d.	1323	1348	1420	1422	1446	1516	1522	1549	1620	1649	1722	1743	1759	1809	1831	1912	...	1958	2055	2155	2205	2217	2300	2337	0018
Banbury .... **114** ◇ d.	1341	1406	...	1440	1504	...	1541	1608	...	1707	1740	1804	...	1832	1849	1931	...	2017	2114	2212	...	2237	2325	2358	0039
Bicester North .... ◇ d.	1354	1422	...	1453	1517	...	|	1621	...	1721	1753	1820	...	...	1905	1944	...	2031	2127	2225	...	2254	...	...	...
High Wycombe .... **128a** ◇ d.	1424	|	...	1515	1544	...	1614	1648	...	1747	1814	1845	...	...	1935	2010	...	2102	2148	2250	...	2319	...	...	...
London Marylebone **128a** ◇ a.	1453	1511	...	1545	1611	...	1643	1715	...	1820	1841	1914	...	...	2008	2037	...	2137	2217	2317	...	2357	...	...	...

		⑥	⑥	⑥	⑥	⑥	⑥		⑥	⑥	⑥	⑥	⑥		⑥	⑥	⑥	⑥		⑥	⑥	⑥	⑥	⑥	⑥
Kidderminster .... ▲ d.		...	...	...	...	0637	0712	...	...	...	...	...	...	...	...	...	...	...	...	...	...	...	...	...	...
Birmingham Snow Hill ....d.	⑥	...	...	...	...	0712	0748	...	...	...	...	...	...	...	...	...	...	...	...	...	...	...	...	...	...
Birmingham Moor Street ......d.		...	...	0615	0637	0716	0752	...	...	0815	0835	0914	0937	...	...	1037	1114	1137	...	...	1237	1337	...	1437	1514
Solihull ....d.		...	...	0624	0646	0725	0801	...	...	0823	0846	0923	0947	...	...	1046	1123	1148	...	...	1246	1347	...	1446	1523
Stratford upon Avon ....d.		...	...	|	|	|	|	...	0755	|	|	|	|	...	1040	|	|	|	...	1240	|	|	1440	|	|
Warwick Parkway ....d.		...	...	0639	0710	0740	0818	...	|	0838	0910	0938	1004	...	|	1110	1138	1204	...	|	1310	1404	|	1510	1538
Warwick ....d.		...	...	0642	0714	0744	|	...	0825	0841	0914	0941	1009	...	1108	1114	1141	1209	...	1308	1314	1409	1508	1514	1541
Leamington Spa .... **114** d.		...	...	0649	0719	0750	0825	...	0832	0846	0919	0947	1015	...	1114	1119	1147	1215	...	1314	1319	1415	1514	1519	1548
Banbury .... **114** ◇ d.		0604	0621	0709	0737	0809	0843	...	...	0906	0937	1005	1035	...	...	1137	1207	1235	...	...	1337	1435	...	1537	1607
Bicester North .... ◇ d.		0620	0635	0723	0754	0822	0856	...	...	0921	0954	1020	1049	...	...	1154	1221	1249	...	...	1354	1449	...	1554	1621
High Wycombe .... **128a** ◇ d.		0650	0706	|	0823	|	0926	...	...	|	1023	|	1122	...	...	1223	|	1322	...	...	1423	1522	...	1623	|
London Marylebone **128a** ◇ a.		0723	0737	0812	0849	0912	0953	...	...	1012	1049	1112	1149	...	...	1250	1312	1349	...	...	1450	1549	...	1650	1712

	⑥		⑥	⑥		⑥		⑥	⑥		⑥	⑥	⑥		⑥	⑥		⑦	⑦	⑦	⑦		⑦	⑦	⑦
Birmingham Snow Hill ....d.	...	...	...	...	...	...	...	...	...	...	...	...	...	...	...	...		...	...	...	...	...	...	...	...
Birmingham Moor Street ......d.	1537	...	...	1637	...	1735	...	...	1835	...	2015	...	2118	...	...	2218		...	...	0828	0847	...	0912	...	0937
Solihull ....d.	1547	...	...	1647	...	1746	...	...	1845	...	2024	...	2127	...	...	2233	⑦	...	...	0837	0855	...	0921	...	0946
Stratford upon Avon ....d.	|	...	1640	|	...	|	...	1840	|	...	|	2040	|	...	2215	|		...	...	|	|	...	|	0936	|
Warwick Parkway ....d.	1604	...	|	1710	...	1804	...	|	1910	...	2039	|	2148	...	|	2255		...	...	0852	0915	...	0937	|	1009
Warwick ....d.	1609	...	1708	1714	...	1809	...	1908	1914	...	2042	2108	2151	...	2235	2258		...	...	0855	0918	...	0941	1001	1014
Leamington Spa .... **114** d.	1615	...	1714	1719	...	1815	...	1914	1919	...	2048	2114	2158	...	2241	2305		...	...	0901	0923	...	0947	1009	1019
Banbury .... **114** ◇ d.	1635	...	...	1737	...	1835	...	...	1937	...	2106	...	2218	...	2302	2327		0750	0834	0918	0941	...	1007	...	1038
Bicester North .... ◇ d.	1649	...	...	1754	...	1849	...	...	1954	...	2119	...	2235	...	...	...		0804	0850	|	0957	...	1021	...	1055
High Wycombe .... **128a** ◇ d.	1722	...	...	1823	...	1922	...	...	2023	...	2145	...	2304	...	...	...		0835	0921	|	1025	...	|	...	|
London Marylebone **128a** ◇ a.	1749	...	...	1849	...	1949	...	...	2050	...	2213	...	2353	...	...	...		0911	0953	1017	1053	...	1112	...	1148

	⑦		⑦	⑦		⑦	⑦		⑦		⑦	⑦		⑦	⑦		⑦	⑦	⑦		⑦	⑦		⑦	⑦
Kidderminster .... ▲ d.	1000	...	1030	...	...	...	...	...	...	...	...	...	...	...	...	...	...	...	...	...	...	...	...	...	...
Birmingham Snow Hill ....d.	1033	...	1108	...	...	...	...	...	...	...	...	...	...	...	...	...	...	...	...	...	...	...	...	...	...
Birmingham Moor Street ......d.	1037	...	1112	1137	...	...	1237	...	1337	...	...	1437	...	1512	1537	...	...	1637	1737	...	...	1837	...	2017	...
Solihull ....d.	1047	...	1121	1147	...	...	1246	...	1347	...	...	1446	...	1521	1547	...	...	1646	1747	...	...	1846	...	2026	...
Stratford upon Avon ....d.	|	...	|	|	...	1236	|	...	|	...	1436	|	...	|	|	...	1636	|	|	...	1836	|	...	|	2036
Warwick Parkway ....d.	1104	...	1137	1204	...	|	1310	...	1404	...	|	1510	...	1537	1604	...	|	1710	1804	...	|	1910	...	2043	|
Warwick ....d.	1109	...	1141	1209	...	1301	1314	...	1409	...	1501	1514	...	1541	1609	...	1701	1714	1809	...	1901	1914	...	2046	2101
Leamington Spa .... **114** d.	1115	...	1147	1215	...	1308	1319	...	1415	...	1508	1519	...	1547	1615	...	1708	1719	1815	...	1908	1919	...	2051	2109
Banbury .... **114** ◇ d.	1134	...	1207	1235	...	...	1337	...	1435	...	...	1537	...	1609t	1635	...	...	1737	1835	...	...	1937	...	2109	2132
Bicester North .... ◇ d.	1148	...	1221	1249	...	...	1354	...	1449	...	...	1554	...	1623	1649	...	...	1754	1849	...	...	1954	...	2121	...
High Wycombe .... **128a** ◇ d.	1121	...	|	1322	...	...	1423	...	1522	...	...	1623	...	|	1722	...	...	1823	1922	...	...	2023	...	|	...
London Marylebone **128a** ◇ a.	1247	...	1312	1350	...	...	1449	...	1549	...	...	1649	...	1717	1749	...	...	1850	1949	...	...	2049	...	2213	...

f – Change at Hatton (a. 1632 / d. 1637).
r – Stourbridge Junction.
t – Arrives 5–6 minutes earlier.

◇ – Additional services operate between these stations.
▲ – Only through services are shown to / from Kidderminster. Regular local trains available. See note ★ on page 107.

CH 2nd class LONDON - HIGH WYCOMBE - OXFORD and LONDON - AYLESBURY 128a

km			②–⑤	Ⓐ	Ⓐ	Ⓐ	Ⓐ	Ⓐ	Ⓐ	Ⓐ	Ⓐ	Ⓐ	Ⓐ	Ⓐ	Ⓐ	Ⓐ	Ⓐ	Ⓐ	Ⓐ	Ⓐ	Ⓐ	Ⓐ	Ⓐ	Ⓐ
0	**London** Marylebone .... **128** d.		0001	...	...	0609	0657	0714	0744	0814	0837	0901	0935	1003	1040	1107	1140	1205	1240	1306	1340	1404	1440	1505
45	High Wycombe .... **128** d.		0029	...	...	0640	0721	0738	0811	|	0906	|	0959	|	1112	|	1212	|	1310	|	1410	|	1513	|
90	Bicester Village .... d.	Ⓐ	0056	0551	0625	0710	0747	0806	0838	0902	0934	0956	1023	1054	1142	1155	1239	1257	1334	1355	1434	1454	1540	1555
103	**Oxford** Parkway .... d.		0105	0602	0634	0722	0755	0817	0846	0911	0944	1007	1032	1103	1151	1206	1248	1306	1342	1404	1443	1504	1549	1604
108	**Oxford** .... a.		0114	0610	0643	0730	0803	0825	0855	0919	0952	1015	1040	1111	1159	1214	1256	1314	1351	1412	1451	1513	1557	1612

	Ⓐ	Ⓐ	Ⓐ	Ⓐ	Ⓐ	Ⓐ	Ⓐ	Ⓐ	Ⓐ	Ⓐ	Ⓐ	Ⓐ	Ⓐ	Ⓐ	Ⓐ a		⑥	⑥	⑥	⑥	⑥	⑥	⑥	⑥
London Marylebone .... **128** d.	1540	1615	1650	1717	1750	1818	1850	1918	1950	2040	2106	2132	2201	2237	2311		0001	0556	0612	0642	0712	0742	0812	0842
High Wycombe .... **128** d.	1613	|	1714	|	1814	|	1916	1950	2022	2110	2145	2204	2228	2318	2346	⑥	0029	0626	0659	0716	0752	0815	0852	0915
Bicester Village .... d.	1639	1703	1740	1810	1840	1905	1943	2023	2047	2133	2216	2235	2256	2345	0017		0056	0655	0734	0750	0823	0847	0923	0950
Oxford Parkway .... d.	1648	1712	1750	1822	1848	1915	1953	2034	2057	2141	2225	2244	2307	2354	0025		0105	0704	0747	0800	0833	0858	0933	1000
Oxford .... a.	1656	1721	1758	1830	1856	1923	2001	2043	2105	2150	2233	2252	2315	0004	0032		0114	0712	0755	0808	0841	0906	0941	1008

	♣	⑥	⑥	⑥	⑥	⑥	⑥	⑥	⑥		⑦	⑦	⑦	⑦	⑦	♣	⑦	⑦	⑦		⑦	⑦
London Marylebone .... **128** d.	and at	1912	1942	2012	2042	2112	2142	2212	2310		...	0742	0812	0842	0912	and at	2042	2112	2142	...	2212	2310
High Wycombe .... **128** d.	the same	1951	2016	2052	2116	2152	2216	2252	2339	⑦	...	0816	0852	0916	0952	the same	2116	2152	2216	...	2252	2340
Bicester Village .... d.	minutes	2022	2050	2123	2150	2223	2250	2323	0010		0749	0850	0923	0950	1023	minutes	2150	2223	2250	...	2323	0010
Oxford Parkway .... d.	past each	2033	2103	2133	2200	2232	2303	2333	0020		0758	0903	0933	1000	1033	past each	2200	2231	2303	...	2333	0020
Oxford .... a.	hour until	2041	2111	2141	2208	2240	2311	2341	0031		0806	0911	0941	1008	1041	hour until	2208	2241	2311	...	2341	0028

		Ⓐ	Ⓐ	Ⓐ	Ⓐ	Ⓐ	Ⓐ	Ⓐ	Ⓐ	Ⓐ	Ⓐ	Ⓐ	Ⓐ	Ⓐ	Ⓐ	Ⓐ	Ⓐ	Ⓐ	Ⓐ	Ⓐ	Ⓐ	Ⓐ	Ⓐ	Ⓐ
Oxford .... d.		0535	0558	0643	0700	0743	0802	0824	0840	0909	0938	1005	1039	1111	1142	1204	1235	1304	1340	1411	1441	1513	1543	1611
Oxford Parkway .... d.		0541	0605	0649	0706	0749	0811	0830	0849	0916	0945	1012	1045	1118	1148	1210	1241	1311	1348	1417	1447	1519	1549	1617
Bicester Village .... d.	Ⓐ	0552	0616	0659	0717	0800	0824	0839	0859	0926	0957	1023	1056	1128	1157	1220	1250	1323	1401	1426	1457	1528	1558	1626
High Wycombe .... **128** d.		0624	0645	0730	0743	0834	0857	0902	0929	|	|	1051	1122	1159	1219	1251	1313	1351	1428	1451	1522	1550	|	1653
London Marylebone .... **128** a.		0701	0729	0800	0825	0906	0936	0940	0959	1020	1047	1124	1157	1235	1258	1323	1343	1423	1508	1525	1601	1626	1647	1723

	Ⓐ	Ⓐ	Ⓐ	Ⓐ	Ⓐ	Ⓐ	Ⓐ	Ⓐ	Ⓐ	Ⓐ	Ⓐ	Ⓐ	Ⓐ		⑥	⑥	⑥	⑥	⑥	⑥	⑥	⑥	
Oxford .... d.	1638	1722	1757	1820	1856	1927	2000	2026	2048	2131	2215	2242	2315		0611	0641	0711	0741	0811	0841	0911	0941	and at
Oxford Parkway .... d.	1644	1728	1803	1826	1902	1938f	2009	2032	2054	2137	2221	2248	2321	⑥	0617	0647	0717	0749	0817	0847	0917	0947	the same
Bicester Village .... d.	1657	1738	1815	1836	1914	1949	2020	2042	2107	2146	2230	2300	2331		0628	0700	0728	0800	0828	0900	0928	1000	minutes
High Wycombe .... **128** d.	|	1809	1838	1906	|	2018	2043	2110	2140	2214	2300	2333	0004		0656	0733	0757	0833	0857	0933	0956	1033	past each
London Marylebone .... **128** a.	1752	1837	1911	1933	2011	2045	2111	2140	2211	2245	2337	0019	...		0733	0809	0839	0909	0941	1009	1039	1109	hour until

	⑥	⑥	⑥	⑥	⑥	⑥		⑦	⑦	⑦		⑦	⑦	⑦	⑦		⑦	⑦	⑦	⑦	⑦	⑦	⑦
Oxford .... d.	2011	2041	2111	2141	2211	2327		0741	0811	0841	...	0911	0941	1011	1041	and at	1941	2011	2041	2111	2141	2211	2327
Oxford Parkway .... d.	2017	2047	2117	2148	2217	2333	⑦	0747	0817	0848	...	0919	0948	1017	1047	the same	1948	2017	2047	2117	2148	2217	2333
Bicester Village .... d.	2028	2059	2128	2200	2227	2346		0757	0828	0900	...	0932	1000	1028	1100	minutes	2000	2028	2100	2128	2200	2227	2346
High Wycombe .... **128** d.	2057	2130	2157	2233	2255	...		|	0857	0933	...	0959	1033	1057	1133	past each	2033	2057	2133	2157	2233	2255	...
London Marylebone .... **128** a.	2139	2204	2239	2309	2337	...		0852	0939	1009	...	1042	1109	1139	1210	hour until	2109	2139	2209	2239	2309	2337	...

LONDON - AYLESBURY (60 km, journey ± 60 minutes)

From London Marylebone: on Ⓐ at 0633*, 0652*, 0727*, 0757*, 0817, 0827, 0857*, 0913, 0927, 1013, 1057*, 1113, 1127, 1157*, 1213, 1227, 1257*, 1310, 1357*, 1413, 1456*, 1513, 1527, 1556, 1611*, 1642*, 1653, 1710, 1730*, 1742, 1758*, 1811, 1831*, 1843, 1859*, 1932, 1956*, 2013, 2023, 2057*, 2127, 2157*, 2211, 2257*, 2322 and 2357*; on ⑥ at 0010, 0653, 0727*, 0757*, 0827, 0857*, 0927, 0957* and at the same minutes past each hour until 1257*, 1357*, 1457*, 1557*, 1627, 1657* and at the same minutes past each hour until 2027, 2057*, 2157*, 2217, 2257*, 2320, 2357; on ⑦ at 0010, 0757* and hourly until 1557*, 1627, 1657* and at the same minutes past each hour until 2027, 2057*, 2157*, 2227, 2257*, 2327, 2345.

From Aylesbury: **on** Ⓐ at 0521*, 0549*, 0607, 0625*, 0638, 0710*, 0730*, 0741, 0802*, 0818*, 0845*, 0923*, 0950, 1020*, 1028, 1050, 1120*, 1150, 1220, 1231, 1250 and at the same minutes past each hour until 1620*, 1629, 1714, 1750*, 1820, 1847*, 1920, 1948*, 2020, 2120*, 2124, 2150 and 2250; on ⑥ at 0515, 0556, 0620*, 0650, 0720*, 0750, 0820*, 0850*, 0920*, 0950, 1020*, 1050, 1120*, 1150, 1220*, 1233, 1320*, 1333, 1420*, 1433, 1520*, 1550 and at the same minutes past each hour until 1920*, 1933, 2020*, 2120*, 2133, 2220*; on ⑦ at 0720*, 0730, 0820*, 0850*, 0920, 0950*, 1020*, 1033, 1120*, 1133, 1220*, 1233, 1320*, 1333, 1420*, 1433, 1520*, 1550 and at the same minutes past each hour until 1920*, 1933, 2020*, 2033, 2120*, 2150, 2250*.

a – To Banbury (Table **128**). Departs 0040.
f – Arrives 1933.
* – Continues to / starts from Aylesbury Vale Parkway (arrives 9–11 minutes after and departs 5 minutes before Aylesbury).
♣ – The 0942, 1142, 1342, 1542, 1742 and 1942 departures from London Marylebone depart Oxford Parkway xx03 and arrive Oxford xx11.

GW Most London trains convey 🍷 LONDON - CHELTENHAM 130

km			Ⓐ	Ⓐ	Ⓐ2	Ⓐ	Ⓐ	Ⓐ	Ⓐ	Ⓐ	Ⓐ	Ⓐ	Ⓐ	Ⓐ	Ⓐ	Ⓐ	Ⓐ	Ⓐ	Ⓐ2	Ⓐ	Ⓐ	Ⓐ2		⑥2	⑥	⑥	⑥
0	**London** Pad....... **132 133** d.		0535	0628	**A**	0727	0828	0928	1028	1128	1228	1328	1428	1528	1630	1730	1830	1928	**C**	2028	2128	...		...	0728	0828	0928
58	Reading.............. **132 133** d.		0600	0653	...	0753	0853	0954	1053	1153	1253	1353	1453	1553	|	|	|	|	...	2053	2153	...		...	0753	0854	0953
85	Didcot Parkway... **132 133** d.	Ⓐ	0614	0707	...	|	0906	1007	1107	1207	1306	1406	1506	1606	1706	1806	1907	2004	...	2106	2206	...	⑥	...	0806	0908	1007
124	**Swindon** .... **132 133** a.		0630	0724	...	0820	0922	1023	1122	1223	1322	1423	1522	1625	1728	1821	1924	2020	...	2122	2222	...		...	0823	0924	1024
	Swindon .... d.		0633	0730	0754	0822	0929	1028	1128	1228	1328	1428	1528	1628	1730	1825	1926	2025	2054	2127	2229	2342		0729	0828	0928	1028
164	Stroud .... d.		0701	0758	0822	0850	0958	1057	1156	1257	1357	1457	1557	1657	1758	1854	1955	2054	2122	2156	2257	0010		0756	0857	0957	1057
183	Gloucester .... a.		0718	0817	0847	0908	1015	1115	1214	1314	1414	1514	1617	1715	1816	1920	2015	2116	2142	2215	2315	0029		0813	0915	1014	1114
	Gloucester .... **138** d.		0725	0823	0854	0917	1021	1121	1220	1322	1420	1521	1624	1722	1822	1926	2023	2123	2157	2226	2321	0034		0818	0919	1019	1119
194	**Cheltenham** Spa...... **138** a.		0733	0832	0903	0925	1031	1130	1228	1331	1428	1530	1632	1731	1831	1935	2032	2132	2205	2234	2331	0043		0827	0929	1031	1129
223	**Worcester** Shrub Hill **138** a.		0758	...	...	...	...	...	...	...	...	...	...	...	...	...	...	2208	...	...	...	...		...	...	...	...

	⑥	⑥	⑥	⑥	⑥	⑥	⑥	⑥	⑥	⑥	⑥2	⑥2		⑦	⑦	⑦2	⑦	⑦	⑦2	⑦	⑦	⑦2	⑦	⑦	⑦2	⑦	⑦2
London Pad....... **132 133** d.	1028	1128	1228	1328	1428	...	1628	1728	1828	1928	...	...		...	...	...	...	...	...	...	...	...	1733	...	...	...	...
Reading.............. **132 133** d.	1053	1153	1253	1353	1453	...	1653	1754	1853	1953	...	...		...	...	...	...	...	...	...	...	...	1758	...	...	...	...
Didcot Parkway... **132 133** d.	1106	1206	1306	1406	1506	...	1706	1809	1906	2006	...	...	⑦	...	...	...	...	...	...	...	...	...	1811	...	...	...	...
Swindon .... **132 133** a.	1123	1224	1323	1423	1523	...	1723	1826	1923	2032	...	...		...	...	...	...	...	...	...	...	...	1828	...	...	...	...
Swindon .... d.	1128	1228	1328	1428	1528	1628	1728	1828	1928	2028	2125	2241		0935	1037	1130	1232	1328	1430	1530	1629	1730	1829	1929	2031	2130	2310
Stroud .... d.	1157	1257	1356	1457	1557	1657	1757	1857	1956	2057	2153	2309		1001	1103	1157	1259	1357	1457	1557	1656	1757	1857	1956	2058	2158	2337
Gloucester .... a.	1214	1314	1414	1514	1614	1714	1815	1915	2013	2115	2213	2329		1019	1122	1219	1318	1417	1522	1617	1718	1818	1916	2018	2121	2218	2359
Gloucester .... d.	1219	1319	1418	1519	1619	1720	1820	1921	2020	2121	2218	...		1027	1127	1223	1322	1425	1525	1623	1723	1822	1923	2024	2124	2224	0002
Cheltenham Spa....... **138** a.	1228	1328	1428	1529	1629	1729	1829	1931	2030	2129	2228	...		1036	1135	1231	1332	1435	1533	1632	1732	1830	1932	2032	2132	2232	0011
Worcester Shrub Hill. **138** a.	...	...	...	...	...	...	...	...	...	...	...	...		...	...	...	...	...	...	...	...	...	...	...	...	...	...

		Ⓐ	Ⓐ	Ⓐ	Ⓐ	Ⓐ	Ⓐ	Ⓐ	Ⓐ	Ⓐ	Ⓐ	Ⓐ	Ⓐ	Ⓐ	Ⓐ2	Ⓐ	Ⓐ	Ⓐ	Ⓐ	Ⓐ2		⑥2	⑥	⑥	⑥2	⑥	⑥
Worcester Shrub Hill. **138** d.		...	...	...	0724	...	...	...	...	...	...	...	...	...	**A**	...	...	...	...	...		...	...	...	...	...	...
Cheltenham Spa....... **138** d.		0456	0553	0648	0758	0859	0959	1059	1159	1259	1359	1459	1559	1659	...	1759	1859	1959	2059	2216		0550	0649	0758	0859	0959	1059
Gloucester .... **138** a.	Ⓐ	0505	0602	0657	0808	0907	1008	1108	1208	1308	1408	1508	1608	1708	...	1807	1909	2008	2107	2225	⑥	0557	0659	0808	0909	1009	1109
Gloucester .... d.		0510	0610	0705	0813	0913	1014	1113	1214	1314	1414	1513	1613	1714	1750	1814	1916	2017	2117	2228		0607	0711	0814	0914	1017	1116
Stroud .... d.		0526	0627	0724	0830	0928	1030	1130	1231	1330	1430	1530	1630	1730	1807	1831	1932	2034	2133	2244		0624	0731	0833	0933	1034	1134
Swindon .... a.		0555	0655	0753	0859	0956	1058	1158	1259	1359	1459	1559	1658	1759	1834	1859	2001	2103	2201	2312		0653	0759	0902	1001	1103	1203
Swindon .... **132 133** d.		0556	0658	0757	0902	0958	1100	1159	1301	1400	1500	1600	1701	1801	...	1902	2003	2104	2203	...		...	0801	0903	...	1104	1204
Didcot Parkway... **132 133** d.		0613	0715	0814	0919	1016	1116	1217	1317	1417	1517	1617	1717	1818	...	1919	2020	2121	2220	...		...	0817	0919	...	1121	1221
Reading.............. **132 133** a.		0625	0728	0826	0932	1028	1129	1229	1330	1429	1530	1629	1729	1830	...	1931	2032	2133	2232	...		...	0830	0933	...	1134	1234
London Pad....... **132 133** a.		0654	0759	0859	1000	1059	1159	1259	1359	1459	1557	1659	1759	1901	...	1959	2101	2207	2304	...		...	0859	0959	...	1159	1259

	⑥	⑥	⑥	⑥2	⑥	⑥	⑥2	⑥	⑥	⑥	⑥2		⑦2	⑦2	⑦	⑦	⑦2	⑦		⑦	⑦2	⑦	⑦2	⑦2	⑦	⑦2	⑦
Worcester Shrub Hill. **138** d.	...	...	...	...	...	...	...	...	...	...	...		...	...	...	...	...	...	...	...	...	...	...	...	...	...	...
Cheltenham Spa....... **138** d.	1159	1259	1359	1459	1559	1659	1759	1859	2001	2101	2132		...	0939	1054	1155	1301	1401	...	1501	1601	1701	1801	1900	2000	2100	2200
Gloucester .... **138** a.	1209	1309	1409	1509	1609	1709	1809	1907	2011	2111	2142	⑦	...	0948	1106	1205	1311	1410	...	1513	1611	1714	1811	1911	2009	2111	2210
Gloucester .... d.	1215	1316	1415	1515	1616	1717	1816	1916	2016	2118	2145		0910	0952	1115	1217	1317	1419	...	1516	1617	1717	1818	1917	2017	2117	2213
Stroud .... d.	1234	1334	1434	1534	1634	1734	1834	1933	2034	2136	2202		0927	1009	1132	1235	1335	1436	...	1534	1636	1734	1835	1934	2034	2134	2232
Swindon .... a.	1302	1402	1502	1602	1702	1802	1902	2002	2102	2204	2230		0955	1036	1201	1303	1403	1504	...	1602	1704	1803	1902	2001	2102	2202	2259
Swindon .... **132 133** d.	1304	1404	1504	...	1704	1804	...	2004	2104	2206	...		...	...	1201	...	...	...	...	1602	...	1804	...	...	...	...	...
Didcot Parkway... **132 133** d.	1320	1420	1520	...	1720	1820	...	2020	2120	2223	...		...	...	1219	...	...	...	...	1620	...	1821	...	...	...	...	...
Reading.............. **132 133** a.	1333	1433	1533	...	1733	1833	...	2033	2133	2236	...		...	...	1231	...	...	...	...	1632	...	1833	...	...	...	...	...
London Pad....... **132 133** a.	1359	1459	1559	...	1759	1859	...	2059	2200	2305	...		...	...	1259	...	...	...	...	1659	...	1858	...	...	...	...	...

A – From / to Salisbury (Tables **134** and **140**).
C – From Westbury (Table **134**).

131 LONDON - OXFORD - WORCESTER - HEREFORD

Most trains convey 🍷 GW

km		Ⓐ	Ⓐ	Ⓐ	Ⓐ	Ⓐ	Ⓐ	Ⓐ	Ⓐ	Ⓐ	Ⓐ	Ⓐ	Ⓐ	Ⓐ	Ⓐ	Ⓐ	Ⓐ	Ⓐ	Ⓐ	Ⓐ	Ⓐ	Ⓐ	Ⓐ	Ⓐ
0	**London** Paddington ▷ d.	...	0505	0550	0650	0750	0850	0950	1050	1150	1250	1350	1450	1520	1550	1658	1734	1757	1858	1950	2050	2150	2250	2318
30	Slough ▷ d.	...	0522	0604	0704	0804	0904	1005	1104	1204	1304	1404	1504	1534	1604u	|	|	|	|	2004	2104	2204	2307	2335
58	Reading ▷ d.	...	0539	0618	0718	0819	0918	1019	1119	1218	1318	1418	1518	1548	1619u	|	1800	|	|	2019	2118	2218	2328	0008b
103	**Oxford** ▷ d.	0510	0607	0653	0748	0844	0945	1045	1145	1245	1344	1445	1545	1615	1645	1746	1824	1848	1945	2045	2143	2245	2359a	0035
148	Moreton in Marsh d.	0535	...	0727	0822	0918	1019	1119	1222	1319	1418	1519	1619	1656	1719	1824	1858	1926	2020	2119	2217	2322	0036	...
172	Evesham d.	0553	...	0756f	0841	0936	1038	1134	1240	1334	1436	1537	1638	1714	1748f	1843	1913	1944	2038	2138	2235	2340	0055	...
187	Worcestershire Parkway d.	0607	...	0809	0854	0949	1051	1146	1253	1346	1449	1550	1651	1727	1801	1856	1923	1956	2051	2151	2248	2353	0106	...
194	**Worcester** Shrub Hill **125 138** a.	0618	...	0817	0904j	0957	1059	1154	1301	1354	1457	1558	1705k	1735	1810	1903	1931	2004	2059k	2159	2256	0002	...	...
195	**Worcester** Foregate St **125** a.	...	...	0820	0917	1000	1102	1158	...	1357	1500	1601	1712	1741	1813	1906	1934	2007	2108	2202	2259	...	...	...
208	Great Malvern **125 138** a.	...	...	0834	0929	1013	1114	1210	...	1409	...	1613	...	...	1830	1924	1947	...	2120	2214t	2311	...	...	...
219	Ledbury **125** a.	...	...	...	...	...	...	1226	...	1423	...	...	...	...	...	...	2001k	...	2138j	2241	...	...	...	...
241	**Hereford** **125** a.	...	...	...	...	...	...	1244	...	1441	...	...	...	...	...	...	2026	...	2204	2258	...	...	...	...

	⑥	⑥	⑥	⑥	⑥	⑥	⑥	⑥	⑥	⑥	⑥	⑥	⑥	⑥	⑥	⑥	⑥	⑦	⑦	⑦	⑦	⑦	⑦
London Paddington ▷ d.	0550	0650	0750	0850	0950	1050	1150	1250	1350	1450	1550	1650	1750	1850	1950	2050	2150	0737v	0837	0921	0942	1046	1146
Slough ▷ d.	0605	0705	0805	0905	1005	1105	1205	1305	1405	1505	1605	1705	1805	1905	2005	2105	2205	0800v	0851	0935	0958	1100	1200
Reading ▷ d.	0619	0720	0820	0920	1019	1119	1219	1319	1419	1519	1619	1719	1819	1919	2019	2119	2219	0819v	0909	0948	1011	1114	1218a
Oxford ▷ d.	0648	0745	0845	0945	1045	1145	1245	1345	1445	1545	1645	1745	1845	1945	2045	2143	2250	0858	0950a	1020	1041	1144	1247
Moreton in Marsh d.	0722	0819	0919	1019	1119	1222	1318	1421	1521	1619	1719	1819	1921	2019	2121	...	2326	0933	1024	...	1117	1218	1321
Evesham d.	0741	0849f	0938	1038	1137	1241	1336	1440	1539	1638	1738	1838	1940	2037	2140	...	2345	0951	1043	...	1137	1236	1340
Worcestershire Parkway d.	0755	0903	0952	1052	1151	1255	1350	1454	1553	1652	1753	1852	1955	2051	2154	...	2359	1005	1056	...	1150	1249	1353
Worcester Shrub Hill **125 138** a.	0802	0910	0959	1059j	1158	1302j	1357	1501j	1600	1659	1802j	1859	2005	2058	2201	...	0006	1014	1103k	...	1158	1256	1400j
Worcester Foregate St **125** a.	0805	0913	1002	1112	1201	1312	1400	1511	1603	1702	1812	1902	2008	2101	2204j	...	...	1017	1111	...	1201	1300	1417
Great Malvern **125 138** a.	0818	0925	1015	1124	1213	1324	1412	...	1615	1714	1829	1914	...	2113k	2224	...	...	1029	1123	...	1213t	1312	1429
Ledbury **125** a.	...	...	...	...	1226	...	1425	...	...	...	...	1928	...	2131r	...	...	...	...	...	...	1239	...	1442
Hereford **125** a	...	...	...	...	1244	...	1443	...	...	...	...	1945	...	2205	...	...	...	...	...	...	1300	...	1500

	⑦	⑦	⑦	⑦	⑦	⑦	⑦	⑦	⑦	⑦
London Paddington ▷ d.	1246	1346	1446	1546	1646	1746	1846	1946	2046	2145
Slough ▷ d.	1300	1400	1500	1600	1700	1800	1900	2000	2100	2159
Reading ▷ d.	1314	1414	1514	1614	1714	1814	1914	2014	2115	2213
Oxford ▷ d.	1344	1444	1544	1645	1745	1844	1945	2046	2144	2242
Moreton in Marsh d.	1419	1519	1618	1720	1819	1918	2020	2121	2217	2316
Evesham d.	1437	1537	1637	1739	1838	1937	2039	2141	2236	2334
Worcestershire Parkway d.	1449	1550	1649	1752	1850	1949	2052	2153	2249	2347
Worcester Shrub Hill **125 138** a.	1457	1558	1657	1801	1858	1957	2103	2202	2258	2356
Worcester Foregate St **125** a.	1501	1601	1700	1804	1901	2000	2109	2205	...	...
Great Malvern **125 138** a.	1515	1617j	1713	1817n	1913	2012	2121	2217	...	...
Ledbury **125** a.	...	1641	...	1842	...	...	2138	...	...	...
Hereford **125** a.	...	1659	...	1859	...	...	2155	...	...	...

	Ⓐ	Ⓐ	Ⓐ	Ⓐ	Ⓐ	Ⓐ	Ⓐ	Ⓐ	Ⓐ
Hereford **125** d.	...	...	...	0449	0523	...	0643	...	...
Ledbury **125** d.	...	...	...	0506	0540	...	0700	...	...
Great Malvern **125 138** d.	...	...	...	0519	0553	...	0713	...	0856
Worcester Foreg'te St **125** d.	...	...	...	0532	0606	...	0726	...	0909
Worcester S Hill **125 138** d.	...	...	0514	0537	0610	0643	0731	0813	0915
Worcestershire Parkway d.	...	...	0521	0543	0616	0649	0738	0819	0921
Evesham d.	...	...	0535	0553	0635a	0700	0751	0834	0935
Moreton in Marsh d.	...	...	0554	0609	0654	0715	0810	0853	0953
Oxford ▷ d.	0520	0600	0632	0648	0732	0753	0849	0932	1032
Reading ▷ a.	0546	0628j	0653	0709	0754	0814	0911	0955	1054
Slough ▷ a.	0606	0651	|	|	|	|	|	1009	1108
London Paddington ▷ a.	0622	0706	0724	0738	0824	0842	0938	1024	1124

	Ⓐ	Ⓐ	Ⓐ	Ⓐ	Ⓐ	Ⓐ	Ⓐ	Ⓐ	Ⓐ	Ⓐ	Ⓐ	Ⓐ	Ⓐ	Ⓐ	Ⓐ	⑥	⑥	⑥	⑥	⑥	⑥	⑥	⑥	⑥
Hereford **125** d.	...	...	...	...	1318	...	1518	...	...	...	...	...	...	...	2200	...	...	0618	0713	...	...	...	...	...
Ledbury **125** d.	...	...	...	...	1335	...	1535	...	...	...	...	...	...	...	2217	...	...	0635	0730	...	...	...	...	...
Great Malvern **125 138** d.	0954	1059	1155	...	1352a	...	1555b	1631	...	...	1905	1945	...	...	2229	...	0554	0654b	0743	...	0850	0958	1050	1155
Worcester Foregate St **125** d.	1008	1112	1209	...	1405	1516	1609	1644	1726	1758	1918	1958	2100	...	2242	...	0608	0708	0756	0825	0904	1012	1104	1209
Worcester Shrub Hill **125 138** d.	1016a	1116	1217a	1316	1414a	1520	1613	1653a	1730	1803	1924	2003	2104	...	2251a	...	0612	0712	0810f	0830	0913a	1017	1115	1215
Worcestershire Parkway d.	1022	1122	1223	1322	1420	1526	1619	1659	1736	1809	|	2009	2110	...	2258	...	0619	0718	0818	0837	0919	1023	1121	1221
Evesham d.	1035	1136	1236	1336	1433	1536	1633	1714	1751	1824	1941	2024	2125	...	2311	...	0635	0732	0833	0851	0933	1037	1135	1235
Moreton in Marsh d.	1054	1154	1255	1354	1452	1552	1653	1748p	1822f	1847a	1956	2045	2146	...	2330	...	0654	0751	0852	0910	0951	1056	1154	1254
Oxford ▷ d.	1132	1232	1332	1432	1532a	1631a	1732	1832a	1902	1932	2032	2132	2232	2305	0011	0632	0732	0832	0932a	0948	1032	1132	1232	1332
Reading ▷ a.	1155	1254	1355	1455	1553	1654	1756	1857	1925	1954	2053	2153	2259	2335	0041	0655	0754	0854	0954	1014	1054	1154	1254	1354
Slough ▷ a.	1209	1308	1409	1509	1607	1708	1811	1911	1939	2009	2107	2207	2325	2357	0057	0709	0807	0908	1007	|	1107	1208	1308	1407
London Paddington ▷ a.	1224	1324	1424	1524	1622	1724	1829	1927	1954	2024	2124	2224	2349	0020	0120	0724	0824	0924	1024	1039	1124	1224	1324	1424

	⑥	⑥	⑥	⑥	⑥	⑥	⑥	⑥	⑥	⑥	⑦	⑦	⑦	⑦	⑦	⑦	⑦	⑦	⑦	⑦	⑦	⑦	⑦	⑦
Hereford **125** d.	...	1318	...	1513	...	...	...	...	2020	...	...	...	...	...	...	1227	1327	...	1531	...	1730	...	...	...
Ledbury **125** d.	...	1335	...	1530	...	...	...	...	2038	...	...	...	...	...	...	1246	1344	...	1548	...	1748	...	...	...
Great Malvern **125 138** d.	...	1355b	1450	1542	1700	1743	1900	...	2055a	2242	...	0858	0955	1050	1155	1300	1356	1458	1600	1658	1801	1857	1957	2040
Worcester Foregate St **125** d.	1305	1409	1504	1555	1714	1804b	1914	2000	2109	2255	0815	0911	1009	1104	1211	1313	1409	1510	1613	1711	1814	1911	2010	2053
Worcester Shrub Hill **125 138** d.	1312	1415	1515b	1613f	1718	1815b	1918	2015b	2115	2302	0820	0915	1013	1108	1213	1317	1414	1515	1617	1715	1818	1915	2014	2059
Worcestershire Parkway d.	1319	1421	1521	1619	1724	1821	1924	2021	2121	2308	0826	0921	1019	1114	1221	1323	1420	1521	1623	1721	1824	1921	2021	2106
Evesham d.	1333	1435	1535	1633	1737	1835	1937	2035	2135	2322	0839	0935	1034	1129	1234	1336	1433	1535	1636	1735	1838	1935	2034	2123
Moreton in Marsh d.	1351	1454	1554	1651	1756	1854	1956	2054	2154	...	0857	0953	1052	1147	1250	1354	1451	1553	1654	1753	1856	1953	2053	2143
Oxford ▷ d.	1431	1531	1632	1732	1832	1932	2032	2132	2236a	...	0930	1030	1130	1230b	1330a	1430	1530	1630	1730	1830	1930	2030	2128	2223
Reading ▷ a.	1453	1553	1654	1754	1854	1954	2054	2154	2304	...	0957	1057	1156	1256	1355	1458	1557k	1657	1757	1856	1955k	2057	2155	2252
Slough ▷ a.	1507	1609	1707	1807	1907	2007	2107	2207	2321	...	1012	1112	1213	1312	1413	1513	1613	1713	1812	1912	2013	2112	2208	2311
London Paddington ▷ a.	1522	1624	1722	1824	1924	2024	2124	2224	2340	...	1029	1129	1229	1328	1429	1528	1629	1729	1828	1929	2028	2129	2224	2340

OTHER SERVICES LONDON - OXFORD

	②–⑤	Ⓐ	Ⓐ	Ⓐ	Ⓐ	and at	Ⓐ	Ⓐ	Ⓐ	Ⓐ	Ⓐ	Ⓐ	Ⓐ	⑥	⑥	⑥	⑥	and at	⑥	⑥	⑥	⑥y	⑥y
London Paddington d.	0032	0505	0720	0820	0920	the same	1420	1620	1828	1930	2020	2120	2220	0032	0520	0620	0720	the same	1920	2020	2119	2218	2250
Slough d.	0050	0522	0734	|	0934	minutes	1434	1634	|	|	2034	2134	|	0050	0536	0635	0735	minutes	1936	2035	2135	2233	2307
Reading d.	0115	0839	0749	0846	0948	past each	1449	1648	|	1955	2049	2148	2245	0115	0550	0649	0749	past each	1951	2049	2153	2251	2332
Oxford a.	0146	0607	0812	0918	1015	hour until	1513	1713	1913	2018	2113	2213	2308	0146	0620	0722	0815	hour until	2016	2113	2223	2318	0008

	⑥y	⑦	⑦	⑦	⑦	⑦	and at	⑦	⑦	⑦	⑦
London Paddington d.	2333	0921	1021	1121	1220	1320	the same	1920	2119	2258	2333
Slough d.	2349	0935	1035	1135	1235	1335	minutes	1935	|	|	0001
Reading d.	0012	0948	1048	1148	1248	1348	past each	1948	2148a	2337	0019
Oxford a.	0042	1020	1120	1220	1323	1419	hour until	2019	2217	*0029**	*0125**

	①	Ⓐ	Ⓐ	Ⓐ	Ⓐ	Ⓐ	and at	Ⓐ
Oxford d.	*0005**	0707	0742	0902	0959	1102	the same	1701
Reading a.	0050	0733	0809	0924	1023	1125	minutes	1724
Slough a.	0116	|	|	|	1038	1139	past each	1738
London Paddington a.	0143	0806	0837	0952	1054	1155	hour until	1757

	Ⓐ	Ⓐ	Ⓐ	Ⓐ	⑥	⑥	and at	⑥	⑥	⑦v	⑦v	⑦z	⑦	⑦	⑦	⑦		⑦	⑦	⑦	⑦	⑦	⑦	⑦
Oxford d.	1802	2006	2102	2202	0550	0701	the same	2102	2200	0750	0824	0855	1055	1155	1255	1355	...	1455	1555	1655	1755	1855	1955	*2305**
Reading a.	1826	2028	2124	2225	0617	0726	minutes	2125	2229	0817	0849	0924	1125	1225	1326	1425	...	1525	1625	1725	1823	1925	2024	0023
Slough a.	1842	2042	2138	2238	0631	0739	past each	2138	2254	0833	0906	0937	1138	1239	1341	1439	...	1539	1639	1739	1839	1938	2038	0045
London Paddington a.	1859	2059	2154	2254	0649	0754	hour until	2153	2314	0850	0921	0953	1154	1254	1359	1456	...	1554	1654	1754	1854	1954	2053	0115

- **a** – Arrives 5–7 minutes earlier.
- **b** – Arrives 8–9 minutes earlier.
- **f** – Arrives 11–15 minutes earlier.
- **j** – Departs 8–11 minutes later.
- **k** – Departs 5–7 minutes later.
- **n** – Departs 1829.
- **p** – Arrives 1732.
- **r** – Departs 2149.
- **t** – Departs 14–15 minutes later.
- **u** – Calls to pick up only.
- **v** – Until Sept. 11.
- **y** – Until Sept. 10.
- **z** – From Sept. 18.
- * – By 🚌 from / to Didcot Parkway.
- ▷ – See panel below main table for additional services London - Oxford and v.v. See Tables **130**, **132** and **133** for other services London - Reading and v.v.

131a SLOUGH - WINDSOR

Journey time 6 minutes 2nd class GW

From Slough:
Ⓐ: 0530, 0549, 0607, 0626, 0650, 0710, 0730, 0750, 0809, 0830, 0856 and every 20 minutes until 2316, 2340.
⑥: 0556, 0616, 0646, 0716, 0746, 0816 and every 20 minutes until 2016, 2046, 2116, 2146, 2214, 2246, 2322, 2352.
⑦: 0822, 0852, 0912 and every 20 minutes until 1852, 1922 and every 30 minutes until 2322.

From Windsor & Eton Central:
Ⓐ: 0539, 0558, 0616, 0640, 0659, 0719, 0739, 0759, 0818, 0839, 0905, 0925 and every 20 minutes untill 2325, 2354.
⑥: 0606, 0626, 0656, 0726, 0756, 0826 and every 20 minutes until 2026, 2056, 2126, 2156, 2224, 2256, 2332.
⑦: 0002, 0832, 0902 and every 20 minutes until 1902, 1932 and every 30 minutes until 2332.

GW — Most trains convey 🍸 — LONDON - BRISTOL - TAUNTON — 132

km		ⒶQ	Ⓐ	Ⓐ	Ⓐ	Ⓐ	Ⓐ	Ⓐ	Ⓐ	Ⓐ	Ⓐ	Ⓐ	Ⓐ	Ⓐ	Ⓐ	Ⓐ	Ⓐ	Ⓐ	Ⓐ	Ⓐ	Ⓐ	Ⓐ	Ⓐ
0	**London** Paddington .... **130 133** d.	0523	0545	0632	0702	0732	0802	0832	0902	0932	1002	1032	1102	1132	1202	1231	1302	1332	1402	1432	1502	1532	1602
58	Reading .... **130 133** d.	0549	0610	0657	0727	0800	0827	0857	0927	0958	1027	1058	1127	1157	1227	1257	1327	1358	1427	1457	1527	1558	1627
85	Didcot Parkway .... **130 133** d.	0603	|	0712	0741	0814	0841	0912	0941	1013	1040	1112	1140	1212	1240	1312	1340	1412	1440	1512	1540	1612	1641
124	Swindon .... **121 130 133** d.	0621	0637	0730	0758	0831	0858	0929	0958	1030	1057	1129	1157	1230	1301	1329	1357	1429	1458	1529	1557	1630	1658
151	Chippenham .... **121** d.	0633	0649	0742	0810	0843	0910	0940	1014	1041	1109	1141	1209	1242	1313	1340	1409	1441	1511	1541	1609	1642	1710
172	Bath .... **140** d.	0646	0705	0757	0823	0856	0923	0953	1027	1054	1122	1154	1223	1256	1326	1353	1423	1454	1524	1554	1623	1655	1723
	Bristol Parkway .... **133** a.	0716t	|	|	|	|	|	|	|	|	|	|	|	|	|	|	|	|	|	|	|	|	|
190	**Bristol** Temple Meads .. **140 110/5/6** a.	0657	0717	0813	0835	0910	0935	1005	1039	1106	1135	1206	1236	1309	1339	1406	1435	1508	1536	1606	1635	1707	1735
221	Weston-super-Mare .... **115 116** a.	...	...	...	...	...	...	...	...	...	...	...	...	...	...	...	...	...	...	1640	...	1742	...
262	**Taunton** .... **110 115 116** a.	...	...	...	...	...	...	...	...	...	...	...	...	...	...	...	...	...	...	...	...	...	...

	Ⓐ	Ⓐ	Ⓐ	Ⓐ	Ⓐ	Ⓐ	Ⓐ	Ⓐ	Ⓐ	Ⓐ	ⒶE	Ⓐ	Ⓐ	⑥	⑥	⑥	⑥	⑥	⑥	⑥	⑥	⑥	⑥
London Paddington .... **130 133** d.	1633	1702	1732	1801	1834	1902	1932	2001	2032	2102	2202	2232	2332	0630	0702	0732	0802	0832	0902	0932	1002	1032	1102
Reading .... **130 133** d.	1658	1727	1757	1828	1859	1927	1958	2027	2057	2127	2227	2259	0005	0655	0727	0757	0827	0859	0927	0958	1027	1057	1127
Didcot Parkway .... **130 133** d.	1712	1741	1811	1841	1913	1941	2011	2040	2112	2140	2241	2313	0020	0709	0740	0812	0840	0913	0940	1013	1040	1112	1140
Swindon .... **121 130 133** d.	1733	1758	1828	1859	1930	1958	2028	2057	2129	2157	2258	2332	0038	0726	0757	0828	0858	0930	0957	1030	1057	1129	1157
Chippenham .... **121** d.	1745	1810	1840	1913	1942	2010	2040	2109	2140	2209	2311	2344	0050	0738	0809	0841	0910	0942	1009	1042	1109	1141	1210
Bath .... **140** d.	1758	1825	1853	1926	1956	2025	2053	2122	2153	2224	2324	2357	0103	0751	0823	0854	0923	0955	1023	1055	1123	1155	1223
Bristol Parkway .... **133** a.	|	|	|	|	|	|	|	|	|	|	|	|	|	|	|	|	|	|	|	|	|	|	|
Bristol Temple Meads... **140 110/5/6** a.	1809	1840	1905	1939	2007	2040	2108	2134	2205	2239	2335	0009	0115	0803	0835	0906	0935	1007	1035	1107	1135	1209	1235
Weston-super-Mare .... **115 116** a.	1842	...	1939	...	2042	...	2150	...	2249	...	0015s	...	...	...	...	...	...	1033	...	...	...	1232	...
Taunton .... **110 115 116** a.	1912	...	2014	...	...	...	...	...	...	...	0044	...	...	...	...	...	...	1105	...	...	...	...	...

	⑥	⑥	⑥	⑥	⑥	⑥	⑥	⑥	⑥	⑥		⑥	⑥	⑥	⑥	⑥	⑥	⑥	⑥	⑥B	⑥	⑥	⑥	⑥
London Paddington .... **130 133** d.	1132	1202	1232	1302	1332	1402	1432	1502	1532	1602	...	1631	1702	1732	1802	1832	1902	1932	2002	2032	2132	2202	2230	2330
Reading .... **130 133** d.	1157	1227	1257	1327	1357	1427	1457	1527	1557	1627	...	1657	1727	1800	1827	1857	1927	1957	2027	2057	2157	2227	2255	0005
Didcot Parkway .... **130 133** d.	1212	1240	1312	1340	1412	1440	1512	1540	1612	1640	...	1712	1740	1815	1840	1912	1940	2012	2040	2112	2210	2240	2309	0020
Swindon .... **121 130 133** d.	1230	1257	1329	1357	1429	1458	1529	1557	1629	1657	...	1729	1757	1832	1857	1929	1957	2028	2057	2129	2227	2257	2326	0038
Chippenham .... **121** d.	1241	1310	1341	1409	1441	1510	1541	1609	1641	1709	...	1740	1809	1844	1909	1941	2009	2040	2109	2140	2239	|	2338	0050
Bath .... **140** d.	1254	1323	1354	1423	1455	1523	1554	1623	1654	1723	...	1753	1823	1857	1923	1956	2022	2053	2122	2153	2253	|	2351	0103
Bristol Parkway .... **133** a.	|	|	|	|	|	|	|	|	|	|	...	|	|	|	|	|	|	|	|	|	|	2319	|	|
Bristol Temple Meads... **140 110/5/6** a.	1306	1335	1406	1435	1509	1535	1606	1635	1706	1735	...	1805	1835	1909	1935	2008	2037	2105	2134	2205	2305	...	0003	0115
Weston-super-Mare .... **115 116** a.	1333	...	1434	...	1540	...	1630	...	1742	...	...	1834	...	1939	...	2039	...	2137	...	2235s	...	...	...	...
Taunton .... **110 115 116** a.	...	...	...	...	...	...	...	...	...	...	...	1906	...	...	...	2112	...	2208	...	2306	...	...	...	...

	⑦B	⑦	⑦	⑦	⑦	⑦	⑦	⑦	⑦	⑦	⑦E	⑦	⑦	⑦E	⑦	⑦	⑦	⑦	⑦	⑦	⑦	⑦	⑦
London Paddington .... **130 133** d.	0813	0900	1030	1130	1230	1330	1430	1500	1530	1600	1630	1700	1730	1800	1830	1900	1930	2030	2130	2200	2237	2258	2333
Reading .... **130 133** d.	0837	0929	1055	1154	1255	1355	1454	1525	1555	1624	1655	1725	1755	1825	1855	1925	1955	2055	2155	2224	2315	2337	0019
Didcot Parkway .... **130 133** d.	0853	0949	1108	1208	1308	1408	1508	1538	1608	1638	1708	1738	|	1838	|	1938	|	|	2208	2238	2329s	2351s	0034s
Swindon .... **121 130 133** d.	0910	1006	1125	1225	1325	1425	1524	1555	1625	1654	1727	1755	1822	1855	1922	1955	2022	2122	2225	2255	2346s	0010s	0052s
Chippenham .... **121** d.	0922	1018	1137	1237	1337	1437	1536	1607	1638	1707	1739	1807	1834	1907	1933	2007	2034	2134	2237	2306	|	0023s	0104s
Bath .... **140** d.	0934	1031	1150	1251	1350	1450	1550	1620	1651	1720	1752	1820	1847	1920	1946	2020	2048	2147	2250	2319	|	0034s	0116s
Bristol Parkway .... **133** a.	|	|	|	|	|	|	|	|	|	|	|	|	|	|	|	|	|	|	|	|	0009	|	|
Bristol Temple Meads... **140 110/5/6** a.	0946	1043	1202	1303	1402	1502	1602	1634	1703	1736	1804	1833	1859	1932	1958	2032	2102	2159	2302	2332	...	0049	0130
Weston-super-Mare .... **115 116** a.	|	1108	1236	...	1433	...	|	...	1733	...	1837	...	1940	|	2039	...	...	2235	...	...	...	...	...
Taunton .... **110 115 116** a.	1026	...	...	...	...	...	1640	...	1804	...	1904	...	...	2008	...	...	...	...	...	...	...	...	...

	Ⓐ	Ⓐ	Ⓐ	Ⓐ	Ⓐ	Ⓐ		Ⓐ	Ⓐ	Ⓐ	Ⓐ	Ⓐ	Ⓐ	Ⓐ	Ⓐ	Ⓐ	Ⓐ		Ⓐ	Ⓐ	Ⓐ	Ⓐ	Ⓐ
Taunton .... **110 115 116** d.	...	...	...	...	...	...	...	...	0655	0723	...	...	...	...	...	...	...	...	...	...	...	...	...
Weston-super-Mare .... **115 116** d.	...	...	...	...	0620	0652	...	...	0724	0754	...	...	...	...	...	...	...	...	...	...	...	...	...
Bristol Temple M .... **140 110/5/6** d.	0453	0525	0547	0630	0700	0730	...	0750	0800	0830	0900	0930	1000	1030	1100	1130	1200	...	1230	1300	1330	1400	1430
Bristol Parkway .... **133** d.	0503	|	|	|	|	|	...	|	|	|	|	|	|	|	|	|	|	...	|	|	|	|	|
Bath .... **140** d.	|	0538	0602	0643	0713	0743	...	0804	0813	0843	0913	0943	1013	1043	1113	1143	1213	...	1243	1313	1343	1413	1443
Chippenham .... **121** d.	|	0552	0615	0656	0726	0756	...	0816	0826	0856	0928	0956	1026	1056	1126	1156	1226	...	1256	1326	1356	1426	1456
Swindon .... **121 130 133** d.	0528	0606	0630	0710	0740	0809	...	0830	|	0910	0945	1010	1040	1111	1140	1211	1240	...	1310	1340	1410	1441	1510
Didcot Parkway .... **130 133** d.	0546	|	0647	0726	|	0827	...	0847	|	0927	1002	1027	1057	1128	1157	1228	1257	...	1327	1357	1428	1457	1527
Reading .... **130 133** a.	0558	0631	0659	0738	|	0839	...	0859	|	0939	1014	1040	1109	1140	1209	1240	1309	...	1339	1409	1440	1509	1539
London Paddington .... **130 133** a.	0626	0659	0729	0809	0829	0908	...	0930	0928	1006	1042	1108	1136	1208	1238	1306	1337	...	1405	1436	1508	1536	1607

	Ⓐ	Ⓐ	Ⓐ	Ⓐ	Ⓐ	Ⓐ		Ⓐ	Ⓐ	Ⓐ	Ⓐ	ⒶB	ⒶD	⑥	⑥	⑥	⑥	⑥		⑥	⑥	⑥B	⑥
Taunton .... **110 115 116** d.	...	...	...	...	...	...	...	...	...	...	...	2003	2117	...	...	...	...	...	...	0657	...	0758	...
Weston-super-Mare .... **115 116** d.	...	...	...	...	...	...	...	1728	...	1829	...	2029	|	...	...	...	0620	...	...	0727	...	0827	...
Bristol Temple Meads... **140 110/5/6** d.	1500	1530	1600	1630	1700	1729	...	1800	1830	1900	2000	2100	2200	0530	0600	0630	0700	0730	...	0800	0830	0900	0930
Bristol Parkway .... **133** d.	|	|	|	|	|	|	...	|	|	|	|	|	|	|	|	|	|	|	...	|	|	|	|
Bath .... **140** d.	1513	1543	1614	1643	1713	1745	...	1813	1843	1913	2013	2113	2213	0543	0613	0643	0713	0744	...	0813	0843	0913	0944
Chippenham .... **121** d.	1526	1556	1626	1657	1726	1757	...	1826	1856	1926	2026	2125	2227	0556	0626	0656	0726	0757	...	0826	0856	0926	0957
Swindon .... **121 130 133** d.	1540	1610	1640	1713	1741	1811	...	1840	1910	1940	2040	2139	2241	0611	0641	0711	0741	0811	...	0841	0912	0941	1011
Didcot Parkway .... **130 133** d.	1557	1627	1657	|	1757	1828	...	1858	1927	1958	2057	2156	2259	0628	0658	0727	0756	0827	...	0857	0927	0956	1026
Reading .... **130 133** a.	1609	1639	1709	1738	1809	1840	...	1910	1939	2010	2109	2208	2310	0641	0711	0740	0810	0841	...	0910	0941	1010	1040
London Paddington .... **130 133** a.	1639	1706	1740	1805	1840	1909	...	1939	2008	2037	2134	2236	2356	0707	0737	0806	0837	0906	...	0936	1006	1036	1106

	⑥	⑥	⑥	⑥	⑥	⑥	⑥	⑥	⑥	⑥	⑥	⑥	⑥	⑥	⑥	⑥	⑥	⑥	⑥	⑥A	⑥	⑥	⑥D	⑥
Taunton .... **110 115 116** d.	...	...	...	...	...	1132	...	...	...	...	...	...	...	...	...	...	...	...	...	1830	...	1958	2119	2140
Weston-super-Mare .... **115 116** d.	...	...	...	...	...	1202	...	1302	...	1402	...	1501	...	1602	...	1702	...	1802	...	1902	...	2029	|	2210
Bristol Temple Meads... **140 110/5/6** d.	1000	1030	1100	1130	1200	1230	1300	1330	1400	1430	1500	1530	1600	1630	1700	1730	1800	1830	1900	1930	2000	2100	2200	2240
Bristol Parkway .... **133** d.	|	|	|	|	|	|	|	|	|	|	|	|	|	|	|	|	|	|	|	|	|	|	|	|
Bath .... **140** d.	1014	1043	1113	1143	1213	1243	1313	1343	1413	1443	1513	1543	1613	1643	1713	1743	1813	1843	1913	1943	2013	2113	2213	2254
Chippenham .... **121** d.	1027	1056	1126	1156	1226	1256	1326	1356	1426	1456	1526	1556	1626	1656	1726	1756	1826	1856	1926	1956	2026	2126	2227	2308
Swindon .... **121 130 133** d.	1041	1111	1141	1211	1241	1311	1341	1411	1441	1511	1541	1611	1641	1711	1741	1811	1841	1911	1941	2011	2041	2140	2241	2322
Didcot Parkway .... **130 133** d.	1056	1126	1156	1226	1256	1326	1356	1426	1456	1526	1556	1626	1656	1726	1756	1826	1856	1926	1956	2026	2056	2156	2257	2339
Reading .... **130 133** a.	1110	1140	1210	1240	1310	1340	1410	1440	1510	1540	1610	1640	1710	1740	1810	1840	1910	1940	2010	2040	2110	2209	2311	2352
London Paddington .... **130 133** a.	1137	1207	1237	1306	1337	1407	1437	1507	1537	1608	1635	1707	1737	1807	1837	1906	1937	2007	2035	2106	2137	2239	2342	0037j

	⑦	⑦	⑦	⑦	⑦	⑦	⑦	⑦	⑦	⑦	⑦	⑦	⑦	⑦	⑦	⑦	⑦	⑦	⑦B		⑦	⑦	⑦E
Taunton .... **110 115 116** d.	...	...	...	...	...	...	...	...	...	...	...	...	...	...	...	1620	...	1704	1757	...	1858	...	2142
Weston-super-Mare .... **115 116** d.	...	...	0829	...	...	...	1131	...	...	1328	...	...	...	1528	...	|	...	1731	1826	...	1927	2028	2204
Bristol Temple Meads... **140 110/5/6** d.	...	0830	0900	...	1000	1100	1200	1230	1300	1400	1430	1500	1530	1600	1630	1700	1730	1800	1900	...	2000	2100	2225
Bristol Parkway .... **133** d.	0834	|	|	1003	|	|	|	|	|	|	|	|	|	|	|	|	|	|	|	...	|	|	|
Bath .... **140** d.	|	0843	0913	|	1013	1113	1213	1243	1313	1413	1443	1513	1544	1614	1643	1713	1743	1813	1913	...	2013	2113	2238
Chippenham .... **121** d.	|	0855	0926	|	1026	1126	1226	1256	1326	1426	1456	1526	1558	1627	1656	1726	1755	1825	1926	...	2026	2125	2251
Swindon .... **121 130 133** d.	0859	0909	0940	1027	1040	1140	1240	1310	1340	1440	1511	1540	1614	1640	1711	1741	1810	1840	1940	...	2040	2139	2305
Didcot Parkway .... **130 133** d.	0914	0926	0956	|	|	1156	1256	1327	1356	1456	1527	1556	...	1656	1727	|	1827	1856	1956	...	2056	2156	2322
Reading .... **130 133** a.	0929	0939	1009	1053	1105	1209	1310	1340	1409	1509	1540	1609	...	1710	1740	1806	1840	1909	2012	...	2111	2209	2335
London Paddington .... **130 133** a.	0955	1007	1036	1120	1136	1235	1336	1406	1435	1536	1609	1636	...	1735	1808	1836	1907	1938	2039	...	2136	2237	0009

A – Until Sept. 10; from Paignton (Table **110**).
B – To/from Exeter St Davids (Table **110**).
D – From Penzance (Tables **110**/**112**).
E – To/from Plymouth (Table **110**).
Q – To Swansea (Table **133**).

a – Via Westbury (Table **110**).
f – Departs 1814.
j – Arrives 0032 from Sept. 17.
r – Arrives 5 minutes earlier.
s – Calls to set down only.
t – Calls at Bristol Parkway after Bristol Temple Meads.

133 LONDON - BRISTOL PARKWAY - CARDIFF - SWANSEA

Most trains convey 🍸 GW

km	Ⓐ	Ⓐ◇	Ⓐ	Ⓐ	Ⓐ	Ⓐ	Ⓐ	Ⓐ	Ⓐ	Ⓐ	Ⓐ	Ⓐ	Ⓐ	Ⓐ	Ⓐ	Ⓐ	Ⓐ	Ⓐ	Ⓐ	Ⓐ	Ⓐ	Ⓐ	Ⓐ	Ⓐ	ⒶG
0	**London** Paddington 130 132 d.	0523	0648	0712	0748	0818	0848	0918	0948	1018	1048	1118	1148	1218	1248	1318	1348	1418	1448	1518	1548	1618	1648	1718	1748
58	Reading 130 132 d.	0549	0713	0739	0813	0843	0913	0943	1013	1043	1113	1143	1213	1243	1313	1343	1413	1443	1513	1543	1613	1643	1713	1743	1813
85	Didcot Parkway 130 132 d.	0603	|	0754	|	|	|	|	|	|	|	|	|	|	|	|	|	|	|	|	|	1658	|	1756	|
124	Swindon 130 132 d.	0621	0741	0812	0841	0910	0941	1011	1041	1111	1140	1210	1240	1310	1340	1410	1440	1510	1540	1610	1640	1715	1742f	1813	1841
180	**Bristol** Parkway 132 d.	0728r	0805	0835	0905	0934	1005	1035	1105	1134	1204	1235	1303	1334	1405	1435	1504	1533	1604	1633	1704	1740	1805	1838	1904
215	Newport ‡ a.	0749	0824	0853	0923	0955	1023	1053	1124	1156	1225	1302	1321	1352	1423	1500	1522	1552	1622	1655	1722	1759	1823	1859	1922
234	**Cardiff** Central ‡ a.	0803	0839	0908	0938	1010	1037	1107	1141	1213	1239	1317	1335	1407	1437	1517	1536	1607	1637	1709	1737	1814	1837	1915	1938
	Cardiff Central 136 d.	0807	0842	...	0942	...	1040	...	1143	...	1242	...	1338	...	1440	...	1539	...	1639	...	1742	1821	1842	1918	1941
266	Bridgend 136 a.	0826	0901	...	1001	...	1059	...	1202	...	1301	...	1357	...	1459	...	1558	...	1658	...	1801	1849	1859	1946	2000
286	Port Talbot 136 a.	0838	0913	...	1013	...	1111	...	1214	...	1313	...	1409	...	1511	...	1610	...	1710	...	1813	1901	1912	1959	2012
295	Neath 136 a.	0845	0920	...	1020	...	1119	...	1222	...	1320	...	1416	...	1519	...	1617	...	1718	...	1820	1908	1919	2006	2019
307	**Swansea** 136 a.	0858	0933	...	1034	...	1131	...	1234	...	1333	...	1429	...	1531	...	1630	...	1730	...	1833	1921	1932	2019	2032

Ⓐ	Ⓐ	Ⓐ	Ⓐ	Ⓐ	⑤	①–④		⑤	①–④	⑤	①–④
London Paddington 130 132 d.	1818	1848	1918	1948	2048	2048	...	2148	2148	2248	2248
Reading 130 132 d.	1843	1913	1943	2013	2113	2113	...	2213	2213	2318	2318
Didcot Parkway 130 132 d.	1857	|	|	|	|	|	...	|	|	2334	2334
Swindon 130 132 d.	1914	1940	2010	2040	2140	2140	...	2240	2240	2351	2351
Bristol Parkway 132 d.	1940	2004	2038f	2105	2203	2203	...	2304	2304	0015	0015
Newport ‡ a.	1958	2025	2057	2123	2223	2232	...	2322	2329	0034	0042
Cardiff Central ‡ a.	2013	2039	2115	2140	2241	2250	...	2337	2347	0047	0100
Cardiff Central 136 d.	2020	2042	2124	2143	2252	2252	...	2351	2351	0050	0103
Bridgend 136 a.	2047	2101	2145	2202	2311	2308	...	0012	0012	0110	0122
Port Talbot 136 a.	2059	2113	2157	2214	2323	2323	...	0024	0024	0135	0143
Neath 136 a.	2106	2120	2204	2221	2330	2330	...	0031	0031	0143	0151
Swansea 136 a.	2118	2133	2217	2234	2343	2343	...	0044	0044	0155	0203

⑥	⑥F	⑥	⑥	⑥K	⑥	⑥	⑥	⑥	⑥	⑥	⑥	⑥	⑥	⑥
London Paddington 130 132 d.	...	0648	0748	0848	0948	1048	1148	1213	1248	1348	1448	1548	1618	1648
Reading 130 132 d.	...	0713	0813	0913	1013	1113	1213	1240	1313	1413	1513	1613	1643	1713
Didcot Parkway 130 132 d.	...	|	|	|	|	|	|	1256	|	|	|	|	1657	|
Swindon 130 132 d.	...	0740	0841	0940	1040	1140	1240	1319	1340	1440	1540	1640	1715	1740
Bristol Parkway 132 d.	0724	0804	0905	1005	1104	1204	1304	1343	1404	1504	1604	1704	1739	1804
Newport ‡ a.	0744	0825	0924	1024	1124	1224	1323	1403	1423	1526	1624	1723	1759	1823
Cardiff Central ‡ a.	0758	0838	0939	1038	1137	1237	1338	1417	1437	1541	1637	1738	1813	1837
Cardiff Central 136 d.	0803	0842	0942	1040	1139	1239	1341	...	1441	1544	1641	1739	...	1840
Bridgend 136 a.	0822	0901	1001	1059	1158	1258	1400	...	1500	1605	1700	1758	...	1859
Port Talbot 136 a.	0835	0914	1013	1111	1210	1310	1412	...	1512	1619	1712	1810	...	1911
Neath 136 a.	0843	0922	1021	1118	1218	1318	1419	...	1520	1627	1719	1818	...	1919
Swansea 136 a.	0855	0934	1033	1131	1230	1330	1432	...	1532	1640	1734	1830	...	1932

⑥	⑥H	⑥	⑥	⑥	⑥	⑥	⑥	⑥
London Paddington 130 132 d.	1718	1748	1818	1848	1915	1948	2048	2202
Reading 130 132 d.	1743	1813	1843	1913	1941	2013	2113	2227
Didcot Parkway 130 132 d.	1757	|	1857	|	1955	|	|	2240
Swindon 130 132 d.	1814	1840	1915	1940	2014	2040	2140	2257
Bristol Parkway 132 d.	1838	1904	1940	2004	2039	2104	2205	2319
Newport ‡ a.	1900	1923	1959	2023	2058	2123	2231	...
Cardiff Central ‡ a.	1914	1940	2013	2039	2111	2138	2250	...
Cardiff Central 136 d.	1919	1942	2015	2040	2113	2140	2251	...
Bridgend 136 a.	1938	2001	2034	2059	2132	2159	2310	...
Port Talbot 136 a.	1950	2013	2046	2111	2144	2211	2322	...
Neath 136 a.	1958	2020	2053	2119	2152	2219	2330	...
Swansea 136 a.	2012	2033	2106	2131	2204	2231	2343	...

⑦	⑦	⑦	⑦H	⑦	⑦	⑦H	⑦	⑦H	⑦	⑦	⑦	⑦	⑦	⑦	⑦	⑦	⑦
London Paddington 130 132 d.	...	0833	0937	1016	1043	1143	1243	1343	1413	1443	1543	1643	1743	1843	1943	2043	2143
Reading 130 132 d.	...	0859	1003	1043	1109	1209	1309	1409	1440	1509	1609	1709	1809	1909	2009	2109	2209
Didcot Parkway 130 132 d.	...	0915	1016	1058	|	|	|	|	1455	|	|	|	|	|	2022	2123	2223
Swindon 130 132 d.	...	0931	1033	1117	1136	1236	1336	1436	1515	1536	1637	1736	1837	1936	2039	2140	2240
Bristol Parkway 132 d.	0858	0955	1100	1146	1201	1300	1400	1459	1539	1601	1702	1800	1901	2000	2103	2205	2302
Newport ‡ a.	0924	1014	1120	...	1221	1321	1419	1525	1558	1620	1725	1820	1921	2021	2122	2224	2321
Cardiff Central ‡ a.	0943	1031	1134	...	1235	1335	1433	1540	1613	1634	1738	1834	1935	2032	2136	2238	2336
Cardiff Central 136 d.	0945	1036	1135	...	1236	1337	1437	1540	...	1637	1740	1838	1936	2036	2137	2239	2338
Bridgend 136 a.	1004	1056	1155	...	1255	1356	1456	1600	...	1659	1759	1857	1955	2055	2156	2258	2357
Port Talbot 136 a.	1017	1108	1207	...	1307	1411	1508	1612	...	1715	1811	1909	2007	2107	2208	2310	0010
Neath 136 a.	1025	1116	1214	...	1315	1419	1516	1620	...	1722	1818	1916	2015	2115	2215	2318	0018
Swansea 136 a.	1036	1129	1229	...	1329	1431	1529	1632	...	1735	1831	1929	2027	2127	2228	2330	0031

Ⓐ	ⒶC	Ⓐ	Ⓐ	Ⓐ	Ⓐ	Ⓐ		Ⓐ	Ⓐ	Ⓐ	ⒶH	Ⓐ	Ⓐ	Ⓐ	Ⓐ	Ⓐ	Ⓐ	Ⓐ	Ⓐ✕	Ⓐ	Ⓐ	Ⓐ	Ⓐ	Ⓐ	Ⓐ
Swansea 136 d.	...	0346	0459	0528	0558	0628	...	0657	0720	0743	0823	...	0923	...	1023	...	1123	...	1223	...	1323	...	1422	...	1523
Neath 136 d.	...	0358	0511	0540	0610	0640	...	0710	0732	0755	0835	...	0935	...	1035	...	1135	...	1235	...	1335	...	1435	...	1535
Port Talbot 136 d.	...	0405	0518	0547	0617	0647	...	0717	0739	0802	0842	...	0942	...	1042	...	1142	...	1242	...	1342	...	1442	...	1542
Bridgend 136 d.	...	0427	0531	0600	0630	0700	...	0730	0752	0815	0855	...	0955	...	1055	...	1155	...	1255	...	1355	...	1455	...	1555
Cardiff Central 136 a.	...	0504	0551	0620	0650	0720	...	0750	0812	0835	0915	...	1015	...	1115	...	1215	...	1315	...	1415	...	1515	...	1615
Cardiff Central ‡ d.	...	0507	0554	0623	0653	0723	...	0755	0817	0841	0918	0951	1018	1041	1118	1150	1218	1254	1318	1353	1418	1454	1518	1554	1618
Newport ‡ d.	...	0525	0607	0637	0706	0737	...	0808	0830	0854	0931	1004	1033	1055	1131	1203	1230	1307	1330	1406	1431	1507	1531	1607	1630
Bristol Parkway 132 d.	0503	0554	0628	0659	0729	0802	...	0829	0856	0916	0956	1024	1056	1124t	1156	1225	1255	1328	1356	1427	1451	1527	1556	1627	1653
Swindon 130 132 d.	0528	0618	0653	0723	0753	0826	...	0853	0920	0940	1021	1048	1121	1149	1220	1249	1320	1352	1420	1451	1517	1551	1620	1651	1719
Didcot Parkway 130 132 d.	0546	0636	|	|	|	|	...	|	|	|	|	1105	|	|	|	|	|	|	|	|	|	|	|	|	1735
Reading 130 132 a.	0558	0648	0718	0749	0818	|	...	0919	0945	1006	1045	1118	1145	1214	1245	1314	1345	1416	1445	1515	1544	1616	1645	1717	1747
London Paddington 130 132 a.	0626	0716	0744	0816	0844	0914	...	0944	1014	1034	1112	1144	1212	1240	1312	1341	1414	1444	1512	1541	1609	1641	1714	1744	1814

	Ⓐ	Ⓐ	Ⓐ	Ⓐ	Ⓐ	①–④	⑤	Ⓐ	⑤	①–④
Swansea 136 d.	...	1623	...	1723	1823	1923	1923	2023	2123	2123
Neath 136 d.	...	1635	...	1735	1835	1935	1935	2035	2135	2135
Port Talbot 136 d.	...	1642	...	1742	1842	1942	1942	2042	2142	2142
Bridgend 136 d.	...	1655	...	1756	1855	1955	1955	2055	2155	2155
Cardiff Central 136 a.	...	1715	...	1816	1915	2017	2017	2115	2215	2215
Cardiff Central ‡ d.	1654	1720	1754	1818	1918	2021	2021	2120	2218	2218
Newport ‡ d.	1707	1735	1807	1831	1931	2034	2034	2133	2233	2233
Bristol Parkway 132 d.	1729	1756	1828	1853	1955	2055	2055	2154	2255	2302
Swindon 130 132 d.	1753	1820	1851	1917	2020	2119	2119	2219	...	...
Didcot Parkway 130 132 d.	|	|	|	1934	|	|	|	|	...	...
Reading 130 132 a.	1817	1847	1916	1946	2044	2144	2144	2243	...	...
London Paddington 130 132 a.	1844	1914	1944	2015	2110	2209	2214	2309	...	...

⑥	⑥	⑥	⑥	⑥	⑥	⑥		⑥	⑥H	⑥	⑥	⑥	⑥K	⑥	⑥
Swansea 136 d.	0356	0525	0552	0623	0644	0723	...	0741	0822	0923	1022	1124	1222	1324	...
Neath 136 d.	0408	0537	0604	0635	0655	0735	...	0753	0834	0935	1034	1136	1234	1336	...
Port Talbot 136 d.	0415	0544	0611	0642	0703	0745	...	0801	0841	0943	1042	1144	1242	1344	...
Bridgend 136 d.	0428	0557	0624	0655	0716	0759	...	0815	0854	0956	1055	1157	1255	1356	...
Cardiff Central 136 a.	0449	0618	0645	0716	0737	0820	...	0838	0915	1017	1116	1218	1316	1417	...
Cardiff Central ‡ d.	0514	0620	0647	0718	0741	0822	...	0841	0918	1019	1118	1221	1318	1421	1441
Newport ‡ d.	0526	0633	0700	0732	0755	0835	...	0855	0934	1032	1133	1234	1332	1434	1455
Bristol Parkway 132 d.	0555	0656	0721	0757	0821	0856	...	0919	0957	1057	1157	1257	1357	1457	1518
Swindon 130 132 d.	0619	0720	0747	0821	0846	0921	...	0947	1021	1121	1221	1321	1421	1521	1546
Didcot Parkway 130 132 d.	0635	|	0803	|	0903	|	...	1004	|	|	|	|	|	|	1605
Reading 130 132 a.	0648	0745	0916	0846	0916	0946	...	1017	1046	1146	1246	1346	1446	1547	1619
London Paddington 130 132 a.	0714	0812	0841	0912	0942	1012	...	1041	1111	1211	1311	1411	1512	1613	1644

⑥	⑥	⑥	⑥	⑥K	⑥	⑥	⑥
Swansea 136 d.	1423	1526	1622	1726	1822	1926	2022
Neath 136 d.	1435	1538	1634	1738	1834	1938	2034
Port Talbot 136 d.	1443	1546	1642	1747	1842	1946	2042
Bridgend 136 d.	1455	1558	1655	1800	1855	1959	2055
Cardiff Central 136 a.	1517	1619	1716	1821	1917	2020	2116
Cardiff Central ‡ d.	1518	1623	1718	1822	1919	2022	2118
Newport ‡ d.	1532	1636	1731	1835	1932	2035	2131
Bristol Parkway 132 d.	1557	1657	1757	1857	1957	2056	2152
Swindon 130 132 d.	1621	1721	1821	1921	2021	2120	2214
Didcot Parkway 130 132 d.	|	|	|	|	|	2136	...
Reading 130 132 a.	1646	1747	1846	1946	2046	2149	...
London Paddington 130 132 a.	1712	1811	1913	2011	2111	2216	...

⑦	⑦	⑦	⑦	⑦	⑦	⑦		⑦	⑦H	⑦	⑦	⑦H	⑦	⑦	⑦H	⑦	⑦	⑦H
Swansea 136 d.	...	0755	...	0837	0923	1022	...	1123	1223	1323	1422	1523	...	1624	1724	1824	1924	2019
Neath 136 d.	...	0807	...	0849	0935	1035	...	1135	1235	1335	1434	1535	...	1636	1736	1836	1936	2031
Port Talbot 136 d.	...	0814	...	0856	0942	1042	...	1142	1242	1342	1441	1542	...	1643	1743	1842	1942	2037
Bridgend 136 d.	...	0827	...	0909	0955	1055	...	1155	1255	1355	1454	1555	...	1656	1756	1856	1956	2051
Cardiff Central 136 a.	...	0848	...	0931	1016	1116	...	1216	1316	1418	1515	1616	...	1717	1817	1917	2017	2112
Cardiff Central ‡ d.	...	0850	...	0935	1020	1120	...	1220	1320	1420	1516	1620	1650	1720	1820	1920	2020	2120
Newport ‡ d.	...	0908	...	0953	1033	1133	...	1233	1334	1433	1529	1633	1705	1733	1835	1934	2033	2133
Bristol Parkway 132 d.	...	0934	1003	1021	1055	1155	...	1255	1355	1455	1555	1655	1727	1755	1858	1955	2055	2155
Swindon 130 132 d.	0838	1000	1027	1045	1118	1219	...	1319	1419	1520	1619	1719	1751	1819	1923	2019	2119	2219
Didcot Parkway 130 132 d.	0855	|	|	1101	|	|	...	|	|	|	|	|	1809	|	|	2036	2135	2236
Reading 130 132 a.	0910	1025	1053	1114	1144	1245	...	1344	1444	1546	1644	1745	1823	1844	1948	2049	2148	2249
London Paddington 130 132 a.	0936	1052	1120	1139	1208	1309	...	1409	1509	1614	1709	1813	1850	1909	2014	2114	2214	2327

C – From Bristol Temple Meads (dep. 0453).
F – From Bristol Temple Meads (dep. 0703).
G – 🛏12 and ✕ London - Carmarthen (Table **136**).
H – To/from Carmarthen (Table **136**).
K – Until Sept. 10 to/from Carmarthen (Table **136**).

f – Arrives 5–7 minutes earlier.
j – Arrives 1414.
r – Arrives 0716.
s – Calls to set down only.
t – Arrives 1115.

◇ – Via Bristol Temple Meads (see Table **132**).
‡ – For additional services see Tables **117**, **118** and **149**.

GW 2nd class — SWINDON - WESTBURY — 134

km			Ⓐ A	Ⓐ	Ⓐ	Ⓐ	Ⓐ	Ⓐ	Ⓐ T	Ⓐ		⑥ F	⑥	⑥	⑥	⑥	⑥	⑥	⑥	⑥	⑥ a		⑦	⑦ E	⑦ G	⑦ C	⑦ H	⑦	⑦
0	**Swindon** .... **132** d.	Ⓐ	0611	0845	1105	1315	1514	1736	1852	2045	⑥	0808	0835	0935	1105	1305	1510	1603	1735	1935	2107	⑦	0914	1141	1341	1544	1744	1929	2125
27	Chippenham **132** d.		0627	0900	1121	1330	1530	1752	1907	2100		0824	0857f	0950	1121	1321	1530f	1618	1750	1950	2122		0930	1156	1356	1559	1759	1945	2140
37	Melksham .... d.		0636	0910	1131	1340	1539	1803	1917	2110		0834	0906	1000	1130	1330	1539	1628	1800	2000	2132		0940	1205	1405	1609	1809	1954	2150
46	Trowbridge.. **140** d.		0646	0919	1140	1349	1549	1812	1927	2119		0843	0916	1009	1140	1340	1549	1637	1809	2009	2141		0949	1214	1414	1618	1818	2004	2159
52	**Westbury** ... **140** a.		0653	0926	1147	1356	1558	1820	1934	2126		0850	0923	1016	1148	1348	1556	1644	1817	2016	2149		0956	1223	1421	1625	1825	2011	2205

		Ⓐ	Ⓐ D	Ⓐ	Ⓐ	Ⓐ	Ⓐ	Ⓐ	Ⓐ	Ⓐ B		⑥	⑥	⑥	⑥	⑥	⑥	⑥	⑥	⑥ F		⑦ W	⑦	⑦ G r	⑦ G t	⑦ C	⑦ C	⑦ C	⑦
Westbury .... **140** d.	Ⓐ	0517	0705	0737	0946	1217	1416	1625	1834	2006	⑥	0744	0834	1007	1205	1405	1505	1636	1835	2117	⑦	0820	1044	1245	1248	1452	1652	1835	2024
Trowbridge .. **140** d.		0523	0711	0743	0952	1223	1422	1631	1840	2012		0750	0840	1013	1211	1411	1511	1642	1841	2123		0826	1049	1252	1255	1458	1658	1841	2030
Melksham .... d.		0533	0721	0753	1002	1233	1432	1641	1850	2022		0800	0850	1023	1221	1423	1521	1652	1851	2133		0836	1100	1301	1306	1508	1708	1851	2040
Chippenham **132** d.		0543	0731	0803	1014	1243	1442	1651	1904	2032		0810	0905f	1038f	1237f	1438	1532	1708f	1905f	2143		0846	1111	1311	1316	1518	1718	1901	2050
Swindon ..... **132** a.		0559	0747	0819	1034	1259	1501	1708	1921	2050		0826	0923	1054	1255	1454	1549	1725	1925	2159		0903	1128	1329	1332	1534	1734	1917	2106

A – To Southampton Central (Table **140**).
B – To Cheltenham Spa (Table **130**).
C – To/from Frome (Table **139**).
D – From Salisbury to Cheltenham Spa (Tables **140** and **130**).
E – Until Oct. 23 conveys (2) to Weymouth (Table **139**).
F – Until Sept. 10 to/from Weymouth (Table **139**).
G – To/from Weymouth (Table **139**).
H – To Salisbury (Table **140**).
K– Until Sept. 10 conveys (2) from Warminster (Table **140**).
T – From Gloucester to Salisbury (Tables **140** and **130**).
W – From Warminster (Table **140**).
a – Runs 58–59 minutes later until Sept. 10.
f – Arrives 5–7 minutes earlier.
r – From Oct. 23.
t – Until Oct. 23.

WELSH LONG DISTANCE BUS SERVICES — 135

Traws Cymru operate several long distance bus services through Wales linking a number of main towns not served by rail services. The principal routes are shown below with the number of through journeys each way each day. For full timings and fares: ✆ +44 (0) 300 200 22 33; www.trawscymru.info

Service T1: Aberystwyth - Aberaeron - Lampeter/Llanbedr - Carmarthen and v.v.: on ⚒ 10 journeys; ⑦ 4 journeys.

Service T2: Aberystwyth - Machynlleth - Dolgellau - Minfford (for Portmeirion) - Porthmadog - Caernarfon - Bangor and v.v.: on ⚒ 7 journeys; ⑦ 2 journeys.

Service T3: Wrexham - Ruabon - Llangollen 🚂 - Corwen 🚂 - Bala 🚂 - Dolgellau - Barmouth and v.v.: on ⚒ 7 journeys; ⑦ 4 journeys.

Service T4: Newtown - Llandrindod Wells - Builth Wells - Brecon - Merthyr Tydfil* (- Cardiff*) and v.v.: on ⚒ 7 journeys; ⑦ 4 journeys.

Service T5: Aberystwyth - Aberaeron - New Quay - Cardigan - Fishguard - Haverfordwest and v.v.: on ⚒ 5 journeys; ⑦ No service.

Service T6: Brecon - Ystradgynlais - Neath - Swansea and v.v.: on ⚒ 10 journeys; ⑦ 5 journeys.

Service T10: Bangor - Betws y Coed - Corwen and v.v.: on ⚒ 5 journeys; ⑦ 3 journeys.

Service T11: Haverfordwest - St Davids - Fishguard and v.v.: on ⚒ 6 journeys; ⑦ No service.

Service T12: Machynlleth - Newtown - Welshpool - Oswestry (- Ruabon - Wrexham) and v.v.: on ⚒ 5 journeys; ⑦ No service.

Service T14: Brecon - Hay-on-Wye - Hereford and v.v.: on ⚒ 4 journeys; ⑦ No service.

Other short workings also operate on most services.

* – Frequent local trains also operate Merthyr Tydfil - Cardiff and v.v.

🚂 – Heritage and Tourist Railways: **Llangollen Railway**: Llangollen - Corwen and v.v. (16km): ✆ +44 (0) 1978 860 979; www.llangollen-railway.co.uk
Bala Lake Railway: (narrow gauge) Bala - Llanuwchllyn and v.v. (7km): ✆ +44 (0) 1678 540 666; www.bala-lake-railway.co.uk

AW 2nd class — CARDIFF - SWANSEA - SOUTH WEST WALES — 136

km			Ⓐ	Ⓐ	Ⓐ	Ⓐ	Ⓐ	Ⓐ	Ⓐ	Ⓐ	Ⓐ	Ⓐ P 🍷	Ⓐ	Ⓐ K 🍷	Ⓐ 🍷	Ⓐ 🍷	Ⓐ 🍷	Ⓐ 🍷	Ⓐ 🍷	Ⓐ 🍷	Ⓐ 🍷	Ⓐ 🍷	Ⓐ 🍷	Ⓐ 🍷	Ⓐ C 🍷	Ⓐ 🍷	Ⓐ 🍷
	Manchester Picc **149**.d.	Ⓐ	...	...	...	...	...	...	...	...	...	...	...	...	...	0630	...	0731	0831	...	0931	1031	1131	...	...	1231	...
0	**Cardiff** Central ..... **134** d.		...	...	...	...	...	...	0535	0631	...	0750	...	0900	...	1006	...	1049	1149	...	1256	1345	1446	...	1514	1546	1602
32	Bridgend .... **134** d.		...	...	...	...	...	...	0606	0659	...	0810	...	0920	...	1026	...	1109	1210	...	1316	1404	1506	...	1533	1606	1622
52	Port Talbot .... **134** d.		...	...	...	...	...	...	0622	0716	...	0825	...	0935	...	1038	...	1124	1222	...	1331	1416	1518	...	1549	1618	1639
61	Neath .... **134** d.		...	...	...	...	...	...	0633	0729	...	0836	...	0945	...	1045	...	1135	1229	...	1341	1424	1525	...	|	1626	1650
73	**Swansea** .... **134** a.		...	...	...	...	...	...	0650	0749	...	0853	...	1002	...	1059	...	1152	1243	...	1357	1437	1539	...	|	1639	1707
73	**Swansea** .... **146** d.		...	...	...	...	...	0545	0654	0753	0817	0908	...	1006	1101	1107	1141	1156	1255	1351	1402	1457	1543	1600	|	1643	1711
91	Llanelli .... **146** d.		...	...	...	...	...	0604	0713	0812	0834	0927	...	1025	1118	1126	1201	1215	1315	1408	1420	1516	1602	1620	1624	1702	1731
124	**Carmarthen** .... a.		...	...	...	...	...	0637	0744	0844	|	0958	...	1054	|	1154	1229	1245c	1340	1439	1450	1542	1635	1648	...	1732	1803
124	**Carmarthen** .... d.		0450	0530	0550	0600	...	0641	0748	0848	|	1003	1055	...	|	1159	1251	...	1345	1444	...	1546	...	1652	...	1736	1807
147	Whitland .... d.		0506	0547	0606	0615	...	0659	0803	0904	0912	1018	1112	...	1153	1215	1308	...	1400	1501	...	1601	...	1709	...	1751	1821
172	Tenby .... d.		|	0624a	|	|	...	0732t	|	0943a	|	|	1143	...	|	|	1345a	...	|	1538a	...	|	...	1765a	...	|	|
191	**Pembroke Dock** ...... a.		|	0656	|	|	...	0807	|	1013	|	|	1216	...	|	|	1417	...	|	1611	...	|	...	1819	...	|	|
166	Clarbeston Road ..... ⊗ d.		0520	...	0620	0630	0720	...	0818	...	0927	1033	...	...	1206	1229	...	...	1415	...	...	1616	...	...	...	1806	1838
174	Haverfordwest .... d.		0532	...	|	0638	|	...	0826	...	|	1041	...	...	|	1238	...	...	1423	...	...	1625	...	...	...	1814	|
189	**Milford Haven** .... a.		0552	...	|	0658	|	...	0843	...	|	1103	...	...	|	1300	...	...	1445	...	...	1643	...	...	...	1836	|
191	**Fishguard** Harbour .. a.		...	...	0645	...	0744	...	...	...	0951	...	...	...	1230	...	...	...	...	...	...	...	...	...	...	...	1902

	Ⓐ 🍷	Ⓐ 🍷	Ⓐ 🍷	Ⓐ	Ⓐ 🍷	Ⓐ	Ⓐ A	Ⓐ 🍷	Ⓐ A	Ⓐ	⑤	①–④	Ⓐ		⑥	⑥	⑥	⑥	⑥	⑥	⑥	⑥ b	⑥ b	⑥ d	⑥ d	⑥ P 🍷	⑥ K 🍷
Manchester Picc **149** . d.	...	1331	1431	...	1531	...	...	1631	...	...	1831	1831	...	⑥	...	...	...	...	...	...	...	...	...	...	...	...	...
Cardiff Central ...... **134** d.	...	1704	1747	1808	1905	...	1941	1948	...	2108	2212	2218	2315		...	...	...	...	...	...	0535	0643	...	0643	0643	0756	0858
Bridgend .... **134** d.	...	1729	1807	1833	1926	...	2001	2007	...	2128	2238	2246	2347		...	...	...	...	...	...	0608	0703	...	0703	0703	0816	0919
Port Talbot .... **134** d.	...	1743	1822	1849	1941	...	2013	2019	...	2145	2250	2259	0003		...	...	...	...	...	...	0623	0718	...	0718	0718	0830	0933
Neath .... **134** d.	...	1755	1829	1901	1952	...	2020	2026	←	2153	2257	|	0016		...	...	...	...	...	...	0634	0729	...	0729	0729	0838	0945
Swansea .... **134** a.	...	1811	1842	1917	2010	...	2032	2041	2032	2208	2311	|	0034		...	...	...	...	...	...	0652	0747	...	0747	0747	0851	1002
Swansea .... **146** d.	1752	1816	1846	*1934*	2013	...	→	2044	2104	2225	2318	|	0051		...	...	...	...	...	0545	0655	0755	...	0752	0752	0902	1005
Llanelli .... **146** d.	1812	1834	1905	*1954*	2032	...	▬	2103	2119	2245	2337	2333	0109s		...	...	...	...	...	0604	0714	0810	...	0812	0812	0921	1023
Carmarthen .... **146** a.	1847	1905	1931	*2029*	2058	...	Ⓐ	2134	2152	2318	0010	0004	0142		...	...	...	...	...	0637	0746	0842	...	0844	0844	0952	1052
Carmarthen .... d.	...	1909	1935	...	...	2103	2110	2142	...	2320f	...	...	...		0449	0530	0550	0600	...	0641	0753	0845	0855	0848	0848	0957	...
Whitland .... d.	...	1924	1950	...	...	2119	2126	2158	...	2336f	...	...	...		0505	0547	0606	0615	...	0700	0808	0900	0911	0907	0908	1014	...
Tenby .... a.	...	1953	|	...	...	|	2154	|	...	|	...	...	...		|	0624a	|	|	...	0733t	|	0942e	|	0942t	|	|	...
Pembroke Dock ...... a.	...	...	|	...	...	|	2225	|	...	|	...	...	...		|	0656	|	|	...	0805	|	1013	|	1013	|	|	...
Clarbeston Road ...... ⊗ d.	...	...	2005	...	...	2134	...	2212	...	2351f	...	...	...		0519	...	0621	0630	0720	...	0823	...	0928	...	0923	1029	...
Haverfordwest .... d.	...	...	2014	...	...	|	...	2223	...	2359f	...	...	...		0531	...	|	0638	|	...	0831	...	|	...	|	1037	...
Milford Haven .... a.	...	...	2036	...	...	|	...	2246	...	0020f	...	...	...		0552	...	|	0658	|	...	0850	...	|	...	|	1059	...
Fishguard Harbour .. a.	...	...	...	...	...	2159	...	...	...	...	...	...	...		...	...	0646	...	0744	...	...	...	0951	...	0947	...	...

	⑥	⑥ 🍷	⑥ 🍷	⑥ A	⑥ 🍷	⑥ 🍷	⑥ 🍷	⑥ 🍷	⑥ 🍷	⑥ 🍷	⑥ 🍷	⑥ 🍷	⑥	⑥ 🍷	⑥ 🍷	⑥ 🍷		⑥ 🍷	⑥ 🍷	⑥ A	⑥	⑥ 🍷	⑥ S	⑥	⑥	⑥	⑥
Manchester Picc **149** . d.	...	...	0630	...	...	0731	0830	...	0931	1031	...	1131	...	1231	...	1331	...	1431	1531	...	...	1631	...	...	1831	...	...
Cardiff Central ...... **134** d.	...	...	1000	1040	...	1059	1204	...	1257	1403	...	1505	1513	1540	1604	1704	...	1804	1903	1919	...	2001	...	2104	2208	2227	*2251*
Bridgend .... **134** d.	...	...	1020	1100	...	1119	1224	...	1318	1424	...	1525	1534	1601	1623	1725	...	1824	1924	1939	...	2021	...	2124	2235	2255	*2311*
Port Talbot .... **134** d.	...	...	1032	1112	...	1134	1235	...	1332	1436	...	1537	1550	1615	1638	1739	...	1839	1939	1952	...	2033	...	2139	2247	2311	*2323*
Neath .... **134** d.	...	...	1039	1119	...	1145	1242	...	1344	1443	...	1544	1601	1622	1646	1751	...	1847	1951	2000	...	|	...	2147	2254	2322	*2331*
Swansea .... **134** a.	...	...	1054c	1131	...	1202	1256	...	1401	1456	...	1600	1620	1635	1659	1807	...	1900	2009	2012	...	|	...	2159	2307	2340	*2343*
Swansea .... **146** d.	...	1059	1105	1139b	1154	1205	1300	1353	1405	1501	1552	1604	...	1639	1704	1811	...	1905	2013	2025	...	|	...	2226	2311	2343	0012
Llanelli .... **146** d.	...	1116	1125	1155b	1214	1224	1319	1410	1423	1520	1609	1623	...	1658	1722	1830	...	1924	2032	2041	...	2103	2140	2246	2330	0003	0031s
Carmarthen .... **146** a.	...	|	1151	1229b	1244	1253c	1345	1440	1452c	1546	1641	1657c	...	1729	1753	1901	...	1950	2058	2109	...	2135	2206	2320	0004	0036	0103
Carmarthen .... d.	1055	|	1156	...	1258	...	1401	1458	...	1550	1700	...	...	1733	1805	1905	...	1957	2100	...	2114	2203	...	...	...	...	...
Whitland .... d.	1111	1151	1215	...	1314	...	1416	1514	...	1605	1716	...	...	1748	1820	1921	...	2013	2115	...	2129	2218	...	...	...	...	...
Tenby .... a.	1145t	|	|	...	1345	...	|	1545	...	|	1747	...	...	|	|	1953	...	|	2143	...	|	|	...	...	...	...	...
Pembroke Dock ...... a.	1219	|	|	...	1418	...	|	1618	...	|	1820	...	...	|	|	2024	...	|	2216	...	|	|	...	...	...	...	...
Clarbeston Road ...... ⊗ d.	...	1204	1230	...	...	...	1431	...	...	1620	...	...	...	1803	1835	...	...	2028	...	...	2143	2236	...	...	...	...	...
Haverfordwest .... d.	...	|	1238	...	...	...	1439	...	...	1628	...	...	...	1811	|	...	...	2036	...	...	|	2244	...	...	...	...	...
Milford Haven .... a.	...	|	1300	...	...	...	1503	...	...	1650	...	...	...	1833	|	...	...	2059	...	...	|	2306	...	...	...	...	...
Fishguard Harbour .. a.	...	1230	...	...	...	...	...	...	...	...	...	...	...	...	1859	...	...	...	...	...	2208	...	...	...	...	...	...

FOR NOTES SEE NEXT PAGE ▶ ▶ ▶

136 CARDIFF - SWANSEA - SOUTH WEST WALES

2nd class AW

	⑦	⑦	⑦	⑦ 🍷	⑦ F🍷	⑦ A	⑦	⑦	⑦ 🍷	⑦ A	⑦ 🍷	⑦ 🍷	⑦ A	⑦	⑦ 🍷	⑦ 🍷	⑦	⑦ 🍷	⑦ 🍷	⑦ 🍷	⑦ 🍷	⑦	⑦ 🍷	⑦	⑦	⑦
Manchester Picc **149** d.	...	...	...	...	...	...	...	...	0930	...	1031	1130	...	...	1232	1330	...	1431	1431	1530	1630	...	1730	1830	...	1930
Cardiff Central ..... **134** d.	...	0804	...	0953	1114	1135	1204	...	1321	1337	1406	1450	1540	...	1602	1708	...	1805	1805	1902	1954	2019	2050	2149	2230	2300
Bridgend ..... **134** d.	...	0827	...	1023	1134	1156	1234	...	1341	1357	1426	1510	1601	...	1622	1729	...	1827	1827	1923	2015	2040	2111	2209	2250	2320
Port Talbot ..... **134** d.	...	0840	...	1039	1147	1208	1248	...	1356	1412	1441	1525	1613	...	1637	1744	...	1843	1843	1938	2030	2055	2126	2224	2303	2336
Neath ..... **134** d.	...	0848	...	1047	1155	1215	|	...	1403	1420	1448	1533	1621	...	1645	1751	...	1851	1851	1945	2037	2103	2134	2231	2312	2345
Swansea ..... **134** a.	...	0901	...	1100	1208	1229	|	...	1418	1431	1503	1548	1632	...	1659	1808	...	1906	1906	2001	2052	2117	2149	2246	2325	2359
Swansea ..... **146** d.	...	▬	1042	1104	1212	1237	|	1401	...	1439	1525	...	1640	1647	1703	...	1837	1916	1916	...	*2058*	2120	...	2250	2336	...
Llanelli ..... **146** d.	...	...	1059	1124	1232	1252	1320	1421	...	1454	1546	...	1655	1707	1723	...	1857	1936	1936	...	*2118*	2140	...	2309	2356	...
Carmarthen ..... a.	...	⑦	1126	1159	1304	1327	1348	1454	...	1528	1611	...	1723	1741	1750	...	1931	2006	2006	...	*2150*	2207	...	2342	0032	...
Carmarthen ..... d.	0955	1019	1130	1202	1308	...	1357	1459	...	...	1615	...	...	1744	1806	...	1935	2012	2012	...	*2155*	2214	...	...	...	...
Whitland ..... d.	1012	1036	1146	1219	1323	...	1413	1516	...	...	1631	...	...	1800	1822	...	1952	2032r	2037r	...	*2211*	2229	...	...	...	...
Tenby ..... d.	|	1106	|	|	|	...	|	1545	...	...	|	...	...	1829	|	...	|	|	2106	...	|	|	...	...	...	...
Pembroke Dock ..... a.	|	1137	|	|	|	...	|	1619	...	...	|	...	...	1903	|	...	|	|	2137	...	|	|	...	...	...	...
Clarbeston Road ..... ⊗ d.	1028	...	1159	1236	1337	...	1428	...	...	...	1646	...	...	...	1837	...	2008	2049	...	...	*2224*	2245	...	...	...	...
Haverfordwest ..... d.	1036	...	|	1244	|	...	1436	...	...	...	1654	...	...	...	1847	...	2017	2057	...	...	|	2253	...	...	...	...
Milford Haven ..... a.	1055	...	|	1303	|	...	1459	...	...	...	1713	...	...	...	1907	...	...	2120	...	...	|	2310	...	...	...	...
Fishguard Harbour .. a.	...	...	1225	...	1401	...	...	...	...	...	...	...	...	...	...	...	...	...	...	...	*2249*	...	...	...	...	...

	Ⓐ	Ⓐ 🍷	Ⓐ	Ⓐ 🍷	Ⓐ	Ⓐ 🍷		Ⓐ	Ⓐ 🍷	Ⓐ S	Ⓐ 🍷	Ⓐ 🍷	Ⓐ	Ⓐ 🍷	Ⓐ 🍷	Ⓐ 🍷	Ⓐ 🍷	Ⓐ S🍷	Ⓐ 🍷	Ⓐ 🍷	Ⓐ 🍷	Ⓐ 🍷	Ⓐ 🍷	Ⓐ P🍷	Ⓐ 🍷	Ⓐ 🍷
Fishguard Harbour .. d.	...	...	...	...	0650	...	...	...	0751	...	...	...	0954	...	...	...	...	...	1250	...	...	...	...	...	...	...
Milford Haven ..... d.	...	...	...	0554	|	0702	...	...	|	...	0908	...	|	...	1105	...	...	...	|	1300	...	...	1507	...	...	...
Haverfordwest ..... d.	...	...	...	0609	|	0717	...	...	|	...	0923	...	|	...	1120	...	...	...	|	1315	...	...	1522	...	...	...
Clarbeston Road ..... ⊗ d.	...	...	...	0617	0714	0725	...	...	0813	...	0931	...	1016	...	1128	...	...	...	1312	1323	...	...	1530	...	...	...
Pembroke Dock ..... d.	...	...	...	|	▬	|	...	0659	|	...	|	0909	|	...	|	1109	...	...	|	|	1309	...	|	...	1506	...
Tenby ..... d.	...	...	...	|	...	|	...	0729	|	...	|	0940	|	...	|	1142t	...	...	|	|	1342t	...	|	...	1537	...
Whitland ..... d.	...	...	...	0632	Ⓐ	0738	...	0757	0827	...	0945	1009	1029	...	1143	1210	...	...	1326	1337	1411	...	1545	...	1607	...
Carmarthen ..... a.	...	...	...	0647	A	0754	...	0813	0842	...	1001	1027	1046	...	1159	1228	...	...	1342	1353	1429	...	1601	...	1624	...
Carmarthen ..... d.	0500	0545	0603	0652	0725	0758	...	0817	0900	...	1005	1030	...	1100	1204	1232	1300	...	1347	1357	1432	1501	1605	...	1627	1655
Llanelli ..... **146** d.	0525	0615	0634	0722	0758	0828	...	0847	0930	0942	1030	1056	...	1130	1229	1259	1330	1357	1411	1422	1459	1531	1630	1644	1653	1725
Swansea ..... **146** a.	|	0635	0653	0741	0814	0847	...	0904	0950	1004	1047	1117	...	1149	1248	1318	1349	1417	|	1442	1518	1551	1650	1702	1717	1744
Swansea ..... **134** d.	|	0638	0710	0749	0823	0851	...	...	0954	...	1051	...	...	1152	1252	...	1354	...	|	1446	...	1554	1654	1705	...	1749
Neath ..... **134** d.	|	0653	0721	0800	0835	0906	...	...	1005	...	1106	...	...	1203	1306	...	1405	...	|	1500	...	1605	1705	1719	...	1804
Port Talbot ..... **134** d.	0558	0704	0729	0807	0842	0917	...	...	1013	...	1118	...	...	1211	1317	...	1413	...	1447	1511	...	1613	1712	1730	...	1815
Bridgend ..... **134** d.	0614	0719	0741	0822	0855	0932	...	...	1028	...	1132	...	...	1226	1332	...	1425	...	1503	1525	...	1625	1724	1745	...	1830
Cardiff Central ..... **134** a.	0651	0747	0805	0847	0915	0953	...	...	1049	...	1153	...	...	1247	1353	...	1446	...	1527	1547	...	1647	1745	1808	...	1852
Manchester Picc **149** a.	...	1111	...	1213	...	1313	...	...	...	...	1513	...	...	1613	1713	...	1813	...	...	1913	...	2019	2107	...	...	2215

	Ⓐ	Ⓐ	Ⓐ	Ⓐ	Ⓐ	Ⓐ	Ⓐ	Ⓐ	Ⓐ	Ⓐ	Ⓐ	⑥	⑥	⑥ 🍷	⑥ 🍷	⑥	⑥ 🍷	⑥	⑥ 🍷	⑥ 🍷	⑥ 🍷		⑥ 🍷	⑥ 🍷	⑥	⑥ 🍷
Fishguard Harbour .. d.	...	...	...	1905	...	...	...	...	2213	...	...	...	...	...	...	...	...	0650	...	...	0751	...	...	...	0954	...
Milford Haven ..... d.	1711	...	...	|	1915	...	2038	...	|	...	2325	0021	...	...	...	...	0554	|	0700	...	|	...	0900	...	|	...
Haverfordwest ..... d.	1726	...	...	|	1930	...	2053	...	|	...	2340	0036	...	...	...	...	0609	|	0716	...	|	...	0915	...	|	...
Clarbeston Road ..... ⊗ d.	1734	...	...	1927	1938	...	2101	...	2235	...	2348	0044	...	...	...	...	0617	0714	0723	...	0813	...	0923	...	1016	...
Pembroke Dock ..... d.	|	1709	...	|	|	...	|	2109	|	2227	|	|	...	...	...	...	|	▬	|	0659	|	...	|	0909	|	...
Tenby ..... d.	|	1740	...	|	|	2010	|	2155g	|	2257	|	|	...	...	...	...	|	...	|	0729	|	...	|	0939	|	...
Whitland ..... d.	1748	1809	...	1940	1952	2037	2115	2224	2251	2325	0003	0057	...	...	...	...	0631	⑥	0737	0756	0827	...	0938	1007	1029	...
Carmarthen ..... a.	1804	1827	...	1957	2008	2053	2132	2243	2308	2343	0020	0116	...	...	...	...	0646	A	0753	0813	0842	...	0954	1025	1046	...
Carmarthen ..... d.	1809	1831	1850	...	2012	2100	...	...	...	...	...	...	0244	0501	0554	0613	0651	0724	0756	0816	0859	...	0959	1029	...	1101
Llanelli ..... **146** d.	1839	1858	1922	...	2037	2130	...	...	...	...	...	...	0307	0526	0624	0643	0721	0757	0826	0844	0929	...	1024	1056	...	1131
Swansea ..... **146** a.	1858	1918	1945	...	2056	2150	...	...	...	...	...	...	0326	|	0644	0703	0740	0814	0845	0902	0949	...	1041	1119	...	1150
Swansea ..... **134** d.	1905	...	1949	...	2100	2154	...	...	...	...	...	...	...	|	0649	0708	0747	0822	0849	...	0954	...	1045	...	...	1159
Neath ..... **134** d.	1920	...	2000	...	2111	2208	...	...	...	...	...	...	...	|	0700	0724	0759	0834	0903	...	1006	...	1100	...	...	1210
Port Talbot ..... **134** d.	1931	...	2007	...	2118	2219	...	...	...	...	...	...	...	0559	0708	0735	0806	0841	0914	...	1014	...	1111	...	...	1218
Bridgend ..... **134** d.	1947	...	2021	...	2131	2233	...	...	...	...	...	...	...	0614	0722	0751	0821	0854	0929	...	1028	...	1126	...	...	1231
Cardiff Central ..... **134** a.	2010	...	2048j	...	2202	2300	...	...	...	...	...	...	...	0642	0746	0831	0847	0915	0950	...	1049	...	1149	...	...	1252
Manchester Picc **149** a.	...	...	...	...	...	...	...	...	...	...	...	...	...	1013	1113	...	1212	...	1313	...	1413	...	1513	...	...	1613

	⑥ A	⑥ 🍷	⑥ 🍷	⑥ 🍷	⑥ 🍷	⑥ 🍷	⑥ 🍷	⑥ 🍷	⑥ 🍷	⑥	⑥ 🍷	⑥ A	⑥ 🍷	⑥	⑥	⑥	⑥	⑥	⑥	⑥	⑥	⑥	⑥	⑦	⑦ 🍷	⑦
Fishguard Harbour .. d.	...	...	...	...	1241	...	...	...	...	...	...	...	...	...	...	...	1900	...	...	...	2212	...	...	...	...	...
Milford Haven ..... d.	...	1101	...	...	|	1300	...	...	1509	...	...	...	...	1706	...	...	|	1912	...	2116	|	...	2308	...	...	...
Haverfordwest ..... d.	...	1116	...	...	|	1315	...	...	1524	...	...	...	...	1721	...	...	|	1927	...	2131	|	...	2323	...	...	...
Clarbeston Road ..... ⊗ d.	...	1124	...	...	1303	1323	...	...	1532	...	...	...	...	1729	...	...	1922	1935	...	2139	2234	...	2331	...	...	...
Pembroke Dock ..... d.	...	|	1108	...	|	|	1309	...	|	...	1509	...	...	|	1712	...	|	|	1913	|	|	2218	|	...	...	...
Tenby ..... d.	...	|	1141t	...	|	|	1344t	...	|	...	1544t	...	...	|	1746t	...	|	|	1956v	|	|	2247	|	...	...	...
Whitland ..... d.	...	1139	1210	...	1316	1337	1413	...	1546	...	1612	...	...	1744	1814	...	1935	1949	2023	2154	2249	2315	2346	...	...	...
Carmarthen ..... a.	...	1155	1227	...	1332	1353	1430	...	1602	...	1631	...	...	1800	1832	...	1952	2005	2039	2211	2305	2333	0004	...	...	...
Carmarthen ..... d.	1128b	1159	1233	1300	1336	1358	1434	1501	1606	...	1634d	1635b	1701	1807	1836	1853	...	2009	2100	...	2309	...	...	...	...	0934
Llanelli ..... **146** d.	1156b	1224	1300	1330	1406	1423	1501	1531	1631	...	1700d	1703b	1731	1836	1902	1925	...	2034	2130	...	2339	...	...	...	...	0959
Swansea ..... **146** a.	1213b	1243	1317	1350	|	1443	1518	1550	1651	...	1721d	1720b	1750	1855	1923	1947	...	2053	2150	...	2359	...	...	...	...	1016
Swansea ..... **134** d.	1222	1247	...	1400	|	1447	...	1555	1658	1712	...	1726	1755	1900	...	1952	...	2057	2153	...	...	...	...	0825	0935	...
Neath ..... **134** d.	1234	1302	...	1411	|	1502	...	1606	1709	1727	...	1738	1806	1911	...	2003	...	2108	2208	...	...	...	...	0836	0946	...
Port Talbot ..... **134** d.	1242	1313	...	1419	1434	1514	...	1614	1717	1739	...	1747	1813	1919	...	2011	...	2115	2219	...	...	...	...	0845	0954	...
Bridgend ..... **134** d.	1255	1328	...	1431	1449	1529	...	1629	1732	1755	...	1800	1827	1933	...	2025	...	2127	2234	...	...	...	...	0902	1009	...
Cardiff Central ..... **134** a.	1316	1349	...	1453	1521	1551	...	1650	1753	1819	...	1821	1848	1956	...	2048	...	2149	2257	...	...	...	...	0924	1031	...
Manchester Picc **149** a.	...	1713	...	1814	...	1913	...	2012	2112	...	...	...	2213	...	...	...	...	...	...	...	...	...	...	1315	1417	...

	⑦ 🍷	⑦ 🍷	⑦	⑦ A	⑦ 🍷	⑦ 🍷	⑦	⑦	⑦ 🍷	⑦ A	⑦ 🍷	⑦	⑦ 🍷	⑦ A	⑦ 🍷	⑦ H🍷	⑦	⑦	⑦ A	⑦ S	⑦	⑦	⑦ F	⑦	⑦	⑦	⑦
Fishguard Harbour .. d.	...	...	...	...	...	...	...	1240	...	...	...	1420	...	...	...	...	...	...	...	...	...	...	...	...	...	2303	...
Milford Haven ..... d.	...	...	...	...	...	1124	...	|	...	...	1330	|	...	...	1531	...	...	1730	...	...	...	1940	...	2135	...	|	2323
Haverfordwest ..... d.	...	...	...	...	...	1139	...	|	...	...	1345	|	...	...	1546	...	...	1745	...	...	...	1955	...	2151	...	|	2338
Clarbeston Road ..... ⊗ d.	...	...	...	...	...	1147	...	1302	...	...	1353	1442	...	...	1554	...	...	1753	...	...	...	2003	...	2159	...	2325	2347
Pembroke Dock ..... d.	...	...	...	...	...	|	1158	|	...	...	|	|	...	...	|	...	1624	|	...	...	1904	|	...	|	2201	|	|
Tenby ..... d.	...	...	...	...	...	|	1228	|	...	...	|	|	...	...	|	...	1654	|	...	...	1934	|	...	|	2231	|	|
Whitland ..... d.	...	...	...	...	...	1202	1258	1315	...	...	1409	1455	...	...	1610	...	1724	1808	...	...	2003	2019	...	2213	2300	2338	0003
Carmarthen ..... a.	...	...	...	...	...	1217	1315	1333	...	...	1426	1512	...	...	1627	...	1742	1825	...	...	2020	2035	...	2230	2320	2355	0023
Carmarthen ..... d.	...	1030	1053	1127	...	1229	1319	1336	...	1417	1434	1517	...	1623	1639	...	1751	...	1920	...	2032	...	2116	2234	...	...	...
Llanelli ..... **146** d.	...	1055	1125	1154	...	1254	1351	1401	...	1451	1459	1549	...	1657	1709	...	1824	...	1954	2005	2104	...	2143	2304	...	...	...
Swansea ..... **146** a.	...	1117	1148	1210	...	1313	1416	|	...	1507	1520	1614	...	1712	1730	...	1849	...	2012	2026	2131	...	2206	2324	...	...	...
Swansea ..... **134** d.	1032	1130	...	1223	1251	1343	...	|	1457	1523	1531	...	1652	1724	1737	1829	*1924*	...	2019	2040	...	...	2210	2329	...	...	...
Neath ..... **134** d.	1043	1141	...	1235	1303	1354	...	1425	1508	1535	1542	...	1703	1736	1748	1841	*1936*	...	2031	2051	...	...	2221	2341	...	...	...
Port Talbot ..... **134** d.	1051	1149	...	1242	1310	1402	...	1434	1515	1542	1549	...	1711	1743	1755	1849	*1942*	...	2037	2059	...	...	2229	2349	...	...	...
Bridgend ..... **134** d.	1107	1204	...	1255	1326	1417	...	1448	1530	1555	1604	...	1726	1756	1810	1906	*1956*	...	2051	2114	...	...	2245	0005	...	...	...
Cardiff Central ..... **134** a.	1130	1227	...	1316	1348	1440	...	1510	1552	1616	1633	...	1749	1817	1833	1929	*2017*	...	2112	2137	...	...	2307	0030	...	...	...
Manchester Picc **149** a.	1515	1614	...	...	1717	1818	...	...	1915	...	2015	...	2115	...	2219	...	...	...	...	...	...	...	...	...	...	...	...

A – To/from London (operated by GW, see Table **134**). Conveys [12] and 🍷.
C – From Holyhead (Tables **149** and **160**).
F – To/from Hereford (Table **149**).
H – To Shrewsbury (Table **149**).
K – From Crewe (Table **149**).
P – To/from Chester (Table **149**).
S – From/to Shrewsbury (Table **146**).

a – Arrives 8–11 minutes earlier.
b – Until Sept. 10.
c – Connects with train in previous column.
d – From Sept. 17.
e – Arrives 0928.
f – ⑤ only.
g – Arrives 2138.

j – Arrives 2043 on ⑤.
r – Arrives 2029.
s – Calls to set down only.
t – Arrives 4–7 minutes earlier.
v – Arrives 1942.

⊗ – Trains call at Clarbeston Road on request (except trains starting or terminating there).

GW 2nd class — WORCESTER - GLOUCESTER - BRISTOL — 138

km		Ⓐ	Ⓐ	Ⓐ	ⒶA	Ⓐ	ⒶE	ⒶE	ⒶB	ⒶE	ⒶB	ⒶK	ⒶE	ⒶB	ⒶE	ⒶE	ⒶB	Ⓐ	ⒶK	Ⓐ	Ⓐ	Ⓐ	Ⓐ
0	**Great Malvern** 125 130 d.		...	...	...	...	...	...	0845	...	1041	...	1242	...	...	...	1643	...	...	...	...	2116	...
13	**Worcester** Foregate St 125 130 d.		...	...	...	...	...	...	0857	...	1053	...	1254	...	1451	...	1655	...	...	1853	...	2129	...
14	**Worcester** Shrub Hill 125 130 d.		0520	...	...	...	0707	*0724*	0900	...	1056	...	1257	...	1456	...	1658	...	...	1857	...	2133	2236
39	Ashchurch for Tewkesbury d.		0537	...	*0631*	...	0724	|	0917	...	1113	...	1314	...	1514	...	1715	1809	...	1913	...	2150	2253
48	Cheltenham Spa ◧ 116 d.		0547	0614	*0640*	...	0734	*0758*	0926	...	1123	...	1324	...	1524	...	1724	1919	...	1923	...	2200	2303
61	**Gloucester** ◧ a.		0556	0623	*0649*	...	0743	*0808*	0935	...	1133	...	1333	...	1535	...	1737	1827	...	1934	...	2209	2313
	Gloucester d.		0604	0626	0700	0731	0748	0842	0941	1040	1141	1242	1338	1440	1540	1641	1741	...	1842	1942	2041	2211	2317
115	**Bristol** Parkway 116 a.		0640	0701	0732	0808	0823	0917	1016	1114	1217	1317	1415	1515	1615	1716	1816	...	1917	2016	2116	2246	2346
124	**Bristol** Temple Meads 116 a.		0653	0716	0746	0827	0835	0932	1028	1126	1229	1329	1428	1528	1627	1728	1829	...	1930	2028	2129	2258	2358

	⑥	⑥	⑥
Great Malvern 125 130 d.		...	...
Worcester Foregate St 125 130 d.		...	...
Worcester Shrub Hill 125 130 d.		...	...
Ashchurch for Tewkesbury d.		...	*0634*
Cheltenham Spa ◧ 116 d.		*0603*	0655
Gloucester ◧ a.		*0612*	0705
Gloucester d.		0617	0708
Bristol Parkway 116 a.		0652	0742
Bristol Temple Meads 116 a.		0708	0754

	⑥	⑥E	⑥B	⑥E	⑥B	⑥B	⑥E	⑥B	⑥C	⑥E	⑥B	⑥K	⑥	⑥	⑥	⑥G
Great Malvern 125 130 d.	0636	...	...	...	...	...	...	...	...	...	...	...	...	...	...	2124
Worcester Foregate St. 125 130 d.	0649	...	0853	...	1053	...	1253	...	1453	...	1653	...	1853	...	...	2137
Worcester Shrub Hill 125 130 d.	0652	...	0856	...	1057	...	1257	...	1457	...	1657	...	1857	...	...	2140
Ashchurch for Tewkesbury d.	0708	...	0913	...	1113	...	1313	...	1513	...	1713	...	1913	...	...	2156
Cheltenham Spa ◧ 116 d.	0718	...	0923	...	1123	...	1323	...	1523	...	1723	...	1923	...	2152	2206
Gloucester ◧ a.	0727	...	0932	...	1132	...	1333	...	1532	...	1732	...	1932	...	2200	2215
Gloucester d.	0735	0840	0941	1041	1141	1241	1341	1441	1541	1641	1741	1841	1940	2111	2205	2217
Bristol Parkway 116 a.	0810	0915	1016	1116	1216	1316	1416	1516	1616	1716	1816	1916	2015	2144	2230	2252
Bristol Temple Meads 116 a.	0830	0928	1029	1128	1228	1328	1428	1528	1628	1728	1828	1928	2027	2158	2240	2304

	⑦	⑦	⑦	⑦	⑦	⑦	⑦	⑦	⑦	⑦
Great Malvern 125 130 d.		...	...	...	...	...	...	...	...	...
Worcester Foregate St. 125 130 d.		...	...	...	1344	1547	1737	1941	...	2158
Worcester Shrub Hill 125 130 d.		...	0957	1154	1357f	1554r	1757j	1953f	...	2218j
Ashchurch for Tewkesbury d.		...	1014	1211	1414	1614	1814	2014	...	2235
Cheltenham Spa ◧ 116 d.		0925	1023	1222	1423	1623	1823	2025	2152	2245
Gloucester ◧ a.		0935	1033	1232	1434	1634	1833	2036	2200	2255
Gloucester d.		0940	1040	1238	1441	1641	1841	2041	2205	2305
Bristol Parkway 116 a.		1016	1116	1312	1516	1714	1916	2116	2230	2341
Bristol Temple Meads 116 a.		1028	1128	1324	1528	1727	1928	2131	2240	2353

	Ⓐ	Ⓐ	Ⓐ	ⒶS	ⒶF	ⒶB	ⒶB	ⒶF	ⒶE	ⒶF	ⒶE	ⒶB	ⒶE	ⒶB	ⒶE	ⒶB	Ⓐ	ⒶA	Ⓐ	Ⓐ	Ⓐ
Bristol Temple Meads 116 d.		...	0610	0624	0742	0837	0939	1041	1137	1238	1339	1439	1538	1640	1738	1842	1938	2008	2057	2144	2246
Bristol Parkway 116 d.		...	0622	0634	0755	0850	0951	1052	1149	1250	1351	1455	1551	1656	1751	1856	1950	2020	2111	2157	2302
Gloucester a.		...	0659	0704	0832	0927	1028	1130	1226	1329	1430	1532	1629	1733	1829	1932	2030	2055	2148	2236	2339
Gloucester ◧ d.		0604	0712	0708	...	0934	...	1138	*1245*	1336	...	1536	*1645*	1738	*1845*	1939	...	*2123*	2151	*2249*	...
Cheltenham Spa ◧ 116 d.		0615	0723	0718	...	0945	...	1148	*1255*	1348	...	1547	*1655*	1750	*1855*	1950	...	*2132*	2201	*2258*	...
Ashchurch for Tewkesbury d.		0623	0732	0725	...	0953	...	1156	*1303*	1356	...	1555	*1703*	1758	*1903*	1958	...	*2141*	2209	...	...
Worcester Shrub Hill 125 130 a.		0640	0750	...	...	1010	...	1212	...	1413	...	1613	...	1820	...	2015t	...	*2208*	2227	...	...
Worcester Foregate St. 125 130 a.		0643	0756	...	...	1016	...	1217	...	1416	...	1617	...	1823	...	2025	...	...	...	...	...
Great Malvern 125 130 a.		...	0810	...	...	1028	...	1229	...	...	...	1629	...	...	...	2040	...	...	...	...	...

	⑥	⑥	⑥	⑥S	⑥
Bristol Temple Meads 116 d.		...	0615	...	0638
Bristol Parkway 116 d.		...	0624	...	0650
Gloucester a.		...	0650	...	0730
Gloucester ◧ d.		0521	0659	0705	0739
Cheltenham Spa ◧ 116 d.		0531	0707	0714	0749
Ashchurch for Tewkesbury d.		0539	...	0722	0757
Worcester Shrub Hill 125 130 a.		0556	...	...	0814c
Worcester Foregate St. 125 130 a.		0559	...	...	0833
Great Malvern 125 130 a.		0616	...	...	...

	⑥F	⑥F	⑥B	⑥B	⑥E	⑥F	⑥E	⑥B	⑥E	⑥B	⑥D	⑥H	⑥B	⑥T	⑥	⑥
Bristol Temple Meads 116 d.	0739	0838	0938	1039	1139	1239	1339	1439	1539	1639	1738	1839	1939	2009	2108	2211
Bristol Parkway 116 d.	0751	0851	0951	1051	1151	1251	1351	1451	1551	1650	1751	1850	1951	2021	2119	2223
Gloucester a.	0830	0929	1028	1129	1230	1329	1430	1529	1630	1728	1830	1928	2029	2057	2157	2259
Gloucester ◧ d.	*0849*	0937	...	1138	*1245*	1338	...	1538	*1645*	1738	...	1938	2036	*2107*	*2218*	...
Cheltenham Spa ◧ 116 d.	*0858*	0948	...	1148	*1255*	1348	...	1548	*1655*	1748	...	1948	2046	*2118*	*2228*	...
Ashchurch for Tewkesbury d.	...	0956	...	1156	*1303*	1356	...	1556	*1703*	1756	...	1956	...	*2125*	...	...
Worcester Shrub Hill 125 130 a.	...	1012t	...	1212	...	1412	...	1612	...	1813	...	2012d	...	...	...	...
Worcester Foregate St. 125 130 a.	...	1020	...	1217	...	1417	...	1616	...	1819	...	2020	...	...	...	...
Great Malvern 125 130 a.	...	...	...	...	...	...	...	...	...	...	...	2032	...	...	...	...

	⑦	⑦	⑦	⑦	⑦	⑦	⑦	⑦	⑦	⑦
Bristol Temple Meads 116 d.		0915	0938	1138	1338	1538	1738	1937	2138	2242
Bristol Parkway 116 d.		0924	0950	1149	1349	1549	1749	1949	2149	2254
Gloucester a.		0950	1026	1228	1431	1630	1829	2030	2226	2330
Gloucester ◧ d.		1002	1038	1236	1438	1637	1839	2036	...	*0002*
Cheltenham Spa ◧ 116 d.		1010	1048	1247	1447	1647	1848	2045	...	*0011*
Ashchurch for Tewkesbury d.		...	1056	1255	1456	1656	1857	2054	...	...
Worcester Shrub Hill 125 130 a.		...	1114	1311t	1516	1720d	1913	2110	...	...
Worcester Foregate St. 125 130 a.		...	...	1321	1519	1719	1919	...	...	...
Great Malvern 125 130 a.		...	...	...	...	...	...	...	...	...

A – To/from Penzance (Tables **115** and **110**).
B – To/from Westbury or Warminster (see Table **140**).
C – Until Sept. 10 to Weymouth (Table **139**); from Sept. 17 to Westbury (Table **140**).
D – Until Sept. 10 from Westbury (Table **139**); from Sept. 17 from Weymouth (Table **139**).
E – To/from Weymouth (Table **139**).
F – From Fareham, Southampton Central, Salisbury or Portsmouth & Southsea (Table **140**).
G – From Sept. 17 extended to Frome (Table **139**).
H – Until Sept. 10 from Weymouth (Table **139**); from Sept. 17 from Warminster (Table **140**).

K – To Frome (Table **139**).
S – To Stansted Airport (Tables **117** and **208**).
T – From Taunton (Table **115**).

c – Departs 0830.
d – Departs 5 minutes later.

f – Arrives 10–11 minutes earlier.
j – Arrives 18 minutes earlier.
r – Arrives 1549.
t – Departs 6–8 minutes later.

◧ – See also Tables **117** and **130**.

GW, SW — BRISTOL - WESTBURY - WEYMOUTH — 139

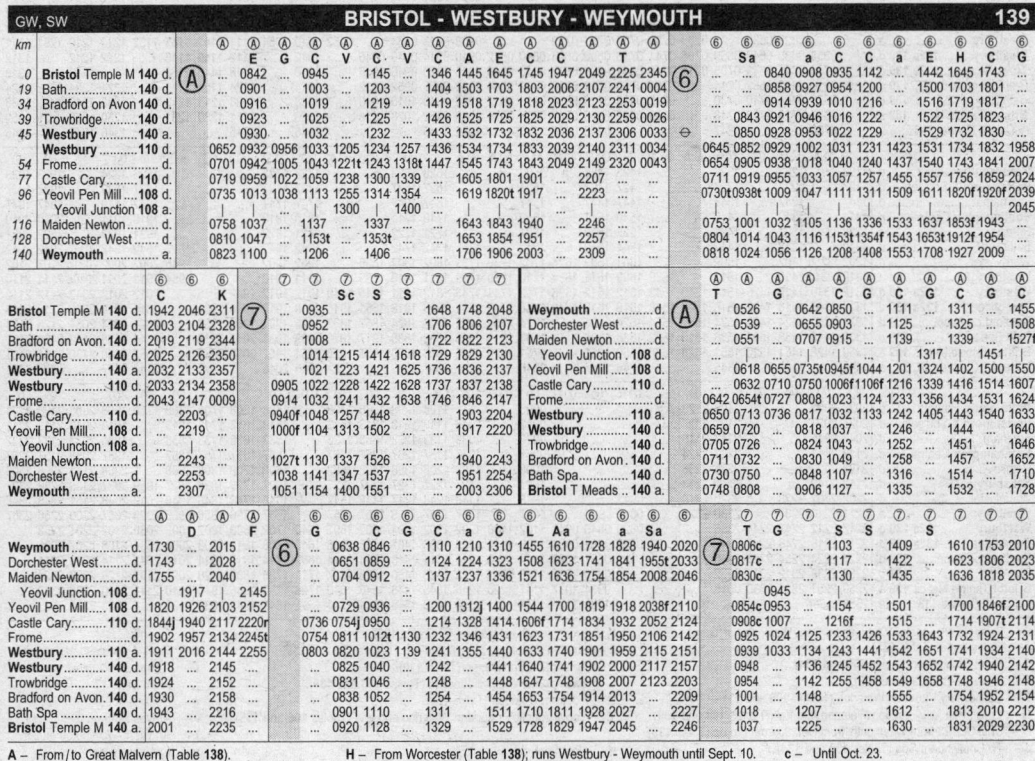

km		Ⓐ	Ⓐ	ⒶE	ⒶG	ⒶC	ⒶV	ⒶC	ⒶV	ⒶC	ⒶA	ⒶE	ⒶC	ⒶC	Ⓐ	ⒶT	Ⓐ
0	**Bristol** Temple M 140 d.		...	0842	...	0945	...	1145	...	1346	1445	1645	1745	1947	2049	2225	2345
19	Bath 140 d.		...	0901	...	1003	...	1203	...	1404	1503	1703	1803	2006	2107	2241	0004
34	Bradford on Avon 140 d.		...	0916	...	1019	...	1219	...	1419	1518	1719	1818	2023	2123	2253	0019
39	Trowbridge 140 d.		...	0923	...	1025	...	1225	...	1426	1525	1725	1825	2029	2130	2259	0026
45	**Westbury** 140 a.		...	0930	...	1032	...	1232	...	1433	1532	1732	1832	2036	2137	2306	0033
	Westbury 110 d.		0652	0932	0956	1033	1205	1234	1257	1436	1534	1734	1833	2039	2140	2311	0034
54	Frome d.		0701	0942	1005	1043	1221t	1243	1318t	1447	1545	1743	1843	2049	2149	2320	0043
77	Castle Cary 110 d.		0719	0959	1022	1059	1238	1300	1339	...	1605	1801	1901	...	2207	...	...
96	Yeovil Pen Mill 108 d.		0735	1013	1038	1113	1255	1314	1354	...	1619	1820t	1917	...	2223	...	...
	Yeovil Junction 108 a.		|	|	...	|	1300	|	1400	...	|	|	|	...	|	...	
116	Maiden Newton d.		0758	1037	...	1137	...	1337	...	...	1643	1843	1940	...	2246	...	...
128	Dorchester West d.		0810	1047	...	1153t	...	1353t	...	...	1653	1854	1951	...	2257	...	...
140	**Weymouth** a.		0823	1100	...	1206	...	1406	...	...	1706	1906	2003	...	2309	...	...

	⑥	⑥	⑥Sa	⑥	⑥a	⑥C	⑥C	⑥a	⑥E	⑥H	⑥C	⑥G
Bristol Temple M 140 d.		...	...	0840	0908	0935	1142	...	1442	1645	1743	...
Bath 140 d.		...	...	0858	0927	0954	1200	...	1500	1703	1801	...
Bradford on Avon 140 d.		...	...	0914	0939	1010	1216	...	1516	1719	1817	...
Trowbridge 140 d.		...	0843	0921	0946	1016	1222	...	1522	1725	1823	...
Westbury 140 a.	⊖	...	0850	0928	0953	1022	1229	...	1529	1732	1830	...
Westbury 110 d.		0645	0852	0929	1002	1031	1231	1423	1531	1734	1832	1958
Frome d.		0654	0905	0938	1018	1040	1240	1437	1540	1743	1841	2007
Castle Cary 110 d.		0711	0919	0955	1033	1057	1257	1455	1557	1756	1859	2024
Yeovil Pen Mill 108 d.		0730t	0938t	1009	1047	1111	1311	1509	1611	1820f	1920f	2039
Yeovil Junction 108 a.		|	|	|	|	|	|	|	|	|	|	2045
Maiden Newton d.		0753	1001	1032	1105	1136	1336	1533	1637	1853f	1943	...
Dorchester West d.		0804	1014	1043	1116	1153t	1354f	1543	1653t	1912f	1954	...
Weymouth a.		0818	1024	1056	1126	1208	1408	1553	1708	1927	2009	...

	⑥C	⑥	⑥K	⑦	⑦	⑦	⑦Sc	⑦S	⑦S	⑦	⑦	⑦
Bristol Temple M 140 d.	1942	2046	2311		...	0935	...	...	...	1648	1748	2048
Bath 140 d.	2003	2104	2328		...	0952	...	...	...	1706	1806	2107
Bradford on Avon. 140 d.	2019	2119	2344		...	1008	...	...	...	1722	1822	2123
Trowbridge 140 d.	2025	2126	2350		...	1014	1215	1414	1618	1729	1829	2130
Westbury 140 a.	2032	2133	2357		...	1021	1223	1421	1625	1736	1836	2137
Westbury 110 d.	2033	2134	2358		0905	1022	1228	1422	1628	1737	1837	2138
Frome d.	2043	2147	0009		0914	1032	1241	1432	1638	1746	1846	2147
Castle Cary 110 d.	...	2203	...		0940f	1048	1257	1448	...	...	1903	2204
Yeovil Pen Mill 108 d.	...	2219	...		1000f	1104	1313	1502	...	...	1917	2220
Yeovil Junction 108 a.	...	|	...		|	|	|	|	...	...	|	|
Maiden Newton d.	...	2243	...		1027t	1130	1337	1526	...	...	1940	2243
Dorchester West d.	...	2253	...		1038	1141	1347	1537	...	...	1951	2254
Weymouth a.	...	2307	...		1051	1154	1400	1551	...	...	2003	2306

	Ⓐ	ⒶT	Ⓐ	ⒶG	Ⓐ	ⒶC	ⒶG	ⒶC	ⒶG	ⒶC	ⒶG	ⒶC
Weymouth d.		...	0526	...	0642	0850	...	1111	...	1311	...	1455
Dorchester West d.		...	0539	...	0655	0903	...	1125	...	1325	...	1508
Maiden Newton d.		...	0551	...	0707	0915	...	1139	...	1339	...	1527f
Yeovil Junction 108 d.		...	|	...	|	|	...	|	1317	|	1451	|
Yeovil Pen Mill 108 d.		...	0618	0655	0735t	0945f	1044	1201	1324	1402	1500	1550
Castle Cary 110 d.		...	0632	0710	0750	1006f	1106f	1216	1339	1416	1514	1607
Frome d.		0642	0654t	0727	0808	1023	1124	1233	1356	1434	1531	1624
Westbury 110 a.		0650	0713	0736	0817	1032	1133	1242	1405	1443	1540	1633
Westbury 140 d.		0659	0720	...	0818	1037	...	1246	...	1444	...	1640
Trowbridge 140 d.		0705	0726	...	0824	1043	...	1252	...	1451	...	1646
Bradford on Avon 140 d.		0711	0732	...	0830	1049	...	1258	...	1457	...	1652
Bath Spa 140 d.		0730	0750	...	0848	1107	...	1316	...	1514	...	1710
Bristol T Meads 140 a.		0748	0808	...	0906	1127	...	1335	...	1532	...	1728

	Ⓐ	ⒶD	Ⓐ	ⒶF	⑥	⑥G	⑥	⑥C	⑥G	⑥C	⑥a	⑥C	⑥L	⑥Aa	⑥	⑥a	⑥Sa	⑥
Weymouth d.	1730	...	2015	...		...	0638	0846	...	1110	1210	1310	1455	1610	1728	1828	1940	2020
Dorchester West d.	1743	...	2028	...		...	0651	0859	...	1124	1224	1323	1508	1623	1741	1841	1955t	2033
Maiden Newton d.	1755	...	2040	...		...	0704	0912	...	1137	1237	1336	1521	1636	1754	1854	2008	2046
Yeovil Junction 108 d.	|	1917	|	2145		...	|	|	...	|	|	|	|	|	|	|	|	|
Yeovil Pen Mill 108 d.	1820	1926	2103	2152		...	0729	0936	...	1200	1312j	1400	1544	1700	1819	1918	2038f	2110
Castle Cary 110 d.	1844j	1940	2117	2220r		0736	0754j	0950	...	1214	1328	1414	1606f	1714	1834	1932	2052	2124
Frome d.	1902	1957	2134	2245t		0754	0811	1012t	1130	1232	1346	1431	1623	1731	1851	1950	2106	2142
Westbury 110 a.	1911	2016	2144	2255		0803	0820	1023	1139	1241	1355	1440	1633	1740	1901	1959	2115	2151
Westbury 140 d.	1918	...	2145	...		...	0825	1040	...	1242	...	1441	1640	1741	1902	2000	2117	2157
Trowbridge 140 d.	1924	...	2152	...		...	0831	1046	...	1248	...	1448	1647	1748	1908	2007	2123	2203
Bradford on Avon. 140 d.	1930	...	2158	...		...	0838	1052	...	1254	...	1454	1653	1754	1914	2013	...	2209
Bath Spa 140 d.	1943	...	2216	...		...	0901	1110	...	1311	...	1511	1710	1811	1928	2027	...	2227
Bristol Temple M 140 a.	2001	...	2235	...		...	0920	1128	...	1329	...	1529	1728	1829	1947	2045	...	2246

	⑦	⑦T	⑦G	⑦	⑦S	⑦S	⑦	⑦S	⑦	⑦	⑦
Weymouth d.		0806c	...	...	1103	...	1409	...	1610	1753	2010
Dorchester West d.		0817c	...	...	1117	...	1422	...	1623	1806	2023
Maiden Newton d.		0830c	...	...	1130	...	1435	...	1636	1818	2035
Yeovil Junction 108 d.		|	0945	...	|	...	|	...	|	|	|
Yeovil Pen Mill 108 d.		0854c	0953	...	1154	...	1501	...	1700	1846f	2100
Castle Cary 110 d.		0908c	1007	...	1216f	...	1515	...	1714	1907t	2114
Frome d.		0925	1024	1125	1233	1426	1533	1643	1732	1924	2131
Westbury 110 a.		0939	1033	1134	1243	1441	1542	1651	1741	1934	2140
Westbury 140 d.		0948	...	1136	1245	1452	1543	1652	1742	1940	2142
Trowbridge 140 d.		0954	...	1142	1255	1458	1549	1658	1748	1946	2148
Bradford on Avon. 140 d.		1001	...	1148	...	...	1555	...	1754	1952	2154
Bath Spa 140 d.		1018	...	1207	...	...	1612	...	1813	2010	2212
Bristol Temple M 140 a.		1037	...	1225	...	...	1630	...	1831	2029	2230

A – From/to Great Malvern (Table **138**).
C – From/to Gloucester (Table **138**).
D – From London Waterloo (Table **108**).
E – From Worcester (Table **138**).
F – To Salisbury (Table **140**).
G – From/to London Waterloo (Tables **108** and **140**).

H – From Worcester (Table **138**); runs Westbury - Weymouth until Sept. 10.
K – From Sept. 17 starts from Great Malvern (Table **138**).
L – To Gloucester (Table **138**); runs Weymouth - Westbury from Sept. 17.
S – From/to Swindon (Table **134**).
T – To/from Cardiff Central (Table **118**).
V – From Basingstoke (Tables **108** and **140**).

a – Until Sept. 10.

c – Until Oct. 23.
f – Arrives 8–10 minutes earlier.
j – Arrives 11–13 minutes earlier.
r – Arrives 2205.
t – Arrives 5–7 minutes earlier.

⊖ – An additional train runs Westbury d.1057 Frome a. 1106 **G**.

140 BRISTOL - WESTBURY - SOUTHAMPTON - PORTSMOUTH and BRIGHTON
2nd class GW, SW

km		⚒	⚒	Ⓐ	ⒶP	⑥	Ⓐ	⑥	ⒶR	⚒	ⒶG	⑥	Ⓐ🍷	⑥F	⚒d	⑥	Ⓐ🍷	Ⓐ	⚒v	⚒	Ⓐ🍷	⑥🍷	⚒A	ⒶG	⑥L	⚒🍷	⚒🍷
	Cardiff Central **118** d.		...	...	...	...	...	...	...	...	...	0629	0628	...	...	0727	0728	...	0827	...	0928	0927	...	...	...	1030	1130
0	**Bristol** Temple Meads **139** d.		...	0500	0510	...	0551	0546	...	0639	...	0723	0722	...	0736	0822	0820	0904	0922	...	1021	1023	1043	...	...	1122	1222
19	Bath Spa **139** d.		...	0513	|	...	0609	0604	...	0658	...	0736	0735	...	0754	0835	0837	0921	0935	...	1035	1037	1101	...	...	1135	1235
34	Bradford on Avon **139** d.		...	0525	0535	...	0626	0620	...	0714	...	0748	0747	...	0810	0847	0849	0933	0947	...	1047	1049	1117	...	...	1147	1247
39	Trowbridge **132a 139** d.		...	0532	0541	...	0632	0626	0646	0720	...	0754	0753	...	0817	0853	0856	0940	0954	...	1053	1055	1123	...	...	1154	1253
45	**Westbury** **132a 139** a.		...	0539	0549	...	0639	0633	0653	0727	...	0801	0800	...	0824	0900	0903	0949	1002	...	1100	1102	1132	...	...	1201	1301
	Westbury d.		0523	0548	...	0601	0641	0648	0655	...	0740	0802	0803	0810	...	0901	0904	0952	1003	1037	1101	1103	...	1139	1143	1202	1301
53	Warminster d.		0531	0556	...	0609	0649	0658	0704	...	0748	0810	0811	0818	...	0911	0912	1001	1011	1045	1111	1113	...	1148	1150	1210	1311
85	**Salisbury** d.		0554	0618	...	0632	0711	0724	0737f	...	0812	0833	0833	0837	...	0933	0934	...	1033	1106	1133	1135	...	1209	1211	1233	1333
112	Romsey d.		...	0637	...	0650	0730	0743	0756	...	...	0852	0852	...	...	0951	0952	...	1051	...	1152	1153	...	...	...	1251	1351
123	**Southampton** Central a.		...	0647	...	0702	0740	0755g	0807	...	...	0902	0902	...	...	1003	1003	...	1103	...	1202	1204	...	...	...	1303	1403
147	Fareham a.		...	0710	...	0727	0803	0824	...	...	...	0926	0927	...	...	1027	1027	...	1127	...	1228	1227	...	...	...	1327	1427
164	**Portsmouth** & Southsea a.		...	0731	...	0746	0822	0844	...	...	...	0946	0947	...	...	1046	1047	...	1147	...	1247	1246	...	...	...	1347	1447
165	**Portsmouth** Harbour a.		...	0738	...	0751	0827	0849	...	...	...	0951	0953	...	...	1051	1052	...	1152	...	1252	1251	...	...	...	1352	1452

	ⒶA	⚒🍷	ⒶT	⑥A	⚒v	ⒶT	⚒v	⑥A	ⒶA	⑥	Ⓐ🍷	Ⓐ	⚒v	Ⓐ	⑥	Ⓐ🍷	ⒶA	⑥A	ⒶC	⑥	Ⓐ🍷	⑥	Ⓐ	⑥	Ⓐ	⑥	Ⓐ
Cardiff Central **118** d.	🍷	1227	...	...	1330	...	1430	...	...	1530	1530	...	1627	...	1727	1727	...	...	...	1827	1830	1929	1930	2029	2030	...	...
Bristol Temple Meads **139** d.	1242	1322	...	1345	1422	...	1522	1542	1545	1622	1622	1706	1722	1810	1822	1824	1843	1845	...	1922	1924	2022	2024	2121	2125	2140	2145
Bath Spa **139** d.	1300	1335	...	1403	1435	...	1535	1600	1603	1635	1635	1724	1735	1827	1835	1837	1901	1903	...	1935	1937	2035	2037	2134	2138	2158	2203
Bradford on Avon **139** d.	1316	1347	...	1419	1447	...	1547	1616	1618	1647	1647	1738	1747	1843	1847	1850	1916	1919	...	1947	1949	2047	2049	2146	2150	2210	2219
Trowbridge **132a 139** d.	1322	1354	...	1425	1453	...	1554	1622	1625	1653	1654	1744	1754	1850	1854	1857	1923	1925	1927	1954	1957	2054	2055	2152	2157	2216	2226
Westbury **132a 139** a.	1329	1401	...	1432	1501	...	1601	1629	1632	1700	1701	1751	1801	1857	1901	1904	1930	1932	1934	2001	2004	2101	2102	2159	2204	2223	2233
Westbury d.	1331	1402	1413	...	1501	1544	1602	1711j	1712	1701	1703	1752	1802	...	1902	1905	...	...	1935	2002	2005	2103	2106	2204	2205	...	2234
Warminster d.	1340	1410	1423	...	1511	1552	1610	1721j	1721	1710	1711	1801	1810	...	1910	1913	...	...	1945	2011	2013	2111	2114	2213	2214	...	2242
Salisbury d.	...	1433	1443	...	1533	1612	1633	...	...	1733	1733	...	1833	...	1933	1933	...	...	2005	2033	2035	2133	2137	2235	2237	...	2302
Romsey d.	...	1451	...	...	1551	...	1651	...	...	1751	1752	...	1851	...	1951	1952	...	...	...	2052	2053	2152	2155	2254	2255	...	2321
Southampton Central a.	...	1503	...	...	1603	...	1703	...	...	1803	1802	...	1903	...	2003	2002	...	...	...	2103	2104	2202	2206	2304	2306	...	2331
Fareham a.	...	1527	...	...	1627	...	1727	...	...	1827	1827	...	1927	...	2027	2027	...	...	...	2127	2126	2226	2241	2327	2330	...	2354
Portsmouth & Southsea a.	...	1547	...	...	1648	...	1747	...	...	1846	1849	...	1947	...	2046	2047	...	...	...	2146	2144	2245	2259	2345	2348	...	0015
Portsmouth Harbour a.	...	1552	...	...	1652	...	1752	...	...	1851	1854	...	1952	...	2051	2052	...	...	...	2151	2149	2250	2304	2350	2353	...	...

	⑥	ⒶE	⚒K	Ⓐ	⑥E	⑦	⑦	⑦T	⑦	⑦	⑦	⑦	⑦	⑦	⑦	⑦	⑦	⑦	⑦	⑦R	⑦	⑦	⑦	⑦	⑦	⑦	⑦
Cardiff Central **118** d.	...	2130	...	...	...		...	...	0918	...	1025	1125	1225	...	1325	1425	...	1525	1625	...	1725	1740	1825	1925	2030	2125	2215
Bristol Temple Meads **139** d.	2215	2225	...	2304	2311		0920	...	1020	1034	1115	1215	1315	1334	1415	1515	1541	1620	1715	...	1815	1840	1915	2015	2127	2230	2315
Bath Spa **139** d.	2233	2241	...	2322	2328		0933	...	1035	1151	1135	1233	1333	1352	1433	1533	1600	1638	1735	...	1830	1858	1930	2033	2145	2248	2329
Bradford on Avon **139** d.	2249	2253	...	2338	2344		0945	...	1047	1107	1147	1249	1345	1404	1449	1545	1616	1650	1747	...	1842	1914	1942	2049	2157	2305	2341
Trowbridge **132a 139** d.	2255	2259	...	2344	2350		0953	...	1054	1113	1153	1255	1352	1410	1455	1552	1623	1656	1753	1818	1850	1920	1949	2055	2203	2311	2348
Westbury **132a 139** a.	2302	2306	...	2351	2357		1000	...	1101	1120	1200	1302	1359	1416	1502	1559	1630	1703	1800	1825	1857	1927	1956	2102	2210	2318	2355
Westbury d.	...	...	2312	...	...		1001	1043	1102	...	1202	1303	1402	1418	1504	1602	...	1705	1802	1827	1901	1929	2000	2103	2211	...	2356
Warminster d.	...	...	2319	...	...		1011	1051	1110	...	1211	1311	1411	1426	1512	1611	...	1714	1810	1835	1909	1937	2009	2111	2219	...	0005
Salisbury d.	...	...	2342	...	...		1033	1112	1133	...	1235	1334	1435	1447	1536	1634	...	1737	1833	1855	1932	2000	2032	2134	2240	...	...
Romsey d.	...	...	...	...	...		1052	...	1151	...	1254	1352	1454	1505	1554	1653	...	1755	1851	...	1950	2018	2051	2152	2300	...	...
Southampton Central a.	...	...	...	...	...		1102	...	1202	...	1304	1403	1504	1516	1605	1703	...	1806	1902	...	2001	2029	2101	2203	2311	...	...
Fareham a.	...	...	...	...	...		1126	...	1226	...	1326	1426	1527	1538	1627	1727	...	1828	1927	...	2026	2057	2126	2226	2334	...	...
Portsmouth & Southsea a.	...	...	...	...	...		1146	...	1246	...	1346	1446	1546	...	1647	1746	...	1848	1947	...	2044	2117	2144	2244	2352	...	...
Portsmouth Harbour a.	...	...	...	...	...		1151	...	1251	...	1351	1451	1551	...	1651	1751	...	1852	1952	...	2050	2123	2149	2249	2356	...	...

	⚒	Ⓐ	⑥A	ⒶA	ⒶE	ⒶJ	ⒶA	⑥A	Ⓐ🍷	⑥	⑥A	ⒶA	Ⓐ🍷	⑥	ⒶA	⑥A	ⒶG	⚒🍷	⑥L	⚒🍷	ⒶA	⑥A	ⒶQ	Ⓐ🍷	⑥	ⒶQ	⑥
Portsmouth Harbour d.		...	...	...	...	...	...	...	0601	0608	...	...	0721	0723	...	...	...	0823	...	0923	🍷	...	...	1023	1023	...	1123
Portsmouth & Sou'sea d.		...	...	...	...	...	...	0539	0605	0612	...	...	0726	0727	...	...	...	0827	...	0927	...	...	...	1027	1027	...	1127
Fareham d.		...	...	0510	...	...	...	0600	0625	0632	...	...	0746	0747	...	...	...	0847	...	0947	...	...	...	1047	1047	...	1147
Southampton Central d.		...	...	0533	...	...	...	0626	0647	0657	...	...	0810	0810	0823	...	...	0910	...	1010	...	...	...	1110	1110	...	1210
Romsey d.		...	...	0545	...	...	...	0638	0659	0711	...	...	0821	0821	0835	...	...	0921	...	1021	...	...	...	1122	1121	...	1221
Salisbury d.		...	0608	0606	...	0635	...	0705f	0720	0730	...	...	0840	0842	0902f	...	0924	0942	1026	1042	1112	1113	1124	1142	1142	1222	1242
Warminster d.		...	0628	0627	...	0655	0730	0728	0741	0750	...	...	0900	0903	0925	...	0944	1002	1046	1102	1132	1133	1144	1202	1202	1243	1302
Westbury a.		...	0637	0636	...	0703	0739	0737	0750	0759	...	...	0908	0913	0934	...	0952	1010	1054	1111	1141	1141	1152	1210	1210	1251	1311
Westbury **132a 139** d.		0558	0638	0640	0659	0705	0741	0738	0800	0805	0840	0842	0910	0914	0940	0940	...	1012	...	1112	1142	1143	...	1212	1212	...	1312
Trowbridge **132a 139** d.		0604	0644	0646	0705	0711	0748	0744	0806	0812	0846	0848	0916	0920	0946	0946	...	1018	...	1118	1148	1150	...	1218	1218	...	1318
Bradford on Avon **139** d.		0610	0650	0652	0711	...	0754	0750	0812	0818	0852	0854	0922	0926	0952	0952	...	1024	...	1124	1154	1156	...	1224	1224	...	1324
Bath Spa **139** d.		0628	0708	0710	0730	...	0812	0808	0829	0834	0910	0912	0936	0940	1010	1010	...	1038	...	1138	1211	1213	...	1238	1240	...	1338
Bristol Temple M **139** a.		0647	0728	0728	0748	...	0830	0827	0847	0847	0928	0930	0950	0952	1028	1028	...	1050	...	1151	1230	1231	...	1250	1252	...	1352
Cardiff Central **118** a.		0750	...	...	0847	...	...	...	0948	0945	...	...	1051	1045	...	...	...	1146	...	1245	...	...	...	1346	1345	...	1445

	Ⓐ🍷	⚒A	⚒v	Ⓐ	⚒v	⑥A	ⒶA	⑥	Ⓐ🍷	⑥R	⚒v	⑥A	ⒶA	⑥	Ⓐ🍷	Ⓐ	⑥A	⑥	Ⓐ🍷	⑥	Ⓐ	⑥T	⑥	Ⓐ🍷	⚒	Ⓐ	⑥
Portsmouth Harbour d.	1123	...	1223	...	1323	...	...	1423	1423	a	1523	j	...	1623	1623	...	...	1723	1723	...	...	...	1823	1824	...	1923	1923
Portsmouth & Sou'sea d.	1127	...	1227	...	1327	...	...	1427	1427	...	1527	...	...	1627	1627	...	...	1727	1727	...	...	...	1827	1829	...	1927	1927
Fareham d.	1147	...	1247	...	1347	...	...	1447	1447	...	1547	...	...	1647	1647	...	...	1747	1747	...	...	...	1847	1849	...	1947	1947
Southampton Central d.	1211	...	1310	...	1410	...	...	1510	1511	...	1609	...	...	1710	1711	...	...	1810	1810	...	...	...	1910	1911	...	2010	2010
Romsey d.	1222	...	1321	...	1421	...	...	1522	1522	...	1621	...	...	1721	1722	...	...	1821	1822	...	...	...	1921	1923	...	2022	2021
Salisbury d.	1242	...	1342	...	1442	...	...	1541	1543	...	1642	...	...	1742	1742	...	...	1842	1842	...	...	1927	1942	1942	2011c	2042	2042
Warminster d.	1302	1325c	1402	...	1502	...	1530	1601	1603	1624	1702	1730	1730	1802	1802	1830	...	1902	1902	...	...	1946	2002	2002	2031c	2103	2102
Westbury a.	1310	1334c	1410	...	1511	...	1539	1609	1611	1634	1710	1739	1739	1811	1810	1839	...	1911	1910	...	...	1954	2011	2011	2040c	2111	2110
Westbury **132a 139** d.	1312	1340	1412	1426	1512	1540	1542	1612	1612	1636	1712	1741	1745	1812	1811	1845	1840	1912	1912	1942	1945	...	2012	2012	2042	2112	2112
Trowbridge **132a 139** d.	1318	1346	1418	1432	1518	1546	1548	1618	1619	1642	1718	1748	1751	1818	1818	1851	1846	1919	1918	1948	1951	...	2018	2018	2048	2118	2118
Bradford on Avon **139** d.	1324	1352	1424	1439	1524	1552	1554	1624	1625	...	1724	1754	1757	1824	1824	1857	1852	1925	1924	1954	1957	...	2024	2024	2054	2125	2124
Bath Spa **139** d.	1338	1410	1438	1502	1538	1610	1612	1638	1638	...	1738	1811	1818	1838	1838	1917	1910	1939	1938	2012	2018	...	2040	2038	2112	2138	2138
Bristol Temple Meads **139** a.	1350	1428	1451	1520	1551	1628	1630	1650	1651	...	1751	1829	1836	1851	1850	1935	1928	1951	1952	2032	2036	...	2052	2050	2130	2151	2151
Cardiff Central **118** a.	1448	...	1547	...	1645	...	...	1746	1747	...	1846	...	...	1947	1949	...	...	2045	2046	...	...	...	2145	2147	...	2258r	2301

	⑥	Ⓐ	Ⓐ	⑥	Ⓐ	⑥	⑦	⑦R	⑦	⑦H	⑦	⑦E	⑦	⑦	⑦	⑦	⑦	⑦	⑦	⑦	⑦	⑦	⑦	⑦	⑦	⑦	⑦
Portsmouth Harbour d.	2023	2023	...	...	2123	2123		...	...	...	0908	...	...	1108	1208	1308	1408	...	1508	1608	1708	1808	...	1908	2008	2108	2204
Portsmouth & Sou'sea d.	2027	2027	...	...	2127	2127		...	...	...	0913	...	1013	1113	1213	1313	1413	...	1513	1613	1713	1813	...	1913	2013	2113	2212
Fareham d.	2047	2045	...	...	2147	2145		...	...	...	0933	...	1033	1133	1233	1333	1433	...	1533	1633	1733	1833	...	1933	2033	2133	2232
Southampton Central d.	2112	2111	...	...	2222	2224		...	...	...	0957	...	1057	1157	1257	1357	1457	...	1557	1657	1757	1857	...	1957	2058	2157	2257
Romsey d.	2123	2122	...	...	2235	2236		...	...	...	1008	...	1108	1208	1308	1408	1508	...	1608	1708	1808	1908	...	2008	2111	2208	2308
Salisbury d.	2142	2142	...	...	2300t	2258		...	...	...	1027	...	1127	1227	1327	1427	1527	...	1627	1727	1828	1927	1959	2027	2130	2228	2327
Warminster d.	2202	2202	2228	...	2320	2318		0811	...	...	1048	...	1148	1248	1347	1448	1547	...	1648	1748	1848	1948	2019	2048	2151	2248	2348
Westbury a.	2211	2210	2237	...	2330	2329		0819	...	...	1057	...	1157	1257	1355	1457	1557	...	1657	1756	1856	1958	2028	2057	2200	2256	2357
Westbury **132a 139** d.	2212	2212	2242	2241	2336	...		0820	0845	0948	1102	1136	1202	1302	1401	1502	1602	1640	1702	1805	1902	2002	2030	2102	2201	2258	...
Trowbridge **132a 139** d.	2218	2218	2248	2247	2342	...		0826	0851	0954	1108	1142	1208	1308	1407	1508	1608	1646	1708	1811	1908	2008	2036	2108	2207	2305	...
Bradford on Avon **139** d.	2224	2224	2254	2253	2348	...		...	0857	1000	1114	1148	1214	1314	1413	1514	1614	1652	1714	1817	1914	2014	2042	2114	2213	2311	...
Bath Spa **139** d.	2238	2238	2312	2311	0002	...		...	0916	1018	1128	1207	1228	1328	1430	1528	1627	1710	1728	1832	1928	2028	2100	2128	2227	2324	...
Bristol Temple Meads **139** a.	2250	2251	2331	2330	0015	...		...	0934	1037	1147	1225	1246	1346	1448	1546	1640	1728	1746	1845	1940	2040	2118	2140	2239	2342	...
Cardiff Central **118** a.	2356	2358r	...	...	...	...		...	1038	1126	1241	...	1340	1440	1545	1641	1744	...	1841	1944	2030	2131	...	2233	2333	...	...

A – From/to Gloucester, Cheltenham Spa, Worcester or Great Malvern (see Table **138**).
C – From Gloucester (Tables **130** and **134**).
E – From/to Frome (Table **139**).
F – Castle Cary - London Waterloo (Tables **108** and **139**).
G – Yeovil Pen Mill - London Waterloo and v.v. (Tables **108** and **139**).
H – Until Oct. 23 from Weymouth; from Oct. 30 from Frome (Table **139**).
J – To Cheltenham Spa (Tables **130** and **134**).

K – From Yeovil Junction on Ⓐ (Table **139**).
L – London Waterloo - Frome and v.v. (Tables **108** and **139**).
P – To London Paddington (Table **110**).
Q – Basingstoke - Yeovil Junction (Tables **108** and **139**).
R – To/from Swindon (Table **134**).
T – Yeovil Junction - London Waterloo and v.v. (Tables **108** and **139**).

a – Until Sept. 10.

c – Ⓐ only.
d – Runs 4 minutes later on Ⓐ.
f – Arrives 9–11 minutes earlier.
j – From Sept. 17.
g – Departs 0803.
r – Arrives xx46 on ⑤.
t – Arrives 5–7 minutes earlier.
v – Conveys 🍷 on Ⓐ.

LM LONDON - NORTHAMPTON - BIRMINGHAM 141

Only selected services are shown. See Table **150** for faster services London - Watford / Milton Keynes / Rugby - Coventry - Birmingham and v.v.

km			Ⓐ	Ⓐ	Ⓐ	Ⓐ	Ⓐ	Ⓐ	Ⓐ	Ⓐ	Ⓐ	Ⓐ	Ⓐ	Ⓐ	Ⓐ	R△	Ⓐ	Ⓐ	Ⓐ	Ⓐ	Ⓐ	Ⓐ	Ⓐ	Ⓐ	Ⓐ
0	**London** Euston 143 d.	Ⓐ	...	...	0534	0612	0715	0723	0749	0816	0849	0915	0949	1015	1049		1615	1652	1715	1752	1816	1852	1915	1953	1952
28	Watford Junction d.		...	...	0555	0632	|	0743	0804	|	0904	|	1004	|	1104	and	|	|	|	|	|	|	|	|	2009
64	Leighton Buzzard d.		...	...	0627	0704	0743	0810	|	0843	|	0942	|	1043	|	at	1643	1720	1743	1820	1843	1920	1942	2021	2034
75	Bletchley d.		...	...	0634	0711	0751	0818	|	0850	|	0949	|	1050	|	the	1650	1727	1750	1827	1850	1927	1950	|	2042
80	Milton Keynes 143 d.		0537	...	0639	0716	0756	0823	0827	0856	0927	0955	1025	1055	1131t	same	1655	1733	1756	1833	1857	1932	1956	2032	2048
106	**Northampton** 143 a.		0553	...	0656	0732	0813	0845	0844	0913	0941	1012	1041	1113	1146	minutes	1713	1751	1813	1849	1914	1949	2013	2048	2109
106	**Northampton** 143 d.		0556	0640	0658	0737	...	...	0856	...	0956	...	1056	...	1156	past	...	1753	...	1856	...	1956	...	2056	...
136	Rugby 143 d.		0619	0703	0721	0759	...	...	0920	...	1020	...	1120	...	1220	each	...	1819	...	1919	...	2020	...	2120	...
154	Coventry 114 d.		0630	0713	0733	0810	...	...	0931	...	1031	...	1131	...	1231	hour	...	1831	...	1931	...	2031	...	2131	...
171	**Birmingham** Int ✈ 114 d.		0649	0732	0751	0829	...	...	0950	...	1050	...	1150	...	1250	until	...	1850	...	1950	...	2050	...	2150	...
185	**Birmingham** New St. 114 a.		0709	0744	0809	0842	...	...	1006	...	1106	...	1206	...	1306		...	1906	...	2005	...	2106	...	2204	...

	Ⓐ	Ⓐ	Ⓐ	Ⓐ	Ⓐ	Ⓐ	Ⓐ		⑥	⑥	⑥	⑥	⑥	⑥	⑥	⑥	⑥	⑥	⑥	⑥	⑥	Q△	⑥	⑥	⑥
London Euston 143 d.	2013	2052	2103	2114	2153	2218	2322	⑥	...	...	0534	...	0624	...	0749	0815	0849	0915	0949	1015	1049		1749	1815	1849
Watford Junction d.	|	|	2126	|	|	2238	2338		...	...	0553	...	0639	...	0804	|	0904	|	1004	|	1104	and	1804	|	1904
Leighton Buzzard d.	2041	2119	2158	2145	2221	2310	0006		...	...	0625	...	0708	...	|	0842	|	0943	|	1043	|	at	|	1843	|
Bletchley d.	2048	|	2205	2152	|	2317	0013		0532	...	0631	...	0715	...	|	0849	0924	0950	1026	1050	|	the	|	1850	|
Milton Keynes 143 d.	2054	2129	2211	2159	2233	2325	0022		0539	...	0637	...	0720	...	0826	0855	0931	0955	1032	1056	1132t	same	1825	1856	1931r
Northampton 143 a.	2110	2146	...	2215	2251	2348	0040		0555	...	0658	...	0737	...	0846	0912	0945	1013	1046	1113	1146	minutes	1840	1913	1947
Northampton 143 d.	...	2156	...	2218	2257	...	...		0556	0641	...	0714	0737	0814	0856	...	0956	...	1056	...	1156	past	1856	...	...
Rugby 143 d.	...	2220	...	2242	2319	...	...		0618	0701	...	0737	0800	0837	0920	...	1020	...	1120	...	1220	each	1920	...	...
Coventry 114 d.	...	2230	...	2253	2330	...	...		0629	0710	...	0750	0811	0850	0931	...	1031	...	1131	...	1231	hour	1931	...	...
Birmingham Int ✈ 114 d.	...	2249	...	2312	2348	...	...		0642	0729	...	0809	0829	0909	0950	...	1050	...	1150	...	1250	until	1950	...	...
Birmingham New St 114 a.	...	2309	...	2332	0007	...	...		0653	0742	...	0823	0842	0923	1006	...	1106	...	1206	...	1306		2006	...	...

	⑥	⑥	⑥	⑥	⑥	⑥	⑥	⑥	⑥		⑦	⑦	⑦	⑦	⑦B	⑦	⑦	⑦	⑦B	⑦	⑦	⑦B	⑦	⑦	⑦	⑦
London Euston 143 d.	1913	1920	1933	1947	2039	2109	2131	2234	2336	⑦	0651	...	0752	0824	0855	...	0924	0955	1001	...	1031	1053	...	1124	1208	1233
Watford Junction d.	|	1936	1954	2005	2055	2128	|	2253	2355		0710	...	0810	0843	0914	...	0944	1011	1019	...	1047	1114	...	1142	1223	1249
Leighton Buzzard d.	|	2001	2026	2035	2127	2158	2209	2320	0028		0738	...	0839	0914	0941	...	1014	1036	1047	...	1113	1143	...	1212	|	1315
Bletchley d.	|	2007	2033	2042	2134	2205	2216	2327	0035		0745	...	0845	0921	0948	...	1021	1043	|	...	|	1150	...	1219	|	1322
Milton Keynes 143 d.	1947	2012	2037	2049	2140	2213	2225	2335	0040		0755	...	0851	0926	0957	...	1027	1051	1058	...	1127	1158	...	1228	1252r	1327
Northampton 143 a.	2005	2026	2055	2106	2155	2231	2245	2353	0102		0812	...	0908	0944	1014	...	1044	1110	1116	...	1150	1216	...	1249	1308	1344
Northampton 143 d.	2005	2035	2057	2118	2204	2241	2254	...	...		...	...	0926	0959	1028	1035	1100	...	1129	1133	*1212*	1217	1235	...	1315	...
Rugby 143 d.	2027	2058	2119	2140	2227	2303	2315	...	...		...	0853	0948	1022	1049	1054	1122	...	1150	1155	*1235*	1239	1258	...	1337	...
Coventry 114 d.	2038	2109	2130	2150	2238	2315	2327	...	...		...	0904	1005r	1033	...	1105	1134	...	...	1206	*1250r*	...	1309	...	1350	...
Birmingham Int ✈ 114 d.	2057	2128	2147	2205	2257	2330	2345	...	...		...	0922	1023	1052	...	1123	1152	...	...	1224	*1309*	...	1321	...	1409	...
Birmingham New St 114 a.	2111	2146	2206	2219	2317	2344	0003	...	...		...	0942	1043	1106	...	1143	1206	...	...	1244	*1323*	...	1341	...	1423	...

	⑦	△	⑦	⑦	⑦	⑦	⑦	⑦	⑦	⑦	⑦	⑦	⑦
London Euston 143 d.	1308		1733	1805	1833	1911	1933	2033	2106	2131	2201	2231	2339
Watford Junction d.	1323	and	1750	1820	1850	|	1950	2050	2124	2147	2221	2252	0001
Leighton Buzzard d.	|	at	1816	|	1916	|	2016	2114	2153	2217	2250	2321	0034
Bletchley d.	|	the	1823	|	1923	|	2023	2121	2200	2224	2257	2328	0041
Milton Keynes 143 d.	1349	same	1828	1848	1928	1948	2028	2131	2209	2232	2306	2336	0049
Northampton 143 a.	1406	minutes	1845	1904	1945	2005	2045	2148	2226	2248	2324	2353	0107
Northampton 143 d.	1415	past	...	1916	...	2009	2056	2157	2238	2251	2332	...	...
Rugby 143 d.	1438	each	...	1940	...	2037	2118	2220	2300	2313	2354	...	...
Coventry 114 d.	1450	hour	...	1950	...	2050	2131	2232	2310	2337f	0004	...	...
Birmingham Int ✈ 114 d.	1509	until	...	2009	...	2109	2149	2250	2320	2356	...	...	...
Birmingham New St 114 a.	1523		...	2024	...	2123	2201	2302	2339	0008	...	...	...

		Ⓐ	Ⓐ	Ⓐ	Ⓐ	Ⓐ	Ⓐ
Birmingham N St 114 d.	Ⓐ	...	...	...	0533	...	0613
Birmingham Int ✈ 114 d.		...	...	...	0548	...	0630
Coventry 114 d.		...	...	0538	0606	...	0648
Rugby 143 d.		...	...	0553	0617	...	0659
Northampton 143 a.		...	...	0614	0638	...	0728
Northampton 143 d.		0415	0505	0623	0639	0658	0738
Milton Keynes 143 d.		0431	0521	0641	0656	0715	0755
Bletchley d.		0436	0526	0646	0701	|	0800
Leighton Buzzard d.		0443	0533	0653	0708	0725	0807
Watford Junction d.		0514	0601	0710	|	|	|
London Euston 143 a.		0539	0625	0725	0738	0803	0838

	Ⓐ	Ⓐ	Ⓐ	Ⓐ	Ⓐ	Ⓐ	Ⓐ	△	Ⓐ	Ⓐ	Ⓐ	Ⓐ	Ⓐ	Ⓐ	Ⓐ	Ⓐ	Ⓐ	Ⓐ	Ⓐ	Ⓐ	Ⓐ		⑥	⑥	⑥
Birmingham New St 114 d.	0653	...	*0733*	0814	0833	...	0933		...	1833	1913	1939	...	2014	2033	2053	2133	2154	2213	2253	2310	⑥	0529	0612	0633
Birmingham Int ✈ 114 d.	0706	...	*0746*	0826	0845	...	0945	and	...	1845	1928	1953	...	2026	2050	2106	2143	2206	2232	2305	2320		0542	0630	0645
Coventry 114 d.	0724	...	*0804*	0846	0904	...	1004	at	...	1904	1948	2012	...	2045	2110	2122	2203	2221	2250	2324	2331		0601	0649	0704
Rugby 143 d.	0735	...	*0816*	0858	0922	...	1015	the	...	1915	1959	2023	...	2056	2124	2133	2213	2233	2301	2334	2344		0612	0700	0714
Northampton 143 a.	0756	...	*0838*	0920	0944	...	1036	same	...	1936	2021	2044	...	2116	2145	2157	2236	2256	2323	2357	0006s		0633	0722	0736
Northampton 143 d.	0805	0824	0905	...	0951	1025	1039	minutes	1925	1941	2027	2048	2113	2118	2148	2207	...	2257	2336	...	|		0638	...	0737
Milton Keynes 143 d.	0822	0841	0922	...	1007	1043	1054	past	1943	1955	2045	2102	2129	2135	2203	2224	...	2313	2352	...	0025		0655	...	0754
Bletchley d.	0827	0846	0927	...	|	1048	|	each	1948	|	2050	|	2135	2140	|	2229	...	2318	2357	...	|		0700	...	|
Leighton Buzzard d.	0834	0853	0934	...	|	1055	|	hour	1955	|	2057	|	2142	2147	|	2236	...	2325	0004	...	|		0707	...	|
Watford Junction d.	0905	|	0959	...	|	|	1116	until	|	2017	|	|	2207	|	|	2301	...	0001	0036	...	0054s		|	...	0816
London Euston 143 a.	0932	0924	1023	...	1042	1126	1131		2027	2033	2128	2138	2224	2217	2246	2330	...	0031	0100	...	0112		0737	...	0836

	⑥	⑥	⑥	⑥	⑥	△	⑥	⑥	⑥	⑥	⑥	⑥	⑥	⑥	⑥	⑥	⑥	⑥	⑥	⑥	⑥	⑥		⑦	⑦
Birmingham New St 114 d.	...	0733	...	...	0833		...	1633	1714	1733	1814	1853	1914	...	1953	2014	...	2053	2114	2155	2210	2245	⑦	...	...
Birmingham Int ✈ 114 d.	...	0745	...	...	0845	and	...	1645	1726	1746	1826	1903	1926	...	2003	2025	...	2103	2125	2207	2229	2257		...	...
Coventry 114 d.	...	0804	...	...	0904	at	...	1704	1748	1804	1848	1922	1948	...	2022	2048	...	2122	2147	2225	2249	2316		...	...
Rugby 143 d.	...	0814	...	...	0914	the	...	1714	1759	1815	1859	1932	1959	...	2032	2058	...	2132	2159	2236	2300	2327		...	...
Northampton 143 a.	...	0836	...	...	0937	same	...	1736	1821	1836	1921	1954	2020	...	2054	2119	...	2154	2220	2303	2321	2355		...	...
Northampton 143 d.	0825	0841	0905	0925	0938	minutes	1725	1738	*1828*	*1904*	1927	2000	2023	2036	2100	2122	2144	2205	2222	...	2330	...		0752	0815
Milton Keynes 143 d.	0842	0855	0922	0942	0953	past	1742	1753	*1844*	*1921*	1944	2017	2038	2051	2116	2139	2201	2221	2239	...	2346	...		0808	0831
Bletchley d.	0847	|	0927	0947	|	each	1747	|	*1849*	*1926*	1949	2022	|	2056	2121	|	2205	2226	2244	...	2351	...		0813	0836
Leighton Buzzard d.	0854	|	0934	0954	|	hour	1754	|	*1856*	*1933*	1956	2029	2047	|	2128	2148	|	2233	|	...	2358	...		0820	0743
Watford Junction d.	|	0918	0959	|	1015	until	|	1815	|	*1959*	2023	2048	2115	2130	2154	2220	2232	2307	2322	...	0020	...		0851	0908
London Euston 143 a.	0926	0938	1022	1025	1035		1825	1835	*1926*	*2022*	2046	2115	2134	2159	2213	2241	2258	2331	2347	...	0040	...		0912	0927

	⑦	⑦	⑦	⑦	⑦	⑦B	⑦	⑦	⑦	⑦	⑦		⑦	⑦	⑦	⑦	⑦	⑦	⑦	⑦	⑦B	⑦	⑦	⑦	⑦
Birmingham New St 114 d.	...	...	0914	0954	1013	...	1050	...	1153	...	1253	and	1753	...	1853	1913	...	1953	2013	...	...	2050	2113	2210	2300
Birmingham Int ✈ 114 d.	...	...	0926	1006	1030	...	1102	...	1203	...	1303	at	1803	...	1903	1932	...	2003	2032	...	...	2102	2131	2228	2312
Coventry 114 d.	...	...	0944	1021	1048	...	1121	...	1225	...	1325	the	1825	...	1921	1945	...	2021	2045	...	...	2120	2144	2247	2323
Rugby 143 d.	...	...	0955	1036	1059	1120	1137	...	1239	...	1337	same	1835	...	1934	1956	...	2032	2055	...	2131	2135	2155	2257	2335
Northampton 143 a.	...	...	1017	1057	1119	1142	1200	...	1300	...	1358	minutes	1856	...	1954	2023	...	2054	2121	...	2153	2203	2217	2318	2356s
Northampton 143 d.	0845	0925	1030	1106	1127	1144	...	1225	1315	1325	1415	past	1856	1925	1955	...	2025	...	...	2127	2155	...	2225	2326	|
Milton Keynes 143 d.	0901	0942	1048	1122	1142	1200	...	1241	1332	1341	1432	each	1913	1941	2012	...	2041	...	...	2143	2211	...	2241	2342	0015s
Bletchley d.	0906	0947	1053	|	1147	1206	...	1246	1337	1346	1437	hour	1918	1946	2017	...	2046	...	...	2148	2216	...	2245	2347	|
Leighton Buzzard d.	0913	0954	1100	|	1154	1213	...	1253	1344	1353	1444	until	1925	1953	2024	...	2053	...	...	2155	2223	...	2252	2354	|
Watford Junction d.	0938	1025	1128	1154	1220	1232	...	1319	1405	1419	1505		1943	2019	2053	...	2124	...	...	2227	2254	...	2323	0025	0045s
London Euston 143 a.	0958	1044	1147	1219	1240	1250	...	1340	1423	1440	1523		2000	2040	2113	...	2144	...	...	2247	2317	...	2343	0045	0103

B – To/from Crewe via Nuneaton (Table **143**).
Q – The 1149 departure from London Euston – Milton Keynes a. 1225, d. 1233, Northampton a. 1253.
R – The 1349 departure from London Euston – Milton Keynes a. 1424, d. 1436, Northampton a. 1450.

f – Arrives 2324.
r – Arrives 5–6 minutes earlier.
s – Stops to set down only.

t – Arrives 7–8 minutes earlier.
△ – Timings may vary ± 3 minutes.

142 NUNEATON - COVENTRY - LEAMINGTON SPA and BEDFORD - BLETCHLEY LM

NUNEATON - COVENTRY - LEAMINGTON SPA

km		Ⓐ	Ⓐ	Ⓐ	Ⓐ	Ⓐ	Ⓐ	Ⓐ		Ⓐ	Ⓐ	Ⓐ	Ⓐ	Ⓐ	Ⓐ	Ⓐ	Ⓐ	Ⓐ	Ⓐ	Ⓐ	Ⓐ	⑥	⑥
0	**Nuneaton** d.		0620	0715	0812	0916	1016	1116	...	1217	1316	1414	1514	1616	1716	1816	1916	2014	2114	2224	2322		...
16	Coventry a.		0639	0735	0833	0936	1038	1139	...	1237	1336	1434	1534	1636	1736	1836	1936	2034	2134	2245	2342		...
16	Coventry 114 d.		0640	0738	0834	0937	1039	1140	...	1238	1337	1435	1537	1637	1737	1837	1937	2035	2136	2247	2343		0546
24	Kenilworth d.		0648	0746	0842	0945	1047	1147	...	1248	1345	1443	1545	1645	1745	1845	1945	2043	2144	2255	2351		0554
32	**Leamington Spa** 114 a.		0655	0753	0852	0953	1055	1155	...	1255	1353	1452	1554	1653	1754	1856	1952	2051	2150	2303	2358		0605

	⑥	⑥	⑥	⑥	⑥	⑥	⑥	⑥	⑥		⑥	⑥	⑥	⑦	⑦	⑦	⑦	⑦		⑦	⑦	⑦	⑦
Nuneaton d.	0619	0716	0816	0916	1016	1116	1216	1316	1416	and	2016	2116	2224		...	...	1213	1313	and	1913	2013	2105	2202
Coventry a.	0639	0736	0836	0936	1036	1136	1236	1337	1436		2036	2136	2244		...	...	1233	1333		1933	2033	2127	2222
										hourly							⑦	⑦	hourly	⑦	⑦	⑦	⑦
Coventry 114 d.	0640	0737	0837	0937	1037	1137	1237	1338	1437		2038	2137	2246		1036	1136	1236	1347		1949	2047	2157	2257
Kenilworth d.	0648	0745	0845	0945	1045	1145	1249	1348	1445	until	2046	2145	2254		1044	1144	1244	1355	until	1957	2055	2205	2305
Leamington Spa 114 a.	0656	0753	0854	0953	1053	1153	1256	1355	1454		2053	2153	2300		1055	1155	1255	1404		2005	2104	2215	2315

	Ⓐ	Ⓐ	Ⓐ	Ⓐ	Ⓐ	Ⓐ	Ⓐ	Ⓐ	Ⓐ	Ⓐ	Ⓐ	Ⓐ	Ⓐ	Ⓐ	Ⓐ		Ⓐ	Ⓐ	Ⓐ	Ⓐ	⑥	⑥	⑥
Leamington Spa 114 d.		0534	0613	0700	0802	0900	1003	1102	1202	1301	1404	1502	1602	1701	1800	...	1902	2001	2101	2206		0534	0608
Kenilworth d.		0542	0620	0707	0809	0907	1010	1109	1209	1309	1411	1508	1609	1708	1807	...	1909	2009	2109	2213		0541	0615
Coventry 114 a.		0550	0627	0714	0816	0915	1017	1116	1216	1316	1419	1516	1616	1716	1815	...	1916	1016	2116	2221		0549	0622
Coventry d.		0552	0634	0716	0817	0917	1018	1117	1217	1316	1419	1516	1620	1717	1817	...	1917	2017	2117	2225		0550	0624
Nuneaton a.		0613	0656	0737	0845	0938	1039	1138	1238	1338	1449	1538	1642	1738	1839	...	1938	2039	2138	2246		0611	0647

	⑥	⑥	⑥	⑥		⑥	⑥	⑦	⑦	⑦	⑦	⑦	⑦		⑦	⑦	⑦	⑦		⑦	⑦	⑦	⑦
Leamington Spa 114 d.	0702	0803	0900	1002	and	2002	2102		1000	1100	1200	1315	1319	and	1915	1919	2015	2019	...	2115	2119	2212	2219
Kenilworth d.	0709	0810	0907	1009		2009	2109		1008	1108	1208		1326			1927		2027	...		2126		2227
Coventry 114 a.	0716	0817	0914	1016	hourly	2016	2116		1016	1116	1216	1326	1339	hourly	1926	1940	2026	2040	...	2126	2140	2223	2237
									⑦			⑦			⑦		⑦			⑦			
Coventry d.	0717	0818	0917	1017	until	2017	2117		1113	...	1239	1339	...	until	1939	...	2039	...	...	2132	...	...	...
Nuneaton a.	0738	0840	0938	1038		2038	2138		1135	...	1300	1400	...		2000	...	2100	...	...	2153	...	...	...

BEDFORD - BLETCHLEY

km		Ⓐ	⑥	⑥	Ⓐ	⑥	Ⓐ	Ⓐ	⑥	Ⓐ	⑥	Ⓐ		⑥	⚒	⑥	Ⓐ	Ⓐ	⑥	Ⓐ	⑥	⚒	Ⓐ
0	**Bedford** d.	0603	0604	0704	0714	0747	0810	0848	0848	0955	1004	1105	...	1114	1155	1255	1258	1355	1355	1455	1455	1555	1648
20	Woburn Sands d.	0634	0635	0735	0745	0818	0841	0919	0919	1026	1035	1136	...	1145	1226	1326	1329	1426	1426	1526	1526	1626	1719
27	**Bletchley** a.	0644	0645	0745	0755	0828	0851	0929	0929	1036	1045	1146	...	1155	1236	1336	1339	1436	1436	1536	1536	1636	1729
	Milton Keynes 142 a.	*0716*	*0720*	*0820*	*0822*	*0852*	*0918*	*0951*	*0954*	*1053*	*1055*	*1200*	...	*1219*	*1254*	*1354*	*1356*	*1451*	*1454*	*1554*	*1554*	*1654*	*1756*

	⑥	⚒	⑥	Ⓐ	⑥	Ⓐ		⚒		⑥	Ⓐ
Bedford d.	1650	1755	1843	1848	1955	1956	...	2112	...	2219	2228
Woburn Sands d.	1721	1826	1914	1921	2026	2027	...	2143	...	2250	2259
Bletchley a.	1731	1836	1924	1931	2037	2038	...	2153	...	2300	2309
Milton Keynes 142 a.	*1754*	*1854*	*1953*	*1957*	*2047*	*2053*	...	*2213*	...	*2317*	*2325*

	⑥	Ⓐ	⑥	Ⓐ	⑥	Ⓐ
Milton Keynes 142 d.	*0435*	*0504*	*0532*	*0552*	*0647*	*0706*
Bletchley d.	0516	0516	0616	0624	0700	0720
Woburn Sands d.	0527	0527	0627	0636	0711	0731
Bedford a.	0558	0558	0658	0708	0742	0802

	⑥	Ⓐ	Ⓐ	⑥		⑥	Ⓐ	⚒	⚒	⚒	⚒	⚒	⚒	⑥		Ⓐ	Ⓐ	⑥	⚒	Ⓐ	⑥	Ⓐ	⑥
Milton Keynes 142 d.	*0747*	*0723*	*0857*	*0856*	...	*0956*	*0955*	*1041*	*1141*	*1242*	*1341*	*1439*	*1541*	*1642*	...	*1655*	*1724*	*1742*	*1842*	*1957*	*1944*	*2056*	*2116*
Bletchley d.	0800	0801	0906	0917	...	1017	1018	1101	1201	1301	1401	1501	1601	1701	...	1705	1738	1756	1901	2025	2025	2132	2132
Woburn Sands d.	0811	0812	0917	0928	...	1028	1029	1112	1212	1312	1412	1512	1612	1712	...	1717	1749	1807	1912	2036	2036	2143	2143
Bedford a.	0842	0843	0948	0959	...	1059	1100	1143	1243	1343	1443	1543	1643	1743	...	1747	1820	1838	1943	2107	2107	2214	2214

143 LONDON - CREWE via Trent Valley LM

See Tables **151 – 154** for other fast services London - Milton Keynes - Stafford - Crewe.

km		⚒	Ⓐ	⑥	Ⓐ	⑥	Ⓐ	⑥	⚒	⚒	⚒	⚒	⚒	⚒	⚒	⚒	⚒	⑥‡	⑥	Ⓐ	Ⓐ‡	⑥	Ⓐ‡	Ⓐ	⑥‡	Ⓐ‡	⑥
0	**London** Euston **141 150** d.		...	...	...	...	0628	0629	0746	0846	0946	1046	1146	1246	1346	1446	1546	1633	1646	1646	1657	1746	1757	1746	1833	1834	1846
28	Watford Junction **141 150** d.		...	...	...	...																					
78	Milton Keynes... **141 150** d.		...	...	...	...	0701	0702	0819	0919	1019	1119	1219	1319	1419	1519	1619		1719	1719		1819		1819			1919
104	Northampton **141** d.		0520	0541	0605	0637																					
135	Rugby **141 150** d.		0542	0602	0627	0657	0729f	0727	0842	0942	1042	1142	1242	1342	1442	1542	1642	1723	1742	1747f		1842		1848f		1923	1942
158	Nuneaton d.		0555	0621f	0640	0711	0742	0741	0855	0955	1055	1155	1255	1355	1455	1555	1655		1755	1801		1855		1900			1955
178	Tamworth (Low Level) d.		0609	0635	0656	0728	0755	0755	0909	1009	1109	1209	1309	1409	1509	1609	1709	1747	1809	1816	1800	1909	1900	1915	1937	1943	2009
188	Lichfield Trent Valley d.		0616	0641	0702	0734	0802	0801	0917	1017	1117	1217	1317	1417	1517	1617	1717	1754	1817	1822	1806	1917	1906	1921	1944	1951	2017
217	Stafford d.		0634	0658	0720	0754	0819	0818	0935	1035	1135t	1235	1341y	1435	1534	1636	1734	1807	1836	1842	...	1935	...	1940			2036
268	**Crewe** a.		0655	0716	0739	0814	0837	0837	0954	1053	1153t	1253	1404y	1454	1553	1654	1754	...	1854	1901	...	1953	...	2003	2013	2017	2054

	①–④	⑤	⑥	Ⓐ‡	Ⓐ	Ⓐ‡	⑥‡	⑥	Ⓐ	Ⓐ	Ⓐ‡	⑦	⑦	⑦	⑦‡	⑦	⑦	⑦	⑦	⑦	⑦	⑦	⑦‡	⑦	⑦	⑦	⑦‡
London Euston . **141 150** d.	1846	1849	1933	1940	1946	2030	2031	2034	2046	2146	2200		...	0855	0917	1001	1053	1243	1343	1443	1543	1643	1718	1743	1846	1947	2025
Watford Junction . **141 150** d.							2046u	2051u					...	0914		1019	1114										
Milton Keynes.... **141 150** d.	1919	1924	2007		2019			2122	2119	2219	2240		...	0957		1058	1158	1320	1419	1519	1619	1719	1742	1819	1922		
Northampton **141** d.		1945											0930	1028j		1129j	1217										
Rugby **141 150** d.	1946	2005	2030		2042		2138	2145	2145	2246	2303		0952	1050		1152	1239	1347	1447f	1542	1647f	1747f		1847f	1947	2048	
Nuneaton d.	2002	2018	2043		2100f			2156	2200	2258	2314		1005	1105	1045	1205	1251	1400	1500	1557	1700	1759		1900	2000	2100	
Tamworth (Low Level) d.	2016	2033	2057	2043	2114	2135	2155	2210	2215	2312	2326s		1020	1119		1219	1305	1415	1515	1612	1715	1813		1915	2015	2115	2132
Lichfield Trent Valley d.	2023	2039	2104	2050	2121	2142	2202	2217	2222	2318	2333s		1026	1126	1102	1225	1311	1421	1521	1618	1721	1819	1824	1921	2022	2121	2139
Stafford d.	2047r	2057	2121	2104	2142	2200		2242f	2244	2346r			1047	1144	1115	1245	1331	1440	1540	1638	1740	1836		1940	2100j	2140	
Crewe a.	2108	2117	2139	2121	2200	2217	2230	2301	2302	0013	0021v		1107	1204	1134	1303	1349	1500	1558	1700	1759	1854	1858	2002	2119	2158	2210

	⚒	⑥	Ⓐ	Ⓐ‡	Ⓐ‡	⑥‡	⑥	Ⓐ	⑥‡	⑥	⑥	Ⓐ	Ⓐ‡	⑥	Ⓐ	⑥		Ⓐ	⑥	⚒	⚒	⚒	⚒	⚒	⚒	⑥‡	⚒
Crewe d.		0539	0546	...	...	...	0624	0714	0754	0725	0745	0816	0829	0833	0933	0933	...	1033	1033	1133	1233	1333	1433	1533	1633	1723	1733
Stafford d.		0559	0608	...	0653	...	0648f	0739f	0815	0748f	0807	0836		0855	0956f	0955	...	1052	1055	1155	1255	1355	1455	1555	1655	1744	1755
Lichfield Trent Valley d.		0616	0626	0640	0708	0712	0705	0757	0830	0805	0826	0853	0900	0913	1013	1013	...	1113	1113	1213	1313	1413	1513	1613	1713	1800	1813
Tamworth (Low Level) d.		0623	0635	0647	0715	0718	0711	0804	0837	0812	0832	0901	0907	0920	1020	1020	...	1120	1120	1220	1320	1420	1520	1620	1720		1820
Nuneaton d.		0639	0650				0726	0818		0827	0847	0916		0935	1036	1035	...	1135	1135	1235	1335	1435	1535	1635	1735		1835
Rugby **141 150** d.		0704r	0710f	0707			0743	0834		0843	0903	0932		0953	1053	1053	...	1153	1154	1253	1353	1453	1553	1653	1753		1853
Northampton **141** a.																	...										
Milton Keynes.... **141 150** a.							0804	0855a		0905c	0924	0954		1015	1113	1114	...	1214	1215	1314	1414	1514	1614	1714	1814		1914
Watford Junction **141 150** a.																	...										
London Euston . **141 150** a.		0759	0808	0802	0823	0823	0840	0937	0944	0950	1000	1030	1018	1052	1150	1150	...	1250	1251	1350	1450	1550	1650	1750	1850	1907	1950

	Ⓐ	⑥	⑥		Ⓐ	Ⓐ	⑥	Ⓐ‡	Ⓐ	Ⓐ	⑦	⑦‡	⑦	⑦	⑦	⑦	⑦	⑦	⑦		⑦	⑦	⑦‡	⑦	⑦	⑦‡	⑦
Crewe d.	1833	1833	1933	...	1935	2038	2038	2125	2131	2152		0853	0952	1123	1216	1316	1416	1516	1616	...	1716	1816	...	1933	2016	2124	2133
Stafford d.	1903r	1855	1952	...	1953	2103f	2058	2145	2149	2213			1020r	1141	1237	1337	1437	1537	1637	...	1737	1837	...	1951	2037	2143	2151
Lichfield Trent Valley d.	1919	1913	2009	...	2010	2121	2115	2200	2206	2230		0924	1037	1158	1254	1354	1454	1554	1654	...	1754	1854	1935	2008	2054	2200	2208
Tamworth (Low Level) d.	1926	1920	2015	...	2017	2128	2122	2207	2213	2236			1044	1205	1300	1400	1500	1600	1700	...	1800	1900		2014	2101	2206	2215
Nuneaton d.	1941	1935	2030	...	2032	2143	2137	2218	2228	2251			1100	1220	1315	1415	1515	1615	1715	...	1815	1915		2029	2115	2218	2230
Rugby **141 150** d.	1956	1951	2047	...	2049	2159	2153	2231	2242	2306			1120	1236	1333	1433	1533	1632	1732	...	1832	1932		2044	2131	2232	2247
Northampton **141** a.		2011	2107	...		2222			2304	2327			1142							...					2153		2312
Milton Keynes.... **141 150** a.	2017	...	...	...	2110	...	2216	2253	...	...		1019	1158	1258	1354	1454	1554	1653	1753	...	1853	1953		2106	2211	2304	...
Watford Junction **141 150** a.		...	...	...	2132	...		2325s	...	...			1232							...				2139	2254	2334s	...
London Euston . **141 150** a.	2053	...	...	...	2148	...	2304	2344	...	...		1104	1250	1349	1433	1533	1633	1732	1832	...	1932	2032	2045	2158	2317	2353	...

a – Departs 0901.
c – Departs 0914.
f – Arrives 5 – 7 minutes earlier.
j – Arrives 13 – 17 minutes earlier.
r – Arrives 8 – 12 minutes earlier.
s – Calls to set down only.
t – On ⑥ Stafford a. 1134, d. 1147, Crewe a. 1211.
u – Calls to pick up only.
v – On ⑤ arrives 0017.
y – On ⑥ Stafford d. 1339, Crewe a. 1357.
‡ – Fast service operated by VT (see Tables **152 – 154** for further details).

LM — BIRMINGHAM - CREWE - LIVERPOOL — 144

km		⚒	Ⓐ	⑥	Ⓐ	⑥	⑥	Ⓐ	Ⓐ	⑥	⚒	Ⓐ	⑥	⚒	⚒	⚒	⚒	⚒	⚒	⚒	⑥	Ⓐ	Ⓐ	⑥
0	**Birmingham** New Street 119 ▷ d.		...	...	0602	0604	0704	0704	0803	0804	0904	1004	1004	1104	1204	1304	1404	1504	1604	1704	1804	1804	1938	1937
19	Wolverhampton 119 ▷ d.		...	...	0622	0620	0724	0723	0821	0825	0922	1022	1022	1122	1222	1322	1422	1522	1622	1722	1822	1822	1957	1957
43	Stafford 119 143 153 d.		...	...	0638	0637	0740	0739	0838	0839	0938	1039	1039	1138	1238	1338	1438	1538	1638	1738	1838	1838	2014	2013
82	**Crewe** 143 153 d.		0604	0615	0658	0658	0758	0800	0858	0859	0959	1059	1058	1159	1259	1357	1459	1558	1658	1758	1859	1859	2035	2034
118	Runcorn 153 d.		0631	0634	0723	0724	0824	0825	0922	0924	1025	1122	1125	1225	1323	1425	1523	1625	1725	1824	1924	1925	2059	2100
131	**Liverpool** South Parkway ‡ a.		0639	0643	0732	0733	0832	0835	0931	0932	1033	1131	1132	1233	1332	1432	1532	1633	1732	1833	1932	1934	2109	2109
140	**Liverpool** Lime Street 153 a.		0651	0654	0742	0742	0842	0844	0940	0942	1044	1140	1143	1243	1341	1443	1542	1643	1743	1843	1942	1945	2118	2118

	⑥	Ⓐ	Ⓐ	⑥	Ⓐ	⑥	Ⓐ	⑦	⑦	⑦	⑦	⑦	⑦	⑦	⑦	⑦	⑦	⑦	⑦	⑦	⑦	⑦	⑦	⑦
Birmingham New Street 119 ▷ d.	2037	2037	2136	2137	2222	2238	2309		...	0942	1042	1139	1235	1335	1435	1535	1635	1735	1835	1935	1952	2053	2142	2200
Wolverhampton 119 ▷ d.	2055	2055	2154	2159	2245	2301	2336		...	1000	1102	1200	1255	1355	1455	1555	1655	1755	1855	1955	2029	2130	2202	2221
Stafford 119 143 153 d.	2111	2112	2213	2219	2301	2317	2355		...	1017	1119	1218	1312	1411	1511	1611	1711	1811	1911	2011	2048	2147	2220	2237
Crewe 143 153 d.	2131	2131	2238	2241	2343	2337	0019		0920	1036	1141	1238	1332	1431	1531	1631	1732	1831	1931	2035	2131	2226	2240	2315
Runcorn 153 d.	2152	2158	2302	...	...	...	...		0946	1102	1204	1304	1356	1457	1554	1657	1757	1857	1954	2101	...	...	2306	...
Liverpool South Parkway ‡ a.	2200	2207	2311	...	...	...	...		0954	1111	1212	1312	1404	1506	1603	1706	1806	1906	2003	2109	...	...	2316	...
Liverpool Lime Street 153 a.	2210	2216	2321	...	...	...	...		1004	1120	1222	1324	1414	1515	1612	1715	1815	1915	2012	2119	...	...	2330	...

	⚒	⑥	Ⓐ	⚒	⚒	Ⓐ	⑥	⑥	Ⓐ	Ⓐ	⑥	⚒	⚒	⑥	Ⓐ	Ⓐ	⑥	⚒	⚒	Ⓐ	⑥	Ⓐ	⑥	Ⓐ
Liverpool Lime Street 153 d.		...	...	0609	0705	0807	0807	0907	0907	1007	1007	1107	1207	1307	1307	1407	1407	1507	1607	1707	1707	1806	1806	1913
Liverpool South Parkway ‡ d.		...	...	0619	0715	0817	0817	0918	0918	1017	1017	1117	1217	1316	1317	1417	1416	1516	1616	1717	1717	1816	1816	1923
Runcorn 153 d.		...	...	0626	0723	0825	0825	0927	0926	1026	1026	1125	1226	1325	1325	1425	1425	1525	1625	1725	1725	1827	1823	1930
Crewe 143 153 d.		0601	0606	0651	0751	0853	0853	0952	0955	1051	1054	1151	1251	1353f	1353	1451	1451	1554	1651	1752	1751	1854	1853	1955
Stafford 119 143 153 d.		0646	0633t	0711	0810	0911	0912	1011	1014	1111	1113	1210	1311	1412	1412	1511	1510	1611	1711	1812	1809	1914	1912	2016
Wolverhampton 119 ▷ a.		0702	0649	0728	0828	0928	0927	1028	1030	1127	1128	1227	1327	1429	1429	1528	1526	1628	1727	1829	1827	1930	1928	2032
Birmingham New Street 119 ▷ a.		0736	0710	0750	0850	0950	0950	1050	1050	1150	1150	1250	1350	1450	1450	1550	1550	1650	1750	1850	1850	1951	1950	2053

	⑥	⑥	Ⓐ	Ⓐ	⑥	Ⓐ	⑥	Ⓐ	⑦	⑦	⑦	⑦	⑦	⑦	⑦	⑦	⑦	⑦	⑦	⑦	⑦	⑦	⑦	⑦
Liverpool Lime Street 153 d.	1913	2004	2034	2134	2134	2235	2217	2335		...	...	1012	1135	1233	1335	1433	1535	1633	1735	1833	1933	2035	2134	2340
Liverpool South Parkway ‡ d.	1923	2015	2044	2144	2144	2247	│	2345		...	...	1022	1145	1243	1345	1443	1545	1643	1745	1843	1943	2045	2144	2352
Runcorn 153 d.	1930	2022	2051	2151	2151	2255	│	2352		...	...	1029	1152	1250	1352	1450	1552	1650	1752	1850	1950	2052	2151	0002
Crewe 143 153 d.	1953	2054	2120	2220	2222	2325	2252	0023		0859	1003	1105t	1219	1319	1419	1519	1619	1719	1819	1919	2019	2119	2221	0030
Stafford 119 143 153 d.	2012	2114	2141	2238	2241	...	...	...		0944	1045	1130f	1239	1339	1439	1539	1638	1738	1838	1938	2039	2138	2242	...
Wolverhampton 119 ▷ a.	2028	2130	2157	2258	2258	...	...	...		1000	1101	1147	1256	1356	1456	1555	1655	1755	1855	1954	2056	2155	2258	...
Birmingham New Street 119 ▷ a.	2050	2150	2217	2319	2319	...	...	...		1037	1137	1213	1315	1415	1514	1613	1713	1814	1914	2014	2116	2214	2316	...

f – Arrives 5–6 minutes earlier. t – Arrives 8–9 minutes earlier. ‡ – 🚌 connections available to / from Liverpool John Lennon Airport ✈. ▷ – See also Tables **145** and **150**.

AW 2nd class — BIRMINGHAM - SHREWSBURY - CHESTER — 145

km		⚒	⑥	Ⓐ	⑥ A	Ⓐ	Ⓐ B	Ⓐ	Ⓐ	⑥ 🍷	Ⓐ 🍷	⑥	Ⓐ	⚒ 🍷	Ⓐ C	⚒ F🍷	⑥ 🍷	⚒ 🍷	⚒ F🍷	⑥ 🍷	Ⓐ 🍷	Ⓐ 🍷	⑥ 🍷	⚒ F🍷	Ⓐ C	⑥ 🍷	Ⓐ 🍷
	London Euston 150 d.		...	...	...	...	...	...	...	...	...	...	...	...	...	...	...	...	...	...	...	...	...	...	...	...	...
0	**Birmingham** Int ✈ d.		...	...	...	...	...	...	...	...	...	...	...	0708	...	0806	...	0906	1006	...	...	1106	1106	1206	...	...	1306
13	**Birmingham** New St d.		...	...	0530	...	...	...	...	0624	0625	...	...	0722	...	0825	...	0925	1025	...	...	1125	1125	1225	...	...	1325
34	Wolverhampton d.		...	...	0548	...	...	...	0610	0644	0644	...	...	0743	...	0845	...	0944	1044	...	...	1144	1144	1244	...	...	1344
59	Telford Central d.		...	...	│	...	...	...	0638	0700	0702	...	...	0800	...	0903	...	1000	1101	...	...	1200	1200	1300	...	...	1401
65	Wellington d.		...	...	│	...	...	...	0646	0707	0709	...	...	0807	...	0910	...	1007	1108	...	...	1207	1207	1307	...	...	1408
81	**Shrewsbury** a.		...	...	│	...	...	...	0700	0721	0724	...	...	0822	...	0925j	...	1021	1123	...	...	1221	1221	1322	...	...	1421
	Aberystwyth 147 a.		...	...	│	...	...	...	...	0921	0921	...	...	│	...	1121	...	│	1322	...	...	│	│	1522	...	...	│
	Cardiff Central 149 d.		...	...	│	...	...	...	...	...	...	0520	0512	│	0645	...	0722	│	...	0923	0922	│	│	...	1122	1123	│
81	**Shrewsbury** d.		0519	0528	│	0557	...	0700	...	...	...	0726	0728	0825	0850	...	0927	1025	...	1127	1130	1225	1225	...	1329	1327	1426
110	Gobowen d.		0540	0548	│	0614	...	0719	...	...	...	0743	0745	0843	0908	...	0944	1043	...	1144	1147	1243	1243	...	1347	1345	1444
122	Ruabon d.		0553	0600	│	0625	...	0731	...	...	...	0755	0757	0855	0921	...	0956	1055	...	1156	1159	1255	1255	...	1400	1357	1456
129	Wrexham General d.		0606f	0608	│	0635	0703	0741	...	...	...	0802	0804	0902	0930	...	1003	1102	...	1203	1209	1305	1302	...	1409	1406	1502
149	**Chester** 160 a.		0623	0630	0642	0658	0720	...	...	...	...	0820	0821	0920	0947	...	1020	1121	...	1221	1226	1322	1320	...	1426	1424	1521
	Holyhead 160 a.		...	...	0819	...	...	...	...	...	...	1019	1009	1112b	1120	...	1217	1324k	...	1419	1419	1522	1514	...	1620	1622	1718

	⑥ 🍷	⚒ F🍷	⚒ 🍷	⑥ 🍷	Ⓐ 🍷	⚒ F🍷	⑥ 🍷	Ⓐ 🍷	⚒	Ⓐ	Ⓐ	Ⓐ C	⚒	⑥ 🍷	Ⓐ	Ⓐ	Ⓐ D🍷	Ⓐ	⑥	⚒ 🍷	⚒	⑥ J	Ⓐ	⚒ M	⑥	Ⓐ	⑥ H
London Euston 150 d.	...	...	...	...	...	...	...	...	...	...	...	...	...	...	...	...	...	...	...	1823	...	...	...	...	...	...	...
Birmingham Int ✈ d.	1306	1406	...	1506	1506	1606	...	...	1706	...	...	...	1806	...	...	...	...	1906	1906	1933	2006	...	...	2106	...	...	...
Birmingham New St d.	1325	1425	...	1525	1525	1625	...	...	1725	...	1734	...	1825	...	...	1834	...	1925	1925	1950	2025	...	...	2125	...	...	2235
Wolverhampton d.	1344	1444	...	1543	1543	1644	...	...	1744	...	1753	...	1844	...	...	1853	...	1945	1944	2018	2044	...	...	2146	...	...	2255
Telford Central d.	1402	1501	...	1600	1600	1701	...	...	1801	...	1820	...	1901	...	...	1914	...	2002	2000	2035	2101	...	...	2203	...	...	2311
Wellington d.	1410	1509	...	1606	1606	1709	...	...	1807	...	1828	...	1909	...	...	1921	...	2009	2007	2042	2108	...	...	2210	...	...	2318
Shrewsbury a.	1424	1524	...	1620	1620	1723	...	...	1823	...	1843	...	1923	...	...	1936	...	2022	2021	2056	2123	...	...	2224	...	...	2332
Aberystwyth 147 a.	│	1721	...	│	│	1921	...	...	│	...	▬	...	2125	...	...	...	...	│	│	...	2336	...	...	│	...	...	▬
Cardiff Central 149 d.	│	...	1322	│	│	...	1523	1523	│	...	...	1716	▬	1723	...	...	1823	│	│	...	...	1941	1941	│	2055	2115	⑥
Shrewsbury d.	1426	...	1529	1625	1625	...	1726	1728	1826	...	...	1909	...	1928	1932	...	2014	2028	2026	...	...	2143	2146	2227	2306	2317	2336
Gobowen d.	1444	...	1546	1643	1643	...	1743	1746	1844	...	...	│	...	1945	1950	...	│	2046	2044	...	...	2200	2204	2245	│	│	2354
Ruabon d.	1456	...	1558	1655	1655	...	1755	1758	1856	...	⑥	│	⑥	1957	2002	...	⊕	2058	2056	...	...	2212	2216	2257	⊕	⊕	0006
Wrexham General d.	1503	...	1608	1702	1702	...	1802	1805	1903	1909	1922	1938	1950	2004	2008	...	│	2105	2103	...	...	2219	2222	2304	│	│	0012
Chester 160 a.	1521	...	1626	1719	1722	...	1820	1822	1922	1927	1939	1958	2008	2024	2028	...	2112	2121	2125	...	...	2236	2243	2320	0023	0027	0030
Holyhead 160 a.	1718	...	1821	1915	1918	...	2025	2020	2126b	...	...	2142	...	2226	2231	...	...	...	...	...	...	...	0043	...	...	*0215*	...

	Ⓐ	⑥	Ⓐ	⑦	⑦	⑦ F🍷	⑦ 🍷	⑦ F🍷	⑦ 🍷	⑦	⑦ F🍷	⑦ 🍷		⑦ 🍷	⑦ F🍷	⑦ 🍷	⑦ 🍷	⑦	⑦	⑦ 🍷	⑦	⑦	⑦	⑦	⑦	⑦	⑦
London Euston 150 d.	...	...	...		...	...	...	...	...	...	...	...	...	...	...	...	...	...	...	1820	...	...	...	...	...	...	...
Birmingham Int ✈ d.	...	...	2304		...	0951	1048	1206	1306	...	1406	...	...	1506	1606	...	1706	1806	1906	1933	2006	2106	...	...	2211	2240	2307
Birmingham New St d.	...	2335	2334		0828	1004	1104	1223	1323	1400	1423	...	...	1523	1624	...	1724	1823	1924	2000	2024	2123	2203	...	2224	2255	2325
Wolverhampton d.	...	2355	0003		0855	1023	1126	1242	1342	1421	1444	...	...	1544	1644	...	1744	1843	1944	2021	2045	2143	2229	...	2243	2316	2349
Telford Central d.	...	0022	0031		0923	1041	1145	1259	1358	1448	1502	...	...	1602	1702	...	1801	1900	2002	2038	2103	2201	2255	...	2303	│	0016
Wellington d.	...	0030	0038		0930	1048	1153	1306	1405	1455	1509	...	...	1609	1709	...	1807	1907	2009	2045	2110	2209	2302	...	2311	│	0024
Shrewsbury a.	...	0045	0053		0943	1103	1207	1320	1419	1510	1523	...	...	1625	1724	...	1821	1921	2023	2100	2124	2223	2315	...	2327	2348	0039
Aberystwyth 147 a.	...	...	...		▬	1321	│	1521	│	...	1723	...	...	│	1920	...	│	2122	│	...	2315	│	▬	...	...	│	...
Cardiff Central 149 d.	...	...	...		⑦	...	│	...	│	...	...	1329	...	│	...	1522	│	...	│	...	▬	│	...	2107	...	│	...
Shrewsbury d.	2340	...	...		1016	...	1219	...	1422	...	...	1533	...	1630	...	1732	1827	...	2026	...	...	2235	...	2319	...	2348	...
Gobowen d.	2358	...	...		1034	...	1237	...	1440	...	...	1551	...	1648	...	1749	1845	...	2044	...	...	│	...	│	...	│	...
Ruabon d.	0010	...	...		1046	...	1249	...	1452	...	...	1603	...	1700	...	1801	1856	...	2056	...	⑦	⊕	⑦	⊕	...	⊕	...
Wrexham General d.	0016	...	...		1053	...	1257	...	1459	...	...	1610	...	1707	...	1809	1906	...	2103	...	2235	│	2337	│	...	│	...
Chester 160 a.	0035	...	...		1112	...	1316	...	1519	...	...	1629	...	1727	...	1826	1925	...	2122	...	2254	2333	2357	0034	...	0044	...
Holyhead 160 a.	0215	...	...		...	...	...	...	...	...	...	1838	...	...	...	2019	2129	...	...	...	...	...	...	...	...	...	...

	⚒	Ⓐ	⑥	⑥ K🍷	Ⓐ K🍷	Ⓐ	⚒	Ⓐ 🍷	⑥	Ⓐ	Ⓐ Q	⑥	⑥ 🍷	Ⓐ C	⑥ Q	Ⓐ Q	Ⓐ	⑥	Ⓐ 🍷	⑥ G🍷	⑥	Ⓐ 🍷	Ⓐ 🍷	⑥ 🍷	⚒ F🍷	⚒ 🍷	⑥ 🍷
Holyhead 160 d.		...	...	...	...	...	...	...	0425	0425	...	...	...	0533	0522	...	0625	0631	...	...	0715	0726	0805	0816	...	0923r	1030
Chester 160 d.		...	...	0416	0422	0532	0547	...	0617	0620	...	...	...	0716	0730	...	0820	0820	...	...	0930	0930	1021	1020	...	1136	1221
Wrexham General d.		...	...	│	│	0547	0605	...	0632	0635	...	...	...	0735	0745	0750	0835	0835	...	...	0946	0945	1035	1035	...	1151	1235
Ruabon d.		...	...	⊕	⊕	0555	▬	...	0639	0642	...	...	...	│	0752	0758	0842	0842	...	...	0952	0952	1042	1042	...	1158	1242
Gobowen d.		...	...	│	│	0608	...	...	0651	0654	...	...	...	│	0804	0810	0854	0854	...	...	1004	1004	1054	1054	...	1210	1254
Shrewsbury a.		...	...	0531	0530	0627	...	...	0710	0714	...	...	...	0806	0824	0828	0913	0913	...	...	1029	1024	1113	1113	...	1230	1313
Cardiff Central 149 a.		...	...	0751	0747	│	...	...	0920	0917	...	...	...	0958	│	│	1116	1116	...	...	│	│	1314	1316	...	│	1526
Aberystwyth 147 d.		...	...	...	...	│	⑥	...	...	...	0526	0529	...	...	│	│	...	...	0728	0729	│	│	...	...	0929	│	...
Shrewsbury d.		0518	0522	...	...	0632	0633	0639	...	...	0731	0732	0819	...	0832	0833	...	...	0931	0931	1034	1031	...	...	1133	1234	...
Wellington d.		0532	0536	...	...	0646	0647	0653	...	...	0746	0746	0833	...	0846	0847	...	...	0945	0945	1048	1046	...	...	1147	1247	...
Telford Central d.		0539	0543	...	...	0653	0653	0700	...	...	0753	0753	0840	...	0853	0853	...	...	0952	0952	1055	1053	...	...	1153	1254	...
Wolverhampton a.		0559	0602	...	...	0712	0712	0717	...	...	0811	0812	0900	...	0912	0911	...	...	1010	1010	1113	1111	...	...	1211	1312	...
Birmingham New St a.		0619	0623	...	...	0733	0733	0747	...	...	0834	0832	0918	...	0935	0932	...	...	1033	1033	1133	1134	...	...	1234	1333	...
Birmingham Int ✈ a.		0649	0649	...	...	0750	0750	0800	...	...	0851	0850	0939	...	0950	0950	...	...	1050	1051	1150	1149	...	...	1250	1350	...
London Euston 150 a.		...	...	...	...	...	...	0913	...	...	...	...	1057	...	...	...	...	...	...	...	...	...	...	...	...	...	...

FOR NOTES SEE NEXT PAGE ▶ ▶ ▶ ▶

145 CHESTER - SHREWSBURY - BIRMINGHAM

2nd class AW

	Ⓐ D🍷	⚒ F🍷	⑥ 🍷	Ⓐ C	Ⓐ 🍷	⑥ 🍷	⚒ F🍷	⚒ 🍷	⑥ 🍷	Ⓐ 🍷	⚒ F🍷	⑥ 🍷	Ⓐ 🍷	Ⓐ	Ⓐ C	⑥	⑥ 🍷	Ⓐ	Ⓐ	⑥	Ⓐ B	⑥	Ⓐ	Ⓐ F	⑥	Ⓐ
Holyhead 160 d.	1041	...	1128	1133	1148	1238	...	1327	1427	1434	...	1525	1538	...	1636	...	1648	...	1728	1728	...	...	...	...	...	1922
Chester 160 d.	1221	...	1335	1316	1338	1420	...	1536	1619	1623	...	1730	1734	...	1822	1825	1833	1834	1917	1931	2022	2020	...	...	...	2119
Wrexham General d.	1239	...	1351	1330	1353	1434	...	1551	1634	1637	...	1745	1750	...	1837	1841	1848	1850	1932	1946	2038	2036	2046	...	...	2135
Ruabon d.	1246	...	1358	1338	1400	1441	...	1558	1641	1644	...	1752	1757	...	1845	...	1855	▬	1939	1953	▬	2043	2053	...	...	2142
Gobowen d.	1258	...	1410	1351	1412	1453	...	1610	1653	1656	...	1804	1809	...	1857	...	1907	...	1951	2005	...	2056	2106	...	...	2154
Shrewsbury a.	1317	...	1430	1416	1431	1512	...	1630	1712	1715	...	1823	1828	...	1921	...	1926	⚒	2013	2026	...	2116	2127	...	...	2214
Cardiff Central 149 a.	1511	...	|	1615	|	1710	...	|	1911	1925	...	|	|	...	2128	...	2130	🍷	...	▬	...	...	...	...	...	|
Aberystwyth 147 d.	...	1128	|	...	|	...	1329	|	...	...	1529	|	|	...	...	...	...	1727	...	Ⓐ	⑥	...	...	1929	1929	|
Shrewsbury d.	...	1333	1433	...	1432	...	1532	1633	...	...	1731	1832	1832	1847	...	...	...	1932	...	2045	2048	...	...	2132	2133	2218
Wellington d.	...	1347	1447	...	1446	...	1545	1647	...	...	1745	1846	1846	1859	...	...	...	1946	...	2057	2101	...	...	2146	2147	2232
Telford Central d.	...	1354	1453	...	1453	...	1553	1654	...	...	1752	1853	1853	1907	...	...	...	1953	...	2107	2108	...	...	2153	2153	2238
Wolverhampton a.	...	1412	1512	...	1511	...	1611	1711	...	...	1810	1912	1912	1937	...	...	...	2012	...	2136	2138	...	...	2212	2212	2255
Birmingham New St a.	...	1433	1533	...	1533	...	1634	1733	...	...	1835	1933	1935	1956	...	...	...	2033	...	2157	2158	...	...	2233	2233	2328
Birmingham Int ✈ a.	...	1450	1550	...	1550	...	1650	1750	...	...	1851	1949	1947	...	...	...	...	2049	...	...	...	...	...	2250	...	...
London Euston 150 a.	...	...	...	...	...	...	...	...	...	...	...	...	...	...	...	...	...	...	...	...	...	...	...	...	...	...

	⑥	Ⓐ	⑥	⚒	⑦	⑦	⑦ 🍷	⑦ 🍷	⑦ 🍷	⑦ 🍷	⑦ 🍷	⑦ F🍷	⑦ 🍷	⑦ 🍷	⑦ F🍷	⑦	⑦ F🍷	⑦	⑦ 🍷	⑦ F🍷	⑦	⑦ 🍷	⑦ F	⑦	⑦	⑦
Holyhead 160 d.	1921	...	...	...		...	...	...	...	...	1020	...	...	...	...	...	...	...	1625	...	...	1826	...	...	...	...
Chester 160 d.	2130	...	...	2232		0813	...	0920	...	1132	1229	...	1334	...	...	1540	...	1731	1826	...	1939	2027	...	2127	2205	2303
Wrexham General d.	2145	...	...	2247		0828	...	0935	...	1148	1244	...	1349	...	...	1556	...	1748	1841	...	1954	|	...	2142	2222	|
Ruabon d.	2152	...	...	2254		▬	...	0942	...	1155	1251	...	1356	...	...	1603	...	1756	1848	...	2001	⊕	...	2149	...	⊕
Gobowen d.	2204	...	...	2306		...	...	0955	...	1207	1303	...	1408	...	...	1615	...	1808	1900	...	2013	|	...	2201	...	|
Shrewsbury a.	2224	...	...	2327		...	...	1014	...	1226	1322	...	1427	...	...	1634	...	1828	1920	...	2033	2120	...	2221	...	0017
Cardiff Central 149 a.	|	...	...	...		⑦	...	|	...	|	1528	...	|	...	...	|	...	|	2130	...	|	|	...	|	...	...
Aberystwyth 147 d.	|	...	...	...		🍷	...	|	0929	|	...	1129	|	*1329*	1329	|	1527	|	...	1727	|	|	1929	|	...	...
Shrewsbury d.	2231	2245	2247	...		0810	0917	1018	1136	1233	...	1330	1430	1524	1531	1638	1732	1831	...	1930	2033	2120	2133	2224	...	...
Wellington d.	2245	2257	2259	...		0824	0931	1032	1149	1247	...	1343	1443	1538	1545	1653	1745	1845	...	1944	2047	|	2147	2238	...	...
Telford Central d.	2251	2305	2307	...		0831	0938	1038	1155	1254	...	1349	1450	1544	1551	1700	1751	1851	...	1950	2054	|	2153	2246	...	...
Wolverhampton a.	2309	2334	2336	...		0850	0957	1056	1213	1312	...	1407	1507	1601	1609	1720	1808	1909	...	2007	2112	2152	2211	2314	...	...
Birmingham New St a.	2331	2352	2354	...		0919	1017	1118	1235	1333	...	1427	1528	1620	1630	1741	1829	1929	...	2029	2133	2211	2232	...	...	...
Birmingham Int ✈ a.	...	...	...	...		0933	1034	1136	1255	1348	...	1451	1552	1639	1651	1756	1847	1951	...	2049	2151	2231	2254	...	...	...
London Euston 150 a.	...	...	...	...		...	...	...	...	...	...	...	...	1759	...	...	...	...	...	...	...	...	...	...	...	...

A – 12 and 🍷 Birmingham New Street - Crewe - Holyhead (Table **151**).
B – 12 and 🍷 London Euston - Wrexham and v.v. (Table **151**).
C – 12 and ✕ Holyhead - Cardiff and v.v.
D – From/to Llanelli (Table **136**).
F – Until Sept. 11 conveys 2 Pwllheli - Birmingham and v.v. (Table **148**).
G – Until Sept. 10 conveys 2 Barmouth - Birmingham (Table **148**).
H – To Crewe (Table **149**).
J – To Llandudno Junction (Table **160**).
K – To Milford Haven (Table **136**).
M – To Manchester Piccadilly (Table **160**).
Q – Also conveys 2 Crewe - Birmingham International (Table **149**).

b – ⑥ only.
f – Arrives 0601.
j – Arrives 0922 on ⑥.
k – Arrives 1316 on ⑥.
r – 0928 on ⑥.

⊕ – Via Crewe (Table **149**).

146 SHREWSBURY - SWANSEA

2nd class AW

km		Ⓐ	⑥	Ⓐ	⑥ 🍷	Ⓐ 🍷	⑦	⑥ 🍷	Ⓐ 🍷	⑦ A	⑥	Ⓐ
0	**Shrewsbury** 149 d.	0446	0516	0556	0904	1009	1204	1358	1405	1620	1757	1824
20	Church Stretton 149 d.	0504	0533	0614	0922	1027	1222	1416	1423	1639	1814	1842
32	Craven Arms 149 d.	0515	0547	0626	0932	1037	1232	1426	1434	1649	1825	1854
52	Knighton d.	0537	0610	0655f	0956	1101	1256	1450	1458	1713	1849	1918
84	**Llandrindod** a.	0612	0648	0734	1034	1140	1335	1529	1537	1750	1928	1957
84	**Llandrindod** d.	▬	0656	0737	1035	1157	1340	1543	1543	1805	1931	1958
110	Llanwrtyd a.	...	0726	0805	1104	1226	1409	1612	1612	1835	2000	2028
110	Llanwrtyd d.	Ⓐ	0727	0811	1109	1228	1411	1614	1626	1836	2012	2032
128	Llandovery d.	0644	0753	0836	1134	1253	1436	1639	1650	1902	2036	2058
146	Llandeilo d.	0705	0814	0858	1156	1315	1458	1701	1712	1923	2057	2119
159	Pantyffynnon d.	0723	0832	0915	1213	1332	1515	1718	1729	1941	2115	2137
178	Llanelli 136 a.	0744	0853	0938	1234	1353	1536	1739	1750	2002	2139	2158
196	**Swansea** 136 a.	0809	|	1004	1257	1417	1602	1807	1815	2026	|	|
211	**Carmarthen** 136 a.	...	0921	...	...	...	...	...	...	...	2206	2228

	⑥	Ⓐ	Ⓐ B	⑥ 🍷	Ⓐ 🍷	⑦	⑥ 🍷	Ⓐ 🍷	⑦	⑥	Ⓐ
Carmarthen 136 d.	...	0447	...	...	...	...	...	...	...	...	...
Swansea 136 d.	0430	|	0601	0914	0927	1110	1310	1435	1535	1816	1830
Llanelli 136 d.	0453	0516	0625	0937	0951	1133	1336	1453	1558	1842	1853
Pantyffynnon d.	0513	0537	0646	0958	1012	1154	1357	1514	1618	1901	1914
Llandeilo d.	0532	0557	0708	1018	1032	1214	1417	1534	1638	1921	1934
Llandovery d.	0553	0619	0730	1039	1054	1236	1439	1556	1700	1942	1956
Llanwrtyd a.	0616	▬	0754	1101	1117	1259	1502	1619	1724	2005	2020
Llanwrtyd d.	0618	...	0812	1111	1118	1301	1504	1626	1725	2009	2035
Llandrindod a.	0646	Ⓐ B	0843	1142	1148	1331	1534	1657	1756	2039	2106
Llandrindod d.	0657	0618	0845	1144	1201	1344	1542	1659	1759	2041	2109
Knighton d.	0734	0703r	0923	1221	1241	1422	1621	1737	1838	2117	2148
Craven Arms 149 d.	0756	0729	0945	1242	1306	1444	1643	1800	1900	2139	2210
Church Stretton 149 d.	0809	0742	0958	1255	1319	1457	1656	1813	1913	2151	2225
Shrewsbury 149 a.	0825	0758	1014	1311	1337	1513	1712	1829	1935	2208	2243

A – To Cardiff Central (Table **136**).
B – To Crewe (Table **149**).

f – Arrives 0648.
r – Arrives 0655.

147 SHREWSBURY - ABERYSTWYTH

2nd class AW

km		⚒	⚒	⚒	⑥	Ⓐ	⚒	Ⓐ	⑥	Ⓐ	⑥	⚒	⚒	⚒	⑥	Ⓐ	⑥	Ⓐ	Ⓐ	⑥	⚒	⑥	Ⓐ	⑦	⑦ 🚌
	Birmingham N Street 145 d.		...	...	0624	0625	0825	...	...	1025	1025	1225	1425	...	1625	1625	...	...	1825	1825	...	2025	2025		
0	**Shrewsbury** d.		...	0625	0729	0727	0930	1029	1029	1127	1129	1328	1528	...	1727	1730	1827	1831	1930	1930	2032	2143	2150		0830
32	Welshpool d.		...	0647	0752	0749	0952	1051	1051	1149	1151	1351	1552	...	1749	1752	1849	1853	1952	1952	2054	2205	2212		0905
54	Newtown d.		...	0702	0807	0804	1007	1106	1106	1204	1206	1406	1607	...	1804	1807	1904	1908	2007	2007	2109	2220	2227		0930
63	Caersws d.		...	0709	0814	0811	1014	1113	1113	1211	1213	1413	1614	...	1811	1814	1911	1915	2014	2014	2116	2227	2234		0945
98	**Machynlleth** a.		...	0742	0845	0843	1045	1141	1142	1242	1244	1444	1645	...	1842	1843	1944	1946	2048	2048	2143	2257	2303		1025
98	**Machynlleth** 148 ▷ d.		0647	0746	0849	0848	1050	1142	1146	1247	1249	1449	1650	1801	1848	1849	1946	1947	2049	2053	2150	2303	2306		1025
104	Dovey Junction 148 ▷ d.		0655	0755	0856	0855	1056	1154	1155	1255	1257	1455	1656	|	1856	1857	1955	1955	2057	2101	2158	2309	2312		1035
118	Borth ▷ d.		0705	0805	0906	0905	1106	1204	1205	1305	1307	1505	1706	|	1906	1907	2005	2005	2107	2111	2208	2319	2322		1055
131	**Aberystwyth** ▷ a.		0721	0822	0921	0921	1121	1220	1221	1322	1322	1522	1721	1829	1921	1921	2022	2020	2122	2125	2222	2335	2336		1120

	⑦	⑦	⑦	⑦	⑦	⑦	⑦	⑦	⑦	⑦
Birmingham N Street 145 d.	...	1004	1223	...	1423	...	1624	...	1823	2024
Shrewsbury d.	1027	1128	1330	1429	1528	1629	1727	1828	1927	2128
Welshpool d.	1051	1150	1352	1451	1551	1651	1749	1850	1949	2150
Newtown d.	1106	1205	1407	1506	1606	1706	1804	1905	2004	2205
Caersws d.	1113	1212	1414	1514	1613	1713	1812	1912	2011	2212
Machynlleth a.	1143	1243	1445	1545	1642	1742	1843	1941	2042	2240
Machynlleth 148 ▷ d.	1143	1248	1449	1546	1647	1743	1847	1942	2047	2245
Dovey Junction 148 ▷ d.	1155	1256	1457	1555	1655	1755	1855	1956	2055	2251
Borth ▷ d.	1205	1306	1507	1615	1706	1805	1905	2006	2105	2301
Aberystwyth ▷ a.	1221	1321	1521	1620	1723	1821	1920	2021	2122	2315

	⚒	Ⓐ	⑥	⑥	Ⓐ	Ⓐ	⑥	Ⓐ	⑥
Aberystwyth ▷ d.		0526	0529	0629	0629	0728	0729	0829	0829
Borth ▷ d.		0541	0544	0644	0644	0743	0744	0844	0844
Dovey Junction 148 ▷ d.		0551	0554	0654	0654	0753	0754	0858	0859
Machynlleth 148 ▷ a.		0559	0602	0702	0702	0801	0805	0906	0907
Machynlleth d.		0602	0603	0703	0705	0805	0808	0906	0908
Caersws d.		0628	0630	0730	0732	0832	0835	0933	0935
Newtown d.		0635	0637	0737	0739	0839	0842	0940	0942
Welshpool d.		0650	0651	0752	0754	0854	0856	0955	0956
Shrewsbury a.		0713	0714	0814	0819	0918	0920	1020	1019
Birmingham New Street 145 a.		0834	0832	...	...	1033	1033	...	...

	⚒	Ⓐ	⑥	⚒	⚒	⚒	Ⓐ	⑥	Ⓐ	⑥	⚒	⑦	⑦	⑦	⑦	⑦	⑦	⑦	⑦	⑦	⑦	⑦	⑦	⑦	⑦
Aberystwyth ▷ d.	0929	1128	1129	1229	1329	1529	1727	1728	1831	1831	1929		0829	0929	1029	1129	1229	1329	1429	1527	1629	1727	1829	1929	2319
Borth ▷ d.	0944	1143	1144	1244	1344	1544	1742	1742	1846	1846	1944		0844	0944	1044	1144	1244	1344	1444	1543	1644	1743	1844	1944	2334
Dovey Junction 148 ▷ d.	0954	1153	1155	1257	1354	1554	1752	1752	1856	1856	1959		0858	0954	1056	1154	1257	1357	1459	1554	1656	1753	1902	1954	2344
Machynlleth 148 ▷ a.	1002	1202	1203	1306	1402	1602	1800	1800	1905	1904	2007		0906	1002	1103	1202	1305	1404	1507	1601	1703	1801	1910	2002	2353
Machynlleth d.	1008	1205	1207	1306	1407	1608	1805	1805	1909	1906	2011		0907	1008	1104	1206	1306	1407	1508	1605	1703	1805	...	2006	...
Caersws d.	1035	1232	1234	1333	1434	1635	1834	1832	1936	1932	2038		0934	1035	1132	1233	1333	1434	1535	1634	1734	1832	...	2033	...
Newtown d.	1042	1239	1241	1340	1441	1642	1841	1839	1943	1939	2045		0941	1042	1139	1240	1340	1441	1542	1641	1741	1839	...	2040	...
Welshpool d.	1056	1254	1255	1354	1455	1656	1856	1855	1957	1957	2100		0956	1057	1154	1254	1354	1456	1556	1655	1755	1854	...	2054	...
Shrewsbury a.	1120	1316	1319	1419	1521	1720	1921	1919	2020	2025	2125		1021	1121	1220	1318	1419	1519	1618	1719	1819	1918	...	2118	...
Birmingham N Street 145 a.	1234	1433	1433	...	1634	1835	2033	2033	...	...	2233		...	1235	...	1427	...	1630	...	1829	...	2029	...	2232	...

▷ – Additional journeys Machynlleth - Aberystwyth and v.v.:
From Machynlleth at 0452 ⚒, 0545 Ⓐ, 0547 ⑥, 0750 ⑦, 0849 ⑦, 0947 ⑦, 1049 ⑦, 1350 ⑦.
From Aberystwyth at 2029 Ⓒ, 2035 ⑥, 2129 Ⓒ, 2132 ⑥, 2229 ⚒, 2338 ⑥, 2339 Ⓐ.

AW 2nd class — MACHYNLLETH - PWLLHELI — 148

The line between Machynlleth and Pwllheli is closed from Sept. 12 for repairs to Barmouth Bridge. A 🚌 replacement service will operate - see lower panel.

Service until September 11

km		⚒	Ⓐ	⑥	⚒	Ⓐ	⑥	⚒	Ⓐ	⑥		Ⓐ	⑥	⚒	⑥	Ⓐ	⑥	Ⓐ	⑦	⑦		⑦	⑦	⑦	⑦
	Birmingham New St **145** d.		...	...	...	*0626*	*0624*	0825	1025	1025	...	1225	1225	1425	1625	1625	*1925**	*1925**		...	...	1004	1223	1423	1624
0	*Shrewsbury* **147** d.		...	...	...	*0727*	*0729*	0930	1127	1129	...	1328	1329	1528	1727	1730	*2032*	*2032*		...	...	1128	1330	1528	1727
6	**Machynlleth** 147 d.		0507	0509	0643	0852	0853	1055	1251	1252	...	1456	1456	1655	1904	1904	2147	2147		1004	...	1251	1453	1650	1855
16	Dovey Junction 147 d.		0513	0515	0649	0858	0859	1101	1257	1258	...	1502	1502	1701	1910	1910	2153	2153		1010	...	1300	1459	1656	1901
22	Aberdovey d.		0526	0528	0702	0911	0912	1114	1310	1311	...	1515	1515	1714	1923	1923	2206	2206		1023	...	1313	1512	1709	1914
22	Tywyn 🚂 a.		0534	0536	0712	0921	0921	1124	1320	1320	...	1525	1525	1725	1933	1933	2216	2216		1030	...	1320	1519	1718	1921
37	Tywyn 🚂 d.		0534	0536	0714	0929	0929	1130	1325	1324	...	1526	1525	1729	1933	1933	2217	2217		1030	...	1324	1531	1729	1924
41	Fairbourne d.		0553	0555	0732	0948	0948	1148	1344	1343	...	1545	1544	1747	1951	1951	2235	2236		1049	...	1343	1549	1747	1943
58	**Barmouth** d.		0606	0608	0747	1001	1001	1201	1357	1356	...	1558	1557	1800	2004	2004	2248	2248		1058	...	1356	1559	1759	1953
58	Harlech a.		...	...	0813	1026	1026	1227	1422	1421	...	1623	1622	1825	2028	2030	2313	2314		1124	...	1422	1624	1825	2018
67	Harlech d.		...	...	0825	1026	1026	1227	1431	1431	...	1628	1629	1833	2029	2030	2314	2314		1125	...	1431	1624	1830	2022
69	Penrhyndeudraeth d.		...	...	0838	1039	1039	1240	1444	1444	...	1640	1641	1845	2041	2043	2327	2327		1138	...	1444	1637	1843	2035
72	Minffordd 160 d.		...	...	0841	1042	1042	1243	1447	1447	...	1644	1645	1849	2045	2047	2330	2331		1142	...	1448	1641	1847	2038
80	**Porthmadog** 160 d.		...	...	0850	1051	1051	1252	1456	1456	...	1652	1653	1857	2053	2055	2337	2339		1154f	...	1456	1647	1855	2044
93	Criccieth d.		...	...	0857	1058	1058	1259	1503	1503	...	1700	1700	1904	2101	2103	2345	2347		1201	...	1503	1654	1902	2052
	Pwllheli a.		...	...	0912	1113	1113	1314	1519	1520	...	1717	1715	1920	2116	2118	2359	0001		1217	...	1519	1710	1918	2107

	⚒	⑥	Ⓐ	⚒	⚒		Ⓐ	⑥	Ⓐ	⑥	⑥	Ⓐ	⚒	Ⓐ	⑥	⑥	Ⓐ	⑦	⑦	⑦		⑦	⑦	⑦	
Pwllheli d.		...	...	0629	0724	...	0934	0934	1137	1137	1338	1338	1537	1742	1742	2026	2026		0934	1128	...	1340	1533	1736	...
Criccieth d.		...	...	0643	0738	...	0948	0948	1151	1151	1352	1352	1551	1756	1756	2040	2040		0948	1142	...	1354	1547	1750	...
Porthmadog 160 d.		...	...	0653	0747	...	0957	0958	1201	1201	1402	1402	1601	1806	1806	2056f	2056f		0958	1157f	...	1406	1557	1800	...
Minffordd 160 d.		...	...	0657	0752	...	1001	1002	1205	1205	1406	1406	1605	1810	1810	2101	2100		1002	1201	...	1410	1601	1805	...
Penrhyndeudraeth d.		...	...	0701	0756	...	1005	1006	1209	1209	1410	1410	1609	1814	1814	2104	2104		1006	1205	...	1414	1605	1809	...
Harlech a.		...	...	0717	0811	...	1022	1023	1226	1224	1427	1427	1626	1830	1830	2120	2119		1023	1219	...	1428	1622	1823	...
Harlech d.		...	...	0717	0821	...	1029	1028	1228	1228	1428	1428	1629	1830	1830	2120	2119		1028	1221	...	1434	1629	1827	...
Barmouth d.		0645	0645	0749	0852f	...	1059	1059f	1255	1255	1455	1455	1656	1857	1857	2147	2146		1101f	1250	...	1501	1656	1854	...
Fairbourne d.		0653	0653	0757	0900	...	1107	1107	1303	1303	1503	1503	1704	1905	1905	2155	2154		1109	1258	...	1509	1704	1903	...
Tywyn 🚂 a.		0714	0714	0817	0922	...	1129	1129	1325	1325	1526	1526	1726	1927	1927	2217	2217		1130	1319	...	1528	1726	1923	...
Tywyn 🚂 d.		0714	0714	0817	0927	...	1130	1130	1325	1325	1526	1526	1727	1934	1934	2217	2217		1130	1320	...	1528	1727	1924	...
Aberdovey d.		0720	0720	0823	0933	...	1136	1136	1331	1331	1532	1532	1733	1940	1941	2223	2223		1136	1326	...	1536	1733	1930	...
Dovey Junction 147 d.		0736	0736	0838	0948	...	1150	1152	1346	1346	1547	1547	1748	1956	1956	2238	2238		1151	1341	...	1551	1749	1948	...
Machynlleth 147 a.		0743	0743	0848	0955	...	1158	1158	1352	1353	1553	1555	1756	2004	2004	2245	2245		1158	1349	...	1559	1757	1955	...
Shrewsbury **147** a.		0920	*0918*	*1020*	1120	...	1316	1319	1519	1521	1719	1720	*1921*	2125	*2125*	...	...		1318	1519	...	1719	1918	2118	...
Birmingham New St **145** a.		1033	*1033*	*1134**	1233	...	1433	1433	1633	1634	1833	1835	*2033*	2233	*2233*	...	...		1427	1630	...	1829	2029	2232	...

Service from September 12

	⚒🚌	⚒🚌	⚒🚌	⚒🚌	⚒🚌		⑦🚌	⑦🚌	⚒🚌	⚒🚌		⑦🚌	⑦🚌	⚒🚌	⚒🚌	⑦🚌	⚒🚌	🚌	🚌	🚌		🚌	🚌	⚒🚌	⚒🚌
Birmingham New St **145** ‡ d.	...	...	...	*0624*	*0624*	...	...	...	*0825*	*0825*	...	*1004*	*1004*	*1025*	*1025*	*1223*	*1223*	*1223*	*1423*	*1423*	...	*1624*	*1624*	*1925**	*1925**
Shrewsbury **147** ‡ d.	...	...	...	*0727*	*0727*	...	...	...	*0930*	*0930*	...	*1128*	*1128*	*1127*	*1127*	*1328*	*1328*	*1328*	*1528*	*1528*	...	*1727t*	*1727t*	*2032*	*2032*
Machynlleth 147 d.	0507	0643	0643	0855	0855	...	1004	1004	1055	1055	...	1255	1255	1255	1255	1455	1455	1455	1655	1655	...	1855	1855	2155	2155
Dovey Junction 147 d.	│	│	│	│	│	...	│	│	│	│	...	│	│	│	│	│	│	│	│	│	...	│	│	│	│
Aberdovey d.	0533	│	0709	│	0921	...	│	1030	│	1121	...	│	1321	│	1321	│	│	1521	│	1721	...	│	1921	│	2221
Tywyn 🚂 a.	0542	0711	0718	0923	0930	...	1032	1039	1123	1130	...	1323	1330	1323	1330	1521	1523	1530	1723	1730	...	1923	1930	2223	2230
Tywyn 🚂 d.	0542	0711	0718	0923	0930	...	1032	1039	1123	1130	...	1323	1330	1323	1330	1521	1523	1530	1723	1730	...	1923	1930	2223	2230
Fairbourne d.	0619	│	0755	│	1007	...	│	1116	│	1207	...	│	1407	│	1407	│	│	1607	│	1807	...	│	2007	│	2307
Barmouth d.	0649	0811	0825	1023	1037	...	1132	1146	1223	1237	...	1423	1437	1423	1437	1621	1623	1637	1823	1837	...	2023	2037	2323	2337
Harlech a.	...	0839	0854	1051	1106	...	1200	1215	1251	1306	...	1451	1506	1451	1506	1649	1651	1706	1851	1906	...	2051	2106	2351	0006
Harlech d.	...	0839	0854	1051	1106	...	1200	1215	1251	1306	...	1451	1506	1451	1506	1649	1651	1706	1851	1906	...	2051	2106	2351	0006
Penrhyndeudraeth d.	...	0853	0908	1105	1120	...	1214	1229	1305	1320	...	1505	1520	1505	1520	1703	1705	1720	1905	1920	...	2105	2120	0006	0020
Minffordd 160 d.	...	0855	0910	1107	1122	...	1216	1231	1307	1422	...	1507	1522	1507	1522	1705	1707	1722	1907	1922	...	2107	2122	0008	0022
Porthmadog 160 d.	...	0900	0915	1112	1127	...	1221	1236	1312	1327	...	1512	1527	1512	1527	1710	1712	1727	1912	1927	...	2112	2127	0013	0027
Criccieth d.	...	0912	0927	1124	1139	...	1233	1248	1324	1339	...	1524	1539	1524	1539	1722	1724	1739	1924	1939	...	2124	2139	0025	0039
Pwllheli a.	...	0932	0947	1144	1159	...	1253	1308	1344	1359	...	1544	1559	1544	1559	1742	1744	1759	1944	1959	...	2144	2159	0045	0059

	⚒🚌	⚒🚌	⚒🚌	⚒🚌	⚒🚌	⚒🚌		🚌	🚌	🚌	🚌	🚌	🚌		🚌	🚌	🚌	🚌		⑦🚌	⑦🚌	⚒🚌	⚒🚌	⚒🚌	⚒🚌
Pwllheli d.	...	...	0548	0603	0648	0703	...	0848	0903	1048	1103	1248	1303	...	1448	1503	1648	1703	...	1737	1752	1848	1903	2025	2040
Criccieth d.	...	...	0608	0623	0708	0723	...	0908	0923	1108	1123	1308	1323	...	1508	1523	1708	1723	...	1757	1812	1908	1923	2045	2100
Porthmadog 160 d.	...	...	0620	0635	0720	0735	...	0920	0935	1120	1135	1320	1335	...	1520	1535	1720	1735	...	1809	1824	1920	1935	2057	2112
Minffordd 160 d.	...	...	0625	0640	0725	0740	...	0925	0940	1125	1140	1325	1340	...	1525	1540	1725	1740	...	1814	1829	1925	1940	2102	2117
Penrhyndeudraeth d.	...	...	0627	0642	0727	0742	...	0927	0942	1127	1142	1327	1342	...	1527	1542	1727	1742	...	1816	1831	1927	1942	2104	2119
Harlech a.	...	...	0641	0656	0741	0756	...	0941	0956	1141	1156	1341	1356	...	1541	1556	1741	1756	...	1830	1845	1941	1956	2118	2133
Harlech d.	...	...	0641	0656	0741	0756	...	0941	0956	1141	1156	1341	1356	...	1541	1556	1741	1756	...	1830	1845	1941	1956	2118	2133
Barmouth d.	0610	0624	0710	0724	0810	0824	...	1010	1024	1210	1224	1410	1424	...	1610	1624	1810	1824	...	1859	1913	2010	2024	2147	2201
Fairbourne d.	0640	│	0740	│	0840	│	...	1040	│	1240	│	1440	│	...	1640	│	1840	│	...	1929	│	2040	│	2217	│
Tywyn 🚂 a.	0717	0724	0817	0824	0917	0924	...	1117	1124	1317	1324	1517	1524	...	1717	1724	1917	1924	...	2006	2013	2117	2124	2254	2301
Tywyn 🚂 d.	0717	0724	0817	0824	0917	0924	...	1117	1124	1317	1324	1517	1524	...	1717	1724	1917	1924	...	2006	2013	2117	2124	2254	2301
Aberdovey d.	0726	│	0826	│	0926	│	...	1126	│	1326	│	1526	│	...	1726	│	1926	│	...	2015	│	2126	│	2303	│
Dovey Junction 147 d.	│	│	│	│	│	│	...	│	│	│	│	│	│	...	│	│	│	│	...	│	│	│	│	│	│
Machynlleth 147 a.	0755	0755	0855	0855	0955	0955	...	1155	1155	1355	1355	1555	1555	...	1755	1755	1955	1955	...	2044	2044	2155	2155	2332	2332
Shrewsbury **147** ‡ a.	*0920*	*0920*	*1020*	*1020*	*1120*	*1120*	...	*1319r*	*1319r*	*1521*	*1521*	*1720*	*1720*	...	*1921*	*1921*	*2125c*	*2125c*	...	...	...	...	...	...	...
Birmingham New St **145** ‡ a.	*1033*	*1033*	*1134**	*1134**	*1234*	*1234*	...	*1433a*	*1433a*	*1634a*	*1634a*	*1835a*	*1835a*	...	*2033a*	*2033a*	*2233*	*2233*	...	...	...	...	...	...	...

a – Arrives 4–6 minutes earlier on ⑦.
c – Arrives 2118 on ⑦.
f – Arrives 4–7 minutes earlier.
r – Arrives 1316 on Ⓐ.
t – Departs 1730 on Ⓐ.
* – Change at Shrewsbury and Machynlleth.
‡ – Connecting services from / to Birmingham and Shrewsbury are by train.
🚂 – Talyllyn Railway (Tywyn Wharf - Abergynolwyn - Nant Gwernol: *12 km*). ✆ 01654 710472. www.talyllyn.co.uk

AW 2nd class — CARDIFF - HEREFORD - CREWE - MANCHESTER — 149

Most Manchester trains continue to / from destinations on Table **136**

km		Ⓐ	②–⑤	Ⓐ	Ⓐ	Ⓐ	Ⓐ R	Ⓐ 🍷	Ⓐ A	Ⓐ	Ⓐ S	Ⓐ 🍷	Ⓐ 🍷	Ⓐ 🍷	Ⓐ 🍷	Ⓐ A	Ⓐ 🍷	Ⓐ 🍷	Ⓐ 🍷	Ⓐ 🍷	Ⓐ 🍷	Ⓐ 🍷	Ⓐ 🍷	Ⓐ 🍷	Ⓐ A	Ⓐ 🍷
0	**Cardiff** Central 134 § d.		0030	0435	0512	0537	...	0635	0645	0750	...	0850	0922	0956	1052	1122	156	1249	1322	1357	1449	1523	1550	1650	1716	1749
19	Newport 134 § d.		0049	0453	0531	0556	...	0648	0659	0805	...	0904	0936	1009	1105	1136	1209	1303	1337	1411	1503	1537	1603	1703	1731	1803
30	Cwmbrân d.		0100	0505	0542	0606	...	0659	0710	0815	...	0914	0947	1020	1116	1147	1220	1314	1347	1422	1513	1547	1614	1714	1742	1813
35	Pontypool & New Inn d.		0106	0511	0548	0612	...	│	0718	0821	...	│	0952	│	│	1154	│	│	1353	│	│	1553	1619	1719	1749	1818
50	Abergavenny d.		0118	0522	0557	0621	...	0714	0729	0830	...	0927	1002	1033	1129	1205	1234	1327	1402	1436	1526	1602	1628	1729	1800	1828
89	**Hereford** d.		0151	0547	0625	0647	...	0739	0754	0857	...	0954	1029	1058	1154	1230	1300	1353	1429	1502	1552	1628	1654	1757	1825	1853
109	Leominster d.		...	0600	0638	0700	...	0752	│	0910	...	1007	│	1111	1207	│	1313	1406	│	1515	1605	1641	1707	1810	│	1906
127	Ludlow d.		...	0611	0649	0711	...	0803	0816	0921	...	1018	1050	1122	1218	1251	1324	1417	1450	1526	1616	1652	1718	1822	│	1917
138	Craven Arms 146 d.		...	0620	0657	0719	0729	0812	│	0929	0945	1026	1058	1131	1227	│	1333	1425	1459	│	1624	1701	1726	1831	│	1926
150	Church Stretton 146 d.		...	0629	0708	0728	0742	0821	│	0938	0958	1035	1107	1140	1236	│	1342	1434	1508	│	1633	1710	1735	1840	│	1935
170	**Shrewsbury** 146 a.		...	0644	0725	0743	0758	0836	0846	0953	1014	1051	1122	1155	1251	1325	1357	1449	1524	1553	1648	1724	1750	1854	1909	1950
170	**Shrewsbury** ¶ d.		...	0646	0728	0746	0800	0836	0850	0956	1017	1051	1130	1157	1251	1329	1357	1452	1529	1556	1649	1728	1751	1858	1909	1950
200	Whitchurch ¶ d.		...	0706	│	0806	0828	0902	│	│	1046	1108	│	│	1308	│	│	1509	│	│	1708	│	1808	1915	│	│
223	**Crewe** ¶ a.		...	0724	│	0824	0852	0924	│	1025	1111	1127	│	1227	1328	│	1427	1528	│	1627	1727	│	1827	1934	│	2021
	Chester **145, 160** a.		...	│	0821	│	...	│	0947	│	...	│	1226	│	│	1426	│	│	1625	│	│	1822	│	│	1958	│
	Holyhead **145, 160** a.		...	│	1009	│	...	│	1120	│	...	│	1419	│	│	1620	│	│	1821	│	│	2020	│	│	2142	│
263	Stockport a.		...	0759	...	0859	...	0959	...	1059	...	1159	...	1259	1359	...	1459	1559	...	1659	1759	...	1859	2007	...	2053
273	**Manchester** Piccadilly a.		...	0809	...	0913	...	1011	...	1111	...	1213	...	1313	1413	...	1513	1613	...	1713	1813	...	1913	2019	...	2107

A – (12) and ✕ Cardiff - Holyhead.
R – From Llandrindod (Table **146**).
S – From Swansea (Table **146**).
V – To Birmingham International (Table **145**).
¶ – Additional journeys Shrewsbury - Whitchurch - Crewe and v.v.:
From Shrewsbury at 0531 Ⓐ, 0548 ⑥, 0825 ⑦, 1019 ⑥, 1026 ⑦, 1224, 1422 ⑦, 1424 ⚒, 1624, 1824 ⑥⑦, 1832 Ⓐ, 2021 ⑦, 2032 ⚒.
From Crewe at 0640 Ⓐ **V**, 0720 ⑥ **V**, 0734 Ⓐ **V**, 0921 ⑦, 1120 ⚒, 1126 ⑦, 1320, 1520 ⑥⑦, 1522 Ⓐ, 1720 ⚒, 1726 ⑦, 1918 ⑦, 2145 ⑦.

149 CARDIFF - HEREFORD - CREWE - MANCHESTER

2nd class AW

Most Manchester trains continue to / from destinations on Table **136**

	Ⓐ 🍷	Ⓐ 🍷	Ⓐ	Ⓐ	Ⓐ	Ⓐ	⑥	⑥	⑥	⑥	⑥ 🍷	⑥ 🍷	⑥ 🍷	⑥ 🍷	⑥ 🍷	⑥ 🍷	⑥ 🍷	⑥ 🍷	⑥ 🍷	⑥ 🍷	⑥ 🍷	⑥ 🍷	⑥ 🍷	⑥ 🍷	⑥ 🍷	⑥ 🍷
Cardiff Central 134 § d.	1823	1855	1941	2015	2115	2155		0435	0520	0537	0652	0722	0752	0851	0923	0955	1053	1123	1155	1255	1322	1355	1456	1523	1555	1654
Newport 134 § d.	1836	1909	1955	2029	2129	2213		0452	0534	0552	0706	0737	0806	0905	0938	1009	1107	1137	1208	1308	1336	1409	1509	1538	1609	1708
Cwmbrân d.	1847	1919	2005	2039	2140	2224		0503	0545	0602	0716	0747	0816	0915	0948	1019	1117	1147	1219	1319	1346	1420	1520	1548	1619	1718
Pontypool & New Inn d.	│	1924	2010	2045	│	2230		0509	0550	0608	│	0753	│	│	0954	│	1123	1153	│	│	1352	│	│	1554	1624	│
Abergavenny d.	1900	1934	2020	2054	2153	2240		0518	0600	0617	0729	0802	0829	0928	1004	1032	1132	1202	1233	1332	1401	1433	1533	1603	1634	1731
Hereford d.	1925	1959	2046	2122	2220	2308		0546	0626	0647d	0755	0830	0855	0954	1030	1058	1158	1228	1258	1358	1427	1459	1559	1629	1700	1757
Leominster d.	│	2012	2059	2135	2233	2321		0559	0639	0700	0808	│	0908	1007	│	1111	1211	│	1311	1411	│	1512	1612	1642	1713	1810
Ludlow d.	1946	2023	2110	2146	2244	2332		0610	0650	0711	0819	0851	0919	1018	1051	1122	1222	1249	1322	1422	1448	1523	1623	1654	1724	1821
Craven Arms 146 d.	│	2032	2118	2154	2253	2342		0618	0659	0719	0827	0859	0927	1026	1100	1130	1230	1257	│	1431	1456	│	1631	│	│	1829
Church Stretton 146 d.	│	2041	2127	2204	2302	2351		0627	0708	0728	0836	0908	0936	1035	1109	│	1239	1307	1337	1441	1505	│	1640	1708	│	1838
Shrewsbury 146 a.	2013	2056	2142	2219	2317	0008		0641	0723	0743	0852	0924	0950	1050	1124	1152	1254	1322	1352	1455	1525	1550	1654	1722	1751	1852
Shrewsbury 145 ¶ d.	2014	2056	2146	2220	2317	0013		0647	0726	0745	0852	0927	0954	1051	1127	1152	1255	1327	1353	1456	1530	1551	1656	1726	1752	1856
Whitchurch ¶ d.	│	2113	│	2245	2343	0039		0707	│	0805	0909	│	1010	1108	│	1209	│	│	1410	│	│	1608	│	│	1808	│
Crewe ¶ a.	2043	2131	│	2307	0005	0104		0725	│	0824	0928	│	1028	1127	│	1227	1327	│	1428	1527	│	1627	1727	│	1827	1927
Chester 145, 160 a.	2112	│	2243	...	0027	...		│	0820	│	│	1020	│	│	1221	│	│	1424	│	│	1626	│	│	1820	│	│
Holyhead 145, 160 a.	...	│	0043	...	...	...		│	1019	│	│	1217	│	│	1419	│	│	1622	│	│	1821	│	│	2025	│	│
Stockport a.	...	2201	...	...	...	...		0758	...	0858	0959	...	1059	1159	...	1259	1359	...	1459	1559	...	1700	1800	...	1859	1959
Manchester Piccadilly a.	...	2215	...	...	...	...		0811	...	0913	1013	...	1113	1212	...	1313	1413	...	1513	1613	...	1713	1814	...	1913	2012

	⑥ 🍷	⑥ 🍷	⑥ 🍷	⑥ J	⑥ 🍷	⑥ 🍷	⑥ N	⑦	⑦	⑦	⑦	⑦ 🍷	⑦ 🍷	⑦ 🍷	⑦ 🍷	⑦ 🍷	⑦ 🍷	⑦ 🍷	⑦ 🍷	⑦ 🍷	⑦ 🍷	⑦ 🍷	⑦	⑦ K	⑦	⑦
Cardiff Central 134 § d.	1723	1756	1851	1941	2012	2055	...		...	0830	0928	1034	1134	1236	1329	1350	1454	1522	1600	1640	1755	1840	1940	...	2107	2319
Newport 134 § d.	1736	1809	1904	1955	2027	2109	...		...	0852	0947	1049	1150	1250	1343	1405	1509	1535	1614	1655	1810	1855	1956	...	2124	2337
Cwmbrân d.	1747	1820	1915	2005	2038	2121	...		...	0903	0959	1103	1206	1306	1353	1415	1524	1546	1628	1709	1824	1909	2010	...	2134	2348
Pontypool & New Inn d.	1752	1825	1920	2011	2043	│	...		...	0909	1005	1109	1212	1311	1359	│	│	1551	│	1715	1830	│	2016	...	2140	2354
Abergavenny d.	1802	1835	1930	2020	2053	2134	...		...	0918	1015	1119	1222	1321	1408	1428	1537	1601	1641	1725	1839	1922	2026	...	2149	0004
Hereford d.	1827	1900	1956	2046	2120	2200	...		...	0947	1045	1149	1252	1349	1435	1454	1604	1627	1707	1753	1906	1950	2054	...	2219	0035
Leominster d.	│	1913	2009	2059	2133	2214	...		...	1001	1058	1202	1305	1403	1448	1507	│	1640	│	1806	1919	2004	2108	...	2232	▬
Ludlow d.	1848	1924	2020	2110	2144	2225	...		...	1012	1110	1213	1317	1414	1459	1518	1626	1651	1729	1817	1931	2015	2119	...	2243	...
Craven Arms 146 d.	1857	│	2029	2118	2153	2233	...		...	1020	│	1223	│	1423	1508	│	│	1659	│	1826	│	2023	2129	...	2252	...
Church Stretton 146 d.	1906	│	2038	2127	2203	2242	...		...	1029	│	1232	│	1433	│	│	│	1708	│	1835	│	2032	2138	...	2301	⑦
Shrewsbury 146 a.	1921	1951	2052	2143	2218	2257	...		...	1046	1141	1249	1347	1449	1529	1553	1654	1722	1755	1850	1959	2047	2156	...	2317	K
Shrewsbury 145 ¶ d.	1928	1952	2056	2143	2219	2306	2335		0955	1048	1147	1250	1349	1453	1533	1554	1654	1732	1756	1854	1959	2050	...	2235	2319	2348
Whitchurch ¶ d.	│	2009	│	│	2244	2332	2359		│	│	│	│	│	│	│	│	│	│	│	│	│	│	...	│	2345	│
Crewe ¶ a.	│	2028	2127	│	2305	2354	0020		1026	1122	1224	1327	1426	1528	│	1627	1727	│	1829	1925	2031	2123	...	2306	0007	0021
Chester 145, 160 a.	2024	│	│	2236	...	0023	...		│	│	*1316*t	│	*1519*t	│	1629	*1727*t	│	1826	*1925*t	│	*2122*t	│	...	2333	0034	0044
Holyhead 145, 160 a.	2226	│	│	...	...	...	...		│	│	│	│	│	│	1838	│	│	2019	*2129*t	│	│	│	...	...	...	...
Stockport a.	...	2100	2158	...	...	...	...		1100	│	1300	1400	1502	1600	...	1700	1801	...	1900	2000	2101	2204	...	...	...	...
Manchester Piccadilly a.	...	2112	2213	...	...	...	...		1120	1207	1315	1417	1515	1614	...	1717	1818	...	1915	2015	2115	2219	...	...	...	...

	Ⓐ	②–⑤	Ⓐ 🍷	Ⓐ	Ⓐ 🍷	Ⓐ	Ⓐ 🍷	Ⓐ A	Ⓐ 🍷	Ⓐ	Ⓐ 🍷	Ⓐ 🍷 S		Ⓐ 🍷	Ⓐ 🍷	Ⓐ 🍷	Ⓐ 🍷	Ⓐ 🍷	Ⓐ 🍷	Ⓐ A	Ⓐ 🍷	Ⓐ 🍷	Ⓐ 🍷	Ⓐ 🍷	Ⓐ 🍷	Ⓐ 🍷
Manchester Piccadilly d.		...	...	...	...	...	0630	...	0731	...	0831	...	...	0931	...	1031	1131	...	1231	...	1331	1431	1531	...	1631	1731
Stockport d.		...	...	...	...	...	0639	...	0739	...	0839	...	...	0939	...	1039	1139	...	1239	...	1339	1439	1539	...	1639	1739
Holyhead 145, 160 d.		...	...	...	...	0425	│	0533	│	0625	│	...	...	│	0805	│	│	1041	│	1133	│	│	│	1434	│	│
Chester 145, 160 d.		...	0422	...	...	0620	│	0716	│	0820	│	...	...	│	1021	│	│	1221	│	1316	│	│	│	1623	│	│
Crewe ¶ d.		...	0450	...	0558	│	0709	│	0809	│	0909	0914	...	1009	│	1109	1209	│	1310	│	1409	1509	1609	│	1710	1812
Whitchurch ¶ d.		...	0509	...	0619	│	│	│	│	│	│	0937	...	│	│	│	│	│	│	│	1429	│	1629	│	│	1831
Shrewsbury 145 ¶ a.		...	0530	...	0646	0714	0743	0806	0841	0913	0939	1006	...	1039	1113	1139	1241	1317	1340	1416	1449	1539	1649	1715	1739	1851
Shrewsbury 146 d.		...	0531	0610	0648	0717	0744	0807	0843	0915	0940	1009	...	1040	1116	1140	1241	1317	1340	1418	1451	1540	1651	1716	1741	1853
Church Stretton 146 d.		...	0546	0626	0703	│	0759	│	0858	0930	│	1027	...	1055	│	1155	│	1332	│	│	1506	1555	1706	1731	1756	1908
Craven Arms 146 d.		...	0554	0634	0711	│	0807	│	0906	0938	│	1037	...	1103	1136	│	│	1340	│	│	1514	1603	1714	1739	1804	1916
Ludlow d.		...	0602	0643	0718	0743	0815	0836	0913	0945	1006	...	...	1110	1143	1209	1308	1348	1407	│	1521	1610	1721	1746	1811	1923
Leominster d.		...	0612	0654	0730	0753	0826	│	0924	│	1016	...	...	1121	│	1219	1320	│	1419	│	1532	1621	1732	1757	1822	1934
Hereford d.		0432	0638d	0710	0748	0810	0844	0901	0944	1010	1034	...	...	1145a	1209	1239	1339	1413	1438	1510	1551	1638	1751	1816	1840	1951
Abergavenny d.		0456	0701	0734	0812	0833	0907	│	1007	1033	1057	...	...	1209	1232	1302	1402	1436	1501	1532	1614	1701	1814	1840	1903	2014
Pontypool & New Inn d.		0509	0712	0745	0822	0843	0918	│	1016	1043	│	...	...	│	1242	│	1412	│	│	│	1624	1711	1824	│	1913	2024
Cwmbrân d.		0516	0717	0750	0828	0848	0924	│	1021	1048	1110	...	...	1222	1247	1315	1417	│	1514	1546	1629	1717	1829	1853	1918	2029
Newport 134 § a.		0535	0732	0801	0840	0900	0938	0944	1032	1101	1121	...	...	1237	1258	1328	1430	1457	1529	1559	1641	1729	1840	1906	1931	2041
Cardiff Central 134 § a.		0604	0747	0818	0856	0917	0959	0958	1047	1116	1143	...	...	1253	1314	1342	1445	1511	1544	1615	1700	1743	1857	1925	1945	2101

	Ⓐ A	Ⓐ	Ⓐ	Ⓐ	Ⓐ	⑥	⑥	⑥ 🍷	⑥ 🍷	⑥	⑥ 🍷	⑥ 🍷	⑥	⑥ 🍷	⑥ 🍷	⑥ 🍷	⑥ 🍷	⑥ 🍷	⑥ 🍷	⑥ 🍷	⑥ 🍷	⑥ 🍷	⑥ 🍷	⑥ 🍷	⑥ 🍷	⑥ 🍷
Manchester Piccadilly d.	...	1831	1931	2031	...		...	...	...	...	0630	0731	...	0830	0931	...	1031	1131	...	1231	1331	...	1431	1531	...	1631
Stockport d.	...	1839	1939	2039	...		...	...	...	...	0639	0740	...	0839	0939	...	1039	1139	...	1239	1339	...	1439	1539	...	1639
Holyhead 145, 160 d.	1636	│	│	│	...		...	...	...	0425	│	│	0631	│	│	0816	│	│	1030	│	│	1238	│	│	1427	│
Chester 145, 160 d.	1822	│	│	│	...		...	0416	...	0617	│	│	0820	│	│	1020	│	│	1221	│	│	1420	│	│	1619	│
Crewe ¶ d.	│	1909	2011	2120	...		...	0450	555	│	0709	0810	│	0910	1010	│	1110	1208	│	1308	1410	│	1510	1610	│	1710
Whitchurch ¶ d.	│	1930	2030	2141	...		...	0509	0616	│	0729	0829	│	│	│	│	│	1227	│	│	1429	│	│	1629	│	1728
Shrewsbury 145 ¶ a.	1921	1957	2049	2208	...		...	0531	0643	0712	0750	0848	0913	0939	1040	1113	1140	1247	1313	1337	1448	1512	1541	1648	1712	1746
Shrewsbury 146 d.	1925	1957	2052	2209	2309		...	0536	0645	0718	0752	0852	0917	0941	1040	1116	1141	1254	1316	1341	1452	1515	1547	1652	1716	1747
Church Stretton 146 d.	1940	2012	2107	2224	2325		...	0551	0700	│	0807	0907	│	0956	1055	│	1156	1309	1331	│	1507	│	1602	1707	│	1802
Craven Arms 146 d.	1949	2020	2115	2232	2333		...	0559	0708	│	0815	0916	│	1004	1103	│	1204	1317	1339	│	1515	│	1610	1715	│	1810
Ludlow d.	1959	2028	2122	2239	2342		...	0606	0715	0744	0822	0924	0945	1011	1111	1142	1211	1324	1346	1407	1523	1541	1617	1722	1742	1817
Leominster d.	│	2038	2133	2250	2353		...	0617	0726	0755	0833	0935	│	1022	1121	│	1222	1335	│	1417	1533	│	1628	1733	│	1828
Hereford d.	2024	2055	2154d	2311	0010		0519	0647z	0744	0814	0851	0952	1011	1040	1139	1209	1239	1352	1414	1433	1549	1606	1647	1750	1807	1848
Abergavenny d.	2047	2123	2217	2334	0034		0843	0710	0807	0837	0914	1015	1034	1103	1203	1232	1302	1416	1438	1456	1612	1629	1710	1813	1830	1911
Pontypool & New Inn d.	│	2133	│	2344	0044		0554	0720	0817	0848	0924	│	1044	│	│	1242	│	│	1448	│	│	1639	1720	1823	1840	1921
Cwmbrân d.	2101	2139	2229	2349	0049		0559	0725	0823	0853	0929	1028	1049	1115	1216	1247	1315	1428	1454	1509	1625	1644	1726	1828	1845	1926
Newport 134 § a.	2114	2151	2244	0002	0102		0610	0737	0836	0905	0940	1039	1100	1128	1229	1258	1329	1440	1505	1521	1637	1655	1739	1841	1856	1938
Cardiff Central 134 § a.	2128	2211	2306f	0022b	0123		0626	0751	0856	0920	0959	1054	1116	1154	1255	1316	1354	1455	1526	1537	1657	1710	1756	1858	1911	1957

	⑥ 🍷	⑥ 🍷	⑥	⑥	⑥	⑥	⑥	⑦	⑦ 🚌	⑦ 🍷 F	⑦ 🍷	⑦ 🍷	⑦ 🍷	⑦ 🍷	⑦ 🍷	⑦ 🍷	⑦ 🍷		⑦ 🍷	⑦ 🍷	⑦ 🍷	⑦ 🍷	⑦	⑦	⑦	⑦
Manchester Piccadilly d.	1731	...	1831	1931	2031	2133	2235		...	...	0930	1031	1130	...	1232	1330	1431	...	1530	1630	1730	...	1830	1930	2031	...
Stockport d.	1739	...	1839	1940	2039	2143	2244		...	...	0941	1040	1143	...	1243	1340	1441	...	1540	1640	1740	...	1840	1940	2040	...
Holyhead 145, 160 d.	│	1648	│	│	│	│	│		...	...	│	│	│	1020	│	│	│	...	│	│	│	1625	│	│	│	...
Chester 145, 160 d.	│	1833	│	│	│	│	│		...	...	*0920*t	│	*1132*t	1229	│	*1334*t	│	...	*1540*t	│	*1731*t	1826	│	*1939*t	│	2303
Crewe ¶ d.	1811	│	1911	2010	2110	2213	2314		...	...	1014	1111	1213	│	1313	1412	1513	...	1613	1713	1813	│	1913	2012	2111	2330
Whitchurch ¶ d.	1830	│	1932	2029	2131	2234	2335		...	...	1033	│	│	│	│	│	│	...	│	│	│	│	│	│	2131	2351
Shrewsbury 145 ¶ a.	1850	1926	1958	2050	2159	2301	0005		...	...	1054	1142	1243	1322	1346	1447	1548	...	1643	1743	1842	1920	1946	2047	2156	0017
Shrewsbury 146 d.	1854	1927	1959	2053	2203	...	...		0750	...	1105	1146	1245	1325	1350	1450	1550	...	1645	1746	1845	1922	1946	2049	2204	...
Church Stretton 146 d.	1909	1942	2014	2108	2218	...	...		0815	...	1121	│	│	1340	│	1506	│	...	1700	│	1900	1938	│	2105	2220	...
Craven Arms 146 d.	1917	1950	2022	2116	2226	...	...		0835	...	1129	│	│	1348	│	1514	│	...	1708	│	1908	1946	│	2113	2228	...
Ludlow d.	1924	1957	2029	2123	2233	...	...		0855	...	1138	1213	1312	1356	1418	1523	1620	...	1716	1814	1916	1954	2014	2122	2236	...
Leominster d.	1935	│	2040	2134	2244	...	...		0920	...	1149	1224	1324	1406	1429	1534	1631	...	1727	1824	│	2004	2024	2133	2246	...
Hereford d.	1952	2027	2057	2153	2301	...	...		0950	1006	1214a	1242	1342	1423	1447	1550	1648	...	1743	1843	1940	2022	2041	2149	2305	...
Abergavenny d.	2015	2050	2120	2216	2324	...	...		...	1030	1237	1306	1405	1446	1510	1614	1712	...	1806	1906	2004	2045	2104	2213	2328	...
Pontypool & New Inn d.	2025	│	2130	2227	2334	...	...		...	1040	1247	1316	1415	1456	│	1625	│	...	1816	1916	│	2056	│	2224	2338	...
Cwmbrân d.	2030	2102	2135	2232	2339	...	...		...	1045	1253	1322	1420	1501	1523	1630	1726	...	1821	1922	2016	2101	2117	2229	2343	...
Newport 134 § a.	2041	2114	2146	2247	2350	...	...		...	1057	1304	1333	1432	1511	1537	1641	1739	...	1835	1935	2028	2113	2127	2240	2356	...
Cardiff Central 134 § a.	2100	2130	2205	2310	0014	...	...		...	1111	1318	1351	1448	1528	1555	1657	1754	...	1853	1951	2046	2130	2144	2257	0017	...

A – 🚌 and ✕ Holyhead - Cardiff Central.
F – To Fishguard Harbour (Table **136**).
J – To Llandudno Junction (Table **160**).
K – From Birmingham Intenational (Table **145**).
N – From Birmingham New St (Table **145**).

S – To Swansea (Table **146**).

a – Arrives 8–9 minutes earlier.
b – 0015 on ⑥ mornings.

d – Arrives 5–7 minutes earlier.
f – 2255 on ⑤.
t – Change at Shrewsbury.
z – Arrives 0633.

¶ – See note ¶ on page 121 for additional journeys Shrewsbury - Whitchurch - Crewe and v.v.:
§ – See also Tables **117** and **118**.

VT Most trains convey 🍸 LONDON - BIRMINGHAM - WOLVERHAMPTON 150

Certain services continue to/from destinations in Table **154**. For slower trains via Northampton see Table **141**.

km			Ⓐ	Ⓐ	Ⓐ	Ⓐ	Ⓐ		Ⓐ	Ⓐ	Ⓐ	Ⓐ	Ⓐ	Ⓐ	ⒶS	Ⓐ	Ⓐ	Ⓐ	Ⓐ	Ⓐ	Ⓐ	Ⓐ	Ⓐ	①-④
0	**London** Euston **143 151/2/3** d.	Ⓐ	0620	0643	0659	0743	0759	and	1459	1543	1623	1643	1723	1743	1823	1843	1919	1943	2019	2043	2103	2139	2230	2330
28	Watford Junction △ d.		0634	|	0714	|	0814	at the	1514	|	1637	|	1737	|	1837	|	|	|	2033	|	|	2154	2245	|
80	Milton Keynes ... **143 151/2/3** d.		|	0713	|	0813	|	same	|	1613	|	1713	|	1813u	|	1913	|	2013	|	2113	2134	2213	2330	0028
133	Rugby d.		0713	|	0751	|	0851	minutes	1551	|	|	|	|	|	|	|	2011	|	2113	|	2157	|	0003	0101
151	Coventry **114** a.		0722	0742	0802	0842	0902	past	1602	1642	1722	1742	1822	1842	1922	1942	2020	2042	2123	2142	2206	2241	0012	0113
168	Birmingham Int ✈ **114** a.		0734	0755	0813	0853	0913	each	1613	1653	1733	1753	1833	1853	1933	1953	2033	2053	2134	2153	2216	2256	0022	0123
182	**Birmingham** New St **114 119** a.		0746	0810	0824	0907	0925	hour	1625	1707	1745	1807	1845	1907	1945	2007	2046	2106	2147	2205	2229	2309	0034	0134
190	Sandwell & Dudley a.		...	0824	...	0924	...	until	...	1724	...	1824	...	1924	1958	2024	2058	2124	2159	2216	2241	2331	|	|
202	**Wolverhampton** **119** a.		...	0837	...	0937	...		...	1737	...	1837	...	1937	2011	2037	2110	2137	2210	2228	2253	2344	0103	0204

	⑤		⑥	⑥	⑥	⑥	⑥	⑥		⑥	⑥	⑥	⑥S	⑥	⑥	⑥	⑥	⑥	⑥	⑥		⑦	⑦	⑦
London Euston **143 151/2/3** d.	2330	⑥	0623	0712	0743	0823	0843	0859	and	1643	1659	1743	1823	1840	1903	1923	1943	2025	2103	2142	⑦	0850	0950	1049
Watford Junction △ d.	|		0637	0726	|	0837	|	0914	at the	|	1714	|	1837	|	|	1937	|	2040	2119	2158		0907	1006	1107
Milton Keynes ... **143 151/2/3** d.	0028		|	|	0813	|	0913	|	same	1713	|	1813	|	1910	|	|	2021	|	2151	2230		0939	1038	1138
Rugby d.	0107		|	0812	|	|	|	0951	minutes	|	1751	|	|	|	1951	|	|	|	2214	2254		1014	1114	1214
Coventry **114** a.	0117		0722	0822	0842	0922	0942	1002	past	1742	1802	1842	1923	1942	2002	2023	2049	2137	2224	2303		1023	1122	1223
Birmingham Int ✈ **114** a.	0127		0733	0833	0853	0933	0953	1013	each	1753	1813	1853	1933	1954	2013	2033	2101	2151	2234	2313		1034	1133	1234
Birmingham New St **114 119** a.	0139		0745	0846	0907	0945	1007	1024	hour	1807	1823	1907	1945	2007	2025	2045	2113	2207	2246	2325		1045	1145	1246
Sandwell & Dudley a.	|		...	...	0924	...	1024	...	until	1824	...	1924	1958	2024	2055	2100	|	2224	2257	2336		1058	1157	...
Wolverhampton **119** a.	0208		...	...	0937	...	1037	...		1837	...	1937	2011	2036	2109	2112	2135	2237	2310	2348		1110	1210	...

	⑦	⑦	⑦	⑦	⑦	⑦	⑦	⑦	⑦	⑦	⑦	⑦	⑦	⑦S	⑦	⑦	⑦	⑦	⑦	⑦	⑦	⑦	⑦	⑦	⑦
London Euston **143 151/2/3** d.	1152	1212	1240	1320	1340	1420	1440	1520	1540	1620	1640	1720	1740	1820	1843	1900	1920	1940	2000	2018	2038	2054	2155	2225	2324
Watford Junction △ d.	1206	1226	|	1334	|	1434	|	1534	|	1634	|	1734	|	1835	|	|	1934	|	|	2032	|	2111	2213	2241	2339
Milton Keynes ... **143 151/2/3** d.	1233	|	1313	|	1413	|	1513	|	1613	|	1713	|	1813	|	1917	|	|	2013	|	|	2117	2146	2248	2314	0013
Rugby d.	1253	1310	|	1417	|	1517	|	1617	|	1717	|	1817	|	|	|	1952	2019	|	2052	|	|	2207	2324	2348	0048s
Coventry **114** a.	1302	1320	1342	1430	1441	1531	1542	1629	1642	1731	1742	1830	1843	1923	1945	2001	2029	2042	2102	2120	22147	2216	2333	2357	0059s
Birmingham Int ✈ **114** a.	1313	1332	1352	1441	1452	1541	1552	1641	1653	1741	1752	1842	1853	1933	1955	2012	2041	2052	2112	2130	2157	2227	2343	0007	0110s
Birmingham New St **114 119** a.	1325	1343	1405	1452	1504	1552	1604	1651	1705	1752	1803	1852	1904	1944	2010	2025	2053	2105	2125	2144	2210	2239	2356	0019	0122s
Sandwell & Dudley a.	...	...	1424	...	1523	|	1624	...	1723	...	1824	...	1924	2008	...	2036	2108	2124	2136	2155	2250	2250	|	|	|
Wolverhampton **119** a.	...	...	1437	...	1537	1623	1637	...	1737	...	1836	...	1937	2020	...	2049	2121	2137	2149	2208	2236	2302	0015	0040	0142

		Ⓐ	Ⓐ	Ⓐ	Ⓐ	Ⓐ	Ⓐ	Ⓐ	ⒶS	ⒶK	Ⓐ	Ⓐ	Ⓐ	Ⓐ	☆	Ⓐ	Ⓐ	Ⓐ	Ⓐ	Ⓐ	Ⓐ	Ⓐ	Ⓐ	Ⓐ
Wolverhampton **119** d.	Ⓐ	0500	0524	0545	0604	0627	0645	0705	0724	0745	...	...	0845	...	and	...	1645	1745	...	1845	...	1945	2046	2146
Sandwell & Dudley d.		|	0534	0555	0615	0638	0656	0715	|	0755	...	...	0855	...	at the	...	1655	1755	...	1855	...	1955	2056	2155
Birmingham New St **114 119** d.		0530	0550	0607	0630	0650	0710	0730	0750	0810	0830	0850	0910	0950	same	1650	1710	1810	1830	1910	1930	2010	2110	2210
Birmingham Int ✈ **114** d.		0540	0600	0618	0640	0701	0721	0743	0801	0819	0841	0900	0920	1000	minutes	1700	1720	1820	1840	1920	1940	2020	2120	2220
Coventry **114** d.		0552	0614	0629	0651	0712	0731	0754	0812	0831	0851	0911	0931	1011	past	1711	1731	1831	1853	1931	1951	2031	2131	2231
Rugby d.		0603	|	|	|	|	|	|	0823	|	0904	|	|	1023	each	1723	|	|	1905	|	2005	2043	|	2245
Milton Keynes ... **143 151/2/3** a.		0622	0641	0656	|	0741s	|	|	|	|	0923	|	0958	|	hour	|	1758	1856	|	1959	|	2105	2158	2306
Watford Junction ▽ a.		0644	|	|	0737	|	|	|	|	0917	|	0958	|	1100	until	1800	|	|	1942	|	2042	2127	2219	2337
London Euston **143 151/2/3** a.		0703	0716	0734	0754	0815	0831	0851	0913	0933	0957	1015	1033	1117		1816	1834	1933	1958	2036	2059	2143	2241	0001

	Ⓐ		⑥	⑥	⑥	⑥	⑥	⑥	⑥	⑥S	⑥	⑥	⑥	⑥		⑥	⑥	⑥	⑥	⑥	⑥		⑦	⑦
Wolverhampton **119** d.	2245	⑥	0546	0606	0645	0706	0745	...	...	0901	0945	...	...	1045	and	1745	...	1845	1945	2045	2109	⑦	0805	0903
Sandwell & Dudley d.	2256		0555	0617	0655	0716	0755	...	...	|	0955	...	...	1055	at the	1755	...	1855	1955	2055	2119		0815	0913
Birmingham New St **114 119** d.	2310		0608	0630	0710	0730	0810	0830	0910	0930	1010	1030	1050	1110	same	1810	1850	1910	2010	2110	2130		0830	0930
Birmingham Int ✈ **114** d.	2320		0618	0641	0720	0740	0820	0840	0920	0940	1020	1040	1100	1120	minutes	1820	1900	1920	2020	2120	2140		0840	0940
Coventry **114** d.	2331		0630	0653	0731	0751	0831	0851	0931	0951	1031	1051	1111	1131	past	1831	1911	1931	2031	2131	2151		0851	0951
Rugby d.	2344		|	|	|	0805	|	|	|	1004	|	1104	1123	|	each	|	1923	1943	2043	2144	2203		0904	1004
Milton Keynes ... **143 151/2/3** a.	0024		0657	|	0759	|	0859	|	0957	|	1058	|	|	1158	hour	1858	|	2005	2105	2205	2224		0936	1037
Watford Junction ▽ a.	0054		0717	0739	|	0841	|	0938	|	1041	|	1140	1200	|	until	|	2002	2033	2137	2235	2311		1007	1111
London Euston **143 151/2/3** a.	0112		0734	0755	0834	0857	0936	0955	1033	1057	1133	1156	1217	1235		1932	2023	2055	2157	2256	2334		1026	1131

	⑦	⑦	⑦	⑦	⑦	⑦	⑦	⑦	⑦	⑦	⑦	⑦	⑦	⑦S	⑦	⑦	⑦	⑦	⑦	⑦	⑦	⑦	⑦	⑦	⑦
Wolverhampton **119** d.	0919	1005	1105	1145	...	1245	...	...	1345	...	1445	...	1545	1604	1645	...	1745	...	1845	...	1945	...	2106	2205	2235
Sandwell & Dudley d.	0930	1015	1114	1155	...	1255	...	...	1355	...	1455	...	1555	|	1655	...	1756	...	1855	...	1955	...	2117	2216	2247
Birmingham New St **114 119** d.	0951	1030	1130	1210	1230	1310	1330	1350	1410	1430	1510	1530	1610	1630	1710	1730	1810	1830	1910	1930	2010	2030	2130	2230	2300
Birmingham Int ✈ **114** d.	1001	1040	1140	1220	1240	1320	1340	1358	1420	1440	1520	1540	1620	1640	1720	1740	1820	1840	1920	1940	2020	2041	2140	2240	2312
Coventry **114** d.	1016	1053	1151	1231	1251	1331	1351	1411	1431	1451	1531	1551	1631	1651	1732	1751	1832	1851	1931	1951	2031	2053	2151	2251	2322
Rugby d.	1028	1105	1205	|	1303	|	1403	1422	|	1503	|	1603	|	1703	|	1803	1843	|	|	2003	|	2105	2204	2304	2335
Milton Keynes ... **143 151/2/3** a.	1105	1137	1224	1259	|	1358	|	|	1458	|	1558	|	1658	|	1758	|	1903	|	1958	|	2100	2127	2235	2336	0015s
Watford Junction ▽ a.	|	1208	|	|	1340	|	1440	|	|	1540	|	1640	|	1740	|	1840	|	1936	|	2041	|	2203	2305	0006	0045
London Euston **143 151/2/3** a.	1203	1225	1301	1336	1359	1436	1459	1515	1536	1559	1636	1659	1735	1759	1835	1859	1940	1955	2035	2059	2148	2224	2323	0028	0103

K – From Manchester (Table **152**).
S – To/from Shrewsbury (Table **145**).
s – Calls to set down only.
u – Calls to pick up only.
☆ – Timings may vary by up to 3 minutes.
△ – Trains call here to pick up only.
▽ – Trains call here to set down only.

VT AW Most trains convey 🍸 LONDON - CHESTER (- HOLYHEAD) 151

km			Ⓐ	Ⓐ	Ⓐa	Ⓐb	Ⓐ	Ⓐ	Ⓐa	Ⓐa	Ⓐ	Ⓐa	Ⓐa	Ⓐb	Ⓐ	Ⓐb	Ⓐa	ⒶG	Ⓐ	ⒶB		⑥A	⑥c	⑥Ld
0	**London** Euston **143 150/2/3/4** d.	Ⓐ	...	*0636*	0810	*0735*	0910	1010	1110	1210	*1240*	1310	1410	*1440*	1610	*1703*	1710	1810	1910	*2107*	⑥	...	0810	*0940*
80	Milton Keynes ... **143 150/2/3/4** d.		...	|	0841	*0806*	0941	1041	1141	1241	|	1341	1441	|	1641u	|	1741u	1841u	1941	*2139*		...	0841	|
254	Crewe **143 152/3/4 160** d.		0625	0823	0950	0950	1048	1148	1248	1350	1424	1448	1548	1644	1749	1855	1855	1954	2054	*0008*		0622	0948	1148
288	**Chester** **160** a.		0644	0848	1010	1010	1109	1208	1308	1411	1449	1508	1608	1708	1808	1915	1915	2013	2119	0040		0642	1007	1208
	Bangor **160** a.		0749	*1049*	1122	1122	1219	1318	*1444*	*1550*	*1643*	*1643*	*1741*	*1848*	1918	*2111*	2029	2125	2230	0147		0748	*1145*	*1340*
	Holyhead **160** a.		0820	*1120*	1156	1156	1249	1346	*1522*	*1620*	*1718*	*1718*	*1821*	*1918*	*2020*	*2142*	2100	2156	2301	0215		0819	*1217*	*1419*

	⑥Lc	⑥	⑥	⑥c	⑥c	⑥	⑥	⑥	⑥		⑦	⑦	⑦	⑦	⑦	⑦	⑦	⑦g	⑦	⑦		⑦	⑦	⑦
London Euston . **143 150/2/3/4** d.	1010	1110	1210	1310	1510	1610	1710	1810	*1907*	⑦	*0810*	*0847*	*0946*	*1116*	*1237*	*1337*	*1437*	1508	1608	1708	...	1808	1908	*2121*
Milton Keynes .... **143 150/2/3/4** d.	1041	1141	1241	1341	1541	1641	1741	1841	|		*0856*	*0934*	*1033*	*1203*	|	|	|	1542	1642	1742	...	1842	1942	|
Crewe **143 152/3/4 160** d.	1148	1248	1351	1448	1648	1748	1850	1948	2100		1042	1127	1227	1327	1434	1527	1627	1651	1750	1901	...	1953	2053	0012
Chester **160** a.	1208	1309	1413	1507	1708	1808	1909	2008	2122		1102	1147	1250	1347	1454	1548	1649	1710	1810	1920	...	2012	2112	0034
Bangor **160** a.	*1340*	*1443*	*1543*	*1646*	*1845*	1919	2021	*2146*	2245		1209	1312	1427	1518	1622	1716	1825	*1917*	*1950*	2034	...	2123	2220	*0145*
Holyhead **160** a.	*1419*	*1514*	*1622*	*1718*	*1915*	1950	2052	*2226*	2317		1240	1340	1458	1557	1655	1758	1859	*1958*	*2019*	2103	...	2154	2251	*0212*

		Ⓐ	Ⓐ	ⒶG	Ⓐa	Ⓐb	Ⓐa	Ⓐa	Ⓐb	Ⓐa	Ⓐ	Ⓐa	Ⓐa	Ⓐb	Ⓐ	Ⓐ	Ⓐb	Ⓐ	Ⓐ	Ⓐ		⑥	⑥c	⑥
Holyhead **160** d.	Ⓐ	...	0448	0551	0655	0655	*0726*	0855	0855	*0923*	*1041*	*1133*	1253	1253	1357	1450	*1538*	*1728*	1826	*1922*	⑥	...	*0425*	0652
Bangor **160** d.		...	0514	0618	0722	0722	*0806*	0922	0922	*1002*	*1110*	*1200*	1321	1321	1425	1518	*1617*	*1807*	1905	2020		...	*0457*	0720
Chester **160** d.		0459	0626	0735	0835	0835	0935	1035	1035	1133	1235	1335	1435	1435	1535	1635	1735	1935	2023	2135		0455	0717	0835
Crewe **143 152/3/4 160** a.		0522	0647	0754	0854	0854	0954	1054	1054	1153	1254	1354	1454	1454	1554	1654	1754	1954	2044	2154		0518	0736	0854
Milton Keynes .... **143 150/2/3/4** a.		*0653*	|	|	1002	|	1102	1202	|	1302	1403	1502	1602	|	1702	1802	|	|	*2254*	*0025*		*0712*	0851	1001
London Euston . **143 150/2/3/4** a.		*0728*	0834	0940	1036	*1100*	1137	1237	*1259*	1339	1440	1538	1636	*1700*	1739	1837	*2003*	*2204*	*2344*	*0112*		*0751*	0928	1036

	⑥	⑥c	⑥d	⑥c	⑥		⑥	⑥	⑥c	⑥c	⑥	⑥	⑥		⑦	⑦g	⑦		⑦	⑦	⑦g	⑦	⑦A	⑦
Holyhead **160** d.	0755	0855	0855	*1030*	*1128*	...	*1238*	1358	*1427*	*1525*	*1648*	*1728*	1825	⑦	0849	*1020*	1150	...	1250	1351	*1530*	*1625*	*1729*	*1826*
Bangor **160** d.	0822	0922	0922	*1102*	*1208*	...	*1305*	1425	*1455*	*1604*	*1715*	*1807*	1904		0917	*1059*	1217	...	1318	1418	*1557*	*1704*	*1756*	*1906*
Chester **160** d.	0933	1035	1035	1235	1335	...	*1435*	1535	1635	1735	1854	1937	2019		1039	1233	1330	...	1433	1533	1735	1835	1938	2037
Crewe **143 152/3/4 160** a.	0952	1054	1054	1254	1354	...	*1454*	1554	1654	1754	1919	2000	2041		1102	1253	1350	...	1454	1552	1753	1853	1958	2056
Milton Keynes .... **143 150/2/3/4** a.	1101	1202	|	1402	1502	...	*1602*	1702	1802	|	|	|	...		|	1402	1501	...	1601	1702	1903	2003	*2138*	*2305*
London Euston . **143 150/2/3/4** a.	1136	1236	*1259*	1436	1538	...	*1637*	1737	1836	*1958*	*2123*	*2218*	...		*1307*	1440	1539	...	1640	1739	1942	2040	*2227*	*2353*

A – From/to Birmingham New Street (Table **145**).
B – Passengers from London and Milton Keynes need to change at Crewe and Chester.
G – Conveys 🛏12 London Euston - Wrexham and v.v. (Table **145**).
L – To Llandudno Junction (Table **160**).
a – From Sept. 12.
b – Until Sept. 9.
c – From Sept. 17.
d – Until Sept. 10.
g – From Sept. 18.
r – Arrives 1328.

152 LONDON - MANCHESTER

Most trains convey 🍸 VT

km			Ⓐ	Ⓐ	Ⓐa	Ⓐ	Ⓐ	Ⓐ	Ⓐ	Ⓐa	Ⓐ	Ⓐ	Ⓐ		Ⓐa	Ⓐ	Ⓐ	Ⓐ	Ⓐ	Ⓐ	Ⓐa	Ⓐ	Ⓐ	Ⓐ	Ⓐ
0	**London** Euston . 150/1/3/4 d.	Ⓐ	...	...	0616	0636	0655	0720	0735	0756	0820	0840	0856	❖♡	1620	1640	1700	1710f	1733t	1800	1820	1834	1857	1922	1940
80	Milton Keynes ...... 150/1/4 d.		...	...	0646	|	0727	0750	0806	|	0850	|	|		1650	|	|	1740f	|	|	1850u	|	|	1953	|
235	Stoke on Trent .... 119 d.		...	...	0745	|	0825	0848	|	0925	0948	|	1025	and at	1748	|	1825	1848	|	1925	1948	|	2025	2050	|
267	Macclesfield .... 119 d.		...	...	0802	|	0841	|	|	0941	|	|	1041	the same	|	|	1841	|	|	1941	|	|	|	2106	|
	Crewe .... 154 d.		0611	0710	|	0812	|	|	0911	|	|	1011	|	minutes	|	1811	|	|	1911	|	|	2018	|	|	2123
	Wilmslow .... d.		0627	0727	|	0827	|	|	0927	|	|	1027	|	past each	|	1827	|	|	1927	|	|	2033	|	|	2138
287	Stockport .... 119 a.		0636	0736	0817	0836	0854	0917	0936	0954	1016	1035	1054	hour until	1816	1835	1854	1916	1935	1954	2016	2042	2056	2118	|
296	**Manchester** Piccadilly 119 a.		0647	0746	0827	0846	0908	0927	0946	1005	1027	1046	1105		1827	1846	1908	1927	1945	2005	2027	2052	2106	2128	2154

	Ⓐ	Ⓐ	Ⓐ	Ⓐ	①–④	⑤		⑥	⑥	⑥	⑥	⑥	⑥	⑥	⑥		⑥	⑥	⑥	⑥	⑥	⑥	⑥	⑥	⑥
London Euston . 150/1/3/4 d.	2000	2040	2100	2136	2200	2200	⑥	0636	0655	0720	0735	0757	0820	0840	0856		1720	1740	1800	1820	1833	1900	1920	1939	2020
Milton Keynes .... 150/1/4 d.	|	|	2131	|	2240	2240		|	0727	0750	0806	|	0850	|	|	and at	1750	|	|	1850	|	|	1950	|	2106
Stoke on Trent .... 119 d.	2126	|	2228	2308	2357s	2355s		|	0829	0848	|	0925	0948	|	1025	the same	1850	|	1925	1948	|	2025	2049	|	2207
Macclesfield .... 119 d.	2142	|	2245	2324	|	|		|	0847	|	|	0941	|	|	1041	minutes	|	|	1941	|	|	2041	|	|	2224
Crewe .... 154 d.	|	2211	|	|	0021s	0017s		0811	|	|	0911	|	|	1011	|	past each	|	1911	|	|	2014	|	|	2124	|
Wilmslow .... d.	|	2227	|	|	|	|		0827	|	|	0927	|	|	1027	|	hour until	|	1927	|	|	2029	|	|	2139	|
Stockport .... 119 a.	2154	2235	2258	2337	0047s	0057s		0835	0902	0916	0935	0954	1017	1035	1054		1916	1935	1954	2016	2038	2054	2121	2148	2237
Manchester Piccadilly 119 a.	2203	2246	2308	2349	0059	0111		0846	0911	0927	0946	1005	1027	1046	1108		1927	1946	2005	2027	2048	2104	2132	2159	2250

	⑥		⑦	⑦	⑦	⑦	⑦	⑦	⑦	⑦	⑦	⑦	⑦	⑦		⑦	⑦	⑦	⑦	⑦	⑦	⑦	⑦	⑦	⑦
London Euston . 150/1/3/4 d.	2101	⑦	0810	0820	0921	1019	1119	1219	1237	1257	1317	1337	1357	1417		1817	1829	1857	1917	1937	1957	2015	2035	2125	2151
Milton Keynes .... 150/1/4 d.	2146		0856	0906	1007	1106	1208	1253	|	|	1350	|	|	1450	and at	1850	|	|	1950	|	|	2048	|	2217	2243
Stoke on Trent .... 119 d.	|		|	1021	1123	1225	1311	1353	|	1426	1451	|	1526	1550	the same	1952	|	2026	2050	|	2126	2150	|	2333	|
Macclesfield .... 119 d.	|		|	1038	1139	1242	1328	|	|	1442	|	|	1542	|	minutes	|	|	2042	|	|	2143	|	|	2351	|
Crewe .... 154 d.	2300		1019	|	|	|	|	|	1413	|	|	1513	|	|	past each	|	2013	|	|	2113	|	|	2222	|	0016s
Wilmslow .... d.	2316		1034	|	|	|	|	|	1428	|	|	1529	|	|	until	|	2029	|	|	2129	|	|	2237	|	|
Stockport .... 119 a.	2326		1043	1050	1152	1255	1341	1420	1438	1455	1519	1538	1555	1622		2020	2038	2056	2119	2138	2159	2221	2246	0003	0039s
Manchester Piccadilly 119 a.	2339		1053	1100	1204	1305	1350	1430	1448	1506	1532	1548	1605	1632		2030	2047	2106	2131	2149	2209	2231	2255	0013	0048

		Ⓐ	Ⓐ	Ⓐ	Ⓐ	Ⓐ	Ⓐ	Ⓐ	Ⓐ	Ⓐ	Ⓐ	Ⓐ	Ⓐa	Ⓐ	Ⓐ	Ⓐ		Ⓐ	Ⓐ	Ⓐ	Ⓐ	Ⓐ	Ⓐ	Ⓐ	Ⓐa
Manchester Piccadilly 119 d.	Ⓐ	0505	0555	0610	0635	0643	0715	0627	0735	0755	0815	0835	0855	0915	0935	0955	♧♥	1635	1655	1715	1735	1755	1815	1835	1855
Stockport .... 119 d.		0513	0603	0618	0643	0652	0724	0636	0744	0804	0824	0844	0903	0924	0944	1003		1644	1704	1724	1744	1804	1824	1844	1904
Wilmslow .... d.		|	0611	|	|	0659	|	|	|	0811	|	|	0911	|	|	1011	and at	|	1711	|	|	1811	|	|	1911
Crewe .... 154 d.		0536	0628	|	|	0717	|	|	|	0829	|	|	0929	|	|	1029	the same	|	1729	|	|	1829	|	|	1929
Macclesfield .... 119 d.		|	|	0631	0656	|	|	0649	0756	|	|	0856	|	|	0956	|	minutes	1656	|	|	1756	|	|	1856	|
Stoke on Trent .... 119 d.		|	|	0648	0712	|	0750	0706	0812	|	0850	0912	|	0950	1012	|	past each	1712	|	1750	1812	|	1850	1912	|
Milton Keynes .... 150/1/4 d.		0653	|	|	|	|	0847	b	|	|	0950	|	|	1047	|	|	until	|	|	1847	|	1934	1948	|	2032
London Euston . 150/1/3/4 a.		0728	0810	0819	0844	0855	0921	0933	0951	1018	1026	1045	1107	1122	1140	1203		1840	1905	1920	1941	2007	2022	2039	2106

	Ⓐ	Ⓐ	Ⓐ	Ⓐ		⑥	⑥	⑥	⑥	⑥	⑥	⑥	⑥	⑥	⑥	⑥		⑥	⑥	⑥	⑥	⑥	⑥	⑥	⑥
Manchester Piccadilly 119 d.	1915	1955	2015	2115	⑥	0525	0555	0610	0635	0655	0715	0735	0755	0815	0835	0855	★	1655	1715	1735	1755	1815	1835	1855	1935
Stockport .... 119 d.	1924	2004	2024	2124		0534	0603	0619	0644	0704	0723	0744	0804	0824	0844	0904		1704	1724	1744	1803	1824	1844	1904	1944
Wilmslow .... d.	|	2011	|	|		0541	0611	|	|	0711	|	|	0811	|	|	0911	and at	1711	|	|	1811	|	|	1911	|
Crewe .... 154 d.	|	2030	|	|		0600	0629	|	|	0729	|	|	0829	|	|	0929	the same	1729	|	|	1828	|	|	1929	|
Macclesfield .... 119 d.	1936	|	2036	2136		|	|	0631	0656	|	|	0756	|	|	0856	|	minutes	|	|	1756	|	|	1856	|	1956
Stoke on Trent .... 119 d.	1953	|	2053	2153		|	|	0648	0712	|	0750	0812	|	0850	0912	|	past each	|	1750	1812	|	1850	1912	|	2012
Milton Keynes .... 150/1/4 d.	2051	2137	2154	2301		0712	0737	|	|	|	0847	|	|	0947	|	|	until	|	1847	|	|	1949	|	|	2112
London Euston . 150/1/3/4 a.	2123	2209	2230	2348		0751	0809	0823	0844	0903	0921	0941	1008	1021	1041	1104		1902	1921	1938	2001	2031	2059	2123	2202

	⑥		⑦	⑦	⑦	⑦	⑦	⑦	⑦	⑦	⑦	⑦	⑦	⑦		⑦	⑦	⑦	⑦	⑦	⑦	⑦	⑦	⑦	⑦
Manchester Piccadilly 119 d.	2035	⑦	0805	0820	0920	1020	1035	1115	1135	1155	1215	1235	1255	1315		1715	1735	1755	1815	1835	1855	1915	1935	2021	2055
Stockport .... 119 d.	2043		0814	0828	0928	1029	1046	1124	1144	1205	1221	1243	1305	1323	and at	1724	1742	1803	1823	1842	1903	1923	1941	2027	2103
Wilmslow .... d.	|		0822	|	|	1037	|	|	|	1213	|	|	1313	|	the same	|	|	1811	|	|	1911	|	|	|	|
Crewe .... 154 d.	|		0843	|	|	1055	|	|	|	1230	|	|	1330	|	minutes	|	|	1829	|	|	1929	|	|	|	|
Macclesfield .... 119 d.	2056		|	0841	0940	|	1057	|	1155	|	|	1255	|	|	past each	|	1755	|	|	1855	|	|	1954	2040	2116
Stoke on Trent .... 119 d.	2112		|	0857	1000	|	1115	1152	1212	|	1249	1312	|	1351	until	1751	1812	|	1851	1912	|	1951	2011	2058	2134
Milton Keynes .... 150/1/4 d.	2212		|	|	1117	|	1222	1249	|	|	1345	|	|	1447		1848	|	|	1948	|	|	2049	|	2200	2251
London Euston . 150/1/3/4 a.	2301		1056	1101	1212	1253	1257	1325	1345	1409	1425	1443	1507	1525		1924	1943	2006	2024	2045	2108	2132	2201	2257	2347

a – From Sept. 12.
b – Via Birmingham New Street (Table **150**).
f – Departs 10 Minutes later from Sept. 12.
s – Calls to set down only.
t – Departs 1740 from Sept. 12.

❖ – The 1140 and 1320 from London do not run until Sept. 12.
♥ – The 1035, 1415 and 1555 from Manchester do not run until Sept. 12.
★ – The 1315 from Manchester departs Milton Keynes 1452, arrives London Euston 1528.

♡ – The 1520 from London also calls at Macclesfield d. 1705.
♧ – Arrival times at London Euston may vary ± 4 minutes.

153 LONDON - LIVERPOOL

Most trains convey 🍸 VT

km			Ⓐ	⑥	Ⓐ	⑥	Ⓐ	⚒	⚒		⚒	⚒		⚒	⚒	⚒	Ⓐ	⑥	⑥	Ⓐ	⑥	Ⓐa	Ⓐ
0	**London** Euston ..... 142/3 150/1/2/4 d.	⚒	0527	0703	0707	0803	0807	0907	1007	...	1107	1207	...	1307	1407	1507	1603	1607	1633	1703	1707	1733	1803
80	Milton Keynes .... 142/3 150/1/2/4 d.		0615	|	|	|	0838	|	|	...	|	|	...	|	|	|	|	|	|	|	|	|	|
135	Rugby .... 142/3 150 d.		|	|	|	0854	|	|	|	...	|	|	...	|	|	|	1654	|	1723	1752	|	1823	1852
155	Nuneaton .... 143 d.		0645	|	|	|	|	|	|	...	|	|	...	|	|	|	|	|	|	|	1803	|	|
215	Stafford .... 143 144 d.		0708	0826	0824	0924	0927	1024	1124	...	1224	1324	...	1424	1524	1624	1724	1724	1808	1824	1827	1857	1924
254	Crewe .... 143 144 151 152 154 d.		0728	0846	0843	0944	|	1043	1143	...	1243	1343	...	1443	1543	1643	1743	1743	|	1844	1847	1917	1943
290	Runcorn .... 144 a.		0745	0900	0900	1000	1000	1100	1200	...	1300	1400	...	1500	1600	1700	1800	1800	1840	1900	1904	1935	2000
312	**Liverpool** Lime Street .... 144 a.		0804	0920	0920	1019	1019	1120	1220	...	1320	1419	...	1519	1620	1720	1820	1820	1857	1921	1922	1952	2020

	⑥		Ⓐ	⑥	Ⓐ	⑥	Ⓐ		⑦	⑦	⑦	⑦	⑦	⑦	⑦	⑦	⑦	⑦	⑦	⑦		⑦	⑦
London Euston ...... 142/3 150/1/2/4 d.	1807	...	1907	1907	2007	2011	2107	⑦	0817	0917	1016	1116	1205	1303	1405	1505	1605	1705	1805	1905	...	2005	2121
Milton Keynes .... 142/3 150/1/2/4 d.	|	...	|	|	|	|	2139		|	|	|	1203	|	|	|	|	|	|	1839	|	...	2039	|
Rugby .... 142 143 150 d.	|	...	|	|	|	2118	|		|	|	|	|	|	|	|	|	|	|	|	|	...	|	|
Nuneaton .... 143 d.	|	...	|	2003	2103	|	2208		0944	1045	1147	|	|	|	|	|	|	1804	|	2004	...	2109	2258
Stafford .... 143 144 d.	1924	...	|	2027	2127	2148	|		1008	1115	1214	1253	1327	1425	1525	1625	1726	|	1929	2029	...	2133	2324
Crewe .... 143 144 151 152 154 d.	1943	...	|	2047	2148	2207	2253		1031	1137	1234	1315	1346	1445	1545	1645	1746	1846	1949	2049	...	2154	2347
Runcorn .... 144 a.	2000	...	2051	2105	2206	2225	2311		1048	1154	1251	1332	1403	1502	1602	1702	1803	1902	2006	2106	...	2211	0006
Liverpool Lime Street .... 144 a.	2019	...	2108	2127	2223	2242	2333		1105	1211	1308	1358	1420	1519	1623	1721	1821	1921	2023	2123	...	2228	0029

		Ⓐ	⑥	Ⓐ	⑥	Ⓐ	⑥	Ⓐ	⑥	⚒	⚒	⚒	⑥	Ⓐ	⑥	Ⓐ	⑥	Ⓐ	⚒	⑥	Ⓐ	Ⓐ	⑥
Liverpool Lime Street .... 144 d.	⚒	0526	0546	0605	0644	0700	0716	0747	0747	0847	0947	1047	1147	1147	1247	1247	1347	1347	1447	1547	1547	1647	1647
Runcorn .... 144 d.		0543	0603	0621	0701	0715u	0733	0803	0803	0903	1003	1103	1203	1203	1303	1303	1403	1403	1503	1603	1603	1703	1703
Crewe .... 143 144 151 152 154 d.		0602	|	|	0720	|	0754	0823	0822	0924	1022	1122	1222	1222	1324	1325	1424	1424	1522	1622	1624	|	1723
Stafford .... 143 144 d.		0621	0635	0653	0739	|	0815	0842	0841	0943	1041	1141	1241	1241	1342	1343	1443	1444	1541	1641	1643	1737	1744
Nuneaton .... 143 d.		|	0659	|	|	|	|	|	0904	|	|	|	|	|	|	|	|	|	|	|	|	|	|
Rugby .... 142 143 150 d.		0653	|	|	|	|	|	|	|	|	|	|	|	|	|	|	|	|	|	|	|	|	|
Milton Keynes .... 142/3 150/1/2/4 d.		0714	|	|	|	|	|	|	|	|	|	|	|	|	|	|	|	|	|	|	|	1825	|
London Euston ...... 142/3 150/1/2/4 a.		0750	0804	0823	0900	0903	0944	1000	1003	1100	1159	1259	1401	1358	1459	1502	1601	1604	1700	1758	1800	1859	1907

	⑥	Ⓐ	Ⓐ	⑥	Ⓐ	⑥	Ⓐ		⑦	⑦	⑦	⑦	⑦	⑦	⑦	⑦	⑦		⑦	⑦	⑦	⑦	⑦
Liverpool Lime Street .... 144 d.	1747	1747	1847	1847	1947	1948	2048	⑦	0818	0838	0938	1038	1147	1247	1347	1447	1547	...	1647	1747	1847	1947	2047
Runcorn .... 144 d.	1803	1803	1903	1903	2003	2005	2104		0835	0854	0954	1054	1205	1305	1405	1505	1605	...	1705	1805	1905	2004	2103
Crewe .... 143 144 151 152 154 d.	1822	1824	1922	1922	2024	2024	2125		0853	0913	1014	1114	1223	1323	1423	1523	1623	...	1723	1823	1923	2024	2124
Stafford .... 143 144 d.	1841	1843	1941	1940	|	2044	2145		|	0932	1033	1136	1243	1343	1443	1543	1643	...	1742	1843	1943	2043	2143
Nuneaton .... 143 d.	|	|	|	|	2102	|	2218		|	0955	1056	1159	|	|	|	|	|	...	|	|	|	|	2218
Rugby .... 142 143 150 d.	|	|	|	|	|	|	2231		|	|	|	|	|	|	|	|	|	...	|	|	|	|	2232
Milton Keynes .... 142/3 150/1/2/4 d.	|	|	|	|	|	|	2254		1020	|	1148	|	|	|	|	|	|	...	|	|	|	2138	2305
London Euston ...... 142/3 150/1/2/4 a.	1958	2003	2103	2113	2204	2218	2344		1104	1134	1229	1307	1403	1503	1603	1703	1803	...	1902	2003	2102	2227	2353

a – From Sept. 12.

u – Calls to pick up only.

TP, VT LONDON, BIRMINGHAM and MANCHESTER - PRESTON - EDINBURGH and GLASGOW 154

km		⚒	Ⓐ	⑥	⑥	⚒	Ⓐ	⚒	Ⓐ	⑥	Ⓐ	⑥	Ⓐ	⑥	Ⓐ	⚒	⑥	⚒	Ⓐ	⑥	⚒	Ⓐ	⑥	⑥	Ⓐ	⑥
0	**London Euston** ... 143 150/1/2/3 d.		...	...	...	...	...	...	...	...	0531	0606	...	...	...	...	...	0730	0643	...	...	0830	0830	0743	0743	...
80	Milton Keynes .... 143 150/1/2/3 d.		...	...	...	...	...	...	...	...	0621	0641	...	...	...	...	...	|	0713	...	...	|	|	0813	0813	...
	Birmingham New St ... 144 150 d.		...	...	...	...	0530	0615	...	...	|	|	0715	...	...	...	0721	|	0815	0815	...	|	|	0915	0915	...
	Wolverhampton............144 150 d.		...	...	...	...	0548	0637	...	...	|	|	0737	...	...	...	0740	|	0837	0837	...	|	|	0937	0937	...
253	Crewe .... 143 144 151 152 153 d.		...	...	0557	...	0622	0709	...	...	0732	0754	0809	...	...	...	0821	|	0909	0909	...	|	|	1009	1009	...
291	Warrington Bank Quay ....d.		...	...	0615	...	0645	0727	...	...	0749	0812	0828	...	...	...	0840	0914	0927	0927	...	1014	1014	1027	1027	...
	Manchester Airport ✈ .156 157 d.		...	...	|	0610	|	|	0710	0710	|	|	|	...	...	0810	|	|	|	|	0910	|	|	|	|	1010
	Manchester Piccadilly 156 157 d.		0457	0500	|	0626	|	|	0726	0726	|	|	|	...	...	0827	|	|	|	|	0926	|	|	|	|	1026
	Liverpool Lime Street ...162 d.		|	|	|	|	|	|	|	|	|	|	|	0812	0812	|	|	|	|	|	|	|	|	|	|	|
310	Wigan North Western..... 157 162 d.		|	|	0625	|	0657	0738	|	|	0800	0823	0839	0843	0844	|	0853	0926	0938	0938	|	1026	1025	1038	1038	|
334	**Preston**........... 156 157 158 162 d.		0536	0535	0639	0704	0713	0753	0803	0803	0815	0838	0855	0900	0900	0903	0911	0941	0952	0953	1006	1041	1041	1054	1103f	1104
	Blackpool North .... 156 162 a.		|	|	...	|	0732	|	|	|	|	|	0920	|	|	|	0930	|	|	|	|	|	|	...	1127	|
368	Lancaster...................... 157 158 d.		0551	0551	...	0720	...	0808	0819	0819	0830	0853	...	|	|	0919	...	0956	1008	1009	1022	1057	1056	...	...	|
398	Oxenholme ....158 d.		0605	0605	...	0734	...	0823	|	|	0844	0907	...	|	|	0933	...	|	1022	1024	1036	1110	1110	...	...	|
450	Penrith....................................d.		0631	0631	...	0759	...	|	0855	0855	|	0933	...	0950	0950	|	...	1032	|	|	1101	1136	1136	...	...	|
478	Carlisle ....214 d.		0650	0649	...	0816	...	0901	0912	0915	0922	0950	...	1009	1007	1013	...	1048	1102	1102	1118	1152	1156r	...	...	1207
519	Lockerbie.................................. d.		0709	0707	...	0835	...	|	0931	0935	|	|	...	1028	1027	1032	...	|	|	|	1138	|	|	...	...	1226
641	**Edinburgh** Waverley.......... △ a.		|	|	...	0938	...	1018	|	|	|	|	...	|	|	1138	...	|	1218	1218	|	|	|	...	...	1332
643	**Glasgow** Central ....214 a.		0820	0822	...	...	...	...	1034	1039	1037	1059	...	1130	1131	...	...	1202	...	...	1241	1304	1308	...	...	...

	Ⓐ	⚒	⚒	⑥	Ⓐ	⑥	Ⓐ	Ⓐ	⑥	⚒	⚒	⚒	⚒	Ⓐ	⑥	Ⓐ	⑥	⚒	Ⓐ	⑥	⚒	⚒	⑥	Ⓐ	⑥	Ⓐ
London Euston ....143 150/1/2/3 d.	...	0930	0843	...	...	1030	1030	0943	0943	...	1130	1043	...	1230	1230	1143	1143	...	1330	1330	1243	...	1430	1430	1343	1343
Milton Keynes........143 150/1/2/3 d.	...	|	0913	...	...	|	|	1013	1013	...	|	1113	...	|	|	1213	1213	...	|	|	1313	...	|	|	1413	1413
Birmingham New St ... 144 150 d.	...	|	1015	...	...	|	|	1115	1115	...	|	1215	...	|	|	1315	1315	...	|	|	1415	...	|	|	1515	1515
Wolverhampton............ 144 150 d.	...	|	1037	...	...	|	|	1137	1137	...	|	1237	...	|	|	1337	1337	...	|	|	1437	...	|	|	1537	1537
Crewe ....143 144 151 152 153 d.	...	|	1109	...	...	|	|	1209	1209	...	|	1309	...	|	|	1409	1409	...	|	|	1508	...	|	|	1609	1609
Warrington Bank Quay ....d.	...	1114	1127	...	...	1214	1214	1227	1227	...	1314	1327	...	1414	1416	1427	1427	...	1514	1514	1527	...	1614	1614	1627	1627
Manchester Airport ✈ 156 157 d.	1010	|	|	1110	1110	|	|	|	|	1210	|	|	1310	|	|	|	|	1410	|	|	|	1510	|	|	|	|
Manchester Piccadilly 156 157 d.	1026	|	|	1126	1126	|	|	|	|	1226	|	|	1326	|	|	|	|	1426	|	|	|	1526	|	|	|	|
Liverpool Lime Street.... 162 d.	|	|	|	|	|	|	|	|	|	|	|	|	|	|	|	|	|	|	|	|	|	|	|	|	|	|
Wigan North Western..... 157 162 d.	|	1125	1138	|	|	1225	1226	1238	1238	|	1325	1338	|	1426	1427	1438	1438	|	1526	1525	1538	|	1625	1626	1638	1638
Preston............156 157 158 162 d.	1104	1141	1153	1204	1204	1241	1241	1259r	1253	1305	1341	1353	1405	1441	1441	1458r	1453	1503	1541	1541	1552	1604	1641	1641	1653	1654
Blackpool North .... 156 162 a.	|	|	|	|	|	|	|	1320	...	|	|	|	|	|	|	1520	...	|	|	|	|	|	|	|	|	1716
Lancaster...................... 157 158 d.	|	1156	1208	1220	1220	1256	1257	...	...	1321	1356	1408	1421	1456	1456	...	...	1519	|	1555	1608	1620	1656	1656	1708	...
Oxenholme .... 158 d.	|	|	1222	1234	1234	1310	1311	...	...	1335	1410	|	1435	1511	1511	...	...	1533	1607	1611	|	1633	|	1711	...	...
Penrith.......................................d.	|	1232	|	1259	|	|	1337	...	...	|	|	1444	1500	1536	1536	...	...	1559	1632	|	1644	1658	1731	1737	...	...
Carlisle ....214 d.	1207	1248	1302	1315	1315	1348	1400r	...	...	1415	1448	1501	1516	1552	1601f	...	...	1616	1649	1650	1702	1715	1748	1752	...	...
Lockerbie.....................................d.	1226	|	|	1335	1335	|	|	...	...	1434c	|	|	1536	|	|	...	...	1634	|	|	|	1734	|	|	...	...
Edinburgh Waverley.......... △ a.	1326	|	1418	|	|	|	|	...	...	1539	|	1618	|	|	|	...	...	1739	|	|	1822	|	|	|	...	...
Glasgow Central ....214 a.	...	1402	...	1438	1439	1500	1516	...	...	...	1600	...	1642	1711	1717	...	...	...	1800	1800	...	1839	1859	1916	...	...

	⚒	⚒	⚒	⚒	⚒	Ⓐ	⑥	⑥	Ⓐ	⚒	Ⓐ	Ⓐ	⑥	Ⓐ	⑥	⑥	Ⓐ	Ⓐ	⑥	Ⓐ	Ⓐ	⑥	Ⓐ	⑤	Ⓐ	⑥
London Euston ....143 150/1/2/3 d.	...	...	1530	1443	...	1630	1630	1543	1543	...	1657	1730	1730	1643	1643	...	...	1757	1830	1830	1743	1743	...	1846	1930	1930
Milton Keynes........143 150/1/2/3 d.	...	...	|	1513	...	|	|	1613	1613	...	|	|	|	1713	1713	...	...	|	|	|	1813u	1813	...	1919	|	|
Birmingham New St ... 144 150 d.	...	...	|	1615	...	|	|	1715	1715	...	|	|	|	1815	1815	...	...	|	|	|	1915	1915	...	|	|	|
Wolverhampton............ 144 150 d.	...	...	|	1637	...	|	|	1737	1737	...	|	|	|	1837	1837	...	...	|	|	|	1937	1937	...	|	|	|
Crewe ....143 144 151 152 153 d.	...	...	|	1709	...	|	|	1809	1809	...	|	|	|	1911r	1908	...	...	|	|	|	2009	2008	...	2043	|	2105
Warrington Bank Quay ....d.	...	...	1714	1727	...	1814	1815	1827	1827	...	1849	1914	1915	1929	1927	...	...	1950	2015	2014	2027	2026	...	2103	2115	2123
Manchester Airport ✈ 156 157 d.	...	1610	|	|	1710	|	|	|	|	1810	|	|	|	|	|	1910	1910	|	|	|	|	|	2007	|	|	|
Manchester Piccadilly 156 157 d.	...	1626	|	|	1727	|	|	|	|	1826	|	|	|	|	|	1926	1926	|	|	|	|	|	2026	|	|	|
Liverpool Lime Street.... 162 d.	1612	|	|	|	|	|	|	|	|	|	|	|	|	|	|	|	|	|	|	|	|	|	|	|	|	|
Wigan North Western..... 157 162 d.	1644	|	1725	1738	|	1826	1826	1838	1838	|	1900	1926	1926	1940	1938	|	|	2003	2026	2026	2038	2037	|	2114	2127	2134
Preston............156 157 158 162 d.	1701	1705	1741	1753	1804	1841	1842	1854	1855	1905	1914	1941	1942	1955	1952	2006	2011	2017	2042	2041	2053	2051	2105	2131	2143	2147
Blackpool North .... 156 162 a.	|	|	|	|	|	|	|	|	1915	|	|	|	|	|	...	|	|	|	|	|	|	...	|	...	|	...
Lancaster...................... 157 158 d.	1718	1723	1756	1808	1820	1857	1856	1909	...	1921	1930	1956	1956	2011	...	2022	2027	2033	2056	2056	2108	...	2121	...	2158	...
Oxenholme .... 158 d.	|	1736	1810	1824	1833	|	1910	1923	...	1935	1945	2010	2010	|	...	2036	2041	...	2111	2111	2124	...	2135	...	2212	...
Penrith.......................................d.	1754	|	|	1849	1859	1932	1936	|	...	2001	2010	|	2036	2050	...	2101	2106	...	2136	2136	|	...	2200	...	2237	...
Carlisle ....214 d.	1811	1816	1848	1906	1915	1948	1953	2002	...	2018	2025	2048	2052	2106	...	2118	2123	...	2152	2151	2203	...	2217	...	2252	...
Lockerbie.....................................d.	|	1835	|	|	1935	|	|	|	...	2037	2044	|	|	|	...	2137	2145	...	2211	2210	|	...	2236	...	|	...
Edinburgh Waverley.......... △ a.	|	1944b	|	2025	|	|	|	|	...	2140	|	|	|	2222	...	|	|	...	|	|	|	...	2341	...	|	...
Glasgow Central ....214 a.	1952e	...	2003	...	2040	2059	2104	2125	...	...	2144	2210	2208	...	...	2240	2248	...	2312	2310	2317	...	...	...	0006	...

	⑥	⑥	Ⓐ	Ⓐ	Ⓐ	⚒	⑥	Ⓐ	⑦	⑦h	⑦d	⑦	⑦	⑦	⑦	⑦	⑦	⑦	⑦	⑦	⑦	⑦	⑦	⑦	⑦	⑦
London Euston ....143 150/1/2/3 d.	1840	...	...	2030	1943	...	2031	2110		...	...	...	...	...	...	...	0847	...	...	0946	...	...	1046	...	...	1228
Milton Keynes........143 150/1/2/3 d.	1910	...	...	|	2013	...	|	|		...	...	...	...	...	...	...	0934	...	...	1033	...	...	1133	...	...	|
Birmingham New St ... 144 150 d.	2015	...	...	|	2115	...	|	|		...	...	0845	0920	...	...	...	|	1020	...	|	1120	...	|	1220	...	|
Wolverhampton............ 144 150 d.	2036	...	...	|	2137	...	|	|		...	...	0904	0938	...	...	...	|	1037	...	|	1137	...	|	1237	...	|
Crewe ....143 144 151 152 153 d.	2109	...	...	2219	2231	...	2231	2259		...	...	0939	1010	...	...	1027	1058	1111	...	1157	1209	...	1258	1309	...	|
Warrington Bank Quay ....d.	...	...	...	2236	...	...	2248	2321		...	...	0956	1028	...	...	1043	1115	1129	...	1214	1227	...	1315	1327	...	1416
Manchester Airport ✈ 156 157 d.	...	2105	2105	|	...	2210	|	|		0905	0905	|	|	...	1010	|	|	|	1110	|	|	...	|	|	1310	|
Manchester Piccadilly 156 157 d.	...	2122	2122	|	...	2225	|	|		0923	0923	|	|	...	1026	|	|	|	1125	|	|	1231v	|	|	1326	|
Liverpool Lime Street.... 162 d.	...	|	|	|	...	|	|	|		|	|	|	|	1012	|	|	|	|	|	|	|	|	|	|	|	|
Wigan North Western..... 157 162 d.	...	|	|	2247	...	2253	2300	2332		|	|	1008	1039	1045	|	1054	1126	1140	|	1225	1238	|	1326	1338	|	1427
Preston............156 157 158 162 d.	...	2200	2217r	2303	...	2309	2316	2350		1005	1019a	1022	1052	1100	1108	1116	1141	1155	1205	1240	1254	1306	1341	1353	1404	1442
Blackpool North .... 156 162 a.	...	...	|	...	...	|	...	...		|	|	...	...	|	|	|	|	|	|	|	...	|	|	|	|	|
Lancaster...................... 157 158 d.	...	...	2237	...	...	2332	...	...		1021	1037	...	...	|	1125	1134	1157	1210	1221	1255	...	1322	1357	1409	1422	1459
Oxenholme .... 158 d.	...	...	...	...	...	...	...	...		1035	|	...	...	|	1139	...	1211	1225	1235	1309	...	1335	1411	|	1436	1513
Penrith.......................................d.	...	...	...	...	...	...	...	...		1100	|	...	...	1149	|	...	1237	|	1301	1335	...	|	1437	1446	1501	|
Carlisle ....214 d.	...	...	...	...	...	...	...	...		1116	1131	...	...	1206	1220	...	1253	1305	1317	1351	...	1416	1452	1503	1517	1550
Lockerbie.....................................d.	...	...	...	...	...	...	...	...		1137	|	...	...	|	1238	...	|	|	1337	|	...	1435	|	|	1537	|
Edinburgh Waverley.......... △ a.	...	...	...	...	...	...	...	...		|	|	...	...	|	1343	...	|	1421	|	|	...	1539	|	1620	|	|
Glasgow Central ....214 a.	...	...	...	...	...	...	...	...		1245	1253	...	...	1323	...	...	1410	...	1445	1507	...	...	1606	...	1643	1707

	⑦	⑦	⑦	⑦	⑦	⑦	⑦	⑦	⑦	⑦	⑦	⑦	⑦	⑦	⑦	⑦	⑦	⑦	⑦	⑦	⑦	⑦	⑦	⑦	⑦	⑦
London Euston ....143 150/1/2/3 d.	...	...	1328	1240	...	1428	1340	...	1528	1440	...	1628	1540	...	...	1728	1640	...	1826	1740	...	1900	1928	2025	1940	2050
Milton Keynes........143 150/1/2/3 d.	...	...	|	1313	...	|	1413	...	|	1513	...	|	1613	...	...	|	1713	...	|	1813	...	|	|	|	2013	2141
Birmingham New St ... 144 150 d.	1319	...	|	1415	...	|	1515	...	|	1615	...	|	1715	...	...	|	1815	...	|	1915	...	2028	|	|	2115	|
Wolverhampton............ 144 150 d.	1338	...	|	1437	...	|	1537	...	|	1637	...	|	1737	...	...	|	1837	...	|	1937	...	2053	|	|	2137	|
Crewe ....143 144 151 152 153 d.	1409	...	|	1509	...	|	1609	...	|	1709	...	|	1809	...	...	|	1908	...	|	2009	...	2126	|	2213	2217	2252
Warrington Bank Quay ....d.	1427	...	1516	1527	...	1616	1627	...	1716	1727	...	1816	1827	...	...	1916	1926	...	2016	2027	...	...	2116	2230	2236	2309
Manchester Airport ✈ 156 157 d.	|	1410	|	|	1510	|	|	1610	|	|	1710	|	|	...	1810	|	|	1910	|	|	2010	...	|	|	|	|
Manchester Piccadilly 156 157 d.	|	1426	|	|	1527	|	|	1626	|	|	1726	|	|	...	1826	|	|	1926	|	|	2026	...	|	|	|	|
Liverpool Lime Street.... 162 d.	|	|	|	|	|	|	|	|	|	|	|	|	|	1812	|	|	|	|	|	|	|	...	|	|	|	|
Wigan North Western..... 156 162 d.	1437	|	1527	1538	|	1627	1638	|	1727	1738	|	1827	1838	1843	|	1927	1938	|	2027	2038	|	...	2127	2241	2247	2320
Preston............156 157 158 162 d.	1452	1505	1542	1553	1607	1642	1652	1706	1742	1753	1807	1842	1853	1859	1904	1942	1953	2007	2042	2053	2103	...	2142	2255	2302	2337
Blackpool North .... 156 162 a.	...	|	|	|	|	|	...	|	|	|	|	|	...	|	|	|	|	|	|	...	|	...	|	...	...	...
Lancaster...................... 157 158 d.	...	1521	1559	1609	1622	1658	...	1721	1758	1809	1823	1858	...	1915	1920	1958	2009	2023	2058	...	2119	...	2158	...	...	...
Oxenholme .... 158 d.	...	|	1613	|	1636	1713	...	1735	1813	1824	1837	1913	...	|	1934	2013	2025	2039	2113	...	2133	...	2213	...	...	...
Penrith.......................................d.	...	1557	|	1645	1701	1738	...	1800	|	1849	1902	1938	...	1953	1959	2038	2051	2105	2138	...	2159	...	2238	...	...	...
Carlisle ....214 d.	...	1614	1651	1702	1719	1753	...	1818	1850	1905	1918	1954	...	2009	2017	2052	2106	2122	2153	...	2214	...	2253	...	...	...
Lockerbie.....................................d.	...	1633	|	|	1738	|	...	1837	|	|	1938	|	...	2028	2036	|	|	2141	|	...	|	...	|	...	...	...
Edinburgh Waverley.......... △ a.	...	1737	|	1820	|	|	...	1940	|	2022	|	|	...	|	2139	|	2228	|	|	...	|	...	|	...	...	...
Glasgow Central ....214 a.	...	...	1806	...	1841	1913	...	...	2005	...	2040	2105	...	2133	...	2205	...	2247	2308	...	2347	...	0005	...	...	...

a – Arrives 1004.
b – Arrives 1939 on ⑥.
c – ⑥ only.
d – Until June 19.
e – Arrives 1932 on ⑥.
f – Arrives 8 – 10 minutes earlier.
h – From June 26.
r – Arrives 5 – 7 minutes earlier.
t – Ⓐ only.
u – Calls to pick-up only.
v – Manchester **Victoria**.

△ – All trains to **Edinburgh** Waverley call at Haymarket 5 – 9 minutes earlier.

154 GLASGOW and EDINBURGH - PRESTON - MANCHESTER, BIRMINGHAM and LONDON

TP, VT

km		Ⓐ	⑥	⚒	⑥	Ⓐ	⚒	Ⓐ	⑥	①	②–⑤	⑥	Ⓐ	Ⓐ	⑥	⚒	⚒	⑥	Ⓐ	⚒	⑥	Ⓐ	Ⓐ	⑥
	Glasgow Central 214 d.	...	...	...	0426	0428	...	...	...	0422	0452	0532	0533	...	...	...	0630	...	...	0709	0737	0737	...	...
	Edinburgh Waverley ▽ d.	...	...	...	|	|	...	...	...	|	|	|	|	...	...	0612	|	0652	0652	|	|	|	...	...
	Lockerbie d.	...	...	...	|	|	...	...	...	0550d	0558	|	|	...	...	0712	0726	|	|	0810	|	|	...	...
	Carlisle 214 d.	...	...	...	0544	0543	...	...	...	0622f	0629f	0647	0647	...	...	0734	0746	0807	0809	0832	0849	0850	...	...
	Penrith d.	...	...	...	0558	0558	...	...	...	0644f	0644	0701	0701	...	...	0749	0800	0822	0824	0847	|	|	...	...
	Oxenholme 158 d.	...	...	...	0621	0621	0626	...	...	0708	0708	0725	0725	...	...	0813	0823	|	|	0911	0923	0924	...	...
	Lancaster 157 158 d.	0513	0538	0628	0636	0636	0643	0658	0658	0723	0723	0739	0739	...	...	0828	0839	0856	0858	0926	0938	0939	...	...
	Blackpool North 156 162 d.	|	|	|	|	|	|	|	|	|	|	|	|	0754	...	|	|	|	|	|	|	|	0947	0954
0	**Preston** 156 157 158 162 d.	0533	0557	0647	0656	0657	0704	0718	0717	0746r	0747f	0800	0800	0817	0817	0847	0859	0917	0919	0947	1000	1000	1017	1017
24	Wigan North Western 157 162 d.	0545	0609	|	0709	0710	0717	0729	0729	|	|	0812	0811	0829	0829	|	0911	0929	0929	|	1011	1011	1029	1029
	Liverpool Lime Street 162 a.	|	|	|	|	|	0757	|	|	|	|	|	|	|	|	|	|	|	|	|	|	|	|	|
59	**Manchester** Piccadilly 156 157 a.	|	|	0724	|	|	...	|	|	0824	0824	|	|	|	|	0924	|	|	|	1024	|	|	|	|
77	**Manchester** Airport ✈ 156 157 a.	|	|	0741	|	|	...	|	|	0841	0841	|	|	|	|	0941	|	|	|	1041	|	|	|	|
	Warrington Bank Quay d.	0556	0620	...	0719	0720	...	0741	0741	...	...	0822	0822	0840	0840	...	0922	0940	0941	...	1022	1023	1040	1040
0	Crewe 143 144 151 152 153 a.	|	|	...	|	|	...	0757	0757	...	...	|	|	0857	0857	...	|	0957	0958	...	|	|	1057	1057
63	Wolverhampton 144 150 a.	|	|	...	|	|	...	0834	0835	...	...	|	|	0934	0933	...	|	1034	1036	...	|	|	1134	1135
82	**Birmingham** New St 144 150 a.	|	|	...	|	|	...	0905	0905	...	...	|	|	1004	1006	...	|	1105	1105	...	|	|	1205	1205
	Milton Keynes 150/1/2/3 a.	|	0738	...	|	|	...	0958	...	...	...	|	|	1058	1058	...	|	1157	1158	...	|	|	1258	1258
	London Euston 143 150/1/2/3 a.	0802	0812	...	0907	0908	...	1033	...	...	...	1014	1008	1134	1133	...	1110	1233	1234	...	1208	1210	1336	1333

	⚒	⚒	⚒	Ⓐ	⑥		⑥	Ⓐ	Ⓐ	⑥	Ⓐ	⑥	⚒	⚒	⚒	⑥	Ⓐ	Ⓐ	⑥	⚒	⚒	⚒	⚒	⚒	⚒
Glasgow Central 214 d.	...	0836	...	0906	0909	...	0937	0940	...	...	...	...	1040	...	1107	1133	1133	...	...	1205	...	1240	...	1309	1335
Edinburgh Waverley ▽ d.	0812	|	0852	|	|	...	|	|	...	...	1012	1012	|	1052	|	|	|	...	...	|	1212	|	1252	|	|
Lockerbie d.	0911	|	|	1010	1012	...	|	|	...	...	1111	1111	|	|	1209	|	|	...	...	1306	1311	|	|	1409	|
Carlisle 214 d.	0933	0949	1008	1034	1035	...	1050	1049	...	...	1133	1135	1149	1207	1233	1248	1249	...	...	1328	1334	1349	1408	1433	1449
Penrith d.	0948	1003	|	1049	1050	...	|	|	...	...	1150	1151	|	|	1248	1302	1303	...	...	1343	1349	|	1422	1448	|
Oxenholme 158 d.	1012	|	1042	1113	1114	...	1124	1123	...	...	1214	1215	1223	1243	1312	|	|	...	...	1407	1413	1424	|	1512	1523
Lancaster 157 158 d.	1027	1038	1057	1128	1129	...	1139	1138	...	...	1229	1230	1238	1257	1327	1337	1338	...	...	1422	1428	1439	1456	1528	1538
Blackpool North 156 162 d.	|	|	|	|	|	...	|	|	1148	...	|	|	|	|	|	|	|	1347	...	|	|	|	|	|	|
Preston 156 157 158 162 d.	1048	1059	1117	1148	1149	...	1159	1159	1218	1217	1249	1250	1259	1317	1347	1359	1359	1417	1420	1442	1448	1459	1517	1548	1559
Wigan North Western 157 162 d.	|	1111	1129	|	|	...	1211	1211	1229	1229	|	|	1310	1329	|	1411	1411	1429	1433	1457	|	1511	1529	|	1611
Liverpool Lime Street 162 d.	|	|	|	|	|	...	|	|	|	|	|	|	|	|	|	|	|	|	|	1541	|	|	|	|	|
Manchester Piccadilly 156 157 a.	1124	|	|	1224	1224	...	|	|	|	|	1323	1323	|	|	1424	|	|	|	|	...	1524	|	|	1624	|
Manchester Airport ✈ 156 157 a.	1141	|	|	1241	1241	...	|	|	|	|	1341	1341	|	|	1441	|	|	|	|	...	1541	|	|	1641	|
Warrington Bank Quay d.	...	1122	1140	...	...	...	1222	1222	1241	1240	...	...	1321	1340	...	1422	1422	1441	1444	...	...	1522	1540	...	1622
Crewe 143 144 151 152 153 a.	...	|	1157	...	...	...	|	|	1257	1259	...	...	|	1357	...	|	|	1457	1458	...	...	|	1558	...	|
Wolverhampton 144 150 a.	...	|	1234	...	...	...	|	|	1335	1333	...	...	|	1436	...	|	|	1535	1535	...	...	|	1634	...	|
Birmingham New St. 144 150 a.	...	|	1305	...	...	...	|	|	1405	1405	...	...	|	1505	...	|	|	1604	1605	...	...	|	1706	...	|
Milton Keynes 150/1/2/3 a.	...	|	1358	...	...	...	|	|	1458	1458	...	...	|	1558	...	|	|	1658	1658	...	...	|	1758	...	|
London Euston 143 150/1/2/3 a.	...	1309	1434t	...	...	...	1410	1411	1535	1535	...	...	1521	1634	...	1608	1610	1736	1734	...	...	1711	1834	...	1809

	Ⓐ	⑥	⑥	Ⓐ	Ⓐ	⑥	Ⓐ	⑥	⚒	Ⓐ	⑥	Ⓐ	⑥	⑥	Ⓐ	Ⓐ	⑥		Ⓐ	⑥	Ⓐ	⑥	Ⓐ	⑥	Ⓐ
Glasgow Central 214 d.	...	...	...	...	1434	1440	...	...	1508	1540	1540	...	...	...	...	1640	1640	...	...	...	1707	1709	1730	1740	...
Edinburgh Waverley ▽ d.	...	...	1410	1412	|	|	1452	1452	|	|	|	...	...	1611	1612	|	|	...	1652	1652	|	|	|	|	...
Lockerbie d.	...	...	1509	1513	|	|	|	|	1609	|	|	...	...	1710	1711	|	|	...	|	|	1810	1810	1826	1833	...
Carlisle 214 d.	...	...	1537f	1539f	1549	1549	1608	1608	1631	1649	1649	...	...	1734	1734	1752	1752	...	1809	1809	1834	1833	1846	1853	...
Penrith d.	...	...	1552	1554	|	|	1621	1622	1646	1703	|	...	...	1749	1749	1806	|	...	|	|	1849	1848	1901	1907	...
Oxenholme 158 d.	...	...	|	|	1624	1624	|	|	1710	|	1724	...	...	1813	1813	1830	1826	...	1843	1844	1913	1912	1925	1930	...
Lancaster 157 158 d.	...	...	1628	1630	1638	1638	1658	1658	1725	1737	1738	...	1758	1829	1829	1844	1841	...	1858	1859	1929	1927	1939	1945	...
Blackpool North 156 162 d.	1547	...	|	|	|	|	|	|	|	|	|	1747	|	|	|	|	|	...	|	|	|	|	|	|	1942
Preston 156 157 158 162 d.	1617	1618	1648	1650	1659	1659	1717	1717	1745	1758	1759	1817	1817	1849	1848	1905	1902	...	1918	1920	1948	1947	2000	2006	2008
Wigan North Western 157 162 d.	1629	1629	|	|	1711	1710	1729	1729	|	1810	1811	1829	1829	|	|	1917	1914	...	1932	1931	|	|	2012	2018	2020
Liverpool Lime Street 162 d.	|	|	|	|	|	|	|	|	|	|	|	|	|	|	|	|	|	...	|	|	|	|	|	|	|
Manchester Piccadilly 156 157 a.	|	|	1724	1724	|	|	|	|	1827	|	|	|	|	1924	1927	|	|	...	|	|	2024	2024	|	|	|
Manchester Airport ✈ 156 157 a.	|	|	1741	1746	|	|	|	|	1846	|	|	|	|	1942	1946	|	|	...	|	|	2043	2040	|	|	|
Warrington Bank Quay d.	1641	1640	...	...	1722	1721	1741	1740	...	1821	1822	1841	1840	...	...	1927	1925	...	1942	1942	...	...	2023	2029	2033
Crewe 143 144 151 152 153 a.	1657	1657	...	...	|	|	1757	1757	...	|	1841	1857	1857	...	...	|	|	...	2000	2001	...	...	2042	2048	2052
Wolverhampton 144 150 a.	1733	1734	...	...	|	|	1835	1833	...	|	|	1935	1934	...	...	|	|	...	2037	2033	...	...	|	|	2132
Birmingham New St. 144 150 a.	1805	1805	...	...	|	|	1905	1906	...	|	|	2005	2006	...	...	|	|	...	2104	2105	...	...	|	|	2152
Milton Keynes 150/1/2/3 a.	1858	1858	...	...	|	|	1959	2005	...	|	|	2105	2105	...	...	2045	2044	...	2158	2205	...	...	2149	2154	...
London Euston 143 150/1/2/3 a.	1933	1932	...	...	1908	1910	2036	2055	...	2010	2027	2143	2157	...	...	2119	2140	...	2241	2256	...	...	2227	2247	...

	⑥	⑥	Ⓐ	Ⓐ	⑥	Ⓐ	⑥	⑥	Ⓐ	Ⓐ	Ⓐ		⑦	⑦	⑦	⑦	⑦	⑦	⑦	⑦	⑦	⑦	⑦	⑦	⑦
Glasgow Central 214 d.	...	...	...	1840	1840	...	...	1846	1911	2006	...		...	...	...	...	...	...	0916	0934	...	...	1013	1038	...
Edinburgh Waverley ▽ d.	...	1811	1811	|	|	1852	1852	|	|	|	2011		...	...	...	...	...	...	|	|	...	1013	|	|	1051
Lockerbie d.	...	1911	1912	|	|	|	|	1955	2008	2104	2112	⑦	...	...	...	...	...	...	1023	|	...	1112	1117	|	|
Carlisle 214 d.	...	1934	1934	1949	1949	2007	2009r	2017	2030	2126	2135		...	...	...	...	...	...	1045	1051	...	1135	1139	1153	1207
Penrith d.	...	1949	1949	|	2003	|	2023	2032	2045	2140	|		...	...	...	...	...	...	1100	1105	...	1149	1154	1207	|
Oxenholme 158 d.	...	2013	2013	2024	2026	2041	2047	2056	2109	2204	2211		...	...	...	...	...	...	1123	1128	...	1213	1218	1231	1243
Lancaster 157 158 d.	...	2028	2029	2038	2041	2056	2102	2111	2125	2219	2226		...	...	...	...	...	...	1138	1143	1158	1228	1235	1245	1257
Blackpool North 156 162 d.	...	|	|	|	|	|	|	|	|	|	|		...	...	...	...	...	...	|	|	|	|	|	|	|
Preston 156 157 158 162 d.	2018	2047	2048	2059	2102	2117	2122	2136f	2144	2240	2252f		0853	0900	1000	1017	1058	1117	1157	1204	1217	1248	1354	1306	1317
Wigan North Western 157 162 d.	2030	|	|	2111	2114	2129	2133	|	|	2253	|		0905	0911	1012	1028	1109	1129	|	1215	1229	|	1308	1318	1329
Liverpool Lime Street 162 d.	|	|	|	|	|	|	|	|	|	|	|		0940	|	|	|	|	|	|	|	|	|	1341	|	|
Manchester Piccadilly 156 157 a.	|	2124	2124	|	|	|	|	2219	2223	|	2338		...	|	|	|	|	|	1241	|	|	1325	...	|	|
Manchester Airport ✈ 156 157 a.	|	2142	2139	|	|	|	|	2237	2245	|	0002		...	|	|	|	|	|	1256	|	|	1340	...	|	|
Warrington Bank Quay d.	2041	...	...	2121	2125	2139	2144	...	...	2303	...		...	0922	1022	1039	1120	1140	...	1226	1240	...	...	1329	1340
Crewe 143 144 151 152 153 a.	2101	...	...	|	2144	2159	2204	...	...	2327	...		...	0941	1041	1059	1139	1159	...	|	1259	...	...	|	1359
Wolverhampton 144 150 a.	2135	...	...	|	2223	2233	2241	...	...	...	...		...	|	|	1134	|	1233	...	|	1332	...	...	|	1433
Birmingham New St. 144 150 a.	2155	...	...	|	2249	2306	2259	...	...	...	...		...	|	|	1155	|	1251	...	|	1405	...	...	|	1505
Milton Keynes 150/1/2/3 a.	...	...	...	2240	...	0024	...	...	...	...	...		...	1110	1206	...	|	...	...	|	1458	...	...	|	1558
London Euston 143 150/1/2/3 a.	...	...	...	2333	...	0112	...	...	...	...	...		...	1209	1243	...	1316	...	...	1416	1536	...	...	1518	1636

	⑦	⑦	⑦	⑦	⑦	⑦	⑦	⑦	⑦	⑦	⑦	⑦	⑦	⑦	⑦	⑦	⑦	⑦	⑦	⑦	⑦	⑦	⑦	⑦	⑦
Glasgow Central 214 d.	1107	1135	...	...	1235	...	1306	1332	...	1405	...	1435	...	1505	1535	...	...	1638	...	1703	1734	...	...	1915	...
Edinburgh Waverley ▽ d.	|	|	...	1212	|	1251	|	|	...	|	1412	|	1451	|	|	...	1614	|	1651	|	|	1813	1851	|	2015
Lockerbie d.	1210	|	...	1311	|	|	1409	|	...	|	1511	|	|	1613	|	...	1713	|	|	1805	1831	1913	|	2017	2114
Carlisle 214 d.	1233	1249	...	1334	1349	1407	1433	1449	...	1523	1534	1549	1607r	1635	1649	...	1736	1751	1807	1828	1851	1936	2004	2038	2137
Penrith d.	1248	|	...	1348	|	1422	1448	|	...	1537	1548	|	1622	1650	|	...	1750	1805	|	1843	1906	1950	2019	2053	|
Oxenholme 158 d.	1312	1323	...	1412	1423	|	1514	1523	...	1601	1612	1623	|	1714	1724	...	1814	1828	1842	1907	1929	2014	2043	2117	2213
Lancaster 157 158 d.	1327	1338	...	1427	1438	1457	1530	1538	...	1616	1627	1638	1657	1729	1738	...	1829	1843	1857	1923	1944	2029	2057	2132	2227
Blackpool North 156 162 d.	|	|	...	|	|	|	|	|	...	|	|	|	|	|	|	...	|	|	|	|	|	|	|	|	|
Preston 156 157 158 162 d.	1347	1359	1418	1447	1459	1517	1549	1559	1620	1638	1647	1659	1718	1748	1759	1817	1849	1904	1917	1943	2005	2049	2118	2151	2246
Wigan North Western 157 162 d.	|	1411	1430	|	1511	1529	|	1611	1633	1650	|	1710	1730	|	1811	1829	|	1915	1929	|	2017	|	2130	|	|
Liverpool Lime Street 162 d.	|	|	|	|	|	|	|	|	|	1726	|	|	|	|	|	|	|	|	|	|	|	|	|	|	|
Manchester Piccadilly 156 157 a.	1426	|	|	1524	|	|	1624	|	|	...	1724	|	|	1825	|	|	1925	|	|	2019	|	2123	|	2227	2322
Manchester Airport ✈ 156 157 a.	1441	|	|	1540	|	|	1640	|	|	...	1740	|	|	1840	|	|	1940	|	|	2039	|	2138	|	2241	2338
Warrington Bank Quay d.	...	1422	1441	...	1522	1540	...	1622	1644	...	...	1721	1741	...	1822	1840	...	1926	1940	...	2027	...	2141	...	...
Crewe 143 144 151 152 153 a.	...	|	1500	...	|	1559	...	|	1702	...	...	|	1800	...	|	1859	...	|	1959	...	2047	...	2200	...	...
Wolverhampton 144 150 a.	...	|	1533	...	|	1632	...	|	1733	...	...	|	1834	...	|	1933	...	|	2033	...	|	...	2233	...	...
Birmingham New St. 144 150 a.	...	|	1605	...	|	1705	...	|	1805	...	...	|	1906	...	|	2005	...	|	2051	...	|	...	2300	...	...
Milton Keynes 150/1/2/3 a.	...	|	1658	...	|	1758	...	|	1903	...	...	|	1958	...	|	2100	...	|	...	...	2152	...	...	...	...
London Euston 143 150/1/2/3 a.	...	1611	1735	...	1711	1835	...	1811	1940	...	...	1911	2035	...	2011	2148	...	2118	...	...	2253	...	...	...	...

d – Arrives 0537.
f – Arrives 7–10 minutes earlier.
r – Arrives 5–6 minutes earlier.
t – Arrives 1437 on ③.
▽ – All trains from **Edinburgh** Waverley call at Haymarket 4–6 minutes later.

EM 2nd class only — CREWE - STOKE - DERBY - NOTTINGHAM — 155

km			⚒	Ⓐ	⑥	⚒	⚒	⚒	⚒	⚒	⚒	⚒	⚒	⚒	⚒	Ⓐ	⑥		⑦	⑦	⑦	⑦	⑦	⑦	⑦	⑦
0	**Crewe** .... d.	Ⓐ	0608	0702	0708	0908	1008v	1108v	1210	1409	1510	1610	1708	1909	2011	2121	2127	⑦	1407	1507	1609	1709	1809	1909	2015	2117
24	Stoke on Trent .... d.		0633	0727	0735	0933	1033	1133	1233	1433	1533	1632	1733	1934	2033	2146	2151		1432	1532	1634	1735	1836	1935	2039	2142
33	Blythe Bridge .... d.		0645	0739	0747	0945	1045	1145	1245	1445	1545	1644	1745	1946	2045	2158	2203		1444	1543	1645	1746	1847	1946	2051	2154
51	Uttoxeter .... d.		0657	0751	0759	0957	1057	1157	1257	1457	1557	1656	1757	1958	2057	2210	2215		1456	1555	1657	1758	1859	1958	2103	2206
82	**Derby** .... 120 172 a.		0720	0816c	0822	1019	1119	1220	1319f	1519n	1619	1719	1820	2020f	2120t	2232a	2238		1518	1617	1720	1820	1921	2020	2125	2229
108	**Nottingham** ..... 120 172 a.		0756	0848	0859	1056	1154	1253	1355	1554	1654	1753j	1853j	2053j	2146t	2302	...		*1555*	*1653*	*1754*	*1854*	*1957*	*2054*	*2154*	*2359*

		⚒	⚒	⑥	Ⓐ	Ⓐ	⑥	⚒	⚒	⚒	⚒	Ⓐ	⚒	⚒	⚒	⚒	⑥	Ⓐ		⑦	⑦	⑦	⑦	⑦	⑦	⑦
Nottingham ...... 120 172 d.	Ⓐ	0716	0816	0917	0916	1016	1016	1216	1316	1416	1516	🚌	1716	1816	1916	2016	2116	2119	⑦	*1416*	*1512*	*1616*	*1716*	*1816*	*1915*	*2016*
Derby .... 120 172 d.		0745	0848	0948r	0948	1047	1048r	1248r	1348	1448	1548j	1645	1746	1848r	1948	2047r	2145	2148		1445	1544	1645	1746	1845	1945	2044
Uttoxeter .... d.		0809	0910	1010	1010	1109	1110	1310	1410	1510	1610	|	1810	1910	2010	2110	2207	2210		1506	1606	1706	1807	1906	2006	2105
Blythe Bridge .... d.		0822	0924	1024	1024	1123	1124	1324	1424	1524	1624	|	1824	1924	2024	2124	2221	2224		1519	1618	1719	1819	1919	2019	2118
Stoke on Trent .... d.		0835	0937	1037	1037	1136	1137	1337	1437	1537	1637	1817	1837	1937	2037	2137	2234	2237		1533	1633	1733	1833	1933	2034	2130
Crewe .... a.		0901	1002	1101	1103	1202	1201	1403	1503	1603	1703	...	1903	2003	2103	2201	2300	2303		1558	1658	1758	1858	1958	2059	2155

a – Departs 2239.
c – Departs 0823.
f – Departs 5–6 minutes later on Ⓐ.
j – Arrives 5–6 minutes earlier on Ⓐ.
n – Departs 4–5 minutes later.
r – Arrives 4–6 minutes earlier.
t – On ⑥ departs Stoke on Trent 2130 and arrives Nottingham 2156.
v – Departs 3 minutes later on Ⓐ.

NT 2nd Class only — MANCHESTER - PRESTON - BLACKPOOL — 156

For other trains Manchester - Preston and v.v. see Tables **154** and **157**.

km			⚒	⚒	⚒	⚒	⚒	⚒	⚒	⚒	⚒	⚒	♣	⚒	⚒	⚒	⚒	Ⓐ	⑥	⚒	⚒	⚒	⑥	Ⓐ	⚒	⚒
0	**Manchester** Airport ✈ .d.	⚒	0446	0542	...	0642	...	0742	...	0844	...	0945	and at	1546	...	1644	...	1745	1746	...	1846	...	1942	1945	...	2042
17	**Manchester** Piccadilly .d.		0504	0601	0630	0701	0730	0800	0831	0901	0930	1001	the same	1601	1630	1701	1731	1803	1801	1830	1901	1930	2000	2003	2030	2102
35	Bolton .... d.		0523	0620	0658r	0721	0750	0820	0851	0921	0950	1020	minutes	1621	1650	1721	1750	1821	1821	1850	1920	1950	2021	2021	2050	2121
67	**Preston** ...... 173a 191 d.		0552	0653	0738	0752	0825	0851	0925	0958	1024	1051	past each	1653z	1737	1754	1826	1859	1852	1925	1951	2025	2051	2052	2127	2151
96	**Blackpool** N .... 191 a.		0619	0720	0801	0820	0849	0918	0946	1023	1048	1118	hour until	1718z	1802	1821	1851	1925	1918	1948	2018	2047	2116	2117	2149	2218

	⚒	⚒	⑥	Ⓐ	⚒	⚒	Ⓐ		⑦🚌	⑦p	⑦y	⑦	⑦	⑦	⑦	⑦	⑦	⑦	⑦	⑦		⑦	⑦	⑦	⑦	⑦
Manchester Airport ✈ .d.	...	2145	...	...	2230c	2309b	2348	⑦	0530	0740	...	0841	0943	1033	...	1110	...	1242	...	1345	and at	1845	1945	2045	2145	2246
Manchester Piccadilly .d.	2131	2159	2230	2231	2254	2330	0009		0555	0800	0804t	0902	1001	1055	1103a	1125	1203a	1301	1302a	1401	the same	1901	2001	2102	2201	2302
Bolton .... d.	2151	2218	2251	2252	2318	2349	0024f		0620s	0819	0819	0923	1020	1115	1120	|	1219	|	1321	1420	minutes	1920	2020	2121	2220	2321
Preston .... 173a 191 d.	2228	2250	2326	2329	2351	0024	0053		0655s	0857	0857	0959	1059	1143	1151	1204	1255	1347	1359	1458	past each	2005n	2056	2159	2303	2356
Blackpool North ... 191 a.	2250	2316	2347	2351	0019	0047	0119		0735	0922	0922	1025	1125	...	1215	...	1319	...	1424	1526	hour until	2030	2122	2225	2329	0022

		⚒	⚒	⚒	⑥	Ⓐ	Ⓐ	⑥	⚒	⚒	Ⓐ	⑥	⚒	⚒	⚒	⚒		⚒	⚒	⚒	⚒	⑥	Ⓐ	⚒	⚒	⚒
Blackpool North ... 191 d.	⚒	0333	0444	0523	0556	0556	0624	0634	0653	0724	0746	0757	0825	0859	0928	0958	and at	1654	1728	1755	1828	1856	1901	1926	1959	2025
Preston .... 173a 191 d.		0357	0509	0549	0620	0621	0650	0700	0720	0751	0823j	0823	0855	0922	0954	1021	the same	1720	1754	1821	1855	1923g	1924	1953	2022	2053
Bolton .... d.		|	0537	0621	0650	0654	0721	0735	0754	0822	0854	0853	0922	0954	1022	1054	minutes	1755	1822	1854	1922	1954	1954	2022	2054	2122
Manchester Piccadilly .a.		0445	0558	0645	0714	0715	0745	0757	0815	0845	0915	0915	0945	1015	1045	1115	past each	1815	1845	1915	1945	2015	2015	2045	2115	2144
Manchester Airport ✈ .a.		0503	0622	...	0732	0732	...	...	0834	...	0934	0935	...	1035	...	1135	hour until	1835	...	1935	...	2033	2033	...	2135	...

	⑥	Ⓐ	Ⓐ	⑥		⚒	⑥	Ⓐ		⑦🚌	⑦🚌	⑦	⑦	⑦	⑦w	⑦	⑦	⑦	⑦	⑦	⑦		⑦	⑦	⑦	⑦
Blackpool North ... 191 d.	2057	2058	2121	2126	...	2223	2307	2319	⑦	0320	0520	0752	...	0900	...	1000	...	1100	...	1151	1250	and at	1949	2050	2151	2222
Preston .... 173a 191 d.	2122	2123	2151	2152	...	2249	2334	2346		0400u	0600u	0818	0912	0926	1009	1026	1109	1126	1157	1220	1318	the same	2016	2119	2219	2249
Bolton .... d.	2153	2154	2224	2224	...	2323	0008	0018		0435u	0635u	0845	|	0958	|	1058	|	1158	|	1254	1353	minutes	2054	2153	2252	2323
Manchester Piccadilly .a.	2214	2219	2246	2247	...	2344	0026	0041		0500u	0700u	0904t	1001	1017a	1056	1117a	1156	1215a	1241	1316	1415	past each	2115	2219	2316	2344
Manchester Airport ✈ .a.	2233	2238	2306	2306	...	0011	0044	0059		0525	0725	...	1024	...	1121	...	1220	...	1256	1332	1432	hour until	2131	2236	2332	...

a – Manchester **Oxford Road**.
b – Ⓐ only.
c – Departs 2234 on Ⓐ.
f – ⑥ mornings only.
g – Arrives 1918.
j – Arrives 0811.
n – Arrives 1958.
p – Until Oct. 23.
r – Arrives 0650.
s – Calls to set down only.
t – Manchester **Victoria**.
u – Calls to pick up only.
w – Until Sept. 11.
y – From Oct. 30.
z – 7 minutes later on Ⓐ.
♣ – The 1045, 1245 and 1445 from Manchester Airport run up to 10 minutes later from Preston.

NT 2nd Class only — MANCHESTER - PRESTON - BARROW IN FURNESS — 157

For other trains Manchester - Preston / Lancaster and v.v. see Tables **154** and **156**.

km			⚒	⚒	⚒	Ⓐ	⑥	⚒D	⚒A	⚒	⚒	⑥D	⑥	⑥A	ⒶD	ⒶA	⚒	⑥g	⚒	Ⓐb	⚒D	⚒A	Ⓐ	⑥	⚒	⚒	⚒D
0	**Manchester** Airport ✈ . d.	⚒	...	0524	...	...	...	0827	...	0927	1028	1128	...	...	1128	...	1228	...	1410	...	1428	...	1528	1528	1626	*1710*	1727
17	**Manchester** Piccadilly . d.		...	0543	...	...	...	0848	...	0948	1047	1147	...	...	1147	...	1247	...	1426	...	1447	...	1547	1547	1647	*1727*	1747
52	Wigan North Western .. d.		...	0616	...	...	...	0921	...	1021	1121t	1216	...	...	1221t	...	1321t	*1427*	|	...	1520t	...	1615	1618	1721y	|	1820
76	**Preston** .... a.		...	0631	...	...	...	0942	...	1042	1142	1232	...	...	1236	...	1335	*1438*	1502	...	1536	...	1632	1634	1743	*1802*	1836
	Preston .... d.		0518	0644	...	...	...	0944	...	1045	1144	1245	1241		1245	...	1345	*1441*	1503	...	1545	1532	1634	1645	1745	*1804*	1845
110	Lancaster .... 174 d.		0538	0702	0736	0823	0823	1002	1013	1102	1202	1303	1255	1301	1302	1313	1402	1513	1518	1524	1603	1612v	1652	1704	1802	1835	1902
120	Carnforth .... 174 d.		0549	0712	0746	0833	0833	...	1023	1112	1212	...	...	1311	...	1323	1412	1522	...	1533	...	1622	1701	1713	1812	1845	...
130	Arnside .... d.		0559	0721	0756	0843	0843	...	1033	1121	1222	...	...	1321	...	1333	1421	1531	...	1543	...	1632	1710	1722	1821	1855	...
135	Grange over Sands ..... d.		0605	0726	0802	0849	0849	...	1039	1127	1227	...	...	1327	...	1339	1427	1537	...	1548	...	1638	1716	1728	1827	1901	...
150	Ulverston .... d.		0621	0741	0818	0903	0905	...	1055	1140	1242	...	...	1343	...	1355	1442	1552	...	1603	...	1654	1731	1743	1842	1917	...
166	**Barrow in Furness** ..... a.		0643	0802	0840	0923	0927	...	1117	1201	1303	...	...	1405	...	1417	1503	1613	...	1625	...	1716	1751	1803	1903	1939	...

	ⒶA	⑥B	⚒	Ⓐ	⑥	⑥	Ⓐ		⑦A	⑦D	⑦A	⑦	⑦	⑦Dc	⑦Dr	⑦A	⑦	⑦	⑦D	⑦A	⑦	⑦	⑦D	⑦	⑦	⑦	⑦
Manchester Airport ✈ .. d.	...	...	1828	...	...	2210	2210	⑦	...	...	...	0935	1033	1132	...	...	1242	1330	1430	...	1530	1630	1730	...	1830	1930	...
Manchester Piccadilly .. d.	...	...	1847	...	...	2225	2225		...	0853z	...	0952	1055	1151	1154j	...	1301	1348	1448	...	1548	1648	1748	...	1848	1948	...
Wigan North Western .... d.	...	...	1919	...	...	2253	2257		...	0920	...	1027	|	1219	1219	...	1333	1421	1517	...	1621t	1718	1818	...	1918	2022t	...
Preston .... a.	...	...	1934	...	...	2308	2313		...	0936	...	1042	1143	1234	1234	...	1347	1437	1532	...	1637	1733	1832	...	1933	2038	...
Preston .... d.	...	...	1944	...	2211	2309	2315		...	0948	...	1043	1146	1245	1245	...	1358	1447	1534	...	1657	1746	1834	...	1947	2046	...
Lancaster .... 174 d.	1913	1913	2002	2208	2232	2328	2333		...	1005	1011	1101	1204	1302	1302	1314	1416	1505	1552	1603	1715	1804	1851	1902	2005	2104	2220
Carnforth .... 174 d.	1923	1923	2011	2218	2242	2337	2342		0855	...	1021	1110	1213	...	...	1324	1425	1514	...	1612	1724	1813	...	1913	2014	2114	2230
Arnside .... d.	1933	1933	2021	2228	2252	2347	2352		0905	...	1031	1119	1223	...	...	1334	1434	1523	...	1622	1734	1822	...	1924	2023	2123	2240
Grange over Sands .... d.	1939	1939	2026	2234	2258	2354	2358		0911	...	1037	1125	1228	...	...	1340	1439	1528	...	1628	1739	1828	...	1930	2029	2128	2246
Ulverston .... d.	1955	1955	2042	2250	2314	0009	0013		0927	...	1053	1140	1243	...	...	1356	1454	1543	...	1644	1754	1843	...	1946	2044	2143	2301
Barrow in Furness ...... a.	2017	2017	2103	2312	2336	0030	0033		0948	...	1115	1201	1304	...	...	1418	1515	1604	...	1706	1815	1903	...	2007	2105	2204	2323

		⚒	⚒	⚒	⚒	⚒	⚒	ⒶD	⑥D	⚒A	⚒	⚒D	⚒A	⚒	⚒b	⚒	ⒶD	⑥D	Ⓐ	⚒A	⚒	⚒	⑥D	ⒶD	Ⓐ	⑥	Ⓐ
Barrow in Furness ...... d.	⚒	0549	0611	0649	0708	0747	0849	...	...	0958	1153	...	1250	1352	1411	1450	...	...	🚌	1646	...	1804	...	...	1855	1903	1945
Ulverston .... d.		0608	0630	0708	0727	0806	0907	...	...	1017	1212	...	1308	1410	1428	1509	...	...	1608	1705	...	1823	...	...	1913	1921	2004
Grange over Sands .... d.		0623	0645	0722	0742	0820	0922	...	...	1032	1227	...	1324	1423	1441	1524	...	...	1647	1720	...	1838	...	...	1929	1937	2019
Arnside .... d.		0628	0651	0727	0749	0825	0927	...	...	1039	1232	...	1330	1429	1446	1529	...	...	...	1727	...	1844	...	...	1935	1943	2024
Carnforth .... 174 d.		0640	0703	0739	0801	0837	0939	...	...	1056t	1244	...	1342	1440	1456	1540	...	...	...	1738	...	1856	...	...	1947	1955	2036
Lancaster .... 174 d.		0651	0716	0748	0812	0847	0950	1032	1048	1108	1251	1348	1353	1450	1507	1548	1643	1647	...	1748	1829	1906	1935	1934	1956	2003	2044
Preston .... a.		0709	...	0806	...	0907	1008	1052	1106	...	1310	1406	...	1508	...	1606	1703	1705	...	...	1848	...	1956	1953	2019	2026	2102
Preston .... d.		0710	...	0808	...	0908	1010	1102	1108	...	1312	1408	...	1510	...	1608	1708	1708	...	...	1848	...	2008	2012	...	...	2104
Wigan North Western .... d.		0725	...	0823	...	0924	1024	1118	1124	...	|	1424	...	1524	...	1623	1724	1723	...	...	|	...	2024	2027	...	...	|
Manchester Piccadilly .. a.		0758	...	0900	...	0957	1057	1157	1157	...	1357	1457	...	1558	...	1658	1758	1757	...	...	1927	...	2058	2058	...	...	2146
Manchester Airport ✈ .. a.		0820	...	0918	...	1017	1117	1217	1217	...	1417	1517	...	1617	...	1717	1818	1817	...	...	1946	...	2119	2120	...	...	2203

	⑥	⑥	Ⓐ	ⒶA	⑥	⑥D		⑦	⑦c	⑦r	⑦	⑦	⑦	⑦	⑦D	⑦Ah	⑦Af	⑦	⑦	⑦D	⑦A	⑦	⑦A	⑦D	⑦	⑦	⑦
Barrow in Furness ...... d.	1945	2042	2045	2145	2146	...	⑦	0753	0841	0841	0905	0950	1052	1141	...	1253	1317	1349	1447	...	1550	1646	1746	...	1851	1952	2046
Ulverston .... d.	2004	2101	2104	2204	2204	...		0812	0859	0859	0922	1008	1110	1200	...	1311	1335	1407	1505	...	1608	1705	1805	...	1909	2011	2105
Grange over Sands .... d.	2019	2116	2119	2219	2220	...		0827	0914	0914	0934	1023	1125	1215	...	1324	1354	1422	1520	...	1624	1720	1820	...	1925	2026	2020
Arnside .... d.	2024	2122	2125	2226	2226	...		0833	0920	0920	0940	1029	1131	1220	...	1330	1359	1428	1526	...	1630	1725	1827	...	1931	2031	2126
Carnforth .... 174 d.	2040t	2134	2137	2238	2238	...		0845	0931	0931	0951	1040	1142	1232	...	1342	1406	1439	1537	...	1642	1737	1841	...	1943	2043	2138
Lancaster .... 174 d.	2047	2143	2147	2246	2246	2305		...	0945t	0945t	1001	1048	1151	1240	1349	1352	1420	1449	1547	1648	1652	1749t	1850	1939	1951	2050	2148
Preston .... a.	2105	2205	...	2309	2310	2324		...	1004	1004	...	1107	1209	1300	1407	...	...	1507	1605	1706	...	1807	...	1958	2014	2108	...
Preston .... d.	2107	...	...	...	...	...		...	1009	1009	...	1109	1211	1309	1408	...	...	1509	1609	1709	...	1809	...	2009	...	2110	...
Wigan North Western .... d.	|	...	...	...	...	...		...	1023	1023	...	1123	|	1323	1424	...	...	1523	1624	1723	...	1823	...	2025	...	2124	...
Manchester Piccadilly .. a.	2148	...	...	...	...	...		...	1056	1052j	...	1156	1256	1354	1456	...	...	1557	1701	1755	...	1900	...	2056	...	2155	...
Manchester Airport ✈ .. a.	2204	...	...	...	...	...		...	1121	...	...	1220	1317	1417	1518	...	...	1617	1718	1818	...	1917	...	2116	...	2213	...

A – From / to Carlisle (Table **159**).
B – To Millom (Table **159**).
D – To / from Windermere (Table **158**).
a – Arrives 1015.
b – From July 18.
c – Until Sept. 11.
f – From June 19.
g – From July 23.
h – Until June 19.
j – Manchester **Oxford Road**.
r – From Sept. 18.
t – Arrives 5–7 minutes earlier.
v – Arrives 1553.
y – ⑥ only. Arrives 1716.
z – From Oct. 30 - Manchester Victoria at 0855.

158 PRESTON - OXENHOLME - WINDERMERE

2nd Class NT

km		⚒	⚒	⚒	⚒	⑥	Ⓐ		Ⓐ	⑥	⚒	⚒	Ⓐ	⑥	⚒		⚒	⚒	⑥	Ⓐ	⚒	⑥	Ⓐ
	Manchester Airport ✈ 157 d.		...	...	...	...	...	...	0827	0828	...	...	1128	1128	...	...	...	1428	...	...	...	1728	1727
	Manchester Piccadilly 157 d.		...	...	...	...	...	...	0848	0848	...	...	1147	1147	...	...	...	1447	...	...	...	1748	1747
	Preston 154 157 d.		...	...	...	...	...	...	0944	0945	...	...	1245	1245	...	...	...	1545	...	...	...	1845	1845
	Lancaster 154 157 d.		0600	...	...	...	...	...	1002	1003	...	...	1302	1313r	...	...	...	1603	...	...	...	1903	1902
0	**Oxenholme** 154 d.		0616	0729	0827	0920	0930	...	1021	1033	1121	1239	1332	1332	1439	...	1537	1631	1736	1742	1829	1922	1922
4	Kendal d.		0621	0733	0831	0924	0934	...	1026	1038	1125	1243	1337	1337	1443	...	1541	1636	1740	1746	1833	1927	1926
16	**Windermere** a.		0636	0748	0846	0939	0949	...	1041	1051	1140	1258	1351	1352	1455	...	1556	1651	1755	1801	1848	1941	1942

	Ⓐ	⑥	Ⓐ	⑦	⑦c	⑦d	⑦		⑦	⑦	⑦y	⑦z		⑦	⑦	⑦		⑦	⑦	⑦		⑦	⑦
Manchester Airport ✈ 157 d.	...	...	...		...	...	...	...	...	...	1132	...	...	...	...	1430	...	...	...	1730	...	...	...
Manchester Piccadilly 157 d.	...	...	...		0855a	0853	...	...	...	...	1151	1154j	...	...	...	1448	...	...	...	1748	...	...	...
Preston 154 157 d.	...	...	...		0948	0948	...	...	...	...	1245	1245	...	...	...	1534	...	...	...	1834	...	...	...
Lancaster 154 157 d.	...	...	...		1006	1006	...	...	...	...	1302	1302	...	...	...	1615f	...	...	...	1851	...	...	...
Oxenholme 154 d.	2120	2206	2222		1030t	1030t	1117	...	1202	1245	1333	1333	...	1422	1529	1631	...	1730	1833	1927	...	2022	2121
Kendal d.	2124	2210	2226		1034	1034	1121	...	1206	1249	1338	1338	...	1426	1533	1636	...	1734	1837	1932	...	2026	2125
Windermere a.	2139	2225	2241		1049	1049	1135	...	1219	1304	1353	1353	...	1441	1548	1651	...	1749	1852	1947	...	2041	2140

	⚒	⚒	⚒	⚒		Ⓐ	⑥	⚒		⚒	⚒		⚒	⚒	Ⓐ	⑥	⚒		⑥	Ⓐ	Ⓐ	⑥	⚒
Windermere d.		0642	0756	0850	...	0956	1008	1057	...	1147	1307	...	1358	1459	1600	1600	1708	...	1802	1805	1856	1857	1948
Kendal d.		0656	0810	0901	...	1010	1022	1111	...	1201	1321	...	1412	1513	1614	1614	1722	...	1816	1819	1910	1911	2002
Oxenholme 154 d.		0701	0815	0906	...	1017	1029	1116	...	1206	1327	...	1417	1518	1627v	1627v	1727	...	1821	1824	1917	1918	2007
Lancaster 154 157 a.		...	...	...	...	1032	1048	...	...	...	1342k	...	...	...	1643	1643	...	...	...	...	1933	1933	...
Preston 154 157 a.		...	...	...	...	1052	1106	...	...	...	1406	...	...	...	1703	1705	...	...	...	...	1953	1956	...
Manchester Piccadilly 157 a.		...	...	...	...	1157	1157	...	...	...	1457	...	...	...	1758	1757	...	...	...	...	2058	2058	...
Manchester Airport ✈ 157 a.		...	...	...	...	1217	1217	...	...	...	1517	...	...	...	1818	1817	...	...	...	...	2120	2119	...

	⑥	Ⓐ	⑥	Ⓐ	⑦	⑦		⑦	⑦	⑦	⑦		⑦	⑦	⑦		⑦	⑦	⑦		⑦	⑦	⑦
Windermere d.	2143	2147	2229	2247		1053	...	1139	1224	1308	1359	...	1446	1554	1659	...	1800	1901	1957	...	2047	2147	...
Kendal d.	2157	2201	2243	2301		1107	...	1153	1236	1322	1413	...	1500	1608	1713	...	1814	1916	2011	...	2101	2201	...
Oxenholme 154 d.	2202	2206	2250	2308		1112	...	1158	1241	1329	1418	...	1505	1615	1718	...	1819	1922	2016	...	2106	2215p	2213
Lancaster 154 157 a.	...	...	2305	2323		...	...	...	...	1344k	...	...	...	1631n	...	...	...	1937	...	...	...	2232	2227
Preston 154 157 a.	...	...	2324	2343		...	...	...	...	1407	...	...	...	1706	...	...	...	1958	...	...	...	2251	2245
Manchester Piccadilly 157 a.	...	...	...	...		...	...	...	...	1456	...	...	...	1755	...	...	...	2056	...	...	...	...	2322
Manchester Airport ✈ 157 a.	...	...	...	...		...	...	...	...	1518	...	...	...	1818	...	...	...	2116	...	...	...	...	2338

a – Manchester **Victoria**.
c – From Oct. 30.
d – Until Oct. 23.
f – Arrives 1552.
j – Manchester **Oxford Road**.
k – Departs 5 minutes later.
n – Departs 1648.
p – Arrives 2206.
r – Arrives 1303.
t – Arrives 1022.
v – Arrives 1619.
y – Until Sept. 11.
z – From Sept. 18.

159 BARROW - WHITEHAVEN - CARLISLE

2nd class NT

km		⚒	⑥	Ⓐ	⚒	⚒	⚒	Ⓐ	⑥	⑥	Ⓐ	⚒	Ⓐ	⑥	⚒	⑥	Ⓐ	⚒	⚒	⑥	Ⓐ	Ⓐ	⚒ B	⚒	⑥	Ⓐ
	Lancaster 157 d.		...	...	...	...	...	...	...	...	...	1013	...	...	...	1301	1313	...	...	...	...	...	1612	...	...	...
0	**Barrow in Furness** d.		...	...	...	0558	0651	0750	0754	0917	0927	1118	1206	1206	1316	1414	1418	1449	1544	1611	1615	...	1717	1807	1857	1912
26	Millom d.		...	...	...	0627	0719	0818	0822	0944	0955	1146	1234	1234	1344	1442	1446	1517	1612	1639	1644	...	1745	1834	1925	1940
47	Ravenglass for Eskdale 🚂 d.		...	...	...	0645	0737	0835	0839	1001	1012	1203	1251	1251	1401	1459	1503	1534	1629	1656	1701	...	1802	1849	1942	1957
56	Sellafield d.		...	...	...	0700	0753	0849	0852	1014	1032r	1217	1303	1303	1413	1512	1515	1547	1641	1708	1712	...	1814	1900	1953	2012r
74	**Whitehaven** d.		...	...	0630	0723	0816	0909	0914	1037	1051	1236	1338	1338	1438	1539	1540	1612r	1701	1729	...	1749	1835	1921	2013	2037
85	Workington d.		0548	0552	0648	0742	0834	0927	0933	1055	1109	1253	1356	1356	1456	1558	1559	1633r	1719	1747	...	1807	1853	1943r	2035r	2055
92	Maryport d.		0556	0600	0656	0750	0843	0936	0941	1103	1117	1301	1404	1404	1505	1607	1608	1643	1728	1756	...	1816	1902	1953	2044	2104
119	Wigton d.		0618	0622	0718	0812	0904	0957	1003	1124	1138	1323	1426	1426	1526	1628	1629	1705	1749	1817	...	1837	1923	2014	2105	2125
138	**Carlisle** a.		0638	0642	0739	0832	0925	1017	1023	1144	1158	1341	1447	1451	1546	1648	1649	1725	1811	1841	...	1857	1943	2034	2125	2145

	⑥	Ⓐ	⑥	Ⓐ	⚒	Ⓐ	⚒	⑦	⑦ a	⑦ a	⑦ b	⑦	⑦	⑦ C	⑦	⑦	⑦		⑦	⑦	⑦	⑦	⑦	⑦	⑦	⑦
Lancaster 157 d.	...	...	1913	1913	...	...	...		...	...	...	...	...	...	1011	...	...	...	1314	...	...	1603	...	...	...	...
Barrow in Furness d.	1944	1944	2018	2018	2110	...	2211		...	...	...	0905	...	0950	1116	1218	1309	...	1419	1455	1558	1717	...	1825	...	1907
Millom d.	2011	2012	2046	2045	2138	...	2239		...	...	...	0933	...	1017	1144	1245	1336	...	1444	1523	1625	1746	...	1853	...	1935
Ravenglass for Eskdale 🚂 d.	2028	...	...	2102	▬	...	...		...	...	...	...	...	1034	1201	1302	1353	...	1459	1541	1642	1803	...	...	...	...
Sellafield d.	2041	...	...	2115	⑥	...	...		...	...	...	...	...	1046	1213	1315	1405	...	1507	1551	1654	1815	...	...	...	...
Whitehaven d.	2102	...	...	2134	2209	2209	...		...	...	...	...	1016	1111	1234	1338	1426	...	1529	1611	1716	1839	1938	...	2030	...
Workington d.	2120	...	...	2152	2227	2227	...		0855	0940	0957	...	1034	1129	1252	1358	1444	...	1547	1629	1734	1857	1956	...	2048	...
Maryport d.	2128	...	...	2200	2236	2236	...		0904	0949	1006	...	1043	1137	1301	1408	1453	...	1556	1637	1743	1906	2005	...	2057	...
Wigton d.	...	...	...	2221	...	2257	...		0925	1010	1027	...	1104	1159	1322	1430	1514	...	1617	1659	1804	1927	2026	...	2118	...
Carlisle a.	...	...	...	2241	...	2317	...		0945	1030	1047	...	1124	1219	1342	1450	1534	...	1637	1719	1824	1947	2046	...	2138	...

	⚒	⚒	⚒	⑥	Ⓐ	⚒	Ⓐ	⑥		Ⓐ	⑥	⚒	Ⓐ	⑥	⚒	⚒		⚒	⚒	Ⓐ	Ⓐ	⑥	⚒	⚒	Ⓐ	⑥
Carlisle d.		...	...	0616	0619	0710	0808	0813	...	0902	0908	1013	1107	1107	1210	1408	...	1441	1512	...	1559	1626	1707	1754	...	1846
Wigton d.		...	...	0635	0636	0731	0826	0831	...	0920	0926	1031	1125	1125	1227	1426	...	1458	1530	...	1617	1644	1725	1812	...	1904
Maryport d.		...	0548	0659	0700	0755	0848	0852	...	0941	0947	1053	1146	1146	1249	1447	...	1520	1551	...	1638	1705	1746	1833	...	1925
Workington d.		...	0558	0710	0711	0806	0858	0902	...	0952	0958	1103	1157	1157	1259	1458	...	1530	1602	...	1648	1715	1757	1844	...	1936
Whitehaven d.		...	0618	0730	0730	0825	0918	0921	...	1012	1017	1123	1216	1216	1319	1518	...	1550	1621	...	1708	1736	1818	1903	...	1956
Sellafield d.		...	0639	0750	0750	0844	0939	0942	...	1031	1037	1147	1238	1240	1340	1538	...	1611	1641	1725	...	1755	1840	1927	...	...
Ravenglass for Eskdale 🚂 d.		...	0650	0801	0801	0854	0949	0952	...	1042	1048	1157	1248	1250	1350	1549	...	1622	1651	1735	...	1805	1849	1939	...	...
Millom d.		0610	0709	0820	0820	0914	1008	1010	...	1101	1107	1216	1307	1309	1409	1608	...	1642	1712	1754	...	1825	1905	2001	2029	...
Barrow in Furness a.		0641	0741	0853	0853	0947	1040	1042	...	1136	1139	1248	1339	1341	1441	1640	...	1714	1745	1826	...	1857	1937	2036	2101	...
Lancaster 157 a.		...	...	...	...	1108	...	...	...	...	...	1353	...	...	...	1748	...	...	...	...	...	...	...	...	...	...

	⑥	⑥	Ⓐ B	⚒	Ⓐ	⑥	⑥	Ⓐ	⑦	⑦	⑦	⑦ a	⑦ b	⑦ a	⑦ b	⑦	⑦	⑦	⑦	⑦	⑦	⑦	⑦	⑦	⑦	⑦
Carlisle d.	...	1909	1909	2000	2055	2106	2149	2201		...	...	0945	...	1023	1041	1106	1207	1324	1401	1510	1616	1710	1810	1910	2010	2110
Wigton d.	...	1927	1927	2018	2113	2124	2206	2219		...	...	1002	...	1041	1058	1124	1225	1342	1419	1528	1634	1728	1828	1928	2028	2128
Maryport d.	...	1948	1948	2039	2134	2145	2227	2241		...	0917	1024	1024	1103	1120	1145	1246	1403	1440	1549	1655	1749	1849	1949	2049	2149
Workington d.	...	1959	1959	2050	2145	2156	2237	2251		...	0927	1033	1033	1113	1130	1156	1258	1414	1451	1600	1706	1800	1900	2000	2100	2200
Whitehaven d.	...	2020	2018	2109	2204	2215	2257	2310		...	0947	1051	1051	1133	1150	1215	1318	1433	1510	1619	1725	1819	1919	2019	2119	2219
Sellafield d.	...	2040	2040	▬	...	...	...	...		...	1007	1109	1109	1151	1208	1239	1337	1451	1529	1642	1744	1840	▬	...	...	...
Ravenglass for Eskdale 🚂 d.	...	2050	2050	⚒	...	...	...	...		...	1017	1119	1119	1201	1218	1249	1347	1501	1539	1652	1754	1850	⑦	...	...	...
Millom d.	2059	2109	2109	2200	...	...	...	...		0950	1036	1137	1137	1219	1236	1308	1406	1517	1557	1711	1814	1909	1925	...	...	...
Barrow in Furness a.	2129	2141	2142	2231	...	...	...	...		1021	1108	1209	1209	1251	1308	1340	1438	1548	1629	1743	1846	1941	1957	...	...	...
Lancaster 157 a.	...	...	2246	...	...	...	...	...		...	...	...	...	1352	1420	...	...	1652	...	1850	...	...	...	...	...	...

B – To/from Preston (Table **157**).
C – From Carnforth (Table **157**).
a – From June 26.
b – Until June 19.
r – Arrives 4–6 minutes earlier.
🚂 – Ravenglass and Eskdale Railway. ✆ 01229 717171. www.ravenglass-railway.co.uk

HOLYHEAD - CHESTER - MANCHESTER 160

AW, VT 2nd class

km	Ⓐ	Ⓐ	Ⓐ	Ⓐ	Ⓐ	Ⓐ	Ⓐ	Ⓐ	Ⓐ	Ⓐ	Ⓐ	Ⓐ	Ⓐ	Ⓐ	Ⓐ	Ⓐ	Ⓐ	Ⓐ	Ⓐ	Ⓐ	Ⓐ	Ⓐ	Ⓐ	Ⓐ	Ⓐ
					P	A			C	AW		P	🍷S		🍷Q	🍷	🍷P	🍷S	🍷	🍷Q	🍷	🍷R	🍷	C	🍷Q
0	**Holyhead** d.	...	...	...	0425	0448	0502	...	0533	0551	...	0625	0655	...	0726	...	0805	0855	...	0923	...	1041	...	1133	1148
40	Bangor d.	...	...	...	0457	0514	0533	...	0600	0618	...	0704	0722	...	0806	...	0855r	0922	...	1002	...	1110	...	1200	1220
	Llandudno ‡ d.	...	...	...	|	|	|	0553	|	|	0641	|	|	0744	|	0846	|	|	0945	|	1045	|	1141	|	|
64	Llandudno Junction ‡ d.	...	0438	...	0515	0532	0556	0607	0621	0636	0650	0726f	0740	0753	0832	0856	0925r	0940	0956	1025	1055	1128	1153	1218	1245
71	Colwyn Bay d.	...	0444	...	0521	0538	0602	0613	0628	0642	0656	0732	0747	0759	0838	0902	0931	0947	1002	1031	1101	1134	1159	1226	1251
88	Rhyl d.	...	0457	...	0530	0549	0613	0626	0640	0653	0708	0741	0758	0812	0849	0914	0940	0958	1013	1042	1113	1143	1212	1237	1300
94	Prestatyn d.	...	0502	...	0536	|	0619	0631	|	0658	0713	0747	0804	0817	0855	0920	0946	1004	1019	1048	1119	1149	1218	1243	1306
136	**Chester** a.	...	0534	...	0608	0617	0650	0705	0712	0726	0744	0816	0831	0848	0927	0951	1016	1031	1051	1118	1151	1217	1249	1312	1334
136	**Chester 151** 190 ♥ d.	0334	0537	0547	...	0626	0653	...	...	0735	0750	...	0835	0851	...	0952	...	1035	1052	...	1152	...	1252	...	...
170	**Crewe 151** ♥ a.	|	0559	|	...	0653	|	...	...	0754	|	...	0854	|	...	|	...	1054	|	...	|	...	|	...	...
165	Warrington Bank Quay 190 d.	|	...	0619	...	...	0720	...	...	...	0819	...	...	0920	...	1020	...	...	1120	...	1220	...	1320	...	...
201	**Manchester** Piccadilly a.	0442	...	0658	...	...	0755	...	...	...	0855	...	...	0954	...	1054	...	...	1154	...	1254	...	1354	...	...
217	**Manchester** Airport a.	0503	...	0717	...	...	0816	...	...	...	0916	...	...	1016	...	1119	...	...	1219	...	1319	...	1419	...	...

	Ⓐ	Ⓐ	Ⓐ	Ⓐ	Ⓐ	Ⓐ	Ⓐ	Ⓐ	Ⓐ	Ⓐ	Ⓐ	Ⓐ	Ⓐ	Ⓐ	Ⓐ	Ⓐ	Ⓐ	Ⓐ	Ⓐ	Ⓐ	Ⓐ	Ⓐ	Ⓐ	Ⓐ	Ⓐ	Ⓐ
	🍷	🍷S	🍷	🍷Q	D	🍷	🍷P	D	🍷		🍷Q		C		T						B	🍷				
Holyhead d.	...	1253	1307	1327	1357	...	1434	1450	...	...	1538	...	1636	...	1728	...	...	1826	...	...	1922	...	...	2032	...	...
Bangor d.	...	1321	1341	1406	1425	...	1501	1518	...	...	1617	...	1703	...	1807	...	...	1905	...	...	2000	2020	...	2100	...	...
Llandudno ‡ d.	...	|	|	|	|	1440	|	|	1544	...	|	1645	|	1744	|	...	1844	|	1937	...	|	|	2044	|	2145	...
Llandudno Junction ‡ d.	1254	1339	1359	1431	1443	1452	1527	1536	1554	1623	1640	1658	1721	1756	1833	1839	1856	1931	1947	...	2023	2038	2056	2129f	2157	...
Colwyn Bay d.	1300	1345	1405	1437	1449	1458	1533	1542	1600	1629	1646	1704	1729	1802	|	1845	1902	1937	1953	...	2029	2044	2102	2135	2203	...
Rhyl d.	1313	1356	1416	1447	1500	1510	1542	1553	1612	1640	1655	1715	1744	1814	|	1856	1914	1946	2004	...	2038	2055	2114	2148	2218	...
Prestatyn d.	1319	1401	1422	1452	|	1516	1548	|	1618	1646	1701	1721	1750	1820	|	1902	1920	1952	2010	...	2044	2101	2120	2153	2224	...
Chester a.	1351	1429	1450	1525	1528	1547	1619	1628	1649	1715	1730	1752	1818	1851	1913	1931	1951	2020	2038	...	2115	2128	2151	2225	2259	...
Chester 151 190 ♥ d.	1352	1435	1452	...	1535	1552	...	1635	1650	...	...	1753	...	1852	...	...	1952	2023	2040	2052	...	2135	2152	2230	2304	2322
Crewe 151 ♥ a.	|	1455	|	...	1554	|	...	1654	|	...	...	|	...	|	...	...	|	2044	2102	|	...	2154	|	2252	2329	|
Warrington Bank Quay 190 d.	1420	...	1520	...	...	1622	...	...	1720	...	...	1820	...	1920	...	...	2020	...	...	2121	...	...	2220	...	...	2350
Manchester Piccadilly a.	1454	...	1555	...	...	1655	...	...	1756	...	...	1855	...	1954	...	...	2054	...	...	2154	...	...	2257	...	...	0022
Manchester Airport a.	1519	...	1619	...	...	1716	...	...	1816	...	...	1919	...	2019	...	...	2117	...	...	...	...	...	2319	...	...	...

	⑥	⑥	⑥	⑥	⑥	⑥	⑥	⑥	⑥	⑥	⑥	⑥	⑥	⑥	⑥	⑥	⑥	⑥	⑥	⑥	⑥	⑥	⑥	⑥	⑥
					P			Q		P	D		Q	D	🍷	🍷P	🍷S	🍷	🍷Q	🍷	P	🍷	🍷Q	🍷	🍷P
Holyhead d.	...	...	...	...	0425	...	...	0522	...	0631	0652	...	0715	0755	...	0816	0855	...	0928	...	1030	...	1128	...	1238
Bangor d.	...	...	...	...	0457	...	...	0601	...	0703	0720	...	0754	0822	...	0855	0922	...	1007	...	1102	...	1208	...	1305
Llandudno ‡ d.	...	...	...	...	|	...	...	|	...	|	|	0744	|	|	0846	|	|	0945	|	1045	|	1144	|	1242	|
Llandudno Junction ‡ d.	...	...	0438	...	0517	0532	...	0625	0644	0722	0738	0753	0821	0840	0856	0921	0940	0955	1033	1055	1122	1154	1233	1255	1323
Colwyn Bay d.	...	...	0444	...	0523	0538	...	0631	0650	0728	0744	0759	0827	0847	0902	0927	0947	1001	1039	1101	1128	1200	1239	1301	1329
Rhyl d.	...	...	0457	...	0534	0553	...	0641	0702	0740	0755	0812	0838	0858	0914	0939	0958	1013	1051	1113	1140	1212	1252	1313	1340
Prestatyn d.	...	...	0502	...	0540	0559	...	0647	0708	0745	0801	0818	0844	0904	0920	0944	1003	1019	1057	1119	1145	1218	1257	1319	1346
Chester a.	...	...	0535	...	0610	0632	...	0718	0738	0816	0828	0849	0915	0931	0951	1015	1029	1051	1129	1151	1217	1250	1329	1351	1417
Chester 151 190 ♥ d.	0336	0452	0535	0552	...	0639	0652	...	0741	...	0835	0852	...	0933	0952	...	1035	1052	...	1152	...	1251	...	1352	...
Crewe 151 ♥ a.	|	|	0558	|	...	0704	|	...	|	...	0854	|	...	0952	|	...	1054	|	...	|	...	|	...	|	...
Warrington Bank Quay 190 d.	|	|	...	0620	...	...	0720	...	0821	...	...	0921	...	...	1020	...	...	1120	...	1220	...	1320	...	1420	...
Manchester Piccadilly a.	0441	0555	...	0657	...	...	0754	...	0854	...	...	0954	...	...	1054	...	...	1154	...	1254	...	1354	...	1454	...
Manchester Airport a.	0502	0616	...	0717	...	...	0816	...	0919	...	...	1019	...	...	1119	...	...	1219	...	1319	...	1419	...	1519	...

	⑥	⑥	⑥	⑥	⑥	⑥	⑥	⑥		⑥	⑥	⑥	⑥	⑥	⑥	⑥	⑥	⑥	⑥	⑥	⑥	⑦	⑦	⑦	⑦
	🍷	🍷Q	D	🍷	🍷P	🍷	🍷Q	🍷		🍷P	🍷	T				B									
Holyhead d.	...	1327	1358	...	1427	...	1525	...	...	1648	...	1728	...	1825	...	1921	...	...	2035	...	...	...	0750	0849	...
Bangor d.	1333	1406	1425	...	1455	...	1604	...	...	1715	...	1807	...	1904	...	2000	...	...	2102	...	...	...	0829	0917	...
Llandudno ‡ d.	|	|	|	1441	|	1544	|	1644	...	|	1744	|	1844	|	1942	|	...	2043	|	2144	...	...	|	|	...
Llandudno Junction ‡ d.	1357	1427	1443	1453	1520	1556	1630	1656	...	1735	1756	1833	1856	1929	1954	2026	...	2054	2133r	2156	...	...	0853	0937	...
Colwyn Bay d.	1403	1433	1450	1459	1526	1602	1636	1702	...	1741	1802	1839	1902	1935	2000	2032	...	2100	2139	2202	...	...	0859	0943	...
Rhyl d.	1415	1446	1500	1511	1537	1614	1648	1714	...	1753	1814	1851	1914	1945	2012	2044	...	2112	2151	2217	...	...	0908	0956	...
Prestatyn d.	1421	1451	|	1517	1543	1620	1653	1720	...	1758	1820	1856	1920	1950	1018	2049	...	2118	2157	2223	...	...	|	1001	...
Chester a.	1452	1526	1527	1548	1615	1651	1725	1751	...	1829	1851	1927	1951	2018	2049	2122	...	2149	2227	2256	...	...	0939	1033	...
Chester 151 190 ♥ d.	1453	...	1535	1549	...	1652	...	1752	...	...	1852	...	1952	2019	2052	...	2152	...	2231	2301	2323	0841	0942	1039	1038
Crewe 151 ♥ a.	|	...	1554	|	...	|	...	|	...	...	|	...	|	2041	|	...	|	...	2253	2327	|	|	|	1102	|
Warrington Bank Quay 190 d.	1521	...	...	1620	...	1720	...	1820	...	...	1920	...	2020	...	2121	...	2220	...	...	...	2350	0908	1010	...	1105
Manchester Piccadilly a.	1555	...	...	1654	...	1754	...	1854	...	...	1954	...	2054	...	2156	...	2255	...	...	...	0023	0943	1044	...	1140
Manchester Airport a.	1619	...	...	1719	...	1819	...	1919	...	...	2019	...	2119	...	...	...	...	...	...	...	...	...	...	...	...

	⑦	⑦	⑦	⑦	⑦	⑦	⑦	⑦	⑦	⑦	⑦	⑦	⑦	⑦	⑦	⑦	⑦	⑦	⑦	⑦	⑦	⑦	⑦	⑦	⑦	⑦
		🍷		🍷P		D		D		D		🍷			🍷P				🍷Q		🍷					
Holyhead d.	...	...	...	1020	...	1150	...	1250	...	1351	...	1430	1530	...	1625	...	1729	...	1826	...	1936	...	...	2033	...	2140
Bangor d.	...	...	...	1059	...	1217	...	1318	...	1418	...	1509	1557	...	1704	...	1756	...	1906	...	2015	...	...	2112	...	2209
Llandudno ‡ d.	1022	...	1107	|	1218	|	1317	|	1420	|	1517	|	|	1644	|	1803	|	1859	|	...	|	...	...	|	2138	|
Llandudno Junction ‡ d.	1032	1037	1117	1123	1228	1235	1327	1336	1430	1436	1527	1534f	1625f	1654	1725	1813	1822	1908	1924	...	2041	...	...	2139	2148	2229
Colwyn Bay d.	...	1043	...	1129	▬	1242	▬	1342	▬	1443	▬	1540	1631	▬	1731	▬	1828	▬	1930	...	2047	...	...	2145	...	2235
Rhyl d.	...	1055	...	1142	...	1253	...	1353	...	1454	...	1553	1644	...	1744	...	1841	...	1943	...	2059	...	...	2156	...	2245
Prestatyn d.	...	1101	...	1147	⑦	1259	...	1359	⑦	1459	⑦	1558	1649	⑦	1749	...	1846	...	1949	...	2104	...	...	2202	...	2251
Chester a.	...	1133	...	1221	🍷	1323	⑦	1426	🍷	1526	🍷	1634	1720	🍷	1822	⑦	1917	⑦	2022	...	2136	...	...	2233	...	2319
Chester 151 190 ♥ d.	...	1134	...	...	1236	1330	1336	1433	1436	1533	1536	1636	1723	1736	...	1836	1927	1935	2027	2036	2138	2143	2206	2237	...*	...
Crewe 151 ♥ a.	...	|	...	...	|	1350	|	1456	|	1552	|	|	1744	|	...	|	1949	|	2049	|	2200	|	|	2301	...	...
Warrington Bank Quay 190 d.	...	1203	...	...	1304	...	1403	...	1503	...	1603	1703	...	1803	...	1903	...	2003	...	2104	...	2210	2233	...	...	...
Manchester Piccadilly a.	...	1239	...	...	1337	...	1440	...	1540	...	1640	1740	...	1837	...	1937	...	2040	...	2140	...	2248	2306	...	...	...
Manchester Airport a.	...	...	...	...	...	...	...	...	...	...	...	...	...	...	...	...	...	...	...	...	...	...	...	...	...	...

CAERNARFON - PORTHMADOG - BLAENAU FFESTINIOG △ A special service is currently operating – see note ❦

km		🚂 GH	🚂 J	🚂 EF KLN	🚂 H	🚂 KL	🚂 GJ	🚂 FK LN	🚂 H	🚂 EF N	🚂 KL	🚂 KL	🚂 FK LN
0	**Blaenau Ffestiniog** d.	...	...	1135	...	1220	...	1340	...	1505	1525	1605	1725
19	Minffordd d.	...	...	1230	...	1320	...	1440	...	1600	1625	1700	1815
22	**Porthmadog** Hbr d.	0940	1050	1245	1255	1335	1415	1455	1540	1615	1640	1715	1830
35	Beddgelert d.	1025	1130	...	1335	...	1455	...	1620	...	...	...	...
42	Rhyd Ddu d.	1100	1200	...	1400	...	1525	...	1645	...	...	...	...
50	Waunfawr d.	1125	1230	...	1430	...	1555	...	1720	...	...	...	...
61	**Caernarfon** a.	1205	1310	...	1510	...	1630	...	1755	...	...	...	...

	🚂 EF KLN	🚂 KL	🚂 FL N	🚂 K	🚂 GH J	🚂 EF KLN	🚂 KL	🚂 H	🚂 FK LN	🚂 GJ	🚂 H
Caernarfon d.	...	...	...	...	1000	...	...	1300	...	1420	1545
Waunfawr d.	...	...	...	...	1030	...	...	1330	...	1450	1615
Rhyd Ddu d.	...	...	...	...	1100	...	...	1400	...	1525	1645
Beddgelert d.	...	...	...	...	1130	...	...	1430	...	1555	1715
Porthmadog Hbr d.	1005	1035	1125	1155	1215	1335	1430	1515	1550	1630	1800
Minffordd d.	1015	1045	1135	1205	...	1345	1440	...	1600	...	...
Blaenau Ffestiniog d.	1120	1150	1240	1320	...	1445	1550	...	1705	...	...

A – Conveys [12] and ✕ to/from London Euston (Table **151**).
B – To/from Birmingham New Street (Tables **145** or **151**).
C – [12] and ✕ Holyhead - Cardiff Central and v.v. (Tables **145** and **149**).
D – Conveys [12] and 🍷 London Euston and v.v. (Table **151**).
E – FR Pink service:
F – FR Blue service:
G – WHR Yellow service:
H – WHR Red service:
J – WHR Blue service:
K – FR Red service:
L – FR Yellow service:
N – FR Green service:
P – To/from Cardiff Central (Tables **145** and **149**).
Q – To/from Birmingham International (Tables **145** or **151**).
R – To/from Llanelli (Tables **149** and **136**).
S – From Sept. 12 conveys [12] and 🍷 to/from London Euston.
T – To/from Shrewsbury (Table **145**).

W – Conveys [12] London - Chester - Wrexham and v.v. (Tables **145** and **151**).
Y – Conveys [12] and 🍷 Crewe - Holyhead.
Z – On Ⓐ Llandudno Junction a. 1238, d. 1240, Llandudno a. 1250.

f – Arrives 5–6 minutes earlier.
g – Until Sept. 9.
n – From Sept. 12.
p – Previous night.
r – Arrives 7–8 minutes earlier.
t – On ①–④ change at Chester.

* – Connection by 🚌.
‡ – For full service Llandudno - Llandudno Junction and v.v. see next page.
♥ – For full service Chester - Crewe and v.v. see next page.
△ – Operators: Ffestiniog Railway and Welsh Highland Railway. ✆ 01766 516024. www.festrail.co.uk
❦ – The service shown is the normal one expected but, owing to current COVID-19 restrictions, a revised and very limited service will be operating. Trains can be boarded at Porthmadog for return journeys to Tan-y-Bwlch, Blaenau Ffestiniog, Beddgelert or Caernarfon and all tickets have to be pre-booked online. A similar offering is available between Caernarfon and Porthmadog. Please see the website above for full details.

160 MANCHESTER - CHESTER - HOLYHEAD

2nd class AW, VT

Ⓐ

	①	②–⑤ T	②–⑤	Ⓐ Y	Ⓐ	Ⓐ	Ⓐ	Ⓐ P	Ⓐ	Ⓐ	Ⓐ C	Ⓐ 🍷	Ⓐ 🍷S	Ⓐ	Ⓐ 🍷	Ⓐ A	Ⓐ 🍷Q	Ⓐ 🍷	Ⓐ A	Ⓐ 🍷P	Ⓐ 🍷	Ⓐ 🍷Q	Ⓐ 🍷	Ⓐ C	Ⓐ 🍷
Manchester Airport d.	...	...	...	...	0533	...	0632	...	...	0734	...	0830	...	...	0935	...	...	1035	...	...	1135	...	1235	...	1335
Manchester Piccadilly d.	2325p	...	0032	...	0548	...	0651	...	...	0751	...	0852	...	...	0953	...	...	1052	...	...	1152	...	1253	...	1353
Warrington Bank Quay **190** d.	2356p	...	|	...	0621	...	0725	...	...	0827	...	0927	...	...	1030	...	...	1126	...	...	1228	...	1328	...	1428
Crewe 151 ♥ d.	|	...	|	0625	|	0656	|	...	0823	|	...	|	0950	...	|	1048	...	|	1148	...	|	...	|	...	|
Chester 151 190 ♥ a.	0026	...	0139	0644	0650	0719	0754	...	0848	0856	...	0956	1010	...	1059	1109	...	1156	1208	...	1258	...	1357	...	1456
Chester d.	0039	0040	...	0644	0655	0721	0755	0825	▬	0859	0952	0959	1014	1027	1103	1115	1124	1157	1210	1231	1303	1326	1358	1430	1457
Prestatyn d.	0104	0106	...	0710	0722	0749	0822	0852	...	0924	|	1025	1040	1054	1126	|	1149	1224	1237	1257	1330	1351	1425	1457	1524
Rhyl d.	0110	0112	...	0716	0728	0755	0828	0858	...	0930	|	1031	1046	1100	1132	1142	1157	1230	1243	1303	1336	1359	1431	1503	1530
Colwyn Bay d.	0121	0123	...	0727	0742	0809	0842	0912	Ⓐ	0944	|	1042	1058	1114	1142	1153	1211	1244	1254	1314	1350	1413	1445	1519	1544
Llandudno Junction ‡ d.	0128	0130	...	0733	0749	0817	0849	0918	0940	0952	1032	1049	1104	1122	1150	1202	1221	1251	1301	1324	1400	1421	1452	1533f	1551
Llandudno ‡ a.	|	|	...	|	0800	|	0900	|	0949	1000	|	|	|	1132	|	|	|	...	|	|	1411	|	1504	|	1603
Bangor d.	0145	0147	...	0750	...	0839	...	0941	...	...	1050	1106	1129r	...	1207	1219	1244	...	1320	1341	...	1444	...	1551	...
Holyhead ▽ a.	0212	0215	...	0820	...	0921	...	1009	...	...	1120	1144	1156	...	1235	1249	1324	...	1346	1419	...	1522	...	1620	...

	Ⓐ 🍷Q	Ⓐ 🍷	Ⓐ 🍷C	Ⓐ 🍷	Ⓐ 🍷Q	Ⓐ 🍷	Ⓐ A	Ⓐ 🍷P	Ⓐ 🍷	Ⓐ	Ⓐ An	Ⓐ 🍷Q	Ⓐ C	Ⓐ	Ⓐ AW	Ⓐ T	Ⓐ	Ⓐ A	Ⓐ	Ⓐ	Ⓐ	Ⓐ P	Ⓐ 🍷	Ⓐ	⑥ T
Manchester Airport d.	...	1435	...	1535	...	1634	...	...	1730	...	...	...	...	1835	...	...	1931	...	2034	...	2132	...	...	2333	...
Manchester Piccadilly d.	...	1452	...	1552	...	1652	...	...	1752	...	...	...	...	1853	...	...	1951	...	2052	...	2150	...	2214	2351	...
Warrington Bank Quay **190** d.	...	1528	...	1626	...	1728	...	...	1830	...	...	...	...	1931	...	...	2027	...	2126	...	2224	...	2249	|	...
Crewe 151 ♥ d.	...	|	...	|	...	|	1749	...	|	...	1855	...	...	|	1954	...	|	2054	|	2136	|	...	|	|	...
Chester 151 190 ♥ a.	...	1556	...	1655	...	1758	1808	...	1858	...	1915	...	...	1959	2013	...	2055	2119	2158	2158	2251	...	2318	0056	...
Chester d.	1525	1557	1629	1656	1726	1759	1810	1826	1902	...	1923	1932	2002	...	2026	2031	...	2125	...	2204	...	2257	...	...	0040
Prestatyn d.	1551	1624	1654	1723	1753	1826	1836	1853	1929	...	1949	2000	|	...	|	2059	...	2151	...	2232	...	2325	...	...	0106
Rhyl d.	1557	1630	1700	1729	1759	1832	1842	1859	1935	...	1955	2006	2031	...	2053	2105	...	2157	...	2238	...	2331	...	...	0112
Colwyn Bay d.	1607	1644	1710	1743	1813	1846	1853	1913	1945	...	2006	2020	2044	...	2104	2119	...	2208	...	2252	...	2345	...	...	0123
Llandudno Junction ‡ d.	1620f	1651	1718	1750	1825f	1853	1900	1919	1956	1959	2013	2030	2054	...	2110	2129	...	2215	...	2300	...	2353	...	...	0130
Llandudno ‡ a.	|	1703	|	1801	|	1905	|	|	|	2009	|	2041	|	...	|	|	...	|	...	|	...	|	...	...	|
Bangor d.	1644	...	1741	...	1848	...	1918	1937	2018	...	2031	...	2111	...	2127	2151	...	2231	...	2324	...	0016	...	...	0147
Holyhead ▽ a.	1718	...	1821	...	1918	...	...	2020	2047	...	2100	...	2142	...	2156	2231	...	2301	...	0002	...	0043	...	...	0215

⑥

	⑥	⑥ 🍷B	⑥	⑥	⑥	⑥ P	⑥	⑥ 🍷Q	⑥ 🍷	⑥ 🍷P	⑥ 🍷	⑥ Y	⑥ 🍷Q	⑥ 🍷	⑥ 🍷S	⑥ 🍷P	⑥ 🍷	⑥ 🍷Q	⑥ 🍷	⑥ 🍷P	⑥ 🍷	⑥ 🍷Q	⑥ 🍷	⑥ 🍷P	⑥ 🍷	⑥ 🍷Q
Manchester Airport d.	...	...	0533	...	0632	...	0732	...	0832	...	0935	...	...	1035	...	...	1135	...	1235	...	1335	...	1435	...	1535	...
Manchester Piccadilly d.	0032	...	0547	...	0651	...	0752	...	0852	...	0952	...	...	1052	...	...	1152	...	1253	...	1353	...	1452	...	1552	...
Warrington Bank Quay **190** d.	|	...	0622	...	0725	...	0828	...	0928	...	1027	...	...	1127	...	...	1228	...	1327	...	1428	...	1526	...	1627	...
Crewe 151 ♥ d.	|	0622	|	0701	|	...	|	...	|	...	|	1048	...	|	1148	...	|	...	|	...	|	...	|	...	|	...
Chester 151 190 ♥ a.	0138	0642	0652	0723	0753	...	0858	...	0957	...	1056	1112	...	1155	1208	...	1256	...	1356	...	1457	...	1555	...	1656	...
Chester d.	...	0644	0656	0725	0754	0824	0859	0924	0958	1024	1056	1115	1126	1156	1210	1225	1257	1324	1357	1428	1458	1525	1556	1630	1656	1724
Prestatyn d.	...	0710	0723	0750	0821	0850	0926	0949	1025	1049	1123	|	1151	1223	1236	1251	1324	1349	1424	1453	1525	1550	1623	1655	1723	1752
Rhyl d.	...	0715	0729	0758	0827	0858	0932	0958	1031	1057	1129	1142	1159	1229	1242	1301f	1330	1357	1430	1502	1531	1558	1629	1701	1729	1758
Colwyn Bay d.	...	0726	0743	0807	0841	0912	0946	1012	1045	1112	1143	1153	1213	1243	1252	1316	1344	1411	1444	1516	1545	1613	1643	1711	1743	1812
Llandudno Junction ‡ d.	...	0732	0750	0817	0848	0922	0953	1021	1052	1122	1151	1200	1220	1250	1258	1323	1353	1420	1455	1526	1552	1623	1650	1719	1751	1822
Llandudno ‡ a.	...	|	0801	|	0859	|	1003	|	1102	|	1201	|	|	|	...	|	1404	|	1504	|	1604	|	1702	|	1801	|
Bangor d.	...	0749	...	0840	...	0945	...	1038	...	1146	...	1216	1237	1314	...	1340	...	1443	...	1543	...	1646	...	1742	...	1846
Holyhead ▽ a.	...	0819	...	0921	...	1019	...	1112	...	1217	...	1246	1316	...	...	1419	...	1514	...	1622	...	1718	...	1821	...	1915

⑥ / ⑦

	⑥ 🍷	⑥ D	⑥ 🍷P	⑥ 🍷	⑥ D	⑥ Q	⑥	⑥ P	⑥	⑥	⑥	⑥ P	⑥	⑥	⑥	⑦	⑦ 🚌	⑦	⑦	⑦ Y	⑦ 🍷	⑦	⑦ 🍷	⑦	⑦ 🍷
Manchester Airport d.	1635	...	...	1735	...	...	1835	...	1931	...	2034	...	2131	...	...	...	...	...	...	...	...	...	...	...	...
Manchester Piccadilly d.	1652	...	...	1752	...	...	1853	...	1952	...	2051	...	2151	2212	2314	...	0718	...	0948	...	1052	...	1156	...	1256
Warrington Bank Quay **190** d.	1727	...	...	1828	...	...	1929	...	2030	...	2130	...	2225	2250	2348	...	0839	...	1020	...	1126	...	1230	...	1332
Crewe 151 ♥ d.	|	1748	...	|	1850	...	|	...	|	2100	|	...	|	|	|	0835	|	0925	|	1042	|	1127	|	1227	|
Chester 151 190 ♥ a.	1756	1808	...	1856	1909	...	1959	...	2059	2122	2158	...	2254	2320	0016	0856	0938	0944	1049	1102	1155	1147	1258	1250	1359
Chester d.	1757	1815	1829	1857	1916	1927	▬	2029	▬	2126	...	2240	▬	...	...	0900	▬	0951	▬	1107	▬	1201	▬	1303	▬
Prestatyn d.	1824	1841	1856	1924	1943	1955	...	2056	...	2154	...	2308	...	...	...	0925	...	1019	...	1131	...	1229	...	1331	...
Rhyl d.	1830	1847	1902	1930	1949	2001	...	2102	...	2200	...	2314	⑥	...	...	0931	...	1025	...	1137	...	1235	...	1337	...
Colwyn Bay d.	1844	1858	1916	1944	2000	2015	⑥	2116	⑥	2214	...	2328	🚌	...	...	0940	⑦	1039	⑦	1148	⑦	1246	⑦	1351	⑦
Llandudno Junction ‡ d.	1851	1904	1926	1951	2006	2023	2030	2130r	2132	2222	...	2334	2348	...	...	0949	1003	1050	1053	1154	1200	1255	1300	1404f	1406
Llandudno ‡ a.	1902	|	|	2001	|	|	2040	|	2143	|	...	...	|	...	...	|	1013	|	1103	|	1210	|	1310	|	1416
Bangor d.	...	1921	1943	...	2023	2045	...	2147	...	2246	...	...	0013	...	...	1006	...	1116	...	1211	...	1312	...	1427	...
Holyhead ▽ a.	...	1950	2025	...	2052	2126	...	2226	...	2317	...	...	0048	...	...	1037	...	1158	...	1240	...	1340	...	1458	...

	⑦ 🍷	⑦ 🍷	⑦ 🍷	⑦ 🍷	⑦	⑦	⑦ 🍷P	⑦ 🍷	⑦	⑦ 🍷	⑦	⑦ 🍷P	⑦	⑦ 🍷	⑦ D	⑦ 🍷Q	⑦	⑦ D	⑦	⑦ D	⑦	⑦	⑦	⑦	⑦	⑦ 🍷
Manchester Airport d.	...	...	...	...	...	...	...	...	...	...	...	...	...	...	...	...	...	...	...	...	...	...	...	...	...	...
Manchester Piccadilly d.	...	1357	...	1457	...	...	...	1557	...	1657	...	...	...	1757	...	...	1857	...	1957	...	2054	...	2157	...	2257	2325
Warrington Bank Quay **190** d.	...	1428	...	1529	...	...	...	1629	...	1729	...	...	...	1827	...	...	1930	...	2031	...	2128	...	2228	...	2331	2356
Crewe 151 ♥ d.	1327	|	1434	|	1527	...	...	|	1627	|	1735	...	1827	|	1901	...	|	1953	|	2053	|	2128	|	2229	|	|
Chester 151 190 ♥ a.	1347	1456	1454	1557	1548	...	...	1657	1649	1757	1755	...	1846	1856	1920	...	2001	2012	2100	2112	2156	2148	2256	2251	2358	0026
Chester d.	1404	▬	1502	▬	1602	...	1636	▬	1702	▬	1802	1830	1852	...	1929	1936	...	2019	▬	2115	...	2201	...	2302	...	0039
Prestatyn d.	1432	...	1530	...	1630	...	1704	...	1730	...	1830	1858	1921	...	1955	2003	...	2045	...	2142	...	2229	...	2330	...	0104
Rhyl d.	1438	...	1536	...	1636	...	1710	...	1736	...	1836	1904	1927	...	2001	2009	...	2051	...	2148	...	2235	...	2336	...	0110
Colwyn Bay d.	1452	⑦	1550	⑦	1650	...	1724	⑦	1750	⑦	1850	1918	1941	...	2012	2023	...	2102	⑦	2159	...	2249	...	2347	...	0121
Llandudno Junction ‡ d.	1501	1504	1600	1604	1700	1705	1734	1740	1802f	1833	1900	1926	1950	...	2019	2033	...	2108	2125	2205	...	2257	...	2354	...	0128
Llandudno ‡ a.	|	1514	|	1614	|	1715	|	1750	|	1843	|	|	|	...	|	|	...	|	2135	|	...	|	...	|	...	|
Bangor d.	1518	...	1623	...	1717	...	1757	...	1825	...	1917	1951	2014	...	2035	2056	...	2125	...	2222	...	2314	...	0017	...	0145
Holyhead ▽ a.	1557	...	1655	...	1758	...	1838	...	1859	...	1958	2019	2044	...	2103	2129	...	2154	...	2251	...	2355	...	0051	...	0212

LLANDUDNO - BLAENAU FFESTINIOG

km		⚒	⚒	⚒	⑦	⑥	Ⓐ	⑦	Ⓐ	⑥	⑦	⑦	⑥	Ⓐ
0	**Llandudno** d.	...	*0708*	1019	1022	1317	1322	1328	1617	1620	*1547*	1859	1903	1905
5	**Llandudno** Junction a.	...	*0718*	1028	1032	1326	1331	1337	1626	1630	*1557*	1908	1911	1914
5	**Llandudno** Junction d.	0530	0728	1031	1034	1329	1334	1340	1629	1633	1615	1915	1918	1923
18	Llanrwst d.	0548	0752	1054	1057	1352	1358	1403	1653	1656	1638	1938	1943	1947
24	Betws y Coed d.	0554	0758	1100	1103	1358	1404	1409	1659	1702	1644	1944	1949	1953
44	**Blaenau Ffestiniog** d.	0624	0832	1134	1136	1432	1437	1441	1732	1735	1716	2016	2025	2027

	⚒	Ⓐ	⑥	⚒Z	⑦	⚒	⑦	⑦	⚒	⑦	⚒
Blaenau Ffestiniog d.	0624	0835	0846	1135	1142	1456	1459	1728	1735	2020	2025
Betws y Coed d.	0650	0902	0913	1202	1208	1523	1525	1755	1802	2047	2052
Llanrwst d.	0656	0908	0919	1208	1214	1529	1531	1801	1808	2053	2058
Llandudno Junction a.	0722	0937	0949	1234	1241	1559	1559	1830	1840	2122	2125
Llandudno Junction d.	*0731*	0940	1006	1237	1244	1604	*1604*	1833	1840	2125	2132
Llandudno a.	*0741*	0949	1015	1247	1254	1615	*1614*	1843	1851	2135	2144

♥ – All trains **Chester** - **Crewe**. Journey time ± 23 minutes.
On ⚒ at 0416⑥, 0422Ⓐ, 0455⑥, 0459Ⓐ, 0535⑥, 0537Ⓐ, 0551, 0626Ⓐ, 0639⑥, 0645Ⓐ, 0717⑥ **D n**, 0735Ⓐ **A**, 0754, 0835Ⓐ **S**, 0835⑥ **D**, 0853, 0933⑥ **D**, 0935 **A n**, 0954, 1035 **S**, 1054, 1133 **A n**, 1154, 1235Ⓐ **A**, 1235⑥ **D n**, 1254, 1335Ⓐ **A n**, 1335⑥ **D**, 1354, 1435Ⓐ **S**, 1435⑥ **D**, 1454, 1535Ⓐ **A**, 1535⑥ **D**, 1554, 1635 **S**, 1654, 1735Ⓐ **g**, 1735⑥ **n**, 1753, 1854, 1935Ⓐ, 1937⑥, 1954, 2019⑥, 2023Ⓐ, 2035⑥, 2040Ⓐ, 2055⑥, 2059Ⓐ, 2128Ⓐ, 2135Ⓐ, 2230, 2301⑥, 2304Ⓐ.
On ⑦ at 0805, 0838, 0857, 0939, 0957, 1039, 1057, 1157, 1223, 1233 **D n**, 1259, 1322, 1330 **D**, 1422, 1433 **D**, 1533 **D**, 1557, 1622, 1657, 1723, 1735 **S**, 1755, 1835 **D**, 1901, 1927, 1938 **B**, 1952, 2027 **Q**, 2037, 2053, 2138, 2152, 2237, 2303 **T**.

‡ – All trains **Llandudno** - **Llandudno Junction**. Journey time ± 10 minutes.
On Ⓐ at 0553, 0641, 0708, 0744, 0802, 0846, 0945, 1020, 1045, 1141, 1252, 1322, 1414, 1440, 1544, 1617, 1645, 1744, 1808, 1844, 1905, 1937, 2016, 2044, 2111, 2145.
On ⑥ at 0708, 0744, 0805, 0846, 0907, 0945, 1010, 1019, 1045, 1108, 1144, 1208, 1242, 1250, 1317, 1408, 1441, 1508, 1544, 1607, 1620, 1644, 1708, 1744, 1808, 1844, 1903, 1913, 1942, 2008, 2043, 2144.
On ⑦ at 1022, 1107, 1139, 1218, 1317, 1328, 1353, 1420, 1517, 1547, 1617, 1644, 1720, 1803, 1859, 2138.

♥ – All trains **Crewe** - **Chester**. Journey time ± 23 minutes.
On ⚒ at 0008②–⑥ **C**, 0012① **C**, 0022① **Q**, 0622⑥ **B**, 0625Ⓐ, 0656Ⓐ, 0701⑥, 0722, 0823, 0924, 0948⑥ **S**, 0950Ⓐ **S**, 1024, 1048Ⓐ **A**, 1048⑥, 1124, 1148Ⓐ **A**, 1148⑥ **S**, 1224, 1248Ⓐ **S**, 1248⑥ **D**, 1324, 1350Ⓐ **A n**, 1351⑥ **D**, 1424, 1448Ⓐ **A n**, 1448⑥ **S**, 1524, 1548Ⓐ **A n**, 1624, 1644Ⓐ **g**, 1648⑥ **S**, 1724, 1748Ⓐ, 1748⑥ **D**, 1824, 1850⑥ **D**, 1855Ⓐ **S**, 1924, 1948⑥ **D**, 1954Ⓐ **A**, 2024, 2047Ⓐ **R**, 2054Ⓐ **A**, 2100⑥, 2136, 2224, 2321⑥, 2330Ⓐ, 2358⑥ **C**.
On ⑦ at 0835, 0925, 1007, 1042, 1104, 1127, 1155, 1227, 1254, 1327, 1357, 1434, 1500, 1527, 1557, 1627, 1651 **D n**, 1735, 1750 **D**, 1827, 1901 **D**, 1926, 1953 **D**, 2027, 2053, 2128, 2203, 2229, 2309 **Q**, 2339.

‡ – All trains **Llandudno Junction** - **Llandudno**. Journey time ± 10 minutes.
On Ⓐ at 0540, 0613, 0651, 0731, 0749, 0821, 0849, 0940, 0952, 1122, 1240, 1305, 1400, 1427, 1452, 1551, 1604, 1651, 1750, 1826, 1840, 1853, 1959, 2030, 2058, 2132.
On ⑥ at 0651, 0731, 0750, 0824, 0848, 0925, 0953, 1006, 1024, 1052, 1123, 1151, 1225, 1237, 1303, 1353, 1425, 1455, 1528, 1552, 1605, 1625, 1650, 1725, 1751, 1825, 1841, 1851, 1928, 1951, 2030, 2132.
On ⑦ at 1003, 1053, 1126, 1200, 1244, 1300, 1340, 1406, 1504, 1534, 1604, 1631, 1705, 1740, 1833, 2125.

← FOR OTHER NOTES SEE PREVIOUS PAGE

CS — Caledonian Sleeper LONDON - SCOTLAND — 161

All trains in this table convey 🛏 (Classic, Club or Double) and (2). Only available for overnight journeys. **Reservation compulsory**. Conveys ✕ and 🍸. All-inclusive fares are available (www.sleeper.scot/tickets). Holders of regular tickets and rail passes may travel in seated accommodation free of charge (R); travel in sleeping accommodation is also possible on payment of the appropriate supplement (a first-class ticket is required for Club or Double rooms). Early booking is recommended.

*See Table **154** for day trains*		⑦	⑦	⑦	Ⓐ	Ⓐ	Ⓐ	⑦	⑦	Ⓐ	Ⓐ
		◐	◐	◐	◐	◐	◐	⊕	⊕	⊕	⊕
London Euston	d.	2100r	2100r	2100r	2115	2115	2115	2330t	2330t	2350	2350
Watford Junction	d.	2118f	2118f	2118f	2134	2134	2134	2349f	2349f	0010	0010
Crewe	d.	2336f	2336f	2336f	2348	2348	2348	|	|	|	|
Preston	d.	0020f	0020f	0020f	0030	0030	0030	|	|	|	|
Carlisle	a.	|	|	|	|	|	|	|	0440f	|	0507
Motherwell	a.	|	|	|	|	|	|	|	0656	|	0656
Glasgow Central ⊠	a.	|	|	|	|	|	|	|	0722	|	0722
Edinburgh Waverley ⊠	a.	|	|	|	|	|	|	0730j	...	0730	...
Dundee **222**	a.	0605	|	|	0605	|	|	...	...	...	...
Aberdeen **222**	a.	0740	|	|	0740	|	|	...	...	...	...
Perth **223**	a.	...	0540	|	...	0540	|	...	...	...	...
Inverness **223**	a.	...	0842	|	...	0842	|	...	...	...	...
Fort William **218**	a.	...	...	0957	...	...	0957	...	...	...	...

*See Table **154** for day trains*		⑦	⑦	Ⓐ	Ⓐ	Ⓐ	Ⓐ	Ⓐ	⑦	⑦	⑦
		⊕	⊕	◧	⊕						
Fort William **218**	d.	...	...	...	...	1950	...	...	1900	...	...
Inverness **223**	d.	...	...	...	...	|	2045	...	|	2026	...
Perth **223**	d.	...	...	...	...	|	2327	...	|	2306	...
Aberdeen **222**	d.	...	...	...	...	|	|	2143	|	|	2143
Dundee **222**	d.	...	...	...	...	|	|	2309	|	|	2309
Edinburgh Waverley	d.	2315k	...	2340	...	|	|	|	|	|	|
Glasgow Central	d.	|	2315z	|	2340	|	|	|	|	|	|
Motherwell	d.	|	2330v	|	2357	|	|	|	|	|	|
Carlisle	d.	|	0144f	|	0145	|	|	|	|	|	|
Preston	a.	|	|	|	|	0431	0431	0431	0429f	0429f	0429f
Crewe	a.	|	|	|	|	0527	0527	0527	0527f	0527f	0527f
Watford Junction	a.	0638f	0638f	0638	0638	|	|	|	|	|	|
London Euston ⊡	a.	0707	0707	0707	0707	0749	0749	0749	0749y	0749y	0749y

f – From June 26.
j – Until June 19 arrives 0444.
k – Until June 19 departs 2325.
r – Until June 19 departs 2030.
t – Until June 19 departs 2134.
v – Until June 19 departs 2202.
y – Until June 19 arrives 0904.
z – Until June 19 departs 2145.
◐ – Sleeping-car passengers may occupy their cabins from 2030.
⊕ – Sleeping-car passengers may occupy their cabins from 2230.
◧ – Sleeping-car passengers may occupy their cabins from 2300.
⊡ – Sleeping-car passengers from Edinburgh and Glasgow may occupy their cabins until 0730.
⊠ – Sleeping-car passengers may occupy their cabins until 0800 following arrival at these stations.

NT 2nd class *See also Table 154* — BLACKPOOL - PRESTON - LIVERPOOL — 162

km		⚒	⑥	Ⓐ	⚒	⚒	⚒	Ⓐ	⑥	⚒	⚒	⚒	⚒	⚒	⚒	⚒	⚒	Ⓐ	⑥	⑥	Ⓐ	⑦	⑦	⑦	⑦
0	**Blackpool** North d.		*0621*	*0624*	0703	0804	1003	...	*1022*	1103	1306	1403	...	1605	1703	1905	2003	2101	2101	2218	2218		0755	0834	0932
28	**Preston** d.		0705	0704	0729	0831	1029	1038	1052	1129	1330	1429	1442	1631	1732	1931	2029	2130	2130	2243	2243		0823	0901	1000
52	Wigan North Western d.		0718	0717	0748	0850	1048	1056	1106	1148	1350	1448	1457	1650	1750	1949	2047	2151	2154	2301	2303		0842	0920	1019
70	St Helens Central d.		0733	0732	0804	0908	1100	1118	|	1201	1402	1500	1517	1704	1803	2002	2100	2204	2207	2318	2320		0857	0937	1035
89	**Liverpool** Lime Street a.		0757	0756	0831	0940	1120	1143	1143	1220	1422	1520	1541	1726	1824	2022	2119	2231	2233	2351	2352		0921	1006	1108

	⑦	⑦	⑦	⑦		⑦	⑦	⑦	⑦
Blackpool North d.	1032	1132	1226	1332		1838	1925	2032	2206
Preston d.	1059	1201	1252	1400	and	1906	1953	2100	2233
Wigan North Western d.	1118	1222	1313	1419	hourly	1925	2012	2119	2258
St Helens Central d.	1135	1239	1329	1436	until	1941	2028	2135	2315
Liverpool Lime Street a.	1207	1308	1405	1506		2010	2057	2208	2344

	⚒	⚒	⑥	Ⓐ	⚒	⚒	⚒	⚒	⚒	⚒
Liverpool Lime Street d.		0636	0812	0812	0836	0936	1136	1212	1236	1436
St Helens Central d.		0653	0829	0831	0853	0953	1153	1230	1253	1453
Wigan North Western d.		0706	0843	0844	0906	1006	1206	1245	1306	1506
Preston a.		0727	0858	0858	0928	1028	1228	1302	1328	1528
Blackpool North a.		0752	*0930*	*0946*	0953	1053	1254	*1346*	1353	1553

	⚒	⚒	⚒	⚒	Ⓐ	⑥	⚒	⚒	Ⓐ	⑥	⑥	Ⓐ	⑦	⑦	⑦	⑦	⑦		⑦	⑦	⑦	⑦	⑦	⑦
Liverpool Lime Street d.	1537	1612	1709	1736	1835	1836	2036	2115	2215	2217	2315	2315		0829	0913	1017	1115		1815	1912	2012	2114	2212	2315
St Helens Central d.	1554	1628	1731	1757	1854	1854	2053	2143	2244	2246	2343	2343		0856	0939	1044	1141	and	1842	1939	2039	2141	2239	2342
Wigan North Western d.	1607	1644	1747	1814	1907	1907	2106	2159	2301	2306	2359	0006		0912	0955	1100	1157	hourly	1858	1955	2055	2157	2256	2358
Preston a.	1628	1700	1809	1835	1928	1929	2127	2221	2322	2328	0021	0027		0933	1016	1121	1219	until	1919	2016	2116	2218	2317	0019
Blackpool North a.	1653	*1802*	*1851*	1900	1953	1955	2154	*2304*	2347	2354	...	*0119*		0959	1041	1146	1244		1944	2041	2143	2243	2342	0044

ME, NT 2nd class — MANCHESTER and LIVERPOOL local services — 163

MANCHESTER - CLITHEROE
Journey time: ± 76–80 minutes *57 km* NT

From Manchester Victoria:
Trains call at Bolton ± 19 and Blackburn ± 50 minutes later.
⚒: 0537, 0741, 0839, 0941 and hourly until 2041, 2140, 2216.
⑦: 0755, 0841, 0945, 1048, 1145 and hourly until 1645, 1757, 1845, 1945, 2112, 2207.

From Clitheroe:
Trains call at Blackburn ± 23 and Bolton ± 54 minutes later:
⚒: 0623, 0647, 0723 and hourly until 1623, 1717, 1823, 1908, 2023, 2123, 2252.
⑦: 0923, 1023 and hourly until 1623, 1719, 1823, 1945, 2023, 2123, 2243.

MANCHESTER - BUXTON
Journey time: ± 56–63 minutes *41 km* NT

From Manchester Piccadilly:
Trains call at Stockport ± 10, Hazel Grove ± 19 and New Mills Newtown ± 33 minutes later.
⚒: 0623, 0721⑥, 0724Ⓐ, 0824, 0924, 1008 and hourly until 1608, 1624, 1724, 1824, 1924, 2024, 2124, 2210, 2307⑥, 2311Ⓐ.
⑦: 0850, 0945, 1045, 1149, 1249, 1351, 1449 and hourly until 2049, 2150, 2248.

From Buxton:
Trains call at New Mills Newtown ± 21, Hazel Grove ± 34 and at Stockport ± 46 minutes later.
⚒: 0600, 0632, 0700, 0734, 0858, 0959, 1058, 1159, 1258, 1359, 1458, 1534, 1658, 1758, 1900, 1947, 2050, 2154, 2256⑥, 2259Ⓐ. **From Oct. 8 all depart 3 minutes earlier.**
⑦: 0811, 0854, 0959, 1056, 1155, 1258, 1354 and hourly until 1954, 2057, 2202, 2255.

CREWE - MANCHESTER AIRPORT ✈
Journey time: ± 42 minutes *37 km* NT

From Crewe:
Trains call at Wilmslow ± 26 minutes
⚒: 0616, 0713, 0817 and hourly until 1917.

From Manchester Airport:
Trains call at Wilmslow ± 14 minutes later.
⚒: 0545, 0704, 0802 and hourly until 1702, 1803, 1903.

MANCHESTER - WIGAN - SOUTHPORT
Journey time: ± 75 minutes *62 km* NT

From Manchester Victoria:
Trains call at Wigan Wallgate ± 35 minutes later.
⚒: 0636, 0720, 0749, 0818**p**, 0850, 0918**p**, 0950, 1018**p**, 1050, 1118**p**, 1148, 1217**p**, 1249 and at the same minutes past each hour until 1849, 1917**p**, 2018**p**, 2126**p**, 2149, 2240.
⑦: 0825, 0926, 1025 and hourly until 2025, 2132.

From Southport:
Trains call at Wigan Wallgate ± 30 minutes later.
⚒: 0617**p**, 0634, 0716**p**, 0730, 0815**p**, 0836, 0916**p**, 0931, 1016**p**, 1036, 1116**p**, 1131, 1216**p**, 1236, 1315**p**, 1331, 1415**p**, 1436, 1517**p**, 1531, 1615**p**Ⓐ, 1617**p**⑥, 1634, 1715**p**, 1731, 1816**p**, 1836, 1917, 2013, 2114, 2218.
⑦: 0842, 0938 and hourly until 2138, 2254.

LIVERPOOL - BIRKENHEAD - CHESTER
Journey time: ± 42 minutes *29 km* ME

From Liverpool Lime Street (Low Level):
Trains call at Liverpool Central ± 2 minutes and Birkenhead Central ± 9 minutes later.
⚒: 0538, 0608, 0643, 0713, 0743, 0755Ⓐ, 0813, 0821Ⓐ, 0843, 0858⑥, 0913, 0928, 0943, 0958 and every 15 minutes until 1858, 1913 and every 30 minutes until 2343.
⑦: 0813, 0843 and every 30 minutes until 2313, 2343.

From Chester:
Trains call at Birkenhead Central ± 33 minutes and Liverpool Central ± 44* minutes later.
⚒: 0555, 0630, 0700, 0722Ⓐ, 0730⑥, 0737Ⓐ, 0752Ⓐ, 0800⑥, 0807Ⓐ, 0815⑥, 0831, 0845 and every 15 minutes until 1830, 1900 and every 30 minutes until 2300.
⑦: 0800, 0830 and every 30 minutes until 2300.

LIVERPOOL - RUNCORN - CHESTER
Journey time: ± 50 minutes *43 km* AW

From Liverpool Lime Street:
Trains call at Liverpool South Parkway ± 9 minutes and Runcorn ± 19 minutes later.
Ⓐ: 0716, 0914, 1136, 1336, 1536, 1739, 2039, 2240.
⑥: 0713, 0914, 1136, 1336, 1535, 1737, 2038, 2220.
⑦: 0945, 1156, 1357, 1557, 1756, 1957, 2137, 2318.

From Chester:
Trains call at Runcorn ± 26 minutes and Liverpool South Parkway ± 35 minutes later.
Ⓐ: 0607, 0810, 1012, 1230, 1430, 1630, 1928, 2129.
⑥: 0605, 0810, 1012, 1230, 1430, 1630, 1942, 2130.
⑦: 0830, 1047, 1247, 1447, 1647, 1847, 2047, 2227.

LIVERPOOL - SOUTHPORT
Journey time: ± 44 minutes *30 km* ME

From Liverpool Central:
⚒: 0608, 0623, 0638, 0653, 0708 and every 15 minutes until 2308, 2323, 2338.
⑦: 0807, 0823, 0853, 0923, 0953, 1007**a**, 1023, 1037**a**, 1053 and at the same minutes past each hour until 2307**a**, 2323, 2337.

From Southport:
⚒: 0538, 0553, 0608, 0623, 0643 and every 15 minutes until 2258, 2318.
⑦: 0758, 0828, 0858, 0928, 0958, 1013**a**, 1028, 1043**a**, 1058 and at the same minutes past each hour until 2243**a**, 2258.

a – Until Sept. 25.
p – Starts/terminates at Manchester **Piccadilly**, not Victoria.
* – Trains FROM Chester call at Liverpool Lime Street, then Liverpool Central.

170 LONDON - LEICESTER - NOTTINGHAM, DERBY and SHEFFIELD

Most trains convey 🍸 EM

km		⚒	②–⑥	Ⓐ	⑥	Ⓐ	Ⓐ	⑥	⑥	Ⓐ	⑥	⚒	⑥	Ⓐ	⑥	Ⓐ	⑥	Ⓐ	⑥	Ⓐ	Ⓐ	⑥	⑥	Ⓐ	⑥	Ⓐ
0	**London** St Pancras 170a d.		0015	...	...	...	0527	...	0530	0559	0600	0605	0630	0632	0633	0635	0702	0702	0705	0705	0730	0732	0735	0735	0802	0803
116	Kettering 170a d.		0141	0524	0526	0606	|	0610	|	|	|	0653	|	|	0721	0727	|	|	0757	0758	|	|	0822	0826	|	|
133	Market Harborough d.		|	0534	0536	0616	|	0620	|	|	|	0704	|	|	0731	0737	|	|	0807	0808	|	|	0832	0836	|	|
159	**Leicester** 189 d.		0236j	0548	0551	0641a	0636	0646a	0639	0706	0707	0719	0734	0742	0745	0750	0807	0809	0821	0825	0840	0837	0846	0849	0906	0909
180	Loughborough 189 d.		|	0558	0601	0652	0645	0656	0649	|	0717	0729	0744	0752	0755	|	|	|	0831	0835	0850	0847	|	|	|	|
191	East Midlands Parkway d.		|	0606	0608	0700	0653	0704	0657	|	0724	0737	0753	0800	|	|	|	|	0838	0842	0857	0854	|	|	|	|
204	**Nottingham** 189 ‡ a.		|	|	|	0713	|	0719	|	|	|	0751	|	|	0811	0815	|	|	0852	0856	|	|	0911	0911	|	|
207	**Derby** 124 a.		0256	0619f	0622f	...	0707	...	0709	0728	0735	...	0806f	0814	...	...	0827	0830	...	...	0911	0908f	...	...	0927	0930
246	Chesterfield 124 ‡ a.		...	0642	0644	...	0725	...	0728	0746	0753	...	0833	0832	...	...	0846	0851	...	...	0929	0930	...	...	0945	0948
265	**Sheffield** 124 ‡ a.		...	0708	0708	...	0738	...	0743	0759	0806	...	0849	0845	...	...	0900	0904	...	...	0942	0945	...	...	1000	1001

	⑥	Ⓐ	⑥	Ⓐ	⑥	Ⓐ	⑥	Ⓐ	⑥	Ⓐ	⚒	⚒	⑥	Ⓐ	⚒	⚒	⚒	⚒	⚒	⚒	⚒	⚒	⚒	⚒	⚒	⚒
London St Pancras 170a d.	0805	0806	0832	0832	0835	0835	0902	0902	0905	0905	0932	0935	1002	1002	1005	1032	1035	1102	1105	1132	1135	1202	1205	1232	1235	1302
Kettering 170a d.	0854	0855	|	|	0922	0926	|	|	0953	0956	|	1022	|	|	1053	|	1122	|	1153	|	1221	|	1253	|	1322	|
Market Harborough d.	0904	0905	|	|	0932	0936	|	|	1003	1006	|	1032	|	|	1103	|	1132	|	1203	|	1231	|	1304	|	1332	|
Leicester 189 d.	0917	0920	0937	0940	0946	0950	1006	1010	1018	1020	1037	1046	1106	1108	1117	1137	1147	1207	1217	1235	1246	1306	1318	1336	1346	1406
Loughborough 189 d.	0927	0930	0947	0950	|	|	|	|	1028	1030	1047	|	|	|	1127	1147	|	|	1227	1247	|	|	1328	1346	|	|
East Midlands Parkway d.	0935	0938	0954	0958	|	|	|	|	1035	1038	1054	|	|	|	1135	1154	|	|	1235	1254	|	|	1335	1354	|	|
Nottingham 189 ‡ a.	0948	0949	|	|	1009	1011	|	|	1049	1050	|	1109	|	|	1150	|	1211r	|	1248	|	1309	|	1350	|	1408	|
Derby 124 a.	...	...	1008	1011	...	...	1027	1030	...	...	1108	...	1127	1129	...	1208	...	1227	...	1308	...	1327	...	1408	...	1428
Chesterfield 124 ‡ a.	...	...	1028	1029	...	...	1045	1049	...	...	1129r	...	1145	1147	...	1228	...	1246	...	1328	...	1346	...	1428	...	1446
Sheffield 124 ‡ a.	...	...	1041	1042	...	...	1058	1105	...	...	1142	...	1158	1201	...	1243	...	1300	...	1343	...	1400	...	1444	...	1500

	⚒	⚒	⚒	⚒	⚒	⚒	⚒	⚒	⚒	Ⓐ	⑥	⚒	⑥	Ⓐ	⑥	Ⓐ	⑥	Ⓐ	⑥	Ⓐ	⑥	Ⓐ	⑥	Ⓐ	⑥	Ⓐ
London St Pancras 170a d.	1305	1332	1335	1402	1405	1432	1435	1502	1505	1532	1532	1535	1602	1602	1605	1605	1632	1632	1635	1635	1702	1702	1705	1705	1732	1732
Kettering 170a d.	1353	|	1422	|	1453	|	1522	|	1552	|	|	1622	|	|	1652	1652	|	|	1722	1726	|	|	1752	1758	|	|
Market Harborough d.	1403	|	1432	|	1503	|	1532	|	1602	|	|	1632	|	|	1704	1703	|	|	1732	1737	|	|	1803	1808	|	|
Leicester 189 d.	1418	1436	1446	1506	1517	1537	1546	1606	1617	1637	1636	1646	1706	1706	1718	1718	1736	1741	1745	1751	1806	1811	1818	1823	1836	1841
Loughborough 189 d.	1428	1446	|	|	1528	1547	|	|	1627	1647	1646	|	|	|	1728	1728	1746	1751	|	|	|	|	1828	1834	1846	1851
East Midlands Parkway d.	1435	1454	|	|	1535	1554	|	|	1634	1654	1654	|	|	|	1735	1737	1753	1758	|	1804	|	|	1835	1841	1854	1859
Nottingham 189 ‡ a.	1448	|	1508	|	1549	|	1609	|	1650	|	|	1709	|	|	1748	1751	|	|	1807	1817	|	|	1848	1855	|	|
Derby 124 a.	...	1508	...	1528	...	1609	...	1628	...	1708	1708f	...	1726	1728	...	...	1807	1813f	...	...	1827	1834	...	...	1909	1912
Chesterfield 124 ‡ a.	...	1527	...	1547	...	1628	...	1646	...	1728	1730	...	1745	1747	...	...	1828	1835	...	...	1845	1852	...	...	1928	1931
Sheffield 124 ‡ a.	...	1542	...	1600	...	1642	...	1700	...	1744	1745	...	1758	1801	...	...	1843	1848	...	...	1900	1916	...	...	1942	1945

	⑥	Ⓐ	⑥	Ⓐ	⑥	Ⓐ	⑥	Ⓐ	⑥	Ⓐ	⑥	Ⓐ	⑥	Ⓐ	⑥	Ⓐ	⑥	Ⓐ	⚒	⑥	Ⓐ	⚒	⚒C	⚒	⚒	⑥
London St Pancras 170a d.	1735	1735	1802	1802	1805	1805	1832	1832	1835	1835	1902	1902	1905	1905	1932	1932	1935	1935	2002	2005	2005	2031	2034	2102	2105	2132
Kettering 170a d.	1822	1826	|	|	1852	1857	|	|	1922	1933j	|	|	1954	1956	|	|	2022	2026	|	2053	2057	|	2121	|	2153	|
Market Harborough d.	1832	1836	|	|	1903	1907	|	|	1932	1944	|	|	2004	2006	|	|	2032	2036	|	2103	2107	|	2131	|	2203	|
Leicester 189 d.	1846	1850	1906	1910	1918	1921	1936	1941	1946	1957	2006	2010	2018	2020	2037	2041	2046	2050	2106e	2117	2123	2136	2146	2206	2218	2236
Loughborough 189 d.	|	|	|	|	1928	1931	1946	1951	|	2007	|	|	2028	2031	2047	2051	|	|	|	2128	2133	2146	|	|	2228	2246
East Midlands Parkway d.	|	1903	|	|	1935	1938	1954	1959	|	|	|	|	2035	2038	2054	2058	2100	2104	|	2136	2141	2154	|	|	2235	2254
Nottingham 189 ‡ a.	1909	1913	|	|	1948	1956	|	|	2009	2025	|	|	2048	2053	|	|	2110	2114	|	2148	2155	|	2207	|	2248	|
Derby 124 a.	...	...	1927	1931	...	...	2007	2012	...	...	2028	2031	...	...	2108	2112	...	...	2131	...	...	2211	...	2228	...	2304
Chesterfield 124 ‡ a.	...	...	1945	1949	...	...	2026	2031	...	...	2047	2051	...	...	2127	2131	...	...	2150	...	...	2230	...	2246	...	2322
Sheffield 124 ‡ a.	...	...	2000	2005	...	...	2040	2047	...	...	2101	2116	...	...	2141	2144	...	...	2204	...	...	2243	...	2301	...	2334

	Ⓐ	Ⓐ	⑥	⑥	Ⓐ	⑥	Ⓐ	Ⓐ	Ⓐ	⑦	⑦	⑦	⑦	⑦	⑦	⑦	⑦	⑦	⑦	⑦	⑦	⑦	⑦	⑦	⑦	⑦
London St Pancras 170a d.	2132	2135	2135	2215	2232	2232	2235	2305	2335		...	0900	0930	1000	1030	1100	1130	1202	1234	1302	1334	1402	1434	1502	1532	1535
Kettering 170a d.	|	2222	2225	2304	|	2319	2322	0037	0055		...	1019	1049	1119	1149	1219	1242	|	1330	|	1433	|	1521	|	1618	1624
Market Harborough d.	|	2232	2235	2314	|	2329	2332	|	|		...	1029	1059	1129	1159	1229	1252	1257	1340	1355	1443	1455	1531	1555	|	1634
Leicester 189 d.	2238	2246	2249	2328	2337	2345	2346	0130j	0198j		1015	1044	1114	1144	1218	1244	1308	1313	1356	1411	1502	1511	1547	1611	1642	1653
Loughborough 189 d.	2248	|	2259	2338	2347	2355	2356	0140	0159		1025	1054	1124	1154	1228	1254	|	1323	1406	1421	1512	1521	1557	1621	1652	1703
East Midlands Parkway d.	2256	2300	2306	2345	2354	0002	0004	0148	0207		1032	1102	1132	1202	1235	1302	|	1330	1414	1428	1519	1529	1605	1629	1659	1711
Nottingham 189 ‡ a.	|	2310	2316	|	|	0018	0022	|	0219		|	1115	|	1214	|	1315	1329	|	1427	|	1533	|	1621	|	|	1723
Derby 124 a.	2309	...	...	2355	0008	0046	...	0201	...		1048	...	1145f	...	1250	...	...	1344v	...	1442v	...	1542f	...	1642v	1713	...
Chesterfield 124 ‡ a.	2328	...	...	...	0026	...	...	...	...		1111	...	1209	...	1310	...	...	1409	...	1510	...	1609	...	1710	1733	...
Sheffield 124 ‡ a.	2341	...	...	...	0039	...	...	...	...		1126	...	1224	...	1327	...	...	1429	...	1527	...	1627	...	1727	1749	...

	⑦	⑦	⑦	⑦	⑦	⑦	⑦	⑦	⑦	⑦	⑦	⑦	⑦	⑦	⑦	⑦	⑦	⑦	⑦	⑦	⑦	⑦	⑦	⑦	⑦	⑦
London St Pancras 170a d.	1602	1605	1632	1635	1702	1705	1732	1735	1802	1805	1832	1835	1902	1905	1932	1935	2002	2005	2032	2035	2102	...	2135	2202	2232	2300
Kettering 170a d.	|	1651	|	1722	|	1751	|	1821	|	1851	|	1921	|	1951	|	2021	|	2051	|	2121	|	...	2230	|	2333	0017
Market Harborough d.	1655	1701	|	1732	|	1801	|	1831	|	1901	|	1931	|	2001	|	2031	|	2101	|	2131	|	...	2240	2256	2343	0027
Leicester 189 d.	1709	1719	1738	1748	1806	1819	1838	1849	1907	1918	1938	1947	2007	2019	2038	2048	2106	2117	2138	2147	2208	2230	2256	2312	2358	0043
Loughborough 189 d.	|	1729	1748	|	|	1829	1848	|	|	1928	1948	|	|	2029	2048	2058	2116	2127	2148	|	2218	2240	2306	|	0008	0053
East Midlands Parkway d.	1723	1736	1755	1802	1820	1836	1855	1902	1920	1935	1955	2001	2020	2036	2055	2105	2124	2135	2155	|	2225	2247	2313	2325	0016	0100
Nottingham 189 ‡ a.	|	1750	|	1815	|	1850	|	1912	|	1950	|	2011	|	2050	|	2115	|	2147	|	2212	|	|	2326	|	0028	|
Derby 124 a.	1733	...	1809f	...	1830	...	1909	...	1930	...	2009	...	2030	...	2109	...	2134	...	2209	...	2239	2257	2350	2339	...	0110
Chesterfield 124 ‡ a.	1751	...	1831	...	1848	...	1928	...	1950	...	2030	...	2049	...	2127	...	2152	...	2227	...	2257	...	...	2357	...	...
Sheffield 124 ‡ a.	1805	...	1846	...	1905	...	1947	...	2005	...	2046	...	2106	...	2141	...	2208	...	2242	...	2316	...	...	0013	...	...

	⚒	②–⑤	①	②–⑤	①	⑥	Ⓐ	⑥	Ⓐ	Ⓐ	⑥	Ⓐ	⚒	⚒	⚒	⑥	Ⓐ	⑥	Ⓐ B	⑥	Ⓐ	⑥	Ⓐ B	⑥	Ⓐ	⑥
Sheffield 124 ‡ d.		...	...	...	...	...	...	...	0458	...	0530	0530	...	0556	...	0633	0630	...	...	0700	0700	...	...	0731	0733	...
Chesterfield 124 ‡ d.		...	...	...	...	...	...	...	0510	...	0542	0542	...	0608	...	0645	0644	...	...	0712	0713	...	...	0743	0745	...
Derby 124 d.		0357	0420	0412	0440	0447	0447	0459	0530	...	0602	0602	...	0628	...	0705	0705	...	...	0732	0733	...	...	0804	0805	...
Nottingham 189 ‡ d.		|	|	|	|	|	0514	0526	|	0549	|	|	0612	|	0649	|	|	0712	0712	|	|	0746	0749	|	|	0812
East Midlands Parkway d.		0410	0433	0422	0453	0500	0527	0536	0543	|	|	0615	0624	0641	0659	|	|	0724	0726	0745	|	|	0759	|	|	0824
Loughborough 189 d.		0417	0441	0430	0500	0508	0534	0543	0550	|	|	|	0632	0648	|	0719	0719	0732	|	0752	0750	|	|	|	0819	0832
Leicester 189 d.		0434j	0452	0446j	0512	0519	0547	0554	0602	0610	0623	0630	0643	0700	0713	0731	0735j	0743	0743	0803	0801	0813	0814	0827	0833	0843
Market Harborough d.		|	0505	|	0525	0533	0600	0608	|	0624	0637	|	0656	|	0727	|	|	0757	0757	|	|	0826	0828	|	|	0857
Kettering 170a d.		0522	|	0535	0535	|	0611	0618	|	0636	0647	|	0706	|	0737	|	|	0807	0808	|	|	0836	0838	|	|	0907
London St Pancras 170a a.		0610	0610	0634	0634	0626	0703	0704	0709	0731	0736	0739	0757	0809	0827	0836	0839	0855	0856	0907	0909	0927	0927	0934	0938	0954

	Ⓐ	Ⓐ	⑥	⚒	⚒	⚒	⚒	⚒	⑥	Ⓐ	⚒	Ⓐ	⑥	⚒	⑥	Ⓐ	⚒	⚒	⚒	⑥	Ⓐ	⚒	⚒	⚒	⚒	⚒
Sheffield 124 ‡ d.	...	0752	0800	...	0835	...	0900	...	0929	0937	...	1000	1001	...	1036	1036	...	1100	...	1130	1137	...	1200	...	1236	...
Chesterfield 124 ‡ d.	...	0812	0812	...	0848	...	0912	...	0941	0949	...	1014	1013	...	1048	1049	...	1112	...	1142	1149	...	1212	...	1249	...
Derby 124 d.	...	0832	0832	...	0909	...	0932	...	1005j	1009	...	1034	1033	...	1108	1110	...	1132	...	1208t	1209	...	1232	...	1309	...
Nottingham 189 ‡ d.	0813	|	|	0850	|	0912	|	0950	|	|	1012	|	|	1050	|	|	1112	|	1150	|	|	1212	|	1250	|	1312
East Midlands Parkway d.	0825	0845	0845	|	|	0924	0945	|	|	|	1024	1047	1046	|	|	|	1124	1145	|	|	|	1225	1245	|	|	1325
Loughborough 189 d.	|	0853	0852	|	|	0932	0953	|	|	|	1032	1054	1053	|	|	|	1132	1152	|	|	|	1232	1252	|	|	1332
Leicester 189 d.	0840	0904	0904	0912	0931	0943	1004	1013	1027	1032	1043	1106	1104	1112	1130	1132	1143	1204	1213	1231	1232	1243	1304	1313	1332	1343
Market Harborough d.	0852	|	|	0926	|	0956	|	1026	|	|	1056	|	|	1125	|	|	1157	|	1226	|	|	1257	|	1326	|	1357
Kettering 170a d.	0911j	|	|	0936	|	1006	|	1036	|	|	1106	|	|	1136	|	|	1207	|	1236	|	|	1307	|	1336	|	1407
London St Pancras 170a a.	1003	1007	1007	1027	1039	1055	1107	1127	1135	1138	1155	1210	1208	1227	1236	1236	1254	1309	1327	1336	1339	1354	1408	1427	1438	1454

	⚒	⚒	⑥	Ⓐ	⚒	⚒	⚒	⑥	Ⓐ	⑥	Ⓐ	⚒	⚒	⑥	Ⓐ	⑥	Ⓐ	⚒	⑥	Ⓐ	⑥	Ⓐ	⑥	Ⓐ	⑥	Ⓐ
Sheffield 124 ‡ d.	1300	...	1336	1337	...	1400	...	1436	1437	...	...	1500	...	1537	1537	...	...	1600	...	...	1637	1637	...	...	1700	1701
Chesterfield 124 ‡ d.	1312	...	1349	1349	...	1412	...	1448	1449	...	...	1512	...	1549	1549	...	...	1613	...	...	1649	1649	...	...	1712	1714
Derby 124 d.	1332	...	1409	1409	...	1432	...	1510	1509	...	...	1532	...	1611j	1609	...	...	1633	...	...	1711j	1709	...	...	1732	1734
Nottingham 189 ‡ d.	|	1350	|	|	1412	|	1449	|	|	1512	1512	|	1550	|	|	1612	1612	|	1650	1650	|	|	1712	1712	|	|
East Midlands Parkway d.	1345	|	|	|	1424	1445	|	|	|	1524	1525	1545	|	|	|	1624	1625	1646	|	|	|	|	1724	1725	1745	1748
Loughborough 189 d.	1352	|	|	|	1432	1452	|	|	|	1532	1533	1552	|	|	|	1632	1632	1653	|	|	|	|	1732	1732	1752	1755
Leicester 189 d.	1404	1413	1431	1432	1443	1504	1512	1532	1532	1543	1544	1604	1612	1632	1630	1643	1643	1704	1713	1715	1733	1730	1743	1745	1804	1806
Market Harborough d.	|	1426	|	|	1456	|	1526	|	|	1556	1558	|	1625	|	|	1656	1657	|	1726	1728	|	|	1756	1758	|	|
Kettering 170a d.	|	1436	|	|	1506	|	1536	|	|	1606	1608	|	1636	|	|	1706	1707	|	1736	1739	|	|	1806	1808	|	|
London St Pancras 170a a.	1507	1527	1536	1538	1554	1608	1627	1636	1639	1654	1656	1710	1727	1736	1740	1754	1803	1809	1827	1827	1836	1840	1854	1905	1907	1910

B – From Lincoln (Table **184**).
C – To Lincoln on Ⓐ (Table **184**).
a – Arrives 11–12 minutes earlier.
d – ②–⑥.
e – Departs 2111 on Ⓐ.
f – Departs 4–7 minutes later.
j – Arrives 4–6 minutes earlier.
r – Arrives 3 minutes earlier on Ⓐ.
t – Arrives 1200.
v – Departs 7–9 minutes later.
‡ – For trains Nottingham - Sheffield and v.v. see Tables **171** and **206**.

EM Most trains convey 🍷 SHEFFIELD, DERBY and NOTTINGHAM - LEICESTER - LONDON 170

	Ⓐ	⑥	Ⓐ	⑥	Ⓐ	⑥	⚒	Ⓐ	⑥	⚒	⚒	⚒	⑥	Ⓐ	⚒	Ⓐ	⑥	⚒	⑥	Ⓐ	⑥	Ⓐ	⑥	⑥	Ⓐ
Sheffield 124‡ d.	...	...	1732	1737	...	...	1800	...	...	1837	...	1900	...	...	1937	...	...	2000	...	...	2030	2037	...	2100	2101
Chesterfield 124‡ d.	...	...	1745	1749	...	...	1812	...	...	1849	...	1912	...	...	1949	...	...	2012	...	...	2042	2049	...	2114	2113
Derby 124 d.	...	...	1808	1811j	...	...	1832	...	...	1909	...	1932	...	...	2010	...	...	2032	...	...	2102	2107	...	2134	2134
Nottingham 189‡ d.	1750	1750	|	|	1810	1812	|	1850	1850	|	1912	|	1950	1949	|	2011	2012	|	2050	2048	|	...	2125	|	|
East Midlands Parkway d.	|	|	|	|	1823	1824	1845	|	|	|	1924	1945	|	|	|	2023	2024	2045	|	2102	2112	...	2137	2149	2147
Loughborough 189 d.	|	|	|	|	1830	1832	1852	|	|	|	1932	1952	|	2004	|	2031	2032	2052	|	2110	2119	...	2145	2157	2154
Leicester 189 d.	1811	1813	1830	1833	1841	1843	1904	1911	1913	1930	1943	2004	2013	2015	2032	2042	2043	2104	2114	2123	2129	...	2156	2207	2206
Market Harborough d.	1824	1826	|	|	1857	1856	|	1925	1926	|	1956	|	2026	2028	|	2056	2056	|	2127	2137	...	...	2209	...	|
Kettering 170a d.	1834	1836	|	|	1907	1906	|	1935	1936	|	2006	|	2036	2038	|	2106	2106	|	2137	2147	...	...	2219	...	|
London St Pancras 170a a.	1926	1927	1936	1936	1954	1954	2009	2027	2027	2038	2054	2108	2126	2134	2139	2156	2154	2208	2234	2239	...	...	2315	...	2316

	Ⓐ	Ⓐ	Ⓐ	⑥	Ⓐ	⚒	⑥	Ⓐ	⑦	⑦	⑦	⑦	⑦	⑦	⑦	⑦	⑦	⑦	⑦	⑦	⑦	⑦	⑦	⑦	⑦
Sheffield 124‡ d.	...	2145	2156	2200	2229	...	2320	2330		...	...	...	...	0823	...	0926	...	...	1052	...	1152	...	1252	1331	...
Chesterfield 124‡ d.	...	2201	2210	2214	2245	...	2332	2354		...	...	...	...	0835	...	0938	...	...	1105	...	1204	...	1304	1344	...
Derby 124 d.	...	2220	2234	2236	2308	...	0006	0015		0700	...	0751	...	0855	...	0958	...	...	1126	...	1225	...	1325	1406	...
Nottingham 189‡ d.	2140	|	...	...	...	2318	...	...		|	0724	|	0821	|	0926	|	1016	1110	|	1209	|	1310	|	|	1410
East Midlands Parkway d.	2156	2233	...	...	...	2332	...	...		0711	0734	0804	0833	0908	0936	1011	1026	1122	1140	1221	1239	1323	1339	1416	1423
Loughborough 189 d.	|	2241	...	...	...	2340	...	...		|	0741	0811	0841	0915	0943	1019	1033	1130	1147	1229	1247	1330	1347	|	1430
Leicester 189 d.	2215j	2252	...	...	...	2353	...	...		0726	0753	0823	0853	0927	0956	1031	1046	1144	1200	1242	1259	1343	1359	1432	1443
Market Harborough d.	2228	2305	...	...	...	...	...	...		0743	0810	0840	0910	0944	1013	1044	1059	1158	1213	1256	1312	1356	1412	|	1456
Kettering 170a d.	2240	2315	...	...	...	...	...	...		0753	0820	0850	0920	0954	1023	1054	1109	1208	|	1306	|	1406	|	|	1506
London St Pancras 170a a.	2352	0022	...	...	...	...	...	...		0915	0942	1012	1041	1112	1141	1211	1219	1256	1308	1353	1408	1455	1508	1539	1555

	⑦	⑦	⑦	⑦	⑦	⑦	⑦	⑦	⑦	⑦	⑦	⑦	⑦	⑦	⑦	⑦	⑦	⑦	⑦	⑦	⑦	⑦	⑦	⑦	⑦
Sheffield 124‡ d.	1351	1432	...	1451	...	1531	...	1551	...	1628	...	1651	...	1728	...	1751	...	...	1851	...	1951	2029	...	...	2236
Chesterfield 124‡ d.	1404	1446	...	1504	...	1544	...	1604	...	1640	...	1703	...	1741	...	1803	...	...	1903	...	2003	2042	...	...	2249
Derby 124 d.	1425	1506	...	1528j	...	1606	...	1628j	...	1701	...	1725	...	1802	...	1826	...	...	1923	...	2025	2103	...	...	2322
Nottingham 189‡ d.	|	|	1506	|	1547	|	1610	|	1647	|	1710	|	1745	|	1810	|	1845	1906	|	1959	|	|	2109	2150	...
East Midlands Parkway d.	1439	1516	1520	1542	1557	1616	1623	1642	1657	1712	1723	1739	1757	1813	1823	1839	1857	1919	1937	2012	2039	2117	2121	2202	...
Loughborough 189 d.	1446	|	1528	1550	|	|	1630	1649	|	1719	1730	1746	|	|	1830	1846	|	1926	1944	2019	2046	2124	2129	2210	...
Leicester 189 d.	1459	1532	1543	1602	1613	1632	1643	1702	1713	1732	1743	1802j	1813	1829	1843	1902j	1913	1943t	1959j	2032	2059	2136	2141	2221	...
Market Harborough d.	1512	|	1556	|	1626	|	1656	|	1726	|	1756	|	1826	1842	1856	|	1926	1956	|	2045	2112	2150	2154	...	...
Kettering 170a d.	|	|	1606	|	1636	|	1706	|	1736	|	1806	|	1836	|	1906	|	1936	2006	|	2055	|	2200	2205	...	...
London St Pancras 170a a.	1608	1639	1655	1709	1727	1739	1755	1809	1827	1839	1855	1909	1927	1939	1955	2009	2027	2055	2108	2155	2208	2303	2310	...	...

j – Arrives 4–5 minutes earlier.
t – Arrives 1937.
‡ – For trains Sheffield - Nottingham see Tables **171** and **206**.

EM Most trains convey 🍷 LONDON - KETTERING - CORBY 170a

See Table **170** for other services London - Kettering and v.v.

km		Ⓐ	dE	Ⓐ	ⒶF	ⒶG	Ⓐ	ⒶG	Ⓐ	ⒶG	Ⓐ	Ⓐ	Ⓐ	Ⓐ	Ⓐ	ⒶA	Ⓐ	Ⓐ	⊠	Ⓐ	Ⓐ	Ⓐ	Ⓐ	Ⓐ
0	**London** St Pancras d.		0015	0545	0559	0605	0617	0635	0647	0705	0718	0749	0818	0847	0915	0945	1015	1045		1617	1647	1717	1747	1817
47	Luton ✈ Parkway d.		0052	0607	|	|	0643	|	0709	|	0742	0811	0841	0912	0937	1007	1037	1107	and at	1639	1709	1741	1812	1842
49	Luton d.		0056	0610	|	|	0646	|	0712	|	0745	0814	0845	0915	0940	1011	1040	1110	the same	1642	1712	1744	1815	1845
80	Bedford d.		0122	0626	|	0639	0701	0711	0728	|	0800	0830	0901	0930	0956	1025	1056	1126	minutes	1658	1728	1800	1830	1901
105	Wellingborough d.		0132	0637	0642	|	0713	|	0739	0751	0811	0841	0912	0942	1007	1036	1107	1137	past each	1709	1739	1811	1842	1912
116	Kettering d.		0141	0646	...	0653	0722	0726	0748	0757	0820	0849	0921	0951	1016	1044	1117	1146	hour until	1718	1748	1820	1851	1920
128	**Corby** a.		...	0654	...	...	0730	...	0756	...	0828	0857	0929	0959	1024	1055	1125	1154		1726	1756	1828	1859	1928

	ⒶA	Ⓐ	Ⓐ	Ⓐ		Ⓐ	Ⓐ	ⒶF	Ⓐ	⑥	⑥E	⑥	⑥F	⑥G	⑥	⑥G	⑥	⑥G	⑥	⑥	⊠	⑥	⑥
London St Pancras d.	1835	1847	1915	1945		2215	2247	2305	2355		0015	0533	0600	0605	0608	0633	0646	0705	0715	0745		2115	2145
Luton ✈ Parkway d.	|	1909	1937	2007	and at	2238	2318	2346	0033		0052	0601	|	|	0630	|	0708	|	0737	0807	and at	2137	2207
Luton d.	|	1912	1940	2010	the same	2241	2321	|	0036		0056	0604	|	|	0633	|	0711	|	0740	0810	the same	2140	2210
Bedford d.	|	1928	1956	2026	minutes	2256	2343	|	0100		0122	0619	|	0638	0649	0706	0727	0739	0756	0826	minutes	2156	2228
Wellingborough d.	|	1939	2007	2037	past each	2308	2355	0021	0111		0132	0630	0642	|	0701	|	0738	0750	0808	0838	past each	2208	2240
Kettering d.	1938f	1948	2016	2047	hour until	2317	0004	0037	0120		0141	0639	...	0652	0710	0720	0748	0756	0816	0846	hour until	2216	2248
Corby a.	1946	1956	2024	2056		2325	0012	...	0128		...	0649	...	...	0718	...	0757	...	0824	0854		2224	2256

	⑥	⑥	⑦	⑦G	⑦F	⑦G	⑦F	⑦G	⑦G	⑦	⑦G	⑦	⑦G	⑦	⑦		⑦	⑦	⑦	⑦	⑦E	⑦	⑦G	⑦E
London St Pancras d.	2218	2235		0900	0930	1000	1030	1100	1130	1214	1234	1314	1334	1414	1444		1944	2014	2044	2114	2135	2212	2232	2300
Luton ✈ Parkway d.	2240	|		0932	1002	1032	1102	1132	1202	1236	1257	1336	1357	1436	1506	and at	2006	2036	2106	2136	2157	2236	2254	2332
Luton d.	2243	|		0936	|	1036	|	1136	|	1239	|	1339	1400	1439	1509	the same	2009	2039	2109	2139	|	2239	|	|
Bedford d.	2259	2316	★	1000	1030	1100	1130	1200	1224	1255	1311	1355	1414	1455	1525	minutes	2025	2055	2125	2155	2211	2255	2313	2358
Wellingborough d.	2310	2335		1012	1042	1112	1142	1212	1235	1307	1323	1407	1426	1507	1537	past each	2037	2107	2137	2207	2223	2307	2325	0010
Kettering d.	2319	|		1018	1048	1118	1148	1218	1241	1316	1329	1416	1432	1516	1547	hour until	2045	2117	2145	2217	2229	2316	2331	0016
Corby a.	2349*	0030*		...	1108	...	1210	1238	...	1324	1356	1424	1454	1525	1555		...	2125	...	2225	...	2324	...	...

	Ⓐ	Ⓐ	ⒶE	Ⓐ	Ⓐ	Ⓐ	Ⓐ	Ⓐ	Ⓐ	Ⓐ	ⒶA	Ⓐ	Ⓐ		Ⓐ	Ⓐ	Ⓐ	Ⓐ	Ⓐ	Ⓐ	ⒶA	Ⓐ	Ⓐ	Ⓐ
Corby d.		0432	...	0539	0611	0639	0710	0740	0809	0840	0848	0910	0939		1204	1240	1310	1340	1410	1440	1508	1541	1611	1642
Kettering d.		0440	0535	0547	0619	0648	0718	0748	0817	0848	0911t	0919	0948	and at	1212	1248	1319	1348	1419	1448	1518	1549	1619	1650
Wellingborough d.		0448	|	0555	0627	0656	0726	0756	0825	0856	|	0927	0956	the same	1220	1256	1327	1356	1427	1456	1528	1557	1627	1658
Bedford d.		0509r	|	0609	0640	0710	0740	0810	0839	0910	|	0940	1010	minutes	1238r	1310	1340	1410	1440	1510	1540	1611	1641	1712
Luton d.		0529	|	0625	0656	0725	0755	0825	0855	0925	|	0956	1025	past each	1255	1325	1356	1425	1456	1525	1555	1627	1657	1727
Luton ✈ Parkway d.		0532	0613	0628	0659	0728	0758	0828	0858	0928	|	0959	1029	hour until	1258	1328	1359	1428	1459	1528	1558	1630	1700	1730
London St Pancras a.		0602	0634	0651	0724	0754	0823	0851	0921	0951	1003	1023	1052		1321	1351	1422	1451	1522	1551	1620	1653	1724	1755

	ⒶG	Ⓐ	ⒶF	Ⓐ	ⒶG	Ⓐ	ⒶG	Ⓐ	Ⓐ	Ⓐ	Ⓐ	Ⓐ	Ⓐ	ⒶG	Ⓐ	⑥	⑥	⑥	⊠	⑥	⑥	⑥G	⑥	⑥G
Corby d.	...	1711	...	1740	...	1806	...	1840	1910	1940	2011	2040	2143	...	2234		0510	0540		2040	2110	...	2140	2201
Kettering d.	1707	1719	...	1749	1808	1815	1834	1848	1919	1949	2019	2049	2152	2240	2243		0519	0549	and at	2048	2119	2137	2148	2219
Wellingborough d.	|	1727	1754	1757	1815	1823	1841	1856	1927	1957	2027	2057	2200	|	2251		0527	0557	the same	2056	2127	|	2156	2227
Bedford d.	1726	1741	|	1810	|	1840r	|	1910	1940	2010	2041	2110	2213	|	2304		0540	0610	minutes	2110	2140	2155	2210	|
Luton d.	|	1756	|	1827	|	1855	|	1925	1956	2025	2056	2126	2229	|	2322		0556	0626	past each	2125	2156	|	2225	|
Luton ✈ Parkway d.	|	1759	|	1832	|	1858	|	1928	1959	2028	2059	2129	2232	2318	2325		0559	0629	hour until	2128	2159	|	2228	|
London St Pancras a.	1803	1822	1840	1855	1905	1921	1926	1951	2022	2051	2122	2152	2255	2352	2356		0623	0652		2151	2222	2234	2251	2315

	⑦	⑦E	⑦G	⑦E	⑦G	⑦F	⑦G	⑦F	⑦G	⑦	⑦	⑦	⑦	⑦	⑦		⑦	⑦	⑦F	⑦	⑦G	⑦	⑦F	⑦G
Corby d.		...	...	...	...	...	1000	1038	...	1141	1227	1310	1341	1410	1440		1910	1940	...	2005	...	2110	2140	...
Kettering d.		0753	0820	0850	0920	0954	1023	1054	1109	1149	1235	1318	1349	1418	1448	and at	1918	1948	...	2018r	2055	2118	2200	2205
Wellingborough d.		0800	0827	0857	0927	1001	1031	1101	1116	1158	1244	1326	1357	1426	1456	the same	1926	1956	...	2026	2102	2126	2207	2213
Bedford d.		0812	0844	0914	0944	1014	1044	1114	1130	1210	1256	1339	1410	1439	1509	minutes	1940	2009	...	2039	2115	2139	2220	2227
Luton d.		0834	|	|	1004	|	1102	|	|	1225	1312	1355	1425	1455	1525	past each	1956	2025	2044	2055	|	2155	2235	2242
Luton ✈ Parkway d.		0838	0906	0936	1008	1039	1106	1135	1153	1228	1315	1358	1428	1458	1528	hour until	1959	2028	|	2058	2131	2158	2238	2246
London St Pancras a.		0915	0942	1012	1041	1112	1141	1211	1219	1252	1339	1422	1452	1522	1552		2023	2052	2108	2122	2155	2223	2303	2310

A – Conveys (12) London St Pancras - Melton Mowbray and v.v. (see panel).
E – To/from Derby (Table **170**).
F – To/from Sheffield (Table **170**).
G – To/from Nottingham (Table **170**).

d – ②–⑤ only.

f – Arrives 1927.
r – Arrives 4–5 minutes earlier.
t – Arrives 0857.

★ – On ⑦ additional trains run from Kettering to Corby at 0945 and 1015.
⊠ – Timings may vary ± 2 minutes.
* – Connection by 🚌.

(LONDON -) CORBY - MELTON MOWBRAY

km		Ⓐ	Ⓐ
	London St Pancras d.	0945	1835
	Kettering d.	1044	1938
0	**Corby** d.	1055	1947
23	Oakham a.	1114	2006
43	**Melton Mowbray** a.	1126	2017

	Ⓐ	Ⓐ
Melton Mowbray d.	0815	1435
Oakham d.	0827	1447
Corby d.	0848	1508
Kettering a.	0857	1517
London St Pancras a.	1003	1620

171 NOTTINGHAM - SHEFFIELD - HUDDERSFIELD and LEEDS — 2nd class NT

NOTTINGHAM - SHEFFIELD - LEEDS

km			⚒	⚒	⚒	⚒	⚒	⚒	⚒		⚒R	⚒	⚒L	⚒	⚒L	⚒	♥	⚒L	⚒	⚒L	⚒	⚒L	⚒	⚒L
0	**Nottingham** 170 206 d.	⚒	...	...	...	0520	...	...	0616	...	...	0718	...	0817	...	0917		...	1717	...	1817	...	1917	...
18	Langley Mill d.		...	...	...	|	...	...	0635	...	...	0737	...	0836	...	0936	and	...	1736	...	1836	...	1936	...
29	Alfreton 206 d.		...	...	...	|	...	...	0643	...	...	0745	...	0844	...	0944	at the	...	1744	...	1844	...	1944	...
45	Chesterfield 170 206 d.		...	...	...	0551	0625	...	0653	...	...	0758	...	0855	...	0955	same	...	1755	...	1856	...	1956	...
64	**Sheffield** 170 206 a.		...	...	...	0615	0642	...	0712	...	...	0816	...	0914	...	1013	minutes	...	1814	...	1914	...	2013	...
64	**Sheffield** 192 193 d.		0528	0602	0619	...	0644	0704	0718	...	0746	0819	0845	0918	0945	1018	past	1744	1818	1846	1918	1945	2018	2045
70	Meadowhall 192 193 d.		0534	0608	0625	...	0650	0710	0724	...	0753	0825	0852	0924	0952	1024	each	1750	1824	1852	1924	1951	2024	2051
90	Barnsley d.		0558	0630	0640	...	0706	0732	0741	...	0808	0840	0909	0940	1011	1040	hour	1808	1838	1910	1940	2011	2040	2109
107	Wakefield Kirkgate d.		0616	0649	0655	...	0723	0750	0756	...	0823	0856	0925	0955	1026	1055	until	1825	1855	1925	1955	2026	2055	2124
130	**Leeds** a.		0644	0724	0720	...	0744	0823	0817	...	0844	0914	0943	1014	1044	1114		1844	1917	1944	2014	2044	2114	2146

	⚒	Ⓐ	⑥	⚒	⚒		⑦	⑦	⑦B	⑦	⑦	⑦		⑦	⑦	⑦	⑦	⑦	⑦	⑦	⑦	⑦	⑦	⑦	⑦
Nottingham 170 206 d.	2017	2115	2212	...	2318	⑦	...	...	0918	...	1017	1118	...	1219	1319	1419	1520	1619	1719	1819	1919	...	2015	2133	2233
Langley Mill d.	2036	2139	2136	...	2336		...	...	0939	...	1035	1136	...	1237	1337	1438	1538	1637	1737	1837	1938	...	2034	2158	2258
Alfreton 206 d.	2044	2147	2144	...	2344		...	...	0947	...	1043	1144	...	1245	1345	1446	1546	1645	1745	1845	1946	...	2042	2206	2306
Chesterfield 170 206 d.	2055	2157	2155	...	2354		...	...	0957	...	1054	1155	...	1256	1356	1457	1557	1656	1757	1856	1957	...	2055	2216	2316
Sheffield 170 206 a.	2114	2216	2214	...	0013		...	...	1016	...	1112	1213	...	1315	1415	1515	1614	1714	1816	1914	2016	...	2114	2234	2335
Sheffield 192 193 d.	2118	2218	2218	2231	...		0839	0917	1017	1051	1116	1216	...	1317	1417	1517	1617	1717	1817	1917	2017	2047	2117	2244	...
Meadowhall 192 193 d.	2124	2224	2224	2237	...		0845	0923	1023	1057	1122	1223	...	1323	1423	1523	1623	1724	1823	1923	2023	2053	2123	2250	...
Barnsley d.	2140	2240	2240	2259	...		0907	0937	1038	1112	1136	1237	...	1337	1437	1537	1637	1738	1837	1937	2037	2115	2137	2312	...
Wakefield Kirkgate d.	2155	2255	2255	2319	...		0925	0954	1053	1130	1152	1253	...	1353	1453	1555	1654	1755	1853	1953	2053	2133	2153	2332	...
Leeds a.	2215	2316	2314	2356	...		0958	1014	1113	1206	1214	1316	...	1414	1514	1614	1714	1814	1914	2016	2114	2206	2215	0006	...

		⚒	⚒	⚒	Ⓐ	⑥	⚒R	⚒L	Ⓐ	⑥	⚒L	⚒	⚒L	⚒	♥	⚒	⚒L	⚒	⚒L	⚒	⚒L	⚒	⚒	⚒
Leeds d.	⚒	...	...	...	...	...	...	0638	0705	0705	0738	0804	0837	0909		1609	1638	1709	1738	1803	1838	1905	1932	2004
Wakefield Kirkgate d.		...	...	...	...	...	...	0655	0723	0722	0756	0821	0855	0925	and	1625	1655	1728	1756	1821	1858	1921	2003	2021
Barnsley d.		...	*0523*	0552	...	...	...	0712	0738	0738	0812	0837	0911	0941	at the	1641	1711	1744	1812	1837	1914	1937	2022	2037
Meadowhall 192 193 d.		...	*0543*	0613	...	...	...	0726	0753	0753	0828	0856	0927	0957	same	1657	1727	1758	1828	1856	1929	1957	2043	2051
Sheffield 192 193 a.		...	*0551*	0621	...	...	...	0733	0801	0801	0836	0904	0934	1004	minutes	1704	1734	1805	1835	1904	1936	2004	2051	2100
Sheffield 170 206 d.		0515	0603	...	0642	0645	0703	...	0803	0803	...	0906	...	1007	past	1706	...	1807	...	1906	...	2006	...	...
Chesterfield 170 206 d.		0530	0619	...	0658	0701	0718	...	0821	0819	...	0922	...	1023	each	1722	...	1823	...	1922	...	2022	...	...
Alfreton 206 d.		0543	0629	...	0709	0712	0729	...	0833	0829	...	0933	...	1033	hour	1733	...	1834	...	1933	...	2033	...	...
Langley Mill d.		0551	0636	...	0717	|	0736	...	0840	0836	...	0940	...	1040	until	1740	...	1841	...	1940	...	2040	...	...
Nottingham 170 206 a.		0612	0700	...	0736	0739	0800t	...	0859	0855	...	0959	...	1058		1758	...	1859	...	1959	...	2059	...	...

	⚒	⚒	Ⓐ	⚒	⑥	Ⓐ	⚒	Ⓐ		⑦	⑦	⑦	⑦		⑦	⑦	⑦	⑦B	⑦	⑦	⑦	⑦	⑦	⑦
Leeds d.	2032	2104	...	2137	...	...	2232	2302	⑦	...	0832	0910	1009		1509	1609	1709	1809	1909	2009	2017	2109	2209	2220
Wakefield Kirkgate d.	2103	2122	...	2154	...	...	2303	2333		...	0903	0926	1025	and	1525	1625	1726	1826	1925	2025	2048	2129	2226	2251
Barnsley d.	2122	2138	...	2211	...	...	2322	2352		...	0921	0942	1041	at the	1541	1641	1742	1842	1941	2041	2106	2145	2241	2309
Meadowhall 192 193 d.	2144	2154	...	2230	...	...	2343	0015		...	0942	0957	1056	same	1557	1657	1757	1857	1956	2056	2132	2159	2255	2331
Sheffield 192 193 a.	2152	2203	...	2240	...	...	2351	0024		...	0949	1004	1104	minutes	1604	1706	1804	1904	2003	2103	2139	2206	2303	2338
Sheffield 170 206 d.	...	2205	2238	...	2256	2338	...	...		0905	...	1007	1106	past	1606	1706	1806	1906	2006	2107	...	2208	*2330*	...
Chesterfield 170 206 d.	...	2221	2253	...	2311	0002	...	...		0921	...	1023	1122	each	1622	1722	1822	1922	2022	2122	...	2224	*2344*	...
Alfreton 206 d.	...	2231	2304	...	2322	|	...	...		0932	...	1033	1132	hour	1632	1732	1833	1933	2032	2133	...	2235	*2355*	...
Langley Mill d.	...	2238	|	...	|	|	...	...		0939	...	1040	1139	until	1639	1739	1840	1940	2039	2140	...	2242	*0002*	...
Nottingham 170 206 a.	...	2258	2327	...	2347	0038	...	...		1002	...	1101	1200		1700	1800	1900	2000	2100	2200	...	2305	*0023*	...

SHEFFIELD - HUDDERSFIELD *'The Penistone Line'*

km			⚒	⚒	⚒		⚒	⚒	⚒		⚒	⚒	⚒		⑦	⑦	⑦L	⑦L	⑦L	⑦L		⑦L	⑦	⑦	⑦	⑦
0	**Sheffield** 192 193 d.	⚒	0537	0630	0735	and	1635	1734	1834	...	1935	2035	2238	⑦	0938	1038	1138	1237	1339	1438	...	1536	1639	1741	1839	1939
6	Meadowhall 192 193 d.		0543	0636	0741		1641	1740	1840	...	1941	2041	2244		0944	1044	1144	1243	1345	1444	...	1542	1645	1747	1845	1945
26	Barnsley d.		0605	0702	0803	hourly	1703	1802	1902	...	2003	2103	2307		1006	1106	1206	1305	1407	1503f	...	1604	1702	1809	1905f	2007
38	Penistone d.		0620	0719	0819		1720	1821	1918	...	2019	2119	2324		1023	1123	1223	1322	1424	1520	...	1621	1719	1825	1922	2024
59	**Huddersfield** a.		0652	0750	0850	until	1751	1852	1949	...	2050	2150	2355		1054	1154	1254	1354	1455	1551	...	1652	1751	1856	1953	2055

		⚒	⚒	⚒	⚒	⚒		⚒	⚒	⚒	⚒	⚒	⚒	⚒		⑦	⑦	⑦L	⑦L	⑦L	⑦L	⑦L	⑦L	⑦	⑦	⑦
Huddersfield d.	⚒	0613	0712	0810	0912	1012	and	1712	1751	1813	1912	2012	2112	2250	⑦	0910	1015	1119	1215	1319	1415	1515	1615	1715	1815	1915
Penistone d.		0644	0743	0842	0943	1043		1743	1826f	1846	1943	2043	2143	2324		0941	1046	1150	1246	1350	1447	1546	1646	1746	1849	1946
Barnsley d.		0701	0800	0859	1000	1100	hourly	1800	1845	1902	2000	2100	2200	2340		0958	1102	1207	1303	1407	1504	1603	1703	1803	1906	2003
Meadowhall 192 193 d.		0722	0822	0921	1022	1121		1821	1909	1923	2021	2121	2221	0002		1018	1117	1228	1319	1428	1521	1626	1721	1826	1920	2023
Sheffield 192 193 a.		0729	0829	0928	1029	1128	until	1828	1919	1932	2028	2129	2229	0009		1028	1125	1236	1328	1437	1529	1634	1729	1833	1929	2032

A – From London St. Pancras (Table **170**).
B – To/from Carlisle (Table **173**).
G – To Gainsborough Central (Table **178**).
D – To Derby (Table **170**).
L – To/from Lincoln (Table **178**).
R – From Retford (Table **178**).
f – Arrives 5 minutes earlier.
r – Arrives 2318 on ⑥.
t – Arrives 0754 on Ⓐ.
v – Ⓐ only.
♥ – Timings may vary ± 3 minutes.

172 NOTTINGHAM - WORKSOP and MATLOCK — 2nd class EM

NOTTINGHAM - WORKSOP *'The Robin Hood Line'*

km			⚒	⚒	⚒	⚒		⚒	Ⓐ	⚒	Ⓐ	⚒		⚒	⚒	⑥		⑦	⑦	⑦	⑦	⑦	⑦	⑦	⑦	⑦
0	**Nottingham** d.	⚒	0517	0625	0725	0824	and	1625	1700	1725	1800	1825	and	2125	2225	2258	⑦	0812	0912	1112	1312	1512	1614	1812	1912	2022
28	Mansfield d.		0551	0701	0802	0902	hourly	1702	1730	1802	1830	1902	hourly	2202	2302	2332		0844	0944	1144	1344	1544	1646	1844	1944	2054
50	**Worksop** a.		0625	0733	0833	0933	until	1733	...	1833	...	1936	until	2236	2337	...		...	...	...	...	...	...	...	...	...

		⚒	⚒	⚒		⚒	Ⓐ	⚒	Ⓐ	⚒	⚒	⚒	Ⓐ	⑥	Ⓐ	⑥	Ⓐ		⑦	⑦	⑦	⑦		⑦	⑦	⑦	⑦
Worksop d.	⚒	0535	0636	0739	and	1639	...	1739	...	1839	1939	2039	2139	2139	2239	2239	2343	⑦	...	...	...	...	...	...	...	...	...
Mansfield d.		0611	0712	0812	hourly	1712	1745	1812	1845	1912	2012	2112	2212	2214	2314	2314	0010		0900	1000	1200	1400	...	1557	1701	1900	2108
Nottingham a.		0650	0750	0850	until	1750	1815	1850	1915	1950	2050	2150	2250	2253	2348	2353	0049		0933	1033	1233	1434	...	1630	1739	1939	2141

NOTTINGHAM - DERBY - MATLOCK

km			⚒	⑥	Ⓐ	⑥	Ⓐ	⚒		⚒	Ⓐ	⑥	⚒	Ⓐ	⑥	⚒	⚒		⑦	⑦	⑦	⑦		⑦	⑦	⑦	⑦	⑦
0	**Nottingham** ‡ d.	⚒	...	0542	...	...	...	...		...	...	...	...	...	...	...	...	⑦	...	0930	1127	1330		1729	1825	1923	2024	2122
26	**Derby** ‡ a.		...	0611	...	...	...	...		...	...	...	...	...	...	...	...		...	0957	1154	1358		1756	1852	1950	2052	2149
26	**Derby** d.		0542	0630	0633	0724	0735	0833	and	1732	1824	1833	1934	2023	2033	2136	2233		0756	0959	1156	1359	and	1758	1854	1951	2053	2153
34	Duffield ◧ d.		0549	0637	0640	0731	0742	0840	hourly	1739	1831	1840	1941	2030	2040	2143	2240		0803	1006	1203	1406	hourly	1805	1901	1958	2100	2200
46	Whatstandwell ◧ d.		0603	0651	0654	0745	0756	0854	until	1753	1845	1854	1955	2044	2054	2157	2254		0817	1020	1217	1420	until	1819	1915	2012	2114	2214
50	Cromford d.		0608	0657	0659	0750	0801	0859		1758	1850	1859	2000	2049	2100	2202	2259		0822	1025	1222	1426		1824	1920	2018	2120	2220
52	Matlock Bath ◧ d.		0611	0959	0702	0753	0804	0902	★	1801	1853	1902	2003	2052	2103	2205	2302		0825	1028	1225	1429	★	1827	1923	2021	2123	2223
53	**Matlock** ◧ a.		0615	0702	0705	0756	0807	0908		1806	1856	1905	2008	2055	2106	2209	2306		0828	1031	1228	1432		1830	1926	2024	2126	2226

		⚒	⚒	⑥	Ⓐ	⚒	⚒	⚒		⚒	⚒	⚒	⚒	⑥	Ⓐ	Ⓐ	⑥	⚒		⑦	⑦	⑦	⑦	⑦		⑦	⑦	⑦
Matlock ◧ d.	⚒	0618	0709	0809	0812	0912	1012	1112		1712	1812	1912	2012	2114	2116	2218	2212	2311	⑦	0839	1038	1237	1442	1540		2042	2144	2256
Matlock Bath ◧ d.		0620	0711	0811	0814	0914	1014	1114	and	1714	1814	1914	2014	2117	2118	2220	2214	2313		0841	1040	1239	1444	1542	and	2044	2146	2258
Cromford d.		0623	0714	0814	0817	0917	1017	1117	hourly	1717	1817	1917	2017	2120	2121	2223	2217	2316		0844	1043	1242	1447	1545	hourly	2047	2149	2301
Whatstandwell ◧ d.		0628	0719	0819	0822	0922	1022	1122	until	1722	1822	1922	2022	2125	2126	2228	2222	2321		0849	1048	1247	1452	1550	until	2052	2154	2306
Duffield ◧ d.		0644	0735	0835	0838	0938	1038	1138		1738	1839	1938	2038	2142	2142	2245	2238	2337		0904	1103	1302	1508	1606		2107	2209	2323
Derby a.		0654	0745	0842	0845	0946	1046	1148	★	1745	1846	1947	2045	2149	2149	2253	2245	2345		0911	1110	1309	1515	1613	★	2114	2216	2330
Derby ‡ d.		...	...	...	...	...	...	...		...	...	...	...	...	...	...	...	2346		0914	1112	1312	1516	1615		2116	2219	2332
Nottingham ‡ a.		...	...	...	...	...	...	...		...	...	...	...	...	...	...	...	0014		0940	1139	1339	1542	1641		2143	2245	2359

f – Arrives 5–7 minutes earlier on ⑥.
r – Arrives 4–6 minutes earlier on Ⓐ.
★ – Timings may vary ± 4 minutes.
‡ – See Tables **120** and **155** for trains Nottingham - Derby and v.v.

◧ – Visitor attractions near these stations:
Duffield: Ecclesbourne Valley Railway (shares National Rail station). ✆ 01629 823076. www.e-v-r.com
Whatstandwell: Crich National Tramway Museum (1.6 km walk). ✆ 01773 854321. www.tramway.co.uk
Matlock Bath: Heights of Abraham (short walk to cable car). ✆ 01629 582365. www.heightsofabraham.com
Matlock: Peak Rail (shares National Rail station). ✆ 01629 580381. www.peakrail.co.uk

LEEDS - SETTLE - CARLISLE — 173

NT 2nd class All ⚒ trains convey 🍸

km			⚒ Ⓐ	⚒ ⑥	⚒	⚒	⚒	⚒		⚒	⚒	⚒	⚒	⚒A	⑦		⑦D	⑦	⑦	⑦	⑦	⑦A
	London Kings Cross 180	d.	...	...	...	...	...	...	...	...	...	...	...	1803	...	...	...	...	...	...	...	1835
0	**Leeds** 174 ▷	d.	0515	0620	0748	0919	1049	1318	...	1518	1648	1818	1949	2039	0859	...	1116	1232	1423	1623	1852	2100
27	Keighley 🚂 174 ▷	d.	0542	0648	0812	0942	1113	1343	...	1543	1713	1842	2012	2101s	0927	...	1139	1255	1447	1647	1916	2119s
42	**Skipton** 174 ▷	d.	0559	0706	0826	0959	1127	1357	...	1559	1727	1856	2027	2119	0945	...	1152	1309	1503	1701	1933	2135
58	Hellifield 174	d.	0615	0720	0840	1013	1141	1409	...	1613	1741	1910	2042	...	0959	...	1205	1323	1517	1713	1945	...
66	**Settle**	d.	0623	0728	0850	1022	1151	1417	...	1620	1749	1919	2050	...	1007	...	1213	1333	1526	1721	1953	...
76	Horton in Ribblesdale	d.	0632	0737	0858	1031	1159	1425	...	1629	1758	1927	2059	...	1016	...	|	1342	1535	1730	2002	...
84	Ribblehead	d.	0640	0745	0906	1039	1207	1433	...	1637	1806	1935	2108	...	1024	...	|	1351	1543	1738	2010	...
93	Dent	d.	0649	0754	0916	1048	1217	1443	...	1646	1815	1944	...	...	1034	...	|	1401	1553	1748	2020	...
99	Garsdale	d.	0655	0800	0921	1054	1222	1448	...	1652	1821	1950	...	...	1040	...	|	1407	1559	1753	2025	...
115	Kirkby Stephen	d.	0707	0812	0934	1106	1235	1501	...	1704	1833	2002	...	...	1053	...	1252	1420	1612	1806	2038	...
132	Appleby	d.	0720	0825	0948	1119	1248	1514	...	1717	1846	2015	...	...	1106	...	1305	1432	1624	1819	2051	...
149	Langwathby	d.	0734	0839	1001	1132	1302	1528	...	1731	1900	2028	...	...	1120	...	|	1446	1638	1833	2105	...
166	Armathwaite	d.	0747	0852	1015	1146	1316	1541	...	1744	1913	2042	...	...	1134	...	|	1500	1652	1847	2119	...
182	**Carlisle**	a.	0802	0907	1030	1201	1331	1602	...	1800	1928	2057	...	...	1152	...	1342	1515	1708	1903	2139	...

		⚒A	⚒ Ⓐ	⚒ ⑥	⚒ ⑥	⚒ Ⓐ	⚒ ⑥	⚒	⚒	⚒	⚒		⚒	Ⓐ	⑥	⚒	⑦	⑦	⑦D	⑦	⑦	⑦
Carlisle	d.	...	0549	...	0753	0824	0927	1058	1340	1450	1618	...	1824	2013	2015	...	0925	1223	1520	1607	1725	1911
Armathwaite	d.	...	0603	...	0808	0838	0941	1112	|	1504	1632	...	1838	2027	2029	...	0939	1237	1534	|	1739	1925
Langwathby	d.	...	0617	...	0822	0852	0955	1126	|	1518	1646	...	1852	2041	2043	...	0953	1251	1548	|	1753	1939
Appleby	d.	...	0631	...	0836	0906	1009	1141	1416	1532	1700	...	1906	2055	2057	...	1007	1305	1602	1644	1808	1953
Kirkby Stephen	d.	...	0644	...	0849	0920	1023	1154	1429	1546	1714	...	1920	2108	2111	...	1021	1319	1615	1657	1822	2007
Garsdale	d.	...	0658	...	0903	0933	1036	1208	|	1559	1727	...	1933	2121	2124	...	1034	1332	1628	|	1835	2020
Dent	d.	...	0703	...	0908	0938	1041	1213	|	1604	1732	...	1938	|	|	...	1040	1338	1633	|	1841	2026
Ribblehead	d.	...	0713	0713	0918	0948	1051	1222	|	1614	1742	...	1948	|	|	2145	1049	1347	1643	|	1850	2035
Horton in Ribblesdale	d.	...	0719	0719	0925	0954	1057	1229	|	1620	1748	...	1954	|	|	2151	1056	1354	1650	|	1857	2042
Settle	d.	...	0727	0727	0933	1002	1105	1237	1506	1628	1756	...	2002	2146	2148	2159	1104	1402	1658	1734	1906	2051
Hellifield 174	d.	...	0736	0736	0941	1011	1113	1244	1514	1637	1805	...	2011	|	|	2208	1113	1411	1707	1742	1913	2059
Skipton 174 ▷	a.	0656	0752	0752	0957	1026	1127	1259	1528	1654	1821	...	2027	2206	2209	2225	1130	1430	1720	1757	1928	2116
Keighley 🚂 174 ▷	a.	0708u	0805	0807	1009	1038	1138	1310	1541	1709	1839	...	2039	2221	2221	2241	1140	1440	1733	1808	1940	2127
Leeds 174 ▷	a.	0733	0834	0835	1034	1107	1204	1338	1605	1738	1908	...	2106	2248	2248	2311	1207	1508	1805	1834	2007	2154
London Kings Cross 180	a.	1000r	...	...	...	...	...	...	...	...	...	...	...	...	...	...	...	...	...	...	...	...

Local trains **Bradford Forster Square - Skipton** and v.v. *30 km*. Journey: ± 38 minutes. Trains call at **Keighley** (± 22 minutes later from Bradford, ± 14 minutes from Skipton).

From Bradford Forster Square: On ⚒ at 0603, 0641, 0711, 0810, 0907, 1011 and hourly until 2011, 2120, 2211, 2311; on ⑦ at 0948 and hourly until 2248.

From Skipton: On ⚒ at 0604, 0709, 0737, 0820, 0904 and hourly until 1704, 1803, 1904, 2004, 2133, 2234; on ⑦ at 0842 and hourly until 2042, 2139.

Other local trains **Leeds - Skipton** and v.v. Journey ± 45 minutes. Trains call at **Keighley** (± 25 minutes later from Leeds, ± 14 minutes from Skipton).

From Leeds: On ⚒ at 0515Ⓐ, 0626, 0656, 0723, 0752⑥, 0825, 0854, 0926 and every 30 minutes until 1656, 1719, 1742, 1755, 1826 and every 30 minutes until 2256, 2320; on ⑦ at 1016, 1126, 1157, 1216, 1316, 1416, 1516, 1611, 1716 and hourly until 2116, 2220, 2323.

From Skipton: On ⚒ at 0545, 0618, 0640, 0701, 0716, 0730, 0744, 0809, 0845, 0917 and every 30 minutes until 2117, 2149, 2247; on ⑦ at 0834, 0912 and hourly until 2012, 2122, 2212, 2315.

A – (12) and 🍸 London Kings Cross - Skipton and v.v. (Table **180**).
D – From / to Nottingham (Table **171**).
r – Arrives 0950 on ⑥.
s – Calls to set down only.
u – Calls to pick up only.
▷ – See panels below main table for other local services (also for services Skipton - Bradford and v.v.).
🚂 – Keighley and Worth Valley Railway (Keighley - Haworth - Oakworth - Oxenhope, *8 km*). ✆ 01535 645214. www.kwvr.co.uk

LEEDS - LANCASTER - MORECAMBE - HEYSHAM — 174

NT 2nd class

km	km			⚒	⚒	⚒		⚒	⚒	⚒		⚒	⑥	Ⓐ	Ⓐ		⑦	⑦		⑦	⑦		⑦
0	0	**Leeds** 173	d.	...	*0626*	0819	...	1018	...	1218	...	1418	1726	1726	1918	...	0831	1033	...	1329	1532	...	1731
27	27	Keighley 🚂 173	d.	...	*0704*	0842	...	1043	...	1243	...	1443	1752	1752	1943	...	0859	1056	...	1352	1555	...	1754
42	42	Skipton 173	d.	0522	0725	0856	...	1057	...	1258	...	1458	1810	1810	2000	...	0917	1110	...	1406	1609	...	1808
58	58	Hellifield 173	d.	0537	0740	0910	...	1111	...	1312	...	1513	1824	1824	2014	...	0931	1124	...	1420	1623	...	1822
66	66	Giggleswick	d.	0548	0750	0921	...	1122	...	1323	...	1523	1834	1834	2025	...	0941	1134	...	1431	1634	...	1833
82	82	Bentham	d.	0603	0805	0935	...	1136	...	1337	...	1538	1849	1849	2040	...	0956	1148	...	1445	1648	...	1847
103	103	Carnforth 157	a.	0622	0826	0956	...	1158	...	1359	...	1559	1911	1911	2102	...	1015	1209	...	1506	1709	...	1908
113		**Lancaster** ❖ 157	a.	0631	*0844*	1006b	...	1211	1249	1409	...	1607a	1920a	1924	2115	...	1027	1219b	...	1518	1721	...	1920
120	112	Morecambe ❖	a.	*0732*	...	1028	...	1225	1259	1423	...	1633	1945	1951	*2145*	...	1039	1240	...	1534	1734	...	1936
127	119	**Heysham** Port	a.	...	...	...	...	...	1317	...	...	...	...	...	...	...	...	1258	...	...	...	...	...

		⚒ Ⓐ	⚒ ⑥	⚒	⚒		⚒	⚒	⚒		⚒		⚒	⑥	Ⓐ	⑦	⑦	⑦		⑦	⑦	
Heysham Port	d.	...	...	...	...	...	...	1320	...	...	...	...	...	...	...	...	1304	...	...	...	...	...
Morecambe ❖	d.	*0602*	*0610*	*0854*	1031	...	1232	1339	1432	...	1731	...	2006	*2115*	*2055*	1049	1322	1540	...	1738	2004	...
Lancaster ❖ 157	d.	0648	0648	0941	1046	...	1245	1349	1448	...	1745	...	2030c	2131	2131	1105	1344c	1552	...	1751	2017	...
Carnforth 157	d.	0658	0658	0951	1056	...	1255	...	1457	...	1756	...	2040	2143	2143	1115	1354	1602	...	1801	2029	...
Bentham	d.	0718	0718	1011	1116	...	1314	...	1517	...	1815	...	2100	2202	2202	1135	1414	1621	...	1820	2048	...
Giggleswick	d.	0734	0734	1027	1132	...	1330	...	1533	...	1831	...	2116	2218	2218	1150	1429	1636	...	1835	2103	...
Hellifield 173	d.	0745	0745	1039	1142	...	1340	...	1543	...	1842	...	2126	2228	2228	1202	1440	1648	...	1847	2115	...
Skipton 173	a.	0802	0802	1056	1157	...	1356	...	1558	...	1858	...	2141	2244	2244	1219	1456	1704	...	1903	2132	...
Keighley 🚂 173	a.	0817	0817	1111	1209	...	1409	...	1610	...	1909	...	2155	...	...	1232	1508	1718	...	1915	2144	...
Leeds 173	a.	0841	0841	1140	1238	...	1437	...	1638	...	1939	...	2222	...	...	1304	1537	1746	...	1944	2209	...

a – Departs 15 – 16 minutes later.
b – Departs 10 minutes later.
c – Arrives 11 – 14 minutes earlier.
🚂 – Keighley and Worth Valley Railway (Keighley - Haworth - Oakworth - Oxenhope, *8 km*). ✆ 01535 645214. www.kwvr.co.uk

❖ – **Full service Lancaster - Morecambe and v.v.**

From Lancaster: On ⚒ at 0517, 0618Ⓐ, 0625⑥, 0723, 0756, 0841, 0923, 1016Ⓐ, 1018⑥, 1050, 1128⑥, 1136Ⓐ, 1214, 1249, 1358, 1413, 1440Ⓐ, 1451⑥, 1523⑥, 1528Ⓐ, 1623, 1643, 1713Ⓐ, 1715⑥, 1750, 1828, 1905, 1935⑥, 1940Ⓐ, 2025⑥, 2038Ⓐ, 2135, 2204Ⓐ, 2206⑥, 2236Ⓐ; on ⑦ at 1030, 1130, 1229, 1339, 1427, 1524, 1630, 1724, 1830, 1925, 2030, 2130.

From Morecambe: On ⚒ at 0602Ⓐ, 0610⑥, 0700, 0741, 0823, 0854, 0941, 1031Ⓐ, 1033⑥, 1115⑥, 1122Ⓐ, 1141⑥, 1152Ⓐ, 1232, 1339, 1422, 1432; 1504, 1543, 1638, 1702Ⓐ, 1704⑥, 1731, 1813, 1841, 1941⑥, 1949Ⓐ, 2006, 2055Ⓐ, 2115⑥, 2149, 2220⑥, 2221Ⓐ, 2252Ⓐ; on ⑦ at 1049, 1145, 1322, 1357, 1441, 1540, 1658, 1738, 1902, 2004, 2105, 2200.

LEEDS - HARROGATE - YORK — 175

NT 2nd class

See Table **180** for through services London - Harrogate and v.v. See Tables **124** and **188** for direct services Leeds - York and v.v.

km			⚒	⚒	⚒	⚒	⚒	⚒	and at	⚒	⚒	⚒	⚒	⚒	⚒	⚒	⚒	⚒	⚒	⚒	⚒	⑦
0	**Leeds**	d.	0605	0633	0732	0801	0829	0859	the same	1529	1559	1659	1729	1749	1809	1828	1859	2006	2029	2129	2339	0906
29	**Harrogate**	d.	0641	0709	0808	0837	0905	0935	minutes	1605	1635	1735	1805	1825	1846	1904	1935	2042	2105	2205	0018	0942
36	Knaresborough	d.	0651	0717	0817	0846	0915	0944	past each	1615	1644	1744	1814	1841f	1855	1914	1944	2051	2114	2214	...	0951
62	**York**	a.	0719	0746	0846*	0915	0944	1011*	hour until	1642	1711	1812	1844	1915	...	1944	2011	2120	2143	2241	...	1019

		⑦	⑦	⑦	⑦	⑦	⑦	⑦	⑦	⑦	⑦	and at	⑦	⑦	⑦	⑦	⑦	⑦	⑦	⑦	⑦	⑦	⑦	⑦
Leeds	d.	0936	1006	1036	1106	1136	1206	1236	1306	1336	1406	the same	1706	1736	1806	1836	1906	1936	2006	2036	2106	2136	2227	2331
Harrogate	d.	1012	1042	1112	1142	1212	1242	1312	1342	1412	1442	minutes	1742	1812	1842	1912	1942	2012	2042	2112	2142	2212	2303	0007
Knaresborough	d.	1021	1051	1121	1151	1221	1251	1321	1351	1421	1451	past each	1751	1821	1851	1921	1951	2021	2051	2121	2151	2221	...	...
York	a.	1058	1126	1152	1220	1253	1325	1355	1425	1453	1523	hour until	1825	1857	1926	1953	2022	2049	2121	...	2218	...	...	...

		⚒	⚒	⚒	⚒	⚒	⚒		⚒	⚒	⚒	⚒		⚒	⚒	⚒	and at	⚒	⚒	⚒	⚒	⚒	⚒
York	d.	...	...	0647	0707	0742	0812	...	0910	0942	1012	1043	...	1110	1142	1211	the same	1642	1712	1743	1842	1911	1944
Knaresborough	d.	...	0654	0714	0736	0807	0837	...	0936	1007	1037	1108	...	1136	1207	1237	minutes	1707	1737	1809	1907	1937	2009
Harrogate	d.	0656	0704	0724	0745	0816	0846	...	0945	1017	1046	1117	...	1146	1216	1246	past each	1716	1746	1819	1917	1946	2019
Leeds	a.	0728	0741	0802	0821	0853	0922	...	1022	1052	1122	1153	...	1222	1252	1322	hour until	1752	1823	1855	1952	2022	2055

		⚒	⚒	⚒	⑦	⑦		⑦	⑦	⑦	⑦		⑦	⑦	⑦		⑦	⑦	⑦	and at	⑦	⑦	⑦
York	d.	2011	2211	2243	...	...	...	0946	...	1046	1116	...	1145	1215	1242	...	1312	1345	1415	the same	2045	2145	...
Knaresborough	d.	2036	2236	2308	...	...	...	1011	1041	1111	1141	...	1211	1241	1311	...	1340	1411	1441	minutes	2111	2211	...
Harrogate	d.	2046	2245	2318	0923	0952	...	1022	1052	1122	1152	...	1222	1252	1323	...	1352	1422	1452	past each	2122	2222	2312
Leeds	a.	2122	2322	2355	0959	1028	...	1058	1128	1158	1228	...	1258	1328	1359	...	1428	1500	1528	hour until	2158	2258	2348

f – Arrives 1834.
* – Arrivals in York may vary ± 3 minutes.

176 PETERBOROUGH - LINCOLN - DONCASTER

2nd class EM

km		Ⓐ	Ⓐ	Ⓐ	ⒶR	Ⓐ	Ⓐ	Ⓐ	Ⓐ	Ⓐ	Ⓐ	Ⓐ	Ⓐ	Ⓐ	Ⓐ	Ⓐ	ⒶR	Ⓐ	⑥	⑥	⑥	⑥	⑥
0	**Peterborough** 180 d.		0632	0731	0832	1028	1100	1226	1321	1416	1510	1626	1710	1818	1926	2000	2104	2310		0634	0734	0836	0936
27	Spalding d.		0652	0751	0852	1048	|	1246	1341	1440f	1530	1646	1730	1838	1946	|	2124	2332		0656	0756	0856	0956
57	Sleaford d.		0714	0813	0918	1117	|	1316	1406	1506	1552	1708	1753	1906f	2008	|	2146	|		0718	0819	0918	1018
91	**Lincoln** 178 180 d.		0743	0845	0948	1148	1202	1349	1435	1536	1621	1740	1823	1938	2037	2103	2215	0016		0747	0851	0947	1049
117	Gainsborough Lea Road 178 d.		...	0907	...	1209	...	1414f	...	...	...	1801	...	1959	...	...	...	...		...	0912	...	1110
151	**Doncaster** a.		...	0934	...	1241	...	1442	...	...	...	1826	...	2025	...	...	...	...		...	0937	...	1136

	⑥	⑥	⑥	⑥	⑥	⑥	⑥	⑥	⑥
Peterborough 180 d.	1100	1202	1358	1528	1642	1829	2000	2050	...
Spalding d.	|	1222	1418	1548	1702	1849	|	2110	...
Sleaford d.	|	1244	1440	1610	1724	1911	|	2132	2218
Lincoln 178 180 d.	1201	1315	1512	1642	1754	1944f	2103	2202	2247
Gainsborough Lea Road 178 d.	...	1336	1533	...	...	2006	...	...	...
Doncaster a.	...	1403	1600	...	...	2032	...	...	...

	Ⓐ	Ⓐ	ⒶR	Ⓐ	Ⓐ	Ⓐ	Ⓐ	Ⓐ
Doncaster d.		...	...	...	0947	...	...	1247
Gainsborough Lea Road 178 d.		...	...	...	1011	...	...	1311
Lincoln 178 180 d.		0612	0709	0822	1035	1142	1234	1335
Sleaford d.		0641	0739	0851	1104	1211	1303	1404
Spalding d.		0701	0759	0912	1124	1231	1323	1424
Peterborough 180 a.		0721	0819	0933	1145	1254	1343	1444

	Ⓐ	Ⓐ	Ⓐ	Ⓐ	Ⓐ	Ⓐ	Ⓐ	Ⓐ	Ⓐ	⑥	⑥	⑥R	⑥	⑥	⑥	⑥	⑥	⑥	⑥	⑥	⑥	⑥	⑥
Doncaster d.	...	1454	...	...	...	...	1847	...	2049		...	...	...	0945	...	...	1146	...	1415	1615	...	...	2046
Gainsborough Lea Road 178 d.	...	1518	...	...	...	...	1911	...	2113		...	...	...	1009	...	...	1210	...	1439	1639	...	...	2110
Lincoln 178 180 d.	1434	1542	1633	1727	1750	1835	1936	2025	2137		0610	0718	0807	1031	1033	1127	1235	1404	1502	1704	1934	2025	2134
Sleaford d.	1503	1611	1708f	|	1820	1905	2009	|	2207		0639	0748	0837	...	1103	|	1304	1434	1532	1736	2003	|	2203
Spalding d.	1523	1631	1728	|	1839	1925	2029	|	2227		0659	0808	0857	...	1123	|	1324	1454	1552	1756	2023	|	...
Peterborough 180 a.	1546	1651	1748	1825	1859	1945	2051	2125	2248		0719	0827	0917	...	1143	1229	1344	1514	1611	1816	2045	2125	...

N – From Nottingham (Table **184**). R – To/from Newark North Gate (Table **189**). f – Arrives 4–5 minutes earlier.

177 HULL - BRIDLINGTON - SCARBOROUGH

2nd class NT

km		⚒	⚒	⚒	⚒A	⚒A	⚒A	★	⚒A	⚒A	⚒	⑦	⑦	⑦A	⑦A	⑦A	⑦A	⑦A	⑦A	⑦A	⑦A	⑦A	⑦A	⑦A
0	**Hull** △ d.		0533	0639	0722	0821	0921		1821	1923	2216		0834	1003	1048	1157	1306	1350	1446	1600	1650	1759	1906	2047
13	Beverley △ d.		|	0653	0736	0837	0935		1835	1937	2230		0848	1019	1102	1213	1320	1407	1502	1616	1707	1815	1920	2101
31	Driffield △ d.		|	0707	0750	0849	0947	and	1847	1949	2244		0904	1034	1117	1228	1335	1422	1517	1631	1722	1830	1935	2116
50	**Bridlington** △ a.		0608	0725	0807	0904	1003	hourly	1903	2004	2301		0920	1051	1134	1246	1352	1439	1535	1649	1740	1848	1952	2133
50	**Bridlington** d.		0609	0730	0809	0905	1003	until	1903	2005	...		0921	1053	1134	1253	1352	1444	1540	1653	1744	1852	1952	...
71	Filey d.		0629	0752	0830	0926	1025		1925	2026	...		0943	1117	1156	1317	1416	1516f	1616r	1717	1816f	1916	2016	...
87	**Scarborough** a.		0646	0810	0847	0943	1042		1942	2043	...		1002	1138	1215	1334	1433	1533	1633	1734	1833	1933	2033	...

	⚒	⚒A	⚒A	⚒B	⚒A	★	⚒A	ⒶA	⑥A		⚒A	⑥	Ⓐ	⑦	ⒶA	⑦	⑦A		⑦A	⑦A	⑦	⑦	⑦
Scarborough d.		0653	...	0815	0901		1801	1900	1900	...	2000	2113	2118		...	1056	1201		1901	2001	...	...	2126
Filey d.		0708	...	0830	0916		1817	1915	1915	...	2017	2128	2133		...	1111	1216		1916	2016	...	...	2141
Bridlington a.		0730	...	0852	0940	and	1840	1938	1939	...	2040	2151	2155		...	1133	1239	and	1939	2039	...	...	2204
Bridlington △ d.		0734	0839	0853	0940	hourly	1840	1938	1940	...	2040	2156	2156		0941	1134	1240	hourly	1940	2040	2124	2144	2204
Driffield △ d.		0750	0852	0909	0953	until	1856	1951	1953	...	2054	2211	2211		0956	1149	1255	until	1955	2055	2139	2157	2220
Beverley △ d.		0805	0905	0923	1006		1908	2004	2005	...	2106	2226	2226		1013	1204	1310		2010	2110	2154	2209	2234
Hull △ a.		0820	0920	0939	1021		1923	2019	2022	...	2121	2241	2241		1026	1220	1325		2025	2125	2210	2225	2250

A – From/to Sheffield (Table **192**).
B – To/from York (Table **179**).
f – Arrives 8–9 minutes earlier.
r – Arrives 1602.
★ – Timings may vary ± 2 minutes.
△ – Additional trains Hull - Bridlington and v.v.:
From Hull on ⚒ at 0558, 0613, 0744, 0800, 0900, 1001, 1101 **B**, 1159 **B**, 1301 **B**, 1359 **B**, 1500 **B**, 1559 **B**, 1701 **B**, 1734, 1801 **B**, 1900 **B**, 2000 **B**, 2022, 2100 Ⓐ **B**, 2116 ⑥; on ⑦ at 1726, 1946 **A**.
From Bridlington at 0645, 0705, 0759, 0910, 1000 **B**, 1100 **B**, 1200 **B**, 1256 **B**, 1400 **B**, 1500 **B**, 1600 **B**, 1700 **B**, 1800 **B**, 1825, 1900 **B**, 2000 **B**, 2058 **B**, 2137, 2233, 2306; on ⑦ at 1823.

178 LINCOLN and CLEETHORPES - SHEFFIELD

2nd class NT

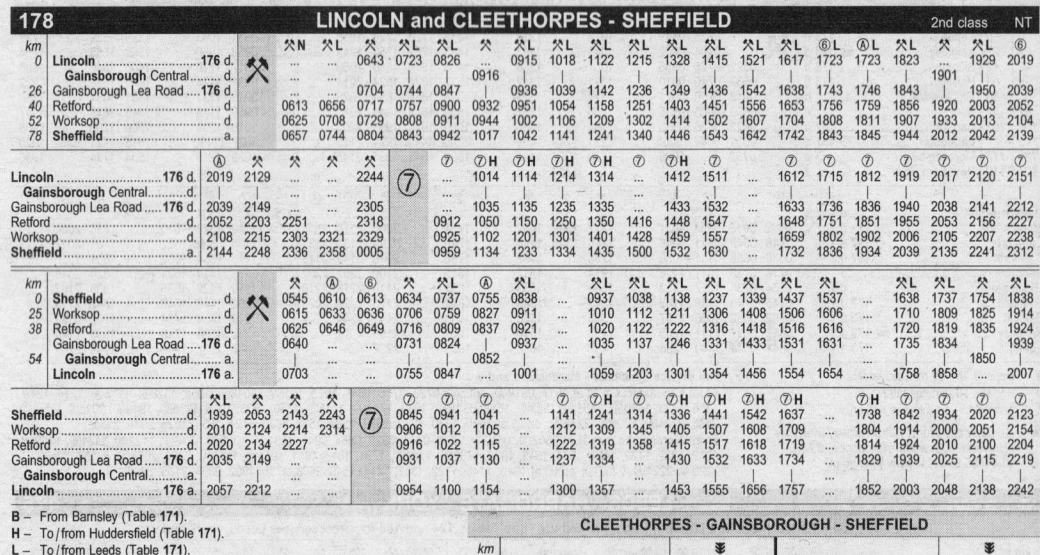

km		⚒	⚒N	⚒L	⚒	⚒L	⚒L	⚒	⚒L	⚒L	⚒L	⚒L	⚒L	⚒L	⚒L	⚒L	⑥L	ⒶL	⚒L	⚒	⚒L	⑥
0	**Lincoln** 176 d.		...	...	0643	0723	0826	...	0915	1018	1122	1215	1328	1415	1521	1617	1723	1723	1823	...	1929	2019
	Gainsborough Central d.		...	...	|	|	|	0916	|	|	|	|	|	|	|	|	|	|	|	1901	|	|
26	Gainsborough Lea Road 176 d.		...	...	0704	0744	0847	|	0936	1039	1142	1236	1349	1436	1542	1638	1743	1746	1843	|	1950	2039
40	Retford d.		0613	0656	0717	0757	0900	0932	0951	1054	1158	1251	1403	1451	1556	1653	1756	1759	1856	1920	2003	2052
52	Worksop d.		0625	0708	0729	0808	0911	0944	1002	1106	1209	1302	1414	1502	1607	1704	1808	1811	1907	1933	2013	2104
78	**Sheffield** a.		0657	0744	0804	0843	0942	1017	1042	1141	1241	1340	1446	1543	1642	1742	1843	1845	1944	2012	2042	2139

	Ⓐ	⚒	⚒	⚒	⚒	⑦	⑦	⑦H	⑦H	⑦H	⑦H		⑦H	⑦		⑦	⑦	⑦	⑦	⑦	⑦	⑦
Lincoln 176 d.	2019	2129	...	...	2244		...	1014	1114	1214	1314	...	1412	1511	...	1612	1715	1812	1919	2017	2120	2151
Gainsborough Central d.	|	|	...	...	|		...	|	|	|	|	...	|	|	...	|	|	|	|	|	|	|
Gainsborough Lea Road 176 d.	2039	2149	...	...	2305		...	1035	1135	1235	1335	...	1433	1532	...	1633	1736	1836	1940	2038	2141	2212
Retford d.	2052	2203	2251	...	2318		0912	1050	1150	1250	1350	1416	1448	1547	...	1648	1751	1851	1955	2053	2156	2227
Worksop d.	2108	2215	2303	2321	2329		0925	1102	1201	1301	1401	1428	1459	1557	...	1659	1802	1902	2006	2105	2207	2238
Sheffield a.	2144	2248	2336	2358	0005		0959	1134	1233	1334	1435	1500	1532	1630	...	1732	1836	1934	2039	2135	2241	2312

km		⚒	⚒	Ⓐ	⑥	⚒	⚒L	Ⓐ	⚒L		⚒L	⚒L	⚒L	⚒L	⚒L	⚒L	⚒L		⚒L	⚒L	⚒	⚒L
0	**Sheffield** d.		0545	0610	0613	0634	0737	0755	0838	...	0937	1038	1138	1237	1339	1437	1537	...	1638	1737	1754	1838
25	Worksop d.		0615	0633	0636	0706	0759	0827	0911	...	1010	1112	1211	1306	1408	1506	1606	...	1710	1809	1825	1914
38	Retford d.		0625	0646	0649	0716	0809	0837	0921	...	1020	1122	1222	1316	1418	1516	1616	...	1720	1819	1835	1924
	Gainsborough Lea Road 176 d.		0640	...	...	0731	0824	|	0937	...	1035	1137	1246	1331	1433	1531	1631	...	1735	1834	|	1939
54	**Gainsborough Central** a.		|	...	...	|	|	0852	|	...	|	|	|	|	|	|	|	...	|	|	1850	|
	Lincoln 176 a.		0703	...	...	0755	0847	...	1001	...	1059	1203	1301	1354	1456	1554	1654	...	1758	1858	...	2007

	⚒L	⚒	⚒	⚒	⑦	⑦	⑦	⑦		⑦	⑦H	⑦	⑦H	⑦H	⑦H	⑦H		⑦H	⑦	⑦	⑦	⑦
Sheffield d.	1939	2053	2143	2243		0845	0941	1041	...	1141	1241	1314	1336	1441	1542	1637	...	1738	1842	1934	2020	2123
Worksop d.	2010	2124	2214	2314		0906	1012	1105	...	1212	1309	1345	1405	1507	1608	1709	...	1804	1914	2000	2051	2154
Retford d.	2020	2134	2227	...		0916	1022	1115	...	1222	1319	1358	1415	1517	1618	1719	...	1814	1924	2010	2100	2204
Gainsborough Lea Road 176 d.	2035	2149	...	...		0931	1037	1130	...	1237	1334	...	1430	1532	1633	1734	...	1829	1939	2025	2115	2219
Gainsborough Central a.	|	|	...	...		|	|	|	...	|	|	...	|	|	|	|	...	|	|	|	|	|
Lincoln 176 a.	2057	2212	...	...		0954	1100	1154	...	1300	1357	...	1453	1555	1656	1757	...	1852	2003	2048	2138	2242

B – From Barnsley (Table **171**).
H – To/from Huddersfield (Table **171**).
L – To/from Leeds (Table **171**).
N – To Nottingham (Table **171**).
r – Arrives 1234.
t – Arrives 1218.
❖ – Service temporarily withdrawn.

CLEETHORPES - GAINSBOROUGH - SHEFFIELD

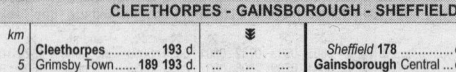

km			❖	
0	**Cleethorpes** 193 d.	...	...	...
5	Grimsby Town 189 193 d.	...	...	...
28	Barnetby 189 193 d.	...	...	...
34	Brigg d.	...	...	...
61	**Gainsborough Central** a.	...	...	...
114	*Sheffield 178* a.	...	...	...

		❖	
Sheffield 178 d.	...	...	...
Gainsborough Central d.	...	...	...
Brigg d.	...	...	...
Barnetby 189 193 d.	...	...	...
Grimsby Town 189 193 d.	...	...	...
Cleethorpes 193 a.	...	...	...

179 HULL - YORK

2nd class NT

km		⚒	⚒	Ⓐ	⑥	⚒	⚒B	⚒S	⚒B	⚒B	⚒B	ⒶB	⑥B	⚒B	⚒B	⚒B	⚒B	⚒B	⚒B	ⒶB	⑥B	⚒B	Ⓐ	⑦	⑦	⑦
0	**Hull** 181 189 d.		0545	0619	0622	0750	0850	0949	1050	1150	1250	1346	1349	1450	1550	1650	1750	1850	1950	2050	2050	2148	...		0831	1039
50	Selby 181 189 d.		0627	0657	0659	0830	0930	1027	1129	1227	1330	1423	1429	1527	1627	1730	1832	1931	2027	2132	2132	2232	2345		0908	1114
84	**York** a.		0659	0731	0731	0902	1002	1103	1204	1249	1400	1444	1450	1602	1650	1801	1907	2002	2101	2204	2210	2303f	0008		0942	1145

	⑦	⑦	⑦	⑦	⑦	⑦	⑦	⑦	⑦	⑦	⑦
Hull 181 189 d.	1131	1234	1335	1421	1535	1635	1735	1835	1935	2021	...
Selby 181 189 d.	1208	1310	1410	1456	1610	1710	1810	1910	2010	2101	2244
York a.	1229	1341	1429	1525	1642	1743	1837	1943	2040	2126	2315

	⚒	⚒	⚒	⑥	Ⓐ	⚒	⚒B	⚒B	⚒B	⚒B
York d.		0536	0615	0730	0730	0845	0945	1045	1145	1242
Selby 181 189 d.		0558	0650	0802	0803	0914	1014	1114	1214	1315
Hull 181 189 a.		0629	0738	0850	0853	0954	1054	1153	1254	1355

	⑥B	ⒶB	⚒B	⚒B	⚒B	⚒B	⚒B	ⒶB	⑥	⚒	⚒	⑦	⑦	⑦	⑦	⑦	⑦	⑦	⑦	⑦	⑦	⑦	⑦	⑦	⑦	⑦
York d.	1343	1345	1443	1546	1644	1745	1845	1941	1941	2144	2247		0851	1001	1049	1152	1250	1351	1453	1551	1651	1751	1849	1955	2052	2151
Selby 181 189 d.	1413	1415	1515g	1618	1713	1815	1914	2011	2011	2214	2319		0921	1021	1119	1213	1321	1420	1516	1620	1720	1812	1918	2018	2114	2222
Hull 181 189 a.	1454	1454	1554	1657	1756	1855	1954	2053	2054	2253	0004		0958	1055	1158	1247	1355	1454	1553	1655	1754	1846	1952	2054	2157	...

B – To/from Bridlington (Table **177**). S – From Scarborough (Table **177**). f – Arrives 2255 on Ⓐ. g – Arrives 1510.

GR Most services convey 🍷 LONDON - LEEDS, YORK, NEWCASTLE and EDINBURGH 180

km			⚒	⚒	⑥	Ⓐ	⚒A	⚒	⑥	⑥	Ⓐ	⑥	Ⓐ	⚒	⚒	⚒	⚒	⚒	Ⓐ	⑥	⚒	⚒	⚒	⚒	⚒	⚒
0	**London** Kings Cross 181/2/3/5 d.		...	...	...	...	...	0555	...	0615	0615	0630	0633	0700	0703	0706	0730	0733	0800	0800	0803	0806	0830	0833	0900	0903
44	Stevenage 185 d.	⚒	...	...	...	...	...	0617	...	0639	0638	0652	0655	|	|	0728	|	0756	|	|	|	|	|	0855	|	|
123	**Peterborough** 185 176 d.		...	...	...	...	...	0648	...	0710	0708	0723	0726	0748	0751	0759	0818	|	|	|	0851	0854	0918	|	0948	0952
170	Grantham 181 d.		...	...	...	...	...	0707	...	0730	0728	0742	0745	|	|	0818	|	0842	|	|	|	0916	|	0941	|	|
193	Newark North Gate 189 d.		...	...	...	...	...	0719	...	0742	0741	|	|	|	|	0832	0846	|	|	|	|	0929	0946	|	|	|
219	**Lincoln** 189 176 a.		...	...	...	...	...	|	...	|	|	|	|	|	|	|	|	|	|	|	|	0956	|	|	|	|
223	Retford 181 d.		...	...	...	...	...	0734	...	0757	0757	|	|	|	|	0847	|	|	|	|	|	...	|	|	|	|
251	**Doncaster** 181 182 d.		...	...	0608	0610	...	0749	...	0813	0812	0818	0818	|	0842	0903	0911	0915	|	|	0943	...	1011	1014	|	1042
283	Wakefield Westgate 124 a.		...	...	|	|	...	0806	...	|	|	0834	0834	|	0859	|	|	0931	|	|	0959	...	|	1031	|	1059
299	**Leeds** 124 175 188 a.		...	...	|	|	0708	0823	...	|	|	0852	0852	|	0916	|	|	0945	|	|	1016	...	|	1047	|	1116
328	Harrogate 175 a.		...	...	|	|	|	▬	...	|	|	...	...	|	...	|	|	1024	|	|	...	...	|	...	|	...
303	**York** 124 183 188 d.		...	...	0635f	0635f	0735	...	...	0835	0835	...	...	0855	...	0930	0935	...	0954f	0955	...	...	1035	...	1054	...
351	Northallerton 183 188 d.		...	...	0655	0655	|	...	...	0856	0855	...	...	|	...	...	|	...	|	|	...	...	1055	...	|	...
374	Darlington 124 188 d.		...	...	0709	0709	0803	...	...	0910	0909	...	...	0924	...	...	1006	...	1023	1024	...	...	1109	...	1123	...
409	Durham 124 188 d.		...	...	0727	0727	0821	...	...	0927	0927	...	...	|	...	...	1025	...	|	|	...	...	1127	...	|	...
432	**Newcastle** 124 188 a.		...	...	0741	0740	0834	Ⓐ	...	0940	0940	...	...	0951	...	...	1039	...	1050	1051	...	...	1140	...	1151	...
	Newcastle 124 188 d.		0622	0704	0744	0742	0847	0856	0911	0946	0946	...	...	0953	...	...	1041	...	1052	1054	...	...	1144	...	1152	...
488	Alnmouth 124 a.		0650	0737	0809	0808	|	|	0944	|	|	...	...	|	...	...	1107	...	|	|	...	...	|	...	|	...
540	Berwick upon Tweed 124 a.		0715	0759	0832	0831	0935	0940	1005	|	|	...	...	1036	...	...	|	...	1135	1137	...	...	|	...	1236	...
632	**Edinburgh** Waverley 124 188 a.		0807	0855	0920	0923	1023	1030	1058	1109	1112	...	...	1128c	...	...	1211	...	1221	1226	...	...	1312	...	1327c	...

	Ⓐ	⑥	⚒	⚒	⚒A	⚒	⚒	⚒	⚒	⑥	Ⓐ	⚒	⚒	⚒	⚒	⚒B	⚒	⚒	⚒	⚒	Ⓐ	⑥	⚒	⑥	Ⓐ	⚒
London Kings Cross 181/2/3/5 d.	0906	0906	0930	0933	1000	1003	1006	1030	1033	1100	1100	1103	1106	1130	1133	1200	1203	1206	1230	1233	1300	1300	1303	1306	1306	1330
Stevenage 185 d.	0928	0929	|	0956	|	|	1028	|	1056	|	|	|	1128	|	1156	|	|	1228	|	1256	|	|	|	1328	1328	|
Peterborough 185 176 d.	0959	1001	1018	|	|	1052	1100	1118	|	|	|	1152	1159	1218	|	|	1252	1300	1318	|	1348	1348	1352	1358	1401	1418
Grantham 181 d.	1020	1021	|	1041	|	|	1120	|	1141	|	|	|	1219	|	1242	|	|	1321	|	1341	|	|	|	1416	1422	|
Newark North Gate 189 d.	1033	1035	1046	|	|	|	1136	1146	|	|	|	|	1232	1246	|	|	|	1337	1346	|	|	|	|	1428	1435	1446
Lincoln 189 176 a.	|	|	|	|	|	|	1202	|	|	|	|	|	|	|	|	|	|	1402	|	|	|	|	|	|	|	|
Retford 181 d.	1049	1050	|	|	|	|	...	|	|	|	|	|	1247	|	|	|	|	...	|	|	|	|	|	1447f	1451	|
Doncaster 181 182 d.	1105	1106	1110	1115	|	1143	...	1211	1214	|	|	1242	1305	1311	1315	|	1343	...	1411	1414	|	|	1443	1505	1506	1511
Wakefield Westgate 124 a.	|	|	|	1131	|	1159	...	|	1230	|	|	1259	|	|	1330	|	1359	...	|	1430	|	|	1459	|	|	|
Leeds 124 175 188 a.	|	|	|	1146	|	1216	...	|	1247	|	|	1316	|	|	1345	|	1416	...	|	1448	|	|	1516	|	|	|
Harrogate 175 a.	|	|	|	1224	|	...	...	|	...	|	|	...	|	|	1424	|	...	...	|	...	|	|	▬	|	|	|
York 124 183 188 d.	1130	1130	1135	...	1155	...	...	1235	...	1254	1255	...	1330	1335	...	1355f	...	...	1435	...	1455	1455	...	1529	1530	1535
Northallerton 183 188 d.	▬	...	|	...	|	...	...	1255	...	|	|	...	...	|	...	|	...	...	1455	...	|	|	...	▬	...	1555
Darlington 124 188 d.	...	...	1206	...	1224	...	...	1309	...	1323	1324	...	...	1408	...	1424	...	...	1509	...	1523	1523	...	...	...	1609
Durham 124 188 d.	...	...	1223	...	|	...	...	1327	...	|	|	...	...	1426	...	|	...	...	1527	...	|	|	...	...	...	1626
Newcastle 124 188 a.	⚒	...	1237	...	1252	...	...	1339	...	1349	1352	...	...	1440	...	1450	...	...	1540	...	1549	1549	⑥	Ⓐ	...	1639
Newcastle 124 188 d.	1206	...	1240	...	1254	...	...	1343	...	1352	1354	...	...	1442	...	1455	...	...	1545	...	1552	1559	1614	1614	...	1641
Alnmouth 124 a.	1241	...	1307	...	|	...	...	|	...	|	|	...	...	1508	...	|	...	...	|	...	|	|	1647	1647	...	1710
Berwick upon Tweed 124 a.	1301	...	|	...	1337	...	...	|	...	1434	1437	...	...	|	...	1538	...	...	|	...	1634	1641	1708	1708	...	|
Edinburgh Waverley 124 188 a.	1356	...	1412	...	1426	...	...	1509	...	1527	1522	...	...	1615	...	1626	...	...	1714a	...	1723	1726	1800	1804	...	1816

	⚒	⚒A	⚒	⚒	⚒	⚒	ⒶK	⑥	Ⓐ	⑥	Ⓐ	⑥	ⒶQ	⚒C	⚒	⑥	ⒶA	⚒	⚒	⚒	⚒G	⑥	Ⓐ	⚒	ⒶH	⑥H
London Kings Cross 181/2/3/5 d.	1333	1400	1403	1406	1430	1433	1500	1500	1503	1503	1506	1506	1525	1530	1533	1600	1600	1603	1606	1630	1633	1700	1700	1703	1718	1718
Stevenage 185 d.	1355	|	|	1428	|	1455	|	|	|	|	1528	1528	|	|	1556	|	|	|	1628	|	1655	|	|	|	|	|
Peterborough 185 176 d.	|	|	1451	1459	1518	|	|	|	1551	1554	1558	1559	|	1618	|	|	|	1652	1700	1718	|	|	|	1751	1810	1810
Grantham 181 d.	1442	|	|	1520	|	1541	|	|	|	|	1617	1618	|	|	1642	|	|	|	1721	|	1742	|	|	|	1829	1829
Newark North Gate 189 d.	|	|	|	1534	1546	|	|	|	|	|	1630	1632	|	1646	|	|	|	|	1737	1746	|	|	|	|	1841	1841
Lincoln 189 176 a.	|	|	|	1601	|	|	|	|	|	|	|	|	|	|	|	|	|	|	1802	|	|	|	|	|	|	|
Retford 181 d.	|	|	|	...	|	|	|	|	|	|	1645	1651f	|	|	|	|	|	|	...	|	1805	|	|	|	|	|
Doncaster 181 182 d.	1515	|	1543	...	1610	1615	|	|	1643	1644	1705f	1707	|	1710	1716	|	|	1741	...	1811	1820	|	|	1843	1908	1904
Wakefield Westgate 124 a.	1531	|	1559	...	|	1632	|	|	1659	1700	|	|	|	|	1734	|	|	1759	...	|	1836	|	|	1900	...	...
Leeds 124 175 188 a.	1545	|	1616	...	|	1651	|	|	1716	1716	|	|	|	|	1749	|	|	1816	...	|	1851	|	|	1917	...	...
Harrogate 175 a.	1625	|	...	...	|	...	|	|	...	...	|	|	|	|	1831	|	|	...	...	|	...	|	|	...	...	...
York 124 183 188 d.	...	1556	...	...	1635	...	1656	1654	...	...	1728	1730	1726f	1735	...	1756f	1756	...	...	1835	...	1855	1857g	...	...	...
Northallerton 183 188 d.	...	|	...	...	1655	...	|	|	...	...	...	...	...	1755	...	|	|	...	...	1856	...	|	|	...	...	...
Darlington 124 188 d.	...	1624	...	...	1708	...	1726	1724	...	...	...	...	...	1809	...	1825	1824	...	...	1910	...	1927	1926	...	...	...
Durham 124 188 d.	...	|	...	...	1725	...	|	|	...	...	...	...	...	1827	...	|	|	...	...	1928	...	|	|	...	...	...
Newcastle 124 188 a.	...	1651	...	...	1740	...	1752	1750	...	...	...	...	...	1841	...	1853	1850	...	...	1941	...	1953	1952	...	...	...
Newcastle 124 188 d.	...	1658	...	...	1743	...	1755	1753	...	...	...	...	...	1843	...	1857	1854	...	...	1945	...	1956	1957	...	...	...
Alnmouth 124 a.	...	|	...	...	|	...	|	|	...	...	...	...	...	1909	...	|	|	...	...	|	...	|	|	...	...	...
Berwick upon Tweed 124 a.	...	1743	...	...	|	...	1838	1836	...	...	...	...	...	|	...	1940	1936	...	...	|	...	2038	2039	...	...	...
Edinburgh Waverley 124 188 a.	...	1830	...	...	1911	...	1922	1929	...	...	...	...	...	2015	...	2025	2020	...	...	2114	...	2123	2124	...	...	...

	Ⓐ	⑥	Ⓐ	⑥	Ⓐ	Ⓐ	⑥	⑥F	ⒶF	⑥	Ⓐ	Ⓐ	⑥	ⒶG	⑥	Ⓐ	⑥	⚒	⚒	①–④	⑤	⑥	⚒P	ⒶD	⑥	Ⓐ
London Kings Cross 181/2/3/5 d.	1730	1730	1733	1733	1748	1800	1800	1803	1803	1818	1818	1830	1830	1833	1833	1900	1900	1903	1906	1930	1930	1930	1933	2000	2000	2003
Stevenage 185 d.	|	|	1755	1755	|	|	|	|	|	|	|	|	|	1855	1856	|	|	|	1928	|	|	|	1955	|	|	|
Peterborough 185 176 d.	1819	1818	|	|	1838	|	|	1851	1855f	1906	1910	1918	1918	|	|	|	|	1951	2000	2018	2018	2018	|	|	2048	2052
Grantham 181 d.	|	|	1842	1841	1906	|	|	|	|	1926	1929	|	|	1943	1943	|	|	|	2021	|	|	|	2041	|	|	|
Newark North Gate 189 d.	1847	1848	|	|	|	|	|	1922	1924	|	|	1947	1947	|	|	|	|	|	2037	2046	2046	2046	|	|	2116	2120
Lincoln 189 176 a.	|	|	|	|	|	|	|	|	|	|	|	|	|	|	|	|	|	|	2103	|	|	|	|	|	|	|
Retford 181 d.	|	|	|	|	1929	|	|	|	|	1949	|	|	|	2006	2007	|	|	|	...	|	|	|	|	|	|	|
Doncaster 181 182 d.	|	|	1916	1916	1944	|	|	1950	1950	2008	|	2012	2012	2022	2022	|	|	2042	...	2111	2111	2112	2114	|	2141	2145
Wakefield Westgate 124 a.	|	|	1935	1932	2000	|	|	2006	2006	2024	|	|	|	2038	2037	|	|	2059	...	|	|	|	2130	|	|	2204
Leeds 124 175 188 a.	|	|	1950	1950	2017	|	|	2021	2021	2041	|	|	|	2054	2055	|	|	2116	...	|	|	|	2147	|	|	2221
Harrogate 175 a.	|	|	2030	...	...	|	|	▬	▬	...	|	|	|	...	2135	|	|	...	...	|	|	|	...	|	|	...
York 124 183 188 d.	1931	1931	...	...	...	1952f	1954	...	...	...	2019	2035	2035	...	...	2057	2054f	...	...	2134	2134	2135	...	2153f	2205	...
Northallerton 183 188 d.	|	|	...	...	...	|	|	...	...	...	2039	|	2055	...	...	|	|	...	...	2154	2154	2155	...	|	|	...
Darlington 124 188 d.	2000	2000	...	...	...	2022	2024	...	...	...	2053	2106	2109	...	...	2126	2125	...	...	2208	2208	2209	...	2222	2234	...
Durham 124 188 d.	2017	2017	...	...	...	|	|	...	...	...	2111	2125	2127	...	...	|	|	...	...	2226	2226	2227	...	2240	2252	...
Newcastle 124 188 a.	2031	2030	...	...	...	2048	2050	⑥	Ⓐ	...	2125	2139	2142	...	...	2153	2153	...	...	2241	2241	2242	...	2254	2307	...
Newcastle 124 188 d.	2033	2034	...	...	...	2051	2055	2059	2101	...	...	2142	...	...	...	2155	...	...	...	...	2241	...	...	...	...	...
Alnmouth 124 a.	2059	|	...	...	...	|	2123	2132	2134	...	...	2210	...	...	...	|	...	...	...	...	2310	...	...	...	...	...
Berwick upon Tweed 124 a.	|	|	...	...	...	2134	2147	2153	2155	...	...	|	...	...	...	2238	...	...	...	...	2334	...	...	...	...	...
Edinburgh Waverley 124 188 a.	2208	2159	...	...	...	2219	2238	2239	2248	...	...	2316	...	...	...	2324	...	...	...	...	0018	...	...	...	...	...

	⑥	⑥	Ⓐ	⑥	Ⓐ	Ⓐ	⑥	Ⓐ	Ⓐ	Ⓐ		⑦	⑦	⑦	⑦	⑦	⑦	⑦	⑦	⑦	⑦	⑦	⑦	⑦A	⑦	⑦
London Kings Cross 181/2/3/5 d.	2003	2030	2033	2100	2100	2133	2200	2200	2300	2333		...	...	...	...	...	...	0848	0900	0903	0922	0930	0933	1000	1003	1007
Stevenage 185 d.	|	|	2055	|	2122	2156	|	|	|	|	⑦	...	...	...	...	...	...	|	|	0925	|	|	0956	|	|	|
Peterborough 185 176 d.	2052	2119	2126	2148	2153	2228	2248	2248	2344s	0016s		...	...	...	...	...	...	|	|	0955	1010	1018	1027	|	1051	1057
Grantham 181 d.	2112	2139	2146	|	|	2248	2307	2308	0012s	0045s		...	...	...	...	...	...	|	|	1014	|	|	1047	|	|	1116
Newark North Gate 189 d.	|	2152	2159	|	2221	2302	2320	2322	0025s	0058s		...	...	...	...	...	...	|	|	1028	|	|	1104f	|	|	1130
Lincoln 189 176 a.	|	|	|	|	|	|	|	|	|	|		...	...	...	...	...	...	|	|	|	|	|	1129	|	|	|
Retford 181 d.	|	2208	|	|	|	2317	2335	|	|	|		...	...	...	...	...	...	|	|	|	|	1056	...	|	|	|
Doncaster 181 182 d.	2145	2224	2224	|	2249f	2337	2350	2352	0053s	0125s		...	...	...	...	...	0937	|	|	1052	1058	1112	...	|	1143f	1155
Wakefield Westgate 124 a.	2204	2240	2240	|	|	2353	0006	|	|	|		...	...	...	...	...	|	|	|	1108	|	|	...	|	|	1211
Leeds 124 175 188 a.	2221	2257	2257	|	|	0010	0023	|	|	0220		...	...	...	...	0830	|	|	|	1122	|	|	...	|	|	1228
Harrogate 175 a.	...	...	...	|	|	...	...	|	|	...		...	...	...	...	|	|	|	|	1200	|	|	...	|	|	...
York 124 183 188 d.	...	...	...	2258	2312	...	...	0020f	0129	...		...	...	...	...	0900	1000	1036	1051	▬	1121	1135	...	1155f	1208f	...
Northallerton 183 188 d.	...	...	...	2319	2343	...	...	0049s	...	...		...	...	...	...	0921	|	|	|	...	|	|	...	|	|	...
Darlington 124 188 d.	...	...	...	2333	2357	...	...	0102s	...	...		...	...	...	...	0935	1029	1105	1119	...	1151	1204	...	1224	1237	...
Durham 124 188 d.	...	...	...	2351	0015	...	...	0120s	...	...		...	...	...	...	0954	1047	1123	|	...	1209	1222	...	|	1255	...
Newcastle 124 188 a.	...	...	...	0005	0044	...	...	0153	...	...		...	...	...	...	1007	1100	1136	1147	⑦	1226	1235	...	1251	1308	...
Newcastle 124 188 d.	...	...	...	...	...	...	...	...	...	...		0845	0915	0919	0945	1010	1102	1139	1152	1156	...	1238	...	1253	1311	...
Alnmouth 124 a.	...	...	...	...	...	...	...	...	...	...		0913	|	0952	1012	1039	|	|	|	1229	...	1303	...	|	|	...
Berwick upon Tweed 124 a.	...	...	...	...	...	...	...	...	...	...		0935	0957	1013	|	1103	1145	|	1234	1250	...	|	...	1337	|	...
Edinburgh Waverley 124 188 a.	...	...	...	...	...	...	...	...	...	...		1027	1047	1103	1112	1158	1231	1308	1318	1347	...	1420	...	1420	1435	...

FOR NOTES SEE PAGE 139 ►►►►

180 LONDON - LEEDS, YORK, NEWCASTLE and EDINBURGH

Most services convey 🍷 GR

	⑦	⑦	⑦	⑦	⑦	⑦	⑦B	⑦	⑦	⑦	⑦	⑦	⑦	⑦	⑦	⑦A	⑦	⑦	⑦	⑦	⑦	⑦	⑦	⑦	⑦	⑦M
London Kings Cross 181/2/3/5 d.	1030	1100	1103	1122	1130	1133	1200	1203	1222	1230	1233	1300	1303	1330	1333	1400	1403	1430	1436	1500	1503	1530	1533	1600	1605	1630
Stevenage 185 d.	|	|	1125	|	|	1155	|	|	|	|	1256	|	1325	|	1356	|	|	|	1457	|	1525	|	1556	|	|	|
Peterborough 185 176 d.	1118	|	1155	|	1218	1225	|	1251	1311	1318	|	|	1356	1418	1427	|	1451	1518	|	|	1555	1619	1627	|	1653	1718
Grantham 181 d.	|	|	1214	1224	|	1244	|	1311	|	|	1343	|	1415	|	1452f	|	1511	|	|	|	1615	1639	1651f	|	1712	|
Newark North Gate 189 d.	1146	|	1228	|	|	1259	|	1324	|	1346	|	|	1429	|	|	|	1524	1546	1555f	|	1628	|	1707	|	1726	1747
Lincoln 189 176 a.	|	|	|	|	|	1325	|	|	|	|	|	|	|	|	|	|	|	|	1622	|	|	|	1732	|	|	|
Retford 181 d.	|	|	|	|	1256	...	|	|	|	|	|	|	|	1456	1520f	|	|	|	...	|	1643	|	...	|	|	|
Doncaster 181 182 d.	1211	|	1252	|	1312	...	|	1350	1359	1411	1420	|	1454	1512	1536	|	1550	1611	...	|	1658	1711	...	|	1752	1811
Wakefield Westgate 124 a.	|	|	1308	|	|	...	|	1406	|	|	1437	|	1510	|	1559	|	1606	|	...	|	1714	|	...	|	1808	|
Leeds 124 175 188 a.	|	|	1324	|	|	...	|	1423	|	|	1454	|	1524	|	1619	|	1623	|	...	|	1728	|	...	|	1826	|
Harrogate 175 a.	|	|	1402	|	|	...	|	...	|	|	...	|	1559	|	...	|	▬	|	...	|	1807	|	...	|	...	|
York 124 183 188 d.	1235	1251f	...	1315	1335	...	1351	...	1421	1434	...	1455	...	1535	...	1553f	...	1634	...	1652f	...	1736f	...	1752f	...	1835
Northallerton 183 188 d.	1255	|	...	1335	|	...	|	...	|	1454	...	|	...	|	...	|	...	1654	...	|	...	|	...	|	...	1855
Darlington 124 188 d.	1309	1320	...	1349	1404	...	1420	...	1450	1508	...	1524	...	1604	...	1622	...	1707	...	1721	...	1805	...	1821	...	1909
Durham 124 188 d.	1327	|	...	1407	1422	...	|	...	1508	1526	...	|	...	1622	...	|	...	1725	...	|	...	1824	...	|	...	1927
Newcastle 124 188 a.	1340	1346	...	1420	1435	...	1447	...	1523	1539	...	1550	...	1635	...	1648	⑦	1739	...	1747	...	1836	...	1847	...	1939
Newcastle 124 188 d.	1342	1349	...	1423	1437	...	1450	...	...	1545	...	1553	...	1638	...	1652	1711	1743	...	1752	...	1842	...	1850	...	1942
Alnmouth 124 a.	|	|	...	|	1502	...	|	...	...	|	...	|	...	1703	...	|	1744	|	...	|	...	1906	...	|	...	|
Berwick upon Tweed 124 a.	|	1431	...	|	|	...	1535	...	...	|	...	1635	...	|	...	1735	1805	|	...	1834	...	|	...	1932	...	|
Edinburgh Waverley 124 188 a.	1508	1516	...	1557	1608	...	1618	...	...	1708	...	1720	...	1808	...	1819	1859	1908	...	1918	...	2010	...	2017	...	2112

	⑦	⑦	⑦	⑦H	⑦	⑦	⑦	⑦	⑦	⑦	⑦F	⑦		⑦	⑦	⑦	⑦G	⑦	⑦	⑦	⑦	⑦	⑦	⑦	⑦	⑦
London Kings Cross 181/2/3/5 d.	1635	1700	1705	1722	1730	1735	1800	1803	1827	1830	1835	1900	...	1903	1906	1930	1935	2000	2005	2035	2100	2105	2135	2200	2205	2235
Stevenage 185 d.	1657	|	|	|	|	1757	|	|	|	|	1857	|	...	|	1928	|	1957	|	|	2057	|	|	2156	|	|	|
Peterborough 185 176 d.	|	|	1753	|	1818	|	1848	1853	|	|	|	|	...	1951	1959	2019	2028	2048	2054	2128	2148	2153	2228	2249	2253	2326s
Grantham 181 d.	1741	|	|	1827	1837	1843	|	|	|	|	1941	|	...	|	2018	|	2047	|	|	2147	|	|	2247	|	2312	2346s
Newark North Gate 189 d.	|	|	1821	1840	|	|	|	1922	|	1946	|	|	...	2019	2034	2048	|	|	|	2201	|	2222	2259	|	2326	2358s
Lincoln 189 176 a.	|	|	|	|	|	|	|	|	|	|	|	|	...	|	2059	|	|	|	|	|	|	|	|	|	|	|
Retford 181 d.	1805	|	|	|	|	|	|	|	|	|	2005	|	...	|	...	|	|	|	2134	|	|	|	2314	|	|	|
Doncaster 181 182 d.	1821	|	1848	1903	1910	1916	|	1949	|	2011	2020	|	...	2044	...	2116f	2121	|	2149	2225	|	2250	2335	2343	2355	0029s
Wakefield Westgate 124 a.	1837	|	1903	...	|	1932	|	2006	|	|	2038	|	...	2102	...	|	2137	|	2205	2241	|	2308	2351	|	|	|
Leeds 124 175 188 a.	1855	|	1919	...	|	1949	|	2021	|	|	2053	|	...	2119	...	|	2152	|	2222	2258	|	2326	0008	|	|	0111
Harrogate 175 a.	...	|	1956	...	|	...	|	2100	|	|	...	|	...	...	...	|	...	|	...	...	|	...	...	|	|	...
York 124 183 188 d.	...	1850	...	...	1937f	...	2000	▬	2025f	2036	...	2053f	...	...	...	2139	...	2156	...	...	2302f	...	...	0012	0020	...
Northallerton 183 188 d.	...	|	...	...	|	...	|	...	|	2056	...	|	...	...	...	|	...	2230	...	...	2337	...	...	0046s	...	...
Darlington 124 188 d.	...	1920	...	...	2007	...	2029	...	2055	2110	...	2122	...	...	...	2222	...	2243	...	...	2350	...	...	0059s	...	...
Durham 124 188 d.	...	|	...	...	2025	...	|	...	2113	2128	...	|	...	...	...	2240	...	2301	...	...	0008	...	...	0117s	...	...
Newcastle 124 188 a.	...	1946	...	...	2038	...	2055	⑦	2128	2141	...	2149	...	...	...	2309	...	2332	...	...	0039	...	...	0149	...	...
Newcastle 124 188 d.	...	1951	...	...	2041	...	2100	2114	...	2145	...	2153	...	...	...	...	...	...	...	...	...	...	...	...	...	...
Alnmouth 124 d.	...	|	...	...	2110	...	|	2147	...	|	...	2221	...	...	...	...	...	...	...	...	...	...	...	...	...	...
Berwick upon Tweed 124 d.	...	2034	...	...	|	...	2142	2208	...	2227	...	2242	...	...	...	...	...	...	...	...	...	...	...	...	...	...
Edinburgh Waverley 124 188 a.	...	2119	...	...	2215	...	2227	2258	...	2312	...	2333	...	...	...	...	...	...	...	...	...	...	...	...	...	...

	⚒	⚒	⚒	Ⓐ	⑥	⚒	⑥	Ⓐ	⚒	⚒	⚒	ⒶJ	⑥	Ⓐ	⑥	⚒	Ⓐ	⑥	Ⓐ	Ⓐ	⑥H	⑥F	ⒶH	ⒶF	⑥	Ⓐ
Edinburgh Waverley 124 188 d.		...	...	...	...	...	...	...	...	...	G	...	...	...	...	...	...	...	...	0540	...	...	...	...	...	...
Berwick upon Tweed 124 d.		...	...	...	...	...	...	...	...	...	...	...	...	...	...	...	...	...	0600	|	...	...	...	...	...	...
Alnmouth 124 d.		...	...	...	...	...	...	...	...	...	...	...	...	...	...	...	...	...	0622	|	...	...	...	...	...	...
Newcastle 124 188 a.		...	...	...	...	...	...	...	...	...	...	...	...	...	...	...	...	...	0652	0702	...	...	...	...	...	←
Newcastle 124 188 d.		...	...	...	...	0445	...	...	0526	...	...	0559	0600	...	...	...	0630	0630	0655	0704	...	...	...	...	0655	0655
Durham 124 188 d.		...	...	...	...	0500	...	...	0539	...	...	0612	0613	...	...	...	0643	0643	→	|	...	...	...	...	0708	0708
Darlington 124 188 d.		...	...	...	...	0517	...	...	0558	...	...	0631	0632	...	...	...	0702	0702	...	|	...	...	...	...	0727	0732j
Northallerton 183 188 d.		...	...	...	...	0528	...	...	0610	...	...	|	|	...	...	...	0714	0714	...	|	...	...	...	...	|	|
York 124 183 185 d.		0440	...	...	...	0600	...	...	0632	...	...	0701	0702	...	...	...	0737	0738	...	|	...	...	...	...	0757	0802
Harrogate 175 d.		|	...	...	...	|	...	...	|	...	...	|	|	...	...	...	|	|	...	|	...	...	...	...	|	|
Leeds 124 175 188 d.		|	0505	0530	0530	|	0605	0605	|	0640	0700	|	|	...	...	0715	|	|	...	|	...	0740	...	0741	|	|
Wakefield Westgate 124 d.		|	0518	0543	0543	|	0618	0618	|	0653	0713	|	|	...	...	0728	|	|	...	|	...	|	...	0754	|	|
Doncaster 181 182 d.		0506	0536	0602	0603	0623	0637	0637	0655	0714	|	|	|	...	...	0747	|	|	...	|	0758	0810	0757	0814	0828	|
Retford 181 d.		|	0550	|	|	|	0652	0651	|	|	|	|	|	...	...	|	|	|	...	|	|	|	|	|	|	0835
Lincoln 189 176 d.		|	|	|	|	|	|	|	|	|	|	|	|	0730	0730	|	|	|	...	|	|	|	|	|	|	|
Newark North Gate 189 d.		0536	0606	0626	0627	0646	0707	0706	|	0738	|	|	|	0758	0759	|	|	|	...	|	0823	0833	0822	0839	|	|
Grantham 181 d.		0548	0617	0638	0640	0658	0719	0719	0727	|	|	|	|	|	|	0819	|	|	...	|	0835	|	0833	|	|	|
Peterborough 185 176 d.		0610	0640	0700	0702	0720	0741	0740	0749	|	|	0813f	0820	0829	0829	|	0845	0850	...	|	0858	0901	|	0908	|	|
Stevenage 185 d.		|	|	|	|	|	|	|	|	|	|	|	|	0858	0900	0905	|	|	...	|	|	|	|	|	|	|
London Kings Cross 181/2/3/5 a.		0701	0731	0750	0753	0810	0831	0831	0840	0853	0901	0909	0910	0923	0923	0931	0936	0939	...	0940	0947	0950	0954	1000	0954	1003

	⑥	Ⓐ	⚒	⑥	ⒶK	⚒	⚒G	⚒	⚒	⚒	Ⓐ	⑥	Ⓐ	⑥	ⒶM	⑥M	⚒	⚒	⑥	Ⓐ	⚒	⚒	⑥	Ⓐ	Ⓐ	⑥
Edinburgh Waverley 124 188 d.	0523	0529	0548	0624	0626	...	...	0655	0730	...	...	...	...	...	0800	0800	0830	...	...	...	...	0900	0930	0930	0933	0933
Berwick upon Tweed 124 d.	0620e	0629	0634	0708	0713	...	...	|	0812	...	...	...	...	...	|	|	0913	...	...	...	...	|	1012	1012	1023	1024
Alnmouth 124 d.	0641	0650	0656	|	|	...	...	|	|	...	...	...	...	...	0901	0901	|	...	...	...	...	|	|	|	1048	1047
Newcastle 124 188 a.	0715	0724	0727	0752	0755	...	...	0824	0855	...	...	...	...	...	0927	0928	0956	...	...	...	...	1024	1056	1055	1122	1121
Newcastle 124 188 d.	▬	▬	0730	0759	0801	...	...	0827	0858	...	...	...	...	...	0930	0930	0959	...	...	...	...	1026	1059	1058	▬	▬
Durham 124 188 d.	...	...	0743	|	|	...	...	0840	|	...	...	...	...	...	0943	0944	|	...	...	...	...	1040	|	|	...	...
Darlington 124 188 d.	...	...	0802	0828	0831	...	...	0859	0927	...	...	...	...	...	1002	1003	1028	...	...	...	...	1100	1127	1128	...	...
Northallerton 183 188 d.	ⒶR	...	|	|	|	...	...	0911	|	...	...	...	...	...	|	|	|	...	...	...	...	1111	|	|	...	⚒
York 124 183 185 d.	0813f	⚒	0832	0858	0901	...	...	0933	0957	...	1002	1002	...	...	1032	1032	1058	...	...	...	...	1133	1158	1158	...	1202
Harrogate 175 d.	|	0737	|	|	|	...	...	|	|	...	|	|	0936	0936	|	|	|	...	...	...	...	|	|	|	⚒	|
Leeds 124 175 188 d.	|	0815	|	|	|	0846	0915	|	|	0945	|	|	1015	1015	|	|	|	1045	...	...	1115	|	|	|	1145	|
Wakefield Westgate 124 d.	|	0830	|	|	|	0858	0928	|	|	0957	|	|	1028	1028	|	|	|	1058	...	...	1128	|	|	|	1158	|
Doncaster 181 182 d.	|	0849	0856	|	|	0919	0947	0956	|	1017	1025	1029	1047	1047	1057	1058	|	1120	...	...	1147	1155	|	|	1218	1225
Retford 181 d.	|	|	|	|	|	|	|	|	|	|	1039	1045	|	|	|	|	|	|	...	...	|	|	|	|	|	1239
Lincoln 189 176 d.	|	|	|	|	|	|	|	|	|	|	|	|	|	|	|	|	|	|	1127	1127	|	|	|	|	|	|
Newark North Gate 189 d.	|	|	0920	|	|	|	|	1020	|	|	1055	1059	|	|	1121	1121	|	|	1159	1156f	|	1219	|	|	|	1255
Grantham 181 d.	|	0921	|	|	|	|	1018	|	|	|	1107	1110	1118	1119	|	|	|	|	1210	1209	1219	|	|	|	|	1307
Peterborough 185 176 d.	|	|	0950	|	|	1009	|	1050	|	1109	1129	1131	|	|	1150	1151	|	1211	1231	1231	|	1247	|	|	1309	1329
Stevenage 185 d.	|	1007	|	|	|	|	1104	|	|	|	1158	1200	1203	1205	|	|	|	|	1300	1300	1305	|	|	|	|	1359
London Kings Cross 181/2/3/5 a.	1022	1031	1041	1049	1052	1101	1131	1139	1150	1204d	1222	1223	1230	1231	1240	1246	1249	1301	1323	1326	1331	1339	1349	1352	1401	1424

	⚒	⚒	⚒A	⚒	⚒	⚒	⚒	⑥B	ⒶB	⚒	Ⓐ	⑥	⚒	Ⓐ	⑥	⚒A	⚒	⚒	⚒	⚒	⚒	⚒	⑥	Ⓐ	⚒	⑥A
Edinburgh Waverley 124 188 d.	...	1000	1030	...	...	...	1100	1130	1130	...	...	...	...	1200	1200	1230	...	...	...	1300	1330	...	...	...	...	1730
Berwick upon Tweed 124 d.	...	|	1112	...	...	...	|	|	|	...	...	...	...	|	|	1313	...	...	...	|	1413	...	...	...	...	1816
Alnmouth 124 d.	...	1100	|	...	...	...	|	|	|	...	...	...	...	1301	1301	|	...	...	...	|	|	...	...	...	...	|
Newcastle 124 188 a.	...	1127	1156	...	...	...	1224	1254	1255	...	...	...	...	1327	1327	1356	...	...	...	1423	1456	...	...	...	...	1900
Newcastle 124 188 d.	...	1129	1158	...	...	...	1226	1257	1258	...	...	...	...	1330	1330	1359	...	...	...	1426	1459	...	...	...	...	1902
Durham 124 188 d.	...	1143	|	...	...	...	1240	|	|	...	...	...	...	1343	1343	|	...	...	...	1440	|	...	...	...	...	|
Darlington 124 188 d.	...	1202	1228	...	...	...	1300	1325	1327	...	...	...	...	1402	1402	1428	...	...	...	1459	1527	...	...	...	...	1932
Northallerton 183 188 d.	...	|	|	...	...	...	1311	|	|	...	...	...	...	|	|	|	...	...	...	1511	|	...	...	...	...	|
York 124 183 185 d.	...	1232	1258	...	...	...	1333	1357	1359	...	1403	1405	...	1432	1432	1458	...	...	...	1533	1557	...	1603	1603	...	2001
Harrogate 175 d.	1136	|	|	...	...	...	|	|	|	...	|	|	1336	|	|	|	...	...	...	|	|	...	|	|	1536	|
Leeds 124 175 188 d.	1215	|	|	1245	...	1315	|	|	|	1345	|	|	1415	|	|	|	1445	...	1515	|	|	1545	|	|	1615	|
Wakefield Westgate 124 d.	1228	|	|	1258	...	1328	|	|	|	1358	|	|	1428	|	|	|	1458	...	1528	|	|	1558	|	|	1628	|
Doncaster 181 182 d.	1247	1255	|	1318	...	1347	1356	|	|	1419	1427	1430	1447	1456	1455	|	1519	...	1547	1556	|	1617	1630	1626	1648	2025
Retford 181 d.	|	|	|	|	...	|	|	|	|	|	1443	1445	|	|	|	|	|	...	|	|	|	|	1644	1641	|	|
Lincoln 189 176 d.	|	|	|	|	1324	|	|	|	|	|	|	|	|	|	|	|	|	1527	|	|	|	|	|	|	|	|
Newark North Gate 189 d.	|	1319	|	|	1354f	|	1420	|	|	|	1457	1500	|	1520	1519	|	|	1554r	|	1620	|	|	1659	1656	|	|
Grantham 181 d.	1318	|	|	|	1407	1418	|	|	|	|	1508	1511	1518	|	|	|	|	1606	1618	|	|	|	1710	1708	1719	|
Peterborough 185 176 d.	|	1350	|	1410	1430	|	1448	|	|	1510	1530	1532	|	1549	1551f	|	1610	1630	|	1650	|	1710	1731	1730	|	2118
Stevenage 185 d.	1405	|	|	|	1459	1505	|	|	|	|	1559	1600	1605	|	|	|	|	1659	1705	|	|	|	1800	1759	1805	2148
London Kings Cross 181/2/3/5 a.	1431	1439	1451	1501	1523	1531	1540	1550	1550	1601	1622	1624	1633	1641	1646	1649	1703	1722	1731	1740	1751	1801	1823	1823	1831	2216

FOR NOTES SEE NEXT PAGE ▶ ▶ ▶ ▶

GR Most services convey 🍷 EDINBURGH - NEWCASTLE - YORK and LEEDS - LONDON 180

	Ⓐ	⑥	⚒	⚒	⚒	⚒	⑥	Ⓐ	⚒	⚒	⚒	⚒	Ⓐ	⑥	Ⓐ	⑥	⚒	Ⓐ	⑥	⚒	Ⓐ	⑥	⑥	Ⓐ	Ⓐ A
Edinburgh Waverley ..**124 188** d.	1400	1400	1408	1430	...	...	...	...	1500	1530	...	...	...	...	1600	1600	1630	...	...	...	1700	1700	...	...	1730
Berwick upon Tweed......... **124** d.	|	|	1457	1512	...	...	...	...	|	1614	...	...	...	...	|	|	1712	...	...	...	|	|	...	...	1816
Alnmouth .... **124** d.	1500	1459	1517	|	...	...	...	...	|	|	...	...	...	...	|	|	|	...	...	...	1800	1800	...	...	|
Newcastle ....**124 188** a.	1528	1527	1554	1558	...	...	...	...	1624	1656	...	...	...	...	1722	1723	1757	...	...	...	1826	1827	...	...	1900
Newcastle ....**124 188** d.	1532	1530	...	1558	...	...	...	...	1626	1659	...	...	...	...	1727	1726	1759	...	...	...	1829	1829	...	...	1902
Durham ....**124 188** d.	1546	1543	...	|	...	...	...	...	1640	|	...	...	...	...	1740	1739	|	...	...	...	1842	1843	...	...	|
Darlington ....**124 188** d.	1605	1603	...	1627	...	...	...	...	1659	1728	...	...	...	...	1759	1758	1828	...	...	...	1900	1902	...	...	1932
Northallerton ....**183 188** d.	|	|	...	|	...	...	...	...	1711	|	...	...	...	...	1810	1810	|	...	...	...	|	|	...	...	|
York ....**124 183 185** d.	1634	1633	...	1658	...	...	...	...	1733	1758	...	1802	...	...	1833	1832	1858	...	...	...	1931	1931	...	...	2001
Harrogate .... **175** d.	|	|	...	|	...	...	...	...	|	|	...	|	1736	1736	|	|	|	...	...	...	|	|	...	...	|
Leeds ....**124 175 188** d.	|	|	...	|	1645	...	1715	1715	|	|	1745	|	1815	1815	|	|	|	1845	1845	1916	|	|	1945	1945	|
Wakefield Westgate....... **124** d.	|	|	...	|	1658	...	1728	1728	|	|	1758	|	1828	1829	|	|	|	1858	1858	1929	|	|	1958	1958	|
Doncaster ....**181 182** d.	1657	1658	...	|	1718	...	1747	1746	1756	|	1818	1825	1848	1847	1855	1855	|	1919	1923f	1948	1953	1954	2017	2017	2027
Retford .... **181** d.	|	|	...	|	|	...	1801	1800	|	|	|	1839	|	|	|	|	|	|	|	|	|	|	|	|	|
Lincoln ....**189 176** d.	|	|	...	|	|	1726	|	|	|	|	|	|	|	|	|	|	|	|	|	|	|	|	|	|	|
Newark North Gate........... **189** d.	1719	1721	...	|	|	1754	|	|	1820	|	|	1855	|	|	1918	1919	|	|	|	|	2016	2019	|	|	|
Grantham .... **181** d.	|	|	...	|	|	1806	1823	1821	|	|	|	1907	1919	1920	|	|	|	|	|	2019	|	|	|	|	|
Peterborough ....**185 176** d.	1750	1749	...	|	1809	1830	|	|	1849	|	1910	1930	|	|	1946	1950	|	2010	2015	|	2045	2051f	2104	2107	2116
Stevenage .... **185** d.	|	|	...	|	|	1859	1909	1906	|	|	|	1959	2005	2005	2015	2020	2030	|	|	2105	2116	2120	|	|	2145
London Kings Cross **181/2/3/5** a.	1841	1846	...	1852	1901	1922	1933	1931	1946c	1953	2001	2023	2028	2031	2039	2046	2055	2059	2109	2131	2139	2146	2154	2200	2209

	⚒	⑥	⑥	Ⓐ	⑥	⚒	Ⓐ	⑥	Ⓐ A	⑤		⑦	⑦	⑦	⑦	⑦	⑦	⑦	⑦	⑦	⑦	⑦	⑦	⑦	⑦ G
Edinburgh Waverley ..**124 188** d.	1734	...	1831	1830	1900	1903t	1936	2000	2100	2200		...	...	...	...	...	...	...	...	...	...	...	...	...	...
Berwick upon Tweed......... **124** d.	1824	...	1913	1920	1946	1954t	2019	2052	2153	2247	⑦	...	...	...	...	...	...	...	...	...	...	...	...	...	...
Alnmouth .... **124** d.	1845	...	|	1943	2008	2014t	2040	2114	2214	2309		...	...	...	...	...	...	...	...	...	...	...	...	...	...
Newcastle ....**124 188** a.	1922	...	1958	2014	2041	2048t	2110	2146	2242	2354		...	...	...	...	...	...	...	...	...	...	...	...	...	...
Newcastle ....**124 188** d.	▬	...	▬	2017	2043	2055	2115	...	2245	...		...	...	0755	...	...	0825	0855	...	...	0925	...	1000	...	...
Durham ....**124 188** d.	...	...	...	2030	2058	2112	2129	...	2259	...		...	...	0809	...	...	0838	0908	...	...	0938	...	|	...	...
Darlington ....**124 188** d.	...	...	...	2049	2118	2131	2148	...	2320	...		...	...	0827	...	...	0856	0927	...	...	0957	...	1028	...	...
Northallerton ....**183 188** d.	...	...	...	|	2131	2142	2200	...	2346s	...		...	...	|	...	...	|	|	...	...	1009	...	|	...	...
York ....**124 183 185** d.	...	...	...	2119	2157	2202	2225	...	0016	...		0800	...	0858	...	...	0925	0958	...	...	1031	...	1058	...	...
Harrogate .... **175** d.	...	...	Ⓐ	|	|	...	|	...	|	...		|	...	|	...	...	|	|	...	0915	|	...	|	...	...
Leeds ....**124 175 188** d.	...	2015	2045	|	|	...	|	...	0045	...		|	0805	|	0840	0905	|	|	0940	1005	|	...	|	1045	1105
Wakefield Westgate....... **124** d.	...	2028	2058	|	|	...	|	...	...	...		|	0818	|	0855	0918	|	|	0953	1018	|	...	|	1059	1118
Doncaster ....**181 182** d.	...	2048	2117	2142	2221	...	2250	...	...	...		0823	0837	|	0920f	0939	|	|	|	1038	1054	...	|	1118	1139
Retford .... **181** d.	⚒	2102	2132	|	...	...	2305	...	...	...		|	0852	|	|	|	|	|	1021	1052	|	...	|	1136	|
Lincoln ....**189 176** d.	2025	|	|	|	...	...	|	...	...	...		|	|	|	|	|	|	|	|	|	|	1055	|	|	|
Newark North Gate........... **189** d.	2051	2118	|	2206	...	...	2320	...	...	...		|	0907	|	|	1002	1009	|	1040f	1107	1118	1121	|	|	1203
Grantham .... **181** d.	2104	2130	2155	2218	...	...	2331	...	...	...		|	0920	|	|	1015	1021	|	|	1118	|	1134	|	|	1216
Peterborough ....**185 176** d.	2128	2150	2217	2239	...	...	2358	...	...	...		0911	0942	1004	1011	1036	1041	1105	1109	1139	1150	1158f	1206	|	1239
Stevenage .... **185** d.	2159	|	2246	2308	...	...	0039s	...	...	...		0941	|	|	|	1107	1112	|	|	|	|	1227	|	|	1309
London Kings Cross **181/2/3/5** a.	2224	2239	2309	2331	...	...	0115	...	...	...		1006	1035	1052	1108	1135	1138	1156	1159	1227	1239	1250	1255	1258	1335

	⑦	⑦	⑦	⑦	⑦	⑦	⑦	⑦	⑦	⑦	⑦	⑦	⑦	⑦	⑦	⑦ A	⑦	⑦	⑦	⑦	⑦ B	⑦	⑦	⑦ A	⑦
Edinburgh Waverley ..**124 188** d.	0900	0930	...	0933	1000	1030	...	1100	1120	1130	...	...	...	1200	1220	1230	...	...	1300	1320	1330	...	1400	1430	1423
Berwick upon Tweed......... **124** d.	|	1013	...	1023	|	1112	...	|	|	1213	...	...	...	|	|	1313	...	...	1343	|	1413	...	|	|	1521
Alnmouth .... **124** d.	|	|	...	1044	1101	|	...	|	|	|	...	...	...	1301	|	|	...	...	|	|	|	...	1501	|	1541
Newcastle ....**124 188** a.	1023	1056	...	1118	1127	1156	...	1223	1246	1256	...	...	...	1327	1347	1356	...	...	1426	1445	1456	...	1528	1553	1612
Newcastle ....**124 188** d.	1027	1100	...	▬	1130	1158	...	1225	1252	1300	...	...	1315	1330	1350	1359	...	1416	1432	1451	1459	...	1531	1555	▬
Durham ....**124 188** d.	1041	|	...	...	1143	|	...	1239	1306	|	...	...	1328	1343	1404	|	...	1429	|	1504	|	...	1544	|	...
Darlington ....**124 188** d.	1100	1129	...	...	1202	1227	...	1258	1324	1330	...	...	1347	1402	|	1431	...	1449	1501	1523	1528	...	1603	1625	...
Northallerton ....**183 188** d.	1112	|	...	...	|	|	...	1310	|	|	...	...	1400	|	|	|	...	1502	|	|	|	...	|	|	...
York ....**124 183 185** d.	1134	1158	...	⑦	1232	1256	...	1332	1356f	1401	...	...	1423	1432	1449	1500	...	1524	1530	1557	1601	...	1633	1658	...
Harrogate .... **175** d.	|	|	...	1115	|	|	...	|	|	|	...	1315	|	|	|	|	...	|	|	|	|	1536	|	|	...
Leeds ....**124 175 188** d.	|	|	...	1205	|	|	1305	|	|	|	...	1405	|	|	|	|	1505	|	|	|	|	1616	|	|	...
Wakefield Westgate....... **124** d.	|	|	...	1218	|	|	1318	|	|	|	...	1418	|	|	|	|	1518	|	|	|	|	1629	|	|	...
Doncaster ....**181 182** d.	1157	|	...	1237	1255	|	1337	1355	|	|	...	1437	1448	1455	|	|	1537	1547	1554	|	|	1648	1656	|	...
Retford .... **181** d.	1211	|	...	|	|	|	|	1410	|	|	...	|	|	|	|	|	|	|	1609	|	|	|	|	|	⑦
Lincoln ....**189 176** d.	|	|	1223	|	|	|	|	|	|	|	1420	|	|	|	|	|	|	|	|	|	|	|	|	|	1650
Newark North Gate........... **189** d.	|	|	1249	1301	1319	|	1401	|	|	|	1446	1500	|	1519	|	|	1601	1611	|	|	|	|	1720	|	1724e
Grantham .... **181** d.	|	|	1302	1313	|	|	1413	|	|	|	1459	1512	|	|	1538	|	1613	|	|	|	|	1719	|	|	1736
Peterborough ....**185 176** d.	1251	|	1324	1335	1351	|	1434	1451	|	|	1523	1534	1538	1551f	|	|	1634	1643	1650	|	|	|	1751	|	1805
Stevenage .... **185** d.	|	|	1354	|	|	|	1504	|	|	|	1554	|	|	|	|	|	1704	|	|	|	|	1804	|	|	1834
London Kings Cross **181/2/3/5** a.	1340	1348	1417	1423	1440	1445	1528	1540	1547	1550	1620	1623	1627	1640	1643	1651	1729	1736	1739	1747	1754	1827	1842	1849	1857

	⑦	⑦	⑦	⑦	⑦	⑦	⑦	⑦	⑦	⑦	⑦	⑦ A	⑦	⑦	⑦	⑦	⑦	⑦	⑦	⑦	⑦	⑦	⑦	⑦ M	⑦
Edinburgh Waverley ..**124 188** d.	...	...	1450	...	1500	1530	...	...	...	1600	1620	1630	...	...	1700	1730	1733	1800	...	1830	1900	1916	2000	2018	2100
Berwick upon Tweed......... **124** d.	...	...	1532	...	|	1612	...	...	...	|	|	1713	...	...	|	1817	1825	|	...	1913	1947	2004	2048	2102	2149
Alnmouth .... **124** d.	...	...	|	...	|	|	...	...	...	1701	|	|	...	...	|	|	1845	1901	...	|	|	2025	2110	|	2210
Newcastle ....**124 188** a.	...	...	1616	...	1623	1656	...	...	...	1727	1747	1756	...	...	1823	1859	1919	1928	...	1956	2030	2058	2141	2148	2237
Newcastle ....**124 188** d.	...	1606	1618	...	1626	1701	...	...	...	1730	1752	1800	...	...	1828	1903	▬	1930	...	2000	2033	2101	2144	...	...
Durham ....**124 188** d.	...	1620	1632	...	1640	|	...	...	...	1743	|	|	...	...	1842	|	...	1944	...	|	2046	2117	2157	...	...
Darlington ....**124 188** d.	...	1639	1650	...	1701	1729	...	...	...	1802	1821	1830	...	...	1901	1930	...	2003	...	2029	2105	2136	2215	...	...
Northallerton ....**183 188** d.	...	1651	|	...	|	|	...	...	...	|	1833	|	...	...	1913	|	...	|	...	|	|	|	2227	...	...
York ....**124 183 185** d.	...	1713	1722	...	1730	1759	...	...	...	1832	1855	1901	...	...	1935	2001	...	2032	...	2100	2135	2214	2301	...	...
Harrogate .... **175** d.	...	|	|	...	|	|	...	1705	...	|	|	|	1800	...	|	|	⑦	|	...	|	|	...	|	...	...
Leeds ....**124 175 188** d.	1645	|	|	1716	|	|	...	1747	1815	|	|	|	1845	1916	|	|	1946	|	2045	|	|	...	|	...	...
Wakefield Westgate....... **124** d.	1658	|	|	1729	|	|	...	1800	1828	|	|	|	1859	1929	|	|	1959	|	2058	|	|	...	|	...	...
Doncaster ....**181 182** d.	1721f	1736	|	1748	1757f	|	...	1818	1847	1855	|	|	1922	1948	1958	|	2020	2055	2117	2126f	2158	...	2324	...	...
Retford .... **181** d.	|	|	|	1802	|	|	...	|	|	|	|	|	|	2002	|	|	|	|	2131	|	|	...	...	...	...
Lincoln ....**189 176** d.	|	|	|	|	|	|	1800	|	|	|	|	|	|	|	|	|	|	|	|	|	|	...	...	...	...
Newark North Gate........... **189** d.	1746	|	1804	|	|	|	1826	1845	|	1919	|	|	1947	|	2022	|	2046	2119	|	2150	2222	...	...	...	...
Grantham .... **181** d.	|	1808	|	1825	1831	|	1839	|	1919	|	1945	|	|	2025	|	2049	|	|	2154	2202	2234	...	...	...	...
Peterborough ....**185 176** d.	1814	|	1833	|	1852	|	1903f	1914	|	1952	|	|	2016	|	2051	2109	2115	2150	2216	2224	2256	...	...	...	...
Stevenage .... **185** d.	|	|	|	1910	|	|	1932	|	2004	|	|	|	|	2110	|	|	|	|	2245	2254	2334s	...	...	...	...
London Kings Cross **181/2/3/5** a.	1905	1917	1922	1935	1942	1947	1959	2006	2028	2042	2049	2053	2106	2135	2140	2158	2205	2239	2310	2318	2359	...	...	...	...

NOTES for pages 137–139.

A – To/from Aberdeen (Table **222**).
B – To/from Inverness (Table **224**).
C – To Glasgow Central on Ⓐ (Table **220**).
D – To Sunderland (a. 2322).
F – To/from Skipton (Table **173**).
G – To/from Bradford Forster Square (Table **182**).
H – To/from Hull (Table **181**).
J – From Sunderland (d. 0539).

K – To/from Stirling (Table **222**).
M – To/from Glasgow Central (Table **220**).
P – To Bradford Forster Square on ⑥ (Table **182**).
Q – To Middlesbrough (a. 1818).
R – From Middlesbrough (d. 0708).

a – Arrives 1710 on ⑥.
c – Arrives 6–8 minutes earlier on Ⓐ.

d – Arrives 4–5 minutes earlier on Ⓐ.
e – Arrives 8 minutes earlier.
f – Arrives 5–7 minutes earlier.
g – Arrives 1849.
j – Arrives 0726.
r – Arrives 1548 on ⑥.
s – Calls to set down only.
t – 8 minutes later on Ⓐ.

First Excel service XL 🚌 PETERBOROUGH - KINGS LYNN 🚌 180a

From **Peterborough** railway station to **Kings Lynn** bus station: Journey 81 minutes. Buses call at **Wisbech** bus station ± 43 minutes later.
⚒: 0704 Ⓐ, 0734, 0809, 0844 and every 30 minutes until 1844, 1944, 2044, 2249: ⑦: 0944, 1044 and hourly until 1944.
From **Kings Lynn** railway station to **Peterborough** bus station: Journey 80 minutes. Buses call at **Wisbech** bus station ± 32 minutes later.
⚒: 0532 Ⓐ, 0602, 0632, 0702, 0732, 0802, 0832, 0902, 0932, 1007 and every 30 minutes until 1707, 1807, 1907, 2127: ⑦: 0807 and hourly until 1807.

181 LONDON - HULL

All trains 🍸 HT

km		Ⓐ	Ⓐ	Ⓐ	Ⓐ	Ⓐ	Ⓐ△	Ⓐ	Ⓐ	⑥	⑥	⑥	⑥	⑥△	⑥	⑥	⑦	⑦	⑦	⑦	⑦△	⑦	⑦
0	**London Kings Cross** 180 d.	0727	0948	1148	1348	1548	1718	1848	2030	0727	0948	1148	1448	1718	1748	1948	1049	1250	1448	1627	1722	1748	1952
170	Grantham 180 d.	0828	1050	1250	1449	1650	1829	1952	2131	0828	1049	1249	1550	1829	1850	2051	1149	1350	1549	1729	1827	1852	2052
223	Retford 180 d.	0852	1111	1311	1512	1712	|	2014	2153	0853	1111	1311	1611	|	1912	2114	1211	1412	1610	1750	|	1914	2114
251	**Doncaster** 180 a.	0905	1126	1326b	1526	1726	1908	2027	2206	0906	1124	1326b	1626	1904c	1925	2127	1227	1426	1627b	1804	1903	1927	2127
280	Selby a.	0923	1143	1346	1543	1743	1927	2047	2223	0923	1143	1346	1644	1928	1943	2145	1244	1443	1646	1821	1922	1944	2144
330	**Hull** 177 a.	0959	1218	1426	1626	1824	2005	2123	2259	0959	1218	1425	1725	2006	2018	2220	1320	1519	1721	1859	2002	2019	2220
343	Beverley 177 a.	...	...	...	...	1842	...	2150	...	...	...	...	...	...	2042	...	...	...	...	...	...	2039	...

	Ⓐ	Ⓐ△	Ⓐ	Ⓐ	Ⓐ	Ⓐ	Ⓐ	Ⓐ	⑥	⑥△	⑥		⑥	⑥	⑥	⑥	⑦	⑦	⑦	⑦		⑦	⑦
Beverley 177 d.	0605	...	0753						0557									1051					
Hull 177 d.	0625	0658	0824	1034	1233	1508	1708	1908	0617	0658	0824	...	1033	1330	1531	1836	0859	1111	1250	1436	...	1621	1847
Selby d.	0701	0734	0901	1109	1308	1543	1745	1945	0652	0735	0901	...	1108	1408	1606	1911	0934	1146	1325	1511	...	1704	1922
Doncaster 180 d.	0721	0757	0923	1126	1325	1605	1804	2004	0710	0758	0925	...	1125	1426	1625	1928	0959	1204	1343	1529	...	1726	1940
Retford 180 d.	0741a	|	0939	1141	1339	1619	1818	2018	|	|	0939	...	1139	1440	1639	1942	1013	1218	1357	1543	...	1740	1954
Grantham 180 d.	0803	0833	1000	1202	1400	1640	1839	2040	0740	0835	1001	...	1200	1501	1701	2004	1035	1239	1418	1606	...	1802	2015
London Kings Cross 180 a.	0914	0954	1108	1307	1507	1746	1945	2146	0847	0947	1107	...	1307	1608	1808	2115	1141	1342	1536	1716	...	1908	2119

a – Arrives 0735. b – Departs 5 minutes later. c – Departs 1912. △ – Operated by GR (Table **180**).

182 LONDON - BRADFORD

All trains 🍸 GC

km		Ⓐ	Ⓐ	Ⓐ	Ⓐ△	Ⓐ△		Ⓐ	⑥	⑥	⑥	⑥△	⑥△	⑥	⑦		⑦	⑦	⑦	⑦△
0	**London Kings Cross** 180 d.	1057	1456	1627	1633	1833	...	1948	1048	1525	1627	1633	1933	1957	1150	...	1550	1853	1927	1935
251	**Doncaster** 180 d.	1235a	1631	1804	1821	2022	...	2119	1222	1702	1802	1820	2114	2134	1321	...	1722	2039b	2100	2121
278	Pontefract Monkhill d.	1258	1655	|	|	|	...	|	|	|	|	|	|	2203	|	...	|	|	|	|
292	Wakefield Kirkgate d.	1314	1714	1831	1838e	2040e	...	2141	1249	1724	1834	1838e	2132e	2220	1346	...	1751	2100	2124	2139e
322	Halifax 190 d.	1347	1746	1905	|	|	...	2226	1321	1757	1905	|	|	2255	1420	...	1821	2133	2158	|
335	**Bradford** Interchange 190 a.	1401	1800	1919	1929f	2129f	...	2242	1335	1812	1918	1929f	2218f	2309	1434	...	1835	2147	2213	2222f

	Ⓐ△	Ⓐ	Ⓐ		Ⓐ△	Ⓐ	Ⓐ	⑥△	⑥		⑥	⑥△	⑥	⑥	⑦	⑦△		⑦	⑦	⑦
Bradford Interchange 190 d.	0630f	0655	0756	...	0843f	1022	1450	0630f	0656	...	0756	0843f	1022	1450	0804	1025f	...	1211	1512	1559
Halifax 190 d.	|	0710	0810	...	|	1037	1503	|	0710	...	0810	|	1037	1503	0817	|	...	1224	1524	1612
Wakefield Kirkgate d.	0713e	0745a	0856	...	0929e	1114	1539	0713e	0745	...	0856	0928e	1114	1539	0849	1118f	...	1258	1602	1644
Pontefract Monkhill d.	|	0759	|	...	|	1132	1554	|	0759	...	|	|	1132	1554	|	|	...	|	|	|
Doncaster 180 d.	|	0831	0930a	...	0948	1203	1622a	|	0831	...	0930a	0947	1203	1622a	0911	1139	...	1321	1625	1711
London Kings Cross 180 a.	0859	1008	1114	...	1131	1344	1808	0901	1008	...	1114	1131	1344	1808	1040	1335	...	1453	1756	1842

a – Arrives 6–8 minutes earlier. b – Arrives 2025. e – Wakefield Westgate. f – Bradford Forster Square. △ – Operated by GR (Table **180**).

182a LONDON - YORK - SUNDERLAND

All trains 🍸 GC

km		①	Ⓐ	Ⓐ	Ⓐ	Ⓐ	Ⓐ	Ⓐ△	⑥	⑥	⑥		⑥	⑥	⑥	⑦	⑦	⑦	⑦	⑦
0	**London Kings Cross** 180 d.	0827	1127	1256	1427	1648	1927	2000	0748	1127	1318	...	1427	1648	1927	0950	1348	1523	1653	1822
303	**York** 180 188 d.	1025a	1323	1451	1618	1845a	2123	2153a	0946	1324	1515	...	1623b	1844	2123	1142	1538	1724	1841	2012
339	Thirsk 188 d.	1043	1340	1514	1635	1902	2140	|	1004	1341	1537	...	1640	1902	2140	1159	1555	1740	1900	2029
351	**Northallerton** 180 188 d.	1059	1349	1523	1644	1910	2149	|	1020	1349	1545	...	1700	1911	2149	1208	1605	1757	1912	2046
375	Eaglescliffe d.	1117	1404	1546	1703	1928	2205	|	1038	1404	1603	...	1717	1929	2206	1225	1624	1814	1932	2103
399	Hartlepool a.	1135	1423	1611	1723	1946c	2223	|	1056	1423	1622	...	1735	1948c	2225	1244	1643	1843	1950	2123
428	**Sunderland** a.	1204	1452	1638	1753	2021	2252	2322	1126	1451	1651	...	1806	2021	2252	1309	1708	1908	2021	2151

	Ⓐ△	Ⓐ	Ⓐ	Ⓐ	Ⓐ		Ⓐ	Ⓐ	⑥	⑥	⑥	⑥	⑥	⑥	⑦	⑦	⑦		⑦	⑦
Sunderland d.	0539	0646	0853	0954	1230	...	1530	1730	0643	0829	0955	1218	1529	1730	0923	1028	1212	...	1414	1812
Hartlepool d.	|	0712	0915	1017	1255	...	1554	1756	0708	0854	1020	1242	1553	1754	0947	1052	1236	...	1439	1836
Eaglescliffe d.	|	0735	0939	1041	1314	...	1615	1819	0735	0915	1042	1301	1613	1814	1007	1111	1257	...	1458	1857
Northallerton 180 188 d.	|	0755	0959	1059	1339	...	1633	1842	0755	0933	1104	1319	1633	1832	1025	1133	1315	...	1515	1920
Thirsk 188 d.	|	0803	1008	1109	1348	...	1643	1852	0804	0946a	1121a	1328	1643	1843	1034	1142	1325	...	1524	1929
York 180 188 d.	0701	0822	1026	1141d	1407	...	1703	1912	0822	1009	1150a	1348	1706a	1902	1054	1208	1347a	...	1547	1949
London Kings Cross 180 a.	0909	1014	1231	1354	1608	...	1908	2107	1014	1214	1350	1544	1906	2059	1241	1355	1542	...	1742	2142

a – Arrives 5–7 minutes earlier. b – Arrives 1614. c – Departs 1954. d – Arrives 1126. △ – Operated by GR (Table **180**).

183 LONDON - NEWCASTLE - EDINBURGH

All trains 🍸 LD

km		Ⓐ	Ⓐ		Ⓐ	Ⓐ		Ⓐ	⑥	⑥	⑥		⑥	⑥	⑦	⑦		⑦	⑦	⑦
0	**London Kings Cross** 180 d.	0545	1045	...	1218	1448	...	2027	0545	1025	1218	...	1548	1827	0852	1023	...	1209	1624	1924
44	Stevenage 180 d.	0610u	|	...	1241u	|	...	|	0610u	|	|	...	|	|	0913u	1045u	...	1235u	|	|
432	**Newcastle** 180 d.	0842	1347	...	1517	1750	...	2308	0841	1318	1518	...	1850	2119	1146c	1316	...	1510a	1925a	2209
632	**Edinburgh** Waverley 180 a.	1008	1522	...	1641	1913	...	0047	1006	1441	1643	...	2015	...	1310	1442	...	1637	2056	2334

	Ⓐ	Ⓐ		Ⓐ	Ⓐ		Ⓐ	⑥	⑥	⑥		⑥	⑥	⑦	⑦		⑦		⑦	⑦
Edinburgh Waverley 180 d.	0623	0911	...	1119	1613	...	1958	0536	0856	1256	...	1525	1756	...	1053	...	1355	...	1549	1853
Newcastle 180 d.	0757c	1052	...	1250	1747c	...	2133	0713a	1022	1422	...	1655	1935a	0820	1220	...	1521	...	1716	2021
Stevenage 180 a.	|	|	...	1520s	2019s	...	0024s	|	1248s	1648s	...	|	2202s	|	|	...	1752s	...	1952s	2258s
London Kings Cross 180 a.	1051	1347	...	1545	2045	...	0105	1004	1314	1714	...	1948	2229	1116	1456	...	1817	...	2015	2320

a – Arrives 9–11 minutes earlier. c – Arrives 5–7 minutes earlier. s – Calls to set down only. u – Calls to pick up down only.

184 SKEGNESS - NOTTINGHAM

2nd class EM

km		⚒	⑥	Ⓐ	Ⓐ	⑥	Ⓐ	⑥	⑥	Ⓐ	⚒	Ⓐ	⑥	⚒	⚒	⚒	⚒	Ⓐ	⑥	⚒	⑥	Ⓐ	⑥	Ⓐ	⚒	⑥	Ⓐ
0	**Skegness** d.	...	...	...	0706	0709	0818	0815	0917	0920	1015	1114	1115	1215	1315	1416	1514	1614	1615	1722	1815	1815	1915	1920	2015	2115	2120
8	Wainfleet d.	...	...	...	0716	0719	0827	0824	0926	0929	1024	1123	1124	1224	1324	1425	1523	1624	1625	1731	1823	1824	1924	1929	2024	2124	2129
38	Boston d.	...	0615	0613	0743	0746	0852	0849	0951	0954	1049	1149	1152	1249	1351	1450	1548	1652	1652	1758	1851	1855f	1949	1954	2049	2151	2154
66	Sleaford d.	...	0637	0635	0810	0812	0915	0913	1016	1017	1113	1218	1215	1313	1415	1514	1614	1716	1714	1821	1915	1920	2016	2017	2114	2213	2217
89	Grantham a.	...	0707	0704	0840	0841	0940	0940	1041	1042	1141	1243	1240	1339	1441	1540	1641	1741	1739	1847	1942	1947	2043	2044	2141	2240	|
89	Grantham 206 d.	0542	0711	0711	0843	0844	0944	0944	1045	1045	1143	1247	1244	1342	1443	1543	1645	1745	1743	1849	1946	1950	2047	2047	2143	2244	|
126	**Nottingham** 206 a.	0625	0750	0750	0923	0919	1019	1019	1120	1120	1220	1322	1318	1417	1522	1621	1719	1822	1819	1923	2025	2030	2121	2121	2221	2316	2305

	⑦	⑦	⑦	⑦	⑦	⑦	⑦	⑦	⑦	⑦	⑦	⑦
Skegness d.	...	1015	1115	1215	1415	1515	1615	1715	1815	1907	2015	2045
Wainfleet d.	...	1024	1124	1224	1424	1524	1624	1724	1824	1916	2024	2054
Boston d.	0915	1052	1151	1252	1453f	1552	1653f	1754f	1853f	1943	2049	2121
Sleaford d.	0938	1115	1213	1315	1515	1614	1715	1816	1916	2007	...	2143
Grantham a.	1005	1142	1240	1342	1542	1641	1742	1843	1943	2034	...	2210
Grantham 206 d.	1010	1147	1245	1347	1547	1645	1747	1847	1947	2038	...	2215
Nottingham 206 a.	1045	1221	1321	1422	1624	1724	1821	1921	2021	2111	...	2252

	⚒	Ⓐ	⑥	⚒	⑥	Ⓐ	⚒	⑥	Ⓐ	⚒
Nottingham 206 d.	0509v	0548	0549	0642	0731	0746	0845	0945	0950	1045
Grantham 206 a.	0552	|	|	0722	0809	0824	0928	|	|	1125
Grantham d.	—	|	|	0725	0812	0827	0931	|	|	1128
Sleaford d.	⚒	0638	0645	0752	0842	0856	0956	1041f	1040	1154
Boston d.	0620	0719c	0720r	0819	0907	0921	1020	1105	1111t	1218
Wainfleet d.	0644	0746	0747	0843	0931	0945	1044	1129	1140	1242
Skegness a.	0656	0759	0759	0856	0942	0957	1057	1141	1151	1254

	⚒	⚒	⚒	⚒	⚒	⑥	Ⓐ	⑥	Ⓐ	⚒	⑥	Ⓐ	⑥	Ⓐ	⑥	⑦	⑦	⑦	⑦	⑦	⑦	⑦	⑦	⑦	⑦	⑦	⑦
Nottingham 206 d.	1145	1245	1345	1445	1545	1650	1645	1747	1748	1846	1945	1948	2045	2049	2141	0830	0850	0950	1150	1250	1350	1450	1550	1650	1747	1830	1945
Grantham 206 a.	1221	1325	1422	1525	1627	1729	1730	1828	1830	1925	2024	2029	2125	2129	2214	0916	0923	1027	1228	1327	1428	1527	1628	1729	1828	1905	2024
Grantham d.	1224	1327	1427	1527	1629	1732	1733	1832	1834	1927	2028	2033	2129	2132	2217	—	0927	1030	1231	1330	1432	1530	1631	1732	1832	1909	2028
Sleaford d.	1250	1354	1453	1553	1655	1758	1803	1857	1901	1956	2053	2058	2154	2158	2243	⑦	0952	1057	1257	1356	1457	1556	1657	1758	1857	1934	2053
Boston d.	1316	1418	1517	1621	1718	1822	1827	1922	1925	2020	2116	2123	2218	2222	...	0920	1017	1120	1321	1420	1524f	1620	1721	1822	1922	1959	2116
Wainfleet d.	1340	1442	1541	1645	1745	1847	1851	1946	1950	2044	...	...	...	...	...	0945	1042	1145	1346	1445	1548	1645	1746	1847	1946	2023	...
Skegness a.	1351	1455	1553	1658	1758	1858	1903	1958	2001	2056	...	...	...	...	...	0956	1053	1156	1357	1455	1600	1656	1757	1858	1958	2035	...

c – Arrives 0701. f – Arrives 4–6 minutes earlier. r – Arrives 0708. t – Arrives 1103. v – Departs 0513 on Ⓐ.

GN, TL KINGS LYNN, CAMBRIDGE and PETERBOROUGH - LONDON - GATWICK ✈ - BRIGHTON 185

KINGS LYNN - CAMBRIDGE - LONDON

km		⚒	Ⓐ	⑥	⑥	Ⓐ	Ⓐ	⑥	Ⓐ	⑥	Ⓐ	Ⓐ	⑥	Ⓐ	⑥	Ⓐ	Ⓐ	⑥	Ⓐ	⑥	Ⓐ	Ⓐ	⑥	Ⓐ
0	**Kings Lynn** d.		0443	...	...	...	0539	0544	0610	...	0618	0641	0644	...	...	0710	...	0744	0748	...	...	0844	0844	...
14	Downham Market d.		0457	...	...	...	0553	0558	0625	...	0635	0655	0658	...	...	0725	...	0758	0802	...	...	0858	0858	...
42	Ely **207 208** d.		0516	0517	0553	...	0613	0617	0642	0653	0653	0714	0717	0729	0747	0744	0800	0817	0825	0853	0845	0917	0917	0947
66	**Cambridge** **207 208** a.		0539	0536	0612	...	0634	0637	0702	0712	0712	0734	0737	0747	0806	0804	0820	0837	0845	0912	0905	0936	0937	1007
66	**Cambridge** d.		0540	0537	0614	0609	0640	0644	0709	0714	0717	0739	0744	0750	0814	0809	0821	0844	0850	0914	0909	0942	0944	1014
159	**London** Kings Cross a.		0633	0633	0703	0703	0733	0733	0803	0803	0825d	0833	0833	0920d	0903	0903	0950d	0933	0948	1003	1004	1033	1034	1105

	⑥	⑥	Ⓐ		⑥	⚒	⚒		⚒	⚒	Ⓐ	⑥	⚒	Ⓐ	⑥	Ⓐ	⑥	⚒	⚒	Ⓐ	⑥	Ⓐ	⑥
Kings Lynn d.	0919	0944	0946	...	1012	1044	...	and at	...	1544	...	...	1644	1716	...	1740	1744	...	1844	...	...	1940	1940
Downham Market d.	0933	0958	1000	...	1028	1058	...	the same	...	1558	...	...	1658	1728	...	1754	1758	...	1858	...	...	1954	1958
Ely **207 208** d.	0954	1017	1018	1053	1053	1117	1153	minutes	1553	1617	1642	1653	1718	1746	1753	1815	1817	1853	1917	1945	1953	2017j	2018
Cambridge **207 208** a.	1013	1037	1038	1112	1112	1138	1213	past each	1613	1637	1702	1712	1737	1805	1812	1836	1837	1913	1937	2006	2012	2038	2037
Cambridge d.	1014	1044	1044	1114	1114	1144	1214	hour until	1614	1644	1708	1714	1742	1808	1814	1844	1844	1914	1944	2014	2014	2044	2044
London Kings Cross a.	1103	1133	1132	1203	1205	1235	1303		1705	1734	1803	1803	1833	1903	1903	1933	1936	2003	2033	2103	2103	2133	2133

	⚒	⚒	⚒	⚒	Ⓐ	⑥	⚒	Ⓐ	⑥	⚒	⑦	⑦	⑦	⑦	⑦		⑦	⑦	⑦	⑦	⑦	⑦	⑦
Kings Lynn d.	...	2040n	...	2140n	...	...	...	2244	2258	...		...	...	...	0825	and	1725	1754	1825	1925	2025	2125	2225
Downham Market d.	...	2058	...	2158	...	...	...	2258	2312	...		...	...	...	0839		1739	1808	1839	1939	2039	2139	2239
Ely **207 208** d.	2053	2117	2153	2217	2246	2253	...	2316	2329	...		...	...	...	0857	hourly	1757	1825	1857	1957	2057	2157	2257
Cambridge **207 208** a.	2113	2137	2212	2237	2306	2312	...	2336	2348	...		...	...	...	0916		1816	1843	1916	2016	2116	2216	2316
Cambridge d.	2114	2144	2214	2244	2314	2314	2335	...	...	2354		0640	0728	0822	0922	until	1822	1844	1922	2022	2122	2222	2320
London Kings Cross a.	2203	2233	2303	2334	0008	0004	0058	...	...	0110		0750	0832	0911	1011		1912	1936	2011	2111	2211	2312	0050

	⚒	①	②–⑥	Ⓐ	⚒	⑥	Ⓐ	⚒	⑥	Ⓐ	⑥	Ⓐ	⑥	Ⓐ	⑥	Ⓐ	Ⓐ	⑥	Ⓐ	⑥	⚒	⑥	Ⓐ	⑥
London Kings Cross d.		0003	0033	...	0503	0542	0542	0603	0642	0642	0712	0712	0742	0740	0812	0810	0842	0842	0910	0912	0942	1012	1012	1042
Cambridge a.		0133	0144	...	0614	0630	0630	0713	0730	0733	0800	0804	0830	0830	0900	0901	0930	0930	1003	1000	1030	1100	1101	1130
Cambridge **207 208** d.		...	...	0550	...	0632	0634	...	0735	0739	0803	0809	0835	0835	0903	0906	0935	0935	1005	1003	1035	1103	1105	1135
Ely **207 208** d.		...	...	0608	...	0655	0653	...	0755	0802j	0823	0830	0855	0856	0923	0926	0956	0955	1025	1023	1055	1123	1125	1155
Downham Market d.		...	...	0624	...	0717	0719	...	0817	0821	...	...	0917	0919	...	...	1019	1017	...	...	1117	...	...	1217
Kings Lynn a.		...	...	0638	...	0731	0733	...	0831	0835	...	...	0935	0934	...	...	1033	1035	...	...	1131	...	...	1231

	Ⓐ	⚒	⚒		⚒	⚒	⑥	Ⓐ	Ⓐ	⑥	Ⓐ	⑥	Ⓐ	⑥	Ⓐ	⑥	Ⓐ	⑥	⑥	Ⓐ	Ⓐ	⑥	Ⓐ
London Kings Cross d.	1042	1112	1142	and at	1512	1542	1612	1612	1639	1642	1709	1712	1739	1742	1809	1812	1839	1842	1912	1912	1907d	1942	1939
Cambridge a.	1133	1201	1230	the same	1600	1630	1700	1704	1732	1730	1805	1800	1832	1830	1903	1900	1932	1930	2000	2005	2015	2030	2033
Cambridge **207 208** d.	1137	1203	1235	minutes	1603	1635	1703	1705	1737	1735	1810	1803	1836	1835	1908	1905	1937	1935	2003	2007	2016	2035	2038
Ely **207 208** d.	1157	1224	1255	past each	1626	1655	1723	1724	1756	1755	1829	1823	1856	1855	1926	1925	1956	1955	2023	2026	2032	2054	2056
Downham Market d.	1217	...	1317	hour until	*1653*p	1717	...	...	1813	1817	...	...	1917	1917	1943	1942	2013	2017	2042	...	2049	2117	2117
Kings Lynn a.	1231	...	1331		*1707*p	1732	...	...	1827	1831	...	...	1931	1931	1957	1956	2027	2031	2056	...	2107	2131	2131

	⑥	Ⓐ	⚒	⑥	Ⓐ	⑥	Ⓐ	⚒	⑥	Ⓐ	⚒	⚒	⑦	⑦	⑦	⑦	⑦		⑦	⑦	⑦	⑦	⑦
London Kings Cross d.	2012	2009	2039	2112	2109	2142	2139	2209	2242	2239	2309	2342		0033	0633	0754	0912	and at	1912	2012	2112	2212	2312
Cambridge a.	2104	2103	2133	2204	2203	2230	2233	2304	2330	2333	0004	0036		0144	0746	0858	0959	the same	2001	2059	2159	2259	0003
Cambridge **207 208** d.	2106	2108	2135	2205	2205	2235	2236	2305	2335	2338	0007	...		...	...	0904	1004	minutes	2004	2104	2204	2304	0006
Ely **207 208** d.	2125	2128	2155	2225	2227	2255	2256	2325	2355	2358	0027	...		...	...	0922	1022	past each	2022	2122	2223	2322	0024
Downham Market d.	2142	...	2217	...	...	2311	2317	...	0011	0014	0043	...		...	...	0939	1039	hour until	2039	2139	2239	2339	0041
Kings Lynn a.	2156	...	2231	...	...	2325	2331	...	0025	0028	0057	...		...	...	0953	1053		2053	2153	2253	2353	0055

PETERBOROUGH and CAMBRIDGE - STEVENAGE - LONDON - GATWICK AIRPORT - HORSHAM and BRIGHTON ❖

km		⚒	⚒	⚒	⚒	⑥	Ⓐ	⚒	⚒	⚒	⚒	♠	⚒	⚒	⚒	⚒	⚒	⚒	⚒	⚒	⚒	⚒	⚒	⚒	⚒	⚒
0	**Peterborough** d.		0324	0419	...	0454	0454	...	0524	...	0554		...	1824	...	1852	1924	...	1955	2024	...	2054	2124	...	2154	2224
28	Huntingdon d.		0338	0433	...	0510	0510	...	0540	...	0610		...	1840	...	1910	1940	...	2010	2040	...	2110	2140	...	2210	2240
	Cambridge d.		|	|	0454	|	|	0524	|	0554	|		1823	|	1853	|	|	1954	|	|	2054	|	|	2154	|	|
79	Stevenage d.		0417	0513	0532	0547	0547	0602	0617	0632	0647	and at	1902	1917	1932	1947	2017	2032	2047	2117	2130	2147	2216	2232	2247	2317
119	Finsbury Park d.		0445	0537	0552	0608	0607	0622	0638	0652	0708		1922	1938	1952	2008	2038	2052	2108	2138	2152	2208	2237	2252	2307	2338
	London Kings Cross a.		0451	|	|	|	|	|	|	|	|	the same	|	|	|	|	|	|	|	|	|	|	|	|	|	2344
122	**London** St Pancras **103** d.		...	0545	0600	0615	0615	0630	0645	0700	0715		1930	1945	2000	2015	2045	2100	2115	2145	2200	2215	2245	2300	2315	...
124	Farringdon **103** d.		...	0549	0604	0619	0619	0634	0649	0704	0719	minutes	1934	1949	2004	2019	2049	2104	2119	2149	2204	2219	2249	2304	2319	...
126	**London** Blackfriars **103** d.		...	0554	0609	0624	0624	0639	0654	0709	0724		1939	1954	2009	2024	2054	2109	2124	2154	2209	2224	2254	2309	2324	...
127	**London** Bridge **103** d.		...	0600	0615	0630	0630	0645	0700	0715	0730	past each	1945	2000	2015	2030	2100	2115	2130	2200	2215	2230	2300	2315	2330	...
143	East Croydon **102 103** d.		...	0616	0629	0646	0646	0659	0716	0729	0746		1959	2016	2029	2046	2116	2129	2146	2216	2229	2246	2316	2329	2346	...
	Redhill **102** d.		...	0637	|	0707	0707	|	0734	|	0807	hour until	|	2037	|	2107	2133	|	2203	2237	|	2303	2333	|	2359	...
153	Gatwick Airport ✈ **102 103** d.		...	0650	0644	0717	0723	0714	0747	0744	0817		2014	2046	2044	2116	2144	2144	2216	2247	2244	2316	2342	2348	0014	...
165	**Horsham** **102** a.		...	0713	|	0739	0746	|	0811	|	0845		|	2109	|	2139	2209	|	2239	2309	|	2339	0005	|	0035	...
	Haywards Heath **103** d.		...	...	0701	...	...	0731	...	0801	...		2031	...	2101	...	...	2201	...	...	2301	...	...	0007	...	...
	Brighton **103** a.		...	...	0722	...	...	0747	...	0817	...		2047	...	2117	...	...	2217	...	...	2317	...	...	0023	...	...

	⚒	⚒	⚒	⚒	⑦	⑦△	⑦△	⑦	⑦	⑦		⑦	⑦	⑦	⑦	⑦
Peterborough d.	...	2254	2320	...		0545	0645	0745	...	0845		...	2045	...	2145	2245
Huntingdon d.	...	2310	2334	...		0601	0659	0759	...	0859		...	2059	...	2159	2259
Cambridge d.	2254	|	|	2354		|	|	|	0828	|		2028	|	2128	|	|
Stevenage d.	2332	2350	0013	0034		0640	0740	0836	0906	0936	and at	2106	2136	2206	2236	2339
Finsbury Park d.	2352	0010	0039	0100		0714	0802	0856	0926	0956		2126	2156	2225	2256	2359
London Kings Cross a.	2359	0018	0046	0110		0722	0810	0902	|	1002	the same	|	2202	|	2302	0005
London St Pancras **103** d.	...	...	...	...		▬	▬	▬	0934	▬		2135	▬	2235	▬	...
Farringdon **103** d.	...	...	...	...					0938	...	minutes	2139	...	2239	...	...
London Blackfriars **103** d.	...	...	...	...		⑦	⑦	⑦	0943	⑦		2144	⑦	2244	...	...
London Bridge **103** d.	...	...	...	...		0719	0819	0921	0951	1021	past each	2151	2221	2251	⑦	...
East Croydon **102 103** d.	...	...	...	...		0735	0835	0935	1005	1035		2205	2235	2305	2323	...
Redhill **102** d.	...	...	...	...		0754	0854	0948	|	1048	hour until	|	2248	|	2342	...
Gatwick Airport ✈ **102 103** d.	...	...	...	...		0809	0909	1003	1021	1103		2221	2303	2321	2351	...
Horsham **102** a.	...	...	...	...		0831	0931	1025	|	1125		|	2325	|	0014	...
Haywards Heath **103** d.	...	...	...	...		...	...	...	1038	...		2238	...	2338	...	...
Brighton **103** a.	...	...	...	...		...	...	...	1054	...		2254	...	2354	...	...

	⚒	①	①	②–⑥	⚒
Brighton **103** d.		...	...	...	...
Haywards Heath **103** d.		...	...	...	...
Horsham **102** d.		...	...	...	...
Gatwick ✈ **102 103** d.		...	...	...	...
Redhill **102** d.		...	...	...	...
East Croydon **102 103** d.		...	...	...	...
London Bridge **103** d.		...	...	...	...
London Blackfriars **103** d.		...	...	...	...
Farringdon **103** d.		...	...	...	...
London St Pancras **103** d.		...	...	...	...
London Kings Cross d.		0032	0132	0136	0518
Finsbury Park d.		0039	0139	0143	0524
Stevenage d.		0113	0221	0210	0545
Cambridge d.		|	|	|	|
Huntingdon d.		0153s	0257s	0247	0624
Peterborough a.		0211	0315	0306	0643

km		⚒	⚒	⚒	⚒	⚒	⑥	Ⓐ	⚒	⚒	⚒	⚒	⚒	⚒	⚒	⚒	⚒	⚒	⚒	⚒	⚒	⚒	⚒	⚒	⚒	♣
0	**Brighton** **103** d.	...	...	...	0506	...	...	0542	...	0605f	...	0637f	...	0707f	...	0734f	...	0807f	...	0837f	...	0912	...	0942	...	
21	Haywards Heath **103** d.	...	...	...	0528	...	...	0601	...	0628	...	0658	...	0728	...	0755	...	0828	...	0858	...	0928	...	0958	...	
	Horsham **102** d.	...	...	...	|	0525	...	|	0555z	|	0623	|	0654	|	0722	|	0755	|	0823	|	0855	|	0925	|	0955	
55	Gatwick Airport ✈ **102 103** d.	...	...	...	0546	0549	0616	0616	0613t	0642	0647	0714	0717	0744	0747	0814	0819	0844	0847	0914	0919	0946	0949	1016	1019	and at
	Redhill **102** d.	...	...	...	|	0559	|	|	0629	|	0659	|	0729	|	0759	|	0829	|	0859	|	0929	|	0959	|	1029	
65	East Croydon **102 103** d.	...	...	...	0601	0615	0631	0631	0645	0701	0716	0731	0746	0801	0816	0831	0846	0901	0916	0931	0945	1001	1015	1031	1045	the same
81	**London** Bridge **103** d.	...	...	...	0616	0631	0646	0646	0700	0716	0731	0746	0801	0816	0831	0846	0901	0916	0931	0946	1001	1016	1031	1046	1101	
82	**London** Blackfriars **103** d.	...	...	...	0622	0637	0652	0652	0706	0822	0737	0752	0807	0822	0837	0852	0907	0922	0937	0952	1007	1022	1037	1052	1107	minutes
84	Farringdon **103** d.	...	...	...	0626	0641	0656	0656	0711	0726	0741	0756	0811	0826	0841	0856	0911	0926	0941	0956	1011	1026	1041	1056	1111	
86	**London** St Pancras **103** d.	...	...	...	0631	0646	0701	0701	0716	0731	0746	0801	0816	0831	0846	0901	0916	0931	0946	1001	1016	1031	1046	1101	1116	past each
	London Kings Cross d.	0548	0533	0618	|	|	|	|	|	|	|	|	|	|	|	|	|	|	|	|	|	|	|	|	|	
90	Finsbury Park d.	0554	0541	0624	0639	0654	0712	0712	0723	0742	0754	0812	0824	0842	0854	0912	0924	0942	0954	1012	1024	1042	1054	1112	1124	hour until
130	Stevenage d.	0614	0602	0644	0702	0714	0733	0733	0743	0803	0814	0833	0844	0903	0914	0933	0944	1003	1014	1033	1044	1103	1114	1133	1144	
179	**Cambridge** d.	|	0644	|	0744	|	0811	0813	|	0840	|	0911	|	0940	|	1011	|	1040	|	1111	|	1140	|	1211	|	
	Huntingdon d.	0650	...	0720	...	0750	...	...	0818	...	0850	...	0920	...	0950	...	1020	...	1050	...	1120	...	1150	...	1220	
	Peterborough a.	0709	...	0735	...	0806	...	...	0834k	...	0905	...	0935	...	1005	...	1039	...	1105	...	1139	...	1205	...	1239	

d – London **Liverpool Street**.
f – On ⑥ departs Brighton 5–8 minutes later.
j – Arrives 5 minutes earlier.
k – 5–6 minutes later on ⑥.
n – Departs 4 minutes later on Ⓐ.
p – Ⓐ only.
s – Calls to set down only.
t – 6 minutes later on ⑥.
z – ⑥ only.
♠ – Timings London Bridge - Horsham / Brighton may vary by up to 4 minutes.
♣ – Timings St. Pancras - Cambridge / Peterborough may vary by up to 3 minutes.
△ – Subject to alteration with partial 🚌 replacement (earlier departures from Peterborough and Huntingdon).
❖ – See Table **180** for fast trains Peterborough - London Kings Cross (operated by GR). See upper panel for other fast trains Cambridge - London Kings Cross and v.v.

NOTE: Table 188 services on ⑥ until July 30 will be found on page 571

185 KINGS LYNN, CAMBRIDGE and PETERBOROUGH - LONDON - GATWICK - BRIGHTON GN, TL

	⚒	⚒	⚒	⚒	⚒	⚒	⚒	⚒	⚒	⚒	⚒	⚒	⚒	⚒	⑦	⑦	⑦	⑦	⑦	⑦	⑦		⑦	⑦	⑦
Brighton 103 d.	1842	...	1912	...	...	2012	...	...	2112	...	...	2212	...	...		...	...	...	*0757*	...	0919		...	2119	...
Haywards Heath 103 d.	1858	...	1928	...	...	2028	...	...	2128	...	...	2228	...	...		...	...	...	*0818*	...	0935		...	2135	...
Horsham 102 d.	│	1855	│	1925	1955	│	2025	2055	│	2125	2155	│	2225	2311		...	0645	0745	│	0845	│		2045	│	2145
Gatwick Airport ✈ 102 103 d.	1916	1919	1946	1949	2019	2046	2049	2119	2146	2149	2219	2246	2249	2335		...	0708	0808	0853	0908	0953	and at	2108	2153	2208
Redhill 102 d.	│	1929	│	1959	2029	│	2059	2129	│	2159	2229	│	2304	2349		...	0724	0824	│	0926	│		2126	│	2226
East Croydon 102 103 d.	1931	1945	2001	2015	2045	2101	2115	2145	2201	2215	2245	2301	2315	0009		...	0739	0839	0909	0939	1009	the same	2139	2208	2239
London Bridge 103 d.	1946	2001	2016	2031	2101	2116	2131	2201	2216	2231	2301	2316	2331	│		...	0757	0857	0925	0957	1025		2155	2225	2255
London Blackfriars 103 d.	1952	2007	2022	2037	2107	2122	2137	2207	2222	2237	2307	2322	2337	0037		...	—	—	0932	—	1032	minutes	—	2231	—
Farringdon 103 d.	1956	2011	2026	2041	2111	2126	2141	2211	2226	2241	2311	2326	2341	0041		...	...	...	0936	...	1036		...	2235	...
London St Pancras 103 d.	2001	2016	2031	2046	2116	2131	2146	2216	2231	2246	2316	2331	2346	0046		...	⑦	⑦	0941	⑦	1041	past each	⑦	2240	⑦
London Kings Cross d.	│	│	│	│	│	│	│	│	│	│	│	│	│	│		0732	0812	0912	│	1012	│		2212	│	2322
Finsbury Park d.	2009	2024	2039	2054	2124	2139	2154	2224	2239	2254	2324	2342	2354	0054		0738	0818	0918	0948	1018	1048	hour until	2218	2248	2328
Stevenage d.	2030	2044	2100	2114	2144	2200	2214	2244	2300	2314	2345	0003	0014	0122		0804	0838	0938	1008	1039	1108		2239	2308	2348
Cambridge d.	2113	│	2140	│	│	2240	│	│	2340	│	│	0040	│	│		│	│	│	1047	│	1147		│	2347	│
Huntingdon d.	...	2120	...	2150	2220	...	2250	2320	...	2350	0020	...	0051	0159		0842	0913	1013	...	1113	...		2313	...	0022
Peterborough a.	...	2135	...	2205	2235	...	2305	2339	...	0009	0039	...	0109	0219		0858	0929	1029	...	1129	...		2331	...	0041

← FOR NOTES SEE PREVIOUS PAGE

188 THE NORTH EAST and YORKSHIRE - MANCHESTER and LIVERPOOL Most trains convey 🍸 TP

km	km		Ⓐ ♠	①	②–⑤	②–⑤	①	Ⓐ	Ⓐ	Ⓐ	Ⓐ	Ⓐ	Ⓐ	Ⓐ A	Ⓐ	Ⓐ	Ⓐ	Ⓐ	Ⓐ	Ⓐ	Ⓐ	Ⓐ	Ⓐ	Ⓐ	Ⓐ
0		**Edinburgh** 124 180 d.		...	...	...	...	...	...	...	...	...	...	...	...	...	...	0529	...	...	...	...	...	...	...
199		**Newcastle** 124 180 d.		...	...	...	...	...	...	0426	...	...	0539	...	...	0640	...	0724	0743	...	...	0844	...	...	0947
222		Durham 124 180 d.		...	...	...	...	...	...	0453	...	...	0551	...	...	0659	...	—	0800	...	...	0900	...	...	0959
257		Darlington 124 180 d.		...	...	...	...	...	...	0511	...	...	0610	...	...	0717	...	...	0818	...	...	0918	...	...	1017
◧	0	Redcar Central 212 d.		...	...	...	...	...	...	│	...	...	│	0603	...	│	0706	...	│	0807	...	│	0907	...	│
◧	12	**Middlesbrough** 212 d.		...	...	...	...	...	...	│	...	...	│	0621y	...	│	0720	...	│	0820	...	│	0921	...	│
279	45	Northallerton 124 180 d.		...	...	...	...	...	...	│	...	...	0620	0650	...	0728	0750	...	0829	0850	...	0929	0950	...	1028
292	—	Thirsk d.		...	...	...	...	...	...	│	...	...	0630	0659	...	│	0758	⚒	│	0859	...	│	0959	...	│
◧	0	**Scarborough** d.		...	...	...	...	...	...	│	...	0534	│	│	0634	│	│	0734	│	│	0834	│	│	0934	│
◧	34	Malton d.		...	...	...	...	...	...	│	...	0601	│	│	0658	│	│	0759	│	│	0859	│	│	0959	│
327	67	**York** 124 180 a.		...	...	...	...	...	...	0542	...	0624	0647	0717	0724	0748	0816	0824	0849	0917	0924	0948	1017	1024	1047
		York 124 d.		0134	0138	0247	0252	...	0458	0544	0618	...	0649	0719	...	0750	0819	0828	0850	0919	...	0950	1020	...	1049
368		**Leeds** 124 a.		0200	0218	0327	0318	...	0542	0622	0642	...	0713	0742	...	0812	0842	0857	0913	0943	...	1012	1042	...	1112
		Leeds 188a d.		0201	0225	0333	0319	...	0545	0630	0645	...	0715	0745	...	0815	0845	...	0915	0945	...	1015	1045	...	1115
383		Dewsbury d.		│	│	│	│	...	0557	0641	0657	...	0727	0757	...	0827	0857	...	0927	0957	...	1027	1057	...	1127
396		Huddersfield 188a d.		0240	0249	0356	0356	...	0608	0651	0707	...	0739	0808	...	0838	0908	...	0938	1008	...	1038	1108	...	1138
436		**Manchester** Victoria d.		│	│	│	│	0554	0640	0722	0739	...	0822v	0839	...	0922v	0939	...	1022v	1039	...	1122v	1140	...	1222v
440		**Manchester** Picc 188a a.		0333	0342	0456	0456	│	0650	│	0749	...	│	0849	...	│	0949	...	│	1049	...	│	1149	...	│
456		**Manchester** Airport ✈ a.		0351	0357	0511	0511	│	0712	│	0810	...	│	0912	...	│	1013	...	│	1113	...	│	1213	...	│
487		**Liverpool** Lime Street a.		...	...	...	...	0634	...	0802	...	...	0901	...	...	1004	...	...	1102	...	...	1202	...	...	1302

	Ⓐ	Ⓐ	Ⓐ	Ⓐ	Ⓐ	Ⓐ	Ⓐ	Ⓐ	Ⓐ	Ⓐ	Ⓐ	Ⓐ	Ⓐ	Ⓐ	Ⓐ	Ⓐ	Ⓐ	Ⓐ	Ⓐ	Ⓐ	Ⓐ	Ⓐ	Ⓐ	Ⓐ	Ⓐ	Ⓐ
Edinburgh 124 180 d.	...	...	...	...	0933	...	...	...	...	...	...	...	...	...	...	...	...	...	...	1410	...	...	...	...	...	...
Newcastle 124 180 d.	...	...	1046	...	1122	1142	...	...	1243	...	...	1343	...	...	1447	...	...	1543	...	1554	1643	...	...	1742	...	...
Durham 124 180 d.	...	...	1058	...	—	1200	...	...	1258	...	...	1359	...	...	1500	...	...	1559	...	—	1659	...	...	1758	...	...
Darlington 124 180 d.	...	...	1116	...	...	1218	...	...	1316	...	...	1417	...	...	1518	...	...	1617	...	...	1717	...	...	1816	...	...
Redcar Central 212 d.	1007	...	│	1107	...	│	1207	...	│	1307	...	│	1407	...	│	1507	...	│	1607	...	│	1707	...	│	1807	...
Middlesbrough 212 d.	1021	...	│	1121	...	│	1221	...	│	1321	...	│	1421	...	│	1521	...	│	1621	...	│	1721	...	│	1821	...
Northallerton 124 180 d.	1050	...	1127	1150	...	1229	1250	...	1327	1350	...	1428	1450	...	1529	1550	...	1628	1650	...	1728	1750	...	1827	1850	...
Thirsk d.	1059	...	│	1159	Ⓐ	│	1259	...	│	1359	...	│	1459	...	│	1559	...	│	1659	Ⓐ	│	1759	...	│	1859	...
Scarborough d.	│	1034	│	│	1134	│	│	1234	│	│	1334	│	│	1434	│	│	1534	│	│	1634	│	│	1734	│	│	1834
Malton d.	│	1059	│	│	1159	│	│	1259	│	│	1359	│	│	1458	│	│	1559	│	│	1659	│	│	1759	│	│	1858
York 124 180 a.	1117	1124	1148	1217	1224	1248	1317	1324	1348	1417	1424	1447	1517	1524	1548	1617	1622	1647	1717	1724	1747	1817	1824	1847	1917	1923
York 124 d.	1120	...	1149	1219	...	1249	1320	...	1350	1419	...	1450	1520	...	1550	1620	1627	1649	1719	...	1749	1818	...	1850	1920	...
Leeds 124 a.	1142	...	1212	1242	...	1312	1343	...	1413	1443	...	1515	1542	...	1612	1642	1657	1712	1743	...	1812	1842	...	1912	1943	...
Leeds 188a d.	1145	...	1215	1245	...	1315	1345	...	1415	1445	...	1516	1545	...	1615	1645	1700	1715	1745	...	1815	1845	...	1915	1945	...
Dewsbury d.	1157	...	1227	1257	...	1326	1357	...	1427	1457	...	1528	1557	...	1627	1657	│	1727	1757	...	1827	1857	...	1927	1957	...
Huddersfield 188a d.	1208	...	1238	1308	...	1338	1408	...	1438	1508	...	1538	1608	...	1638	1708	1718	1738	1808	...	1838	1908	...	1938	2008	...
Manchester Victoria d.	1239	...	1322v	1339	...	1422v	1440	...	1522v	1540	...	1622v	1639	...	1722v	1739	1750	1818y	1839	...	1924f	1939	...	2014	2037	...
Manchester Picc 188a a.	1249	...	│	1349	...	│	1449	...	│	1549	...	│	1649	...	│	1749	...	│	1849	...	│	1949	...	│	2048	...
Manchester Airport ✈ a.	1313	...	│	1413	...	│	1513	...	│	1613	...	│	1713	...	│	1813	...	│	1913	...	│	2013	...	│	2111	...
Liverpool Lime Street a.	...	...	1404	...	...	1501	...	...	1605	...	...	1702	...	...	1802	...	...	1859	...	...	2003	...	...	2053	...	...

	Ⓐ	Ⓐ	Ⓐ	Ⓐ	Ⓐ	Ⓐ A	Ⓐ	Ⓐ	Ⓐ	Ⓐ	Ⓐ	Ⓐ	Ⓐ A	⑦ ♥	⑦	⑦	⑦	⑦	⑦	⑦	⑦	⑦	⑦	⑦	⑦	⑦
Edinburgh 124 180 d.	...	...	1734	...	...	...	1911	...	...	...	...	...	...		...	...	...	...	...	...	...	...	...	...	...	...
Newcastle 124 180 d.	1843	...	1922	2006	...	...	2058	...	...	2201	...	...	...		...	...	0749	...	...	0836	...	...	0939	...	...	1047
Durham 124 180 d.	1900	...	—	2018	...	...	2115	...	...	2214	...	...	...		...	...	0801	...	...	0849	...	...	0954	...	...	1059
Darlington 124 180 d.	1917	...	...	2036	...	...	2133	...	...	2232	...	...	...		...	...	0819	...	...	0907	...	...	1010	...	...	1117
Redcar Central 212 d.	│	1906	...	│	...	2022	│	2107	...	│	2204	...	2319		...	...	│	...	...	│	...	...	│	1004	...	│
Middlesbrough 212 d.	│	1920	...	│	...	2035	│	2121	...	│	2218	...	2332		...	...	│	...	...	│	0919	...	│	1018	...	│
Northallerton 124 180 d.	1928	1950	...	│	...	2103	2143	2151	...	2243	2248	...	2359		...	...	│	...	...	0918	0947	...	1021	1050	...	1128
Thirsk d.	│	1958	Ⓐ	│	...	2111	│	2159	...	│	2256	...	0008		...	...	│	...	...	0928	0955	...	│	1058	...	│
Scarborough d.	│	│	1934	│	2020	│	│	│	2134	│	│	2245	│		...	...	│	...	0835	│	│	0934	│	│	1034	│
Malton d.	│	│	1959	│	2046	│	│	│	2158	│	│	2311	│		...	...	│	...	0859	│	│	0959	│	│	1059	│
York 124 180 a.	1947	2017	2024	2102	2113	2131	2202	2221	2225	2302	2318	2335	0034		...	...	0845	...	0924	0947	1013	1023	1043	1115	1124	1147
York 124 d.	1949	2019	...	2105	2115	—	...	...	2231	...	—	2339	...		...	0818	0848	0917	...	0949	1018	...	1046	1117	...	1149
Leeds 124 a.	2012	2042	...	2127	2155	Ⓐ	...	...	2258	...	Ⓐ	0005	...		...	0841	0912	0943	...	1012	1041	...	1110	1143	...	1212
Leeds 188a d.	2014	2045	...	2130	2201	2206	...	...	2300	...	2305	0010	...		...	...	0915	0946	...	1015	1045	...	1115	1145	...	1215
Dewsbury d.	2027	2057	...	2142	│	2217	...	...	│	...	2316	0028t	...		...	...	0927	0958	...	1027	1057	...	1127	1157	...	1227
Huddersfield 188a d.	2038	2108	...	2151	2219	2226	...	...	2318	...	2329	│	...		...	...	│	1008	...	│	1107	...	│	1208	...	│
Manchester Victoria d.	2123v	2157j	...	2226	2257	│	...	...	2352	...	│	│	...		0924	...	1024y	1040	...	1124y	│	...	1223y	│	...	1323y
Manchester Picc 188a a.	│	2207	...	│	2307	2308	...	...	0001	...	0010	0107	...		│	...	│	...	...	│	1142	...	│	1241	...	│
Manchester Airport ✈ a.	│	2228	...	│	2328	...	...	...	0017	...	...	...	...		│	...	│	...	...	│	...	...	│	...	...	│
Liverpool Lime Street a.	2202	...	...	2313	...	...	...	...	...	...	...	...	...		1002	...	1102	...	...	1202	...	...	1302	...	...	1401

	⑦	⑦	⑦	⑦	⑦	⑦	⑦	⑦	⑦	⑦	⑦	⑦	⑦	⑦	⑦	⑦	⑦	⑦	⑦	⑦	⑦	⑦	⑦	⑦	⑦	⑦
Edinburgh 124 180 d.	...	0933	...	...	...	...	...	...	...	...	...	...	...	...	...	...	1423	...	...	...	...	...	...	...	...	1733
Newcastle 124 180 d.	...	1118	1143	...	...	1244	...	...	1343	...	...	1447	...	...	1543	...	1612	1644	...	...	1743	...	...	1843	...	1919
Durham 124 180 d.	...	—	1200	...	...	1257	...	...	1359	...	...	1459	...	...	1600	...	—	1700	...	...	1759	...	...	1859	...	—
Darlington 124 180 d.	...	...	1218	...	...	1316	...	...	1416	...	...	1517	...	...	1618	...	...	1718	...	...	1815	...	...	1917	...	...
Redcar Central 212 d.	1104	...	│	1205	...	│	1304	...	│	1402	...	│	1504	...	│	1604	...	│	1704	...	│	1801	...	│	1904	...
Middlesbrough 212 d.	1118	...	│	1219	...	│	1318	...	│	1415	...	│	1518	...	│	1618	...	│	1718	...	│	1815	...	│	1919	...
Northallerton 124 180 d.	1150	...	1229	1249	...	1327	1349	...	│	1447	...	1529	1549	...	1629	│	...	1729	1750	...	1827	1844	...	1928	1950	...
Thirsk d.	1158	⑦	│	1257	...	│	1357	...	│	1455	...	│	1559	...	│	1655	⑦	│	1759	...	│	1853	...	│	1958	⑦
Scarborough d.	│	1134	│	│	1234	│	│	1334	│	│	1434	│	│	1534	│	│	1634	│	│	1734	│	│	1834	│	│	1934
Malton d.	│	1159	│	│	1259	│	│	1359	│	│	1459	│	│	1559	│	│	1659	│	│	1759	│	│	1858	│	│	1959
York 124 180 a.	1215	1224	1248	1314	1324	1346	1414	1424	1442	1513	1524	1548	1616	1625	1647	1715	1724	1748	1816	1824	1846	1911	1924	1950	2016	2024
York 124 d.	1217	...	1250	1316	...	1348	1416	...	1448	1515	...	1550	1618	1629	1648	1717	...	1750	1819	...	1849	1916	...	1951	2018	...
Leeds 124 a.	1243	...	1313	1343	...	1411	1443	...	1511	1543	...	1612	1643	1657	1712	1744	...	1813	1843	...	1913	1943	...	2014	2043	...
Leeds 188a d.	1245	...	1315	1345	...	1415	1445	...	1515	1545	...	1615	1645	1700	1715	1745	...	1815	1845	...	1915	1945	...	2015	2045	...
Dewsbury d.	1256	...	1326	1356	...	1426	1457	...	1526	1557	...	1627	1657	│	1726	1757	...	1827	1857	...	1927	1957	...	2027	2057	...
Huddersfield 188a d.	1308	...	│	1408	...	│	1508	...	│	1608	...	│	1708	1718	│	1808	...	│	1907	...	│	2008	...	│	2108	...
Manchester Victoria d.	│	...	1424y	│	...	1523y	│	...	1623y	│	...	1723y	│	│	1823y	│	...	1923y	│	...	2023y	│	...	2124y	│	...
Manchester Picc 188a a.	1342	...	│	1442	...	│	1543	...	│	1644	...	│	1742	1752	│	1842	...	│	1942	...	│	2043	...	│	2143	...
Manchester Airport ✈ a.	...	...	│	...	...	│	...	...	│	...	...	│	...	...	│	...	...	│	...	...	│	...	...	│	...	...
Liverpool Lime Street a.	...	...	1502	...	...	1600	...	...	1701	...	...	1801	...	...	1901	...	...	2001	...	...	2101	...	...	2202	...	...

A – From Saltburn (Table **212**).
f – Arrives 1908.
j – Arrives 2139
v – Arrives 13 minutes earlier.
y – Arrives 6–10 minutes earlier.
♠ – Service valid until Sept. 9
♥ – Service valid until July 31.

NOTE: *Table **188** services on ⑥ until July 30 will be found on page 571*

TP Most trains convey 🍸 THE NORTH EAST and YORKSHIRE - MANCHESTER and LIVERPOOL 188

	⑦	⑦	⑦	⑦	⑦		⑦	⑦	⑦	⑦	⑦A
Edinburgh 124 180 d.	...	...	...	1916	...	...	...	...	...	...	...
Newcastle 124 180 d.	2006	...	...	2101	...	...	...	...	...	...	...
Durham 124 180 d.	2018	...	...	2117	...	...	...	...	...	...	...
Darlington 124 180 d.	2036	...	...	2136	...	...	...	...	...	...	...
Redcar Central 212 d.	|	2005	...	|	...	...	2104	...	2157	...	2319
Middlesbrough 212 d.	|	2019	...	|	...	...	2119	...	2211	...	2332
Northallerton 124 180 d.	|	2050	...	|	...	...	2148	...	2241	...	|
Thirsk d.	|	2058	...	|	...	...	2157	...	2249	...	|
Scarborough d.	|	|	2034	|	2134	...	|	...	|	2245	|
Malton d.	|	|	2058	|	2158	...	|	...	|	2311	|
York 124 180 a.	2102	2117	2125	2214	2225	...	2225	...	2313	2335	0035
York 124 d.	2105	...	2128	...	2226	...	...	...	2315	2339	...
Leeds 124 a.	2127	...	2156	...	2254	...	...	...	2341	0005	...
Leeds 188a d.	2130	...	2200	...	2257	...	...	2305	2344	0007	...
Dewsbury d.	2142	...	|	...	2308	...	...	2316	2356	|	...
Huddersfield 188a d.	|	...	2218	...	2318	...	...	2329	|	|	...
Manchester Victoria d.	2252f	...	|	...	|	...	...	|	0042	|	...
Manchester Picc. 188a a.	|	...	2252	...	2352	...	...	0006	0049	0121	...
Manchester Airport ✈ a.	|	...	...	...	0012	...	...	...	...	...	...
Liverpool Lime Street a.	2333	...	...	...	...	...	...	...	...	...	...

		①	②–⑤	①	②–⑤	①	②–⑤	Ⓐ	Ⓐ	Ⓐ
Liverpool Lime Street d.		...	...	...	...	...	...	...	...	...
Manchester Airport ✈ d.	Ⓐ	...	...	0038	0038	...	...	...	...	0419
Manchester Picc 188a d.		...	...	0053	0053	0242	0242	...	...	0433
Manchester Victoria d.		0001	0005	|	|	|	|	...	...	|
Huddersfield 188a d.		0028	0101	|	|	0349g	0349g	...	...	0529c
Dewsbury d.	♠	|	|	|	|	|	|	...	...	|
Leeds 188a a.		0105	0120	0206	0223	0408	0408	...	...	0550
Leeds 124 d.		0107	0124	0211	0235	0420	0420	...	...	0552
York 124 a.		0134	0202	0238	0314	0446	0459	...	...	0615
York 124 180 d.		...	...	...	...	▬	...	0505	0618	0617
Malton d.		...	...	...	...	...	...	|	|	0641
Scarborough a.		...	...	...	...	...	...	|	|	0707
Thirsk d.		...	...	...	...	...	...	0528	|	...
Northallerton 124 180 d.		...	...	...	...	...	...	0536	0637	...
Middlesbrough 212 a.		...	...	...	...	...	...	0634	|	...
Redcar Central 212 a.		...	...	...	...	...	...	0647	|	...
Darlington 124 180 d.		...	...	...	...	...	...	0558‡	0650	...
Durham 124 180 d.		...	...	...	...	Ⓐ	...	...	0706	...
Newcastle 124 180 a.		...	...	...	...	0704	...	...	0723	...
Edinburgh 124 180 a.		...	...	...	...	0855	...	...	...	...

	Ⓐ	Ⓐ	Ⓐ	Ⓐ	Ⓐ	Ⓐ	Ⓐ	Ⓐ	Ⓐ	Ⓐ	Ⓐ	Ⓐ	Ⓐ	Ⓐ	Ⓐ	Ⓐ	Ⓐ	Ⓐ	Ⓐ	Ⓐ	Ⓐ	Ⓐ	Ⓐ	Ⓐ	Ⓐ	Ⓐ
Liverpool Lime Street d.	...	...	...	...	...	0552	...	0654	0724	...	...	0754	...	0854	...	...	0954	...	...	1054	...	...	1154	...	...	1254
Manchester Airport ✈ d.	...	...	...	0537	...	|	0635	|	|	...	0747	|	0835	|	...	0940	|	...	1040	|	...	1140	|	...	1240	|
Manchester Picc. 188a d.	...	...	...	0557	...	|	0656	|	|	...	0805	|	0856	|	...	0957	|	...	1057	|	...	1157	|	...	1257	|
Manchester Victoria d.	...	...	...	0615c	...	0645c	0715	0730	0800	...	0815	0845c	0915	0946f	...	1015	1045f	...	1115	1146f	...	1215c	1245f	...	1315	1346f
Huddersfield 188a d.	...	...	...	0646	...	0717	0746	0800	0828	...	0846	0917	0946	1017	...	1045	1117	...	1146	1217	...	1246	1317	...	1346	1417
Dewsbury d.	...	...	...	0657	...	0727	0757	|	0838	...	0857	0927	0957	1027	...	1057	1127	...	1157	1227	...	1257	1327	...	1357	1427
Leeds 188a a.	...	...	...	0710	...	0740	0810	0822	0850	...	0910	0940	1010	1040	...	1110	1140	...	1210	1240	...	1310	1340	...	1410	1440
Leeds 124 d.	...	...	...	0714	...	0743	0813	0827	0852	0927	0914	0942	1014	1042	...	1114	1142	...	1214	1242	...	1314	1342	...	1414	1442
York 124 a.	...	...	...	0736	...	0805	0836	0856	0914	0956	0936	1004	1036	1105	...	1136	1204	...	1236	1305	...	1336	1404	...	1436	1504
York 124 180 d.	0639	0702	0710	0739	0803	0806	0839	0900	0916	1000	0939	1006	1039	1107	1117	1139	1206	1217	1239	1307	1317	1339	1406	1417	1439	1507
Malton d.	|	0727	|	|	0828	|	|	0925	|	1025	|	|	|	|	1142	|	|	1242	|	|	1342	|	|	1442	|	|
Scarborough a.	|	0753	|	|	0852	|	|	0949	|	1051	|	|	|	|	1206	|	|	1306	|	|	1406	|	|	1506	|	|
Thirsk d.	0656	...	|	0756	...	|	0856	...	|	...	0956	|	1056	|	...	1156	|	...	1256	|	...	1357	|	▬	1456	|
Northallerton 124 180 d.	0705	...	0729	0808	...	0826	0906	...	0935	...	1007	1026	1105	1126	...	1205	1225	...	1305	1326	...	1407	1426	...	1507	1526
Middlesbrough 212 a.	0735	...	|	0838	...	|	0936	...	|	...	1037	|	1135	|	...	1236	|	...	1335	|	...	1437	|	...	1537	|
Redcar Central 212 a.	0749	...	|	0849	...	|	0947	...	|	...	1049	|	1146	|	...	1247	|	...	1347	|	...	1449	|	...	1549	|
Darlington 124 180 d.	...	...	0742	...	...	0839	▬	...	0948	...	...	1039	▬	1139	...	...	1238	...	...	1340	...	...	1439	...	...	1539
Durham 124 180 d.	...	...	0800	...	...	0855	Ⓐ	...	1005	...	...	1055	Ⓐ	1155	...	...	1254	...	...	1357	...	...	1455	Ⓐ	...	1555
Newcastle 124 180 a.	...	...	0817	...	...	0911	0919	...	1017	...	...	1113	1206	1210	...	...	1312	...	...	1411	...	...	1513	1614	...	1613
Edinburgh 124 180 a.	...	...	...	...	...	...	1101	...	...	...	...	...	1352	...	...	...	...	...	...	...	...	...	...	1804	...	...

	Ⓐ	Ⓐ	Ⓐ	Ⓐ	Ⓐ	Ⓐ	Ⓐ	Ⓐ	Ⓐ	Ⓐ	ⒶA	Ⓐ	Ⓐ	Ⓐ	Ⓐ	Ⓐ	Ⓐ	Ⓐ	Ⓐ	ⒶA	Ⓐ	Ⓐ	Ⓐ	Ⓐ	Ⓐ	Ⓐ
Liverpool Lime Street d.	...	...	1354	...	...	...	1454	...	1554	...	...	1654	...	...	1754	...	...	...	1854	...	1954	...	...	2108	...	...
Manchester Airport ✈ d.	...	1340	|	...	1440	...	|	1540	|	...	1640	|	...	1740	|	...	1840	...	|	1938	|	...	2037	|	2135	2239
Manchester Picc. 188a d.	...	1357	|	...	1457	1529	|	1557	|	...	1656	|	...	1757	|	...	1857	...	|	1959	|	...	2056	|	2155	2258
Manchester Victoria d.	...	1415c	1446f	...	1515	|	1545	1615c	1646f	...	1715c	1745f	...	1815	1846f	...	1915	...	1945f	2015	2045f	...	2115	2145	2215	2315
Huddersfield 188a d.	...	1446	1515	...	1546	1601	1617	1646	1717	...	1745	1817	...	1846	1917	...	1946	...	2017	2046	2117	...	2148	2217	2246	2351
Dewsbury d.	...	1457	1527	...	1557	|	1627	1657	1726	...	1757	1827	...	1857	1927	...	1956	...	2027	2057	2127	...	2158	2227	2257	0008
Leeds 188a a.	...	1510	1540	...	1610	1621	1640	1710	1739	...	1810	1840	...	1910	1940	...	2010	...	2040	2110	2140	...	2212	2241	2310	0027
Leeds 124 d.	...	1514	1542	...	1614	1627	1642	1713	1742	...	1812	1842	...	1914	1942	...	2014	...	2050	2114	2142	...	2223	2243	2313	0031
York 124 a.	...	1536	1604	...	1636	1655	1705	1736	1805	...	1836	1907	...	1937	2004	...	2037	...	2128	2136	2208	...	2259	2307	2340	0111
York 124 180 d.	1517	1539	1607	1617	1639	1700	1706	1739	1806	1817	1839	1908	1917	1939	2007	2017	2041	2117	2130	2139	2221	2217	2301	2307	...	...
Malton d.	1542	|	|	1642	|	1725	|	|	|	1842	|	|	1942	|	|	2042	|	2142	|	|	|	2242	2326	|	...	...
Scarborough a.	1606	|	|	1706	|	1751	|	|	|	1906	|	|	2006	|	|	2106	|	2206	|	|	|	2308	2352	|	...	...
Thirsk d.	...	1556	|	...	1656	...	|	1756	1823	...	1856	|	▬	1957	|	...	2057	...	|	2156	|	...	...	2329	...	...
Northallerton 124 180 d.	...	1607	1626	...	1706	...	1726	1805	1831	...	1905	1927	...	2008	2026	...	2107	...	2200	2205	2240	...	...	2338	...	...
Middlesbrough 212 a.	...	1637	|	...	1737	...	|	1835	|	...	1935	|	...	2038	|	...	2137	...	|	2235	|	...	...	|	...	...
Redcar Central 212 a.	...	1649	|	...	1749	...	|	1846	|	...	1946	|	...	2049	|	...	2149	...	|	2246	|	...	...	|	...	...
Darlington 124 180 d.	...	...	1639	...	...	...	1739	...	1844	...	...	1940	...	...	2039	...	...	...	2215	...	2253	...	...	2352	...	...
Durham 124 180 d.	...	...	1700	...	...	...	1755	...	1901	...	...	1957	Ⓐ	...	2055	...	...	...	2231	...	2309	...	...	0009	...	...
Newcastle 124 180 a.	...	...	1718	...	...	...	1810	...	1918	...	...	2011	2101	...	2113	...	...	...	2244	...	2326	...	...	0040	...	...
Edinburgh 124 180 a.	...	...	...	...	...	...	...	...	...	...	...	...	2248	...	...	...	...	...	...	...	...	...	...	...	...	...

	⑤h	⑤k	①–④		⑦	⑦	⑦	⑦	⑦	⑦	⑦	⑦	⑦	⑦	⑦	⑦	⑦	⑦	⑦	⑦	⑦	⑦	⑦	⑦	⑦	⑦
Liverpool Lime Street d.	...	...	...		...	...	...	...	...	...	...	...	0854	...	...	0951	...	...	1051	...	...	1151	...	...	1251	...
Manchester Airport ✈ d.	2339	2343	2339	⑦	...	...	...	...	...	...	...	...	|	...	...	|	...	...	|	...	...	|	...	...	|	...
Manchester Picc. 188a d.	2355	0004	2355		...	...	...	...	...	0827	...	0916	|	...	1015	|	...	1113	|	...	1213	|	...	1314	|	...
Manchester Victoria d.	0005	|	0005		...	...	...	...	...	|	...	|	0937c	...	|	1037c	...	|	1137c	...	|	1237c	...	|	1337c	...
Huddersfield 188a d.	0034	0034	0101		...	...	...	...	...	0901	...	0945	|	...	1045	|	...	1146	|	...	1246	|	...	1346	|	...
Dewsbury d.	|	|	|	♥	...	...	...	...	...	0915	...	0957	1027	...	1055	1126	...	1157	1226	...	1257	1327	...	1357	1427	...
Leeds 188a a.	0111	0111	0120		...	...	...	...	...	0928	...	1010	1040	...	1108	1139	...	1210	1239	...	1310	1340	...	1410	1440	...
Leeds 124 d.	0113	0113	0124		...	...	0845	...	...	0930	...	1014	1042	...	1114	1141	...	1214	1241	...	1314	1345	...	1412	1441	...
York 124 a.	0139	0139	0202		...	...	0907	...	...	1000	...	1036	1105	...	1136	1203	...	1236	1304	...	1337	1410	...	1435	1504	...
York 124 180 d.	...	...	...		0842	0900	▬	0918	0937	1003	1007	1040	1108	1117	1139	1204	1217	1239	1306	1317	1339	1412	1417	1437	1507	1517
Malton d.	...	...	...		|	0925	...	|	|	1028	|	|	|	1142	|	|	1242	|	|	1342	|	|	1442	|	|	1542
Scarborough a.	...	...	...		|	0953	...	|	|	1054	|	|	|	1208	|	|	1308	|	|	1408	|	|	1508	|	|	1608
Thirsk d.	...	...	...		0859	...	...	|	0954	...	|	1100	|	...	|	|	...	1256	|	...	1356	|		1455	|	▬
Northallerton 124 180 d.	...	...	...		0907	...	...	|	1008	...	1026	1111	1127	...	1201	|	...	1305	1325	...	1405	|	...	1504	1526	...
Middlesbrough 212 a.	...	...	...		0937	...	...	|	1038	...	|	1141	|	...	1231	|	...	1335	|	...	1435	|	...	1534	|	...
Redcar Central 212 a.	...	...	...		0949	...	...	|	1050	...	|	1153	|	...	1243	|	...	1346	|	...	1446	|	...	1545	|	...
Darlington 124 180 d.	...	...	...		...	...	...	0946	...	...	1039	▬	1140	...	...	1232	...	...	1338	...	...	1440	...	...	1539	...
Durham 124 180 d.	...	...	...		...	...	⑦	1002	...	...	1055	⑦	1156	...	...	1249	...	...	1355	...	...	1457	...	...	1555	⑦
Newcastle 124 180 a.	...	...	...		...	...	0919	1018	...	...	1113	1156	1212	...	...	1304	...	...	1410	...	...	1514	...	...	1610	1711
Edinburgh 124 180 a.	...	...	...		...	...	1103	...	...	...	...	1347	...	...	...	...	...	...	...	...	...	...	...	...	...	1859

	⑦	⑦	⑦	⑦	⑦	⑦	⑦	⑦	⑦	⑦	⑦	⑦	⑦	⑦	⑦	⑦	⑦	⑦	⑦A	⑦	⑦	⑦	⑦	⑦	⑦	⑦
Liverpool Lime Street d.	...	1351	...	...	...	1450	...	1551	...	...	1651	...	...	1751	...	...	1851	...	...	...	1951	...	2108	...	...	...
Manchester Airport ✈ d.	...	|	...	...	...	|	...	|	...	...	|	...	...	|	...	...	|	...	...	...	|	...	|	...	...	...
Manchester Picc. 188a d.	1415	|	...	1510	...	|	1614	|	...	1714	|	...	1814	|	...	1914	|	...	2010	...	|	2114	|	2215	2245	2352
Manchester Victoria d.	|	1437c	...	|	...	1528	|	1637c	...	|	1737c	...	|	1837c	...	|	1937c	...	|	...	2037c	|	2148	|	|	|
Huddersfield 188a d.	1446	|	...	1546	1601	|	1646	|	...	1746	|	...	1846	|	...	1946	|	...	2046	...	|	2146	|	2246	2317	0028c
Dewsbury d.	1457	1527	...	1557	|	1627f	1657	1727	...	1757	1827	...	1857	1927	...	1957	2027	...	2057	...	2127	2156	|	2257	2327	|
Leeds 188a a.	1510	1540	...	1610	1621	1640	1710	1740	...	1810	1840	...	1910	1940	...	2010	2040	...	2111	...	2140	2209	2241	2310	2340	0105
Leeds 124 d.	1513	1542	...	1613	1627	1642	1714	1742	...	1814	1842	...	1914	1942	...	2014	2042	...	2112	...	2143	2214	2243	2314	2342	0107
York 124 a.	1535	1605	...	1635	1656	1705	1736	1805	...	1836	1905	...	1937	2005	...	2037	2105	...	2134	...	2207	2236	2308	2341	0010	0134
York 124 180 d.	1541	1607	1617	1639	1700	1707	1739	1807	1817	1839	1907	1917	1941	2007	2017	2041	2121	2117	2136	2201	...	2241	2309	...	...	...
Malton d.	|	|	1642	|	1725	|	|	|	1842	|	|	1942	|	|	2042	|	|	2142	|	2226	...	2306	|	...	...	...
Scarborough a.	|	|	1708	|	1751	|	|	|	1908	|	|	2008	|	|	2108	|	|	2208	|	2252	...	2334	|	...	...	...
Thirsk d.	1604	|	...	1656	...	|	1756	|	...	1856	|	▬	1958	|	...	2057	|	...	2158	...	...	...	2333	...	...	...
Northallerton 124 180 d.	|	1626	...	1705	...	1726	1805	1826	...	1905	1926	...	2007	2026	...	2106	|	...	2207	...	...	...	2343	...	...	...
Middlesbrough 212 a.	1641	|	...	1735	...	|	1835	|	...	1935	|	...	2037	|	...	2135	|	...	2236	...	...	...	|	...	...	...
Redcar Central 212 a.	1653	|	...	1747	...	|	1846	|	...	1946	|	...	2049	|	...	2147	|	...	2247	...	...	...	|	...	...	...
Darlington 124 180 d.	...	1639	...	...	...	1739	...	1839	...	...	1939	...	...	2039	...	...	2156	...	...	...	...	...	2357	...	...	...
Durham 124 180 d.	...	1655	...	...	...	1755	...	1855	...	...	1955	⑦	...	2055	...	...	2213	...	...	...	...	...	0014	...	...	...
Newcastle 124 180 a.	...	1713	...	...	...	1810	...	1913	...	...	2010	2114	...	2115	...	...	2225	...	...	...	...	...	0044	...	...	...
Edinburgh 124 180 a.	...	...	...	...	...	...	...	...	...	...	...	2258	...	...	...	...	...	...	...	...	...	...	...	...	...	...

A – To/from Saltburn (Table **212**).
c – Arrives 5–8 minutes earlier.
f – Arrives 11–15 minutes earlier.
g – Arrives 0334.
h – Until July 29.
k – From Aug. 5.
r – Arrives 0315.
v – Arrives 1608.
♠ – Service valid until Sept 9.
♥ – Service valid until July 31.
‡ – Arrival time. Departs 0607. Calls before Middlesbrough.

188a HULL - MANCHESTER TP

km		⚒	⑥	Ⓐ	⚒	⚒	⑥	Ⓐ	⚒	⚒		⚒	⚒	⚒	⑥	Ⓐ	Ⓐ	⑥	⚒	Ⓐ	⑥	⚒	⚒	⚒	⚒	⚒
0	**Hull** d.		0446	0505	0604	0705	0807	0807	0908	1008	...	1106	1206	1308	1407	1407	1503	1508	1608	1704	1708	1808	1903	2008	2107	2208
34	Selby d.		0522	0542	0637	0740	0840	0840	0940	1040	...	1138	1241	1340	1440	1440	1536	1540	1640	1737	1740	1840	1938	2041	2140	2240
83	**Leeds** 188 d.		0607r	0607	0707	0807	0907	0907	1007	1107	...	1207	1307	1407	1507	1507	1607	1607	1707	1807	1807	1907	2002c	2106	2205	2305
111	Huddersfield 188 d.		0625	0625	0725	0825	0925	0925	1025	1125	...	1225	1325	1424	1525	1525	1625	1625	1725	1825	1825	1925	2025	2127	2225	2329
140	Stalybridge d.		0654	0654	0754	0854	0943v	0949r	1044v	1143v	...	1243v	1343v	1443v	1543v	1550r	1654	1654	1754	1854	1854	1954	2054	2156	2252	2354
152	**Manchester** Piccadilly 188 a.		0711	0711	0812	0912	1004v	1005	1104a	1204a	...	1304a	1402a	1504a	1604a	1612	1709	1714	1810	1912	1909	2012	2113	2214	2308	0011

	⑦	⑦	⑦	⑦	⑦	⑦	♠	⑦	⑦	⑦	⑦
Hull d.		0808	0908	1009	1106	1209	and at	1908	2009	2106	2208
Selby d.		0841	0940	1041	1139	1241	the same	1940	2041	2138	2240
Leeds 188 d.		0907	1007	1107	1207	1307	minutes	2007	2107	2207	2305
Huddersfield 188 d.		0925	1025	1125	1225	1325	past each	2025	2127	2227	2329
Stalybridge d.		0953	1054	1154	1254	1354	hour until	2054	2156	2256	2351
Manchester Piccadilly 188 a.		1010	1110	1210	1309	1409		2109	2211	2311	0006

	⚒	⚒	⚒	⚒	⚒	⑥	Ⓐ	Ⓐ	⑥
Manchester Picc 188 d.		0535	0627	0728	0830	0930	0935	1030	1035j
Stalybridge d.		0549	0645	0745	0845	0945	0950	1050r	1050j
Huddersfield 188 d.		0614	0712	0812	0912	1012t	1012	1112	1112
Leeds 188 d.		0636	0734	0834	0934	1034	1034	1134	1134
Selby d.		0708	0754	0857	0958	1057	1057	1157	1157
Hull a.		0742	0834	0931	1034	1131	1131	1231	1231

	⚒	⚒	⚒	⚒	⚒	⚒	⚒	⚒	⚒	⚒	⚒	⚒	⑦	⑦	⑦	⑦	⑦		⑦	⑦	⑦	⑦	⑦	⑦	⑦
Manchester Piccadilly 188 d.	1135j	1235j	1335j	1435j	1535j	1630	1730	1830	1930	2030	2130	2230		...	0831	0927	1030	and at	1630	1730	1830	1930	2030	2127	2228
Stalybridge d.	1150j	1250j	1350j	1450j	1550j	1645	1745	1845	1945	2045	2145	2245		...	0844	0944	1044	the same	1644	1744	1844	1944	2044	2140	2244
Huddersfield 188 d.	1212	1312	1412	1509	1612	1712	1812	1912	2012	2112	2212	2312		...	0912	1012	1112	minutes	1712	1812	1912	2012	2112	2210	2312
Leeds 188 d.	1234	1335	1434	1533	1634	1735	1834	1934	2033	2134	2241r	2334		0836	0934	1034	1134	past each	1734	1834	1934	2034	2134	2237r	2331
Selby d.	1257	1357	1457	1557	1659	1800	1859	1957	2057	2200	2313	2354		0900	1002	1102	1159	hour until	1800	1900	2000	2059	2200	2313	...
Hull a.	1331	1431	1531	1631	1733	1837	1933	2034	2135	2236	2348	0029		0934	1037	1137	1236		1839	1936	2034	2136	2237	2347	...

a – 7 minutes later on ⑥ until July 20.
c – Departs 2007 on ⑥.
j – 5 minutes earlier on ⑥ until July 30.
r – Arrives 5–7 minutes earlier.
t – Arrives 7 minutes earlier from Aug. 6.
v – 10–11 minutes later on ⑥ until July 30.
♠ – Timings may be up to 3 minutes earlier.

189 GRIMSBY - LINCOLN - NEWARK - NOTTINGHAM - LEICESTER 2nd class EM

km		Ⓐ	Ⓐ	Ⓐ‡	ⒶL	Ⓐ	ⒶL	Ⓐ	Ⓐ‡		Ⓐ	Ⓐ	Ⓐ	Ⓐ	Ⓐ	Ⓐ	Ⓐ	Ⓐ	Ⓐ	Ⓐ	Ⓐ	Ⓐ	Ⓐ	Ⓐ
0	**Grimsby** Town 178 193 d.		...	0507	...	...	...	...	0558	...	...	0741	0839	...	1041	1241	...	1438	🚌	1641	...	1838	...	...
22	Barnetby 178 193 d.		...	0526	...	...	...	...	0616	...	...	0801	0858	...	1100	1300	...	1457	...	1700	...	1857	...	...
46	Market Rasen d.		...	0542	...	...	...	...	0632	...	...	0819	0914	...	1115	1315	...	1512	...	1715	...	1913	...	...
70	**Lincoln** 180 d.		0516	0601	0614	...	0640	...	0652	...	0747	0838	0935	1035	1135	1336	1437	1535f	1634	1738	1837	1932	2048	...
96	Newark Castle ♧ d.		0558	...	0642	...	0714f	...	0721n	...	0814	0906	1003	1104	1203	1404	1504	1558	1729	1808	1902	2001	2114	...
124	**Nottingham** ♧ a.		0634	...	0706	...	0739	...	...	...	0839	0927	1025	1125	1225	1426	1526	1626	...	1835	1925	2022	2141	...
	Nottingham 170 d.		...	...	0712	0727	0749	0824	...	...	...	0929	1027	1127	1227	1427	1528	1628	...	1837	1927	2024	...	2158
138	E Midlands Parkway 170 d.		...	...	0726	0744	0759	0842	...	...	...	0945	1043	1143	1243	1444	1544	1644	...	1853	1944	2042	...	2215
148	Loughborough 170 d.		...	...	|	0753	|	0852	...	...	...	0954	1052	1152	1252	1452	1553	1653	...	1902	1953	2050	...	2223
168	**Leicester** 170 a.		...	...	0740	0817	0812	0916	...	...	...	1017	1114	1214	1314	1515	1615	1715	...	1924	2018	2112	...	2248

	Ⓐ	Ⓐ‡	⑥	⑥	⑥	⑥‡	⑥	⑥	⑥	⑥‡		⑥	⑥	⑥		⑥	⑥	⑥		⑥	⑥‡	⑥	⑥	⑥
Grimsby Town 178 193 d.	...	2206		...	...	0642	...	0838	...	1038	...	1240	...	1438	...	1638	...	1839	...	...	1959	...	...	...
Barnetby 178 193 d.	...	2225		...	...	0702	...	0857	...	1057	...	1259	...	1457	...	1657	...	1859	...	...	2018	...	...	...
Market Rasen d.	...	2242		...	...	0717	...	0912	...	1112	...	1314	...	1512	...	1712	...	1914	...	...	2032	...	...	...
Lincoln d.	...	2306f		0518	0634	0739	0839	0933	1036	1133	...	1335	1437	1533	...	1731	1830	1934	...	2042	2051	...	2142	...
Newark Castle ♧ d.	...	2332		0600	0658	0806	0907	1003	1104	1202	...	1403	1506	1605	...	1759	1858	2003	...	2110	...	...	2210	...
Nottingham ♧ a.	...	0003		0636	0725	0828	0928	1027	1127	1226	...	1425	1527	1630	...	1825	1925	2029	...	2140	...	...	2240	...
Nottingham 170 d.	2320	...		*0649*	0726	0831	0929	1030	1129	1227	...	1427	1529	1632	...	1827	1927	2033	...	2149	...	2233	...	2318
E Midlands Parkway 170 d.	2333	...		*0659*	0744	0848	0946	1047	1148	1244	...	1444	1546	1649	...	1844	1944	2050	...	2206	...	2249	...	2332
Loughborough 170 d.	2341	...		|	0753	0856	0955	1055	1156	1253	...	1452	1554	1658	...	1852	1952	2058	...	2214	...	2258	...	2340
Leicester 170 a.	2353	...		*0712*	0815	0918	1017	1117	1218	1315	...	1515	1617	1720	...	1915	2015	2120	...	2237	...	2320	...	2351

	Ⓐ	Ⓐ§	Ⓐ	Ⓐ	Ⓐ	Ⓐ	Ⓐ	Ⓐ	Ⓐ	Ⓐ	Ⓐ	Ⓐ		Ⓐ	Ⓐ	Ⓐ§		Ⓐ§	Ⓐ	ⒶL		ⒶT	Ⓐ	Ⓐ
Leicester 170 d.		...	...	...	0638	0742	0841	0944	1043	1143	1243	1338	...	1539	1643	1743	...	1944	2041	2146	...	2130	...	2251
Loughborough 170 d.		...	...	...	0704	0804	0903	1007	1104	1205	1305	1403	...	1603	1705	1805	...	2006	2103	|	...	2152	...	2310
E Midlands Parkway 170 d.		...	...	...	0713	0813	0912	1016	1114	1214	1314	1413	...	1613	1714	1816	...	2015	2113	|	...	2210r	...	2318
Nottingham 170 a.		...	...	...	0732	0830	0928	1033	1132	1231	1331	1432	...	1632	1731	1833	...	2030	2131	2207	...	2227	...	2334
Nottingham ♧ d.		...	0539	0637	0737	0835	...	1035	1133	1235	1334	1435	...	1634	1735	1835	...	2032	2132	2215	...	...	2237	...
Newark Castle ♧ d.		...	0606	0659	0803	0903	...	1101f	1157	1301f	1356	1500	...	1701	1804	1902	...	2100	2204	2243	...	...	2310	...
Lincoln d.		0458	0636	0736r	0836	0933	...	1131	1227	1332	1425	1532	...	1732	1834	1932	...	2130	2234	2313	...	...	23379	...
Market Rasen d.		0514	0653	0752	...	0949	...	1147	...	1348	...	1548	...	1748	...	1948	...	2146	...	...	...	...	...	...
Barnetby 178 193 a.		0530	0708	0808	...	1005	...	1202	...	1403	...	1604	...	1804	...	2004	...	2201	...	...	...	...	...	...
Grimsby Town 178 193 a.		0549	0730	0829	...	1026	...	1223	...	1424	...	1625	...	1826	...	2026	...	2223	...	...	...	...	...	...

	⑥	⑥§	⑥	⑥	⑥	⑥		⑥§	⑥	⑥		⑥	⑥	⑥		⑥	⑥	⑥§	⑥		⑥	⑥	⑥	⑥
Leicester 170 d.		...	...	...	...	0643	...	...	0843	0943	...	1042	1143	1243	...	1343	1543	1643	1742	...	1943	2043	2143	2333
Loughborough 170 d.		...	...	...	...	0706	...	...	0905	1005	...	1104	1205	1305	...	1405	1605	1705	1804	...	2005	2105	2205	2344
E Midlands Parkway 170 d.		...	...	...	...	0715	...	...	0916	1014	...	1113	1213	1313	...	1413	1614	1715	1813	...	2013	2114	2214	2352
Nottingham 170 a.		...	...	...	...	0734	...	...	0933	1036	...	1135	1233	1334	...	1433	1631	1733	1832	...	2029	2130	2230	0008
Nottingham ♧ d.		...	0513	0555	...	0736	...	...	0934	1038	...	1138	1238	1338	...	1440	1633	1738	1834	...	2031	2132	...	...
Newark Castle ♧ d.		...	0535	0630	...	0800	...	0817n	0957	1101	...	1201	1301	1400	...	1503	1700	1803	1902	...	2057	2206	...	...
Lincoln d.		0520	0559	0659	0731	0830	...	0841	1026	1131	...	1230	1333	1429	...	1534	1731	1834	1931	...	2127	2229	...	...
Market Rasen d.		0536	...	...	0747	...	...	0857	...	1147	...	...	1349	...	...	1549	1746	1850	...	...	...	...	...	...
Barnetby 178 193 a.		0552	...	...	0802	...	...	0912	...	1202	...	...	1404	...	...	1605	1802	1906	...	...	...	...	...	...
Grimsby Town 178 193 a.		0613	...	...	0823	...	...	0936	...	1225	...	...	1428	...	...	1628	1825	1930	...	...	...	...	...	...

	⑦	⑦	⑦	⑦	⑦	⑦	⑦	⑦	⑦	⑦	⑦	⑦	⑦	⑦	⑦	⑦
Cleethorpes d.		...	...	...	...	...	1331	...	...	...	...	1823	...	...	2050	...
Grimsby Town 178 193 d.		...	...	...	...	...	1339	...	...	...	...	1831	...	...	2058	...
Barnetby 178 193 d.		...	...	...	...	...	1358	...	...	...	...	1850	...	...	2117	...
Market Rasen d.		...	...	...	...	...	1413	...	...	...	...	1905	...	...	2133	...
Lincoln d.		0900	1032	1124	1238	1338	1438f	1524	1635	1738	1852	1932c	2027	2103	2152	2251
Newark Castle d.		0929	1059	1153	1306	1405	1507	1553	1705	1808	1921	2001	2056	2132	...	2320
Nottingham a.		1005	1124	1230	1332	1430	1544	1617	1740	1836	1957	2025	2121	2200	...	2356

	⑦	⑦	⑦	⑦	⑦		⑦	⑦	⑦	⑦		⑦	⑦	⑦	⑦	⑦
Nottingham d.		0933	1024	1125	1227	...	1337	1427	1536	1628	...	1727	1853	1930	2027	2230
Newark Castle d.		1009	1048	1201	1251	...	1401	1503	1601	1652	...	1803	1917	1955	2051	2306
Lincoln d.		1040	1115	1232	1317	...	1427	1534	1638r	1723	...	1836	1947	2025	2123	2336
Market Rasen d.		...	1131	...	...	...	...	...	1654	...	...	1852	...	...	...	...
Barnetby 178 193 d.		...	1146	...	...	...	...	...	1710	...	...	1907	...	...	...	...
Grimsby Town 178 193 a.		...	1209	...	...	...	...	...	1733	...	...	1930	...	...	...	...
Cleethorpes a.		...	1219	...	...	...	...	...	1742	...	...	1942	...	...	...	...

G – From/to Cleethorpes (see table above).
L – To/from London St Pancras (Table **170**).
N – To Nottingham (Table **184**).
P – To/from Peterborough (Table **176**).
T – From Peterborough (Table **208**).

c – Arrives 1924.
f – Arrives 4–6 minutes earlier.
n – Newark North Gate.
r – Arrives 8–11 minutes earlier.

‡ – From Cleethorpes (departs 8 minutes earlier).
§ – To Cleethorpes (arrives 8–10 minutes after Grimsby Town).

LINCOLN - NEWARK NORTH GATE

See Table **180** for through services London Kings Cross - Newark - Lincoln and v.v.

km		Ⓐ	ⒶN	Ⓐ	ⒶG	Ⓐ	Ⓐ	ⒶP	Ⓐ	Ⓐ	Ⓐ	Ⓐ	Ⓐ	ⒶP	⑥	⑥N	⑥	⑥	⑥	⑥	⑥	⑥
0	**Lincoln** d.		0516	0600	0652	0730	0911	1002	1127	1324	1527	1727	2025	2233		0518	0608	0730	0744	1004	1127	1204
26	**Newark** North Gate a.		0545	0629	0721	0755	0939	1030	1151	1348	1551	1751	2049	2301		0547	0636	0756	0811	1030	1152	1230

	⑥	⑥	⑥	⑥	⑥	⑥	⑥	⑥	⑥	⑥	⑦	⑦	⑦	⑦	⑦	⑦	⑦	⑦	⑦	⑦	⑦	⑦
Lincoln d.	1324	1411	1527	1605	1655	1726	1801	1912	2025	2135		0835	1106	1223	1248	1427	1545	1710	1915	1958	2126	2230
Newark North Gate a.	1348	1437	1551	1631	1721	1750	1827	1939	2049	2203		0857	1130	1247	1312	1449	1609	1734	1937	2021	2155	2259

	Ⓐ	ⒶP	Ⓐ	Ⓐ	Ⓐ	Ⓐ	Ⓐ	Ⓐ	Ⓐ		Ⓐ	Ⓐ	Ⓐ	⑥	⑥P	⑥G	⑥	⑥	⑥	⑥	⑥	⑥
Newark North Gate d.		0637	0742	0929	0948	1039	1137	1337	1535	...	1737	2037	2315		0646	0817	0931	1040	1136	1235	1337	1452
Lincoln a.		0707	0811	0954	1017	1108	1202	1402	1601	...	1802	2103	2344		0712	0838	0956	1107	1201	1302	1402	1417

	⑥	⑥	⑥	⑥	⑥		⑥	⑥	⑥	⑦	⑦	⑦	⑦	⑦	⑦	⑦	⑦	⑦	⑦	⑦	⑦	⑦
Newark North Gate d.	1534	1642	1727	1737	1839	...	1944	2037	2211		0915	1140	1259	1335	1455	1555	1644	1755	1945	2028	2210	2321
Lincoln a.	1559	1709	1753	1802	1906	...	2010	2103	2240		0946	1204	1325	1401	1520	1622	1714	1820	2007	2051	2236	2351

♧ – Additional journeys Newark Castle - Nottingham and v.v.
Journey time: 28–36 minutes.
From Newark Castle on Ⓐ at: 0627, 0736, 0841, 0936, 1136, 1243, 1343, 1436, 1639, 1736, 1845, 1945.
On ⑥ at: 0736, 0841, 0940, 1136, 1243, 1343, 1438, 1636, 1736, 1835, 1941.
From Nottingham on Ⓐ at: 0543, 0650, 0757, 0851, 1058, 1157, 1255, 1358, 1556, 1656, 1752, 1851.
On ⑥ at: 0650, 0758, 0901, 1059, 1155, 1256, 1355, 1556, 1656, 1758, 1854.

NT 2nd class LEEDS - BRADFORD - HALIFAX - MANCHESTER - CHESTER 190

Additional trains run Leeds - Bradford - Manchester Victoria and v.v. on ⚒.

km		⚒	⚒	⚒	⚒	⚒	⚒	⚒	⚒	⚒	⚒	⑥	Ⓐ	⚒	⚒	⚒	⚒	⚒	⚒	⚒	⑦	⑦	♣	⑦
0	**Leeds** 191 d.	0542	0642	0742	0842	0942	1042	1142	1242	1342	1442	1542	1542	1642	1742	1840	1940	2042	2142	2242	0819	0918		2319
15	**Bradford** Interchange. 191 d.	0603	0704	0803	0904	1004	1104	1204	1303	1403	1504	1604	1604	1704	1803	1905	2003	2103	2203	2303	0839	0939		2339
28	Halifax 191 d.	0617	0717	0817	0917	1017	1117	1217	1317	1417	1517	1617	1617	1717	1817	1917	2017	2116	2217	2316	0850	0950	and	2350
42	Hebden Bridge 191 d.	0632	0733	0833	0933	1033	1133	1233	1333	1433	1533	1633	1633	1732	1833	1933	2033	2132	2232	2332	0902	1002		0002
49	Todmorden 191a d.	0639	0739	0840	0940	1040	1140	1240	1340	1440	1540	1640	1640	1739	1840	1940	2040	2140	2239	2338	0908	1008	hourly	0008
63	Rochdale 191a d.	0650	0751	0850	0951	1051	1151	1251	1351	1451	1551	1651	1655	1750	1851	1951	2051	2151	2251	2352	0921	1021		0020
80	**Manchester** Victoria. 191a a.	0706	0806	0905	1005	1106	1205	1306	1405	1506	1605	1705	1712	1805	1905	2005	2106	2206	2308	0009	0935	1035	until	0034
113	Warrington Bank Quay 160 d.	0744a	0843	0947a	1043	1139	1239f	1345	1439	1539	1639	1737	1746	1844a	1942	2043	2151	...	...	...	...	...		...
142	**Chester** 160 a.	0808	0907	1015	1107	1205	1305	1407	1505	1615j	1705	1805	1815	1913	2005	2105	2217	...	...	...	...	...		...

	⚒	⚒	⚒	⚒	⚒	⚒	⚒	⚒	⚒	⚒	⚒	⚒	Ⓐ	⑥	Ⓐ	⑥	⚒	⚒	⚒	⚒	⚒	⑦	♥	⑦
Chester 160 d.	...	...	0617r	0720	0823	0922	1025	1125	1225	1322v	1422	1519	1615	1623	1717	1721	1825	1922	2021	...	...	...		...
Warrington Bank Quay. 160 d.	...	...	0646	0747	0849	0946	1046	1146	1246	1346	1446	1545f	1645k	1645	1740	1746	1847t	1946	2047	...	...	...		...
Manchester Victoria .. 191a d.	0545	0632	0719	0821	0921	1021	1121	1221	1321	1421	1521	1622	1722	1722	1820	1822	1921	2019	2121	2156	2256	0854	and	2254
Rochdale 191a d.	0606	0645	0734	0835	0933	1033	1133	1233	1333	1433	1533	1636	1739	1739	1835	1834	1933	2031	2133	2210	2310	0907		2307
Todmorden 191a d.	0623	0658	0743	0845	0943	1043	1143	1243	1343	1443	1543	1646	1748	1748	1848	1848	1943	2041	2143	2221	2321	0919	hourly	2319
Hebden Bridge 191 d.	0631	0704	0750	0851	0950	1050	1150	1250	1350	1450	1550	1652	1754	1754	1855	1854	1949	2050	2150	2227	2327	0925		2325
Halifax 191 d.	0646	0719	0805	0906	1005	1105	1205	1305	1405	1505	1605	1706	1809	1809	1910	1910	2004	2105	2205	2239	2338	0938	until	2338
Bradford Interchange .. 191 d.	0702	0737	0820	0921	1022	1123f	1221	1321	1421	1521v	1621	1722	1825	1825	1926	1926	2021	2122	2221	2254	2353	0954		2354
Leeds 191 a.	0724	0800	0841	0943	1043	1143	1242	1343	1442	1545	1642	1743	1844	1845	1947	1947	2043	2143	2245	2315	0015	1015		0014

a – Arrives 6–8 minutes earlier on Ⓐ.
f – Arrives 5 minutes earlier.
j – 1605 on Ⓐ.
k – Arrives 1637.
r – 0625 on ⑥.
t – 1852 on Ⓐ.
v – 3 minutes later on ⑥.
♥ – The 1154 from Manchester Victoria departs Todmorden 1223, Hebden Bridge 1229, Halifax 1244, Bradford Interchange 1300 and arrives Leeds 1320.
♣ – The 1918 from Leeds departs Bradford Interchange 1942, Halifax 1954, Hebden Bridge 2007, Todmorden 2014, Rochdale 2029 and arrives Manchester Victoria 2045.

NT 2nd class YORK - LEEDS - BLACKBURN - BLACKPOOL 191

km		⚒	⚒	⚒	⚒	⚒	⚒	⚒	⊡	⚒	⚒	⚒	⚒	⚒	⑦	⑦	⑦	⑦		⑦	⑦	⑦	⑦	⑦
0	**York** 124 188 d.	0519	0612	0713	0822	0923	1023	1123		1822	1922	2023	2123	2219	0921	1021	1122	1221		1723	1822	1920	2023	2121
41	**Leeds** 124 188 190 d.	0557	0657	0755	0857	0957	1058	1156		1857	1957	2057	2156	2257	0957	1057	1157	1257		1757	1857	1957	2057	2157
56	**Bradford** Interchange. 190 d.	0616	0717	0816	0916	1017	1121	1217	and	1917	2017	2117	2216	2317	1016	1117	1217	1317	and	1817	1917	2017	2117	2217
69	Halifax 190 d.	0627	0728	0827	0927	1028	1132	1229		1928	2028	2128	2227	2328	1027	1129	1229	1329		1829	1929	2029	2129	2229
83	Hebden Bridge 190 d.	0641	0739	0838	0938	1039	1142	1240	hourly	1940	2039	2141	2238	2340	1042	1143	1243	1343	hourly	1843	1943	2043	2144	2246
103	Burnley Manchester Road . d.	0705	0804	0903f	1003	1103	1203	1303		2003	2103	2203	2303f	2359	1103	1203	1303	1403		1903	2003	2102	2205	2308
113	Accrington d.	0714	0813	0912	1012	1112	1212	1312	until	2012	2112	2212	2312	0008	1112	1213	1313	1414	until	1914	2013	2113	2214	2317
123	**Blackburn** d.	0723	0821	0921	1021	1120	1221	1320		2020	2121	2220	2321	0021	1123	1222	1324	1424		1923	2027f	2124	2224	2326
142	**Preston** 156 a.	0745	0844	0939	1039	1138	1239	1338		2039	2141	2240	2339	...	1141	1239	1341	1443		1940	2044	2141	2242	2343
171	**Blackpool** North 156 a.	0809	0907	1002	1102	1202	1302	1403		2103	2205	2304	0005	...	1206	1303	1405	1507		2005	2108	2205	2306	0008

	⚒	⚒	⚒	⚒	⚒	⚒	⊖	⚒	⚒	⚒	⚒	Ⓐ	⑦	⑦	⑦	⑦	⑦	⑦	⑦	⊡	⑦	⑦	⑦	⑦
Blackpool North 156 d.	0520	0621	0721	0821	0921	1022		1822	1922	2022	2118	2202	...	...	0918	1023	1117	1217	1318		1818	1918	2020	2119
Preston 156 d.	0545	0646	0746	0845	0946	1046		1846	1946	2046	2142	2226	...	...	0947	1047	1143	1241	1342		1842	1942	2044	2143
Blackburn d.	0603	0703	0803	0903	1003	1103	and	1903	2003	2103	2158	2243	...	0904	1004	1104	1200	1257	1358	and	1858	1959	2102	2200
Accrington d.	0611	0711	0811	0911	1011	1111		1911	2011	2111	2206	2251	...	0912	1012	1112	1208	1305	1406		1906	2007	2109	2208
Burnley Manchester Road d.	0620	0720	0820	0920	1020	1120	hourly	1920	2020	2120	2215	2300	...	0921	1021	1121	1217	1314	1415	hourly	1915	2016	2118	2217
Hebden Bridge 190 d.	0642	0742	0842	0942	1042	1141		1941	2042	2141	2236	2323	...	0942	1042	1141	1238	1336	1437		1937	2037	2140	2238
Halifax 190 d.	0653	0753	0853	0953	1053	1152	until	1952	2053	2152	2247	2334	0858	0956	1056	1156	1252	1350	1452	until	1952	2051	2155	2253
Bradford Interchange .. 190 d.	0709	0807	0907	1007	1107	1206		2007	2107	2207	2302	2347	0914	1011	1111	1210	1307	1405	1506		2007	2106	2209	2308
Leeds 124 188 190 a.	0730r	0826	0928	1028	1127	1229		2026	2129	2227	2324	...	0935	1029	1128	1228	1327	1426	1526		2026	2125	2227	2326
York 124 188 a.	0800	0900	1000	1100	1200	1301		2100	2201	2304	0001	...	1013	1101	1200	1300	1359	1501	1600		2059	2200	2257	2356

f – Arrives 5–6 minutes earlier.
r – Departs 0737.
⊡ – Timings may vary ± 4 minutes.
⊖ – On ⑥ no departure from Blackpool at 1222; departs 1219 - other timings as shown.

NT 2nd class MANCHESTER - BURNLEY - BLACKBURN 191a

km		⚒	⚒	⚒	⚒	⊡	⚒	⚒	⚒	⚒	⚒	⚒	⑦	⑦	⑦	⊡	⑦	⑦	⑦	⑦	⑦	⑦
0	**Manchester** Victoria d.	0600	0704	0904	1004		1704	1904	2004	2104	2204	2304	0833	0858	1000		1700	1802	1900	2000	2100	2202
17	Rochdale d.	0614	0718	0921	1020	and	1720	1920	2018	2118	2217	2318	0854	0919	1021	and	1721	1822	1920	2021	2121	2222
31	Todmorden d.	0629	0735	0935	1034	hourly	1736	1934	2033	2136	2235	2333	0909	0935	1036	hourly	1736	1837	1935	2036	2136	2237
45	Burnley Manchester Road d.	0645	0751	0951	1050		1752	1950	2049	2152	2251	2349	0925	0951	1052		1752	1853	1951	2052	2152	2253
54	Accrington d.	0655	0801	1001	1100	until	1802	2000	2059	2202	2301	0001	0936	1002	1103	until	1803	1903	2001	2103	2203	2303
63	**Blackburn** a.	0706	0812	1012	1111		1813	2010	2111	2213	2313	0012	0952	1018	1118		1818	1918	2016	2119	2219	2318

	⚒	⚒	⚒	⚒		⚒	⚒		⚒	⚒	⚒	⚒	⚒	⑦	⑦	⑦h		⑦h	⑦	⑦	⑦	⑦
Blackburn d.	0619	0714	0818	1019		1319	1519		1819	2017	2120	2219	2319	0748	0812	0912		1912	2017	2113	2213	2300
Accrington d.	0627	0721	0827	1027	and	1327	1527	and	1827	2025	2130	2227	2327	0756	0821	0921	and	1921	2026	2122	2222	2308
Burnley Manchester Road d.	0638	0732	0838	1038	hourly	1338	1538	hourly	1838	2036	2141	2238	2338	0807	0832	0932	hourly	1932	2037	2133	2233	2319
Todmordon d.	0654	0749	0854	1054		1354	1554		1855	2052	2157	2254	2354	0824	0848	0948		1948	2055	2149	2249	2335
Rochdale d.	0707	0804	0907	1107	until	1407	1607	until	1910	2109	2214	2311	0009	0838	0903	1003	until	2003	2109	2204	2304	2349
Manchester Victoria a.	0724	0824f	0924	1124		1424	1624		1924	2123	2229	2333	0023	0859	0924	1024		2024	2132	2225	2325	0011

f – On ⑥ arrives 0818.
h – Until July 31 runs 8 minutes later throughout.
⊡ – Timings may vary ± 1–3 minutes. On ⚒ the 1304 from Manchester does not run.

NT 2nd class HULL - DONCASTER - SHEFFIELD 192

km		⚒	⚒	⚒	⚒B	⚒A	⚒B	⚒B		⚒B	ⒶB	⑥B	⑥B	ⒶB	⚒	⑦	⑦	⑦A	⑦	⑦	⑦B		⑦B	⑦	⑦
0	**Hull** 181 d.	0519	0631	0721	0828	0925	1023	1125		1926	2021	2026	2125	2126	2245	0845	0927	1029	1125	1229	1329		2129	2157	2253
17	Brough d.	0531	0643	0733	0841	0937	1035	1137	and	1938	2033	2038	2137	2138	2257	0902	0939	1041	1137	1241	1341	and	2141	2214	2310
38	Goole d.	0550	0658	0749	0856	0954	1050	1154	hourly	1954	|	|	2152	2153	2313	0918	0954	1056	1154	1256	1356	hourly	2156	2230	2326
66	**Doncaster** 181 a.	0612	0719	0818	0919	1019	1112	1219		2020	2113	2119	2214	2215	2339	0943	1019	1119	1217	1321	1420		2219	2258	2356
66	**Doncaster** 193 d.	0614	0720	0822	0920	1021	1115	1220	until	2021	2117	2121	2216	2217	2343	...	1021	1122	1219	1323	1421	until	2221	...	...
90	Meadowhall 193 d.	0634	0739	0840	0940	1038	1137	1237		2040	2135	2139	2233	2237	0008	...	1039	1144	1237	1341	1439		2242	...	...
96	**Sheffield** 193 a.	0642	0746	0848	0949	1048	1148	1249		2049	2143	2150	2241	2245	0017	...	1049	1151	1248	1348	1449		2250	...	...

	⚒B	⚒B	▽⊙	⚒B	⚒	Ⓐ	⑥	⚒C	⚒	⚒	⑦B	⑦B	⑦B	⑦B	⑦B	⑦B	⑦B	⑦B	⑦B	⑦B	⑦A	⑦A	⑦	⑦	⑦
Sheffield 193 d.	0542	0655		1757	1856	1957	1957	2056	2157	2300	0836	0925	1025	1134	1225	1324	1425	1525	1625	1725	1825	1925	2026	2126	2225
Meadowhall 193 d.	0548	0703	and	1803	1902	2003	2003	2102	2203	2306	0843	0931	1031	1141	1231	1331	1432	1531	1632	1731	1831	1931	2032	2132	2231
Doncaster 193 a.	0612	0724	hourly	1824	1922	2022	2022	2123	2222	2325	0903	0950	1050	1200	1250	1350	1453	1550	1654	1750	1850	1950	2049	2150	2250
Doncaster 181 d.	0614	0726		1826	1923	2024	2029	2123	2225	2328	0905	0952	1054	1203	1255	1352	1500	1552	1655	1802	1852	1951	2052	2152	2252
Goole d.	0638	0746	until	1847	1941	|	|	2142	2244	2347	0924	1011	1113	1223	1314	1411	1519	1611	1718	1824	1911	2011	2116	2211	2317
Brough d.	0659	0801		1904	1959	2102	2106	2157	2302	0002	0939	1026	1128	1240	1329	1426	1534	1626	1734	1839	1926	2025	2134	2227	2337
Hull 181 a.	0719	0816		1917	2013	2116	2123	2213	2315	0015	0952	1040	1142	1254	1342	1439	1548	1639	1748	1852	1939	2041	2148	2241	2355

A – From/to Bridlington (Table 177).
B – From/to Scarborough (Table 177).
C – To Bridlington on ⑥ (Table 177).
▽ – Timings may vary by ± 3 minutes.
⊙ – On ⑥ the 0957 from Sheffield departs Doncaster 1030, Goole 1050, Brough 1106. and arrives Hull 1119.

193 CLEETHORPES - DONCASTER - SHEFFIELD - MANCHESTER TP

km		⚒	⚒	⚒	⚒	⚒	⚒	⚒		⚒	⚒	⚒	Ⓐ	⑦	⑦	⑦	⑦	⑦		⑦	⑦	⑦	⑦
0	**Cleethorpes** 178 d.	...	...	...	0504	0624	0727	0824	◧	1824	1924	2024	2124	...	...	...	0926	1024	⊖	1827	1924	2024	2114
5	Grimsby Town 178 189 d.	...	...	...	0512	0632	0735	0832		1832	1932	2032	2132	...	...	...	0934	1032		1835	1932	2032	2122
29	Barnetby 178 189 d.	...	...	...	0532	0652	0755	0852		1852	1952	2052	2152	...	...	...	0953	1052	and	1855	1952	2052	2142
48	Scunthorpe d.	...	...	...	0547	0708	0811	0908	and	1908	2008	2108	2208	...	...	...	1011	1108	hourly	1908	2008	2108	2158
85	**Doncaster** a.	...	...	...	0625	0738	0841	0938		1941	2038	2138	2238	...	...	...	1039	1140		1941	2038	2142	2228
85	**Doncaster** 192 d.	...	...	0536	0626	0742	0843	0942	hourly	1942	2042	2143	2244	...	...	0945	1044	1143	until	1942	2043	2144	2229
109	Meadowhall 192 d.	...	...	0557	0654	0759	0902	1002		2003	2104	2202	|	...	...	1005	1102	1200		2001	2103	2203	|
115	**Sheffield** 192 a.	...	...	0607	0705	0806	0909	1009	until	2009	2109	2209	2323	...	...	1012	1110	1209		2008	2109	2210	2300
115	**Sheffield** 206 d.	0325j	0508	0609	0707	0808	0911	1011		2011	2111	2210	...	0751	0911	1014	1111	1211		2011	2111	2213	...
175	Stockport 206 a.	|	|	0653	0752	0852	0952	1052		2052	2152	2255	...	0834	0953	1055	1155	1253		2052	2155	2301	...
184	**Manchester** Piccadilly 206 a.	0452j	0608	0703	0803	0902	1002	1105		2101	2206	2305	...	0844	1003	1105	1210	1305		2102	2206	2311	...
200	**Manchester** Airport ✈ a.	0523	...	...	...	...	...	...		...	...	2323t	...	...	...	...	...	...		...	...	...	...

	⚒	⚒	⚒	⚒	⚒		⚒	⚒	⚒	⚒	⑥	Ⓐ	Ⓐ	⑦	⑦	⑦	⑦	⑦		⑦	⑦	⑦	⑦
Manchester Airport ✈ d.	...	0554	...	...	...	♥	...	...	...	2052t	...	...	2330	...	...	...	...	...	♠	...	...	...	...
Manchester Piccadilly 206 d.	...	0615	0718	0818	1018		1818	1918	2018	2118	2217	2220	2350	0813	0910	1013	1119	1219		2018	2119	2219	2319
Stockport 206 d.	...	0626	0728	0828	1028		1828	1928	2028	2128	|	|	|	0823	0919	1023	1129	1228		2028	2128	2227	2328
Sheffield 206 a.	...	0706	0810	0909	1108	and	1908	2008	2109	2208	2307	2309	0126	0908	1008	1107	1209	1309	and	2109	2211	2309	0010
Sheffield 192 d.	0521	0708	0811	0911	1111		1911	2011	2111	2211	2309	2312	...	0910	1010	1110	1210	1310		2111	2212	2311	...
Meadowhall 192 d.	|	0715	0817	0917	1117	hourly	1917	2017	2117	2217	|	|	...	0916	1016	1116	1216	1316	hourly	2117	2218	|	...
Doncaster 192 a.	0551	0732	0836	0937	1135		1937	2035	2140	2235	2335	2354	...	0936	1036	1136	1234	1335		2135	2236	2340	...
Doncaster d.	0553	0733	0838	0939	1137	until	1938	2037	2144	2238	...	...	...	0938	1038	1139	1237	1337	until	2137	2239	...	...
Scunthorpe d.	0619	0801	0904	1005	1203		2003	2103	2211	2313	...	...	...	1004	1104	1205	1303	1403		2204	2305	...	...
Barnetby 178 189 d.	0636	0817	0919	1020	1218		2018	2118	2227	2328	...	...	...	1019	1120	1220	1318	1417		2219	2320	...	...
Grimsby Town 178 189 d.	0702	0844	0940	1042	1243		2040	2140	2250	2350	...	...	...	1041	1144	1242	1342	1442		2241	2344	...	...
Cleethorpes 178 a.	0716	0853	0952	1054	1255		2052	2152	2305	0003	...	...	...	1053	1154	1254	1352	1453		2253	2354	...	...

j – On ① departs Sheffield 0345, arrives Manchester Piccadilly 0437.
t – Ⓐ only.

♥ – The 1318 from Manchester to Cleethorpes does not run.
♠ – The 1519 from Manchester to Cleethorpes does not run.
◧ – The 0924 and 1324 from Cleethorpes to Manchester do not run.
⊖ – The 1126 from Cleethorpes to Manchester does not run.

194 SHEFFIELD - MANCHESTER (Hope Valley service) 2nd class only NT

km		⚒	Ⓐ	⑥	Ⓐ	⑥	⚒	⑥	Ⓐ	⚒	⚒	⚒	⚒	Ⓐ	⑥	⚒		⑥	Ⓐ	⚒	⚒	⚒	⚒	⚒	⚒
0	**Sheffield** 193 d.	...	0618	0620	0710	0712	0728j	0812	0832	0914	1014	1114	1214	1314	1314	1414	...	1514	1546	1614	1714	1814	1914	2014	2114
16	Grindleford d.	...	0633	0635	0728	0728	|	0827	|	0929	1029	1128	1228	1326	1328	1429	...	1528	1559	1629	1729	1829	1929	2028t	2128
18	Hathersage d.	...	0638	0639	0732	0732	|	0831	|	0932	1032	1132	1232	|	1332	1432	...	1532	1603	1632	1732	1832	1932	2031	2131
24	Hope d.	...	0646	0647	0740	0739	|	0838	|	0940	1040	1139	1239	1335	1339	1440	...	1539	1609	1640	1740	1840	1940	2037	2138
32	Edale d.	...	0653	0654	0747	0747	|	0846	0857	0947	1047	1147	1247	|	1347	1447	...	1547	|	1647	1747	1847	1947	2044	2145
41	Chinley d.	0648	0701	0702	0756	0755	0803	0854	0905	0955	1055	1155	1255	1348	1355	1457	...	1555	1621	1655	1755	1855	1955	2052	2152
67	**Manchester** Piccadilly 193 a.	0732	0736	0736	0834	0834	0836	0934	0941	1034	1132	1232	1332	1431	1432	1534	...	1631	1702	1734	1832	1934	2036n	2131	2230

	⑥	Ⓐ	Ⓐ	⑦	⑦	⑦	⑦		⑦	⑦
Sheffield 193 d.	2224	2247	2327	0914	1017	1115	1214		2014	2216
Grindleford d.	2238	2302	2342	0928	1031	1129	1228	and	2028	2231
Hathersage d.	2242	2306	2345	0932	1034	1133	1232		2032	2234
Hope d.	2249	2313	2353	0939	1041	1140	1239	hourly	2039	2242
Edale d.	2256	2321	2359	0947	1048	1147	1346		2046	2249
Chinley d.	2304	2329	0008	0955	1055	1156	1355	until	2055	2258
Manchester Piccadilly 193 a.	2341	0018	0036	1032	1132	1240a	1434		2134	2337

	⚒	⚒	Ⓐ	⑥	⚒	Ⓐ	⑥	⚒
Manchester Picc 193 d.	0546	0638	0713	0749	0849	0942	0949	1049
Chinley d.	0615	0713	0748	0824	0923	1015	1023	1123
Edale d.	0623	0722	0756	0832	0932	1024	1032	1132
Hope d.	0630	0729	0802	0839	0938	1031	1038	1138
Hathersage d.	0637	0736	0809	0846	0945	1039	1045	1145
Grindleford d.	0641	0740	0813	0850	0949	1043	1049	1149
Sheffield 193 a.	0659	0804f	0832	0905	1005	1059	1106	1206

		⚒	⚒	⚒	⚒	⚒	⚒	Ⓐ	⑥	⚒	⑥	Ⓐ	⚒	⑦	⑦g	⑦h	⑦h	⑦g	⑦	A	⑦	⑦	⑦
Manchester Piccadilly 193 d.		1549	1642	1649	1742	1749	1849	1949	1949	2049	2119	2122	2228	0743	0829	0845	0931	0944	1045		1945	2045	2213
Chinley d.	and	1624	1709	1724	1809	1824	1924	2022	2024	2123	2157	2212	2254	0821	0905	0921	1008	1020	1121	and	2021	2118	2246
Edale d.		1633	|	1732	|	1832	1932	|	2032	2131	...	|	2302	0830	0914	0930	1017	1029	1130	hourly	2029	2127	2254
Hope d.	hourly	1639	|	1739	|	1839	1939	2034	2039	2138	...	2225	2308	0837	0920	0936	1023	1036	1136	until	2036	2132	2300
Hathersage d.		1645	|	1746	|	1846	1946	2039	2046	2145	...	2232	2316	0844	0927	0943	1030	1043	1143		2043	2139	2305
Grindleford d.	until	1649	|	1750	|	1850	1950	|	2050	2149	...	|	2320	0848	0931	0947	1034	1047	1147	▽	2047	2143	2310
Sheffield 193 a.		1706	1739	1807	1842c	1907	2006	2057	2106	2210	...	2252	2336	0905	0948	1004	1051	1104	1205		2102	2202	2326

A – From Sept. 18 the 1245 departure from Manchester Piccadilly is retimed to depart at 1252.
a – Until Sept. 11 arrives 1232.
c – Arrives 1836 on ⑥.
f – Arrives 0759 on ⑥.
g – Until Sept. 11.
h – From Sept. 18.
j – Departs 0734 on ⑥.
n – Arrives 2031 on Ⓐ.
t – Ⓐ only.
▽ – Timings may vary by ± 4 minutes.

200 LONDON - HARWICH, IPSWICH and NORWICH Most Norwich trains convey 🍸 LE

km		Ⓐ 2P	Ⓐ	Ⓐ	Ⓐ 2	Ⓐ	Ⓐ C	Ⓐ	Ⓐ	Ⓐ	Ⓐ	Ⓐ 2	Ⓐ	Ⓐ	Ⓐ 2	Ⓐ	Ⓐ	Ⓐ	Ⓐ	Ⓐ	Ⓐ	Ⓐ 2	Ⓐ	Ⓐ	Ⓐ 2
0	**London** Liverpool Street d.	...	...	0600	0616	0625	...	0700	0730	0755	0830	0900	0930	1000	1030	1100	1130	1200	1230	1300	1330	1400	1430	1500	1530
48	Chelmsford d.	...	...	0630	0651	0656	...	|	0802	|	0902	|	1003	|	1104	|	1201	|	1301	|	1401	|	1502	|	1559
84	Colchester d.	0540	*0615*	0649	0714	0719	...	0748	0822	0847	0923	0947	1021	1046	1123	1147	1221	1247	1320	1348	1420	1447	1521	1548	1620
97	Manningtree ★ d.	0549	*0623*	0657	0722	0727	...	0756	0830	0855	0931	0955	1029	1054	1131	1155	1229	1255	1328	1356	1428	1455	1528	1556	1628
112	**Harwich** Int'l ★ d.	|	|	|	0740	|	0745	|	|	|	|	|	|	|	|	|	|	|	|	|	|	|	|	|	|
115	**Harwich** Town ★ a.	|	|	|	0745	|	|	|	|	|	|	|	|	|	|	|	|	|	|	|	|	|	|	|	|
111	**Ipswich** 205 d.	0600	0639	0710	...	0739	0819v	0811f	0843	0906	0943	1008	1042	1106	1143	1207	1241	1306	1339	1407	1439	1506	1539	1607	1640
130	Stowmarket 205 d.	0612	0650	0721	...	0750	0834	0822	0855	|	0953	|	1053	|	1154	|	1252	|	1351	|	1450	|	1551	|	1651
153	Diss d.	...	0702	0733	...	0802	...	0834	0907	0927	1005	1028	1104	1126	1206	1227	1304	1329	1403	1427	1502	1529	1603	1629	1703
185	**Norwich** a.	...	0722	0752	...	0820	...	0852	0924	0945	1022	1048	1122	1144	1225	1245	1322	1346	1420	1445	1519	1546	1620	1647	1720

	Ⓐ	Ⓐ	Ⓐ	Ⓐ 2	Ⓐ	Ⓐ	Ⓐ 2	Ⓐ	Ⓐ 2	Ⓐ 2	Ⓐ 2	Ⓐ	Ⓐ 2	Ⓐ 2	Ⓐ 2	Ⓐ	Ⓐ 2L	Ⓐ 2	Ⓐ	Ⓐ 2	Ⓐ	Ⓐ 2	Ⓐ	⑥ 2P	⑥ 2
London Liverpool Street d.	1600	1630	1700	1702	1730	1750	1802	1830	1845	1902	1908	1930	2000	2002	2030	2100	...	2102	2130	2200	2230	2302	2330	...	...
Chelmsford d.	|	|	|	1733	|	|	1833	|	1919	|	1941	|	|	2035	2100	|	...	2134	2200	2228	2303	2334	0001	...	...
Colchester d.	1646	1718	|	1759	|	1843	1901	1920	1957	1948	2011	2020	2050	2105	2121	2147	...	2204	2220	2247	2322	0004	0021	0540	0610
Manningtree ★ d.	1654	1726	1749	1806	1827	1851	1909	1928	2005	1956	2019	2029	2058	2113	2129	2155	...	2212	2229	2255	2330	0012	0029	0548	0618
Harwich Int'l ★ d.	|	|	|	|	|	|	|	|	2023	|	|	|	|	|	|	|	2147	2227	|	|	|	|	|	|	|
Harwich Town ★ a.	|	|	|	|	|	|	|	|	...	|	|	|	|	|	|	|	|	...	|	|	|	|	|	|	|
Ipswich 205 d.	1707	1737	1800	1819	1840	1903	1923	1940	...	2009	2030	2041	2109	2126	2141	2207	2213	...	2243v	2307	2342	0030	0045r	0600	0629
Stowmarket 205 d.	1719	1748	1811	...	1851	1914	...	1951	...	2020	...	2052	2120	...	2152	2218	...	...	2255	...	2353	...	0057	0611	...
Diss d.	1731	1800	1823	...	1903	1927	...	2003	...	2032	...	2104	2132	...	2204	2230	...	...	2307	...	0009	...	0110	...	...
Norwich a.	1750	1819	1841	...	1923	1946	...	2023	...	2050	...	2121	2149	...	2221	2248	...	...	2326	...	0027	...	0133	...	...

C – To Cambridge (Table **205**).
P – To Peterborough (Table **205**).
L – To Lowestoft (Table **201**).
f – Arrives 0806.
r – Arrives 0039.
t – Arrives 1737.
v – Arrives 4 minutes earlier.

LE Most Norwich trains convey 🍸 LONDON - HARWICH, IPSWICH and NORWICH 200

	⑥ 2	⑥	⑥	⑥ C	⑥ 2	⑥	⑥	⑥	⑥	⑥ 2	⑥	⑥		⑥ 2	⑥	⑥	⑥	⑥	⑥	⑥	⑥ 2	⑥	⑥	⑥ 2	⑥	⑥
London Liverpool Street d.	0534	...	0630	...	0636	0700	0730	0800	0830	0900	0930	1000	...	1030	1102	1130	1200	1230	1300	1330	1400	1430	1500	1530	1600	1630
Chelmsford d.	0610	...	0701	...	0710	|	0801	|	0901	|	1001	|	...	1101	|	1201	|	1301	|	1401	|	1501	|	1601	|	1701
Colchester d.	0643	...	0720	...	0738	0747	0820	0847	0920	0947	1020	1047	...	1120	1147	1220	1247	1320	1347	1420	1448	1520	1547	1620	1647	1720
Manningtree ★ d.	0651	...	0728	...	0746	0755	0828	0855	0928	0955	1028	1055	...	1128	1155	1228	1255	1328	1355	1428	1456	1528	1555	1628	1655	1728
Harwich Int'l ★ d.	|	...	|	0750	0805	|	|	|	|	|	|	|	...	|	|	|	|	|	|	|	|	|	|	|	|	|
Harwich Town ★ a.	|	...	|	|	...	|	|	|	|	|	|	|	...	|	|	|	|	|	|	|	|	|	|	|	|	|
Ipswich 205 d.	0702	0710	0739	0821f	...	0806	0839	0906	0939	1006	1039	1106	...	1139	1209	1239	1306	1339	1409v	1439	1507	1539	1606	1639	1706	1739
Stowmarket 205 d.	...	0721	0751	0835	...	|	0851	|	0951	|	1051	|	...	1151	|	1251	|	1351	|	1451	|	1551	|	1651	1717	1751
Diss d.	...	0733	0803	...	...	0826	0903	0928	1003	1026	1103	1126	...	1203	1230	1303	1326	1403	1429	1503	1526	1603	1626	1703	1729	1803
Norwich a.	...	0752	0820	...	...	0843	0920	0945	1020	1043	1120	1143	...	1220	1247	1320	1343	1420	1447	1520	1544	1620	1644	1720	1748	1820

	⑥	⑥	⑥	⑥	⑥ 2	⑥	⑥ 2	⑥ 2	⑥ 2	⑥ 2L	⑥ 2	⑥ 2	⑥	⑥ 2	⑥	⑥ 2	⑥
London Liverpool Street d.	1700	1730	1800	1830	1902	1930	1936	2000	2030	...	2100	2102	2130	2200	2230	2302	2330
Chelmsford d.	|	1801	|	1901	|	2001	2009	|	2101	...	|	2134	2201	2228	2301	2335	2359
Colchester d.	1747	1820	1847	1920	1947	2020	2032	2047	2120	...	2148	2204	2220	2248	2320	0005	0021
Manningtree ★ d.	1755	1828	1855	1928	1955	2028	2040	2055	2128	...	2156	2212	2228	2256	2328	0013	0029
Harwich Int'l ★ d.	|	|	|	|	|	|	2055	|	|	2138	|	2227	|	|	|	|	|
Harwich Town ★ a.	|	|	|	|	|	|	...	|	|	|	|	...	|	|	|	|	|
Ipswich 205 d.	1806	1839	1906	1939	2008	2039	...	2106	2139	2204	2207	...	2239	2307	2339	0024	0041
Stowmarket 205 d.	|	1851	|	1951	|	2051	...	|	2151	...	...	...	2251	...	2351	...	0052
Diss d.	1826	1903	1928	2003	2028	2103	...	2126	2203	...	...	...	2303	...	0003	...	0105
Norwich a.	1843	1920	1946	2020	2046	2120	...	2143	2220	...	...	...	2320	...	0020	...	0122

⑦	⑦ 2	⑦ 2	⑦	⑦ 2	⑦ 2C	⑦	⑦ 2P	⑦ 2
London Liverpool Street d.	0644	...	...	...	...	0810	...	0907
Chelmsford d.	0725	...	...	...	...	|	...	0942
Colchester d.	0748	0813	...	0818	...	0916	0925	1011
Manningtree ★ d.	0756	0821	...	0827	...	0924	0933	1019
Harwich Int'l ★ d.	0811	|	...	0844	0850	|	|	|
Harwich Town ★ a.	...	|	...	0849	|	|	|	|
Ipswich 205 d.	...	0832	0842	...	0920c	0936	0955t	1030
Stowmarket 205 d.	...	...	0853	...	0934	0947	1006	...
Diss d.	...	...	0905	...	...	0959	...	...
Norwich a.	...	...	0924	...	...	1017	...	...

	⑦	⑦ 2	⑦	⑦ 2	⑦ 2	⑦		⑦ 2	⑦	⑦ 2	⑦ 2	⑦	⑦	⑦ 2	⑦	⑦ 2	⑦ 2	⑦	⑦ 2	⑦ 2	⑦	⑦ 2	⑦	⑦ 2	⑦
London Liverpool Street d.	0930	1007	1030	1100	1107	1130	and	1707	1730	1800	1807	1830	1900	1907	1930	2000	2007	2030	...	2107	2130	2207	2230	2307	2330
Chelmsford d.	|	1042	|	|	1142	|	at	1742	|	|	1842	|	|	1942	|	2032	2042	|	...	2142	|	2242	|	2342	|
Colchester d.	1017	1111	1117	1144	1211	1217	the	1811	1817	1844	1911	1917	1944	2011	2017	2055	2111	2117	...	2211	2217	2311	2317	0011	0017
Manningtree ★ d.	1025	1119	1125	|	1219	1225	same	1819	1825	|	1919	1925	1952	2019	2025	2103	2119	2125	...	2219	2225	2319	2326	0019	0026
Harwich Int'l ★ d.	|	|	|	|	|	|	minutes	|	|	|	|	|	|	|	|	2119	|	|	2138	|	|	|	|	|	|
Harwich Town ★ a.	|	|	|	|	|	|	past	|	|	|	|	|	|	|	|	...	|	|	|	|	|	|	|	|	|
Ipswich 205 d.	1036	1133	1137	1201	1230	1236	each	1830	1836	1901	1930	1936	2003	2030	2036	...	2130	2136	2204	2231	2236	2331	2338	0031	0038
Stowmarket 205 d.	1048	...	1148	1213	...	1248	hour	...	1848	1912	...	1948	2014	...	2048	...	...	2148	...	...	2248	...	2349	...	0050
Diss d.	1100	...	1200	1225	...	1300	until	...	1900	1924	...	2000	2026	...	2100	...	...	2200	...	...	2300	...	0001	...	0103
Norwich a.	1117	...	1218	1242	...	1318		...	1917	1941	...	2017	2044	...	2117	...	...	2217	...	...	2318	...	0019	...	0120

Ⓐ	Ⓐ 2	Ⓐ 2	Ⓐ	Ⓐ	Ⓐ 2	Ⓐ L	Ⓐ 2	Ⓐ 2	Ⓐ	Ⓐ 2	Ⓐ	Ⓐ 2	Ⓐ		Ⓐ	Ⓐ	Ⓐ	Ⓐ	Ⓐ	Ⓐ 2	Ⓐ	Ⓐ	Ⓐ 2	Ⓐ	Ⓐ
Norwich d.	...	0500r	0525r	0600r	...	...	0624r	...	0702r	...	0726	0803	0830	...	0903	0932	1000	1030	1100	1132	1200	1232	1300	1330	1401
Diss d.	...	0518r	0543r	0618r	...	...	0642r	...	0720	...	0744	0820	0847	...	0920	0949	1017	1047	1117	1149	1217	1249	1317	1348	1418
Stowmarket 205 d.	...	0531r	0556r	0631	...	...	0655	...	0733	...	0756	0832	|	...	0932	|	1029	|	1129	|	1229	|	1329	|	1430
Ipswich 205 d.	0512	0544	0609	0644	0652	0658	0708	...	0748	...	0813	0844	0910	...	0945	1010	1041	1110	1142	1210	1242	1310	1341	1410	1442
Harwich Town ★ d.	|	|	|	|	|	|	|	...	|	0755	|	|	|	...	|	|	|	|	|	|	|	|	|	|	|
Harwich Int'l ★ d.	|	|	|	|	|	0725	|	0724	|	0800	|	|	|	...	|	|	|	|	|	|	|	|	|	|	|
Manningtree ★ d.	0523	0555	0619	0654	0702	...	0719	0738	0757	0817	0822	0853	0919	...	0954	1019	1051	1119	1151	1219	1251	1319	1350	1419	1451
Colchester d.	0533	0606	0630	0705	0713	...	0730	0748	0808	0835t	0832	0903	0930	...	1004	1030	1101	1130	1201	1230	1301	1330	1400	1430	1502
Chelmsford d.	0556	|	|	|	0742	...	|	0815	|	0857	|	0921	|	...	1022	|	1118	|	1218	|	1319	|	1419	|	1519
London Liverpool Street a.	0632	0654	0722	0758	0819	...	0823	0855	0858	0938	0925	1000	1019	...	1055	1118	1151	1215	1251	1315	1351	1416	1451	1517	1551

	Ⓐ	Ⓐ	Ⓐ	Ⓐ	Ⓐ 2	Ⓐ	Ⓐ	Ⓐ 2	Ⓐ	Ⓐ	Ⓐ 2	Ⓐ	Ⓐ 2	Ⓐ C	Ⓐ	Ⓐ 2P	Ⓐ	Ⓐ 2	Ⓐ	Ⓐ 2P	Ⓐ 2	Ⓐ 2
Norwich d.	1430	1500	1530	1600	1630	1703	1730	1800	1832	1900	1932	2000	...	...	2032	...	2102	...	2202	...	...	2305
Diss d.	1447	1517	1548	1617	1648	1720	1747	1817	1849	1917	1949	2017	...	...	2049	...	2119	...	2219	...	...	2323
Stowmarket 205 d.	|	1529	|	1629	|	1733	1759	1829	|	1929	|	2029	...	2047	|	2115	2131	...	2231	2310	...	2335
Ipswich 205 d.	1509	1543	1610	1642	1710	1749	1811	1842	1910	1942	2010	2045c	...	2103	2110	2128	2144	2223	2243	2322	...	2349
Harwich Town ★ d.	|	|	|	|	|	|	|	|	|	|	|	|	...	|	|	|	|	|	|	|	2328	...
Harwich Int'l ★ d.	|	|	|	|	|	|	|	|	|	|	|	|	2045	2129	|	|	|	|	|	|	2333	...
Manningtree ★ d.	1519	1553	1619	1652	1719	|	1820	1852	1920	1953	2020	2054	2058	...	2120	2138	2153	2233	2253	2331	2350	...
Colchester d.	1530	1603	1630	1704	1730	1806	1830	1903	1930	2002	2030	2103	2112c	...	2130	2150	2203	2243	2303	2340	2359	...
Chelmsford d.	|	1621	|	1721	|	1823	|	1921	|	2020	|	2121	2140	...	|	...	2221	2309	2325	...	...	...
London Liverpool Street a.	1615	1657	1718	1758	1820	1858	1916	1953	2020	2054	2119	2155	2214	...	2218	...	2255	2348	0003	...	...	...

⑥	⑥ 2	⑥	⑥
Norwich d.	0500	0532	0600
Diss d.	0517	0549	0617
Stowmarket 205 d.	0529	|	0629
Ipswich 205 d.	0541	0610	0641
Harwich Town ★ d.	|	|	|
Harwich Int'l ★ d.	|	|	|
Manningtree ★ d.	0551	0620	0651
Colchester d.	0601	0630	0701
Chelmsford d.	0619	|	0719
London Liverpool Street a.	0651	0715	0751

	⑥ L	⑥ 2	⑥ 2	⑥	⑥	⑥ 2	⑥	⑥	⑥	⑥	⑥	⑥		⑥ 2	⑥	⑥	⑥ 2	⑥	⑥	⑥	⑥	⑥	⑥	⑥ 2	⑥	⑥
Norwich d.	...	0632	...	0700	0732	0800	0832	0903	0932	1000	1032	1100	...	1132	1200	1232	1300	1332	1400	1432	1500	1532	1600	1630	1703	1730
Diss d.	...	0649	...	0717	0749	0817	0849	0920	0949	1017	1049	1117	...	1149	1217	1249	1317	1349	1417	1449	1517	1549	1617	1647	1720	1747
Stowmarket 205 d.	...	|	...	0729	|	0829	|	0932	|	1029	|	1129	...	|	1229	|	1329	|	1429	|	1529	|	1629	|	1732	1759
Ipswich 205 d.	0659	0710	...	0741	0810	0841	0910	0944	1010	1041	1110	1141	...	1210	1241	1310	1341	1410	1441	1510	1541	1610	1641	1709	1744	1811
Harwich Town ★ d.	|	|	...	|	|	|	|	|	|	|	|	|	...	|	|	|	|	|	|	|	|	|	|	|	|	|
Harwich Int'l ★ d.	0727	|	0720	|	|	|	|	|	|	|	|	|	...	|	|	|	|	|	|	|	|	|	|	|	|	|
Manningtree ★ d.	...	0720	0733	0751	0820	0851	0920	0954	1019	1051	1119	1151	...	1219	1251	1320	1351	1419	1451	1519	1551	1619	1651	1719	1754	1820
Colchester d.	...	0730	0743	0801	0830	0901	0930	1003	1030	1101	1130	1201	...	1230	1301	1330	1401	1430	1501	1530	1601	1630	1701	1730	1803	1830
Chelmsford d.	...	|	0809	0819	|	0919	|	1021	|	1119	|	1219	...	|	1319	|	1419	|	1519	|	1619	|	1719	|	1821	|
London Liverpool Street a.	...	0815	0846	0851	0915	0951	1015	1053	1115	1151	1215	1251	...	1315	1351	1415	1451	1515	1551	1615	1651	1715	1751	1815	1853	1915

	⑥ 2	⑥	⑥	⑥ 2		⑥	⑥ 2	⑥ 2C	⑥ 2	⑥ 2P	⑥	⑥ 2	⑥ 2	⑥	⑥ 2P	⑥	⑥ 2
Norwich d.	1800	1832	1900	...	...	2000	...	...	...	...	2100	...	...	2200	...	...	2305
Diss d.	1817	1849	1917	...	...	2017	...	...	...	...	2117	...	...	2217	...	...	2323
Stowmarket 205 d.	1829	|	1929	...	...	2029	...	2046	...	2115	2129	...	...	2229	2310	...	2335
Ipswich 205 d.	1841	1910	1941	2009	...	2041	...	2101	2109	2128	2141	2152	2223	2241	2323	...	2346
Harwich Town ★ d.	|	|	|	|	...	|	|	|	|	|	|	|	|	|	|	2326	...
Harwich Int'l ★ d.	|	|	|	|	...	|	2045	2125	|	|	|	|	|	|	|	2331	...
Manningtree ★ d.	1851	1919	1951	2019	...	2051	2058	...	2119	2137	2151	2202	2233	2251	2332	2348	...
Colchester d.	1901	1930	2001	2029	...	2101	2112c	...	2129	2148	2201	2212	2243	2301	2342	2357	...
Chelmsford d.	1919	|	2019	|	...	2119	2140	...	|	...	2219	2240	2309	2324	...	...	...
London Liverpool Street a.	1951	2015	2051	2115	...	2151	2214	...	2215	...	2251	2313	2345	2358	...	...	...

⑦	⑦ 2	⑦	⑦ 2	⑦ 2	⑦	⑦ 2	⑦ 2	⑦
Norwich d.	...	0657	...	...	0800	0825	...	0900
Diss d.	...	0714	...	...	0817	0842	...	0917
Stowmarket 205 d.	...	0725	...	...	0829	0854	...	0929
Ipswich 205 d.	...	0737	0752	0811	0841	0906	0911	0941
Harwich Town ★ d.	...	|	|	|	|	|	|	|
Harwich Int'l ★ d.	0720	|	0815	|	|	|	|	|
Manningtree ★ d.	0733	0746	...	0821	0851	|	0921	0951
Colchester d.	0742	0756	...	0830	0900	0922	0930	1000
Chelmsford d.	0804	|	...	0859	|	|	0959	|
London Liverpool Street a.	0858	0900	...	0935	0947	1007	1035	1047

		⑦ 2	⑦	⑦ 2	⑦ 2	⑦	⑦	⑦ 2	⑦	⑦ 2	⑦	⑦ 2	⑦ 2P	⑦	⑦ 2	⑦ 2	⑦	⑦ 2C	⑦ 2	⑦ 2P	⑦	⑦ 2	⑦	⑦ 2	⑦ 2
Norwich d.	and	...	1500	1523	...	1600	1623	...	1700	...	1800	...	...	1900	...	...	2000	...	...	...	2100	...	2205	...	2305
Diss d.	at	...	1517	1540	...	1617	1640	...	1717	...	1817	...	...	1917	...	...	2017	...	...	...	2117	...	2222	...	2322
Stowmarket 205 d.	the	...	1529	1552	...	1629	1652	...	1729	...	1829	...	1912	1929	...	...	2029	2046	...	2111	2129	...	2234	...	2334
Ipswich 205 d.	same	1511	1541	1605	1611	1641	1705	1711	1741	1811	1841	1911	1925	1941	2011	...	2041	2103	2111	2123	2141	2211	2246	...	2346
Harwich Town ★ d.	minutes	|	|	|	|	|	|	|	|	|	|	|	|	|	|	...	|	|	|	|	|	|	|	2254	...
Harwich Int'l ★ d.	past	|	|	|	|	|	|	|	|	|	|	|	|	|	|	2030	|	2126	|	|	|	|	|	2259	...
Manningtree ★ d.	each	1521	1551	|	1621	1651	|	1721	1751	1821	1851	1921	1934	1951	2021	2043	2051	...	2120	2132	2151	2221	2255	2315	...
Colchester d.	hour	1530	1600	1621	1630	1700	1721	1730	1800	1830	1900	1930	1943	2000	2030	2052	2100	...	2130	2142	2200	2230	2304	2325	...
Chelmsford d.	until	1559	|	|	1659	|	|	1759	|	1859	|	1959	...	|	2059	2110	|	...	2159	...	|	2259	2325	...	...
London Liverpool Street a.		1635	1647	1709	1735	1747	1809	1835	1847	1935	1947	2035	...	2047	2135	2144	2147	...	2235	...	2247	2335	2359	...	...

C – To/from Cambridge (Table **205**).
P – To/from Peterborough (Table **205**).
L – To/from Lowestoft (Table **201**).

c – Arrives 5–6 minutes earlier.
f – Arrives 0817.
r – Departs 3–5 minutes later until Oct. 7.
t – Arrives 8–11 minutes earlier.

★ – All trains Manningtree - Harwich International - Harwich Town and v.v.
Manningtree - Harwich Town: on Ⓐ at 0553, 0701, 0722, 0801, 0859 and hourly until 1759, 1901, 2000, 2101, 2200, 2300, 2335; on ⑥ at 0556, 0659 and hourly until 2259, 2335; on ⑦ at 0827 and hourly until 2227.
Harwich Town - Manningtree on Ⓐ at 0524, 0626, 0728, 0755, 0828, 0926 and hourly until 1826, 1928, 2028, 2128, 2228, 2328; on ⑥ at 0626 and hourly until 2326; on ⑦ at 0854 and hourly until 2254.

201 IPSWICH - LOWESTOFT
2nd class only LE

km		Ⓐ	Ⓐ	Ⓐ		Ⓐ	Ⓐ	Ⓐ	Ⓐ	Ⓐ		Ⓐ H	⑥	◧	⑥ H	⑦	⑦	⑦	⑦	and in	⑦	⑦	⑦
0	**Ipswich** d.	0620	0734	0916		1516	1554	1717	1813	1917		2216	0716		2215	1008	1110	1208	1310	the same	2011	2108	2202
17	Woodbridge d.	0637	0753	0931	and	1531	1618f	1732	1830	1932	and	2231	0731	and	2230	1025	1125	1225	1325	pattern	2025	2125	2219
36	Saxmundham d.	0744r	0815	0953	hourly	1553	1640	1754	1851	1954	hourly	2253	0753	hourly	2252	1047	1147	1247	1347	every	2047	2147	2240
65	Beccles d.	0815	0846	1024	until	1624	1718f	1825	1925	2025	until	2324	0824	until	2323	1118	1218	1318	1418	**two** hours	2118	2218	2311
79	**Lowestoft** a.	0833	0906	1042		1642	1736	1843	1943	2043		2342	0844		2341	1136	1236	1336	1436	until	2136	2236	2330

	Ⓐ H	Ⓐ	Ⓐ	Ⓐ	Ⓐ	Ⓐ	Ⓐ		Ⓐ	Ⓐ	Ⓐ	Ⓐ	Ⓐ	Ⓐ	Ⓐ	⑥		⑥	⑦	⑦	⑦	⑦		⑦
Lowestoft d.	0524	0614	0640	0727	0907	1007	1106		1506	1606	1702	1807	1907	2007	2107	0606		2106	0805	0905	1005	1100		2000
Beccles d.	0540	0630	0656	0743	0924	1025	1124	and	1524	1624	1725f	1825	1925	2025	2125	0624	and	2124	0821	0921	1021	1121t	and	2021t
Saxmundham d.	0611	0702	0727	0815	0955	1056	1155	hourly	1555	1705f	1756	1856	1956	2056	2156	0655	hourly	2155	0852	0952	1052	1152	hourly	2052
Woodbridge d.	0634	0725	0750	0838	1017	1118	1217	until	1617	1726	1818	1918	2018	2118	2218	0717	until	2217	0914	1014	1114	1214	until	2114
Ipswich a.	0652	0743	0808	0856	1036	1136	1235		1636	1743	1836	1936	2036	2136	2235	0734		2235	0931	1031	1131	1231		2131

H – To/from Harwich International (Table **200**). **f** – Arrives 6–8 minutes earlier. **r** – Arrives 0658. ◧ – The 1616 departure from Ipswich arrives Lowestoft at 1750.

203 NORWICH and IPSWICH local services
2nd class LE

NORWICH - GREAT YARMOUTH
Journey time ± 32 minutes *30 km (33 km via Reedham)*

From Norwich: Trains noted '**r**' call at **Reedham** 18–21 minutes later.

Ⓐ: 0506, 0611, 0652, 0736**r**, 0836, 0906**a**, 0936, 1025**a**, 1036, 1136**r**, 1236, 1318**a**, 1336, 1425**a**, 1440, 1536, 1640, 1706, 1736, 1840, 1940, 2040, 2140, 2300.

⑥: 0530**r**, 0636, 0706, 0736**r**, 0809, 0836, 0906**b**, 0936, 0955**b**, 1024**b**, 1036, 1120**b**, 1136**r**, 1216**b**, 1235, 1318**b**, 1336, 1418**b**, 1436, 1518**b**, 1536, 1640, 1706, 1736, 1806, 1840, 1940, 2040, 2140, 2300.

⑦: 0736**r**, 0845 and the service repeats at the same times **every 2 hours** until 2136**r**, 2236.

From Great Yarmouth: Trains noted '**r**' call at **Reedham** 12–14 minutes later.

Ⓐ: 0543, 0624, 0658, 0732, 0817, 0917, 0952**a**, 1017, 1113**a**, 1117, 1217, 1317, 1352**a**, 1417, 1517**r**, 1545**a**, 1617, 1717, 1747**r**, 1817, 1917, 2017, 2117, 2217, 2334**r**.

⑥: 0615, 0717, 0745, 0817, 0847, 0917, 0947**b**, 1017, 1041**b**, 1115**b**, 1117, 1157**b**, 1217, 1255**b**, 1317, 1355**b**, 1417, 1455**b**, 1512**r**, 1555**b**, 1617, 1717, 1747**r**, 1817, 1847**r**, 1917, 2017, 2117, 2217, 2334**r**.

⑦: 0817**r**, 0922 and the service repeats at the same times **every 2 hours** until 2217**r**, 2317**r**.

NORWICH - LOWESTOFT
Journey time ± 43 minutes *38 km*

From Norwich: Trains noted '**r**' call at **Reedham** 18–21 minutes later.

Ⓐ: 0536**r**, 0627**r**, 0645**r**, 0755**r**, 0855, 1005**r**, 1058, 1205**r**, 1255, 1405**r**, 1455**r**, 1550**r**, 1658**r**, 1750**r**, 1902**r**, 2005**r**, 2105**r**, 2205**r**, 2240**r**.

⑥: 0540**r**, 0650**r**, 0750**r**, 0855, 1005**r**, 1058, 1205**r**, 1258, 1405**r**, 1458**r**, 1555**r**, 1657**r**, 1750**r**, 1905**r**, 2005**r**, 2105**r**, 2205**r**, 2240**r**.

⑦: 0725, 0805**r**, 0905, 1005**r**, 1105, 1205**r**, 1305, 1405**r**, 1505, 1605**r**, 1705, 1805**r**, 1905, 2005**r**, 2058**r**.

From Lowestoft: Trains noted '**r**' call at **Reedham** 20–23 minutes later.

Ⓐ: 0542**r**, 0635**r**, 0733**r**, 0750**r**, 0850**r**, 0948**r**, 1057, 1148**r**, 1257, 1348**r**, 1457, 1548**r**, 1648**r**, 1748**r**, 1848**r**, 1955**r**, 2057, 2148**r**, 2248**r**, 2330**r**.

⑥: 0638**r**, 0740**r**, 0848**r**, 0948**r**, 1057, 1148**r**, 1257, 1348**r**, 1457, 1548**r**, 1648**r**, 1748**r**, 1848**r**, 1955**r**, 2057, 2148**r**, 2248**r**, 2330**r**.

⑦: 0858, 0946**r**, 1105, 1146**r**, 1305, 1346**r**, 1505, 1546**r**, 1705, 1746**r**, 1905, 1946**r**, 2105, 2146**r**, 2335**r**.

NORWICH - SHERINGHAM (🚂)
Journey time ± 57 minutes *49 km*

From Norwich:
Trains call at **Hoveton and Wroxham** 🚂 ± 15 minutes, and **Cromer** ± 45 minutes later.

⚒: 0510 Ⓐ, 0520 ⑥, 0540 Ⓐ, 0545 ⑥, 0715, 0821, 0945, 1045 and hourly until 1745, 1854, 1955, 2115, 2245 ①–④, 2305 ⑤⑥.

⑦: 0836, 0945, 1036, 1145, 1236, 1345, 1436, 1545, 1636, 1745, 1836, 1945, 2036.

From Sheringham:
Trains call at **Cromer** ± 11 minutes, and **Hoveton and Wroxham** 🚂 ± 39 minutes later.

⚒: 0007 ⑥, 0621 ⑥, 0631 Ⓐ, 0716, 0822, 0944, 1047, 1144, 1247, 1344, 1447, 1546, 1649, 1749, 1852, 1956, 2110, 2217, 2347 ①–④ (also 0553 Ⓐ from Cromer).

⑦: 0007, 0942, 1041, 1142, 1241, 1342, 1441, 1542, 1641, 1742, 1841, 1942, 2041, 2142.

IPSWICH - FELIXSTOWE
Journey time ± 25 minutes *25 km*

From Ipswich:

Ⓐ: 0504, 0604, 0714, 0825, 0857, 0958 and hourly until 2058, 2228.

⑥: 0558, 0658, 0758 and hourly until 2058, 2228.

⑦: 0955, 1055 and hourly until 1955.

From Felixstowe:

Ⓐ: 0534, 0636, 0747, 0854, 0928 and hourly until 2128, 2301.

⑥: 0628, 0728, 0828 and hourly until 2128, 2258.

⑦: 1025, 1125 and hourly until 2025.

a – ①⑤ July 18 - Sept. 2.
b – Until Sept. 10.
r – Via Reedham.

🚂 – Heritage and Tourist railways:
NORTH NORFOLK RAILWAY: Sheringham - Holt and v.v. *8 km*. ✆ 01263 820800. www.nnrailway.co.uk
BURE VALLEY STEAM RAILWAY: Wroxham - Aylsham and v.v. ✆ 01263 733858. www.bvrw.co.uk

204 IPSWICH - CAMBRIDGE and PETERBOROUGH
2nd class only LE

km		Ⓐ	⑥	⚒C	Ⓐ	⑥	Ⓐ	⑥	⑥	Ⓐ	ⒶH	⑥H	⚒	⑥	Ⓐ	⚒	⚒	Ⓐ	⑥	⚒	⚒	Ⓐ	⑥	⚒	⚒	⑥	Ⓐ
0	**Ipswich** 200 d.	0510	0511	0600	0617	0619	0656	0720	0758	0801	0819	0821	0921	0958	1001	1021	1121	1156	1200	1221	1321	1358	1402	1420	1521	1558	1600
19	Stowmarket 200 d.	0522	0525	0611	0631	0633	0710	0735	0809	0812	0834	0835	0936	1009	1012	1035	1135	1207	1211	1235	1335	1409	1412	1435	1535	1609	1612
42	Bury St Edmunds d.	0543	0548	0629	0653	0654	0732	0758	0829	0830	0857	0859	0959	1029	1030	1059	1159	1228	1229	1259	1359	1429	1429	1459	1559	1629r	1629
65	Newmarket d.	0602	0607	|	0713	0718r	0751	0818	|	|	0918	0918	1019	|	|	1118	1219	|	|	1318	1419	|	|	1518	1619	|	|
88	**Cambridge** 208 a.	0627	0630	|	0737	0740	0818	0841	|	|	0941	0940	1041	|	|	1141	1240	|	|	1341	1440	|	|	1541	1640	|	|
73	Soham d.	...	...	0649	...	...	...	...	0849	0850	...	...	...	1050	1049	...	...	1251	1249	...	...	1449	1449	...	...	1650	1650
82	Ely 208 a.	...	...	0657	...	...	...	...	0858	0859	...	...	...	1059	1058	...	...	1259	1258	...	...	1458	1458	...	...	1659	1659
108	March 208 a.	...	...	0715	...	...	...	...	0917	0917	...	...	...	1117	1116	...	...	1318	1317	...	...	1517	1517	...	...	1717	1717
132	**Peterborough** 208 a.	...	...	0738	...	...	...	...	0939	0940	...	...	...	1140	1139	...	...	1340	1339	...	...	1540	1539	...	...	1740	1739

	⚒	⚒	Ⓐ	⑥	⚒	Ⓐ		⑥	⑥	Ⓐ	⚒	⚒	⚒	⑦	⑦a	⑦	⑦H	⑦C	⑦	⑦	⑦		⑦	⑦	⑦	⑦
Ipswich 200 d.	1621	1721	1742	1758	1821	1914	...	1921	2000	2001	2021	2120	2221	0736	0755	0820	0920	0955	1020	1120	1155		1755	1820	1920	2105
Stowmarket 200 d.	1635	1736	1755	1809	1835	1927	...	1935	2011	2013	2035	2135	2235	0750	0807	0834	0934	1006	1034	1134	1207	and in	1807	1834	1934	2119
Bury St Edmunds d.	1658	1758	1825f	1829r	1859	1959t	...	1959	2029	2030	2059	2159	2256	0811	0824	0857	0957	1023	1057	1157	1225	the same	1825	1857	1957	2140
Newmarket d.	1718	1818	|	|	1918	2019	...	2019	|	|	2118	2219	...	0830	|	0914	1017	|	1116	1217	|	pattern	|	1916	2017	2159
Cambridge 208 a.	1741	1840	|	|	1940	2041	...	2041	|	|	2140	2242	...	0854	|	0937	1039	|	1138	1239	|	every	|	1938	2039	2224
Soham d.	...	...	1846	1849	...	...	...	...	2049	2051	...	...	...	...	0843	...	...	1042	...	...	1244	**two** hours	1844	...	...	...
Ely 208 a.	...	...	1857	1858	...	...	...	...	2058	2059	...	...	...	...	0852	...	...	1051	...	...	1253	until	1853	...	...	...
March 208 a.	...	...	1917	1917	...	...	...	...	2117	2117	...	...	...	...	0911	...	...	1111	...	...	1311		1911	...	...	...
Peterborough 208 a.	...	...	1940	1939	...	...	...	...	2139	2139	...	...	...	...	0934	...	...	1133	...	...	1334		1934	...	...	...

	Ⓐ	⚒	Ⓐ	⑥	Ⓐ	⑥		⚒	⑥	Ⓐ	⚒	⚒	⚒	⚒		⚒	⚒	⚒	⚒	⚒	⚒		⑥	Ⓐ	⑥	Ⓐ	⚒
Peterborough 208 d.	...	...	...	...	...	...	...	0750	...	...	...	0950	...	...	...	1150	...	...	1350	...	...	...	1551	1550	...	...	...
March 208 d.	...	...	...	...	...	...	...	0809	...	...	...	1009	...	...	...	1209	...	...	1409	...	...	...	1610	1609	...	...	...
Ely 208 d.	...	...	...	...	...	...	...	0831	...	...	...	1031	...	...	...	1232	...	...	1431	...	...	...	1631	1631	...	...	...
Soham d.	...	...	...	...	...	...	...	0838	...	...	...	1039	...	...	...	1239	...	...	1438	...	...	...	1639	1639	...	...	...
Cambridge 208 d.	...	...	0641	0642	0743	0746	...	|	0847	0847	0947	|	1047	1147	...	|	1247	1347	|	1447	1547	...	|	|	1646	1646	1746
Newmarket d.	...	...	0702	0703	0804	0807	...	|	0907	0907	1008	|	1107	1208	...	|	1307	1408	|	1507	1608	...	|	|	1707	1707	1807
Bury St Edmunds d.	0530	0625	0726r	0726r	0826	0826	...	0859	0926	0926	1026	1100	1126	1226	...	1300	1326	1426	1459	1526	1626	...	1700	1659	1727	1727	1827
Stowmarket 200 d.	0550	0645	0746	0747	0847	0847	...	0914	0947	0947	1047	1115	1147	1247	...	1315	1347	1447	1514	1547	1647	...	1715	1714	1747	1748	1847
Ipswich 200 a.	0605	0701	0801	0802	0902	0902	...	0927	1002	1004	1102	1128	1202	1302	...	1328	1402	1502	1527	1602	1702	...	1727	1727	1802	1804	1902

	⑥	Ⓐ	⑥	Ⓐ	⚒H	ⒶC	⑥C	⚒		⚒	ⒶC	⑥C	⚒	⑦	⑦	⑦a	⑦	⑦	⑦		⑦C	⑦	⑦H	⑦C	⑦	⑦
Peterborough 208 d.	1751	1750	...	...	...	1950	1952	...	...	...	2146	2147	...	...	...	0950	...	...	1144	★	1741	...	...	1945	...	...
March 208 d.	1810	1809	...	...	...	2009	2011	...	...	...	2205	2206	...	...	...	1009	...	...	1203		1800	...	...	2004	...	...
Ely 208 d.	1831	1831	...	...	...	2032	2032	...	...	...	2227	2227	...	...	...	1031	...	...	1228	and in	1829	...	...	2027	...	...
Soham d.	1839	1839	...	...	...	2039	2040	...	...	...	2234	2235	...	...	...	1039	...	...	1236	the same	1836	...	...	2035	...	...
Cambridge 208 d.	|	|	1847	1847	1947	|	|	2047	...	2147	|	|	2247	0900	0945	|	1045	1145	|	pattern	|	1845	1945	|	2045	2250
Newmarket d.	|	|	1907	1907	2008	|	|	2107	...	2208	|	|	2308	0926	1006	|	1105	1206	|	every	|	1905	2006	|	2106	2311
Bury St Edmunds d.	1900	1859	1926	1926	2026	2100	2100	2126	...	2226	2255	2255	2328	0946	1024	1059	1124	1224	1257	**two** hours	1857	1924	2024	2056	2126	2331
Stowmarket 200 d.	1915	1915	1947	1947	2046	2115	2115	2147	...	2247	2310	2310	2348	1006	1045	1114	1145	1245	1312	until	1912	1945	2046	2111	2145	2350
Ipswich 200 a.	1927	1927	2002	2004	2102	2128	2126	2202	...	2302	2321	2321	0002	1023	1100	1127	1200	1300	1325		1924	2000	2103	2123	2200	0005

C – To/from Colchester (Table **200**).
H – To/from Harwich International (Table **200**).
a – Until Sept. 11.
f – Arrives 1817.
r – Arrives 4–5 minutes earlier.
t – Arrives 1948.
★ – Peterborough d. 1350 (not 1344), then March d. 1409, Ely d. 1432, Soham d. 1439, Bury St Edmunds d. 1500, Stowmarket d. 1515, Ipswich a. 1527.

EM 2nd class NORWICH - NOTTINGHAM - SHEFFIELD - MANCHESTER - LIVERPOOL 206

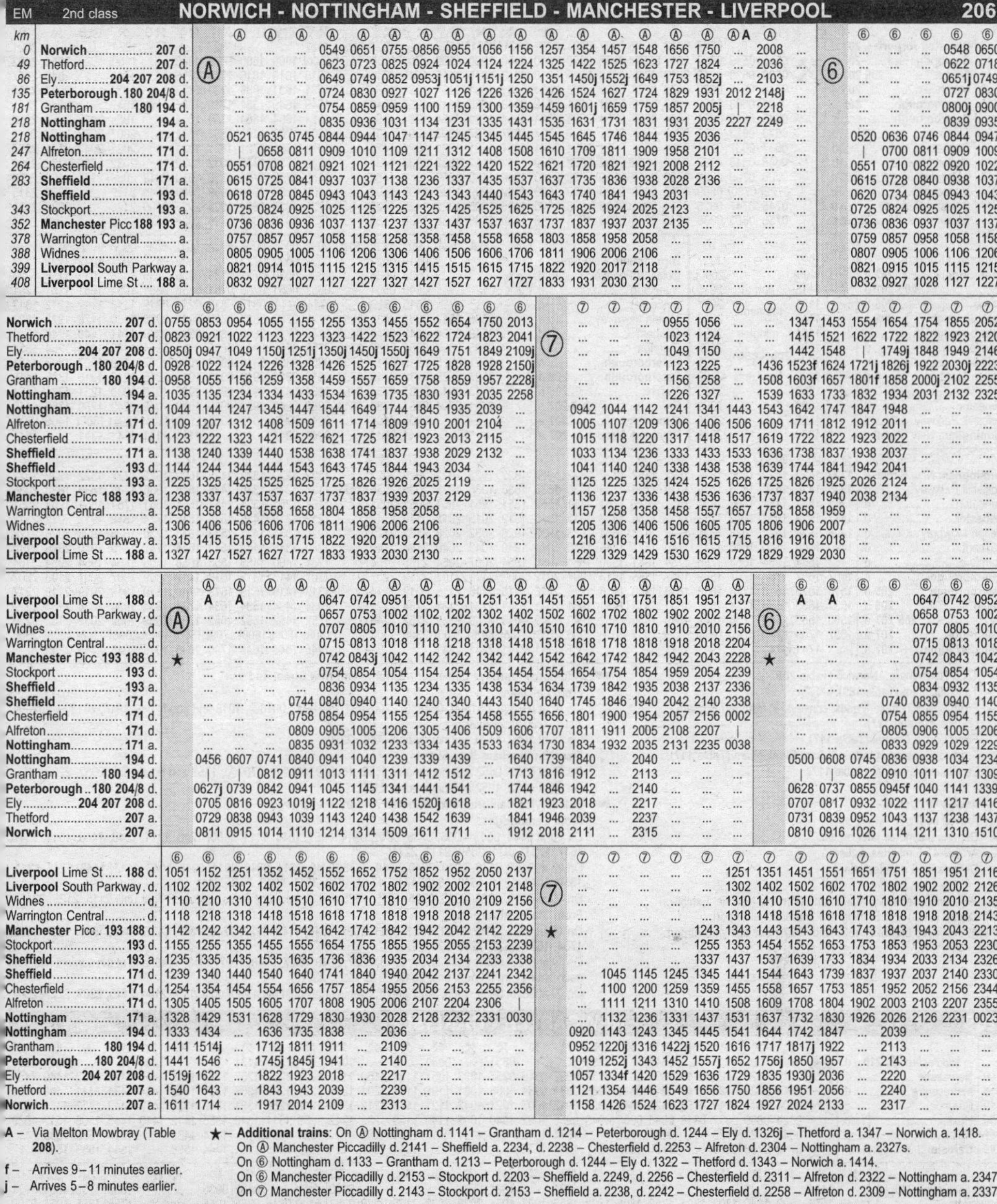

km			Ⓐ	Ⓐ	Ⓐ	Ⓐ	Ⓐ	Ⓐ	Ⓐ	Ⓐ	Ⓐ	Ⓐ	Ⓐ	Ⓐ	Ⓐ	Ⓐ	Ⓐ	Ⓐ	Ⓐ A	Ⓐ			⑥	⑥	⑥	⑥	⑥
0	**Norwich** 207 d.		...	...	...	0549	0651	0755	0856	0955	1056	1156	1257	1354	1457	1548	1656	1750	...	2008	...		...	...	...	0548	0650
49	Thetford 207 d.	Ⓐ	...	...	...	0623	0723	0825	0924	1024	1124	1224	1325	1422	1525	1623	1727	1824	...	2036	...	⑥	...	...	...	0622	0718
86	Ely 204 207 208 d.		...	...	...	0649	0749	0852	0953j	1051j	1151j	1250	1351	1450j	1552j	1649	1753	1852j	...	2103	...		...	...	...	0651j	0749f
135	**Peterborough** 180 204/8 d.		...	...	...	0724	0830	0927	1027	1126	1226	1326	1426	1524	1627	1724	1829	1931	2012	2148j	...		...	...	...	0727	0830
181	Grantham 180 194 d.		...	...	...	0754	0859	0959	1100	1159	1300	1359	1459	1601j	1659	1759	1857	2005j	|	2218	...		...	...	...	0800j	0900
218	**Nottingham** 194 a.		...	...	...	0835	0936	1031	1134	1231	1335	1431	1535	1631	1731	1831	1931	2035	2227	2249	...		...	...	...	0839	0935
218	**Nottingham** 171 d.		0521	0635	0745	0844	0944	1047	1147	1245	1345	1445	1545	1645	1746	1844	1935	2036	...	...	...		0520	0636	0746	0844	0947
247	Alfreton 171 d.		|	0658	0811	0909	1010	1109	1211	1312	1408	1508	1610	1709	1811	1909	1958	2101	...	...	...		|	0700	0811	0909	1009
264	Chesterfield 171 d.		0551	0708	0821	0921	1021	1121	1221	1322	1420	1522	1621	1720	1821	1921	2008	2112	...	...	...		0551	0710	0822	0920	1022
283	**Sheffield** 171 a.		0615	0725	0841	0937	1037	1138	1236	1337	1435	1537	1637	1735	1836	1938	2028	2136	...	...	...		0615	0728	0840	0938	1037
	Sheffield 193 d.		0618	0728	0845	0943	1043	1143	1243	1343	1440	1543	1643	1740	1841	1943	2031	...	...	...	...		0620	0734	0845	0943	1043
343	Stockport 193 a.		0725	0824	0925	1025	1125	1225	1325	1425	1525	1625	1725	1825	1924	2025	2123	...	...	...	...		0725	0824	0925	1025	1125
352	**Manchester** Picc 188 193 a.		0736	0836	0936	1037	1137	1237	1337	1437	1537	1637	1737	1837	1937	2037	2135	...	...	...	...		0736	0836	0937	1037	1137
378	Warrington Central a.		0757	0857	0957	1058	1158	1258	1358	1458	1558	1658	1803	1858	1958	2058	...	...	...	...	...		0759	0857	0958	1058	1158
388	Widnes a.		0805	0905	1005	1106	1206	1306	1406	1506	1606	1706	1811	1906	2006	2106	...	...	...	...	...		0807	0905	1006	1106	1206
399	**Liverpool** South Parkway a.		0821	0914	1015	1115	1215	1315	1415	1515	1615	1715	1822	1920	2017	2118	...	...	...	...	...		0821	0915	1015	1115	1215
408	**Liverpool** Lime St 188 a.		0832	0927	1027	1127	1227	1327	1427	1527	1627	1727	1833	1931	2030	2130	...	...	...	...	...		0832	0927	1028	1127	1227

	⑥	⑥	⑥	⑥	⑥	⑥	⑥	⑥	⑥	⑥	⑥	⑥		⑦	⑦	⑦	⑦	⑦	⑦	⑦	⑦	⑦	⑦	⑦	⑦	⑦	⑦
Norwich 207 d.	0755	0853	0954	1055	1155	1255	1353	1455	1552	1654	1750	2013		...	...	...	0955	1056	...	...	1347	1453	1554	1654	1754	1855	2052
Thetford 207 d.	0823	0921	1022	1123	1223	1323	1422	1523	1622	1724	1823	2041	⑦	...	...	...	1023	1124	...	...	1415	1521	1622	1722	1822	1923	2120
Ely 204 207 208 d.	0850j	0947	1049	1150j	1251j	1350j	1450j	1550j	1649	1751	1849	2109j		...	...	...	1049	1150	...	...	1442	1548	|	1749j	1848	1949	2146
Peterborough 180 204/8 d.	0928	1022	1124	1226	1328	1426	1525	1627	1725	1828	1928	2150j		...	...	...	1123	1225	...	1436	1523f	1624	1721j	1826j	1922	2030j	2223
Grantham 180 194 d.	0958	1055	1156	1259	1358	1459	1557	1659	1758	1859	1957	2228j		...	...	...	1156	1258	...	1508	1603f	1657	1801f	1858	2000j	2102	2255
Nottingham 194 a.	1035	1135	1234	1334	1433	1534	1639	1735	1830	1931	2035	2258		...	...	...	1226	1327	...	1539	1633	1733	1832	1934	2031	2132	2325
Nottingham 171 d.	1044	1144	1247	1345	1447	1544	1649	1744	1845	1935	2039	...		0942	1044	1142	1241	1341	1443	1543	1642	1747	1847	1948	...	...	...
Alfreton 171 d.	1109	1207	1312	1408	1509	1611	1714	1809	1910	2001	2104	...		1005	1107	1209	1306	1406	1506	1609	1711	1812	1912	2011	...	...	...
Chesterfield 171 d.	1123	1222	1323	1421	1522	1621	1725	1821	1923	2013	2115	...		1015	1118	1220	1317	1418	1517	1619	1722	1822	1923	2022	...	...	...
Sheffield 171 a.	1138	1240	1339	1440	1538	1638	1741	1837	1938	2029	2132	...		1033	1134	1236	1333	1433	1533	1636	1738	1837	1938	2037	...	...	...
Sheffield 193 d.	1144	1244	1344	1444	1543	1643	1745	1844	1943	2034	...	...		1041	1140	1240	1338	1438	1538	1639	1744	1841	1942	2041	...	...	...
Stockport 193 a.	1225	1325	1425	1525	1625	1725	1826	1926	2025	2119	...	...		1125	1225	1325	1424	1525	1626	1725	1826	1925	2026	2124	...	...	...
Manchester Picc 188 193 a.	1238	1337	1437	1537	1637	1737	1837	1939	2037	2129	...	...		1136	1237	1336	1438	1536	1636	1737	1837	1940	2038	2134	...	...	...
Warrington Central a.	1258	1358	1458	1558	1658	1804	1858	1958	2058	...	...	...		1157	1258	1358	1458	1557	1657	1758	1858	1959	...	...	...	...	...
Widnes a.	1306	1406	1506	1606	1706	1811	1906	2006	2106	...	...	...		1205	1306	1406	1506	1605	1705	1806	1906	2007	...	...	...	...	...
Liverpool South Parkway a.	1315	1415	1515	1615	1715	1822	1920	2019	2119	...	...	...		1216	1316	1416	1516	1615	1715	1816	1916	2018	...	...	...	...	...
Liverpool Lime St 188 a.	1327	1427	1527	1627	1727	1833	1933	2030	2130	...	...	...		1229	1329	1429	1530	1629	1729	1829	1929	2030	...	...	...	...	...

		Ⓐ	Ⓐ	Ⓐ	Ⓐ	Ⓐ	Ⓐ	Ⓐ	Ⓐ	Ⓐ	Ⓐ	Ⓐ	Ⓐ	Ⓐ	Ⓐ	Ⓐ	Ⓐ	Ⓐ	Ⓐ		⑥	⑥	⑥	⑥	⑥	⑥	⑥
Liverpool Lime St 188 d.		A	A	...	...	0647	0742	0951	1051	1151	1251	1351	1451	1551	1651	1751	1851	1951	2137		A	A	...	...	0647	0742	0952
Liverpool South Parkway d.	Ⓐ	...	...	...	...	0657	0753	1002	1102	1202	1302	1402	1502	1602	1702	1802	1902	2002	2148	⑥	...	...	...	...	0658	0753	1002
Widnes d.		...	...	...	...	0707	0805	1010	1110	1210	1310	1410	1510	1610	1710	1810	1910	2010	2156		...	...	...	...	0707	0805	1010
Warrington Central d.		...	...	...	...	0715	0813	1018	1118	1218	1318	1418	1518	1618	1718	1818	1918	2018	2204		...	...	...	...	0715	0813	1018
Manchester Picc 193 188 d.	★	...	...	...	...	0742	0843j	1042	1142	1242	1342	1442	1542	1642	1742	1842	1942	2043	2228	★	...	...	...	...	0742	0843	1042
Stockport 193 d.		...	...	...	...	0754	0854	1054	1154	1254	1354	1454	1554	1654	1754	1854	1959	2054	2239		...	...	...	...	0754	0854	1054
Sheffield 193 a.		...	...	...	...	0836	0934	1135	1234	1335	1438	1534	1634	1739	1842	1935	2038	2137	2336		...	...	...	...	0834	0932	1135
Sheffield 171 d.		...	...	...	0744	0840	0940	1140	1240	1340	1443	1540	1640	1745	1846	1940	2042	2140	2338		...	...	...	0740	0839	0940	1140
Chesterfield 171 d.		...	...	...	0758	0854	0954	1155	1254	1354	1458	1555	1656	1801	1900	1954	2057	2156	0002		...	...	...	0754	0855	0954	1155
Alfreton 171 d.		...	...	...	0809	0905	1005	1206	1305	1406	1509	1606	1707	1811	1911	2005	2108	2207	|		...	...	...	0805	0906	1005	1206
Nottingham 171 a.		...	...	...	0835	0931	1032	1233	1334	1435	1533	1634	1730	1834	1932	2035	2131	2235	0038		...	...	...	0833	0929	1029	1229
Nottingham 194 d.		0456	0607	0741	0840	0941	1040	1239	1339	1439	...	1640	1739	1840	...	2040	...	...	...		0500	0608	0745	0836	0938	1034	1234
Grantham 180 194 d.		|	|	0812	0911	1013	1111	1311	1412	1512	...	1713	1816	1912	...	2113	...				|	|	0822	0910	1011	1107	1309
Peterborough 180 204/8 d.		0627j	0739	0842	0941	1045	1145	1341	1441	1541	...	1744	1846	1942	...	2140	...				0628	0737	0855	0945f	1040	1141	1339j
Ely 204 207 208 d.		0705	0816	0923	1019j	1122	1218	1416	1520j	1618	...	1821	1923	2018	...	2217	...				0707	0817	0932	1022	1117	1217	1416
Thetford 207 a.		0729	0838	0943	1039	1143	1240	1438	1542	1639	...	1841	1946	2039	...	2237	...				0731	0839	0952	1043	1137	1238	1437
Norwich 207 a.		0811	0915	1014	1110	1214	1314	1509	1611	1711	...	1912	2018	2111	...	2315	...				0810	0916	1026	1114	1211	1310	1510

	⑥	⑥	⑥	⑥	⑥	⑥	⑥	⑥	⑥	⑥	⑥	⑥		⑦	⑦	⑦	⑦	⑦	⑦	⑦	⑦	⑦	⑦	⑦	⑦	⑦	⑦
Liverpool Lime St 188 d.	1051	1152	1251	1352	1452	1552	1652	1752	1852	1952	2050	2137		...	...	...	...	...	1251	1351	1451	1551	1651	1751	1851	1951	2116
Liverpool South Parkway d.	1102	1202	1302	1402	1502	1602	1702	1802	1902	2002	2101	2148		...	...	...	...	...	1302	1402	1502	1602	1702	1802	1902	2002	2126
Widnes d.	1110	1210	1310	1410	1510	1610	1710	1810	1910	2010	2109	2156	⑦	...	...	...	...	...	1310	1410	1510	1610	1710	1810	1910	2010	2135
Warrington Central d.	1118	1218	1318	1418	1518	1618	1718	1818	1918	2018	2117	2205		...	...	...	...	...	1318	1418	1518	1618	1718	1818	1918	2018	2143
Manchester Picc 193 188 d.	1142	1242	1342	1442	1542	1642	1742	1842	1942	2042	2142	2229	★	...	...	...	...	1243	1343	1443	1543	1643	1743	1843	1943	2043	2213
Stockport 193 d.	1155	1255	1355	1455	1555	1654	1755	1855	1955	2055	2153	2239		...	...	...	...	1255	1353	1454	1552	1653	1753	1853	1953	2053	2230
Sheffield 193 a.	1235	1335	1435	1535	1635	1736	1836	1935	2034	2134	2233	2338		...	...	...	...	1337	1437	1537	1639	1733	1834	1934	2033	2134	2326
Sheffield 171 d.	1239	1340	1440	1540	1640	1741	1840	1940	2042	2137	2241	2342		...	1045	1145	1245	1345	1441	1544	1643	1739	1837	1937	2037	2140	2330
Chesterfield 171 d.	1254	1354	1454	1554	1656	1757	1854	1955	2056	2153	2255	2356		...	1100	1200	1259	1359	1455	1558	1657	1753	1851	1952	2052	2156	2344
Alfreton 171 d.	1305	1405	1505	1605	1707	1808	1905	2006	2107	2204	2306	|		...	1111	1211	1310	1410	1508	1609	1708	1804	1902	2003	2103	2207	2355
Nottingham 171 a.	1328	1429	1531	1628	1729	1830	1930	2028	2128	2232	2331	0030		...	1132	1236	1331	1437	1531	1637	1732	1830	1926	2026	2126	2231	0023
Nottingham 194 d.	1333	1434	...	1636	1735	1838	...	2036	...					0920	1143	1243	1345	1445	1541	1644	1742	1847	...	2039	...		
Grantham 180 194 d.	1411	1514j	...	1712j	1811	1911	...	2109	...					0952	1220j	1316	1422j	1520	1616	1717	1817j	1922	...	2113	...		
Peterborough 180 204/8 d.	1441	1546	...	1745j	1845j	1941	...	2140	...					1019	1252j	1343	1452	1557j	1652	1756j	1850	1957	...	2143	...		
Ely 204 207 208 d.	1519j	1622	...	1822	1923	2018	...	2217	...					1057	1334f	1420	1529	1636	1729	1835	1930j	2036	...	2220	...		
Thetford 207 a.	1540	1643	...	1843	1943	2039	...	2239	...					1121	1354	1446	1549	1656	1750	1856	1951	2056	...	2240	...		
Norwich 207 a.	1611	1714	...	1917	2014	2109	...	2313	...					1158	1426	1524	1623	1727	1824	1927	2024	2133	...	2317	...		

A – Via Melton Mowbray (Table **208**).

f – Arrives 9 – 11 minutes earlier.

j – Arrives 5 – 8 minutes earlier.

★ – **Additional trains**: On Ⓐ Nottingham d. 1141 – Grantham d. 1214 – Peterborough d. 1244 – Ely d. 1326j – Thetford a. 1347 – Norwich a. 1418.
On Ⓐ Manchester Piccadilly d. 2141 – Sheffield a. 2234, d. 2238 – Chesterfield d. 2253 – Alfreton d. 2304 – Nottingham a. 2327s.
On ⑥ Nottingham d. 1133 – Grantham d. 1213 – Peterborough d. 1244 – Ely d. 1322 – Thetford d. 1343 – Norwich a. 1414.
On ⑥ Manchester Piccadilly d. 2153 – Stockport d. 2203 – Sheffield a. 2249, d. 2256 – Chesterfield d. 2311 – Alfreton d. 2322 – Nottingham a. 2347.
On ⑦ Manchester Piccadilly d. 2143 – Stockport d. 2153 – Sheffield a. 2238, d. 2242 – Chesterfield d. 2258 – Alfreton d. 2309 – Nottingham a. 2337.

LE 2nd Class STANSTED AIRPORT - CAMBRIDGE - NORWICH 207

km			Ⓐ	⑥	Ⓐ	⑥	⚒	Ⓐ	⑥	Ⓐ	⑥	⚒	⚒	⚒	⚒	Ⓐ	⑥	Ⓐ	⑥	⑥	Ⓐ	⑥	Ⓐ	⑥	Ⓐ	⚒
0	**Stansted Airport** ✈ 208 d.	⚒	...	...	...	0648	0748t	...	0848	...	0948	1048	1148	1248	1348	1448	1448	1537	1548	1648	1648	1748	1754	1848	...	1948t
40	**Cambridge** 208 d.		0602	0605	0700	0720	0819	0913	0930r	1014	1020	1120	1220	1320	1420	1520	1520	1616	1620	1720	1729	1820	1830	1921	1925	2020
63	Ely 206 208 d.		0619	0622	0717	0738	0837	0930	0950f	1030	1037	1137	1237	1337	1436	1537	1537	1633	1637	1737	1748	1837	1849	1937	1944	2036
100	Thetford 206 d.		0643	0646	0744	0806	0900	0953	1015	1054	1101	1201	1301	1401	1501	1600	1603	1657	1701	1801	1811	1900	1912	2001	2008	2100
123	Attleborough d.		0702	0704	0803	0824	0915	1008	1030	1109	1117	1216	1316	1416	1516	1616	1618	1713	1716	1816	1826	1915	1927	2016	2023	2115
133	Wymondham d.		0709	0711	0812	0832	0925	1015	1038	1116	1124	1224	1324	1424	1524	1623	1625	1720	1724	1824	1833	1923	1934	2023	2030	2122
149	**Norwich** 206 a.		0723	0725	0826	0846	0940	1029	1052	1131	1139	1243	1339	1440	1540	1637	1639	1737	1740	1839	1848	1936	1948	2036	2044	2136

	⚒	⑥	Ⓐ		⑦	⑦	⑦		⑦	⑦	⑦
Stansted Airport ✈ 208 d.	2048t	2210	2210	⑦	0818	1009	1109		1909	2009	2118
Cambridge 208 d.	2120	2255v	2257r		0851	1050j	1150j	and at	1950j	2048f	2151
Ely 206 208 d.	2136	2311	2313		0908	1107	1207	the same	2007	2105	2208
Thetford 206 d.	2200	2335	2337		0934	1133	1231	minutes	2031	2128	2231
Attleborough d.	2215	2350	2352		0949	1148	1246	past each	2046	2143	2246
Wymondham d.	2222	2357	2359		0956	1155	1253	hour until	2053	2150	2253
Norwich 206 a.	2236	0010	0012		1013	1213	1313		2109	2205	2313

		⑥	Ⓐ	⑥	Ⓐ	⑥	Ⓐ	⑥	Ⓐ	⚒
Norwich 206 d.	⚒	0527	0533	0627	0633	0727	0730	0827	0833	0927
Wymondham d.		0539	0545	0639	0645	0739	0742	0839	0845	0939
Attleborough d.		0546	0552	0646	0652	0746	0749	0846	0852	0946
Thetford 206 d.		0600	0606	0700	0706	0800	0803	0900	0906	1000
Ely 206 208 d.		0627	0632	0727	0734f	0827	0828	0927	0932	1027
Cambridge 208 a.		0647	0650	0744	0753	0844	0851	0944	0949	1045
Stansted ✈ 208 a.		0724	...	0824	...	0924	...	1024	1024	1124

	⑥	Ⓐ	⚒	Ⓐ	⑥	⚒	⚒	⑥	Ⓐ	⑥	Ⓐ	⑥	Ⓐ	Ⓐ	⑥	⚒	⑥	Ⓐ	⚒		⑦	⑦		⑦	⑦
Norwich 206 d.	1027	1033	1127	1228	1229	1327	1427	1521	1527	1627	1627	1721	1727	1823	1827	1927	2110	2112	2240	⑦	0903	1003	and at	2003	2208
Wymondham d.	1039	1045	1139	1240	1242	1339	1439	1533	1539	1639	1639	1733	1739	1835	1839	1939	2122	2124	2252		0915	1015	the same	2015	2220
Attleborough d.	1046	1052	1146	1247	1249	1346	1446	1540	1546	1646	1648	1742	1746	1842	1846	1946	2129	2131	2259		0922	1022	minutes	2022	2227
Thetford d.	1100	1106	1200	1301	1304	1400	1500	1558	1600	1700	1702	1800	1809f	1856	1900	2000	2143	2145	2313		0936	1036	past each	2036	2241
Ely 206 208 d.	1127	1131	1227	1328	1331	1427	1527	1627	1627	1727	1727	1827	1837	1926	1927	2027	2208	2210	2338		1003	1103	hour until	2103	2306
Cambridge 208 a.	1145	1149	1244	1346	1349	1444	1546	1644	1645	1744	1745	1844	1856	1946	1944	2045	2225	2227	2357		1021	1121		2120	2324
Stansted Airport ✈ 208 a.	1224	1224	1324	1424	1424	1524	1624	1724	1724	1824		1924	...	...	2024	2124	...	...	...		1103	1204		2203	...

– Arrives 6 minutes earlier. f – Arrives 4 minutes earlier. r – Arrives 11 – 12 minutes earlier. t – ⑥ only. v – Arrives 2245.

208 STANSTED AIRPORT ✈ - CAMBRIDGE - PETERBOROUGH - LEICESTER - BIRMINGHAM XC

km		Ⓐ	⑥	⑥	Ⓐ	Ⓐ	⑥	Ⓐ	⑥	⚒	⚒	⚒🍷	⚒🍷	⚒🍷		⚒🍷	⑥🍷	Ⓐ🍷	⚒🍷	⚒🍷	⚒G	⚒	ⒶB	⚒	Ⓐ
0	**Stansted Airport** ✈ **207** d.	...	...	0527	0527	0612	0627	0721	0727	0821f	0921f	1027	...	1227	...	1427	...	...	1627	...	...	1821f	...	...	2021
40	**Cambridge** **207** d.	0515	0515	0557	0557	0657c	0658	0800	0800	0900	1000	1100	1200	1300j	...	1500j	1600	1600	1700j	1800	...	1900j	...	1958	2102
64	Ely **205 207** d.	0530	0530	0612	0612	0712	0713	0815	0815	0915	1015	1115	1215	1315	...	1515	1615	1615	1715	1815	...	1915	...	2015	2117
89	March **205** d.	0546	0546	0630	0630	0728	0729	0833	0831	0931	1031	1131	1231	1331	...	1531	1631	1633	1731	1833	...	1931	...	2031	2134
113	**Peterborough** **205** a.	0608	0608	0652	0652	0750	0751	0851	0849	0949	1050	1149	1250	1349	...	1549	1649	1651	1749	1851	...	1949	...	2049	2151
	Peterborough d.	0610	0610	0654	0654	0754	0754	0854	0854	0954	1054	1154	1254	1354	...	1554	1654	1654	1754	1854	...	1954	2012	2054	2200
131	Stamford d.	0623	0623	0707	0707	0807	0807	0907	0907	1007	1107	1207	1307	1407	...	1607	1707	1707	1807	1907	...	2007	2028	2107	2213
154	Oakham d.	0637	0637	0721	0721	0821	0821	0921	0921	1021	1121	1221	1321	1421	...	1621	1721	1721	1821	1921	...	2021	2043	2121	2227
174	Melton Mowbray d.	0648	0648	0732	0732	0832	0832	0932	0932	1032	1132	1232	1332	1432	...	1632	1732	1732	1832	1932	...	2032	2056	2132	2238
197	**Leicester** d.	0706	0708	0750	0750	0850	0850	0950	0950	1050	1150	1250	1350	1450	...	1650	1750	1750	1850	1950	2018	2050	2117	2150	2256
227	Nuneaton d.	0729j	0730j	0809	0816	0909	0909	1009	1009	1109	1209	1309	1409	1509	...	1709	1809	1816	1909	2009	2045	2109	...	2209	2315
244	Coleshill Parkway △ d.	0745	0747	0825	0831	0925	0925	1025	1025	1125	1225	1325	1425	1525	...	1725	1825	1831	1925	2025	2100	2125	...	2225	2331
259	**Birmingham** New Street a.	0758	0803	0838	0845	0938	0938	1038	1038	1138	1238	1338	1438	1538	...	1738	1838	1845	1938	2038	2116	2139	...	2238	2344

	⑦		⑦
Stansted Airport ✈ **207** d.	1027	⊖	1927
Cambridge **207** d.	1100j		2000j
Ely **205 207** d.	1115	and at	2015
March **205** d.	1131	the same	2031
Peterborough **205** a.	1149		2049
Peterborough d.	1154	minutes	2054
Stamford d.	1207	past each	2107
Oakham d.	1221		2121
Melton Mowbray d.	1232	hour until	2132
Leicester d.	1250		2150
Nuneaton d.	1309		2209
Coleshill Parkway △ d.	1325		2225
Birmingham New Street a.	1339		2238

	ⒶA	⑥A	Ⓐ	⑥	⚒A	Ⓐ🍷	⑥🍷	Ⓐ🍷	⑥🍷	ⒶC	⑥E	Ⓐ🍷	⑥🍷	⚒🍷	⚒🍷
Birmingham New Street d.	...	...	0519	0522	...	0622	0622	0722	0722	0822	0822	1022	1022	1122	1222
Coleshill Parkway △ d.	...	...	0533	0536	...	0636	0636	0735	0736	0836	0836	1036	1036	1136	1236
Nuneaton d.	...	...	0549	0551	...	0651	0651	0750	0751	0853	0851	1051	1051	1151	1251
Leicester d.	...	...	0615	0615j	...	0714j	0714j	0818	0813	0914	0912	1113	1112	1212	1312
Melton Mowbray d.	0536	0542	0631	0631	0654	0730	0730	0837	0829	0931	0928	1130	1128	1228	1328
Oakham d.	0549	0554	0643	0643	0706	0742	0742	0849	0841	0942	0940	1141	1140	1240	1340
Stamford d.	0605	0607	0657	0657	0719	0756	0756	0903	0855	0956	0954	1155	1154	1254	1354
Peterborough a.	0621	0625	0710	0710	0736	0809	0809	0916	0909	1010	1007	1209	1207	1307	1407
Peterborough **205** d.	0627	0628	0713	0713	0737	0819	0816	0919	0916	1012	1015	1215	1216	1316	1416
March **205** a.	0643	0643	0731	0731	0754	0834	0831	0934	0931	1028	1030	1230	1231	1331	1431
Ely **205 207** a.	0701	0704	0753	0753	0814	0853	0849	0952	0950	1049	1048	1249	1250	1350	1449
Cambridge **207** a.	...	...	0808	0809	...	0913	0905t	1012	1006	1105t	1104t	1305t	1306t	1406	1505t
Stansted Airport ✈ **207** a.	...	...	0841	0841	...	0944	0941	...	...	1141	1141	1341	1341	...	1541

	⚒🍷	Ⓐ🍷	⑥🍷	⚒	Ⓐ	⑥	Ⓐ	Ⓐ	⑥	Ⓐ	⑥	Ⓐ	⑥	Ⓐ	⑥	⑦🍷	⑦🍷	⑦🍷	⑦	⑦	⑦	⑦	⑦	⑦	⑦
Birmingham New Street d.	1322	1422	1422	1522	1622	1622	1652	1722	1722	1822	1822	1922	1922	2022	2022	1122	1222	1322	1422	1522	1622	1722	1822	1922	2022
Coleshill Parkway △ d.	1336	1436	1436	1536	1636	1636	1706	1736	1736	1836	1836	1936	1936	2036	2036	1136	1236	1336	1436	1536	1636	1736	1836	1936	2036
Nuneaton d.	1351	1451	1451	1551	1651	1651	1725j	1751	1751	1852	1851	1951	1951	2051	2051	1151	1251	1351	1451	1551	1651	1751	1851	1951	2051
Leicester d.	1412	1512	1512	1612	1713	1712	1756	1817	1812	1916	1912	2015	2012	2116	2112	1212	1318	1416	1516	1616	1714	1812	1912	2012	2112
Melton Mowbray d.	1428	1528	1528	1628	1730	1728	1816	1834	1828	1933	1928	2032	2028	2132	2128	1228	1334	1433	1533	1633	1730	1828	1928	2028	2128
Oakham d.	1440	1540	1540	1640	1741	1740	1827	1846	1840	1944	1940	2043	2040	2144	2140	1240	1346	1444	1544	1644	1742	1840	1940	2040	2140
Stamford d.	1454	1554	1554	1654	1755	1754	1841	1900	1854	1958	1954	2057	2054	2158	2154	1254	1400	1458	1558	1658	1756	1854	1954	2054	2154
Peterborough a.	1507	1607	1607	1707	1809	1807	1855	1913	1907	2012	2007	2111	2107	2212	2207	1307	1413	1512	1613	1712	1809	1907	2007	2108	2207
Peterborough **205** d.	1516	1620	1616	1716	1813	1816	1900	1916	1916	2016	2016	2116	2116	2219	2214	1319	1419	1519	1619	1719	1819	1919	2019	2119	2217
March **205** a.	1531	1635	1631	1734	1831	1831	1915	1931	1931	2031	2031	2131	2131	2234	2229	1334	1434	1534	1634	1734	1834	1934	2034	2134	2232
Ely **205 207** a.	1550	1653	1649	1756	1849	1849	1935	1952	1949	2049	2049	2149	2149	2252	2248	1352	1452	1552	1652	1752	1852	1952	2052	2152	2250
Cambridge **207** a.	1607	1709	1705t	1816a	1905t	1905t	1951	2010	2006	2106t	2105t	2205t	2205t	2309	2304	1408t	1509t	1608t	1709t	1808t	1909t	2008t	2108t	2208t	2306
Stansted Airport ✈ **207** a.	...	1741	1741	...	1941	1941	...	...	...	2141	2141	2241	2241	...	...	1445	1545	1645	1745	1845	1945	2045	2145	2245	...

A – [2] Nottingham - Norwich (Table **206**).
B – To Nottingham (Table **189**).
C – From Bristol Temple Meads; conveys 🍷 from Birmingham (Tables **116** and **117**).
D – From Cardiff Central (Table **117**).
E – From Gloucester; conveys 🍷 from Birmingham (Table **117**).
G – To Gloucester on Ⓐ (Table **117**).

a – Arrives 1812 on Ⓐ.
c – Arrives 0647.
f – Departs 6 minutes later on ⑥.
j – Arrives 4–5 minutes earlier.
t – Departs 5–6 minutes later.

△ – 🚌 connections available to and from the National Exhibition Centre (NEC) and Birmingham International Airport.
⊖ – 🍷 conveyed on 1527, 1627 and 1727 from Stansted Airport.

☛ **Additional journeys Leicester - Birmingham New Street and v.v.**
From Leicester:
On ⚒ at 0548⑥, 0618Ⓐ, 0648, 0722Ⓐ, 0817, 0915Ⓐ, 0918⑥, 1018 and hourly until 1918, 2018⑥, 2020Ⓐ, 2118, 2220⑥, 2226Ⓐ.
On ⑦ at 1020, 1120 and hourly until 2020, 2220.
From Birmingham New Street:
On ⚒ at 0552, 0652 and hourly until 1552, 1609Ⓐ, 1652⑥, 1709Ⓐ, 1752 and hourly until 2052, 2222.
On ⑦ at 0952, 1052 and hourly until 2152.

☛ **Full service Cambridge to Stansted Airport ✈ and v.v.**
From Cambridge:
On Ⓐ at 0444, 0517, 0635, 0735, 0811, 0914, 0951, 1048, 1111, 1150, 1248, 1311, 1348, 1448, 1511, 1547, 1647, 1711, 1911, 2050, 2111, 2211.
On ⑥ at 0451, 0540, 0610, 0640, 0649, 0736, 0748, 0811, 0848, 0911, 0948, 1048, 1111, 1148, 1248, 1311, 1350, 1448, 1511, 1548, 1648, 1711, 1748, 1848, 1911, 1948, 2048, 2111, 2211
On ⑦ at 0739, 0825, 0915, 0925, 1015, 1025 and at the same times past each hour until 2115, 2125, 2215.
From Stansted Airport:
On Ⓐ at 0527, 0612, 0721, 0821, 0921, 1027, 1048, 1148, 1227, 1248, 1348, 1427, 1448, 1537, 1627, 1648, 1754, 1821, 2021, 2210, 2227, 2257.
On ⑥ at 0527, 0627, 0648, 0727, 0748, 0827, 0848, 0927, 0948, 1027, 1048, 1148, and at the same times past each hour every 2 hours until 2048, 2210, 2227, 2327.
On ⑦ at 0818, 0909, 1009, 1027 and the same times past each hour until 2027, 2104, 2118, 2209, 2227, 2304.

209 NEWCASTLE - CARLISLE 2nd class NT

km		⚒	⚒	⚒	⚒H	⚒S	⚒	⚒	⚒	⚒	⚒	⚒	⚒	⚒	⚒	⚒	⚒	⚒	⚒	⚒	⚒	⚒	⚒	Ⓐ	⑥	⚒K
	Middlesbrough **210** d.	...	...	...	...	0649	...	0731	...	...	0831	...	0931	...	...	1031	...	...	1131	...	...	1231	...	...	...	1331
0	**Newcastle** d.	0542	0620	0725	0740	0805	0823	0857	0923	0946	0957	1023	1057	1123	1150	1159	1223	1239	1257	1323	1340	1355	1423	1433	1440	1456
6	Metrocentre d.	0549	0629	0734	0748	0814	0831	0906	0931	0954	1006	1031	1106	1131	1201	1208	1231	1247	1306	1331	1348	1404	1431	1441	1448	1505
19	Prudhoe d.	0604	0644	0749	0758	0825	0846	0921	0942	1007	1021	1042	1121	1142	1212	1223	1242	1259	1321	1342	1359	1419	1442	1452	1459	1520
36	Hexham d.	0624	0659	0802	0818	0838	0905	0940	0955	1022	1040	1055	1140	1155	1232	1242	1255	1311	1340	1355	1412	1440	1455	1505	1512	1539
62	Haltwhistle d.	0643	0722	0825	...	0857	0928	...	1014	1042	...	1114	...	1214	1253	...	1314	1334	...	1414	1435	...	1514	1528	1535	...
99	**Carlisle** a.	0712	0758	0859	...	0934f	1001	...	1044	1116	...	1146	...	1244	1327	...	1346	1406	...	1444	1508	...	1544	1559	1607	...

	⚒	⚒	⚒	⚒	⚒	⚒	⚒	⚒	⚒	⚒K	⚒	⚒	Ⓐ	⑥	⚒	⑥	Ⓐ	⑦	⑦	⑦	✥W	⑦	⑦K	⑦	⑦
Middlesbrough **210** d.	...	1431	...	...	...	...	1631	...	...	1731	...	1831	...	...	...	...	2130	...	0832	0930		1630	1730	1831	1931
Newcastle d.	1540	1556	1623	1640	1703	1723	1756	1808	1823	1855	1923	1951	2023	2033	2125	2238	2253	0845	0955	1055	and at	1755	1855	1955	2100
Metrocentre d.	1548	1605	1631	1648	1713	1731	1805	1817	1831	1904	1931	2003	2031	2041	2133	2247	2302	0853	1003	1103	the same	1803	1903	2003	2109
Prudhoe d.	1559	1620	1642	1703	1728	1746	1821	1833	1846	1919	1946	2019c	2046	2056	2148	2302	2317	0908	1017	1115	minutes	1818	1915	2018	2124
Hexham d.	1612	1639	1655	1722	1747	1805	1840	...	1905	1938	2005	...	2105	2115	2207	2321	2336	0927	1037	1135	past each	1837	1934	2037	2143
Haltwhistle d.	1632	...	1714	1745	...	1828	...	...	1928	...	2028	...	2126	2136	2230	...	...	0950	1100	1156	hour until	1858	1957	2100	2206
Carlisle a.	1707	...	1744	1817	...	1901	...	...	2002	...	2102	...	2156	2211	2305	...	...	1024	1134	1232		1935	2028	2134	2240

	⚒S	⚒	⑥	Ⓐ	⚒	⚒	⚒	⚒	⚒	⚒	⚒	⚒	⚒	⚒	⚒	⚒K	⚒	⚒	⚒	⚒	⚒	⚒	⚒	⚒	⚒	⚒
Carlisle d.	...	...	0557	0557	0632	0659	0725	0803	0820	...	0922	0952	...	1023	1054	...	1125	1152	...	1253	...	1332	1355	...	1437	1454
Haltwhistle d.	...	...	0629	0629	0703	0731	0754	0833	0852	...	0957	1020	...	1053	1122	...	1157	1220	...	1321	...	1404	1423	...	1507	1522
Hexham d.	0609	0637	0652	0652	0725	0754	0814	0857	0918	0956	1018	1040	1055	1118	1142	1156	1218	1240	1255	1341	1356	1425	1443	1456	1530	1542
Prudhoe d.	0626	0655	0704	0710	0742	0811	0826	0914	0930	1013	1030	1052	1112	1130	1154	1213	1230	1252	1312	1353	1413	1437	1455	1513	1542	1554
Metrocentre d.	0641	0710	0720	0726	0758	0827	0846	0930	0944	1029	1044	1104	1128	1144	1208	1228	1244	1304	1328	1405	1429	1449	1507	1529	1555	1606
Newcastle a.	0652	0720	0733	0736	0809	0839	0854	0945v	0955	1039	1054	1112	1138	1153	1222	1238	1255	1313	1339	1413	1439	1457	1516	1539	1603	1615
Middlesbrough **210** a.	0818t	...	0855	0858	...	...	...	...	...	1159	...	...	1259	...	...	1400	...	...	1459	...	1559	...	...	1659	...	...

	⚒K	Ⓐ	⑥	⚒	⚒	⚒	⚒	⚒	⚒	⚒	Ⓐ	⑥	⚒	⚒	⚒	⑥	Ⓐ	⑦	⑦	✥U	⑦	⑦	⑦	⑦	⑦
Carlisle d.	...	1521	1527	1552	...	1622	...	1724	1753	...	1839	1849	...	2009	2204	...	...	0844	0954		1652	1754	1848	1948	2038
Haltwhistle d.	...	1553	1559	1620	...	1652	...	1756	1821	...	1912	1921	...	2037	2236	...	...	0916	1022	and at	1724	1822	1920	2020	2110
Hexham d.	1556	1614	1620	1640	1656	1716	1759	1820	1841	1856	1935	1943	2000	2101	2259	2327	2341	0940	1046	the same	1745	1846	1941	2043	2133
Prudhoe d.	1613	1626	1632	1652	1713	1728	1817	1832	1853	1913	1947	1955	2018	2118	2317	2345	2359	0957	1103	minutes	1802	1903	1958	2101	2151
Metrocentre d.	1629	1638	1644	1704	1729	1740	1832	1844	1905	1929	1959	2007	2033	2134	2332	2357	0013	1013	1117	past each	1817	1917	2014	2116	2206
Newcastle a.	1639	1646	1652	1715	1739	1751	1842	1853	1914	1939	2008	2016	2042	2143	2342	0006	0024	1022	1126	hour until	1826	1926	2023	2125	2216
Middlesbrough **210** a.	1759	...	...	...	1859	...	2004	...	...	2105	...	...	2205	2303	...	...	...	...	1249		1948	2048	2148	2248	...

H – From Hartlepool (Table **210**).
K – From/to Whitby (Tables **210** and **211**).
S – To/from Saltburn (Tables **210** and **212**).

U – The 1054 and 1354 departures from Carlisle continue to Whitby (Tables **210** and **211**).
W – The 1430 departure from Middlesbrough starts from Whitby (Tables **210** and **211**).

c – ⑥ only.
f – 0929 on Ⓐ.

r – Arrives 5 minutes earlier.
t – Arrives 0810 on Ⓐ.
v – Arrives 0940 on ⑥.

✥ – Timings may vary by ± 4 minutes.

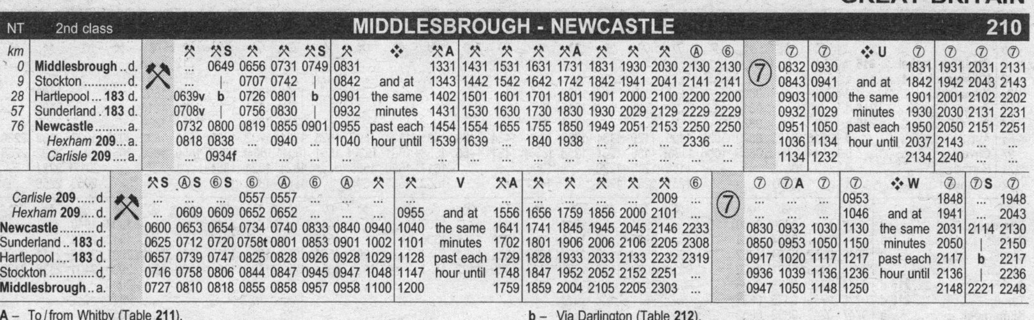

NT 2nd class MIDDLESBROUGH - NEWCASTLE 210

km		⚒	⚒S	⚒	⚒	⚒S	⚒	❖	⚒A	⚒	⚒	⚒	⚒A	⚒	⚒	⚒	Ⓐ	⑥	⑦	⑦	❖U	⑦	⑦	⑦	⑦
0	**Middlesbrough** .. d.	...	0649	0656	0731	0749	0831		1331	1431	1531	1631	1731	1831	1930	2030	2130	2130	0832	0930		1831	1931	2031	2131
9	Stockton .... d.	...	|	0707	0742	|	0842	and at	1343	1442	1542	1642	1742	1842	1941	2041	2141	2141	0843	0941	and at	1842	1942	2043	2143
28	Hartlepool ... **183** d.	0639v	b	0726	0801	b	0901	the same	1402	1501	1601	1701	1801	1901	2000	2100	2200	2200	0903	1000	the same	1901	2001	2102	2202
57	Sunderland . **183** d.	0708v	|	0756	0830	|	0932	minutes	1431	1530	1630	1730	1830	1930	2029	2129	2229	2229	0932	1029	minutes	1930	2030	2131	2231
76	**Newcastle** .... a.	0732	0800	0819	0855	0901	0955	past each	1454	1554	1655	1755	1850	1949	2051	2153	2250	2250	0951	1050	past each	1950	2050	2151	2251
	Hexham **209** ... a.	0818	0838	...	0940	...	1040	hour until	1539	1639	...	1840	1938	...	...	...	2336	...	1036	1134	hour until	2037	2143	...	...
	Carlisle **209** .... a.	...	0934f	...	...	...	...		...	...	...	...	...	...	...	...	...	...	1134	1232		2134	2240	...	...

	⚒S	ⒶS	⑥S	⑥	Ⓐ	⑥	Ⓐ	⚒	⚒	V	⚒A	⚒	⚒	⚒	⚒	⚒	⑥	⑦	⑦A	⑦	⑦	❖W	⑦	⑦S	⑦
Carlisle **209** ..... d.	...	...	...	0557	0557	...	...	...	...		...	...	...	...	...	2009	...	...	...	...	0953		1848	...	1948
Hexham **209** .... d.	...	0609	0609	0652	0652	...	...	...	0955	and at	1556	1656	1759	1856	2000	2101	...	...	...	...	1046	and at	1941	...	2043
Newcastle .... d.	0600	0653	0654	0734	0740	0833	0840	0940	1040	the same	1641	1741	1845	1945	2045	2146	2233	0830	0932	1030	1130	the same	2031	2114	2130
Sunderland .. **183** d.	0625	0712	0720	0758t	0801	0853	0901	1002	1101	minutes	1702	1801	1906	2006	2106	2205	2308	0850	0953	1050	1150	minutes	2050	|	2150
Hartlepool .... **183** d.	0657	0739	0747	0825	0828	0926	0928	1029	1128	past each	1729	1828	1933	2033	2133	2232	2319	0917	1020	1117	1217	past each	2117	b	2217
Stockton .... d.	0716	0758	0806	0844	0847	0945	0947	1048	1147	hour until	1748	1847	1952	2052	2152	2251	...	0936	1039	1136	1236	hour until	2136	|	2236
Middlesbrough .. a.	0727	0810	0818	0855	0858	0957	0958	1100	1200		1759	1859	2004	2105	2205	2303	...	0947	1050	1148	1250		2148	2221	2248

A – To/from Whitby (Table **211**).
S – To/from Saltburn (Table **212**).
U – The 1430 and 1730 departures from Middlesbrough start from Whitby (Table **211**).
V – The 1156 departure from Hexham continues to Whitby (Table **211**).
W – The 1054 and 1354 departures from Carlisle continue to Whitby (Table **211**).
b – Via Darlington (Table **212**).
f – 0929 on Ⓐ.
r – Ⓐ only.
t – Arrives 0752.
v – 4 minutes later on ⑥.
❖ – Timings between Carlisle and Newcastle and v.v. may vary by ± 4 minutes.

NT 2nd class MIDDLESBROUGH and PICKERING - WHITBY 211

km		⚒	⑦D	⚒	⑦B	⑦C	⚒H	⑦C	⚒H	⚒🚌	⚒🚌
0	**Middlesbrough** .... d.	0654	0841	1019	1050	1349	1404	1651	1800	2043	2042
18	Battersby .... d.	0736r	0912	1050	1131r	1424	1437	1726	1831	|	2146
41	Glaisdale .... d.	0810	0946	1124	1205	1458	1511	1759	1905	|	2225
46	Grosmont .... d.	0818	0954	1132	1213	1506	1519	1807	1913	|	2234
56	**Whitby** .... a.	0838	1012	1151	1231	1524	1538	1826	1931	2150	2257

	⚒	⑦D	⚒H	⑦C	⑦C	⚒H	⑦D	⚒	⚒🚌	⚒🚌
Whitby .... d.	0845	1022	1159	1249	1550	1558	1834	1942	2224	2223
Grosmont .... d.	0902	1039	1216	1306	1608	1616	1851	1959	|	2248
Glaisdale .... d.	0913	1050	1227	1317	1618	1627	1902	2010	|	2257
Battersby .... d.	0948	1126	1303	1353	1655	1703	1938	2046	|	2335
Middlesbrough .... a.	1015	1152	1330	1429	1728	1730	2004	2113	2330	0045

km		🚂		🚂		🚂			🚂		
0	**Pickering** .... d.	...	...	0920	...	1200	...	...	1500	...	...
29	Grosmont .... a.	...	...	1025	...	1305	...	...	1605	...	...
29	Grosmont .... d.	0915	...	1040	...	1315	...	...	1630	...	...
39	**Whitby** .... a.	0945	...	1110	...	1345	...	...	1655	...	...

	🚂		🚂	🚂		🚂			🚂	
Whitby .... d.	1000	...	1235	...	...	1400	...	...	1710	...
Grosmont .... a.	1025	...	1300	...	...	1425	...	...	1735	...
Grosmont .... d.	1035	...	...	1330	...	1430	...	...	1740	...
Pickering .... a.	1140	...	...	1440	...	1540	...	...	1840	...

B – From Newcastle (Table **210**).
C – To/from Carlisle (Tables **209** and **210**).
D – To/from Darlington (Table **212**).
H – To/from Hexham (Table **210**).
r – Arrives 14–15 minutes earlier.
🚂 – Daily services will run April 4 - October 30 2022. National Rail tickets **not** valid. An amended service operates on most ⑦ and on certain other dates - please confirm with operator. The North Yorkshire Moors Railway. ✆ 01751 472508. www.nymr.co.uk

NT 2nd class BISHOP AUCKLAND - DARLINGTON - MIDDLESBROUGH - SALTBURN 212

km		⚒	⚒	⚒N	⚒B	⚒	⚒		⚒	⚒M	⑦A	⑦	⑦	⑦	♥	⑦	⑦		⑦	⑦N	⑦M	⑦
0	**Bishop Auckland** .... d.	...	...	...	a	0726	0826		2126	...	...	...	0814	0924		1924	2024	...	...	...	...	...
4	Shildon .... d.	...	...	...	...	0732	0832	and at	2132	...	...	...	0820	0930		1930	2030	...	...	...	...	...
8	Newton Aycliffe .... d.	...	...	...	...	0736	0836	the same	2136	...	...	...	0824	0934	and at	1934	2034	...	...	...	...	...
19	**Darlington** .... a.	...	...	...	...	0753	0853	minutes	2153	...	...	...	0841	0951	the same	1951	2051	...	...	...	...	...
19	**Darlington** .... ▶ d.	0614	0628	...	...	0755	0855	past each	2155	...	0809	...	0842	0952	minutes	1952	2053	...	2127	2157	...	2252
43	**Middlesbrough 188** ▶ d.	0646t	0709v	0729	0811	0826	0923	hour until	2223	2236	0836	0845	0910	1020	past each	2020	2120	...	2156	2222	2237	2319
55	Redcar Central. **188** ▶ d.	0656	0721	0741	0823	0838	0935		2235	2247	...	0857	0922	1032	hour until	2032	2132	...	...	2234	2247	...
63	**Saltburn** .... ▶ a.	0710	0735	0755	0838	0854	0949		2249	2257	...	0911	0936	1048		2046	2147	...	...	2248	2256	...

	⚒M	⚒	⚒C	⚒	⚒N	⚒		⚒	⚒Y	⚒	ⒶY	⑦	⑦	⑦	⑦	⑦	⑦A	⑦	♥	⑦	⑦A	⑦
Saltburn .... ▷ d.	0554	...	0622	0659	0722	0759		1959	2008	2059	2310	...	...	...	0957	1057	...	1157		1857	...	1957
Redcar Central **188** ▷ d.	0603	...	0635	0712	0735	0812	and at	2012	2022	2112	2319	...	...	...	1010	1110	...	1210		1910	...	2010
Middlesbrough 188 ▷ d.	0614	...	0649	0727	0749	0825	the same	2025	2033	2125	2330	...	0823	0923	1023	1123	1153	1223	and at	1923	2005	2023
Darlington .... ▷ a.	...	...	0717	0755	0818	0853	minutes	2053	...	2153	...	...	0851	0951	1051	1152	1223	1251	the same	1951	2033	2052
Darlington .... d.	...	0644	...	0756	...	0855	past each	2055	...	...	...	0740	0852	0952	1053	1154	...	1253	minutes	1953	...	...
Newton Aycliffe .... d.	...	0659	...	0811	...	0910	hour until	2110	...	...	...	0755	0907	1007	1108	1209	...	1308	past each	2008	...	...
Shildon .... d.	...	0704	...	0816	...	0915		2115	...	...	...	0800	0912	1012	1113	1214	...	1313	hour until	2013	...	...
Bishop Auckland ...... a.	...	0710	...	0822	...	0921		2121	...	...	...	0806	0918	1019	1119	1220	...	1319		2019	...	...

A – To/from Whitby (Table **211**).
B – From Hexham (Table **210**).
C – To Carlisle (Table **210**).
M – To/from Manchester (Table **188**).
N – To/from Newcastle (Table **210**).
Y – To York (Table **188**).
a – Runs 7 minutes later on ⑥.
t – Arrives 5 minutes earlier.
v – Arrives 0658.
♥ – Timings may vary by ± 3 minutes.
▶ – Additional trains Darlington - Middlesbrough - Saltburn. From Darlington on ⚒ at 0822 and hourly until 2022.
▷ – Additional trains Saltburn - Middlesbrough - Darlington. From Saltburn on ⚒ at 0822 and hourly until 2122, 2159, 2259; on ⑦ at 2057, 2157, 2257.

SR 2nd class CARLISLE - DUMFRIES - GLASGOW 214

km		⚒	⚒	⚒	⚒	⚒	⑥	Ⓐ	Ⓐ	⑥	⚒	⚒	⚒	⑥	Ⓐ	⚒	⚒	⚒	⑥	Ⓐ	⚒	Ⓐ
	Newcastle **210** .... d.	...	...	...	...	...	...	...	...	...	...	...	...	...	...	...	...	...	...	...	...	...
0	**Carlisle** .... **154** d.	...	...	0607	0700	0809	0908	0916	0958	0958	1112	1212	1306	1407	1408	1506	1608	1727	1757	1758	1920	...
16	Gretna Green .... d.	...	...	0620	0712	0821	0920	0928	1010	1010	1124	1224	1318	1419	1422	1518	1621	1743	1808	1810	1932	...
28	Annan .... d.	...	...	0628	0728b	0829	0928	0936	1021	1017	1132	1232	1326	1428	1431	1526	1630	1755	1817	1819	1940	...
53	**Dumfries** .... d.	...	...	0647	0744	0848	0945	0953	1040	1046g	1149	1351	1343	1453t	1453b	1543	1653b	1812	1835	1837	1957	2049
124	Auchinleck .... d.	...	...	0735	...	0936	...	...	1129	1137	...	1339	...	1541	1541	...	1741	...	1924	1926	...	2139
146	**Kilmarnock** .... ▽ d.	0620	0652	0755	...	0955	...	...	1156f	1157	...	1357	...	1559	1559	...	1759	...	1957r	1957r	...	2157
185	**Glasgow** Central .... **154** ▽ a.	0711	0734	0836	...	1037	...	...	1234	1234	...	1437	...	1636	1636	...	1839	...	2035	2037	...	2237

	⑥	⚒	⚒	⑦	⑦	⑦	⑦	⑦
Newcastle **210** .... d.	...	...	...	...	...	...	...	...
Carlisle .... **154** d.	...	2111	2310	1312	1512	1712	1912	2126
Gretna Green .... d.	...	2123	2321	1323	1523	1723	1923	2137
Annan .... d.	...	2131	2329	1331	1531	1731	1931	2145
Dumfries .... d.	2049	2148	2350	1350	1549	1749	1950	2203
Auchinleck .... d.	2139	...	...	1438	...	...	2038	...
Kilmarnock .... ▽ d.	2157	...	...	1456	...	...	2057	...
Glasgow Central .... **154** ▽ a.	2234	...	...	1543	...	...	2135	...

	⚒	⚒	⚒	⑥	⚒	⑥	⚒	⚒
Glasgow Central .... **154** ▽ d.	...	...	...	...	0707	...	0913	...
Kilmarnock .... ▽ d.	...	...	...	...	0755a	...	0953	...
Auchinleck .... d.	...	...	...	...	0811	...	1009	...
Dumfries .... d.	0457	0604	0715	0758	0901	1002	1100	1159
Annan .... d.	0512	0619	0730	0813	0916	1017	1115	1214
Gretna Green .... d.	0521	0628	0739	0822	0927	1026	1124	1223
Carlisle .... **154** a.	0535	0641	0754	0837	0943	1039	1140	1236
Newcastle **210** .... a.	...	...	...	...	...	...	...	...

	⚒	⚒	⚒	⚒	Ⓐ	⑥	Ⓐ	⑥		⚒	⚒	⚒	Ⓐ	Ⓐ	Ⓐ	⑥	⚒	⑦	⑦	⑦	⑦	⑦
Glasgow Central .... **154** ▽ d.	1113	...	1313	...	1513	1513	1611	1613	...	...	1728	1913	2017	2113	...	2213	2313	...	...	1503	...	2206
Kilmarnock .... ▽ d.	1154	...	1355	...	1553	1558b	1654	1654	...	...	1825	1953	2054	2157	...	2253	0002	...	...	1552	...	2243
Auchinleck .... d.	1210	...	1412	...	1610	1615	1711	1711	...	...	1842	2010	...	2214	...	2309	...	...	...	1608	...	2300
Dumfries .... d.	1304	1358	1501	1602	1707c	1707	1800	1800	...	1905	1930	2100	...	2302	2307	2359	...	1301	1501	1701	1902	2350
Annan .... d.	1320	1413	1517	1617	1722	1722	1816	1816	...	1920	...	2116	...	...	2322	0014	...	1316	1516	1716	1917	0005
Gretna Green .... d.	1328	1422	1525	1626	1731	1731	1824	1824	...	1929	...	2124	...	...	2331	0023	...	1325	1525	1727	1926	0014
Carlisle .... **154** a.	1341	1436	1539	1639	1744	1744	1838	1841	...	1943	...	2139	...	...	2343	0036	...	1338	1538	1739	1939	0027
Newcastle **210** .... a.	...	...	...	...	...	...	...	...	...	...	...	...	...	...	...	...	...	...	...	...	...	...

a – Arrives 0749.
b – Arrives 5–6 minutes earlier.
c – Arrives 1658.
f – Arrives 1145.
g – Arrives 1035.
r – Arrives 1942.
t – Arrives 1446.
▽ – Additional hourly services are available.

215 GLASGOW and KILMARNOCK - STRANRAER

2nd class SR

km		⚒	⚒	⚒	⚒	⑦	Ⓐ	⑥	⚒	⑦	Ⓐ	⑥	Ⓐ	⑥	⑦	⚒	⑥	Ⓐ	⑦	Ⓐ	⑥	⚒	⑦	⚒	⚒
0	**Glasgow** Central ..... **216** d.	...	...	...	...	...	...	...	...	...	...	...	...	...	...	...	...	...	...	1712	1713	...	...	...	...
39	**Kilmarnock 214** .... a.	...	...	...	...	...	...	...	...	...	...	...	...	...	...	...	...	...	...	1752	1751	...	...	...	...
39	**Kilmarnock** .... d.	...	...	0801	...	...	...	...	1202	...	...	...	...	...	...	...	1701	1702	...	1803	1803	...	...	2108	...
56	Troon .... **216** d.	...	...	0814	...	...	...	...	1215	...	...	...	...	...	...	...	1713	1714	...	1816	1816	...	...	2120	...
64	**Ayr** 🚌 ⊠ .... **216** a.	...	...	0827	...	...	...	...	1224	...	...	...	...	...	...	...	1728	1730	...	1828	1830	...	...	2130	...
64	**Ayr** .... d.	0615	0725	0829	1029	1106	1129	1134	1226	1306	1424	1429	1531	1534	1506	1625	1734	1732	1805	1830	1832	2025	1927	2132	2230
97	Girvan .... d.	0641	0756f	0855	1056	1136f	1156	1201	1253	1336f	1451	1455	1558	1601	1536f	1651	1804f	1804f	1835f	1856	1858	2051	1953	2202	2256
121	Barrhill .... d.	...	0815	...	...	1156	1215	1220	...	1356	...	...	1617	1620	1555	...	1824	1824	1854	...	...	...	2017f	2221	...
162	**Stranraer** .... a.	...	0851	...	...	1231	1250	1255	...	1431	...	...	1652	1655	1631	...	1858	1858	1930	...	...	...	2053	2256	...

	Ⓐ	⑥	⑥	Ⓐ		⚒	⚒	⚒	⑦	⚒	⑦	Ⓐ	⑥		⚒	⑦	⚒	⚒	⑦	⑥	Ⓐ	⚒	⑦	⚒	⚒
Stranraer .... d.	...	...	0700	0700	...	...	0901	...	1041	...	1241	1302	1302	...	...	1441	...	1709	1740	...	...	1908	1940	...	...
Barrhill .... d.	...	...	0734	0734	...	...	0935	...	1116	...	1316	1336	1336	...	...	1515	...	1744	1814	...	...	1942	2015	...	...
Girvan .... d.	0646	0652	0754	0752	...	0900	0953	1100	1134	1300	1334	1351	1354	...	1500	1534	1656	1802	1833	1912	1912	2001	2033	2111	2305
Ayr .... a.	0713	0719	0821	0822	...	0928	1023	1128	1202	1327	1402	1422	1422	...	1529	1601	1723	1835	1901	1939	1944	2030	2101	2138	2332
Ayr 🚌 ⊠ .... **216** d.	0714	0723	0823	0823	...	...	...	...	...	...	...	...	...	...	...	...	1725	...	...	...	...	2030	...	...	...
Troon .... **216** d.	0725	0733	0835	0835	...	...	...	...	...	...	...	...	...	...	...	...	1735	...	...	...	...	2041	...	...	...
Kilmarnock .... a.	0747	0747	0852	0852	...	...	...	...	...	...	...	...	...	...	...	...	1755	...	...	...	...	2057	...	...	...
Kilmarnock 214 .... d.	...	...	0856	0856	...	...	...	...	...	...	...	...	...	...	...	...	...	...	...	...	...	...	...	...	...
Glasgow Central ..... **216** a.	...	...	0936	0939	...	...	...	...	...	...	...	...	...	...	...	...	...	...	...	...	...	...	...	...	...

f – Arrives 4 – 5 minutes earlier.

⊠ – 🚌 connections operate between Ayr station and Cairnryan ferry port for pre-booked Rail & Sail ticket holders (see www.stenaline.co.uk/rail). For ⛴ Cairnryan - Belfast timings, see Table **2002**.

216 GLASGOW - AYR, ARDROSSAN and LARGS

SR

Typical off-peak journey time in hours and minutes
READ DOWN ↓ READ UP ↑

Journey times may be extended during peak hours on Ⓐ (0600 - 0900 and 1600 - 1900) and also at weekends.
The longest journey time by any train is noted in the table heading.

GLASGOW CENTRAL - AYR

Longest journey: 1 hour 04 minutes SR

km	△				△
0	0h00	↓	**Glasgow** Central ......d.		0h49
43	0h25		Kilwinning ....d.	↑	0h22
48	0h29	↓	Irvine ....d.		0h18
56	0h37		Troon..........................d.	↑	0h11
61	0h41	↓	Prestwick Airport ✈ ..d.		0h07
67	0h52		**Ayr**............................a.	↑	0h00

From Glasgow Central: On ⚒ at 0015 ②–⑥, 0602, 0630, 0700, 0730, 0800, 0830, 0900, 0932, 1000, 1030Ⓐ, 1104, 1134, 1200Ⓐ, 1204⑥, 1304, 1403, 1434, 1531Ⓐ, 1534⑥, 1600⑥, 1628, 1730⑥, 1734Ⓐ, 1747Ⓐ, 1804, 1900, 1930, 2000⑥, 2030, 2130, 2230, 2300⑥, 2330.
On ⑦ at 0900 and every 30 minutes until 1900, 2000, 2100, 2200, 2300, 2330.

From Ayr: On ⚒ at 0607⑥, 0615Ⓐ, 0650, 0715⑥, 0718Ⓐ, 0734 Ⓐ, 0741, 0805, 0829, 0853, 0936, 1007, 1036, 1108, 1134Ⓐ, 1140⑥, 1206, 1236, 1306, 1336, 1406, 1452, 1523, 1548, 1622, 1714, 1747, 1824, 1912, 1941Ⓐ, 1945⑥, 2045, 2145, 2300.
On ⑦ at 0845 and every 30 minutes until 1945, 2045, 2145, 2300.

△ – Trains at 0015⚒ - 0800⚒ and 1834⚒ - 2330⚒ and all day on ⑦ call additionally at Paisley Gilmour Street. Additional slower trains also run.

GLASGOW CENTRAL - ARDROSSAN - LARGS

Longest journey: 1 hour 10 minutes SR

km					
0	0h00	↓	**Glasgow** Central ......d.	↑	0h59
12	0h10		Paisley Gilmour St ....d.		0h46
43	0h29	↓	Kilwinning ....d.	↑	0h25
50	0h38		**Ardrossan** Sth Beach ..d.		0h17
64	0h49	↓	Fairlie ....d.	↑	0h05
69	0h56		**Largs** ....a.		0h00

From Glasgow Central:
On ⚒ at 0614, 0715, 0848 and hourly until 1548, 1630, 1715 ⑥, 1725 Ⓐ, 1749, 1852, 1945, 2045, 2145, 2245, 2315 ①–④⑥, 2345 ⑤.
On ⑦ at 0940 and hourly until 2140, 2242.

From Largs:
On ⚒ at 0642, 0722 Ⓐ, 0742, 0833 Ⓐ, 0853 ⑥, 0953 and hourly until 1553, 1648, 1733, 1852, 1954Ⓐ, 2001⑥, 2054, 2152, 2253.
On ⑦ at 0854 and hourly until 2154, 2300.

218 GLASGOW - OBAN, FORT WILLIAM and MALLAIG

2nd class; most trains convey 🍸 SR

km		⚒	⚒	⚒A	Ba	⚒	⚒	⑦g	⑦	⑦	Bc	⚒	Bb	⑦	⑦	⚒	⚒	Ⓐ	⚒	⑦	⑦	⚒	①–④	⑤	⑥
	Edinburgh **220** .... d.	...	...	0450	...	...	...	0808	...	...	...	...	...	...	...	...	...	...	...	...	...	...	...	...	...
0	**Glasgow** Queen Street... d.	...	0520	0548‡	...	0821	0821	|	...	0956	...	1036	...	1220	1220	1222	1222	...	1634	1821	1821	1823	1823	1823	1823
16	Dalmuir .... d.	...	0538	0605	...	0841	0841	0928u	...	1016	...	1059	...	1234	1234	1243	1243	...	1658	1836	1836	1842	1842	1842	1842
26	Dumbarton Central.......... d.	...	0547	0616	...	0852	0852	|	...	1026	...	1108	...	1247	1247	1253	1253	...	1707	1845	1845	1851	1851	1851	1851
40	Helensburgh Upper .... d.	...	0603	0633	...	0907	0907	0950	...	1041	...	1127	...	1306f	1306f	1308	1308	...	1722	1905f	1905f	1906	1906	1906	1906
51	Garelochhead .... d.	...	0614	0646	...	0918	0918	1002	...	1052	...	1140	...	1318	1318	1319	1319	...	1733	1916	1916	1917	1917	1917	1917
68	Arrochar & Tarbet .... d.	...	0634	0709	...	0938	0938	1022	...	1112	...	1200	...	1338	1338	1339	1339	...	1757f	1936	1936	1937	1937	1937	1937
81	Ardlui .... d.	...	0652f	0724x	...	0951	0951	1036	...	1128	...	1214	...	1356f	1356f	1356	1356	...	1810	1951	1951	1951	1951	1951	1951
95	**Crianlarich** .... a.	...	0708	0745	...	1007	1007	1052	...	1145	...	1230	...	1412	1412	1412	1412	...	1826	2007	2007	2007	2007	2007	2007
95	**Crianlarich** .... d.	...	0718	0747	...	1015	1021	1053	...	1147	...	1233	...	1418	1424	1418	1424	...	1829	2014	2020	2014	2020	2020	2020
	Dalmally .... d.	...	0751f	|	...	1042	|	1120	...	1215	...	1259	...	1444	|	1444	|	1705	1855	2040	|	2040	|	|	|
	Taynuilt .... d.	...	0811	|	...	1103	|	1143	...	1239f	...	1320	...	1504	|	1505	|	1724	1919	2100	|	2102	|	|	|
162	**Oban** .... a.	...	0835	|	...	1127	|	1207	...	1304	...	1343	...	1527	|	1528	|	1747	1942	2124	|	2126	|	|	|
115	Bridge of Orchy.............. d.	...	...	0818	...	...	1048	...	...	...	...	...	...	...	1449	...	1449	...	...	...	2047	...	2045	2045	2045
140	Rannoch .... d.	...	...	0845	...	...	1109	...	...	...	...	...	...	...	1512	...	1512	...	...	...	2108	...	2105	2105	2108
177	Roy Bridge .... d.	...	...	0931x	...	...	1148	...	...	...	...	...	...	...	1550	...	1550	...	...	...	2146	...	2146	2146	2146
183	Spean Bridge .... d.	...	...	0939	...	...	1155	...	...	...	...	...	...	...	1556	...	1556	...	...	...	2153	...	2153	2156	2153
197	**Fort William** .... a.	...	...	0957	...	...	1208	...	...	...	...	...	...	...	1609	...	1609	...	...	...	2206	...	2206	2209	2206
197	**Fort William** .... d.	0830	...	...	1015	...	1212	...	1212	...	1245	...	1440	...	1619	...	1619	...	...	...	2214	...	2211	2214	2212
223	Glenfinnan .... d.	0905	...	...	|	...	1246	...	1246	...	|	...	|	...	1655	...	1655	...	...	...	2247	...	2247	2247	2246
251	Arisaig .... d.	0938	...	...	|	...	1319	...	1319	...	|	...	|	...	1728	...	1728	...	...	...	2320	...	2320	2320	2319
259	Morar .... d.	0946	...	...	|	...	1327	...	1327	...	|	...	|	...	1736	...	1736	...	...	...	2328	...	2328	2328	2327
264	**Mallaig** .... a.	0953	...	...	1226	...	1338	...	1338	...	1501	...	1642	...	1743	...	1743	...	...	...	2339	...	2339	2339	2338

	⚒	⚒	⚒	⚒	⚒	⑦	⑦	Ⓐ	Ba	⑦	⑥	Ⓐ		⑦g	⚒	⚒	⑦	⑦	Bc	⑦A	⑦	⚒	Bb	⚒	ⒶA
Mallaig .... d.	...	0603	...	...	1010	...	1006	...	1410	...	...	...	...	...	1605	...	1601	...	1645	...	1815	1815	1840	...	...
Morar .... d.	...	0613	...	...	1017	...	1017	...	|	...	...	...	...	...	1612	...	1612	...	|	...	1822	1822	|	...	...
Arisaig .... d.	...	0623	...	...	1027	...	1026	...	|	...	...	...	...	...	1621	...	1621	...	|	...	1831	1831	|	...	...
Glenfinnan .... d.	...	0655	...	...	1101	...	1059	...	|	...	...	...	...	...	1654	...	1654	...	|	...	1904	1904	|	...	...
Fort William .... a.	...	0729	...	...	1134	...	1132	...	1603	...	...	...	...	...	1728	...	1728	...	1853	...	1937	1937	2032	...	...
Fort William .... d.	...	0744	...	...	1140	...	1140	...	...	...	...	...	...	...	1737	...	1737	...	...	1900	...	...	—	...	1950
Spean Bridge .... d.	...	0757	...	...	1156	...	1156	...	...	...	...	...	...	...	1751	...	1751	...	...	1918	...	...	...	...	2009
Roy Bridge .... d.	...	0804	...	...	1202	...	1202	...	...	...	...	...	...	...	1757	...	1757	...	...	1926x	...	...	...	...	2017x
Rannoch .... d.	...	0847f	...	...	1242	...	1242	...	...	...	...	...	...	...	1838	...	1838	...	...	2015	...	...	...	...	2108
Bridge of Orchy .... d.	...	0907	...	...	1303	...	1303	...	...	...	...	...	...	...	1858	...	1858	...	...	2046	...	...	...	...	2137
Oban .... d.	0521	|	0857	1211	|	1211	|	1441	...	1611	1611	1611	...	1704	|	1811	|	1811	...	|	...	...	...	2039	|
Taynuilt .... d.	0544	|	0920	1235	|	1238	|	1506	...	1638	1634	1634	...	1732	|	1833	|	1833	...	|	...	...	...	2101	|
Dalmally .... d.	0603	|	0940	1300f	|	1259	|	1526	...	1658	1654	1654	...	1755	|	1856	|	1856	...	|	...	...	...	2120	|
Crianlarich .... a.	0631	0931	1008	1332	1327	1326	1332	1554	...	1726	1722	...	...	1823	1922	1927	1922	1927	...	2116	...	...	...	2148	2207
Crianlarich .... d.	0633	0933	1014	1337	1337	1337	1337	1556	...	1727	1724	...	...	1824	1932	1932	1932	1932	...	2117	...	...	...	2148	2209
Ardlui .... d.	0651	0952f	1029	1355	1355	1355	1355	1611	...	1743	1742	...	...	1841	1952	1952	1952	1952	...	2138x	...	...	...	2204	2228x
Arrochar & Tarbet .... d.	0710f	1006	1043	1409	1409	1409	1409	1627	...	1757	1756	...	...	1855	2006	2006	2006	2006	...	2156	...	...	...	2218	2245
Garelochhead .... d.	0730	1032f	1104	1431	1431	1429	1429	1649	...	1819	1819	...	...	1719	2026	2026	2026	2026	...	2222	...	...	...	2238	2311
Helensburgh Upper .... d.	0742	1044	1117	1444	1444	1440	1440	1700	...	1831	1831	...	...	1930	2039	2039	2040	2040	...	2238	...	...	...	2250	2324
Dumbarton Central .... d.	0757	1058	1130	1459	1459	1454	1454	1713	...	1847	1844	...	...	|	2052	2052	2054	2054	...	2254	...	...	...	2303	2339
Dalmuir .... d.	|	1108	1139	1512	1512	1505	1505	1724	...	1858	1853	...	...	1955s	2103	2103	2104	2104	...	2305	...	...	...	2313	2351
Glasgow Queen Street... a.	0842	1133	1156	1534	1534	1526	1526	1744	...	1920	1919	...	...	|	2125	2125	2120	2120	...	2328¶	...	...	...	2332	0015¶
Edinburgh **220** .... a.	...	...	...	...	...	...	...	...	...	...	...	...	...	2113	...	...	...	...	...	0024	...	...	...	...	0111

A – 🅁. 🛏2 (limited accommodation), 🛏 1, 2 cl. and ✕ London Euston - Fort William and v.v. (Table **161**).

B – THE JACOBITE – 🚂. 🅁. National Rail tickets **not** valid. To book ✆ 0333 996 6720 or visit www.westcoastrailways.co.uk

a – Apr. 4 - Oct. 28.

b – ⑥ May 7 - Sept. 24.

c – Ⓑ May 2 - Sept. 30.

f – Arrives 5 – 7 minutes earlier.

g – June 26 - Aug. 28.

r – 0844 on ⑥.

s – Calls to set-down only.

u – Calls to pick-up only.

x – Calls on request.

‡ – Low-level platforms. Calls to pick up only.

¶ – Low-level platforms. Calls to set down only.

SCOTTISH ISLAND FERRIES 219

Caledonian MacBrayne Ltd operates numerous ferry services linking the Western Isles of Scotland to the mainland and to each other. Principal routes – some of which are seasonal – are listed below (see also the map on page **90**). Service frequencies, sailing-times and reservations: ✆ +44 (0)800 066 5000; fax +44 (0)1475 635 235; www.calmac.co.uk

Ardrossan – Brodick (Arran)
Ardrossan – Campbeltown (Kintyre)
Barra – Eriskay
Claonaig – Lochranza (Arran)
Colintraive – Rhubodach (Bute)
Fionnphort – Iona (Iona)
Gallanach - Kerrera (Kerrera)
Gourock - Dunoon
Kennacraig – Port Ellen (Islay)
Largs – Cumbrae (Cumbrae)
Leverburgh (Harris) – Berneray (North Uist)
Lochaline – Fishnish (Mull)
Mallaig – Armadale (Skye)
Mallaig – Eigg, Muck, Rum and Canna
Mallaig – Lochboisdale (South Uist)
Oban – Castlebay (Barra)
Oban – Coll and Tiree
Oban – Colonsay, Port Askaig (Islay) and Kennacraig
Oban – Craignure (Mull)
Oban – Lismore
Portavadie (Cowal & Kintyre) – Tarbert (Loch Fyne)
Sconser (Skye) – Raasay
Tayinloan – Gigha
Tobermory (Mull) – Kilchoan
Uig (Skye) – Lochmaddy (North Uist)
Uig (Skye) – Tarbert (Harris)
Ullapool – Stornoway (Lewis)
Wemyss Bay – Rothesay (Bute)

EDINBURGH - GLASGOW 220

GR, SR, XC

EDINBURGH - FALKIRK - GLASGOW QUEEN STREET

km			⚒	⚒	⚒	Ⓐ	⚒	Ⓐ	⚒	Ⓐ	⚒	Ⓐ	⚒	Ⓐ	⚒	⚒	⊠	⚒	⚒	Ⓐ	⚒	Ⓐ	⚒	Ⓐ	⚒	Ⓐ
0	**Edinburgh** Waverley... d.	⚒	0600	0645	0715	0730	0745	0800	0815	0830	0845	0900	0915	0930	0945	1015	and at	1545	1615	1630	1645	1700	1715	1730	1745	1800
2	Haymarket................. d.		0604	0651	0719	0735	0750	0805	0820	0835	0850	0905	0921	0935	0950	1021	the same	1549	1621	1634	1650	1705	1720	1734	1749	1805
28	Linlithgow................... d.		0618	0704	0732	|	0804	|	0835	|	0907	|	0936	|	1003	1036	minutes	1605	1634	|	1708	|	1734	|	1807	|
41	Falkirk High................ d.		0628	0714	0742	0756	0814	0829	0845	0853	0917	0923	0946	0955	1013	1046	past each	1614	1644	1652	1718	1724	1744	1755	1817	1825
76	**Glasgow** Queen Street a.		0648	0737	0807	0821	0838	0853	0907	0915	0938	0948	1007	1021	1035	1107	hour until	1637	1707	1714	1739	1748	1808	1818	1838	1848

	⚒	Ⓐ	⚒	⚒	⚒	⊠	⚒	⚒	⚒	⚒		⑦	⑦	⑦		⑦	⑦	⑦	⑦	☆⊡	⑦	⑦	⑦	⑦	⑦
Edinburgh Waverley.... d.	1815	1830	1845	1915	1945	and at	2215	2245	2315	2345	⑦	0800	0830	0900	...	0930	1000	1030	1100	and at	2130	2200	2230	2300	2330
Haymarket.................. d.	1820	1835	1850	1921	1949	the same	2219	2250	2321	2350		0804	0834	0904	...	0936	1004	1034	1104	the same	2134	2204	2235	2304	2334
Linlithgow.................. d.	1834	|	1905	1937	2004	minutes	2233	2307	2335	0004		0824	0854	0924	...	0954	1022	1047	1117	minutes	2147	2217	2248	2317	2347
Falkirk High............... d.	1843	1855	1915	1946	2014	past each	2243	2316	2345	0013		0834	0902	0934	...	1004	1032	1055	1127	past each	2155	2227	2256	2327	2357
Glasgow Queen Street. a.	1906	1918	1936	2006	2034	hour until	2304	2338	0012	0037		0856	0924	0954	...	1024	1053	1115	1148	hour until	2215	2247	2316	2348	0019

		⚒	⚒	⚒	Ⓐ	⚒	Ⓐ	⚒	Ⓐ	⚒	Ⓐ	⚒	Ⓐ	⚒	⚒	⚒	☆❖	⚒	⚒	Ⓐ	⚒	Ⓐ	⚒	Ⓐ	⚒	Ⓐ
Glasgow Queen Street. d.	⚒	0600	0645	0715	0730	0745	0800	0815	0830	0845	0900	0915	0930	0945	1015	1045	and at	1545	1615	1630	1645	1700	1715	1730	1745	1800
Falkirk High............... d.		0619	0704	0735	0756	0804	0822	0835	0855	0907	0922	0935	0954	1006	1035	1105	the same	1604	1634	1652	1707	1722	1736	1752	1806	1822
Linlithgow.................. d.		0629	0714	0745	|	0814	|	0845	|	0916	|	0945	|	1016	1045	1115	minutes	1614	1645	|	1716	|	1745	|	1816	|
Haymarket.............. ▽ a.		0642	0731	0800	0816	0832	0846	0859	0918	0929	0940	1003	1016	1032	1059	1128	past each	1631	1658	1719	1729	1749	1801	1818	1831	1850
Edinburgh Waverley.... a.		0649	0737	0805	0823	0838	0852	0904	0924	0934	0945	1008	1023	1037	1104	1133	hour until	1636	1704	1724	1734	1754	1808	1824	1838	1855

	⚒	Ⓐ	⚒	⚒	⚒	⚒	⚒	⚒	⚒	⚒	⚒	⚒	⚒		⑦	⑦	⑦	⑦	⑦	⑦	⑦	★⊙	⑦	⑦	⑦	⑦
Glasgow Queen Street. d.	1815	1830	1845	1915	1945	2015	2045	2115	2145	2215	2245	2315	2345	⑦	0756	0830	0900	0930	1000	1030	1100	and at	2200	2230	2300	2330
Falkirk High............... d.	1834	1853	1904	1934	2005	2036	2104	2135	2206	2236	2305	2334	0005		0816	0849	0919	0950	1020	1050	1120	the same	2220	2250	2320	2350
Linlithgow.................. d.	1844	|	1916	1946	2015	2046	2113	2144	2216	2245	2314	2344	0014		0826	0859	0927	0959	1030	1059	1127	minutes	2227	2259	2327	2359
Haymarket.............. ▽ a.	1858	1917	1929	2001	2028	2059	2128	2159	2231	2301	2330	2357	0028		0848	0919	0946	1017	1048	1112	1145	past each	2240	2312	2340	0012
Edinburgh Waverley.... a.	1903	1922	1934	2008	2033	2104	2133	2204	2236	2309	2338	0003	0036		0853	0924	0952	1022	1053	1117	1150	hour until	2246	2318	2345	0017

EDINBURGH - MOTHERWELL - GLASGOW CENTRAL

km			⑥	Ⓐ	⚒2		⚒2		ⒶA	⑥A		Ⓐ2	⑥2		⚒A	ⒶB		⚒2		⑦A	⑦A	⑦B
0	**Edinburgh** Waverley.............. d.	⚒	0624	0626	0742	...	1550	...	1713	1712	...	1748	1748	...	1912	2019	...	2313	⑦	1712	1914	2120
2	Haymarket.............................. d.		0629	|	0746	...	1554	...	1717	1717	...	1753	1753	...	1917	2024	...	2317		1717	1918	2125
71	Motherwell.............................. a.		0705	0705	0834	...	1639	...	1756	1757	...	1848	1903	...	1954	2102	...	0022		1753	1956	2203
92	**Glasgow** Central..................... a.		0724	0725	0857	...	1658	...	1812	1814	...	1912	1934	...	2017	2126	...	...		1813	2015	2224

		⚒2	⚒B		⚒2		⚒A		⚒		ⒶA	⑥		⚒2		⑥		Ⓐ		⑦A		⑦
Glasgow Central.......................d.	⚒	...	0648	...	0705	...	0748	...	1145	...	1900	1900	...	1947	...	2105	...	2105	⑦	1900	...	2058
Motherwell.................................d.		0559	0704	...	0721	...	0807	...	1203	...	1916	1915	...	2009	...	|	...	2123		1915	...	2118
Haymarket..................................a.		0711	0747	...	0820	...	0850	...	1254	...	1954	1953	...	2056	...	2155	...	|		1958	...	2203
Edinburgh Waverley...................a.		0716	0753	...	0827	...	0855	...	1259	...	1959	2000	...	2101	...	2201	...	2221		2004	...	2208

☛ Trains also run **Edinburgh Waverley - Bathgate - Airdrie - Glasgow Queen Street Low Level** (up to four trains per hour on Ⓐ; two per hour on ⑥⑦).
☛ Trains also run **Edinburgh Waverley - Shotts - Glasgow Central** (one train per hour on ⚒; every two hours on ⑦).

A – To/from destinations on Tables **116** and **124**.
B – To/from London Kings Cross (Table **180**).

⊙ – The 1230, 1530 and 1730 from Glasgow arrive Haymarket 1319, 1618 and 1817 and Edinburgh 1324, 1623 and 1823 respectively.
⊡ – The 1530 and 1730 from Edinburgh arrive Glasgow 1620 and 1820 respectively.
❖ – The 1315 from Glasgow arrives Haymarket 1404 and Edinburgh 1410.

⊠ – Timings may vary by ± 3 minutes.
☆ – Timings may vary by ± 4 minutes.
★ – Timings may vary by ± 5 minutes.
▽ – Trains call to set down only.

GLASGOW and EDINBURGH - DUNDEE - ABERDEEN 222

GR, SR, XC

🍸 conveyed on most trains with first class seating.

km		⚒ 2G	⚒ A	⚒ 2E	⚒	⚒	⚒	⚒	⚒ 2	⚒	⚒	⚒ 2	⚒	⚒	⚒ 2	⚒ 2	⑦	⚒ 2	⚒	⚒	⚒ 2	⚒ 2	⑦	⚒	⚒ 2	⑦	⑦	⚒
0	**Edinburgh** Waverley **223/4** d.	...	...	...	...	0530	...	...	0600	0630	...	0700	0730	...	...	0801	0804	...	0830	...	...	0901	0908	0930	...	0915	...	...
2	Haymarket............ **223/4** d.	...	...	...	...	0535	...	...	0604	0635	...	0706	0735	...	...	0807	0809	...	0835	...	...	0905	0913	0935	...	0920	...	...
42	Kirkcaldy................. **223** d.	...	0516s	...	...	0604	...	...	0645	0703	...	0747	|	...	...	0846	|	...	|	...	...	0946	0950	|	...	1005	...	...
54	Markinch................. **223** d.	...	|	...	...	0613	...	...	0654	|	...	0756	|	...	...	0855	|	...	|	...	...	0955	|	|	...	1014	...	...
82	Leuchars.................. △ d.	...	0544s	...	...	0634	...	...	0714	0726	...	0816	0827	...	...	0919	|	...	0932	...	...	1015	1015	1026	...	1035	...	...
	Glasgow Queen St. **223** d.	...	|	...	...	|	...	0551	|	|	...	|	|	0741	...	|	|	0810	|	0841	...	|	|	|	0908	|	0933	0941
	Stirling.............. **223/4** d.	...	|	...	...	|	...	0621	|	|	...	|	|	0809	...	|	|	0838	|	0909	...	|	|	|	0944	|	1010	1011
	Perth................... **223** d.	...	|	0600	...	|	0636	0658	|	|	0755t	|	|	0847f	...	|	|	0914	|	0950	...	|	|	|	1021	|	1048	1046f
95	**Dundee**........................d.	0539	0605s	0625	0642	0649	0706f	0725	0728	0743	0824f	0831	0843	0909	0929	0933	0920	0939	0947	1012	1025	1029	1030	1041	1046	1051	1111	1114f
112	Carnoustie......................d.	0556	0622s	0640	|	0703	0722	0736	...	|	0841	...	|	|	0946	...	|	...	|	|	1039	...	|	|	...	|	1126	|
123	Arbroath..........................d.	0603	0631s	0647	|	0712	0731	0744	...	0800	0849	...	0900	0925	0954	...	|	...	1007	1028	1047	...	1047	1058	...	1107	1134	1130
145	Montrose.........................d.	0619	0648s	0702	|	0727	...	0758	...	0814	...	...	0914	0939	...	...	|	...	1021	1044	...	...	1103	1112	...	1122	1148	1148
184	Stonehaven.......................d.	0645	0715s	0726	|	0751	...	0819	...	0835	...	...	0935	|	...	...	|	...	1042	|	...	...	1127	1133	...	1144	1212	|
210	**Aberdeen**.........................a.	0706	0740	0746	0756	0812	...	0842	...	0852	...	...	0956	1015	...	...	1029	...	1105	1122	...	...	1147	1150	...	1206	1234	1238

	⚒ 2	⚒ 2	⚒ C	⚒	⑦	⑦	⚒ 2	⚒ 2	⚒	⑦ 2	⚒	⑦	⚒ 2	⚒ 2	⑦	⚒	⑦	⚒ 2	⚒ 2	⚒	⑦ 2	⚒	⑦	⚒ 2	⚒ 2	⚒ C	⚒ 2	⑦ C
Edinburgh Waverley **223/4** d.	...	1000	1027	...	...	1050	...	1100	1130	1132	...	...	...	1201	1241	...	...	...	1300	1330	1336	...	...	...	1400	1430	...	1433
Haymarket............ **223/4** d.	...	1005	1033	...	...	1054	...	1104	1135	1136	...	...	...	1205	1246	...	...	...	1304	1335	1340	...	...	...	1405	1435	...	1439
Kirkcaldy................. **223** d.	...	1046	1105	...	...	1123	...	1145	|	1208	...	...	...	1246	1315	...	...	...	1345	|	1412	...	...	...	1447	1507	...	1511
Markinch................. **223** d.	...	1055	|	...	...	|	...	1154	|	1217	...	...	...	1255	|	...	...	...	1354	|	1421	...	...	...	1457	|	...	|
Leuchars.................. △ d.	...	1115	1130	...	...	1147	...	1214	1225	1239	...	...	...	1315	1338	...	...	...	1414	1428	1443	...	...	...	1518	1531	...	1536
Glasgow Queen St. **223** d.	...	|	|	1041	1045	|	...	|	|	|	1141	1145	...	|	|	1240	1243	...	|	|	|	1340	1345	...	|	|	1412	|
Stirling.............. **223/4** d.	...	|	|	1109	1112	|	...	|	|	|	1210	1212	...	|	|	1313	1310	...	|	|	|	1408	1412	...	|	|	1446	|
Perth................... **223** d.	...	|	|	1140	1145	|	...	|	|	|	1244	1247	...	|	|	1344	1344	...	|	|	|	1445f	1450	...	|	|	1528	|
Dundee........................d.	1124	1129	1146	1203	1211	1211r	1224	1228	1240	1255	1307	1310	1324	1330	1353	1407	1408	1424	1431	1443	1457	1514f	1512	1527	1532	1550	1553	1552
Carnoustie......................d.	1141	...	|	|	|	|	1240	...	|	...	|	|	1338	...	|	|	|	1440	...	|	...	|	1524	1541	...	|	...	|
Arbroath..........................d.	1149	...	1203	1220	1227	1227	1249	...	1259	...	1324	1326	1346	...	1409	1424	1425	1449	...	1500	...	1534	1531	1549	...	1607	...	1609
Montrose.........................d.	...	...	1219	1234	1242	1242	...	...	|	...	1338	1341	...	...	1423	1438	1439	...	...	|	...	1548	1545	...	...	1623	...	1625
Stonehaven.......................d.	...	...	1243	|	1304	1304	...	...	1331	...	|	1403	...	...	1447	|	1500	...	...	1534	...	|	1606	...	...	1646	...	1649
Aberdeen.........................a.	...	...	1302	1310	1322	1322	...	...	1348	...	1414	1422	...	...	1505	1517	1517	...	...	1553	...	1629	1627	...	...	1706	...	1710

A – 🅁. 🛏 1, 2 class and 🚃2 London Euston - Aberdeen. Departs London previous day. Train stops to set down only. See also Table **161**.
C – From destinations on Table **180**.
E – To Inverurie (Table **225**).
G – To Inverness (Table **225**).
f – Arrives 5–8 minutes earlier.
r – Arrives 1200.
t – Ⓐ only.
s – Stops to set down only.

222 GLASGOW and EDINBURGH - DUNDEE - ABERDEEN

GR, SR, XC

🍷 conveyed on most trains with first class seating.

	Ⓐ	⚒	⑦	⚒	⚒	⚒	⑦	⚒	⑦	⚒	⚒	⑦	Ⓐ	⚒	⑦	⚒	⚒	⚒	⑦	⑦	⚒	⚒	Ⓐ	⑦	⚒	⚒	⑦
	G	2		2		2	2			2	2			2			2	2		2		2			2	D	D
Edinburgh Waverley **223/4** d.	...	...	...	1500	1530	...	1534	...	...	...	1600	1607	1630	...	...	...	...	1700	1705	1734	1730	...	...	...	1750	1813	1813
Haymarket **223/4** d.	...	...	...	1504	1535	...	1538	...	...	...	1604	1611	1635	...	...	...	...	1704	1710	1739	1738	...	...	...	1757	1817	1817
Kirkcaldy **223** d.	...	...	...	1545	|	...	1610	...	...	...	1645	1642	|	...	...	...	...	1745	1740	1811	|	...	...	...	1840	|	|
Markinch **223** d.	...	...	...	1554	|	...	1623	...	...	...	1654	1651	|	...	...	...	...	1754	|	1820	|	...	...	...	1848	|	|
Leuchars △ d.	...	...	...	1614	1626	...	1645	...	...	...	1714	1710	1726	...	...	...	...	1817	1803	1842	1832	...	...	...	1909	|	|
Glasgow Queen St. **223** d.	1439	...	1450	|	|	1511	|	1539	1545	...	|	|	|	1610	1645	1638	...	|	|	|	|	1710	1741	1745	|	|	|
Stirling **223/4** d.	1509	...	1519	|	|	1542	|	1609	1612	...	|	|	|	1640	1712	1705	...	|	|	|	|	1745u	1814	1814	|	|	|
Perth **223** d.	1541	...	1556	|	|	1630	|	1643	1648	...	|	|	|	1720	1742	1746f	...	|	|	|	|	1830f	1850f	1847	|	|	|
Dundee d.	1604	1618	1619	1628	1641	1654	1659	1705	1710	1725	1729	1725	1742	1754f	1805	1809	1831	1832	1818	1856	1856f	1855	1913	1910	1923	1936	1934f
Carnoustie d.	|	1634	|	...	|	...	...	|	|	1741	...	1740	|	1816	|	|	1853	...	|	...	|	...	1924	1922	...	|	|
Arbroath d.	1621	1643	1635	...	1659	...	...	1722	1726	1750	...	1747	1807f	1824	1821	1834	1902	...	1835	...	1913	...	1932	1929	...	|	|
Montrose d.	1635	...	1649	...	1713	...	...	1736	1741	...	...	1801	1822	...	1835	1851	...	...	1849	...	1927	...	1947	1944	...	|	|
Stonehaven d.	|	...	1710	...	1737	...	...	1757	1806	...	...	1824	1845	...	1856	|	...	...	1910	...	1948	...	2011	2010	...	|	|
Aberdeen a.	1713	...	1727	...	1755	...	...	1815	1825	...	...	1842	1904	...	1918	1931	...	...	1927	...	2005	...	2029	2029	...	2046	2043

	⑦	⚒	⚒	⚒	⚒	⚒	⑦	Ⓐ	⚒	⚒	⚒	⑦	⚒	Ⓐ	⚒	⑦	⚒	⚒	⚒	⚒	⑦	⚒	⑦	⑥	Ⓐ	⚒	⑦
	C	C	2		2	2	2	C		2			2	C			2	2				2	2	2	2	2	2
Edinburgh Waverley **223/4** d.	1835	1835	...	...	...	1900	1915	1927	1931	...	...	...	2000	2034	...	2100	2100	...	2131	...	...	2200	2228	...	...	2300	...
Haymarket **223/4** d.	1841	1840	...	...	...	1905	1919	1933	1937	...	...	...	2004	2039	...	2105	2104	...	2136	...	...	2204	2232	...	...	2304	...
Kirkcaldy **223** d.	1913	1913	...	...	...	1946	2002	|	|	...	...	...	2047	2111	...	2134	2147	...	2204	...	...	2247	2315	...	...	2347	...
Markinch **223** d.	|	|	...	...	...	1954	2011	|	|	...	...	...	2055	|	...	2143	2155	...	|	...	...	2258	2324	...	...	2356	...
Leuchars △ d.	1937	1940	...	...	...	2015	2032	|	2027	...	...	...	2116	2139	...	2204	2216	...	2227	...	...	2322	2345	...	...	0016	...
Glasgow Queen St. **223** d.	|	|	1810	1841	...	|	|	|	|	1909	1937	1944	|	|	2040	|	|	...	|	2140	2145	|	|	2305	2310	|	2344
Stirling **223/4** d.	|	|	1843	1909	...	|	|	2012	|	1946	2004	2011	|	|	2108	|	|	...	|	2209	2212	|	|	2334	2339	|	0020
Perth **223** d.	|	|	1926	1944	...	|	|	...	|	2026	2043v	2049	|	|	2145	|	|	...	|	2246	2249	|	|	0012	0018	|	0100
Dundee d.	1953	1957	1950	2008	2015	2029	2048	...	2045	2052	2111f	2112	2133	2154	2212	2219	2230	2236	2255	2308	2312	2338	2359	...	0044	0032	...
Carnoustie d.	|	|	...	|	2032	...	...	...	|	...	2123	|	...	|	2224	|	...	2253	|	2325	2323	...	...	...	...	...	...
Arbroath d.	2010	2015	...	2025	2040	...	...	...	2102	...	2131	2128	...	2212	2231	2239	...	2301	2311	2332	2330	...	...	...	...	...	...
Montrose d.	2026	2030	...	2039	...	...	...	...	2116	...	2150	2142	...	2228	2246	2253	...	...	2325	2347	2345	...	...	...	...	...	...
Stonehaven d.	2050	2053	...	|	...	...	...	...	|	...	2214	2206	...	2252	|	2314	...	...	2347	0012	0006	...	...	...	...	...	...
Aberdeen a.	2110	2113	...	2121	...	...	...	...	2153	...	2234	2224	...	2311	2324	2335	...	...	0009	0032	0023	...	...	...	...	...	...

km		⚒	⚒	⚒	⚒	⚒	⚒	⚒	⚒	⚒	⚒	⚒	⚒	⚒	⚒	⑦	⚒	⚒	⚒	⚒	⑦	⚒	⚒	⚒	⚒	⚒	Ⓐ
		2	2		2	2			2	2	2		2	G	2			C	2	D	2	2	2			2	2
0	**Aberdeen** d.	0507	...	...	...	...	0534	0557	0616	...	...	0639	...	0708	...	...	0738	0752	...	0820	...	...	...	0854	0904	...	...
26	Stonehaven d.	0526	...	...	...	...	|	0613	0635	...	...	0655	...	0727	...	...	0754	0811	...	0837	...	...	...	|	0920	...	...
65	Montrose d.	0552	...	...	...	...	0609	0635	0700	...	...	0715	...	0747	...	...	0814	0833	...	0859	...	...	...	0927	0940	...	...
87	Arbroath d.	▬	...	...	...	0606	0624	0649	▬	0711	...	0730	0743	0801	...	...	0829	0850	...	0914	...	...	0922	0941	0955	...	*1006*
97	Carnoustie d.	⚒	...	...	...	0613	|	0656	⑦2	0718	...	|	0750	|	...	...	|	|	...	|	...	...	0929	|	|	...	*1013*
115	**Dundee** d.	2	0540	0548	0635	0638	0648	0715f	0724	0735	0740	0752	0815	0826	0840	0845	0850	0908	0915	0933	0925	0942	0943	0959	1013	1018	1040
149	**Perth** **223** d.	0516	|	0613	|	...	0711	|	|	...	|	0814	0842k	|	|	0907	0912	|	0940	|	|	|	...	1021	|	1430	|
202	Stirling **223/4** d.	0554	|	0652	|	...	0754	|	|	...	|	0848	0920k	|	|	0941	0946	|	1018	|	|	|	...	1051	|	1122	|
249	**Glasgow** Queen St. **223** a.	0639	|	0724	|	...	0832	|	|	...	|	0925	0956	|	|	1015	1015	|	1053	|	|	|	...	1120	|	1153	|
	Leuchars △ d.	...	0553	...	0651	...	...	0727	0737	...	0753	...	...	|	0853	...	...	0922	...	|	0938	0956	...	...	1026	...	1053
	Markinch **223** d.	...	0615	...	0716	...	...	|	0759	...	0815	...	...	|	0914	...	...	|	...	|	1000	1018	...	...	|	...	1114
	Kirkcaldy **223** d.	...	0631	...	0727	...	...	|	0810	...	0826	...	...	|	0925	...	...	0947	...	|	1011	1028	...	...	|	...	1125
	Haymarket **223/4** a.	...	0713	...	0809	...	...	0828j	0858	...	0908	...	...	0930	1007	...	...	1019	...	1047	1055	1111	...	...	1114	...	1209a
	Edinburgh Waverley **223/4** a.	...	0721	...	0814	...	...	0833j	0903	...	0913	...	...	0935	1012	...	...	1026	...	1054	1100	1117	...	...	1122	...	1214a

	⑦	⚒	⑦	⚒	⚒	⑦	⑦	⚒	⚒	⑦	⚒	⚒	⚒	⑦	⚒	⑦	⚒	⑦	⚒	⚒	⑦	⚒	⑦	⑦	⚒	⚒	⚒
			C	C	2	2	2	2						D	2	E		C	2		2	2				2	
Aberdeen d.	0930	0944	0947	0952	...	...	...	...	...	1033	1048	1101	...	1110	...	1131	1145	1147	...	1207	...	...	1230	1244	1255	...	1313
Stonehaven d.	0946	|	1006	1011	...	...	...	...	...	1049	|	1117	...	1127	...	1148	|	1206	...	1223	...	...	1247	1304	|	...	|
Montrose d.	1009	1021f	1028	1033	...	...	...	...	...	1109	1124	1137	...	1149	...	1208	1221	1228	...	1245	...	...	1308	1329	1328	...	1346
Arbroath d.	1024	1036	1045	1050	...	...	...	1102	...	1124	1138	1152	...	1204	*1210*	1222	1235	1245	...	1259	...	*1308*	1323	1343	1342	...	1401
Carnoustie d.	1031	|	|	|	...	...	...	1109	...	|	|	|	...	|	*1217*	|	|	|	...	|	...	*1315*	|	1350	|	...	|
Dundee d.	1050	1055	1104	1109	1115	...	1120	1126	1140	1142	1156	1210	1215	1222	1240	1240	1253	1304	1310	1317	1320	1340	1343	1406	1400	1414	1419
Perth **223** d.	1111	1120	|	|	1141	...	|	...	|	1215r	1218	|	1240	|	|	1307	1315	|	1345y	|	|	|	1407	|	1422	1440	|
Stirling **223/4** d.	1146	1152	|	|	1227	1152	|	...	|	1248	1248	|	1317	|	|	1343	1345	|	1423	|	|	|	1442	|	1451	1521	|
Glasgow Queen St. **223** a.	1214	1221	|	|	1301	|	|	...	|	1315	1321	|	1353	|	|	1413	1415	|	1454	|	|	|	1510	|	1521	1554	|
Leuchars △ d.	...	...	1118	1123	...	|	1133	...	1153	...	...	1223	...	|	1253	...	...	1318	...	1329	1333	1353	...	1419	...	...	1431
Markinch **223** d.	...	...	|	|	...	|	1155	...	1214	...	...	|	...	|	1314	...	...	|	...	|	1356	1414	...	|	...	...	|
Kirkcaldy **223** d.	...	...	1143	1148	...	|	1206	...	1225	...	...	|	...	|	1325	...	...	1344	...	|	1406	1425	...	1446	...	...	|
Haymarket **223/4** a.	...	...	1216	1219	...	1231	1240	...	1307	...	...	1314	...	1336	1408	...	...	1420	...	1418	1440	1507	...	1517	...	...	1520
Edinburgh Waverley **223/4** a.	...	...	1222	1225	...	1236	1245	...	1312	...	...	1320	...	1343	1413	...	...	1426	...	1426c	1445	1512	...	1523	...	...	1526

	⚒	⑦	⚒	⑦	⚒	⚒	⑦	⚒	⚒	⑦	⚒	⚒	⚒	⑦	⑦	⚒	⚒	⚒	⚒	⚒	⑦	⚒	⚒	⚒	⑦	⑦	⚒
	2			C		2	2	2	2			C	2			2			2		2	2	2	2			2
Aberdeen d.	...	1334	1343	1347	1356	...	...	...	...	1433	1445	1452	...	1508	1531	...	...	1535	...	1604	...	...	...	1630	1631	1704	...
Stonehaven d.	...	1350	|	1406	1413	...	...	...	...	1450	|	1511	...	1528	1548	...	...	|	...	1620	...	...	...	|	1647	1720	...
Montrose d.	...	1410	1423	1428	1437f	...	...	...	...	1511	1518	1533	...	1549	1612	...	...	1612	...	1648	...	...	...	1713f	1707	1743	...
Arbroath d.	*1409*	1425	1437	1445	1452	...	...	1504	...	1526	1532	1550	...	1603	1626	1559	...	1627	...	1703	...	...	1712	1728	1722	1758	*1817*
Carnoustie d.	*1416*	|	|	|	|	...	...	1511	...	|	|	|	...	1610	|	1606	...	|	...	1710	...	...	1719	|	|	|	*1824*
Dundee d.	1440	1443	1456	1503	1510	1515	1515	1528	1542	1545	1554f	1609	1616	1624	1644	1624	1638	1647	1707	1724	1721	1740	1736	1750	1740	1817	1847
Perth **223** d.	|	1504	1518	|	|	1541	|	...	|	1609	1615	|	1646f	|	1706	...	|	1713f	1738f	|	|	|	...	1811	1801	|	|
Stirling **223/4** d.	|	1544	1548	|	|	1621	|	...	|	1643	1644s	|	1726	|	1740	...	|	1747	1817	|	|	|	...	1843	1834	|	|
Glasgow Queen St. **223** a.	|	1612	1619	|	|	1656	|	...	|	1712	1718	|	1758	|	1809	...	|	1822	1852	|	|	|	...	1914	1909	|	|
Leuchars △ d.	1453	...	...	1517	1522	...	1528	...	1555	...	...	1624	...	1637	...	...	1651	...	...	1736	1734	1753	...	...	...	1829	1900
Markinch **223** d.	1514	...	...	|	|	...	1551	...	1616	...	...	|	...	|	...	...	1713	...	...	|	1757	1816	...	...	...	|	1921
Kirkcaldy **223** d.	1525	...	...	1543	|	...	1601	...	1627	...	...	1649	...	1704	...	...	1724	...	...	|	1807	1827	...	...	...	1852	1932
Haymarket **223/4** a.	1607	...	...	1618	1611e	...	1635	...	1710	...	...	1719	...	1734	...	...	1807	...	...	1824	1841	1906	...	...	...	1921	2015
Edinburgh Waverley **223/4** a.	1612	...	...	1624	1618e	...	1640	...	1715	...	...	1725	...	1740	...	...	1813	...	...	1829	1846	1913	...	...	...	1926	2024

	⚒	⚒	⚒	⑦	Ⓐ	⑦	⚒	⚒	⚒	⑦	⚒	⚒	⑦	⚒	⚒	⑦	⚒	⚒	⚒	⚒	⚒	⚒	⑦	⚒	Ⓑ	⚒	⑦
		2	2		C	2		2	2			2			2			2			2	2			B		2
Aberdeen d.	1741	...	...	1745	1818	...	1840	...	...	1904	1915	...	1946	1947	...	2008	2010	...	2044	2106	...	...	2130	2135	2143	2228	2226
Stonehaven d.	1757	...	...	1801	1837	...	|	...	...	1921	1931	...	2006	|	...	2024	2026	...	2103	|	...	...	2147	2152	2201u	2247	2246
Montrose d.	1822	...	...	1824	1859	...	1916	...	...	1945	1956	...	2030f	2020	...	2047	2048	...	2128	2139	...	...	2208	2213	2226u	2311	2310
Arbroath d.	1836	...	1846	1839	1916	...	1930	...	1938	1959	2010	...	2045	2037	2051	2102	2103	...	2142	2154	...	2205	2223	2228	2244u	2325	2324
Carnoustie d.	|	...	1853	|	|	...	|	...	1944	2006	2016	...	|	|	2058	|	|	...	|	|	...	2211	|	|	2253u	2332	2331
Dundee d.	1856	1914	1911	1858	1934	1916	1948	1953	2002	2023	2030	2044	2103	2101	2113	2120	2121	2149	2201	2212	2231	2229	2241	2248	2309u	2349	2348
Perth **223** d.	1918	1946y	...	1920	|	|	2014	|	...	|	|	|	2128f	2122	...	|	|	|	2223	|	|	...	|	|	|	0012t	0011
Stirling **223/4** d.	1949	2027	...	1953	|	|	2045	|	...	|	|	|	2203	2152	...	|	|	|	2253	|	|	...	|	|	|	...	...
Glasgow Queen St. **223** a.	2022	2056	...	2021	|	|	2114	|	...	|	|	|	2238	2222	...	|	|	|	2321	|	|	...	|	|	|	...	...
Leuchars △ d.	...	...	...	...	1948	1929	...	2005	...	2036	2043	2057	...	...	...	2132	2135	2202	...	2224	2244	...	|	|	2328u	...	...
Markinch **223** d.	...	...	...	...	|	1951	...	2027	...	|	|	2118	...	...	...	2154	2157	2224	...	|	2305	...	|	|	|	...	...
Kirkcaldy **223** d.	...	...	...	...	2013	2002	...	2037	...	2102	|	2129	...	...	...	2203	2206	2234	...	|	2316	...	|	|	2359u	...	...
Haymarket **223/4** a.	...	...	...	...	2043	2047	...	2124	...	2133	2143	2213	...	...	...	2231	2241	2318	...	2322	0001	...	2355	0005	...	...	...
Edinburgh Waverley **223/4** a.	...	...	...	...	2049	2052	...	2129	...	2138	2149	2221	...	...	...	2238	2246	2324	...	2329	0006	...	0001	0010	...	...	...

B – 🅁. 🛏 1, 2 class and 🚃2 Aberdeen - London Euston. Train stops to pick up only. See also Table **161**.
C – From/to destinations on Table **180**.
D – From/to destinations on Table **124**.
E – From Inverurie (Table **225**).
G – To/from Inverness (Table **225**).

a – 4 minutes earlier on Ⓐ.
b – Arrives 1359 on ⑥.
c – Arrives 1422 on ⑥.
e – 4–6 minutes earlier on ⑥.
f – Arrives 5–7 minutes earlier.
g – Arrives 1624.

h – Arrives 2103.
j – 9 minutes earlier on ⑥.
k – 4–6 minutes later on Ⓐ.
r – Arrives 1202.
s – Stops to set down only.
t – Ⓐ only.

u – Stops to pick up only.
v – Arrives 2033.
y – Arrives 8 minutes earlier.

△ – Frequent 🚌 connections available to/from **St Andrews.** Journey 10 minutes. Operator: Stagecoach (routes 42, 94, 99).

SR 2nd class — EDINBURGH - TWEEDBANK — 222a

km		⚒	⚒	⚒	⚒	⚒	⚒	⚒	⚒	⚒	⚒		⚒	⚒	⚒	⚒	⚒	⚒	⚒	⚒	⚒	⚒	Ⓐ	⑥	⑥
0	**Edinburgh** Waverley ..... d.		0610	0641	0714	0740	0811	0843	0914	0942	1011	...	1043	1111	1143	1212	1243	1310	1343	1413	1442	1511	1540	1543	1613
13	Eskbank ..... d.		0632	0703	0733	0802	0832	0902	0934	1004	1034	...	1103	1132	1203	1233	1302	1332	1403	1433	1502	1532	1603	1602	1634
15	Newtongrange ..... d.		0635	0706	0736	0805	0835	0905	0937	1007	1037	...	1106	1135	1206	1236	1305	1335	1406	1436	1505	1535	1606	1605	1637
53	Galashiels ..... d.		0706	0737	0808	0836	0906	0937	1008	1038	1108	...	1137	1206	1237	1307	1336	1406	1437	1507	1536	1607	1636	1636	1708
57	**Tweedbank** ..... a.		0710	0741	0812	0840	0910	0941	1012	1043	1114	...	1143	1211	1242	1311	1342	1410	1443	1511	1540	1611	1642	1640	1712

	Ⓐ	⚒	⚒	Ⓐ	⑥	⑥	Ⓐ	⚒	⚒	⚒	⚒	⚒	⚒	⑦	⑦	⑦	⑦	⑦	⑦	⑦	⑦	⑦		⑦	⑦
Edinburgh Waverley ..... d.	1619	1643	1715	1740	1744	1816	1816	1842	1943	2043	2143	2242	2343		0912	1011	1113	1212	1312	1411	1515	1611	and hourly until	2212	2311
Eskbank ..... d.	1638	1704	1735	1805	1804	1835	1838	1904	2004	2102	2202	2302	0003		0931	1031	1132	1231	1331	1432	1534	1631		2232	2330
Newtongrange ..... d.	1641	1707	1738	1808	1807	1838	1841	1907	2007	2105	2205	2305	0006		0932	1034	1135	1234	1334	1435	1537	1634		2235	2333
Galashiels ..... d.	1712	1738	1809	1839	1838	1909	1912	1938	2037	2136	2236	2336	0037		1005	1105	1206	1305	1405	1507	1608	1705		2306	0004
Tweedbank ..... a.	1716	1744	1814	1843	1842	1913	1916	1943	2043	2140	2243	2341	0043		1009	1109	1210	1309	1409	1512	1612	1710		2310	0009

	⚒	⚒	⚒	⚒	⚒	⚒	⚒	⚒	⑥	Ⓐ	⚒	⚒	⚒	⚒	⚒	Ⓐ	⑥	⚒	⚒	⚒	⚒	Ⓐ	⑥	⚒	⚒
Tweedbank ..... d.		0549	0620	0650	0719	0749	0819	0850	0921	0921	0951	1019	1049	1119	1149	1218	1219	1249	1319	1350	1419	1447	1450	1519	1549
Galashiels ..... d.		0553	0624	0654	0723	0753	0823	0854	0925	0925	0955	1023	1053	1123	1153	1222	1223	1253	1323	1354	1423	1451	1454	1523	1553
Newtongrange ..... d.		0622	0653	0723	0752	0822	0852	0923	0954	0954	1024	1052	1122	1152	1222	1251	1252	1322	1352	1423	1452	1520	1523	1552	1622
Eskbank ..... d.		0625	0656	0726	0755	0825	0855	0926	0957	0957	1027	1055	1125	1155	1225	1254	1255	1325	1355	1426	1455	1523	1526	1555	1625
Edinburgh Waverley ..... a.		0647	0720	0746	0817	0848	0915	0948	1019	1023	1048	1118	1148	1218	1250	1315	1321	1349	1419	1448	1518	1545	1549	1618	1651

	⑥	Ⓐ	⑥	Ⓐ	⑥	Ⓐ	⚒		⚒	⚒	⑥	Ⓐ	⚒	Ⓐ	⑥	⚒	⚒	⑦	⑦	⑦	⑦	⑦		⑦	⑦
Tweedbank ..... d.	1619	1621	1650	1650	1719	1722	1749	...	1820	1849	1921	1923	2019	2114	2119	2219	2319		0848	0947	1047	1147	and hourly until	2143	2247
Galashiels ..... d.	1623	1625	1654	1654	1723	1726	1753	...	1824	1853	1925	1927	2023	2118	2123	2223	2323		0852	0951	1051	1151		2147	2251
Newtongrange ..... d.	1652	1655	1723	1723	1752	1755	1822	...	1854	1922	1954	1956	2052	2147	2152	2252	2352		0921	1020	1120	1220		2213	2320
Eskbank ..... d.	1655	1658	1726	1726	1755	1758	1825	...	1857	1925	1957	1959	2055	2150	2155	2255	2355		0924	1023	1123	1223		2216	2323
Edinburgh Waverley ..... a.	1715	1724	1746	1751	1819	1819	1849	...	1919	1948	2019	2023	2118	2210	2217	2319	0020		0943	1042	1143	1245		2243	2343

SR — EDINBURGH and GLASGOW - PERTH - INVERNESS — 223

Most Inverness trains convey 🍸.

km			⚒A	⚒2	⚒	⚒2	⚒	①	②–⑥	⚒2	⑦	⑦	⚒2	Ⓐ	⑥	⚒	⚒	⑦2	⑦	⚒2	⚒2	⚒	⚒2	⚒	⑦	⚒2	⑦
0	**Edinburgh** Waverley 222/4 d.	...	...	0635	...	0735	...	...	0837	0841	...	0925	0936	...	...	...	1033	1035	...	1038	1135	...	1235	1330	...	1334	1354
2	Haymarket 222/4 d.	...	...	0639	...	0739	...	...	0842	0845	...	0930	0940	...	...	...	1037	1039	...	1042	1139	...	1239	1335	...	1339	1358
42	Kirkcaldy 222 d.	...	...	0722	...	0822	...	...	|	0928	...	|	1023	...	...	...	|	|	...	1125	1222	...	1322	|	...	1422	|
54	Markinch 222 d.	...	...	0731	...	0831	...	...	|	0937	...	|	1032	...	...	...	|	|	...	1135	1231	...	1331	|	...	1431	|
	Glasgow Queen St. 222 d.	...	...	|	0707	|	0841	...	|	|	0933	|	|	1007	1008	1041	|	|	1111	|	|	1207	|	|	1345	|	|
	Stirling 222/4 d.	...	0458	|	0734	|	0909	...	0931	|	1010	1022	|	1035	1035	1109	1117	1123	1141	|	|	1236	|	1416	1412	|	1440
91	**Perth** 222 d.	...	0540	0805	0811	0907	0948	0953	1002	1009	1045	1056	1107	1116r	1116f	1137	1156	...	1221	1209	1303	1312	1410	1450	1448	1512	1512
116	Dunkeld & Birnam d.	...	0601	...	0834f	...	...	1009	1019	...	...	1112	...	1138f	1140r	...	1213	...	1239	...	...	1329	...	1507	...	...	1530
137	Pitlochry d.	...	0615	...	0847	...	...	1033g	1033	...	...	1130f	...	1152	1153	...	1228	...	1253	...	...	1342	...	1521	...	...	1544
148	Blair Atholl d.	...	0627	...	0856	...	...	|	|	...	...	1140	...	|	|	...	1238	...	|	...	...	|	...	1531	...	...	1553
186	Dalwhinnie d.	...	0659	...	0921	...	...	|	|	...	...	1205	...	|	|	...	1303	...	|	...	...	|	...	1556	...	...	1622f
202	Newtonmore d.	...	0710	...	0931	...	...	|	|	...	...	1216	...	|	|	...	1314	...	|	...	...	|	...	1607	...	...	1632
207	Kingussie d.	0647	0717	...	0939	...	...	1115	1115	...	...	1221	...	1236	1238	...	1319	...	1337	...	...	1426	...	1612	...	...	1637
226	Aviemore 🚂 d.	0700	0743	...	0951	...	...	1129	1129	...	...	1233	...	1250	1250	...	1334	...	1349	...	...	1438	...	1626	...	...	1649
237	Carrbridge d.	0715c	0754	...	1001	...	...	|	|	...	...	1242	...	|	|	...	1343	...	1401f	...	...	|	...	1635	...	...	1658
282	**Inverness** a.	0748	0842	...	1028	...	...	1201	1201	...	...	1318	...	1326	1326	...	1415	...	1429	...	...	1523	...	1703	...	...	1725

	⑦P	⚒2	⚒	⑦	⚒2	⑦	⚒	⑥K	ⒶK	⚒2	⑦	⑦K	⑦2	⚒	⚒	⚒2	⑦P	⑦2	⚒2	⑦2	⚒	⚒	⚒2	⚒2	⚒2	⑦2	⚒2
Edinburgh Waverley 222/4 d.	...	1435	...	...	1535	1552	...	1633	1633	1635	...	1632	1750	...	1733	1736	...	1806	1840	1855	...	1938	2045	2145	2245n	2235	2318
Haymarket 222/4 d.	...	1440	...	...	1539	1557	...	1638	1638	1639	...	1637	1754	...	1738	1741	...	1810	1844	1859	...	1944	2049	2149	2249n	2240	2322
Kirkcaldy 222 d.	...	1524	...	...	1622	|	...	|	|	1722	...	|	1826	...	|	1826	...	|	1927	|	...	|	2125	2222	2326	|	|
Markinch 222 d.	...	1533	...	...	1631	|	...	|	|	1731	...	|	1836	...	|	1835	...	|	1936	2003	...	|	2134	2232	2335	|	0023
Glasgow Queen St. 222 d.	1438	|	1507	1545	|	|	1638	|	|	|	1645	|	|	1741	|	|	1803	|	|	|	1906	|	|	|	|	|	|
Stirling 222/4 d.	1508	|	1534	1612	|	1639	1705	1719	1719	|	1712	1722	|	1814	1821	|	1835	1910	|	|	1937	2020	|	|	|	2333	|
Perth 222 d.	1546	1612	1617a	1646	1709	1711	1741	1754	1757f	1810	1741	1801f	1906	1845	1903b	1910	1912	1945	2012e	2034	2028b	2057f	2208	2308	0006	0011	0054
Dunkeld & Birnam d.	|	...	1636	...	...	1727	...	|	|	...	...	|	...	...	|	...	1929	...	...	...	2046	2116	...	...	...	...	...
Pitlochry d.	1614	...	1650	...	...	1741	...	1824	1827	...	...	1831	...	...	1934	...	1942	...	...	...	2100	2130	...	...	...	...	...
Blair Atholl d.	|	...	1700	...	...	|	...	|	|	...	...	|	...	...	|	...	1952	...	...	...	|	2140	...	...	...	...	...
Dalwhinnie d.	|	...	|	...	...	|	...	|	|	...	...	|	...	...	|	...	2017	...	...	...	2137f	2211r	...	...	...	...	...
Newtonmore d.	|	...	|	...	...	|	...	|	|	...	...	|	...	...	|	...	2028	...	...	...	|	2222	...	...	...	...	...
Kingussie d.	1656	...	1735	...	...	1824	...	1910	1913	...	...	1916	...	...	2017	...	2033	...	...	...	2153	2227	...	...	...	...	...
Aviemore 🚂 d.	1709	...	1749	...	...	1837	...	1926	1930f	...	...	1932	...	...	2032	...	2046	...	...	...	2205	2239	...	...	...	...	...
Carrbridge d.	|	...	1758	...	...	|	...	|	|	...	...	|	...	...	|	...	2056	...	...	...	|	2248	...	...	...	...	...
Inverness a.	1745	...	1826	...	...	1910	...	2004	2007	...	...	2009	...	...	2124t	...	2126	...	...	...	2239	2316	...	...	...	...	...

	⚒2	⚒2	⚒2	⚒2	⚒2	⚒	⑦2	⚒	⑦2	⑦2	⚒K	⚒2	⑦2	①	②–⑥	⚒2	⚒	⑦K	⚒	⑦	⑦	⑦	⚒	⚒	⚒2	⑦	⚒2
Inverness d.	...	...	...	0536	...	0645	...	...	...	...	0755	...	...	0845	0845	...	0942	0940	...	...	1053	...	1051	...	...	1238	...
Carrbridge d.	...	...	...	0603	...	|	...	...	...	...	|	...	...	0913	0913	...	|	1011	...	...	|	...	|	...	...	1310	...
Aviemore 🚂 d.	...	...	...	0613	...	0722	...	...	...	...	0832	...	...	0922	0922	...	1030	1022	...	...	1128	...	1130	...	...	1319	...
Kingussie d.	...	...	...	0624	...	0736	...	...	...	...	0845	...	...	0938f	0938f	...	1042	1035	...	...	1139	...	1143	...	...	1338f	...
Newtonmore d.	...	...	...	0629	...	|	...	...	...	...	|	...	...	0943	0943	...	|	1040	...	...	|	...	|	...	...	1342	...
Dalwhinnie d.	...	...	...	0641	...	|	...	...	...	...	|	...	...	0955	0955	...	|	|	...	...	1152	...	|	...	...	|	...
Blair Atholl d.	...	...	...	0712r	...	0809	...	...	...	...	|	...	...	|	|	...	|	1117f	...	...	|	...	1216	...	...	1414	...
Pitlochry d.	...	...	...	0727f	...	0819	...	...	...	...	0928	...	...	1026	1033r	...	1122v	1127	...	...	1223	...	1230	...	...	1425	...
Dunkeld & Birnam d.	...	...	...	0740	...	0834	...	...	...	...	|	...	...	1040	1047	...	|	1141	...	...	1238	...	1242	...	...	1437	...
Perth 222/4 d.	0600	0619	0716	0759	0804	0855	0850	0917	0917	0936	0958	1014	1010	1105r	1105	1115	1155	1201	1211	1215	1257	1307	1305f	1315	1324	1456	1427
Stirling 222 d.	|	|	|	0842	|	0934	|	|	0954	|	1033	|	1047	1145	1145	|	1235	1238	|	1248	1328	1343	1337	1345	|	1534	|
Glasgow Queen St. 222 a.	|	|	|	0920	|	|	|	|	|	|	|	|	|	1214	1214	|	1311	|	|	1315	|	1413	|	1415	|	1607	|
Markinch 222 d.	0631	0646	0752	...	0837	|	0919	0946	|	1007	|	1051	|	...	...	1148	...	|	1250	...	|	...	|	...	1353	...	1456
Kirkcaldy 222 d.	|	0657	0804	...	0849	|	0930	0958	|	|	|	1103	|	...	...	1159	...	|	1301	...	|	...	|	...	1404	...	1508
Haymarket 222/4 a.	0733	0742	0850	...	0947	1009	1018	1042	1045	1113	1108	1147	1138	...	...	1244	...	1314	1346	...	1405	...	1421	...	1449	...	1553
Edinburgh Waverley 222/4 a.	0738	0747	0855	...	0953	1015	1023	1047	1050	1118	1114	1154	1143	...	...	1249	...	1320	1355	...	1410	...	1429	...	1454	...	1558

	⚒	⚒	⚒	⑦	⚒2	⑦	⚒	⚒2	⑦	⑦	⚒	⚒	⑦	⑦2	⚒2	⚒	⚒2	⚒	⚒	⑦	⑦	⚒	Ⓐ	⑥	⚒	⑦B	ⒶB
Inverness d.	1248	...	...	1326	...	...	1449	...	1522	...	...	1545	1626	...	...	1726	...	1853	...	1852	...	...	2023	2023	...	2026	2045
Carrbridge d.	1325	...	...	|	...	...	|	...	|	...	...	1616	1658f	...	...	1759f	...	|	...	1925	...	...	2058	2058	...	|	|
Aviemore 🚂 d.	1334	...	...	1407	...	...	1525	...	1557	...	...	1634r	1708	...	...	1808	...	1933r	...	1934	...	...	2107	2107	...	2119	2136
Kingussie d.	1346	...	...	1418	...	...	1537	...	1608	...	...	1646	1720	...	...	1820	...	1945	...	1946	...	...	2119	2119	...	2133	2150
Newtonmore d.	1351	...	...	|	...	...	|	...	|	...	...	1651	|	...	...	|	...	|	...	1951	...	...	2123	2123	...	2141	2155
Dalwhinnie d.	1402	...	...	|	...	...	|	...	|	...	...	1703	|	...	...	|	...	|	...	2002	...	...	2137	2135	...	2154	2211
Blair Atholl d.	|	...	...	|	...	...	|	...	|	...	...	1725	1753	...	...	|	...	|	...	2025	...	...	2201	2157	...	2222	2235
Pitlochry d.	1433	...	...	1459	...	...	1618	...	1650	...	...	1735	1803	...	...	1905	...	2030	...	2035	...	...	2215	2208	...	2232	2246
Dunkeld & Birnam d.	1446	...	...	|	...	...	1637f	...	1704	...	...	1750	1820	...	...	1920	...	2047	...	2049	...	...	2227	2220	...	2248	2303
Perth 222/4 d.	1507	1518	1523	1529	1621	1609	1705b	1721	1722	1801	1804	1820b	1839	...	1913	1939	2004	2105	2122	2119b	2128	2218	2246	2239	2313	2306	2327
Stirling 222 a.	1541	1548	|	1558	|	1643	1740	|	1752	1834	|	1853	1910	1919	|	2017	|	2136	2152	2151	2203	|	2319	2319	|	2353	0012
Glasgow Queen St. 222 a.	|	1619	|	|	|	1712	1814	|	|	1909	|	1922	1942	|	|	2044	|	|	2222	|	2238	|	2359	2359	|	...	...
Markinch 222 a.	|	...	1554	|	1652	...	...	1801	|	...	1833	...	...	|	1943	...	2039	|	...	|	...	2248	...	...	2341	...	...
Kirkcaldy 222 a.	|	...	1606	|	1703	...	...	1812	|	...	1845	...	...	|	1955	...	2050	|	...	|	...	2300	...	...	2352	...	...
Haymarket 222/4 a.	1627	...	1652	1638	1749	...	...	1848	1831	...	1929	...	...	2002	2042	...	2127	2221	...	2234	...	2333	...	...	0028	...	...
Edinburgh Waverley 222/4 a.	1633	...	1657	1647	1754	...	...	1858	1837	...	1934	...	...	2007	2048	...	2133	2226	...	2241	...	2342	...	...	0033	...	...

A – [R]. 🛏 1, 2 class and (2) London Euston - Inverness (departs London previous day). Station calls are to set down only. See also Table **161**.
B – [R]. 🛏 1, 2 class and (2) Inverness - London Euston. Train stops to pick up only. See Table **161**.
K – From / to London Kings Cross (Table **180**)
P – To Elgin (Table **225**).

a – Arrives 1604.
b – Arrives 10 – 12 minutes earlier.
c – Arrives 0709.
e – Arrives 2008 on Ⓐ.
f – Arrives 4 – 6 minutes earlier.
g – Arrives 1022.
h – 0942 on ⑥.

j – Arrives 0800 on Ⓐ.
n – Departs 5 minutes later on Ⓐ.
r – Arrives 7 – 9 minutes earlier.
t – Arrives 2114 on ⑥.
v – Departs 1127 on Ⓐ.

🚂 – Strathspey Railway (Aviemore - Boat of Garten - Broomhill, *14 km*). ✆ 01479 810725. www.strathspeyrailway.co.uk

224 EDINBURGH - STIRLING — 2nd class only — SR

km			⚒	⚒	⚒	⚒	⚒	⚒	⚒	⚒	⚒	⚒	⚒	⚒	⚒	⚒	⚒	⚒	⚒	⚒	⚒	⚒	⚒	⚒	⚒
0	**Edinburgh** Waverley **222/3** d.	⚒	0518	0533	0604	0633	0703	0734	0804	0834	0906	0935	1003	1036	1103	1133	1203	1233	1304	1337	1403	1433	1505	1535	1603
2	Haymarket .... **222/3** d.		0523	0537	0608	0637	0707	0739	0809	0838	0910	0939	1007	1041	1108	1138	1207	1238	1308	1341	1407	1437	1509	1539	1607
28	Linlithgow........................d.		0542	0557	0628	0657	0727	0758	0830	0858	0929	0959	1027	1100	1127	1157	1226	1257	1327	1400	1427	1452	1528	1558	1628
41	Falkirk Grahamston............d.		0553	0612**f**	0638	0707	0738	0812	0841	0908	0940	1012	1038	1111	1140	1208	1240	1312**f**	1341	1411	1438	1510	1540	1611	1638
58	**Stirling** .... **222/3** a.		0606	0628	0656	0721	0757	0829	0858	0923	0957	1028	1056	1126	1156	1222	1258	1328	1356	1425	1501	1526	1558	1626	1652

	⚒	⚒	⚒	⚒	⚒	⚒	⚒	⚒	⚒	⚒	⑥	Ⓐ		⑦	⑦	⑦	⑦	⑦	⑦	⑦	⑦	⑦	⑦	⑦	⑦
Edinburgh Waverley . **222/3** d.	1638	1704	1736	1803	1835	1904	2003	2103	2204	2303	2332	2334	⑦	0935	1035	1112	1134	1205	1234	1305	1336	1406	1437	1507	1536
Haymarket .... **222/3** d.	1642	1709	1742	1808	1839	1908	2007	2107	2208	2307	2336	2339		0939	1039	1116	1138	1211	1239	1309	1341	1410	1441	1511	1540
Linlithgow .... d.	1701	1730	1801	1829	1901	1928	2027	2126	2227	2326	2356	2359		1004	1058	1135	1159	1231	1258	1329	1402	1431	1502	1531	1601
Falkirk Grahamston............ d.	1714	1742	1814	1841	1914	1939	2037	2137	2241	2337	0006	0009		1015	1109	1146	1210	1244	1311	1339	1413	1441	1515	1542	1611
Stirling .... **222/3** a.	1728	1800	1828	1859	1929	1954	2051	2150	2257	2350	0021	0023		1029	1123	1200	1224	1259	1325	1355	1427	1456	1530	1556	1625

	⑦	⑦	⑦	⑦	⑦	⑦	⑦	⑦	⑦	⑦
Edinburgh Waverley . **222/3** d.	1606	1636	1705	1734	1806	1835	1936	2035	2135	2235
Haymarket .... **222/3** d.	1610	1641	1709	1738	1810	1839	1940	2039	2139	2240
Linlithgow .... d.	1631	1702	1731	1757	1832	1901	2001	2058	2158	2301
Falkirk Grahamston............ d.	1641	1712	1741	1808	1844	1912	2011	2109	2213**f**	2314
Stirling .... **222/3** a.	1656	1730	1757	1822	1901	1926	2025	2123	2227	2331

		⚒	⚒	⚒	⚒		⚒	⚒	⚒	⚒
Stirling .... **222/3** d.	⚒	0538	0608	0635	0704	...	0729	0810	0832	0908
Falkirk Grahamston.......... d.		0552	0622	0650	0719	...	0743	0824	0846	0922
Linlithgow........................ d.		0603	0633	0701	0730	...	0754	0835	0856	0933
Haymarket .... **222/3** a.		0622	0651	0720	0751	...	0812	0854	0915	0952
Edinburgh Waverley **222/3** a.		0627	0656	0725	0756	...	0818	0859	0920	0957

	⚒	⚒	⚒	⚒	⚒	⚒	⚒	⚒		⚒	⚒	⚒	⚒	⚒	⚒	⚒	⚒	⚒	⚒	⚒	⚒	⚒	⚒	⚒	⚒
Stirling .... **222/3** d.	0940	1003	1038	1104	1134	1204	1240	1304	...	1331	1403	1438	1503	1534	1603	1633	1700	1734	1803	1828	1902	1940	2001	2037	2143
Falkirk Grahamston............ d.	0955	1017	1053	1118	1148	1218**r**	1254	1319	...	1347	1418	1452	1518	1548	1617	1647	1713	1752	1817	1844	1917	1954	2015	2052	2157
Linlithgow .... d.	1006	1028	1103	1130	1200	1230	1304	1329	...	1358	1429	1503	1529	1559	1628	1657	1724	1804	1827	1855	1927	2004	2026	2103	2208
Haymarket .... **222/3** a.	1025	1046	1121	1151	1220	1251	1325	1348	...	1417	1451	1521	1550	1620	1646	1716	1742	1823	1846	1913	1949	2023	2044	2122	2227
Edinburgh Waverley . **222/3** a.	1030	1052	1126	1156	1225	1256	1330	1353	...	1423	1456	1528	1556	1627	1652	1721	1748	1828	1852	1918	1954	2028	2049	2127	2233

	⚒	⚒		⑦	⑦	⑦	⑦	⑦	⑦	⑦	⑦	⑦	⑦	⑦	⑦		⑦	⑦	⑦	⑦	⑦	⑦	⑦	⑦	⑦
Stirling .... **222/3** d.	2236	2325	⑦	0910	0954	1047	1109	1152	1208	1254	1308	1350	1418	1450	1518	...	1550	1618	1650	1718	1818	1919	2018	2108	2218
Falkirk Grahamston............ d.	2250	2342		0924	1011	1104	1123	1206	1222	1311	1322	1404	1432	1507	1532	...	1604	1632	1704	1732	1832	1933	2032	2123	2233
Linlithgow .... d.	2301	2352		0935	1023	1116	1134	1217	1233	1321	1333	1415	1443	1518	1543	...	1615	1643	1715	1742	1843	1944	2043	2133	2243
Haymarket .... **222/3** a.	2319	0011		1000	1045	1138	1152	1235	1251	1342	1353	1433	1501	1538	1601	...	1633	1701	1736	1801	1901	2002	2103	2152	2302
Edinburgh Waverley . **222/3** a.	2324	0016		1005	1050	1143	1158	1240	1256	1347	1358	1438	1506	1546	1606	...	1639	1706	1742	1806	1906	2007	2108	2158	2307

f – Arrives 5 minutes earlier.

r – Departs 1224 on Ⓐ.

225 ABERDEEN - ELGIN - INVERNESS — 2nd class only — SR

km			⚒	⚒	⚒G	⚒D	⚒F	⚒G	⚒	⚒🍷	⚒	⚒🍷	⚒	⚒G	⚒🍷	⚒	⚒B	⚒🍷	⚒🍷	⚒H	⚒		⑦G	⑦G	⑦G	⑦G	⑦🍷
0	**Aberdeen** ....¶ d.	⚒	...	...	0617	0718	0730	0823	0841	1010	...	1156	...	1341	1525	...	1727	1818	2018	2200	2249	⑦	1003	1300	1524	1800	2128
10	Dyce ✈ ....¶ d.		...	...	0625	0727	0739	0831	0850	1019	...	1205	...	1349	1534	...	1736	1827	2027	2208	2258		1012	1309	1532	1809	2137
22	Kintore ....¶ d.		...	...	0635	0735	0747	0840	▬	1027	...	1213	...	1359	1542	...	|	1835	2035	2218	2306		1020	1317	1542	1817	2145
27	**Inverurie**...............¶ d.		...	...	0641	0742	0753	0846	...	1034	...	1219	...	1405	1549	...	1748	1842	2041	2224	2313		1026	1323	1547	1823	2151
44	Insch.........................d.		...	...	0654	0755	...	0859	...	1048	...	1233	...	1419	1605	...	1801	1855	2054	2237	...		1039	1335	1600	1836	2202
65	Huntly ....d.		...	...	0713	0811	...	0915	...	1104	...	1250	...	1438	1622	...	1817	1911	2111	2254	...		1055	1352	1616	1852	2223
85	Keith ....d.		...	...	0728	0826	...	0930	⚒	1119	...	1304	...	1453	1643	...	1832	1926	2126	2309	...		1110	1407	1637	1907	2238
114	**Elgin**.......................d.		0700	0722	0748	0849	...	0953	1051	1140	1236	1325	1421	1523**t**	1709**f**	1759	1853	1946	2149	2329	...		1130	1427	1659	1928	2258
137	Forres ....d.		0713	0736	0801	0902	...	1006	1104	1153	1249	1338	1434	1536	1722	1812	1906	1959	2204	2342	...		1143	1440	1712	1941	2311
149	Nairn.........................d.		0724	0747	0811	0914	...	1018	1117	1205	1300	1351	1447	1547	1734	1823	1918	2010	2215	2352	...		1154	1451	1726**f**	1952	2322
173	**Inverness** ....a.		0744	0808	0831	0935	...	1036	1137	1226	1320	1411	1507	1607	1755	1843	1939	2030	2235	0012	...		1214	1511	1749	2014	2342

		⚒A	⚒G	⚒	⚒	⚒🍷	⚒	⚒G	⚒	⚒🍷	⚒	⚒🍷	⚒🍷	⚒	⚒G	⚒H	⚒	⚒	⚒		⑦G	⑦G	⑦G	⑦G	⑦C	⑦🍷	⑦C
Inverness................ d.	⚒	0456	0556	...	0703	0855	1002	1057	1146	1239	1331	1430	1528	1624	1713	1805	1859	2038	2133	⑦	1000	1231	1530	1704	1800	2104	2143
Nairn .... d.		0516	0615	...	0724	0915	1018	1115	1206	1300	1351	1447	1548	1645	1734	1824	1919	2057	2152		1019	1251	1548	1723	1819	2122	2202
Forres....................... d.		0526	0626	...	0735	0930	1029	1126	1217	1311	1402	1458	1559	1656	1744	1835	1930	2108	2203		1030	1302	1558	1734	1830	2132	2213
Elgin .... d.		0539	0638	...	0757**j**	0953**j**	1043	1139	1231	1325	1415	1511	1619**f**	1709	1801**f**	1855**f**	1943	2122	2216		1043	1314	1611	1747	1842	2145	2226
Keith......................... d.		0558	0658	...	0818	1013	...	1200	...	1346	...	1532	1639	...	1821	1915	...	...	2236		1103	1334	1632	1808	...	2206	...
Huntly....................... d.		0612	0712	0747	0839	1028	...	1214	...	1400	...	1546	1654	...	1845	1938	...	...	2253		1123	1352**f**	1647	1822	...	2221	...
Insch .... d.		0628	0728	0803	0859	1048	...	1234	...	1420	...	1605	1710	...	1900	1954	...	...	2309		1139	1408	1703	1838	...	2237	...
Inverurie .... ¶ d.		0640	0740	0815	0911	1100	...	1246	...	1432	...	1617	1722	...	1913	2006	...	...	2321		1151	1420	1715	1850	...	2249	...
Kintore.................. ¶ d.		0646	0746	0820	0917	1106	...	1251	...	1437	...	1623	1727	...	1919	2012	...	...	2327		1156	1426	1720	1856	...	2255	...
Dyce ✈ .... ¶ d.		0656	0756	0830	0926	1115	...	1300	...	1447	...	1632	1737	...	1928	2021	...	...	2336		1205	1435	1729	1904	...	2303	...
Aberdeen............. ¶ a.		0705	0805	0839	0936	1125	...	1309	...	1456	...	1641	1749	...	1938	2036	...	...	2346		1214	1444	1738	1914	...	2313	...

A – [12] Inverness - Edinburgh (Table **222**).
B – [12] and 🍷 from Glasgow Queen St (Table **222**).
C – [12] and 🍷 Glasgow Queen Street - Inverness - Elgin (Table **223**).
D – From Dundee (Table **222**).
E – [12] to Glasgow Queen Street (Table **222**).
F – To/from Montrose (Table **222**).

G – Conveys [12] and 🍷.
H – Conveys [12].

f – Arrives 5–8 minutes earlier.
j – Arrives 10 minutes earlier.
t – Arrives 1511.

¶ – Additional trains Aberdeen - Dyce - Kintore - Inverurie and v.v.:
From Aberdeen on ⚒ at 0749, 0858, 0950, 1042, 1109, 1141, 1226, 1252, 1311, 1400, 1436, 1504, 1542, 1600, 1625, 1657, 1739, 1757, 1900, 1927, 1957, 2058, 2141, 2249; On ⑦ at 1033, 1225, 1428, 1550, 1649, 2034.
From Inverurie on ⚒ at 0651, 0718, 0758, 0845, 0956, 1031, 1129, 1200, 1217, 1258, 1328, 1356, 1451, 1517, 1546, 1625, 1644, 1702, 1746, 1820, 1845, 1929, 2025, 2049, 2129, 2218;
On ⑦ at 1104 **E**, 1255, 1458, 1619, 1730, 2102.

SR 2nd class — INVERNESS - THURSO, WICK and KYLE OF LOCHALSH — 226

km		⚒	⚒	⚒ 🍷	⚒	⚒	⚒	⚒ 🍷	⚒	⚒	⚒		⚒ 🍷	⚒		⑦	⑦	⑦		⑦	⑦ 🍷	⑦ a	⑦
0	**Inverness** d.	0700	0855	1041	1056	1143	1335	1400	1450	1712	1754	...	1831	2129	...	0940	1059	1253	...	1533	1754	1754	2108
16	Beauly d.	0715	0910	|	1113	1200	1350	1415	1505	1727	1809	...	1846	2144	...	0955	1115	1308	...	1548	1809	1809	2123
21	Muir of Ord d.	0723	0916	1101	1119	1209	1356	1423	1511	1733	1815	...	1855	2150	...	1001	1121	1314	...	1556	1815	1815	2129
30	Dingwall d.	0739	0929	1112	1132	1221	1411	1437	1524	1747	1829	...	1908	2203	...	1014	1134	1327	...	1609	1831	1833	2142
49	Garve d.	|	0952	|	1155	...	1433	|	|	|	1855	...	|	|	...	|	1158	|	...	|	|	1855	|
75	Achnasheen d.	|	1018	|	1221	...	1504f	|	|	|	1922	...	|	|	...	|	1225	|	...	|	|	1922	|
104	Strathcarron d.	|	1048	|	1253	...	1533	|	|	|	1953r	...	|	|	...	|	1255	|	...	|	|	1951	|
116	Stromeferry d.	|	1105	|	1310	...	1550	|	|	|	2010	...	|	|	...	|	1312	|	...	|	|	2008	|
124	Plockton d.	|	1117	|	1322	...	1602	|	|	|	2022	...	|	|	...	|	1324	|	...	|	|	2020	|
133	**Kyle of Lochalsh** a.	|	1130	|	1335	...	1615	|	|	|	2035	...	|	|	...	|	1347	|	...	|	|	2033	|
51	Invergordon d.	0758	...	1130	...	...	...	1454	1541	1804	...	...	1927	2220	...	1032	...	1345	...	1626	1848	...	2200
71	Tain d.	0817	...	1149	...	...	...	1513	...	1824	...	...	1946	2239	...	1050	...	1403	...	...	1907	...	2218
93	Ardgay d.	0833	...	1205	...	...	...	1529	...	1839	...	...	2002	...	...	...	...	...	...	...	1923	...	...
108	Lairg d.	0853	...	1221	...	...	...	1545	...	...	...	...	2018	...	...	...	...	...	...	...	1942	...	...
136	Golspie d.	0918	...	1246	...	...	...	1610	...	...	...	...	2043	...	...	...	...	...	...	...	2007	...	...
146	Brora d.	0929	...	1257	...	...	...	1621	...	...	...	...	2053	...	...	...	...	...	...	...	2018	...	...
163	Helmsdale d.	0947	...	1312	...	...	...	1636	...	...	...	...	2108	...	...	...	...	...	...	...	2033	...	...
201	Forsinard d.	1021	...	1346	...	...	...	1712	...	...	...	...	2142	...	...	...	...	...	...	...	2107	...	...
237	Georgemas Jcn a.	1045	...	1410	...	...	...	1736	...	...	...	...	2206	...	...	...	...	...	...	...	2131	...	...
248	**Thurso** a.	1059	...	1424	...	...	...	1750	...	...	...	...	2220	...	...	...	...	...	...	...	2145	...	...
248	**Thurso** d.	1102	...	1427	...	...	...	1753	...	...	...	...	2223	...	...	...	...	...	...	...	2148	...	...
237	Georgemas Jcn d.	1114	...	1439	...	...	...	1805	...	...	...	...	2235	...	...	...	...	...	...	...	2200	...	...
260	**Wick** a.	1131	...	1456	...	...	...	1822	...	...	...	...	2252	...	...	...	...	...	...	...	2217	...	...

	⚒	⚒	⚒		⚒	⚒ 🍷	⚒	⚒	⚒	⚒	⚒ 🍷	⚒	⚒ 🍷	⚒	⚒	⑦	⑦ a	⑦		⑦ 🍷	⑦	⑦	⑦
Wick d.	...	...	...	...	0618	0802	...	...	...	...	1234	...	1600	...	...	...	...	...	...	1158	...	...	...
Georgemas Jcn. d.	...	...	...	...	0636	0820	...	...	...	...	1252	...	1618	...	...	...	...	...	...	1216	...	...	...
Thurso a.	...	...	...	...	0646	0830	...	...	...	...	1302	...	1628	...	...	...	...	...	...	1226	...	...	...
Thurso d.	...	...	...	...	0650	0834	...	...	...	...	1306	...	1632	...	...	...	...	...	...	1230	...	...	...
Georgemas Jcn. d.	...	...	...	...	0703	0847	...	...	...	...	1319	...	1645	...	...	...	...	...	...	1243	...	...	...
Forsinard d.	...	...	...	...	0727	0913	...	...	...	...	1347	...	1711	...	...	...	...	...	...	1309	...	...	...
Helmsdale d.	...	...	...	...	0800	0946	...	...	...	...	1421	...	1744	...	...	...	...	...	...	1342	...	...	...
Brora d.	...	...	...	...	0816	1002	...	...	...	...	1436	...	1800	...	...	...	...	...	...	1358	...	...	...
Golspie d.	...	...	...	...	0825	1012	...	...	...	...	1447	...	1810	...	...	...	...	...	...	1408	...	...	...
Lairg d.	...	0626	...	...	0852	1038	...	...	...	...	1512	...	1835	...	...	...	...	...	...	1433	...	...	...
Ardgay d.	0614	0643	...	...	0907	1054	...	...	...	...	1530	...	1851	1929	...	...	...	...	...	1449	...	...	...
Tain d.	0630	0659	...	...	0923	1110	...	...	...	...	1546	...	1907	1947	2244	1055	...	1408	...	1505	...	...	2223
Invergordon d.	0649	0719	...	...	0942	1131	...	...	...	1551	1610t	...	1925	2006	2303	1114	...	1427	...	1524	1631	...	2242
Kyle of Lochalsh d.	|	|	0611	...	|	|	...	1208	1346	|	|	1713	|	|	|	|	1020	|	...	|	|	1509	|
Plockton d.	|	|	0626	...	|	|	...	1221	1359	|	|	1726	|	|	|	|	1033	|	...	|	|	1525	|
Stromeferry d.	|	|	0638	...	|	|	...	1233	1411	|	|	1738	|	|	|	|	1045	|	...	|	|	1537	|
Strathcarron d.	|	|	0657	...	|	|	...	1252	1434t	|	|	1757	|	|	|	|	1103	|	...	|	|	1556	|
Achnasheen d.	|	|	0726	...	|	|	...	1320	1503	|	|	1826	|	|	|	|	1131	|	...	|	|	1624	|
Garve d.	|	|	0753	...	|	|	...	1347	1529	|	|	1852	|	|	|	|	1157	|	...	|	|	1651	|
Dingwall d.	0708	0738	0816	...	1001	1153	1245	1410	1552	1611	1630	1918	1942	2025	2321	1135	1220	1445	...	1542	1649	1714	2300
Muir of Ord d.	0722	0751	0830	...	1014	1207	1258	1422	1604	1624	1644	1931	1954	2038	2334	1148	1232	1457	...	1555	1702	1726	2313
Beauly d.	0728	0757	0835	...	1020	1212	1304	1427	1609	1629	1649	1936	|	2043	2339	1153	1237	1502	...	1600	1707	1732	2318
Inverness a.	0743	0812	0850	...	1038	1227	1321	1442	1627	1646	1706	1951	2012	2058	2354	1208	1252	1517	...	1615	1722	1747	2333

a – Until Sept. 25. f – Arrives 1459. r – Arrives 1950. t – Arrives 5–6 minutes earlier.

Valid until Sept. 25 — 🚌 INVERNESS - ULLAPOOL - STORNOWAY — 227

	①–⑥ 🚌	①–⑥ ⛴		①–⑤ 🚌	①–⑤ ⛴		⑦ 🚌	⑦ ⛴	⑥ 🚌	⑥ ⛴
Inverness d.	0810	...	...	1500	...	...	1610	...	1640	...
Garve d.	0844	...	...	1534	...	...	1644	...	1714	...
Ullapool a.	0930	...	...	1620	...	...	1730	...	1800	...
Ullapool d.	...	1030	...	...	1730	...	...	1830	...	1900
Stornoway a.	...	1300	...	...	2000	...	...	2100	...	2130

	①–⑥ ⛴	①–⑥ 🚌		①–⑤ ⛴	①–⑤ 🚌		⑦ ⛴	⑦ 🚌	⑥ ⛴	⑥ 🚌
Stornoway d.	0700	...	...	1400	...	...	1500	...	1530	...
Ullapool a.	0930	...	...	1630	...	...	1730	...	1800	...
Ullapool d.	...	0950	...	...	1650	...	...	1750	...	1820
Garve d.	...	1032	...	...	1732	...	...	1832	...	1903
Inverness a.	...	1110	...	...	1810	...	...	1910	...	1940

☛ Latest passenger check-in for ⛴ is 30 minutes before departure.

Operators: 🚌 Scottish Citylink (service **961**). www.citylink.co.uk ✆ +44 (0) 871 266 3333.
⛴ Caledonian MacBrayne. www.calmac.co.uk ✆ +44 (0) 800 066 5000.

🚌 INVERNESS - FORT WILLIAM - OBAN — 228

Service number	919	918	919	915	919	919	919	918	919	919	920
Inverness bus station d.	0900	1000	1100	...	1200	1300	1400	1500	1715	1815	2015
Fort Augustus bus stance d.	1004	1104	1204	...	1304	1404	1504	1604	1819	1919	2116
Invergarry Jct. bus bay A82 d.	1018	1118	1218	1253j	1318	1418	1518	1618	1833	1933	2128
Fort William bus station a.	1105	1205	1305	1340	1405	1505	1605	1705	1917	2017	2205
Service number											
		①–⑥						①–⑥			
Fort William bus station d.	...	1230	...	...	...	...	...	1750	...	...	...
Ballachulish Tourist Office d.	...	1300	...	...	...	...	...	1820	...	...	...
Oban Station Road a.	...	1403	...	...	...	...	...	1923	...	...	...

Service number	919	919	919	918	919	919	915	919	919	919	918
				①–⑥							①–⑥
Oban Station Road d.	...	...	...	0930	...	...	...	...	...	...	1557
Ballachulish Tourist Office d.	...	...	...	1034	...	...	...	...	...	...	1701
Fort William bus station a.	...	...	...	1105	...	...	...	...	...	...	1732
Service number				919							919
Fort William bus station d.	0730	0930	1030	1130	1230	1330	1350	1430	1530f	1630	1740
Invergarry Jct. bus bay A82 d.	0814	1014	1114	1214	1314	1414	1434j	1514	1627	1714	1824
Fort Augustus bus stance d.	0828	1028	1128	1228	1328	1428	...	1528	1641	1728	1838
Inverness bus station a.	0935	1135	1235	1335	1435	1535	...	1635	1748	1835	1942

f – Departs 1543 on ⑤ during school term and ①–⑦ during school holidays. Check locally for school dates.
j – On A87 at Invergarry Hotel.

Operator: Scottish Citylink. www.citylink.co.uk ✆ +44 (0) 871 266 3333.

✆ +44 (0) 1624 662525 — ISLE OF MAN RAILWAYS — 229

km	*Manx Electric Railway*	A	A	A		A	A	A	A	A	A
0	**Douglas** Derby Castle ‡ d.	0940	1010	1040	...	1140	1240	1340	1410	1510	1610
4	Groudle d.	0950	1020	1050	...	1150	1250	1350	1420	1520	1620
11	Laxey d.	1010	1040	1110	...	1210	1310	1410	1440	1540	1640
29	**Ramsey** a.	1055	...	1155	...	1255	1355	1455	1525	1625	...

	A	A	A	A		A	A	A		A	A
Ramsey d.	1110	1140	1240	1340	...	1440	1510	1540	...	...	1640
Laxey d.	1155	1225	1325	1425	...	1525	1555	1625	...	1655	1725
Groudle d.	1213	1243	1343	1443	...	1543	1613	1643	...	1713	1743
Douglas Derby Castle ‡ a.	1225	1255	1355	1455	...	1555	1625	1655	...	1725	1755

km	*Snaefell Mountain Railway*	B	B	B		B	B	B	
0	**Laxey** d.	1015	1045	1115	and at the same minutes past	1445	1515	1545	...
8	**Summit** a.	1045	1115	1145	each hour until	1515	1545	1615	...

	B	B	B		B	B	B		
Summit d.	1110	1140	1210	and at the same minutes past	1540	1610	1640	...	...
Laxey a.	1140	1210	1240	each hour until	1610	1640	1710	...	...

km	*Isle of Man Steam Railway*	CE	E	C	E	C	E	C	E	E	D✕
0	**Douglas** Railway Station ‡ d.	0950	1120	1150	1250	1350	1430	1550	1600	1730	1745
9	Santon ⊠ d.	1011	1141	1211	1311	1411	1451	1611	1621	1751	1806
13	Ballasalla d.	1020	1150	1220	1320	1420	1500	1620	1630	1800	1815
16	Castletown d.	1027	1157	1227	1327	1427	1507	1627	1637	1807	1822
25	**Port Erin** a.	1050	1220	1250	1350	1450	1530	1650	1700	1830	1845

	D✕	CE	E	C	E	C	E	C	E	E	D✕
Port Erin d.	0745	1000	1130	1200	1300	1400	1445	1600	1615	1745	1915
Castletown d.	0807	1027	1157	1227	1327	1427	1507	1627	1637	1807	1942
Ballasalla d.	0815	1035	1205	1235	1335	1435	1515	1635	1645	1815	1949
Santon ⊠ d.	|	1047	1217	1247	1347	1447	1527	1647	1657	1827	|
Douglas Railway Station ‡ a.	0845	1105	1235	1305	1405	1505	1545	1705	1715	1845	2030

A – June 1 – Sept. 18, 20 – 25, 27 – 30, Oct. 1, 2, 4 – 9, 11 – 16, 18 – 23, 25 – 30. May 30 – June 9 a greatly enhanced service operates. On ③⑤ July 9 - Sept. 10 additional late afternoon/eveming services also run - please check locally.
B – June 3 – 6, 10 – 13, 19, 20, 26, 27, July 1 – 4, then ②③⑤⑥⑦ July 6 - Sept. 12.
C – June 3 – 6, 10 – 13, 19, 20, 26, 27, July 2, 3, 4, 8 – 12, then ①④⑤⑦ July 15 - Sept. 12.
D – ⑤ June 4, July 2, Aug. 6, Sept. 3. Reservation essential.
E – ⑥ July 17 - Sept. 11.

⊠ – All trains call on request.
‡ – 🚌 services **1**, **1A**, **1H**, **2**, **2A**, **11**, **11A**, **12**, **12A**, connect Derby Castle and Lord Street Bus Station which is near the Steam Railway Station.

IRELAND

SEE MAP PAGE 86

Operators: Iarnród Éireann (**IÉ**), www.irishrail.ie Northern Ireland Railways (**NIR**), www.translink.co.uk Bus Éireann, www.buseireann.ie Ulsterbus, www.translink.co.uk and Dublin Area Rapid Transit (**DART**), www.irishrail.ie Most cross-border services are jointly operated.

Timings: **Rail: NIR** services are valid from June 14, 2021 until further notice. **IÉ** services are valid from March 21, 2021 until further notice. **DART** services are valid until further notice.
Bus: Ulsterbus services are valid until further notice. **Bus Éireann** services are valid until further notice.

Rail services: Except for *Enterprise* cross-border expresses (for details, see Table **230** below), **all trains** convey *Standard* (2nd) class seating. Most express trains in the Republic of Ireland, as noted in the tables, also have first class accommodation.
On public holiday dates in the **Republic of Ireland**, DART trains run as on Sundays; outer-suburban services to or from Drogheda and Dundalk do not run. Other services may be amended, though most main-line trains run normally. All services are subject to alteration during the Christmas, New Year and Easter holiday periods.

Bus services: **Bus Éireann** and **Ulsterbus**: services are shown in detail where there is no comparable rail service; only basic information is given for other routes. Buses do not always call at the rail station, but usually stop nearby. Where possible the stop details are given in the station bank or as a footnote. On longer routes, a change of bus may be required – please check with the driver. At holiday times bus travellers should consult detailed leaflets or seek further information from the operator. **Bus Éireann**: ✆ +353 1 836 6111 (Dublin) or + 353 21 450 8188 (Cork); **Ulsterbus**: ✆ + 028 9033 3000 (Translink, Belfast). **Dublin Busáras** (bus station) is a 5 minute walk from Dublin Connolly station.

The Dublin Tram service (Luas) connects Dublin Connolly and Heuston stations at frequent intervals. Journey time is 14 minutes, depending on traffic conditions. See Dublin City Plan on page 31.

230 BELFAST - DUNDALK - DUBLIN

NIR, IÉ

Enterprise express trains (*E*) convey Standard (2nd) class and Plus (1st) class seating. 🍸 (Café Bar and trolley service) and ✕ (at-seat meal service in Plus) currently not available.

km		Ⓐ	Ⓐ	Ⓐ	⑥	Ⓐ	Ⓐ	⚒ 2	⑥	⚒	⚒ (*E*)	⑥	⚒ ♥	Ⓐ	⑥	⚒ (*E*)	⚒	Ⓐ	⑥	⚒ 2	⑥	Ⓐ	⑥	⚒ (*E*)	Ⓐ	⑥
0	**Belfast** LP ♣ .. § d.	...	...	...	...	...	0600	0650	...	0736j	0800	...	...	0959	1031t	1035	...	1159	1231t	1235	...	1329	1401t	1405	...	...
13	Lisburn § d.	...	...	...	...	...	0629	|	...	0803	|	...	...	1034	1041	|	...	1234	1241	|	...	1404	1411	|	...	...
42	Portadown § d.	...	...	...	...	...	0652	0721	...	0826	0831	...	...	1057	1105	1108	...	1257	1305	1306	...	1427	1435	1436	...	...
71	Newry d.	...	...	...	...	...	*0724*	0742	...	...	0853	...	...	...	...	1127	...	...	...	1327	...	▬	...	1458	...	...
95	**Dundalk** d.	0540	0630	0705	0705	...	...	0800	0810	...	0912	1015	1050	...	...	1146	1245	...	...	1346	...	Ⓐ	...	1518	...	...
131	Drogheda d.	0604	0655	0730	0730	0758	...	0822	0835	...	|	1040	1114	...	...	1207	1310	...	...	1407	1420	1450	...	1540	1550	1610
148	Balbriggan d.	0619	0712	0746	0746	0814	...	|	0851	...	|	1055	1128	...	...	|	1326	...	...	|	1436	1506	...	|	1605	1626
154	Skerries d.	0625	0718	0752	0752	0820	...	|	0857	...	|	1101	1134	...	...	|	1332	...	...	|	1442	1512	...	|	1611	1632
168	Malahide d.	0641	0736	0807	0807	0835	...	|	0913	...	|	1116	1149	...	...	|	1347	...	...	|	1457	1527	...	|	1627	1647
183	**Dublin** Connolly .. a.	0658	0759	0830	0830	0858	...	0900	0934	...	1005	1139	1209	...	...	1240	1411	...	...	1440	1518	1548	...	1620	1648	1707

	Ⓐ	⑥	⚒ (*E*)	⚒	Ⓐ	⑥	⑥	⚒ 2	⑥	⚒	Ⓐ	⚒ (*E*)	Ⓐ	⑥	Ⓐ	⑥	⑦	⑦	⑦ (*E*)	⑦ (*E*)	⑦ (*E*)	⑦ (*E*)		⑦ (*E*)		
Belfast LP ♣ ... § d.	1541	1601t	1605	...	1709	1731t	...	1805	...	1929	...	2005	2159	2222	2259	2322	...	...	0900	1105	1305	1605	...	1905	...	...
Lisburn § d.	1611	1611	|	...	1731	1741	...	|	...	2004	...	|	2234	2245	2334	2345	...	...	0913	|	|	|	...	|	...	...
Portadown § d.	1635	1635	1639	...	1759	1806	...	1839	...	2027	...	2039	2258	2310	2357	0009	...	...	0940	1136	1336	1636	...	1936	...	...
Newry d.	...	...	1701	...	1824	1830	...	1901	...	...	...	2101	2322	2334	...	...	...	...	1001	1158	1358	1658	...	1958	...	...
Dundalk d.	...	...	1720	...	...	...	...	1920	...	...	2040	2120	...	...	...	...	...	0930	1019	1217	1417	1717	...	2017	...	...
Drogheda d.	...	...	1741	1802	...	...	1850	1941	2010	...	2105	2141	...	...	...	...	...	0955	1040	1239	1439	1740	...	2040	...	...
Balbriggan d.	...	...	|	1818	...	...	1906	|	2026	...	2121	|	...	...	...	...	...	1010	|	|	|	|	...	|	...	...
Skerries d.	...	...	|	1824	...	...	1912	|	2032	...	2127	|	...	...	...	...	...	1016	|	|	|	|	...	|	...	...
Malahide d.	...	...	|	1839	...	...	1927	|	2047	...	2142	|	...	...	...	...	...	1031	|	|	|	|	...	|	...	...
Dublin Connolly .. a.	...	...	1817	1902	...	...	1949	2015	2105	...	2201	2215	...	...	...	...	...	1053	1120	1315	1515	1815	...	2115	...	...

	Ⓐ	⑥	Ⓐ	Ⓐ	⚒ (*E*)	⚒	⚒ w	⚒ 2	⚒	⑥	⚒	⚒ (*E*)	⚒	⚒	⚒ (*E*)	⑥	⚒	⚒ 2	⚒	Ⓐ	⑥	Ⓐ	⚒ (*E*)	⚒	⚒	⑥
Dublin Connolly .. d.	...	...	...	0715	0735	...	0850	0930	...	1000	1105	1120	...	1250	1320	1350	1445	1520	1544	...	...	1628	1650	...	...	1715
Malahide d.	...	...	...	0729	|	...	0910	|	...	1024	1124	|	...	1305	|	1406	1504	|	1604	...	...	1646	|	...	...	1738
Skerries d.	...	...	...	0744	|	...	0924	|	...	1038	1140	|	...	1320	|	1420	1518	|	1618	...	...	1701	|	...	...	1754
Balbriggan d.	...	...	...	0749	|	...	0930	|	...	1044	1150	|	...	1325	|	1426	1524	|	1624	...	...	1706	|	...	...	1800
Drogheda d.	...	...	...	0805	0807	...	0948	1006	...	1101	1210	1156	...	1344	1356	1444	1543	1553	1647	...	...	1724	|	...	...	1817
Dundalk d.	...	...	...	...	0830	...	1018	1028	...	...	1235	1218	...	...	1418	▬	...	1615	...	...	...	1749	1748	...	...	1841
Newry d.	0635	0708	*0730*	...	0848	...	...	1046	...	...	...	1239	...	...	1436	...	...	1632	...	...	...	...	1806	...	1850	...
Portadown § d.	0700	0733	0800	...	0909	0915	...	1108	1115	...	...	1304	1315	...	1458	1515	...	1655	...	1705	1715	...	1828	1845	1915	...
Lisburn § a.	0724	0755	0824	...	|	0937	...	|	1137	...	...	|	1337	...	|	1537	...	|	...	1729	1738	...	|	1907	1937	...
Belfast LP ♣ ... § a.	0745	0805t	0846	...	0945	1010	...	1145	1210f	...	...	1335	1410f	...	1535	1613f	...	1726	...	1738t	1748t	...	1905	1940	2010	...

	Ⓐ	Ⓐ	⑥	Ⓐ	⑥	⚒ (*E*)	⚒	⚒ ▲	⑥	⚒ 2	⚒	①–④	⑤	⚒	⚒			⑦ (*E*)	⑦ (*E*)	⑦ (*E*)	⑦ (*E*)		⑦ (*E*)		⑦	
Dublin Connolly .. d.	1721	...	...	1809	1840	1900	...	1920	2020	2050	...	2146	2146	2246	2347	...	...	1000	1200	1400	1600	...	1900	...	2135	...
Malahide d.	|	...	...	1830	1855	|	...	1940	2040	|	...	2209	2209	2304	0008	...	...	|	|	|	|	...	|	...	2157	...
Skerries d.	1758	...	...	1844	1909	|	...	1954	2054	|	...	2223	2223	2319	0022	...	...	|	|	|	|	...	|	...	2211	...
Balbriggan d.	1804	...	...	1850	1915	|	...	2000	2100	|	...	2229	2229	2324	0028	...	...	|	|	|	|	...	|	...	2217	...
Drogheda d.	1821	...	...	1908	1930	1934	...	2018	2118	2128	...	2247	2247	2321	0049	...	...	1032	1232	1432	1632	...	1933	...	2237	...
Dundalk d.	1846	...	...	1932	...	1955	...	...	...	2150	...	...	2312	0009	0115	...	...	1054	1254	1454	1654	...	1955	...	2301	...
Newry d.	1912	1950	...	...	...	2013	...	...	...	2207	...	...	...	...	...	...	...	1112	1312	1512	1712	...	2013	...	...	...
Portadown § d.	...	2015	2015	...	...	2033	2045	...	...	2228	2245	...	...	...	...	...	...	1133	1333	1533	1733	...	2033	...	...	...
Lisburn § a.	...	2037	2037	...	...	|	2107	...	...	|	2307	...	...	...	...	...	...	|	|	|	|	...	|	...	...	...
Belfast LP ♣ ... § a.	...	2110	2110	...	...	2105	2140	...	...	2300	2340	...	...	...	...	...	...	1208	1408	1608	1808	...	2108	...	...	...

f – On ⑥ terminates at Belfast Great Victoria Street 22–25 mins. earlier.
j – 7 minutes earlier on ⑥.
t – Belfast **Great Victoria Street**.
w – From Rosslare on Ⓐ, from Gorey on ⑥; see Table **237**.
▲ – 7 – 10 minutes later on Ⓐ.
♥ – 15 – 21 minutes later on ⑥.
§ – Other local trains run Belfast - Lisburn - Portadown and v.v.
♣ – Belfast Lanyon Place (formerly Central Station).

231 BELFAST - LARNE and BANGOR

NIR

From Belfast LP ♣ – Ⓐ: 0655 **H**, 0750 **H**, 0855 **H** and hourly until 1355 **H**, 1455, 1555 **H**, 1643 **H**, 1744, 1825 **H**, 2025 **H**, 2225 **H**, 2325 **H**.
⑥: 0725 **H**, and every **two** hours until 2125 **H**, 2225 **H**, 2325 **H**.
⑦: 0955 **H**, and every **two** hours until 2155 **H**.

From Larne Town – Ⓐ: 0608 **S**, 0648 **S**, 0758 **S** and hourly until 1458 **S**, 1556, 1623, 1738 **S**, 1828, 1928 **S**, 2128 **S**.
⑥: 0628 **S**, 0728 **S**, 0828 **S**, and every **two** hours until 2228 **S**.
⑦: 0858 **S**, and every **two** hours until 2058 **S**.

Trains call at: Carrickfergus 27 - 29 minutes from Belfast and 28 - 31 minutes from Larne and Whitehead 38 - 40 minutes from Belfast, 18 - 21 minutes from Larne.

Trains marked **H** arrive Larne **Harbour** 4 minutes after Larne **Town**. Trains marked **S** depart Larne **Harbour** 3 minutes before Larne **Town**. Journey time Belfast Central - Larne Harbour 57 - 65 mins.

A frequent train service operates between Belfast Lanyon Place ♣ and Bangor. Journey time 30–31 minutes. 20 km. Approximate timings from Belfast ①–⑥: 2 per hour at xx12 and xx42 minutes past each hour, ⑦: xx42. Approximate timings from Bangor ①–⑥: 2 per hour at xx25 and xx55 minutes past each hour, ⑦: xx25.

♣ – Belfast Lanyon Place (formerly Central Station).

232 🚌 BELFAST - ENNISKILLEN and ARMAGH

Ulsterbus **251**, **261**

From Belfast ★ to Enniskillen (Bus Stn) (journey time 2 hours 15 mins)
Ⓐ: 0805, 0905 and hourly until 1905, 2005.
⑥: 1005, 1205, 1405, 1505, 1605, 1805, 2005.
⑦: 1605, 2005.

From Enniskillen (Bus Stn) to Belfast ★
Ⓐ: 0725, 0825, and hourly until 1625, 1725, 1825 ◧.
⑥: 0725, 0925, 1125, 1225, 1325, 1525, 1725.
⑦: 1225, 1525, 1725.

From Belfast ★ to Armagh (Bus Stn) (journey time 1 hour 25 mins)
Ⓐ: 0800, 0945, 1045, 1145, 1245, 1345, 1445, 1645, 1715, 1745, 1845, 1945, 2115.
⑥: 1045, 1245, 1445, 1745, 1845, 2005.
⑦: 1335, 1735, 2015, 2200.

From Armagh (Bus Stn) to Belfast ★
Ⓐ: 0630, 0715, 0805, 0905, 1005, 1105, 1205, 1305, 1505, 1605, 1705, 1805.
⑥: 0730, 0905, 1105, 1305, 1605, 1705.
⑦: 1210, 1410, 1610, 1830, 2015.

Buses call at Portadown (Market Street) 40 - 75 minutes from Belfast and Portadown (Northern Bank) 20–30 minutes from Armagh (Bus Stn).

◧ – Change at Dungannon; arrive Europa Buscentre 2140.
★ – Europa Buscentre / Great Victoria St. Rail Station.

NIR — BELFAST - LONDONDERRY and PORTRUSH — 233

km		Ⓐ	⚒	⚒	⚒	⚒	⚒	❖	⚒	⚒	⚒		⑦	⑦	⑦	⑦	⑦		⑦	⑦	⑦	⑦		
	Belfast GVSt. ★ d.	0605	...	0710	...	0810	...	and at the	2110	...	2240	...	...	...	0910	...	1010	and at the	1910	...	2010	2110	...	...
0	**Belfast** LP ♣ d.	0615	...	0720	...	0820	...	same	2120	...	2250	...	...	...	0920	...	1020	same	1920	...	2020	2120	...	...
33	Antrim d.	0643	...	0747	...	0847	...	minutes	2247	...	2317	...	...	...	0947	...	1047	minutes	1947	...	2047	2147	...	...
52	Ballymena d.	0657	...	0803	...	0903	...	past every	2203	...	2330	...	...	...	1003	...	1103	past every	2003	...	2103	2200	...	...
97	**Coleraine** d.	0743	0745	0843	0845	0943	0945	hour	2243	2245	0005	...	0845	0945	1043	1045	1143	**two** hours	2043	2045	2143	2235	...	...
107	Portrush a.	|	0757	|	0857	|	0957	until	|	2257	...	...	0857	0957	|	1057	1157	until	|	2057	2157	...	...	...
151	**Londonderry** a.	0822	...	0922	...	1022	...		2322	...	...	...	...	...	1122	...	...		2122	...	...	...	...	...

	Ⓐ	⚒	Ⓐ	Ⓐ	⑥	⑥	⚒	⚒	❖	⚒	⚒	⚒	Ⓐ	⑥	⚒	⑦	⑦	⑦		⑦	⑦	⑦	⑦	⑦
Londonderry d.	...	...	0612	...	...	0642	...	0738	and at the	...	2038	...	2138	2138	...	...	...	0938	and at the	...	...	1938	...	...
Portrush d.	...	0605	|	0705	0700	|	0803	|	same	2103	|	2203	|	|	2303	0905	1003	|	same	1905	2003	|	2103	2203
Coleraine d.	0550	0621	0652	0719	0712	0721	0815	0819	minutes	2115	2119	2215	2219	2216	2315	0920	1015	1019	minutes	1919	2015	2019	2119	2215
Ballymena d.	0626	0700	0730	0800	...	0800	...	0900	past every	...	2200	...	2300	...	...	1000	...	1100	past every	2000	...	2100	2200	...
Antrim d.	0642	0714	0747	0814	...	0814	...	0914	hour	...	2214	...	2316	...	...	1014	...	1114	**two** hours	2014	...	2114	2214	...
Belfast LP ♣ a.	0710	0742	0816	0839	...	0841	...	0939	until	...	2239	...	2339	...	...	1039	...	1139	until	2039	...	2139	2239	...
Belfast GVSt. ★ a.	...	0752	0826	0851	...	0850	...	0950		...	2250	...	...	...	...	1050	...	1150		2050	...	2150	...	...

★ – Belfast GVSt. (Belfast Great Victoria St.) is the nearest station to Belfast City Centre and the Europa Buscentre is adjacent. ♣ – Belfast Lanyon Place (formerly Central Station).
❖ – 1010 depart from Belfast GVSt. runs to Portrush, arrives 1155. 1238 Ⓐ dep. Londonderry: change at Coleraine for Belfast.

Ulsterbus 212 express 🚌 service, Belfast - Londonderry. Journey time: 1 hour 40 minutes.
Ⓐ: 0630, 0700 and every 30 minutes until 1900, 1930 then 2030, 2130, 2300.
⑥: 0645, 0900, 1000, 1030 and every 30 minutes until 1900, 1930 then 2030, 2130, 2300.
⑦: 0830, 1030, 1100 and every 30 minutes until 1930 then 2030, 2130, 2215, 2300.

Ulsterbus 212 express 🚌 service, Londonderry - Belfast. Journey time: 1 hour 45 minutes.
Ⓐ: 0415, 0530, 0600, and every 30 minutes until 1700 then 1800, 1930, 2100, 2200, 2300.
⑥: 0645, 0730, 0800 and every 30 minutes until 1630, 1700 then 1800, 1930, 2100, 2200, 2300.
⑦: 0700, 0800, 0900, 0930 and every 30 minutes to 1730, 1800, 1900, 2100.

Ulsterbus X3, X4 — 🚌 DUBLIN - LONDONDERRY — 234

	X4	X3	X4	X3	X4	X4	X3	X4	
Dublin Busáras d.	0630	1000	1100	1215	1515	1800	2015	2230	...
Dublin Airport ✈ △ d.	0650	1020	1120	1235	1535	1820	2035	2250	...
Monaghan d.	|	1205	|	1420	|	|	2220	|	...
Omagh ▽ a.	|	1300	|	1515	|	|	2315	|	...
Strabane ▽ a.	|	1330	|	1545	|	|	2345	|	...
Londonderry a.	1035	1400	1505	1615	1920	2155	0015	0155	...

	X4	X4	X4	X3	X4	X3	X3	X4	
Londonderry d.	0130	0415	0550	0700	0950	1200	1500	1730	...
Strabane △ d.	|	|	|	0730	|	1230	1530	|	...
Omagh △ d.	|	|	|	0800	|	1300	1600	|	...
Monaghan d.	|	|	|	0905	|	1405	1705	|	...
Dublin Airport ✈ ▽ a.	0500	0800	0935	1040	1335	1540	1840	2115	...
Dublin Busáras a.	0520	0820	0955	1100	1355	1600	1900	2135	...

△ – Buses call here to pick up only. ▽ – Buses call here to set down only. ☛ The calling point in each town is the bus station unless otherwise indicated.

Bus Éireann 30, X30 — 🚌 DUBLIN - DONEGAL — 234a

Dublin Busáras d.	0630	0800	0930	1100	1230	1400	1530	1700	1830	2000	2300	0030
Dublin Airport ✈ △ d.	0650	0820	0950	1120	1250	1420	1550	1720	1850	2020	2320	0050
Virginia d.	0755	0925	1055	1225	1355	1525	1655	1825	1955	2125	0025	0155
Cavan d.	0835	0955	1135	1255	1435	1555	1735	1855	2035	2155	0055	0235
Enniskillen d.	0925	1040	1225	1340	1525	1640	1825	1940	2125	2240	0140	0325
Ballyshannon d.	1010	1120	1310	1420	1610	1720	1910	2020	2210	2320	0220	0410
Donegal ⊡ a.	1030	1135	1330	1435	1630	1735	1930	2035	2230	2335	0235	0430

Donegal ⊡ d.	0100	0400	0530	0700	0830	1000	1130	1300	1430	1600	1730	1900
Ballyshannon d.	0120	0420	0550	0720	0850	1020	1150	1320	1450	1620	1750	1920
Enniskillen d.	0200	0500	0635	0800	0935	1100	1235	1400	1535	1700	1835	2000
Cavan d.	0240	0540	0735	0840	1035	1140	1335	1440	1635	1740	1935	2040
Virginia d.	0310	0610	0805	0910	1105	1210	1405	1510	1705	1810	2005	2110
Dublin Airport ✈ ▽ a.	0415	0715	0910	1015	1210	1315	1510	1615	1810	1915	2110	2215
Dublin Busáras a.	0435	0735	0930	1035	1230	1335	1530	1635	1830	1935	2130	2235

△ – Buses call here to pick up only. ▽ – Buses call here to set down only. ⊡ – Donegal **Abbey Hotel**.

Bus Éireann 51, 64, 480 — 🚌 LONDONDERRY - GALWAY and GALWAY - CORK — 235

	⚒									⑤⑦
Londonderry d.	...	...	...	0715	0915	1110	...	1530	1830	...
Letterkenny d.	...	...	...	0755	0957	1150	...	1610	1910	...
Donegal (Abbey Hotel) d.	...	0635	...	0840	1040	1240	...	1655	1955	...
Ballyshannon d.	...	0655	...	0900	1100	1300	...	1715	2015	...
Sligo d.	0600	0740	0800	1000	1200	1400	1600	1815	2105	2115
Ireland West Airport Knock d.	|	...	0905	1105	1305	1500	1705	|	...	|
Knock d.	0724	...	0924	1125	1324	1520	1725	1920	...	2230
Claremorris (Dalton St.) d.	|	...	|	1135	|	1530	1735	|	...	2240
Galway (Bus Station) ❖ a.	0900	...	1045	1240	1445	1635	1840	2040	...	2345

Galway (Bus Station) ❖ d.	...	...	0705	0805		1705	1805	1905	2005
Ennis d.	...	...	0820	0920		1820	1920	2020	2120
Shannon Airport ✈ d.	...	...	0850	0950	and	1850	1950	2050	2150
Limerick (Colbert Rail Station) a.	...	...	0920	1020	hourly	1920	2020	2120	2220
Limerick (Colbert Rail Station) d.	0725	0835	0935	1035	until	1935	2035	...	...
Mallow (Town Park) d.	0830	0940	1040	1140		2040	2140	...	...
Cork a.	0915	1025	1125	1225		2125	2225	...	...

Cork d.	...	...	0725	0825		1725	1825	1925	2055
Mallow (Town Park) d.	...	...	0800	0900		1800	1900	2000	2130
Limerick (Colbert Rail Station) a.	...	...	0910	1010	and	1910	2010	2110	2240
Limerick (Colbert Rail Station) d.	0725	0825	0925	1025	hourly	1925	2025	...	...
Shannon Airport ✈ d.	0755	0855	0955	1055	until	1955	2055	...	...
Ennis d.	0825	0925	1025	1125		2025	2125	...	...
Galway (Bus Station) ❖ a.	0945	1045	1145	1245		2145	2245	...	...

	⚒	⚒		⚒						⑤
Galway (Bus Station) ❖ d.	0600	...	0845	1030	...	1200	*1410*	1600	1810	...
Claremorris (Dalton St.) d.	0700	...	|	1135	...	1305	|	|	1911	...
Knock d.	0710	...	1005	1145	...	1315	*1530*	1725	1921	...
Ireland West Airport Knock d.	0730	...	1025	1205	...	1335	*1550*	1745	|	...
Sligo d.	0845	0855	1145	1310	1330	1500	1710	1905	2040	2100
Ballyshannon d.	...	0945	1232	...	1417	1547	1757	1952	...	2147
Donegal (Abbey Hotel) d.	...	1015	1252	...	1437	1607	1817	2012	...	2207
Letterkenny d.	...	1110	1340	...	1525	1655	1905	2100	...	2250
Londonderry a.	...	1145	1420	...	1605	1735	1945	2140	...	2330

❖ – Change buses at Galway. Minimum connection time 45 minutes. ☛ The calling point in each town is the bus station unless otherwise indicated.

236 DUBLIN - SLIGO IÉ

km		Ⓐ 🍷	⚒ 🍷	⚒ 🍷	⚒ 🍷	⚒ 🍷	A 🍷	⚒ 🍷	Ⓐ	Ⓐ	⚒ 🍷	Ⓐ		⑦ 🍷		⑦ 🍷		⑦ 🍷	B 🍷	⑦ 🍷		⑦ 🍷	
0	**Dublin** Connolly d.	0655	0905	1100	1300	1500	1600	1710	1717	1815	1915	2047	...	0905	...	1300	...	1500	1600	1710	...	1905	...
26	Maynooth d.	0731	0937	1136	1336	1536	1639	1744	1802	1858	1954	2129	...	0938	...	1336	...	1536	1637	1745	...	1944	...
83	Mullingar d.	0813	1018	1217	1418	1617	1720	1825	1851	1941	2034	2215	...	1019	...	1418	...	1617	1718	1825	...	2025	...
125	**Longford** d.	0853	1048	1249	1450	1647	1750	1855	1924	2012	2112	...	...	1050	...	1450	...	1648	1747	1858	...	2055	...
143	Dromod d.	0906	1101	1303	1504	1700	1804	1908	...	...	2124	...	...	1104	...	1504	...	1701	1804	1914	...	2106	...
159	Carrick on Shannon d.	0919	1114	1316	1517	1712	1816	1920	...	...	2136	...	...	1117	...	1517	...	1713	1818	1928	...	2118	...
173	Boyle d.	0933	1128	1329	1529	1724	1828	1931	...	...	2148	...	...	1139	...	1539	...	1732	1832	1941	...	2130	...
219	**Sligo** a.	1017	1216	1416	1616	1807	1905	2016	...	...	2225	...	...	1215	...	1615	...	1808	1907	2016	...	2207	...

	Ⓐ	Ⓐ	Ⓐ 🍷	⚒ 🍷	⚒ 🍷	⚒ 🍷	⚒ 🍷	⚒ 🍷	C 🍷	Ⓐ 🍷	⚒ 🍷		⑦ 🍷		⑦ 🍷		⑦ 🍷		⑦ 🍷		B 🍷		⑦ 🍷
Sligo d.	...	...	0540	0640	0905	1105	1305	1505	1655	1650	1900	...	0905	...	1105	...	1305	...	1505	...	1630	...	1905
Boyle d.	...	...	0612	0712	0937	1137	1337	1537	1729	1729	1937	...	0939	...	1138	...	1338	...	1538	...	1705	...	1942
Carrick on Shannon d.	...	...	0624	0726	0951	1151	1350	1550	1742	1742	1950	...	0951	...	1151	...	1350	...	1550	...	1719	...	1953
Dromod d.	...	...	0635	0738	1003	1203	1402	1602	1806	1806	2002	...	1003	...	1203	...	1402	...	1602	...	1731	...	2005
Longford d.	0538	0615	0649	0751	1016	1216	1415	1615	1825	1825	2015	...	1016	...	1216	...	1415	...	1615	...	1748	...	2018
Mullingar d.	0612	0649	0719	0821	1055	1254	1454	1654	1903	1905	2044	...	1055	...	1245	...	1454	...	1654	...	1826	...	2051
Maynooth d.	0655	0730	0810	0904	1136	1334	1535	1743	1944	1950	2125	...	1136	...	1326	...	1535	...	1742	...	1906	...	2132
Dublin Connolly a.	0740	0818	0849	0940	1209	1409	1608	1822	2015	2030	2159	...	1209	...	1358	...	1610	...	1814	...	1940	...	2205

A – ⚒ (Ⓐ June 6 - Aug. 30). B – ⑦ (not June 7 - Aug. 30). C – ⑥ (not June 6 - Aug. 30).

☛ **Shaded services are temporarily suspended.**

236a BALLYBROPHY - ROSCREA - LIMERICK IÉ

km		Ⓐ	⚒ 🍷	⚒		⚒h ◇🍴	⚒	⑦ 🍷	⑦		
0	**Dublin** Heuston d.	...	0900	...	...	1800	...	1825	...	...	...
107	Ballybrophy d.	...	0958	1008	...	1856	1905	1936	1942	...	...
123	Roscrea d.	...	...	1028	...	...	1928	|	2003	...	...
154	Nenagh d.	0745	...	1110	...	...	2011	|	2044	...	...
199	**Limerick** Colbert a.	0845	...	1210	...	...	2115	2043	2153	...	...

	⚒	⚒ 🍷		⚒	⚒ ◇🍷	⑦	⑦ 🍷			
Limerick Colbert d.	0625	0740	...	1655	...	1720	1820	...	...	...
Nenagh d.	0735	|	...	1751	...	1816	|	...	...	...
Roscrea d.	0816	|	...	1831	...	1856	|	...	...	...
Ballybrophy d.	0840	0849	...	1855	1901	1921	1924	...	...	...
Dublin Heuston a.	...	0953	...	...	2000	...	2031	...	...	...

h – 🍴 on Ⓐ, 🍷 on ⑥. ◇ – Also conveys 1st class.

☛ **Shaded services are temporarily suspended.**

237 DUBLIN - ROSSLARE IÉ

km		⚒		⑥	Ⓐ		Ⓐ 🍷	⑥ 🍷		Ⓐ	Ⓐ	Ⓐ 🍷	⑥ 🍷		⑦	⑦		⑦ 🍷		⑦ 🍷			
0	**Dublin Connolly** ▲ d.		...	0805	0933	...	1333	1336	...	1633	1733	1835	1838	...		1025	...	1345	...	1845	...	...	...
11	Dún Laoghaire ▲ d.		...	0825	0957	...	1358	1357	...	1658	1758	1859	1856	...		1043	...	1406	...	1906	...	...	...
21	Bray ▲ d.		...	0845	1020	...	1422	1417	...	1722	1822	1920	1917	...		1103	...	1427	...	1927	...	...	...
47	Wicklow d.		...	0913	1045	...	1447	1445	...	1749	1849	1947	1946	...		1130	...	1450	...	1953	...	...	...
80	Arklow d.		...	0940	1114	...	1515	1511	...	1818	1921	2014	2013	...		1157	...	1517	...	2020	...	...	...
97	Gorey d.		...	0953	1127	...	1528	1525	...	1831	1935	2027	2026	...		1209	...	1529	...	2032	...	...	...
126	Enniscorthy d.		...	1013	1147	...	1547	1545	...	1856	1956	2047	2046	...		1229	...	1552	...	2052	...	...	...
150	**Wexford** d.		...	1034	1207	...	1608	1606	...	1917	2016	2110	2107	...		1251	...	1614	...	2114	...	...	...
160	Rosslare Strand d.		...	1052	1225	...	1625	1624	...	1933	2034	...	2124	...		1309	...	1633	...	2132	...	...	...
166	**Rosslare** Europort a.		...	1059	1231	...	1633	1632	...	1941	2042	...	2133	...		1317	...	1641	...	2140	...	...	...

	⚒	Ⓐ	Ⓐ y	⑥	Ⓐ 🍷	⑥ 🍷		⚒ 🍷		Ⓐ	⑥		⑦		⑦ 🍷		⑦ 🍷		⑦				
Rosslare Europort d.		...	0535	...	0720	0720	...	1255	...	1730	1755	...		...	0940	...	1420	...	1805	...	...	...	...
Rosslare Strand d.		...	0540	...	0726	0726	...	1301	...	1736	1801	...		...	0946	...	1426	...	1811	...	...	...	...
Wexford d.		...	0557	...	0743	0745	...	1320	...	1753	1819	...		...	1005	...	1447	...	1831	...	...	...	...
Enniscorthy d.		...	0620	...	0804	0806	...	1339	...	1813	1840	...		...	1026	...	1508	...	1852	...	...	...	...
Gorey d.		0550	0643	0645	0825	0827	...	1400	...	1836	1901	...		...	1046	...	1531	...	1912	...	...	...	...
Arklow d.		0602	0657	0701	0838	0840	...	1413	...	1849	1914	...		...	1059	...	1545	...	1925	...	...	...	...
Wicklow d.		0632	0730	0735	0905	0913	...	1446	...	1916	1945	...		...	1129	...	1612	...	1954	...	...	...	...
Bray ▲ d.		0659	0759	0805	0929	0940	...	1510	...	1943	2009	...		...	1155	...	1637	...	2016	...	...	...	...
Dún Laoghaire ▲ d.		0720	0819	0825	0949	0955	...	1530	...	2000	2024	...		...	1210	...	1651	...	2031	...	...	...	...
Dublin Connolly ▲ a.		0748	0847	0847	1019	1016	...	1556	...	2028	2049	...		...	1229	...	1712	...	2048	...	...	...	...

y – To Dundalk; see Table **230**. ▲ – Additional surburban trains (*DART*) run Howth - Dublin Connolly - Dún Laoghaire - Bray. Trains run every 10 - 15 mins. on ⚒, every 20 - 30 mins. on ⑦.

238 DUBLIN - KILKENNY - WATERFORD IÉ

km		⚒	⚒ 🍷		⚒ 🍷		⚒ 🍷	⚒ 🍷	⑤ 🍷	⚒ 🍷	⚒ 🍷	⚒ 🍷	Ⓐ	⑦		⑦ 🍷		⑦ 🍷		⑦ 🍷		⑦ 🍷	
0	**Dublin Heuston** △ d.		0720	...	1015	...	1315	1510	1615	1640	1735	1835	2015		...	0910	...	1410	...	1745	...	1840	...
48	Kildare △ d.		0751	...	1040	...	|	1538	|	1715	1805	1903	2100		...	0939	...	1438	...	1813	...	1904	...
72	Athy d.		0807	...	1100	...	1356	1555	1656	1735	1825	1922	2114		...	0957	...	1457	...	1832	...	1927	...
90	Carlow d.		0822	...	1112	...	1409	1606	1725	1747	1837	1938	2127		...	1010	...	1509	...	1844	...	1939	...
106	Muine Bheag d.		0835	...	1123	...	1421	1618	|	1759	1848	1949	...		...	1024	...	1521	...	1858	...	1951	...
130	**Kilkenny** a.		0900	...	1140	...	1438	1635	|	1817	1905	2007	...		...	1042	...	1541	...	1917	...	2009	...
130	**Kilkenny** d.		0903	...	1144	...	1443	1640	|	1821	1910	2012	...		...	1047	...	1545	...	1921	...	2014	...
147	Thomastown d.		0919	...	1155	...	1459	1656	|	1831	1920	2022	...		...	1057	...	1556	...	1932	...	2024	...
179	**Waterford** a.		0944	...	1223	...	1530	1721	1813	1904	1948	2054	...		...	1126	...	1624	...	2001	...	2054	...

	⚒	Ⓐ	⚒ 🍷	Ⓐ 🍷	⚒ 🍷		⚒ 🍷	⚒ 🍷	⚒ 🍷	⑤⑥	⚒ 🍷	Ⓐ	⑦		⑦ 🍷		⑦ 🍷		⑦ 🍷		⑦ 🍷		
Waterford d.		...	0555	0700	0750	...	1100	1305	1450	1605	1825	...		...	0905	...	1240	...	1510	...	1805	...	...
Thomastown d.		...	0619	|	0809	...	1119	1324	1511	|	1846	...		...	0924	...	1259	...	1530	...	1824	...	...
Kilkenny a.		...	0634	|	0824	...	1134	1339	1525	|	1900	...		...	0939	...	1314	...	1544	...	1839	...	...
Kilkenny d.		...	0637	|	0828	...	1141	1343	1530	|	1911	...		...	0943	...	1318	...	1548	...	1843	...	...
Muine Bheag d.		...	0651	0742	0844	...	1155	1357	1545	|	1931	...		...	0957	...	1332	...	1603	...	1859	...	...
Carlow d.		0630	0703	0755	0856	...	1207	1411	1557	1700	1943	2135		...	1010	...	1343	...	1615	...	1910	...	...
Athy d.		0641	0715	0809	0908	...	1219	1423	1622	1713	1956	2146		...	1024	...	1355	...	1627	...	1926	...	...
Kildare △ d.		0659	0734	|	0927	...	1239	1441	1642	1730	2015	2202		...	1043	...	1414	...	1646	...	1946	...	...
Dublin Heuston △ a.		0743	0807	0900	1000	...	1316	1521	1712	1806	2046	2248		...	1122	...	1454	...	1724	...	2024	...	...

△ – For additional trains Dublin - Kildare and v.v, see Tables **240**, **245**.

239 LIMERICK - WATERFORD IÉ

km			⚒ 🍷	⚒			⚒	⚒	s	
0	**Limerick Colbert** d.	...	0855	...	...	...	1750	...	...	...
35	**Limerick Junction** d.	...	0921	0940	...	...	1822	1840	...	...
40	Tipperary d.	...	...	0954	...	...	...	1854	...	...
62	Cahir d.	...	...	1019	...	...	...	1919	...	...
79	Clonmel d.	...	...	1038	...	...	...	1938	...	...
101	Carrick on Suir d.	...	...	1103	...	...	...	2003	...	...
124	**Waterford** a.	...	...	1125	...	...	...	2025	...	...

		⚒	⚒			⚒	⚒		
Waterford d.	...	0720	...	...	...	1625	...	...	...
Carrick on Suir d.	...	0745	...	...	...	1650	...	...	...
Clonmel d.	...	0807	...	...	...	1712	...	...	...
Cahir d.	...	0826	...	...	...	1731	...	...	...
Tipperary d.	...	0848	...	...	...	1753	...	...	...
Limerick Junction a.	...	0903	0935	...	...	1808	1830	...	...
Limerick Colbert a.	...	...	1002	...	...	...	1855	...	...

IÉ DUBLIN - GALWAY, BALLINA and WESTPORT 240

km		⚒	⚒ 🍷	⚒ 🍷	⚒ 🍷	⚒ 🍷	⚒ 🍷	⚒ 🍷	⚒ 🍷	⚒ 🍷	⚒ 🍷	⚒	⚒ 🍷	⚒ 🍷	⚒ 🍷	⚒ 🍷	⑦ 🍷	⑦	⑦ 🍷	⑦ 🍷	⑦ 🍷	⑦ 🍷	⑦ 🍷	⑦ 🍷	⑦ 🍷	⑦
0	**Dublin Heuston 245** d.	...	0735	...	0925	1125	1245	1325	1445	1535	1630	1710	1730	1815	1830	1935	0800	...	1140	1340	1440	1540	1635	1830	1845	2030
48	Kildare **245** d.	...	0800	...	|	|	|	|	|	|	1658	1738	|	|	|	|	0825	...	1205	1409	|	|	|	1901	1914	|
67	Portarlington **245** d.	...	0814	...	1001	1200	1321	1403	1522	1613	|	1755	1812	|	1913	2009	0839	...	1219	1423	1516	|	1713	1915	1928	2107
93	Tullamore d.	...	0830	...	1018	1217	1338	1422	1541	1631	1726	1812	1829	1907	|	2031	0856	...	1244	1447	1540	1633	1731	1932	1953	2123
129	**Athlone** d.	0650	0905	0915	1050	1241	1404	1447	1605	1659	1749	1845	1858	1929	1952	2102	0922	0940	1309	1512	1605	1658	1802	2000	2022	2149
152	Ballinasloe d.	0707	0920**k**	|	1105	1258	|	1503	|	1714	1808	...	1914	|	2008	2118	0938	|	1324	|	1622	|	1819	|	2037	2204
187	Athenry **242** d.	0733	0948**k**	|	1127	1322	|	1524	|	1738	1832	...	1936	|	2029	2141	1004	|	1346	|	1645	|	1848	|	2059	2224
208	**Galway 242** a.	0751	1006**k**	|	1152	1344	|	1545	|	1759	1852	...	2001	|	2053	2204	1024	|	1405	|	1708	|	1908	|	2119	2244
160	Roscommon d.	▬	...	0938	▬	...	1429	▬	1629	▬	▬	...	...	1958	▬	...	▬	1002	▬	1537	...	1732	▬	2023	▬	...
186	Castlerea d.	...	...	0957	...	...	1448	...	1648	...	...	...	...	2017	...	...	...	1021	...	1556	...	1751	...	2042	...	...
204	Ballyhaunis d.	...	...	1010	...	...	1501	...	1702	...	...	...	...	2030	...	...	...	1034	...	1610	...	1804	...	2055	...	...
222	Claremorris d.	⚒	...	1024	⚒	...	1515	⚒	1716	⚒	⚒	...	...	2044	⚒	...	⑦	1048	⑦	1626	...	1820	⑦	2109	⑦	...
240	Manulla Junction § d.	0737	...	1036	1039	...	1528	1532	1729	1732	1838	...	...	2057	2100	...	0813	1102	1105	1640	...	1834	1837	2122	2125	...
273	**Ballina** a.	0805	...	|	1106	...	|	1600	|	1800	1906	...	...	|	2128	...	0841	|	1133	|	...	|	1905	|	2153	...
246	Castlebar d.	...	...	1043	...	...	1535	...	1736	...	...	...	...	2109	...	...	...	1109	...	1647	...	1841	...	2129	...	...
264	**Westport** a.	...	...	1056	...	...	1557	...	1756	...	...	...	...	2126	...	...	...	1127	...	1708	...	1906	...	2149	...	...

	Ⓐ	Ⓐ	Ⓐ 🍷	⚒ 🍷	⚒	⚒ 🍷	⚒	⚒ 🍷	⚒ 🍷	⚒	⚒ 🍷	⚒	⚒	⚒ 🍷	⚒ 🍷	⚒	⑦	⑦ 🍷	⑦	⑦	⑦ 🍷	⑦ 🍷	⑦ 🍷	⑦ 🍷	⑦	⑦ 🍷
Westport d.	...	...	0520	...	...	0715	...	0945	...	...	1310	...	...	1820	...	...	...	0750	...	...	1330	...	1550	...	...	1750
Castlebar d.	...	...	0532	...	...	0728	...	0957	...	...	1323	...	...	1833	...	...	...	0803	...	...	1343	...	1603	...	...	1803
Ballina d.	...	...	|	...	0705	|	0935	|	...	1300	|	1455	1805	|	...	2027	0740	|	1030	1310	|	...	|	...	1735	|
Manulla Junction § d.	...	...	|	...	0733	0736	1003	1005	...	1328	1330	1525	1833	1839	...	2055	0808	0811	1058	1338	1349	...	1610	...	1803	1809
Claremorris d.	...	...	0550	...	▬	0750	▬	1020	...	▬	1344	▬	▬	1852	...	▬	▬	0825	▬	▬	1402	...	1624	...	▬	1822
Ballyhaunis d.	...	...	0603	...	...	0804	...	1033	...	...	1357	...	...	1905	...	...	...	0839	...	...	1416	...	1643	...	...	1840
Castlerea d.	...	...	0616	...	⚒	0818	⚒	1046	...	Ⓐ	1410	⚒	⚒	1919	...	...	⑦	0853	⑦	⑦	1430	...	1658	...	⑦	1853
Roscommon d.	...	...	0634	...	🍷	0838	🍷	1105	...	🍷	1432	🍷	🍷	1939	...	Ⓐ	🍷	0913	🍷	🍷	1451	...	1718	...	🍷	1913
Galway 242 d.	...	0525	|	0625	0730	|	0930	|	1105	1305	|	1505	1720	|	1920	2215	0805	|	1100	1300	|	1505	|	1700	1800	|
Athenry **242** d.	...	0543	|	0640	0748	|	0948	|	1128	1320	|	1520	1738	|	1937	2234	0821	|	1118	1317	|	1523	|	1718	1818	|
Ballinasloe d.	...	0606	|	|	0808	|	1012	|	1149	1345	|	1547	1805	|	2006	2300	0845	|	1141	1346	|	1546	|	1743	1845	|
Athlone d.	0520	0624	0700	0716	0826	0903	1028	1131	1208	1407	1458	1605	1828	2011	2031	2315	0902	0938	1159	1403	1516	1606	1747	1804	1903	1937
Tullamore d.	0544	0648	0723	0738	0849	0930	1056	1156	1237	1440	1524	1634	1850	2035	2056	...	0933	1002	1223	1429	1541	1633	1811	1830	1930	2014
Portarlington **245** d.	0602	0707	0741	|	0907	0949	1114	1224	1256	1508	1548	1652	1915	2053	2114	...	0951	1022	1243	1447	1601	1652	1829	1851	1957	2032
Kildare **245** d.	0614	0723	0754	0811	|	|	|	|	|	|	|	1706	1928	|	|	...	1001	|	1255	|	|	1706	1844	1906	|	|
Dublin Heuston 245 a.	0659	0759	0831	0843	0950	1027	1154	1304	1339	1548	1629	1740	2001	2136	2154	...	1037	1104	1328	1528	1642	1737	1915	1941	2041	2111

f – ⑤ only. **j** – Also runs on ⑥. **k** – Change at Athlone on ⑤. **§** – Passenger transfer point only. ☛ **Shaded services are temporarily suspended.**

IÉ LIMERICK JUNCTION - LIMERICK - GALWAY 242

km		⚒	⚒	⚒	⚒	⚒	⚒		⑦	⑦	⑦	⑦
0	**Limerick Jct 243** d.	...	...	...	...	...	...	...	...	1137	...	...
35	**Limerick ¶ 245** d.	0555	0920	1420	1630	1805	1950	...	0900	1203	1555	1815
74	Ennis **245** d.	0649**x**	1000	1501	1710	1844	2029	...	0942	1307	1636	1856
103	Gort d.	0713	1022	1523	...	1931	2051	...	1004	1331	1702	1923
132	Athenry **240** d.	0743	1054	1554	...	2009	2119	...	1035	1400	1733	1954
152	**Galway 240** a.	0809	1113	1615	...	2032	2142	...	1055	1423	1751	2012

	⚒	⚒	⚒	⚒	⚒	⚒	⚒	⑦	⑦	⑦	⑦
Galway 240 d.	...	0615	1025	1345	...	1750	...	0825	1155	1610	1830
Athenry **240** d.	...	0633	1044	1408	...	1817	...	0843	1214	1633	1853
Gort d.	...	0704	1117	1435	...	1844	...	0912	1244	1703	1924
Ennis **245** d.	0650	0735	1141	1503	1720	1908	2035	0936	1307	1726	1947
Limerick ¶ 245 a.	0730	0820	1222	1542	1800	1949	2115	1020	1345	1805	2027
Limerick Jct 243 a.	...	...	...	...	...	...	...	...	1422	...	...

x – Arrive 0635. **¶** – Limerick Colbert. ☛ **Shaded services are temporarily suspended.**

IÉ LIMERICK JUNCTION - LIMERICK 243

Shuttle service connecting with main-line trains. *35 km.* Journey time : 25 - 40 minutes. For through services to or from Dublin Heuston see Table **245**.

From Limerick Junction ⚒: 0806, 0836, 0935, 1040, 1250, 1438, 1636, 1839, 2040, 2243.
⑦: 1136, 1333, 1547, 1732, 1844, 2030, 2300.

From Limerick Colbert ⚒: 0530, 0615, 0725, 0900, 0950, 1055, 1250, 1455, 1650, 1750, 1850, 2055.
⑦: 1050, 1250, 1505, 1645, 1750, 1950, 2220.

IÉ (DUBLIN -) CORK - MALLOW - TRALEE 244

km			⚒	⚒	⚒	⚒	⚒	⚒	Ⓐ ◇✕	⑥ 🍷	⚒			⑦	⑦ ◇🍷	⑦	⑦	⑦	⑦	⑦			
0	**Cork 245** d.	...	0625	0900	...	*1225*	*1425*	*1625*	...	...	2100	...	...	0855	*1010*	1215	1450	*1625*	1850	...	...	...	...
	Dublin **245** d.	...	|	*0700*	*0900*	*1100*	*1300*	*1500*	1705	1705	*1900*	...	...	|	0830	*1000*	*1300*	*1400*	*1700*	1905	...	...	...
34	**Mallow 245** d.	...	0651	0920	1120	1320	1520	1725	1916	1916	2120	...	...	0921	1035	1251	1529	1724	1930	2112	...	...	...
66	Millstreet d.	...	0716	0948	1143	1348	1543	1747	1940	1940	2148	...	...	0944	1101	1316	1553	1748	1953	2137	...	...	...
100	Killarney d.	...	0747	1019	1220	1420	1620	1820	2020	2020	2216	...	...	1014	1134	1347	1625	1826	2031	2208	...	...	...
134	**Tralee** a.	...	0826	1058	1258	1458	1658	1858	2058	2058	2255	...	...	1050	1221	1423	1704	1901	2109	2247	...	...	...

		①	②–⑤	⚒	⚒	⚒	⚒	⚒	⚒	⚒			⑦		⑦ 🍷	⑦ 🍷	⑦	⑦	⑦ 🍷	⑦			
Tralee d.	...	0445	0555	0705	0905	1105	1305	1505	1705	1905	...	...	0710	...	1150	1350	1510	1710	1750	1915	...	...	...
Killarney d.	...	0519	0629	0744	0939	1139	1339	1539	1739	1939	...	...	0740	...	1224	1430	1543	1744	1828	1949	...	...	...
Millstreet d.	...	0545	0655	0814	1010	1210	1410	1610	1810	2010	...	...	0814	...	1253	1459	1614	1810	1857	2020	...	...	...
Mallow 245 d.	...	0609	0729**z**	0842	1038	1238	1438	1638	1843	2043	...	...	0841	...	1321	1527	1643	1836	1927	2046	...	...	...
Dublin **245** a.	...	*0822*	*0930*	1047	*1258*	*1458*	*1659*	*1904*	*2104*	*2259*	...	...	*1053*	...	1530	1739	*1854*	*2057*	2133	|	...	...	...
Cork 245 a.	...	*0720*	0750	*0915*	*1145*	*1344*	*1537*	*1737*	1905	2104	...	...	0914	...	*1352*	*1632*	1727	1907	*2037*	2115	...	...	...

CORK - COBH Journey time: 24 minutes *19 km.*
⚒ 0600 ⑥, 0700, 0800, 0900, 1000, then hourly until 1600, 1700, 1800, 1900 Ⓐ, 2000, 2100.
† 0800, 0900, 1100, 1200, 1300, 1430, 1600, 1700, 1800, 1940, 2100, 2200.

COBH - CORK
⚒ 0630 ⑥, 0730, 0830, 0930, 1030, then hourly until 1630, 1730, 1830, 1930 Ⓐ, 2030, 2130.
† 0830, 0930, 1130, 1230, 1330, 1500, 1630, 1730, 1830, 2030, 2130, 2230.

CORK - MIDLETON Journey time: 24 mins. *19 km.*
⚒ 0615, 0715, 0815, 0915, 1015, then hourly until 2015, 2115.
0815, 0915, 1115, 1215, 1415, 1615, 1715, 1815, 2015.

MIDLETON - CORK
⚒ 0645, 0745, 0845, 0945, 1045, then hourly until 2045, 2145.
† 0845, 0945, 1145, 1245, 1445, 1645, 1745, 1845, 2045.

z – Arrive 0718. ◇ – Also conveys 🚃. ☛ **Shaded services are temporarily suspended.**

245 DUBLIN - LIMERICK, TRALEE and CORK IÉ

All catering services are temporarily suspended. First class is reduced on many services.

km			⚒h ◇✕	⚒	⚒ ◇🍷	⚒	⚒ ◇🍷	⚒	⚒ ◇🍷	⚒	⚒ ◇🍷	⚒	⚒ ◇🍷	⚒	⚒ ◇🍷	⚒	⚒ ◇🍷	⚒	⚒ ◇🍷	⚒ 🍷	⚒ 🍷	⚒	⚒ ◇🍷	⚒
0	**Dublin Heuston** 240 d.		0700	...	0800	...	0900	...	1000	...	1100	...	1200	...	1300	...	1400	...	1500	1525	1530	...	1600	...
48	Kildare 240 d.		|	...	|	...	|	...	|	...	|	...	|	...	|	...	|	...	|	1612	1559	...	|	...
67	Portarlington 240 d.		|	...	|	...	|	...	|	...	|	...	|	...	|	...	|	...	|	1626	1610	...	|	...
82	Portlaoise d.	⚒	0746	...	|	...	0944	...	1044	...	1144	...	1244	...	1344	...	1444	...	|	1637	1620	...	|	...
107	Ballybrophy d.		|	...	|	...	1000	...	|	...	|	...	|	...	|	...	1500	...	|	...	1635	...	|	...
127	Templemore d.		|	...	0904	...	|	...	|	...	1208	...	|	...	|	...	|	...	|	...	1648	...	|	...
139	Thurles d.		0815	...	0914	...	1017	...	1113	...	1217	...	1314	...	1414	...	1518	...	1610	...	1656	...	1711	...
172	**Limerick Junction** § d.		0835	0836	0932	0935	1035	1040	1131	1136	1235	1250	1332	1336	1432	1436	1536	1540	1629	...	|	...	1730	1735
208	**Limerick Colbert** § 242 a.		|	0904	|	1003	|	1107	|	1204	|	1324	|	1404	|	1504	|	1608	|	...	1741	1805	|	1803
**	Ennis 242 a.		|	*0959*	|	...	|	...	|	1310	|	...	|	1455	|	...	|	1710	|	...	...	1843	|	...
208	Charleville d.		|	...	|	...	1059	...	|	...	1258	...	|	...	|	...	|	...	1651	...	...	...	|	...
232	**Mallow** 244 d.		0909	...	1007	...	1114	...	1205	...	1314	...	1407	...	1506	...	1610	...	1707	...	...	...	1804	...
	Tralee 246 a.		*1058*	...	|	...	|	...	|	...	*1458*	...	|	...	|	...	|	...	*1858*	...	...	...	|	...
266	**Cork** 244 a.		0937	...	1037	...	1145	...	1237	...	1344	...	1437	...	1537	...	1642	...	1737	...	...	...	1837	...

	⚒ 🍷	Ⓐ ◇✕	⑥ ◇🍷	Ⓐ ◇✕	⑥ 🍷	⚒	⚒ 🍷	Ⓐ ◇✕	⑥ ◇🍷	⚒	⚒ ◇🍷	⚒	⚒	⚒			⑦ ◇🍷	⑦	⑦	⑦ ◇🍷	⑦	⑦	⑦ 🍷	
Dublin Heuston 240 d.	1625	1700	1700	1705	1705	...	1725	1800	1800	...	1900	...	2100	...	...		0830	...	...	1000	...	...	1125	...
Kildare 240 d.	|	|	|	|	|	...	1754	|	|	...	|	...	|	...	...		|	...	...	|	...	...	1153	...
Portarlington 240 d.	1700	|	|	|	|	...	1805	|	|	...	|	...	|	...	...	⑦	|	...	...	|	...	...	1205	...
Portlaoise d.	1712	|	|	|	|	...	1815	|	|	...	1946	...	2144	...	...		0913	...	...	1044	...	...	1215	...
Ballybrophy d.	1729	|	|	1800	1800	...	1829	1857	1857	...	2001	...	|	...	...		|	...	...	|	...	...	1230	...
Templemore d.	1740	|	|	1812	1812	...	1842	|	|	...	2014	...	|	...	...		|	...	...	|	...	...	1244	...
Thurles d.	1750	|	|	1820	1820	...	1851	1915	1915	...	2022	...	2214	...	...		0941	...	...	1114	...	...	1253	...
Limerick Junction § d.	1813	1827	1827	|	|	1836	|	1933	1933	1937	2040	2040	2235	2243	...		1003	1008	...	1132	...	1136	|	...
Limerick Colbert § 242 a.	1840	|	|	|	|	1902	1940	|	|	2005	|	2107	|	2311	...		|	1035	...	|	...	1204	1340	...
Ennis 242 a.	...	|	|	|	|	...	*2031*	|	|	2110	|	...	|	...	...		|	1125	...	|	...	*1306*	...	...
Charleville d.	...	|	|	1858	1858	...	...	|	|	...	2104	...	|	...	...		1022	...	...	|	...	...	...	...
Mallow 244 d.	...	1859	1859	1916	1916	...	...	2008	2008	...	2119	...	2307	...	...		1037	...	1045	1206	1251	...	...	...
Tralee 246 a.	...	|	|	2058	2058	...	...	|	|	...	*2251*	...	|	...	...		1221	...	|	|	1423	...	...	...
Cork 244 a.	...	1932	1932	...	...	...	...	2037	2037	...	2148	...	2337	...	...		...	...	1106	1237	...	...	...	...

	⑦ ◇🍷	⑦	⑦ ◇🍷	⑦ 🍷	⑦ ◇🍷	⑦ ◇🍷	⑦ 🍷	⑦ ◇🍷	⑦	⑦	⑦ ◇🍷	⑦ 🍷	⑦ 🍷	⑦	⑦ ◇🍷	⑦	⑦	⑦	⑦ 🍷		⑦	⑦		
Dublin Heuston 240 d.	1200	...	1300	1325	1400	1500	1525	1600	...	...	1700	1800	1825	...	1900	1905	...	...	1925	...	2100	2110	...	...
Kildare 240 d.	|	...	|	1353	|	|	1553	|	...	...	|	|	1857	...	|	|	...	...	1950	...	|	2142	...	...
Portarlington 240 d.	|	...	|	1405	|	|	1605	|	...	...	|	|	1911	...	|	1942	...	...	2015	...	2136	2153	...	...
Portlaoise d.	|	...	|	1415	|	|	1615	|	...	...	|	|	1921	...	|	|	...	...	2026	...	|	2204	...	...
Ballybrophy d.	|	...	|	1430	|	|	1630	|	...	...	|	|	1936	...	|	|	...	...	2040	...	|	|	...	...
Templemore d.	|	...	|	1443	|	|	1643	|	...	...	|	|	1947	...	|	|	...	...	2052	...	|	|	...	...
Thurles d.	1309	...	1409	1452	1509	1609	1652	1709	...	...	1809	1908	1955	...	2009	2018	...	...	2101	...	2213	2233	...	...
Limerick Junction § d.	1329	1333	|	|	1529	|	|	1729	1732	...	|	1929	|	...	|	2040	2047	...	|	...	2235	|	...	...
Limerick Colbert § 242 a.	|	1401	|	1540	*1614*	|	1740	|	1759	1815	|	*2004*	2043	2050	|	|	2114	...	2149	...	*2328*	2320	...	...
Ennis 242 a.	|	...	|	*1636*	|	|	...	|	...	1855	|	|	...	2129	|	|	...	...	...	...	|	...	...	...
Charleville d.	|	...	1450	...	|	|	...	1751	...	...	|	|	...	...	|	2059	...	...	...	...	|	...	...	...
Mallow 244 d.	1402	...	1505	...	1600	1702	...	1806	...	...	1900	2000	...	...	2101	2115	...	2125	...	...	2307	...	...	...
Tralee 246 a.	|	...	|	...	*1901*	|	...	|	...	...	|	|	...	...	|	2248	...	|	...	...	|	...	...	...
Cork 244 a.	1434	...	1532	...	1632	1728	...	1837	...	...	1927	2034	...	...	2127	...	...	2150	...	...	2337	...	...	...

		⚒	⑥ 🍷	Ⓐ 🍷	Ⓐ 🍷	⚒ 🍷	⚒	Ⓐ ◇✕	⑥ ◇🍷	⚒	⚒ 🍷	⚒	⚒	⚒	Ⓐ ✕	⑥ 🍷	⚒	⚒ ◇🍷	⚒	⚒ ◇🍷	⚒	⚒ ◇🍷	⚒	⚒ ◇🍷
Cork 244 d.		...	0545	0545	0615	...	...	0700	0700	...	...	...	...	...	...	...	...	0925	...	1025	...	1125	...	1225
Tralee 246 d.		...	|	|	|	...	...	|	|	...	...	0705	...	...	0705	0705	...	|	...	|	...	|	...	*1105*
Mallow 244 d.	⚒	...	0609	0609	|	...	...	0722	0722	...	...	0844	...	...	0843	0843	...	0946	...	1046	...	1146	...	1246
Charleville d.		...	0623	0623	|	...	...	|	|	...	...	...	...	...	0858	0858	...	|	...	1102	...	|	...	|
Ennis 242 d.		...	|	|	|	...	...	|	|	0650	...	...	0745	...	|	|	...	|	...	|	...	|	*1147*	|
Limerick Colbert § 242 d.		0530	|	*0615*	|	0640	0725	|	|	0730	0740	...	0826	0900	|	|	0950	|	1055	|	1150	|	1250	|
Limerick Junction § d.		0558	0644	0644	|	|	0753	0755	0755	...	|	...	...	0926	0918	0918	1019	1022	1123	1125	1220	1222	1321	1324
Thurles d.		0615	0701	0701	|	0722	...	0814	0814	...	0823	...	...	...	|	|	...	1041	...	|	...	1241	...	|
Templemore d.		0624	|	|	|	0731	...	|	|	...	0832	...	...	...	|	|	...	|	...	1148	...	|	...	1346
Ballybrophy d.		0636	|	|	|	0742	...	|	|	...	0844	...	...	...	|	|	...	|	...	|	...	1259	...	|
Portlaoise d.		0654	|	|	|	0800	...	|	|	...	0902	...	...	...	|	|	...	1113	...	|	...	1317	...	1413
Portarlington 240 d.		|	|	|	|	0810	...	|	|	...	|	...	...	...	|	|	...	|	...	|	...	|	...	|
Kildare 240 d.		0718	|	|	|	0824	...	|	|	...	|	...	...	...	|	|	...	|	...	|	...	|	...	|
Dublin Heuston 240 a.		0750	0820	0820	0830	0857	...	0931	0931	...	0957	...	...	...	1047	1047	...	1200	...	1258	...	1406	...	1500

	⚒	⚒ ◇🍷	⚒	⚒	⚒ ◇🍷	⚒	⚒ ◇🍷	⚒	⚒ ◇🍷	⚒	⚒ ◇🍷	⚒	⚒	⚒ ◇🍷	Ⓐ ◇🍷	⚒	⚒ ◇🍷			⑦ 🍷	⑦ 🍷	⑦	⑦ 🍷	
Cork 244 d.	...	1325	...	...	1425	...	1525	...	1625	...	1725	...	...	1825	1925	...	2025	...		...	0825	...	...	...
Tralee 246 d.	...	|	...	...	|	...	|	...	*1505*	...	|	...	...	|	|	...	*1905*	...		...	*0710*	...	...	...
Mallow 244 d.	...	1345	...	...	1446	...	1546	...	1646	...	1746	...	...	1846	1947	...	2047	...	⑦	...	0846	...	...	...
Charleville d.	...	|	...	...	1502	...	|	...	1702	...	|	...	...	1902	|	...	|	...		...	0902	...	...	...
Ennis 242 d.	...	|	1325	...	|	1503	|	...	|	...	|	1720	...	|	|	1908	|	...		...	|	0942	...	...
Limerick Colbert § 242 d.	1350	|	1407	1455	|	1550	|	1650	|	1750	|	1800	1850	|	|	1948	*2055*	...		0825	|	1022	1025	...
Limerick Junction § d.	1420	1422	...	1524	1524	1622	1624	1718	1724	1822	1823	...	1918	1924	2024	...	2128	...		|	0924	...	|	...
Thurles d.	...	1440	...	...	1543	...	1641	...	1742	...	1841	...	...	1943	2042	...	2145	...		0908	|	...	1108	...
Templemore d.	...	|	...	...	|	...	|	...	1752	...	|	...	...	1952	|	...	|	...		0917	|	...	1117	...
Ballybrophy d.	...	|	...	...	|	...	|	...	|	...	1859	...	...	|	|	...	|	...		0929	|	...	1129	...
Portlaoise d.	...	1513	...	...	|	...	1713	...	1818	...	1917	...	...	2019	2114	...	2217	...		0946	|	...	1146	...
Portarlington 240 d.	...	|	...	...	|	...	|	...	|	...	|	...	...	|	|	...	|	...		0956	|	...	1155	...
Kildare 240 d.	...	|	...	...	|	...	|	...	|	...	|	...	...	|	|	...	|	...		1014	|	...	1211	...
Dublin Heuston 240 a.	...	1559	...	...	1659	...	1801	...	1906	...	2004	...	...	2106	2200	...	2303	...		1043	1053	...	1240	...

	⑦ ◇🍷	⑦ 🍷	⑦ ◇🍷	⑦ 🍷	⑦	⑦ ◇🍷	⑦ 🍷	⑦ ◇🍷	⑦ 🍷	⑦	⑦ ◇🍷	⑦ 🍷	⑦ ◇🍷	⑦	⑦ ◇🍷	⑦ 🍷	⑦	⑦ ◇🍷	⑦ 🍷	⑦	⑦ ◇🍷			
Cork 244 d.	1025	...	1225	...	...	1325	...	1425	...	...	1525	...	1625	...	1725	...	...	1825	...	...	1925	...	...	...
Tralee 246 d.	|	...	|	1150	...	*1150*	...	|	1345	...	|	...	*1510*	...	|	...	...	|	1750	...	|	...	...	...
Mallow 244 d.	1046	...	1246	1321	...	1346	...	1445	1528	...	1546	...	1646	...	1746	...	...	1846	1926	...	1946	...	...	...
Charleville d.	1102	...	1302	1337	...	|	...	1501	1543	...	|	...	1702	...	|	...	...	1902	|	...	|	...	...	...
Ennis 242 d.	|	...	|	|	1308	|	...	|	|	...	|	...	|	...	|	*1726*	...	|	|	*1900*	|	...	...	...
Limerick Colbert § 242 d.	*1050*	1225	*1250*	|	1354	|	1420	|	|	1550	|	1620	|	1750	|	1820	1845	|	|	1950	|	...	...	...
Limerick Junction § d.	1124	|	1323	1356	1422	1423	|	|	|	1618	1620	|	|	1819	1820	|	1914	1923	1958	2018	2020	...	...	...
Thurles d.	1143	1308	1342	1414	...	1441	1504	1538	1618	...	1639	1703	1740	...	1839	1902	...	1942	2017	...	2039	...	...	...
Templemore d.	|	1317	|	|	...	|	1513	|	|	...	|	1712	|	...	|	1911	...	|	|	...	|	...	...	...
Ballybrophy d.	|	1329	|	|	...	|	1526	|	|	...	|	1725	|	...	|	1924	...	|	|	...	|	...	...	...
Portlaoise d.	|	1346	|	|	...	|	1542	|	|	...	|	1743	|	...	|	1940	...	2014	|	...	2111	...	...	...
Portarlington 240 d.	|	1355	|	|	...	|	1551	|	1657	...	|	1752	|	...	|	1949	...	|	|	...	|	...	...	...
Kildare 240 d.	|	1411	|	|	...	|	1601	|	1711	...	|	1807	|	...	|	1959	...	|	|	...	|	...	...	...
Dublin Heuston 240 a.	1257	1440	1458	1533	...	1558	1632	1655	1742	...	1756	1837	1854	...	1955	2031	...	2059	2132	...	2158	...	...	...

◇ – Also conveys [1st class]. § – Also Table **243**. ** – Limerick - Ennis: *39 km*.

☛ Shaded services are temporarily suspended.

FRANCE

SEE MAP PAGES 164 and 165

Operator: Société Nationale des Chemins de Fer Français (SNCF), unless otherwise shown.

Services: Most long distance trains convey first and second class accommodation; many regional services are now second class only (travel classes are not usually indicated in our tables). *TGV* (*Train à Grande Vitesse*) high-speed trains have a bar car selling drinks, light meals and refreshments (some short-distance services have only vending machines). Selected international *TGV* trains have an at-seat meal service in first class. Certain other long-distance trains, branded *Intercités*, also offer a refreshment service, often from a trolley wheeled through the train. Regional and local trains (outside Paris) are classified *TER* (*Transport Express Régional*). Domestic overnight trains convey modern couchettes (four-berth in first class, six-berth in second class) and reclining seats (second class only). Couchette compartments for the exclusive use of women are available on request. Note that all luggage placed on luggage racks must be labelled. The regular *TGV* network is branded ***inOui***. SNCF subsidiary ***Ouigo*** operate an extensive network of low-cost high-speed services, together with some traditional loco-hauled services (branded ***Ouigo Classique***). Tickets for Ouigo services are only available via its website.

Timings: **Valid July 2 - August 28, 2022** except where shown. Amended services operate on and around public holidays; whilst we try to show holiday variations, passengers are advised to confirm train times locally before travelling during these periods. Public holidays in 2022 are Jan. 1, Easter Monday (Apr. 18), May 1, May 8, Ascension Day (May 26), Whit Monday (June 6), July 14, Aug. 15, Nov. 1, Nov. 11, Dec. 25. Services may be subject to alteration December 12 - January 2. **Engineering work** can often affect schedules; major changes are shown in the tables where possible but other changes may occur at short notice.

Tickets: Seat reservation is compulsory for travel by *TGV* and overnight trains (also other trains shown with 🅁), and is also available for a small fee on many other long-distance trains. Advance reservation is recommended for travel to ski resorts during the winter sports season. **Special fares** (which include a seat reservation) are payable for travel by *TGV* trains, night trains and other services with compulsory reservation (pass holders must pay a special supplement to use these services). In north-eastern France regional tickets are valid on *TGV* services for many local journeys (without prior reservation) on payment of a €3 TER-GV supplement (this is indicated in the relevant tables where applicable). All rail tickets (except passes) must be date-stamped before boarding the train using the self-service validating machines (composteurs) at the platform entrances. Note that where two *TGV* units are coupled together, they will often carry different train numbers for reservation purposes.

Note: *TGV* services **Lille Europe - Charles de Gaulle ✈ - Marne-la-Vallée - Lyon / Bordeaux / Rennes / Nantes** are shown in the International section (Table **11**).

TGV NORD — 250

SERVICE UNTIL JULY 17. See pages 559 and 560 for service July 18 - August 28.

HIGH-SPEED TRAINS. For Paris Charles de Gaulle ✈ - Lille services see Table **11**. For Paris - Calais, Boulogne and Rang du Fliers services see page 166.
Journeys to / from Paris are 🅁 with supplement. For other journeys, *TGV* and ♣ trains are classified *TER-GV* and require a Grande Vitesse supplement, €3 valid all day, 🅁 not required.

PARIS - LILLE FLANDRES

km		TGV 7001	TGV 7007	TGV 7011	TGV 7015	TGV 7023	TGV 7025	TGV 7027	TGV 7031	TGV 7035	TGV 7037	TGV 7043	TGV 7045	TGV 7047	TGV 7053	TGV 7057	TGV 7061	TGV 7065	TGV 7069	TGV 7073	TGV 7077	TGV 7081	TGV 7085	TGV 7087	TGV 7087	TGV 7297
		①–⑤	⚒	①–④		⑥	Ⓑ	⑥	⑤–⑦	⑥⑦	①–⑤	①–⑥	⑦	Ⓐ		Ⓐ	⑤⑦	Ⓐ		⑤⑦	①–⑤	⑦	⑥	⑦	⑤	①–⑤
		t		e	f	g	h	j	k	m	n	d			p		q		r	s	t		j	r	s	◧
0	**Paris** Nord d.	0646	0746	0816	0845	0946	1016	1046	1146	1246	1315	1446	1516	1546	1646	1716	1746	1816	1846	1916	1946	2016	2046	2116	2116	2149
227	**Lille** Flandres a.	0748	0848	0918	0954	1048	1118	1148	1248	1348	1418	1548	1618	1648	1748	1818	1848	1918	1948	2018	2048	2118	2148	2218	2219	2309

	TGV 7200	TGV 7200	TGV 7002	TGV 7006	TGV 7010	TGV 7014	TGV 7020	TGV 7026	TGV 7028	TGV 7030	TGV 7032	TGV 7038	TGV 7040	TGV 7044	TGV 7046	TGV 7052	TGV 7060	TGV 7064	TGV 7068	TGV 7072	TGV 7076	TGV 7078	TGV 7082	TGV 7084	TGV 7086
	②–⑤	①	Ⓐ	①–⑥	①–⑤		①–⑥	①–⑥	⑦	⑥	①–⑤	②–⑥	⑦	Ⓐ	⑥⑦	Ⓑ		⑦	Ⓑ	Ⓐ	⑤–⑦	①⑤		⑤	⑦
	u ⊡	v ●			t	d	p	f		g	h	w	r		j	x		r	t		y	s	A	s	r
Lille Flandres d.	0534	0552	0638	0712	0742	0812	0912	1012	1042	1112	1142	1312	1342	1442	1512	1612	1712	1742	1812	1842	1912	1942	2012	2042	2112
Paris Nord a.	0717	0708	0747	0814	0844	0914	1014	1114	1144	1214	1244	1414	1444	1544	1614	1714	1814	1844	1914	1944	2014	2044	2114	2144	2214

PARIS - VALENCIENNES, LILLE EUROPE and DUNKERQUE

km		♣	TGV 7155	TGV 7355	TGV 7159	TGV 7359	TGV 7163	TGV 7363		TGV 7165	TGV 7265	TGV 7365	TGV 7369	TGV 7171	TGV 7371	TGV 7173	TGV 7273	♣		TGV 7375	♣	TGV 7177	TGV 7277	TGV 7377	TGV 7181	TGV 7183
		Ⓐ	Ⓐ	①–⑤	⑥	⑥	⑦	⑦		Ⓐ	Ⓐ	⑥	Ⓐ	⑥	⑦	①–⑤	⑤	Ⓐ		⑥	Ⓐ	⑦	⑦	Ⓐ	Ⓐ	⑥
		B		t	z	g						g		z		t				j						z
0	**Paris** Nord d.	...	0752	0752	0852	0852	0952	0952	...	1052	1052	1052	1222	1352	1352	1428	1428	...	...	1552	...	1652	1652	1652	1752	1752
179	Arras a.	...	0840	0840	0941	0941	1041	1041	...	1141	1141	1140	1310	1441	1440	1517	1517	...	...	1640	...	1741	1741	1740	1840	1840
179	Arras d.	0718	0844	0851	0944	0951	1044	1051	...	1145	1149	1151	1314	1444	1451	1521	1535	...	...	1651	...	1744	1748	1751	1844	1844
199	Lens a.	|	|	0902	|	1002	|	1102	...	|	|	1203	1327	|	1502	1534	|	...	...	1702	...	|	|	1802	|	|
204	Douai a.	|	0858	|	0958	|	1058	|	...	1158	|	|	|	1458	|	1604	|	...	...	|	...	1758	|	|	1858	1858
240	**Valenciennes** a.	|	0935	|	1035	|	1135	|	...	1235	|	|	|	1535	|	1631	|	...	...	|	...	1835	|	|	1935	1935
218	Béthune a.	|	...	0916	...	1016	...	1116	...	...	|	1216	1342	...	1516	...	|	...	...	1716	...	...	|	1816	...	...
	Lille Europe a.	0737	...	|	...	|	...	|	...	...	1208	|	|	...	|	...	1605	...	...	|	...	...	1807	|	...	...
	Lille Europe d.	0750	...	|	...	|	...	|	...	...	1220	|	|	...	|	...	...	1650	...	|	1750	...	1820	|	...	...
252	Hazebrouck a.	|	...	0939	...	1039	...	1139	...	...	|	1239	1405	...	1539	...	...	|	...	1739	|	...	|	1839	...	...
292	**Dunkerque** a.	0820	...	1004	...	1104	...	1204	...	...	1251	1304	1430	...	1604	...	...	1720	...	1804	1820	...	1851	1904	...	...

	TGV 7283	TGV 7185	TGV 7385	TGV 7289	TGV 7289	TGV 7189	TGV 7389	TGV 7391	TGV 7295	TGV 7195
	⑥	Ⓐ	Ⓑ	⑥	⑤	⑦	Ⓒ	Ⓐ	⑦	⑦
	g		x		s					
Paris Nord d.	1752	1852	1852	1952	1952	1952	1952	2022	2152	2152
Arras a.	1840	1940	1940	2041	2041	2042	2042	2111	2240	2240
Arras d.	1848	1944	1951	2044	2044	2044	2051	2121	2244	2248
Lens a.	|	|	2002	|	|	|	2102	2135	|	|
Douai a.	|	1958	|	|	|	2058	|	|	|	2302
Valenciennes a.	|	2035	|	|	|	2135	|	|	|	2338
Béthune a.	|	...	2016	|	|	...	2116	2151	|	...
Lille Europe a.	1907	...	|	2107	2117	...	|	|	2307	...
Lille Europe d.	1920	...	|	...	...	...	|	|	...	...
Hazebrouck a.	|	...	2039	...	...	...	2139	2214	...	...
Dunkerque a.	1951	...	2104	...	...	...	2204	2242	...	...

	TGV 7104	TGV 7304	TGV 7106		TGV 7208	TGV 7212		TGV 7312	TGV 7116	TGV 7218
	Ⓐ	Ⓐ	①–⑤		Ⓐ	⑦		⑥	①–⑥	⑦
			t					g	¶	
Dunkerque d.	...	0556	...	...	0656	...	...	0756	...	1125
Hazebrouck d.	...	0620	...	...	|	...	...	0820	...	|
Lille Europe a.	...	|	...	...	0729	...	...	|	...	1157
Lille Europe d.	...	|	...	...	0740	0851	...	|	...	1205
Béthune d.	...	0643	...	...	|	|	...	0843	...	|
Valenciennes d.	0616	|	0657	...	|	|	...	|	1016	|
Douai d.	0651	|	0735	...	|	|	...	|	1051	|
Lens d.	|	0657	|	...	|	|	...	0857	|	|
Arras a.	0706	0710	0752	...	0801	0912	...	0911	1105	1225
Arras d.	0718	0718	0756	...	0808	0918	...	0918	1118	1230
Paris Nord a.	0808	0808	0847	...	0859	1011	...	1011	1208	1320

	TGV 7320	TGV 7520	TGV 7322	TGV 7124		TGV 7324	TGV 7326	TGV 7226	TGV 7130		TGV 7330	TGV 7230	TGV 7134	TGV 7334	TGV 7238		♣	TGV 7142	TGV 7342	TGV 7242		TGV 7344	TGV 7144	TGV 7546	TGV 7346
	Ⓐ	Ⓐ	⑥	⑦		⑦	⑥	⑥	Ⓑ		Ⓐ	⑦	①–⑤	⑦	Ⓐ		Ⓐ	⑥⑦	⑦	⑥		⑥	⑦	Ⓐ	①–⑤
			g				j	g	x			r	t				B	z		g		g			t
Dunkerque d.	1211	...	1256	...	...	1356	1456	...	...	...	1556	...	...	1656	1808	...	1834	...	1856	1900	...	1956	...	...	2028
Hazebrouck d.	1234	...	1320	...	...	1420	1520	...	...	...	1620	...	...	1720	|	...	|	...	1920	|	...	2020	...	...	2054
Lille Europe a.	|	...	|	...	...	|	|	...	...	...	|	...	...	|	1840	...	1910	...	|	1931	...	|	...	...	|
Lille Europe d.	|	1303	|	...	...	|	|	1551	...	...	|	1651	...	|	1851	...	1922	...	|	1936	...	|	...	2102	|
Béthune d.	1257	|	1343	...	...	1443	1544	|	...	...	1643	|	...	1743	|	...	|	...	1943	|	...	2043	...	|	2120
Valenciennes d.	|	|	|	1416	...	|	|	|	1616	...	|	|	1716	|	|	...	|	1916	|	|	...	|	2016	|	|
Douai d.	|	1323	|	1451	...	|	|	|	1651	...	|	|	1753	|	|	...	|	1951	|	|	...	|	2051	2134	|
Lens d.	1313	|	1357	|	...	1457	1558	|	|	...	1657	|	|	1757	|	...	|	|	1957	|	...	2057	|	|	2137
Arras a.	1330	1337	1409	1505	...	1511	1611	1614	1706	...	1710	1713	1805	1810	1913	...	1941	2007	2010	1959	...	2110	2105	2148	2152
Arras d.	1341	1341	1418	1518	...	1518	1618	1618	1718	...	1718	1718	1818	1818	1918	...	...	2018	2018	2018	...	2118	2118	2201	2201
Paris Nord a.	1432	1432	1508	1610	...	1610	1708	1708	1808	...	1808	1808	1908	1908	2008	...	...	2108	2108	2108	...	2208	2208	2253	2253

Other TER-GV trains	♣	♣		♣	♣	♣	♣		♣	♣
	Ⓐ	Ⓐ		Ⓐ	Ⓐ	Ⓐ	Ⓐ		Ⓐ	Ⓐ
Lille Europe d.	0656	0750	...	0850	1050	1321	1550	...	1750	1850
Dunkerque a.	0733	0820	...	0920	1120	1352	1620	...	1820	1920

Other TER-GV trains	♣	♣		♣	♣	♣	♣		♣	♣
	Ⓐ	Ⓐ		Ⓐ	⊖	Ⓐ	Ⓐ		Ⓐ	Ⓐ
Dunkerque d.	0800	0904	...	1000	1300	1446	1600	...	1700	1834
Lille Europe a.	0831	0935	...	1031	1331	1517	1631	...	1731	1910

A – ②③④⑦ (also July 15; not July 13, 14).
B – 🚌12 Amiens (d. 0642 / a. 2018) - Dunkerque and v.v.
d – Not July 15.
e – Not July 13.
f – Not July 6.
g – Also July 14.
h – Not July 6, 14.
j – Also July 14; not July 16.
k – Also July 13, 14; not July 15.
m – Also July 14; not July 17.
n – Not July 13, 14.
p – Not July 15, 16.
q – Also July 13, 16; not July 15.
r – Not July 17.
s – Also July 13; not July 15.
t – Not July 14, 15.
u – Until July 8.
v – Also July 12, 13, 15.
w – Not July 6, 15.
x – Not July 14.
y – Also July 13, 14; not July 15, 17.
z – Also July 14; not July 2.
⊖ – ①–⑥ (not July 2, 9, 16).
◧ – To Roubaix (a. 2333) and Tourcoing (a. 2338). Via Arras (a. 2239).
⊡ – Via Arras (d. 0615). From July 5 calls at Tourcoing (d. 0505), Roubaix (d. 0510).
● – From Tourcoing (d. 0521) and Roubaix (d. 0526). Via Arras (d. 0619).
⊝ – Via Douai (see Paris - Dunkerque Table).
⊕ – Full name is Rang du Fliers - Verton - Berck.
◇ – Not July 2, 9, 16
¶ – Not July 2.
♣ – TER à Grande Vitesse (*TER-GV*) service via high-speed line.
TGV – High-speed train. 🅁. 🍷.

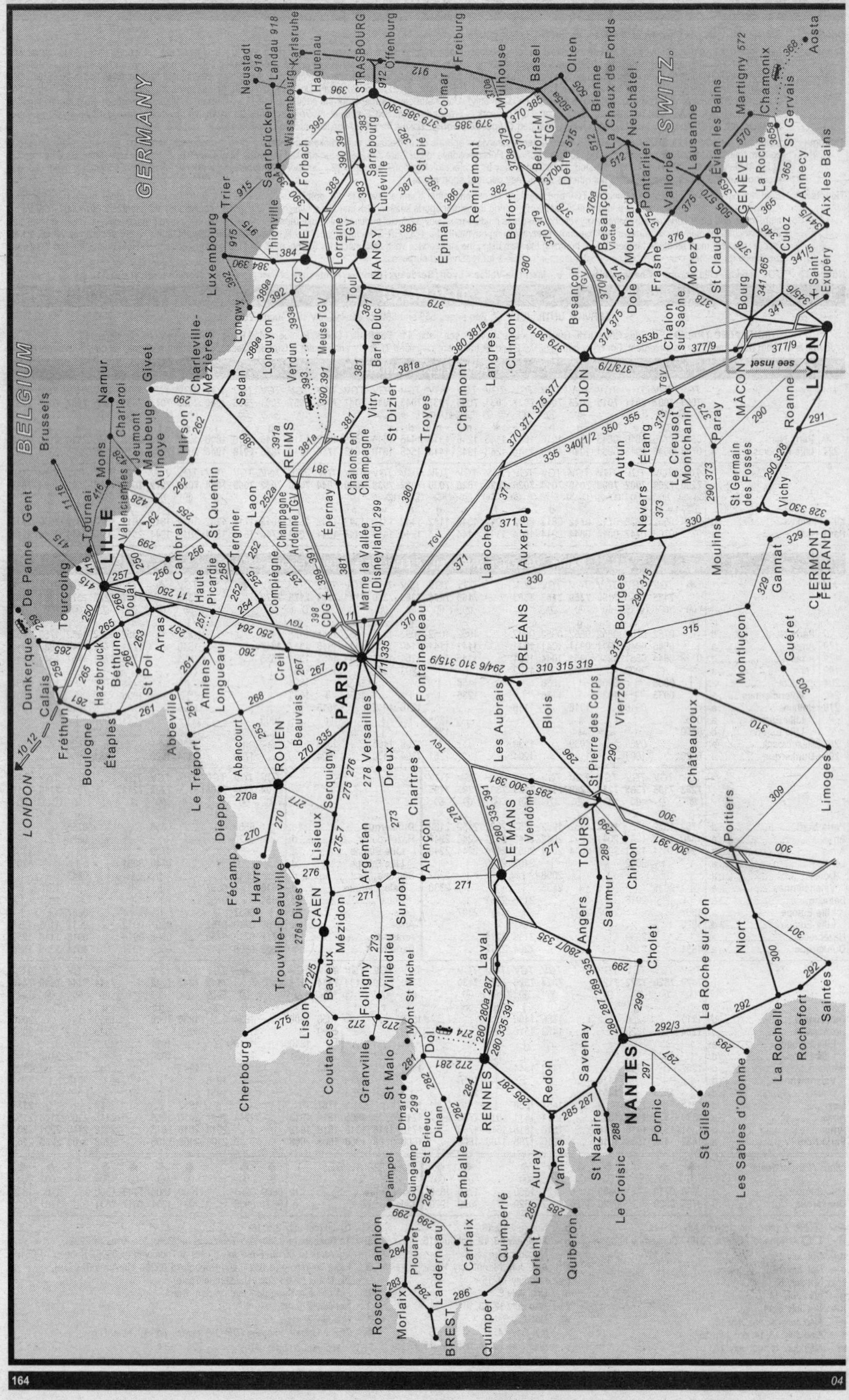

BELGIUM
GERMANY
SWITZ.
LONDON
Dunkerque
Calais
Fréthun
Boulogne
Étaples
Hazebrouck
Béthune
St Pol
Arras
Douai
Tourcoing
De Panne
Gent
Brussels
Tournai
Mons
Namur
Charleroi
Jeumont
Maubeuge
Aulnoye
Valenciennes
LILLE
Cambrai
St Quentin
Hirson
Givet
Charleville-Mézières
Sedan
Longwy
Longuyon
Luxembourg
Trier
Thionville
METZ
Saarbrücken
Forbach
Wissembourg
Neustadt
Landau
Karlsruhe
Haguenau
STRASBOURG
Offenburg
Freiburg
Colmar
Mulhouse
Basel
Olten
Bienne
La Chaux de Fonds
Neuchâtel
Pontarlier
Vallorbe
Lausanne
Évian les Bains
Martigny
Chamonix
Aosta
St Gervais
La Roche
Annecy
Aix les Bains
GENÈVE
Culoz
Bourg
Saint Exupéry
LYON
see inset
MÂCON
Chalon sur Saône
Dijon
DIJON
Dole
Mouchard
Frasne
Morez
St Claude
Besançon
Besançon TGV
Viotte
Belfort
Belfort-M. TGV
Delle
Remiremont
Épinal
St Dié
Lunéville
Sarrebourg
NANCY
Toul
Lorraine TGV
Verdun
Meuse TGV
Bar le Duc
St Dizier
Vitry
Châlons en Champagne
REIMS
Champagne Ardenne TGV
Épernay
Laon
Tergnier
Haute Picardie
Amiens
Longueau
Abbeville
Le Tréport
Compiègne
Creil
Beauvais
CDG
Marne la Vallée (Disneyland)
PARIS
Troyes
Chaumont
Langres
Culmont
Laroche
Auxerre
Fontainebleau
Autun
Étang
Le Creusot
Montchanin
Paray
Nevers
Moulins
St Germain des Fossés
Vichy
Roanne
CLERMONT FERRAND
Gannat
Montluçon
Guéret
Limoges
Bourges
Vierzon
Châteauroux
ORLÉANS
Les Aubrais
Blois
St Pierre des Corps
TOURS
Vendôme
Chinon
Poitiers
Saumur
Angers
LE MANS
Chartres
Dreux
Versailles
Serquigny
ROUEN
Abancourt
Dieppe
Fécamp
Le Havre
Trouville-Deauville
Dives
Lisieux
CAEN
Mézidon
Argentan
Surdon
Alençon
Bayeux
Lison
Cherbourg
Coutances
Folligny
Villedieu
Granville
Mont St Michel
Dol
St Malo
Dinard
Dinan
RENNES
Laval
St Brieuc
Guingamp
Paimpol
Lamballe
Lannion
Plouaret
Morlaix
Roscoff
Landerneau
BREST
Carhaix
Quimper
Quimperlé
Lorient
Auray
Quiberon
Vannes
Redon
Savenay
St Nazaire
Le Croisic
NANTES
Pornic
Cholet
La Roche sur Yon
St Gilles
Les Sables d'Olonne
Niort
La Rochelle
Rochefort
Saintes
TGV

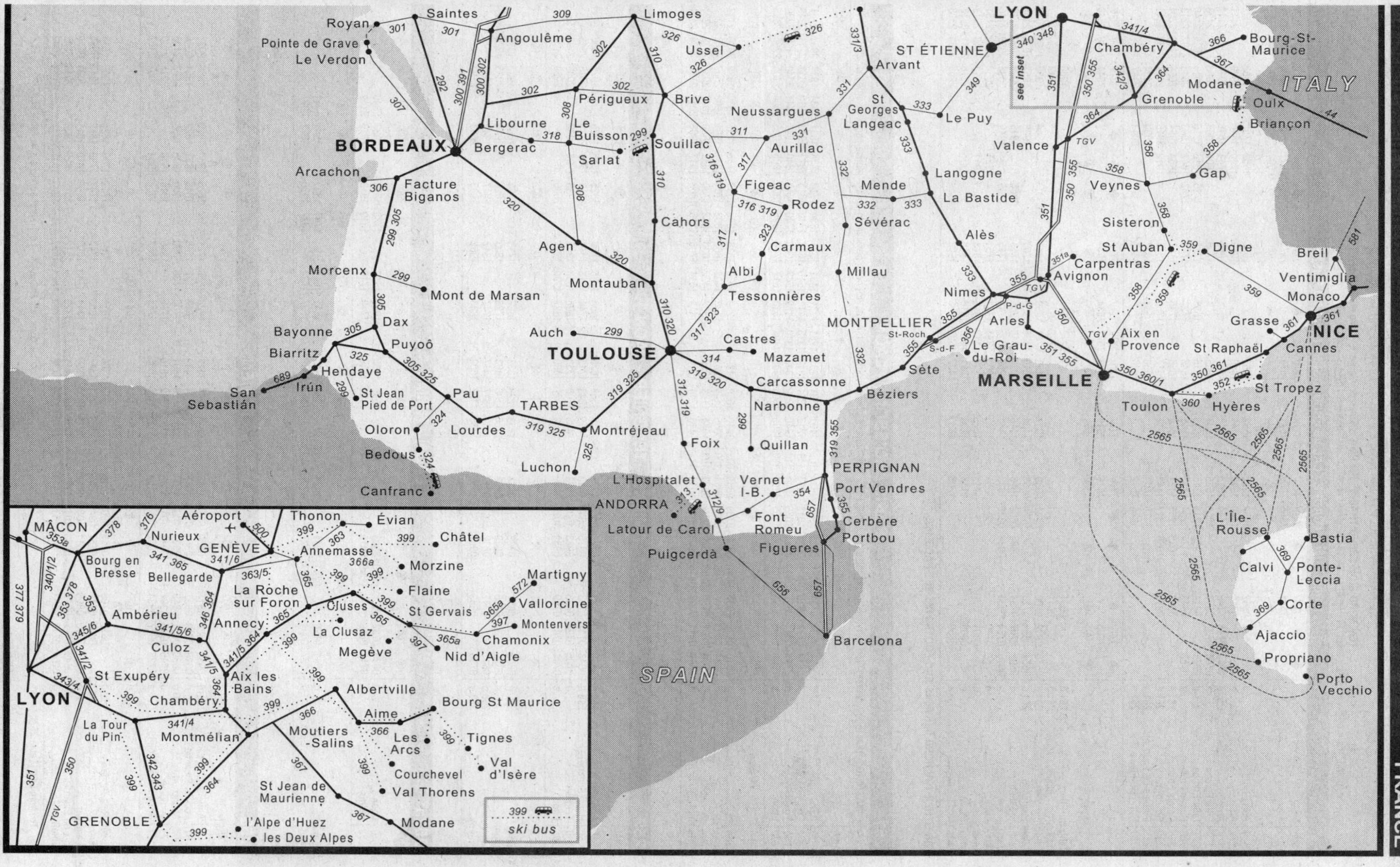
ITALY
SPAIN
ANDORRA
see inset
ski bus
LYON
ST ÉTIENNE
MARSEILLE
NICE
TOULOUSE
BORDEAUX
MONTPELLIER
PERPIGNAN
TARBES
Royan
Pointe de Grave
Le Verdon
Saintes
Angoulême
Limoges
Ussel
Brive
Périgueux
Libourne
Bergerac
Le Buisson
Sarlat
Souillac
Cahors
Agen
Montauban
Arcachon
Facture Biganos
Mont de Marsan
Morcenx
Dax
Puyoô
Bayonne
Biarritz
Hendaye
Irún
San Sebastián
St Jean Pied de Port
Pau
Lourdes
Oloron
Bedous
Canfranc
Luchon
Montréjeau
Auch
Foix
L'Hospitalet
Latour de Carol
Puigcerdà
Vernet I-B.
Font Romeu
Figueres
Barcelona
Portbou
Cerbère
Port Vendres
Quillan
Narbonne
Carcassonne
Béziers
Sète
Castres
Mazamet
Albi
Tessonnières
Carmaux
Rodez
Figeac
Aurillac
Neussargues
Millau
Sévérac
Mende
St Georges Langeac
Arvant
Le Puy
Langogne
La Bastide
Alès
Nimes
Arles
Le Grau-du-Roi
Avignon
Carpentras
Valence
Veynes
Gap
Briançon
Oulx
Modane
Grenoble
Chambéry
Bourg-St-Maurice
Sisteron
St Auban
Digne
Aix en Provence
Toulon
Hyères
St Raphaël
St Tropez
Cannes
Grasse
Monaco
Ventimiglia
Breil
Bastia
Ponte-Leccia
Corte
L'Île-Rousse
Calvi
Ajaccio
Propriano
Porto Vecchio
St-Roch
S-d-F
P-d-G
TGV
MÂCON
Bourg en Bresse
Nurieux
Bellegarde
Aéroport
GENÈVE
Thonon
Évian
Annemasse
Châtel
Morzine
La Roche sur Foron
Cluses
Flaine
St Gervais
Megève
La Clusaz
Annecy
Aix les Bains
Culoz
Ambérieu
St Exupéry
Chambéry
Montmélian
La Tour du Pin
GRENOBLE
l'Alpe d'Huez
les Deux Alpes
St Jean de Maurienne
Modane
Moutiers-Salins
Albertville
Aime
Les Arcs
Bourg St Maurice
Tignes
Val d'Isère
Courchevel
Val Thorens
Chamonix
Nid d'Aigle
Montenvers
Vallorcine
Martigny

250 TGV NORD

SERVICE UNTIL JULY 17. See pages 559 and 560 for service July 18 - August 28.

TGV NORD HIGH-SPEED TRAINS. For Paris Charles de Gaulle ✈ - Lille services see Table **11**.
Journeys to / from Paris are 🅁 with supplement. For other journeys, *TGV* and ♣ trains are classified *TER-GV* and require a Grande Vitesse supplement, €3 valid all day, 🅁 not required.

PARIS - LILLE EUROPE - CALAIS - BOULOGNE - RANG DU FLIERS

km		♣ Ⓐ	♣ Ⓐ B	*TGV* 7551 Ⓐ		♣ Ⓐ	*TGV* 7565 ⑥ g	*TGV* 7569 Ⓐ		*TGV* 7571 ⑥ g		*TGV* 7571 ⑦		♣ Ⓐ		*TGV* 7575 ⑥ j		♣ Ⓐ	*TGV* 7577 Ⓐ	*TGV* 7581 Ⓐ		*TGV* 7585 ⑦	♣ ①–⑥ ◇	*TGV* 7591 Ⓐ
0	**Paris** Nord d.	...	...	0652	...	...	1052	1222	...	1352	...	1352	...	...	...	1552	...	...	1652	1752	...	1852	...	2022
179	Arras a.	...	...	0741	...	...	1140	1310	...	1441	...	1440	...	...	...	1640	...	...	1740	1840	...	1940	...	2111
179	Arras d.	0643	0718	0745	...	...	1144	1318	...	1448	...	1444	...	...	...	1644	...	...	1744	1848	...	1944	...	2117
227	**Lille** Europe a.	0704	0737	0807	...	...	1205	1338	...	1507	...	1505	...	...	...	1706	...	...	1807	1908	...	2006	...	2138
227	**Lille** Europe d.	0721	...	0814	...	0955	1215	1345	...	1515	...	1515	...	1655	...	1718	...	1725	1815	1915	...	2015	2035	2145
326	**Calais** Fréthun a.	0753	...	0843	...	1024	1244	1413	...	1545	...	1545	...	1724	...	1746	...	1753	1842	1943	...	2043	2102	2213
326	**Calais** Fréthun **261** d.	...	...	0853	...	1035	1255	1424	...	1554	...	1556	...	1735	...	1757	...	...	1854	1954	...	2054	2113	2224
360	**Boulogne** Ville **261** a.	...	...	0915	...	1055	1317	1443	...	1617	...	1617	...	1755	...	1818	...	...	1912	2015	...	2117	2133	2244
387	Étaples-Le Touquet **261** a.	...	...	...	...	...	1336	1501	...	...	...	1636	...	...	...	1837	...	...	...	2033	...	2136	...	...
398	**Rang du Fliers** ⊕ **261** a.	...	...	...	...	...	1346	1512	...	...	...	1646	...	...	...	1847	...	...	...	2043	...	2147	...	...

	♣ Ⓐ	*TGV* 7508 Ⓐ	♣ Ⓐ		♣ Ⓐ	♣ ⑥ ◇	*TGV* 7516 ①–⑥		*TGV* 7518 ⑦		*TGV* 7520 Ⓐ ⊖	*TGV* 7522 ⑥	*TGV* 7534 Ⓑ x		*TGV* 7534 ⑥ g		♣ Ⓐ	♣ Ⓐ B	♣ Ⓐ		*TGV* 7544 Ⓒ	*TGV* 7546 Ⓐ ⊖	*TGV* 7546 ⑦
Rang du Fliers ⊕ **261** d.	...	...	0631	...	...	...	...	...	...	...	...	1212	1611	...	...	...	...	...	...	...	1906	...	...
Étaples-Le Touquet **261** d.	...	...	0641	...	...	...	...	...	...	...	...	1223	1621	...	...	...	...	...	...	...	1917	...	...
Boulogne Ville **261** d.	0530	0632	0700	...	...	0731	0930	...	1037	...	1153	1241	1639	...	1641	...	...	...	1844	...	1935	1955	2040
Calais Fréthun **261** a.	0554	0655	0723	...	...	0754	0955	...	1104	...	1215	1305	1705	...	1706	...	...	...	1908	...	1957	2017	2105
Calais Fréthun d.	0605	0707	0734	...	0806	0808	1006	...	1115	...	1230	1316	1715	...	1715	...	1806	...	1918	...	2009	2029	2116
Lille Europe a.	0640	0734	0804	...	0835	0835	1035	...	1145	...	1259	1345	1744	...	1745	...	1835	...	1946	...	2036	2056	2145
Lille Europe d.	...	0740	...	...	...	...	1051	...	1205	...	1303	1351	1751	...	1751	...	...	1921	...	...	2052	2102	2151
Arras a.	...	0801	...	...	...	...	1113	...	1225	...	1337	1412	1813	...	1813	...	...	1941	...	...	2113	2148	2213
Arras d.	...	0805	...	...	...	...	1118	...	1230	...	1341	1418	1818	...	1818	...	...	...	...	...	2118	2201	2218
Paris Nord a.	...	0859	...	...	...	...	1208	...	1320	...	1432	1508	1908	...	1908	...	...	...	...	...	2208	2253	2308

FOR OTHER TGV NORD SERVICES AND FOOTNOTES SEE PAGE 163.

251 PARIS - SOISSONS - LAON

WARNING! Due to engineering work services in this table are subject to a high number of variations which it has not been possible to show - please check all times locally.

km		Ⓐ	Ⓐ	⑥	Ⓒ	Ⓐ	Ⓒ	Ⓐ	⑥	Ⓐ	⑥	Ⓐ	†		⚒	Ⓐ		Ⓒ	Ⓐ	⑥	Ⓐ	Ⓐ		⚒
0	**Paris** Nord d.	0634	0704	0731	0831	0834	0931	0934	1031	1131	1131	1231	1231	1331	1431	1531	1634	1732	1734	1831	1834	1934	2031	2131
61	Crépy-en-Valois d.	0713	0813	0810	0911	0914	1013	1013	1111	1212	1211	1312	1313	1411	1516	1612	1713	1813	1813	1913	1913	2012	2111	2210
105	Soissons d.	0741	0841	0837	0941	0941	1039	1041	1139	1240	1239	1340	1340	1439	1542	1640	1740	1840	1840	1941	1941	2040	2139	2239
140	**Laon** a.	0805	0905	0901	1005	1005	1105	1105	1205	1305	1305	1405	1404	1513	1617	1713	1805	1905	1905	2005	2005	2105	2205	2305

	Ⓐ	Ⓐ	Ⓐ	⑥	Ⓐ	Ⓒ	†	⚒	†	⑥				Ⓐ	Ⓐ	Ⓒ	Ⓐ	Ⓒ	Ⓐ	Ⓐ	Ⓐ		⑤⑥
Laon d.	0510	0539	0637	0642	0738	0739	0839	0939	0940	1039	1139	...	1239	1339	1538	1539	1637	1736	1737	1839	1939	2039	2137
Soissons d.	0534	0603	0701	0706	0802	0803	0904	1003	1005	1104	1203	...	1303	1403	1602	1603	1701	1801	1801	1903	2003	2103	2202
Crépy-en-Valois d.	0604	0632	0730	0736	0830	0832	0933	1032	1034	1133	1232	...	1332	1432	1630	1632	1730	1832	1830	1932	2032	2132	2231
Paris Nord a.	0640	0711	0808	0816	0908	0912	1015	1113	1113	1214	1314	...	1414	1514	1708	1715	1808	1917	1908	2013	2113	2214	2314

252 AMIENS - TERGNIER - LAON

km		①	⑥	Ⓐ		Ⓐ	Ⓒ	Ⓑ		⑥	†	⑥		Ⓐ	Ⓐ	⑥		Ⓑ	⑥	①–④		⑤	†	
0	**Amiens** **258** d.	0558	0625	0625	...	0825	0858	1225	...	1325	1558	1625	...	1658	1725	1758	...	1825	1858	1925	...	1925	1958	...
59	Ham (Somme) **258** d.	0643	0712	0713	...	0913	0943	1313	...	1415	1643	1713	...	1744	1813	1844	...	1913	1943	2013	...	2013	2043	...
80	Tergnier d.	0705	0726	0733	...	0933	1005	1333	...	1433	1705	1733	...	1805	1833	1905	...	1933	2005	2032	...	2033	2105	...
108	**Laon** a.	0731	0747	0759	...	0959	1027	1359	...	1459	1727	1800	...	1827	1900	1927	...	2000	2027	...	...	2059	2127	...

	⚒		⚒		⚒		†		Ⓐ	†	⚒				Ⓐ		Ⓐ		Ⓐ		Ⓒ	⑤	
Laon d.	0603	...	0657	...	0733	...	0833	...	1158	1223	1333	...	1657	...	1733	...	1755	...	1855	...	1933	1955	...
Tergnier d.	0629	...	0726	...	0803	...	0903	...	1226	1303	1403	...	1726	...	1803	...	1826	...	1926	...	2003	2026	...
Ham (Somme) **258** d.	0647	...	0747	...	0817	...	0919	...	1247	1317	1417	...	1747	...	1817	...	1847	...	1947	...	2019	...	...
Amiens **258** a.	0733	...	0833	...	0902	...	1002	...	1333	1402	1502	...	1833	...	1902	...	1933	...	2033	...	2102	...	...

252a LAON - REIMS

km		Ⓐ	Ⓐ		Ⓐ	Ⓒ		Ⓒ	Ⓐ		⑥	†		⑥	Ⓐ		Ⓑ	Ⓐ		Ⓒ	Ⓐ			
0	**Laon** d.	0633	0733	...	0810	0833	...	1033	1333	...	1335	1433	...	1633	1640	...	1733	1833	...	1933	2040	...	...	...
52	**Reims** a.	0719	0819	...	0849	0919	...	1119	1419	...	1421	1519	...	1719	1719	...	1819	1919	...	2019	2119	...	...	...

	Ⓐ	Ⓐ		⑥	Ⓒ		†	Ⓐ		⑥	Ⓐ		Ⓒ	Ⓐ		Ⓐ	⑥		Ⓑ	Ⓐ			
Reims d.	0641	0726	...	0741	0941	...	1141	1241	...	1244	1441	...	1541	1641	...	1741	1833	...	1841	1941	...	...	...
Laon a.	0727	0804	...	0827	1027	...	1227	1327	...	1329	1520	...	1627	1727	...	1827	1920	...	1927	2027	...	...	...

253 AMIENS - ROUEN

km		Ⓐ	Ⓐ	Ⓐ A		⑥ A	†	Ⓐ		Ⓐ A	⑥	†		†	Ⓐ	Ⓐ		Ⓐ	Ⓒ A	Ⓐ		Ⓐ A	Ⓐ	
0	**Amiens** d.	0558	0658	0817	...	0830	0928	1028	...	1216	1254	1428	...	1628	1658	1728	...	1828	1830	1859	...	1930	2028	...
31	Poix de Picardie d.	0618	0719	0837	...	0851	0948	1048	...	1237	1314	1449	...	1648	1722	1748	...	1848	1852	1922	...	1951	2048	...
52	Abancourt ◧ d.	0630	0731	0849	...	0904	1000	1100	...	1249	1326	1501	...	1700	1736	1800	...	1900	1905	1935	...	2003	2100	...
73	Serqueux d.	0645	0745	0901	...	0917	1017	1115	...	1301	1342	1515	...	1715	...	1815	...	1915	1918	...	...	2015	2115	...
121	**Rouen** Rive-Droite a.	0725	0827	0934	...	0952	1056	1153	...	1335	1426	1555	...	1755	...	1852	...	1952	1954	...	...	2052	2152	...

	Ⓐ	Ⓐ	⑥ A		Ⓐ A	†	Ⓐ		Ⓐ A	Ⓐ	⑥		Ⓐ	Ⓐ	⑥ A		† A	Ⓐ	Ⓐ A		Ⓒ	Ⓐ	
Rouen Rive-Droite d.	...	0619	0708	...	0718	0908	1016	...	1125	1213	1306	...	1611	...	1707	...	1712	1719	1825	...	1909	1913	...
Serqueux d.	...	0656	0747	...	0757	0947	1056	...	1159	1251	1344	...	1656	...	1747	...	1747	1756	1859	...	1947	1955	...
Abancourt ◧ d.	0625	0710	0800	...	0811	1001	1111	...	1211	1305	1359	...	1711	1746	1800	...	1800	1810	1911	...	2001	2010	...
Poix de Picardie d.	0641	0722	0812	...	0823	1013	1122	...	1223	1317	1411	...	1723	1800	1812	...	1812	1822	1923	...	2013	2022	...
Amiens a.	0705	0742	0833	...	0843	1032	1143	...	1243	1338	1432	...	1742	1824	1832	...	1833	1842	1943	...	2032	2042	...

A – To / from Lille (Table **257**).

◧ – For connections with Beauvais - Le Tréport services see Table **268**.

AMIENS - COMPIÈGNE 254

km		Ⓐ	Ⓐ	⑥	†	Ⓐ	Ⓐ	⑥	†	†	⑥	Ⓐ	⑥	†	⑤	Ⓒ	Ⓐ	Ⓐ	Ⓒ	Ⓐ	†	⑥	Ⓐ	†	⑥
0	**Amiens** 260 d.	0547	0617	0659	0734	0734	0855	0914	0932	1118	1127	1229	1247	1330	1608	1618	1639	1703	1733	1752	1906	1926	1930	2019	2037
5	Longueau 260 d.	|	|	|	|	0740	|	0920	0938	|	|	1235	1253	1336	|	|	|	1709	1739	|	1915	|	|	2025	2043
36	Montdidier d.	0618	0652	0730	0805	0814	0928	0954	1009	1148	1157	1307	1324	1407	1638	1648	1710	1743	1811	1827	1941	1956	2003	2056	2115
76	**Compiègne** a.	0647	0728	0759	0835	0851	0955	1030	1042	1217	1226	1342	1359	1440	1708	1717	1737	1820	1844	1904	2009	2025	2029	2130	2148

	Ⓐ	Ⓐ	Ⓐ	⑥	†	Ⓐ	Ⓐ	⑥	†	Ⓐ	⑥	†	⑥	†	Ⓐ	Ⓒ	Ⓐ	Ⓒ	Ⓐ	Ⓐ	⑥	†	†	⑥
Compiègne d.	0544	0620	0659	0700	0738	0744	0903	0918	0936	1059	1104	1119	1247	1333	1444	1620	1644	1736	1751	1831	1904	1913	2022	2041
Montdidier d.	0619	0653	0739	0731	0806	0814	0928	0953	1010	1125	1131	1147	1323	1408	1513	1648	1711	1811	1827	1904	1931	1940	2056	2116
Longueau 260 d.	0652	|	0820	|	0829	|	|	1022	1039	|	|	|	1353	1438	|	|	|	1841	1859	|	|	|	2126	2146
Amiens 260 a.	0658	0726	0826	0759	0834	0845	1000	1028	1044	1156	1203	1218	1359	1444	1544	1718	1744	1847	1905	1934	2003	2009	2131	2151

PARIS - COMPIÈGNE - ST QUENTIN - CAMBRIAI and MAUBEUGE 255

km		⑥	⚒	Ⓐ	Ⓐ	Ⓐ	⑥	Ⓒ		⑥	Ⓐ	Ⓒ	Ⓐ	⚒	Ⓐ	†	⑥	⑥	Ⓑ	Ⓐ d	†	Ⓐ e	⑥	⑥	Ⓐ
0	**Paris** Nord ◧ d.	...	...	...	0637	0719	...	0734	0834	...	0919	1019	1034	...	...	...	1219	...	1234	1307	1319	1319	...	1419	1434
51	Creil ◧ d.	...	...	...	0705	|	...	0805	0905	...	|	|	1105	...	1148	...	|	...	1306	|	|	|	...	|	1505
84	**Compiègne** ◧ d.	...	0628	...	0727	0800	0804	0828	0928	...	1000	1100	1128	...	1228	1235	1300	1304	1329	1400	1400	1400	1404	1500	1528
108	Noyon d.	...	0649	...	0741	|	0829	0842	0942	...	|	|	1142	...	1253	1259	|	1328	1343	|	|	|	1429	|	1542
124	Chauny d.	...	0701	...	0752	|	0840	0852	0952	...	|	|	1153	...	1307	1313	|	1341	1353	|	|	|	1443	|	1552
131	Tergnier d.	...	0710	0744	0800	|	0850	0901	1001	...	|	|	1202	...	1313	1319	|	1350	1401	|	|	|	1450	|	1601
154	**St Quentin** 256 d.	0624	0729	0759	0813	0835	0909	0914	1014	1024	1033	1134	1216	1224	1332	1337	1333	1409	1414	1435	1433	1435	1509	1534	1614
181	Busigny 256 d.	0645	...	0820	...	|	...	...	...	1045	...	|	|	1245	...	...	...	...	...	|	...	|	...	|	...
207	**Cambrai** Ville 256 a.	|	...	|	...	|	...	...	...	|	...	|	|	|	...	...	...	...	...	|	...	|	...	|	...
217	Aulnoye Aymeries 262 d.	0711	...	0846	...	0906	...	...	...	1111	...	1210	1247	1316	...	...	...	...	...	1506	...	1506	...	1606	...
229	**Maubeuge** 262 a.	...	...	...	...	0918	...	...	...	...	...	1220	1257	...	...	...	...	...	...	1518	...	1518	...	1618	...

	Ⓒ	Ⓐ	Ⓐ	Ⓐ	⑥	Ⓐ		Ⓒ	Ⓐ	⚒	Ⓐ	Ⓐ	Ⓒ	Ⓐ	†	Ⓐ		Ⓐ	Ⓒ	Ⓐ	†	Ⓐ	Ⓐ	Ⓒ
Paris Nord ◧ d.	...	...	...	...	1634	1634	1719	...	...	...	1734	1819	...	1834	1834	...	1919	...	...	1934	2019	2034	2134	2237
Creil ◧ d.	...	...	...	...	1700	1705	|	...	...	...	1805	|	...	1905	1905	...	|	...	...	2005	|	2105	2208	2305
Compiègne ◧ d.	...	1628	...	1704	1723	1728	1800	...	...	1804	1828	1900	1904	1928	1928	...	2000	2004	2008	2028	2100	2129	2230	2328
Noyon d.	...	1653	...	1729	1737	1742	|	...	...	1828	1842	|	1928	1942	1942	...	|	2028	2032	2042	|	2142	2244	2342
Chauny d.	...	1706	...	1742	1749	1752	|	...	...	1841	1852	|	1941	1952	1953	...	|	2043	2044	2053	|	2153	2255	2352
Tergnier d.	...	1713	...	1751	1757	1801	|	...	1844	1850	1901	|	1950	2001	2001	2004	|	2049	2051	2101	|	2201	2302	0001
St Quentin 256 d.	1624	1732	1733	1809	1810	1814	1835	1842	1859	1909	1914	1935	2009	2014	2015	2020	2035	2109	2109	2114	2135	2214	2314	0014
Busigny 256 d.	1645	...	1755	...	1826	...	|	1903	1920	...	...	1952	...	...	2034	2040	|	...	...	...	|	...	...	...
Cambrai Ville 256 a.	|	...	|	...	1849	...	|	|	|	...	...	2015	...	...	2056	|	|	...	...	...	|	...	...	...
Aulnoye Aymeries 262 d.	1711	...	1824	...	...	...	1906	1930	1946	...	...	...	...	...	...	2101	2106	...	...	...	2206	...	...	...
Maubeuge 262 a.	...	...	...	...	...	...	1918	...	...	...	...	...	...	...	...	...	2118	...	...	...	2218	...	...	...

	Ⓐ	Ⓐ	⑥	Ⓐ	Ⓐ	Ⓑ	⑥	Ⓐ	Ⓐ	Ⓑ	⚒	⑥	Ⓐ	⚒	†	Ⓐ	⑥	Ⓐ	⑥	Ⓐ	⑥	Ⓐ	⚒	†
Maubeuge 262 d.	...	...	...	...	...	...	...	...	0642	...	...	...	...	0742	0842	...	...	...	1042	...	...	1142	...	...
Aulnoye Aymeries 262 d.	...	...	...	...	...	...	...	0605	0653	...	...	0729	0729	0754	0854	...	...	...	1053	...	1129	1154	...	...
Cambrai Ville 256 d.	...	...	...	...	0536	...	0606	|	|	...	...	|	|	|	|	...	...	...	|	...	|	|	...	1207
Busigny 256 d.	...	...	...	...	0600	...	0630	0636	|	...	...	0754	0758	|	|	...	...	...	|	...	1153	|	...	1232
St Quentin 256 d.	0446	0545	0546	0552	0621	0646	0646	0658	0724	0746	0752	0814	0818	0825	0925	0946	1001	1046	1124	1152	1214	1225	1246	1248
Tergnier d.	0503	0600	0602	0611	|	0701	0702	0716	|	0802	0810	...	...	|	|	1001	1016	1100	|	1210	...	|	1301	1303
Chauny d.	0511	0608	0608	0617	|	0707	0709	...	|	0808	0817	...	...	|	|	1008	1023	1106	|	1217	...	|	1308	1309
Noyon d.	0522	0619	0620	0630	|	0718	0720	...	|	0820	0829	...	...	|	|	1019	1034	1117	|	1229	...	|	1319	1320
Compiègne ◧ d.	0536	0633	0635	0654	0701	0732	0735	...	0758	0834	0854	...	...	0900	0959	1033	1049	1131	1158	1254	...	1300	1333	1335
Creil ◧ d.	0600	0658	0659	...	|	0756	0759	...	|	0857	...	...	...	|	|	1059	1112	1158	|	...	...	|	1359	1359
Paris Nord ◧ a.	0628	0727	0728	...	0747	0827	0827	...	0841	0926	...	...	...	0947	1042	1126	1140	1226	1241	...	...	1344	1426	1428

	Ⓐ	⑥	⑥	⑥	Ⓐ	†	†	Ⓐ		Ⓐ	†	Ⓐ		†	Ⓐ	Ⓒ	Ⓒ	Ⓐ		Ⓐ	⚒	†	†	†
Maubeuge 262 d.	...	...	...	...	...	...	1442	1542	...	...	1637	...	...	...	...	...	1737	1742	...	...	...	...	1952	...
Aulnoye Aymeries 262 d.	1219	...	1329	...	...	...	1454	1554	...	...	1649	...	...	...	1721	1729	1749	1753	...	1845	...	1943	2004	...
Cambrai Ville 256 d.	|	...	|	...	...	...	|	|	...	...	|	...	...	...	|	|	|	|	...	|	...	|	|	...
Busigny 256 d.	1249	...	1353	...	...	...	|	|	...	...	|	...	...	...	1746	1754	|	|	...	1915	...	2008	|	...
St Quentin 256 d.	1309	1352	1414	1425	1445	1452	1525	1625	1645	1652	1723	1746	...	1752	1807	1815	1823	1824	1852	1936	1945	2028	2034	2046
Tergnier d.	...	1411	...	|	1500	1511	|	|	1700	1711	|	1802	...	1811	1821	...	|	|	1911	1949	2000	...	|	2102
Chauny d.	...	1417	...	|	1507	1517	|	|	1707	1720	|	1809	...	1817	...	...	|	|	1920	...	2007	...	|	2108
Noyon d.	...	1429	...	|	1519	1529	|	|	1718	1733	|	1820	...	1829	...	...	|	|	1933	...	2018	...	|	2120
Compiègne ◧ d.	...	1454	...	1500	1533	1554	1600	1659	1732	1754	1756	1835	...	1854	...	...	1858	1858	1954	...	2033	...	2108	2135
Creil ◧ d.	...	...	...	|	1558	...	|	|	1756	...	|	1859	...	...	...	...	|	|	...	...	2055	...	|	2156
Paris Nord ◧ a.	...	...	...	1543	1627	...	1644	1742	1828	...	1841	1930	...	...	...	...	1941	1941	...	...	2126	...	2153	2226

d – July 4 – 15.
e – July 18 - Aug. 26.

◧ – Other trains **Paris - Compiègne** at 0640 ⑥, 0737 Ⓐ, 0837 †, 0849 ⑥, 1037 Ⓐ, 1249 ⑥, 1337 Ⓐ, 1537 Ⓐ, 1637 ⚒, 1737 †, 1749 ⚒, 1822 Ⓐ, 1837 ⚒, 1937, 2037 †, 2149 ⑥, 2222 Ⓐ.

Other trains **Compiègne - Paris** at 0510 Ⓐ, 0606 ⚒, 0709 ⑥, 0716 Ⓐ, 0810 Ⓒ, 1107 Ⓑ, 1110 ⑥, 1202, 1507 ⑥, 1608 Ⓑ, 1706 Ⓒ, 1707 Ⓐ, 1807 Ⓑ, 1907 Ⓐ, 1910 ⑥, 2007 Ⓐ.

LILLE - DOUAI - CAMBRAI - ST QUENTIN 256

km		Ⓐ ⊖	⑥ ⊖	Ⓐ	Ⓐ	⑥	Ⓐ	Ⓐ	Ⓒ	† ⊖	Ⓒ	Ⓐ	Ⓐ		Ⓒ	Ⓒ	Ⓐ	Ⓐ	Ⓐ	Ⓒ	Ⓐ	Ⓐ	A	Ⓒ	Ⓐ
0	**Lille** Flandres 257 d.	...	...	...	0723	0805	0823	0923	1005	...	1205	1223	1323	...	1405	1605	1623	*1653*	1723	1805	1823	1923	1923	2005	2023
34	Douai 257 d.	...	...	...	0747	0829	0847	0947	1029	...	1229	1247	1347	...	1429	1629	1647	1725	1747	1829	1847	1947	1947	2029	2047
66	Cambrai Ville ⊡ d.	0536	0606	0632	0832	0855	0932	1032	1055	1207	1255	1332	1432	...	1455	1655	1732	1807	1832	1856	1932	2032	2032	2109	2132
82	Caudry d.	0550	0620	0645	0845	0907	0945	1045	1107	1221	1307	1345	1445	...	1507	1707	1745	1824	1845	1908	1945	...	2045	2121	2145
92	Busigny 255 d.	0600	0630	0654	0854	0916	0954	1054	1116	1232	1316	1354	1454	...	1516	1716	1755	1836	1854	1917	1955	...	2054	2130	2154
119	**St Quentin** 255 a.	0619	0644	0714	0914	0936	1010	1110	1140	1246	1336	1410	1510	...	1540	1736	1811	1856	1910	1937	2010	...	2110	2150	2210

	①	Ⓐ	Ⓐ	Ⓐ	Ⓒ	Ⓐ	Ⓒ		Ⓐ	Ⓒ	Ⓐ	Ⓒ	Ⓐ	Ⓒ	Ⓐ	Ⓒ		Ⓐ	⑥ ⊖	Ⓐ	Ⓒ	Ⓐ ⊖	Ⓐ	† ⊖
St Quentin 255 d.	0450	0550	0650	0702	0710	0750	0924	...	0950	1110	1150	1324	1450	1524	1650	1724	...	1746	1810	1850	1910	1935	1950	2015
Busigny 255 d.	0506	0606	0706	0723	0730	0806	0946	...	1006	1131	1206	1346	1506	1546	1706	1746	...	1808	1826	1906	1931	1952	2008	2034
Caudry d.	0516	0616	0716	0736	0739	0816	0955	...	1016	1140	1216	1355	1516	1555	1716	1755	...	1816	1837	1916	1940	2002	2016	2044
Cambrai Ville ⊡ d.	0540	0638	0738	0805	0801	0838	1010	...	1038	1202	1238	1410	1538	1610	1738	1810	...	1838	1849	1938	2002	2015	2038	2056
Douai 257 a.	0616	0716	0816	0835	0835	0916	1035	...	1116	1235	1316	1435	1616	1635	1816	1835	...	1916	...	2016	2035	...	2116	...
Lille Flandres 257 a.	0637	0737	0837	*0907*	0855	0937	1055	...	1137	1255	1337	1455	1637	1655	1837	1855	...	1937	...	2037	2058	...	2137	...

A – Ⓐ July 4 – 22; ⑤ July 29 - Aug. 26 (also Aug. 16 – 18).
⊖ – 2 Cambrai - St Quentin - Paris and v.v. (Table **255**).

⊡ – Other trains **Douai - Cambrai Ville** at 0727 Ⓐ, 0731 ⑥, 0827 Ⓐ, 0931 Ⓒ, 1127 Ⓐ, 1131 Ⓒ, 1327 Ⓐ, 1331 Ⓒ, 1531 Ⓒ, 1627 Ⓐ, 1731 Ⓒ, 1827 Ⓐ, 1926 Ⓒ, 1927 Ⓐ.

Other trains **Cambrai Ville - Douai** at 0633 Ⓐ, 0659 ⑥, 0703 Ⓐ, 0859 Ⓒ, 0953 Ⓒ, 1003 Ⓐ, 1059 Ⓒ, 1259 Ⓒ, 1303 Ⓐ, 1459 Ⓒ, 1603 Ⓐ, 1659 Ⓒ, 1803 Ⓐ, 1900 ⑥, 1903 Ⓐ.

257 LILLE - DOUAI - ARRAS - AMIENS and PARIS

For *TGV* and *TER-GV* trains Lille Europe / Douai - Arras and v.v. via the high-speed line see Table **250**.

km		Ⓐ	Ⓐ	⑥	Ⓐ	Ⓒ	Ⓐ	Ⓐ	Ⓒ	Ⓐ	Ⓐ	Ⓒ	Ⓐ	Ⓒ	Ⓐ	Ⓐ	⑥	†	Ⓐ	Ⓐ	Ⓒ	Ⓐ	Ⓐ	Ⓒ
			A	A				A									A	A	A					
0	**Lille** Flandres ... **256** d.	0553	0653	0705	0753	0905	0953	1053	1105	1153	1253	1305	1353	1505	1553	1653	1705	1705	1753	1853	1905	1953	2058	2108
34	Douai ... **256** d.	0615	0715	0726	0816	0926	1016	1116	1126	1216	1316	1326	1416	1532	1616	1716	1726	1726	1816	1916	1926	2016	2122	2132
59	Arras ... d.	0632	0731	0742	0832	0942	1032	1132	1141	1232	1332	1341	1432	1547	1632	1732	1742	1742	1832	1932	1943	2032	2136	2147
96	Albert ... d.	0653	0750	0802	0851	1002	1051	1150	1202	1251	1354	1402	1451	1608	1652	1752	1802	1802	1850	1953	2004	2053	2156	2207
127	**Amiens** ... a.	0710	0810	0823	0910	1023	1110	1210	1225	1310	1412	1423	1510	1627	1710	1812	1823	1823	1910	2010	2023	2110	2214	2227

	Ⓐ	⑥	Ⓐ	Ⓐ	†	⑥	Ⓐ	Ⓒ	Ⓐ	Ⓐ	Ⓒ	Ⓐ	Ⓒ	Ⓐ	Ⓐ	Ⓒ	Ⓐ	Ⓐ	Ⓒ	Ⓐ	Ⓐ	Ⓒ	Ⓐ
						A	A					A							A		A		
Amiens ... d.	0550	0637	0650	0750	0837	0838	0850	1037	1050	1150	1237	1250	1435	1450	1550	1637	1650	1750	1837	1850	1950	2037	2101
Albert ... d.	0607	0658	0707	0810	0858	0858	0909	1058	1108	1207	1258	1310	1454	1508	1608	1658	1708	1808	1858	1908	2010	2058	2121
Arras ... d.	0629	0720	0729	0829	0920	0921	0929	1120	1129	1229	1321	1329	1515	1529	1629	1720	1729	1829	1920	1929	2029	2123	2140
Douai ... **256** d.	0644	0736	0744	0844	0936	0935	0944	1136	1145	1244	1336	1344	1531	1545	1645	1736	1747	1845	1936	1945	2044	2138	2155
Lille Flandres ... **256** a.	0707	0755	0807	0907	0955	0955	1007	1155	1207	1307	1355	1407	1553	1607	1707	1755	1807	1907	1955	2007	2107	2158	2217

WEEKEND TER SERVICE LILLE - ARRAS - PARIS

	Ⓒ	Ⓒ		Ⓒ	Ⓒ
Lille Flandres ... **256** d.	0914	1914	**Paris** Nord ... d.	1022	1828
Douai ... **256** d.	0934	1936	Creil ... d.	1048	1857
Arras ... d.	0950	1951	Longueau ... d.	1124	1935
Longueau ... d.	1026	2026	Arras ... d.	1157	2010
Creil ... d.	1101	2106	Douai ... **256** d.	1211	2029
Paris Nord ... a.	1126	2129	**Lille** Flandres ... **256** a.	1232	2051

🚌 AMIENS - TGV HAUTE-PICARDIE 🚌

SNCF 🚌 service Ⓡ. Journey 45 minutes.
From **Amiens** at 0500*, 0645, 1055, 1710.
From **TGV Haute-Picardie** at 1000, 1354, 1854, 2035.
For *TGV* departures and arrivals at TGV Haute-Picardie see Table **11**.

A – To / from Rouen (Table **253**).

* – May not run daily.

258 AMIENS - ST QUENTIN

km		Ⓐ	⚒	†	⚒		Ⓐ	Ⓐ	Ⓒ	Ⓐ
0	**Amiens** ... **252** d.	0646	0746	1046	1246	...	1646	1746	1846	1946
59	Ham (Somme) ... **252** d.	0722	0822	1122	1322	...	1722	1822	1922	2022
76	**St Quentin** ... a.	0742	0842	1142	1342	...	1742	1842	1942	2042

	Ⓐ	⚒		Ⓐ	†	⚒		⚒	†
St Quentin ... d.	0614	0716	...	0816	0916	1216	...	1816	2016
Ham (Somme) ... **252** d.	0633	0738	...	0838	0938	1238	...	1838	2038
Amiens ... **252** a.	0714	0814	...	0914	1014	1314	...	1914	2114

259 CALAIS - DUNKERQUE - DE PANNE

km		Ⓐ	⑥	Ⓐ	Ⓐ		⑥	Ⓐ	Ⓐ	Ⓐ
0	**Calais** Ville ... d.	0602	0701	0702	0804	...	1201	1302	1547	1835
23	Gravelines ... d.	0624	0723	0724	0826	...	1222	1325	1605	1856
46	**Dunkerque** ... a.	0647	0747	0747	0849	...	1247	1349	1626	1919

	Ⓐ	⑥	Ⓐ	⑥	Ⓐ	Ⓐ	Ⓐ	Ⓐ	Ⓐ
					d	🚌 e			
Dunkerque ... d.	0600	0658	0703	1258	1301	1301	1730	1830	1930
Gravelines ... d.	0624	0722	0724	1322	1325	1354	1754	1854	1954
Calais Ville ... a.	0643	0742	0743	1342	1345	1436	1813	1915	2013

d – July 4 – 8.
e – July 11 - Aug. 26.

🚌 **DUNKERQUE - LEFFRINCKOUCKE - ADINKERKE (DE PANNE STATION)** Operator: DK'BUS (www.dkbus.com).
Route C2 runs Dunkerque Gare - Leffrinckoucke (Fort Des Dunes). Every 10 minutes (every 30 minutes on ⑦). Journey 22 minutes.
Route 20 runs Leffrinckoucke (Fort Des Dunes) - Bray Dunes - Gare d'Adinkerke - De Panne. Hourly. Journey 33 minutes.
Connects at De Panne station with coastal tram service (Table **406**).

260 PARIS - AMIENS

km		Ⓐ	⚒	Ⓐ	Ⓑ	⑥	⑥	Ⓐ		Ⓒ	Ⓒ	⑥	Ⓐ	†	Ⓐ	⑥		†	⑥	B	C	†	Ⓐ	⑥
0	**Paris** Nord ... **255** d.	0604	0704	0731	0804	0807	0831	0907	...	0907	0931	1031	1031	1107	1134	1150	...	1204	1307	1323	1331	1331	1352	1431
51	Creil ... **255** d.	0631	0731	0758	0830	0841	|	0941	...	0941	|	|	|	1141	1200	1219	...	1230	1341	|	|	|	1435	|
66	Clermont-de-l'Oise ... d.	0642	0742	|	0842	0856	|	0959	...	0956	|	|	|	1156	1212	|	...	1241	1355	|	|	|	1445	|
81	St Just en Chaussée ... d.	0652	0752	|	0853	0913	|	1008	...	1013	|	|	|	1213	1223	|	...	1252	1408	|	|	|	1455	|
126	Longueau ... **254** d.	0716	0817	0834	0917	0945	0930	1038	...	1045	1032	1132	1132	1242	1246	1257	...	1316	1437	1438	1432	1432	1519	1529
131	**Amiens** ... **254** a.	0722	0822	0838	0922	0951	0933	1043	...	1051	1037	1136	1136	1247	1252	1302	...	1322	1443	1445	1436	1436	1524	1533
	Boulogne Ville **261** ... a.	...	...	0956	...	...	1052	...	...	...	1155	1256	1255	...	...	...	...	...	...	1601	1556	1556	...	1653
	Calais Ville **261** ... a.	...	...	...	...	...	1126	...	...	...	1229	1327	1332	...	...	...	...	...	...	...	...	1626	...	1725

	⑤	†	⚒	Ⓐ	Ⓐ		Ⓒ	Ⓐ	⑥	Ⓐ	†			Ⓐ	Ⓐ				⑥	Ⓐ	†		D
Paris Nord ... **255** d.	1519	1531	1604	1631	1704	...	1707	1707	1731	1731	1749	...	1804	1831	1904	1907	1931	...	2004	2004	2031	2107	2228
Creil ... **255** d.	1547	|	1631	1657	1730	...	1739	1741	|	|	|	...	1830	|	1930	1941	|	...	2030	2033	|	2142	2258
Clermont-de-l'Oise ... d.	1557	|	1642	|	1742	...	1755	1758	|	|	|	...	1842	|	1942	1958	|	...	2041	2044	|	2158	2310
St Just en Chaussée ... d.	1607	|	1653	|	1753	...	1813	1813	|	|	|	...	1853	|	1953	2013	|	...	2052	2053	|	2207	2320
Longueau ... **254** d.	1629	1630	1717	1733	1817	...	1846	1845	1831	1833	1852	...	1917	1932	2017	2045	2032	...	2116	2117	2133	2236	2344
Amiens ... **254** a.	1635	1633	1722	1737	1822	...	1851	1851	1835	1838	1856	...	1922	1938	2022	2051	2036	...	2122	2122	2138	2242	2350
Boulogne Ville **261** ... a.	...	1752	...	1857	...	...	...	...	1955	...	2015	...	...	...	...	...	2154	...	...	...	...	...	...
Calais Ville **261** ... a.	...	1824	...	1930	...	...	...	...	2027	...	2047	...	...	...	...	...	2224	...	...	...	...	...	...

	Ⓐ f	Ⓐ	⑥		Ⓐ	Ⓐ	Ⓒ		Ⓐ	⚒	Ⓐ		Ⓐ		Ⓐ		Ⓑ	⑥	†		Ⓐ	⑥	Ⓒ
Calais Ville **261** ... d.	...	...	...	...	...	...	...	...	...	...	...	...	...	...	0636	...	...	...	...	...	...	...	0936
Boulogne Ville **261** ... d.	...	...	...	...	...	...	...	...	...	...	...	...	...	...	0704	...	...	...	...	...	...	...	1002
Amiens ... **254** d.	0417	0502	0524	...	0538	0604	0613	...	0621	0638	0704	...	0722	0738	0822	...	0837	0909	0916	...	1008	1034	1123
Longueau ... **254** d.	0422	0509	0530	...	0544	0611	0619	...	0628	0645	0711	...	0730	0745	0829	...	0844	0916	0922	...	1015	1041	1129
St Just en Chaussée ... d.	0452	0539	0559	...	0608	0639	0647	...	|	0708	0741	...	|	0808	|	...	0908	0946	0952	...	1040	1105	|
Clermont-de-l'Oise ... d.	0504	0550	0608	...	0618	0659	0703	...	|	0718	0759	...	|	0818	|	...	0919	1000	1001	...	1050	1115	|
Creil ... **255** d.	0519	0606	0629	...	0631	0720	0720	...	|	0731	0819	...	|	0831	|	...	0931	1018	1018	...	1102	1126	|
Paris Nord ... **255** a.	0553	0642	0709	...	0656	0756	0754	...	0731	0800	0856	...	0832	0904	0930	...	1000	1053	1055	...	1132	1156	1229

	Ⓐ	⑥	⚒		†				Ⓐ	†			Ⓐ	†		Ⓒ	Ⓒ	Ⓐ		E	†	Ⓐ f	
Calais Ville **261** ... d.	...	1138	...	...	...	...	1436	...	...	1536	...	...	...	1638	...	...	1736	1738	...	...	1936	...	...
Boulogne Ville **261** ... d.	1104	1203	...	...	...	...	1504	...	...	1602	...	...	...	1704	...	...	1802	1804	...	...	2005	...	...
Amiens ... **254** d.	1223	1323	1435	...	1538	1602	1622	...	1722	1723	1737	...	1822	1822	...	1902	1922	1938	...	2038	2125	2138	...
Longueau ... **254** d.	1229	1329	1442	...	1545	1608	1628	...	1729	1729	1744	...	1830	1830	...	1908	1929	1944	...	2045	2132	2144	...
St Just en Chaussée ... d.	|	|	1506	...	1608	1637	|	...	|	|	1808	...	|	|	...	1951	|	2007	...	2109	|	2209	...
Clermont-de-l'Oise ... d.	|	|	1516	...	1617	1656	|	...	|	|	1818	...	|	|	...	2002	|	2017	...	2118	|	2220	...
Creil ... **255** d.	|	|	1527	...	1628	1716	|	...	|	|	1829	...	|	|	...	2018	|	2027	...	2128	|	2230	...
Paris Nord ... **255** a.	1338	1429	1558	...	1656	1753	1729	...	1831	1829	1858	...	1929	1929	...	2056	2029	2056	...	2202	2229	2259	...

B – ④⑤ (also July 4, 6, 11, 13; not July 14).
C – ①–③ July 18 - Aug. 24 (also July 5).
D – † July 3 – 24; daily July 25 - Aug. 28.
E – ⑦ July 3 – 17; ⑥ July 18 - Aug. 28.
f – July 25 - Aug. 26.

(PARIS -) AMIENS - BOULOGNE - CALAIS 261

For *TGV* services see Table **250**. Alternative connections Paris - Calais are available by changing at Lille or Hazebrouck (Tables **250** / **265**).

km		⑥	Ⓐ	Ⓐ	Ⓐ	Ⓐ	Ⓒ	Ⓐ	Ⓐ	⑥	Ⓐ	⑥	Ⓐ	Ⓐ	⑥	Ⓒ	Ⓐ	†	⑥	Ⓐ	Ⓐ	⚒	⑥	A
	Paris Nord **260** d.	...	...	...	...	...	...	...	...	...	0731	...	...	...	0831	0931	...	...	1031	1031	...	...	...	1323
0	**Amiens** d.	0537	0548	...	0648	0653	0737	0708	0808	0837	0840	0842	0853	...	0935	1039	1048	1137	1139	1139	1248	1308	1337	1445
45	Abbeville d.	0605	0616	...	0716	0727	0805	0753	0853	0905	0806	0925	0927	...	1001	1105	1116	1204	1205	1205	1316	1353	1404	1511
58	Noyelles sur Mer 🚂 d.	0614	0625	...	0725	...	0814	...	...	0914	0915	...	...	...	1010	1114	1125	1213	1214	1214	1325	...	1413	1520
85	Rang du Fliers-Verton-Berck d.	0632	0644	0649	0743	...	0833	...	...	0933	0933	...	...	1019	1029	1132	1144	1232	1233	1233	1344	...	1432	1539
96	Étaples-Le Touquet d.	0640	0652	0657	0751	...	0841	...	...	0941	0941	...	...	1027	1037	1140	1152	1240	1241	1241	1352	...	1440	1546
123	**Boulogne** Ville d.	0703	0710	0722	0808	...	0902	...	...	1001	0956	...	...	1050	1054	1157	1209	1303	1258	1257	1409	...	1502	1601
130	Wimille-Wimereux d.	0710	|	0730	|	...	0910	...	...	1009	...	...	...	1057	|	|	|	1310	|	|	|	...	1509	...
140	Marquise-Rinxent d.	0717	0722	0737	0820	...	0917	...	...	1016	...	...	...	1104	1104	1207	1221	1317	|	|	1421	...	1516	...
157	**Calais** Fréthun d.	0734	|	0759	|	...	0933	...	...	1032	...	...	...	1121	|	|	|	1333	|	|	|	...	1532	...
165	**Calais** Ville a.	0748	0748	0809	0841	...	0943	...	...	1042	...	...	...	1133	1126	1229	1242	1343	1327	1332	1443	...	1541	...

	B	†	Ⓐ	⑥	†	Ⓐ	Ⓑ	Ⓐ	†	Ⓐ	Ⓐ		Ⓒ	Ⓐ	Ⓐ	Ⓐ	Ⓐ	⑥	†		Ⓐ	Ⓐ	
Paris Nord **260** d.	1331	1331	...	1431	...	...	...	...	1531	...	...	...	...	1631	...	...	...	1731	1749	...	...	...	1931
Amiens d.	1439	1439	1508	1536	1537	1548	1608	...	1635	1708	...	...	1737	1740	1753	1808	...	1837	1858	1908	1947	1953	2038
Abbeville d.	1505	1505	1542	1603	1605	1616	1653	...	1702	1753	...	...	1805	1806	1826	1853	...	1903	1924	1953	2015	2026	2105
Noyelles sur Mer 🚂 d.	1514	1514	...	1612	1614	1625	...	...	1710	...	...	...	1814	1815	...	...	...	1913	1933	...	2024	...	2113
Rang du Fliers-Verton-Berck d.	1533	1533	...	1630	1633	1644	...	1649	1728	...	1746	...	1833	1833	...	...	1849	1932	1952	...	2043	...	2132
Étaples-Le Touquet d.	1541	1541	...	1638	1641	1652	...	1657	1737	...	1754	...	1841	1841	...	...	1857	1940	2000	...	2051	...	2139
Boulogne Ville d.	1556	1558	...	1655	1702	1709	...	1722	1754	...	1817	...	1902	1858	...	...	1920	1957	2017	...	2108	...	2155
Wimille-Wimereux d.	...	|	...	|	1710	|	...	1730	|	...	1824	...	1910	|	...	...	1927	|	|	...	|	...	|
Marquise-Rinxent d.	...	|	...	|	1717	1721	...	1737	|	...	1832	...	1917	|	...	...	1935	|	|	...	2119	...	|
Calais Fréthun d.	...	|	...	|	1733	|	...	1800	|	...	1848	...	1933	|	...	...	1951	|	|	...	|	...	|
Calais Ville a.	...	1626	...	1725	1742	1742	...	1809	1824	...	1857	...	1943	1930	...	...	2000	2027	2047	...	2141	...	2224

	Ⓐ	C	Ⓐ	Ⓐ	Ⓐ	⑥	Ⓐ		Ⓐ	Ⓐ	⑥	Ⓐ	Ⓐ	Ⓒ	Ⓐ		Ⓒ	Ⓒ	Ⓐ	⚒	⑥	Ⓐ	⑥
Calais Ville d.	...	0420	...	0520	...	...	...	...	0636	...	0711	0720	0758	0811	0920	...	0936	1010	...	...	1138	1146	1211
Calais Fréthun d.	...	|	...	|	...	...	...	...	|	...	0720	|	0807	0820	|	...	|	1019	...	...	|	1156	1220
Marquise-Rinxent d.	...	0437	...	0537	...	...	...	...	|	...	0731	0737	0825	0831	0939	...	|	1030	...	...	|	1207	1231
Wimille-Wimereux d.	...	|	...	|	...	...	...	...	|	...	0738	|	0832	0838	|	...	|	1037	...	...	|	1214	1238
Boulogne Ville d.	...	0450	...	0550	...	...	...	...	0704	...	0747	0750	0841	0847	0952	...	1002	1046	1104	...	1203	1222	1247
Étaples-Le Touquet d.	...	0509	...	0609	...	...	...	...	0719	...	0808	0809	0906	0907	1009	...	1018	1106	1119	...	1219	1245	1307
Rang du Fliers-Verton-Berck d.	...	0518	...	0617	...	...	...	...	0727	...	0817	0818	0913	0916	1018	...	1027	1115	1127	...	1227	...	1316
Noyelles sur Mer 🚂 d.	...	0535	...	0635	...	...	...	...	0745	...	0835	0835	...	0934	1035	...	1045	1133	1145	...	1245	...	1334
Abbeville d.	0537	0545	0606	0644	0649	0706	0739	...	0754	0806	0844	0845	...	0943	1045	...	1054	1142	1154	1206	1254	...	1343
Amiens a.	0607	0611	0651	0711	0735	0751	0813	...	0820	0851	0910	0911	...	1010	1111	...	1120	1210	1220	1251	1320	...	1410
Paris Nord **260** a.	...	...	...	...	...	...	...	...	0930	...	...	...	...	...	...	...	1229	...	1338	...	1429	...	...

	Ⓐ 🚌 d	Ⓐ e	⚒	†		Ⓐ	Ⓐ	†	Ⓐ	Ⓐ	⑥		†		Ⓐ	Ⓒ	Ⓐ	Ⓐ	Ⓐ	Ⓐ	⑥	Ⓐ	†
Calais Ville d.	1241	1305	1320	...	1436	...	1520	1536	...	1605	1614	...	1638	...	1705	1736	1738	...	1820	1907	1911	1920	1936
Calais Fréthun d.	1305	1314	1330	...	|	...	|	|	...	1615	1623	...	|	...	1715	|	|	...	|	1916	1920	|	|
Marquise-Rinxent d.	1326	1325	1342	...	|	...	1537	|	...	1626	1634	...	|	...	1733	|	|	...	1837	1928	1931	1937	|
Wimille-Wimereux d.	1345	1332	1349	...	|	...	|	|	...	1633	1641	...	|	...	1740	|	|	...	|	1935	1938	|	|
Boulogne Ville d.	1411	1340	1357	...	1504	...	1550	1602	...	1640	1650	...	1704	...	1747	1802	1804	...	1850	1953	1947	1950	2005
Étaples-Le Touquet d.	1509	1403	1418	...	1519	...	1609	1618	...	1703	1710	...	1719	...	1812	1818	1819	...	1909	2019	2008	2009	2021
Rang du Fliers-Verton-Berck d.	...	...	1426	...	1527	...	1617	1627	...	1711	1719	...	1727	...	1819	1827	1827	...	1918	2027	2017	2018	2029
Noyelles sur Mer 🚂 d.	...	...	1447	...	1545	...	1635	1645	...	...	1737	...	1745	...	...	1845	1845	...	1935	...	2035	2035	2047
Abbeville d.	...	...	1458	1507	1554	1606	1644	1654	1706	...	1746	...	1754	1806	...	1854	1854	1906	1945	...	2044	2045	2056
Amiens a.	...	...	1527	1552	1620	1651	1711	1720	1751	...	1813	...	1820	1849	...	1922	1920	1951	2011	...	2110	2111	2122
Paris Nord **260** a.	...	...	...	...	1729	...	...	1829	...	...	...	...	1929	...	...	2029	2056	...	...	...	...	...	2229

🚌 ABBEVILLE - LE TRÉPORT 🚌

🚌 number **732**. Subject to alteration during school holiday periods. *37 km.* Journey 70 minutes (* – 50 minutes):
From **Abbeville** at 0641 Ⓐ, 0820 ⑥, 0830 Ⓐ, 1125 Ⓒ *, 1220 ⚒, 1411 ⚒, 1520 Ⓑ, 1620 ⑥, 1735 Ⓐ, 1825 ⑥ *, 1825 Ⓐ, 1920 ⑥, 1930 Ⓐ, 1937 †, 2030 ⑤.
From **Le Tréport** at 0436 Ⓐ *, 0608 Ⓐ, 0624 ⑥, 0714 Ⓐ, 0819 ⑥, 0914 Ⓐ, 0929 Ⓒ, 1219 ⚒, 1319 ⑥, 1624 Ⓐ, 1655 † *, 1715 Ⓐ, 1729 Ⓒ, 1800 Ⓐ, 1919 ⑥.

A – ④⑤ (also July 4, 6, 11, 13; not July 14).
B – ①–③ July 18 - Aug. 24 (also July 5).
C – Ⓐ July 4 – 29; ① Aug. 1 – 22 (not Aug. 15).
d – July 11 - Aug. 26.
e – July 4 – 8.
🚂 – *Chemin de fer de la Baie de Somme.* www.chemindefer-baiedesomme.fr. Cayeux sur Mer - Saint Valery sur Somme - Noyelles sur Mer - Le Crotoy. Noyelles sur Mer station is adjacent to the SNCF station.

LILLE - MAUBEUGE and CHARLEVILLE MÉZIÈRES 262

km		Ⓐ	Ⓐ	Ⓐ 🚌	Ⓐ	Ⓐ	Ⓐ	Ⓐ		Ⓐ	⑥	⑥	⑥ 🚌	Ⓐ	Ⓐ	Ⓐ		Ⓐ	⑥	Ⓐ	Ⓐ 🚌	†	Ⓐ	Ⓐ
0	**Lille** Flandres d.	0535	0605	...	...	0635	...	0705	...	...	0705	...	...	0735	0805	...	...	0835	0835	0905	...	0905	...	...
48	Valenciennes d.	0612	0642	...	...	0710	...	0742	...	0751	0753	...	...	0812	0842	0851	...	0912	0913	0942	...	0950	0951	1051
82	Aulnoye Aymeries **255** d.	0637	0718	...	0721	...	0745	0818	...	0821	0822	0830	...	0837	0908	0921	...	0937	0938	1018	...	1020	1021	1120
94	**Maubeuge** **255** a.	0647	|	...	0731	...	|	|	...	0831	0833	|	...	0847	...	0931	...	0947	0949	|	...	1032	1031	1131
104	**Jeumont** a.	...	|	...	0739	...	|	|	...	0839	0842	|	...	...	...	0939	...	...	0958	|	...	1042	1039	1140
94	Avesnes d.	...	0729	...	...	...	0801	0829	...	...	...	0840	...	...	...	...	...	...	...	1029	...	...	...	...
123	Hirson a.	...	0753	0803	...	...	0830	0853	...	...	...	0904	0914	...	...	...	...	...	...	1053	1103	...	...	...
184	**Charleville-Mézières** a.	...	...	0903	...	...	...	...	...	...	...	...	1014	...	...	...	...	...	...	...	1203	...	...	...

	Ⓒ	Ⓒ	Ⓐ	Ⓒ	Ⓐ	Ⓒ	Ⓒ		Ⓐ	Ⓐ 🚌	Ⓐ	Ⓐ	Ⓒ	Ⓒ	Ⓐ		Ⓐ	Ⓐ	Ⓐ	Ⓒ	Ⓒ	⑥ 🚌	Ⓐ
Lille Flandres d.	1035	...	1205	1205	1235	...	1235	...	1305	...	...	1335	1435	...	1535	...	1605	...	1635	1635	...	...	...
Valenciennes d.	1114	...	1242	1253	1312	...	1314	...	1342	...	1351	1412	1514	...	1612	...	1642	1651	1712	1713	...	...	...
Aulnoye Aymeries **255** d.	1139	1145	1318	1322	1337	1347	1348	...	1418	...	1422	1437	1539	1602	1637	...	1718	1721	1737	1738	1745	...	1745
Maubeuge **255** a.	1150	|	|	1333	1347	1357	|	...	|	...	1433	1447	1551	|	1647	...	|	1731	1747	1749	|	...	|
Jeumont a.	1158	|	|	1342	...	1407	|	...	|	...	1441	...	1559	|	...	...	|	1739	...	1758	|	...	|
Avesnes d.	...	1155	1329	...	...	...	1359	...	1429	...	...	...	...	1611	...	...	1729	...	...	...	1755	...	1801
Hirson a.	...	1219	1353	...	...	...	1421	...	1453	1503	...	...	...	1636	...	...	1753	...	...	...	1819	1829	1830
Charleville-Mézières a.	...	...	...	...	...	...	1503	...	...	1603	...	...	...	...	...	...	...	...	...	...	...	1929	...

	Ⓐ d	Ⓐ e	Ⓐ	Ⓒ	Ⓐ	Ⓐ	Ⓐ 🚌	Ⓐ	⑥	Ⓒ	† 🚌		Ⓐ	Ⓒ	Ⓐ	Ⓐ	†	Ⓐ	Ⓐ	Ⓐ	Ⓒ	Ⓐ	Ⓐ
Lille Flandres d.	1705	1705	...	1705	1735	1805	...	...	1805	...	...	...	1835	1835	1905	...	1905	1935	2005	2035	2035	2105	2135
Valenciennes d.	1742	1742	1751	1753	1812	1842	...	1851	1853	...	...	...	1912	1914	1942	1951	1951	2012	2042	2112	2114	2142	2212
Aulnoye Aymeries **255** d.	1818	1818	1821	1823	1837	|	...	1921	1922	1948	...	...	1937	1939	2018	2020	2022	2037	2118	2137	2139	2218	2237
Maubeuge **255** a.	|	|	1835	1833	1845	|	...	1931	1933	|	...	...	1945	1950	|	2031	2033	2045	|	2147	2150	|	2246
Jeumont a.	|	|	1847	1842	1854	|	...	1939	1942	|	...	...	1954	1959	|	2039	2042	2054	|	...	2159	|	2254
Avesnes d.	1829	1829	...	...	...	1910	...	...	...	1958	...	...	...	...	2029	...	...	...	2129	...	...	2229	...
Hirson a.	1852	1852	...	...	...	1929	1938	...	...	2022	2032	...	...	...	2053	...	...	...	2153	...	...	2253	...
Charleville-Mézières a.	1931	1950	...	...	...	...	2038	...	...	...	2132	...	...	...	...	...	...	...	...	...	...	...	...

FOR RETURN SERVICE AND FOOTNOTES SEE NEXT PAGE →

262 CHARLEVILLE MÉZIÈRES and MAUBEUGE - LILLE

	Ⓐ	⑥	Ⓐ	Ⓐ	Ⓐ	⑥	⑥		Ⓐ	Ⓐ	⑥	Ⓐ	Ⓐ	Ⓐ	Ⓐ		⑥	Ⓒ	⑥	†	Ⓐ	Ⓐ	Ⓐ
														🚌			🚌						
Charleville-Mézières d.	...	...	...	...	...	...	...	...	...	0625	...	...	...	0657	...	...	0731	...	...	...	...	...	...
Hirson d.	...	...	...	0633	...	0641	...	...	...	0709	...	...	...	0757	0807	...	0831	0841	...	...	...	...	0907
Avesnes d.	...	...	...	0653	...	0705	...	...	...	0733	...	...	...	...	0832	...	...	0905	...	...	...	...	0932
Jeumont d.	0606	0618	0621	|	0639	|	...	...	...	|	0718	...	0821	...	|	...	...	|	0902	0902	...	0921	|
Maubeuge 255 d.	0614	0626	0629	|	0651	|	0711	...	0713	|	0726	0813	0828	...	|	...	...	|	0911	0911	0913	0928	|
Aulnoye Aymeries 255 d.	0625	0640	0642	|	0709	0715	0723	...	0725	0752	0740	0825	0842	...	0852	...	...	0915	0924	0924	0925	0942	0952
Valenciennes d.	0650	0709	0709	0720	0738	...	0747	...	0750	0820	0809	0850	0909	...	0920	...	...	...	0947	0945	0950	1009	1020
Lille Flandres a.	0725	0755	...	0755	...	...	0825	...	0825	0855	0855	0925	...	...	0955	...	...	...	1025	...	1025	...	1055

	Ⓐ	Ⓒ	†	⑥	Ⓐ	Ⓐ	Ⓐ		⑥	Ⓒ	Ⓒ	Ⓐ	Ⓐ	Ⓒ	Ⓒ		Ⓐ	Ⓐ	Ⓐ	Ⓐ	⑥	Ⓐ	Ⓐ
					🚌				🚌									🚌					
Charleville-Mézières d.	...	...	...	...	0957	...	...	...	1131	...	...	...	...	...	...	...	...	1357	...	...	...	...	...
Hirson d.	...	1041	...	...	1057	1107	...	...	1231	1241	...	1342	...	1443	...	...	...	1457	1507	...	...	...	1622
Avesnes d.	...	1105	...	...	...	1132	...	...	...	1305	...	1408	...	1507	...	...	...	...	1532	...	...	...	1650
Jeumont d.	...	|	1102	1118	...	|	1221	...	...	|	1302	|	...	|	1502	...	1521	...	|	...	1618	1621	|
Maubeuge 255 d.	...	|	1110	1126	...	|	1229	...	...	|	1310	|	1413	|	1510	...	1528	...	|	1613	1627	1628	|
Aulnoye Aymeries 255 d.	1052	1115	1122	1140	...	1152	1242	...	...	1315	1323	1417	1425	1517	1523	...	1542	...	1552	1625	1640	1642	1705
Valenciennes d.	1120	...	1146	1209	...	1220	1309	...	...	...	1347	...	1450	...	1547	...	1609	...	1620	1650	1709	1709	...
Lille Flandres a.	1155	...	1225	1255	...	1255	...	...	...	...	1425	...	1525	...	1625	...	...	...	1655	1725	1755	...	...

	Ⓐ	†	Ⓒ	⑥	Ⓐ		†	Ⓐ	Ⓐ	Ⓒ	Ⓐ		Ⓐ	Ⓐ	Ⓒ	Ⓐ	Ⓐ		Ⓐ	Ⓐ	†	Ⓐ	Ⓐ
		🚌															🚌						
Charleville-Mézières d.	...	1536	...	...	...	...	...	...	...	...	...	...	...	...	1801	...	1757	...	...	...	...	...	...
Hirson d.	...	1636	1646	...	...	...	...	1707	...	...	...	...	1807	...	1841	...	1857	...	1907	...	...	2007	2107
Avesnes d.	...	...	1710	...	...	...	...	1732	...	...	...	...	1832	...	1904	...	...	...	1932	...	...	2032	2132
Jeumont d.	1654	...	|	1702	...	...	1718	|	...	1818	1821	...	|	1906	|	1921	...	...	|	2006	2025	|	|
Maubeuge 255 d.	1701	...	|	1710	1713	...	1726	|	1813	1827	1828	...	|	1914	|	1928	...	...	|	2014	2034	|	|
Aulnoye Aymeries 255 d.	1713	...	1719	1725	1725	...	1740	1752	1825	1842	1842	...	1852	1925	1923	1942	...	...	1952	2025	2048	2052	2152
Valenciennes d.	1739	...	...	1748	1750	...	1809	1820	1850	1911	1909	...	1920	1950	1947	2009	...	...	2020	2050	2118	2120	2218
Lille Flandres a.	...	...	...	1825	1825	...	1855	1855	1925	1956	...	...	1955	2025	2025	...	...	...	2055	2125	2202	2155	...

d – July 11 - Aug. 26. e – July 4 – 8.

FOR RETURN SERVICE SEE PREVIOUS PAGE.

263 ÉTAPLES - ST POL - ARRAS

km		Ⓐ	⑥	Ⓐ		⑥	Ⓒ	Ⓐ		⑥	†	Ⓐ		⑥	†	Ⓐ		Ⓐ	†	⑥		Ⓐ	Ⓒ	Ⓐ
0	**Étaples Le Touquet** d.	0515	0539	0626	...	0737	0831	0835	...	1107	1153	1320	...	1349	1452	1526	...	1626	1637	1647	...	1737	1754	1901
12	Montreuil sur Mer d.	0525	0549	0636	...	0747	0841	0845	...	1117	1203	1330	...	1359	1502	1536	...	1636	1647	1657	...	1747	1804	1911
33	Hesdin d.	0549	0615	0706	...	0813	0911	0905	...	1147	1233	1400	...	1425	1528	1556	...	1700	1711	1717	...	1817	1830	1941
61	**St Pol sur Ternoise** a.	0614	0642	0733	...	0840	0938	0929	...	1214	1300	1427	...	1452	1555	1620	...	1725	1736	1742	...	1844	1857	2008

	Ⓐ	Ⓐ		Ⓒ	†		Ⓐ	⑥		†	Ⓐ		⑥	Ⓐ		†	Ⓐ		Ⓐ	⑥		†	
St Pol sur Ternoise d.	0521	0636	...	0844	1033	...	1040	1117	...	1203	1330	...	1531	1632	...	1641	1747	...	1913	2017	...	2023	...
Hesdin d.	0547	0704	...	0909	1100	...	1105	1145	...	1231	1358	...	1558	1658	...	1709	1815	...	1939	2044	...	2051	...
Montreuil sur Mer d.	0607	0730	...	0933	1126	...	1125	1211	...	1257	1424	...	1624	1718	...	1735	1841	...	1959	2110	...	2117	...
Étaples Le Touquet a.	0616	0739	...	0942	1135	...	1134	1220	...	1306	1433	...	1633	1727	...	1744	1850	...	2008	2119	...	2125	...

	Ⓐ	⑥	Ⓐ		⑥	Ⓐ	†		†	Ⓐ	Ⓐ		⑥	Ⓐ	Ⓐ		⑥	†	Ⓐ		Ⓒ	Ⓐ	
	🚌	🚌	🚌		🚌	🚌	🚌		🚌	🚌	🚌		🚌	🚌	🚌		🚌	🚌	🚌		🚌	🚌	
St Pol sur Ternoise d.	0630	0653	0753	...	0851	0942	0945	...	1307	1340	1442	...	1517	1629	1733	...	1752	1805	1835	...	1910	1935	...
Arras a.	0747	0810	0910	...	0956	1059	1102	...	1424	1457	1559	...	1622	1746	1838	...	1857	1922	1940	...	1955	2040	...

	Ⓐ	Ⓐ	⑥	⑥	†		Ⓐ	⑥	†	Ⓐ	⑥		†	Ⓐ	⑥	Ⓐ	⑥		Ⓐ	†	Ⓐ	⑥	†
	🚌	🚌	🚌	🚌	🚌		🚌	🚌	🚌	🚌	🚌		🚌	🚌	🚌	🚌	🚌		🚌	🚌	🚌	🚌	🚌
Arras d.	0519	0651	0734	0847	0915	...	0928	0945	1038	1203	1350	...	1532	1623	1721	1746	1839	...	1848	1914	1950	2008	2015
St Pol sur Ternoise a.	0620	0750	0833	1004	1025	...	1027	1044	1155	1320	1507	...	1631	1740	1820	1903	1938	...	2005	2013	2107	2107	2058

265 ARRAS and LILLE - HAZEBROUCK - DUNKERQUE and CALAIS

See Table **250** for *TGV* and *TER-GV* services.

km		Ⓐ	Ⓐ	Ⓐ	Ⓐ		⑥	Ⓐ	⑥	Ⓐ		⑥	Ⓐ	Ⓐ		Ⓐ	Ⓐ	Ⓒ	Ⓒ		Ⓐ	Ⓒ	Ⓐ	Ⓐ
	Arras d.	...	...	0553	...	...	...	0615	...	...	...	0705	...	...	...	0715	...	...	0805	...	...	...	...	0815
	Lens d.	...	...	0609	...	...	...	0633	...	...	...	0723	...	...	...	0733	...	...	0823	...	...	...	...	0833
	Béthune d.	...	...	0626	...	...	...	0655	...	...	...	0741	...	...	...	0755	...	...	0841	...	...	...	...	0855
	Lillers d.	...	...	0635	...	...	...	0704	...	...	...	0750	...	...	...	0804	...	...	0850	...	...	...	...	0904
0	**Lille** Flandres d.	...	0613	|	0623	...	0639	|	0705	0713	...	|	0723	0740	...	|	0813	0813	|	...	0823	0839	0840	|
22	Armentières d.	...	0628	|	0644	...	0653	|	0721	0728	...	|	0744	0754	...	|	0828	0829	|	...	0844	0853	0854	|
47	Hazebrouck a.	...	0646	0652	0710	...	0711	0721	0746	0746	...	0806	0810	0814	...	0821	0846	0854	0906	...	0910	0910	0914	0921
47	Hazebrouck d.	0623	0648	0654	...	...	0712	0723	0747	0748	...	...	...	0816	...	0823	0848	0854	...	...	...	0912	0916	0923
87	**Dunkerque** a.	|	|	0728	...	...	|	|	0820	|	...	...	...	0848	...	|	|	0928	...	...	...	|	0948	|
68	St Omer d.	0641	0701	...	...	...	0725	0741	...	0801	...	...	...	...	...	0841	0901	...	...	...	...	0925	...	0941
109	**Calais** Ville a.	0718	0728	...	...	...	0756	0818	...	0828	...	...	...	...	...	0919	0928	...	...	...	...	0955	...	1018

	Ⓐ	Ⓒ	Ⓐ	Ⓒ		Ⓐ	Ⓒ	Ⓒ	Ⓐ		Ⓐ	Ⓒ	Ⓐ		Ⓐ	Ⓒ	Ⓒ	Ⓐ		⑥	Ⓐ	Ⓒ	Ⓒ
Arras d.	...	...	...	1005	...	...	...	...	...	...	...	...	1215	...	1255	...	1305	...	...	...	...	...	1506
Lens d.	...	...	...	1023	...	...	...	...	...	...	...	...	1233	...	1309	...	1323	...	...	...	...	...	1523
Béthune d.	...	...	...	1041	...	...	...	...	...	...	...	...	1255	...	1326	...	1341	...	...	...	...	...	1540
Lillers d.	...	...	...	1050	...	...	...	...	...	...	...	...	1304	...	1335	...	1350	...	...	...	...	...	1549
Lille Flandres d.	0923	0939	1013	|	...	1023	1039	1139	1213	...	1240	1243	|	...	|	1313	|	1323	...	1339	1413	1439	|
Armentières d.	0944	0953	1028	|	...	1044	1053	1153	1228	...	1254	1258	|	...	|	1329	|	1344	...	1353	1428	1453	|
Hazebrouck a.	1010	1011	1046	1106	...	1110	1111	1211	1246	...	1314	1317	1321	...	1350	1354	1406	1409	...	1412	1446	1511	1606
Hazebrouck d.	...	1012	1048	...	...	...	1112	1212	1248	...	1316	1317	1323	...	1352	1354	...	...	...	1414	1448	1512	...
Dunkerque a.	...	1044	|	...	...	...	|	1244	|	...	1348	|	|	...	1426	1428	...	...	...	1445	|	|	...
St Omer d.	...	...	1101	...	...	...	1125	...	1301	...	...	1330	1341	...	...	...	...	...	...	...	1501	1525	...
Calais Ville a.	...	...	1129	...	...	...	1156	...	1328	...	...	1402	1418	...	...	...	...	...	...	...	1528	1556	...

	Ⓒ	Ⓐ	Ⓐ	Ⓐ		Ⓐ	⑥	†	Ⓐ		Ⓐ	Ⓐ	Ⓐ		Ⓐ	Ⓒ	⑥	Ⓐ		Ⓐ	Ⓐ	Ⓐ	Ⓐ
Arras d.	...	...	...	...	...	...	...	...	...	...	1615	...	...	...	1655	1707	...	...	...	...	1712	...	...
Lens d.	...	...	...	...	...	...	...	...	...	...	1633	...	...	...	1709	1724	...	...	...	...	1735	...	...
Béthune d.	...	...	...	...	...	...	...	...	...	...	1655	...	...	...	1726	1741	...	...	...	...	1759	...	...
Lillers d.	...	...	...	...	...	...	...	...	...	...	1704	...	...	...	1735	1750	...	...	...	...	1812	...	...
Lille Flandres d.	1539	1540	...	1553	...	1613	1639	1640	1640	...	|	1653	1713	...	|	|	1739	1740	...	...	|	1753	1813
Armentières d.	1553	1554	...	1613	...	1628	1653	1653	1654	...	|	1713	1728	...	|	|	1753	1754	...	...	|	1813	1828
Hazebrouck a.	1613	1614	...	1640	...	1646	1711	1711	1714	...	1721	1740	1746	...	1751	1806	1811	1814	...	...	1835	1840	1846
Hazebrouck d.	1613	1615	1623	...	...	1648	1712	1712	1715	...	1723	...	1748	...	1759	...	1812	1816	...	1823	...	...	1848
Dunkerque a.	1648	1648	|	...	...	|	|	|	1748	...	|	...	|	...	1838	...	1844	1848	...	|	...	...	|
St Omer d.	...	...	1641	...	...	1701	1725	1725	...	...	1741	...	1801	...	...	...	...	...	...	1841	...	...	1901
Calais Ville a.	...	...	1718	...	...	1728	1755	1755	...	...	1818	...	1828	...	...	...	...	...	...	1919	...	...	1928

FOR ADDITIONAL TRAINS AND FOOTNOTES SEE NEXT PAGE →

ARRAS and LILLE - HAZEBROUCK - DUNKERQUE and CALAIS 265

See Table **250** for *TGV* and *TER-GV* services.

		Ⓒ	Ⓐ		Ⓒ	Ⓐ	Ⓐ		Ⓐ	Ⓒ		Ⓒ	Ⓐ	Ⓐ		Ⓐ	Ⓒ		Ⓐ f	Ⓐ 🚌 h	Ⓐ g		Ⓒ	Ⓐ 🚌 j
Arras	d.	...	1755	...	...	...	...	...	...	1905	...	...	1915	...	...	1955	...	...	...	...	...	...	...	...
Lens	d.	...	1811	...	...	...	...	...	...	1923	...	...	1933	...	...	2012	...	...	...	...	...	...	...	...
Béthune	d.	...	1829	...	...	...	...	...	...	1941	...	...	1955	...	...	2030	...	...	...	...	...	...	...	...
Lillers	d.	...	1838	...	...	...	...	...	...	1950	...	...	2004	...	...	2040	...	...	...	...	...	...	...	...
Lille Flandres	d.	1813	|	...	1839	1840	1853	...	1913	|	...	1939	|	1953	...	|	2039	...	2040	2011	2113	...	2139	2113
Armentières	d.	1829	|	...	1853	1854	1913	...	1928	|	...	1953	|	2013	...	|	2053	...	2054	2043	2128	...	2153	2145
Hazebrouck	a.	1854	1854	...	1911	1914	1940	...	1946	2006	...	2011	2021	2040	...	2058	2111	...	2114	2128	2146	...	2211	2230
Hazebrouck	d.	1854	1859	...	1912	1916	...	...	1948	...	...	2012	2023	...	...	2100	2112	...	2116	...	2148	...	2212	...
Dunkerque	a.	1928	1938	...	|	1948	...	...	|	...	...	2044	|	...	...	2138	|	...	2148	...	|	...	2244	...
St Omer	d.	...	...	...	1925	...	...	...	2001	...	...	...	2041	...	...	...	2125	...	...	...	2201	...	...	...
Calais Ville	a.	...	...	...	1956	...	...	...	2029	...	...	...	2118	...	...	...	2156	...	...	...	2228	...	...	...

		Ⓐ	⑥	Ⓐ	Ⓐ	Ⓐ		Ⓐ	⑥	⑥	Ⓐ	⑥		Ⓐ	Ⓐ	Ⓐ	Ⓐ	⑥		Ⓒ	Ⓒ	Ⓐ	Ⓐ	Ⓐ
Calais Ville	d.	...	...	0529	...	...	...	...	0606	...	...	...	...	0629	...	0642	...	...	...	...	...	0731	...	...
St Omer	d.	...	...	0557	...	...	...	...	0636	...	...	...	...	0658	...	0719	...	...	...	...	...	0800	...	...
Dunkerque	d.	...	0531	|	...	...	...	0612	|	...	0627	0633	...	|	...	|	0712	0717	...	...	0731	|	...	0812
Hazebrouck	a.	...	0605	0613	...	...	...	0644	0648	...	0700	0705	...	0713	...	0736	0744	0748	...	...	0804	0812	...	0845
Hazebrouck	d.	0538	0605	0613	0620	0623	...	0645	0650	0654	0702	0706	...	0713	0721	0738	0745	0749	...	0755	0804	0814	0820	0846
Armentières	d.	|	0630	0632	0647	|	...	0705	0707	|	|	0731	...	0731	0747	|	0804	0807	...	|	0830	0832	0846	0904
Lille Flandres	a.	|	0647	0647	0708	|	...	0720	0723	|	|	0748	...	0747	0808	|	0820	0823	...	|	0847	0847	0907	0920
Lillers	d.	0557	...	...	...	0645	...	...	...	0711	0718	...	...	...	...	0757	...	...	...	0812	...	...	...	...
Béthune	d.	0607	...	...	...	0700	...	...	...	0721	0728	...	...	...	...	0807	...	...	...	0822	...	...	...	...
Lens	d.	0628	...	...	...	0726	...	...	...	0738	0746	...	...	...	...	0828	...	...	...	0839	...	...	...	...
Arras	a.	0645	...	...	...	0747	...	...	...	0755	0800	...	...	...	...	0845	...	...	...	0856	...	...	...	...

		Ⓒ	Ⓐ	Ⓐ	Ⓐ	Ⓐ		Ⓒ	Ⓒ	Ⓒ	Ⓐ	Ⓐ		Ⓑ	⑥	Ⓒ	Ⓐ	Ⓐ		Ⓐ	Ⓒ	Ⓐ	Ⓒ	Ⓐ
Calais Ville	d.	0806	0831	...	0842	...	...	...	...	1006	...	1031	...	...	...	...	1131	...	...	...	1206	...	...	...
St Omer	d.	0836	0859	...	0919	...	...	...	...	1036	...	1059	...	...	...	...	1159	...	...	...	1236	...	...	...
Dunkerque	d.	|	|	...	|	0911	...	0915	...	|	...	|	...	1112	1116	...	|	...	...	...	|	1232	1232	...
Hazebrouck	a.	0848	0913	...	0936	0944	...	0948	...	1049	...	1113	...	1144	1148	...	1213	...	...	...	1249	1307	1305	...
Hazebrouck	d.	0850	0914	0920	0938	0946	...	0948	0954	1051	1108	1113	...	1145	1148	1154	1213	1221	...	1238	1250	...	1305	1320
Armentières	d.	0907	0932	0946	|	1005	...	1006	|	1107	|	1131	...	1204	1206	|	1232	1247	...	|	1308	...	1330	1346
Lille Flandres	a.	0923	0947	1007	|	1020	...	1021	|	1124	|	1147	...	1220	1221	|	1247	1308	...	|	1323	...	1347	1407
Lillers	d.	...	...	...	0957	...	...	...	1010	...	1124	...	...	...	...	1211	...	...	...	1257	...	...	...	...
Béthune	d.	...	...	...	1007	...	...	...	1020	...	1134	...	...	...	...	1221	...	...	...	1307	...	...	...	...
Lens	d.	...	...	...	1028	...	...	...	1038	...	1152	...	...	...	...	1238	...	...	...	1328	...	...	...	...
Arras	a.	...	...	...	1045	...	...	...	1056	...	1205	...	...	...	...	1255	...	...	...	1345	...	...	...	...

		Ⓐ	⑥	Ⓐ	†	⑥		Ⓐ	Ⓐ	Ⓐ	Ⓒ	Ⓒ		Ⓐ	Ⓒ	Ⓐ	Ⓐ	Ⓐ		⑥	Ⓐ	Ⓒ	Ⓒ	Ⓐ
Calais Ville	d.	1242	...	...	1406	1411	...	...	1429	...	...	...	...	...	1606	1631	1642	...	...	...	...	...	...	...
St Omer	d.	1319	...	...	1436	1440	...	...	1458	...	...	...	...	...	1636	1659	1719	...	...	...	...	...	...	...
Dunkerque	d.	|	1316	...	|	|	...	1432	|	1512	1517	...	...	1612	|	|	|	1712	...	1715	...	...	1732	1732
Hazebrouck	a.	1336	1348	...	1448	1453	...	1506	1513	1544	1548	...	...	1644	1648	1713	1736	1744	...	1748	...	...	1805	1806
Hazebrouck	d.	...	1348	1421	1449	1454	...	1508	1513	1545	1549	1554	...	1645	1650	1714	1738	1746	...	1748	1751	1754	1805	1808
Armentières	d.	...	1406	1447	1507	1511	...	|	1532	1604	1607	|	...	1704	1707	1732	|	1805	...	1807	1817	|	1830	|
Lille Flandres	a.	...	1421	1508	1522	1528	...	|	1547	1620	1623	|	...	1720	1723	1747	|	1820	...	1821	1838	|	1847	|
Lillers	d.	...	...	...	...	...	...	1524	...	...	...	1611	...	...	...	...	1757	...	...	...	...	1811	...	1824
Béthune	d.	...	...	...	...	...	...	1534	...	...	...	1621	...	...	...	...	1807	...	...	...	...	1820	...	1834
Lens	d.	...	...	...	...	...	...	1552	...	...	...	1638	...	...	...	...	1828	...	...	...	...	1838	...	1852
Arras	a.	...	...	...	...	...	...	1607	...	...	...	1657	...	...	...	...	1845	...	...	...	...	1855	...	1905

		Ⓐ	Ⓐ	Ⓒ	Ⓐ		Ⓐ	Ⓐ	Ⓒ	Ⓐ		Ⓒ	Ⓐ	Ⓐ		Ⓐ	Ⓐ	Ⓐ g	Ⓒ		Ⓐ 🚌 j	Ⓐ	Ⓐ f	Ⓐ 🚌 j
Calais Ville	d.	1731	1742	1805	...	...	1842	...	...	...	...	...	...	1931	...	1942	...	...	2006	...	...	2030	2030	...
St Omer	d.	1759	1819	1834	...	...	1918	...	...	...	...	...	...	1959	...	2019	...	...	2036	...	...	2057	2057	...
Dunkerque	d.	|	|	|	...	...	|	1912	1915	...	...	...	1932	|	...	|	2012	2012	|	...	...	|	|	...
Hazebrouck	a.	1813	1836	1848	...	...	1937	1944	1947	...	...	...	2006	2013	...	2036	2045	2045	2048	...	...	2113	2113	...
Hazebrouck	d.	1813	1838	1848	1851	...	...	1946	1948	1951	...	1954	2008	2013	...	...	...	2046	2050	...	2059	...	2113	2133
Armentières	d.	1832	|	1906	1917	...	...	2005	2006	2017	...	|	|	2032	...	...	...	2105	2107	...	2144	...	2132	2218
Lille Flandres	a.	1847	|	1921	1938	...	...	2020	2021	2038	...	|	|	2047	...	...	...	2120	2123	...	2216	...	2147	2250
Lillers	d.	...	1857	...	...	...	...	...	...	...	...	2011	2024	...	...	...	...	...	...	...	...	...	...	...
Béthune	d.	...	1907	...	...	...	...	...	...	...	...	2021	2034	...	...	...	...	...	...	...	...	...	...	...
Lens	d.	...	1928	...	...	...	...	...	...	...	...	2038	2052	...	...	...	...	...	...	...	...	...	...	...
Arras	a.	...	1945	...	...	...	...	...	...	...	...	2056	2105	...	...	...	...	...	...	...	...	...	...	...

f – July 25 – Aug. 26.
g – Aug. 16 – 26.
h – July 11 – 22.
j – July 4 – 22.

FOR ADDITIONAL SERVICES SEE PREVIOUS PAGE.

ST POL SUR TERNOISE - BÉTHUNE - LILLE 266

km			Ⓐ	Ⓐ	⑥	Ⓐ	Ⓐ	Ⓐ	⑥	Ⓐ	Ⓐ	Ⓐ	†		⑥	Ⓐ	Ⓐ 🚌	Ⓐ	⑥	⑥	Ⓐ 🚌	†	Ⓐ	Ⓐ	⑥
0	**St Pol sur Ternoise**	d.	...	0544	...	...	0639	...	0702	...	0739	...	...	...	...	...	0801	...	0904	0959	1001	1004	...	...	1202
32	Béthune	d.	0549	0618	0636	0649	0710	0718	0736	0749	0810	0818	0836	...	0838	0849	0908	0918	0938	1033	1108	1038	1118	1149	1236
74	**Lille** Flandres	a.	0644	0654	0729	0744	...	0754	0829	0844	...	0854	0929	...	0918	0944	...	0954	1018	1116	...	1118	1154	1244	1329

		†	Ⓐ	†	Ⓐ	⑥	Ⓐ	†	Ⓐ	⑥	Ⓐ 🚌	Ⓐ		Ⓐ	Ⓐ	Ⓒ	Ⓐ	Ⓐ	Ⓒ	Ⓐ 🚌	Ⓒ	Ⓐ	Ⓐ	Ⓐ
St Pol sur Ternoise	d.	...	1215	...	1444	1503	...	1601	...	...	1628	...	...	...	1744	1802	...	...	...	1828	1859	...	...	...
Béthune	d.	1236	1249	1438	1518	1536	1549	1635	1649	1738	1735	1745	...	1749	1818	1836	1845	1849	1938	1935	1931	1945	1949	2045
Lille Flandres	a.	1329	1344	1518	1554	1617	1644	1718	1744	1818	...	1824	...	1844	1854	1929	1924	1944	2018	...	...	2024	2044	2124

		Ⓐ 🚌	Ⓐ	Ⓐ 🚌	⑥	Ⓐ	Ⓐ 🚌	Ⓒ	⑥	Ⓐ	Ⓐ	†		Ⓐ	⑥	†	Ⓐ	Ⓐ 🚌	⑥	Ⓐ	†	⑥	Ⓐ	Ⓐ
Lille Flandres	d.	...	0615	...	0642	0706	...	...	0731	0806	...	0831	...	0906	0954	1042	1115	...	1142	1215	1231	1231	1306	1406
Béthune	d.	0700	0712	0725	0722	0742	0752	0810	0824	0842	0922	0924	...	0942	1035	1124	1212	1222	1222	1312	1324	1326	1349	1442
St Pol sur Ternoise	a.	0807	...	0832	...	...	0859	0842	...	...	0954	...	...	...	1106	1156	...	1329	...	...	...	1358	1421	...

		†	Ⓐ	⑥	Ⓐ	⑥	†	Ⓐ 🚌	Ⓐ	Ⓐ	⑥	Ⓐ		Ⓐ	⑥	Ⓐ	Ⓐ	†	Ⓐ	Ⓐ	⑥	Ⓐ	Ⓐ	Ⓒ
Lille Flandres	d.	1442	1515	1542	1606	1631	1642	...	1715	1736	1742	...	...	1815	1831	1836	1906	...	1915	1936	1942	2015	2036	2042
Béthune	d.	1522	1612	1628	1644	1724	1724	1725	1812	1815	1822	1832	...	1912	1935	1915	1944	1950	2012	2024	2028	2112	2116	2112
St Pol sur Ternoise	a.	...	...	1700	1715	...	1756	1832	...	...	...	1904	...	...	2007	...	2016	2021	...	...	2100	...	...	...

267 PARIS - BEAUVAIS - CREIL

km		Ⓐ	⑥	Ⓐ	Ⓐ	Ⓒ	Ⓐ	Ⓒ	Ⓐ			⚒		⑥	Ⓐ	Ⓒ	Ⓐ	⑥	Ⓐ	†	⑥	Ⓐ	⚒	Ⓑ	Ⓒ
0	**Paris** Nord ... d.	0607	0631	0637	0737	0801	0847	0901	1001	1101	1201	1301	1401	1601	1607	1701	1707	1801	1807	1844	1901	1907	2001	2101	2201
	Persan-Beaumont ... d.	0637	0710	0709	0809	0835	0924	0936	1036	1136	1236	1336	1436	1637	1637	1738	1738	1837	1837	1928	1937	1937	2037	2137	2241
80	**Beauvais** ... a.	0720	0751	0751	0851	0918	1005	1018	1118	1218	1318	1418	1518	1720	1720	1820	1820	1920	1920	2009	2020	2020	2119	2218	2322

	⚒	Ⓐ	Ⓒ	Ⓐ	Ⓐ	Ⓐ	Ⓒ	⚒	†		⚒		⚒		⚒	Ⓐ		Ⓐ		⑥	†	Ⓐ	Ⓒ	†
Beauvais ... d.	0540	0613	0627	0640	0710	0740	0744	0840	0940	1040	1140	1240	1340	1440	1640	1710	1740	1810	1843	1940	1951	2010	2040	2140
Persan-Beaumont ... d.	0623	|	0709	0723	|	0823	0827	0923	1023	1123	1223	1323	1423	1521	1723	1754	1823	1854	1923	2022	2032	2053	2123	2223
Paris Nord ... a.	0657	0725	0742	0755	0825	0855	0857	0957	1057	1157	1257	1357	1457	1557	1757	1825	1857	1925	1957	2057	2107	2128	2159	2257

km		Ⓐ	Ⓐ	⑥	Ⓐ	Ⓐ	Ⓐ	Ⓐ	⑥	†	Ⓐ	⑥	Ⓐ		†	Ⓐ	⑥	⚒	Ⓐ	Ⓐ	Ⓒ	Ⓐ	Ⓐ	†	⑥
0	**Beauvais** ... d.	0529	0609	0633	0646	0657	0753	0822	0920	0930	0947	1044	1143	...	1255	1300	1305	1609	1650	1736	1737	1804	1850	2025	2045
37	**Creil** ... a.	0615	0644	0714	0725	0749	0833	0906	1007	1007	1023	1121	1224	...	1334	1351	1352	1645	1743	1819	1826	1856	1934	2112	2132

	Ⓐ	Ⓐ	⑥	Ⓐ	†	Ⓐ	⑥	Ⓐ	Ⓐ	†	⑥	Ⓐ		Ⓐ	⑥	Ⓒ	Ⓐ	Ⓐ	⑥	Ⓐ	Ⓐ	Ⓐ	Ⓒ	Ⓐ
Creil ... d.	0642	0721	0726	0755	0830	0900	0927	1034	1132	1200	1212	1310	...	1359	1403	1645	1656	1718	1743	1753	1829	1906	1915	1948
Beauvais ... a.	0735	0811	0815	0839	0911	0937	1008	1110	1211	1240	1252	1349	...	1449	1450	1724	1739	1807	1825	1841	1916	1955	2004	2024

268 BEAUVAIS - LE TRÉPORT

km		Ⓐ	⑥	Ⓐ	Ⓒ	⚒	Ⓐ	†	Ⓐ	⑥	⑤⑥
0	**Beauvais** ... d.	...	...	0743	0935	1235	1541	1835	1839	1849	2035
49	Abancourt ⊖ ... d.	0648	0742	0828	1025	1325	1634	1931	1926	1936	2125
103	Eu ... d.	0732	0826	0912	1109	1409	1718	2016	2011	2021	2209
106	**Le Tréport** ... a.	0736	0831	0916	1120	1420	1722	2020	2015	2025	2216

	Ⓐ	⑥	†	⑥	Ⓐ		Ⓐ	⑥	Ⓐ	†
Le Tréport ... d.	0551	0647	0735	0935	0954	1229	1538	1735	1751	1835
Eu ... d.	0556	0652	0740	0940	0959	1234	1543	1740	1756	1840
Abancourt ⊖ ... d.	0641	0737	0826	1026	1044	1323	1629	1826	1856	1926
Beauvais ... a.	0725	0822	0912	1112	1129	1412	1713	1912	1946	2012

⊖ – For connections to / from Rouen see Table **253**.

270 PARIS - ROUEN - LE HAVRE

JULY 11 - AUGUST 12. WARNING! Services in this table are subject to frequent variations - please confirm all schedules locally.

km		⑥	Ⓐ	Ⓐ	A	Ⓐ	B	⑥	Ⓐ	⑥	Ⓐ	Ⓒ		Ⓐ	Ⓒ		⑥ C	Ⓒ	Ⓒ	Ⓒ	Ⓐ	Ⓒ	Ⓒ	Ⓐ
0	**Paris** St Lazare ... d.	...	...	...	0542	...	0553	...	0646	0655	0708	0710	...	0736	0740	0815	0840	0908	...	0932	0945	1008	1040	1051
57	Mantes la Jolie ... d.	...	...	...	|	...	0646	...	|	|	|	|	...	0842	0849	|	|	|	...	1043	1050	|	|	|
79	Vernon-Giverny ... d.	...	...	...	|	...	0702	...	0809	0805	|	|	...	0905	0911	|	|	|	...	1107	1107	|	1203	|
111	Val de Reuil ... d.	...	...	...	|	...	0722	...	0828	0824	|	|	...	0924	0930	|	|	|	...	1127	1126	|	1222	|
126	Oissel ... d.	...	...	...	|	...	0734	...	0840	0833	|	|	...	0934	0939	|	|	|	...	1136	1135	|	1231	|
140	**Rouen** Rive-Droite ... d.	0607	0608	0640	0722	0729	0745	0807	0850	0843	0903	0858	...	0946	0949	0958	1029	1104	1110	1145	1145	1203	1242	1255
178	Yvetot ... d.	0631	0633	0705	0747	0754	...	0834	...	...	0927	0919	...	...	...	1020	...	1127	1135	...	...	1224	...	1316
203	Bréauté-Beuzeville ... d.	0644	0648	0719	0802	0809	...	0847	...	...	0940	0932	...	...	...	1034	...	1142	1148	...	...	1237	...	1329
228	**Le Havre** ... a.	0700	0704	0735	0818	0832	...	0903	...	...	1004	0946	...	...	...	1050	...	1201	1205	...	...	1251	...	1344

	⑥	Ⓐ	⑥	Ⓒ	Ⓐ			⑥	Ⓐ	Ⓒ			Ⓐ	⑥	⑥	Ⓐ	①③⑤	Ⓒ	Ⓐ	Ⓐ	Ⓒ	Ⓐ	Ⓐ
Paris St Lazare ... d.	1108	...	...	1132	1143	1209	1308	...	1321	1338	1410	...	1504	1510	...	...	1535	1540	1555	1605	1610	...	1634
Mantes la Jolie ... d.	|	...	...	1248	1252	|	|	...	1429	1448	|	...	|	|	...	...	1651	1648	|	1721	|	...	1740
Vernon-Giverny ... d.	|	...	...	1311	1314	|	|	...	1445	1511	|	...	|	|	...	...	1708	1711	|	1738	|	...	1802
Val de Reuil ... d.	|	...	...	1330	1334	|	|	...	1505	1530	|	...	|	|	...	...	1726	1731	|	1759	|	...	1822
Oissel ... d.	|	...	...	1338	1344	|	|	...	1514	1539	|	...	|	|	...	...	1735	1741	|	1811	|	...	1834
Rouen Rive-Droite ... d.	1259	1302	1307	1348	1354	1401	1458	1510	1535	1548	1559	...	1700	1659	1709	1735	1745	1750	1759	1821	1804	1835	1846
Yvetot ... d.	|	1329	1334	...	...	1422	1519	1535	...	...	1620	...	1721	|	1733	1800	...	...	1820	...	1825	1900	...
Bréauté-Beuzeville ... d.	|	1343	1347	...	...	1436	1533	1548	...	...	1634	...	1735	|	1746	1815	...	...	1833	...	1838	1915	...
Le Havre ... a.	1341	1400	1403	...	...	1451	1548	1604	...	...	1650	...	1749	1742	1802	1831	...	...	1847	...	1852	1931	...

	⑥	†	Ⓐ	Ⓒ	Ⓒ	Ⓐ	Ⓒ	Ⓐ		Ⓐ	Ⓒ		Ⓐ	Ⓒ	Ⓐ	Ⓒ	Ⓐ	Ⓒ	Ⓐ	†	⑤	Ⓒ	Ⓒ
Paris St Lazare ... d.	1640	1640	1642	1710	...	1710	1740	1745	1806	1835	1839	...	1900	1910	1936	1940	2007	2010	2039	2039	2055	2110	2139
Mantes la Jolie ... d.	1748	|	|	|	...	1824	1848	1858	|	|	|	...	|	|	2046	2049	|	|	2144	|	|	|	2232
Vernon-Giverny ... d.	1806	1805	|	|	...	1846	1911	1920	|	2009	2005	...	|	|	2103	2111	|	|	2205	2205	|	|	2250
Val de Reuil ... d.	1825	1825	|	|	...	1905	1930	1939	|	2028	2025	...	|	|	2123	2130	|	|	2225	2224	|	|	2309
Oissel ... d.	1834	1834	|	|	...	1914	1939	1948	|	2037	2034	...	|	|	2133	2139	|	|	2234	2234	|	|	2318
Rouen Rive-Droite ... d.	1844	1844	1901	1902	1907	1924	1948	1958	2003	2047	2044	...	2106	2101	2144	2148	2159	2204	2244	2244	2251	2301	2328
Yvetot ... d.	...	...	1921	|	1932	...	...	...	2024	...	...	...	|	|	...	...	2220	2225	...	...	|	|	...
Bréauté-Beuzeville ... d.	...	...	1934	|	1945	...	...	...	2038	...	...	...	|	|	...	...	2233	2238	...	...	|	|	...
Le Havre ... a.	...	...	1947	1944	2001	...	...	...	2053	...	...	...	2151	2143	...	...	2249	2252	...	...	2335	2343	...

	Ⓐ	Ⓐ	⑥	Ⓐ	Ⓐ	Ⓐ	Ⓐ		Ⓐ	†	⑥	⑥	Ⓐ	†	⑥		Ⓐ	Ⓒ	Ⓐ	Ⓐ	Ⓐ	Ⓒ	⑥
Le Havre ... d.	...	...	...	0514	...	...	0600	...	0619	...	...	0632	...	0703	0706	...	0709	...	...	0734	0805	0807	...
Bréauté-Beuzeville ... d.	...	...	...	0529	...	...	0617	...	0634	...	...	0650	...	0718	0721	...	0723	...	...	0751	0819	0821	...
Yvetot ... d.	...	...	...	0543	...	...	0633	...	0648	...	...	0704	...	0732	0735	...	0737	...	...	0807	0833	0836	...
Rouen Rive-Droite ... d.	0501	0541	0604	0609	0632	0647	0658	...	0714	0717	0717	0730	0738	0755	0800	...	0803	0805	0807	0832	0901	0900	0917
Oissel ... d.	0512	0551	0614	|	0644	0703	...	...	|	0727	0727	...	0749	|	|	...	|	0816	0817	...	|	|	0927
Val de Reuil ... d.	0523	0600	0623	|	0653	0711	...	...	|	0736	0736	...	0758	|	|	...	|	0825	0826	...	|	|	0936
Vernon-Giverny ... d.	0544	0621	0647	|	0713	0731	...	...	|	0756	0756	...	0819	|	|	...	|	0845	0847	...	|	|	0956
Mantes la Jolie ... d.	0605	0639	0711	|	0731	0757	...	...	|	0814	|	...	0844	|	|	...	|	0911	0912	...	|	|	1014
Paris St Lazare ... a.	0716	0750	0813	0813	0842	0905	...	...	0921	0912	0913	...	0947	0932	0948	...	0959	1013	1017	...	1057	1046	1118

	Ⓐ	Ⓒ	Ⓒ	Ⓒ	Ⓐ		⑥			†	Ⓐ	Ⓒ		Ⓐ	Ⓒ		⚒	⚒	Ⓒ		Ⓐ		Ⓒ
Le Havre ... d.	...	0847	0906	...	...	1005	...	...	1030	1114	...	...	1208	...	...	...	1233	1314	...	1407	1433	1508	...
Bréauté-Beuzeville ... d.	...	0904	0921	...	...	1019	...	...	1048	|	...	...	1222	...	...	...	1250	|	...	1422	1450	1522	...
Yvetot ... d.	...	0917	0935	...	...	1033	...	...	1102	|	...	...	1237	...	...	...	1304	|	...	1436	1504	1536	...
Rouen Rive-Droite ... d.	0941	0942	0959	1013	1022	1100	1117	...	1128	1159	1210	1215	1301	1317	1320	...	1328	1359	1411	1459	1528	1559	1613
Oissel ... d.	0953	...	|	1023	1032	|	1127	...	...	|	1220	1225	|	1327	1330	...	...	|	1421	|	...	|	1623
Val de Reuil ... d.	1004	...	|	1032	1041	|	1136	...	...	|	1229	1234	|	1336	1339	...	...	|	1430	|	...	|	1632
Vernon-Giverny ... d.	1027	...	|	1052	1101	|	1156	...	...	|	1250	1254	|	1356	1359	...	...	|	1452	|	...	|	1652
Mantes la Jolie ... d.	1044	...	|	1116	1118	|	1215	...	...	|	|	1316	|	1414	|	...	...	|	|	|	...	|	1716
Paris St Lazare ... a.	1158	...	1148	1213	1218	1246	1318	...	...	1343	1412	1413	1448	1519	1518	...	...	1548	1613	1648	...	1751	1813

	Ⓐ	Ⓐ	Ⓒ	Ⓐ	Ⓒ		Ⓐ		Ⓒ	Ⓐ	Ⓒ	† C	Ⓐ	Ⓒ	Ⓐ		Ⓒ	Ⓐ	Ⓒ	Ⓐ	Ⓒ	Ⓒ	Ⓒ
Le Havre ... d.	...	1602	1609	...	...	1706	...	...	...	1802	1806	...	...	1908	1910	...	...	1931	1933	2008	2013	...	2108
Bréauté-Beuzeville ... d.	...	1616	1624	...	...	1721	...	...	...	1817	1821	...	...	1922	1927	...	...	1948	1950	2023	|	...	2124
Yvetot ... d.	...	1630	1638	...	...	1735	...	...	...	1831	1835	...	...	1936	1942	...	...	2004	2004	2038	|	...	2138
Rouen Rive-Droite ... d.	1615	1654	1701	1701	1717	1759	1804	...	1811	1854	1859	1916	1917	1959	2010	...	2011	2028	2029	2101	2105	2117	2201
Oissel ... d.	1625	...	|	1711	1727	|	1814	...	1821	|	|	|	1927	|	|	...	2021	...	...	|	|	2127	|
Val de Reuil ... d.	1634	...	|	1723	1736	|	1827	...	1830	|	|	|	1936	|	|	...	2030	...	...	|	|	2136	|
Vernon-Giverny ... d.	1654	...	|	1743	1758	|	1848	...	1852	|	|	|	1956	|	|	...	2052	...	...	|	|	2156	|
Mantes la Jolie ... d.	|	...	|	1807	|	|	1912	...	1917	|	|	|	2014	|	|	...	2116	...	...	|	|	2214	|
Paris St Lazare ... a.	1809	...	1848	1916	1918	1953	2021	...	2018	2036	2059	2118	2131	2148	2157	...	2205	...	...	2243	2242	2258	2333

A – ①②④ July 11–28 (not July 14); ①–⑤ Aug. 1–12.

B – ①③④⑤.

C – To / from Dieppe (Table **270a**).

FÉCAMP - LE HAVRE 270

Additional 🚌 services operate Fécamp - Bréauté-Beuzeville and v.v. For other trains Bréauté-Beuzeville - Le Havre and v.v. see previous page.

km		Ⓐ	†	⚒		⚒	†	†		⑥	⚒	†		†	⑥	†		⑥	Ⓑ			Ⓑ		
0	**Fécamp** d.	0645	0733	0752	...	0933	0933	1133	...	1134	1333	1333	...	1533	1534	1633	...	1733	1735	1833	...	1933	...	...
20	Bréauté-Beuzeville d.	0707	0754	0814	...	0955	0954	1154	...	1156	1355	1354	...	1554	1556	1655	...	1754	1756	1855	...	1954	...	...
45	**Le Havre** a.	0729	...	0836	...	1017	...	...	...	1218	1417	...	...	...	1618	1717	...	...	1818	1917	...	...	...	...

		⚒	†	⑥		†				Ⓒ	Ⓐ	Ⓒ				⚒		†	Ⓐ	†		Ⓑ		
	Le Havre d.	0830	...	1037	...	...	...	1237	...	1437	1637	...	...	1737	...	1837	...	...	1937	...	...	...	...	...
	Bréauté-Beuzeville d.	0855	1001	1101	...	1101	...	1301	...	1501	1701	1701	...	1801	...	1901	...	1901	2001	2001	...	2101	...	...
	Fécamp a.	0915	1021	1121	...	1121	...	1321	...	1521	1721	1721	...	1821	...	1921	...	1921	2021	2021	...	2121	...	...

ROUEN - DIEPPE 270a

km		⚒	Ⓐ	Ⓐ	⚒	Ⓐ	⑥ A	†		⑥	Ⓐ	Ⓒ		⚒	Ⓐ	Ⓐ	†	⚒		Ⓑ	Ⓐ	⑥	Ⓐ	
0	**Rouen** Rive-Droite d.	0646	0710	0746	0910	1010	1031	1046	1210	1246	1347	1410	...	1610	1646	1708	1710	1746	1810	1846	1910	1912	2010	2124
63	**Dieppe** a.	0747	0800	0847	0959	1059	1117	1147	1259	1349	1447	1459	...	1659	1747	1759	1759	1847	1859	1947	2000	1959	2059	2218

		Ⓐ	Ⓐ	⑥	⚒	Ⓐ	Ⓒ	Ⓐ	Ⓐ	⚒	†			⚒	Ⓐ		†	Ⓐ	⑥	Ⓐ	† A	Ⓐ	Ⓒ	Ⓑ
	Dieppe d.	0517	0605	0617	0702	0715	0746	0802	0815	1002	1017	1202	...	1315	1402	1602	1704	1715	1801	1815	1825	1902	1915	2002
	Rouen Rive-Droite a.	0601	0716	0718	0751	0817	0832	0851	0916	1052	1116	1251	...	1416	1451	1651	1751	1816	1851	1916	1913	1951	2017	2051

A – To / from Paris (Table **270**).

CAEN - ALENÇON - LE MANS - TOURS 271

km		Ⓐ	Ⓐ	⑥	Ⓐ	Ⓐ 🚌	Ⓒ	Ⓐ 🚌		Ⓒ 🚌	⑥	Ⓒ	Ⓐ	Ⓐ	Ⓒ 🚌	Ⓑ		Ⓐ	†	Ⓐ	⑥	†	†	🚌
0	**Caen** 275 277 d.	0606	0703	0716	0741	...	0903	0930	...	...	1050	1251	1254	1452	...	...	...	1649	1650	1748	1752	1752	2026	...
23	Mézidon 275 277 d.	0621	0717	0731	0756	...	0918	|	...	...	1105	1306	1309	1507	...	...	...	1704	1705	1804	1807	1808	2041	...
67	Argentan 273 d.	0648	0748	0758	0832	...	0943	1030	...	...	1132	1335	1336	1534	...	...	...	1731	1733	1833	1834	1834	2105	...
82	Surdon 273 d.	0658	0757	0807	0841	0924	|	|	...	1045	1141	1344	1354	1543	1543	...	...	1741	|	1842	1843	1844	|	2147
91	Sées d.	0705	0805	0814	0848	0934	|	|	...	1055	1148	1352	1352	1550	1553	...	...	1748	1747	1849	1850	1851	2118	2157
111	Alençon ◇ d.	0720	0820	0828	0904	0957	1009	1115	...	1118	1202	1408	1408	1605	1616	1618	...	1804	1802	1904	1904	1908	2132	2220
166	**Le Mans** ◇ a.	0810	0911	0914	0941	...	1039	1230	...	...	1238	1447	1445	1641	...	1711	...	1838	1838	1938	1938	1941	2208	...
	Tours (below) a.	...	...	...	1050	...	1153	...	...	...	...	1550	1550	...	...	...	...	...	...	...	...	2048	...	...

		①	⑥ 🚌	Ⓐ	⑥	Ⓐ		⑥ 🚌	Ⓐ 🚌	†	⑥	Ⓐ		⑥	† 🚌	⑤ 🚌	Ⓐ	Ⓐ		Ⓒ	⚒	† 🚌	†	†
	Tours (below) d.	...	...	...	...	...	...	...	...	0919	0901	1109	...	...	...	...	...	1634	...	1633	...	...	...	1914
	Le Mans ◇ d.	0613	...	0725	0735	0824	...	...	0915	1025	1029	1213	...	1326	...	1350	1635	1741	...	1741	1824	...	1943	2020
	Alençon ◇ d.	0653	0710	0758	0825	0900	...	0942	1030	1102	1101	1254	...	1414	1445	1505	1722	1820	...	1822	1905	1933	2015	2051
	Sées d.	0705	0733	0810	0837	0916	...	1005	|	1115	1113	1307	...	1426	1508	|	1735	1832	...	1834	1917	1956	2027	2104
	Surdon 273 d.	0712	0743	0817	0844	0923	...	1015	|	1122	1120	1314	...	1433	1518	|	1742	1839	...	1841	1924	2006	2035	|
	Argentan 273 d.	0722	...	0828	0854	0933	...	...	1115	1132	1131	1324	...	1443	...	1550	1751	1849	...	1851	1934	...	2045	2118
	Mézidon 275 277 d.	0747	...	0854	0920	0958	...	...	|	1157	1154	1351	...	1509	...	|	1817	1914	...	1916	2000	...	2111	2140
	Caen 275 277 a.	0801	...	0909	0934	1012	...	...	1215	1211	1208	1406	...	1523	...	1650	1831	1927	...	1932	2014	...	2125	2155

km		⚒	Ⓐ	Ⓐ		Ⓐ	Ⓒ	⚒			Ⓒ	Ⓐ			Ⓐ	Ⓐ			†	⚒		⑥ 🚌	†	Ⓐ
	Caen (above) d.	...	...	...	...	0741	0903	...	...	...	1251	1254	...	...	...	...	...	...	...	...	...	...	1752	...
0	**Le Mans** d.	0618	0647	0732	...	0951	1042	1207	...	1251	1451	1451	...	1651	1716	1816	...	1851	1915	1916	...	...	1947	1951
49	Château du Loir d.	0649	0734	0803	...	1021	1110	1254	...	1324	1521	1520	...	1723	1804	1904	...	1923	2000	2004	...	2015	2017	2022
96	St Pierre des Corps a.	|	...	|	...	|	1148	...	...	|	|	|	...	|	...	...	...	|	|	...	...	|	|	|
99	**Tours** a.	0728	...	0832	...	1050	1153	...	...	1353	1550	1550	...	1753	...	...	...	1953	2038	...	...	2105	2048	2100

		①	①	②–⑤	Ⓐ	Ⓐ	⑥	Ⓐ	⑥	†	†	Ⓐ		Ⓐ	⑥	⑤	Ⓐ	Ⓒ	Ⓐ	Ⓐ	Ⓐ	†	†	⑤†
	Tours d.	0522	0558	...	0609	...	0737	0756	0901	0919	1029	1109	...	1229	1229	1407	1515	1633	1634	1727	1829	...	1914	2129
	St Pierre des Corps d.	|	|	...	|	...	|	|	0917	|	|	|	...	|	|	|	|	|	|	|	|	...	|	|
	Château du Loir d.	0551	0627	0630	0648	0753	0807	0826	0949	0948	1059	1139	...	1259	1311	1437	1543	1702	1703	1809	1859	1909	1945	2159
	Le Mans a.	0637	0715	0719	0738	0841	0853	0857	1020	1018	1131	1210	...	1331	1359	1508	1613	1733	1733	1856	1931	1958	2016	2231
	Caen (above) a.	...	...	...	...	...	...	...	1208	1211	...	1406	...	...	...	...	...	1932	1927	...	...	...	2155	...

◇ – Other trains **Alençon - Le Mans** at 0546 ①, 0618 Ⓐ, 0648 Ⓐ, 0747 Ⓐ, 1244 ⑥, 1248 Ⓐ, 1718 Ⓐ, 1818 Ⓐ, 1918 †; **Le Mans - Alençon** at 0646 Ⓐ, 0749 Ⓐ, 1253 Ⓐ, 1326 †, 1653 Ⓐ, 1753 Ⓐ, 1902 Ⓐ, 1956 ⚒.

☛ At Le Mans 🚌 services use the Gare Routière (bus station) adjacent to the railway station.

CAEN - COUTANCES - GRANVILLE - RENNES 272

At Caen and Rennes 🚌 services use the bus station (gare routière) adjacent to the railway station.

km		Ⓐ	Ⓐ 🚌	Ⓐ	⑥	Ⓐ	†	Ⓒ	Ⓐ	Ⓒ	Ⓒ	Ⓐ	Ⓒ	⑥ 🚌	Ⓐ	Ⓐ 🚌	Ⓐ	Ⓒ	† 🚌	Ⓑ 🚌	Ⓐ	Ⓒ	Ⓐ	†
0	**Caen** 275 ◧ d.	0601	0730	0801	0810	0910	0910	1010	1110	1210	...	1309	1512	...	1611	1615	1710	1712	1715	...	1810	1909	1912	2013
30	Bayeux 275 ◧ d.	0623	|	0823	0827	0927	0927	1027	1127	1227	...	1331	1534	...	1633	|	1732	1734	|	...	1832	1931	1934	2036
57	Lison 275 ◧ d.	0640	|	0841	0841	0941	0941	1041	1141	1241	...	1348	1552	...	1650	|	1749	1752	|	...	1849	1948	1951	2052
75	Saint Lô ◧ d.	0655	|	0856	0856	0956	0956	1056	1156	1256	...	1403	1605	...	1705	|	1804	1805	|	...	1904	2003	2004	2105
105	Coutances ◧ d.	0722	|	0917	0918	1018	1022	1118	1218	1318	...	1424	1627	...	1726	|	1831	1827	|	...	1925	2025	2027	2126
143	**Granville** a.	0749	|	*1005**	0945	1044	1048	1144	1244	1344	...	*1515**	1653	...	*1813**	|	1859	1853	|	...	1951	2051	*2116**	...
143	**Granville** 273 d.	0759	|	...	0958	...	1058	...	1258	...	1414	...	...	1703	...	|	...	...	|	1909	...	...	...	...
157	Folligny 273 d.	0810	|	...	1009	...	1109	...	1309	...	1424	...	...	|	...	|	...	...	|	|	...	...	...	...
176	Avranches d.	0824	0900	...	1023	...	1123	...	1323	...	1438	...	...	1733	...	1745	...	...	1845	1939	...	...	...	...
198	Pontorson ⊡ d.	0842	|	...	1041	...	1141	...	1341	...	1457	...	...	|	...	|	...	...	|	|	...	...	...	...
219	Dol de Bretagne 281 d.	0900	|	...	1058	...	1158	...	1358	...	1514	...	...	|	...	|	...	...	|	|	...	...	...	...
277	**Rennes** 281 a.	0933	1020	...	1133	...	1233	...	1431	...	1549	...	...	1853	...	1905	...	...	2005	2059	...	...	...	...

		Ⓐ	Ⓐ	⑥	Ⓐ 🚌	†	Ⓐ	†	⑥ 🚌	⑥	B	C	† 🚌	Ⓐ	Ⓒ	Ⓒ	Ⓒ	Ⓐ 🚌	Ⓐ	Ⓐ 🚌	Ⓒ	Ⓐ	Ⓒ	Ⓐ
	Rennes 281 d.	...	...	...	0730	...	...	...	0805	...	...	...	1004	1126	...	1406	...	1513	...	1615	...	...	1726	1757
	Dol de Bretagne 281 d.	...	...	...	|	...	...	...	|	...	...	...	|	1159	...	1438	...	|	...	|	...	...	1759	1830
	Pontorson ⊡ d.	...	...	...	|	...	...	...	|	...	...	...	|	1215	...	1458	...	|	...	|	...	...	1817	1847
	Avranches d.	...	...	...	0851	...	...	...	0925	...	...	...	1124	1231	...	1516	...	1633	...	1735	...	...	1834	1905
	Folligny 273 d.	...	...	...	|	...	...	...	|	...	...	...	|	1246	...	1530	...	|	...	|	...	...	1849	1924
	Granville 273 a.	...	...	...	|	...	...	...	0955	...	...	...	1154	1256	...	1540	...	1703	...	|	...	...	1900	1939
	Granville d.	0604	0655	0805	|	0905	*0939**	0955	...	1005	...	*1139**	...	1307	1405	...	1600	...	1713	|	1800	...	1910	1956
	Coutances ◧ d.	0631	0731	0832	|	0932	1031	1032	...	1032	1218	1231	...	1337	1432	...	1628	...	1740	|	1828	1840	1938	2026
	Saint Lô ◧ d.	0654	0755	0855	|	0955	1055	1055	...	1055	1242	1255	...	1402	1455	...	1650	...	1803	|	1850	1903	2002	2047
	Lison 275 ◧ d.	0707	0808	0908	|	1008	1108	1108	...	1108	1255	1308	...	1415	1508	...	1703	...	1816	|	1903	1916	2015	2100
	Bayeux 275 ◧ d.	0724	0825	0925	|	1025	1125	1125	...	1125	1312	1325	...	1429	1525	...	1720	...	1830	|	1920	1934	2029	2114
	Caen 275 ◧ a.	0746	0847	0947	1020	1047	1147	1147	...	1147	1334	1347	...	1446	1547	...	1742	...	1847	1905	1942	1956	2046	2133

B – ①–④ July 11 - Aug. 11 (not July 13, 14).

C – ⑤ (also July 4 – 7, 13, Aug. 16 – 18, 22 – 25).

* – Connection by 🚌.

◧ – Other trains Caen - Coutances at 0701 Ⓐ, 1010 Ⓐ, 1156 **B**, 1210 **C**; Coutances - Caen at 0549 Ⓐ, 0628 ⑥, 0831 Ⓐ, 1533 Ⓐ, 1641 Ⓐ.

⊡ – Full name is Pontorson - Mont St Michel (*10 km* from Mont St Michel).

273 PARIS - DREUX - GRANVILLE

Suburban trains run Paris - Dreux and v.v. approximately hourly. For connections Surdon - Alençon and v.v. see Table **271**.

km		Ⓐ	Ⓐ ◧	Ⓒ		Ⓒ ◧	†		Ⓐ				⑥		⑤	⑤	Ⓒ		Ⓐ	①–④		⑤	Ⓐ	Ⓒ
0	**Paris** Montparnasse ...... **278** d.	0732	0732	0850	...	0850	0927	...	0945	1054	1354	...	1527	...	1528	1613	1645	...	1713*	1813	...	1813	1943	1950
17	Versailles Chantiers .... **278** d.	|	|	0904	...	0904	|	...	|	|	|	...	|	...	|	|	|	...	|	1827	...	1826	|	2003
82	**Dreux** .... d.	0820	0820	0942	...	0942	1014	...	1033	|	1440	...	1614	...	|	|	|	...	|	1914	...	1914	2044	2044
118	Verneuil sur Avre .... d.	0840	0840	1001	...	1001	1036	...	1056	1157	1459	...	1637	...	|	1731	1751	...	1831	1936	...	1936	2103	2103
142	L'Aigle .... d.	0854	0854	1015	...	1015	1050	...	1109	1211	1513	...	1650	...	1642	1745	1805	...	1845	1950	...	1950	2117	2117
183	Surdon .... **271** d.	0915	0915	1036	...	1036	1114	...	1131	|	1534	...	1715	...	|	1806	1826	...	1906	2011	...	2014	2138	2138
198	Argentan .... **271** d.	0926	0926	1046	...	1046	1124	...	1143	1241	1545	...	1724	...	1711	1816	1838	...	1917	2021	...	2026	2149	2149
226	Briouze .... d.	0942	0942	1102	...	1102	1140	...	...	|	1601	...	...	...	|	|	|	...	1934	...	...	2043	2205	2205
243	Flers .... d.	0953	0953	1113	...	1113	1151	...	...	1305	1612	...	...	...	1734	1839	1901	...	1947	...	...	2053	2216	2215
272	Vire .... d.	1010	1010	1129	...	1129	1207	...	...	1321	1629	...	...	...	1750	1855	1919	...	2003	...	...	2109	2232	2232
298	Villedieu les Poêles .... d.	1025	1025	1144	...	1144	1223	...	...	1336	1644	...	...	...	1806	1911	1935	...	2019	...	...	2125	2247	2248
	Pontorson - Mont St Michel a.	|	1121	|	...	1240	|	...	...	|	|	...	...	...	|	|	|	...	|	...	...	|	|	|
313	Folligny .... **272** d.	1043	...	1202	...	...	1233	...	...	|	|	...	...	...	|	|	|	...	2029	...	...	2134	|	|
328	**Granville** .... **272** a.	1053	...	1212	...	...	1243	...	...	1354	1702	...	...	...	1824	1931	1952	...	2039	...	...	2144	2305	2305
		①	⑥	②–⑤	†	Ⓐ		⑥	†		⑥	Ⓐ		⚒	†		†	†		Ⓒ	Ⓒ ◧	Ⓐ	Ⓐ ◧	†
	Granville .... **272** d.	0450	...	...	...	0555	...	0625	0655	0900	...	...	...	1154	1400	1553	1705	...	...	1830	...	1838	...	1953
	Folligny .... **272** d.	|	...	...	...	|	...	|	|	|	...	...	...	|	|	|	|	...	...	1853	...	1901	...	2004
	Pontorson - Mont St Michel .... d.	|	...	...	...	|	...	|	|	|	...	...	...	|	|	|	|	...	...	|	1804	|	1814	|
	Villedieu les Poêles .... d.	0508	...	...	...	0613	...	0643	0713	0918	...	...	...	1212	1418	1611	1723	...	...	1903	1903	1911	1911	2014
	Vire .... d.	0523	...	...	...	0628	...	0658	0728	0933	...	...	...	1228	1433	1627	1738	...	...	1919	1919	1927	1927	2029
	Flers .... d.	0540	...	...	...	0645	...	0715	0745	0950	...	...	...	1245	1450	1645	1755	...	...	1936	1936	1944	1944	2047
	Briouze .... d.	0551	...	...	...	0656	...	0726	0756	|	...	...	...	1256	1501	|	1806	...	...	1947	1947	1955	1955	2058
	Argentan .... **271** d.	0609	0610	0612	0639	0714	...	0744	0814	1016	1209	1218	...	1314	1519	1713	1824	1934	...	2007	2007	2013	2013	2116
	Surdon .... **271** d.	0618	0619	0622	0648	0723	...	0753	0823	1025	1218	1227	...	1323	1528	|	|	1943	...	2016	2016	2022	2022	|
	L'Aigle .... d.	0642	0643	0643	0713	0744	...	0815	0845	1047	1242	1248	...	1345	1549	1743	1851	2007	...	2039	2039	2044	2044	2144
	Verneuil sur Avre .... d.	0656	0657	0656	0726	0757	...	0828	0858	1101	1256	1301	...	1358	1603	1758	|	2021	...	2053	2053	2057	2057	2157
	Dreux .... d.	0718	0719	0717	0748	0817	...	0849	0919	|	1318	1323	...	1419	|	|	|	2043	...	2115	2115	2117	2117	2216
	Versailles Chantiers .... **278** d.	0805	|	0804	|	|	...	|	|	|	|	|	...	|	|	|	|	2121	...	|	|	|	|	2254
	Paris Montparnasse .... **278** a.	0816*	0809	0816*	0835	0917	...	0939	1010	1210	1410	1415*	...	1510	1716	1915	2010	2132	...	2211	2211	2206	2206	2312

◧ – 🚌 connnection available to / from Mont St Michel △ (a. 1201 Ⓐ / 1320 Ⓒ, d. 1724 Ⓒ / 1734 Ⓐ).
△ – Mont St Michel Le Verger - for more information see Table **274**.
* – Paris **Vaugirard** (5 – 10 minute walk from Montparnasse main concourse).

274 🚌 RENNES - MONT ST MICHEL 🚌

Keolis Armor

km																		
0	**Rennes** gare routière .... d.	0945	1045	1245	...	...	...	...	...	...	**Mont St Michel** .... d.	1120	1600	1800	...	...	...	...	...	...
68	**Mont St Michel** .... a.	1055	1155	1355	...	...	...	...	...	...	**Rennes** gare routière .... a.	1230	1710	1910	...	...	...	...	...	...

Operator: Keolis Armor (www.keolis-armor.com). Rail tickets and passes not valid. The gare routière at Rennes and Dol are adjacent to the rail stations. At Mont St Michel the coach terminates at Le Verger close to the tourist information office. A free *Passeur* motorised shuttle service operates along the causeway to Mont St Michel itself taking 25 minutes (or 45 minutes walk, *2.4 km*). Horse-drawn shuttles (*Maringotes*) taking 35 minutes are also available, fee payable.

275 PARIS - CAEN - CHERBOURG

JULY 11 - AUGUST 12. WARNING! Services in this table are subject to frequent variations - please confirm all schedules locally.
Other services: Paris - Lisieux Table **276**; Lisieux - Caen Table **277**; Mézidon - Caen Table **271**. Additional local trains run Paris - Evreux and v.v.

km		①	Ⓐ	Ⓐ	Ⓐ	Ⓐ	A	⑥	†	†	⑥	Ⓐ	⑤	①–④	Ⓒ	Ⓐ	Ⓒ	⑤	①–④	①②④	Ⓒ	Ⓒ	⑤	Ⓐ	Ⓒ	Ⓐ
0	**Paris** St Lazare .... d.	0032	...	...	...	...	0547	...	...	0735	0735	0748	0819	...	0821	0919	0920	...	...	1018	1035	1127	1140	1213	1238	1317
108	Evreux .... d.	0237	...	...	...	0609	0707	...	...	|	|	0924	|	...	|	1048	|	...	...	|	|	|	|	|	|	1452
160	Bernay .... d.	0314	...	...	...	0647	0732	...	...	|	|	0952	|	...	|	1113	|	...	...	|	|	|	|	|	|	1518
191	Lisieux .... ⊡ d.	0339	...	0609	...	0703	0747	...	...	|	|	1009	|	...	|	1129	|	...	...	|	|	|	|	|	|	1533
216	Mézidon .... ⊡ d.	|	...	0623	...	0718	|	...	...	|	|	|	|	...	|	|	|	...	...	|	|	|	|	|	|	|
239	**Caen** .... **272** ⊡ d.	0407	0550	0642	0653	0736	0812	0824	0924	0959	1001	1034	1055	1101	1101	1154	1159	1224	1229	1248	1303	1359	1410	1456	1502	1555
269	Bayeux .... **272** d.	0425	0607	...	0710	...	0832	0840	0940	...	1017	...	1112	1118	1118	...	...	1241	1246	1305	1320	...	...	1515	1518	...
296	Lison .... **272** d.	0440	0620	...	0723	...	0846	0854	0954	...	1031	...	1126	1132	1132	...	...	1254	1259	1319	1334	...	...	1531	1532	...
314	Carentan .... d.	0453	0631	...	0734	...	0858	0905	1005	...	1042	...	1137	1142	1143	...	...	1305	1310	1330	1345	...	...	1541	1543	...
343	Valognes .... d.	0509	0646	...	0749	...	0912	0920	1020	...	1057	...	1151	1157	1157	...	...	1320	1325	1344	1358	...	...	1556	1557	...
371	**Cherbourg** .... a.	0525	0701	...	0804	...	0928	0935	1035	...	1113	...	1207	1213	1213	...	...	1335	1340	1400	1413	...	...	1612	1613	...
		Ⓐ	Ⓒ	⑤	Ⓒ	①–④	Ⓐ	†	Ⓐ	Ⓐ	Ⓒ	Ⓒ	Ⓐ	⑥	†	Ⓒ	Ⓐ	†	⑤	①–④	†	⑥	⑤	①–④	Ⓒ	Ⓒ
	Paris St Lazare .... d.	...	1350	1420	1440	...	1526	1535	...	1629	1635	1655	1722	1725	1725	1825	1831	1855	1923	1923	1925	1925	2020	2020	2030	2206
	Evreux .... d.	...	1534	|	|	...	|	|	...	1805	|	1836	|	|	|	|	2014	2035	|	2103	|	2111	|	2201	|	2334
	Bernay .... d.	...	1601	|	|	...	|	|	...	1830	|	1902	|	|	|	|	2039	2101	|	2128	|	2136	|	2226	|	0001
	Lisieux .... ⊡ d.	...	1616	|	|	...	|	|	1831	1845	|	1917	|	|	|	|	2054	2117	|	2143	|	2151	|	2241	|	0017
	Mézidon .... ⊡ d.	...	|	|	|	...	|	|	1845	|	|	|	|	|	|	|	|	|	|	|	|	|	|	|	|	|
	Caen .... **272** ⊡ d.	1626	1640	1700	1701	1705	1802	1759	1903	1910	1901	1940	2006	1959	2003	2101	2118	2140	2158	2206	2203	2214	2257	2306	2301	0041
	Bayeux .... **272** d.	1642	...	1716	1718	1722	1818	...	...	1927	1918	...	2023	...	2020	2118	2135	...	2214	...	...	...	2314	2322	2318	...
	Lison .... **272** d.	1656	...	1730	1732	1736	1832	...	...	1941	1932	...	2037	...	2034	2132	2149	...	2228	...	...	...	2328	2336	2332	...
	Carentan .... d.	1707	...	1741	1742	1746	1842	...	...	1952	1943	...	2048	...	2045	2143	2159	...	2239	...	...	...	2339	2347	2343	...
	Valognes .... d.	1722	...	1755	1757	1801	1857	...	...	2005	1957	...	2102	...	2059	2157	2213	...	2254	...	...	...	2353	0001	2357	...
	Cherbourg .... a.	1737	...	1810	1813	1816	1913	...	...	2021	2013	...	2118	...	2114	2213	2228	...	2310	...	...	...	0008	0015	0013	...
		Ⓐ	Ⓐ	⑥	Ⓐ	Ⓒ	Ⓐ	Ⓐ	Ⓒ	Ⓐ	Ⓒ	Ⓐ	Ⓒ		⑥	Ⓐ	Ⓐ	Ⓒ	⑤	Ⓒ	⑤	Ⓒ	⑥	Ⓐ	①–④	⑤
	Cherbourg .... d.	...	...	...	0555	0636	0642	...	...	...	...	0841	0853	...	...	...	1044	1050	...	...	1130	...	...	...	1229	1241
	Valognes .... d.	...	...	...	0611	0652	0658	...	...	...	...	0857	0909	...	...	...	1100	1106	...	...	1146	...	...	...	1245	1258
	Carentan .... d.	...	...	...	0624	0705	0711	...	...	...	...	0912	0925	...	...	...	1114	1121	...	...	1200	...	...	...	1259	1311
	Lison .... **272** d.	...	...	...	0635	0716	0722	...	...	...	...	0923	0936	...	...	...	1124	1132	...	...	1211	...	...	...	1309	1322
	Bayeux .... **272** d.	...	...	...	0650	0730	0737	...	...	...	...	0938	0950	...	...	...	1138	1147	...	...	1225	...	...	...	1323	1337
	Caen .... **272** ⊡ d.	0458	0612	0652	0709	0749	0756	0829	0830	0859	0910	0957	1008	...	1112	1120	1157	1206	...	...	1244	1308	1312	1320	1342	1355
	Mézidon .... ⊡ d.	|	|	|	|	|	|	|	|	|	|	|	|	...	1131	1139	|	|	...	...	|	|	1331	1339	|	|
	Lisieux .... ⊡ d.	0522	0636	0716	|	|	|	0853	0853	|	|	|	|	...	1145	1153	|	|	1240	1245	1307	|	1345	1353	1404	|
	Bernay .... d.	0537	0651	0731	|	|	|	0908	0908	|	|	|	|	...	...	...	|	|	1255	1303	1322	|	...	...	1421	|
	Evreux .... d.	0603	0718	0758	|	|	|	0935	0935	|	|	|	|	...	...	...	|	|	1322	1333	1349	|	...	...	1450	|
	Paris St Lazare .... a.	0741	0855	0943	0942	1033	1044	1114	1113	1202	1143	1225	1241	...	...	...	1424	1443	1459	1513	1525	1543	...	...	1619	1619
		Ⓒ	⑤	Ⓒ	⑥	⑤	Ⓒ	Ⓐ	⑥	Ⓐ	Ⓒ	Ⓐ	Ⓒ		Ⓐ	Ⓒ	Ⓐ	†	Ⓐ	⚒	Ⓒ	⑥	B	†	⑥	†
	Cherbourg .... d.	1253	...	...	1354	1446	1451	...	...	...	...	...	...	...	1643	1651	...	...	1755	...	1846	...	1918	1948	...	2034
	Valognes .... d.	1309	...	...	1410	1502	1508	...	...	...	...	...	...	...	1659	1707	...	...	1811	...	1902	...	1934	2004	...	2050
	Carentan .... d.	1325	...	...	1425	1517	1522	...	...	...	...	...	...	...	1713	1721	...	...	1825	...	1916	...	1947	2018	...	2104
	Lison .... **272** d.	1336	...	...	1436	1528	1533	...	...	...	...	...	...	...	1724	1732	...	...	1836	...	1927	...	1958	2029	...	2115
	Bayeux .... **272** d.	1350	...	...	1450	1543	1547	...	...	...	...	...	...	...	1738	1746	...	...	1850	...	1941	...	2012	2043	...	2129
	Caen .... **272** ⊡ d.	1409	1414	1430	1508	1601	1606	1620	1635	1657	1707	...	...	...	1757	1805	1835	1903	1909	1937	2000	2028	2030	2103	2107	2147
	Mézidon .... ⊡ d.	|	|	|	|	|	|	1638	1654	|	|	...	...	...	|	|	1854	|	|	1956	|	|	|	|	|	|
	Lisieux .... ⊡ d.	|	1437	1453	|	|	|	1651	1708	|	|	1743	1753	...	|	|	1908	|	1933	2010	|	2051	2052	|	|	|
	Bernay .... d.	|	1452	1508	|	|	|	...	...	|	|	1759	1809	...	|	|	...	|	1948	...	|	2106	2107	|	|	|
	Evreux .... d.	|	1519	1535	|	|	|	...	...	|	|	1826	1836	...	|	|	...	|	2015	...	|	2133	2134	|	|	|
	Paris St Lazare .... a.	1643	1659	1713	1743	1840	1843	...	...	1940	1943	2006	2013	...	2031	2047	...	2143	2141	...	2215	2247	2155	2328	2328	2358

A – ①③④⑤.
B – ①②④⑤.

⊡ – Other trains **Lisieux - Caen** at 0647 Ⓐ, 0742 ⑥, 0753 Ⓐ, 1104 Ⓐ, 1159 ⑥, 1204 Ⓐ, 1359 ⑥, 1404 Ⓐ, 1700 Ⓐ, 1742 ⑥, 1744 Ⓐ; from **Caen - Lisieux** at 0635 Ⓐ, 0745 Ⓐ, 1020 Ⓐ, 1740 Ⓐ.

PARIS - LISIEUX - TROUVILLE DEAUVILLE 276

JULY 11 - AUGUST 12. WARNING! Services in this table are subject to frequent variations - please confirm all schedules locally.

km		Ⓐ	⑥	Ⓐ	†	⑤	⑥	Ⓐ	†	⑤	⑥	Ⓐ		Ⓒ	Ⓐ	Ⓐ	Ⓒ	Ⓐ	Ⓒ		①–④	†	⑤	†
						d														A				
0	**Paris** St Lazare .... 275 d.	...	...	...	...	0655	0813	...	0855	0937	0955	1150	...	1154	...	1529	1556	...	1755	1810	...	...	1928	1955
108	Evreux.......................... 275 d.	...	...	...	...	0834	0939	...	1035	1114	1134	1331	...	1334	...	1713	1734	...	1935	1953	...	...	2112	2134
160	Bernay.......................... 275 d.	...	...	...	...	0901	1006	...	1101	1140	1202	1356	...	1359	...	1739	1802	...	2002	2019	...	...	2137	2200
191	**Lisieux**........................ 275 d.	0723	0735	0830	0844	0917	1023	1050	1117	1156	1219	1413	...	1416	1714	1755	1820	1853	2018	2034	2100	2145	2153	2216
209	Pont l'Évêque ....d.	0738	0748	0843	0857	0929	1037	1103	1129	1208	1232	1426	...	1428	1730	1808	1833	1906	2032	2046	2114	2158	2204	2228
221	**Trouville-Deauville** ....a.	0747	0757	0852	0906	0938	1046	1112	1139	1217	1241	1436	...	1437	1739	1817	1842	1915	2041	2055	2123	2207	2213	2237

	Ⓐ	Ⓐ	Ⓐ	Ⓐ	Ⓒ	Ⓐ	Ⓒ	⑤	Ⓒ		⑤	Ⓒ	Ⓐ	Ⓐ	Ⓒ	Ⓐ	Ⓒ	Ⓐ	†	⑥	①–④	†	†
Trouville-Deauville ....d.	0556	0651	0730	0759	0811	1020	1025	1219	1220	1349	1622	1631	1644	1721	1731	1756	1821	1920	1921	1952	2012	2020	2121
Pont l'Évêque ....d.	0605	0700	0738	0808	0820	1029	1037	1228	1232	1358	1631	1640	1654	1730	1741	1808	1833	1929	1931	2001	2022	2032	2131
Lisieux...................................... 275 d.	0617	0714	0750	0822	0833	1041	1050	1240	1245	1412	1643	1653	1708	1743	1753	1822	1846	1941	1943	2014	2033	2044	2143
Bernay.. 275 d.	...	...	0807	...	...	1057	1107	1255	1303	...	1659	1709	...	1759	1809	...	1903	...	1959	...	...	2100	2201
Evreux... 275 d.	...	...	0833	...	...	1124	1135	1322	1333	...	1725	1736	...	1826	1836	...	1932	...	2026	...	...	2127	2227
Paris St Lazare .... 275 a.	...	...	1012	...	...	1259	1313	1459	1513	...	1903	1913	...	2006	2013	...	2113	...	2201	...	...	2247	2353

A – ①③④⑤.

d – July 22 - Aug. 12.

TROUVILLE DEAUVILLE - DIVES CABOURG 276a

From **Trouville-Deauville** at 0902Ⓐ, 1053⚒, 1153†, 1253⚒, 1453, 1622†, 1642⑥, 1742†, 1826Ⓐ, 1853⑥, 1902†, 2028⑤**e**, 2044①–④, 2053Ⓒ, 2104⑤**f**. Journey 30 minutes.

From **Dives-Cabourg** at 0516Ⓐ, 0942, 1141⚒, 1241†, 1338⚒, 1532Ⓒ, 1638Ⓐ, 1702†, 1742⑥, 1822†, 1926Ⓐ, 1942Ⓒ. Journey 30 minutes.

e – Until July 8.

f – From July 15.

ROUEN - LISIEUX - CAEN 277

At Caen 🚌 services use the bus station (gare routière) adjacent to the railway station.

km		Ⓐ	Ⓐ	⑥		Ⓐ	Ⓐ	Ⓒ		Ⓐ	Ⓐ	Ⓒ		Ⓐ	Ⓐ	†		Ⓒ	Ⓐ	Ⓒ		Ⓐ	Ⓒ	Ⓐ
						g	h			🚌				🚌										
0	**Rouen** Rive Droite.................d.	0600	0702	0703	...	0759	0807	1007	...	1007	1206	1207	...	1407	1606	1607	...	1657	1706	1807	...	1809	1904	1909
23	Elbeuf-St Aubin........................d.	0617	0719	0718	...	0820	0822	1022	...	|	1222	1222	...	|	1622	1622	...	1714	1721	1822	...	1824	1919	1924
73	Serquigny ....d.	0651	|	|	...	|	|	|	...	|	1255	1255	...	|	1650	|	...	1749	1757	1900	...	1857	|	|
83	Bernay........................... 275 d.	0658	0755	0753	...	0853	0855	1055	...	|	1304	1304	...	|	1658	1655	...	1757	1804	1907	...	1907	1952	1957
114	Lisieux........................... 275 d.	0714	0811	0809	...	0909	0912	1111	...	|	1321	1320	...	|	1714	1712	...	1813	1821	1924	...	1924	2009	2014
139	Mézidon.................. 271 275 d.	0728	0826	0824	...	0924	0926	1126	...	|	1335	1334	...	|	1729	1727	...	1827	1835	1939	...	1938	2024	2029
162	**Caen** .... 271 275 a.	0742	0840	0838	...	0938	0940	1140	...	1147	1353	1348	...	1547	1742	1741	...	1841	1852	1953	...	1952	2038	2043

	Ⓐ	Ⓐ	⑥		Ⓐ	Ⓐ	Ⓒ		Ⓐ	Ⓒ	Ⓐ		Ⓐ	†	Ⓐ		Ⓒ		Ⓐ		Ⓐ	⑥	†
						🚌					🚌								g		h		
Caen .... 271 275 d.	0551	0709	0711	...	0803	1006	1006	...	1203	1206	1406	...	1606	1610	1702	...	1706	1805	1858	...	1904	1906	2006
Mézidon.......................... 271 275 d.	0605	0724	0725	...	0817	|	1020	...	1217	1220	|	...	1620	1625	1715	...	1720	1819	1911	...	1917	1919	2020
Lisieux.. 275 d.	0619	0739	0740	...	0832	|	1034	...	1232	1235	|	...	1635	1639	1729	...	1735	1833	1925	...	1931	1933	2033
Bernay... 275 d.	0636	0756	0757	...	0849	|	1051	...	1249	1251	|	...	1652	1657	1746	...	1752	1850	1942	...	1948	1950	2049
Serquigny ....d.	0643	0804	0804	...	|	|	1100	...	1257	1300	|	...	1700	|	|	...	1759	|	|	...	|	|	|
Elbeuf-St Aubin.....................................d.	0719	0836	0836	...	0921	|	1136	...	1332	1336	|	...	1735	1729	1821	...	1833	1922	2020	...	2022	2022	2122
Rouen Rive Droite..............................a.	0737	0856	0851	...	0938	1146	1153	...	1352	1353	1546	...	1752	1744	1838	...	1851	1943	2038	...	2037	2039	2137

g – July 11 - Aug. 12.

h – July 4–8, Aug. 16–19, 22–26.

PARIS - CHARTRES - LE MANS 278

For *TGV* trains Paris - Le Mans via the high-speed line see Table **280**. Additional trains run Nogent le Rotrou - Le Mans and v.v.

km		①⑦	Ⓐ		⚒	⚒	Ⓐ		Ⓐ	Ⓒ							⚒		†				Ⓐ	Ⓒ
0	**Paris** Montparnasse ....d.	0002	0533	...	0609	0636	0709	...	0739	0809	...	0906	1009	1106	...	1209	1306	...	1306	1409	1506	...	1609	1609
17	Versailles Chantiers..............d.	0019	0546	...	0625	0652	0725	...	0755	0823	...	0922	1025	1122	...	1225	1322	...	1322	1425	1522	...	1625	1625
48	Rambouillet............................d.	0044	0606	...	0645	0712	0745	...	0815	0845	...	0940	1045	1141	...	1245	1342	...	1342	1445	1542	...	1645	1645
88	**Chartres** ....d.	0123	0643	...	0724	0738	0829	...	0856	0924	...	1007	1124	1208	...	1324	1409	...	1410	1524	1610	...	1724	1729
149	Nogent le Rotrou ....d.	...	...	...	...	0814	0922	...	...	...	...	1042	...	1245	...	...	1444	...	1449	...	1648	...	...	1825
211	**Le Mans**...............................a.	...	...	...	...	0850	...	...	...	...	...	1122	...	1325	...	...	1522	...	...	...	1724	...	...	1917

	Ⓐ	Ⓐ		⑥	Ⓑ	Ⓒ		Ⓐ	Ⓐ		Ⓑ		Ⓐ		Ⓐ			Ⓐ		Ⓑ			Ⓐ
																				j			
Paris Montparnasse ....d.	1624	1639	...	1705	1705	1709	...	1724	1739	...	1805	1809	1824	...	1839	1906	...	1939	2009	2106	...	2209	2302
Versailles Chantiers ....d.	1640	1655	...	1722	1722	1725	...	1740	1755	...	1822	1825	1840	...	1855	1922	...	1955	2025	2123	...	2225	2318
Rambouillet..d.	1700	1715	...	1741	|	1745	...	1800	1815	...	|	1845	1900	...	1915	1941	...	2015	2045	2142	...	2245	2345
Chartres..d.	1729	1754	...	1808	1807	1824	...	1828	1854	...	1906	1924	1929	...	1953	2009	...	2054	2124	2209	...	2324	0020
Nogent le Rotrou ....d.	1824	...	...	1847	1845	...	...	1922	...	...	1944	...	2023	...	...	2046	...	...	...	2244	...	...	...
Le Mans..a.	1914	...	...	1925	1922	...	...	...	...	...	2022	...	...	...	...	2128	...	...	...	2322	...	...	...

	Ⓐ	⑥	①		Ⓐ	⚒	Ⓐ			Ⓐ	⚒		Ⓐ		Ⓐ		⚒	Ⓐ	⚒		†		
			k																				
Le Mans..d.	...	...	0338	...	...	...	...	...	...	0538	...	...	...	...	0630	...	...	0638	0734	...	...	...	0937
Nogent le Rotrou ....d.	...	...	0415	...	...	...	0534	...	...	0615	...	...	0635	...	0707	...	...	0730	0811	...	0815	...	1014
Chartres..d.	0405	0451	0452	...	0535	0605	0631	...	0635	0658	0705	...	0732	0735	0751	...	0805	0834	0852	...	0852	0935	1052
Rambouillet..d.	0446	0519	0521	...	0616	0646	0701	...	0716	|	0746	...	0801	0816	0819	...	0846	0903	0919	...	0919	1016	1119
Versailles Chantiers ....d.	0506	0540	0541	...	0638	0708	0724	...	0738	0741	0808	...	0824	0838	0841	...	0908	0925	0939	...	0940	1037	1141
Paris Montparnasse ....a.	0520	0553	0553	...	0650	0720	0735	...	0750	0753	0820	...	0835	0850	0853	...	0920	0936	0954	...	0953	1050	1153

					†	⚒			Ⓐ		Ⓐ		Ⓒ	Ⓐ	Ⓐ						Ⓐ	†	†
Le Mans..d.	...	1133	...	...	...	1338	...	...	...	1535	...	...	...	...	...	...	1738	...	1938	...	...	...	2138
Nogent le Rotrou ....d.	...	1210	...	...	1413	1415	...	...	...	1612	1637	...	...	...	...	...	1813	1842	2015	...	...	...	2213
Chartres..d.	1135	1251	1335	...	1452	1452	1535	...	1639	1651	1735	...	1735	1805	1835	...	1852	1938	2052	...	2121	2131	2252
Rambouillet..d.	1216	1320	1416	...	1519	1519	1616	...	|	1719	1816	...	1816	1846	|	...	1919	2019	2119	...	2158	2211	2318
Versailles Chantiers ....d.	1238	1341	1438	...	1540	1541	1638	...	|	1741	1838	...	1838	1908	|	...	1941	2040	2141	...	2224	2229	2339
Paris Montparnasse ....a.	1250	1353	1450	...	1553	1553	1650	...	1737	1753	1850	...	1850	1920	1944	...	1953	2052	2153	...	2238	2248	2353

OUIGO TRAINS PARIS - LE MANS - NANTES ★

	⑦	
Paris Austerlitz .... d.	0729	1408
Juvisy .... d.	0745	1423
Massy-Palaiseau........................ d.	|	1444
Versailles Chantiers .... d.	|	1503
Chartres .... d.	|	1544
Le Mans .... d.	0958	1649
Angers St-Laud.......................... d.	1053	1737
Nantes .... a.	1137	1820

	①–⑤	
Nantes .... d.	0737	1245
Angers St-Laud.......................... d.	0820	1328
Le Mans .... d.	0911	1415
Chartres .... d.	1025	1518
Versailles Chantiers .... d.	|	1553
Massy-Palaiseau........................ d.	1147	1613
Juvisy .... d.	1203	|
Paris Austerlitz .... a.	1219	1653**b**

SUBURBAN TRAINS PARIS - VERSAILLES

- **RER Line C**: Paris Austerlitz - - Versailles Château Rive Gauche. Journey 40 minutes.
- **RER Line L**: Paris St Lazare - Versailles Rive Droite. Journey 35–40 minutes.
- **RER Line N**: Paris Montparnasse - Versailles Chantiers. Journey 13–27 minutes.

Trains run every 15–30 mins. 0600 - 2400 (2100 Line **C**). Line **C** serves St Michel Notre Dame. Detailed schedules can be found at www.transilien.com.

The Château is approx 600 metres from Château Rive Gauche station, approx 1400 metres from Rive Droite station and approx 1600 metres from Chantiers station.

b – Paris **Bercy**.

j – Until Aug. 14 (also Aug. 15, 19, 21, 26, 28).

k – Also ②–⑤ July 5 - Aug. 12.

★ – *Ouigo Classique*. Low-cost traditional loco-hauled train. Internet booking only at www.ouigo.com. Outline timings – services may not run on all days shown (please confirm timings when booking). For other *Ouigo* trains Paris - Nantes via St Pierre des Corps, see Table **296**.

280 TGV BRETAGNE - PAYS DE LA LOIRE

TGV timings may vary by a few minutes - please check your reservation. See Table **280a** for TER regional services Le Mans - Nantes / Rennes.

PARIS - LE MANS - RENNES

km		*TGV* **8081**	*TGV* **8605**	*TGV* **7601**	*TGV* **8691**	*TGV* **8707**	*TGV* **8083**	*TGV* **8611**	*TGV* **8615**	*TGV* **8711**	*TGV* **8715**	*TGV* **8051**	*TGV* **8619**	*TGV* **8719**	*TGV* **8719**	*TGV* **8085**	*TGV* **8623**	*TGV* **8723**	*TGV* **7603**	*TGV* **8629**	*TGV* **8729**	*TGV* **8631**	*TGV* **8067**	*TGV* **8639**
		①⑥	⚒			Ⓑ				Ⓑ	⑥		①–⑥		⑦						⑥	⑤		
		d	◧	⊡⊠		e				e	f		g	A	h			B	⊠	C	f	j		B
0	**Paris** Montparnasse d.	0706	0735	0748	0856	0856	1000	1000	1056	1056	1056	1215	1259	1259	1300	1356	1443	1443	1523	1656	1656	1657	1715	1759
	Le Mans d.	|	0836	|	|	|	|	|	|	|	|	1313	|	|	|	|	|	|	1628	|	|	|	1813	|
	Laval d.	0821	|	0914	|	|	|	|	|	|	|	1344	|	|	|	|	1556	1556	|	|	|	|	1844	|
	Vitré d.	0841	|	|	|	|	|	|	|	|	|	|	|	|	|	|	|	|	|	|	|	|	|	|
364	**Rennes** a.	0903	0922	0939	1025	1025	1125	1125	1225	1225	1225	1409	1425	1425	1425	1525	1625	1625	1713	1825	1825	1825	1909	1925
	To:	*Mal*	*Bre*	—	*Lan*	*Qui*	*Mal*	*Bre*	*Bre*	*Qui*	*Qui*	—	*Bre*	*Qui*	*Qui*	*Mal*	*Bre*	*Qui*	—	*Bre*	*Qui*	*Bre*	—	*Bre*

	TGV **8731**	*TGV* **8735**	*TGV* **8093**	*TGV* **8033**	*TGV* **8093**	*TGV* **8093**	*TGV* **8641**	*TGV* **8739**	*TGV* **8075**	*TGV* **8059**	*TGV* **8059**	*TGV* **8035**	*TGV* **8751**	*TGV* **8751**	*TGV* **8649**	*TGV* **8751**	*TGV* **8073**	*TGV* **8097**	*TGV* **8655**	*TGV* **8755**	*TGV* **8063**	*TGV* **8065**	*TGV* **8791**
		⑤	⑤			⑤			⑤	⑤	⑥		⑦	①–④	⑤	⑤	⑦	⑤	⑤	⑤		⑦	⑤
	B	j	j	B	D	j	C	C	k	m	f	B	E	F	j	j	h	j	j	j	C	h	j
Paris Montparnasse d.	1759	1800	1815	1815	1815	1815	1856	1856	1858	1915	1915	1957	1957	1957	1959	1959	2015	2020	2054	2054	2115	2215	2215
Le Mans d.	|	|	|	|	|	|	|	|	2000	2013	2013	|	|	|	|	|	2113	2117	|	|	2213	2313	2313
Laval d.	|	|	|	1929	1929	|	|	|	2032	2044	2044	|	|	|	|	|	2144	2146	|	|	2244	2344	2344
Vitré d.	|	|	|	1949	1949	|	|	|	2052	|	2105	|	|	|	|	|	2205	|	|	|	|	|	0005
Rennes a.	1925	1926	1942	2009	2009	1942	2025	2025	2114	2109	2125	2125	2125	2125	2125	2125	2225	2211	2225	2225	2309	0009	0025
To:	*Qui*	*Qui*	*Mal*	—	*Mal*	*Mal*	*Bre*	*Qui*	—	—	—	—	*Qui*	*Lor*	*Bre*	*Qui*	—	*Mal*	*Bre*	*Qui*	—	—	*Lor*

km		*TGV* **8072**	*TGV* **8680**	*TGV* **8050**	*TGV* **8080**	*TGV* **8602**	*TGV* **8702**	*TGV* **8702**	*TGV* **8052**	*TGV* **8604**	*TGV* **8606**	*TGV* **8706**		*TGV* **7606**	*TGV* **8610**	*TGV* **8710**	*TGV* **8084**	*TGV* **8620**	*TGV* **8620**	*TGV* **8720**	*TGV* **8622**	*TGV* **8056**	*TGV* **8722**	*TGV* **8074**
		①–⑤	①	⑥	①–⑤			⑤	Ⓑ	①	①–⑥	①–⑥						②–⑥	①		Ⓑ	⑥		Ⓑ
		p	s	f	p	A	A	j	e	s	g	g		⊠	t	v		u	s		e	f	C	e
	From:	—	*Bri*	—	*Mal*	*Bre*	*Qui*	*Qui*	—	*Bre*	*Bre*	*Qui*		—	*Bre*	*Qui*	*Mal*	*Bre*	*Bre*	*Qui*	*Bre*	—	*Qui*	—
0	**Rennes** d.	0534	0635	0650	0701	0735	0735	0735	0748	0835	0935	0935	...	1018	1135	1135	1248	1335	1335	1335	1435	1436	1535	1630
	Vitré d.	0556	|	|	|	|	|	|	|	|	|	|	...	|	|	|	|	|	|	|	|	|	|	1657
	Laval d.	0616	0704	0719	|	|	|	|	0816	|	1003	1003	...	|	|	|	1317	|	|	|	|	|	|	1718
169	**Le Mans** d.	0648	|	0750	0745	|	|	|	0848	|	|	|	...	|	|	|	1348	|	|	|	|	|	|	1748
371	**Paris** Montparnasse a.	0752	0823	0854	0851	0910	0910	0911	0951	1009	1123	1123	...	1145	1312	1312	1452	1509	1509	1509	1612	1613	1712	1849

	TGV **8630**	*TGV* **8086**	*TGV* **8792**	*TGV* **8628**	*TGV* **8690**	*TGV* **8694**	*TGV* **8730**	*TGV* **7608**	*TGV* **8636**	*TGV* **8636**	*TGV* **8636**		*TGV* **8088**	*TGV* **8640**	*TGV* **8734**	*TGV* **8642**	*TGV* **8092**	*TGV* **8692**	*TGV* **8646**	*TGV* **8746**	*TGV* **8096**	*TGV* **8652**	*TGV* **8752**
		⑥⑦	①–④	⑤		⑤	Ⓑ		①–④	⑤	⑦				⑦	⑤	⑦	⑦		①–⑥	⑦	⑦	⑦
	C	q	w	j	H	j	e	⊙⊠	g	j	h		r	B	h	j	h	h	G	g	h	h	h
From:	*Bre*	*Mal*	*Lor*	*Bre*	*Lan*	*Lan*	*Qui*	—	*Bre*	*Bre*	*Bre*		*Mal*	*Bre*	*Qui*	*Bre*	*Mal*	*Lan*	*Bre*	*Qui*	*Mal*	*Bre*	*Qui*
Rennes d.	1635	1635	1635	1635	1735	1735	1735	1752	1835	1835	1835	...	1835	1935	1935	1935	2035	2035	2135	2135	2148	2235	2235
Vitré d.	|	|	|	|	|	|	|	|	|	|	|	...	|	|	|	|	|	|	|	|	|	|	|
Laval d.	|	|	|	|	|	|	|	1819	|	|	|	...	|	2002	2002	2007	|	|	|	|	2216	|	|
Le Mans d.	|	|	|	|	|	|	|	1849	|	|	|	...	|	|	|	|	|	|	|	|	2251	|	|
Paris Montparnasse a.	1812	1812	1812	1813	1910	1910	1910	1958	2010	2011	2011	...	2011	2120	2120	2124	2212	2212	2310	2311	2354	0011	0011

PARIS - LE MANS - NANTES

km		*TGV* **8911**	*TGV* **8911**	*TGV* **8803**	*TGV* **7621**	*TGV* **8913**	*TGV* **8973**	*TGV* **8917**	*TGV* **8871**	*TGV* **8975**	*TGV* **8807**	*TGV* **8921**	*TGV* **8977**	*TGV* **8875**	*TGV* **7623**	*TGV* **8923**	*TGV* **8879**	*TGV* **8881**	*TGV* **8817**	*TGV* **8905**	*TGV* **8927**	*TGV* **8819**	*TGV* **8821**	*TGV* **8931**
		⑥	①–⑤	①–⑥				⑥	Ⓑ	①–④	⑤⑥		⑤–⑦	①–④			①–⑤		①–⑤	①–④	⑤	⑥⑦	⑤	
			g⊖	g	⊠			f	e	w	x		y	w	●⊠		z		a	w	j	q	j	
0	**Paris** Montparnasse d.	0643	0643	0744	0835	0939	0939	1039	1039	1223	1223	1252	1326	1335	1429	1447	1535	1635	1723	1751	1752	1752	1823	1843
	Le Mans d.	|	|	|	0936	1037	1037	1136	1136	|	|	|	1426	1432	1536	|	1631	1731	|	|	|	|	|	|
254	Sablé d.	|	|	0850	|	|	|	|	|	|	|	|	1448	1454	|	|	|	|	|	|	|	|	|	1949
302	Angers St Laud d.	0811	0815	0912	1016	1116	1116	1214	1216	|	|	1417	1511	1516	1617	1611	1712	1814	|	1917	1916	1916	|	2012
390	**Nantes** a.	0852	0850	0950	1054	1154	1154	1254	1254	1419	1419	1454	1549	1554	1658	1650	1750	1858	1921	1954	1954	1954	2019	2050
	To:	*Cro*	*Cro*	—	—	*Cro*	*Sab*	*Cro*	—	*Sab*	—	*Cro*	*Sab*	—	—	*Cro*	—	—	—	*Naz*	*Cro*	—	—	*Cro*

	TGV **8985**	*TGV* **8823**	*TGV* **8887**	*TGV* **8935**	*TGV* **8937**	*TGV* **8825**	*TGV* **8827**	*TGV* **8939**
		⑤		⑤	⑤	⑥⑦		⑤
		j	B	j	j	q	B	j
Paris Montparnasse d.	1843	1927	1939	1939	2045	2052	2152	2152
Le Mans d.	|	|	2038	2041	|	|	|	|
Sablé d.	1949	|	|	|	|	|	|	|
Angers St Laud d.	2012	|	2118	2122	2211	2218	2316	2316
Nantes a.	2050	2123	2155	2202	2250	2255	2354	2353
To:	*Sab*	—	—	*Cro*	*Cro*	—	—	*Cro*

	TGV **8860**	*TGV* **8900**		*TGV* **8802**	*TGV* **8804**		*TGV* **8910**	*TGV* **8804**
	①–⑤	①–⑤		①–④			①	⑤
	p	p		z	K		s	j
From:	—	*Naz*		—	—		*Cro*	—
Nantes d.	0509	0605	...	0640	0705	...	0705	0709
Angers St Laud d.	0548	0644	...	|	0744	...	0744	0748
Sablé d.	0611	|	...	|	|	...	|	|
Le Mans d.	0634	|	...	|	|	...	|	|
Paris Montparnasse a.	0736	0815	...	0845	0914	...	0915	0927

km		*TGV* **8808**	*TGV* **8912**	*TGV* **8972**	*TGV* **7622**	*TGV* **8916**	*TGV* **8812**	*TGV* **8876**		*TGV* **8922**	*TGV* **8880**	*TGV* **8984**	*TGV* **8816**	*TGV* **8926**	*TGV* **7624**	*TGV* **8818**		*TGV* **8928**	*TGV* **8986**	*TGV* **8930**	*TGV* **8932**	*TGV* **8988**	*TGV* **8934**	*TGV* **8936**
		①–⑥					①–⑤				⑥⑦		Ⓑ			⑦		⑦	①–⑥	⑦	①–⑥	⑦	⑦	⑦
		g			⊠		p				q		e		⊕⊠	h		h	g	h	g	h	h	h
	From:	—	*Cro*	*Sab*	—	*Cro*	—	—		*Cro*	—	*Sab*	—	*Cro*	—	—		*Cro*	*Sab*	*Cro*	*Cro*	*Sab*	*Cro*	*Cro*
0	**Nantes** d.	0808	0905	1105	1140	1203	1305	1405	...	1505	1605	1705	1740	1805	1809	1840	...	1856	1905	2002	2005	2105	2205	2244
88	Angers St Laud d.	0848	0944	1144	1219	|	1344	1444	...	1544	1644	1744	|	1844	1848	|	...	1945	1944	2042	2044	2144	2245	|
136	Sablé d.	|	|	|	|	|	|	|	...	|	|	|	|	1907	|	|	...	|	|	|	|	|	|	|
191	**Le Mans** d.	|	1026	1226	|	|	|	1526	...	1626	1726	|	|	|	|	|	...	2025	|	2124	2126	|	|	|
393	**Paris** Montparnasse a.	1018	1128	1329	1343	1414	1514	1628	...	1728	1833	1916	1945	2019	2024	2046	...	2128	2115	2228	2230	2319	0020	0049

To / From:
Bre – Brest (Table **284**). *Cro* – Le Croisic (Table **288**). *Lor* – Lorient (Table **285**). *Naz* – St Nazaire (Table **288**). *Sab* – Les Sables-d'Olonne (Table **293**).
Bri – St Brieuc (Table **284**). *Lan* – Lannion (Table **284**). *Mal* – St Malo (Table **281**). *Qui* – Quimper (Table **285**).

A – ①②③④⑥ (also July 15; not July 13, Aug. 15).
B – ①②③④⑦ (not July 13, 14).
C – ①②③④⑥⑦ (also July 15; not July 13).
D – ②③④ (not July 13, 14, Aug. 16).
E – ⑦ (also ①–④ Aug. 1 – 18).
F – ①–④ July 4 – 28 (also Aug. 22 – 25; not July 13, 14).
G – ①②③④⑦ until Aug. 21 (also Aug. 28; not July 13, 14).
H – ①②③④⑦ (also July 15, Aug. 20, 27; not July 13, 14).
K – ②③④⑥⑦ (also July 15, Aug. 15; not July 13, Aug. 16).

a – Not July 14, 15, 25 – 28, Aug. 1 – 4, 8 – 11, 15.
d – Also July 14, 15, Aug. 16; not July 15.
e – Not July 14, 15.
f – Also July 14, 15.
g – Not Aug. 15.
h – Also Aug. 15.
j – Also July 13; not July 15.
k – From July 22 (also July 13).
m – Not July 15.
p – Not July 14, 15, Aug. 15.
q – Also July 14, 15, Aug. 15.
r – Not Aug. 21, 28.
s – Also July 16; not July 15.
t – Until Aug. 20 (also Aug. 27).
u – Not Aug. 16.
v – Until Aug. 19 (also Aug. 20, 27).
w – Not July 13, 14, Aug. 15.
x – Also July 14.
y – Also July 13, 14, Aug. 15.
z – Not July 13, 14, 25 – 29, Aug. 1 – 15.
◧ – Also calls at Massy TGV (d. 0747).
⊡ – Also calls at Massy TGV (d. 0800).
⊖ – Also calls at Massy TGV (d. 0655).
● – Also calls at Massy TGV (d. 1443).
⊙ – Also calls at Massy TGV (d. 1943).
⊕ – Also calls at Massy TGV (d. 2014).
⊠ – OUIGO low-cost TGV service. Internet booking only (www.ouigo.com).
TGV – High-speed train. Ⓡ. 🍸.

LE MANS - NANTES and RENNES 280a

TER regional services. For *TGV* services see Table **280**. Additional trains are available Le Mans - Sablé sur Sarthe and v.v.

km		Ⓐ	Ⓐ	Ⓐ	⑥ A	Ⓐ	† A	Ⓐ	Ⓐ B	Ⓐ		Ⓐ		⑤	⚒	Ⓐ	Ⓐ C	Ⓒ	Ⓐ	Ⓐ	†	Ⓐ	Ⓐ	†
0	**Le Mans** d.	0547	0616	0641	0700	0706	0725	0741	0753	1042	1227	1309	...	1541	1643	1700	1741	1747	1800	1840	1900	1906	1941	2045
49	Sablé sur Sarthe **287** d.	0609	0645	0711	0725	0731	0746	0811	0828	1106	1259	1332	...	1611	1706	1731	1811	1820	1831	1901	1921	1931	2011	2108
97	Angers St Laud **287** d.	0632	0725	0733	0804	0808	0809	0835	0906	1130	1335	1355	...	1633	1730	1808	1836	1858	1906	1935	1944	2005	2033	2133
185	**Nantes** **287** a.	0715	...	0815	0846	...	0850	0915	...	1215	...	1440	...	1715	1816	...	1917	...	...	2015	2027	...	2115	2215

	Ⓐ	Ⓐ	Ⓐ	⚒		Ⓐ	Ⓐ		⚒		⚒	Ⓐ	†		Ⓐ	Ⓐ	Ⓐ	Ⓑ		⑥	Ⓑ	Ⓐ	Ⓒ A
Nantes **287** d.	...	0609	0644	...	...	0744	...	1144	...	...	1544	...	1644	...	1644	...	1744	...	...	...	1844	...	2110
Angers St Laud **287** d.	0552	0704	0727	0752	...	0827	0855	1227	1252	...	1627	1704	1727	...	1728	1752	1827	1852	...	1852	1929	1950	2154
Sablé sur Sarthe **287** d.	0630	0727	0751	0827	...	0854	0929	1253	1330	...	1652	1739	1750	...	1754	1828	1854	1928	...	1929	1953	2028	2216
Le Mans a.	0656	0755	0818	0900	...	0916	0955	1316	1402	...	1716	1810	1812	...	1816	1900	1916	1954	...	2002	2016	2054	2238

km		Ⓐ	Ⓐ	⑥		Ⓐ	Ⓐ	⑥		†	⚒	†		⑥	⑤	Ⓑ		Ⓐ	Ⓐ	Ⓐ			Ⓐ	Ⓑ
0	**Le Mans** d.	0630	0650	0704	...	0717	0818	0925	...	1117	1220	1441	...	1521	1531	1620	...	1643	1720	1749	...	1820	1920	2024
90	Laval **287** d.	0723	0754	0752	...	0811	0909	1015	...	1207	1322	1532	...	1610	1619	1711	...	1732	1814	1853	...	1911	2020	2115
125	Vitré **287** d.	0749	...	...	...	...	...	...	...	...	...	...	...	...	1638	...	...	1800	...	...	...	...	...	...
163	**Rennes** **287** a.	0821	...	...	...	...	...	...	...	...	...	...	...	...	1717	...	...	1832	...	...	...	...	...	...

	Ⓐ	Ⓐ	Ⓐ		Ⓐ	⚒	Ⓒ		Ⓐ	Ⓐ	Ⓒ		⑤	⑥	Ⓑ		Ⓐ	⑥	†		Ⓐ	Ⓐ	†
Rennes **287** d.	...	...	...	...	0629	...	...	...	...	...	...	...	...	...	...	...	...	...	...	...	...	...	...
Vitré **287** d.	...	...	...	...	0652	...	...	...	...	...	...	...	...	...	...	...	...	...	...	...	...	...	...
Laval **287** d.	0604	0641	0659	...	0720	0804	0925	...	0941	1245	1247	...	1545	1622	1644	...	1750	1844	1904	...	1904	1944	2008
Le Mans a.	0706	0734	0804	...	0814	0855	1015	...	1034	1354	1338	...	1634	1712	1734	...	1853	1934	1954	...	2014	2034	2058

A – To/from Le Croisic (Table **288**). B – To/from Chartres (Table **278**). C – To/from Le Croisic on ⑤ (Table **288**).

PARIS - RENNES - ST MALO 281

TGV timings may vary by a few minutes - please check your reservation.

km		*TGV* 8081 ①⑥ d	*TGV* 8083	*TGV* 8085	*TGV* 8093 ⑤ e	*TGV* 8093 D	*TGV* 8097 ⑤ e
	Paris Montparnasse **280** d.	0706	1000	1356	1815	1815	2020
0	**Rennes** **272** d.	0906	1133	1529	1853	2013	2215
58	Dol **272** d.	0940	1208	|	2029	2045	2246
81	**St Malo** a.	0954	1221	1611	2043	2100	2300

	TGV 8080 ①-⑤ f	*TGV* 8084	*TGV* 8086 ⑥⑦	*TGV* 8088 g	*TGV* 8092 ⑦ h	*TGV* 8096 ⑦ h
St Malo d.	0608	1159	1539	1742	1938	2101
Dol **272** d.	0623	|	1555	1758	1954	|
Rennes **272** a.	0655	1242	1625	1829	2025	2144
Paris Montparnasse **280** a.	0851	1452	1812	2011	2212	2354

	Ⓐ	⚒	Ⓒ	Ⓐ		†	⚒		Ⓐ	⑥	Ⓐ	⚒	†	†	Ⓐ		⑥	Ⓐ	†	Ⓐ	⑥	Ⓐ	Ⓒ
Rennes **272** d.	0635	0735	0935	0935	1138	1235	1235	...	1435	1435	1539	1635	1635	1735	1735	...	1735	1804	1835	1835	1835	1936	2040
Dol **272** d.	0714	0813	1011	1013	1217	1311	1319	...	1514	1521	1620	1713	1714	1811	1813	...	1816	1846	1914	1917	1921	2015	2119
St Malo a.	0730	0829	1025	1029	1233	1325	1335	...	1530	1535	1636	1729	1730	1825	1829	...	1832	1905	1928	1933	1935	2031	2135

	⑥	Ⓐ	Ⓐ	Ⓐ	†	⑥	Ⓐ			⚒	⑥	Ⓑ	⑤	①-④	Ⓐ		Ⓒ	Ⓒ	Ⓐ	Ⓐ	Ⓒ	Ⓐ	Ⓒ
St Malo d.	0619	0627	0658	0758	0822	0827	0837	...	1030	1227	1316	1323	1424	1530	1630	...	1634	1730	1730	1830	1832	2030	2032
Dol **272** d.	0635	0643	0716	0817	0836	0843	0851	...	1046	1243	1332	1339	1440	1546	1646	...	1648	1746	1746	1846	1846	2046	2046
Rennes **272** a.	0721	0725	0756	0856	0913	0925	0925	...	1125	1325	1418	1418	1519	1625	1725	...	1725	1825	1825	1925	1925	2125	2125

D – ②③④ (not July 13, 14, Aug. 16).
d – Also July 14, 15, Aug. 16; not July 15.
e – Also July 13; not July 15.
f – Not July 14, 15, Aug. 15.
g – Not Aug. 21, 28.
h – Also July 14, 15, Aug. 16; not July 15.
TGV – High-speed train. 🅁. 🍷.

DOL - DINAN - ST BRIEUC 282

DOL - DINAN

km		Ⓐ	⑥	⚒	†	⚒		Ⓐ	⑥	⑤	E	⑤
0	**Dol** d.	0821	0846	0945	1110	1324	1724	1925	1928	2035	2052	2255
32	**Dinan** a.	0844	0906	1005	1130	1344	1752	1952	1948	2055	2112	2315

	Ⓐ 🚌 j	Ⓐ k	Ⓐ	⑥	Ⓐ	Ⓒ	⚒		Ⓐ	Ⓒ	Ⓐ m
Dinan d.	0545	0558	0737	0802	0914	1014	1211	1527	1836	1846	2003
Dol a.	0610	0618	0805	0830	0934	1041	1231	1547	1902	1906	2023

DINAN - ST BRIEUC **JULY 2 – 29**

km		Ⓐ 🚌	Ⓐ 🚌		⚒ 🚌	🚌		Ⓐ 🚌	Ⓒ 🚌		Ⓐ 🚌	Ⓐ 🚌
0	**Dinan** d.	0605	0620	...	0640	1205	...	1620	1715	...	1810	1820
41	Lamballe **284** d.	0718	|	...	0750	1315	...	1730	1825	...	1917	|
62	**St Brieuc** . **284** a.	...	0720	...	0825	1350	...	1805	1900	...	...	1920

	Ⓐ 🚌	Ⓐ 🚌	⚒ 🚌	Ⓐ 🚌	Ⓒ 🚌		Ⓐ 🚌	Ⓐ 🚌	Ⓐ 🚌	Ⓐ 🚌	Ⓒ 🚌
St Brieuc .... **284** d.	0640	...	0845	1330	1615	...	1715	...	1835	...	1910
Lamballe ..... **284** d.	|	0635	0920	1405	1650	...	|	1740	|	1835	1945
Dinan a.	0740	0742	1030	1515	1800	...	1815	1853	1935	1948	2055

DINAN - ST BRIEUC **JULY 30 – AUGUST 28**

km		Ⓐ 🚌	Ⓐ 🚌		⚒			Ⓐ	Ⓒ		Ⓐ 🚌	Ⓐ 🚌
0	**Dinan** d.	0605	0620	...	0714	1205	...	1621	1743	...	1810	1820
41	Lamballe ... **284** d.	0718	|	...	0804	1255	...	1711	1834	...	1917	|
62	**St Brieuc** . **284** a.	...	0720	...	0820	1311	...	1727	1849	...	...	1920

	Ⓐ 🚌	Ⓐ 🚌	⚒	Ⓐ	Ⓒ	Ⓐ 🚌	Ⓐ 🚌	Ⓐ	Ⓐ 🚌	Ⓐ 🚌	Ⓒ
St Brieuc .... **284** d.	0640	...	0846	1325	1615	1715	...	1751	1835	...	1859
Lamballe ..... **284** d.	|	0635	0902	1341	1631	|	1740	1807	|	1835	1915
Dinan a.	0740	0742	0951	1430	1720	1815	1853	1856	1935	1948	2004

E – ①②③④⑦. j – July 4–29. k – Aug. 1–26. m – Runs 13 minutes later on ①–④.

🚌 MORLAIX - ROSCOFF 🚌 283

Until July 7	⚒	Ⓐ	⑥		⚒	Ⓐ	⑥		Ⓒ	Ⓐ	†		⚒	Ⓐ n	⚒		Ⓐ	†	⚒			⑤	
Morlaix, Gare SNCF d.	0655	0755	0800	...	0950	1110	1115	...	1430	1430	1540	...	1540	1625	1655	...	1745	1820	1820	...	2015	2055	...
St Pol de Léon, Ti Kastelliz ⊡ d.	0720	0825	0825	...	1010	1130	1135	...	1450	1450	1600	...	1605	1700	1720	...	1810	1840	1847	...	2035	2115	...
Roscoff, Ferry d.	0735	0840	0840	...	1025	1145	1150	...	|	1505	|	...	|	|	|	...	|	1855	1902	...	2050	2130	...
Roscoff, Quai d'Auxerre ⊙ a.	0740	0845	0845	...	1030	1150	1155	...	1505	1510	1615	...	1620	1715	1735	...	1825	1900	1907	...	2055	2135	...

Until July 7	⚒	⚒		⚒	Ⓐ		†	⑥			Ⓐ n		⑥	Ⓐ m		†	⑥		Ⓐ	Ⓒ		Ⓐ	
Roscoff, Quai d'Auxerre ⊙ d.	0655	0745	...	0845	1155	...	1200	1200	...	1350	1600	...	1600	1650	...	1650	1705	...	1720	1900	...	1900	...
Roscoff, Ferry d.	|	|	...	0850	|	...	|	|	...	|	|	...	|	|	...	|	1710	...	1725	|	...	1905	...
St Pol de Léon, Ti Kastelliz ⊡ d.	0710	0800	...	0905	1210	...	1215	1215	...	1405	1615	...	1615	1705	...	1705	1725	...	1740	1915	...	1920	...
Morlaix, Gare SNCF a.	0735	0825	...	0925	1237	...	1235	1240	...	1425	1635	...	1635	1725	...	1725	1750	...	1805	1935	...	1940	...

m – School holidays only.
n – Not during School holidays.
⊡ – 300 metres from railway station.
⊙ – 400 metres from railway station.

284 (PARIS -) RENNES - LANNION and BREST

TGV timings may vary by a few minutes - please check your reservation. For services Guingamp - Carhaix / Paimpol and v.v. see Table **299**.

km										*TGV* **8605**			*TGV* **8691**				*TGV* **8611**					*TGV* **8615**				
		Ⓐ	⑥	Ⓐ	Ⓐ	Ⓐ	Ⓐ	Ⓐ		⚒	⚒	⑥		†	Ⓐ	⑥		Ⓐ		⑥	†		⑥	Ⓑ	⚒	
	Paris Montparnasse **280** d.	...	...	...	...	...	...	...	...	0735	...	...	0856	...	...	...	1000	...	...	...	...	1056	...	...	...	...
0	**Rennes** d.	...	...	...	...	0635	0702	0735	...	0926	...	0935	1032	1036	1043	1043	1129	...	...	...	...	1229	...	...	1239	1335
80	Lamballe **282** d.	...	...	...	...	0728	0742	0831	...	|	...	1029	|	1125	1120	1120	|	...	...	...	...	1308	...	...	1337	1412
101	St Brieuc **282** d.	...	...	...	0728	0743	0754	0845	...	1016	...	1043	1124	1137	1113	1133	1215	...	...	...	...	1321	...	...	1354	1424
132	Guingamp d.	...	...	...	0746	...	0810	...	...	1033	1048	...	1142	...	1149	1149	|	...	...	...	...	1338	...	...	...	1441
	Lannion d.	0604	...	...	|	...	|	...	...	|	|	...	|	...	|	|	|	...	...	1228	1236	|	...	...	...	|
158	Plouaret-Trégor d.	0627	...	...	0800	...	0824	...	...	|	1103	...	|	...	|	1203	|	...	...	1252	1300	1353	1359	1408	...	|
175	**Lannion** a.	|	...	...	0818	...	|	...	...	|	1119	...	1213	...	|	|	|	...	...	|	|	|	1416	1425	...	|
189	Morlaix d.	0650	0710	0751	...	...	0842	...	...	1102	...	...	...	...	1218	1222	1254	1310	...	1310	1317	1411	...	...	...	1510
	Landivisiau d.	0707	0724	0813	...	...	0857	...	...	|	...	...	...	...	1234	1239	|	1325	...	1326	1332	|	...	...	...	1525
230	Landerneau **286** d.	0719	0736	0825	...	...	0908	...	...	|	...	...	...	...	1244	1250	|	1337	...	1338	1342	|	...	...	...	1536
248	**Brest** **286** a.	0735	0751	0841	...	...	0920	...	...	1135	...	...	...	...	1256	1302	1326	1354	...	1352	1354	1444	...	...	...	1550

	TGV **8619**												*TGV* **8623**												*TGV* **8629**
	①–⑥ d	Ⓐ	†	⑤	⑥	†	Ⓒ		⑤	⑥	①–④	⑤		†	Ⓐ	⑥	†		⚒	Ⓐ	Ⓐ	Ⓒ	⑥	Ⓐ	A
Paris Montparnasse **280** d.	1259	...	...	...	...	...	...	...	...	...	...	...	1443	...	...	...	...	...	...	...	...	...	...	...	1656
Rennes d.	1429	...	1435	1435	1439	1439	...	...	...	...	...	1536	1629	...	...	...	1635	...	1635	...	1735	1735	...	1739	1829
Lamballe **282** d.	|	...	1512	1525	1516	1527	...	...	...	...	...	1613	|	...	...	...	1726	...	1728	...	1813	1813	...	1837	|
St Brieuc **282** d.	1516	...	1525	1537	1529	1541	...	...	...	...	...	1626	1718	...	1730	1732	1737	...	1740	...	1826	1826	...	1849	1916
Guingamp d.	1533	...	1542	...	1546	...	...	...	...	...	...	1642	1734	1742	1753	1750	...	...	...	...	1842	1842	...	...	1933
Plouaret-Trégor d.	|	...	1556	...	1600	...	1610	...	...	...	...	|	|	1757	1810	1805	...	...	...	...	|	1856	1912	...	|
Lannion a.	|	...	|	...	|	...	1627	...	...	...	...	|	|	1813	1826	1821	...	...	...	...	|	|	1929	...	|
Morlaix d.	1602	1610	1614	...	1618	...	...	...	1657	1710	1710	1712	1803	...	...	...	...	...	...	1810	1912	1915	...	...	2002
Landivisiau d.	|	1624	1630	...	1633	...	...	...	1711	1725	1725	1728	|	...	...	...	...	...	...	1825	1927	1931	...	...	|
Landerneau **286** d.	|	1636	1641	...	1644	...	...	...	1723	1737	1737	1738	|	...	...	...	...	...	...	1837	1938	1941	...	...	|
Brest **286** a.	1635	1654	1653	...	1658	...	...	...	1739	1751	1754	1752	1838	...	...	...	...	...	...	1849	1950	1953	...	...	2035

	TGV **8631**					*TGV* **8635**	*TGV* **8695**		*TGV* **8639**							*TGV* **8641**			*TGV* **8645**		*TGV* **8649**			*TGV* **8655**	*TGV* **8657**
	⑤ e		Ⓐ	⑥	Ⓐ	⑤ e	⑤ e		B	†	⑥	①–④	†	⑤	⑤	A	⑥–④		⑤ e	⑤	⑤ e	⑤	†	⑤ e	⑦ f
Paris Montparnasse **280** d.	1657	...	...	...	...	1748	1748	...	1759	...	...	...	...	...	...	1856	...	...	1907	...	1959	...	...	2054	2359
Rennes d.	1829	...	1835	1837	...	|	|	...	1929	1935	1936	...	...	1939	...	2029	...	...	|	2040	2129	...	2135	2229	|
Lamballe **282** d.	1907	...	1928	1932	...	|	|	...	|	2025	2013	...	...	2015	...	2108	...	...	|	2117	2210	...	2212	|	|
St Brieuc **282** d.	1921	...	1940	1944	...	2004	2010	...	2017	2037	2025	2026	...	2027	...	2121	...	...	2116	2130	2224	...	2224	2316	0423
Guingamp d.	1938	1945	...	...	...	|	2028	...	2034	...	2042	2042	2043	2044	2054	2137	...	...	|	2146	2241	...	2241	2333	0440
Plouaret-Trégor d.	|	2000	...	...	...	|	|	...	|	...	2056	2056	2058	2058	2109	2152	2158	...	|	2200	2256	2258	2255	|	|
Lannion a.	|	2016	...	...	...	|	2057	...	|	...	|	2112	2115	|	2125	|	2215	...	|	|	|	2315	|	|	|
Morlaix d.	2006	...	...	...	2014	2046	...	...	2103	...	2115	...	...	2116	...	2211	...	...	|	2219	2313	...	2313	0002	0515
Landivisiau d.	|	...	...	...	2029	|	...	...	|	...	2130	...	...	2132	...	|	...	...	|	2234	|	...	2329	|	|
Landerneau **286** d.	|	...	...	...	2041	|	...	...	|	...	2141	...	...	2142	...	2236	...	...	|	2245	2338	...	2339	|	0539
Brest **286** a.	2039	...	...	...	2053	2118	...	...	2136	...	2154	...	...	2154	...	2248	...	...	2221	2258	2350	...	2353	0035	0552

	TGV **8680**		*TGV* **8602**				*TGV* **8604**				*TGV* **8606**				*TGV* **8610**							*TGV* **8620**	*TGV* **8620**		
	① g	Ⓐ	C	Ⓐ	Ⓐ	Ⓐ	① g	Ⓐ	Ⓐ	⑥	①–⑥ d	⚒	†		d	⑥	Ⓑ	⑥	Ⓐ	⑥	Ⓐ	②–⑥ j	① g	Ⓐ	⑥
Brest **286** d.	...	...	0518	0541	...	...	0627	0700	...	...	0718	0800	...	...	0905	0941	1040	...	...	...	...	1119	1128	...	...
Landivisiau d.	...	...	|	0552	...	...	|	0717	...	...	|	0814	...	...	|	0952	1051	...	...	...	...	|	|	...	...
Landerneau **286** d.	...	...	|	0602	...	...	|	0729	...	...	|	0827	...	...	0918	1002	1101	...	...	...	...	|	|	...	...
Morlaix d.	...	...	0551	0618	...	...	|	0743	...	...	0751	0843	...	...	0941	1018	1117	...	...	...	...	1151	|	...	...
Lannion d.	...	...	|	|	...	0626	|	▬	0731	0740	|	...	...	0935	|	|	|	...	...	1129	1138	|	|	1231	...
Plouaret-Trégor d.	...	...	|	0634	...	0642	|	⑥	0747	0756	|	...	...	0951	0959	1035	1134	...	...	1145	1153	|	|	1247	...
Guingamp d.	...	...	0620	0649	...	0658	|		0802	0809	0820	...	...	...	1015	1049	1148	...	...	...	1207	1220	|	1301	...
St Brieuc **282** d.	0538	0616	0637	0706	0715	0721	0737	0806	...	0828	0837	...	0907	...	1032	1105	1205	1206	1209	...	1223	1237	1237	...	1303
Lamballe **282** d.	0550	0627	|	0717	0726	...	|	0817	...	...	|	...	0918	...	1044	1117	1217	1220	1223	...	...	|	|	...	1317
Rennes a.	0629	0721	0725	0759	0820	...	0825	0913	...	...	0925	...	1007	...	1125	1159	1259	1321	1321	...	...	1325	1325	...	1418
Paris Montparnasse **280** a.	0823	...	0910	...	...	...	1009	...	...	...	1123	...	...	...	1312	...	...	...	...	...	...	1509	1509	...	...

		TGV **8622**									*TGV* **8630**	*TGV* **8628**					*TGV* **8690**	*TGV* **8694**	*TGV* **8632**				*TGV* **8636**		*TGV* **8636**
	†	Ⓑ k	Ⓐ	⑥	†	Ⓒ	⑤	①–④	⑥	①–④	A	⑤ e			Ⓒ	⑤	D	⑤ e	① g	Ⓐ	†	Ⓐ	①–④ d	⑤	⑤ e
Brest **286** d.	...	1218	1245	...	...	1301	1304	1308	1400	...	1414	1431	...	...	1458	1500	...	...	1530	...	...	1600	1618	...	1618
Landivisiau d.	...	|	1302	...	...	1312	1315	1319	1413	...	|	|	...	...	1509	1511	...	...	|	...	...	1616	|	...	|
Landerneau **286** d.	...	|	1314	...	...	1322	1325	1329	1425	...	|	|	...	...	1519	1521	...	...	|	...	...	1628	|	...	|
Morlaix d.	...	1251	1328	...	...	1338	1340	1344	1439	...	1446	1505	...	...	1535	1536	...	...	1603	...	...	1643	1650	...	1649
Lannion d.	...	|	...	1329	1332	|	|	|	...	1442	|	|	...	1520	|	|	1545	1545	|	...	...	...	|	1634	|
Plouaret-Trégor d.	...	|	...	1345	1348	1355	1356	1401	...	1458	1504	|	...	1536	1552	|	|	|	|	...	...	...	|	1650	1708
Guingamp d.	...	1320	...	...	...	1410	1411	1415	...	...	1519	|	...	...	1607	1606	1615	1615	1632	...	...	...	|	...	1724
St Brieuc **282** d.	1311	1337	...	...	...	1427	1427	1432	...	...	1536	|	1610	...	1624	1624	1633	1633	1650	1714	1718	...	1738	...	1742
Lamballe **282** d.	1323	|	...	...	...	1439	1438	1443	...	...	1548	|	1624	...	1636	1635	|	1645	1702	1728	1730	...	|	...	|
Rennes a.	1414	1425	...	...	...	1519	1519	1525	...	...	1629	1629	1717	...	1715	1721	1725	1725	|	1821	1821	...	1825	...	1825
Paris Montparnasse **280** a.	...	1612	...	...	...	...	...	...	...	...	1812	1813	...	...	...	...	1910	1910	1919	...	...	...	2010	...	2011

	TGV **8636**							*TGV* **8640**		*TGV* **8642**			*TGV* **8644**				*TGV* **8692**					*TGV* **8646**	*TGV* **8648**		*TGV* **8652**
	⑦ m	†	⚒	Ⓐ	Ⓒ	Ⓐ	⑤	B	⑥	⑤ e	†	Ⓐ	⑦ m	Ⓐ	⑥	†	⑦ m	Ⓐ	①–④	⑤	Ⓒ	E	⑤⑥ n	†	⑦ m
Brest **286** d.	1622	1641	...	1648	...	...	1706	1713	1713	1718	1730	1740	1802	1806	1808	1809	...	1859	...	...	...	1918	1918	...	2013
Landivisiau d.	|	1652	...	1704	...	...	1717	|	1724	|	1741	1754	|	1818	1822	1820	...	1912	...	...	...	|	|	...	|
Landerneau **286** d.	|	1702	...	1717	...	...	1727	|	1734	|	1751	1804	|	1828	1834	1830	...	1924	...	...	...	|	|	...	|
Morlaix d.	1654	1718	...	1734	...	...	1743	1746	1750	1753	1806	1818	|	1843	1848	1846	...	1945	...	...	...	1951	1952	...	2048
Lannion d.	|	|	...	...	1734	1735	|	|	|	|	|	|	|	|	|	|	1855	...	1932	1932	1937	|	|	2037	|
Plouaret-Trégor d.	|	1736	...	...	1750	1751	1800	|	1808	|	1830	1846	|	1900	1912	|	|	▬	1948	1948	1953	|	|	2053	|
Lannion a.	|	|	...	...	|	|	|	|	|	|	1847	1903	|	|	1929	|	|	†	|	|	|	|	|	|	|
Guingamp d.	|	1751	...	...	1805	1805	1815	1816	1823	1823	...	...	|	1915	...	1915	1925		2002	2003	2008	2020	2021	2107	2117
St Brieuc **282** d.	1740	1808	1814	...	...	1823	1832	1833	1840	1841	...	...	1913	1932	...	1932	1943	2018	2017	...	...	2037	2039	...	2134
Lamballe **282** d.	|	1819	1928	...	...	...	1842	1846	1851	|	...	...	|	1943	...	1943	|	2029	...	...	...	|	2052	...	2146
Rennes a.	1825	1859	1921	...	...	...	1925	1925	1930	1929	...	...	|	2025	...	2025	2029	2121	...	...	...	2125	|	...	2225
Paris Montparnasse **280** a.	2011	...	...	...	...	...	...	2120	...	2127	...	...	2132	...	...	...	2212	...	...	...	...	2310	2305	...	0011

A – ①②③④⑥⑦ (also July 15; not July 13).
B – ①②③④⑦ (not July 13, 14).
C – ①②③④⑥ (also July 15; not July 13, Aug. 15).
D – ①②③④⑦ (also July 15, Aug. 20, 27; not July 13, 14).
E – ①②③④⑦ until Aug. 21 (also Aug. 28; not July 13, 14).

d – Not Aug. 15.
e – Also July 13; not July 15.
f – Also Aug. 15; not Aug. 14.
g – Also July 16; not July 15.
j – Not Aug. 16.

k – Not July 14, 15.
m – Also Aug. 15.
n – Also July 13, 14.

TGV – High-speed train. 🅁. 🍷.

RENNES and NANTES - QUIMPER 285

TGV timings may vary by a few minutes - please check your reservation.

km													*TGV*	*TGV*					*TGV*	*TGV*	*TGV*				
													8703	**8707**					**7667**	**8711**	**8715**				
		Ⓐ	Ⓐ	Ⓐ	Ⓐ	Ⓐ	⑥	Ⓐ	⑥	⑥	†	†	⑥	Ⓑ	⑥	†	Ⓐ	Ⓐ		Ⓑ	⑥	Ⓐ	†	⑥	Ⓒ
													d	**e**					**A** ⊠	**e**	**d**				
0	*Paris Montparnasse* **280** d.	...	...	...	...	...	...	...	...	...	...	...	0830	0856	...	...	...	...	...	1056	1056	...	...	...	...
365	**Rennes** d.	0621	...	...	0705	...	0841	0935	...	0941	0953	...	|	1029	...	1135	...	1135	1154	1232	1232	1241	...	...	1241
	Nantes 288 d.	|	0614	0643	|	0714	|	|	0925	|	|	0930	|	|	1114	|	1118	|	|	|	|	|	1220	1224	|
	Savenay 288 d.	|	0637	0709	|	0737	|	|	0946	|	|	1005	|	|	1139	|	1140	|	|	|	|	|	1254	1245	|
437	Redon d.	0706	0711	0747	0747	0810	0923	1011	1023	1023	1035	1039	|	1106	1210	1211	1217	1217	|	|	|	1325	1325	1320	1331
492	Vannes ⊖ d.	0737	...	0815	0815	...	0954	1037	1052	1052	1106	...	1102	1131	...	1240	1245	1245	1253	1330	1330	1356	...	...	1401
511	Auray ⊖ d.	*0756*	...	0828	0828	...	...	1049	1104	1104	1119	...	1115	1144	...	1252	1258	1258	1306	1343	1343	...	...	...	...
545	Lorient ⊖ d.	*0826*	...	0849	0849	...	...	1108	1125	1125	|	...	1134	1204	...	1313	1318	1318	1333	1402	1402	...	...	...	...
565	Quimperlé d.	...	...	0901	0901	...	...	1120	1137	1137	◧	...	1148	|	...	1325	1331	1331	|	1415	|	...	...	...	...
612	**Quimper** a.	...	...	0929	0929	...	...	1148	1205	1205	...	...	1212	1244	...	1353	1359	1359	1410	1441	1437	...	...	...	...

								TGV	*TGV*	*TGV*				*TGV*	*TGV*										
								8719	**8719**	**8721**				**8723**	**8725**										
	†	Ⓐ	†	Ⓐ	⑥	⑥	⑤		⑦	⑤	⑤	†	Ⓐ		⑤⑥	†	⚒	Ⓒ	Ⓐ	Ⓐ		Ⓐ	①–④	†	⑤
								B	**f**	**g**				**C**	**h**			**D**							
Paris Montparnasse **280** d.	...	...	...	...	...	...	...	1259	1300	1305	...	...	...	1443	1505	...	...	...	...	...	...	...	...	...	...
Rennes d.	...	...	1335	...	...	1335	1341	1432	1432	|	1441	1441	1605	1632	|	1640	1641	...	...	1705	1735	...	1743	...	1743
Nantes 288 d.	1256	1256	|	1314	1318	|	|	|	|	|	|	|	|	|	|	|	|	1700	1649	|	|	1714	|	1719	|
Savenay 288 d.	|	|	|	1337	1340	|	|	|	|	|	|	|	|	|	|	|	|	|	1710	|	|	1738	|	1753	|
Redon d.	1342	1340	1412	1410	1417	1417	1426	|	|	|	1518	1534	1641	|	|	1716	1725	1743	1747	1747	1812	1814	1826	1827	1832
Vannes ⊖ d.	1411	1409	1440	...	1446	1446	1456	1530	1530	1530	1546	1608	1709	1731	1731	1745	1801	1809	1816	1816	1838	...	1857	...	1902
Auray ⊖ d.	|	1421	1452	...	1458	1458	...	1543	1543	1543	1558	...	1721	1745	1745	1757	...	|	1828	1828	1850	...	...	...	...
Lorient ⊖ d.	1437	1442	1514	...	1519	1519	...	1602	1602	1602	1620	...	1743	1804	1804	1819	...	1836	1850	1850	1909	...	...	...	...
Quimperlé d.	|	1454	1526	...	1531	1531	...	|	|	|	1632	...	1756	|	|	1831	...	|	1902	1902	1922	...	...	...	...
Quimper a.	1512	1522	1554	...	1559	1559	...	1637	1637	1637	1700	...	1825	1837	1837	1859	...	1915	1930	1930	1950	...	...	...	...

		TGV		*TGV*						*TGV*	*TGV*				*TGV*	*TGV*				*TGV*	*TGV*	*TGV*	*TGV*	*TGV*	*TGV*
		8727		**8729**						**8731**	**8735**				**8739**	**8747**				**8751**	**8751**	**8751**	**8753**	**8755**	**8791**
	Ⓐ	⑤	⚒	⑥	⑤	①–④	Ⓒ	⑤	Ⓐ		⑤	⑥	⑥	Ⓑ		⑤	Ⓐ	†	⑤	⑦	①–④	⑤	⑤	⑤	⑤
	D	**g**		**d**						**C**	**g**				**E**	**g**				**F**	**G**	**g**	**g**	**g**	**g**
Paris Montparnasse **280** d.	...	1644	...	1656	...	...	...	...	...	1759	1800	...	...	...	1856	1923	...	...	...	1957	1957	1959	2014	2054	2215
Rennes d.	...	|	...	1832	1841	1841	1841	1845	...	1932	1931	...	1941	1941	2032	|	...	...	2055	2132	2132	2132	|	2232	0029
Nantes 288 d.	1757	|	1814	|	|	|	|	|	1914	|	|	1926	|	|	|	|	2014	2014	|	|	|	|	|	|	|
Savenay 288 d.	|	|	1838	|	|	|	|	|	1937	|	|	1947	|	|	|	|	2037	2049	|	|	|	|	|	|	|
Redon d.	1842	1858	1910	|	1918	1925	1930	1941	2010	|	|	2024	2024	2025	2108	|	2112	2123	2140	2208	2208	2208	2220	|	|
Vannes ⊖ d.	1909	1925	...	1930	1943	1956	2004	2012	...	2030	2031	2053	2053	2101	2134	2143	...	...	2211	2234	2234	2234	2246	2330	0128
Auray ⊖ d.	1921	1941	...	1943	1955	...	...	...	...	|	2044	2105	2105	...	2147	|	...	...	...	2247	2247	2247	2259	2343	0141
Lorient ⊖ d.	1940	2002	...	2002	2014	...	...	...	...	2056	2103	2125	2125	...	2205	2209	...	...	...	2305	2303	2305	2319	0002	0157
Quimperlé d.	|	2015	...	|	2026	...	...	...	...	|	|	2138	2138	...	2219	|	...	...	...	2319	...	2319	2333	|	...
Quimper a.	2015	2045	...	2037	2054	...	...	...	...	2130	2138	2206	2206	...	2248	2241	...	...	...	2348	...	2348	0001	0037	...

			TGV	*TGV*										*TGV*				*TGV*							*TGV*
			8702	**8702**										**8706**				**8710**							**8720**
	Ⓐ	Ⓐ		⑤	Ⓐ	Ⓐ	Ⓐ	⚒	Ⓐ	⑥	Ⓐ	Ⓐ	Ⓐ	①–⑥	†	Ⓒ	Ⓐ		Ⓐ	⑥	Ⓐ	†	⚒	⑥	
			B	**g**										**j**		**D**	**D**	**k**							
Quimper d.	...	...	0512	0512	0534	0534	...	...	0636	...	...	...	0704	0724	...	0850	0852	0911	0949	1038	...	...	...	...	1130
Quimperlé d.	...	...	0541	0541	0600	0600	...	...	0703	...	...	...	0734	|	...	|	|	0941	1016	1105	...	...	...	...	|
Lorient ⊖ d.	...	...	0556	0556	0613	0613	...	...	0716	...	...	0737	0749	0759	...	0925	0926	0955	1028	1118	...	...	...	1143	1204
Auray ⊖ d.	...	...	0613	0614	0633	0633	...	...	0737	...	...	0806	...	0817	...	|	|	1013	1049	1139	...	...	...	1209	|
Vannes ⊖ d.	0601	...	0627	0627	0646	0646	0704	...	0748	0753	...	0820	...	0830	...	0952	0952	1026	1101	1150	1201	1201	...	1220	1231
Redon d.	0632	0642	0654	0654	0720	0726	0734	0744	0819	0824	0846	...	...	|	0932	1021	1021	1053	1133	1221	1232	1231	1249	...	|
Savenay 288 d.	|	0717	|	|	|	0751	|	0819	|	|	0920	...	...	|	1004	|	|	|	|	|	|	|	1321	...	|
Nantes 288 a.	|	0744	|	|	|	0816	|	0842	|	|	0944	...	...	|	1039	1104	1104	|	1216	|	|	|	1344	...	|
Rennes a.	0721	...	0729	0729	0755	...	0819	...	0856	0913	...	...	...	0929	...	...	...	1129	...	1257	1319	1321	...	...	1329
Paris Montparnasse **280** a.	...	...	0910	0911	...	...	...	...	...	...	...	...	...	1123	...	...	...	1312	...	...	...	...	...	...	1509

								TGV					*TGV*			*TGV*	*TGV*		*TGV*						
								8722					**8792**			**8726**	**8730**		**7662**						
	⑥	Ⓐ	†	Ⓐ	Ⓐ	⑥	Ⓐ		†	Ⓒ	⑤	†	①–④	†	⑥	⑥	Ⓑ	Ⓐ		Ⓐ	Ⓐ	Ⓐ	Ⓒ	Ⓐ	Ⓒ
								E					**m**			**d**	**e**		**A** ⊠						
Quimper d.	...	...	1159	1159	1159	1236	1247	1319	1336	1403	1402	...	...	...	...	1509	1515	...	1532	...	...	1558	1610	...	...
Quimperlé d.	...	...	1225	1226	1226	1303	1317	|	1403	1430	1429	...	...	...	...	1538	1545	...	|	...	...	1625	1637	...	...
Lorient ⊖ d.	...	1219	1238	1239	1239	1316	1332	1355	1416	1443	1442	...	1458	...	...	1557	1559	...	1610	...	1620	1638	1650	...	...
Auray ⊖ d.	...	1245	1259	1259	1259	1336	...	1413	1436	1501	1503	...	1516	...	...	1616	1617	...	1635	...	1646	1659	1708	...	...
Vannes ⊖ d.	1258	1259	1311	1311	1311	1349	...	1426	1449	1513	1514	...	1529	1556	1605	1629	1630	...	1649	1657	1701	1711	1720	...	...
Redon d.	1328	...	1342	1346	1353	1420	...	1453	1520	1541	1545	1549	|	1627	1636	|	|	1649	|	1728	...	1742	1748	1752	1759
Savenay 288 d.	|	...	|	|	1419	|	...	|	|	|	|	1618	|	|	|	|	|	1720	|	|	...	|	|	1823	1831
Nantes 288 a.	|	...	|	|	1442	1504	...	|	1604	|	|	1642	|	|	|	|	|	1744	|	|	...	|	|	1846	1854
Rennes a.	1418	...	1418	1421	...	...	...	1529	...	1619	1621	...	1625	1717	1719	|	1729	...	1803	1814	...	1819	1825	...	...
Paris Montparnasse **280** a.	...	...	...	...	...	...	...	1712	...	...	...	...	1812	...	...	1906	1910	...	...	...	...	...	...	...	...

			TGV					*TGV*			*TGV*	*TGV*					*TGV*	•				*TGV*	*TGV*	*TGV*	*TGV*
			8732					**8734**			**8740**	**8740**					* **8742**					**8744**	**8746**	**8794**	**8752**
	Ⓑ	Ⓐ	⑦	⑥	Ⓐ	Ⓑ	⑥	⑦	⑤	†	⑤			⑥	⑥	Ⓐ	⑦	†	†	Ⓐ	Ⓐ	⑦	①–⑥	⑦	⑦
			f					**f**			**g**	**H**					**f**					**f**	**j**	**f**	**f**
Quimper d.	...	...	1656	...	1703	...	...	1711	1715	...	1747	1747	...	1754	1754	...	1818	1834	1834	1835	1835	1907	1920	...	2024
Quimperlé d.	...	...	|	...	1733	...	...	1740	1742	⊡	|	|	...	1821	1821	...	|	1901	1901	1901	1901	|	|	...	|
Lorient ⊖ d.	...	1715	1731	1737	1748	...	...	1755	1755	|	1822	1822	...	1834	1834	...	1853	1914	1914	1914	1914	1943	1955	2029	2059
Auray ⊖ d.	...	1745	|	1804	...	...	...	1813	1814	1832	1840	1840	...	1855	1855	...	1911	1935	1935	1934	1934	2001	2013	2048	2117
Vannes ⊖ d.	...	1759	1757	1815	...	1804	1809	1826	1826	1845	1852	1852	...	1906	1906	...	1924	1946	1946	1946	1946	2014	2026	2102	2130
Redon d.	1849	...	|	...	...	1834	1840	1854	1854	1917	1919	|	...	1941	1944	1946	|	2021	2034	2021	2027	2041	2053	|	|
Savenay 288 d.	1921	...	|	...	...	|	|	|	|	|	|	|	...	|	2009	2018	|	|	2107	|	2053	|	|	|	|
Nantes 288 a.	1944	...	|	...	...	|	|	|	|	|	|	|	...	|	2032	2041	|	|	2141	|	2116	|	|	|	|
Rennes a.	...	...	|	...	...	1919	1923	1930	1930	1956	|	|	...	2016	...	...	|	2056	...	2056	...	|	2129	|	2229
Paris Montparnasse **280** a.	...	...	2029	...	...	...	...	2120	...	...	2128	2131	...	...	...	...	2200	...	...	...	...	2251	2311	2334	0011

A – To / from Paris Charles de Gaulle ✈ (Table **11**).
B – ①②③④⑥ (also July 15; not July 13, Aug. 15).
C – ①②③④⑦ (not July 13, 14).
D – To / from Brest (Table **286**).
E – ①②③④⑥⑦ (also July 15; not July 13).
F – ⑦ (also ①–④ Aug. 1–18).
G – ①–④ July 4–28 (also Aug. 22–25; not July 13, 14).
H – ①②③④⑥ (also July 15; not July 14, Aug. 15).

d – Also July 14, 15.
e – Not July 14, 15.
f – Also Aug. 15.
g – Also July 13; not July 15.
h – Also July 13, 14.
j – Not Aug. 15.
k – Until Aug. 19 (also Aug. 20, 27).
m – Not July 13, 14, Aug. 15.

◧ – To Quiberon (a. 1210).
⊡ – From Quiberon (d. 1741).

⊖ – Other trains **Vannes - Lorient** at 0640 Ⓐ, 0742 Ⓐ, 0840 ⑥, 1214 Ⓐ, 1645 ⑥, 1740 Ⓐ, 1845 Ⓐ, 2153 ⑤; **Lorient - Vannes** at 0648 Ⓐ, 1210 Ⓐ, 1810 Ⓐ.

⊠ – OUIGO low-cost TGV service. Internet booking only (www.ouigo.com).

TGV – High-speed train. Ⓡ. 🍸.

AURAY - QUIBERON. Journey 50 minutes.
From Auray at 0831, 1017, 1119, 1208, 1402, 1507, 1612, 1735 Ⓐ, 1751 Ⓒ, 1911, 2010.
From Quiberon at 0924, 1115, 1309, 1352, 1457, 1602, 1725 Ⓐ, 1741 Ⓒ, 1901, 2006, 2116.

286 BREST - QUIMPER

km		Ⓐ	Ⓒ A	Ⓐ A	Ⓐ	Ⓐ		⑥	†	Ⓐ	†	⑥		⑥	†	Ⓐ	⑥	Ⓐ		†	⑥	Ⓐ	Ⓐ	†
0	**Brest** 284 d.	0631	0747	0749	0837	1000	...	1056	1156	1233	1335	1344	...	1432	1527	1625	1626	1735	...	1745	1757	1839	1942	2002
18	Landerneau 284 d.	0643	|	|	0849	1012	...	1108	1208	1245	1347	1356	...	1444	1539	1640	1638	1746	...	1757	1809	1851	1954	2014
72	Châteaulin d.	0729	|	|	0933	1052	...	1148	1248	1331	1431	1436	...	1528	1623	1720	1718	1832	...	1837	1849	1937	2044	2054
102	**Quimper** a.	0750	0848	0850	0954	1113	...	1209	1309	1352	1452	1457	...	1549	1644	1741	1739	1853	...	1858	1910	1958	2105	2115

		Ⓐ	Ⓐ	⑥	Ⓐ	⑥		†	Ⓐ	⑥	Ⓐ	†		⑥	†	†	⑥	Ⓐ		Ⓐ	Ⓐ	Ⓒ A	Ⓐ A	†
	Quimper d.	0605	0706	0802	0910	1000	...	1030	1207	1223	1308	1408	...	1505	1600	1654	1655	1657	...	1809	1914	1917	2022	2141
	Châteaulin d.	0626	0731	0832	0931	1021	...	1051	1228	1244	1333	1429	...	1526	1621	1715	1720	1722	...	1830	1935	|	|	2202
	Landerneau 284 d.	0706	0820	0911	1006	1100	...	1130	1308	1323	1412	1508	...	1605	1700	1754	1759	1809	...	1915	2017	|	|	2241
	Brest 284 a.	0719	0833	0923	1018	1112	...	1142	1321	1335	1424	1520	...	1617	1712	1806	1811	1822	...	1928	2030	2019	2123	2253

A – To / from Nantes (Table **285**).

287 RENNES - NANTES

Other journeys Rennes - Nantes and v.v. are possible by changing trains at Redon (see both directions of Table **285**).

km		Ⓐ		⚒		Ⓒ		⚒		Ⓐ		†		⑥		Ⓐ		†		†		⚒		
0	**Rennes** d.	0737	...	0837	...	1037	...	1237	...	1337	...	1437	...	1637	...	1739	...	1745	...	1837	...	1837	...	1937
145	**Nantes** a.	0855	...	0955	...	1153	...	1354	...	1453	...	1553	...	1754	...	1854	...	1900	...	1952	...	1953	...	2055

		Ⓐ		⑥		Ⓒ		⚒		†		Ⓐ	⑥	Ⓐ		Ⓐ		Ⓒ		Ⓑ		⚒		†
	Nantes d.	0706	...	0806	...	1010	...	1206	...	1306	...	1406	1506	1606	...	1706	...	1713	...	1804	...	1906	...	2005
	Rennes a.	0829	...	0923	...	1123	...	1323	...	1423	...	1523	1623	1723	...	1825	...	1830	...	1923	...	2025	...	2123

SLOWER TRAINS VIA SABLÉ SUR SARTHE

km		Ⓐ	Ⓐ	Ⓐ	Ⓐ	Ⓐ	⑥	⑥		Ⓐ	Ⓒ	Ⓐ		Ⓐ	Ⓐ	†		①–④	⑤ B	Ⓐ	Ⓒ	Ⓐ	Ⓐ	†
0	**Rennes** 280a d.	0556	0629	0652	0656	0744	0800	0854	...	0907	1056	1056	1156	1256	1456	1556	...	1657	1657	1701	1756	1801	1856	1942
38	Vitré 280a d.	0616	0652	0716	0726	0814	0830	0916	...	0927	1116	1116	1226	1316	1516	1616	...	1717	1717	1730	1817	1830	1916	2002
73	Laval 280a d.	0637	0719	0737	0752	0840	0855	0937	...	0948	1137	1137	1252	1337	1537	1637	...	1737	1737	1756	1837	1856	1937	2021
126	Sablé sur Sarthe a.	0700	...	0800	...	...	...	1000	...	1009	1200	1200	...	1400	1600	1700	...	1800	1800	...	1901	...	2000	2042
126	Sablé sur Sarthe 280a d.	0711	...	0811	...	...	...	1006	...	1011	1206	1206	...	1406	1611	1706	...	1813	1811	...	1907	...	2011	2043
174	Angers St Laud 280a d.	0733	...	0835	...	...	...	1030	...	1033	1230	1229	...	1430	1633	1730	...	1836	1836	...	1930	...	2033	2106
262	**Nantes** 280a a.	0815	...	0915	...	...	...	1115	...	1115	1315	1315	...	1515	1715	1815	...	1917	1917	...	2014	...	2115	2146

		Ⓐ	Ⓐ	Ⓐ	Ⓐ	⑥	Ⓐ	⑥		Ⓐ	Ⓒ		Ⓐ	Ⓐ	⑤	Ⓐ		†	Ⓐ	Ⓒ	Ⓐ	Ⓒ	Ⓐ	Ⓑ
	Nantes 280a d.	...	0544	...	...	...	0744	0844	...	0944	1044	...	1148	1339	...	1544	...	1544	...	...	...	1744	1744	1944
	Angers St Laud 280a d.	...	0627	...	...	...	0827	0928	...	1027	1127	...	1230	1421	...	1627	...	1627	...	...	...	1827	1827	2027
	Sablé sur Sarthe 280a a.	...	0649	...	...	...	0849	0949	...	1049	1149	...	1252	1443	...	1649	...	1649	...	...	...	1849	1849	2049
	Sablé sur Sarthe d.	...	0655	...	...	...	0857	0959	...	1057	1157	...	1257	1455	...	1657	...	1657	...	...	...	1857	1857	2057
	Laval 280a d.	0636	0718	0723	0800	0904	0920	1021	...	1120	1220	1300	1320	1520	1619	1720	...	1720	1732	1804	1904	1920	1920	2120
	Vitré 280a d.	0702	0740	0749	0825	0931	0941	1041	...	1141	1241	1327	1341	1541	1638	1741	...	1741	1800	1830	1930	1941	1942	2141
	Rennes 280a a.	0732	0801	0821	0857	1000	1001	1102	...	1201	1301	1357	1401	1601	1717	1803	...	1804	1832	1901	2000	2001	2004	2201

B – To / from Le Croisic (Table **288**).

288 NANTES - ST NAZAIRE - LE CROISIC

TGV timings may vary by a few minutes - please check your reservation.

km		Ⓐ	Ⓐ	Ⓐ	⑥	Ⓐ	Ⓐ	*TGV* 8911 ⑥		*TGV* 8911 ①–⑤ d	⑥ C	† C	Ⓐ	Ⓒ D	Ⓒ	*TGV* 8913		Ⓐ	*TGV* 8917 ⑥ e	Ⓐ	Ⓒ	*TGV* 8921	Ⓐ	Ⓐ
	Paris M'nasse 280 d.	...	...	...	...	...	...	0643	...	0643	...	...	...	...	...	0939	...	...	1039	...	...	1252	...	...
0	**Nantes** 285 d.	0638	0710	0738	0746	0810	0838	0858	...	0856	0904	0906	1005	1015	1110	1200	...	1238	1300	1310	1410	1500	1507	1636
39	Savenay 285 d.	0702	0732	0802	0820	0832	0902	|	...	|	0926	0927	1027	1038	1132	|	...	1302	|	1332	1440	|	1529	1701
64	**St Nazaire** d.	0724	0748	0824	0843	0848	0924	0933	...	0933	0945	0941	1043	1056	1148	1236	...	1324	1338	1348	1457	1536	1545	1723
79	Pornichet d.	...	0800	...	0856	0900	...	0945	...	0945	1000	0954	1055	1110	1200	|	...	...	1351	1400	1510	|	1600	...
83	La Baule Escoublac d.	...	0808	...	0906	0908	...	0953	...	0953	1008	1003	1102	1122	1207	1253	...	...	1400	1408	1518	1553	1607	...
90	**Le Croisic** a.	...	0821	...	0919	0921	...	1006	...	1006	1020	1015	1116	1139	1221	1303	...	...	1412	1421	1530	1605	1621	...

		TGV 8923	Ⓐ	Ⓐ	⑥ E	Ⓐ	† E	Ⓐ		⑥	†	⑤ F	⑤	①–④	*TGV* 8905 ①–④ f	*TGV* 8927 ⑤ g		⑤⑥ D	*TGV* 8931	⑤	*TGV* 8935 ⑤ g	⑥–④	*TGV* 8937 ⑤ g	*TGV* 8939 ⑤ g
	Paris Montparnasse 280 d.	1447	...	...	...	...	...	...	...	...	...	...	...	...	1751	1752	...	...	1843	...	1939	...	2045	2152
	Nantes 285 d.	1655	1710	1738	1804	1808	1808	1838	...	1846	1910	1919	1923	1938	1959	2000	...	2010	2056	2137	2206	2213	2256	2359
	Savenay 285 d.	|	1732	1802	1826	1832	1830	1902	...	1919	1932	1944	1956	2002	|	|	...	2032	|	2206	|	2239	|	|
	St Nazaire d.	1731	1748	1824	1842	1847	1844	1924	...	1946	1947	2012	2017	2024	2035	2036	...	2049	2132	2223	2242	2256	2336	0036
	Pornichet d.	1743	1800	...	1852	1900	1854	...	...	1959	1959	2022	...	...	...	2048	...	2101	|	2234	2254	2307	|	|
	La Baule Escoublac d.	1751	1808	...	1907	1908	1911	...	...	2007	2007	2029	...	...	...	2055	...	2109	2149	2240	2302	2313	2354	0054
	Le Croisic a.	1810	1821	...	1919	1921	1923	...	...	2019	2021	2042	...	...	...	2107	...	2122	2158	2252	2314	2326	0003	0103

		TGV 8900 ①–⑤ h	⚒	*TGV* 8910 j	Ⓐ	Ⓐ	Ⓐ	Ⓒ D	Ⓐ	*TGV* 8912	Ⓐ	Ⓐ		†	⑥	*TGV* 8916	Ⓒ	Ⓐ	Ⓐ	Ⓐ	*TGV* 8922	Ⓐ	†	Ⓐ
	Le Croisic d.	...	0539	0555	...	0639	...	0724	0739	0755	...	0839	...	0934	0939	1047	1153	...	1239	...	1350	1439	1539	1539
	La Baule Escoublac d.	...	0552	0607	...	0652	...	0745	0752	0807	...	0852	...	0946	0952	1103	1208	...	1252	...	1402	1452	1552	1552
	Pornichet d.	...	0559	|	...	0659	...	0756	0759	|	...	0859	...	0955	0959	1110	1215	...	1259	...	|	1459	1559	1559
	St Nazaire d.	0522	0611	0623	0635	0711	0735	0811	0811	0824	0835	0911	...	1007	1011	1123	1227	1235	1311	1335	1421	1511	1611	1613
	Savenay 285 d.	|	0625	|	0657	0725	0757	0827	0825	|	0857	0925	...	1021	1026	|	1250	1257	1325	1357	|	1526	1625	1631
	Nantes 285 a.	0559	0648	0659	0721	0748	0821	0848	0848	0859	0921	0948	...	1043	1048	1157	1323	1321	1348	1421	1459	1548	1648	1654
	Paris Montparnasse 280 a.	0815	...	0915	...	...	...	...	...	1125	...	...	...	...	...	1414	...	...	...	...	1728	...	...	...

		Ⓐ	Ⓐ	*TGV* 8926	Ⓐ	†	⑥	*TGV* 8928 ⑦ k	Ⓐ	†	⑥ D	Ⓐ		*TGV* 8930 ⑦ k	*TGV* 8932 ①–⑥ d	† D	Ⓐ	Ⓒ C	⑤	†	⑥	*TGV* 8934 ⑦ k	*TGV* 8936 ⑦ k	⑥
	Le Croisic d.	...	1639	1653	...	1723	1723	1739	...	1811	1820	1839	...	1846	1855	1855	1939	1951	...	2039	2039	2052	2135	2135
	La Baule Escoublac d.	...	1652	1706	...	1737	1736	1753	...	1823	1841	1852	...	1902	1909	1905	1952	2008	...	2052	2053	2107	2147	2148
	Pornichet d.	...	1659	|	...	1744	1743	|	...	1830	1853	1859	...	1908	|	1924	1959	2016	...	2059	2101	2114	|	2154
	St Nazaire d.	1635	1711	1722	1735	1755	1754	1811	1835	1842	1908	1911	...	1922	1925	1939	2011	2027	2108	2111	2112	2126	2203	2206
	Savenay 285 d.	1657	1725	|	1757	1812	1817	|	1857	1901	1924	1925	...	|	|	1956	2025	2042	2126	2125	2126	|	|	2222
	Nantes 285 a.	1721	1748	1759	1821	1835	1850	1850	1921	1934	1947	1948	...	1956	2000	2018	2048	2104	2159	2148	2148	2159	2238	2245
	Paris Montparnasse 280 a.	...	...	2019	...	...	...	2128	...	...	...	...	...	2228	2230	...	...	...	...	...	...	0020	0049	...

C – To / from Le Mans (Table **280a**).
D – To / from Orléans (Tables **289** and **296**).
E – To / from Tours (Table **289**).
F – [2] Le Mans - Le Croisic; [2] Rennes - Le Croisic.

d – Not Aug. 15.
e – Also July 14, 15.
f – Not July 13, 14, Aug. 15.
g – Also July 13; not July 15.

h – Not July 14, 15, Aug. 15.
j – Also July 16; not July 15.
k – Also Aug. 15.
TGV – High-speed train. [R]. 🍸.

NANTES - ANGERS - TOURS 289

TGV and *INTERCITÉS* timings may vary by a few minutes - please check your reservation. See Table **335** for *TGV* trains Nantes - Lyon via Le Mans.
Additional local trains run Saumur - Tours and v.v. Frequent connecting services operate St Pierre des Corps - Tours and v.v. (journey 5 minutes).

km		★ 4402	*TGV* 5326 ① d	*TGV* 5306	★ 4406	*TGV* 5320				
0	**Nantes** 280 d.	0540	0740	1144	1344	1640	...	...	...	...
88	Angers St Laud 280 d.	0621	0821	1223	1427	1722	...	...	...	...
132	Saumur Rive Droit d.	0649	|	|	1449	1746	...	...	...	...
202	**St Pierre des Corps** a.	0730	0915	1318	1530	1822	...	...	...	...
	Massy TGV a.	|	1010	1424	|	1922	...	...	...	...
	Lyon Part Dieu **290** a.	1315	1230	1630	2122	2130	...	...	...	...
	Marseille St Charles **355** a.	...	1423	1823	...	...	...	...	...	...
	Montpellier ⊡ **355** a.	...	...	...	...	...	...	...	...	...

	TGV 5487 A	*TGV* 5224 Be	★ 4504	★ 4506 ⑥⑦	★ 4506 ①–⑤	*TGV* 5358			
Montpellier ⊡ **355** d.	...	...	...	...	...	1624	...	...	...
Marseille St Charles **355** d.	...	...	...	...	...	|	...	...	...
Lyon Part Dieu **290** d.	...	...	0938	1531	1534	1830	...	...	...
Massy TGV d.	1050	1212	|	|	|	2041	...	...	...
St Pierre des Corps d.	1143	1309	1543	2116	2116	2135	...	...	...
Saumur Rive Droit d.	|	|	1616	2159	2212	2208	...	...	...
Angers St Laud 280 d.	1240	1403	1638	2223	2245	2231	...	...	...
Nantes 280 a.	1319	1442	1720	2303	2327	2307	...	...	...

TER REGIONAL TRAINS NANTES - TOURS

km		Ⓐ	Ⓐ	Ⓐ	Ⓐ	Ⓒ	Ⓐ	Ⓐ	Ⓐ		①–④	⑤	Ⓐ	Ⓐ	Ⓐ	Ⓒ	Ⓐ	Ⓐ	Ⓐ	†	Ⓐ	⑥	†	†
	Le Croisic **288** d.	...	...	...	...	0724	...	...	...	...	...	...	...	...	...	...	...	...	...	...	...	1820	1855	...
0	**Nantes** 280a 287 d.	*0544*	*0644*	0713	*0744*	0910	0913	*0944*	1113	*1148*	*1417*	*1417*	*1544*	1613	*1644*	1644f	1711	*1744*	1813	1813	...	2009	2028	2213
88	Angers St Laud 280a 287 d.	0635	0735	0756	0833	0959	0956	1035	1156	1235	1535	1536	1635	1657	1735	1735	1758	1835	1856	1858	1936	2056	2118	2255
132	Saumur Rive Droit a.	0709	0811	0815	0911	1019	1019	1110	1215	1310	1611	1610	1711	1719	1811	1811	1821	1910	1915	1917	2011	2116	2140	2315
132	Saumur Rive Droit ⊖ d.	0710	...	0816	...	1023	1020	1111	1216	1311	...	1611	...	1720	...	1819	1822	...	1916	1918	...	2120	2142	2316
199	**Tours** ⊖ a.	0749	...	0849	...	1056	1054	1201	1249	1401	...	1700	...	1801	...	1859	1902	...	1948	1958	...	2154	2215	2349
	Orléans **296** a.	...	...	1008	...	1209	...	...	1405	...	...	...	...	...	...	...	...	...	2101	...	...	2308	2325	...

	Ⓐ	Ⓐ	†	Ⓐ	Ⓐ	Ⓒ	Ⓐ	†	Ⓐ	⚒	Ⓐ	Ⓒ	⑥	†	Ⓐ	Ⓐ	Ⓐ	①–④	⑤⑥	†	⚒	†	⑤
Orléans **296** d.	...	...	...	...	0702	0705	...	...	1121	...	...	...	...	...	...	...	...	1658	1658	1801	...	...	...
Tours ⊖ d.	...	...	...	0656	0810	0820	0901	...	1237	1242	*1400*	1500	1612	1612	1612	...	1739	1810	1810	1909	1839	1853	2105
Saumur Rive Droit ⊖ a.	...	...	...	0738	0841	0852	0938	...	1309	1331	*1448*	1537	1651	1651	1651	...	1829	1841	1841	1940	1929	1933	2143
Saumur Rive Droit d.	0620	0702	0724	0739	0842	0856	0941	1148	1310	1347	1537	1540	1652	1652	1652	1748	1848	1842	1842	1941	1948	1948	2144
Angers St Laud 280a d.	0658	0738	0800	0804	0904	0927	1018	1224	1333	1423	1604	1603	1715	1715	1716	1824	1859	1904	1904	2004	2024	2024	2219
Nantes 280a a.	0746	*0842*	*0850*	0846	0946	1010	*1115*	*1315*	1415	*1515*j	1646	1646	1758	1758	1758	*1917*	1924	1946	1946	2046	*2115*j	*2146*	...
Le Croisic **288** a.	...	...	*1015*	...	...	1139	...	...	...	...	...	...	1919	1923	...	...	...	...	2122	...	...	...	...

A – To/from Strasbourg (Table **391**).
B – To/from Lille (Table **11**).
C – ①②③④⑥.
d – Not July 11.
e – Not July 9, 10, 17.
f – Connecting train runs on † only.
j – Connecting train runs on Ⓐ only.

⊡ – Montpellier Sud-de-France.
⊖ – Also **Saumur - Tours** at 0605 Ⓐ, 0629 ⚒, 0700 Ⓐ, 0800, 1630 †, 1643 ⑥, 1802 Ⓑ, 2010 †; **Tours - Saumur** at 0615 Ⓐ, 1400, 1440 ⑤, 2001 Ⓑ, 2107 **C**, 2212 †.
★ – *INTERCITÉS*.
TGV – High-speed train. Ⓡ. 🍸.

TOURS - BOURGES - NEVERS - MOULINS - LYON 290

SERVICE UNTIL AUGUST 21. *INTERCITÉS* timings may vary by a few minutes. See Table **335** for *TGV* trains Nantes/Tours - Massy - Lyon and v.v.

km		⑥	Ⓐ		4402 ★	⚒	†	Ⓒ 🚌	Ⓐ		⑥	Ⓒ 🚌	Ⓐ 🚌			4406 ★	Ⓐ	Ⓒ 🚌	Ⓒ	Ⓐ	Ⓐ	⑥	†	Ⓐ
	Nantes **289** d.	...	...	...	0540	...	...	...	...	...	...	...	...	...	...	1344	...	...	...	...	...	...	...	...
0	**Tours** d.	0640	0650	...	|	0851	0851	1005	1051	...	1205	1220	1230	1250	1450	|	1650	1725	1733	1750	1852	1852	1932	1949
3	St Pierre des Corps d.	0648	0658	...	0733	0858	0858	|	1058	...	1212	|	|	1256	1458	1531	1657	|	1740	1758	1859	1859	1939	2012
	Bléré-la-Croix d.	0703	0713	...	|	0921	0920	|	1125	...	1227	|	|	1319	1520	|	1720	|	1803	1819	1921	1921	2001	2018
32	Chenonceaux d.	0709	0719	...	|	0928	*0940**	|	1130	...	1232	|	|	1326	1526	|	1727	|	1810	1824	1926	1926	2006	|
	St-Aignan-Noyers d.	0727	0737	...	|	0946	*1020**	1110	1148	...	1249	1325	1335	1344	1550	|	1750	1830	1827	1846	1951	1951	2028	*2105**
	Les Aubrais-Orléans d.	|	|	...	0840	|	|	|	|	...	...	|	|	...	▬	1644	...	|	...	...	...	|	...	|
113	Vierzon 315 d.	*0850**	*0900**	...	0922	*1115**	*1135**	1215	*1315**	1330	...	1440	1440	...	...	1741	...	1945	...	...	...	*2100**	...	*2220**
145	**Bourges** 315 a.	...	*0950**	...	0945	...	...	...	...	1347	...	...	...	...	...	1758	...	...	...	...	...	...	...	▬
145	**Bourges** 315 d.	▬	▬	...	0947	...	...	...	...	1349	...	...	...	...	...	1759	...	...	...	...	...	...	...	...
214	**Nevers** 315 a.	...	Ⓐ	...	1025	...	...	...	...	1428	...	...	...	...	...	1839	...	...	...	...	...	...	...	...
214	**Nevers** 330 d.	...	0531	0834	1036	...	...	...	...	1438	...	...	...	...	1818	1849	...	...	...	...	...	...	...	...
274	**Moulins-sur-Allier** . 330 373 d.	⚒	0607	0910	1108	...	...	...	...	1509	...	...	...	...	1900	1919	...	...	...	...	...	...	...	†
	Digoin 373 d.		0649	0951	|	...	...	...	...	1551	...	...	...	...	...	|	...	...	...	...	...	...	...	...
	Paray le Monial 373 d.	0535	0702	1020	|	...	...	...	...	1605	...	...	...	...	...	|	...	...	...	...	...	...	...	2008
315	St Germain des Fossés . 330 d.	|	|	|	1133	...	...	...	...	|	...	...	...	...	...	1941	...	...	...	...	...	...	...	|
325	Vichy 330 d.	|	|	|	|	...	...	...	...	|	...	...	...	...	...	|	...	...	...	...	...	...	...	|
381	Roanne 328 d.	|	|	|	1211	...	...	...	...	|	...	...	...	...	...	2020	...	...	...	...	...	...	...	|
474	**Lyon** Part Dieu 328 a.	0722	|	1204	1315	...	...	...	...	1752	...	...	...	...	...	2126	...	...	...	...	...	...	...	2200
479	**Lyon** Perrache 328 a.	0733	0850	1217	1327	...	...	...	...	1803	...	...	...	...	...	2134	...	...	...	...	...	...	...	2214

km		⚒	Ⓐ	⑥	Ⓒ 🚌 h	⚒	Ⓐ	Ⓒ 🚌	Ⓐ	⑥		4504 ★		🚌		Ⓐ		🚌	⚒	4506 ★ ⑥⑦	4506 ★ ①–⑤	Ⓐ		Ⓐ
0	**Lyon** Perrache 328 d.	...	...	...	...	...	...	...	...	...	...	0925	...	...	1146	...	...	...	...	1520	1521	1700	1807	1916
5	**Lyon** Part Dieu 328 d.	...	...	...	...	...	...	...	...	...	...	0938	...	...	1159	...	...	...	...	1531	1534	|	1820	1928
	Roanne 328 d.	...	...	...	...	...	...	...	...	...	...	1043	...	...	|	...	...	...	...	1635	1639	|	|	|
	Vichy 330 d.	...	...	...	...	...	...	...	...	...	...	|	...	...	|	...	...	...	...	|	|	|	|	|
	St Germain des Fossés . 330 d.	...	...	...	...	...	...	...	...	...	...	1122	...	...	|	...	...	...	...	1714	1718	|	|	|
129	Paray le Monial 373 d.	...	...	...	...	...	...	...	...	...	...	|	...	...	1338	...	...	...	...	|	|	1850	2005	2110
140	Digoin 373 d.	...	...	...	...	...	...	...	...	...	...	|	...	...	1351	...	...	...	...	|	|	▬	2017	▬
196	**Moulins-sur-Allier** . 330 373 d.	0654	0723	...	...	0854	...	...	...	...	...	1143	...	...	1439	...	...	...	...	1736	1739	...	2109	...
256	**Nevers** 330 a.	0737	0801	...	...	0926	...	...	...	...	...	1211	...	...	1514	...	...	...	...	1805	1807	...	2144	...
256	**Nevers** 315 d.	▬	▬	...	...	▬	...	...	...	...	...	1220	...	...	1521	...	...	...	...	1811	1813	...	...	...
325	**Bourges** 315 a.	...	...	...	...	...	...	...	...	...	...	1259	...	...	1559	...	...	...	...	1849	1853	...	...	†
325	**Bourges** 315 d.	...	...	...	...	...	...	...	...	...	...	1301	...	...	1559	...	...	...	...	1851	1855	...	...	🚌
357	Vierzon 315 d.	⚒	Ⓐ	...	0800	⑥	...	1050	*1100**	...	...	1323	...	1615	1619	...	...	1815	...	1913	1916	†	...	2025
	Les Aubrais-Orléans d.	...	...	...	|	...	...	|	|	...	...	1430	...	|	...	...	...	|	...	2007	2017	...	...	|
	St-Aignan-Noyers d.	0631	0757	0848	0915	1010	1112	1205	1242	1307	1408	|	1611	1730	...	1807	1908	1930	2006	|	|	2044	...	2130
438	Chenonceaux d.	0657	0818	0911	0945	1033	1135	1235	1300	1325	1431	|	1634	|	...	1835	1930	|	2031	|	|	2108	...	|
	Bléré-la-Croix d.	0703	0823	0917	|	1038	1140	|	1305	1330	1436	|	1640	|	...	1841	1936	|	2036	|	|	2114	...	|
467	St Pierre des Corps a.	0728	0838	0933	|	1100	1201	|	1320	1345	1458	1540	1703	|	...	1903	2004	|	2057	2106	2107	2134	...	|
470	**Tours** a.	0735	0845	0940	1035	1107	1208	1325	1327	1352	1505	|	1710	1835	...	1910	2012	2035	2104	|	|	2141	...	2235
	Nantes **289** a.	...	...	...	...	...	...	...	...	...	...	1720	...	...	...	...	...	...	...	2303	2327	...	...	...

ADDITIONAL 🚌 SERVICES TOURS - VIERZON - BOURGES

	⑤ 🚌	Ⓐ 🚌	Ⓐ 🚌	† 🚌					
Tours d.	1720	1730	1830	1930	...	...	...	...	...
Vierzon d.	1905	1935	2025	2115	...	...	...	...	...
Bourges a.	...	...	...	2205	...	...	...	...	...

	Ⓐ 🚌	Ⓐ 🚌	🚌	⑤ 🚌					
Bourges d.	0500	...	1515	...	...	...	...	...	...
Vierzon d.	0550	0710	1605	1810	...	...	...	...	...
Tours a.	0755	0905	1750	1955	...	...	...	...	...

h – Runs 10 minutes later on †.
★ – *INTERCITÉS*.
* – Connection by 🚌.

291 ROANNE - ST ÉTIENNE

km																							
		Ⓐ	Ⓐ d	⚒	Ⓐ d		⚒	Ⓐ	Ⓒ	Ⓐ	⚒	Ⓐ		Ⓐ d	Ⓑ	⑥		Ⓐ		†	† e		
0	**Roanne** d.	0526	0556	0630	0656	...	0726	0826	0855	0956	1056	1226	1356	1456	1556	1656	...	1726	1826	1926	2026	...	...
80	**St Étienne** Châteaucreux a.	0637	0707	0743	0807	...	0837	0937	1009	1107	1207	1337	1507	1607	1707	1807	...	1837	1937	2037	2137	...	...

	Ⓐ d	⚒	⚒	†		Ⓐ	⑥	Ⓐ				Ⓐ		Ⓐ	Ⓐ		d	Ⓐ		†		
St Étienne Châteaucreux d.	0553	0623	0723	0823	...	0853	0953	1123	1223	...	1453	1555	1653	1723	1753	...	1823	1853	1955	2053	...	...
Roanne a.	0704	0734	0834	0934	...	1004	1104	1234	1334	...	1604	1705	1804	1834	1904	...	1934	2004	2105	2204	...	...

d – Until July 13. e – Until July 10.

292 NANTES - LA ROCHELLE - BORDEAUX

INTERCITÉS timings may vary by a few minutes.

km																									
											3831				3833										
		Ⓐ	Ⓐ	⚒	Ⓐ	Ⓐ	Ⓐ		Ⓐ	⚒	★		Ⓒ	Ⓐ	★	⑥	Ⓒ	Ⓐ	Ⓐ	†	Ⓐ	†	Ⓐ	†	Ⓐ
0	**Nantes** 293 d.	...	...	...	...	...	...	...	...	...	0755	...	...	...	1155	...	...	...	...	...	...	...	...	...	...
77	La Roche sur Yon 293 d.	...	...	...	...	...	...	...	...	...	0836	...	...	...	1236	...	...	...	...	...	...	...	...	...	...
113	Luçon d.	...	...	...	...	...	...	...	...	...	0900	...	...	...	1300	...	...	...	...	...	...	...	...	...	...
	La Rochelle P Dauphine d.	...	...	...	0538	...	...	...	0759	0844	|	...	1226	1228	|	1409	...	1504	...	1601	...	...	1639	...	1706
180	**La Rochelle** Ville d.	...	0501	0528	0550	0611	0632	0724	0806	0852	0943	1133	1234	1235	1343	1417	1510	1512	...	1609	1628	...	1647	1709	1713
209	Rochefort d.	...	0530	0550	0622	0640	0701	0747	0835	0921	1005	1156	1303	1304	1405	1445	1534	1540	...	1638	1650	...	1722	1731	1742
253	Saintes d.	0538	...	0620	0702	...	...	0817	0910	...	1034	1226	...	1339	1434	...	1606	...	1620	1712	1720	1720	1800	1802	...
	Angoulême 301 a.	|	...	|	0809	...	...	|	...	...	|	|	...	...	|	...	|	...	|	...	|	|	1901	|	...
	Jonzac d.	0617	...	0658	...	...	...	0856	...	...	1111	1306	...	...	1511	...	1650	...	1658	...	1758	1800	...	1846	...
376	**Bordeaux** St Jean a.	0727	...	0805	...	...	...	1004	...	...	1207	1410	...	...	1607	...	1759	...	1804	...	1904	1904	...	1958	...

	3835				3837				
	★	Ⓐ	⚒	†	★	Ⓐ	†	Ⓐ	Ⓐ
Nantes 293 d.	1555	...	...	...	1755	...	...	...	1935
La Roche sur Yon 293 d.	1636	...	...	...	1836	...	...	...	2031
Luçon d.	1700	...	...	...	1900	...	...	...	2100
La Rochelle Porte Dauphine d.	|	1804	1843	1843	|	2021	2108	2128	|
La Rochelle Ville d.	1743	1811	1850	1851	1943	2028	2135	2135	2140
Rochefort d.	1805	1840	1919	1919	2005	2057	2205	2205	...
Saintes d.	1834	1914	1954	...	2034	2132	2239	2239	...
Angoulême 301 a.	|	...	...	...	|	...	...	...	...
Jonzac d.	1911	...	...	...	2111	...	...	...	...
Bordeaux St Jean a.	2008	...	...	...	2203	...	...	...	...

	Ⓐ	Ⓐ	Ⓐ	Ⓐ	Ⓐ	⚒	Ⓐ	Ⓐ	Ⓐ
Bordeaux St Jean d.	...	...	...	...	...	...	0556	...	0656
Jonzac d.	...	...	...	...	...	...	0657	...	0754
Angoulême 301 a.	...	...	...	...	...	...	|	0641	|
Saintes d.	...	...	0549	...	...	0716	0740	0756	0843
Rochefort d.	0543	...	0625	0646	0706	0751	...	0831	0911
La Rochelle Ville d.	0612	0619	0654	0714	0737	0822	...	0902	0933
La Rochelle Porte Dauphine a.	...	|	...	...	0743	0828	...	0907	...
Luçon d.	...	0659	...	...	...	...	...	...	...
La Roche sur Yon 293 d.	...	0724	...	...	...	...	...	...	...
Nantes 293 a.	...	0805	...	...	...	...	...	...	...

	3852				3854				3856										3858					
	★	⑥	Ⓐ	⑥	★	Ⓐ			★	Ⓐ	⑥	⑤	Ⓐ			Ⓐ	†	Ⓐ	★	†	Ⓐ		Ⓐ	†
Bordeaux St Jean d.	0755	...	...	0847	0955	...	...	1256	1355	...	...	1456	...	1547	...	...	...	1656	1755	...	...	1856	1956	2008
Jonzac d.	0843	...	...	0946	1043	...	...	1357	1443	...	...	1555	...	1646	...	...	...	1759	1843	...	...	1957	2057	2106
Angoulême 301 a.	|	...	...	|	|	...	...	|	|	...	...	|	...	|	1659	...	...	|	|	...	...	|	|	|
Saintes d.	0927	...	1004	1030	1127	1204	...	1443	1527	...	...	1640	1646	1732	1805	...	1844	1844	1927	...	1959	2043	2143	2154
Rochefort d.	0956	1021	1039	1100	1156	1239	1306	1512	1556	1614	1706	...	1721	1801	1840	1901	1919	...	1956	2022	2034	2112	2212	2224
La Rochelle Ville d.	1019	1057	1110	1123	1219	1310	1346	1534	1619	1648	1736	...	1752	1828	1910	1930	1949	...	2019	2056	2104	2134	2234	2246
La Rochelle Porte Dauphine a.	|	1102	1116	...	|	1316	1350	...	|	1654	1742	...	1757	1833	1916	...	1955	...	|	2102	2110	...	...	...
Luçon d.	1100	...	...	...	1300	...	...	...	1700	...	...	...	...	...	...	...	...	...	2100	...	...	...	...	...
La Roche sur Yon 293 d.	1124	...	...	...	1324	...	...	...	1724	...	...	...	...	...	...	...	...	...	2124	...	...	...	...	...
Nantes 293 a.	1205	...	...	...	1405	...	...	...	1805	...	...	...	...	...	...	...	...	...	2205	...	...	...	...	...

★ – *INTERCITÉS*.

293 NANTES - LES SABLES D'OLONNE

TGV timings may vary by a few minutes - please check your reservation.

km																										
										TGV 8973					*TGV* 8975	*TGV* 8977								*TGV* 8985		
		Ⓐ	Ⓐ	Ⓐ		Ⓒ	Ⓒ	A			⑥	Ⓑ		⑤	①–④ f	⑤–⑦ g		①–④	Ⓐ	†		⚒	⑤–⑦			⑤†
	Paris Montparnasse 280 d.	...	...	...	...	...	...	...	...	0939	...	...	...	...	1223	1326	...	...	...	...	...	...	...	1843	...	...
0	**Nantes** 292 d.	0635	0735	0935	...	0935	1035	1108	...	1205	1308	1308	...	1428	1430	1600	...	1640	1735	1808	...	1907	2008	2105	...	2213
77	La Roche sur Yon 292 a.	0726	0828	1026	...	1026	1125	1200	...	1246	1400	1400	...	1513	1511	1645	...	1730	1825	1900	...	2000	2100	2145	...	2304
77	La Roche sur Yon d.	0728	0838	1028	...	1028	1127	1202	...	1249	1402	1402	...	1515	1514	1647	...	1732	1827	1904	...	2002	2102	2148	...	2306
114	**Les Sables d'Olonne** a.	0759	0907	1057	...	1101	1153	1232	...	1315	1432	1434	...	1540	1539	1713	...	1811	1859	1934	...	2032	2132	2214	...	2335

							TGV 8972	*TGV* 8972					*TGV* 8984						*TGV* 8986				*TGV* 8988		
	①	Ⓐ	⑥	Ⓑ		Ⓐ	Ⓐ	Ⓒ	⚒					Ⓐ	①–④		†	⑤	①–⑥ h	Ⓑ		⚒	⑦ j	†	⑥
Les Sables d'Olonne d.	0523	0620	0719	0727	...	0809	0940	0944	1028	...	1201	1401	1544	1601	1701	...	1716	1724	1744	1827	...	1928	1944	2028	2225
La Roche sur Yon a.	0549	0649	0748	0757	...	0836	1004	1008	1058	...	1232	1431	1608	1630	1730	...	1746	1753	1808	1857	...	1957	2008	2057	2251
La Roche sur Yon 292 d.	0551	0658	0750	0759	...	0838	1006	1010	1059	...	1234	1433	1610	1632	1736	...	1748	1755	1810	1859	...	1959	2010	2059	2253
Nantes 292 a.	0650	0754	0846	0854	...	0930	1050	1054	1154	...	1325	1526	1654	1725	1828	...	1845	1850	1854	1954	...	2054	2054	2154	2340
Paris Montparnasse 280 a.	...	...	...	...	...	...	1329	1328	...	...	...	...	1916	...	...	...	...	...	2115	...	...	...	2319	...	...

A – ①②③④⑥.

f – Not July 13, 14, Aug. 15.

g – Also July 13, 14, Aug. 15.

h – Not Aug. 15.

j – Also Aug. 15.

TGV – High-speed train. 🅁. 🍷.

294 PARIS - LES AUBRAIS - ORLÉANS

km																										
		Ⓐ	Ⓐ	⚒	Ⓐ	⚒	†		⚒	†	⚒		⚒		Ⓑ		Ⓐ	Ⓐ	Ⓒ	Ⓐ	Ⓒ	Ⓒ	Ⓐ	Ⓐ	Ⓒ	①–④ B
0	**Paris** Austerlitz 296 315 d.	0541	0626	0652	0826	0926	1024	1122	1222	1324	1326	1526	1626	...	1725	1723	1755	1826	1827	1924	1925	1949	1953	2023	2122	2305
119	Les Aubrais-Orléans 296 315 a.	0714	0727	0827	0924	1027	1157	1226	1354	1425	1424	1624	1724	...	1824	1851	1855	1924	1925	2025	2024	2116	2117	2125	2224	0016
121	**Orléans** a.	0720	0734	0833	0932	1034	1203	1234	1400	1432	1432	1632	1732	...	1832	1857	1902	1932	1933	2032	2032	2122	2123	2132	2232	0023

	⑥	Ⓐ	Ⓐ	Ⓐ	Ⓐ	Ⓐ	⑥	⚒	Ⓒ	Ⓐ	†	⚒		⚒	⚒		⑤†	⚒	†	⑥		Ⓐ	Ⓐ	†	⚒
Orléans d.	0455	0459	0556	0625	0656	0727	0738	0828	0925	0927	1027	1125	...	1247	1324	1530	1625	1724	1827	1829	1823	1927	1937	2027	2127
Les Aubrais-Orléans 296 315 d.	0502	0506	0603	0632	0703	0734	0745	0835	0932	0934	1032	1132	...	1253	1331	1536	1631	1730	1834	1836	1830	1934	1944	2033	2134
Paris Austerlitz 296 315 a.	0606	0607	0708	0737	0809	0839	0915	0945	1037	1040	1208	1237	...	1424	1437	1646	1740	1834	1948	1952	2015	2040	2120	2138	2242

B – Departs Paris 2239 on ②③ July 19 - Aug. 10.

PARIS - TOURS 295

TGV services via high-speed line. Timings may vary by a few minutes - please check your reservation for confirmed timings.
See Table **300** for *TGV* services Paris - Vendôme-Villiers - St Pierre des Corps and v.v. See Table **296** for TER regional services Paris Austerlitz - Blois - Tours and v.v.

km		*TGV*	*TGV*	*TGV*	*TGV*	*TGV*	*TGV*	*TGV*	*TGV*	*TGV*
		8301	**8335**	**8311**	**8313**	**8315**	**8317**	**8319**	**8321**	**8323**
		⑥	**8303**	⑤		①–⑤	①–⑤	Ⓑ	①–⑥	⑦
		d		**e**		**f**	**f**	**g**	**h**	**j**
0	**Paris** Montparnasse .... d.	0729	1230	1529	1631	1730	1756	1831	1931	2100
162	Vendôme-Villiers TGV .... d.	0816	1316	1614	1716	1816	1843	1916	2016	2146
221	St Pierre des Corps .... a.	0835	1335	1633	1735	1835	1907	1935	2035	2205
224	**Tours** .... a.	0844	1344	1641	1743	1847	1915	1944	2043	2218

	TGV	*TGV*	*TGV*	*TGV*	*TGV*	*TGV*	*TGV*	*TGV*	*TGV*
	8300	**8306**	**8308**	**8310**	**8314**	**8316**	**8318**	**8320**	**8324**
	①–⑤	①–⑤	①–⑤	①–⑥		⑤	⑤⑦		⑦
	f	**f**	**k**	**h**		**e**	**m**		
Tours .... d.	0554	0642	0752	0813	1213	1617	1709	1856	2115
St Pierre des Corps .... d.	0602	0654	0802	0825	1225	1625	1724	1904	2123
Vendôme-Villiers TGV .... d.	0624	0715	|	0846	1246	1646	1746	1924	2144
Paris Montparnasse .... a.	0721	0805	0906	0937	1337	1737	1837	2015	2236

d – Also July 14, 15.
e – Also July 13; not July 15.
f – Not July 14, 15, Aug. 15.
g – Not ①–④ July 25 - Aug. 11.
h – Not Aug. 15.
j – Also Aug. 15.
k – Not July 14, 15, July 25 - Aug. 15.
m – Also July 13, Aug. 15; not July 15.
TGV – High-speed train. Ⓡ. 🍷.

ORLÉANS and PARIS - BLOIS - TOURS 296

See Table **295** for direct *TGV* services Paris Montparnasse - Tours and v.v. See Table **300** for other *TGV* services Paris Montparnasse - St Pierre des Corps and v.v.
Frequent trains run St Pierre des Corps - Tours and v.v. (journey time 5 minutes) and Les Aubrais-Orléans - Orléans and v.v. (journey time 4 minutes).

km		⑥	Ⓐ	Ⓐ	Ⓒ	Ⓐ	⑥	Ⓐ	†	Ⓐ	Ⓐ	†	⑥	Ⓐ	⑥	†	†	Ⓐ	⑥	Ⓐ	⑥	Ⓒ	Ⓐ	⑥	Ⓐ
				A	**B**															**A**					
0	**Orléans** .... d.	0642	0642	0702	0705	0708	0742	0744	0744	0754	...	...	...	0842	0946	...	1042	1042	1044	1121	1225	1242	1242	...	...
	Paris Austerlitz .... ◧ d.	|	|	|	|	|	|	|	|	|	0726	0726	0726	|	|	0845	|	|	|	|	|	|	|	1238	1258
	Les Aubrais-Orléans .... ◧ d.	|	|	|	|	|	|	|	|	|	0825	0825	0825	|	|	0950	|	|	|	|	|	|	|	1335	1405
27	Beaugency .... d.	0700	0701	0717	|	0730	0801	0802	0803	0824	|	0843	0845	0901	1004	1008	1101	1101	1102	|	1255	1301	1301	1355	|
59	Blois .... d.	0719	0720	0732	0736	0751	0820	0822	0823	0852	0856	0904	0908	0920	1023	1030	1120	1120	1122	1152	1314	1320	1320	1416	1435
91	Amboise .... d.	0738	0739	|	|	0810	0838	0840	0845	...	0916	0923	0929	0938	1042	1050	1139	1143	1141	|	...	1339	1343	1437	1454
112	St Pierre des Corps .... a.	0749	0751	0755	0759	0825	0851	0851	0900	...	0930	0936	0942	0949	1053	1104	1150	1154	1152	1219	...	1350	1357	1449	1517
115	**Tours** .... a.	0756	0758	0802	0809	0832	0858	0858	0907	...	0937	0943	0949	0957	1100	1111	1157	1201	1159	1226	...	1356	1404	1456	1524

	⚒	†	Ⓐ		①–⑥	Ⓐ	†	Ⓐ	⑥	†	⚒	†	⑥	Ⓐ	Ⓑ	Ⓐ	Ⓐ		⑤	⑥–④	Ⓑ	†	⑤	⑥
					C					**A**						**n**								
Orléans .... d.	1442	1442	1539	1642	1658	1702	1735	1742	1742	1801	1808	...	...	...	1842	1909	...	1941	2041	2042	2142	...	...	...
Paris Austerlitz .... ◧ d.	|	|	|	|	|	|	|	|	|	|	|	1734	1734	1737	|	|	1837	|	|	|	|	2304	2307	2307
Les Aubrais-Orléans .... ◧ d.	|	|	|	|	|	|	|	|	|	|	|	1836	1836	1836	|	|	1936	|	|	|	|	0005	0006	0008
Beaugency .... d.	1501	1501	1558	1701	1714	1732	1805	1801	1803	|	1838	|	1854	|	1901	1938	|	2000	2100	2101	2201	|	|	|
Blois .... d.	1520	1521	1618	1720	1731	1751	1824	1820	1826	1829	1857	1902	1916	1902	1920	1958	2003	2019	2120	2120	2220	0032	0032	0039
Amboise .... d.	1538	1540	1636	1738	|	...	...	1838	1847	|	...	1918	1936	1918	1938	...	2018	2038	2138	2138	2238	0048	0049	0055
St Pierre des Corps .... a.	1551	1553	1650	1749	1753	...	...	1850	1901	1852	...	1930	1948	1930	1950	...	2032	2049	2149	2149	2249	0100	0101	0107
Tours .... a.	1557	1559	1656	1756	1800	...	...	1858	1908	1859	...	1937	1955	1937	1957	...	2039	2056	2156	2156	2256	0108	0108	0114

km		Ⓐ	Ⓐ	Ⓐ	⑥	Ⓐ	Ⓐ	⑥	Ⓐ	⚒	Ⓐ	†	⑥		⑥	†	Ⓐ	Ⓐ	Ⓒ	Ⓒ	⑥	Ⓐ	†	⑥	⑥
																	A			**B**					
0	**Tours** .... d.	0501	...	0601	0605	0612	...	0630	0701	...	0740	0743	0744	...	0834	0842	0859	0940	1003	1106	1113	1113	1114	1201	...
3	St Pierre des Corps .... d.	0508	...	0608	0612	0620	...	0637	0708	...	0747	0750	0750	...	0842	0850	0907	0947	1009	1116	1121	1121	1121	1208	...
24	Amboise .... d.	0519	...	0620	0623	0631	...	0649	0719	...	0758	0802	0803	...	0856	0903	0918	0958	1021	|	1133	1134	1133	1219	...
56	Blois .... d.	0539	0553	0640	0645	0649	0654	0711	0740	0803	0818	0821	0823	...	0922	0929	0934	1019	1040	1142	1155	1152	1154	1239	1254
88	Beaugency .... d.	0558	0611	0658	0705	|	0713	0732	0759	0822	0836	0839	0842	...	0948	0955	|	1039	1058	|	1215	|	1214	1257	1321
115	Les Aubrais-Orléans .... ◧ a.	|	|	|	0724	0724	|	|	|	|	|	|	|	...	1011	1014	|	|	|	|	1234	1224	1232	|	|
234	**Paris** Austerlitz .... ◧ a.	|	|	|	0835	0834	|	|	|	|	|	|	|	...	1116	1116	|	|	|	|	1349	1333	1349	|	|
	Orléans .... a.	0618	0640	0718	...	...	0742	0752	0818	0851	0855	0858	0900	...	...	...	1008	1102	1117	1209	...	...	...	1316	1351

	Ⓐ	Ⓐ	Ⓐ	Ⓒ	⑤†	Ⓐ	†		†	Ⓐ	⑥	Ⓑ	Ⓐ	⑥	Ⓐ	Ⓒ		⑥–④	⑤	Ⓐ	Ⓐ	Ⓐ	⑥	†
		A												**p**						**A**			**B**	**B**
Tours .... d.	1223	1259	1355	1401	1501	1512	1557	...	1602	...	1700	1701	1713	...	1801	1804	...	1901	1904	2000	2101	2201	2204	2225
St Pierre des Corps .... d.	1230	1307	1402	1408	1508	1520	1605	...	1609	...	1708	1708	1720	...	1808	1811	...	1909	1911	2008	2108	2208	2213	2234
Amboise .... d.	1242	|	1414	1420	1520	1532	1619	...	1620	...	1720	1720	1733	...	1820	1827	...	1920	1922	2019	2120	2220	|	|
Blois .... d.	1304	1335	1435	1440	1540	1553	1641	...	1640	1701	1740	1740	1754	1802	1840	1850	...	1940	1942	2035	2140	2240	2240	2258
Beaugency .... d.	1325	|	1455	1458	1559	|	1701	...	1658	1728	1759	1758	|	1829	1859	1911	...	1958	2000	|	2158	2258	|	|
Les Aubrais-Orléans .... ◧ a.	|	|	|	|	|	1620	1720	...	|	|	|	|	1821	|	|	1930	...	|	|	|	|	|	|	|
Paris Austerlitz .... ◧ a.	|	|	|	|	|	1724	1730	...	|	|	|	|	1924	|	|	2039	...	|	|	|	|	|	|	|
Orléans .... a.	1346	1405	1518	1518	1618	...	...	...	1717	1758	1818	1818	...	1858	1919	...	...	2018	2020	2101	2218	2318	2308	2325

OUIGO TRAINS PARIS - BLOIS - NANTES ★

	①–⑤	⑥	
Paris Austerlitz .... d.	0729	0752	1743
Juvisy .... d.	0744	0807	1802
Les Aubrais-Orléans ... d.	0836	0856	1900
Blois .... d.	0905	0928	1928
St Pierre des Corps .... d.	0936	0958	1956
Saumur .... d.	1024	1030	2029
Angers St-Laud .... d.	1053	1053	2053
Nantes .... a.	1138	1138	2133

	⑥⑦		
Nantes .... d.	0813	1911	...
Angers St-Laud .... d.	0859	1956	...
Saumur .... d.	0922	2018	...
St Pierre des Corps . d.	1001	2102	...
Blois .... d.	1032	2129	...
Les Aubrais-Orléans. d.	1110	2159	...
Juvisy .... d.	1203	2252	...
Paris Montparnasse. a.	1218	2308	...

A – To / from Nantes (Table **289**).
B – To / from Le Croisic (Tables **289** and **288**).
C – To Nantes on ①–④, to Le Croisic on ⑤⑥ (Tables **289** and **288**).
n – Until July 8 and from Aug. 22.
p – Also July 4–8, Aug. 22–26.
◧ – See also Tables **294** and **315**.
★ – *Ouigo Classique*. Low-cost traditional loco-hauled train. Outline timings – services may not run on all days shown (please confirm timings when booking). Internet booking only at www.ouigo.com. For other *Ouigo* trains Paris - Nantes via Le Mans, see Table **278**.

NANTES - PORNIC and ST GILLES CROIX DE VIE 297

km		Ⓐ	Ⓐ	Ⓒ	Ⓒ		Ⓐ	⑥	⑥	†		Ⓐ	Ⓒ		Ⓐ		Ⓐ	Ⓒ		Ⓐ	Ⓒ	Ⓐ	Ⓐ
0	**Nantes** .... d.	0707	0707	0909	0909	...	1009	1009	1109	1109	...	1113	1209	...	1229	1309	1429	1509	...	1511	1609	1616	1616
24	Ste Pazanne .... d.	0747	0751	0945	0948	...	1042	1042	1142	1142	...	1146	1240	...	1302	1342	1459	1542	...	1543	1642	1654	1657
54	**Pornic** .... a.	0815	|	1013	|	...	1110	|	1210	|	...	|	1308	...	1330	|	|	1610	...	1611	|	|	1725
63	Challans .... d.	...	0815	...	1011	...	...	1106	...	1206	...	1210	...	...	...	1405	1522	...	...	...	1705	1716	...
84	**St Gilles Croix de Vie** .... a.	...	0832	...	1028	...	...	1122	...	1223	...	1227	...	...	...	1422	1538	...	...	...	1722	1733	...

	Ⓐ	⑥	†	Ⓐ		†	⑥	Ⓐ	Ⓐ		Ⓐ	⑤		①–④ 🚌	⑤	⑥	†		①–④	⑤	Ⓑ	⑤ 🚌
Nantes .... d.	1708	1709	1709	1739	...	1805	1809	1814	1844	...	1915	1935	...	1945	2009	2009	2009	...	2015	2035	2109	2220
Ste Pazanne .... d.	1739	1743	1743	1811	...	1838	1842	1851	1921	...	1948	2008	...	2030r	2040	2042	2042	...	2046	2106	2141	2250r
Pornic .... a.	|	|	1810	1839	...	|	1910	|	1949	...	|	2036	...	|	|	|	2110	...	2114	2134	|	|
Challans .... d.	1804	1806	...	...	...	1901	...	1916	...	...	2011	...	...	2110	2103	2105	...	...	...	...	2204	2328
St Gilles Croix de Vie .... a.	1821	1822	...	...	...	1918	...	1934	...	...	2028	...	...	2142	2120	2122	...	...	...	...	2221	2359

r – Ste Pazanne **Rue de Vigneau**.

FOR RETURN SERVICE SEE NEXT PAGE →

297 ST GILLES CROIX DE VIE and PORNIC - NANTES

		Ⓐ	Ⓐ	Ⓐ	Ⓐ	Ⓐ		⑥	⑥	Ⓐ	†		†	⑥	Ⓐ	Ⓒ	Ⓐ		Ⓐ		Ⓐ	⑥	† 🚌
St Gilles Croix de Vie	d.	0539	...	0639	...	0733	...	...	0733	...	...	...	0903	0907	0939	...	1042	...	...	1239	...	...	1350
Challans	d.	0556	...	0656	...	0749	...	...	0750	...	...	...	0919	0924	0955	...	1059	...	...	1256	...	...	1422
Pornic	d.	|	0627	|	0716	|	...	0740	|	0825	0909	...	|	|	|	1050	|	...	1150	|	1348	1350	|
Ste Pazanne	d.	0618	0656	0718	0745	0812	...	0818	0818	0853	0949	...	0949	0947	1018	1118	1121	...	1219	1318	1416	1418	1502r
Nantes	a.	0650	0728	0750	0816	0844	...	0850	0850	0924	1020	...	1020	1020	1050	1150	1151	...	1250	1350	1450	1450	1542
		⑥	†	Ⓒ	Ⓐ	Ⓐ		Ⓒ	Ⓐ	†	⑥		Ⓐ	Ⓐ	⑥	Ⓐ	Ⓒ		Ⓒ	†	†	⑥	⑥
St Gilles Croix de Vie	d.	1439	...	1539	1547	...	...	...	...	1736	...	...	1744	1834	1839	...	...	...	1933	2039	...	...	2135
Challans	d.	1456	...	1556	1603	...	...	...	...	1752	...	...	1802	1850	1856	...	...	...	1949	2056	...	...	2152
Pornic	d.	|	1450	|	|	1625	...	1650	1741	|	1750	...	|	|	|	1849	1940	...	|	|	2125	2130	|
Ste Pazanne	d.	1518	1518	1618	1625	1655	...	1718	1810	1815	1818	...	1824	1923	1918	1923	2018	...	2018	2118	2153	2155	|
Nantes	a.	1550	1550	1650	1656	1729	...	1750	1836	1846	1850	...	1856	1955	1950	1955	2050	...	2050	2150	2225	2220	2235

FOR RETURN SERVICE AND FOOTNOTES SEE PREVIOUS PAGE.

299 OTHER LOCAL SERVICES

ANGERS - CHOLET — Journey 41 – 50 minutes *60 km*

From Angers at 0619 Ⓐ, 0723 Ⓐ, 0823 Ⓐ, 0923 ⑥, 1023 Ⓐ, 1123, 1254 ⚒, 1622 Ⓐ, 1757 Ⓐ, 1822 ⑥, 1823 Ⓐ, 1926 Ⓐ, 1954 †, 2026 ⚒, 2031 †, 2131 ⑤, 2238 †.

From Cholet at 0550 Ⓐ, 0610 Ⓐ, 0645 Ⓐ, 0649 ⑥, 0711 Ⓐ, 0749 Ⓐ, 0849, 1049 Ⓐ, 1149 ⑥, 1234 Ⓐ, 1355, 1748 Ⓐ, 1751 Ⓒ, 1840 †, 1849 Ⓐ, 1919 Ⓐ, 1924 Ⓒ, 2154 †.

BAYONNE - ST JEAN PIED DE PORT — *50 km*

		Ⓐ	Ⓒ	Ⓐ	Ⓐ	Ⓒ	Ⓒ	Ⓐ	Ⓐ	Ⓒ	Ⓐ	Ⓒ
Bayonne	d.	0641	0829	0850	1027	1124	1420	1435	1709	1820	1835	2053
Cambo les Bains	d.	0710	0854	0921	1051	1149	1445	1502	1736	1845	1905	2118
St Jean P de Port	a.	0745	0929	0955	...	1224	1520	1538	1811	1920	1940	2153
			Ⓐ	Ⓐ	Ⓒ	Ⓐ	Ⓐ	Ⓒ	Ⓒ	Ⓐ	Ⓐ	Ⓒ
St Jean P de Port	d.	0631	...	0842	0940	...	1226	1240	1635	1657	1826	1938
Cambo les Bains	d.	0709	0815	0920	1016	1156	1304	1316	1711	1737	1904	2014
Bayonne	a.	0734	0839	0945	1040	1221	1329	1340	1735	1802	1929	2039

BORDEAUX - MONT DE MARSAN — *147 km*

	Ⓐ	Ⓒ	⚒		Ⓐ	Ⓒ	Ⓐ	Ⓐ	Ⓒ	⑥
Bordeaux St Jean **305** d.	0557	0836	1045	1245	1444	1544	1644	1738	1745	1944
Facture Biganos.... **305** d.	0623	0902	1110	1310	1510	1610	1709	1810	1810	2010
Morcenx **305** d.	0701	0940	1148	1349	1549	1648	1746	1848	1848	2049
Mont de Marsan a.	0730	1003	1211	1418	1613	1711	1816	1912	1917	2113

	Ⓐ	†	Ⓐ		Ⓐ	Ⓐ	⑥
Bordeaux St Jean **305** d.	1944	2028	2031	**Mont de Marsan** d.	0524	0739	0844
Facture Biganos.... **305** d.	2009	2053	|	Morcenx **305** d.	0545	0812	0910
Morcenx **305** d.	2049	2132	2128	Facture Biganos **305** d.	|	0851	0948
Mont de Marsan a.	2115	2155	2148	**Bordeaux** St J.. **305** a.	0650	0920	1016

			Ⓐ	Ⓐ	Ⓒ	Ⓒ	Ⓐ	Ⓐ	Ⓒ	Ⓐ
Mont de Marsan d.	1047	1242	1444	1545	1547	1739	1742	1841	1944	2046
Morcenx **305** d.	1113	1314	1513	1614	1614	1805	1812	1914	2010	2113
Facture Biganos.... **305** d.	1151	1352	1551	1651	1654	1847	1850	1952	2048	2151
Bordeaux St Jean **305** a.	1216	1420	1620	1714	1717	1916	1916	2016	2117	2218

CARCASSONNE - LIMOUX - QUILLAN

km			Ⓐ 🚌	⚒	⑥ 🚌	Ⓐ 🚌	Ⓒ 🚌		⚒	⚒ 🚌	† 🚌	⚒	⚒ 🚌
0	**Carcassonne**	d.	0635	0720	0800	0800	0915	...	1025	...	1230	1227	...
26	Limoux	d.	0725	0748	0845	0847	0955	...	1054	1117	1310	1256	1301
54	**Quillan**	a.	0813	...	0935	0938	1045	...	...	1205	1400	...	1345
			🚌	⚒	⚒ 🚌	Ⓐ 🚌	⚒		⚒ 🚌	Ⓐ 🚌	† 🚌	⚒	⚒ 🚌
	Carcassonne	d.	1415	1600	...	1715	1736	...	...	1820	1905	1907	...
	Limoux	d.	1450	1629	1635	1810	1805	...	1810	1915	1945	1936	1941
	Quillan	a.	1535	...	1725	1900	...	...	1900	2005	2035	...	2025
			⚒ 🚌	⚒	Ⓐ 🚌	Ⓐ 🚌	⚒		Ⓒ 🚌	Ⓐ 🚌	⚒ 🚌	⚒	† 🚌
	Quillan	d.	0545	...	0620	0705	...	...	0745	0820	1026	...	1100
	Limoux	d.	0629	0639	0655	0750	0800	...	0819	0903	1110	1135	1135
	Carcassonne	a.	...	0709	0750	...	0830	...	0910	0950	...	1204	1220
			Ⓒ 🚌	Ⓐ 🚌	⚒ 🚌	⚒	⚒ 🚌		⚒	Ⓑ 🚌	⑥ 🚌	⚒	⚒ 🚌
	Quillan	d.	1245	1245	1356	...	1545	...	...	1710	1725	...	1820
	Limoux	d.	1319	1326	1440	1450	1625	...	1640	1745	1800	1820	1854
	Carcassonne	a.	1410	1420	...	1520	...	...	1710	1840	...	1849	1950

CHARLEVILLE MÉZIÈRES - GIVET — Journey 60 – 65 minutes *64 km*

From Charleville Mézières at 0635 Ⓐ **d**, 0705 **e**, 0735, 0835, 0935, 1035 **f**, 1135, 1235, 1335, 1434, 1535, 1635, 1705 Ⓐ **d**, 1735, 1805 Ⓐ **d**, 1835, 1936, 2035.

From Givet at 0519 Ⓐ **d**, 0550 **e**, 0620 Ⓐ, 0651 **g**, 0720 **e**, 0727 Ⓐ **d**, 0820, 0920, 1020, 1028 Ⓐ **d**, 1120 **f**, 1150 Ⓐ **d**, 1220 **h**, 1320, 1420 **h**, 1427 Ⓐ **d**, 1519, 1620, 1719, 1820, 1920.

Subject to alteration July 2, 3, 9, 10.

DINARD - ST MALO

🚌 : Approximately hourly on Ⓐ (fewer on Ⓒ). Journey 21 – 26 minutes. *11 km.* Operator: Breizgo (en Ille-et-Vilaine). Route **16**.

⛴ : *Le Bus de Mer* passenger ferry operates a frequent daily servjce. Journey 10 minutes. Operator: Compagnie Corsaire (compagniecorsaire.com).

GUINGAMP - CARHAIX — Journey 65 – 70 minutes *56 km*

From Guingamp at 0750 Ⓐ, 1042 ⚒, 1340 Ⓐ, 1343 Ⓒ, 1540 ①–④, 1745 ⚒, 1940 Ⓒ, 2030 ⑤, 2045 ①–④, 2207 ⑤.

From Carhaix at 0626 Ⓐ, 0905 ⚒, 1200 Ⓑ, 1228 ⑥, 1258 ⑤, 1353 ①–④, 1505, 1803 †, 1910 Ⓐ.

GUINGAMP - PAIMPOL — Journey: 47 – 53 minutes *47 km*

From **Guingamp** at 0817 Ⓐ, 1153, 1401, 1737 †, 1739 ⚒, 1950 †, 2007 Ⓐ, 2202 ⑤.

From **Paimpol** at 0720 Ⓐ, 0916, 1304, 1515, 1834 †, 1906 Ⓐ, 1916 ⑥.

LILLE - LENS — Journey 42 – 46 minutes *39 km*

From Lille Flandres on Ⓐ at 0647, 0726, 0739, 0747, 0809, 0847, 0909, 1047, 1109, 1147, 1209, 1247, 1347, 1509, 1547, 1609, 1647, 1709, 1739, 1747, 1809, 1847, 1909, 1947, 2047; on ⑥ at 0650, 0811, 0819, 0948, 1206, 1219, 1319, 1357, 1548, 1606, 1719, 1819, 1948, 2006, 2053; on † at 0819, 0948, 1148, 1206, 1319, 1448, 1606, 1648, 1819, 1948, 2006, 2053.

From Lens on Ⓐ at 0540, 0614, 0640, 0710, 0714, 0740, 0814, 0840, 0952, 1110, 1114, 1210, 1214, 1310, 1314, 1440, 1614, 1640, 1714, 1740, 1814, 1840, 1940, 2014; on ⑥ at 0626, 0700, 0713, 0735, 0754, 1035, 1108, 1200, 1300, 1435, 1508, 1700, 1835, 1908, 2035; on † at 0754, 1035, 1108, 1200, 1435, 1508, 1635, 1800, 1908, 1935,

Subject to alteration on † Aug. 7 – 28.

NANTES - CHOLET — Journey 52 – 70 minutes *65 km*

From Nantes at 0628 Ⓐ, 0728 ⚒, 0829 **j**, 1100 ⑥ 🚌, 1129 Ⓐ, 1259 ⚒, 1535 ⑥ 🚌, 1547 Ⓐ, 1620 Ⓐ 🚌, 1729 Ⓐ, 1829 Ⓑ, 1929 ⚒, 2035 †.

From Cholet at 0605 Ⓐ, 0640 Ⓐ, 0744 ⚒, 1010 **j**, 1240 ⚒, 1420 ⑥ 🚌, 1444 Ⓐ, 1610 Ⓐ, 1655 ⑥ 🚌, 1711 Ⓑ, 1745 Ⓐ 🚌, 1853 ⚒, 1935 †.

PARIS - DISNEYLAND (Marne la Vallée - Chessy) — *32 km*

Trains run approximately every 15 – 30 minutes 0500 - 2400 on RER Line A: Châtelet les Halles - Gare de Lyon - Marne la Vallée Chessy (for Disneyland).

Operator: RATP. For *TGV* services serving Marne la Vallée see Tables **11** and **391**.

Journey: 39 minutes.

SOUILLAC - SARLAT 🚌 — *30 km*

From Souillac Gare SNCF at 0650 ①–⑤, 0840 †, 0940 ⑥, 1340, 1945 ①–⑤.

From Sarlat Gare SNCF at 0612 ①–⑤, 1222 ①–⑤, 1232 Ⓒ, 1310 ③, 1643 ①②④⑤, 1737 Ⓒ, 1815 ①–⑤.

🚌 (Nouvelle Aquitaine Cars Régionaux Ligne 6). Journey 40 – 45 minutes.

Warning! *Service is amended during school holiday periods.*

TOULOUSE - AUCH — Journey 85 – 95 minutes *88 km*

From Toulouse Matabiau at 0624 **k**, 0724 Ⓐ, 0824, 1024 **m**, 1224, 1424, 1524 Ⓐ, 1624, 1724 Ⓐ, 1824 **n**, 2024, 2125 Ⓐ 🚌.

From Auch at 0603 ⚒, 0705 Ⓐ, 0805 ◧, 0905 Ⓐ, 1005, 1205, 1406, 1605, 1705 Ⓐ, 1805, 1919 Ⓐ 🚌, 2005.

TOURS - CHINON — Journey 46 – 54 minutes *49 km*

From Tours at 0640 ⚒ 🚌, 0729 Ⓐ, 0820 † 🚌, 0931 ⚒, 1220 † 🚌, 1232 ⚒, 1505 **p**, 1631 Ⓐ, 1732 Ⓐ, 1805 ⚒ 🚌, 1901 Ⓐ, 1902 Ⓒ, 1957 Ⓑ.

From Chinon at 0624 Ⓐ, 0657 ⚒, 0730 Ⓐ 🚌 **q**, 0739 Ⓐ **r**, 0839 Ⓐ, 0935 ⚒ 🚌, 1003 † 🚌, 1109 ⚒, 1339, 1604 † 🚌, 1609 Ⓐ **r**, 1739 ⚒, 1841 Ⓑ, 2003 †, 2022 ⚒ 🚌.

VALENCIENNES - CAMBRAI — Journey 50 minutes *40 km*

From Valenciennes at 0649 ⚒, 0749 Ⓐ 🚌, 0823 ⑥, 0949 Ⓐ **d**, 1223 ⑥, 1249 Ⓐ, 1649 Ⓐ **d**, 1649 Ⓐ **s** 🚌, 1723 Ⓒ, 1749 Ⓐ, 1835 Ⓐ **d** 🚌, 1849 Ⓐ **s**, 1930 Ⓒ.

From Cambrai Ville at 0549 Ⓐ, 0635 Ⓐ 🚌, 0649 ⑥, 0749 ⚒, 1149 Ⓐ **d**, 1249 ⚒, 1649 Ⓐ **s** 🚌, 1649 Ⓐ **d**, 1749 Ⓐ **d** 🚌, 1749 Ⓐ **s**, 1850 Ⓒ.

- **d** – Until July 8.
- **e** – ⑥ until July 9; ⚒ from July 11.
- **f** – ⑥ until July 9; daily from July 10.
- **g** – Ⓐ until July 8; † from July 10.
- **h** – † until July 10; daily from July 11.
- **j** – Ⓑ until July 13; † July 24 - Aug. 14; Ⓑ from Aug. 15.
- **k** – ⚒ until July 16; ⑥ from July 23.
- **m** – Daily until July 17; Ⓒ from July 23.
- **n** – ⒸⒸ untl July 17; daily from July 18.
- **p** – Daily until July 10; Ⓒ July 14 - Aug. 21; Daily from Aug. 22.
- **q** – July 11 - Aug. 19.
- **r** – Until July 8 and from Aug. 22.
- **s** – July 11 - Aug. 26.
- ◧ – Terminates at Toulouse Arenes on Ⓐ from July 18.

PARIS - POITIERS - LA ROCHELLE and BORDEAUX 300

Subject to alteration July 2, 3, 9, 15, 16, 23, 24, Aug, 6, 7, 13 – 15, 20 – 28. *TGV* timings may vary by a few minutes - please check your reservation.
Frequent connecting services operate St Pierre des Corps - Tours and v.v. Journey time 5 minutes.

PARIS - BORDEAUX NON-STOP SERVICES

km																										
		TGV	*TGV*	*TGV*	*TGV*	*TGV*	*TGV*	*TGV*	*TGV*	*TGV*	*TGV*	*TGV*	*TGV*	*TGV*	*TGV*	*TGV*	*TGV*	*TGV*	*TGV*	*TGV*	*TGV*	*TGV*	*TGV*	*TGV*	*TGV*	*TGV*
		8571	**8503**	**8531**	**7671**	**8537**	**8572**	**8473**	**8505**	**8541**	**8547**	**8574**	**8261**	**8475**	**8509**	**8549**	**8590**	**8267**	**8517**	**8551**	**8593**	**8477**	**8477**	**8213**	**8519**	**8523**
		①–⑥	①–⑥	①–⑥					①–④	①–⑥	①–④		⑥	⑦	Ⓑ		⑤		①–⑥	①–⑥		⑤	①–④	⑤		⑤
		d	**d**	**d**	**A** ⊠	**B**			**e**	**d**	**e**			**f**	**g**	**B**	**h**	**B**	**d**	**d**		**h**	**e**	**h**	**B**	**h**
0	**Paris** Montparnasse .... d.	0637	0711	0711	0911	1011	1011	1111	1111	1211	1406	1406	1511	1511	1511	1611	1611	1711	1711	1811	1811	1847	1848	1911	1911	2006
537	**Bordeaux** St Jean .... a.	0848	0914	0914	1116	1214	1214	1314	1314	1414	1614	1614	1714	1714	1714	1814	1814	1914	1914	2014	2014	2054	2051	2114	2114	2214
	To:	*Tar*	*Tou*	*Hen*	*Tou*	*Hen*	*Tar*	*Arc*	*Tou*	*Hen*	*Hen*	*Tar*	—	*Arc*	*Tou*	*Hen*	*Tar*	—	*Tou*	*Hen*	*Tar*	*Arc*	*Arc*	—	*Tou*	*Tou*

To: *Arc – Arcachon (Table* ***306****). Hen – Hendaye (Table* ***305****). Tar – Tarbes (Table* ***305****). Tou – Toulouse (Table* ***320****).*

PARIS - POITIERS - LA ROCHELLE and BORDEAUX

km																										
		TGV	*TGV*	*TGV*	*TGV*	*TGV*		*TGV*	*TGV*	*TGV*	*TGV*	*TGV*	*TGV*		*TGV*	*TGV*	*TGV*	*TGV*	*TGV*	*TGV*		*TGV*	*TGV*	*TGV*	*TGV*	*TGV*
		8431	**8371**	**8483**	**8331**	**8533**		**8533**	**8471**	**7669**	**8373**	**9802**	**5450**		**8375**	**8437**	**8379**	**8379**	**8377**	**8335**		**8333**	**7673**	**7653**	**8361**	**8485**
		⑤⑥						⑤	⑥		⑥		①–⑥				⑤	⑦		①–④		⑤⑥			⑤–⑦	
		j				**B C**		**C h**	**D k**	**E** ⊠	**k**	**F**	**G m**				**h**	**f**	**H**	**e**		**j**	⊡ ⊠	⊠	**n**	
0	**Paris** Montparnasse ... **295** d.	0602	0653	0653	0729	0801	...	0801	0801	...	0826	...	...	...	0915	1006	1219	1219	1219	1230	...	1231	1237	1330	1342	1419
	Vendôme-Villiers TGV **295** d.	|	|	|	0816	|	...	|	|	...	|	...	...	...	|	|	|	|	|	1316	...	1316	|	|	|	|
	St Pierre des Corps .... **295** a.	0700	|	|	0835	|	...	|	|	...	|	...	...	...	1013	1106	|	1317	1317	1335	...	1335	|	1428	|	1519
	St Pierre des Corps .... d.	0704	|	|	0842	|	...	|	|	0910	|	1010	1010	...	1017	1110	|	1320	1321	1339	...	1348	|	1431	|	1523
	Châtellerault .... d.	|	|	|	0910	|	...	|	|	|	|	|	|	...	|	|	|	|	|	1425	...	1420	|	|	|	|
	Futuroscope .... d.	|	|	|	0924	|	...	|	|	|	|	|	|	...	|	|	|	|	|	1440	...	1436	|	|	|	|
318	**Poitiers** .... a.	0735	0809	0811	0933	0917	...	0917	0917	0940	0945	1040	1040	...	1050	1140	1337	1353	1352	1447	...	1444	|	1503	|	1554
318	**Poitiers** .... d.	0738	0813	0823	...	0920	...	0920	0920	0943	0954	1043	1043	...	1053	1143	1340	1355	1354	...	...	...	|	1506	|	1557
398	Niort .... d.	|	0903	|	...	|	...	|	|	|	1041	|	|	...	1144	|	1428	1442	1439	...	...	...	|	|	1541	|
465	**La Rochelle** Ville .... a.	|	0944	|	...	|	...	|	|	|	1120	|	|	...	1225	|	1505	1523	1526	...	...	...	|	|	1621	|
	Angoulême .... d.	0826	...	0906	...	|	...	|	|	1026	...	1126	1126	...	...	1226	...	...	...	...	...	...	1437	|	...	1638
	Libourne .... d.	|	...	0949	...	|	...	|	|	|	...	|	|	...	...	|	...	...	...	...	...	...	|	|	...	1717
540	**Bordeaux** St Jean .... a.	0902	...	1011	...	1018	...	1018u	1018	1102	...	1202	1202	...	...	1302	...	...	...	...	...	...	1514	1607	...	1736

km																										
		TGV	*TGV*	*TGV*	*TGV*		*TGV*	*TGV*	*TGV*	*TGV*		*TGV*	*TGV*	*TGV*	*TGV*	*TGV*		*TGV*	*TGV*	*TGV*	*TGV*		*TGV*	*TGV*	*TGV*	*TGV*
		8363	**8447**	**5454**	**8449**		**8343**	**8389**	**8367**	**8367**		**8451**	**8391**	**8491**	**8345**	**5240**		**8393**	**7659**	**8395**	**8495**		**8455**	**8347**	**8461**	**8461**
					①–④		⑤	⑦	①–⑤	⑥		⑤	Ⓑ		①–⑤					⑤⑦	⑤⑦			Ⓑ	⑤	⑦
				G	**e**		**h**	**f**	**d**			**h**	**g** ◧		**p**	**J**			⊠	**q**	**q**		**B**	**g**	**r**	
0	**Paris** Montparnasse ... **295** d.	1544	1606	...	1706	...	1706	1706	1730	1734	...	1744	1827	1827	1831	...	...	1919	1944	2025	2025	...	2039	2100	2140	2201
	Vendôme-Villiers TGV **295** d.	|	|	...	|	...	|	|	1815	1819	...	|	|	|	1916	...	...	|	|	|	|	...	|	2146	|	|
	St Pierre des Corps .... **295** a.	|	|	...	|	...	|	|	1835	1839	...	|	|	|	1935	...	...	2018	|	|	|	...	|	2205	2237	2259
	St Pierre des Corps .... d.	|	|	1810	|	...	|	|	1839	1846	...	|	|	|	1945	2010	...	2022	|	|	|	...	|	2209	2241	2303
	Châtellerault .... d.	|	|	|	1823	...	1823	|	|	|	...	|	|	|	2013	|	...	|	|	|	|	...	|	2237	|	|
	Futuroscope .... d.	|	|	|	|	...	|	|	|	|	...	|	|	|	|	|	...	|	|	|	|	...	|	|	|	|
	Poitiers .... a.	|	1725	1840	1845	...	1845	1845	|	|	...	|	1945	1945	2031	2040	...	2055	|	2146	2146	...	|	2253	2311	2333
	Poitiers .... d.	|	1728	1843	1849	...	...	1848	|	|	...	|	1949	1954	...	2043	...	2058	|	2147	2154	...	|	...	2315	2337
394	Niort .... d.	1740	|	|	|	...	...	1935	1946	2004	...	|	2041	|	...	|	...	2145	|	2245	|	...	|	...	|	|
461	**La Rochelle** Ville .... a.	1825	|	|	|	...	...	2012	2028	2046	...	|	2123	|	...	|	...	2226	|	2344	|	...	|	...	|	|
	Angoulême .... d.	...	1809	1926	1930	...	...	...	...	...	...	1933	...	2037	...	2126	...	...	2131	...	2237	...	2229	...	2357	0020
	Libourne .... d.	...	|	|	|	...	...	...	...	...	...	|	...	2120	...	|	...	...	|	...	2320	...	|	...	|	|
	Bordeaux St Jean .... a.	...	1844	2002	2006	...	...	...	...	...	...	2008	...	2142	...	2202	...	...	2207	...	2346	...	2306	...	0036	0059

TER REGIONAL SERVICES TOURS - POITIERS - ANGOULÊME and LA ROCHELLE

For TER services Angoulême - Bordeaux see Table **302**.

km																										
		Ⓐ	Ⓐ	Ⓐ		Ⓐ	⚒	⚒		Ⓐ	Ⓐ	⑥		Ⓐ	†	Ⓒ		⑥	Ⓐ	Ⓐ			⑥			
																			t	🚌 **v**						
0	**Tours** .... d.	...	...	...	...	...	0615	...	...	...	0735	...	...	...	...	...	...	...	...	...	...	...	...	1221	...	...
68	Châtellerault .... d.	...	...	...	...	0630	0710	...	...	0741	0827	0838	...	0839	0901	...	...	1031	...	...	...	...	...	1308	...	...
90	Futuroscope .... d.	...	...	...	...	0655	0722	...	...	0806	0841	0902	...	0904	0916	...	...	1055	...	...	...	...	...	1331	...	...
101	**Poitiers** .... a.	...	...	...	...	0704	0729	...	...	0815	0849	0910	...	0913	0924	...	...	1104	...	...	...	...	...	1341	...	...
101	**Poitiers** .... d.	0559	0618	0635	...	0707	...	0752	...	0818	...	0912	...	...	...	1004	...	...	1216	1216	...	1223	1314	...	...	...
166	Ruffec .... d.	|	0653	|	...	0746	...	|	...	0856	...	0948	...	...	...	|	...	...	1303	1400	...	|	1357	...	...	...
213	**Angoulême** .... a.	|	0725	|	...	0816	...	|	...	0925	...	1018	...	...	...	|	...	...	1335	1500	...	|	1425	...	...	...
181	Niort .... d.	0653	...	0744	...	...	...	0851	...	...	...	...	...	...	...	1059	...	...	...	...	...	1324	...	...	...	...
248	**La Rochelle** Ville .... a.	0739	...	0836	...	...	...	0937	...	...	...	...	...	...	...	1144	...	...	...	...	...	1409	...	...	...	...

	Ⓐ	Ⓐ	Ⓐ		Ⓒ	Ⓐ			Ⓐ	⑥			†	Ⓐ	Ⓐ		Ⓐ	Ⓑ			Ⓐ	⑥	†		
Tours .... d.	...	...	...	...	...	...	...	...	1624	...	...	...	...	...	1722	...	...	...	1820	...	...	...	2016	...	...
Châtellerault .... d.	...	...	...	...	...	1639	...	...	1712	1721	...	...	...	1727	1809	...	1839	...	1907	...	1939	1952	2103	...	...
Futuroscope .... d.	...	...	...	...	...	1703	...	...	1725	1746	...	...	...	1751	1823	...	1904	...	1920	...	2003	2016	2116	...	...
Poitiers .... a.	...	...	...	...	...	1714	...	...	1732	1755	...	...	...	1800	1831	...	1913	...	1928	...	2013	2026	2123	...	...
Poitiers .... d.	1523	1618	1613	...	1716	1716	1709	...	...	...	1757	...	1802	1804	...	...	1917	1912	...	...	...	...	...	...	...
Ruffec .... d.	|	1701	|	...	1759	1759	|	...	...	...	|	...	1847	1849	...	...	2000	|	...	...	...	...	...	...	...
Angoulême .... a.	|	1731	|	...	1828	1830	|	...	...	...	|	...	1916	1920	...	...	2030	|	...	...	...	...	...	...	...
Niort .... d.	1613	...	1724	...	...	...	1809	...	...	...	1858	...	...	...	...	...	...	2014	...	...	...	...	...	...	...
La Rochelle Ville .... a.	1656	...	1809	...	...	...	1900	...	...	...	1943	...	...	...	...	...	...	2055	...	...	...	...	...	...	...

A – To Toulouse (Table **320**).
B – ①②③④⑦ (not July 13, 14).
C – To Hendaye (Table **305**).
D – To Arcachon (Table **306**).
E – From Tourcoing (Table **11**).
F – From Brussels (Table **11**).
G – From Strasbourg (Table **391**).
H – ①②③④⑥ (also July 15; not July 13, Aug. 15).
J – From Lille (Table **11**).

d – Not Aug. 15.
e – Not July 13, 14, Aug. 15.
f – Also July 13, 14, Aug. 15.
g – Not July 14, 15.
h – Also July 13; not July 15.
j – Also July 13, 14.
k – Also July 14, 15.
m – Also July 10; not July 2 – 8, Aug. 15.
n – Also July 13, 14, Aug. 15; not July 16.
p – Not July 14, 15, ①–④ July 25 - Aug. 15.
q – Also July 13, Aug. 15; not July 15.
r – Not July 1, 15.
t – Until July 29.
u – Calls to pick up only.
v – From Aug. 1.

◧ – Uses train number **8397** on certain dates.
⊡ – Does not call at Angoulême Aug. 8 – 12.
⊠ – OUIGO low-cost TGV service. Internet booking only at www.ouigo.com.

TGV – High-speed train. Ⓡ. 🍸.

FOR RETURN SERVICES SEE NEXT PAGE →

300 BORDEAUX and LA ROCHELLE - POITIERS - PARIS

Subject to alteration July 2, 3, 9, 15, 16, 23, 24, Aug, 6, 7, 13–15, 20–28. *TGV* timings may vary by a few minutes - please check your reservation.
Frequent connecting services operate St Pierre des Corps - Tours and v.v. Journey time 5 minutes.

BORDEAUX - PARIS NON-STOP SERVICES

	TGV	*TGV*	*TGV*	*TGV*	*TGV*	*TGV*	*TGV*	*TGV*	*TGV*	*TGV*	*TGV*	*TGV*	*TGV*	*TGV*	*TGV*	*TGV*	*TGV*	*TGV*	*TGV*	*TGV*	*TGV*	*TGV*	*TGV*	*TGV*	*TGV*
	8478	**8402**	**8404**	**8502**	**8530**	**8560**	**8504**	**8534**	**8562**	**8508**	**8536**	**8581**	**8583**	**8472**	**7672**	**8472**	**8542**	**8542**	**8544**	**8514**	**8516**	**8585**	**8550**	**8587**	**8589**
	①–⑥			①–⑥	Ⓑ	①–⑥		①–⑥	⑦	①–⑤	①–⑤	①–⑥		①–⑥		⑦	⚒	†	①–④	⑤–⑦	①–⑤	⑦		①–⑤	⑦
	d	A		d	e	d		d	f	g	g	d	h		B ⊠				j	k	g	f		m	f
From:	*Arc*	—	—	*Tou*	*Hen*	*Tar*	*Tou*	*Hen*	*Tar*	*Tou*	*Hen*	*Tar*	*Tar*	*Arc*	*Tou*	*Arc*	*Hen*	*Hen*	*Hen*	*Tou*	*Tou*	*Tar*	*Hen*	*Tar*	*Tar*
Bordeaux St Jean ... d.	0644	0712	0746	0846	0946	0946	1046	1213	1213	1245	1347	1347	1546	1641	1646	1713	1730	1742	1846	1846	1946	1946	2050	2050	2212
Paris Montparnasse ... a.	0858	0922	1006	1056	1155	1155	1256	1426	1426	1456	1557	1557	1756	1900	1849	1927	1949	1956	2101	2101	2157	2157	2301	2300	0024

*To: Arc – Arcachon (Table **306**). Hen – Hendaye (Table **305**). Tar – Tarbes (Table **305**). Tou – Toulouse (Table **320**).*

BORDEAUX and LA ROCHELLE - POITIERS - PARIS

km		*TGV*	*TGV*	*TGV*		*TGV*	*TGV*	*TGV*		*TGV*	*TGV*	*TGV*		*TGV*	*TGV*	*TGV*		*TGV*	*TGV*	*TGV*		*TGV*	*TGV*	*TGV*		
		8430	**8480**	**8370**		**5260**	**8432**	**8632**		**8362**	**7652**	**5440**		**8484**	**8376**	**7656**		**9820**	**8378**	**8470**		**8512**	**8380**	**8380**		
		①	①–⑤	①–⑥				Ⓐ		Ⓒ										⑥			①–④	⑤–⑦		
		n	g	d		C	p				⊠	D				⊠		E		F q		B	r	t		
0	**Bordeaux** St Jean ... d.	0546	0518	...	...	0558	0658	...	...	...	0850	0858	...	1018	...	1158	...	1258	...	1446	...	1446	...	...	...	...
	Libourne ... d.	|	0542	...	...	|	|	...	...	...	|	|	...	1042	...	|	...	|	...	|	...	|	...	...	...	...
114	Angoulême ... d.	0628	0623	...	...	0636	0736	...	...	...	0929	0935	...	1124	...	1233	...	1336	...	1523	...	1523	...	...	...	...
	La Rochelle Ville ... d.	|	|	0539	...	|	|	0824	...	0847	|	|	...	|	1044	1236	...	|	1347	|	...	|	1528	1539	...	...
	Niort ... d.	|	|	0621	...	|	|	0906	...	0929	|	|	...	|	1126	|	...	|	1430	|	...	|	1607	1616	...	...
	Poitiers ... a.	|	0704	0708	...	0716	0817	|	...	|	1009	1017	...	1204	1209	|	...	1418	1515	|	...	|	1702	1708	...	...
	Poitiers ... d.	|	0714	0714	...	0719	0820	|	...	|	1012	1019	...	1215	1215	|	...	1419	1518	|	...	|	1707	1709	...	...
	Futuroscope ... d.	|	|	|	...	|	|	|	...	|	|	|	...	|	|	|	...	|	|	|	...	|	|	|	...	...
	Châtellerault ... d.	|	|	|	...	|	|	|	...	|	|	|	...	|	|	|	...	|	|	|	...	|	|	|	...	...
	St Pierre-des-Corps ... a.	|	|	|	...	0750	0851	1009	...	1032	|	1051	...	1248	1248	1348	...	1450	1557	|	...	|	|	|	...	...
	St Pierre des Corps ... **295** d.	|	|	|	...	...	0854	1013	...	1036	|	...	...	1252	1252	1342	...	...	1601	|	...	|	|	|	...	...
	Vendôme-Villiers TGV **295** d.	|	|	|	...	...	|	|	...	|	|	...	...	|	|	|	...	...	|	|	...	|	|	|	...	...
542	**Paris** Montparnasse ... **295** a.	0819	0840	0840	...	...	1001	1119	...	1140	1138	...	...	1358	1358	1439	...	...	1706	1716	...	1716	1841	1841	...	...

	TGV	*TGV*	*TGV*		*TGV*	*TGV*	*TGV*		*TGV*	*TGV*	*TGV*		*TGV*	*TGV*	*TGV*		*TGV*	*TGV*	*TGV*		*TGV*	*TGV*	*TGV*		
	5444	**8488**	**8364**		**7660**	**8442**	**8388**		**8450**	**8388**	**8386**		**8386**	**8394**	**8476**		**7674**	**8454**	**8392**		**8454**	**8392**	**8396**		
						⑦	⑦			⑤	①		⑥	⑦	⑦			⑦	⑦		⑤	⑤	⑦		
	D v				G ⊠	f	f			t	w			f	F f		B ⊠	f	f		t	x	f		
Bordeaux St Jean ... d.	1558	1618	...	...	1658	1753	...	...	1830	...	...	...	...	...	2011	...	2045	2058	...	...	2107	...	...	...	...
Libourne ... d.	|	1642	...	...	|	|	...	...	|	...	...	...	...	...	|	...	|	|	...	...	|	...	...	...	...
Angoulême ... d.	1636	1725	...	...	1737	1833	...	...	1909	...	...	...	...	...	2049	...	2123	2139	...	...	2149	...	...	...	...
La Rochelle Ville ... d.	|	|	1701	...	|	|	1814	...	|	1917	1911	...	1925	1947	|	...	|	|	2101	...	|	2058	2150	...	...
Niort ... d.	|	|	1743	...	|	|	1851	...	|	1954	1952	...	2007	2029	|	...	|	|	2143	...	|	2143	2228	...	...
Poitiers ... a.	1717	1805	|	...	1817	|	1958	...	2000	|	|	...	|	2111	|	...	|	2226	2230	...	2231	2233	2311	...	...
Poitiers ... d.	1720	1809	|	...	1820	|	2004	...	2004	|	|	...	|	2114	|	...	|	2236	2236	...	2239	2239	2314	...	...
Futuroscope ... d.	|	|	|	...	|	|	|	...	|	|	|	...	|	|	|	...	|	|	|	...	|	|	|	...	...
Châtellerault ... d.	|	|	|	...	|	|	|	...	|	|	|	...	|	|	|	...	|	|	|	...	|	|	|	...	...
St Pierre-des-Corps ... a.	1750	|	|	...	1850	1938	2037	...	2043	2115	2116	...	2115	|	2148	...	|	2308	2308	...	2312	2310	|	...	...
St Pierre des Corps ... **295** d.	...	|	|	...	...	1945	2039	...	2043	2119	2120	...	2119	|	2152	...	|	2311	2311	...	2313	2313	|	...	...
Vendôme-Villiers TGV ... **295** d.	...	|	|	...	...	|	|	...	|	|	|	...	|	|	|	...	|	|	|	...	|	|	|	...	...
Paris Montparnasse ... **295** a.	...	1937	1941	...	...	2051	2144	...	2151	2223	2224	...	2224	2241	2256	...	2308	0016	0016	...	0018	0018	0040	...	...

TER REGIONAL SERVICES LA ROCHELLLE and ANGOULÊME - POITIERS - TOURS

For TER services Bordeaux - Angoulême see Table **302**.

	Ⓐ	Ⓐ	Ⓐ	①		⚒	Ⓐ	⑥	Ⓐ		⑥	†	Ⓐ	Ⓐ				⑥	†			Ⓐ y	Ⓐ	Ⓒ	Ⓐ
La Rochelle Ville ... d.	...	...	...	0556	...	...	...	...	0623	...	0633	...	...	0715	0753	...	...	...	...	...	...	...	1225	1225	...
Niort ... d.	...	...	...	0636	...	...	...	...	0710	...	0713	...	...	0756	0838	...	...	...	...	...	...	...	1309	1310	...
Angoulême ... d.	...	...	...	|	...	...	0614	...	|	...	|	...	0731	|	|	...	0826	...	1032	...	...	1230	|	|	...
Ruffec ... d.	...	...	...	|	...	...	0641	...	|	...	|	...	0758	|	|	...	0854	...	1059	...	...	1303	|	|	...
Poitiers ... a.	...	...	...	0732	...	...	0741	...	0809	...	0802	...	0846	0857	0930	...	0947	...	1147	...	...	1354	1404	1412	...
Poitiers ... d.	0548	0608	0658	...	...	0736	0743	0748	...	...	...	0830	...	...	...	...	...	0948	...	1235	...	...	...	...	1500
Futuroscope ... d.	0558	0616	0708	...	...	0744	0752	0758	...	...	...	0837	...	...	...	...	...	0957	...	1245	...	...	...	...	1508
Châtellerault ... d.	0622	0627	0731	...	...	0755	0816	0822	...	...	...	0850	...	...	...	...	...	1022	...	1309	...	...	...	...	1520
Tours ... a.	...	0716	...	...	...	0844	...	...	...	...	...	...	...	...	...	...	...	...	...	1406	...	...	...	...	1609

	Ⓐ 🚌 z	⑥	Ⓐ	⚒			Ⓐ	Ⓐ	†		Ⓐ	Ⓐ	Ⓒ	⑥	†			Ⓐ	†	Ⓐ		⚒	Ⓐ	Ⓑ 🚌	⑤†
La Rochelle Ville ... d.	...	...	...	...	...	...	1550	...	...	...	...	1709	1713	...	1751	...	...	1757	...	...	...	1833	...	...	1925
Niort ... d.	...	...	...	...	...	...	1634	...	...	...	...	1757	1758	...	1836	...	...	1842	...	...	...	1918	...	...	2010
Angoulême ... d.	1230	1343	...	...	...	...	|	1628	1642	...	1732	|	|	...	|	...	1838	|	...	...	...	|	1930	...	|
Ruffec ... d.	1330	1409	...	...	...	...	|	1658	1709	...	1759	|	|	...	|	...	1905	|	...	...	...	|	1957	...	|
Poitiers ... a.	1516	1457	...	...	...	...	1735	1740	1752	...	1840	1900	1900	...	1937	...	1946	1953	...	...	...	2014	2039	...	2100
Poitiers ... d.	...	...	1547	1638	...	1732	...	1746	...	...	1845	...	...	1909	...	...	...	...	1955	2001	...	...	...	2055	...
Futuroscope ... d.	...	...	1557	1648	...	1740	...	1755	...	...	1857	...	...	1918	...	...	...	...	2005	2011	...	...	...	2113	...
Châtellerault ... d.	...	...	1621	1712	...	1753	...	1820	...	...	1917	...	...	1943	...	...	...	...	2026	2032	...	...	...	2142	...
Tours ... a.	...	...	...	...	...	1851	...	...	...	...	...	...	...	...	...	...	...	...	2107	2113	...	...	...	...	...

A – July 4–8, 11–13, 18–22, Aug. 16–19, 22–26.
B – From Toulouse (Table **320**).
C – To Lille (Table **11**).
D – To Strasbourg (Table **391**).
E – To Brussels (Table **11**).
F – From Arcachon (Table **306**).
G – To Paris Charles de Gaulle ✈, Lille or Tourcoing (Table **11**).

d – Not Aug. 15.
e – Not July 14, 15.
f – Also Aug. 15.
g – Not July 14, 15, Aug. 15.
h – Not July 2, 4–8, 11–13, 15.
j – Not July 13, 14, Aug. 15.
k – Also July 13, 14, Aug. 15.

m – Also July 14, 15, Aug. 15.
n – Also Aug, 16; not Aug. 15.
p – Not Aug. 22–25.
q – Also July 14, 15.
r – Also July 15; not July 13.
t – Also July 13; not July 15.
v – Not July 2–8.
w – Also July 14, 15, Aug. 16, 23–25; not Aug. 15.
x – Not July 15.
y – Until July 29.
z – From Aug. 1.
⊠ – OUIGO low-cost TGV service. Internet booking only at www.ouigo.com.
TGV – High-speed train. Ⓡ. 🍸.

ANGOULÊME and NIORT - SAINTES - ROYAN 301

km			Ⓐ	Ⓐ	Ⓐ	Ⓐ	Ⓐ	†			⑥		⚒	Ⓐ	Ⓐ	Ⓐ	†			⚒		Ⓐ			Ⓐ
0	**Angoulême**	d.	...	0641	...	...	0732	...	0941	...	...	1103	...	...	1307	...	1448	...	...	1503	1659	...	...	1822	1859
49	Cognac	d.	...	0724	...	...	0817	...	1021	...	...	1143	...	...	1346	...	1526	...	...	1544	1742	...	...	1905	1939
	Niort	d.	0637	|	...	...	|	0915	|	...	0959	|	1152	1252	|	...	|	...	1450	|	|	...	1749	|	|
75	**Saintes**	a.	0746	0744	...	←	0835	1020	1040	...	1107	1201	1256	1359	1405	←	1544	...	1554	1603	1802	...	1908	1930	1957
75	**Saintes**	d.	...	→	0751	0756	0843	1023	1046	...	1110	1209	1259	→	...	1426	1555	...	...	1612	1805	1811	1916	...	...
	La Rochelle Ville **292**	a.	...	...	|	0900	|	|	|	...	|	|	|	...	...	|	|	...	...	|	1908	|	|	...	...
111	**Royan**	a.	...	...	0818	...	0910	1049	1112	...	1139	1239	1326	...	...	1453	1626	...	...	1641	...	1838	1946	...	...

		Ⓐ			†		⑤		
Angoulême	d.	...	1940	...	...	...	...	2145	...
Cognac	d.	...	2025	...	...	...	...	2224	...
Niort	d.	1840	|	...	1959	...	2055	|	...
Saintes	a.	1959	2045	...	2104	...	2159	2244	...
Saintes	d.	...	2052	...	2113	...	2202	2253	...
La Rochelle Ville **292**	a.	...	|	...	|	...	|	|	...
Royan	a.	...	2118	...	2139	...	2228	2319	...

		Ⓐ	Ⓐ	⑥	Ⓐ	Ⓐ	Ⓐ	Ⓐ	⑥
Royan	d.	...	0537	...	0619	...	0721	0721	...
La Rochelle Ville **292**	d.	...	|	...	|	0550	|	|	...
Saintes	a.	...	0603	...	0645	0657	0747	0747	...
Saintes	d.	0555	0612	0630	0647	0702	0750	0753	0753
Niort	a.	0711	|	|	0803	|	0856	|	|
Cognac	d.	...	0634	0648	...	0723	...	0815	0815
Angoulême	a.	...	0719	0725	...	0809	...	0855	0856

km			⑥	Ⓐ	Ⓒ	⚒	⚒	⑥	†	⚒			Ⓑ		†	Ⓐ	Ⓐ	Ⓐ	⚒	†	†	⚒	†	†	⑤
0	**Royan**	d.	0740	0919	0927	...	1121	...	1221	1221	...	1520	...	...	1606	1621	1719	...	...	1736	1845	1929	1929	...	...
	La Rochelle Ville **292**	d.	|	|	|	...	|	...	|	|	...	|	...	...	|	|	|	1639	...	|	|	|	|	...	...
36	**Saintes**	a.	0806	0946	0953	...	1148	...	1247	1249	...	1546	...	...	1633	1650	1745	1756	...	1806	1911	1955	1955	...	...
36	**Saintes**	d.	0809	0959	0959	1008	1156	1157	1250	1300	1324	1555	1609	...	1640	1658	...	1800	1805	1809	1918	2001	2001	2007	2018
116	**Niort**	a.	0915	|	|	1115	|	|	1402	1407	|	|	1714	...	|	|	...	|	1915	1916	|	|	|	2113	2125
	Cognac	d.	...	1022	1022	...	1215	1215	...	...	1347	1615	...	...	1659	1717	...	1822	...	...	1937	2021	2021	...	...
	Angoulême	a.	...	1100	1100	...	1254	1254	...	...	1425	1653	...	...	1741	1800	...	1901	...	...	2017	2100	2104	...	...

BORDEAUX - ANGOULÊME, PÉRIGUEUX, BRIVE and LIMOGES 302

For *TGV* services Bordeaux - Angoulême see Table **300**.

km			Ⓐ	Ⓐ	⑥	Ⓐ	Ⓐ	Ⓐ	Ⓐ A	⚒	†	⚒	⑥	Ⓐ	†	Ⓐ	Ⓒ	Ⓒ	Ⓐ	Ⓐ	Ⓐ A	Ⓒ	Ⓐ	Ⓐ	Ⓐ
0	**Bordeaux** St Jean	d.	...	...	...	...	0550	0607	0626	0650	0723	0725	0827	0831	0950	1027	1027	...	1127	...	1227	1227	1249	1327	...
37	Libourne	d.	...	...	...	...	0615	0628	0649	0715	0745	0748	0853	0853	0916	1051	1049	...	1149	...	1252	1251	1314	1350	...
53	Coutras	d.	...	...	...	...	0627	0637	0658	0727	|	0758	0903	0903	1028	|	1059	...	1159	...	1303	1303	1326	|	...
135	**Angoulême**	a.	...	...	...	...	0715	|	|	0815	|	|	|	|	1116	|	|	...	|	...	|	|	1421	|	...
93	Mussidan	d.	...	...	...	...	...	0706	0727	...	|	0819	0932	0931	...	|	1127	...	1227	...	1333	1332	...	|	...
129	**Périgueux**	a.	...	...	...	...	...	0728	0754	...	0830	0838	0955	0953	...	1137	1149	...	1249	...	1355	1354	...	1435	...
129	**Périgueux**	◧ d.	0431	0600	0630	0706	...	0738	0757	...	0837	0845	0958	...	...	1144	...	1223	...	1314	1358	1401	...	1442	1528
203	**Brive la Gaillarde**	◧ a.	|	|	|	|	...	|	0855	...	|	|	1049	...	...	|	...	|	...	|	1450	|	...	|	|
166	Thiviers	d.	0459	0633	0702	0739	...	0804	...	...	0900	0910	...	...	...	1206	...	1255	...	1354	...	1423	...	1504	1555
228	**Limoges** Benedictins	a.	0544	0724	0747	0826	...	0845	...	...	0939	0951	...	...	...	1249	...	1340	...	1440	...	1501	...	1545	1648

			†	⑥	Ⓐ	Ⓐ		Ⓐ	Ⓒ	Ⓐ	Ⓐ	†	Ⓐ	†	Ⓐ	⑥		Ⓐ	Ⓐ	†	†	Ⓐ	⑥	
Bordeaux St Jean	d.	1427	...	...	1527	...	1627	...	...	1650	1725	1727	1800	1827	1827	1831	1851	1902	1925	1927	...	2027	2027	2126
Libourne	d.	1453	...	...	1552	...	1650	...	...	1715	1753	1752	1825	1854	1850	1854	1919	1925	1953	1955	...	2050	2049	2150
Coutras	d.	1502	...	...	1602	...	1659	...	...	1727	1802	1801	1835	|	1900	|	1931	|	2002	2004	...	2100	2058	2200
Angoulême	a.	|	...	...	|	...	|	...	...	1815	|	|	|	|	|	|	2022	|	|	|	...	|	|	|
Mussidan	d.	1531	...	...	1630	...	1727	...	...	...	1832	1829	1904	|	1928	|	...	|	2031	2033	...	2128	2128	2228
Périgueux	a.	1553	...	...	1652	...	1749	...	...	...	1854	1851	1926	1939	1953	1939	...	2012	2052	2055	...	2150	2150	2250
Périgueux	◧ d.	...	1559	1609	...	1702	...	1807	1826	...	1901	...	1929	1946	...	1946	...	2020	...	2058	2129	...	2153	...
Brive la Gaillarde	◧ a.	...	|	|	...	|	...	|	|	...	|	...	2025	|	...	|	...	|	...	2149	|	...	2244	...
Thiviers	d.	...	1627	1637	...	1733	...	1843	1854	...	1924	...	...	2010	...	2010	...	2042	...	...	2158	...	...	...
Limoges Benedictins	a.	...	1718	1728	...	1825	...	1929	1939	...	2007	...	...	2051	...	2051	...	2127	...	...	2245	...	...	...

		Ⓐ	Ⓐ	⑥	Ⓐ	Ⓐ	Ⓐ	Ⓐ	Ⓐ	⚒	Ⓑ	⑥ A		⑥	Ⓐ	⚒	†	⚒	†	Ⓐ	Ⓒ	Ⓐ A	Ⓐ	Ⓐ
Limoges Benedictins	d.	...	...	...	...	...	0550	...	...	0610	...	...	...	...	0713	0830	...	...	0929	1012	1054	...	...	1139
Thiviers	d.	...	...	...	...	...	0631	...	...	0700	...	...	...	...	0802	0908	...	...	1010	1054	1135	...	...	1230
Brive la Gaillarde	◧ d.	...	...	...	0534	...	|	...	...	|	...	0735	...	...	|	|	...	...	|	|	|	1116	...	|
Périgueux	◧ a.	...	...	...	0625	...	0655	...	...	0733	...	0826	...	...	0829	0929	...	...	1030	1118	1157	1207	...	1259
Périgueux	d.	0535	0605	0608	0626	...	0702	0730	...	...	0805	0829	...	...	...	0937	...	1005	1037	1125	1204	1210	...	...
Mussidan	d.	0557	0630	0630	0652	...	0726	0753	...	...	0827	0852	...	...	...	|	...	1027	|	1145	1227	1233	...	...
Angoulême	d.	|	|	|	|	0645	|	|	0745	...	|	|	...	0840	...	|	0944	|	|	|	|	|	1236	...
Coutras	d.	0625	0658	0658	0721	0735	0757	0821	0834	...	0856	0921	...	0928	...	|	1033	1055	|	|	1256	1302	1326	...
Libourne	d.	0636	0708	0709	0731	0748	0807	0832	0848	...	0908	0931	...	0940	...	1031	1045	1106	1131	1215	1306	1312	1340	...
Bordeaux St Jean	a.	0659	0732	0732	0758	0810	0835	0859	0910	...	0932	0958	...	1007	...	1100	1110	1132	1157	1243	1328	1335	1409	...

		Ⓐ	Ⓒ	Ⓒ	Ⓐ		Ⓐ	Ⓐ	†	Ⓐ	⑥			Ⓐ		Ⓒ	Ⓐ		†	Ⓐ	⑥	†	Ⓐ	†
Limoges Benedictins	d.	...	1206	...	1257	...	1552	...	1620	1626	1630	...	...	1726	...	1814	1831	...	1922	2017	2028	2110	2210	2310
Thiviers	d.	...	1253	...	1336	...	1635	...	1706	1714	1716	...	...	1812	...	1855	1925	...	2011	2106	2113	2159	2255	2356
Brive la Gaillarde	◧ d.	...	|	...	|	...	|	...	|	|	|	1707	...	|	...	|	|	...	|	|	|	|	|	|
Périgueux	◧ a.	...	1319	...	1400	...	1659	...	1731	1744	1741	1759	...	1837	...	1915	1958	...	2036	2131	2139	2225	2321	0021
Périgueux	d.	1319	...	1406	1407	1605	1706	...	...	...	...	1802	...	1844	...	1922	...	2005	...	...	...	...	...	...
Mussidan	d.	1341	...	1428	1430	1629	1729	...	...	...	...	1828	...	|	...	|	...	2027	...	...	...	...	...	...
Angoulême	d.	|	...	|	|	|	|	1745	...	...	...	|	...	|	1855	|	...	|	...	...	...	...	...	...
Coutras	d.	1409	...	1456	1459	1658	1758	1834	...	...	...	1857	...	|	1945	|	...	2055	...	...	...	...	...	...
Libourne	d.	1420	...	1507	1509	1708	1809	1848	...	...	...	1907	...	1931	1958	2009	...	2106	...	...	...	...	...	...
Bordeaux St Jean	a.	1441	...	1532	1536	1732	1832	1910	...	...	...	1930	...	1957	2023	2032	...	2132	...	...	...	...	...	...

PÉRIGUEUX - BRIVE - TULLE

		Ⓐ	⑥	Ⓐ		Ⓐ	†	⑥			Ⓐ	⑥		† B	Ⓐ	†		①-④	⑤⑥	Ⓐ		†	Ⓐ	⑥
Bordeaux St Jean (above)	d.	...	...	...	...	0626	...	0827	...	...	1227	...	...	...	...	...	...	...	...	1800	...	1927	...	2027
Périgueux	d.	0628	0628	0734	...	0757	0948	0958	...	1237	1358	1600	...	1600	1633	1759	...	1801	1801	1929	...	2058	2106	2153
Brive la Gaillarde	a.	0731	0732	0836	...	0855	1049	1049	...	1339	1450	1702	...	1702	1751	1907	...	1904	1907	2025	...	2149	2207	2244
Brive la Gaillarde **326**	d.	...	0735	...	...	0859	...	...	...	...	1453	...	...	1713	...	...	...	1912	...	...	...	...	...	...
Tulle **326**	a.	...	0801	...	...	0924	...	...	...	...	1518	...	...	1741	...	...	...	1937	...	...	...	...	...	...

		Ⓐ	Ⓐ	⑥		⑥	Ⓐ	Ⓒ		Ⓐ	†	Ⓐ		⑥	†	Ⓐ			⑤ B	☐		† B	†	Ⓐ
Tulle **326**	d.	...	...	...	...	0707	...	0819	...	1047	...	...	...	1220	...	...	...	...	1743	...	...	1744	...	...
Brive la Gaillarde **326**	a.	...	...	...	...	0732	...	0845	...	1113	...	...	...	1248	...	...	...	...	1810	...	...	1812	...	...
Brive la Gaillarde	d.	0534	0622	0625	...	0735	0746	0848	...	1116	1127	1250	...	1251	1414	1640	...	1707	1813	1814	...	1815	1936	1938
Périgueux	a.	0625	0725	0726	...	0826	0852	0950	...	1207	1227	1354	...	1355	1515	1746	...	1759	1917	1917	...	1917	2039	2039
Bordeaux St Jean (above)	a.	0758	...	...	...	0958	...	...	...	1335	...	...	...	...	...	...	...	1930	...	...	...	...	...	...

A – To/from Tulle (see lower part of Table).
B – To/from Ussel (Table **326**).

◧ – See lower part of Table for additional services.
☐ – ①②③④⑥.

303 LIMOGES - MONTLUÇON

km		Ⓐ	Ⓐ		Ⓐ	⑥		†	Ⓐ		Ⓐ 🚌	Ⓒ		Ⓐ	Ⓐ		Ⓐ			†			
0	**Limoges** Benedictins d.	0551	0729	...	0910	1011	...	1115	1311	...	...	1527	...	1609	1710	...	1812	2014	...	2103	...	...	...
78	Guéret d.	0701	0835	...	1011	1109	...	1217	1419	...	1425	1641	...	1722	1820	...	1921	2119	...	2215	...	...	...
156	**Montluçon** Ville a.	...	...	...	1104	1201	...	1311	...	...	1533	1742	...	1822	...	...	...	...	...	...	...	...	...

	Ⓐ		Ⓐ 🚌		Ⓐ		Ⓐ		⑥		⚒				Ⓐ		Ⓐ		†			
Montluçon Ville d.	...	...	0554	...	...	...	0739	...	0840	...	...	...	1546	...	...	...	...	...	1840	...	...	...
Guéret d.	0618	...	0700	...	0711	...	0840	...	0941	...	1240	...	1640	...	1738	...	1839	...	1941	...	...	...
Limoges Benedictins a.	0728	...	...	...	0817	...	0946	...	1047	...	1349	...	1746	...	1847	...	1949	...	2048	...	...	...

305 BORDEAUX - TARBES, HENDAYE

TGV services are subject to alteration July 15, 16, 23, 24, Aug, 6, 7, 13, 14, 20, 21. *TGV* timings may vary by a few minutes - please check your reservation.
For overnight trains Paris - Lourdes - Hendaye see Table **319**. For connections Hendaye - Irún see Table **689**.

km		Ⓐ	Ⓐ	Ⓐ	⚒	Ⓐ				*TGV* **8571** ①–⑥ d	*TGV* **8531** ①–⑥ d	⚒	*TGV* **8533** Ⓑ e	⑥	†	†	*TGV* **8535** ⑥ f		⚒	⑤	⚒	*TGV* **8537**	*TGV* **8572**		
	Paris Montparnasse **300** d.	...	...	...	...	...	...	...	...	0637	0711	...	0801	...	...	...	0923	...	...	...	...	1011	1011	...	...
0	**Bordeaux** St Jean **299 306** d.	...	0510	...	...	...	0816	0816	...	0854	0920	...	1024	1019	1028	...	|	...	...	...	...	1220	1220	1319	...
40	Facture Biganos **299 306** d.	...	0533	...	...	...	0838	0838	...	|	|	...	|	1040	1050	...	|	...	...	...	...	|	|	1341	...
109	Morcenx **299** d.	...	0611	...	...	...	0915	0915	...	|	|	...	|	1122	1123	...	|	...	...	...	...	|	|	1412	...
148	Dax a.	...	0630	...	...	...	0934	0934	...	1003	1028	...	1132	1144	1141	...	1231	...	...	...	...	1328	1328	1431	...
148	Dax d.	0614	0637	0703	0802	0815	0941	0945	...	1006	1032	1042	1135	1147	1144	1146	1235	...	1242	1242	1310	1332	1336	1438	1442
179	Puyoô **325** d.	|	|	|	|	0833	|	1004	...	|	|	|	|	|	|	1203	|	...	1300	1300	|	|	|	|	1500
193	Orthez **325** d.	|	|	|	|	0843	|	1015	...	|	|	|	|	|	|	1214	|	...	1310	1310	|	|	1404	|	1511
233	Pau **325** d.	|	|	|	|	0907	|	1039	...	1055	|	|	|	|	|	1237	|	...	1333	1336	|	|	1528	|	1535
272	Lourdes **325** d.	|	|	|	|	...	|	...	...	1131	|	|	|	|	|	1305	|	...	...	1405	|	|	1503	|	...
293	**Tarbes** **325** a.	|	|	|	|	...	|	...	...	1147	|	|	|	|	|	1320	|	...	...	1419	|	|	1519	|	...
199	**Bayonne** d.	0658	0721	0748	0846	...	1014	...	...	...	1106	1130	1207	1224	1231	...	1306	...	...	...	1356	1406	...	1510	...
209	Biarritz d.	0707	0729	0757	0855	...	1023	...	...	...	1118	1140	1220	1233	1240	...	1318	...	...	...	1406	1418	...	1519	...
222	St Jean de Luz d.	0723	0743	0812	0911	...	1039	...	...	...	1134	1155	1236	1249	1256	...	1334	...	...	...	1422	1434	...	1535	...
235	**Hendaye** a.	0736	0754	0826	0924	...	1053	...	...	...	1147	1208	1251	1302	1310	...	1347	...	...	...	1435	1447	...	1548	...

	TGV **8541**	⑥	⑥	Ⓑ	Ⓑ	Ⓐ	*TGV* **8547** g	Ⓐ		*TGV* **8574**			*TGV* **8549** Ⓑ h	*TGV* **8590** ⑤ j	**14155** Ⓐ A	⚒				B	**14157** Ⓒ A	⑤	⑥	*TGV* **8551**	*TGV* **8593**
Paris Montparnasse **300** d.	1211	...	...	...	...	...	1406	...	...	1406	...	...	1611	1611	...	...	...	...	...	...	...	...	...	1811	1811
Bordeaux St Jean **299 306** d.	1420	1436	1436	1438	1438	...	1620	...	...	1620	1718	1718	1820	1820	...	...	1846	...	1846	...	...	...	...	2020	2020
Facture Biganos **299 306** d.	|	1458	1458	1500	1500	...	|	...	...	|	1743	1743	|	|	...	...	1910	...	1910	...	...	...	...	|	|
Morcenx **299** d.	|	1529	1529	1531	1531	...	|	...	...	|	1820	1820	|	|	...	...	1947	...	1947	...	...	...	...	|	|
Dax a.	1528	1548	1548	1550	1550	...	1728	...	...	1728	1839	1839	1928	1928	...	...	2006	...	2006	...	...	...	...	2130	2130
Dax d.	1532	1557	1601	1557	1601	1706	1732	1744	...	1736	1846	1850	1932	1936	...	1944	2013	...	2017	2044	...	2057	2115	2132	2136
Puyoô **325** d.	|	|	1619	|	1619	|	|	|	...	|	|	1908	|	|	...	|	|	...	2035	|	...	|	|	|	|
Orthez **325** d.	|	|	1630	|	1630	|	|	|	...	1804	|	1919	|	|	...	|	|	...	2045	|	...	|	|	|	2204
Pau **325** d.	|	|	1654	|	1654	|	|	|	...	1827	|	1943	|	2023	...	|	|	...	2108	|	...	|	|	|	2227
Lourdes **325** d.	|	|	...	|	...	|	|	|	...	1903	|	...	|	2059	...	|	|	...	2137	|	...	|	|	|	2303
Tarbes **325** a.	|	|	...	|	...	|	|	|	...	1919	|	...	|	2115	...	|	|	...	2152	|	...	|	|	|	2319
Bayonne d.	1606	1629	...	1629	...	1751	1806	1829	...	...	1920	...	2006	...	2020	2028	2045	...	...	2126	2138	2139	2157	2206	...
Biarritz d.	1618	1638	...	1638	...	1800	1818	1838	...	...	1929	...	2018	...	2029	2038	2054	...	...	...	2147	...	...	2218	...
St Jean de Luz d.	1634	1654	...	1654	...	1816	1834	1853	...	...	1945	...	2034	...	2043	2053	2110	...	...	...	2201	...	...	2234	...
Hendaye a.	1647	1707	...	1707	...	1829	1852	1906	...	...	1959	...	2047	...	2055	2106	2123	...	...	...	2213	...	...	2247	...

	Ⓐ	Ⓐ	Ⓐ	①	Ⓐ	⑥	Ⓐ	Ⓐ	Ⓐ	*TGV* **8560** ①–⑥ d	*TGV* **8530** k	Ⓒ	Ⓐ	Ⓐ	Ⓐ	*TGV* **8562** ⑦ m	*TGV* **8534**	⚒	*TGV* **8581** ①–⑥ d	**14142** A	*TGV* **8536** k		Ⓐ		*TGV* **8540** n
Hendaye d.	...	0450	...	...	0545	0549	0627	...	0653	...	0712	...	...	0810	0916	...	0933	1010	...	1019	1110	1227	...	1410	1312
St Jean de Luz d.	...	0502	...	...	0557	0601	0639	...	0705	...	0726	...	...	0822	0929	...	0946	1022	...	1030	1123	1239	...	1422	1325
Biarritz d.	...	0514	...	...	0609	0613	0651	...	0717	...	0739	...	...	0834	0941	...	0959	1034	...	1040	1136	1251	...	1434	1338
Bayonne ⊡ d.	...	0528	...	...	0622	0627	0705	...	0731	...	0754	...	...	0848	0954	...	1014	1048	...	1052	1151	1305	...	1448	1354
Tarbes **325** d.	...	|	...	0528	|	|	|	0630	|	0647	|	...	...	|	|	0855	|	|	1043	...	|	|	1342	|	|
Lourdes **325** d.	...	|	...	0543	|	|	|	0645	|	0704	|	...	...	|	|	0920	|	|	1106	...	|	|	1356	|	|
Pau **325** d.	0504	|	0610	0610	|	|	|	0713	|	0731	|	0827	0818	|	|	0948	|	|	1134	...	|	|	1424	|	|
Orthez **325** d.	0528	|	0635	0635	|	|	|	0738	|	0754	|	0850	0842	|	|	|	|	|	|	...	|	|	1447	|	|
Puyoô **325** d.	0539	|	0645	0645	|	|	|	0750	|	|	|	0901	0853	|	|	|	|	|	|	...	|	|	1458	|	|
Dax ⊡ a.	0557	0601	0703	0703	0707	0711	0749	0808	0815	0822	0826	0919	0916	0920	1038	1040	1046	1120	1221	...	1223	1349	1516	1520	1426
Dax d.	0609	0609	0715	0715	0715	0714	...	...	...	0830	0830	0922	0928	0928	...	1049	1049	1128	1228	...	1228	...	1528	1528	1431
Morcenx **299** d.	0629	0629	0734	0734	0734	0734	...	...	...	|	|	0942	0947	0947	...	|	|	1148	|	...	|	...	1547	1547	|
Facture Biganos **299 306** d.	0706	0706	0811	0811	0811	0812	...	...	...	|	|	1014	1019	1019	...	|	|	1219	|	...	|	...	1619	1619	|
Bordeaux St Jean **299 306** a.	0731	0731	0835	0835	0835	0836	...	...	...	0940	0940	1035	1041	1041	...	1208	1208	1241	1341	...	1341	...	1641	1641	1540
Paris Montparnasse **300** a.	...	...	...	...	...	...	...	...	...	1155	1155	...	...	...	...	1426	1426	...	1557	...	1557	...	...	...	1756

	TGV **8583** p	*TGV* **8542** ⚒	*TGV* **8542** †	Ⓐ	Ⓐ	*TGV* **8544**	Ⓐ	Ⓒ	⑥	*TGV* **8585** ⑦ m	Ⓐ	Ⓐ	†	†	Ⓐ	*TGV* **8550**	*TGV* **8587** ①–⑤ q	①–④	⑤	⑤	⑥	⑥	†	*TGV* **8589** ⑦ m	⚒
Hendaye d.	...	1458	1509	1507	...	1612	1653	1654	...	...	...	1708	...	1749	1753	1812	...	...	...	1847	...	1909	1913	...	2008
St Jean de Luz d.	...	1510	1522	1519	...	1625	1705	1707	...	...	...	1720	...	1801	1806	1825	...	...	...	1859	...	1922	1926	...	2021
Biarritz d.	...	1523	1535	1531	...	1638	1717	1719	...	...	...	1732	...	1813	1818	1839	...	...	...	1911	...	1935	1938	...	2032
Bayonne ⊡ d.	...	1538	1550	1545	...	1654	1731	1733	...	...	...	1746	...	1826	1832	1854	...	...	...	1925	...	1950	1951	...	2046
Tarbes **325** d.	1240	|	|	|	...	|	|	|	...	1632	...	|	1700	|	|	|	1740	...	...	|	1840	|	|	1920	|
Lourdes **325** d.	1304	|	|	|	...	|	|	|	...	1655	...	|	1714	|	|	|	1803	...	...	|	1855	|	|	1937	|
Pau **325** d.	1331	|	|	|	1624	|	|	|	1722	1725	1723	|	1747	|	|	|	1831	1907	1907	|	1923	|	|	2005	|
Orthez **325** d.	1354	|	|	|	1648	|	|	|	1746	1750	1747	|	1810	|	|	|	1854	1931	1931	|	1947	|	|	|	|
Puyoô **325** d.	|	|	|	|	1658	|	|	|	1757	|	1758	|	1821	|	|	|	|	1942	1942	|	1957	|	|	|	|
Dax ⊡ a.	1422	1606	1618	1617	1716	1725	1815	1806	1815	1818	1816	1820	1839	1858	1916	1926	1922	2000	2000	2004	2016	2020	2024	2052	2129
Dax d.	1431	1611	1623	1622	...	1728	...	1809	...	1827	1828	1828	1842	1900	...	1928	1931	...	2012	2012	2028	2028	2026	2055	...
Morcenx **299** d.	|	|	|	1642	...	|	...	1829	...	|	1847	1847	1901	1920	...	|	|	...	2033	2033	2048	2048	2045	|	...
Facture Biganos **299 306** d.	|	|	|	1720	...	|	...	1906	...	|	1919	1919	1933	1952	...	|	|	...	2115	2115	2119	2119	2117	|	...
Bordeaux St Jean **299 306** a.	1540	1724	1736	1743	...	1840	...	1929	...	1936	1941	1941	2001	2022	...	2040	2040	...	2143	2143	2141	2141	2146	2202	...
Paris Montparnasse **300** a.	1756	1949	1956	...	...	2101	...	...	...	2157	...	...	...	...	...	2301	2300	...	...	...	...	...	...	0024	...

A – To/from Toulouse (Table **325**).
B – ①②③④⑦.

d – Not Aug. 15.
e – Not July 14, 15, 24, Aug. 7, 14, 21.
f – Also July 14, 15.
g – Not July 15.
h – Not July 14, 15.
j – Also July 13; not July 15.

k – Not Aug. 21–26.
m – Also Aug. 15.
n – Not Aug. 22–26.
p – Not July 2, 4–8, 11–13, 15.
q – Not July 14, 15, Aug. 15.

⊡ – Other trains Bayonne - Dax at 0705⑥, 1637⑤†.

TGV – High-speed train. Ⓡ. 🍷.

BORDEAUX - ARCACHON 306

TGV timings may vary by a few minutes - please check your reservation. Additional TER services operate during peak hours.

km							*TGV* 8471 ⑥ d				*TGV* 8473					*TGV* 8475 ⑦ e				*TGV* 8477 ①–④ f	*TGV* 8477 ⑤ g			⚒
		Ⓐ	Ⓑ																					
	Paris Montparnasse **300** d.	...	...	...	...	...	0801	...	...	...	1111	...	...	...	...	1511	...	...	...	1848	1847	...	...	...
0	**Bordeaux** St Jean d.	0604	0704	0804	0904	1004	1024	1104	1204	1304	1324	1404	1504	1604	1704	1724	1804	1904	2004	2057	2100	2104	2204	2304
40	Facture Biganos d.	0633	0733	0833	0933	1033	1048	1133	1233	1333	1350	1433	1533	1633	1733	1750	1833	1935	2033	2119	2121	2133	2233	2333
56	La Teste a.	0650	0750	0850	0950	1050	|	1150	1250	1350	|	1450	1550	1650	1750	|	1850	1952	2050	|	2135	2150	2250	2350
59	**Arcachon** a.	0654	0754	0854	0956	1054	1103	1154	1254	1354	1405	1454	1554	1654	1756	1804	1854	1957	2054	2134	2139	2156	2256	2354

	TGV 8478 ⚒	⚒		⚒							*TGV* 8470 ⑥ d			*TGV* 8472 ①–⑥		*TGV* 8472 ⑦				*TGV* 8476 ⑦ e			
Arcachon d.	0600	0606	0634	0706	0806	0906	1006	1106	1202	1306	1354	1404	1506	1557	1606	1629	1704	1806	1906	1919	2006	2106	2206
La Teste d.	|	0610	0638	0710	0810	0910	1010	1110	1206	1310	|	1409	1510	|	1610	|	1708	1810	1910	1925	2010	2110	2210
Facture Biganos d.	0617	0627	0655	0727	0827	0927	1027	1127	1225	1327	1410	1427	1527	1613	1627	1645	1725	1827	1927	1939	2027	2127	2227
Bordeaux St Jean a.	0640	0656	0725	0756	0856	0956	1056	1156	1256	1356	1436	1456	1556	1635	1656	1709	1757	1856	1956	2005	2056	2159	2256
Paris Montparnasse **300** a.	0858	...	...	...	...	...	...	...	...	...	1716	...	...	1900	...	1927	...	...	...	2256	...	...	...

d – Also July 14, 15.
e – Also Aug. 15.
f – Not July 13, 14, Aug. 15.
g – Also July 13; not July 15.
TGV – High-speed train. Ⓡ. 🍷.

BORDEAUX - LE VERDON - POINTE DE GRAVE 307

km			⚒	Ⓐ 🚌	Ⓐ	Ⓒ	†	Ⓐ 🚌		Ⓐ	Ⓒ	Ⓐ 🚌	Ⓐ	Ⓐ 🚌	Ⓐ	Ⓒ		⑥	†		Ⓐ		Ⓐ	†
0	**Bordeaux** St Jean d.	0759	0859	0900	...	1014	1059	1100	...	...	1156	1200	...	1300	...	1359	...	1458	1558	1659	1758	1858	1958	2024
19	Blanquefort d.	0824	0922	1005	1022	1032	1121	1205	...	1222	1222	1305	1322	1305	1422	1422	...	1522	1622	1722	1822	1922	2021	2049
35	Margaux d.	0842	0941	...	1041	1046	1142	...	...	1242	1242	...	1342	...	1442	1442	...	1541	1642	1742	1841	1942	2042	2107
57	Pauillac d.	0904	1002	...	1104	1104	1203	...	...	1304	1304	...	1404	...	1504	1504	...	1601	1704	1804	1901	2004	2103	2126
76	Lesparre d.	0919	1018	...	1119	1119	1218	...	...	1319	1319	...	1418	...	1519	1519	...	1615	1718	1819	1916	2019	2119	2141
102	Soulac sur Mer d.	0941	...	...	1141	1141	...	...	...	1341	1341	...	...	...	1541	1541	...	...	...	1842	...	2041	2141	...
109	**Le Verdon** a.	0948	...	...	1149	1148	...	...	...	1348	1348	...	...	...	1548	1548	...	...	...	1849	...	2048	2148	...
112	**Pointe de Grave** a.	0952	...	...	1153	1152	...	...	...	1352	1352	...	...	...	1552	1552	...	...	...	1853	...	...	...	...

	⚒	Ⓐ	⑥	Ⓐ	Ⓐ 🚌	Ⓒ	Ⓐ		Ⓐ 🚌	⑥	Ⓐ	Ⓐ 🚌	Ⓒ	Ⓐ	Ⓐ 🚌		Ⓒ	①–④	⑤	Ⓒ	Ⓒ	Ⓐ	
Pointe de Grave d.	...	...	...	1014	...	1014	...	...	...	...	1214	...	1214	1414	...	...	1414	...	...	...	1714	1714	1914
Le Verdon d.	...	0653	0818	1018	...	1018	...	...	...	...	1218	...	1218	1418	...	...	1418	...	...	...	1718	1718	1918
Soulac sur Mer d.	...	0700	0825	1025	...	1025	...	...	...	...	1225	...	1225	1425	...	...	1425	...	...	...	1725	1725	1925
Lesparre d.	0622	0722	0847	1048	...	1048	1152	...	...	1152	1248	...	1248	1448	...	...	1448	1628	1628	1647	1748	1747	1947
Pauillac d.	0639	0740	0905	1105	...	1105	1209	...	...	1209	1305	...	1302	1505	...	...	1505	1643	1643	1705	1805	1805	2005
Margaux d.	0659	0802	0927	1127	...	1127	1228	...	...	1228	1327	...	1327	1527	...	...	1527	1702	1702	1727	1823	1827	2027
Blanquefort d.	0723	0823	0949	1148	1155	1148	1248	...	1255	1249	1348	1355	1349	1547	1555	...	1548	1721	1721	1749	1836	1849	2049
Bordeaux St Jean a.	0745	0844	1011	...	1300	1212	...	...	1400	1311	...	1500	1411	...	1700	...	1611	1749	1803	1811	1853	1911	2111

⛴ **POINTE DE GRAVE - ROYAN**. Sailing time approximately 20 minutes. ✆ 0974 500 033. www.transgironde.fr
January - June and September - December: Up to 9 sailings daily. **July and August**: Every 40 – 50 minutes 0630 - 2030 (0715 - 2115 from Royan).

PÉRIGUEUX - LE BUISSON - AGEN 308

km		Ⓐ	⚒	†	Ⓐ	Ⓒ	Ⓐ	Ⓐ	Ⓒ		Ⓐ	†	⚒	⑥	Ⓐ	Ⓑ	⑥	①–④	①–④	⑤	†	⑥	①–④	†	⑤
0	**Périgueux** d.	...	...	...	...	0827	0834	0940	1214	...	1251	1434	1519	1639	1648	...	...	1733	...	1821	1831	1838	2000	2005	2028
40	Les Eyzies d.	...	...	...	...	0855	0909	1009	1249	...	1326	1509	1547	1715	1722	...	...	1808	...	1858	1859	1913	2035	2040	2103
57	Le Buisson **318** d.	...	...	...	...	0913	0926	1027	1306	...	1343	1526	1605	1731	1739	...	...	1828	...	1916	1917	1930	2052	2057	2120
90	**Sarlat** **318** a.	...	...	...	...	|	...	|	...	...	...	...	|	...	...	...	...	1857	...	|	|	...	...	...	...
108	Monsempron Libos d.	0632	0757	0825	0954	1005	...	1118	...	1329	...	...	1655	...	...	1803	1848	...	1924	2009	2007	...	...	...	...
152	**Agen** a.	0719	0845	0910	1040	1048	...	1201	...	1414	...	...	1740	...	...	1851	1934	...	2015	2054	2051	...	...	...	...

	Ⓐ		Ⓐ	Ⓐ	Ⓐ	Ⓒ	Ⓐ			Ⓒ	Ⓐ	⚒	†	†	⑥	Ⓐ		†	Ⓐ	A	⑤	Ⓑ	⑥	⑤
Agen d.	...	...	0615	0741	0900	0920	...	...	1231	...	...	1435	...	1600	...	1638	...	1705	...	1748	1748	1907	1946	2106
Monsempron Libos d.	...	...	0700	0827	0943	1004	...	...	1317	...	...	1518	...	1643	...	1724	...	1751	...	1832	1833	1953	2032	2152
Sarlat **318** d.	0549	...	...	...	|	|	...	...	...	...	...	|	...	|	...	...	...	...	...	...	|	...	...	...
Le Buisson **318** d.	0620	0720	...	...	1036	1055	1138	...	...	1333	1442	1609	1627	1734	1739	...	...	...	1839	...	1924	...	...	...
Les Eyzies d.	0637	0737	...	...	1054	1112	1155	...	...	1350	1459	1626	1644	1752	1756	...	...	...	1857	...	1941	...	...	...
Périgueux a.	0712	0811	...	...	1123	1139	1229	...	...	1424	1533	1654	1718	1821	1830	...	...	...	1931	...	2015	...	...	...

A – ①②③④⑥.

LIMOGES - ANGOULÊME and POITIERS 309

km		Ⓐ 🚌	Ⓐ 🚌	Ⓐ	Ⓐ	⚒ 🚌		⑥	†	⑥ 🚌		† 🚌		Ⓐ 🚌	†	⚒	Ⓐ 🚌		Ⓐ	⑥ 🚌		⑤† 🚌	Ⓐ
0	**Limoges** Benedictins d.	0520	0650	0700	0756	0820	...	0900	1007	1140	1212	1240	...	1400	1510	1609	1700	...	1715	1750	1808	1810	1914
	St Junien d.	0600	0730	0742	0839	0900	...	0938	1045	1220	1253	1320	...	1440	1548	1647	1740	...	1757	1830	1849	1850	1957
	Saillat Chassenon a.	|	|	...	0845	|	...	0944	1051	|	1259	|	...	|	1554	1652	|	...	...	|	1855	|	2003
122	**Angoulême** a.	0720	0850	...	...	1020	...	...	...	1350	...	1440	...	1600	...	...	1900	...	...	1950	...	2010	...

	Ⓐ	Ⓐ 🚌	Ⓐ	Ⓐ 🚌	Ⓐ		⑥	†	⑥ 🚌	Ⓐ 🚌				Ⓐ	⑥ 🚌			Ⓐ 🚌	† 🚌	Ⓐ 🚌	† 🚌	⑤⑥ 🚌
Angoulême d.	...	0610	...	0740	...	...	...	...	1140	1240	...	...	...	...	1700	...	...	1750	1900	2000	2100	2100
Saillat Chassenon d.	0649	|	...	|	0855	...	1000	1103	|	|	1403	...	1704	...	|	1902	...	|	|	|	|	|
St Junien d.	0656	0730	0754	0900	0902	...	1007	1110	1300	1400	1410	...	1711	1808	1830	1909	...	1910	2020	2120	2220	2240
Limoges Benedictins a.	0736	0810	0832	0940	0940	...	1043	1146	1340	1440	1448	...	1751	1845	1910	1950	...	1950	2100	2200	2300	2320

km		Ⓐ	Ⓐ		⑥	Ⓐ		Ⓒ			Ⓐ	Ⓒ		Ⓐ	Ⓒ		†	Ⓐ		Ⓐ	⑤†		
0	**Limoges** Benedictins d.	0447	0558	...	0755	0843	...	0938	...	...	1244	1344	...	1544	1648	...	1742	1744	...	1844	1948	...	...
139	**Poitiers** a.	0654	0754	...	0956	1034	...	1132	...	...	1455	1545	...	1754	1837	...	1950	1951	...	2054	2144	...	...

	Ⓐ	Ⓐ		⑥	†		⑥	Ⓐ		Ⓒ	Ⓐ		⑥	†		Ⓐ	Ⓐ		⑥	Ⓑ		
Poitiers d.	0543	0829	...	0835	0930	...	1024	1230	...	1333	1433	...	1634	1723	...	1733	1831	...	1848	2033	...	...
Limoges Benedictins a.	0741	1024	...	1030	1122	...	1217	1431	...	1524	1635	...	1831	1927	...	1936	2036	...	2046	2227	...	...

310 PARIS - LIMOGES - TOULOUSE

Warning! *INTERCITÉS* (★) services are subject to minor, but complex, variations and timings shown may vary by up 7 minutes on certain dates (earlier departures possible; please check your reservation for confirmed timings). See Table **320** for *TGV* services Paris - Agen - Toulouse and v.v.

km		★ 3605	★ 3615	★ 3615	★ 3619	★ 3621		★ 3625	★ 3629	★ 3635	★ 3645	★ 3645		★ 3655	★ 3655	★ 3665	★ 3665	★ 3675		★ 3685	★ 3685	3751	3751	3751
		⚒	†	Ⓐ		Ⓐ		Ⓒ	†	Ⓒ				Ⓒ	Ⓐ	Ⓒ	Ⓐ	Ⓐ		Ⓒ	Ⓐ	■ 🅁	■ 🅁	■ 🅁
											d	e										A	B	C
0	**Paris** Austerlitz .... **294 315** d.	0639	0739	0740	0829	0939	...	1041	1140	1241	1439	1439	...	1635	1639	1736	1740	1840	...	1933	1939	2145	2212	2212
119	Les Aubrais-Orléans. **294 315** d.	0740	|	|	0935	|	...	|	1240	|	1541	1541	...	|	|	|	|	|	...	|	|	2248	2334	2319
200	Vierzon .... **315** d.	0816	0910	0914	|	|	...	1210	|	|	1617	1617	...	|	|	1913	1913	2011	...	2112	2112	|	|	|
236	Issoudun .... d.	|	|	|	|	1129	...	1230	|	|	|	|	...	1827	1827	|	|	2030	...	|	|	|	|	|
263	Châteauroux .... d.	0849	0942	0945	1044	1144	...	1248	1345	1441	1649	1648	...	1842	1842	1944	1944	2046	...	2143	2143	|	|	|
294	Argenton sur Creuse .... d.	|	0958	|	|	1200	...	|	|	1457	|	|	...	|	|	2000	2000	|	...	2159	2159	|	|	|
341	La Souterraine .... d.	|	1025	1024	1122	1225	...	|	1422	1522	|	|	...	1919	1919	|	|	2123	...	2224	2224	|	|	|
400	**Limoges** Benedictins .... a.	0955	1100	1058	1157	1300	...	1402	1456	1557	1754	1800	...	1954	1954	2055	2055	2158	...	2258	2300	|	|	|
400	**Limoges** Benedictins .... d.	0957	1103	1100	1200	1301	...	1405	1459	1557	1759	1800	...	1956	1956	2058	2058	2159	...	2300	2300	|	|	|
459	Uzerche .... d.	|	1144	1138	|	1339	...	1442	|	|	|	|	...	2033	2033	|	|	2237	...	|	|	|	|	|
499	**Brive la Gaillarde** .... a.	1101	1209	1207	1304	1407	...	1507	1603	1700	1901	1910	...	2103	2103	2200	2200	2308	...	0005	0008	|	|	|
499	**Brive la Gaillarde** .... d.	1104	...	...	1305	1407	...	...	...	1700	1905	1911	...	...	...	2200	2200	...	...	...	...	|	|	|
536	Souillac .... d.	1129	...	...	1330	1432	...	...	...	1724	1931	1939	...	...	...	2226	2226	...	...	...	...	|	|	0355
559	Gourdon .... d.	1145	...	...	1347	1448	...	...	...	1741	1948	1956	...	...	...	2243	2243	...	...	...	...	|	|	0422
600	Cahors .... d.	1212	...	...	1414	1521	...	...	...	1814	2015	2025	...	...	...	2313	2313	...	...	...	...	|	0448	0501
639	Caussade .... d.	1239	...	...	|	...	...	...	...	...	2041	2054	...	...	...	...	...	...	...	...	...	|	|	0539
662	Montauban .... **320** d.	1256	...	...	1455	...	...	...	...	...	2056	2111	...	...	...	...	...	...	...	...	...	0600	0601	0603
713	**Toulouse** Matabiau .... **320** a.	1322	...	...	1523	...	...	...	...	...	2123	2137	...	...	...	...	...	...	...	...	...	0642	0642	0642

	3750	★ 3604	★ 3614	★ 3624	★ 3628		★ 3634	★ 3638	★ 3642	★ 3644	★ 3648		★ 3650	★ 3652	★ 3654	★ 3654	★ 3674		★ 3664	★ 3674	★ 3684	★ 3684	★ 3694
	■ 🅁	Ⓐ		⚒	†		⚒	†	Ⓐ	⑥	†		Ⓒ	Ⓐ	†	⑥	Ⓐ		†	Ⓒ	⑥	Ⓑ	
Toulouse Matabiau .... **320** d.	2218	...	...	...	...	...	...	...	0629	0738	...	...	1031	1133	...	...	...	...	...	...	...	...	1635
Montauban .... **320** d.	2253	...	...	...	...	...	...	...	0700	0804	...	...	1057	1200	...	...	...	...	...	...	...	...	1702
Caussade .... d.	2314	...	...	...	...	...	...	...	0714	0818	...	...	|	|	...	...	...	...	...	...	...	...	1716
Cahors .... d.	2346	...	...	...	...	...	0641	0730	0745	0847	...	...	1139	1241	1241	1245	1437	...	...	...	...	...	1745
Gourdon .... d.	0017	...	...	...	...	...	0708	0758	0812	0914	...	...	1207	1308	1308	1312	1504	...	...	...	...	...	1813
Souillac .... d.	0037	...	...	...	...	...	0725	0815	0829	0931	...	...	1225	1326	1325	1329	1521	...	...	...	...	...	1830
Brive la Gaillarde .... a.	|	...	...	...	...	...	0752	0840	0856	0957	...	...	1251	1352	1350	1354	1546	...	...	...	...	...	1856
Brive la Gaillarde .... d.	|	0353	0458	0601	0701	...	0753	0843	0900	1001	1106	...	1254	1355	1353	1357	1549	...	1558	1659	1755	1800	1859
Uzerche .... d.	|	|	0524	|	|	...	0819	0908	|	|	1132	...	|	|	1420	1424	1615	...	|	|	1823	1826	|
Limoges Benedictins .... a.	|	0456	0602	0701	0802	...	0858	0944	0959	1102	1208	...	1353	1455	1456	1504	1652	...	1701	1759	1859	1902	2002
Limoges Benedictins .... d.	|	0456	0604	0704	0805	...	0859	0947	1004	1107	1211	...	1356	1458	1459	1507	1655	...	1704	1802	1902	1905	2003
La Souterraine .... d.	|	0527	|	0735	|	...	0932	1018	|	|	|	...	1426	1529	1533	1537	1727	...	|	|	1933	1936	|
Argenton sur Creuse .... d.	|	|	0655	|	0856	...	0955	|	|	|	1304	...	|	|	|	|	1751	...	1755	1853	1957	|	|
Châteauroux .... d.	|	0605	0712	0812	0913	...	1013	1055	1109	1214	1322	...	1504	1607	1611	1615	1809	...	1812	1910	2014	2014	2108
Issoudun .... d.	|	0620	|	|	|	...	|	1111	|	|	1338	...	|	|	1626	|	1825	...	|	1926	|	|	|
Vierzon .... **315** d.	|	0642	0746	0848	|	...	|	|	1143	1249	|	...	|	|	1648	1648	1848	...	1846	1948	2049	2049	2142
Les Aubrais-Orléans .... **294 315** a.	0540	|	|	|	1021	...	|	|	1220	1324	|	...	1619	1718	|	|	|	...	|	|	|	|	2217
Paris Austerlitz .... **294 315** a.	0650	0822	0926	1025	1122	...	1227	1303	1323	1430	1531	...	1719	1829	1820	1819	2031	...	2018	2121	2238	2238	2327

TER REGIONAL SERVICES ORLÉANS - LIMOGES

	⚒	⚒	Ⓐ	⚒	†		⚒	Ⓒ	⚒	Ⓐ	Ⓐ		Ⓐ	⑥	Ⓑ	Ⓐ	⑥	†	Ⓐ	Ⓐ	⚒	Ⓐ	Ⓐ
Orléans .... **315** d.	...	...	0650	0750	...	0912	...	1050	1312	...	1412	...	...	...	1612	...	1650	1652	1712	...	1749	...	1849
Vierzon .... **315** d.	...	0645	0746	0846	...	1002	1050	1146	1414	...	1508	...	1652	...	1702	1734	1748	1747	1800	1835	1843	1934	1946
Issoudun .... d.	...	0709	0810	0907	...	...	1111	1208	1435	...	...	...	1713	...	...	1755	1810	1809	...	1856	...	1955	2007
Châteauroux .... d.	0639	0726	0828	0925	1010	...	1125	1225	1458	1656	...	...	1730	1806	...	1810	1828	1827	...	1910	...	2010	2025
Argenton sur Creuse .... d.	0654	0742	0844	0941	1026	...	1141	1242	...	1712	...	...	1756	1822	...	1825	1852	1903	...	1927	...	2025	...
La Souterraine .... d.	0721	0811	...	...	1056	...	1210	...	...	1739	...	...	...	1853	...	1853	...	1932	...	...	...	2052	...
Limoges Benedictins .... a.	0808	0843	...	...	1140	...	1255	...	...	1815	...	...	...	1939	...	1940	...	2009	...	...	...	2138	...

	Ⓐ	②–⑤	⑥	①	⚒	⚒	†	Ⓐ	Ⓐ	⑥	Ⓐ	Ⓐ	Ⓒ	Ⓑ		Ⓑ	Ⓐ	Ⓒ	⑥	⚒	Ⓐ	Ⓐ	Ⓑ
Limoges Benedictins .... d.	...	...	...	0541	0722	...	0822	0822	...	...	1322	...	1322	...	...	1622	...	...	1622	1722	...	...	1822
La Souterraine .... d.	...	...	...	0612	0806	...	0906	0908	...	...	1406	...	1406	...	...	1705	...	...	1708	1805	...	...	1909
Argenton sur Creuse .... d.	...	0642	0642	0642	0833	0918	0934	0937	1208	...	1433	...	1434	1612	...	1732	...	...	1737	1832	...	1913	1938
Châteauroux .... d.	0635	0721	0721	0721	0850	0936	0949	0952	1226	1235	1450	...	1449	1629	1732	1748	...	...	1753	1849	...	1932	1953
Issoudun .... d.	0651	0739	0739	0739	0905	0953	...	...	1242	1252	1505	...	...	1646	1748	1803	...	...	...	1903	...	1948	...
Vierzon .... **315** d.	0714	0805	0805	0805	0926	1015	...	...	1307	1315	1526	1657	...	1714	1814	1824	1855	1859	...	1925	1957	2014	...
Orléans .... **315** a.	0809	0900	0902	0902	...	1110	...	...	1402	1410	...	1747	...	1810	1910	...	1947	1947	...	...	2047	2110	...

TER REGIONAL SERVICES LIMOGES - BRIVE LA GAILLARDE

	Ⓐ		Ⓐ		⚒		⑥		†		⚒		⑥		Ⓐ		Ⓐ		Ⓑ		Ⓐ		
Limoges Benedictins .... d.	0620	...	0701	...	0735	...	0907	...	1007	...	1223	...	1604	...	1634	...	1715	...	1836	...	1933	...	...
Uzerche .... d.	0708	...	0751	...	0826	...	0957	...	1057	...	1313	...	1654	...	1724	...	1805	...	1924	...	2023	...	...
Brive la Gaillarde .... a.	0741	...	0823	...	0857	...	1030	...	1130	...	1346	...	1727	...	1757	...	1838	...	1958	...	2056	...	...

	Ⓐ		Ⓐ		Ⓐ		⑥				Ⓐ		⑥		Ⓐ		Ⓑ		Ⓑ				
Brive la Gaillarde .... d.	0608	...	0650	...	0801	...	0801	...	1225	...	1649	...	1732	...	1804	...	1910	...	2011	...	...	...	...
Uzerche .... d.	0638	...	0719	...	0830	...	0831	...	1255	...	1717	...	1801	...	1833	...	1940	...	2039	...	...	...	...
Limoges Benedictins .... a.	0728	...	0808	...	0916	...	0920	...	1345	...	1755	...	1851	...	1923	...	2029	...	2118	...	...	...	...

TER REGIONAL SERVICES BRIVE LA GAILLARDE - TOULOUSE

	Ⓐ	Ⓐ	†	⑥		Ⓐ	Ⓐ	Ⓒ	Ⓐ		⚒	†			⚒	†	⚒	†		Ⓐ	⚒	†	⑥
Brive la Gaillarde .... d.	...	0621	...	0624	...	0726	...	0824	0917	...	...	1024	...	...	1424	...	...	1628	...	1727	...	1824	2024
Souillac .... d.	...	0647	...	0649	...	0751	...	0849	0941	...	...	1048	...	...	1449	...	...	1651	...	1750	...	1849	2049
Gourdon .... d.	...	0702	...	0705	...	0807	...	0905	0957	...	...	1103	...	...	1505	...	...	1706	...	1805	...	1905	2105
Cahors .... d.	0630	0730	0732	0732	...	0834	0931	0932	1022	...	1132	1130	1332	...	1532	1532	1732	1732	...	1831	1933	1932	2132
Caussade .... d.	0658	0759	0800	0800	...	0900	1000	0959	...	...	1200	1158	1400	...	1559	1601	1800	1800	...	1859	2001	2000	2159
Montauban .... **320** d.	0715	0817	0817	0817	...	0916	1017	1017	...	...	1217	1216	1417	...	1616	1618	1817	1817	...	1916	2018	2017	2217
Toulouse Matabiau .... **320** a.	0743	0846	0858	0858	...	0943	1058	1058	...	...	1258	1258	1458	...	1658	1659	1858	1858	...	1957	2058	2058	2258

	Ⓐ	Ⓐ	Ⓒ		Ⓐ	Ⓒ		Ⓐ				Ⓒ	Ⓒ		①–④ ◧	⑤ ◧		Ⓐ	Ⓒ		Ⓐ	Ⓐ	Ⓒ
Toulouse Matabiau .... **320** d.	0604	0649	0701	...	0901	0901	...	...	1101	...	1301	1501	1701	...	1717	1717	...	1817	1901	...	1917	2007	2101
Montauban .... **320** d.	0646	0727	0742	...	0943	0943	...	...	1143	...	1343	1543	1742	...	1745	1745	...	1847	1943	...	1946	2046	2142
Caussade .... d.	0701	0742	0758	...	0958	0958	...	...	1158	...	1358	1557	1757	...	1800	1801	...	1902	1958	...	2001	2101	2157
Cahors .... d.	0731	0811	0827	...	1026	1027	...	1037	1227	...	1427	1625	1826	...	1830	1831	...	1931	2028	...	2030	2130	2226
Gourdon .... d.	0757	...	...	...	...	1052	...	1103	...	...	1454	1652	...	...	1857	1858	...	1956	2054	...	...	...	...
Souillac .... d.	0812	...	...	...	...	1108	...	1119	...	...	1510	1709	...	...	1913	1914	...	2012	2110	...	...	...	...
Brive la Gaillarde .... a.	0836	...	...	...	...	1136	...	1143	...	...	1537	1736	...	...	1940	1940	...	2037	2136	...	...	...	...

A – Ⓐ July 4 – 15.
B – ①–④ from July 18 (not Aug. 15).
C – ⑥⑦ July 2 – 17; ⑤⑥⑦ July 22 - Aug. 28 (also Aug. 15).

d – From July 18.
e – Until July 17.

◧ – Does not run Toulouse - Montauban on ①–⑤ July 4 – 15.
★ – *INTERCITÉS*. 🅁.
■ – *INTERCITÉS DE NUIT*. 🛏 1, 2 cl. and 2nd class seated. Overnight journeys only.
Timings and running days vary. For confirmed days of running and timings please consult the SNCF journey planner: www.oui.sncf/billet-train.

BRIVE - AURILLAC — 311

km		Ⓐ	⑥	Ⓐ	Ⓒ		Ⓒ		Ⓐ 🚌	
0	**Brive la Gaillarde** .... **316** d.	1125	1131	1413	1531	...	1715	1935	...	2216
27	St Denis-près-Martel ...... **316** d.	1148	1200	1437	1600	...	1742	2002	2010	2242
102	**Aurillac** .... a.	1315	1323	1604	1727	...	1912	...	2201	0005

	Ⓐ	⑥	Ⓐ	Ⓒ	Ⓐ	†	Ⓐ	Ⓒ	A
Aurillac .... d.	0515	0620	0620	1036	1150	1434	1538	1517	1704
St Denis-près-Martel ... **316** d.	0638	0744	0744	1201	1317	1601	1705	1643	1830
Brive la Gaillarde ...... **316** a.	0705	0809	0812	1229	1344	1626	*1736*	1710	1851

A – To / from Neussargues (Table **331**).

TOULOUSE and PARIS - LATOUR DE CAROL — 312

For overnight trains Paris - Latour de Carol see Table **319**. For *Le Petit Train Jaune* Latour de Carol - Villefranche see Table **354**. For services Latour de Carol - Barcelona see Table **656**.

km		Ⓐ		Ⓒ	Ⓐ	①⑤	Ⓒ	Ⓐ	Ⓐ	Ⓒ	Ⓐ	Ⓒ	Ⓑ	Ⓐ	Ⓒ	Ⓐ d	Ⓐ e	Ⓐ	Ⓒ	Ⓐ	Ⓒ	Ⓒ	Ⓐ	⑦–④ 🚌
0	**Toulouse** Matabiau .... ◧ d.	0647	0747	0847	0947	1047	1047	1216	1247	1247	1347	1347	1447	1547	1547	1647	1717	1747	1747	1847	1847	1947	2047	2145
65	Pamiers .... ◧ d.	0744	0843	0945	1046	1146	1145	1317	1346	1346	1443	1444	1546	1644	1644	1745	1820	1845	1846	1946	1945	2049	2150	2311
83	Foix .... ◧ d.	0800	0902	1001	1101	1159	1203	1334	1400	1402	1501	1505	1601	1659	1659	1803	1837	1859	1902	2003	2000	2108	2205	2337
123	Ax-les-Thermes .... d.	0840	0942	1039	1142	...	1243	1415	...	1440	1540	1546	...	1740	1745	1842	1917	1940	1944	2043	...	2151	...	0024
144	L'Hospitalet ⊖ .... d.	...	1008	...	1207	...	1308	...	...	...	1605	1617	...	1806	1815	...	...	...	2011	2108	...	...	...	...
163	**Latour de Carol** .... a.	...	1031	...	1229	...	1330	...	...	...	1628	1640	...	1829	1837	...	...	...	2033	2130	...	...	...	...

	⚒	⚒	Ⓐ	Ⓒ		Ⓐ	①⑤	Ⓒ		Ⓐ	Ⓒ	Ⓐ	Ⓒ	Ⓐ	Ⓒ	Ⓐ	Ⓐ	Ⓒ	Ⓐ	Ⓒ	Ⓒ	Ⓐ	†
Latour de Carol .... d.	...	...	...	...	0727	...	...	...	1033	...	...	1333	1333	...	1526	...	1633	...	...	1725	...	1833	2040
L'Hospitalet ⊖ .... d.	...	...	...	...	0749	...	...	...	1054	...	...	1354	1355	...	1547	...	1653	...	...	1746	...	1854	2105
Ax-les-Thermes .... d.	...	0614	0718	...	0817	0922	...	1018	1121	1218	1222	1420	1422	1614	1615	...	1719	1720	...	1816	...	1920	2133
Foix .... ◧ d.	0558	0656	0759	0800	0903	1003	1100	1104	1204	1259	1305	1502	1504	1658	1658	1731	1805	1802	1901	1901	2001	2002	2211
Pamiers .... ◧ d.	0615	0713	0816	0817	0918	1020	1117	1118	1220	1316	1321	1518	1518	1715	1715	1746	1819	1818	1917	1917	2019	2018	2226
Toulouse Matabiau .... ◧ a.	0716	0814	0914	0914	1014	1115	1214	1214	1314	1414	1414	1614	1614	1814	1814	1848	1916	1916	2014	2014	2114	2114	2314

d – Until July 15.
e – From July 18.

◧ – Other trains **Toulouse - Foix** at 0716 Ⓐ, 1647 Ⓒ, 1816 Ⓐ, 1947 Ⓐ; **Foix - Toulouse** at 0627 Ⓐ, 0728 Ⓐ, 1401 Ⓐ, 1602 Ⓑ.
⊖ – Full name is L'Hospitalet-près-l'Andorre.

🚌 ANDORRA 🚌 — 313

Toulouse Matabiau ...... d.	1100	1500	2000
Toulouse Airport ✈ ...... d.	1130	1530	2030
Andorra bus station...... a.	1500	1900	2400

Andorra bus station... d.	0500	1000	1500
Toulouse Airport ✈ .. d.	0830	1330	1830
Toulouse Matabiau... a.	0845	1345	1845

Andorra bus station...... d.	0620	and	2120
Soldeu .... d.	0700	hourly	2200
Pas de la Casa .... a.	0715	until	2215

Pas de la Casa .... d.	0720	and	2120
Soldeu .... d.	0745	hourly	2145
Andorra bus station.. a.	0815	until	2215

Operated by ANDBUS ✆ +34 973 984 016. www.andorrabybus.com.

☐ – Operated by Cooperativa Interurbana (service L4). Additional services operate on ①–⑥.

TOULOUSE - CASTRES - MAZAMET — 314

km		Ⓐ		⚒		†						Ⓐ		† 🚌		Ⓐ e		B				⑤ 🚌		
0	**Toulouse** Matabiau .... d.	0541	...	0750	...	0840	...	1143	...	1344	...	1543	...	1546	...	1643	...	1740	...	1847	...	1940	...	2043
86	Castres......... a.	0654	...	0903	...	0956	...	1251	...	1451	...	1656	...	1722	...	1749	...	1854	...	1959	...	2103	...	2157
86	Castres......... d.	0704	...	0913	...	1002	...	1301	...	1501	...	1702	...	1723	...	1759	...	1908	...	2009	...	2104	...	2203
105	**Mazamet** .... a.	0722	...	0930	...	1020	...	1320	...	1520	...	1720	...	1753	...	1817	...	1926	...	2027	...	2134	...	2221

	Ⓐ		Ⓐ		Ⓐ				Ⓑ		⚒		† 🚌						Ⓐ		B		
Mazamet .... d.	0527	...	0551	...	0635	...	0737	...	1028	...	1231	...	1305	...	1432	...	1729	...	1823	...	1940	...	...
Castres......... a.	0544	...	0608	...	0652	...	0756	...	1045	...	1249	...	1334	...	1449	...	1747	...	1840	...	1957	...	...
Castres......... d.	0551	...	0614	...	0658	...	0802	...	1051	...	1255	...	1335	...	1455	...	1753	...	1858	...	2003	...	...
Toulouse Matabiau .... a.	0701	...	0730	...	0806	...	0910	...	1201	...	1402	...	1505	...	1602	...	1906	...	2008	...	2114	...	...

B – Daily until July 17; Ⓒ from July 23.
e – From July 18.

PARIS and ORLÉANS - VIERZON - BOURGES - NEVERS and MONTLUÇON — 315

km		Ⓐ	⚒	Ⓐ 🚌	⚒	⑥		Ⓐ	⑥	Ⓐ	⑤	C	†	⚒ D		Ⓐ	Ⓐ	†	Ⓐ	Ⓐ	Ⓐ	Ⓑ	⑤		①–④
0	**Paris** Austerlitz .... **310** d.	...	...	...	0708	...	...	...	...	...	...	1143	1204	1204	...	...	...	...	...	...	...	1708	...	...	...
	Orléans .... **310** d.	0612	0712	...	|	...	0912	...	...	...	1212	|	|	|	...	1412	1612	1612	...	1651	1712	|	...	1814	...
119	Les Aubrais-Orléans..... **310** d.	|	|	...	0807	...	|	...	...	...	|	1248	1307	1310	...	|	|	|	...	|	|	1807	...	|	...
178	Salbris .... d.	0648	0749	...	0836	...	0949	...	...	...	1249	|	|	|	...	1452	1648	1649	...	1730	1748	1836	...	1850	...
200	Vierzon Ville......... **290 310** d.	0703	0803	0823	0851	0856	1004	1018	1022	...	1304	1323	1344	1346	...	1510	1703	1704	...	1747	1803	1851	...	1904	1923
232	**Bourges** .... **290** a.	0729	0823	|	0908	|	1023	|	|	...	1323	1340	1403	1407	...	1538	1722	1723	...	1814	1822	1910	...	1926	|
	Bourges .... **290** d.	0731	...	|	...	|	...	|	|	1228	...	...	...	...	1419	...	1725	...	1740	...	1825	...	1924	...	|
	Nevers .... **290** a.	0819	...	|	...	|	...	|	|	|	...	...	...	...	|	...	1813	...	|	...	1913	...	|	...	|
291*	St Amand-Montrond-Orval...d.	...	...	|	...	0950	...	1120	1128	1316	...	...	...	...	1508	...	...	...	1832	...	...	...	2021	...	2021
341*	**Montluçon** .... a.	...	...	0958	...	1035	...	1204	1212	...	...	...	...	...	1552	...	...	...	1925	...	...	...	2105	...	2105

	†	Ⓐ	Ⓒ	Ⓐ		⑤ f	†	⑤ g	⑤†
Paris Austerlitz .... **310** d.	...	...	1903	1908	...	2059	2108	2109	...
Orléans .... **310** d.	...	1912	|	|	...	|	|	|	...
Les Aubrais-Orléans .... **310** d.	...	|	2009	2008	...	2203	2207	2213	...
Salbris .... d.	...	1948	2036	2036	...	2235	2234	2238	...
Vierzon Ville .... **290 310** d.	...	2003	2051	2051	...	2250	2251	2253	2259
Bourges .... **290** a.	...	2022	2108	2108	...	2308	2308	2311	|
Bourges .... **290** d.	1940	...	...	...	2119	...	...	...	|
Nevers .... **290** a.	|	...	...	...	|	...	...	...	|
St Amand-Montrond-Orval......... d.	2029	...	...	...	2204	...	...	...	2353
Montluçon .... a.	2121	...	...	...	2250	...	...	...	0038

	Ⓐ	⚒	⚒	⑥	Ⓐ 🚌	⑥	Ⓐ	Ⓐ 🚌	Ⓐ
Montluçon .... d.	...	0521	...	0600	0603	...	...	0630	...
St Amand-Montrond-Orval......... d.	...	0606	...	0645	|	...	...	0738	...
Nevers .... **290** d.	...	|	...	|	|	...	0647	|	0745
Bourges .... **290** a.	...	|	...	|	|	...	0734	|	0832
Bourges .... **290** d.	0635	|	0650	|	|	0736	0737	|	0835
Vierzon Ville......... **290 310** d.	0657	0659	0710	0738	0738	0757	0759	0835	0857
Salbris .... d.	0710	...	0723	...	...	0810	0812	...	0910
Les Aubrais-Orléans......... **310** a.	|	...	0752	...	...	|	|	...	|
Orléans .... **310** a.	0747	...	|	...	...	0847	0848	...	0947
Paris Austerlitz .... **310** a.	...	...	0853	...	...	...	...	...	...

	⑥	Ⓑ	†	⚒	Ⓐ	⑥	Ⓐ	†	Ⓐ	Ⓐ	⑥	Ⓐ	Ⓐ	Ⓐ	Ⓒ		Ⓐ	Ⓒ	Ⓐ	Ⓐ	†	†	†	⑤ 🚌
Montluçon .... d.	0801	0808	...	...	0957	1040	...	...	...	...	...	...	...	...	...	1710	...	...	1739	...	...	1906	...	1847
St Amand-Montrond-Orval......... d.	0848	0855	...	...	1044	1125	...	...	1354	...	...	...	...	...	...	1756	...	...	1834	...	...	1952	...	2007
Nevers .... **290** d.	|	|	...	...	|	|	1245	...	|	...	...	...	1645	1741	...	|	...	...	|	1845	1920	|	...	|
Bourges .... **290** a.	0932	0941	...	...	|	|	1332	...	1441	...	...	...	1733	1831	...	1841	...	...	1922	1933	1958	2038	...	|
Bourges .... **290** d.	...	...	0949	0949	|	|	1335	1349	...	1552	1555	1635	1736	1832	1835	...	1851	1857	...	1936	2000	...	2052	|
Vierzon Ville .... **290 310** d.	...	...	1008	1008	1137	1220	1357	1408	...	1611	1616	1657	1757	1855	1859	...	1910	1918	...	1957	2016	...	2111	2134
Salbris .... d.	...	...	|	|	...	...	1412	1422	...	1625	1631	1710	1810	1910	1910	...	1925	1933	...	2010	...	...	2125	...
Les Aubrais-Orléans .... **310** a.	...	...	1041	1047	...	...	|	1447	...	1650	1658	|	|	|	|	...	1952	2000	...	|	...	...	2150	...
Orléans .... **310** a.	...	...	|	|	...	...	1451	|	...	|	|	1747	1847	1947	1947	...	|	|	...	2047	...	...	|	...
Paris Austerlitz .... **310** a.	...	...	1150	1152	...	...	...	1550	...	1754	1806	...	...	...	...	...	2054	2110	...	...	...	...	2253	...

C – July 4–7, 25–28, Aug. 16–18.
D – Not July 4–7, 18–21, 25–28, Aug. 8–11, 16–18.
f – July 22 - Aug. 5.
g – July 1, 8, 15, Aug. 12, 19, 26.
* – Via Bourges (Montluçon is *327 km* for trains not calling at Bourges).

316 BRIVE - FIGEAC - RODEZ

For overnight trains Paris - Rodez - Albi see Table **319**.

km		⑥	Ⓐ	Ⓑ	Ⓐ	Ⓒ	Ⓐ	Ⓐ		Ⓑ
0	**Brive la Gaillarde** ...... **311** d.	0541	0546	0744	1119	1321	1435	1707	1935	2225
27	St Denis-près-Martel... **311** d.	0606	0610	0814	1143	1345	1503	1743	2003	2249
45	Rocamadour-Padirac........d.	0622	0626	0830	1158	1400	1519	1759	2018	2304
53	Gramat.............................d.	0629	0633	0837	1205	1407	1527	1806	2025	2311
88	Figeac....................... **317** d.	0657	0703	0904	1235	1434	1556	1835	2053	2338
94	Capdenac................... **317** d.	0707	0713	0914	1245	1443	1607	1845	2103	2348
109	Viviez-Decazeville.............d.	0722	0728	0931	1259	1458	1622	1900	2118	0003
161	**Rodez**..............................a.	0810	0814	1017	1344	1542	1708	1945	2203	0048

	Ⓐ	⑥	†	Ⓐ	Ⓒ	Ⓐ	Ⓐ	Ⓒ	Ⓐ	Ⓒ	
Rodez ....d.	0611	0720	0810	0845	1049	1054	1254	1410	1502	1614	1741
Viviez-Decazeville..............d.	0656	0805	0855	0930	1133	1138	1343	1459	1550	1659	1826
Capdenac.................. **317** d.	0715	0822	0913	0947	1150	1155	1401	1516	1608	1716	1844
Figeac...................... **317** d.	0722	0829	0920	0955	1157	1202	1409	1523	1616	1723	1852
Gramat..............................d.	0750	0855	0947	1022	1224	1229	1438	1550	1645	1752	1918
Rocamadour-Padirac ....d.	0757	0902	0954	1029	1231	1236	1445	1556	1653	1759	1925
St Denis-près-Martel.. **311** d.	0813	0917	1009	1045	1247	1252	1502	1612	1710	1815	1941
Brive la Gaillarde ... **311** a.	0837	0941	1033	1109	1310	1315	1526	1635	1736	1838	2007

317 AURILLAC - FIGEAC - TOULOUSE

km		①	Ⓐ	⚒ 🚌			⚒	⚒ 🚌			⚒ 🚌	Ⓐ			🚌			Ⓐ 🚌	🚌			Ⓐ	Ⓐ 🚌	
0	**Aurillac**...............................d.	...	...	0629	...	...	0824	...	...	...	1025	...	...	1224	...	...	...	1335	1630	...	...	1801	1840	...
65	Figeac......................... **316** d.	0544	...	0749	...	...	0939	0949	...	...	1145	...	...	1339	1347	...	...	1455	1750	...	...	1916	1957	...
71	Capdenac..................... **316** d.	0559	0612	0804	...	0814	...	1004	...	1014	1200	1211	...	...	1402	1412	...	1510	1805	1815	...	...	2008	...
100	Villefranche de Rouergue......d.	...	0640	...	...	0845	...	...	...	1044	...	1239	...	...	...	1445	...	...	...	1845	...	...	...	...
117	Najac...................................d.	...	0655	...	...	0900	...	...	...	1059	...	1254	...	...	...	1500	...	...	...	1900	...	...	...	...
170	Gaillac........................ **323** d.	...	0742	...	...	0948	...	...	...	1145	...	1341	...	...	...	1546	...	...	...	1949	...	...	...	...
224	**Toulouse** Matabiau....... **323** a.	...	0831	...	...	1031	...	...	...	1223	...	1423	...	...	...	1623	...	...	...	2031	...	...	...	...

	⚒	⚒ 🚌	Ⓐ	Ⓐ			⚒ 🚌	⚒ 🚌			🚌		Ⓐ 🚌			Ⓐ 🚌	Ⓒ 🚌	Ⓐ		Ⓐ 🚌		Ⓒ 🚌	Ⓐ 🚌
Toulouse Matabiau .... **323** d.	...	...	0653	...	...	0857	...	...	1303	...	...	...	...	...	1704	...	...	1811	...	...	1909	...	...
Gaillac .... **323** d.	...	...	0742	...	...	0937	...	...	1341	...	...	...	...	...	1743	...	...	1850	...	...	1949	...	...
Najac...d.	...	...	0829	...	...	1028	...	...	1428	...	...	...	...	...	1829	...	...	1937	...	...	2035	...	...
Villefranche de Rouergue.................d.	...	...	0844	...	...	1043	...	...	1444	...	...	...	...	...	1844	...	...	1953	...	...	2051	...	...
Capdenac .... **316** d.	...	0815	0915	...	...	1109	1115	1315	1511	...	1521	...	1649	...	1912	1917	1917	2020	...	2026	2118	2123	2123
Figeac .... **316** d.	0614	0830	0921	1000	...	...	1130	1330	...	...	1536	1546	1704	...	...	1932	1932	...	...	2041	...	2138	2138
Aurillac..a.	0729	0950	...	1115	...	...	1250	1450	...	...	...	1701	1824	...	...	2052	...	...	...	2201	...	2258	...

318 BORDEAUX - LIBOURNE - BERGERAC - SARLAT

km		⚒	⚒	Ⓐ	Ⓐ	Ⓐ		Ⓐ		Ⓐ	Ⓒ	Ⓐ	Ⓐ	Ⓒ	Ⓒ	Ⓐ		Ⓐ		Ⓐ		⑤		⑤
0	**Bordeaux** St Jean.. **300 302** d.	...	0551	0720	0742	0842	0942	1042	...	1142	1142	1242	1342	1342	1542	1542	...	1642	1742	1837	1942	1942	2132	2227
37	Libourne .... **300 302** d.	...	0623	0744	0806	0906	1006	1107	...	1210	1206	1306	1406	1406	1608	1607	...	1706	1806	1901	2007	2007	2157	2251
45	St Émilion..............................d.	...	0630	0751	0813	0913	1013	1115	...	1217	1214	1313	1413	1413	1615	1616	...	1713	1813	1909	2014	2014	2205	2258
77	Ste Foy la Grande ....d.	...	0701	0821	0839	0938	1040	1138	...	1241	1242	1337	1441	1437	1643	1643	...	1741	1839	1941	2040	2040	2228	2321
99	**Bergerac**...............................d.	0615	0719	0840	0859	0952	1058	1154	...	1255	1300	1359	1500	1456	1702	1703	...	1802	1858	1959	2054	2057	2244	2337
135	Le Buisson .... **308** d.	0648	...	...	0934	...	1131	...	...	...	...	1434	...	1529	...	1738	...	...	1933	...	...	2129	...	...
168	**Sarlat**........................... **308** a.	0717	...	...	1003	...	1202	...	...	...	...	1503	...	1559	...	1807	...	...	2003	...	...	2158	...	...

	Ⓐ	⑥	⚒	⚒	Ⓐ	Ⓐ	†	⑥	†	Ⓐ	⑥	Ⓐ	Ⓒ	Ⓐ	Ⓐ	Ⓐ	Ⓒ		Ⓐ	Ⓐ	Ⓒ	Ⓐ	
Sarlat.................................. **308** d.	...	...	...	0619	...	0740	0755	...	...	...	0912	...	...	1104	...	1248	1256	...	...	1712	1714	...	1905
Le Buisson .... **308** d.	...	...	...	0651	...	0810	0825	...	...	...	0944	...	...	1135	...	1320	1326	...	...	1743	1747	...	1936
Bergerac...d.	0532	0604	0621	0726	0803	0859	0859	0904	1004	1009	1021	1104	1205	1209	1258	1359	1403	1622	1721	1820	1824	1904	2009
Ste Foy la Grande ....d.	0548	0620	0640	0743	0822	0919	0916	0922	1020	1023	1041	1121	1222	1224	1317	1420	1420	1644	1742	1840	1843	1921	2024
St Émilion...d.	0612	0646	0708	0814	0848	0947	0943	0950	1046	1047	1107	1148	1249	1250	1348	1448	1446	1714	1814	1910	1907	1946	2047
Libourne .... **300 302** d.	0620	0654	0716	0821	0856	0955	0952	0958	1053	1054	1115	1155	1256	1258	1356	1455	1453	1722	1821	1917	1914	1953	2055
Bordeaux St Jean............ **300 302** a.	0647	0718	0739	0844	0920	1018	1018	1021	1118	1118	1138	1218	1319	1322	1418	1519	1518	1747	1844	1941	1940	2018	2118

319 OVERNIGHT TRAINS PARIS - RODEZ, HENDAYE, LATOUR DE CAROL and CERBÈRE

INTERCITÉS DE NUIT – 🛏 1, 2 cl. and 💺2. Overnight journeys only. For services to Toulouse see Table **310**.

Timings and running days may vary. For confirmed days of running and timings please consult the SNCF journey planner: www.oui.sncf/billet-train.

	3755	3755	3741	3971	3737	3741	3971	3737	3755	3755
	①–⑤		①–⑤	①–⑤	①–⑤					⑤
	Ⓡ A	Ⓡ B	Ⓡ A	Ⓡ A	Ⓡ A	Ⓡ C	Ⓡ C	Ⓡ C	Ⓡ C	Ⓡ D
Paris Austerlitz .... d.	1939	1939	2114	2114	2114	2141	2141	2141	2212	2212
Les Aubrais-Orléans .... d.	|	|	2224	2224	2224	2249	2249	2249	2334	2334
St Denis-près-Martel............ a.	0354	0354	|	|	|	|	|	|	0354	0354
Rocamadour-Padirac .... a.	0411	0411	|	|	|	|	|	|	0411	0411
Gramat................................... a.	0418	0418	|	|	|	|	|	|	0418	0418
Figeac.................................... a.	0449	0449	|	|	|	|	|	|	0449	0449
Capdenac............................... a.	0458	0458	|	|	|	|	|	|	0458	0458
Viviez-Decazeville.................. a.	0513	0513	|	|	|	|	|	|	0513	0513
Rodez.................................... a.	0607	0607	|	|	|	|	|	|	0607	0607
Carmaux .... a.	...	0728	|	|	|	|	|	|	...	0728
Albi Ville .... a.	...	0748	|	|	|	|	|	|	...	0748
Tarbes .... a.	...	...	0720	|	|	0720	|	|	...	...
Lourdes .... a.	...	...	0737	|	|	0737	|	|	...	...
Pau.. a.	...	...	0806	|	|	0806	|	|	...	...
Orthez .... a.	...	...	0830	|	|	0830	|	|	...	...
Dax... a.	...	...	0900	|	|	0900	|	|	...	...
Bayonne .... a.	...	...	0958	|	|	0958	|	|	...	...
Biarritz .... a.	...	...	1010	|	|	1010	|	|	...	...
St Jean de Luz .... a.	...	...	1026	|	|	1026	|	|	...	...
Hendaye .... a.	...	...	1040	|	|	1040	|	|	...	...
Pamiers.............................. a.	...	...	...	0711	|	...	0711	|	...	...
Foix...................................... a.	...	...	...	0726	|	...	0726	|	...	...
Ax-les-Thermes .... a.	...	...	...	0814	|	...	0814	|	...	...
L'Hospitalet ⊖ .... a.	...	...	...	0845	|	...	0845	|	...	...
Latour de Carol................. a.	...	...	...	0912	|	...	0912	|	...	...
Castelnaudary........................... a.	...	...	...	...	0555	...	...	0555	...	...
Carcassonne .... a.	...	...	...	...	0633	...	...	0633	...	...
Lézignan.................................... a.	...	...	...	...	0655	...	...	0655	...	...
Narbonne................................... a.	...	...	...	...	0710	...	...	0710	...	...
Perpignan.................................. a.	...	...	...	...	0831	...	...	0831	...	...
Argelès sur Mer .... a.	...	...	...	...	0851	...	...	0851	...	...
Collioure .... a.	...	...	...	...	0857	...	...	0857	...	...
Port Vendres .... a.	...	...	...	...	0902	...	...	0902	...	...
Banyuls sur Mer......................... a.	...	...	...	...	0908	...	...	0908	...	...
Cerbère................................... a.	...	...	...	...	0917	...	...	0917	...	...
Portbou .... a.	...	...	...	...	...	...	...	...	...	...

	3754	3754	3736	3972	3972		3742	3742	3756	3758
		⑦		Ⓒ	Ⓐ		⑦		①–④	
	Ⓡ C	Ⓡ	Ⓡ ◧	Ⓡ ◧	Ⓡ ◧		Ⓡ E	Ⓡ F	Ⓡ G	Ⓡ H
Portbou.............................. d.	...	...	...	...	...	...	...	...	...	...
Cerbère............................... d.	...	...	1907	...	...	...	...	...	...	...
Banyuls sur Mer..................... d.	...	...	1916	...	...	...	...	...	...	...
Port Vendres.......................... d.	...	...	1923	...	...	...	...	...	...	...
Collioure .... d.	...	...	1928	...	...	...	...	...	...	...
Argelès sur Mer .... d.	...	...	1935	...	...	...	...	...	...	...
Perpignan .... d.	...	...	1957	...	...	...	...	...	...	...
Narbonne................................. d.	...	...	2113	...	...	...	...	...	...	...
Lézignan .... d.	...	...	2128	...	...	...	...	...	...	...
Carcassonne............................ d.	...	...	2148	...	...	...	...	...	...	...
Castelnaudary......................... d.	...	...	2207	...	...	...	...	...	...	...
Latour de Carol............... d.	...	...	|	1918	1925	...	...	...	...	...
L'Hospitalet ⊖ .... d.	...	...	|	1944	1951	...	...	...	...	...
Ax-les-Thermes .... d.	...	...	|	2018	2020	...	...	...	...	...
Foix .... d.	...	...	|	2109	2110	...	...	...	...	...
Pamiers............................... d.	...	...	|	2124	2124	...	...	...	...	...
Hendaye........................... d.	...	...	|	|	|	...	1823	1903	...	...
St Jean de Luz...................... d.	...	...	|	|	|	...	1835	1915	...	...
Biarritz .... d.	...	...	|	|	|	...	1847	1927	...	...
Bayonne .... d.	...	...	|	|	|	...	1902	1942	...	...
Dax....................................... d.	...	...	|	|	|	...	1956	2037	...	...
Orthez................................... d.	...	...	|	|	|	...	2024	2107	...	...
Pau....................................... d.	...	...	|	|	|	...	2047	2134	...	...
Lourdes................................. d.	...	...	|	|	|	...	2115	2202	...	...
Tarbes .... d.	...	...	|	|	|	...	2131	2219	...	...
Albi Ville .... d.	...	2050	|	|	|	...	|	|	...	...
Carmaux .... d.	...	2113	|	|	|	...	|	|	...	...
Rodez .... d.	2238	2238	|	|	|	...	|	|	2238	2238
Viviez-Decazeville.................. d.	2329	2329	|	|	|	...	|	|	2329	2329
Capdenac............................... d.	2347	2347	|	|	|	...	|	|	2347	2347
Figeac................................... d.	2356	2356	|	|	|	...	|	|	2356	2356
Gramat.................................. d.	0027	0027	|	|	|	...	|	|	0027	0027
Rocamadour-Padirac .... d.	0034	0034	|	|	|	...	|	|	0034	0034
St Denis-près-Martel............. d.	0051	0051	|	|	|	...	|	|	0051	0051
Les Aubrais-Orléans............ a.	0540	0540	0610	0610	0610	...	0610	0610	|	|
Paris Austerlitz .... a.	0650	0650	0720	0720	0720	...	0720	0720	0822	0926

A – July 4 – 15.
B – July 8, 13.
C – ⑥⑦ July 2 – 17; daily July 18 - Aug. 28.
D – July 22 - Aug. 26.
E – July 3 – 24.
F – ①–⑥ July 2 – 23; daily July 25 - Aug. 28. Note ◧ applies.
G – ①–④ July 4 – 12.
H – July 8, 13 – 15.
◧ – Arrives Les Aubrais and Paris 10 – 15 minutes later on ①–⑤ July 4 – 15.
⊖ – Full name is L'Hospitalet-près-l'Andorre.

BORDEAUX - TOULOUSE - NARBONNE 320

For overnight trains Paris - Cerbère - Portbou see Table **319**. *TGV* and *INTERCITÉS* timings may vary by a few minutes - please check your reservation.

km		★ 4651	TGV 6871	★ 4655	★ 4657	TGV 8503		★ 4659	TGV 7671	★ 4661	TGV 8505	TGV 6873		★ 4663	TGV 6875	TGV 7673	★ 4665		TGV 8509	★ 4669	TGV 8517	TGV 8519	TGV 8523
		①–⑤ d				①–⑥ e			⊠							⊠				Ⓑ A f			⑤ g
	Paris Montparnasse **300** d.	...	...	...	...	0711	...	...	0911	...	1111	...	...	...	...	1237	...	...	1511	...	1711	1911	2006
0	**Bordeaux** St Jean d.	...	...	0628	0828	0924	...	1028	1122	1228	1320	...	...	1428	...	1520	1628	...	1720	1828	1920	2120	2226
79	Marmande d.	...	...	|	0907	|	...	|	|	|	|	...	...	|	...	|	|	...	|	1906	|	|	|
136	Agen d.	...	...	0732	|	1027	...	1132	1227	1332	1426	...	...	1533	...	1626	1733	...	|	|	2027	2226	2330
206	Montauban d.	...	...	0810	1010	|	...	1210	1305	1409	1505	...	...	1611	...	1705	1811	...	|	2011	2105	2305	|
257	**Toulouse** Matabiau a.	...	...	0837	1037	1134	...	1237	1331	1435	1531	...	...	1640	...	1742	1837	...	1923	2037	2131	2331	0031
257	**Toulouse** Matabiau d.	0641	0744	0842	1046	...	...	1246	...	1443	...	1541	...	1646	1744	...	1846	...	...	2046	...	...	...
348	Carcassonne d.	0727	0828	0930	1131	...	...	1331	...	1530	...	1628	...	1728	1828	...	1931	...	...	2129	...	...	...
407	**Narbonne** a.	0755	0858	0958	1157	...	...	1359	...	1557	...	1656	...	1757	1856	...	1957	...	...	2159	...	...	...
	Montpellier Sud-de-France **355** a.	|	1000	|	|	...	...	|	...	|	...	|	...	|	2003	...	|	...	...	...	...	...	...
	Montpellier St Roch **355** a.	0849	|	1052	1251	...	...	1453	...	1651	...	1754	...	1853	|	...	2052	...	...	...	...	...	...
	Marseille St Charles **355** a.	1029	|	1232	1437	...	...	1636	...	1838	...	|	...	2045	|	...	2233	...	...	...	...	...	...
	Lyon Part Dieu **350** a.	...	1150	...	...	...	...	...	...	...	...	1950	...	...	2150	...	...	...	...	...	...	...	...

	TGV 8502	TGV 8504	★ 4752	TGV 8508	TGV 6821	★ 4756	TGV 8512	★ 4758	TGV 6823	TGV 6823	TGV 7672	★ 4760	TGV 6823	TGV 8514	★ 4762	TGV 8516	TGV 7674	★ 4764	TGV 8522	★ 4766	TGV 6825	★ 4770
	①–⑥ e		①–⑥ A h	Ⓑ d ◧					Ⓒ j	Ⓒ k	⊠		Ⓐ	⑤–⑦ m		Ⓑ d	⊠	B	⑦ n			①–⑤ p
Lyon Part Dieu **350** d.	...	...	...	...	0636	...	...	...	0910	0920	...	...	1210	...	...	...	...	...	...	...	1810	...
Marseille St Charles **355** d.	...	...	...	...	|	0718	...	0928	|	|	...	1122	|	...	1327	...	...	1528	...	1724	|	1928
Montpellier St Roch **355** d.	...	...	0706t	...	0845	0907	...	1106	1117	1123	...	1307	1412	...	1506	...	...	1707	...	1907	2012	2108
Montpellier Sud-de-France **355** d.	...	...	|	...	|	|	...	|	|	|	...	|	|	...	|	...	...	|	...	|	|	|
Narbonne d.	...	...	0802	...	0948	1001	...	1201	1210	1236	...	1400	1506	...	1602	...	...	1802	...	2004	2109	2208
Carcassonne d.	...	...	0833	...	1019	1031	...	1231	1241	1309	...	1431	1536	...	1632	...	...	1832	...	2034	2140	2238
Toulouse Matabiau a.	...	...	0915	...	1101	1115	...	1315	1330	1415	...	1515	1619	...	1715	...	...	1915	...	2117	2222	2321
Toulouse Matabiau d.	0624	0828	0924	1038	...	1124	1232	1323	...	...	1425	1524	...	1628	1724	1728	1825	1924	2003	2125	...	...
Montauban d.	0657	0857	0950	|	...	1150	|	1350	...	...	1457	1550	...	|	1750	1757	1857	1950	|	2151	...	...
Agen d.	0735	0935	1027	|	...	1228	1335	|	...	...	1536	1628	...	1731	1828	1835	1936	|	|	2229	...	...
Marmande d.	|	|	|	|	...	|	|	1454	...	...	|	|	...	|	|	|	|	2055	|	|	...	...
Bordeaux St Jean a.	0840	1040	1132	1240	...	1333	1440	1534	...	...	1640	1733	...	1837	1932	1940	2040	2135	2206	2334	...	...
Paris Montparnasse **300** a.	1056	1256	...	1456	...	...	1716	...	...	...	1849	...	...	2101	...	2157	2308	...	0024	...	...	...

TER REGIONAL TRAINS **BORDEAUX - AGEN**

km		Ⓐ	①	⚒		Ⓐ	⚒	Ⓐ		Ⓒ	⚒	†		Ⓐ	⚒	Ⓑ			Ⓑ	⑥		Ⓑ	
0	**Bordeaux** St Jean d.	...	0604	0655	...	0727	0833	1033	...	1133	1333	1433	...	1533	1633	1733	...	1832	1931	2047	...	2133	...
79	Marmande d.	0650	0650	0750	...	0813	0919	1120	...	1223	1419	1519	...	1619	1719	1819	...	1919	2024	2133	...	2219	...
136	**Agen** a.	0726	0726	0826	...	0849	0955	1155	...	1258	1456	1556	...	1656	1755	1855	...	1955	2101	2210	...	2255	...

	Ⓐ	⚒	Ⓐ		Ⓐ		Ⓒ		Ⓐ	Ⓐ	Ⓒ		Ⓐ		Ⓑ		⚒	①–④	⑤†		⑤	Ⓒ
Agen d.	0534	0610	0709	...	0810	0910	1104	...	1204	1306	1310	...	1406	1604	1710	...	1804	1912	1912	...	2001	2001
Marmande d.	0610	0647	0744	...	0845	0944	1138	...	1239	1341	1345	...	1440	1639	1744	...	1839	1947	1947	...	2036	2036
Bordeaux St Jean a.	0659	0733	0833	...	0933	1033	1227	...	1327	...	1433	...	1528	1727	1833	...	1927	...	2037	...	...	2124

TER REGIONAL TRAINS **AGEN - TOULOUSE**

km		Ⓐ	⑥	Ⓐ		Ⓐ q	Ⓐ q	Ⓐ r		Ⓒ	Ⓐ							Ⓐ	Ⓒ	Ⓐ		Ⓒ	Ⓐ
0	**Agen** d.	0554	0628	0656	...	0656	0744	0756	...	0828	0853	1032	...	1202	1432	1632	...	1752	1828	1856	...	2032	2055
70	Montauban d.	0641	0716	0742	...	0744	0832	0844	...	0916	0941	1120	...	1250	1520	1721	...	1840	1916	1944	...	2121	2143
121	**Toulouse** Matabiau a.	0719	0744	...	...	0811	0911	0911	...	0944	1011	1148	...	1318	1547	1749	...	1907	1944	2011	...	2148	2211

	Ⓐ	⑥	Ⓐ		Ⓐ	Ⓒ					Ⓐ r		Ⓒ	Ⓐ	Ⓐ		Ⓒ	Ⓐ	Ⓒ		Ⓐ	
Toulouse Matabiau d.	0604	0605	0649	...	0753	0812	1012	...	1212	1434	1556	...	1607	1649	1749	...	1817	1841	2007	...	2007	...
Montauban d.	0639	0634	0723	...	0822	0841	1040	...	1241	1503	1637	...	1637	1718	1818	...	1845	1917	2036	...	2042	...
Agen a.	0728	0728	0812	...	0909	0929	1128	...	1328	1551	1724	...	1723	1805	1905	...	1930	2005	2124	...	2130	...

TER REGIONAL TRAINS **TOULOUSE - CARCASSONNE - NARBONNE**

km		Ⓐ A	Ⓐ	Ⓐ	Ⓐ r	Ⓒ	Ⓐ	Ⓐ q		Ⓐ	Ⓒ	Ⓐ	Ⓐ	Ⓒ	Ⓐ		Ⓐ	Ⓒ	Ⓐ	Ⓐ	Ⓒ	Ⓐ	A
0	**Toulouse** Matabiau d.	...	0605	0657	0718	0718	0749	0808	...	0918	0918	1008	1118	1118	1205	...	1318	1318	1416	1513	1513	1605	1650
55	Castelnaudary d.	...	0651	0742	0759	0759	0833	0854	...	0959	0958	1054	1159	1159	1251	...	1359	1359	1504	1555	1555	1651	1735
91	**Carcassonne** d.	0642	0714	0804	0821	0821	0855	0914	...	1020	1020	1116	1220	1221	1313	...	1421	1421	1525	1617	1618	1714	1757
128	Lézignan d.	0701	0734	...	0839	0839	...	...	...	1039	1039	...	1238	1238	...	...	1439	1439	...	1636	1637	1734	1815
150	**Narbonne** a.	0714	0748	...	0851	0851	...	...	...	1051	1051	...	1251	1251	...	...	1451	1451	...	1649	1649	1748	1827
	Perpignan **355** a.	...	...	...	0950	0948	...	...	...	1150	1148	...	1350	1350	...	...	1550	1549	...	1748	1750	...	...
	Cerbère **355** a.	...	...	...	...	1031	...	...	...	...	1231	...	...	1430	...	...	...	1631	...	...	1829	...	...
	Portbou **355** a.	...	...	...	...	...	...	...	...	...	...	...	...	1445	...	...	...	...	...	...	1845	...	...

	①–④	⑤–⑦	Ⓐ	Ⓐ	Ⓐ	C	Ⓐ
Toulouse Matabiau d.	1718	1718	1749	1805	1851	1920	2005
Castelnaudary d.	1759	1759	1840	1855	1943	2001	2053
Carcassonne d.	1820	1820	1902	1917	2003	2023	2113
Lézignan d.	1839	1839	1921	...	...	2042	...
Narbonne a.	1851	1851	1933	...	...	2054	...
Perpignan **355** a.	1950	1950	...	...	...	2150	...
Cerbère **355** a.	...	2031	...	...	...	...	...
Portbou **355** a.	...	...	...	...	...	...	...

	Ⓐ q	Ⓐ r	Ⓐ q	Ⓐ r	Ⓐ	⚒	⚒ A	Ⓐ
Portbou **355** d.	...	...	...	...	...	...	...	...
Cerbère **355** d.	...	...	...	...	...	...	...	...
Perpignan **355** d.	...	...	...	...	...	0604	...	...
Narbonne d.	...	...	0559	0559	...	0657	0729	0809
Lézignan d.	...	...	0612	0612	...	0711	0741	0821
Carcassonne d.	0556	0600	0631	0631	0702	0732	0801	0841
Castelnaudary d.	0618	0622	0651	0651	0723	0752	0822	0902
Toulouse Matabiau a.	0707	0712	0732	...	0813	0830	0912	0948

	Ⓐ	Ⓒ	Ⓐ	Ⓐ	†	⑥	Ⓐ	Ⓐ	Ⓒ	Ⓐ	Ⓐ	Ⓒ	Ⓐ	Ⓐ	Ⓐ	Ⓒ	Ⓐ A	Ⓐ	Ⓐ	Ⓐ	Ⓒ	Ⓒ
Portbou **355** d.	...	...	...	...	...	0903	...	...	...	...	...	...	...	...	...	...	...	...	...	...	...	...
Cerbère **355** d.	0724	...	...	...	0921	0924	...	...	...	...	...	1324	...	...	...	1514	...	...	...	...	1719	...
Perpignan **355** d.	0807	...	...	1007	1007	1007	...	1204	...	...	1406	1411	...	...	1603	1601	...	...	...	1810	1810	...
Narbonne d.	0909	0909	...	1109	1109	1111	...	1306	1307	...	1509	1510	...	1641	1655	1656	1727	1811	1829	1906	1907	2009
Lézignan d.	0922	0922	...	1122	1122	1124	...	1319	1322	...	1522	1522	...	1654	1709	1709	1740	1824	1842	1922	1922	2022
Carcassonne d.	0942	0941	1040	1142	1142	1143	1244	1339	1341	1445	1543	1542	1636	1713	1730	1729	1801	1843	1902	1942	1942	2042
Castelnaudary d.	1003	1002	1101	1203	1203	1203	1306	1400	1401	1505	1603	1602	1658	1734	1750	1750	1822	1903	...	2003	2003	2103
Toulouse Matabiau a.	1042	1042	1145	1242	1242	1242	1351	1439	1439	1551	1642	1642	1740	1819	1830	1830	1907	1949	...	2042	2042	2143

A – To / from Montpellier, Beziers or Nîmes (Table **355**).
B – Daily July 2 – 23; ①–⑤ July 25 - Aug. 26.
C – Daily July 2 – 17; Ⓐ July 18 - Aug. 26.
d – Not July 14, 15.
e – Not Aug. 15.
f – Not July 14, 15, Aug. 14.
g – Also July 13; not July 15.
h – Not July 15, 16, Aug. 15.

j – Until July 17.
k – From July 23.
m – Not July 2, 8, 15.
n – Also Aug. 15.
p – Not July 14, 15, Aug. 15.
q – Until July 15.
r – From July 18.
t – ① only (not Aug. 15).

◧ – Subject to alteration Aug. 24 – 26.
⊠ – OUIGO low-cost TGV service. Internet booking only at www.ouigo.com.
★ – *INTERCITÉS*. 🅁.
TGV – High-speed train. 🅁. 🍷.

323 TOULOUSE - ALBI - RODEZ

km		⑥ 🚌	Ⓐ			①⑤		Ⓐ					Ⓐ		Ⓐ		Ⓐ		Ⓐ	†	⚒		† 🚌
0	**Toulouse** Matabiau ... 317 d.	0022	0606	0725	0917	1005	1116	1231	...	1307	1411	1635	1712	1736	1752	...	1815	1837	1914	1914	1928	2123	2325
54	Gaillac ... 317 d.	0122	0648	0811	1004	1051	1200	1321	...	1358	1458	1726	1757	1822	1842	...	1905	1922	2005	2005	2020	2209	0025
75	**Albi** Ville ... d.	0152	0703	0825	1024	1104	1217	1341	...	1417	1512	1745	1819	1836	1902	...	1924	1936	2028	2029	2040	2230	0055
92	Carmaux ... d.	...	0721	0843	1041	1122	1234	1358	...	1433	1530	1802	...	1854	1918	...	...	1954	...	2045	2056	2246	...
158	**Rodez** ... a.	...	0823	0946	...	1220	1336	...	...	...	1631	...	...	1957	...	...	...	2056	...	2146	2157	...	...

	Ⓐ	⚒	A	Ⓐ		Ⓐ	⑥	Ⓐ	†					Ⓐ	Ⓐ				Ⓐ		†	⚒
Rodez ... d.	...	...	...	...	...	0618	0633	0739	...	0834	1021	...	...	1224	...	1430	...	1636	1725	1844	2102	2113
Carmaux ... d.	0522	0557	0557	0617	0644	0722	0736	0844	0844	0933	1123	...	1144	1322	1454	1531	1650	1734	1825	1955	2210	2212
Albi Ville ... d.	0540	0614	0614	0635	0704	0742	0756	0903	0903	0951	1141	...	1201	1342	1513	1549	1707	1754	1845	2012	2231	2231
Gaillac ... 317 d.	0559	0631	0632	0657	0725	0756	0811	0918	0918	1004	1200	...	1223	1358	1533	1602	1726	1808	1906	2032	2244	2244
Toulouse Matabiau ... 317 a.	0648	...	0720	0743	0820	0836	0851	1000	1000	1044	1239	...	1312	1437	1619	1641	1820	1852	1954	2119	2324	2324

A – ⚒ July 4–16; ⑥ July 23 - Aug. 27.

324 PAU - OLORON - CANFRANC

For connections to Zaragoza (Spain) see Table **670**.

km		Ⓒ	Ⓐ		Ⓐ 🚌	⚒		🚌	†			Ⓒ 🚌			🚌					🚌			
0	**Pau** ... d.	0702	0715	...	...	0915	...	...	1045	...	1208	...	...	1436	...	...	1600	1740	...	...	1905	...	2029
36	Oloron-Ste-Marie ... d.	0738	0751	...	0810	0951	...	...	1121	...	1248	1310	...	1512	...	...	1636	1816	...	...	1941	...	2104
61	Bedous (Gare) ... d.	0815	0828	...	0843	1028	...	1035	1158	...	...	1343	...	1549	1551	...	1713	1853	...	1856	2018	...	...
77	Urdos (Douane) 🏛 ... d.	...	...	...	0905	...	...	1057	...	...	...	1405	...	...	1613	...	...	...	...	1918	...	...	...
96	**Canfranc** (Gare) ... a.	...	...	...	0923	...	...	1115	...	...	...	1423	...	...	1631	...	...	...	...	1936	...	...	...

	⑥	Ⓐ		Ⓒ	Ⓐ			🚌					🚌				🚌			Ⓐ 🚌		Ⓒ 🚌
Canfranc (Gare) ... d.	...	...	...	...	...	...	...	1124	...	...	...	...	1516	...	...	...	1741	...	...	1950	...	2001
Urdos (Douane) 🏛 ... d.	...	...	...	...	...	...	...	1141	...	...	...	...	1533	...	...	...	1758	...	...	2020	...	2018
Bedous (Gare) ... d.	...	...	...	0701	0713	...	0913	1204	...	1206	...	...	1555	1557	...	1738	1821	...	1904	2046	...	2041
Oloron-Ste-Marie ... d.	0616	0629	...	0742	0755	...	0955	...	...	1248	1516	...	...	1639	...	1820	...	...	1945	2122	...	2117
Pau ... a.	0652	0704	...	0818	0831	...	1031	...	...	1324	1552	...	...	1715	...	1859	...	...	2021	...	...	...

325 TOULOUSE - TARBES - PAU - BAYONNE

km		Ⓐ	⚒	Ⓐ			Ⓐ			14141			14143 B		Ⓐ	Ⓒ	14151	Ⓐ		Ⓐ	Ⓒ	Ⓐ	
0	**Toulouse** Matabiau ... d.	...	...	0631	...	...	0642	0731	0831	0937	...	1016	1137	...	1233	1236	1337	1431	...	...	1431	1442	1531
91	St Gaudens ... d.	...	...	0732	...	...	0755	0834	0935	|	...	1120	1230	...	1339	1339	1427	1528	...	...	1535	1555	1629
104	Montréjeau ... d.	...	...	0741	...	...	0804	0843	0943	1032	...	1129	|	...	1348	1348	|	1537	...	...	1543	1604	1638
121	Lannemezan ... d.	...	...	0754	...	...	...	0855	0956	|	...	1141	|	...	1400	1400	|	1550	...	...	1556	...	1650
158	**Tarbes** ... 305 d.	...	0606	0822	...	...	...	0922	1021	1110	...	1207	1312	...	1426	1426	1509	1617	...	1621	1622	...	1718
179	Lourdes ... 305 d.	...	0622	0837	...	...	...	0937	...	1126	...	...	1328	...	...	...	1525	...	...	1637	...	...	1734
218	**Pau** ... 305 d.	0542	0656	0905	0913	...	...	1006	...	1154	...	...	1357	...	...	...	1553	...	...	1711	...	...	1803
258	Orthez ... 305 d.	0607	0719	...	0939	...	...	...	...	1216	...	...	1419	...	...	...	1616	...	...	1736	...	...	...
272	Puyoô ... 305 d.	0617	0741	...	0951	...	...	...	...	|	...	...	|	...	...	...	|	...	...	1746	...	...	...
323	**Bayonne** ... a.	0654	0824	...	1028	...	...	...	...	1310	...	...	1501	...	...	...	1659	...	...	1826	...	...	...

	Ⓐ	†	Ⓒ		14155 Ⓐ C	Ⓐ d	Ⓐ e		Ⓐ	14157 Ⓒ C	Ⓐ		Ⓐ d	Ⓒ		Ⓐ d	Ⓐ e	Ⓐ d		Ⓒ		† 🚌
Toulouse Matabiau ... d.	...	...	1631	...	1637	1642	1701	...	1731	1738	1742	...	1831	1831	...	1842	1842	1931	...	1931	2031	2200
St Gaudens ... d.	...	...	1735	...	|	1755	1816	...	1829	|	1855	...	1929	1933	...	1955	1955	2034	...	2038	2134	2340
Montréjeau ... d.	...	...	1743	...	|	1804	1825	...	1838	|	1904	...	1938	1942	...	2004	2005	2043	...	2047	2143	|
Lannemezan ... d.	...	...	1756	...	1745	...	...	...	1850	1855	...	...	1950	1954	...	...	2017	2058	...	2101	2156	|
Tarbes ... 305 d.	...	1757	1821	...	1809	...	...	...	1919	1932	...	...	2018	2020	...	...	2044	2125	...	2130	2221	0043
Lourdes ... 305 d.	...	1813	...	...	1825	...	...	...	1934	1956	...	...	...	...	...	...	...	2140	...	2147	...	0118
Pau ... 305 d.	1816	1847	...	...	1853	...	...	...	2003	2024	...	...	...	...	...	...	...	2209	...	2215	...	0213
Orthez ... 305 d.	1840	1912	...	...	1916	...	...	...	...	2046	...	...	...	...	...	...	...	...	...	...	...	...
Puyoô ... 305 d.	1851	1922	...	...	|	...	...	...	...	|	...	...	...	...	...	...	...	...	...	...	...	...
Bayonne ... a.	1934	2001	...	...	1959	...	...	...	...	2128	...	...	...	...	...	...	...	...	...	...	...	...

	Ⓐ	Ⓐ		Ⓐ	⚒	Ⓐ		⑥	Ⓐ		Ⓒ	Ⓐ		14140	Ⓐ		Ⓒ					14142 C
Bayonne ... d.	...	...	...	...	...	...	...	...	...	...	...	0603	...	0703	...	...	...	0733	...	...	...	1102
Puyoô ... 305 d.	...	...	...	...	...	...	...	...	...	...	...	0647	...	|	...	...	...	0811	...	...	...	|
Orthez ... 305 d.	...	...	...	...	...	...	...	...	...	...	...	0657	...	0747	...	...	...	0823	...	...	...	1147
Pau ... 305 d.	...	...	...	...	...	0559	...	...	...	...	0659	0721	...	0811	...	...	...	0847	0959	...	...	1211
Lourdes ... 305 d.	...	...	...	...	...	0628	...	...	...	...	0728	0755	...	0839	...	...	...	...	1028	...	...	1239
Tarbes ... 305 d.	...	...	...	0554	...	0644	...	0650	0741	...	0744	0811	...	0855	0947	...	0947	...	1044	...	1143	1255
Lannemezan ... d.	...	...	...	0611	...	0711	...	0716	0807	...	0811	...	...	|	1013	...	1013	...	1111	...	1208	|
Montréjeau ... d.	0523	0559	...	0624	0659	0723	...	0729	0819	...	0824	...	...	|	1025	...	1025	...	1123	...	1220	1330
St Gaudens ... d.	0531	0608	...	0632	0708	0732	...	0737	0828	...	0832	...	...	0936	1034	...	1034	...	1132	...	1228	|
Toulouse Matabiau ... a.	0644	0721	...	0729	0821	0829	...	0838	0929	...	0930	...	...	1028	1133	...	1132	...	1229	...	1329	1427

					Ⓐ	14148		Ⓒ	Ⓐ		14150	Ⓒ		Ⓑ	Ⓐ		Ⓐ	⑤	Ⓐ		†	Ⓒ
Bayonne ... d.	...	...	...	...	...	1503	...	...	...	...	1703	...	...	1735	...	...	1840	1840	...	...	...	1911
Puyoô ... 305 d.	...	...	...	...	...	|	...	...	...	...	|	...	...	1813	...	...	1917	1917	...	...	...	1949
Orthez ... 305 d.	...	...	...	...	...	1546	...	...	...	...	1747	...	...	1823	...	...	1928	1928	...	...	...	1959
Pau ... 305 d.	1255	...	...	...	...	1611	...	...	1657	...	1811	...	...	1847	1855	...	1952	1952	...	...	1959	2024
Lourdes ... 305 d.	1325	...	...	...	...	1639	...	...	1726	...	1839	...	...	...	1924	...	...	2026	...	...	2028	2058
Tarbes ... 305 d.	1341	1445	...	1541	...	1655	...	1741	1742	...	1855	1938	...	...	1940	...	...	2042	...	...	2044	2113
Lannemezan ... d.	1407	1512	...	1606	...	1721	...	1806	1809	...	|	2003	...	...	2007	...	...	...	...	...	2113	...
Montréjeau ... d.	1420	1525	...	1619	1659	|	...	1819	1821	...	|	2016	...	...	2019	...	...	...	2109	...	2126	...
St Gaudens ... d.	1428	1533	...	1627	1708	|	...	1827	1830	...	1938	2024	...	...	2028	...	...	...	2117	...	2134	...
Toulouse Matabiau ... a.	1529	1631	...	1729	1821	1827	...	1929	1929	...	2027	2129	...	...	2129	...	...	...	2230	...	2230	...

🚌 MONTRÉJEAU - LUCHON 🚌

	Ⓐ			Ⓒ	⚒		Ⓐ	Ⓒ	Ⓐ	
Montréjeau ... d.	0751	0859	1139	1357	1425	...	1600	1815	1847	2057
Luchon ... a.	0839	0947	1227	1445	1514	...	1648	1903	1935	2145

	Ⓐ	⑥	Ⓐ	†	⚒	†	Ⓐ	Ⓒ	⚒	Ⓒ	Ⓐ	Ⓒ	Ⓐ
Luchon ... d.	0617	0914	0923	1019	1114	1248	1453	1514	1605	1708	1715	1916	1946
Montréjeau ... d.	0707	1004	1013	1109	1204	1338	1543	1604	1655	1758	1808	2006	2036

B – Not July 4–8, 11–13, 15, 21.
C – To / from Hendaye (Table **305**).
d – Until July 15.
e – From July 18.

BRIVE LA GAILLARD and LIMOGES - USSEL - CLERMONT FERRAND 326

Subject to confimation from October 31

BRIVE and LIMOGES - USSEL

km		① g	Ⓐ C	②–⑤ r	① g	⑦ d	①–⑥ w	⑦ d	⑥ s	Ⓐ 🚌		Ⓑ n⊗	⑥ s		①–④ m	⑦ d⊙	⑤ f	B	⑤ f	Ⓒ	①–④ m	⑤ f	①–④ m	⑤ f	⑦ d	⑤ f	Ⓑ n
	Périgueux **302** d.	...	...	...	...	...	...	...	...	...	...	...	...	...	...	1600	...	...	...	...	...	...	...	...	...	...	...
0	**Brive la Gaillarde** . **302** ◧ d.	...	0616	0619	0622	1005	...	...	1109	1106	...	1328	1347	...	1711	1713	1751	...	...	1849	1849	1910t	...	...	1932	2111	...
26	Tulle **302** ◧ a.	...	0641	0645	0648	1030	...	...	1137	1146	...	1353	1412	...	1736	1741	1816	...	...	1914	1914	1935t	...	...	1957	2137	...
26	Tulle d.	...	0649	0654	0656	1038	...	...	1145	1146	...	1411	1422	...	1744	1748	1822	...	...	1921	1921	1942	...	...	2003	2144	...
	Limoges d.	0546	|	|	|	|	1014	1014	|	|	1307	|	|	...	|	|	|	1807	1807	|	|	|	1912	1912	|	|	2118
79	Meymac d.	0718	0743	0748	0754	1133	1146	1148	1238	1254	1446	1504	1517	...	1838	1842	1916	1948	2000j	2017	2018	2040	2049	2054	2056	2236	2248
92	**Ussel** a.	0730	0754	0800	0806	1145	1157	1159	1249	1316	1458	1516	1528	...	1850	1853	1927	1959	2012	2029	2030	2051	2100	2105	2109	2247	2301

km		Ⓐ ⊡	Ⓐ	⑥ s	① g	Ⓐ C	⑥ s		A	Ⓑ n⊗		⑥ s	⑤ f	⑦ d	⑤⑦ h	⑥	①–④ z	⑦ d	⑤ f	⑤ f	Ⓐ 🚌	⑥s 🚌	Ⓐ		①–④ m	⑤ f	⑦ d
0	**Ussel** d.	0537	0616	0659	0740	0803	0950	1046	1205	1235	1253	1310	1522	1524	1546	1622	1625	1629	1631	1714	1725	1725	...	1756	1926	1946	2002
13	Meymac d.	0550	0629	0712	0756	0816	1003	1059	1218	1257	1307	1323	1535	1537	1602	1634	1637	1642	1643	1727	1749	1749	...	1809	1939	2002	2018
111	**Limoges** a.	|	0811	0853	0936	0950	|	1239	1354	|	1444	|	|	|	1740	|	|	|	|	|	|	|	...	1958	|	|	|
	Tulle a.	0643	...	...	...	...	1056	...	...	1350	...	1416	1628	1629	...	1727	1731	1737	1736	1818	1858	1858	...	...	2034	2058	2115
	Tulle **302** ◧ d.	0650	...	...	...	...	1103	...	...	1357	...	1426	1635	1636	...	1734	1738	1744	1743	1826	...	1858	1950	...	2041	2105	2122
	Brive la Gaillarde . **302** ◧ a.	0717	...	...	...	...	1129	...	...	1424	...	1452	1700	1702	...	1801	1804	1812	1810	1851	...	1933	2016	...	2107	2130	2147
	Périgueux **302** a.	...	...	...	...	...	...	...	...	...	...	...	...	...	...	...	...	1917	1917	...	...	...	...	...	...	...	...

🚌 USSEL - CLERMONT FERRAND 🚌

	🚌 ① g	🚌 ⚒	🚌 †	🚌 Ⓑ	🚌 ⑥	🚌 Ⓒ		🚌 ⑤ f	🚌 Ⓑ		
Ussel d.	0537	0818	1008	1204	1302	1521	...	1932	2045	...	...
Laqueuille a.	0617	0858	1048	1244	1342	1601	...	2012	2125	...	...
Clermont Ferrand a.	*0722*	*1003*	*1205*	1344	1442	*1705*	...	2112	2225	...	...

	🚌	🚌	🚌 †	🚌 ⑥	🚌 Ⓐ	🚌 ⑤† e	🚌 ⚒		🚌	🚌 ⑤ f
Clermont Ferrand d.	1010	1253	...	...	...	1413	1517	...	1756	*1948*
Laqueuille d.	1110	1353	1358	1418	1426	1513	1617	...	1856	2053
Ussel a.	1150	...	1438	1458	1506	1553	1657	...	1936	2131

A – ①②③④⑥ (not July 13, Aug. 15, Nov. 1, 10).
B – ①②③④⑥⑦ (also Nov. 11; not July 13, Nov. 10).
C – July 4 - Aug. 26.
d – Also Aug. 15, Nov. 1.
e – Also July 13, Nov. 10.
f – Also July 13, Nov. 10; not Nov. 11.
g – Also Nov. 2; not July 4 - Aug. 22, Oct. 31.
h – Also July 13, Aug. 15, Nov. 1, 10.
j – Arrives 1947.
m – Not July 13, 14, Aug. 15, Nov. 1, 10.
n – Not July 14, Nov. 11.
r – Not July 5 - Aug. 26, Nov. 1, 2, 11.
s – Also July 14, Nov. 11.
t – 3 minutes **earlier** on July 1, 8, 13, 15.
w – Not Aug. 15, Nov. 1.
z – Not July 4 - Aug. 25, Nov. 1, 10.
⊙ – Runs 5–9 minutes **earlier** Brive - Ussel on Aug. 15, Nov. 1.
⊡ – Runs 5–6 minutes **earlier** July 4 - Aug. 26.
⊗ – Subject to alteration on ①–④ Oct. 17–27.
◧ – Additional local trains run Brive - Tulle and v.v.

CLERMONT FERRAND - LYON 328

For rail journeys Clermont Ferrand - St Étienne and v.v., travel via Roanne (see Table **291** for connecting services).

km		Ⓐ △	⚒		Ⓐ	⚒	⚒	†	⚒	Ⓐ	⚒		⊖				Ⓐ		Ⓑ	⚒	Ⓑ			Ⓑ	† A
0	**Clermont Ferrand 329 330** d.	...	...	...	...	...	0600	...	...	0701	...	...	0857	...	...	1157	...	1357	1457	...	...	1657	...	1757	1957
14	Riom-Châtel-Guyon **329 330** d.	...	...	...	...	...	0609	...	...	|	...	...	0907	...	...	1207	...	1407	1507	...	...	1707	...	1807	2007
55	Vichy **330** d.	...	...	...	...	...	0632	...	...	|	...	...	0930	...	...	1230	...	1430	1530	...	...	1730	...	1830	2030
129	Roanne **290** d.	0505	0550	0604	0635	0648	0720	0720	0735	|	0835	0935	1018	1135	1250	1318	1450	1518	1618	1650	1750	1818	1850	1918	2118
171	Tarare d.	0540	0630	0645	0711	0727	0756	0800	0811	|	0911	1011	1048	1211	1331	1348	1531	1548	1648	1731	1831	1848	1931	1948	2148
222	**Lyon** Part Dieu **290** a.	0622	|	0727	0752	|	0835	0852	0852	0917	0952	1052	1122	1252	|	1422	|	1623	1722	|	|	1922	|	2022	2222
227	**Lyon** Perrache **290** a.	0634	0723	0738	0803	0824	0851	0903	0903	0928	1003	1104	1133	1303	1424	1433	1624	1634	1733	1824	1924	1933	2024	2033	2233

	⚒		⚒		⊖			Ⓐ		⚒			Ⓐ	⚒					Ⓐ	Ⓐ	Ⓐ		B	⊕	⊕
Lyon Perrache **290** d.	0627	0657	0757	0957	1127	1157	1235	1336	1427	1457	1557	1627	1636	1657	1727	1736	1757	1827	1836	1857	1927	1936	1957	2027	2057
Lyon Part Dieu **290** d.	0638	0708	0808	1008	1138	1208	|	1347	1438	1508	1608	1638	|	1708	1738	|	1808	1838	|	1908	1938	|	2008	2038	2108
Tarare d.	0713	0803	0850	1050	1213	1250	1330	1438	1514	1550	1650	1713	1730	1750	1813	1830	1850	1913	1930	1950	|	2030	2050	2113	2150
Roanne **290** d.	0746	0844	0925	1125	1246	1325	1410	1517	1546	1625	1725	1746	1810	1825	1846	1910	1925	1946	2010	2025	|	2110	2125	2146	2225
Vichy **330** d.	0831	...	...	...	1331	...	...	...	1631	...	...	1831	...	...	1931	...	...	2031	...	...	|	...	...	2231	...
Riom-Châtel-Guyon **329 330** d.	0855	...	...	...	1355	...	...	...	1655	...	...	1855	...	...	1955	...	...	2055	...	...	|	...	...	2255	...
Clermont Ferrand .. **329 330** a.	0904	...	...	...	1404	...	...	...	1704	...	...	1904	...	...	2004	...	...	2104	...	...	2154	...	...	2304	...

A – From July 3.
B – ⑦ to July 10; Ⓑ from July 14.
△ – Retimed June 13–24 as follows: Roanne d. 0515, Tarare d. 0550, Lyon Perrache a. 0639 (not calling at Lyon Part Dieu).
⊖ – Not Sept. 5–9, 12–16, 19–23.
⊕ – Not June 13–17, 20–24.

CLERMONT FERRAND - NEUSSARGUES - AURILLAC 331

Table temporarily relocated from page 196. Readers are advised to confirm timings locally.

km		Ⓐ 🚌	⑥ 🚌	🚌	H 🚌	J	🚌¶	🚌	K 🚌	M 🚌	†v	†v 🚌	N 🚌	M	M 🚌	B 🚌	†	🚌	D 🚌	E	E	⑤r	⑤r 🚌	†s	†s 🚌	C 🚌
0	**Clermont Ferrand** ... **333** d.	*0542*t	*0734*t	*1038*t	*1246*t	1303	...	*1648*t	*1748*t	*1748*t	1757	...	*1757*t	1844	...	*1844*t	1957	...	*2012*t	2012	...	2123	...	2141	...	*2141*t
36	Issoire **333** d.	*0610*t	*0803*t	*1106*t	*1312*t	1329	...	*1716*t	*1816*t	*1816*t	1825	...	*1825*t	1912	...	*1912*t	2025	...	*2040*t	2040	...	2151	...	2209	...	*2209*t
61	Arvant **333** d.	0636	0826	1129	1336	1348	...	1741	1843	*1838*t	1844	...	1849	1931	...	1936	2045	...	2105	2105	...	2211	...	2229	...	2234
85	Massiac-Blesle d.	0652	0842	1145	1352	1408	...	1757	1858	1902	1904	...	1904	1951	...	1951	2106	...	2118	2125	...	2232	...	2249	...	2250
111	**Neussargues** d.	0723	0913	1216	1423	1429	1445	1828	1930	1933	1924	1929	1936	2012	2017	2023	2126	2131	2150	2145	2150	2252	2257	2310	2315	2321
120	Murat (Cantal) d.	0738	0928	1231	...	...	1500	1843	1945	1948	...	1944	1951	...	2032	2038	...	2146	2205	...	2205	...	2312	...	2330	2336
131	Le Lioran d.	0750	0940	1243	...	...	1512	1855	1957	2000	...	1956	2003	...	2044	2050	...	2158	2217	...	2217	...	2324	...	2342	2348
168	**Aurillac** a.	0837	1027	1330	...	...	1559	1942	2044	2047	...	2043	2050	...	2131	2137	...	2245	2304	...	2304	...	0011	...	0029	0035

	P 🚌	Q 🚌	Q		Ⓐ 🚌		🚌		🚌‡	J	H 🚌		🚌		A 🚌	M 🚌		A 🚌	F 🚌	G	N 🚌	†v 🚌	†v			
Aurillac d.	0512	0517	...	...	0713	...	0956	...	1312	...	...	...	1607	...	1707	1707	...	1846	1856	...	1917	1920	...	...	...	...
Le Lioran d.	0559	0604	...	...	0800	...	1043	...	1359	...	...	...	1654	...	1754	1754	...	1933	1943	...	2004	2007	...	...	...	...
Murat (Cantal) d.	0611	0616	...	...	0812	...	1055	...	1411	...	...	...	1706	...	1806	1806	...	1945	1955	...	2016	2019	...	...	...	...
Neussargues d.	0626	0631	0641	...	0827	...	1110	...	1426	1436	1431	...	1721	...	1821	1821	...	2000	2010	2020	2031	2034	2044	...	...	...
Massiac-Blesle d.	0657	...	0703	...	0858	...	1141	...	...	1457	1503	...	1752	...	1852	1852	...	2032	...	2042	2103	...	2107	...	...	...
Arvant **333** d.	0713	...	0723	...	0914	...	1157	...	...	1517	1518	...	1808	...	1908	*1921*t	...	2047	...	2102	2118	...	2128	...	...	...
Issoire **333** d.	*0743*t	...	0743	...	*0950*t	...	*1225*t	...	...	1536	*1546*t	...	*1837*t	...	*1939*t	*1939*t	...	*2115*t	...	2120	*2146*t	...	2146	...	...	...
Clermont Ferrand ... **333** a.	*0817*t	...	0817	...	*1019*t	...	*1254*t	...	...	1600	*1611*t	...	*1905*t	...	*2007*t	*2007*t	...	*2142*t	...	2147	*2215*t	...	2215	...	...	...

A – ①–④ to July 28 (also July 22, 29; not July 14).
B – ①②③④⑥ to July 13; ①–⑥ July 16 - Sept. 1; ①②③④⑥ Sept. 3 - Oct. 1; ⑥ from Oct. 8.
C – ⑤⑦ Aug. 5–28 (also July 13, Aug. 15).
D – ③ to July 27; Ⓐ Aug. 1 - Sept. 1; ③ Sept. 7–28.
E – ①②④⑤ to July 29 (not July 14); ①②④⑤ Sept. 2–30; Ⓐ from Oct. 3.
F – ⑤ to July 15 (not July 1); Ⓐ from Aug. 1.
G – ⑤ to July 15; Ⓐ from Sept. 2 (not Sept. 7, 14, 21, 28).
H – ①–④ to July 7; ①–④ Sept. 19–29.
J – ⑤–⑦ to July 17 (also July 23, 24, 30, 31); ⑤–⑦ Sept. 3–25; daily from Sept. 30.
K – ①–④ to July 13; ①–⑤ July 18 - Aug. 26; ①–④ Aug. 29 - Sept. 29.
L – Daily to July 10 (also July 15–17, 23, 24, 30, 31, Sept. 3, 4, 9–11); daily from Sept. 16.
M – ⑤ to July 15; ⑤ Sept. 2–30; Ⓐ from Oct. 3.
N – July 14, Aug. 7, 14, 15, 21, 28 only.
P – ④ to July 28 (not July 14); ⚒ Aug. 2 - Sept. 2.
Q – ①②③⑤⑥ to Aug. 1; ⚒ from Sept. 3 (not Sept. 8, 15, 22, 29).
r – Not July 8 - Aug. 26.
s – Also July 8, 15, 22, 29; not Aug. 7–28.
t – Connection is by train.
v – Not July 14, Aug. 7, 14, 15, 21, 28.
¶ – Runs 5 minutes **earlier** July 11 - Aug. 12.
‡ – Runs 6 minutes **earlier** July 11 - Aug. 12.

329 MONTLUÇON - CLERMONT FERRAND

km		⑥	Ⓐ	Ⓐ		②–⑤	Ⓐ		Ⓑ		†
					e	r 🚌					
0	**Montluçon 327** d.	...	0557	0701	0828	0844	1036	1220	1701	1843	1936
13	Commentry d.	...	0608	0712	0840	0909	1047	1233	1714	1856	1947
67	Gannat **327** d.	0705	0706	0807	0927	1012	1134	1326	1805	1949	2042
94	Riom-Châtel-Guyon ▷ d.	0729	0729	0825	0943	1045	1153	1345	1831	2010	2101
108	**Clermont Ferrand** ▷ a.	0741	0741	0835	0952	1110	1202	1354	1840	2019	2110

	Ⓐ	①		⚒		Ⓑ	⚒	Ⓑ	⑤	†
		g							f	
Clermont Ferrand ▷ d.	0604	0635	0733	1216	1349	1648	1746	1910	2007	2012
Riom-Châtel-Guyon ▷ d.	0614	0645	0747	1228	1401	1702	1758	1923	2017	2022
Gannat **327** d.	0630	0707	0808	1246	1426	1727	1824	1950	2037	2043
Commentry d.	0721	0811	0857	1343	...	1822	1917	2040	2128	2134
Montluçon 327 a.	0734	0823	0907	1353	...	1832	1927	2053	2138	2144

e – ①⑥⑦ (also July 14, Aug. 16, Nov. 1, 2, 11).
f – Also July 13, Nov. 10; not Nov. 11.
g – Also Aug. 16, Nov. 2; not Aug. 15.
r – Not July 14, Aug. 16, Nov. 1, 2, 11.
▷ – See also Tables **328** and **330**.

330 PARIS - NEVERS - CLERMONT FERRAND

Intercités timings may vary by up to 5 minutes. Paris arrival times may be up to 15 minutes later on Oct. 15, 16, Nov. 19, 20.
Southbound TER timings may vary by up to 3 minutes Oct. 10 – 30. On July 16, Sept. 3, 4 services may run from / to Paris Gare de Lyon (not Bercy).

km									5951	5955				5959	5963		5967		5971	5973		5979	5977	5983	5983
									🅁★	🅁★				🅁★	🅁★		🅁★		🅁★	🅁★		🅁★	🅁★	🅁★	🅁★
		⚒	⚒	Ⓐ	⚒	Ⓐ	⚒	Ⓑ	①–⑥		⚒	⚒	Ⓐ			Ⓐ	⑤	Ⓑ		Ⓐ	†		Ⓐ		⑤
		⊖							b	⊕		⊗D	⊗	⊗			f			r		J	r	H	f
0	**Paris** Bercy ▶ d.	...	...	...	...	...	...	...	0657	0857	...	...	...	1257	1357	...	1457	...	1557	1657	...	1752	1757	1857	1857
254	**Nevers** ‡ ▶ d.	...	...	*0531*	...	...	0700	...	0900	1059	...	...	...	1500	1600	...	1659	...	1800	1900	...	2004	|	2100	2100
314	Moulins sur Allier ‡ d.	0508**g**	0554	0622	0642	0714	0743	0812	0931	1130	1215	1306	1415	1531	1633	1644	1712	1732	1812	1832	1933	1937	2036	|	2131	2131
355	St Germain des Fossés ‡ d.	0537	0617	0650	0709	0742	0808	0835	|	|	1239	1334	1440	|	|	1710	1740	|	1840	|	|	2001	|	|	|	2151
365	Vichy ▷ d.	0546	0625	0659	0718	0751	0816	0844	0958	1157	1249	1343	1449	1558	1659	1719	1749	1759	1849	1858	1959	2010	2103	|	2157	2200
406	Riom - Châtel-Guyon ▷ d.	0609	0650	0723	0742	0815	0839	0908	1022	1221	1312	1407	1513	1622	1724	1743	1812	1824	1913	1922	2024	2033	2127	|	2221	2225
420	**Clermont Ferrand** ▷ a.	0618	0659	0731	0751	0824	0848	0917	1031	1230	1321	1420	1522	1631	1733	1752	1821	1833	1922	1931	2033	2042	2136	2115	2230	2234

	5950	5950	5954		5958					5962		5966			5970	5974		5978			5982		5986		5990	
	🅁★	🅁★	🅁★		🅁★					🅁★		🅁★			🅁★	🅁★		🅁★			🅁★		🅁★		🅁★	
	①	②–⑤	Ⓐ	Ⓐ	⑥	Ⓐ	Ⓐ	⚒	Ⓐ		⑥	①–⑥	⚒	⚒		⑦	Ⓐ		Ⓐ	Ⓐ	Ⓑ		⑦			
	g	p	r		k							b⊗	⊗	⊗		e					h	E	e			
Clermont Ferrand ▷ d.	0524	0527	0552	0614	0626	0641	0717	0744	0808	0829	0842	1027	1043	1241	1327	1427	1538	1627	1642	1712	1727	1741	1832	1842	1927	2026
Riom - Châtel-Guyon ▷ d.	0535	0538	|	0623	0636	0651	0726	0753	0821	0839	0851	1038	1052	1251	1338	1437	1548	1638	1651	1721	1738	1750	1843	1851	1938	2035
Vichy ▷ d.	0559	0602	|	0646	0700	0713	0747	0818	0843	0904	0915	1102	1114	1313	1402	1501	1610	1702	1713	1743	1802	1812	1907	1913	2002	2057
St Germain des Fossés ‡ d.	0611	|	|	0657	|	0724	0758	0831	0855	|	0925	|	1127	1324	|	|	1622	|	1724	1754	|	1823	|	1925	|	2108
Moulins sur Allier ‡ d.	0630	0629	|	0723	0727	0750	0823	0854	...	0931	0950	1129	1153	1350	1429	1528	1650	1729	1750	1817	1829	1850	1933	1950	2029	2132
Nevers ‡ ▶ d.	0659	0659	|	0801	0756	...	...	0926	...	1000	...	1159	...	...	1459	1559	...	1759	...	...	1859	...	2001	...	2059	...
Paris Bercy ▶ a.	0857	0857	0903	...	1007	...	...	...	...	1157	...	1357	...	...	1657	1800	...	1957	...	...	2057	...	2157	...	2257	...

ADDITIONAL TER TRAINS PARIS - NEVERS

km			Ⓐ			⚒	⚒		Ⓐ	Ⓐ	Ⓒ	Ⓐ	⑦
					L								
0	**Paris** Bercy d.	...	0711	0911	...	...	1412	...	1702	1802	1804	1902	2004
119	Montargis d.	...	0816	1011	...	...	1512	...	1811	1911	1910	2011	2110
155	Gien d.	...	0837	1034	...	...	1534	...	1834	1934	1931	2033	2132
196	Cosne d.	0736	0903	1100	1236	1336	1600	1747	1900	2000	1957	2059	2158
228	La Charité d.	0801	0923	1117	1301	1401	1619	1812	1917	2017	2015	2118	2215
254	**Nevers** a.	0825	0944	1141	1325	1425	1640	1836	1939	2041	2035	2138	2235

	Ⓐ	Ⓐ	⑥	Ⓐ	Ⓐ			Ⓐ	⑦	⚒		
			k									◧
Nevers d.	0451	0551	0622	0721	0835	1021	1233	1421	1622	1635	1821	1924
La Charité d.	0513	0613	0644	0742	0858	1042	1257	1443	1645	1658	1842	1951
Cosne d.	0530	0630	0702	0802	0924	1102	1323	1500	1702	1724	1902	2016
Gien d.	0555	0655	0727	0826	...	1126	...	1525	1727	...	1926	...
Montargis d.	0620	0720	0752	0850	...	1150	...	1550	1753	...	1950	...
Paris Bercy a.	0727	0827	0850	0954	...	1249	...	1649	1851	...	2049	...

D – Not July 25 - Aug. 26, Sept. 3. From Dijon (Table **373**).
E – Daily to July 24; ⑥ July 30 - Aug. 20; daily from Aug. 26. To Dijon on Ⓑ (Table **373**).
H – ①②③④⑥⑦ (also July 15, Nov. 11; not July 13, Nov. 10).
J – ⑦ to June 26; Ⓑ July 3 - Aug. 28 (not July 14, 15); ⑦ from Sept. 4 (also Nov. 1).
L – Daily to July 8; Ⓑ July 10 - Aug. 26; daily from Aug. 28.

b – Not Aug. 15, Nov. 1.
e – Also Aug. 15, Nov. 1.
f – Also July 13, Nov. 10; not July 15, Nov. 11.
g – ① (also Aug. 16, Nov. 2; not Aug. 15, Oct. 31).
h – Not July 14, 15, Oct. 31, Nov. 11.
k – Also July 14, Nov. 11.
p – Not July 14, 15, Aug. 16, Nov. 1, 2, 11.
r – Not July 4 - Aug. 26, Oct. 31.

★ – *INTERCITÉS*. 🍸. Subject to alteration July 15 – 17, Sept. 3, 4.
◧ – On Ⓐ Nevers d. 1934, La Charité d. 1959, Cosne a. 2023.
⊕ – Subject to alteration Nov. 14 – 18.
⊗ – Subject to alteration Nov. 14 – 18, 21 – 25.
⊖ – Runs 4 – 8 minutes **earlier** from Oct. 31.
▶ – For additional trains see panel below main table.
▷ – See also Tables **328** and **329**.
‡ – See also Table **290**.

331 CLERMONT FERRAND - NEUSSARGUES - AURILLAC

This table is temporarily relocated to page 195

332 (CLERMONT FERRAND -) NEUSSARGUES - BÉZIERS

RAIL SERVICES IN THIS TABLE ARE VALID TO JULY 10 AND FROM AUGUST 13. Please check locally for amended service July 11 - August 12.

km						🚌		🚌		🚌	🚌
		⚒	⚒	Ⓐ	⚒	⚒		⑤	⑤		Ⓑ
							⊕	f	d		w
0	**Clermont Ferrand 331** d.	...	...	...	...	1050	1303j	...	...	1650	2130
111	**Neussargues** 331 d.	...	...	...	...	|	1436	...	...	|	|
130	St Flour ⊖ d.	...	...	...	...	|	1457	1557	...	|	|
168	St Chély d'Apcher d.	...	...	...	1130t	1225	1537	1620	1627r	1830	2300
201	Marvejols ★ d.	...	...	...	1207	|	1615e	...	1705	|	|
	Mende ★ a.	...	...	...	|	1340	|	...	|	1945	0015
243	Sévérac le Château d.	...	...	...	1257	▬	1702e	...	1754	▬	...
273	Millau a.	...	...	...	1329	...	1735e	...	1826	†	...
273	Millau d.	0551	...	...	1330	...	1738	...	1828	2105	...
352	Bédarieux d.	0712	0842	1243	1449	1727	1858	...	1946	2229	...
394	**Béziers** a.	0745	0915	1317	1522	1801	1931	...	2019	2301	...

	🚌									
	⚒	⚒	⚒		⑤	Ⓐ			⑦	⑤
				⊙	d			N	hM	d
Béziers d.	...	0637	0757	0935	...	1200	1643	1821	1901	1901
Bédarieux d.	...	0713	0829	1011	...	1232	1715	1859	1944	1947
Millau a.	...	0832	▬	1127	...	▬	▬	2016	2054	2104
Millau d.	...	0836	🚌	1129	1341	🚌	🚌	...	2059	▬
Sévérac le Château d.	...	0906		1159	1411	A	B	...	2132	...
Mende ★ d.	0700	|	0950	|	|	1525	1600	...	|	🚌
Marvejols ★ d.	|	0954	|	1249	1458	|	|	...	2222	†
St Chély d'Apcher d.	0820	1030t	1115	1327	1535r	1645	1720	...	2259r	2309
St Flour ⊖ d.	|	...	|	1406	...	|	|	...	...	2339
Neussargues 331 a.	|	...	|	1426	...	|	|	...	...	...
Clermont Ferrand 331 a.	1000	...	1300	1600j	...	1825	1900	...	...	...

OTHER 🚌 LINKS. See Tables **331** and **333** for connecting rail services Clermont Ferrand - Arvant / Massiac and v.v.

	🚌	🚌	🚌	🚌	🚌	🚌	🚌	🚌	🚌	🚌
	Ⓐ	Ⓐ	⑥	⚒			Ⓑ	⑤f‡	Ⓐ◧	†
Clermont Ferrand 331 333 d.	...	...	...	1048	...	...	...	...	2125	2148
Arvant 331 333 d.	...	0741	0826	|	...	...	...	...	|	|
Massiac-Blesle 331 d.	0711	0758	0843	|	1150	1808	1910	2130	|	|
St Flour ⊖ d.	0735	0824	0909	1213	1214	1833	1935	2155	2250	2313

	🚌	🚌	🚌	🚌	🚌	🚌	🚌	🚌	🚌
	⚒	⚒		†	v	⑤f	⚒	Ⓐ◐	†
St Flour ⊖ d.	0628	0845	1104	1645	1718	1728	1745	1825	1930
Massiac-Blesle 331 a.	0653	|	1128	|	1742	|	|	1850	|
Arvant 331 333 a.	...	|	...	|	...	1808	|	...	|
Clermont Ferrand 331 333 a.	...	1010	...	1810	...	...	1910	...	2055

A – Ⓐ Aug. 29 - Oct. 28.
B – Daily to Aug. 28; Ⓒ Sept. 3 - Oct. 23; daily from Oct. 29.
D – ⑥⑦ July 2 – 10, Ⓒ Aug. 13 – 28.
E – ②–⑤ from Aug. 30 (not Nov. 1, 2, 11).
H – ①–⑥ July 2 – 9; ⚒ Aug. 12 – 27.
J – ①–④ from Aug. 29 (also Oct. 28, Nov. 4; not Nov. 1, 10).
M – From Montpellier (Table **355**).
N – ①②③④⑥⑦ (also July 8, Aug. 12, 19, 26, Oct. 28, Nov. 4, 11; not Nov. 10).

d – Also Nov. 10; not July 8 - Aug. 26, Oct. 28, Nov. 4, 11.
e – 8 – 10 minutes **earlier** Aug. 13 – 31, Sept. 1, 3, 5 – 8, 10, 12 – 15.
f – Also July 13, Nov. 10; not Nov. 11.
h – ⑦ (not July 10 - Aug. 28, Oct. 23, 30).
j – ⑤–⑦ to July 10; ⑤–⑦ Sept. 16 – 25; daily from Sept. 30.
n – Not Nov. 11.
r – Not Sept. 2 – 11.
t – Not Aug. 13 - Sept. 16.
v – Not July 8, 13, 15, 22, 29, Aug. 5, 12, 19, 26.

w – Runs 20 minutes later on †.

‡ – Runs 6 minutes earlier from Nov. 4.
◧ – Runs 20 minutes later July 4 - Aug. 26.
◐ – Runs 3 minutes earlier on ①–④ to July 13 and ①–⑤ July 18 – 29.
⊖ – St Flour - Chaudes Aigues.
⊙ – Does not run Marvejols - Neussargues - Clermont Ferrand Aug. 13 - Sept. 15.
⊕ – Does not run Clermont Ferrand - Neussargues - Marvejols Aug. 13 - Sept. 15.
⊗ – Departs 2125 and operated by 🚌 on June 12.
◇ – By 🚌 on June 12.
★ – Connecting rail services Marvejols - Mende and v.v. (*35 km*, journey 42 – 49 minutes).
From Marvejols at 0700 ②–⑤ **E**, 0750 **D**, 1351 **H**, 1722 ⑤ **d** and 2228 ⑦ **h** ◇.
From Mende at 1118 **H**, 1613 ⑤ **d**, 1730 **J** and 2127 ⑦ **h** ⊗.
△ – Additional 🚌 journeys Bédarieux - Béziers and v.v.:
From Bédarieux at 0615 ⚒, 0710 †, 1215 †, 1313 ⑥, 1615 † and 1635 ⚒.
From Béziers at 1049 †, 1205 ⑥, 1430 †, 1530 ⚒, 1740 ⚒ and 2045 ⑤ **n**.

☛ *Bus services in this table are operated on behalf of SNCF. Rail tickets valid.*

CLERMONT FERRAND - LE PUY EN VELAY and NÎMES — 333

SERVICE FROM JUNE 25

km						🚌		🚌							🚌		🚌				🚌			🚌	🚌	
		Ⓐ	Ⓐ		Ⓐ	Ⓐ	⑥	⑥	①	Ⓒ	Ⓒ	Ⓒ						Ⓒ	Ⓐ			⚒	⑤	Ⓐ	⑤	†
				H	⊗				k	D	D	D	G										f		f	
0	**Clermont Ferrand 331** d.	...	0542	...	0645v	...	0734	...	...	0918	...	...	...	0949	...	1253z	...	1430	1448	1640	...	1758	1858	1901	*2012*t	2118
36	Issoire **331** d.	...	0610	...	0714	...	0803	...	...	0948	...	...	...	1017	...	1321v	...	1509	1520	1708	...	1826	1926	1941	*2040*t	2146
61	Arvant **331** d.	...	0629	...	0735	...	0822	...	...	1008	...	...	...	1036	...	1342v	...	1532	1542	1727	...	1845	1945	2028	2104	2205
71	Brioude d.	...	0638	...	0744	...	0831	...	...	1017	...	...	...	1044	...	1351	1357	1540	1550	1737	...	1854	1954	2045	2119	2214
95	St Georges d'Aurac d.	...	0706	...	0804	...	0850	...	...	1040	...	...	...	1109	...	|	|	━	━	1805n	1807	1918	2019	|	|	2238
103	Langeac d.	...	|	...	0812	0817	0858	0902	...	1055	...	...	...	|	...	1419	|	...	...	1813	|	|	|	|	2157	|
147	**Le Puy en Velay** a.	...	0757	...	|	0903	|	0948	...	|	...	...	...	1201	...	|	1505	⑤†	...	|	1857	2010	2110	2205	2243	2329
170	Langogne d.	...	━	...	0938	━	1027	...	1115	1227	...	1244	...	...	...	1546	...	c	♣	1943n	...	...	...	...	...	...
47•	**Mende** d.	0447	⑥w	0838	|	†	|	...	|	...	1127	|	1147	...	1445	|	...	1654	1834r	|	...	...	...	...	...	...
188	La Bastide-St Laurent d.	0600	0706	0949	1007	1013	1047	...	1135	...	1236	1307	1306n	...	1553	1610	...	1807	1942	2014n	...	...	...	...	...	...
241	Grand Combe la Pise d.	0709	0811	...	1106	1114	1147	...	1234	...	...	1413	1410	...	...	1712	...	1912	...	2118	...	...	...	...	...	...
254	Alès d.	0726	0828	...	1124	1132	1205	...	1252	...	...	1430	1430‡	...	...	1729	...	1932	...	2134	...	...	...	...	...	...
303	**Nîmes** Centre a.	0801	0901	...	1157	1204	1238	...	1331	...	...	1503	1502‡	...	...	1802	...	2006	...	2206	...	...	...	...	...	...

						🚌		🚌				🚌					🚌		🚌		🚌	🚌				🚌
	Ⓐ	⑥	①	②–⑤	⚒	Ⓐ	①	†			⑥	Ⓐ	⑥	†	Ⓒ							Ⓐ	†	Ⓑ		
			g	d			m		⊖	♥			D	D	D							◇				
Nîmes Centre d.	...	...	...	...	...	...	0716	...	0816	...	...	...	0953	1017	...	1215	...	...	...	1418	...	...	...	1658	1815	...
Alès d.	...	...	...	...	...	...	0751	...	0850	...	...	...	1029	1052	...	1251	...	...	...	1453	...	...	...	1749b	1852	...
Grand Combe la Pise d.	...	...	...	...	...	...	0812	...	0906	...	...	...	1046	1112	...	1308	...	...	...	1510	...	...	...	1813n	1911	...
La Bastide-St Laurent d.	...	...	...	...	...	...	0916	...	1005	1009	...	...	1157	1214	...	1418j	1419	...	...	1609	1614	...	...	1916	2016j	2017
Mende a.	...	...	...	...	...	...	|	...	|	1117	...	...	|	|	...	1528	|	...	...	|	1722	...	...	|	2126	|
Langogne d.	...	...	...	...	...	...	0935	...	1028	...	...	...	1217	1234	1252	...	1443	...	...	1629	...	...	...	1940	...	2041
Le Puy en Velay d.	...	...	0523	0609	0808	0945	━	1059	|	...	1210	1218	...	...	|	...	...	1601	1654	|	...	1910	1950	|	...	...
Langeac d.	...	...	|	|	|	|	...	|	1153	...	|	|	...	...	1421	...	...	|	|	1754	...	|	|	2103	...	...
St Georges d'Aurac d.	...	...	0616	0702	0900	|	⚒	|	1201	...	1303	|	...	...	1429	...	...	1654	1743	1804	...	|	2043	2111	...	...
Brioude d.	0555	0630	0641	0723	0921	1049	1104	1203	1220	...	1324	1324	...	...	1449	...	...	1715	...	1823	...	2018	2104	2130	...	...
Arvant **331** d.	0603	0638	0649	0732	0930	...	1112	...	1229	...	1333	1339	...	...	1457	...	...	1724	...	1832	...	2035	2112	2138	...	...
Issoire **331** d.	0623	0658	0710	0753	0950	...	1132	...	1250	...	1354	1421	...	...	1517	...	...	1745	...	1851	...	*2115*t	2133	2158	...	...
Clermont Ferrand 331 a.	0655	0738	0742	0822	1019	...	1211	...	1318	...	1422	1501	...	...	1547	...	...	1812	...	1917	...	*2142*t	2200	2226	...	...

A – ①②③④⑥⑦ (also Nov. 11; not July 13, Nov. 10).
B – Ⓑ to Sept. 9; daily from Sept. 11.
D – Until Sept. 11.
E – ②–⑥ (also July 11, 18, 25, Aug. 1, 8, 22, 29, Oct. 24, 31; not July 14, Nov. 1, 11).
G – Ⓐ to Sept. 9; daily from Sept. 12.
H – Ⓑ (daily June 26 - Sept. 2). By 🚌 on Ⓐ w; by train (Mende d. 0840) on † (daily July 2 - Aug. 28).

b – Arrives 1734.
c – Also Nov. 10; not ⑤ July 8 - Aug. 26, Oct. 28, Nov. 4.
d – Not July 14, Aug. 16, Nov. 1, 2, 11.
e – Not July 13, 14, Aug. 15, Nov, 1, 10.
f – Also July 13, Nov. 10; not Nov. 11.
g – Also Aug. 16, Nov. 2; not Aug. 15.
j – Arrives 4–5 minutes earlier.
k – Not July 11 - Aug. 29, Oct. 10–31.
m – Not July 11 - Aug. 29, Oct. 24, 31.
n – Arrives 7–11 minutes earlier.
r – 1832 on ⑤ (also Nov. 10; not July 8 - Aug. 26, Oct. 28, Nov. 4, 11).
t – By train Clermont Ferrand - Arvant.
v – 1–2 minutes **earlier** Aug. 1–19.
w – Not July 4 - Aug. 27.
z – 1246 Aug. 1–19.

‡ – 3 minutes later on ①–④ July 11 - Aug. 25 (not July 13, 14, Aug. 15).
◇ – Connecting train Arvant - Clermont runs 5 minutes later on certain dates.
⊗ – Subject to alteration on ①–⑤ Oct. 10–28.
⊖ – Subject to alteration on ②–⑤ Oct. 11–28.
♣ – By train on ⑤ (also Nov. 10; not July 8 - Aug. 26, Oct. 28, Nov. 4, 11); by 🚌 on other dates.
♥ – By train on ⚒ July 2 - Aug. 27; by 🚌 on other dates.
• – Distance from La Bastide.
▶ – Other trains Alès - Nîmes (journey time 32–41 minutes).
From Alès at 0556 Ⓐ **w**, 0625 Ⓐ, 0652, 0802 ⚒, 0828, 0929, 1031 Ⓐ, 1227 Ⓐ, 1252, 1528 **A**, 1530 ⑤ **f**, 1640 Ⓐ, 1836 Ⓐ and 1932.
From Nîmes at 0613 Ⓐ, 0651 Ⓐ **w**, 0717 **E**, 0751 Ⓐ, 0921 Ⓐ, 1017 **B**, 1118 ⑤ **f**, 1119 ①–④ **e**, 1317 Ⓐ, 1517 Ⓐ, 1617, 1731 ⚒, 1925 Ⓐ and 2117.

TGV services LYON - MASSY - LE MANS - RENNES and NANTES — 335

Timings may vary by a few minutes – please check your reservation. Subject to alteration Oct. 29 - Nov. 1. See Table **290** for slower services via Bourges.

	TGV 5350	*TGV* 5381	*TGV* 5350		*TGV* 5384	*TGV* 5384	*TGV* 5382	*TGV* 5382		*TGV* 5354		*TGV* 5386	*TGV* 5357		*TGV* 5358	*TGV* 5358	*TGV* 5388							
		Ⓐ	Ⓐ			Ⓒ		⑤		Ⓐ														
	K	s	t		E		C	f		s			C		N	y	R							
Marseille St Charles **350** d.	...	...	...	...	...	...	0831	...	...	...	...	1435	1435	...	...	...	...	...	...	...	...	...	...	...
Avignon TGV **350** d.	...	...	...	...	...	...	0908	...	...	...	...	1518	1518	...	...	...	...	...	...	...	...	...	...	...
Montpellier St-Roch **355** d.	...	...	...	...	0828	0838	|	...	...	...	...	|	|	...	1624	1624	...	...	...	...	...	...	...	...
Valence TGV **355** d.	...	...	...	...	|	|	0942	...	...	...	...	|	|	...	1743	1743	...	...	...	...	...	...	...	...
Lyon Perrache d.	0617	0617	0617	...	|	|	|	1016	...	1516	...	|	|	...	|	|	1816	...	...	...	...	...	...	...
Lyon Part Dieu d.	0630	0630	0630	...	1030	1030	1030	1030	...	1530	...	1630	1630	...	1830	1830	1830	...	...	...	...	...	...	...
Massy TGV d.	0842	0842	0850	...	1242	1242	1242	1242	...	1742	...	1841	1841	...	2041	2041	2044	...	...	...	...	...	...	...
St Pierre des Corps a.	|	|	0940	...	|	|	|	|	...	|	...	|	|	...	|	2131	|	...	...	...	...	...	...	...
Le Mans **280** a.	0929	0929	|	...	1329	1329	1329	1329	...	1829	...	1929	1929	...	|	|	2132	...	...	...	...	...	...	...
Laval **280** a.	|	1001	|	...	|	|	|	|	...	|	...	2004	|	...	|	|	|	...	...	...	...	...	...	...
Rennes **280** a.	|	1030	|	...	1417	1417	1417	1417	...	|	...	2030	|	...	|	|	2220	...	...	...	...	...	...	...
Saumur Rive Droit a.	|	...	|	...	...	...	...	...	...	|	...	...	|	...	|	2205	...	...	...	...	...	...	...	...
Angers St Laud **280** a.	1009j	...	1039	...	...	...	...	...	...	1910	...	...	2014	...	2156	2228	...	...	...	...	...	...	...	...
Nantes **280** a.	1050j	...	1122	...	...	...	...	...	...	1950	...	...	2054	...	2235	2307	...	...	...	...	...	...	...	...

	TGV 5300	*TGV* 5300		*TGV* 5332		*TGV* 5304	*TGV* 5304	*TGV* 5334		*TGV* 5306	*TGV* 5306	*TGV* 5306		*TGV* 5336	*TGV* 5336		*TGV* 5341	*TGV* 5338	*TGV* 5338		*TGV* 5320			
	①	②–⑤					Ⓒ							①	⑤				①–④					
	g	p		△		R	w	R		C z	A	Q		g	f		C	D	m		B			
Nantes **280** d.	0450	0455	...	...	...	0854	0909	...	...	1144	1209	1217	...	...	...	...	...	...	...	...	1640	...	...	...
Angers St Laud **280** d.	0529	0533	...	...	...	0933	0948	...	...	1223	1248	1256	...	...	...	...	...	...	...	...	1722	...	...	...
Saumur Rive Droit d.	0551	|	...	...	...	|	|	...	...	|	|	|	...	...	...	...	...	...	...	...	1746	...	...	...
Rennes **280** d.	|	|	...	0740	...	|	|	0923	...	|	|	|	...	1348	1348	...	1529	1529	1540	...	|	...	...	...
Laval **280** d.	|	|	...	|	...	|	|	|	...	|	|	|	...	1415	1415	...	1557	1557	|	...	|	...	...	...
Le Mans **280** d.	|	|	...	0830	...	1030	1030	1030	...	|	1330	|	...	|	|	...	1630	1630	1630	...	|	...	...	...
St Pierre des Corps d.	0628	0628	...	|	...	|	|	|	...	1322	|	|	...	|	|	...	|	|	|	...	1826	...	...	...
Massy TGV d.	0727	0727	...	0927	...	1126	1126	1126	...	1427	1427	1427	...	1528	1528	...	1728	1728	1728	...	1926	...	...	...
Lyon Part Dieu a.	0930	0930	...	1130	...	1330	1330	1330	...	1630	1630	1630	...	1730	1730	...	1930	1930	1930	...	2130	...	...	...
Lyon Perrache a.	|	|	...	|	...	|	|	1349	...	|	|	|	...	1748	|	...	|	|	1947	...	2143	...	...	...
Valence TGV **355** a.	1013	1013	...	|	...	1410	1410	...	...	|	|	|	...	...	1811	...	2016	|	...	...	...	...	...	...
Montpellier St-Roch **355** a.	1119•	1119•	...	|	...	1527	1527h	...	...	|	|	|	...	...	1935	...	2139	|	...	...	...	...	...	...
Avignon TGV **350** a.	...	...	...	1242	...	...	...	...	...	1751	1751	1751	...	...	...	...	...	2039	...	...	...	...	...	...
Marseille St Charles **350** a.	...	...	...	1323	...	...	...	...	...	1823	1823	1823	...	...	...	...	...	2115	...	...	...	...	...	...

MARSEILLE - LYON - LE HAVRE

	TGV 5376 d		*TGV* 5316 e
Marseille St Charles d.	1536	**Le Havre** d.	0749
Avignon TGV d.	1607	**Rouen** Rive Droite d.	0842
Valence TGV d.	1645	Mantes la Jolie d.	0929
Lyon Part Dieu d.	1730	Versailles Chantiers d.	1004
Massy-Palaiseau a.	1938	Massy-Palaiseau d.	1028
Versailles Chantiers a.	1955	**Lyon** Part Dieu a.	1230
Mantes la Jolie a.	2029	Valence TGV a.	1312
Rouen Rive Droite a.	2114	Avignon TGV a.	1350
Le Havre a.	2205	**Marseille** St Charles a.	1423

A – ①–⑤ to July 1; Ⓐ from Aug. 29 (not Oct. 31).
B – Ⓑ to June 24; daily June 26 - Sept. 2; Ⓑ from Sept. 4 (not Oct. 31, Nov. 11).
C – ⑥⑦ to June 26; daily July 2 - Aug. 28; Ⓒ from Sept. 3 (also Oct. 31).
D – ⑤–⑦ to June 26; daily July 1 - Aug. 28; ⑤–⑦ from Sept. 2 (also Oct. 31, Nov. 1, 10).
E – ① to June 27; Ⓐ July 4 - Aug. 26; ① from Aug. 29 (also Nov. 2).
K – ⑥ to June 25; daily July 2 - Aug. 28; ⑥ Sept. 3 - Oct. 1; ①–⑥ Oct. 5–31; ⑥ from Nov. 5 (also Nov. 11).
N – Runs on Nov. 26 only.
Q – Runs on Nov. 27 only.
R – July 2 - Aug. 28.

d – Not June 24, 25, July 1–4, 14–31, Aug. 1–20, 26, 27, Nov. 11, 12.
e – Not June 12, 25, 26, July 2–5, 15–31, Aug. 1–21, 27, 28, Nov. 12, 13.
f – Also Nov. 10; not July 8 - Aug. 26, Nov. 11.
g – Also Nov. 2; not July 4 - Aug. 22, Oct. 31.
h – 1538 on Oct. 8, 9, 15, 16, 29, 30, Nov. 5, 6, 26, 27.
j – On ①–⑤ Oct. 5–28 arrives Angers 1016, Nantes 1058. On Ⓐ July 4 - Aug. 26 arrives Nantes 1054.
m – Not July 4 - Aug. 25, Oct. 31, Nov. 1, 10.
p – Not July 5 - Aug. 26, Nov. 1, 2, 11.
s – Not July 4 - Aug. 26, Oct. 31.
t – Not July 4 - Aug. 26, Oct. 5–31.
w – Also Oct. 31; not July 2 - Aug. 28.
y – Not Nov. 26.
z – Not Nov. 27.

TGV – High-speed train. Ⓡ. 🍸.

• – Montpellier **Sud de France**.
△ – On Oct. 30 departs Rennes 0755 and does not call at Le Mans.

340 PARIS - LYON

TGV trains

For Charles de Gaulle ✈ - Marne la Vallée - Lyon see Table **11**. For Paris - Lyon St Exupéry ✈ see Table **342**. For Paris - Lyon - Milano see Table **44**.
Timings may vary by up to 5 minutes (please check your reservation for confirmed timings). Services to/from St Étienne are subject to alteration Oct. 29–31, Nov. 1, 11–13.

km		*TGV* **6601**	*TGV* **6641**	*TGV* **7801**	*TGV* **6641**	*TGV* **6603**	*TGV* **6643**	*TGV* **6605**	*TGV* **6605**	*TGV* **6681**	*TGV* **6607**	*TGV* **6607**	*FR* **6651**	*TGV* **6609**	*TGV* **6611**	*TGV* **6613**	*TGV* **7803**	*TGV* **6685**	*TGV* **6615**	*TGV* **6617**	*TGV* **6657**	*FR* **6653**	*TGV* **6619**	*TGV* **6621**	*TGV* **6659**	*TGV* **6687**
		Ⓐ	②–⑤	①⑥	①	①–⑥	Ⓐ	⑦	⑥	①–⑥		Ⓒ									⑤				①–④	
		v	s	⊠	c	b	z	e	d	b		w	♠		A		⊠		B		f	♠			m	
0	**Paris** Gare de Lyon **341/2** d.	0549	0625	0625	0640	0656	0730	0751	0752	0752	0850	0850	0859	0958	1100	1152	1228	1250	1250	1350	1426	1430	1456	1549	1625	1658
303	Le Creusot TGV d.	0714	|	|	|	|	|	0919	0917	0917	|	|	|	|	|	1317	|	|	|	1517	|	|	|	1714	|	|
363	Mâcon Loché TGV **341/2** a.	|	|	|	|	|	|	|	|	|	|	|	|	|	|	|	|	|	|	|	|	|	|	1732	|	|
427	**Lyon** Part-Dieu a.	0756	0826	0826	0841	0856	0926	0956	0956	0956	1047	1047	1056	1156	1256	1356	1426	1456	1456	1556	1619	1627	1656	1803	1822	1856
	St Étienne Châteaucreux a.	|	|	|	|	|	|	|	|	1049	...	|	|	|	|	|	|	1549	|	|	|	|	|	|	...	1949
432	**Lyon** Perrache a.	0809	0839	0839	0854	0909	0939	1009	1009	...	...	1100	1109	1209	1309	1409	1439	...	1509	1609	1638	1643	1709	1816	...	...

	TGV **6623**	*TGV* **6663**	*TGV* **6627**	*TGV* **7805**	*TGV* **6665**	*TGV* **6689**	*TGV* **6629**	*TGV* **6669**	*TGV* **6631**	*FR* **6655**	*TGV* **6633**	*TGV* **6635**
					Ⓑ						Ⓑ	⑤⑦
	D	E		⊠	q		F	G		♠	h	t
Paris Gare de Lyon **341/2** d.	1658	1726	1749	1830	1846	1857	1857	1926	1954	2000	2048	2158
Le Creusot TGV d.	|	|	1917	|	|	|	|	|	|	|	2211	|
Mâcon Loché TGV **341/2** a.	|	|	|	|	|	2032	2032	|	|	|	2230	|
Lyon Part-Dieu a.	1856	1926	1956	2027	2042	2058	2058	2126	2152	2156	2256	2356
St Étienne Châteaucreux a.	|	|	|	|	|	2149	|	|	|	|	|	|
Lyon Perrache a.	1909	1939	2009	2039	2055	...	2117	2139	2205	2209	2309	0009

	TGV **6640**	*TGV* **6602**	*TGV* **6642**	*FR* **6650**	*TGV* **6644**	*TGV* **6604**	*TGV* **6690**	*TGV* **6648**	*TGV* **6693**
	①	Ⓐ	Ⓐ		①–④		①–⑥		
	g	v	z	♠	m	H	b	R	
Lyon Perrache d.	0521	0551	0613	0621	0641	0649	...	0720	...
St Étienne C ⊡ d.	|	|	|	|	|	|	0612	|	0643
Lyon Part-Dieu d.	0534	0603	0626	0634	0654	0702	0702	0734	0734
Mâcon Loché TGV **341/2** d.	0601	0629	|	|	|	|	|	|	|
Le Creusot TGV d.	0623	0650	|	|	|	|	|	|	|
Paris Gare de Lyon **341/2** a.	0751	0813	0823	0833	0850	0900	0900	0931	0931

	TGV **6608**	*TGV* **6610**	*TGV* **7802**	*TGV* **6612**	*TGV* **6614**	*TGV* **6616**	*FR* **6652**	*TGV* **6616**	*TGV* **6618**	*TGV* **6694**	*TGV* **6620**	*TGV* **6622**	*TGV* **7804**	*TGV* **6624**	*TGV* **6664**	*TGV* **6626**	*FR* **6654**	*TGV* **6668**	*TGV* **6696**	*TGV* **6628**	*TGV* **6638**	*TGV* **6630**	*TGV* **6632**	*TGV* **6634**	*TGV* **7806**	*TGV* **6676**
						Ⓐ		Ⓒ							Ⓑ			⑤⑦			①–④				⑤⑦	⑤⑦
			⊠		p	v	♠	w	J				⊠		h		♠	y			m	L	N	k	⊠	t¶
Lyon Perrache d.	0751	0851	0921	0951	1051	...	1142	1151	1251	...	1351	1451	1541	1551	1621	1651	1711	1721	...	1751	...	1851	1951	2051	2121	2151
St Étienne Châteaucreux d.	|	|	|	|	|	...	|	|	|	1211	|	|	|	|	|	|	|	|	1643	|	...	|	|	|	|	|
Lyon Part-Dieu d.	0804	0902	0932	1004	1101	1132	1155	1204	1304	1304	1404	1504	1554	1604	1634	1704	1722	1734	1734	1804	1838	1904	2004	2104	2134	2204
Mâcon Loché TGV **341/2** d.	|	|	|	|	|	|	|	|	|	|	|	|	|	|	|	|	|	|	|	|	|	|	|	|	|	|
Le Creusot TGV d.	0846	|	|	1046	|	|	|	|	|	|	1446	|	|	1645	|	|	|	|	|	1846	|	|	|	2146	|	2249
Paris Gare de Lyon **341/2** a.	1008	1101	1130	1209	1300	1330	1357	1401	1501	1501	1610	1701	1751	1808	1833	1900	1921	1932	1932	2008	2036	2100	2202	2308	2332	0011

A – Daily to July 4; ①⑤⑥⑦ July 8 - Aug. 22 (also July 13, 14, Aug. 16); daily from Aug. 26.
B – Daily to July 2; ①⑤⑥ July 4–23 (also July 13, 14); ⑤ July 29 - Aug. 26 (also Aug. 22, 27); daily from Aug. 29.
D – ②–⑦ to June 26; ②–⑤ June 28 - July 22 (not July 14, 15); ②–⑦ from Aug. 23 (also Oct. 31; not Aug. 27, 28, Nov. 2).
E – ①–⑤ to July 4 (also July 8, 11, 13, 18, 22, Aug. 22); Ⓐ from Aug. 26 (not Oct. 31).
F – ⑥ to June 25; ⑤ July 8 - Aug. 26 (also Aug. 13; not Aug. 15); ⑥ from Sept. 3 (also Oct. 31, Nov. 11).
G – Ⓑ to July 3 (also July 8, 10, 13, 17, 22, 24); Ⓑ from Aug. 26 (not Oct. 31, Nov. 11).
H – ①–⑥ to July 1; ①–⑤ July 4–25 (also Aug. 1, 8, 16; not July 14, 15); ①–⑥ from Aug. 22 (not Aug. 27, Nov. 1).
J – Daily to July 1; ①–⑤ July 4–25 (also Aug. 1, 8, 16; not July 14, 15); daily from Aug. 22 (not Aug. 27, 28).
L – Ⓑ to July 3; ⑤⑦ July 8 - Aug. 26 (also July 13, Aug. 15; not July 15); daily from Aug. 28.
N – Ⓑ to June 24; daily June 26 - July 24; Ⓒ July 30 - Aug. 21; Ⓑ from Aug. 22 (also Aug. 27; not Oct. 31, Nov. 11).
R – ① to June 27; ⑥ July 30 - Aug. 20; ①⑥ from Aug. 29 (also Nov. 2, 11).

b – Not Aug. 15, Nov. 1.
c – Not July 25 - Aug. 15, Oct. 31.
d – Also Oct. 31, Nov. 11; not July 2 - Aug. 27.
e – Also Aug. 15, Nov. 1.
f – Also Nov. 10; not July 8 - Aug. 26, Nov. 11.
g – Also Nov. 2; not July 4 - Aug. 22, Oct. 31.
h – Not July 14, 15, Oct. 31, Nov. 11.
k – Not July 2, 9, 14–16, 23, 30, Aug. 6, 13, 20, 27.
m – Not July 4 - Aug. 25, Oct. 31, Nov. 1, 10.
p – Not July 25–29, Aug. 1–5, 8–12, 16–19.
q – Not July 14, 15, 25–28, Aug. 1–4, 8–11, 16–18, Oct. 31, Nov. 11.
s – Not July 14, 15, 26–29, Aug. 2–19, Nov. 1, 11.
t – Also July 13, Aug. 15, Nov. 1, 10; not July 15, Nov. 11.
u – Not July 3 - Aug. 28, Oct. 31, Nov. 11.
v – Not July 15, Oct. 31.
w – Also July 15, Oct. 31.
y – Also Nov. 1, 10; not July 3 - Aug. 28, Nov. 11.
z – Not July 15, July 25 - Aug. 19, Oct. 31.

TGV – High-speed train. 🅁. 🍸.
FR – Italian high-speed train. 🅁. 🍸.

⊡ – St Étienne Châteaucreux.
♠ – *Frecciarossa* Italian high-speed train. Special fares. 🅁. 🍸.
¶ – On July 13, Nov. 1 Le Creusot d. 2246, Paris a. 0008.
⊠ – OUIGO low-cost TGV service. Internet bookings only at www.ouigo.com

341 PARIS - GENÈVE and ANNECY

Timings may vary by up to 5 minutes (please check your reservation for confirmed timings). Certain services are subject to alteration Aug. 13–15 and Oct. 29 - Nov. 1.

km		*TGV* **9761**	*TGV* **6931**	*TGV* **9241**	*TGV* **9763**		*TGV* **9765**	*TGV* **6939**		*TGV* **9773**	*TGV* **6941**		*TGV* **9775**	*TGV* **9249**		*TGV* **9777**	*TGV* **6947**		*TGV* **9781**	*TGV* **6951**	*TGV* **6953**	*TGV* **9789**	*TGV* **9789**
		①–⑥	①–⑥																		⑤		
		d	b	M				H						M			B			C	f	D	A
0	**Paris** Gare de Lyon **340 342 366** d.	0615	0646	0646	0817	...	1017	1047	...	1217	1246	...	1416	1443	...	1616	1646	...	1817	1842	1950	2018	2018
363	Mâcon Loché TGV **340 342** d.	|	0825	0825	|	...	|	1225	...	|	1425	...	|	|	...	|	1825	...	|	|	|	|	|
406	Bourg-en-Bresse **365 376** d.	0811	|	|	1011	...	1211	|	...	1411	|	...	1611	|	...	1811	|	...	2010	|	|	2212	|
	Lyon St Exupéry TGV ✈ **342** d.	|	|	|	|	...	|	|	...	|	|	...	|	1638	...	|	|	...	|	2042	|	|	◐
439	Nurieux-Brion **376** a.	|	|	|	|	...	|	|	...	|	|	...	|	|	...	|	|	...	2037	|	|	|	|
470	Bellegarde **346** a.	0900	|	|	1100	...	1300	|	...	1500	|	...	1700	|	...	1900	|	...	2100	|	|	2300	|
503	**Genève** **346 505 570** a.	0929	|	|	1129	...	1329	|	...	1529	|	...	1729	|	...	1929	|	...	2129	|	|	2329	0044
	Lausanne **505 570** a.	1014	|	|	...	...	...	|	...	...	|	...	1814	|	...	2014	|	...	...	|	|	...	...
	Chambéry **345 364 366** a.	...	0939	0939	...	...	...	1339	...	...	1539	...	...	1740	...	...	1941	...	...	2139	2240	...	...
	Aix les Bains **345 364** a.	...	1000	...	...	...	...	1400	...	...	1600	...	...	...	...	...	2000	...	...	2200j	2300	...	...
	Annecy **345 364** a.	...	1028	...	...	...	...	1429	...	...	1630	...	...	...	...	...	2028	...	...	2228j	2328	...	...

km		*TGV* **6960**	*TGV* **9760**		*TGV* **9764**		*TGV* **6964**	*TGV* **9768**		*TGV* **9770**		*TGV* **6974**	*TGV* **9774**		*TGV* **6978**	*TGV* **9776**		*TGV* **6980**	*TGV* **9780**		*TGV* **9782**	*TGV* **6986**	*TGV* **9784**
		①–⑥																⑦			①–④		
		b	E									G						e			L		J
0	**Annecy** **345 364** d.	0532	...	...	...	...	0932	...	...	...	...	1332	...	...	1533	...	...	1732	...	...	...	1932	...
39	Aix les Bains **345 364** d.	0600	...	...	...	...	1000	...	...	...	...	1401	...	...	1600	...	...	1832*	...	...	...	2001	...
53	**Chambéry** **345 364 366** d.	0622	...	...	...	...	1022	...	...	...	...	1422	...	...	1622	...	...	1818	...	...	...	2022	...
	Lausanne **505 570** d.	|	...	...	...	...	|	0945	...	...	...	|	1345	...	|	...	...	|	...	...	1844	|	1945
	Genève **346 505 570** d.	|	0629	...	0829	...	|	1029	...	1229	...	|	1429	...	|	1629	...	|	1829	...	1942	|	2029
	Bellegarde **346** d.	|	0701	...	0900	...	|	1102	...	1302	...	|	1502	...	|	1702	...	|	1902	...	2017	|	2102
	Nurieux-Brion **376** d.	|	|	...	0925	...	|	|	...	|	...	|	|	...	|	|	...	|	|	...	|	|	|
144	Lyon St Exupéry TGV ✈ **342** d.	|	|	...	|	...	|	|	...	|	...	|	|	...	|	|	...	|	|	...	|	|	|
	Bourg-en-Bresse **365 376** d.	|	0751	...	0952	...	|	1151	...	1351	...	|	1551	...	|	1752	...	|	1951	...	2107	|	2152
222	Mâcon Loché TGV **340 342** d.	0735	|	...	|	...	1136	|	...	|	...	1539	|	...	1735	|	...	1955	|	...	|	2137	|
585	**Paris** Gare de Lyon **340 342 366** a.	0913	0942	...	1144	...	1313	1342	...	1546	...	1717	1743	...	1912	1946	...	2131	2143	...	2306	2316k	2345

A – ⑤⑦ June 10 - July 1; ⑤⑦ Sept. 4 - Oct. 7 (not Sept. 9, 16). Departs Paris 2028 on Oct. 2. Arrives Lausanne up to 20 minutes earlier on certain dates.
B – Daily to Sept. 2; Ⓑ from Sept. 4 (not Nov. 11).
C – Ⓑ to June 24; daily from June 26.
D – ⑤⑦ July 3 - Sept. 2 (also Sept. 9; not Aug. 14); Ⓑ from Oct. 9 (not Oct. 30, 31).
E – ①–⑥ to July 2; ①⑥ July 4 - Aug. 22 (not Aug. 15); ①–⑥ from Aug. 27.
G – Ⓑ to July 1; daily from Aug. 29.
H – Daily to July 1; ⑦ July 3 - Aug. 21 (also Aug. 15); ④–⑦ from Aug. 28 (also Oct. 31, Nov. 1).
J – ⑤⑦ to Nov. 6 (also July 14, Oct. 31, Nov. 1; not Aug. 14, Sept. 16); Ⓑ from Nov. 10.
L – ①–④ July 4 - Aug. 25 (not July 14); ①–④ Oct. 10 - Nov. 9 (not Oct. 31, Nov. 1).
M – 🚄12 Paris - Milano (Table **44**). Special fares.

b – Not Aug. 15, Nov. 1.
d – Not Aug. 15.
e – Also Aug. 15, Nov. 1.
f – Also July 13, Nov. 10; not July 15, Nov. 11.
j – On ⑦ from Sept. 4 (also Nov. 1) arrives Aix les Bains 2203, Annecy 2232.
k – 2338 on Sept. 23, 30.

TGV – High-speed train. 🅁. 🍸.

* – Calls at Aix les Bains after Chambéry
◐ – Diverted via Dijon and Vallorbe.

PARIS - GRENOBLE 342

Timings may vary by up to 5 minutes (please check your reservation for confirmed timings).

km		TGV 6901 ① g	TGV 6905	TGV 6911 H	TGV 6311 C	TGV 6917 A	TGV 6919	TGV 6921 Ⓐ r	TGV 6923 B	TGV 6925 ①–⑥ b¶	TGV 6927 D	TGV 6929 Q
0	**Paris** Gare de Lyon ..... **350/1** d.	0624	0743	0942	0953	1141	1443	1642	1741	1842	1940	2032
441	Lyon St Exupéry ✈ ...... **350/1** a.	0824	0939	1136	1146	1334	1634	1834	1934	2034	2134	2225
441	Lyon St Exupéry ✈ .... d.	0831	0946	1140	1150	1338	1644	1838	1938	2038	2138	2231
553	**Grenoble** .... a.	0942	1048	1242	1342	1442	1746	1942	2042	2142	2242f	2343

	TGV 6900 ①–④ M	TGV 6902 R	TGV 6906 ①–⑥ b	TGV 6908		TGV 6910 Av	TGV 6920 Ⓑ h	TGV 6922 B		TGV 6924		TGV 6928 ⑦ e
Grenoble .... d.	0519	0619t	0817	1019	...	1317	1519	1719	...	1919	...	2119
Lyon St Exupéry ✈ .... a.	0619	0719	0922	1121	...	1420	1621	1821	...	2021	...	2221
Lyon St Exupéry ✈ ...... **350/1** d.	0623	0723	0927	1125	...	1425	1625	1825	...	2025	...	2225
Paris Gare de Lyon ...... **350/1** a.	0817	0917	1120	1318	...	1618	1818	2018	...	2218	...	0018

A – ①⑤⑥⑦ (also Nov. 1, 2, 10); runs daily July 1 - Aug. 29.
B – Ⓑ to June 24; daily June 26 - Sept. 2; Ⓑ from Sept. 4 (not Oct. 31, Nov. 11).
C – June 13 – 17, 20 – 24, Oct. 10 – 14, 17 – 21 only.
D – ④⑦ to June 30; Ⓑ July 3 - Sept. 1 (not July 14, 15); ⑦–④ from Sept. 4 (not Oct. 31, Nov. 10).
H – ①–⑥ to July 1 (not June 13 – 17, 20 – 24); Ⓑ from Aug. 29 (not Oct. 10 – 14, 17 – 21, 31, Nov. 11).
M – ①–④ from Aug. 29 (not Oct. 31, Nov. 1, 10). On Aug. 30, 31 runs with train number **6308** and departs Grenoble 0442.
Q – ⑤⑦ to July 3; ⑦ July 10 - Aug. 28 (also July 13, Aug. 15); ⑤⑦ from Sept. 4 (also Nov. 1, 10; not Nov. 11). On Sept. 9, 16, 23 runs with train number **6915** and arrives Grenoble 0010.
R – ①–⑤ to June 24; ①–⑥ June 27 - Aug. 27 (not Aug. 15); ①–⑤ from Aug. 29 (not Oct. 31, Nov. 1, 11).
b – Not July 2 - Aug. 27, Nov. 1.
e – Also Aug. 15, Nov. 1.
f – Arrives 2316 July 4 – 8, 11, 12 and on Ⓐ Aug. 1 – 31.
g – ① from Aug. 29 (also Nov. 2; not Oct. 31). On Nov. 14, 21 Paris d. 0634.
h – Not July 3 - Aug. 28, Oct. 31, Nov. 11.
r – Not July 4 - Aug. 26, Oct. 31.
t – 0612 July 18 - Sept. 2.
v – Not Oct. 7.
TGV – High-speed train. Ⓡ. 🍸.
¶ – On Aug. 29, 30, 31 runs with train number **6315** and arrives Paris 2231.

LYON - GRENOBLE 343

Warning! Timings may vary by up to 3 minutes.

km		⚒	Ⓐ		Ⓐ		Ⓐ		Ⓐ z	z	z			Ⓐ			Ⓐ		Ⓐ	△	▽	⑦ r	⑥ 🚌	⑤⑦ t 🚌	🚌
0	**Lyon** Part-Dieu .. **344** d.	0615	0643	0714	0743	0814	0844	0916	0944	1014	1116	1216	1316	1343	and at	1816	1844	1916	1945	2014	2116	2214	2216	2315	2314
41	Bourgoin-Jallieu . **344** d.	0645	0712	0744	0812	0844	0912	0945	1013	1044	1144	1245	1344	1413	the same	1845	1912	1944	2013	2044	2145	2244	2307	|	0005
56	La Tour du Pin ... **344** d.	0654	0723	0754	0823	0853	0923	0954	1024	1054	1154	1254	1354	1424	minutes	1854	1924	1954	2024	2054	2154	2254	|	|	0025
104	Voiron .... d.	0724	0755	0824	0854	0923	0955	1024	1054	1124	1224	1324	1423	1454	past each	1924	1954	2024	2054	2124	2224	2324	|	|	0115
129	**Grenoble** .... a.	0738	0809	0839	0909	0937	1009	1039	1109	1139	1239	1339	1439	1509	hour until	1939	2009	2039	2109	2139	2239	2339	0015	0045	0150

	⚒ k	Ⓐ			Ⓐ		z	z			Ⓐ		Ⓐ		Ⓐ		Ⓐ		Ⓐ		🚌			⑦ r	⑥ 🚌
Grenoble .... d.	0522	0552	0622	and at	0951	1022	1122	1222	1322	1422	1452	1522	1552	1622	1652	1722	1752	1822	1852	1922	1947	2022	...	2122	2123
Voiron .... d.	0539	0608	0639	the same	1007	1039	1139	1239	1338	1437	1507	1538	1608	1639	1708	1739	1808	1839	1908	1939	|	2038	...	2139	2153
La Tour du Pin ..... **344** d.	0607	0637	0707	minutes	1036	1107	1208	1308	1407	1506	1535	1607	1636	1707	1737	1807	1837	1906	1937	2006	|	2106	...	2206	2238
Bourgoin-Jallieu ... **344** d.	0618	0648	0717	past each	1046	1116	1218	1317	1416	1516	1545	1616	1647	1716	1748	1816	1848	1917	1946	2017	|	2116	...	2217	2300
Lyon Part-Dieu .... **344** a.	0646	0716	0744	hour until	1114	1144	1246	1345	1444	1544	1613	1644	1715	1744	1816	1844	1915	1944	2014	2044	2116	2144	...	2246	2400

k – Not Aug. 2 – 6, 9 – 13, 17 – 20, 23 – 27, 30, 31.
r – Also June 13 – 17, 20 – 24, Nov. 11.
t – Also July 13, 14, Aug. 15, Nov. 1, 10.
z – Not June 13 – 17, 20 – 24, Oct. 10 – 14, 17 – 21.
△ – Subject to alteration on Ⓐ Aug. 1 – 31.
▽ – Subject to alteration July 4 – 8, 11, 12 and on Ⓐ Aug. 1 – 31.

LYON - CHAMBÉRY 344

Warning! Timings may vary by up to 3 minutes.

km		Ⓐ 🚌	⚒	⚒			Ⓐ ⊙	Ⓒ				⚒		Ⓐ					Ⓒ	Ⓐ		Ⓐ		A	⑦–④ B 🚌
0	**Lyon** Part Dieu . **343/5** d.	0620	0650	0750	0850	0950	1034	1050	...	1150	1250	1350	1450	1550	1649	1750	1850	...	1948	1949	...	2047	...	2147	2150
41	Bourgoin-Jallieu ... **343** d.	|	0717	0818	0917	1018	|	1117	...	1218	1318	1418	1518	1618	1718	1818	1918	...	2015	2018	...	2118	...	2218	|
56	La Tour du Pin ..... **343** d.	|	0728	0828	0928	1028	|	1128	...	1228	1328	1428	1528	1628	1728	1828	1928	...	2026	2028	...	2129	...	2228	|
106	**Chambéry** .... **345** a.	0750	0817	0920	1016	1121	1158	1217	...	1321	1417	1518	1617	1717	1817	1917	2017	...	2118	2118	...	2217	...	2317	2320

	⚒	⚒			Ⓑ	⑥ M	Ⓐ		Ⓒ		Ⓐ v⊙	①–⑤ C⊙	⑥				Ⓒ	Ⓐ				Ⓑ	Ⓑ		
Chambéry .... **345** d.	0544	0644	0744	...	0835	0836	0944	...	1031	...	1129	1137	1144	...	1234	1344	1435	1444	...	1544	1634	1744	1841	1944	2034
La Tour du Pin ...... **343** d.	0633	0731	0831	...	0930	0932	1031	...	1132	...	|	|	1231	...	1332	1431	1535	1541	...	1631	1731	1831	1932	2031	2132
Bourgoin-Jallieu .... **343** d.	0644	0743	0843	...	0942	0944	1043	...	1142	...	|	|	1243	...	1343	1443	1545	1551	...	1643	1742	1843	1943	2043	2143
Lyon Part Dieu .. **343/5** a.	0710	0810	0910	...	1010	1010	1110	...	1210	...	1300	1302	1310	...	1410	1510	1610	1618	...	1710	1810	1910	2010	2110	2210

A – ⑤⑥ to June 25; daily from July 1.
B – ⑦–④ until June 30.
C – Sept. 12 – 30 only.
M – From Bourg St Maurice (Table **366**).
v – Not Sept. 12 – 30.
⊙ – Via Aix les Bains (Table **345**).

LYON - AIX LES BAINS - ANNECY 345

km		🚌 Ⓐ	Ⓐ	⚒	⚒	🚌 †	⚒	Ⓐ ⊗	🚌 Ⓐ	Ⓒ	Ⓐ	Ⓐ	🚌 †	⚒	🚌 Ⓐ		🚌 Ⓐ	Ⓐ		Ⓐ		Ⓑ			⊖
0	**Lyon** Part Dieu ..... **344 346** d.	0608	...	...	0708	0708	0808	0908	1008	1008	1034	...	1208	1208	1308	1408	1508	...	1608	...	1708	1808	...	1908	2108
46	Ambérieu .... **346** d.	|	0614	0714	0733	|	0833	0933	|	1033	|	1214	|	1233	|	1433	|	1614	1633	...	1733	1833	1914	1933	2133
96	Culoz .... **346** d.	|	0652	0752	0804	|	|	|	|	|	|	1252	|	|	|	|	|	1652	|	1752	|	|	1952	|	2204
118	Aix les Bains ....a.	|	0711	0811	0819	0835	0918	1018	|	1117	1145	1311	|	1318	|	1518	|	1711	1718	1811	1818	1918	2011	2018	2218
118	Aix les Bains .... **364** d.	|	0713	0813	*0835*	0835	0925	1025	|	1125	1148	1313	|	1325	|	1525	|	1713	*1735*e	1813	*1835*	*1934*	2013	2025	2225
132	**Chambéry** .... **344 364** a.	|	0725	0825	|	|	|	|	|	|	1158	1325	|	|	|	|	|	1725	|	1825	|	|	2025	|	|
157	**Annecy** .... **364** a.	0759	...	...	*0915*	0910	1007	1105	1159	1209	...	...	1359	1405	1459	1605	1659	...	*1814*e	...	*1915*	*2015*	...	2107	2307

	Ⓐ	Ⓐ	⚒	Ⓐ	⚒	🚌 †	🚌 Ⓐ	Ⓒ	Ⓐ ⊗	Ⓐ v	①–⑤ C	⑥	🚌 Ⓑ	⚒			Ⓐ		🚌 ⑥		Ⓑ	Ⓐ		🚌 Ⓐ	†
Annecy .... **364** d.	...	0553	0653	...	*0742*e	0800	0900	0953	1051	...	...	1153	1200	...	1351	1550	...	*1642*b	1700	...	*1744*	...	*1842*k	2000	2053
Chambéry .... **344 364** d.	0534	|	|	0734	|	|	|	|	|	1129	1137	|	|	1234	|	|	1634	|	|	1734	|	1834	|	|	|
Aix les Bains .... **364** a.	0547	0634	0735	0747	*0823*e	|	|	1034	1134	1143	1147	1234	|	1247	1434	1633	1647	*1723*b	|	1747	*1823*	1847	*1923*k	|	2132
Aix les Bains .... d.	0549	0641	0742	0749	0841	|	|	1041	1141	1146	1150	1241	|	1249	1441	1640	1649	1739	|	1749	1841	1849	1941	|	2141
Culoz .... **346** d.	0608	|	|	0808	|	|	|	|	|	1204	1206	|	|	1308	|	1656z	1707	1755	|	1808	|	1908	|	|	|
Ambérieu .... **346** d.	0646	0728	0828	0846	0928	|	|	1128	1228	1236	1238	1328	|	1346	1527	1727	...	1828	|	1846	1928	1945	2028	|	2228
Lyon Part Dieu .... **344 346** a.	...	0752	0852	...	0952	0952	1052	1152	1252	1300	1302	1352	1352	...	1552	1752	...	1852	1852	...	1952	...	2052	2152	2252

C – Sept. 12 – 30 only.

b – Not ⑥.
e – Not Sept. 12 – 16, 19 – 23, 26 – 30, Oct. 3 – 7.
k – Daily to Aug. 7; ⑥⑦ from Aug. 13 (also Aug. 15).
v – Not Sept. 12 – 30.
z – † only.

⊗ – Subject to alteration on ①–⑤ Oct. 3 – 14.
⊖ – Subject to alteration on ⑦–④ Oct. 2 – 13.

346 LYON - BELLEGARDE - GENÈVE

Warning! Subject to alteration October 29 – 31.

km																								
															TGV 9750									
		①-⑤	①-⑤	⑥	①-⑤	①-⑥			⚒		①-⑤			⊗	R	①-⑤		①-⑤	Ⓑ	①-⑤		①-⑤	①-⑤	
	Marseille St Charles **350** ... d.	...	...	...	...	...	...	...	...	...	...	...	...	...	1353	...	...	...	...	...	...	...	...	...
0	**Lyon** Part Dieu **345** d.	...	...	...	...	0638	...	0838	0938	1038	...	1238	...	1438	1545	...	1638	...	1738	...	1834	...	...	2038
50	Ambérieu **345** d.	...	...	...	...	0703	...	0903	1003	1103	...	1303	...	1503	|	...	1703	...	|	...	|	...	...	2103
102	Culoz **345 364** d.	...	...	...	...	0740	...	0940	1034	1140	...	1340	...	1540	|	...	1740	...	1840	...	1940	...	...	2140
135	Bellegarde **364** a.	...	...	...	...	0804	...	1004	1059	1204	...	1404	...	1604	1707s	...	1804	...	1904	...	2004	...	...	2204
135	Bellegarde **364** d.	0552	0625	0652	0725	0807	...	1007	1107	1207	1245	1407	...	1607	|	1725	1807	1825	1907	1925	2007	2025	2125	2207
168	**Genève** **364** a.	0629	0658	0729	0758	0835	...	1035	1135	1235	1318	1435	...	1635	1743	1758	1835	1858	1935	1958	2035	2100	2200	2235

						TGV 9758																		
	①-⑤	⚒	①-⑥	⚒		R		©	Ⓐ	①-⑤	⚒			①-⑤	⑦ Q	①-⑤	†	⚒	①-⑤	①-⑤	†	⚒	①-⑤	①-⑤
Genève **364** d.	0502	0514	0602	0614	0714	0742	0930	1130	1130	1202	1225	1330	1530	1602	1625	1702	1714	1730	1802	1902	1914	1930	2018	2118
Bellegarde **364** a.	0537	0546	0637	0646	0746	|	0958	1158	1200	1237	1254	1358	1558	1637	1652	1737	1746	1758	1837	1937	1946	1958	2053	2153
Bellegarde **364** d.	...	0552	...	0650	0752	0812u	1001	1201	1205	...	1258	1401	1601	...	1655	...	1752	1801	...	...	1952	2001	...	...
Culoz **345 364** d.	...	0619	...	0715	0819	|	1026	1223	1227	...	1323	1426	1626	...	|	...	1819	1826	...	...	2019	2026	...	...
Ambérieu **345** d.	...	0658	...	0755	0858	|	|	1300	1302	...	1358	1458	1658	...	|	...	1858	1858	...	...	2058	2058	...	...
Lyon Part Dieu **345** a.	...	0722	...	0822	0922	0926	1122	1324	1326	...	1422	1522	1722	...	1811	...	1922	1922	...	...	2122	2122	...	...
Marseille St Charles **350** .... a.	...	...	...	...	...	1125	...	...	...	...	...	...	...	...	...	...	...	...	...	...	...	...	...	...

Q – Until Oct. 23.
R – July 2 - Aug. 28 only.

s – Calls to set down only.
u – Calls to pick up only.

TGV – High-speed train. 🅁. 🍷.

⊗ – Subject to alteration on ①-⑤ June 20 - July 1.

348 LYON - ST ÉTIENNE

TER services

Timings may vary by 1 – 2 minutes until June 26. Departure times from St Étienne and St Chamond (of trains heading to Lyon) may be up to 3 minutes **earlier** from Sept. 26. For *TGV* trains Paris - St Étienne see Table **340**. **Warning!** Subject to alteration on Oct. 29 – 31, Nov. 1, 11 – 13.

km																								
		⚒	Ⓐ	⚒	⚒	Ⓐ	Ⓐ			Ⓐ	Ⓐ	⚒		Ⓐ			Ⓐ	⚒		Ⓐ			Ⓐ	⚒
0	**Lyon** Part-Dieu d.	...	0624	...	0654	...	0724	...	0754	...	0824	...	0854	0924	...	0954	1024	...	1054	1124	...	1154	1224	...
	Lyon Perrache d.	0531	|	0631	|	0701	|	0731	|	0801	|	0831	|	|	0931	|	|	1031	|	|	1131	|	|	1231
22	Givors Ville d.	0558	0641	0658	0711	0728	0741	0758	0811	0828	0841	0858	0911	0941	0958	1011	1041	1058	1111	1141	1158	1211	1241	1258
47	St Chamond d.	0618	0702	0718	0732	0748	0802	0818	0832	0848	0902	0918	0932	1002	1018	1032	1102	1118	1132	1202	1218	1232	1302	1318
59	**St Étienne** Châteaucreux a.	0627	0711	0727	0741	0757	0811	0827	0841	0857	0911	0927	0941	1011	1027	1041	1111	1127	1141	1211	1227	1241	1311	1327

		Ⓐ			Ⓐ	⚒		Ⓐ			Ⓐ	Ⓐ	⚒		Ⓐ	Ⓐ			Ⓐ	Ⓐ	⚒		Ⓐ	Ⓐ
Lyon Part-Dieu d.	1254	1324	...	1354	1424	...	1454	1524	...	1554	...	1624	...	1654	...	1724	...	1754	...	1824	...	1854	...	1924
Lyon Perrache d.	|	|	1331	|	|	1431	|	|	1531	|	1601	|	1631	|	1701	|	1731	|	1801	|	1831	|	1901	|
Givors Ville d.	1311	1341	1358	1411	1441	1458	1511	1541	1558	1611	1628	1640	1657	1711	1728	1741	1758	1811	1828	1841	1858	1911	1928	1941
St Chamond d.	1332	1402	1418	1432	1502	1518	1532	1602	1618	1632	1648	1700	1718	1731	1748	1802	1818	1832	1848	1902	1918	1932	1948	2002
St Étienne Châteaucreux a.	1341	1411	1427	1441	1511	1527	1541	1611	1627	1641	1657	1711	1727	1741	1757	1811	1827	1841	1857	1911	1927	1941	1957	2011

				⚒	Ⓑ	⑥⑦ c	⑥⑦ d	①-④ m 🚌	🚌 ¶	
Lyon Part-Dieu d.	...	1954	2024	...	2124	2224	2324	2324	0024	...
Lyon Perrache d.	1931	|	|	2031	|	|	|	|	|	...
Givors Ville d.	1958	2011	2041	2058	2141	2241	2341	2353	0053	...
St Chamond d.	2018	2032	2102	2118	2202	2302	0002	0022	0122	...
St Étienne Châteaucreux a.	2027	2041	2111	2127	2211	2311	0011	0037	0137	...

	Ⓐ	Ⓐ	Ⓐ	Ⓐ	⚒	Ⓐ	Ⓐ	⚒
St Étienne Châteaucreux ▷ d.	0521	0534	0549	0604	0619	0634	0649	0704
St Chamond ▷ d.	0530	0543	0558	0613	0628	0643	0658	0713
Givors Ville d.	0550	0603	0619	0633	0649	0703	0719	0733
Lyon Perrache a.	|	0631	|	0701	|	0731	|	0801
Lyon Part-Dieu a.	0606	...	0636	...	0706	...	0736	...

		Ⓐ	Ⓐ			Ⓐ	Ⓐ	⚒		Ⓐ			Ⓐ	⚒		Ⓐ			Ⓐ	⚒		Ⓐ		
St Étienne Châteaucreux ▷ d.	0719	0734	0749	0804	0819	0834	0849	0904	0919	0949	1004	1019	1049	1104	1119	1149	1204	1219	1249	1304	1319	1349	1404	1419
St Chamond ▷ d.	0728	0743	0758	0813	0828	0843	0858	0913	0928	0958	1013	1028	1058	1113	1128	1158	1213	1228	1258	1313	1328	1358	1413	1428
Givors Ville d.	0749	0803	0819	0833	0849	0903	0919	0933	0949	1019	1033	1049	1119	1133	1149	1219	1233	1249	1319	1333	1349	1419	1433	1449
Lyon Perrache a.	|	0831	|	0901	|	0931	|	1001	|	|	1101	|	|	1201	|	|	1301	|	|	1401	|	|	1501	|
Lyon Part-Dieu a.	0806	...	0836	...	0906	...	0936	...	1006	1036	...	1106	1136	...	1206	1236	...	1306	1336	...	1406	1436	...	1506

	Ⓐ	⚒		Ⓐ			Ⓐ	Ⓐ	⚒		Ⓐ	Ⓐ			Ⓐ	Ⓐ	⚒					Ⓑ		⑥⑦ e
St Étienne Châteaucreux ▷ d.	1449	1504	1519	1549	1604	1619	1634	1649	1704	1720j	1734	1750	1804	1819	1834	1849	1904	1919	2004	2019	...	2119	...	2219
St Chamond ▷ d.	1458	1513	1528	1558	1613	1628	1643	1658	1713	1730j	1743	1759	1813	1828	1843	1858	1913	1928	2013	2028	...	2128	...	2228
Givors Ville d.	1519	1533	1549	1619	1633	1649	1703	1719	1733	1749	1803	1819	1833	1849	1903	1919	1933	1949	2033	2049	...	2149	...	2249
Lyon Perrache a.	|	1601	|	|	1701	|	1731	|	1801	|	1831	|	1901	|	1931	|	2001	|	2101	|	...	|	...	|
Lyon Part-Dieu a.	1536	...	1606	1636	...	1706	...	1736	...	1806	...	1836	...	1906	...	1936	...	2006	...	2106	...	2206	...	2308

c – Also June 13 – 17, 21, July 14, 15, Nov. 1; not June 12, 20, 22 – 24, July 10, 24, Aug. 28, Sept. 25, Oct. 2, 23, Nov. 6.
d – Also June 17, July 14, 15, Nov. 1; not June 12, July 10, 24, Aug. 28, Sept. 18, 25, Oct. 2, 23, Nov. 6.
e – Also June 13 – 17, 21, July 14, 15 and ⑤ from Sept. 23; not June 12, July 10, 24, Aug. 28, Sept. 4, 25, Oct. 2, 23, Nov. 6.
j – 8 minutes earlier Sept. 26 - Oct. 28.
m – ①-④ (not July 13, 14, Aug. 15, Nov. 1, 10). **Subject to confirmation**.

▷ – Departure times from St Étienne and St Chamond may be up to 3 minutes **earlier** from Sept. 26.
¶ – **Subject to confirmation**.

349 ST ÉTIENNE - LE PUY

km																
		Ⓐ	⚒			Ⓐ ◇	⑥	◇			Ⓐ	©	Ⓐ	Ⓐ		
0	**St Étienne** Châteaucreux d.	0530	0648	...	0850	0958	1100	1252	...	1557	1717	1750	1805	1856	2009	2200
15	Firminy d.	0549	0710	...	0908	1015	1117	1309	...	1613	1733	1807	1828	1913	2032	2223
88	**Le Puy en Velay** a.	0723	0826	...	1022	1121	1225	1424	...	1720	1848	1917	1936	2021	2137	2326

	Ⓐ	Ⓐ	⚒	Ⓐ			⑥	Ⓑ ◇		◇				Ⓑ	©	Ⓑ
Le Puy en Velay d.	0432	0542	0642	0738	0842	...	1033	1042	...	1237	...	1613	...	1736	1840	1940
Firminy d.	0537	0648	0753	0851	0949	...	1148	1148	...	1351	...	1726	...	1851	1949	2055
St Étienne Châteaucreux a.	0559	0705	0810	0908	1006	...	1205	1205	...	1408	...	1743	...	1907	2007	2111

◇ – Subject to alteration on ①-⑤ Oct. 10 – 28.

PARIS / LYON - AVIGNON - MARSEILLE - TOULON - NICE 350

This page shows *TGV* services from / to Paris (see next page for services from / to / via Lyon). For other *TGV* trains Paris - Valence TGV and v.v., see Table **355**. For *TGV* trains Paris - Valence Ville - Avignon Centre, see Table **351**. For regional TER services Marseille - Nice, also overnight service Paris - Nice, see Table **361**. Paris departure times may be up to 3 minutes later and arrivals up to 4 minutes earlier from Sept. 12 (please check your reservation).

km		*TGV*	*TGV*		*TGV*	*TGV*	*TGV*		*TGV*	*TGV*	*TGV*	*TGV*		*TGV*		*TGV*	*TGV*		*TGV*	*TGV*		*TGV*	*TGV*
		7829	**6101**		**7851**	**6161**	**6103**		**6173**	**6155**	**6173**	**6155**		**6107**		**6165**	**6109**		**6175**	**6111**		**6167**	**7825**
			Ⓐ			①–④																⑤	
		⊠	**v**		⊠	**H**			**S**	**S**	**w**	**w**							**G**			**M**	⊠
0	**Paris** Gare de Lyon .... **342 351 355** d.	0600	0636	...	0717	0735	0739	...	0824	0824	0907	0907	...	0936	...	1026	1039	...	1106	1136	...	1207	1236
441	Lyon St Exupéry ✈ .... **342 351** d.	|	|	...	0913	|	|	...	|	|	|	|	...	|	...	|	|	...	|	|	...	|	|
527	Valence TGV .... **355** d.	|	|	...	|	|	|	...	|	|	|	|	...	|	...	|	|	...	|	|	...	|	|
657	**Avignon** TGV .... d.	0846	0922	...	|	1030	1022	...	1105	1105	|	|	...	1222	...	1306	1322	...	|	1422	...	1451	1522
731	Aix en Provence TGV .... d.	0913**p**	0945	...	1021	|	1045	...	|	|	|	|	...	1245	...	|	1345	...	|	1445	...	|	1545
750	**Marseille** St Charles .... a.	0925	0957	...	|	|	1057	...	|	|	1211	1211	...	1257	...	|	1357	...	1411	1457	...	|	1558
750	**Marseille** St Charles .... **360 361** d.	...	...	...	|	|	...	...	|	|	1227	1227	...	...	...	|	...	...	1427	...	...	|	...
817	**Toulon** .... **360 361** a.	...	...	...	1110	1142	...	...	1209	1209	1311	1311	...	...	...	1411	...	...	1512	...	...	1609	...
	Toulon .... **361** d.	...	...	...	1114	1146	...	...	1213	1225	1315	1324	...	...	...	1415	...	...	1516	...	...	1613	...
	Hyères .... **360** a.	...	...	...	|	|	...	...	|	1240	|	1340	...	...	...	|	...	...	|	...	...	|	...
885	Les Arcs-Draguignan .... **361** a.	...	...	...	|	|	...	...	|	...	|	...	...	...	...	1452	...	...	|	...	...	|	...
911	St Raphaël-Valescure .... **361** a.	...	...	...	1207	1242	...	...	1304	...	1409	...	...	...	...	1509	...	...	1610	...	...	1705	...
943	**Cannes** .... **361** a.	...	...	...	1234	1312	...	...	1338	...	1435	...	...	...	...	1533	...	...	1635	...	...	1730	...
954	Antibes .... **361** a.	...	...	...	1247	1324	...	...	1349	...	1447	...	...	...	...	1546	...	...	1647	...	...	1742	...
974	**Nice** .... **361** a.	...	...	...	1307	1340	...	...	1407	...	1507	...	...	...	...	1607	...	...	1707	...	...	1807	...

	TGV	*TGV*	*TGV*	*TGV*	*TGV*		*TGV*	*TGV*		*TGV*	*TGV*		*TGV*		*TGV*	*TGV*	*TGV*	*TGV*		*TGV*	*TGV*		*TGV*
	7827	**6163**	**6077**	**6171**	**6077**		**6117**	**7853**		**6121**	**6181**		**6123**		**6153**	**6127**	**6187**	**6129**		**6131**	**6131**		**6137**
			6177	⑥	**6177**										Ⓑ		⑤			②–④			
	⊠	**N**		**Q**				⊠		**B**					**h**		**f**			**r**	**D**		**A**
Paris Gare de Lyon .... **342 351 355** d.	1439	1447	1507	1522	...	...	1537	1607	...	1638	1707	...	1736	...	1825	1839	1908	1936	...	2009	2036	...	2138
Lyon St Exupéry ✈ .... **342 351** d.	|	|	|	|	...	...	|	1807**p**	...	|	|	...	|	...	|	|	|	|	...	|	|	...	|
Valence TGV .... **355** d.	|	|	|	|	...	...	|	|	...	|	|	...	|	...	|	|	|	|	...	|	|	...	|
Avignon TGV .... d.	1722	|	|	|	...	...	1822	|	...	1922	|	...	2022	...	|	2122	2149	2220	...	2251	2322	...	0025
Aix en Provence TGV .... d.	1745	|	|	|	...	...	1845	|	...	1945	|	...	2045	...	2122	2145	|	2243	...	2315	2346	...	0049
Marseille St Charles .... a.	1757	|	1811	|	←	...	1857	|	...	1957	2011	...	2057	...	|	2157	|	2255	...	2327	2358	...	0102
Marseille St Charles .... **360 361** d.	...	|	1827	|	1827	...	...	|	...	...	2027	...	...	...	|	...	|	...	...	...	...	...	...
Toulon .... **360 361** a.	...	1811	→	1905	1911	...	...	2011	...	...	2111	...	...	...	2212	...	2258	...	...	...	...	...	...
Toulon .... **361** d.	...	1815	...	1909	1915	...	...	2016	...	...	2115	...	...	...	...	...	2302	...	...	...	...	...	...
Hyères .... **360** a.	...	|	...	|	|	...	...	|	...	...	|	...	...	...	...	...	|	...	...	...	...	...	...
Les Arcs-Draguignan .... **361** a.	...	|	...	|	|	...	...	2053	...	...	|	...	...	...	...	...	|	...	...	...	...	...	...
St Raphaël-Valescure .... **361** a.	...	1909	...	2005	2009	...	...	|	...	...	2209	...	...	...	...	...	2351	...	...	...	...	...	...
Cannes .... **361** a.	...	1934	...	2029	2035	...	...	2134	...	...	2235	...	...	...	...	...	0016	...	...	...	...	...	...
Antibes .... **361** a.	...	1947	...	2041	2047	...	...	2147	...	...	2247	...	...	...	...	...	0028	...	...	...	...	...	...
Nice .... **361** a.	...	2007	...	2107	2107**z**	...	...	2209	...	...	2307	...	...	...	...	...	0046	...	...	...	...	...	...

	TGV		*TGV*	*TGV*	*TGV*		*TGV*		*TGV*		*TGV*	*TGV*		*TGV*	*TGV*	*TGV*		*TGV*	*TGV*	*TGV*		*TGV*	*TGV*
	6102		**6136**	**6150**	**6106**		**7858**		**6112**		**7822**	**6188**		**7820**	**6116**	**6170**		**6074**	**6120**	**6176**		**6122**	**6166**
	Ⓐ		①–④	Ⓐ														**6174**					⑦
	v		**m**	**v**			⊠				⊠	**C**		⊠		**K**			**J**				**R**
Nice .... **361** d.	...	...	...	...	...	...	0552	...	...	...	...	0752	...	...	...	0952	...	1053	...	1153	...	...	1220
Antibes .... **361** d.	...	...	...	...	...	...	0610	...	...	...	...	0810	...	...	...	1009	...	1110	...	1210	...	...	1236
Cannes .... **361** d.	...	...	...	...	...	...	0624	...	...	...	...	0824	...	...	...	1023	...	1124	...	1224	...	...	1251
St Raphaël-Valescure .... **361** d.	...	...	...	...	...	...	|	...	...	...	...	0849	...	...	...	1049	...	1149	...	1249	...	...	1320
Les Arcs-Draguignan .... **361** d.	...	...	...	...	...	...	0704	...	...	...	...	|	...	...	...	|	...	|	...	|	...	...	|
Hyères .... **360** d.	...	...	...	...	...	...	|	...	...	...	...	|	...	...	...	|	...	|	...	|	...	...	|
Toulon .... **361** a.	...	...	...	...	...	...	0742	...	...	...	...	0942	...	...	...	1144	...	1244	...	1343	...	...	1430
Toulon .... **360 361** d.	...	...	...	0549	...	...	0746	...	...	...	...	0946	...	...	...	1148	...	1248	...	1347	...	...	1434
Marseille St Charles .... **360 361** a.	...	...	...	|	...	...	|	...	...	...	...	|	...	...	...	|	...	1332	...	|	...	...	|
Marseille St Charles .... d.	0520	...	0602	|	0659	...	|	...	0902	...	0936	|	...	1144	1202	|	...	1349	1402	|	...	1502	|
Aix en Provence TGV .... d.	0535	...	0618	0643	0715	...	0840	...	0917	...	|	|	...	1158	1218	|	...	|	1418	1441	...	1518	|
Avignon TGV .... d.	0557	...	0641	0705	0738	...	|	...	0940	...	1007	1056	...	1221	1240	1258	...	|	1440	|	...	1540	1556
Valence TGV .... **355** d.	|	...	|	|	|	...	|	...	|	...	1043	|	...	1255	|	|	...	|	|	|	...	|	|
Lyon St Exupéry ✈ .... **342 351** d.	|	...	|	|	|	...	|	...	|	...	1111	|	...	1321	|	|	...	|	|	|	...	|	|
Paris Gare de Lyon .... **342 351 355** a.	0842	...	0921	0952	1018	...	1134	...	1221	...	1304	1338	...	1514	1524	1536	...	1652	1721	1736	...	1823	1838

	TGV		*TGV*		*TGV*	*TGV*		*TGV*		*TGV*	*TGV*		*TGV*	*TGV*	*TGV*	*TGV*		*TGV*	*TGV*				
	6124		**7856**		**6162**	**6128**		**7824**		**6168**	**6132**		**6180**	**6134**	**6186**	**6186**		**6144**	**6186**				
					①–④									⑦		⑦		⑦					
			⊠		**H**			⊠						**e**	**U**			**e**	**T**				
Nice .... **361** d.	...	...	1352	...	1416	...	...	...	...	1553	...	...	1652	...	1753	1754	...	...	1850	...	...	...	...
Antibes .... **361** d.	...	...	1410	...	1433	...	...	...	...	1610	...	...	1710	...	1810	1809	...	...	1911	...	...	...	...
Cannes .... **361** d.	...	...	1424	...	1448	...	...	...	...	1624	...	...	1724	...	1824	1821	...	...	1926	...	...	...	...
St Raphaël-Valescure .... **361** d.	...	...	1449	...	1513	...	...	...	...	1649	...	...	|	...	1849	1845	...	...	1953	...	...	...	...
Les Arcs-Draguignan .... **361** d.	...	...	|	...	|	...	...	...	...	1706	...	...	1806	...	|	|	...	...	|	...	...	...	...
Hyères .... **360** d.	1432	...	|	...	|	...	...	...	...	|	...	...	|	...	|	|	...	...	|	...	...	...	...
Toulon .... **361** a.	1448	...	1542	...	1606	...	...	...	...	1744	...	...	1844	...	1944	1945	...	...	2046	...	...	...	...
Toulon .... **360 361** d.	1452	...	1546	...	1610	...	...	...	...	1748	...	...	1848	...	1948	1949	...	...	2050	...	...	...	...
Marseille St Charles .... **360 361** a.	1536	...	|	...	|	...	...	...	...	1832	...	...	1932	...	|	|	...	...	|	...	...	...	...
Marseille St Charles .... d.	1549	...	|	...	|	1702	...	1732	...	1845	1902	...	1949	2002	|	|	...	2102	|	...	...	...	...
Aix en Provence TGV .... d.	1608	...	1641	...	|	1718	...	1746	...	|	1918	...	|	2017	|	|	...	2117	|	...	...	...	...
Avignon TGV .... d.	1630	...	|	...	1727	1740	...	1810	...	|	1940	...	|	2042	2056	2059	...	2139	2200	...	...	...	...
Valence TGV .... **355** d.	|	...	|	...	|	|	...	|	...	|	|	...	|	|	|	|	...	|	|	...	...	...	...
Lyon St Exupéry ✈ .... **342 351** d.	|	...	|	...	|	|	...	|	...	|	|	...	|	|	|	|	...	|	|	...	...	...	...
Paris Gare de Lyon .... **342 351 355** a.	1916	...	1936	...	2033	2022	...	2053	...	2152	2223	...	2252	2323	2334	2351	...	0023	0043	...	...	...	...

A – ⑤⑦ to July 1; ⑤ July 8 - Aug. 26 (also July 13; not July 15); ⑤⑦ from Sept. 2 (also Nov. 1, 10; not Nov. 11).
B – Ⓑ to June 24; daily June 26 - Sept. 2; Ⓑ from Sept. 4 (not Oct. 31, Nov. 11).
C – Daily to Oct. 2; Ⓒ from Oct. 8 (also Oct. 31).
D – ①⑤⑥⑦ (also July 13, 14, Aug. 16, Nov. 1, 2, 10).
G – Daily until Oct. 1; ⑤⑥ from Oct. 7 (also Oct. 31, Nov. 10).
H – ①–④ July 4 - Aug. 25 (not July 13, 14, Aug. 15).
J – Daily to July 1; Ⓑ July 3 - Aug. 26 (not July 14, 15); daily from Aug. 28.
K – ⑥⑦ to June 26; daily July 2 - Aug. 28.
M – ⑤ July 8 - Aug. 26 (also July 13; not July 15).
N – ⑤⑥ to June 25; daily July 1 - Aug. 28.
Q – ⑥ July 2 - Aug. 27 (also July 14, 15).
R – ⑦ July 3 - Aug. 28 (also Aug. 15).
S – July 2 - Aug. 28.
T – Runs on Aug. 15 only.
U – Runs on Nov. 1 only.

e – Also Aug. 15, Nov. 1.
f – Also July 13, Nov. 10; not July 15, Nov. 11.
h – Not July 14, 15, Oct. 31, Nov. 11.
m – Also ⑦ July 3 - Aug. 28; not July 13, 14, Oct. 31, Nov. 1, 10.
p – Arrives 6 minutes earlier.
r – Not July 13, 14, Aug. 16, Nov. 1, 2, 10.
v – Not July 15, Oct. 31.
w – Not July 2 - Aug. 28.
z – 2111 on ⑥ July 2 - Aug. 27 (also July 14, 15).

TGV – High-speed train. 🅁. 🍷.

⊠ – OUIGO low-cost TGV service. Internet bookings only at www.ouigo.com.

350 PARIS / LYON - AVIGNON - MARSEILLE - TOULON - NICE

This page shows *TGV* services from / to / via Lyon (see previous page for services from / to Paris Gare de Lyon).
Timings may vary by up to 4 minutes (please check your reservation).

km		*TGV*	*TGV*		*TGV*	*TGV*	*TGV*	*TGV*	*TGV*	*TGV*	*TGV*	*TGV*	*TGV*	*TGV*	*TGV*	*TGV*	*TGV*		*TGV*	*TGV*	*TGV*	*TGV*	*TGV*
		6801	**7811**		**6811**	**7831**	**5102**	**9758**	**5110**	**9810**	**9810**	**5332**	**5113**	**5316**	**9877**	**6803**	**7841**		**7835**	**5306**	**5306**	**9830**	**5537**
							①–⑥		①–⑥	⑦	①–⑥		⑥							**C**	**B**		
			⊠		**U**	⊠	**b**	**A**	**b**	**e**	**b**		**k**	**mH**	**L**		⊠		⊠				**E**
	Brussels Midi **11** d.	...	...	...	...	...	...	...	...	0637	0702f	...	...	...	...	...	...	...	...	...	...	1317	...
	Lille Europe **11** d.	...	...	...	...	...	0550t	...	...	0725	|	...	0902	...	...	...	...	...	...	...	...	1403	...
	Lille Flandres **11** d.	...	...	...	...	...	|	...	0645j	|	|	...	|	...	...	...	1138x	...	1301x	...	...	|	...
	Charles de Gaulle ✈ **11** d.	...	...	...	...	0659	0653	...	0827	0827	0827	...	0958	...		...	|	...	1357	...	...	1457	...
	Marne la Vallée-Chessy **11** d.	...	...	...	...	0715	0709	...	0841	0841	0841	...	1011	...	...	...	1248	...	1412	...	...	1510	...
	Nantes **335** d.	...	...	...	...	|	|	...	|	|	|	...	|	...	...	...	|	...	|	1144	1209	|	...
	Rennes **335** d.	...	...	...	...	|	|	...	|	|	|	0740	|	...	...	...	|	...	|	|	|	|	...
	Massy TGV **335** d.	...	...	...	...	|	|	...	|	|	|	0927	|	1028z	...	...	|	...	|	1427	1427	|	...
	Metz **379** d.	...	...	...	...	|	|	...	|	|	|	|	|	|	0810	...	|	...	|	|	|	|	...
	Strasbourg **379** d.	...	...	...	...	|	|	...	|	|	|	|	|	|	0903	...	|	...	|	|	|	|	1336
	Dijon Ville **379** d.	...	...	...	...	|	|	...	|	|	|	|	|	|	1125	...	|	...	|	|	|	|	1620
	Genève **346** d.	...	...	...	...	|	|	0742	|	|	|	|	|	|	|	...	|	...	|	|	|	|	|
0	**Lyon** Part Dieu ▶ d.	0628	0706	...	0806	|	0906	0941	1036	1036	1036	1136	1210	1236	1310	1406	|	...	1608	1636	1636	1706	1806
	Lyon St Exupéry ✈ d.	|	|	...	|	|	|	|	|	|	|	|	|	|	|	|	1438	...	|	|	|	|	|
104	Valence TGV ▶ d.	0704	|	...	0851	|	|	|	1119	1119	1119	|	1256	1318	1352	|	|	...	|	1719	1719	|	|
	Avignon TGV d.	0739	0811	...	0930	0950	1012	1049	1153	1153	1153	1247	1331	1353	1430	1510	1531	...	1713	1754	1754	1811	1911
	Aix en Provence TGV d.	0801	0833	...	0953	1012	1034	1113	|	|	|	1309	|	|	1453	1533	1553	...	|	|	|	1834	1933
	Marseille St Charles a.	0815	0846	...	1006r	1024	1046	1125	1223	1223	1223	1323	1401	1423	1506	1545	1606	...	1741	1823	1823	1849	1945
	Marseille St Charles **360 361** d.	0827	...	...	...	...	...	...	...	...	...	...	...	...	...	1557	...	...	...	...	...	...	1957
	Toulon **360 361** d.	0916	...	...	...	...	...	...	...	...	...	...	...	...	...	1647	...	...	...	...	...	...	2046
	Les Arcs-Draguignan **361** a.	0953	...	...	...	...	...	...	...	...	...	...	...	...	...	1725	...	...	...	...	...	...	2124
	St Raphaël-Valescure **361** a.	1009	...	...	...	...	...	...	...	...	...	...	...	...	...	1742	...	...	...	...	...	...	2141
	Cannes **361** a.	1035	...	...	...	...	...	...	...	...	...	...	...	...	...	1807	...	...	...	...	...	...	2206
	Antibes **361** a.	1047	...	...	...	...	...	...	...	...	...	...	...	...	...	1819	...	...	...	...	...	...	2218
	Nice **361** a.	1107	...	...	...	...	...	...	...	...	...	...	...	...	...	1837	...	...	...	...	...	...	2237

	TGV	*TGV*	*TGV*	*TGV*		*TGV*	*TGV*	*TGV*	
	7845	**5338**	**9580**	**9835**		**5124**	**5124**	**5126**	
		D		⑥		⑤	⑦	①–④	
	⊠		**F**	**k**		**q**	**p**	**s**	
Brussels Midi **11** d.	...	...	...	1617	...	...	...	...	...
Lille Europe **11** d.	...	...	...	1703	...	1826	...	1823	...
Lille Flandres **11** d.	1541y	...	...	|	...	|	1823	|	...
Charles de Gaulle ✈ **11** d.	1706	...	...	1757	...	1928	1928	1959	...
Marne la Vallée-Chessy **11** d.	1722	...	...	1811	...	1952	1952	2012	...
Nantes **335** d.	|	...	...	|	...	|	|	|	...
Rennes **335** d.	|	1529	...	|	...	|	|	|	...
Massy TGV **335** d.	|	1728	...	|	...	|	|	|	...
Metz **379** d.	|	|	...	|	...	|	|	|	...
Strasbourg **379** d.	|	|	1614	|	...	|	|	|	...
Dijon Ville **379** d.	|	|	|	|	...	|	|	|	...
Genève **346** d.	|	|	|	|	...	|	|	|	...
Lyon Part Dieu ▶ d.	|	1936	2006	2010	...	2154	2154	2206	...
Lyon St Exupéry ✈ d.	1913	|	|	|	...	|	|	|	...
Valence TGV ▶ d.	|	|	|	2055	...	|	|	|	...
Avignon TGV d.	2007	2042	2111	2131	...	2305	2305	2311	...
Aix en Provence TGV d.	2029	2103	2136	2153	...	2329	2329	2335	...
Marseille St Charles a.	2041	2115	2149	2208	...	2341	2341	2347	...
Marseille St Charles **360 361** d.	...	...	...	...	...	...	...	...	...
Toulon **360 361** d.	...	...	...	...	...	...	...	...	...
Les Arcs-Draguignan **361** a.	...	...	...	...	...	...	...	...	...
St Raphaël-Valescure **361** a.	...	...	...	...	...	...	...	...	...
Cannes **361** a.	...	...	...	...	...	...	...	...	...
Antibes **361** a.	...	...	...	...	...	...	...	...	...
Nice **361** a.	...	...	...	...	...	...	...	...	...

	TGV	*TGV*	*TGV*		*TGV*	*TGV*		*TGV*
	7838	**9854**	**6860**		**9583**	**5382**		**5516**
			Ⓐ			**C**		
	⊠		**d**		**F**			**E**
Nice **361** d.	...	...	...	...	...	...	...	0652
Antibes **361** d.	...	...	...	...	...	...	...	0709
Cannes **361** d.	...	...	...	...	...	...	...	0722
St Raphaël-Valescure **361** d.	...	...	...	...	...	...	...	0746
Les Arcs-Draguignan **361** d.	...	...	...	...	...	...	...	0803
Toulon **360 361** d.	...	...	...	...	...	...	...	0847
Marseille St Charles **360 361** a.	...	...	...	...	...	...	...	0931
Marseille St Charles d.	0613	0636	0714	...	0810	0831	...	0945
Aix en Provence TGV d.	0628	0651	|	...	0826	|	...	1000
Avignon TGV d.	0650	0716	0746	...	0848	0908	...	1025
Valence TGV ▶ d.	|	|	0821	...	|	0942	...	|
Lyon St Exupéry ✈ a.	0741	|	|	...	|	|	...	|
Lyon Part Dieu ▶ a.	|	0820	0856	...	0954	1020	...	1128
Genève **346** a.	|	|	...	...	|	|	...	|
Dijon Ville **379** a.	|	|	...	...	|	|	...	1325
Strasbourg **379** a.	|	|	...	...	1343	|	...	1554
Metz **379** a.	|	|	...	...	...	|	...	...
Massy TGV **335** a.	|	|	...	...	...	1234	...	...
Rennes **335** a.	|	|	...	...	...	1417	...	...
Nantes **335** a.	|	|	...	...	...	...	...	...
Marne la Vallée-Chessy **11** a.	0933	1017	...	...	...	...	...	...
Charles de Gaulle ✈ **11** a.	|	1032	...	...	...	...	...	...
Lille Flandres **11** a.	1044g	|	...	...	...	...	...	...
Lille Europe **11** a.	...	1127	...	...	...	...	...	...
Brussels Midi **11** a.	...	1211	...	...	...	...	...	...

	TGV		*TGV*	*TGV*		*TGV*	*TGV*	*TGV*	*TGV*	*TGV*	*TGV*	*TGV*	*TGV*	*TGV*	*TGV*	*TGV*	*TGV*	*TGV*	*TGV*		*TGV*		
	7842		**5166**	**9866**		**9750**	**5192**	**5386**	**5356**	**9868**	**5376**	**9896**	**7832**	**9882**	**6850**	**7836**	**7836**	**7816**	**6862**		**6852**		
			Ⓐ	Ⓒ			⑥		**C**	①–⑥						**T**	**R**						
	⊠		**v**	**w**		**A**	**a**			**b**	**nH**	**L**	⊠			⊠	⊠	⊠	**Y**				
Nice **361** d.	...	...	...	...	...	...	...	...	...	...	...	...	...	...	1453	...	...	...	...	...	1723	...	...
Antibes **361** d.	...	...	...	...	...	...	...	...	...	...	...	...	...	...	1511	...	...	...	...	...	1741	...	...
Cannes **361** d.	...	...	...	...	...	...	...	...	...	...	...	...	...	...	1524	...	...	...	...	...	1754	...	...
St Raphaël-Valescure **361** d.	...	...	...	...	...	...	...	...	...	...	...	...	...	...	1550	...	...	...	...	...	1820	...	...
Les Arcs-Draguignan **361** d.	...	...	...	...	...	...	...	...	...	...	...	...	...	...	1606	...	...	...	...	...	1836	...	...
Toulon **360 361** d.	...	...	...	...	...	...	...	...	...	...	...	...	...	...	1648	...	...	...	...	...	1918	...	...
Marseille St Charles **360 361** a.	...	...	...	...	...	...	...	...	...	...	...	...	...	...	1731	...	...	...	...	...	2002	...	...
Marseille St Charles d.	1002	...	1210	1210	...	1353	1410	1435	1435	1510	1536	1602	1644	1710	1745	1815	1815	1836	1910	...	2014	...	...
Aix en Provence TGV d.	1017	...	1226	1226	...	1407	1426	1451	1451	1526	|	1616	|	1726	1759	1829	1829	1841	1926	...	2029	...	...
Avignon TGV d.	1040	...	1248	1248	...	1429	1448	1518	1518	1548	1607	1638	1719	1748	1821	1851	1851	1917	1948	...	2051	...	...
Valence TGV ▶ d.	|	...	|	|	...	|	|	|	|	|	1645	1713	|	|	|	|	|	|	|	...	2126	...	...
Lyon St Exupéry ✈ a.	1131	...	|	|	...	|	|	|	|	|	|	|	1810	|	|	|	|	|	|	...	|	...	...
Lyon Part Dieu ▶ a.	|	...	1354	1354	...	1535	1554	1622	1622	1654	1720	1750	|	1854	1925	1954	1954	2020	2053	...	2202	...	...
Genève **346** a.	|	...	|	|	...	1743	|	|	|	|	|	|	|	|	...	|	|	...	...	...	...	...	...
Dijon Ville **379** a.	|	...	|	|	...	...	|	|	|	|	|	1937	|	|	...	|	|	...	...	...	...	...	...
Strasbourg **379** a.	|	...	|	|	...	...	|	|	|	|	|	2201	|	|	...	|	|	...	...	...	...	...	...
Metz **379** a.	|	...	|	|	...	...	|	|	|	|	|	2254‡	|	|	...	|	|	...	...	...	...	...	...
Massy TGV **335** a.	|	...	|	|	...	...	|	1834	1834	|	1938z	...	|	|	...	|	|	...	...	...	...	...	...
Rennes **335** a.	|	...	|	|	...	...	|	2030	|	|	...	...	|	|	...	|	|	...	...	...	...	...	...
Nantes **335** a.	|	...	|	|	...	...	|	...	2054	|	...	...	|	|	...	|	|	...	...	...	...	...	...
Marne la Vallée-Chessy **11** a.	1317	...	1548	1549	...	...	1748	...	...	1847	...	...	2007	2050	...	2149	2147	...	...	...	...	...	...
Charles de Gaulle ✈ **11** a.	1331	...	1602	1603	...	...	1802	...	...	1902	...	...	2022	2103	...	2204	2202	...	...	...	...	...	...
Lille Flandres **11** a.	1430x	...	|	|	...	...	1944	...	...	|	...	...	...	|	...	...	2301	...	...	...	...	...	...
Lille Europe **11** a.	...	...	1657	1657	...	...	...	...	...	1956	...	...	...	2159	...	...	...	...	...	...	...	...	...
Brussels Midi **11** a.	...	...	...	1743	...	...	...	...	...	2043	...	...	...	2243	...	...	...	...	...	...	...	...	...

A – July 2 - Aug. 28.
B – ①–⑤ to July 1; Ⓐ from Aug. 29 (not Oct. 31).
C – ⑥⑦ to June 26; daily July 2 - Aug. 28; Ⓒ from Sept. 3 (also Oct. 31).
D – ⑤–⑦ to June 26; daily July 1 - Aug. 28; ⑤–⑦ from Sept. 2 (also Oct. 31, Nov. 1, 10).
E – From / to Nancy (Table **379**).
F – From / to Frankfurt (Table **47**).
H – From / to Rouen and Le Havre (Table **335**).
L – From / to Luxembourg (Table **379**).
R – ①–⑤ from Oct. 24 (also Nov. 5, 6, 12, 13, 19, 20).
T – Daily to Oct. 23 (also Oct. 29, 30 and ⑥⑦ from Nov. 26). To Tourcoing (a. 2309).
U – ①⑥ to June 27; ①④⑤⑥⑦ July 2 - Aug. 22 (also July 13, Aug. 16); daily from Aug. 25.
Y – ⑤⑦ to July 1; daily from Aug. 29.

a – Also July 14, 15, Nov. 11.
b – Not Aug. 15, Nov. 1.
d – Not June 14 – 16, 21 – 23, 28 – 30, July 15, Oct. 31.
e – Also Aug. 15, Nov. 1.
f – 0700 on ⑥ to Sept. 10 (also July 21, Nov. 11, 12, 19); 0652 on July 14.
g – Not Aug. 6, 7, 13, 14, 20, 21, 27, 28.
j – 0653 on June 25, July 2, 9, Nov. 11, 12, 19. On Aug. 13 departs 0636 from Lille **Europe**.
k – Also July 14, 15, Oct. 31, Nov. 11.
m – Not June 12, 25, 26, July 2, 3, 15 – 31, Aug. 1 – 21, 27, 28, Nov. 12, 13.
n – Not June 24, 25, July 1, 2, 14 – 31, Aug. 1 – 20, 26, 27, Nov. 11, 12.
p – Also Aug. 15; not Aug. 14.
q – Also July 13, Aug. 14, Oct. 31; not Aug. 15, Nov. 11.
r – 1010 on ① (not Aug. 15).
s – Not July 13, 14, Aug. 15, Oct. 31, Nov. 1.
t – ① to July 11; ①–⑥ from July 18 (not Aug. 15, Nov. 1).

v – Not July 15.
w – Also July 15.
x – Not Aug. 13 – 15.
y – Not Aug. 13, 14.
z – Massy **Palaiseau**.

TGV – High-speed train. 🅁. 🍸.

‡ – Arrival times may be up to 90 minutes later (see Table **379**).
⊠ – OUIGO low-cost TGV service. Internet bookings only at www.ouigo.com.
▶ – For other trains Valence TGV - Lyon and Paris see Table **355**. For Valence Ville - Lyon see Table **351**.

LYON - VALENCE - AVIGNON - MARSEILLE via 'classic' line 351

See Table **350** for *TGV* services Paris / Lyon - Valence TGV - Avignon TGV - Marseille, Table **355** for *TGV* services Paris / Lyon - Valence TGV - Montpellier.
TGV timings may vary by up to 5 minutes (please check your reservation for confirmed timings). All TER trains are 2nd class only except through services between Lyon and Marseille.
Warning! Subject to alteration on June 18. Services Avignon - Miramas - Marseille and v.v. are subject to alteration on Nov. 12.

km		Ⓐ	Ⓐ	Ⓒ	Ⓐ	Ⓒ	Ⓐ	Ⓐ	⚒	Ⓒ	⚒		Ⓐ	Ⓐ	Ⓒ	⊗	*TGV* 6191 ①–⑥ D	*TGV* 6191 ①–⑥ E			⚒ ⊗	⊗	⊗	⊗	*TGV* 6193 G
	Paris Gare de Lyon § d.	...	...	...	...	...	...	...	...	...	...	...	...	...	...	...	0743	0743	...	...	...	...	...	...	1141
	Lyon St Exupéry TGV ✈ § d.	...	...	...	...	...	...	...	...	...	...	...	...	...	...	...	0938	0943	...	...	...	...	...	...	1343
	Lyon Perrache d.	...	...	...	...	...	...	...	0538	...	...	...	0738	...	...	...	|	|	...	...	...	...	...	...	|
0	**Lyon** Part-Dieu d.	...	...	...	...	...	...	...	|	...	0620	0720	|	...	...	0820	|	|	0920	...	1020	...	1120	1220	|
32	Vienne d.	...	...	...	...	...	...	...	0600	...	0641	0741	0800	...	...	0839	|	|	0941	...	1039	...	1141	1241	|
87	Tain-l'Hermitage-Tournon d.	...	...	...	...	...	...	...	0638	...	0720	0824	0838	...	...	0911	|	|	1023	...	1118	...	1214	1324	|
105	**Valence** Ville a.	...	...	...	...	...	...	...	0650	...	0731	0835	0850	...	...	0923	1006	1011	1034	...	1130	...	1225	1334	1411
105	**Valence** Ville d.	...	...	...	0557	0557	0635c	0658	...	0658j	▬	0838	...	0913	0913	...	1009	1014	1036	...	1131	1205	...	1337	1414
150	Montélimar d.	...	...	...	0626	0628	0703	0726	...	0728	...	0901	...	0941	0942	...	1033	1039	1059	...	1159	1234	...	1401	1437
202	Orange d.	...	...	...	0701	0716	0737	0801	...	0803	Ⓐ	0936	...	1017	1019	...	1101	1106	1132	...	1233	1316	...	1436	1505
230	**Avignon** Centre a.	...	...	...	0726	0741	0802	0823	...	0825		0951	...	1040	1043	...	1116	1120	1147	...	1252	1342	...	1452	1519
230	**Avignon** Centre d.	0550	0650	0656	...	0756	0805	...	...	0828	0856	0958	...	1049	1053	...	1119z	1123y	...	1155	...	1345	...	1458	1524
265	Arles **355** d.	0609	0709	0714	...	0812	0822	...	...	0855	0914	1017	...	1113	1112	...	1148z	1148y	...	1212	...	1402	...	1516	1543
299	Miramas **355** d.	0630	0731	0735	...	0835	0846	...	...	0921	0935	1041	...	1135	1135	...	1213z	1222y	...	1233	...	1424	...	1539	1601
328	Vitrolles (for ✈) ⊖ **355** d.	0648	0748	0756	...	0856	0902	...	...	0943	0956	1058	...	1156	1156	...	...	...	...	1254	...	1446	...	1556	...
351	**Marseille** St Charles **355** a.	0706	0811	0819	...	0919	0920	...	...	1010	1019	1116	...	1219	1219	...	...	...	...	1319	...	1510	...	1615	...

	⊗	⚒ ⊗	①–④ m	⑤ f⊗	Ⓒ		①–④ m		⑤–⑦ v	Ⓑ	Ⓐ	⚒		Ⓐ		⑤ pA		Ⓐ		Ⓑ	*TGV* 6195 Ⓑ h				
Paris Gare de Lyon § d.	...	...	...	...	...	...	...	...	...	...	...	...	...	...	...	...	...	...	...	...	1741	...	...	...	...
Lyon St Exupéry TGV ✈ § d.	...	...	...	...	...	...	...	...	...	...	...	...	...	...	...	...	...	...	...	...	1943	...	...	...	...
Lyon Perrache d.	...	1338	...	...	...	...	...	...	...	...	1538	...	1638	...	...	...	1738	1810	...	1838	|	...	1938	...	...
Lyon Part-Dieu d.	1320	|	...	...	...	1420	...	1520	1520	...	|	1620	|	...	1720	...	|	|	1820	|	|	1920	|	2020	2120
Vienne d.	1341	1359	...	...	...	1440	...	1540	1540	...	1558	1640	1700	...	1741	...	1758	1831	1840	1858	|	1940	2000	2041	2141
Tain-l'Hermitage-Tournon d.	1419	1436	...	...	...	1512	...	1622	1622	...	1637	1720	1738	...	1824	...	1837	1909	1920	1937	|	2023	2038	2124	2224
Valence Ville a.	1430	1447	...	...	...	1523	...	1632	1632	...	1647	1731	1750	...	1834	...	1847	1920	1931	1947	2011	2033	2050	2135	2235
Valence Ville d.	1432	▬	...	1525t	1525t	▬	1625c	▬	1634	1702	1702	1733	▬	1802	1837	1857	1901	...	1933	▬	2014	2035	▬	...	...
Montélimar d.	1459	...	...	1554t	1555t	...	1651	...	1658	1730	1730	1801	...	1830	1900	1923	1931	...	2001	...	2037	2057	...	...	...
Orange d.	1534	Ⓐ	...	1629t	1631t	⑤	1725	Ⓒ	1732	1804	1804	1836	Ⓐ	1904	1935	1956	2004	...	2036	Ⓐ	2105	2130	⑦	...	...
Avignon Centre a.	1552		...	1651t	1654t	f	1750		1758	1827	1827	1852		1927	1951	2015	2027	...	2052		2119	2148	u	...	...
Avignon Centre d.	...	1556	1654	1654	1656	1750	1752	1756	...	...	...	...	1856	...	2001	...	...	...	...	2100	2123	...	2156	...	...
Arles **355** d.	...	1614	1713	1713	1717	1809	1809	1814	...	...	...	...	1914	...	2020	...	...	...	...	2118	2142	...	2214	...	...
Miramas **355** d.	...	1635	1735	1735	1742	1830	1831	1836	...	...	...	...	1935	...	2044	...	...	...	...	2139	2201	...	2238	...	...
Vitrolles (for ✈) ⊖ **355** d.	...	1655	1757	1756	1801	1848	1847	1856	...	...	...	...	1956	...	2100	...	...	...	...	2200	...	...	2259	...	...
Marseille St Charles **355** a.	...	1719	1819	1819	1819	1906	1906	1919	...	...	...	...	2019	...	2119	...	...	...	...	2223	...	...	2321	...	...

	Ⓐ	Ⓐ	⚒	⚒	⚒	†	⚒	⚒	Ⓐ	⚒	*TGV* 6194 ①–⑥ b	Ⓐ	⊗	Ⓐ ⊗	Ⓐ	⊗	⊖	⊗	Ⓒ		⊗	*TGV* 6196 G	⚒		Ⓑ
Marseille St Charles **355** d.	...	...	...	...	...	...	...	...	...	...	...	...	0652	...	0741	...	0840	...	0940	1040	...	...	...	1140	...
Vitrolles (for ✈) ⊖ **355** d.	...	...	...	...	...	...	...	...	...	...	...	...	0711	...	0804	...	0904	...	1004	1103	...	...	...	1204	...
Miramas **355** d.	...	...	...	...	...	...	...	...	...	...	0645	...	0730	...	0825	...	0926	...	1026	1124	...	...	...	1226	...
Arles **355** d.	...	...	...	...	...	...	...	...	...	...	0706	...	0752	...	0848	...	0948	...	1048	1145	...	...	...	1248	...
Avignon Centre a.	...	...	...	...	...	...	...	...	...	...	0724	...	0808	...	0906	...	1005	...	1106	1202	...	...	...	1305	...
Avignon Centre d.	...	...	...	...	0534	...	0610	...	0634	0702	0728	0734	0810	...	...	...	1008	...	...	...	1212	1232	...	1307r	...
Orange d.	...	...	...	...	0555	...	0626	...	0654	0724	0747	0757	0826	...	...	...	1032	...	...	...	1228	1249	...	1330r	...
Montélimar d.	...	0532	...	...	0630	...	0700	...	0729	0800	0815	0832	0900	...	...	...	1107	...	...	...	1302	1315	...	1405r	...
Valence Ville a.	...	0603	...	...	0700	...	0723	...	0759	0828	0840	0902	0922	...	...	...	1134	...	...	...	1326	1339	...	1434c	...
Valence Ville d.	0540	0610	0625	0640	0709	0710	0725	0740	0808	0830	0843	...	0925	1035	...	1125	...	1230	...	...	1330	1342	1430	...	1509
Tain-l'Hermitage-Tournon d.	0551	0621	0637	0651	0720	0721	0737	0751	0821	0840	|	...	0936	1047	...	1137	...	1241	...	...	1342	|	1442	...	1521
Vienne d.	0629	0659	0721	0729	0758	0759	0821	0830	0859	0920	|	...	1020	1120	...	1221	...	1319	...	...	1424	|	1519	...	1559
Lyon Part-Dieu a.	|	|	0740	|	|	|	0840	|	|	0940	|	...	1040	1140	...	1240	...	1340	...	...	1448	|	1540	...	|
Lyon Perrache a.	0650	0720	...	0750	0820	0820	...	0850	0920	...	|	...	...	...	...	...	...	...	...	...	...	|	...	...	1620
Lyon St Exupéry TGV ✈ § a.	...	...	...	...	...	...	...	...	...	...	0913	...	...	...	...	...	...	...	...	...	...	1413	...	...	...
Paris Gare de Lyon § a.	...	...	...	...	...	...	...	...	...	...	1120	...	...	...	...	...	...	...	...	...	...	1618	...	...	...

		⚒		Ⓑ	Ⓒ	Ⓐ	Ⓒ		Ⓐ		Ⓐ	*TGV* 6198 ①–⑥ b¶	*TGV* 6198 ⑦ e	Ⓑ		⑦ dA	Ⓒ	Ⓐ	Ⓐ		Ⓒ	Ⓐ	⚒		
Marseille St Charles **355** d.	1251	...	1340	...	1440	...	...	...	1540	...	...	...	...	...	1649	...	...	1715	1749	...	1832	1853	...	...	2041
Vitrolles (for ✈) ⊖ **355** d.	1310	...	1404	...	1503	...	...	...	1603	...	...	...	...	...	1711	...	...	1737	1812	...	1857	1912	...	...	2104
Miramas **355** d.	1328	...	1426	...	1524	...	...	...	1624	...	...	1659	1659	...	1730	...	...	1757	1831	...	1919	1931	...	...	2126
Arles **355** d.	1351	...	1448	...	1545	...	...	...	1645	...	...	1719	1719	...	1752	...	...	1821	1851	...	1941	1951	...	...	2148
Avignon Centre a.	1408	...	1505	...	1602	...	...	...	1703	...	...	1737	1737	...	1809	...	...	1839	1907	...	1958	2008	...	...	2206
Avignon Centre d.	1410	...	1508	...	...	1610	1610	...	...	1707	1726	1738	1738	...	1811	1831	1837	1841	...	1922	2002	2010	...	...	...
Orange d.	1426	...	1531	...	...	1626	1626	...	...	1726	1749	1755	1755	...	1826	1854	1900	1906	...	1945	2025	2031	...	...	...
Montélimar d.	1500	...	1607	...	...	1658	1700	...	...	1800	1831	1822	1822	...	1900	1929	1935	1948	...	2018	2100	2106	...	...	...
Valence Ville a.	1522	...	1636	...	...	1722	1724	...	...	1829	1858	1846	1846	...	1922	1958	2006	2017	...	2047	2132	2132	...	...	...
Valence Ville d.	1525	1609	...	1709	...	1725	1727	1809	...	1831	...	1849	1849	1910	1925	...	...	...	...	2049	...	...	2140	...	...
Tain-l'Hermitage-Tournon d.	1536	1621	...	1721	...	1737	1738	1821	...	1843	...	|	|	1921	1936	...	...	...	...	2100	...	...	2151	...	...
Vienne d.	1620	1659	...	1759	...	1821	1821	1859	...	1920	...	|	|	1959	2020	...	...	...	...	2134	...	...	2231	...	...
Lyon Part-Dieu a.	1640	|	...	|	...	1840	1840	|	...	1940	...	|	|	|	2040	...	...	...	...	2157	...	...	2250n	...	...
Lyon Perrache a.	...	1720	...	1820	...	...	...	1920	...	...	...	|	|	2020	...	...	...	...	...	...	...	...	...	...	...
Lyon St Exupéry TGV ✈ § a.	...	...	...	...	...	...	...	...	...	...	...	|	1917	...	...	...	...	...	...	...	...	...	...	...	...
Paris Gare de Lyon § a.	...	...	...	...	...	...	...	...	...	...	...	2112	2117	...	...	...	...	...	...	...	...	...	...	...	...

A – To / from Annecy (Table **364**).
D – ①–⑥ from Sept. 12 (not Nov. 1).
E – ①–⑥ until Sept. 10 (not Aug. 15).
G – ①⑤⑥⑦ to June 27; daily July 1 - Aug. 29; ①⑤⑥⑦ Sept. 2 – 11; ⑥⑦ Sept. 17 - Oct. 2; ①⑤⑥⑦ from Oct. 8 (also Nov. 1, 2, 10).

b – Not Aug. 15, Nov. 1.
c – From July 4.
d – Also July 14, Aug. 15.
f – Not Nov. 11.
h – Not July 14, 15, Oct. 31, Nov. 11.
j – 0655 on June 12, 18, 25, July 2.
m – Not July 14, Aug. 15, Nov. 1.
n – Arrives 2259 on ①④ Aug. 18 - Sept. 15; arrives 2257 on Sept. 6.
p – Also July 13, Nov. 10; not Nov. 11.

r – ①–④ to June 30; daily from July 4.
t – From July 8.
u – Also Aug. 15, Nov. 1, 11.
v – Also July 14, Aug. 15, Nov. 1.
y – ②–④ until June 30. Arrives Miramas 1210 on June 14, 21, 28.
z – ①–⑤ Sept. 12 - Oct. 7.

TGV – High-speed train. Ⓡ. 🍷.

⊗ – Subject to alteration or cancellation on ①–⑤ Sept. 12 - Oct. 7.
⊖ – Does not run Avignon - Valence Sept. 12 - Oct. 7.
¶ – Also calls at Mâcon-Loché TGV (a. 1933, d. 1936).
§ – See Table **342** for full service Paris - Lyon St Exupéry and v.v.
⊖ – Vitrolles Aéroport Marseille-Provence ✈. A shuttle bus runs to the airport terminal (journey time: 5 minutes).

351a AVIGNON TGV - AVIGNON CENTRE - CARPENTRAS

km		⚒	Ⓐ	Ⓐ	r	r	Ⓐr	Ⓒ	r						Ⓐ		Ⓐ					†			
0	**Avignon** TGV ◇ d.	0611	0638	0708	0738	0809	0908	1008	1108	1211	1308	1408	1508	1608	...	1708	1738	1808	1908	2008	...	2208	...	...	...
4	**Avignon** Centre ◇ d.	0619	0651	0717	0750	0818	0917	1017	1117	1217	1317	1417	1517	1617	1652	1717	1751	1817	1917	2017	...	2217	...	...	...
31	**Carpentras** a.	0648	0720	0748	0820	0848	0948	1048	1148	1245	1348	1448	1548	1648	1720	1748	1820	1848	1948	2048	...	2248	...	...	...

	⚒			Ⓐ		Ⓐ				r	r		r	r	r		Ⓐ							
Carpentras d.	0606	...	0706	0735	0806	0835	0906	1006	...	1206	1306	...	1435	1506	1606	1706	1735	1806	1906	2006	2106	...	...	...
Avignon Centre ◇ a.	0636	...	0736	0808	0836	0908	0936	1036	...	1236	1336	...	1509	1536	1636	1736	1808	1836	1936	2036	2136	...	...	...
Avignon TGV ◇ a.	0644	...	0744	0817	0844	0917	0944	1044	...	1244	1344	...	1517	1544	1644	1744	1817	1844	1944	2044	2144	...	...	...

r – Not Sept. 12–16, 19–23, 26–30, Oct. 3–7.

⊗ – Subject to alteration on ①–⑤ from Oct. 24.

◇ – **Full service** Avignon TGV - Avignon Centre and v.v. (journey 4–6 minutes):
From Avignon TGV at 0608 †, 0611 ⚒, 0638, 0708, 0738 Ⓐ, 0809 **r**, 0838, 0908 **r**, 0938, 1008 **r**, 1038 ⊗, 1108, 1138, 1211 **r**, 1238 ⊗, 1308, 1337, 1408, 1438 ⊗, 1508, 1538, 1608, 1638, 1708, 1738 Ⓐ, 1808, 1838, 1908, 1937, 2008, 2033, 2108 and 2208. **From Avignon Centre** at 0539 Ⓐ, 0611 Ⓒ, 0639, 0720 Ⓐ, 0739, 0810, 0839, 0911, 0939, 1011 ⊗, 1039, 1109, 1139, 1211 Ⓐ ⊗, 1214 Ⓒ, 1239 **r**, 1311, 1339 **r**, 1411 ⊗, 1439, 1512 **r**, 1539 **r**, 1611 ⊗, 1639 **r**, 1710, 1739, 1811 Ⓐ, 1839, 1911, 1939, 2011, 2039 and 2139.

352 🚌 TOULON - ST TROPEZ - ST RAPHAËL

🚌 route **7802**: **Toulon** Gare Routière (adjacent to railway station) → **St Tropez** Gare Routière. *84 km.* Journey 1 hr 40 m - 1 hr 45 m.
From Toulon at 0620 ⚒, 0900 ⚒, 1130, 1530 ⚒ and 1815. **From St Tropez** at 0600 ⚒, 1230 ⚒, 1630, 1730 ⚒ and 1830 ⚒.

🚌 route **7601**: **St Tropez** Gare Routière → **St Raphaël** Gare Routière (adjacent to railway station). *35 km* Journey 1 hr 20 m - 1 hr 30 m.
From St Tropez at 0630, 0730 and hourly until until 1930; then 2045.
From St Raphaël at 0615, 0715, 0815, 0915, 1115, 1315, 1415, 1515, 1615, 1715, 1800, 1915 and 2015.

Operator: ZOU! ✆ 0 809 400 013
https://zou.maregionsud.fr

☛ Route **7601** is subject to confirmation from July 8.

353 LYON - BOURG EN BRESSE

Local stopping trains via Villars-les-Dombes. See Table **378** for services via Ambérieu.

km		Ⓐ	Ⓐ n	⚒	Ⓐ	† 🚌	Ⓐ 🚌	⚒	Ⓐ		Ⓐ	⚒	Ⓐ		Ⓐ n	⚒	Ⓐ		Ⓐ n	⚒	⚒	E	⑤⑦ f		Ⓐ 🚌
0	**Lyon** Perrache d.	0601	0631	0701	0801	...	...	1001	1101	1201	1301	1401	1501	1601	1643	1701	1731	1801	1843	1901	2001	2101	2117	...	...
5	**Lyon** Part Dieu d.	0612	0642	0712	0812	0812	0912	1012	1112	1212	1312	1412	1512	1612	1654	1712	1742	1812	1854	1912	2012	2112	2129	...	2220
65	**Bourg en Bresse** a.	0714	0741	0814	0914	0933	1033	1114	1214	1314	1414	1514	1614	1714	1746	1814	1845	1914	1946	2014	2114	2214	2228	...	2341

	Ⓐ	⚒	† 🚌	Ⓐ	⚒	Ⓐ n		Ⓐ n	⚒	Ⓐ 🚌			Ⓐ	⚒	Ⓐ	Ⓐ 🚌			⚒		Ⓐ			Ⓑ
Bourg en Bresse d.	0517	0547	0557	0617	0647	0715	0747	0815	0847	0927	...	1047	1147	1247	1347	1427	...	1547	1647	1747	1847	1947	...	2047
Lyon Part Dieu a.	0618	0648	0718	0718	0748	0807	0848	0907	0948	1048	...	1148	1248	1348	1448	1548	...	1648	1748	1848	1948	2048	...	2148
Lyon Perrache a.	0630	0659	...	0729	0759	0818	0859	0918	0959	...	...	1159	1259	1359	1459	...	...	1659	1759	1859	1959	2059	...	2159

E – ①②③④⑥ (not July 13, 14, Aug. 15, Nov. 1, 10). **f** – Also July 13, 14, Aug. 15, Nov. 1, 10. **n** – Not July 15 - Aug. 26.

353a MÂCON - BOURG EN BRESSE - AMBÉRIEU

km		🚌 Ⓒd	Ⓐn	🚌 Ⓒd	Ⓐn		🚌		🚌 Ⓐ	🚌 A	Ⓐn	🚌	Ⓐn	🚌 A	🚌	🚌 A	Ⓐn	Ⓐn	🚌 Ⓒd	🚌 A	Ⓐn	🚌 Ⓒd	Ⓐn	🚌 A	🚌 Ⓐ	🚌 Ⓒ
0	**Mâcon** Ville d.	...	0704	0727	0804	...	0904	...	1104	...	...	...	1304	1304	1504	...	...	1704	1704	...	1804	1804	1904	1904	2004	2104
37	Bourg en Bresse a.	...	0732	0829	0833	...	1006	...	1206	...	...	...	1334	1406	1606	...	...	1732	1806	...	1832	1906	1932	2006	2106	2137
37	Bourg en Bresse **378** d.	0716	0734	...	...	0844	...	1044	...	1216	1234	1316	...	...	...	1616	1628	1734	...	1816	1834	*1916*	1934	...	...	...
68	**Ambérieu** **378** a.	0755	0758	...	...	0902	...	1102	...	1255	1258	1355	...	...	...	1655	1653	1758	...	1855	1858	*1955*	1958	...	...	...

	🚌 A	Ⓐn	🚌 A	🚌	Ⓐn	🚌 Ⓒd	🚌	🚌 Ⓐ	🚌 A	Ⓐn	🚌	Ⓐn	🚌 Ⓒd	🚌	🚌	Ⓐn	🚌 Ⓒd	Ⓐn	🚌 A	Ⓐn	🚌 Ⓒd	🚌 A		Ⓐn	🚌 Ⓒd‡	🚌
Ambérieu **378** d.	...	0655	0705	...	0805	0805	*0905*v	...	...	...	1205	1305	1305	...	1505	...	...	1701	1705	1805	1805	...	1859	1910	...	2111
Bourg en Bresse **378** a.	...	0718	0745	...	0829	0845	*0945*v	...	...	...	1245	1329	1345	...	1545	...	...	1724	1745	1828	1845	...	1917	1932	...	2151
Bourg en Bresse d.	0650	0719	...	0750	...	...	0950	1050	1215	1228	...	...	...	1350	...	1628	1650	1725	*1750*	1829	...	1850	...	1934	1950	...
Mâcon Ville a.	0753	0747	...	0853	...	...	1053	1153	1318	1257	...	...	...	1453	...	1657	1753	1753	*1853*	1857	...	1953	...	2003	2053	...

A Ⓐ July 15 - Aug. 26; Ⓐ Oct. 24 - Nov. 4.
d – Runs daily July 14 - Aug. 28 and Oct. 22 - Nov. 6.
n – Not July 15 - Aug. 26, Oct. 24 - Nov. 4.
v – ⚒ only.
‡ – 5 minutes later on dates in note **A**.

353b DIJON - BOURG EN BRESSE

km		Ⓐn		Ⓒr		z		Ⓐn		
0	**Dijon** Ville d.	0644	...	0844	...	1244	...	1744	1856	...
30	St Jean de Losne d.	0717	...	0917	...	1311	...	1818	1923	...
86	Louhans d.	0755	...	0956	...	1347	...	1857	1959	...
140	**Bourg en Bresse** a.	0828	...	1028	...	1419	...	1928	2030	...

	Ⓐn			⚒z			†		
Bourg en Bresse d.	0532	0632	...	1137	...	1737	1832	...	...
Louhans d.	0605	0705	...	1210	...	1810	1905	...	...
St Jean de Losne d.	0644	0744	...	1247	...	1847	1944	...	...
Dijon Ville a.	0716	0816	...	1315	...	1915	2016	...	...

n – Not Oct. 31. **r** – Also Oct. 31. **z** – Not Nov. 7–10.

354 PERPIGNAN - VILLEFRANCHE - LATOUR DE CAROL

km		Ⓐ	Ⓐ	Ⓐz	Ⓐv	Ⓐv	Ⓐv	Ⓐ	Ⓐ	Ⓐ	
0	**Perpignan** d.		0707	0906	1106	1306	1506	1716	1816	1916	...
40	Prades-Molitg les Bains d.		0750	0948	1148	1348	1548	1758	1902	1958	...
46	**Villefranche-Vernet les Bains** a.		0758	0956	1156	1356	1556	1806	1910	2006	...

	Ⓒ	†C	D	Ⓒ	Ⓒ	Ⓒ	Ⓒ	Ⓒ	†	†		
Perpignan d.		0800	0806	1006	1206	1406	1606	1806	1906	2006	...	...
Prades-Molitg les Bains d.		0845	0851	1048	1248	1448	1648	1848	1951	2048	...	...
Villefranche-Vernet les Bains a.		0852	0858	1056	1256	1456	1656	1856	1958	2056	...	...

	Ⓐ	Ⓐ	Ⓐ	Ⓐ	Ⓐz	Ⓐv	Ⓐv	Ⓐv	Ⓐ	
Villefranche-Vernet les Bains d.		0604	0704	0805	1004	1204	1404	1604	1814	...
Prades-Molitg les Bains d.		0612	0712	0813	1012	1212	1412	1612	1822	...
Perpignan a.		0654	0754	0854	1055	1254	1454	1654	1904	...

	Ⓒ	⑥	⑥	Ⓒ	Ⓒ	Ⓒ	Ⓒ	Ⓒ	Ⓒ			
Villefranche-Vernet les Bains d.		0704	0805	0904	1104	1304	1504	1704	1904	...	...	...
Prades-Molitg les Bains d.		0712	0813	0912	1112	1312	1512	1712	1912	...	...	...
Perpignan a.		0754	0854	0954	1154	1354	1554	1754	1954	...	...	...

VILLEFRANCHE - LATOUR DE CAROL *Petit Train Jaune* Narrow gauge, 2nd class. In summer most trains include open sightseeing carriages.

SERVICE MAY 26 - JULY 1 AND AUGUST 29 - SEPTEMBER 25

km									
0	**Villefranche-Vernet les Bains** d.	0857	1002	...	1349	1546	...	1749	...
28	Mont Louis la Cabanasse d.	1025	1129	...	1507	1709	...	1908	...
35	Font Romeu-Odeillo-Via d.	1044	1156	...	1526	1728	...	1934	...
56	Bourg Madame d.	...	1255	...	...	...	...	2032	...
63	**Latour de Carol** a.	...	1311	...	...	...	...	2048	...

Latour de Carol d.	0826	...	...	...	1511	...	...	...
Bourg Madame d.	0846	...	...	...	1532	...	...	...
Font Romeu-Odeillo-Via d.	0958	1104	...	1545	1643	1748	...	...
Mont Louis la Cabanasse d.	1030	1135	...	1614	1715	1818	...	...
Villefranche-Vernet les Bains a.	1140	1251	...	1727	1829	1928	...	...

SERVICE JULY 2 - AUGUST 28

km									
0	**Villefranche-Vernet les Bains** d.	0902	1006	...	1333	1527	...	1745	...
28	Mont Louis la Cabanasse d.	1039	1144	...	1505	1716	...	1919	...
35	Font Romeu-Odeillo-Via d.	1058	1208	...	1524	1735	...	1941	...
56	Bourg Madame d.	...	1303	...	...	...	...	2037	...
63	**Latour de Carol** a.	...	1321	...	...	...	...	2055	...

Latour de Carol d.	0839	...	...	...	1518	...	...	...
Bourg Madame d.	0900	...	...	...	1538	...	...	...
Font Romeu-Odeillo-Via d.	1008	1115	...	1541	1646	1754	...	...
Mont Louis la Cabanasse d.	1041	1141	...	1609	1719	1822	...	...
Villefranche-Vernet les Bains a.	1155	1252	...	1725	1833	1940	...	...

C – July 3 - Aug. 28.
D – ⑥⑦ to June 26; ⑥ July 2 - Aug. 27; Ⓒ from Sept. 3.
v – Not Oct. 10–21.
z – Not Sept. 26 - Oct. 28.

PARIS, LYON and MARSEILLE - MONTPELLIER - PERPIGNAN - PORTBOU 355

TGV services from / to Paris. Timings may vary by up to 5 minutes (please check your reservation). Subject to alteration Oct. 29 - Nov. 1.

km	All services [R]	*TGV*	*TGV*	*TGV*	*TGV*	*TGV*	*TGV*	*TGV*	*TGV*	*TGV*	*TGV*	*TGV*	*TGV*	*TGV*	*TGV*	*TGV*	*TGV*	*TGV*	*TGV*	*TGV*	*TGV*	*TGV*	*TGV*
		7871	**6271**	**6221**	**6221**	**6221**	**6273**	**6273**	**9713**	**6275**	**7885**	**7875**	**9715**	**6035**	**6035**	**6277**	**6223**	**6223**	**6279**	**6225**	**6225**	**6225**	**6281**
				①–⑥		⑦	⑤	⑥															
		⊠	A	r	R	g	E	C			⊠	⊠	K	♣	♥	S		Z		O	N	P	B
0	**Paris** Gare de Lyon .... **342 351** d.	0609	0711	0812	0812	0843	0912	0912	1010	1111	1213	1410	1512	1512	1512	1611	1711	1711	1811	1912	1912	1912	2012
441	Lyon St Exupéry ✈ .... **342 351** d.	|	|	|	|	|	|	|	|	|	|	1608	|	|	|	|	|	|	|	|	|	|	|
527	Valence TGV .... d.	0827	0927	1027	1027	1059	1127	1127	1227	1327	1426	|	1727	1727	1727	1827	1927	1927	2027	2127	2127	2127	2227
676	**Nîmes** Pont-du-Gard .... d.	|	1006	|	|	|	1206	1206	|	1406	1506	|	|	|	|	1906	|	|	2106	|	|	|	2306
686	**Nîmes** Centre .... d.	0914	|	1114	1114	1146	|	|	1314	|	|	1714	1815	1815	1815	|	2014	2014	|	2214	2214	2214	|
	Montpellier Saint-Roch .... a.	0942	|	1142	1142	1214	|	|	1341	|	|	1741	1841	1841	1841	|	2043	2043	|	2242	2242	2242	|
	Montpellier Saint-Roch .... d.	...	|	1147	1147	1219	|	|	1346	|	|	...	1846	1846	...	|	...	2046	|	...	2247	2247	|
730	**Montpellier** Sud-de-France .... a.	...	1026	|	|	|	1225	1225	|	1426	1526	...	|	|	...	1926	...	|	2126	...	|	|	2326
	Montpellier Sud-de-France .... d.	...	1032	|	|	|	...	1231	|	1432	...	...	|	|	...	1932	...	|	2132	...	|	|	...
759	Sète .... d.	...	1050	1204	1204	1236	...	1249	1404	1452	...	...	1904	1904	...	1950	...	2104	2150	...	2304	2304	...
782	Agde .... d.	...	1107	1221	1221	1253	...	1305	1421	1507	...	...	1920	1920	...	2007	...	2120	2207	...	2321	2321	...
803	Béziers .... d.	...	1122	1232	1235	1307	...	1319	1435	1522	...	...	1935	1935	...	2022	...	2135	2222	...	2332	2335	...
829	**Narbonne** .... a.	...	1136	...	1249	1321	...	1333	1449	1536	...	...	1949	1949	...	2036	...	2149	2236	...	...	2349	...
892	**Perpignan** .... a.	...	1212	...	1325	1357	...	1408	1525	1612	...	...	2025	2025	...	2112	...	2225	2312	...	...	0025	...
	Barcelona Sants **13 657** .... a.	...	...	...	...	...	...	...	1654	...	...	...	2154	...	...	...	...	...	...	...	...	...	...

All services [R]	*TGV*	*TGV*	*TGV*	*TGV*	*TGV*	*TGV*	*TGV*	*TGV*	*TGV*	*TGV*	*TGV*	*TGV*	*TGV*	*TGV*	*TGV*	*TGV*	*TGV*	*TGV*	*TGV*	*TGV*	*TGV*	*TGV*	*TGV*
	6200	**6250**	**6250**	**6252**	**6202**	**7872**	**6254**	**6254**	**6256**	**9708**	**9702**	**6210**	**6210**	**6258**	**6258**	**6204**	**7882**	**6036**	**9704**	**7876**	**6260**	**6206**	**6206**
		①		①–④			⑥	⑦															⑤
	F	a	⊖	Q		⊠	C	D	▽	⊗	▽	⊗	W	G		J	⊠	U	L	⊠		♠	H
Barcelona Sants **13 657** .... d.	...	...	...	...	...	...	...	...	...	0910	1000	...	...	...	...	...	...	...	1400	...	...	...	...
Perpignan .... d.	...	...	...	...	0733	...	0933	0947	1044	1045	1133	...	1133	1245	...	1333	...	1533	1533	...	1745	1833	...
Narbonne .... d.	...	...	...	...	0810	...	1010	1025	1122	1122	1210	...	1210	1323	...	1409	...	1610	1610	...	1822	1912	...
Béziers .... d.	...	0538	...	...	0827	...	1027	1042	1139	1139	1226	...	1226	1339	1339	1425	...	1627	1627	...	1839	1929	...
Agde .... d.	...	0553	...	...	0841	...	1041	1056	1153	1153	1240	...	1240	1353	1353	1439	...	1641	1641	...	1853	1944	...
Sète .... d.	...	0610	...	...	0856	...	1057	1113	1210	1210	1256	...	1256	1410	1410	1455	...	1657	1657	...	1910	2000	...
Montpellier Sud-de-France .... a.	...	0626	...	...	|	...	1113	1128	1226	1226	|	...	|	1426	1426	|	...	|	|	...	1926	|	...
Montpellier Sud-de-France .... d.	...	0633	0633	0733	|	...	1120	1135	1233	1233	|	...	|	1433	1433	|	1633	|	|	...	1933	|	...
Montpellier Saint-Roch .... a.	...	|	|	|	0911	...	|	|	|	|	1311	...	1311	|	|	1511	|	1713	1713	...	|	2017	...
Montpellier Saint-Roch .... d.	0517	|	|	|	0918	1020	|	|	|	|	1318	1318	1318	|	|	1518	|	1718	1718	1817	|	2024	2025
Nîmes Centre .... d.	0547	|	|	|	0949	1051	|	|	|	|	1349	1349	1349	|	|	1549	|	1749	1749	1850	|	2057	2057
Nîmes Pont-du-Gard .... d.	|	0655	0655	0755	|	|	1143	1158	1255	1255	|	|	|	1455	1455	|	1655	|	|	|	1955	|	|
Valence TGV .... d.	0635	0735	0735	0835	1034	|	1223	1238	1335	1335	1435	1435	1435	1535	1535	1635	1735	1835	1835	1936	2035q	2142	2142
Lyon St Exupéry ✈ .... **342 351** d.	|	|	|	|	|	1154	|	|	|	|	|	|	|	|	|	|	|	|	|	|	|	|	|
Paris Gare de Lyon .... **342 351** a.	0848	0947	0947	1047	1246	1346	1434	1450	1551	1549	1647	1647	1647	1746	1746	1848	1949	2048	2048	2147	2247q	2354	2354

TGV and *AVE* services from / to / via Lyon.
Timings may vary by up to 5 minutes (please check your reservation). Subject to alteration Oct. 29 - Nov. 1.

All services [R]	*TGV*		*TGV*	*TGV*	*TGV*	*TGV*	*TGV*	*TGV*	*TGV*	*TGV*	*TGV*		*TGV*	*TGV*	*AVE*		*TGV*	*TGV*	*TGV*	*TGV*	*TGV*	*TGV*	*TGV*
	6821		**6823**	**6823**	**5300**	**5521**	**7867**	**6823**	**6823**	**9812**	**6823**		**5304**	**9826**	**9743**		**9879**	**5336**	**6825**	**5120**	**5341**	**9836**	**9836**
			©	©	Ⓐ			©			Ⓐ							⑤					⑤⑥
			▷	△	n		⊠T	⊕	Y		v		M				X	f		⊡	M		d
Brussels Midi **11** .... d.	...	...	...	...	...	...	...	...	...	0817	...	...	...	1017	...	...	...	...	...	...	...	1617	1617
Lille Europe **11** .... d.	...	...	...	...	...	...	...	...	...	0902	...	...	...	1103	...	...	...	...	...	1602	...	1703	1703
Charles de Gaulle ✈ **11** .... d.	...	...	...	...	...	...	0852	...	...	0958	...	...	...	1157	...	...	...	...	...	1656	...	1757	1757
Marne la Vallée - Chessy **11** .... d.	...	...	...	...	...	...	0910	...	...	1011	...	...	...	1211	...	...	...	...	...	1710	...	1811	1811
Metz **379** .... d.	...	...	...	...	...	0551k	|	...	...	|	...	...	...	|	...	...	1210	...	...	|	...	|	|
Strasbourg **379** .... d.	...	...	...	...	...	0700	|	...	...	|	...	...	...	|	...	...	1303	...	...	|	...	|	|
Dijon Ville **379** .... d.	...	...	...	...	...	0923	|	...	...	|	...	...	...	|	...	...	1525	...	...	|	...	|	|
Nantes **335** .... d.	...	...	...	...	0455j	|	|	...	...	|	...	...	0909t	|	...	...	|	...	...	|	...	|	|
Rennes **335** .... d.	...	...	...	...	|	|	|	...	...	|	...	...	|	|	...	...	|	1348	...	|	1529	|	|
Massy TGV .... d.	...	...	...	...	0727	|	|	...	...	|	...	...	1126	|	...	...	|	1528	...	|	1728	|	|
Lyon Part Dieu .... **350** d.	0636	...	0910	0920	0936	1104	1110	1126	1157	1210	1210	...	1336	1410	1435	...	1710	1736	1810	1910	1942	2010	2010
Lyon St Exupéry ✈ .... d.	|	...	|	|	|	|	|	|	|	|	|	...	|	|	|	...	|	|	|	|	|	|	|
Valence TGV .... **350** d.	0716	...	0953	1000	1018	|	1151	1202	1241	1251	1251	...	1413	1451	1511	...	1751	1816	1851	1951	2019	2051	2051
Nîmes Pont-du-Gard .... d.	|	...	|	|	1058	|	1232	|	|	|	|	...	|	1532	|	...	1832	|	|	|	|	|	|
Nîmes Centre .... d.	0808	...	1044	1049	|	1226	|	1249	1330	1338	1338	...	1500e	|	1557	...	|	1904	1939	2043	2112	2138	2138
Montpellier Saint-Roch .... a.	0840	...	1112	1119	|	1254	|	1316	1403	1405	1405	...	1527e	|	1624	...	|	1935	2006	2108	2139	2208	2208
Montpellier Saint-Roch .... d.	0845	...	1117	1123	|	...	|	1321	1412	...	1412	...	...	|	1628	...	|	...	2012	...	...	...	2211
Montpellier Sud-de-France .... a.	|	...	|	|	1119	...	1253	|	|	...	|	...	...	1553	|	...	1853	...	|	...	...	...	|
Montpellier Sud-de-France .... d.	|	...	|	|	...	...	...	|	|	...	|	...	...	...	|	...	...	...	|	...	...	...	|
Sète .... d.	0906	...	|	|	...	...	...	|	|	...	|	...	...	...	|	...	...	...	2029	...	...	...	2228
Agde .... d.	|	...	|	|	...	...	...	|	|	...	|	...	...	...	|	...	...	...	|	...	...	...	2245
Béziers .... d.	0932	...	1158	1215	...	...	...	1359	1450	...	1450	...	...	...	1715	...	...	...	2053	...	...	...	2259
Narbonne .... a.	0945	...	1211	1233	...	...	...	1412	1503	..	1503	...	...	...	1728	...	...	...	2106	...	...	...	2312
Toulouse Matabiau **320** .... a.	1101	...	1330	1415	...	...	...	1531	1619	...	1619	...	...	...	|	...	...	...	2222	...	...	...	|
Perpignan .... a.	...	...	...	...	...	...	...	...	...	...	...	...	...	...	1806	...	...	...	...	...	...	...	2359
Barcelona Sants **13 657** .... a.	...	...	...	...	...	...	...	...	...	...	...	...	...	...	1932	...	...	...	...	...	...	...	...

A – ①–⑤ to June 24; daily June 27 - Sept. 2; Ⓐ from Sept. 5 (not Oct. 31).
B – ③④⑤⑦ to July 1; ⑤ July 8 - Aug. 26 (also July 13; not July 15); ⑤⑦ from Sept. 2 (also Nov. 1, 10; not Nov. 11).
C – ⑥ July 2 - Aug. 27 (also July 14).
D – ⑦ July 3 - Aug. 28 (also Aug. 15).
E – ⑤ July 8 - Aug. 26 (also July 13; not July 15).
F – ①–⑤ to July 1; ①⑤ July 4 - Aug. 26 (also July 13, Aug. 16; not July 15, Aug. 15); Ⓐ from Aug. 29 (not Oct. 31).
G – ⑥⑦ to June 26; ⑤⑦ July 3 - Aug. 28 (also July 13, Aug. 15; not July 15); © from Sept. 3 (also Oct. 31).
H – ⑤ to July 1; ⑤ from Sept. 2 (also Nov. 10; not Nov. 11). Arrives Paris 7–21 minutes later Sept. 23 - Oct. 21 and from Nov. 18.
J – Ⓑ to June 24; daily June 26 - Sept. 2; Ⓑ from Sept. 4 (not Oct. 31, Nov. 11).
K – June 14 - Sept. 30.
L – June 15 - Oct. 1.
M – ⑥⑦ to June 26; daily July 2 - Aug. 28; © from Sept. 3 (also Oct. 31).
N – ⑤⑦ to Aug. 21 (also July 13, Aug. 15; not July 15); Ⓑ from Aug. 26 (not Nov. 11).
O – Ⓑ to June 24; daily June 26 - Sept. 2; Ⓑ from Sept. 4 (not Nov. 11).
P – ⑤ to June 24; ⑤⑦ July 1 - Aug. 28 (also July 13, Aug. 15; not July 15); ⑤ from Sept. 2 (also Oct. 31, Nov. 10; not Nov. 11).
Q – ①–④ July 4 - Aug. 25 (not July 13, 14, Aug. 15).
R – ①–⑥ to Aug. 27; ⑤ from Sept. 2 (also Nov. 1, 10; not Nov. 11).
S – Daily to July 3; ⑤–⑦ July 8 - Aug. 21 (also July 13, 14, Aug. 15); daily from Aug. 26.
T – From Tourcoing (Table **11**).
U – Daily to Aug. 28; ⑤⑦ from Sept. 2 (also Nov. 1, 10; not Nov. 11).
W – ⑦ to June 26; © from Sept. 3 (also Oct. 31).
X – From Luxembourg (Table **379**).
Y – Runs on July 15 only.
Z – ⑤⑥ to June 25; daily July 1 - Aug. 28; ⑤⑥ from Sept. 2 (also Oct. 31, Nov. 10).

a – Also Nov. 2; not July 4 - Aug. 22, Oct. 31.
d – Also July 13, 14, Nov. 10.
e – 11 minutes later on Oct. 8, 9, 15, 16, 29, 30, Nov. 5, 6, 26, 27.
f – Also Nov. 10; not July 8 - Aug. 26, Nov. 11.
g – Not Oct. 30.
j – 0450 on ① (also Nov. 2; not Oct. 31).
k – 0503 on ②–⑥ from Nov. 29.
n – Not July 4 - Aug. 26, Oct. 31.
q – On ①–④ until Aug. 25 (not July 13, 14, Aug. 15) departs Valence 2045, arrives Paris 2300.
r – Also Oct. 30.
t – 0854 July 2 - Aug. 28.
v – Not July 15, Oct. 31.

TGV – High-speed train. [R]. 🍷.
AVE – Spanish high-speed train. [R]. 🍷.

⊡ – ④⑤⑦ (also July 13, Aug. 15, Nov. 1; not July 14, 15, Nov. 11).
♥ – ⑤–⑦ to June 26; daily July 1 - Aug. 28; ⑤⑦ from Sept. 2 (also Nov. 1, 10; not Nov. 11).
♣ – ⑥ to June 25; ①–⑥ July 2 - Aug. 27 (not Aug. 15).
♠ – ⑦ to June 26; ⑤–⑦ July 2 - Aug. 28 (also July 13, 14, Aug. 15); ⑦ from Sept. 4 (also Nov. 1). Timings may vary by up to 12 minutes (please check your reservation).
⊖ – ①⑤ to July 1; ⑥ July 2 - Aug. 27 (also July 14, 15); ① from Aug. 29 (also Nov. 2; not Oct. 31).
⊕ – © from Oct. 1 (also Oct. 31). Timings may vary by up to 20 minutes on certain dates (please check your reservation).
▷ – Until July 17.
△ – July 23 - Sept. 25.
▽ – July 2 - Aug. 28.
⊗ – Not July 2 - Aug. 28.
⊠ – OUIGO low-cost TGV service. Internet bookings only at www.ouigo.com

355 PARIS, LYON and MARSEILLE - MONTPELLIER - PERPIGNAN - PORTBOU

TGV and *AVE* services from / to / via Lyon.
Timings may vary by up to 5 minutes (please check your reservation). Subject to alteration Oct. 29 - Nov. 1.

All services 🅁	*TGV* 5156 ①⑤ m	*TGV* 9898 X		*TGV* 5384 A	*TGV* 5384 ©	*TGV* 9862 ⑥⑦ c	*TGV* 9862 ①–⑤ h		*TGV* 6871		*AVE* 9736	*TGV* 5158 ⑥ y		*TGV* 5500	*TGV* 7860 ⊠	*TGV* 9864 ①–⑥ b	*TGV* 9864 ⑦ e		*TGV* 5358	*TGV* 5182		*TGV* 6873		*TGV* 6875
Barcelona Sants **13 657** d.	...	...	...	...	...	...	...	...	...	...	0815	...	...	...	...	...	...	...	...	...	...	...	...	...
Perpignan d.	...	...	...	...	...	0702	...	...	...	...	0941	...	...	...	...	...	...	...	...	...	...	...	...	...
Toulouse Matabiau **320** d.	...	...	...	...	...	|	...	...	0744	...	|	...	...	...	...	...	...	...	...	...	...	1541	...	1744
Narbonne d.	...	...	...	...	...	0745	...	...	0859	...	1019	...	...	...	...	...	...	...	...	...	...	1659	...	1859
Béziers d.	...	...	...	...	...	0805	...	...	0915	...	|	...	...	...	...	...	...	...	...	...	...	1714	...	1915
Agde d.	...	...	...	...	...	0820	...	...	|	...	|	...	...	...	...	...	...	...	...	...	...	|	...	|
Sète d.	...	...	...	...	...	0838	...	...	0940	...	|	...	...	...	...	...	...	...	...	...	...	1739	...	1946
Montpellier Sud-de-France a.	...	...	...	...	...	|	...	...	1000	...	|	...	...	...	...	...	...	...	...	...	...	|	...	2003
Montpellier Sud-de-France d.	...	...	...	...	...	|	0910	...	1007	...	|	...	...	...	1407	...	...	...	...	1710	...	|	...	2010
Montpellier Saint-Roch a.	...	...	...	...	...	0853	|	...	|	...	1121	...	...	...	|	...	...	...	...	|	...	1754	...	|
Montpellier Saint-Roch d.	0524	0629	...	0828	0838	0858	|	...	|	...	1125	1151	...	1358	|	1452	1452	...	1624	|	...	1758	...	|
Nîmes Centre d.	0555	0658	...	0905	0908	0927	|	...	|	...	1200	1223	...	1429	|	1521	1521	...	1655	|	...	1828	...	|
Nîmes Pont-du-Gard d.	|	|	...	|	|	|	0932	...	1030	...	|	|	...	|	1429	|	|	...	|	1732	...	|	...	2033
Valence TGV **350** d.	0645	0748	...	|	|	1015	1015	...	1114	...	1246	1314	...	|	|	1615	1620	...	1743	1815	...	1915	...	2115
Lyon St Exupéry ✈ a.	|	|	...	|	|	|	|	...	|	...	|	|	...	|	1527	|	|	...	|	|	...	|	...	|
Lyon Part Dieu **350** a.	0722	0824	...	1024	1024	1050	1050	...	1150	...	1322	1351	...	1550	|	1650	1654	...	1820	1850	...	1950	...	2150
Massy TGV a.	|	|	...	1234	1234	|	|	...	...	...	...	|	...	|	|	|	|	...	2033	|	...	...	...	...
Rennes **335** a.	|	|	...	1417	1417	|	|	...	...	...	...	|	...	|	|	|	|	...	|	|	...	...	...	...
Nantes **335** a.	|	|	...	...	...	|	|	...	...	...	...	|	...	|	|	|	|	...	2307	|	...	...	...	...
Dijon Ville **379** a.	|	0958	...	...	...	|	|	...	...	...	...	|	...	1740	|	|	|	...	...	|	...	...	...	...
Strasbourg **379** a.	|	1221	...	...	...	|	|	...	...	...	...	|	...	2013	|	|	|	...	...	|	...	...	...	...
Metz **379** a.	|	1324	...	...	...	|	|	...	...	...	...	|	...	2115	|	|	|	...	...	|	...	...	...	...
Marne la Vallée - Chessy **11** a.	0919	...	...	...	...	1247	1247	...	...	...	...	1549	...	...	1723	1847	1847	...	...	2050	...	...	...	...
Charles de Gaulle ✈ **11** a.	0934	...	...	...	...	1302	1302	...	...	...	...	1603	...	...	1740	1902	1902	...	...	2103	...	...	...	...
Lille Europe **11** a.	1040f	...	...	...	...	1431	1424	...	...	...	...	1657	...	...	1903•	1956	1956	...	...	2159	...	...	...	...
Brussels Midi **11** a.	...	...	...	...	...	1519	1533	...	...	...	...	...	...	...	...	2043	2043	...	...	...	...	...	...	...

AVE and *INTERCITÉS* services from / to Marseille. Timings may vary by up to 4 minutes (please check your reservation). Subject to alteration on June 18, Oct. 29 – 31, Nov. 1, 12.

km	All services 🅁	4752 ①–⑥ d★	4756 ★	*AVE* 9731 ■	4758 ★	4760 ★	4762 n ★	4764 ★△	4766 ★	4770 Ⓐv ★
0	**Marseille** St Charles .. **350/1** d.	...	0718	0802	0928	1122	1327	1528	1724	1928
19	Aix en Provence TGV .. **350** d.	...	|	0818	|	|	|	|	|	|
53	Avignon TGV **350** d.	...	|	0840	|	|	|	|	|	|
	Arles **351** d.	...	0810	|	|	1211	|	|	|	|
135	**Nîmes** Centre d.	0636g	0837	0908	1036	1237	1435	1637	1837	2038
	Montpellier Saint-Roch a.	0702g	0903	0935	1103	1303	1503	1704	1903	2104
	Montpellier Saint-Roch d.	0706g	0907	0939	1106	1307	1506	1707	1907	2108
	Sète d.	|	0923	|	|	1323	|	|	|	|
	Béziers d.	0745	|	1017	1145	|	1545	1746	1948	2151
	Narbonne a.	0759	0958	1030	1159	1357	1559	1759	2001	2205
	Toulouse Matabiau **320** a.	0915	1115z	|	1315	1515	1715	1915	2117	2321
	Bordeaux St Jean **320** a.	1132	1333z	|	1534	1733	1932	2135	2334	...
	Perpignan a.	...	...	1108	...	...	...	...	...	...
	Barcelona Sants **13 657** a.	...	...	1234	...	...	...	...	...	...

All services 🅁	4651 Ⓐv ★	4655 n ★	4657 ★	4659 ★	4661 ★	4663 ★	*AVE* 9724 ■	4665 ★	4669 D ★	4669 ⒶB ★
Barcelona Sants **13 657** d.	...	...	...	...	...	...	1636	...	...	...
Perpignan d.	...	...	...	...	...	...	1802	...	...	...
Bordeaux St Jean **320** d.	...	0628	0828	1028z	1228	1428	|	1628	1828	1828
Toulouse Matabiau **320** d.	0641	0842	1046	1246z	1443	1646	|	1846	2046	2046
Narbonne d.	0758	1000	1200	1402	1600	1800	1843	2000	2200	2200
Béziers d.	0814	1016	|	1418	1616	1815	1859	2015	|	2213
Sète d.	|	|	1236	|	|	|	|	|	2236	...
Montpellier Saint-Roch a.	0849	1052	1251	1453	1651	1853	1945	2052	2252	...
Montpellier Saint-Roch d.	0853	1055	1254	1457	1654	1857	1950	2055	2256	...
Nîmes Centre d.	0923	1125	1325	1526	1722	1926	2025	2125	2322	...
Arles **351** d.	|	|	1349	|	1744	|	|	|	...	...
Avignon TGV **350** a.	|	|	|	|	|	|	2047	|	...	...
Aix en Provence TGV **350** a.	|	|	|	|	|	|	2111	|	...	...
Marseille St Charles **350/1** a.	1029	1232	1437	1636	1838	2045j	2126	2233	...	...

TER services. See above and page 205 for *TGV*, *AVE* and *INTERCITÉS* services. See Table **319** for overnight *Intercités de Nuit* service Paris - Portbou.
Timings may vary by 1 – 2 minutes. Subject to alteration on June 18, Oct. 29 – 31, Nov. 1, 12.

km		⚒	Ⓐ	⚒	Ⓐ	Ⓐ	Ⓐ	⚒	Ⓐ	©	†	Ⓐ	© J	© k	Ⓐ	Ⓐ	Ⓐ		⚒	Ⓐ s	Ⓐ	Ⓑ	© k	© J	Ⓐ
0	**Marseille** St Charles .... **351** d.	...	...	...	...	...	...	...	...	...	...	...	...	...	...	0617	...	...	...	...	...	...	...	...	...
23	Vitrolles Aéroport Marseille ‡ d.	...	...	...	...	...	...	...	...	...	...	...	...	...	...	0637	...	...	...	...	...	...	...	...	...
52	Miramas **351** d.	...	...	...	...	...	...	...	...	...	...	...	...	...	...	0655	...	...	...	...	...	...	...	...	...
86	Arles **351** d.	...	...	...	...	...	...	...	...	...	...	...	...	...	...	0715	...	...	...	...	...	...	...	...	...
	Avignon Centre d.	...	...	...	...	...	...	...	0614	...	...	0635	...	...	...	|	0715	...	0735	...	...	0835	...	...	...
100	Tarascon-sur-Rhône d.	...	...	...	...	...	...	...	0626	...	...	0652	...	...	...	0724	0727	...	0749	...	...	0851	...	...	...
118	**Nîmes** Pont-du-Gard d.	...	...	...	...	...	...	...	0636	...	...	0704	...	...	...	0734	0738	...	0802	...	...	0906	...	...	...
128	**Nîmes** Centre d.	...	0505r	0540t	...	0614	0644	0649	0649	...	0714	0716	...	...	...	0746	0751	...	0816	...	0846	0918	...	...	...
154	Lunel d.	...	0523r	0557t	...	0631	0702	0709	0709	...	0732	0734	...	...	...	0804	0810	...	0834	...	0904	0935	...	...	...
178	**Montpellier** Saint-Roch a.	...	0542r	0615t	...	0649	0720	0733	0733	...	0750	0752	...	...	...	0822	0835	...	0852	...	0922	0953	...	...	...
	Montpellier Saint-Roch d.	...	0550	0618	...	0653	0724	...	0737	0754	0754	0756	...	...	...	0826	0837	...	0855	...	0926	0956	...	...	...
198	Frontignan d.	...	0602	0629	...	0705	0741	...	0754	0805	0805	0808	...	...	...	0838	0854	...	0906	...	0938	1008	...	...	...
205	Sète d.	...	0610	0636	...	0712	0748	...	0800	0812	0812	0815	...	...	...	0845	0859	...	0913	...	0944	1015	...	...	...
228	Agde d.	...	0625	0653	...	0726	0804	...	...	0827	0827	0829	...	...	...	0859	...	...	0928	...	0958	1029	...	...	...
249	Béziers d.	...	0638	0709	...	0738	0819	...	...	0840	0840	0842	...	...	...	0912	...	...	0941	...	1011	1041	...	...	...
	Toulouse Matabiau **320** d.	...	|	|	...	|	|	...	...	|	|	|	...	0718	0718q	|	...	...	|	...	|	|	0918	0918	0918
275	**Narbonne** a.	...	0652	0726	...	0754	0836	...	...	0854	0854	0856	...	0851	0851q	0926	...	...	0954	...	1025	1057	1052	1051	1051
	Narbonne d.	0704	0704	0729	0735	0806	...	...	...	...	...	...	...	0902	0904	...	...	1005	1005	...	▬	...	1105	1104	1104
	Toulouse Matabiau **320** a.	|	|	0912	|	|	...	...	...	...	...	...	...	|	|	...	...	|	|	...	...	...	|	|	|
296	Port la Nouvelle d.	0717	0717	...	0748	0819	...	...	...	...	...	...	...	0917	0918	...	...	1018	1018	...	...	...	1118	1118	1118
330	Rivesaltes d.	0741	0741	...	0811	0842	...	...	...	...	...	...	...	0941	0943	...	...	1041	1041	...	©	...	1141	1142	1143
338	**Perpignan** a.	0748	0748	...	0817	0848	...	...	...	...	...	...	...	0948	0950	...	...	1048	1048	...	J	...	1146	1148	1150
	Perpignan d.	0755	0755	...	...	0855	...	...	...	...	...	...	0920	0955	...	...	...	...	...	1055	1100	...	1153	1155	...
360	Argelès sur Mer d.	0811	0811	...	...	0911	...	...	...	...	...	...	0937	1011	...	...	...	...	...	1111	1116	...	1208	1211	...
365	Collioure d.	0816	0816	...	...	0916	...	...	...	...	...	...	0942	1016	...	...	...	...	...	1116	1122	...	1213	1216	...
368	Port Vendres d.	0820	0820	...	...	0920	...	...	...	...	...	...	0946	1020	...	...	...	...	...	1120	1125	...	1217	1219	...
373	Banyuls sur Mer d.	0825	0825	...	...	0925	...	...	...	...	...	...	0951	1025	...	...	...	...	...	1125	1131	...	1222	1225	...
380	Cerbère **657** a.	0831	0831	...	...	0931	...	...	...	...	...	...	0957	1031	...	...	...	...	...	1131	1137	...	1228	1231	...
382	**Portbou** **657** a.	0845	0845	...	...	0945	...	...	...	...	...	...	...	1045	...	...	...	...	...	1145	1151	...	1245	...	...

A – ① to June 27; Ⓐ July 4 - Aug. 26; ① from Aug. 29 (also Nov. 2).
B – Ⓐ until Sept. 9 (not July 15).
D – ⑦ to Sept. 4 (not Aug. 14); Ⓑ from Sept. 11 (not Oct. 30, 31, Nov. 11).
J – July 2 - Aug. 28.
X – To Luxembourg (Table **379**).

b – Not Aug. 15, Nov. 1.
c – ⑥⑦ (also July 14, 15, Nov. 11). Timings vary by up to 19 minutes on July 15. Also runs on Nov. 1 from Montpellier Saint-Roch to Paris.
d – Not July 15, 16, Aug. 15, Oct. 31, Nov. 1, 12.
e – Also Aug. 15, Nov. 1.
f – Lille **Flandres**.
g – ① to Sept. 5 (not Aug. 15); ①–⑥ from Sept. 12 (not Oct. 31, Nov. 1, 12).
h – Not July 14, 15, Nov. 1, 11.
j – 2037 on ⑦ (also Nov. 1; not Aug. 14).
k – Not July 2 - Aug. 28.
m – Also Aug. 16, Nov. 2; not July 15, Aug. 15, Oct. 31, Nov. 11.
n – Not Oct. 23.

q – Until July 15 depart Toulouse *0657* and change trains at Carcassonne (a. *0804*, d. 0821).
r – ① to Sept. 5 (not Aug. 15); Ⓐ from Sept. 12.
s – Not Nov. 7 – 10, 14 – 18.
t – Ⓐ to Sept. 9; ⚒ from Sept. 12.
v – Not July 15, Oct. 31.
y – Also July 14, Nov. 11; not July 16, Nov. 12.
z – Not Nov. 21 – 25, 28 – 30, Dec. 1, 2.

TGV – High-speed train. 🅁. 🍸.
AVE – Spanish high-speed train. 🅁. 🍸.

• – Not Aug. 13, 14. Lille **Flandres**.
△ – Runs up to 4 minutes later Marseille - Toulouse on ⑥⑦.
■ – (12) Marseille - Barcelona - Madrid and v.v.
‡ – Vitrolles Aéroport Marseille-Provence ✈. A shuttle bus runs to the airport terminal (journey time: 5 minutes). See also Table **351**.
★ – *INTERCITÉS*. 🅁. 🍸.
⊠ – OUIGO low-cost TGV service. Internet bookings only at www.ouigo.com

PORTBOU - PERPIGNAN - MONTPELLIER - MARSEILLE, LYON and PARIS 355

TER services. See pages 205 and 206 for *TGV*, *AVE* and *INTERCITÉS* services. See Table **319** for overnight *Intercités de Nuit* services Paris - Portbou and Cerbère - Paris. Timings may vary by up to 3 minutes. Subject to alteration on June 18, Oct. 29–31, Nov. 1, 12.

km			Ⓐ	Ⓐ	Ⓒ	Ⓐ	Ⓒ		Ⓐ	Ⓐ	Ⓒ	Ⓐ		B	⑥ k	Ⓐ	Ⓒ	Ⓐ	Ⓐ	Ⓐ	Ⓐ	Ⓒ k	⑥ J	D
	Marseille St Charles 351 d.	0820	...	...	...	...	...	...	...	...	...	...	1218	...	...	...	...	...	...	...	...	...	...	...
	Vitrolles Aéroport Marseille ‡ d.	0838	...	...	...	...	...	...	...	...	...	...	1237	...	...	...	...	...	...	...	...	...	...	...
	Miramas 351 d.	0855	...	...	...	...	...	...	...	...	...	...	1255	...	...	...	...	...	...	...	...	...	...	...
	Arles 351 d.	0915	...	...	...	...	...	...	...	...	...	...	1314	...	...	...	...	...	...	...	...	...	...	...
0	**Avignon** Centre d.	|	...	1023	1043	...	...	1135	1214	...	...	...	|	1335	1335	...	...	...	...	...	...	1535	1535	1535
21	Tarascon-sur-Rhône d.	0924	...	1036	1056	...	...	1149	1226	...	...	...	1323	1348	1349	...	...	...	...	...	...	1547	1547	1549
39	**Nîmes** Pont-du-Gard d.	0934	...	1048	1108	...	...	1202	1237	...	...	...	1333	1401	1401	...	...	...	...	...	...	1559	1559	1601
49	**Nîmes** Centre d.	0946	...	1100	1120	...	...	1214	1249	...	...	...	1345	1413	1412	1514	...	...	...	1546	...	1612	1612	1614
	Lunel d.	1005	...	1118	1138	...	...	1231	1308	...	...	...	1402	1431	1431	1532	...	...	...	1602	...	1631	1631	1632
	Montpellier Saint-Roch a.	1023	...	1136	1156	...	...	1249	1334	...	...	...	1419	1449	1449	1550	...	...	...	1619	...	1648	1648	1650
	Montpellier Saint-Roch d.	*1037*	1050	1151	1200	...	...	1253	...	1351	...	...	1422	1453	1453	1554	...	...	...	1622	...	1652	1652	1654
	Frontignan d.	*1049*	1102	1204	1211	...	...	1305	...	1404	...	...	1439	1504	1505	1605	...	...	...	1633	...	1704	1704	1706
	Sète d.	*1054*	1109	1211	1218	...	...	1312	...	1412	...	...	1456**z**	1511	1512	1612	...	...	...	1640	...	1711	1711	1713
	Agde d.	...	1124	1228	1233	...	...	1327	...	1427	...	...	1512	1526	1527	1627	...	...	...	1654	...	1726	1726	1727
	Béziers d.	...	1138	1243	1246	...	...	1340	...	1441	...	...	1527	1539	1540	1640	...	...	...	1708	...	1740	1740	1740
	Toulouse Matabiau **320** d.	...	|	|	|	1118	1118	|	...	|	1318	1318	|	|	|	|	1513	1513**h**	...	|	...	|	|	|
	Narbonne a.	...	1154	1256	1301	1251	1251	1354	...	1455	1451	1451	1543	1554	1555	1654	1649	1649**h**	...	1724	...	1754	1754	1754
	Narbonne d.	...	1205	▬	...	1304	1304	1406	...	...	1504	1502	...	1606	1604	▬	1706	1704	...	1727	1738	1804	1804	1805
	Toulouse Matabiau **320** a.	...	|	...	...	|	|	|	...	...	|	|	...	|	|	...	|	|	...	1907	|	|	|	|
	Port la Nouvelle d.	...	1218	...	...	1318	1318	1419	...	...	1519	1518	...	1619	1617	...	1720	1717	...	...	1750	1817	1817	1817
	Rivesaltes d.	...	1241	Ⓒ	...	1343	1344	1442	...	...	1543	1543	...	1642	1641	Ⓐ	1744	1742	...	...	1813	1841	1841	1841
	Perpignan a.	...	1248	J	...	1350	1350	1448	...	...	1549	1550	...	1648	1648		1750	1748	...	...	1820	1848	1848	1848
	Perpignan d.	...	1255	1255	...	...	1355	1455	...	...	1555	...	...	1655	...	1728	1755	...	1755	...	1828	...	1853	1855
	Argelès sur Mer d.	...	1311	1311	...	...	1410	1511	...	...	1611	...	...	1711	...	1744	1810	...	1811	...	1844	...	1908	1911
	Collioure d.	...	1316	1316	...	...	1415	1516	...	...	1616	...	...	1716	...	1750	1815	...	1816	...	1850	...	1913	1916
	Port Vendres d.	...	1320	1320	...	...	1419	1520	...	...	1620	...	...	1720	...	1753	1818	...	1819	...	1853	...	1917	1920
	Banyuls sur Mer d.	...	1325	1325	...	...	1424	1525	...	...	1625	...	...	1725	...	1759	1823	...	1824	...	1859	...	1922	1925
	Cerbère 657 a.	...	1331	1331	...	...	1430	1531	...	...	1631	...	...	1731	...	1805	1829	...	1830	...	1905	...	1928	1931
	Portbou 657 a.	...	1345	1345	...	...	1445**k**	1545	...	...	1640**k**	...	...	1745	...	...	1845	...	1845	...	...	...	...	1945

	Ⓐ	Ⓐ k	Ⓐ		⑤–⑦ p	Ⓑ	Ⓐ	⑦ A	Ⓐ k	Ⓐ k	C	Ⓐ	⚒	Ⓐ	†	Ⓐ			⑥ J		Ⓑ d	①–④ E⊗	F⊗	G⊗
Marseille St Charles 351 d.	...	...	...	...	...	...	...	...	...	1620	1620	...	...	...	...	...	...	...	...	1819	...	...	...	...
Vitrolles Aéroport Marseille ‡ d.	...	...	...	...	...	...	...	...	...	1639	1639	...	...	...	...	...	...	...	...	1838	...	...	...	...
Miramas 351 d.	...	...	...	...	...	...	...	...	...	1655	1655	...	...	...	...	...	...	...	...	1855	...	...	...	...
Arles 351 d.	...	...	...	...	...	...	...	...	...	1715	1715	...	...	...	...	...	...	...	...	1915	...	...	...	...
Avignon Centre d.	...	...	...	...	...	...	1643	...	...	|	|	1722	1732	1732	1733	1815	1835	...	...	|	1943	2132	2143**e**	...
Tarascon-sur-Rhône d.	...	...	...	...	...	...	1656	...	...	1724	1724	|	1744	1744	1746	1827	1849	...	...	1924	1956	|	|	...
Nîmes Pont-du-Gard d.	...	...	...	...	...	...	1708	...	...	1734	1734	|	1756	1756	1757	1839	1901	...	...	1935	2008	|	|	...
Nîmes Centre d.	...	1644	1648	...	...	1719	1719	...	...	1746	1746	1751	1808	1808	1808	1849	1913	...	...	1946	2019	2159	2219	2219**t**
Lunel d.	...	1702	1715	...	...	1737	1737	...	1742	1804	1807	1814	1831	1831	1831	1917	1931	...	...	2005	2037	2216	2237	2237**t**
Montpellier Saint-Roch a.	...	1720	1730	...	...	1755	1755	...	1806	1822	1826	1831	1849	1849	1850	1930	1949	...	...	2022	2054	2235	2255	2255**t**
Montpellier Saint-Roch d.	1712	1724	1733	...	...	1759	1759	1804	1809	1826	1834	...	1853	1853	1854	1936	1953	...	...	2026	2058	2259	2259	2259
Frontignan d.	1728	1735	1750	...	...	1811	1811	1815	1826	1837	1851	...	1905	1905	1906	1953	2005	...	...	2037	2110	2310	2310	2310
Sète d.	1735	1742	1755	...	...	1818	1818	1823	1832	1844	1857	...	1912	1912	1913	2002	2012	...	...	2044	2116	2317	2317	2317
Agde d.	1752	1759	1811**v**	...	...	1832	1832	1837	1848	1900	1913	...	1927	1927	1927	2018	2026	...	...	2059	2131	2332	2332	2332
Béziers d.	1807	1813	1824**v**	...	...	1845	1845	1847	1903	1914	1928	...	1941	1941	1941	2033	2040	...	...	2113	2144	2347	2347	2347
Toulouse Matabiau **320** d.	|	|	|	1718	1718	|	|	...	|	|	|	...	|	|	|	|	|	1920**r**	...	|	|	|	|	|
Narbonne a.	1823	1827	1838**v**	1851	1851	1859	1859	...	1922	1930	1946	...	1955	1955	1955	2049	2054	2054**r**	...	2132	2158	0003	0003	0003
Narbonne d.	1835	...	...	1901	1901	...	...	...	...	...	...	...	...	2004	2004	▬	...	2104	...	...	2204	...	...	...
Toulouse Matabiau **320** a.	|	...	...	|	|	...	...	...	...	...	...	...	...	|	|	...	...	|	...	...	|	...	...	...
Port la Nouvelle d.	1848	...	...	1917	1917	...	...	...	...	...	...	...	...	2017	2017	...	...	2118	...	...	2217	...	...	...
Rivesaltes d.	1911	...	...	1943	1943	...	...	...	...	...	...	...	...	2040	2040	†	...	2143	...	...	2240	...	...	...
Perpignan a.	1917	...	...	1950	1950	...	...	...	...	...	...	...	...	2047	2047	J	...	2150	...	...	2246	...	...	...
Perpignan d.	...	...	...	...	1954	...	...	...	...	...	...	...	...	2052	...	2130	...	...	2209	...	...	...	...	...
Argelès sur Mer d.	...	...	...	...	2010	...	...	...	...	...	...	...	...	2107	...	2147	...	...	2226	...	...	...	...	...
Collioure d.	...	...	...	...	2015	...	...	...	...	...	...	...	...	2112	...	2152	...	...	2231	...	...	...	...	...
Port Vendres d.	...	...	...	...	2019	...	...	...	...	...	...	...	...	2116	...	2156	...	...	2235	...	...	...	...	...
Banyuls sur Mer d.	...	...	...	...	2024	...	...	...	...	...	...	...	...	2121	...	2201	...	...	2240	...	...	...	...	...
Cerbère 657 a.	...	...	...	...	2031	...	...	...	...	...	...	...	...	2127	...	2207	...	...	2246	...	...	...	...	...
Portbou 657 a.	...	...	...	...	...	...	...	...	...	...	...	...	...	...	...	...	...	...	...	...	...	...	...	...

	Ⓐ	Ⓐ		Ⓐ	Ⓐ	Ⓐ △	Ⓐ J	Ⓐ k	Ⓐ	⑥	Ⓐ	⚒	Ⓒ	Ⓐ J	Ⓐ k	Ⓐ ●	Ⓐ	Ⓒ	Ⓒ	Ⓐ	Ⓐ	Ⓐ	Ⓒ	Ⓐ
Portbou 657 d.	...	...	...	...	...	...	...	...	...	...	...	...	...	...	...	...	...	...	...	...	...	...	...	...
Cerbère 657 d.	...	...	...	...	...	...	...	...	...	...	0522	...	...	...	...	...	...	...	...	0624	0654	0724	0724	...
Banyuls sur Mer d.	...	...	...	...	...	...	...	...	...	...	0528	...	...	...	...	...	...	...	...	0630	0701	0731	0730	...
Port Vendres d.	...	...	...	...	...	...	...	...	...	...	0534	...	...	...	...	...	...	...	...	0636	0706	0736	0736	...
Collioure d.	...	...	...	...	...	...	...	...	...	...	0537	...	...	...	...	...	...	...	...	0640	0710	0739	0739	...
Argelès sur Mer d.	...	...	...	...	...	...	...	...	...	...	0542	...	...	...	...	...	...	...	...	0645	0715	0745	0745	...
Perpignan a.	...	...	...	...	...	...	...	...	...	...	0558	...	...	...	...	...	...	...	...	0700	0731	0800	0800	...
Perpignan d.	...	...	...	...	...	0538	...	...	...	...	▬	0604	...	...	...	...	0638	0707	...	0707	0738	0807	0807	...
Rivesaltes d.	...	...	...	...	...	0545	...	...	...	...	...	0610	...	...	...	...	0644	0714	...	0714	0744	0814	0814	...
Port la Nouvelle d.	...	...	...	...	...	0608	...	...	...	...	...	0635	...	...	...	...	0708	0738	...	0738	0808	0838	0837	...
Toulouse Matabiau **320** d.	...	...	...	...	...	|	...	...	...	...	Ⓐ	|	...	...	...	...	|	|	...	|	|	|	|	...
Narbonne a.	...	...	...	...	...	0622	...	...	...	...	k	0648	...	...	...	...	0722	0751	...	0751	0822	0851	0851	...
Narbonne d.	...	...	0530	...	0554	...	0625	0630	...	0630	0636	0657	0654	0658	0702	0717	...	...	0801	0803	0827	0909	0904	0904
Toulouse Matabiau **320** a.	...	...	|	...	|	...	|	|	...	|	|	0830	|	|	|	|	...	...	|	|	|	1042	|	|
Béziers d.	0446	...	0546	...	0609	...	0642	0646	...	0646	0653	...	0712	0713	0717	0735	...	...	0815	0820	0843	...	0921	0921
Agde d.	0500	...	0600	...	0624	...	0655	0659	...	0659	0707	...	0727	0727	0730	0749	...	...	0828	0832	0856	...	0933	0933
Sète d.	0516	...	0617	...	0640	...	0713	0714	...	0714	0724	...	0743	0742	0744	0806	...	...	0842	0847	0912	...	0947	0948
Frontignan d.	0522	...	0622	...	0645	...	0719	0719	...	0719	0730	...	0748	0747	0750	0812	...	...	0848	0852	0917	...	0952	0953
Montpellier Saint-Roch a.	0533	...	0634	...	0702	...	0730	0731	...	0731	0747	...	0804	0804	0802	0828	...	...	0859	0903	0929	...	1004	1005
Montpellier Saint-Roch d.	0537	...	0637	0641	0706	...	0733	0734	0738	0739	0749	...	0808	0806	0806	0832	...	...	0902	0906	...	...	1008	1008
Lunel d.	0552	...	0651	0656	0723	...	0748	0749	0754	0755	0810	...	0825	0823	0823	0849	...	...	0919	0923	...	...	1025	1025
Nîmes Centre d.	0611	0645	0713	0727	0745	...	0812	0813	0824	0826	...	...	0846	0845	0845	0905	...	...	0940	0941	...	...	1046	1046
Nîmes Pont-du-Gard d.	0622	0655	0724	0736	0755	...	0822	0823	|	0836	...	...	0855	0855	0855	...	...	...	0949	...	...	...	1056	1056
Tarascon-sur-Rhône d.	0631	0706	0733	0746	0806	...	0833	0833	|	0847	...	...	0906	0906	0906	...	...	...	0959	...	...	...	1107	1107
Avignon Centre a.	|	0719	|	0759	0818	...	|	|	0900	0900	...	...	0918	0920	0918	...	...	...	|	...	...	...	1119	1119
Arles 351 d.	0640	...	0741	...	...	...	0842	0842	...	...	...	...	...	...	...	...	...	...	1008	...	...	...	...	...
Miramas 351 d.	0701	...	0802	...	...	...	0902	0903	...	...	...	...	...	...	...	...	...	...	1031	...	...	...	...	...
Vitrolles Aéroport Marseille ‡ d.	0718	...	0818	...	...	...	0921	0921	...	...	...	...	...	...	...	...	...	...	1048	...	...	...	...	...
Marseille St Charles 351 a.	0737**f**	...	0836	...	...	...	0940	0940	...	...	...	...	...	...	...	...	...	...	1106	...	...	...	...	...

A – ⑦ (not July 10 - Aug. 28, Oct. 23, 30). To St Chély d'Apcher (Table **332**).
B – Ⓑ (daily June 26 - Sept. 2).
C – Ⓒ (daily July 2 - Aug. 28).
D – ①–⑤ to June 24; Ⓑ June 27 - Sept. 2; Ⓐ from Sept. 5.
E – ①–④ to Sept. 8 (also Aug. 26; not July 13, 14, Aug. 15).
F – ⑤ to Aug. 19 (also July 13); Ⓐ from Sept. 12.
G – ⑤⑥† to Aug. 21 (also Aug. 27, 28, Sept. 3, 4); daily from Sept. 10.
J – July 2 - Aug. 28.

d – Runs daily Avignon - Nîmes Centre.
e – 2148 until July 15.
f – Arrives 0745 July 19–22, 26–29, Aug. 15 and on ②–⑤ Sept. 20 - Oct. 28.
h – From Sept. 26 Toulouse d. 1518, Narbonne a. 1652.
k – Not July 2 - Aug. 28.
p – Also July 13, 14, Aug. 15, Nov. 1, 10.
r – Daily to July 22; Ⓐ July 25 - Aug. 26; daily from Aug. 29.
t – 22–25 minutes **earlier** on July 14, Aug. 15.
v – Sète - Narbonne July 4 - Aug. 26 only.

z – Arrives 1444.

⊗ – Does not run Béziers - Narbonne on ①–⑤ Aug. 22 - Oct. 7, ①–⑥ Oct. 10–28.
△ – Runs 5 minutes **earlier** July 4 - Aug. 26.
● – From Carcassonne (d. 0642) and Lezignan (d. 0700).
‡ – Vitrolles Aéroport Marseille-Provence ✈. A shuttle bus runs to the airport terminal (journey time: 5 minutes). For additional trains see Table **351**.

FRANCE

355 PORTBOU - PERPIGNAN - MONTPELLIER - MARSEILLE, LYON and PARIS

TER services. See pages 205 and 206 for *TGV*, *AVE* and *INTERCITÉS* services. See Table **319** for overnight *Intercités de Nuit* service Cerbère - Paris.
Timings may vary by up to 3 minutes. Subject to alteration on June 18, Oct. 29–31, Nov. 1, 12.

	Ⓐ s	Ⓐ	†	⑥		Ⓐ	© J	Ⓐ s	Ⓐ	Ⓐ	Ⓐ	©	Ⓐ	† J	⚒	H	Ⓐ	©		Ⓐ	⑥ k	B		⚒
Portbou 657 d.	...	...	...	0903	...	...	...	1004	...	...	...	1104k	...	1204	1204	...	...	1303k	...	...	...	1404	...	...
Cerbère 657 d.	0825	...	0921	0924	...	...	1012	1025	...	...	...	1125	...	1225	1225	...	...	1324	...	...	...	1425	...	...
Banyuls sur Mer d.	0832	...	0928	0930	...	...	1018	1031	...	...	...	1131	...	1231	1231	...	...	1331	...	...	...	1431	...	...
Port Vendres d.	0837	...	0933	0936	...	...	1024	1037	...	...	...	1136	...	1236	1236	...	...	1336	...	...	...	1437	...	...
Collioure d.	0841	...	0937	0939	...	...	1027	1040	...	...	...	1140	...	1240	1240	...	...	1339	...	...	...	1440	...	...
Argelès sur Mer d.	0846	...	0942	0945	...	...	1033	1045	...	...	...	1145	...	1245	1245	...	...	1345	...	...	...	1445	...	...
Perpignan a.	0902	...	0958	1000	...	...	1048	1101	...	...	...	1200	...	1300	1300	...	...	1404	...	...	...	1501	...	...
Perpignan d.	0909	1007	1007	1007	...	...	...	...	1111	...	1204	1207	...	...	1307	...	1406	1411	...	...	1507	1507	...	...
Rivesaltes d.	0915	1014	1014	1014	...	...	...	...	1118	...	1210	1214	...	...	1314	...	1413	1417	...	...	1514	1514	...	...
Port la Nouvelle d.	0938	1040	1040	1038	...	...	...	...	1140	...	1235	1238	...	...	1337	...	1437	1440	...	...	1537	1538	...	...
Toulouse Matabiau 320 d.	|	|	|	|	...	...	...	...	|	...	|	|	...	...	|	...	|	|	...	...	|	|	...	...
Narbonne a.	0952	1054	1054	1057z	...	...	...	...	1153	...	1248	1252	...	...	1351	...	1451	1452	...	...	1550	1551	...	...
Narbonne d.	...	1109	1109	1111z	1104	...	...	...	1203	1232	1306	1303	1304	...	▬	1428	1509	1510	1504	...	1553	1604	1630	...
Toulouse Matabiau 320 a.	...	1242	1242	1242	|	...	...	...	|	|	1439	|	|	...	...	|	1642	1642	|	...	|	|	|	...
Béziers d.	...	...	...	...	1119	...	...	...	1219	1251	...	1318	1318	...	...	1445	...	...	1519	...	1607	1620	1645	...
Agde d.	...	...	...	...	1131	...	...	...	1231	1304	...	1331	1331	...	...	1500	...	...	1531	...	1631v	1632	1658	...
Sète d.	...	...	...	...	1146	...	...	...	1246	1324	...	1346	1346	...	...	1516	...	...	1546	1606	1646	1647	1712	...
Frontignan d.	...	...	...	...	1151	...	...	...	1251	1329	...	1351	1351	...	©	1522	...	...	1551	1613	1652	1652	1718	...
Montpellier Saint-Roch a.	...	...	...	...	1203	...	...	...	1303	1346	...	1403	1403	...	k	1535	...	...	1603	1632	1703	1704	1730	...
Montpellier Saint-Roch d.	...	...	...	...	1207	1232	...	...	1306	...	...	1407	1407	...	1537	1538	...	...	1607	1636	1706	1707	1734	1739
Lunel d.	...	...	...	...	1224	1254	...	...	1323	...	...	1423	1423	...	1553	1554	...	...	1624	1656	1722	1724	1751	1759
Nîmes Centre d.	...	...	...	...	1245	1320	...	...	1344	...	...	1445	1445	...	1614	1612	...	...	1645	1715	1743	1745	1812	1822
Nîmes Pont-du-Gard d.	...	...	...	...	1255	|	...	...	1355	...	...	1455	1455	...	1623	1623	...	...	1655	1725	1753	1755	1822	1831
Tarascon-sur-Rhône d.	...	...	...	...	1306	|	...	...	1406	...	...	1506	1506	...	1632	1632	...	...	1705	1737	1806	1806	1831	1842
Avignon Centre a.	...	...	...	...	1318	1354	...	...	1418	...	...	1518	1518	...	|	|	...	...	1717	1752	1818	1819	|	1854
Arles 351 d.	...	...	...	...	...	...	...	...	...	...	...	...	...	...	1641	1641	...	...	...	...	...	...	1841	...
Miramas 351 d.	...	...	...	...	...	...	...	...	...	...	...	...	...	...	1702	1702	...	...	...	...	...	...	1903	...
Vitrolles Aéroport Marseille ‡ d.	...	...	...	...	...	...	...	...	...	...	...	...	...	...	1719	1719	...	...	...	...	...	...	1919	...
Marseille St Charles 351 a.	...	...	...	...	...	...	...	...	...	...	...	...	...	...	1737	1737	...	...	...	...	...	...	1937	...

	Ⓐ	© J	© k		Ⓐ k	Ⓐ J		Ⓐ	©	Ⓐ	© n	⑦ J	Ⓐ	†	H	© k	©	⑤ F	A	Ⓐ	† J	⑥ J	† J	⑥ J
Portbou 657 d.	...	...	1455	...	...	...	1604	...	...	...	1657k	...	...	...	1804	...	1904	...	...	2004	2014	...	...	...
Cerbère 657 d.	...	1514	1514	...	...	...	1625	...	...	...	1720	1725	...	...	1825	...	1925	...	...	2025	2035	2113	2217	2313
Banyuls sur Mer d.	...	1521	1522	...	...	...	1631	...	...	...	1727	1731	...	...	1831	...	1931	...	...	2031	2041	2119	2223	2319
Port Vendres d.	...	1527	1528	...	...	...	1637	...	...	...	1733	1736	...	...	1837	...	1937	...	...	2037	2047	2125	2229	2325
Collioure d.	...	1531	1532	...	...	...	1640	...	...	...	1737	1740	...	...	1840	...	1940	...	...	2040	2050	2128	2232	2328
Argelès sur Mer d.	...	1537	1538	...	...	...	1645	...	...	...	1743	1745	...	...	1845	...	1945	...	...	2045	2055	2134	2238	2334
Perpignan a.	...	1554	1556	...	...	...	1701	...	...	...	1800	1800	...	...	1901	...	2001	...	...	2101	2118	2149	2253	2349
Perpignan d.	1603	1601	1603	...	...	...	1707	...	...	1810	1810	1810	...	...	1907	1907	2007	2017	2017	...	...	...	...	...
Rivesaltes d.	1609	1608	1610	...	...	...	1714	...	...	1816	1816	1816	...	...	1914	1914	2014	2025	2025	...	...	...	...	...
Port la Nouvelle d.	1633	1632	1634	...	...	...	1737	...	...	1840	1839	1839	...	...	1938	1937	2037	2053	2053	...	...	...	...	...
Toulouse Matabiau 320 d.	|	|	|	...	...	...	|	1650p	1650p	|	|	|	...	...	|	|	|	|	|	...	...	...	...	...
Narbonne a.	1646	1646	1646	...	...	...	1751	1827	1827	1852	1851	1851	...	...	1951	1951	2051	2107	2107	...	...	...	...	...
Narbonne d.	1655	1656	1656	1704	1724	1724	1804	1830	1830	1906	1907	1909	1904	1904	2004	2006	2102	2111	2124	...	...	...	...	...
Toulouse Matabiau 320 a.	1830	1830	1830	|	|	|	|	|	|	2042	2042	2042	|	|	|	|	|	|	|	...	...	...	...	...
Béziers d.	...	...	...	1720	1742	1741	1821	1845	1845	...	...	...	1921	1921	2025	2021	2118	2130	2142	...	...	...	...	...
Agde d.	...	...	...	1733	1756	1757	1833	1859	1859	...	...	...	1935	1935	2037	2033	2130	2146	2156	...	...	...	...	...
Sète d.	...	...	...	1747	1813	1814	1848	1914	1914	...	...	...	1951	1951	2051	2049	2145	2202	2213	...	...	...	...	...
Frontignan d.	...	...	...	1753	1819	1820	1853	1919	1920	...	...	...	1957	1957	2056	2054	2150	2207	2218	...	...	...	...	...
Montpellier Saint-Roch a.	...	...	...	1804	1832	1834	1905	1930	1932	...	...	...	2008	2008	2107	2109	2202	2218	2229	...	...	...	...	...
Montpellier Saint-Roch d.	...	...	...	1807	1835	1837	1910	1934	1936	...	...	...	2012	2012	2110	2113	2206r	2222	2233t	...	...	...	...	...
Lunel d.	...	...	...	1823	1849	1859	1927	1957	1959	...	...	...	2027	2029	2126	2129	2223r	2239	2250t	...	...	...	...	...
Nîmes Centre d.	...	...	...	1846	1905	1919	1948	2016	2016	...	...	...	2048	2048	2145	2147	2242r	2256	2308t	...	...	...	...	...
Nîmes Pont-du-Gard d.	...	...	...	1855	...	...	1958	...	...	...	...	...	2058	...	...	...	...	...	...	...	...	...	...	...
Tarascon-sur-Rhône d.	...	...	...	1907	...	...	2009	...	...	...	...	...	2109	...	...	...	...	...	...	...	...	...	...	...
Avignon Centre a.	...	...	...	1920	...	...	2021	...	...	...	...	...	2121	...	...	...	...	...	...	...	...	...	...	...
Arles 351 d.	...	...	...	...	...	...	...	...	...	...	...	...	...	...	...	...	...	...	...	...	...	...	...	...
Miramas 351 d.	...	...	...	...	...	...	...	...	...	...	...	...	...	...	...	...	...	...	...	...	...	...	...	...
Vitrolles Aéroport Marseille ‡ d.	...	...	...	...	...	...	...	...	...	...	...	...	...	...	...	...	...	...	...	...	...	...	...	...
Marseille St Charles 351 a.	...	...	...	...	...	...	...	...	...	...	...	...	...	...	...	...	...	...	...	...	...	...	...	...

A – ①–④ until Sept. 8 (not July 13, 14, Aug. 15); Ⓐ from Sept. 12.
B – Ⓑ (daily June 26 - Sept. 2).
F – ⑤ until Sept. 9 (also July 13).
H – Ⓐ (daily June 27 - Sept. 2).
J – July 2 - Aug. 28.

k – Not July 2 - Aug. 28.
n – Not ⑦ July 3 - Aug. 28.
p – 1655 July 18 - Sept. 25.

r – Not July 14, Aug. 15.
s – Not Nov. 7 – 10, 14 – 18.
t – From Sept. 12.
v – Arrives 1618.
z – From Oct. 1 Narbonne a. 1054, d. 1113.

‡ – Vitrolles Aéroport Marseille-Provence ✈. A shuttle bus runs to the airport terminal (journey time: 5 minutes). See also Table **351**.

356 NÎMES - LE GRAU-DU-ROI

JUNE 25 - AUGUST 28

km		©							©	Ⓐ			©					①–⑥	⑦		©	Ⓐ
0	**Nîmes** Centre d.	0902	1030	...	1310	1408	...	1733	1852	1854	...	Le Grau-du-Roi d.	1017	...	1257	...	1618	1731	1731	1845	2005	2006
39	Aigues-Mortes d.	0950	1112	...	1350	1446	...	1826	1939	1938	...	Aigues-Mortes d.	1026	...	1306	...	1627	1739	1739	1853	2014	2015
45	Le Grau-du-Roi a.	0957	1119	...	1357	1453	...	1833	1946	1946	...	**Nîmes** Centre a.	1118	...	1356	...	1710	1831	1833	1939	2102	2101

FROM AUGUST 29

km		Ad		⑥⑦ C		A							Ⓐ e		Ad		⑥⑦ C		A			
0	**Nîmes** Centre d.	1030	...	1253	...	1733	...	...	...	...	...	Le Grau-du-Roi d.	0636	...	1145	...	1618	...	1844	...	...	...
39	Aigues-Mortes d.	1112	...	1334	...	1826	...	...	...	...	...	Aigues-Mortes d.	0644	...	1154	...	1627	...	1852	...	...	...
45	Le Grau-du-Roi a.	1119	...	1341	...	1833	...	...	...	...	...	**Nîmes** Centre a.	0732	...	1239	...	1710	...	1940	...	...	...

A – Daily Aug. 29 - Sept. 30; Ⓐ from Oct. 3.
C – ⑥⑦ Sept. 3 – 25 (not Sept. 4).

d – Not Oct. 17 – 28.
e – Runs 17 minutes later on Oct. 18, 25, Nov. 8.

BRIANÇON - GAP - GRENOBLE, VALENCE and MARSEILLE 358

SERVICE FROM JULY 4

km		Ⓐ 2	⑥ 2	Ⓐ	Ⓐ	②–⑤ d	① g	⚒	⑥	Ⓒ	Ⓑ ⊗	🚌 ⑤–① q			Ⓒ	⚒	Ⓐ ⊗		⑥ L	⑤†		🚌 ⑤⑥	Ⓑ		5790 N
0	**Briançon** d.	...	...	...	...	...	0444	...	0510	...	0609	...	0827	...	0856	...	1047	1247	1321	1424	1512	...	...	1726	2000
13	L'Argentière les Écrins d.	...	...	...	...	...	0457	...	0523	...	0621	...	0840	...	0908	...	1059	1259	1333	1436	1525	...	...	1739	2016
28	Montdauphin-Guillestre d.	...	...	...	...	...	0508	...	0534	...	0631	...	0850	...	0918	...	1110	1310	1346	1446	1537	...	...	1750	2029
45	Embrun d.	...	...	...	...	...	0523	...	0549	...	0648	...	0905	...	0933	...	1127	1331	1403	1501	1552	...	...	1806	2048
82	**Gap** a.	...	...	...	...	...	0555	...	0622	...	0725	...	0937	...	1005	...	1158	1404	1440	1533	1624	...	...	1836	|
82	**Gap** d.	...	...	0507	0537	0555	0557	*0553**	0624	0626**h**	0730	0750	0940	*0958**	1008	*1158**	1201	1407	1510	1536	1627	1645	*1656**	1839	2129
109	Veynes-Dévoluy a.	...	...	0527	0556	0614	0616	*0623**	0653	0656**h**	0750	0815	0958	*1023**	1027	*1223**	1220	1427	1532	1557	1647	1710	*1721**	1858	|
109	Veynes-Dévoluy d.	...	...	0530	0559	0617	0619	*0623**	0654	0659**p**	0755	0815	1001	*1023**	1030	*1223**	1223	1430	1535	1600	1650	1710	*1721**	1901	2203
	Vif a.	...	...	|	|	|	|	*0812**	|	|	|	|	|	*1212**	|	*1412**	|	|	|	|	|	|	*1910**	|	|
	Vif d.	...	...	|	|	|	|	0822	|	|	|	|	|	1222	|	1422	|	|	|	|	|	|	1920	|	|
	Grenoble a.	...	...	|	|	|	|	0846	|	|	|	0955**r**	|	1246	|	1446	|	|	|	|	|	1850**r**	1944	|	|
172	Die d.	...	...	|	|	0711	0714	...	0747	|	0903	...	|	...	1131	...	1324	|	1642	|	1750	...	...	|	2311
209	Crest d.	...	...	|	|	0747	0751	...	0823	|	0940	...	|	...	1208	...	1359	|	1716	|	1827	...	...	|	2347
244	**Valence** Ville **364** a.	...	...	|	|	0819	0823	...	0852	|	1015	...	|	...	1240	...	1429	|	1748	|	1903	...	...	|	|
	Valence TGV a.	...	...	|	|	0832	0833	...	0902	|	1027	...	|	...	1251	...	1441	|	1805	|	1912	...	...	|	|
	Paris Austerlitz a.	...	...	|	|	...	...	...	...	|	...	...	|	...	...	...	...	|	...	|	...	...	...	|	0755
159	Sisteron d.	0547	0555	0614	0644	...	...	...	...	0743	...	...	1044	...	...	...	...	1516	...	1641	...	...	...	1946	...
176	Château Arnoux - St Auban d.	0600	0609	0628	0658	...	...	...	...	0757	...	...	1058	...	...	...	...	1530	...	1654	...	...	...	1959	...
209	Manosque-Gréoux d.	0624	0634	0654	0727	...	...	...	...	0821	...	...	1127	...	...	...	...	1556	...	1718	...	...	...	2028	...
278	Aix en Provence ▷ d.	0708	0722	0739	0810	...	...	...	...	0910	...	...	1210	...	...	...	...	1640	...	1809	...	...	...	2111	...
315	**Marseille** St Charles ▷ a.	0749	0807	0819	0848	...	...	...	...	0949	...	...	1249	...	...	...	...	1719	...	1849	...	...	...	2149	...

km		5789 N		⚒			⚒	🚌 Ⓒ	⑥ L	Ⓒ			🚌 Ⓒ	⊗	◇		🚌 ⑤ w	⊗	⑤† ⊗	◇	Ⓑ 2	⑥	Ⓑ	Ⓑ	⑤†
	Marseille St Charles ▷ d.	...	...	...	0741	...	...	...	...	...	...	1311	...	...	...	1641	...	...	...	...	1741	1741	1841	...	...
	Aix en Provence ▷ d.	...	...	...	0825	...	...	...	...	...	...	1354	...	...	...	1724	...	...	...	...	1824	1824	1924	...	...
	Manosque-Gréoux d.	...	...	...	0909	...	...	...	...	...	...	1437	...	...	...	1808	...	...	...	...	1909	1907	2005	...	...
	Château Arnoux - St Auban d.	...	...	...	0933	...	...	...	...	...	...	1501	...	...	...	1832	...	...	...	...	1932	1930	2031	...	...
	Sisteron d.	...	...	...	0946	...	...	...	...	...	...	1517	...	...	...	1849	...	...	...	...	1945	1947	2046	...	...
	Paris Austerlitz d.	2051	...	...	|	...	...	...	...	...	...	|	...	...	...	|	...	...	...	...	...	|	|	...	...
	Valence TGV d.	|	...	...	|	...	1011	...	1200	...	...	|	...	1433	...	|	...	1749	1749	...	...	|	|	1951	1951
	Valence Ville **364** d.	|	...	...	|	...	1021	...	1213	...	...	|	...	1448	...	|	...	1758	1758	...	...	|	|	2000	2000
	Crest d.	0437	...	...	|	...	1053	...	1247	...	...	|	...	1521	...	|	...	1829	1829	...	...	|	|	2034	2034
	Die d.	0513	...	...	|	...	1133	...	1324	...	...	|	...	1558	...	|	...	1904	1904	...	...	|	|	2109	2109
0	**Grenoble** d.	|	...	0810	|	1010	|	1055**r**	|	1210	1310	|	1455**r**	|	1610	|	1805**r**	|	|	1810	...	|	|	|	|
	Vif a.	|	...	0840	|	1033	|	|	|	1240	1338	|	|	|	1633	|	|	|	|	1833	...	|	|	|	|
	Vif d.	|	...	*0851**	|	*1043**	|	|	|	*1251**	*1348**	|	|	|	*1644**	|	|	|	|	*1844**	...	|	|	|	|
109	Veynes-Dévoluy a.	0621	...	*1021**	1029	*1213**	1232	1235	1425	*1421**	*1518**	1558	1635	1658	*1814**	1930	1945	1958	1958	*2014**	...	2030	2125	2209	2209
	Veynes-Dévoluy d.	|	...	*1021**	1032	*1213**	1235	1235	1428	*1421**	*1518**	1601	1635	1701	*1814**	1934	1945	2001	2001	*2014**	...	2033	2128	2212	2212
	Gap a.	0651	...	*1046**	1051	*1238**	1254	1300	1447	*1446**	*1543**	1621	1700	1724	*1839**	1955	2010	2021	2021	*2039**	...	2054	2156	2233	2233
	Gap d.	|	...	...	1054	...	1257	...	1449	...	...	1630	...	1727	...	1959	...	...	2054	...	...	2057	...	...	2236
	Embrun d.	0730	...	...	1128	...	1330	...	1522	...	...	1707	...	1807	...	2049**t**	...	...	2133	...	...	2133	...	...	2307
	Montdauphin-Guillestre d.	0749	...	...	1143	...	1345	...	1539	...	...	1725	...	1822	...	2105	...	...	2148	...	...	2148	...	...	2322
	L'Argentière les Écrins d.	0803	...	...	1154	...	1356	...	1551	...	...	1740	...	1832	...	2116	...	...	2159	...	...	2200	...	...	2333
	Briançon a.	0822	...	...	1207	...	1407	...	1602	...	...	1751	...	1844	...	2127	...	...	2210	...	...	2211	...	...	2344

OTHER LOCAL TRAINS MARSEILLE - AIX EN PROVENCE (2nd class)

From Marseille St Charles at 0623 Ⓐ, 0653, 0711 Ⓐ, 0723 Ⓐ, 0753, 0811 Ⓐ, 0823 Ⓐ, 0853, 0923 Ⓐ, 0941 Ⓐ, 0953 Ⓒ, 1053 Ⓒ, 1123 Ⓐ, 1153, 1223 Ⓐ, 1253, 1323 Ⓐ, 1353, 1423 Ⓐ, 1453, 1523, 1553 Ⓐ, 1611 Ⓐ, 1623 Ⓐ, 1653, 1711 Ⓐ, 1723, 1753, 1811 Ⓐ, 1823 Ⓐ, 1853, 1923 Ⓐ, 1953, 2023 Ⓐ, 2053 and 2153.

From Aix en Provence at 0623 Ⓐ, 0641 Ⓐ, 0653, 0722 Ⓐ, 0753, 0823, 0840 Ⓐ, 0853 ⚒, 0923 Ⓐ, 0953, 1053 Ⓒ, 1123 Ⓐ, 1153, 1223 Ⓐ, 1253, 1322 Ⓐ, 1353, 1423 Ⓐ, 1455, 1523 Ⓐ, 1553, 1622 Ⓐ, 1653, 1710 Ⓐ, 1723 Ⓐ, 1740 Ⓐ, 1753, 1823, 1853 Ⓐ, 1923, 1953 Ⓐ, 2023, 2127 Ⓒ, 2200 Ⓐ, 2247 Ⓐ and 2253 Ⓒ.

L – July 9 - Aug. 27 only.
N – Conveys 🛏 1, 2 cl. and (2) (reclining). Ⓡ. For overnight journeys only. **Timings may vary.** May not run on certain nights. For confirmed days of running and timings please consult the SNCF journey planner: www.sncf.com

d – Not July 14, 15, Aug. 16, Nov. 1, 2, 11.
g – Also July 15, Aug. 16, Nov. 2; not Aug. 15.
h – † only.
p – 0702 on ⑥.

q – Also July 14, Nov. 1.
r – Grenoble gare routière (bus station).
t – Arrives 2036.
w – Not Nov. 11.

* – By 🚌.
⊗ – Journeys to / from Valence are subject to alteration on ①–⑤ Sept. 12 - Oct. 7.
▷ – For other local trains see panel below main table.

🚌 BRIANÇON - MODANE

Ⓡ	Ⓒ	Ⓒ	Ⓐ	
Briançon rail station d.	0650	1245	1445	1645
Modane rail station . a.	0830	1425	1625	1825

Ⓡ	Ⓒ			
Modane rail station . d.	1115	...	1715	1915
Briançon rail station a.	1240	...	1840	2040

✆ 0809 400 013 https://zou.maregionsud.fr

NICE - ANNOT - DIGNE 359

2nd class only

km	CP ▲		⑦ ◇				Ⓑ
0	**Nice** (Gare CP) d.	0655	0837	0920	1300	1710	1809
	Plan du Var d.	0736	0918	1002	1342	1751	1850
41	Villars sur Var d.	0755	0938	1021	1401	1810	1909
58	Puget Théniers d.	0818	1001	1044	1424	1833	1933
64	Entrevaux d.	0828	1011	1054	1434	1843	1943
78	Annot d.	0847	1027	1112	1452	1904	1959
96	Thorame Haute d.	0911	...	1136	1516	1927	...
106	St André les Alpes d.	0925	...	1151	1531	1940	...
150	**Digne** ★ a.	1022	...	1248	1628	2037	...

CP ▲	⚒				⑦ ◇	
Digne ★ d.	...	0710	1052	1432	...	1735
St. André les Alpes. d.	...	0809	1152	1532	...	1829
Thorame Haute d.	...	0823	1206	1546	...	1841
Annot d.	0542	0848	1230	1610	1640	1903
Entrevaux d.	0600	0906	1248	1628	1658	1921
Puget Théniers d.	0610	0916	1258	1638	1708	1932
Villars sur Var d.	0631	0937	1319	1659	1729	1953
Plan du Var d.	0652	0959	1341	1720	1750	2014
Nice (Gare CP) a.	0731	1038	1420	1803	1828	2053

🚂 *TRAIN DES PIGNES* steam train, **2022**
⑦ May 8 - Oct. 30 ⊠
Puget Théniers 1100 → Annot 1220
Annot 1530 → Puget Théniers 1615
Also calls at Entrevaux
www.traindespignes.fr

🚌 LER route 26, operated by Autocars Payan.

	🚌 ⚒	🚌		🚌		🚌		🚌	
Digne △ d.	0455	0730	...	1145	...	1335	...	1630	...
Digne (Gare) d.	0500	0740	...	1155	...	1345	...	1640	...
Manosque-Gréoux (Gare) d.	0600	0845	...	1300	...	1450	...	1750	...
Aix en Provence TGV a.	0700	0945	...	1400	...	1550	...	1850	...
Aéroport Marseille ✈ a.	0715	1000	...	1415	...	1605	...	1905	...

	🚌 ⚒		🚌		🚌		🚌		🚌
Aéroport Marseille ✈ d.	0950	...	1255	...	1540	...	1830	...	2110
Aix en Provence TGV d.	1020	...	1325	...	1610	...	1900	...	2135
Manosque-Gréoux (Gare) a.	1125	...	1430	...	1715	...	2005	...	2225
Digne (Gare) a.	1225	...	1530	...	1815	...	2100	...	2315
Digne △ a.	1235	...	1540	...	1825	...	2105	...	2320

△ – Gare Routière (bus station).
▲ – Narrow gauge railway, operated by Chemins de Fer de Provence. **All services are operated by 🚌 between St André les Alpes and Digne until further notice.**
★ – 🚌 Digne - Sisteron and v.v. LER route 37. Journey time: 60 minutes.
From Digne (Gare CP) at 0755 ⚒, 1140, 1245 ⚒, 1610 ⑤, 1720 ⊡ and 1835.
From Sisteron (Gare SNCF) at 0640 ⚒, 1105 ⚒, 1250 ⚒, 1605 and 1845.

⊠ – Also July 15, 22, 29, Aug. 4, 5, 11, 12, 18, 19, 25, 26, Nov. 5.
On Sept. 18, Nov. 5 runs Puget - Annot - Le Fugeret (a. 1300) and v.v. – return train departs Le Fugeret 1525 (on Sept. 18) / 1535 (on Nov. 5), Annot 1710 (on Sept. 18) / 1640 (on Nov. 5), arrives Puget 1755 (on Sept. 18) / 1725 (on Nov. 5).
⊡ – Daily except ⑤.
◇ – ⑦ June 19 - Oct. 30.

360 MARSEILLE - TOULON - HYÈRES

km																									
		Ⓐ	Ⓐ		Ⓐ		Ⓐ			Ⓒ		Ⓐ	Ⓐ	Ⓒ		Ⓐ	6155 ♥A		Ⓒ		Ⓐ	6155 ♥h	Ⓐ	Ⓒ	
	Paris Gare de Lyon 350 ... d.	...	...	...	...	...	...	...	...	...	...	...	...	...	...	...	0824	...	...	...	...	0907	...	...	...
0	**Marseille** St Charles .... 361 d.	0532g	0602	0632	0704	0732	0802	0832	0932	0932	1002	1002	1025	1032	1102	1102	|	1132	1132	1202	1202	1227	1222	1232	1302
27	Cassis • d.	0555g	0625	0655	0727	0755	0825	0855	0955	0955	1025	1025	1100	1055	1125	1125	|	1155	1155	1225	1225	|	1256	1255	1325
37	La Ciotat d.	0603g	0633	0703	0734	0803	0833	0903	1003	1003	1033	1033	1108	1103	1133	1133	|	1203	1203	1233	1233	|	1303	1303	1333
51	Bandol d.	0615g	0645	0715	0747	0815	0845	0915	1015	1015	1045	1045	1121	1115	1145	1145	|	1215	1215	1245	1245	|	1316	1315	1345
67	**Toulon** 361 a.	0632g	0702	0732	0801	0832	0902	0932	1032	1032	1102	1102	1137	1132	1202	1202	1209	1232	1232	1302	1302	1311	1332	1332	1402
67	**Toulon** d.	0635	0705	0735	...	0835	...	0935	...	1035	...	1105	...	1135	...	1205	1225	...	1235	...	1305	1324	...	...	...
87	**Hyères** a.	0657	0727	0757	...	0857	...	0957	...	1057	...	1127	...	1157	...	1227	1240	...	1257	...	1327	1340	...	...	...

	Ⓐ	Ⓐ	Ⓒ		Ⓐ	Ⓐ	Ⓒ		Ⓐ		Ⓒ		Ⓐ		Ⓐ		Ⓐ		Ⓐ		Ⓐ		D	E	E
Paris Gare de Lyon 350 ... d.	...	...	...	...	...	...	...	...	...	...	...	...	...	...	...	...	...	...	...	...	...	...	...	...	...
Marseille St Charles ..... 361 d.	1302	1327	1332	1403	1403	1427	1432	1502	1502	1532	1532	1602	1602	1632	1702	1732	1802	1832	1902	1932	1943	2032	2107	2132	2232
Cassis • d.	1325	1402	1356	1427	1427	1458	1455	1525	1525	1555	1555	1625	1625	1655	1725	1755	1825	1855	1925	1956	2024	2055	2131	2155	2255
La Ciotat d.	1333	1409	1403	1434	1434	1506	1503	1533	1533	1603	1603	1633	1633	1703	1733	1803	1833	1903	1933	2003	2032	2103	2139	2203	2303
Bandol d.	1345	1422	1416	1447	1447	1519	1515	1545	1545	1615	1615	1645	1645	1715	1745	1815	1845	1915	1945	2016	2045	2115	2152	2215	2315
Toulon 361 a.	1402	1439	1432	1502	1502	1535	1532	1602	1602	1632	1632	1702	1702	1732	1802	1832	1902	1932	2002	2032	2102	2132	2207	2232	2332
Toulon d.	1405	...	1435	...	1505	...	1535	...	1605	...	1635	...	1705	1735	1805	1835	1905	1935	...	2035	...	2135	...	...	...
Hyères a.	1427	...	1457	...	1527	...	1557	...	1627	...	1657	...	1727	1757	1827	1857	1927	1957	...	2057	...	2157	...	...	...

		Ⓐ	Ⓐ	Ⓐ		Ⓐ	Ⓐ	Ⓐ		Ⓐ		Ⓒ			Ⓒ		Ⓐ	Ⓒ	Ⓐ	Ⓒ	Ⓐ	Ⓐ	Ⓒ	Ⓒ	Ⓐ
Hyères d.	...	...	0602	...	0632	...	0702	...	0732	0802	0832	...	0932	...	1032	...	1102	1132	...	...	1202	...	1232	...	1302
Toulon a.	...	...	0623	...	0653	...	0723	...	0753	0823	0853	...	0953	...	1053	...	1123	1153	...	...	1223	...	1253	...	1323
Toulon 361 d.	0556	0622	0626	0652	0656	0720	0726	0752	0756	0826	0856	0924	0956	1026	1056	1126	1126	1156	1156	1226	1226	1256	1256	1326	1326
Bandol d.	0612	|	0642	|	0712	|	0742	|	0812	0842	0912	0939	1012	1042	1112	1142	1142	1211	1212	1242	1242	1312	1312	1342	1342
La Ciotat d.	0624	0644	0654	0714	0724	0740	0754	0814	0824	0854	0924	0950	1024	1054	1123	1154	1154	1223	1224	1254	1254	1324	1323	1354	1354
Cassis • d.	0632	|	0702	|	0732	|	0802	|	0832	0902	0932	0958	1032	1102	1133	1202	1202	1230	1232	1302	1302	1332	1333	1402	1402
Marseille St Charles ..... 361 a.	0657	0715	0727	0745	0757	0811	0827	0845	0857	0927	0957	1027	1057	1127	1157	1227	1227	1257	1257	1327	1335	1357	1357	1427	1436
Paris Gare de Lyon 350 ... a.	...	...	...	...	...	...	...	...	...	...	...	...	...	...	...	...	...	...	...	...	...	...	...	...	...

		Ⓒ	Ⓐ	6124 ♥	Ⓐ		Ⓐ		Ⓒ	Ⓐ	Ⓐ	Ⓒ	Ⓐ	Ⓐ	Ⓒ	Ⓐ		Ⓐ						E	Ⓒk
Hyères d.	...	1402	1402	1432	...	...	1502	...	1532	1602	...	1631	1702	...	1732	1802	1832	...	1932	...	2032	...	2132	2132	...
Toulon a.	...	1423	1423	1448	...	...	1523	...	1553	1623	...	1652	1723	...	1753	1823	1853	...	1953	...	2053	...	2153	2153	...
Toulon 361 d.	1356	1426	1426	1452	1456	1526	1526	1556	1556	1626	1652	1655	1726	1756	1756	1826	1856	1926	1956	...	2056	...	...	2156	2227
Bandol d.	1412	1442	1442	|	1512	1542	1542	1612	1612	1642	1706	1710	1742	1812	1812	1842	1912	1942	2012	...	2112	...	...	2212	2243
La Ciotat d.	1424	1454	1454	|	1524	1554	1554	1624	1624	1654	1718	1721	1756	1824	1823	1854	1924	1954	2024	...	2124	...	...	2224	2255
Cassis • d.	1432	1502	1502	|	1532	1602	1602	1632	1632	1702	1725	1729	1803	1832	1833	1902	1932	2002	2032	...	2132	...	...	2232	2303
Marseille St Charles..... 361 a.	1457	1527	1541	1536	1557	1627	1627	1657	1657	1727	1753	1757	1828	1857	1857	1927	1957	2027	2057	...	2157	...	...	2257	2329
Paris Gare de Lyon 350 ... a.	...	...	...	1916	...	...	...	...	...	...	...	...	...	...	...	...	...	...	...	...	...	...	...	...	...

A – July 2 - Aug. 28.
D – ①-④ (not July 14, Aug. 15, Nov. 1).
E – ⑤-⑦ (also July 14, Aug. 15, Nov. 1).
g – ① (also July 15, Aug. 16, Nov. 2; not Aug. 15).
h – Not July 2 - Aug. 28. Departs Paris 0909 from Sept. 12.
k – Not Sept. 25, Oct. 2, 9, 16, 23, 30.
• – Cassis station is located 4 km from Cassis town.
♥ – *TGV* high-speed train. 🄡. 🍷.

361 MARSEILLE - TOULON - CANNES - NICE - MONACO - VENTIMIGLIA

Local *TER* services. See Table **350** for long-distance *TGV* services.

km																									
				Ⓑ		①-⑤	①-⑤	⑥⑦	①-⑤	①-⑤	①-⑤	⑥⑦	①-⑤	①-⑤			①-⑤		Ⓐ	⑥⑦ e	①-⑤ d		5771 ★		
0	**Marseille** St Charles .... 360 d.	...	...	...	...	...	...	...	...	...	...	...	...	...	...	...	...	...	...	0557	0549r	...	...	...	...
	Paris Austerlitz d.	...	...	...	...	...	...	...	...	...	...	...	...	...	...	...	...	...	...	|	|	...	2051	...	...
67	**Toulon** 360 d.	...	...	...	...	...	...	...	...	...	...	...	...	...	...	...	...	...	0619	0644	0644	...	0713	...	...
100	Carnoules d.	...	...	...	...	...	...	...	...	...	...	...	...	...	...	...	...	...	0652	|	0706	...	|	...	...
135	Les Arcs-Draguignan d.	...	...	...	...	...	...	...	...	0555	...	...	0626	...	...	0635	...	...	0720	0730	0729	...	0755	...	0809
158	Fréjus d.	...	...	...	...	...	...	...	...	0609	...	...	0639	...	...	0648	...	...	...	|	0741	...	|	...	0822
161	St Raphaël-Valescure d.	...	...	...	...	...	...	...	...	0614	...	...	0644	...	...	0652	...	...	...	0746	0746	...	0813	...	0826
165	Boulouris sur Mer d.	...	...	...	...	...	...	...	...	|	...	...	|	...	...	0656	...	...	...	|	|	...	|	...	0830
◧	Grasse d.	...	...	...	...	...	...	...	...	|	0623	...	|	...	0653	|	...	0723	...	|	|	0753	|	0823	|
193	**Cannes** d.	...	...	0522	...	0552	0612	0622	0624	0644	0652	0654	0712	...	0722	0730	0744	0752	...	0812	0814	0822	0838	0852	0904
202	Juan les Pins d.	...	...	0532	...	0602	0620	0632	0633	0651	0702	0703	0720	...	0731	...	0751	0802	...	|	0822	0831	|	0902	...
204	Antibes d.	...	...	0535	...	0605	0624	0635	0636	0656	0705	0706	0724	...	0735	...	0756	0805	...	0823	0826	0835	0850	0905	...
213	Cagnes sur Mer d.	...	...	0546	...	0616	0631	0646	0647	0703	0716	0717	0731	...	0746	...	0803	0816	...	|	0833	0846	|	0916	...
219	Nice St Augustin ✈ ⊡ d.	...	...	0556	...	0626	0639	0656	0657	0710	0726	0727	0739	...	0756	...	0810	0826	...	0836	0841	0856	|	0926	...
224	**Nice** Ville a.	...	...	0603	...	0633	0646	0703	0704	0718	0733	0734	0746	←	0803	...	0818	0833	...	0843	0848	0903	0908	0933	...
	Nice Ville d.	0536	0606	0606	0636	0636	0649	0706	0707	0721	0750	0737	0749	0750	0806	...	0821	0836	...	...	0851	0906	...	0936	...
229	Villefranche sur Mer d.	0544	0614	0614	0644	0644	0657	0714	0715	0729	→	0745	0757	0758	0814	...	0829	0844	...	...	0859	0914	...	0944	...
231	Beaulieu sur Mer d.	0547	0618	0618	0648	0648	0700	0718	0718	0732	...	0748	0800	0801	0817	...	0832	0847	...	...	0902	0917	...	0947	...
234	Eze d.	0551	0621	0621	0651	0651	|	0721	0722	|	...	0752	|	0805	0821	...	|	0851	...	...	|	0921	...	0951	...
240	**Monaco-Monte Carlo** d.	0602	0632	0632	0702	0702	0711	0732	0732	0743	...	0802	0811	0816	0832	...	0843	0902	...	...	0913	0932	...	1002	...
244	Cap Martin-Roquebrune d.	0607	0637	0637	0707	0707	|	0737	0737	|	...	0807	|	0821	0837	...	|	0907	...	...	|	0937	...	1007	...
249	Menton d.	0615	0645	0645	0715	0715	0721	0745	0744	0754	...	0815	0821	0829	0845	...	0853	0915	...	...	0923	0945	...	1015	...
259	**Ventimiglia** a.	0631	0701	0701	0731	0731	...	0801	...	0810	...	0831	...	0845	0901	...	...	0931	...	...	...	1001	...	1031	...

				Ⓐ			①-⑤		⑥⑦									Ⓐ						①-⑤	
Marseille St Charles..... 360 d.	...	...	...	...	0757	...	...	...	...	...	...	0957	...	...	...	...	...	...	1157	...	...	...	...	...	...
Toulon 360 d.	...	...	0724	0819	0844	...	...	...	...	...	...	1044	...	...	1119	...	...	1216	1244	...	...	...	...	...	...
Carnoules d.	...	...	0757	0852	|	...	...	...	...	...	...	|	...	...	1152	...	...	1249	|	...	...	...	...	...	...
Les Arcs-Draguignan d.	...	...	0826	0922	0930	...	0935	...	...	...	1105	1130	...	...	1220	1235	...	1320	1330	...	...	...	...	...	...
Fréjus d.	...	...	...	...	|	...	0948	...	...	...	1118	|	...	...	▬	1248	...	...	|	...	...	...	...	...	...
St Raphaël-Valescure d.	...	...	...	...	0946	...	0952	...	...	...	1122	1146	...	...	...	1252	...	...	1346	...	...	...	1452	...	...
Boulouris sur Mer d.	...	...	...	...	|	...	0956	...	...	...	1126	|	...	...	...	1256	...	...	|	...	...	...	1456	...	...
Grasse d.	0853	0923t	...	...	|	0953z	|	1023	...	...	|	|	1153	...	1253	|	...	...	|	1353	...	1453	|	...	...
Cannes d.	0922	0952	...	...	1011	1022	1030	1052	1122	1152	1200	1211	1222	1253	1322	1330	1352	...	1411	1422	1453	1522	1530	1544	1553
Juan les Pins d.	0931	1002	...	...	|	1031	...	1102	1132	1202	...	|	1231	1302	1331	...	1402	...	|	1431	1502	1531	...	1551	1602
Antibes d.	0935	1005	...	...	1021	1035	...	1105	1135	1205	...	1221	1235	1305	1335	...	1405	...	1421	1435	1505	1535	...	1556	1605
Cagnes sur Mer d.	0946	1016	...	...	|	1046	...	1116	1146	1216	...	|	1246	1316	1346	...	1416	...	|	1446	1516	1546	...	1603	1616
Nice St Augustin ✈ ⊡ d.	0956	1026	...	...	1033	1055	...	1126	1156	1226	...	1233	1256	1326	1356	...	1426	...	1433	1456	1526	1556	...	1610	1626
Nice Ville a.	1003	1033	...	...	1041	1103	...	1133	1203	1233	...	1241	1303	1333	1403	...	1433	...	1441	1502	1533	1603	...	1618	1633
Nice Ville d.	1006	1036	...	...	...	1106	...	1136	1206	1236	...	...	1306	1336	1406	...	1436	...	...	1505	1536	1606	...	1621	1636
Villefranche sur Mer d.	1014	1044	...	...	...	1114	...	1144	1214	1244	...	...	1314	1344	1414	...	1444	...	...	1514	1544	1614	...	1629	1644
Beaulieu sur Mer d.	1017	1047	...	...	...	1118	...	1147	1218	1247	...	...	1318	1347	1418	...	1447	...	...	1517	1547	1617	...	1632	1647
Eze d.	1021	1051	...	...	...	1121	...	1151	1221	1251	...	...	1321	1351	1421	...	1451	...	...	1521	1551	1621	...	|	1651
Monaco-Monte Carlo d.	1032	1102	...	...	...	1132	...	1202	1232	1302	...	...	1332	1401	1432	...	1502	...	...	1532	1601	1632	...	1643	1702
Cap Martin-Roquebrune d.	1037	1107	...	...	...	1137	...	1207	1237	1307	...	...	1337	1406	1437	...	1507	...	...	1537	1606	1637	...	|	1706
Menton d.	1045	1115	...	...	...	1145	...	1215	1245	1315	...	...	1345	1414	1445	...	1515	...	...	1545	1614	1645	...	1653	1714
Ventimiglia a.	1101	1131	...	...	...	1201	...	1231	1301	1331	...	...	1401	1431	1501	...	1531	...	...	1601	1631	1701	...	...	1731

d – Not Aug. 15, Nov. 1.
e – Also Aug. 15, Nov. 1.
r – 0548 on ①.
t – ①-⑤ only.
z – ⑥⑦ only.

★ – Conveys 🛏 1, 2 cl. and 💺 (reclining). Also calls at Marseille-Blancarde (a. 0625). 🄡. For overnight journeys only.
Timings may vary. For confirmed timings and days of running, please consult the SNCF journey planner: www.sncf.com
◧ – Grasse - Cannes is *17 km*.
⊡ – Situated approximately 800 metres from Nice ✈ terminal building.

MARSEILLE - TOULON - CANNES - NICE - MONACO - VENTIMIGLIA 361

Local *TER* services. See Table **350** for long-distance *TGV* services.

		①–⑤				①–⑤		①–⑤				Ⓐ		①–⑤	⑥⑦					Ⓐ				①–⑤	
Marseille St Charles 360 d.	...	...	...	...	1457	...	...	...	...	...	...	...	1627	...	...	...	...	...	...	1715	1757	...	...	...	...
Toulon 360 d.	...	...	1420	...	1544	...	...	...	...	...	...	1619	1712	...	...	...	1715	...	...	1819	1844	...	...	...	...
Carnoules d.	...	...	1453	...	|	...	...	...	...	...	...	1652	|	...	...	...	1747	...	...	1852	1906	...	...	...	...
Les Arcs-Draguignan d.	...	...	1521	1605	1630	...	...	...	...	1705	...	1720	1800	...	...	...	1817	1835	...	1920	1930	...	...	2005	...
Fréjus d.	...	...	▬	1618	|	...	...	...	...	1718	...	...	|	...	...	...	...	1848	...	...	|	...	...	2018	...
St Raphaël-Valescure d.	...	...	...	1622	1646	...	...	...	...	1722	...	...	1816	...	...	...	...	1852	...	...	1946	...	...	2022	...
Boulouris sur Mer d.	...	...	...	1626	|	...	...	...	...	1726	...	...	|	...	...	...	...	1856	...	...	|	...	...	2026	...
Grasse d.	1553	...	...	|	|	...	1653	...	1723	|	1753	...	|	1823	...	1853	...	|	1923	...	|	1953	...	|	2053
Cannes d.	1622	1644	1653	1704	1711	1717	1722	1746	1752	1800	1822	...	1841	1852	1853	1922	...	1930	1952	...	2011	2022	2052	2100	2122
Juan les Pins d.	1631	1651	1702	...	|	1725	1731	1753	1802	...	1831	...	|	1902	1902	1931	...	...	2002	...	|	2031	2102	...	2131
Antibes d.	1635	1656	1705	...	1721	1729	1735	1758	1805	...	1835	...	1851	1905	1905	1935	...	...	2005	...	2021	2035	2105	...	2135
Cagnes sur Mer d.	1646	1703	1716	...	|	1736	1746	1805	1816	...	1846	...	|	1916	1916	1946	...	...	2016	...	|	2046	2116	...	2146
Nice St Augustin ✈ ⊡ d.	1656	1710	1726	...	1733	1743	1756	1812	1826	...	1856	...	1903	1926	1925	1956	...	...	2026	...	2033	2056	2126	...	2156
Nice Ville a.	1703	1718	1733	...	1742	1750	1803	1820	1833	...	1903	...	1911	1933	1933	2003	...	...	2033	...	2041	2103	2133	...	2203
Nice Ville d.	1706	1721	1736	...	...	1753	1806	1823	1836	...	1906	...	...	1936	1936	2006	...	...	2036	...	...	2106	2136	...	2206
Villefranche sur Mer d.	1714	1729	1744	...	...	1801	1814	1831	1844	...	1914	...	...	1944	1944	2014	...	...	2044	...	...	2114	2144	...	2214
Beaulieu sur Mer d.	1717	1732	1747	...	...	1805	1817	1834	1847	...	1917	...	...	1947	1947	2017	...	...	2047	...	...	2117	2147	...	2217
Eze d.	1721	|	1751	...	...	|	1821	|	1851	...	1921	...	...	1951	1951	2021	...	...	2051	...	...	2121	2151	...	2221
Monaco-Monte Carlo d.	1732	1743	1802	...	...	1815	1832	1845	1902	...	1932	...	...	2002	2001	2032	...	...	2102	...	...	2132	2202	...	2232
Cap Martin-Roquebrune d.	1737	|	1806	...	...	|	1837	|	1907	...	1937	...	...	2007	2006	2037	...	...	2107	...	...	2137	2207	...	2237
Menton d.	1745	1753	1814	...	...	1826	1845	1855	1915	...	1945	...	...	2015	2014	2045	...	...	2115	...	...	2145	2215	...	2245
Ventimiglia a.	1801	...	1831	...	...	...	1901	...	1931	...	2001	...	...	2031	2031	2101	...	...	2131	...	...	2201	2231p	...	2301p

	⑥⑦	⑤	①–⑤	⑥⑦	⑤–⑦			⑤–⑦	⑤	Ⓒ	⑥⑦
Marseille St Charles 360 d.	...	...	...	...	...	...	...	...	2103	2115	...
Toulon 360 d.	...	...	...	...	...	...	1945	...	2147	2202	...
Carnoules d.	...	...	...	...	...	...	2019	...	|	|	...
Les Arcs-Draguignan d.	2035	...	2105	...	...	...	2047	...	2230	2248	...
Fréjus d.	2048	...	2118	...	...	...	...	...	|	|	...
St Raphaël-Valescure d.	2052	...	2123	...	...	...	...	...	2247	2304	...
Boulouris sur Mer d.	2056	...	|	...	...	...	...	...	|	|	...
Grasse d.	|	2122	|	2123z	2153	2153	...	...	|	|	2323
Cannes d.	2130	2145	2152	2152	2222	2222	...	2252	2312	2329	2352
Juan les Pins d.	...	2153	2202	2202	2231	2231	...	2302	|	|	0002
Antibes d.	...	2157	2205	2205	2235	2235	...	2305	2322	2339	0005
Cagnes sur Mer d.	...	2204	2216	2216	2246	2246	...	2316	|	|	0016
Nice St Augustin ✈ ⊡ d.	...	2212	2226	2226	2256	2256	...	2326	2335	2351	0026
Nice Ville a.	...	2219	2233	2233	2303	2303	...	2333	2341	2359	0033
Nice Ville d.	...	...	2236r	...	2306	...	...	2336	...	...	...
Villefranche sur Mer d.	...	...	2244r	...	2314	...	...	2344	...	...	...
Beaulieu sur Mer d.	...	...	2248r	...	2317	...	...	2347	...	...	...
Eze d.	...	...	2251r	...	2321	...	...	2351	...	...	...
Monaco-Monte Carlo d.	...	...	2302r	|	2332	...	...	0002	...	...	...
Cap Martin-Roquebrune d.	...	...	2307r	|	2337	...	...	0007	...	...	...
Menton d.	...	...	2314r	|	2344	...	...	0014	...	...	...
Ventimiglia a.	...	...	...	...	...	...	...	...	...	...	...

	Ⓐ	⑥	Ⓐ	Ⓐ	①–⑤	①–④			Ⓐ
Ventimiglia d.	...	...	...	...	...	...	...	...	...
Menton d.	...	...	...	...	...	0514	...	...	...
Cap Martin-Roquebrune d.	...	...	...	...	...	0520	...	...	...
Monaco-Monte Carlo d.	...	...	...	...	...	0528	...	...	...
Eze d.	...	...	...	...	...	0536	...	...	...
Beaulieu sur Mer d.	...	...	...	...	...	0540	...	...	...
Villefranche sur Mer d.	...	...	...	...	...	0543	...	...	...
Nice Ville a.	...	...	...	...	...	0553	...	...	...
Nice Ville d.	...	...	...	0520	0526	▬	0556	0620	...
Nice St Augustin ✈ ⊡ d.	...	...	...	0528	0533	...	0603	0628	...
Cagnes sur Mer d.	...	...	...	|	0543	...	0613	|	...
Antibes d.	...	...	...	0540	0554	...	0624	0640	...
Juan les Pins d.	...	...	...	|	0557	...	0627	|	...
Cannes d.	...	...	...	0556	0610	...	0640	0653	...
Grasse a.	...	...	...	|	0638	...	0708	|	...
Boulouris sur Mer d.	...	...	...	|	▬	...	▬	|	...
St Raphaël-Valescure d.	...	...	...	0617	...	...	...	0716	...
Fréjus d.	...	...	...	|	Ⓐ	...	Ⓐ	|	...
Les Arcs-Draguignan d.	0538	0542	0608	0633	0638	0638	0708	0733	0738
Carnoules d.	0606	0610	0636	|	0706	0710	0736	|	0806
Toulon 360 a.	0639	0642	0709	0713	0739	0739	0809	0815	0839
Marseille St Charles 360 a.	0745	...	...	0811	0845	...	...	0903	...

						①–⑤		①–⑤			①–⑤			①–⑤				⑥⑦		Ⓐ					⑥⑦
Ventimiglia d.	...	0525t	0555b	...	0625	...	0655	...	...	0725	...	...	0755	...	0825	0855	0925	0955	...	...	1025	...	1055	1125	1125
Menton d.	...	0544	0614	...	0644	0704	0714	0734	...	0744	0804	...	0814	0834	0844	0914	0944	1014	...	...	1044	...	1114	1144	1144
Cap Martin-Roquebrune d.	...	0550	0620	...	0650	|	0720	|	...	0750	|	...	0820	|	0850	0920	0950	1020	...	...	1050	...	1120	1150	1150
Monaco-Monte Carlo d.	...	0558	0628	...	0658	0716	0728	0746	...	0758	0816	...	0828	0846	0858	0928	0958	1028	...	...	1058	...	1128	1158	1158
Eze d.	...	0606	0636	...	0706	|	0736	|	...	0806	|	...	0836	|	0906	0936	1006	1036	...	...	1106	...	1136	1206	1206
Beaulieu sur Mer d.	...	0610	0640	...	0710	0725	0740	0755	...	0810	0825	...	0840	0855	0910	0940	1010	1040	...	...	1110	...	1140	1210	1210
Villefranche sur Mer d.	...	0613	0643	...	0713	0728	0743	0758	...	0813	0828	...	0843	0858	0913	0943	1013	1044	...	...	1113	...	1143	1213	1213
Nice Ville a.	...	0625	0653	...	0723	0738	0753	0808	...	0825	0838	...	0853	0908	0923	0953	1024	1056	...	...	1125	...	1153	1223	1223
Nice Ville d.	...	0628	0656	...	0726	0741	0756	0811	0820	0828	0841	...	0856	0911	0926	0956	1027	1059	1120	...	1128	...	1156	...	1226
Nice St Augustin ✈ ⊡ d.	...	0633	0703	...	0733	0746	0803	0816	0828	0833	0846	...	0903	0916	0933	1006	1033	1106	1128	...	1133	...	1203	...	1233
Cagnes sur Mer d.	...	0643	0713	...	0743	0754	0813	0824	|	0843	0854	...	0913	0924	0943	1013	1043	1116	|	...	1143	...	1213	...	1243
Antibes d.	...	0654	0724	...	0754	0803	0824	0833	0840	0854	0903	...	0924	0933	0954	1024	1054	1127	1140	...	1154	...	1224	...	1254
Juan les Pins d.	...	0657	0727	...	0757	0806	0827	0836	|	0857	0906	...	0927	0936	0957	1027	1057	1130	|	...	1157	...	1227	...	1257
Cannes d.	0658	0710	0740	0758	0810	0815	0840	0845	0853	0910	0915	0929	0940	0945	1010	1038	1108	1141	1153	...	1210	1228	1240	...	1308
Grasse a.	|	0738	0808	|	0838	...	0908t	...	|	0938	...	|	1008z	...	1038	...	...	...	|	...	1238	|	1308	...	...
Boulouris sur Mer d.	0733	...	...	0833	▬	...	...	...	|	...	...	1003	...	...	...	...	...	...	|	...	...	1303	▬	...	...
St Raphaël-Valescure d.	0737	...	...	0837	...	...	...	...	0916	...	...	1007	...	...	...	...	...	...	1216	...	...	1307	...	...	...
Fréjus d.	0741	...	...	0841	...	...	...	...	|	...	...	1011	...	...	...	...	...	...	|	...	...	1311	...	...	...
Les Arcs-Draguignan d.	0754	...	...	0854	0908	...	...	...	0933	...	...	1024	...	...	...	...	...	...	1233	1238	...	1324	1338	...	...
Carnoules d.	...	...	...	...	0936	...	...	...	|	...	...	...	...	...	...	...	...	...	|	1306	...	...	1406	...	...
Toulon 360 a.	...	...	...	...	1009	...	...	...	1015	...	...	...	...	...	...	...	...	...	1315	1339	...	...	1439	...	...
Marseille St Charles 360 a.	...	...	...	...	...	...	...	...	1103	...	...	...	...	...	...	...	...	...	1403	...	...	...	...	...	...

													Ⓐ				Ⓒ		①–⑤		①–⑤		①–⑤ d	⑥⑦ e	①–⑤
Ventimiglia d.	1155	...	...	1225	1255	...	1325	1355	...	1425	1455	...	...	...	1525	...	...	1555	...	1625	1645	1655z	...	...	
Menton d.	1214	...	...	1244	1314	...	1344	1414	...	1444	1514	...	...	...	1544	...	...	1614	1634	1644	1704	1714	1734	...	
Cap Martin-Roquebrune d.	1220	...	...	1250	1320	...	1350	1420	...	1450	1520	...	...	...	1550	...	...	1620	|	1650	|	1720	|	...	
Monaco-Monte Carlo d.	1228	...	...	1258	1328	...	1358	1428	...	1458	1528	...	...	...	1558	...	...	1628	1646	1658	1716	1728	1747	...	
Eze d.	1236	...	...	1306	1336	...	1406	1436	...	1506	1536	...	...	...	1606	...	...	1636	|	1706	|	1736	|	...	
Beaulieu sur Mer d.	1240	...	...	1310	1340	...	1410	1440	...	1510	1540	...	...	...	1610	...	...	1640	1655	1710	1725	1740	1755	...	
Villefranche sur Mer d.	1243	...	...	1313	1343	...	1413	1443	...	1513	1543	...	...	...	1613	...	...	1643	1658	1713	1728	1743	1759	...	
Nice Ville a.	1253	...	...	1323	1353	...	1425	1453	...	1523	1553	...	...	...	1625	...	...	1653	1708	1723	1738	1755	1808	...	
Nice Ville d.	1256	1320	...	1326	1356	1420	1428	1456	...	1526	1556	1620	...	...	1628	...	...	1656	1711	1726	1741	1758	1811	1819	...
Nice St Augustin ✈ ⊡ d.	1303	1328	...	1333	1403	1428	1433	1503	...	1533	1603	1628	...	...	1633	...	...	1703	1716	1733	1746	1803	1817	1828	...
Cagnes sur Mer d.	1313	|	...	1343	1413	|	1443	1513	...	1543	1613	|	...	...	1643	...	...	1713	1724	1743	1754	1813	1825	|	...
Antibes d.	1324	1340	...	1354	1424	1440	1454	1524	...	1554	1624	1640	...	...	1654	...	...	1724	1733	1754	1803	1824	1833	1840	...
Juan les Pins d.	1337	|	...	1357	1427	|	1457	1527	...	1557	1627	|	...	...	1657	...	...	1727	1736	1757	1806	1827	1836	|	...
Cannes d.	1338	1353	1358	1410	1440	1453	1508	1540	1554	1610	1640	1653	...	1657	1710	1728	...	1740	1745	1810	1818	1840	1848	1853	1853
Grasse a.	...	|	|	1438	1508	|	▬	1608	|	1638	1708	|	...	|	1738	|	...	1808t	...	1838	|	1908	|	|	|
Boulouris sur Mer d.	...	|	1432	...	...	|	...	...	1629	...	...	|	...	1733	...	1803	...	...	...	...	|	...	|	|	1928
St Raphaël-Valescure d.	...	1416	1436	...	...	1516	...	...	1633	...	...	1716	...	1737	...	1807	...	...	...	...	1846	...	1915	1916	1932
Fréjus d.	...	|	...	...	...	|	...	...	1637	...	...	|	...	1741	...	1811	...	...	...	...	1850	...	1919	|	1936
Les Arcs-Draguignan d.	...	1434	...	...	...	1533	1638	...	1650	...	...	1733	1738	1754	...	1824	1839	...	...	...	1903	...	1933	1933	1949
Carnoules d.	...	|	...	...	...	|	1706	...	...	...	...	|	1806	...	...	...	1911	...	...	...	...	...	1954	|	...
Toulon 360 a.	...	1515	...	...	...	1615	1739	...	...	...	...	1815	1839	...	...	...	1942	...	...	...	...	...	2015	2015	...
Marseille St Charles 360 a.	...	1602	...	...	...	1703	...	...	...	...	...	1903	...	...	...	...	...	...	...	...	...	...	2103	2101	...

b – Not ⑥.
d – Not Aug. 15, Nov. 1.
e – Also Aug. 15, Nov. 1.
p – ⑤–⑦ only.
r – Not ⑤.
t – ①–⑤ only.
z – ⑥⑦ only.

⊡ – Situated approximately 800 metres from Nice ✈ terminal building.

361 VENTIMIGLIA - MONACO - NICE - CANNES - TOULON - MARSEILLE

Local *TER* services. See Table **350** for long-distance *TGV* services.

	⑥⑦		①–⑤		5772 ★	⑥⑦ e	①–⑤ d		①–⑤			①–⑤					⑤–⑦			⑥⑦		⑤–⑦		⑥⑦	⑤–⑦
Ventimiglia d.	...	1725	...	1755	...	...	...	1825	...	...	1855	...	1925	1955	2025	2055	...	2144	...	...	2155	...	2255	2255	2325
Menton d.	...	1744	1804	1814	...	...	1839	1844	1904	...	1914	1934	1944	2014	2044	2114	...	2204	...	...	2213	2243	2314	2314	2344
Cap Martin-Roquebrune d.	...	1750	|	1820	...	...	|	1852	|	...	1920	|	1950	2020	2050	2120	...	2210	...	...	...	2249	2320	2320	2350
Monaco-Monte Carlo d.	...	1758	1816	1828	...	...	1852	1859	1916	...	1928	1946	1958	2028	2058	2128	...	2215	2228	2228	...	2257	2328	2328	2358
Eze d.	...	1806	|	1836	...	...	|	1907	|	...	1936	|	2006	2036	2106	2136	...	...	2236	2236	...	2305	2336	2336	0006
Beaulieu sur Mer d.	...	1810	1825	1840	...	...	1903	1911	1925	...	1940	1955	2010	2040	2110	2140	...	...	2240	2240	...	2309	2340	2340	0010
Villefranche sur Mer d.	...	1813	1828	1843	...	...	1906	1914	1928	...	1943	1958	2013	2043	2113	2143	...	...	2243	2243	...	2312	2343	2343	0013
Nice Ville a.	...	1823	1838	1853	...	...	1917	1923	1938	...	1953	2008	2023	2053	2123	2153	...	...	2253	2253	...	2323	2353	2353	0023
Nice Ville d.	...	1826	1841	1856	1916	1920	1920	1926	1941	...	1956	2011	2026	2056	2126	2156	2226	...	...	2256	...	...	...	2356	...
Nice St Augustin ✈ ⊡ d.	...	1833	1846	1903	|	1927	1925	1933	1946	...	2003	2017	2033	2103	2133	2203	2233	...	...	2303	...	...	...	0003	...
Cagnes sur Mer d.	...	1843	1854	1913	|	|	1934	1943	1954	...	2013	2025	2043	2113	2143	2213	2243	...	...	2313	...	...	...	0013	...
Antibes d.	...	1854	1903	1924	1934	1942	1943	1954	2003	...	2024	2033	2054	2124	2154	2224	2254	...	...	2324	...	...	...	0024	...
Juan les Pins d.	...	1857	1906	1927	|	|	1946	1957	2006	...	2027	2036	2057	2127	2157	2227	2257	...	...	2327	...	...	...	0027	...
Cannes d.	1858	1908	1915	1940	1948	1957	1957	2010	2015	2028	2038	2048	2110	2138	2208	2240	2310	...	...	2338	...	...	...	0038	...
Grasse a.	|	...	...	2008p	|	|	|	2038	...	|	...	|	2138	...	...	2308z	2337z	...	...	...	...	...	...	...	...
Boulouris sur Mer d.	1933	...	...	...	|	|	|	...	...	2103	...	2122	...	...	...	...	...	...	...	...	...	...	...	...	...
St Raphaël-Valescure d.	1937	...	...	...	2013	2020	2024	...	...	2107	...	2126	...	...	...	...	...	...	...	...	...	...	...	...	...
Fréjus d.	1941	...	...	...	|	|	2027	...	...	2111	...	2130	...	...	...	...	...	...	...	...	...	...	...	...	...
Les Arcs-Draguignan d.	1954	...	...	...	2030	2037	2041	...	...	2124	...	2142	...	...	...	...	...	...	...	...	...	...	...	...	...
Carnoules d.	...	...	...	...	|	2057	2102	...	...	...	...	...	...	...	...	...	...	...	...	...	...	...	...	...	...
Toulon 360 a.	...	...	...	...	2113	2118	2123	...	...	...	...	...	...	...	...	...	...	...	...	...	...	...	...	...	...
Paris Austerlitz a.	...	...	...	...	0755	|	|	...	...	...	...	...	...	...	...	...	...	...	...	...	...	...	...	...	...
Marseille St Charles 360 a.	...	...	...	...	...	2206	2213	...	...	...	...	...	...	...	...	...	...	...	...	...	...	...	...	...	...

d – Not Aug. 15, Nov. 1.
e – Also Aug. 15, Nov. 1.
p – ⑤–⑦ only.
z – ⑥⑦ only.

★ – Conveys 🛏 1, 2 cl. and (2) (reclining). Also calls at Marseille-Blancarde (d. 2157). [R]. For overnight journeys only. **Timings may vary**. For confirmed timings and days of running, please consult the SNCF journey planner: www.sncf.com

⊡ – Situated approximately 800 metres from Nice ✈ terminal building.

363 BELLEGARDE and GENÈVE - ANNEMASSE - ÉVIAN LES BAINS

See Table **346** for connecting trains Lyon Part Dieu - Bellegarde and v.v. French holiday dates apply.

km				①–⑤	①–⑤			①–⑤			Ⓑ	⑥⑦	①–⑤	🚌 ①–⑤		Ⓒ	🚌 Ⓐ	Ⓑ					*TGV* 6503 C	*TGV* 6503 A
	Paris Gare de Lyon 341 d.	...	...	...	...	...	...	...	...	...	...	...	...	...	...	...	...	...	...	...	...	...	1029	1028
	Bellegarde 365 d.	...	...	...	0715	...	...	...	...	0815	0915	...	...	...	...	1015	1012	1115	...	...	1215	...	1343	1342
0	**Genève** 365 ‡ d.	0632	...	0702	|	0732	0802	...	0832	|	|	0932	0932	...	1032	|	|	|	1132	1232	|	1332	|	|
9	Genève Eaux Vives 365 ‡ d.	0647	...	0717	|	0747	0817	...	0847	|	|	0947	0947	...	1047	|	|	|	1147	1247	|	1347	|	|
17	Annemasse 365 ‡ a.	0655	...	0725	0755	0755	0825	...	0855	0855	0955	0955	0955	...	1055	1055	1102	1155	1155	1255	1255	1355	1419	1418
17	Annemasse d.	...	0700	0731	...	0801	...	0830	...	0900	...	1001	1001	...	...	1100	1102	...	1201	...	1300	1401	1427	1427
47	Thonon les Bains d.	...	0730	0800	...	0830	...	0901	...	0930	...	1030	1029	1034	...	1130	1147	...	1230	...	1330	1430	1500	1509
56	**Évian les Bains** a.	...	0738	0808	...	0838	...	0908	...	0938	...	1038	...	1054	...	1138	1207	...	1238	...	1338	1438	1507	1516

						①–⑤			①–⑤			①–⑤							⊗⊖	⊗	⊙		⊗	🚌 ⑤
Paris Gare de Lyon 341 d.	...	...	...	...	...	...	...	...	...	...	...	...	...	...	...	...	...	...	...	...	...	...	...	...
Bellegarde 365 ‡ d.	...	1415	...	...	1615	...	1715	...	...	...	1815	...	1915	...	...	...	2015	2115	...	...	2215	...	...	2312
Genève 365 ‡ d.	1432	|	1532	1632	|	1702	|	1732	1802	1832	|	1902	|	1932	...	2032	|	|	2132	2232	|	...	2332	|
Genève Eaux Vives 365 ‡ d.	1447	|	1547	1647	|	1717	|	1747	1817	1847	|	1917	|	1947	...	2047	|	|	2147	2247	|	...	2347	|
Annemasse 365 a.	1455	1455	1555	1655	1655	1725	1755	1755	1825	1855	1855	1925	1955	1955	...	2055	2055	2155	2155	2255	2255	...	2355	0000
Annemasse d.	...	1500	1601	...	1700	1731	...	1801	1831	...	1900	1931	...	2001	...	...	2100	...	2201	...	2300	...	...	0000
Thonon les Bains d.	...	1530	1630	...	1730	1800	...	1830	1900	...	1930	2000	...	2030	...	...	2130	...	2230	...	2330	...	...	0045
Évian les Bains a.	...	1538	1638	...	1738	1808	...	1838	1908	...	1938	2008	...	2038	...	...	2138	...	2238	...	2338	...	...	0105

	①–⑥		①–⑤			①–⑤			①–⑤				Ⓒ	Ⓐ		🚌 ①–⑤	⑥⑦		①–⑤				⑥⑦	①–⑤
Évian-les-Bains d.	0521	...	0551	0621	...	0648	0721	...	0751	0821	...	0921	1021	1021	...	1050	1121	...	...	...	1221	...	1251	1321
Thonon-les-Bains d.	0530	...	0600	0630	...	0700	0730	...	0800	0830	...	0930	1030	1030	...	1110	1130	...	1141	...	1230	...	1300	1330
Annemasse a.	0559	...	0629	0659	...	0729	0759	...	0829	0859	...	0959	1059	1059	...	1155	1159	...	1214	...	1259	...	1329	1359
Annemasse 365 ‡ d.	0605	0605	0635	0705	0705	0735	0805	0805	0835	0905	0905	1005	1105	1112	1105	1155	1205	1205	...	1220	1305	1305	1335	1405
Genève Eaux Vives 365 ‡ d.	0613	|	0643	|	0713	0743	0813	|	0843	|	0913	1013	|	|	1113	|	1213	1213	...	1228	|	1313	1343	1413
Genève 365 ‡ a.	0627	|	0657	|	0727	0757	0827	|	0857	|	0927	1027	|	|	1127	|	1227	1227	...	1242	|	1327	1357	1427
Bellegarde 365 a.	...	0642	...	0742	...	...	...	0842	...	0942	...	...	1142	1157	...	1245	...	...	...	...	1342	...	...	...
Paris Gare de Lyon 341 a.	...	...	...	...	...	...	...	...	...	...	...	...	...	...	...	...	...	...	...	...	...	...	...	...

	Ⓑ	*TGV* 6504 ⑦ H		Ⓒ			Ⓑ			*TGV* 6506 ⑦ D	①–⑤	*TGV* 6506 ⑥ G	①–⑤	①–⑤	*TGV* 6506 ⑦ E	①–⑥					⊙	⊗	Ⓑ ⊖	⊗
Évian-les-Bains d.	...	1318	1421	1421	...	1521	...	1621	...	1643t	1651	1702	1721	...	1739	1751	1821	...	1921	...	2021	...	2151	...
Thonon-les-Bains d.	...	1332	1430	1430	...	1530	...	1630	...	1654t	1700	1713	1730	...	1749	1800	1830	...	1930	...	2030	...	2200	...
Annemasse a.	...	1358	1459	1459	...	1559	...	1659	...	1719	1729	1738	1759	...	1814	1829	1859	...	1959	...	2059	...	2230	...
Annemasse 365 ‡ d.	1405	1422	...	1505	1505	1605	1605	1705	1705	1733	1735	1758	1805	1805	1817	1835	1905	1905	2005	2005	2105	2105	...	2235
Genève Eaux Vives 365 ‡ d.	|	|	...	|	1512	1613	|	|	1713	|	1743	|	1813	|	|	1843	|	1913	2013	|	|	2113	...	2243
Genève 365 ‡ a.	|	|	...	|	1527	1627	|	|	1727	|	1757	|	1827	|	|	1857	|	1927	2027	|	|	2127	...	2257
Bellegarde 365 a.	1442	1511	...	1542	...	...	1642	1742	...	1814	...	1838	...	1842	1852	...	1942	...	...	2042	2142	...	...	...
Paris Gare de Lyon 341 a.	...	1801r	...	...	...	...	...	...	...	2109j	...	2208	...	...	2209	...	...	...	...	...	...	...	...	...

A – Runs on July 14, 15, Aug. 15, Oct. 31, Nov. 11 only. Departs Paris 0954 on Nov. 11, 1032 on Aug. 15, 1043 on Oct. 31.
C – ⑥⑦ July 2 - Aug. 28 (also June 18, 25); ⑥ from Sept. 3. Departs Paris 1015 on Aug. 14, 1018 on Oct. 29.
D – ⑦ from Sept. 18 (also July 14, 15, Aug. 15, Nov. 1).
E – ⑦ until Sept. 11.
G – ⑥ July 2 - Aug. 27. Arrives Paris 2143 on Aug. 13.
H – ⑦ (also Aug. 15, Nov. 1). Departure times are up to 21 minutes later on Aug. 15, Nov. 1.

j – 2113 on Aug. 15, Nov. 1; 2126 on July 14, 15.
r – 1757 from Sept. 18; 1812 on Aug. 14, 15, Oct. 30, Nov. 1.
t – 3 minutes earlier on July 14, 15, Aug. 15, Nov. 1.

TGV – High-speed train. [R]. 🍸. Timings may vary by a few minutes – please check your reservation.

⊙ – Subject to alteration on ①–⑤ Oct. 3 – 28 (also Oct. 2).
⊖ – Subject to alteration on ①–⑤ Oct. 10 – 28.
⊗ – Subject to alteration on ①–④ July 18 - Aug. 18.
‡ – Frequent additional services (every 15 minutes during the day) operate Genève - Annemasse and v.v.

GENÈVE and ANNECY - CHAMBÉRY - GRENOBLE - VALENCE 364

SERVICE FROM JULY 4. Timings may vary by 1–2 minutes. **WARNING!** Until July 3 timings may vary and certain services do not run – please check locally.

km																									
		Ⓐ	⚒	Ⓐ	⚒		⚒ ⊗	Ⓐ	⚒	⊗		Ⓒ	Ⓒ	⊗	⊖	Ⓒ	⊗					Ⓐ	A	Ⓑ	Ⓐ
0	**Genève** 341 346 d.	...	...	...	...	...	...	...	0659	...	...	...	...	1000	...	...	...	1159	...	...	...	1459	...	...	...
33	Bellegarde 341 346 d.	...	...	...	...	...	...	...	0729	...	...	...	...	1029	...	...	...	1229	...	...	...	1529	...	...	...
66	Culoz 346 d.	...	...	...	...	...	...	...	|	...	...	...	...	|	...	...	...	|	...	...	...	|	...	...	...
	Annecy 341 345 d.	...	...	...	0542	...	0642	0719	|	0742	0842	0842	0953	|	1042	1142	...	|	1242	1344	1442	|	1542	1642	1718
88	Aix les Bains 341 345 d.	...	...	...	0626	...	0726	0803	0807	0826	0926	0926	1034	1107	1126	1226	...	1307	1326	1426	1526	1607	1626	1726	1802
102	**Chambéry** 341 345 a.	...	...	...	0637	...	0737	0814	0818	0837	0937	0937	...	1118	1137	1237	...	1316	1337	1437	1537	1618	1637	1737	1812
102	**Chambéry** d.	...	0540	*0601*r	0640	...	0740	...	0821	0840	...	0940	...	1121	1140	1240	1240	1319	1340	1440	1540	1621	1640	1740	...
116	Montmélian d.	...	0551	*0611*r	0651	...	0751	...	|	0851	...	0951	...	|	1151	1251	1251	|	1351	1451	1551	|	1651	1751	...
165	**Grenoble** a.	...	0627	*0653*r	0727	...	0827	...	0902	0927	...	1027	...	1202	1227	1327	1327	1402	1427	1527	1627	1702	1727	1827	...
165	**Grenoble** ▷ d.	0558	0630	0705t	0730	0730	0830	...	...	0930	...	1030	...	1205	1230	1330	1330	...	1430	1530	1630	1705	1730	1830	...
242	Romans-Bourg de Péage d.	0658	0730	0758	0830	0830	0931	...	...	1031	...	1131	...	1258	1330	1431	1431	...	1531	1631	1731	1758	1831	1931	...
249	Valence TGV d.	0707	0739	0807	0839	0839	0939	...	...	1039	...	1139	...	1307	1338	1443f	1443f	...	1539	1643f	1739	1807	1843f	1943f	...
259	**Valence** Ville a.	0715	0746	0815	0847	0847	0947	...	...	1047	...	1147	...	1315	1345	1451	1451	...	1547	1651	1746	1814	1851	1951	...

		⑤–⑦ k		⚒	E	Ⓐ			🚐
Genève 341 346 d.	1642	1642	...	...	...	...	1842	...	...
Bellegarde 341 346 d.	1711	1711	...	...	...	...	1911	...	...
Culoz 346 d.	1746	1746	...	...	...	...	1946	...	...
Annecy 341 345 d.	|	|	1744	...	1842	1903	|	1946	2038
Aix les Bains 341 345 d.	1806	1806	1826	...	1926	1949	2007	2026	2136
Chambéry 341 345 a.	1816	1816	1837	...	1937	1958	2018	2037	2208
Chambéry d.	1819	1819	1840	...	1940	...	2021	2040	...
Montmélian d.	|	|	1851	...	1951	...	|	2051	...
Grenoble a.	1900	1900	1927	...	2027	...	2102	2127v	...
Grenoble ▷ d.	...	1904	1930	1940	2030	...	...	...	...
Romans-Bourg de Péage d.	...	1958	2031	2058	2131	...	...	...	...
Valence TGV d.	...	2007	2039	2107	2139	...	...	...	...
Valence Ville a.	...	2015	2047	2115	2147	...	...	...	...

	①–⑤	⚒	⚒ n	Ⓐ	Ⓐ	B	①–⑥	Ⓐ		Ⓐ	
Valence Ville d.	...	...	...	...	...	0524	...	...	...	0614	0644
Valence TGV d.	...	...	...	...	...	0532	...	...	...	0623	0655
Romans-Bourg de Péage d.	...	...	...	...	...	0540	...	...	...	0631	0703
Grenoble a.	...	...	...	...	...	0648	...	...	...	0730	0755
Grenoble d.	0507	...	0536	...	0632	...	0658	...	0733	0733	0758
Montmélian d.	0544	...	0624	...	0710	...	|	...	0810	0810	|
Chambéry a.	0554	...	0633	...	0719	...	0739	...	0819	0819	0839
Chambéry 341 345 d.	0557	0620	...	0645	0722	...	0742	0800	0822	0822	0842
Aix les Bains 341 345 d.	0609	0635	...	0658	0735	...	0755	0812	0835	0835	0855
Annecy 341 345 a.	|	0715	...	0733	0815	...	|	0855	0915	0915	|
Culoz 346 d.	0632	...	...	...	...	...	|	...	...	...	|
Bellegarde 341 346 d.	0702	...	...	...	...	...	0833	...	...	...	0933
Genève 341 346 a.	0731	...	...	...	...	...	0900	...	...	...	1000

	Ⓐ	Ⓒ	Ⓐ	Ⓐ	⊗			Ⓐ ⊖	Ⓒ	⊗	⊗	⊗	⊗			Ⓐ					C A	Ⓐ D	Ⓒ	🚐	† H
Valence Ville d.	0714	0814	0814	0914	1013	...	...	1208	1213	1313	1348	1412	1513	1613	1648	...	1713	1748	1813	1912	2013	2114	2114	...	2214
Valence TGV d.	0723	0823	0823	0923	1022	...	...	1219	1223	1323	1358	1423	1523	1623	1657	...	1722	1757	1822	1921	2023	2123	2123	...	2223
Romans-Bourg de Péage d.	0732	0832	0832	0931	1031	...	...	1230	1232	1331	1406	1432	1531	1631	1705	...	1730	1805	1831	1930	2031	2131	2131	...	2231
Grenoble a.	0830	0929	0928	1030	1130	...	...	1330	1330	1430	1455	1530	1629	1729	1755	...	1830	1855	1929	2029	2130	2226	2230	...	2330
Grenoble d.	▬	0932	0931	...	1133	1158	1233	1333	1333	1433	1458	1533	1633	1733	1758	...	1833	*1906*	1933	2033	2133	...	2233	...	...
Montmélian d.	...	1009	1009	...	1210	|	1310	1410	1410	1510	|	1610	1710	1810	|	...	1910	*1950*	2010	2110	2210	...	2310	...	...
Chambéry a.	...	1018	1018	...	1219	1239	1319	1419	1419	1519	1539	1619	1719	1819	1839	...	1919	*1959*	2020	2119	2219	...	2319	...	...
Chambéry 341 345 d.	⚒	1020	1020	...	1222	1242	1322	1422	1422	1522	1542	1622	1722	1822	1842	1901	1922	...	2025	2122	2222	...	...	2330	...
Aix les Bains 341 345 d.	0925	1035	1035	...	1235	1255	1335	1437	1437	1534	1555	1636	1735	1835	1855	1912	1934	...	2037	2134	2235	...	...	2350	...
Annecy 341 345 a.	1007	1113	1115	...	1315	|	1416	1515	1515	1615	|	1714	1814	1915	|	1958	2015	...	2115	2215	2315	...	...	0022	...
Culoz 346 d.	...	...	...	...	...	|	...	...	...	...	|	...	...	...	|	...	...	...	...	...	...	...	...	...	...
Bellegarde 341 346 d.	...	...	...	...	...	1333	...	...	...	...	1633	...	...	...	1933	...	...	...	...	...	...	...	...	...	...
Genève 341 346 a.	...	...	...	...	...	1400	...	...	...	...	1700	...	...	...	2001	...	...	...	...	...	...	...	...	...	...

A – To / from Avignon on dates in Table **351**.
B – ⚒ to Aug. 20; ① from Aug. 22.
C – Ⓑ to July 31; ⑦ from Aug. 7 (also Aug. 15).
D – Until July 29.
E – Daily until Aug. 7; ⑥⑦ from Aug. 13 (also Aug. 15).
H – Until Oct. 30.

f – Arrives 5–6 minutes earlier.
k – Also July 13, 14, Aug. 15, Nov. 1, 10.
n – Not July 14 - Aug. 31.
r – Not July 14 - Aug. 26.
t – 0659 July 18 - Sept. 2.
v – 2138 on Ⓐ Aug. 1–31.

⊗ – Subject to alteration on ①–⑤ Sept. 12 - Oct. 7.
⊖ – Subject to alteration on ①–⑤ Sept. 12 - Oct. 21.
▷ – Grenoble departures may be 1–2 minutes **earlier** July 18 - Sept. 4.

NANCY - ÉPINAL - REMIREMONT 386

TABLE TEMPORARILY RELOCATED FROM PAGE 225. **AMENDED SERVICE AUGUST 2 - OCTOBER 7**. See page 225 for service to August 1 and from October 8. Subject to alteration on Sept. 10, 11, 17, 18. Northbound timings Remiremont → Épinal → Nancy may vary by up to 9 minutes Sept. 3–30 (see note ⊠).

km																											
																						2571					
		Ⓐ	Ⓐ	⚒ n	⚒ ⊗	Ⓐ n	Ⓒ	Ⓐ ⊗	n	⑥	Ⓐ ⊗	⑥	†	Ⓐ n	⚒ ⊗	†	Ⓐ	⊗	⚒	⑥	n	♥	Ⓒ	n	Ⓐ		Ⓐ n
	Paris Est **390** d.	...	...	...	...	...	...	...	...	...	...	...	...	...	...	...	...	...	...	...	...	1223	...	...	...	...	...
0	**Nancy** d.	0555	0618	0655	0720	0755	0820	0818v	0856	0920	0930	1020	1020	1055	1117	1120	1155	1217	1255	1320	1320	1406	1420	1520	1555	1620	1655
74	Épinal a.	0659	0720	0759	0824	0859	0913	0918	1000	1024	1023z	1111	1122	1159	1218	1211	1257	1318f	1359	1422k	1424	1448	1524h	1621	1659	1724	1759
74	Épinal d.	...	0721	...	0826	...	0915	0920	...	...	1025z	...	1124	...	1220	...	...	1320f	...	1424k	1425r	1451	...	1623	...	1726t	...
100	**Remiremont** a.	...	0754	...	0900	...	0938	0954	...	...	1055z	...	1158	...	1254	...	...	1354f	...	1458k	1459r	1512	...	1657	...	1800t	...

						2573					
			⚒	Ⓐ n		♥¶	◧		⑥	Ⓐ ▽	†
Paris Est **390** d.	...	...	...	...	...	1810	...	...	...	...	...
Nancy d.	1720	1756	1820	1857	1920	1958	2020	2117	2205	2220	2257
Épinal a.	1824	1900	1924	2004	2018x	2045	2124	2218	2310	2339	0004
Épinal d.	1826	...	1926g	...	2020n	2048	...	2220	...	...	...
Remiremont a.	1900	...	2000g	...	2054n	2114	...	2254	...	...	...

			2574									2578
SEE NOTE ⊠	Ⓐ	⚒ n	⚒j ♥	†	⚒	⚒ ◐	Ⓐ	⑥	Ⓐ		Ⓐ n	† ♥
Remiremont d.	...	0511t	0600	...	0615	...	0710y	...	...	0811	...	0859
Épinal a.	...	0541t	0621	...	0643	...	0741y	...	...	0841	...	0920
Épinal d.	0500	0543	0624	0643	0645	0703	0743	0746	0803	0843	0903	0923
Nancy a.	0559	0640	0705	0740	0740	0805	0840	0844	0902	0940	1002	1004
Paris Est **390** a.	...	...	0846	...	...	...	...	...	...	...	...	1150

														2580													
SEE NOTE ⊠	⚒ n	†	Ⓐ ⊗	Ⓐ n	Ⓒ	⚒	⊗	Ⓐ	Ⓐ n	⑥	⊗	Ⓒ ⊖	Ⓐ n	♥		Ⓐ	⚒	†	Ⓑ		⑥	Ⓐ	†	Ⓐ n	⑥	Ⓐ n	†
Remiremont d.	0911t	...	1011	...	1035	...	1211	...	1311	...	1411	...	1514	1558	1611c	...	1711n	...	1811	...	1910	1911	1928	...	2002	2011	...
Épinal a.	0941t	...	1041	...	1104	...	1241e	...	1340	...	1441	...	1542	1621	1641c	...	1741n	...	1841	...	1931	1941	1949	...	2030	2041	...
Épinal d.	0943	0955	1043	1103	1106	1143q	1243e	1318	1342	1355	1443p	1543	1544	1623	1643	1703	1743	1755	1843	1903	1933	1943	1951	2003	2032	2043	2138
Nancy a.	1040	1040	1140	1202	1202	1240	1340	1405	1436	1440	1540	1640	1640	1706	1739	1802	1840	1840	1940	2002	2033	2040	2042	2102	2127	2146	2235
Paris Est **390** a.	...	...	...	...	...	...	...	...	...	...	...	...	...	1846	...	...	...	...	...	...	...	...	...	...	...	...	...

c – Ⓒ (also Oct. 7).
e – On † Épinal a. 1240, d. 1241.
f – On ⑥ Épinal a. 1323, d. 1325, Remiremont a. 1358.
g – Not Aug. 6, 13, 20.
h – 1511 on †.
j – Not Sept. 12, 19, 24.
k – 4 minutes earlier on Sept. 24, Oct. 1.
n – Not Aug. 2–5, 8–12, 15–19.
p – 1446 on Ⓐ.
q – 1139 on ⑥.
r – ⚒ only.

t – Ⓐ only.
v – 0821 Sept. 5–30.
x – 2024 on Ⓐ Aug. 2–19.
y – Not Sept. 5–30.
z – 3 minutes later Oct. 4–7.

¶ – On Ⓒ Épinal a. 2043, d. 2046, Remiremont a. 2108.
◧ – On ⑥ Nancy d. 2025, Épinal a. 2116.
◐ – On ⑥ Épinal d. 0708, Nancy a. 0804.
⊖ – On ⑥ Épinal d. 1552, Nancy a. 1637.
⊗ – Subject to alteration Aug. 2–5.

▽ – Not ①–④ Sept. 12–29. By 🚐 until Sept. 9. By train (Nancy d. 2220, Épinal a. 2324) on Sept. 16, 23, 30, Oct. 3–7.
⊠ – Northbound timings Remiremont - Épinal - Nancy may vary by up to 9 minutes Sept. 3–30 (earlier departures possible). Southbound timings Nancy - Épinal - Remiremont are unchanged during this period.
♥ – *TGV* train. 🅁. 🍸.

365 BELLEGARDE / GENÈVE / ANNECY - LA ROCHE SUR FORON - ST GERVAIS

See panel below main table for *TGV* services from / to Paris.

km																									
		①–⑤	Ⓑ	Ⓐ			Ⓑ	①–⑤				Ⓑ	①–⑤	Ⓒ		⑥		Ⓑ	①–⑤			⑥⑦		①–⑤	
										◇⊗		⊗	🚌		⊗	🚌		⊗	🚌		⊗			🚌	
	Lyon Part-Dieu **346** d.	...	...	...	...	...	...	...	...	...	...	...	...	...	...	...	...	...	...	...	...	...	...	...	...
0	**Bellegarde** 363 d.	...	...	...	...	...	...	0715	0815	...	...	0915	1012	1015	...	1110	...	1115	1212	1215	...	...	...	...	1415
	Genève 363 ▷ d.	...	0547	...	0632	0732	...	|	|	0832	0932	|	|	|	1032	|	1132	|	|	|	1232	1232	1332	...	|
	Genève Eaux Vives **363** ▷ d.	...	0602	...	0647	0747	...	|	|	0847	0947	|	|	|	1047	|	1147	|	|	|	1247	1247	1347	...	|
38	Annemasse **363** ▷ a.	...	0610	...	0655	0755	...	0755	0855	0855	0955	0955	|	1055	1055	|	1155	1155	|	1255	1255	1255	1355	...	1455
38	Annemasse ▷ d.	...	0619	...	0702	...	0802	0802	...	0902	...	1002	|	...	1102	|	...	1202	|	...	1302	1302	━━	1405	...
•	**Annecy** ▷ d.	...	|	...	|	...	|	|	...	|	...	|	|	...	|	|	...	|	|	...	|	|	...	|	...
55	La Roche sur Foron ▷ a.	...	0638	...	0719	...	0819	0819	...	0919	...	1019	1103	...	1119	1201	...	1219	1303	...	1319	1319	①–⑥	1432	...
55	La Roche sur Foron d.	0624	...	0655	0724	...	0824	0824	...	0924	...	1024	1103	...	1124	1201	...	1224	1303	...	1324	1324	🚌	1432	...
77	Cluses (Haute-Savoie) d.	0653	...	0724	0753	...	0853	0853	...	0953	...	1053	1147	...	1153	1245	...	1253	1347	...	1352	1353	1400	1516	...
96	Sallanches Megève d.	0710	...	0739	0810	...	0910	0910	...	1010	...	1110	1211	...	1210	1309	...	1310	1411	...	...	1410	1424	1540	...
102	**St Gervais-les-Bains** a.	0715	...	0744	0816	...	0916	0916	...	1016	...	1116	1227	...	1216	1325	...	1316	1427	...	...	1416	1440	1556	...

		Ⓐ			①–⑤			①–⑤	①–⑤				①–⑤							⑥	Ⓑ		⑤	⑦–④	⑤f
	⊖⊗			⊙	⊡																🚌	▲		🚌	🚌
Lyon Part-Dieu **346** d.	...	...	...	...	...	...	...	...	...	...	...	...	...	...	...	...	...	...	...	...	...	...	...	...	...
Bellegarde 363 d.	...	...	...	...	...	1615	...	...	...	...	1715	...	...	1815	...	...	1915	2015	...	...	2015	...	2115	2115	2212
Genève 363 ▷ d.	1432	...	*1532*	1547	...	|	1632	1647	...	1732	|	1747	...	|	1832	1932	|	|	2032	2032	|	2132	|	|	|
Genève Eaux Vives **363** ▷ d.	1447	...	*1547*	1602	...	|	1647	1702	...	1747	|	1802	...	|	1847	1947	|	|	2047	2047	|	2147	|	|	|
Annemasse **363** ▷ a.	1455	...	*1555*	1610	...	1655	1655	1710	...	1755	1755	1810	...	1855	1855	1955	1955	2055	2055	2055	2105	2155	2155	|	|
Annemasse ▷ d.	1502	...	1602	1619	...	...	1702	1719	...	...	1802	1819	...	...	1902	...	2002	...	...	2102	2105	...	2202	|	|
Annecy ▷ d.	|	...	|	|	1552	...	|	|	1652	...	|	|	1752	...	|	...	|	...	...	|	|	...	|	|	|
La Roche sur Foron ▷ a.	1519	...	1619	1638	1633	...	1719	1738	1733	...	1819	1838	1833	...	1919	...	2019	...	...	2119	2132	...	2219	2206	2303
La Roche sur Foron d.	1524	1612	1624	...	1645	...	1724	...	1745	...	1824	...	1845	...	1924	...	2024	...	...	2124	2132	...	2224	2206	2303
Cluses (Haute-Savoie) d.	1553	1638	1655	...	1710	...	1753	...	1810	...	1853	...	1910	...	1953	...	2053	...	...	2153	2216	...	2253	2250	2347
Sallanches Megève d.	1610	1655	1710	...	1724	...	1810	...	1823	...	1910	...	1923	...	2010	...	2110	...	...	2210	2240	...	2310	2314	0011
St Gervais-les-Bains a.	1616	1701	1716	...	1729	...	1816	...	1829	...	1916	...	1929	...	2016	...	2116	...	...	2216	2256	...	2316	2330	0027

			①–⑤				①–⑤				①–⑤				Ⓐ		①–⑤	⑥⑦			⑥	Ⓑ	Ⓒ	Ⓐ	①–⑥
	‡															⊙	🚌				🚌	⊗			🚌
St Gervais-les-Bains d.	0450	...	0520	...	0549	...	0633	...	0649	...	0733	...	0749	...	0803	...	0819	0849	...	...	0935	0949	...	...	1030
Sallanches Megève d.	0455	...	0525	...	0555	...	0638	...	0654	...	0739	...	0755	...	0811	...	0835	0854	...	...	0951	0955	...	...	1046
Cluses (Haute-Savoie) d.	0511	...	0541	...	0611	...	0654	...	0711	...	0753	...	0811	...	0825	...	0854	0911	...	...	1015	1011	...	...	1110
La Roche sur Foron a.	0537	...	0603	...	0637	...	0716	...	0737	...	0816	...	0837	...	0849	...	0934	0937	...	...	1059	1037	...	...	1154
La Roche sur Foron ▷ d.	0541	...	...	0623	0641	...	0727	0723	0741	...	0827	0823	0841	...	...	0923	0934	0941	...	...	1059	1041	...	...	1154
Annecy ▷ a.	|	...	...	|	|	...	0806	|	|	...	0906	|	|	...	...	|	|	|	...	...	|	|	...	...	|
Annemasse ▷ a.	0558	...	...	0640	0658	...	...	0740	0758	...	...	0840	0858	...	...	0942	1001	0958	...	...	|	1058	...	...	|
Annemasse **363** ▷ d.	0605	0605	...	0650	0705	0705	...	0750	0805	0805	...	0850	0905	0905	...	0950	...	...	1005	...	|	1105	1105	1112	|
Genève Eaux Vives **363** ▷ d.	|	0613	...	0658	0713	|	...	0758	|	0813	...	0858	0913	|	...	0958	...	...	1013	...	|	1113	|	|	|
Genève 363 ▷ a.	|	0627	...	0712	0727	|	...	0812	|	0827	...	0912	0927	|	...	1012	...	...	1027	...	|	1127	|	|	|
Bellegarde 363 a.	0642	...	...	...	...	0742	...	...	0842	...	...	...	...	0942	...	...	...	...	...	...	1150	...	1142	1157	1245
Lyon Part-Dieu **346** a.	...	...	...	...	...	...	...	...	...	...	...	...	...	...	...	...	...	...	...	...	...	...	...	...	...

			⑥	Ⓑ		Ⓑ		①–⑤	⑥⑦	Ⓒ	Ⓑ				①–⑤		Ⓐ	Ⓑ					Ⓑ		
	⊗		🚌	⊗		⊗		🚌			⊗													¶	▲
St Gervais-les-Bains d.	1049	...	1130	1149	...	1249	...	1309	1349	...	1449	...	1549	...	1648	...	1718	...	1749	...	1849	...	1949	...	...
Sallanches Megève d.	1054	...	1146	1155	...	1254	...	1325	1355	...	1454	...	1555	...	1654	...	1725	...	1755	...	1854	...	1954	...	...
Cluses (Haute-Savoie) d.	1111	...	1210	1211	...	1311	...	1349	1411	...	1511	...	1611	...	1711	...	1738	...	1811	...	1911	...	2011	...	...
La Roche sur Foron a.	1137	...	1254	1237	...	1337	...	1433	1437	...	1537	...	1637	...	1737	...	1807	...	1837	...	1937	...	2037	...	...
La Roche sur Foron ▷ d.	1141	...	1254	1241	...	1341	...	1433	1441	...	1541	...	1641	...	1741	...	...	1823	1841	...	1941	...	2041	...	...
Annecy ▷ a.	|	...	|	|	...	|	...	|	|	...	|	...	|	...	|	...	...	|	|	...	|	...	|	...	...
Annemasse ▷ a.	1158	...	|	1258	...	1358	...	1500	1458	...	1558	...	1658	...	1758	...	...	1840	1858	...	1958	...	2058	...	...
Annemasse **363** ▷ d.	...	1205	|	1305	1305	1405	1405	1500	1505	1505	1605	1605	1705	1705	1805	1805	...	1850	1905	1905	2005	2005	...	2105	2105
Genève Eaux Vives **363** ▷ d.	...	1213	|	1313	|	|	1413	|	1513	|	|	1613	1713	|	|	1813	...	1858	1913	|	|	2013	...	|	2113
Genève 363 ▷ a.	...	1227	|	1327	|	|	1427	|	1527	|	|	1627	1727	|	|	1827	...	1912	1927	|	|	2027	...	|	2127
Bellegarde 363 a.	...	...	1345	...	1342	1442	...	1550	...	1540	1642	...	...	1742	1842	...	...	...	...	1942	2042	...	...	2142	...
Lyon Part-Dieu **346** a.	...	...	...	...	...	...	...	...	...	...	...	...	...	...	...	...	...	...	...	...	...	...	...	...	...

ANNECY - ANNEMASSE - GENÈVE

	①–⑤		①–⑤		①–⑤			Ⓑ		Ⓑ		①–⑤	⑦	①–⑤	⑥⑦	Ⓑ	①–⑤			Ⓑ	①–⑤			Ⓑ	
							⊙	⊡	⊡	⊡	⊡					⊡	⊡								▲
Annecy d.	*0510**	0544	*0610**	0644	*0710**	0744	0844	0944	1044	1144	1244	*1340**	1344	*1440**	1444	1544	1552	...	1644	1744	1752	...	1844	1944	2044
La Roche sur Foron a.	|	0619	|	0719	|	0819	0919	1019	1119	1219	1319	|	1419	|	1519	1619	1633	...	1719	1819	1833	...	1919	2019	2119
La Roche sur Foron d.	|	0623	|	0723	|	0823	0923	1023	1123	1223	1323	|	1423	|	1523	1623	...	1641	1723	1823	...	1841	1923	2023	2123
Annemasse a.	*0610**	0640	*0710**	0740	*0810**	0840	0942	1040	1140	1240	1340	*1440**	1440	*1540**	1540	1640	...	1658	1740	1840	...	1858	1940	2040	2140
Annemasse ◧ d.	0620	0650	0720	0750	0820	0850	0950	1050	1150	1250	1350	1450	1450	1550	1550	1650	...	1705	1750	1850	...	1905	1950	2050	2150
Genève Eaux Vives ◧ d.	0628	0658	0728	0758	0828	0858	0958	1058	1158	1258	1358	1458	1458	1558	1558	1658	...	1713	1758	1858	...	1913	1958	2058	2158
Genève ◧ a.	0642	0712	0742	0812	0842	0912	1012	1112	1212	1312	1412	1512	1512	1612	1612	1712	...	1727	1812	1912	...	1927	2012	2112	2212

	Ⓑ		①–⑤		Ⓑ		Ⓑ		⑦	①–⑤		⑦	①–⑤			①–⑤	⑥⑦	①–⑤		①–⑤			Ⓑ	⑥	⑥⑦
						⊡	⊡	⊡			⊡			⊡	⊙								▲		
Genève ◧ d.	0547	0632	...	0647	0747	0847	0947	1047	1147	1147	1247	1347	1347	1447	1547	1647	1647	1717	1747	1817	1847	1947	2047	2047	2148
Genève Eaux Vives ◧ d.	0602	0647	...	0702	0802	0902	1002	1102	1202	1202	1302	1402	1402	1502	1602	1702	1702	1732	1802	1832	1902	2002	2102	2102	2203
Annemasse ◧ a.	0610	0655	...	0710	0810	0910	1010	1110	1210	1210	1310	1410	1410	1510	1610	1710	1710	1740	1810	1840	1910	2010	2110	2110	2211
Annemasse d.	0619	0702	...	0719	0819	0919	1019	1119	1219	*1220**	1319	1419	*1420**	1519	1619	1719	*1720**	*1750**	1819	*1850**	1919	2019	2119	*2120**	*2220**
La Roche sur Foron a.	0638	0719	...	0738	0838	0938	1038	1138	1238	|	1338	1438	|	1538	1638	1738	|	|	1838	|	1938	2038	2138	|	|
La Roche sur Foron d.	0642	...	0727	0742	0842	0942	1042	1142	1242	|	1342	1442	|	1542	1642	1742	|	|	1842	|	1942	2042	2142	|	|
Annecy a.	0716	...	0806	0816	0916	1016	1116	1216	1316	*1320**	1416	1516	*1520**	1616	1716	1816	*1820**	*1850**	1916	*1950**	2016	2116	2216	*2220**	*2320**

TGV services. Timings may vary by a few minutes (please check your reservation). For other services Paris - Bellegarde, see Table **341**.

	TGV **6467**	*TGV* **6467**		*TGV* **6473**						
		⑥		⑥						
	D	**C**		**E**						
Paris Gare de Lyon d.	0637	0640	...	1029	...	...	...	...	...	...
Bellegarde a.	0927	0957	...	1339	...	...	...	...	...	...
Annemasse a.	1027	1034	...	1419	...	...	...	...	...	...
Cluses (Haute-Savoie) a.	1110	1136	...	1509	...	...	...	...	...	...
Sallanches Megève a.	1123	1150	...	1528	...	...	...	...	...	...
St Gervais-les-Bains a.	1132	1201	...	1536	...	...	...	...	...	...

	TGV **6482**		*TGV* **6484**	*TGV* **6484**						
	⑥			⑥						
	E		**D**	**C**						
St Gervais-les-Bains d.	1300	...	1606	1631	...	...	...	...	...	...
Sallanches Megève d.	1311	...	1614	1639	...	...	...	...	...	...
Cluses (Haute-Savoie) d.	1325	...	1635	1700	...	...	...	...	...	...
Annemasse d.	1420	...	1734	1758	...	...	...	...	...	...
Bellegarde d.	1505	...	1818	1846	...	...	...	...	...	...
Paris Gare de Lyon a.	1813	...	2126	2208	...	...	...	...	...	...

C – ⑥ July 2 - Aug. 27.
D – Runs on July 14 only.
E – ⑥ July 2 - Aug. 27 (also July 14, 15).

f – Also Nov. 10; not Nov. 11.

TGV – High-speed train. Ⓡ. 🍸.

* – By 🚌.
⊖ – Change trains at Annemasse on ①–⑤.

◇ – Change trains at Annemasse on ⑥.
▲ – Subject to alteration on ①–④ July 18 - Aug. 18.
⊡ – Subject to alteration on ①–⑤ Sept. 19 - Oct. 7.
⊗ – Subject to alteration on ①–⑤ Sept. 26 - Oct. 14.
⊙ – Subject to alteration Oct. 3 – 7.
¶ – Subject to alteration on ①–⑤ Oct. 3 – 28 (also Oct. 2).
‡ – Subject to alteration on ①–⑤ Oct. 17 - Nov. 4.
• – Annecy to La Roche sur Foron is 39 km.
▷ – For other trains Genève - Annemasse - La Roche sur Foron - Annecy see panel below main table (see also note ◧).
◧ – Frequent services (every 15 minutes during the day) operate Genève - Annemasse and v.v.

ST GERVAIS - CHAMONIX - VALLORCINE (- MARTIGNY) 365a

Mont-Blanc Express. **SERVICE UNTIL OCTOBER 2.** For full details of journeys Vallorcine - Martigny and v.v., see Table **572**.

km																									
												A					ⒶE								
0	**St Gervais** d.	0628	0705	0808	...	0928	1028	1128	1228	1328	1428	1528	...	...	1628	1728	1805f	1828	1928	2028	...	...	...	...	...
9	Les Houches d.	0654	0733	0836	...	0954	1054	1154	1254	1354	1454	1554	...	...	1654	1754	1833f	1854	1954	2054	...	...	...	...	...
20	**Chamonix** Mont-Blanc a.	0713	0750	0852	...	1013	1113	1213	1313	1413	1513	1613	...	...	1713	1813	1851	1913	2013	2113	...	...	...	...	...
20	**Chamonix** Mont-Blanc d.	0728	0828	0928	...	1028	1128	1228	1328	1428	1528	1628	...	1657	1728	1828	1857	1928	2028	...	...	...	...	...	...
24	Les Tines d.	0737	0837	0937	...	1037	1137	1237	1337	1437	1537	1637	...	1705	1737	1837	1905	1937	2037	...	...	...	...	...	...
28	Argentière Haute Savoie d.	0748	0846	0946	...	1046	1146	1246	1346	1446	1546	1646	...	1716	1746	1846	1916	1946	2046	...	...	...	...	...	...
35	**Vallorcine** a.	0803	0901	1001	...	1101	1201	1301	1401	1501	1601	1701	...	1731	1801	1901	1931	2001	2101	...	...	...	...	...	...
	Change trains																								
35	**Vallorcine** ★ 572 d.	0810	0910	1010	...	1110	1210	1310	1410	1510	1610	...	1710	...	1810	1910	...	2010	2110	...	...	...	...	...	...
56	**Martigny** 572 a.	0859	0959	1059	...	1159	1259	1359	1459	1559	1659	...	1759	...	1859	1959	...	2059	2159	...	...	...	...	...	...

										A		A	D		A	D		A	D				
Martigny 572 d.	...	...	0718	0818	0918	1018	1118	1218	1318	...	1518	...	...	1618	...	...	1718	...	...	1818	1918	...	...	...
Vallorcine ★ 572 a.	...	...	0805	0905	1005	1105	1205	1305	1405	...	1605	...	...	1705	...	...	1805	...	...	1905	2005	...	...	...
Change trains																								
Vallorcine d.	0640	0710	0810	0910	1010	1110	1210	1310	1410	1510	...	1610	1610	...	1710	1710	...	1810	1810	1910	2010	...	...	...
Argentière Haute Savoie d.	0654	0727	0827	0927	1027	1127	1227	1327	1427	1527	...	1627	1627	...	1727	1727	...	1827	1827	1927	2027	...	...	...
Les Tines d.	0703	0737	0837	0937	1037	1137	1237	1337	1437	1537	...	1637	1637	...	1737	1737	...	1837	1837	1937	2037	...	...	...
Chamonix Mont-Blanc a.	0710	0745	0845	0945	1045	1145	1245	1345	1445	1545	...	1645	1645	...	1745	1745	...	1845	1845	1945	2045	...	...	...
Chamonix Mont-Blanc ▷ d.	0715	0755	0855	0955	1055	1155	1255	1355	1455	1555	...	1655	1715	...	1755	1815	...	1855	1915	1955	...	...	...	...
Les Houches d.	0732	0814	0914	1014	1114	1214	1314	1414	1514	1614	...	1714	1732	...	1814	1832	...	1914	1932	2014	...	...	...	...
St Gervais a.	0757	0840	0940	1040	1140	1240	1340	1440	1540	1640	...	1740	1757	...	1840	1857	...	1940	1957	2040	...	...	...	...

A – June 18 - Sept. 18.
D – Until June 17 and from Sept. 19.
E – Ⓐ to July 1 / from Sept. 1.

f – 3–4 minutes later June 20 - July 1 and Sept. 1–16.

▷ – Certain Chamonix departure times are 1 minute earlier until June 17.
★ – 🛃 is at Le Châtelard Frontière (see Table **572**).

(PARIS -) CHAMBÉRY - ALBERTVILLE - BOURG ST MAURICE 366

See panel below main table for *TGV* services from / to Paris. **Warning!** Subject to alteration on Aug. 19–26, Oct. 29, 30.

km																									
		🚌 Ⓐ	Ⓐ	🚌 Ⓐ		🚌 Ⓐ		D		E		🚌 Ⓐ		D		Ⓐ	⚒		🚌 Ⓐ	H	🚌 ①–④ J				🚌 ⚒
	Lyon Part Dieu **344** d.	...	...	...	...	...	...	...	...	...	...	...	...	...	...	...	...	...	...	...	...	...	...	...	...
	Aix les Bains **345 364** d.	...	...	...	...	...	...	...	...	1119r	...	...	...	...	...	...	...	1719t	...	...	...	...	...	...	...
0	**Chambéry** **345 364 367** d.	0551	0630	...	...	0808	...	0951	...	1131	...	1236	...	1355	...	1531	1631	1731	1832	1930	1932	...	2045	...	2200
13	Montmélian **367** d.	0621	0641	...	...	0838	...	1002	...	1141	...	|	...	1408	...	1541	1641	1741	|	1941	|	...	2055	...	2230
25	St Pierre d'Albigny **367** d.	0639	0650	...	...	0853	...	1013	...	1150	...	|	...	1417	...	1550	1650	1750	|	1950	|	...	2104	...	2245
48	Albertville a.	0717	0715	...	...	0918	...	1042	...	1215	...	1336	...	1440	...	1615	1715	1815	1921	2015	2021	...	2129	...	2310
48	Albertville d.	0717	0722	...	...	0918	...	1049	...	1222	...	1336	...	1447	...	1622	1722	1822	1921	2022	2021	...	2136	...	2310
76	**Moûtiers-Salins** d.	0747	0748	0845	...	0948	...	1113	...	1250	...	1406	...	1510	...	1650	1750	1850	1953	2050	2053	...	2204	...	2345
91	Aime la Plagne d.	0802	...	0900	...	1003	...	1127	...	1307	...	|	...	1525	...	1707	1807	1907	2009	2107	2109	...	2221	...	0000
98	Landry d.	0812	...	0910	...	1013	...	1135	...	1316	...	|	...	1533	...	1716	1816	1916	2019	2116	2119	...	2230	...	0011
105	**Bourg St Maurice** a.	0824	...	0922	...	1025	...	1142	...	1323	...	1436	...	1540	...	1723	1823	1923	2034	2123	2134	...	2237	...	0025

	🚌 Ⓐ		⚒		Ⓑ	⑥		🚌 †	🚌 Ⓐ	Ⓐ F	🚌 Ⓐ		D		E		D		🚌 Ⓐ			🚌 Ⓐ		
Bourg St Maurice d.	0419	...	0538	...	0638	0638	...	0717	0757	...	0841	...	1038	...	1218	...	1416	...	1514	...	1638	1702	...	1838
Landry d.	|	...	0546	...	0646	0646	...	0728	0808	...	0852	...	1046	...	1226	...	1424	...	1527	...	1646	1713	...	1846
Aime la Plagne d.	|	...	0554	...	0654	0654	...	0740	0820	...	0904	...	1054	...	1234	...	1432	...	1539	...	1654	1725	...	1854
Moûtiers-Salins d.	0449	...	0612	...	0712	0712	...	0802	0837	0847	0921	...	1113	...	1251	...	1453	...	1557	...	1713	1742	...	1913
Albertville a.	0524	...	0638	...	0738	0738	...	0847	...	0916	0956	...	1138	...	1315	...	1515	...	1632	...	1738	1817	...	1938
Albertville d.	0524	...	0645	...	0745	0745	...	0847	...	0923	0956	...	1145	...	1322	...	1522	...	1632	...	1745	1817	...	1945
St Pierre d'Albigny **367** d.	0544	...	0709	...	0810	0812	...	0915	...	0948	1026	...	1210	...	1351	...	1549	...	|	...	1810	1843	...	2010
Montmélian **367** d.	0559	...	0719	...	0819	0820	...	0930	...	0957	1041	...	1219	...	1359	...	1558	...	|	...	1819	1858	...	2019
Chambéry **345 364 367** a.	0629	...	0728	...	0828	0829	...	1000	...	1007	1111	...	1228	...	1408	...	1609	...	1723	...	1828	1928	...	2028
Aix les Bains **345 364** a.	...	...	0740n	...	0840t	|	...	...	...	...	...	...	...	...	...	...	...	...	...	...	1841t	...	...	...
Lyon Part Dieu **344** a.	...	...	...	...	...	1010	...	...	...	...	...	...	...	...	...	...	...	...	...	...	...	...	...	...

TGV services. For other services Paris - Chambéry, see Table **341**.

	TGV 6419 ⑥ B
Paris Gare de Lyon d.	0735
Chambéry a.	1058
Albertville a.	1143
Moûtiers-Salins a.	1213
Aime la Plagne a.	1232
Landry a.	1243
Bourg St Maurice a.	1253

	TGV 6434 C	*TGV* 6434 ⑥ B
Bourg St Maurice d.	1448	1448
Landry d.	1457	1457
Aime la Plagne d.	1509	1509
Moûtiers-Salins d.	1535	1537
Albertville d.	1602	1609
Chambéry d.	1655	1700
Paris Gare de Lyon a.	2000	2001

B – ⑥ July 2 - Aug. 27 (also July 14; not Aug. 20).
C – Runs on July 15 only.
D – Ⓒ to Aug. 15 (also July 15); daily Aug. 27 - Sept. 25; ⑥⑦ Oct. 1–16; daily from Oct. 22.
E – ⑥ to Aug. 13 (also July 15); ①–⑥ Aug. 27 - Sept. 24; ⑥ Oct. 1–15; ⚒ from Oct. 29.
F – From July 11.
H – ⑤⑥ to Oct. 29 (also July 13); ⚒ from Oct. 31.
J – ①–④ to Oct. 27 (not July 13, 14, Aug. 15).

n – ②–⑤ to Oct. 28 (not July 14, Aug. 16); Ⓐ from Oct. 31.
r – ①–⑤ Aug. 29 - Sept. 23 (also July 15); Ⓐ from Oct. 24.
t – Ⓐ only.

TGV – High-speed train. Ⓡ. 🍷.

367 CHAMBÉRY - MODANE

Subject to alteration on Oct. 29 - Nov. 1. See Table **44** for *TGV* services Paris - Modane - Milano and v.v.

km																								
				🚌	*TGV*		🚌	🚌	🚌			🚌	🚌						🚌				🚌	🚌
					6401																			
		⚒	Ⓐ	Ⓐ	⑥		Ⓐ	Ⓐ	Ⓐ	Ⓒ	Ⓒ	Ⓐ	Ⓐ	Ⓐ	⚒	Ⓑ	⑥	Ⓒ	Ⓐ	⑤†	†	Ⓐ	⑥	⑤
					B	**D**	**E**								**z**		**z**	**z**		**v**				**f**
	Paris Gare de Lyon **341** d.	...	...	...	0735	...	...	...	...	...	...	...	...	...	...	...	...	...	...	...	...	...	...	...
	Lyon Part Dieu **344** d.	...	...	...	|	...	...	...	...	...	...	...	...	...	...	...	...	...	...	...	...	...	...	...
0	**Chambéry** **364 366** d.	0636	0736	0833	1110	1136	1136	1236	1236	1248	1351	1354	1354	1651	1751	1836	1836	1949	1954	2036	2136	2149	2154	2255
14	Montmélian **364 366** d.	0646	0745	|	|	1146	|	|	1256	1258	1402	|	1414	1701	1801	1846	1845	1959	|	2047	2145	2159	2224	2325
26	St Pierre d'Albigny **366** d.	0656	0753	|	|	1156	|	|	1312	1307	1412	|	1430	1709	1809	1854	1854	2007	|	2056	2154	2207	2240	2341
61	St Avre la Chambre d.	0727	0824	0956	1146	1226	1228	1328	1403	1338	1444	1446	1521	1740	1840	1922	1931	2038	2046	2126	2224	2237	2315	0016
71	St Jean de Maurienne d.	0735	0833	1011	1157	1243	1243	1343	1418	1347	1453	1501	1536	1749	1849	1931	1939	2047	2101	2135	2232	2245	2330	0035
83	St Michel-Valloire d.	0745	0843	1027	1211	1254	1250	1350	1434	1358	1506	1508	1552	1759	1859	1940	1951	2058	2117	2145	2243	2255	2346	0047
99	**Modane** a.	0758	0856	1047	1226	1307	1310	1410	1454	1413	1520	1528	1612	1812	1912	1954	2005	2111	2137	2159	2256	2309	0006	0107

	🚌		🚌		🚌	🚌					🚌	🚌			🚌	🚌	*TGV*	*TGV*						
																	6406	**6406**						
	Ⓐ	⚒	†	⚒	Ⓐ	Ⓐ	Ⓐ	Ⓐ	Ⓒ	Ⓒ	Ⓐ	Ⓐ		Ⓒ	Ⓐ	Ⓐ		⑥		Ⓐ	Ⓒ	Ⓐ		Ⓑ
						E	**H**	**G**	**w**								**S**	**A**	**z**		**z**			
Modane d.	0436	0600	0552	0700	0753	0931	0933	0933	0958**j**	1158	1146	1210	...	1340	1346	1349	1440	1526	1614	1721	1802	1832	...	2007
St Michel-Valloire d.	0456	0616	0612	0716	0813	0951	0949	0949	1014**j**	1214	1206	1230	...	1357	1406	1409	1457	1542	1630	1737	1818	1848	...	2021
St Jean de Maurienne d.	0512	0626	0628	0727	0829	1007	1000	1005	1024**j**	1225	1222	1246	...	1408	1422	1425	1509	1556	1640	1747	1829	1858	...	2031
St Avre la Chambre d.	0527	0635	0643	0735	0844	1022	1022	1025	1033**j**	1236	1237	1301	...	1423	1437	1440	1519	1606	1649	1756	1837	1907	...	2039
St Pierre d'Albigny **366** d.	|	0705	0734	0806	|	|	1056	1102	1103	1307	|	1352	...	1503	|	1531	|	|	1719	1830	1907	1937	...	2106
Montmélian **364 366** d.	|	0714	0750	0814	|	|	1105	1111	1111	1316	|	1408	...	1514	|	1547	|	|	1728	1840	1916	1945	...	2115
Chambéry **364 366** a.	0629	0723	0820	0824	1007	1114	1113	1120	1120	1325	1329	1428	...	1523	1529	1607	1554	1645	1737	1849	1924	1955	...	2124
Lyon Part Dieu **344** a.	...	...	...	...	...	...	...	...	...	...	...	...	...	...	...	...	|	|	...	...	...	...	...	...
Paris Gare de Lyon **341** a.	...	...	...	...	...	...	...	...	...	...	...	...	...	...	...	...	1859	2001	...	...	...	...	...	...

A – ⑥ July 2 - Aug. 27 (also July 14, 15; not July 16). Departure times are 6 – 7 minutes earlier on July 14.
B – ⑥ July 2 - Aug. 27 (also July 14).
D – Daily to Oct. 2; ⑥⑦ Oct. 8 – 23; daily from Nov. 5.
E – Oct. 3 - Nov. 4.
G – Until Sept. 30.
H – From Nov. 7.
S – Runs on July 16 only.

f – Also July 13, Nov. 10; not Nov. 11.
j – On July 3 departs Modane 0939, St Michel-Valloire 0954, St Jean de Maurienne 1005, St Avre la Chambre 1023.
v – Also July 13, Nov. 10.
w – Not July 17.
z – Not July 16.

TGV – High-speed train. Ⓡ. 🍷.

368 🚌 CHAMONIX - MONT BLANC TUNNEL - COURMAYEUR

SAT / Arriva Italia

By 🚌. Journey 45 minutes. **Please check for latest coronavirus restrictions / international travel requirements. Service confirmed until September 11.**
Dec. 18 - Apr. 18: From Chamonix (Avenue de Courmayeur) at 0830, 0930, 1615, 1730. From Courmayeur (Piazzale Monte Bianco) at 0815, 0945, 1615, 1730.
Apr. 19 - June 24: From Chamonix (Avenue de Courmayeur) at 0830, 1815. From Courmayeur (Piazzale Monte Bianco) at 0945, 1700.
June 25 - Sept. 11: From Chamonix (Avenue de Courmayeur) at 0830, 1245, 1530, 1800. From Courmayeur (Piazzale Monte Bianco) at 0945, 1145, 1545, 1800.
Sept. 12 - Dec. 2: From Chamonix (Avenue de Courmayeur) at 0830, 1815. From Courmayeur (Piazzale Monte Bianco) at 0945, 1700.

🚌 COURMAYEUR - PRÉ ST DIDER - AOSTA

Arriva Italia

Courmayeur △ d.	0645	0745	0835	0935	and	1935	2035	2135	...	...
Pré St Didier d.	0653	0753	0843	0943	hourly	1943	2043	2143	...	...
Aosta ⊡ a.	0745	0845	0935	1035	until	2035	2135	2235	...	...

Aosta ⊡ d.	0645	0745	0845	0945	1045	1145	1245	1335	1445	and	2145
Pré St Didier d.	0737	0837	0937	1037	1137	1237	1337	1427	1537	hourly	2237
Courmayeur △ a.	0745	0845	0945	1045	1145	1245	1345	1435	1545	until	2245

△ – P. le Monte Bianco.
⊡ – Autostazione (bus station).

369 CORSICAN RAILWAYS

Narrow gauge. 2nd class.

SUMMER SERVICE JUNE 27 - SEPTEMBER 4

km																											
		⚒			Ⓐ					⚒	⚒			⚒	⚒					Ⓐ				Ⓐ	⑥	Ⓑ**b**	⚒
0	**Bastia** d.	0620	0700	0740	0835	...	...	0858	0929	1031	...	...	1208	1320	1430	...	...	1520	1545	...	1700	...	...	1710	1802	1820	1930
10	Biguglia d.	0635	0716	0754	0850	...	...	0911	0943	1046	...	...	1223	1335	1445	...	...	1534	1600	...	1713	...	...	1727	1819	1835	1945
22	Casamozza d.	0649	0730	0811	0904	...	...	0929	0959	1101	...	...	1238	1349	1459	...	...	1549	1615	...	1729	...	...	1742	1835	1854	1959
47	Ponte Leccia d.	▬	▬	0848	...	...	...	1010	1036	▬	...	...	▬	...	▬	...	...	1624	▬	...	1811	1815	...	...	...	1931	...
98	Ile Rousse d.	...	...	|	...	0830	1030	1125	|	...	...	1305	...	...	...	1455	1730	|	...	...	|	1930	2010	...	...	|	...
120	**Calvi** a.	...	...	|	...	0915	1115	1200	|	...	...	1350	...	...	...	1540	1815	|	...	...	|	2005	2055	...	...	|	...
74	Corté d.	...	...	0931	...	...	...	...	1115	...	1337	...	...	...	...	...	...	1704	...	...	1851	...	...	...	...	2005	...
90	Vivario d.	...	...	1002	...	...	...	...	1146	...	1408	...	...	...	...	...	...	1735	...	...	1922	...	...	...	...	...	...
107	Vizzavona d.	Ⓐ	Ⓐ	1024	...	...	...	...	1207	⚒	1429	...	Ⓐ	...	⚒	...	...	1758	⚒	...	1942	...	...	...	...	...	...
145	Mezzana d.	0655	0825	1115	...	...	...	...	1255	1325	1520	...	1615	...	1745	...	...	1846	1910	2000	2030	...	...	...	...	...	...
158	**Ajaccio** a.	0715	0845	1135	...	...	...	...	1315	1345	1540	...	1635	...	1805	...	...	1906	1930	2020	2050	...	...	...	...	...	...

	⚒	⚒			Ⓐ				Ⓐ			⚒		⚒	⚒		Ⓐ				Ⓐ		⚒			⚒	Ⓐ
Ajaccio d.	...	...	...	...	0630	0725	...	...	0800	0911	...	...	...	1052	1215	...	...	...	...	1457	1550	1646	1715	...	...	1815	1935
Mezzana d.	...	...	...	...	0650	0746	...	...	0820	0932	...	...	...	1116	1235	...	...	...	...	1521	1610	1707	1735	...	...	1835	1955
Vizzavona d.	...	...	...	...	▬	0836	...	...	▬	1023	...	...	...	1208	▬	...	...	...	...	1611	▬	1757	▬	...	...	...	...
Vivario d.	...	...	...	...	...	0855	...	...	...	1042	...	...	...	1227	...	...	...	...	...	1630	...	1816	...	...	...	...	...
Corté d.	...	0627	...	...	...	0932	...	...	...	1116	...	...	...	1257	...	...	...	...	...	1705	...	1852	...	...	...	...	...
Calvi d.	...	|	...	0640	...	|	0730	0930	...	|	...	...	1210	...	...	...	...	1400	1550	|	...	|	...	1630	1830	...	...
Ile Rousse d.	...	|	...	0726	...	|	0815	1015	...	|	...	...	1255	...	...	...	...	1445	1626	|	...	|	...	1715	1915	...	...
Ponte Leccia d.	...	0701	...	0850**e**	Ⓐ	1011**c**	...	...	⚒	1150	...	...	...	...	⚒	...	...	...	1740	1744**c**	⑥	1930	⚒	...	...	...	...
Casamozza d.	0700	0738	0756	0928	0945	1048	...	...	1117	1225	1246	1354	...	...	1510	1620	1746	...	...	1822	1845	2005	2016	...	...	...	...
Biguglia d.	0716	0754	0812	0943	1000	1103	...	...	1131	1240	1300	1408	...	...	1524	1634	1800	...	...	1838	1859	2019	2030	...	...	...	...
Bastia a.	0733	0811	0829	0958	1015	1117	...	...	1146	1253	1315	1423	...	...	1540	1649	1815	...	...	1851	1914	2032	2045	...	...	...	...

b – Not Aug. 14. Does not run Casamozza - Corté on July 13.
c – Arrives 6 minutes earlier.
e – Arrives 0840.

TGV Rhin-Rhône PARIS - DIJON - BESANÇON - MULHOUSE - BASEL 370

Regional TER services: Table **371** Paris - Dijon; Table **374** Dijon - Besançon; Table **378** Besançon - Belfort; Table **378a** Belfort - Mulhouse; Table **385** Mulhouse - Basel.
TGV timings may vary by up to 5 minutes (please check your reservation). **Warning!** Certain services are subject to alteration on ⑥⑦ Sept. 24 - Oct. 23.

km		*TGV* 6701	*TGV* 9203	*TGV* 9261	*TGV* 6703	*TGV* 6703	*TGV* 9211	*TGV* 6705	*TGV* 9269	*TGV* 9213		*TGV* 9215	*TGV* 6743	*TGV* 9219	*TGV* 6745	*TGV* 6709	*TGV* 9277	*TGV* 9223	*TGV* 6711	*TGV* 6713	*TGV* 6715	*TGV* 6753	*TGV* 6753
		Ⓐ	①–⑥		Ⓒ	Ⓐ d									Ⓑ				①–⑥	⑦		⑤	⑦
		v		L	z	v⊙	d g		g L	g		a g	R		h		L		b	e	T	f	U
0	**Paris** Gare de Lyon .... **375** d.	0651	0722	0756	0920	0926	1021	1120	1156	1222	...	1421	1451	1621	1652	1721	1755	1821	1852	1919	2022	2120	2122
212	Montbard .... d.	0757	|	|	1027	|	|	|	|	|	...	|	1557	|	1757	|	|	|	1957	|	|	2227	2226
287	**Dijon** Ville .... **375** a.	0832	|	0930	1100	1104	1157	1257	1331	1357	...	|	1632	|	1832	1857	1930	1957	2033	2057	2159	2300	2301
287	**Dijon** Ville .... **375 377 379** d.	0836	|	0934	1104	1113	1201	1301	1334	1401	...	|	1636	|	1836	1901	1933	2001	2036	2101	2201	2304	2305
333	Dole .... **375** a.	|	|	0957	|	|	|	|	1357	|	...	|	1659	|	1859	|	1955	|	|	|	|	2328	|
364	**Besançon** Franche-Comté TGV. **379** d.	0909	|	...	1133	1144	|	1330	...	|	...	|	|	|	|	1930	...	|	2109	2131	2231	|	2338
377	Besançon Viotte .... a.	0921	|	...	|	|	|	|	...	|	...	|	1728	|	1928	|	...	|	|	|	|	2354	2350
446	Belfort Montbéliard TGV .... **379** d.	...	0941	...	1157	1208	|	1354	...	|	...	1640	...	1841	...	1954	...	|	2133	2155	2255	...	...
491	**Mulhouse** .... **379** a.	...	1003	...	1222	1244	1303	1417	...	1504	...	1703	...	1903	...	2017	...	2104	2158	2220	2323	...	...
525	**Basel** SBB .... a.	...	1026	...	...	...	1326	...	...	1526	...	1726	...	1926	...	...	...	2126	...	...	...	...	...
	Zürich HB **510** .... ▲ a.	...	1126	...	...	...	1426	...	...	1626	...	1826c	...	2026	...	...	...	2226	...	...	...	...	...

	TGV 6760	*TGV* 6700	*TGV* 6700	*TGV* 6762	*TGV* 9264	*TGV* 6702	*TGV* 9264	*TGV* 9206	*TGV* 9206		*TGV* 9210	*TGV* 6704	*TGV* 9218	*TGV* 9268		*TGV* 9222	*TGV* 6706	*TGV* 9226	*TGV* 9270	*TGV* 6708	*TGV* 9230	*TGV* 6766	*TGV* 6766
	Ⓐ		⑥														Ⓑ				Ⓑ	⑤	⑦
	v	Y	k	r	D		g L	g	E		s g		g	g L		g	h		m L			w	e
Zürich HB **510** .... ▲ d.	...	...	...	...	...	...	...	0734	0734	...	0934	...	1134	...	...	1334	...	1534	...	...	1734	...	...
Basel SBB .... d.	...	...	...	...	...	...	...	0834	0834	...	1034	...	1234	...	...	1434	...	1634	...	...	1834	...	...
Mulhouse .... **379** d.	...	0539	0541	...	...	0741	...	0856	0859	...	1056	1158	1256	...	...	1456	1541	1656	...	1741	1856	...	...
Belfort Montbéliard TGV .... **379** d.	...	0604	0606	...	...	0806	...	0920	|	...	|	1223	1320	...	...	|	1606	|	...	1806	1920	...	...
Besançon Viotte .... d.	0533	|	|	0636	...	|	...	|	|	...	|	|	|	...	...	|	|	|	...	|	|	1933	1950
Besançon Franche-Comté TGV.. **379** d.	|	0627	0629	0652	...	0829	...	|	|	...	|	1246	|	...	...	|	1629	|	...	1829	|	|	2003
Dole .... **375** d.	0558	|	|	|	0814	|	0902	|	|	...	|	|	|	1400	...	|	|	|	1800	|	|	1956	|
Dijon Ville .... **375 377 379** a.	0621	0657	0657	0720	0840	0858	0926	|	|	...	1157	1314	|	1424	...	1557	1657	1757	1824	1857	|	2025	2029
Dijon Ville .... **375** d.	0625	0701	0702	0724	0844	0900	0930	|	|	...	1201	1318	|	1428	...	1601	1701	1801	1827	1901	|	2031	2033
Montbard .... d.	0701	|	|	0800	|	|	|	|	|	...	|	1402	|	|	...	|	1737	|	|	|	|	|	|
Paris Gare de Lyon .... **375** a.	0805	0839	0839	0908t	1021	1038	1105	1139	1204	...	1342	1506	1541	1605	...	1741	1843	1941	2006	2041	2138	2209	2213

LOCAL CONNECTING TRAINS BESANÇON FRANCHE-COMTÉ TGV - BESANÇON VIOTTE

km		⚒				Ⓐ n	Ⓒ q	Ⓐ	Ⓒ					Ⓑ					⑦ e	①–⑥ b			N
0	Besançon Viotte .... d.	0604	...	0807	...	0955	1010	1123	1140	1226	1338	1415	1515	1608	...	1735	1807	1905	1928	1937	2047	...	2210
13	Besançon Franche-Comté TGV ...... a.	0619	...	0820	...	1010	1025	1136	1153	1237	1355	1431	1528	1619	...	1748	1822	1920	1941	1953	2059	...	2225

	⚒		Ⓐ	Ⓒ									Ⓑ				①–⑥ b	⑦ e		①–⑥ b	⑦ e		N
Besançon Franche-Comté TGV .... d.	0635	...	0837	0852	...	1104	1211	...	1339	1416	1454	1539	1637	...	1807	1837	1937	1946	2022	2115	2138	...	2241
Besançon Viotte .... a.	0655	...	0852	0907	...	1117	1224	...	1354	1429	1509	1553	1652	...	1822	1854	1952	2001	2037	2128	2151	...	2256

D – ①–④ Sept. 26 - Oct. 13. From Frasne (Table **375**).
E – Runs Sept. 26 – 29, Oct. 3 – 6, 10 – 13 only.
L – *TGV Lyria.* To / from Lausanne (Table **375**).
N – Ⓑ to July 3; ⑤⑦ July 8 - Aug. 21 (also July 13, Aug. 15; not July 15); Ⓑ from Aug. 26.
R – ⑤⑦ to Aug. 21 (also July 13, Aug. 15; not July 15); Ⓑ from Aug. 26 (not Oct. 31, Nov. 11).
T – Ⓑ to July 3; ⑤⑦ July 8 - Aug. 28 (also July 13, Aug. 15; not July 15); ④⑤⑦ from Sept. 1 (also Nov. 1; not Nov. 11).
U – ⑦ from July 3 (also Aug. 15, Nov. 1).
Y – ①–⑤ to July 4; ① July 11 - Aug. 22 (also Aug. 16; not Aug. 15); Ⓐ from Aug. 29 (not Oct. 31).

a – Not Aug. 1 – 27.
b – Not Aug. 15, Nov. 1.
c – ⑥⑦ only.
d – Not June 13, 14.
e – Also Aug. 15, Nov. 1.
f – Also July 13, Nov. 10; not July 15, Nov. 11.
g – Not ①–④ Sept. 26 - Oct. 13.
h – Not July 14, 15, Oct. 31, Nov. 11.
k – Also July 14, 15, Oct. 31, Nov. 11.

m – Not Oct. 17 – 20, 24 – 27.
n – Not Oct. 31.
p – Not Sept. 25, Oct. 2, 9, 16, 23.
q – Also Oct. 31; not Nov. 11.
r – Not June 12, 19, 26.
s – Not Aug. 2 – 28.
t – 0917 on July 16.
v – Not July 15, Oct. 31.
w – Also Nov. 10; not July 8 - Aug. 26, Nov. 11.
z – Also July 15, Oct. 31.

TGV – High-speed train. 🅁 🍸.

⊙ – On ①–④ Sept. 26 - Oct. 13 Paris d. 0922, Dijon a. 1057, d. 1101, Besançon Franche-Comté d. 1131, Belfort Montbéliard d. 1156, Mulhouse a. 1219. Sept. 19 – 22, Oct. 17 – 20, 24 Paris d. 0947, Dijon a. 1125, d. 1129, Besançon Franche-Comté d. 1158, Belfort Montbéliard d. 1221, Mulhouse a. 1244. On June 15 departs Paris 0920.
▲ – Journeys to / from Zürich are subject to alteration until July 24.

MULHOUSE - FREIBURG 370a

km		①–⑤ a							🚌	
0	**Mulhouse** .... d.	0633	0831	1031	1231	1431	1631	1831	2015	...
19	Neuenburg 🏛 .... d.	0651	0852	1051	1251	1451	1651	1851	2044	...
22	Müllheim (Baden) .... a.	0655	0856	1055	1255	1455	1655	1855	2052	...
51	Müllheim (Baden) .... **912** d.	*0705*	*0904*	*1104*n	*1306*	*1501*	*1707*	*1907*	...	2104
51	**Freiburg** (Brsg) Hbf ...... **912** a.	*0724*	*0924*	*1124*n	*1325*	*1523*	*1726*	*1926*	...	2124

	①–⑤ a	①–⑥	⑦							🚌
Freiburg (Brsg) Hbf ... **912** d.	*0627*	*0918*	0936	*1034*	*1238*	*1432*	*1632*	*1832*	2033	...
Müllheim (Baden) ...... **912** a.	*0648*	*0936*	0956	*1052*	*1257*	*1451*	*1651*	*1851*	2052	...
Müllheim (Baden) .... d.	0703	0945	0956	1103	1308	1506	1706	1906	...	2103
Neuenburg 🏛 .... d.	0708	0950	1000	1108	1313	1511	1711	1911	...	2109
Mulhouse .... a.	0727	1012	1019	1127	1332	1530	1730	1930	...	2135

a – Not Nov. 1.

n – On ⑦ (also Oct. 3, Nov. 1) Müllheim d. *1102*, Freiburg a. *1121*.

BELFORT - BELFORT MONTBÉLIARD TGV - DELLE 370b

See Table **515** for full service Meroux - Delle - Biel/Bienne and v.v. French holiday dates apply.

km		Ⓐ n	E	⚒	Ⓐ w	Ⓐ w	G		Ⓐ w	H		⚒		Ⓐ w		Ⓐ w	†	⑥ k	Ⓐ w	Ⓑ n		Ⓑ n	Ⓐ w	⚒	†	D
0	**Belfort** Ville .... d.	0445	0548	...	0704	0748	*0748*	*0848*	*1002*	1142	...	1248	...	1348	...	1543	1548	1602	1644	1729	*1848*	*1948*	2021	2121	2148	...
7	Meroux TGV ⊡ .... a.	0454	0557	...	0712	0756	*0757*	*0857*	*1011*	1150	...	1257	...	1357	...	1551	1557	1611	1652	1736	*1857*	*1957*	2030	2130	2157	...
7	Meroux TGV ⊡.. **515** d.	0455	...	0603	0714	0759	0803	0903	1103	...	1203	...	1303	...	1403	1552	...	1612	1659	1737	1903	2003	...	...	...	2203
21	**Delle** 🏛 .... **515** a.	0512	...	0618	0731	0816	0818	0918	1118	...	1218	...	1318	...	1418	1610	...	1631	1715	1757	1918	2018	...	...	...	2218
	Biel/Bienne **515** ..... a.	...	...	0741	...	...	0941	1041	1241	...	1341	...	1441	...	1541	...	...	...	...	...	2041	2141	...	...	...	...

	⚒ D	Ⓐ w	⚒	Ⓐ w	G			Ⓐ w		E		Ⓐ w		Ⓐ w	†	E	†	Ⓑ n		Ⓑ n	Ⓐ w	⚒		†	†	Ⓐ n
Biel/Bienne **515** ...... d.	...	...	...	...	0619	0719	...	0919	1019	...	1119	...	1219	...	1519	...	...	...	1719	1819	...	...	2019	...	...	...
Delle 🏛 .... **515** d.	0540	...	0655	0740	0740	0840	...	1040	1140	...	1240	...	1340	1440	1640	1640	...	1742	1840	1940	...	...	2140	...	2226	2248
Meroux TGV ⊡ ...**515** a.	0556	...	0711	0756	0756	0856	...	1056	1156	...	1256	...	1356	1456	1656	1655	...	1759	1856	1956	...	...	2156	...	2243	2304
Meroux TGV ⊡ .... d.	...	0602	0713	0758	*0808*	...	0943	*1102*	...	1229	...	1320	*1402*	1501	...	1658	1702	1800	*1902*	*2006*	2047	2140	...	2202	2307	2307
Belfort Ville .... a.	...	0611	0723	0807	*0817*	...	0952	*1111*	...	1239	...	1329	*1411*	1511	...	1711	1711	1809	*1913*	*2015*	2056	2149	...	2211	2317	2316

D – To / from Delémont (Table **515**).
E – ⚒ to July 2; ⑥ July 9 - Aug. 27; ⚒ from Aug. 29.
G – ⑥ to July 2; ⚒ July 4 - Aug. 27; ⑥ from Sept. 3 (also Oct. 31).
H – Daily to July 3; ⑥⑦ July 9 - Aug. 21; daily from Aug. 27.

k – Also Oct. 31.
n – Not Oct. 31.
w – Not July 4 - Aug. 26, Oct. 31.

⊡ – Meroux station platforms are located directly above Belfort-Montbéliard TGV station.

371 PARIS - SENS - AUXERRE and DIJON *TER services*

For *TGV* services Paris - Dijon see Table **370**. **Warning!** Subject to alteration Sept. 24 - Oct. 7 (also July 16, Sept. 3, 4, 17, 18).

km		Ⓐ n	⚒	⚒	⚒	Ⓐ	Ⓐ n	Ⓑ	⑥			⑥	Ⓐ	⑥	Ⓑ	Ⓒ	Ⓐ	Ⓐ 🚌		Ⓐ	Ⓒ	Ⓒ		†	Ⓐ	Ⓑ n ⊗ ¶
0	**Paris** Bercy d.	...	...	...	...	0611	...	...	...	0733	...	0833	0835	...	...	0920	0921	...	...	1033	1033	...	1233**f**	...	...	...
113	Sens d.	...	...	0622	...	0721	...	...	...	0831	...	0932	0933	...	...	1027	1031	...	...	1132	1132	...	1331	...	...	...
147	Joigny d.	...	...	0649	...	0747	...	...	...	0849	...	0949	0950	...	...	1047	1048	...	...	1149	1149	...	1348	...	...	...
	Auxerre d.	0535	0636	|	...	|	*0739*	0835	0837	|	...	|	|	1037	1039	|	|	...	...	|	|	*1139*	|	1336	1337	...
156	Laroche Migennes a.	0553	0654	0656	...	0755	*0752*	0853	0852	0855	...	0955	0956	1054	1053	1055	1055	...	...	1155	1155	*1152*	1355	1352	1351	...
156	Laroche Migennes d.	0558	...	0659	0707	0757	0800	...	...	0859	0906	1005	1005	...	...	1059	...	1110	1107	1158	1205	1200	1405	...	...	1400
175	**Auxerre** a.	|	...	|	0725	0810	|	...	...	|	0919	1018	1018	...	...	|	...	|	1125	1211	1218	|	1418	...	...	|
197	Tonnerre d.	0625	...	0723	...	...	0824	...	...	0923	...	...	...	...	...	1123	...	1219	...	...	...	1223	...	...	...	1425
243	Montbard d.	0650	...	0750	...	...	0849	...	...	0949	...	...	...	...	...	1150	...	1317	...	...	...	1250	...	...	...	1450
315	**Dijon** Ville a.	0727	...	0827	...	...	0927	...	...	1027	...	...	...	...	...	1233	...	1446	...	...	...	1328	...	...	...	1527
	Lyon Part Dieu **377** a.	...	...	1044	...	...	...	...	...	1244	...	...	...	...	...	1444	...	...	...	...	...	...	...	...	...	...

		⚒		Ⓐ n	Ⓐ n	†				⑥	Ⓑ	Ⓑ n	†	⑥	Ⓐ	⑤⑥ k	† r	①–④ m	⚒ ⊙	†	⑥	†	Ⓐ	†	Ⓐ	Ⓑ n
Paris Bercy d.	...	1333	...	1433	...	...	...	1533	...	1627	1627**e**	...	...	...	...	1727	1729	1728	...	...	1827	1827	1827	...	...	...
Sens d.	...	1432	...	1531	...	...	...	1631	...	1732	1732	...	...	...	...	1832	1832	1833	...	...	1930	1932	1931	...	...	...
Joigny d.	...	1450	...	1548	...	...	...	1649	...	1748	1748	...	...	...	...	1849	1849	1850	...	...	1948	1948	1948	...	...	...
Auxerre d.	1435	|	...	|	1535	*1537*	1635	|	...	|	|	1728	1832	1837	1839	|	|	|	...	...	|	|	|	1943	1946	...
Laroche Migennes a.	1453	1456	...	1555	1551	*1552*	1653	1655	...	1755	1755	1744	1846	1852	1853	1855	1855	1856	...	...	1955	1955	1955	1956	2002	...
Laroche Migennes d.	...	1459	1507	1605	1600	1600	...	1659	1705	1757	1805	1759	...	...	...	1859	1859	1900	1905	1916	1957	2005	*2010*	...	...	2011
Auxerre a.	...	|	1525	1618	|	|	...	|	1722	1810	1818	|	...	...	...	|	|	|	1919	1934	2010	2018	*2025*	...	...	|
Tonnerre d.	...	1523	...	...	1626	1626	...	1723	...	...	...	1826	...	...	...	1923	1923	1924	...	...	...	...	...	...	...	2035
Montbard d.	...	1549	...	...	1650	1650	...	1749	...	...	...	1851	...	...	...	1949	1949	1950	...	...	...	...	...	...	...	2101
Dijon Ville a.	...	1627	...	...	1727	1727	...	1827	...	...	...	1927	...	...	...	2027	2027	2029	...	...	...	...	...	...	...	2139
Lyon Part Dieu **377** a.	...	1844	...	...	...	...	...	2044	...	...	...	...	...	...	...	...	2244	2244	...	...	...	...	...	...	...	...

	Ⓐ	⑥	†	Ⓐ	Ⓒ	⑤–⑦	①–④			△	
Paris Bercy d.	...	...	...	1928	1929	...	...	2033	...	2233	...
Sens d.	...	...	...	2035	2032	...	...	2133	...	2348	...
Joigny d.	...	...	...	2052	2049	...	...	2150	...	0016	...
Auxerre d.	2035	2036	2038	|	|	...	...	|	...	|	...
Laroche Migennes a.	2053	2053	2054	2058	2055	...	...	2156	...	0024	...
Laroche Migennes d.	...	...	...	2102	2059	2106	2107	2158	...	...	...
Auxerre a.	...	...	...	|	|	2119	2125	2212	...	...	...
Tonnerre d.	...	...	...	2126	2123	...	...	...	...	...	...
Montbard d.	...	...	...	2152	2149	...	...	...	...	...	...
Dijon Ville a.	...	...	...	2230	2227	...	...	...	...	...	...
Lyon Part Dieu **377** a.	...	...	...	...	...	...	...	...	...	...	...

	Ⓐ		Ⓐ	⑥	Ⓐ		⚒	Ⓐ	⑥	⚒
Lyon Part Dieu **377** d.	...	...	...	...	...	...	...	...	...	...
Dijon Ville d.	...	...	...	...	...	...	...	0532	0533	...
Montbard d.	...	...	...	...	...	...	...	0611	0612	...
Tonnerre d.	...	...	...	...	...	...	...	0637	0638	...
Auxerre d.	0450	...	0535	0550	...	...	0636	|	|	...
Laroche Migennes a.	0503	...	0553	0603	...	...	0654	0700	0701	...
Laroche Migennes d.	0505	...	...	0604	0604	...	...	0704	0703	0707
Auxerre a.	|	...	...	|	|	...	...	|	|	0725
Joigny d.	0513	...	...	0612	0612	...	...	0711	0710	...
Sens d.	0530	...	...	0630	0630	...	...	0729	0727	...
Paris Bercy a.	0633	...	...	0727	0734	...	...	0832	0827	...

	Ⓑ	⚒	†	Ⓑ	⑥	⚒		Ⓐ n	⑥ w	⚒	⑥ w	Ⓑ n	Ⓐ ⊖	Ⓒ			Ⓐ n⊗	Ⓒ w	†	Ⓐ	⑥		⊗		Ⓐ	Ⓒ
Lyon Part Dieu **377** d.	...	...	...	...	...	0516**g**	...	...	...	...	...	...	...	0716	...	...	...	...	...	...	...	...	1116	...	...	...
Dijon Ville d.	0631	...	...	...	...	0733	...	0833	0833	...	...	...	...	0933	...	...	1207	1230	...	...	...	...	1329	...	...	...
Montbard d.	0708	...	...	...	...	0811	...	0909	0910	...	...	...	...	1011	...	...	1306	1310	...	...	...	...	1409	...	...	...
Tonnerre d.	0733	...	...	...	...	0837	...	0933	0936	...	...	...	...	1037	...	...	1331	1336	...	...	...	...	1437	...	...	...
Auxerre d.	|	0739	0747	0835	0837	|	...	|	|	0950	1037	1039	...	|	...	1139	|	|	1336	1337	1340	1435	|	...	*1535*	1537
Laroche Migennes a.	0800	0752	0800	0853	0852	0900	...	1000	1000	1002	1054	1053	...	1100	...	1152	1356	1400	1352	1351	1354	1453	1501	...	*1551*	1552
Laroche Migennes d.	0807	0805	0805	...	...	0904	0906	*1005*	1012	1005	...	...	1104	1104	1107	1204	*1405*	*1405*	1402	1402	1402	...	1505	1507	1604	1605
Auxerre a.	0825	|	|	...	...	|	0919	*1018*	1028	|	...	...	|	|	1125	|	*1418*	*1418*	|	|	|	...	|	1525	|	|
Joigny d.	...	0813	0813	...	...	0911	...	...	...	1012	...	...	1111	1111	...	1212	...	...	1410	1410	1410	...	1512	...	1611	1613
Sens d.	...	0830	0830	...	...	0929	...	...	...	1030	...	...	1129	1129	...	1229	...	...	1428	1429	1428	...	1531	...	1629	1630
Paris Bercy a.	...	0935	0927	...	...	1027	...	...	...	1133**h**	...	...	1227	1227	...	1327	...	...	1527	1527**c**	1527	...	1637•	...	1725	1726

				Ⓑ n	G	Ⓐ H	†	⑥	Ⓐ		⚒ ⊙	†	Ⓑ	†	Ⓐ	⑥	†	Ⓐ	Ⓐ	⑥	†		⑤–⑦	①–④		Ⓑ n
Lyon Part Dieu **377** d.	...	1316	...	...	...	...	...	...	...	1516	...	...	...	...	...	...	...	...	...	...	...	1716	...	...	...	...
Dijon Ville d.	...	1533	...	1633	...	...	...	...	...	1732	...	...	1833	...	...	1833	...	...	...	...	...	1933	...	...	...	2037
Montbard d.	...	1611	...	1710	...	...	...	...	...	1811	...	...	1910	...	...	1910	...	...	...	...	...	2011	...	...	...	2129
Tonnerre d.	...	1637	...	1736	...	...	...	...	...	1837	...	...	1935	...	...	1935	...	...	...	...	...	2037	...	...	...	2154
Auxerre d.	1635	|	...	|	1741	1742	1832	1837	1839	|	...	...	|	...	...	|	1943	1946	2035	2036	2038	|	...	...	...	|
Laroche Migennes a.	1653	1700	...	1759	1754	1754	1846	1852	1853	1900	...	...	2000	...	...	2004	1956	2002	2053	2053	2054	2100	...	...	...	2221
Laroche Migennes d.	...	1704	1705	*1805*	1805	1820	...	...	...	1904	1905	1916	...	2005	2010	2009	2005	2005	...	...	...	2104	2106	2107	...	2228
Auxerre a.	...	|	1722	*1818*	|	|	...	...	...	|	1919	1934	...	2018	2025	2027	|	|	...	...	...	|	2119	2125	...	2244
Joigny d.	...	1711	...	...	1813	1828	...	...	...	1911	...	...	...	...	...	...	2013	2013	...	...	...	2111	...	...	...	...
Sens d.	...	1729	...	...	1830	1854	...	...	...	1929	...	...	...	...	...	...	2039	2040	...	...	...	2129	...	...	...	...
Paris Bercy a.	...	1827	...	...	1925	2001	...	...	...	2027	...	...	...	...	...	...	2148	2148	...	...	...	2227	...	...	...	...

LOCAL TRAINS PARIS - LAROCHE MIGENNES For faster trains see the main part of Table **371** above. **Warning!** Subject to alteration Sept. 24 - Oct. 7 (also Sept. 17, 18).

km								†	⚒				Ⓐ n	Ⓒ	Ⓐ	Ⓐ n	Ⓒ w	Ⓐ n	Ⓐ n	Ⓒ	Ⓐ		Ⓐ	Ⓒ		❖
0	**Paris** Gare de Lyon d.	0646	0746	0846	...	1046	1146	1246	1246	1346	1446	1546	1621	1646	1712	1721	1746	1812	1821	1846	1912	1946	2046	2046	2146	2246
45	Melun d.	0713	0810	0912	...	1112	1213	1313	1313	1413	1512	1613	1648	1712	|	1748	1812	|	1848	1912	|	2013	2113	2113	2213	2313
60	Fontainebleau-Avon d.	0726	0823	0925	...	1125	1226	1326	1326	1426	1525	1626	1701	1725	|	1801	1825	|	1901	1925	|	2026	2126	2126	2226	2326
79	Montereau d.	0745	0844	0945	...	1145	1244	1345	1345	1444	1545	1644	1722	1746	1805	1822	1845	1905	1922	1945	2005	2046	2144	2146	2244	2344
113	Sens a.	0813	...	1013	...	1213	...	1413	1413	...	1613	...	1750	1813	1833	1850	1913	1933	1950	2013	2033	2112	...	2213	...	...
113	Sens d.	0833	...	1033	...	1215	...	1415	1436	...	1633	...	1752	1833	1835	1852	1933	1935	1952	2033	2035	2114	...	2215	...	...
147	Joigny d.	0900	...	1100	...	1243	...	1442	1503	...	1701	...	1820	1900	1902	1920	2000	2002	2020	2100	2102	2142	...	2243	...	...
156	**Laroche Migennes** a.	0908	...	1108	...	1250	...	1450	1510	...	1708	...	1827	1909	1909	1927	2010	2009	2027	2108	2109	2149	...	2250	...	...

		Ⓐ	⑥ w	Ⓐ n	Ⓐ n	Ⓒ w	Ⓐ n	Ⓐ n	†	⑥ w							⚒	†		⚒	†	Ⓐ	Ⓒ			
Laroche Migennes d.	0410	0450	0510	0539	0550	0610	0639	0650	...	0650	0750	1010	...	1210	...	1410	...	1450	1550	...	1650	1750	1810	...	...	...
Joigny d.	0417	0457	0517	0546	0558	0617	0646	0658	...	0658	0758	1017	...	1217	...	1417	...	1458	1558	...	1658	1758	1817	...	...	...
Sens a.	0443	0523	0543	0610	0625	0643	0710	0725	...	0725	0825	1043	...	1243	...	1443	...	1525	1625	...	1725	1825	1844	...	...	...
Sens d.	0445	0525	0545	0612	0627	0645	0713	0727	...	0745	0845	1045	...	1245	...	1445	...	1545	1645	...	1745	1845	1846	...	...	...
Montereau d.	0516	0555	0616	0644	0657	0715	0743	0757	0814	0815	0916	1116	1214	1316	1414	1515	1613	1616	1716	1814	1816	1916	1916	2013	2114	2215
Fontainebleau-Avon d.	0534	|	0633	0701	|	0734	0800	|	0832	0834	0934	1134	1232	1334	1432	1534	1630	1633	1734	1832	1834	1934	1934	2031	2132	2231
Melun d.	0547	|	0648	0715	|	0747	0815	|	0845	0847	0947	1147	1247	1347	1447	1547	1645	1645	1747	1847	1847	1946	1947	2045	2145	2245
Paris Gare de Lyon a.	0613	0648	0713	0743	0748	0813	0843	0848	0913	0913	1013	1213	1313	1413	1513	1613**j**	1713	1713	1813	1913	1913	2013**b**	2013	2113	2213	2313

G – Ⓒ to Aug. 21; daily from Aug. 27.
H – Until Aug. 26.

b – Paris **Bercy**.
c – On Aug. 9, 10 arrives Paris **Gare de Lyon** (not Bercy).
e – On Aug. 9, 10 departs Paris **Gare de Lyon** (not Bercy).
f – On June 29, 30, Aug. 24, 25 departs Paris **Gare de Lyon** (not Bercy).
g – ① (also July 15, Aug. 16, Nov. 2, 12; not Aug. 15, Oct. 31).
h – 1140 on July 27, 28; 1149 June 13 – 17, 20 – 24, Sept. 12 – 16, 19 – 23.
j – On ⑤ (also July 13, Nov. 10; not Nov. 11) arrives Paris **Bercy** (not Gare de Lyon).
k – Also July 13, Oct. 31, Nov. 10; not Nov. 11.
m – Not July 13, 14, Aug. 15, Oct. 31, Nov. 1, 10.

n – Not Oct. 31.
r – Not July 14.
w – Also Oct. 31.

⊗ – Not ①–⑤ Sept. 12 - Oct. 14.
△ – Timings may vary by up to 7 minutes on certain dates.
• – On ⑤ (also July 13) arrives Paris **Gare de Lyon** 1633 (not Paris Bercy).
⊙ – On Ⓐ July 11 - Aug. 26 Laroche d. 1907, Auxerre a. 1925.
¶ – Runs 10 – 24 minutes later on certain dates.
⊖ – Runs 21 – 26 minutes later on June 27, 30.
❖ – Subject to alteration.

DIJON and CHALON SUR SAÔNE - MONTCHANIN - NEVERS 373

WARNING! Subject to alteration July 25 - Aug. 26 (also on Sept. 3).

km		Ⓐ n	Ⓐ vn	Ⓐ n	Ⓐ n	⚒	⚒	Ⓑ n		⚒n ⊗⊖		⊗	Ⓐ n⊗	⚒ v	⚒	Ⓑ n	Ⓑ n	⚒	⚒	Ⓐ n	Ⓑ vn	Ⓐ n	†		
0	**Dijon** Ville ..... 377 d.	...	...	0612	0646	...	0712	0812	...	1012	...	1212	1236	...	1412	...	1612	...	1712	1748	...	1812	1812	...	1912
37	Beaune ..... 377 d.	...	...	0631	0706	...	0731	0831	...	1031	...	1231	1255	...	1431	...	1631	...	1731	1807	...	1831	1831	...	1931
	Chalon sur Saône ... 377 d.	...	*0556*	│	│	0708	│	│	...	│	...	│	│	1410	│	1610	│	1710	│	│	1810	│	│	1910	│
	Chagny ..... 377 d.	...	0622	│	│	0722	│	│	...	│	...	│	│	1422	│	1622	│	1722	│	│	1821	│	│	1922	│
81	**Montchanin** ..... d.	...	0648	0658	0732	0748	0758	0858	...	1102	...	1258	1322	1448	1458	1648	1658	1748	1758	1834	1847	1857	1858	1948	1958
89	Le Creusot Ville ..... d.	...	...	0705	0739	...	0805	0905	...	1109	...	1305	1329	...	1505	...	1705	...	1805	1841	...	1904	1905	...	2005
111	Étang ..... ★ d.	0605	...	0721	│	...	0821	0921	...	1125	...	1321	│	...	1521	...	1721	...	1821	│	...	1919	1921	...	2021
	Autun ..... ★ a.	│	...	│	│	...	│	│	...	│	...	│	│	...	│	...	│	...	│	│	...	...	│	...	│
179	Decize ..... d.	0647	...	0803	0831	...	0903	1003	...	1207	...	1403	1420	...	1603	...	1803	...	1903	1932	...	...	2003	...	2103
216	**Nevers** ..... a.	0719	...	0829	0853	...	0929	1029	...	1233	...	1429	1443	...	1629	...	1829	...	1929	1955	...	...	2029	...	2129

km		Ⓐ n	① g	⚒	⚒	⚒	Ⓐ n	Ⓑ n	Ⓐ vn			⊗	Ⓐ n⊗	Ⓐ n	Ⓐ vn		Ⓑ n	⑥ r	Ⓑ n	Ⓑ n	Ⓐ n	⑥ r	⑥ r	Ⓐ n	Ⓑ n⊖
	Nevers ..... d.	...	0531	...	0631	...	0704	0731	...	0931**k**	...	1131	1153	1331	...	1531	...	...	1731	...	1844	1844	...	1848	1939
	Decize ..... d.	...	0556	...	0657	...	0729	0757	...	0957**k**	...	1157	1219	1357	...	1556	...	...	1757	...	1908	1909	...	1920	2004
0	Autun ..... ★ d.	...	│	...	│	...	│	│	...	│	...	│	│	│	...	│	...	...	│	...	│	│	...	│	│
15	Étang ..... ★ d.	0639	0639	...	0740	...	│	0840	...	1040**k**	...	1240	│	1440	...	1639	...	...	1840	...	│	1953	...	2002	2048
▬	Le Creusot Ville ..... d.	0655	0655	...	0755	...	0820	0855	...	1055	...	1255	1312	1455	...	1655	...	...	1855	...	2004	2009	...	...	2103
0	**Montchanin** ..... d.	0702	0702	0712	0803	0812	0827	0903	0912	1103	1112	1303	1319	1503	1512	1702	1712	1812	1903	1912	2011	2016	2022	...	2117
29	Chagny ..... 377 d.	│	│	0739	│	0839	│	│	0939	│	1139	│	│	│	1539	│	1739	1839	│	1939	│	│	2048	...	│
44	**Chalon sur Saône** ... 377 a.	│	│	0750	│	0850	│	│	0950	│	1150	│	│	│	1550	│	1750	1850	│	1950	│	│	2058	...	│
	Beaune ..... 377 d.	0728	0728	...	0829	...	0853	0929	...	1129	...	1329	1345	1529	...	1727	...	...	1929	...	2037	2042	...	...	2144
	Dijon Ville ..... 377 a.	0748	0748	...	0848	...	0914	0950	...	1148	...	1348	1404	1548	...	1748	...	...	1948	...	2056	2100	...	...	2203

MONTCHANIN - PARAY LE MONIAL - MOULINS SUR ALLIER

km		Ⓐ n	⚒ ⊗	†	⚒ n⊗	v	⚒	Ⓑ n		Ⓑ vn	
	Dijon Ville (see above) ..... d.	...	...	...	1012	...	...	...	...	...	...
0	**Montchanin** ..... ▷ d.	0708	0808	0908	1106	1308	1508	1708	1808	1908	2008
15	Montceau les Mines ..... ▷ d.	0722	0822	0922	1120	1322	1522	1722	1822	1922	2022
50	Paray le Monial ..... **290** ▷ d.	0752	0851	0952	1154	1351	1552	1752	1851	1951	2051
61	Digoin ..... **290** d.	...	...	...	1206	...	...	...	...	...	...
117	**Moulins sur Allier** ..... **290** a.	...	...	...	1257	...	...	...	...	...	...
	Clermont Ferrand **330** ..... a.	...	...	...	1420	...	...	...	...	...	...

	Ⓐ n	⚒		⊗	⚒ v		Ⓑ n		Ⓑ n
Clermont Ferrand **330** ... d.	...	...	...	...	...	...	...	...	1741
Moulins sur Allier ..... **290** d.	...	...	...	...	...	...	...	...	1903
Digoin ..... **290** d.	...	...	...	...	...	...	...	...	1948
Paray le Monial ..... **290** ▷ d.	0608	0708	1008	1211	1408	1608	1808	1908	2008
Montceau les Mines ..... ▷ d.	0638	0738	1038	1238	1438	1638	1838	1938	2039
Montchanin ..... ▷ a.	0652	0752	1052	1252	1452	1652	1852	1952	2052
Dijon Ville (see above) .. a.	...	...	...	...	...	...	...	...	2203

g – Also Aug. 16, Nov. 2; not Aug. 15, Oct. 31.
k – 2 minutes earlier on ⑥.
n – Not Oct. 31.
r – Also Oct. 31.
v – Not July 4–8, 11–13, 15, 18–22, 25–29, Aug 1–5, 8–12, 16–19, 22–26.

⊖ – Conveys 12 Dijon - Montchanin - Clermont Ferrand and v.v. (see panel below main table).
⊗ – Subject to alteration Oct. 17–21, 24–28.
▷ – Additional journeys Montchanin - Paray and v.v. on Ⓐ n: **From Montchanin** at 1608. **From Paray le Monial** at 1708.
★ – 🚌 **ÉTANG - AUTUN** and v.v. Journey time 21 minutes: **From Étang** at 0643 ① **g**, 0725 Ⓐ **n**, 0825 ⑥, 0925 Ⓑ **n**, 1045 Ⓐ **n**, 1245 Ⓒ **r**, 1325, 1525 Ⓐ **n**, 1645 ⚒, 1725 Ⓑ **n**, 1825 ⚒, 1845 Ⓐ **n**, 1925 Ⓑ **n**, 2010 Ⓐ **n** and 2055 †. **From Autun** at 0534 Ⓐ **n**, 0608 Ⓐ **n**, 0649 Ⓐ **n**, 0704 ① **g**, 0809 Ⓐ **n**, 0850 †, 1009, 1216, 1449 Ⓐ **n**, 1608, 1749 ⚒, 1809 Ⓑ **n**, 1849 †, 1922 ⑥ **r** and 1950 †.

DIJON - DOLE - BESANÇON 374

For *TGV* services see Table **370** (Paris - Dijon - Besançon - Basel) and Table **379** (Strasbourg - Besançon - Dijon). On Oct. 31 services run as on ⑥.

km		Ⓐ		Ⓐ		Ⓐ						Ⓐ		Ⓐ	Ⓐ		Ⓐ		Ⓐ		Ⓐ			Ⓑ			
0	**Dijon** Ville ..... 375 d.	0509	0614	0640	0709	0740	0813	0909	1011	1109	1209	1309	1344	1409	1509	1540	1609	1640	1709	1739	1809	1840	1909	1940	2009	2109	2210
32	Auxonne ..... d.	0529	0636	0659	0730	0759	0834	0929	1030	1129	1231	1329	1406	1429	1529	1602	1629	1702	1729	1801	1829	1902	1929	2001	2029	2129	2231
46	Dole Ville ..... 375 d.	0539	0646	0709	0740	0809	0844	0939	1040	1139	1241	1339	1416	1439	1539	1613	1639	1712	1739	1812	1839	1912	1939	2012	2039	2139	2241
91	**Besançon** Viotte .. a.	0604	0722	0734	0814	0834	0914	1004	1105	1204	1314	1404	1450	1504	1604	1647	1704	1746	1804	1846	1904	1946	2004	2046	2104	2204	2316

	Ⓐ		Ⓐ	Ⓐ				Ⓐ				Ⓐ		Ⓐ					Ⓑ		Ⓐ		Ⓐ		Ⓐ		
Besançon Viotte .. d.	0456	0556	0625	0656	0712	0756	0856	0912	0956	1056	...	1206	1225	1256	1356	1456	1556	1612	1656	1712	1756	1812	1856	1912	1956	2056	2156
Dole Ville ..... 375 d.	0530	0623	0659	0722	0745	0824	0922	0945	1022	1122	...	1233	1259	1322	1422	1522	1622	1647	1722	1745	1822	1845	1922	1946	2022	2122	2221
Auxonne ..... d.	0539	0631	0708	0731	0754	0832	0931	0954	1031	1131	...	1242	1308	1330	1430	1531	1631	1657	1731	1754	1831	1854	1931	1955	2031	2131	2231
Dijon Ville ..... 375 a.	0602	0651	0730	0751	0815	0852	0951	1015	1051	1151	...	1301	1330	1351	1451	1552	1652	1720	1751	1815	1851	1915	1951	2018	2051	2151	2251

PARIS - DIJON - LAUSANNE and NEUCHÂTEL 375

TGV timings may vary by up to 5 minutes (please check your reservation for confirmed timings). **Warning!** *TGV* services via Dijon are subject to alteration on ⑥⑦ Sept. 24 - Oct. 23.

km										*TGV* **9761**	*TGV* **9261**				*TGV* **9269**		*TGV* **9775**						*TGV* **9777**	*TGV* **9277**	
		①–⑤ a¶	①–⑤ a	①–⑤ a	①–⑤ a	Ⓐ n	⑥ r	Ⓐ n	Ⓐ n	①–⑥ d					⊡			①–⑤ a	①–⑤ a	①–⑤ a¶	Ⓐ n				
0	**Paris** Gare de Lyon ..... 370 d.	...	...	...	...	...	...	...	...	0615	0756	...	...	...	1156	...	1416	...	...	...	...	...	1616	1755	...
287	**Dijon** Ville ..... 370 374 d.	...	...	...	...	...	...	*0509*	*0640*	│	0934	...	...	*1011*	1334	...	│	...	...	...	...	1734	│	1933	...
333	Dole Ville ..... 374 376 d.	...	...	...	...	...	0613	0616	0715	│	1000	...	1014	1114	1400	...	│	...	...	...	...	1815**h**	│	1957	...
359	Arc-et-Senans ..... d.	...	...	...	...	...	0631	0640	│	│	│	...	1035	1133	│	...	│	...	...	...	...	1834	│	│	...
365	Mouchard ..... 376 d.	...	...	...	...	...	0645	0648	0740	│	│	...	1041	1142	│	...	│	...	...	...	...	1844	│	2015	...
389	Andelot ..... 376 d.	...	...	...	...	...	0704	0706	...	◐	│	...	1102	1204	│	...	◐	...	...	...	...	1903	◐	│	...
410	Frasne ..... d.	0523	...	0620	...	0717	0719	...	...	│	1044	1053	...	1219	1444	1453	│	1644	...	1718	1806	1918	│	2044	2053
426	Pontarlier 🏛 ..... a.	│	...	│	...	0732	0735	...	...	│	│	1104	...	1234	│	1504	│	│	...	1729	1822	1933	│	│	2104
490	**Neuchâtel** ..... a.	│	...	│	...	...	...	...	...	│	│	1153	...	...	│	1553	│	│	...	...	...	...	│	│	2153
434	Vallorbe 🏛 ..... ▷ a.	0542	0547	0638	0647	...	...	...	...	│	1057	...	...	...	1457	...	│	1711	1747	...	...	...	│	2057	...
480	**Lausanne** ..... ▷ a.	...	0635	...	0735	...	...	...	...	1014	1152	...	...	...	1536	...	1814	...	1835	...	...	...	2014	2137	...

							TGV **9264**		*TGV* **9264**	*TGV* **9768**				*TGV* **9268**	*TGV* **9774**				*TGV* **9270**					*TGV* **9782**	*TGV* **9784**
	①–⑤ a¶	Ⓐ n	⚒	①–⑤ a		①–⑤ a	D		⊡		†	⚒		⊡			①–⑤ a¶		⊗	①–⑤ a	①–⑤ a	Ⓐ n		①–④ L	J
Lausanne ..... ▷ d.	...	...	...	...	0601	...	...	...	0723	0945	...	...	...	1223	1345	1601	...	...	1623	1634	...	...	...	1844	1945
Vallorbe 🏛 ..... ▷ d.	...	...	...	0559	0648	0655	...	...	0800	│	...	...	...	1300	│	1648	1652	...	1700	1719	1726	...	...	│	│
Neuchâtel ..... d.	...	...	...	│	...	│	...	0706	│	│	...	...	1206	│	│	...	│	1606	│	...	│	...	...	│	│
Pontarlier 🏛 ..... d.	0509	0555	...	│	...	│	...	0755	│	│	...	1128	1255	│	│	...	│	1655	│	...	│	1736	1829	│	│
Frasne ..... d.	0519	0611	...	0615	...	0711	0717	0806	0815	│	...	1145	1306	1315	│	...	1710	1706	1715	...	1744	1752	1845	│	│
Andelot ..... 376 d.	...	0624	0759	...	...	...	│	...	│	◐	1203	1203	...	│	◐	...	...	...	│	...	...	...	1901	◐	◐
Mouchard ..... 376 d.	...	0646	0817	...	...	...	0755	...	0845	│	1220	1221	...	│	│	...	...	...	│	...	...	...	1918	│	│
Arc-et-Senans ..... d.	...	0651	0823	...	...	...	│	...	│	│	1226	1226	...	│	│	...	...	...	│	...	...	...	1924	│	│
Dole Ville ..... 374 376 d.	...	0729**k**	0841	...	...	...	0814	...	0902	│	1245	1245	...	1400	│	...	...	...	1800	...	...	...	1940	│	│
Dijon Ville ..... 370 374 d.	...	0755	...	...	...	...	0844	...	0930	│	*1330*	*1330*	...	1428	│	...	...	...	1827	...	...	...	*2018*	│	│
Paris Gare de Lyon ..... 370 a.	...	...	...	...	...	...	1021	...	1105	1342	...	...	...	1605	1743	...	...	...	2006	...	...	...	...	2306	2345

D – ①–④ Sept. 26 - Oct. 13.
J – ⑤⑦ to Nov. 6 (also July 14, Oct. 31, Nov. 1; not Aug. 14, Sept. 16); Ⓑ from Nov. 10.
L – ①–④ July 4 - Aug. 25 (not July 14); ①–④ Oct. 10 - Nov. 9 (not Oct. 31, Nov. 1).

a – Not Aug. 1.
d – Not Aug. 15.
h – Arrives 1800.
k – Arrives 0708.
n – Not Oct. 31.
r – Also Oct. 31.

TGV – *TGV Lyria*. High-speed train. Ⓡ. 🍸.

¶ – 12 Pontarlier - Frasne - Vallorbe and v.v.
⊡ – Not ①–④ Sept. 26 - Oct. 13.
⊗ – Not Oct. 17–20, 24–27.
◐ – Via Genève (Table **341**).
▷ – Additional local services Vallorbe - Lausanne and v.v. (journey time ±50 minutes): **From Vallorbe** at 0510 and hourly until 2110; then 2210 ⑤⑥, 2212 ⑦–④, 2304 ①–⑤ and 2310 ⑥⑦. **From Lausanne** at 0501 and hourly until 2301.

376 DOLE / BESANÇON - MOREZ - ST CLAUDE - BOURG EN BRESSE

km		⑥ r	Ⓐ n	Ⓒ r			🚌 ⑤ f	⑤ f	D	⑤⑦ w	🚌 ⊖	🚌 ⑤⑦ w
0	**Dole** Ville .... **375** d.	0613	0616	...	1014	*1114*	1612	...	1815	...	...	...
	Besançon ◇ . **378** d.	|	|	...	|	|	|	1639	|	...	...	...
26	Arc-et-Senans **375/8** d.	0631	0640	...	1035	*1133*	|	1702	1834	...	...	...
32	Mouchard .... **375/8** d.	0645	0648	...	1041	*1142*	1659	1709	1844	...	...	2045
56	Andelot .... **375** d.	0703	0710	0710	1107	1209	...	1734	1902	1910	1910	|
70	Champagnole .... d.	...	0740j	0740j	1120	1221	...	1746	...	1923	1930	2127
105	Morez .... d.	...	0831	0832	1212	1312	...	1844	...	2015	2017	2209
128	**St Claude** .... a.	...	0857	0859	1240	1340	...	1912	...	2042	2057	2249

	① g	⚒ ns		⑤ f	🚌 ⑤ f	①–④ p	🚌 Ⓐ n		Ⓑ	
St Claude .... d.	0443	0617	0954	1511	...	1551	...	1723	1723	...
Morez .... d.	0516	0649	1029	1543	...	1626	...	1757	1757	...
Champagnole .... d.	0603	0736	1147t	1631	...	1712	1735	1845	1845	...
Andelot .... **375** a.	0613	0753	1158	1642	...	...	1755	1856	1856k	1901
Mouchard .... **375/8** a.	0636	0816	*1220*	1705	1715	...	1825	...	1925	1917
Arc-et-Senans ...... **375/8** a.	*0650*	0822	*1225*	1713	|	...	|	...	1930	1923
Besançon-Viotte . **378** a.	|	|	|	1738	|	...	|	...	1957	|
Dole Ville .... **375** a.	*0708*	0841	*1245*	...	1802	...	1912	...	...	1940

ST CLAUDE - OYONNAX - BOURG EN BRESSE *Rail services are subject to alteration Oct. 29 – 31*

km		⚒	⚒	🚌	🚌 ⚒	Ⓐ	🚌	🚌 ⚒	🚌 Ⓐ	🚌	🚌	†
0	**St Claude** ..... 🚌 ⊠ d.	*0550*a	*0645*	*0840*	*0940*	*1140*	*1235*c	*1440*a	...	*1630*a	*1725*	...
32	Oyonnax .... 🚌 ⊠ d.	*0626*a	*0721*	*0916*	*1016*	*1216*	*1311*c	*1516*a	...	*1706*a	*1801*	...
32	Oyonnax .... d.	0636	0733	0925	1025	1238	1320	1525	1610	1725	1810	1837
45	Brion Montréal ⊡ ..... d.	0651	0748	0942	1042	1254	1343	1542	1634	1742	1827	1853
48	Nurieux Brion .... d.	0655	0752	|	|	1257	|	|	|	|	|	1856
81	**Bourg en Bresse** ▷ a.	0734	0833	1022	1122	1337	1423	1622	1714	1822	1907	1933
	Lyon Part Dieu .... ▷ a.	0830	...	...	...	...	...	...	...	...	...	...

	🚌 Ⓐ	Ⓐ	🚌 ⑥	🚌	🚌 ⚒	🚌 ⚒	Ⓑ		🚌	🚌 Ⓑ
Lyon Part Dieu .... ▷ d.	...	...	...	...	...	...	...	...	...	...
Bourg en Bresse ...... ▷ d.	0645	0840e	0850	1030	1235	1430	1730	1839	1930	2025
Nurieux Brion .... d.	|	0924	|	|	|	|	1811	1916	|	|
Brion Montréal ⊡ .... d.	0725	0928	0930	1110	1315	1510	1815	1920	2010	2105
Oyonnax .... a.	0742	0944	0947	1134	1332	1527	1829	1934	2027	2129
Oyonnax .... 🚌 ⊠ d.	*0750*	*0955*	*0955*	*1143*	*1340*	*1535*	*1838*a	*1948*a	*2038*	...
St Claude .... 🚌 ⊠ a.	*0826*	*1031*	*1031*	*1219*	*1416*	*1611*	*1914*a	*2024*a	*2114*	...

D – From Dijon (d. 1734).

a – Ⓐ only.
c – ⑥⑦ only.
e – 0844 until Oct. 28.
f – Also July 13, Nov. 10; not Nov. 11.
g – Also Aug. 16, Nov. 2; not Aug. 15, Oct. 31.
j – Arrives 19 minutes earlier.
k – Departs 1908.
n – Not Oct. 31.
p – Not July 4 - Aug. 25, Oct. 24 – 31, Nov. 1 – 3, 10.
r – Also Oct. 31.

s – By 🚌 in amended timings on Ⓐ July 4 - Aug. 26 and Ⓐ Oct. 24 - Nov. 4 (St Claude d. 0528, Morez d. 0603, Champagnole d. 0653, Andelot a. 0713, Mouchard a. 0743, Arc-et-Senans a. 0756, Dole a. 0852).
t – Arrives 1115.
w – Also July 13, 14, Aug. 15, Nov. 1, 10.

⊖ – ①②③④⑥ (not July 13, 14, Aug. 15, Nov. 1, 10).
⊠ – All services St Claude - Oyonnax and v.v. are by 🚌.
⊡ – Brion Montréal la Cluse.
◇ – Besançon-Viotte.
▷ – See Tables **353** and **378** for full service Bourg en Bresse - Lyon and v.v.

376a BESANÇON - LE LOCLE - LA CHAUX DE FONDS

km		①–⑤ a	①–⑤ a		Ⓐ n	Ⓐ n		b	b	Ⓐ n	
0	**Besançon** Viotte .... d.	...	...	...	0609	0704	0931	1409	...	1737	1934
32	La Valdahon .... d.	0449	0542	...	0649	0752	1015	1449	1543	1830	2019
66	Morteau .... d.	0528	0627	0728	*0745**	*0843**	1055	1528	1628	1906	2058
79	Le Locle .... **512** d.	0544	0644	0744	...	...	1113	1544	1644	...	2114
87	**La Chaux de Fonds 512** a.	0553	0653	0753	...	...	1122	1553	1653	...	2123

	①–⑤ a	Ⓐ n	①–⑤ a		b				Ⓐ n	Ⓐ n	
La Chaux de Fonds .. **512** d.	0600	...	0700	0800	1200	1600	1700	...	...	2131
Le Locle .... **512** d.	0606	...	0709	0809	1209	1609	1709	...	...	2140
Morteau .... d.	0622	*0700**	0724	0826	1226	1626	1726	*1817**	1913	2157
La Valdahon .... d.	0700	0803	...	0904	1303	1704	1803	1906	1952	2234e
Besançon Viotte .... a.	0737	0850	...	0943	1343	1750	1853	1950	2037	...

a – Not Aug. 1.
b – Not Oct. 17 – 21, 24 – 28.
e – ⑦–④.

n – Not Oct. 31.

* – By 🚌.

377 DIJON - CHALON SUR SAÔNE - MÂCON - LYON

TER Services

For *TGV* services Dijon - Lyon, see Table **379**. Journeys from / to Paris are subject to alteration Sept. 24 - Oct. 7 (also July 16, Sept. 3, 4, 17, 18).

km		Ⓐ	⚒	Ⓐ n		⚒	Ⓐ n	S		Ⓐ n			Ⓐ n	⚒		Ⓐ n			†	Ⓐ n	Ⓐ	Ⓒ p			Ⓐ n
	Paris Bercy **371** .... d.	...	...	...	...	...	...	...	...	...	0733	...	...	...	0920c	...	...	...	...	...	...	...	1333r	...	...
0	**Dijon** Ville .... **373** d.	...	...	0541	0640	0725	0741	0840	0850	0941	1041	...	1141	1144	1240	1341	1350	1441	...	1541	...	1550	1641	...	1741
37	Beaune .... **373** d.	...	...	0602	0700	0752	0802	0900	0920	1002	1102	...	1202	1211	1301	1402	1420	1502	...	1602	...	1620	1702	...	1801
52	Chagny .... d.	...	...	0612	0710	0801	0812	0911	0931	1012	1112	...	1212	1221	1311	1412	1431	1512	...	1612	...	1631	1712	...	1812
67	**Chalon sur Saône** .... d.	...	...	0623	0723	0816	0823	0923	0946	1023	1123	...	1223	1233	1323	1423	1446	1523	...	1623	...	1654b	1723	...	1823
125	Mâcon Ville .... d.	0558	0635	0657	0757	...	0857	0957	...	1057	1157	1235	1257	1312	1357	1457	...	1557	1656	1657	1737	1733	1757	1836	1857
163	Villefranche sur Saône .... d.	0631	0706	0721	0821	...	0921	1021	...	1121	1221	1306	1321	...	1421	1521	...	1621	1720	1721	1806	...	1821	1906	1921
197	**Lyon** Part Dieu .... a.	0700	|	0744	0844	...	0944	1044	...	1144	1244	|	1344	...	1444	1544	...	1644	1744	1744	|	...	1844	|	1944
	Lyon Perrache .... a.	...	0732	...	...	...	...	...	...	...	...	1332	...	...	...	...	...	...	...	...	1832	...	...	1932	...

			Ⓐ n	⑥ p	†	⑤ f	† j	①–④ m	⚒	
Paris Bercy **371** .... d.	...	1533	...	...	...	...	1729	1728	...	...
Dijon Ville .... **373** d.	1752	1841	1941	1950	2011	2041	2041	2043	2050	2212
Beaune .... **373** d.	1821	1902	2002	2020	2039	2102	2102	2103	2120	2241
Chagny .... d.	1833	1912	2012	2031	2050	2112	2112	2113	2131	2254
Chalon sur Saône .... d.	1847	1923	2023	2046	2104	2123	2123	2124	2140	2307
Mâcon Ville .... d.	...	1957	2057	...	...	2157	2157	2157	...	...
Villefranche sur Saône ..... d.	...	2021	2121	...	...	2221	2221	2222	...	...
Lyon Part Dieu .... a.	...	2044	2144	...	...	2244	2244	2244	...	...
Lyon Perrache .... a.	...	...	...	...	...	...	2300	...	...	...

	⚒	Ⓑ n	⚒	① g	⚒	Ⓐ n		Ⓐ n		Ⓐ
Lyon Perrache .... d.	...	...	...	0500	...	0605	...	...	...	0728
Lyon Part Dieu .... d.	...	...	...	0516	...	0616	0716	...	...	|
Villefranche sur Saône ...... d.	...	...	...	0541	...	0641	0741	...	...	0755
Mâcon Ville .... d.	...	...	0605	0605	...	0704	0805	0818	...	0824
Chalon sur Saône .... d.	0556	0614	0639	0639	0714	0739	0839	0856	0913	...
Chagny .... d.	0606	0624	0649	0649	0724	0749	0849	0906	0923	...
Beaune .... **373** d.	0615	0635	0700	0700	0737	0800	0900	0915	0941	...
Dijon Ville .... **373** a.	0639	0707	0724	0724	0807	0819	0919	0942	1011	...
Paris Bercy **371** .... a.	...	...	1027	1027	...	...	1227c	...	...	...

	Ⓐ n				Ⓐ n			Ⓐ n		Ⓐ	Ⓐ n			Ⓐ n			⚒	Ⓐ	Ⓐ n	†	Ⓐ		Ⓐ n		Ⓐ
Lyon Perrache .... d.	...	0828	...	...	...	...	...	...	...	1328	...	...	...	...	...	...	1724	1736	...	...	1836	...	...	2106	2204
Lyon Part Dieu .... d.	0816	|	0916	...	1016	1116	...	1216	1316	|	1416	1516	...	1616	1716	...	|	1747	1816	...	1847	1916	2016	2117	2215
Villefranche sur Saône ..... d.	0841	0855	0941	...	1041	1141	...	1241	1341	1355	1441	1541	...	1641	1741	...	1756	1812	1841	...	1912	1941	2041	2142	2240
Mâcon Ville .... d.	0905	0924	1004	...	1104	1204	...	1305	1405	1425	1504	1605	...	1704	1805	1823c	1825	1834	1904	1924	1934	2004	2104	2204	2303
Chalon sur Saône .... d.	0939	...	1039	1114	1139	1238	1248	1339	1439	...	1539	1639	1714	1739	1839	1914	...	...	1939	2001	...	2039	2139	...	...
Chagny .... d.	0949	...	1049	1124	1149	1248	1303	1349	1449	...	1549	1649	1724	1749	1849	1929	...	...	1949	2011	...	2049	2149	...	...
Beaune .... **373** d.	1000	...	1100	1137	1200	1259	1315	1400	1500	...	1600	1659	1736	1800	1900	1941	...	...	1959	2020	...	2100	2200	...	...
Dijon Ville .... **373** a.	1019	...	1119	1207	1219	1319	1344	1419	1519	...	1619	1720	1807	1819	1919	2010	...	...	2019	2051	...	2119	2219	...	...
Paris Bercy **371** .... a.	...	...	...	...	...	1637•	...	...	1827	...	...	2027	...	...	2227	...	...	...	...	...	...	...	...	...	...

PARIS - DIJON - LYON

Ouigo Classique. Low-cost traditional loco-hauled train. Internet bookings only: www.ouigo.com. Timings may vary (please check when booking).

		Ⓒ	Ⓐ
Paris Bercy ★ .... d.	1202	1811	1816
Melun .... d.	1237	1843	1846
Dijon Ville .... a.	1504	2102	2102
Dijon Ville .... d.	1507	2105	2105
Chalon sur Saône .... d.	1543	2147	2147
Mâcon Ville .... d.	1614	2220	2220
Lyon Part Dieu .... a.	1652	2300	2300
Lyon Perrache .... a.	1704	...	...

	Ⓐ	Ⓒ	
Lyon Perrache .... d.	0603	0631	1810
Lyon Part Dieu .... d.	|	|	|
Mâcon Ville .... d.	0641	0709	1856
Chalon sur Saône .... d.	0717	0739	1943
Dijon Ville .... a.	0812	0812	2023
Dijon Ville .... d.	0815	0815	2028
Melun .... a.	1020	1022	2233
Paris Bercy ★ .... a.	1053	1056	2309

S – From Sens on ⚒ (Table **371**).

b – Arrives 1646.
c – Ⓒ only.
f – Also July 13, Nov. 10; not Nov. 11.
g – Also July 15, Aug. 16, Nov. 2, 12; not Aug. 15, Oct. 31.
j – Not July 14.
m – Not July 13, 14, Aug. 15, Oct. 31, Nov. 1, 10.
n – Not Oct. 31.
p – Also Oct. 31.
r – ⚒ only.

• – Not ①–⑤ Sept. 12 - Oct. 14. Arrives Paris Gare de Lyon 1633 (not Paris Bercy) on ⑤ (also July 13).
★ – Paris departure / arrival station may vary on certain dates (please check when booking).

LYON - LONS-LE-SAUNIER - BESANÇON - BELFORT 378

See Table **379** for *TGV* services Lyon - Besançon Franche-Comté TGV - Belfort Montbéliard TGV.

km		⚒	⚒	Ⓐ jn	Ⓐ	Ⓐ n		Ⓒ r	Ⓐ n			Ⓐ	⚒	⚒			Ⓐ n		Ⓒ r	Ⓐ n	Ⓑ n	Ⓒ r		Ⓐ n	⑤⑦ v
0	**Lyon** Perrache .... **353** d.	...	...	...	0601	...	0712	...	...	...	...	1301	...	1401	...	...	...	...	1617	1617	1717	1817	1817	*1901*	2117
5	**Lyon** Part-Dieu.... **353** d.	...	...	...	0612	...	0725	0942	0942	...	...	1312	...	1412	...	...	...	...	1629t	1630	1730	1830	1830	*1912*	2129
	Ambérieu..................‡ d.	...	...	...	|	...	|	|	|	...	...	|	...	|	...	...	...	...	|	|	1758	1859	1859	|	|
65	Bourg-en-Bresse **353** ‡ d.	...	...	...	0714	0719	0821	1021	1021	...	...	1414	1419	1514	1524	...	...	...	1719	1719	1819	1919	1919	2040	2230
129	**Lons-le-Saunier**.........d.	0544	0616	0645	▬	0800	0859	1101	1103	...	1215	▬	1502	▬	1604	...	1701	1715	1801	1801	1859	2001	2001	2122	2313
178	Mouchard ....d.	0627	0702	0722	...	0839	0937	1139	1139	...	1302	...	1538	...	1641	...	1737	1802	1838	1838	...	2041	2041	...	...
184	Arc-et-Senans.............d.	0634	0707	0729	Ⓐ	0845	0943	1145	1146	...	1307	⚒	1544	...	1647	...	1742	1807	1843	1843	...	2046	2046	...	...
218	**Besançon** Viotte ....a.	0710	0742	0755	n	0909	1009	1209	1210	...	1342		1609	...	1711	...	1809	1842	1909	1909	...	2109	2109	...	...
218	**Besançon** Viotte ... ▷ d.	0714	...	...	0814	...	1014	...	1214	1232	...	1514	...	1614	...	1732	1814j	...	...	1914	...	2112	...	...	...
297	Montbéliard............▷ d.	0810	...	...	0909	...	1111	...	1310	1341	...	1610	...	1710	...	1841	1910j	...	...	2010	...	2210	...	...	...
315	**Belfort** Ville...........▷ a.	0824	...	...	0924	...	1125	...	1324	1356	...	1624	...	1724	...	1856	1924j	...	...	2024	...	2224	...	...	...

	⚒	Ⓐ n	Ⓐ n		Ⓐ n	Ⓐ jn	⚒			⚒	⚒	Ⓐ				Ⓐ n	⑥ r	Ⓐ n	†	Ⓐ n	Ⓐ jn		Ⓐ n		
Belfort Ville ....▷ d.	...	...	0535	...	0604	0636	0736	...	0936	...	...	...	...	1204	1336	...	1536	1536	1536	1636	...	...	*1736*	1836	2036
Montbéliard.............▷ d.	...	...	0549	...	0618	0650	0750	...	0950	...	...	...	...	1220	1350	...	1550	1550	1550	1650	...	...	*1750*	1850	2050
Besançon Viotte .....▷ a.	...	...	0646	...	0725	0746	0846	...	1046	...	...	...	...	1328	1446	...	1646	1646	1646	1746	...	...	*1849*	1946	2146
Besançon Viotte ....d.	...	0601	...	0651	0728	...	0851	0851	...	1051	...	...	1312	▬	1451	1529	1651	1651	1651	▬	1751	1818	1900	1951	...
Arc-et-Senans.............d.	...	0633	...	0716	0755	...	0914	0914	...	1113	...	...	1345	...	1514	1601	1715	1715	1715	...	1813	1852	1932	2014	...
Mouchard ....d.	...	0640	...	0722	0801	...	0920	0920	...	1120	...	...	1354	...	1520	1608	1721	1721	1721	Ⓐ	1821	1900	1938	2021	...
Lons-le-Saunier..........d.	0601	0730	...	0801	0841	...	1001	1001	...	1159	1302	...	1436	...	1603	1647	1759	1803	1803		1859	1945	2022	2102	...
Bourg-en-Bresse **353** ‡ d.	0645	...	...	0844	...	...	1044	1044	...	...	1342	1347	1518	1547	1644	...	...	1843	1846	1847	...	...	...	2144	...
Ambérieu..................‡ d.	|	...	...	0905	...	...	1104	1104	...	...	...	|	...	|	|	...	...	...	|	|	...	...	...	|	...
Lyon Part-Dieu..... **353** a.	0731	...	...	0930	...	...	1130	1130	...	...	...	1448	...	1648	1730	...	...	...	1937	1948	...	...	...	2230	...
Lyon Perrache .... **353** a.	0743	...	...	...	...	...	1143	1143	...	...	...	1459	...	1659	1744	...	...	...	...	1959	...	...	...	2243	...

OTHER SERVICES **BESANÇON - BELFORT**

	Ⓐn	Ⓐn	Ⓑn	†		Ⓐn	Ⓐn	Ⓒr		Ⓐn		Ⓐn
Besançon Viotte .... d.	0532	0614	0632	0712	0732	1114	1314	1332	1632	1716	1832	2014
Montbéliard...................d.	0641	0715	0741	0810	0841	1210	1410	1441	1741	1812	1941	2111
Belfort Ville...................a.	0656	0729	0756	0824	0856	1224	1424	1456	1756	1826	1956	2126

	Ⓒr	Ⓐn	Ⓐn	Ⓐn	Ⓐn				
Belfort Ville.............d.	0604	0704	0836	1136	1236	1304	1704	1819	1936
Montbéliard.............d.	0620	0720	0850	1150	1251	1320	1720	1833	1950
Besançon Viotte .....a.	0728	0828	0946	1246	1348	1428	1828	1943	2046

j – Not July 4 - Aug. 26.
n – Not Oct. 31.
r – Also Oct. 31.
t – 1630 on † (also Oct. 31).
v – Also July 13, 14, Aug. 15, Nov. 1, 10.
‡ – See also Table **353a**.
▷ – See also panel below main table.

Local trains BELFORT - MULHOUSE 378a

See also Table ***380***

	Ⓐ	⚒	Ⓐ m	⚒	Ⓐ	Ⓒ	Ⓐ m	Ⓐ	Ⓒ	Ⓐ m	Ⓐ	Ⓒ	Ⓐ	Ⓒ	Ⓐ m	Ⓐ	m	Ⓐ	†	Ⓐ	⚒ m	†	Ⓐ	Ⓐ m	⑥	† A	Ⓐ 🚌
Belfort Ville......d.	0531	0555	0631	0701	0733	0736	0806	0906	1004	1006	1206	1210	1304	1404	1506	1606	1706	1736	1800	1806	1848	1900	1907	2006	2016	2055	2055
Altkirch ....d.	0551	0620	0653	0723	0755	0758	0826	0926	1024	1026	1226	1234	1326	1427	1526	1626	1726	1758	1822	1828	1910	1922	1929	2026	2036	2117	2146
Mulhouse.........a.	0609	0637	0710	0740	0811	0815	0839	0939	1039	1039	1239	1247	1339	1442	1539	1639	1740	1810	1839	1840	1922	1939	1940	2040	2050	2133	2209

	Ⓐ	⚒	Ⓐ m	Ⓐ			Ⓐ m	Ⓐ m	Ⓒ	Ⓐ	Ⓐ m	Ⓒ		Ⓐ		†	⚒	Ⓐ m	Ⓐ	m	Ⓐ	Ⓐ	m	Ⓐ	m		Ⓐ 🚌
Mulhouse.........d.	0620	0650	0723	0804	0823	...	0923	1023	1122	1220	1310	1315	...	1423	...	1559	1619	1650	1719	1750	1823	1904	1929	2020	2056	...	2220
Altkirch ....d.	0632	0704	0734	0818	0835	...	0935	1035	1136	1235	1322	1332	...	1435	...	1616	1636	1707	1736	1807	1838	1918	1946	2037	2110	...	2244
Belfort Ville......a.	0653	0727	0758	0841	0857	...	0956	1056	1159	1256	1343	1354	...	1456	...	1639	1700	1730	1800	1831	1901	1941	2009	2100	2131	...	2335

A – Runs 8–10 minutes later from Aug. 28.
m – Not July 18–22, 25–29, Aug. 1–5, 8–12, 16–19.

LUXEMBOURG - METZ - STRASBOURG - DIJON - LYON 379

Timings may vary by up to 5 minutes – please check your reservation for confirmed timings. **Warning!** Subject to alteration on Sept. 17, 18, Oct. 1.

km		*TGV* **5521**	*TGV* **9877**		*TGV* **9879**	*TGV* **5537**		*TGV* **9580** ♣	
0	**Luxembourg** ....**384** d.	...	0724k	...	1124n	...	...	...	...
34	Thionville ....**384** d.	...	0748c	...	1148	...	...	...	...
64	**Metz** .... **383 384** d.	0551j	0810	...	1210	...	...	...	...
	Nancy ....▷ d.	|	|	...	|	1226v	...	...	...
209	**Strasbourg**......................**383** a.	0646	0859	...	1257	1329v	...	...	...
209	**Strasbourg**......................**385** d.	0700	0903	...	1303	1336	...	1614	...
274	Colmar...............................**385** d.	|	0932	...	1331	|	...	|	...
315	**Mulhouse**.................. **370 385** d.	0757	1001	...	1400	1434h	...	1709	...
360	Belfort Montbéliard TGV.........**370** d.	0821	1026	...	1425	1503h	...	1734	...
442	**Besançon** Franche-Comté TGV **370** d.	0844	1049	...	1448	1536	...	1758	...
519	**Dijon** Ville...................... **370** ▷ a.	0911	1116	...	1516	1604	...	|	...
519	**Dijon** Ville.........................**377** d.	0923	1125	...	1525	1620	1752	|	...
556	Beaune ....**377** d.	|	|	...	|	|	1821	|	...
586	**Chalon sur Saône** ....**377** d.	|	|	...	|	|	1847	1856	...
644	Mâcon Ville ....**377** d.	1022	|	...	|	1721	...	|	...
716	**Lyon** Part Dieu .... **11 377** a.	1100	1304	...	1656	1756	...	1956	...
	Lyon Perrache..............................a.	|	|	...	|	|	...	|	...
	Valence TGV **350**.....................a.	|	1347	...	1746	|	...	|	...
	Avignon TGV **350**....................a.	|	1427	...	|	1908	...	2109	...
	Aix en Provence TGV **350**......a.	|	1450	...	|	1930	...	2133	...
	Marseille St Charles **350** ....a.	|	1506	...	|	1945	...	2149	...
	Nice Ville **360**.........................a.	|	...	...	|	2237	...	...	...
	Nîmes Centre **355** ....a.	1223	...	...	1829•	...	...	...	...
	Montpellier Saint-Roch **355**........a.	1254	...	...	1853•	...	...	...	...

	TGV **9898**	*TGV* **9583** ♣		*TGV* **5516**		*TGV* **5500**		*TGV* **9896**
Montpellier Saint-Roch **355**..............d.	0629	...	...	...	...	1358	...	...
Nîmes Centre **355** ....d.	0658	...	...	...	...	1429	...	...
Nice Ville **360**...................................d.	|	...	...	0652	...	|	...	...
Marseille St Charles **350** ....d.	|	0810	...	0945	...	|	...	1602
Aix en Provence TGV **350**..................d.	|	0826	...	1000	...	|	...	1616
Avignon TGV **350**...............................d.	|	0848	...	1025	...	|	...	1638
Valence TGV **350**...............................d.	0748	|	...	|	...	|	...	1713
Lyon Perrache.......................................d.	|	|	...	|	...	|	...	|
Lyon Part Dieu .... **11 377** d.	0834	1004	...	1134	...	1604	...	1804
Mâcon Ville ....**377** d.	|	|	...	1212	...	1642	...	|
Chalon sur Saône ....**377** d.	|	1106	1114	1244	...	|	...	|
Beaune ....**377** d.	|	|	1137	1306	...	|	...	|
Dijon Ville.....................................**377** a.	0958	|	1207	1325	...	1740	...	1937
Dijon Ville................................ **370** ▷ d.	1007	|	...	1337	...	1750	...	1946
Besançon Franche-Comté TGV ... **370** d.	1035	1203	...	1409	...	1822	...	2015
Belfort Montbéliard TGV...................**370** d.	1058	1227	...	1433	...	1847	...	2038
Mulhouse............................. **370 385** d.	1123	1255	...	1459	...	1912	...	2103
Colmar...**385** d.	1153	|	...	1527	...	1944q	...	2130z
Strasbourg ....**385** a.	1221	1343	...	1554	...	2013	...	2201
Strasbourg ....**383** d.	1229	...	...	1600	...	2024	...	2207
Nancy ....▷ a.	|	...	...	1702e	...	|	...	|
Metz .... **383 384** a.	1324	...	...	...	...	2115	...	2254x
Thionville ....**384** a.	1348	...	...	...	...	...	...	2319r
Luxembourg ....**384** a.	1415p	...	...	...	...	...	...	2349t

c – Not ①–⑤ July 18 - Aug. 12, Aug. 16–19, 22–26.
e – 1713 on ①–⑤ Sept. 5–30; 1740 on Sept. 10, 11, 17, 18, 24.
h – 3–7 minutes later on ⑥.
j – 0503 on ②–⑥ from Nov. 29.
k – Not July 16 - Aug. 28.
n – Not July 16 - Aug. 28. Amended departure times: 1052 on June 25, 26; 1051 on July 2, 3; 1059 July 11–15, ①–⑤ Aug. 29 - Sept. 16, ①–⑤ Oct. 17–31, Nov. 2–4, 14–18, 21–25.
p – Not July 16 - Aug. 28. Arrives 1444 on July 2, 3.
q – Ⓐ July 11 - Aug. 26.
r – Not June 13–17, 20–24, 27–30, July 1, 4–8, July 15 - Aug. 28, Oct. 10–14, 17–21, Nov. 7–10, 14–18, 21–25, 28–30, Dec. 1, 2, 5–9. Amended arrival times: 0017 Oct. 24–28; 0103 on Oct. 31, Nov. 1, 4, 11; 0109 on Nov. 2, 3.
t – Not July 15 - Aug. 28, Oct. 10–14, 17–21, Nov. 14–18, 21–25, 28–30, Dec. 1, 2, 5–9. Amended arrival times: 0019 on June 25, 26; 0029 on July 2, 3; 0042 on Oct. 24–28; 0128 on Oct. 31, Nov. 1, 4, 11; 0134 on Nov. 2, 3; 0145 on ①–⑤ until July 8 and Oct. 7–10.

v – Not Sept. 10, 11, 17, 18, 24, Oct. 2. Departs Nancy 1211 Aug. 2 - Oct. 7.
x – On ①–⑤ until July 8, ①–⑤ Oct. 10–21, ①–⑤ Oct. 31 - Nov. 11 and ①–⑤ from Nov. 28 arrives 0024 (the following morning); arrives 2355 Oct. 24–28; arrives 2353 on ①–⑤ Nov. 14–25.
z – Does not call at Colmar on Ⓐ July 11 - Aug. 26.

TGV – High-speed train. 🅁. 🍷.

♣ – From / to Frankfurt (Tables **47** and **912**).
▷ – See panel below main table for other TER services Nancy - Dijon and v.v.
• – Arrives Nîmes **Pont-du-Gard** (not Centre) and Montpellier **Sud-de-France** (not Saint-Roch).

TER services **NANCY - NEUFCHÂTEAU - DIJON**

	⑥⑦	Ⓐ	
Nancy .... **382** d.	0754	0854	1654
Toul.............................. **382** d.	0816	0915	1713
Neufchâteau ....d.	0842	0939	1737
Culmont Chalindrey ....a.	0934	...	1827
Culmont Chalindrey ... **381a** d.	0942	...	1834
Dijon .... **381a** a.	1031	...	1927

	Ⓐ	⑥⑦	
Dijon .... **381a** d.	...	1057	2005
Culmont Chalindrey ... **381a** a.	...	1142	2053
Culmont Chalindrey ....d.	...	1152	2058
Neufchâteau ....d.	0652	1241	2151
Toul.............................. **382** a.	0720	1308	2220
Nancy .... **382** a.	0744	1329	2239

380 PARIS - TROYES - MULHOUSE

SERVICE UNTIL AUGUST 21. Timings may vary by up to 6 minutes on certain dates (earlier departures possible). Subject to alteration on July 2, 3. This route is currently subject to frequent variations so readers are strongly advised to confirm timings locally before travelling.

km		Ⓐ	⚒	Ⓐ	Ⓐ D	⑥	Ⓐ	Ⓐ	⑥	Ⓐ	Ⓒ	⑦ e	⑥ d	Ⓐ ♣	L	⑥	Ⓐ A	Ⓒ B	⚒	Ⓒ ⊙		Ⓐ	Ⓐ	Ⓒ	Ⓐ
0	**Paris** Est ... d.	...	...	...	...	...	0542	0635	0642	0742	0742	0842	0842	0842	0942t	1042t	1142	1142	1242	1342	...	1442	...	1512	1512
110	Nogent sur Seine ... d.	...	...	...	...	...	0644	0733	0744	0840	0842	0940	0940	0944	1040	1140	1241	1240	1340	1440	...	1545	...	1610	1610
129	Romilly sur Seine ... d.	...	...	...	...	...	0656	0744	0755	0851	0853	0951	0951	0955	1051	1151	1252	1251	1351	1451	...	1556	...	1621	1621
166	**Troyes** ... d.	...	...	...	0504	0639	0724	0805	0815	0911	0916	1011	1019	1015	1113	1211	1312	1314	1412	1515	...	1617	...	1643	1650
221	Bar sur Aube ... d.	...	...	...	0535	0709	0754	0837	0845	...	0946	1041	1049	1045	▬	▬	1342	1344	▬	1545	...	1648	...	1713	1720
262	Chaumont ... **381a** d.	...	...	...	0557	0730	0816	0859	0906	...	1008	1102	1111	1106	...	...	1403	1405	...	1606	...	1710	...	1734	1741
296	Langres ... **381a** d.	...	...	...	0621	0753	0838	0920	0929	...	1031	1122	1131	1129	...	...	1424	1429	...	1633	...	1739	...	1755	1803r
307	Culmont Chalindrey ... **381a** d.	...	...	...	0629	0800	0846	0930	0937	...	1038	1131	1140	1136	Ⓐ	...	1432	1436	Ⓐ	1642	...	1751	...	1803	1811r
380	Vesoul ... d.	0639	0739	0839	...	...	...	1010	...	...	...	1210	1219	...	1239	1339	...	...	1639	1721	1739	1830	1839	...	...
410	Lure ... **382** d.	0656	0756	0856	...	...	...	1027	...	...	...	1227	1237	...	1256	1356	...	...	1656	1738	1756	...	1856	...	...
442	**Belfort** Ville ... **378a 382** d.	0725	0825	0925	...	...	...	1047	...	...	...	1248	1257	...	1325	1425	...	...	1725	1756	1825	...	1925	...	...
490	**Mulhouse** ... **378a** a.	...	...	...	...	...	...	1118	...	...	...	1316	1323v	...	...	...	...	...	...	...	...	...	...	...	...

	† w	⚒ z	Ⓐ	⚒	Ⓑ	G	⑤† H	F	⑤† Q	Ⓑ	♥
Paris Est ... d.	1642	1642	1712	1742	1812	1842	1842	1842	1842	1942	2042
Nogent sur Seine ... d.	1740	1740	1814	1841	1914	1942	1943	1942	1943	2040	2140
Romilly sur Seine ... d.	1751	1751	1825	1852	1925	1953	1954	1953	1954	2051	2151
Troyes ... d.	1811	1815	1844	1911	1946	2013	2014	2017	2020	2111	2216
Bar sur Aube ... d.	1840	1845	...	...	...	2043	2044	2048	2052	...	2246
Chaumont ... **381a** d.	1901	1906	...	...	...	2104	2105	2111	2114	...	2307
Langres ... **381a** d.	1922	1928	...	...	...	2125	2127	2135	2136	...	2332
Culmont Chalindrey ... **381a** d.	1934	1935	...	...	...	2134	2134	2143	2145	...	2340
Vesoul ... d.	2015	2015	...	...	...	2214	...	...	2225	...	...
Lure ... **382** d.	2032	2032	...	...	...	2231	...	...	2242	...	...
Belfort Ville ... **378a 382** d.	2051	2052	...	...	...	2251	...	...	2302	...	...
Mulhouse ... **378a** a.	2117	2118	...	...	...	2317	...	...	2328	...	...

	Ⓐ	⑥	Ⓐ	⚒	Ⓐ	Ⓐ N	⑥	Ⓑ J	Ⓑ M
Mulhouse ... **378a** d.	...	...	...	...	...	...	...	...	0516
Belfort Ville ... **378a 382** d.	...	...	...	...	...	...	...	...	0544
Lure ... **382** d.	...	...	...	...	...	...	...	...	0602
Vesoul ... d.	...	...	...	...	...	...	...	...	0619
Culmont Chalindrey . **381a** d.	...	...	...	...	0543	...	0610	0656	0659
Langres ... **381a** d.	...	...	...	...	0551	...	0619	0705	0707
Chaumont ... **381a** d.	...	...	...	...	0612	...	0640	0726	0729
Bar sur Aube ... d.	...	...	...	...	0633	...	0701	0746	0749
Troyes ... d.	0514	0544	0610	0647	0710	0743	0746j	0817	0819
Romilly sur Seine ... d.	0534	0604	0630	0707	0730	0804	0807	0836	0840
Nogent sur Seine ... d.	0546	0616	0642	0719	0741	0816	0819	0848	0851
Paris Est ... a.	0646	0716	0746	0816	0846	0916	0916	0946	0946

	⑥	Ⓐ	⚒	◇	Ⓐ	Ⓒ	Ⓐ ♣	Ⓐ	Ⓒ	†	⚒ ♣	⚒	⑤	①–④ m	C	Ⓒ ◧	⑤	①–④ m	Ⓐ		Ⓐ	⑥	†	Ⓑ u	Ⓑ
Mulhouse ... **378a** d.	...	...	...	0746	...	...	...	...	...	1230	...	...	...	...	...	1522	1535	1535	...	...	...	...	...	...	...
Belfort Ville ... **378a 382** d.	...	0635	0735	0813	0935	...	...	...	...	1259	...	1335	...	...	...	1551	1604	1604	1635	1735	...	1809	1815	...	1839
Lure ... **382** d.	...	0704	0804	0832	1004	...	...	...	...	1318	...	1404	...	...	...	1610	1622	1622	1704	1804	...	1827	1832	...	1908
Vesoul ... d.	...	0721	0821	0848	1021	...	...	...	...	1335	...	1421	...	...	...	1629	1640	1639	1721	1821	1844	1844	1849	...	1925
Culmont Chalindrey ... **381a** d.	0723	▬	...	0929	▬	1126	1225	...	1325	1423	1426	▬	1547	1551	...	1725h	1722	1730f	▬	...	1924	1925	1930	2108	...
Langres ... **381a** d.	0731	...	...	0937	...	1134	1233	...	1334	1432	1434	...	1555	1600	...	1734	1730	1739	...	...	1933	1933	1938	2117	...
Chaumont ... **381a** d.	0753	⚒	...	0958	...	1155	1255	...	1355	1453	1455	⑥	1617	1620	...	1755	1751	1800	...	...	1953	1954	1959	2138	...
Bar sur Aube ... d.	0814		...	1018	L	1216	1315	...	1416	1513	1516		1637	1641	...	1816	1812	1820	P	...	2014	2014	2019	2159	...
Troyes ... d.	0844	0944	...	1049	1144	1247	1345	1444	1447	1543	1546	1647	1714	1717	1742	1845	1848	1849	1948	...	2047	2047	2049	2228	...
Romilly sur Seine ... d.	0903	1004	...	1108	1204	1307	1404	1503	1507	1602	1605	1707	1734	1737	1803	1904	1908	1908	2008	...	2108	2108	2108	...	...
Nogent sur Seine ... d.	0915	1015	...	1120	1216	1319	1416	1515	1519	1613	1617	1719	1746	1749	1816	1916	1920	1920	2020	...	2120	2120	2120	...	...
Paris Est ... a.	1016	1116	...	1217	1316	1416	1516	1616	1616	1716	1716	1816	1846	1846	1916	2016	2016	2016	2116	...	2216k	2216	2216	...	...

A – To Dijon Ville (a. 1520). Does not run Troyes - Culmont - Dijon June 13 - July 1 (also on July 7, 8).
B – To Dijon Ville on ⑥ (a. 1525).
C – ⑥⑦ to June 26; daily from July 9.
D – To Dijon Ville (a. 0741).
F – ①②③④⑥ July 18 - Aug. 18 (not Aug. 15).
G – ①②③④⑥ to July 16 (also Aug. 20; not July 14).
H – ⑤† July 22 - Aug. 19.
J – Ⓑ July 18 - Aug. 19. Departure times are 2–4 minutes later on Ⓐ.
L – ⚒ to July 16; ⑥ from July 23.
M – Ⓑ to July 17 (also Aug. 21).
N – From July 11.
P – Ⓑ to July 17; † from July 24.
Q – ⑤† to July 17 (also Aug. 21).
d – Also July 14.
e – Also Aug. 15.
f – Arrives 1719.
h – Arrives 1711.
j – Arrives 0731.
k – 2223 Aug. 16–19.
m – Not July 14, Aug. 15.
r – 9 minutes later on ⑤.
t – 6–8 minutes earlier on July 30.
u – Not Aug. 16–19.
v – 1338 on July 14.
w – Not June 19.
z – Also June 19.
⊙ – Runs 4–8 minutes earlier Troyes - Belfort on July 14.
♥ – Does not run Troyes - Culmont Aug. 16–19.
♣ – Does not run Troyes - Culmont and v.v on ①–⑤ June 13 - July 1 (also on July 7, 8).
◇ – Runs up to 11 minute earlier on June 18, 19. Does not run Mulhouse - Troyes on ①–⑤ until July 1 (also on July 7, 8).
◧ – Until June 26 departure times Mulhouse - Vesoul are 9–13 minutes later.

381 PARIS - CHÂLONS EN CHAMPAGNE - BAR LE DUC - NANCY and ST DIZIER

TER services

SERVICE UNTIL OCTOBER 8. Timings may vary by up to 5 minutes on certain dates (earlier departures possible). Subject to alteration on June 18, 19, 25, 26, July 9, 10, 16, 17, 30, 31, Aug. 6, 7.

km		Ⓐ	Ⓐ ⊗	⑥	Ⓐ	⑥ △	†	Ⓐ ⊖	⑥ a	⑥	†	Ⓐ A	⑥	Ⓐ E	Ⓒ	⑥	Ⓐ	Ⓐ M	Ⓐ	† ▽	⑥	⑥ R	Ⓐ
0	**Paris** Est ... **390** d.	...	0636	...	0736	0835	0836	0836	0936	1023	1036	1036	1136	1236	1236	1436	1436	...	1634	1635	1636	...	1736
95	Château Thierry ... d.	...	0731	...	0826	0923	0931	0931	1031	1118	1131	1131	1231	1331	1331	1531	1531	...	1721	1728	1731	...	1831
142	Épernay ... ♠ d.	0644	0759	0830	0854	0951	0959	0959	1059	1146	1159	1159	1259	1359	1359	1559	1559	1614	1749	1802	1759	1815	1859
	Champagne-Ardenne TGV ... **390** d.	|	|	|	|	|	|	|	|	|	|	|	|	|	|	|	|	|	|	|	|	|	|
172*	**Châlons en Champagne** ... **381a** d.	0704	0823t	0846	0912	1011	1017	1023t	1115	1204	1215	1217	1316	1415	1417	1615	1619	1632	1806	1832	1816	1831	1917
205	Vitry le François ... **381a** d.	0723	0842	0904	0931	1030	1035	1042	...	1222	...	1235	1334	...	1436	...	1635	1649	1823	1850	1834	1849	1935
234	**St Dizier** ... **381a** a.	|	0901	|	|	|	|	1101	...	1242	...	|	|	...	1455	...	1655	|	|	|	|	|	1955
255	**Bar le Duc** ... ♣ d.	0754	...	0930	0957	1100	1059	...	...	...	...	1301	1359	...	...	...	...	1715	1847	1920	1859	1914	...
295	Commercy ... ♣ d.	0815	...	0955	1019	1121	...	...	...	...	...	...	...	...	...	...	...	...	1908	1943	...	1935	...
321	Toul ... ♣ d.	0830	...	1013	1040	1141	...	...	...	...	...	...	...	...	...	...	...	...	1924	2006	...	1953	...
354	**Nancy** ... ♣ a.	0854	...	1036y	1100	1203	...	...	...	...	...	...	...	...	...	...	...	...	1944	2024	...	2030	...
	Strasbourg **383** ... a.	...	...	...	1234	1344	...	...	...	...	...	...	...	...	...	...	...	...	2121	2202	...	...	...

	† Q		2785 Ⓑ h♥	Ⓐ	⑤	Ⓒ	①–④ m	⑤	† ⊡	
Paris Est ... **390** d.	...	1836	1928	1936	1936	2036	2136	2136	2236	...
Château Thierry ... d.	...	1931	|	2031	2031	2131	2231	2232	2331	...
Épernay ... ♠ d.	1912	1959	|	2059	2059	2159	2259	2259	2359	...
Champagne-Ardenne TGV ... **390** d.	|	|	2011	|	|	|	|	|	|	...
Châlons en Champagne ... **381a** d.	1930	2017	2035	2115	2117	2218	2315	2317	0015	...
Vitry le François ... **381a** d.	1947	2035	2055	...	2135	...	...	2334	...	...
St Dizier ... **381a** a.	|	2055	|	...	|	...	...	|	...	...
Bar le Duc ... ♣ d.	2014	...	2119	...	2155	...	...	2359	...	...
Commercy ... ♣ d.	2039	...	...	...	...	...	...	...	...	...
Toul ... ♣ d.	2058	...	...	...	...	...	...	...	...	...
Nancy ... ♣ a.	2128	...	...	...	...	...	...	...	...	...
Strasbourg **383** ... a.	...	...	...	...	...	...	...	...	...	...

	Ⓐ	⚒	2778 ①–⑥ b♥	Ⓐ	Ⓒ	Ⓐ	†
Strasbourg **383** ... d.	...	...	...	...	...	0444	...
Nancy ... ♣ d.	...	...	...	...	...	0616	...
Toul ... ♣ d.	...	...	...	...	...	0640	...
Commercy ... ♣ d.	...	...	...	...	...	0659	...
Bar le Duc ... ♣ d.	...	...	0610	...	...	0722	...
St Dizier ... **381a** d.	...	0533	|	0633	0709	|	...
Vitry le François ... **381a** d.	...	0553	0636	0653	0730	0752	...
Châlons en Champagne ... **381a** d.	0511	0611	0655	0711	0748	0812	0941
Champagne-Ardenne TGV ... **390** a.	|	|	0715	|	|	|	|
Épernay ... ♠ d.	0530	0629	|	0729	0806	0830	1007
Château Thierry ... d.	0559	0659	|	0759	0835	0859	1036
Paris Est ... **390** a.	0653	0753	0801	0853	0923	0953	1123

	⑥	Ⓐ D		⑥ ▽	†	Ⓐ C	⑥	Ⓐ B	⑥ a	Ⓒ	Ⓐ	Ⓒ wN	†	Ⓐ	⑥	Ⓐ	† d	†	† ▽	Ⓐ	⑥		⑤
Strasbourg **383** ... d.	...	...	...	0819	...	...	...	...	...	...	...	...	...	...	...	...	...	...	1619	1619	...	...	...
Nancy ... ♣ d.	...	...	...	1004	...	...	...	...	...	...	...	1434	...	...	...	...	...	1620	1746	1746	...	...	2035
Toul ... ♣ d.	...	...	...	1025	...	...	...	...	...	...	...	1458	...	...	...	...	...	1647	1808	1808	...	...	2059
Commercy ... ♣ d.	...	...	...	1040	...	...	...	...	...	...	...	1512	...	...	...	...	...	1710	1825	1825	...	...	2113
Bar le Duc ... ♣ d.	0909	...	...	1103	1109	...	...	1327	1409	...	...	1534	...	...	...	...	...	1735	1847	1850	1909	...	2135
St Dizier ... **381a** d.	|	0933	...	|	|	1133	...	|	|	1516	...	|	...	1633	...	1733	1743	|	|	|	|	...	|
Vitry le François ... **381a** d.	0933	0953	...	1128	1133	1153	...	1352	1433	1534	...	1602	...	1653	...	1753	1802	1806	1911	1913	1932	...	2200
Châlons en Champagne ... **381a** d.	0951	1011	...	1149	1151	1212	1248	1411	1451	1551	1612	1619	1650	1712	1750	1812	1824	1830	1932	1932	1949	...	2217
Champagne-Ardenne TGV ... **390** a.	|	|	...	|	|	|	|	|	|	|	|	|	|	|	|	|	|	|	|	|	|	...	|
Épernay ... ♠ d.	1009	1029	...	1207	1209	1229	1307	1429	1509	1608	1629	1637	1707	1729	1807	1829	1848	1852	1949	1949	2009	...	2235
Château Thierry ... d.	1036	1059	...	1235	1236	1259	1336	1459	1536	1634	1659	...	1736	1759	1836	1859	1924	...	2020	2020	2036	...	...
Paris Est ... **390** a.	1123	1153	...	1323	1323	1353	1423	1553	1623	1724	1753	...	1823	1853	1923	1953	2023	...	2123	2123	2123	...	...

FOR NOTES AND OTHER TER SERVICES BETWEEN BAR LE DUC AND NANCY, SEE NEXT PAGE →

PARIS - CHÂLONS EN CHAMPAGNE - BAR LE DUC - NANCY and ST DIZIER 381

OTHER TER SERVICES **BAR LE DUC - NANCY**. **SERVICE UNTIL OCTOBER 8**. Timings may vary by up to 3 minutes.

	Ⓐ	Ⓐ		⑥H	Ⓐ	⑥r		†	Ⓐ		Ⓐ	ⒶJ	†	ⒶK		ⒶK	⑥		ⒶK	†	Ⓐ	Ⓐ	⑥¶		†		Ⓐv
Bar le Duc ....d.	0554	0610e	...	0725	0726	0726	...	0925	0950	...	1125	1211	1225	1300	...	1425	1425	...	1523	1525	1625	1726	1724	...	1825	...	2125
Commercy........d.	0615	0637e	...	0746	0746	0757	...	0956	1013	...	1145	1236	1246	1320	...	1446	1446	...	1543	1546	1646	1747	1749	...	1846	...	2146
Toul..................d.	0630	0658e	...	0801	0801	0813	...	1011	1033	...	1200	1301	1301	1342	...	1501	1501	...	1605	1601	1701	1803	1808	...	1909	...	2200
Nancy ....a.	0654	0725	...	0825	0825	0837	...	1036	1056	...	1225	1324	1325	1406	...	1525	1525	...	1628	1625	1725	1828	1836	...	1936	...	2223

	⑥	Ⓐ	⑥	Ⓐv		Ⓐv	†	ⒶK	ⒶK	ⒶJ	Ⓒ		ⒶJ	Ⓐv	Ⓐv	⑥	Ⓐ	Ⓐ		⑥	Ⓑv		⑥	Ⓐ		†	Y
Nancy ....d.	0646	0735	0758	0834	...	0934	1002	1035	1133	1234	1234	...	1334	1435	1535	1607	1635	1707	...	1802	1834	...	1934	1935	...	2032	2035
Toul..................d.	0710	0759	0825	0858	...	0958	1026	1059	1157	1258	1300	...	1400	1459	1559	1631	1659	1733	...	1826	1858	...	2000	2000	...	2056	2059
Commercy........d.	0724	0814	0839	0912	...	1012	1040	1113	1211	1312	1319	...	1419	1513	1613	1646	1713	1752	...	1840	1912	...	2021	2019	...	2111	2113
Bar le Duc ....a.	0745	0834	0901	0933	...	1033	1101	1134	1232	1333	1345	...	1445	1534	1633	1707	1734	1818	...	1900	1934	...	2048	2044	...	2131	2134

A – Ⓐ until Sept. 23. Does not run Épernay - Bar le duc June 13 - July 7. Does not run Châlons - Bar le Duc July 11–13, 18, 19, Sept. 12–16, 19–23.
B – Ⓐ until Sept. 23 (not July 11–13). Does not run Bar le Duc - Épernay June 13 - July 7. Does not run Bar le Duc - Châlons July 18, 19, Sept. 12–16, 19–23.
C – Not July 11–13. Does not run St Dizier - Épernay June 13–17, 20–24, July 4–7. Does not run St Dizier - Châlons July 18, 19, Sept. 19 - Oct. 7.
D – Not Sept. 26–30. Does not run St Dizier - Châlons Sept. 19–23, Oct. 3–7. Arrives Paris 9–11 minutes later on June 28, Aug. 23.
E – Not Oct. 6, 7. Does not run Épernay - Châlons June 13–17, 20–24, July 4–7.
H – July 6 - Oct. 1.
J – Until Aug. 26.
K – Ⓐ until July 15 (also Aug. 22–26).
M – Ⓐ from July 8 (not July 18, 19). To Metz (a. 1814).
N – To Reims (a. 1708).
Q – From Reims (d. 1836).
R – Not Sept. 10 - Oct. 1. From Reims (d. 1743 Aug. 6 - Sept. 3, 1749 to July 30 / from Oct. 8).
Y – ①-④ (not July 14, Aug. 15).

a – Not July 2.
b – Not Aug. 15, Nov. 1.
d – Not July 3.
e – 6–8 minutes earlier Aug. 30 - Sept. 2.
h – Not Oct. 31, Nov. 11.
m – Not July 14, Aug. 15.
r – Not July 6 - Oct. 1.
t – Arrives 8 minutes earlier.
v – Not July 18–22, 25–29, Aug. 1–5, 8–12, 16–19.
w – Not Sept. 24, Oct. 1.
y – 1043 Sept. 10–24.
z – Not Aug. 15.

⊗ – Does not run Châlons - St Dizier Sept. 19–23.
⊖ – Does not run Châlons - St Dizier June 13–24, July 4–7, 11–13, 18, 19, Sept. 19 - Oct. 7.
△ – Subject to alteration Sept. 10 - Oct. 1.
▽ – Subject to alteration Sept. 10–24.
⊡ – Runs 15–16 minutes earlier on July 3.
¶ – Runs 14–20 minutes **earlier** Sept. 10–24.
* – *188 km* via high-speed line.
♣ – See panel above for other TER services Bar le Duc - Nancy and v.v.
♥ – *TGV* train. 🅁. 🍷.
♠ – **ÉPERNAY - REIMS**. *31 km*. Journey: 34–40 minutes.
From Épernay at 0532①**z**, 0632Ⓐ**s**, 0642⑥, 0649Ⓐ, 0732Ⓐ, 0802⚒, 0832Ⓐ, 0902Ⓐ**s**, 1002, 1102Ⓐ, 1202, 1301Ⓐ, 1402, 1432Ⓐ**s**, 1602, 1632Ⓐ**s**, 1702Ⓐ, 1732Ⓐ**s**, 1802, 1832Ⓐ, 1902Ⓐ, 2002 and 2102⑤.
From Reims at 0448①**z**, 0548Ⓐ, 0648Ⓐ, 0718⚒**s**, 0748Ⓐ, 0818Ⓐ**s**, 0848Ⓐ, 0918Ⓒ, 0948Ⓐ, 1048Ⓐ, 1118Ⓒ, 1148Ⓐ, 1248⚒, 1318†, 1348Ⓐ, 1418Ⓐ, 1518Ⓒ, 1548Ⓐ**s**, 1618Ⓐ, 1648Ⓐ, 1718**s**, 1748Ⓐ, 1818Ⓐ**s**, 1848Ⓐ, 1918Ⓒ, 1948Ⓐ and 2048⑤.

REIMS - CHÂLONS EN CHAMPAGNE - DIJON 381a

SERVICE UNTIL OCTOBER 8. Timings may vary by up to 4 minutes Sept. 12 - Oct. 7 (earlier departures possible). **Warning!** Subject to alteration Aug. 12–15 and ⑥⑦ Sept. 17 - Oct. 2.

km		Ⓐv	Ⓐ	Ⓐ	Ⓒ	Ⓐv	Ⓐv¶		Ⓐ	Ⓒ	Ⓐ◇	⚒	Ⓐ⊗	Ⓒ	Ⓐ	Ⓒ	Ⓐ	Ⓐ	†	⑥	Ⓐ	Ⓐ	Ⓒ	Ⓐ	Ⓐ
0	**Reims**..........d.	...	0620	0705	0735	0740	0835	0935	1035	1135	1135	1234	1335	1335	1438	1505	1535	1635	1735	1735	1735	1835	1935	1935	2035
58	**Châlons en Champagne**........a.	...	0655	0750	0810	0815	0911	1021	1110	1211	1211	1319	1410	1412	1525	1543	1611	1711	1819	1819	1819	1919	2012	2019	2110
58	**Châlons en Champagne**. **381** d.	...	0657	...	0823	...	0924	...	...	1224	1224	...	1423	...	...	1549	1624	1724	1825	1825	1825	1925	...	2025	...
91	Vitry le François.......... **381** d.	...	0718	...	0841	...	0943	...	...	1243	1243	...	1443	...	...	1608	1643	1743	1844	1844	1844	1943	...	2043	...
120	St Dizier.......... **381** d.	0622	0737	...	0901	...	1003	...	...	1303	1303	...	1503	...	...	1630	1703	1803	1905	1905	1903	2003	...	2101	...
193	Chaumont.......... **380** d.	0719	0824	...	0955	...	1057	...	...	1349	1357	...	1550	...	...	1719	1749	1857	2001	2002	...	2050	...	...	...
227	Langres.......... **380** d.	0743	...	...	...	...	...	...	...	...	...	...	1614	...	...	...	...	...	2024	2025	...	2114	...	...	...
238	Culmont Chalindrey... **379 380** d.	0751	...	...	...	...	...	...	...	...	...	...	1626	...	...	...	...	...	2033	2032	...	2122	...	...	...
315	**Dijon** Ville.......... **379** a.	...	...	...	...	...	...	...	...	...	...	...	1711	...	...	...	...	...	2119	...	...	...	...	...	...

	Ⓐ	Ⓐ	⑥	Ⓐ	Ⓒ	Ⓐ	Ⓐ	Ⓒ	Ⓐ	Ⓐ⊡	Ⓒ	Ⓐ	Ⓐ⊖	Ⓒ	Ⓐ	⑥	v⊕	Ⓐ	Ⓐ	Ⓒ	Ⓐv	Ⓐ	Ⓐw		Ⓐ
Dijon Ville.......... **379** d.	...	...	...	...	...	...	...	...	...	...	...	...	...	...	...	...	...	...	...	...	...	...	...	...	1805
Culmont Chalindrey .... **379 380** d.	...	...	...	0535	...	0630	...	0730	...	...	...	...	...	...	...	...	...	...	...	...	...	...	1639	...	1907
Langres.......... **380** d.	...	...	...	0544	...	0639	...	0738	...	...	...	...	...	...	...	...	...	...	...	...	...	...	1648	...	1916
Chaumont.......... **380** d.	...	...	...	0606	...	0701	...	0800	...	1009	...	...	1201	1209	...	...	1409	...	...	...	...	...	1710	1802	1937
St Dizier.......... **381** d.	...	0557	...	0657	...	0758	...	0857	...	1057	...	...	1257	1257	...	...	1457	...	...	...	...	...	1757	1859	2024
Vitry le François.......... **381** d.	...	0617	...	0717	...	0817	...	0917	...	1117	...	...	1317	1317	...	...	1517	...	...	...	...	...	1817	1919	2044
Châlons en Champagne . **381** a.	...	0637	...	0737	...	0836	...	0935	...	1137	...	...	1337	1334	...	...	1535	...	...	...	...	...	1837	1936	2104
Châlons en Champagne .... d.	0611	0646	0646	0741	0800	0849	0939	0948	1051	1150	1200	1241	1350	1347	1441	1450	1550	1611	1711	1741	1750	1811	1850	1949	2106
Reims.......... a.	0655	0730	0732	0825	0837	0924	1026	1025	1128	1225	1239	1325	1425	1425	1525	1525	1625	1655	1755	1827	1825	1855	1925	2025	2142

v – Not July 18–22, 25–29, Aug. 1–5, 8–12, 16–19.
w – Not July 18–22, 25–29, Aug. 1–5, 8–12, 16–19, Sept. 12 - Oct. 7.

¶ – Does not run Châlons - Chaumont Sept. 19 - Oct. 7.
◇ – Does not run Châlons - Chaumont July 11–13, Sept. 12 - Oct. 7.
⊗ – Does not run Châlons - Dijon July 11–13, Oct. 3–7. Does not run Chaumont - Dijon Sept. 27–30.
⊡ – Does not run Chaumont - Châlons July 18, 19, Sept. 19 - Oct. 7.

⊖ – Does not run Chaumont - Châlons July 18, 19, Sept. 12 - Oct. 7.
⊕ – Does not run Chaumont - Châlons July 11–13, Sept. 12–16, 19–23, 26–30.

☛ Other services Reims - Châlons en Champagne and v.v.:
From Reims at 0809Ⓐ, 1605Ⓐ**v**, 1705Ⓐ**v**, 1805Ⓐ**v** and 2222⑦.
From Châlons en Champagne at 0720Ⓐ**v**, 0820Ⓐ**v** and 1650Ⓐ**v**.

STRASBOURG - ST DIÉ - ÉPINAL - BELFORT 382

STRASBOURG - ST DIÉ - ÉPINAL

km		Ⓐ	Ⓐ	Ⓐ	Ⓐ	Ⓐr	Ⓐn	Ⓐr	Ⓐ	Ⓐ	Ⓐ	Ⓐ	Ⓐ	Ⓐ	
0	**Strasbourg**..........▷ d.		...	0532	0653	0905	...	1202	1424r	...	1629	1657	1757	1857	...
9	Entzheim Aéroport ✈..........▷ d.		...	0540	0700	0913	...	1210	1431r	...	1637	1705	1807	1905	...
19	Molsheim..........▷ d.		...	0547	0709	0921	...	1219	1440r	...	1645	1715	1815	1913	...
87	**St Dié**..........a.		...	0720	0824	1034	...	1333	1548r	...	1757	1848	1926	2025	...
	St Dié..........d.		0618	0730	0831n	1046n	1234	1341n	1556	1703	1805	...	1933	...	...
147	**Épinal**..........a.		0713	0824	0927n	1139n	1325	1433n	1652	1758	1858	...	2025	...	...

	⑥	⑥	⑥	⑥	⑥	⑥	⑥	⑥	⑥
Strasbourg..........▷ d.		...	0644	0817	1210	...	1405	1620	...
Entzheim Aéroport ✈..........▷ d.		...	0652	0824	1217	...	1413	1628	...
Molsheim..........▷ d.		...	0700	0832	1225	...	1421	1636	...
St Dié..........a.		...	0800	0950	1326	...	1523	1752	...
St Dié..........d.		0628	0806	1000	1333	1437	1536	...	1830
Épinal..........a.		0723	0857	1052	1424	1533	1629	...	1923

	⑥	⑥		†	†	†	†	†	†	†
Strasbourg..........▷ d.	1729	1815	...		0746	0934	1350	1646	1729	1901
Entzheim Aéroport ✈..........▷ d.	1736	1823	...		0753	0945	1359	1654	1741	1909
Molsheim..........▷ d.	1744	1831	...		0801	0958	1407	1703	1755	1917
St Dié..........a.	1905	1940	...		0903	1113	1511	1811	1915	2021
St Dié..........d.	...	1946	...		0912	1120	1518	1821	...	2035
Épinal..........a.	...	2037	...		1004	1215	1611	1915	...	2127

	Ⓐ	Ⓐ	Ⓐ	Ⓐ	Ⓐr	Ⓐn	Ⓐn	Ⓐr	Ⓐ
Épinal..........d.		...	0615	0730	0833n	1045	...	1232n	1503n
St Dié..........a.		...	0709	0827	0924n	1139	...	1327n	1553n
St Dié..........d.		0546	0723	0835r	0931	...	1208	1336	1600
Molsheim..........▷ d.		0719	0833	0944r	1045	...	1321	1437	1711
Entzheim Aéroport ✈..........▷ d.		0729	0840	0952r	1052	...	1328	1444	1720
Strasbourg..........▷ a.		0738	0848	0959r	1100	...	1336	1453	1730

	Ⓐ	Ⓐ	Ⓐ	Ⓐ		⑥	⑥	⑥	⑥	⑥	⑥	⑥	⑥	⑥	
Épinal..........d.	1556	1703	1837	2035	...		0704	0803	0904	1105	1435	1610	1725	2054	...
St Dié..........a.	1653	1753	1929	2125	...		0756	0858	0955	1156	1526	1702	1815	2144	...
St Dié..........d.	...	1801	1940	...	...		0803	0905	1003	1203	1533	1709	1821	...	...
Molsheim..........▷ d.	...	1916	2046	...	...		0911	1016	1112	1314	1643	1820	1930	...	...
Entzheim Aéroport ✈..........▷ d.	...	1923	2053	...	...		0919	1024	1120	1322	1650	1827	1937	...	...
Strasbourg..........▷ a.	...	1931	2101	...	...		0928	1032	1128	1330	1658	1835	1945	...	...

	†	†	†	†	†	†	†	†	†
Épinal..........d.		...	0807	1017	1330	...	1630	1725	1925
St Dié..........a.		...	0900	1110	1422	...	1721	1818	2018
St Dié..........d.		0707	0906	1116	...	1521	1727	1830	2024
Molsheim..........▷ d.		0821	1015	1225	...	1629	1829	1948	2128
Entzheim Aéroport ✈..........▷ d.		0829	1022	1232	...	1636	|	1955	2135
Strasbourg..........▷ a.		0840	1032	1242	...	1646	1842	2005	2145

ÉPINAL - BELFORT

km		Ⓐz		Ⓐz		D	B 🚌				
0	**Épinal**..........d.	0626	...	0958	...	1457	1457	...	1858	...	...
58	Luxeuil les Bains..........d.	0714	...	1043	...	1543	1616	...	1943	...	...
76	Lure.......... **380** d.	0727	...	1056	...	1556	1641	...	1956	...	...
108	**Belfort** Ville.......... **380** a.	0755	...	1125	...	1625	1726	...	2025	...	...

	Ⓐz		D	B 🚌		C	A	⑦		
Belfort Ville.......... **380** d.	0605	...	1105	1105	...	1702	1705	1705	...	2005
Lure.......... **380** d.	0633	...	1134	1220	...	1731	1734	1737	...	2034
Luxeuil les Bains..........d.	0645	...	1147	1248	...	1744	1747	1750	...	2047
Épinal..........a.	0734	...	1234	1412	...	1830	1834	1834	...	2134

A – ①-⑤ (not Aug. 15, Oct. 31).
B – Runs Oct. 17–21, 24–28 only.
C – Runs on Aug. 15 only.
D – Not Oct. 17–21, 24–28.

n – Not July 25 - Aug. 12, Sept. 26–30, Oct. 3–7, 24–28, 31, Nov. 2–4.
r – Not Sept. 26–30, Oct. 3–7, 24–28, 31, Nov. 2–4.
z – Not Oct. 31.

▷ – Additional trains run Strasbourg - Entzheim Aéroport (300 metres from terminal) - Molsheim and v.v.: 3–4 per hour on Ⓐ, 1–2 per hour on ⑥, hourly on †.

383 METZ and NANCY - STRASBOURG

For faster *TGV* services Paris - Strasbourg, see Table **390**. Services in this table are subject to timing variations – see note ⊠ for further details. Readers are advised to confirm timings locally.

km	SEE NOTE ⊠	Ⓐ n	TGV 5521 [R]	Ⓐ	⑥	Ⓐ	⚒	⚒ ■	⚒	TGV 9877 [R]	Ⓐ	⑥ ■	† ●	Ⓐ d	Ⓐ	Ⓒ	⑥ ■	TGV 2587 ⑦ e [R]	Ⓐ	† ▲	TGV 9879 [R]	⑥ ●	Ⓐ	⚒	Ⓐ	⑥
0	**Metz** d.	...	0551f	...	...	...	0642	...	0747	0810	...	...	...	...	0934	0940	...	...	...	...	1210	...	...	1247	...	...
	Paris Est **381** d.	...	|	...	...	...	|	...	|	|	...	...	...	...	|	|	...	0910	0736	...	|	0835	...	|	...	...
Δ	**Nancy** **387** d.	...	|	...	...	0612	|	0714	|	|	0814	0814	0814	0914	|	|	1014	1054	1104	1116	|	1206	1214	|	1316	...
	Lunéville **387** d.	...	|	...	...	0630	|	0732	|	|	0832	0832	0833	0932	|	|	1038	|	1124	1134	|	1226	1232	|	1334	...
88	Sarrebourg d.	0535z	|	0617	0634	0654	|	0758	0849	|	0855	0855	0857	0955	|	|	1101	1135	1147	1157	|	1251	1258	1349	1356	1357
91	Réding d.	0540z	|	0622	0638	0658	0729	|	...	|	0859	|	|	|	1024	1030	|	|	|	|	|	|	|	...	|	1401
114	Saverne d.	0555	|	0641	0654	0714	0746	0815	...	|	0915	0915	0917	1014	1041	1046	1120	1155	1205	1216	|	1309	1315	...	1412	1417
159	**Strasbourg** a.	0634	0646	0708	0734	0741	0811	0841	...	0859	0941	0941	0943	1041	1111	1114	1145	1217	1234	1245	1257	1344	1341	...	1440	1456

SEE NOTE ⊠	Ⓐ	Ⓑ ■	⑥ ●	Ⓐ	Ⓐ	†	† ■	Ⓐ	Ⓑ	⑥	⚒ ●	Ⓐ	Ⓐ	Ⓑ	Ⓐ	Ⓑ	⚒ ●	† ■	⑥	Ⓐ	†	Ⓐ	⑥ ●	† ■	†	TGV 2583 Ⓑ ¶ [R]
Metz d.	1342	...	...	...	...	1552	...	1617	1642	1647	...	1724	1746	...	1817	1842	...	...	1934	...	1947	1947	...	...	2043	...
Paris Est **381** d.	|	...	...	...	...	|	...	|	|	|	...	|	|	...	|	|	...	...	|	1635	|	|	...	1635	|	1943
Nancy **387** d.	|	1415	1416	1514	1614	|	1614	|	|	|	1716	|	|	1814	|	|	1916	1916	|	1946	|	|	2016	2035	|	2124
Lunéville **387** d.	|	1433	1440	1534	1632	|	1632	|	|	|	1733	|	|	1832	|	|	1934	1934	|	2007	|	|	2034	2059	|	2146
Sarrebourg d.	|	1456	1504	1558	1655	1654	1658	1718	|	1749	1759	1824	1849	1856	1918	|	1957	1957	2033	2034	2049	2055	2057	2122	|	2211
Réding d.	1430	1500r	|	|	1659	...	|	...	1729	...	|	1828	...	|	...	1930	|	|	|	|	...	|	|	|	2130	|
Saverne d.	1445	1515	1523	1616	1715	...	1715	...	1744	...	1816	1846	...	1915	...	1948	2017	2016	2050	2053	...	2112	2114	2138	2144	2229
Strasbourg a.	1511	1541	1549	1641	1741	...	1741	...	1811	...	1841	1911	...	1941	...	2019	2042	2044	2114	2121	...	2140	2141	2202	2209	2252

SEE NOTE ⊠	Ⓐ	TGV 2584 ①–⑥ b [R]	⚒	Ⓐ	Ⓐ	Ⓐ	Ⓐ	⑥ ■	⚒	Ⓑ ●	⑥ ■	⑥ ■	†	Ⓐ	⑥ ■	† ▲	⑥	Ⓐ	Ⓐ	⚒	⊖	TGV 9898 [R]	Ⓑ	⑥	Ⓐ	⑥
Strasbourg d.	0444	0541	...	0615	...	0649	0719	0717	0749	0816	0819	0926	0949	1017	1017	1019	...	...	1118	1149	1217	1229	1249	1255	1315	...
Saverne d.	0507	0606	...	0643	...	0712	0745	0748	0814	0845	0846	0953	1015	1043	1043	1044	...	...	1145	1215	1243	|	1315	1333	1343	...
Réding d.	|	|	...	|	...	0727	|	|	0828	|	|	|	1029	1058	|	|	...	...	|	1229	|	|	1329	|	|	...
Sarrebourg d.	0524	0624	0636	0700	0703	|	0801	0806	|	0904	0903	1010	|	1102	1102	1100	1111	1136	1203	|	1302	|	|	1349	1359	1411
Lunéville **387** d.	0549	0649	|	0725	|	|	0826	0831	|	0927	0928	1033	|	1125	1125	1125	|	|	1226	|	1325	|	|	...	1421c	|
Nancy **387** a.	0612	0709	|	0744	|	|	0844	0848	|	0945	0954	1051	|	1144	1144	1144	|	|	1244	|	1344	|	|	...	1440c	|
Paris Est **381** a.	0953	0846	|	...	|	|	...	...	|	...	1323	...	|	...	...	...	|	|	...	|	...	|	|	...	...	|
Metz a.	...	...	0736	...	0752	0816	...	...	0916	...	...	...	1115	...	...	...	1211	1236	...	1317	...	1324	1416	...	...	1511

SEE NOTE ⊠	⑥ ●	Ⓐ	Ⓐ	⑥ ●	TGV 2588 ⑦ e [R]	Ⓐ	Ⓑ ■	†	Ⓐ	Ⓑ ■	⑥ ●	⑥	Ⓐ	†	Ⓐ	⚒ ●	† ■	⑥	†	Ⓐ	Ⓐ	Ⓒ ⊖	Ⓐ	TGV 5500 [R]	Ⓐ w	TGV 9896 [R]
Strasbourg d.	1419	1426	1514	1519	1546	...	1619	...	1649	1719	1719	...	1749	1749	...	1816	1818	1849	1849	1918	...	1949	1949	2024	2105	2207
Saverne d.	1446	1454	1543	1544	1611	...	1643	...	1715	1744	1746	...	1815	1820	...	1843	1845	1913	1917	1944	...	2015	2018	|	2133	|
Réding d.	|	|	|	|	|	...	|	...	1731	|	1801	...	1832	1834	...	1858r	|	1926	|	1959	...	|	2034	|	|	|
Sarrebourg d.	1503	1513	1601	1600	1632	1636	1701	1708	1742	1803	1805	1808	|	|	1836	1902	1904	|	1942	2003	2008	2030	2038	|	2150	|
Lunéville **387** d.	1527	1536	1625	1626	|	|	1724	|	|	1827	1829	|	|	|	|	1925	1927	|	|	2025	|	2056	...	|	...	|
Nancy **387** a.	1544	1554	1644	1644	1710	|	1743	|	|	1847	1847	|	|	|	|	1944	1946	|	|	2044	|	2114	...	|	...	|
Paris Est **381** a.	...	...	...	...	1846	|	2123	|	|	...	...	|	|	|	|	...	...	|	|	...	|	...	...	|	...	|
Metz a.	...	...	...	...	...	1736	...	1813	1833	...	...	1911	1919	1921	1936	...	...	2015	2031	...	2058	...	...	2115	...	2254t

b – Not July 15, Aug. 15, Sept. 10, 12, 17, 24, Oct. 3, Nov. 1.
c – Not Aug. 4–22.
d – Not Aug. 1–3, 29–31, Sept. 1–16.
e – Also Aug. 15, Nov. 1; not Sept. 11, 18, Oct. 2.
f – 0503 on ②–⑥ from Nov. 29.
n – Not July 18–22, 25–29, Aug. 1–5, 8–12, 16–19.
r – Ⓐ only.
t – Arrives up to 90 minutes later on ①–⑤ until July 8 and ①–⑤ from Oct. 10.

w – Not Aug. 22 - Sept. 30.
z – Not Aug. 23, 26.

TGV – High-speed train. [R]. 🍷. Timings may vary – please check your reservation.

● – Subject to alteration on ⑥⑦ Sept. 10 - Oct. 2.
■ – Subject to alteration on ⑥⑦ Sept. 10–24.
▲ – Subject to alteration on Sept. 11, 18, Oct. 2.
⊖ – Subject to alteration on Sept. 10, 11, 17, 18, 24, Oct. 1.

¶ – Subject to alteration on Sept. 11, 12, 18, 23, Oct. 2, 23, 30, Nov. 6, 13. Does not call at Saverne on June 12, 19, ①–⑤ Aug. 8 - Sept. 2, Oct. 24–26, 31, Nov. 1, 2, 20, 27, Nov. 4.
⊠ – Timings may vary may by up to 10 minutes (earlier departures possible). Services are particularly affected as follows: from/to Metz until July 10 and from Oct. 10; from Nancy to Strasbourg until June 19 and Aug. 2 - Oct. 7; from Strasbourg to Nancy until June 19 and Sept. 5–30. Services from/to Paris are subject to alteration on June 18, 19, 25, 26, July 9, 10, 16, 17, 30, 31, Aug. 6, 7.
Δ – Nancy - Sarrebourg: *80 km*.

384 Regional trains NANCY - METZ - LUXEMBOURG

Timings may vary by up to 3 minutes. French holiday dates apply, but with variations on June 23 (see shaded box below). See Table **390** for *TGV* trains Paris - Metz - Luxembourg.

km		Ⓐ	Ⓐ	⚒	Ⓐ		Ⓐ n	Ⓐ		⚒	Ⓐ n	n	Ⓐ	†	⑥	Ⓐ n		❖	Ⓐ n			Ⓐ n	⑥
0	**Nancy** d.	0528	0620r	0650	0720	0750	0806	0820	0828	0850	0920	0950	1020	1028	1049	1120	1150	and at the same	2020	2050	2150	2237	2250
28	Pont-à-Mousson d.	0553	0637	0707	0737	0807	0823	0837	0853	0907	0937	1007	1037	1053	1107	1137	1207	minutes past	2037	2107	2207	2303	2307
37	Pagny sur Moselle d.	0603	0644	0714	0744	0814	0830	0845	0903	0915	0945	1015	1045	1103	1115	1145	1215	each hour until	2045	2115	2215	2310	2315
57	**Metz** a.	0621	0658	0728	0758	0828	0844	0858	0921	0928	0958	1028	1058	1121	1128	1158	1228		2058	2128	2228	2328	2328

	Ⓐ	⚒	Ⓐ	Ⓑ	⑥	Ⓐ		Ⓐ n	⚒	Ⓐ n		Ⓐ n	⚒	Ⓐ n		Ⓐ n	⊠	Ⓐ n			Ⓑ n	Ⓐ n	Ⓒ
Metz d.	0602	0632	0702	0732	0734	0803	0832	0902	0932	1002	1033	1102	1132	1202	1232	1302	and at the same	2002	2032	2039	2132	2225	2232
Pagny sur Moselle d.	0615	0645	0715	0745	0747	0816	0845	0915	0945	1016	1045	1115	1145	1215	1245	1315	minutes past	2015	2045	2057	2145	2244	2245
Pont-à-Mousson d.	0623	0653	0723	0753	0754	0823	0853	0923	0953	1023	1053	1123	1153	1222	1253	1323	each hour until	2023	2053	2106	2153	2251	2253
Nancy a.	0640	0710	0740	0810	0811	0840	0911	0940	1010	1041	1111	1140	1210	1240	1310	1340		2040	2110	2132	2210	2319	2310

(NANCY -) METZ - LUXEMBOURG. Subject to alteration July 15 - Aug. 28 (also on June 25, 26, July 2, 3, Nov. 12, 13, 19, 20).
Timings may vary by up to 4 minutes (earlier departures possible). **Readers planning journeys on this route are strongly advised to confirm timings before travelling.**

km		Ⓐ	Ⓐ	⚒	Ⓐ	⚒	Ⓐ		Ⓐ n	⚒	†	†	Ⓐ	⑥	⚒				Ⓐ	Ⓐ	n	Ⓐ		Ⓐ n		Ⓐ
	Nancy ★ d.	...	...	...	0620r	0650	0720	0750	...	0850k	...	0950	...	...	1049k	1150	1250	1350	...	1450	...	...	1550	...	1650	1720
0	**Metz** d.	0533	0603	0633	0703	0733	0803	0833	0903	0932	0946	1030	1030	1042	1132	1233	1333	1433	1446	1533	1546	1603	1633	1703	1730	1803
18	Hagondange d.	0545	0615	0645	0715	0745	0815	0845	0918	0945	1002	1045	1045	1105	1145	1245	1345	1445	1502	1545	1602	1617	1645	1715	1745	1815
30	Thionville d.	0557	0627	0657	0727	0757	0827	0857	0936	0957	1018	1057	1057	1119	1157	1257	1357	1457	1518	1557	1618	1635	1657	1727	1757	1827
64	**Luxembourg** a.	0622	0652	0722	0752	0822	0852	0922	1003	1022	1045	1122	1122	1145	1222	1322	1422	1522	1545	1622	1645	1703	1722	1752	1822	1852

	n	Ⓐ			⚒ n	†	Ⓒ	Ⓐ	⑥	†
Nancy ★ d.	1750c	1822	1850c	1950c	2050k	...	2150	...	...	...
Metz d.	1833	1903	1933	2033	2133	2146	2232	2246	2314	2316
Hagondange d.	1845	1918	1945	2045	2145	2202	2244	2302	2331	2332
Thionville d.	1857	1934	1957	2057	2157	2218	2257	2318	2347	2344
Luxembourg a.	1922	2003	2022	2122	2222	2245	2322	2345	0014	...

	Ⓐ	⚒	Ⓐ	Ⓐ	Ⓐ	⑥	Ⓐ	Ⓐ		Ⓐ		⚒	Ⓐ n
Luxembourg d.	0516	0539k	0546	...	0616	0628	...	0709	0739	0809	0816	0839	...
Thionville d.	0544	0604	0613	0634	0645	0656	0700	0734	0804	0834	0845	0904	0924
Hagondange d.	0556	0616	0624	0646	0656	0712	0712	0746	0816	0846	0856	0916	0934
Metz a.	0614	0627	0641	0657	0714	0732	0727	0757	0827	0857	0914	0927	0952
Nancy ★ a.	...	0710	...	0740	...	0811	0810	0840	0911c	...	...	1010k	1041

		Ⓒ	Ⓐ		Ⓐ n		Ⓐ n		Ⓑ n	⑥	Ⓐ		Ⓐ			Ⓑ	⑥	Ⓐ	Ⓒ	Ⓐ n	Ⓑ	Ⓐ n	Ⓐ	n	Ⓐ n	Ⓒ z
Luxembourg d.	0939	1016	1039	1139	1209	1239	1258	1339	1416	1439	1439	1539	1558	1639	1739	1839	1839	1858	1939	2009	2016	2039	2116	2139	2239	2256
Thionville d.	1004	1043	1105	1204	1235	1304	1334	1404	1445	1504	1506	1604	1627	1704	1804	1904	1906	1929	2004	2034	2045	2104	2145	2204	2304	2324
Hagondange d.	1015	1054	1116	1216	1245	1316	1346	1416	1456	1516	1517	1616	1637	1716	1816	1916	1917	1940	2016	2046	2056	2116	2156	2216	2316	2337
Metz a.	1030	1114	1127	1228	1257	1328	1359	1429	1514	1528	1531	1627	1648	1727	1827	1927	1931	1957	2027	2057	2114	2127	2214	2227	2327	2354
Nancy ★ a.	1111	...	1210	1310	...	1410	...	1510c	...	1610	...	1710c	...	1810	1910	2010	2013	...	2110	...	...	2210	...	2310c	...	...

c – Ⓒ only.
k – ⑥ only.
n – Not July 18–22, 25–29, Aug. 1–5, 8–12, 16–19.
r – 0616 Sept. 5–30.
z – Not July 14, Sept. 4, Oct. 9.

❖ – Nancy d. 1746 (not 1750) June 12–17 and ①–⑤ Sept. 5–30. The 1620, 1720, 1822 and 1920 from Nancy also run July 18 - Aug. 19.
⊠ – The 1432 from Metz runs on Ⓒ only. On ⑥ Metz d. 1934 (not 1932) and then runs 3–4 minutes later to Nancy (a. 2013). The 1702, 1802 and 1902 from Metz also run July 18 - Aug. 19.
★ – See upper panel for full service Nancy - Metz and v.v.

PUBLIC HOLIDAY ALTERATIONS

On June 23 (public holiday in Luxembourg) many services to/from Luxembourg operate as on Ⓒ/†. On July 14, Nov. 11 (public holidays in France) many services to/from Luxembourg operate as on Ⓐ/⚒. ***Please check locally if travelling on these dates.***

385 STRASBOURG - MULHOUSE - BASEL

French holiday dates apply

For *TGV* trains Paris - Strasbourg - Colmar see Table 390. For *TGV* trains Luxembourg - Metz - Strasbourg - Mulhouse - Lyon - Marseille / Montpellier see Table 379.

km		Ⓐ	Ⓐ	⚒	Ⓐ	⑥ 2	Ⓐ	Ⓒ	Ⓐ	Ⓒ 2		Ⓐ	⑥ 2		Ⓐ	⑥ 2	⚒	† 2	Ⓐ		Ⓐ	Ⓒ 2		Ⓐ	⑥ 2		Ⓐ
0	**Strasbourg** d.	...	0515	0551	0621	0621	0651	0651	0721	0721	0751	0821	0821	0851	0921	0921	0951	0951	1021	1051	1121	1121	1151	1220	1221	1251	1321
43	Sélestat d.	...	0539	0611	0641	0648	0711	0711	0741	0746	0811	0841	0846	0911	0941	0946	1011	1016	1041	1111	1141	1146	1211	1242	1247	1311	1341
65	Colmar d.	...	0551	0623	0653	0701	0723	0723	0753	0758	0823	0853	0858	0923	0953	0958	1023	1028	1053	1123	1153	1158	1223	1254	1259	1323	1353
106	**Mulhouse** ‡ d.	0546	0616	0646	0716	0730	0746	0749f	0816	0825	0846	0916	0925	0946	1016	1025	1046	1055	1116	1146	1216	1225	1246	1315	1325	1346	1416
133	St Louis (Haut Rhin) ‡ d.	0600	0630	0700	0730	...	0800	0812	0830	...	0900	0930	...	1000	1030	...	1100	...	1130	1200	1230	...	1300	...	...	1400	1430
140	**Basel** SBB ‡ a.	0608	0638	0708	0738	...	0808	0820	0840	...	0908	0938	...	1008	1040	...	1108	...	1138	1208	1240	...	1308	...	...	1408	1440

	⚒	† 2	⑥ 2		Ⓐ	⑥ 2		Ⓑ	⑥ 2		Ⓐ	⑥ 2		Ⓑ	⑥ 2		Ⓑ	⑥ 2		Ⓑ	⑥ 2	Ⓐ 2	⚒	† 2	2	† 2	⚒ 2
Strasbourg d.	1351	1351	1421	1451	1521	1521	1551	1621	1621	1651	1721	1721	1751	1821	1821	1851	1921	1921	1951	2021	2021	2051	2121	2121	2221	2251	2320
Sélestat d.	1411	1416	1446	1511	1541	1546	1610	1641	1646	1711	1741	1746	1811	1841	1846	1911	1941	1946	2011	2041	2046	2118	2141	2146	2246	2311	2346
Colmar d.	1423	1428	1458	1523	1553	1558	1622	1653	1658	1723	1753	1758	1823	1853	1858	1923	1953	1958	2023	2053	2058	2131	2153	2158	2259	2323	0000
Mulhouse ‡ d.	1446	1455	1525	1546	1616	1625	1646	1716	1725	1746	1816	1825	1846	1916	1925	1946	2016	2020	2046	2116	2125	2158	2216	2224	2324	2344	0022j
St Louis (Haut Rhin) ‡ d.	1500	...	...	1600	1630	...	1700	1730	...	1800	1830	...	1900	1930	...	2000	2030	...	2100	2130	...	...	2230	...	...	...	...
Basel SBB ‡ a.	1508	...	...	1608	1640	...	1710	1738	...	1808	1840	...	1908	1938	...	2008	2038	...	2108	2138	...	...	2238	...	...	...	...

	Ⓐ 2	⑥ 2	Ⓐ	Ⓐ		† 2	⑥ 2	Ⓐ		⑥ 2	Ⓐ		Ⓐ		⑥ 2		⑥ 2	Ⓐ	† 2	⚒	Ⓐ		Ⓐ		Ⓐ	† 2	⚒
Basel SBB ‡ d.	...	...	0521	0537	0621	...	...	0651	0721	...	0751	0821	0851	0921	...	1021	...	1051	...	1121	1151	1221	1251	1321	...	...	1421
St Louis (Haut Rhin) ‡ d.	...	...	0530	0546	0630	...	...	0700	0730	...	0800	0830	0900	0930	...	1030	...	1100	...	1130	1200	1230	1300	1330	...	...	1430
Mulhouse ‡ d.	0457	0534	0546	0601	0646	0700	0704	0716	0746	0803	0816	0846	0916	0946	1004	1046	1104	1116	1134	1146	1216	1246	1316	1346	1414	1434	1446
Colmar d.	0518	0602	0606	0629	0706	0726	0732	0736	0806	0830	0836	0906	0936	1006	1032	1106	1132	1136	1202	1206	1236	1306	1336	1406	1435	1502	1506
Sélestat d.	0530	0613	0619	0642	0719	0738	0743	0749	0819	0843	0849	0919	0949	1019	1043	1119	1143	1149	1213	1219	1249	1319	1349	1419	1447	1513	1519
Strasbourg a.	0556	0639	0639	0709	0739	0804	0809	0809	0839	0909	0910	0939	1009	1039	1109	1139	1209	1209	1239	1239	1309	1339	1409	1439	1509	1539	1539

	⑥ 2	Ⓐ	† 2	⚒	⑥ 2	Ⓐ		†	⑥ 2	Ⓐ		⑥	Ⓑ		⑥ 2	Ⓐ		⑥ 2	Ⓑ	† 2	⚒ d	⑥ 2	Ⓐ d	†	Ⓐ	⑥ 2	Ⓑ 2◇
Basel SBB ‡ d.	...	1451	...	1521	...	1551	1621	1639	...	1651	1721	...	1751	1821	...	1851	1921	...	1951	...	2021	...	2038	2121	2151	...	...
St Louis (Haut Rhin) ‡ d.	...	1500	...	1530	...	1600	1630	1648	...	1700	1730	...	1800	1830	...	1900	1930	...	2000	...	2030	...	2046	2130	2200	...	...
Mulhouse ‡ d.	1514	1516	1534	1546	1604	1616	1646	1702	1704	1716	1746	1804	1816	1846	1904	1916	1946	2004	2016	2034	2046	2110	2114f	2146	2216	2234	2330
Colmar d.	1535	1536	1602	1606	1632	1636	1706	1730	1732	1736	1806	1832	1836	1906	1932	1936	2006	2032	2036	2102	2106	2138	2136	2206	2236	2302	2359
Sélestat d.	1547	1549	1613	1619	1643	1649	1719	1742	1743	1749	1819	1843	1849	1919	1943	1949	2019	2043	2049	2113	2119	2150	2148	2219	2249	2313	0012
Strasbourg a.	1609	1609	1639	1639	1709	1709	1739	1809	1809	1809	1839	1909	1909	1939	2009	2009	2039	2109	2109	2139	2139	2215	2214	2239	2309	2339	0040

d – Runs daily Basel - Mulhouse.
f – Arrives 5 minutes earlier.
j – 0051 on the mornings ②–⑥ June 21 - July 2 (by 🚌 from Colmar). Arrives up to 5 minutes later on certain other dates.
n – Not July 18–22, 25–29, Aug. 1–5, 8–12, 16–19.
◇ – On † Mulhouse d. 2338, Colmar d. 0003, Sélestat d. 0015, Strasbourg a. 0040. Minor timing variations may apply on certain other dates.
* – 1643 on July 14, Aug. 15, Nov. 1, 11.

‡ – **Other local stopping trains** Mulhouse - Basel and v.v. (journey 30–32 minutes):
From Mulhouse at 0449①–⑤n, 0549①–⑤, 0619①–⑥, 0649①–⑤n, 0719①–⑥, 0749, 0819①–⑤n, 0919, 1049①–⑤n, 1119, 1219①–⑤n, 1320, 1419①–⑥n, 1519⑥⑦, 1549①–⑤, 1620①–⑥, 1649①–⑤n, 1719①–⑥, 1749①–⑤, 1819n, 1849①–⑤, 1919①–⑥, 1949Ⓑn and 2019①–⑤.
From Basel SBB at 0608①–⑤n, 0638①–⑤, 0708①–⑥, 0738①–⑤n, 0808①–⑥, 0839, 1039, 1138①–⑤n, 1239, 1338①–⑤n, 1439⑥⑦, 1538①–⑥, 1608①–⑤n, 1639*①–⑥, 1708①–⑤, 1738n, 1808①–⑤, 1839①–⑥, 1908Ⓑn, 1938①–⑤, 2138①–⑤n and 2238①–⑤.

386 NANCY - ÉPINAL - REMIREMONT

SERVICE JUNE 19 - AUGUST 1 AND FROM OCTOBER 8. See page 213 for amended service August 2 - October 7. **Warning!** Subject to alteration on Oct. 22.

km		Ⓐ	Ⓐ	⚒ n	⚒ ⊗	Ⓐ n	Ⓒ	Ⓐ ⊙	Ⓑ n⊕	⑥	Ⓐ ⊙	⑥	†	Ⓐ n⊕	†	⚒ ⊙	Ⓐ ⊕	⊡⊙	⚒ ⊕	n	2571 ♥	†	⚒	n	Ⓐ		Ⓐ n
	Paris Est 390 d.	...	...	...	...	...	...	...	...	...	...	...	...	...	...	...	...	...	...	...	1223	...	...	...	...	...	...
0	**Nancy** d.	0555	0620	0655	0720	0755	0820	0820	0856	0920	0930	1020	1020	1055	1120	1120	1155	1220	1255	1320	1406	1420	1420	1520	1555	1620	1655
74	Épinal a.	0653	0720	0753	0818	0853	0909	0918	0954	1018	1022	1105	1118	1153	1205	1218	1251	1321	1353	1418	1448	1505	1518	1618	1653	1718	1753
74	Épinal d.	...	0721	...	0820	...	0911	0920	...	...	1024	...	1120	...	...	1220	...	1323	...	1420r	1451	...	1520t	1620	...	1720t	...
100	**Remiremont** a.	...	0754	...	0854	...	0934	0954	...	...	1054	...	1154	...	...	1254	...	1357	...	1454r	1512	...	1554t	1654	...	1754t	...

			⚒	Ⓐ n		2573 ♥	◧	△	⑥	Ⓐ ▽	†
Paris Est 390 d.	...	...	...	...	...	1810	...	...	...	...	...
Nancy d.	1720	1756	1820v	1857	1920	1958	2020	2120	2205	2220	2255
Épinal a.	1818	1854	1918	1953	2018	2039	2118	2218	2304	2318	2358
Épinal d.	1820	...	1920z	...	2020n	2042	...	2220	...	...	...
Remiremont a.	1854	...	1954z	...	2054n	2108	...	2254	...	...	...

	Ⓐ	⚒ n	2574 ⚒ ♥	†	⚒	⚒ ◐	Ⓐ	⑥	Ⓐ		Ⓐ n	2578 † ♥
Remiremont d.	...	0511t	0600	...	0615f	...	0710	...	...	0811	...	0859
Épinal a.	...	0541t	0621	...	0643f	...	0741	...	...	0841	...	0920
Épinal d.	0500	0543	0624	0643	0645	0703	0743	0746	0803	0843	0903	0923
Nancy a.	0559	0640	0705	0740	0740	0802	0840	0844	0902	0940	1002	1004
Paris Est 390 a.	...	...	0846	...	...	...	...	...	...	...	...	1150

	⚒ n⊕	†	Ⓐ ⊙	Ⓐ n⊕	Ⓒ	⚒ ⊕	⊙	Ⓐ ⊕	Ⓐ n⊕	⑥	⊙	Ⓒ ⊖	Ⓐ n	2580 ♥		Ⓐ	⚒	†	Ⓑ		⑥	Ⓐ B	†	Ⓐ n	⑥	Ⓐ n	†
Remiremont d.	0911t	...	1011	...	1035	...	1211	...	1311	...	1411	...	1514	1558	1611	...	1711n	...	1811	...	1910	1911	1928	...	2002	2011	...
Épinal a.	0941t	...	1041	...	1104	...	1241e	...	1340	...	1441	...	1542	1621	1641	...	1741n	...	1841	...	1931	1941	1949	...	2030	2041	...
Épinal d.	0943	0955	1043	1103	1106	1143q	1243e	1321	1342	1355	1443p	1543	1544	1623	1643	1703	1743	1755	1843	1903	1933	1943	1951	2003	2032	2043	2138
Nancy a.	1040	1040	1140	1202	1202	1240	1340	1408	1436	1440	1540	1640	1640	1706	1739	1802	1840	1840	1940	2002	2033	2040	2040j	2102	2127	2146	2235
Paris Est 390 a.	...	...	...	...	...	...	...	...	...	...	...	...	...	1846	...	...	...	...	...	...	...	...	...	...	...	...	...

B – From June 24.
e – On † Épinal a. 1240, d. 1241.
f – Not June 25.
j – 2042 until July 31.
n – Not July 18–22, 25–29, Aug. 1.
p – 1446 on Ⓐ.
q – 1139 on ⑥.
r – ⚒ only.
t – Ⓐ only.
v – 1818 on ⑥ until July 16.
z – Not July 23, 30.
◧ – On ⑥ Nancy d. 2025, Épinal a. 2110.
◐ – On ⑥ Épinal d. 0708, Nancy a. 0804.
⊖ – On ⑥ Épinal d. 1552, Nancy a. 1637.
⊡ – Runs 3–4 minutes **earlier** on ⑥. On † Épinal a. 1318, d. 1320, Remiremont a. 1354.
⊗ – Subject to alteration July 25–29, Aug. 1.
⊕ – Subject to alteration Oct. 17–21, 24–28.
⊙ – Subject to alteration July 25–29, Aug. 1, Oct. 17–21, 24–28.
△ – By 🚌 June 20–24 (Nancy d. 2101, Épinal d. 2225, Remiremont a. 2308).
▽ – By 🚌 June 20–24, July 25–29, Aug. 1 (Nancy d. 2220, Épinal a. 2339).
♥ – *TGV* train. Ⓡ. 🍷.

387 NANCY - LUNÉVILLE - ST DIÉ

SERVICE UNTIL AUGUST 1 AND FROM OCTOBER 8. The service from August 2 to October 7 will be shown in the August and Autumn editions.

km		Ⓐ n	Ⓐ b		⑥	Ⓐ	Ⓐ n	⑥	†	Ⓐ w	⑥	⑥	⑥	†	Ⓐ		⑥	Ⓐ n	2591 ⑦ e♥	Ⓐ	⑥	Ⓐ n	⑥	†	Ⓐ	⑥	Ⓐ
	Paris Est 390 d.	...	...	...	...	...	...	...	...	...	...	...	...	...	...	...	...	...	1358	...	...	...	...	...	...	...	...
0	**Nancy** 383 d.	0542	0649	0750	0855	0859	0926	0949	0955	1027	1052	1150	1250	1252	1310	1411	1450	1450	1552	1550	1553	1649	1652	1652	1711	1750	1751
33	Lunéville 383 d.	0604	0711	0811	0914	0921	0951	1008	1014	1100	1112	1210	1311	1313	1331	1429	1510	1511	1614	1610	1614	1710	1711	1710	1730	1813	1811
84	**St Dié** a.	0703	0755	0855	0953	1003	1031	1051	1055	1143	1151	1249	1353	1355	1415	1513	1549	1553	1647	1655	1655	1755	1749	1759	1831	1853	1856

	†	Ⓐ	⑥	Ⓐ n	2593 ①–⑤ v♥	⑥	†	Ⓐ n	①–⑤ A	2595 ⑦ e♥	Ⓐ ▲
Paris Est 390 d.	...	...	...	...	1810	...	...	...	...	2010	...
Nancy 383 d.	1759	1850	1854	1911	1954	2003	2005	2002	2002	2153	2159
Lunéville 383 d.	1819	1914	1914	1931	|	2024	2024	2032	2037	2215	2220
St Dié a.	1900	1953	2002	2029	2046	2103	2107	2116	2127	2244	2258

	Ⓐ		⑥	Ⓐ	Ⓐ	† ◇	2596 ⚒j ♥	Ⓐ	Ⓐ	⑥	Ⓐ n	Ⓒ
St Dié d.	0505	...	0600	0606	0631	0702	0715	0732	0805	0810	0905	0907
Lunéville 383 d.	0546	...	0641	0652	0729	0744	|	0830	0849	0852	0951	0950
Nancy 383 a.	0605	...	0700	0714	0749	0803	0809	0848	0910	0910	1012	1008
Paris Est 390 a.	...	...	...	...	...	...	0946	...	...	...	...	...

A – July 18 - Aug. 1 only.
b – Not Aug. 1.
e – Also Nov. 1.
j – Not July 15, 16.
n – Not July 18–22, 25–29, Aug. 1.
v – Not July 14, 15, Oct. 31, Nov. 1, 11.
w – Not Oct. 10–14.
▲ – July 25 - Aug. 1 operated by 🚌 (Nancy d. 2159, Lunéville d. 2239, St Dié a. 2343).
◇ – Runs 5–6 minutes earlier on July 14, Nov. 1, 11.
♥ – *TGV* train. Ⓡ. 🍷.

387 NANCY - LUNÉVILLE - ST DIÉ

SERVICE UNTIL AUGUST 1 AND FROM OCTOBER 8. The service August 2 - October 7 will be shown in later editions.

																2598									
	⑥	Ⓐ	Ⓒ	⑥	Ⓐ	Ⓒ		⑥	Ⓐ	⑥	Ⓐ n	†	⑥	Ⓐ	Ⓐ n	⑥	⑦ e♥	†	Ⓐ	⑥	⑥	†	Ⓐ	†	Ⓐ n	⑥
St Dié d.	1000	1046	1107	1206	1226	1253	...	1401	1442	1520	1557	1557	1610	1632	1705	1707	1711	1732	1805	1809	1908	1925	1930	1959	2005	2015
Lunéville **383** d.	1037	1131	1149	1248	1310	1348	...	1446	1530	1600	1639	1641	1652	1730	1749	1749	1745	1814	1850	1852	1947	2010	2031	2047	2052	2100
Nancy **383** a.	1055	1152	1210	1312	1333	1410	...	1504	1550	1618	1658	1658	1709	1748	1808	1810	1804	1833	1908	1912	2006	2032	2049	2108	2108	2120
Paris Est 390 a.	...	...	...	...	...	...	...	...	...	...	...	...	...	...	...	...	1950	...	...	...	...	...	...	...	...	...

e – Also Nov. 1. n – Not July 18–22, 25–29, Aug. 1. ♥ – *TGV* train. 🅁. 🍷.

389 PARIS - REIMS - CHARLEVILLE MÉZIÈRES - SEDAN

Services Reims - Charleville - Sedan and v.v. are subject to alteration on Sept. 24, 25. *TGV* services are subject to alteration on Dec. 3, 4.

km								*TGV* 2707				*TGV* 2709	*TGV* 2715					*TGV* 2719				*TGV* 2721		
		Ⓐ	⑥	Ⓐ n	Ⓐ	⑥	Ⓐ n	Ⓐ s	⑥	Ⓐ	†	①–⑥ b⊗	⑦ e	Ⓐ	⑥	†	⚒ n⊖	E	⑥	Ⓐ ⊖	Ⓐ n⊖	⑦ e	Ⓐ ⊖	Ⓒ
0	**Paris** Est **390** d.	...	...	...	...	...	...	0739	...	...	...	0828	0828	...	...	...	...	1028	...	...	...	1128	...	...
136	Champagne Ardenne TGV **390 391a** d.	...	...	...	...	...	0740	|	0810	0810	...	|	|	...	0910	1010	1010	|	1110	1110	1140	|	1210	1210
147	**Reims** **391a** a.	...	...	...	...	...	0752	0825	0821	0822	...	0914	0914	...	0923	1022	1022	1114	1121	1122	1152	1214	1222	1221
147	**Reims** d.	0630	0630	0700	0735	0745	0800	...	0829	0830	0830	0919	0919	0930	0930	1030	1030	...	1129	1130	1200	...	1230	1229
186	Rethel d.	0654	0653	0724	0759	0809	0824	...	0852	0854	0553	0942	0942	0954	0954	1053	1054	...	1152	1154	1224	...	1254	1252
235	**Charleville-Mézières** a.	0725	0726	0751	0830	0841	0851	...	0925	0926	0925	1010	1011	1026	1026	1125	1126	...	1226	1226	1251	...	1326	1325
235	**Charleville-Mézières** **389a** d.	0730	0731	...	0835	0846	...	...	0930	0931	0930	1019x	...	1031x	1031	...	1131x	...	1231	1231x	...	...	1331x	1330k
255	**Sedan** **389a** a.	0751	0755	...	0856	0905	...	...	0957	0951	0958	1035x	...	1051x	1049	...	1150x	...	1254	1257x	...	...	1351x	1357k

				TGV 2733				*TGV* 2743					*TGV* 2747			*TGV* 2751	*TGV* 2753				*TGV* 2757	*TGV* 2759		*TGV* 2765
	Ⓐ ⊖	⑥	Ⓐ ⊖	⑤⑥ d		Ⓒ	Ⓐ	Ⓑ h		Ⓐ n		Ⓐ n			Ⓐ n	D	⑤ f	⚒	†	⚒	⑤⑦ t	B	Ⓐ	⑤⑦ t
Paris Est **390** d.	...	...	...	1258	...	...	...	1528	...	...	...	...	1728	...	...	1828	1828	...	...	...	2028	2058	...	2128
Champagne Ardenne TGV **390 391a** d.	1240	1310	1310	|	1410	1510	1518	|	1610	1640	1710	1740	|	1810	1840	|	|	1910§	2010	2016	|	|	...	|
Reims **391a** a.	1252	1321	1322	1344	1422	1522	1527	1614	1622	1652	1722	1752	1814	1822	1852	1913	1914	1922§	2021	2028	2114	2144	...	2214
Reims d.	1300	1329	1330	...	1430	1525y	1530	...	1630	1700	1730	1800	...	1830	1900	1919	1920	1930	2029	2030	...	*2200*‡	2200	2219
Rethel d.	1324	1352	1354	...	1454	1553	1553	...	1653	1724	1754	1824	...	1853	1924	1943	1943	1954	2053	2054	...	|	2224	2242
Charleville-Mézières a.	1351	1425	1426	...	1525	1625	1626	...	1725	1751	1825	1856	...	1926	1951	2010	2011	2026	2124	2127	...	*2320*‡	2256	2310
Charleville-Mézières **389a** d.	...	1430	1431q	...	1530q	1630k	1631	...	1730	1800	1830	...	...	1931r	...	2019	...	2031	2130	...	...	...	...	2319
Sedan **389a** a.	...	1452	1457q	...	1551q	1651k	1651	...	1755	1825	1852	...	...	1956r	...	2035	...	2051	2157	...	...	...	...	2335

SEE NOTE ⊠		*TGV* 2706				*TGV* 2712		*TGV* 2714		*TGV* 2716		*TGV* 2720				*TGV* 2722	*TGV* 2726					*TGV* 2730	*TGV* 2738	
	Ⓐ	Ⓐ v	Ⓐ n	Ⓐ	⑥	Ⓐ v	Ⓐ	①–⑥ b	⚒	Ⓐ s	Ⓐ n	⑦ e	⚒ n		⚒	H	⑥ u	⊖	Ⓐ n⊖	⚒ ⊖	Ⓐ n⊖	Ⓐ v⊙	⑦ e	⚒ ⊖
Sedan **389a** d.	...	...	0534	0605	0604	...	0638	0649	0704p	...	0734	0753	0800a	0910z	1010	...	1053j	1110x	...	1204x	...	1252x	...	1310x
Charleville-Mézières **389a** a.	...	...	0600	0624	0629	...	0657	0703	0730	...	0800	0807	0826a	0930	1030	...	1107j	1130x	...	1232x	...	1306x	...	1330x
Charleville-Mézières d.	0535	...	0608	0629	0634	...	0704	0715	0735	...	0808	0817	0831	0935	1035	...	1117	1135	1208	1237	1304	1316	...	1335
Rethel d.	0607	...	0636	0702	0706	...	0737	0747	0808	...	0836	0847	0905	1008	1108	...	1147	1208	1236	1309	1337	1346	...	1408
Reims a.	0631	...	0700	0726	0729	...	0800	0809	0831	...	0900	0909	0930	1031	1131	...	1209	1231	1300	1333	1401	1408	...	1431
Reims **391a** d.	0636	0644	0705	0736	0739	0744	0805	0814	0836	0844	0905	0914	0935	1036	1136	1202	1215	1236	1305	1338	1405	1414	1415	1436
Champagne Ardenne TGV **390 391a** d.	0648	|	0718	0748	0751	|	0818	|	0848	|	0918	|	0948	1048	1148	|	|	1248	1318	1350	1418	|	|	1448
Paris Est **390** a.	...	0731	...	...	...	0831	...	0901	...	0931	...	1001	...	...	...	1248	1301	...	...	...	...	1501	1501	...

SEE NOTE ⊠				*TGV* 2750		*TGV* 2752	*TGV* 2754							*TGV* 2756		*TGV* 2760		*TGV* 2762						*TGV* 2766
	†	⑥	Ⓐ ⊖	⑥ u		Ⓐ v	⑦ e	†	Ⓐ	⑥	Ⓐ n	J	†	⑤⑦ t	Ⓐ	B		G	Ⓐ	⑥	Ⓐ	Ⓒ	Ⓐm n	⑦ e
Sedan **389a** d.	1310	1406	1410x	...	1510q	...	...	...	1610q	1607	1634	1710	1710	...	1734	...	1810c	...	*1834*n	...	*1904*	2010g	*2019*•	2053
Charleville-Mézières **389a** a.	1338	1430	1430x	...	1530q	...	...	...	1630q	1631	1700	1730	1735	...	1800	...	1830	...	*1900*n	...	*1931*	2034	*2034*•	2107
Charleville-Mézières d.	1343	1435	1435	...	1535	...	1617	1635	1635	1636	1708	1735	1740	...	1808	...	1835	...	1908	1934	2005	2039	2105	2117
Rethel d.	1415	1508	1508	...	1608	...	1647	1707	1708	1711	1736	1808	1815	...	1836	...	1908	...	1934	2008	2037	2113	2137	2147
Reims a.	1440	1534	1531	...	1631	...	1709	1731	1731	1736	1800	1831	1840	...	1859	...	1931c	...	2000	2033	2100	2139	2201	2209
Reims **391a** d.	1445	1538	1536	1614	1636	1714	1715	1736	1736	1739	1805	1836	1847	1844	1904§	1914	1936c	1944	...	...	...	...	...	2214
Champagne Ardenne TGV **390 391a** d.	1456	1550	1548	|	1648	|	|	1748	1748	1750	1818	1848	1858	|	1918§	|	1948c	|	...	...	...	...	...	|
Paris Est **390** a.	...	...	...	1701	...	1801	1801	...	...	...	...	...	...	1931	...	2001	...	2031	...	...	...	...	...	2301

B – ①②③④⑥ (also July 15, Nov. 11; not July 13, Aug. 15, Nov. 1, 10).
D – ①②③④⑥⑦ (also July 15, Nov. 11; not July 13, Nov. 10).
E – ①–⑥ to July 16 (not July 11–13); ⑥ July 23 - Aug. 20; ①–⑥ from Aug. 27 (not Nov. 1).
G – ⑤⑦ to July 8 (also July 13); ⑤ July 22 - Aug. 26; ⑤⑦ from Sept. 2 (also Nov. 1, 10; not Nov. 11).
H – Ⓑ to July 10; ⑦ July 17 - Aug. 21 (also Aug. 15); Ⓑ from Aug. 28 (not Oct. 31, Nov. 11).
J – ⑤⑥ to July 9; ⚒ from July 11.

a – Ⓐ only.
b – Not Aug. 15, Nov. 1.
c – On ⑥ Sedan d. 1805, Reims a. 1934, d. 1939, Champagne Ardenne a. 1951.
d – Also July 13, 14, Oct. 31, Nov. 10; not July 22, 29, Aug. 5, 12, 19, 26.
e – Also Aug. 15, Nov. 1.
f – Also July 13, Nov. 10; not July 15, Nov. 11.
g – 2012 on †.
h – Not July 14, 15, Oct. 31, Nov. 11.
j – Not Oct. 31.
k – ⑥ only.
m – Not Sept. 19 - Oct. 21.
n – Not July 18–22, 25–29, Aug. 1–5, 8–12, 16–19.
p – 0710 on ⑥.
q – Not Oct. 17–21, 24–28, 31, Nov. 2–4, 7–10.
r – Not ⑥.
s – Not July 11 - Aug. 26, Oct. 31.
t – Also July 13, Aug. 15, Nov. 1, 10; not July 15, Nov. 11.
u – Also July 14, 15, Oct. 31, Nov. 11.
v – Not July 15, Oct. 31.
x – Not Sept. 5–9, 12–16, Oct. 17–21, 24–28, 31, Nov. 2–4, 7–10, 14–18, 21–25, 28–30, Dec. 1, 2.
y – 1529 on †.
z – 0904 on †.

TGV – High-speed train. 🅁. 🍷.
‡ – ⑥ only. By 🚌.
§ – Not June 13–16, 20–23, 27–30, July 4–7.
• – Not June 17, 24, July 1, 8.
⊗ – Operated by 🚌 Reims - Sedan Oct. 24–28 (Reims d. 0924, Rethel d. 1016, Charleville a. 1059, Sedan a. 1132).
⊙ – Operated by 🚌 Sedan - Reims Oct. 24–28 (Sedan d. 1157, Charleville d. 1230, Rethel d. 1318, Reims a. 1404).
⊖ – Subject to alteration Oct. 24–28.
⊠ – Timings of TER services Sedan - Charleville - Reims - Champagne Ardenne may vary by up to 5 minutes from Sept. 19 (earlier departures possible).

389a CHARLEVILLE MÉZIÈRES - LONGUYON - LONGWY and THIONVILLE

km		Ⓐ J	Ⓐ n	Ⓐ	Ⓐ n	Ⓐ	⑥	Ⓐ J⊗	†		Ⓐ k	†	
0	**Charleville-Mézières** **389** d.	0521	...	0621	...	...	0914	1121	1337	...	1721	1818	...
20	**Sedan** **389** d.	0537	...	0637	...	...	0932	1137	1403	...	1740	1835	...
69	Montmédy d.	0610	...	0710	...	...	1003	1211	1434	...	1811	1906	...
	Longwy **392** d.	|	0615	|	...	0815	|	|	|	...	|	|	...
91	Longuyon **392** a.	0625	0627	0725	...	0827	1016	1225	1447	...	1825	1920	...
91	Longuyon **392** d.	0630	0630	0730	0729	0828	1021	1230z	1452	...	1830	1921	2000
	Longwy **392** a.	0643	|	0743	|	|	1033	1243z	1504	...	1843	|	2012
132	Hayange d.	...	0702	...	0801	0901	...	...	...	...	...	1954	...
140	**Thionville** a.	...	0710	...	0810	0910	...	...	...	...	...	2002	...

	Ⓐ J	Ⓐ n		Ⓐ Jz⊖	⑥		†	Ⓐ	Ⓐ	Ⓐ n	Ⓐ k	†
Thionville d.	...	0635	...	...	...	...	1621	1710	...	1841	...	...
Hayange d.	...	0643	...	...	...	...	1629	1718	...	1849	...	...
Longwy **392** d.	0654	|	...	1316	1422	...	|	|	1816	|	1916	2022
Longuyon **392** a.	0706	0716	...	1329	1435	...	1659	1750	1829	1921	1929	2034
Longuyon **392** d.	0711	...	...	1334	1440	...	1700	1751	1834	1922	1934	2039
Longwy **392** a.	|	...	...	|	|	...	|	1805	|	1936	|	|
Montmédy d.	0725	...	...	1349	1454	...	1713	...	1848	...	1948	2053
Sedan **389** d.	0756	...	...	1420	1528	...	1745	...	1919	...	2019	2126
Charleville-Mézières **389** a.	0811	...	...	1439v	1547	...	1803	...	1935	...	2034	2147

J – From July 11.
k – Not June 17, 24, July 1, 8.
n – Not July 18 - Aug. 19.
v – Not Sept. 5–16.
z – Not Sept. 19–30.
⊗ – Subject to alteration Sept. 5–9, 12–16 and from Oct. 17.
⊖ – Subject to alteration from Oct. 17.

TGV EST EUROPÉEN 390

Timings may vary by up to 5 minutes – please check your reservation. **Warning!** Subject to alteration on Dec. 3, 4. Luxembourg services are subject to alteration July 15 - Aug. 28 (see note ❦).

PARIS - STRASBOURG - COLMAR

km		ICE	TGV	TGV	TGV	TGV	TGV	TGV	ICE		TGV	TGV	TGV	TGV	TGV	ICE	TGV	TGV	TGV	TGV	TGV	TGV	TGV	TGV	TGV	TGV
		9571	**9561**	**2363**	**2407**	**2407**	**2365**	**7691**	**9573**		**2421**	**9575**	**2369**	**2431**	**2371**	**9563**	**9577**	**7693**	**2443**	**2443**	**9591**	**9579**	**2377**	**2465**	**2465**	**2471**
			①-⑥	①-⑥	⑥		①-⑤		◐		⑤-⑦		①-⑤	⑤	⑦		⑧		⑤⑦	①-④				⑥⑦	①-⑤	⑤⑦
				b	D	E	y	⊠			c		v	f	e		⊙	⊠	a	n	F	⊙		w	v★	s
0	**Paris** Est d.	0655	0720	0720	0738	0758	0925	1004	1055	...	1255	1355	1355	1455	1455	1520	1555	1607	1639	1655	1725	1755	1855	2025	2025	2155
304	Lorraine TGV d.	|	|	|	|	|	|	|	|	...	|	|	|	|	|	|	|	◇	|	|	|	|	|	2142	2149	|
439	**Strasbourg** a.	0841	0906	0906	0942	0958	1111	1150	1241	...	1444	1541	1541	1641	1641	1709	1741	1849	1831	1841	1913	1941	2041	2218	2225	2341
439	**Strasbourg** 385 d.	0846	0912	0916	...	...	1117	...	1246	...	...	1546	1555	...	1646	1713	1746	...	...	...	...	1946	2046	...	...	...
	Stuttgart Hbf **32** a.	1004	|	|	...	...	|	...	1405	...	...	1704	|	...	|	|	1904	...	...	...	...	2104	|	...	...	...
	Frankfurt Hbf **30 912** a.	...	1058	|	...	...	|	...	...	...	...	...	|	...	|	1858	...	...	...	...	...	...	|	...	...	...
482	Sélestat 385 a.	...	...	|	...	...	|	...	...	...	...	...	|	...	|	...	...	...	...	...	...	...	2104	...	...	...
504	**Colmar** 385 a.	...	...	0942	...	...	1143	...	...	...	...	...	1626	...	1712	...	...	...	...	...	...	...	2118	...	...	...

	TGV	TGV	TGV	TGV	TGV	TGV	TGV	ICE	TGV	TGV	ICE	ICE	TGV	TGV	TGV	TGV	ICE	TGV	TGV	TGV	TGV	TGV	TGV	TGV	TGV	TGV
	2400	**2404**	**2350**	**9590**	**9578**	**9588**	**2352**	**9568**	**2356**	**9576**	**9566**	**9574**	**7692**	**2430**	**2358**	**2440**	**9572**	**2362**	**2450**	**2454**	**2364**	**9560**	**7694**	**9570**	**2470**	**2474**
	①	①-⑤	①-⑥	①-⑤	①-⑥	⑥⑦	⑦	⑧	①-⑥		⑥			⑥	①-⑤		◧	①-⑤	⑥⑦	①-⑤	⑦				⑤	⑦
	g	v	b	uF		⊖F	e		b	⊙			⊠	x	y	G		v	w	v	e		⊠		f¶	e♥
Colmar 385 d.	...	...	0638	...	...	...	0737	...	1001	...	...	...	...	...	1401	...	...	1645	...	...	1745	...	...	...	...	...
Sélestat 385 d.	...	...	0652	...	...	...	0749	...	|	...	...	...	...	...	|	...	...	|	...	...	|	...	...	...	...	...
Frankfurt Hbf **30 912** d.	...	...	|	...	...	...	|	0656	|	...	0856	...	...	...	|	...	...	|	...	...	|	1656	...	...	...	...
Stuttgart Hbf **32** d.	...	...	|	...	0652	...	|	|	|	0910	|	1052	...	...	|	...	1453	|	...	...	|	|	...	1852	...	...
Strasbourg 385 a.	...	...	0713	...	0813	...	0808	0847	1031	1037	1047	1213	...	...	1435	...	1612	1713	...	...	1813	1848	...	2013	...	...
Strasbourg d.	0614	0641	0720	0747	0819j	0820	0820	0852	1044	1044	1052	1219	1247	1446	1448	1546	1617	1717	1717	1817	1819	1855	2003	2020	2047	2152
Lorraine TGV d.	|	|	0759	|	|	|	|	|	|	|	|	|	◇	|	|	|	|	|	|	|	|	|	◇	|	|	|
Paris Est a.	0805	0835	0916	0935	1005	1005	1005	1038	1231	1231	1238	1405‡	1517	1635	1635	1735	1805	1905§	1913r	2012	2012	2041	2231	2205	2235	2340

PARIS - METZ - LUXEMBOURG

km		TGV	TGV		TGV		TGV		TGV		TGV	TGV		TGV		TGV	TGV		TGV	TGV	TGV		TGV
		2601	**2801**		**2807**		**2815**		**2817**		**2613**	**7693**		**2833**		**2625**	**2625**		**2839**	**2839**	**2843**		**2647**
		①	①-⑤		①-⑥											⑤	①-④				⑥⑦		⑤⑦
		g	v		b						J	⊠				t	m		⊗	A	w		z
0	**Paris** Est d.	0658	0728	...	0813	...	1040	...	1340	...	1540	1607	...	1740	...	1840	1840	...	1939	2010	2038	...	2140
136	Champagne-Ardenne TGV d.	|	|	...	0856	...	|	...	|	...	|	|	...	|	...	|	1922	...	|	|	|	...	|
236	Meuse TGV a.	|	|	...	|	...	|	...	|	...	|	|	...	|	...	|	|	...	|	|	|	...	|
315	**Metz** 383 384 a.	0824	0851	...	0944	...	1204	...	1504	...	1704	1733	...	1904	...	2004	2011	...	2104	2134	2202	...	2304
345	Thionville ❦ 384 a.	...	0916	...	1007	...	1227	...	1527	...	...	...	...	1927	...	...	...	...	2127	...	2227	...	...
379	**Luxembourg** ❦ 384 a.	...	0944	...	1032	...	1252	...	1552	...	...	...	...	1952	...	...	...	...	2152	...	2252	...	...

	TGV	TGV	TGV	TGV	TGV		TGV	TGV		TGV		TGV	TGV		TGV		TGV	TGV		TGV		TGV	TGV
	2650	**2852**	**2852**	**2654**	**2854**		**2656**	**2860**		**2864**		**7692**	**2870**		**2872**		**2680**	**2680**		**2886**		**2892**	**7694**
	①-⑤	⑤	①-⑤	⑥			①-⑤	⑥⑦										⑦				⑦	
	v	N	L	M	Q		v	w				⊠					R	e				e	⊠
Luxembourg ❦ 384 d.	...	0559	0559	...	0640	...	...	0759	...	1010	...	...	1410	...	1610	...	...	...	...	1847	...	2010	...
Thionville ❦ 384 d.	...	0623	0623	...	0703	...	...	0823	...	1034	...	...	1432	...	1634	...	...	...	...	1912	...	2035	...
Metz 383 384 d.	0623	0650	0650	0726	0726	...	0850	0850	...	1056	...	1352	1505	...	1656	...	1728	1747	...	1942	...	2057	2106
Meuse TGV d.	|	|	0720	|	|	...	0920	0920	...	|	...	|	|	...	|	...	|	|	...	|	...	|	|
Champagne-Ardenne TGV d.	|	|	|	|	|	...	|	|	...	|	...	|	|	...	|	...	1820	1839	...	2032	...	|	|
Paris Est a.	0750	0820	0820	0850	0850	...	1020	1020	...	1220	...	1517	1631	...	1820	...	1901	1920	...	2114	...	2221	2231

PARIS - NANCY (-STRASBOURG)

Certain trains continue beyond Nancy to Épinal and Remiremont (Table **386**) or to Lunéville and St Dié (Table **387**).

km		TGV	TGV	TGV	TGV	TGV	TGV	TGV	TGV		TGV	TGV	TGV	TGV	TGV	TGV	TGV	TGV	TGV	TGV	TGV	TGV	TGV		TGV
		2501	**2503**	**2407**	**2407**	**2503**	**2503**	**2587**	**2505**		**2571**	**2509**	**2591**	**2509**	**2513**	**2513**	**2515**	**2573**	**2785**	**2583**	**2519**	**2595**	**2465**		**2527**
		①-⑤	⑥	⑥		⑥	①-⑤	⑦	①-⑥			①-⑤	⑦	⑥	①-⑤	⑦	①-⑤		⑧	⑧	⑥	⑦	①-⑤		⑤⑦
		v	T	D	E	D	v	e	b			v	e	k	d	e	v		h B		k	e	v★		z
0	**Paris** Est d.	0710	0738	0738	0758	0758	0838	0910	1013	...	1223	1358	1358	1458	1558	1610	1713	1810	1928	1943	2009	2010	2025	...	2113
136	Champagne-Ardenne TGV d.	0752	0821	0821	0841	0841	0921	|	|	...	1306	1441	1441	1541	1647	1653	|	|	2008	|	|	|	|	...	|
236	Meuse TGV d.	|	|	0848	0908	|	|	1014	|	...	|	1508	1508	1608	|	|	|	1913	...	|	2112	2113	2128	...	|
330	**Nancy** 383 a.	0848	0916	|	|	0936	1016	1048	1144	...	1400	1544	1544	1644	1744	1748	1844	1948	...	2118	2152	2147	|	...	2244
	Strasbourg 383 a.	...	...	0942	0958	...	...	1217	...	...	...	...	...	...	...	...	...	...	...	2252	...	...	2225	...	...

	TGV	TGV	TGV	TGV	TGV	TGV	TGV		TGV	TGV		TGV	TGV	TGV	TGV	TGV	TGV	TGV	TGV	TGV	TGV	TGV	TGV	TGV	TGV
	2530	**2778**	**2404**	**2574**	**2584**	**2596**	**2534**		**2536**	**2578**		**2540**	**2542**	**2544**	**2580**	**2588**	**2450**	**2362**	**2548**	**2598**	**2454**	**2364**	**2550**	**2550**	**2552**
	①-⑤	①-⑥	①-⑤	⚒		⚒	†		⚒	†			⑤⑦	①-⑤		⑦	⑥	①-④	①-⑥	⑦	①-⑤	⑦	①-⑤	⑥⑦	⑦
	v	b B	v		Y								q	v		e	k	H	b	e	v	e	v	w	e
Strasbourg 383 d.	...	...	0641	...	0541	...	...	...	...	...	...	...	...	...	...	1546	1717	1717	...	...	1817	1819	...	...	...
Nancy 383 d.	0611	...	|	0716	0716	0816	0816	...	1011	1011	...	1255	1430	1611	1716	1716	|	|	1811	1811	|	|	1940	2016	2116
Meuse TGV d.	|	...	0733	|	|	|	|	...	|	|	...	1332	|	|	|	|	|	|	1848	1849	|	|	|	|	|
Champagne-Ardenne TGV d.	|	0718	|	|	|	|	|	...	1108	1108	...	|	|	1708	|	|	1830	1830	|	|	1930	1930	2038	2118	|
Paris Est a.	0746	0801	0835	0846	0846	0946	0946	...	1150	1150	...	1433	1601	1750	1846	1846	1913	1913	1950	1950	2012	2012	2119	2200	2246

PARIS - SAARBRÜCKEN (- FRANKFURT)

km		TGV		ICE		ICE		TGV	ICE	
		9551		**9553**		**9555**		**9559**	**9557**	
						⑧		⑥	⑧	
0	**Paris** Est d.	0906	...	1310	...	1710	...	1906	1906	...
372	Forbach 🏛 a.	1045	...	|	...	|	...	2047	2047	...
383	**Saarbrücken** Hbf a.	1056	...	1457	...	1857	...	2057	2057	...
	Frankfurt (Main) Hbf **919** a.	1259	...	1659	...	2059	...	2259	2259	...

	ICE	ICE	ICE	ICE	ICE		TGV		ICE
	9558	**9586**	**9556**	**9554**	**9554**		**9552**		**9550**
	①-⑤	⑥	①-⑤	⑥	⑦				⑧
Frankfurt (Main) Hbf **919** d.	0556	0656	0856	1056	1056	...	1256	...	1856
Saarbrücken Hbf d.	0801	0903	1101	1303	1303	...	1503	...	2101
Forbach 🏛 d.	0811	0914	|	|	1314	...	1514p	...	2112
Paris Est a.	0951*	1053*	1252	1454	1454	...	1654	...	2252

A – ①-⑤ July 11 - Aug. 26 (not July 15, Aug. 15).
B – To / from Bar le Duc (Table **381**).
D – ⑥ until July 9 (also July 14, 15).
E – ⑧ to July 13; daily from July 16.
F – From / to Freiburg (Brsg) Hbf (Table **32**).
G – ⑤⑦ to July 10 (also July 13); ⑧ July 17 - Aug. 28; ⑤⑦ from Sept. 2 (also Nov. 1, 10; not Nov. 11).
H – ①-④ July 11 - Aug. 25 (not July 13, 14, Aug. 15).
J – ⑧ to July 13; ⑤⑦ July 17 - Aug. 21 (also Aug. 15); ⑧ from Aug. 26 (not Oct. 31, Nov. 11).
L – ①-⑤ from Aug. 29 (not Oct. 31, Nov. 1, 11).
M – ⑥ (also ②-⑤ July 19 - Aug. 12; not Aug. 16).
N – ⑤ to July 8 (also July 13).
Q – ①-④ to July 14 (also July 14; not July 13); ① July 18 - Aug. 22 (also Aug. 16; not Aug. 15); ①-⑤ from Aug. 29 (not Nov. 1).
R – ①-⑤ to July 8 (also July 13); ⑤ July 22 - Aug. 26; ①-⑤ from Aug. 29 (not Oct. 31, Nov. 1, 11).
T – ⑥ from July 16 (also Oct. 31, Nov. 11).
Y – ①-⑥ (not July 15, Aug. 15, Sept. 10, 12, 17, 24, Oct. 3, Nov. 1).

a – Also July 13, Nov. 1, 10; not July 15 - Aug. 28, Nov. 11.
b – Not Aug. 15, Nov. 1.
c – Also July 13, 14, Aug. 15, Oct. 31, Nov. 1, 10.
d – Not July 14 - Aug. 26, Oct. 31, Nov. 1, 11.
e – Also Aug. 15, Nov. 1.
f – Also July 13, Nov. 10; not July 15, Nov. 11.
g – Also Nov. 2; not July 11 - Aug. 22, Oct. 31.
h – Not Oct. 31, Nov. 11.
j – 0820 on ⑥ (also July 14, 15, Aug. 15, Oct. 31, Nov. 1, 11; not July 2).
k – Also July 14, 15, Oct. 31, Nov. 11.
m – Not July 13, 14, Aug. 15, Oct. 31, Nov. 1.
n – Not July 11 - Aug. 25, Oct. 31, Nov. 1, 10.
p – ⑥ from July 16.
q – Also July 13, Aug. 15, Nov. 1, 10; not July 15, 22, 29, Aug. 5, 12, 19, 26, Nov. 11.
r – 1905 on ⑦ (also Aug. 15, Nov. 1).
s – Also July 13, Aug. 15, Nov. 1, 10; not July 15, Sept. 2, 9, 16, 23, Nov. 11.
t – Also July 13; not July 15, Nov. 11.
u – Not July 14, 15, Oct. 31, Nov. 11.
v – Not July 14, Aug. 15, Oct. 31, Nov. 1, 11.
w – Also July 14, 15, Aug. 15, Oct. 31, Nov. 1, 11.
x – Also July 11 – 15, 22, 29, Aug. 5, 12, 19, 26, Oct. 31, Nov. 11.
y – Not July 11 - Aug. 26, Oct. 31, Nov. 1, 11.
z – Also July 13, Aug. 15, Nov. 1, 10; not July 15, Nov. 11.

TGV – High-speed train. 🄡. 🍸.
ICE – German high-speed train. 🄡. ✕.

* – 7 – 9 minutes later until July 9.
‡ – 1413 on Oct. 3, 4, 5.
§ – 1913 on ①-④ July 11 - Aug. 25 (not July 13, 14, Aug. 15).
⊖ – ⑥⑦ (also July 14, 15, Oct. 31, Nov. 11). Train number **9584** on ⑥ (also July 14, 15, Oct. 31, Nov. 11).
¶ – Not Sept. 2. Arrives Paris 2242 on Aug. 19, 26.
◧ – Runs as *TGV* **9592** on ⑥.
◐ – Runs as *TGV* **9593** on ⑥.
⊙ – To / from München (Table **32**).
★ – Runs 10 minutes later July 4 - Aug. 26.
♥ – On June 26, July 24, 31, Aug. 7, Nov. 1 departs Strasbourg 2047, arrives Paris 2240.
⊗ – Not ①-⑤ July 11 - Aug. 12, Aug. 16 – 19, 22 – 26.
❦ – Journeys to / from Thionville and Luxembourg are subject to alteration July 15 - Aug. 28 (also on June 25, 26, July 2, 3, Nov. 12, 13, 19, 20).
◇ – Via Metz.
⊠ – OUIGO low-cost TGV. Internet bookings only: www.ouigo.com

391 STRASBOURG - BRUSSELS, NANTES, RENNES and BORDEAUX

Timings may vary by up to 4 minutes – please check your reservation.

	TGV	TGV	TGV	TGV	TGV	TGV	TGV	TGV	TGV	TGV	TGV	TGV	TGV
	9890	**5420**	**5450**	**5470**	**5487**	**5487**	**5487**	**5470**	**5487**	**5454**	**9894**	**5488**	**5473**
	⑦	①–⑥										Ⓑ	Ⓑ
	e	r◇	P	Ⓑh	Q	N	R	⑥k	⑥k			w	B
Strasbourg d.	0556	0556	0613	0731	0731	0731	0731	0741	0741	1420	1512	1731	1731
Lorraine TGV ★ d.	0636	0636	0652	0809	0809	0809	0809	0820	0820	1501	1550	1810	1810
Meuse TGV ★ d.	0657	0657	0712	|	|	|	|	|	|	1524	|	1831	1831
Champagne-Ardenne TGV a.	0722	0722	0738	0847	0847	0847	0847	0858	0858	1548	1627	1856	1856
Champagne-Ardenne TGV d.	0728	0728	0746	0858	0858	0858	0858	0901	0901	1558	1630	1900	1900
Paris Charles de Gaulle ✈ a.	0758	0758	|	0928	0928	0928	0928	0931	0931	|	1701	|	|
Paris Charles de Gaulle ✈ d.	0806	0811	|	0946	0946	0946	0946	0946	0946	|	1707	|	|
Lille Europe a.	0858	0907	|	|	|	|	|	|	|	|	1757	|	|
Brussels Midi/Zuid a.	0943j	...	|	|	|	|	|	|	|	|	1843	|	|
Marne la Vallée - Chessy § a.	...	...	0816	0958	0958	0958	0958	0958	0958	1628	...	1928	1928
Marne la Vallée - Chessy § d.	...	...	0832	1002	1002	1002	1002	1002	1002	1632	...	1932	1932
Massy TGV a.	...	...	0904	1034	1034	1034	1034	1034	1034	1704	...	2004	2004
St Pierre des Corps a.	...	...	1006	|	|	1140	|	|	1140	1800	...	|	|
Le Mans a.	...	...	|	1129	|	|	1145	1129	|	|	...	2100	2100
Angers a.	...	...	|	|	1205	1234	1234	|	1234	|	...	2140	|
Nantes a.	...	...	|	|	1247	1319	1319	|	1319	|	...	2220	|
Rennes a.	...	...	|	1217	...	...	...	1217	...	|	...	...	2154
Poitiers a.	...	...	1040	...	...	...	...	...	...	1840	...	...	...
Angoulême a.	...	...	1123	...	...	...	...	...	...	1923	...	...	...
Bordeaux St Jean a.	...	...	1202	...	...	...	...	...	...	2002	...	...	...

	TGV		TGV	TGV	TGV		TGV	TGV	TGV	TGV	TGV	TGV	TGV
	9870		**5482**	**5464**	**5440**		**5466**	**5460**	**5480**	**5480**	**5444**	**9872**	**9872**
			①–⑥	①–⑥								⑤–⑦	①–④
			b	H			J	L	D	E	P	c	d
Bordeaux St Jean d.	...	...	...	...	0858v	...	...	...	...	...	1558	...	...
Angoulême d.	...	...	...	...	0936	...	...	...	...	...	1636	...	...
Poitiers d.	...	...	...	...	1019	...	...	...	...	...	1720	...	...
Rennes d.	...	...	...	0840	|	...	1431	1431	...	...	|	...	...
Nantes d.	...	...	0809f	|	|	...	|	|	1535	1535	|	...	...
Angers d.	...	...	0848f	|	|	...	|	|	1616	1616	|	...	...
Le Mans d.	...	...	0930	0930	|	...	1530	1530c	1657	1657	|	...	...
St Pierre des Corps d.	...	...	|	|	1054	...	|	|	|	|	1754	...	...
Massy TGV d.	...	...	1026	1026	1155	...	1627	1628	1755	1755	1855	...	...
Marne la Vallée - Chessy § a.	...	...	1055	1055	1224	...	1657	1657	1827	1827	1927	...	...
Marne la Vallée - Chessy § d.	...	...	1100	1100	1228	...	1704	1703	1831	1831	1931	...	...
Brussels Midi/Zuid d.	0717	...	|	|	|	...	|	|	|	|	|	1817	1917
Lille Europe d.	0801	...	|	|	|	...	|	|	|	|	|	1903	2003
Paris Charles de Gaulle ✈ a.	0853	...	1110	1110	|	...	|	1713	1841	1841	|	1954	2054
Paris Charles de Gaulle ✈ d.	0859	...	1123	1123	|	...	|	1728	1856	1856	|	2002	2113
Champagne-Ardenne TGV a.	0928	...	1153	1153	1255	...	1732	1759	1929	1929	1959	2031	2143
Champagne-Ardenne TGV d.	0931	...	1156	1156	1258	...	1735	1810	1935	1943	2002	2034	2146
Meuse TGV ★ a.	1000	...	|	|	1323	...	|	|	2000	2008	2026	|	|
Lorraine TGV ★ a.	1025	...	1233	1233	1348	...	1814	1848	2025	2029	2047	2119	2224
Strasbourg a.	1105	...	1313	1313	1431	...	1901	1934g	2105	2109	2127	2158	2304

B – ⑧ July 13 - Aug. 28 (not July 14).
D – From July 3.
E – Until July 2.
H – ①–⑥ July 14 - Aug. 27 (not Aug. 15).
J – ⑤⑦ to July 3; daily July 8 - Aug. 28; ⑤⑦ from Sept. 2 (also Nov. 1, 10; not Nov. 11).
L – ①②③④⑥ to July 7; ①②③④⑥ from Aug. 29 (also Nov. 11; not Nov. 1, 10). On Oct. 29, 31 Rennes d. 1453 and does not call at Le Mans.
N – ⑧ to Oct. 4 (not July 14, 15); ⑦ from Oct. 9 (also Nov. 1–4, Dec. 5–9; not Nov. 27).
P – July 9 - Aug. 28 only.
Q – ①–⑤ Oct. 5–28; ①④ Nov. 7 - Dec. 1.
R – ②③⑤ Nov. 8 - Dec. 2 (also Nov. 27; not Nov. 11).

b – Not Aug. 15, Nov. 1, 12.
c – Also July 13, 14, Aug. 15, Oct. 31, Nov. 1, 10.
d – Not July 13, 14, Aug. 15, Oct. 31, Nov. 1, 10.
e – Also July 15, 16, Aug. 15, Nov. 1, 12.
f – 6 minutes **earlier** July 2 - Aug. 27.
g – 1928 on ⑥ (also Nov. 11).
h – Not July 14, 15, Oct. 31, Nov. 11.
j – 0953 on June 12, 19, 26.
k – Also July 14, 15, Oct. 31, Nov. 11.
r – Not July 15, 16, Aug. 15, Nov. 1, 12.
v – 0825 on June 12.
w – Not Oct. 31, Nov. 11.

TGV – High-speed train. 🅁. 🍷.

◇ – Also calls at Haute Picardie (a. 0837, d. 0840).
§ – Station for Disneyland Paris.
★ – Connecting 🚌 services operate on the following routes:
Nancy - Lorraine TGV (journey 35 minutes);
Metz - Lorraine TGV (journey 25 minutes);
Verdun - Meuse TGV (journey 25 minutes).

391a REIMS - CHAMPAGNE ARDENNE TGV

Timings of certain services from Reims to Champagne-Ardenne vary by 1–2 minutes from Sept. 19 (earlier departures possible). Timings may vary by up to 4 minutes on Sept. 24.

	⑥	Ⓐ	Ⓐ	Ⓐ	⑥	Ⓑ	⚒	Ⓐ	Ⓐn	Ⓐ		Ⓐ	⚒	Ⓐ		Ⓐ	†	⚒	Ⓐ	⚒	†	⚒z	Ⓐ	
Reims d.	0635	0636	0705	0736	0739	0805	0836	0905	0935	1005	1036	1105	1136	1206	1236	1305	1335	1338	1405	1436	1445	1536	1605	1636
Champagne-Ardenne TGV a.	0649	0648	0718	0748	0751	0818	0848	0918	0948	1018	1048	1118	1148	1219	1248	1318	1346	1350	1418	1448	1456	1548	1618	1648

	Ⓐ	Ⓑ	⑥	Ⓐ	⚒m	†	Ⓐm	Ⓑ	⑥	Ⓐ	†
Reims d.	1705	1736	1739	1805	1836	1847	1904	1936	1939	2035	2105
Champagne-Ardenne TGV a.	1718	1748	1750	1818	1848	1858	1918	1948	1951	2048	2119

	⚒	Ⓐn	⚒	Ⓑ	⚒	Ⓐ	n
Champagne-Ardenne TGV d.	0710	0740	0810	0840	0910	0940	1010
Reims a.	0722	0752	0822	0852	0923	0952	1022

	Ⓐ	⚒	Ⓐn		Ⓐ		Ⓐ		Ⓐ	Ⓒ	Ⓐ			Ⓐ		Ⓐn		Ⓐn	m	Ⓐm	†	⚒	Ⓐ	†
Champagne-Ardenne TGV d.	1040	1110	1140	1210	1240	1310	1340	1410	1440	1510	1518	...	1610	1640	1710	1740	1810	1840	1910	1940	2010	2016	2110	2147
Reims a.	1052	1122	1152	1222	1252	1322	1352	1422	1452	1522	1527	...	1622	1652	1722	1752	1822	1852	1922	1952	2021	2028	2122	2159

m – Not June 13–16, 20–23, 27–30, July 4–7.
n – Not July 18–22, 25–29, Aug. 1–5, 8–12, 16–19.
z – 2 minutes later on ⑥.

392 LONGWY - NANCY / LUXEMBOURG

LONGWY - NANCY ⊖

km		Ⓐn	⚒	Ⓒ	G 🚌	ⒶE	J¶ 🚌	H 🚌	ⒶD	Ⓒ	⑦w V	†
0	**Longwy** 389a d.	0543	0647	1047	1155	1247k	1233	1355	1447k	1647	...	1921
16	Longuyon 389a d.	0556	0700	1100	1221	1300k	1259	1421	1500k	1701	...	1936
57	Conflans-Jarny d.	0630	0730	1130	1320	1330	1358	1520	1530	1730	1927	2009
100	Pont-à-Mousson 384 d.	0700	0800	1200	...	1400	1452	...	1600	1800	1959	2040
128	**Nancy** 384 a.	0720	0820	1220	...	1420	1525	...	1620	1820	2016	2100

	⚒L	G 🚌	M	H 🚌	J 🚌	†	Ⓐ		⑤f V
Nancy 384 d.	0839	...	1239	...	1239	1639	1739	1839	1944
Pont-à-Mousson 384 d.	0859	...	1259	...	1312	1659	1800	1901	2003
Conflans-Jarny d.	0930	0936	1330	1335	1406	1730	1830	1930	2031
Longuyon 389a d.	1000k	1035	1400k	1433	1504	1759	1900	2000	...
Longwy 389a a.	1012k	1102	1412k	1500	1531	1812	1912	2012	...

LONGWY - LUXEMBOURG (see note ⊠)

km		①–⑤	①–⑥	①–⑤	①–⑥	①–⑤	①–⑤	①–⑤	①–⑤	①–⑤	①–⑤	①–⑤	①–⑤	⑥	①–⑤	①–⑤	①–⑥
		b	b	b	b	b	b	b◇	b◇	b	b	b	b		b	b	b
0	**Longwy** d.	0620	0651	0720	0751	0820	0851	1321	1351	1651	1721	1751	1821	1851	*1851*	*1921*	1951
8	Rodange 🏛 ⊡ d.	0629	0659	0729	0759	0829	0859	1329	1359	1659	1729	1759	1829	1859	1910	1940	1959
10	Pétange ⊡ a.	0633	0703	0733	0803	0833	0903	1333	1403	1703	1733	1803	1833	1903	1914	1944	2003
27	**Luxembourg** ⊡ a.	0657	0727	0757	0827	0857	0927	1357	1427	1727	1757	1827	1857	1927	1940	2010	2027

	①–⑤	①–⑥	①–⑤	①–⑥	①–⑤	①–⑤		①–⑤	①–⑤	①–⑤	①–⑤	①–⑤	①–⑤	①–⑥	①–⑤	①–⑥
	b	b	b	b	b	b		b◇	b◇	b	b	b	b	b	b	b
Luxembourg ⊡ d.	*0520*	0604	*0620*	0704	0734	0804	...	1204	1234	1604	1634	1704	1734	1804	1834	1904
Pétange ⊡ d.	*0544*	0627	*0644*	0727	0757	0827	...	1227	1257	1627	1657	1727	1757	1827	1857	1927
Rodange 🏛 ⊡ d.	0602	0632	0702	0732	0802	0832	...	1232	1302	1632	1702	1732	1802	1832	1902	1932
Longwy a.	0609	0639	0709	0739	0809	0839	...	1239	1309	1639	1709	1739	1809	1839	1909	1939

LONGWY - METZ 🚌 service (journey 55 minutes):
From Longwy at 0505 Ⓐ, 0630 Ⓐ, 0740, 0945 ⚒, 1235 ⑥, 1242 Ⓐ, 1335 †, 1445 ⚒, 1545 Ⓐ, 1615 ⑥, 1634 Ⓑ, 1745 ⑥, 1825 Ⓐ, 1925 Ⓐ and 1930 Ⓒ.
From Metz at 0631 Ⓐ, 0834 Ⓐ, 0920 ⚒, 1020 †, 1220 ⚒, 1430 ⑥, 1520 Ⓑ, 1620 ⚒, 1720 Ⓐ, 1820 Ⓐ, 1830 Ⓒ, 2021 Ⓐ, 2030 ⑥, 2120 †, 2215 ⑥ and 2237 Ⓐ.

D – Ⓐ June 20 - Oct. 7.
E – Ⓐ June 20 - Oct. 7 (not July 18 - Aug. 19).
G – ①–⑤ July 1–8; ①–⑤ Sept. 19–30.
H – ①–⑤ June 27 - July 8; ①–⑤ Sept. 19–30.
J – June 13–17 and ①–⑤ Oct. 10–28.
L – ⚒ June 18 - Oct. 8 (not July 18 - Aug. 20); ⑥ from Oct. 15.
M – Daily June 18 - Oct. 9; ⑥⑦ from Oct. 15.
V – From / to Verdun (Table **393a**).

b – Not June 23, Aug. 15, Nov. 1.
f – Not July 15 - Aug. 26.
k – Not June 27–30, July 1, 4–8, Sept. 19–23, 26–30.
n – Not July 18 - Aug. 19.
w – Not July 10 - Aug. 21.

¶ – An additional 🚌 service runs on dates in note **J** two hours later.
◇ – Subject to alteration June 27 - July 8 and Sept. 19–30.
⊠ – Subject to alteration Aug. 20 - Sept. 3. Longwy timings may vary by up to 3 minutes (earlier departures possible).
⊡ – Additional trains run Rodange - Luxembourg and v.v. (see Table **449**).
⊖ – Journeys between Longwy and Nancy are also possible via Metz (see the Longwy - Metz 🚌 panel together with Table **384**).

393 🚌 CHÂLONS EN CHAMPAGNE - VERDUN 🚌

Journey time: 1 hour 48 minutes

From Châlons en Champagne at 0820 Ⓐ, 1025 Ⓒ, 1230 Ⓐ, 1425 Ⓒ, 1430 Ⓐ, 1830 Ⓐ, 1840 †, 2025 Ⓒ and 2030 Ⓐ.
From Verdun at 0512 Ⓐ, 0742 Ⓒ, 1014 Ⓐ, 1209 Ⓐ, 1222 Ⓒ, 1509 Ⓐ, 1622 †, 1732 †, 1734 Ⓐ and 1742 ⑥.

VERDUN - METZ 393a

km		⑥	Ⓐ	Ⓐ	z △	Ⓐn ▽	Ⓐn ▽	Ⓐn	⑥	Ⓐ	⑦k N	†
0	**Verdun** d.	...	0635	0737	1037	1237	1437	1637	1637	1813	1849	1939
40	Conflans-Jarny d.	0627	0720	0815	1115	1315	1515	1715	1715	1850	1926	2016
66	Hagondange . **384** d.	0705	|	0847	1147	1347	1547	1742	1747	|	...	|
84	**Metz** **384** a.	0717	0801	0903	1209	*1414*	1601	*1757*r	1801	1924	...	2050

	Ⓐ	P	⑥	Ⓐn △	Ⓐn ▽	Ⓒz	Ⓐ	†	Ⓐ	⑥	⑤f N
Metz **384** d.	0605	*0833*t	0855	1038	1238	1255	1637	1637	1821	1851	...
Hagondange **384** d.	|	0911	0909	1051	1251	1311	1651	1653	|	1905	...
Conflans-Jarny d.	0643	0943	0943	1123	1323	1343	1723	1731	1853	1939	2036
Verdun a.	0721	1019	1019	1158	1400	1419	1800	*1819*	1929	2015	2112

N – To/from Nancy (Table **392**).
P – ① to July 4; Ⓐ from July 11. Subject to alteration from Oct. 17.

f – Not July 15 - Aug. 26.
k – Not July 10 - Aug. 21.
n – Not July 18 - Aug. 19.

r – *1759* July 11 – 15, Aug. 22 – 26.
t – *0832* July 11 - Aug. 26.
z – Not Oct. 9.

△ – Subject to alteration on ①–⑤ until July 8 and on Ⓐ from Oct. 10.
▽ – Subject to alteration until June 20 (also on June 27, July 4) and from Oct. 10.

METZ - FORBACH - SAARBRÜCKEN 394

French holiday dates apply

SERVICE JULY 11 - OCTOBER 9

Warning! Until July 10 timings may vary (earlier departures / later arrivals possible; connections at Forbach may not apply) and certain services do not run.

km		Ⓐn	⑥	Ⓐ	Ⓐ	Ⓐ	⑥	⚒	†	⑥	Ⓐn	Ⓐ	Ⓒ	Ⓐn	Ⓒ	Ⓐ	⚒	Ⓐn	Ⓐ	†	⑥	⚒n		Ⓐ	Ⓐ	Ⓒ	Ⓐ
0	**Metz** d.	0538	0603	0636	0704	0738	0738	0838	0838	0934	0938	1038	1038	1138	1238	1238	1338	1438	1538	1538	1538	1638	...	1713	1735	1738	1813
50	St Avold d.	0609	0640	0708	0739	0810	0812	0910	0910	1011	1010	1111	1112	1209	1312	1312	1410	1510	1610	1612	1612	1709	...	1747	1812	1812	1851
70	Forbach a.	0624	0656	0724	0753	0826	0826	0926	0926	1026	1024	1126	1126	1226	1325	1326	1426	1525	1626	1626	1626	1726	...	1801	1828	1826	1904
70	Forbach d.	*0631*	0659	*0731*	...	*0831*	...	0930	*0931*	...	*1031*	1130	*1131*	*1231*	1329	*1331*	*1431*	*1531*	*1631*	*1631*	1632	...	1731	...	*1831*	*1831*	...
81	**Saarbrücken** a.	*0642*	0709	*0742*	...	*0842*	...	0940	*0942*	...	*1042*	1140	*1142*	*1242*	1340	*1342*	*1442*	*1542*	*1642*	*1642*	1642	...	1742	...	*1842*	*1842*	...

	⑤	k	Ⓑ	Ⓐn	Ⓐ	Ⓒ	Ⓐ	Ⓐ	⑥⑦	†	Ⓐ	Ⓐ
Metz d.	1829	1838	...	1910	1938	1938	2038	...	2135	2238	2238	...
St Avold d.	1906	1910	...	1946	2010	2012	2110	...	2210	2310	2310	...
Forbach a.	1922	1926	...	1959	2026	2026	2126	...	2226	2326	2326	...
Forbach d.	...	...	1931	...	*2031*	*2031*	*2131*	2244	...	2330	...	2344
Saarbrücken a.	...	...	1942	...	*2042*	*2042*	*2142*	2255	...	2340	...	2355

	Ⓐ	Ⓐ	⑥	Ⓐ	Ⓐ	⚒	Ⓐ	Ⓑ	⑥	Ⓐ	⑥	Ⓐ
Saarbrücken d.	0446	...	0450	...	0616	...	...	*0716*	0721	...	...	0816
Forbach a.	0456	...	0500	...	0626	...	...	*0726*	0731	...	...	0826
Forbach d.	...	0503	0503	0607	...	0633	0707	0733	0733	0801	0834	...
St Avold d.	...	0519	0520	0621	...	0647	0723	0749	0749	0815	0850	...
Metz a.	...	0550	0550	0656	...	0720	0756	0820	0820	0846	0920	...

	Ⓐn	Ⓐ	n	Ⓐ	Ⓐ	Ⓒ	Ⓐn	⑥	Ⓐ	†	⑥	Ⓐ	⑥	†	Ⓐ		Ⓐn	⑥	Ⓐ	†	⑦	①–⑥	n	Ⓑ	Ⓐ	Ⓐ	Ⓐ
Saarbrücken d.	...	0921	*1016*	*1116*	1221	...	*1316*	1321	*1416*	1421	*1416*	*1516*	1521	*1616*	*1616*	*1716*	...	*1816*	*1816*	*1816*	*1916*	*1916*	*2016*	2116	...	2225	2325
Forbach a.	...	0931	*1026*	*1126*	1230	...	*1326*	1331	*1426*	1431	*1426*	*1526*	1531	*1626*	*1626*	*1726*	...	*1826*	*1826*	*1826*	*1926*	*1926*	*2026*	2126	...	2235	2335
Forbach d.	0835	0933	1033	1133	1232	1233	1333	1333	1433	1433	1435	1534	1533	1633	1633	1733	1808	1833	1835	1835	1933	1934	2033	...	2134	...	...
St Avold d.	0850	0949	1049v	1149	1246	1247	1349	1349	1449	1447	1449	1549	1547	1647	1649	1749	1824	1847	1851	1849	1948	1949	2049t	...	2150	...	...
Metz a.	0920	1022	1120	1220	1320	1320	1420	1420	1520	1520	1522	1620	1620	1720	1720	1820	1856	1920	1924	1925	2020	2020	2120	...	2220	...	...

k – Not ⑤.
n – Not July 18 – 22, 25 – 29, Aug. 1 – 5, 8 – 12, 16 – 19.

t – 2047 on ⑥.
v – 1047 on Ⓒ.

STRASBOURG - SAARBRÜCKEN 395

French holiday dates apply

km		Ⓐn	Ⓐ⊙		⚒⊙		†	⚒⊗		Ⓐ n⊖		⊗		Ⓑ n⊖		⑥	Ⓐ	Ⓑ	Ⓐn	⚒	†	Ⓐ	⑥	Ⓐ	†
0	**Strasbourg** d.	0545	0645	...	0745	...	0845	0945	...	1145	...	1245	...	1445	...	1545	1545	1645	1715	1745j	1815	1845	1945	1955	2000
71	Diemeringen a.	0637	0737	...	0837	...	0937	1037	...	1237	...	1337	...	1537	...	1637	1637	1736	1807	1837	1907	1937	2037	2047	2055
97	Sarreguemines 🚉 ▲ a.	0705	0805	...	0905	...	1005	1105	...	1305	...	1405	...	1605	...	1705	1705	1805	1835	1905	1935	2005	2105	2115	2123
115	**Saarbrücken** Hbf ▲ a.	...	...	...	0927	...	1027	...	...	1327	...	...	...	...	...	1727	...	...	...	...	...	...	2127	...	...

	Ⓐ	Ⓐn	⚒	Ⓐn	⚒	†	⚒⊗		†	⚒⊗		⚒⊗	†		⑥	Ⓐ n⊖		Ⓐ⊙	Ⓑn	Ⓑ	⑥	Ⓑ		⑥ 🚌
Saarbrücken Hbf ▲ d.	...	...	...	...	...	0654t	...	...	...	0954	...	...	1154	...	...	1354	...	...	...	...	1754	...	...	...
Sarreguemines 🚉 ▲ d.	0452	0543	0613	0643	0713	0714	0813	...	1014	1014	...	1213	1214	...	1414	1414	...	1513	1613	1713	1814	1822	...	1910
Diemeringen d.	0521	0611	0642	0712	0742	0743	0842	...	1042	1043	...	1242	1243	...	1442	1443	...	1541	1641	1742	1843	1850	...	1940
Strasbourg a.	0621	0712	0738	0807	0837	0837	0937	...	1137	1137	...	1337	1337	...	1537	1537	...	1637	1737	1837	1937	1945	...	2115

SAARBAHN LIGHT RAIL SERVICE **S1 SARREGUEMINES - SAARBRÜCKEN** ⊡

	⚒	Ⓐ	⚒	Ⓐ				
Sarreguimes (Bahnhof) d.	0516	0546	0616	0646	0716	hourly ◐	2316	0016
Saarbrücken Hbf a.	0545	0615	0645	0715	0745	until	2345	0045

	⚒	Ⓐ	⚒	Ⓐ	⚒	Ⓐ			
Saarbrücken Hbf d.	0440	0510	0540	0610	0640	0710	0740	hourly ◧	2340
Sarreguimes (Bahnhof) a.	0510	0540	0610	0640	0710	0740	0810	until	0010

j – 1744 on ①–⑤ June 27 - July 8.
n – Not July 18 – 22, 25 – 29, Aug. 1 – 5, 8 – 12, 16 – 19.
t – Not July 14, Aug. 15, Nov. 1, 11.

⊗ – Subject to alteration Aug. 1 – 5, 8 – 12, Oct. 24 – 28, 31, Nov. 2 – 4.
⊙ – Subject to alteration Aug. 1 – 5, 8 – 12.
⊖ – Subject to alteration Oct. 24 – 28, 31, Nov. 2 – 4.

▲ – For additional light rail service Sarreguemines - Saarbrücken see below main table.
⊡ – Operated by Saarbahn (www.saarbahn.de). In Saarbrücken also serves city centre.
◐ – Every 30 minutes 0716 - 0916 and 1216 - 2116 on Ⓐ, 0816 - 1816 on ⑥, 1216 - 1816 on †.
◧ – Every 30 minutes 0740 - 0840 and 1140 - 2040 on Ⓐ, 0740 - 1740 on ⑥, 1140 - 1740 on †.

STRASBOURG - WISSEMBOURG 396

Additional trains run Strasbourg - Haguenau and v.v.

See Table **918** for connecting trains Wissembourg - Neustadt (Weinstr) and v.v.

km		⚒	Ⓐ	⑥	⑥	†	Ⓐ ¶	⑥	Ⓐn ‡	⑥	†	Ⓐ ¶	⑥	Ⓐn ¶	†	⑥	Ⓐ	†	Ⓐ	⑥	†	Ⓐn	Ⓐ	Ⓑ	Ⓑ	⑥	Ⓐ
0	**Strasbourg** d.	0618	0735	0751	0851	0921	0935	1055	1121	1205	1251	1251	1351	1405	1451	1551	1621	1651	1721	1721	1721	1751	1821	1851	1921	1951	2035
34	Haguenau a.	0639	0808	0824	0914	0942	0957	1118	1143	1229	1312	1313	1414	1427	1514	1614	1644	1713	1741	1742	1755	1814	1842	1913	1943	2015	2109
66	**Wissembourg** a.	0716	0840	0853	0943	1010	1025	1145	1212	1309	1341	1347	1443	1456	1543	1643	1714	1742	1815	1816	1823	1854	1915	1951z	2022t	2048	*2151*b

	Ⓐ	Ⓐ	⑥	Ⓐ	⑥	†	Ⓐ	⑥	⑥	Ⓐ ¶	†	†	Ⓐn ‡	⑥	⑥	†	Ⓐ ¶	⑥	Ⓐn ¶	†	Ⓐ	⑥	Ⓐ	⑥	†	Ⓐn	†
Wissembourg d.	0607	0640	0641	0730	0742	0844	0848	0948	1037	1038	1045	1147	1230	1237	1347	1349	1402	1545	1551	1647	1741	1744	1821	1837	1838	1921	2049
Haguenau d.	0643	0714	0716	0804	0812	0914	0915	1015	1103	1104	1113	1214	1301	1304	1414	1416	1429	1612	1618	1714	1818	1815	1848	1902	1913	1947	2115
Strasbourg a.	0711	0741	0738	0830	0837	0938	0939	1041	1138	1141	1138	1237	1324	1338	1440	1439	1453	1638	1645	1737	1845	1839	1916	1937	1937	2010	2138

b – By 🚌 from Haguenau.
n – Not July 18 – 22, 25 – 29, Aug. 1 – 5, 8 – 12, 16 – 19.

t – 2018 on †.
z – 1942 on †.

¶ – Subject to alteration Oct. 10 – 21.
‡ – Subject to alteration on ①②④⑤ Oct. 10 – 21.

397 PRIVATE TOURIST RAILWAYS

MER DE GLACE - TRAIN DE MONTENVERS

✆ 04.50.53.22.75. www.compagniedumontblanc.fr

From Chamonix (200 metres from SNCF station) to Montenvers 'Mer de Glace' (altitude 1913 metres). Journey time: 20 minutes. Services run every 30 minutes (except Oct. 16 - Nov. 7 when an hourly service operates). A more frequent service (every 20 minutes) is provided during periods of high demand. **No service Oct. 3–21 and Nov. 7–20.**

A cable car takes visitors to the ice grotto inside the glacier (please check for opening dates).

Dec. 18 - Mar. 18: from Chamonix 1000 - 1600; returning until 1630.
Mar. 19 - Apr. 30: from Chamonix 1000 - 1630; returning until 1700.
May 1 - July 8: from Chamonix 0830 - 1630 ‡; returning until 1700.
July 9 - Aug. 28: from Chamonix 0830 - 1700; returning until 1730.
Aug. 29 - Sept. 18: from Chamonix 0830 - 1630 ‡; returning until 1700.
Sept. 19 - Oct. 2: from Chamonix 0930 - 1600; returning until 1630.
Oct. 22 - Nov. 6: from Chamonix 0930 - 1600; returning until 1630.

‡ – Departure from Chamonix at 0900 (also 0930 return service) runs if sufficient demand.

PANORAMIQUE DES DÔMES

Electric rack railway from the foot to the summit of Le puy de Dôme. Journey: 15 minutes. **2022 service**. No service Mar. 21–25. www.panoramiquedesdomes.fr

Until Mar. 20 (does **not** run on ①②): Hourly departures 1000 - 1700, returning 1030 - 1730.
Mar. 26 - June 30: Departures every 40 minutes 0900 - 1900, returning 0920 - 1920.
July 1 - Aug. 31: Departures every 20 minutes 0900 - 2000, returning 0920 - 2020.
Sept. 1 - Nov. 6: Departures every 40 minutes 0900 - 1900, returning 0920 - 1920.
From Nov. 9 (does **not** run on ①②): Hourly departures 1000 - 1700, returning 1030 - 1730.

TRAMWAY DU MONT BLANC

The highest rack railway in France. www.compagniedumontblanc.fr
✆ 04.50.53.22.75.

Winter: December 18, 2021 - March 27, 2022 (not Mar. 7–11, 14–18, 21–25).
Runs from St Gervais Le Fayet (opposite SNCF station) to Bellevue (altitude 1794 metres). Journey 60 minutes.

Mondays to Fridays until March 4 (not school holidays):
Depart St Gervais: 0900, 1100, 1310, 1430.
Depart Bellevue: 1000, 1200, 1430, 1620 (until Feb. 4), 1640 (from Feb. 7).

Saturdays and Sundays (also during school holidays):
Depart St Gervais: 0900, 1000, 1100, 1310, 1410, 1510.
Depart Bellevue: 1000, 1100, 1200, 1410, 1510, 1620 (until Jan. 30), 1640 (from Feb. 5).

Summer: June 11 - September 18, 2022
From St Gervais Le Fayet (opposite SNCF station) to Nid d'Aigle (altitude 2372 metres). Journey 70–80 minutes.

June 11 - July 8 and August 29 - September 18
Depart St Gervais: 0820, 0930, 1030¶, 1110, 1230, 1340¶, 1445, 1525.
Depart Nid d'Aigle: 0940, 1050, 1205¶, 1240, 1355, 1505¶, 1615, 1640.

July 9 - August 28:
Depart St Gervais: 0700, 0800, 0910¶, 0945, 1100, 1210¶, 1315, 1355, 1515¶, 1620, 1700.
Depart Nid d'Aigle: 0815, 0920, 1040¶, 1110, 1225, 1330¶, 1450, 1525, 1635¶, 1755, 1815.

¶ – Subject to cancellation (please check locally).

398 PARIS - PARIS AÉROPORTS

See page 31 for plan of central Paris

CHARLES DE GAULLE - PARIS

VAL shuttle train: air terminals - RER / TGV station.

Roissyrail (RER line B): Aéroport Charles de Gaulle 2 TGV - Paris Châtelet les Halles. Frequent service 0450 - 2400.

Journey time from Charles de Gaulle:

Gare du Nord	35 minutes
Châtelet les Halles ★	38 minutes
St Michel Notre Dame	40 minutes
Antony (for Orly, see middle panel)	58 minutes

★ Cross - platform interchange with *RER* for Gare de Lyon.

ORLY - PARIS (*VAL + RER B*)

VAL light rail: Orly Sud - Orly Ouest - Antony (7 minutes). Frequent service ① - ⑤: 0600 - 2230; ⑦: 0700 - 2300. Cross platform interchange with RER line B (below).

RER line B: Antony - Paris. Frequent service 0510 - 0010.

Journey time from Antony:

St Michel Notre Dame	20 minutes
Châtelet les Halles ☆	25 minutes
Gare du Nord	29 minutes

☆ Interchange with *RER* for Gare de Lyon.

ORLY - PARIS (*Orlyrail*)

🚌: Orly (Ouest and Sud) - Pont de Rungis Aéroport d'Orly station. Frequent shuttle service.

RER line C: Pont de Rungis Aéroport d'Orly - Paris. Every 15 minutes approx. 0500 - 2330 (0530 - 2400 from Paris).

Journey time from Pont de Rungis Aéroport d'Orly:

Paris Austerlitz	24 minutes
St Michel Notre Dame	27 minutes
Musée d'Orsay	31 minutes
Champ de Mars Tour Eiffel	39 minutes

399 🚌 SAVOIE SKI BUSES

Winter 2020 / 2021

A network of bus services links the airports at Genève and Lyon with most ski resorts in the Savoie area during the ski season. A selection of services is shown below but details should be confirmed before booking. Further details of services from Genève can be found on the Genève bus station website www.gare-routiere.com where online bookings can be made; for telephone bookings ✆ +41 22 732 02 30. Bookings can also be made through the websites and offices of the operators and at tourist offices in the ski resorts.

A minimum of one hour should be allowed between aircraft and bus and vice versa. Reservation is recommended or compulsory, and in most cases journeys from the resort to the airport should be confirmed at the local tourist office or bus station (generally 24 or 48 hours in advance) when timings will be given. Most services do not operate on December 25.

🚌 GENÈVE AÉROPORT - ST GERVAIS - CHAMONIX

Departures from Genève Gare Routière and Genève ✈ (Arrivals terminal) to St Gervais (Gare SNCF) and Chamonix Sud (Ave Courmayeur) at least six times daily. Journey 2 hours 10 minutes. Operator: www.ouibus.com. Connections at St Gervais Gare SNCF are available to / from St Gervais (Le Pont), Combloux, Megève, Praz sur Arly and Les Contamines.

🚌 GENÈVE AÉROPORT - TARENTAISE SKI RESORTS

🚌 Genève ✈ (Secteur International) - Moûtiers - Aime - Bourg St Maurice - Tignes - Val d'Isère. Journey approximately 4 hours. Reservations: www.altibus.com

Connections (with through fares) are available to most ski resorts in the area, including Pralognan, Brides les Bains, St Martin de Belleville, Les Ménuires, Val Thorens, Méribel, La Tania, Le Praz, Courchevel, Plagne and Les Arcs. Additional direct services are operated by Voyages Loyet to St Martin de Belleville, Les Ménuires and Val Thorens.

🚌 OTHER SERVICES FROM GENÈVE AÉROPORT ✈

GRENOBLE Daily services to Grenoble. Connections available to l'Alpe d'Huez, Stations de l'Isère, Briancon and Serre Chevalier. Reservations: www.ouibus.com
AVORIAZ via Thonon (connections for Abondance and Châtel), Saint Jean d'Aulps, Morzine. Runs on ⑥ during ski season. Reservations www.sat-autocars.com
LA CLUSAZ via Le Grand Bornand, St Jean de Sixt. Runs on ⑤⑥⑦ during ski season. Reservations www.ballanfat-autocars.fr
For further ski resorts see www.altibus.com

🚌 LYON ✈ / CHAMBÉRY ✈ - SAVOIE SKI RESORTS

Bus services operate from Lyon St Exupéry airport and Chambéry airport to most Savoie ski resorts from late December to mid April. Book on-line at www.altibus.com or ✆ +33 479 68 32 96. Reservations are compulsory, at least 48 hours in advance.

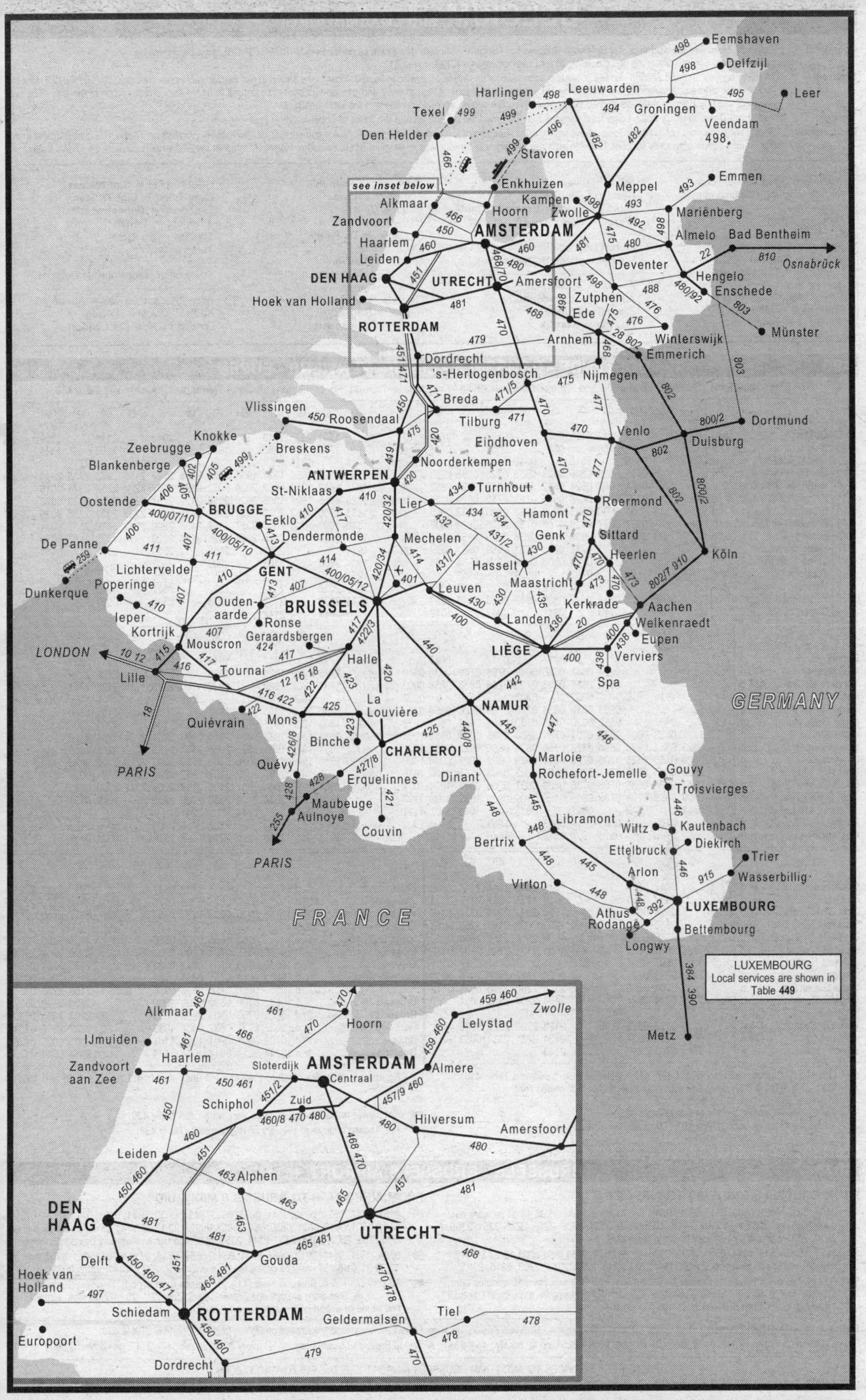
Eemshaven
Delfzijl
Leer
Harlingen
Leeuwarden
Groningen
Veendam
Texel
Den Helder
Stavoren
Enkhuizen
Emmen
see inset below
Alkmaar
Hoorn
Kampen
Zwolle
Meppel
Mariënberg
Zandvoort
AMSTERDAM
Almelo
Bad Bentheim
Haarlem
Osnabrück
Leiden
Deventer
DEN HAAG
UTRECHT
Amersfoort
Hengelo
Enschede
Hoek van Holland
Zutphen
Ede
Münster
ROTTERDAM
Arnhem
Winterswijk
Emmerich
Dordrecht
's-Hertogenbosch
Nijmegen
Breda
Vlissingen
Roosendaal
Tilburg
Dortmund
Venlo
Knokke
Eindhoven
Duisburg
Zeebrugge
Breskens
Blankenberge
Noorderkempen
ANTWERPEN
St-Niklaas
Turnhout
Oostende
Lier
BRUGGE
Hamont
Roermond
Eeklo
Dendermonde
Mechelen
Genk
Sittard
De Panne
Heerlen
Köln
Lichtervelde
Hasselt
GENT
Dunkerque
Poperinge
Leuven
Maastricht
Oudenaarde
BRUSSELS
Kerkrade
Aachen
Ieper
Ronse
Landen
Welkenraedt
Kortrijk
Geraardsbergen
Eupen
LONDON
Mouscron
Halle
LIÈGE
Verviers
Lille
Tournai
Spa
GERMANY
La Louvière
NAMUR
Quiévrain
Mons
Binche
CHARLEROI
PARIS
Quévy
Marloie
Gouvy
Rochefort-Jemelle
Troisvierges
Erquelinnes
Dinant
Maubeuge
Aulnoye
Libramont
Wiltz
Kautenbach
Couvin
Diekirch
Bertrix
Ettelbruck
Trier
Arlon
Wasserbillig
PARIS
Virton
Athus
LUXEMBOURG
FRANCE
Rodange
Bettembourg
Longwy
LUXEMBOURG
Local services are shown in Table 449
Metz
Alkmaar
Hoorn
Lelystad
Zwolle
IJmuiden
Haarlem
Zandvoort aan Zee
Sloterdijk
AMSTERDAM
Centraal
Almere
Schiphol
Zuid
Hilversum
Amersfoort
Leiden
Alphen
DEN HAAG
UTRECHT
Delft
Gouda
Hoek van Holland
Schiedam
ROTTERDAM
Tiel
Geldermalsen
Europoort
Dordrecht

BELGIUM and LUXEMBOURG

Operators: **Belgium**: Nationale Maatschappij der Belgische Spoorwegen / Société Nationale des Chemins de fer Belges (NMBS / SNCB). www.belgianrail.be
Luxembourg: Société Nationale des Chemins de fer Luxembourgeois (CFL). www.cfl.lu

Services: All trains convey first and second classes of seating accommodation unless otherwise indicated. Most trains shown in our Belgian tables are classified *IC* (InterCity). Trains for two or more different destinations are sometimes linked together for part of their journey and passengers should be careful to board the correct portion of the train. The line numbers used by Belgian Railways in their public timetables are shown as small numbers in the table headings.

Timings: Valid **until December 10, 2022**. Local train services may be amended on and around the dates of public holidays (see page 4).

Reservations: Seat reservations are not available for journeys wholly within Belgium or Luxembourg. Reservations are compulsory for international journeys on *Thalys*, *ICE* and *Eurostar* trains (for timings see International section). Supplements are not payable for journeys in Belgium or Luxembourg. However, a higher level of fares is payable on *Thalys* trains.

Dutch-language forms of some **French-language** Belgian names

Aarlen = **Arlon**
Aat = **Ath**
Bergen = **Mons**
Doornik = **Tournai**
Duinkerke = **Dunkerque** (France)
Hoei = **Huy**
Luik = **Liège**
Moeskroen = **Mouscron**
Namen = **Namur**
Nijvel = **Nivelles**
Rijsel = **Lille** (France)
's Gravenbrakel = **Braine le Comte**
Wezet = **Visé**

French-language forms of some **Dutch-language** Belgian names

Anvers = **Antwerpen**
Audenarde = **Oudenaarde**
Bruges = **Brugge**
Courtrai = **Kortrijk**
Dixmude = **Diksmuide**
Furnes = **Veurne**
Gand = **Gent**
Hal = **Halle**
La Panne = **De Panne**
Lierre = **Lier**
Louvain = **Leuven**
Malines = **Mechelen**
Menin = **Menen**
Ostende = **Oostende**
Renaix = **Ronse**
Roulers = **Roeselare**
Saint Nicolas = **Sint Niklaas**
Saint Trond = **Sint Truiden**
Termonde = **Dendermonde**
Tirlemont = **Tienen**
Tongres = **Tongeren**
Ypres = **Ieper**

Some other places outside Belgium

Aken / Aix la Chapelle = **Aachen**
Keulen / Cologne = **Köln**
Londen / Londres = **London**

400 OOSTENDE - BRUSSELS - LIÈGE - VERVIERS - EUPEN

Lines 50a, 36, 37

For *Thalys* trains Paris - Brussels - Liège - Köln and *ICE* trains Brussels - Köln - Frankfurt see Table **21**. For connections Verviers - Welkenraedt - Aachen see Table **438**

km			Ⓐ	Ⓐ	Ⓐ	Ⓐ	Ⓐ	Ⓐ	Ⓐ	Ⓐ ⊡	Ⓐ		Ⓐ	Ⓐ	Ⓐ	Ⓐ	Ⓐ	Ⓐ	Ⓐ	Ⓐ	Ⓐ	Ⓐ △	Ⓐ	Ⓐ △	
0	**Oostende** ▶ d.	Ⓐ	...	...	0442	...	0536	...	0636	...	0743		...	1741	...	1843	...	1943	...	2043	...	2143	...	2309	...
22	Brugge ▷ d.		...	...	0458	...	0551	...	0652	...	0758		...	1756	...	1858	...	1958	...	2058	...	2158	...	2324	...
	Kortrijk **410** d.		...	0419	|	0518	|	0619	|	0717	|	and	1719	|	1819	|	1919	|	2020	|	2119	|	2219	|	...
62	Gent Sint-Pieters ▷ d.		...	0455	0523	0555	0623	0655	0723	0755	0823	at	1755	1823	1855	1923	1955	2023	2055	2123	2155	2223	2255	2349	...
114	**Brussels** Midi / Zuid ▷ a.		...	0524	0552	0624	0652	0724	0752	0824	0852	the	1824	1852	1924	1952	2024	2052	2124	2152	2224	2252	2324	0018	...
114	**Brussels** Midi / Zuid d.		...	0526	0555	0628	0655	0728	0755	0828	0855	same	1828	1855	1927	1955	2026	2055	2127	2157	2228	2257	2328	0020	...
116	Brussels Central d.		...	0531	0600	0633	0700	0733	0800	0833	0900	minutes	1833	1900	1932	2000	2031	2100	2132	2202	2233	2302	2333	0025	...
118	Brussels Nord d.		...	0537	0607	0639	0706	0739	0806	0839	0907	past	1840	1907	1938	2007	2037	2107	2138	2208	2237	2308	2337	0031	...
148	Leuven d.		...	0554	0625	0658	0726	0758	0826	0858	0926	each	1859	1926	1954	2026	2054	2126	2154	2226	...	2326	...	0050	...
221	**Liège** Guillemins a.		...	...	0701	0732	0759	0831	0859	0931	0959	hour	1931	1959	...	2059	...	2159	...	2259	...	0021	...	0144	...
221	**Liège** Guillemins d.		...	...	0704	0735	0803	0836	0903	0934	1003	until	1934	2003	...	2103	...	2203	...	2303	...	0024	...	...	...
241	Pepinster **438** d.		...	...	|	0752	|	0854	|	0953	|		1953	|	...	|	...	|	...	|	...	|	...	...	...
245	**Verviers** Central **438** d.		...	...	0723	0800	0822	0901	0922	1000	1022		2000	2022	...	2122	...	2222	...	2322	...	0043	...	...	...
258	Welkenraedt **438** a.		0636	...	0734	0812	0833	0912	0933	1011	1033		2011	2033	...	2133	...	2233	...	2333	...	0053	...	...	...
264	**Eupen** a.		0643	...	0743	...	0842	...	0942	...	1042		...	2042	...	2142	...	...	...	...	...	...	...	...	...

		Ⓐ	Ⓐ △	Ⓐ	Ⓐ	Ⓐ	Ⓐ	Ⓐ	Ⓐ	Ⓐ	Ⓐ	Ⓐ ⊙		Ⓐ	Ⓐ	Ⓐ	Ⓐ	Ⓐ	Ⓐ	Ⓐ	Ⓐ	Ⓐ	Ⓐ △		
Eupen d.	Ⓐ	...	...	...	...	...	0617	...	0717	...	0817	...		1717	...	1817	...	1918	...	2017	...	2117	2221	...	...
Welkenraedt **438** d.		...	...	...	0524	0543	0626	0649	0725	0746	0825	0848		1725	1748	1825	...	1926	...	2025	...	2125	2229	...	...
Verviers Central **438** d.		...	...	...	0535	0556	0638	0702	0738	0803	0838	0902	and	1738	1802	1838	...	1939	...	2038	...	2138	2241	...	...
Pepinster **438** d.		...	...	...	|	0602	|	0708	|	0809	|	0908	at	|	1808	|	...	|	...	|	...	|	|	...	...
Liège Guillemins a.		...	...	...	0553	0619	0656	0725	0756	0826	0856	0925	the	1756	1825	1856	...	1957	...	2056	...	2156	2300	...	...
Liège Guillemins d.		...	0437	...	0558	0628	0701	0730	0801	0829	0901	0928	same	1801	1827	1901	...	2001	...	2101	...	2201	2304	...	...
Leuven d.		...	0533	0604	0635	0704	0735	0806	0835	0904	0933	1003	minutes	1833	1903	1933	2004	2034	2104	2134	2204	2234	2359	...	...
Brussels Nord d.		0523	0551	0623	0655	0723	0756	0824	0856	0922	0951	1021	past	1851	1921	1951	2023	2055	2123	2155	2223	2255	0018	...	...
Brussels Central d.		0528	0556	0628	0700	0728	0801	0829	0901	0927	0956	1026	each	1856	1926	1956	2028	2100	2128	2200	2228	2300	0023	...	...
Brussels Midi / Zuid a.		0532	0600	0632	0704	0732	0805	0833	0905	0931	1000	1030	hour	1900	1930	2000	2032	2104	2132	2204	2232	2304	0027	...	...
Brussels Midi / Zuid ▷ d.		0537	0604	0635	0708	0736	0808	0837	0908	0937	1004	1037	until	1904	1937	2004	2037	2108	2137	2208	2237	2308	0030	...	...
Gent Sint-Pieters ▷ d.		0609	0639	0709	0739	0808	0839	0909	0939	1009	1039	1109		1939	2009	2039	2109	2139	2209	2239	2309	2340	0101	...	...
Kortrijk **410** a.		0641	|	0742	|	0841	|	0941	|	1041	|	1141		|	2041	|	2141	|	2241	|	2341	|	|	...	...
Brugge ▷ d.		...	0703	...	0803	...	0903	...	1003	...	1103	...		2003	...	2103	...	2203	...	2303	...	0008	0126	...	...
Oostende ▶ a.		...	0716	...	0816	...	0916	...	1016	...	1116	...		2016	...	2116	...	2216	...	2316	...	0021	0139	...	...

		Ⓒ	Ⓒ	Ⓒ		Ⓒ	Ⓒ	Ⓒ	Ⓒ △	Ⓒ △
Oostende ▶ d.	Ⓒ	...	0442	0544		1844	1944	2044	2144	2308
Brugge ▷ d.		...	0457	0559		1859	1959	2059	2159	2323
Gent Sint-Pieters ▷ d.		...	0524	0624		1924	2024	2124	2224	2348
Brussels Midi / Zuid ▷ a.		...	0553	0653		1953	2053	2153	2253	0018
Brussels Midi / Zuid d.		...	0556	0656	and	1956	2056	2156	2256	0020
Brussels Central d.		...	0601	0701		2001	2101	2201	2301	0025
Brussels Nord d.		...	0607	0707	hourly	2007	2107	2207	2307	0031
Leuven d.		...	0626	0727		2027	2127	2226	2326	0050
Liège Guillemins a.		...	0702	0800	until	2100	2200	2300	0021	0142
Liège Guillemins d.		...	0704	0804		2104	2204	2304	0024	...
Pepinster **438** d.		...	|	|		|	|	|	|	...
Verviers Central **438** d.		...	0723	0823		2123	2223	2323	0043	...
Welkenraedt **438** a.		0636	0734	0834		2134	2234	2334	0053	...
Eupen a.		0643	0743	0843		2143	...	...	...	...

	Ⓒ △	Ⓒ	Ⓒ	Ⓒ	Ⓒ		Ⓒ	Ⓒ	Ⓒ △
Eupen d.	...	...	...	0717	0817		2017	2117	2221
Welkenraedt **438** d.	...	0522	0627	0726	0826		2026	2126	2229
Verviers Central **438** d.	...	0535	0639	0739	0839		2039	2139	2241
Pepinster **438** d.	...	|	|	|	|		|	|	|
Liège Guillemins a.	...	0553	0656	0756	0856	and	2056	2156	2300
Liège Guillemins d.	0438	0557	0700	0800	0900		2100	2200	2304
Leuven d.	0533	0633	0733	0833	0933	hourly	2133	2233	2359
Brussels Nord d.	0553	0651	0751	0851	0951		2151	2251	0018
Brussels Central d.	0558	0656	0756	0856	0956	until	2156	2256	0023
Brussels Midi / Zuid a.	0602	0700	0800	0900	1000		2200	2300	0027
Brussels Midi / Zuid ▷ d.	0605	0703	0803	0903	1003		2203	2303	0030
Gent Sint-Pieters ▷ d.	0637	0737	0837	0937	1037		2237	2337	0101
Brugge ▷ d.	0701	0801	0901	1001	1101		2301	0001	0126
Oostende ▶ a.	0714	0814	0914	1014	1114		2314	0014	0139

▶ – Oostende - Brugge: see also Tables **407**, **410**; Oostende - Gent see also Table **410**.
△ – Via Landen (Table **430**) between Leuven and Liège (not high-speed line). May vary due to engineering work.
▷ – For Brugge - Gent - Brussels see also Table **405**.
⊡ – Trains from Kortrijk at 0817 and 1019 terminate at Leuven.
⊙ – No trains from Welkenraedt at 1048 or 1348 (they start from Leuven at 1207 and 1503).

☛ *For slower trains Brussels - Liège via Landen see Table **430**.*
*For Aachen change at Verviers or Welkenraedt (Table **438**).*

401 BRUSSELS - BRUSSELS AIRPORT ✈

Line 36c

FROM BRUSSELS MIDI / ZUID TO AIRPORT ✈

Ⓐ: 0404, 0436, 0451, 0509, 0515, 0536, 0545, 0551 then at 09 15 23 36 45 51 minutes past each hour until 2051 then 2109, 2115, 2123, 2139, 2151, 2209, 2215, 2223, 2251, 2309, 2315, 2323. Certain timings vary by up to 3 minutes.

Ⓒ: 0451, 0509, 0539, 0544, 0551, 0609, 0623, 0639, 0644, 0651 then at 09 15 23 39 44 51 minutes past each hour until 2139, 2151, 2209, 2215, 2223, 2251, 2309, 2315, 2351.

☛ All services call at Brussels Central 4 minutes later and Brussels Nord 10 minutes later. Journey time to airport: from Brussels Midi / Zuid 20 – 27 minutes, from Brussels Centraal 16 – 23 minutes, from Brussels Nord 10 – 17 minutes.

FROM AIRPORT ✈ TO BRUSSELS MIDI / ZUID

Ⓐ: 0431, 0513, 0524, 0530, 0541, 0603, 0613, 0624, 0630, 0641, 0701, 0713, 0724, 0730, 0741, 0801, 0813, 0824, 0830, 0841, 0853 then at 02 13 25 30 41 53 mins past each hour until 2253, 2302, 2324, 2330, 2341, 2353, 0002. Certain timings vary by up to 3 minutes.

Ⓒ: 0524, 0531, 0541, 0613, 0624, 0631, 0641, 0657, 0713, 0724, 0731, 0741, 0757 then at 13 25 31 41 53 57 minutes past each hour until 2257, 2331, 2341, 2352, 0031.

☛ All services call at Brussels Nord (11 – 18 minutes from airport), Brussels Centraal (16 – 23 minutes from airport) and Brussels Midi / Zuid (21 – 28 minutes from airport). Full name of airport is Brussels Airport - Zaventem.

EUROPEAN QUARTER: Brussels Luxembourg - Brussels Schumann - Brussels Airport. Journey 18 – 21 minutes. Hourly journeys on Ⓐ run from / to Charleroi (Table **420**).
Brussels Luxembourg to Airport: on Ⓐ every 30 minutes 0654 – 2254, on Ⓒ hourly 0441 – 2341. Airport to Brussels Luxembourg: on Ⓐ every 30 minutes 0547 – 2147, on Ⓒ hourly 0604 – 0104.

FOR DIRECT SERVICES TO AND FROM BRUSSELS AIRPORT SEE THE FOLLOWING TABLES:
Aalst **412**, Antwerpen **420 / 432**, Brugge **405**, Charleroi **420**, Denderleeuw **412**, Gent **405**, Hasselt **432**, Kortrijk **407**, Leuven **430 / 432**, Mechelen **432**, Mons **422**, Namur **440**, Tournai **417**.

ZEEBRUGGE - BRUGGE — 402

Line 50a

km		Ⓐ	Ⓐ	Ⓐ	Ⓐ	Ⓐ		Ⓐ	Ⓐ	Ⓐ	Ⓐ	Ⓐ		
0	Zeebrugge Strand ❦ d.	Ⓐ	...	...	...	...	and	...	...	...	...	...	...	...
0	Zeebrugge Dorp ❦ d.		0707	0807	0907	1007	hourly	1607	1707	1807	1907	2007	...	...
15	Brugge a.		0724	0824	0924	1024	until	1624	1724	1824	1924	2024	...	...

		Ⓒ	Ⓒ	Ⓒ		Ⓒ	Ⓒ	Ⓒ	
Zeebrugge Strand ❦ d.	Ⓒ	0807	0907	1007	and	1807	1907	2007	...
Zeebrugge Dorp ❦ d.		|	|	|	hourly	|	|	|	...
Brugge a.		0825	0925	1025	until	1825	1925	2025	...

		Ⓐ	Ⓐ	Ⓐ	Ⓐ		Ⓐ	Ⓐ	Ⓐ	Ⓐ	Ⓐ	Ⓐ		
Brugge d.	Ⓐ	0636	0736	0836	0936	and	1436	1536	1636	1736	1836	1936	...	...
Zeebrugge Dorp ❦ a.		0653	0753	0853	0953	hourly	1453	1453	1653	1753	1853	1953	...	...
Zeebrugge Strand ❦ a.		...	...	...	...	until	...	...	...	...	...	...	...	...

		Ⓒ	Ⓒ	Ⓒ		Ⓒ	Ⓒ	Ⓒ	
Brugge d.	Ⓒ	0736	0836	0936	and	1736	1836	1936	...
Zeebrugge Dorp ❦ a.		|	|	|	hourly	|	|	|	...
Zeebrugge Strand ❦ a.		0754	0854	0954	until	1754	1854	1954	...

❦ – On certain high summer dates during July and August trains on Ⓐ serve Zeebrugge Strand (not Zeebrugge Dorp). Please enquire locally.

☛ Most trains continue beyond Brugge as stopping services to Gent (not shown). Change at Brugge for Brussels and faster service to Gent (Tables **400**/**405**).

KNOKKE and BLANKENBERGE - BRUGGE - GENT - BRUSSELS — 405

Line 50a

For additional trains Brugge - Gent - Brussels see Table **400**. For Brugge - Gent (- Antwerpen) see Table **410**.

km			Ⓐ	Ⓐ	Ⓐ	Ⓐ ◧	Ⓐ		Ⓐ	Ⓐ	Ⓐ	Ⓐ
0	**Knokke** d.	Ⓐ	...	...	...	0505	...	and	2006	...	2121	2221
•	Blankenberge d.		...	...	...	|	0550	at	|	2050	|	|
22	Brugge a.		...	...	...	0527	0605	the	2028	2106	2143	2243
22	Brugge d.		0407	0429	0510	0529	0607	same	2031	2109	...	...
62	**Gent** Sint-Pieters d.		0438	0500	0538	0600	0636	minutes	2100	2138	...	...
119	**Brussels** Midi/Zuid a.		0508	0529	0607	0629	0705	past	2129	2207	...	...
121	Brussels Central a.		0515	0540	0615	0640	0714	each	2140	2215	...	...
123	Brussels Nord a.		0520	0545	0620	0645	0719	hour	2145	2220	...	...
135	**Brussels Airport** ✈ a.		▽	0557	▽	0657	▽	until	2157	▽	...	...

		Ⓒ	Ⓒ	Ⓒ	Ⓒ	Ⓒ	Ⓒ		Ⓒ	Ⓒ	Ⓒ n
Knokke d.	Ⓒ	...	...	...	...	0707	...	and	2007	...	2221
Blankenberge d.		...	...	...	...	|	0754	at	|	2054	|
Brugge a.		...	...	...	...	0728	0807	the	2028	2107	2243
Brugge d.		0510	0610	...	0710	0731	0810	same	2031	2110	...
Gent Sint-Pieters d.		0539	0639	0702	0739	0802	0839	minutes	2102	2139	...
Brussels Midi/Zuid a.		0608	0708	0731	0808	0831	0908	past	2131	2208	...
Brussels Central a.		0616	0716	0743	0816	0843	0916	each	2143	2216	...
Brussels Nord a.		0621	0721	0748	0821	0848	0921	hour	2148	2221	...
Brussels Airport ✈ a.		▽	▽	0802	▽	0902	▽	until	2202	▽	...

		Ⓐ n	Ⓐ	Ⓐ ❦	Ⓐ		Ⓐ	Ⓐ	Ⓐ	Ⓐ	Ⓐ	Ⓐ	Ⓐ
Brussels Airport ✈ d.	Ⓐ	...	▽	0603	▽	and	2003	▽	2103	▽	2203	▽	2302
Brussels Nord d.		...	0540	0615	0640	at	2015	2040	2115	2140	2215	2240	2315
Brussels Central d.		...	0545	0620	0645	the	2020	2045	2120	2145	2220	2245	2320
Brussels Midi/Zuid d.		...	0553	0629	0653	same	2029	2053	2129	2153	2229	2253	2331
Gent Sint-Pieters d.		...	0625	0702	0726	minutes	2102	2125	2202	2225	2302	2325	0003
Brugge a.		...	0650	0730	0751	past	2130	2150	2230	2250	2330	2350	0030
Brugge d.		0633	0653	0733	0753	each	2133	2153	2233	...	...	...	...
Blankenberge a.		|	0709	|	0809	hour	|	2209	|	...	...	...	...
Knokke a.		0654	...	0754	...	until	2154	...	2254	...	...	...	...

		Ⓒ n	Ⓒ n	Ⓒ	Ⓒ		Ⓒ	Ⓒ	Ⓒ	Ⓒ
Brussels Airport ✈ d.	Ⓒ	...	...	0657	▽	and	2057	▽	▽	▽
Brussels Nord d.		...	...	0712	0740	at	2112	2140	2240	2340
Brussels Central d.		...	...	0717	0745	the	2117	2145	2245	2345
Brussels Midi/Zuid d.		...	...	0726	0752	same	2126	2152	2252	2352
Gent Sint-Pieters d.		...	...	0802	0823	minutes	2202	2223	2324	0023
Brugge a.		...	...	0830	0848	past	2230	2248	2349	0048
Brugge d.		0733	0751	0833	0851	each	2233	2251	...	...
Blankenberge a.		|	0804	|	0904	hour	|	2304	...	...
Knokke a.		0754	...	0854	...	until	2254	...	...	...

n – An additional journey runs one hour earlier.

▽ – To/from Leuven, Hasselt/Genk (Table **430**).

• – Blankenburg - Brugge: *15 km*.

◧ – No journeys on Ⓐ at 1006, 1106 (local trains run Knokke to Brugge at 1006, 1105).

❦ – 0701Ⓐ, 1203Ⓐ and 1303Ⓐ from Brussels Airport require a change at Brugge for Knokke.

KNOKKE - OOSTENDE - DE PANNE (Coastal Tramway) — 406

De Lijn 'Kusttram'

KNOKKE railway station - **OOSTENDE** railway station *Journey 65 minutes*

Ⓐ: 0445, 0545, 0645, 0715, 0735, 0755, 0825, 0840, 0855, 0910, 0925, and every 15 minutes until 1800, 1815, 1830, 1845, 1900, 1920, 1945, 2002, 2024, 2124, 2224, 2324.

Ⓒ: 0445⑥, 0545, 0645, 0715, 0755⑥, 0825, 0840⑥, 0855, 0910, 0925, 0940, 0955, 1010 and every 15 minutes until 1845, 1900, 1920, 1940, 2002, 2024, 2124, 2224, 2324.

Calls at Heist (+6 minutes), Zeebrugge (+13 minutes), Blankenberge (+25 minutes).

OOSTENDE railway station - **DE PANNE** railway station *Journey 79 minutes*

Ⓐ: 0452, 0552, 0652, 0707, 0727, 0740, 0752, 0822, 0842, 0902, 0917, 0932, 0947, 1002, 1017 and every 15 minutes until 1832, 1902, 1932, 2027, 2127, 2227, 2327.

Ⓒ: 0452⑥, 0552⑥, 0652, 0707⑥, 0727, 0740⑥, 0752, 0822, 0842, 0902, 0917, 0932, 0947, 1002 and every 15 minutes until 1837, 1907, 1937, 2007, 2027, 2127, 2227, 2327.

Calls at Middelkerke (+23 minutes), Nieuwpoort (+41 minutes), Koksijde (+60 minutes).

DE PANNE railway station - **OOSTENDE** railway station *Journey 79 minutes*

Ⓐ: 0419, 0519, 0619, 0716, 0734, 0816, 0831, 0846, 0901 and every 15 minutes until 1701, 1716, 1731, 1746, 1819, 1836, 1854, 1909, 1924, 1949, 2014, 2114, 2214, 2314.

Ⓒ: 0419⑥, 0519⑥, 0619, 0716, 0734⑥, 0816, 0831, 0846⑥, 0901 and every 15 minutes until 1701, 1716, 1731, 1746, 1803, 1819, 1836, 1854, 1909, 1924, 1944, 2014, 2114, 2214, 2314.

Calls at Koksijde (+19 minutes), Nieuwpoort (+38 minutes), Middelkerke (+56 minutes).

OOSTENDE railway station - **KNOKKE** railway station *Journey 65 minutes*

Ⓐ: 0452, 0532, 0552, 0632, 0652, 0712, 0732, 0752, 0812, 0832, 0852, 0915, 0937, 0952, 1007, 1022 and every 15 minutes until 1907, 1937, 2007, 2037, 2127, 2227, 2327.

Ⓒ: 0452⑥, 0532⑥, 0632⑥, 0652, 0732, 0752, 0812, 0832, 0852, 0915, 0937, 0952, 1007, 1022 and every 15 minutes until 1852, 1907, 1937, 2007, 2037, 2127, 2227, 2327.

A change of tram may be necessary at Oostende. In July and August trams run every 10 minutes during the day.

Connections with rail services are available at Knokke (Table **405**), Zeebrugge (Table **402**), Blankenberge (Table **405**), Oostende (Tables **400/07/10**) and De Panne (Table **411**).

OOSTENDE - BRUGGE - KORTRIJK - BRUSSELS — 407

Lines 66, 89

For direct trains Oostende - Brugge - Brussels via Gent (also Kortrijk - Gent - Brussels) see Table **400**. For direct trains Brugge - Brussels - Brussels Nationaal ✈ see Table **405**.

km			Ⓐ	Ⓐ	Ⓐ	Ⓐ	Ⓐ	Ⓐ	Ⓐ	Ⓐ	Ⓐ	Ⓐ		Ⓐ	Ⓐ	Ⓐ
0	**Oostende** ▷ d.	Ⓐ	...	...	...	...	0557	...	...	0657	0758	0858		1958	2058	2158
22	Brugge ▷ d.		...	...	...	...	0614	...	...	0714	0814	0914		2014	2114	2214
39	Torhout d.		...	...	...	...	0630	...	...	0731	0830	0930		2030	2130	2230
44	Lichtervelde § d.		...	...	...	...	0636	...	...	0736	0836	0936		2036	2136	2236
52	Roeselare d.		...	...	...	...	0644	...	...	0745	0844	0944	and	2044	2144	2244
73	**Kortrijk** a.		...	...	...	...	0706	...	...	0805	0905	1005		2105	2205	2305
73	**Kortrijk** d.		0512	0543	0611	0644	0711	0744	0811	0817	0912	1012	hourly	2112	2212	...
98	Oudenaarde d.		0533	0603	0631	0704	0731	0803	0832	|	0933	1033		2133	2233	...
115	Zottegem d.		0547	0617	0645	0717	0745	0818	0847	◇	0947	1047	until	2147	2247	...
136	Denderleeuw d.		0605	0638	0705	0739	0804	0837	0905	|	1005	1105		2205	2305	...
158	**Brussels** Midi/Zuid a.		0620	0656	0720	0756	0819	0853	0920	0924	1020	1120		2220	2320	...
160	Brussels Central a.		0627	0705	0727	0805	0827	0900	0927	0932	1027	1127		2227	2327	...
162	Brussels Nord a.		0632	0710	0732	0810	0831	0905	0932	0937	1032	1132		2232	2332	...
174	**Brussels Airport** ✈ a.		0647	...	0747	...	0847	...	0947	...	1047	1147		2247	2347	...

		Ⓒ	Ⓒ	Ⓒ	Ⓒ		Ⓒ	Ⓒ n
Oostende ▷ d.	Ⓒ	...	...	...	0648		1948	2148
Brugge ▷ d.		...	...	...	0705		2005	2205
Torhout d.		...	...	...	0721		2021	2221
Lichtervelde § d.		...	...	...	0735		2035	2235
Roeselare d.		...	...	...	0743	and	2043	2243
Kortrijk a.		...	...	...	0803		2103	2303
Kortrijk d.		0511	0611	0711	0811	hourly	2111	...
Oudenaarde d.		0531	0631	0731	0831		2131	...
Zottegem d.		0547	0647	0747	0847	until	2147	...
Denderleeuw d.		0605	0705	0805	0905		2205	...
Brussels Midi/Zuid a.		0620	0720	0820	0920		2220	...
Brussels Central a.		0627	0727	0827	0927		2227	...
Brussels Nord a.		0632	0732	0832	0932		2232	...
Brussels Airport ✈ a.		0646	0746	0846	0946		2246	...

		Ⓐ	Ⓐ	Ⓐ	Ⓐ		Ⓐ	Ⓐ	Ⓐ	Ⓐ	Ⓐ	Ⓐ	Ⓐ	Ⓐ	Ⓐ	Ⓐ
Brussels Airport ✈ d.	Ⓐ	...	...	0513	0613		1613	...	1713	1813	...	1913	2013	2113	2213	...
Brussels Nord d.		...	...	0527	0627		1627	1653	1727	1827	1921	1927	2027	2127	2227	2319
Brussels Central d.		...	...	0532	0632		1632	1658	1732	1832	1926	1932	2032	2132	2232	2323
Brussels Midi/Zuid d.		...	...	0539	0639		1639	1705	1739	1839	1937	1939	2039	2139	2242	2329
Denderleeuw d.		...	...	0558	0658		1658	1724	1758	1858	|	1958	2058	2158	2302	2348
Zottegem d.		...	...	0615	0715	and	1715	1745	1815	1915	◇	2015	2115	2215	2319	0014
Oudenaarde d.		...	...	0630	0731		1732	1759	1832	1932	|	2032	2132	2232	2333	0030
Kortrijk a.		...	...	0647	0749	hourly	1749	1816	1849	1949	2041	2049	2151	2249	2351	...
Kortrijk d.		0455	0555	0655	0755		1755	...	1855	1955	2055	...	2155	...	...	...
Roeselare d.		0517	0617	0716	0817	until	1817	...	1917	2017	2117	...	2217	...	...	...
Lichtervelde § d.		0525	0625	0725	0825		1825	...	1925	2025	2125	...	2225	...	...	...
Torhout d.		0530	0630	0730	0830		1830	...	1930	2030	2130	...	2230	...	...	...
Brugge ▷ a.		0545	0645	0745	0845		1845	...	1945	2045	2146	...	2246	...	...	...
Oostende ▷ a.		0602	0702	0802	0902		1902	...	2002	2102	2202	...	2302	...	...	...

		Ⓒ	Ⓒ		Ⓒ	Ⓒ	Ⓒ	Ⓒ
Brussels Airport ✈ d.	Ⓒ	...	0613		1913	2013	2113	2213
Brussels Nord d.		...	0627		1927	2027	2127	2227
Brussels Central d.		...	0632		1932	2032	2132	2232
Brussels Midi/Zuid d.		...	0639		1939	2039	2139	2239
Denderleeuw d.		...	0658		1958	2058	2158	2258
Zottegem d.		...	0715	and	2015	2115	2215	2315
Oudenaarde d.		...	0731		2031	2131	2231	2331
Kortrijk a.		...	0749	hourly	2049	2149	2249	2349
Kortrijk d.		0657	0757		2057	2157	...	...
Roeselare d.		0718	0818	until	2118	2218	...	...
Lichtervelde § d.		0735	0835		2135	2235	...	...
Torhout d.		0740	0840		2140	2240	...	...
Brugge ▷ a.		0755	0855		2156	2255	...	...
Oostende ▷ a.		0810	0910		2211	2310	...	...

n – An additional journey runs one hour earlier.

◇ – Via Gent (Table **400**). To Leuven/from Welkenraedt.

▷ – See also Tables **400** and **410**.

§ – On Ⓒ trains arrive 10 minutes earlier.

ADDITIONAL TRAINS *Journey 47 minutes*
Brugge - Kortrijk: Ⓐ hourly 0557 - 2257; Ⓒ every 2 hours 0737 - 1937.
Kortrijk - Brugge: Ⓐ hourly 0516 - 2116; Ⓒ every 2 hours 0635 - 2035.

410 POPERINGE - KORTRIJK - GENT - ANTWERPEN

Lines 69, 75, 59

km			Ⓐ	Ⓐ	Ⓐ	Ⓐ				Ⓐ										Ⓐ	Ⓐ	Ⓐ			
0	**Poperinge**	d.	...	0407	...	...	0507	...		...	1909	...	2007	...	2107	...	2207	...		0549	0649	0735	...	...	...
10	Ieper	d.	...	0415	...	...	0515	...		...	1917	...	2015	...	2115	...	2215	...		0558	0658	0743	...	...	...
23	Comines / Komen	d.	...	0425	...	...	0525	...	and	...	1927	...	2025	...	2125	...	2225	...		0608	0708	0753	...	...	...
32	Menen	d.	...	0434	...	...	0534	...	at	...	1936	...	2034	...	2134	...	2234	...		0618	0718	0802	...	...	...
43	**Kortrijk**	a.	...	0450	...	...	0550	...	the	...	1952	...	2050	...	2150	...	2250	...	A	0633	0734	0817	...	...	...
43	**Kortrijk**	d.	...	0458	...	...	0558	...	same	...	1959	...	2058	...	2158	...	2258	...	L	0641	0741	...	...	...	...
	Oostende	▷ d.	...	|	...	...	|	0610	minutes	...	|	2010	|	2110	|	2210	|	...	S	|	|	...	...	...	...
	Brugge	▷ d.	...	|	...	△	|	0625	past	△	|	2025	|	2125	|	2225	|	...	O	|	|	...	...	...	...
85	**Gent** Sint-Pieters	▷ a.	...	0524	...	0607	0624	0649	each	2009	2024	2049	2124	2149	2224	2249	2324	...		...	...	...	...	...	...
85	**Gent** Sint-Pieters	d.	0427	0527	0553	0611	0627	0653	hour	2011	2027	2053	2127	2153	2227	2253	2327	...		0711	0811	...	...	...	...
112	Lokeren	d.	0449	0549	0615	0633	0649	0715	until	2033	2049	2115	2149	2215	2249	2315	2349	...		▽	▽	...	...	...	...
125	Sint-Niklaas	d.	0500	0600	0626	0645	0700	0726		2045	2100	2126	2200	2226	2300	2326	2400	...		...	...	...	...	...	...
148	Antwerpen Berchem	a.	0517	0617	0648	0704	0717	0748		2104	2117	2148	2217	2248	2317	2348	0018	...		...	...	...	...	...	...
151	**Antwerpen** Centraal	a.	0523	0623	0654	0710	0723	0754		2110	2123	2154	2223	2254	2323	2354	0023	...		...	...	...	...	...	...

		Ⓐ					Ⓐ			Ⓐ				Ⓐ				Ⓐ	Ⓒ			Ⓐ	Ⓐ	Ⓐ	
Antwerpen Centraal	d.	0437	0506	0537	0606	0637	0649	0706	0737	0751		2006	2037	2051	2106	2137	2237	2337	2337	...		...	...	...	...
Antwerpen Berchem	d.	0442	0512	0543	0612	0643	0654	0712	0743	0756		2012	2043	2056	2112	2143	2243	2343	2343	...		...	...	...	...
Sint-Niklaas	d.	0502	0536	0602	0636	0702	0715	0736	0802	0817	and	2035	2102	2117	2136	2202	2302	0002	0002	...		...	...	...	...
Lokeren	d.	0512	0546	0612	0646	0712	0725	0746	0812	0828	at	2046	2112	2128	2146	2212	2312	0012	0012	...		...	▽	▽	...
Gent Sint-Pieters	a.	0533	0606	0633	0706	0732	0748	0807	0833	0848	the	2106	2133	2148	2206	2233	2333	0033	0033	...	A	...	1637	1744	...
Gent Sint-Pieters	▷ d.	0536	0609	0636	0711	0736	0753	0810	0836	0853	same	2110	2136	2152	2210	2236	2336	...	0039	...	L	...	1641	1748	...
Brugge	▷ a.	|	0635	|	0734	|	△	0835	|	△	minutes	2135	|	△	2235	|	|	...	|	...	S	...	|	|	...
Oostende	▷ a.	|	0650	|	0749	|	...	0850	|	...	past	2150	|	...	2250	|	|	...	|	...	O	...	|	|	...
Kortrijk	a.	0601	...	0701	...	0801	...	...	0901	...	each	...	2201	...	...	2301	0011	...	0113	...		...	1710	1819	...
Kortrijk	d.	0604	...	0708	...	0810	...	...	0910	...	hour	...	2210	...	...	2310	...	...	...	...		1641	1719	1822	...
Menen	d.	0620	...	0724	...	0826	...	...	0926	...	until	...	2226	...	...	2326	...	...	...	...		1656	1735	1838	...
Comines / Komen	d.	0629	...	0733	...	0835	...	...	0935	...		...	2235	...	...	2334	...	...	...	...		1705	1746	1849	...
Ieper	d.	0639	...	0743	...	0845	...	...	0945	...		...	2245	...	...	2345	...	...	...	...		1715	1756	1859	...
Poperinge	a.	0647	...	0751	...	0853	...	...	0953	...		...	2253	...	...	2353	...	...	...	...		1722	1804	1907	...

ADDITIONAL TRAINS KORTRIJK - GENT

			Ⓐ§		Ⓐ§		Ⓒ		Ⓒ
Kortrijk	d.	Ⓐ	0419	hourly	2219	Ⓒ	0523	hourly	2223
Gent Sint-Pieters	a.		0452	until	2252		0554	until	2254

			Ⓐ§		Ⓐ§		Ⓒ		Ⓒ
Gent Sint-Pieters	d.	Ⓐ	0609	hourly	2309	Ⓒ	0606	hourly	2306
Kortrijk	a.		0641	until	2341		0637	until	2337

△ – From / to De Panne (Table **411**).
▽ – To / from Brussels (Table **400**).
▷ – See also Table **400** (also **407** Oostende - Brugge).
§ – Most journeys continue to / from Brussels (Table **400**).
☛ *Between Kortrijk and Antwerpen most trains are attached to Lille - Kortrijk - Antwerpen trains (Table **415**).*

411 DE PANNE - LICHTERVELDE - GENT

Line 73

km				Ⓐ		Ⓐ ◧		Ⓒ △		Ⓒ △
0	**De Panne** §	d.	Ⓐ	0452		1852	Ⓒ	0552		2052
5	Veurne	d.		0501	and	1901		0601	and	2101
20	Diksmuide	d.		0513		1913		0613		2113
39	Lichtervelde	d.		0530	hourly	1930		0630	hourly	2130
56	Tielt	d.		0542		1943		0642		2142
86	**Gent** Sint-Pieters	a.		0607	until	2009		0707	until	2207
	Antwerpen 410	a.		0710		2110		|		|
	Brussels Midi / Zuid	a.		...		...		0812		2312
	Brussels Airport ✈	a.		...		...		0835		2335

			Ⓐ ◐		Ⓐ		Ⓒ △		Ⓒ △
Brussels Airport ✈	d.	Ⓐ	...		...	Ⓒ	0524		2025
Brussels Midi / Zuid	d.		...		...		0548		2048
Antwerpen 410	d.		0649	and	2051		|	and	|
Gent Sint-Pieters	d.		0753		2152		0653		2153
Tielt	d.		0819	hourly	2220		0719	hourly	2219
Lichtervelde	d.		0832		2232		0732		2232
Diksmuide	d.		0849	until	2249		0749	until	2249
Veurne	d.		0901		2301		0801		2301
De Panne §	a.		0908		2308		0808		2308

△ – To / from Leuven or Landen (Table **430**). Runs Gent - Brussels and v.v. via Aalst (Table **412**).
◧ – Also De Panne - Gent at 1952Ⓐ, 2052Ⓐ.
◐ – Also Gent - De Panne at 0553Ⓐ, 0653Ⓐ.
§ – De Panne railway station is situated in Adinkerke. Connection available with the coastal tramway (Table **406**).

412 GENT - AALST - DENDERLEEUW - BRUSSELS

Line 50

For direct trains Gent - Brussels see Tables 400 and 405

km			Ⓐ	Ⓐ △	Ⓐ	Ⓒ	△		Ⓐ	Ⓒ	△
0	**Gent** Sint-Pieters	d.	0441	0512	0541	0541	0612	and at	2141	2141	2213
28	Aalst	d.	0513	0543	0613	0612	0643	the same	2213	2212	2243
35	Denderleeuw	d.	0523	0553	0623	0625	0653	minutes	2223	2225	2254
58	**Brussels** Midi / Zuid	a.	0541	0611	0641	0642	0711	past	2241	2242	2312
60	Brussels Central	a.	0548	0618	0648	0649	0718	each	2248	2249	2318
62	Brussels Nord	a.	0553	0623	0653	0654	0723	hour	2253	2254	2323
74	**Brussels Airport** ✈	a.	⊡	0635	⊡	...	0736	until	⊡	...	2335

		Ⓐ △	Ⓐ	Ⓒ	△	Ⓐ		Ⓒ	△	Ⓐ
Brussels Airport ✈	d.	0524	⊡	...	0624	⊡	and at	...	2224	⊡
Brussels Nord	d.	0537	0607	0606	0637	0707	the same	2206	2237	2307
Brussels Central	d.	0541	0612	0610	0641	0712	minutes	2210	2241	2312
Brussels Midi / Zuid	d.	0549	0619	0618	0649	0719	past	2218	2249	2319
Denderleeuw	d.	0609	0639	0642	0709	0739	each	2242	2309	2339
Aalst	d.	0619	0648	0651	0719	0748	hour	2251	2319	2349
Gent Sint-Pieters	a.	0647	0718	0719	0747	0818	until	2319	2347	0019

△ – To / from Leuven or Landen (Table **430**). On Ⓒ most journeys run from / to De Panne (Table **411**).
⊡ – To / from Hasselt or Tongeren (Table **431**).

413 EEKLO - GENT - OUDENAARDE - RONSE

Line 86

km				Ⓐ		Ⓐ‡		Ⓒ		Ⓒ	⑥‡
0	**Eeklo**	d.	Ⓐ	0510		2011	Ⓒ	0711	and hourly	1911	2011
27	**Gent** St-Pieters	a.		0545	and	2045		0745	on ⑥,	1945	2045
27	**Gent** St-Pieters	d.		0557	hourly	2057		0757	every two	1957	2057
52	Oudenaarde	a.		0627	until	2127		0827	hours on †	2027	2127
52	Oudenaarde	d.		0633	△	2135		0835	until	2035	2135
66	**Ronse**	a.		0644		2146		0846		2046	2146

			Ⓐ		Ⓐ		Ⓒ		Ⓒ	⑥§
Ronse	d.	Ⓐ	0515		2014	Ⓒ	0714	and hourly	1914	2014
Oudenaarde	a.		0526	and	2025		0725	on ⑥,	1925	2025
Oudenaarde	d.		0533	hourly	2033		0733	every two	1933	2033
Gent St-Pieters	a.		0603	until	2103		0803	hours on †	2003	2103
Gent St-Pieters	d.		0615	▽	2115		0815	until	2015	2115
Eeklo	a.		0649		2149		0849		2049	2149

△ – Also Gent - Ronse at 1628Ⓐ, 1728Ⓐ.
▽ – Also Ronse - Gent at 0547Ⓐ, 0647Ⓐ, 2114Ⓐ, 2214Ⓐ.
‡ – Also Eeklo - Gent - Oudenaarde at 2111Ⓐ, 2111Ⓒ, 2211Ⓐ.
§ – Also Ronse - Gent at 2114Ⓒ.

414 GENT - MECHELEN - LEUVEN

Line 53

For Mechelen - Leuven via Brussels Nationaal ✈ see Table 432

km				Ⓐ	Ⓐ	Ⓐ	Ⓐ	Ⓐ	Ⓐ	Ⓐ		Ⓐ	Ⓐ	Ⓐ	Ⓐ			Ⓒ	Ⓒ	Ⓒ	Ⓒ		Ⓒ	Ⓒ	Ⓒ
0	**Gent** St-Pieters	d.	Ⓐ	0421	...	...	0521	0557	...	0619	and at	2057	...	2121	2157	...	Ⓒ	...	0659	...	0759	and at	...	2200	...
30	Dendermonde	d.		0500	0524	...	0600	0624	...	0700	the same minutes	2124	...	2200	2224	...		...	0728	...	0828	the same minutes	...	2228	...
57	Mechelen	d.		0528	0548	0622	0628	0648	0722	0728	past each	2148	2222	2228	2253	...		0736	0754	0836	0854	past each	2236	2254	2336
82	**Leuven**	a.		...	0614	0655	...	0714	0755	...	hour until	2214	2255	...	2319	...		0806	...	0906	...	hour until	2306	...	0006

			Ⓐ	Ⓐ	Ⓐ	Ⓐ	Ⓐ	Ⓐ	Ⓐ		Ⓐ	Ⓐ	Ⓐ	Ⓐ		Ⓒ	Ⓒ	Ⓒ	Ⓒ	Ⓒ		Ⓒ	Ⓒ	Ⓒ	Ⓒ
Leuven	d.	Ⓐ	0505	0546	...	0605	0646	...	0705	and at	2146	...	2205	2246	Ⓒ	...	...	0654	...	0754	and at	...	2054	2154	2254
Mechelen	d.		0539	0615	0632	0639	0715	0732	0739	the same minutes	2215	2232	2239	2315		0606	0706	0723	0806	0823	the same minutes	2106	2123	2223	2323
Dendermonde	d.		...	0640	0702	...	0740	0802	...	past each	2240	2302	...	2336		0634	0734	...	0834	...	past each	2134	...	...	...
Gent St-Pieters	a.		...	0703	0739	...	0804	0839	...	hour until	2303	2339	...	...		0701	0801	...	0901	...	hour until	2201	...	...	...

Line 75 LILLE - MOUSCRON - KORTRIJK - (GENT - ANTWERPEN) 415

A change at Kortrijk may be necessary on certain journeys. Lille - Mouscron is subject to alteration on French and Belgian public holidays

km		Ⓐ	⚒	⚒	Ⓐ					Ⓐ		Ⓒ	Ⓐ	Ⓒ	⑥	Ⓑ		Ⓐ	⚒	†					
		n			n					n								n							
0	**Lille** Flandres ▷ d.	0627	0709	0809	0830	0909	1009	1109	1209	1227	1309	1403	1409	1509	1603	1609	1709	1727	1809	1803	1909	2009	2109	2209	...
10	Roubaix ▷ d.	0637	0723	0823	0840	0919	1019	1119	1219	1241	1319	1418	1419	1519	1618	1619	1723	1737	1822	1818	1919	2019	2119	2219	...
12	Tourcoing 🚌 ▷ d.	0641	0727	0827	0844	0924	1024	1124	1224	1245	1324	1422	1424	1524	1622	1624	1727	1741	1827	1822	1924	2024	2124	2224	...
18	Mouscron a.	...	0733	0833	...	0929	1029	1129	1229	...	1329	1427	1430	1530	1627	1630	1733	...	1832	1827	1930	2029	2129	2229	...
18	Mouscron **417** d.	...	0736	0836	...	0936	1036	1136	1236	...	1336	1436	1436	1536	1636	1636	1736	...	1836	1833	1936	2036	2136	2236	...
30	**Kortrijk** **417** a.	...	0745	0845	...	0945	1045	1145	1245	...	1345	1445	1445	1545	1645	1646	1745	...	1845	1845	1945	2045	2145	2245	...
	Gent Sint-P. **410** a.	...	0824	0924	...	1024	1124	1224	1324	...	...	1524	1524	1624	1724	1724	1824	...	1924	1924	2024	2124	2224	2324	...
	Antwerpen **410** a.	...	0923	1023	...	1123	1223	1323	1423	...	...	1623	1623	1723	1823	1823	1923	...	2023	2023	2123	2223	2323	0023	...

	⚒	Ⓐ	Ⓐ	⑥		Ⓐ			⚒	†		Ⓐ						Ⓐ							
		n				n						n						n							
Antwerpen **410** d.	...	...	...	...	0637	...	0737	0837	0937	...	1037	...	1137	1237	1337	1437	1537	...	1637	1737	1837	1937	2037	2137	...
Gent Sint-P. **410** d.	...	...	...	...	0736	...	0836	0936	1036	...	1136	...	1236	1336	1436	1536	1636	...	1736	1836	1936	2036	2136	2236	...
Kortrijk **417** d.	0613	...	0713	0713	0813	...	0913	1001	1113	1113	1213	...	1313	1401	1513	1613	1713	...	1813	1913	2013	2113	2201	2301	...
Mouscron **417** a.	0623	...	0723	0723	0824	...	0923	...	1123	1123	1223	...	1323	...	1523	1623	1723	...	1823	1923	2023	2123	...	...	...
Mouscron d.	0630	...	0727	0730	0827	...	0930	...	1130	1130	1230	...	1327	...	1530	1630	1727	...	1827	1930	2030	2130	...	...	...
Tourcoing 🚌 ▷ d.	0637	0720	0733	0736	0833	0916	0937	...	1137	1137	1237	1320	1333	...	1537	1637	1733	1816	1833	1937	2037	2137	...	...	...
Roubaix ▷ d.	0641	0724	0737	0740	0837	0920	0941	...	1141	1141	1241	1324	1337	...	1541	1641	1737	1821	1837	1941	2041	2141	...	...	...
Lille Flandres ▷ a.	0651	0733	0751	0754	0851	0929	0951	...	1151	1151	1251	1333	1351	...	1551	1651	1751	1830	1851	1951	2051	2151	...	...	...

n – Not Dec. 20 - 31.

▷ – Frequent services Lille Flandres - Lille Europe - Roubaix / Tourcoing are operated by the Lille *VAL* métro (Line 2) or by tram.

☛ *Between Kortrijk and Antwerpen these trains are attached to Poperinge - Kortrijk - Gent - Antwerpen trains (Table **410**).*

Lines 78, 118 LILLE - TOURNAI - MONS 416

km			Ⓐ	Ⓐ	Ⓐ	Ⓐ	Ⓐ	Ⓐ	Ⓐ	Ⓐ	Ⓐ	Ⓐ	Ⓐ	Ⓐ	Ⓐ	Ⓐ	Ⓐ	Ⓐ	Ⓐ	Ⓐ	Ⓐ	Ⓐ	Ⓐ	Ⓐ	Ⓐ
					d		d														◇				
0	**Lille** Flandres § d.	Ⓐ	...	0601	...	0708	...	0728	0808	0908	1008	...	1208	1308	...	1508	1608	1708	1732	1808	1908	2008	...	...	2208
	Mouscron **417** d.		0519	|	0619	|	0714	|	|	|	|	...	|	|	...	|	|	|	|	|	|	|	...	...	|
25	**Tournai** **417** a.		0541	0630	0640	0738	0735	0755	0837	0936	1036	...	1237	1336	...	1536	1636	1736	1805	1836	1937	2036	...	...	2236
25	**Tournai** d.		0542	...	0643	0743	0743	...	0843	0943	1043	1143	1243	1343	1443	1543	1643	1743	...	1843	1943	2043	2143	2228	...
64	Saint-Ghislain d.		0603	...	0703	0803	0803	...	0903	1003	1103	1203	1303	1403	1503	1603	1703	1803	...	1903	2003	2104	2203	2259	...
73	**Mons** a.		0613	...	0713	0813	0813	...	0913	1013	1113	1213	1313	1413	1513	1613	1713	1813	...	1913	2013	2113	2214	2313	...
	Charleroi Sud **425** a.		0647	...	0747	0847	0847	...	0947	1047	1147	1247	1347	1447	1547	1647	1747	1847	...	1947	2047	2147	2247	...	...
	Namur **425** a.		0721	...	0821	0921	0921	...	1021	1121	1221	1321	1421	1521	1621	1721	1821	1921	...	2021	2121	2221	2321	...	...

		Ⓐ	Ⓐ	Ⓐ	Ⓐ	Ⓐ	Ⓐ	Ⓐ	Ⓐ	Ⓐ	Ⓐ	Ⓐ	Ⓐ	Ⓐ	Ⓐ	Ⓐ	Ⓐ	Ⓐ	Ⓐ	Ⓐ	Ⓐ	Ⓐ	Ⓐ	Ⓐ	Ⓐ
				◇					◇								k		k			◇			
Namur **425** d.	Ⓐ	...	...	...	0540	...	0640	0740	0840	0940	1040	1140	1240	1340	1440	...	1540	1540	1640	...	1740	1840	1940	2040	2140
Charleroi Sud **425** d.		...	...	...	0612	...	0712	0812	0912	1012	1112	1212	1312	1412	1512	...	1612	1612	1712	...	1812	1912	2012	2112	2212
Mons d.		0452	...	0550	0646	...	0746	0846	0946	1046	1146	1246	1346	1446	1546	...	1646	1646	1746	...	1846	1946	2046	2146	2246
Saint-Ghislain d.		0505	...	0603	0656	...	0756	0856	0956	1056	1156	1256	1356	1456	1556	...	1656	1656	1757	...	1857	1956	2056	2156	2256
Tournai a.		0532	...	0634	0715	...	0815	0915	1015	1115	1215	1315	1415	1515	1615	...	1715	1715	1818	...	1918	2015	2115	2215	2321
Tournai **417** d.		...	0622	0644	0722	0803	0821	0921	1021	1121	1221	1321	...	1521	1621	1649	1718	1723	1824	1822	1923	2021	2121	...	...
Mouscron **417** a.		...	|	|	|	|	|	|	|	|	|	|	...	|	|	|	1739	|	1845	|	|	|	|	...	...
Lille Flandres § a.		...	0652	0719	0752	0832	0852	0952	1052	1152	1252	1352	...	1552	1652	1722	...	1752	...	1852	1952	2052	2152	...	...

		Ⓒ	Ⓒ	Ⓒ		Ⓒ	Ⓒ	Ⓒ	
Mouscron **417** d.	Ⓒ	0613	0713	0813		2013	2113	2213	...
Tournai **417** d.		0629	0729	0829	and	2029	2129	2229	...
Saint-Ghislain d.		0659	0759	0859	hourly	2059	2159	2259	...
Mons a.		0712	0812	0912	until	2112	2212	2312	...
Charleroi Sud **425** a.		0751	0851	0951		2151	2251	...	...
Namur **425** a.		0830	0930	1030		2230	2330	...	...
Liège Guillemins **442** a.		0920	1020	1120		2320	...	...	...

		Ⓒ	Ⓒ	Ⓒ	Ⓒ		Ⓒ	Ⓒ	
Liège Guillemins **442** d.	Ⓒ	...	...	0640	0740		1940	2040	...
Namur **425** d.		...	0630	0730	0830	and	2030	2130	...
Charleroi Sud **425** d.		0609	0709	0809	0909	hourly	2109	2209	...
Mons d.		0648	0748	0848	0948	until	2148	2248	...
Saint-Ghislain d.		0702	0802	0902	1002		2202	2301	...
Tournai **417** a.		0730	0830	0930	1030		2230	2330	...
Mouscron **417** a.		0746	0846	0946	1046		2246	2346	...

		⑥	⑥	Ⓒ		Ⓒ	Ⓒ	Ⓒ	
Lille Flandres § d.	Ⓒ	0649	0749	0849	hourly	1949	2049	2149	...
Tournai a.		0721	0821	0921	until	2021	2121	2221	...

		⑥	⑥	Ⓒ		Ⓒ	Ⓒ	Ⓒ	
Tournai d.	Ⓒ	0636	0736	0836	hourly	1936	2036	2144	...
Lille Flandres § a.		0708	0809	0908	until	2008	2108	2213	...

d – From Kortrijk (depart 0606 and 0702).
k – To Kortrijk (arrive 1750 and 1855).

◇ – Change trains at Tournai.
§ – 🚌 between Lille and Tournai = Blandain.

Lines 94, 60 KORTRIJK - MOUSCRON - TOURNAI - BRUSSELS - SINT NIKLAAS 417

For direct trains Kortrijk - Brussels see Table **400** (via Gent) and Table **407** (via Oudenaarde)

km			Ⓐ	Ⓐ	Ⓐ	Ⓐ	Ⓐ	Ⓐ	Ⓐ	Ⓐ	Ⓐ	Ⓐ	Ⓐ	Ⓐ	Ⓐ		Ⓐ	Ⓐ	Ⓐ		Ⓒ		Ⓒ
0	**Kortrijk** **415** d.	Ⓐ	...	...	...	...	...	...	...	...	0636	...	...	0737	...		2035	...	2135	Ⓒ	...		...
13	Mouscron **415/6** d.		...	...	...	...	0545	0603	...	...	0648	0702	...	0747	...		2046	...	2146		...		...
32	**Tournai** **416** d.		0444	0509	0544	0557	0609	0628	0644	0657	0710	0728	0744	0809	0844	and	2109	2144	2209		0544		2244
50	Leuze d.		0457	0523	0557	0611	0623	0640	0657	0711	0723	0740	0757	0823	0857	at	2123	2157	2223		0558		2258
62	Ath d.		0507	0534	0607	0621	0634	0650	0707	0721	0734	0750	0807	0833	0907	the	2134	2207	2234		0608	and	2308
100	Halle d.		0537	0603	0637	|	0703	|	0737	|	0803	|	0837	0902	0937	same	2203	2237	2303		0637		2337
116	**Brussels** Midi / Zuid a.		0548	0613	0648	0700	0715	0728	0748	0800	0815	0828	0848	0914	0948	minutes	2215	2248	2315		0648	hourly	2348
116	**Brussels** Midi / Zuid d.		0551	0618	0651	0702	0718	0730	0751	0802	0818	0830	0853	0917	0951	past	2218	2251	2318		0651		2351
118	Brussels Central d.		0556	0623	0656	0707	0723	0735	0756	0807	0823	0835	0858	0922	0956	each	2223	2256	2323		0656	until	2356
120	Brussels Nord d.		0604	0629	0704	0711	0729	0739	0802	0813	0829	0839	0905	0929	1004	hour	2229	2304	2329		0704		0004
132	**Brussels Airport** ✈ a.		0624	|	0724	n	|	...	0824	n	|	...	0924	|	1024	until	|	2324	|		0724		0024
154	Dendermonde d.		...	0656	...	...	0756	...	...	...	0856	...	...	0956	...		2256	...	0012		...		...
168	Lokeren **410** a.		...	0721	...	...	0821	...	...	...	0921	...	...	1021	...		2321	...	...		...		...
181	**Sint-Niklaas** **410** a.		...	0736	...	...	0836	...	...	...	0936	...	...	1036	...		2336	...	...		...		...

		Ⓐ	Ⓐ	Ⓐ	Ⓐ	Ⓐ		Ⓐ	Ⓐ	Ⓐ	Ⓐ	Ⓐ	Ⓐ	Ⓐ		Ⓐ	Ⓐ	Ⓐ	Ⓐ		Ⓒ		Ⓒ
Sint-Niklaas **410** d.	Ⓐ	...	...	0524	...	0624		...	1924	...	2024	...	2124	2224		...	...	...	...	Ⓒ	...		...
Lokeren **410** d.		...	...	0539	...	0639		...	1939	...	2039	...	2139	2239		...	...	...	...		...		...
Dendermonde d.		...	...	0603	...	0703	and	...	2003	...	2103	...	2203	2303		...	...	...	...		...		...
Brussels Airport ✈ d.		...	0541	|	0641	|	at	1941	|	2041	|	2141	|	|		n	...	n	...		0541		2241
Brussels Nord d.		...	0601	0633	0701	0732	the	2001	2034	2101	2133	2201	2233	2333	A	1549	1616	1649	1717		0600	and	2300
Brussels Central d.		...	0606	0638	0706	0737	same	2006	2039	2106	2138	2206	2238	2338	L	1554	1621	1654	1722		0605		2305
Brussels Midi / Zuid a.		...	0610	0642	0710	0741	minutes	2010	2043	2110	2142	2210	2242	2342	S	1558	1625	1658	1726		0609	hourly	2309
Brussels Midi / Zuid d.		0513	0613	0646	0713	0747	past	2013	2047	2113	2147	2213	2247	2347	O	1600	1627	1700	1728		0613		2313
Halle d.		0524	0624	0658	0724	0758	each	2024	2058	2124	2158	2224	2258	2358		|	|	|	|		0624	until	2324
Ath d.		0553	0653	0729	0753	0829	hour	2053	2129	2153	2226	2253	2329	0026		1640	1706	1740	1806		0654		2354
Leuze d.		0602	0702	0739	0802	0839	until	2102	2139	2202	...	2302	2339	...		1650	1717	1750	1816		0704		0004
Tournai **416** d.		0615	0715	0753	0815	0853		2115	2152	2215	...	2315	2350	...		1702	1730	1802	1829		0715		0016
Mouscron **415/6** d.		...	...	0816	...	0916		...	2215	...	...	...	...	...		...	1754	...	1853		...		...
Kortrijk **415** a.		...	...	0826	...	0926		...	2224	...	...	...	...	...		...	...	...	...		...		...

n – To/from Namur and Liège via Brussels Luxembourg (Table **440**).

419 ROOSENDAAL - ESSEN - ANTWERPEN *Line 12*

km			Ⓐ	Ⓐ ♡	Ⓐ	Ⓐ ♡	Ⓐ	Ⓐ ♡	Ⓐ		Ⓐ ♡	Ⓐ	Ⓐ	Ⓐ		Ⓒ	Ⓒ	Ⓒ		Ⓒ	Ⓒ
0	**Roosendaal** d.	Ⓐ	...	...	0621	...	0721	...	...	and at the		...	2221	2321	Ⓒ	...	0721	0821	and	2121	2221
8	Essen 🏛 d.		0504	0546	0630	0646	0730	0746	0805	same minutes	2046	2146	2230	2330		0629	0730	0830	hourly	2130	2230
26	Kapellen d.		0521	0606	0651	0706	0751	0806	0823	past each	2106	2206	2251	2351		0651	0751	0851	until	2151	2251
41	**Antwerpen** Centraal a.		0536	0622	0610	0722	0710	0722	0841	hour until	2122	2222	2310	0010		0710	0810	0910		2210	2310

		Ⓐ ♡	Ⓐ	Ⓐ	Ⓐ ♡	Ⓐ	Ⓐ		Ⓐ ♡	Ⓐ	Ⓐ ♡	Ⓐ	Ⓐ ♡		Ⓒ	Ⓒ	Ⓒ		Ⓒ	Ⓒ	Ⓒ
Antwerpen Centraal d.	Ⓐ	0537	0550	0619	0637	0650	0719	and at the	2037	2050	2137	2150	2237	Ⓒ	0550	0650	0750	and	2150	2305	0005
Kapellen d.		0555	0610	0637	0655	0710	0737	same minutes	2055	2110	2155	2210	2255		0610	0710	0810	hourly	2210	2325	0025
Essen 🏛 d.		0612	0631	0655	0712	0731	0755	past each	2112	2131	2212	2230	2312		0631	0731	0831	until	2231	2345	0045
Roosendaal a.		...	0638	...	...	0738	...	hour until	...	2138	...	2238	...		0638	0738	0838		2238	...	...

♡ – To/from Brussels (Table **420**); most continue to/from Charleroi.

420 BREDA - ANTWERPEN - BRUSSELS - CHARLEROI *Lines 25, 124*

For *Thalys* services Paris - Brussels - Antwerpen - Amsterdam see Table **18**. For additional trains Antwerpen - Brussels Nationaal ✈ see Table **432**.

km			Ⓐ	Ⓐ	Ⓐ	Ⓐ	Ⓐ	Ⓐ ♡	Ⓐ	Ⓐ	Ⓐ ♡	Ⓐ	Ⓐ ♡	Ⓐ	Ⓐ ♥	Ⓐ ♡	Ⓐ	Ⓐ ♡	△	Ⓐ	Ⓐ ♥	Ⓐ ♡	Ⓐ	Ⓐ
0	**Breda** 🏛 d.	Ⓐ	...	...	...	...	...	...	...	...	...	...	...	...	0742	...	...	...		...	2042	...	...	...
33	Noorderkempen (Brecht) d.		...	...	...	...	...	...	...	0701	...	...	...	...	0801	...	...	...		...	2101	...	...	...
57	**Antwerpen** Centraal a.		...	...	...	...	...	...	...	0717	...	...	...	...	0816	...	...	...	and	...	2116	...	...	...
57	**Antwerpen** Centraal 432 d.		0454	...	0554	0625	0637	0654	0708	0719	0725	0737	0754	0808	0819	0825	0836	0854	at	2106	2119	2125	2154	2205
59	Antwerpen Berchem d.		0459	...	0559	0630	0642	0659	0713	0724	0730	0742	0759	0813	0825	0830	0842	0859	the	2111	2125	2130	2159	2210
81	Mechelen 432 d.		0514	...	0614	0644	0704	0714	0735	0739	0744	0804	0814	0835	0839	0844	0904	0914	same	2133	2139	2144	2214	2247
	Brussels Airport ✈ 432 a.		|	...	|	|	|	|	|	0751	|	|	|	|	0850	|	|	|	minutes	|	2150	|	|	|
101	Brussels Nord d.		0532	0602	0632	0702	0724	0732	0756	...	0802	0824	0832	0856	0908	0902	0924	0932	past	2154	2208	2202	2232	2317
103	Brussels Central d.		0537	0607	0637	0707	0729	0737	0801	...	0807	0829	0837	0901	0913	0907	0929	0937	each	2159	2213	2207	2237	2321
105	**Brussels** Midi/Zuid a.		0541	0611	0641	0711	0733	0741	0805	...	0811	0833	0841	0905	0917	0911	0933	0941	hour	2203	2217	2211	2241	2325
105	**Brussels** Midi/Zuid d.		0545	0615	0645	0715	...	0745	...	...	0815	...	0845	...	...	0915	...	0945	until	...	...	2215	2245	2332
134	Nivelles d.		0611	0641	0711	0740	...	0811	...	...	0841	...	0911	...	...	0941	...	1011		...	...	2241	2311	|
160	**Charleroi** Sud a.		0636	0706	0736	0808	...	0836	...	...	0906	...	0936	...	...	1006	...	1036		...	...	2306	2336	0027

	Ⓐ ♥	Ⓐ	Ⓐ	Ⓐ	Ⓐ ♥	Ⓐ ♡			Ⓒ	Ⓒ	Ⓒ	Ⓒ	Ⓒ	Ⓒ	Ⓒ	Ⓒ ♥	Ⓒ		Ⓒ	Ⓒ ♥	Ⓒ	Ⓒ	Ⓒ ♥	
Breda 🏛 d.	2142	...	...	...	2242	...	...	Ⓒ	...	...	...	...	...	...	...	0742	...		...	2142	...	...	2242	...
Noorderkempen (Brecht) d.	2201	...	...	...	2301	...	...		...	...	...	...	...	...	...	0801	...		...	2201	...	...	2301	...
Antwerpen Centraal a.	2216	...	...	...	2316	...	...		...	...	...	...	...	...	...	0816	...	and	...	2216	...	...	2316	...
Antwerpen Centraal 432 d.	2219	2225	2254	2305	2319	2325	...		...	0540	0609	0640	0709	0740	0809	0819	0840	at	2209	2219	2240	2309	2319	...
Antwerpen Berchem d.	2225	2230	2259	2310	2325	2330	...		...	0545	0614	0645	0714	0745	0814	0825	0845	the	2214	2225	2245	2314	2325	...
Mechelen 432 d.	2239	2244	2314	2347	2339	2344	...		...	0603	0632	0703	0732	0803	0832	0839	0903	same	2232	2239	2303	2332	2339	...
Brussels Airport ✈ 432 a.	2250	|	|	|	2350	|	...		...	|	|	|	|	|	|	0850	|	minutes	|	2250	|	|	2350	...
Brussels Nord d.	2308	2302	2332	0013	0008	0002	...		0555	0623	0655	0723	0755	0823	0855	0907	0923	past	2255	2307	2323	2355	0006	...
Brussels Central d.	2313	2307	2337	0017	0013	0007	...		0559	0627	0659	0727	0759	0827	0859	0912	0927	each	2259	2312	2327	2359	0011	...
Brussels Midi/Zuid a.	2317	2311c	2341	0021	0017	0011c	...		0603	0631	0703	0731	0803	0831	0903	0916	0931	hour	2303	2316	2331	0003	0015	...
Brussels Midi/Zuid d.	...	...	...	0024	...	...	...		0606	...	0706	...	0806	...	0906	...	...	until	2306	...	...	...	...	...
Nivelles d.	...	...	...	|	...	...	...		0633	...	0733	...	0832	...	0933	...	...		2333	...	...	...	...	...
Charleroi Sud a.	...	...	...	0122	...	...	...		0656	...	0756	...	0857	...	0956	...	...		2358	...	...	...	...	...

		Ⓐ ♡	Ⓐ	Ⓐ	Ⓐ ⊡	Ⓐ ♥	Ⓐ ♡	Ⓐ	Ⓐ	Ⓐ	Ⓐ ♥	Ⓐ ♡	Ⓐ	Ⓐ	Ⓐ	Ⓐ ♥	Ⓐ ♡		Ⓐ	Ⓐ ♥	Ⓐ ♡	Ⓐ	Ⓐ	Ⓐ ♥
Charleroi Sud d.	Ⓐ	...	...	...	0426	...	...	...	0523	...	...	0552	...	0623	...	...	0654		...	...	1854	...	1923	...
Nivelles d.		...	...	...	0455	...	...	...	0551	...	...	0620	...	0651	...	...	0720		...	...	1920	...	1951	...
Brussels Midi/Zuid a.		...	...	...	0535	...	...	...	0616	...	...	0645	...	0716	...	...	0745	and	...	...	1945	...	2016	...
Brussels Midi/Zuid d.		0449	0519	0526	0538	0545	0549	0556	0619	0626	0645	0649	0659	0718	0726	0744	0747	at	1926	1945	1949	1956	2019	2045
Brussels Central d.		0454	0524	0531	0542	0550	0554	0601	0624	0631	0650	0654	0704	0723	0731	0749	0752	the	1931	1950	1954	2001	2024	2050
Brussels Nord d.		0502	0530	0538	0549	0556	0602	0608	0630	0638	0656	0702	0710	0730	0738	0756	0802	same	1938	1956	2002	2008	2030	2056
Brussels Airport ✈ 432 d.		|	|	|	|	0611	|	|	|	|	0711	|	|	|	|	0811	|	minutes	|	2011	|	|	|	2111
Mechelen 432 d.		0518	0546	0558	0617	0624	0618	0629	0646	0658	0724	0718	0731	0746	0758	0824	0818	past	1958	2024	2018	2029	2046	2124
Antwerpen Berchem d.		0531	0559	0619	0651	0638	0631	0649	0659	0719	0738	0731	0752	0759	0819	0838	0831	each	2019	2038	2031	2049	2059	2138
Antwerpen Centraal 432 a.		0535	0603	0623	0655	0642	0635	0653	0703	0723	0742	0735	0756	0803	0823	0842	0835	hour	2023	2042	2035	2053	2103	2142
Antwerpen Centraal d.		...	...	...	...	0644	...	...	...	...	0744	...	...	...	...	0844	...	until	...	2044	...	...	...	2144
Noorderkempen (Brecht) d.		...	...	...	...	0701	...	...	...	...	0801	...	...	...	...	0901	...		...	2101	...	...	...	2201
Breda 🏛 a.		...	...	...	...	0718	...	...	...	...	0818	...	...	...	...	0918	...		...	2118	...	...	...	2218

	Ⓐ ♡	Ⓐ	Ⓐ ♡	Ⓐ	Ⓐ	Ⓐ	Ⓐ	Ⓐ		Ⓒ ♥	Ⓒ	Ⓒ	Ⓒ ♥	Ⓒ	Ⓒ		Ⓒ ♥	Ⓒ	Ⓒ	Ⓒ	Ⓒ	Ⓒ	Ⓒ	⑥ ⊡
Charleroi Sud d.	1954	2023	2054	2123	2154	...	2223	...	Ⓒ	...	0505	...	...	0605	...		...	2005	...	2105	...	2205	...	...
Nivelles d.	2020	2051	2120	2151	2220	...	2251	...		...	0531	...	...	0631	...		...	2031	...	2131	...	2231	...	2304
Brussels Midi/Zuid a.	2045	2116	2145	2216	2245	...	2317	...		...	0556	...	...	0656	...	and	...	2056	...	2156	...	2257	...	2340
Brussels Midi/Zuid d.	2049	2119	2149	2219	2249	2256	2319	2356		0544	0600	0628	0644	0700	0728	at	2044	2100	2128	2200	2228	2300	2328	2342
Brussels Central d.	2054	2124	2154	2224	2254	2301	2324	0001		0549	0604	0632	0649	0704	0732	the	2049	2104	2132	2204	2232	2304	2332	2346
Brussels Nord d.	2102	2132	2202	2230	2302	2308	2328	0008		0556	0610	0638	0656	0710	0738	same	2056	2110	2138	2210	2238	2310	2338	2353
Brussels Airport ✈ 432 d.	|	|	|	|	|	|	...	|		0611	|	|	0711	|	|	minutes	2111	|	|	|	|	|	|	|
Mechelen 432 d.	2118	2148	2218	2246	2318	2329	...	0029		0624	0630	0659	0724	0730	0759	past	2124	2130	2159	2230	2259	2330	2359	0019
Antwerpen Berchem d.	2131	2201	2231	2259	2331	2350	...	0049		0638	0647	0716	0738	0747	0816	each	2138	2147	2216	2247	2316	2347	0016	0051
Antwerpen Centraal 432 a.	2135	2205	2235	2303	2335	2354	...	0053		0642	0651	0720	0742	0751	0820	hour	2142	2151	2220	2251	2320	2351	0020	0055
Antwerpen Centraal d.	...	...	...	...	...	...	...	...		0644	...	...	0744	...	...	until	2144	...	...	...	...	...	...	...
Noorderkempen (Brecht) d.	...	...	...	...	...	...	...	...		0701	...	...	0801	...	...		2201	...	...	...	...	...	...	...
Breda 🏛 a.	...	...	...	...	...	...	...	...		0718	...	...	0818	...	...		2218	...	...	...	...	...	...	...

c – Connects with train to Charleroi in preceding column.

△ – No service from Antwerpen at 2036.
♥ – From/to Amsterdam or Den Haag via Rotterdam (Table **18**).
♡ – From/to Essen (Belgium), Table **419**.
⊡ – Local train.

BRUSSELS AIRPORT ✈ - CHARLEROI

Runs Ⓐ only

	Ⓐ		Ⓐ	
Brussels Airport ✈ d.	0547		2147	...
Brussels Schuman d.	0603	and	2203	...
Brussels Luxembourg d.	0610	hourly	2210	...
Nivelles d.	0652	until	2252	...
Charleroi Sud a.	0721		2321	...

	Ⓐ		Ⓐ	
Charleroi Sud d.	0539		2139	...
Nivelles d.	0608	and	2208	...
Brussels Luxembourg d.	0654	hourly	2254	...
Brussels Schuman d.	0657	until	2257	...
Brussels Airport ✈ a.	0712		2312	...

421 CHARLEROI - MARIEMBOURG - COUVIN *Line 132*

km			Ⓐ	Ⓐ	Ⓐ		Ⓐ	Ⓐ		Ⓒ		⑥
0	**Charleroi** Sud d.	Ⓐ	0547	0704	0818		1918	2212	Ⓒ	0816		2216
18	Berzée d.		0609	0728	0837	every	1937	2230		0836	every	2236
22	Walcourt d.		0621	0736	0844	hour	1944	2237		0846	**two**	2246
35	Philippeville d.		0635	0750	0859	until	1959	2251		0900	hours	2300
48	Mariembourg ▲ d.		0647	0802	0911	△	2011	2303		0912	until	2312
53	**Couvin** a.		0653	0808	0917		2017	2309		0918		2318

		Ⓐ	Ⓐ		Ⓐ	Ⓐ		Ⓒ		Ⓒ
Couvin d.	Ⓐ	0730	0839		1439	2039	Ⓒ	0640		2040
Mariembourg ▲ d.		0739	0848	every	1448	2048		0651	every	2049
Philippeville d.		0751	0900	hour	1500	2100		0702	**two**	2101
Walcourt d.		0805	0915	until	1514	2115		0716	hours	2115
Berzée d.		0810	0929	▽	1519	2121		0723	until	2122
Charleroi Sud a.		0830	0940		1545	2141		0745		2144

△ – Also from Charleroi Sud at 1644, 1721, 1741, 1821, 2016, 2116 (no journey at 1718).
▽ – Also from Couvin at 0434, 0457, 0540, 0615, 0638, 1604, 1642, 1804, 1840, 1939.

▲ – For MARIEMBOURG - TREIGNES heritage railway operated by *Chemin de Fer à Vapeur des 3 Vallées* (CFV3V). For days of running and timings see www.cfv3v.eu

BRUSSELS - MONS - QUIÉVRAIN 422

Lines 96, 97

km		Ⓐ	Ⓐ ◇	Ⓐ	Ⓐ ◇	Ⓐ		Ⓐ ◇	Ⓐ	Ⓐ ◇	Ⓐ	Ⓐ ◇	Ⓐ	Ⓐ ◇	Ⓐ	Ⓐ ◇	Ⓐ		Ⓒ		Ⓒ
0	**Brussels Airport** ✈ d.	0530	...	0630	...	0730		...	1930	...	2030	...	2130	...	2230	...	2330	...	0531		2231
12	Brussels Nord 423 d.	0543	0613	0643	0712	0743	and	1913	1943	2013	2043	2113	2143	2213	2243	2313	2343	...	0543		2243
14	Brussels Central 423 d.	0548	0618	0648	0717	0748	at	1918	1948	2018	2048	2118	2148	2218	2248	2318	2348	...	0548		2248
16	**Brussels Midi / Zuid** 423 d.	0556	0625	0655	0725	0756	the	1925	1956	2025	2055	2125	2156	2225	2256	2325	2356	...	0556	and	2256
32	Halle 423 d.	|	0635	|	0735	|	same	1935	|	2035	|	2135	|	2235	|	2335	|	...	|	hourly	|
45	Braine-le-Comte 423 d.	0617	0647	0718	0747	0819	minutes	1947	2017	2047	2118	2147	2217	2247	2317	2347	0017	...	0617	until	2317
51	Soignies d.	0623	0654	0724	0753	0825	past	1953	2023	2053	2124	2154	2223	2253	2323	2353	0023	...	0624		2324
76	**Mons** a.	0643	0713	0743	0812	0844	each	2012	2043	2112	2143	2213	2243	2312	2343	0012	0043	...	0643		2343
76	**Mons** d.	...	0715	...	0814	...	hour	2014	...	2114	...	2215	...	2314	...	...	...	...	⊡		⊡
86	Saint-Ghislain a.	...	0729	...	0829	...	until	2028	...	2128	...	2229	...	2328	...	...	...	...	⊡		⊡
96	**Quiévrain** a.	...	0750	...	0849	...		2047	...	...	...	...	...	...	...	...	...	...	⊡		⊡

	Ⓐ	Ⓐ ◇	Ⓐ	Ⓐ ◇	Ⓐ	Ⓐ ◇	Ⓐ	Ⓐ ◇	Ⓐ		Ⓐ ◇	Ⓐ	Ⓐ ◇	Ⓐ	Ⓐ			Ⓒ		Ⓒ	
Quiévrain d.	...	...	...	0513	...	0613	...	0713	...		1913	...	2013	...	...	...	...	⊡		⊡	...
Saint-Ghislain d.	...	...	...	0531	...	0631	...	0731	...	and	1931	...	2031	...	...	...	...	⊡		⊡	...
Mons a.	...	...	...	0545	...	0645	...	0745	...	at	1945	...	2045	...	...	...	...	⊡		⊡	...
Mons d.	0419	0448	0519	0548	0618	0648	0718	0748	0819	the	1948	2019	2048	2119	2219	...	...	0518		2218	...
Soignies d.	0440	0509	0540	0609	0639	0709	0739	0809	0840	same	2009	2040	2109	2140	2240	...	...	0540		2240	...
Braine-le-Comte 423 d.	0447	0516	0547	0616	0645	0716	0745	0816	0847	minutes	2016	2047	2116	2147	2247	...	...	0547	and	2247	...
Halle 423 d.	|	0526	|	0626	|	0727	|	0827	|	past	2026	|	2126	|	|	...	...	|	hourly	|	...
Brussels Midi / Zuid 423 a.	0506	0535	0605	0635	0703	0736	0804	0836	0905	each	2035	2105	2135	2205	2305	...	...	0605	until	2305	...
Brussels Central 423 a.	0513	0542	0613	0642	0710	0742	0810	0842	0913	hour	2042	2113	2142	2213	2313	...	...	0613		2313	...
Brussels Nord 423 a.	0518	0547	0618	0647	0715	0747	0815	0847	0918	until	2047	2118	2147	2218	2318	...	...	0618		2318	...
Brussels Airport ✈ a.	0531	...	0631	...	0728	...	0828	...	0931		...	2131	...	2231	2331	...	...	0631		2331	...

◇ – From / to Liège via Landen (Table **430**).

⊡ – MONS - QUIÉVRAIN LOCAL TRAINS ON Ⓒ: from Mons hourly 0654Ⓒ - 2054Ⓒ, from Quiévrain hourly 0737Ⓒ - 2137Ⓒ.

BRUSSELS - LA LOUVIÈRE - BINCHE 423

Lines 96, 108

For additional trains Brussels - Halle - Braine-le-Comte see Table **422**

km		Ⓐ		Ⓐ	Ⓐ	Ⓐ	Ⓒ		Ⓒ
0	**Brussels** Nord d.	0618		2018	2118	2218	0618		2218
2	Brussels Central d.	0623		2023	2123	2223	0622		2222
4	**Brussels** Midi / Zuid d.	0630	and	2030	2130	2230	0630	and	2230
20	Halle d.	0641	hourly	2041	2141	2241	0643	hourly	2243
33	Braine-le-Comte d.	0658	until	2058	2158	2256	0700	until	2300
52	**La Louvière** Centre d.	0718		2118	2218	...	0721		2321
55	La Louvière Sud a.	0722		2122	2222	...	0725		2325
64	**Binche** a.	0739		2139	...	...	0748		2348

	Ⓐ		Ⓐ	Ⓒ	Ⓒ		Ⓒ
Binche d.	0521		2120	0512	0612		2212
La Louvière Sud d.	0538		2138	0535	0635		2235
La Louvière Centre d.	0544	and	2144	0541	0641	and	2241
Braine-le-Comte d.	0606	hourly	2206	0604	0704	hourly	2304
Halle d.	0620	until	2220	0620	0720	until	2320
Brussels Midi / Zuid a.	0630		2230	0630	0730		2330
Brussels Central a.	0637		2237	0636	0736		2336
Brussels Nord a.	0642		2242	0641	0741		2341

On Ⓐ trains run beyond Brussels to / from Turnhout (Table **434**).

BRUSSELS - GERAARDSBERGEN 424

Lines 94, 123 (S6)

km		Ⓐ		Ⓐ	Ⓒ		Ⓒ
0	**Brussels** Nord d.	0442		2042	0742		2042
2	Brussels Centraal d.	0446	and	2046	0746	and	2046
4	**Brussels** Midi / Zuid d.	0453	hourly	2053	0753	hourly	2053
18	Halle d.	0504	until	2104	0804	until	2104
33	Edingen d.	0515		2115	0815		2115
49	**Geraardsbergen** a.	0534		2134	0834		2134

	Ⓐ		Ⓐ	Ⓒ		Ⓒ
Geraardsbergen d.	0425		2025	0725		2025
Edingen d.	0446	and	2046	0746	and	2046
Halle d.	0458	hourly	2057	0758	hourly	2058
Brussels Midi / Zuid a.	0507	until	2107	0807	until	2107
Brussels Centraal a.	0513		2113	0813		2113
Brussels Nord a.	0518		2118	0818		2118

MONS - CHARLEROI - NAMUR 425

Lines 118, 130

km		Ⓐ	Ⓐ	Ⓐ	Ⓐ ♡	Ⓐ	Ⓐ ◇	Ⓐ		Ⓐ	Ⓐ	Ⓐ	Ⓐ	Ⓐ	Ⓐ	Ⓒ	Ⓒ ♡	Ⓒ ♡		Ⓒ ♡	Ⓒ ♡
	Tournai 416 d.	...	...	...	0542	...	0643	...	and at	1943	...	2043	...	2143	...	...	0629	0729		2029	2129
0	**Mons** d.	0437	...	0539	0615	0639	0715	0739	the same	2015	2039	2116	2139	2216	2239	0614	0714	0814		2114	2214
20	La Louvière Sud d.	0453	...	0558	0631	0657	0731	0758	minutes	2031	2058	2131	2158	2231	2259	0632	0732	0832	and	2132	2232
41	**Charleroi** Sud d.	0513	0550	0619	0650	0719	0750	0819	past	2050	2119	2150	2217	2250	2317	0653	0754	0854	hourly	2154	2254
56	Tamines d.	0527	0602	0632	0704	0732	0804	0832	each	2104	2132	2204	2232	2304	...	0708	0809	0909	until	2209	2309
78	**Namur** a.	0549	0621	0649	0721	0749	0821	0849	hour	2121	2149	2221	2253	2321	...	0730	0830	0930		2230	2330
	Liège Guillemins 442 a.	0636	...	0736	...	0836	...	0936	until	...	2236	...	...	...	...	0820	0920	1020		2320	...

	Ⓐ	Ⓐ	Ⓐ ◇	Ⓐ	Ⓐ ◇	Ⓐ	Ⓐ ◇		Ⓐ	Ⓐ	Ⓐ	Ⓐ	Ⓐ	Ⓐ	Ⓐ	Ⓒ ♡	Ⓒ ♡	Ⓒ ♡		Ⓒ ♡	Ⓒ
Liège Guillemins 442 d.	...	...	...	0524	...	0624	...	and at	1923	...	2023	...	2123	...	2223	...	...	0640		2040	2140
Namur d.	...	0507	0540	0612	0640	0712	0740	the same	2012	2040	2112	2140	2211	2240	2312	...	0630	0730		2130	2230
Tamines d.	...	0530	0557	0631	0657	0731	0757	minutes	2031	2057	2131	2157	2232	2257	2333	...	0653	0752	and	2152	2252
Charleroi Sud d.	0443	0545	0612	0645	0712	0745	0812	past	2045	2112	2145	2212	2251	2310	2352	0609	0709	0809	hourly	2209	2307
La Louvière Sud d.	0505	0606	0629	0706	0730	0806	0830	each	2106	2129	2206	2229	2309	...	...	0630	0730	0830	until	2230	...
Mons a.	0521	0621	0644	0721	0744	0821	0844	hour	2121	2144	2221	2244	2330	...	...	0646	0746	0846		2246	...
Tournai 416 a.	...	...	0715	...	0815	...	0915	until	...	2215	...	2321	...	...	...	0730	0830	0930		2330	...

◇ – Certain journeys run from / to Lille Flandres (Table **416**).

♡ – From / to Mouscron (Table **416**).

MONS - QUÉVY 426

Line 96

km		Ⓐ	Ⓐ	Ⓐ		Ⓐ	Ⓐ§	Ⓐ§	Ⓐ	Ⓐ	Ⓐ
0	Mons d.	0723	0822	0922	hourly	1622	1729	1811	1922	2022	2122
18	Quévy a.	0738	0838	0938	until	1638	1748	1831	1938	2038	2138

	Ⓐ	Ⓐ‡	Ⓐ	Ⓐ	Ⓐ‡	Ⓐ	Ⓐ		Ⓐ	Ⓐ
Quévy d.	0513	0549	0613	0644	0705	0813	0914	hourly	1915	2013
Mons a.	0539	0615	0638	0709	0731	0839	0939	until	1941	2039

§ – From Brussels (depart Brussels Midi 1640 and 1717).

‡ – To Brussels (arrive Brussels Midi 0703 and 0820).

No service on Ⓒ.

CHARLEROI - ERQUELINNES 427

Line 130a

29*km*. Journey time: 41 – 47 minutes on Ⓐ; 38 – 40 minutes on Ⓒ. Trains call at Thuin (*14km*, 15 – 17 minutes from Charleroi; *15km*, 20 minutes from Erquelinnes).

From Charleroi Sud on Ⓐ at 0528, 0640, 0721, 0751, 0840, 0949, 1044, 1144, 1244, 1344, 1444, 1544, 1616, 1649, 1725, 1744, 1844, 1946 and 2044.

From Charleroi Sud on Ⓒ at 0614, 0814 and every **two** hours until 2014.

From Erquelinnes on Ⓐ at 0459, 0558, 0619, 0657, 0735, 0807, 0857, 1000, 1057, 1157, 1257, 1357, 1457, 1558, 1628, 1701, 1756, 1858, 2000 and 2057.

From Erquelinnes on Ⓒ at 0705, 0905 and every **two** hours until 2105.

☛ Jeumont (France) is approximately 2 km from Erquelinnes station (for Jeumont - Lille see Table **262**).

CROSS-BORDER SERVICES 428

	Ⓐ	Ⓐ	⑥	⑥	†	†	Ⓐ	Ⓒ	Ⓒ
Namur d.	0501	...	0619	...	0719	...	1346	1616	...
Charleroi Sud d.	0542	...	0652	...	0755	...	1435	1646	...
Mons d.	|	0615	|	0715	|	0815	|	|	1706
Maubeuge 🏛 a.	0623	|	0730	|	0830	|	1523	1720	|
Aulnoye-Aymeries 🏛 a.	...	0642	...	0742	...	0842	...	...	1733

	Ⓐ	Ⓐ		Ⓒ	Ⓒ		Ⓐ	Ⓒ	Ⓒ
Aulnoye-Aymeries 🏛 d.	...	0917	...	...	1220	...	...	...	2115
Maubeuge 🏛 d.	0930	|	...	1232	|	...	1932	2131	|
Mons a.	|	0955	...	|	1300	...	|	|	2155
Charleroi Sud a.	1010	...	...	1307	...	...	2010	2206	...
Namur a.	1054	...	...	1340	...	...	2041	2240	...

☛ *Subject to cancellation; please check locally.*

Trains call only at the stations shown. For connections Maubeuge - Paris and Aulnoye - Paris see Table **255**.

430 BRUSSELS - LANDEN - HASSELT, GENK and LIÈGE

Lines 36, 21

For direct services Brussels - Liège via high-speed line see Table **400**. For other services Brussels - Hasselt on Ⓐ (via Aarshot) see Table **431**.

km			Ⓐ ♡	Ⓐ	Ⓐ •	Ⓐ ♡	Ⓐ △	Ⓐ •		Ⓐ ♡	Ⓐ △	Ⓐ •	Ⓐ ♡	Ⓐ △					Ⓐ	Ⓐ	Ⓐ	Ⓐ	Ⓐ	
0	**Brussels** Midi/Zuid d.	Ⓐ	0511	0515	0538	0611	0615	0638		2111	2114	2138	2211	2215	...	...	...		1603	1631	1707	1731	1801	...
2	Brussels Central d.		0516	0519	0543	0616	0619	0643	and	2116	2118	2143	2216	2219	...	...	...		1608	1636	1712	1736	1806	...
4	Brussels Nord d.		0522	0525	0549	0622	0625	0649	at	2122	2125	2149	2222	2225	...	...	...		1614	1642	1718	1742	1812	...
16	**Brussels Airport** ✈ d.		|	0537	|	|	0637	|	the	|	2137	|	|	2237	...	...	...	A	|	|	|	|	|	...
33	Leuven d.		0541	0553	0610	0641	0653	0710	same	2142	2153	2210	2241	2253	...	...	...	L	1635	1703	1737	1803	1832	...
64	Tienen d.		0555	0609	0624	0655	0709	0724	minutes	2155	2209	2224	2255	2309	...	...	...	S	1649	1717	1752	1817	1846	...
64	Landen d.		0606	0622	0635	0706	0722	0735	past	2206	2222	2235	2306	2322	...	...	...	O	1700	1729	1803	1829	1855	...
75	Sint-Truiden d.		0615	...	|	0717	...	|	each	2215	...	|	2315	...	...	...	...		|	1744	|	1845	...	...
92	**Hasselt** a.		0630	...	|	0731	...	|	hour	2230	...	|	2330	...	...	...	...		|	1800	|	1901	...	...
108	Genk a.		0651	...	|	0751	...	|	until	2251	...	|	...	...	...	...	...		|	...	|	1923	...	...
103	**Liège** Guillemins a.		...	...	0706	...	...	0809		...	...	2306	...	...	...	...	...		1737	...	1837	...	...	...

		Ⓒ ♡	Ⓒ	Ⓒ ♡	Ⓒ	Ⓒ △	Ⓒ ♡	Ⓒ	Ⓒ △		Ⓒ ♡	Ⓒ	Ⓒ △	Ⓒ ♡	Ⓒ △	Ⓒ b	Ⓒ △	Ⓒ b						
Brussels Midi/Zuid d.	Ⓒ	0612	...	0712	...	0715	0812	...	0815		2112	...	2115	2212	2215	2256	2315	0020	...	...	...	...	...	...
Brussels Central d.		0617	...	0717	...	0719	0817	...	0819	and	2117	...	2119	2217	2219	2301	2319	0025	...	...	...	...	...	...
Brussels Nord d.		0623	...	0723	...	0725	0823	...	0825	at	2123	...	2125	2223	2225	2307	2325	0031	...	...	...	...	...	...
Brussels Airport ✈ d.		|	...	|	...	0738	|	...	0843	the	|	...	2138	|	2238	|	2338	|	...	...	...	...	...	...
Leuven d.		0642	...	0742	...	0754	0842	...	0859	same	2142	...	2154	2242	2254	2326	2352	0050	...	...	...	...	...	...
Tienen d.		0656	...	0756	...	0810	0856	...	0915	minutes	2156	...	2210	2256	2310	2341	...	0103	...	...	...	...	...	...
Landen d.		0707	0712	0807	0812	0823	0907	0912	0928	past	2207	2212	2223	2307	2323	2352	...	0114	...	...	...	...	...	...
Sint-Truiden d.		0716	|	0816	|	...	0916	|	...	each	2216	|	...	2316	...	|	...	|	...	...	...	...	...	...
Hasselt a.		0731	|	0831	|	...	0931	|	...	hour	2231	|	...	2331	...	|	...	|	...	...	...	...	...	...
Genk a.		0751	|	0851	|	...	0951	|	...	until	2251	|	...	2351	...	|	...	|	...	...	...	...	...	...
Liège Guillemins a.		...	0754	...	0854	...	...	0954	...		...	2255	...	...	...	0021	...	0142	...	...	...	...	...	...

		Ⓐ △	Ⓐ ♡	Ⓐ b	Ⓐ •	Ⓐ △	Ⓐ ♡	Ⓐ •	Ⓐ	Ⓐ △	Ⓐ ♡	Ⓐ •	Ⓐ △		Ⓐ ♡	Ⓐ •	Ⓐ			Ⓐ	Ⓐ	Ⓐ	Ⓐ	
Liège Guillemins d.	Ⓐ	...	...	0437	0455	...	...	0552	...	...	...	0655	...		...	2155	...	...		...	0623	...	0724	...
Genk d.		...	...	|	|	...	0507	|	0534	...	0607r	|	...	and	2107	|	...	...		...	|	0637	|	...
Hasselt d.		...	0428	|	|	...	0528	|	0555	...	0628	|	...	at	2128	|	...	...		...	|	0700	|	...
Sint-Truiden d.		...	0444	|	|	...	0544	|	0616	...	0644	|	...	the	2144	|	...	...	A	...	|	0718	|	...
Landen d.		0435	0455	0508	0528	0535	0555	0625	0629	0633	0655	0727	0735	same	2155	2228	2235	...	L	0642	0701	0732	0801	...
Tienen d.		0452	0507	0520	0539	0552	0607	0636	0644	0650	0707	0739	0752	minutes	2207	2239	2252	...	S	0655	0713	0744	0813	...
Leuven d.		0508	0521	0533	0553	0608	0621	0652	0659	0707	0722	0753	0808	past	2221	2253	2308	...	O	0709	0727	0759	0827	...
Brussels Airport ✈ a.		0521	|	|	|	0621	|	|	|	0721	|	|	0821	each	|	|	2321	...		|	|	|	|	...
Brussels Nord a.		0534	0538	0549	0611	0634	0638	0710	0717	0734	0740	0813	0834	hour	2238	2311	2334	...		0726	0745	0817	0845	...
Brussels Central a.		0540	0544	0555	0617	0640	0644	0716	0723	0739	0748	0819	0839	until	2244	2317	2340	...		0732	0751	0823	0851	...
Brussels Midi/Zuid a.		0545	0549	0600	0622	0645	0649	0721	0728	0744	0753	0824	0844		2249	2322	2345	...		0737	0756	0828	0856	...

		Ⓒ △	Ⓒ b	Ⓒ △	Ⓒ △	Ⓒ ♡	Ⓒ △	Ⓒ	Ⓒ ♡	Ⓒ △	Ⓒ	Ⓒ ♡	Ⓒ △		Ⓒ	Ⓒ ♡	Ⓒ △	Ⓒ	Ⓒ ♡	Ⓒ	Ⓒ	Ⓒ ♡	Ⓒ b	
Liège Guillemins d.	Ⓒ	...	0438	...	...	...	...	0705	...	...	0805	...	...		2005	...	...	2105	...	...	2204	...	2304	...
Genk d.		...	|	...	...	...	...	|	0707	...	|	0807	...	and	|	2003	...	|	2107	...	|	2203	|	...
Hasselt d.		...	|	...	...	0630	...	|	0728	...	|	0830	...	at	|	2028	...	|	2128	...	|	2230	|	...
Sint-Truiden d.		...	|	...	...	0645	...	|	0744	...	|	0845	...	the	|	2044	...	|	2144	...	|	2245	|	...
Landen d.		...	0506	0535	0635	0656	0735	0746	0755	0835	0846	0856	0936	same	2046	2055	2135	2146	2155	2235	2246	2256	2333	...
Tienen d.		...	0517	0552	0652	0708	0752	...	0807	0852	...	0908	0953	minutes	...	2107	2152	...	2207	2252	...	2308	2345	...
Leuven d.		0507	0533	0608	0708	0721	0808	...	0821	0908	...	0921	1009	past	...	2121	2208	...	2221	2308	...	2321	2359	...
Brussels Airport ✈ a.		0521	|	0621	0721	|	0821	...	|	0921	...	|	1022	each	...	|	2221	...	|	2321	...	|	|	...
Brussels Nord a.		0534	0550	0634	0735	0738	0835	...	0838	0935	...	0938	1034	hour	...	2138	2234	...	2238	2334	...	2338	0016	...
Brussels Central a.		0540	0557	0640	0740	0744	0840	...	0844	0940	...	0944	1040	until	...	2144	2240	...	2244	2340	...	2344	0022	...
Brussels Midi/Zuid a.		0545	0602	0645	0745	0749	0845	...	0849	0945	...	0949	1045		...	2149	2245	...	2249	2345	...	2349	0027	...

b – From/to Brugge and Oostende (Table **400**).
r – Journey at 0907 departs Genk at 0852 (arrives Hasselt 0912).
♡ – From/to Brugge and Gent, Table **405** (most trains also from/to Blankenberge).
△ – From/to Gent via Aalst, Table **412** (on Ⓒ most trains also from/to De Panne, Table **411**).
• – From/to Mons and Quiévrain (Table **422**).

431 BRUSSELS - AARSCHOT - HASSELT - TONGEREN

Line 35

No service on Ⓒ via this route. For other trains Brussels - Hasselt (via Landen) see Table **430**.

km			Ⓐ	Ⓐ	Ⓐ		Ⓐ	Ⓐ	Ⓐ
	Gent **412** ▷ d.	Ⓐ	0441	0541	0639		1941	2041	2141
0	**Brussels** Midi/Zuid d.		0544	0644	0743		2044	2144	2244
2	Brussels Central d.		0549	0649	0748	and	2049	2149	2249
4	Brussels Nord d.		0555	0655	0755	hourly	2055	2155	2255
46	Aarschot **432** d.		0621	0721	0821	until	2121	2221	2321
63	Diest **432** d.		0634	0734	0834		2134	2234	2334
84	**Hasselt** **432** a.		0648	0748	0848		2148	2248	2348
110	Tongeren **435** a.		0721	0821	0921		2221	...	...

		Ⓐ	Ⓐ	Ⓐ	Ⓐ		Ⓐ	Ⓐ
Tongeren **435** d.	Ⓐ	...	0538	0635	0738r		2038	2138
Hasselt **432** d.		0511	0611	0711	0811		2111	2211
Diest **432** d.		0527	0627	0727	0827	and	2127	2227
Aarschot **432** d.		0541	0641	0741	0841	hourly	2141	2241
Brussels Nord a.		0605	0705	0805	0905	until	2205	2305
Brussels Central a.		0611	0711	0812	0911		2211	2311
Brussels Midi/Zuid a.		0616	0716	0817	0916		2216	2316
Gent **412** ▷ a.		0718	0818	0919	1019		2319	0019

r – Journey from Tongeren at 1938 requires a change at Hasselt.
▷ – Gent to Brussels is via Aalst and Denderleeuw (Table **412**).

432 ANTWERPEN - BRUSSELS NATIONAAL ✈ - AARSCHOT - HASSELT

Lines 35, 36c, 16

For Antwerpen - Hasselt via Mol see Table **434**. For additional trains Brussels Nationaal ✈ - Leuven see Table **430**.

km	*Via Airport*		Ⓐ		Ⓐ		Ⓒ		Ⓒ	Ⓒ
0	**Antwerpen** Centraal . **420** d.	Ⓐ	0449		2249	Ⓒ	0536		2136	2236
24	Mechelen **420** d.		0508		2308		0556		2156	2256
40	**Brussels Airport** ✈ . **420** d.		0521	and	2321		0610	and	2210	2310
59	Leuven d.		0542	hourly	2342		0633	hourly	2233	2333
75	Aarschot d.		0556	until	2356		0647	until	2247	2347
92	Diest d.		0609		0009		0706		2306	0006
113	**Hasselt** a.		0622		0022		0723		2323	0023

		Ⓐ		Ⓐ		Ⓒ ‡	Ⓒ		Ⓒ
Hasselt d.	Ⓐ	0436		2236	Ⓒ	...	0637		2237
Diest d.		0450		2250		...	0655		2255
Aarschot d.		0502	and	2302		...	0714	and	2314
Leuven d.		0524	hourly	2324		0536	0736	hourly	2336
Brussels Airport ✈ .. **420** a.		0539	until	2339		0550	0750	until	2350
Mechelen **420** a.		0552		2352		0604	0804		0004
Antwerpen Centraal.. **420** a.		0611		0011		0624	0824		0024

km	*Via Lier*		Ⓐ		Ⓐ		Ⓒ		Ⓒ	Ⓒ
0	**Antwerpen** Centraal d.	Ⓐ	0617		2017	Ⓒ	0628		2128	2228
14	Lier d.		0635	and	2035		0643	and	2143	2243
41	Aarschot d.		|	hourly	|		0717	hourly	2217	2317
59	Diest d.		0704	until	2104		0727	until	2230	2330
80	**Hasselt** a.		0717		2117		0743		2243	2343

		Ⓐ		Ⓐ		Ⓒ	Ⓒ		Ⓒ
Hasselt d.	Ⓐ	0541		1941	Ⓒ	0618	0718		2218
Diest d.		0555	and	1955		0633	0733	and	2233
Aarschot d.		|	hourly	|		0655	0755	hourly	2255
Lier d.		0626	until	2026		0717	0817	until	2317
Antwerpen Centraal a.		0642		2042		0731	0831		2331

km	*Via Lier*		Ⓐ		Ⓐ		Ⓒ		Ⓒ	
0	**Antwerpen** Centraal d.	Ⓐ	0632	and	2232	Ⓒ	0645	and	2245	...
14	Lier d.		0648	hourly	2249		0705	hourly	2305	...
41	Aarschot d.		0712	until	2312		0735	until	2335	...
57	**Leuven** a.		0724		2324		0748		2348	...

		Ⓐ		Ⓐ		Ⓒ		Ⓒ	
Leuven d.	Ⓐ	0636	and	2036	Ⓒ	0612	and	2212	...
Aarschot d.		0650	hourly	2050		0626	hourly	2226	...
Lier d.		0713	until	2113		0657	until	2257	...
Antwerpen Centraal a.		0728		2128		0715		2315	...

‡ – Also at 0636.

Line 15 — BRUSSELS and ANTWERPEN - LIER - TURNHOUT / HASSELT / HAMONT — 434

km			Ⓐ	Ⓐ	Ⓐ	Ⓐ	Ⓐ	Ⓐ	
	Brussels Midi / Zuid ▷ d.	Ⓐ	...	...	...	0633	...	...	
	Brussels Central ▷ d.		...	...	...	0638	...	...	
	Brussels Nord ▷ d.		...	...	...	0644	...	...	and
	Mechelen ▷ d.		...	...	...	0705	...	...	at
0	**Antwerpen** Centraal d.		0547	0609	0646	|	0709	0747	the
2	Antwerpen Berchem d.		0552	0615	0652	|	0715	0752	same
15	Lier d.		0603	0626	0703	0723	0727	0803	minutes
34	Herentals d.		0622	0643	0722	0738	0743	0822	past
	Turnhout a.		0637	|	0737	0753	|	0837	each
46	Geel d.		...	0655	...	...	0755	...	hour
56	Mol a.		...	0702	...	...	0802	...	until
99	**Hasselt** a.		...	0752r	...	...	0852r	...	
77	Overpelt a.		...	0722	...	...	0826	...	
79	Neerpelt a.		...	0726	...	...	0828	...	
87	**Hamont** a.		...	0738	...	...	0838	...	

	Ⓐ	Ⓐ	Ⓐ	Ⓐ	Ⓐ	Ⓐ	Ⓐ	Ⓐ	Ⓐ	Ⓐ	Ⓐ	Ⓐ	Ⓐ	
Brussels Midi / Zuid ▷ d.	1833	...	...	1933	...	...	2033	...	...	2133	...	2233	...	...
Brussels Central ▷ d.	1838	...	...	1938	...	...	2038	...	...	2138	...	2238	...	...
Brussels Nord ▷ d.	1844	...	...	1944	...	...	2044	...	...	2144	...	2244	...	...
Mechelen ▷ d.	1904	...	...	2004	...	...	2104	...	...	2204	...	2304	...	...
Antwerpen Centraal d.	|	1909	1947	|	2009	2047	|	2109	2147	|	2225	|	2325	...
Antwerpen Berchem d.	|	1915	1952	|	2015	2052	|	2115	2152	|	2230	|	2330	...
Lier d.	1922	1927	2003	2022	2027	2103	2122	2127	2203	2222	2244	2322	2345	...
Herentals d.	1938	1943	2022	2038	2043	2122	2138	2143	2222	2238	2306	2338	0007	...
Turnhout a.	1953	|	2037	2053	|	2137	2153	|	2237	2253	|	2353	|	...
Geel d.	...	1955	...	...	2055	...	...	2155	...	...	2318	...	0019	...
Mol a.	...	2002	...	...	2102	...	...	2202	...	...	2325	...	0026	...
Hasselt a.	...	2052r	...	...	2153r	...	...	2253r	...	...	|	...	...	...
Overpelt a.	...	2026	...	...	2122	...	...	2222	...	...	2342	...	...	...
Neerpelt a.	...	2028	...	...	2126	...	...	2226	...	...	2345	...	...	...
Hamont a.	...	2038	...	...	2138	...	...	2238	...	...	...	...	...	...

km			Ⓐ	Ⓐ	Ⓐ	Ⓐ	Ⓐ	Ⓐ	Ⓐ	Ⓐ	Ⓐ	Ⓐ	Ⓐ	
	Hamont d.	Ⓐ	...	...	...	0528	...	...	0619	...	...	0719	...	
	Neerpelt d.		...	...	...	0538	...	...	0634	...	...	0734	...	
	Overpelt d.		...	...	...	0541	...	...	0638	...	...	0738	...	and
	Hasselt d.		...	...	...	|	...	...	0607s	...	...	0707s	...	at
	Mol d.		0458	...	...	0558	...	...	0658	...	...	0758	...	the
	Geel d.		0506	...	...	0606	...	...	0707	...	...	0807	...	same
0	**Turnhout** d.		|	0458	0521	|	0604	0621	|	0704	0721	|	0804	minutes
18	Herentals d.		0520	0523	0543	0620	0623	0640	0720	0723	0740	0820	0823	past
38	Lier d.		0535	0539	0558	0635	0639	0657	0735	0739	0757	0835	0839	each
	Antwerpen Berchem a.		0545	|	0608	0645	|	0707	0745	|	0807	0845	|	hour
	Antwerpen Centraal a.		0551	|	0613	0651	|	0713	0751	|	0813	0851	|	until
55	Mechelen ▷ d.		...	0558	...	...	0658	...	...	0758	...	...	0858	
75	Brussels Nord ▷ a.		...	0616	...	...	0716	...	...	0816	...	...	0916	
77	Brussels Central ▷ a.		...	0622	...	...	0722	...	...	0822	...	...	0922	
79	**Brussels** Midi / Zuid ▷ a.		...	0627	...	...	0727	...	...	0827	...	...	0927	

	Ⓐ	Ⓐ	Ⓐ	Ⓐ	Ⓐ	Ⓐ	Ⓐ	Ⓐ	
Hamont d.	...	1919	...	...	2019	...	2119	...	...
Neerpelt d.	...	1934	...	...	2030	...	2130	...	...
Overpelt d.	...	1938	...	...	2033	...	2133	...	...
Hasselt d.	...	1907s	...	...	2008s	...	2108s	2208	...
Mol d.	...	1958	...	...	2058	...	2158	2253	...
Geel d.	...	2007	...	...	2106	...	2206	...	...
Turnhout d.	1921	|	2004	2021	|	2104	|	...	...
Herentals d.	1943	2020	2023	2043	2120	2123	2220	...	...
Lier d.	1958	2035	2039	2058	2135	2139	2235	...	...
Antwerpen Berchem a.	2008	2045	|	2108	2145	|	2245	...	...
Antwerpen Centraal a.	2013	2051	|	2113	2151	|	2251	...	...
Mechelen ▷ d.	...	...	2058	...	...	2158	...	...	...
Brussels Nord ▷ a.	...	...	2116	...	...	2216	...	...	...
Brussels Central ▷ a.	...	...	2122	...	...	2222	...	...	...
Brussels Midi / Zuid ▷ a.	...	...	2127	...	...	2227	...	...	...

		Ⓒ	Ⓒ	Ⓒ	Ⓒ		Ⓒ	Ⓒ △	Ⓒ ▽	Ⓒ
Antwerpen C. d.	Ⓒ	0609	0709	0753	0809		2009	2053	2109	2309
Ant. Berchem d.		0615	0715	0759	0815	and	2015	2059	2115	2315
Lier d.		0627	0727	0810	0827	at	2027	2110	2127	2327
Herentals d.		0643	0743	0832	0843	the	2043	2132	2143	2343
Turnhout a.		|	|	0847	|	same	|	2147	|	|
Geel d.		0655	0755	...	0855	minutes	2055	...	2155	2355
Mol a.		0702	0802	...	0902	past	2102	...	2202	0002
Hasselt a.		0752x	0852x	...	0952x	each	2152x	...	|	|
Overpelt a.		0726	0826	...	0926	hour	2126	...	2226	0026
Neerpelt a.		0728	0828	...	0928	until	2128	...	2228	0028
Hamont a.		0738	0838	...	0938		2138	...	2238	0038

		Ⓒ ⊙	Ⓒ ⊡	Ⓒ	Ⓒ	Ⓒ		Ⓒ	Ⓒ	Ⓒ	Ⓒ	Ⓒ
Hamont d.	Ⓒ	0628	...	0719	...	0819		...	2019	...	2119	...
Neerpelt d.		0637	...	0730	...	0830	and	...	2030	...	2130	...
Overpelt d.		0640	...	0733	...	0833	at	...	2033	...	2133	...
Hasselt d.		|	...	|	...	0808z	the	...	2008z	...	2108z	...
Mol d.		0658	...	0758	...	0858	same	...	2058	...	2158	...
Geel d.		0706	...	0806	...	0906	minutes	...	2106	...	2206	...
Turnhout d.		|	0717	|	0817	|	past	2017	|	2117	|	2217
Herentals d.		0720	0733	0820	0833	0920	each	2033	2120	2133	2220	2233
Lier d.		0735	0752	0835	0852	0935	hour	2052	2135	2152	2235	2252
Ant. Berchem a.		0745	0801	0845	0901	0945	until	2101	2145	2201	2245	2301
Antwerpen C. a.		0751	0808	0851	0908	0951		2108	2151	2208	2251	2308

r – Portion for Hasselt is detached from the main train at Mol (departs Mol xx07 or xx08).
s – Portion from Hasselt attaches to the main train at Mol (arrives Mol xx53; Hamont portion arrives xx49).
x – Hourly on ⑥. On ⑦ Hasselt is served every **two** hours (from Antwerpen even hours 0609 - 2009). Note **r** applies.
z – Hourly on ⑥. On ⑦ Hasselt is served every **two** hours (departing on even hours 0808 - 2008). Note **s** applies.

▷ – See also Table **420**.
△ – Also at 2153, 2253, 2353.
▽ – Also at 2209.
⊡ – Also at 0617.
⊙ – Also runs Mol - Antwerpen at 0449 and Neerpelt - Antwerpen at 0537.

☛ *On Ⓐ Turnhout trains run beyond Brussels to / from Binche (Table **423**).*

Line 34 — LIÈGE - HASSELT — 435

km			Ⓐ ◇		Ⓐ ◇		Ⓒ ♡		Ⓒ ♡
0	**Liège** Guillemins d.	Ⓐ	0723	and	2123	Ⓒ	0615	and	2115
27	Tongeren 431 d.		0759	hourly	2159		0652	hourly	2152
53	**Hasselt** 431 a.		0823	until	2223		0715	until	2215

		Ⓐ ◇		Ⓐ ◇		Ⓒ ♡		Ⓒ ♡	Ⓒ ♡	Ⓒ ♡
Hasselt 431 d.	Ⓐ	0637	and	2037	Ⓒ	0546	and	2046	2146	2246
Tongeren 431 d.		0701	hourly	2101		0610	hourly	2110	2209	2309
Liège Guillemins a.		0737	until	2137		0647	until	2147	...	...

◇ – From / to Maastricht (Table **436**).

♡ – Most journeys on Ⓒ run beyond Hasselt to / from Antwerpen (Table **432**).

Line 40 — LIÈGE - MAASTRICHT — 436

km			Ⓐ	Ⓐ	Ⓐ ◇	Ⓐ ◇		Ⓐ ◇	Ⓐ ◇	Ⓐ					⑥	Ⓒ	Ⓒ	Ⓒ		Ⓒ	Ⓒ		
0	**Liège** Guillemins d.	Ⓐ	0609	0640	0740	0840	and	2040	2140	2240	...	...	...	Ⓒ	0608	0708	0808	0908	and	2108	2208	...	...
19	Visé 🏛 d.		0627	0658	0758	0858	hourly	2058	2158	2258	...	...	...		0626	0726	0826	0926	hourly	2126	2226	...	...
32	**Maastricht** a.		0642	0713	0813	0913	until	2113	2213	2313	...	...	...		0642	0742	0842	0942	until	2142	2242	...	...

		Ⓐ	Ⓐ	Ⓐ ◇	Ⓐ	Ⓐ ◇	Ⓐ ◇		Ⓐ ◇	Ⓐ	Ⓐ	Ⓐ		⑥	Ⓒ	Ⓒ	Ⓒ		Ⓒ	Ⓒ			
Maastricht d.	Ⓐ	...	...	0648	...	0748	0848	and	2048	2148	2248	2348	Ⓒ	0718	0818	0918	1018	and	2218	2318	...	...	...
Visé 🏛 d.		0615	0644	0703	0727	0803	0903	hourly	2103	2203	2303	0003		0733	0833	0933	1033	hourly	2233	2333	...	...	...
Liège Guillemins a.		0633	0703	0721	0746	0821	0921	until	2121	2221	2321	0021		0752	0852	0952	1052	until	2252	2352	...	...	...

◇ – To / from Hasselt (Table **435**).

Lines 37, 44 — SPA - VERVIERS - AACHEN — 438

For international trains Brussels - Aachen and beyond see Tables **20** / **21**.

km		Ⓐ	Ⓐ	Ⓐ ⊡				Ⓐ	Ⓒ	Ⓒ
0	Spa Géronstère d.	...	0601	0638	0738		1938	2038	2038	2138
1	**Spa** d.	...	0604	0641	0741	and	1941	2041	2041	2141
13	Pepinster d.	...	0626	0700	0800	hourly	2000	2100	2100	2200
17	**Verviers** Central a.	...	0631	0705	0805	until	2005	2105	2106	2205
17	**Verviers** Central 400 d.	...	...	0726	0827		2027	2127	2127	2227
31	Welkenraedt 🏛 400 d.	0640	...	0741	0841		2041	2140	2141	2240
50	**Aachen** Hbf a.	0656	...	0756	0856		2056	...	2156	...

		Ⓐ	Ⓒ				Ⓐ	Ⓒ △
Aachen Hbf d.	...	0704	...	0804		2004	2104	2104
Welkenraedt 🏛 400 d.	0620	0720	0721	0820	and	2020	2119	2121
Verviers Central 400 a.	0633	0733	0734	0833	hourly	2033	...	2134
Verviers Central d.	0654	0754	0754	0854	until	2054	...	2154
Pepinster d.	0701	0801	0801	0901		2101	...	2201
Spa d.	0720	0820	0820	0920		2120	...	2220
Spa Géronstère a.	0722	0822	0822	0922		2122	...	2222

△ – Also 2204Ⓒ to Welkenraedt.

⊡ – Runs daily Welkenraedt - Aachen.

440 BRUSSELS - NAMUR - DINANT

Lines 161, 154

km			Ⓐ	Ⓐ	Ⓐ	Ⓐ	Ⓐ	Ⓐ	Ⓐ	Ⓐ		Ⓐ	Ⓐ	Ⓐ	Ⓐ	Ⓐ			Ⓐ	Ⓐ			
	Brussels Airport ✈ d.	Ⓐ	...	...	...	0616	...	...	0716	...		...	2116	...	...	...	...		...	...	...	...	...
0	**Brussels** Midi / Zuid d.		...	0533	0602	|	0633	0702	|	0733	and	2102	|	2133	2202	2233	...		1608	1641	...	...	...
2	Brussels Central d.		...	0538	0607	|	0638	0707	|	0738	at	2107	|	2138	2207	2238	...	A	1613	1646	...	...	...
4	**Brussels** Nord d.		...	0544	0612	|	0644	0713	|	0744	the	2112	|	2144	2212	2244	...	L	1621	1652	...	...	...
9	Brussels Schuman d.		...	0552	0620	0633	0652	0721	0733	0752	same	2120	2133	2152	2220	2252	...	S	1629	1700	...	...	...
10	Brussels Luxembourg d.		...	0556	0625	0638	0656	0725	0738	0756	minutes	2125	2138	2156	2225	2256	...	O	1634	1704	...	...	...
33	Ottignies d.		...	0617	0649	0702	0717	0748	0802	0817	past	2149	2202	2217	2249	2321	...		1656	1726	...	...	...
48	Gembloux d.		...	0630	0702	0714	0730	0802	0814	0830	each	2202	2214	2230	2302	2333	...		1709	1739	...	...	...
65	**Namur** a.		...	0643	0716	0727	0743	0816	0827	0843	hour	2216	2227	2243	2316	2346	...		1722	1752	...	...	...
65	**Namur** ▷ d.		0631	0645	0718	0731	0749	0818	0831	0847	until	2218	2231	2247	2318	2348	...		1724	...	...	...	...
	Liège Guillemins **442** a.		|	◇	0809	|	◇	0909	|	◇		2309	|	◇	0009	◇	...		◇	...	...	...	...
93	**Dinant** ▷ a.		0703	...	...	0803	...	...	0903	...		...	2303	...	...	...	...		...	...	...	...	...

		Ⓐ	Ⓐ	Ⓐ	Ⓐ	Ⓐ	Ⓐ	Ⓐ	Ⓐ	Ⓐ		Ⓐ	Ⓐ	Ⓐ	Ⓐ	Ⓐ			Ⓐ	Ⓐ	Ⓐ		
Dinant ▷ d.	Ⓐ	...	...	...	...	0557	...	...	0657	...		...	2057	...	2137	...	...		...	...	...	...	...
Liège Guillemins **442** d.		...	◇	0450	◇	|	0550	◇	|	0650	and	◇	|	2050	|	◇	...		◇	...	◇	...	...
Namur ▷ a.		...	0518	0543	0613	0627	0643	0713	0728	0743	at	2114	2129	2143	2208	2214	...	A	0637	...	0737	...	...
Namur d.		0424	0520	0545	0616	0633	0645	0716	0734	0745	the	2118	2133	2145	...	2218	...	L	0639	0709	0739	...	...
Gembloux d.		0436	0533	0601	0631	0648	0701	0731	0748	0801	same	2133	2148	2201	...	2233	...	S	0653	0725	0753	...	...
Ottignies d.		0449	0545	0613	0643	0700	0714	0744	0800	0814	minutes	2145	2200	2213	...	2245	...	O	0706	0737	0806	...	...
Brussels Luxembourg d.		0519	0607	0636	0705	0722	0736	0806	0822	0836	past	2206	2222	2236	...	2306	...		0727	0758	0827	...	...
Brussels Schuman d.		0522	0610	0639	0708	0726	0739	0809	0826	0839	each	2209	2226	2239	...	2309	...		0730	0801	0830	...	...
Brussels Nord a.		0529	0618	0647	0716	|	0747	0817	|	0847	hour	2217	|	2247	...	2317	...		0738	0809	0838	...	...
Brussels Central a.		0534	0624	0652	0722	|	0752	0823	|	0852	until	2223	|	2252	...	2323	...		0744	0815	0844	...	...
Brussels Midi / Zuid a.		0539	0629	0657	0727	|	0757	0828	|	0857		2228	|	2257	...	2328	...		0749	0820	0849	...	...
Brussels Airport ✈ a.		...	...	...	...	0743	...	...	0843	...		...	2243	...	...	...	...		...	...	...	...	...

		Ⓒ	Ⓒ	Ⓒ	Ⓒ		Ⓒ	Ⓒ	Ⓒ	Ⓒ	Ⓒ
Brussels Midi / Zuid d.	Ⓒ	0603	0632	0703	0732	and	2103	2132	2203	2232	2332
Brussels Central d.		0607	0637	0707	0737	at	2107	2137	2207	2237	2337
Brussels Nord d.		0614	0643	0714	0743	the	2114	2143	2214	2243	2343
Brussels Schuman d.		0622	0651	0722	0751	same	2122	2151	2222	2251	2352
Brussels Luxembourg d.		0627	0655	0727	0755	minutes	2127	2155	2227	2255	2356
Ottignies d.		0648	0717	0748	0817	past	2148	2217	2248	2317	0017
Gembloux d.		0700	0730	0800	0830	each	2200	2230	2300	2329	0030
Namur a.		0712	0743	0812	0843	hour	2212	2243	2313	2342	0043
Namur ▷ d.		0715	0747	0815	0847	until	2215	2247	...	...	...
Dinant ▷ a.		0747	◇	0847	◇		2247	◇	...	...	...

		Ⓒ	Ⓒ	Ⓒ	Ⓒ	Ⓒ		Ⓒ	Ⓒ
Dinant ▷ d.	Ⓒ	...	...	...	0613	◇	and	2113	◇
Namur ▷ a.		...	...	...	0644	0713	at	2144	2213
Namur d.		0515	0547	0618	0647	0718	the	2147	2218
Gembloux d.		0530	0602	0633	0702	0733	same	2202	2232
Ottignies d.		0542	0614	0645	0714	0745	minutes	2214	2245
Brussels Luxembourg d.		0606	0636	0706	0736	0806	past	2236	2306
Brussels Schuman d.		0609	0639	0709	0739	0809	each	2239	2309
Brussels Nord a.		0617	0646	0717	0746	0817	hour	2246	2317
Brussels Central a.		0623	0652	0723	0752	0823	until	2252	2323
Brussels Midi / Zuid a.		0628	0657	0728	0757	0828		2257	2328

◇ – To / from Arlon, Luxembourg or other destinations in Table **445**.

▷ – See also Table **448**.

442 NAMUR - LIÈGE

Line 125

km			Ⓐ	Ⓐ	Ⓐ	Ⓐ	Ⓐ	Ⓐ		Ⓐ	Ⓐ	Ⓐ	Ⓐ	Ⓐ		Ⓒ	Ⓒ	Ⓒ ▽	Ⓒ ▽		Ⓒ ▽	Ⓒ ▽	Ⓒ ▽
	Mons **425** d.	Ⓐ	0437	...	0539	...	0639	...	and at	1939	...	2039	...	...	Ⓒ	...	0614	0714	0814		1914	2014	2114
	Charleroi Sud **425** d.		0513	...	0619	...	0719	...	the	2019	...	2119	...	...		...	0653	0754	0854		1954	2054	2154
	Brussels Midi / Zuid **440** . § d.		|	...	|	0602	|	0702	same	|	2002	|	2102	2202		...	|	|	|	and	|	|	|
0	**Namur** d.		0552	0618	0652	0718	0752	0818	minutes	2052	2118	2152	2218	2318		0634	0732	0832	0932	hourly	2032	2132	2232
20	Andenne d.		0606	0632	0706	0732	0806	0832	past	2106	2132	2206	2232	2332		0647	0747	0847	0947	until	2047	2147	2247
31	Huy d.		0615	0645	0715	0745	0815	0845	each	2114	2145	2214	2245	2345		0658	0758	0858	0958		2058	2158	2258
60	**Liège** Guillemins a.		0636	0709	0735	0809	0835	0909	hour	2135	2209	2235	2309	0009		0720	0820	0920	1020		2120	2220	2320
63	Liège St Lambert a.		0646	0720	0746	0820	0846	0920	until	2146	2220	2246	2320	0020		0729	0829	0929	1029		2129	2229	2329

		Ⓐ	Ⓐ	Ⓐ	Ⓐ	Ⓐ	Ⓐ	Ⓐ		Ⓐ	Ⓐ	Ⓐ	Ⓐ	Ⓐ		Ⓒ ▽	Ⓒ ▽	Ⓒ ▽	Ⓒ ▽		Ⓒ ▽	Ⓒ	Ⓒ
Liège St Lambert d.	Ⓐ	0438	0513	0538	0613	0638	0713	0738	and at	2013	2038	2113	2138	2213	Ⓒ	0630	0730	0830	0930		2030	2130	2230
Liège Guillemins d.		0450	0524	0550	0624	0650	0724	0750	the	2024	2050	2123	2150	2223		0640	0740	0840	0940		2040	2140	2240
Huy d.		0513	0546	0613	0646	0713	0746	0813	same	2046	2113	2146	2213	2246		0702	0802	0902	1002	and	2102	2202	2302
Andenne d.		0527	0555	0627	0655	0727	0755	0827	minutes	2055	2127	2155	2227	2255		0713	0813	0913	1013	hourly	2113	2213	2313
Namur a.		0543	0608	0643	0708	0743	0808	0843	past	2108	2143	2208	2243	2308		0726	0826	0926	1026	until	2126	2226	2326
Brussels Midi / Zuid **440** .. § a.		0657	|	0757	|	0857	|	0957	each	|	2257	|	...	|		|	|	|	|		|	|	...
Charleroi Sud **425** a.		...	0643	...	0743	...	0843	...	hour	2143	...	2246	...	2352		0806	0906	1007	1107		2207	2307	...
Mons **425** a.		...	0721	...	0821	...	0921	...	until	2221	...	2330	...	...		0846	0946	1046	1146		2246	...	...

§ – For direct trains Brussels - Liège see Table **400**.

▽ – From / to Mouscron via Tournai (Table **416**).

☛ On Ⓒ trains continue beyond Liège to / from Liers.

445 (BRUSSELS) - NAMUR - LUXEMBOURG

Line 162

km			Ⓐ	Ⓐ	Ⓐ	Ⓐ		Ⓐ	Ⓐ	Ⓐ	Ⓐ		Ⓐ	Ⓐ	Ⓐ	Ⓐ		Ⓒ		Ⓒ	Ⓒ	Ⓒ	
	Brussels Midi / Zuid **440** ... d.	Ⓐ	...	...	0533	0633		1933	2033	2133	2233		...	1608	...	1807	Ⓒ	0632		1932	2032	2132	...
	Brussels Nord **440** d.		...	...	0544	0644		1944	2044	2144	2244		...	1621	...	1821		0643		1943	2043	2143	...
	Brussels Luxembourg **440** . d.		...	...	0556	0656		1956	2056	2156	2256		...	1634	...	1833		0655		1955	2055	2155	...
0	**Namur** d.		0536	0601	0645	0749	and	2047	2147	2247	2348	A	1557	1724	1822	1922		0747	and	2047	2147	2247	...
29	Ciney d.		0558	0622	0707	0808	hourly	2107	2207	2305	0005	L	1629	1759	1857	1939		0806	hourly	2106	2207	2306	...
52	Marloie d.		0616	0644	0722	0823	until	2122	2222	...	...	S	1654	1815	1914	2000		0822	until	2122	2222	2322	...
58	Rochefort-Jemelle d.		0622	0649	0729	0829	⊡	2129	2227	...	...	O	1659	1820	1920	2005		0829	⊡	2129	2227	2327	...
90	Libramont d.		0656	0718	0756	0856		2156	...	...	...		...	...	...	...		0856		2156	...	...	...
137	Arlon a.		0722	0750	0822	0922		2222	...	...	...		...	...	...	...		0922		2222	...	...	...
137	Arlon ▷ d.		0729	0800	0829	0929		2229	...	...	...		...	...	...	...		0929		2229	...	...	...
165	**Luxembourg** ▷ a.		0750	0826	0850	0950		2250	...	...	...		...	...	...	...		0950		2250	...	...	...

		Ⓐ	Ⓐ	Ⓐ	Ⓐ	Ⓐ	Ⓐ	Ⓐ	Ⓐ		Ⓐ	Ⓐ	Ⓐ	Ⓐ	Ⓐ				Ⓒ	Ⓒ		Ⓒ	Ⓒ
Luxembourg ▷ d.	Ⓐ	...	...	...	*0510*	...	*0610*	0710	0810		1910	2010	2110	2210	2310	...	Ⓒ	...	0610	0710		2010	*2110*
Arlon ▷ a.		...	...	...	*0531*	...	*0631*	0731	0831		1931	2031	2131	2231	2331	...		...	0631	0731		2031	*2131*
Arlon d.		...	0436	...	0536	...	0636	0736	0836		1936	2036	2136	...	...	...		...	0637	0736		2036	2137
Libramont d.		...	0510	...	0608	...	0709	0809	0909	and	2009	2109	2208	...	...	...		...	0708	0809	and	2109	2209
Rochefort-Jemelle d.		...	0534	0554	0633	0640	0733	0833	0933	hourly	2033	2133	2232	...	...	...		0633	0733	0833	hourly	2133	2232
Marloie d.		...	0540	0602	0639	0648	0739	0839	0939	until	2039	2139	2237	...	...	...		0639	0739	0839	until	2139	...
Ciney d.		0502	0557	0620	0656	0721	0755	0856	0956	♡	2056	2156	...	...	...	...		0656	0756	0856	♡	2156	...
Namur a.		0518	0613	0637	0713	0737	0813	0914	1014		2114	2214	...	...	...	...		0713	0813	0913		2213	...
Brussels Luxembourg **440** .. a.		0606	0702	0725	0804	0825	0904	1004	1104		2204	2304	...	...	...	...		0804	0904	1004		2304	...
Brussels Nord **440** a.		0618	0716	0738	0817	0838	0917	1017	1117		2217	2317	...	...	...	...		0817	0917	1017		2317	...
Brussels Midi / Zuid **440** a.		0629	0727	0749	0828	0849	0928	1028	1128		2228	2328	...	...	...	...		0828	0928	1028		2328	...

⊡ – A change of train at Arlon is also required for the following departures from Brussels Ⓐ – 0833, 1532, 1632, 1733; ⑦ – 1032, 1332, 1432, 1832.

♡ – A change of train at Arlon is also required for the departures from Luxembourg Ⓐ 1210; ⑥ – 0810; ⑦ – 0610, 1410, 1510, 1610, 1710, 1810.

▷ – Additional local trains run Arlon - Kleinbettingen 🚍 - Luxembourg (journey time: 20 – 30 minutes).

LIÈGE - GOUVY - CLERVAUX - LUXEMBOURG 446

Line 43/L10

km																									
		Ⓐ	Ⓒ				A		A		A		A		A		A		A		A				
0	**Liège** Guillemins .. **447** d.	...	...	...	...	0607	0707	0807	0907	1007	1107	1207	1307	1407	1507	1607	1707	1807	1907	2007	2107	2207	...	...	...
23	Rivage **447** d.	...	...	...	...	0631	0731	0831	0931	1031	1131	1231	1331	1431	1531	1631	1731	1831	1931	2031	2131	2231	...	...	...
31	Aywaille d.	...	...	...	...	0640	0740	0840	0940	1040	1140	1240	1340	1440	1540	1640	1740	1840	1940	2040	2140	2240	...	...	...
58	Trois-Ponts d.	...	...	...	...	0702	0802	0902	1002	1102	1202	1302	1402	1502	1602	1702	1802	1902	2002	2102	2202	2302	...	...	...
70	Vielsalm d.	...	...	...	...	0712	0812	0912	1012	1112	1212	1312	1412	1512	1612	1712	1812	1912	2014	2114	2214	2312	...	...	...
81	Gouvy 🏨 d.	...	...	0524a	0624a	0724	0824	0924	1024	1124	1224	1324	1424	1524	1624	1724	1824	1924	2024	2124	2224	2321	...	...	...
91	Troisvierges d.	0435	0505	0535	0635	0735	0835	0935	1035	1135	1235	1335	1435	1535	1635	1735	1835	1935	2035	2135	2235	...	...	...	...
99	**Clervaux** d.	0444	0514	0545	0644	0744	0844	0944	1044	1144	1244	1344	1444	1544	1644	1744	1844	1944	2044	2144	2244	...	...	...	...
114	Kautenbach d.	0501	0531	0601	0701	0801	0901	1001	1101	1201	1301	1401	1501	1601	1701	1801	1901	2001	2101	2201	2301	...	...	...	...
129	Ettelbruck d.	0516	0546	0616	0716	0816	0916	1016	1116	1216	1316	1416	1516	1616	1716	1816	1916	2016	2116	2216	2316	...	...	...	...
141	Mersch d.	0528	0556	0626	0726	0828	0928	1028	1128	1228	1328	1428	1528	1628	1728	1828	1928	2028	2128	2228	2328	...	...	...	...
160	**Luxembourg** a.	0546	0615	0644	0743	0846	0946	1046	1146	1246	1346	1446	1546	1646	1746	1846	1946	2046	2146	2246	2346	...	...	...	...

	Ⓐ	Ⓐ	B	B		B		B		B		B		B		B		B							
Luxembourg d.	...	...	0516	0616	0716	0816	0916	1016	1116	1216	1316	1416	1516	1616	1716	1816	1916	2016	2116	2216	2316	...	...	...	...
Mersch d.	...	...	0533	0633	0733	0833	0933	1033	1133	1233	1333	1433	1533	1633	1733	1833	1933	2033	2133	2233	2333	...	...	...	...
Ettelbruck d.	...	...	0545	0645	0745	0845	0945	1045	1145	1245	1345	1445	1545	1645	1745	1845	1945	2045	2145	2245	2345	...	...	...	...
Kautenbach d.	...	...	0559	0659	0759	0859	0959	1059	1159	1259	1359	1459	1559	1659	1759	1859	1959	2059	2159	2300	0000	...	...	...	...
Clervaux d.	...	...	0616	0716	0816	0916	1016	1116	1216	1316	1416	1516	1616	1716	1816	1916	2016	2116	2216	2316	0016	...	...	...	...
Troisvierges d.	...	...	0633	0733	0833	0933	1033	1133	1233	1333	1433	1533	1633	1733	1833	1933	2033	2133	2233	2324	0024	...	...	...	...
Gouvy 🏨 d.	0505	0544	0644	0744	0844	0944	1044	1144	1244	1344	1444	1544	1644	1744	1844	1944	2044	2144	2244	...	...	...	...	...	...
Vielsalm d.	0516	0553	0653	0753	0853	0953	1053	1153	1253	1353	1453	1553	1653	1753	1853	1953	2053	2153	2253	...	...	...	...	...	...
Trois-Ponts d.	0528	0603	0703	0803	0903	1003	1103	1203	1303	1403	1503	1603	1703	1803	1903	2003	2103	2203	2303	...	...	...	...	...	...
Aywaille d.	0550	0624	0724	0824	0924	1024	1124	1224	1324	1424	1524	1624	1724	1824	1924	2024	2124	2224	2324	...	...	...	...	...	...
Rivage **447** d.	0558	0632	0732	0832	0932	1032	1132	1232	1332	1432	1532	1632	1732	1832	1932	2032	2132	2232	2332	...	...	...	...	...	...
Liège Guillemins ... **447** a.	0621	0654	0754	0854	0954	1054	1154	1254	1354	1454	1554	1654	1754	1854	1954	2054	2154	2254	2354	...	...	...	...	...	...

A – Runs ①–⑤ (not Belgian holidays) Liège - Troisvierges; daily Troisvierges - Luxembourg.
B – Runs daily Luxemourg - Troisvierges; ①–⑤ (not Belgian holidays) Troisvierges - Liège.

a – ①–⑤ (not Belgian holidays).

ADDITIONAL TRAINS TROISVIERGES - CLERVAUX - LUXEMBOURG:
From Troisvierges hourly 0405Ⓐ - 2205Ⓐ. From Luxembourg hourly 0544Ⓐ - 2344Ⓐ.

CONNECTING TRAINS KAUTENBACH - WILTZ (journey 12–14 minutes):
From Kautenbach: On Ⓐ every 30 minutes 0532 - 2302; on Ⓒ hourly 0602, 0702, 0804 - 0004.
From Wiltz: On Ⓐ every 30 minutes 0416 - 2246; on Ⓒ hourly 0546 - 0746 and 0842 - 2242.

LIÈGE - MARLOIE - ROCHEFORT JEMELLE 447

Line 43

km																							
			Ⓐ	Ⓐ		Ⓐ	Ⓐ	Ⓐ	Ⓐ	Ⓐ	Ⓐ	Ⓐ	Ⓐ		Ⓒ	Ⓒ	Ⓒ	Ⓒ	Ⓒ	Ⓒ	Ⓒ	Ⓒ	
	Liège St Lambert ◇ d.	Ⓐ	0606	0703		1603	1633	1703	1803	1903	2003	2103	2203	Ⓒ	0805	1005	1205	1405	1605	1805	2005	2205	...
0	**Liège** Guillemins **446** d.		0616	0716	and	1616	1647	1716	1816	1916	2016	2116	2216		0816	1016	1216	1416	1616	1816	2016	2216	...
23	Rivage **446** d.		0643	0743	hourly	1643	1716	1743	1843	1943	2043	2143	2243		0843	1043	1243	1443	1643	1843	2043	2243	...
43	Barvaux d.		0705	0805	until	1705	1738	1805	1905	2005	2105	2205	2305		0905	1105	1305	1505	1705	1905	2105	2305	...
65	Marloie **445** a.		0723	0823		1723	1758	1823	1923	2023	2123	2223	2323		0923	1123	1323	1523	1723	1923	2123	2323	...
71	**Rochefort-Jemelle** **445** a.		...	...		...	1807	...	...	...	2130	2231	2331		...	...	...	...	...	...	...	2331	...

		Ⓐ	Ⓐ	Ⓐ	Ⓐ	Ⓐ	Ⓐ	Ⓐ		Ⓐ	Ⓐ			Ⓒ	Ⓒ	Ⓒ	Ⓒ	Ⓒ	Ⓒ	Ⓒ	Ⓒ		
Rochefort-Jemelle **445** d.	Ⓐ	0426	0526	0603	0628	...	...	...		...	...	...	Ⓒ	0728	...	...	...	...	...	...	...	...	...
Marloie **445** d.		0435	0535	0613	0635	0735	0835	0935	and	1935	2035	...		0735	0935	1135	1335	1535	1735	1935	2135	...	...
Barvaux d.		0452	0552	0631	0652	0752	0852	0952	hourly	1952	2052	...		0752	0952	1152	1352	1552	1752	1952	2152	...	...
Rivage **446** d.		0515	0615	0654	0715	0815	0915	1015	until	2015	2115	...		0815	1015	1215	1415	1615	1815	2015	2215	...	...
Liège Guillemins **446** a.		0543	0643	0722	0743	0843	0943	1043		2043	2143	...		0843	1043	1243	1443	1643	1843	2043	2243	...	...
Liège St Lambert ◇ a.		0555	0655	0736	0755	0855	0955	1055		2055	2155	...		0854	1054	1254	1454	1654	1854	2054	2254	...	...

◇ – Most trains continue beyond Liège St Lambert to/from Liers.

ARDENNES LOCAL SERVICES 448

Lines 154, 166, 165

km			Ⓐ	Ⓐ		Ⓐ		Ⓒ		Ⓒ
0	**Namur** **440** d.	Ⓐ	0555	0655		1955	Ⓒ	0555		1955
28	Dinant **440** d.		0627	0727		2027		0627	and	2027
43	Houyet d.		0647	0747	and	2047		0647	every	2047
52	Beauraing d.		0656	0756	hourly	2056		0656	**two**	2056
100	Bertrix a.		0734	0834	until	2134		0734	hours	2134
100	Bertrix d.		0741	0841		2141		0741	until	2141
108	**Libramont** a.		0751	0851		2151		0751		2151

		Ⓐ	Ⓐ		Ⓐ		Ⓒ		Ⓒ
Libramont d.	Ⓐ	0609	0709		1909	Ⓒ	0709		1909
Bertrix a.		0618	0718		1918		0718	and	1918
Bertrix d.		0624	0724	and	1924		0724	every	1924
Beauraing d.		0702	0802	hourly	2002		0802	**two**	2002
Houyet d.		0712	0812	until	2012		0812	hours	2012
Dinant **440** d.		0731	0831		2031		0831	until	2031
Namur **440** a.		0802	0902		2102		0902		2102

km			Ⓐ		Ⓐ	Ⓐ‡		Ⓒ		Ⓒ
0	**Libramont** d.	Ⓐ	0657		2057	2157	Ⓒ	0757	and	2157
8	Bertrix d.		0707	and	2107	2206		0807	every	2207
33	Florenville d.		0721	hourly	2121	...		0821	**two**	2221
57	Virton d.		0740	until	2140	...		0840	hours	2240
85	Athus ▷ d.		0802		2201	...		0901	until	2301
98	**Arlon** a.		0819		2218	...		0918		2318

		Ⓐ		Ⓐ			Ⓒ		Ⓒ
Arlon d.	Ⓐ	0642		2141	...	Ⓒ	0541		1941
Athus ▷ d.		0701	and	2201	...		0601	and	2001
Virton d.		0722	hourly	2222	...		0622	every	2022
Florenville d.		0739	until	2239	...		0639	**two**	2039
Bertrix d.		0754		2254	...		0654	hours	2054
Libramont a.		0804		2304	...		0704	until	2104

▷ – Athus - Luxembourg: see Table **449**. ‡ – Also 2257Ⓐ to Bertrix.

LUXEMBOURG – local services 449

Operator: CFL

		⚒		⚒		†		†		†
Luxembourg **446** d.	⚒	0455	every	2255	†	0455	and	1155	every	2255
Ettelbruck **446** d.		0536	30	2336		0536	hourly	1236	30	2336
Diekirch a.		0542	minutes	2342		0542	until	1242	mins	2342

		⚒		⚒		†		†		†
Diekirch d.	⚒	0450	every	2320	†	0550	and	1050	every	2320
Ettelbruck **446** d.		0456	30	2326		0556	hourly	1056	30	2326
Luxembourg ... **446** a.		0538	minutes	0008		0638	until	1138	minutes	0008

		⚒		⚒		†		†		†
Luxembourg d.	⚒	0520	every	2350	†	0550	and	1150	every	2350
Pétange d.		0544	30	0014		0614	hourly	1214	30	0014
Rodange d.		0550	minutes	0020		0620	until	1220	minutes	0020
Athus (Belgium) .. ▷ a.		0555		0025		0625		1225		0025

		⚒		⚒		†		†		†
Athus (Belgium). ▷ d.	⚒	0435	every	2335	†	0635	and	1135	every	2335
Rodange d.		0440	30	2340		0640	hourly	1140	30	2340
Pétange d.		0445	mins	2345		0645	until	1145	minutes	2345
Luxembourg a.		0510		0010		0710		1210		0010

Luxembourg → Bettembourg → Esch-sur-Alzette → Pétange → **Rodange** (journey 12 mins to Bettembourg, 25 mins to Esch, 45–50 mins to Pétange, 50–55 mins to Rodange):
⚒: 0521 and approx every 30 minutes to 1921, 1932 and every 30 minutes to 2332, 0002.
†: 0502, 0521, 0602 and hourly to 1102.

Rodange → Pétange → Esch-sur-Alzette → Bettembourg → **Luxembourg** (5–7 mins to Pétange, 26–32 mins to Esch, 39–45 mins to Bettembourg, 50–55 mins to Luxembourg):
⚒: 0451, 0551, 0921, 0951 and every 30 minutes to 1251, 1421 to 1621, 1921.
†: 0432, 0532.

Luxembourg → **Wasserbillig** (journey 35–42 minutes):
Trains run approx. every 30 minutes (some continue to Trier, Table **915**).

Wasserbillig → **Luxembourg** (journey 35–42 minutes):
Trains run approx. every 30 minutes (some from Trier, Table **915**).

Luxembourg → **Kleinbettingen** (journey 18–19 minutes) ⊠:
Ⓐ: 0525 and approx. every 30 minutes to 2055, 2120, 2220, 2320 (not 0922, 1122, 1922).
Ⓒ: 0545 and hourly to 2245.

Kleinbettingen → **Luxembourg** (journey 18–19 minutes) ⊠:
Ⓐ: 0441 and approx. every 30 mins to 1946, 2045, 2116, 2150, 2250, 2350 (not 1015, 1215).
Ⓒ: 0615 and hourly to 2315.

Bettembourg → Dudelange → **Volmerange-les-Mines** (journey 17 minutes):
Approx. every 30 mins. On † runs only to Dudelange Usines, hourly (afternoon every 30 mins).

Volmerange-les-Mines → Dudelange → **Bettembourg** (journey 14 minutes):
Approx. every 30 mins. On † runs from Dudelange Usines, hourly (afternoon every 30 mins).

▷ – For connections to/from Arlon see Table **448**.

⊠ – Certain trains continue to/from Arlon.

NETHERLANDS

SEE MAP PAGE 231

Operator: NS – Nederlandse Spoorwegen (unless otherwise indicated) www.ns.nl

Services: Trains convey first- and second-class seated accommodation, unless otherwise indicated in the tables. Some trains consist of portions for two or more destinations, and passengers should be careful to join the correct part of the train. The destination of each train portion is normally indicated beside the entrance doors.

Timings: Valid **until December 10**, 2022.

Holidays: Unless otherwise indicated, services marked ⚒ do not run on ⑦ or on Dec. 25, Jan. 1, Apr. 18;
those marked Ⓐ do not run on ⑥⑦ or on Apr. 18, 27, May 26, June 6;
those marked † run on ⑦ and on Dec. 25, Jan. 1, Apr. 18;
those marked Ⓒ run on ⑥⑦ and on Apr. 18, 27, May 26, June 6.

No trains, other than international services, will run between ± 2000 hours on Dec. 31 and ± 0200 on Jan. 1.

Tickets: A nationwide smartcard system called *OV-chipkaart* is used for all public transport in the Netherlands. Personalised and anonymous cards are available (€7.50 on-line, €10.50 paper application) which can be loaded and topped up with travel credit. Disposable single use cards can also be purchased from ticket machines and ticket offices for full fare single / return journeys and day tickets (a €1 supplement is payable for single use cards). You must always check-in and check-out your OV-chipkaart for each journey. Alternatively, e-tickets for full fare single and return journeys may be purchased on-line and printed yourself.

Supplements: A supplement is payable for journeys on *Intercity direct* services (except for local journeys Amsterdam - Schiphol and Rotterdam - Breda), also for internal journeys on *ICE* trains between Amsterdam and Arnhem. In both cases the single journey supplement is €2.60 (off-peak discounts are available). Supplements may be purchased from special Supplement Pillars (using your OV-chipkaart) or from ticket machines.

450 AMSTERDAM - DEN HAAG - ROTTERDAM - ROOSENDAAL - VLISSINGEN

For *Intercity direct* services via the high-speed line, see Table **451**. For services via Amsterdam Zuid and Schiphol ✈, see Table **460**.

For Night Network services Amsterdam - Rotterdam and v.v., see Table **454**. For International services to / from Brussels, see Table **18**.

km		④⑤z	⊖	⊖	④⑤z	⑥⑦e		Ⓐ	Ⓐ	Ⓐ	Ⓐ	⑥k	⚒	Ⓐ	Ⓒ		Ⓐ	Ⓒ		✣ and at the same minutes past each hour until	Ⓐ	Ⓒ	
0	**Amsterdam** Centraal ...... **461** d.	0005	0005	0035	0035	0105	...	...	...	...	...	...	0535	0605	...	0635	0705	0705	0735		1905	1905	1935
5	Amsterdam Sloterdijk ...... d.	0010	0010	0040	0040	0110	...	...	...	...	...	...	0540	0610	...	0640	0710	0710	0740		1910	1910	1940
19	**Haarlem** ...... **461** d.	0021	0021	0051	0051	0121	...	...	...	...	...	...	0551	0621	...	0651	0721	0721	0751		1921	1921	1951
47	Leiden Centraal ...... a.	0040	0040	0110	0110	0140	...	...	...	...	...	...	0610	0640	...	0710	0740	0740	0810		1940	1940	2010
47	Leiden Centraal ...... **460** d.	0043	0045	0115	0115	0145	...	...	...	...	...	...	0615	0645	...	0715	0745	0745	0815		1945	1945	2015
63	**Den Haag** HS ...... **460 471** d.	0056	0059	0129	0130	0157	...	...	...	...	...	...	0629	0659	...	0729	0759	0759	0829		1959	1959	2029
71	Delft ...... **460 471** d.	0102	0105	0135	...	...	...	...	...	...	...	...	0635	0705	...	0735	0805	0805	0835		2005	2005	2035
81	Schiedam Centrum ...... **460** d.	0110	0113	0144	...	...	...	...	...	...	...	...	0643	0713	...	0743	0813	0813	0843		2013	2013	2043
85	**Rotterdam** Centraal **460 471** a.	0115	0118	0150	...	...	...	...	...	...	...	...	0648	0718	...	0748	0818	0818	0848		2018	2018	2048
85	**Rotterdam** Centraal **460 471** d.	...	...	...	...	...	...	...	...	...	0621	...	0651	0721	...	0751	0821	0821	0851		2021	2021	2051
105	Dordrecht ...... **460 471** d.	...	...	...	...	...	...	...	...	...	0637	...	0707	0737	...	0807	0837	0837	0907		2037	2037	2107
143	**Roosendaal** ...... a.	...	...	...	...	...	...	...	...	...	0700	...	0730	0800	...	0830	0900	0900	0930		2100	2100	2130
143	**Roosendaal** ...... d.	...	...	...	...	...	...	0527	0606	0636	0703	0706	0736	0803	0806	0836	0903	0906	0936		2103	2106	2136
156	Bergen op Zoom ...... d.	...	...	...	...	...	...	0537	0615	0645	0712	0715	0745	0812	0815	0845	0912	0915	0945		2112	2115	2145
193	Goes ...... d.	...	...	...	...	...	...	...	0646	0716	0732	0746	0816	0832	0846	0916	0932	0946	1016		2132	2146	2216
212	Middelburg ...... d.	...	...	...	...	...	...	...	0701	0731	0744	0801	0831	0844	0901	0931	0944	1001	1031		2144	2201	2231
218	**Vlissingen** ...... a.	...	...	...	...	...	...	...	0709	0739	0751	0809	0839	0851	0909	0939	0951	1009	1039		2151	2209	2239

Amsterdam Centraal ...... **461** d.	2005	2035	2105	2135	2205	2235	2305	2335	...
Amsterdam Sloterdijk ...... d.	2010	2040	2110	2140	2210	2240	2310	2340	...
Haarlem ...... **461** d.	2021	2051	2120	2151	2221	2251	2321	2351	...
Leiden Centraal ...... a.	2040	2110	2140	2210	2240	2310	2340	0010	...
Leiden Centraal ...... **460** d.	2045	2115	2145	2215	2245	2315	2345	0015	...
Den Haag HS ...... **460 471** d.	2059	2129	2159	2229	2259	2329	2359	0029	...
Delft ...... **460 471** d.	2105	2135	2205	2235	2305	2335	0005	0035	...
Schiedam Centrum ...... **460** d.	2113	2143	2213	2243	2313	2343	0013	0043	...
Rotterdam Centraal **460 471** a.	2118	2148	2218	2248	2318	2348	0018	0048	...
Rotterdam Centraal **460 471** d.	2121	2151	2221	2251	2321	2351	0021	0051	...
Dordrecht ...... **460 471** d.	2137	2207	2237	2307	2337	0007	0037	0107	...
Roosendaal ...... a.	2200	2230	2300	2330	2400	0030	0109j	0139h	...
Roosendaal ...... d.	2206	2236	2306	2336	0006	...	...	...	...
Bergen op Zoom ...... d.	2215	2245	2315	2345	0015	...	...	...	...
Goes ...... d.	2246	2316	2346	0016	0046	...	...	...	...
Middelburg ...... d.	2301	2331	0001	0031	0101	...	...	...	...
Vlissingen ...... a.	2309	2339	0009	0039	0109	...	...	...	...

	A	④v	⚒	Ⓐ	⚒	Ⓐ		Ⓐ	⚒
Vlissingen ...... d.	...	...	...	...	...	...	...	0540	...
Middelburg ...... d.	...	...	...	...	...	...	...	0546	...
Goes ...... d.	...	...	...	...	...	...	...	0558	...
Bergen op Zoom ...... d.	...	...	...	...	...	0547	...	0617	...
Roosendaal ...... a.	...	...	...	...	...	0557	...	0627	...
Roosendaal ...... d.	...	...	...	0531	...	0601	...	0631	0631
Dordrecht ...... **460 471** d.	...	...	...	0554	0554	0624	0624	0654	0654
Rotterdam Centraal ...... **460 471** a.	...	...	...	0608	0608	0638	0638	0708	0708
Rotterdam Centraal ...... **460 471** d.	0512	0516	0542	0612	0612	0642	0642	0712	0712
Schiedam Centrum ...... **460** d.	0517	0520	0546	0616	0616	0646	0646	0716	0716
Delft ...... **460 471** d.	0524	0528	0554	0624	0624	0654	0654	0724	0724
Den Haag HS ...... **460 471** d.	0533	0536	0603	0633	0633	0703	0703	0733	0733
Leiden Centraal ...... **460** a.	0545	0548	0615	0645	0645	0715	0715	0745	0745
Leiden Centraal ...... d.	0550	0550	0620	0650	0650	0720	0720	0750	0750
Haarlem ...... **461** d.	0610	0610	0640	0710	0710	0740	0740	0810	0810
Amsterdam Sloterdijk ...... d.	0619	0619	0649	0719	0719	0749	0749	0819	0819
Amsterdam Centraal ...... **461** a.	0625	0625	0655	0725	0725	0755	0755	0825	0825

		⑥k	Ⓐ		⚒		Ⓒ	Ⓐ		and at the same minutes past each hour until	Ⓒ	Ⓐ											
Vlissingen ...... d.	...	0551	0610	...	0621	...	0651	0710	0721		1851	1910	1921	1951	2021	2051	2121	2151	2221	2251	2321	...	...
Middelburg ...... d.	...	0559	0616	...	0629	...	0659	0716	0729		1859	1916	1929	1959	2029	2059	2129	2159	2229	2259	2329	...	...
Goes ...... d.	...	0614	0628	...	0644	...	0714	0728	0744		1914	1928	1944	2014	2044	2114	2144	2214	2244	2314	2344	...	...
Bergen op Zoom ...... d.	...	0644	0647	...	0714	...	0744	0747	0814		1944	1947	2014	2044	2114	2144	2214	2244	2314	2344	0014	...	...
Roosendaal ...... a.	...	0654	0657	...	0724	...	0754	0757	0824		1954	1957	2024	2054	2124	2154	2224	2254	2324	2354	0024	...	...
Roosendaal ...... d.	...	0701	0701	...	0731	...	0801	0801	0831		2001	2001	2031	2101	2131	2201	2231	2301	2331	0001	...	...	...
Dordrecht ...... **460 471** d.	0654	0724	0724	0724	0754	0754	0824	0824	0854		2024	2024	2054	2124	2154	2224	2254	2324	2354	0024	...	...	...
Rotterdam Centraal **460 471** a.	0708	0738	0738	0738	0808	0808	0838	0838	0908		2038	2038	2108	2138	2208	2238	2308	2338	0008	0038	...	...	...
Rotterdam Centraal **460 471** d.	0712	0742	0742	0742	0812	0812	0842	0842	0912		2042	2042	2112	2142	2212	2242	2312	2342	0012	...	...	...	...
Schiedam Centrum ...... **460** d.	0716	0746	0746	0746	0816	0816	0846	0846	0916		2046	2046	2116	2146	2216	2246	2316	2346	0016	...	...	...	...
Delft ...... **460 471** d.	0724	0754	0754	0754	0824	0824	0854	0854	0924		2054	2054	2124	2154	2224	2254	2324	2354	0024	...	...	...	...
Den Haag HS ...... **460 471** d.	0733	0803	0803	0803	0833	0833	0903	0903	0933		2103	2103	2133	2203	2233	2303	2333	0003	0033	...	...	...	...
Leiden Centraal ...... **460** a.	0745	0815	0815	0815	0845	0845	0915	0915	0945		2115	2115	2145	2215	2245	2315	2345	0015	0045	...	...	...	...
Leiden Centraal ...... d.	0750	0820	0820	0820	0850	0850	0920	0920	0950		2120	2120	2150	2220	2250	2320	2350	0020	0050	...	...	...	...
Haarlem ...... **461** d.	0810	0840	0840	0840	0910	0910	0940	0940	1010		2140	2140	2210	2240	2310	2340	0010	0040	0110	...	...	...	...
Amsterdam Sloterdijk ...... d.	0819	0849	0849	0849	0919	0919	0949	0949	1019		2149	2149	2219	2249	2319	2349	0019	0049	0119	...	...	...	...
Amsterdam Centraal ...... **461** a.	0825	0855	0855	0855	0925	0925	0955	0955	1025		2155	2155	2225	2255	2325	2355	0025	0055	0125	...	...	...	...

AMSTERDAM - DEN HAAG CENTRAAL

km		Ⓐ	Ⓐ	Ⓐ	Ⓐ	⚒	⚒	⚒	⚒	⚒	⚒			and at the same minutes past each hour until									
0	**Amsterdam** Centraal ...... **461** d.	0620	0650	0720	0750	0820	0850	0920	0950	1020	1050	1120	1150		1820	1850	1920	1950	2020	2050	2120	2150	...
5	Amsterdam Sloterdijk ...... d.	0625	0655	0725	0755	0825	0855	0925	0955	1025	1055	1125	1155		1825	1855	1925	1955	2025	2055	2125	2155	...
19	**Haarlem** ...... **461** d.	0637	0707	0737	0807	0837	0907	0937	1007	1037	1107	1137	1207		1837	1907	1937	2007	2037	2107	2137	2207	...
47	Leiden Centraal ...... a.	0657	0727	0757	0827	0857	0927	0957	1027	1057	1127	1157	1227		1857	1927	1957	2027	2057	2127	2157	2227	...
47	Leiden Centraal ...... **460** d.	0659	0729	0759	0829	0859r	0929r	0959r	1029r	1059r	1129r	1159t	1229t		1859t	1929t	2001	2031	2101	2131	2201	2231	...
62	**Den Haag** Centraal ...... **460** a.	0710	0740	0810	0840	0910r	0940r	1010r	1040r	1110r	1140r	1210t	1240t		1910t	1940t	2012	2042	2112	2142	2212	2242	...

	Ⓐ	Ⓐ	Ⓐ	Ⓐ	⚒	⚒	⚒	⚒	⚒	⚒			and at the same minutes past each hour until										
Den Haag Centraal ...... **460** d.	0618	0649	0719	0749	0817f	0847f	0917f	0947f	1017f	1047f	1117f	1147f		1817f	1847f	1917	1947	2017	2047	2117	2147	2217	...
Leiden Centraal ...... **460** a.	0631	0701	0731	0801	0829f	0859f	0929f	0959f	1029f	1059f	1129f	1159f		1829f	1859f	1929	1959	2029	2059	2129	2159	2229	...
Leiden Centraal ...... d.	0633	0703	0733	0803	0833	0903	0933	1003	1033	1103	1133	1203		1833	1903	1933	2003	2033	2103	2133	2203	2233	...
Haarlem ...... **461** d.	0655	0725	0755	0825	0855	0925	0955	1025	1055	1125	1155	1225		1855	1925	1955	2025	2055	2125	2155	2225	2255	...
Amsterdam Sloterdijk ...... d.	0704	0734	0804	0834	0834	0934	1004	1034	1104	1134	1204	1234		1904	1934	2004	2034	2104	2134	2204	2234	2304	...
Amsterdam Centraal ...... **461** a.	0710	0740	0810	0840	0840	0940	1010	1040	1110	1140	1210	1240		1910	1940	2010	2040	2110	2140	2210	2240	2310	...

A – ①②③⑤ (not Apr. 18, 27, June 6).

e – Also Apr. 28, May 27, June 7; not Dec. 26, Jan. 2.
f – 2 minutes later on Ⓐ.
h – Mornings of ④–⑦ (also June 7; not Dec. 26, Jan. 2).
j – Mornings of ①–③ (also Dec. 26, Jan. 2; not June 7).
k – Also Apr. 27, May 26, June 6; not Dec. 25, Jan. 1.
r – 2 minutes later on ⑥ (also Apr. 27, May 26, June 6; not Dec. 25, Jan. 1).

t – 2 minutes later on Ⓒ.
v – Not May 26.
z – Not Apr. 28, May 27.

⊖ – ①②③⑥⑦ (also Apr. 28, May 27).
✣ – On Ⓐ Amsterdam Centraal d. 0804 / 0834 / 0904 (not 0805 / 0835 / 0905; Amsterdam Sloterdijk departures are also 1 minute earlier).

AMSTERDAM - ROTTERDAM - BREDA 451

Intercity direct services via the high-speed line. Supplement payable (except for local journeys Amsterdam - Schiphol and Rotterdam - Breda).

km		1010	910	9212	912	1014	914	9216	916	1018	918	9220	920	1022	922	9224	924	1026	926	9228	928	1030	930	9232	932
		⚒	⚒	B c	⚒	⚒		B		⚒		B		⚒		B		⚒		B		⚒		B	
0	**Amsterdam** Centraal .... d.	0553	0608	0628	0638	0655	0708	0728	0738	0755	0808	0828	0838	0855	0908	0928	0938	0953	1008	1028	1038	1055	1108	1128	1138
17	**Schiphol** + ... d.	0610	0623	0643	0653	0710	0723	0743	0753	0810	0823	0843	0853	0910	0923	0943	0953	1010	1023	1043	1053	1110	1123	1143	1153
70	**Rotterdam** Centraal ...... a.	0636	0649	0709	0719	0736	0749	0809	0819	0836	0849	0909	0919	0936	0949	1009	1019	1036	1049	1109	1119	1136	1149	1209	1219
70	**Rotterdam** Centraal ...... d.	...	0652	0711	0722	...	0752	0811	0822	...	0852	0911	0922	...	0952	1011	1022	...	1052	1111	1122	...	1152	1211	1222
117	**Breda** .... a.	...	0715	0734	0745	...	0815	0834	0845	...	0915	0934	0945	...	1015	1034	1045	...	1115	1134	1145	...	1215	1234	1245

	1034		1070	970	9272	972	974	976	978
					B				
Amsterdam Centraal ... d.	1153	and at the same minutes past each hour until	2053	2108	2128	2138	2208	2238	2308
Schiphol + ... d.	1210		2110	2123	2143	2153	2223	2253	2323
Rotterdam Centraal .... a.	1236		2136	2149	2209	2219	2249	2319	2349
Rotterdam Centraal .... d.	...		...	2152	2211	2222	2252	...	2352
Breda .... a.	...		...	2215	2234	2245	2315	...	0015

	1003	1005	905	1007	907	907	9211	909	1011	911
	⚒	⚒	⚒	⚒	⚒		B		⚒	
Breda .... d.	...	...	0645	...	0715	...	0726	0745	...	0815
Rotterdam Centraal .... a.	...	...	0708	...	0738	...	0750	0808	...	0838
Rotterdam Centraal .... d.	0624	0651	0711	0724	0741	0741	0754	0811	0824	0841
Schiphol + ... d.	0651	0718	0738	0751	0808	0808	0821	0838	0851	0908
Amsterdam Centraal .... a.	0705	0732	0752	0805	0822	0822	0835	0852	0905	0922

	9215	913	1015	915	9219	917	1019	919	9223	921	1023	923	9227	925	1027		963	9267	965	1067	967	9271	969	971
	B		⚒		B		⚒		B		⚒		B					B				B		
Breda .... d.	0826	0845	...	0915	0926	0945	...	1015	1026	1045	...	1115	1126	1145	...	and at the same minutes past each hour until	2115	2126	2145	...	2215	2226	2245	2315
Rotterdam Centraal .... a.	0850	0908	...	0938	0950	1008	...	1038	1050	1108	...	1138	1150	1208	...		2138	2149	2208	...	2238	2249	2308	2338
Rotterdam Centraal .... d.	0854	0911	0924	0941	0954	1011	1024	1041	1054	1111	1124	1141	1154	1211	1224		2141	2158	2211	2224	2241	2258	2311	2341
Schiphol + ... d.	0921	0938	0951	1008	1021	1038	1051	1108	1121	1138	1151	1208	1221	1238	1251		2208	2224	2238	2251	2308	2324	2338	0008
Amsterdam Centraal ... a.	0935	0952	1007	1022	1035	1051	1105	1122	1135	1152	1205	1222	1235	1251	1305		2222	2238	2252	2305	2322	2338	2352	0022

B – To/from Brussels (Table **18**).

c – Not Jan. 1.

Local trains AMSTERDAM CENTRAAL - SCHIPHOL 452

See Table **451** for *Intercity direct* trains (which can be used without payment of a supplement between Amsterdam Centraal and Schiphol).

From Amsterdam Centraal

0511 ⑥ **k**, 0515 Ⓐ, 0531 ⚒, 0541 Ⓐ, 0543 ⑥ **k**, 0601 ⚒, 0611, 0631, 0641, 0701, 0711, 0731, 0741 and at 01, 11, 31 and 41 minutes past each hour until 0001, 0011, 0031, 0041.

k – Also Apr. 27, May 26, June 6.

From Schiphol + Journey time: 17 – 18 minutes

0531 Ⓐ, 0541, 0552 Ⓐ, 0611, 0632 ⚒, 0641, 0702, 0711, 0732, 0741 and at 02, 11, 32 and 41 minutes past each hour until 2302, 2311, 2332, 2341; then 0002, 0011, 0041.

UTRECHT - AMSTERDAM - ROTTERDAM - EINDHOVEN Night Network 454

	⑥⑦s	⑥⑦s		③	③	H	④t		③w	③w	G	④v		③w	③w	G	④v		③w	③w	L		†		†	
Utrecht Centraal .... d.	...	...	...	...	0115	0116c	0110	...	...	0216	0216e	0210	...	...	0316	0316f	0310	...	...	0416	0416h	...	0505	...	0605	...
Amsterdam Centraal ... d.	...	...	...	...	0146	0146	0146	...	...	0246	0246	0246	...	...	0346	0346	0346	...	...	0446	0446	...	0543	...	0639	...
Schiphol + ... d.	...	...	...	0203	|	0205	0205	...	0303	|	0305	0305	...	0403	|	0405	0405	...	0503	|	0505	...	0556	...	...	...
Leiden Centraal .... d.	...	...	...	0219	0223j	0223	0223	...	0319	0323j	0324	0323	...	0419	0423j	0424	0423	...	0519	0523j	0523	...	0615	...	...	...
Den Haag HS .... d.	...	...	...	...	0238	0238	0244j	...	...	0338	0338	0344j	...	...	0438	0438	0444j	...	...	0538	0538	...	0628	...	...	...
Delft .... d.	...	...	...	...	0245	0245	|	...	...	0345	0345	|	...	...	0445	0445	|	...	...	0545	0545	...	0634	...	...	...
Rotterdam Centraal .... d.	0002	0102	...	...	0258	0258	0326	...	...	0358	0358	0426	...	...	0458	0458	0526	...	...	0558	0558	...	0646	...	...	...
Dordrecht .... d.	0017	0118	...	...	...	...	...	...	...	...	...	...	...	...	...	...	...	...	...	...	...	...	...	...	...	...
Breda .... d.	0036	0141	...	...	...	...	...	...	...	...	...	...	...	...	...	...	...	...	...	...	...	...	...	...	...	...
Tilburg .... d.	0054	0155	...	...	...	...	...	...	...	...	...	...	...	...	...	...	...	...	...	...	...	...	...	...	...	...
Eindhoven Centraal .... a.	0117	0217	...	...	...	...	...	...	...	...	...	...	...	...	...	...	...	...	...	...	...	...	...	...	...	...

		M	①②z	③	③		④t	⑥⑦s	G	③w	③w		④v	⑥⑦s	G	③w	③w		④v	G	③w	③w		Ⓒ		†
Eindhoven Centraal .... d.	...	...	...	...	...	...	...	0030	...	...	...	...	...	0130	...	...	...	...	...	...	...	...	...	...	...	...
Tilburg .... d.	...	...	...	...	...	...	...	0102	...	...	...	...	...	0202	...	...	...	...	...	...	...	...	...	...	...	...
Breda .... d.	...	...	...	...	...	...	...	0120	...	...	...	...	...	0220	...	...	...	...	...	...	...	...	...	...	...	...
Dordrecht .... d.	...	...	...	...	...	...	...	0139	...	...	...	...	...	0239	...	...	...	...	...	...	...	...	...	...	...	...
Rotterdam Centraal .... d.	...	0056	0100	0100	...	...	0132	0151	0200	0200	...	...	0232	0251	0300	0300	...	...	0332	0400	0400	...	...	0500	...	0600
Delft .... d.	...	0106	0112	0113	...	...	|	...	0213	0213	...	...	|	...	0312	0313	...	...	|	0413	0413	...	...	0512	...	0613
Den Haag HS .... d.	...	0132p	0129j	0129j	...	...	0223j	...	0222	0222	...	...	0323j	...	0323	0322	...	...	0423j	0422	0422	...	...	0523	...	0622
Leiden Centraal .... d.	...	0145	0145	0145	0147	...	0245j	...	0245j	0245j	0240	...	0345j	...	0345j	0345j	0340	...	0445j	0445	0445j	0440	...	0545j	...	0646j
Schiphol + ... a.	...	0201	0201	|	0203	...	0301	...	0301	|	0257	...	0401	...	0401	|	0357	...	0501	0501	|	0457	...	0601	...	0704
Amsterdam Centraal ... a.	0118	0217	0217	0217	...	...	0317	...	0317	0317	...	...	0417	...	0417	0417	...	...	0516	0516	0517	...	...	0617	...	0722
Utrecht Centraal .... a.	0148	0248r	0248	0248	...	...	0358	...	0348y	0348	...	...	0458	...	0448y	0448	...	...	0558	0548y	0548	...	...	0659	...	...

G – ①②⑤⑥⑦ (also Apr. 27, May 26).
H – ①②⑤⑥⑦ (also Apr. 28).
L – ①②④⑤⑥⑦ (also Apr. 27).
M – ④–⑦ (also June 7; not Dec. 26, Jan. 2).

c – 0110 on ⑤ (not May 27).
e – 0210 on ⑤.
f – 0310 on ⑤†.
h – 0410 on ④⑤† (not May 26).
j – Arrives 7 – 10 minutes earlier.
p – Arrives 0113.
r – 0258 on ④⑤ (not Apr. 28, May 27).
s – Also Apr. 28, May 27, June 7; not Dec. 26, Jan. 2.
t – Not Apr. 28.
v – Not May 26.
w – Not Apr. 27.
y – 5 minutes later on †; 10 minutes later on ⑤.
z – Also Dec. 26, Jan. 2; not June 7.

ALMERE - UTRECHT 457

km		Ⓐ	Ⓐ	Ⓐ	⚒	†	Ⓐ		⚒			⚒					A	④d				
0	**Almere** Centrum .... d.	0551	0621	0651	0721	0721	0751	0821	0851	and at the same minutes past each hour until	1921	1951	2021	...	2121	...	2221	2221	...	2321	...	...
20	Naarden-Bussum .... **480** d.	0612	0642	0712	0742	0742	0812	0842	0912		1942	2012	2042	...	2142	...	2242	2242	...	2342	...	...
26	Hilversum .... **480** d.	0618	0648	0718	0748	0748	0818	0848	0918		1948	2018	2048	2118	2148	2218	2248	2253	2318	2348	0018	0048
43	**Utrecht** Centraal .... a.	0636	0705	0735	0805	0806	0835	0905	0935		2005	2035	2106	2136	2206	2236	2306	2312	2336	0006	0036	0106

	⑥⑦c		Ⓐ	⚒	Ⓐ	⚒		⚒			⚒						④d	A				
Utrecht Centraal .... d.	0054	...	0626	0656	0726	0756	0826	0856	and at the same minutes past each hour until	1926	1956	2024	2054	2124	2154	2224	2247	2254	2324	2354	...	...
Hilversum .... **480** d.	0113	...	0643	0713	0743	0813	0843	0913		1943	2013	2043	2112	2143	2212	2243	2306	2312	2343	0013	...	...
Naarden-Bussum .... **480** d.	0121	...	0651	0721	0751	0821	0851	0921		1951	2021	2051	...	2151	...	2251	...	...	2351	0021	...	...
Almere Centrum .... a.	0138	...	0708	0738	0808	0838	0908	0938		2008	2038	2108	...	2208	...	2308	...	...	0008	0038	...	...

A – ①②③⑤⑥⑦ (also May 26).
c – Also Apr. 28, May 27, June 7; not Dec. 26, Jan. 2.
d – Not May 26.

AMSTERDAM - ALMERE - ZWOLLE 459

See Table **460** for fast services via Amsterdam Zuid

km		Ⓐ	Ⓐ	⑥k	Ⓐ	Ⓐ	⚒	Ⓐ	⚒	†	⚒	⚒					⊠								
0	**Amsterdam** Centraal .. d.	...	...	...	0553	0608	...	0623	0638	...	0653	0708	0723	0738	0753	0808	and at the same minutes past each hour until	2223	2238	2253	2308	2323	2338	2353	0008
14	Weesp .... d.	...	...	...	0610	|	...	0640	|	...	0710	|	0740	|	0810	|		2240	|	2310	|	2340	|	0010	|
30	**Almere** Centrum .. **460** d.	...	...	...	0625	0628	...	0655	0658	...	0725	0728	0755	0758	0825	0828		2255	2258	2325	2328	2355	2358	0024	0028
36	Almere Buiten ...... **460** d.	...	...	...	0631	...	...	0701	...	...	0731	...	0801	...	0831	...		2301	...	2331	...	0001	...	0030	...
54	**Lelystad** Centrum **460** d.	0541	0611	0640	0654	...	0724	0724	...	0741	0754	...	0824	...	0854	...		2324	...	2354	...	0020	...	0050	...
75	Dronten .... d.	0553	0623	0652	0706	...	0736	0736	...	0753	0806	...	0836	...	0906	...		2336	...	0006	...	...	...	...	...
88	Kampen Zuid .... d.	0602	0632	0701	0714	...	0744	0744	...	0802	0814	...	0844	...	0914	...		2344	...	0015	...	...	...	...	...
104	**Zwolle** .... **460** a.	0613	0643	0712	0724	...	0754	0754	...	0813	0824	...	0854	...	0924	...		2354	...	0024	...	...	...	...	...

	Ⓐ	Ⓐ		Ⓐ		Ⓐ		⚒		⚒													⑥⑦c		
Zwolle .... **460** d.	...	...	...	...	0537a	...	0607a	...	0637a	...	0707r	...	0737r	...	0807	...	0837	and at the same minutes past each hour until	...	2237	...	2307	...	2337	0007
Kampen Zuid .... d.	...	...	...	...	0546a	...	0617a	...	0646a	...	0717r	...	0746r	...	0817	...	0846		...	2247	...	2317	...	2346	0017
Dronten .... d.	...	...	...	...	0555a	...	0625a	...	0655a	...	0725r	...	0755r	...	0825	...	0855		...	2255	...	2325	...	2355	0025
Lelystad Centrum ... **460** d.	0514	...	0540	...	0610	...	0640	...	0710	...	0740	...	0810	...	0840	...	0910		...	2310	...	2340	...	0010	0037
Almere Buiten .... **460** d.	0528	...	0558	...	0628	...	0658	...	0728	...	0758	...	0828	...	0858	...	0928		...	2328	...	2358	...	0028	...
Almere Centrum .... **460** d.	0536	0602	0606	0632	0636	0702	0706	0732	0736	0802	0806	0832	0836	0902	0906	0932	0936		2332	2336	0002	0006	0032	0036	...
Weesp .... d.	0551	|	0621	|	0651	|	0721	|	0751	|	0821	|	0851	|	0921	|	0951		|	2351	|	0021	|	0051	...
Amsterdam Centraal ... a.	0608	0622	0637	0652	0707	0722	0737	0753	0807	0822	0837	0852	0908	0922	0937	0952	1008		2352	0007	0022	0037	0052	0108	...

a – Ⓐ only.
c – Also Apr. 28, May 27, June 7; not Dec. 26, Jan. 2.
k – Also Apr. 27, May 26, June 6; not Dec. 25, Jan. 1.
r – ⚒ only.
⊠ – Amsterdam Centraal d. 0907/1707 (not 0908/1708).

460 DEN HAAG - SCHIPHOL - AMSTERDAM ZUID - ALMERE - ZWOLLE

For services Amsterdam Centraal - Almere - Zwolle and v.v., see Table 459. For services via Amersfoort and Utrecht, see Table 481.

km		⑥k	Ⓐ	⚒	Ⓐ	⚒	Ⓐ		Ⓐ		Ⓐ		⚒◧		⚒◧		⚒◧		⚒◧		⚒◧		⚒◧		◐
	Dordrecht 450 d.	...	...	...	...	...	0604	...	0634	...	0704	...	0734	...	0804	...	0834	...	0904	...	0934	...	1004	...	1034
	Rotterdam Centraal 450 d.	...	...	...	0551	...	0621	...	0651	...	0721	...	0751	...	0821	...	0851	...	0921	...	0951	...	1021	...	1051
	Schiedam Centrum 450 d.	...	...	...	0556	...	0626	...	0656	...	0726	...	0756	...	0826	...	0856	...	0926	...	0956	...	1026	...	1056
	Delft 450 d.	...	...	...	0604	...	0634	...	0704	...	0734	...	0804	...	0834	...	0904	...	0934	...	1004	...	1034	...	1104
	Den Haag HS 450 d.	...	...	...	0613	...	0643	...	0713	...	0743	...	0813	...	0843	...	0913	...	0943	...	1013	...	1043	...	1113
0	**Den Haag** Centraal 450 d.	...	0533	0603	|	0633	|	0703	|	0733	|	0803	|	0833	|	0903	|	0933	|	1003	|	1033	|	1103	|
15	Leiden Centraal 450 d.	...	0547	0617	0627	0647	0657	0717	0727	0747	0757	0817	0827	0847	0857	0917	0927	0947	0957	1017	1027	1047	1057	1117	1127
42	**Schiphol** ✈ d.	...	0605	0635	0644	0705	0714	0735	0744	0805	0818	0835	0848	0904	0918	0935	0948	1004	1018	1035	1048	1104	1118	1135	1144
51	**Amsterdam** Zuid d.	...	0612	0642	0656	0712	0726	0742	0756	0812	0826	0842	0856	0912	0926	0942	0956	1012	1026	1042	1056	1112	1126	1142	1156
56	Duivendrecht d.	...	|	|	0701	|	0731	|	0801	|	0831	|	0901	|	0931	|	1001	|	1031	|	1101	|	1131	|	1201r
80	**Almere** Centrum 459 d.	...	0632	0702	0719	0732	0749	0802	0819	0832	0849	0902	0919	0932	0949	1002	1019	1032	1049	1102	1119	1132	1149	1202	1219r
86	**Almere** Buiten 459 d.	...	|	|	0724	|	0754	|	0824	|	0854	|	0924	|	0954	|	1024	|	1054	|	1124	|	1154	|	1224r
104	**Lelystad** Centrum 459 d.	0640	0647	0717	0736	0749	0806	0817	0836	0847	0906	0917	0936	0947	1006	1017	1036	1047	1106	1117	1136	1147	1206	1217	1236r
154	**Zwolle** 459 a.	0712	0713	0743	...	0813	...	0843	...	0913	...	0943	...	1013	...	1043	...	1113	...	1143	...	1213	...	1243	...
	Leeuwarden **482** a.	...	|	0843	...	|	...	0943	...	|	...	1043	...	|	...	1143	...	|	...	1243	...	|	...	1343	...
	Groningen **482** a.	...	0812	...	...	0912	...	...	...	1012	...	...	...	1112	...	...	...	1212	...	...	...	1312	...	...	...

		◐			◐		◐																	
Dordrecht 450 d.	...	1104		...	1734	...	1804	...	1839	...	1909	...	1939	...	2009	...	2039	...	2109	...	2139	...	...	...
Rotterdam Centraal 450 d.	...	1121		...	1751	...	1821	...	1857	...	1927	...	1957	...	2027	...	2057	...	2127	...	2157	...	...	...
Schiedam Centrum 450 d.	...	1126		...	1756	...	1826	...	1901	...	1931	...	2001	...	2031	...	2101	...	2132	...	2201	...	...	...
Delft 450 d.	...	1134	and at	...	1804	...	1834	...	1909	...	1939	...	2009	...	2039	...	2109	...	2139	...	2209	...	...	...
Den Haag HS 450 d.	...	1143		...	1813	...	1843	...	1918	...	1948	...	2018	...	2048	...	2118	...	2148	...	2218	...	...	...
Den Haag Centraal 450 d.	1133	|	the same	1803	|	1833	|	1903	|	1933	|	2003	|	2033	|	2103	|	2133	|	2203	|	2233	2303	2333
Leiden Centraal 450 d.	1147	1157		1817	1827	1847	1857	1917	1931	1947	2001	2017	2031	2047	2101	2117	2131	2147	2201	2217	2231	2247	2317	2347
Schiphol ✈ d.	1205	1214	minutes	1835	1844	1905	1914	1935	1949	2005	2019	2035	2049	2105	2119	2135	2149	2205	2219	2235	2249	2305	2335	0003
Amsterdam Zuid d.	1212	1226		1842	1856	1912	1926	1942	1956	2012	2026	2042	2056	2112	2126	2142	2156	2212	2226	2242	2256	2312	2342	...
Duivendrecht d.	|	1231r	past each	|	1901r	|	1931r	|	...	|	...	|	...	|	...	|	...	|	...	|	...	|	|	...
Almere Centrum 459 d.	1232	1249r		1902	1919r	1932	1949r	2002	...	2032	...	2102	...	2132	...	2202	...	2232	...	2302	...	2332	0002	...
Almere Buiten 459 d.	|	1254r	hour until	|	1924r	|	1954r	|	...	|	...	|	...	|	...	|	...	|	...	|	...	|	|	...
Lelystad Centrum 459 d.	1247	1306r		1917	1936r	1947	2006r	2017	...	2047	...	2117	...	2147	...	2217	...	2247	...	2317	...	2347	0017	...
Zwolle 459 a.	1313	...		1943	...	2013	...	2043	...	2113	...	2143	...	2213	...	2243	...	2313	...	2343	...	0015	0043	...
Leeuwarden **482** a.	|	...		1943	...	|	...	2143	...	|	...	2243	...	|	...	2351	...	|	...	0051	...	|	0151c	...
Groningen **482** a.	1412	...		...	...	2112	...	...	...	2212	...	...	...	2312	...	...	...	0023	...	...	...	0123	...	...

	⚒	Ⓐ	Ⓐ	Ⓐz	Ⓐ		Ⓐ	⚒z	⑥k	⚒		⑥k	Ⓐ		⚒■		⚒■		⚒■		⚒■		●		●
Groningen **482** d.	...	...	...	...	...	...	...	0533b	...	...	...	...	...	0648h	...	...	...	0748t	...	...	...	0848	...	...	...
Leeuwarden **482** d.	...	...	...	...	...	0507a	...	|	...	...	0617a	...	...	|	...	0717v	...	|	...	0817	...	|	...	0917	...
Zwolle 459 d.	...	...	...	0547	...	0617a	...	0647	...	...	0717r	...	...	0747	...	0817	...	0847	...	0917	...	0947	...	1017	...
Lelystad Centrum 459 d.	...	0543	...	0613	0624	0643a	0654	0713	...	0724	0743r	...	0754	0813	0824	0843	0854	0913	0924	0943	0954	1013	1024r	1043	1054r
Almere Buiten 459 d.	...	|	...	|	0636	|	0706	|	...	0736	|	...	0806	|	0836	|	0906	|	0936	|	1006	|	1036r	|	1106r
Almere Centrum 459 d.	...	0558	...	0628	0642	0658	0712	0728	...	0742	0758	...	0812	0828	0842	0858	0912	0928	0942	0958	1012	1028	1042r	1058	1112r
Duivendrecht d.	...	|	...	|	0659	|	0729	|	...	0759	|	...	0829	|	0859	|	0929	|	0959	|	1029	|	1059r	|	1129r
Amsterdam Zuid d.	...	0618	0639	0648	0709	0718	0739	0748	0805	0809	0818	0835	0839	0848	0908	0918	0938	0948	1005	1018	1039	1048	1109	1118	1139
Schiphol ✈ d.	0556	0626	0647	0656	0717	0726	0747	0756	0812	0817	0826	0842	0847	0856	0916	0926	0946	0956	1012	1026	1047	1057	1117	1126	1147
Leiden Centraal 450 d.	0615	0645	0705	0715	0735	0745	0805	0815	0830	0835	0845	0900	0905	0915	0935	0945	1005	1015	1030	1045	1105	1115	1135	1145	1205
Den Haag Centraal 450 a.	0626	0656	|	0726	|	0756	|	0826	|	|	0856	|	|	0926	|	0956	|	1026	|	1056	|	1126	|	1156	|
Den Haag HS 450 d.	...	...	0717	...	0747	...	0817	...	0842	0847	...	0912	0914	...	0944	...	1017	...	1044	...	1117	...	1147	...	1217
Delft 450 d.	...	...	0725	...	0755	...	0825	...	0850	0855	...	0920	0925	...	0955	...	1025	...	1055	...	1125	...	1155	...	1225
Schiedam Centrum 450 d.	...	...	0733	...	0803	...	0833	...	0858	0903	...	0928	0933	...	1003	...	1033	...	1103	...	1133	...	1203	...	1233
Rotterdam Centraal 450 a.	...	...	0738	...	0808	...	0838	...	0903	0908	...	0933	0938	...	1008	...	1038	...	1108	...	1138	...	1208	...	1238
Dordrecht 450 a.	...	...	0756	...	0826	...	0856	...	0923	0926	...	0953	0956	...	1026	...	1056	...	1126	...	1156	...	1226	...	1256

			●		●																			⑤⑥k
Groningen **482** d.		...	...	1648	...	...	...	1748	...	...	...	1848	...	...	...	1948	...	...	2048	...	2148	...	2248	2326
Leeuwarden **482** d.		1617	...	|	...	1717	...	|	...	1817	...	|	...	1917	...	|	...	2017	|	2117	|	2217	|	|
Zwolle 459 d.		1717	...	1747	...	1817	...	1847	...	1917	...	1947	...	2017	...	2047	...	2117	2147	2217	2247	2317	2347	0037
Lelystad Centrum 459 d.	and at	1743	1754r	1813	1824r	1843	...	1913	...	1943	...	2013	...	2043	...	2113	...	2143	2213	2243	2313	2343	0013	0108
Almere Buiten 459 d.		|	1806r	|	1836r	|	...	|	...	|	...	|	...	|	...	|	...	|	|	|	|	|	|	|
Almere Centrum 459 d.	the same	1758	1812r	1828	1842r	1858	...	1928	...	1958	...	2028	...	2058	...	2128	...	2158	2228	2258	2328	2358	0028	0122
Duivendrecht d.		|	1829r	|	1859r	|	...	|	...	|	...	|	...	|	...	|	...	|	|	|	|	|	|	|
Amsterdam Zuid d.	minutes	1818	1838	1848	1909	1918	1935	1948	2005	2018	2035	2048	2105	2118	2135	2148	2205	2218	2248	2318	2348	0018	0048	0142‡
Schiphol ✈ d.		1826	1846	1856	1917	1926	1942	1956	2012	2026	2042	2056	2112	2126	2142	2156	2212	2226	2256	2326	2356	0026	0056	...
Leiden Centraal 450 d.	past each	1845	1905	1915	1935	1945	2000	2015	2030	2045	2100	2115	2130	2145	2200	2215	2230	2245	2315	2345	0015	0045	0115	...
Den Haag Centraal 450 a.		1856	|	1926	|	1956	|	2026	|	2056	|	2126	|	2156	|	2226	|	2256	2326	2356	0026	0056	0126c	...
Den Haag HS 450 d.	hour until	...	1917	...	1947	...	2012	...	2042	...	2112	...	2142	...	2212	...	2242	...	...	...	...	...	...	...
Delft 450 d.		...	1925	...	1955	...	2020	...	2050	...	2120	...	2150	...	2220	...	2250	...	...	...	...	...	...	...
Schiedam Centrum 450 d.		...	1933	...	2003	...	2028	...	2058	...	2128	...	2158	...	2228	...	2258	...	...	...	...	...	...	...
Rotterdam Centraal 450 a.		...	1938	...	2008	...	2033	...	2103	...	2133	...	2203	...	2233	...	2303	...	...	...	...	...	...	...
Dordrecht 450 a.		...	1958	...	2026	...	2053	...	2123	...	2153	...	2223	...	2253	...	2323	...	...	...	...	...	...	...

a – Ⓐ only.
b – 0548 on ⑥ (also Apr. 27, May 26, June 6; not Dec. 25, Jan. 1).
c – Mornings of ⑥⑦ (also Apr. 28, May 27, June 7; not Dec. 26, Jan. 2).
h – 0637 on ⑥ (also Apr. 27, May 26, June 6: not Dec. 25, Jan. 1).
k – Also Apr. 27, May 26, June 6; not Dec. 25, Jan. 1.

r – ⚒ only.
t – 0737 on †.
v – 0707 on †.
z – Runs daily Schiphol - Den Haag Centraal.

◧ – Runs 4–6 minutes later Dordrecht - Schiphol on ⑥k.
◐ – Runs 4–6 minutes later Dordrecht - Schiphol on ©.
■ – Runs 3–5 minutes **earlier** Amsterdam Zuid - Dordrecht on ⑥k.
● – Runs 3–5 minutes **earlier** Amsterdam Zuid - Dordrecht on ©.
‡ – Amsterdam **Centraal**.

461 AMSTERDAM - HAARLEM - HOORN and ZANDVOORT AAN ZEE

km		Ⓐ¶	Ⓐ	⑥k	Ⓐ	©	Ⓐ	⑥k			✣														
	Amsterdam C ⊙ 450 d.	0526	0556	...	0626	0626k	0656	0656	0726	0756		1726	1756	1826	1856	1926	1956	2026	2056	2126	2156	2226	2256	2326	2356
0	**Haarlem** 450 d.	0545	0615	...	0645	0645	0715	0715	0745	0815		1745	1815	1845	1915	1945	2015	2045	2115	2145	2215	2245	2315	2345	0015
11	Beverwijk d.	0602	0632	...	0702	0702	0732	0732	0802	0832	and every	1802	1832	1902	1932	2002	2032	2102	2132	2202	2232	2302	2332	0002	0031
22	Castricum 466 d.	0615	0645	0649	0715	0719	0745	0749	0815	0845	30 minutes	1815	1845	1919j	1949j	2019	2049	2119	2149	2219	2249	2319	2349	0019	0049
34	**Alkmaar** 466 a.	0626	0656	0700	0726	0730	0756	0800	0826	0856	until	1826	1856	1930j	2000j	2030	2100	2130	2200	2230	2300	2330	2400	0030	0101
34	**Alkmaar** 466 d.	0631	0701	0701	0731	0731	0801	0801	0831	0901		1831	1901	1931	2001	2031	...	2131	...	2231	...	2331	...	0031t	...
40	Heerhugowaard 466 d.	0639	0709	0709	0739	0739	0809	0809	0839	0909		1839	1909	1939	2009	2039	...	2139	...	2239	...	2339	...	0039t	...
57	**Hoorn** a.	0654	0724	0724	0754	0754	0824	0824	0854	0924		1854	1924	1954	2024	2054	...	2154	...	2254	...	2354	...	0054t	...

	Ⓐ	⚒	⑥k	Ⓐ	©	Ⓐ																	◇		
Hoorn d.	...	...	...	0606	...	0636	0706	0736r	0806	0836r	0906	0936	1006		1736	1806	1836	1906	1936	2006	...	2106	...	2206	2306
Heerhugowaard 466 d.	...	...	...	0621	...	0651	0721	0751r	0821	0851r	0921	0951	1021		1751	1821	1851	1921	1951	2021	...	2121	...	2221	2321
Alkmaar 466 a.	...	...	...	0629	...	0659	0729	0759r	0829	0859r	0929	0959	1029	and every	1759	1829	1859	1929	1959	2029	...	2129	...	2229	2329
Alkmaar 466 d.	0530	0600	0630	0634	0700	0704	0734y	0804j	0834j	0904j	0934j	1004	1034	30 minutes	1804	1834	1900	1930	2000	2030	2100	2130	2200	2230	2330
Castricum 466 d.	0540	0610	0640	0644	0710	0714	0744y	0814j	0844j	0914j	0944j	1014	1044	until	1814	1844	1910	1940	2010	2040	2110	2140	2210	2240	2340
Beverwijk d.	0558	0628	0658	0658	0728	0728	0758	0828	0858	0929	0958	1028	1058		1828	1958	1928	1958	2028	2058	2129	2158	2228	2258	2358
Haarlem 450 d.	0617	0647	0717	0717	0747	0747	0817	0847	0917	0948	1017	1047	1117		1847	1917	1947	2017	2047	2117	2148	2217	2247	2317	0017
Amsterdam C ⊙ 450 a.	0635	0706	0735	0735	0806	0805	0836	0906	0935	1006	1035	1105	1135		1905	1935	2006	2035	2105	2135	2206	2235	2305	2335	0035

km										
	Amsterdam C ⊙ d.	0641a	0711r	0741r	0811	0841	and every	2311	2341	0011
0	**Haarlem** d.	0700	0730	0800	0830	0900	30 minutes	2330	2400	0030
8	**Zandvoort** aan Zee a.	0710	0740	0810	0840	0910	until	2340	0010	0040

	Ⓐ	Ⓐ	⚒	⚒						
Zandvoort aan Zee d.	0550	0620	0650	0720	0750	0820	0850	and every	2320	2350
Haarlem d.	0602	0632	0702	0732	0802	0832	0902	30 minutes	2332	0002
Amsterdam C ⊙ a.	0620	0650	0720	0750	0820	0850	0920	until	2350	0020

a – Ⓐ only.
j – 4 minutes earlier on †.
k – ⑥ (also Apr. 27, May 26, June 6; not Dec. 25, Jan. 1).

r – ⚒ only.
t – Mornings of ⑥⑦ (also Apr. 28, May 27, June 7; not Dec. 26, Jan. 2).
y – 4 minutes earlier on ⑥k.

◇ – Also at 2300 and 0000 from Alkmaar to Amsterdam.
¶ – 3 minutes later Amsterdam - Alkmaar on ④⑤ (not May 26).

✣ – The 0726, 0756, 0826 and 0856 from Amsterdam run 4 minutes later Castricum - Alkmaar on †.
⊙ – Amsterdam Centraal. All trains also call at Amsterdam Sloterdijk (5 minutes from Centraal).

LEIDEN - ALPHEN - UTRECHT and GOUDA — 463

Additional services run on Ⓐ

km		Ⓐ	⚒	⚒								
0	**Leiden** Centraal ....d.	0553	0623	0653	0723	0753	and every	2323	2353	0023	...	...
15	Alphen a/d Rijn ....d.	0607	0637	0707	0737	0807	30 minutes	2337	0007	0037	...	...
34	Woerden ....d.	0625	0655	0725	0755	0825	until	2355	0025	0055	...	...
50	**Utrecht** Centraal ....a.	0635	0705	0735	0805	0835		0005	0035	0105	...	...

	Ⓐ	⚒	⚒									
Utrecht Centraal..........d.	0555	0625	0655	0725	0755	and every	2325	2355	0025	...	...	...
Woerden..........................d.	0606	0636	0706	0736	0806	30 minutes	2336	0006	0036	...	...	...
Alphen a/d Rijn ....d.	0624	0654	0724	0754	0824	until	2354	0024	0054	...	...	...
Leiden Centraal ....a.	0637	0707	0737	0807	0837		0007	0037	0107	...	...	...

ALPHEN A/D RIJN - GOUDA and v.v. *17 km.* Journey: 22–29 minutes.

From Alphen a/d Rijn at 0609 Ⓐ, 0639 Ⓐ, 0709 ⚒, 0739 ⚒, 0809, 0839 and every 30 minutes until 0009, 0039; then 0108.

From Gouda at 0551 Ⓐ, 0628 ⚒, 0658 ⚒, 0728, 0758, 0821, 0858, 0928, 0958, 1021, 1058, 1128, 1158, 1221, 1258, 1328, 1358, 1421, 1458, 1528, 1558, 1621 Ⓒ, 1628 Ⓐ, 1658, 1728, 1758, 1821 Ⓒ, 1828 Ⓐ, 1858, 1928, 1958, 2021, 2058, 2128, 2158, 2221 Ⓐ, 2228 Ⓒ, 2258, 2328, 2358 and 0028.

AMSTERDAM - GOUDA - ROTTERDAM — 465

For fast trains **Amsterdam** - **Rotterdam**, see Tables **450** and **451**. For other trains **Gouda** - **Rotterdam**, see Table **481**.

km		Ⓐ	⚒	⚒	⚒					
0	**Amsterdam** Centraal .....d.	0549	0619	0649	0719	0749	0819		2319	2349
6	Amsterdam Amstel ....d.	0558	0628	0658	0728	0758	0828	and every	2328	2358
9	Duivendrecht ....d.	0601	0631	0701	0731	0801	0831	30 minutes	2331	0001
27	Breukelen ....d.	0618	0648	0718	0748	0818	0848		2348	0018
40	Woerden ....d.	0628	0658	0728	0758	0828	0858	until	2358	0028
56	**Gouda** ....d.	0641	0711	0741	0811	0841	0911		0011	0041
70	Rotterdam Alexander .....d.	0654	0724	0754	0824	0854	0924		0024	0054
80	**Rotterdam** Centraal.......a.	0704	0734	0804	0834	0904	0934		0034	0104

	Ⓐ	Ⓐ	⚒	⚒					
Rotterdam Centraal.... d.	0524	0554	0624	0654	0724	0754		2254	2324
Rotterdam Alexander.... d.	0535	0605	0635	0705	0735	0805	and every	2305	2335
Gouda .... d.	0549	0619	0649	0719	0749	0819	30 minutes	2319	2349
Woerden .... d.	0601	0632	0702	0732	0802	0832		2331	0001
Breukelen...................... d.	0611	0641	0711	0741	0811	0841	until	2341	0011
Duivendrecht.................. d.	0628	0658	0728	0758	0828	0858		2358	0028
Amsterdam Amstel......... d.	0632	0702	0732	0802	0832	0902		0002	0032
Amsterdam Centraal.. a.	0641	0711	0741	0811	0841	0911		0011	0041

AMSTERDAM - ALKMAAR - DEN HELDER — 466

Timings may vary by ± 1 minute

km		⑥⑦c		Ⓐ	⚒	Ⓐ	Ⓐ					†	⚒									
	Nijmegen **468**..............d.	2343p	...	...	...	...	...	0536a	0613r	0643r	0713	0736	0743	0813	0843		2013	2043	2113	2143	2213	2243
	Arnhem Centraal **468**........d.	0001	...	...	...	...	...	0602a	0632r	0702r	0732	0801	0802	0832	0902		2032	2101	2131	2201	2231	2301
0	**Amsterdam** Centraal **461 470** d.	0109	...	0529	...	0609	0639	0709	0739	0809	0839	0909	0909	0939	1009	and every	2139	2209	2239	2309	2339	0009
5	Amsterdam Sloterdijk **461 470** d.	0115	...	0535	...	0615	0645	0715	0745	0815	0845	0915	0915	0945	1015	30 minutes	2145	2215	2245	2315	2345	0015
12	Zaandam..............................d.	0122	...	0542	...	0622	0652	0722	0752	0822	0852	0922	0922	0952	1022		2152	2222	2252	2322	2352	0022
29	Castricum........................ **461** d.	0134	...	0606	...	0634	0704	0734	0804	0834	0904	0934	0934	1004	1034	until	2204	2234	2304	2334	0004	0034
41	**Alkmaar**................ **461 470** a.	0146	...	0618	...	0646	0716	0746	0816	0846	0916	0946	0946	1016	1046		2216	2246	2316	2346	0016	0046
41	**Alkmaar**.......................... **461** d.	...	...	0619	0649	0649	0719	0749	0819	0849	0919	0949	0949	1019	1049		2219	2249	2319	2349	0019	0049b
48	Heerhugowaard.............. **461** d.	...	...	0628	0658	0658	0728	0757	0828	0858	0928	0958	0958	1028	1058		2228	2258	2328	2358	0028	0058b
83	**Den Helder**..........................a.	...	...	0656	0726	0726	0756	0826	0856	0926	0956	1026	1026	1056	1126		2256	2326	2356	0033	0056	0126b

		Ⓐ	†	⑥k	Ⓐ	Ⓐ	⚒	Ⓐm														
Den Helder ....d.	...	0504	...	...	0534	0604	0634	0646	0704	0734	0804	0834	0904	0934		2004	2034	2104	2134	2204	2304	2357
Heerhugowaard .... **461** d.	...	0531	...	...	0601	0631	0701	0715	0731	0801	0831	0901	0931	1001		2031	2101	2131	2201	2231	2331	0023
Alkmaar .... **461** a.	...	0541	...	...	0611	0641	0711	0724	0741	0811	0841	0911	0941	1011	and every	2041	2111	2141	2211	2241	2341	0031
Alkmaar .... **461 470** d.	0502	0544	0603	0600	0614	0644	0714	0727	0744	0814	0844	0914	0944	1014	30 minutes	2044	2114	2144	2214	2244	2344	0032
Castricum .... **461** d.	0512	0555	0614	0610	0625	0655	0725	0735	0755	0825	0855	0925	0955	1025		2055	2125	2155	2225	2255	2355	0042
Zaandam ....d.	0536	0608	0635	|	0638	0708	0738	0749	0808	0838	0908	0938	1008	1038	until	2108	2138	2208	2238	2308	0008	0103
Amsterdam Sloterdijk. **461 470** d.	0541	0615	0641	0700	0645	0715	0745	0755	0815	0845	0915	0945	1015	1045		2115	2145	2215	2245	2315	0015	0109
Amsterdam Centraal. **461 470** a.	0547	0621	0647	0705	0651	0721	0751	0801	0821	0851	0921	0951	1021	1051		2121	2151	2221	2251	2321	0021	0116
Arnhem Centraal **468** ....a.	...	0729	...	...	0759	0829	0859	...	0929	0959	1029	1059	1129	1159		2229	2259	2330	2400	0030	0132	...
Nijmegen **468** ....a.	...	0747	...	...	0817	0847	0917	...	0947	1017	1047	1117	1147	1217		2247	2317	2347	0024	0049	0152z	...

a – Ⓐ only.
b – Mornings of ①④⑤⑥⑦ (also Apr. 19, June 7).
c – Also Apr. 28, May 27, June 7; not Dec. 26, Jan. 2.
k – Also Apr. 27, May 26, June 6; not Dec. 25, Jan. 1.
m – To Maastricht (Table **470**).
p – Previous day.
r – ⚒ only.
z – Mornings of ①②③④⑥⑦ (also May 27).

AMSTERDAM and SCHIPHOL ✈ - ARNHEM - NIJMEGEN — 468

Timings may vary by ± 1 minute

Many trains from / to Amsterdam Centraal start from / continue to Den Helder (see Table **466**). For international trains **Amsterdam** – **Arnhem** – **Köln**, see Table **28**.

km			Ⓐ	Ⓐ	Ⓐ	Ⓐ	⑥k	Ⓐ	Ⓐ	⚒	⚒	Ⓐ		⚒		⑥k	Ⓐ		⚒		⚒		⚒	
0	**Amsterdam** Centraal...... **470** d.	0024	...	...	*0610*	...	*0626*	0624	*0641*	...	0654	...	0724	...	0754	...	...	0824	...	0854	...	0924	...	0954
6	Amsterdam Amstel .... **470** d.	0033	...	...	*0618*	...	|	0633	*0649*	...	0703	...	0733	...	0803	...	...	0833	...	0903	...	0933	...	1003
	Schiphol ✈ .... **470** d.	|	...	...	|	0618	|	|	|	...	|	0703	|	0733	|	0803	0803	|	0833	|	0903	|	0933	|
	Amsterdam Zuid......... **470** d.	|	...	...	|	0626	|	|	|	...	|	0711	|	0741	|	0810	0811	|	0841	|	0911	|	0941	|
39	**Utrecht** Centraal............ **470** a.	0051	...	...	*0637*	0648	*0651*	0651	*0707*	...	0721	0738	0751	0808f	0821	0833	0840	0851	0908f	0921	0938f	0951	1008f	1021
39	**Utrecht** Centraal.......................d.	0053	0553	0623	0639	...	0653	0653	0709	0709	0723	0743	0753	0813f	0823	0839	0844	0853	0913f	0923	0943f	0953	1013f	1023
79	Ede-Wageningen ....d.	0119	0620	0650	0703	...	0719	0719	0733	0733	0749	0804	0819	0834	0849	0903	0905	0919	0934	0949	1004	1019	1034	1049
96	**Arnhem** Centraal.......................a.	0132	0630	0700	0714	...	0729	0729	0744	0744	0759	0815	0829	0845	0859	0914	0916	0929	0945	0959	1015	1029	1045	1059
96	**Arnhem** Centraal............. **475** d.	0135z	0635	0705	0720	...	0735	0735	0750	...	0805	0820	0835	0850	0905	0920	0920	0935	0950	1005	1020	1035	1050	1105
114	**Nijmegen**........................... **475** a.	0152z	0647	0717	0732	...	0747	0747	0802	...	0817	0832	0847	0902	0917	0932	0932	0947	1002	1017	1032	1047	1102	1117

Amsterdam Centraal...... **470** d.	...	1024	...	1054		...	1854	...	1924	...	1954	...	2024	...	2054	...	2124	...	2154	...	2224	2254	2324
Amsterdam Amstel.......... **470** d.	...	1033	...	1103	and at	...	1903	...	1933	...	2003	...	2033	...	2103	...	2133	...	2203	...	2233	2303	2333
Schiphol ✈ .... **470** d.	1003	|	1033	|	the same	1833	|	1903	|	1933	|	2003	|	2033	|	2103	|	2133	|	2203	|	|	|
Amsterdam Zuid.......... **470** d.	1011	|	1041	|		1841	|	1911	|	1940	|	2010	|	2040	|	2110	|	2140	|	2210	|	|	|
Utrecht Centraal............ **470** a.	1038j	1051	1108j	1121	minutes	1908j	1921	1938j	1951	2004	2021	2034	2051	2104	2121	2134	2151	2204	2221	2234	2251	2321	2351
Utrecht Centraal.......................d.	1043j	1053	1114j	1123	past each	1914j	1923	1943j	1953	2009	2023	2039	2053	2109	2123	2139	2153	2209	2223	2239	2253	2323	2353
Ede-Wageningen ....d.	1104	1119	1135	1149	hour until	1935	1949	2004	2019	2033	2049	2103	2119	2133	2149	2203	2219	2233	2248	2303	2320	2350	0020
Arnhem Centraal.......................a.	1115	1129	1146	1159		1946	1959	2015	2029	2044	2059	2114	2129	2144	2159	2214	2229	2244	2259	2314	2330	2400	0030
Arnhem Centraal............. **475** d.	1120	1135	1150	1205		1950	2005	2020	2035	2050	2105	2120	2135	2150	2205	2220	2235	2250	2305	2320	2335	0005	0035
Nijmegen........................... **475** a.	1132	1147	1202	1217		2002	2017	2032	2047	2102	2117	2132	2147	2202	2217	2232	2247	2302	2317	2332	2347	0024	0049

km		Ⓐ	⚒	Ⓐ	Ⓐ	⚒	†	⚒	⚒	†	⚒		⚒	†	⚒	⚒		⚒						
	Nijmegen .... **475** d.	...	...	0536	...	0613	...	0628a	0643	...	0658a	0713	0728a	0736	0743	0758a	0813	0828	0843	0858	0913	0928	0943	
	Arnhem Centraal......... **475** a.	...	...	0556	...	0626	...	0640a	0656	...	0710a	0726	0740a	0756	0756	0810a	0826	0840	0856	0910	0926	0940	0956	and at
	Arnhem Centraal.......................d.	0546	...	0602	0616	0632	...	0645	0702	...	0715	0732	0745	0801	0802	0815	0832	0845	0902	0915	0932	0945	1002	the same
	Ede-Wageningen......................d.	0556	...	0612	0626	0642	...	0655	0712	...	0725	0742	0755	0811	0812	0825	0842	0855	0912	0925	0942	0955	1012	
	Utrecht Centraal.......................a.	0621	...	0637	0651	0707	...	0717r	0737	...	0747r	0807	0817r	0838	0837	0847r	0907	0917r	0937	0947t	1007	1017t	1037	minutes
0	**Utrecht** Centraal............ **470** d.	0626	0639	0639	0656	0709	0708	0722r	0739	0738	0752r	0809	0822r	0839	0839	0852r	0909	0922r	0939	0952t	1009	1022t	1039	
36	**Amsterdam** Zuid...... **470** d.	0651	|	|	0721	|	|	0751	|	|	0821	|	0851	|	|	0921	|	0951	|	1021	|	1051	|	past each
45	**Schiphol** ✈ .... **470** a.	0657	|	|	0727	|	|	0757	|	|	0827	|	0857	|	|	0927	|	0957	|	1027	|	1057	|	hour until
	Amsterdam Amstel....... **470** d.	...	0657	0657	...	0727	0729	...	0757	0759	...	0827	...	0857	0857	...	0927	...	0957	...	1027	...	1057	
	Amsterdam Centraal... **470** a.	...	0705	0705	...	0735	0737	...	0805	0807	...	0835	...	0905	0905	...	0935	...	1005	...	1035	...	1105	

															†			†							⑤⑥k
Nijmegen .... **475** d.	1728	1743	1758	1813	1828	1843	1858	1913	1928	1943	1958	2013	2028	2043	2058	2113	...	2128	2143	...	2213	2243	2313	2343	2343
Arnhem Centraal.......... **475** a.	1740	1756	1810	1826	1840	1856	1910	1926	1940	1956	2010	2026	2041	2056	2110	2126	...	2140	2156	...	2226	2256	2326	2356	2356
Arnhem Centraal.......................d.	1745	1802	1815	1832	1846	1902	1916	1932	1946	2002	2016	2032	2046	2101	2116	2131	...	2146	2201	...	2231	2301	2331	0001	0001
Ede-Wageningen ....d.	1755	1812	1825	1842	1856	1912	1926	1942	1956	2012	2026	2042	2056	2111	2126	2141	...	2156	2211	...	2241	2311	2341	0011	0011
Utrecht Centraal.......................a.	1817t	1837	1847t	1907	1921	1937	1951	2007	2021	2037	2051	2107	2121	2138	2151	2208	...	2221	2238	...	2308	2338	0008	0038	0038
Utrecht Centraal............ **470** d.	1822t	1839	1852t	1909	1926	1939	1956	2009	2026	2039	2056	2109	2126	2139	2156	2209	2212	2226	2239	2242	2309	2339	*0023*	...	0039
Amsterdam Zuid....... **470** d.	1851	|	1921	|	1951	|	2021	|	2051	|	2121	|	2151	|	2221	|	2235n	2251	|	2305	|	|	|	...	|
Schiphol ✈ .... **470** a.	1857	|	1927	|	1957	|	2027	|	2057	|	2127	|	2157	|	2227	|	2241n	2257	|	2314	|	|	|	...	|
Amsterdam Amstel........ **470** d.	...	1857	...	1927	...	1957	...	2027	...	2057	...	2127	...	2157	...	2227	...	...	2257	...	2327	2357	*0043*	...	0100
Amsterdam Centraal.... **470** a.	...	1905	...	1935	...	2005	...	2035	...	2105	...	2135	...	2205	...	2235	...	...	2305	...	2335	0005	*0051*	...	0107

a – Ⓐ only.
f – 4 minutes **earlier** on ⑥ (also Apr. 27, May 26, June 6; not Dec. 25, Jan. 1).
j – 1–5 minutes **earlier** on Ⓒ.
k – Also Apr. 27, May 26, June 6; not Dec. 25, Jan. 1.
n – 3 minutes later on ⑥ (also Apr. 27, May 26, June 6; not Dec. 25, Jan. 1).
r – 4 minutes later on ⑥ (also Apr. 27, May 26, June 6; not Dec. 25, Jan. 1).
t – 4 minutes later on Ⓒ.
z – ①②③④⑥⑦ (also May 27).

470 ENKHUIZEN - AMSTERDAM - EINDHOVEN - MAASTRICHT, VENLO and HEERLEN

ENKHUIZEN / ALKMAAR - AMSTERDAM CENTRAAL - EINDHOVEN - MAASTRICHT / HEERLEN *Timings may vary by ± 1 minute*

km		Ⓐ	Ⓐ	Ⓐ	⚒	⚒	Ⓐ	Ⓐ	Ⓒ	⑥k	Ⓐ◇	Ⓐ	Ⓒ	Ⓐ◇	Ⓐd	Ⓒ	Ⓐ◇	⚒	†	⚒◇	⚒	†	⚒◇	⚒	†	⚒◇
0	**Enkhuizen** d.	...	...	0509	...	0539	0539	...	...	0609	0609	...	0639	0639	...	0709k	0709	...	0739	0739	...	0809	0809	...	0839	0839
18	Hoorn d.	...	...	0534	...	0604	0604	...	...	0634	0639	...	0704	0709	...	0734k	0739	...	0804	0809	...	0834	0839	...	0904	0909
	Alkmaar 466 d.	...	...	|	...	|	|	0627	...	|	|	0657	|	|	0727	|	|	0757	|	|	0827	|	|	0857	|	|
57	Amsterdam Sloterdijk 466 d.	...	...	0600	...	0630	0630	0655	...	0700	0705	0725	0730	0735	0755	0800k	0805	0825	0830	0835	0855	0900	0905	0925	0930	0935
62	**Amsterdam** Centraal 466 a.	...	...	0606	...	0636	0636	0701	...	0706	0711	0731	0736	0741	0801	0806k	0811	0831	0836	0841	0901	0906	0911	0931	0936	0941
62	**Amsterdam** Centraal 468 d.	...	...	0610	...	▬	0641	0705	...	0710	0715	0735	0740	0745	0804	0811	0816	0835	0840	0845	0905	0910	0914	0935	0940	0945
68	Amsterdam Amstel 468 d.	...	...	0618	...	...	0649	0713	...	0718	0723	0743	0748	0753	0812	0819	0824	0843	0848	0853	0913	0918	0922	0943	0948	0953
101	**Utrecht** Centraal 468 d.	...	0609	0639	...	...	0709	0733	...	0739	0744	0803	0809	0814	0833	0839	0844	0903	0909	0914	0933	0939	0944	1003	1009	1014
149	's-Hertogenbosch d.	...	0639	0709	...	...	0739	0806	...	0809	0815	0836	0839	0845	0906	0909	0915	0936	0939	0945	1006	1009	1015	1036	1039	1045
181	**Eindhoven** Centraal a.	...	0658	0728	...	Ⓒ	0758	0824	...	0828	0834	0854	0858	0904	0924	0928	0934	0954	0958	1004	1024	1028	1034	1054	1058	1104
181	**Eindhoven** Centraal d.	0629	0659	0729	0729	0757	0759	0827	0829	0829	0838	0857	0859	0908	0927	0929	0938	0957	0959	1008	1027	1029	1038	1057	1059	1108
210	Weert d.	0646	0716	0746	0746	0815	0816	0845	0846	0846	0856	0915	0916	0926	0945	0946	0956	1015	1016	1026	1045	1046	1056	1115	1116	1126
234	Roermond d.	0700	0730	0800	0800	0830	0830	0900	0900	0900	0910	0930	0930	0940	1000	1000	1010	1030	1030	1040	1100	1100	1110	1130	1130	1140
258	Sittard ★ d.	0716	0746	0816	0816	0846	0846	0916	0916	0916	0926	0946	0946	0956	1016	1016	1026	1046	1046	1056	1116	1116	1126	1146	1146	1156
277	**Heerlen** ★ a.	|	|	|	|	|	|	|	|	|	0941	|	|	1011	|	|	1041	|	|	1111	|	|	1141	|	|	1211
280	**Maastricht** a.	0730	0800	0830	0830	0900	0900	0930	0930	0930	...	1000	1000	...	1030	1030	...	1100	1100	...	1130	1130	...	1200	1200	...

	⚒	†	⚒◇											†	⚒	†	†	⚒	†							
Enkhuizen ◧ d.	...	0909	0909	...	0939	...	1009	and at the same minutes past each hour until	...	1739	...	1809	...	1839	1839	...	1909	1909	1939	2009	2039	2109	2139	2209	2239
Hoorn ◧ d.	...	0934	0939	...	1009	...	1039		...	1809	...	1839	...	1904	1909	...	1934	1939	2004	2036	2104	2134	2204	2234	2304
Alkmaar 466 d.	0927	|	|	0957	|	1027	|		1757	|	1827	|	1857	|	|	1927	|	|	|	|	|	|	|	|	|
Amsterdam Sloterdijk 466 ◧ d.	0955	1000	1005	1025	1035	1055	1105		1825	1835	1855	1905	1925	1930	1935	1955	2000	2005	2030	2100	2130	2200	2230	2300	2330
Amsterdam Centraal 466 ◧ a.	1001	1006	1011	1031	1041	1101	1111		1831	1841	1901	1911	1931	1936	1941	2001	2006	2011	2036	2106	2136	2206	2236	2306	2336
Amsterdam Centraal 468 d.	1005	1010	1014	1034	1046	1105	1114		1834	1846	1905	1914	1935	1940	1945	2005	2010	2014	2040	2110	2140	2210	2240	2310	2340
Amsterdam Amstel 468 d.	1013	1018	1022	1042	1054	1113	1122		1842	1854	1913	1922	1943	1948	1953	2013	2018	2022	2048	2118	2148	2218	2248	2317	2347
Utrecht Centraal 468 d.	1033	1039	1044	1103	1114	1133	1144		1903	1914	1933	1944	2003	2009	2014	2033	2039	2044	2109	2139	2209	2239	2309	2339	0009
's-Hertogenbosch d.	1106	1109	1115	1136	1145	1206	1215		1935	1945	2005	2015	2036	2039	2045	2106	2109	2115	2139	2209	2239	2309	2339	0009	0039
Eindhoven Centraal a.	1124	1128	1134	1154	1204	1224	1234		1954	2004	2024	2034	2054	2058	2104	2125	2128	2134	2158	2228	2258	2328	2358	0028	0058
Eindhoven Centraal d.	1127	1129	1138	1157	1208	1227	1238		1957	2008	2027	2038	2057	2059	2108	2127	2129	2138	2159	2229	2259	2329	2359	...	...
Weert d.	1145	1146	1156	1215	1226	1245	1256		2015	2026	2045	2056	2115	2116	2126	2145	2146	2156	2216	2246	2316	2346	0016	...	...
Roermond d.	1200	1200	1210	1230	1240	1300	1310		2030	2040	2100	2110	2130	2130	2140	2200	2200	2210	2230	2300	2330	0000	0030	...	...
Sittard ★ d.	1216	1216	1226	1246	1256	1316	1326		2046	2056	2116	2126	2146	2146	2156	2216	2216	2226	2246	2316	2346	0016	0046	...	...
Heerlen ★ a.	|	|	1241	|	1311	|	1341		|	2111	|	2141	|	|	2211	|	|	2241	|	|	|	|	|	...	...
Maastricht a.	1230	1230	...	1300	...	1330	...		2100	...	2130	...	2200	2200	...	2230	2230	...	2300	2330	2400	0030	0100	...	...

	Ⓐ		Ⓐ	Ⓐ	Ⓐ	Ⓒ	Ⓐ	Ⓐ	Ⓒ	Ⓐ	Ⓐ	Ⓒ	Ⓐ	⚒	†	⚒	⚒	†	⚒	⚒	†	⚒				
Maastricht d.	...	...	...	0531	...	...	0601	...	0631k	0631	...	0701k	0701	...	0731	0731	...	0801	0801	...	0831	0831	...	0901	...	0931
Heerlen ★ d.	...	...	...	|	0549	...	|	0619	|	|	0649	|	|	0719	|	|	0749	|	|	0819	|	|	0849	|	0919	|
Sittard ★ d.	...	...	...	0547	0605	...	0617	0635	0647k	0647	0705	0717k	0717	0735	0747	0747	0805	0817	0817	0835	0847	0847	0905	0917	0935	0947
Roermond d.	...	...	...	0602	0620	...	0632	0650	0702k	0702	0720	0732k	0732	0750	0802	0802	0820	0832	0832	0850	0902	0902	0920	0932	0950	1002
Weert d.	...	...	...	0616	0634	...	0646	0704	0716k	0716	0734	0746k	0746	0804	0816	0816	0834	0846	0846	0904	0916	0916	0934	0946	1004	1016
Eindhoven Centraal a.	...	...	...	0632	0651	...	0702	0721	0732k	0732	0751	0802k	0802	0821	0832	0832	0851	0902	0902	0921	0932	0932	0951	1002	1021	1032
Eindhoven Centraal d.	0534	0604a	0627	0636	0657	0704k	0706	0727	0734	0736	0757	0804	0806	0827	0834	0836	0857	0904	0906	0927	0934	0936	0957	1006	1027	1036
's-Hertogenbosch d.	0553	0623a	0648	0658	0718	0723k	0728	0748	0753	0758	0818	0823	0828	0848	0853	0858	0918	0923	0928	0948	0953	0958	1018	1028	1048	1058
Utrecht Centraal 468 d.	0623	0653r	0718	0729	0749	0753k	0759	0819	0823	0829	0849	0853	0859	0919	0923	0929	0949	0953	0959	1019	1023	1029	1049	1059	1119	1129
Amsterdam Amstel 468 d.	0641	0711r	0736	0747	0807	0811k	0817	0837	0841	0847	0908	0911	0917	0937	0941	0947	1007	1011	1017	1037	1041	1047	1107	1117	1137	1147
Amsterdam Centraal 468 a.	0649	0719r	0744	0755	0815	0819k	0825	0845	0849	0855	0917	0919	0925	0945	0949	0955	1015	1019	1025	1045	1049	1055	1115	1125	1145	1155
Amsterdam Centraal 466 ◧ d.	0653	0723	0749	0759	0819	0823	0829	0849	0853	0859	0919	0923	0929	0949	0953	0959	1019	1023	1029	1049	1053	1059	1119	1129	1149	1159
Amsterdam Sloterdijk 466 ◧ d.	0659	0729	0755	0805	0825	0829	0835	0855	0859	0905	0925	0929	0935	0955	0959	1005	1025	1029	1035	1055	1059	1105	1125	1135	1155	1205
Alkmaar 466 a.	|	|	|	0833	|	|	0903	|	|	0933	|	|	1003	|	|	1033	|	|	1103	|	|	1133	|	1203	|	1233
Hoorn ◧ d.	0729	0759	0829	...	0859	0859	...	0929	0929	...	0959	0959	...	1029	1029	...	1059	1059	...	1129	1129	...	1159	...	1229	...
Enkhuizen ◧ a.	0753	0823	0853	...	0923	0923	...	0953	0953	...	1023	1023	...	1053	1053	...	1123	1123	...	1153	1153	...	1223	...	1253	...

						†⊙	⚒	†	†⊙	⚒	†	†⊙	⚒	†	†⊙	⚒	†	†	⚒	†					
Maastricht ◐ d.	and at the same minutes past each hour until	...	1631	...	1701	...	1731	1731	...	1801	1801	...	1831	1831	...	1901	1901	...	1931	1931	2001	2031	2101	2131	2201
Heerlen ★ d.		1619	|	1649	|	1719	|	|	1749	|	|	1819	|	|	1849	|	|	1919	|	|	|	|	|	|	|
Sittard ★ ◐ d.		1635	1647	1705	1717	1735	1747	1747	1805	1817	1817	1835	1847	1847	1905	1917	1917	1935	1947	1947	2017	2047	2117	2147	2217
Roermond ◐ d.		1650	1702	1720	1732	1750	1802	1802	1820	1832	1832	1850	1902	1902	1920	1932	1932	1950	2002	2002	2032	2102	2132	2202	2232
Weert ◐ d.		1704	1716	1734	1746	1804	1816	1816	1834	1846	1846	1904	1916	1916	1934	1946	1946	2004	2016	2016	2046	2116	2146	2216	2246
Eindhoven Centraal ◐ a.		1721	1732	1751	1802	1821	1832	1832	1851	1902	1902	1921	1932	1932	1951	2002	2002	2021	2032	2032	2102	2132	2202	2232	2302
Eindhoven Centraal d.		1727	1736	1757	1806	1827	1834	1836	1857	1904	1906	1927	1934	1936	1957	2004	2006	2027	2034	2036	2104	2134	2204	2234	2304
's-Hertogenbosch d.		1748	1758	1818	1828	1848	1853	1858	1918	1923	1928	1948	1953	1958	2018	2023	2028	2048	2053	2058	2123	2153	2223	2253	2323
Utrecht Centraal 468 d.		1819	1829	1849	1859	1919	1923	1929	1949	1953	1959	2019	2023	2029	2049	2053	2059	2119	2123	2129	2153	2223	2253	2323	2353
Amsterdam Amstel 468 d.		1837	1847	1907	1917	1937	1941	1947	2007	2011	2017	2037	2041	2047	2107	2111	2117	2137	2141	2147	2211	2241	2313	2343	0013
Amsterdam Centraal 468 a.		1845	1855	1915	1925	1945	1949	1955	2015	2019	2025	2045	2049	2055	2115	2119	2125	2145	2149	2155	2219	2249	2321	2351	0021
Amsterdam Centraal 466 d.		1849	1859	1919	1929	1949	1953	1959	2019	2023	2029	2049	2053	2059	2119	2123	2129	2149	2153	2159	2223	2253	2323	2353	0023
Amsterdam Sloterdijk 466 d.		1855	1905	1925	1935	1955	1959	2005	2025	2029	2035	2055	2059	2105	2125	2129	2135	2155	2159	2205	2229	2259	2329	2359	0029
Alkmaar 466 a.		|	1933	|	2003	|	|	2033	|	|	2103	|	|	2133	|	|	2203	|	|	2233	|	|	|	|	|
Hoorn d.		1929	...	1959	...	2029	2029	...	2059	2059	...	2129	2129	...	2159	2159	...	2229	2229	...	2259	2329	2359	0026	0105
Enkhuizen a.		1953	...	2023	...	2053	2053	...	2123	2123	...	2153	2153	...	2223	2223	...	2253	2253	...	2323	2353	0023	...	0127c

SCHIPHOL - AMSTERDAM ZUID - EINDHOVEN - VENLO *Timings may vary by ± 1 minute*

km		Ⓐ	Ⓐ	Ⓐ	⚒	⚒	Ⓐ	⑥k	Ⓐ															
0	**Schiphol** ✈ 468 d.	...	...	...	...	...	0618	0645	0648	0718j	0748j	and at the same minutes past each hour until	1818j	1848j	1918j	1949	2019	2049	2119	2149	2219	...	2249	2318j	2348j
9	**Amsterdam** Zuid 468 d.	...	...	...	...	...	0626	0655	0656	0726	0756		1826	1856	1926	1956	2026	2056	2126	2156	2226	...	2256	2325	2355
45	**Utrecht** Centraal 468 a.	...	...	...	...	...	0648	0718	0718	0748	0818		1848	1918	1948	2018	2048	2118	2148	2218	2248	...	2318	2348	0018
45	**Utrecht** Centraal d.	...	...	0609	...	...	0654	▬	0724	0754	0824		1854	1924	1954	2024	2054	2125	2154	2224	2254	*2309*	*2339*	*0009*	...
93	's-Hertogenbosch d.	...	...	0639	...	...	0725	...	0755	0825	0854		1924	1954	2024	2054	2124	2154	2224	2254	2324	*2339*	*0009*	*0039*	...
125	**Eindhoven** Centraal a.	...	...	0658	...	...	0743	...	0813	0843	0913		1943	2013	2043	2113	2143	2213	2243	2313	2343	*2358*	*0028*	*0058*	...
125	**Eindhoven** Centraal d.	0619	0649	...	0719	0749	0749	0819	0819	0849	0919		1949	2019	2049	2119	2149	2219	2249	2319	...	0019	...	...	...
138	Helmond d.	0628	0658	...	0728	0758	0758	0828	0828	0858	0928		1958	2028	2058	2128	2158	2228	2258	2328	...	0028	...	...	...
176	**Venlo** a.	0658	0728	...	0758	0828	0828	0858	0858	0928	0958		2028	2058	2128	2158	2228	2258	2328	2358	...	0058	...	...	...

	Ⓐ	Ⓐ	Ⓐ	⚒																†	⚒	†	⚒		
Venlo d.	...	0533	0603	0633	0703	0733	0803	0833	0903	0933	and at the same minutes past each hour until	1633	1703	1733	1803	1833	1903	1933	2003	2033	2033	2103	2103	...	...
Helmond d.	...	0602	0632	0702	0732	0802	0832	0902	0932	1002		1702	1732	1802	1832	1902	1932	2002	2032	2102	2102	2132	2132	...	...
Eindhoven Centraal a.	...	0611	0641	0711	0741	0811	0841	0911	0941	1011		1711	1741	1811	1841	1911	1941	2011	2041	2111	2111	2141	2141	...	...
Eindhoven Centraal d.	0547	0617	0647	0717	0747	0817	0847	0917	0947	1017		1717	1747	1817	1847	1917	1947	2017	2047	2117	▬	2147	▬	*2204*	*2234*
's-Hertogenbosch d.	0608	0638	0708	0738	0808	0838	0908	0938	1008	1038		1738	1808	1838	1908	1938	2008	2038	2108	2138	...	2208	...	*2223*	*2253*
Utrecht Centraal a.	0635	0705	0735	0805	0839	0905	0935	1005	1035	1105		1805	1835	1904	1934	2004	2034	2104	2134	2205	⚒	2235	⚒	*2251*	*2321*
Utrecht Centraal 468 d.	0642	0712	0742	0812	0842	0912	0942	1012	1042	1112		1812	1842	1912	1942	2012	2042	2112	2142	2212	2212	2242	2242	2312	2342
Amsterdam Zuid 468 d.	0705	0735	0805	0835	0908	0938	1008	1038	1108t	1138t		1838t	1908t	1935	2005	2035	2105	2135	2205	2235	2235v	2305	2305	2335v	0005
Schiphol ✈ 468 a.	0711	0741	0811	0841	0914	0944	1014	1044	1114t	1144t		1844t	1914t	1941	2011	2041	2111	2141	2211	2241	2241v	2314	2314	2341v	0011

Local stopping trains SITTARD - HEERLEN - KERKRADE (operated by Arriva)

km		⚒										
0	Sittard d.	0618a	0648r	0718r	0748	0818	0848	and every 30 minutes until	2318	2348	0018
19	Heerlen a.	0638a	0708r	0738r	0808	0838	0908		2338	0008	0038
19	Heerlen d.	0640	0713	0740	0813	0840	0913		2340	0013	...
28	Kerkrade Centrum a.	0654	0726	0754	0826	0854	0926		2354	0026	...

	⚒	⚒								
Kerkrade Centrum d.	0607a	0637	0707r	0737	0807	0837	and every 30 minutes until	2307	2337	0007
Heerlen a.	0621a	0651	0721r	0751	0821	0851		2321	2351	0021
Heerlen d.	0622	0652	0722	0752	0822	0852		2322	2352	0022
Sittard a.	0642	0712	0742	0812	0842	0912		2342	0012	0042

a – Ⓐ only.
c – Mornings of ⑥⑦ (also Apr. 28, May 27, June 7; not Dec. 26, Jan. 2).
d – From Den Helder (Table **466**).
j – 3 minutes earlier on ⑥**k**.
k – ⑥ (also Apr. 27, May 26, June 6; not Dec. 25, Jan. 1).
r – ⚒ only.

t – 3 minutes earlier on †.
v – 3 minutes later on ⑥**k**.

◇ – Runs daily Eindhoven - Heerlen.
⊙ – Runs daily Heerlen - Eindhoven.
★ – See also Sittard - Heerlen - Kerkrade panel.

◧ – Additional trains Enkhuizen - Hoorn - Amsterdam and v.v.: **From Enkhuizen** at 2309 and 2339. **From Amsterdam Centraal** at 0623 Ⓐ and 0753 ⑥**k**.
◐ – Additional trains Maastricht - Sittard - Eindhoven: **From Maastricht** at 2301 and 0001.

DEN HAAG - EINDHOVEN 471

km		Ⓐ	⚒	⚒	Ⓐ★	⚒	⚒							★								
0	**Den Haag** Centraal ▷ d.	...	...	0546a	...	...	0616	...	0646r	...	0716	...	0746		...	2216	...	2246	...	...	...	...
2	**Den Haag** HS 450 460 d.	0523	...	0553a	...	...	0623	...	0653r	...	0723	...	0753	and at	...	2223	...	2253	...	...	*2329*	...
10	Delft 450 460 d.	0530	...	0600a	...	...	0630	...	0700r	...	0730	...	0800		...	2230	...	2300	...	...	*2335*	...
24	**Rotterdam** Centraal 450 451 460 d.	0544	...	0614	...	...	0644	...	0714	...	0744	...	0814	the same	...	2244	...	2314	...	...	*2352*	...
◐	Dordrecht 450 460 ★ d.	|	0558	|	0620	0628	|	0658	|	0728	|	0758	|	minutes	2228	|	2258	|	2328	...	|	2358
71	Breda 451 ★ a.	0607	0621	0637	0640	0651	0707	0721	0737	0751	0807	0821	0837		2251	2307	2321	2337	2351	...	0015	0021
71	Breda 475 d.	0608	0623a	0638	0645	0653	0708	0723r	0738	0753	0808	0823	0838	past each	2253	2308	2323	2338	2353	...	...	0023
92	Tilburg 475 d.	0623	0642a	0653	0658	0712	0723	0742r	0753	0812	0823	0842	0853	hour until	2312	2323	2342	2353	0012	0038	...	0042
	's-Hertogenbosch 475 a.	|	0658a	|	|	0728	|	0758r	|	0828	|	0858	|		2328	|	2358	|	0028	|	...	0058
129	**Eindhoven** Centraal a.	0645	...	0715	0725	...	0745	...	0815	...	0845	...	0915		...	2345	...	0015	...	0107	...	...

	Ⓐ	⚒	Ⓐ	⚒	⚒	⚒	⚒				Ⓐ♥					♥						
Eindhoven Centraal d.	0544	...	0614	...	0644	...	0714	...	0744	...	0803	0814	...	0844	...		2244	...	2314	...	2344	...
's-Hertogenbosch 475 d.	|	0603a	|	0633a	|	0703	|	0733r	|	0803	|	|	0833	|	0903		|	2303	|	2333	|	...
Tilburg 475 d.	0609	0619a	0639	0649a	0709	0719	0739	0749r	0809	0819	0831	0839	0849	0909	0919	and at	2309	2319	2339	2349	0009	...
Breda 475 a.	0621	0637a	0651	0707a	0721	0737	0751	0807r	0821	0837	0843	0851	0907	0921	0937	the same	2321	2337	2351	0007	0021	...
Breda 451 ★ d.	0623	0639	0653	0709	0723	0739	0753	0809	0823	0839	0850	0853	0909	0923	0939		2323	2339	2353	0009	0023	0039
Dordrecht 450 460 ★ a.	|	0702	|	0732	|	0802	|	0832	|	0902	0912	|	0932	|	1002	minutes	|	0002	|	0032	|	0102
Rotterdam Centraal 450 451 460 d.	0648	...	0718	...	0748	...	0818	...	0848	...	...	0918	...	0948	...	past each	2348	...	0018	...	0051*	...
Delft 450 460 d.	0659	...	0729	...	0759	...	0829	...	0859	...	...	0929	...	0959	...		2359	...	0029	...	...	...
Den Haag HS 450 460 a.	0706	...	0736	...	0806	...	0836	...	0906	...	...	0936	...	1006	...	hour until	0006	...	0036	...	...	...
Den Haag Centraal a.	0714	...	0742	...	0812	...	0842	...	0912t	...	...	0942	...	1012	...		0012	...	0042	...	...	...

a – Ⓐ only.
r – ⚒ only.
t – 0915 on †.

* – 0046 on the morning of ⑥⑦ (also Apr. 28, May 27, June 7; not Dec. 26, Jan. 2.
◐ – Dordrecht - Breda is 30 km.

▷ – Den Haag Centraal departure times are 2 minutes later on Ⓐ 0648 - 1948.
★ – Additional direct services Dordrecht - Eindhoven: From Dordrecht at 0920 Ⓐ, 1320 Ⓐ and 1720 Ⓐ.
♥ – Additional direct services Eindhoven - Dordrecht: From Eindhoven at 1203 Ⓐ, 1603 Ⓐ and 2007 Ⓐ.

MAASTRICHT - HEERLEN - AACHEN 473

Operated by **Arriva** (NS tickets valid)

km		①–⑤ d	⑥ k	①–⑤ d		①–⑥ e				
0	**Maastricht** 472 d.	...	...	0619	...	0719	0819	and	2319	...
11	Valkenburg 472 d.	...	...	0630	...	0730	0830	hourly	2330	...
24	**Heerlen** 472 d.	0543	0643	0643	0743	0743	0843	until	2343	...
34	Herzogenrath 🚌 802 a.	0559	0659	0659	0759	0759	0859		2359	...
48	**Aachen** Hbf 802 a.	0613	0713	0714	0813	0813	0913		0013	...

	①–⑤ d	①–⑥ e		⊠			
Aachen Hbf 802 d.	0546	0645	0746	and	2246	...	2345
Herzogenrath 🚌 802 d.	0600	0700	0800	hourly	2300	...	0000
Heerlen 472 a.	0613	0713	0813	until	2313	...	0013
Valkenburg 472 a.	0629	0729	0829		2329	...	...
Maastricht 472 a.	0640	0740	0840		2340	...	...

Other trains MAASTRICHT - HEERLEN

km		Ⓐ	⚒	⚒						
0	**Maastricht** d.	0537	0607	0637	0707	0737	and every	0007	0037	...
11	Valkenburg d.	0550	0620	0650	0720	0750	30 minutes	0020	0050	...
24	**Heerlen** d.	0607	0637	0707	0737	0807	until	0037	0107	...

	Ⓐ	⚒	⚒					
Heerlen d.	0523	0553	0623	0653	0723	and every	2353	0023
Valkenburg d.	0540	0610	0640	0710	0740	30 minutes	0010	0040
Maastricht a.	0554	0624	0654	0724	0754	until	0024	0054

d – Not Apr. 18, 27, May 26, June 6.
k – Also Apr. 27, May 26, June 6; not Dec. 25, Jan. 1.
e – Not Dec. 25, Jan. 1, Apr. 18.
⊠ – Aachen Hbf d. 1243/1543/1743 (not 1246/1546/1746); other timings follow the regular pattern.

ROOSENDAAL - 's-HERTOGENBOSCH - NIJMEGEN - ARNHEM - ZWOLLE 475

km		Ⓐ	Ⓐ	Ⓐ	Ⓐ	⚒	⚒	Ⓐ	†	⑥k	Ⓐ	†	⚒	†	⚒									
0	**Roosendaal** d.	...	...	...	...	...	...	0527	...	...	0557	...	0627	0654	0657	0727	0757		2127	2157	2227	...	2257	2327
23	Breda 471 d.	...	...	...	...	...	...	0550	...	...	0620	...	0650	0713	0720	0750	0820		2150	2220	2250	...	2320	2350
44	Tilburg 471 d.	...	...	...	...	...	...	0603	...	...	0633	...	0703	0733	0733	0803	0833		2203	2233	2303	...	2333	0003
67	**'s-Hertogenbosch** 471 a.	...	...	...	...	...	...	0619	...	...	0649	...	0719	0749	0749	0819	0849		2219	2249	2319	...	2349	0019
67	**'s-Hertogenbosch** d.	...	...	0532	...	...	...	0624	...	...	0654	...	0724	0754	0754	0824	0854	and every	2224	2254	2324	...	2354	...
86	Oss d.	...	...	0550	...	...	...	0635	...	...	0705	...	0735	0805	0805	0835	0905	30 minutes	2235	2305	2335	...	0005	...
110	**Nijmegen** a.	...	...	0613	...	...	...	0652	...	...	0722	...	0752	0822	0822	0852	0922	until	2252	2322	2352	...	0022	...
110	**Nijmegen** 468 d.	...	...	0616	0624	...	0654	0654	*0713*	*0716*	0724	*0736*	0754	0824	0824	0854	0924		2254	2324	2354	0002	0024	...
129	**Arnhem** Centraal 468 a.	...	...	0634	0637	...	0707	0707	*0726*	*0734*	0737	*0756*	0807	0837	0837	0907	0937		2307	2337	0007	0019	0037	...
129	**Arnhem** Centraal d.	...	0559	...	0641	...	0711	0711	0730	0741	0741	0811	0811	0841	0841	0911	0941		2311	2341	...	0025	...	...
145	Dieren d.	...	0619	...	0653	...	0723	0723	0750	0753	0753	0823	0823	0853	0853	0923	0953		2323	2353	...	0044	...	...
159	Zutphen d.	0603	0633	...	0703	0703	0733	0733	0803	0803	0803	0833	0833	0903	0903	0933	1003		2333	0003	...	0054	...	...
174	Deventer d.	0616	0646	...	0716	0716	0746	0746	0816	0816	0816	0846	0846	0916	0916	0946	1016		2346	0016	...	...	...	...
204	**Zwolle** a.	0641	0711	...	0741	0741	0811	0811	0841	0841	0841	0911	0911	0941	0941	1011	1041		0011	0041	...	...	...	...

	Ⓐ	Ⓐ	Ⓐ	Ⓐ		Ⓐ	Ⓐ	⚒		⚒		⚒												
Zwolle d.	...	...	...	...	...	...	...	...	...	0620a	...	0650a	0720r	0750	0820	0850		2120	2150	2220	2250	...	2320	2350
Deventer d.	...	...	...	...	...	...	...	...	...	0645a	...	0715a	0745r	0815	0845	0915		2145	2215	2245	2315	...	2345	0015
Zutphen d.	...	...	...	...	...	0547	0607	...	...	0658	...	0728	0758	0828	0858	0928		2158	2228	2258	2328	...	2358	0028
Dieren d.	...	...	...	...	...	0559	0618	...	...	0707	...	0737	0807	0837	0907	0937		2207	2237	2307	2337	...	0007	0037
Arnhem Centraal a.	...	...	...	...	...	0619	0636	...	...	0719	...	0749	0819	0849	0919	0949		2219	2249	2319	2349	...	0019	0049
Arnhem Centraal 468 d.	...	...	...	0553	...	0623	0641	0653	...	0723	0753	0753	0823	0853	0923	0953	and every	2223	2253	2323	2353	...	*0035*	...
Nijmegen 468 a.	...	...	...	0606	...	0636	0659	0706	...	0736	0806	0806	0836	0906	0936	1006	30 minutes	2236	2306	2336	0006	...	*0049*	...
Nijmegen d.	...	...	...	0609	...	0639	▬	0709	...	0739	0809	0809	0839	0909	0939	1009	until	2239	2309	2339	...	0027	...	...
Oss d.	...	...	...	0625	...	0655	...	0725	...	0755	0825	0825	0855	0925	0955	1025		2255	2325	2355	...	0049	...	...
's-Hertogenbosch a.	...	...	...	0637	...	0707	...	0737	...	0807	0837	0837	0907	0937	1007	1037		2307	2337	0007	...	0107	...	...
's-Hertogenbosch 471 d.	...	...	0612	0642	0712r	0712	0742	0742	0812	0812	0842	0842	0912	0942	1012	1042		2312	2342	0012	...	...	...	...
Tilburg 471 d.	0549	...	0628	0658	0728r	0728	0758	0758	0828	0828	0858	0858	0928	0958	1028	1058		2328	2358	0028	...	...	...	...
Breda 471 d.	0607	0615	0645	0715	0745	0745	0815	0815	0845	0845	0915	0915	0945	1015	1045	1115		2345	0015	0049	...	...	...	...
Roosendaal a.	...	0633	0703	0733	0803	0803	0833	0833	0903	0903	0933	0933	1003	1033	1103	1133		0003	0033	0107	...	...	...	...

a – Ⓐ only.
k – Also Apr. 27, May 26, June 6; not Dec. 25, Jan. 1.
r – ⚒ only.

ARNHEM and ZUTPHEN - WINTERSWIJK 476

Operated by **Arriva** (NS tickets valid) 2nd class only

km	⊠	Ⓐ	⚒	⚒		⚒		⚒		⚒		⚒					⊡				Ⓐ				
0	**Arnhem** Cen... d.	0605	0705	0731	0805	0835	0902	0935	1005	1035	1105	1131	1205	1235	1305	1331	and at the same	1905	1931	2005	2031	2105	2205	2305	0005
14	Zevenaar d.	0620	0720	0750	0820	0850	0920	0950	1020	1050	1120	1150	1220	1250	1320	1350	minutes past	1920	1950	2020	2050	2120	2220	2320	0020
30	Doetinchem d.	0637	0737	0807	0837	0907	0937	1007	1037	1107	1137	1207	1237	1307	1337	1407	each hour until	1937	2007	2037	2107	2137	2237	2337	0037
64	**Winterswijk** a.	0710	0810	0840	0910	0940	1010	1040	1110	1140	1210	1240	1310	1340	1410	1440		2010	2042	2110	2140	2210	2310	0010	0110

⊠	Ⓐ	Ⓐ	⚒	Ⓐ		⚒		⚒		⚒		⚒		⚒							Ⓐ		Ⓐ		
Winterswijk d.	0520	0550	0620	0650	0720	0750	0820	0850	0920	0950	1020	1050	1120	1150	1220	1250	and at the same	1920	1950	2020	2050	2120	2150	2220	2320
Doetinchem d.	0553	0623	0653	0723	0753	0823	0853	0923	0953	1023	1053	1123	1153	1223	1253	1323	minutes past	1953	2023	2053	2123	2153	2223	2253	2353
Zevenaar d.	0609	0640	0710	0740	0810	0840	0910	0940	1010	1040	1110	1140	1210	1240	1310	1340	each hour until	2010	2040	2110	2140	2210	2240	2310	0010
Arnhem Cen a.	0624	0655	0725	0754	0825	0856	0925	0955	1025	1055	1125	1155	1225	1255	1325	1355		2025	2055	2125	2155	2225	2255	2325	2325

km		Ⓐ	Ⓐ	Ⓐ	⑥k	Ⓐ		Ⓐ		Ⓐ		Ⓐ		Ⓐ							Ⓐ				
0	**Zutphen** d.	0632	0702	0732	0737	0802	0837	0907	0937	1007	1037	1107	1137	1207	1237	1307	and at the same	1937	2007	2038	2107	2138j	2237	2337	0020
22	Ruurlo d.	0648	0718	0748	0751	0818	0851	0921	0951	1021	1051	1121	1151	1221	1251	1321	minutes past	1951	2021	2052	2121	2152	2252	2352	0034
43	**Winterswijk** a.	0707	0737	0807	0810	0840	0911	0940	1011	1040	1111	1140	1211	1240	1311	1340	each hour until	2011	2040	2111	2140	2211	2311	0011	0055

	Ⓐ	Ⓐ	⑥k	Ⓐ	Ⓐ	Ⓒ	Ⓐ		Ⓐ		Ⓐ		Ⓐ		Ⓐ							Ⓐ			
Winterswijk d.	0555	0617	0620	0647	0717	0720	0747	0820	0850	0920	0950	1020	1050	1120	1150	1220	1250	and at the same	1920	1950	2020	2050	2120	2220	2320
Ruurlo d.	0612	0635	0638	0705	0735	0738	0805	0838	0908	0938	1008	1038	1108	1138	1208	1238	1308	minutes past	1938	2008	2038	2108	2138	2238	2338
Zutphen a.	0628	0651	0653	0721	0751	0753	0821	0853	0923	0953	1023	1053	1123	1153	1223	1253	1323	each hour until	1953	2023	2054	2124	2154	2254	2354

j – 2137 on †.
k – Also Apr. 27, May 26, June 6; not Dec. 25, Jan. 1.
w – Also Apr. 28, May 27, June 7; not Dec. 26, Jan. 2.
⊡ – Arnhem d. 1435/1635/1835 (not 1431/1631/1831).

⊠ – Additional journeys Arnhem Centraal - Winterswijk and v.v.:
From Arnhem at 0035 ⑦ **w**, 0140 ⑦ **w**, 0635 Ⓐ, 2135 Ⓐ, 2235 Ⓐ and 2335 Ⓐ.
From Winterswijk at 0020 ⑦ **w** and 2250 Ⓐ.
Additional trains run Arnhem - Doetinchem and v.v.

477 NIJMEGEN - VENLO - ROERMOND

Operated by **Arriva** (NS tickets valid)

km		⚒	⚒								
0	**Nijmegen** d.	0538a	0608a	0638r	0708r	0738	0808	and every 30 minutes until	2238	2308	2338
24	Boxmeer d.	0601a	0631a	0701r	0731r	0801	0831		2301	2331	0001
39	Venray d.	0615a	0645a	0715r	0745r	0815	0845		2315	2345	0015
61	**Venlo** d.	0633	0703	0733	0803	0833	0903		2333	0003	0031
84	**Roermond** a.	0655	0725	0755	0825	0855	0925		2355	0025	...

	⚒	⚒								
Roermond d.	...	0603a	0633a	0703r	0733r	0803	0833	and every 30 minutes until	2233	2303
Venlo d.	0559	0629	0659	0729	0759	0829	0859		2259	2329
Venray d.	0615	0645	0715	0745	0815	0845	0915		2315	2345
Boxmeer d.	0630	0700	0730	0800	0830	0900	0930		2330	0000
Nijmegen a.	0652	0722	0752	0822	0852	0922	0952		2352	0022

☛ Additional journeys: **Venlo** → **Roermond** at 0533 Ⓐ and 0603 Ⓐ; **Nijmegen** → **Venlo** at 0008; **Venlo** → **Nijmegen** at 0529 Ⓐ; **Roermond** → **Venlo** at 2333, 0003 and 0033.

a – Ⓐ only. r – ⚒ only.

478 ARNHEM - TIEL - GELDERMALSEN - UTRECHT and 's-HERTOGENBOSCH

km		Ⓐ	Ⓐ	⚒	⚒					
0	**Tiel** d.	0553	0623	0653	0723	0753	0823	and every 30 minutes until	2323	2353
12	Geldermalsen a.	0604	0634	0704	0734	0804	0834		2334	0004
38	**Utrecht** Centraal a.	0638	0708	0738	0808	0838	0908		0007	0037

	Ⓐ	Ⓐ	⚒						
Utrecht Centraal d.	0552	0622	0652	0722	0752	and every 30 minutes until	2322	2352	...
Geldermalsen d.	0624	0654	0724	0754	0824		2354	0024	...
Tiel a.	0635	0705	0735	0805	0835		0005	0035	...

km		Ⓐ	Ⓐ	⚒						
0	Geldermalsen d.	0612	0641	0711	...	0741	0811	and every 30 minutes until	2342	0012
22	**'s-Hertogenbosch** a.	0628	0657	0728	...	0758	0828		2358	0028

	Ⓐ	⚒	⚒					
's-Hertogenbosch d.	0603	0633	0703	0733	0803	and every 30 minutes until	2333	0003
Geldermalsen a.	0618	0648	0718	0748	0818		2348	0018

ARNHEM - TIEL and v.v. Operated by **Arriva** (NS tickets valid). 2nd class only. *44 km*. Journey time: 35 – 36 minutes.

From Arnhem at 0039 ⑦ **w**, 0638 Ⓐ, 0708 Ⓐ, 0738 Ⓐ, 0808 Ⓐ, 0838 ⚒, 0908 Ⓐ, 0938, 1008 Ⓐ, 1038, 1138, 1238, 1338, 1408 Ⓐ, 1438, 1508 Ⓐ, 1538, 1608 Ⓐ, 1638, 1708 Ⓐ, 1738, 1808 Ⓐ, 1838, 1938, 2038, 2138, 2238 and 2338. **From Tiel** at 0617 Ⓐ, 0647 Ⓐ, 0717 Ⓐ, 0747 ⚒, 0817 Ⓐ, 0847, 0917 Ⓐ, 0947, 1047, 1147, 1247, 1317 Ⓐ, 1347, 1417 Ⓐ, 1447, 1517 Ⓐ, 1547, 1617 Ⓐ, 1647, 1717 Ⓐ, 1747, 1847, 1947, 2017 Ⓐ, 2047, 2147, 2247 and 2347 ⑥ **k**.

k – Also Apr. 27, May 26, June 6; not Dec. 25, Jan. 1. w – Also Apr. 28, May 27, June 7; not Dec. 26, Jan. 2.

479 DORDRECHT - GELDERMALSEN

Operated by **R-net** (NS tickets valid); 2nd class only

km		Ⓐ	⚒z	⚒z	Ⓒ	Ⓐ	Ⓒ	Ⓐ	Ⓒ	Ⓐ	Ⓒ	Ⓐ		Ⓒ	Ⓐ	Ⓒ	Ⓐ	Ⓐ	Ⓒ						
0	**Dordrecht** d.	0512	0546	0616	0641	0646	0711	0716	0741	0748	0811	0818	and every 30 minutes until	1911	1918	1941	1948	2005	2011	2037f	2111	2141	and every 30 minutes until	2341	0011
10	Sliedrecht d.	0523	0558	0628	0653	0658	0723	0728	0753	0800	0823	0830		1923	1930	1953	2000	2021	2023	2053	2123	2153		2353	0023
24	Gorinchem d.	0541	0615	0645	0710	0715	0740	0745	0810	0815	0840	0845		1940	1945	2010	2014	2042	2040	2110	2140	2210		0010	0040
49	**Geldermalsen** a.	0605	0637	0707	0734	0737	0804	0807	0834	0837	0904	0907		2004	2008	2034	2038	2106	2104	2134	2204	2234		0034	0104

	⑥k	Ⓐ	Ⓒ	Ⓐ	Ⓒ	Ⓐ	Ⓒ	Ⓐ	Ⓒ	Ⓐ		Ⓒ	Ⓐ	Ⓒ	Ⓐ	Ⓒ	Ⓐ								
Geldermalsen d.	...	0613	0640k	0643	0710k	0713	0740	0743	0810	0813	and every 30 minutes until	1840	1843	1910	1913	1940	1943	2010j	2040j	2110	2140	and every 30 minutes until	0010	0040	0108
Gorinchem d.	0639	0644	0709	0714	0739	0746	0809	0816	0839	0846		1909	1916	1939	1946	2009	2016	2039	2109	2139	2209		0039	0109	0130
Sliedrecht d.	0653	0658	0723	0728	0753	0800	0823	0830	0853	0900		1923	1930	1953	2000	2023	2031	2053	2123	2153	2223		0053	0123	0144
Dordrecht a.	0705	0710	0735	0740	0805	0812	0835	0842	0905	0912		1935	1942	2005	2012	2035	2043	2105	2135	2205	2235		0105	0135	0155

f – 2041 on Ⓒ. j – 2 – 3 minutes later on Ⓐ. k – ⑥ (also Apr. 27, May 26, June 6; not Dec. 25, Jan. 1). z – Runs 3 – 5 minutes **earlier** on ⑥ (also Apr. 27, May 26, June 6).

480 AMSTERDAM and SCHIPHOL ✈ - AMERSFOORT - DEVENTER - ENSCHEDE

AMSTERDAM CENTRAAL - AMERSFOORT

km		⑥⑦c	⑥⑦c		F	Ⓐ	Ⓐ	Ⓐ	⚒			Ⓐ		⚒					❖					
0	**Amsterdam** Centraal d.	0030	0100	...	0502	0600	0611	0630	0641	0700	0711	0730	0741	0800	0811	0830	0841	0900	and at the same minutes past each hour until	2241	2300	2311	2330	2341
14	Weesp d.	|	|	...	|	|	0629	|	0659	|	0729	|	0759	|	0829	|	0859	|		2259	|	2329	|	2359
23	Naarden-Bussum 457 d.	|	|	...	|	|	0635	|	0705	|	0735	|	0805	|	0835	|	0905	|		2305	|	2335	|	0005
29	Hilversum 457 d.	0052	0122	...	0525	0622	0645	0652	0715	0722	0745	0752	0815	0822	0845	0852	0915	0922		2315	2322	2345	2352	0015
36	Baarn d.	|	|	...	|	|	0650	|	0720	|	0750	|	0820	|	0850	|	0920	|		2320	|	2350	|	0020
45	**Amersfoort** Centraal a.	0104	0134	...	0537	0634	0658	0704	0728	0734	0758	0804	0828	0834	0858	0904	0928	0934		2328	2334	2358	0004	0028

		Ⓐ	Ⓐ	Ⓐ		Ⓐ		⚒		⚒		⚒				◇	◇					⑤⑥k		
Amersfoort Centraal d.	0448	0531	0601	0626	0631	0656	0701	0726	0731	0756	0801	0826	0831	0856	0901	0926	and at the same minutes past each hour until	2231	2256	2301	2326	2331	2356	0001
Baarn d.	0455	0538	0608	|	0638	|	0708	|	0738	|	0808	|	0838	|	0908	|		2238	|	2308	|	2338	|	0008
Hilversum 457 d.	0502	0545	0615	0640	0645	0710	0715	0740	0745	0810	0815	0840	0845	0910	0915	0940		2245	2310	2315	2340	2345	0010	0015
Naarden-Bussum 457 d.	0511	0555	0625	|	0655	|	0725	|	0755	|	0825	|	0855	|	0925	|		2255	|	2325	|	2355	|	0025
Weesp d.	0521	0603	0633	|	0703	|	0733	|	0803	|	0833	|	0903	|	0933	|		2303	|	2333	|	0003	|	0033
Amsterdam Centraal a.	0537	0619	0649	0700	0719	0730	0750	0800	0819	0830	0849	0900	0919	0930	0949	1000		2319	2330	2349	2400	0019	0030	0049

SCHIPHOL ✈ - AMSTERDAM ZUID - AMERSFOORT - ENSCHEDE

km		Ⓐ	Ⓐ	⚒H	⚒	⚒	H				H				H			H			H			⑤⑥k
0	**Schiphol** ✈ d.	0538	0608	...	0638	0708	...	0738	...	0808	...	0838	and at the same minutes past each hour until	2108	...	2138	2208	...	2238	2308	...	...	2338	2338
9	Amsterdam Zuid d.	0545	0615	...	0645	0715	...	0745	...	0815	...	0845		2115	...	2145	2215	...	2245	2315	...	...	2345	2345
14	Duivendrecht d.	0550	0620	...	0650	0720	...	0750	...	0820	...	0850		2120	...	2150	2220	...	2250	2320	...	...	2350	2350
37	Hilversum d.	0607	0637	...	0707	0737	...	0807	...	0837	...	0907		2137	...	2207	2237	...	2307	2337	...	...	0007	0007
53	**Amersfoort** Centraal a.	0618	0648	...	0718	0748	...	0818	...	0848	...	0918		2148	...	2218	2248	...	2318	2348	...	...	0018	0018
53	**Amersfoort** Centraal d.	0622	...	0652	0722	...	0752	0822	...	...	0852	0922		...	2152	2222	...	2252	2322	...	2352	...	...	0024
96	Apeldoorn d.	0647	...	0717	0747	...	0817	0847	...	...	0917	0947		...	2217	2247	...	2317	2347	...	0017	...	...	0049
111	**Deventer** d.	0700	...	0730	0800	...	0830	0900	...	...	0930	1000		...	2230	2300	...	2330	0000	...	0030	...	...	0100
149	Almelo 492 d.	0725	...	0755	0825	...	0855	0925	...	...	0955	1025		...	2255	2325	...	2355	0025	...	0055	...	...	0125
164	**Hengelo** 492 a.	0737	...	0806	0836	...	0906	0936	...	...	1006	1036		...	2306	2336	...	0006	0036	...	0106	...	...	0136
172	**Enschede** 492 a.	0745	...	0814	0844	...	0914	0944	...	...	1014	1044		...	2314	2344	...	0014	0044	...	0114	...	...	0144

	ⒶH	Ⓐ	Ⓐ	⚒	ⒶH	⚒H		⚒		⚒H	H		⚒		H				H			J		
Enschede 492 d.	0446	...	0516	...	0546	...	...	0616	...	0646	...	...	0716	...	0746	...	0816	and at the same minutes past each hour until	2146	...	2216	2246	...	...
Hengelo 492 d.	0454	...	0524	...	0554	...	...	0624	...	0654	...	...	0724	...	0754	...	0824		2154	...	2224	2254	...	...
Almelo 492 d.	0506	...	0536	...	0606	...	...	0636	...	0706	...	...	0736	...	0806	...	0836		2206	...	2236	2306	...	...
Deventer d.	0532	...	0602	...	0632	0632	...	0702	...	0732	0732	...	0802	0802	0832	...	0902		2232	...	2302	2332	...	...
Apeldoorn d.	0544	...	0614	...	0644	0644	...	0714	...	0744	0744	...	0814	0814	0844	...	0914		2244	...	2314	2344	...	...
Amersfoort Centraal a.	0608	...	0638	...	0708	0708	...	0738	...	0808	0808	...	0838	0838	0908	...	0938		2308	...	2338	0008	...	...
Amersfoort Centraal d.	...	0611	0641	0641	...	...	0711	0741	0741	...	...	0811	0841	0841	...	0911	0941		...	2311	2341	...	0011	...
Hilversum d.	...	0624	0654	0654	...	...	0724	0754	0754	...	...	0824	0854	0854	...	0924	0954		...	2324	2354	...	0024	...
Duivendrecht d.	...	0640	0710	0710	...	...	0740	0810	0810	...	...	0840	0910	0910	...	0940	1010		...	2340	0010	...	0040	...
Amsterdam Zuid a.	...	0645	0715	0715	...	...	0745	0815	0815	...	...	0845	0915	0915	...	0945	1015		...	2345	0015	...	0045	...
Schiphol ✈ a.	...	0652	0722	0722	...	...	0752	0822	0822	...	...	0852	092	0922	...	0952	1022		...	2352	0022	...	0052	...

Through trains AMSTERDAM CENTRAAL - DEVENTER - HENGELO

	⑥⑦c	F♥	v♥		♥	Ⓐ	♥⊡	Ⓐ	♥	Ⓐ		Ⓒ	♥	E♥	⑥k
Amsterdam Centraal d.	0030	0502	0700	0900	0910	1000	1100	1200	1300	1400	1500	1700	1710	1900	1900
Hilversum d.	0052	0525	0722	0922	0932	1022	1122	1222	1322	1422	1522	1722	1732	1922	1922
Amersfoort Centraal d.	0106	0540	0736	0936	0945	1036	1136	1236	1336	1436	1536	1736	1745	1936	1936
Apeldoorn d.	0132	0605	0801	1001	1010	1101	1201	1301	1401	1501	1601	1801	|	2001	2001
Deventer d.	0142	0617	0818	1012	1022	1112	1218	1312	1418	1512	1618	1812	1821	2018	2019
Almelo d.	...	0642	0845	...	1047	...	1245	...	1445	...	1645	...	1847	2045	2046
Hengelo a.	...	0653	0856	...	1057	...	1256	...	1456	...	1656	...	1857	2056	2056

	⑥k	G♥	Ⓐ	L♥	†	Ⓐ	♥	Ⓐ	♥⊖	Ⓐ	♥		♥	♥	n♥
Hengelo d.	...	0803	...	0903	0904	...	1103	...	1303	...	1502	...	1703	1903	2103
Almelo d.	...	0816	...	0916	0916	...	1116	...	1316	...	1514	...	1716	1916	2116
Deventer d.	0847	0848	0918	0948	0948	1047	1148	1247	1348	1447	1538	1547	1748	1948	2148
Apeldoorn d.	0900	0900	0929	1000	1000	1100	1200	1300	1400	1500	|	1600	1800	2000	2200
Amersfoort Centraal d.	0926	0926	0656	1026	1026	1126	1226	1326	1426	1526	1616	1626	1826	2026	2226
Hilversum d.	0940	0940	1010	1040	1040	1140	1240	1340	1440	1540	1629	1640	1840	2040	2240
Amsterdam Centraal a.	1000	1000	1030	1100	1100	1200	1300	1400	1500	1600	1650	1700	1900	2100	2300

♥ – *IC* service to / from Germany via Bad Bentheim. Conveys 🍸. See Table **22** for further details.

E – Ⓑ to Apr. 10 (not Dec. 24, 31); ⑦ Apr. 17 - Aug. 28 (also Apr. 18, June 6); Ⓑ from Sept. 4 (not Oct. 3).
F – ①–⑥ Apr. 11 - Sept. 3 (not Apr. 18, June 6).
G – ① Apr. 11 - Aug. 29 (also Apr. 19, June 7; not Apr. 18, June 6).
H – From / to Den Haag (Table **481**).
J – Continues to Den Haag on dates in Table **481**.
L – ①–⑥ (not Dec. 25, Jan. 1, Apr. 18, June 6).

c – Also Apr. 28, May 27, June 7; not Dec. 26, Jan. 2.
k – Also Apr. 27, May 26, June 6; not Dec. 25, Jan. 1.
n – Not Dec. 24, 31. v – Not Dec. 25, Jan. 1.

⊡ – June 12 - Aug. 21 runs up to 10 minutes later.
⊖ – June 12 - Aug. 21 runs up to 12 minutes **earlier** and does not call at Apeldoorn.
❖ – The 1900 from Amsterdam runs on dates as shown in the Amsterdam Centraal - Hengelo panel.
◇ – The 0926 from Amersfoort runs on ⚒ only (subsequent services from Amersfoort at xx26 run daily).

Timings may vary by ± 1 minute

ROTTERDAM and DEN HAAG - UTRECHT - ZWOLLE 481

km		Ⓐ	⚒	⚒	Ⓐ	Ⓐ	Ⓐ	⚒	⚒	⚒	⚒	⚒d	Ⓐ	⚒	⚒	⚒		Ⓐ	⚒	⚒			⚒	⚒	
0	**Rotterdam** Centraal d.	...	...	0605a	...	0620	...	0635	...	0650	...	0705	...	...	0720	...	0735	...	...	0750	...	0805	...	0820	...
10	Rotterdam Alexander d.	...	...	0613a	...	0628	...	0643	...	0658	...	0713	...	...	0728	...	0743	...	...	0758	...	0813	...	0828	...
◧	**Den Haag** Centraal d.	...	0555a	|	0610	|	0625	|	0640	|	0655	|	0710	0710	|	0725	|	0740	0740	|	0755	|	0810	|	0825
24	Gouda d.	...	0614a	0624a	0629	0639	0644	0654	0659	0709	0714	0724	0729	0729	0739	0744	0754	0759	0759	0809	0814	0824	0829	0839	0844
56	**Utrecht** Centraal a.	...	0632a	0642a	0647	0658	0702	0712	0717	0728	0732	0742	0747	0747	0759	0802	0812	0817	0817	0828	0832	0842	0847	0858	0902
56	**Utrecht** Centraal d.	0618	0637	0648	0651	...	0707	0718	0721a	...	0737	0748	0751	...	...	0807	0818	0821	...	...	0837	0848	0851a	...	0907
77	**Amersfoort** Centraal a.	0631	0650	0701	0704	...	0720	0732	0734a	...	0750	0802	0804	...	...	0820	0832	0834	...	...	0850	0902	0904a	...	0920
77	**Amersfoort** Centraal 480 d.	0634	0652	0704	0706	...	...	0734	...	...	0752	0804	0806	...	...	...	0834	0836	...	...	0852	0904	...	...	...
	Deventer 480 a.	|	0728	|	0742	...	...	|	...	...	0828	|	0842	...	...	...	|	0912	...	...	0928	|	...	...	...
	Enschede 480 a.	|	0814	|	...	...	...	|	...	...	0914	|	...	...	...	...	|	...	...	...	1014	|	...	...	...
144	**Zwolle** a.	0709	...	0739	...	...	...	0809	...	...	...	0839	...	...	...	...	0909	...	...	...	...	0939	...	...	...
	Leeuwarden 482 a.	0813	...	|	...	...	...	0913	...	...	...	|	...	...	...	...	1013	...	...	...	...	|	...	...	...
	Groningen 482 a.	...	...	0842	...	...	...	...	...	...	...	0942	...	...	...	...	...	...	...	...	...	1042	...	...	...

		⚒	⚒			⚒	⚒			⚒	⚒			⚒	⚒			⚒	⚒						
Rotterdam Centraal d.	0835	...	0850	...	0905	...	0920	...	0935	...	0950	...	1005	...	1020	...	1035	...	1050	...	1105	...	1120	...	1135
Rotterdam Alexander d.	0843	...	0858	...	0913	...	0928	...	0943	...	0958	...	1013	...	1028	...	1043	...	1058	...	1113	...	1128	...	1143
Den Haag Centraal d.	|	0840	|	0855	|	0910	|	0925	|	0940	|	0955	|	1010	|	1025	|	1040	|	1055	|	1110	|	1125	|
Gouda d.	0854	0859	0909	0914	0924	0929	0939	0944	0954	0959	1009	1014	1024	1029	1039	1044	1054	1059	1109	1114	1124	1129	1139	1144	1154
Utrecht Centraal a.	0912	0917	0928	0932	0942	0947	0958	1002	1012	1017	1028	1032	1042	1047	1058	1102	1112	1117	1128	1132	1142	1147	1158	1202	1212
Utrecht Centraal d.	0918	0921a	...	0937	0948	0951a	...	1007	1018	1021a	...	1037	1048	1051a	...	1107	1118	1121a	...	1137	1148	1151a	...	1207	1218
Amersfoort Centraal a.	0932	0934a	...	0950	1002	1004a	...	1020	1032	1034a	...	1050	1102	1104a	...	1120	1132	1134a	...	1150	1202	1204a	...	1220	1232
Amersfoort Centraal 480 d.	0934	...	...	0952	1004	...	...	...	1034	...	...	1052	1104	...	...	...	1134	...	...	1152	1204	...	...	...	1234
Deventer 480 a.	|	...	...	1028	|	...	...	...	|	...	...	1128	|	...	...	...	|	...	...	1228	|	...	...	...	|
Enschede 480 a.	|	...	...	1114	|	...	...	...	|	...	...	1214	|	...	...	...	|	...	...	1314	|	...	...	...	|
Zwolle a.	1009	...	...	...	1039	...	...	...	1109	...	...	...	1139	...	...	...	1209	...	...	...	1239	...	...	...	1309
Leeuwarden 482 a.	1113	...	...	...	|	...	...	...	1213	...	...	...	|	...	...	...	1313	...	...	...	|	...	...	...	1413
Groningen 482 a.	...	...	...	...	1142	...	...	...	...	...	...	...	1242	...	...	...	...	...	...	...	1342	...	...	...	...

				⊡																				
Rotterdam Centraal d.	...	1150	...	and at the same minutes past each hour until	1905	...	1920	...	1935	...	1950	...	2005	...	2020	...	2035	...	2050	...	2105	...	2135	...
Rotterdam Alexander d.	...	1158	...		1913	...	1928	...	1943	...	1958	...	2013	...	2028	...	2043	...	2058	...	2113	...	2143	...
Den Haag Centraal d.	1140	|	1155		|	1910	|	1925	|	1940	|	1955	|	2010	|	2025	|	2040	|	2055	|	2125	|	2155
Gouda d.	1159	1209	1214		1924	1929	1939	1944	1954	1959	2009	2014	2024	2029	2039	2044	2054	2059	2109	2114	2124	2144	2154	2214
Utrecht Centraal a.	1217	1228	1232		1942	1947	1959	2002	2012	2017	2028	2032	2042	2047	2058	2102	2112	2117	2128	2132	2142	2202	2212	2232
Utrecht Centraal d.	1221a	...	1237		1948	1951a	...	2007	2019	...	...	2037	2049	...	...	2107	2119	...	...	2137	2148	2207	2219	2237
Amersfoort Centraal a.	1234a	...	1250		2002	2004a	...	2020	2032	...	...	2050	2102	...	...	2120	2132	...	...	2150	2202	2220	2232	2250
Amersfoort Centraal 480 d.	...	...	1252		2004	...	...	...	2034	...	...	2052	2104	...	...	...	2134	...	...	2152	2204	...	2234	2252
Deventer 480 a.	...	...	1328		|	...	...	...	|	...	...	2128	|	...	...	...	|	...	...	2228	|	...	|	2328
Enschede 480 a.	...	...	1414		|	...	...	...	|	...	...	2214	|	...	...	...	|	...	...	2314	|	...	|	0014
Zwolle a.	...	...	...		2039	...	...	...	2109	...	...	...	2139	...	...	...	2209	...	...	...	2239	...	2309	...
Leeuwarden 482 a.	...	...	...		|	...	...	...	2213	...	...	...	|	...	...	...	2313	...	...	...	|	...	0013	...
Groningen 482 a.	...	...	...		2142	...	...	...	...	...	...	...	2242	...	...	...	...	...	...	...	2342	...	...	...

Rotterdam Centraal d.	2205	...	2235	...	2305	...	2335	...	0005
Rotterdam Alexander d.	2213	...	2243	...	2313	...	2343	...	0013
Den Haag Centraal d.	|	2225	|	2255	|	2325	|	2355	|
Gouda d.	2224	2244	2254	2314	2324	2344	2354	0014	0024
Utrecht Centraal a.	2242	2302	2312	2332	2342	0002	0012	0032	0042
Utrecht Centraal d.	2248	2307	2319	2337	2348	0009	0019	0037	0048
Amersfoort Centraal a.	2302	2320	2332	2350	0001	0022	0032	0050	0102
Amersfoort Centraal 480 d.	2304	...	2334	2352	0004	...	...	...	0106c
Deventer 480 a.	|	...	|	0028	|	...	...	...	|
Enschede 480 a.	|	...	|	0114	|	...	...	...	|
Zwolle a.	2339	...	0009	...	0046	...	...	...	0141c
Leeuwarden 482 a.	|	...	...	...	|	...	...	...	|
Groningen 482 a.	0042	...	...	...	0201b	...	...	...	0254e

	Ⓐ	Ⓐ	Ⓐ	Ⓐ	Ⓐ	Ⓐ	Ⓐ	Ⓐ	⚒	⚒	⚒
Groningen 482 d.	...	...	...	...	...	...	...	...	...	...	...
Leeuwarden 482 d.	...	...	...	...	...	...	...	...	...	...	...
Zwolle d.	...	...	...	...	...	...	...	0550	...	...	...
Enschede 480 d.	...	...	...	...	0446	...	...	|	...	...	...
Deventer 480 d.	...	...	...	...	0532	...	...	|	...	...	...
Amersfoort Centraal 480 a.	...	...	...	...	0608	...	...	0625	...	...	...
Amersfoort Centraal d.	...	...	...	...	0610	...	0626	0629	0640a	...	0656a
Utrecht Centraal a.	...	...	...	...	0623	...	0639	0642	0653a	...	0709a
Utrecht Centraal d.	0558	0603	0613	0618	0628	0633	0643	0648	0658	0703	0713
Gouda d.	0617	0622	0632	0637	0647	0652	0702	0707	0717	0722	0732
Den Haag Centraal a.	0636	|	0651	|	0706	|	0721	|	0736	|	0751
Rotterdam Alexander d.	...	0631	...	0646	...	0701	...	0716	...	0731	...
Rotterdam Centraal a.	...	0640	...	0655	...	0710	...	0725	...	0740	...

	⚒	Ⓐ	⚒	⚒	⚒	Ⓐ	⚒	⚒	⚒	⑥k	Ⓐ		⚒		⚒	⚒	Ⓐ			⚒	⚒	Ⓐ			⚒
Groningen 482 d.	...	0503t	...	...	...	...	...	...	...	...	...	...	0606	...	...	...	...	...	...	...	...	...	0718z	...	...
Leeuwarden 482 d.	...	|	...	...	...	...	0547a	...	...	...	...	...	|	...	...	...	...	0647r	...	...	...	...	|	...	...
Zwolle d.	...	0620	...	...	...	...	0650	...	...	...	...	...	0720	...	...	...	...	0750	...	...	...	...	0820	...	...
Enschede 480 d.	...	|	0546a	...	...	...	|	...	...	...	...	...	|	0646r	...	...	...	|	...	...	...	...	|	0746	...
Deventer 480 d.	...	|	0632	...	...	0647	|	...	...	...	0717	...	|	0732	...	...	0747	|	...	...	...	0818	|	0832	...
Amersfoort Centraal 480 a.	...	0655	0708	...	...	0724	0725	...	...	...	0754	...	0755	0808	...	...	0824	0825	...	...	...	0854	0855	0908	...
Amersfoort Centraal d.	...	0659	0710	...	...	0726	0729	0740	...	...	0756	...	0759	0810	...	...	0826	0829	0840	...	...	0856	0859	0910	...
Utrecht Centraal a.	...	0712	0723	...	...	0739	0742	0753	...	...	0809	...	0812	0823	...	...	0839	0842	0853	...	...	0909	0912	0923	...
Utrecht Centraal d.	0718	0718	0728	0733	0743	0743	0748	0758	0803	0813	0813	0818	0818	0828	0833	0843	0843	0848	0858	0903	0913	0913	0918	0928	0933
Gouda d.	0737	0737	0747	0752	0802	0802	0807	0817	0822	0832	0834	0837	0837	0847	0852	0902	0902	0907	0917	0922	0932	0932	0937	0947	0952
Den Haag Centraal a.	|	|	0806	|	0821	0821	|	0836	|	0851	0852	|	|	0908n	|	0921	0921	|	0936	|	0951	0951	|	1006	|
Rotterdam Alexander d.	0746	0746	...	0801	...	...	0816	...	0831	...	...	0846	0846	...	0901	...	...	0916	...	0931	...	...	0946	...	1001
Rotterdam Centraal a.	0755	0755	...	0810	...	...	0825	...	0840	...	...	0855	0855	...	0910	...	...	0925	...	0940	...	...	0955	...	1010

	⚒	Ⓐ			⚒	⚒			⚒	⚒			⚒									⊖		
Groningen 482 d.	...	...	...	...	...	...	0818	...	...	...	...	...	...	...	0918	...	...	...	...	...	...	and at the same minutes past each hour until	...	...
Leeuwarden 482 d.	...	...	0747v	...	...	...	|	...	...	...	0847	...	...	...	|	...	...	...	0947	...	...		...	1747
Zwolle d.	...	...	0850	...	...	...	0920	...	...	...	0950	...	...	...	1020	...	...	...	1050	...	...		...	1850
Enschede 480 d.	...	...	|	...	...	...	|	0846	...	...	|	...	...	...	|	0946	...	...	|	...	...		...	|
Deventer 480 d.	...	0847	|	...	...	...	|	0932	...	...	|	...	...	...	|	1032	...	...	|	...	...		...	|
Amersfoort Centraal 480 a.	...	0924	0925	...	...	...	0955	1008	...	...	1025	...	...	...	1055	1108	...	...	1125	...	...		...	1925
Amersfoort Centraal d.	...	0926	0929	0940	...	0956a	0959	1010	...	1026a	1029	1040	...	1056a	1059	1110	...	1126a	1129	1140	...		1926a	1929
Utrecht Centraal a.	...	0939	0942	0953	...	1009a	1012	1023	...	1039a	1042	1053	...	1109a	1112	1123	...	1139a	1142	1153	...		1939a	1942
Utrecht Centraal d.	0943	0943	0948	0958	1003	1013	1018	1028	1033	1043	1048	1058	1103	1113	1118	1128	1133	1143	1148	1158	1203		1943	1948
Gouda d.	1002	1002	1007	1017	1022	1032	1037	1047	1052	1102	1107	1117	1122	1132	1137	1147	1152	1202	1207	1217	1222		2002	2007
Den Haag Centraal a.	1020	1021	|	1036	|	1051	|	1106	|	1121	|	1136	|	1151	|	1206	|	1221	|	1236	|		2020	|
Rotterdam Alexander d.	...	...	1016	...	1031	...	1046	...	1101	...	1116	...	1131	...	1146	...	1201	...	1216	...	1231		...	2016
Rotterdam Centraal a.	...	...	1025	...	1040	...	1055	...	1110	...	1125	...	1140	...	1155	...	1210	...	1225	...	1240		...	2025

																									⑥⑦c
Groningen 482 d.	...	...	...	1818	...	...	...	...	...	1918	...	...	...	2018	...	...	...	2118	...	...	...	2218	...	...	...
Leeuwarden 482 d.	...	...	...	|	...	...	...	1847	...	|	...	1947	...	|	...	2047	...	|	...	2147	...	|	...	2236	...
Zwolle d.	...	...	...	1920	...	...	...	1950	...	2020	...	2050	...	2120	...	2150	...	2220	...	2250	...	2320	...	2350	...
Enschede 480 d.	...	...	...	|	1846	...	...	|	...	|	1946	|	...	|	2046	|	...	|	2146	|	...	|	2246	|	...
Deventer 480 d.	...	...	...	|	1932	...	...	|	...	|	2032	|	...	|	2132	|	...	|	2232	|	...	|	2332	|	...
Amersfoort Centraal 480 a.	...	...	...	1955	2008	...	...	2025	...	2055	2108	2125	...	2155	2208	2225	...	2255	2308	2325	...	2355	0008	0025	...
Amersfoort Centraal d.	1940	...	1956a	1959	2010	...	...	2028	2040	2059	2110	2128	2140	2159	2210	2228	2240	2259	2310	2328	2340	2358	0010	0028	*0040*
Utrecht Centraal a.	1953	...	2009a	2012	2023	...	...	2041	2053	2112	2123	2141	2153	2212	2223	2241	2253	2312	2323	2341	2353	0012	0023	0041	*0053*
Utrecht Centraal d.	1958	2003	2013	2018	2028	2033	2043	2048	2058	2118	2128	2148	2158	2218	2228	2248	2258	2318	2328	2348	2358	0018	0028c	...	0118
Gouda d.	2017	2022	2032	2037	2047	2052	2102	2107	2117	2137	2147	2207	2217	2237	2247	2307	2317	2337	2347	0007	0017	0037	0047c	...	0137
Den Haag Centraal a.	2036	|	2051	|	2106	|	2121	|	2136	|	2206	|	2236	|	2306	|	2336	|	0006	|	0036	|	0106c	...	|
Rotterdam Alexander d.	...	2031	...	2046	...	2101	...	2116	...	2146	...	2216	...	2246	...	2316	...	2346	...	0016	...	0046	...	...	0146
Rotterdam Centraal a.	...	2040	...	2055	...	2110	...	2125	...	2155	...	2225	...	2255	...	2325	...	2355	...	0025	...	0055	...	...	0155

a – Ⓐ only.
b – Mornings of ②–⑦ (not Dec. 26, Jan. 2, Apr. 19).
c – Mornings of ⑥⑦ (also Apr. 28, May 27, June 7; not Dec. 26, Jan. 2).
d – Runs daily Amersfoort - Groningen.
e – Mornings of ⑥ only.
k – Also Apr. 27, May 26, June 6; not Dec. 25, Jan. 1.

n – 0906 on ©.
r – ⚒ only.
t – 0505 on ①④⑤.
v – 0736 on †.
z – 0706 on ©.

⊡ – The 1540, 1610, 1640, 1710 and 1740 from Den Haag Centraal continue to Deventer on Ⓐ (arriving 37 – 45 minutes after Amersfoort).
⊖ – On Ⓐ the 1446 and 1646 from Enschede arrive Den Haag Centraal 2 minutes later.
◧ – Den Haag to Gouda is 28 km.

482 ZWOLLE - GRONINGEN and LEEUWARDEN

Timings may vary by ± 1 minute

km		⑥		Ⓐ	Ⓐ	Ⓐ L	Ⓐ	Ⓐ	Ⓐ	⚒ M	⚒		Ⓐ	⚒	Ⓐ	⚒	⚒			⚒	Ⓑ n	⑥ k	⚒	† N
	Rotterdam Centraal **481** d.	0005	...	...	...	...	...	...	...	...	...	...	...	...	...	...	0605a	...	...	...	...	...	...	...
	Utrecht Centraal **481** d.	0048	...	...	...	...	...	...	...	...	...	...	...	...	0618	...	0648	...	...	...	...	...	...	...
	Amersfoort Centraal **481** d.	0106	...	...	...	...	...	...	...	...	...	...	...	...	0634	...	0704	...	...	...	...	...	...	...
	Den Haag Centraal **460** d.	|	...	...	...	...	...	...	...	...	...	...	0533	...	|	...	|	...	...	0603	...	...	0633	...
	Schiphol + **460** d.	|	...	...	...	...	...	...	...	...	...	...	0605	...	|	...	|	...	...	0635	...	...	0705	...
	Amsterdam Zuid **460** d.	|	...	...	...	...	...	...	...	...	...	...	0612	...	|	...	|	...	...	0642	...	...	0712	...
	Zwolle **460 481** a.	0141	...	...	...	...	...	...	...	...	...	...	0713	...	0709	...	0739	...	...	0743	...	...	0813	...
0	**Zwolle** d.	0145	...	0548	0552	0615	0618	0622	0645	0648	0652	...	0715	0718	0718	0722	0745	0745	0748	0748	0752	0752	0815	0815
27	Meppel d.	0201	...	0604	0608	0630	0634	0638	|	0704	0707	...	|	0734	0734	0738	|	|	0804	0804	0807	0807	|	|
41	Steenwijk d.	|	...	0613	|	|	0643	|	|	0713	|	...	|	0743	0743	|	|	|	0813	0813	|	|	|	|
65	Heerenveen d.	|	...	0629	|	|	0656	|	|	0726	|	...	|	0756	0756	|	|	|	0826	0826	|	|	|	|
94	**Leeuwarden** a.	|	...	0651	|	|	0713	|	|	0743	|	...	|	0814	0813	|	|	|	0843	0843	|	|	|	|
47	Hoogeveen d.	0213	...	...	0619	0643	...	0649	|	...	0719	...	|	...	...	0749	|	|	...	...	0819	0819	|	|
77	Assen d.	0232	...	...	0637	0702	...	0707	0725	...	0737	...	0755	...	...	0807	0825	0825	...	...	0837	0841	0855	0855
104	**Groningen** a.	0254	...	...	0657	0723	...	0727	0742	...	0757	...	0812	...	...	0827	0842	0842	...	...	0857	0901	0912	0912

		⚒	⚒	⚒						⚒						⚒ ◐							
Rotterdam Centraal **481** d.	...	0635	...	0705	...	...	...	...	0735	...	0805	...	...	...	0835	...		1805	...	...	...	1835	...
Utrecht Centraal **481** d.	...	0718	...	0748	...	...	...	...	0818	...	0848	...	...	...	0918	...	and at	1848	...	...	...	1918	...
Amersfoort Centraal **481** d.	...	0734	...	0804	0804	...	...	...	0834	...	0904	...	...	...	0934	...		1904	...	...	...	1934	...
Den Haag Centraal **460** d.	...	|	...	|	|	0703	...	0733	|	...	|	0803	...	0833	|	...	the	|	1803	...	1833	|	...
Schiphol + **460** d.	...	|	...	|	|	0735	...	0805	|	...	|	0835	...	0905	|	...	same	|	1835	...	1905	|	...
Amsterdam Zuid **460** d.	...	|	...	|	|	0742	...	0812	|	...	|	0842	...	0912	|	...		|	1842	...	1912	|	...
Zwolle **460 481** a.	...	0809	...	0839	0839	0843	...	0913	0909	...	0939	0943	...	1013	1009	...	minutes	1939	1943	...	2013	2009	...
Zwolle d.	0818	0818	0822	0845	0845	0848	0852	0915	0918	0922	0945	0948	0952	1015	1018	1022		1945	1948	1952	2015	2018	2022
Meppel d.	0833	0833	0838	|	|	0904	0908	|	0933	0938	|	1004	1008	|	1033	1038	past	|	2004	2007	|	2033	2038
Steenwijk d.	0843	0843	|	|	|	0913	|	|	0943	|	|	1013	|	|	1043	|	each	|	2013	|	|	2043	|
Heerenveen d.	0856	0856	|	|	|	0926	|	|	0956	|	|	1026	|	|	1056	|		|	2026	|	|	2056	|
Leeuwarden a.	0913	0913	|	|	|	0943	|	|	1013	|	|	1043	|	|	1113	|	hour	|	2043	|	|	2113	|
Hoogeveen d.	...	...	0849	|	|	...	0919	|	...	0949	|	...	1019	|	...	1049	until	|	...	2019	|	...	2049
Assen d.	...	...	0907	0925	0925	...	0937	0955	...	1011	1025	...	1037	1055	...	1107		2025	...	2037	2055	...	2107
Groningen a.	...	...	0927	0942	0942	...	0957	1012	...	1031	1042	...	1057	1112	...	1127		2042	...	2057	2112	...	2127

																							⚒ ⊖	⑤⑥ k
Rotterdam Centraal **481** d.	1905	...	...	...	1935	...	2005	...	...	...	2035	...	2105	...	...	2135	...	2205	...	...	...	...	2305	...
Utrecht Centraal **481** d.	1948	...	...	...	2019	...	2049	...	...	...	2119	...	2148	...	...	2219	...	2248	...	...	...	...	2348	...
Amersfoort Centraal **481** d.	2004	...	...	...	2034	...	2104	...	...	...	2134	...	2204	...	...	2234	...	2304	...	...	...	...	0004	...
Den Haag Centraal **460** d.	|	1903	...	1933	|	...	|	2003	...	2033	|	...	|	2103	2133	|	...	|	2203	...	2233	...	|	2303
Schiphol + **460** d.	|	1935	...	2005	|	...	|	2035	...	2105	|	...	|	2135	2205	|	...	|	2235	...	2305	...	|	2335
Amsterdam Zuid **460** d.	|	1942	...	2012	|	...	|	2042	...	2112	|	...	|	2142	2212	|	...	|	2242	...	2312	...	|	2342
Zwolle **460 481** a.	2039	2043	...	2113	2109	...	2139	2143	...	2213	2209	...	2239	2243	2313	2309	...	2339	2343	...	0013	...	0046	0043
Zwolle d.	2045	2048	2052	2115	2118	2122	2145	2148	2152	2215	2218	2222	2245	2248	2315	2318	...	2345	2348	...	0015	...	0049	0048
Meppel d.	|	2104	2108	|	2133	2138	|	2204	2208	|	2233	2238	|	2304	2330	2334	...	|	0004	...	0031	...	0105	0104
Steenwijk d.	|	2113	|	|	2143	|	|	2213	|	|	2243	|	|	2313	|	2343	...	|	0013	...	|	...	|	0113
Heerenveen d.	|	2126	|	|	2156	|	|	2226	|	|	2256	|	|	2329	|	2356	...	|	0028	...	|	...	|	0128
Leeuwarden a.	|	2143	|	|	2213	|	|	2243	|	|	2313	|	|	2351	|	0013	...	|	0051	...	|	...	|	0151
Hoogeveen d.	|	...	2119	|	...	2149	|	...	2219	|	...	2250	|	...	2343	...	...	|	...	...	0043	...	0117	...
Assen d.	2125	...	2137	2155	...	2207	2225	...	2237	2255	...	2307	2325	...	0002	...	...	0025	...	...	0102	...	0137	...
Groningen a.	2142	...	2157	2212	...	2227	2242	...	2257	2312	...	2327	2342	...	0023	...	...	0042	...	...	0123	...	0201	...

	Ⓐ	Ⓐ		Ⓐ	Ⓐ	⑥ k	Ⓐ	⚒	Ⓐ	⚒	⑥ k	Ⓑ n	Ⓐ	†	⚒	Ⓒ	Ⓐ	⚒	†	⚒	†	⚒	⚒	
Groningen d.	...	0503t	...	...	0533	0548	...	0606	0632	...	0637	0648	0702	...	...	0706	0718	0732	...	...	0737	0748	0802	...
Assen d.	...	0527	...	...	0556	0604	...	0628	0652	...	0658	0704	0722	...	...	0728	0734	0752	...	...	0758	0804	0822	...
Hoogeveen d.	...	0547	...	...	0617	|	...	0647	0710	...	0717	|	0740	...	...	0747	|	0810	...	...	0817	|	0840	...
Leeuwarden d.	0507	|	...	0547	|	|	0617	|	|	0647	|	|	|	0707	0717	|	|	|	0736	0747	|	|	|	0817
Heerenveen d.	0529	|	...	0604	|	|	0634	|	|	0704	|	|	|	0729	0734	|	|	|	0759	0804	|	|	|	0834
Steenwijk d.	0546	|	...	0617	|	|	0647	|	|	0717	|	|	|	0746	0747	|	|	|	0816	0817	|	|	|	0847
Meppel d.	0555	0559	...	0626	0630	|	0656	0700	0722	0726	0730	|	0752	0755	0756	0800	|	0822	0826	0826	0830	|	0852	0856
Zwolle a.	0612	0615	...	0642	0645	0645	0712	0715	0738	0742	0745	0745	0808	0812	0812	0815	0815	0838	0842	0842	0845	0845	0908	0912
Zwolle **460 481** d.	0617	0620	...	0650	0647	0647	0717	0720	...	0750	0747	0747	...	0817	0817	0820	0820	...	0850	0850	0847	0847	...	0917
Amsterdam Zuid **460** a.	0717	|	...	|	0747	0747	0817	|	...	|	0847	0847	...	0917	0917	|	|	...	|	|	0947	0947	...	1017
Schiphol + **460** a.	0724	|	...	|	0754	0754	0824	|	...	|	0854	0854	...	0924	0924	|	|	...	|	|	0954	0954	...	1024
Den Haag Centraal **460** a.	0756	|	...	|	0826	0826	0856	|	...	|	0926	0926	...	0956	0956	|	|	...	|	|	1026	1026	...	1056
Amersfoort Centraal **481** a.	...	0655	...	0725	...	...	...	0755	...	0825	...	...	...	...	...	0855	0855	...	0925	0925	...	...	...	...
Utrecht Centraal **481** a.	...	0712	...	0742	...	...	...	0812	...	0842	...	...	...	...	...	0911	0912	...	0941	0942	...	...	...	...
Rotterdam Centraal **481** a.	...	0755	...	0825	...	...	...	0855	...	0925	...	...	...	...	...	0955	0955	...	1025	1025	...	...	...	...

					⚒ ◧		⊠																
Groningen d.	0818	0832	...	0848	0902	...		1718	1732	...	1748	1802	...	1818	1832	...	1848	1902	...	1918	1932	...	1948
Assen d.	0834	0852	...	0904	0922	...	and at	1734	1752	...	1804	1822	...	1834	1852	...	1904	1922	...	1934	1952	...	2004
Hoogeveen d.	|	0910	...	|	0940	...		|	1810	...	|	1840	...	|	1910	...	|	1940	...	|	2010	...	|
Leeuwarden d.	|	|	0847	|	|	0917	the	|	|	1747	|	|	1817	|	|	1847	|	|	1917	|	|	1947	|
Heerenveen d.	|	|	0904	|	|	0934	same	|	|	1804	|	|	1834	|	|	1904	|	|	1934	|	|	2004	|
Steenwijk d.	|	|	0917	|	|	0947		|	|	1817	|	|	1847	|	|	1917	|	|	1947	|	|	2017	|
Meppel d.	|	0922	0926	|	0952	0956	minutes	|	1822	1826	|	1852	1856	|	1922	1926	|	1952	1956	|	2022	2026	|
Zwolle a.	0915	0938	0942	0945	1008	1012		1815	1838	1842	1845	1908	1912	1915	1938	1942	1945	2008	2012	2015	2038	2042	2045
Zwolle **460 481** d.	0920	...	0950	0947	...	1017	past	1820	...	1850	1847	...	1917	1920	...	1950	1947	...	2017	2020	...	2050	2047
Amsterdam Zuid **460** a.	|	...	|	1047	...	1117	each	|	...	|	1947	...	2017	|	...	|	2047	...	2117	|	...	|	2147
Schiphol + **460** a.	|	...	|	1054	...	1124		|	...	|	1954	...	2024	|	...	|	2054	...	2124	|	...	|	2154
Den Haag Centraal **460** a.	|	...	|	1126	...	1156	hour	|	...	|	2026	...	2056	|	...	|	2126	...	2156	|	...	|	2226
Amersfoort Centraal **481** a.	0955	...	1025	...	...	...	until	1855	...	1925	...	...	...	1955	...	2025	...	...	...	2055	...	2125	...
Utrecht Centraal **481** a.	1012	...	1042	...	...	...		1912	...	1942	...	...	...	2012	...	2041	...	...	...	2112	...	2141	...
Rotterdam Centraal **481** a.	1055	...	1125	...	...	...		1955	...	2025	...	...	...	2055	...	2125	...	...	...	2155	...	2225	...

																	Ⓑ n	⑥ k					⑤⑥ k	J
Groningen d.	1958	...	2018	2032	...	2048	2102	...	2118	2132	...	2148	...	2202	...	2218	2228	2230	...	2248	...	...	2326	2328
Assen d.	2023	...	2034	2052	...	2104	2122	...	2134	2152	...	2204	...	2222	...	2234	2253	2253	...	2304	...	...	2348	2353
Hoogeveen d.	2040	...	|	2110	...	|	2140	...	|	2210	...	|	...	2240	...	|	2310	2310	...	|	...	...	0007	0010
Leeuwarden d.	|	2017	|	|	2047	|	|	2117	|	|	2147	|	...	|	2217	|	|	|	2236	|	...	2324	|	|
Heerenveen d.	|	2034	|	|	2104	|	|	2134	|	|	2204	|	...	|	2234	|	|	|	2259	|	...	2346	|	|
Steenwijk d.	|	2047	|	|	2117	|	|	2147	|	|	2217	|	...	|	2247	|	|	|	2316	|	...	0003	|	|
Meppel d.	2052	2056	|	2122	2126	|	2152	2156	|	2222	2226	|	...	2252	2256	|	2322	2322	2326	|	...	0012	0019	0022
Zwolle a.	2108	2112	2115	2138	2142	2145	2208	2212	2215	2238	2242	2245	...	2308	2312	2315	2338	2338	2342	2345	...	0028	0035	0038
Zwolle **460 481** d.	...	2117	2120	...	2150	2147	...	2217	2220	...	2250	2247	...	...	2317	2320	...	...	2350	2347	...	...	0037	...
Amsterdam Zuid **460** a.	...	2217	|	...	|	2247	...	2317	|	...	|	2347	...	...	0017	|	...	...	|	0047	...	...	0142‡	...
Schiphol + **460** a.	...	2224	|	...	|	2254	...	2324	|	...	|	2354	...	...	0024	|	...	...	|	0054	...	...	...	...
Den Haag Centraal **460** a.	...	2256	|	...	|	2326	...	2356	|	...	|	0026	...	...	0056	|	...	...	|	0126c	...	...	...	...
Amersfoort Centraal **481** a.	...	...	2155	...	2225	...	...	...	2255	...	2325	...	...	...	...	2355	...	...	0025	...	...	...	...	...
Utrecht Centraal **481** a.	...	...	2212	...	2241	...	...	...	2312	...	2341	...	...	...	...	0012	...	...	0041	...	...	...	...	...
Rotterdam Centraal **481** a.	...	...	2255	...	2325	...	...	...	2355	...	0025	...	...	...	...	0055	...	...	...	...	...	...	...	...

J – ①②③④⑦ (also Dec. 25, Jan. 1; not Apr. 27, May 26, June 6).
L – From Lelystadt Centrum (d. 0541).
M – From Lelystadt Centrum on Ⓐ (d. 0611).
N – From Lelystadt Centrum (d. 0741).

a – Ⓐ only.
c – Mornings of ⑥⑦ (also Apr. 28, May 27, June 7; not Dec. 26, Jan. 1).
k – Also Apr. 27, May 26, June 6; not Dec. 25, Jan. 1.
n – Also Dec. 25, Jan. 1; not Apr. 27, May 26, June 6.

t – 0505 on ①④⑤.

⊖ – Timings Zwolle - Groningen may vary by up to 3 minutes (earliest departures shown).
⊠ – Groningen d. 0928 (not 0932). On ⚒ Groningen d. 1328 (not 1332). On ②⑤ Groningen d. 1630 (not 1632).
◐ – The 1522, 1622, 1722, 1822 and 1922 from Zwolle run daily. The 1822 from Zwolle departs Assen 1911, arrives Groningen 1931.
◧ – The 1602 and 1702 from Groningen run daily.
‡ – Amsterdam **Centraal**.

For traffic arrangements on Dutch holiday dates, see page 242

OLDENZAAL - HENGELO - ZUTPHEN 488

Operated by **Blauwnet** (NS tickets valid) 2nd class only

km		Ⓐ	†	Ⓐ	⚒			⚒								Ⓑn		⚒	†		⚒	†		D	
0	**Oldenzaal** ★ d.	0602	...	0632	0702	0732	and at	1402	1432	1502	1532	and at	2002	2032	2102	2132	2132	2202	2232	2232	2302	2332	2332	0002	0032
11	**Hengelo** ★ a.	0612	...	0642	0712	0742	the same	1412	1442	1512	1542	the same	2012	2042	2112	2142	2142	2212	2242	2242	2312	2342	2342	0012	0042
11	**Hengelo** d.	0616	...	0646	0716	0746	minutes	1416	1446	1516	1546	minutes	2016	2046	2116	2146	...	2216	2246	...	2316	2346	...	0016	0046
26	Goor d.	0630	0700	0700	0730	0800	past each	1430	1500	1530	1600	past each	2030	2100	2130	2200	...	2230	2300	...	2330	2400	...	0030	0100
39	Lochem d.	0639	0709	0709	0739	0809	hour until	1439	1509	1539	1609	hour until	2039	2109	2139	2209	...	2239	2309	...	2339	...	...	0039	...
56	**Zutphen** a.	0653	0721	0723	0753	0823		1453	1523	1553	1623		2053	2122	2153	2223	...	2253	2321	...	2353	...	...	0051	...

	Ⓐ	Ⓐ	Ⓐ	⚒	Ⓐ		⚒		⚒			⚒									Ⓐ				D
Zutphen d.	...	...	0609	...	0636	...	0706j	0736t	0806	0836t	and at	1306	1336t	1406	1436t	1506	1536	and at	2006	2036	2106	2136	2236t	2336t	0009
Lochem d.	...	...	0621	...	0651	...	0721	0751	0821	0851	the same	1321	1351	1421	1451	1521	1551	the same	2021	2051	2121	2151	2251	2350	0021
Goor d.	0530	0600	0630	0630	0700	0700	0730	0800	0830	0900	minutes	1330	1400	1430	1500	1530	1600	minutes	2030	2100	2130	2200	2300	0000	0029
Hengelo a.	0544	0614	0644	0644	0714	0714	0744	0814	0844	0914	past each	1344	1414	1444	1514	1544	1614	past each	2044	2114	2144	2214	2314	0014	...
Hengelo ★ d.	0548	0618	0648	0648	0718	0718	0748	0818	0848	0918	hour until	1348	1418	1448	1518	1548	1618	hour until	2048	2118	2148	2218	2318	0018	...
Oldenzaal ★ a.	0558	0628	0658	0658	0728	0728	0758	0828	0858	0928		1358	1428	1458	1528	1558	1628		2058	2128	2158	2228	2328	0028	...

D – Mornings of ②–⑦ (not Dec. 26, Jan. 2, Apr. 19).
j – 0709 on ⑥ (also Apr. 27, May 26, June 6).
n – Also Dec. 25, Jan. 1; not Apr. 27, May 26, June 6.
t – 3 minutes later on †.
★ – See Table **811** for other journeys Bad Bentheim - Oldenzaal - Hengelo and v.v.

ZWOLLE - ENSCHEDE 492

Operated by **Blauwnet** (NS tickets valid)

km		Ⓐ	Ⓐ	⚒	⚒						
0	**Zwolle** d.	0551	0621	0651	0721	0751	0822	and at	2251	2321	2351
18	Raalte d.	0608	0636	0708	0736	0808	0836	the same	2308	2336	0008
32	Nijverdal d.	0618	0647	0718	0747	0818	0847	minutes	2318	2347	0018
44	Almelo 480 d.	0630	0700	0730	0800	0830	0900	past each	2330	0000	0030
59	Hengelo 480 d.	0647	0717	0747	0817	0847	0917	hour until	2348	0018	0044z
67	**Enschede** 480 a.	0656	0726	0756	0826	0856	0926		2357	0027	0053z

	Ⓐ	Ⓐ	Ⓐ	⚒	⚒					
Enschede 480 d.	0506	0534	0604	0634	0704	0734	0804	and at	2304	2334
Hengelo 480 d.	0517	0547	0617	0647	0717	0747	0817	the same	2317	2346
Almelo 480 d.	0530	0600	0630	0700	0730	0800	0830	minutes	2330	0000
Nijverdal d.	0543	0616	0643	0716	0743	0816	0843	past each	2343	0016
Raalte d.	0554	0624	0654	0724	0754	0824	0854	hour until	2354	0024
Zwolle a.	0609	0638	0709	0739	0809	0838	0909		0009	0039

z – 4 minutes later on the mornings of ③⑤⑥⑦ (also Apr. 28, June 7; not Dec. 26, Jan. 2).
☛ Timings may vary by ± 1 minute. Additional trains run on Ⓐ.

ZWOLLE - EMMEN 493

Operated by **Blauwnet** (NS tickets valid)

km		Ⓐ	Ⓐ	Ⓐ	⑥k	Ⓐ																	⚒	⚒	D
0	**Zwolle** d.	0553	0623	0653	0653	0723	0753	0823	0853	0923	and at	1523	1553	1623	1653	1723	1753	1823	1853	and at	2223	2253	2323	2356	0023
23	Ommen d.	0607	0637	0707	0707	0737	0807	0837	0907	0937	the same	1537	1607	1637	1707	1737	1807	1837	1907	the same	2237	2307	2337	0010	0037
34	Mariënberg d.	0614	0644	0714	0714	0744	0814	0844	0914	0944	minutes	1544	1614	1644	1714	1743	1814	1844	1914	minutes	2244	2314	2344	0017	0044
55	Coevorden d.	0630	0700	0730	0735	0800	0835	0900	0935	1000	past each	1600	1635	1700j	1735	1800j	1835	1900	1935	past each	2300	2335	2400	0036	0101
75	**Emmen** a.	0653	0723	0753	0753	0815	0853	0915	0953	1015	hour until	1615	1653	1715j	1753	1815j	1853	1915	1952	hour until	2315	2353	0015	0053	0119

	Ⓐ	Ⓐ	Ⓐ		Ⓐ	⑥k																	⚒		⚒	D
Emmen d.	0512	0542	0610	0638v	0708	0716	0738z	0816	0838	and at	1616	1638	1708f	1738	1808f	1838	1916	1938	2016	2038	2116	2138	2216	2238	2316	0019
Coevorden d.	0530	0600	0630	0700	0730	0732	0800	0832	0900	the same	1632	1700	1730f	1800	1830f	1900	1932	2000	2032	2100	2132	2200	2232	2300	2333	0036
Mariënberg d.	0546	0616	0646	0716	0746	0746	0816	0846	0916	minutes	1646	1716	1746	1816	1846	1916	1946	2016	2046	2116	2146	2216	2246	2316	2349	0052
Ommen d.	0553	0623	0653	0723	0753	0753	0823	0853	0923	past each	1653	1723	1753	1823	1853	1923	1953	2023	2053	2123	2153	2223	2253	2323	2356	0059
Zwolle a.	0608	0638	0708	0738	0808	0808	0838	0908	0938	hour until	1708	1738	1808	1838	1908	1938	2008	2038	2108	2138	2208	2238	2308	2338	0011	0114

D – Mornings of ②–⑦ (not Dec. 26, Jan. 2, Apr. 19).
f – On Ⓒ departs Emmen 8 minutes later, Coevorden 2 minutes later.
j – On Ⓐ departs Coevorden 5 minutes later, arrives Emmen 8 minutes later.
k – Also Apr. 27, May 26, June 6; not Dec. 25, Jan. 1.
v – 0642 on Ⓒ.
z – 0742 on †.

LEEUWARDEN - GRONINGEN 494

Operated by **Arriva** (NS tickets valid)

km		Ⓐ	⚒	Ⓐ		⚒	Ⓐ			⚒	⚒				⚒	⚒										
0	**Leeuwarden** d.	0551	0621	0647	0651	0721	0747	0751	0817	0821	0847	0851	and at the same	1917	1921	1947	1951	2017	2051	2117	2151	2217	2251	2317	2351	0051
25	Buitenpost d.	0614	0644	|	0714	0744	|	0814	0833	0844	|	0914	minutes past	1933	1944	|	2014	2033	2114	2133	2214	2233	2314	2333	0014	0114
54	**Groningen** a.	0636	0706	0721	0736	0806	0821	0836	0851	0906	0921	0936	each hour until	1951	2006	2021	2036	2051	2136	2151	2236	2251	2336	2351	0036	0136

	Ⓐ	⚒	Ⓐ		Ⓐ	⚒	Ⓐ		⚒	⚒				⚒	⚒										
Groningen d.	0554	0624	0639	0654	0709	0724	0739	0754	0809	0824	0839	0854	and at the same	1909	1924	1939	1954	2039	2054	2139	2154	2239	2254	2339	2354	0054
Buitenpost d.	0616	0646	0656	0716	|	0746	0756	0816	|	0846	0856	0916	minutes past	|	1946	1956	2016	2056	2116	2156	2216	2256	2316	2356	0016	0116
Leeuwarden a.	0640	0710	0713	0740	0743	0810	0813	0840	0843	0910	0913	0940	each hour until	1943	2010	2013	2040	2113	2140	2213	2240	2313	2340	0013	0040	0140

GRONINGEN - BAD NIEUWESCHANS - LEER 495

Operated by **Arriva** (NS tickets valid); 2nd class only

km		Ⓐ	Ⓐ	⚒	⚒	†		⚒	⚒	†	Ⓐ	⚒	Ⓐ	Ⓐ	†	⚒	†	⚒					
0	**Groningen** 498 d.	0514	0606	0617	0647	0653	and at	1717	1747	1753	1807	1817	1837	1847	1853	1917	1953	1953	2053	2153	2253	2353	0022
15	Hoogezand-Sappemeer 498 d.	0530	|	0633	0703	0709	the same	1733	1803	1809	|	1833	|	1903	1909	1933	2009	2010	2109	2209	2309	0009	0038
34	Winschoten d.	0548	0635	0650	0721	0730	minutes	1750	1821	1830	1835	1850	1905	1921	1930	1950	2030	2035	2130	2230	2331	0028	0056
46	**Bad Nieuweschans** ▣ d.	0559	...	0701	...	0740	past each	1801	...	1840	...	1901	...	...	1940	2001	2040	2045	2140	2240	2341	...	0106
56	Weener ▣ a.	0608	...	0710	...	0749	hour until	1810	...	1849	...	1910	...	...	1949	2010	2049	2054	2149	2249	...	...	...

	Ⓐ	Ⓐ	Ⓐ	⚒	†	⚒	⚒	†	⚒	⚒		†	⚒	⚒	†	⚒	†	⚒					
Weener ▣ d.	...	...	0618	...	...	0715	...	0810	0818	...	and at	1810	1818	...	1910	1918	2010	2015	2110	2210	2310	...	...
Bad Nieuweschans ▣ d.	...	...	0628	...	...	0725	0800a	0820	0828	...	the same	1820	1828	...	1920	1928	2020	2025	2120	2220	2320	0005	0110
Winschoten d.	0538	0608	0640	0710f	0733	0740	0810	0834	0840	0910	minutes	1834	1840	1910	1934	1940	2034	2040	2134	2234	2334	0016	0119
Hoogezand-Sappemeer 498 d.	0555	0625	0656	0726	0749	0756	0826	0851	0856	0926	past each	1851	1856	1926	1951	1956	2051	2056	2151	2251	2351	0034	0136
Groningen 498 a.	0612	0642	0713	0743	0807	0813	0843	0908	0913	0943	hour until	1908	1913	1943	2008	2013	2108	2113	2208	2308	0008	0051	0153

	①–⑥ d 🚌	①–⑥ d 🚌	⑦b 🚌	①–⑥ d 🚌		⑦b 🚌	①–⑥ d 🚌	🚌	🚌	🚌			①–⑥ d 🚌	🚌		🚌
Groningen d.	...	...	...	...	and at the same	...	...	...	...	...	...	A	0630	0830	and every	2030
Weener ▣ d.	0612	0712	0800	0812	minutes past	2000	2012	2100	2200	2300	...	L S	|	|	two hours	|
Leer a.	0632	0732	0820	0832	each hour until	2020	2032	2123	2223	2323	...	O	0725	0925	until	2125

	①–⑥ d 🚌	①–⑥ d 🚌	⑦b 🚌	①–⑥ d 🚌		⑦b 🚌	①–⑥ d 🚌	🚌	🚌	🚌			①–⑥ d 🚌	🚌		🚌
Leer d.	0542	0642	0730	0742	and at the same	1930	1942	2030	2130	2230	...	A L	0730	0930	and every	2130
Weener ▣ a.	0602	0702	0750	0802	minutes past	1942	2002	2054	2154	2254	...	S	|	|	two hours	|
Groningen a.	...	...	...	...	each hour until	...	...	...	...	...	...	O	0825	1025	until	2225

a – Ⓐ only.
b – Also Dec. 25, Jan. 1, Apr. 18, June 6.
d – Not Dec. 25, Jan. 1, Apr. 18, June 6.
f – 0709 on ⑥ (also Apr. 27, May 26, June 6).

☛ Dutch running dates apply for rail services (see page 242).

LEEUWARDEN - STAVOREN 496

Operated by **Arriva** (NS tickets valid); 2nd class only

km		Ⓐ	Ⓐ	⚒	Ⓐ	Ⓐ		⚒	⚒		⚒			⚒		⚒	Ⓐ		⚒	Ⓐ		⚒	Ⓐ	
0	**Leeuwarden** d.	0523	0553	0623	0653	0707	0723	0723	0753	0823	0853	and at the same	1423	1453	1523	1553	1553	1623	1653	1653	1723	1753	1753	1823
22	Sneek a.	0542	0612	0642	0712	0725	0742	0742	0812	0842	0912	minutes past	1442	1512	1542	1612	1612	1642	1712	1712	1742	1812	1812	1842
22	Sneek d.	0546	0616	0646	0716	...	...	0746	...	0846	...	each hour until	1446	...	1546	...	1616	1646	...	1716	1746	...	1816	1846
51	**Stavoren** a.	0613	0643	0713	0743	...	...	0813	...	0913	...		1513	...	1613	...	1643	1713	...	1743	1813	...	1843	1913

	⚒		⚒								⑤⑥k
Leeuwarden d.	1853	1923	1953	2023	...	2123	...	2223	...	2323	2323
Sneek a.	1912	1942	2012	2042	...	2142	...	2242	...	2341	2342
Sneek d.	...	1946	...	2046	...	2146	...	2246	...	...	2346
Stavoren a.	...	2013	...	2113	...	2213	...	2313	...	...	0013

	⑥⑦c		Ⓐ	Ⓐ	⚒	Ⓐ	⚒			⚒	⚒	Ⓐ
Stavoren d.	0018	...	...	...	...	0618	0648	...	...	0718	...	0748
Sneek a.	0044	...	...	...	...	0644	0714	...	...	0744	...	0814
Sneek d.	0046	...	0548	0618	0648	0648	0718	...	0748	0748	0818	0818
Leeuwarden a.	0108	...	0608	0638	0708	0708	0738	...	0808	0808	0838	0838

		⚒	⚒			⚒		⚒	Ⓐ		⚒	Ⓐ		⚒	Ⓐ		⚒						
Stavoren d.	...	0818	...	0918	and at the same	...	1618	...	1648	1718	...	1748	1818	...	1848	1918	...	2018	...	2118	...	2218	...	2318
Sneek a.	...	0844	...	0944	minutes past	...	1644	...	1714	1744	...	1814	1844	...	1914	1944	...	2044	...	2144	...	2244	...	2345
Sneek d.	0848	0848	0918	0948	each hour until	1618	1648	1718	1718	1748	1818	1818	1848	1918	1918	1948	2018	2048	...	2148	...	2248	...	2348
Leeuwarden a.	0908	0908	0938	1008		1638	1708	1738	1738	1808	1838	1838	1908	1938	1938	2008	2038	2108	...	2208	...	2308	...	0008

c – Also Apr. 28, May 27, June 7; not Dec. 26, Jan. 2.
k – Also Apr. 27, May 26, June 6; not Dec. 25, Jan. 1.

497 SCHIEDAM - HOEK VAN HOLLAND

Services are operated by *Rotterdamse Elektrische Tram N.V.* (RET). Local RET fares apply.

Metro line **B**: (Nesselande -) Schiedam Centrum - Hoek van Holland. Journey time: 24 minutes. All services call at Vlaardingen Centrum and Maassluis Centrum.

Departures from Schiedam Centrum:

On Ⓐ at 0018, 0518, 0548, 0603, 0619, 0641, 0648, 0718, 0736, 0756, 0816 and every 20 minutes until 1856; 1917, 1948, 2018 and every 30 minutes until 2348.

On ⑥ at 0018, 0619, 0648, 0718 and every 30 minutes until 1118; 1133, 1156, 1216, 1236 and every 20 minutes until 1816; 1847, 1918, 1948 and every 30 minutes until 2348.

On ⑦ at 0018, 0748, 0818 and every 30 minutes until 2348.

Departures from Hoek van Holland Haven:

On Ⓐ at 0018, 0048, 0547, 0617, 0631, 0651, 0711 and every 20 minutes until 1851; 1918, 1929, 1948, 2018 and every 30 minutes until 2348.

On ⑥ at 0018, 0048, 0648, 0718 and every 30 minutes until 1048; 1111, 1131, 1151 and every 20 minutes until 1851; 1918, 1948 and every 30 minutes until 2348.

On ⑦ at 0018, 0048, 0747, 0817 and every 30 minutes until 1847; 1918, 1948 and every 30 minutes until 2348.

498 OTHER BRANCH LINES

ALMELO – MARIËNBERG Operated by **Blauwnet** (NS tickets valid) *19 km.* Journey time: 17 – 19 minutes.

From Almelo:
0618 Ⓐ, 0648 Ⓐ, 0718 Ⓐ, 0748 ⚒, 0818 Ⓐ, 0848, 0948, 1048, 1148, 1248, 1318 ⚒, 1348, 1418 ⚒, 1448, 1518 ⚒, 1548, 1618 ⚒, 1648, 1718 ⚒, 1748, 1818 ⚒, 1848, 1948, 2048, 2148, 2248 and 2350.

From Mariënberg:
0555 Ⓐ, 0625 Ⓐ, 0655 Ⓐ, 0725 ⚒, 0755 Ⓐ, 0825, 0855 Ⓐ, 0925, 1025, 1125, 1225, 1325, 1355 ⚒, 1425, 1455 ⚒, 1525, 1555 ⚒, 1625, 1655 ⚒, 1725, 1755 ⚒, 1825, 1925, 2025, 2125, 2225 and 2325.

AMERSFOORT – EDE-WAGENINGEN Operated by **Connexxion** (NS tickets valid) *34 km.* Journey time: 35 – 38 minutes.

From Amersfoort Centraal:
0509 Ⓐ, 0535 ⚒, 0609 ⚒, 0639 ⚒, 0709, 0739, 0809, 0839 and every 30 minutes until 2339.
All trains call at Barneveld Centrum (17 minutes from Amersfoort)

From Ede-Wageningen:
0553 Ⓐ, 0623 ⚒, 0653 ⚒, 0723 ⚒, 0753, 0823, 0853 and every 30 minutes until 0023.
All trains call at Barneveld Centrum (20 minutes from Ede-Wageningen)

APELDOORN – ZUTPHEN Operated by **Arriva** (NS tickets valid) *18 km.* Journey time: 13 – 20 minutes.

From Apeldoorn:
0636 Ⓐ, 0705 Ⓐ, 0735 Ⓐ, 0805 Ⓐ, 0806 ⑥ **k**, 0811 †, 0823 Ⓒ, 0835 Ⓐ, 0905 Ⓐ, 0906 Ⓒ, 0923 Ⓒ, 0935 Ⓐ and at 05 Ⓐ, 06 Ⓒ, 23 Ⓒ and 35 Ⓐ minutes past each hour until 1905 Ⓐ, 1906 Ⓒ, 1923 Ⓒ, 1935 Ⓐ; then 2004, 2024, 2101, 2123, 2201, 2223, 2301, 2323, 0001.

From Zutphen:
0612 Ⓐ, 0636 Ⓐ, 0706 Ⓐ, 0736 Ⓐ, 0737 Ⓒ, 0754 Ⓒ, 0806 Ⓐ, 0836 Ⓐ, 0837 Ⓒ, 0854 Ⓒ and at 06 Ⓐ, 36 Ⓐ, 37 Ⓒ and 54 Ⓒ minutes past each hour until 1806 Ⓐ, 1836 Ⓐ, 1837 Ⓒ, 1854 Ⓒ; then 1906 Ⓐ, 1935 Ⓐ, 1937 Ⓒ, 2007, 2037, 2105, 2137, 2205, 2237, 2305 and 2337.

GRONINGEN – DELFZIJL Operated by **Arriva** (NS tickets valid) *38 km.* Journey time: 37 – 38 minutes. 2nd class only.

From Groningen:
0518 Ⓐ, 0548 ⚒, 0618, 0648 ⚒, 0718, 0748 ⚒ and at 18 and 48 ⚒ minutes past each hour until 2018, 2048 ⚒; then 2118, 2218, 2318 and 0031.

From Delfzijl:
0600 Ⓐ, 0630 ⚒, 0700, 0730 ⚒, 0800, 0830 ⚒ and at 00 and 30 ⚒ minutes past each hour until 2100, 2130 ⚒; then 2200, 2300, 0002 and 0113.

GRONINGEN – EEMSHAVEN ⊡ Operated by **Arriva** (NS tickets valid) *36 km.* Journey time: 51 – 53 minutes. 2nd class only.

From Groningen:
0622 **A**, 0752 **B**, 0852 ⚒ **C**, 0922 † **C**, 1052 **D**, 1122 ⚒ **E**, 1222 **C**, 1422 † **E**, 1522 **C**, 1652 ⑥ **F**, 1722 ①–⑥ **H** and 1822 **C**.

From Eemshaven:
0719 **A**, 0849 **B**, 0949 ⚒ **C**, 1019 † **C**, 1149 **D**, 1219 ⚒ **E**, 1319 **C**, 1519 † **E**, 1619 **C**, 1749 ⑥ **F**, 1819 ①–⑥ **H** and 1919 **C**.

GRONINGEN – VEENDAM 🚂 Operated by **Arriva** (NS tickets valid) *29 km.* Journey time: 28 minutes. 2nd class only.

From Groningen:
0459 Ⓐ, 0529 Ⓐ, 0559 ⚒, 0629 ⚒, 0659 ⚒, 0723 †, 0729 ⚒, 0759 ⚒, 0823 †, 0829 ⚒ and at 59 ⚒, 23 † and 29 ⚒ minutes past each hour until 1859 ⚒, 1923 †, 1930 ⚒; then 2023, 2123, 2223, 2323 and 0042.
All trains call at Hoogezand-Sappemeer (16 minutes from Groningen)

From Veendam:
0532 Ⓐ, 0602 Ⓐ, 0632 ⚒, 0702 ⚒, 0732 ⚒, 0802 ⚒, 0808 †, 0832 ⚒, 0902 ⚒, 0908 †, 0932 ⚒ and at 02 ⚒, 08 † and 32 ⚒ minutes past each hour until 1902 ⚒, 1908 †, 1932 ⚒; then 2002 ⚒, 2008 †, 2108, 2208, 2308, 2400 and 0116.
All trains call at Hoogezand-Sappemeer (12 minutes from Veendam)

LEEUWARDEN – HARLINGEN Haven ★ Operated by **Arriva** (NS tickets valid) *26 km.* Journey time: 25 – 30 minutes. 2nd class only.

From Leeuwarden:
0540 Ⓐ, 0550 Ⓐ, 0620 Ⓐ, 0640 ⑥ **k**, 0650 ⚒, 0720, 0748 Ⓐ, 0750 Ⓒ, 0820, 0848 Ⓐ, 0850 Ⓒ, 0920, 0950 and every 30 minutes until 2020; then 2120, 2220 and 2320.

From Harlingen Haven:
0612 Ⓐ, 0642 Ⓐ, 0712 ⚒, 0742 ⚒, 0812, 0842 and every 30 minutes until 2112; then 2149, 2249 and 2349.

ZWOLLE – KAMPEN Operated by **Blauwnet** (NS tickets valid) *13 km.* Journey time: 11 minutes.

From Zwolle:
0547 Ⓐ, 0617 Ⓐ, 0647 ⚒, 0717, 0747 and every 30 minutes until 0017.

From Kampen:
0602 Ⓐ, 0632 Ⓐ, 0702 ⚒, 0732, 0802, 0832 and every 30 minutes until 0032.

A – ⚒ Apr. 1 - June 18; daily June 20 - Oct. 30.
B – ⑥ until Mar. 26 (not Dec. 25, Jan. 1); ①–⑥ June 24 - Aug. 27; ⑥ from Nov. 5.
C – Apr. 1 - Oct. 30.
D – ⚒ Dec. 13 - Mar. 31; ⑥ June 25 - Aug. 27; ①–⑥ from Oct. 31.
E – Until Mar. 31 and from Oct. 31.
F – ⑥ until Mar. 26 (not Dec. 25, Jan. 1); ⑥ from Nov. 5.
H – June 24 - Aug. 27.
k – Also Apr. 27, May 26, June 6; not Dec. 25, Jan. 1.

⊡ – For 🚢 to / from Borkum. See www.ag-ems.de for latest timings. Additional trains run Groningen - Roodeschool and v.v.
★ – For 🚢 to / from Terschelling and Vlieland. All trains also call at Harlingen (station for the town centre), 3 minutes from Harlingen Haven.
🚂 – Station for *Museumspoorlijn S.T.A.R.* Steam trains operate to / from Stadskanaal on ⑦ May - September. www.stadskanaalrail.nl

499 OTHER 🚌 and 🚢 LINES

ALKMAAR – LEEUWARDEN 🚌 *Arriva Qliner* route **350** Journey time: 1 hr 41 m – 2 hrs 28 m

From Alkmaar rail station:
On Ⓐ at 0526, 0622, 0722, 0825, 0928, 1028, 1128, 1228, 1328, 1427, 1527, 1622, 1719, 1827, 1929, 2029 and 2129.
On ⑥ at 0630, 0730, 0828, 0928 and hourly until 1728; then 1830, 1930, 2030 and 2130.
On † at 0831, 0931, 1031, 1131, 1231, 1329, 1429 and hourly until 2229.

From Leeuwarden bus station:
On Ⓐ at 0609, 0709, 0812, 0912 and hourly until 1712; then 1817, 1918, 2018, 2118 and 2218.
On ⑥ at 0716, 0816, 0913, 1013 and hourly until 1613; then 1714, 1818, 1919, 2019, 2119 and 2219.
On † at 0817, 0917, 1017, 1117, 1213, 1313, 1413, 1513, 1613, 1713, 1817, 1918, 2018, 2118 and 2218.

DEN HELDER – TEXEL 🚢 *TESO*: ✆ +31 (0) 222 36 96 00 Journey time: 20 minutes

🚌 route **33**: Den Helder rail station (departs 18 minutes before ships sail) to Havenhoofd.
From Den Helder Havenhoofd: 0630 ⚒, 0730 ⚒, 0830 and hourly until 2130.

From Texel ('t Horntje ferryport): 0600 ⚒, 0700 ⚒, 0800 and hourly until 2100.
🚌 route **33**: Den Helder Havenhoofd to rail station (journey: 7 minutes).

ENKHUIZEN – STAVOREN 🚢 *Rederij V & O* ▲: ✆ +31 (0) 228 32 66 67 Journey time: ± 90 minutes

From Enkuizen Spoorhaven: 0845 **A**, 1245 **A**, 1645 **A**.

From Stavoren: 1025 **A**, 1425 **A**, 1825 **A**.

VLISSINGEN – BRESKENS 🚢 *Westerschelde Ferry* ▲ Journey time: 23 minutes
0545 Ⓐ, 0645 Ⓐ, 0748, 0848 and hourly until 1948.
Additional sailings operate June - August.

BRESKENS ferryport – **BRUGGE** rail station 🚌 *Connexxion* **42** Journey time: 84 minutes
0614 Ⓐ, 0714 Ⓐ, 0715 ⑥, 0815, 0915, 1015 and hourly until 2215.

BRUGGE rail station – **BRESKENS** ferryport 🚌 *Connexxion* **42** Journey time: 82 minutes
0648 ⚒, 0748 ⚒, 0848, 0948 and hourly until 1948; then 2048 ⚒.

BRESKENS – VLISSINGEN 🚢 *Westerschelde Ferry* ▲ Journey time: 23 minutes
0612 Ⓐ, 0712 Ⓐ, 0818, 0918 and hourly until 1918.
Additional sailings operate June - August.

A – Daily Apr. 29 - Oct. 2 (also Apr. 23, 24).

▲ – Conveys foot passengers, cycles and mopeds only.

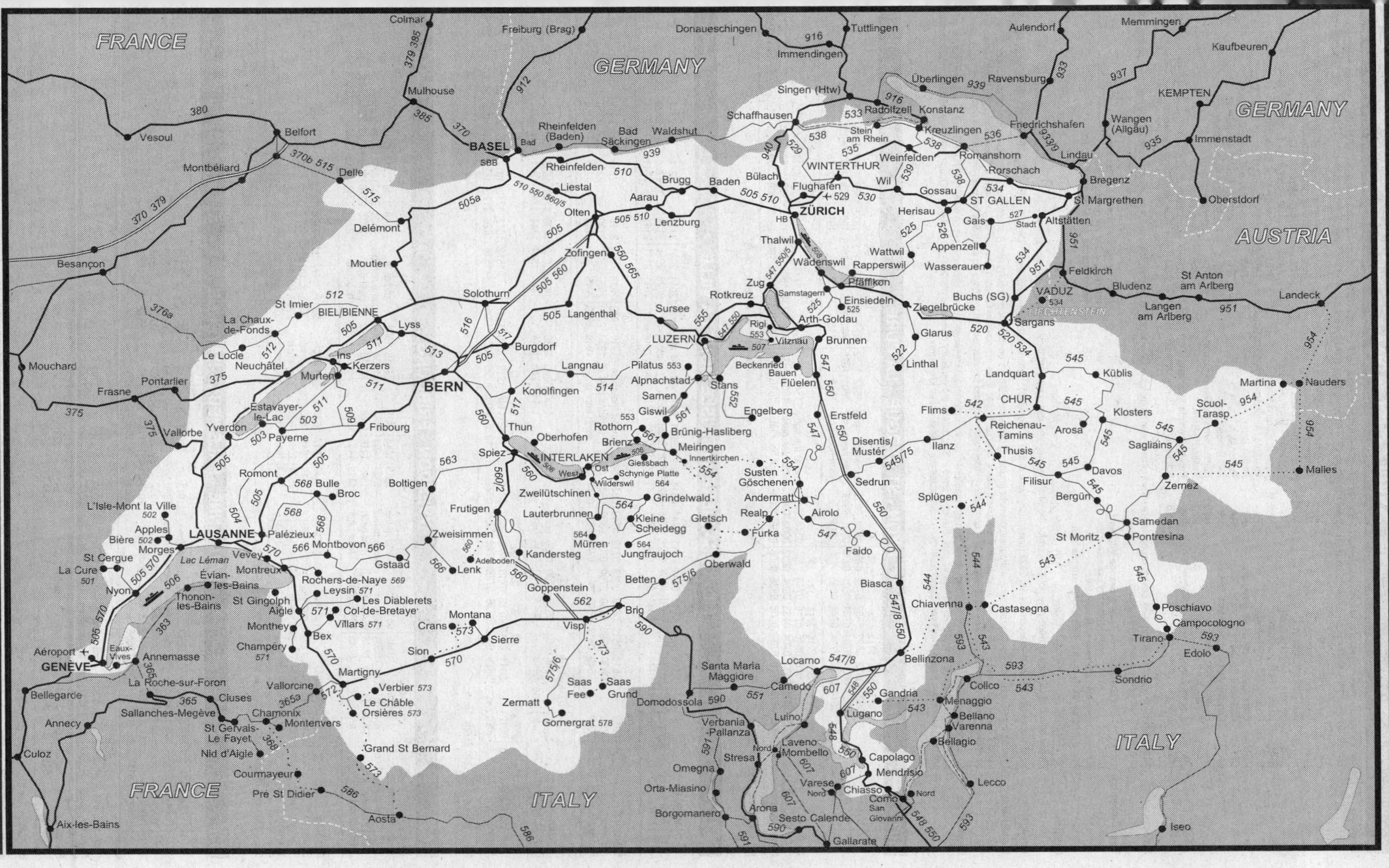

A list of scenic rail routes will be found on page 40

SWITZERLAND

Operators: There are numerous operators of which Schweizerische Bundesbahnen (SBB)/Chemins de fer Fédéraux (CFF)/Ferrovie Federali Svizzere (FFS) is the principal: www.sbb.ch. Bus services are provided by PostAuto/Autopostale (PA): www.postauto.ch. Table headings show the operators' initials; abbreviations used in the European Rail Timetable are:

AB	Appenzeller Bahnen	MGB	Matterhorn Gotthard Bahn	SBS	Schweizerische Bodensee-Schifffahrtsgesellschaft
BLM	Bergbahn Lauterbrunnen - Mürren	MOB	Montreux - Oberland Bernois	SGV	Schifffahrtsgesellschaft des Vierwaldstättersees
BLS	BLS Lötschbergbahn	MThB	Mittelthurgau Bahn	SMC	Sierre - Montana - Crans
BOB	Berner Oberland Bahnen	MVR	Montreux - Vevey Riviera	SNCF	Société Nationale des Chemins de Fer Francais
BRB	Brienz - Rothorn Bahn	NStCM	Nyon-St Cergue-Morez	SOB	Schweizerische Südostbahn
BSB	Bodensee-Schiffsbetriebe	PA	PostAuto / Autopostale / AutoDaPosta	THURBO	an alliance of MThB and SBB
CGN	Compagnie Générale de Navigation	PB	Pilatus Bahn	TMR	Transports de Martigny et Régions
CP	CarPostal Suisse	RA	RegionAlps	TPC	Transports Publics du Chablais
FART	Ferrovie Autolinee Regionali Ticinesi	RB	Rigi Bahnen	TPF	Transports Publics Fribourgeois
FS	Ferrovie dello Stato	RBS	Regionalverkehr Bern - Solothurn	URh	Untersee und Rhein
GGB	Gornergrat Bahn	RhB	Rhätische Bahn	WAB	Wengernalpbahn
JB	Jungfraubahn	RM	Regionalverkehr Mittelland	ZB	Zentralbahn
MBC	Morges - Bière - Cossonay	SBB	Schweizerische Bundesbahnen	ZSG	Zürich Schifffahrtsgesellschaft

Services: All trains convey first and second class seating except where shown otherwise in footnotes or by a '1' or '2' in the train column. For most local services you must be in possession of a valid ticket before boarding your train.

Train Categories:

TGV	French high-speed **Train à Grande Vitesse**.	*IC*	**InterCity** quality internal express train.
ICE	German high-speed **InterCity Express** train.	*IR*	**InterRegio** fast inter-regional train.
RJ	Austrian high-speed **Railjet** train.	*RE*	**RegioExpress** semi-fast regional train.
EC	**EuroCity** quality international express train.		

Catering: ✕ – Restaurant; ⊗ – Bistro; (🍸) – Bar coach; 🍸 – Minibar.
Please note that catering facilities may not be open for the whole journey and may vary from those shown in our tables.

Timings: Valid **December 12, 2021 - December 10, 2022** (unless otherwise stated in the table). National public holidays are on Dec. 25, Jan. 1, Apr. 15, 18, May 26, June 6, Aug. 1.

Supplements: Most internal Swiss journeys can be made without supplement (including domestic journeys on international services). A supplement is payable on a small number of trains (mainly tourist services) and these are indicated in the relevant tables. Special 'global' fares are payable for international *TGV* journeys between Switzerland and France with compulsory reservation. A supplement is payable and compulsory reservation required for international journeys on *EC* trains between Switzerland and Italy.

Reservations: As well as compulsory reservations for international journeys mentioned above, optional seat reservations are also available on other *ICE*, *RJ*, *EC* and *IC* trains. Reservation is recommended for travel in first class panorama cars. Standard fares in Switzerland are generally calculated according to distance, although artificially inflated tariff-kilometres are used on certain routes. However, distances shown in our tables are always actual kilometres.

501 NYON - ST CERGUE - LA CURE

Narrow gauge 2nd class only NStCM

km		Ⓐj	⚒jz	⚒jz	jz		⚒							⚒		⚒		Ⓐj		Ⓐj				
0	**Nyon** d.	0522	0552	0622	0652	0722	0752	0822	0852	and at the same	1522	1552	1622	1652	1722	1752	1822	1852	1922	1952	2052	2209	...	2339
19	St Cergue d.	0559	0631	0701	0731	0801	0830	0901	0928	minutes past	1601	1628	1701	1728	1801	1828	1901	1928	2001	2028	2131	2240	...	0010
27	**La Cure** a.	*0614*	0644	0714	0744	0815	...	0915	...	each hour until	1615	...	1715	...	1815	...	1915	...	2015	...	2144	...	...	...

	Ⓐj		Ⓐj	⚒jz	⚒jz	jz	⚒							⚒		⚒		Ⓐj						
La Cure d.	...	...	*0616*	0646	0716	0746	...	0844	...	and at the same	1544	...	1644	...	1744	...	1844	...	1944	2044	...	2148	...	...
St Cergue d.	0533	0604	0633	0704	0733	0804	0832	0902	0932	minutes past	1602	1632	1702	1732	1802	1832	1902	1932	2002	2102	...	2202	2249	0019
Nyon a.	0608	0638	0708	0738	0808	0838	0908	0938	1008	each hour until	1638	1708	1738	1808	1838	1908	1938	2008	2038	2138	...	...	2323	0053

j – Not Sept. 19.

z – Change trains at St Cergue on Ⓐ.

502 MORGES - BIÈRE and L'ISLE MONT LA VILLE

Narrow gauge 2nd class only MBC

km			⑥⑦k		⚒	⚒		⚒		⚒		Ⓐ			Ⓐ								
0	**Morges** d.	0011	0116	...	0611	0641	0711	0741	0811	0841	0911	0941	and at the same	2011	2041	2111	...	2211	...	2311	...	...	...
12	Apples a.	0028	0133	...	0628	0658	0728	0758	0828	0858	0928	0958	minutes past	2028	2058	2128	...	2228	...	2328	...	...	...
19	**Bière** a.	0041	0146	...	0641	0711	0741	0811	0841	0911	0941	1011	each hour until	2041	2111	2141	...	2241	...	2341	...	...	...

	⑥⑦k		⚒	⚒		⚒		⚒		Ⓐ			Ⓐ										
Bière d.	0019	...	0519	0549	0619	0649	0719	0749	0819	0849	and at the same	1919	1949	2019	...	2119	...	2219	...	2319	...	...	...
Apples d.	0030	...	0530	0600	0630	0700	0730	0800	0830	0900	minutes past	1930	2000	2030	...	2130	...	2230	...	2330	...	...	...
Morges a.	0049	...	0549	0619	0649	0719	0749	0819	0849	0919	each hour until	1949	2019	2049	...	2149	...	2249	...	2349	...	...	...

km		⑥⑦k	⑥⑦k			Ⓐ		Ⓐ					Ⓐ											
0	Apples d.	0030	0134	...	0630	0700	0730	0800	...	0930	...	1130	1200	1230	...	1430	1530	1630	1730	1830	1930	2030	...	2230	2330
11	L'Isle Mont la Ville a.	0044	0148	...	0644	0712	0744	0812	...	0944	...	1144	1212	1244	...	1444	1544	1644	1744	1844	1944	2044	...	2244	2344

	⑥⑦k			Ⓐ	Ⓒ	Ⓐ	Ⓐ	Ⓒ	Ⓐ			Ⓐ	Ⓒ	Ⓐ										
L'Isle Mont la Ville d.	0012	...	0614	0645	0712	0715	0745	0812	0815	...	1012	1145	1212	1215	1312	...	1512	1612	1712	1812	1912	2012	2112	...	2312
Apples a.	0026	...	0628	0658	0726	0728	0758	0826	0828	...	1026	1158	1226	1228	1326	...	1526	1626	1726	1826	1926	2026	2126	...	2326

k – Not Dec. 26, Jan. 2, Apr. 16.

503 YVERDON - FRIBOURG

SBB

km		⑥⑦c																		⑥⑦c		
0	**Yverdon** d.	0048	...	0448	0518	0548	and at the	1318	1348	1418	...	1518	1548	and at the	2118	2148	2218	2248	2318	...	...	...
18	Estavayer-le-Lac d.	0104	...	0504	0534	0604	same minutes	1334	1404	1434	...	1534	1604	same minutes	2134	2204	2234	2304	2334	...	...	...
28	Payerne d.	0114	...	0516	0546	0616	past each	1346	1416	1446	...	1546	1616	past each	2146	2216	2246	2316	2344	0016	...	...
50	**Fribourg** a.	...	...	0543	0613	0643	hour until	1413	1443	1513	...	1613	1643	hour until	2213	2243	2313	2348	...	0043	...	...

Fribourg d.	...	0517	0547	and at the	1317	1347	...	1447	1517	1547	and at the	2217	2247	2317	2338	...	...	...	...	...	...	...
Payerne d.	0515	0545	0615	same minutes	1345	1415	...	1515	1545	1615	same minutes	2245	2315	2345	0007	...	...	...	...	...	...	...
Estavayer-le-Lac d.	0524	0554	0624	past each	1354	1424	...	1524	1554	1624	past each	2254	2324	2354	0016	...	...	...	...	...	...	...
Yverdon a.	0543	0613	0643	hour until	1413	1443	...	1543	1613	1643	hour until	2313	2343	0013	0035	...	...	...	...	...	...	...

c – Mornings of ⑥⑦ (also Apr. 15, 18, May 26, 27, June 6, Aug. 1).

504 LAUSANNE - PALÉZIEUX - PAYERNE

SBB

km		⑥⑦c			⚒			⚒														
0	**Lausanne** 505 d.	0133	...	0513	...	and at the	1913	...	2013	...	2113	...	2213	...	2313	...	...	...	...	...	...	...	...
21	Palézieux 505 d.	0155	...	0530	0603	same minutes	1930	2003	2030	...	2130	...	2230	...	2330	...	...	...	...	...	...	...	...
38	Moudon d.	0213	...	0552	0623	past each	1952	2023	2052	...	2152	...	2252	...	2352	...	...	...	...	...	...	...	...
58	**Payerne** a.	0232	...	0613	0643	hour until	2013	2043	2113	...	2213	...	2313	...	0013	...	...	...	...	...	...	...	...
	Kerzers 511 a.	...	...	0656	...		2056	...	2156	...	2256	...	2356	...	...	...	...	...	...	...	...	...	...

	⚒			⚒																			
Kerzers 511 d.	...	0504	and at the	...	1904	...	2004	...	2104	...	2204	...	...	...	...	...	...	...	...	...	...	...	...
Payerne d.	0517	0547	same minutes	1917	1947	...	2047	...	2147	...	2247	...	2347	...	...	...	...	...	...	...	...	...	...
Moudon d.	0537	0605	past each	1937	2005	...	2105	...	2205	...	2305	...	0005	...	...	...	...	...	...	...	...	...	...
Palézieux 505 d.	0557	0629	hour until	1957	2029	...	2129	...	2229	...	2329	...	0029	...	...	...	...	...	...	...	...	...	...
Lausanne 505 a.	...	0648		...	2048	...	2148	...	2248	...	2348	...	0048	...	...	...	...	...	...	...	...	...	...

c – Also Apr. 15, 18, May 26, 27, June 6, Aug. 1.

SBB GENÈVE - LAUSANNE - BERN / BIEL - ZÜRICH 505

km		RE 18493	IR 2503	IR 2155	IR 2155	IR 2353	IR 2353	IC 703	IC 1507	IR 2159	IC 507	IR 2357	IR 2505	IR 2505	IC 805	IR 2809	IC 705	IC 1509	IR 1805	IC 509	IR 2359	IR 2507	IC 807	RE 18455
			⑥⑦	②–⑦	①	①	②–⑦					Ⓐ		①										
				e	d	d C	e C	✕	✕		R✕	§			✕	⊙	✕	✕		R✕	C◇	🍷	B✕	
						◇	◇																	
0	Genève Aéroport ✈ 570 d.	0011	...	...	...	...	...	...	...	...	...	...	...	...	...	...	...	...	...	...	...	...	...	0510
6	**Genève** 570 d.	0020	...	...	...	...	...	...	...	...	...	...	...	...	...	...	...	...	0449	...	...	...	...	0520
27	Nyon 570 d.	0036	...	...	...	...	...	...	...	...	...	...	...	...	...	...	...	...	0504	...	...	...	...	0536
53	Morges 570 d.	0055	...	...	...	...	...	...	...	...	...	...	...	...	...	...	...	...	0523	...	...	...	...	0555
66	**Lausanne** 570 a.	0108	...	...	...	...	...	...	...	...	...	...	...	...	...	...	...	...	0537	...	...	...	...	0608
66	**Lausanne** d.	...	0130	...	...	...	...	...	...	...	...	...	...	0444	...	...	...	...	━━	0542	...	0544	...	━━
	Yverdon d.	...	|	...	...	...	...	...	...	...	...	...	...	|	...	...	...	...	...	0606	...	|	...	...
	Neuchâtel d.	...	|	...	...	...	...	...	...	...	...	...	...	|	...	...	...	...	...	0626	...	|	...	...
	Biel / Bienne a.	...	|	...	...	...	...	...	...	...	...	...	...	|	...	...	...	...	...	0642	...	|	...	...
	Biel / Bienne d.	...	|	...	...	...	...	...	0516	...	0543	...	...	|	...	...	...	0616	...	0644	...	|	...	...
	Solothurn d.	...	|	...	...	...	...	...	0534	...	0601	...	...	|	...	...	...	0634	...	0701	...	|	...	...
87	Palézieux d.	...	0146	...	...	...	...	...	|	...	|	...	...	0500	...	...	...	|	*IR*	|	...	0600	...	*IR*
106	Romont 568 d.	...	0202	...	...	...	...	...	|	...	|	...	...	0516	...	...	...	|	**2161**	|	...	0616	...	**2811**
132	Fribourg 568 d.	...	0219	...	...	...	...	...	|	...	|	...	0534	0534	...	...	0604	|		|	...	0634	...	
163	**Bern** 568 a.	...	...	...	...	...	...	...	|	...	|	...	0556	0556	...	...	0626	|		|	...	0656	...	⊙
163	**Bern** d.	...	...	0418h	*0359z*	*0431z*	0438t	0529j	|	...	|	0538	0600	0600	0602	0607	0631	|	0633	|	0638	0700	0702	0707
	Luzern **565** a.	...	...	|	|	|	|	|	|	...	|	|	0701	0701	|	|	|	|	|	|	|	0801	|	|
186	Burgdorf d.	...	...	|	|	0454	0454t	|	|	...	|	0553	...	...	|	0621	|	|	|	|	0653	...	|	0721
210	Langenthal d.	...	...	|	|	0512	0512	|	|	...	|	0612	...	...	|	0641	|	|	|	|	0712	...	|	0741
230	**Olten** a.	...	...	0444	0444	0524	0524	0555	0557	...	0618	0624	...	...	0628	0654	|	0657	0700	0718	0724	...	|	0754
230	**Olten** d.	...	...	0446	0446	0526	0526	0557	0559	0602	0620	0626	...	...	0631	...	|	0659	0702	0720	0730	...	|	...
243	Aarau 510 d.	...	...	0456	0456	0536	0536	|	|	0614	0631	0640	...	...	|	...	|	|	0714	0731	|	...	|	...
253	Lenzburg 510 d.	...	...	0503	0503	0542	0542	|	|	|	|	0647	...	...	|	...	|	|	|	|	|	...	|	...
	Brugg 510 d.	...	...	|	|	|	|	|	|	0630	|	|	...	...	|	...	|	|	0730	|	|	...	|	...
	Baden 510 a.	...	...	|	|	|	|	|	|	0638	|	|	...	...	|	...	|	|	0738	|	|	...	|	...
285	**Zürich** HB 510 a.	...	...	0528	0528	0606	0606	0628	0630	0654	0656	0713	...	...	0702	...	0728	0730	0754	0756	0806	...	0758	...
	Zürich Flughafen ✈ **530/5** a.	...	...	0541	0541	...	...	0651	0642a	...	0712	...	...	...	0714	...	0751	...	...	0812	...	...	0814	...
	St Gallen **530** a.	...	...	...	...	...	...	0752	0732a	...	0802	...	...	...	|	...	0852	...	...	0902	...	...	|	...
	Romanshorn **535** a.	...	...	...	...	...	...	...	...	...	...	...	...	...	0812	...	...	...	...	...	...	...	0912	...

km		IC 1511	IC 707	IR 2163		IR 2509	IC 511	IC 809	RE 18457	IC 1513	IC 709	IR 2165		IR 2511	IC 513	IC 811	RE 18459	IC 1515	IC 711	IR 2167		IR 2513	IC 515	IC 813
		✕	✕			🍷	R✕	B✕		✕	✕			🍷	R✕	B✕		✕	✕			🍷	R✕	B✕
	Genève Aéroport ✈ 570 d.	...	...	...	...	0549	0602	...	0611	...	0632	...	...	0649	0705	...	...	...	0732	...	...	0749	0805	...
	Genève 570 d.	...	0542	...	...	0559	0612	...	0620	...	0642	...	...	0659	0715	...	0720	...	0742	...	...	0759	0815	...
	Nyon 570 d.	...	|	...	...	0613	0626	...	0636	...	|	...	...	0713	|	...	0736	...	|	...	...	0813	|	...
0	Morges 570 d.	...	|	...	...	0630	0642	...	0655	...	|	...	...	0730	0742	...	0755	...	|	...	...	0830	0842	...
	Lausanne 570 a.	...	0617	...	...	0641	|	...	0708	...	0717	...	...	0741	|	...	0808	...	0817	...	...	0841	|	...
0	**Lausanne** d.	0615	0620	...	0630	0644	|	...	━━	0715	0720	...	0730	0744	|	...	━━	0815	0820	...	0830	0844	|	...
39	Yverdon d.	0637	|	...	0659	|	0706	...	...	0737	|	...	0759	|	0806	...	...	0837	|	...	0859	|	0906	...
75	Neuchâtel d.	0658	|	...	━━	|	0726	...	...	0758	|	...	━━	|	0826	...	...	0858	|	...	━━	|	0926	...
105	**Biel / Bienne** a.	0715	|	...	...	|	0743	...	...	0815	|	...	...	|	0843	...	...	0915	|	...	...	|	0943	...
105	**Biel / Bienne** d.	0717	|	...	...	|	0746	...	...	0817	|	...	...	|	0846	...	...	0917	|	...	...	|	0946	...
130	Solothurn d.	0734	|	...	...	|	0801	...	...	0834	|	...	...	|	0901	...	...	0934	|	...	...	|	1001	...
	Palézieux d.	|	|	...	*IR*	0700	|	...	*IR*	|	|	...	*IR*	0800	|	...	*IR*	|	|	...	*IR*	0900	|	...
	Romont 568 d.	|	|	...	**2361**	0716	|	...	**2813**	|	|	...	**2363**	0816	|	...	**2815**	|	|	...	**2365**	0916	|	...
	Fribourg 568 d.	|	0704	...		0734	|	...		|	0804	...		0834	|	...		|	0904	...		0934	|	...
	Bern 568 a.	|	0726	...	C⊡	0756	|	...	⊙	|	0826	...	C◇	0856	|	...	⊙	|	0926	...	C⊡	0956	|	...
	Bern d.	|	0731	0733	0738	0800	|	0802	0807	|	0831	0833	0838	0900	|	0902	0907	|	0931	0933	0938	1000	|	1002
	Luzern **565** a.	|	|	|	|	0901	|	|	|	|	|	|	|	1001	|	|	|	|	|	|	|	1101	|	|
	Burgdorf d.	|	|	|	0753	...	|	|	0821	|	|	|	0853	...	|	|	0921	|	|	|	0953	...	|	|
	Langenthal d.	|	|	|	0812	...	|	|	0841	|	|	|	0912	...	|	|	0941	|	|	|	1012	...	|	|
165	**Olten** a.	0757	|	0800	0824	...	0818	|	0854	0857	|	0900	0924	...	0918	|	0954	0957	|	1000	1024	...	1018	|
165	**Olten** d.	0759	|	0802	0830	...	0820	|	...	0859	|	0902	0930	...	0920	|	...	0959	|	1002	1030	...	1020	|
178	Aarau 510 d.	|	|	0814	|	...	0831	|	...	|	|	0914	|	...	0931	|	...	|	|	1014	|	...	1031	|
	Lenzburg 510 d.	|	|	|	|	...	|	|	...	|	|	|	|	...	|	|	...	|	|	|	|	...	|	|
196	Brugg 510 d.	|	|	0830	|	...	|	|	...	|	|	0930	|	...	|	|	...	|	|	1030	|	...	|	|
205	Baden 510 a.	|	|	0838	|	...	|	|	...	|	|	0938	|	...	|	|	...	|	|	1038	|	...	|	|
227	**Zürich** HB 510 a.	0830	0828	0854	0906	...	0856	0858	...	0930	0928	0954	1006	...	0956	0958	...	1030	1028	1054	1106	...	1056	1058
	Zürich Flughafen ✈ **530/5** a.	0842a	0851	...	...	...	0912	0914	...	...	0951	...	...	...	1012	1014	...	...	1051	...	...	...	1112	1114
	St Gallen **530** a.	0932a	0952	...	...	...	1002	|	...	...	1052	...	...	...	1102	|	...	...	1152	...	...	...	1202	|
	Romanshorn **535** a.	...	...	...	...	...	...	1012	...	...	...	...	...	...	...	1112	...	...	...	...	...	...	...	1212

	RE 18461	IC 1517	IC 713	IR 2169		IR 2515	IC 517	IC 815	RE 18463	IC 1519	IC 715	IR 2171		IR 2517	IC 519	IC 817	RE 18465	IC 1521	IC 717	IR 2173		IR 2519	IC 521	IC 819
		✕	✕			🍷	R✕	B✕		✕	✕			🍷	R✕	B✕		✕	✕			🍷	R✕	B✕
Genève Aéroport ✈ 570 d.	...	...	0832	...	...	0849	0905	...	...	...	0932	...	...	0949	1005	...	...	...	1032	...	...	1049	1105	...
Genève 570 d.	0820	...	0842	...	...	0859	0915	...	0920	...	0942	...	...	0959	1015	...	1020	...	1042	...	...	1059	1115	...
Nyon 570 d.	0836	...	|	...	...	0913	|	...	0936	...	|	...	...	1013	|	...	1036	...	|	...	...	1113	|	...
Morges 570 d.	0855	...	|	...	...	0930	0942	...	0955	...	|	...	...	1030	1042	...	1056	...	|	...	...	1130	1142	...
Lausanne 570 a.	0908	...	0917	...	...	0941	|	...	1008	...	1017	...	...	1041	|	...	1108	...	1117	...	...	1141	|	...
Lausanne d.	━━	0915	0920	...	0930	0944	|	...	━━	1015	1020	...	1030	1044	|	...	━━	1115	1120	...	1130	1144	|	...
Yverdon d.	...	0937	|	...	0959	|	1006	...	...	1037	|	...	1059	|	1106	...	...	1137	|	...	1159	|	1206	...
Neuchâtel d.	...	0958	|	...	━━	|	1026	...	...	1058	|	...	━━	|	1126	...	...	1158	|	...	━━	|	1226	...
Biel / Bienne a.	...	1015	|	...	...	|	1043	...	...	1115	|	...	...	|	1143	...	...	1215	|	...	...	|	1243	...
Biel / Bienne d.	...	1017	|	...	...	|	1046	...	...	1117	|	...	...	|	1146	...	...	1217	|	...	...	|	1246	...
Solothurn d.	...	1034	|	...	...	|	1101	...	...	1134	|	...	...	|	1201	...	...	1234	|	...	...	|	1301	...
Palézieux d.	*IR*	|	|	...	*IR*	1000	|	...	*IR*	|	|	...	*IR*	1100	|	...	*IR*	|	|	...	*IR*	1200	|	...
Romont 568 d.	**2817**	|	|	...	**2367**	1016	|	...	**2819**	|	|	...	**2369**	1116	|	...	**2821**	|	|	...	**2371**	1216	|	...
Fribourg 568 d.		|	1004	...		1034	|	...		|	1104	...		1134	|	...		|	1204	...		1234	|	...
Bern 568 a.	⊙	|	1026	...	C◇	1056	|	...	⊙	|	1126	...	C◇	1156	|	...	⊙	|	1226	...	C◇	1256	|	...
Bern d.	1007	|	1031	1033	1038	1100	|	1102	1107	|	1131	1133	1138	1200	|	1202	1207	|	1231	1233	1238	1300	|	1302
Luzern **565** a.	|	|	|	|	|	1201	|	|	|	|	|	|	|	1301	|	|	|	|	|	|	|	1401	|	|
Burgdorf d.	1021	|	|	|	1053	...	|	|	1121	|	|	|	1153	...	|	|	1221	|	|	|	1253	...	|	|
Langenthal d.	1041	|	|	|	1112	...	|	|	1141	|	|	|	1212	...	|	|	1241	|	|	|	1312	...	|	|
Olten a.	1054	1057	|	1100	1124	...	1118	|	1154	1157	|	1200	1224	...	1218	|	1254	1257	|	1300	1324	...	1318	|
Olten d.	...	1059	|	1102	1130	...	1120	|	...	1159	|	1202	1230	...	1220	|	...	1259	|	1302	1330	...	1320	|
Aarau 510 d.	...	|	|	1114	|	...	1131	|	...	|	|	1214	|	...	1231	|	...	|	|	1314	|	...	1331	|
Lenzburg 510 d.	...	|	|	|	|	...	|	|	...	|	|	|	|	...	|	|	...	|	|	|	|	...	|	|
Brugg 510 d.	...	|	|	1130	|	...	|	|	...	|	|	1230	|	...	|	|	...	|	|	1330	|	...	|	|
Baden 510 a.	...	|	|	1138	|	...	|	|	...	|	|	1238	|	...	|	|	...	|	|	1338	|	...	|	|
Zürich HB 510 a.	...	1130	1128	1154	1206	...	1156	1158	...	1230	1228	1254	1306	...	1256	1258	...	1330	1328	1354	1406	...	1356	1358
Zürich Flughafen ✈ **530/5** a.	...	...	1151	...	...	...	1212	1214	...	...	1251	...	...	...	1312	1314	...	...	1351	...	...	...	1412	1414
St Gallen **530** a.	...	...	1252	...	...	...	1302	|	...	...	1352	...	...	...	1402	|	...	...	1452	...	...	...	1502	|
Romanshorn **535** a.	...	...	...	...	...	...	...	1312	...	...	...	...	...	...	...	1412	...	...	...	...	...	...	...	1512

B – From Brig (Table **560**).
C – To Chur (Table **520**).
R – To Rorschach (Table **530**).

a – Ⓐ only.
d – Not Apr. 18, June 6, Aug. 1.
e – Also Apr. 18, June 6, Aug. 1.

h – 0404 on Mar. 26, 27, May 21, 22, June 21–24, 28–30, July 1, Sept. 17, 18, Oct. 4–7, 11–14, 29, 30.
j – 0513 on Feb. 7, 28, Mar. 26, 27, 28, May 9, 16, 21, 22, 23, June 13, 20–24, 27–30, July 1, 25, Sept. 5, 17, 18, 19, Oct. 3–7, 10–14, 29, 30, 31, Nov. 7, 28, Dec. 5.
t – 2 minutes earlier on Ⓒ.
z – Change trains at Zollikofen (departs Zollikofen 11 minutes later).

§ – Runs as *RE* **4509** Olten - Zürich.
⊙ – Operated by BLS.
◇ – Operated by SOB.
⊡ – Operated by SBB on Ⓐ, by SOB on Ⓒ.

505 GENÈVE - LAUSANNE - BERN / BIEL - ZÜRICH SBB

	RE 18467	IC 1523	IC 719	IR 2175		IR 2521	IC 523	IC 821	RE 18469	IC 1525	IC 721	IR 2177		IR 2523	IC 525	IC 823	RE 18471	IC 1527	IC 723	IR 2179		IR 2525	IC 527	IC 825
		✕	✕			🍷	R✕	B✕		✕	✕			🍷	R✕	B✕		✕	✕			🍷	R✕	B✕
Genève Aéroport + 570 d.	...	...	1132	...	...	1149	1205	...	...	...	1232	...	...	1249	1305	...	...	...	1332	...	...	1349	1405	...
Genève 570 d.	1120	...	1142	...	...	1159	1215	...	1220	...	1242	...	...	1259	1315	...	1320	...	1342	...	...	1359	1415	...
Nyon 570 d.	1136	...	|	...	...	1213	|	...	1236	...	|	...	...	1313	|	...	1336	...	|	...	...	1413	|	...
Morges 570 d.	1155	...	|	...	...	1230	1242	...	1256	...	|	...	...	1330	1342	...	1355	...	|	...	...	1430	1442	...
Lausanne 570 a.	1208	...	1217	...	...	1241	|	...	1308	...	1317	...	...	1341	|	...	1408	...	1417	...	...	1441	|	...
Lausanne d.	▬	1215	1220	...	1230	1244	|	...	▬	1315	1320	...	1330	1344	|	...	▬	1415	1420	...	1430	1444	|	...
Yverdon d.	...	1237	|	...	1259	|	1306	...	...	1337	|	...	1359	|	1406	...	...	1437	|	...	1459	|	1506	...
Neuchâtel d.	...	1258	|	...	▬	|	1326	...	...	1358	|	...	▬	|	1426	...	...	1458	|	...	▬	|	1526	...
Biel / Bienne a.	...	1315	|	...	...	|	1343	...	...	1415	|	...	...	|	1443	...	...	1515	|	...	...	|	1543	...
Biel / Bienne d.	...	1317	|	...	...	|	1346	...	...	1417	|	...	...	|	1446	...	...	1517	|	...	...	|	1546	...
Solothurn d.	...	1334	|	...	...	|	1401	...	...	1434	|	...	...	|	1501	...	...	1534	|	...	...	|	1601	...
Palézieux d.	*IR*	|	|	...	*IR*	1300	|	...	*IR*	|	|	...	*IR*	1400	|	...	*IR*	|	|	...	*IR*	1500	|	...
Romont 568 d.	**2823**	|	|	...	**2373**	1316	|	...	**2825**	|	|	...	**2375**	1416	|	...	**2827**	|	|	...	**2377**	1516	|	...
Fribourg 568 d.		|	1304	...		1334	|	...		|	1404	...		1434	|	...		|	1504	...		1534	|	...
Bern 568 a.	⊙	|	1326	...	C ◇	1356	|	...	⊙	|	1426	...	C ◇	1456	|	...	⊙	|	1526	...	C ⊡	1556	|	...
Bern d.	1307	|	1331	1333	1338	1400	|	1402	1407	|	1431	1433	1438	1500	|	1502	1507	|	1531	1533	1538	1600	|	1602
Luzern 565 a.	|	|	|	|	|	1501	|	|	|	|	|	|	|	1601	|	|	|	|	|	|	|	1701	|	|
Burgdorf d.	1321	|	|	|	1353	...	|	|	1421	|	|	|	1453	...	|	|	1521	|	|	|	1553	...	|	|
Langenthal d.	1341	|	|	|	1412	...	|	|	1441	|	|	|	1512	...	|	|	1541	|	|	|	1612	...	|	|
Olten a.	1354	1357	|	1400	1424	...	1418	|	1454	1457	|	1500	1524	...	1518	|	1554	1557	|	1600	1624	...	1618	|
Olten d.	...	1359	|	1402	1430	...	1420	|	...	1459	|	1502	1530	...	1520	|	...	1559	|	1602	1630	...	1620	|
Aarau 510 d.	...	|	|	1414	|	...	1431	|	...	|	|	1514	|	...	1531	|	...	|	|	1614	|	...	1631	|
Lenzburg 510 d.	...	|	|	|	|	...	|	|	...	|	|	|	|	...	|	|	...	|	|	|	|	...	|	|
Brugg 510 d.	...	|	|	1430	|	...	|	|	...	|	|	1530	|	...	|	|	...	|	|	1630	|	...	|	|
Baden 510 a.	...	|	|	1438	|	...	|	|	...	|	|	1538	|	...	|	|	...	|	|	1638	|	...	|	|
Zürich HB 510 a.	...	1430	1428	1454	1506	...	1456	1458	...	1530	1528	1554	1606	...	1556	1558	...	1630	1628	1654	1706	...	1656	1658
Zürich Flughafen + 530/5 a.	...	...	1451	...	...	...	1512	1514	...	...	1551	...	...	...	1612	1614	...	1642a	1651	...	...	...	1712	1714
St Gallen 530 a.	...	...	1552	...	...	...	1602	|	...	...	1652	...	...	...	1702	|	...	1732a	1752	...	...	...	1802	|
Romanshorn 535 a.	...	...	...	...	...	...	...	1612	...	...	...	...	...	...	...	1712	...	...	...	...	...	...	...	1812

	RE 18473	IC 1529	IC 725	IR 2181		IR 2527	IC 529	IC 827	RE 18475	IC 1531	IC 727	IR 2183		IR 2529	IC 531	IC 829	RE 18477	IC 1533	IC 729	IR 2185		IR 2531	IC 533	IC 831
		✕	✕			🍷	R✕	B✕		✕	✕			🍷	R✕	B✕		✕	✕			🍷	✕	B✕
Genève Aéroport + 570 d.	...	...	1432	...	...	1449	1505	...	...	...	1532	...	...	1549	1605	...	...	...	1632	...	...	1649	1705	...
Genève 570 d.	1420	...	1442	...	...	1459	1515	...	1520	...	1542	...	...	1559	1615	...	1620	...	1642	...	...	1659	1715	...
Nyon 570 d.	1436	...	|	...	...	1513	|	...	1536	...	|	...	...	1613	|	...	1636	...	|	...	...	1713	|	...
Morges 570 d.	1456	...	|	...	...	1530	1542	...	1555	...	|	...	...	1630	1642	...	1655	...	|	...	...	1730	1742	...
Lausanne 570 a.	1508	...	1517	...	...	1541	|	...	1608	...	1617	...	...	1641	|	...	1708	...	1717	...	...	1741	|	...
Lausanne d.	▬	1515	1520	...	1530	1544	|	...	▬	1615	1620	...	1630	1644	|	...	▬	1715	1720	...	1730	1744	|	...
Yverdon d.	...	1537	|	...	1559	|	1606	...	...	1637	|	...	1659	|	1706	...	...	1737	|	...	1759	|	1806	...
Neuchâtel d.	...	1558	|	...	▬	|	1626	...	...	1658	|	...	▬	|	1726	...	...	1758	|	...	▬	|	1826	...
Biel / Bienne a.	...	1615	|	...	...	|	1643	...	...	1715	|	...	...	|	1743	...	...	1815	|	...	...	|	1843	...
Biel / Bienne d.	...	1617	|	...	...	|	1646	...	...	1717	|	...	...	|	1746	...	...	1817	|	...	...	|	1846	...
Solothurn d.	...	1634	|	...	...	|	1701	...	...	1734	|	...	...	|	1801	...	...	1834	|	...	...	|	1901	...
Palézieux d.	*IR*	|	|	...	*IR*	1600	|	...	*IR*	|	|	...	*IR*	1700	|	...	*IR*	|	|	...	*IR*	1800	|	...
Romont 568 d.	**2829**	|	|	...	**2379**	1616	|	...	**2831**	|	|	...	**2381**	1716	|	...	**2833**	|	|	...	**2383**	1816	|	...
Fribourg 568 d.		|	1604	...		1634	|	...		|	1704	...		1734	|	...		|	1804	...		1834	|	...
Bern 568 a.	⊙	|	1626	...	C ◇	1656	|	...	⊙	|	1726	...	C ⊡	1756	|	...	⊙	|	1826	...	C ◇	1856	|	...
Bern d.	1607	|	1631	1633	1638	1700	|	1702	1707	|	1731	1733	1738	1800	|	1802	1807	|	1831	1833	1838	1900	|	1902
Luzern 565 a.	|	|	|	|	|	1801	|	|	|	|	|	|	|	1901	|	|	|	|	|	|	|	2001	|	|
Burgdorf d.	1621	|	|	|	1653	...	|	|	1721	|	|	|	1753	...	|	|	1821	|	|	|	1853	...	|	|
Langenthal d.	1641	|	|	|	1712	...	|	|	1741	|	|	|	1812	...	|	|	1841	|	|	|	1912	...	|	|
Olten a.	1654	1657	|	1700	1724	...	1718	|	1754	1757	|	1800	1824	...	1818	|	1854	1857	|	1900	1924	...	1918	|
Olten d.	...	1659	|	1702	1730	...	1720	|	...	1759	|	1802	1830	...	1820	|	...	1859	|	1902	1930	...	1920	|
Aarau 510 d.	...	|	|	1714	|	...	1731	|	...	|	|	1814	|	...	1831	|	...	|	|	1914	|	...	1931	|
Lenzburg 510 d.	...	|	|	|	|	...	|	|	...	|	|	|	|	...	|	|	...	|	|	|	|	...	|	|
Brugg 510 d.	...	|	|	1730	|	...	|	|	...	|	|	1830	|	...	|	|	...	|	|	1930	|	...	|	|
Baden 510 a.	...	|	|	1738	|	...	|	|	...	|	|	1838	|	...	|	|	...	|	|	1938	|	...	|	|
Zürich HB 510 a.	...	1730	1728	1754	1806	...	1756	1758	...	1830	1828	1854	1906	...	1856	1858	...	1930	1928	1954	2006	...	1956	1958
Zürich Flughafen + 530/5 a.	...	...	1751	...	...	...	1812	1814	...	1842a	1851	...	...	...	1912	1914	...	...	1951	...	...	...	2012	2014
St Gallen 530 a.	...	...	1852	...	...	...	1902	|	...	1932a	1952	...	...	...	2002	|	...	...	2052	...	...	...	2102	|
Romanshorn 535 a.	...	...	...	...	...	...	...	1912	...	...	...	...	...	...	...	2012	...	...	...	...	...	...	...	2112

	RE 18479	IC 1535	IC 731	IR 2187		IR 2533	IC 535	IC 833	RE 18481	IC 1537	IC 733	IR 2189		IR 2535	IC 537	IC 835	RE 18483	IC 1539	IC 735 ⑤⑥	IC 735 ⑦–④	IR 2191		IR 2537	IC 539
		✕	✕			🍷	✕	B✕		✕	✕				✕	B✕		◐	n✕	r✕	✕			◐
Genève Aéroport + 570 d.	...	...	1732	...	...	1749	1805	...	...	...	1832	...	...	1849	1905	...	...	...	1932	1932	...	...	1949	2005
Genève 570 d.	1720	...	1742	...	...	1759	1815	...	1820	...	1842	...	...	1859	1915	...	1920	...	1942	1942	...	...	1959	2015
Nyon 570 d.	1736	...	|	...	...	1813	|	...	1836	...	|	...	...	1913	|	...	1936	...	|	|	...	...	2013	|
Morges 570 d.	1756	...	|	...	...	1830	1842	...	1855	...	|	...	...	1930	1942	...	1955	...	|	|	...	...	2030	2042
Lausanne 570 a.	1808	...	1817	...	...	1841	|	...	1908	...	1917	...	...	1941	|	...	2008	...	2017	2017	...	...	2041	|
Lausanne d.	▬	1815	1820	...	1830	1844	|	...	▬	1915	1920	...	1930	1944	|	...	▬	2015	2020	2020	...	2030	2044	|
Yverdon d.	...	1837	|	...	1859	|	1906	...	...	1937	|	...	1959	|	2006	...	...	2037	|	|	...	2059	|	2106
Neuchâtel d.	...	1858	|	...	▬	|	1926	...	...	1958	|	...	▬	|	2026	...	...	2058	|	|	...	▬	|	2126
Biel / Bienne a.	...	1915	|	...	...	|	1943	...	...	2015	|	...	...	|	2043	...	...	2115	|	|	...	...	|	2143
Biel / Bienne d.	...	1917	|	...	...	|	1946	...	...	2017	|	...	...	|	2046	...	...	2117	|	|	...	...	|	2146
Solothurn d.	...	1934	|	...	...	|	2001	...	...	2034	|	...	...	|	2101	...	...	2134	|	|	...	...	|	2201
Palézieux d.	*IR*	|	|	...	*IR*	1900	|	...	*IR*	|	|	...	*IR*	2000	|	...	*IR*	|	|	|	...	*IR*	2100	|
Romont 568 d.	**2835**	|	|	...	**2385**	1916	|	...	**2837**	|	|	...	**2387**	2016	|	...	**2839**	|	|	|	...	**2389**	2116	|
Fribourg 568 d.		|	1904	...		1934	|	...		|	2004	...		2034	|	...		|	2104	2104	...		2134	|
Bern 568 a.	⊙	|	1926	...	C ◇	1956	|	...	⊙	|	2026	...	◇	2056	|	...	⊙	|	2126	2126	...	◇	2156	|
Bern d.	1907	|	1931	1933	1938	2000	|	2002	2007	|	2031	2033	2038	2100	|	2102	2107	|	2131	2131	2133n	2138	2200	|
Luzern 565 a.	|	|	|	|	|	2101	|	|	|	|	|	|	|	2201	|	|	|	|	|	|	|	|	2301	|
Burgdorf d.	1921	|	|	|	1953	...	|	|	2021	|	|	|	2053	...	|	|	2121	|	|	|	|	2154	...	|
Langenthal d.	1941	|	|	|	2012	...	|	|	2041	|	|	|	2112	...	|	|	2141	|	|	|	|	2212	...	|
Olten a.	1954	1957	|	2000	2024	...	2018	|	2054	2057	|	2100	2124	...	2118	|	2154	2157	|	2157	2200n	2225	...	2218
Olten d.	...	1959	|	2002	2030	...	2020	|	...	2059	|	2102	...	...	2120	|	...	2159n	|	2200	2202	...	...	2220
Aarau 510 d.	...	|	|	2014	|	...	2031	|	...	|	|	2114	...	...	2131	|	...	|	|	|	2214	...	...	2231
Lenzburg 510 d.	...	|	|	|	|	...	|	|	...	|	|	|	...	...	|	|	...	|	|	|	|	...	...	|
Brugg 510 d.	...	|	|	2030	|	...	|	|	...	|	|	2130	...	...	|	|	...	|	|	|	2230	...	...	|
Baden 510 a.	...	|	|	2038	|	...	|	|	...	|	|	2138	...	...	|	|	...	|	|	|	2238	...	...	|
Zürich HB 510 a.	...	2030	2028	2054	2106	...	2056	2058	...	2130	2128	2154	...	...	2156	2158	...	2230n	2228	2231	2254	...	...	2256
Zürich Flughafen + 530/5 a.	...	...	2051	...	...	...	...	2114	...	...	2151	...	...	...	...	2214	...	...	2251	2251	...	...	...	...
St Gallen 530 a.	...	...	2152	...	...	...	...	|	...	...	2252	...	...	...	...	|	...	...	2352	2352	...	...	...	...
Romanshorn 535 a.	...	...	...	...	...	...	...	2212	...	...	...	...	...	...	...	2312	...	...	...	...	...	...	...	...

B – From Brig (Table **560**).
C – To Chur (Table **520**).
R – To Rorschach (Table **534**).

a – Ⓐ only.
n – ⑤⑥ (not Dec. 24, 25, Jan. 1, Apr. 15).
r – Also Dec. 24, 25, Jan. 1, Apr. 15.

◐ – Conveys ✕ until Biel/Bienne.
⊙ – Operated by BLS.
◇ – Operated by SOB.
⊡ – Operated by SBB on Ⓐ, by SOB on Ⓒ.

SBB — GENÈVE - LAUSANNE - BERN / BIEL - ZÜRICH — 505

	IC 837	RE 18485	IC 1541	IC 737		RE 18439	IR 2539	IR 2539	IC 839	IC 541	RE 4793	RE 18487	IC 1543	IC 739	RE 18441	IR 2541	IC 841	IC 543	RE 18489	IC 1545	RE 18443	IR 2543	RE 18491	IC 1547
			▽					⑤⑥																
			◐	✕						◐			◐	◧						D				★
Genève Aéroport ✈ .... 570 d.	...	...	...	2032	...	...	...	2049	...	2102k	...	...	...	...	...	...	...	...	2210	...	2241r	...	2311	...
Genève .... 570 d.	...	2020	...	2042	...	2050	...	2059	...	2112k	...	2120	...	...	2150	...	...	...	2220	...	2250t	...	2320	...
Nyon .... 570 d.	...	2036	...	|	...	2106	...	2113	...	2126k	...	2136	...	...	2206	...	...	...	2236	...	2306	...	2336	...
Morges .... 570 d.	...	2056	...	|	...	2125	...	2130	...	2142	...	2156	...	...	2225	...	...	...	2256	...	2325	...	2355	...
Lausanne .... 570 a.	...	2108	...	2117	...	2138	...	2141	...	|	...	2208	...	...	2238	...	...	...	2310	...	2338	...	0010	...
Lausanne .... d.	...	▬	2115	2120	2130	...	2144	2144	...	|	...	▬	2215	2220	...	2244	...	...	▬	2315	...	2344	▬	0015
Yverdon .... d.	...	...	2137	|	2159	...	|	|	...	2206	...	...	2237	|	...	|	...	...	...	2337	...	|	...	0037
Neuchâtel .... d.	...	...	2158	|	▬	...	|	|	...	2226	...	...	2258	|	...	|	...	...	...	2358	...	|	...	0058
Biel / Bienne .... a.	...	...	2215	|	...	...	|	|	...	2243	...	...	2315	|	...	|	...	...	...	0017	...	|	...	0115
Biel / Bienne .... d.	...	...	2217	|	...	...	|	|	...	2246	...	...	2317	|	...	|	...	2346	...	...	...	|	...	▬
Solothurn .... d.	...	...	2234	|	...	...	|	|	...	2305	...	...	2334	|	...	|	...	0005	...	...	...	|	...	...
Palézieux .... d.	...	*IR*	|	|	*IR*	...	2200	2200	...	|	...	*IR*	|	|	...	2300	...	|	*IR*	...	...	0000	*IC*	*IR*
Romont .... 568 d.	...	**2841**	|	|	**2351**	...	2216	2216	...	|	...	**2845**	|	|	...	2316	...	|	**2399**	...	...	0016	**843**	**2847**
Fribourg .... 568 d.	...		|	2204		...	2234	2234	...	|	...		|	2304	...	2334	...	|		...	...	0034	⑥⑦	⑥⑦
Bern .... 568 a.	...	⊙	|	2226		...	2256	2256	...	|	...	⊙	|	2326	...	2356	...	|	◇	...	...	0100	h	h ⊙
Bern .... d.	2202	2207	|	2231	2233	...	2300	2300	2302	|	...	2305	|	2331	...	...	0002	|	0007	...	...	...	0106	0109
Luzern **565** .... a.	|	|	|	|	|	...	0001	0001	|	|	...	|	|	|	...	...	|	|	|	...	...	...	|	|
Burgdorf .... d.	|	2223	|	|	2251	...	...	...	|	|	...	2321	|	|	...	...	|	|	0023	...	...	...	|	0125
Langenthal .... d.	|	2242	|	|	2312	...	...	...	|	|	...	2341	|	|	...	...	|	|	0042	...	...	...	|	0144
Olten .... a.	2228	2254	2257	2257	2325	...	...	...	2328	2330	...	2355	2357	2357	...	...	0028	0030	0055	...	...	...	0132	0157
Olten .... d.	2230	...	2302	2300	...	...	...	...	2330	2333	2335	...	...	0002	...	...	0035	0037	...	...	...	...	0134	...
Aarau .... 510 d.	|	...	2314	|	...	...	...	...	|	2344	2345	...	...	0012	...	...	|	0047	...	...	...	...	0145	...
Lenzburg .... 510 d.	|	...	|	|	...	...	...	...	|	|	|	...	...	0019	...	...	|	0054	...	...	...	...	|	...
Brugg .... 510 d.	|	...	2330	|	...	...	...	...	|	|	0003	...	...	|	...	...	|	|	...	...	...	...	|	...
Baden .... 510 a.	|	...	2338	|	...	...	...	...	|	|	0013	...	...	|	...	...	|	|	...	...	...	...	|	...
Zürich HB .... 510 a.	2302	...	2354	2331	...	...	...	...	0001	0010	0042	...	...	0040	...	...	0106	0114	...	...	...	...	0210	...
Zürich Flughafen ✈ **530/5** . a.	2314	...	...	...	...	...	...	...	...	...	...	...	...	...	...	...	...	...	...	...	...	...	...	...
St Gallen **530** .... a.	|	...	...	...	...	...	...	...	...	...	...	...	...	...	...	...	...	...	...	...	...	...	...	...
Romanshorn **535** .... a.	0012	...	...	...	...	...	...	...	...	...	...	...	...	...	...	...	...	...	...	...	...	...	...	...

km ♥		RE 18400	RE 18402	RE 18450	RE 18404	RE 18452	IC 504	IR 2504		IC 702	IC 1504	RE 18454	IR 2806	IR 2506	IR 2352	IC 704	IC 1506	IR 2808	IC 804	IR 2508	IR 2354	IC 508	IR 2158	IC 706
		⑥⑦											Ⓐ											
										✕	✕		⊙		◇	✕	⊖	⊙	B ✕	🍸	⊡	✕		✕
	Romanshorn .... d.	...	...	...	...	...	...	...	...	...	...	...	...	...	...	...	...	...	...	...	...	...	...	...
	St Gallen **530** .... d.	...	...	...	...	...	...	...	...	...	...	...	...	...	...	...	...	...	...	...	...	...	...	0507
	Zürich Flughafen ✈ **530/5** . d.	...	...	...	...	...	...	...	...	...	...	...	...	...	...	...	...	...	...	...	...	...	...	0608
0	**Zürich** HB .... 510 d.	...	...	...	...	...	...	...	...	...	...	...	...	...	...	0519	...	...	0602	...	0553	0604	0606	0632
	Baden .... 510 d.	...	...	...	...	...	...	...	...	...	...	...	...	...	...	|	...	...	|	...	|	|	0621	|
	Brugg .... 510 d.	...	...	...	...	...	...	...	...	...	...	...	...	...	...	|	...	...	|	...	|	|	0632	|
32	Lenzburg .... 510 d.	...	...	...	...	...	...	...	...	...	...	...	...	...	...	0540	...	...	|	...	|	|	|	|
42	Aarau .... 510 d.	...	...	...	...	...	...	...	...	...	...	...	...	...	...	0548	...	...	|	...	|	0630	0646	|
55	**Olten** .... a.	...	...	...	...	...	...	...	...	...	...	...	...	...	...	0557	...	...	|	...	0628	0638	0655	|
55	**Olten** .... d.	...	...	...	...	...	...	...	...	...	...	...	0506	...	0536	0602	0602	0606	|	...	0636	0640	0656	|
	Langenthal .... d.	...	...	...	...	...	...	...	...	...	...	...	0518	...	0548	|	|	0618	|	...	0648	|	|	|
	Burgdorf .... d.	...	...	...	...	...	...	...	...	...	...	...	0538	...	0606	|	|	0638	|	...	0706	|	|	|
	Luzern **565** .... d.	...	...	...	...	...	...	...	...	...	...	...	|	...	|	|	|	|	|	0600	|	|	|	|
117	**Bern** .... a.	...	...	...	...	...	...	...	...	...	...	...	0553	...	0621	0628	|	0653	0658	0700	0721	|	0724	0728
	Bern .... 568 d.	...	...	...	...	...	...	0504	...	0534	...	...	▬	0604	▬	0634	|	▬	...	0704	...	|	▬	0734
	Fribourg .... 568 d.	...	...	...	...	...	...	0526	...	0556	...	...	...	0626	...	0656	|	...	...	0726	...	|	...	0756
	Romont .... 568 d.	...	...	...	...	...	...	0544	...	|	...	...	*IC*	0644	...	|	|	...	...	0744	...	|	...	|
	Palézieux .... d.	...	...	...	...	...	...	0600	...	|	...	...	**1606**	0700	...	|	|	...	...	0800	...	|	...	|
	Solothurn .... d.	...	...	...	...	...	...	|	...	|	...	...		|	...	|	0626	...	...	|	...	0658	...	|
	Biel / Bienne .... a.	...	...	...	...	...	...	|	...	|	...	...	D ✕	|	...	|	0643	...	...	|	...	0713	...	|
	Biel / Bienne .... d.	...	...	...	...	...	0516	|	...	|	0545	...	0616	|	...	|	0645	*RE*	...	|	...	0716	...	|
	Neuchâtel .... d.	...	...	...	...	...	0534	|	...	|	0603	...	0634	|	...	|	0703	**18456**	...	|	...	0734	...	|
	Yverdon .... d.	...	...	...	...	...	0554	|	0558	|	0623	...	0654	|	0658	|	0723		...	|	...	0754	0758	|
	Lausanne .... a.	...	...	...	...	...	|	0616	0628	0640	0645	...	|	0716	0728	0740	0745		...	0816	...	|	0828	0840
	Lausanne .... 570 d.	0251	0351	0451	0521	0551	|	0619	...	0643	...	0651	|	0719	...	0743	...	0751	...	0819	...	|	...	0843
	Morges .... 570 d.	0303	0404	0505	0535	0605	0618	0629	...	|	...	0705	0718	0729	...	|	...	0805	...	0829	...	0818	...	|
	Nyon .... 570 d.	0324	0425	0525e	0555	0625	|	0646	...	|	...	0725	|	0746	...	|	...	0825	...	0846	...	|	...	|
	Genève .... 570 a.	0339	0442	0540e	0610	0640	0647	0701	...	0718	...	0740	0747	0801	...	0818	...	0840	...	0901	...	0847	...	0918
	Genève Aéroport ✈ .... 570 a.	...	0456	0548e	...	...	0656	0711	...	0727	...	...	0756	0811	...	0827	...	...	...	0911	...	0856	...	0927

km ♥		IC 1508	IR 2810	IC 806	IR 2510	IR 2356	IC 510	IR 2160	IC 708	IC 1510	IR 2812	IC 808	IR 2512	IR 2358	IC 512	IR 2162	IC 710	IC 1512	IR 2814	IC 810	IR 2514	IR 2360	IC 514	IR 2164
		✕	⊙	B ✕	🍸	C ◇	R ✕		✕	✕	⊙	B ✕	🍸	C ⊡	R ✕		✕	✕	⊙	B ✕	🍸	C ◇	R ✕	
	Romanshorn **535** .... d.	...	...	0548	...	...	...	...	...	...	...	0648	...	...	...	...	...	...	...	0748	...	...	...	...
	St Gallen **530** .... d.	...	...	|	...	...	0558	...	0607	0628a	...	|	...	...	0658	...	0707	...	...	|	...	...	0758	...
	Zürich Flughafen ✈ **530/5** . d.	...	...	0645	...	...	0648	...	0708	0718a	...	0745	...	...	0748	...	0808	...	...	0845	...	...	0848	...
	Zürich HB .... 510 d.	0630	...	0702	...	0653	0704	0706	0732	0730	...	0802	...	0753	0804	0806	0832	0830	...	0902	...	0853	0904	0906
	Baden .... 510 d.	|	...	|	...	|	|	0722	|	|	...	|	...	|	|	0822	|	|	...	|	...	|	|	0922
	Brugg .... 510 d.	|	...	|	...	|	|	0732	|	|	...	|	...	|	|	0832	|	|	...	|	...	|	|	0932
	Lenzburg .... 510 d.	|	...	|	...	|	|	|	|	|	...	|	...	|	|	|	|	|	...	|	...	|	|	|
	Aarau .... 510 d.	|	...	|	...	|	0730	0746	|	|	...	|	...	|	0830	0846	|	|	...	|	...	|	0930	0946
	Olten .... a.	0700	...	|	...	0728	0738	0755	|	0800	...	|	...	0828	0838	0855	|	0900	...	|	...	0928	0938	0955
0	**Olten** .... d.	0702	0706	|	...	0736	0740	0756	|	0802	0806	|	...	0836	0840	0856	|	0902	0906	|	...	0936	0940	0956
	Langenthal .... d.	|	0718	|	...	0748	|	|	|	|	0818	|	...	0848	|	|	|	|	0918	|	...	0948	|	|
	Burgdorf .... d.	|	0738	|	...	0806	|	|	|	|	0838	|	...	0906	|	|	|	|	0938	|	...	1006	|	|
	Luzern **565** .... d.	|	|	|	0700	|	|	|	|	|	|	|	0800	|	|	|	|	|	|	|	0900	|	|	|
	Bern .... a.	|	0753	0758	0800	0821	|	0824	0828	|	0853	0858	0900	0921	|	0924	0928	|	0953	0958	1000	1021	|	1024
	Bern .... 568 d.	|	▬	...	0804	...	|	▬	0834	|	▬	...	0904	...	|	▬	0934	|	▬	...	1004	...	|	▬
	Fribourg .... 568 d.	|	...	...	0826	...	|	...	0856	|	...	...	0926	...	|	...	0956	|	...	...	1026	...	|	...
	Romont .... 568 d.	|	...	...	0844	...	|	...	|	|	...	...	0944	...	|	...	|	|	...	...	1044	...	|	...
	Palézieux .... d.	|	...	...	0900	...	|	...	|	|	...	...	1000	...	|	...	|	|	...	...	1100	...	|	...
36	Solothurn .... d.	0726	...	...	|	...	0758	...	|	0826	...	...	|	...	0858	...	|	0926	...	...	|	...	0958	...
61	**Biel / Bienne** .... a.	0743	...	...	|	...	0813	...	|	0843	...	...	|	...	0913	...	|	0943	...	...	|	...	1013	...
	Biel / Bienne .... d.	0745	*RE*	...	|	...	0816	...	|	0845	*RE*	...	|	...	0916	...	|	0945	*RE*	...	|	...	1016	...
	Neuchâtel .... d.	0803	**18458**	...	|	...	0834	...	|	0903	**18460**	...	|	...	0934	...	|	1003	**18462**	...	|	...	1034	...
	Yverdon .... d.	0823		...	|	...	0854	0858	|	0923		...	|	...	0954	0958	|	1023		...	|	...	1054	1058
	Lausanne .... a.	0845		...	0916	...	|	0928	0940	0945		...	1016	...	|	1028	1040	1045		...	1116	...	|	1128
	Lausanne .... 570 d.	...	0851	...	0919	...	|	...	0943	...	0951	...	1019	...	|	...	1043	...	1051	...	1119	...	|	...
	Morges .... 570 d.	...	0905	...	0929	...	0918	...	|	...	1005	...	1029	...	1018	...	|	...	1105	...	1129	...	1118	...
	Nyon .... 570 d.	...	0925	...	0946	...	|	...	|	...	1025	...	1046	...	|	...	|	...	1125	...	1146	...	|	...
	Genève .... 570 a.	...	0940	...	1001	...	0947	...	1018	...	1040	...	1101	...	1047	...	1118	...	1140	...	1201	...	1147	...
	Genève Aéroport ✈ .... 570 a.	...	...	...	1011	...	0956	...	1027	...	...	...	1111	...	1056	...	1127	...	...	...	1211	...	1156	...

B – To Brig (Table **560**).
C – From Chur (Table **520**).
D – From / to Delémont (Table **505a**).
R – From Rorschach (Table **530**).

a – Ⓐ only.
e – 3 minutes later on Ⓐ.

h – Mornings of ⑥⑦ (not Dec. 25, 26, Jan. 2, Apr. 16).
k – ⑤⑥ only.
r – ⑦–④ only. Departs 2236 Mar. 20 - Aug. 28.
t – Departs 2245 on ⑦–④ Mar. 20 - Aug. 28.

★ – Runs 3 – 4 minutes later on the mornings of ①–⑤.
▽ – Runs as *IR* **2193** Olten - Zürich.

◐ – Conveys ✕ until Biel/Bienne.
⊖ – Conveys ✕ from Biel/Bienne.
◧ – Conveys ✕ Lausanne - Bern.
⊙ – Operated by BLS.
◇ – Operated by SOB.
⊡ – Operated by SBB on Ⓐ, by SOB on Ⓒ.
♥ – Kilometres via the high-speed line.

505 ZÜRICH - BIEL / BERN - LAUSANNE - GENÈVE SBB

	IC 712	IC 1514	IR 2816	IC 812	IR 2516	IR 2362	IC 516	IR 2166	IC 714	IC 1516	IR 2818	IC 814	IR 2518	IR 2364	IC 518	IR 2168	IC 716	IC 1518	IR 2820	IC 816	IR 2520	IR 2366	IC 520	IR 2170
	✕	✕	⊙	B✕	🍸	C◇	R✕		✕	✕	⊙	B✕	🍸	C◇	R✕		✕	✕	⊙	B✕	🍸	C◇	R✕	
Romanshorn 535 d.	...	...	...	0848	...	...	...	...	...	...	...	0948	...	...	...	...	...	...	...	1048	...	...	...	...
St Gallen 530 d.	0807	...	...	│	...	...	0858	...	0907	...	...	│	...	...	0958	...	1007	...	...	│	...	...	1058	...
Zürich Flughafen + 530/5 d.	0908	...	...	0945	...	...	0948	...	1008	...	...	1045	...	...	1048	...	1108	...	...	1145	...	...	1148	...
Zürich HB 510 d.	0932	0930	...	1002	...	0953	1004	1006	1032	1030	...	1102	...	1053	1104	1106	1132	1130	...	1202	...	1153	1204	1206
Baden 510 d.	│	│	...	│	...	│	│	1022	│	│	...	│	...	│	│	1122	│	│	...	│	...	│	│	1222
Brugg 510 d.	│	│	...	│	...	│	│	1032	│	│	...	│	...	│	│	1132	│	│	...	│	...	│	│	1232
Lenzburg 510 d.	│	│	...	│	...	│	│	│	│	│	...	│	...	│	│	│	│	│	...	│	...	│	│	│
Aarau 510 d.	│	│	...	│	...	│	1030	1046	│	│	...	│	...	│	1130	1146	│	│	...	│	...	│	1230	1246
Olten a.	│	1000	...	│	...	1028	1038	1055	│	1100	...	│	...	1128	1138	1155	│	1200	...	│	...	1228	1238	1255
Olten d.	│	1002	1006	│	...	1036	1040	1056	│	1102	1106	│	...	1136	1140	1156	│	1202	1206	│	...	1236	1240	1256
Langenthal d.	│	│	1018	│	...	1048	│	│	│	│	1118	│	...	1148	│	│	│	│	1218	│	...	1248	│	│
Burgdorf d.	│	│	1038	│	...	1106	│	│	│	│	1138	│	...	1206	│	│	│	│	1238	│	...	1306	│	│
Luzern 565 d.	│	│	│	│	1000	│	│	│	│	│	│	│	1100	│	│	│	│	│	│	│	1200	│	│	│
Bern a.	1028	│	1053	1058	1100	1121	│	1124	1128	│	1153	1158	1200	1221	│	1224	1228	│	1253	1258	1300	1321	│	1324
Bern 568 d.	1034	│	▬	...	1104	...	│	▬	1134	│	▬	...	1204	...	│	▬	1234	│	▬	...	1304	...	│	▬
Fribourg 568 d.	1056	│	...	...	1126	...	│	...	1156	│	...	...	1226	...	│	...	1256	│	...	...	1326	...	│	...
Romont 568 d.	│	│	...	...	1144	...	│	...	│	│	...	...	1244	...	│	...	│	│	...	...	1344	...	│	...
Palézieux d.	│	│	...	...	1200	...	│	...	│	│	...	...	1300	...	│	...	│	│	...	...	1400	...	│	...
Solothurn d.	│	1026	...	...	│	...	1058	...	│	1126	...	...	│	...	1158	...	│	1226	...	...	│	...	1258	...
Biel/Bienne a.	│	1043	...	...	│	...	1113	...	│	1143	...	...	│	...	1213	...	│	1243	...	...	│	...	1313	...
Biel/Bienne d.	│	1045	*RE*	...	│	...	1116	...	│	1145	*RE*	...	│	...	1216	...	│	1245	*RE*	...	│	...	1316	...
Neuchâtel d.	│	1103	**18464**	...	│	...	1134	...	│	1203	**18466**	...	│	...	1234	...	│	1303	**18468**	...	│	...	1334	...
Yverdon d.	│	1123		...	│	...	1154	1158	│	1223		...	│	...	1254	1258	│	1323		...	│	...	1354	1358
Lausanne a.	1140	1145		...	1216	...	│	1228	1240	1245		...	1316	...	│	1328	1340	1345		...	1416	...	│	1428
Lausanne 570 d.	1143	...	1151	...	1219	...	│	...	1243	...	1251	...	1319	...	│	...	1343	...	1351	...	1419	...	│	...
Morges 570 d.	│	...	1205	...	1229	...	1218	...	│	...	1305	...	1329	...	1318	...	│	...	1405	...	1429	...	1418	...
Nyon 570 d.	│	...	1225	...	1246	...	│	...	│	...	1325	...	1346	...	│	...	│	...	1425	...	1446	...	│	...
Genève 570 a.	1218	...	1240	...	1301	...	1247	...	1318	...	1340	...	1401	...	1347	...	1418	...	1440	...	1501	...	1447	...
Genève Aéroport + 570 a.	1227	...	...	...	1311	...	1256	...	1327	...	...	...	1411	...	1356	...	1427	...	...	...	1511	...	1456	...

	IC 718	IC 1520	IR 2822	IC 818	IR 2522	IR 2368	IC 522	IR 2172	IC 720	IC 1522	IR 2824	IC 820	IR 2524	IR 2370	IC 524	IR 2174	IC 722	IC 1524	IR 2826	IC 822	IR 2526	IR 2372	IC 526	IR 2176
	✕	✕	⊙	B✕	🍸	C◇	R✕		✕	✕	⊙	B✕	🍸	C⊡	R✕		✕	✕	⊙	B✕	🍸	C◇	R✕	
Romanshorn 535 d.	...	...	...	1148	...	...	...	...	...	...	...	1248	...	...	...	...	...	...	...	1348	...	...	...	...
St Gallen 530 d.	1107	...	...	│	...	...	1158	...	1207	...	...	│	...	...	1258	...	1307	...	...	│	...	...	1358	...
Zürich Flughafen + 530/5 d.	1208	...	...	1245	...	...	1248	...	1308	...	...	1345	...	...	1348	...	1408	...	...	1445	...	...	1448	...
Zürich HB 510 d.	1232	1230	...	1302	...	1253	1304	1306	1332	1330	...	1402	...	1353	1404	1406	1432	1430	...	1502	...	1453	1504	1506
Baden 510 d.	│	│	...	│	...	│	│	1322	│	│	...	│	...	│	│	1422	│	│	...	│	...	│	│	1522
Brugg 510 d.	│	│	...	│	...	│	│	1332	│	│	...	│	...	│	│	1432	│	│	...	│	...	│	│	1532
Lenzburg 510 d.	│	│	...	│	...	│	│	│	│	│	...	│	...	│	│	│	│	│	...	│	...	│	│	│
Aarau 510 d.	│	│	...	│	...	│	1330	1346	│	│	...	│	...	│	1430	1446	│	│	...	│	...	│	1530	1546
Olten a.	│	1300	...	│	...	1328	1338	1355	│	1400	...	│	...	1428	1438	1455	│	1500	...	│	...	1528	1538	1555
Olten d.	│	1302	1306	│	...	1336	1340	1356	│	1402	1406	│	...	1436	1440	1456	│	1502	1506	│	...	1536	1540	1556
Langenthal d.	│	│	1318	│	...	1348	│	│	│	│	1418	│	...	1448	│	│	│	│	1518	│	...	1548	│	│
Burgdorf d.	│	│	1338	│	...	1406	│	│	│	│	1438	│	...	1506	│	│	│	│	1538	│	...	1606	│	│
Luzern 565 d.	│	│	│	│	1300	│	│	│	│	│	│	│	1400	│	│	│	│	│	│	│	1500	│	│	│
Bern a.	1328	│	1353	1358	1400	1421	│	1424	1428	│	1453	1458	1500	1521	│	1524	1528	│	1553	1558	1600	1621	│	1624
Bern 568 d.	1334	│	▬	...	1404	...	│	▬	1434	│	▬	...	1504	...	│	▬	1534	│	▬	...	1604	...	│	▬
Fribourg 568 d.	1356	│	...	...	1426	...	│	...	1456	│	...	...	1526	...	│	...	1556	│	...	...	1626	...	│	...
Romont 568 d.	│	│	...	...	1444	...	│	...	│	│	...	...	1544	...	│	...	│	│	...	...	1644	...	│	...
Palézieux d.	│	│	...	...	1500	...	│	...	│	│	...	...	1600	...	│	...	│	│	...	...	1700	...	│	...
Solothurn d.	│	1326	...	...	│	...	1358	...	│	1426	...	...	│	...	1458	...	│	1526	...	...	│	...	1558	...
Biel/Bienne a.	│	1343	...	...	│	...	1413	...	│	1443	...	...	│	...	1513	...	│	1543	...	...	│	...	1613	...
Biel/Bienne d.	│	1345	*RE*	...	│	...	1416	...	│	1445	*RE*	...	│	...	1516	...	│	1545	*RE*	...	│	...	1616	...
Neuchâtel d.	│	1403	**18470**	...	│	...	1434	...	│	1503	**18472**	...	│	...	1534	...	│	1603	**18474**	...	│	...	1634	...
Yverdon d.	│	1423		...	│	...	1454	1458	│	1523		...	│	...	1554	1558	│	1623		...	│	...	1654	1658
Lausanne a.	1440	1445		...	1516	...	│	1528	1540	1545		...	1616	...	│	1628	1640	1645		...	1716	...	│	1728
Lausanne 570 d.	1443	...	1451	...	1519	...	│	...	1543	...	1551	...	1619	...	│	...	1643	...	1651	...	1719	...	│	...
Morges 570 d.	│	...	1505	...	1529	...	1518	...	│	...	1605	...	1629	...	1618	...	│	...	1705	...	1729	...	1718	...
Nyon 570 d.	│	...	1525	...	1546	...	│	...	│	...	1625	...	1646	...	│	...	│	...	1725	...	1746	...	│	...
Genève 570 a.	1518	...	1540	...	1601	...	1547	...	1618	...	1640	...	1701	...	1647	...	1718	...	1740	...	1801	...	1747	...
Genève Aéroport + 570 a.	1527	...	...	...	1611	...	1556	...	1627	...	...	...	1711	...	1656	...	1727	...	...	...	1811	...	1756	...

	IC 724	IC 1526	IR 2828	IC 824	IR 2528	IR 2374	IC 528	IR 2178	IC 726	IC 1528	IR 2830	IC 826	IR 2530	IR 2376	IC 530	IR 2180	IC 728	IC 1530	IR 2832	IC 828	IR 2532	IR 2378	IC 532	IR 2182
	✕	✕	⊙	B✕	🍸	C⊡	R✕		✕	✕	⊙	B✕	🍸	C◇	R✕		✕	✕	⊙	B✕		C◇	R✕	
Romanshorn 535 d.	...	...	...	1448	...	...	...	...	...	...	...	1548	...	...	...	...	...	...	...	1648	...	...	...	...
St Gallen 530 d.	1407	...	...	│	...	...	1458	...	1507	...	...	│	...	...	1558	...	1607	1628a	...	│	...	...	1658	...
Zürich Flughafen + 530/5 d.	1508	...	...	1545	...	...	1548	...	1608	...	...	1645	...	...	1648	...	1708	1718a	...	1745	...	...	1748	...
Zürich HB 510 d.	1532	1530	...	1602	...	1553	1604	1606	1632	1630	...	1702	...	1653	1704	1706	1732	1730	...	1802	...	1753	1804	1806
Baden 510 d.	│	│	...	│	...	│	│	1622	│	│	...	│	...	│	│	1722	│	│	...	│	...	│	│	1822
Brugg 510 d.	│	│	...	│	...	│	│	1632	│	│	...	│	...	│	│	1732	│	│	...	│	...	│	│	1832
Lenzburg 510 d.	│	│	...	│	...	│	│	│	│	│	...	│	...	│	│	│	│	│	...	│	...	│	│	│
Aarau 510 d.	│	│	...	│	...	│	1630	1646	│	│	...	│	...	│	1730	1746	│	│	...	│	...	│	1830	1846
Olten a.	│	1600	...	│	...	1628	1638	1655	│	1700	...	│	...	1728	1738	1755	│	1800	...	│	...	1828	1838	1855
Olten d.	│	1602	1606	│	...	1636	1640	1656	│	1702	1706	│	...	1736	1740	1756	│	1802	1806	│	...	1836	1840	1856
Langenthal d.	│	│	1618	│	...	1648	│	│	│	│	1718	│	...	1748	│	│	│	│	1818	│	...	1848	│	│
Burgdorf d.	│	│	1638	│	...	1706	│	│	│	│	1738	│	...	1806	│	│	│	│	1838	│	...	1906	│	│
Luzern 565 d.	│	│	│	│	1600	│	│	│	│	│	│	│	1700	│	│	│	│	│	│	│	1800	│	│	│
Bern a.	1628	│	1653	1658	1700	1721	│	1724	1728	│	1753	1758	1800	1821	│	1824	1828	│	1853	1858	1900	1921	│	1924
Bern 568 d.	1634	│	▬	...	1704	...	│	▬	1734	│	▬	...	1804	...	│	▬	1834	│	▬	...	1904	...	│	▬
Fribourg 568 d.	1656	│	...	...	1726	...	│	...	1756	│	...	...	1826	...	│	...	1856	│	...	...	1926	...	│	...
Romont 568 d.	│	│	...	...	1744	...	│	...	│	│	...	...	1844	...	│	...	│	│	...	...	1944	...	│	...
Palézieux d.	│	│	...	...	1800	...	│	...	│	│	...	...	1900	...	│	...	│	│	...	...	2000	...	│	...
Solothurn d.	│	1626	...	...	│	...	1658	...	│	1726	...	...	│	...	1758	...	│	1826	...	...	│	...	1858	...
Biel/Bienne a.	│	1643	...	...	│	...	1713	...	│	1743	...	...	│	...	1813	...	│	1843	...	...	│	...	1913	...
Biel/Bienne d.	│	1645	*RE*	...	│	...	1716	...	│	1745	*RE*	...	│	...	1816	...	│	1845	*RE*	...	│	...	1916	...
Neuchâtel d.	│	1703	**18476**	...	│	...	1734	...	│	1803	**18478**	...	│	...	1834	...	│	1903	**18480**	...	│	...	1934	...
Yverdon d.	│	1723		...	│	...	1754	1758	│	1823		...	│	...	1854	1858	│	1923		...	│	...	1954	1958
Lausanne a.	1740	1745		...	1816	...	│	1828	1840	1845		...	1916	...	│	1928	1940	1945		...	2016	...	│	2058
Lausanne 570 d.	1743	...	1751	...	1819	...	│	...	1843	...	1851	...	1919	...	│	...	1943	...	1951	...	2019	...	│	...
Morges 570 d.	│	...	1805	...	1829	...	1818	...	│	...	1905	...	1929	...	1918	...	│	...	2005	...	2029	...	2018	...
Nyon 570 d.	│	...	1825	...	1846	...	│	...	│	...	1925	...	1946	...	│	...	│	...	2025	...	2046	...	│	...
Genève 570 a.	1818	...	1840	...	1901	...	1847	...	1918	...	1940	...	2001	...	1947	...	2018	...	2040	...	2101	...	2047	...
Genève Aéroport + 570 a.	1827	...	...	...	1911	...	1856	...	1927	...	...	...	2011	...	1956	...	2027	...	...	...	2111	...	2056	...

B – To Brig (Table 560).
C – From Chur (Table 520).
R – From Rorschach (Table 530).

a – Ⓐ only.

⊙ – Operated by BLS.
◇ – Operated by SOB.
⊡ – Operated by SBB on Ⓐ, by SOB on Ⓒ.

SBB ZÜRICH - BIEL / BERN - LAUSANNE - GENÈVE 505

	IC 730	IC 1532	IR 2834	IC 830	IR 2534	IR 2380	IC 534	IR 2184	RE 18436		IC 732	IR 1734	IC 1534	IR 2836	IC 832	IR 2536	IR 2382	IC 536	RE 18438	IR 2186	IC 734	IC 1536	IR 2838	IC 834
									⑦–④			⑤⑥												
	✕	✕	⊙	B✕		C◇	R✕				✕		✕	⊙	✕		C◇	R◐			✕	◐	⊙	✕
Romanshorn **535** d.	...	...	...	1748	...	...	...	...	...	...	...	...	...	...	1848	...	...	...	...	...	...	...	...	1948
St Gallen **530** d.	1707	...	...	|	...	...	1758	...	...	...	1807	...	1828a	...	|	...	...	1858	...	...	1907	...	...	|
Zürich Flughafen ✈ **530/5** d.	1808	...	...	1845	...	...	1848	...	...	...	1908	...	1918a	...	1945	...	...	1948	...	...	2008	...	...	2045
Zürich HB **510** d.	1832	1830	...	1902	...	1853	1904	1906	...	...	1932	...	1930	...	2002	...	1953	2004	...	2006	2032	2030	...	2102
Baden **510** d.	|	|	...	|	...	|	|	1922	...	...	|	...	|	...	|	...	|	|	...	2022	|	|	...	|
Brugg **510** d.	|	|	...	|	...	|	|	1932	...	...	|	...	|	...	|	...	|	|	...	2032	|	|	...	|
Lenzburg **510** d.	|	|	...	|	...	|	|	|	...	...	|	...	|	...	|	...	|	|	...	|	|	|	...	|
Aarau **510** d.	|	|	...	|	...	|	1930	1946	...	...	|	...	|	...	|	...	|	2030	...	2046	|	|	...	|
Olten a.	|	1900	...	|	...	1928	1938	1955	...	...	|	...	2000	...	|	...	2028	2038	...	2055	|	2100	...	|
Olten d.	|	1902	1906	|	...	1936	1940	1956	...	...	|	...	2002	2006	|	...	2036	2040	...	2056	|	2102	2106	|
Langenthal d.	|	|	1918	|	...	1948	|	|	...	...	|	...	|	2018	|	...	2048	|	...	|	|	|	2118	|
Burgdorf d.	|	|	1938	|	...	2006	|	|	...	...	|	...	|	2038	|	...	2106	|	...	|	|	|	2138	|
Luzern **565** d.	|	|	|	|	1900	|	|	|	...	...	|	...	|	|	|	2000	|	|	...	|	|	|	|	|
Bern a.	1928	|	1953	1958	2000	2021	|	2024	...	...	2028	...	|	2053	2058	2100	2121	|	...	2124	2128	|	2153	2158
Bern **568** d.	1934	|	▬	...	2004	...	|	▬	...	...	2034	...	|	▬	▬	2104	...	|	...	▬	2134	|	▬	▬
Fribourg **568** d.	1956	|	...	...	2026	...	|	...	...	...	2056	...	|	...	...	2126	...	|	...	...	2156	|	...	...
Romont **568** d.	|	|	...	...	2044	...	|	...	...	...	|	...	|	...	...	2144	...	|	...	...	|	|	...	...
Palézieux d.	|	|	...	...	2100	...	|	...	...	...	|	...	|	...	...	2200	...	|	...	...	|	|	...	...
Solothurn d.	|	1926	...	...	|	...	1958	...	...	...	|	...	2026	...	...	|	...	2058	...	...	|	2126	...	...
Biel / Bienne a.	|	1943	...	...	|	...	2013	...	...	...	|	...	2043	...	...	|	...	2113	...	...	|	2143	...	...
Biel / Bienne d.	|	1945	*RE*	...	|	...	2016	*RE*	...	...	|	...	2045	*RE*	*RE*	|	...	2116	...	...	|	2145	*RE*	*RE*
Neuchâtel d.	|	2003	**18482**	...	|	...	2034	**18436**	...	...	|	...	2103	**18484**	**18484**	|	...	2134	...	...	|	2203	**18486**	**18486**
Yverdon d.	|	2023		...	|	...	2054	⑤⑥	...	2058	|	...	2123	⑤⑥	⑦–④	|	...	2154	...	2158	|	2223	⑤⑥	⑦–④
Lausanne a.	2040	2045		...	2116	...	|		...	2128	2140	...	2145			2216	...	|	...	2228	2240	2245		
Lausanne **570** d.	2043	...	2051	...	2119**k**	...	|	2121	2121	...	...	2148	...	2151	2151	...	...	|	2221	...	2243**k**	...	2251	2251
Morges **570** d.	|	...	2105	...	2129**k**	...	2118	2135	2135	...	...	2159	...	2205	2205	...	...	2218	2235	...	|	...	2305	2305**r**
Nyon **570** d.	|	...	2129**e**	...	2146**k**	...	|	2155	2204	...	...	2216	...	2225	2229	...	...	2233**k**	2255**t**	...	|	...	2325	2329**r**
Genève **570** a.	2118	...	2144**e**	...	2201**k**	...	2147**k**	2210	2222	...	...	2231	...	2240	2244	...	...	2247**k**	2310**t**	...	2318**k**	...	2340	2344**r**
Genève Aéroport ✈ **570** a.	2127	...	...	...	2211**k**	...	...	2218	2230	...	...	2241	...	...	2257	...	...	...	2318**t**	...	2327**k**	...	2348	2352**r**

	IR 2538	IR 2386	RE 18440	IC 538	IR 2188	IC 736	IC 1538	IR 2840	IC 836	IR 2540	IR 2394	IC 540	IR 2190	IC 738	IC 838	IR 2502	IR 2502	IR 2396	IC 542	IR 2192	IC 740	IC 842	IR 2846	IC 844
			⑦–④																				⑥⑦	⑥⑦
				R		✕		⊙			◇			✕			★	◇					h⊙	h
Romanshorn **535** d.	...	...	...	...	...	...	...	...	2048	...	...	...	...	...	2148	...	...	...	...	...	...	...	...	...
St Gallen **530** d.	...	...	...	1958	...	2007	...	...	|	...	...	...	...	2107	|	...	...	...	...	...	...	...	...	...
Zürich Flughafen ✈ **530/5** d.	...	...	...	2048	...	2108	...	...	2145	...	...	...	...	2208	2245	...	...	...	...	...	...	...	...	...
Zürich HB **510** d.	...	2055	...	2104	2106	2132	2130	...	2202	...	...	2204	2206	2232	2302	...	...	...	2304	2306	2332	0002	...	0102
Baden **510** d.	...	|	...	|	2122	|	|	...	|	...	...	|	2222	|	|	...	...	...	|	2322	|	|	...	|
Brugg **510** d.	...	|	...	|	2132	|	|	...	|	...	...	|	2232	|	|	...	...	...	|	2332	|	|	...	|
Lenzburg **510** d.	...	|	...	|	|	|	|	...	|	...	...	|	|	|	|	...	...	...	|	|	|	|	...	|
Aarau **510** d.	...	|	...	2130	2146	|	|	...	|	...	...	2230	2246	|	|	...	...	...	2330	2346	|	|	...	|
Olten a.	...	2128	...	2138	2155	|	2200	...	2232	...	...	2238	2256	2302	2332	...	...	...	2338	2356	0002	0032	...	0132
Olten d.	...	2136	...	2140	2156	|	2202	2206	2235	...	2237	2240	▬	2304	2335	...	...	2337	2340	▬	0004	0035	0037	0135
Langenthal d.	...	2148	...	|	|	|	|	2218	|	...	2249	|	...	|	|	...	...	2349	|	...	|	|	0050	|
Burgdorf d.	...	2209	...	|	|	|	|	2236	|	...	2309	|	...	|	|	...	...	0009	|	...	|	|	0110	|
Luzern **565** d.	2100	|	...	|	|	|	|	|	|	2200	|	|	...	|	|	...	...	|	|	...	|	|	|	|
Bern a.	2200	2226	...	|	2224	2228	|	2253	2302	2300	2326	|	...	2331	0002	...	...	0026	|	...	0031	0102**g**	0126	0204
Bern **568** d.	2204	▬	...	|	...	2234	|	▬	▬	2308	...	|	...	▬	...	0008	0008	...	|	...	...	...	...	...
Fribourg **568** d.	2226	...	...	|	...	2256	|	...	...	2330	...	|	...	...	...	0032	0033	...	|	...	...	...	...	...
Romont **568** d.	2244	...	...	|	...	...	|	...	...	2348	...	|	...	...	...	...	0050	...	|	...	...	...	...	...
Palézieux d.	2300	...	...	|	...	...	|	...	...	0004	...	|	...	...	...	...	0106	...	|	...	...	...	...	...
Solothurn d.	|	...	...	2158	...	...	2226	...	...	|	...	2257	...	...	...	...	|	...	0005	...	...	...	...	...
Biel / Bienne a.	|	...	...	2213	...	...	2243	...	...	|	...	2314	...	...	...	...	|	...	0022	...	...	...	...	...
Biel / Bienne d.	|	*RE*	...	...	...	...	2245	*RE*	*RE*	|	...	2316	*RE*	*RE*	...	...	|	...	0024**h**	*RE*	...	...	...	...
Neuchâtel d.	|	**18440**	...	...	...	...	2303	**18488**	**18488**	|	...	2334	**18442**	**18442**	...	...	|	...	0042**h**	**18446**	...	...	...	...
Yverdon d.	|	⑤⑥	...	...	...	...	2323	⑤⑥	⑦–④	|	...	2354	①–⑤	⑥⑦	...	...	|	...	0102**h**	⑥⑦	...	...	...	...
Lausanne a.	2316		...	...	...	...	2345			0020	...	0016			...	...	0122	...	0125**h**	...	...	...	...	...
Lausanne **570** d.	...	2321	2321	...	...	...	...	2351	2351	...	...	...	0025	0051	...	...	...	...	...	0135	...	...	...	...
Morges **570** d.	...	2335	2335	...	...	...	...	0004	0005	...	...	...	0039	0105	...	...	...	...	...	0148	...	...	...	...
Nyon **570** d.	...	2355	2359	...	...	...	...	0024	0029	...	...	...	0059	0125	...	...	...	...	...	0208	...	...	...	...
Genève **570** a.	...	0010	0014	...	...	...	...	0040	0044	...	...	...	0114	0140	...	...	...	...	...	0224	...	...	...	...
Genève Aéroport ✈ **570** a.	...	0018	0022	...	...	...	...	0048	...	...	...	...	...	...	...	...	...	...	...	...	...	...	...	...

B – To Brig (Table **560**).
C – From Chur (Table **520**).
R – From Rorschach (Table **530**).

a – Ⓐ only.
e – 4 minutes earlier on ⑤⑥.
g – On the mornings of ① (not Apr. 18, June 6, Aug. 1) change trains at Zollikofen (a. 0109, d. *0112*), Bern a. *0120*.
h – Mornings of ⑥⑦ (not Dec. 25, 26, Jan. 2, Apr. 16).
k – ⑤⑥ only.

n – Not Dec. 24, 25, Jan. 1, Apr. 15.
r – Mar. 20 - Aug. 28 Morges d. 2304, Nyon d. 2334, Genève a. 2349, Genève Aéroport a. 2357.
t – 4–11 minutes later on ⑦–④.

★ – Mornings of ①⑥⑦.
◐ – Conveys ✕ until Biel/Bienne.
⊙ – Operated by BLS.
◇ – Operated by SOB.

SBB BIEL/BIENNE and PORRENTRUY - BASEL 505a

km		IC 1545				IC 1607			IC 1609			IC 1611				IC 1637			IC 1639			IC 1641		
			⑥⑦																					
		L	c					D			D				D			D			D			
0	**Biel / Bienne** **515** d.	0019	0121	...	...	0549	...	0619	0649	...	0719	0749	and at	...	2019	2049	...	2119	2149	...	2219	2249	...	2319
24	Moutier **515** d.	0039	0138	...	...	0608	...	0638	0708	...	0738	0808	the same	...	2038	2108	...	2138	2208	...	2238	2308	...	2338
	Porrentruy **515** d.	|	|	...	0508	|	0610	|	|	0710	|	|	minutes	2010	|	|	2110	|	|	2210	|	|	2310	|
35	Delémont **515** a.	0048	0148	...	0539	0618	0639	0648	0718	0739	0748	0818	past each	2039	2048	2118	2139	2148	2218	2239	2248	2318	2339	2348
	Delémont d.	...	...	...	0543	0623	0643	...	0723	0743	...	0823	hour until	2043	...	2123	2143	...	2223	2243	...	2323	2343	...
74	**Basel** SBB a.	...	...	...	0623	0655*	0723	...	0755*	0823	...	0855*		2123	...	2155*	2223	...	2255*	2323	...	2358*	0028	...

			IC 1606			IC 1608			IC 1610				IC 1636			IC 1638			IC 1640		IC 1642			
																						⑤⑥		
			G	D			D			D				D			D					k		
Basel SBB d.	...	0457	...	...	0537	0603	...	0637	0703	...	0737	and at	2003	...	2037	2103	...	2137	2203	2237	2303	...	2342	0042
Delémont a.	...	0537	...	...	0617	0637	...	0717	0737	...	0817	the same	2037	...	2117	2137	...	2217	2237	2317	2337	...	0022	0122
Delémont **515** d.	0512	*0551*	0542	0612	0621	0642	0712	0721	0742	0812	0821	minutes	2042	2112	2121	2142	2212	2221	2242	2321	*2351*	2342	0023	...
Porrentruy **515** a.	|	*0620*	|	|	0650	|	|	0750	|	|	0850	past each	|	|	2150	|	|	2250	|	2350	*0020*	|	0052	...
Moutier **515** d.	0522	...	0552	0622	...	0652	0722	...	0752	0822	...	hour until	2052	2122	...	2152	2222	...	2252	...	...	2354	...	...
Biel / Bienne **515** d.	0541	...	0610	0641	...	0710	0741	...	0810	0841	...		2110	2141	...	2210	2241	...	2310	...	...	0013	...	...

D – To / from Delle (Table **515**).
G – To Genève Aéroport (Table **505**).
L – From Lausanne (Table **505**).
c – Not Dec. 25, 26, Jan. 2, Apr. 16.
k – Not Dec. 24, 25, Jan. 1, Apr. 15.
* – Arrives xx53 until July 24.

506 LAC LÉMAN CGN

GENÈVE - YVOIRE - LAUSANNE ⊡

	⛴ B	⛴ G	A	⛴ G	ⒸE	⛴ B	⛴ G		⛴ J	⛴ E	
Genève Mont-Blanc... d.	1045	1045	1235	...	...	1445	1445	...	...	...	...
Genève Jardin-Anglais d.	|	|	|	1235	...	|	|	...	1900	...	...
Nyon d.	1205	1205	1345	|	...	|	|	...	|	...	...
Yvoire (France) d.	1225	1245t	...	1400	1445	1607	1615	...	2032	2037	...
Morges d.	...	1356	...	...	1556	...	1726	...	...	2152	...
Lausanne-Ouchy a.	...	1433	...	...	1633	...	1801	...	...	2230	...

	⛴ B	⛴ G	A	H	⛴ E	ⒸE	⛴ G	⛴ B		⛴ E	⛴ J
Lausanne-Ouchy... d.	...	1055	...	...	...	1255	1455	...	...	1855	...
Morges d.	...	1131	...	...	...	1331	1531	...	...	1931	...
Yvoire (France) d.	1245	1245	...	1405	1405	1441	1645	1645	...	2030	2035
Nyon d.	1312	1312	1350	|	|	...	1712	1712	...	...	2055
Genève Jardin-Ang. a.	|	|	|	1520	1520	...	|	|	...	...	2220
Genève Mont-Blanc a.	1305	1430	1505	...	...	...	1835	1835	...	...	...

LAUSANNE - ST GUINGOLPH

	D	⛴ E	D	A		⛴ C	E	AD		E	⛴ H	A	⛴ E	AD		⛴ D	E	⛴ E	A	D		⛴ E		⛴ D		
Lausanne-Ouchy d.	0910	0940	←	...	...	1040	1040	...	...	1240	1240	1240	1245	...	...	1445	1450	1545	...	...	...	1650	...	1810	...	...
Vevey-Marché d.	1000	|	1002	...	...	1131	1131	1145	...	|	|	1338	|	1345	...	|	|	|	1545	1545	...	1745	...	1857	...	...
Vevey-La Tour d.	→	|	|	...	...	...	...	1150	...	1333	1343	|	|	1350	...	|	1543	|	1550	1550	...	|	...	|	...	...
Montreux d.	...	|	1025	...	...	...	...	1220	...	...	...	|	|	1420	...	|	...	|	1620	1620	...	1808	...	1917	...	...
Territet d.	...	|	|	...	...	...	...	1227	...	...	...	|	|	1427	...	|	...	|	1627	1627	...	|	...	...	...	...
Château-de-Chillon d.	...	|	1035	...	...	...	...	1235	...	...	...	|	|	1435	...	|	...	|	1635	1635	...	|	...	...	...	...
Villeneuve d.	...	|	1043	...	...	...	...	1243	...	...	...	1404	|	1443	...	|	...	|	1643	1643	...	1822	...	...	...	...
Bouveret d.	...	|	1105	1105	...	...	...	1305	...	...	...	...	|	1505	...	|	...	|	1705	1705	...	1844	...	...	...	...
St Gingolph a.	...	1030	1118	1118	...	...	...	1318	...	...	...	...	1335	1518	...	1535	...	1635	...	1718	...	...	...	...	...	...

	E		⛴ C	E	⛴ E	AD		AD	⛴ H	E		⛴ E	A		AD	E		⛴ D		⛴ E	D		⛴ D			
St Gingolph d.	...	...	...	...	1030	1118	...	1318	...	...	...	1335	...	...	1518	...	...	1535	...	1635	1718	...	...	...	...	...
Bouveret d.	0905	...	...	...	1043	|	...	|	...	...	...	1348	...	...	|	...	...	1548	...	1648	|	...	...	...	...	...
Villeneuve d.	|	...	...	...	1104	|	...	|	...	...	...	1409	1409	...	|	...	...	|	...	1709	|	...	...	...	...	...
Château-de-Chillon d.	|	...	...	...	1112	|	...	|	...	...	...	1417	1417	...	|	...	...	1617	...	1717	1744	...	...	...	...	...
Territet d.	|	...	...	...	|	|	...	|	...	...	...	|	|	...	|	...	...	|	...	|	|	...	...	...	...	...
Montreux d.	0930	...	...	...	1130	|	...	|	...	...	...	1430	1430	...	|	...	...	1630	...	1730	1755	...	1927	...	...	...
Vevey-La Tour d.	|	...	...	...	|	|	...	|	1345	1345	...	|	|	...	|	1545	...	|	...	|	|	...	|	...	...	...
Vevey-Marché d.	0952	...	1135	1135	1152	1140	...	1340	1352	1352	...	1452	1452	...	1540	1552	...	1652	...	1752	1815	...	|	...	...	...
Lausanne-Ouchy a.	1037	...	1227	1227	1237	...	...	...	1442	1442	...	1537	1555	...	...	1644	...	1755	...	1842	1907	...	2030	...	...	...

LAUSANNE - ÉVIAN-LES-BAINS (France) *See notes ⊡ and ⊠*

	L									M	N
Lausanne-Ouchy d.	0740	0925	1100	1230	1400	1530	1715	1840	2000	2130	2235
Évian les Bains a.	0815	1000	1135	1305	1435	1605	1750	1915	2035	2150	2255

	L									M	N
Évian les Bains d.	0820	1005	1145	1315	1445	1615	1800	1920	2045	2200	2256
Lausanne-Ouchy a.	0855	1040	1220	1350	1520	1650	1835	1955	2120	2220	2345

A – ⑦ to Apr. 10 (also Dec. 25, Jan. 1; not Dec. 26); ⑦ from Oct. 23.
B – Ⓐ Apr. 19 - June 17; ①–⑤ Sept. 5 - Oct. 14 (not Sept. 19).
C – Ⓒ Apr. 15 - June 18; ⑥⑦ Sept. 10 - Oct. 16 (also Sept. 19).
D – Daily Apr. 15 - Oct. 16.
E – Daily June 19 - Sept. 4.
G – Ⓒ Apr. 15 - June 12; daily June 18 - Sept. 4; ⑥⑦ Sept. 10 - Oct. 16 (also Sept. 19).
H – Daily Apr. 15 - June 18 and Sept. 5 - Oct. 26.
J – Daily May 21 - Sept. 24.
L – ⚒ to June 11; daily June 13 - Sept. 10; ①–⑥ from Sept. 12 (not Sept. 19).
M – Ⓐ to Apr. 14; ⚒ Apr. 16 - June 11; daily June 13 - Sept. 10; ①–⑥ Sept. 12 - Oct. 15 (not Sept. 19); ①–⑤ from Oct. 17.
N – Ⓐ to June 17; daily June 19 - Sept. 9; ①–⑤ from Sept. 12 (not Sept. 19).

P – ①–⑥ June 20 - Sept. 3 (not Aug. 1).
Q – Mornings of Ⓑ June 21 - Sept. 4 (not Aug. 2)

r – Not Sept. 19.
t – Arrives 1225.

⊡ – Swiss holiday dates apply.
⊠ – Additional sailings: **From Lausanne** at 0455 ⚒ **r**, 0620 ⚒ **r** and 2350 **P**. **From Évian-les-Bains** at 0010 **Q**, 0540 ⚒ **r** and 0700 ⚒ **r**.
⛴ – Normally operated by historic steamship.

Operator: CGN – Compagnie Générale de Navigation ✆ +41 (0) 848 811 848 (www.cgn.ch).

507 VIERWALDSTÄTTERSEE SGV

SERVICE MAY 26 - SEPTEMBER 11

	Ⓐ	C		⛴	⛴ †		⛴ D	⛴	⛴	⊙					⊡
Luzern (Bahnhofquai) d.	0620	0812	...	0912	0940	1012	1040	1112	1212	1312	1412	1512	1612	1712	1912
Verkehrshaus Lido d.	|	0822	...	0922	|	1022	|	1122	1222	1322	1422	1522	1622	1722	1922
Weggis d.	0659	0853	...	0953	1024	1053	1124	1153	1253	1353	1453	1553	1653	1753	1953
Vitznau d.	...	0910	...	1010	1040	1110	1142	1210	1310	1410	1510	1610	1710	1810	2010
Beckenried d.	...	0926	...	1027	1123	1127	1158	1227	1327	1427	1527	1627	1800	1835	2031
Gersau d.	...	...	...	1045	...	1145	|	1245	1345	1445	1545	1645	1817	|	...
Treib d.	...	...	1002	1102	...	1202	1226	1302	1402	1502	1602	1702	1834	1902	...
Brunnen d.	...	...	1011	1111	...	1211	1235	1311	1411	1511	1611	1711	1841	1909	...
Rütli d.	...	...	1021	1121	...	1221	1245	1321	1421	1521	1621	1721	...	...	...
Sisikon d.	...	...	|	|	...	|	1256	1332	|	|	1632	1732	...	...	...
Tellsplatte d.	...	...	1045	|	...	|	1319	1339	|	|	1639	1739	...	...	...
Bauen d.	...	...	1035*	1135	...	1235	1308*	|	1435	1535	|	1749	...	...	...
Flüelen a.	...	...	1057	1155	...	1255	1335	1355	1455	1555	1655	1808	...	...	...

	Ⓐ	C			⛴ †		⛴		⛴ D	⛴	⛴	⊙		⊡	
Flüelen d.	...	...	...	0948	...	1100	1200	1300	1340	1400	1500	1600	1700	...	...
Bauen d.	...	...	...	1008	...	1121	|	1321	|	1421	|	1621	1721	...	...
Tellsplatte d.	...	...	...	1018	...	|	1216	|	1356	|	1516	|	|	...	...
Sisikon d.	...	...	...	1025	...	|	1224	|	|	|	1524	|	|	...	...
Rütli d.	...	...	...	1036	...	1136	1236	1336	1411	1436	1536	1636	1736	...	...
Brunnen d.	...	...	0919	1049	...	1149	1249	1349	1424	1449	1549	1649	1749	...	...
Treib d.	...	...	0927	1057	...	1157	1257	1357	1432	1457	1557	1657	1757	...	...
Gersau d.	...	...	0942	1114	...	1214	1314	1414	|	1514	1614	1714	1814	...	...
Beckenried d.	...	0932	1000	1132	1135	1232	1332	1432	1500	1532	1632	1732	1832	2032	...
Vitznau d.	...	0949	1049	1149	|	1249	1349	1449	1521	1549	1649	1749	1849	|	...
Weggis d.	0707	1005	1105	1205	|	1305	1405	1505	1538	1605	1705	1805	1905	2057	...
Verkehrshaus Lido d.	|	1035	|	1235	|	1335	1435	1535	|	1635	1735	1835	1935	2135	...
Luzern (Bahnhofquai) a.	0742	1047	1147	1247	1235	1347	1447	1547	1623	1647	1747	1847	1947	2147	...

		†			C		†								
Luzern (Bahnhofquai) d.	0938	1000	1038	1200	1238	1338	1400	1438	...	...	...	...	...	...	...
Verkehrshaus Lido d.	0948	1010	1048	1210	1248	1348	1410	1448	...	...	...	...	...	...	...
Küssnacht am Rigi d.	|	1053	|	1253	|	|	1453	|	...	...	...	...	...	...	...
Kehrsiten Dorf d.	|	...	1131	...	|	1409	...	1531	...	...	...	...	...	...	...
Hergiswil d.	1016	...	1146	...	|	1424	...	1548	...	...	...	...	...	...	...
Stansstad d.	1025	...	|	...	1314	1433	...	1558	...	...	...	...	...	...	...
Alpnachstad a.	1046	...	1210	...	1335	1455	...	1621	...	...	...	...	...	...	...

	†				C	†									
Alpnachstad d.	...	1057	1222	...	1347	...	1510	1637	...	...	...	...	...	...	...
Stansstad d.	...	1119	|	...	1409	...	1532	1700	...	...	...	...	...	...	...
Hergiswil d.	...	1129	1247	...	1419	...	|	1710	...	...	...	...	...	...	...
Kehrsiten Dorf d.	...	1144	|	...	1434	...	1544	|	...	...	...	...	...	...	...
Küssnacht am Rigi d.	1055	|	|	1255	|	1455	|	|	...	...	...	...	...	...	...
Verkehrshaus Lido d.	|	1205	1316	1333	1502	|	1605	|	...	...	...	...	...	...	...
Luzern (Bahnhofquai) a.	1153	1217	1328	1345	1514	1547	1617	1745	...	...	...	...	...	...	...

C – Ⓒ (daily July 9 - Aug. 21).
D – † (daily July 9 - Aug. 21).

* – Calls at Bauen before Tellsplatte.
⊙ – Operated by ⛴ on Ⓒ (daily July 9 - Aug. 21).
⊡ – Operated by ⛴ on ⑤⑥.

⛴ – Normally operated by historic steamship.

Operator: SGV – Schifffahrtsgesellschaft Vierwaldstättersee ✆ +41 (0)41 367 67 67 (www.lakelucerne.ch).

OTHER SWISS LAKES 508

ZÜRICHSEE (operator: ZSG)

	B	†w	C	A	D	L		D	E	E
Zürich (Bürkliplatz) d.	0920	1010	1020	1120	1120	1220	1320	1420	1520	1730
Erlenbach d.	0956	ǀ	ǀ	ǀ	1156	ǀ	1356	ǀ	1556	ǀ
Thalwil d.	ǀ	ǀ	1054	1154	ǀ	1254	ǀ	1454	ǀ	1805
Wädenswil d.	1038	1118	ǀ	ǀ	1238	ǀ	1438	ǀ	1638	1900
Rapperswil a.	1125	...	1220	1320	1325	1420	1525	1620	1725	1950

	†w	U	C	A	D	L		D	C	E
Rapperswil d.	...	1135	1230	1330	1335	1430	1535	1630	1735	1955
Wädenswil d.	1119	1220	ǀ	ǀ	1420	ǀ	1620	ǀ	1820	2046
Thalwil d.	ǀ	ǀ	1357	1457	ǀ	1557	ǀ	1757	ǀ	2133
Erlenbach d.	ǀ	1302	ǀ	ǀ	1502	ǀ	1702	ǀ	1902	ǀ
Zürich (Bürkliplatz) a.	1230	1335	1430	1530	1535	1630	1735	1830	1935	2210

THUNERSEE (operator: BLS)

	F	⑦H	G		K⛴	F	J	F	M⛴	
Thun d.	0840	0940	0940	1140	1240	1340	1440	1540	1840	...
Oberhofen d.	ǀ	1003	1003	1203	1303	1403	1503	1603	1903	...
Spiez d.	0928	1024	1028	1228	1328	1428	1551	1628	1928	...
Beatenbucht d.	0954	...	1102	1302	1402	1502	1624	1702	2002	...
Interlaken West a.	1049	...	1149	1349	1449	1549	...	1749	...	...

	⑦H		F	G		K⛴	J	F	F	M⛴
Interlaken West d.	...	...	1110	1210	1410	1510	...	1610	1810	...
Beatenbucht d.	...	...	1158	1258	1458	1558	1625	1658	1910	2003
Spiez d.	1026	...	1234	1334	1534	1634	1653	1734	1934	2034
Oberhofen d.	1047	...	1257	1357	1557	1657	ǀ	ǀ	1957	2057
Thun a.	1110	...	1320	1420	1620	1720	1750	1809	2015	2120

BRIENZERSEE (operator: BLS)

	S	N	S⛴	P	N	S⛴	P		T⛴	
Interlaken Ost d.	0907	1007	1107	1207	1307	1407	1507	...	1907	...
Iseltwald d.	0952	1046	1152	1246**z**	1352	1452	1546**z**	...	1952	...
Brienz a.	1020	1120	1220	1320	1420	1520	1620	...	2020	...

	S	N	S⛴	P	N	S⛴	P		T⛴	
Brienz d.	1040	1140	1240	1340	1440	1540	1640	...	2040	...
Iseltwald d.	1117	1208	1308	1408	1517	1608	1708	...	2108	...
Interlaken Ost a.	1153	1253	1353	1453	1553	1653	1753	...	2153	...

A – Until Apr. 2 and from Oct. 24.
B – © Apr. 3 - June 26; daily July 1 - Aug. 31; ⑥⑦ Sept. 3 - Oct. 23.
C – © Apr. 3–24; daily Apr. 30 - Oct. 2; ⑥⑦ Oct. 8–23.
D – Apr. 3 - Oct. 23.
E – May 1 - Sept. 30.
F – May 26 - Oct. 23.
G – Apr. 9 - Nov. 13.
H – ⑦ Dec. 12 - Apr. 3; ⑦ Nov. 20 - Dec. 4.
J – Apr. 9 - May 25 and Oct. 24 - Nov. 13.
K – Daily Dec. 25 - Jan. 2; © May 7–22; daily May 26 - Oct. 23.
L – July 1 - Aug. 31.
M – ⑥ May 7–21; ②–⑥ May 26 - Sept. 17.
N – Apr. 9 - May 25 and Sept. 19 - Oct. 23.
P – Apr. 2 - Oct. 23.
S – May 26 - Sept. 18.
T – ⑥ June 25 - Aug. 27.
U – © May 1 - June 26; daily July 1 - Aug. 31; ⑥⑦ Sept. 3–25.
w – Not Dec. 26, Jan. 2.
z – 6 minutes later Apr. 9 - May 25 and Sept. 19 - Oct. 23.

⛴ – Operated by historic steamship.

Operators:
BLS – Schifffahrt Berner Oberland ✆ +41 (0) 58 327 48 11 (www.bls.ch).
ZSG – Zürichsee Schifffahrtsgesellschaft ✆ +41 (0) 44 487 13 33 (www.zsg.ch).

TPF FRIBOURG - MURTEN - INS - NEUCHÂTEL 509

km		⚒	⚒								
0	**Fribourg** d.	0457	0531	0601	0631	and at the	2101	2131	2201	2231	2334
22	Murten d.	0529	0602	0632	0702	same minutes	2132	2202	2232	2302	0005
32	Ins 511 d.	0540	0612	0644	0712	past each	2144	2212	2244	2314	0017**z**
45	**Neuchâtel** 511 a.	...	0625	...	0725	hour until	...	2225	...	...	...

	⚒		⚒						
Neuchâtel 511 d.	*0532*	...	0634	...	0734	and at the	...	2234	...
Ins 511 d.	0546	0612	0646	0712	0746	same minutes	2212	2246	2319
Murten d.	0556	0626	0656	0726	0756	past each	2226	2256	2330
Fribourg a.	0630	0700	0730	0800	0830	hour until	2300	2330	0001

z – Murten - Ins on the mornings of ⑥⑦ only.

SBB BASEL - ZÜRICH 510

Non-stop *IC*, *ICE* and *TGV* services.

km		*IC* 551	*IC* 1251	*IC* 559	*IC* 1253	*IC* 561	*ICE* 3	*IC* 1255	*IC* 563	*ICE* 271 1271	*IC* 565	*IC* 767	*TGV* 9203	*IC* 769	*IC* 569	*IC* 771	*IC* 591	*IC* 571	*ICE* 71	*TGV* 9211	*IC* 775	*IC* 575	*ICE* 73	*TGV* 9213	*EC* 9	*IC* 579	*ICE* 75
							①–⑤	⑥⑦									Ⓐ	©									
			✕	✕	✕	✕	L✕	c✕	✕	G✕	✕	✕	P⊗	✕	✕		✕	✕	G✕	P⊗	✕	✕	G✕	P⊗	G✕	✕	G✕
0	**Basel** SBB d.	0533	0606	0633	0706	0733	0806	0806	0833	0906	0933	1006	1033	1106	1133	1206	1233	1233	1306	1333	1406	1433	1506	1533	1606	1633	1706
91	**Zürich** HB a.	0626	0700	0726	0800	0826	0900	0900	0926	1000	1026	1100	1126	1200	1226	1300	1326	1326	1400	1426	1500	1526	1600	1626	1700	1726	1800
	Chur 520 a.	...	...	0852	0923**a**	0952	1023**z**	1023	1052	1123	1152	...	...	...	1352	...	...	1452	1523	...	...	1652	...	...	...	1852	1923

	IC 581	*IC* 595	*TGV* 9215	*IC* 783	*IC* 583	*ICE* 77	*TGV* 9219	*IC* 787	*IC* 587	*ICE* 79	*TGV* 9223	*IC* 791	*IC* 793	
	Ⓐd	T	S									⑤⑥	⑤⑥	
	✕		P⊗		✕	G✕	P⊗	✕	✕	G	P⊗	k	k	
Basel SBB d.	1733	1733	1733	1806	1833	1906	1933	2006	2033	2106	2133	2206	2306	...
Zürich HB a.	1826	1826	1826	1900	1926	2000	2026	2100	2126	2200	2226	2300	2400	...
Chur 520 a.	1952	...	...	...	2052	...	...	...	2252**r**	...	...	...	...	...

	ICE 78		*IC* 556	*IC* 556	*IC* 760	*TGV* 9206	*ICE* 76	*IC* 560	*IC* 764
				⚒					
	G		✕	✕	✕	P	G	✕	✕
Chur 520 d.	...	...	...	0508	...	...	...	0708	...
Zürich HB d.	0559	...	0634	0634	0659	0734	0759	0834	0859
Basel SBB a.	0653	...	0728	0728	0753	0828	0853	0928	0953

	IC 552	*TGV* 9210	*ICE* 74	*IC* 564	*EC* 8	*TGV* 9218	*ICE* 72	*IC* 568	*IC* 772	*TGV* 9222	*ICE* 70	*IC* 572	*IC* 776	*TGV* 9226	*IC* 576	*ICE* 272 292	*TGV* 9230	*IC* 782	*IC* 580	*ICE* 4	*IC* 582		*IC* 584	*IC* 1260	*IC* 1258		*IC* 792
	Q	R																									⑤⑥
		P	G	✕	G✕	P	G	✕	✕	P	G	✕		P	✕	G	P	✕	✕	G	✕		✕				k
Chur 520 d.	...	...	...	0908	...	...	1037	1108	...	...	1237	1308	...	...	1508	...	...	...	1708	...	1808	...	1908	...	2008	...	...
Zürich HB d.	0934	0934	0959	1034	1059	1134	1159	1234	1259	1334	1359	1434	1459	1534	1634	1659	1734	1759	1834	1859	1934	...	2034	2059	2134	...	2259
Basel SBB a.	1028	1028	1053	1128	1153	1228	1253	1328	1353	1428	1453	1528	1553	1628	1728	1753	1828	1853	1928	1953	2028	...	2128	2153	2228	...	2353

IR and *RE* services

km																							
0	**Basel** SBB d.	0437	...	0511	0537	0543	...	and at	1911	1937	1943	...	2011	2043	...	2111	2143	...	2211	2243	...	2311	...	0011
17	Rheinfelden d.	0450	...	0525	0550	ǀ	...	the same	1925	1950	ǀ	...	2025	ǀ	...	2125	ǀ	...	2225	ǀ	...	2325	...	0025
57	Brugg 505 d.	0520	...	0600	0620	ǀ	...	minutes	2000	2020	ǀ	...	2100	ǀ	...	2200	ǀ	...	2300	ǀ	...	0000	...	0100
66	Baden 505 d.	0529	...	0608	0629	ǀ	...	past each	2008	2029	ǀ	...	2108	ǀ	...	2208	ǀ	...	2308	ǀ	...	0008	...	0108
	Liestal d.	ǀ	...	ǀ	ǀ	0554	...	hour until	ǀ	ǀ	1954	...	ǀ	2054	...	ǀ	2154	...	ǀ	2254	...	ǀ	...	ǀ
	Aarau 505 d.	ǀ	...	ǀ	ǀ	0623	0654		ǀ	ǀ	2023	2054	ǀ	2123	2154	ǀ	2223	2254	ǀ	2323	...	ǀ	...	ǀ
	Lenzburg 505 d.	ǀ	...	ǀ	ǀ	0630	0701		ǀ	ǀ	2030	2101	ǀ	2130	2201	ǀ	2230	2301	ǀ	2330	...	ǀ	...	ǀ
88	**Zürich** HB 505 530 535 a.	0549	...	0624	0649	0652	0722		2024	2049	2052	2122	2124	2152	2222	2224	2252	2322	2324	2352	...	0024	...	0124
	Zürich Flughafen ✈ 530 535 a.	0604	...	...	0704	...	...		...	2104	...	...	...	...	...	...	...	...	...	...	...	...	...	...

km		⑥⑦j																						
	Zürich Flughafen ✈ 530 535 d.	...	...	...	...	0556	...	...	...	0656	...	...	and at	...	2056	...	...	...	...	...	...	...	...	...
0	**Zürich** HB 505 530 535 d.	0108	0508	0535	0608	0610	0636	0638	0708	0710	0736	0738	the same	2108	2110	2136	2138	2208	2236	2238	2308	2336	2338	0008
32	Lenzburg 505 d.	0129	0529	ǀ	0629	ǀ	ǀ	0659	0729	ǀ	ǀ	0759	minutes	2129	ǀ	ǀ	2159	2229	ǀ	2259	2329	ǀ	2359	0029
41	**Aarau** 505 d.	0136	0536	ǀ	0636	ǀ	ǀ	0705	0736	ǀ	ǀ	0805	past each	2136	ǀ	ǀ	2205	2236	ǀ	2305	2336	ǀ	0005	0036
77	Liestal d.	0202	0602	ǀ	0702	ǀ	ǀ	...	0802	ǀ	ǀ	...	hour until	2202	ǀ	ǀ	...	2302	ǀ	...	0002	ǀ	...	0102
	Baden 505 d.	ǀ	ǀ	0551	ǀ	0632	0652	...	ǀ	0732	0752	...		ǀ	2132	2152	...	ǀ	2252	...	ǀ	2352	...	ǀ
	Brugg 505 d.	ǀ	ǀ	0600	ǀ	0641	0702	...	ǀ	0741	0802	...		ǀ	2141	2202	...	ǀ	2302	...	ǀ	0002	...	ǀ
	Rheinfelden d.	ǀ	ǀ	0634	ǀ	0713	0734	...	ǀ	0810	0834	...		ǀ	2210	2234	...	ǀ	2334	...	ǀ	0034	...	ǀ
91	**Basel** SBB a.	0213	0613	0650	0713	0732	0748	...	0813	0824	0850	...		2213	2224	2248	...	2313	2348	...	0013	0048	...	0113

G – International service from / to stations in Germany (see Table **912**).
L – ①–⑤ (not Dec. 24, 31, Apr. 15, 18, June 6, Oct. 3). From Karlsruhe (Table **912**).
P – From / to Paris (Table **370**). Ⓡ for international journeys.
Q – Until Mar. 28 and Aug. 2–28.
R – Mar. 29 - Aug. 1 and from Aug. 29.
S – ⑥⑦ Apr. 2 - July 31 (also Apr. 15, 18, May 26, 27, June 6); ⑥⑦ from Aug. 28.
T – ⑥⑦ Dec. 12–19; daily Dec. 25 - Jan. 2; ⑥⑦ Jan. 8 - Mar. 27; ⑥⑦ Aug. 6–27 (also Aug. 1).
a – Ⓐ only.
c – ⑥⑦ (also Dec. 24, 31, Apr. 15, 18, June 6, Oct. 3). Does not run Zürich - Chur on Dec. 24, 31, Oct. 3.
d – Not Dec. 27–31, May 27.
j – Not Dec. 25, 26, Jan. 2, Apr. 16.
k – Not Dec. 24, 25, Jan. 1, Apr. 15.
r – ⑦–④ (also Dec. 25, Jan. 1, Apr. 15).
z – May 26 and Aug. 1 only.

511 BERN - PAYERNE and NEUCHÂTEL SBB, BLS

km			⚒	Ⓐ		C				C			D		C				C					
0	**Bern** d.	...	...	...	*0534*	0553	0608	0608	*0634*	0653	0708	0708		*2134*	2153	2208	2208	*2234*	2253	2308	2308	2339	...	0008	0008
22	Kerzers ▲ d.	0504	...	0532	0604	0611	0631	0634	0704	0711	0731	0734	and at	2204	2211	2231	2234	2304	2311	2331	2334	0005	...	0034	0036
	Murten d.	0521f	0542	0542	0621f	|	|	0643	0721f	|	|	0743	the same	2221f	|	|	2243	2321f	|	|	2342	|	...	|	0045
	Avenches d.	0529	0549	0549	0629	|	|	0649	0729	|	|	...	minutes	2229	|	|	...	2329	|	|	2350	|	...	|	...
	Payerne a.	0541	0557	0557	0641	|	|	0657	0741	|	|	...	past each	2241	|	|	...	2341	|	|	0001	|	...	|	...
	Lausanne **504** a.	0648	...	...	0748	|	|	...	0848	|	|	...	hour until	2348	|	|	...	...	|	|	...	|	...	|	...
30	Ins **508** d.	...	...	...	...	0617	0640	...	...	0717	0740	...		...	2217	2240	...	...	2317	2340	...	0013	...	0041	...
43	**Neuchâtel** **508** a.	...	...	...	...	0627	0656	...	...	0727	0756	...		...	2227	2256	...	...	2327	2356	...	0026	...	0056	...

km		C		⚒		C		Ⓐ			C				E	C				C					
	Neuchâtel **508** d.	0532	...	...	0601	0632	...	0656	...	0701	0732	...	...	0801		2232	...	...	2301	2332	...	...	...	...	0009
	Ins **508** d.	0543	...	...	0617	0642	...	0708	...	0717	0742	...	...	0817	and at	2242	...	...	2317	2342	...	...	...	...	0025
	Lausanne **504** d.	|	...	...	|	|	0513	|	...	|	|	0613	...	|	the same	|	2113	...	|	|	2213	...	...	...	|
0	**Payerne** d.	|	...	0600	|	|	0618	|	0700	|	|	0718	...	|	minutes	|	2218	...	|	|	2318	...	...	0006	|
11	Avenches d.	|	...	0609	|	|	0630	|	0708	|	|	0730	...	|	past each	|	2230	...	|	|	2330	...	...	0017	|
18	Murten d.	|	0617	0617	|	|	0647f	|	0717	|	|	0747f	0817	|	hour until	|	2247f	2317	|	|	2347f	...	...	0025	|
26	Kerzers ▲ d.	0549	0630	0630	0630	0649	0656	0719	0730	0730	0749	0756	0830	0830		2249	2256	2330	2330	2349	2356	0004	...	0038	0038
	Bern a.	0607	0652	0652	0652	0707	*0726*	0738	0752	0752	0807	*0826*	0852	0852		2307	*2326*	2352	2352	0007	...	0030	...	0103	0103

C – To/from La Chaux de Fonds (Table **512**).
D – The 0804 from Kerzers departs Murten 0815 (not 0821).
E – 1413 from Lausanne on Ⓐ: Avenches d. 1537, Murten a. 1545.
f – Arrives 8–9 minutes earlier.
▲ – Connecting services **KERZERS - LYSS**. *17 km.* Journey: 19–20 minutes
From **Kerzers**: 0606 and hourly until 2306.
From **Lyss**: 0535 and hourly until 2235; then 2336 and 0009.

512 NEUCHÂTEL and BIEL/BIENNE - LA CHAUX DE FONDS - LE LOCLE SBB, BLS

NEUCHÂTEL - LA CHAUX DE FONDS - LE LOCLE

km					⊠											
	Bern **511** d.	...	...	0553	and at	...	1853	...	1953	...	2053	...	2153	...	2253	...
0	**Neuchâtel** d.	0529	0600	0629	the same	1900	1929	2000	2029	2100	2129	2200	2229	2300	2329	0000
29	**La Chaux de Fonds** a.	0557	0627	0657	minutes	1927	1957	2027	2057	2127	2157	2227	2257	2327	2357	0027
	La Chaux de Fonds d.	*0607*	0631	*0707*	past each	1931	*2003*	2037	*2103*	2137	*2203*	2237	*2303*	2337	...	0037
37	**Le Locle** a.	*0615*	0640	*0715*	hour until	1940	*2011*	2046	*2111*	2146	*2211*	2246	*2311*	2346	...	0046

Le Locle d.	*0451*	0520	and at	*2251*	2320
La Chaux de Fonds a.	*0459*	0529	the same	*2259*	2329
La Chaux de Fonds d.	0502	0532	minutes	2302	2332
Neuchâtel a.	0530	0600	past each	2330	2400
Bern **511** a.	0607	...	hour until	2007	...

BIEL/BIENNE - LA CHAUX DE FONDS

km		Ⓐ												
0	**Biel/Bienne** d.	0518	0547	0620	0647	and at the same	1820	1847	1920	1947	2047	2147	2247	2347
28	St Imier d.	0600	0613	0700	0713	minutes past	1900	1913	2000	2017	2117	2217	2317	0017
44	**La Chaux de Fonds** a.	0617	0628	0717	0728	each hour until	1917	1928	2017	2034	2134	2234	2334	0034

	Ⓐ												A	B
La Chaux de Fonds d.	0441	0532	0542	0632	0642	and at the same	1932	1942	2042	2142	2242	...	2342	2342
St Imier d.	0457	0545	0559	0645	0659	minutes past	1945	1959	2059	2159	2259	...	2359	2359
Biel/Bienne a.	0539	0612	0640	0712	0741	each hour until	2012	2041	2141	2241	2341	...	0041	0047

A – ⑦–④ (also Dec. 25, Jan. 1, Apr. 15).
B – ⑤⑥ (not Dec. 25, Jan. 1, Apr. 15).
⊠ – Certain connecting trains La Chaux de Fonds (d. *xx07*) - Le Locle (a. *xx15*) run 4 minutes earlier (subsequent departures from La Chaux de Fonds are at *0807*, *0903*, *1003*, *1103*, *1207*, *1303*, *1403*, *1503*, *1607*, *1707*, *1803* and *1903*).

513 BERN - BIEL SBB

km			⑥⑦n		Ⓐ																		
0	**Bern** d.	0012	0112	...	0500	0530	...	0612	0642	and at the same	2012	2042	...	2112	2132	...	2212	2232	...	2312	2332	...	...
23	Lyss d.	0030	0135	...	0522	0552	...	0630	0700	minutes past	2030	2100	...	2130	2154	...	2230	2254	...	2330	2354	...	...
34	**Biel/Bienne** a.	0038	0143	...	0535	0605	...	0638	0708	each hour until	2038	2108	...	2138	2207	...	2238	2307	...	2338	0007	...	...

	⑥⑦n																					
Biel/Bienne d.	0026	...	0518	0552	...	0622	0652	and at the same	2022	2052	...	2122	2154	...	2222	2254	...	2322	2354	...	...	...	...
Lyss d.	0035	...	0531	0601	...	0631	0701	minutes past	2031	2101	...	2131	2207	...	2231	2307	...	2331	0007	...	...	...	...
Bern a.	0052	...	0554	0618	...	0648	0718	each hour until	2048	2118	...	2148	2230	...	2248	2330	...	2348	0030	...	...	...	...

n – Not Dec. 26, Jan. 2, Apr. 16.
☛ Additional stopping services operate.

514 BERN - LUZERN via Langnau BLS

For fast services via Zofingen see Table **565**.

km											
0	**Bern** d.	0536a	...	0612	0636	and at	2136	...	2212	2236	2342
21	Konolfingen d.	0552a	...	0634	0652	the same	2152	...	2234	2252	0005
38	Langnau d.	0606	0636	0652	0706	minutes	2206	2236	2252	2306	0023
75	Wolhusen d.	0645	0720	...	0745	past each	2245	2320	...	2345	...
96	**Luzern** a.	0703	0743	...	0803	hour until	2303	2343	...	0010	...

	Ⓐ										
Luzern d.	0450	...	0557	...	0616	and at	2157	...	2216	2257	...
Wolhusen d.	0514	...	0616	...	0644	the same	2215	...	2244	2315	...
Langnau d.	0554	0607	0654	0707	0721	minutes	2254	2307	2321	2351	0007
Konolfingen d.	0607	0626	0707	0726	...	past each	2307	2326	...	...	0026
Bern a.	0626	0648	0726	0748	...	hour until	2326	2348	...	...	0049

a – Ⓐ only.
☛ Additional stopping services operate.

515 BIEL/BIENNE - DELÉMONT - DELLE - MEROUX SBB

km																								
0	**Biel/Bienne** 505a d.	...	...	...	...	0619	0719	0819	0919	1019	1119	1219	1319	1419	1519	1619	1719	1819	1919	2019	2119	2219	...	2319
24	Moutier 505a d.	...	...	...	...	0638	0738	0838	0938	1038	1138	1238	1338	1438	1538	1638	1738	1838	1938	2038	2138	2238	...	2338
35	Delémont 505a d.	0417	0449	...	0551	0651	0751	0851	0951	1051	1151	1251	1351	1451	1551	1651	1751	1851	1951	2051	2151	2251	...	2351
63	Porrentruy 505a d.	0448	0520	...	0621	0721	0821	0921	1021	1121	1221	1321	1421	1521	1621	1721	1821	1921	2021	2121	2221	2321	...	0020
75	**Delle** ▦ a.	0506	0536	...	0640	0738	0838	0938	1038	1138	1238	1338	1438	1540	1638	1738	1838	1938	2040	2138	2238	2340	...	...
75	**Delle** ▦ 370b d.	...	0540r	...	...	0740k	0840	0940	1040e	1140	1240	1340	...	...	1640v	1740t	1840	1940b	...	2140	2240v	...	...	...
89	Meroux TGV ⊡ 370b d.	...	0556r	...	...	0756k	0856	0956	1056e	1156	1256	1356	...	...	1656v	1756t	1856	1956b	...	2156	2256v	...	...	...

Meroux TGV ⊡ 370b d.	...	...	...	0603r	...	0803k	0903	1003	1103e	1203	1303	1403	...	...	1703v	1803t	1903	2003b	...	...	2203	2303v	...	...
Delle ▦ 370b a.	...	...	...	0618r	...	0818k	0918	1018	1118e	1218	1318	1418	...	...	1718v	1818t	1918	2018b	...	...	2218	2318v	...	...
Delle ▦ d.	...	...	0517	0620	0719	0820	0920	1020	1120	1220	1320	1420	1519	1619	1720	1820	1920	2020	2119	...	2220	2320	...	0022
Porrentruy 505a d.	0436	...	0540	0640	0740	0840	0940	1040	1140	1240	1340	1440	1540	1640	1740	1840	1940	2040	2140	...	2240	2340	...	0041
Delémont 505a d.	0512	...	0612	0712	0812	0912	1012	1112	1212	1312	1412	1512	1612	1712	1812	1912	2012	2112	2212	...	2309	0009	...	0110
Moutier 505a a.	0521	...	0621	0721	0821	0921	1021	1121	1221	1321	1421	1521	1621	1721	1821	1921	2021	2121	2221	...	...	...	...	...
Biel/Bienne 505a a.	0541	...	0641	0741	0841	0941	1041	1141	1241	1341	1441	1541	1641	1741	1841	1941	2041	2141	2241	...	...	...	...	...

b – Ⓑ (not Oct. 31).
e – ①–⑤ (not Apr. 18, May 26, June 6, July 4 - Aug. 26, Oct. 31, Nov. 1, 11).
k – ⑥ to July 2; ①–⑥ July 4 - Aug. 27 (not July 14, Aug. 15); ⑥ from Sept. 3 (also Oct. 31).
r – ①–⑥ (not Apr. 18, May 26, June 6, July 14, Aug. 15, Nov. 1, 11).
t – ⑥ (also Oct. 31).
v – ⑦ (also Apr. 18, May 26, June 6, July 14, Aug. 15, Nov. 1, 11).
⊡ – Meroux station platforms are located directly above the Belfort-Montbéliard TGV platforms.

516 BERN - SOLOTHURN Narrow gauge. RBS

km		⚒	⚒												Ⓐ	Ⓐ	Ⓐ	Ⓐ	Ⓐ	Ⓐ	Ⓐ	Ⓐ	Ⓐ
0	**Bern** RBS d.	0513	0550	0605	0635	and at the same	2205	2235	2308	2338	0011	...	Additional	0620	0650	0720	0750	0820	1650	1720	1750	1820
14	Jegenstorf d.	0532	0603	0618	0648	minutes past	2218	2248	2321	2351	0030	...	services	0633	0703	0733	0803	0833	1703	1733	1803	1833
34	**Solothurn** a.	0556	0627	0642	0712	each hour until	2242	2312	2345	0015	0054	...	on Ⓐ	0657	0727	0757	0827	0857	1727	1757	1827	1857

												Ⓐ	Ⓐ	Ⓐ	Ⓐ	Ⓐ		Ⓐ	Ⓐ	Ⓐ	Ⓐ	Ⓐ
Solothurn d.	0518	0549	0619	0649	and at the same	2219	2249	2320	2350	...	Additional	0604	0634	0704	0734	0804	...	1634	1704	1734	1804	1834
Jegenstorf d.	0542	0612	0642	0712	minutes past	2242	2312	2343	0013	...	services	0627	0657	0727	0757	0827	...	1657	1727	1757	1827	1857
Bern RBS a.	0556	0626	0656	0726	each hour until	2256	2326	2357	0031	...	on Ⓐ	0641	0711	0741	0811	0841	...	1711	1741	1811	1841	1911

BLS SOLOTHURN - BURGDORF - THUN 517

km		⚒	Ⓐ	⚒																				
0	**Solothurn** d.	...	...	0514	0542	0611	0646	0717	and at	1846	1917	1946	2017	...	...	2117	...	...	2217	...	...	2317	...	0009
5	Biberist Ost d.	...	...	0520	0547	0616	0650	0722	the same	1850	1922	1950	2022	...	...	2122	...	...	2222	...	...	2322	...	0014
21	**Burgdorf** a.	...	...	0545	0612	0645	0712	0745	minutes	1912	1945	2012	2045	...	...	2145	...	...	2245	...	...	2345	...	0039
21	**Burgdorf** 505 d.	0448	0515	0551	0625	0651	0725	0751	past each	1925	1951	2025	2051	*2049*	2125	2151	*2149*	2225	2251	*2249*	2325	2351	*2349*	▬
28	Hasle-Rüegsau d.	0501	0525	|	0638	|	0738	|	hour until	1938	|	2038	|	2102	2138	|	2202	2238	|	2302	2338	|	0001	...
46	Konolfingen a.	0522	0549	|	0700	|	0800	|		2000	|	2100	|	2123	2200	|	2223	2300	|	2323	2400	|	0023	...
46	Konolfingen d.	*0528*	0558	|	0701	|	0801	|		2001	|	2101	|	...	2201	|	...	2301	|	...	0001	|	...	0036
	Bern 505 560 a.	|	|	0611	|	0711	|	0811		|	2011	|	2111	...	|	2211	...	|	2311	...	|	0011	...	|
61	**Thun** 560 a.	*0549*	0619	0651	0719	0751	0819	0851		2019	2051	2119	2151	...	2219	2251	...	2319	2351	...	0019	0059	...	0057

				Ⓐ																					
Thun 560 d.	...	0502	...	0532	0608	0639	and at	1808	1839	...	1908	1939	...	2008	2039	...	2108	2139	...	2208	2239	...	2308	2339	*0003*
Bern 505 560 d.	...	0550	...	|	0650	|	the same	1850	|	...	1950	|	...	2050	|	...	2150	|	...	2250	|	...	2350	|	|
Konolfingen a.	...	|	...	0553	|	0658	minutes	|	1858	...	|	1958	...	|	2058	...	|	2158	...	|	2258	...	|	2358	*0024*
Konolfingen d.	...	|	...	0600	|	0700	past each	|	1900	*1936*	|	2000	*2036*	|	2100	*2136*	|	2200	*2236*	|	2300	*2336*	|	0000	0037
Hasle-Rüegsau d.	...	|	...	0622	|	0722	hour until	|	1922	2001	|	2022	2101	|	2122	2201	|	2222	2301	|	2322	0001	|	0022	0058
Burgdorf 505 a.	...	0608	...	0632	0708	0732		1908	1932	2011	2008	2032	2111	2108	2132	2211	2208	2232	2311	2308	2332	0011	0008	0032	0107
Burgdorf d.	0528	0615	0647	0647	0715	0747		1915	1947	...	2015	...	...	2115	...	...	2215	...	...	2315	...	...	0015	...	...
Biberist Ost d.	0550	0635	0706	0706	0735	0806		1935	2006	...	2035	...	...	2135	...	...	2235	...	...	2335	...	...	0035	...	...
Solothurn a.	0557	0642	0713	0713	0742	0813		1942	2013	...	2042	...	...	2142	...	...	2242	...	...	2342	...	...	0042	...	...

SBB ZÜRICH - SARGANS - CHUR 520

km		*IR* 2395 ⑥⑦ z◇		*IR* 2353 B◇	*IC* 557 ✕	*RJX* 161 E✕	*IC* 911 ✕	*IR* 2355 ◇(🍸)	*IC* 559 ✕	*IC* 1253 Ⓐ ✕	*IC* 913 Ⓒ ✕	*IR* 2359 B◇	*IC* 561 ✕	*EC* 163 E✕	*IC* 1255 Ⓒ ‡✕	*IR* 2361 B⊡	*IC* 563 ✕	*ICE* 271 1271 G✕	*IR* 2363 B◇	*IC* 565 ✕	*RJX* 165 H✕	*IR* 2365 B⊡	*IC* 567 ✕	*IC* 921 ✕	*IR* 2367 B◇
	Basel SBB 510 d.	...	...	...	...	...	...	...	0633	0706	...	...	0733	...	0806	...	0833	0906	...	0933	...	...	...	...	...
0	**Zürich** HB 522 555 d.	0020	...	0612	0638	0640	0707	0712	0738	0807	0807	0812	0838	0840	0907	0912	0938	1007	1012	1038	1040	1112	1138	1207	1212
12	Thalwil 555 d.	0028	...	0621	|	|	|	0721	|	|	|	0821	|	|	|	0921	|	|	1021	|	|	1121	|	|	1221
24	Wädenswil 522 d.	0037	...	0631	|	|	|	0731	|	|	|	0831	|	|	|	0931	|	|	1031	|	|	1131	|	|	1231
33	Pfäffikon 522 d.	0045	...	0641	|	|	|	0741	|	|	|	0841	|	|	|	0941	|	|	1041	|	|	1141	|	|	1241
57	Ziegelbrücke 522 d.	0100	...	0659	|	|	|	0759	|	|	|	0859	|	|	|	0959	|	|	1059	|	|	1159	|	|	1259
90	**Sargans** 534 d.	0120	...	0723	0733	0736	0803	0823	0833	0903	0903	0923	0933	0936	1003	1023	1033	1103	1123	1133	1136	1223	1233	1303	1323
106	Buchs 534 a.	|	...	|	|	0748	|	|	|	|	|	|	|	0948	|	|	|	|	|	|	1148	|	|	|	|
103	Landquart 534 545 d.	0131	...	0734	0742	...	0813	0834	0842	0913	0913	0934	0942	...	1013	1034	1042	1113	1134	1142	...	1234	1242	1313	1334
116	**Chur** 534 545 a.	0138	...	0743	0752	...	0823	0843	0852	0923	0923	0943	0952	...	1023	1043	1052	1123	1143	1152	...	1243	1252	1323	1343

	IC 569 ✕	*RJX* 167 J✕	*IR* 2369 B◇	*IC* 571 ✕	*ICE* 71 G✕	*IR* 2371 B◇	*IC* 573	*RJX* 169 E✕	*IR* 2373 B◇	*IC* 575 ✕	*IC* 929 ✕	*IR* 2375 B◇	*IC* 577 ✕	*RJX* 367 E✕	*IC* 931 Ⓑ ✕	*IR* 2377 B⊡	*IC* 579 ✕	*ICE* 75 G✕	*IR* 2379 B◇	*IC* 581 ✕	*RJX* 369 E✕	*IR* 2381 B⊡	*IC* 583 ✕	*IR* 2383 B◇	*IC* 585 ✕
Basel SBB 510 d.	1133	...	...	1233c	1306	...	...	...	...	1433	...	...	...	...	...	...	1633	1706	...	1733t	...	...	1833	...	...
Zürich HB 522 555 d.	1238	1240	1312	1338	1407	1412	1438	1440	1512	1538	1607	1612	1638	1640	1707	1712	1738	1807	1812	1838	1840	1912	1938	2012	2038
Thalwil 555 d.	|	|	1321	|	|	1421	|	|	1521	|	|	1621	|	|	|	1721	|	|	1821	|	|	1921	|	2021	|
Wädenswil 522 d.	|	|	1331	|	|	1431	|	|	1531	|	|	1631	|	|	|	1731	|	|	1831	|	|	1931	|	2031	|
Pfäffikon 522 d.	|	|	1341	|	|	1441	|	|	1541	|	|	1641	|	|	|	1741	|	|	1841	|	|	1941	|	2041	|
Ziegelbrücke 522 d.	|	|	1359	|	|	1459	|	|	1559	|	|	1659	|	|	|	1759	|	|	1859	|	|	1959	|	2059	|
Sargans 534 d.	1333	1336	1423	1433	1503	1523	1533	1536	1623	1633	1703	1723	1733	1736	1803	1823	1833	1903	1923	1933	1936	2023	2033	2128	2133
Buchs 534 a.	|	1348	|	|	|	|	|	1548	|	|	|	|	|	1748	|	|	|	|	|	|	1948	|	|	|	|
Landquart 534 545 d.	1342	...	1434	1442	1513	1534	1542	...	1634	1642	1713	1734	1742	...	1813	1834	1842	1913	1934	1942	...	2034	2042	2138	2142
Chur 534 545 a.	1352	...	1443	1452	1523	1543	1552	...	1643	1652	1723	1743	1752	...	1823	1843	1852	1923	1943	1952	...	2043	2052	2147	2152

	NJ 465 R N		*IR* 2385 B◇	*IC* 597 ⑤⑥ k	*IC* 587 ⑦–④ r	*NJ* 467 R W		*IR* 2391 ◇	*IC* 589	*IR* 2393 ⊙	
Basel SBB 510 d.	...	...	...	...	2033	...	...	...	...	...	...
Zürich HB 522 555 d.	2040	...	2112	2138	2138	2140	...	2212	2238	2312	...
Thalwil 555 d.	|	...	2121	|	|	|	...	2221	|	2321	...
Wädenswil 522 d.	|	...	2131	|	|	|	...	2231	|	2331	...
Pfäffikon 522 d.	|	...	2141	|	|	|	...	2241	|	2341	...
Ziegelbrücke 522 d.	|	...	2159	|	|	|	...	2259	|	0000	...
Sargans 534 d.	2136	...	2228	2233	2233	2236	...	2328	2336	0031	...
Buchs 534 a.	2148	...	|	|	|	2248	...	|	|	|	...
Landquart 534 545 d.	...	...	2238	2242	2242	...	...	2339	2349	0042	...
Chur 534 545 a.	...	...	2247	2252	2252	...	...	2348	2357	0051	...

	IC 556 ⚒	*IR* 2356 B◇		*IC* 558	*IR* 2358 B⊡	*IC* 912 Ⓐ ✕	*NJ* 466 R W	*IC* 560	*IR* 2360 B◇
Chur 534 545 d.	0508	0516	...	0608	0616	0637	...	0708	0716
Landquart 534 545 d.	0518	0525	...	0618	0625	0647	...	0718	0725
Buchs 534 d.	|	|	...	|	|	|	0712	|	|
Sargans 534 d.	0527	0535	...	0627	0635	0655	0724	0727	0735
Ziegelbrücke 522 d.	|	0600	...	|	0700	|	|	|	0800
Pfäffikon 522 d.	|	0619	...	|	0719	|	|	|	0819
Wädenswil 522 d.	|	0629	...	|	0729	|	|	|	0829
Thalwil 555 d.	|	0639	...	|	0739	|	|	|	0839
Zürich HB 522 555 a.	0622	0648	...	0722	0748	0753	0820	0822	0848
Basel SBB 510 a.	0728	...	...	...	...	...	...	0928	...

	NJ 464 R N	*IC* 562 ✕	*IR* 2362 B◇	*IC* 916 ✕	*IC* 564 ✕	*IR* 2364 B◇	*RJX* 366 E✕	*IC* 566 ✕	*IR* 2366 B◇	*ICE* 72 G	*IC* 568 ✕	*IR* 2368 B◇	*RJX* 368 E✕	*IC* 570 ✕	*IR* 2370 B⊡	*ICE* 70 G	*IC* 572 ✕	*IR* 2372 B◇	*RJX* 160 J✕	*IC* 574 ✕	*IR* 2374 B⊡	*IC* 928 ✕	*IC* 576 ✕	*IR* 2376 B◇	*IC* 930 † ✕
Chur 534 545 d.	...	0808	0816	0837	0908	0916	...	1008	1016	1037	1108	1116	...	1208	1216	1237	1308	1316	...	1408	1416	1437	1508	1516	1537
Landquart 534 545 d.	...	0818	0825	0847	0918	0925	...	1018	1025	1047	1118	1125	...	1218	1225	1247	1318	1325	...	1418	1425	1447	1518	1525	1547
Buchs 534 d.	0812	|	|	|	|	|	1011	|	|	|	|	|	1211	|	|	|	|	|	1411	|	|	|	|	|	|
Sargans 534 d.	0824	0827	0835	0855	0927	0935	1023	1027	1035	1055	1127	1135	1223	1227	1235	1255	1327	1335	1423	1427	1435	1455	1527	1535	1555
Ziegelbrücke 522 d.	|	|	0900	|	|	1000	|	|	1100	|	|	1200	|	|	1300	|	|	1400	|	|	1500	|	|	1600	|
Pfäffikon 522 d.	|	|	0919	|	|	1019	|	|	1119	|	|	1219	|	|	1319	|	|	1419	|	|	1519	|	|	1619	|
Wädenswil 522 d.	|	|	0929	|	|	1029	|	|	1129	|	|	1229	|	|	1329	|	|	1429	|	|	1529	|	|	1629	|
Thalwil 555 d.	|	|	0939	|	|	1039	|	|	1139	|	|	1239	|	|	1339	|	|	1439	|	|	1539	|	|	1639	|
Zürich HB 522 555 a.	0920	0922	0948	0953	1022	1048	1120	1122	1148	1153	1222	1248	1320	1322	1348	1353	1422	1448	1520	1522	1548	1553	1622	1648	1653
Basel SBB 510 a.	...	...	...	1128	...	...	...	...	...	1253	1328	...	...	...	...	1453	1528	...	...	...	...	...	1728	...	...

	RJX 162 H✕	*IC* 578 ✕	*IR* 2378 B◇	*IC* 1256	*IC* 580 ✕	*IR* 2380 B◇	*IC* 934 ✕	*EC* 164 E✕	*IC* 582 ✕	*IR* 2382 B◇	*IC* 936 ✕	*IC* 584 ✕	*IR* 2384 ⊡		*RJX* 166 E✕	*IC* 1258	*IR* 2388 ◇		*IC* 588 ✕	*IR* 2390 ⊡		*RJX* 168 E✕	*IR* 2392 ◇		*IR* 2398 ⑤⑥ v◇
Chur 534 545 d.	...	1608	1616	1637	1708	1716	1737	...	1808	1816	1837	1908	1916	...	...	2008	2016	...	2108	2114	...	...	2214	...	2314
Landquart 534 545 d.	...	1618	1625	1647	1718	1725	1747	...	1818	1825	1847	1918	1925	...	...	2018	2025	...	2118	2122	...	...	2222	...	2322
Buchs 534 d.	1611	|	|	|	|	|	|	1811	|	|	|	|	|	...	2011	|	|	...	|	|	...	2211	|	...	|
Sargans 534 d.	1623	1627	1635	1655	1727	1735	1755	1823	1827	1835	1855	1927	1935	...	2023	2027	2035	...	2127	2135	...	2223	2235	...	2337
Ziegelbrücke 522 d.	|	|	1700	|	|	1800	|	|	|	1900	|	|	2000	...	|	|	2100	...	|	2200	...	|	2300	...	0000
Pfäffikon 522 d.	|	|	1719	|	|	1819	|	|	|	1919	|	|	2019	...	|	|	2119	...	|	2219	...	|	2319	...	0019
Wädenswil 522 d.	|	|	1729	|	|	1829	|	|	|	1929	|	|	2029	...	|	|	2129	...	|	2229	...	|	2329	...	0029
Thalwil 555 d.	|	|	1739	|	|	1839	|	|	|	1939	|	|	2039	...	|	|	2139	...	|	2239	...	|	2339	...	0039
Zürich HB 522 555 a.	1720	1722	1748	1753	1822	1848	1853	1920	1922	1948	1953	2022	2048	...	2120	2122	2148	...	2222	2248	...	2320	2348	...	0048
Basel SBB 510 a.	...	...	...	...	1928	...	...	...	2028	...	...	2128	...	...	...	2228	...	...	...	...	...	...	...	...	...

Other connecting services **SARGANS - BUCHS**

Sargans d.	0500	0536	and at the same minutes past	2200	2236	2300	2339	0000
Buchs a.	0512	0545	each hour until	2212	2245	2312	2347	0012

	⚒								
Buchs d.	0512	0615	0647	and at the same minutes past	2315	2347	0018	0047
Sargans a.	0524	0624	0701	each hour until	2325	0001	0028	0101

B – From/to Bern (Table **505**). Most convey (🍸).
E – International service to/from stations in Austria (Tables **86** and **951**).
G – International service from/to stations in Germany (Tables **73** and **912**).
H – 12 ✕ Budapest - Wien - Zürich and v.v. (Table **86**).
J – 12 ✕ Bratislava - Wien - Zürich and v.v. (Table **86**).
N – 🛏 1, 2 cl. ▬ 2 cl. and 2 Zürich - Graz and v.v. Also conveys through cars to/from Zagreb (Table **86**).

W – 🛏 1, 2 cl. ▬ 2 cl. and 2 Zürich - Wien - Budapest and v.v. (Table **86**).

c – Ⓒ only.
k – Not Dec. 25, Jan. 1, Apr. 15.
r – Also Dec. 25, Jan. 1, Apr. 15.
t – Ⓐ (not Dec. 27–31, May 27).

v – Not Dec. 24, 25, Jan. 1, Apr. 15.
z – Not Dec. 12, 25, 26, Jan. 2, Apr. 16.

‡ – Runs as *ICE* **3** on May 26, Aug. 1.
◇ – Operated by SOB.
⊡ – Operated by SBB on Ⓐ, by SOB on Ⓒ.
⊙ – Operated by SBB on ⑦–④ **r**, by SOB on ⑤⑥ **k**.

522 (ZÜRICH -) ZIEGELBRÜCKE - LINTHAL — SBB, SOB

km												
	Zürich HB .... 520 d.	...	...	...	0643		1743	...	1843	...		...
	Wädenswil .... 520 d.	...	...	...	0700	and	1800	...	1900	...	and	...
	Pfäffikon .... 520 d.	...	...	...	0706		1806	...	1906	...		...
0	**Ziegelbrücke** ...... 520 d.	0430	0530	0630	0730	hourly	1830	1903	1930	2003	hourly	2303
11	Glarus .... d.	0446	0546	0646	0746		1846	1916	1946	2016		2316
16	Schwanden .... d.	0459	0559	0659	0759	until	1859	1929	1954	2029	until	2329
27	**Linthal** .... a.	0516	0616	0716	0816		1916	1946	...	2046		2346

	Ⓐ								
Linthal .... d.	0442	0542		1842	...	1946	2012		0012
Schwanden .... d.	0504	0604	and	1904	1934	2004	2034	and	0034
Glarus .... d.	0513	0615		1915	1943	2015	2043		0043
Ziegelbrücke .... 520 a.	0526	0629	hourly	1929	1956	2029	2056	hourly	0056
Pfäffikon .... 520 a.	0551	0651		1951	...	...	...		...
Wädenswil .... 520 a.	0559	0659	until	1959	...	...	...	until	...
Zürich HB .... 520 a.	0617	0717		2017	...	...	...		...

525 LUZERN - ARTH GOLDAU - ST GALLEN — SOB

km			*IR*			*IR*					*IR*			*IR*				*IR*		*IR*		*IR*		
			2009			**2011**					**2013**			**2015**	⊠			**2039**		**2041**		**2043**		
			V			**V**					**V**			**V**				**V**					⑤⑥ k	
0	**Luzern** .... 547 550 d.	...	...	...	...	...	0539	...	...	0639	...	...	...	0739		...	...	1939	...	*2039*	...	*2139*	*2218*	*2218*
16	Küssnacht am Rigi...... d.	...	...	...	...	...	0558	...	...	0658	...	...	...	0800	and at	...	...	2000	...	*2059*	...	*2159*	|	|
28	**Arth Goldau 547 550** a.	...	...	...	...	...	0610	...	...	0710	...	...	...	0811		...	...	2011	...	*2111*	...	*2211*	*2245*	*2245*
28	**Arth Goldau** .... d.	...	...	...	...	...	*0619*	...	...	*0713*	...	...	...	0816	the same	...	...	2016	...	2116	...	2216	2315	2315
	Einsiedeln .... ● d.	0516	...	0541**r**	0616	...	|	0645	0711	|	...	0746	0811	|		1946	2011	|	2111	|	2211	|	|	|
48	Biberbrugg .... ● d.	0523	0537**a**	0550**r**	0625	0637	*0647*	0652	0725**f**	*0735*	0737	0752	0825**f**	0837	minutes	1952	2025**f**	2037	2125**f**	2137	2225**f**	2237	2339	2339
54	Samstagern .... ● d.	0533	|	0601	0633	|	...	0701	0733	...	|	0801	0833	|		2001	2033	|	2133	2144	2233	2244	2348	2348
62	Pfäffikon .... d.	0546	0554**a**	0616	0646	0654	...	0716	0746	...	0754	0816	0846	0854	past each	2016	2046	2054	2146	2154	2246	2254	0001	0001
66	**Rapperswil** .... a.	0553	0600**a**	0623	0653	0700	...	0723	0753	...	0800	0823	0853	0900		2023	2053	2100	2153	2200	2253	2303	0006	0006
66	**Rapperswil** .... d.	...	0603	...	...	0703	...	...	...	...	0803	...	...	0903	hour until	...	...	2103	...	2203	...	2303	0006	...
94	Wattwil .... d.	...	0627	...	...	0727	...	...	...	...	0827	...	...	0927		...	...	2127	...	2227	...	2327	0029	...
117	Herisau .... d.	...	0647	...	...	0747	...	...	...	...	0847	...	...	0947		...	...	2147	...	2247	...	2347	0048	...
125	**St Gallen** .... a.	...	0655	...	...	0755	...	...	...	...	0855	...	...	0955		...	...	2155	...	2255	...	2355	0056	...

				IR			*IR*				*IR*				*IR*			*IR*		*IR*		*IR*	*IR*	*IR*
				2006			**2008**				**2010**		⊠		**2034**			**2036**		**2038**		**2040**	**2042**	**2044**
	Ⓐ			**V**			**V**				**V**				**V**									
St Gallen .... d.	...	...	...	0505	...	...	0605	...	...	...	0705	...		...	1905	...	...	2005	...	2105	...	2205	2305	0005
Herisau .... d.	...	...	...	0513	...	...	0613	...	...	...	0713	...	and at	...	1913	...	...	2013	...	2113	...	2213	2313	0013
Wattwil .... d.	...	...	...	0532	...	...	0632	...	...	...	0732	...		...	1932	...	...	2032	...	2132	...	2232	2332	0032
Rapperswil .... a.	...	...	...	0557	...	...	0657	...	...	...	0757	...	the same	...	1957	...	...	2057	...	2157	...	2257	2357	0057
Rapperswil .... d.	0506	...	0536	0559	0606	...	0659	...	0706	0736	0759	0806		1936	1959	2006	2036	2059	2106	2159	2206	2257	0006	...
Pfäffikon .... d.	0511	...	0541	0603	0611	...	0703	...	0711	0741	0803	0811	minutes	1941	2003	2011	2041	2103	2111	2203	2211	2301	0011	...
Samstagern .... ● d.	0523	...	0555	|	0625	...	|	...	0725	0755	|	0825		1955	|	2025	2055	2112	2125	2212	2225	2313	0023	...
Biberbrugg .... ● d.	0531	...	0603	0619	0638**j**	0637	0719	0721	0739**j**	0805	0820	0839**j**	past each	2005	2020	2039**j**	2105	2120	2139**j**	2222	2239**j**	2322	...	...
Einsiedeln .... ● a.	|	...	|	▬	0645	|	▬	|	0746	0812	|	0846		2012	|	2046	2112	|	2146	|	2246	|	...	...
Arth Goldau .... a.	*0604*	...	*0630*	...	...	0704	...	0745	...	...	0845	...	hour until	...	2045	...	...	2145	...	2248	...	2349	...	...
Arth Goldau . 547 550 d.	...	0620	...	0646	...	*0715*	0746	*0815*	...	...	0849	...		...	2049	...	...	*2149*	...	*2315*	...	...	...	...
Küssnacht am Rigi ...... d.	...	0632	...	0700	...	|	0800	|	...	...	0901	...		...	2101	...	...	*2201*	...	|	...	...	...	...
Luzern .... 547 550 a.	...	0653	...	0721	...	*0741*	0821	*0841*	...	...	0921	...		...	2121	...	...	*2221*	...	*2341*	...	...	...	...

EINSIEDELN - BIBERBRUGG - WÄDENSWIL

km		Ⓐ							and at			
0	**Einsiedeln** .... d.	0454	0524	0557	0624	0657	0724	0759	the same	2224	2259	2324
6	Biberbrugg .... d.	0501	0532	0607	0632	0707	0732	0807	minutes	2232	2307	2332
11	Samstagern .... d.	0509	0541	0617	0641	0717	0741	0817	past each	2241	2317	2341
17	**Wädenswil** .... a.	0518	0550	0626	0640	0726	0750	0826	hour until	2250	2326	2350

	Ⓐ					and at			
Wädenswil .... d.	0541	0610	0634	0710	0734	the same	2310	2334	0015
Samstagern ... d.	0550	0617	0641	0717	0741	minutes	2317	2341	0025
Biberbrugg ..... d.	0558	0626	0651	0726	0752	past each	2326	2352	0033
Einsiedeln .... a.	0606	0633	0657	0733	0759	hour until	2333	2359	0040

V – VORALPEN EXPRESS – Most convey (🍷).
a – Ⓐ only.
f – Arrives 7 minutes earlier.
j – Arrives 4 – 5 minutes earlier.
k – Also Apr. 14, 17, May 25, 26, June 5, July 31, Oct. 31; not Dec. 24, 25.
r – On Ⓒ departs Einsiedeln 0546, Biberbrugg 0552.
⊠ – Train numbers increase by 2 each hour.
● – See panel below main table for services Einsiedeln - Samstagern - Wädenswil and v.v.

526 GOSSAU - APPENZELL - WASSERAUEN — Narrow gauge. AB

km		Ⓐ	e																								
0	**Gossau** ...... ▷ d.	0551	0621	0651	0721	0751	and at	1021	1051	1121	1151	1221	1321	1351	1421	1451	1521	1551	1621	1651	1721	1751	1851	1951	2051	2151
5	Herisau .... ▷ d.	0558	0628	0658	0728	0758	the same	1028	1058	1128	1158	1228	1328	1358	1428	1458	1528	1558	1628	1658	1728	1758	1858	1958	2058	2158
15	Urnäsch ...... ▷ d.	0613	0643	0713	0743	0813	minutes	1043	1113	1143	1213	1243	1343	1413	1443	1513	1543	1613	1643	1713	1743	1813	1913	2013	2113	2213
26	**Appenzell** ... ▷ a.	0630	0700	0730	0800	0830	past each	1100	1130	1200	1230	1300	1400	1430	1500	1530	1600	1630	1700	1730	1800	1830	1930	2030	2130	2230
32	**Wasserauen** ... a.	0643	0712	0743	0812**t**	0842	hour until	1112**t**	1142	1212	1242	1312	1412	1442**t**	1512	1542**t**	1612	1642	1712	1742	1812	1842	*1946**	*2046**	*2146*‡	...

Wasserauen .... d.	...	0648**a**	0718**e**	0748	0818**t**	and at	1118**t**	1148	1218	1248	1318	1418	1448**t**	1518	1548**t**	1618	1648	1718	1748	1818	1848	...	*1947**	*2047**	*2147*‡	...
Appenzell ... ▷ d.	0630	0700	0730	0800	0830	the same	1130	1200	1230	1300	1330	1430	1500	1530	1600	1630	1700	1730	1800	1830	1900	1930	2000	2100	2200	2300
Urnäsch .... ▷ d.	0645	0715	0745	0815	0845	minutes	1145	1215	1245	1315	1345	1445	1515	1545	1615	1645	1715	1745	1815	1845	1915	1945	2015	2115	2215	2315
Herisau .... ▷ d.	0702	0732	0802	0832	0902	past each	1202	1232	1302	1332	1402	1502	1532	1602	1632	1702	1732	1802	1832	1902	1932	2002	2032	2132	2232	2332
Gossau .... ▷ a.	0708	0738	0808	0838	0908	hour until	1208	1238	1308	1338	1408	1508	1538	1608	1638	1708	1738	1808	1838	1908	1938	2008	2038	2138	2238	2338

a – Ⓐ only.
e – Ⓐ to Apr. 22; ⚒ Apr. 25 - Nov. 4; ①–⑤ from Nov. 7.
t – Apr. 30 - Oct. 30.
* – By 🚌 from / to Appenzell.
‡ – Apr. 30 - Oct. 30. By 🚌 from / to Appenzell.
▷ – **Additional journeys** Gossau - Appenzell:
From Gossau at 1251, 1821, 1921, 2021, 2251 and 2351.
From Appenzell at 0500 ⚒, 0530 Ⓑ, 0600 **e** and 1400.

527 ST GALLEN - APPENZELL — Narrow gauge rack railway. AB

km		⑥⑦	⑥⑦	⑥⑦		⚒	Ⓒ	Ⓐ		⑥	Ⓐ						♣							
		z 🚌	z 🚌	z 🚌						h														
0	**St Gallen** .... d.	0026	0137	0243	...	0520	0550	0550	0620	0650	0650	0720	0750	...	0826	0856	and every	2226	2256	...	2326	...	...	...
7	Teufen .... d.	0038	0149	0255	...	0534	0604	0604	0634	0704	0704	0734	0804	...	0841	0911	30 minutes	2241	2311	...	2341	...	...	...
14	Gais ▲ .... d.	0048	0159	0305	...	0547	0617	0619	0647	0717	0719	0747	0817	...	0854	0924	until	2254	2324	...	2354	...	...	...
20	**Appenzell** .... a.	0059	0210	0316	...	0558	0628	0630	0658	0728	0730	0758	0828	...	0905	0935		2305	2335	...	0005	...	...	...

	⑥⑦	⑥⑦		⚒		Ⓐ	⚒		Ⓐ						♠						⑤⑥		
	z 🚌	z 🚌	...																		k 🚌		
Appenzell .... d.	0104	0210	...	0508	0538	0558	0608	0638	0658	0708	0738	...	0814	0844	and every	2214	2244	...	2314	...	2353	...	...
Gais ▲ .... d.	0113	0219	...	0521	0551	0607	0621	0651	0707	0721	0751	...	0827	0857	30 minutes	2227	2257	...	2327	...	0002	...	...
Teufen .... d.	0123	0229	...	0534	0604	0618	0634	0704	0718	0734	0804	...	0840	0910	until	2240	2310	...	2340	...	0012	...	...
St Gallen .... a.	0137	0243	...	0550	0620	0633	0650	0720	0733	0750	0820	...	0856	0926		2256	2326	...	2356	...	0026	...	...

h – Not Dec. 25, Jan. 1.
k – Also Apr. 14, 17, May 25, 26, June 5, July 31, Oct. 31; not Dec. 24, 25.
z – Also Apr. 15, 18, May 26, 27, June 6, Aug. 1, Nov. 1; not Dec. 25, Jan. 1.
♣ – On Ⓐ the 1726 and 1826 from St Gallen run 2 minutes later Gais - Appenzell.
♠ – On Ⓐ the 1714 and 1814 from Appenzell depart Gais 3 minutes **earlier**. On Ⓐ Appenzell d. 1747 / 1847 (not 1744 / 1844).
▲ – Rail service **Gais - Altstätten Stadt** and v.v. *8 km*. Journey time: 20 – 23 minutes. **Operator**: AB.
From **Gais** at 0620 Ⓐ, 0720, 0824 and hourly until 1824; then 1924 🚌 and 2024 🚌.
From **Altstätten Stadt** at 0654 Ⓐ, 0754, 0900 and hourly until 1900; then 2000 🚌 and 2100 🚌.
A connecting 🚌 service operates Altstätten Stadt - Altstätten SBB station (in Table **534**).
Journey time: 6 minutes.

529 WINTERTHUR - SCHAFFHAUSEN — SBB

km																							
0	**Winterthur** .... d.	0542	0606	0619	0642	and at the same	2106	2119	2142	2206	2242	2306	2342	0012	...	...	...	...	...	...	...	...
26	Schloss Laufen am Rheinfall. d.	0606	0630	|	0706	minutes past	2130	|	2206	2230	2306	2330	0006	0036	...	...	...	...	...	...	...	...
30	**Schaffhausen** .... a.	0613	0638	0646	0713	each hour until	2138	2146	2213	2238	2313	2338	0013	0043	...	...	...	...	...	...	...	...

Schaffhausen .... d.	0515	0521	0546	and at the same	2015	2021	2046	2121	2146	2221	2246	2321	2347	...	...	...	...	...	...	...	...
Schloss Laufen am Rheinfall .... d.	|	0526	0550	minutes past	|	2026	2050	2126	2150	2226	2250	2326	2351	...	...	...	...	...	...	...	...
Winterthur .... a.	0542	0554	0619	each hour until	2042	2054	2119	2154	2219	2254	2319	2354	0023	...	...	...	...	...	...	...	...

SBB ZÜRICH - ST GALLEN 530

km		IR 3251			IR 3253		IC 701	IC 505	IR 3255	IC 1507	IC 703	IC 507	IR 3257	EC 97	IC 705	IC 509	IR 3259	IC 1511	IC 707	IC 511	IR 3261	EC 99	IC 709	IC 513
										Ⓐ				A				Ⓐ						
							✕	✕		✕	✕	✕		M✕	F✕	✕		✕	✕	✕		M✕	✕	✕
	Genève **505** ▷ d.	...	...	...	...	...	...	...	...	...	...	...	...	...	...	...	...	...	0542	0612	...	...	0642	0715
	Lausanne **505** d.	...	...	...	...	...	...	...	...	...	...	...	...	...	...	0542	...	0615	0620	|	...	...	0720	|
	Biel/Bienne **505** d.	...	...	...	...	...	...	...	...	0516	...	0543	...	...	...	0644	...	0717	|	0746	...	...	|	0846
	Bern **505** d.	...	...	...	...	...	...	...	...	|	0529j	|	...	...	0631	|	...	|	0731	|	...	...	0831	|
0	**Zürich** HB ● **535** d.	...	...	...	...	...	0539	0603	0609	0633	0639	0703	0709	0733	0739	0803	0809	0833	0839	0903	0909	0933	0939	1003
10	**Zürich** Flughafen ✈ ● **535** d.	...	...	...	...	...	0553	0613	0623	0643	0653	0713	0723	0743	0753	0813	0823	0843	0853	0913	0923	0943	0953	1013
30	Winterthur **535** d.	...	...	0511	...	...	0608	0629	0638	0659	0708	0729	0738	0758	0808	0829	0838	0859	0908	0929	0938	0958	1008	1029
57	Wil d.	0456	...	0542	0556	...	0626	|	0656	|	0726	|	0756	|	0826	|	0856	|	0926	|	0956	|	1026	|
78	Gossau d.	0515	...	...	0615	...	0645	|	0715	|	0745	|	0815	|	0845	|	0915	|	0945	|	1015	|	1045	|
87	**St Gallen** **534** a.	0522	...	...	0622	...	0652	0702	0722	0732	0752	0802	0822	0830	0852	0902	0922	0932	0952	1002	1022	1030	1052	1102
103	Rorschach **534** a.	0539	...	...	0639	...	...	0721	0739	...	...	0821	0839	...	...	0921	0939	...	...	1021	1039	...	...	1121
	Chur **534** a.	0648	...	...	0748	...	...	...	0848	...	...	...	0948	...	...	...	1048	...	...	...	1148	...	...	...

	IR 3263	IC 711	IC 515	IR 3265	EC 191	IC 713	IC 517	IR 3267	IC 715	IC 519	IR 3269	EC 193	IC 717	IC 521	IR 3271	IC 719	IC 523	IR 3273	IC 721	IC 525	IR 3275	IC 1527	IC 723	IC 527
												A										Ⓐ		
		✕	✕		M✕	✕	✕		✕	✕		M✕	✕	✕		✕	✕		✕	✕		✕	✕	✕
Genève **505** ▷ d.	...	0742	0815	...	...	0842	0915	...	0942	1015	...	...	1042	1115	...	1142	1215	...	1242	1315	...	...	1342	1415
Lausanne **505** d.	...	0820	|	...	...	0920	|	...	1020	|	...	...	1120	|	...	1220	|	...	1320	|	...	1415	1420	|
Biel/Bienne **505** d.	...	|	0946	...	...	|	1046	...	|	1146	...	...	|	1246	...	|	1346	...	|	1446	...	1517	|	1546
Bern **505** d.	...	0931	|	...	...	1031	|	...	1131	|	...	...	1231	|	...	1331	|	...	1431	|	...	|	1531	|
Zürich HB ● **535** d.	1009	1039	1103	1109	1133	1139	1203	1209	1239	1303	1309	1333	1339	1403	1409	1439	1503	1509	1539	1603	1609	1633	1639	1703
Zürich Flughafen ✈ ● **535** d.	1023	1053	1113	1123	1143	1153	1213	1223	1253	1313	1323	1343	1353	1413	1423	1453	1513	1523	1553	1613	1623	1643	1653	1713
Winterthur **535** d.	1038	1108	1129	1138	1158	1208	1229	1238	1308	1329	1338	1358	1408	1429	1438	1508	1529	1538	1608	1629	1638	1659	1708	1729
Wil d.	1056	1126	|	1156	|	1226	|	1256	1326	|	1356	|	1426	|	1456	1526	|	1556	1626	|	1656	|	1726	|
Gossau d.	1115	1145	|	1215	|	1245	|	1315	1345	|	1415	|	1445	|	1515	1545	|	1615	1645	|	1715	|	1745	|
St Gallen **534** a.	1122	1152	1202	1222	1230	1252	1302	1322	1352	1402	1422	1430	1452	1502	1522	1552	1602	1622	1652	1702	1722	1732	1752	1802
Rorschach **534** a.	1139	...	1221	1239	...	...	1321	1339	...	1421	1439	...	...	1521	1539	...	1621	1639	...	1721	1739	...	...	1821z
Chur **534** a.	1248	...	...	1348	...	...	...	1448	...	...	1548	...	...	...	1648	...	...	1748	...	...	1848	...	...	...

	IR 3277	EC 197	IC 725	IC 529	IR 3279	IC 1531	IC 727	IC 531	IR 3281	EC 199	IC 729	IC 533	IR 3283	IC 731	IR 3285	IC 733	IR 3287	IC 735	IR 3289			IR 3293		
		¶				Ⓐ																		
		M✕	✕	✕		✕	✕	✕	S	M✕	✕	✕		✕		✕				◇				
Genève **505** ▷ d.	...	...	1442	1515	...	...	1542	1615	...	...	1642	1715	...	1742	...	1842	...	1942	...	...	...	...	...	...
Lausanne **505** d.	...	...	1520	|	...	1615	1620	|	...	...	1720	|	...	1820	...	1920	...	2020	...	...	...	...	...	...
Biel/Bienne **505** d.	...	...	|	1646	...	1717	|	1746	...	...	|	1846	...	|	...	|	...	|	...	...	...	...	...	...
Bern **505** d.	...	...	1631	|	...	|	1731	|	...	...	1831	|	...	1931	...	2031	...	2131	...	...	...	...	...	...
Zürich HB ● **535** d.	1709	1733	1739	1803	1809	1833	1839	1903	1909	1933	1939	2003	2009	2039	2109	2139	2209	2239	2309	2339	...	0017	...	...
Zürich Flughafen ✈ ● **535** d.	1723	1743	1753	1813	1823	1843	1853	1913	1923	1943	1953	2013	2023	2053	2123	2153	2223	2253	2323	2353	...	0030	...	...
Winterthur **535** d.	1738	1758	1808	1829	1838	1859	1908	1929	1938	1958	2008	2029	2038	2108	2138	2208	2238	2308	2338	0009	...	0045	...	...
Wil d.	1756	|	1826	|	1856	|	1926	|	1956	|	2026	|	2056	2126	2156	2226	2256	2326	2356	0031	...	0103	...	...
Gossau d.	1815	|	1845	|	1915	|	1945	|	2015	|	2045	|	2115	2145	2215	2245	2315	2345	0015	0048	...	0120	...	...
St Gallen **534** a.	1822	1830	1852	1902	1922	1932	1952	2002	2022	2030	2052	2102	2122	2152	2222	2252	2322	2352	0022	0055	...	0128	...	...
Rorschach **534** a.	1839	...	...	1921	1939	...	...	2021	2039	...	...	...	...	...	...	...	...	...	...	...	...	...	...	...
Chur **534** a.	1948	...	...	...	2048	...	...	...	...	...	...	...	...	...	...	...	...	...	...	...	...	...	...	...

	IR 3292				IR 3252	IC 706	IR 3254	IC 510	IC 708	IC 1510	IR 3256	IC 512	IC 710	EC 290	IR 3258	IC 514	IC 712	IR 3260	IC 516	IC 714	EC 198	IR 3262	IC 518	IC 716
		⑥⑦	⑥⑦							Ⓐ				①–⑤										
		c◇	c			✕		✕	✕	✕	S	✕	✕	L✕		✕	✕		✕	✕	M✕		✕	✕
Chur **534** d.	...	...	...	...	...	...	...	...	...	...	...	...	...	...	0611	...	...	0711	...	...	...	0811	...	...
Rorschach **534** d.	...	...	...	...	...	...	...	0539	...	...	0621	0639	...	...	0721	0739	...	0821	0839	...	...	0921	0939	...
St Gallen **534** d.	0037	...	...	...	0437	0507	0537	0558	0607	0628	0637	0658	0707	0729	0737	0758	0807	0837	0858	0907	0929	0937	0958	1007
Gossau d.	0044	...	...	...	0444	0514	0544	|	0614	|	0644	|	0714	|	0744	|	0814	0844	|	0914	|	0944	|	1014
Wil d.	0102	0105	...	...	0504	0534	0604	|	0634	|	0704	|	0734	|	0804	|	0834	0904	|	0934	|	1004	|	1034
Winterthur **535** d.	...	0127	0135	...	0524	0554	0624	0633	0654	0703	0724	0733	0754	0803	0824	0833	0854	0924	0933	0954	1003	1024	1033	1054
Zürich Flughafen ✈ ● **535** a.	...	...	|	...	0536	0606	0636	0646	0706	0716	0736	0746	0806	0816	0836	0846	0906	0936	0946	1006	1016	1036	1046	1106
Zürich HB ● **535** a.	...	...	0158	...	0551	0621	0651	0657	0721	0727	0751	0757	0821	0827	0851	0857	0921	0951	0957	1021	1027	1051	1057	1121
Bern **505** a.	...	...	...	...	...	0728	...	|	0828	|	...	|	0928	...	...	|	1028	...	|	1128	...	...	|	1228
Biel/Bienne **505** a.	...	...	...	...	...	|	...	0813	|	0843	...	0913	|	...	...	1013	|	...	1113	|	...	...	1213	|
Lausanne **505** a.	...	...	...	...	...	0840	...	|	0940	0945	...	|	1040	...	...	|	1140	...	|	1240	...	...	|	1340
Genève **505** ▷ a.	...	...	...	...	...	0918	...	0947	1018	...	...	1047	1118	...	...	1147	1218	...	1247	1318	...	...	1347	1418

	IR 3264	IC 520	IC 718	EC 196	IR 3266	IC 522	IC 720	IR 3268	IC 524	IC 722	IR 3270	IC 526	IC 724	IR 3272	IC 528	IC 726	EC 192	IR 3274	IC 530	IC 728	IC 1530	IR 3276	IC 532	IC 730
				A													A				Ⓐ			
		✕	✕	M✕		✕	✕		✕	✕		✕	✕		✕	✕	M✕		✕	✕	✕		✕	✕
Chur **534** d.	0911	...	...	...	1011	...	...	1111	...	...	1211	...	...	1311	...	...	...	1411	...	...	...	1511	...	...
Rorschach **534** d.	1021	1039	...	...	1121	1139	...	1221	1239	...	1321	1339	...	1421	1439	...	...	1521	1539	...	...	1621	1639	...
St Gallen **534** d.	1037	1058	1107	1129	1137	1158	1207	1237	1258	1307	1337	1358	1407	1437	1458	1507	1529	1537	1558	1607	1628	1637	1658	1707
Gossau d.	1044	|	1114	|	1144	|	1214	1244	|	1314	1344	|	1414	1444	|	1514	|	1544	|	1614	|	1644	|	1714
Wil d.	1104	|	1134	|	1204	|	1234	1304	|	1334	1404	|	1434	1504	|	1534	|	1604	|	1634	|	1704	|	1734
Winterthur **535** d.	1124	1133	1154	1203	1224	1233	1254	1324	1331	1354	1424	1433	1454	1524	1533	1554	1603	1624	1633	1654	1703	1724	1733	1754
Zürich Flughafen ✈ ● **535** a.	1136	1146	1206	1216	1236	1246	1306	1336	1346	1406	1436	1446	1506	1536	1546	1606	1616	1636	1646	1706	1716	1736	1746	1806
Zürich HB ● **535** a.	1151	1157	1221	1227	1251	1257	1321	1351	1357	1421	1451	1457	1521	1551	1557	1621	1627	1651	1657	1721	1727	1751	1757	1821
Bern **505** a.	...	|	1328	...	...	|	1428	...	|	1528	...	|	1628	...	|	1728	...	...	|	1828	|	...	|	1928
Biel/Bienne **505** a.	...	1313	|	...	...	1413	|	...	1513	|	...	1613	|	...	1713	|	...	...	1813	|	1843	...	1913	|
Lausanne **505** a.	...	|	1440	...	...	|	1540	...	|	1640	...	|	1740	...	|	1840	...	...	|	1940	1945	...	|	2040
Genève **505** ▷ a.	...	1447	1518	...	...	1547	1618	...	1647	1718	...	1747	1818	...	1847	1918	...	...	1947	2018	...	...	2047	2118

	EC 190	IR 3278	IC 534	IC 732	IC 1534	IR 3280	IC 536	IC 734	EC 98	IR 3282	IC 538	IC 736		IR 3284		IC 738	EC 96	IR 3286	EC 96		IR 3288		IR 3290	
					Ⓐ												A		B					
	M✕		✕	✕	✕		✕	✕	M✕		✕	F✕				✕	M✕		M✕	◇				
Chur **534** d.	...	1611	...	...	...	1711	...	...	...	1811	...	...	...	1911	...	...	...	2011	...	...	...	...	...	...
Rorschach **534** d.	...	1721	1739z	...	...	1821	1839	...	...	1921	1939	...	...	2021	...	...	...	2121	...	...	...	...	...	...
St Gallen **534** d.	1729	1737	1758	1807	1828	1837	1858	1907	1929	1937	1958	2007	...	2037	...	2107	2129	2137	2158	2213	2237	...	2337	...
Gossau d.	|	1744	|	1814	|	1844	|	1914	|	1944	|	2014	...	2044	...	2114	|	2144	|	2222	2244	...	2344	...
Wil d.	|	1804	|	1834	|	1904	|	1934	|	2004	|	2034	...	2104	...	2134	|	2204	|	2239	2304	...	0004	...
Winterthur **535** d.	1803	1824	1833	1854	1903	1924	1933	1954	2003	2024	2033	2054	...	2124	...	2154	2203	2224	2233	2301	2324	...	0028	...
Zürich Flughafen ✈ ● **535** a.	1816	1836	1846	1906	1916	1936	1946	2006	2016	2036	2046	2106	...	2136	...	2206	2216	2236	2246	2314	2336	...	0040	...
Zürich HB ● **535** a.	1827	1851	1857	1921	1927	1951	1957	2021	2027	2051	2057	2121	...	2151	...	2221	2227	2251	2257	2325	2351	...	0053	...
Bern **505** a.	...	...	|	2028	|	...	|	2128	...	...	|	2228	...	...	...	2331	...	...	...	...	...	...	...	...
Biel/Bienne **505** a.	...	...	2013	|	2043	...	2113	|	...	...	2213	...	...	...	...	...	...	...	...	...	...	...	...	...
Lausanne **505** a.	...	...	|	2140	2145	...	|	2240	...	...	...	...	...	...	...	...	...	...	...	...	...	...	...	...
Genève **505** ▷ a.	...	...	2147k	...	...	...	2247k	2318k	...	...	...	...	...	...	...	...	...	...	...	...	...	...	...	...

A – From Apr. 11.
B – Until Apr. 10.
F – From/to Fribourg (Table **505**).
L – From Lindau (Table **75**).
M – From/to München (Table **75**).
S – From/to Sargans (Table **534**).

c – Also Apr. 15, 18, May 26, 27, June 6, Aug. 1; not Dec. 25, 26.
j – 0513 on Feb. 7, 28, Mar. 26, 27, 28, May 9, 16, 21, 22, 23, June 13, 20 – 24, 27 – 30, July 1, 25, Sept. 5, 17, 18, 19, Oct. 3 – 7, 10 – 14, 29, 30, 31, Nov. 7, 28, Dec. 5.
k – ⑤⑥ only.
z – Change trains at St Gallen on Ⓐ.

¶ – Until Apr. 10 runs with train number **1197** and terminates at St Gallen.
◇ – Operated by THURBO.
▷ – Most Genève services start from/continue to Genève Aéroport (see Table **505**).
● – Frequent services operate **Zürich - Zürich Flughafen** and v.v. (up to 13 trains per hour 0600 - 2400).

533 SCHAFFHAUSEN - KREUZLINGEN (URh)

	✕A		✕B		✕A		✕A		
Schaffhausen d.	0910	...	1110	...	1318	...	1518	...	...
Stein am Rhein d.	1115	...	1315	...	1523	...	1723	...	...
Kreuzlingen Hafen a.	1355	...	1555	...	1805	...	2005j	...	...

	✕A		✕D	✕F		✕A		✕E	
Kreuzlingen Hafen d.	0900	...	1100	1200	...	1427	...	1627	...
Stein am Rhein d.	1130	...	1330	1530h	...	1657	...	1857	...
Schaffhausen a.	1245	...	1445	1645	...	1815	...	2015j	...

A – ④–① Apr. 15 – 24; daily Apr. 28 - Oct. 2.
B – ⑦ Apr. 17 - June 19 (also Apr. 15, 18, May 26, June 6, 16); daily June 25 - Sept. 11 (also Sept. 18, 25); daily Oct. 2 – 16.
D – ④–① Apr. 15 – 24; daily Apr. 28 - Oct. 16.
E – ⑦ Apr. 17 - June 19 (also Apr. 15, 18, May 26, June 6, 16); daily June 26 - Sept. 11 (also Sept. 18, 25, Oct. 2).
F – ④ June 30 - Sept. 8.
h – Arrives 1425.
j – Not Aug. 13.

534 WIL - ST GALLEN - BUCHS - CHUR (SBB)

km		IR 3251	IR 3253	IR 3255	IR 3257	EC 97	IR 3259	IR 3261	EC 99	IR 3263	IR 3265	EC 191	IR 3267	IR 3269	EC 193	IR 3271	IR 3273	IR 3275	IR 3277	EC 197	IR 3279	IR 3281	EC 199				
		W	W			AM			M			M			AM					AM			M	◇	◇	◇	◇
	Zürich HB **530** d.	...	...	0609	0709	0733	0809	0909	0933	1009	1109	1133	1209	1309	1333	1409	1509	1609	1709	1733	1809	1909	1933	...	...	...	...
0	**St Gallen** 530 d.	0525	0625	0725	0825	0832	0925	1025	1032	1125	1225	1232	1325	1425	1432	1525	1625	1725	1825	1832	1925	2025	2032	2125	2225	2325	0026
16	Rorschach 530 d.	0539	0639	0739	0839	|	0939	1039	|	1139	1239	|	1339	1439	|	1539	1639	1739	1839	|	1939	2039	|	2139	2239	2339	0043
27	**St Margrethen** d.	0547	0647	0747	0847	0849	0947	1047	1049	1147	1247	1249	1347	1447	1449	1547	1647	1747	1847	1849	1947	2047	2049	2147	2247	2347	0053
39	Altstätten d.	0559	0659	0759	0859	...	0959	1059	...	1159	1259	...	1359	1459	...	1559	1659	1759	1859	...	1959	2059	...	2200	2300	0002	0107
65	**Buchs** 520 d.	0615	0715	0815	0915	...	1015	1115	...	1215	1315	...	1415	1515	...	1615	1715	1815	1915	...	2015	2115	...	2215	2315	0018	...
81	Sargans ⊖ 520 a.	0624	0724	0824	0924	...	1024	1124	...	1224	1324	...	1424	1524	...	1624	1724	1824	1924	...	2024	2124	...	2225	2325	0028	...
93	Landquart 520 a.	0638	0737	0837	0937	...	1037	1137	...	1237	1337	...	1437	1537	...	1637	1737	1837	1937	...	2037	*2137*	...	*2237*	*2338*	*0041*	...
107	**Chur** 520 a.	0648	0748	0848	0948	...	1048	1148	...	1248	1348	...	1448	1548	...	1648	1748	1848	1948	...	2048	*2147*	...	*2247*	*2348*	*0051*	...

	IR 3256	EC 290	IR 3258	IR 3260	EC 198	IR 3262	IR 3264	EC 196	IR 3266	IR 3268	IR 3270	IR 3272	EC 192	IR 3274	IR 3276	EC 190	IR 3278	IR 3280	EC 98	IR 3282	IR 3284	EC 96	IR 3286	EC 96			
		L			M			AM					AM			M			M			AM		BM	◇	◇	◇
Chur 520 d.	*0508*r	...	0611	0711	...	0811	0911	...	1011	1111	1211	1311	...	1411	1511	...	1611	1711	...	1811	1911	...	2011	...	*2114*	*2214*	*2301*
Landquart 520 d.	*0518*r	...	0621	0721	...	0821	0921	...	1021	1121	1221	1321	...	1421	1521	...	1621	1721	...	1821	1921	...	2021	...	*2122*	*2222*	*2309*
Sargans ⊖ 520 d.	0536	...	0636	0736	...	0836	0936	...	1036	1136	1236	1336	...	1436	1536	...	1636	1736	...	1836	1936	...	2036	...	2136	2236	2339
Buchs 520 d.	0545	...	0645	0745	...	0845	0945	...	1045	1145	1245	1345	...	1445	1545	...	1645	1745	...	1845	1945	...	2045	...	2145	2245	2348
Altstätten d.	0601	...	0701	0801	...	0901	1001	...	1101	1201	1301	1401	...	1501	1601	...	1701	1801	...	1901	2001	...	2101	...	2201	2301	0003
St Margrethen d.	0613	0710	0713	0813	0910	0913	1013	1110	1113	1213	1313	1413	1510	1513	1613	1710	1713	1813	1910	1913	2013	2110	2113	2118	2213	2313	0013
Rorschach 530 d.	0621	|	0721	0821	|	0921	1021	|	1121	1221	1321	1421	|	1521	1621	|	1721	1821	|	1921	2021	|	2121	|	2221	2321	0021
St Gallen 530 a.	0635	0728	0735	0835	0928	0935	1035	1128	1135	1235	1335	1435	1528	1535	1635	1728	1735	1835	1928	1935	2035	2128	2135	2155	2234	2334	0034
Zürich HB **530** a.	0751	0827	0851	0951	1027	1051	1151	1227	1251	1351	1451	1551	1627	1651	1751	1827	1851	1951	2027	2051	2151	2227	2251	2257	...	...	...

🚌 FELDKIRCH (AUSTRIA) - VADUZ (LIECHTENSTEIN) - SARGANS 🚌. Line number 11.

	①–⑤ z	①–⑥ v	①–⑥ v																					
Feldkirch (Bahnhof) d.	...	...	...	...	0624	0654	and at the	1724	1754	1824	1854	1924	1954	2024	2054	2124	2154	2224	2254	...	...	...	...	...
Schaan (Bahnhof) d.	0515	0530	0600	0630	0700	0730	same minutes	1800	1830	1900	1930	2000	2030	2100	2130	2200	2230	2300	2330	...	...	...	...	...
Vaduz Post d.	0526	0541	0611	0641	0711	0741	past each	1811	1841	1909	1941	2009	2041	2109	2141	2209	2239	2309	2339	...	...	...	...	...
Sargans (Bahnhof) a.	0557	0612	0642	0712	0742	0812	hour until	1842	1912	...	2012	...	2112	...	2212	...	...	...	...	...	...	...	...	...

	①–⑤ z	①–⑥ v		①–⑤ z		①–⑤ z			①–⑤ z															
Sargans (Bahnhof) d.	...	...	...	0544	...	0614	0644	...	0714	0744	0814	and at the	1844	1914	1944	...	2044	...	2144	...	2244	...	...	...	...
Vaduz Post d.	0518	0548	0618	0618	0648	0648	0718	0748	0748	0818	0848	same minutes	1918	1948	2018	2048	2118	2148	2218	2248	2318	...	...	...	...
Schaan (Bahnhof) d.	0530	0600	0630	0630	0700	0700	0730	0800	0800	0830	0900	past each	1930	2000	2030	2100	2130	2200	2230	2300	2326	...	...	...	...
Feldkirch (Bahnhof) a.	0606	0636	0706	0706	0736	0736	0806	0836	0836	0906	0936	hour until	2006	2036	2106	2136	2206	2236	2306	2336	...	...	...	...	...

A – From Apr. 11.
B – Until Apr. 10.
L – ①–⑤ only. From Lindau (Table **75**).
M – 🚆12 ✕ Zürich - Bregenz - München and v.v.
W – From Wil (Table **530**).
r – ⚒ only.
v – Also Feb. 27; not Dec. 24, 25, Jan. 6, Feb. 2, Apr. 18, May 26, June 6, 16, Aug. 15, Sept. 8, Nov. 1, Dec. 8.
z – Not Dec. 24, 31, Jan. 6, Feb. 2, Apr. 15, 18, May 26, June 6, 16, Aug. 15, Sept. 8, Nov. 1, Dec. 8.
◇ – Operated by THURBO.
⊖ – See panel below main table for 🚌 links to/from Vaduz (Liechtenstein).

535 ZÜRICH - KONSTANZ and ROMANSHORN (SBB, THURBO)

km			RE 2103		IC 803		IR 2107		IC 805		IR 2109		IC 807		IR 2111		IC 809		IR 2113			IC 831		IR 2135		IC 833
		◇	Ⓐ	R	✕	◇		R	✕	◇		R	✕	◇		R	✕	◇		R	⊡⊠	✕	◇		R	✕
	Brig **560** d.	...	...	...	...	...	...	...	...	...	...	...	0546	...	...	...	0648	...	...	...		1748	...	...	...	1848
	Bern **505 560** d.	...	...	...	...	...	...	...	0602	...	...	...	0702	...	...	...	0802	...	...	...	and at	1902	...	...	...	2002
	Luzern **555** d.	...	...	...	...	...	0535	...	|	...	0635	...	|	...	0735	...	|	...	0835	...		|	...	1935	...	|
0	**Zürich** HB ‡530 d.	...	*0525*	...	0605	...	0635	...	0705	...	0735	...	0805	...	0835	...	0905	...	0935	...	the same	2005	...	2035	...	2105
10	**Zürich** Flug ✈ ‡530 d.	...	|	...	0616	...	0646	...	0716	...	0746	...	0816	...	0846	...	0916	...	0946	...	minutes	2016	...	2046	...	2116
30	Winterthur 530 d.	...	0601	...	0631	...	0701	...	0731	...	0801	...	0831	...	0901	...	0931	...	1001	...		2031	...	2101	...	2131
46	Frauenfeld d.	...	0612	...	0642	...	0712	...	0742	...	0812	...	0842	...	0912	...	0942	...	1012	...	past each	2042	...	2112	...	2142
64	Weinfelden 538/9 d.	0606	0625	0627	0655	0706	0725	0727	0755	0806	0825	0827	0855	0906	0925	0927	0955	1006	1025	1027	hour until	2055	2106	2125	2127	2155
87	Kreuzlingen a.	0631	0643	|	|	0731	0743	|	|	0831	0843	|	|	0931	0943	|	|	1031	1043	|		|	2131	2143	|	|
88	**Konstanz** a.	0634	0650	|	|	0742	0750	|	|	0834	0850	|	|	0934	0950	|	|	1034	1050	|		|	2134	2150	|	|
86	**Romanshorn** 538/9 a.	...	...	0642	0712	...	...	0742	0812	...	...	0842	0912	...	...	0942	1012	...	...	1042		2112	...	...	2142	2212

		IR 2137		IC 835		IR 2139		IC 837		RE 2145	RE 3547	
	◇		R		◇	¶	R		◇	◇	◇	◇
Brig **560** d.	...	...	...	1948	...	...	...	...	...	...	...	...
Bern **505 560** d.	...	...	...	2102	...	...	...	2202	...	...	...	...
Luzern **555** d.	...	...	...	|	...	...	...	|	...	...	...	...
Zürich HB ‡530 d.	...	2135	...	2205	...	2235	...	2305	...	2339	0008	...
Zürich Flug ✈ ‡530 d.	...	2146	...	2216	...	2246	...	2316	...	2353	0019	...
Winterthur 530 d.	...	2201	...	2231	...	2301	...	2331	...	0008	0034	...
Frauenfeld d.	...	2212	...	2242	...	2312	...	2342	...	0018	0045	...
Weinfelden 538/9 d.	2206	2225	2227	2255	2306	2325	2327	2355	0006	0030	0100	0106
Kreuzlingen a.	2231	2243	|	|	2331	2343	|	|	0030	0048	|	0130
Konstanz a.	2234	2250	|	|	2334	2350	|	|	0034	0051	|	0135
Romanshorn 538/9 a.	...	...	2242	2312	...	...	2342	0012	...	...	0117	...

		IR 2106		IC 806		IR 2108		IC 808	⊡✣
	R		◇	✕	R		◇	✕	
Romanshorn 538/9 d.	0517	...	...	0548	0617	...	...	0648	
Konstanz d.	|	0509	0524	|	|	0609	0624	|	and at
Kreuzlingen d.	|	0516	0527	|	|	0616	0627	|	
Weinfelden 538/9 d.	0533	0536	0554	0606	0633	0636	0654	0706	the same
Frauenfeld d.	...	0548	...	0618	...	0648	...	0718	minutes
Winterthur 530 d.	...	0601	...	0631	...	0701	...	0731	
Zürich Flughafen ✈ ‡530 a.	...	0614	...	0644	...	0714	...	0744	past each
Zürich HB ‡530 a.	...	0625	...	0655	...	0725	...	0755	hour until
Luzern **555** d.	...	0725	...	|	...	0825	...	|	
Bern **505 560** a.	...	...	...	0758	...	...	...	0858	
Brig **560** a.	...	...	...	0911	...	...	...	1011	

		IR 2130		IC 830		IR 2132		IC 832		IR 2134		IC 834		IR 2136		IC 836		IR 2138		IC 838		RE 2142		IC 840		RE 2146	
	R		◇	✕	R		◇	✕	R		◇	✕	R		◇	✕	R	§	◇		R	◇	◇		R	◇	◇
Romanshorn 538/9 d.	1717	...	...	1748	1817	...	...	1848	1917	...	...	1948	2017	...	...	2048	2117	...	...	2148	2217	...	...	2248	2317	...	...
Konstanz d.	|	1709	1724	|	|	1809	1824	|	|	1909	1924	|	|	2009	2024	|	|	2109	2124	|	|	2209	2224	|	|	2309	0009
Kreuzlingen d.	|	1716	1727	|	|	1816	1827	|	|	1916	1927	|	|	2016	2027	|	|	2116	2127	|	|	2216	2227	|	|	2316	0020
Weinfelden 538/9 d.	1733	1736	1754	1806	1833	1836	1854	1906	1933	1936	1954	2006	2033	2036	2054	2106	2133	2136	2154	2206	2233	2236	2254	2306	2333	2336	0047
Frauenfeld d.	...	1748	...	1818	...	1848	...	1918	...	1948	...	2018	...	2048	...	2118	...	2148	...	2218	...	2248	...	2318	...	2348	...
Winterthur 530 d.	...	1801	...	1831	...	1901	...	1931	...	2001	...	2031	...	2101	...	2131	...	2201	...	2231	...	2259	...	2331	...	2359	...
Zürich Flug ✈ ‡530 a.	...	1814	...	1844	...	1914	...	1944	...	2014	...	2044	...	2114	...	2144	...	2214	...	2244	...	|	...	2344	...	|	...
Zürich HB ‡530 a.	...	1825	...	1855	...	1925	...	1955	...	2025	...	2055	...	2125	...	2155	...	2225	...	2255	...	*2340*	...	2355	...	*0040*	...
Luzern **555** d.	...	1925	...	|	...	2025	...	|	...	2125	...	|	...	...	...	|	...	...	...	|	...	...	...	...	...	...	...
Bern **505 560** a.	...	...	...	1958	...	...	...	2058	...	...	...	2158	...	...	...	2302	...	...	...	0002	...	...	...	...	...	...	...
Brig **560** a.	...	...	...	2111	...	...	...	...	...	...	...	...	...	...	...	...	...	...	...	...	...	...	...	...	...	...	...

R – To/from Rorschach (Table **538**). Operated by THURBO.
§ – On ①②③④⑦ (also Dec. 25, Jan. 1, Apr. 15) runs as *RE* **2140** ◇.
¶ – On ①②③④⑦ (also Dec. 25, Jan. 1, Apr. 15) runs as *RE* **2141** ◇.
✣ – The 1609 from Konstanz terminates at Zürich HB.
⊠ – Passengers travelling on the 1635 from Luzern must change trains at Zürich HB.
⊡ – Train numbers increase by 2 each hour.
‡ – Frequent services operate **Zürich - Zürich Flughafen** and v.v. (up to 13 trains per hour 0600 - 2400).
◇ – Operated by THURBO.

BSB/SBS — ROMANSHORN - FRIEDRICHSHAFEN car ferry service — 536

	h	h	e	e			f	f
						and		
Romanshorn Fähre .... d.	0524	0624	0724	0824	0924	hourly	1824	1924	2024
Friedrichshafen Autoquai . a.	0608	0708	0808	0908	1008	until	1908	2008	2108

	h	h	e	e				f	f
						and			
Friedrichshafen Autoquai .. d.	0521	0621	0721	0821	0921	hourly	1821	1921	2021
Romanshorn Fähre .... a.	0605	0705	0805	0905	1005	until	1905	2005	2105

e – ①–⑥ to Mar. 26 (not Dec. 24, 25, 31, Jan. 1); daily Mar. 28 - Nov. 5; ①–⑥ from Nov. 7.
f – ①–⑤ to Mar. 25 (not Dec. 24 - Jan. 7); daily Mar. 28 - Nov. 4; ①–⑤ from Nov. 7.
h – ①–⑤ (not Dec. 24 - Jan. 7, Apr. 15, 18, May 26, June 6, Aug. 1).

Operator: BSB / SBS ✆ 071 466 78 88.

THURBO — SCHAFFHAUSEN - ROMANSHORN - RORSCHACH and ST GALLEN — 538

km								⚒																
0	**Schaffhausen** .... d.	...	...	...	...	...	...	...	...	0519	...	0549	...	...	0619	...	and at	1949	...	...	2019	...	2049	...
20	Stein am Rhein .... d.	...	...	...	...	0512	...	...	...	0542	...	0612	...	...	0642	...	the same	2012	...	...	2042	...	2112	...
46	**Kreuzlingen** .... d.	0445	...	0515	...	0545	...	...	...	0615	...	0645	...	...	0715	...	minutes	2045	...	...	2115	...	2145	...
	Konstanz .... d.	|	...	|	...	|	...	...	0609	|	...	|	...	0709	|	...	past each	|	...	2109	|	...	|	...
47	Kreuzlingen Hafen .... d.	0447	...	0517	...	0547	...	...	0612	0617	...	0647	...	0712	0717	...	hour until	2047	...	2112	2117	...	2147	...
	Weinfelden .... **535 539** d.	|	...	|	...	|	...	0557	|	|	0627	|	*0655*	|	|	0727		|	*2055*	|	|	2127	|	*2155*
65	**Romanshorn**.... **535 539** a.	0512	...	0542	...	0612	...	0612	0625	0642	0642	0712	*0712*	0725	0742	0742		2112	*2112*	2125	2142	2142	2212	*2212*
65	**Romanshorn**................ d.	0514	0516	0544	0546	0614	0616	0616	0626	0644	0646	0714	0716	0726	0744	0746		2114	2116	2126	2144	2146	2214	2216
	St Gallen .... a.	0541	|	0611	|	0641	|	|	0644	0711	|	0741	|	0744	0811	|		2141	|	2144	2211	|	2241	|
73	Arbon .... a.	...	0525	...	0555	...	0625	0625	...	...	0655	...	0725	...	...	0755		...	2125	...	...	2155	...	2225
80	**Rorschach** .... a.	...	0536	...	0606	...	0636	0636	...	...	0706	...	0736	...	...	0806		...	2136	...	...	2206	...	2236

											⑥⑦j
Schaffhausen............... d.	2119	...	2149	...	2219	...	2249	...	2319	2349	...
Stein am Rhein .... d.	2142	...	2212	...	2242	...	2312	...	2342	0012	...
Kreuzlingen .... d.	2215	...	2245	...	2315	...	2345	...	0015	0043	0105
Konstanz .... d.	|	...	|	...	|	...	|	...	|	...	|
Kreuzlingen Hafen.......... d.	2217	...	2247	...	2317	...	2347	...	0017	...	0107
Weinfelden..... **535 539** d.	|	2227	|	*2255*	|	2327	|	*2355*	|	...	|
Romanshorn.... **535 539** a.	2242	2242	2312	*2312*	2342	2342	0012	*0012*	0042	...	0128
Romanshorn................ d.	2244	2246	2314	2316	2344	2346	0014	0017	...	...	*0134*
St Gallen................... a.	2311	|	2341	|	0011	|	0041	|	...	...	*0158*
Arbon .... a.	...	2255	...	2325	...	2355	...	0025	...	...	...
Rorschach .... a.	...	2306	...	2336	...	0006	...	0036	...	...	...

				Ⓐ					
Rorschach..................... d.	...	...	...	...	...	0454	...	0524	...
Arbon .... d.	...	...	...	...	...	0504	...	0534	...
St Gallen...................... d.	...	...	...	...	...	|	...	|	0519
Romanshorn .... a.	...	...	...	...	...	0513	...	0542	0546
Romanshorn ...... **535 539** d.	...	...	...	0448	...	0517	0518	*0548*	0548
Weinfelden....... **535 539** a.	...	...	...	|	...	0533	|	*0605*	|
Kreuzlingen Hafen .... d.	...	...	...	0510	...	...	0540	...	0610
Konstanz .... a.	...	...	...	|	...	...	|	...	|
Kreuzlingen................... d.	0446	...	0516	0516	...	...	0546	...	0616
Stein am Rhein................ d.	0516	...	0546	0546	...	...	0616	...	0646
Schaffhausen................ a.	0541	...	0613	0613	...	...	0643	...	0713

																							⑤⑥k			
Rorschach .... d.	0554	...	...	0624	...	0654	...	and at	...	2124	...	2154	...	2224	...	2254	...	...	2324	...	...	...	2354	...
Arbon .... d.	0604	...	...	0634	...	0704	...	the same	...	2134	...	2204	...	2234	...	2304	...	...	2334	...	...	...	0004	...
St Gallen..................... d.	|	0549	0615	|	0619	|	0649	minutes	2115	|	2119	|	2149	|	2219	|	2249	...	|	2319	2319	...	|	2349
Romanshorn.................. a.	0613	0616	0633	0643	0646	0713	0716	past each	2133	2143	2146	2213	2216	2243	2246	2313	2316	...	2343	2346	2346	...	0013	0016
Romanshorn.... **535 539** d.	0617	0618	0633	*0648*	0648	0717	0718	hour until	2133	*2148*	2148	2217	2218	*2248*	2248	2317	2318	...	...	2348	2348	...	...	0018
Weinfelden..... **535 539** a.	0633	|	|	*0705*	|	0733	|		|	*2205*	|	2233	|	*2305*	|	2333	|	...	...	|	|	...	...	|
Kreuzlingen Hafen .... d.	...	0640	0647	...	0710	...	0740		2147	...	2210	...	2240	...	2310	...	2340	...	...	0010	0010	...	...	0040
Konstanz .... a.	...	|	0650	...	|	...	|		2150	...	|	...	|	...	|	...	|	...	...	|	|	...	...	|
Kreuzlingen .... d.	...	0646	...	...	0716	...	0746		...	...	2216	...	2246	...	2316	...	2346	...	...	0013	0016	...	...	0044
Stein am Rhein .... d.	...	0716	...	...	0746	...	0816		...	...	2246	...	2316	...	2346	...	0016	...	...	...	0046	...	...	...
Schaffhausen................ a.	...	0743	...	...	0813	...	0843		...	...	2313	...	2343	...	0013	...	0043	...	...	...	0111	...	...	...

j – Mornings of ⑥⑦ (also Apr. 15, 18, May 26, 27, 24, June 6, Aug. 1; not Dec. 25, 26).
k – Also Apr. 14, 17, May 25, 26, June 5; not Dec. 24, 25, Jan. 1.

THURBO — ROMANSHORN - WEINFELDEN - WIL — 539

km			Ⓐ			Ⓐ					
0	**Romanshorn** ‡ d.	...	0507	0537	and at the same	1907	1937	2037	2137	2237	2337
22	Weinfelden.... ‡ d.	0502	0532	0602	minutes past	1932	2002	2102	2202	2302	0002
41	**Wil**.................. a.	0527	0557	0627	each hour until	1957	2027	2127	2227	2327	0027

	Ⓐ			Ⓐ					
Wil .... d.	0502	0532	and at the same	1902	1932	2032	2132	2232	2332
Weinfelden..... ‡ a.	0530	0600	minutes past	1930	2000	2100	2200	2300	2400
Romanshorn ‡ a.	0553	0623	each hour until	1953	2023	2123	2223	2323	0023

‡ – See also Tables **535** and **538**.

PA — CHUR - FLIMS — 542

🚌 **Chur** (Postautostation) - **Flims** Dorf (Post). Journey time: 26–41 minutes. Additional journeys operate until Apr. 18 and June 11 - Oct. 23.

From **Chur** at 0603 ⚒, 0638 Ⓐ, 0658, 0728, 0758, 0828, 0858 and at 28 and 58 minutes past each hour until 1828, 1858; then 1928, 2000, 2100, 2200 and 2300.

From **Flims** Dorf at 0521 ⚒, 0555 Ⓐ, 0618, 0707 Ⓐ, 0721, 0751, 0821, 0851, 0921, 0951, 1021, 1051, 1121, 1156, 1236, 1306 Ⓐ, 1321, 1351 and at 21 and 51 minutes past each hour until 1921, 1951; then 2018, 2118, 2218 and 2318.

PA, RhB* — ST MORITZ and TIRANO - CHIAVENNA - LUGANO — 543

				P[R]	B[R]					
St Moritz, Bahnhof .... d.	0815	0915	1020	1025	...	1115	❖	1715	1915	2015
Silvaplana......................... d.	0827	0927	1032	1034u	...	1127		1727	1926	2026
Sils / Segl Maria, Posta .... d.	0836	0936	1041	1041u	...	1136	and	1736	1934	2034
Maloja, Posta.................. d.	0848	0948	1053	1053u	...	1148		1748	1945	2045
Castasegna 🏛 .... d.	0929	1029	1134	1126u	...	1229	hourly	1829	2024	2124
Chiavenna, Stazione ...... d.	0953	1053	1158	1206u	...	1253		1853	2048	2139
Tirano, Stazione.......... d.	...	...	...	|	1420	...	until	...	...	...
Menaggio .... d.	...	...	...	1311	|	...		...	...	...
Lugano, Stazione ◐ .... a.	...	...	...	1416	1730	...		...	...	...

							B[R]	P[R]		
Lugano, Stazione ◐......... d.	...	...	...		...	...	1000	1531	...	...
Menaggio .... d.	...	...	...		...	...	|	1618	...	...
Tirano, Stazione .... a.	...	...	...	and	...	...	1300	|	...	...
Chiavenna, Stazione........ d.	0709	...	0907		1607	1707	...	1725s	1807	1914
Castasegna 🏛 .... d.	0725	0823	0923	hourly	1623	1723	...	|	1823	1930
Maloja, Posta.................. d.	0811	0911	1011		1711	1811	...	1823s	1911	2011
Sils / Segl Maria, Posta ..... d.	0824	0924	1024	until	1724	1824	...	1834s	1924	2024
Silvaplana........................ d.	0832	0932	1032		1732	1832	...	1840s	1932	2032
St Moritz, Bahnhof........... a.	0841	0941	1041		1741	1845	...	1856	1945	2045

A – June 18 - Oct. 23.
B – *Bernina Express*: ④–⑦ Feb. 17 - Mar. 27; daily Mar. 31 - Oct. 30; ④–⑦ Nov. 3–27.
P – *Palm Express*: ⑤–⑦ to June 5 (also Dec. 20–23, 27–30, Apr. 18, May 26, June 6); daily June 10 - Oct. 23; ⑤–⑦ from Oct. 28.
s – Stops to set down only.
u – Stops to pick up only.
❖ – The 1515 from St Moritz runs 6 minutes later Maloja - Chiavenna.
◐ – 🏛 is at Gandria.
* – **Operators**: Tirano - Lugano RhB. ✆ (081) 288 65 65; St Moritz - Chiavenna - Lugano PA. ✆ (058) 341 34 92.

☛ **Additional journeys** St Moritz - Chiavenna and v.v. **From St Moritz** at 0720 and 1815 **A**. **From Chiavenna** at 0615 and 2014 **A**.

PA — CHUR - BELLINZONA and CHIAVENNA — 544

km				S A	B[R] A	B[R]	B[R]		S A	B[R] ⑥A	B[R]										S A			B[R]		
0	**Chur** Postautostation .... d.	0658	...	...	0758	0808	0858	...	...	0958	1008	1058	...	1208	1258	...	1408	1458	...	1608	...	1658	...	1808	...	2008
40	Thusis Bahnhof .... ⊡ d.	0725	0735	...	0825	0835	0925	0935	...	1025	1035	1125	1135	1235	1325	1335	1435	1525	1535	1635	...	1725	1735	1835	1935	2035
64	Splügen Dorf..................... d.	0754	0816	0820	|	0906	0954	1016	1020	|	1106	1154	1216	1306	1354	1416	1506	1554	1616	1706	1715	1754	1816	1906	2016	2106
	San Bernardino Villaggio ..... a.	0810	0836	|	0910	0924	1010	1036	|	1110	1124	1210	1236	1324	1410	1436	1524	1610	1636	1724	|	1810	1836	1924	2036	2124
	Chiavenna Stazione ◐ .... a.	|	...	1020	|	|	|	...	1220	|	|	|	...	|	|	...	|	|	...	|	1915	|	...	|	...	|
179	**Bellinzona** Stazione .... a.	0904	...	...	1004	1020	1104	...	...	1204	1220	1304	...	1420	1504	...	1620	1704	...	1820	...	1904	...	2020	...	2220

				S A												S A	B[R]		B[R]	S A	B[R]	B[R] A		B[R]	⑥A	
Bellinzona Stazione .... d.	...	...	0742	...	...	0856	0942	...	1056	1142	...	1256	1342	...	1456	...	1542	...	1656	...	1742	1756	...	1856	1956	2056
Chiavenna Stazione ◐.. d.	...	...	|	0745	...	|	|	...	|	|	...	|	|	...	|	1445	|	...	|	1645	|	|	...	|	|	|
San Bernardino Villaggio... d.	0633	0722	0833	|	0922	0952	1033	1122	1152	1233	1322	1352	1433	1522	1552	|	1633	1722	1752	|	1833	1852	1922	1952	2052	2152
Splügen Dorf...................... d.	0653	0743	0853	0940	0943	1010	1053	1143	1210	1253	1343	1410	1453	1543	1610	1640	1653	1743	1810	1840	1853	1910	1943	2010	2112	2212
Thusis Bahnhof .... ⊙ a.	0728	0823	0928	...	1023	1039	1128	1223	1239	1328	1423	1439	1528	1623	1639	...	1728	1823	1839	...	1928	1939	2023	2039	2145	2245
Chur Postautostation .... a.	0753	...	0953	...	...	1104	1153	...	1304	1353	...	1504	1553	...	1704	...	1753	...	1904	...	1953	2004	...	2104	2210	23[illegible]

A – June 11 - Oct. 23.
B – San Bernardino Route Express.
S – Splügen Pass service.
⊡ – Stops to pick up only.
⊙ – Stops to set down only.
◐ – 🏛 is at Splügen Pass.

Reservations: ✆ +41 58 341 34 87 up to one hour before departure from ori[illegible]

For *Glacier Express* services, see Table **575**

545 RHÄTISCHE BAHN (RhB) services

Narrow gauge

DISENTIS / MUSTÉR - CHUR - LANDQUART - KLOSTERS - SCUOL TARASP / DAVOS

km																									
		Ⓐ M	⚒	⚒	⚒	Ⓐ		Ⓐ				⚒	M ❖			❖				M			Ⓑ M		
0	**Disentis / Mustér** d.	...	...	...	...	...	...	...	...	...	0544	0615	...	...	0644		...	...	1444	...	...	1544	...	...	1644
12	Trun d.	...	...	...	...	...	...	...	...	...	0602	0631	...	...	0702		...	...	1502	...	...	1602	...	...	1702
30	Ilanz d.	...	...	...	...	...	...	0524	...	...	0624	0653	...	...	0724		...	...	1524	...	...	1624	...	...	1724
49	Reichenau-Tamins d.	...	...	...	...	...	...	0549	...	...	0649	0718	...	...	0749	and at	...	...	1549	...	...	1649	...	...	1749
59	**Chur** a.	...	...	...	...	...	...	0603	...	...	0703	0732	...	...	0803		...	...	1602	...	...	1702	...	...	1802
59	**Chur** 520 534 d.	...	...	...	...	...	...	0621	...	...	0721	...	...	...	0821	the same	...	...	1621	...	...	1721	...	...	1821
73	**Landquart** 520 534 a.	...	...	...	...	...	...	0641	...	...	0741c	...	...	...	0841c		...	...	1641c	...	...	1741c	...	...	1841c
73	**Landquart** d.	0454	0513	...	0534	0620	0647	0647	...	0747	0750	...	0820	0847	0850	minutes	1620	1647	1650	1720	1747	1750	1820	1847	1850
94	Küblis d.	0514	0539	...	0608	0646	0714	0714	...	0810	0814	...	0843	0910	0914		1643	1710	1714	1743	1810	1814	1843	1910	1914
103	Klosters Dorf d.	|	0553	...	0623	0659	0727	0727	...	0823	|	...	|	0923	|	past each	|	1723	|	|	1823	|	|	1923	|
105	**Klosters** Platz a.	0528	0556	...	0626	0702	0730	0730	...	0825	0830	...	0858	0926	0930		1658	1726	1730	1758	1825	1830	1858	1925	1930
105	**Klosters** Platz 🚗 d.	...	0558	0627	0631	0703	0731	0731	0732	0829	0831	...	0902	0929	0931	hour until	1702	1729	1731	1802	1829	1831	1902	1929	1931
120	**Davos** Dorf d.	...	0630	0652	|	0726	|	|	0754	0853	|	...	0929	0953	|		1729	1753	|	1826	1853	|	1926	1953	|
123	**Davos** Platz a.	...	0633	0657	|	0729	|	|	0757	0857	|	...	0933	0957	|		1733	1757	|	1829	1857	|	1929	1957	|
127	Sagliains ¶ 🚗 a.	...	...	...	0658	...	0758	0758	...	...	0854	...	...	...	0954		...	...	1754	...	...	1854	...	...	1954
136	Ardez ⊗ a.	...	...	...	0709	...	0809	0809	...	...	0907	...	...	...	1007		...	...	1807	...	...	1907	...	...	2007
144	**Scuol-Tarasp** a.	...	...	...	0718	...	0818	0818	...	...	0915	...	...	...	1015		...	...	1815	...	...	1915	...	...	2015

	zR			⑤ f								
Disentis / Mustér d.	...	1744	...	...	1844	...	1944	...	2044	...	2224	...
Trun d.	...	1802	...	...	1902	...	2002	...	2102	...	2239	...
Ilanz d.	...	1824	...	...	1924	...	2024	...	2124	...	2259	...
Reichenau-Tamins d.	...	1849	...	...	1949	...	2049	...	2149	...	2323	...
Chur a.	...	1902	...	...	2002	...	2102	...	2203	...	2333	...
Chur 520 534 d.	...	1921	...	...	▬	...	▬	...	▬	...	▬	...
Landquart 520 534 a.	...	1941	...	←	...	...	...	...	...	...	...	...
Landquart d.	1920	1950f	1947	1950	...	2047	...	2147	...	2247	...	2355
Küblis d.	1943	→	2013	2017	...	2113	...	2215	...	2313	...	0021
Klosters Dorf d.	|	...	2026	|	...	2126	...	2233	...	2326	⑤⑥	0033
Klosters Platz a.	1958	...	2029	2031	...	2129	...	2236	...	2329	e	0036
Klosters Platz 🚗 d.	2002	...	2030	2035	2035	2130	2135	2238	2238	2330	2335	0037
Davos Dorf d.	2026	...	2054	|	|	2154	|	2301	|	2354	|	0059
Davos Platz a.	2030	...	2058	|	|	2158	|	2305	|	2358	|	0105
Sagliains ¶ 🚗 a.	...	...	...	2058	2058	...	2158	...	2258	...	2358	...
Ardez ⊗ a.	...	...	...	2109	2109	...	2209	...	2309	...	0009	...
Scuol-Tarasp a.	...	...	...	2118	2118	...	2218	...	2318	...	0018	...

	⚒	⚒		Ⓐ Q	⚒	⊙	Ⓐ	⚒		
Scuol-Tarasp d.	...	...	...	...	0541	...	...	0641	...	...
Ardez ⊗ d.	...	...	...	...	0549	...	...	0649	...	...
Sagliains ¶ 🚗 d.	...	...	...	...	0603	...	...	0703	...	...
Davos Platz d.	...	0500	...	...	|	0600	0610	|	0700	...
Davos Dorf d.	...	0504	...	...	|	0604	0614	|	0704	...
Klosters Platz 🚗 a.	...	0526	...	...	0622	0626	0639	0723	0727	...
Klosters Platz d.	...	0528	...	0556	...	0628	0647	...	0728	...
Klosters Dorf d.	...	0531	...	|	...	0631	0650	...	0731	...
Küblis d.	...	0545	...	0614	...	0645	0714	...	0745	...
Landquart a.	...	0613	...	0643	...	0713	0739	...	0813	...
Landquart 520 534 d.	...	...	0619r	...	...	0717	...	...	...	0817
Chur 520 534 a.	...	...	0636r	...	...	0735	...	...	...	0835
Chur d.	0611	...	0652	...	...	0756	...	...	...	0856
Reichenau-Tamins d.	0624	...	0702	...	...	0805	...	...	...	0905
Ilanz d.	0653	...	0733	...	...	0833	...	...	...	0933
Trun d.	0715	...	0754	...	...	0854	...	...	...	0954
Disentis / Mustér a.	0731	...	0811	...	...	0911	...	...	...	1011

		⊙	⊡			M	⊗			M			Ⓒ M								P			...	...
Scuol-Tarasp d.	...	0741	...	0841	...	...		1641	...	...	1741	...	...	1841	...	...	1941	2041	...	...	*2141*	...		...	...
Ardez ⊗ d.	...	0749	...	0849	...	...		1649	...	...	1749	...	...	1849	...	...	1949	2049	...	...	*2150*	...		...	...
Sagliains ¶ 🚗 d.	...	0803	...	0903	...	...		1703	...	...	1803	...	...	1903	...	...	2003	2103	...	...	2203	...		...	...
Davos Platz d.	0730	|	0802	|	0902	0926	and at	|	1702	1726	|	1802	1830	|	1902	2000	|	|	2100	2150	|	2222		...	...
Davos Dorf d.	0734	|	0806	|	0906	0930		|	1706	1730	|	1806	1834	|	1906	2004	|	|	2103	2154	|	2226	A	...	...
Klosters Platz 🚗 a.	0757	0822	0827	0923	0929	0955	the same	1723	1729	1754	1823	1827	1854	1923	1929	2027	2023	2123	2127	2218	2221	2250		...	...
Klosters Platz d.	0759	0825	0831	0925	0931	0959		1725	1731	1759	1825	1831	1859	1925	1931	▬	2029	▬	2128	▬	2222	2253	L	...	...
Klosters Dorf d.	|	|	0834	|	0934	|	minutes	|	1734	|	|	1834	|	|	1934	...	2032	...	2132	...	2225	2257		...	...
Küblis d.	0815	0844	0850	0944	0950	1016		1744	1750	1816	1844	1850	1916	1944	1950	...	2046	...	2145	...	2239	2312	S	...	...
Landquart a.	0837	0910	0913	1010	1013c	1037	past each	1810	1813c	1837	1910	1913c	1937	2010	2013	...	2113	...	2213	...	2305	2335		...	...
Landquart 520 534 d.	...	0917	0917	1017	...	...		1817	...	...	1917	...	...	...	...	2017	...	...	▬	...	▬	...	O	...	...
Chur 520 534 a.	...	0935	0935	1035	...	...	hour until	1835	...	...	1935	...	...	...	...	2035	...	...	...	...	...	...		...	...
Chur d.	...	0956	0956	1056	...	...		1856	...	...	1956	...	...	...	...	2059	...	2159	...	2259	...	...		1725	1825
Reichenau-Tamins d.	...	1005	1005	1105	...	...		1905	...	...	2005	...	...	...	...	2112	...	2211	🚌	2311	🚌	...		|	|
Ilanz d.	...	1033	1033	1133	...	...		1933	...	...	2033	...	...	...	...	2141	...	2235	2237	2335	2337	...		1802	1902
Trun d.	...	1054	1054	1154	...	...		1954	...	...	2054	...	...	...	...	2200	...	...	2259	...	2359	...		1824	1924
Disentis / Mustér a.	...	1111	1111	1211	...	...		2011	...	...	2111	...	...	...	...	2215	...	...	2318	...	0018	...		1841	1941

SCUOL TARASP and KLOSTERS - ST MORITZ and PONTRESINA

km																										
		Ⓐ		⚒	†	⚒								Ⓒ				Ⓒ				Ⓒ				
0	**Scuol-Tarasp** d.	...	...	0601	0641	*0641*	...	*0741*	0834	...	0934	...	1034	...	1134	...	1234	...	1334	...	1434	...	1534	...	1634	1734
8	Ardez ⊗ d.	...	...	0612	0649	*0649*	...	*0749*	0843	...	0943	...	1043	...	1143	...	1243	...	1343	...	1443	...	1543	...	1643	1743
	Landquart ◐ d.	0454	...	|	|	|	...	|	|	0820	|	0920	|	1020	|	1120	|	1220	|	1320	|	1420	|	1520	|	|
	Klosters Platz d.	0530	...	|	|	|	...	|	|	0900	|	1000	|	1100	|	1200	|	1300	|	1400	|	1500	|	1600	|	|
17	Sagliains ¶ a.	|	...	|	0701	*0701*	...	*0801*	0854	|	0954	|	1054	|	1154	|	1254	|	1354	|	1454	|	1554	|	1654	1754
	Sagliains ¶ d.	|	...	|	0703	0703	...	0803	0855	|	0955	|	1055	|	1155	|	1255	|	1355	|	1455	|	1555	|	1655	1755
19	Susch ⊗ d.	0553	...	0625	0705	0705	...	0805	0858	0919	0958	1019	1058	1119	1158	1219	1258	1319	1358	1419	1458	1519	1558	1619	1658	1758
25	Zernez ⊖ d.	0602	...	0633	0713	0713	...	0813	0907	0929	1007	1026	1107	1129	1207	1226	1307	1329	1407	1426	1507	1529	1607	1626	1707	1807
42	Zuoz d.	0622	0633r	0654	0733	0733	0757r	0834	0927	0956	1027	1046	1127	1156	1227	1246	1327	1356	1427	1446	1527	1557	1627	1646	1727	1827
52	Samedan a.	0633	0646r	0707	0746	0746	0811r	0847	0942	1009	1042	1057	1142	1207	1242	1257	1342	1407	1442	1457	1542	1608	1642	1657	1742	1842
52	Samedan ▲ d.	0636	0648	0709	0748	0748	0812	0850	0948	1010	1048	1059	1148	1209	1248	1259	1348	1409	1448	1459	1548	1609	1648	1659	1748	1848
	St Moritz ▲ a.	0643	|	0716	|	|	0819	|	|	1019	|	1109	|	1217	|	1309	|	1417	|	1509	|	1617	|	1709	|	|
57	**Pontresina** a.	...	0657	...	0757	0757	...	0857	0957	...	1057	...	1157	...	1257	...	1357	...	1457	...	1557	...	1657	...	1757	1857

			Ⓑ						⑤⑥ e		
Scuol-Tarasp d.	...	1834	...	1934	...	2041	...	2141	2241	...	...
Ardez ⊗ d.	...	1843	...	1943	...	2049	...	2150	2249	...	...
Landquart ◐ d.	1720	|	1820	|	1920z	|	...	|	|	...	...
Klosters Platz d.	1800	|	1900	|	2000	|	...	|	|	...	...
Sagliains ¶ a.	|	1854	|	1954	|	2101	...	2201	2301	...	...
Sagliains ¶ d.	|	1855	|	1955	|	...	2103	2203	...	2303	...
Susch ⊗ d.	1819	1858	1919	1958	2020	...	2105	2206	...	2306	...
Zernez ⊖ d.	1826	1907	1926	2007	2032	...	2113	2213	...	2313	...
Zuoz d.	1846	1927	1946	2027	2054	...	2133	2233	...	2333	...
Samedan a.	1857	1942	1959	2042	2107	...	2146	2246	...	2345	...
Samedan ▲ d.	1859	1948	2001	2048	...	...	2150	2250	...	2346	...
St Moritz ▲ a.	1909	|	2009	|	...	...	|	|	...	2354	...
Pontresina a.	...	1957	...	2057	...	...	2157	2257	...	...	...

	Ⓐ	⚒	⚒	†	†T 🚌	⚒					Ⓒ
Pontresina d.	...	...	0542	0558	...	...	0702	0802	...	0902	...
St Moritz ▲ d.	...	0445	|	|	...	...	|	|	0845	|	0937
Samedan ▲ a.	...	0452	0548	0604	...	...	0708	0808	0853	0908	0944
Samedan d.	0453	0513	0553	0608	...	0608	0713	0813	0858	0913	0945
Zuoz d.	0506	0526	0607	0622	...	0622	0726	0827	0910	0927	0956
Zernez ⊖ d.	0526	0546	...	0646	...	0646	0746	0849	0929	0949	1029
Susch ⊗ d.	0533	0553	...	0653	0655	0653	0753	0858	0937	0958	1037
Sagliains ¶ a.	|	0556	...	0656	|	0656	0756	0901	|	1001	|
Sagliains ¶ d.	|	0601	...	0703	|	*0658*	*0758*	0902	|	1002	|
Klosters Platz a.	0551	|	...	0723	|	|	|	|	0957	|	1057
Landquart ◐ a.	0643	|	...	...	|	|	|	|	1037	|	1137
Ardez ⊗ d.	...	0612	...	...	0709	*0709*	*0809*	0914	...	1014	...
Scuol-Tarasp a.	...	0623	...	...	0717	*0718*	*0818*	0923	...	1023	...

				Ⓒ				Ⓒ								Ⓒ									⑤⑥ e	
Pontresina d.	1002	...	1102	...	1202	...	1302	...	1402	...	1502	...	1602	...	1702	...	1802	1902	2002	...	2102	...	2202	...	2302	2302
St Moritz ▲ d.	|	1047	|	1137	|	1247	|	1337	|	1447	|	1537	|	1647	|	1737	|	|	|	...	|	...	|	...	|	|
Samedan ▲ a.	1008	1055	1108	1144	1208	1255	1308	1344	1408	1455	1508	1544	1608	1655	1708	1744	1808	1908	2007	...	2107	...	2208	...	2308	2308
Samedan d.	1013	1058	1113	1145	1213	1258	1313	1345	1413	1458	1513	1545	1613	1658	1713	1745	1813	1913	2013	...	2113	...	2213	...	2313	▬
Zuoz d.	1027	1110	1127	1156	1227	1310	1327	1356	1427	1510	1527	1559	1627	1710	1727	1756	1827	1927	2027	...	2127	...	2227	...	2327	...
Zernez ⊖ d.	1049	1129	1149	1229	1249	1329	1349	1429	1449	1529	1549	1629	1649	1729	1749	1829	1849	1949	2046	...	2146	...	2246	...	2346	...
Susch ⊗ d.	1058	1137	1158	1237	1258	1337	1358	1437	1458	1537	1558	1637	1658	1737	1758	1837	1858	1958	2053	...	2153	...	2253	...	2353	⑤⑥
Sagliains ¶ a.	1101	|	1201	|	1301	|	1401	|	1501	|	1601	|	1701	|	1801	|	1901	2001	2056	...	2156	...	2256	...	2356	e
Sagliains ¶ d.	1102	|	1202	|	1302	|	1402	|	1502	|	1602	|	1702	|	1802	|	1902	2002	...	2058	2203	2158	...	2258	...	2358
Klosters Platz a.	|	1157	|	1257	|	1357	|	1457	|	1557	|	1657	|	1757	|	1857	|	|	...	|	2221	|	...	|	...	|
Landquart ◐ a.	|	1237	|	1337	|	1437	|	1537	|	1637	|	1737	|	1837	|	1937	|	|	...	|	2305	|	...	|	...	|
Ardez ⊗ d.	1114	...	1214	...	1314	...	1414	...	1514	...	1614	...	1714	...	1814	...	1914	2014	...	2109	...	2209	...	2309	...	0009
Scuol-Tarasp a.	1123	...	1223	...	1323	...	1423	...	1523	...	1623	...	1723	...	1823	...	1923	2023	...	2118	...	2218	...	2318	...	0018

FOR NOTES SEE NEXT PAGE →

Narrow gauge

RHÄTISCHE BAHN (RhB) services 545

CHUR - ST MORITZ

km																										
							951						955													
			⚒	⚒	⚒								W									D		⑤⑥		
							B 🅁						B 🅁											d		
0	**Chur**	d.	0428	0509	0604	0658	0758	0832	0858	0958	1058	1158	1258	1333	1358	1458	1558	1658	1758	1858	1958	2056	2056	2156	2156	2256	0001
10	Reichenau-Tamins	d.	0440	0518	0617	0709	0809	|	0909	1009	1109	1209	1309	|	1409	1509	1609	1709	1809	1909	2009	2108	2108	2209	2209	2306	0011
27	Thusis	d.	0502	0541	0640	0729	0829	|	0929	1029	1129	1229	1329	1404	1429	1529	1629	1729	1829	1929	2029	2133	2133	2231	2233	2329	0034
41	Tiefencastel	d.	▬	0557	▬	0746	0846	0918	0946	1046	1146	1246	1346	1428	1446	1546	1646	1746	1846	1946	2046	2149	2149	...	2249	▬	...
51	**Filisur**	d.	...	0613	...	0801	0901	0933	1001	1101	1201	1301	1401	|	1501	1601	1701	1801	1901	2001	2101	2204	2204	...	2304	...	...
59	Bergün / Bravuogn	d.	...	0630	...	0814	0914	0947	1014	1114	1214	1314	1414	1457	1514	1614	1714	1814	1914	2014	2114	2216	2217	...	2315	...	...
72	Preda	d.	...	0647	...	0832	0932	|	1032	1132	1232	1332	1432	|	1532	1632	1732	1832	1932	2032	2132	...	2234	...	2331	...	...
84	**Samedan**	a.	...	0700	...	0846	0945	|	1045	1145	1245	1345	1445	|	1545	1645	1745	1845	1945	2045	2145	...	2248	...	2344	...	...
84	**Samedan**	d.	0556	*0709*	0749	0853	0949	|	1049	1149	1249	1349	1449	|	1549	1649	1749	1849	1949	2049	2149	...	2250	...	...	2346	...
	Pontresina	a.	|	|	|	|	|	1020	|	|	|	|	|	1534	|	|	|	|	|	|	|	...	|	...	...	|	...
87	Celerina	d.	0601	*0713*	0753	0856	0953	...	1053	1153	1253	1353	1453	...	1553	1653	1753	1853	1953	2053	2153	...	2253	...	...	2350	...
89	**St Moritz**	a.	0606	*0716*	0800	0901	1000	...	1100	1200	1300	1400	1500	...	1600	1700	1800	1900	2000	2100	2200	...	2300	...	...	2354	...

											950							952								
											W												⑤⑥			
	⚒	⚒	Ⓐ	⚒	†						B 🅁							B 🅁					d			
St Moritz	d.	...	...	...	0541	...	0558	0702	0802	0902	1002	...	1102	1202	1302	1402	1502	1602	...	1702	1802	1902	2002	2102	2102	2202	2359
Celerina	d.	...	...	...	0545	...	0601	0706	0805	0905	1005	...	1105	1205	1305	1405	1505	1605	...	1705	1805	1905	2005	2105	2105	2205	0003
Pontresina	d.	...	...	...	|	...	|	|	|	|	|	1032	|	|	|	|	|	|	1624	|	|	|	|	|	|	|	|
Samedan	a.	...	...	...	0548	...	0605	0709	0809	0909	1009	|	1109	1209	1309	1409	1509	1609	|	1709	1809	1909	2009	2108	2108	2209	0007
Samedan	d.	...	...	...	0550	...	0607	0715	0815	0915	1015	|	1115	1215	1315	1415	1515	1615	|	1715	1815	1915	2015	2115	▬	▬	▬
Preda	d.	...	...	...	0603	...	0620	0729	0829	0929	1029	|	1129	1229	1329	1429	1529	1629	|	1729	1829	1929	2029	2131	...	...	...
Bergün / Bravuogn	d.	...	...	0539	0620	...	0637	0747	0847	0947	1047	1114	1147	1247	1347	1447	1547	1647	1704	1747	1847	1947	2047	2148	...	...	...
Filisur	d.	...	...	0553	0634	...	0651	0801	0901	1001	1101	1126	1201	1301	1401	1501	1601	1701	1718	1801	1901	2001	2101	2201	...	...	...
Tiefencastel	d.	...	...	0610	0651	...	0707	0815	0915	1015	1115	1145	1215	1315	1415	1515	1615	1715	1732	1815	1915	2015	2116	2217	...	...	...
Thusis	d.	0509	0608	0627	0709	0728	0728	0833	0933	1033	1133	1204	1233	1333	1433	1533	1633	1733	1749	1833	1933	2033	2133	2233	2233	2336	0040
Reichenau-Tamins	d.	0534	0632	0653	|	0753	0753	0852s	0952s	1052s	1152s	|	1252s	1352s	1452s	1552s	1652s	1752s	|	1852s	1952s	2052s	2157	2255	2255	2357	0102
Chur	a.	0548	0646	0705	0742	0805	0805	0904	1004	1104	1204	1239	1304	1404	1504	1604	1704	1804	1820	1904	2004	2104	2209	2310	2310	0010	0112

ST MORITZ - TIRANO

km																											
									971		951				973			955		975							
						⚒			W						W			W		V						Ⓐ	
								△	A 🅁	▷	B 🅁	△			A 🅁	◇	▽▷	B 🅁	△	A 🅁	▷		🚌		🚌		
0	**St Moritz**	d.	...	...	...	...	0748	0848	0917	0948	...	1048	1148	1248	1317	1348	1448	...	1548	1614	1648	1748	...	1848	...	1948	2020
6	**Pontresina**	a.	...	...	...	...	0757	0857	0925	0957	...	1057	1157	1257	1325	1357	1457	...	1557	1622	1657	1757	...	1857	...	1957	2029
6	**Pontresina**	d.	...	...	...	0702	0808	0904	0928	1008	1022	1104	1208	1304	1328	1408	1504	1541	1605	1623	1704	1808	...	1904	...	2004	▬
12	Morteratsch ⊗	d.	...	...	...	0711	0818	0913	|	1018	|	1113	1218	1313	|	1418	1513	|	1618	|	1713	1818	...	1913	...	2013	...
17	Bernina Diavolezza ⊗	d.	...	...	...	0720	0828	0923	|	1028	1040	1123	1228	1323	|	1428	1523	1606	1628	1639	1723	1828	...	1922	...	2022	...
22	Ospizio Bernina	d.	...	...	...	0731	0838	0933	|	1038	|	1133	1238	1333	|	1438	1533	1619	1638	1652	1733	1838	...	1932	...	2032	...
27	Alp Grüm	a.	...	...	...	0740	0849	0942	1006	1049	1059	1142	1249	1342	1407	1449	1542	1628	1649	1700	1742	1848	...	1942	...	2041	...
27	Alp Grüm	d.	...	...	...	0744	0853	0944	1018	1053	1115	1144	1253	1344	1418	1453	1544	1640	1653	1716	1744	1853	...	1946	...	2046	...
44	**Poschiavo**	a.	...	...	...	0830	0941	1022	1054	1141	1201	1222	1341	1422	1453	1541	1622	1715	1741	1800	1822	1932	...	2023	...	2123	🚌
44	**Poschiavo**	d.	0620	0742	0834	0834	0942	1023	1056	1142	1210	1223	1342	1423	1455	1542	1623	1724	1742	1801	1823	...	1934	...	2034	...	2134
48	Le Prese	d.	0627	0749	0841	0841	0949	1030	1103	1149	1221	1230	1349	1430	1502	1549	1630	1732	1749	|	1830	...	1940	...	2040	...	2140
51	Miralago ⊗	d.	0633	0754	0847	0847	0954	1035	|	1154	|	1235	1354	1435	|	1554	1635	|	1754	|	1835	...	1944	...	2044	...	2144
54	Brusio ⊗	d.	0642	0802	0857	0857	1002	1043	|	1202	|	1243	1402	1443	|	1602	1643	|	1802	|	1843	...	1948	...	2048	...	2148
58	Campocologno 🏛	d.	0654	0814	0908	0908	1014	1052	|	1214	|	1252	1414	1452	|	1614	1652	|	1814	|	1852	...	1952	...	2052	...	2152
61	**Tirano**	a.	0703	0823	0917	0917	1023	1100	1132	1223	1249	1300	1423	1500	1531	1623	1700	1759	1823	1839	1900	...	2000	...	2100	...	2200

							950			972				974		952			976								
			⚒				W			V				W					W								
				🚌			B 🅁	◇	▽▷	A 🅁	△	▷	▷	A 🅁		B 🅁	△	△	A 🅁				🚌		🚌	🚌	🚌
Tirano	d.	...	...	0653	...	0741	0806	0900	0941	1006	1100	1141	1300	1317	1341	1424	1500	1541	1606	1700	1741	1900	...	1939	2002	2102	2202
Campocologno 🏛	d.	...	...	0659	...	0752	|	0908	0952	|	1108	1152	1308	|	1352	|	1508	1552	|	1708	1752	1910	...	1947	2008	2108	2208
Brusio ⊗	d.	...	...	0706	...	0802	|	0916	1002	|	1116	1202	1316	|	1402	|	1516	1602	|	1716	1802	1920	...	1956	2012	2112	2212
Miralago ⊗	d.	...	...	0710	...	0810	|	0923	1010	|	1123	1210	1323	|	1410	|	1523	1610	|	1723	1810	1927	...	2003	2015	2115	2215
Le Prese	d.	...	...	0712	...	0815	0835	0928	1015	1041	1128	1215	1328	1344	1415	1455	1528	1615	1640	1728	1815	1932	...	2007	2018	2218y	2218y
Poschiavo	a.	...	...	0728	...	0825	0845	0936	1025	1047	1136	1225	1336	1353	1425	1506	1536	1625	1647	1736	1825	1940	...	2016	2028	2128y	2228y
Poschiavo	d.	...	0628	...	0732	0828	0847	0937	1028	1050	1137	1228	1337	1357	1428	1510	1537	1628	1648	1737	1828	...	2005	...	...	...	...
Alp Grüm	a.	...	0706	...	0811	0906	0923	1010	1106	1126	1210	1306	1410	1442	1506	1544	1610	1706	1727	1810	1906	...	|	...	...	...	...
Alp Grüm	d.	...	0708	...	0813	0908	0948	1013	1108	1142	1213	1308	1413	1459	1508	1545	1613	1708	1742	1813	1908	...	|	...	...	...	...
Ospizio Bernina	d.	...	0715	...	0820	0915	0958	1020	1115	|	1220	1315	1420	|	1515	|	1620	1715	|	1820	1915	...	2036	...	...	...	...
Bernina Diavolezza ⊗	d.	...	0726	...	0833	0927	|	1033	1127	1200	1233	1327	1433	1517	1527	|	1633	1727	|	1833	1927	...	2041	...	...	...	...
Morteratsch ⊗	d.	...	0738	...	0844	0940	|	1044	1140	|	1244	1340	1444	|	1540	|	1644	1740	|	1844	1940	...	2047	...	...	...	...
Pontresina	a.	...	0748	...	0856	0951	1028	1053	1151	1225	1253	1351	1453	1534	1551	1622	1653	1751	1815	1853	1951	...	2057	...	...	...	...
Pontresina	d.	0801	0801	...	0901	1001	...	1101	1201	1227	1301	1401	1501	1536	1601	...	1701	1801	1817	1901	2001	...	S	...	...	...	...
St Moritz	a.	0811	0811	...	0911	1011	...	1111	1211	1235	1311	1411	1511	1545	1611	...	1711	1811	1825	1911	2011	...	...	...	...	...	...

DAVOS - FILISUR

km			⚒			♣					
0	Davos Platz	d.	0605	...	0731	and hourly	2031	...	...	...	...
16	Filisur	a.	0630	...	0756	until	2056	...	...	...	...

		⚒			♣						
Filisur	d.	0634	...	0804	and hourly	2104	...	...	...	...	...
Davos Platz	a.	0658	...	0829	until	2129	...	...	...	...	...

CHUR - AROSA

km			⚒								●
0	**Chur**	d.	0508	0620	0708	and	1908	2006	2100	...	2300
18	Langwies	d.	0550	0705	0750	hourly	1950	2044	2140	...	2341
26	**Arosa**	a.	0609	0722	0809	until	2009	2102	2157	...	2358

		⚒	Ⓐ	Ⓒ							
Arosa	d.	0549	0623	0649	0749	and	1849	1949	...	2107	2203
Langwies	d.	0605	0638	0705	0805	hourly	1905	2004	...	2123	2219
Chur	a.	0653	0720	0753	0853	until	1953	2045	...	2205	2300

A – BERNINA EXPRESS – (12) [panorama car] 🍷. 🅁. Supplement payable.
B – BERNINA EXPRESS – (12) [panorama car] 🍷 Chur - Pontresina - Tirano and v.v. 🅁. Supplement payable.
D – Daily to Mar. 13; ⑤⑥ from Mar. 18 (also Apr. 14, May 25; not Apr. 15).
M – Conveys (12) Landquart - Klosters - St Moritz and v.v. (see lower panel on page 268).
P – From Pontresina (see lower panel on page 268).
Q – From Samedan (see lower panel on page 268).
R – On Ⓒ conveys (12) Landquart - Klosters - Samedan (see lower panel on page 268).

S – Continues to Samedan (a. 2104).
T – May 15 - Oct. 30.
U – May 7 - Oct. 30.
V – Dec. 26 - Jan. 2, Apr. 15 - Oct. 30 and Dec. 7–10.
W – May 14 - Oct. 30.

c – Connects with train in previous column.
d – Also Apr. 14, May 25; not Dec. 24, 25, Jan. 1, Apr. 15.
e – ⑤⑥ (also Dec. 26–30, Apr. 14, May 25; not Dec. 24, 25, Apr. 15).

f – ⑤ (not Apr. 15).
r – ⚒ only.
s – Calls to set down only.
y – On ⑥ (also Apr. 14, May 25, July 31) departs Le Prese 3 minutes later, arrives Poschiavo 7 minutes later.
z – Change trains at Klosters Platz on Ⓐ.

⊙ – Change trains at Landquart on †.
⊡ – Change trains at Landquart on ⚒.
⊗ – Request stop.
◐ – See upper panel on page 268.

▷ – Conveys open car June 27 - Sept. 4 (subject to fine weather).
△ – Conveys panorama car (🅁) until Mar. 27.
◇ – Conveys panorama car (🅁) Jan. 6 - Mar. 27.
▽ – Conveys panorama car (🅁) until Mar. 27 and from Oct. 31.
❖ – The 1020, 1220 and 1420 from Landquart run on Ⓒ only.
⊠ – The 1026, 1226 and 1426 from Davos Platz run on Ⓒ only. See later columns for additional journeys Chur - Disentis.
▲ – See Chur - St Moritz panel on page 269 for connecting trains Samedan - St Moritz and v.v.
♣ – Variations May 14 - Oct. 30: The 1031 and 1531 from Davos are retimed to depart at 1018 and 1518 (Filisur a. 1053, 1553); the 1104 and 1604 from Filisur are retimed to depart at 1106, 1606 (Davos a. 1150, 1650). These retimed services are operated with historic rolling stock (including open cars).
● – Operated by 🚌 in similar timings on ①–④ Apr. 19 - Nov. 24 (not May 25, 26, June 6, Aug. 1).
¶ – Sagliains station can only be used for changing trains.
⊖ – 🚌 **ZERNEZ - MALLES**. Operator: AutoDaPosta ✆ +41 (0) 81 856 10 90. Journey ± 1 h 30 m. **From Zernez** at 0715, 0815, 0915, 1015 **U**, 1032, 1115, 1215 **U**, 1315, 1415 **U**, 1515, 1615, 1715 and 1815 **U**. **From Malles / Mals** at 0610, 0803, 0903, 1003 **U**, 1103, 1203 **U**, 1303, 1403 **U**, 1503, 1545 **U**, 1603, 1703, 1803 and 1903.
🚗 – Car-carrying operates operates Klosters Selfranga - Sagliains and v.v. ✆ +41 (0) 81 288 37 37 (www.rhb.ch/en/car-transporter).

547 LUZERN and ZÜRICH - BELLINZONA - LOCARNO (via Gotthard pass) SBB, SOB

See Table **550** for faster services via the Gotthard and Ceneri Base tunnels.

km				*IC*		*IC*			*EC*		*IC*		*IC*		*IC*		*IC*		*IC/IR*		*IC*		*IC/IR*	*IR*	
		C	(🍷)	◇	(🍷)	◇	(🍷)		◇	(🍷)	◇	(🍷)	◇	(🍷)	◇	(🍷)	◇	(🍷)	◇	(🍷)	◇	(🍷)	◇	◇	
	Basel SBB **565** d.	...	...	0503	...	...	0603		1503	...	...	1603	1703	...	...	1803	1903	...	...	2003	2103	...	...	2203	...
	Luzern **525 550** d.	...	...	0618	...	...	0718		1618	...	...	1718	1818	...	...	1918	2018	...	...	2118	2218	...	...	2318	...
0	**Zürich** HB **550** d.	...	...	|	0605	0705	|		|	1605	1705	|	|	1805	1905	|	|	2005	2105	|	|	2205	2305	|	...
29	Zug **550** d.	...	...	|	0630	0730	|		|	1630	1730	|	|	1830	1930	|	|	2030	2130	|	|	2230	2330	|	...
45	**Arth-Goldau 525 550** a.	...	...	0645	0645	0745	0745	and in	1645	1645	1745	1745	1845	1845	1945	1945	2145	2045	2145	2145	2245	2245	2345	2345	...
45	**Arth-Goldau** **550** d.	...	...	▬	0654	▬	0754	the same	▬	1654	▬	1754	▬	1854	▬	1954	▬	2054	▬	2154	...	2254	...	...	2355
53	Schwyz d.	...	...	...	0702	...	0802		...	1702	...	1802	...	1902	...	2002	...	2102	...	2202	...	2302	...	...	0002
56	Brunnen d.	...	...	...	0706	...	0806	pattern	...	1706	...	1806	...	1906	...	2006	...	2106	...	2206	...	2306	...	...	0005
68	Flüelen d.	...	...	...	0715	...	0815		...	1715	...	1815	...	1915	...	2015	...	2115	...	2215	...	2315	...	...	0015
71	Altdorf **550** d.	...	...	...	0718	...	0818	every **two**	...	1718	...	1818	...	1918	...	2018	...	2118	...	2218	...	2318	...	...	0017
77	**Erstfeld** d.	...	0625	...	0725	...	0825	hours until	...	1725	...	1825	...	1925	...	2025	...	2125	...	2224	...	2324	...	...	0024
106	Göschenen d.	...	0651	...	0751	...	0851		...	1751	...	1851	...	1951	...	2051	...	2151	...	...	...	...	...	...	...
122	Airolo d.	0612	0702	...	0802	...	0902		...	1802	...	1902	...	2002	...	2102	...	2202	...	...	...	...	...	...	...
142	Faido d.	0630	0721	...	0821	...	0921		...	1821	...	1921	...	2021	...	2121	...	2221	...	...	...	...	...	...	...
168	Biasca **548** d.	0655	0745j	...	0845j	...	0945j		...	1845j	...	1945j	...	2045j	...	2145j	...	2245j	...	...	...	...	...	...	...
187	**Bellinzona** **548 550** a.	0709	0800j	...	0900j	...	1000j		...	1900j	...	2000j	...	2100j	...	2200j	...	2300j	**e**	...	...	...	...	...	...
187	**Bellinzona** ▷ d.	*0719*	0804	0819	0904	0919	1004		1819	1904	1919	2004	2019	...	2119	...	2219	...	2319	...	...	...	...	...	...
208	**Locarno** ▷ a.	*0744*	0825	0844	0925	0944	1025		1844	1925	1944	2025	2044	...	2144	...	2244	...	2344	...	...	...	...	...	...

km			*IC*		*IC*																				
		(🍷)	◇	(🍷)	◇			(🍷)		(🍷)		(🍷)		(🍷)			(🍷)		(🍷)					**e**	**e**
	Locarno ▷ d.	...	...	...	...	0435	0515	...	0615	...	0715	0735	0815	0835	0915		1935	2015	2035	2115	2145	2215	2245	2315	2345
	Bellinzona ▷ a.	...	...	...	...	0501	0541	...	0641	...	0741	0755	0841	0855	0941		1955	2041	2055	2141	2211	2241	2311	2341	0011
	Bellinzona **548 550** d.	...	0507	...	...	...	...	0559	▬	0659f	▬	0759f	▬	0859f	▬		1959f	▬	2059f	▬	▬	▬	▬	...	...
	Biasca **548** d.	...	0521	...	...	...	...	0614	...	0714f	...	0814f	...	0914f	...		2014f	...	2114f	...	...	...	...	...	...
	Faido d.	...	|	...	...	...	...	0639	...	0739	...	0839	...	0939	...	and in	2039	...	2139	...	...	...	...	...	...
	Airolo d.	...	|	...	...	...	...	0658	...	0758	...	0858	...	0958	...		2058	...	2158	...	...	...	...	...	...
	Göschenen d.	...	|	...	...	...	...	0709	...	0809	...	0909	...	1009	...	the same	2109	...	2209	...	...	...	...	...	...
	Erstfeld d.	0531	|	0631	...	...	...	0734	...	0834	...	0934	...	1034	...	pattern	2134	...	2234	...	...	...	...	...	...
	Altdorf **550** d.	0537	0550	0637	...	...	...	0739	...	0839	...	0939	...	1039	...		2139	...	2239	...	...				
	Flüelen d.	0541	|	0641	...	...	...	0744	...	0844	...	0944	...	1044	...	every **two**	2144	...	2244	...	...	2309	...	...	...
	Brunnen d.	0554	|	0654	...	...	...	0755	...	0855	...	0955	...	1055	...	hours until	2155	...	2255	...	2307	2320	...	...	...
	Schwyz d.	0558	|	0658	...	...	...	0759	*IC*	0859	*IC*	0959	*IC*	1059	*EC*		2159	*IC*	2259	*IC*	2310	2323	...	...	...
	Arth-Goldau **550** a.	0607	0611	0707	...	...	...	0807	◇	0907	◇	1007	◇	1107	◇		2207	◇	2307	◇	2319	2331	...	...	...
0	**Arth-Goldau 525 550** d.	0615	0615	0715	0715	...	...	0815	0815	0915	0915	1015	1015	1115	1115		2215	2215	2315	2315	2320	2332	...	...	...
	Zug **550** a.	|	0630	0730	|	...	...	|	0830	0930	|	|	1030	1130	|		|	2230	2330	|	|	2353	2358	...	...
	Zürich HB **550** a.	|	0655	0755	|	...	...	|	0855	0955	|	|	1055	1155	|		|	2255	2355	|	|	...	0025	...	...
28	**Luzern** **525 550** a.	0641	...	...	0741	...	...	0841	...	...	0941	1041	...	...	1141		2241	...	...	2341	2353	...	...	...	...
	Basel SBB **565** a.	0656	...	...	0856	...	...	0956	...	...	1056	1156	...	...	1256		2400	...	...	0102	...	...	...	...	...

C – To Chiasso (Table **548**).

e – Daily to Jan. 15; ①–⑥ Jan. 17 - May 28 (also Feb. 27, Apr. 17, May 1); daily May 30 - Aug. 28; ⑤⑥ from Sept. 2.
f – 2 minutes **earlier** June 16 - Aug. 28.
j – 2 minutes later June 16 - Aug. 28.

◇ – See also Table **550**.
◧ – ②–⑦ Apr. 15 - Oct. 16 (also Apr. 18, June 6, Aug. 1). Conveys panorama car. Supplement payable.
▷ – Other services Bellinzona - Locarno and v.v.: **From Bellinzona** at 0449, 0519, 0549, 0619, 0649, 0749 and hourly until 2149; then 2249**e**. **From Locarno** at 0545, 0645 and hourly until 2045.

GOTTHARD PANORAMA EXPRESS

	3093		3092
	◧🍷		◧🍷
Arth-Goldau d.	1340	**Lugano** d.	0918
Flüelen d.	1409	**Bellinzona** d.	0948
Göschenen d.	1458	Airolo d.	1042
Airolo d.	1515	Göschenen d.	1059
Bellinzona a.	1612	Flüelen d.	1140
Lugano a.	1641	**Arth-Goldau** a.	1200

548 Local services BIASCA and LOCARNO - LUGANO - MILANO SBB, FSS

km										**A**														
0	Biasca **547** d.	...	...	0515	...	0555	...	0625	...	0655	...	0721**d**	...	0755	...	0825		...	1925	...	1955	...	2025	...
19	**Bellinzona** **547** a.	...	...	0529	...	0609	...	0639	...	0709	...	0735**d**	...	0809	...	0839		...	1939	...	2009	...	2039	...
19	**Bellinzona** **607** d.	0433	0517	0532	...	0616	...	0641**r**	...	0716	...	0746	...	0816	...	0846	and at	...	1946	...	2016	...	2046	...
	Locarno d.	|	|	|	0555	|	0625	|	0655	|	0725	|	0755	|	0825	|	the same	1925	|	1955	|	2025	|	2055
	Cadenazzo ⊗ **607** d.	|	|	|	0609	|	0639	|	0709	|	0739	|	0809	|	0839	|		1939	|	2009	|	2039	|	2109
48	**Lugano** **607** a.	0505	0551	0604	0624	0635	0654	0658**r**	0724	0735	0754	0805	0824	0835	0854	0905	minutes	1954	2005	2024	2035	2054	2105	2124
48	**Lugano** **607** d.	0506	0602j	0606	...	0636	0702j	0706	0725	0736	0802j	0806	0825	0836	0902j	0906	past each	2002j	2006	2025	2036	2102j	2106	...
67	Mendrisio **607** d.	0532	0619	0632	...	0658	0719	0732	0742	0758	0819	0832	0841	0858	0919	0932		2019	2032	2041	2058	2119	2132	...
74	**Chiasso** **607** a.	0540	0626	0640	...	0706	0726	0740	0750	0806	0826	0840	0949	0906	0926	0940	hour until	2026	2040	2049	2106	2126	2140	...
74	**Chiasso** 🏛 **607** d.	0543	0631	0647	...	...	0731	0743	...	...	0831	0843	...	...	0931	0943		2031	2043	...	...	...	...	...
78	Como S. Giovanni **607** d.	0554	0636	0654	...	...	0736	0750	...	...	0836	0850	...	...	0936	0950		2036	2050	...	...	...	...	...
125	**Milano** Centrale a.	...	0717	...	...	...	0817	...	...	...	0917	...	...	...	1017	...		2117	...	...	...	...	...	...

Biasca **547** d.	2055	...	2125	...	2155	...	2225	...	2255	...	2325
Bellinzona **547** a.	2109	...	2139	...	2209	...	2239	...	2309	...	2339
Bellinzona **607** d.	2116	...	2146	...	2216	...	2246	...	2316	...	2346
Locarno d.	|	2125	|	2155	|	2225	|	2255	|	2325**e**	|
Cadenazzo ⊗ **607** d.	|	2139	|	2209	|	2239	|	2309	|	2339	|
Lugano **607** a.	2135	2154	2205	2224	2235	2254	2305	2324	2335	2354	0005
Lugano **607** d.	2136	2155	2206	...	2236	2255	2306	...	2336	2355	0006
Mendrisio **607** d.	2158	2216	2232	...	2258	2316	2332	...	2358	0016	0032
Chiasso **607** a.	2206	2225	2240	...	2306	2325	2340	...	0006	0025	0041
Chiasso 🏛 **607** d.	...	...	...	...	...	...	...	...	...	...	...
Como S. Giovanni **607** d.	...	...	...	...	...	...	...	...	...	...	...
Milano Centrale a.	...	...	...	...	...	...	...	...	...	...	...

Milano Centrale d.	...	...	...	...	...	...	...	...	...
Como S. Giovanni **607** d.	...	...	...	0511	...	...	...	...	0611
Chiasso 🏛 **607** a.	...	...	...	0517	...	...	...	...	0617
Chiasso **607** d.	0402**b**	...	0452	0520	...	0534	0554	...	0620
Mendrisio **607** d.	0411	...	0500	0530	0534	0543	0604	...	0634
Lugano **607** a.	0431	...	0520	...	0554	0604	0624	...	0654
Lugano **607** d.	0432	...	0521	...	0603	0605	0625	0635	0655
Cadenazzo ⊗ **607** d.	|	...	|	...	|	0620	|	0650	|
Locarno a.	|	...	|	...	|	0635	|	0705	|
Bellinzona **607** a.	0503	...	0554	...	0619	...	0643	...	0713
Bellinzona **547** d.	0509	...	0556	...	0620	...	0650	...	0720
Biasca **547** a.	0524	...	0610	...	0637	...	0707	...	0737

km																								
	Milano Centrale d.	...	...	...	...	0643	...		...	...	1943	...	...	...	2043	...	...	...	2143	...	...	...	2243**c**	...
	Como S. Giovanni **607** d.	...	...	...	0710	0724	...		...	2010	2024	...	...	2110	2124	...	...	...	2224	...	...	...	2324**c**	...
	Chiasso 🏛 **607** a.	...	...	...	0717	0729	...	and at	...	2017	2029	...	...	2117	2129	...	...	...	2229	...	...	...	2329**c**	...
	Chiasso **607** d.	0634	0654	0711	0720	0734	0754	the same	2011	2020	2034	2054	...	2120	2134	2154	...	2220	2234	2254	...	2320	2334	2354
	Mendrisio **607** d.	0642	0704	0718	0734	0742	0804		2018	2034	2042	2104	...	2134	2142	2204	...	2234	2243	2304	...	2334	2243	0004
	Lugano **607** a.	0658**k**	0724	0734	0754	0758**k**	0824	minutes	2034	2054	2058**k**	2124	...	2154	2158**k**	2224	...	2254	2304	2324	...	2354	0004	0024
0	**Lugano** **607** d.	0705	0725	0735	0755	0805	0825	past each	2035	2055	2105	2125	2135	2155	2205	2225	2235	2255	2305	2325	2335	2355	0005	0025
30	Cadenazzo ⊗ **607** d.	0720	|	0750	|	0820	|		2050	|	2120	|	2150	|	2220	|	2250	|	2320	|	2350	|	0020	|
42	**Locarno** a.	0735	|	0805	|	0835	|	hour until	2105	|	2135	|	2205	|	2235	|	2305**e**	|	2335**e**	|	0005**g**	|	0035**g**	|
	Bellinzona **607** a.	...	0743	...	0813	...	0843		...	2113	...	2143	...	2213	...	2243	...	2313	...	2343	...	0026	...	0056
	Bellinzona **547** d.	...	0750	...	0820	...	0850		...	2120	...	2150	...	2220	...	2250	...	2320	...	2350	...	...	...	...
	Biasca **547** a.	...	0807	...	0837	...	0907		...	2137	...	2207	...	2237	...	2307	...	2337	...	0007	...	...	...	...

A – From Airolo (Table **547**).

b – Not ①.
c – ⑥⑦ only.
d – 4 minutes later on ⑥⑦ (also Jan. 6, Apr. 18, May 26, June 6, 16, 29, Aug. 15, Nov. 1, Dec. 8).

e – Daily to Jan. 15; ①–⑥ Jan. 17 - May 28 (also Feb. 27, Apr. 17, May 1); daily May 30 - Aug. 28; ⑤⑥ from Sept. 2.
g – To Locarno on mornings until Jan. 16, ⑥⑦ Jan. 22 - Feb. 20 (also Feb. 25), ①②③⑥⑦ Feb. 26 - Mar. 6, ⑥⑦ Mar. 12 - May 29 (also Apr. 15, 18, 19, May 2, 27), daily June 4 - Aug. 29 and ⑥⑦ from Sept. 3.
j – 7 minutes earlier June 16 - Aug. 28.

k – 6 minutes later June 16 - Aug. 28.
r – June 16 - Aug. 28 Bellinzona d. 0646 Lugano a. 0705.

⊗ – Trains do not call at Cadenazzo June 16 - Aug. 28.

SBB, FS — ZÜRICH and LUZERN - LUGANO - MILANO (via Gotthard and Ceneri Base Tunnels) — 550

See Table **547** for slower services via the classic Gotthard route.

km		IR 2409	IC 659	EC 311	IR 2311	IC 861	EC 313	IR 2413	IC 663	EC 307	IR 2315	IC 865	EC 315	IR 2417	IC 667	EC 327	IR 2319	IC 869	EC 317	IR 2421	EC 151	IR 2323	IC 873	EC 319
				◧			◧			◧			◧			◧			◧					◧
		★	🍴	V🍴	★	🍴	🍴	★	🍴	B🍴	★	🍴	🍴	★	🍴	G🍴	★	🍴	🍴	★	F🍴	★	🍴	¶🍴
0	**Zürich** HB ... 547 555 d.	0605	...	0633	...	0705	0733	0805	...	0833	...	0905	0933	1005	...	1033	...	1105	1133	1205	...	...	1305	1333
29	Zug ... 547 555 d.	0630	...	0700	...	0730	0800	0830	...	0900	...	0930	1000	1030	...	1100	...	1130	1200	1230	...	...	1330	1400
	Basel SBB **565** ... d.	|	0503	|	0603	|	|	|	0703	|	0803	|	|	|	0903	|	1003	|	|	|	1103	1203	|	|
	Luzern ... 525 547 d.	|	0618	|	0718	|	⊙	|	0818	⊙	0918	|	⊙	|	1018	⊙	1118	|	⊙	|	1218	1318	|	⊙
45	**Arth-Goldau** ... 525 547 a.	0645	0645	0716	0745	0745	0816	0845	0845	0916	0945	0945	1016	1045	1045	1116	1145	1145	1216	1245	1245	1345	1345	1416
45	**Arth-Goldau** ... 547 d.	...	0649	0718	...	0749	0818	...	0849	0918	...	0949	1018	...	1049	1118	...	1149	1218	...	1249	...	1349	1418
51	Altdorf ... 547 d.	...	|	|	...	0808	|	...	|	|	...	1008	|	...	|	|	...	1208	|	...	|	...	1408	|
165	Bellinzona ... ▲ 547 a.	...	0742	0812	...	0842	0912	...	0942	1012	...	1042	1112	...	1142	1212	...	1242	1312	...	1342	...	1442	1512
165	Bellinzona ... 548 607 d.	...	0744	0814	...	0844	0914	...	0944	1014	...	1044	1114	...	1144	1214	...	1244	1314	...	1344	...	1444	1514
186	**Lugano** ... 548 607 a.	...	0758	0830	...	0858	0930	...	0958	1030	...	1058	1130	...	1158	1230	...	1258	1330	...	1358	...	1458	1530
186	**Lugano** ... 548 607 d.	...	...	0832	...	...	0932	...	...	1032	...	...	1132	...	...	1232	...	...	1332	...	1410**h**	...	...	1532
212	**Chiasso** 🏛 ... 548 607 d.	...	...	0902	...	...	1002**t**	...	...	1102	...	...	1202	...	...	1302	...	...	1402**t**	...	1455	...	...	1602
216	Como S. Giovanni ... 548 607 d.	...	...	0910	...	...	1010	...	...	1110	...	...	1210	...	...	1310	...	...	1410	...	1503	...	...	1610
263	**Milano** Centrale ... 548 a.	...	...	0950	...	...	1050	...	...	|	...	...	1250	...	...	|	...	...	1450	...	1555**g**	...	...	1650
	Milano Rogoredo ... a.	...	...	...	...	...	...	...	...	1230	...	...	...	...	...	1418	...	...	...	...	...	...	...	...

	IR 2425	IC 675	IR 2327	IC 877	EC 321	IR 2429	EC 153	IR 2331	IC 881	EC 323	IR 2433	IC 683	IR 2335	IC 885	EC 325	IR 2437	IC 687	IC 1487	IR 2339	IC 889	IR 2441	IC 691	IC 893	IC 895
					◧					◧					◧			⑥⑦		①–⑤			Ⓐ	⑥
	★	🍴	★	🍴	🍴	★	🍴	★	🍴	🍴	★	🍴	★	🍴	🍴	★	🍴	🍴	★	🍴	★	🍴		e
Zürich HB ... 547 555 d.	1405	...	...	1505	1533	1605	...	...	1705	1733	1805	...	...	1905	1933	2005	...	2033	...	2105	2205	...	2305	2333
Zug ... 547 555 d.	1430	...	...	1530	1600	1630	...	...	1730	1800	1830	...	...	1930	2000	2030	...	2100	...	2130	2230	...	2330	0000
Basel SBB **565** ... d.	|	1303	1403	|	|	|	1503	1603	|	|	|	1703	1803	|	|	|	1903	|	2003	|	|	2103	|	|
Luzern ... 525 547 d.	|	1418	1518	|	⊙	|	1618	1718	|	⊙	|	1818	1918	|	⊙	|	2018	|	2118	|	|	2218	|	|
Arth-Goldau ... 525 547 a.	1445	1445	1545	1545	1616	1645	1645	1745	1745	1816	1845	1845	1945	1945	2016	2045	2045	2116	2145	2145	2245	2245	2345	0015
Arth-Goldau ... 547 d.	...	1449	...	1549	1618	...	1649	...	1749	1818	...	1849	...	1949	2018	...	2049	2118	...	2149	...	2249	2349	0016
Altdorf ... 547 d.	...	|	...	1608	|	...	|	...	1808	|	...	|	...	2008	|	...	|	2137	...	2208	...	|	0008	0034
Bellinzona ... ▲ 547 a.	...	1542	...	1642	1712	...	1742	...	1842	1912	...	1942	...	2042	2112	...	2142	2212	...	2242	...	2342	0047	0115
Bellinzona ... 548 607 d.	...	1544	...	1644	1714	...	1744	...	1844	1914	...	1944	...	2044	2114	...	2144	2214	...	2244	...	2344	...	...
Lugano ... 548 607 a.	...	1558	...	1658	1730	...	1758	...	1858	1930	...	1958	...	2058	2130	...	2158	2230	...	2258	...	2358	...	...
Lugano ... 548 607 d.	...	...	...	...	1732	...	1810**h**	...	...	1932	...	...	...	...	2132	...	2202	2232	...	2302	...	0002	...	...
Chiasso 🏛 ... 548 607 d.	...	...	...	...	1802	...	1855	...	...	2002	...	...	...	...	2202	...	2230	2257	...	2330	...	0030	...	...
Como S. Giovanni ... 548 607 d.	...	...	...	...	1810	...	1903	...	...	2010	...	...	...	...	2210	...	...	...	...	...	...	...	...	...
Milano Centrale ... 548 a.	...	...	...	...	1850	...	1950	...	...	2050	...	...	...	...	2250	...	...	...	...	...	...	...	...	...
Milano Rogoredo ... a.	...	...	...	...	...	...	...	...	...	...	...	...	...	...	...	...	...	...	...	...	...	...	...	...

	IC 862	IR 2308	IC 664	IR 2410	IC 866	IR 2312	IC 668	IR 2414	EC 312	IC 870	IR 2316	EC 156	IR 2418	EC 314	IC 874	IR 2320	EC 158	IR 2422	EC 316	IC 878	IR 2324	IC 680	IR 2426	EC 318
									◧					◧			◧		◧					◧
		★		★	🍴	★	🍴	★	🍴	🍴	★	🍴	★	🍴	🍴	★	🍴	★	🍴	🍴	★	🍴	★	🍴
Milano Rogoredo ... d.	...	...	...	...	...	...	...	...	...	...	...	...	...	...	...	...	...	...	...	...	...	...	...	...
Milano Centrale ... 548 d.	...	...	...	...	...	...	...	...	0710	...	...	0810	...	0910	...	...	1005**g**	...	1110	...	...	...	...	1310
Como S. Giovanni ... 548 607 d.	...	...	...	...	...	...	...	...	0754	...	...	0904	...	0950	...	...	1059	...	1150	...	...	...	...	1350
Chiasso 🏛 ... 548 607 d.	...	...	0530	...	...	...	...	...	0805	...	...	0924**r**	...	1005**t**	...	...	1124**r**	...	1205	...	...	...	...	1405**t**
Lugano ... 548 607 a.	...	...	0558	...	...	...	...	...	0828	...	...	0950**r**	...	1028	...	...	1150**r**	...	1228	...	...	...	...	1428
Lugano ▷ ... 548 607 d.	...	...	0600	...	0702	...	0802	...	0830	0902	...	1002	...	1030	1102	...	1202	...	1230	1302	...	1402	...	1430
Bellinzona ... 548 607 a.	...	...	0615	...	0716	...	0816	...	0845	0916	...	1016	...	1045	1116	...	1216	...	1245	1316	...	1416	...	1445
Bellinzona ... ▲ 547 d.	0507	...	0618	...	0718	...	0818	...	0847	0918	...	1018	...	1047	1118	...	1218	...	1247	1318	...	1418	...	1447
Altdorf ... 547 d.	0550	...	|	...	0750	...	|	...	|	0950**z**	...	|	...	|	1150**z**	...	|	...	|	1350**z**	...	|	...	|
Arth-Goldau ... 547 a.	0611	...	0711	...	0811	...	0911	...	0942	1011	...	1111	...	1142	1211	...	1311	...	1342	1411	...	1511	...	1542
Arth-Goldau ... 525 547 d.	0615	0615	0715	0715	0815	0815	0915	0915	0945	1015	1015	1115	1115	1145	1215	1215	1315	1315	1345	1415	1415	1515	1515	1545
Luzern ... 525 547 a.	|	0641	0741	|	|	0841	0941	|	⊙	|	1041	1141	|	⊙	|	1241	1341	|	⊙	|	1441	1541	|	⊙
Basel SBB **565** ... a.	|	0756	0856	|	|	0956	1056	|	|	|	1156	1256	|	|	|	1356	1456	|	|	|	1556	1656	|	|
Zug ... 547 555 a.	0630	...	...	0730	0830	...	...	0930	1000	1030	...	...	1130	1200	1230	...	...	1330	1400	1430	...	...	1530	1600
Zürich HB ... 547 555 a.	0655	...	...	0755	0855	...	...	0955	1027	1055	...	...	1155	1227	1255	...	...	1355	1427	1455	...	...	1555	1627

	IC 882	IR 2328	IR 2682	IC 1482	IC 684	IR 2430	EC 320	IC 886	IR 2332	EC 308	IC 688	IR 2434	EC 322	IC 890	IR 2336	EC 310	IC 692	IR 2438	EC 324	IC 894	IR 2340	EC 326	IC 696	IR 2442
			Ⓐ	Ⓒ			◧			◧			‡◧			◧			◧			◧		
	🍴	★		🍴	🍴	★	🍴	🍴	★	V🍴	🍴	★	🍴	🍴	★	G🍴	🍴	★	🍴	🍴	★	B🍴		★
Milano Rogoredo ... d.	...	...	...	...	...	...	...	...	...	...	...	...	...	...	...	1742	...	...	...	...	...	1937	...	...
Milano Centrale ... 548 d.	...	...	...	...	...	...	1510	...	...	1610	...	...	1710	...	...	|	...	...	1910	...	...	|	...	...
Como S. Giovanni ... 548 607 d.	...	...	...	...	...	...	1550	...	...	1650	...	...	1750	...	...	1850	...	...	1950	...	...	2050	...	...
Chiasso 🏛 ... 548 607 d.	...	...	...	...	...	...	1605	...	...	1705	...	...	1805	...	...	1905	...	...	2005	...	...	2105	...	...
Lugano ... 548 607 a.	...	...	...	...	...	...	1628	...	...	1728	...	...	1828	...	...	1928	...	...	2028	...	...	2128	...	...
Lugano ▷ ... 548 607 d.	1502	...	...	1530	1602	...	1630	1702	...	1730	1802	...	1830	1902	...	1930	2002	...	2030	2102	...	2130	2202	...
Bellinzona ... 548 607 a.	1516	...	...	1545	1616	...	1645	1716	...	1745	1816	...	1845	1916	...	1945	2016	...	2045	2116	...	2145	2216	...
Bellinzona ... ▲ 547 d.	1518	...	...	1547	1618	...	1647	1718	...	1747	1818	...	1847	1918	...	1947	2018	...	2047	2118	...	2147	2218	...
Altdorf ... 547 d.	1550**z**	...	...	|	|	...	|	1750**z**	...	|	|	...	|	1950**z**	...	|	|	...	|	2150**z**	...	|	|	...
Arth-Goldau ... 547 a.	1611	...	...	1642	1711	...	1742	1811	...	1842	1911	...	1942	2011	...	2042	2111	...	2142	2211	...	2242	2311	...
Arth-Goldau ... 525 547 d.	1615	1615	1645	1645	1715	1715	1745	1815	1815	1845	1915	1915	1945	2015	2015	2045	2115	2115	2145	2215	2215	2245	2315	2315
Luzern ... 525 547 a.	|	1641	|	⊙	1741	|	⊙	|	1841	⊙	1941	|	⊙	|	2041	⊙	2141	|	|	|	2241	|	2341	|
Basel SBB **565** ... a.	|	1756	|	|	1856	|	|	|	1956	|	2056	|	|	|	2156	|	2300	|	|	|	2400	|	0102	|
Zug ... 547 555 a.	1630	...	1700	1700	...	1730	1800	1830	...	1900	...	1930	2000	2030	...	2100	...	2130	2200	2230	...	2300	...	2330
Zürich HB ... 547 555 a.	1655	...	1727	1727	...	1755	1827	1855	...	1927	...	1955	2027	2055	...	2127	...	2155	2227	2255	...	2327	...	2355

B – To/from Bologna (Table **600**).
G – To/from Genova (Table **610**).
F – From Frankfurt (Table **912**).
V – To/from Venezia (Table **605**).

e – Not Dec. 25, Jan. 1.
g – Milano **Porta Garibaldi**.
h – 9 minutes earlier June 16 - Aug. 28.
r – 6–8 minutes later June 16 - Aug. 28.
t – Until Sept. 4.
z – Not June 16 - Aug. 28.

¶ – Train number **329** on ⑤–⑦ (also Apr. 18, May 26, June 6, Aug. 1).
‡ – Train number **332** on ⑤–⑦ (also Apr. 18, May 26, June 6, Aug. 1).
▷ – June 16 - Aug. 28 Lugano departures at xx02 are retimed to xx01.
◧ – Supplement payable in Italy and for international journeys.
★ – Operated by SOB. See Table **547** for full details.
⊙ – See Table **525** for connecting service from/to Luzern.
▲ – For connecting services Bellinzona - Locarno and v.v. see Table **547**.

FART — LOCARNO - DOMODOSSOLA — 551

km				C		C		C 🍸			V 🍸		C 🍸	V 🍸		V 🍸		V 🍸		C 🍸				⑤⑦	
0	**Locarno** ... d.	0538	...	0648	0709	0748	0809	0848	...	0951	1048	1118	1148	1248	1348	1448	1513	1548	1619	1648	...	1748	1819	1848	1920
20	Camedo 🏛 ... d.	0619	...	0724	0750	0824	0850	0924	...	1041	1124**u**	1204	1224	1324**u**	1432	1524**u**	1554	1624	1704	1724	...	1824	1905	1925	2000
26	Re ... d.	...	...	0740	...	0840**x**	...	0940**x**	...	1058	1140**x**	...	1240**x**	1340**x**	...	1540**x**	...	1640**x**	...	1740**x**	...	1840**x**	...	1941**x**	...
34	S. Maria Maggiore ... d.	...	...	0753	...	0853**x**	...	0953**x**	...	1111	1153**x**	...	1253**x**	1353**x**	...	1553**x**	...	1653**x**	...	1753**x**	...	1852**x**	...	1955**x**	...
53	**Domodossola** ... a.	...	...	0836	...	0936	...	1036	...	1150	1236	...	1336	1436	...	1636	...	1736	...	1836	...	1936	...	2036	...

						C 🍸	C	V 🍸	V 🍸			V 🍸				V 🍸		C 🍸		C		C			C ⑤⑦
Domodossola ... d.	...	...	...	...	0825	0925	1003	1025	1125	...	1225	1325	...	...	...	1525	...	1625	...	1725	...	1900	...	1925	2025
S. Maria Maggiore ... d.	...	...	...	...	0910**x**	1010**x**	1045	1110**x**	1210**x**	...	1310	1410**x**	...	...	...	1610**x**	...	1710**x**	...	1810	...	1943	...	2013	2109**x**
Re ... d.	...	...	...	...	0922**x**	1022**x**	1057	1122**x**	1222**x**	...	1322	1422**x**	...	...	...	1622**x**	...	1722**x**	...	1822	...	1955	...	2026	2122**x**
Camedo 🏛 ... d.	0625	0656	0756	0856	0939	1038	1109	1139	1239	1255	1339	1438**s**	1447	...	1607	1638**s**	1723	1739	...	1839	1924	2009**s**	2019	2043**s**	2137**s**
Locarno ... a.	0708	0741	0841	0941	1019	1117	1155	1217	1317	1341	1421	1519	1535	...	1655	1717	1808	1819	...	1919	2009	2046	2106	2124	2217

C – CENTOVALLI EXPRESS.
V – TRENO PANORAMICO VIGEZZO VISION – Conveys panorama car. Supplement payable.
s – Stops to set down only.
u – Stops to pick up only.
x – Stops only on request.

552 LUZERN - STANS - ENGELBERG

Narrow gauge rack railway. ZB

km		E			E				E			E		🚌				🚌					T	T
0	**Luzern** 561 d.	0504	0527	0557	0610	0627		2057	2110	2127	2157	2210	2227	...	2257	2310	2327	...	2357	0032	0102		0836	0936
9	Hergiswil 561 d.	0514	0540	0610	|	0640	and at	2110	|	2140	2210	|	2240	...	2310	2318	2340	...	0010	0045	0115	EXTRA	0847	0947
11	Stansstad d.	0518	0544	0614	|	0644	the same	2114	|	2144	2214	|	2244	...	2314	2322	2344	...	0014	0050	0119	SERVICES	0851	0951
14	Stans d.	0522	0548	0618	0624	0648	minutes	2118	2124	2148	2218	2224	2248	...	2318	2326	2348	...	0018	0054	0123	▶▶▶	0854	0954
18	Dallenwil d.	0529	0552	...	0629	0652	past each	...	2129	2152	...	2229	2252	2255	2322	...	2352	2355	0022	0059	...		|	|
21	Wolfenschiessen d.	0533	0557	...	0633	0657	hour until	...	2133	2157	...	2233	2257	|	...	...	2357	|	0027	0103	...		|	|
33	**Engelberg** ⊡ a.	0553	...	...	0653	...		...	2153	...	...	2253	...	2316	...	...	...	0016	...	...	...		0921	1021
			🚌			E				E			E			E		🚌		🚌			T	T
	Engelberg ⊡ d.	...	0500	...	...	0602	...		...	2102	...	...	2202	...	...	2302	...	2330	...	0018	...		1624	1724
	Wolfenschiessen d.	0452	|	0522	0601	0622	...	and at	2101	2122	...	2201	2222	...	2301	2322	...	|	0001	|	0038	EXTRA	|	|
	Dallenwil d.	0455	0523	0527	0604	0629	...	the same	2104	2129	...	2204	2229	...	2304	2329	2334	2353	0004	0038	0041	SERVICES	|	|
	Stans d.	0501	...	0532	0610	0634	0640	minutes	2110	2134	2140	2210	2234	2240	2310	2334	2340	...	0010	...	0047	▶▶▶	1701	1801
	Stansstad d.	0505	...	0535	0614	|	0644	past each	2114	|	2144	2214	|	2244	2314	|	2344	...	0014	...	0051		1705	1805
	Hergiswil 561 d.	0509	...	0540	0618	|	0648	hour until	2118	|	2148	2218	|	2248	2318	|	2348	...	0018	...	0055		1709	1809
	Luzern 561 a.	0522	...	0549	0632	0649	0702		2132	2149	2202	2232	2249	2302	2332	2349	0002	...	0032	...	0109		1719	1819

E – LUZERN - ENGELBERG EXPRESS. Conveys panorama cars.
T – SKI UND WANDER EXPRESS. ⑥⑦ Dec. 12 - Mar. 27 (also Dec. 27–31); ⓒ May 14 - Oct. 30.
⊡ – Station for Titlis, accessible by cable-car.

553 MOUNTAIN RAILWAYS IN CENTRAL SWITZERLAND

RB (2nd class only)

ARTH-GOLDAU - RIGI KULM

km						C					C	F
0	Arth-Goldau d.	0755	0908	1008	1108	1208	1308	1423	1523	1623	1723	1823
9	Rigi Kulm a.	0840	0947	1047	1147	1247	1347	1502	1602	1702	1802	1902

				C						C	F
Rigi Kulm d.	0858	1001	1101	1201	1301	1416	1516	1616	1716	1816	1916
Arth-Goldau a.	0948	1048	1148	1248	1348	1503	1603	1703	1803	1903	2003

RIGI KULM - VITZNAU

km										D 🚂	⑦A	E 🚂														
0	Rigi Kulm d.	...	...	0900	1000	1100	1200	1300	1400	1415	1430	1430	1500	1600	1700	...	1820t	...	2000t	...	2240h	...	...	...	...	...
2	Rigi Staffelhöhe d.	0715	...	0910	1010	1110	1210	1310	1410	1428	1446	1447	1510	1610	1710	...	1830	...	2010	...	2250	...	...	...	...	...
7	Vitznau a.	0749	...	0940	1040	1140	1240	1340	1440	1506	1513	1539	1540	1640	1740	...	1900	...	2040	...	2320	...	...	...	...	...

						⑦A	D 🚂		E 🚂	⑦A															
Vitznau d.	0635	...	0815	0915	1015	1050	1051	1115	1116	1150	1215	1315	1415	1515	1615	...	1740	...	1915	...	2205	...	...	...	...
Rigi Staffelhöhe d.	0659	...	0837	0937	1037	1115	1158	1137	1217	1215	1237	1337	1437	1537	1637	...	1801	...	1937	...	2227	...	...	...	...
Rigi Kulm a.	...	...	0847	0947	1047	1125	1221	1147	1234	1225	1247	1347	1447	1547	1647	...	1811g	...	1947g	...	2237h	...	...	...	...

ALPNACHSTAD - PILATUS KULM. Narrow gauge rack railway. *5 km*. Journey time: 30 minutes uphill, 40 minutes downhill. **Operator**: PB ✆ 041 329 11 11.
Services run daily May 26 - November 20 (weather permitting). **No winter service**.
From **Alpnachstad** at 0810 **r**, 0850, 0935, 1015, 1055, 1135, 1220, 1300, 1345, 1425, 1505, 1550, 1630 **r** and 1710 **r**.
From **Pilatus Kulm** at 0845 **r**, 0930, 1010, 1050, 1130, 1215, 1255, 1340, 1420, 1500, 1545, 1625, 1705 **r** and 1745 **r**.

BRIENZ - BRIENZER ROTHORN. Narrow gauge rack railway. *8 km*. Most services operated by 🚂. Journey time: 55–60 minutes uphill, 60–70 minutes downhill.
Operator: BRB, ✆ 033 952 22 22. Services run **June 5 - October 24** (subject to demand and weather conditions on the mountain). Extra trains may run at busy times. **No winter service**.
From **Brienz**: 0736 **†B**, 0836, 0940, 1045, 1145, 1258, 1358, 1458 and 1636.
From **Brienzer Rothorn**: 0906 **†B**, 0938, 1115, 1220, 1328, 1428, 1528, 1628 and 1740.

A – ⑦ May 22 - Sept. 4.
B – † July 3 - Sept. 25.
C – Daily Dec. 18 - Mar. 6; ⓒ Mar. 12 - Apr. 24; daily Apr. 30 - Oct. 23; ⑥⑦ from Oct. 29.
D – June 5, July 3, 24, Aug. 21, Sept. 4, Oct. 2 only.
E – Jan. 30, Feb. 27 only.
F – ⑤ to Apr. 8 (also Apr. 14, 22); ⑤–⑦ Apr. 29 - Oct. 28 (also May 25, 26, June 6, 15, 16, Aug. 1, 15); ⑤ from Nov. 4.
g – ⑤⑥ Dec. 31 - Mar. 5; daily Apr. 30 - Oct. 23; ⑤⑥ Oct. 28 - Dec. 3.
h – ⑤⑥ Apr. 30 - May 14; daily May 20 - Sept. 4; ⑤⑥ Sept. 9 - Oct. 22.
r – May 26 - Oct. 30.
t – Apr. 30 - Oct. 23.
🚂 – Steam train. Supplement payable for uphill journeys **to** Rigi Kulm (no supplement for downhill journeys). Reservations: ✆ 041 399 87 87. Website: www.rigi.ch

554 🚌 MEIRINGEN - ANDERMATT

PA

Service operates **June 25 - October 16** (no winter service). Reservations: ✆ +41 (0) 848 100 222.

							ⓒ				
Meiringen Bahnhof d.	...	0850	...	0925	...	1050	1055	1325	1325	1520	...
Steingletscher, Susten d.	...	0944	1000	|	...	|	1149	|	1425	|	...
Susten Passhöhe d.	...	▬	1010	|	...	|	...	|	1435	|	...
Göschenen Bahnhof d.	...	...	1049	|	...	|	...	|	1514	|	...
Grimsel Passhöhe d.	0912	...	|	1055	...	1205	...	1440	|	1635	...
Gletsch Post d.	0922	...	|	1105	...	1215	...	1450	|	1645	...
Oberwald Bahnhof a.	0937	...	|	1120	...	1230	...	1505	|	1700	...
Oberwald Bahnhof d.	...	0942	|	...	1220	...	...	...	|	...	*1704*
Gletsch Post a.	...	0954	|	...	1232	...	...	...	|	...	*1716*
Gletsch Post d.	...	0954	|	...	1318	...	...	...	|	...	1720
Furka Passhöhe d.	...	1010	|	...	1340	...	...	...	|	...	1740
Realp Post d.	...	...	|	...	1404	...	...	...	|	...	1804
Andermatt Bahnhof a.	...	...	1104	...	1423	...	...	...	1529	...	1823

						ⓒ					
Andermatt Bahnhof d.	...	...	...	0830	...	...	...	...	1534	1551	...
Realp Post d.	...	...	...	0842	...	...	...	...	1546	|	...
Furka Passhöhe d.	...	...	...	0906	...	...	...	...	1610	|	...
Gletsch Post a.	...	...	...	0935	...	...	...	...	1639	|	...
Gletsch Post d.	...	...	...	1005	...	...	...	...	*1645*	|	...
Oberwald Bahnhof a.	...	...	...	1020	...	...	...	...	*1700*	|	...
Oberwald Bahnhof d.	...	...	0845	...	1030	...	1250	1530	...	|	1704
Gletsch Post d.	...	...	0857	...	1042	...	1302	1542	...	|	1716
Grimsel Passhöhe d.	...	...	0911	...	1113	...	1333	1613	...	|	1733
Göschenen Bahnhof d.	0911	...	...	...	|	...	|	|	...	1611	|
Susten Passhöhe d.	0946	...	...	...	|	...	|	|	...	1646	|
Steingletscher, Susten d.	0956	1000	...	...	|	1150	|	|	...	1720	|
Meiringen Bahnhof a.	...	1051	...	...	1214	1241	1434	1714	...	1811	1834

555 ZÜRICH FLUGHAFEN ✈ - ZÜRICH - LUZERN

SBB (train category *IR*)

km		A	⑥⑦b	⑥⑦d	⑥⑦c	⑥⑦c	⑥⑦c												Ⓐe			Ⓐe		
	Konstanz 535 d.	...	...	...	...	...	...	...	...	...	0509	...	0609	...	0709		...	1509	...	...	...	...	...	1709
0	**Zürich** Flughafen ✈ ‡ d.	...	...	...	...	...	...	...	...	...	0615	...	0715	...	0815	and at	...	1615	...	...	...	...	...	1815
10	**Zürich** HB 520 ‡ d.	0008	0010	0035	0135	0235	0335	...	0535	0610	0635	0710	0735	0810	0835	the same	1610	1635	1639	1710	1735	1739	1810	1835
22	Thalwil 520 d.	0017	|	0045	|	|	|	...	0545	|	0645	|	0745	|	0845	minutes	|	1645	|	|	1745	|	|	1845
39	Zug d.	0035	0032	0102	0157	0257	0357	...	0603	0632	0703	0732	0803	0832	0903	past each	1632	1703	1712	1732	1803	1812	1832	1903
49	Rotkreuz d.	0046	|	0109	0206	0306	0406	...	0611	|	0711	|	0811	|	0911	hour until	|	1711	1722	|	1811	1822	|	1911
67	**Luzern** a.	0107	0051	0123	0223	0323	0423	...	0625	0651	0725	0751	0825	0851	0925		1651	1725	1739	1751	1825	1839	1851	1925

Konstanz 535 d.	...	1809	...	1909	...	...	...	...	...	...
Zürich Flughafen ✈ ‡ d.	...	1915	...	2015	...	...	...	...	...	...
Zürich HB 520 ‡ d.	1910	1935	2010	2035	2110	2135	2210	2235	2310	2335
Thalwil 520 d.	|	1945	|	2045	|	2145	|	2245	|	2345
Zug d.	1932	2003	2032	2103	2132	2203	2232	2303	2332	0003
Rotkreuz d.	|	2011	|	2111	|	2211	|	2311	|	0011
Luzern a.	1951	2025	2051	2125	2151	2225	2251	2325	2351	0025

	⑥⑦c	⑥⑦c	⑥⑦c	⑥⑦d					Ⓐe	
Luzern d.	0035	0135	0235	0335	...	0452	0535	0609	0620	0635
Rotkreuz d.	0048	0151	0251	0351	...	0513	0548	|	0635	0648
Zug d.	0057	0200	0300	0400	...	0526	0558	0629	0647	0658
Thalwil 520 d.	0114	0216	0316	0416	...	0543	0614	|	|	0714
Zürich HB 520 ‡ a.	0123	0225	0325	0425	...	0555	0625	0650	0720	0725
Zürich Flughafen ✈ ‡ a.	...	...	...	...	...	...	0644	...	...	0744
Konstanz 535 d.	...	...	...	...	...	...	0750	...	...	0850

		Ⓐe																						
Luzern d.	0709	0720	0735	0809	0835		1509	1535	1609	1635	1709	1735	1809	1835	1909	1935	2009	2035	2109	2135	2209	2235	2309	2335
Rotkreuz d.	|	0735	0748	|	0848	and at	|	1548	|	1648	|	1748	|	1848	|	1948	|	2048	|	2148	|	2248	|	2348
Zug d.	0729	0747	0758	0829	0858	the same	1529	1558	1629	1658	1729	1758	1829	1858	1929	1958	2029	2058	2129	2158	2229	2258	2329	2358
Thalwil 520 d.	|	|	0814	|	0914	minutes	|	1614	|	1714	|	1814	|	1914	|	2014	|	2114	|	2214	|	2314	|	0014
Zürich HB 520 ‡ a.	0750	0820	0825	0850	0925	past each	1550	1625	1650	1725	1750	1825	1850	1925	1950	2025	2050	2125	2150	2225	2250	2325	2350	0025
Zürich Flughafen ✈ ‡ a.	...	...	0844	...	0944	hour until	...	1644	...	...	...	1844	...	1944	...	2044	...	...	...	...	...	...	...	...
Konstanz 535 d.	...	...	0950	...	1050		...	1750	...	...	...	1950	...	2050	...	2150	...	...	...	...	...	...	...	...

A – ①–⑤ (also Dec. 26, Jan. 2, Apr. 16).
b – Not Dec. 26, Jan. 2, Apr. 16.
c – Also Apr. 15, 18, May 26, 27, June 6, Aug. 1; not Dec. 25, 26.
d – Also Apr. 15, 18, May 26, 27, June 6, Aug. 1; not Dec. 12, 25, 26.
e – Not Dec. 27–31, July 25 - Aug. 5.
‡ – See also Tables **530** and **535**. Frequent services operate **Zürich - Zürich Flughafen** and v.v. (up to 13 trains per hour 0600 - 2400).

SBB BASEL - BERN - INTERLAKEN and BRIG 560

See Table **562** for services via Kandersteg.

km		IC 993		IC 955	IC 802	IC 1057	IC 957	IC 804	EC 51	IC 951	IC 959	IC 806	IC 333	IC 953	IC 961	IC 808	IC 1063	IC 963	IC 810	IC 1065	IC 965	IC 812	EC 53	IC 967	IC 814	IC 1069
		⑥⑦ z			✕	✕	⊗	✕	◧ ✕	Ⓐ H ⊗	J ⊗	✕	✕	Ⓐ H ✕	J ✕	✕	✕	✕	✕	⊗	✕	✕	◧ ✕	⊗	✕	✕
	Romanshorn **535** d.	...	...	...	...	...	...	...	...	...	...	0548	...	...	...	0648	...	...	0748	...	...	0848	...	...	0948	...
	Zürich Flughafen ✈ **535** d.	...	...	...	...	...	...	...	...	...	...	0645	...	...	...	0745	...	...	0845	...	...	0945	...	...	1045	...
	Zürich HB **505** d.	...	...	...	...	...	...	0602	...	...	...	0702	...	...	...	0802	...	...	0902	...	...	1002	...	...	1102	...
0	**Basel** SBB **565** d.	...	...	...	...	0522	0556	|	0628	*0656*	0656	|	0728	*0756*	0756	|	0828	0856	|	0928	0956	|	1028	1056	|	1128
39	Olten **505 565** d.	...	...	...	...	0558	0629	|	0658	*0729*	0729	|	0758	*0829*	0829	|	0858	0929	|	0958	1029	|	1058	1129	|	1158
101	**Bern** **505** a.	...	...	...	...	0626	0656	0658c	0726	*0756*	0756	0758c	0826	*0856*	0856	0858c	0926	0956	0958c	1026	1056	1058c	1126	1156	1158c	1226
101	**Bern** d.	0109	...	0604	0607	0634	0704	0707	0734	0804	0804	0807	0834	0904	0904	0907	0934	1004	1007	1034	1104	1107	1134	1204	1207	1234
132	Thun d.	0136	...	0624	0626	0654	0724	0726	0754	0824	0824	0826	0854	0924	0924	0926	0954	1024	1026	1054	1124	1126	1154	1224	1226	1254
142	**Spiez** ▷ d.	0147	...	0634	0636	0704	0734	0736	0805	0834	0834	0836	0904	0934	0934	0936	1005	1034	1036	1104	1134	1136	1205	1234	1236	1304
158	Interlaken West ▷ a.	0202	...	0651	|	0722	0751	|	|	0851	0851	|	0922	0951	0951	|	|	1051	|	1122	1151	|	|	1251	|	1322
160	**Interlaken** Ost ▷ a.	0208	...	0658	|	0728	0758	|	|	0858	0858	|	0928	0958	0958	|	|	1058	|	1128	1158	|	|	1258	|	1328
197	Visp **570** d.	...	...	...	0703	...	...	0803	0833	...	...	0903	...	...	...	1003	1033	...	1103	...	...	1203	1233	...	1303	...
206	**Brig** **570 590** a.	...	...	...	0711	...	...	0811	0841	...	...	0911	...	...	...	1011	1040	...	1111	...	...	1211	1241	...	1311	...
	Domodossola 🏛 **590** a.	...	...	...	...	...	...	...	0912	...	...	...	...	...	...	...	...	...	...	...	...	...	1312	...	...	...
	Milano Centrale **590** a.	...	...	...	...	...	...	...	1040	...	...	...	...	...	...	...	...	...	...	...	...	...	1440	...	...	...

	ICE 275	IC 816	EC 57	IC 971	IC 818	IC 1073	EC 7	IC 820	IC 1075	IC 975	IC 822	IC 1077	IC 977	IC 824	IC 1079	IC 979	IC 826	EC 59	ICE 371	IC 828	IC 1083	IC 983	IC 830	IC 1085	ICE 373	IC 1087
	G✕	✕	◧ ✕	⊗	✕	✕	G✕	✕	✕	✕	✕	⊗	⊗	✕	⊗	✕	✕	◧ ✕	G✕	✕	⊗	✕	✕	✕	G✕	①–⑥ ✕
Romanshorn **535** d.	...	1048	...	...	1148	...	...	1248	...	...	1348	...	...	1448	...	...	1548	...	...	1648	...	...	1748	...	...	...
Zürich Flughafen ✈ **535** d.	...	1145	...	...	1245	...	...	1345	...	...	1445	...	...	1545	...	...	1645	...	...	1745	...	...	1845	...	...	...
Zürich HB **505** d.	...	1202	...	...	1302	...	...	1402	...	...	1502	...	...	1602	...	...	1702	...	...	1802	...	...	1902	...	...	...
Basel SBB **565** d.	1156	|	1228	1256	|	1328	1356	|	1428	1456	|	1528	1556	|	1628	1656	|	1728	1756	|	1828	1856	|	1928	1956	2028
Olten **505 565** d.	1229	|	1258	1329	|	1358	1429	|	1458	1529	|	1558	1629	|	1658	1729	|	1758	1829	|	1858	1929	|	1958	2029	2058
Bern **505** a.	1256	1258c	1326	1356	1358c	1426	1456	1458c	1526	1556	1558c	1626	1656	1658c	1726	1756	1758c	1826	1856	1858c	1926	1956	1958c	2026	2056	2126
Bern d.	1304	1307	1334	1404	1407	1434	1504	1507	1534	1604	1607	1634	1704	1707	1734	1804	1807	1834	1904	1907	1934	2004	2007	2034	2107	2134
Thun d.	1324	1326	1354	1424	1426	1454	1524	1526	1554	1624	1626	1654	1724	1726	1754	1824	1826	1854	1924	1926	1954	2024	2026	2054	2126	2154
Spiez ▷ d.	1334	1336	1405	1434	1436	1504	1534	1536	1605	1634	1636	1704	1734	1736	1805	1834	1836	1905	1934	1936	2004	2034	2036	2105	2137	2205
Interlaken West ▷ a.	1352	|	|	1451	|	1522	1551	|	|	1651	|	1722	1751	|	|	1851	|	|	1952	|	2022	2050	|	|	2154	|
Interlaken Ost ▷ a.	1358	|	|	1458	|	1528	1558	|	|	1658	|	1728	1758	|	|	1858	|	|	1958	|	2028	2056	|	|	2159	|
Visp **570** d.	...	1403	1433	...	1503	...	...	1603	1633	...	1703	...	...	1803	1833	...	1903	1933	...	2003	...	...	2103	2133	...	2233
Brig **570 590** a.	...	1411	1441	...	1511	...	...	1611	1640	...	1711	...	...	1811	1841	...	1911	1941	...	2011	...	...	2111	2141	...	2241
Domodossola 🏛 **590** a.	...	...	1512	...	...	...	...	...	...	...	...	...	...	...	...	...	...	2012	...	...	...	...	...	...	...	...
Milano Centrale **590** a.	...	...	1640	...	...	...	...	...	...	...	...	...	...	...	...	...	...	2140	...	...	...	...	...	...	...	...

	IC 1089	IC 987	IC 1091	IC 1093	IC 1095	IC 989	IC 1097	RE 4293	IC 838	IC 991
	⑦ ✕			①–⑥ ⊖	⑦					
Romanshorn **535** d.	...	...	...	...	...	...	...	...	...	...
Zürich Flughafen ✈ **535** d.	...	...	...	...	...	...	...	...	...	...
Zürich HB **505** d.	...	...	...	...	...	...	...	...	...	...
Basel SBB **565** d.	2028	2056	2128	...	...	2156	2228	...	*2258*	...
Olten **505 565** d.	2058	2129	2158	...	...	2229	2258	...	2335	...
Bern **505** a.	2126	2156	2226	...	...	2256	2326	...	0002	...
Bern d.	2134	2207	...	2234	2234	2308	2339	...	...	0008
Thun d.	2154	2226	...	2254	2254	2327	2359	...	...	0030
Spiez ▷ d.	2205	2237	...	2305	2305	2338	0009	0013	...	0040
Interlaken West ▷ a.	|	2252	...	|	|	2355	0024	|	...	0056
Interlaken Ost ▷ a.	|	2258	...	|	⊙	2400	0030	⊙	...	0101
Visp **570** d.	|	...	...	2336	|	...	...	|	...	...
Brig **570 590** a.	2303	...	...	2344	0013	...	...	0123	...	...
Domodossola 🏛 **590** a.	...	...	...	...	...	...	...	...	...	...
Milano Centrale **590** a.	...	...	...	...	...	...	...	...	...	...

	IC 956	IC 1056	ICE 372	IC 807	IC 1058	IC 960	IC 952	IC 809	IC 1060	IC 962	IC 952
		✕	G✕	⊖✕	⊗	J ⊗	Ⓐ H ⊗	✕	✕	J ✕	Ⓐ H ✕
Milano Centrale **590** d.	...	...	...	...	...	...	...	...	...	...	...
Domodossola 🏛 **590** d.	...	...	...	...	...	...	...	...	...	...	...
Brig **570 590** d.	...	...	...	0546	...	...	...	0648	0718	...	...
Visp **570** d.	...	...	...	0554	...	...	...	0657	0727	...	...
Interlaken Ost ▷ d.	0458	0531	0558	|	0630	0700	0700	|	|	0800	0800
Interlaken West ▷ d.	0503	0536	0603	|	0635	0705	0705	|	|	0805	0805
Spiez ▷ d.	0520	0554	0622	0625	0654	0722	0722	0725	0754	0822	0822
Thun d.	0530	0604	0633	0636	0704	0733	0733	0736	0804	0833	0833
Bern a.	0552	0624	0652	0654c	0724	0752	0752	0754c	0824	0852	0852
Bern **505** d.	0604	0636	0704	0702	0736	0804	*0804*	0802	0836	0904	*0904*
Olten **505 565** a.	0630	0703	0730	|	0803	0830	*0830*	|	0903	0930	*0930*
Basel SBB **565** a.	0701	0732	0801	|	0832	0901	*0901*	|	0932	1001	*1001*
Zürich HB **505** a.	...	...	...	0758	...	...	...	0858	...	...	...
Zürich Flug ✈ **535** a.	...	...	...	0814	...	...	...	0914	...	...	...
Romanshorn **535** a.	...	...	...	0912	...	...	...	1012	...	...	...

	IC 811	IC 1062	IC 964	IC 813	EC 50	ICE 278	IC 815	IC 1066	IC 968	IC 817	IC 1068	EC 6	IC 819	IC 1070	IC 972	IC 821	EC 52	IC 974	IC 823	IC 1074	ICE 376	IC 825	IC 1076	IC 978	IC 827	IC 1078
	✕	⊗	✕	✕	◧ ✕	G✕	✕	⊗	✕	✕	✕	G✕	✕	✕	⊗	✕	◧ G✕	⊗	✕	✕	G✕	✕	✕	⊗	¶ ✕	✕
Milano Centrale **590** d.	...	...	...	...	0720	...	...	...	...	...	...	...	...	...	...	...	1120	...	...	...	...	...	...	...	...	...
Domodossola 🏛 **590** d.	...	...	...	...	0848	...	...	...	...	...	...	...	...	...	...	...	1248	...	...	...	...	...	...	...	...	...
Brig **570 590** d.	0748	...	...	0848	0918	...	0948	...	...	1048	1118	...	1148	...	...	1248	1318	...	1348	...	...	1448	1518	...	1548	...
Visp **570** d.	0757	...	...	0857	0927	...	0957	...	...	1057	1127	...	1157	...	...	1257	1327	...	1357	...	...	1457	1527	...	1557	...
Interlaken Ost ▷ d.	|	0830	0900	|	|	1000	|	1030	1100	|	|	1200	|	1230	1300	|	|	1400	|	1430	1500	|	|	1600	|	1630
Interlaken West ▷ d.	|	0835	0905	|	|	1005	|	1035	1105	|	|	1205	|	1235	1305	|	|	1405	|	1435	1505	|	|	1605	|	1635
Spiez ▷ d.	0823	0854	0922	0923	0954	1022	1023	1054	1122	1123	1154	1222	1223	1254	1322	1323	1354	1422	1423	1454	1522	1523	1554	1622	1623	1654
Thun d.	0834	0904	0933	0934	1004	1033	1034	1104	1133	1134	1204	1233	1234	1304	1333	1334	1404	1433	1434	1504	1533	1534	1604	1633	1634	1704
Bern a.	0854c	0924	0952	0954c	1024	1052	1054c	1124	1152	1154c	1224	1252	1254c	1324	1352	1354c	1424	1452	1454c	1524	1552	1554c	1624	1652	1654c	1724
Bern **505** d.	0902	0936	1004	1002	1036	1104	1102	1136	1204	1202	1236	1304	1302	1336	1404	1402	1436	1504	1502	1536	1604	1602	1636	1704	1702	1736
Olten **505 565** a.	|	1003	1030	|	1103	1130	|	1203	1230	|	1303	1330	|	1403	1430	|	1503	1530	|	1603	1630	|	1703	1730	|	1803
Basel SBB **565** a.	|	1032	1101	|	1132	1201	|	1232	1301	|	1332	1401	|	1432	1501	|	1532	1601	|	1632	1701	|	1732	1801	|	1832
Zürich HB **505** a.	0958	...	...	1058	...	...	1158	...	...	1258	...	...	1358	...	...	1458	...	...	1558	...	...	1658	...	...	1758	...
Zürich Flughafen ✈ **535** a.	1014	...	...	1114	...	...	1214	...	...	1314	...	...	1414	...	...	1514	...	...	1614	...	...	1714	...	...	1814	...
Romanshorn **535** a.	1112	...	...	1212	...	...	1312	...	...	1412	...	...	1512	...	...	1612	...	...	1712	...	...	1812	...	...	1912	...

	IC 980	IC 829	EC 54	EC 54	IC 982	IC 831	IC 1082	IC 984	IC 833	IC 1084	IC 986	IC 835	EC 56	IC 336	IC 837	IC 1088	IC 338	IC 990	IC 839	IC 1090	IC 1096	IC 992	IC 1092	IC 841		IC 1094
	✕	‡ ✕	Ⓐ ◧ ✕	Ⓒ ◧ ✕	✕	§ ✕	⊗	⊗	✕	⊗	✕	✕	◧ ✕							①–⑥			⑦			⑤⑥ k
Milano C **590** d.	...	...	1520	1520	...	...	...	...	...	...	...	...	1820	...	...	...	...	...	...	...	...	...	...	...	...	...
Domodossola 🏛 **590** d.	...	...	1648	1648	...	...	...	...	...	...	...	...	1948	...	...	...	...	...	...	...	...	...	...	...	...	...
Brig **570 590** d.	...	1648	1718	1720	...	1748	...	...	1848	1918	...	1948	2019	...	...	2118	...	...	...	2218	...	...	2226	...	...	...
Visp **570** d.	...	1657	1727	1729	...	1757	...	...	1857	1927	...	1957	2028	...	...	2127	...	...	...	2227	...	...	|	...	...	...
Interlaken Ost ▷ d.	1700	|	|	|	1800	|	1830	1900	|	|	2000	|	|	2100	...	|	...	2200	...	|	...	2300	|	...	...	2333
Interlaken West ▷ d.	1705	|	|	|	1805	|	1835	1905	|	|	2005	|	|	2105	...	|	...	2205	...	|	...	2305	|	...	...	2338
Spiez ▷ d.	1722	1723	1754	1756	1822	1823	1854	1922	1923	1954	2022	2023	2054	2122	...	2154	...	2222	...	2254	...	2322	2325	...	...	2357
Thun d.	1733	1734	1804	1807	1833	1834	1904	1933	1934	2004	2033	2034	2104	2133	...	2204	...	2233	...	2304	...	2333	2336	...	...	0007
Bern a.	1752	1754c	1824	1828	1852	1854c	1924	1952	1954c	2024	2052	2054c	2124	2152	...	2224	...	2252	...	2324	...	2352	2354	...	...	0027
Bern **505** d.	1804	1802	1836	1836	1904	1902	1936	2004	2002	2036	2104	2102	2136	...	2202	...	2236	...	2302	...	2336	...	...	0002	...	...
Olten **505 565** a.	1830	|	1903	1903	1930	|	2003	2030	|	2103	2130	|	2203	...	2228	...	2303	...	2328	...	0003	...	...	0028	...	...
Basel SBB **565** a.	1901	|	1932	1932	2001	|	2032	2101	|	2132	2201	|	2232	...	*2300*	...	2337	...	*2400*	...	0037	...	...	*0102*	...	...
Zürich HB **505** a.	...	1858	...	...	...	1958	...	...	2058	...	...	2158	...	...	...	...	...	...	...	...	...	...	...	...	...	...
Zürich Flughafen ✈ **535** a.	...	1914	...	...	...	2014	...	...	2114	...	...	2214	...	...	...	...	...	...	...	...	...	...	...	...	...	...
Romanshorn **535** a.	...	2012	...	...	...	2112	...	...	2212	...	...	2312	...	...	...	...	...	...	...	...	...	...	...	...	...	...

G – From/to stations in Germany (Table **912**).
H – Ⓐ May 2 - Sept. 9.
J – Daily to May 1; Ⓒ May 7 - Sept. 4; daily from Sept. 10.

c – Connects with train in previous column.
k – ⑤⑥ (not Dec. 24, 25, Jan. 1, Apr. 15).
z – ⑥⑦ (not Dec. 25, 26, Jan. 2, Apr. 16).

⊙ – Via Kandersteg (Table **562**).
⊖ – Also calls at Frutigen (Table **562**).
¶ – Runs 1–2 minutes later Spiez - Bern on ⑦ Jan. 9 - Mar. 20.
§ – Runs 1–2 minutes later Spiez - Bern on ⑦ Jan. 9 - Mar. 13.
‡ – Runs 1–2 minutes later Spiez - Bern on ⑦ Jan. 2 - Apr. 10 and ⑦ June 19 - Oct. 23 (also May 29, June 6).
◧ – Supplement payable for journeys to/from Milano.

▷ – Other trains Spiez - Interlaken West - Interlaken Ost and v.v. (operated by BLS): **From Spiez** at 0555, 0805, 1005, 1205, 1405, 1605, 1805 and 1905. **From Interlaken Ost** at 0730, 0930, 1130, 1330, 1530, 1730 and 1930.

561 LUZERN - INTERLAKEN

Narrow gauge rack railway. ZB

km																								
		Ⓐ	Ⓐ			L			L				L			L			L			L		
0	**Luzern** 552 d.	...	...	...	0542	0606	0612	0642	0706	0712	0742		1706	1712	1742	1806	1812	1842	1906	1912	1942	2006	2012	2042
9	Hergiswil 552 d.	...	...	...	0554	│	0624	0654	│	0724	0754		│	1724	1754	│	1824	1854	│	1924	1954	│	2024	2054
13	Alpnachstad ⊙ d.	...	...	...	0559	│	0629	0659	│	0729	0759	and at	│	1729	1759	│	1829	1859	│	1929	1959	│	2029	2059
15	Alpnach Dorf d.	...	...	...	0601	│	0631	0701	│	0731	0801		│	1731	1801	│	1831	1901	│	1931	2001	│	2031	2101
21	Sarnen d.	...	...	...	0609	0624	0639	0709	0724	0739	0809	the same	1724	1739	1809	1824	1839	1909	1924	1939	2009	2024	2039	2109
23	Sachseln d.	...	...	...	0613	0628	0643	0713	0728	0743	0813		1728	1743	1813	1828	1843	1913	1928	1943	2013	2028	2043	2113
29	Giswil d.	...	...	...	0621	0637	0651	0721	0737	0751	0821	minutes	1737	1751	1821	1837	1851	1921	1937	1951	2021	2037	2051	2121
36	Lungern d.	...	...	...	▬	0651	...	▬	0751	...	▬		1751	...	▬	1851	...	...	1951	▬	...	2051	▬	...
40	Brünig Hasliberg d.	...	...	...	...	0703	...	...	0803	...	...	past each	1803	...	...	1903	...	...	2003	...	...	2103	...	...
45	**Meiringen** ● a.	...	...	...	...	0716	...	...	0816	...	...		1816	...	...	1916	...	...	2016	...	...	2116	...	...
45	**Meiringen** ● d.	0515	0545	0614	0651	0722	...	0751	0822	...	0851	hour until	1822	...	1851	1922	...	...	...	2020	...	...	2120	...
58	**Brienz** ⊡ d.	0527	0556	0628	0702	0733	...	0802	0837	...	0902		1837	...	1902	1935	...	...	...	2032	...	...	2132	...
65	Oberried d.	0537	0608	0639	0712	0744	...	0812	│	...	0912		│	...	1912	1944	...	...	...	2042	...	...	2142	...
74	**Interlaken** Ost a.	0550	0620	0651	0724	0754	...	0824	0855	...	0924		1855	...	1924	1955	...	...	...	2055	...	...	2155	...

			⑤⑥								
	L		k								
Luzern 552 d.	2106	2112	...	2142	2212	2242	2312	2342	0012	0042	...
Hergiswil 552 d.	│	2124	...	2154	2224	2254	2324	2354	0024	0056	...
Alpnachstad ⊙ d.	│	2129	...	2159	2229	2259	2329	2359	0029	0100	...
Alpnach Dorf d.	│	2131	...	2201	2231	2301	2331	0001	0031	0102	...
Sarnen d.	2124	2139	...	2209	2239	2309	2339	0009	0039	0110	...
Sachseln d.	2128	2143	...	2213	2243	2313	2343	0013	0043	0113	...
Giswil d.	2137	2151	...	2221	2251	2321	2351	0021	0051	0121	...
Lungern d.	2151	▬	...	...	...	...	...	...	...	...	...
Brünig Hasliberg d.	2203	...	...	...	...	...	...	...	...	...	...
Meiringen ● a.	2216	...	...	...	...	...	...	...	...	...	...
Meiringen ● d.	...	2220	2320	...	...	...	...	...	...	...	...
Brienz ⊡ d.	...	2232	2332	...	...	...	...	...	...	...	...
Oberried d.	...	2242	2342	...	...	...	...	...	...	...	...
Interlaken Ost a.	...	2255	2355	...	...	...	...	...	...	...	...

	⑥⑦							Ⓐ		
	z					L			L	
Interlaken Ost d.	0006	...	...	...	...	...	...	0557	...	...
Oberried d.	0017	...	...	...	...	...	...	0609	...	...
Brienz ⊡ d.	0026	...	...	...	...	...	...	0618	...	...
Meiringen ● a.	0039	...	...	...	...	...	...	0631	...	...
Meiringen ● d.	...	...	...	...	...	0541	...	▬	0641	...
Brünig Hasliberg d.	...	...	...	...	...	0551	...	...	0651	...
Lungern d.	...	...	...	...	...	0604	...	...	0704	...
Giswil d.	...	...	0505	0535	0605	0621	0635	0705	0721	0735
Sachseln d.	...	...	0513	0543	0613	0629	0643	0713	0729	0743
Sarnen d.	...	...	0519	0549	0619	0635	0649	0719	0735	0749
Alpnach Dorf d.	...	...	0524	0554	0624	│	0654	0724	│	0754
Alpnachstad ⊙ d.	...	...	0529	0559	0629	│	0659	0729	│	0759
Hergiswil 552 d.	...	...	0535	0603	0633	│	0703	0733	│	0803
Luzern 552 a.	...	...	0547	0617	0647	0655	0717	0747	0755	0817

	Ⓐ																							
		L			L				L			L			L △									
Interlaken Ost d.	0627	0704	...	0733	0804	...	0833		1804	...	1833	1904	...	1933	2004	...	2104	...	...	2204	...	...	2304	...
Oberried d.	0640	0714	...	0745	│	...	0844		│	...	1844	│	...	1946	2015	...	2115	...	...	2215	...	...	2315	...
Brienz ⊡ d.	0650	0725	...	0754	0825	...	0854	and at	1825	...	1854	1925	...	1956	2025	...	2124	...	...	2224	...	...	2324	...
Meiringen ● a.	0703	0735	...	0807	0835	...	0907		1835	...	1907	1935	...	2009	2036	...	2137	...	...	2237	...	...	2337	...
Meiringen ● d.	▬	0741	...	▬	0841	...	▬	the same	1841	...	▬	1941	...	▬	2041	...	...	...	...	...	...	...	...	...
Brünig Hasliberg d.	...	0751	...	...	0851	...	...		1851	...	...	1951	...	...	2051	...	...	...	...	...	...	...	...	...
Lungern d.	...	0804	...	...	0904	...	...	minutes	1904	...	...	2004	...	...	2104	...	...	...	...	...	...	...	...	...
Giswil d.	0805	0821	0835	0905	0921	0935	1005		1921	1935	2005	2021	2035	2105	2121	2135	...	2205	2235	...	2305	2335	...	0005
Sachseln d.	0813	0829	0843	0913	0929	0943	1013	past each	1929	1943	2013	2029	2043	2113	2129	2143	...	2213	2243	...	2313	2343	...	0013
Sarnen d.	0819	0835	0849	0919	0935	0949	1019		1935	1949	2019	2035	2049	2119	2135	2149	...	2219	2249	...	2319	2349	...	0019
Alpnach Dorf d.	0824	│	0854	0924	│	0954	1024	hour until	│	1954	2024	│	2054	2124	│	2154	...	2224	2254	...	2324	2354	...	0024
Alpnachstad ⊙ d.	0829	│	0859	0929	│	0959	1029		│	1959	2029	│	2059	2129	│	2159	...	2229	2259	...	2329	2359	...	0029
Hergiswil 552 d.	0833	│	0903	0933	│	1003	1033		│	2003	2033	│	2103	2133	│	2203	...	2233	2303	...	2333	0003	...	0033
Luzern 552 a.	0847	0855	0917	0947	0955	1017	1047		1955	2017	2047	2055	2117	2147	2155	2217	...	2247	2317	...	2347	0017	...	0047

L – LUZERN - INTERLAKEN EXPRESS. (12) [panorama cars]. The following services convey ✕: From Luzern 0806 - 1506 (0706 - 1706 May 14 - Oct. 30). From Interlaken 1004 - 1704 (0904 - 1904 May 14 - Oct. 30).

k – ⑤⑥ (not Dec. 25, Jan. 1, Apr. 15).
z – ⑥⑦ (not Dec. 26, Jan. 2, Apr. 16).

△ – Change trains at Meiringen on ④ (except on May 26).
⊙ – Station for Pilatusbahn (Table **553**).
⊡ – Station for Brienz Rothorn Bahn (Table **553**).

● – Rail service **Meiringen - Innertkirchen** and v.v. Narrow gauge. 2nd class only. *5 km.* Journey time: 11 minutes. **Operator**: ZB.
From Meiringen at 0612 Ⓐ, 0634 Ⓐ, 0656, 0718 Ⓐ, 0745, 0818 Ⓐ, 0845, 0945, 1045, 1118 Ⓐ, 1145, 1218 Ⓐ, 1245, 1318 Ⓐ, 1345, 1445, 1545, 1618 Ⓐ, 1645, 1718 Ⓐ, 1745, 1818 Ⓐ, 1845, 1918 Ⓐ, 1945, 2045, 2145 and 2245 ⑤⑥ **k**.
From Innertkirchen Kraftwerk at 0558 Ⓐ, 0623 Ⓐ, 0629 Ⓒ, 0645 Ⓐ, 0707, 0729 Ⓐ, 0802, 0829 Ⓐ, 0902, 1002, 1102, 1129 Ⓐ, 1202, 1229 Ⓐ, 1302, 1329 Ⓐ, 1402, 1502, 1602, 1629 Ⓐ, 1702, 1729 Ⓐ, 1802, 1829 Ⓐ, 1902, 1929 Ⓐ, 2002, 2102 and 2202 ⑤⑥ **k**.

562 BERN - SPIEZ - BRIG (via Lötschberg pass)

BLS

Services from/to Bern (except *IC*/*EC* trains) also convey (12) Bern - Spiez - Zweisimmen (Table **563**).
Passengers from Bern and Thun should ensure they join the correct portion for their destination. See Table **560** for faster services via the Lötschberg Base Tunnel.

km																									
																		IC 1085		*IC* 1087/9		*IC* 1093	*IC* 1095	*IC* 1097	
													Ⓐ	Ⓒ								①–⑥	⑦		
0	**Bern** 560 d.	...	0639	0739	0839	0939	1039	1139	1239	1339	1439	1539	1639	1639	1739	1839	1939	2034	...	2134	...	2234	2234	2339	...
31	Thun 560 d.	...	0701	0801	0901	1001	1101	1201	1301	1401	1501	1601	1701	1701	1801	1901	2001	2054	...	2154	...	2254	2254	2359	...
41	**Spiez** 560 a.	...	0710	0810	0910	1010	1110	1210	1310	1410	1510	1610	1710	1710	1810	1910	2010	2102	...	2202	...	2302	2302	0008	...
41	**Spiez** d.	0612	0712	0812	0912	1012	1112	1212	1312	1412	1512	1612	1712	1712	1812	1912	2012	2105	2112	2205	2212	2305	2305	...	0013
55	Frutigen ● d.	0625	0725	0825	0925	1025	1125	1225	1325	1425	1525	1625	1725	1725	1825	1925	2025	│	2125	│	2225	2317	2317	...	0025
72	Kandersteg 🚗 d.	0641	0741	0841	0941	1041	1141	1241	1341	1441	1541	1641	1741	1741	1841	1941	2041	│	2141	│	2241	│	2335	...	0042
89	Goppenstein 🚗 d.	0655	0755	0855	0955	1055	1155	1255	1355	1455	1555	1655	1755	1755	1855	1955	2055	│	2155	│	2255	│	2348	...	0055
115	**Brig** 560 a.	0720	0822	0920	1022	1120	1222	1320	1422	1520	1622	1720	1820	1822	1920	2022	2122	2141	2220	2241v	2322	2344	0013	...	0123
	Domodossola 590 a.	0754	...	0954	...	1154t	...	1354	...	1554	...	1754	1854	...	1954	...	...	...	2254	...	...	...	...	...	...

		IC 807																*IC* 1084			*EC* 56		*IC* 1088		*IC* 992
		R ✕			Ⓒ	Ⓐ													Ⓒ	Ⓐ					
Domodossola 590 d.	0437	...	...	0558	...	0658	0758	...	0958	...	1158t	...	1358	...	1558	...	1758	...	...	1858	1948	1958	...	...	...
Brig 560 d.	0514	0546	...	0636	0734	0736	0836	0934	1036	1134	1236	1334	1436	1534	1636	1734	1836	1918	1934	1936	2019	2036	2118	2205	...
Goppenstein 🚗 d.	0538	│	...	0700	0800	0800	0900	1000	1100	1200	1300	1400	1500	1600	1700	1800	1900	│	2000	2000	│	2100	│	2231	...
Kandersteg 🚗 d.	0553	│	←	0715	0815	0815	0915	1015	1115	1215	1315	1415	1515	1615	1715	1815	1915	│	2015	2015	│	2115	│	2247	...
Frutigen ● d.	0609	0612	0631	0731	0831	0831	0931	1031	1131	1231	1331	1431	1531	1631	1731	1831	1931	│	2031	2031	│	2131	│	2303	...
Spiez a.	→	0624	0644	0744	0844	0844	0944	1044	1144	1244	1344	1444	1544	1644	1744	1844	1944	1953	2044	2044	2053	2144	2153	2316	...
Spiez 560 d.	...	0625	0650	0750	0850	0850	0950	1050	1150	1250	1350	1450	1550	1650	1750	1850	...	1954	...	...	2054	...	2154	...	2322
Thun 560 a.	...	0634	0658	0758	0858	0858	0958	1058	1158	1258	1358	1458	1558	1658	1758	1858	...	2003	...	...	2103	...	2203	...	2332
Bern 560 a.	...	0654	0721	0821	0921	0921	1021	1121	1221	1321	1421	1521	1621	1721	1821	1921	...	2024	...	...	2124	...	2224	...	2352

R – (12) Brig - Zürich - Romanshorn.

t – ③–⑦ only.
v – 2303 on ⑦.

🚗 – Car-carrying shuttle available. ✆ +41 (0) 58 327 41 14.
www.bls.ch/en/fahren/unterwegs-mit/autoverlad/kandersteg-goppenstein

● – 🚌 **SERVICE FRUTIGEN - ADELBODEN**. 20 km. Journey ±30 minutes.
Operator: Autoverkehr Frutigen-Adelboden (AFA). ✆ +41 (0) 33 673 74 74.
From Frutigen at 0615 Ⓐ, 0633, 0700 Ⓐ, 0733, 0800, 0833, 0900 Ⓒ, 0933, 1000 Ⓒ, 1033, 1133 and hourly until 1533; then 1603 Ⓒ, 1633, 1700, 1733, 1800, 1833, 1900 Ⓐ, 1933, 2033, 2133, 2233 and 2325.
From Adelboden (Post) at 0537 Ⓐ, 0552, 0622 Ⓐ, 0652, 0725, 0752, 0825 Ⓒ, 0852, 0925 Ⓒ, 0952, 1052 and hourly until 1452; then 1525 Ⓒ, 1552, 1625, 1652, 1725, 1752, 1825 Ⓐ, 1852, 1952, 2052, 2152 and 2225.

BLS — INTERLAKEN - SPIEZ - ZWEISIMMEN — 563

km																								
						Ⓒ													Ⓐ				Ⓐ	
	Interlaken Ost ◇ **560** d.	...	...	...	...	...	...	...	...	...	...	...	...	...	...	...	...	...	...	...	...	...	...	...
	Bern **560 562** △ d.	...	0639	...	0739	...	0839	...	0939	1039	...	1139	1239	...	1339	1439	...	1539	...	1639	...	1739	...	1839
0	**Spiez** **560** d.	0612	0712	0738	0812	0838	0912	0938	1012	1112	1138	1212	1312	1338	1412	1512	1538	1612	1638	1712	1738	1812	1838	1912
11	Erlenbach im Simmental d.	0629	0729	0753	0829	0853	0929	0953	1029	1129	1153	1229	1329	1353	1429	1529	1553	1629	1653	1729	1753	1829	1853	1929
26	Boltigen d.	0649	0749	0811	0849	0911	0949	1011	1049	1149	1211	1249	1349	1411	1449	1549	1611	1649	1711	1749	1811	1849	1911	1949
35	**Zweisimmen** a.	0659	0759	0820	0859	0920	0959	1020	1059	1159	1220	1259	1359	1420	1459	1559	1620	1659	1720	1759	1820	1859	1920	1959

Interlaken Ost ◇ **560** d.	...	...	...	...	...	...	...	...	...
Bern **560 562** △ d.	1939	...	...	...	...	...	...	...	...
Spiez **560** d.	2012	2106	...	2206	...	2306	...	0013	...
Erlenbach im Simmental d.	2029	2121	...	2221	...	2321	...	0029	...
Boltigen d.	2049	2141	...	2241	...	2341	...	0048	...
Zweisimmen a.	2059	2152	...	2252	...	2352	...	0059	...

	Ⓐ	Ⓐ	Ⓒ	Ⓐ		Ⓐ				
Zweisimmen d.	0539	0554	0602	0639	0702	0739	0802	...	0902	0939
Boltigen d.	0548	0603	0611	0648	0711	0748	0811	...	0911	0948
Erlenbach im Simmental d.	0605	0622	0630	0705	0730	0805	0830	...	0930	1005
Spiez **560** a.	0621	0639	0647	0721	0747	0821	0847	...	0947	1021
Bern **560 562** a.	...	0721	0721	...	0821	...	0921	...	1021	...
Interlaken Ost ◇ **560** a.	...	...	...	...	...	...	...	...	...	...

														Ⓒ										
Zweisimmen d.	1002	...	1102	1139	1202	...	1302	1339	1402	...	1502	1539	1602	1639	1702	1739	1802	1902	2002	2104	2204	2304	...	0010
Boltigen d.	1011	...	1111	1148	1211	...	1311	1348	1411	...	1511	1548	1611	1648	1711	1748	1811	1911	2012	2114	2214	2314	...	0020
Erlenbach im Simmental d.	1030	...	1130	1205	1230	...	1330	1405	1430	...	1530	1605	1630	1705	1730	1805	1830	1930	2031	2134	2234	2334	...	0042
Spiez **560** a.	1047	...	1147	1221	1247	...	1347	1421	1447	...	1547	1621	1647	1721	1747	1821	1847	1947	2047	2150	2250	2350	...	0058
Bern **560 562** a.	1121	...	1221	...	1321	...	1421	...	1521	...	1621	...	1721	...	1821	...	1921	...	...	...	...	...	...	...
Interlaken Ost ◇ **560** a.	...	...	...	...	...	...	...	...	...	...	...	...	...	...	...	...	...	...	...	...	...	...	...	...

◇ – Trains also call at Interlaken West.

△ – Trains from Bern convey portions for Zweisimmen and Brig - please ensure you join the correct portion.

Narrow gauge rack railway. BOB, WAB, JB — INTERLAKEN - KLEINE SCHEIDEGG - JUNGFRAUJOCH — 564

INTERLAKEN - LAUTERBRUNNEN / GRINDELWALD

km																							
																	🚌	🚌					
0	**Interlaken** Ost d.	0605	0605	0635	0635		2005	2005	2035	2035	2105	2105	...	2205	2205	...	2304	2305	...	...	...	...	...
3	Wilderswil ⊡ d.	0610	0610	0640	0640	and every	2010	2010	2040	2040	2110	2110	...	2210	2210	...	2311	2312	...	...	...	...	...
8	Zweilütschinen d.	0616	0617	0646	0647	30 minutes	2016	2017	2046	2047	2116	2117	...	2216	2217	...	2318	2319	...	...	...	...	...
	Grindelwald Terminal 🚡 a.	|	0635	|	0705		|	2035	|	2105	|	2135	...	|	2235	...	2325	|	...	...	...	...	...
19	**Grindelwald** a.	|	0639	|	0709	until	|	2039	|	2109	|	2139	...	|	2239	...	...	2337	...	...	...	...	...
	Lauterbrunnen ⊙ a.	0625	...	0655	...		2025	...	2055	...	2125	...	...	2225	...	...	...	...	...	...	...	...	...

km																								
																		🚌	🚌		🚌			
0	**Lauterbrunnen** ⊙ d.	...	0532	...	0602	...	0632		...	2002	...	2032	...	...	2132	...	...	2230	...	2330	...	...	...
	Grindelwald d.	0518	|	0548	|	0618	|	and every	1948	|	2018	|	...	2118	|	...	2218	|	...	|	...	...	...
	Grindelwald Terminal 🚡 d.	0522	|	0552	|	0622	|	30 minutes	1952	|	2022	|	...	2122	|	...	|	|	...	|	...	...	...
4	Zweilütschinen d.	0542	0542	0612	0612	0642	0642		2012	2012	2042	2042	...	2142	2142	...	2236	2236	...	2336	...	...	...
9	Wilderswil ⊡ d.	0548	0548	0618	0618	0648	0648	until	2018	2018	2048	2048	...	2148	2148	...	2243	2245	...	2345	...	...	...
12	**Interlaken** Ost a.	0552	0552	0623	0623	0653	0653		2023	2023	2053	2053	...	2153	2153	...	2252	2254	...	2354	...	...	...

GRINDELWALD - KLEINE SCHEIDEGG *No service May 9 – 20 and Oct. 17 – 28*

km																							
			b			b		b	f		f		f	f									
0	**Grindelwald** d.	0745	0815	0845	and at the same	1615	1645	1715	1715	1745	1745	1815	1845	1915	...	...	...	...	...	...	...	...	...
1	Grindelwald Grund d.	0753	0823	0853	minutes past	1623	1653	1720	1723	1750	1753	1820	1850	1920	...	...	...	...	...	...	...	...	...
9	**Kleine Scheidegg** a.	0817	0847	0917	each hour until	1647	1717	...	1747	...	1817	...	...	...	...	...	...	...	...	...	...	...	...

		b		b		b			b			f	f									
Kleine Scheidegg d.	...	...	...	0831	0901	0931	and at the same	1601	1631	1701	1731	1801	1831	...	...	...	...	...	...	...	...	...
Grindelwald Grund d.	0736	0806	0836	0906	0936	1006	minutes past	1636	1706	1736	1806	1836	1906	...	...	...	...	...	...	...	...	...
Grindelwald a.	0740	0810	0840	0910	0940	1010	each hour until	1640	1710	1740	1810	1840	1910	...	...	...	...	...	...	...	...	...

LAUTERBRUNNEN - WENGEN - KLEINE SCHEIDEGG (SEE NOTE ▲)

km																									
0	**Lauterbrunnen** ⊙ d.	0524	0600	0630	0700	0730	0800	0830	0900	0930	1000	1030	1100	1130	1200	1230	1300	1330	1400	1430	1500	1530	1600	1630	1700
4	Wengen a.	0535	0611	0641	0711	0741	0811	0841	0911	0941	1011	1041	1111	1141	1211	1241	1311	1341	1411	1441	1511	1541	1611	1641	1711
4	Wengen ▲ d.	...	...	...	...	0746	0816j	0846	0916j	0946	1016j	1046	1116j	1146	1216j	1246	1316j	1346	1416	1446j	1516	1546j	1616	1646j	1716f
11	**Kleine Scheidegg** ▲ a.	...	...	...	...	0808	0838j	0908	0938j	1008	1038j	1108	1138j	1208	1238j	1308	1338j	1408	1438	1508j	1538	1608j	1638	1708j	1738f

Lauterbrunnen ⊙ d.	1730	1800	1830	and every	2100	2130	2230	2330	...
Wengen a.	1741	1811	1841	30 minutes	2111	2141	2241	2341	...
Wengen ▲ d.	1746f	...	...	until	...	...	...	...	...
Kleine Scheidegg ▲ a.	1808f	...	...		...	...	...	...	...

Kleine Scheidegg ▲ d.	...	...	...	...	...	...	...	0814j	0844	0914j
Wengen ▲ a.	...	...	...	...	...	...	...	0839j	0909	0939j
Wengen d.	0504	0540	0613	0643	0713	0743	0813	0843	0913	0943
Lauterbrunnen ⊙ a.	0517	0553	0626	0656	0726	0756	0826	0856	0926	0956

Kleine Scheidegg ▲ d.	0944	1014j	1044	1114j	1144	1214j	1244	1314	1344j	1414	1444j	1514	1544j	1614	1644j	1714	1744f	1814f	...	...	...	...	...	...	...
Wengen ▲ a.	1009	1039j	1109	1139j	1209	1239j	1309	1339	1409j	1439	1509j	1439	1609j	1639	1709j	1739	1809f	1839f	...	...	...	...	...	...	...
Wengen d.	1013	1043	1113	1143	1213	1243	1313	1343	1413	1443	1513	1443	1613	1643	1713	1743	1813	1843	1913	1943	2013	2043	2113	2213	2313
Lauterbrunnen ⊙ a.	1026	1056	1126	1156	1226	1256	1326	1356	1426	1456	1526	1556	1626	1656	1726	1756	1826	1856	1926	1956	2026	2056	2126	2226	2326

KLEINE SCHEIDEGG - JUNGFRAUJOCH *Subject to alteration Oct. 31 - Nov. 11*

km																								
		a	a	a															n	e	a	a	a	
0	**Kleine Scheidegg** d.	...	...	*0827*	*0857*	*0927*e	*0957*	*1027*e	*1057*	*1127*e	*1157*	*1227*e	*1257*	*1327*e	*1357*	*1427*e	*1457*	*1527*e	*1557*	1627	...	*1657*	1727	...
	Grindelwald Terminal 🚡 d.	...	...	|	|	|	|	|	|	|	|	|	|	|	|	|	|	|	|	|	...	|	|	...
2	Eigergletscher 🚡 a.	...	...	*0832*	*0902*	*0932*e	*1002*	*1032*e	*1102*	*1132*e	*1202*	*1232*e	*1302*	*1332*e	*1402*	*1432*e	*1502*	*1532*e	*1602*	1632	...	*1702*	1732	...
2	Eigergletscher d.	0745	0815	0845	0915	0945	1015	1045	1115	1145	1215	1245	1315	1345	1415	1445	1515	1545	1615	...	1645	1715	...	...
9	**Jungfraujoch** a.	0811	0841	0911	0941	1011	1041	1111	1141	1211	1241	1311	1341	1411	1441	1511	1541	1611	1641	...	1711	1741	...	...

	a	a		a	e															n	a	a	a	
Jungfraujoch d.	0817	0847	...	0917	...	0947	1017	1047	1117	1147	1217	1247	1317	1347	1417	1447	1517	1547	1617	1647	...	1717	1747	...
Eigergletscher a.	0841	0911	...	0941	...	1011	1041	1111	1141	1211	1241	1311	1341	1411	1441	1511	1541	1611	1641	1711	...	1741	1811	...
Eigergletscher 🚡 d.	*0846*	...	0916	...	0946	*1016*	*1046*e	*1116*	*1146*e	*1216*	*1246*e	*1316*	*1346*e	*1416*	*1446*e	*1516*	*1546*e	*1616*	*1646*e	...	1716	*1746*	...	...
Grindelwald Terminal 🚡 a.	|	...	|	...	|	|	|	|	|	|	|	|	|	|	|	|	|	|	|	...	|	|	...	...
Kleine Scheidegg a.	*0854*	...	0924	...	0954	*1024*	*1054*e	*1124*	*1154*e	*1224*	*1254*e	*1324*	*1354*e	*1424*	*1454*e	*1524*	*1554*e	*1624*	*1654*e	...	1724	*1754*	...	...

a – July 2 - Aug. 14.
b – Dec. 18 - Apr. 24, July 2 - Oct. 16 and Oct. 29 - Nov. 13.
e – Dec. 18 - Apr. 24 and July 2 - Oct. 16.
f – June 18 - Oct. 16.
j – Dec. 18 - Apr. 24 and May 21 - Oct. 16.
n – Apr. 23 - Oct. 30.
r – June 25 - Oct. 16.

* – Via Wengen (*28 km* via Grindelwald).
◇ – Additional journeys available until Apr. 24 and July 2 - Oct. 9.
▲ – No service Wengen - Kleine Scheidegg and v.v. Apr. 25 - May 6 and Oct. 31 - Dec. 2.

🚡 – *Eiger Express* gondola service Grindelwald Terminal - Eigergletscher and v.v. Journey time 20 minutes. Regular departures as follows: Until Apr. 22 0800 - 1650; Apr. 23 - July 1 0800 - 1720; July 2 - Aug. 14 0715 - 1820; Aug. 15 - Nov. 6 0800 - 1720; Nov. 7 – 11 closed for maintenance.

⊙ – Cableway **Lauterbrunnen - Grütschalp**, and narrow gauge railway **Grütschalp - Mürren**. Total distance: *5 km*. Operator: BLM. Journey time: 20 minutes including connection. **No service May 2 – 20 and Oct. 10 – 28.**
From Lauterbrunnen at 0613, 0631, 0701, 0731, 0801, 0838, 0908, 0938 and every 30 minutes ◇ until 1938.
From Mürren at 0606, 0636, 0706, 0736, 0806, 0828, 0858, 0928, 0958 and every 30 minutes ◇ until 1858.

Cableway **Mürren - Schilthorn**. Operates Dec. 12 - Apr. 24 and Apr. 30 - Oct. 30.
Operator: Schilthornbahn ✆ +41 33 826 00 07.
From Mürren at 0810, 0840 and every 30 minutes until 1610.
From Schilthorn at 0903, 0933 and every 30 minutes until 1633.

⊡ – Narrow gauge rack railway operates **May 26 - Oct. 23 Wilderswil - Schynige Platte**. *7 km*. Journey time: 52 minutes. Operator: BOB. **Service may be reduced In bad weather**.
From Wilderswil at 0725, 0805 **r**, 0845, 0925, 1005, 1045, 1125, 1205, 1245, 1325, 1405, 1445, 1525, 1605 and 1645.
From Schynige Platte at 0821, 0901 **r**, 0941, 1021, 1101, 1141, 1221, 1301, 1341, 1421, 1501, 1541, 1621, 1701 and 1753.

565 BASEL and BERN - LUZERN

SBB, SOB

km		IR 2349	IC 659	IR 2457	RE 4709	IR 2505	IR 2311	IR 2459	RE 4711	IR 2507	IC 663	IR 2461	RE 4713	IR 2509	IR 2315	IR 2463	RE 4715	IR 2511	IC 667	IR 2465	RE 4717	IR 2513	IR 2319	IR 2467	RE 4719	IR 2515
		⑥⑦ t	✕	Ⓐ			★ L			🍷	✕			🍷	★ L			🍷	✕			🍷	★ L			🍷
0	**Basel** SBB 560 d.	0100	0503	...	...	...	0603	0616	...	...	0703	0716	...	...	0803	0816	...	...	0903	0916	...	...	1003	1016	...	...
14	Liestal d.	0110	|	...	...	...	|	0627	...	...	|	0727	...	...	|	0827	...	...	|	0927	...	...	|	1027	...	...
21	Sissach d.	0116	|	...	...	...	|	0633	...	...	|	0733	...	...	|	0833	...	...	|	0933	...	...	|	1033	...	...
39	**Olten** 560 d.	0137h	0530	0549	0606	...	0630	0649	0706	...	0730	0749	0806	...	0830	0849	0906	...	0930	0949	1006	...	1030	1049	1106	...
	Genève Aéroport ✈ 505 d.	|	|	|	|	...	|	|	|	...	|	|	|	0549	|	|	|	0649	|	|	|	0749	|	|	|	0849
	Genève 505 d.	|	|	|	|	...	|	|	|	...	|	|	|	0559	|	|	|	0659	|	|	|	0759	|	|	|	0859
	Lausanne 505 d.	|	|	|	|	0444g	|	|	|	0544	|	|	|	0644	|	|	|	0744	|	|	|	0844	|	|	|	0944
	Bern d.	|	|	|	|	0600	|	|	|	0700	|	|	|	0800	|	|	|	0900	|	|	|	1000	|	|	|	1100
47	Zofingen d.	0144	|	0558	0613	0629	|	0658	0713	0729	|	0758	0813	0829	|	0858	0913	0929	|	0958	1013	1029	|	1058	1113	1129
69	Sursee d.	0158	|	0611	0631	0642	|	0711	0731	0742	|	0811	0831	0842	|	0911	0931	0942	|	1011	1031	1042	|	1111	1131	1142
95	**Luzern** a.	0216	0605	0630	0655	0701	0705	0730	0755	0801	0805	0830	0855	0901	0905	0930	0955	1001	1005	1030	1055	1101	1105	1130	1155	1201
	Lugano 550 △ a.	...	0758	...	...	...	...	...	...	...	0958	...	...	...	...	...	...	...	1158	...	...	...	...	...	...	...

	EC 151	IR 2469	RE 4721	IR 2517	IR 2323	IR 2471	RE 4723	IR 2519	IC 675	IR 2473	RE 4725	IR 2521	IR 2327	IR 2475	RE 4727	IR 2523	EC 153	IR 2477	RE 4729	IR 2525	IR 2331	IR 2479	RE 4731	IR 2527	IC 683	IR 2481
	F✕			🍷	★ L			🍷	✕			🍷	★ L			🍷	M✕			🍷	★ L			🍷	✕	
Basel SBB 560 d.	1103	1116	...	...	1203	1216	...	...	1303	1316	...	...	1403	1416	...	...	1503	1516	...	...	1603	1616	...	...	1703	1716
Liestal d.	|	1127	...	...	|	1227	...	...	|	1327	...	...	|	1427	...	...	|	1527	...	...	|	1627	...	...	|	1727
Sissach d.	|	1133	...	...	|	1233	...	...	|	1333	...	...	|	1433	...	...	|	1533	...	...	|	1633	...	...	|	1733
Olten 560 d.	1130	1149	1206	...	1230	1249	1306	...	1330	1349	1406	...	1430	1449	1506	...	1530	1549	1606	...	1630	1649	1706	...	1730	1749
Genève Aéroport ✈ 505 d.	|	|	|	0949	|	|	|	1049	|	|	|	1149	|	|	|	1249	|	|	|	1349	|	|	|	1449	|	|
Genève 505 d.	|	|	|	0959	|	|	|	1059	|	|	|	1159	|	|	|	1259	|	|	|	1359	|	|	|	1459	|	|
Lausanne 505 d.	|	|	|	1044	|	|	|	1144	|	|	|	1244	|	|	|	1344	|	|	|	1444	|	|	|	1544	|	|
Bern d.	|	|	|	1200	|	|	|	1300	|	|	|	1400	|	|	|	1500	|	|	|	1600	|	|	|	1700	|	|
Zofingen d.	|	1158	1213	1229	|	1258	1313	1329	|	1358	1413	1429	|	1458	1513	1529	|	1558	1613	1629	|	1658	1713	1729	|	1758
Sursee d.	|	1211	1231	1242	|	1311	1331	1342	|	1411	1431	1442	|	1511	1531	1542	|	1611	1631	1642	|	1711	1731	1742	|	1811
Luzern a.	1205	1230	1255	1301	1305	1330	1355	1401	1405	1430	1455	1501	1505	1530	1555	1601	1605	1630	1655	1701	1705	1730	1755	1801	1805	1830
Lugano 550 △ a.	1358	...	...	...	...	...	...	...	1558	...	...	...	...	...	...	...	1758	...	...	...	...	...	...	...	1958	...

	RE 4733	IR 2529	IR 2335	IR 2483	RE 4735	IR 2531	IC 687	IR 2485	RE 4737	IR 2533	IR 2339	IR 2487	RE 4739	IR 2535	IC 691	IR 2489	RE 4741	IR 2537	IR 2343	IR 2491	RE 4743	IR 2539	IR 2345	IR 2493	RE 4745	IR 2347
		🍷	★ B			🍷	C✕			🍷	★ E				C✕				★ A	⑤⑥ s				⑤⑥ s		★
Basel SBB 560 d.	...	...	1803	1816	...	...	1903	1916	...	...	2003	2016	...	...	2103	2116	...	...	2203	2216	...	...	2258	2316	...	0004
Liestal d.	...	...	|	1827	...	...	|	1927	...	...	|	2027	...	...	|	2127	...	...	|	2227	...	...	2308	2327	...	0014
Sissach d.	...	...	|	1833	...	...	|	1933	...	...	|	2033	...	...	|	2133	...	...	|	2233	...	...	|	2333	...	|
Olten 560 d.	1806	...	1830	1849	1906	...	1930	1949	2006	...	2030	2049	2106	...	2130	2149	2206	...	2230	2249	2307	...	2330j	2348	0007	0035j
Genève Aéroport ✈ 505 d.	|	1549	|	|	|	1649	|	|	|	1749	|	|	|	1849	|	|	|	1949	|	|	|	2049k	|	...	|	|
Genève 505 d.	|	1559	|	|	|	1659	|	|	|	1759	|	|	|	1859	|	|	|	1959	|	|	|	2059k	|	...	|	|
Lausanne 505 d.	|	1644	|	|	|	1744	|	|	|	1844	|	|	|	1944	|	|	|	2044	|	|	|	2144	|	...	|	|
Bern d.	|	1800	|	|	|	1900	|	|	|	2000	|	|	|	2100	|	|	|	2200	|	|	|	2300	|	...	|	|
Zofingen d.	1813	1829	|	1858	1913	1929	|	1958	2013	2029	|	2058	2113	2129	|	2158	2213	2229	|	2256	2314	2329	|	...	0014	0042
Sursee d.	1831	1842	|	1911	1931	1942	|	2011	2031	2042	|	2111	2131	2142	|	2211	2231	2242	|	...	2332	2342	|	...	0033	0056
Luzern a.	1855	1901	1905	1930	1955	2001	2005	2030	2055	2101	2105	2130	2155	2201	2205	2230	2255	2301	2305	...	2355	0001	0005	...	0055	0116
Lugano 550 △ a.	...	...	...	...	...	...	2158	...	...	...	...	...	...	...	2358	...	...	...	...	...	...	...	...	...	...	...

km		IR 2344	IR 2304	RE 4706	IR 2456	IR 2306	IR 2508	RE 4708	IR 2458	IR 2308	IR 2510	RE 4710	IR 2460	IC 664	IR 2512	RE 4712	IR 2462	IR 2312	IR 2514	RE 4714	IR 2464	IC 668	IR 2516	RE 4716	IR 2466	IR 2316
		⑥⑦ t	★				🍷			★ E	🍷			C	🍷			★ B	🍷			✕	🍷			★ L
	Lugano 550 △ d.	...	...	...	...	...	...	...	...	...	...	...	...	0600	...	...	...	...	...	...	...	0802‡	...	...	...	...
0	**Luzern** d.	0047	0454	0458	0530a	0554	0600	0605	0630	0654	0700	0705	0730	0754	0800	0805	0830	0854	0900	0905	0930	0954	1000	1005	1030	1054
26	Sursee d.	0107	|	0524	0548a	|	0618	0627	0648	|	0718	0727	0748	|	0818	0827	0848	|	0918	0927	0948	|	1018	1027	1048	|
48	Zofingen d.	0120	|	0545	0603a	|	0632	0645	0703	|	0732	0745	0803	|	0832	0845	0903	|	0932	0945	1003	|	1032	1045	1103	|
111	**Bern** a.	|	|	|	|	|	0700	|	|	|	0800	|	|	|	0900	|	|	|	1000	|	|	|	1100	|	|	|
	Lausanne 505 a.	|	|	|	|	|	0816	|	|	|	0916	|	|	|	1016	|	|	|	1116	|	|	|	1216	|	|	|
	Genève 505 a.	|	|	|	|	|	0901	|	|	|	1001	|	|	|	1101	|	|	|	1201	|	|	|	1301	|	|	|
	Genève Aéroport ✈ 505 a.	|	|	|	|	|	0911	|	|	|	1011	|	|	|	1111	|	|	|	1211	|	|	|	1311	|	|	|
	Olten 560 d.	0137h	0530	0552	0612	0630	...	0652	0712	0730	...	0752	0812	0830	...	0852	0912	0930	...	0952	1012	1030	...	1052	1112	1130
	Sissach d.	|	|	...	0627	|	...	...	0727	|	...	...	0827	|	...	...	0927	|	...	...	1027	|	...	...	1127	|
	Liestal d.	0153	|	...	0634	|	...	...	0734	|	...	...	0834	|	...	...	0934	|	...	...	1034	|	...	...	1134	|
	Basel SBB 560 a.	0204	0556	...	0645	0656	...	...	0745	0756	...	...	0847	0856	...	...	0947	0956	...	...	1045	1056	...	...	1145	1156

	IR 2518	RE 4718	IR 2468	EC 156	IR 2520	RE 4720	IR 2470	IR 2320	IR 2522	RE 4722	IR 2472	EC 158	IR 2524	RE 4724	IR 2474	IR 2324	IR 2526	RE 4726	IR 2476	IC 680	IR 2528	RE 4728	IR 2478	IR 2328	IR 2530	RE 4730
	🍷			M✕	🍷			★ L	🍷			M✕	🍷			★ L	🍷			✕	🍷			★ L	🍷	
Lugano 550 △ d.	...	...	...	1002‡	...	...	...	...	...	...	...	1202‡	...	...	...	...	...	...	...	1402‡	...	...	...	...	...	...
Luzern d.	1100	1105	1130	1154	1200	1205	1230	1254	1300	1305	1330	1354	1400	1405	1430	1454	1500	1505	1530	1554	1600	1605	1630	1654	1700	1705
Sursee d.	1118	1127	1148	|	1218	1227	1248	|	1318	1327	1348	|	1418	1427	1448	|	1518	1527	1548	|	1618	1627	1648	|	1718	1727
Zofingen d.	1132	1145	1203	|	1232	1245	1303	|	1332	1345	1403	|	1432	1445	1503	|	1532	1545	1603	|	1632	1645	1703	|	1732	1745
Bern a.	1200	|	|	|	1300	|	|	|	1400	|	|	|	1500	|	|	|	1600	|	|	|	1700	|	|	|	1800	|
Lausanne 505 a.	1316	|	|	|	1416	|	|	|	1516	|	|	|	1616	|	|	|	1716	|	|	|	1816	|	|	|	1916	|
Genève 505 a.	1401	|	|	|	1501	|	|	|	1601	|	|	|	1701	|	|	|	1801	|	|	|	1901	|	|	|	2001	|
Genève Aéroport ✈ 505 a.	1411	|	|	|	1511	|	|	|	1611	|	|	|	1711	|	|	|	1811	|	|	|	1911	|	|	|	2011	|
Olten 560 d.	...	1152	1212	1230	...	1252	1312	1330	...	1352	1412	1430	...	1452	1512	1530	...	1552	1612	1630	...	1652	1712	1730	...	1752
Sissach d.	...	...	1227	|	...	...	1327	|	...	...	1427	|	...	...	1527	|	...	...	1627	|	...	...	1727	|	...	...
Liestal d.	...	...	1234	|	...	...	1334	|	...	...	1434	|	...	...	1534	|	...	...	1634	|	...	...	1734	|	...	...
Basel SBB 560 a.	...	...	1245	1256	...	...	1345	1356	...	...	1445	1456	...	...	1545	1556	...	...	1645	1656	...	...	1745	1756	...	...

	IR 2480	IC 684	IR 2532	RE 4732	IR 2482	IR 2332	IR 2534	RE 4734	IR 2484	IC 688	IR 2536	RE 4736	IR 2486	IR 2336	IR 2538	RE 4738	IR 2488	IC 692	IR 2540	RE 4740	IR 2490	IR 2340	IR 2542	RE 4742	IC 696	RE 4744
		✕	🍷			★ L				✕				★ L			⑤⑥ s	✕			⑤⑥ s	★ L				
Lugano 550 △ d.	...	1602‡	...	...	...	...	...	...	...	1802‡	...	...	...	...	...	...	...	2002‡	...	...	...	...	...	...	2202‡	...
Luzern d.	1730	1754	1800	1805	1830	1854	1900	1905	1930	1954	2000	2005	2030	2054	2100	2105	2130	2154	2200	2205	...	2254	2300	2305	2354	0005
Sursee d.	1748	|	1818	1827	1848	|	1918	1927	1948	|	2018	2027	2048	|	2118	2127	2148	|	2218	2227	...	|	2318	2327	|	0028
Zofingen d.	1803	|	1832	1845	1903	|	1932	1945	2003	|	2032	2045	2103	|	2132	2145	2203	|	2232	2245	2303	|	2332	2345	|	0046
Bern a.	|	|	1900	|	|	|	2000	|	|	|	2100	|	|	|	2200	|	|	|	2300	|	|	|	2400	|	|	|
Lausanne 505 a.	|	|	2016	|	|	|	2116	|	|	|	2216	|	|	|	2316	|	|	|	0020	|	|	|	...	|	|	|
Genève 505 a.	|	|	2101	|	|	|	2201k	|	|	|	...	|	|	|	...	|	|	|	...	|	|	|	...	|	|	|
Genève Aéroport ✈ 505 a.	|	|	2111	|	|	|	2211k	|	|	|	...	|	|	|	...	|	|	|	...	|	|	|	...	|	|	|
Olten 560 d.	1812	1830	...	1852	1912	1930	...	1952	2012	2030	...	2052	2112	2130	...	2152	2212	2233j	...	2253	2312	2333j	...	2353	0035h	0055
Sissach d.	1827	|	...	...	1927	|	...	...	2027	|	...	...	2127	|	...	...	2227	|	...	...	2327	|	...	...	|	...
Liestal d.	1834	|	...	...	1934	|	...	...	2034	|	...	...	2134	|	...	...	2234	2249	...	...	2334	2349	...	...	0051	...
Basel SBB 560 a.	1845	1856	...	...	1945	1956	...	...	2045	2056	...	...	2145	2156	...	...	2245	2300	...	...	2345	2400	...	...	0102	...

A – To Arth-Goldau (Table **547**).
B – To / from Bellinzona via Göschenen (Table **547**).
C – To / from Chiasso (Table **550**).
E – To / from Erstfeld (Table **547**).
F – [12] ✕ Frankfurt - Basel - Luzern - Milano ◧.
L – To / from Locarno via Göschenen (Table **547**).
M – To / from Milano ◧ (Table **550**).

a – Ⓐ only.
g – ① only.
h – Arrives 7 – 9 minutes earlier.
j – Arrives 5 minutes earlier.
k – ⑤⑥ only.
s – Not Dec. 25, Jan. 1, Apr. 15.
t – Not Dec. 25, 26, Jan. 2, Apr. 16.

‡ – 1 minute earlier June 16 - Aug. 28.
★ – Operated by **SOB**. Conveys (🍷).
◧ – Supplement payable for journeys to / from Italy.

Narrow gauge. MOB — LENK - ZWEISIMMEN - MONTREUX — 566

km		2201	2203	2205	2207	2209	2211	2213	2115	2415	2217	2119	2419	2221	2223	2423	2225	2227	2427	2229	2231	2431	2233	2235	2237	2239	2241
							P	P	P		P	B		P	P		P	P		B							
0	**Zweisimmen** ‡ d.	...	...	0502a	0602	0702	0802	0902	1002	1030	1102	1202	1230	1302	1402	1430	1502	1602	1630	1702	1802	1830	1902	2002	2102	2202	2302
9	Saanenmöser ‡ d.	...	...	0518a	0618	0718	0818	0918	1018	1044	1118	1218	1244	1318	1418	1444	1518	1618	1644	1718	1818	1844	1918	2018	2118	2218	2318
11	Schönried ‡ d.	...	...	0522a	0622	0722	0822	0922	1022	1048	1122	1222	1248	1322	1422	1448	1522	1622	1648	1722	1822	1848	1922	2022	2122	2222	2322
16	**Gstaad** ‡ d.	...	0435	0535	0635	0735	0835	0935	1035	1056	1135	1235	1256	1335	1435	1456	1535	1635	1656	1735	1835	1856	1935	2035	2135	2235	2335
19	Saanen d.	...	0439	0539	0639	0739	0839	0939	1039	...	1139	1239	...	1339	1439	...	1539	1639	...	1739	1839	...	1939	2039	2139	2239	2339
23	Rougemont d.	...	0444	0544	0644	0744	0844	0944	1044	...	1144	1244	...	1344	1444	...	1544	1644	...	1744	1844	...	1944	2044	2144	2244	2344
29	Châteaux d'Oex d.	0432	0500	0600	0700	0800	0900	1000	1100	...	1200	1300	...	1400	1500	...	1600	1700	...	1800	1900	...	2000	2100	2200	2300	2359
40	**Montbovon** d.	0449	0521	0621	0721	0821	0921	1021	1121	...	1221	1321	...	1421	1521	...	1621	1721	...	1821	1921	...	2021	2121	2221	2321	...
51	Les Avants § d.	0513	0546	0646	0746	0846	0946	1046	1146	...	1246	1346	...	1446	1546	...	1646	1746	...	1846	1946	...	2046	2146	2246	2346	...
55	Chamby ⊗ § d.	0519	0552	0652	0752	0852	0952	1052	1152	...	1252	1352	...	1452	1552	...	1652	1752	...	1852	1952	...	2052	2152	2252	2352	...
58	Chernex § d.	0527	0601	0701	0801	0901	1001	1101	1201	...	1301	1401	...	1501	1601	...	1701	1801	...	1901	2001	...	2101	2201	2301	0001	...
62	**Montreux** § a.	0538	0611	0711	0811	0911	1011	1111	1211	...	1311	1411	...	1511	1611	...	1711	1811	...	1911	2011	...	2113	2213	2313	0013	...

	2202	2204	2206	2208	2408	2110	2212	2412	2214	2216	2416	2218	2220	2420	2222	2224	2424	2226	2326	2228	2230	2232	2234	2236	2238	2240	2242
	Ⓐ																		Ⓐ d								
						P	P		B	P		P	P		P	B		P		P	P						
Montreux § d.	...	0450	0550	0650	...	0750	0850	...	0950	1050	...	1150	1250	...	1350	1450	...	1550	1622	1650	1750	1850	1950	2050	2150	2250	2350
Chernex § d.	...	0500	0600	0700	...	0800	0900	...	1000	1100	...	1200	1300	...	1400	1500	...	1600	1631	1700	1800	1900	2000	2100	2200	2300	0000
Chamby ⊗ § d.	...	0503	0603	0703	...	0803	0903	...	1003	1103	...	1203	1303	...	1403	1503	...	1603	1635	1703	1803	1903	2003	2103	2203	2303	0003
Les Avants § d.	...	0513	0613	0713	...	0813	0913	...	1013	1113	...	1213	1313	...	1413	1513	...	1613	1656v	1713	1813	1913	2013	2113	2213	2313	0013
Montbovon d.	...	0545	0645	0745	...	0845	0945	...	1045	1145	...	1245	1345	...	1445	1545	...	1645	1717	1745	1845	1945	2045	2145	2245	2345	0045
Châteaux d'Oex d.	0458	0601	0701	0801	...	0901	1001	...	1101	1201	...	1301	1401	...	1501	1601	...	1701	1733	1801	1901	2001	2101	2201	2301	0001	0100
Rougemont d.	0512	0615	0715	0815	...	0915	1015	...	1115	1215	...	1315	1415	...	1515	1615	...	1715	...	1815	1915	2015	2115	2215	2315	0015	...
Saanen d.	0517	0620	0720	0820	...	0920	1020	...	1120	1220	...	1320	1420	...	1520	1620	...	1720	...	1820	1920	2020	2120	2220	2320	0020	...
Gstaad ‡ d.	0522	0625	0725	0825	0903	0925	1025	1103	1125	1225	1303	1325	1425	1504	1525	1625	1704	1725	...	1825	1925	2025	2125	2225	2325	0023	...
Schönried ‡ d.	0532	0634	0734	0834	0911	0934	1034	1111	1134	1234	1311	1334	1434	1513	1534	1634	1713	1734	...	1834	1934	2034	2134	2234	2334	...	...
Saanenmöser ‡ d.	0536	0640	0740	0840	0916	0940	1040	1116	1140	1240	1316	1340	1440	1516	1540	1640	1716	1740	...	1840	1940	2040	2140	2240	2340	...	...
Zweisimmen ‡ a.	0550	0657	0757	0857	0929	0957	1057	1129	1157	1257	1329	1357	1457	1530	1557	1657	1730	1757	...	1857	1957	2057	2157	2257	2357	...	...

LENK - ZWEISIMMEN ★

km																											
		Ⓐ		Ⓐ				Ⓒ		Ⓒ		Ⓐ									Ⓐ		Ⓐ				
0	**Lenk** d.	0611	0634	0705	0737	0837	0937	1005	1037	1105	1137	1205	1237	1305	1337	1437	1537	1605	1637	1737	1805	1837	1905	1937	2037	2137	2237
13	**Zweisimmen** a.	0629	0652	0723	0755	0855	0955	1023	1055	1123	1155	1223	1255	1323	1355	1455	1555	1623	1655	1755	1823	1855	1923	1955	2055	2155	2255

	Ⓐ		Ⓐ				Ⓒ		Ⓒ			Ⓐ								Ⓐ		Ⓐ					⑤⑥
Zweisimmen d.	0550	0611	0634	0705	0805	0905	0937	1005	1037	1105	1137	1205	1237	1305	1405	1505	1537	1605	1705	1737	1805	1837	1905	2005	2105	2205	2305
Lenk a.	0608	0629	0652	0723	0823	0923	0955	1023	1055	1123	1155	1223	1255	1323	1423	1523	1555	1623	1723	1755	1823	1855	1923	2023	2123	2223	2323

B – GOLDEN PASS BELLE ÉPOQUE – Conveys Belle Époque carriages.
P – GOLDEN PASS PANORAMIC – Conveys panorama cars.

a – Ⓐ only.
d – Runs daily Montreux - Les Avants.
s – Also Apr. 15, May 26, June 6, Aug. 1, Sept. 19.
t – Not Dec. 25, Jan. 1, Apr. 15.
v – Arrives 1643.

⊗ – Chamby is a request stop.

‡ – Additional local trains Zweisimmen - Gstaad and v.v.
From Zweisimmen at 0630 Ⓐ, 0730 Ⓐ, 0830, 1530 Ⓒ and 1730.
From Gstaad at 0504 Ⓐ, 0704 Ⓐ, 0804 Ⓐ, 1603 Ⓒ and 1904 ⑤⑥ **t**.

§ – Additional local trains Les Avants - Montreux and v.v.:
From Les Avants at 0619, 0719 and hourly until 2019.
From Montreux at 0050 ⑥⑦ **s**, 0622, 0722 and hourly until 2022.

★ – Additional trains Lenk - Zweisimmen and v.v.
From Lenk at 0532 Ⓐ and 2337 ⑤⑥. **From Zweisimmen** at 0511 Ⓐ.

Narrow gauge. 2nd class only. TPF — MONTBOVON - BULLE - PALÉZIEUX — 568

MONTBOVON - BULLE

km																			
			Ⓐ	✕							Ⓐ🚌	✕🚌	🚌	🚌		🚌			
0	**Montbovon** d.	SERVICE TO	0545	0645	0718	0845	and	2045	...	SERVICE	0542	0642	0718	0842	and	2042	...	...	...
13	Gruyères d.	JAN. 30 AND	0607	0707	0738	0907	hourly	2107	...	FROM JAN. 31	0559	0659	0735	0859	hourly	2059	...	...	...
17	**Bulle** ▽ a.	FROM JUNE 26	0615	0715	0748	0915	until	2115	...	TO JUNE 25	0614	0714	0750	0914	until	2114	...	...	...

		Ⓐ	✕								Ⓐ🚌	✕🚌	🚌	🚌		🚌			
Bulle ▽ d.	SERVICE TO	0445	0545	0645	0748	0845	and	1945	...	SERVICE	0445	0545	0645	0745	and	1945	...	...	...
Gruyères d.	JAN. 30 AND	0452	0552	0652	0755	0852	hourly	1952	...	FROM JAN. 31	0456	0556	0656	0756	hourly	1956	...	...	...
Montbovon a.	FROM JUNE 26	0513	0613	0713	0816	0913	until	2013	...	TO JUNE 25	0517	0617	0717	0817	until	2017	...	...	...

BULLE - PALÉZIEUX

km																							
		✕	Ⓐ B	Ⓐ A		Ⓐ B	Ⓐ A			Ⓐ B	Ⓐ A								⑤⑥				
0	**Bulle** ▽ d.	0519	0546	0551	0616	0646	0651	and at the	1816	1846	1851	1916	...	2016	...	2116	...	2216	...	2316	...	...	...
20	Châtel-St Denis a.	0542	0610	0614	0640	0710	0714	same minutes	1840	1910	1914	1940	...	2040	...	2140	...	2240	...	2340	...	...	...
20	Châtel-St Denis d.	0543	0614	0614	0644	0714	0714	past each	1844	1914	1914	1944	...	2044	...	2144	...	2244	...	2344	...	...	...
24	**Palézieux** a.	0556	0626	0626	0656	0726	0726	hour until	1856	1926	1926	1956	...	2056	...	2156	...	2256	...	2356	...	...	...

	⑥⑦		✕	Ⓐ A	Ⓐ B		Ⓐ A	Ⓐ B			Ⓐ A	Ⓐ B											
Palézieux d.	0010	...	0604	0633	0634	0704	0733	0734	and at the	1904	1933	1934	2004	...	2104	...	2204	...	2304	...	...	...	...
Châtel-St Denis a.	0020	...	0614	0642	0644	0714	0742	0744	same minutes	1914	1942	1944	2014	...	2114	...	2214	...	2314	...	...	...	...
Châtel-St Denis d.	0021	...	0618	0643	0648	0718	0743	0748	past each	1918	1943	1948	2018	...	2118	...	2218	...	2318	...	...	...	...
Bulle ▽ a.	0046	...	0644	0708	0714	0744	0808	0814	hour until	1944	2008	2014	2044	...	2144	...	2244	...	2344	...	...	...	...

BULLE - ROMONT - FRIBOURG - BERN

km																							
0	**Bulle** ▽ d.	0520	0550	0620	0650	0720	0750	0820	0850	and at the	1820	1850	1920	1950	2020	2050	2120	2150	2220	2250	2320	2350	...
18	Romont **505** a.	0537	0607	0637	0707	0737	0807	0837	0907	same minutes	1837	1907	1937	2007	2037	2107	2137	2207	2237	2307	2337	0007	...
44	Fribourg **505** a.	0555	0625	0655	0725	0755	0825	0855	0925	past each	1855	1925	1955	2025	2055	2125	2155	2225	2255	2325	2355	0025	...
75	**Bern** **505** a.	...	0651z	...	0751y	...	0851y	...	0951z	hour until	...	1951z	...	...	...	...	...	...	...	...	...	...	...

	Ⓐ																						
Bern **505** d.	...	...	...	...	0709z	...	0809y	...	0909y	...	1009z	and at the	...	2009z	...	...	...	...	...	...	...	...	...
Fribourg **505** d.	0534	0604	0634	0704	0734	0804	0834	0904	0934	1004	1034	same minutes	2004	2034	2104	2134	2204	2234	2304	2334	...	0007	...
Romont **505** d.	0553	0623	0653	0723	0753	0823	0853	0923	0953	1023	1053	past each	2023	2053	2123	2153	2223	2253	2323	2353	...	0036	...
Bulle ▽ a.	0611	0641	0711	0741	0811	0841	0911	0941	1011	1041	1111	hour until	2041	2111	2141	2211	2241	2311	2341	0011	...	0053	...

A – Until June 25.
B – From June 26.

y – Daily to May 1; Ⓒ May 7 - Sept. 11; daily from Sept. 26.
z – Not Sept. 12–25.

▽ – 🚌 **Bulle - Broc and v.v.**: Journey 15 minutes. All services also call at Broc Village.
From Bulle at 0619 Ⓐ, 0719, 0819 and hourly until 1919.
From Broc Fabrique at 0625 Ⓐ, 0725, 0825 and hourly until 1925.

Narrow gauge rack railway. 2nd class only. MVR — MONTREUX - CAUX - ROCHERS DE NAYE — 569

Services do not run Caux - Rochers de Naye and v.v. on ①② Jan. 10 - Feb. 15 and ①② Feb. 28 - Mar. 29.

km													
0	**Montreux** d.	0547	0644	0744	0817	and	1517	1617	1717	1817	1917	and	2317
3	Glion ▲ d.	0558	0655	0755	0829	hourly	1529	1629	1729	1829	1927	hourly	2327
5	Caux a.	0607	0704	0804	0839	until	1539	1639	1739	1839	1936	until	2336
10	**Rochers de Naye** a.	...	...	...	0906		1606	1706b	1806b	...	...		...

Rochers de Naye d.	...	...	...	0911	and	1611	1711b	1811b		...	and	...
Caux d.	0612	0712	0812	0941	hourly	1641	1741	1841	...	1946	hourly	2346
Glion ▲ d.	0625	0725	0829	0953	until	1653	1753	1853	...	1958	until	2258
Montreux a.	0637	0737	0841	1006		1706	1806	1906	...	2011		2311

b – May 20 - Oct. 30.

▲ – Funicular railway operates **Glion** - **Territet** and v.v. Journey: 6 minutes. **Operator**: MVR ✆ 021 989 81 90. No service Apr 26–28, Oct. 17–22. Simultaneous departures from both **Glion** and **Territet** at 0512, 0527, 0542, 0557 and every 15 minutes until 2057; then 2112 and every 30 minutes until 0042.
Note: Local stopping trains run hourly from Territet to Montreux, Vevey, Lausanne and Aigle.

SWITZERLAND

570 GENÈVE - LAUSANNE - SION - BRIG

SBB

km		IR 1705 ①–⑤	IR 1805		RE 18455	EC 35 ◧ ✕	IR 1707	IR 1807	RE 18457	IR 1709	IR 1809	RE 18459	EC 37 ◧¶ V✕	IR 1711	IR 1811	RE 18461 △	IR 1713	❖	IR 1829	RE 18479 △	IR 1731	IR 1831	RE 18481	EC 41 ◧ ✕
0	**Genève** Aéroport ✈ ..... **505** d.	...	...	...	0510	...	0519	...	0611	0619	0701	...	...	0719	0801	...	0819		1701	...	1719	1801	...	...
6	**Genève** ..... **505** d.	...	0449	...	0520	0539	0529	0609	0620	0629	0711	0720	0739	0729	0811	0820	0829		1711	1720	1729	1811	1820	1839
27	Nyon ..... **505** d.	...	0504	...	0536	|	0544	|	0636	0644	|	0736	|	0744	|	0836	0844		|	1736	1744	|	1836	|
53	Morges ..... **505** d.	...	0523	...	0555	|	0600	|	0655	0700	|	0755	|	0800	|	0855	0900		|	1756	1800	|	1855	|
66	**Lausanne** ..... **505** a.	...	0537	...	0608	0614	0612	0647	0708	0712	0747	0808	0814	0812	0847	0908	0912	and at	1747	1808	1812	1847	1908	1914
66	**Lausanne** ..... ▷ d.	0507	0547	0601	0611	0618	0621	0650	0711	0721	0750	0811	0818	0821	0850	0911	0921		1750	1811	1821	1850	1911	1918
84	Vevey ..... ▷ d.	0523	0602	0618	0626	|	0636	0705	0726	0736	0805	0826	|	0836	0905	0926	0936	the same	1805	1826	1836	1905	1926	|
91	**Montreux** ..... ▷ d.	0531	0609	0627	0632	0637	0643	0711	0732	0743	0811	0832	0837	0843	0911	0932	0943		1811	1832	1843	1911	1932	1937
95	Villeneuve ..... ▷ d.	|	|	0631	|	|	|	|	0736	|	|	|	|	|	|	0936	|	minutes	|	1836	|	|	|	|
105	Aigle ..... ▷ d.	0542	0620	0638	0642	|	0653	0722	0743	0754	0822	0842	|	0853	0922	0943	0953		1822	1843	1853	1922	1942	|
114	Bex ..... d.	0549	|	...	0648	|	|	|	0749	|	|	0848	|	|	|	0949	|	past each	|	1849	|	|	1948	|
118	St Maurice ..... d.	0558	0629	...	0653	|	|	0732	0753	|	0832	0853	|	|	0932	0953	|		1832	1853	|	1932	1953	|
133	Martigny ..... d.	0609	0640	...	...	|	0711	0743	...	0811	0843	...	|	0911	0943	...	1011	hour until	1843	...	1911	1943	...	|
158	**Sion** ..... d.	0623	0655	...	...	0712	0725	0757	...	0825	0857	...	0912	0925	0957	...	1025		1857	...	1925	1957	...	2012
174	Sierre / Siders ..... d.	0634	0705	...	...	|	0735	0807	...	0835	0908	...	|	0935	1008	...	1035		1908	...	1935	2008	...	|
184	Leuk ..... d.	0641	0713	...	...	|	0743	|	...	0843	|	...	|	0943	|	...	1043		|	...	1943	|	...	|
203	Visp ..... **560** d.	0654	0725	...	...	|	0755	0825	...	0855	0925	...	|	0955	1025	...	1055		1925	...	1955	2025	...	|
212	**Brig** ..... **560** a.	0701	0732	...	...	0740	0802	0832	...	0902	0932	...	0940	1002	1032	...	1102		1932	...	2002	2032	...	2040
·	*Milano Centrale* **590** ..... a.	...	...	...	...	0940	...	...	...	...	...	...	1140	...	...	...	...		...	...	...	...	...	2240

	IR 1733	IR 1833	RE 18483	IR 1735	IR 1835	RE 18485	IR 1737 ⑤⑥	IR 1737 ⑦–④	IR 1837 ⑦–④	IR 1837 ⑤⑥	RE 18487 ⑤⑥	RE 18487	IR 1739 ⑤⑥	RE 3579 ⑤⑥	IR 1739 ⑦–④	RE 3579 ⑦	IR 1839 ⑤⑥	IR 1839 ⑦–④	IR 1741 ⑤⑥	IR 1841 ⑦–④	IR 1743			EC 39 ◧ ✕	IR 1927 Ⓐ n
Genève Aéroport ✈ ..... **505** d.	1816**t**	1901	...	1919	2001	...	2019	2019	...	2058	...	...	2119	...	...	...	2201	2149**c**	2219	2249	*2311*	...		...	...
Genève ..... **505** d.	1826**t**	1911	1920	1929	2011	2020	2029	2029	2104	2108	2120	2120	2129	...	...	...	2211	2159**c**	2229	2259	*2320*	...		1339	1704
Nyon ..... **505** d.	1841**t**	|	1936	1944	|	2036	2044	2044	2119	|	2136	2136	2144	...	...	...	|	2214**c**	2244	2313	*2336*	...		|	|
Morges ..... **505** d.	1900	|	1955	2000	|	2056	2100	2100	2135	|	2156	2156	2200	...	...	...	|	2229**c**	2300	2330	*2355*	...		|	1738
Lausanne ..... **505** a.	1912	1947	2008	2012	2047	2108	2112	2112	2147	2147	2208	2208	2212	...	...	...	2247	2241**c**	2312	2341	*0010*	...	A	1414	1751
Lausanne ..... ▷ d.	1921	1950	2011	2021	2050	2110	2121	2121	2149	2150	2211	...	2221	...	2226	...	2250	2300	2321	2344	0025	...		1418	1756
Vevey ..... ▷ d.	1936	2005	2026	2036	2105	2125	2136	2136	2204	2205	2226	...	2236	...	2243	...	2305	2315	2336	2359	0040	...	L	|	1811
Montreux ..... ▷ d.	1943	2011	2032	2043	2111	2130	2143	2143	2211	2211	2232	...	2243	...	2250	...	2311	2321	2343	0005	0047	...		1437	1818
Villeneuve ..... ▷ d.	|	|	2036	|	|	2135	|	|	|	|	2236	...	|	...	|	...	|	|	|	|	|	...	S	|	1823
Aigle ..... ▷ d.	1953	2022	2043	2053	2122	2142	2153	2153	2222	2222	2243	...	2253	...	2300	...	2322	2332	2353	0016	0057	...		|	1832
Bex ..... d.	|	|	2049	|	|	2148	|	|	|	|	2249	...	|	...	2308	...	|	|	0000	0023	0104	...	O	|	1839
St Maurice ..... d.	|	2032	2053	|	2132	2153	|	2203	2232	2232	2253	...	|	...	2316	...	2332	2342	0006	0029	0110	...		|	1844
Martigny ..... d.	2011	2043	...	2111	2143	...	2211	2214	2243	2243	...	...	2311	...	2329	...	2343	2353	0016	0040	0120	...		|	1858
Sion ..... d.	2025	2057	...	2125	2157	...	2225	2228	2259	2257	...	...	2324	2330	2343	2347	2357	0007	0031	0054	0134	...		1513	1916
Sierre / Siders ..... d.	2035	2108	...	2135	2208	...	2235	2238	2310	2308	...	...	...	2340	2354**z**	2357	0008	0018	0041	0104	...	...		|	...
Leuk ..... d.	2043	|	...	2143	|	...	2243	2246	|	|	...	...	...	2347	|	0004	|	0025	0048	0112	...	...		|	...
Visp ..... **560** d.	2055	2125	...	2155	2225	...	2255	2258	2327	2325	...	...	...	2359	0011**z**	0016	0025	0038	0100	0124	...	...		|	...
Brig ..... **560** a.	2102	2132	...	2202	2232	...	2302	2306	2338	2332	...	...	...	0004	0018**z**	0021	0032	0045	0108	0132	...	...		1540	...
Milano Centrale **590** ..... a.	...	...	...	...	...	...	...	...	...	...	...	...	...	...	...	...	...	...	...	...	...	...		1740	...

	RE 3590 ⑥⑦		IR 1702	IR 1804	IR 1704	RE 18454	IR 1904 Ⓐ n	IR 1806	IR 1706	RE 18456	IR 1808	IR 1708	RE 18458	IR 1810	IR 1710	RE 18460 △	⊛	IR 1830	IR 1730	RE 18480	IR 1832	IR 1732	EC 36 ◧‡ ✕	RE 18482
Milano Centrale **590** ..... d.	...	...	...	...	...	...	...	...	...	...	...	...	...	...	...	...		...	...	...	...	...	1720	...
Brig ..... **560** d.	...	...	...	0420	*0438*	...	...	0524	0557	...	0624	0657	...	0726	0757	...		1726	1757	...	1826	1857	1916	...
Visp ..... **560** d.	...	...	...	0429	*0444*	...	...	0532	0606	...	0632	0706	...	0735	0806	...		1735	1806	...	1835	1906	|	...
Leuk ..... d.	...	...	...	0439	*0500*	...	...	0542	0616	...	0642	0716	...	|	0816	...		|	1816	...	|	1916	|	...
Sierre / Siders ..... d.	...	...	...	0447	*0507*	...	...	0550	0623	...	0650	0723	...	0750	0823	...	and at	1750	1823	...	1850	1923	|	...
Sion ..... d.	...	...	0424	0458	0529	...	0550	0601	0634	0637**a**	0701	0734	...	0801	0834	...		1801	1834	...	1901	1934	1947	...
Martigny ..... d.	...	...	0438	0513	0543	...	0605	0616	0648	0652**a**	0716	0748	...	0816	0848	...	the same	1816	1848	...	1916	1948	|	...
St Maurice ..... d.	0039	...	0449	0524	0554	0604	0616	0627	|	0704	0727	|	0804	0827	|	0904		1827	|	1904	1927	|	|	2001
Bex ..... d.	0043	...	0454	0529	0559	0608	0622	|	|	0708	|	|	0808	|	|	0908	minutes	|	|	1908	|	|	|	2011
Aigle ..... ▷ d.	0049	...	0502	0538	0606	0615	0630	0638	0706	0715	0738	0806	0815	0837	0906	0915		1837	1906	1915	1937	2006	|	2018
Villeneuve ..... ▷ d.	0056	...	|	|	|	0622	|	|	|	0722	|	|	0822	|	|	0922	past each	|	|	1922	|	|	|	|
Montreux ..... ▷ d.	0100	...	0513	0548	0617	0627	0641	0648	0717	0727	0748	0817	0827	0848	0917	0927		1848	1917	1927	1948	2017	2023	2028
Vevey ..... ▷ d.	0108	...	0522	0555	0624	0633	0649	0655	0724	0733	0755	0824	0833	0855	0924	0933	hour until	1855	1924	1933	1955	2024	|	2033
Lausanne ..... ▷ a.	0123	...	0537	0610	0639	0649	0704	0710	0739	0749	0810	0839	0849	0910	0939	0949		1910	1939	1949	2010	2039	2042	2049
Lausanne ..... **505** d.	*0135*	...	0548	0613	0648	0651	0708	0713	0748	0751	0813	0848	0851	0913	0948	0951		1913	1948	1951	2013	2048	2045	2051
Morges ..... **505** d.	*0148*	...	0559	|	0659	0705	0724	|	0759	0805	|	0859	0905	|	0959	1005		|	1959	2005	|	2059	|	2105
Nyon ..... **505** d.	*0208*	...	0616	|	0716	0725	|	|	0816	0825	|	0916	0925	|	1016	1025		|	2016	2025	|	2116	|	2129**f**
Genève ..... **505** a.	*0224*	...	0631	0650	0731	0740	0756	0750	0831	0840	0850	0931	0940	0950	1031	1040		1950	2031	2040	2050	2131	2121	2144**f**
Genève Aéroport ✈ ..... **505** a.	...	...	0641	0659	0741	...	...	0759	0841	...	0859	0941	...	0959	1041	...		1959	2041	...	2059	2141**k**	...	...

	IR 1834 ⑤⑥	IR 1834 ⑦–④	IR 1734 ⑤⑥	IR 1734	RE 18484 ⑤⑥	RE 18484 ⑦–④	IR 1836 ⑤⑥	IR 1836 ⑦–④	IR 1736 ⑤⑥	IR 1736	EC 42 ⑤⑥ ◧V	⑦–④	RE 18486 ⑤⑥	RE 18486 ⑦–④	IR 1838 ⑤⑥	EC 44 ⑦–④ ◧V	RE 18488 ⑤⑥	RE 18488 ⑦–④	IR 1840 ⑤⑥	IR 1840 ⑦–④	RE 18442 ①–⑤			EC 32 ◧ ✕	EC 34 ◧ ✕
Milano Centrale **590** ..... d.	...	...	...	...	...	...	...	...	...	...	1920	...	...	...	...	1920	...	...	...	...	...	...		0820	1320
Brig ..... **560** d.	1926	1926	1957	1957	...	...	2026	2026	2057	2057	2116	...	...	...	2126	2126	...	...	2226	2226	...	...		1016	1516
Visp ..... **560** d.	1935	1935	2006	2006	...	...	2035	2035	2106	2106	|	...	...	...	2135	2135	...	...	2235	2235	...	...		|	|
Leuk ..... d.	|	|	2016	2016	...	...	|	|	2116	2116	|	...	...	...	|	|	...	...	|	|	...	...		|	|
Sierre / Siders ..... d.	1950	1950	2023	2023	...	...	2050	2050	2123	2123	|	...	...	...	2150	|	...	...	2250	2250	...	...	A	|	|
Sion ..... d.	2001	2001	2034	2034	...	...	2101	2101	2134	2134	2147	...	...	...	2201	2159	...	...	2301	2301	...	...		1047	1547
Martigny ..... d.	2016	2016	2048	2048	...	...	2116	2116	2148	2148	|	...	...	...	2216	2215	...	...	2316	2316	...	...	L	|	|
St Maurice ..... d.	2027	2027	|	|	2104	2104	2127	2127	|	|	|	2149	2201	...	2227	2227	2304	...	2327	2327	...	...		|	|
Bex ..... d.	|	|	|	|	2108	2109	|	|	|	|	|	2153	2211	...	|	|	2309	...	|	|	...	...	S	|	|
Aigle ..... ▷ d.	2037	2037	2106	2106	2115	2115	2137	2137	2206	2206	|	2217	2218	...	2237	2237	2315	...	2337	2337	...	...		|	|
Villeneuve ..... ▷ d.	|	|	|	|	2122	2122	|	|	|	|	|	2224	|	...	|	|	2322	...	|	|	...	...	O	|	|
Montreux ..... ▷ d.	2048	2048	2117	2117	2127	2129	2148	2148	2217	2217	2223	2231	2228	...	2248	2248	2327	...	2348	2348	...	...		1123	1623
Vevey ..... ▷ d.	2055	2055	2124	2124	2133	2135	2155	2155	2224	2224	|	2240	2233	...	2255	2255	2333	...	2355	2357	...	...		|	|
Lausanne ..... ▷ a.	2110	2110	2139	2139	2149	2149	2210	2210	2239	2239	2242	...	2249	...	2310	2310	2349	...	0010	0012	...	...		1142	1642
Lausanne ..... **505** d.	2113	2113	2148	...	2151	2151	2213	2213	2248	...	2245	...	2251	2251	2313	2312	2351	2351	0013	...	0025	...		1145	1645
Morges ..... **505** d.	|	2124	2159	...	2205	2205	|	2224	2259	...	|	...	2305	2305**r**	|	2324	0004	0005	|	...	0039	...		|	|
Nyon ..... **505** d.	|	2140**e**	2216	...	2225	2229	|	2240**e**	2316	...	|	...	2325	2329**r**	|	2339**e**	0024	0029	|	...	0059	...		|	|
Genève ..... **505** a.	2150	2155**e**	2231	...	2240	2244	2250	2254**e**	2331	...	2321	...	2340	2344**r**	2350	2354**e**	0040	0044	0050	...	0114	...		1221	1721
Genève Aéroport ✈ ..... **505** a.	2159	2204**e**	2241	...	...	2257	2259	2303**e**	2341	...	...	...	2348	2352**r**	2359	0003**e**	0048	...	...	...	...	...		...	...

V – [12] and ✕ Genève - Milano - Venezia and v.v.

a – Ⓐ only.
c – 6 minutes later Mar. 20 - Aug. 28.
e – 5 – 12 minutes later Mar. 20 - Apr. 7.
f – 4 minutes earlier on ⑤⑥.
k – ⑤⑥ only.
n – Not Dec. 27 - 31.
r – Mar. 20 - Aug. 28 Morges d. 2304, Nyon d. 2334, Genève a. 2349, Genève Aéroport a. 2357.
t – 3 minutes later on ©.
z – Sion - Brig on ①-④ only.

❖ – Train numbers increase by 2 each hour. See later columns for additional trains within the hourly pattern. The 1320 from Genève does not call at Villeneuve.
⊛ – Train numbers increase by 2 each hour. See later columns for additional trains within the hourly pattern. Timing variations for St Maurice to Genève services: St Maurice d. 1101 / 1601 (not 1104 / 1604) then retimed at Bex (d. 1111 / 1611), Aigle (d. 1118 / 1618), not calling at Villeneuve.
△ – Timings may vary by 1 – 2 minutes on certain dates.
▷ – Hourly stopping trains also run Lausanne - Aigle and v.v.
◧ – Supplement payable for journeys from / to Italy.
‡ – Train number **46** on ©.
¶ – Train number **47** on ©.

Local services from VEVEY, AIGLE and BEX — 571

2nd class only

VEVEY - BLONAY - LES PLÉIADES: Narrow gauge (rack Blonay - Les Pléiades). **Operator**: MVR. Additional services run Vevey - Blonay and v.v. on Ⓐ. On Sept. 19 services run as on Ⓒ.

km																							
			Ⓐ		Ⓐ		Ⓐ		Ⓒ			❖											
0	Vevey d.	0556	...	0641	...	0711	0726	0741	...	0811	0841	and at the same	1811	1841	1911	1941	2011	2041	2111	2141	2211	2241	2341
6	Blonay a.	0612	0615	0657	0700	0727	0742	0757	0803	0827	0857	minutes past	1827	1857	1927	1957	2027	2057	2127	2157	2227	2257	2357
10	Les Pléiades a.	...	0627	...	0712	...	0759	...	0819	...	0919	each hour until	...	1919	...	...	...	...	...	...	...	...	...

				Ⓐ			Ⓐ		Ⓐ		Ⓒ										
Les Pléiades d.	...	...	...	0637	...	...	0719	...	0802	...	0835	...	...	0935	and at the same	...	1935	...	...	...	...	...
Blonay d.	0531	0601	0631	0657	0701	0731	0746	0801	0826	0831	0859	0901	0931	1001	minutes past	1931	2001	2031	2116	2131	2216	2316
Vevey a.	0546	0616	0646	...	0716	0746	0801	0816	...	0846	...	0916	0946	1016	each hour until	1946	2016	2046	2131	2146	2231	2331

AIGLE - LEYSIN: Narrow gauge rack railway. *6 km*. Journey time: 29–39 minutes. The Leysin terminus station is Grand Hotel, but all trains also call at Feydey station. **Operator**: TPC.

From Aigle at 0545, 0656 Ⓒ, 0756 Ⓒ, 0805 Ⓐ, 0856, 0956 and hourly until 2256.
Also **Aigle - Leysin Feydey** at 0622 Ⓐ, 0713 Ⓐ, 0832 Ⓒ, 1532 Ⓒ, 1732 Ⓐ and 1832 Ⓐ.

From Leysin Grand Hotel at 0521, 0619 Ⓐ, 0653 Ⓒ, 0753 Ⓒ, 0853, 0953 and hourly until 1653; then 1727 Ⓐ, 1753 Ⓒ, 1853, 1953, 2053, 2153, 2253 and 2329.
Also **Leysin Feydey - Aigle** at 0654 Ⓐ, 0746 Ⓐ, 0932 Ⓒ, 1632 Ⓒ, 1759 Ⓐ and 1916 Ⓐ.

AIGLE - LES DIABLERETS: Narrow gauge. *23 km*. Journey time: 50–54 minutes. **Operator**: TPC.

From Aigle at 0525, 0625, 0725, 0829, 0929 and hourly until 2229.

From Les Diablerets at 0607, 0707, 0734, 0834 and hourly until 2234.

AIGLE - CHAMPÉRY: Narrow gauge rack railway. 2nd class only. **Operator**: TPC. Additional trains operate Aigle - Monthey and v.v. on ⚒.

km																										
		A			⚒																	⑤⑥t		⑤⑥t		⑤⑥t
0	**Aigle** d.	0022	...	...	0507	0620	0732	0828	0932	1028	1132	1228	1332	1428	1532	1628	1728	1828	1928	2033	2130	2233	2233	2303	2303	2358
11	Monthey Ville a.	0041	...	...	0526	0639	0752	0849	0952	1049	1152	1249	1352	1449	1552	1649	1749	1849	1949	2052	2149	2252	2252	2322	2322	0017
11	Monthey Ville d.	...	...	0510	0528	0641	0800	0851	1000	1100	1200	1251	1400	1451	1600	1700	1800	1900	1951	2100	2151	2259	...	2324	...	...
23	**Champéry** a.	...	...	0543	0601	0717	0833	0924	1033	1133	1233	1324	1433	1524	1633	1733	1833	1933	2024	2133	2224	2332	...	2357	...	...

	⚒			⚒	Ⓐ		⚒																	⑤⑥t
Champéry d.	...	...	0602	...	0627	...	0656	0756	0903	0956	1056	1156	1303	1356	1503	1556	1656	1756	1856	2003	2056	...	2203	2226	2337
Monthey Ville a.	...	...	0635	...	0701	...	0730	0830	0937	1030	1130	1230	1337	1430	1537	1630	1730	1830	1930	2037	2130	...	2237	2259	0010
Monthey Ville d.	0439	0540	0640	0705	0705	0739	0739	0837	0940	1037	1140	1237	1340	1437	1540	1637	1737	1837	1937	2040	2137	...	2240	2302	...
Aigle a.	0459	0600	0701	0729	0729	0800	0800	0857	1000	1057	1200	1257	1400	1457	1600	1657	1757	1857	1957	2100	2157	...	2300	2322	...

BEX - VILLARS-SUR-OLLON - COL-DE-BRETAYE: Narrow gauge rack railway. 2nd class only. **Operator**: TPC. Additional trains operate Villars - Col-de-Bretaye and v.v. (see note ⊡).

km																										
															C			D				D				
0	**Bex** d.	0625	0715	0802	0902	1002	1102	1202	1311	...	1402	1502	1602	1702	1702	1802	...	1902	2002	2102	...	2202	...	...	...	...
3	Bévieux ⊗ d.	0635	0725	0812	0912	1012	1112	1212	1321	...	1412	1512	1612	1712	1712	1812	...	1912	2012	2112	...	2212	...	...	...	...
12	Villars-sur-Ollon a.	0703	0753	0840	0940	1040	1140	1240	1349	...	1440	1540	1640	1740	1740	1840	...	1940	2040	2140	...	...	...	...	...	...
12	Villars-sur-Ollon d.	...	0805	0850	0950	1050	1150	1250	...	1420	1450	1550	1650	1750	...	...	1914	...	...	...	2204	...	...	...	...	...
17	**Col-de-Bretaye** a.	...	0823	0908	1008	1108	1208	1308	...	1438	1508	1608	1708	1808	...	...	1932	...	...	...	2222	...	...	...	...	...

															C		D			D				
Col-de-Bretaye d.	...	...	...	...	0845	0945	1045	1145	1215	...	1345	1445	1545	1645	1745	1815	...	1935	...	...	2230	...	...	...	...
Villars-sur-Ollon a.	...	...	...	...	0905	1005	1105	1205	1235	...	1405	1505	1605	1705	1805	1835	...	1955	...	...	2250	...	...	...	...
Villars-sur-Ollon d.	0516	0618	0709	0813	0913	1013	1113	1213	...	1304	1413	1513	1613	1713	1813	...	1913	...	2013	2113	...	...	...	...	...
Bévieux ⊗ d.	0548	0650	0741	0845	0945	1045	1145	1245	...	1336	1445	1545	1645	1745	1845	...	1945	...	2045	2145	...	...	...	...	...
Bex a.	0600	0702	0753	0857	0957	1057	1157	1257	...	1348	1457	1557	1657	1757	1857	...	1957	...	2057	2157	...	...	...	...	...

A – ①–⑤ (also Dec. 26, Jan. 2, Apr. 16).
C – Daily Dec. 18 - Mar. 27 and July 2 - Aug. 28; ⑥⑦ Sept. 3–25.
D – Daily July 2 - Aug. 28; ⑥ Sept. 3–24.
t – Not Dec. 25, Jan. 1, Apr. 15.

❖ – Certain Les Pléiades arrivals are up to 7 minutes later on Ⓐ.
⊗ – Trains call at Bévieux on request.
⊡ – Additional trains operate Villars - Col-de-Bretaye and v.v. Dec. 18 - Mar. 27 and July 27 - Aug. 28.

MARTIGNY - VALLORCINE — 572

TMR (2nd class only). Narrow gauge rack railway

For services Vallorcine - Chamonix - St Gervais and v.v. see Table **365a**.

km										
0	**Martigny** d.	0518	0618	0718		1918	2018	2118	...	...
7	Salvan d.	0535	0635	0735	and	1935	2035	2135	...	...
9	Les Marécottes d.	0538	0638	0738	hourly	1938	2038	2138	...	...
14	Finhaut d.	0551	0651	0750	until	1950	2050	2150	...	...
18	Le Châtelard Frontière 🏛 d.	0600	0700	0800		2000	2100	2200	...	...
21	**Vallorcine** a.	...	...	0805		2005	...	...	...	...

	Ⓐ		Ⓐ						
Vallorcine d.	...	...	...	...	0810		2110	...	...
Le Châtelard Frontière 🏛 d.	0515	0615	0641	0715	0815	and	2115	2215	...
Finhaut d.	0525	0625	0651	0725	0825	hourly	2125	2225	...
Les Marécottes d.	0538	0638	0703	0738	0838	until	2138	2237	...
Salvan d.	0541	0641	0707	0741	0841		2141	2241	...
Martigny a.	0601	0701	0730	0801	0901		2201	2301	...

SION VALLEY RESORTS — 573

MARTIGNY - ORSIÈRES▲ and LE CHÂBLE. *19 km*. Journey time: 24–28 minutes for both routes. **Operator**: RA.

From Martigny at 0605, 0715, 0749, 0815, 0849, 0915, 0949, 1015, 1049, 1149 **e**, 1249, 1349, 1449, 1549, 1615 **g**, 1649, 1715 **g**, 1749, 1815 **g**, 1849, 1915 **g**, 1949, 2015 **g**, 2049, 2152 and 2319.

From Orsières / Le Châble ◇ at 0532, 0636, 0708, 0744, 0820, 0844, 0920, 0944, 1020, 1044, 1144 **f**, 1255, 1344, 1444, 1544, 1620 **g**, 1644, 1720 **g**, 1744, 1820 **g**, 1844, 1920 **g**, 1944, 2020 **g**, 2044 and 2240.

🚌 **LE CHÂBLE - VERBIER**. Journey time: ± 25 minutes. **Operator**: PA.

From Le Châble Gare at 0648 Ⓐ **h**, 0748 ①† **r**, 1039 Ⓒ, 1145 Ⓐ **h**, 1321 Ⓒ, 1600 Ⓐ **h**, 1621 Ⓒ, 1721 Ⓐ **h**, 1821 Ⓒ and 1948.

From Verbier Post at 0607 Ⓐ **h**, 0717 Ⓐ **h**, 0817, 1117 Ⓒ, 1217 Ⓐ **h**, 1417 Ⓒ, 1650, 1750 Ⓐ **h**, 1850 Ⓒ and 2017.

🚌 **MARTIGNY - AOSTA** via Grand St Bernard tunnel. Journey time: ± 1 hour 50 minutes. **Operator**: TMR / SAVDA.

From Martigny Gare at 0830 ②⑤ and 1830 ②⑤⑦.

From Aosta Autostazione at 1100 ②⑤ and 1600 ②⑤⑦.

🚌 **SION - CRANS-SUR-SIERRE**. Journey time: ± 45 minutes. On Mar. 19, June 16, Aug. 15, Nov. 1, Dec. 8 services run as on ⑦. On Apr. 15 services run as on Ⓐ. **Operator**: PA.

From Sion Gare at 0610 Ⓐ, 0645 ⚒, 0745, 0840 ⚒, 0905 Ⓐ, 1000, 1045 ⚒, 1145 Ⓒ, 1150 Ⓐ, 1230 ⚒, 1345, 1510, 1540 Ⓐ, 1648 ⚒, 1710 †, 1810, 1910 and 2105 ⚒.

From Crans-sur-Sierre Post at 0643, 0700 Ⓐ, 0740 ⚒, 0835, 0930 ⚒, 1005 Ⓐ, 1050, 1135 ⚒, 1235 Ⓒ, 1245 Ⓐ, 1335 ⚒, 1545, 1605 Ⓐ, 1635, 1805, 1905 and 2005 ⚒.

SIERRE - MONTANA. Funicular railway temporarily closed until December 11. Selected 🚌 services are shown below. Journey time: ± 40 minutes. **Operator**: SMC.

From **Sierre** at 0614, 0714, 0740 and at 14 and 40 minutes past each hour until 1914, 1940; then 2040.

From **Montana** Gare: 0605, 0640 and at 05 and 40 minutes past each hour until 1805, 1840; then 1920, 1940 and 2040.

🚌 **BRIG - SAAS-FEE**. Journey time: 68–89 minutes. Services call at **Visp** (Bahnhof Süd) ± 20 minutes from Brig, and **Saas Grund** (Post) ± 10 minutes from Saas Fee. **Operator**: PA.

From Brig Bahnhof at 0420, 0515, 0545 and every 30 minutes until 1115; then 1140, 1215, 1247, 1315, 1345 and every 30 minutes until 1845; then 1945, 2045 and 2215.

From Saas-Fee Busterminal at 0530, 0600, 0630, 0700, 0730, 0752, 0822, 0852 and every 30 minutes until 1852; then 1930, 1957, 2130 and 2330.

e – Departs 1200 on ③ (except Dec. 22, 29, Mar. 2, Apr. 20, June 29 - Aug. 17, Oct. 19, 26).
f – Departs Orsières 1138 (Le Châble 1142) on ③ (except Dec. 22, 29, Mar. 2, Apr. 20, June 29 - Aug. 17, Oct. 19, 26).
g – Not Sept. 30 - Oct. 9.
h – Not June 16, Aug. 15, Nov. 1, Dec. 8.
r – Also Mar. 19, June 16, Nov. 1, Dec. 8.
◇ – Orsières departure times shown; departures from Le Châble are usually 1–2 minutes later.
▲ – Journeys to / from Orsières require a change of trains at Sembrancher.

575 GLACIER EXPRESS — MGB, RhB*

Glacier Express through services. [R]. Supplement payable. For local services see Tables 545 and 576. Narrow gauge railway (part rack).

km		WINTER SERVICE ▶▶▶ Dec. 12 to May 13	902 [R] ✕	904 [R] A ✕	SUMMER SERVICE ▶▶▶ May 14 to Oct. 23	900 [R] ✕	902 [R] ✕	904 [R] ✕	906 [R] ✕
0	**Zermatt** d.		0852	0952		0752	0852	0952	...
45	**Brig** Bahnhofplatz a.		1010	1110		0910	1010	1110	...
45	**Brig** Bahnhofplatz d.		1018	1118		0918	1018	1118	1418
113	**Andermatt** a.		1146	1246		1046	1146	1246	1546
113	**Andermatt** d.		1154	1254		1054	1154	1254	1554
142	**Disentis / Mustér** a.		1256	1356		1154	1256	1356	1654
142	**Disentis / Mustér** d.		1311	1411		1219	1311	1411	1711
201	**Chur** ▽ a.		1424	1524		1324	1424	1524	1824
242	Tiefencastel ▽ a.		1528	1628		...	1528	1628	1946
252	**Filisur** ▽ a.		1543	1643		...	1543	1643	2001
285	**Samedan** ▽ a.		1631	1731		...	1631	1731	2049
290	**St Moritz** a.		1637	1737		...	1637	1737	2100

	WINTER SERVICE ▶▶▶ Dec. 12 to May 13	923 [R] ✕	925 [R] A ✕	SUMMER SERVICE ▶▶▶ May 14 to Oct. 23	901 [R] ✕	903 [R] ✕	905 [R] ✕	907 [R] ✕
St Moritz d.		0851	0948		0702	0851	0948	...
Samedan △ d.		0901	0958		0715	0901	0958	...
Filisur △ d.		0949	1048		0801	0949	1048	...
Tiefencastel △ d.		1007	1107		0815	1007	1107	...
Chur △ d.		1105	1216		0926	1105	1216	1426
Disentis / Mustér a.		1218	1328		1027	1218	1328	1527
Disentis / Mustér d.		1237	1337		1037	1237	1337	1537
Andermatt a.		1352	1452		1152	1352	1452	1652
Andermatt d.		1354	1454		1208	1408	1508	1708
Brig Bahnhofplatz a.		1540	1640		1340	1540	1640	1840
Brig Bahnhofplatz d.		1550	1650		...	1550	1650	1850
Zermatt a.		1710	1810		...	1710	1810	2010

All Glacier Express trains convey (12) [panorama cars]. Reservations can be made at any Swiss station. Reservations for ✕ are obligatory and must be made in advance of travel: RhB, ✆ 081 288 65 65. Meals are served between 1100 and 1330 at your seat. Further information: www.glacierexpress.ch

A – Apr. 10 - May 13.
△ – Calls to pick up only.
▽ – Calls to set down only.

* – Operators: MGB: Zermatt - Brig - Andermatt - Disentis; RhB: Disentis - Chur - St Moritz.

576 Local services ZERMATT - BRIG - ANDERMATT - DISENTIS (also ANDERMATT- GÖSCHENEN) — MGB

Narrow gauge railway (part rack). For *Glacier Express* through services see Table 575

ZERMATT - VISP - BRIG

km							🚌				🚌												
0	**Zermatt** d.	0537	0613	0637	0737	0813	...	0837	and at the same minutes past each hour until	1713	...	1737	1813	1837	1913	1937	2013	...	2113	...	2213	...	...
8	Täsch d.	0548	0625	0648	0748	0825	...	0848		1725	...	1748	1825	1848	1925	1948	2025	...	2125	...	2223	...	...
21	St Niklaus d.	0613	0650	0713	0813	0850	...	0913		1750	...	1813	1850	1913	1950	2013	2050	...	2150	...	2244	...	...
29	Stalden-Saas d.	0635	0710	0735	0835	0910	...	0935		1810	...	1835	1910	1935	2010	2035	2110	...	2210	...	2305	...	...
36	Visp a.	0646	0722	0746	0846	0922	...	0946		1822	...	1846	1922	1946	2022	2046	2122	...	2222	...	2316	...	...
36	Visp 560 570 d.	0650	0725	0750	*0908*	...	0925	*1008*		...	1825	*1908*	1925	1950	2025	2050	2125	...	2225	...	2318	...	...
45	**Brig** Bahnhofplatz 560 570 a.	0702	0737	0802	*0920*	...	0937	*1020*		...	1837	*1920*	1937	2002	2037	2102	2137	...	2237	...	2328	...	...

									🚌				🚌							①–⑥	⑦	
Brig Bahnhofplatz 560 570 d.	0517	0552	0627	0652	0727	0752	0827	*0838*	0927	...	and at the same minutes past each hour until	*1738*	1827	...	*1838*	...	1952	...	2052	...	2227	2317	...
Visp 560 570 a.	0528	0603	0638	0703	0738	0803	0838	*0850*	0938	...		*1750*	1838	...	*1850*	...	2003	...	2103	...	2238	2328	...
Visp d.	0530	0608	0641	0708	0741	0808	0841	0908	...	0941		1808	...	1841	1908	...	2008	...	2108	...	2241	2329	...
Stalden-Saas d.	0539	0618	0651	0718	0751	0818	0851	0918	...	0951		1818	...	1851	1918	...	2018	...	2118	...	2249	2338	...
St Niklaus d.	0555	0636	0711	0736	0811	0836	0911	0936	...	1011		1836	...	1911	1936	...	2036	...	2136	...	2308	2355	...
Täsch d.	0620	0700	0736	0800	0836	0900	0936	1000	...	1036		1900	...	1936	2000	...	2100	...	2200	...	2336	0017	...
Zermatt a.	0635	0714	0751	0814	0851	0914	0951	1014	...	1051		1914	...	1951	2014	...	2114	...	2214	...	2348	0028	...

VISP - BRIG - ANDERMATT

km				△				①–⑥	⑦	
	Visp d.	...	0708	and hourly until	1908	2008	2108	2238	2255	...
0	**Brig** Bahnhofplatz d.	0623	0723		1923	2023	2123	2250	2316	...
7	Mörel d.	0633	0733		1933	2033	2133	2300	2325	...
10	Betten d.	0639	0739		1939	2039	2139	2306	2332	...
17	Fiesch d.	0656	0756		1956	2056	2155	2323	2349	...
41	Oberwald 🚗 d.	0742	0842		2042	2139	*2235**	...	...	...
59	Realp 🚗 ⊗ d.	0805	0905		2105	...	...	...	...	...
68	**Andermatt** a.	0820	0920		2120	...	...	...	...	...

										①–⑥	⑦
Andermatt d.	...	...	0737	and hourly until	1637	1737	1837	1925	2025	...	...
Realp 🚗 ⊗ d.	...	...	0750		1650	1750	1850	1936	2036	...	...
Oberwald 🚗 d.	*0613**	0712	0812		1712	1812	1912	1956	2056	*2250**	*2250**
Fiesch d.	0655	0755	0855		1755	1855	1955	2031	2131	2325	2353
Betten d.	0715	0815	0915		1815	1915	2015	2048	2148	2344	0010
Mörel d.	0722	0822	0922		1822	1922	2022	2057	2157	2351	0017
Brig Bahnhofplatz a.	0733	0833	0933		1833	1933	2033	2106	2206	0001	0026
Visp a.	0750	0850	0950		1850	*1950*	*2050*	2138	*2222*	...	...

ANDERMATT - GÖSCHENEN

km																								
	Realp d.	...	0616	...	...	0731	...	0831	...	0931	...	...	and at the same minutes past each hour until	...	...	...	1831	...	...	...	...	...	2131	2231
0	**Andermatt** d.	0550	0629	0650	0729	0750	0829	0850	0929	0950	1029	1050		1729	1750	1829	1850	1929	1950	2029	2050	2129	2150	2250
4	**Göschenen** a.	0605	0644	0705	0744	0806	0844	0906	0944	1006	1044	1106		1744	1806	1844	1906	1944	2006	2044	2106	2144	2206	2306

Göschenen d.	0608	0654	0712	0754	0812	0854	0912	0954	and at the same minutes past each hour until	1612	1654	1712	1754	1812	1854	1912	1954	2012	2054	2112	2154	2212	2312
Andermatt a.	0618	0706	0722	0806	0822	0906	0922	1006		1622	1706	1722	1806	1822	1906	1922	2006	2022	2106	2122	2206	2222	2322
Realp a.	...	0721	...	0821	...	0921	...	...		...	...	...	1821	...	...	...	...	...	2121	...	2221	...	...

ANDERMATT - DISENTIS

km		B				🚌 k	🚌 A	🚌	
0	**Andermatt** 🚗 d.	0621	0728	and hourly until	1928	...	2124	...	...
10	Oberalppass d.	0639	0750		1950	...	2139	...	...
19	Sedrun 🚗 d.	0707	0816		2016	2101	2201	2201	...
29	**Disentis / Mustér** a.	0627	0839		2039	2118	2218	2218	...

	B			✣		🚌	🚌 A	🚌 k		🚌
Disentis / Mustér d.	0620	0708r	0814	and hourly until	1914	2022	2022	2122	...	2222
Sedrun 🚗 d.	0637	0731	0831		1931	2039	2040	2139	...	2239
Oberalppass d.	0657	0753	0853		1953	...	2102	...	...	...
Andermatt 🚗 a.	0722	0822	0922		2022	...	2117	...	...	...

REALP - FURKA - OBERWALD ⊡

km		H		H 🚂		H		D 🚂		
0	**Realp** DFB d.	0915	...	1020	...	...	...	1420	...	...
7	Furka DFB a.	0940	...	1105	...	...	...	1505	...	...
7	Furka DFB d.	0950	...	1130	...	...	...	1530	...	...
13	Gletsch d.	1020	...	1210	...	1320	...	1610	...	...
18	**Oberwald** a.	1045	...	1235	...	1345	...	1635	...	...

	E 🚂		H		H 🚂		H	H			
Oberwald d.	1050	...	1145	...	1350	...	1445	...	...	...	...
Gletsch d.	1120	...	1205	...	1420	...	1505	1615	...	...	...
Furka DFB a.	1155	...	...	...	1455	...	...	1640	...	...	...
Furka DFB d.	1220	...	...	...	1520	...	...	1650	...	...	...
Realp DFB a.	1305	...	...	...	1605	...	...	1720	...	...	...

A – May 1 - Oct. 31.
B – May 14 - Oct. 23.
D – ④–⑥ June 23 - Sept. 24 (also Aug. 14).
E – ⑤–⑦ June 24 - Sept. 25 (also Aug. 15).
H – ④–⑦ June 23 - Sept. 25 (also Aug. 15).

k – To Apr. 30 and from Nov. 1.
r – 0714 May 14 - Oct. 23.
* – By 🚌 from / to Flesch.
⊗ – Realp is a request stop.
🚂 – Steam train. [R]. Special fares.

⊡ – Summer only tourist service. Special fares. Operator: Dampfbahn Furka-Bergstrecke ✆ 0848 000 144. www.dfb.ch
△ – The 0908 and 1808 departures from Visp require a change of trains at Brig.
✣ – The 1514 from Disentis departs Oberalppass 1551 (not 1553).
🚗 – Car-carrying shuttle available. ✆ +41 (0) 848 642 442. www.matterhorngotthardbahn.ch

578 ZERMATT - GORNERGRAT — Narrow gauge rack railway. GGB

Journey 33 minutes uphill, 44 minutes downhill, *9 km. Services are liable to be suspended in bad weather.*

Service until April 24

From Zermatt: 0824, 0848, 0912*, 0936*, 1000*, 1024*, 1048*, 1112, 1136, 1200, 1224, 1248, 1312, 1336, 1400, 1424, 1448, 1512, 1536, 1600, 1624, 1724, 1824 and 1924¶.

From Gornergrat: 0735, 0907, 0931, 0955, 1019, 1043, 1107, 1131, 1155, 1219, 1243, 1307, 1331, 1355, 1419, 1443, 1507, 1531, 1555, 1619, 1638, 1718, 1818, 1918 and 2007¶.

Service April 25 - June 10

From Zermatt: 0700, 0824, 0912, 1000, 1048, 1136, 1224, 1312, 1400, 1448, 1536, 1624 and 1724.

From Gornergrat: 0735, 0907, 0955, 1043, 1131, 1219, 1307, 1355, 1443, 1531, 1619, 1718 and 1818.

¶ – Until Apr. 18.

* – Duplicated non-stop journey available until Apr. 18 (journey time 29 minutes).

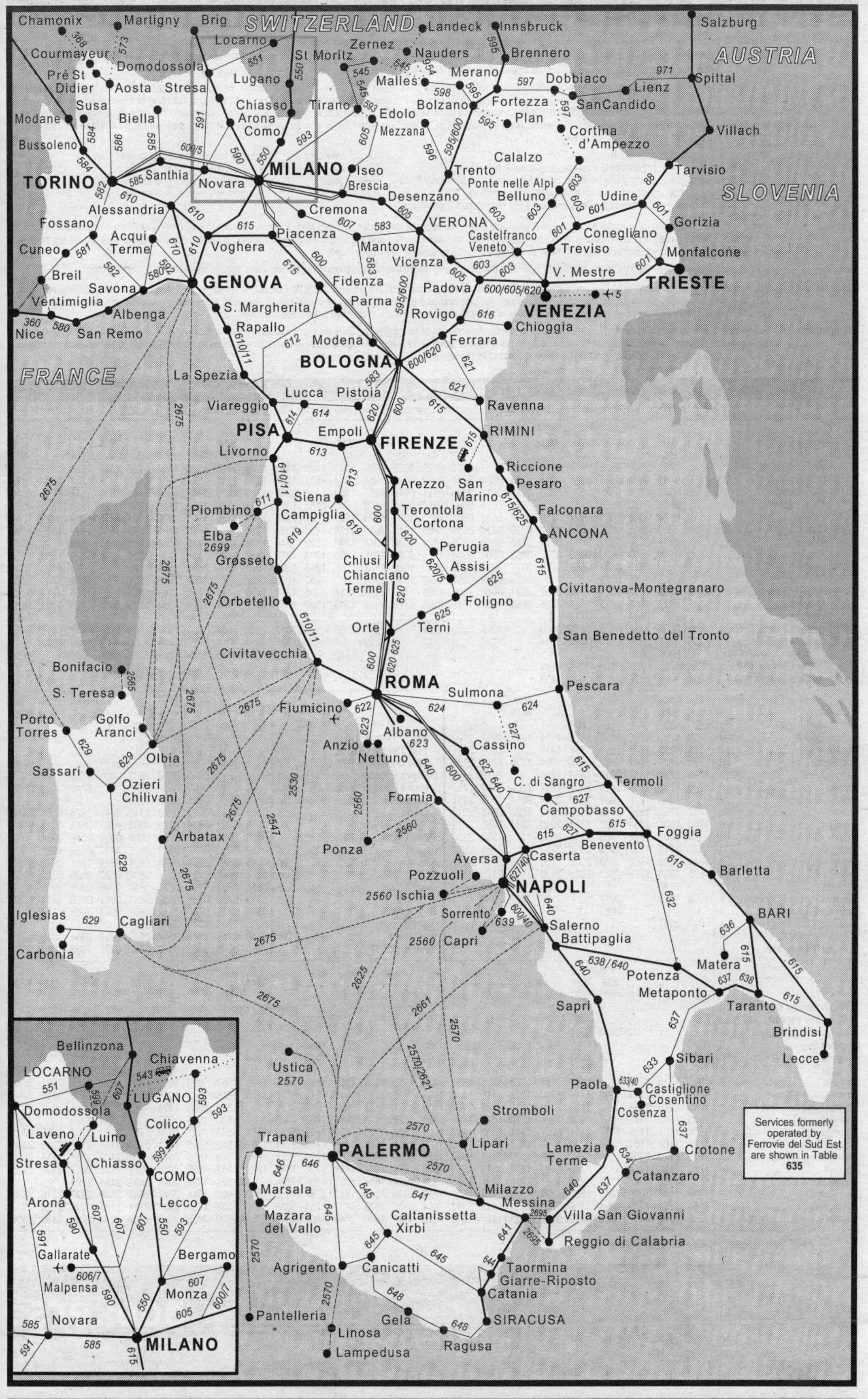

ITALY

Operator: Services are operated by Trenitalia, a division of Ferrovie dello Stato Italiane S.p.a. (FS), unless otherwise noted: www.trenitalia.com.
Trenord is a joint venture between Trenitalia and Ferrovie Nord Milano (LeNord) that operates local services, mainly in the Lombardia region: www.trenord.it.
Nuovo Trasporto Viaggiatori (NTV) is an open-access operator providing alternative services over the high-speed network: www.italotreno.it.

Services: All trains convey First and Second classes of travel unless otherwise shown by a figure "2" at the top of the column, or in a note in the Table heading. Four classes of accommodation is available on Frecciarossa (*FR*) services: Executive, Business, Premium and Standard class. Overnight sleeping car (🛏) or couchette (▬) trains do not necessarily convey seating accommodation or may convey only second class seats - refer to individual footnotes. Excelsior sleeping cars offer en-suite facilities. Descriptions of sleeping and couchette cars appear on page 10. Refreshment services (✕ or 🍷) where known, may only be available for part of the journey, and may be added to or taken away from trains during the currency of the timetable.

Train Categories: There are 9 categories of express train:

EC	**EuroCity**	international express; supplement payable.
FA	**Frecciargento**	tilting trains used on both high-speed and traditional lines.
FB	**Frecciabianca**	fast premium fare services using traditional lines.
FR	**Frecciarossa**	fast premium fare services using high-speed lines.
IC	**InterCity**	internal day express; supplement payable.
ICN	**InterCity Notte**	internal night express.
ITA	**.italo**	high-speed service (operated by NTV).
RJ	**Railjet**	Austrian express; supplement payable.

Timings: Owing to the late availability of summer schedules, we have only been able to check timings for selected long-distance services in Italy (mainly high-speed services operated by Trenitalia). Other long-distance services and all regional timings have not been checked and are valid **until June 11**, although major alterations from June 12 are not expected. However, readers using this edition to plan journeys in Italy are advised to confirm all timings locally.

Tickets: Tickets must be date-stamped by the holder before boarding the train using the self-service validating machines – this applies to all tickets except passes.

Reservations: Reservations are **compulsory** for all journeys by services for which a train category (*EC, FA, FB, FR, IC, ICN, ITA, RJ*) is shown in the timing column and passengers boarding without a prior reservation may be surcharged. Reservations for sleeping and couchette car accommodation on domestic night trains are valid only when presented with personal identification. *ITA* services are 'global' price trains with compulsory reservation - Trenitalia tickets are not valid.

Supplements: Supplements are calculated according to class of travel and total distance travelled (minimum 10km, maximum 3000km), and are payable on all *EC* and *IC* trains, regardless of the number of changes of train. A higher fare (including supplement) is payable for travel by *FA*, *FB* and *FR* trains. Some trains are only available to passengers holding long distance tickets and the restrictions applying to these are noted in the tables.

580 VENTIMIGLIA - GENOVA

Trains without numbers are 2nd class only. Local trains run Savona - Genova and v.v. every 30 mins. Ⓐ/hourly Ⓒ, journey 65–70 minutes.

km		*IC*				*IC*							*IC*				*IC*				*FB*			
		655				**505**							**745**				**655**				**8655**			
		⚒		Ⓐ	Ⓐ				Ⓐ	Ⓒ	Ⓐ					Ⓐ	†			Ⓐ				Ⓐ
0	**Ventimiglia** 🏛 d.	0451	0509	0530	0550	0641	0700	0757	0828	0925	0928	0957	1103	1128	1157	1228	1303	1328	1357	1428	1510	1528	1557	1628
5	Bordighera d.	0458	0516	0537	0558	0648	0709	0804	0837	0933	0937	1004	1111	1137	1204	1237	1311	1337	1404	1437	|	1537	1604	1637
16	San Remo d.	0508	0524	0545	0606	0658	0718	0812	0846	0941	0946	1012	1120	1146	1212	1246	1320	1346	1412	1446	1523	1546	1612	1646
24	Taggia Arma d.	0514	0530	0551	0612	|	0724	0819	0853	0947	0953	1019	|	1152	1219	1253	1326	1353	1419	1453	|	1553	1619	1653
39	Imperia d.	0524	0540	0601	0622	0710	0734	0829	0904	0957	1004	1029	1132	1202	1229	1304	1336	1404	1429	1504	1535	1604	1629	1704
46	Diano d.	|	0545	0606	0627	0717	0739	0835	0910	1003	1010	1035	1138	1208	1235	1310	|	1410	1435	1510	1541	1610	1635	1710
61	Alassio d.	0537	0556	0622	0644	0730	0755	0848	0926	1021	1026	1048	1152	1225	1248	1326	1352	1426	1448	1526	1552	1626	1648	1726
67	Albenga d.	0545	0603	0630	0650	0737	0803	0855	0934	1027	1034	1055	1200	1234	1255	1334	1400	1434	1455	1534	1600	1634	1655	1734
76	Loano d.	|	0612	0651	0659	|	0817	0903	0948	1040	1048	1103	|	1248	1303	1348	|	1448	1503	1548	|	1648	1703	1748
79	Pietra Ligure d.	|	0616	0655	|	|	0823	0908	0957	1050	1057	1108	|	1257	1308	1357	|	1457	1508	1557	|	1657	1708	1800
85	Finale Ligure Marina d.	0600	0623	0701	0708	0752	0831	0914	1005	1059	1105	1114	1214	1305	1314	1405	1414	1505	1514	1605	1617	1705	1714	1805
108	**Savona** d.	0617	0645	0719	0724	0805	0852	0933	1025	1125	1125	1133	1233	1325	1333	1425	1432	1525	1533	1625	1633	1725	1733	1825
120	Varazze d.	|	0654	|	0732	|	...	|	...	...	...	|		...	|	...		...	|	...	|	...	|	...
151	**Genova** Piazza Principe § a.	0655	0738	0805	0812	0850	...	1021	...	...	...	1217	1305	...	1417	...	1504	...	1617	...	1705	...	1817	...
154	**Genova** Brignole a.	|	|	0813	0820	0859	...	1029	...	...	...	1225	|	...	1425	...	|	...	1625	...	|	...	1825	...
	Milano Centrale **610** a.	0900	0935	...	...	|	...	...	...	...	...	...	1455	...	...	...	1653	...	...	...	1855	...	...	...
	Pisa Centrale **610** a.	...	...	...	...	1101	...	...	...	...	...	...	...	...	...	...	...	...	...	...	...	...	...	...
	Roma Termini **610** a.	...	...	...	...	1433	...	...	...	...	...	...	...	...	...	...	...	...	...	...	...	...	...	...

	IC	*IC*					*FB*		
	681	**681**					**8659**		
	Ⓐ	Ⓒ			Ⓐ				
Ventimiglia 🏛 d.	1703	1703	1728	1757	1828	1924	1943	1957	2120
Bordighera d.	1711	1711	1737	1804	1837	1932	|	2004	2128
San Remo d.	1720	1720	1746	1812	1846	1941	1956	2012	2136
Taggia Arma d.	1726	1726	1753	1819	1853	1946	|	2019	2142
Imperia d.	1736	1736	1804	1829	1904	1957	2008	2029	2152
Diano d.	|	|	1810	1835	1910	2003	2014	2035	2157
Alassio d.	1752	1752	1826	1848	1926	2019	2027	2048	2212
Albenga d.	1800	1800	1834	1855	1934	2040	2034	2055	2219
Loano d.	|	1808	1848	1903	1948	2055	|	2103	2230
Pietra Ligure d.	|	1813	1857	1908	1957	2059	|	2108	2234
Finale Ligure Marina d.	1814	1820	1905	1914	2005	2106	2047	2114	2242
Savona d.	1833	1835	1925	1933	2025	2126	2106	2133	2305
Varazze d.	|	1843	...	|	...	...	|	2146	...
Genova Piazza Principe § a.	1908	1908	...	2017	...	...	2142	2224	...
Genova Brignole a.	|	|	...	2025	...	...	|	2232	...
Milano Centrale **610** a.	2057	2057	...	...	...	...	2340	...	...
Pisa Centrale **610** a.	...	...	...	...	...	...	...	...	...
Roma Termini **610** a.	...	...	...	...	...	...	...	...	...

									FB
									8639
	Ⓐ	Ⓐ			⚒	†	Ⓐ		
Roma Termini **610** d.	...	...	...	...	...	...	...	...	...
Pisa Centrale **610** d.	...	...	...	...	...	...	...	...	...
Milano Centrale **610** d.	...	...	...	...	...	...	...	...	0710
Genova Brignole d.	...	...	0515	0600	0638	...	0737	...	|
Genova Piazza Principe § d.	...	...	0522	0607	0646	...	0745	...	0858
Varazze d.	...	...	0605	0653	0729	...	|	...	|
Savona d.	0503	0545	0621	0710	0745	0745	0828	0855	0931
Finale Ligure Marina d.	0519	0601	0636	0729	0801	0801	0843	0915	0943
Pietra Ligure d.	0526	0607	0642	0737	0807	0807	0849	0924	|
Loano d.	0530	0612	0647	0742	0812	0812	0853	0928	|
Albenga d.	0546	0631	0704	0804	0824	0824	0901	0940	0957
Alassio d.	0557	0645	0711	0811	0832	0832	0908	0951	1007
Diano d.	0610	0701	0725	0825	0846	0846	0920	1009	1021
Imperia d.	0615	0705	0732	0832	0851	0851	0928	1014	1028
Taggia Arma d.	0625	0717	0742	0842	0901	0901	0938	1024	|
San Remo d.	0631	0723	0748	0848	0906	0906	0945	1030	1042
Bordighera d.	0640	0733	0756	0857	0915	0915	0954	1039	|
Ventimiglia 🏛 a.	0650	0745	0803	0903	0922	0922	1003	1047	1054

				IC	*IC*											*FB*				*IC*			*IC*	*IC*
				659	**659**											**8643**				**675**			**518**	**689**
	Ⓐ	Ⓒ		Ⓐ	Ⓒ	Ⓐ			Ⓐ		Ⓐ	Ⓒ	Ⓐ				Ⓐ							
Roma Termini **610** d.	...	...	...	...	...	...	...	...	...	...	...	...	...	...	...	...	...	...	...	...	...	...	1557	...
Pisa Centrale **610** d.	...	...	...	...	...	...	...	...	...	...	...	...	...	...	...	...	...	...	...	...	...	...	1903	...
Milano Centrale **610** d.	...	...	...	0910	0910	...	...	...	...	...	...	...	...	...	...	1510	...	...	...	1705	...	...	|	2005
Genova Brignole d.	0935	...	...	|	|	...	1135	...	...	1335	...	...	...	1535	...	|	...	1735	...	|	1935	...	2129	|
Genova Piazza Principe § d.	0943	...	...	1058	1058	...	1143	...	...	1343	...	...	...	1543	...	1658	...	1743	...	1858	1943	...	2137	2158
Varazze d.	|	...	...	|	1123	...	|	...	...	|	...	...	...	|	...	|	...	|	...	|	|	...	|	|
Savona d.	1028	1028	1055	1131	1131	1157	1228	1255	1357	1428	1455	1455	1557	1628	1655	1731	1757	1828	1855	1931	2028	2055	2207	2232
Finale Ligure Marina d.	1043	1043	1115	1143	1144	1218	1243	1315	1418	1443	1515	1515	1618	1643	1715	1743	1818	1843	1915	1943	2046	2115	2219	2245
Pietra Ligure d.	1049	1049	1124	|	1153	1224	1249	1324	1424	1449	1524	1524	1624	1649	1724	|	1824	1849	1924	|	2051	2124	|	|
Loano d.	1053	1053	1128	|	1159	1228	1253	1328	1428	1453	1528	1528	1628	1653	1728	|	1828	1853	1928	|	2054	2128	|	|
Albenga d.	1101	1101	1139	1157	1211	1237	1301	1339	1437	1501	1539	1539	1637	1701	1739	1757	1837	1901	1939	1957	2102	2139	2235	2301
Alassio d.	1108	1108	1151	1208	1226	1249	1308	1349	1449	1508	1551	1551	1649	1708	1751	1807	1849	1908	1951	2004	2108	2151	2243	2308
Diano d.	1120	1120	1209	|	|	1306	1320	1406	1506	1520	1609	1609	1706	1720	1809	1821	1906	1920	2007	|	2120	2207	2255	2319
Imperia d.	1128	1128	1214	1223	1240	1311	1328	1411	1511	1528	1614	1614	1711	1728	1814	1828	1911	1928	2012	2024	2128	2212	2302	2326
Taggia Arma d.	1138	1138	1224	1234	1250	1321	1338	1421	1521	1538	1624	1624	1721	1738	1824	|	1921	1938	2021	2034	2138	2221	|	|
San Remo d.	1145	1145	1230	1241	1257	1327	1345	1428	1527	1545	1630	1630	1727	1745	1830	1842	1927	1945	2027	2041	2145	2227	2315	2339
Bordighera d.	1154	1154	1239	1251	1306	1337	1354	1437	1537	1554	1639	1639	1737	1754	1839	|	1937	1954	2037	2051	2154	2237	2324	2349
Ventimiglia 🏛 a.	1203	1203	1247	1258	1312	1349	1403	1447	1549	1603	1647	1650	1749	1803	1847	1854	1949	2003	2047	2058	2203	2250	2330	2356

§ – Local services may use the underground platforms.

VENTIMIGLIA and NICE - CUNEO — 581

2nd class

Subject to alteration on French and Italian public holidays.

km																								
		①–⑤														①–⑤					①–⑤	①–⑤ 🚌		
	Ventimiglia d.	...	...	...	...	...	...	...	...	1044	...	...	...	...	...	...	...	...	...	1837	...	...	...	...
0	**Nice** Ville d.	0543	...	0730	0756	...	...	0830	...	|	1209	...	...	...	1456	1646	...	1720	...	|	1810	...	1912	1943
34	Sospel d.	0657	...	0826	0852	...	...	0931	...	|	1307	...	...	...	1552	1745	...	1818	...	|	1920	...	2020	2038
43	Breil sur Roya a.	0709	...	0838	0904	...	...	0943	...	1120	1319	...	...	...	1604	1757	...	1830	...	1916	1932	...	2032	2050
43	Breil sur Roya d.	...	...	...	...	...	...	0959	...	1121	1321	...	...	...	1608	...	...	...	...	1918	...	1935	...	...
71	Tende d.	...	0800	...	...	0940	...	1105	1120	1220	1425	1510	...	1650	1718	...	1830	...	...	2017	...	2034	...	...
89	Limone 582 d.	...	0830	...	...	1010	...	...	1150	1247	...	1546	...	1720	...	...	1900	...	...	2046	...	...	...	...
118	**Cuneo** 582 a.	...	...	...	...	...	...	...	...	1319	...	...	...	...	...	...	...	...	...	2119	...	...	...	...

km																								
		①–⑥	①–⑤	①–⑥	Ⓑ													🚌 ①–⑤				⑥⑦ 🚌	①–⑤ 🚌	
0	**Cuneo** 582 d.	...	...	...	...	...	0641	...	...	...	...	...	...	...	...	1441	...	...	...	...	...	...	...	...
29	Limone 582 d.	...	...	...	...	0700	0721	...	0850	...	1038	...	...	...	1420	1517	1600	...	...	...	1740	...	...	...
47	Tende d.	...	...	...	...	0730	0750	...	0920	...	1108	1143	...	1437	1450	1544	1630	1630	...	1728	1810	1815	1845	...
76	Breil sur Roya a.	...	...	...	...	...	0848	...	...	...	...	1249	...	1537	...	1643	...	1730	...	1827	...	1922	1926	...
76	Breil sur Roya d.	0541	0610	0645	0725	...	0849	0918	...	1100	...	1254	...	1539	...	1645	...	...	1732	1832	...	...	...	1936
	Sospel d.	0553	0622	0657	0737	...	|	0931	...	1112	...	1307	...	1552	...	|	...	...	1745	1846	...	...	...	1948
	Nice Ville a.	0648	0715	0803	0832	...	|	1033	...	1206	...	1405	...	1650	...	|	...	...	1844	1947	...	...	...	2046
96	**Ventimiglia** a.	...	...	...	...	...	0925	...	...	...	...	...	...	...	...	1723	...	...	...	...	...	...	...	...

TORINO - CUNEO, LIMONE and SAVONA — 582

2nd class

km																								
				⚒			⚒				⚒		Ⓑ		⚒			Ⓐ	†					
0	**Torino** Porta Nuova d.	...	0525	...	0625	...	0641	0722	...	...	...	0825	...	0925	...	1025	...	...	...	1125	...	1225	...	1325
52	Savigliano d.	...	0603	...	0703	...	0734	0803	...	...	...	0903	...	1003	...	1103	...	...	...	1203	...	1303	...	1403
64	Fossano d.	...	0612	0622	0713	0725	0745	0812	...	...	0822	0913	0925	1012	1022	1113	...	...	1125	1212	1222	1313	1325	1412
90	Cuneo 581 d.	0550	0636	|	|	0750	...	0836	...	0841	|	|	0950	1036	|	|	...	1150	1150	1236	|	|	1350	1436
119	**Limone** 581 a.	0628	...	|	|	0826	...	...	...	0919	|	|	1028	...	|	|	...	1228	1228	...	1240	|	1428	...
83	Mondovi d.	...	...	0640	0728	...	...	...	...	...	0840	0928	...	...	1040	1128	...	...	...	...	1300	1328	...	...
103	Ceva d.	...	...	0700	0742	...	...	...	...	...	0900	0942	...	...	1100	1142	...	...	...	...	1329	1342	...	...
132	S.Giuseppe di Cairo d.	...	...	0730	0813	...	...	...	...	...	0929	1013	...	...	1129	1213	...	...	...	...	...	1413	...	...
153	**Savona** a.	...	...	0752	0836	...	...	...	...	...	...	1036	...	...	...	1236	...	...	...	...	...	1436	...	...

	⚒							Ⓐ		Ⓐ			Ⓐ	Ⓐ		⚒				⚒		⚒	
Torino Porta Nuova d.	...	1425	...	1525	...	...	1625	...	1725	...	...	...	1750	...	1825	...	1855	...	1925	1955	2025	...	2125
Savigliano d.	...	1503	...	1603	...	...	1703	...	1803	...	...	...	1829	...	1903	...	1931	...	2003	2032	2103	...	2203
Fossano d.	1422	1513	1525	1612	1622	...	1713	1725	1812	...	1822	...	1837	1845	1913	1925	1941	...	2012	2041	2113	2125	2212
Cuneo 581 d.	|	|	1550	1636	|	...	|	1750	1836	1841	|	...	1901	|	|	1950	|	...	2036	|	|	2150	2236
Limone 581 a.	|	|	1628	...	|	...	|	1828	...	1919	|	...	...	|	|	2028	|	...	...	|	|	...	...
Mondovi d.	1440	1528	...	...	1640	...	1728	...	...	...	1840	...	...	1858	1928	...	1956	...	...	2100	2128	...	...
Ceva d.	1500	1542	...	...	1700	...	1742	...	...	...	1900	...	...	1912	1942	...	2018	...	...	2120	2142	...	...
S.Giuseppe di Cairo d.	1529	1613	...	...	1729	...	1813	...	...	...	1929	...	...	...	2013	...	2049	...	...	...	2213	...	...
Savona a.	...	1636	...	...	...	...	1836	...	...	...	...	...	...	...	2036	...	2112	...	...	...	2236	...	...

				⚒	⚒	⚒	⚒		⚒	Ⓐ	†			⚒	†	⚒				Ⓐ		Ⓑ	
Savona d.	...	...	0531	...	...	...	...	...	...	...	...	...	0731	0808	...	...	...	...	0931	...	...	...	1131
S.Giuseppe di Cairo d.	...	...	0553	...	...	0631	...	...	...	...	...	...	0753	0831	0831	...	...	...	0953	1031	...	...	1153
Ceva d.	...	...	0617	...	0650	0700	...	...	...	0738	...	...	0817	0900	0900	...	...	...	1017	1100	...	...	1217
Mondovi d.	...	...	0632	...	0706	0720	...	...	...	0752	...	...	0832	0920	0920	...	...	...	1032	1120	...	...	1232
Limone 581 d.	...	...	|	...	|	|	0640	...	...	|	0732	...	|	|	|	0840	...	0932	|	|	...	1132	|
Cuneo 581 d.	0524	0612	|	0654	|	|	0719	0724	0751	|	0812	...	|	|	|	0919	0924	1012	|	|	1124	1212	|
Fossano d.	0544	0635	0644	0714	0722	0738	...	0744	0814	0805	0835	...	0844	0938	0938	...	0944	1035	1044	1138	1144	1235	1244
Savigliano d.	0552	...	0652	0722	0731	...	...	0752	0822	...	...	...	0852	...	...	...	0952	...	1052	...	1152	...	1252
Torino Porta Nuova a.	0635	...	0735	0805	0815	...	...	0835	0905	...	...	...	0935	...	...	...	1035	...	1135	...	1235	...	1335

	⚒		Ⓑ						⚒					⚒	†	Ⓐ		Ⓐ				⚒	
Savona d.	...	...	...	1330	...	...	...	1531	...	...	...	...	1731	1800	...	...	...	...	1931	...	...	...	2131
S.Giuseppe di Cairo d.	1231	...	...	1353	1431	...	...	1553	1631	...	...	...	1753	1831	1831	...	...	...	1953	2031	...	...	2153
Ceva d.	1300	...	...	1417	1500	...	...	1617	1700	...	...	...	1817	1900	1900	...	...	...	2017	2100	...	...	2217
Mondovi d.	1320	...	...	1432	1520	...	...	1632	1720	...	...	...	1832	1920	1920	...	...	...	2032	2120	...	...	2232
Limone 581 d.	|	...	1332	|	|	...	1532	|	|	...	1732	...	|	|	|	1840	...	1932	|	|	...	2132	|
Cuneo 581 d.	|	1324	1412	|	|	1524	1612	|	|	1724	1812	...	|	|	|	1919	1924	2012	|	|	2124	2212	|
Fossano d.	1338	1344	1435	1444	1538	1544	1635	1644	1738	1744	1835	...	1844	1938	1938	...	1944	2035	2044	2138	2144	2235	2244
Savigliano d.	...	1352	...	1452	...	1552	...	1652	...	1752	...	...	1852	...	...	...	1952	...	2052	...	2152	...	2252
Torino Porta Nuova a.	...	1435	...	1535	...	1635	...	1735	...	1835	...	...	1935	...	...	...	2035	...	2135	...	2235	...	2340

MANTOVA and PORRETTA TERME — 583

2nd class

BOLOGNA - PORRETTA TERME
59 km Journey 60–72 minutes

From **Bologna** Centrale: 0544⚒, 0627⚒, 0702, 0804⚒, 0904, 1004⚒, 1104, 1204, 1304, 1404, 1504, 1604, 1704, 1735, 1804, 1835Ⓐ, 1904, 1936Ⓐ, 2004, 2104, 2204.

From **Porretta Terme**: 0500⚒, 0542, 0608, 0640, 0718, 0750⚒, 0822, 0922⚒, 1022, 1122⚒, 1222, 1322, 1422, 1522, 1622, 1720, 1821, 1921, 2021, 2050Ⓐ, 2122Ⓐ.

MANTOVA - MODENA
61 km Journey 60–90 minutes

From **Mantova**: 0535⚒, 0629, 0732⚒, 0829, 0929, 1129, 1229⚒, 1329, 1429⚒, 1529, 1629⚒, 1729, 1829⚒, 1929, 2029⚒, 2129.

From **Modena**: 0547⚒, 0630⚒, 0707, 0807⚒, 0907, 1107†, 1207⚒, 1307, 1407⚒, 1507, 1607⚒, 1707, 1807⚒, 1907, 2007, 2107⚒, 2207.

PORRETTA TERME - PISTOIA
40 km Journey 60–75 minutes

From **Porretta Terme**: 0655⚒, 0715, 0926⚒, 1322, 1524, 1824.

From **Pistoia**: 0600, 0823⚒, 1220, 1420, 1721, 1926.

VERONA - MANTOVA
37 km Journey 45–50 minutes

From **Verona** Porta Nuova: 0631⚒, 0731⚒, 0831⚒, 0931, 1231⚒, 1331, 1431⚒, 1531, 1631⚒, 1731, 1831⚒, 1931, 2031⚒, 2131†.

From **Mantova**: 0629⚒, 0729⚒, 0829, 0929⚒, 1229, 1329⚒, 1429, 1529⚒, 1629, 1729⚒, 1829, 1929⚒, 2029.

584 TORINO - SUSA and BARDONECCHIA

2nd class

For Italy - France *Frecciarossa* and *TGV* services via Oulx and Modane see Table **44**. For domestic high-speed trains see Table **600**.

km		⚒	⚒	†	⚒	⚒		⚒	†	⚒	⚒		⚒	†	⚒	⚒		⚒	†	⚒	⚒		⚒	†
0	**Torino** Porta Nuova d.	0445	0515	0545	0545	0615	0645	0715	0745	0745	0815	0845	0915	0945	0945	1015	1045	1115	1145	1145	1215	1245	1315	1345
46	Bussoleno d.	0543	0559	0632	0643	0659	0743	0759	0832	0843	0859	0943	0959	1032	1043	1059	1143	1159	1232	1243	1259	1343	1359	1432
54	**Susa** a.	0553	|	|	0653	|	0753	|	|	0853	|	0953	|	|	1053	|	1153	|	|	1253	|	1353	|	|
76	Oulx-Claviere ▲ d.	...	0628	0701	...	0728	...	0828	0901	...	0928	...	1028	1101	...	1128	...	1228	1301	...	1328	...	1428	1501
87	**Bardonecchia** ♣ a.	...	0641	0714	...	0741	...	0841	0914	...	0941	...	1041	1114	...	1141	...	1241	1314	...	1341	...	1441	1514
107	**Modane** 🏨 ♣ a.	...	...	...	...	...	...	...	...	...	...	...	...	...	...	...	...	...	...	...	...	...	...	...

	⚒	⚒		⚒	†	⚒	⚒		⚒	†	⚒	⚒		⚒	†	⚒	⚒		⚒	†	⚒	⚒	
Torino Porta Nuova d.	1345	1415	1445	1515	1545	1545	1615	1645	1715	1745	1745	1815	1845	1915	1945	1945	2015	2045	2115	2145	2145	2215	2245
Bussoleno d.	1443	1459	1543	1559	1632	1643	1659	1743	1759	1832	1843	1859	1943	1959	2032	2043	2059	2143	2159	2232	2243	2259	2342
Susa a.	1453	|	1553	|	|	1653	|	1753	|	|	1853	|	1953	|	|	2053	|	2153	|	|	2253	|	...
Oulx-Claviere-Sestriere ▲ d.	...	1528	...	1628	1701	...	1732	...	1828	1901	...	1928	...	2028	2101	...	2128	...	2228	2301	...	2328	...
Bardonecchia ♣ a.	...	1541	...	1641	1714	...	1745	...	1841	1914	...	1941	...	2041	2114	...	2141	...	2241	2314	...	2341	...
Modane 🏨 ♣ a.	...	...	...	...	...	...	...	...	...	...	...	...	...	...	...	...	...	...	...	...	...	...	...

	†	⚒	†	⚒	⚒	⚒	⚒	†	⚒		⚒	⚒	†	⚒		⚒	⚒	†	⚒		⚒	⚒	†
Modane 🏨 ♣ d.	...	...	...	...	...	...	...	...	...	...	...	...	...	...	...	...	...	...	...	...	...	...	...
Bardonecchia ♣ d.	...	...	0509	0521	...	0621	...	0648	0721	...	0821	...	0848	0921	...	1021	...	1048	1121	...	1215	...	1248
Oulx-Claviere-Sestriere ▲ d.	...	...	0522	0534	...	0634	...	0701	0734	...	0834	...	0901	0934	...	1034	...	1101	1134	...	1227	...	1301
Susa d.	0439	0509	|	|	0609	|	0709	|	|	0809	|	0909	|	|	1009	|	1109	|	|	1209	|	1309	|
Bussoleno d.	0449	0519	0549	0601	0619	0701	0719	0728	0801	0819	0901	0919	0928	1001	1019	1101	1119	1128	1201	1219	1301	1319	1328
Torino Porta Nuova a.	0545	0615	0645	0645	0715	0745	0815	0815	0845	0915	0945	1015	1015	1045	1115	1145	1215	1215	1245	1315	1345	1415	1415

	⚒		⚒	⚒	†	⚒		⚒	⚒	†	⚒		⚒	⚒	†	⚒		⚒	⚒	†	⚒		⚒
Modane 🏨 ♣ d.	...	...	...	...	...	...	...	...	...	...	...	...	...	...	...	...	...	...	...	...	...	...	...
Bardonecchia ♣ d.	1321	...	1421	...	1448	1521	...	1621	...	1648	1721	...	1821	...	1848	1921	...	2015	...	2048	2121	...	2221
Oulx-Claviere-Sestriere ▲ d.	1334	...	1434	...	1501	1534	...	1634	...	1701	1734	...	1834	...	1901	1934	...	2027	...	2101	2134	...	2234
Susa d.	|	1409	|	1509	|	|	1609	|	1709	|	|	1809	|	1909	|	|	2009	|	2109	|	|	2209	|
Bussoleno d.	1401	1419	1501	1519	1528	1601	1619	1701	1719	1728	1801	1819	1901	1919	1928	2001	2019	2101	2119	2128	2201	2219	2301
Torino Porta Nuova a.	1445	1515	1545	1615	1615	1645	1715	1745	1815	1815	1845	1915	1945	2015	2015	2045	2115	2145	2215	2215	2245	2317	2345

▲ – Station for Cesana, Claviere and Sestriere.

♣ – A cross-border 🚌 service is available Bardonecchia - Modane and v.v. Journey time 30 minutes. www.gherra.it
From **Bardonecchia** at 0800 Ⓐ, 1200 Ⓐ, 1500 Ⓐ, 1900 Ⓐ. From **Modane** at 0730 Ⓐ, 0930 Ⓐ, 1330 Ⓐ, 1630 Ⓐ.

585 TORINO - MILANO

For Italy - France *Frecciarossa* and *TGV* services via Oulx and Modane see Table **44**. For domestic high-speed trains see Table **600**.

km											*ICN* **795** ✣A									*IC* **509**		*ICN* **797** ✣B		
0	**Torino** Porta Nuova **586** d.	0454	0554	0654	0754	0854	...	1054	1154	1254	1335	1354	...	1454	1554	1654	1754	1854	...	1905	1954	2030	2054	...
6	**Torino** Porta Susa **586** d.	0505	0605	0705	0805	0905	...	1105	1205	1305	1345u	1405	...	1505	1605	1705	1805	1905	...	1916u	2005	2040u	2105	...
29	Chivasso **586** d.	0520	0620	0720	0820	0920	...	1120	1220	1320	|	1420	...	1520	1620	1720	1820	1920	...	|	2020	|	2120	...
60	Santhià d.	0538	0638	0738	0838	0938	...	1138	1238	1338	|	1438	...	1538	1638	1738	1838	1938	...	|	2038	|	2138	...
79	Vercelli d.	0549	0649	0749	0849	0949	...	1149	1249	1349	1424	1449	...	1549	1649	1749	1849	1949	...	2001	2049	2120	2149	...
101	Novara d.	0605	0705	0805	0905	1005	...	1205	1305	1405	1443	1505	...	1605	1705	1805	1905	2005	...	2015	2105	2137	2205	...
140	Rho Fiera Milano d.	0633	0733	0833	0933	1033	...	1233	1333	1433	|	1533	...	1633	1733	1833	1933	2033	...	|	2133	|	2233	...
153	**Milano** Centrale a.	0645	0745	0845	0945	1045	...	1245	1345	1445	1532g	1545	...	1645	1745	1845	1945	2045	...	2055	2145	2210g	2245	...

		IC **508**		*ICN* **798** ✣B									*ICN* **794** ✣A										
Milano Centrale d.	0615	0620	0715	0658g	0815	...	0915	1115	1215	1315	1415	...	1428g	1515	1615	1715	1815	...	1915	2015	2115	2215	...
Rho Fiera Milano d.	0625	|	0725	|	0825	...	0925	1125	1225	1325	1425	...	|	1525	1625	1725	1825	...	1925	2025	2125	2225	...
Novara d.	0656	0702	0756	0802	0856	...	0956	1156	1256	1356	1456	...	1518	1556	1656	1756	1856	...	1956	2056	2156	2256	...
Vercelli d.	0709	0716	0809	0816	0909	...	1009	1209	1309	1409	1509	...	1533	1609	1709	1809	1909	...	2009	2109	2209	2309	...
Santhià d.	0721	|	0821	|	0921	...	1021	1221	1321	1421	1521	...	|	1621	1721	1821	1921	...	2021	2121	2221	2321	...
Chivasso **586** d.	0742	|	0842	|	0942	...	1042	1242	1342	1442	1542	...	|	1642	1742	1842	1942	...	2042	2142	2242	2342	...
Torino Porta Susa **586** a.	0754	0805s	0854	0905s	0954	...	1056	1254	1354	1454	1554	...	1613s	1654	1754	1854	1954	...	2054	2154	2254	2354	...
Torino Porta Nuova **586** a.	0806	0820	0906	0920	1006	...	1108	1306	1406	1506	1606	...	1625	1706	1806	1906	2006	...	2106	2206	2306	0006	...

km	2nd class	⚒	⚒	⚒	Ⓐ	†		⚒	Ⓐ	Ⓐ	Ⓐ	⚒		†	Ⓐ	⚒	†	⚒		Ⓐ	⚒	†	⚒	Ⓐ
0	**Santhià** d.	0650	0750	0850	0950	0950	...	1150	1250	1350	1450	1550	...	1550	1650	1750	1750	1850	...	1915	1950	1950	2050	2150
27	**Biella S. Paola** a.	0718	0818	0918	1018	1015	...	1218	1318	1418	1518	1618	...	1615	1718	1818	1815	1918	...	1935	2018	2015	2118	2218

2nd class	⚒	⚒	†	Ⓐ	⚒		Ⓐ	Ⓐ	Ⓐ	†	⚒		Ⓐ	†	⚒	⚒	†		⚒	⚒		⚒	Ⓐ
Biella S. Paola d.	0651	0751	0848	0851	0951	...	1151	1251	1351	1448	1451	...	1551	1648	1651	1751	1848	...	1851	1951	...	2051	2151
Santhià a.	0713	0813	0912	0913	1013	...	1213	1313	1413	1512	1513	...	1613	1712	1713	1813	1912	...	1913	2013	...	2113	2213

A – 🛏 1, 2 cl., 🛌 2 cl. (4 berth) Torino - Reggio di Calabria and v.v.
B – 🛏 1, 2 cl., 🛌 2 cl. (4 berth) Torino - Salerno and v.v.

g – Milano **Porta Garibaldi**.

s – Stops to set down only.
u – Stops to pick up only.

✣ – Running days, timings and numbers of *ICN* trains may vary - please check your reservation. For confirmed timings please consult the *Trenitalia* journey planner at www.trenitalia.com

586 TORINO - AOSTA

2nd class

km		⚒	†	⚒	†	⚒	†	⚒	†	⚒	†	⚒	†	†	⚒	⚒	†	⚒	†	⚒	†	⚒	†	⚒	†
0	**Torino** Porta Nuova **585** d.	0525	0525	0725	0725	0825	0825	0925	0925	1125	1125	1325	1325	1425	1425	1625	1625	1725	1725	1825	1825	2025	2025	2225	2225
6	**Torino** Porta Susa **585** d.	0534	0534	0734	0734	0834	0834	0934	0934	1134	1134	1334	1334	1434	1434	1634	1634	1734	1734	1834	1834	2034	2034	2234	2234
29	Chivasso **585** d.	0552	0552	0752	0752	0852	0852	0952	0952	1152	1152	1352	1352	1452	1452	1652	1652	1752	1752	1852	1852	2052	2052	2252	2352
62	Ivrea a.	0613	0613	0822	0822	0922	0922	1022	1022	1222	1222	1422	1422	1517	1522	1722	1722	1822	1817	1922	1922	2122	2122	2322	2322
62	Ivrea d.	0614	0614	0823	0823	0923	0923	1023	1023	1223	1223	1423	1423	1518	1523	1723	1723	1823	1818	1923	1923	2123	2123	2323	2323
79	Pont Saint Martin d.	0634	0637	0837	0842	0937	0937	1037	1037	1237	1237	1437	1437	1537	1537	1737	1737	1837	1837	1937	1942	2137	2142	2337	2337
91	Verrès d.	0646	0650	0848	0855	0948	0950	1048	1050	1248	1250	1448	1450	1550	1548	1748	1750	1848	1850	1948	1955	2148	2155	2348	2350
104	Chatillon-Saint Vincent d.	0700	0702	0900	0913	1000	1002	1100	1102	1300	1302	1500	1502	1602	1600	1800	1802	1900	1902	2000	2013	2200	2207	0000	0002
129	**Aosta** a.	0720	0722	0920	0934	1020	1022	1120	1122	1320	1322	1520	1522	1622	1620	1820	1822	1920	1922	2020	2034	2220	2227	0020	0022

	†	⚒	⚒	†	†	⚒	†	⚒	⚒	†	⚒	†	⚒	†	⚒	†	⚒	†	⚒	†	†	⚒	⚒	†
Aosta d.	0537	0540	0640	0641	0737	0740	0837	0840	1040	1041	1240	1241	1440	1441	1540	1541	1740	1741	1840	1841	1937	1940	2040	2044
Chatillon-Saint Vincent d.	0558	0600	0700	0702	0758	0800	0858	0900	1100	1102	1300	1302	1500	1502	1600	1602	1800	1802	1900	1902	1958	2000	2100	2106
Verrès d.	0611	0612	0718	0714	0811	0812	0911	0912	1112	1114	1312	1314	1512	1514	1612	1614	1812	1814	1912	1914	2011	2012	2112	2118
Pont Saint Martin d.	0623	0622	0728	0726	0823	0822	0923	0922	1122	1126	1322	1326	1522	1526	1622	1626	1822	1826	1922	1926	2023	2026	2122	2130
Ivrea a.	0640	0640	0740	0740	0840	0840	0940	0940	1140	1140	1340	1340	1540	1540	1640	1640	1840	1840	1940	1940	2040	2040	2140	2140
Ivrea d.	0641	0641	0741	0741	0841	0841	0941	0941	1141	1141	1341	1341	1541	1541	1641	1641	1841	1841	1941	1941	2041	2041	2141	2141
Chivasso **585** a.	0706	0706	0806	0806	0906	0906	1006	1006	1206	1206	1406	1406	1606	1606	1706	1706	1906	1906	2006	2006	2106	2106	2206	2206
Torino Porta Susa **585** a.	0725	0725	0830	0825	0925	0925	1025	1025	1225	1225	1425	1425	1625	1625	1725	1725	1925	1925	2025	2025	2125	2125	2225	2225
Torino Porta Nuova **585** a.	0735	0735	0840	0835	0935	0935	1035	1035	1235	1235	1435	1435	1635	1635	1735	1735	1935	1935	2035	2035	2135	2135	2235	2235

BRIG - STRESA - MILANO 590

EC services convey ✕ and are 🅁 (inclusive of supplement). Services between Brig and Milano are subject to alteration Aug. 28 - Sept. 20.

km		*EC* 35	*EC* 51	*EC* 37	*EC* 47	*EC* 53	*EC* 57	*EC* 39	*EC* 59	*EC* 41	
				①–⑤	⑥⑦						
				V	V						
	Genève **570** d.	0539	...	0739	0739	...	...	1339	...	1839	...
	Lausanne **570** d.	0618	...	0818	0818	...	...	1418	...	1918	...
	Basel **560** d.	|	0628	|	|	1028	1228	|	1728	|	...
	Bern **560** d.	|	0734	|	|	1134	1334	|	1834	|	...
0	**Brig** 🏛 d.	0744	0844	0944	0944	1244	1444	1544	1944	2044	...
42	**Domodossola** 🏛 § a.	0812	0912	1012	|	1312	1512	1612	2012	2112	...
42	**Domodossola** d.	0817	0917	1017	|	1317	1517	1617	2017	2117	...
81	Stresa d.	0841	0941	|	|	|	1541	1641	|	2141	...
124	Gallarate d.	|	|	1107	1107	1407	|	|	2107	|	...
167	**Milano** Centrale a.	0940	1040	1140	1140	1440	1640	1740	2140	2240	...

	EC 50	*EC* 32	*EC* 52	*EC* 34	*EC* 54	*EC* 36	*EC* 46	*EC* 56	*EC* 42	*EC* 44
						①–⑤	⑥⑦		⑤⑥	⑦–④
			F						V	V
Milano Centrale d.	0720	0820	1120	1320	1520	1720	1720	1820	1920	1920
Gallarate d.	0754	|	|	|	1554	|	|	|	1954	1954
Stresa d.	|	0920	1220	1420	|	1820	1820	1920	|	|
Domodossola a.	0843	0943	1243	1443	1643	1843	|	1943	2043	2043
Domodossola 🏛 § d.	0848	0948	1248	1448	1648	1848	|	1948	2048	2048
Brig 🏛 a.	0916	1014	1316	1514	1716	1914	1914	2016	2114	2114
Bern **560** a.	1024	|	1424	|	1824	|	|	2124	|	|
Basel **560** a.	1132	|	1532	|	1932	|	|	2232	|	|
Lausanne **570** a.	...	1142	...	1642	...	2042	2042	...	2242	2310
Genève **570** a.	...	1221	...	1721	...	2121	2121	...	2321	2354

LOCAL TRAINS **DOMODOSSOLA - MILANO** (SEE NOTE ♠)

km						⚒	†	⚒		⚒				⚒			⚒					⚒			⚒
0	**Domodossola** d.	0456	0556	0601	0654	0720	0801	...	0856	...	1001	1201	1256	...	1401	1456	...	1601	1656	1801	1856	...	2001	2056	...
30	Verbània-Pallanza d.	0516	0616	0627	0716	0743	0827	...	0916	...	1027	1227	1316	...	1427	1516	...	1627	1716	1827	1916	...	2027	2116	...
35	Baveno d.	|	|	0632	|	|	0832	...	|	...	1032	1232	|	...	1432	|	...	1632	|	1832	|	...	2032	|	...
39	Stresa d.	0523	0623	0636	0723	0751	0836	...	0923	...	1036	1236	1323	...	1436	1523	...	1636	1723	1836	1923	...	2036	2123	...
56	Arona d.	0537	0637	0704	0737	0806	0906	0906	0937	1006	1106	1306	1337	1406	1506	1537	1606	1706	1737	1906	1937	2006	2106	2137	2206
82	Gallarate d.	0559	0659	0733	0759	0835	0935	0935	0959	1035	1135	1335	1359	1435	1535	1559	1635	1735	1759	1935	1959	2035	2135	2159	2235
89	Busto Arsizio FS d.	0605	0705	0739	0805	0841	0941	0941	1005	1041	1141	1341	1405	1441	1541	1605	1641	1741	1805	1941	2005	2041	2141	2205	2241
112	Rho-Fiera Milano d.	0621	0721	0801	0821	0901	1001	1001	1021	1101	1200	1401	1421	1501	1601	1621	1701	1801	1821	2001	2020	2101	2201	2221	2301
123	**Milano** P Garibaldi a.	|	|	0814	|	0914	1014	1014	|	1114	1214	1414	|	1514	1614	|	1714	1814	|	2014	|	2114	2214	|	2314
125	**Milano** Centrale a.	0637	0737	...	0835	...	...	...	1035	...	...	...	1435	...	...	1635	...	...	1837	...	2037	...	...	2235	...

					⚒			⚒			⚒			⚒				⚒			⚒		⚒	
Milano Centrale d.	...	0725	...	0825	...	0925	...	...	1325	...	...	1525	...	...	1725	...	1825	...	1925	...	...	2125	...	...
Milano Porta Garibaldi d.	0612	|	0746	|	0846	|	1146	1246	|	1346	1446	|	1546	1646	|	1746	|	1846	|	1946	2046	|	2146	2246
Rho-Fiera Milano d.	0623	0736	0757	0836	0857	0936	1157	1257	1336	1357	1457	1536	1557	1657	1736	1757	1836	1857	1936	1957	2057	2136	2157	2257
Busto Arsizio FS d.	0644	0754	0818	0854	0918	0954	1218	1318	1354	1418	1518	1554	1618	1718	1754	1818	1854	1918	1954	2018	2118	2154	2218	2318
Gallarate d.	0650	0800	0824	0900	0924	1000	1224	1324	1400	1424	1524	1600	1624	1724	1800	1824	1900	1924	2000	2024	2124	2200	2224	2324
Arona d.	0721	0820	0854	0920	0954	1020	1254	1354	1420	1454	1554	1620	1654	1754	1820	1854	1920	1954	2020	2054	2154	2220	2254	2354
Stresa d.	0741	0833	0915	0933	...	1033	1315	...	1433	1515	...	1633	1715	...	1833	1915	1933	...	2033	2115	...	2233	...	...
Baveno d.	0745	|	0919	|	...	|	1319	...	|	1519	...	|	1719	...	|	1919	|	...	|	2119	...	|	...	...
Verbània-Pallanza d.	0750	0842	0924	0942	...	1042	1324	...	1442	1524	...	1642	1724	...	1842	1924	1942	...	2042	2124	...	2242	...	...
Domodossola a.	0823	0904	0959	1004	...	1104	1359	...	1504	1551	...	1704	1759	...	1904	1959	2004	...	2104	2159	...	2304	...	...

OTHER TRAINS **BRIG - DOMODOSSOLA**

km						Ⓐ						③–⑦										Ⓐ				
0	**Brig** 🚗 d.	0022	...	0522	...	0622	...	0722	...	0922	...	1122	...	1322	...	1522	...	1722	...	1822	...	1922	...	2222
23	Iselle di Trasquera § 🚗 d.	0036	...	0536	...	0636	...	0736	...	0936	...	1136	...	1336	...	1536	...	1736	...	1836	...	1936	...	2236
42	**Domodossola** a.	0055	...	0554	...	0654	...	0754	...	0954	...	1154	...	1354	...	1554	...	1754	...	1854	...	1954	...	2254

					Ⓐ						③–⑦								Ⓐ				
Domodossola d.	0437	...	0558	...	0658	...	0758	...	0958	...	1158	...	1358	...	1558	...	1758	...	1858	...	1958	...	2258
Iselle di Trasquera § 🚗 d.	0456	...	0616	...	0716	...	0816	...	1016	...	1216	...	1416	...	1616	...	1816	...	1916	...	2016	...	2316
Brig 🚗 a.	0511	...	0633	...	0733	...	0833	...	1033	...	1233	...	1433	...	1633	...	1833	...	1933	...	2033	...	2333

F – To Frankfurt (Tables **560** and **912**).
V – To / from Venezia (Table **605**).
s – Calls to set down only.
u – Calls to pick up only.

♠ – Most services (2) only. Certain trains are operated by Trenord.
§ – Ticket point is **Iselle**.
🚗 – Car-carrying shuttle available. www.bls.ch.

DOMODOSSOLA and ARONA - NOVARA - ALESSANDRIA 591

2nd class

km		Ⓐ	⚒			⚒	⚒				
0	**Domodossola** d.	0520	0617	0648	1245	1343	1545	1747	1848	...	...
38	Omegna d.	0614	0657	0752	1337	1444	1641	1842	1940	...	...
44	Pettenasco d.	0621	0704	0759	1343	1451	1648	1849	1947	...	...
47	Orta-Miasino d.	0626	0712	0804	1351	1456	1653	1854	1952	...	...
60	Borgomanero d.	0641	0724	0815	1406	1507	1704	1905	2004	...	...
90	**Novara** a.	0716	0754	0843	1437	1541	1740	1943	2039	...	...

	⚒		†	⚒			⚒			
Novara d.	0546	0645	1223	1345	1515	1734	1915	...	...	...
Borgomanero d.	0621	0725	1249	1420	1550	1811	1950	...	...	...
Orta-Miasino d.	0645	0740	1306	1432	1608	1826	2006	...	...	...
Pettenasco d.	0649	0744	1311	1437	1613	1831	2011	...	...	...
Omegna d.	0656	0751	1318	1443	1619	1843	2018	...	...	...
Domodossola a.	0748	0849	1417	1542	1714	1938	2114	...	...	...

ARONA - NOVARA

km		⚒	⚒	†A	Ⓐ	⚒	⚒	⚒	†A	⚒	†
0	**Arona** d.	0648	0748	0915	1348	1548	1748	1848	1915	1948	2115
20	Oleggio d.	0712	0812	0932	1412	1612	1812	1912	1932	2012	2132
37	**Novara** a.	0732	0832	0948	1432	1632	1832	1932	1948	2032	2148

	⚒	Ⓐ	†B	⚒	⚒	⚒	†B	⚒	⚒	†
Novara d.	0650	0750	0812	1423	1523	1723	1812	1823	1923	2012
Oleggio d.	0713	0813	0826	1441	1541	1741	1826	1841	1941	2026
Arona a.	0739	0839	0845	1512	1612	1812	1845	1912	2012	2045

NOVARA - ALESSANDRIA

km		⚒	⚒	⚒◧	⚒◧	⊡	⚒	Ⓐ	†	Ⓐ	
0	**Novara** d.	0608	0708	0808	0908	1208	1408	1708	1827	1908	2027
25	Mortara a.	0632	0732	0832	0932	1235	1432	1732	1854	1932	2054
25	Mortara d.	0632	0732	0832	0932	*1328*	1432	1732	*1900*	1932	*2100*
67	**Alessandria** a.	0717	0815	0915	1015	*1415*	1515	1815	*1943*	2020	*2143*

	⚒	Ⓐ	†	⚒		⚒	†	⚒		Ⓐ
Alessandria d.	0511	0609	0645	0645	1245	1545	1645	1845	1945	2045
Mortara a.	0555	0653	0728	0738	1328	1633	1728	1928	2028	2128
Mortara d.	*0612*	*0705*	0728	*0828*	1328	*1728*	1728	1928	2028	2128
Novara a.	*0640*	*0733*	0752	*0852*	1352	*1752*	1752	1952	2052	2152

A – Additional services Arona - Novara at 1115†, 1315†, 1515†, 1715†.
B – Additional services Novara - Arona at 1012†, 1212†, 1412†, 1612†.

◧ – Subject to alteration until Mar. 4.
⊡ – Runs 15 – 17 minutes later on ⚒.

ACQUI TERME 592

2nd class

km					⚒	⚒			⚒	⚒	
0	**Alessandria** d.	...	0740	0935	1140	...	1340	1540	1740	1940	...
34	**Acqui Terme** d.	0545	0817	1017	1217	1324	1417	1617	1817	2017	...
84	S. Giuseppe di Cairo d.	0652	0922	1122	1322	1437	1522	1722	1922	2122	...
105	**Savona** a.	0717	0947	1150	1347	1500	1547	1748	1947	2147	...

	⚒	⚒	⚒	†		⚒				
Savona d.	0611	0800	0959	1010	1207	1407	1611	1811	2000	...
S. Giuseppe di Cairo d.	0639	0839	1039	1039	1239	1439	1639	1839	2039	...
Acqui Terme a.	0736	0937	1136	1136	1336	1536	1736	1936	2137	...
Alessandria a.	0820	...	1220	1220	1420	1620	1820	2020	...	...

km		C	⚒						Ⓐ		C
0	**Acqui Terme** d.	0607	0703	0917	1117	1217	1317	1617	1717	1817	2040
59	**Genova** P Principe a.	0727	0825	1043	1243	1343	1443	1743	1843	1942	2157
61	**Genova** Brignole a.	0735	0833	1051	1251	1351	1451	1751	1851	1950	2206

	D		⚒			Ⓐ				D
Genova Brignole d.	0706	0913	1013	1113	1313	1413	1613	1813	1913	2035
Genova P Principe d.	0714	0921	1021	1121	1321	1421	1621	1821	1921	2043
Acqui Terme a.	0835	1039	1139	1239	1439	1539	1739	1939	2039	2202

C – Additional services Acqui Terme - Genova Brignole at 0520 Ⓐ, 0740 Ⓐ, 1417 Ⓐ.

D – Additional services Genova Brignole - Acqui Terme at 0605 Ⓐ, 1213 Ⓐ, 1713 Ⓐ

593 MILANO - COLICO - TIRANO and COLICO - CHIAVENNA

Trenord

Additional local trains are available Milano Porta Garibaldi - Lecco and v.v. (line S8), and Lecco - Sondrio and v.v.

km																							
		2	⚒ 🚌													🚌				🚌		2	2
0	**Milano** Centrale d.	...	...	0620	0720	0820	0920	...	1020	1220	1320	1420	1620	1720	...	1820	...	1920	2020	...	2120	2252	2322
12	Monza d.	...	...	0632	0732	0832	0932	...	1032	1232	1332	1432	1632	1732	...	1832	...	1932	2032	...	2132	2309	2339
50	Lecco d.	...	...	0702	0802	0902	1002	...	1102	1302	1402	1502	1702	1802	...	1902	...	2002	2102	...	2202	2354	0024
72	Varenna-Esino d.	...	...	0725	0825	0925	1025	...	1125	1325	1425	1525	1725	1825	...	1925	...	2025	2125	...	2231	...	...
75	Bellano-Tartavalle Terme d.	...	...	0730	0830	0930	1030	...	1130	1330	1430	1530	1730	1830	...	1930	...	2030	2130	...	2240	...	...
89	**Colico** a.	...	...	0747	0847	0947	1047	...	1147	1347	1447	1547	1747	1847	...	1947	...	2047	2147	...	2256	...	...
130	Sondrio a.	0520	0641	0820	0920	1020	1120	...	1220	1420	1520	1620	1820	1921	1930	2020	...	2119	2221	2225	2330	...	...
156	**Tirano** a.	0555	0722	0852	0952	1052	1205	...	1252	1452	1605	1652	1852	...	2012	2052	...	2152	...	2307	...	...	...

	†	⚒																			2	2
Tirano d.	...	...	...	...	0612	0700	...	0908	1108	...	1208	1308	...	1508	1608	...	1708	1808	1908	...	...	...
Sondrio d.	0431	0441	0531	...	0641	0741	...	0941	1141	...	1241	1341	...	1541	1641	...	1741	1841	1941	2041	...	...
Colico d.	0502	0516	0602	0609	0715	0815	...	1015	1215	...	1315	1415	...	1615	1715	...	1815	1915	2015	2115	...	...
Bellano-Tartavalle Terme d.	0517	0532	0617	0629	0730	0830	...	1030	1230	...	1330	1430	...	1630	1730	...	1830	1930	2030	2130	...	...
Varenna-Esino d.	0522	0537	0622	0638	0735	0835	...	1035	1235	...	1335	1435	...	1635	1735	...	1835	1935	2035	2135	...	...
Lecco d.	0549	0601	0655	0719	0801	0901	...	1101	1301	...	1401	1501	...	1701	1801	...	1901	2001	2101	2201	2206	2306
Monza d.	0623	0627	0727	0755	0827	0927	...	1127	1327	...	1427	1527	...	1727	1827	...	1927	2027	2127	2227	2250	2350
Milano Centrale a.	0640	0640	0740	0807	0840	0940	...	1140	1340	...	1440	1540	...	1740	1840	...	1940	2040	2140	2240	2308p	0008p

COLICO - CHIAVENNA

2nd class

km																								
			†	⚒	⚒		†	⚒		⚒			⚒		⚒			⚒		Ⓐ 🚌		⚒		🚌
0	**Colico** d.	0545	0706	0706	0810	...	0812	0845	1004	1045	...	1204	1245	1404	1445	...	1604	1645	1804	1820	...	1852	2004	2120
27	**Chiavenna** a.	0617	0731	0737	0835	...	0843	0917	1035	1117	...	1235	1317	1435	1517	...	1635	1717	1835	1856	...	1923	2035	2155

	Ⓐ 🚌		⚒	†		⚒	⚒		⚒			⚒		⚒			⚒		⚒		†	⚒
Chiavenna d.	0512	0625	0703	0739	...	0745	0843	0925	1043	...	1125	1243	1325	1443	...	1525	1643	1725	1847	...	1925	1931	2043
Colico a.	0548	0656	0735	0804	...	0809	0915	0956	1115	...	1156	1315	1356	1515	...	1556	1715	1756	1919	...	1956	2002	2115

d – Also Ⓐ during school holidays.
e – Schooldays only.
p – Milano **Porta Garibaldi**.

🚌 TIRANO - EDOLO

	⚒	⚒	⚒	⑥ d	e
Tirano Stazione d.	0840	1040	1435	1635	1700
Aprica S Pietro d.	0920	1120	1515	1720	1745
Edolo a.	0945	1145	1540	1745	1810

	⚒	⚒	⚒	⚒	⚒
Edolo d.	0615	0915	1115	1515	1715
Aprica S Pietro d.	0650	0940	1140	1540	1740
Tirano Stazione a.	0730	1020	1220	1620	1820

595 INNSBRUCK - BOLZANO / BOZEN - VERONA - BOLOGNA

For high-speed trains Bolzano - Verona - Milano / Bologna / Roma and v.v. see Table **600**. For other local trains see next page.
Journeys from/to München are subject to alteration until Aug. 5. Services between Innsbruck and Brennero are subject to alteration Aug. 20 - Sept. 11.

km							*EC*	*EC*			*EC*			*EC*		*EC*		*EC*			*ICN*	*RJX*	
		2	2	2	2	2	**81**	**1281**	2	2	**83**	2		**85**	2	**87**	2	**89**	2	2	**763**	**185**	2
			⚒			⚒	①–⑤	⑥⑦													⑥⑦		
							✕ ♠	✕ ♠			✕ ♠♦			✕ ♠		✕ ♠		✕ ♠			✣♦	✕ ♦	
	München Hbf **951** d.	...	...	...	...	...	0734	0734	...	...	0934	...	...	1134	...	1334	...	1534	...	...	...	...	...
0	**Innsbruck** Hbf d.	...	...	...	0549	...	0924	0924	...	...	1124	...	...	1324	...	1524	...	1724	...	...	...	2004	2105
37	**Brennero / Brenner** 🏛 a.	...	...	...	0629	...	1000	1000	...	...	1200	...	...	1400	...	1600	...	1800	...	...	...	2040	2145
37	**Brennero / Brenner** 🏛 d.	...	...	0608	0632	0708	1014	1010	1038	...	1214	1300	...	1414	1508	1614	1708	1814	...	1908	...	2050	2151
60	Vipiteno / Sterzing d.	...	...	0627	0652	0727	|	|	1057	...	|	1320	...	|	1527	|	1727	|	...	1927	...	2116	2210
78	Fortezza / Franzensfeste d.	...	0536	0645	0709	0745	1046	1046	1115	...	1246	1338	...	1446	1545	1646	1745	1846	...	1945	...	2134	2228
89	Bressanone / Brixen d.	...	0545	0655	0719	0755	1056	1056	1125	...	1256	1348	...	1456	1555	1656	1755	1856	...	1955	...	2144	2238
99	Chiusa / Klausen d.	...	0553	0703	0728	0803	|	|	1133	...	|	1356	...	|	1603	|	1803	|	...	2003	...	|	2246
127	**Bolzano / Bozen** a.	...	0617	0729	0753	0829	1127	1127	1159	...	1327	1423	...	1527	1629	1727	1829	1927	...	2029	...	2215	2310
127	**Bolzano / Bozen** 600 d.	0500	0620	0731	...	0831	1131	1131	...	1231	1331	1425	...	1531	1631	1731	1831	1931	...	2031	2130	...	2315
143	Ora / Auer d.	0512	0633	0743	...	0843	|	|	...	1243	|	1437	...	|	1643	|	1843	|	...	2043	2144	...	|
165	Mezzocorona d.	0525	0650	0756	...	0856	|	|	...	1256	|	1450	...	|	1656	|	1856	|	...	2056	2200	...	|
182	Trento 600 d.	0537	0705	0810	...	0910	1204	1204	...	1310	1404	1504	...	1604	1710	1804	1910	2004	...	2110	2216	...	0009
206	Rovereto 600 d.	0551	0720	0825	...	0925	1219	1219	...	1325	1419	1519	...	1619	1725	1819	1925	2019	...	2125	2232	...	...
274	**Verona** Porta Nuova 600 a.	0646	0814	0914	...	1014	1256	1256	...	1414	1458	1614	...	1658	1814	1858	2014	2056	←	2214	2316	...	...
274	**Verona** Porta Nuova 600 d.	0703	...	...	...	...	1313	1313	...	1426	1522	1626	...	1710	1826	1915	→	...	2104	...	2336	...	...
388	**Bologna** Centrale 600 a.	0837	...	...	...	...	1410	|	...	1558	1619	1758	...	|	1958	2016	...	...	2230	...	⊖	...	...
	Venezia Santa Lucia **605** a.	...	...	...	...	...	...	1428	...	...	...	...	...	1825	...	...	...	...	...	...	|	...	...
	Roma Termini **620** a.	...	...	...	...	...	...	...	...	...	...	...	...	...	...	...	...	...	...	...	0606	...	...

			RJX	*ICN*			*EC*	*EC*				*EC*		*EC*		*EC*	*EC*				
	2		2	**184**	**764**	2	2	**88**	**86**	2	2		**84**	2	**82**	2	**80**	**1280**	2	2	2	2
	Ⓐ				⑤⑥					Ⓐ	Ⓒ			Ⓐ			①–⑤	⑥⑦		Ⓐ		
				✕ ♦	✣♦			✕ ♠	✕ ♠				✕ ♠♦		✕ ♠		✕ ♠	✕ ♠				
Roma Termini **620** d.	...	...	...	...	2300	...	...	...	...	...	...	...	...	...	...	...	...	...	...	...	...	...
Venezia S Lucia **605** d.	...	...	...	...	|	...	...	...	...	...	...	...	...	...	1335	...	...	1535	...	...	...	...
Bologna Centrale 600 d.	...	...	...	...	●	0605	...	0745	...	...	1010	...	1152	1205	|	1410	1550	|	1610	...	1810	2005
Verona Porta Nuova 600 a.	...	...	...	...	0530	0743	...	0847	...	...	1135	...	1247	1335	1450	1535	1645	1650	1735	...	1935	2135
Verona Porta Nuova 600 d.	...	...	...	...	0600	...	0750	0901	1101	1150	1150	...	1301	1350	1501	1550	1701	1701	1750	...	1950	2155
Rovereto 600 d.	...	...	...	...	0701	...	0839	0943	1143	1239	1239	...	1343	1439	1543	1639	1743	1743	1839	...	2039	2246
Trento 600 d.	0528	...	0640	...	0717	...	0854	0959	1159	1254	1254	...	1359	1454	1559	1654	1759	1759	1854	...	2054	2301
Mezzocorona d.	0544	...	|	...	0730	...	0905	|	|	1305	1305	...	|	1505	|	1705	|	|	1905	...	2105	2312
Ora / Auer d.	0603	...	|	...	0747	...	0919	|	|	1319	1319	...	|	1519	|	1719	|	|	1919	...	2119	2326
Bolzano / Bozen 600 a.	0618	...	0728	...	0805	...	0930	1031	1231	1330	1330	...	1431	1530	1631	1730	1831	1831	1930	...	2130	2339
Bolzano / Bozen d.	0632	...	0732	0750	...	...	0932	1034	1234	1332	1332	...	1434	1532	1634	1732	1834	1834	1932	2032	2132	...
Chiusa / Klausen d.	0655	...	0755	|	...	...	0955	|	|	1355	1355	...	|	1555	|	1755	|	|	1955	2055	2155	...
Bressanone / Brixen d.	0703	...	0803	0818	...	...	1003	1104	1304	1403	1403	...	1504	1603	1704	1803	1904	1904	2003	2103	2203	...
Fortezza / Franzensfeste d.	0715	...	0815	0829	...	...	1015	1115	1315	1415	1415	...	1515	1615	1715	1815	1915	1915	2015	2115	2215	...
Vipiteno / Sterzing d.	0733	...	0833	0847	...	...	1033	|	|	1433	1433	...	|	1633	|	1833	|	|	2033	2133	2233	...
Brennero / Brenner 🏛 a.	0752	...	0852	0910	...	...	1056	1148	1348	1456	1456	...	1548	1656	1748	1856	1948	1948	2056	2151	2256	...
Brennero / Brenner 🏛 d.	...	...	0902	0920	...	...	...	1200	1400	...	...	...	1600	...	1800	...	2000	2000	...	2154	...	...
Innsbruck Hbf a.	...	...	0938	0956	...	...	...	1236	1436	...	...	...	1636	...	1836	...	2036	2036	...	2230	...	...
München Hbf **951** a.	...	...	...	...	...	...	...	1427	1627	...	...	...	1827	...	2026	...	2227	2227	...	...	...	...

♦ – **NOTES** (LISTED BY TRAIN NUMBER)

83 – (12) ✕ München - Bolgona (- Rimini a. 1733 May 26 - Sept. 10).
84 – (12) ✕ (May 27 - Sept. 11 : Rimini d. 1034 -) Bolgona - München.
184 – (12) ✕ Bolzano - Innsbruck - Wien. *Railjet* service (Tables **950** / **951**).
185 – (12) ✕ Wien - Innsbruck - Bolzano. *Railjet* service (Tables **950** / **951**).
763 – From Bolzano on ⑥⑦: 🛏 1, 2 cl., ▬ 2 cl. (4 berth) (2) Bolzano - Roma.
764 – From Roma on ⑤⑥: 🛏 1, 2 cl., ▬ 2 cl. (4 berth) (2) Roma - Bolzano.

⊖ – Via Orvieto (d. 0510).
● – Via Orte (d. 2341) and Orvieto (d. 0013).
♠ – Also available to passengers without reservation.
✣ – Running days, timings and numbers of *ICN* trains may vary - please check your reservation. For confirmed timings please consult the *Trenitalia* journey planner at www.trenitalia.com.

2nd class INNSBRUCK - BRENNERO - BOLZANO - MERAN, VERONA and BOLOGNA 595

Local trains - for long distance trains and through trains Brennero - Bolzano - Verona - Bologna see previous page.
Innsbruck - Brennero trains are subject to alteration on and around Austrian holiday dates.

INNSBRUCK - BRENNERO

km																								
			①–⑥	A				①–⑥													B	①–⑥		
0	**Innsbruck** Hbf d.	0005	0519	0549	0619	0649	0749	0819	0849	0949	1049	1149	1249	1349	1449	1549	1649	1749	1849	1949	2105	2205	2305	...
18	Matrei d.	0022	0537	0607	0636	0706	0806	0836	0906	1006	1106	1206	1306	1406	1506	1606	1706	1806	1906	2006	2123	2222	2322	...
23	Steinach in Tirol d.	0027	0542	0612	0641	0711	0811	0841	0911	1011	1111	1211	1311	1411	1511	1611	1711	1811	1911	2011	2128	2227	2327	...
37	**Brennero / Brenner** 🏛 a.	0044	0559	0629	0658	0728	0828	0858	0928	1028	1128	1228	1328	1428	1528	1628	1728	1828	1928	2028	2145	2244	2344	...

		①–⑥		①–⑥			B														C		
Brennero / Brenner 🏛 d.	0527	0558	0628	0703	0733	0833	0902	0933	1033	1133	...	1233	1333	1433	1533	1633	1733	1833	1933	2033	2154	2303	...
Steinach in Tirol d.	0546	0617	0647	0720	0750	0850	0917	0950	1050	1150	...	1250	1350	1450	1550	1650	1750	1850	1950	2050	2209	2320	...
Matrei d.	0550	0621	0651	0724	0754	0854	0921	0954	1054	1154	...	1254	1354	1454	1554	1654	1754	1854	1954	2054	2213	2324	...
Innsbruck Hbf a.	0607	0638	0708	0742	0811	0911	0938	1013	1111	1213	...	1311	1413	1511	1613	1711	1813	1911	2011	2111	2230	2341	...

BRENNERO - BOLZANO - MERANO

km																								
		⚒	Ⓐ	A	⚒	†		Ⓐ	⚒	Ⓒ									Ⓐ				D	
0	**Brennero / Brenner** 🏛 d.	0534	...	0702	...	0708	0738	0808	...	0838	0938	1038	1138	1238	1338	1438	1538	1638	...	1738	1838	1938	...	2108
23	Vipiteno / Sterzing d.	0553	...	0723	...	0727	0757	0827	...	0857	0957	1057	1157	1257	1357	1457	1557	1657	...	1757	1857	1957	...	2127
41	Fortezza / Franzensfeste d.	0611	0640	0739	0715	0745	0815	0845	...	0915	1015	1115	1215	1315	1415	1515	1615	1715	...	1815	1915	2015	2122	2145
52	Bressanone / Brixen d.	0621	0649	0749	0725	0755	0825	0855	...	0925	1025	1125	1225	1325	1425	1525	1625	1725	...	1825	1925	2025	2130	2155
62	Chiusa / Klausen d.	0629	0657	0758	0733	0803	0833	0903	...	0933	1033	1133	1233	1333	1433	1533	1633	1733	...	1833	1933	2033	2138	2203
90	**Bolzano / Bozen** a.	0653	0723	0823	0759	0829	0859	0929	...	0959	1059	1159	1259	1359	1459	1559	1659	1759	...	1859	1959	2059	2159	2229
90	**Bolzano / Bozen** ◧ d.	0655	0735	...	0801	...	0901	...	0935	1001	1101	1201	1301	1401	1501	1601	1701	1801	1835	1901	2001	2101	2203	...
122	**Merano / Meran** ◧ a.	0743	0815	...	0845	...	0945	...	1015	1045	1145	1245	1345	1445	1545	1645	1745	1845	1915	1945	2044	2144	2244	...

	⚒	⚒	†	⚒		⚒			Ⓒ								Ⓐ				C	†	
Merano / Meran ◧ d.	...	0600	...	0633	0713	0746	0816	0916	1016	1116	1216	1316	1416	1516	1616	1716	1746	1816	1916	...	1942	2046	2146
Bolzano / Bozen ◧ a.	...	0646	...	0718	0800	0826	0900	1000	1100	1200	1300	1400	1500	1600	1700	1800	1825	1900	1958	...	2031	2126	2226
Bolzano / Bozen d.	0602	0702	0702	...	0802	...	0902	1002	1102	1202	1302	1402	1502	1602	1701	1802	1827	1902	...	2002	2031	...	...
Chiusa / Klausen d.	0625	0725	0725	...	0825	...	0925	1025	1125	1225	1325	1425	1525	1625	1722	1825	1849	1925	...	2025	2056	...	...
Bressanone / Brixen d.	0633	0733	0733	...	0833	...	0933	1033	1133	1233	1333	1433	1533	1633	1730	1833	1857	1933	...	2033	2105	...	...
Fortezza / Franzensfeste d.	0645	0745	0745	...	0845	...	0945	1045	1145	1245	1345	1445	1545	1645	1745	1845	1907	1945	...	2045	2115	...	...
Vipiteno / Sterzing d.	0703	0803	0803	...	0903	...	1003	1103	1203	1303	1403	1503	1603	1703	1803	1903	1932	2003	...	2103	2133	...	...
Brennero / Brenner 🏛 a.	0722	0822	0822	...	0922	...	1022	1122	1222	1322	1422	1522	1622	1722	1822	1922	1953	2022	...	2122	2151	...	...

BOLZANO - PLAN 🚌

Service 350 (♥)																							
	⚒																						
Bolzano / Bozen bus station d.	0628	0728	...	0828	0928	...	1028	1128	...	1228	1328	...	1428	1528	...	1628	1728	...	1828	1928	...	...	...
Ponte Gardena / Waidbruck d.	0657	0757	...	0857	0957	...	1057	1157	...	1257	1357	...	1457	1557	...	1657	1757	...	1857	1957	...	...	...
Ortisei / St Ulrich d.	0727	0827	...	0927	1027	...	1127	1227	...	1327	1427	...	1527	1627	...	1727	1827	...	1927	2027	...	...	...
Santa / St Cristina d.	0736	0836	...	0936	1036	...	1136	1236	...	1336	1436	...	1536	1636	...	1736	1836	...	1936	2036	...	...	...
Selva / Wolkenstein d.	0748	0848	...	0948	1048	...	1148	1248	...	1348	1448	...	1558	1658	...	1748	1848	...	1948	2048	...	...	...
Plan a.	0752	0852	...	0952	1052	...	1152	1252	...	1352	1452	...	1552	1652	...	1752	1852	...	1952	2052	...	...	...

Service 350 (♥)																							
Plan d.	0634	0732	...	0834	0934	...	1034	1134	...	1234	1334	...	1434	1534	...	1634	1734	...	1834	...	...	...	...
Selva / Wolkenstein d.	0637	0735	...	0837	0937	...	1037	1137	...	1237	1337	...	1437	1537	...	1637	1737	...	1837	...	...	...	...
Santa / St Cristina d.	0649	0749	...	0849	0949	...	1049	1149	...	1249	1349	...	1449	1549	...	1649	1749	...	1849	...	...	...	...
Ortisei / St Ulrich d.	0701	0801	...	0901	1001	...	1101	1201	...	1301	1401	...	1501	1601	...	1701	1801	...	1901	...	...	...	...
Ponte Gardena / Waidbruck a.	0729	0829	...	0929	1029	...	1129	1229	...	1329	1429	...	1529	1629	...	1729	1829	...	1929	...	...	...	...
Bolzano bus station a.	0757	0857	...	0957	1057	...	1157	1257	...	1357	1457	...	1557	1657	...	1757	1857	...	1957	...	...	...	...

BOLZANO - VERONA

km																								
		Ⓐ	⚒		Ⓐ	Ⓒ		Ⓒ		⚒		Ⓐ			Ⓐ		Ⓐ	Ⓐ			Ⓐ		†	
0	**Bolzano / Bozen** d.	0536	0634	0736	0836	0936	...	1031	1136	1236	1336	1434	...	1536	1636	1736	1836	1906	...	1936	2036	...	2136	...
16	Ora / Auer d.	0555	0651	0755	0855	0955	...	1043	1155	1255	1355	1452	...	1555	1655	1755	1855	1927	...	1955	2055	...	2155	...
38	Mezzocorona d.	0616	0712	0816	0916	1016	...	1056	1216	1316	1416	1513	...	1616	1716	1816	1916	1942	...	2016	2116	...	2216	...
55	Trento d.	0633	0733	0833	0937	1033	...	1110	1233	1333	1433	1535	...	1633	1733	1833	1933	1955	...	2033	2133	...	2233	...
79	Rovereto d.	0647	0747	0847	0951	1047	...	1125	1247	1347	1452	1549	...	1647	1747	1847	1947	2010	...	2047	2147	...	2247	...
147	**Verona** Porta Nuova a.	0751	0854	0954	1058	1151	...	1214	1351	1454	1551	1655	...	1751	1854	1951	2051	2108	...	2151	2251	...	2348	...

	⚒	⚒	Ⓐ	⚒			Ⓐ	⑥	†	⚒			⚒		Ⓐ			Ⓐ		Ⓐ		Ⓐ	
Verona Porta Nuova d.	0520	0606	0627	0706	...	0806	0850	0906	0953	1106	...	1206	1306	1406	1506	1606	...	1706	1806	1906	2006	2106	...
Rovereto d.	0607	0707	0732	0807	...	0907	0937	1007	1042	1207	...	1307	1407	1507	1607	1707	...	1807	1907	2007	2107	2207	...
Trento d.	0632	0732	0749	0832	...	0932	0952	1032	1057	1232	...	1332	1432	1532	1632	1732	...	1832	1932	2032	2132	2232	...
Mezzocorona d.	0646	0746	0802	0846	...	0946	1005	1046	1108	1246	...	1346	1446	1546	1646	1746	...	1846	1946	2046	2146	2246	...
Ora / Auer d.	0706	0806	0817	0906	...	1006	1020	1106	1122	1306	...	1406	1506	1606	1706	1806	...	1906	2006	2106	2206	2306	...
Bolzano / Bozen a.	0724	0823	0830	0923	...	1023	1039	1123	1133	1323	...	1423	1523	1623	1723	1823	...	1923	2023	2123	2223	2327	...

VERONA - BOLOGNA

km																								
			⚒			Ⓒ					†			⚒			⚒							
0	**Verona** Porta Nuova d.	0518	0605	...	0703	1026	...	1226	1326	...	1345	1426	...	1514	1626	...	1717	1826	...	2104	...	...	...	...
114	**Bologna** Centrale a.	0653	0739	...	0837	1151	...	1358	1458	...	1524	1558	...	1655	1758	...	1857	1958	...	2230	...	...	...	...

					Ⓒ		⚒	Ⓐ		Ⓒ						Ⓑ							
Bologna Centrale d.	0605	0710	...	0810	1010	...	1110	1205	...	1210	1410	...	1610	1810	...	1910	2005	...	2105	...	...	...	...
Verona Porta Nuova a.	0743	0835	...	0935	1135	...	1240	1335	...	1338	1535	...	1735	1935	...	2048	2135	...	2235	...	...	...	...

A – 🚌2 Innsbruck - Bolzano.
B – 🚌2 Innsbruck - Trento and v.v.
C – 🚌2 Merano - Innsbruck.
D – 🚌2 Lienz - Merano (Table **597**).

◧ – Additional trains: Bolzano - Merano at 0545⚒, 0624⚒, 0655†, 0735⑥, 0801†, 0935⚒, 1135⚒, 1335⚒, 1635Ⓐ; Merano - Bolzano at 0846⚒, 1046⚒, 1246⚒, 1446⚒, 1946Ⓐ.

♥ – For more information www.suedtirolmobil.info.

596 TRENTO - MALÉ - MEZZANA
Trentino Trasporti

Mezzocorona Ferrovia is adjacent to Mezzocorona FS station. Operator: Trentino Trasporti www.trentinotrasporti.it.

km			⚒	⚒	⚒	⚒	⚒	⚒	⚒	⚒	⚒	⚒	⚒	⚒	⚒	⚒			†	†	†	†	†	†	†	†
													◧	◧	◧	◧										
0	**Trento** d.	⚒	0710	0812	0931	1027	1106	1202	1341	1454	1554	1718	1727	1809	1842	1935	...	†	0610	0810	1010	1210	1410	1610	1810	2010
17	Mezzocorona Ferrovia d.		0742	0841	0957	1054	1133	1230	1408	1521	1623	1739	1754	1835	1908	2001	...		0637	0837	1037	1237	1437	1637	1837	2037
22	Mezzolombardo d.		0755	0849	1006	1102	1141	1238	1416	1528	1631	1746	1802	1843	1916	2008	...		0644	0844	1044	1244	1444	1644	1844	2044
45	Cles d.		0833	0927	1042	1139	1222	1318	1454	1607	1708	1819	1840	1917	1953	2044	...		0722	0922	1122	1322	1522	1722	1922	2122
56	Malé d.		0859	0953	1107	1204	1250	1345	1522	1638	1736	1840	1905	1935	2016	2104	...		0746	0946	1146	1346	1546	1746	1944	2144
66	**Mezzana** a.		0915	1009	1123	1220	1309	1406	1540	1654	1752	1857	...	...	...	...	...		0803	1003	1203	1403	1603	1803	...	...

			⚒	⚒	⚒	⚒	⚒	⚒	⚒	⚒	⚒	⚒	⚒	⚒	⚒	⚒			†	†	†	†	†	†	†	†
					⊡							⊡														
	Mezzana d.	⚒	0611	0656	...	0925	1021	1136	1230	1345	1423	...	1619	1716	1806	1925	...	†	...	0842	1042	1242	1442	1642	1842	...
	Malé d.		0630	0716	0823	0943	1039	1154	1252	1407	1441	1509	1639	1735	1825	1943	...		0600	0900	1100	1300	1500	1700	1900	2000
	Cles d.		0649	0755	0849	1008	1105	1223	1320	1434	1508	1530	1707	1801	1852	2008	...		0624	0924	1124	1324	1524	1724	1924	2024
	Mezzolombardo d.		0722	0832	0928	1045	1142	1302	1401	1514	1547	1604	1747	1842	1931	2044	...		0701	1001	1201	1401	1601	1801	2001	2101
	Mezzocorona Ferrovia d.		0727	0840	0935	1053	1149	1310	1409	1522	1554	1609	1755	1849	1938	2052	...		0708	1008	1208	1408	1608	1808	2008	2108
	Trento a.		0749	0906	1002	1121	1216	1338	1436	1547	1620	1630	1823	1915	2004	2118	...		0734	1034	1234	1434	1634	1834	2034	2134

◧ – Other trains Trento - Malé at 0611⚒, 1243⚒, 1326⚒, 1634⚒.

⊡ – Other trains Malé - Trento at 0530⚒, 0644⚒, 1530⚒.

597 FORTEZZA / FRANZENSFESTE - S. CANDIDO / INNICHEN - LIENZ
2nd class ÖBB, SAD

Trains to Lienz are subject to alteration on and around Italian and Austrian holiday dates.

km		Ⓐ																			Ⓐ	Ⓐ		Ⓐ	Ⓐ
0	**Fortezza / Franzensfeste** d.	0547	...	0650	0750	0850	0950	1050	1150	1250	1350	1450	1550	1650	1750	1850	1950	2050	...		0617	0720	and at	1820	1920
33	Brunico / Bruneck d.	0630	...	0730	0830	0930	1030	1130	1230	1330	1430	1530	1630	1730	1830	1930	2030	2130	...	A	0700	0800	the same	1900	2000
61	Dobbiaco / Toblach d.	0706	...	0806	0906	1006	1106	1206	1306	1406	1506	1606	1706	1806	1906	2006	2106	2206	...	L	0736	0836	minutes	1936	2036
65	**S. Candido / Innichen** a.	0710	...	0810	0910	1010	1110	1210	1310	1410	1510	1610	1710	1810	1910	2010	2110	2210	...	S	0740	0840	past each	1940	2040
65	**S. Candido / Innichen** 🏛 d.	...	0716	0816	0916	1016	1116	1216	1316	1416	1516	1616	1716	1816	1916	2016	...	...	...	O	...	...	hour until	...	...
78	Sillian 🏛 d.	...	0730	0830	0930	1030	1130	1230	1330	1430	1530	1630	1730	1830	1930	2030	...	...	...		...	...	⊖	...	...
108	**Lienz** a.	...	0809	0909	1009	1109	1209	1309	1409	1509	1609	1709	1809	1909	2009	2109	...	...	...		...	...		...	...

		Ⓐ	-⚒													D					Ⓐ	Ⓐ		Ⓐ	Ⓐ
	Lienz d.	...	...	0550	0645	0750	0850	0950	1050	1150	1250	1350	1450	1550	1650	1750	1850	1950	...		...	...	and at	...	...
	Sillian d.	...	...	0630	0730	0830	0930	1030	1130	1230	1330	1430	1530	1630	1730	1830	1930	2030	...	A	...	...	the same	...	...
	S. Candido / Innichen 🏛 a.	...	...	0643	0743	0843	0943	1043	1143	1243	1343	1443	1543	1643	1743	1843	1943	2043	...	L	...	...	minutes	...	...
	S. Candido / Innichen 🏛 d.	0521	0550	0650	0750	0850	0950	1050	1150	1250	1350	1450	1550	1650	1750	1850	1950	2050	...	S	0620	0720	past each	1720	1820
	Dobbiaco / Toblach d.	0526	0555	0655	0755	0855	0955	1055	1155	1255	1355	1455	1555	1655	1755	1855	1955	2055	...	O	0625	0725	hour until	1725	1825
	Brunico / Bruneck d.	0600	0631	0731	0831	0931	1031	1131	1231	1331	1431	1531	1631	1731	1831	1931	2031	2131	...		0701	0801	⊖	1801	1901
	Fortezza / Franzensfeste a.	0634	0710	0810	0910	1010	1110	1210	1310	1410	1510	1610	1710	1810	1910	2010	2110	2210	...		0740	0840		1840	1940

🚌 DOBBIACO / TOBLACH - CORTINA 🚌

Service **445** (♠)	⚒								
Dobbiaco / Toblach bus station d.	0705	0905	1105	1405	1605	1805	...	...	...
Dobbiaco / Toblach Bahnhof d.	0710	0910	1110	1410	1610	1810	...	...	...
Cortina a.	0755	0955	1155	1455	1655	1855	...	...	...

Service **445** (♠)	⚒								
Cortina d.	0805	1005	1305	1505	1705	1905	...	...	...
Dobbiaco / Toblach Bahnhof d.	0845	1045	1345	1545	1745	1945	...	...	...
Dobbiaco / Toblach bus station a.	0850	1050	1350	1550	1750	1950	...	...	...

D – (2) Lienz - Merano (Table **595**).

♠ – For more information www.suedtirolmobil.info.

⊖ – Trains from Fortezza at 0820 - 1720 and from San Candido at 0820 - 1720 run additionally on © Dec. 12 - Mar. 27 and June 18 - Sept. 4.

598 MERANO / MERAN - MALLES / MALS
2nd class SAD

'Ferrovia della Val Venosta'. Operator: SAD www.sad.it.

km		⚒																								
0	**Merano / Meran** d.	*0532**	*0636**	*0710**	*0749**	*0819**	*0919**	*0949**	*1019**	*1119**	*1149**	*1219**	*1319**	*1349**	*1419**	*1519**	*1549**	*1619**	*1719**	*1749**	*1819**	*1919**	*1949**	*2049**	*2149**	*2249**
	Töll d.	0548	0652	0731	0802	0835	0931	1002	1035	1131	1202	1235	1331	1402	1435	1531	1602	1635	1731	1802	1835	1931	2000	2100	2200	2300
37	Silandro / Schlanders d.	0623	0729	0810	0832	0910	1010	1032	1110	1210	1232	1310	1410	1432	1504	1610	1632	1710	1810	1832	1910	2010	2032	2132	2232	2332
60	**Malles / Mals** a.	0653	0754	0838	0855	0938	1038	1055	1138	1238	1255	1338	1438	1455	1538	1638	1655	1738	1838	1855	1938	2038	2055	2155	2255	2355

		⚒																								
	Malles / Mals d.	0518	0540	0616	0701	0720	0820	0903	0920	1020	1103	1120	1220	1303	1320	1420	1503	1520	1620	1703	1720	1820	1903	1920	2020	2120
	Silandro / Schlanders d.	0540	0603	0641	0727	0748	0848	0927	0948	1048	1127	1148	1248	1327	1348	1448	1527	1548	1648	1727	1748	1848	1927	1948	2048	2148
	Töll d.	0612	0637	0716	0757	0825	0925	0957	1025	1125	1157	1225	1325	1357	1425	1525	1557	1625	1725	1757	1825	1925	1957	2025	2125	2225
	Merano / Meran a.	*0626**	*0651**	*0734**	*0813**	*0843**	*0943**	*1013**	*1043**	*1143**	*1213**	*1243**	*1343**	*1413**	*1443**	*1543**	*1613**	*1643**	*1743**	*1813**	*1843**	*1943**	*2013**	*2043**	*2143**	*2243**

* – Connection by 🚌.

599 ITALIAN LAKES (LAGO MAGGIORE, GARDA, COMO)

Lago Maggiore: ⛴ services link Arona, Stresa, Baveno, Laveno, Luino and Locarno throughout the year on an irregular schedule.
Operator: Navigazione sul Lago Maggiore, P. le Baracca 1, 28041 Arona, Italy. ✆ +39 (0)322 233 200. www.navigazionelaghi.it

Lago di Garda: ⛴ services link Desenzano, Peschiera, Garda, Salo, Gardone and Riva, (April to October only), on an irregular schedule with a very limited service at other times.
Operator: Navigazione sul Lago di Garda, Piazza Matteotti 1, 25015 Desenzano del Garda, Italy. ✆ +39 (0)30 914 9511. www.navigazionelaghi.it

Lago di Como: ⛴ services link Como, Bellagio, Menaggio, Varenna, Bellano and Colico (April to September only) on an irregular schedule.
Operator: Navigazione Lago di Como, Via Per Cernobbio 18, 22100 Como, Italy. ✆ +39 (0)31 579 211. www.navigazionelaghi.it

Hydrofoil service (valid until March 26, 2022):

	⚒	⚒	†	⚒	⚒	⚒	⚒	†	⚒	⚒	
Como d.	0710	0733	1110	1225	1335	1425	1530	1540	1710	1810	1910
Tremezzo d.	0749	0819	1146	1302	1422	1512	1607	1617	1759	1859	1947
Bellagio d.	|	0813r	1155	1309	1432	1522	1614	1624	1806	1906	1953
Menaggio d.	0757	0808	1202	1316	1440	1530	1621	1631	1814	1921	1959
Bellano d.	...	...	1211	...	1456	...	1633	...	1830	...	2011
Colico a.	...	...	1238	...	1528	...	1700	...	1902	...	2038

	⚒	⚒	†	⚒	⚒	⚒	†	⚒	⚒	†	⚒
Colico d.	0606	...	0636	...	...	...	1355	...	1605	...	1730
Bellano d.	0628	...	0658	...	...	...	1422	...	1638	...	1757
Menaggio d.	0641	0650	0711	0808	0900	1316	1434	1530	1655	1706	1810
Bellagio d.	0647	0659	0717	0814	0909	1330	1442	1546	1704	1714	1817
Tremezzo d.	0653	0705	0723	0820	0915	1336	1448	1552	1710	1720	1823
Como a.	0730	0751	0800	0857	1005	1412	1525	1645	1800	1800	1900

r – Via Menaggio.

Italo, Trenitalia

HIGH-SPEED SERVICES 600

All trains Ⓡ and 🍷. *FA*, *FB* and *FR* trains are operated by Trenitalia (www.trenitalia.com). *ITA* trains are operated by Italo (www.italotreno.it).
Trenitalia tickets and passes are not valid on Italo trains. Trains may use different numbers for part of their journey.

km		*FR*	*ITA*	*FR*	*FR*	*FR*	*FR*	*ITA*	*FR*	*FR*	*ITA*	*ITA*	*FR*	*FR*	*ITA*	*FR*	*ITA*	*FR*	*FB*	*ITA*	*ITA*	*FR*	*FR*	*ITA*
		9503	**9907**	**9401**	**9303**	**9603**	**9511**	**9967**	**9605**	**8505**	**8113**	**9969**	**9403**	**9607**	**8951**	**9515**	**9971**	**9604**	**8801**	**8903**	**9915**	**9405**	**9611**	**8953**
		①–⑥				Ⓐ		①–⑥	⚒								①–⑥							
							L				**R**								**L**		**A**			
0	**Torino** Porta Nuova....... **605** d.	...	...	...	...	...	...	...	...	...	...	...	...	0550	...	...	0600	...	...	...	0625	...	0650	...
6	**Torino** Porta Susa △.... **605** d.	...	...	...	...	...	...	...	...	...	...	...	...	0600	...	...	0610	...	...	...	0635	...	0700	...
	Bergamo .... d.	...	...	...	...	...	...	...	0545	...	...	...	...	│	0543	...	│	...	...	...	│	...	│	...
	Brescia...................... **605** d.	...	...	...	...	...	...	...	│	...	...	...	...	│	0627	...	│	0642	...	...	│	...	│	...
	Desenzano-Sirmione .. **605** d.	...	...	...	...	...	...	...	│	...	...	...	...	│	0643	...	│	│	...	...	│	...	│	...
	Peschiera del Garda... **605** d.	...	...	...	...	...	...	...	│	...	...	...	...	│	0652	...	│	│	...	...	│	...	│	...
	Bolzano / Bozen..... **595** d.	...	...	...	...	...	...	...	│	0512	...	...	...	│	│	...	│	│	...	...	│	...	│	0642
	Trento.................... **595** d.	...	...	...	...	...	...	...	│	0543	...	...	...	│	│	...	│	│	...	...	│	...	│	0714
	Rovereto................. **595** d.	...	...	...	...	...	...	...	│	0557	...	...	...	│	│	...	│	│	...	...	│	...	│	0728
	Verona Porta Nuova .. **595** a.	...	...	...	...	...	...	...	│	0640	...	...	...	│	0711	...	│	│	...	...	│	...	│	0810
	Verona Porta Nuova .. **605** d.	...	...	...	...	...	...	...	│	0652	...	...	...	│	0722	...	│	│	...	...	│	...	│	0822
148	**Milano** Centrale........... **605** a.	...	...	...	...	...	...	...	0625	│	...	...	...	0650	│	...	0657	0720	...	...	0730	...	0750	│
148	**Milano** Centrale.................. d.	...	0540	...	0545	0600	0610	0615	0635	│	0640	0645	...	0700	│	0710	0715	0730	...	...	0740	...	0800	│
158	Milano Rogoredo .... d.	...	0550	...	0557**u**	│	0620**u**	0626	│	│	│	│	...	│	│	0720**u**	0726	│	...	...	│	...	│	│
299	Reggio Emilia AV................. d.	...	0628	...	│	│	0656	│	│	│	0728	│	...	│	│	0756	│	│	...	...	0828	...	│	│
	Venezia Santa Lucia .... d.	...	│	0526	│	│	│	│	│	│	│	│	0626	│	│	│	│	│	0653	0705	│	0726	│	│
	Venezia Mestre △ .... **620** d.	...	│	0538	│	│	│	│	│	│	│	│	0638	│	│	│	│	│	0705	0717	│	0738	│	│
	Padova .... **620** d.	...	│	0556	│	│	│	│	│	│	│	│	0656	│	│	│	│	│	0723	0735	│	0756	│	│
	Rovigo .... **620** d.	...	│	0617	│	│	│	│	│	│	│	│	│	│	│	│	│	│	0747	│	│	0816	│	│
	Ferrara...................... **620** d.	...	│	│	│	│	│	│	│	│	│	│	0729	│	│	│	│	│	0805	0811	│	│	│	│
363	**Bologna** Centrale ● ..... **620** a.	...	0654	0659	0809	0704	0724	│	│	0744	0754	0749	0759	0804	0814	0824	│	0834	0842	0839	0854	0859	0904	0914
363	**Bologna** Centrale ● ..... **620** d.	...	0657	0702	0812	0707	0727	│	│	0747	0757	0752	0802	0807	0817	0827	│	0837	...	0842	0857	0902	0907	0917
455	**Firenze** SMN................ **620** a.	...	0735	0739	0850	│	0804	│	│	0824	0835	│	0839	│	0854	0904	│	│	...	0920	0935	0939	│	0954
455	**Firenze** SMN................ **620** d.	0600	0743	0748	0859	│	0814	│	│	0833	0843	│	0848	│	0903	0914	│	│	...	0928	0943	0948	│	1003
	Roma Tiburtina............ **620** a.	0739	0910	0914**s**	1023**s**	│	0940	│	│	0959**s**	1009	0949	1014	│	│	1039	│	│	...	1054	1109	1114	│	│
716	**Roma** Termini .... **620** a.	0749	0919	0930	1035	0910	0950	0924	0934	1010	1019	1000	1025	1011	1035	1049	1025	1040	...	1105	1119	1122	1110	1135
716	**Roma** Termini .... **640** d.	0800	0930	...	...	0925	...	0941	0953	...	1030	...	1035	1025	...	1100	1040	1053	...	1115	...	1135	1125	...
926	**Napoli** Afragola .... a.	0856**s**	1027	...	...	│	...	│	1051**s**	...	│	...	│	│	...	1156	1139	1148**s**	...	│	...	│	│	...
938	**Napoli** Centrale .... **640** a.	0913	1043	...	...	1033	...	1053	1103	...	1143	...	1148	1133	...	1213	1153	1203	...	1228	...	1248	1233	...
938	**Napoli** Centrale .... **640** d.	...	...	...	...	...	...	...	...	...	1200	...	...	...	...	1225	1205	...	...	...	...	...	...	...
988	**Salerno**....................... **640** a.	...	...	...	...	...	...	...	...	...	1242	...	...	...	...	1302	1250	...	...	...	...	...	...	...

	FR	*ITA*	*FR*	*ITA*	*FR*	*FA*	*ITA*	*FR*	*ITA*	*FR*	*FR*	*ITA*	*FR*	*ITA*	*ITA*	*FR*	*FR*	*FR*	*ITA*	*ITA*	*ITA*	*FR*	*FR*	
	9519	**9973**	**9613**	**8905**	**8507**	**9466**	**9919**	**9583**	**9975**	**9409**	**9617**	**8907**	**8503**	**9923**	**9923**	**9411**	**9311**	**9527**	**9977**	**8909**	**9927**	**9413**	**9623**	
			Ⓑ											①–⑥									Ⓐ	
		G				**T**		**R**		**U**		**U**								**T**				
Torino Porta Nuova....... **605** d.	0700	...	...	...	...	...	0730	0800	...	...	...	...	...	0830	...	...	0840	...	...	...	0930	...	...	...
Torino Porta Susa △.... **605** d.	0710	...	...	...	...	...	0740	0810	...	...	...	...	...	0840	...	...	0850	...	...	...	0940	...	...	...
Bergamo .... d.	│	...	...	...	...	...	│	│	...	...	...	...	0800	│	...	...	│	...	...	...	│	...	...	...
Brescia...................... **605** d.	│	...	...	...	...	...	│	│	...	...	...	...	0847	│	...	...	│	...	...	...	│	...	...	...
Desenzano-Sirmione ... **605** d.	│	...	...	...	...	...	│	│	...	...	...	...	│	│	...	...	│	...	...	...	│	...	...	...
Peschiera del Garda.... **605** d.	│	...	...	...	...	...	│	│	...	...	...	...	0909	│	...	...	│	...	...	...	│	...	...	...
Bolzano / Bozen...... **595** d.	│	...	...	...	0712	...	│	│	...	...	...	...	│	│	...	...	│	...	...	...	│	...	...	...
Trento...................... **595** d.	│	...	...	...	0743	...	│	│	...	...	...	...	│	│	...	...	│	...	...	...	│	...	...	...
Rovereto.................. **595** d.	│	...	...	...	0757	...	│	│	...	...	...	...	│	│	...	...	│	...	...	...	│	...	...	...
Verona Porta Nuova ... **595** a.	│	...	...	...	0840	...	│	│	...	...	...	...	0924	│	...	...	│	...	...	...	│	...	...	...
Verona Porta Nuova ... **605** d.	│	...	...	...	0852	...	│	│	...	...	...	...	0937	│	...	...	│	...	...	...	│	...	...	...
Milano Centrale............ **605** a.	0800	...	...	...	│	...	0830	0902	...	...	...	...	│	0930	...	...	│	...	...	...	1030	...	...	...
Milano Centrale.................. d.	0810	0815	0830	...	│	...	0840	0910	0915	...	0930	...	│	0940	0940	...	│	1010	1015	...	1040	...	1058	...
Milano Rogoredo .... d.	0820	0826	│	...	│	...	0850	0920	0926	...	0940**u**	...	│	0950	0950	...	1004	1020**u**	1026	...	1050	...	│	...
Reggio Emilia AV................. d.	0856	│	│	...	│	...	0928	0956	│	...	│	...	│	1028	1028	...	1042	1056	│	...	1128	...	│	...
Venezia Santa Lucia .... d.	│	│	│	0805	│	...	│	│	│	...	│	...	│	│	│	0926	│	│	│	...	│	1026	│	...
Venezia Mestre △ ...... **620** d.	│	│	│	0817	│	0834	│	│	│	0840	│	0920	│	│	│	0938	│	│	│	1017	│	1038	│	...
Padova....................... **620** d.	│	│	│	0835	│	0850	│	│	│	0856	│	0935	│	│	│	0956	│	│	│	1035	│	1056	│	...
Rovigo....................... **620** d.	│	│	│	0857	│	│	│	│	│	│	│	│	│	│	│	│	│	│	│	│	│	│	│	...
Ferrara...................... **620** d.	│	│	│	│	│	│	│	│	│	0929	│	1011	│	│	│	1028	│	│	│	1110	│	1129	│	...
Bologna Centrale ● ...... **620** a.	0924	│	0934	0939	0944	0949	0954	1024	│	0959	│	1039	1044	1054	1054	1058	1109	1124	│	1139	1154	1159	1204	...
Bologna Centrale ● ...... **620** d.	0927	│	0937	0942	0947	0952	0957	1027	│	1002	│	1042	1047	1057	1057	1101	1112	1127	│	1142	1157	1202	1207	...
Firenze SMN................. **620** a.	1004	│	│	1020	1024	│	1035	1104	│	1039	│	1120	1124	1135	1135	1139	1150	1204	│	1220	1235	1239	│	...
Firenze SMN................. **620** d.	1014	│	│	1028	1033	│	1043	1114	│	1048	│	1128	1133	1143	1143	1148	1159	1214	│	1228	1243	1248	│	...
Roma Tiburtina............. **620** a.	1139	│	│	1154	1159**s**	1149**s**	1209	1240	│	1214	│	1254	│	1309	1309	1314	1322	1340	│	1354	1409	1414	│	...
Roma Termini................ **620** a.	1149	1125	1140	1205	1210	1200	1219	1249	1225	1225	1240	1305	1305	1319	1319	1325	1335	1349	1325	1405	1419	1425	1410	...
Roma Termini................ **640** d.	1200	1140	1155	...	...	...	1230	1300	1240	1250	...	1330	...	...	...	1335	1353	1400	1340	1415	1430	1438	1425	...
Napoli Afragola .... a.	1257	1237	1250**s**	...	...	...	1327	1356	│	│	...	│	...	...	...	│	1448**s**	1456	1437	│	1527	│	│	...
Napoli Centrale .... **640** a.	1315	1253	1310	...	...	...	1343	1413	1353	1403	...	1443	...	...	...	◧	1503	1512	1453	1528	1543	1548	1533	...
Napoli Centrale .... **640** d.	1325	...	...	...	...	...	...	1425	...	...	...	1455	...	...	...	...	...	1525	...	...	...	...	...	...
Salerno........................ **640** a.	1406	...	...	...	...	...	...	1504	...	...	...	1530	...	...	...	...	...	1606	...	...	...	...	...	...

	FR	*ITA*	*FR*	*ITA*	*ITA*	*FR*	*FA*	*FR*	*FR*	*ITA*	*ITA*	*FR*	*FR*	*ITA*	*ITA*	*ITA*	*FR*	*ITA*	*FR*	*ITA*	*FR*	*ITA*	*FA*	*ITA*
	9587	**9979**	**9625**	**8911**	**9931**	**9415**	**9721**	**9535**	**9535**	**9981**	**9935**	**8419**	**9631**	**9983**	**8913**	**9939**	**9421**	**8959**	**9543**	**9985**	**9639**	**8915**	**8519**	**8153**
			Ⓐ			⚒	①–⑤						Ⓑ											
	R							**d**	**e**			**R**				**Af**					**R**		**S**	**R**
Torino Porta Nuova....... **605** d.	1000	...	...	...	...	...	...	1100	1100	...	1130	...	...	...	...	1220	...	...	1300	...	...	...	...	1320
Torino Porta Susa △.... **605** d.	1010	...	...	...	...	...	...	1110	1110	...	1141	...	...	...	...	1230	...	...	1310	...	...	...	...	1330
Bergamo .... d.	│	...	...	...	...	...	...	│	│	...	│	...	...	...	...	│	...	...	│	...	...	...	...	│
Brescia...................... **605** d.	│	...	...	...	...	...	...	│	│	...	│	...	...	...	...	│	...	1329	│	...	...	...	...	│
Desenzano-Sirmione ... **605** d.	│	...	...	...	...	...	...	│	│	...	│	...	...	...	...	│	...	1343	│	...	...	...	...	│
Peschiera del Garda.... **605** d.	│	...	...	...	...	...	...	│	│	...	│	...	...	...	...	│	...	1352	│	...	...	...	...	│
Bolzano / Bozen...... **595** d.	│	...	...	...	...	...	0845	│	│	...	│	...	...	...	...	│	...	│	│	...	...	...	1312	│
Trento...................... **595** d.	│	...	...	...	...	...	0919	│	│	...	│	...	...	...	...	│	...	│	│	...	...	...	1343	│
Rovereto.................. **595** d.	│	...	...	...	...	...	0934	│	│	...	│	...	...	...	...	│	...	│	│	...	...	...	1357	│
Verona Porta Nuova ... **595** a.	│	...	...	...	...	...	1020	│	│	...	│	...	...	...	...	│	...	1411	│	...	...	...	1440	│
Verona Porta Nuova ... **605** d.	│	...	...	...	...	...	1032	│	│	...	│	...	...	...	...	│	...	1422	│	...	...	...	1452	│
Milano Centrale............ **605** a.	1102	...	...	...	...	...	1145	1202	1202	...	1230	...	...	...	...	1330	...	│	1402	...	...	...	│	1430
Milano Centrale.................. d.	1110	1115	1125	...	1140	...	...	1210	1210	1215	1240	...	1258	1315	...	1340	...	│	1410	1420	1430	...	│	1440
Milano Rogoredo .... d.	1120	1126	1138**u**	...	1150	...	...	1220	1220	1226	1250	...	│	1326	...	│	...	│	1420	1426	│	...	│	│
Reggio Emilia AV................. d.	1156	│	│	...	1228	...	...	1256	1256	│	1328	...	│	│	...	1428	...	│	1456	│	│	...	│	1528
Venezia Santa Lucia .... d.	│	│	│	1105	│	1126	...	│	│	│	│	1226	│	│	1305	│	1326	│	│	│	│	1405	│	│
Venezia Mestre △ ...... **620** d.	│	│	│	1117	│	1138	...	│	│	│	│	1238	│	│	1317	│	1338	│	│	│	│	1417	│	│
Padova....................... **620** d.	│	│	│	1135	│	1156	...	│	│	│	│	1256	│	│	1335	│	1356	│	│	│	│	1435	│	│
Rovigo....................... **620** d.	│	│	│	1157	│	│	...	│	│	│	│	│	│	│	│	│	1417	│	│	│	│	│	│	│
Ferrara...................... **620** d.	│	│	│	│	│	1229	...	│	│	│	│	1329	│	│	1411	│	│	│	│	│	│	1511	│	│
Bologna Centrale ● ...... **620** a.	1224	│	1234	1239	1254	1259	...	1324	1324	│	1354	1359	1404	│	1439	1454	1459	1514	1524	│	1534	1539	1544	1554
Bologna Centrale ● ...... **620** d.	1227	│	1237	1242	1257	1302	...	1327	1327	│	1357	1402	1407	│	1442	1457	1502	1517	1527	│	1537	1542	1547	1557
Firenze SMN................. **620** a.	1304	│	│	1320	1335	1339	...	1404	1404	│	1435	1439	│	│	1520	1535	1539	1554	1604	│	│	1620	1624	1635
Firenze SMN................. **620** d.	1314	│	│	1328	1343	1348	...	1414	1414	│	1443	1448	│	│	1528	1543	1548	1603	1614	│	│	1628	1633	1643
Roma Tiburtina............. **620** a.	1440	│	│	1454	1509	1514**s**	...	1540	│	│	1609	1614	1604	│	1653	1709	1714	│	1740	│	│	1754	1759	1809
Roma Termini................ **620** a.	1449	1425	1443	1505	1519	1525	...	1549	1549	1525	1619	1624	1615	1625	1705	1719	1724	1735	1749	1730	1740	1805	1810	1819
Roma Termini................ **640** d.	1500	...	1453	1515	1530	...	...	1600	1600	1540	1630	1635	1625	...	1715	...	1735	...	1800	...	1753	1815	1820	1830
Napoli Afragola .... a.	1556	...	1548**s**	│	1625	...	...	1656**s**	1656**s**	│	1727	1736	│	...	1817	...	│	...	1856	...	1848	│	1921	1928
Napoli Centrale .... **640** a.	1612	...	1603	1628	1643	...	...	1712	1712	1653	1743	│	1733	...	│	...	1848	...	1912	...	│	1928	│	│
Napoli Centrale .... **640** d.	1625	...	...	...	1700	...	...	...	...	...	...	│	...	...	│	...	...	...	1925	...	│	...	│	│
Salerno........................ **640** a.	1706	...	...	...	1739	...	...	...	...	...	...	1809	...	...	1854	...	...	...	2005	...	1919	...	1948	2011

FOR FOOTNOTES SEE NEXT PAGE →

600 HIGH-SPEED SERVICES

Italo, Trenitalia

All trains 🅁 and 🍸. *FA, FB* and *FR* trains are operated by Trenitalia (www.trenitalia.com). *ITA* trains are operated by Italo (www.italotreno.it). Trenitalia tickets and passes are not valid on Italo trains. Trains may use different numbers for part of their journey.

	FR	*FR*	*FR*	*ITA*	*FR*	*FA*	*ITA*	*ITA*	*FR*	*FR*	*ITA*	*FR*	*ITA*	*FR*	*ITA*	*FR*	*ITA*	*FR*	*FR*	*FR*	*FR*	*ITA*	*FR*
	9425	**9641**	**9547**	**9987**	**9643**	**8815**	**8919**	**9947**	**9427**	**9645**	**8963**	**9551**	**9989**	**9647**	**8923**	**8525**	**9951**	**9431**	**9325**	**9325**	**9555**	**9991**	**9651**
					⑧														①–④	⑤–⑦			
			N			**L**						**B**										**C**	
Torino Porta Nuova .... **605** d.	...	1350	...	...	...	...	...	1430	...	1450	...	...	...	...	...	...	1530	...	1540	⊕	...	...	...
Torino Porta Susa △ .... **605** d.	...	1400	...	...	...	...	...	1440	...	1500	...	...	...	...	...	...	1540	...	1550	1550	...	...	...
Bergamo .... d.	...	|	...	...	...	...	...	|	...	|	...	...	...	...	...	...	|	...	|	|	...	...	...
Brescia .... **605** d.	...	|	...	...	...	...	...	|	...	|	...	...	...	...	...	...	|	...	|	|	...	...	...
Desenzano-Sirmione .... **605** d.	...	|	...	...	...	...	...	|	...	|	...	...	...	...	...	...	|	...	|	|	...	...	...
Peschiera del Garda .... **605** d.	...	|	...	...	...	...	...	|	...	|	...	...	...	...	...	...	|	...	|	|	...	...	...
Bolzano / Bozen .... **595** d.	...	|	...	...	...	...	...	|	...	|	1442	...	...	...	...	1512	|	...	|	|	...	...	...
Trento .... **595** d.	...	|	...	...	...	...	...	|	...	|	1514	...	...	...	...	1543	|	...	|	|	...	...	...
Rovereto .... **595** d.	...	|	...	...	...	...	...	|	...	|	1528	...	...	...	...	1557	|	...	|	|	...	...	...
Verona Porta Nuova .... **595** a.	...	|	...	...	...	...	...	|	...	|	1610	...	...	...	...	1640	|	...	|	|	...	...	...
Verona Porta Nuova .... **605** d.	...	|	...	...	...	...	...	|	...	|	1620	...	...	...	...	1652	|	...	|	|	...	...	...
Milano Centrale .... **605** a.	...	1450	...	...	...	...	...	1530	...	1550	|	...	...	...	...	|	1630	...	|	|	...	...	...
Milano Centrale .... d.	...	1458	1510	1515	1525	...	...	1540	...	1558	|	1610	1615	1630	...	|	1640	...	|	|	1710	1715	1735
Milano Rogoredo .... d.	...	|	1520u	1526	1538u	...	...	1550	...	|	|	1620u	1626	1640u	...	|	1650	...	1704	1704	1720u	1726	|
Reggio Emilia AV .... d.	...	|	1556	|	|	...	...	1628	...	|	|	1656	|	|	...	|	1728	...	1742	1742	1756	|	|
Venezia Santa Lucia .... d.	1426	|	|	|	|	1452	1505	|	1526	|	|	|	|	|	1605	|	|	1626	|	|	|	|	|
Venezia Mestre △ .... **620** d.	1438	|	|	|	|	1504	1517	|	1538	|	|	|	|	|	1617	|	|	1638	|	|	|	|	|
Padova .... **620** d.	1456	|	|	|	|	1521	1535	|	1556	|	|	|	|	|	1635	|	|	1656	|	|	|	|	|
Rovigo .... **620** d.	|	|	|	|	|	1546	|	|	|	|	|	|	|	|	1656	|	|	1717	|	|	|	|	|
Ferrara .... **620** d.	1529	|	|	|	|	1602	1611	|	1629	|	|	|	|	|	|	|	|	|	|	|	|	|	|
Bologna Centrale ● .... **620** a.	1559	1604	1624	|	1634	1637	1639	1654	1659	1704	1714	1724	|	|	1739	1744	1754	1759	1809	1809	1824	|	|
Bologna Centrale ● .... **620** d.	1602	1607	1627	|	1637	...	1642	1657	1702	1707	1717	1727	|	|	1742	1747	1757	1802	1812	1812	1827	|	|
Firenze SMN .... **620** a.	1639	|	1704	|	|	...	1720	1735	1739	|	1754	1804	|	|	1820	1824	1835	1839	1850	1850	1904	|	|
Firenze SMN .... **620** d.	1648	|	1714	|	|	...	1728	1743	1748	|	1803	1814	|	|	1828	1833	1843	1848	1859	1859	1914	|	|
Roma Tiburtina .... **620** a.	1814	|	1840	|	|	...	1854	1909	1914	|	|	1940	|	|	1954	1959	2009	2014	2024	2024	2043	|	|
Roma Termini .... **620** a.	1825	1810	1849	1825	1840	...	1905	1919	1925	1910	1935	1949	1925	1940	2005	2010	2019	2025	2035	2035	2050	2025	2034
Roma Termini .... **640** d.	1835	...	1900	1840	1853	...	1915	1930	1935	...	...	2000	1940	...	2015	2025	2030	2035	2053	2053	2100	...	...
Napoli Afragola .... a.	|	...	1956	|	1948s	...	|	2025	|	...	...	2056	2038	...	|	|	2125	|	2148s	2148s	2156	...	...
Napoli Centrale .... **640** a.	1948	...	2010	1953	2003	...	2028	2043	2048	...	...	2113	2053	...	2145	2133	2143	2148	2203	2203	2212	...	...
Napoli Centrale .... **640** d.	...	...	2020	...	...	...	2040	2055	2101	...	...	2125	...	...	...	...	2155	...	...	...	2223	...	...
Salerno .... **640** a.	...	...	2057	...	...	...	2117	2132	2138	...	...	2205	...	...	...	...	2232	...	...	...	2300	...	...

	ITA	*FA*	*ITA*	*ITA*	*FR*	*FR*	*ITA*	*FR*	*ITA*	*FR*	*FA*	*ITA*	*ITA*	*FR*	*FR*	*FR*	*ITA*	*FR*	*FR*	*FR*	*FR*	*ITA*	*ITA*
	8925	**8527**	**9955**	**9993**	**9433**	**9653**	**8967**	**9559**	**9995**	**9657**	**8529**	**9959**	**9997**	**9435**	**9329**	**9663**	**9961**	**9437**	**9437**	**9567**	**9567**	**9963**	**8163**
													⑧		⑧		⑧	①–⑥	⑦	⑧	⑥⑦	①–⑤	⑥⑦
															P								
Torino Porta Nuova .... **605** d.	...	...	1630	...	...	...	...	1700	...	...	...	1720	...	...	1750	...	...	...	...	1900	1900	1925	1925
Torino Porta Susa △ .... **605** d.	...	...	1640	...	...	...	...	1710	...	...	...	1730	...	...	1800	...	...	...	...	1910	1910	1935	1935
Bergamo .... d.	...	1600	|	...	...	...	...	|	...	...	...	|	...	...	|	...	...	...	...	|	|	|	|
Brescia .... **605** d.	...	1700	|	...	...	...	1729	|	...	...	...	|	...	...	|	...	...	...	...	|	|	|	|
Desenzano-Sirmione .... **605** d.	...	|	|	...	...	...	1743	|	...	...	...	|	...	...	|	...	...	...	...	|	|	|	|
Peschiera del Garda .... **605** d.	...	1725	|	...	...	...	1752	|	...	...	...	|	...	...	|	...	...	...	...	|	|	|	|
Bolzano / Bozen .... **595** d.	...	|	|	...	...	...	|	|	...	...	1710	|	...	...	|	...	...	...	...	|	|	|	|
Trento .... **595** d.	...	|	|	...	...	...	|	|	...	...	1743	|	...	...	|	...	...	...	...	|	|	|	|
Rovereto .... **595** d.	...	|	|	...	...	...	|	|	...	...	1757	|	...	...	|	...	...	...	...	|	|	|	|
Verona Porta Nuova .... **595** a.	...	1741	|	...	...	...	1811	|	...	...	1840	|	...	...	|	...	...	...	...	|	|	|	|
Verona Porta Nuova .... **605** d.	...	1752	|	...	...	...	1822	|	...	...	1852	|	...	...	|	...	...	...	...	|	|	|	|
Milano Centrale .... **605** a.	...	|	1730	...	...	...	|	1802	...	...	|	1830	...	...	1850	...	...	...	...	2002	2002	2030	2030
Milano Centrale .... d.	...	|	1740	1745	...	1758	|	1810	1820	1830	|	1840	1845	...	1900	1925	1940	...	...	2010	2010	2040	2040
Milano Rogoredo .... d.	...	|	1750	|	...	|	|	1820	1829	|	|	|	|	...	|	1938u	1950	...	...	2020	2020	|	|
Reggio Emilia AV .... d.	...	|	1828	|	...	|	|	1856	|	|	|	1928	|	...	1942	|	2028	...	...	2056	2056	2128	2128
Venezia Santa Lucia .... d.	1705	|	|	|	1726	|	|	|	|	|	|	|	|	1826	|	|	|	1926	1926	|	|	|	|
Venezia Mestre △ .... **620** d.	1717	|	|	|	1738	|	|	|	|	|	|	|	|	1838	|	|	|	1938	1938	|	|	|	|
Padova .... **620** d.	1735	|	|	|	1756	|	|	|	|	|	|	|	|	1856	|	|	|	1956	1956	|	|	|	|
Rovigo .... **620** d.	|	|	|	|	|	|	|	|	|	|	|	|	|	|	|	|	|	|	|	|	|	|	|
Ferrara .... **620** d.	1811	|	|	|	1829	|	|	|	|	|	|	|	|	1929	|	|	|	2029	2029	|	|	|	|
Bologna Centrale ● .... **620** a.	1839	1844	1854	1849	1859	1904	1914	1924	|	1934	1944	1954	1949	1959	2009	2034	2054	2059	2059	2124	2124	2154	2154
Bologna Centrale ● .... **620** d.	1842	1847	1857	1852	1902	1907	1917	1927	|	1937	1947	1957	1952	2002	2012	2037	2057	2102	2102	2127	2127	2157	2157
Firenze SMN .... **620** a.	1920	1924	1935	|	1939	|	1954	2004	|	|	2024	2035	|	2039	2050	|	2135	2139	2139	2204	2204	2235	2235
Firenze SMN .... **620** d.	1928	1933	1943	|	1948	|	2003	2014	|	|	2033	2043	|	2048	...	|	2143	2148	2148	2214	2214	2243	2243
Roma Tiburtina .... **620** a.	2054	2059s	2109	2049	2114s	|	2132	2140	|	|	2159s	2209	2149	2214	...	|	2309	2314s	2347s	2340s	0016s	0009	0052
Roma Termini .... **620** a.	2105	2110	2119	2100	2125	2110	2143	2149	2125	2140	2210	2219	2200	2225	...	2240	2319	2325	2356	2349	0025	0019	0102
Roma Termini .... **640** d.	2115	...	2130	...	...	2125	2205	2200	2140	2153	...	2230	...	2235	...	2250	...	...	...	...	...	...	...
Napoli Afragola .... a.	|	...	2225	...	...	|	|	2256s	2237	2248s	...	|	...	2334s	...	|	...	...	...	...	...	...	...
Napoli Centrale .... **640** a.	2228	...	2243	...	...	2233	2318	2312	2253	2303	...	2343	...	2348	...	2359	...	...	...	...	...	...	...
Napoli Centrale .... **640** d.	...	...	...	...	...	2245	...	...	...	...	...	...	...	...	...	...	...	...	...	...	...	...	...
Salerno .... **640** a.	...	...	...	...	...	2322	...	...	...	...	...	...	...	...	...	...	...	...	...	...	...	...	...

NOTES for pages 289 and 290.

A – To Bari (Tables **615**).
B – To Battipaglia (Table **640**).
C – To Caserta (Table **615**).
G – From Genova (Table **610**).
L – To Lecce (Tables **615**).
N – To Taranto (Tables **615**).
P – To Perugia (Table **620**).
R – To Reggio di Calabria (Table **640**).
S – To Sibari (Tables **640**).
T – From Trieste (Table **601**).
U – From Udine (Table **601**).

d – ②③④⑥.
e – ①⑤⑦.
f – Train **8139** on ©.
s – Calls to set down only.
u – Calls to pick up only.

◧ – To Fiumicino Aeroporto ✈ (a. 1407).
⊕ – From Bardonecchia (d. 1440) and Oulx (d. 1451).
△ – Most trains call to pick up only.
● – Most services use underground platforms 16–19; allow a minimum of 10 minutes when connecting with services from / to the main station.

Italo, Trenitalia

HIGH-SPEED SERVICES 600

All trains 🄡 and 🍸. *FA, FB* and *FR* trains are operated by Trenitalia (www.trenitalia.com). *ITA* trains are operated by Italo (www.italotreno.it). Trenitalia tickets and passes are not valid on Italo trains. Trains may use different numbers for part of their journey.

km		*FR*	*ITA*	*FR*	*FR*	*FR*	*ITA*	*ITA*	*FR*	*FR*	*ITA*	*FR*	*ITA*	*FR*	*FA*	*ITA*	*FR*	*FR*	*ITA*	*FR*	*FR*	*ITA*	*FR*	*ITA*
		9782	**9900**	**9600**	**9300**	**9400**	**9904**	**8900**	**9508**	**9606**	**9966**	**9404**	**9908**	**9608**	**8502**	**9968**	**9512**	**9610**	**8954**	**9304**	**9304**	**9970**	**9406**	**9912**
			①–⑥		①–⑥	①–⑥	①–⑥			①–⑤	①–⑥			①–⑥				①–⑥		①–④	⑤–⑦			
					P																			
	Salerno 640 d.	...	...	...	...	...	...	...	...	...	...	...	...	0515	...	...	...	...	...	...	...	...	...	...
	Napoli Centrale 640 a.	...	...	...	...	...	...	...	...	...	...	...	...	│	...	...	...	...	...	...	...	...	...	...
	Napoli Centrale 640 d.	...	...	...	...	...	...	...	...	0500	...	...	0514	│	...	0535	0545	...	0550	0523	0523	0602	0609	0620
	Napoli Afragola d.	...	...	...	...	...	...	...	...	0515u	...	...	0529	0542	...	0550	0602u	...	│	⊖	⊖	0616	│	│
0	**Roma** Termini 640 a.	...	...	...	...	...	...	...	...	0610	...	...	0630	0640	...	0646	0700	...	0705	0715	0715	0720	0725	0730
4	**Roma** Termini 620 d.	...	...	...	...	0535	0540	0555	0600	0625	0630	0635	0640	0650	0650	0705	0710	0720	0725	0725	0725	0730	0735	0740
261	**Roma** Tiburtina 620 d.	...	...	...	...	0545u	0550	0605	0610u	│	0640	0645u	0650	│	0700u	│	0720	│	│	0735	0735	0740	0745	0750
—	**Firenze** SMN 620 a.	...	...	...	...	0711	0717	0731	0746	│	│	0811	0817	│	0827	│	0846	│	0857	0901	0901	│	0911	0917
	Firenze SMN 620 d.	...	...	...	0710	0720	0725	0739	0755	│	│	0820	0825	│	0836	│	0855	│	0905	0910	0910	│	0920	0925
	Bologna Centrale ● 620 a.	...	...	...	0748	0758	0803	0818	0833	│	0838	0858	0903	0853	0913	0908	0933	0923	0943	0948	0948	│	0958	1003
0	**Bologna** Centrale ● 620 d.	...	...	...	0751	0801	0806	0821	0836	│	0841	0901	0906	0856	0916	0911	0936	0926	0946	0951	0951	│	1001	1006
47	Ferrara 620 d.	...	...	...	│	0829	│	0849	│	│	│	0929	│	│	│	│	│	│	│	│	│	│	1029	│
79	Rovigo 620 d.	...	...	...	│	│	│	│	│	│	│	│	│	│	│	│	│	│	│	│	│	│	│	│
123	Padova 620 d.	...	...	...	│	0906	│	0927	│	│	│	1006	│	│	│	│	│	│	│	│	│	│	1106	│
151	**Venezia** Mestre ▽ 620 a.	...	...	...	│	0923	│	0942	│	│	│	1023	│	│	│	│	│	│	│	│	│	│	1123	│
160	**Venezia** Santa Lucia a.	...	...	...	│	0934	│	0955	│	│	│	1034	│	│	│	│	│	│	│	│	│	│	1134	│
	Reggio Emilia AV d.	...	...	...	0813	...	0830	...	0900	│	│	...	0930	│	│	│	1000	│	│	1013	1013	│	...	1030
	Milano Rogoredo a.	...	...	...	│	...	0908	...	0938	│	│	...	│	│	│	│	1038s	1020s	│	│	│	1032	...	│
	Milano Centrale a.	...	...	...	0858	...	0920	...	0950	0924	0945	...	1020	0958	│	1015	1050	1035	│	1058	1058	1045	...	1120
	Milano Centrale 605 d.	0653	0730	0753	0910	...	0930	...	1002	...	...	...	1030	...	│	...	...	...	│	1110	1110	...	...	1130
114	**Verona** Porta Nuova 605 a.	│	│	│	│	...	│	...	│	...	...	...	│	...	1008	...	...	...	1038	│	│	...	...	│
114	**Verona** Porta Nuova 595 d.	│	│	│	│	...	│	...	│	...	...	...	│	...	1020	...	...	...	1050	│	│	...	...	│
182	Rovereto 595 d.	│	│	│	│	...	│	...	│	...	...	...	│	...	1103	...	...	...	1132	│	│	...	...	│
206	Trento 595 d.	│	│	│	│	...	│	...	│	...	...	...	│	...	1117	...	...	...	1146	│	│	...	...	│
261	**Bolzano / Bozen** 595 a.	│	│	│	│	...	│	...	│	...	...	...	│	...	1151	...	...	...	1218	│	│	...	...	│
137	Peschiera del Garda 605 d.	│	│	│	│	...	│	...	│	...	...	...	│	...	...	...	...	...	...	│	│	...	...	│
151	Desenzano-Sirmione 605 d.	│	│	│	│	...	│	...	│	...	...	...	│	...	...	...	...	...	...	│	│	...	...	│
179	**Brescia** 605 a.	│	│	│	│	...	│	...	│	...	...	...	│	...	...	...	...	...	...	│	│	...	...	│
229	**Bergamo** a.	│	│	│	│	...	│	...	│	...	...	...	│	...	...	...	...	...	...	│	│	...	...	│
	Torino Porta Susa ▽ 605 a.	0743	0818	0845	0959	...	1018	...	1051	...	...	...	1124	...	...	...	...	...	...	1159	1208	...	...	1229
	Torino Porta Nuova 605 a.	0757	0830	0857	1010	...	1030	...	1103	...	...	...	1135	...	...	...	...	...	...	1210	⊙	...	...	1240

	ITA	*ITA*	*FR*	*FR*	*ITA*	*FR*	*ITA*	*FR*	*FR*	*ITA*	*ITA*	*FR*	*FR*	*FR*	*ITA*	*FR*	*ITA*	*ITA*	*FR*	*FR*	*FR*	*FR*	*ITA*	*FA*
	8904	**9972**	**9516**	**9616**	**8956**	**9490**	**9918**	**9618**	**8506**	**8906**	**9974**	**9520**	**9620**	**9414**	**9922**	**8508**	**8908**	**9976**	**9524**	**9624**	**9310**	**9416**	**9924**	**8509**
				①–⑥																				
		C	**B**																					**S**
Salerno 640 d.	...	...	0550	...	...	0610	0620	...	...	...	...	0651	...	0713	0720	...	...	...	0744	...	...	...	...	0913
Napoli Centrale 640 a.	...	...	0628	...	...	0647	0658	...	...	...	...	0730	...	0753	0758	...	...	...	0822	...	...	...	...	│
Napoli Centrale 640 d.	0610	...	0640	0655	0702	0709	0720	...	0730	...	0740	0745	...	0809	0820	...	0830	...	0840	...	0855	...	0920	│
Napoli Afragola d.	│	...	0658	0710u	│	│	0735	...	│	...	│	0801	...	│	0835	...	│	...	0858	...	0908u	...	0933	0941
Roma Termini 640 a.	0735	...	0755	0804	0815	0820	0830	...	0840	...	0851	0900	...	0925	0930	...	0945	...	0955	...	1008	...	1030	1040
Roma Termini 620 d.	0755	0805	0810	0820	0825	0835	0840	0850	0850	0855	0905	0910	0920	0935	0943	0950	0955	1005	1010	1020	1025	1035	1040	1050
Roma Tiburtina 620 d.	0805	│	0820	│	│	0845	0850	│	0900u	0905	│	0920	│	0945	0951	1000u	1005	│	1020	│	1035	1045u	1050	1100
Firenze SMN 620 a.	0931	│	0946	│	0957	1011	1017	│	1027	1031	│	1046	│	1111	1117	1127	1131	│	1146	│	1201	1211	1217	1227
Firenze SMN 620 d.	0939	│	0955	│	1005	1020	1025	│	1036	1039	│	1055	│	1120	1125	1136	1139	│	1155	│	1210	1220	1225	1236
Bologna Centrale ● 620 a.	1018	1008	1033	1023	1043	1058	1103	1053	1113	1118	1108	1133	│	1158	1203	1213	1218	1208	1233	1223	1248	1258	1303	1313
Bologna Centrale ● 620 d.	1021	1011	1036	1026	1046	1101	1106	1056	1116	1121	1111	1136	│	1201	1206	1216	1221	1211	1236	1226	1251	1301	1306	1316
Ferrara 620 d.	│	│	│	│	│	│	│	│	│	1149	│	│	│	1229	│	│	1249	│	│	│	│	1329	│	│
Rovigo 620 d.	1106	│	│	│	│	1145	│	│	│	│	│	│	│	│	│	│	│	│	│	│	│	│	│	│
Padova 620 d.	1127	│	│	│	│	1206	│	│	│	1227	│	│	│	1306	│	│	1327	│	│	│	│	1406	│	│
Venezia Mestre ▽ 620 a.	1142	│	│	│	│	1223	│	│	│	1242	│	│	│	1323	│	│	1342	│	│	│	│	1423	│	│
Venezia Santa Lucia a.	1155	│	│	│	│	1234	│	│	│	1255	│	│	│	1334	│	│	1355	│	│	│	│	1434	│	│
Reggio Emilia AV d.	...	│	1100	│	│	...	1130	│	│	...	│	1200	│	...	1230	│	...	│	1300	│	1315	...	1330	│
Milano Rogoredo a.	...	│	1138	1120s	│	...	1208	│	│	...	│	1238s	1218s	...	1308	│	...	│	1338s	1320s	1355	...	1410	│
Milano Centrale a.	...	1115	1150	1135	│	...	1220	1158	│	...	1215	1250	1230	...	1320	│	...	1315	1350	1335	│	...	1420	│
Milano Centrale 605 d.	...	...	1202	...	│	...	1230	...	│	...	...	...	...	...	1330	│	...	...	...	...	│	...	1430	│
Verona Porta Nuova 605 a.	...	...	│	...	1138	...	│	...	1208	...	...	...	...	...	│	1308	...	...	...	...	│	...	│	1408
Verona Porta Nuova 595 d.	...	...	│	...	1149	...	│	...	1220	...	...	...	...	...	│	1320	...	...	...	...	│	...	│	1420
Rovereto 595 d.	...	...	│	...	│	...	│	...	1303	...	...	...	...	...	│	│	...	...	...	...	│	...	│	1503
Trento 595 d.	...	...	│	...	│	...	│	...	1317	...	...	...	...	...	│	│	...	...	...	...	│	...	│	1517
Bolzano / Bozen 595 a.	...	...	│	...	│	...	│	...	1348	...	...	...	...	...	│	│	...	...	...	...	│	...	│	1548
Peschiera del Garda 605 d.	...	...	│	...	1207	...	│	...	...	...	...	...	...	...	│	1336	...	...	...	...	│	...	│	...
Desenzano-Sirmione 605 d.	...	...	│	...	1216	...	│	...	...	...	...	...	...	...	│	│	...	...	...	...	│	...	│	...
Brescia 605 a.	...	...	│	...	1231	...	│	...	...	...	...	...	...	...	│	1400	...	...	...	...	│	...	│	...
Bergamo a.	...	...	│	...	...	...	│	...	...	...	...	...	...	...	│	1500	...	...	...	...	│	...	│	...
Torino Porta Susa ▽ 605 a.	...	...	1249	...	...	...	1318	...	...	...	...	...	...	...	1418	...	...	...	...	...	1508	...	1520	...
Torino Porta Nuova 605 a.	...	...	1300	...	...	...	1330	...	...	...	...	...	...	...	1430	...	...	...	...	...	1520	...	1530	...

	ITA	*ITA*	*FR*	*FR*	*FR*	*ITA*	*FA*	*ITA*	*ITA*	*FR*	*ITA*	*FR*	*ITA*	*FR*	*ITA*	*ITA*	*FR*	*FR*	*FR*	*ITA*	*ITA*	*FA*	*FR*	*FR*
	8912	**9978**	**9514**	**9628**	**8418**	**9928**	**8816**	**8914**	**9980**	**9532**	**8960**	**9420**	**9932**	**9634**	**8916**	**9982**	**9584**	**9636**	**9422**	**8146**	**9984**	**9751**	**9540**	**9640**
				①–⑤													①–④	①–⑤				①–⑤		Ⓑ
			N		**R**	**A**	**L**										**R**			**R**				
Salerno 640 d.	0838	...	0846	...	0954	...	...	...	...	...	...	...	...	...	...	...	1051	...	...	1122	...	...	...	...
Napoli Centrale 640 a.	0923	...	0928	...	│	...	...	...	...	...	...	...	...	...	...	...	1127	...	...	1158	...	...	...	...
Napoli Centrale 640 d.	0935	...	0940	0955	│	...	...	...	1035	1040	...	1109	1120	1130	...	1135	1140	1155	1209	1215	...	...	1240	1255
Napoli Afragola d.	│	...	0958	1010u	1020	...	...	...	│	1057u	...	│	1135	│	...	│	1158	1210u	│	1230	...	...	1258u	1310u
Roma Termini 640 a.	1045	...	1055	1105	1125	...	...	...	1145	1200	...	1219	1230	1239	...	1245	1300	1305	1320	1330	...	...	1355	1405
Roma Termini 620 d.	1055	1105	1110	1120	1135	1140	...	1155	1205	1210	1225	1236	1240	1250	1255	1305	1310	1320	1335	1340	1405	...	1410	1420
Roma Tiburtina 620 d.	1105	│	1120	│	1145	1150	...	1205	│	1220	│	1245	1250	│	1305	│	1320	│	1345	1350	│	...	1420	│
Firenze SMN 620 a.	1231	│	1246	│	1311	1317	...	1331	│	1346	1357	1411	1417	│	1431	│	1446	│	1511	1517	│	...	1546	│
Firenze SMN 620 d.	1239	│	1255	│	1320	1325	...	1339	│	1355	1405	1420	1425	│	1439	│	1455	│	1520	1525	│	...	1555	│
Bologna Centrale ● 620 a.	1318	1308	1333	1323	1358	1403	...	1418	│	1433	1443	1458	1503	1453	1518	1508	1533	│	1558	1603	│	...	1633	│
Bologna Centrale ● 620 d.	1321	1311	1336	1326	1401	1406	1418	1421	│	1436	1446	1501	1506	1456	1521	1511	1536	│	1601	1606	│	...	1636	│
Ferrara 620 d.	1349	│	│	│	1429	│	1440	│	│	│	│	│	│	│	1552	│	│	│	1629	│	│	...	│	│
Rovigo 620 d.	│	│	│	│	│	│	1457	1506	│	│	│	1545	│	│	│	│	│	│	│	│	│	...	│	│
Padova 620 d.	1427	│	│	│	1506	│	1533	1527	│	│	│	1606	│	│	1627	│	│	│	1706	│	│	...	│	│
Venezia Mestre ▽ 620 a.	1442	│	│	│	1523	│	1556	1542	│	│	│	1623	│	│	1642	│	│	│	1723	│	│	...	│	│
Venezia Santa Lucia a.	1455	│	│	│	1534	│	1608	1555	│	│	│	1634	│	│	1655	│	│	│	1734	│	│	...	│	│
Reggio Emilia AV d.	...	│	1400	│	...	1435	...	...	│	1500	│	...	1530	│	...	│	1600	│	...	1635	│	...	1700	│
Milano Rogoredo a.	...	│	1438	1420s	...	│	...	...	1502	1538	│	...	1608	│	...	│	1638	1618s	...	│	1702	...	1738s	1718s
Milano Centrale a.	...	1415	1450	1435	...	1520	...	...	1515	1550	│	...	1620	1558	...	1615	1650	1635	...	1720	1715	...	1750	1730
Milano Centrale 605 d.	...	...	1502	...	...	1530	...	...	...	1602	│	...	...	...	...	...	1702	...	...	1730	...	1745	...	...
Verona Porta Nuova 605 a.	...	...	│	...	...	│	...	...	...	│	1538	...	...	...	...	...	│	...	...	│	...	1858	...	...
Verona Porta Nuova 595 d.	...	...	│	...	...	│	...	...	...	│	1549	...	...	...	...	...	│	...	...	│	...	1920	...	...
Rovereto 595 d.	...	...	│	...	...	│	...	...	...	│	│	...	...	...	...	...	│	...	...	│	...	2003	...	...
Trento 595 d.	...	...	│	...	...	│	...	...	...	│	│	...	...	...	...	...	│	...	...	│	...	2017	...	...
Bolzano / Bozen 595 a.	...	...	│	...	...	│	...	...	...	│	│	...	...	...	...	...	│	...	...	│	...	2048	...	...
Peschiera del Garda 605 d.	...	...	│	...	...	│	...	...	...	│	1607	...	...	...	...	...	│	...	...	│	...	...	...	...
Desenzano-Sirmione 605 d.	...	...	│	...	...	│	...	...	...	│	1616	...	...	...	...	...	│	...	...	│	...	...	...	...
Brescia 605 a.	...	...	│	...	...	│	...	...	...	│	1631	...	...	...	...	...	│	...	...	│	...	...	...	...
Bergamo a.	...	...	│	...	...	│	...	...	...	│	...	...	...	...	...	...	│	...	...	│	...	...	...	...
Torino Porta Susa ▽ 605 a.	...	...	1549	...	...	1629	...	...	...	1649	...	...	...	...	...	...	1749	...	...	1824	...	...	...	...
Torino Porta Nuova 605 a.	...	...	1600	...	...	1640	...	...	...	1700	...	...	...	...	...	...	1800	...	...	1835	...	...	...	...

FOR FOOTNOTES SEE NEXT PAGE →

600 HIGH-SPEED SERVICES

Italo, Trenitalia

All trains 🄡 and 🍷. *FA, FB* and *FR* trains are operated by Trenitalia (www.trenitalia.com). *ITA* trains are operated by Italo (www.italotreno.it). Trenitalia tickets and passes are not valid on Italo trains. Trains may use different numbers for part of their journey.

	FR	FR	ITA	FR	ITA	ITA	FR	FR	FR	FR	FR	ITA	ITA	FR	FR	FR	FR	ITA	FR	ITA	ITA	FR	FR	FR
	9796	9423	9940	9642	8918	9986	9544	9644	9320	9320	9426	9946	9988	9588	9648	9480	9428	9948	8524	8920	9990	9552	9652	9430
																							⑧	
					T				g	h				R		T				U				U
Salerno 640 d.	...	...	...	...	...	...	1250	...	...	...	...	...	1343	1354	...	...	...	...	...	...	...	1445	...	...
Napoli Centrale 640 a.	...	...	...	...	...	...	1328	...	...	...	...	...	1423	1428	...	...	...	...	...	...	...	1523	...	...
Napoli Centrale 640 d.	...	⊡	1320	1330	1335	...	1340	...	1355	1355	1410	1420	1435	1440	1500	...	1509	1520	...	1535	...	1540	1555	1609
Napoli Afragola d.	...	|	1335	|	|	...	1354	...	1409u	1409u	|	1435	|	1458	1515u	...	|	1535	...	|	...	1558	1610u	|
Roma Termini 640 a.	...	1425	1430	1440	1446	...	1455	...	1505	1505	1520	1530	1550	1555	1610	...	1620	1630	...	1645	...	1700	1705	1719
Roma Termini 620 d.	...	1435	1440	1450	1455	1505	1510	1520	1525	1525	1535	1540	1610	1610	1625	1630	1635	1640	1650	1655	1705	1710	1720	1735
Roma Tiburtina 620 d.	...	1445	1450	|	1505	|	1520	|	1535	|	1545	1550	|	1620	|	1640u	1645	1650	1700u	1705	|	1720	|	1845
Firenze SMN 620 a.	...	1611	1617	|	1631	|	1646	|	1701	1701	1711	1717	|	1746	|	|	1811	1817	1827	1831	|	1846	|	1911
Firenze SMN 620 d.	...	1620	1625	|	1639	|	1655	|	1710	1710	1720	1725	|	1755	|	|	1820	1825	1836	1839	|	1855	|	1920
Bologna Centrale ● 620 a.	...	1658	1703	1653	1718	1708	1733	|	1748	1748	1758	1803	|	1833	|	1838	1858	1903	1913	1918	1908	1933	1923	1958
Bologna Centrale ● 620 d.	...	1701	1706	1656	1721	1711	1736	|	1751	1751	1801	1806	|	1836	|	1841	1901	1906	1916	1921	1911	1936	1926	2001
Ferrara 620 d.	...	|	|	|	1752	|	|	|	|	|	1829	|	|	|	|	|	1929	|	|	1949	|	|	|	|
Rovigo 620 d.	...	1745	|	|	|	|	|	|	|	|	|	|	|	|	|	|	|	|	|	|	|	|	|	2045
Padova 620 d.	...	1806	|	|	1827	|	|	|	|	|	1906	|	|	|	|	1942	2006	|	|	2025	|	|	|	2106
Venezia Mestre ▽ 620 a.	...	1823	|	|	1842	|	|	|	|	|	1923	|	|	|	|	1956	2023	|	|	2040	|	|	|	2123
Venezia Santa Lucia a.	...	1834	|	|	...	|	|	|	|	|	1934	|	|	|	|	...	2034	|	|	...	|	|	|	...
Reggio Emilia AV d.	...	...	1730	|	...	|	1800	|	1813	1813	...	1835	|	1900	|	...	...	1930	|	...	|	2000	|	...
Milano Rogoredo a.	...	...	1808	|	...	|	1838s	1818s	|	|	...	1908	1902	1938	|	...	...	2008	|	...	|	2038	|	...
Milano Centrale a.	...	...	1820	1800	...	1815	1850	1830	1900	1900	...	1920	1915	1950	1924	...	...	2020	|	...	2015	2050	2030	...
Milano Centrale 605 d.	1753	...	1830	1810	...	...	...	...	1910	1910	...	1930	...	2002	...	...	...	...	|	...	...	2102	2053	...
Verona Porta Nuova 605 a.	|	...	|	|	...	...	...	...	|	|	...	|	...	|	...	...	...	...	2008	...	...	|	|	...
Verona Porta Nuova 595 d.	|	...	|	|	...	...	...	...	|	|	...	|	...	|	...	...	...	...	2020	...	...	|	|	...
Rovereto 595 d.	|	...	|	|	...	...	...	...	|	|	...	|	...	|	...	...	...	...	2103	...	...	|	|	...
Trento 595 d.	|	...	|	|	...	...	...	...	|	|	...	|	...	|	...	...	...	...	2117	...	...	|	|	...
Bolzano / Bozen 595 a.	|	...	|	|	...	...	...	...	|	|	...	|	...	|	...	...	...	...	2148	...	...	|	|	...
Peschiera del Garda 605 d.	|	...	|	|	...	...	...	...	|	|	...	|	...	|	...	...	...	...	...	...	...	|	|	...
Desenzano-Sirmione 605 d.	|	...	|	|	...	...	...	...	|	|	...	|	...	|	...	...	...	...	...	...	...	|	|	...
Brescia 605 a.	|	...	|	|	...	...	...	...	|	|	...	|	...	|	...	...	...	...	...	...	...	|	|	...
Bergamo a.	|	...	|	|	...	...	...	...	|	|	...	|	...	|	...	...	...	...	...	...	...	|	2143	...
Torino Porta Susa ▽ 605 a.	1848	...	1918	1859	...	...	...	...	1959	1959	...	2018	...	2049	...	...	...	...	...	...	...	2149	...	...
Torino Porta Nuova 605 a.	1900	...	1930	1910	...	...	...	...	2010	2010	...	2030	...	2100	...	...	...	...	...	...	...	2200	...	...

	ITA	FR	FB	ITA	ITA	FR	FR	ITA	FR	ITA	FR	ITA	FR	FR	ITA	FR	ITA	FR	FR	FR	ITA	ITA	ITA	FR
	9952	9658	8828	8922	9965	9556	9660	8966	9432	9956	9662	9994	8528	9560	8968	9434	8160	9668	9330	9330	9996	9964	8166	9568
																		⑧	⑤⑥	⑦–④	⑧	⑥⑦	①–⑤	⑧
	A	R	L		G									L			R							
Salerno 640 d.	...	1617	...	...	...	...	...	...	...	1625	...	...	...	...	...	...	1722	...	...	...	...	1814	1814	...
Napoli Centrale 640 a.	...	|	...	...	...	...	...	...	...	1705	...	...	...	...	...	...	1758	...	...	...	...	1858	1858	...
Napoli Centrale 640 d.	...	|	...	1635	1620	1640	1655	...	1704	1720	1725	1730	...	...	1755	1809	1820	1830	...	...	1835	1920	1920	1940
Napoli Afragola d.	...	1641	...	|	|	1658u	1709u	...	|	1734	|	1748	...	...	|	|	|	|	...	...	|	1935	1935	1958u
Roma Termini 640 a.	...	1740	...	1745	1730	1755	1805	...	1815	1830	1835	1846	...	...	1910	1920	1930	1940	...	...	1946	2030	2030	2055
Roma Termini 620 d.	1740	1750	...	1755	1805	1810	1820	1825	1835	1840	1850	1905	1850	1911	1925	1935	1940	1950	1950	1950	2005	2040	2040	2110
Roma Tiburtina 620 d.	1750	|	...	1805	|	1819	|	|	1845	1850	|	|	1900u	1920	|	1945	1950	|	2000u	2000u	|	2050	2050	2120
Firenze SMN 620 a.	1917	|	...	1931	|	1946	|	1957	2032	2017	|	|	2027	2046	2057	2111	2117	|	2127	2127	|	2217	2217	2258
Firenze SMN 620 d.	1925	|	...	1939	|	1955	|	2005	2041	2025	|	|	2036	2055	2105	2120	2125	|	2136	2136	|	2225	2225	...
Bologna Centrale ● 620 a.	2003	1953	...	2018	|	2033	2023	2043	2118	2103	2053	2108	2113	2133	2143	2158	2203	2153	2213	2213	|	2303	2303	...
Bologna Centrale ● 620 d.	2006	1956	2018	2021	|	2036	2026	2046	2121	2106	2056	2111	2116	2136	2146	2201	2206	2156	2216	2216	|	2306	2306	...
Ferrara 620 d.	|	|	2042	|	|	|	|	|	2152	|	|	|	|	|	|	2229	|	|	|	|	|	|	|	...
Rovigo 620 d.	|	|	2108	2101	|	|	|	|	|	|	|	|	|	|	|	|	|	|	|	|	|	|	|	...
Padova 620 d.	|	|	2140	2127	|	|	|	|	2229	|	|	|	|	|	|	2306	|	|	|	|	|	|	|	...
Venezia Mestre ▽ 620 a.	|	|	2156	2142	|	|	|	|	2242	|	|	|	|	|	|	2323	|	|	|	|	|	|	|	...
Venezia Santa Lucia a.	|	|	2208	2155	|	|	|	|	2255	|	|	|	|	|	|	2334	|	|	|	|	|	|	|	...
Reggio Emilia AV d.	2030	|	...	...	|	2100	|	|	...	2130	|	|	|	2200	|	...	2235	|	|	|	|	2330	2330	...
Milano Rogoredo a.	|	|	...	...	2103	2138s	|	|	...	2208	|	|	|	2238s	|	...	|	|	|	|	2302	0008	0030	...
Milano Centrale a.	2120	2100	...	...	2115	2150	2130	|	...	2220	2200	2215	|	2250	|	...	2320	2300	0015	0035	2315	0020	0040	...
Milano Centrale 605 d.	2130	...	...	...	...	...	2145	|	...	...	2210	2230	|	...	|	...	...	...	...	...	...	...	...	...
Verona Porta Nuova 605 a.	|	...	...	...	...	...	|	2138	...	...	|	|	2208	...	2238	...	...	...	...	...	...	...	...	...
Verona Porta Nuova 595 d.	|	...	...	...	...	...	|	2150	...	...	|	|	2220	...	2249	...	...	...	...	...	...	...	...	...
Rovereto 595 d.	|	...	...	...	...	...	|	2232	...	...	|	|	|	...	|	...	...	...	...	...	...	...	...	...
Trento 595 d.	|	...	...	...	...	...	|	2246	...	...	|	|	|	...	|	...	...	...	...	...	...	...	...	...
Bolzano / Bozen 595 a.	|	...	...	...	...	...	|	2318	...	...	|	|	|	...	|	...	...	...	...	...	...	...	...	...
Peschiera del Garda 605 d.	|	...	...	...	...	...	|	...	...	...	|	|	|	...	2307	...	...	...	...	...	...	...	...	...
Desenzano-Sirmione 605 d.	|	...	...	...	...	...	|	...	...	...	|	|	|	...	2316	...	...	...	...	...	...	...	...	...
Brescia 605 a.	|	...	...	...	...	...	2223	...	...	...	|	|	2300	...	2331	...	...	...	...	...	...	...	...	...
Bergamo a.	|	...	...	...	...	...	...	...	...	...	|	|	2340	...	0010	...	...	...	...	...	...	...	...	...
Torino Porta Susa ▽ 605 a.	2229	...	...	...	...	...	...	...	...	...	2259	2319	...	...	...	...	...	...	...	...	...	...	...	...
Torino Porta Nuova 605 a.	2240	...	...	...	...	...	...	...	...	...	2310	2330	...	...	...	...	...	...	...	...	...	...	...	...

NOTES for pages 291 and 292.

A – From Bari (Tables **615**).
B – From Battipaglia (Table **640**).
C – From Caserta (Table **615**).
G – To Genova (Table **610**).
L – From Lecce (Tables **615**).
N – From Taranto (Tables **615**).
P – From Perugia (Table **620**).
R – From Reggio di Calabria (Table **640**).
S – From Sibari (Tables **640**).
T – To Trieste (Table **601**).
U – To Udine (Table **601**).

g – ①②③⑥.
h – ④⑤⑦.
s – Calls to set down only.
u – Calls to pick up only.

⊡ – From Fiumicino Aeroporto ✈ (a. 1353).
⊖ – Via Cassino (d. 0605).
⊙ – To Oulx (a. 1312) and Bardonecchia (a. 1325).
▽ – Most trains call to set down only.
● – Most services use underground platforms 16 – 19; allow a minimum of 10 minutes when connecting with services from / to the main station.

VENEZIA - UDINE and TRIESTE 601

For Venezia / Udine / Trieste - Ljubljana trains see Table **87**. For Udine - Villach trains see Table **88**.

km		*ICN* 774	*FR* 9707	*IC* 588	*ITA* 8918	*FR* 9480	*IC* 592	*FR* 9759		
		A✣			B					
	Roma Termini **600 620** ...... d.	2235	...	1022	1455	1630	1530	...	...	...
	Bologna C **600 620** .... d.	0333	...	1446	1721	1841	2000	...	...	...
	Torino P Nuova **605** .... d.	|	...	|	|	|	|	1840	...	...
	Milano Centrale **605** .... d.	|	0745	|	|	|	|	|	...	...
	Milano P Garibaldi **605** ... d.	|	|	|	|	|	|	1943	...	...
0	**Venezia** Mestre .... d.	0525	1011	1640	1855	2010	2151	2205	...	...
33	S. Dona di Piave-Jesolo .... ◧ d.	|	1039	1705	|	|	2212	|	...	...
60	Portogruaro-Caorle .... d.	|	1057	1728	1947	|	2237	|	...	...
74	Latisana-Lignano-Bibione ...... d.	●	1108	1739	1959	|	2249	2242	...	...
103	Cervignano-Aquileia-Grado ... d.	|	1126	1757	|	|	2307	2301	...	...
115	Trieste Airport ✈ .... d.	|	1135	1807	|	2125	2317	2310	...	...
–	Gorizia Centrale ⊡ .... d.	0816	|	|	|	|	|	|	...	...
120	Monfalcone .... d.	0834	1142	1814	2030	|	2324	2317	...	...
148	**Trieste** Centrale .... a.	0901	1205	1837	2053	2155	2347	2340	...	...

	FR 9712	*FR* 9466	*IC* 584	*ITA* 8902	*IC* 594	*FA* 9758	*ICN* 770		
				B			A✣		
Trieste Centrale .... d.	0600	0642	0721	0810	1227	1705	1950	...	...
Monfalcone .... d.	0625	|	0747	0834	1252	1730	2014	...	...
Gorizia Centrale ⊡ .... d.	|	|	|	|	|	|	2038	...	...
Trieste Airport ✈ .... d.	0631	0707	0753	|	1258	1736	|	...	...
Cervignano-Aquileia-Grado. d.	0639	|	0802	|	1307	1743	|	...	...
Latisana-Lignano-Bibione ... d.	0655	|	0822	0904	1324	1759	●	...	...
Portogruaro-Caorle .... d.	|	|	0834	0914	1334	1809	|	...	...
S. Dona di Piave-Jesolo . ◧ d.	|	|	0852	|	1352	1825	|	...	...
Venezia Mestre .... a.	0741	0819	0919	0955	1414	1850	2315	...	...
Milano P Garibaldi **605** a.	0955	|	|	|	|	|	|	...	...
Milano Centrale **605** .... a.	|	|	|	|	|	2115	|	...	...
Torino P Nuova **605** .... a.	1058	|	|	|	|	...	|	...	...
Bologna C **600 620** .... a.	...	0949	1112	1139	1614	...	0109	...	...
Roma Termini **600 620** ... a.	...	1200	1535	1405	2040	...	0635	...	...

km		*ICN* 774	*RJ* 132	*RJ* 130	*ITA* 8994	*ITA* 8920	*FA* 9755	*FR* 9430		
		A✣				C		C		
	Roma Termini **600 620** ...... d.	2235	...	...	...	1655	...	1735	...	...
	Bologna C **600 620** .... d.	0333	...	...	...	1921	...	2001	...	...
	Milano Centrale **605** .... d.	|	...	...	1735	|	1845	|	...	...
0	**Venezia** Santa Lucia .... d.	0548	0955	1555	|	|	|	|	...	...
9	**Venezia** Mestre .... d.	|	1007	1607	2000	2051	2110	2137	...	...
30	Treviso Centrale .... d.	0614	1030	1630	2028	2109	2130	2156	...	...
57	Conegliano .... d.	0636	|	|	2046	2127	2148	2215	...	...
74	Sacile .... d.	0654	|	|	|	|	|	|	...	...
87	Pordenone .... d.	0705	1107	1707	2106	2147	2208	2236	...	...
136	**Udine** .... a.	0743	1144	1744	2140	2217	2237	2305	...	...
	Wien Hbf **88** .... a.	...	1735	2335	...	...	...	...	...	...

	FA 9713	*FR* 9409	*ITA* 8971	*ITA* 8907	*RJ* 131	*RJ* 133	*ICN* 770		
		C		D			A✣		
Wien Hbf **88** .... d.	...	...	...	...	0625	1225	...	...	...
Udine .... d.	0615	0647	0716	0727	1218	1818	2059	...	...
Pordenone .... d.	0646	0721	0749	0800	1251	1851	2133	...	...
Sacile .... d.	|	|	|	|	|	|	2143	...	...
Conegliano.......................... d.	0706	0750	0812	0823	|	|	2156	...	...
Treviso Centrale................. d.	0731	0813	0831	0845	1332	1932	2215	...	...
Venezia Mestre .... a.	0749	0825	0855	0908	1353	1953	|	...	...
Venezia Santa Lucia......... a.	|	|	|	|	1405	2005	2238	...	...
Milano Centrale **605** .... a.	1015	|	1125	|	...	...	|	...	...
Bologna C **600 620** .... a.	...	0959	...	1039	...	...	0109	...	...
Roma Termini **600 620** ... a.	...	1225	...	1305	...	...	0635	...	...

km																								
		⚒																					Ⓑ	
0	**Venezia** Santa Lucia .... d.	...	...	...	0639	0739	...	0939	1039	...	1239	1339	...	1439	1539	...	1639	1739	...	1839	1939	...	2101	2239
9	**Venezia** Mestre .... d.	...	0551	...	0651	0751	...	0951	1051	...	1251	1351	...	1451	1551	...	1651	1751	...	1851	1951	...	2114	2251
42	S. Dona di Piave-Jesolo .... ◧ d.	...	0615	...	0715	0815	...	1015	1115	...	1315	1415	...	1515	1615	...	1715	1815	...	1915	2015	...	|	2315
69	Portogruaro-Caorle .... d.	0529	0635	...	0735	0835	...	1035	1135	...	1335	1435	...	1535	1635	...	1735	1835	...	1935	2035	...	|	2335
83	Latisana-Lignano-Bibione ...... d.	0540	0646	...	0746	0846	...	1046	1146	...	1346	1446	...	1546	1646	...	1746	1846	...	1946	2046	...	2154	2346
101	S. Giorgio di Nogaro.............. d.	0552	0658	...	0758	0858	...	1058	1158	...	1358	1458	...	1558	1658	...	1758	1858	...	1958	2058	...	2204	2358
112	Cervignano-Aquileia-Grado ... d.	0601	0707	...	0807	0907	...	1107	1207	...	1407	1507	...	1607	1707	...	1807	1907	...	2007	2107	...	2212	0007
124	Trieste Airport ✈ .... d.	0609	0715	...	0815	0915	...	1115	1215	...	1415	1515	...	1615	1715	...	1815	1915	...	2015	2115	...	2220	0015
129	Monfalcone .... d.	0615	0721	...	0821	0921	...	1121	1221	...	1421	1521	...	1621	1721	...	1821	1921	...	2021	2121	...	2226	0021
157	**Trieste** Centrale .... a.	0642	0744	...	0844	0944	...	1144	1244	...	1444	1544	...	1644	1744	...	1844	1944	...	2044	2144	...	2255	0044

																			Ⓐ			
Trieste Centrale .... d.	0516	0616	...	0716	0816	...	0916	1216	...	1316	1416	...	1516	1616	...	1716	1816	...	1916	2016	...	2116	2206
Monfalcone .... d.	0540	0640	...	0740	0840	...	0940	1240	...	1340	1440	...	1540	1640	...	1740	1840	...	1940	2040	...	2140	2229
Trieste Airport ✈ .... d.	0545	0645	...	0745	0845	...	0945	1245	...	1345	1446	...	1545	1645	...	1745	1845	...	1945	2045	...	2145	2234
Cervignano-Aquileia-Grado .... d.	0553	0653	...	0753	0853	...	0953	1253	...	1353	1453	...	1553	1653	...	1753	1853	...	1953	2053	...	2153	2242
S. Giorgio di Nogaro............................ d.	0601	0701	...	0801	0901	...	1001	1301	...	1401	1501	...	1601	1701	...	1801	1901	...	2001	2101	...	2201	2249
Latisana-Lignano-Bibione .... d.	0614	0714	...	0814	0914	...	1014	1314	...	1414	1514	...	1614	1714	...	1814	1914	...	2014	2114	...	2214	2300
Portogruaro-Caorle .... d.	0625	0725	...	0825	0925	...	1025	1325	...	1425	1525	...	1625	1725	...	1825	1925	...	2025	2124	...	2224	2310
S. Dona di Piave-Jesolo .... ◧ d.	0643	0743	...	0843	0943	...	1043	1343	...	1443	1543	...	1643	1743	...	1843	1943	...	2043	*2203*	...	*2302*	2327
Venezia Mestre .... a.	0709	0809	...	0909	1009	...	1109	1409	...	1509	1609	...	1709	1809	...	1909	2009	...	2109	*2238*	...	*2338*	2350
Venezia Santa Lucia......................... a.	0721	0821	...	0921	1021	...	1121	1421	...	1521	1621	...	1721	1821	...	1921	2021	...	2121	*2251*	...	*2351*	...

km																								
		Ⓐ	Ⓐ	Ⓐ	⚒		⚒	†					Ⓐ			Ⓐ	†		Ⓐ		†			
0	**Venezia** Santa Lucia .... d.	0501	0513	0601	0701	...	0713	0801	1001	1201	...	1401	1501	1601	...	1701	1701	1801	1901	...	1901	2001	2201	2301
9	**Venezia** Mestre .... d.	0514	0526	0614	0714	...	0726	0814	1014	1214	...	1414	1514	1614	...	1714	1714	1814	1914	...	1914	2014	2214	2314
30	Treviso Centrale .... d.	0534	0552	0634	0734	...	0752	0834	1034	1234	...	1434	1534	1634	...	1734	1734	1834	1934	...	1934	2034	2235	2335
57	Conegliano .... d.	0552	0619	0652	0752	...	0819	0852	1052	1252	...	1452	1552	1652	...	1752	1752	1852	1952	...	1952	2052	2253	2353
74	Sacile .... d.	0603	0634	0703	0803	...	0834	0903	1103	1303	...	1503	1603	1703	...	1803	1803	1903	2003	...	2003	2103	2304	0004
87	Pordenone .... d.	0615	0648	0715	0815	...	0848	0915	1115	1315	...	1515	1615	1715	...	1815	1815	1915	2015	...	2015	2115	2316	0016
136	**Udine** .... a.	0651	0728	0751	0851	...	0928	0951	1151	1351	...	1551	1651	1751	...	1851	1851	1951	2051	...	2051	2151	2353	0053
136	**Udine** .... d.	0654	0732	*0806*	0854	...	0938	0954	1154	1354	...	1554	1654	1754	...	1854	*1908*	1954	*2120*	...	2120	2154	2355	...
169	Gorizia Centrale ⊡ .... d.	0718	0803	|	0918	...	1009	1018	1218	1418	...	1618	1718	1818	...	1918	*1939*	2018	*2151*	...	2151	2218	0026	...
192	Monfalcone .... d.	0739	0827	*0845*	0939	...	1033	1039	1239	1439	...	1639	1739	1839	...	1939	*2003*	2041	*2215*	...	2215	2239	0049	...
219	**Trieste** Centrale .... a.	0802	0856	*0908*	1002	...	1102	1102	1302	1502	...	1702	1802	1902	...	2002	*2032*	2104	*2244*	...	2244	2302	0118	...

		⚒	⚒			†			Ⓐ		⚒		Ⓐ			Ⓐ	Ⓐ			Ⓐ		Ⓐ	
Trieste Centrale .... d.	...	0528	0548	0658	...	*0728*	0858	1058	1128	...	*1222*	1258	1328	...	1458	*1552*	*1558*	1658	...	1758	1858	*1928*	2032
Monfalcone .... d.	...	0558	0618	0722	...	*0758*	0922	1122	1158	...	*1246*	1322	1358	...	1522	*1616*	*1628*	1722	...	1822	1922	*1958*	2058
Gorizia Centrale ⊡ .... d.	...	0620	0645	0743	...	*0820*	0943	1143	1220	...	|	1343	1420	...	1543	|	*1650*	1743	...	1843	1943	*2020*	2120
Udine .... a.	...	0652	0719	0806	...	*0852*	1006	1206	1252	...	*1324*	1406	1452	...	1606	*1654*	*1722*	1806	...	1906	2006	*2052*	2152
Udine .... d.	0601	0658	0732	0809	...	0909	1009	1209	1305	...	1332	1409	1509	...	1609	1709	1732	1809	...	1909	2009	2109	2209
Pordenone .... d.	0636	0737	0811	0844	...	0944	1044	1244	1340	...	1411	1444	1544	...	1644	1744	1811	1844	...	1944	2044	2144	2244
Sacile .... d.	0647	0752	0825	0855	...	0955	1055	1255	1351	...	1425	1455	1555	...	1655	1755	1825	1855	...	1955	2055	2155	2254
Conegliano .... d.	0659	0803	0841	0907	...	1007	1107	1307	1403	...	1441	1507	1607	...	1707	1807	1841	1907	...	2007	2107	2207	2307
Treviso Centrale .... d.	0723	0823	0907	0927	...	1027	1127	1327	1423	...	1507	1527	1627	...	1727	1825	1907	1927	...	2027	2127	2227	2327
Venezia Mestre .... a.	0746	0846	0934	0946	...	1046	1146	1346	1444	...	1534	1546	1646	...	1746	1846	1934	1946	...	2046	2146	2246	2346
Venezia Santa Lucia......................... a.	0759	0859	0947	0959	...	1059	1159	1359	1459	...	1547	1559	1659	...	1759	1859	1947	1959	...	2059	2159	2259	2359

🚋 service **Trieste** (Piazza Oberdan) - **Villa Opicina** (Stazione Trenovia) and v.v. *Linea Tranviaria*. Operator: Trieste Trasporti S.p.A. Service currently suspended, replacement 🚌 (Line **2**).
From **Trieste**: 0711, 0731, 0751 and every 20 minutes until 2011. From **Villa Opicina**: 0700, 0720, 0740 and every 20 minutes until 2000. Journey 15 minutes.
Walking times: Trieste Centrale railway station - Piazza Oberdan ± 10 minutes; Villa Opicina Stazione Trenovia - Villa Opicina railway station ± 20 minutes.

A – 🛏 1, 2 cl., 🛏 2 cl. (4 berth) 2 Trieste - Udine - Venezia - Roma and v.v.
B – 12 🍷 Napoli - Milano - Venezia - Trieste and v.v. (Table **600**).
C – 12 🍷 Napoli - Roma - Bologna - Venezia - Udine and v.v. (Table **600**).
D – 12 🍷 Udine - Venezia - Bologna - Roma - Napoli - Salerno (Table **600**).

◧ – A 🚌 service operates 0600 - 1930 to Lido di Jesolo; 1 – 2 per hour. Journey 35 minutes.
● – Via Udine and Venezia (see Udine - Venezia sub-table).

⊡ – An international 🚌 service operates between Gorizia Centrale and Nova Gorica (Slovenia; bus stop 100 metres from station on Italian side) stations. Total journey time ± 20 minutes.
✣ – Running days, timings and numbers of *ICN* trains may vary - please check your reservation. For confirmed timings please consult the *Trenitalia* journey planner at www.trenitalia.com.

603 NORTH EAST ITALY LOCAL SERVICES

2nd class

BELLUNO - CALALZO (see note △)

km																								
		⚒			†B	©A		Ⓐ	©			⚒						Ⓑ						
0	**Belluno** d.	0730	0830	...	0911	...	...	0930	1030	...	1330	1430	...	1530	1730	...	1930	2030	...	...	...	...	...	...
7	Ponte nelle Alpi-Polpet a.	0738	0838	...	0919	...	...	0938	1038	...	1338	1438	...	1538	1738	...	1938	2038	...	...	...	...	...	...
7	Ponte nelle Alpi-Polpet d.	0739	0839	...	0920	0939	...	0939	1039	...	1339	1439	...	1539	1739	...	1939	2039	...	...	...	...	...	...
44	**Calalzo** ● a.	0827	0927	...	1010	1027	...	1027	1127	...	1427	1527	...	1627	1827	...	2027	2127	...	...	...	...	...	...

	⚒				⚒			Ⓑ		⑥	Ⓑ		©A	⚒		†B							
Calalzo ● d.	0628	0728	...	0928	1228	...	1328	1528	...	1628	1728	...	1740	...	...	1758	1828	...	1928	...	...	...	...
Ponte nelle Alpi-Polpet a.	0708	0808	...	1008	1308	...	1408	1608	...	1708	1808	...	1825	...	...	1841	1908	...	2008	...	...	...	...
Ponte nelle Alpi-Polpet d.	0710	0810	...	1010	1310	...	1410	1610	...	1710	1810	...	...	1839	...	1842	1910	...	2010	...	...	...	...
Belluno a.	0718	0818	...	1018	1318	...	1418	1618	...	1718	1818	...	...	1847	...	1849	1918	...	2018	...	...	...	...

CALALZO - CORTINA

km	🚌 service 30 (♠)																							
		⚒		⚒			⚒	⑥		Ⓐ	⚒	⚒		†	⚒				⚒	†		⚒	⚒	
0	**Calalzo** Stazione FS d.	0622	0658	0740	...	0820	0935	1100	...	1118	1215	1310	...	1400	1410	1450	...	1635	1745	1835	...	1905	2035	...
35	**Cortina** Autostazione a.	0718	0756	0838	...	0918	1033	1158	...	1216	1313	1408	...	1458	1508	1548	...	1733	1843	1933	...	2003	2128	...

🚌 service 30 (♠)																							
	⚒	⚒	⚒		⚒	⚒	⚒		⚒		⚒		⚒		⚒		⚒	⚒	⚒		⚒	⚒	
Cortina Autostazione d.	0545	0623	0650	...	0820	0930	1115	...	1220	1240	1315	...	1402	1505	1620	...	1705	1755	1920	...	1940	2010	...
Calalzo Stazione FS a.	0643	0721	0748	...	0918	1028	1213	...	1318	1338	1413	...	1500	1603	1718	...	1803	1853	2018	...	2035	2103	...

VENZIA - CONEGLIANO - BELLUNO

km																								
		⚒		Ⓐ	©A			Ⓐ🚌	Ⓐ🚌			⚒				Ⓐ		⚒			Ⓐ	†		🚌
0	**Venezia** Santa Lucia d.	...	...	0743	0748	...	0843	...	...	...	...	...	...	...	...	1443	...	1643	1743	...	1843	...	1931	...
9	**Venezia** Mestre d.	...	...	0756	0800	...	0856	...	...	...	...	...	...	...	...	1456	...	1656	1756	...	1856	...	1944	...
30	Treviso Centrale d.	...	...	0822	0821	...	0922	...	...	...	...	...	...	...	...	1522	...	1722	1822	...	1922	...	2007	...
57	**Conegliano** d.	0639	0741	0840	0841	...	0940	1040	1140	1241	...	1341	...	1441	...	1540	1641	1740	1846	...	1940	1941	2031	2201
71	Vittorio Veneto d.	0657	0802	0902	0902	...	1002	1103	1203	1302	...	1402	...	1502	...	1602	1702	1802	1903	...	2002	2002	2047	2224
98	Ponte nelle Alpi-Polpet a.	0731	0831	0931	0931	...	1031	1148	1248	1331	...	1431	...	1531	...	1631	1731	1831	1931	...	2031	2031	2115	2309
98	Ponte nelle Alpi-Polpet d.	0739	0839	0939	...	...	1039	1148	1248	1339	...	1439	...	1539	...	1639	1739	1839	1939	...	2039	2039	2116	2310
105	**Belluno** a.	0747	0847	0947	...	...	1047	1201	1301	1347	...	1447	...	1547	...	1647	1747	1847	1947	...	2047	2047	2124	2322

	⚒	⚒	†	⚒			Ⓐ🚌		Ⓐ🚌		Ⓐ				⚒	Ⓐ	Ⓐ	©		©A	Ⓐ		🚌
Belluno d.	0536	0615	0620	0720	...	0820	0920	1020	1120	...	1220	1320	1420	...	1520	1620	1720	1720	...	...	1820	1920	2020
Ponte nelle Alpi-Polpet a.	0544	0623	0628	0728	...	0828	0933	1028	1133	...	1228	1328	1428	...	1528	1628	1728	1728	...	...	1828	1928	2032
Ponte nelle Alpi-Polpet d.	0545	0624	0633	0733	...	0833	0933	1033	1133	...	1233	1333	1433	...	1533	1633	1733	1733	...	1833	1833	1933	2033
Vittorio Veneto d.	0613	0656	0701	0759	...	0901	1011	1101	1211	...	1301	1401	1501	...	1601	1701	1801	1801	...	1904	1904	2001	2111
Conegliano d.	0631	0712	0718	0817	...	0921	1041	1119	1241	...	1318	1418	1521	...	1618	1721	1818	1819	...	1919	1925	2018	2141
Treviso Centrale d.	0653	0737	...	0837	...	0940	...	1137	...	...	...	...	1540	...	...	1740	...	1838	...	1940	1951	...	...
Venezia Mestre a.	0716	0804	...	0904	...	1004	...	1204	...	...	...	...	1604	...	...	1804	...	1904	...	2004	2016	...	...
Venezia Santa Lucia a.	0729	0817	...	0917	...	1017	...	1217	...	...	...	...	1617	...	...	1817	...	1917	...	2017	2029	...	...

PADOVA - CASTELFRANCO VENETO - MONTEBELLUNA

km																								
			⚒	†B			†		⚒C	⚒			⚒		⚒		ⒶC		Ⓑ				C	🚌
0	**Padova** d.	0604	0704	0723	0804	...	0904	1104	1125	1204	...	1304	1404	1504	1604	...	1625	1704	1804	1904	...	2004	2125	2246
31	Castelfranco Veneto d.	0636	0736	0751	0836	...	0936	1136	1152	1236	...	1336	1436	1536	1636	...	1652	1736	1836	1936	...	2036	2156	2347
48	**Montebelluna** a.	0652	0752	0805	0852	...	0952	1153	1205	1252	...	1352	1452	1552	1652	...	1705	1752	1852	1952	...	2052	2209	0017

	⚒C		⚒	†C			⚒C	†			⚒		⚒C	⚒			⚒	Ⓑ				†B	
Montebelluna d.	0541	0708	0808	0808	...	0908	0946	1008	1208	...	1308	1408	1457	1508	...	1608	1708	1808	1908	...	2008	2017	2108
Castelfranco Veneto d.	0554	0725	0825	0825	...	0925	0959	1025	1225	...	1325	1425	1510	1525	...	1625	1725	1825	1925	...	2025	2032	2125
Padova a.	0628	0756	0856	0853	...	0956	1033	1056	1256	...	1356	1456	1534	1556	...	1656	1756	1856	1956	...	2056	2128	2156

TRENTO - BASSANO DEL GRAPPA

km																								
		⚒		⚒				⚒		⚒		⚒				⚒		⚒				⚒		
0	**Trento** d.	0505	...	0535	...	0605	...	0905	...	1105	...	1205	...	1305	...	1605	...	1635	...	1705	...	1805	...	1905
31	Levico Terme d.	0552	...	0622	...	0652	...	0952	...	1152	...	1252	...	1352	...	1652	...	1722	...	1752	...	1852	...	1952
44	Borgo Valsugana Centro d.	0608	...	0641	...	0710	...	1008	...	1208	...	1308	...	1408	...	1708	...	1737	...	1808	...	1908	...	2008
97	**Bassano del Grappa** a.	0712	...	...	...	0816	...	1116	...	1316	...	1416	...	1516	...	1816	...	...	...	1916	...	2016	...	2116

	⚒		⚒		⚒		†		⚒		⚒		⚒				⚒						
Bassano del Grappa d.	0500	...	0725	...	0825	...	0925	...	1125	...	1325	...	1425	...	1525	...	...	...	1925	...	2025	...	2125
Borgo Valsugana Centro d.	0558	...	0828	...	0928	...	1028	...	1228	...	1428	...	1528	...	1628	...	1828	...	2028	...	2128	...	2228
Levico Terme d.	0612	...	0842	...	0942	...	1042	...	1242	...	1442	...	1542	...	1642	...	1842	...	2042	...	2142	...	2242
Trento a.	0659	...	0929	...	1029	...	1129	...	1329	...	1529	...	1629	...	1729	...	1929	...	2129	...	2229	...	2329

TREVISO - MONTEBELLUNA - BELLUNO (♡)

km																								
		⚒			†B	⚒		Ⓐ	⚒C		†	⚒						ⒶC						C
0	**Treviso** d.	0535	0635	...	...	0735	...	0935	...	...	1135	1235	...	1335	1435	...	1535	...	...	1735	1835	...	1935	...
21	Montebelluna d.	0600	0700	...	0806	0800	...	1000	1206	...	1200	1300	...	1400	1500	...	1600	1706	...	1800	1900	...	2000	2210
56	Feltre d.	0639	0739	...	0839	0839	...	1039	1239	...	1239	1339	...	1439	1539	...	1639	1739	...	1839	1939	...	2039	2249
87	**Belluno** a.	0715	0815	...	0910	0915	...	1115	1315	...	1315	1415	...	1515	1615	...	1715	1815	...	1915	2015	...	2115	2325

	⚒C	Ⓐ	⚒		⚒	†C			⚒C	†				⚒C			⚒	Ⓑ			†B		
Belluno d.	0434	...	0534	...	0634	0634	0734	...	0834	0834	1034	...	1234	1334	1434	...	1534	1634	1734	...	1850	1834	1934
Feltre d.	0505	...	0613	...	0713	0713	0813	...	0912	0913	1113	...	1313	1413	1513	...	1613	1713	1813	...	1832	1913	2013
Montebelluna d.	0540	0601	0701	...	0801	0756	0901	...	0945	1001	1201	...	1401	1456	1601	...	1701	1801	1901	...	2016	2001	2101
Treviso Centrale a.	...	0625	0725	...	0825	...	0925	...	...	1025	1225	...	1425	...	1625	...	1725	1825	1925	...	...	2025	2125

VENEZIA - CASTELFRANCO VENETO - BASSANO DEL GRAPPA

km									
		⚒	⚒	⚒					
0	**Venezia** Santa Lucia d.	0527	0557	0627	0657	0757	and	2057	2157
9	**Venezia** Mestre d.	0540	0609	0640	0709	0809	hourly	2109	2210
45	Castelfranco Veneto d.	0628	0646	0728	0746	0846	until	2146	2252
64	**Bassano del Grappa** a.	0644	0711	0744	0811	0911		2211	2314

	⚒	⚒		⚒				
Bassano del Grappa d.	0521	0546	0621	0646	0721	and	2021	2121
Castelfranco Veneto d.	0545	0604	0646	0704	0746	hourly	2046	2146
Venezia Mestre a.	0621	0650	0721	0750	0821	until	2121	2226
Venezia Santa Lucia a.	0633	0703	0733	0803	0833		2133	2239

VICENZA - CASTELFRANCO VENETO - TREVISO

km																								
		⚒			⚒	†		Ⓐ			⚒			⚒			⚒	⚒						
0	**Vicenza** d.	0614	0714	...	0814	0914	...	1114	1214	...	1314	1414	...	1514	1614	...	1714	1814	...	1914	2014	...	...	...
24	Cittadella d.	0639	0739	...	0839	0939	...	1139	1239	...	1339	1439	...	1539	1639	...	1739	1839	...	1939	2039	...	...	...
36	Castelfranco Veneto d.	0655	0755	...	0855	0955	...	1155	1255	...	1355	1455	...	1555	1655	...	1755	1855	...	1955	2055	...	...	...
60	**Treviso** Centrale a.	0722	0822	...	0922	1022	...	1222	1322	...	1422	1522	...	1622	1722	...	1822	1922	...	2022	2122	...	...	...

	⚒	⚒			⚒		†	Ⓑ		⚒			⚒			⚒			⚒				
Treviso Centrale d.	0538	0638	...	0738	0838	...	0938	1138	...	1238	1338	...	1438	1538	...	1638	1738	...	1838	2038	...	...	...
Castelfranco Veneto d.	0607	0707	...	0807	0907	...	1007	1207	...	1307	1407	...	1507	1607	...	1707	1807	...	1907	2107	...	...	...
Cittadella d.	0621	0721	...	0821	0921	...	1021	1221	...	1321	1421	...	1521	1621	...	1721	1821	...	1921	2121	...	...	...
Vicenza a.	0646	0746	...	0846	0946	...	1046	1246	...	1346	1446	...	1546	1646	...	1746	1846	...	1946	2146	...	...	...

A – Venezia - Ponte nelle Alpi-Polpet - Calalzo and v.v.
B – Padova - Montebelluna - Belluno - Calalzo and v.v. (see note ♡).
C – Padova - Montebelluna - Belluno and v.v. (see note ♡).

△ – Additional 🚌 services available.
♡ – Subject to confirmation from Feb. 21.
♠ – Operator: Dolomitibus. www.dolomitibus.it.
● – Full name of station is Calalzo-Pieve di Cadore-Cortina.

TORINO - MILANO - VERONA - VENEZIA 605

🍷 on all *FA*, *FR* and *ITA* trains

km		*ITA*	*FA*	*FA*	*FR*	*ITA*	*EC*	*ITA*	*FA*	*EC*	*EC*	*ITA*	*FA*	*ITA*	*FA*	*FA*	*EC*	*FA*	*ITA*	*FA*	*ITA*	*FA*	*ITA*
		8973	**9707**	**9709**	**9710**	**8977**	**311**	**8981**	**9723**	**1281**	**37/47**	**8983**	**9731**	**8987**	**9735**	**9741**	**85**	**9747**	**8993**	**9751**	**8995**	**9755**	**8997**
		④–①								⑥⑦				④–①				①–⑥		①–⑤			
					A		B			C ♠	D						C ♠			E			
0	**Milano** Centrale **600** d.	0735	0745	0815	0845	0935	1005	1135	1145	...	1205	1235	1345	1435	1445	1545	...	1645	1735	1745	1835	1845	1935
83	Brescia **600** d.	0813	0823	0853	0923	1013	1053	1213	1223	...	1253	1313	1423	1513	1523	1623	...	1723	1813	1823	1913	1923	2013
111	Desenzano-Sirmione **600** d.	0826	|	0908	|	|	|	1227	1238	...	|	1327	|	|	1538	|	...	|	1827	|	|	|	2027
125	Peschiera del Garda ‡ **600** d.	|	0844	|	0944	1034	1114	|	|	...	1314	|	1444	1533	|	1644	...	1744	|	1844	1934	1944	|
148	**Verona** Porta Nuova **600** a.	0847	0858	0928	0958	1047	1128	1247	1258	...	1328	1347	1458	1547	1558	1658	...	1758	1847	1858	1947	1958	2047
148	**Verona** Porta Nuova d.	0849	0900	0930	1000	1049	1130	1249	1300	1313	1330	1349	1500	1549	1600	1700	1710	1800	1849	...	1949	2000	2049
200	Vicenza d.	0917	0927	0957	1027	1117	1157	1317	1327	1338s	1357	1417	1527	1617	1627	1727	1735s	1827	1917	...	2017	2027	2117
230	Padova **600** d.	0934	0946	1016	1046	1134	1216	1334	1346	1358s	1416	1434	1546	1634	1646	1746	1756s	1846	1934	...	2034	2046	2134
258	**Venezia** Mestre **600** a.	0952s	1000	1030s	1100s	1152s	1230s	1352s	1400s	1414s	1430s	1452s	1600s	1652s	1700s	1800s	1812s	1900	1950	...	2052s	2100	2152s
267	**Venezia** Santa Lucia **600** a.	1003	|	1042	1112	1203	1242	1403	1412	1428	1442	1503	1612	1703	1712	1812	1825	1912	|	...	2103	|	2203
	Udine **601** a.	...	|	...	...	...	...	...	...	...	...	...	...	...	...	...	...	...	2140	...	...	2237	...
	Trieste Centrale **601** a.	...	1205	...	...	...	...	...	...	...	...	...	...	...	...	...	...	...	...	...	...	...	...

	ITA	*FA*	*FA*	*FR*	*ITA*	*ITA*	*FA*	*FA*	*ITA*	*FA*	*EC*	*EC*	*FA*	*ITA*	*ITA*	*EC*	*FA*	*ITA*	*EC*	*FA*	*ITA*	*FA*
	8970	**9706**	**9708**	**9713**	**8974**	**8976**	**9721**	**9724**	**8978**	**9728**	**308**	**82**	**9736**	**8984**	**8986**	**1280**	**9744**	**8988**	**42/44**	**9748**	**8993**	**9758**
		①–⑥					①–⑤		④–①							⑥⑦					④–①	
							E				B	C ♠				C ♠	A		D			
Trieste Centrale **601** d.	...	...	...	...	...	...	...	...	...	...	...	...	...	...	...	...	...	...	...	...	...	1705
Udine **601** d.	...	...	...	0615	...	0716	...	...	...	...	...	...	...	...	...	...	...	...	...	...	...	|
Venezia Santa Lucia **600** d.	0557	0648	0718	|	0757	|	...	1048	1057	1148	1318	1335	1348	1357	1457	1535	1548	1557	1618	1648	1757	|
Venezia Mestre **600** d.	0609u	0700u	0730u	0800	0809u	0909	...	1100u	1109u	1200u	1330u	1347u	1400u	1409u	1509u	1547u	1600u	1609u	1630u	1700u	1809u	1900
Padova **600** d.	0626	0716	0746	0816	0826	0926	...	1116	1126	1216	1346	1403u	1416	1426	1526	1603u	1616	1626	1646	1716	1826	1916
Vicenza d.	0644	0734	0804	0834	0844	0944	...	1134	1144	1234	1404	1424u	1434	1444	1544	1624u	1634	1644	1704	1734	1844	1934
Verona Porta Nuova a.	0710	0800	0830	0900	0910	1010	...	1200	1210	1300	1430	1450	1500	1510	1610	1650	1700	1710	1730	1800	1910	2000
Verona Porta Nuova **600** d.	0712	0802	0832	0902	0912	1012	1032	1202	1212	1302	1432	...	1502	1512	1612	...	1702	1712	1732	1802	1912	2002
Peschiera del Garda ‡ **600** d.	|	|	0848	|	0926	|	1048	|	1226	1318	1448	...	|	|	1626	...	|	|	1748	|	1926	2018
Desenzano-Sirmione **600** d.	0733	0823	|	0923	|	1033	|	1223	|	|	|	...	1523	1533	|	...	1723	1733	|	1823	|	|
Brescia **600** d.	0749	0839	0909	0939	0949	1049	1109	1239	1249	1339	1509	...	1539	1549	1649	...	1739	1749	1809	1839	1949	2039
Milano Centrale **600** a.	0825	0915	0945	1015	1025	1125	1145	1315	1325	1415	1555	...	1615	1625	1725	...	1815	1825	1855	1915	2025	2115

	FR	*FR*	*FR*					
	9743	**9753**	**9759**					
Torino Porta Nuova **600** d.	1508	1710	1840	...	...	...	...	...
Torino Porta Susa **600** d.	1518u	1720u	1850u	...	...	...	...	...
Rho-Fiera Milano d.	1556	1756	1926	...	...	...	...	...
Milano Porta Garibaldi a.	1610	1810	1940	...	...	...	...	...
Milano Porta Garibaldi d.	1613	1813	1943	...	...	...	...	...
Brescia **600** d.	1653	1853	2023	...	...	...	...	...
Desenzano-Sirmione **600** d.	1708	1908	|	...	...	...	...	...
Peschiera del Garda ‡ **600** d.	|	|	|	...	...	...	...	...
Verona Porta Nuova **600** a.	1728	1928	2053	...	...	...	...	...
Verona Porta Nuova d.	1730	1930	2055	...	...	...	...	...
Vicenza d.	1757	1957	|	...	...	...	...	...
Padova **600** d.	1816	2016	|	...	...	...	...	...
Venezia Mestre **600** a.	1830s	2030s	2155	...	...	...	...	...
Venezia Santa Lucia **600** a.	1842	2042	|	...	...	...	...	...
Trieste Centrale **601** a.	...	...	2340	...	...	...	...	...

	FR	*FR*	*FR*					
	9702	**9712**	**9716**					
Trieste Centrale **601** d.	...	0600	...	...	...	...	...	...
Venezia Santa Lucia **600** d.	0618	|	0818	...	...	...	...	...
Venezia Mestre **600** d.	0630u	0749	0830u	...	...	...	...	...
Padova **600** d.	0646	|	0846	...	...	...	...	...
Vicenza d.	0704	|	0904	...	...	...	...	...
Verona Porta Nuova a.	0730	0844	0930	...	...	...	...	...
Verona Porta Nuova **600** d.	0732	0846	0932	...	...	...	...	...
Peschiera del Garda ‡ **600** d.	0748	|	0948	...	...	...	...	...
Desenzano-Sirmione **600** d.	|	|	|	...	...	...	...	...
Brescia **600** d.	0809	|	1009	...	...	...	...	...
Milano Porta Garibaldi a.	0847	0955	1047	...	...	...	...	...
Milano Porta Garibaldi d.	0850	0958	1050	...	...	...	...	...
Rho-Fiera Milano d.	0903	|	1103	...	...	...	...	...
Torino Porta Susa **600** a.	0938s	1046s	1138s	...	...	...	...	...
Torino Porta Nuova **600** a.	0950	1058	1150	...	...	...	...	...

MILANO - VERONA - VENEZIA LOCAL TRAINS

2nd class Trenord

	Ⓐ	⚒	⚒	†					Ⓒ														
Milano Centrale d.	...	...	...	...	0625	0725	0825	...	0925	...	1125	1225	1325	1425	1525	1625	1725	1825	1925	2025	2125	2225	2325
Milano Lambrate d.	...	...	...	...	0633	0733	0833	...	0933	...	1133	1233	1333	1433	1533	1633	1733	1833	1933	2033	2133	2233	2333
Treviglio d.	...	...	...	...	0656	0756	0856	...	0956	...	1156	1256	1356	1456	1556	1656	1756	1856	1956	2056	2156	2256	2356
Brescia d.	...	...	0631	...	0733	0833	0933	...	1033	...	1233	1333	1433	1533	1633	1733	1833	1933	2033	2133	2233	2333	0033
Desenzano-Sirmione d.	...	...	0654	...	0749	0849	0949	...	1049	...	1249	1349	1449	1549	1649	1749	1849	1949	2049	2149	2249	2349	0049
Peschiera del Garda ‡ d.	...	...	0703	...	0758	0858	0958	...	1058	...	1258	1359	1458	1558	1658	1758	1858	1958	2058	2158	2258	2358	0058
Verona Porta Nuova a.	...	...	0720	...	0817	0917	1017	...	1115	...	1317	1417	1517	1617	1717	1817	1917	2017	2117	2217	2317	0017	0117
			|																				
Verona Porta Nuova d.	0522	0622	0722	0722	0822	0922	1022	1122	...	1222	1322	1422	1522	1622	1722	1822	1922	2041	...	2222	...	...	...
Vicenza d.	0603	0703	0803	0803	0903	1003	1103	1203	...	1303	1403	1503	1603	1703	1803	1903	2003	2141	...	2303	...	...	...
Padova **600** d.	0622	0722	0822	0822	0922	1022	1122	1222	...	1322	1422	1522	1622	1722	1822	1922	2022	2210	...	2322	...	...	...
Venezia Mestre **600** a.	0637	0737	0837	0837	0937	1037	1137	1237	...	1337	1437	1537	1637	1737	1837	1937	2037	2243	...	2337	...	...	...
Venezia Santa Lucia **600** a.	0650	0750	0850	0850	0950	1050	1150	1250	...	1350	1450	1550	1650	1750	1850	1950	2050	2256	...	2350	...	...	...

			⚒		⚒							Ⓐ											Ⓒ
Venezia Santa Lucia **600** d.	...	...	0504	...	0610	...	0710	0810	0910	1010	1110	1210	...	1310	1410	1510	1610	1710	1810	1910	2010	2110	2134
Venezia Mestre **600** d.	...	...	0517	...	0623	...	0723	0823	0923	1023	1123	1223	...	1323	1423	1523	1623	1723	1823	1923	2023	2123	2147
Padova **600** d.	...	...	0553	...	0640	...	0740	0840	0940	1040	1140	1240	...	1340	1440	1540	1640	1740	1840	1940	2040	2140	2220
Vicenza d.	...	...	0620	...	0658	...	0758	0858	0958	1058	1158	1258	...	1358	1458	1558	1658	1758	1858	1958	2058	2158	2252
Verona Porta Nuova a.	...	...	0720	...	0738	...	0838	0938	1038	1138	1238	1338	...	1438	1538	1638	1738	1838	1938	2038	2138	2238	2334
										Ⓒ													
Verona Porta Nuova d.	0543	0643	...	0743	...	0840	...	0943	...	1143	1243	...	1343	1443	1543	1643	1743	1843	1943	2043	2143	...	...
Peschiera del Garda ‡ d.	0557	0657	...	0757	...	0859	...	0957	...	1157	1257	...	1357	1457	1557	1657	1757	1857	1957	2057	2157	...	...
Desenzano-Sirmione d.	0607	0707	...	0807	...	0909	...	1007	...	1207	1307	...	1407	1507	1607	1707	1807	1907	2007	2107	2207	...	...
Brescia d.	0628	0728	...	0828	...	0928	...	1028	...	1228	1328	...	1428	1528	1628	1728	1828	1928	2028	2128	2228	...	...
Treviglio d.	0705	0801	...	0905	...	1005	...	1105	...	1305	1405	...	1505	1605	1705	1805	1905	2005	2105	2205	2305	...	...
Milano Lambrate d.	0728	0828	...	0928	...	1028	...	1128	...	1328	1428	...	1528	1628	1728	1828	1928	2028	2128	2228	2328	...	...
Milano Centrale a.	0735	0835	...	0935	...	1035	...	1135	...	1335	1435	...	1535	1635	1735	1835	1935	2035	2135	2235	2335	...	...

BRESCIA - EDOLO

2nd class Trenord

km		⚒	†						Ⓐ	
0	**Brescia** d.	0555	0707	0907	1107	1307	1507	1707	1758	1907
	Iseo d.	0633	0733	0933	1133	1333	1533	1733	1831	1933
103	**Edolo** ⊖ a.	0834	0907	1107	1307	1507	1707	1907	2018	2107

	⚒	⚒							†
Edolo ⊖ d.	0554	0647	0754	0954	1154	1354	1554	1754	1954
Iseo d.	0731	0833	0931	1131	1331	1531	1731	1931	2136
Brescia a.	0754	0903	0954	1154	1354	1554	1754	1954	2200

A – (12) 🍷 Genova - Venezia and v.v.
B – (12) ✕ Zürich - Milano - Venezia and v.v. [R] inclusive of supplement.
C – (12) ✕ München - Verona - Venezia and v.v.
D – (12) 🍷 Genève - Milano - Venezia and v.v. [R] inclusive of supplement.
E – (12) 🍷 Milano - Bolzano and v.v.

s – Stops to set down only.
u – Stops to pick up only.
♠ – Also available to passengers without reservation.
‡ – Station for Gardaland Park. Free shuttle bus available.
⊖ – For 🚌 Edolo - Tirano see Table **593**.

606 MILANO MALPENSA AEROPORTO ✈ — Trenord

Milano Centrale d.	0525	0555	0625	and at	1955	2025	2125	2225	2325
Milano Porta Garibaldi d.	0535	0605	0635	the same	2005	2035	2135	2235	2335
Milano Bovisa d.	0542	0612	0642	minutes	2012	2042	2142	2242	2342
Busto Arsizio FN d.	0607	0637	0707	past each	2037	2107	2207	2307	0007
Malpensa Aeroporto T1 ✈ a.	0616	0646	0716	hour until	2046	2116	2216	2316	0016

Malpensa Aeroporto T1 ✈ d.	0543	0613	0643	and at	2043	2113	2143	2243
Busto Arsizio FN d.	0552	0622	0652	the same	2052	2122	2152	2252
Milano Bovisa a.	0618	0648	0718	minutes	2118	2148	2218	2318
Milano Porta Garibaldi a.	0625	0655	0725	past each	2125	2155	2225	2325
Milano Centrale a.	0637	0707	0737	hour until	2137	2207	2237	2335

All services below operate as *Malpensa Express*. Special fare payable.

Milano Cadorna d.	0457	0527	0557	0627	and at the same	2157	2227	2257	2327
Milano Bovisa d.	0503	0533	0603	0633	minutes	2203	2233	2303	2333
Busto Arsizio FN d.	0525	0555	0625	0655	past each	2225	2255	2325	2355
Malpensa Aeroporto T1 ✈ a.	0534	0604	0634	0704	hour until	2234	2304	2334	0004

Malpensa Aeroporto T1 ✈ d.	0556	0626	0656	0726	and at the same	2256	2326	2356
Busto Arsizio FN d.	0603	0633	0703	0733	minutes	2303	2333	0003
Milano Bovisa a.	0626	0656	0726	0756	past each	2326	2356	0026
Milano Cadorna a.	0633	0703	0733	0803	hour until	2333	0003	0033

607 MILANO LOCAL SERVICES — Trenord

Subject to alteration on and around Italian and Swiss public holidays. See Table **548** for services Locarno - Cadenazzo - Lugano and v.v.

MILANO and MALPENSA AEROPORTO - PORTO CERESIO, COMO and BELLINZONA

km																							
				①–⑥			①–⑥			①–⑥				①–⑥						①–⑥			①–⑥
0	**Milano** Porta Garibaldi d.	...	...	...	...	0532	...	...	0632	...	...	0732		...	...	1932	...	2032	...	2104	...	2234	...
13	Rho-Fiera Milano d.	...	...	...	...	0543	...	...	0643	...	...	0743	and	...	...	1943	...	2043	...	2117	...	2247	...
	Malpensa Aeroporto T1 ✈ d.	...	...	...	...	|	...	0619	|	...	0719	|	at	...	1919	|	2019	|	2119	|	2219	|	2319
	Busto Arsizio FN d.	...	...	...	...	|	...	0630	|	...	0730	|	the	...	1930	|	2030	|	2130	|	2230	|	2330
36	Busto Arsizio FS d.	...	...	...	...	0559	...	0638	0701	...	0738	0801	same	...	1938	2001	2038	2101	2138	2143	2238	2313	2338
44	Gallarate d.	...	...	...	...	0605	...	0644	0707	...	0744	0807	minutes	...	1944	2007	2044	2107	2144	2150	2244	2320	2344
63	Varese d.	0500	0525	0536	0606	0625	0636	0706	0725	0736	0806	0825	past	1936	2006	2025	2106	2125	2206	2217	2306	2347	0006
77	**Porto Ceresio** a.	|	0545	|	|	0645	|	|	0745	|	|	0845	each	|	|	2045	|	2145	|	...	|	...	|
75	Stabio d.	0516	...	0553	0623	...	0653	0723	...	0753	0823	...	hour	1953	2023	...	2123	...	2223	...	2323	...	0023
79	Mendrisio **550** a.	0520	...	0602	0627	...	0702	0727	...	0802	0827	...	until	2002	2027	...	2127	...	2227	...	2327	...	0027
86	Chiasso **550** a.	|	...	0610	|	...	0710	|	...	0810	|	...		2010	|	...	|	...	|	...	|	...	|
90	**Como** San Giovanni a.	|	...	0624	|	...	0724	|	...	0824	|	...		2024	|	...	|	...	|	...	|	...	|
98	Lugano **550** a.	0554	...	...	0654	...	...	0754e	...	...	0854	...		...	2054	...	2154	...	2254	...	2354	...	0054
127	**Bellinzona** **550** a.	0619	...	...	0713	...	...	0813e	...	...	0913	...		...	2113	...	2213	...	2313	...	0026	...	0126

km																							
				①–⑥			①–⑥			①–⑥			①–⑥				①–⑥						
108	**Bellinzona** **550** d.	...	0431	...	...	0532	...	...	0641	...	...	0746	...		...	1846	...	...	1946	...	...	...	2046
79	Lugano **550** d.	...	0506	...	...	0606	...	...	0706	...	...	0806	...	and	...	1906	...	...	2006	...	...	...	2106
71	**Como** San Giovanni d.	...	|	0541	...	|	0636	...	|	0736	...	|	0836	at	...	|	1936	...	|	...	...	...	|
67	Chiasso **550** d.	...	|	0550	...	|	0650	...	|	0750	...	|	0850	the	...	|	1950	...	|	...	...	...	|
60	Mendrisio **550** d.	...	0533	0603	...	0633	0703	...	0733	0803	...	0833	0903	same	...	1933	2003	...	2033	...	...	...	2133
56	Stabio d.	...	0537	0607	...	0637	0707	...	0737	0807	...	0837	0907	minutes	...	1937	2007	...	2037	...	...	...	2137
	Porto Ceresio d.	0516	|	|	0616	|	|	0716	|	|	0816	|	|	past	1916	|	|	2016	|	...	2116	...	|
44	Varese d.	0536	0600	0624	0636	0700	0724	0736	0800	0824	0836	0900	0924	each	1936	2000	2024	2036	2100	...	2136	2143	2200
25	Gallarate d.	0552	0616	...	0704	0716	...	0752	0816	...	0852	0916	...	hour	1952	2016	...	2052	2116	...	...	2210	2216
17	Busto Arsizio FS d.	0558	0625	...	|	0725	...	0758	0825	...	0858	0925	...	until	1958	2025	...	2058	2125	...	...	2216	2225
	Busto Arsizio FN d.	|	0631	...	|	0731	...	|	0831	...	|	0931	...		|	2031	...	|	2131	...	...	|	2231
0	**Malpensa** Aeroporto T1 ✈ a.	|	0641	...	|	0741	...	|	0841	...	|	0941	...		|	2041	...	|	2141	...	...	|	2241
	Rho-Fiera Milano d.	0616	...	...	0731	...	...	0816	...	...	0916	...	...		2016	...	...	2116	...	...	...	2241	...
	Milano Porta Garibaldi a.	0628	...	...	0741	...	...	0828	...	...	0928	...	...		2028	...	...	2128	...	...	...	2255	...

GALLARATE - LUINO - CADENAZZO - BELLINZONA

km																								
		①–⑥				①–⑤			⑥–③								①–⑤			①–⑥				
0	**Gallarate** d.	0608	...	...	...	0719	...	0842	...	...	...	...	...	1519	1719	...	1842	1919	...	1942	2219	...	...	...
31	Laveno Mombello d.	0644	...	...	...	0800	...	0927	...	...	...	...	...	1601	1801	...	1927	2001	...	2027	2301	...	...	...
46	**Luino** d.	0703	0718	...	...	0815	...	0943	1118	...	...	1318	...	1615	1815	...	1943	2015	...	2043	2315	...	...	...
59	Pino-Tronzano 🏛 d.	...	0730	...	...	...	...	...	1130	...	...	1330	...	...	...	...	...	...	...	...	...	...	...	...
77	**Cadenazzo** a.	...	0756	...	0801	...	...	...	1156	...	1201	1356	...	...	...	...	...	...	...	...	...	...	...	...
86	**Bellinzona** a.	...	...	...	0811	...	...	...	...	...	1211	...	...	...	...	...	...	...	...	...	...	...	...	...

	①–⑥	①–⑤		⑥⑦	①–⑤		①–⑥			⑥–③												
Bellinzona d.	...	...	...	...	...	...	...	0949	...	...	1149	...	...	...	...	...	...	...	...	1949	...	...	...
Cadenazzo d.	...	...	...	...	...	...	...	0959	...	1004	1159	...	1204	...	...	...	...	...	...	1959	...	2004	...
Pino-Tronzano 🏛 d.	...	...	...	...	...	...	...	...	...	1028	...	...	1228	...	...	...	...	...	...	...	...	2028	...
Luino d.	0500	0534	...	0604	0619	...	0718	...	...	1042	...	...	1242	1345	...	1545	1745	...	1945	...	...	2042	2045
Laveno Mombello d.	0516	0550	...	0617	0640	...	0733	...	...	...	...	...	...	1400	...	1600	1800	...	2000	...	...	...	2100
Gallarate a.	0552	0629	...	0651	0718	...	0805	...	...	...	...	...	...	1441	...	1641	1841	...	2041	...	...	...	2141

MILANO - CREMONA - MANTOVA

km											
0	**Milano** Centrale d.	0620	0820	1020	1220	1420	1620	1715	1820	1915	2020
60	Codogno d.	0702	0902	1102	1302	1502	1702	1758	1902	1958	2102
88	Cremona d.	0730	0930	1130	1330	1530	1730	1823	1930	2023	2130
151	**Mantova** a.	0818	1018	1218	1418	1618	1818	1918	2018	2118	2218

Mantova d.	0518	0607	0642	0842	1042	1242	1442	1642	1842	2042
Cremona d.	0613	0653	0730	0930	1130	1330	1530	1730	1930	2130
Codogno d.	0639	0718	0753	0953	1153	1353	1553	1753	1953	2153
Milano Centrale a.	0730	0810	0842	1040	1240	1440	1640	1840	2040	2240

MILANO - BERGAMO — *56 km* Journey 55–60 minutes 2nd class

From **Milano** Centrale at 0535, 0605, 0705, 0805, 0905, 1005, 1105, 1205, 1305, 1405, 1505, 1605, 1705, 1805, 1905, 2005, 2105, 2205, 2340.

From **Bergamo** at 0500, 0602, 0702, 0735 Ⓐ, 0802, 0902, 0957 Ⓒ, 1002 Ⓐ, 1057 Ⓒ, 1102 Ⓐ, 1202, 1302, 1402, 1502, 1602, 1702, 1802, 1902, 2002, 2102, 2202, 2300 Ⓒ.

MILANO - COMO LAGO — *46 km* Journey: 1 hour. 2nd class

From **Milano** Cadorna: 0543 Ⓐ, 0643, 0743 and hourly until 2043, 2143, 2243.

From **Como** Lago: 0516, 0616, 0716 and hourly until 2016, 2116, 2216.

Additional services operate on ⚒. A reduced service may operate in peak summer.

MILANO - VARESE - LAVENO — *72 km* Journey: 87–107 mins 2nd class

From **Milano** Cadorna: 0609 ⚒, 0639, 0752, 0839, 0939, 1039, 1139, 1239, 1352, 1439, 1539, 1652, 1722 Ⓐ, 1752, 1822 Ⓐ, 1852, 1922 Ⓐ, 1939 Ⓒ, 2039.

From **Laveno-Mombello** FN: 0538 Ⓐ, 0608 ⚒, 0638, 0708 ⚒, 0738, 0808 Ⓐ, 0838, 0938, 1038, 1138, 1238, 1338, 1438, 1538, 1638, 1738, 1838, 1938, 2038.

A reduced service may operate in peak summer.

e – On ①–⑤ arrives Lugano 0747, Bellinzona 0807.

TORINO and MILANO - GENOVA - PISA - ROMA 610

🍷 on all *EC, FA, FB, FR* and *ITA* trains

km		*IC* 501	*FB* 8601	*FA* 8583 ①–⑥ ♦	*FB* 8605	*FA* 8551 ①–⑥	*IC* 651	*IC* 503	*IC* 505	*FB* 8639	*IC* 657 Ⓐ	*IC* 657 Ⓒ	*IC* 659 Ⓐ	*IC* 659 Ⓒ	*FB* 8613	*IC* 511	*IC* 665	*FB* 8619
0	**Torino** Porta Nuova d.	...	...	...	...	...	...	0605	...	...	...	...	...	...	...	1040	...	...
56	Asti d.	...	...	...	...	...	...	0641	...	...	...	...	...	...	...	1113	...	...
91	Alessandria d.	...	...	...	...	...	...	0702	...	...	...	...	...	...	...	1136	...	...
112	Novi Ligure d.	...	...	...	...	...	...	0718	...	...	...	...	...	...	...	|	...	...
	Milano Centrale d.	...	...	...	...	...	0610	|	...	0710	0805	0805	0910	0910	...	|	1210	1310
	Pavia d.	...	...	...	...	...	0635	|	...	0735	0835	0835	0935	0935	...	|	1235	1335
	Voghera d.	...	...	...	...	...	|	|	...	0751	0851	0851	|	|	...	|	|	|
	Tortona d.	...	...	...	...	...	0659	|	A	|	|	|	0959	0959	...	|	1259	|
166	**Genova** Piazza Principe a.	...	...	...	...	...	0744	0803	|	0844	0944	0944	1044	1044	...	1221	1344	1437
166	**Genova** Piazza Principe d.	...	0515	0553	0705	0738	0747	...	0853	|	0947	0947	|	|	1210	1224	1347	1502
169	**Genova** Brignole d.	...	0522u	0600u	0712u	0746u	0756	...	0901	A	0956	0956	A	A	1217u	1233	1356	1512
194	S. Margherita-Portofino d.	...	|	|	|	|	0824	...	|	...	1016	1016	...	...	|	|	1416	|
196	Rapallo d.	...	|	|	0737	0817	0829	...	0922	...	1021	1021	...	...	|	1304	1421	1537
205	Chiavari d.	...	0547	|	0746	|	0838	...	0931	...	1030	1030	...	...	1246	1313	1430	1546
212	Sestri Levante d.	0505	|	|	|	|	0845	...	0938	...	1038	1038	...	...	|	1321	1438	|
235	Levanto d.	0522	|	|	|	|	0901	...	|	...	1100	1100	...	...	|	|	1501	|
240	Monterosso d.	0528	|	|	|	|	0907	...	|	...	1107	1107	...	...	|	|	1507	|
256	La Spezia Centrale d.	0544	0618	0651	0816	0855	0923	...	1011	...	1123	1123	...	...	1316	1352	1521	1616
272	Sarzana d.	0557	|	|	|	|	|	...	|	...	|	|	...	...	|	|	...	|
282	Carrara-Avenza d.	0606	|	|	|	|	|	...	|	...	|	1141	...	...	|	1411	...	|
289	Massa Centro d.	0614	0638	|	0836	|	0945	...	1033	...	1145	1148	...	...	1336	1419	...	1636
310	Viareggio d.	0628	0650	|	0848	|	1000	...	1046	...	1200	1209	...	...	1348	1434	...	1648
331	**Pisa** Centrale a.	0644	0704	0730	0904	0947	1017	...	1101	...	1217	1223	...	...	1404	1447	...	1704
331	**Pisa** Centrale d.	0647	0707	0733	0907	0950	1020	...	1111	...	1220	1226	...	...	1407	1450	...	1707
	Firenze Campo di Marte d.	|	|	0826	|	0846	|	...	|	...	|	|	...	...	|	|	...	|
351	**Livorno** Centrale a.	0701	0720	|	0920	|	1035	...	1124	...	1235	1240	...	...	1420	1502	...	1720
351	**Livorno** Centrale d.	0703	0722	|	0922	|	...	...	1126	...	1255	1255	...	...	1422	1504	...	1722
385	Cecina d.	0728	|	|	|	|	...	...	1150	...	1326	1323	...	...	|	|	...	|
420	Campiglia Marittima d.	0747	0757	|	0957	|	...	...	|	...	1350	1341	...	...	1457	1540	...	1757
437	Follonica d.	0758	|	|	|	|	...	...	1215	...	1401	1352	...	...	|	1552	...	|
479	Grosseto d.	0819	0824	|	1024	|	...	...	1235	...	1433	1425	...	...	1524	1614	...	1824
589	Civitavecchia d.	0924	0916	|	1116	|	...	...	1326	...	...	...	...	...	1616	1708	...	1916
660	**Roma** Ostiense a.	1015	|	|	|	|	...	...	1420s	...	...	...	...	...	|	1752	...	|
667	**Roma** Termini a.	|	1003	0945t	1203	1210	...	...	1433	...	...	...	...	...	1703	1803	...	2003
	Napoli Centrale **640** a.	1229	...	...	...	...	...	...	...	...	...	...	...	...	...	2029	...	...
	Salerno **640** a.	...	...	...	...	...	...	...	...	...	...	...	...	...	...	2124	...	...

	IC 669	*EC* 327 ⊖♦	*FB* 8643	*FB* 8623	*IC* 673	*FA* 8591	*IC* 675	*IC* 679	*FA* 9745 ♦	*IC* 519	*IC* 685	*IC* 689	*ICN* 1963 ❖♦	*IC* 687	*ITA* 9965 ♦	*ICN* 799 B ❖♦	*ICN* 799 C ❖♦
Torino Porta Nuova d.	...	...	...	1520	...	...	...	...	...	1805	...	...	...	...	...	2015	2155
Asti d.	...	...	...	1600	...	...	...	...	...	1841	...	...	...	...	...	2056	2236
Alessandria d.	...	...	...	1616	...	...	...	...	...	1902	...	...	...	...	...	2116	2259
Novi Ligure d.	...	...	...	|	...	...	...	...	...	1916	...	...	...	...	...	|	|
Milano Centrale d.	1405	1420r	1510	|	1605	...	1705	1805	1825	|	1905	2005	2010	2110	2130	|	|
Pavia d.	1435	1441	1535	|	1635	...	1735	1835	1857	|	1935	2035	2041	2135	|	|	|
Voghera d.	1451	|	1551	|	1651	...	1751	1851	|	|	1951	2051	2057	2151	|	|	|
Tortona d.	|	1513	|	|	|	...	|	1902	|	|	|	|	2108	|	|	|	|
Genova Piazza Principe a.	1544	1552	1644	1700	1744	...	1844	1944	1955s	2002s	2044	2144	2153	2240	2309s	2204	2350
Genova Piazza Principe d.	1547	...	|	1705	1747	1835	|	1947	1955s	2002s	2047	|	2156	2243	2311s	2207	2353
Genova Brignole d.	1556	...	A	1712	1756	1842u	A	1956	2003	2012	2056	A	2205	2252	2318	2216	0002
S. Margherita-Portofino d.	|	...	...	|	1816	|	...	2016	...	...	|	...	|	2315	...	|	|
Rapallo d.	1621	...	...	1737	1821	|	...	2021	...	...	2126	...	|	2320	...	2241	0028
Chiavari d.	1630	...	...	1746	1830	|	...	2030	...	...	2135	...	|	2329	...	2250	0038
Sestri Levante d.	1638	...	...	|	1838	|	...	2038	...	...	2142	...	|	2341	...	|	|
Levanto d.	1701	...	...	|	1901	|	...	2100	...	...	|	...	|	2357	...	|	|
Monterosso d.	1707	...	...	|	1907	|	...	2107	...	...	|	...	|	0003	...	|	|
La Spezia Centrale d.	1724	...	...	1816	1923	1948	...	2123	...	...	2223	...	2309	0018	...	2352	0127
Sarzana d.	|	...	...	1828	|	2000	...	|	...	...	2235	...	|	...	...	|	|
Carrara-Avenza d.	1746	...	...	|	1941	|	...	|	...	...	2243	...	|	...	...	|	|
Massa Centro d.	1754	...	...	1840	1949	2012	...	2145	...	...	2250	...	|	...	...	|	|
Viareggio d.	1808	...	...	1852	2002	|	...	2200	...	...	2303	...	2341	...	...	|	|
Pisa Centrale a.	1824	...	...	1908	2017	2036	...	2217	...	...	2317	...	2356	...	...	0048	0216
Pisa Centrale d.	1826	...	...	1911	2020	2038	...	2220	...	...	2320	...	2359	...	...	0108	0221
Firenze Campo di Marte d.	|	...	...	|	|	2131	...	|	...	...	|	...	|	...	...	|	|
Livorno Centrale a.	1840	...	...	1924	2035	|	...	2235	...	...	2335	...	0014	...	...	0128	0237
Livorno Centrale d.	...	...	...	1926	...	|	...	...	...	...	...	...	0017	...	...	0240	0240
Cecina d.	...	...	...	1948	...	|	...	...	...	...	...	...	|	...	...	|	|
Campiglia Marittima d.	...	...	...	2006	...	|	...	...	...	...	...	...	|	...	...	|	|
Follonica d.	...	...	...	|	...	|	...	...	...	...	...	...	|	...	...	|	|
Grosseto d.	...	...	...	2033	...	|	...	...	...	...	...	...	|	...	...	0407	0407
Civitavecchia d.	...	...	...	2124	...	|	...	...	...	...	...	...	|	...	...	0500	0500
Roma Ostiense a.	...	...	...	|	...	|	...	...	...	...	...	...	|	...	...	0543	0543
Roma Termini a.	...	...	...	2218	...	2256	...	...	...	...	...	...	|	...	...	|	|
Napoli Centrale **640** a.	...	...	...	...	...	...	...	...	...	...	...	...	|	...	...	0817	0817
Salerno **640** a.	...	...	...	...	...	...	...	...	...	...	...	...	0613	...	...	0911	0911

km		2	2	*ICN* 757 ❖♦
0	**Torino** Porta Nuova d.	...	...	2050
56	Asti d.	...	...	2129
91	Alessandria d.	...	...	2152
	Genova Brignole d.	1117	1706	|
	Genova Piazza Principe d.	1125	1714	|
113	Tortona d.	1241	1851	2207
130	Voghera d.	1253	1902	2218
188	Piacenza a.	1340	1947	2255
335	**Bologna** Centrale a.	*1525*	2125	0022

	ICN 754 ❖♦	2	2
Bologna Centrale d.	0535	0633	*1150*
Piacenza d.	0710	0809	1409
Voghera d.	0757	0856	1456
Tortona d.	0808	0907	1507
Genova Piazza Principe a.	|	1014	1612
Genova Brignole a.	|	1024	1620
Alessandria d.	0825	...	...
Asti d.	0847	...	...
Torino Porta Nuova a.	0925	...	...

♦ – **NOTES** (LISTED BY TRAIN NUMBER)

310 – [12] ✕ Genova - Milano - Zürich (Table **550**).
327 – [12] ✕ Zürich - Milano - Genova (Table **550**).
754 – 1, 2 cl., 2 cl. (4 berth) Lecce - Torino.
757 – 1, 2 cl., 2 cl. (4 berth) Torino - Lecce.
796 – 1, 2 cl., 2 cl. (4 berth) and [2] Salerno - Torino.
799 – 1, 2 cl., 2 cl. (4 berth) and [2] Torino - Salerno.
1962 – 1, 2 cl., 2 cl. (4 berth) Siracusa - Milano; 1, 2 cl., 2 cl. (4 berth) Palermo (**1964**) - Messina - Milano.
1963 – 1, 2 cl., 2 cl. (4 berth) Milano - Siracusa; 1, 2 cl., 2 cl. (4 berth) Milano - Messina (**1965**) - Palermo.
8583 – [12] 🍷 Genova - Roma (**8586**) - Fiumicino Airport ✈ (a. 1022).
8596 – [12] 🍷 Fiumicino Airport ✈ (**8595**, d. 1953) - Roma - Genova.
9710 – [12] 🍷 Genova - Milano (**9711**) - Venezia.
9745 – [12] 🍷 Venezia (**9744**) - Milano - Genova.
9965 – [12] 🍷 Napoli - Milano - Genova.
9973 – [12] 🍷 Genova - Milano - Napoli.

A – To / from Ventimiglia (Table **580**).
B – ①–⑤ until Mar. 15.
C – ⑥⑦ until Mar. 13; daily from Mar. 16.
r – Milano **Rogoredo**.
⊖ – [R] for international journeys.
❖ – Running days, timings and numbers of *ICN* trains vary - please check your reservation. For confirmed timings please consult the *Trenitalia* journey planner at www.trenitalia.com.

s – Calls to set down only.
t – Roma **Tiburtina**.
u – Calls to pick up only.

610 ROMA - PISA - GENOVA - MILANO and TORINO

🍷 on all *EC*, *FA*, *FB*, *FR* and *ITA* trains

km		*ICN* 796 ⑥⑦ ❖♦	*ITA* 9973 ♦	*IC* 652	*IC* 500	*FA* 9710 ♦		*ICN* 796 ③–⑤ ❖♦	*ICN* 796 ①② ❖♦	*IC* 655 ①–⑥	*IC* 658	*ICN* 1962 ⑥⑦ ❖♦		*IC* 662	*IC* 504	*ICN* 1962 ①–⑤ ❖♦	*FA* 8588	*IC* 666		*FB* 8606	*IC* 745	*IC* 670	*IC* 655 †
	Salerno **640** d.	2052	...	...	...	...	...	2052	2052	...	...	2333	...	...	...	2333	...	...	...	...	...	...	...
	Napoli Centrale **640** d.	2146	...	...	...	...	...	2146	2146	...	...	|	...	...	...	|	...	...	...	...	...	...	...
0	**Roma** Termini d.	|	...	...	...	...	...	|	|	...	...	|	...	...	...	|	0625	...	...	0657	...	...	...
7	**Roma** Ostiense d.	0011	...	...	...	...	...	0011	0017	...	...	|	...	...	...	|	|	...	...	|	...	...	...
81	Civitavecchia d.	0053	...	...	...	...	...	0130	0130	...	...	|	...	...	...	|	|	...	...	0746	...	...	...
188	Grosseto d.	0153	...	...	...	...	...	0232	0232	...	...	|	...	...	...	|	|	...	...	0839	...	...	...
230	Follonica d.	|	...	...	...	...	...	|	|	...	...	|	...	...	...	|	|	...	...	|	...	...	...
247	Campiglia Marittima d.	|	...	...	...	...	...	|	|	...	...	|	...	...	...	|	|	...	...	0905	...	...	...
282	Cecina d.	|	...	...	...	...	...	|	|	...	...	|	...	...	...	|	|	...	...	0920	...	...	...
316	**Livorno** Centrale a.	0306	...	...	...	...	...	0345	0345	...	...	0540	...	...	...	0628	|	...	...	0939	...	...	...
316	**Livorno** Centrale d.	0309	...	...	...	...	...	0348	0348	...	0525	0540	...	0625	...	0628	|	0835	...	0941	...	1124	...
	Firenze Campo di Marte d.	|	...	...	...	...	...	|	|	...	|	|	...	|	...	|	0754	|	...	|	...	|	...
336	**Pisa** Centrale a.	0323	...	...	...	...	...	0402	0402	...	0539	0557	...	0639	...	0647	0848	0855	...	0953	...	1139	...
336	**Pisa** Centrale d.	0326	...	...	...	...	...	0405	0405	...	0542	0557	...	0642	...	0647	0850	0857	...	0956	...	1142	...
357	Viareggio d.	|	...	...	...	...	...	|	|	...	0557	0617	...	0657	...	0707	|	0923	...	1012	...	1200	...
378	Massa Centro d.	|	...	...	...	...	...	|	|	...	0613	|	...	0709	...	|	0916	0937	...	1025	...	1212	...
385	Carrara-Avenza d.	|	...	...	...	...	...	|	|	...	|	|	...	0716	...	|	|	0950	...	|	...	1219	...
395	Sarzana d.	|	...	...	...	...	...	|	|	...	|	|	...	0724	...	|	|	|	...	|	...	|	...
411	La Spezia Centrale d.	0425	...	0456	...	...	...	0504	0504	...	0638	0654	...	0738	...	0758	0939	1035	...	1046	...	1238	...
418	Monterosso d.	|	...	0514	...	...	...	|	|	...	0654	|	...	|	...	|	|	1055	...	|	...	1255	...
423	Levanto d.	|	...	0521	...	...	...	|	|	...	0700	|	...	0757	...	|	|	1102	...	|	...	1302	...
446	Sestri Levante d.	|	...	0540	...	...	...	|	|	...	0716	|	...	0814	...	|	|	1124	...	|	...	1324	...
453	Chiavari d.	0512	...	0552	...	...	...	0606	0606	...	0724	|	...	0824	...	|	|	1132	...	1117	...	1332	...
462	Rapallo d.	0521	...	0601	...	...	...	0618	0618	...	0733	|	...	0833	...	|	|	1141	...	|	...	1341	...
464	S. Margherita-Portofino d.	|	...	0607	...	...	...	|	|	...	0739	|	...	|	...	|	|	|	...	|	...	1346	...
498	**Genova** Brignole d.	0555	0608	0635	0648	0658	...	0704	0704	A	0810	0830	...	0909	...	0927	1038s	1210	...	1145	A	1410	A
501	**Genova** Piazza Principe a.	0601	0614u	0641	0656u	0705u	...	0710	0710	|	0816	0839	...	0915	...	0936	1045	1216	...	1150	|	1416	|
501	**Genova** Piazza Principe d.	0606	0614u	0644	0656u	0705u	...	0713	0713	0719	0819	0839	...	0918	0923	0936	...	1219	...	1159	1319	1419	1520
573	Tortona d.	|	|	|	|	|	...	|	|	|	0900	0930	...	|	|	1016	...	|	...	|	|	|	|
590	Voghera d.	|	|	0734	|	|	...	|	|	0808	0911	0944	...	1008	|	1028	...	1308	...	|	1408	1508	1608
616	Pavia d.	|	|	0751	|	0806	...	|	|	0825	0927	1014	...	1025	|	1050	...	1325	...	|	1425	1525	1625
655	**Milano** Centrale a.	|	0805	0822	|	0835	...	|	|	0900	1000	1120	...	1055	|	1120	...	1353	...	|	1455	1553	1653
	Novi Ligure d.	|	...	...	0734	...	...	|	|	...	...	...	...	...	|	...	...	...	...	|	...	...	...
	Alessandria d.	0657	...	...	0748	...	...	0813	0813	...	...	...	...	...	1010	...	...	...	...	1244	...	...	...
	Asti d.	0723	...	...	0807	...	...	0833	0833	...	...	...	...	...	1029	...	...	...	...	1302	...	...	...
	Torino Porta Nuova a.	0810	...	...	0845	...	...	0910	0910	...	...	...	...	...	1110	...	...	...	...	1340	...	...	...

	IC 510	*EC* 310 ⊖♦	*IC* 674	*FB* 8616		*FB* 8655	*IC* 680	*FB* 8620	*IC* 681 Ⓐ		*IC* 681 Ⓒ	*IC* 684 Ⓒ	*IC* 684 Ⓐ	*FB* 8659		*IC* 518	*FA* 8556 Ⓑ	*FB* 8626	*FB* 8630		*FA* 8596 Ⓑ ♦	*IC* 522
Salerno **640** d.	0626	...	...	...	...	...	...	...	...	...	...	...	...	...	...	...	...	...	...	...	...	...
Napoli Centrale **640** d.	0731	...	...	...	...	...	...	...	...	...	...	...	...	...	...	...	...	...	...	...	...	1731
Roma Termini d.	0957	...	...	1157	...	...	...	1357	...	...	...	...	...	...	...	1557	1650	1657	1827	...	2035t	|
Roma Ostiense d.	1007	...	...	|	...	...	...	|	...	...	...	...	...	...	...	1607	|	|	|	...	|	1943
Civitavecchia d.	1047	...	...	1246	...	...	...	1446	...	...	...	...	...	...	...	1647	|	1746	1916	...	|	2023
Grosseto d.	1139	...	...	1339	...	...	...	1539	...	...	...	1604	1610	...	...	1739	|	1838	2007	...	|	2121
Follonica d.	1158	...	...	|	...	...	...	|	...	...	...	1624	1631	...	...	1759	|	|	|	...	|	2141
Campiglia Marittima d.	1209	...	...	1405	...	...	...	1605	...	...	...	1636	1642	...	...	|	|	1907	2032	...	|	2151
Cecina d.	|	...	...	|	...	...	...	|	...	...	...	1655	1700	...	...	1823	|	|	|	...	|	2210
Livorno Centrale a.	1243	...	...	1438	...	...	...	1638	...	...	...	1716	1722	...	...	1844	|	1938	2105	...	|	2234
Livorno Centrale d.	1245	...	1324	1440	...	...	...	1640	...	...	...	1718	1724	...	...	1846	|	1940	2107	...	|	2236
Firenze Campo di Marte d.	|	...	|	|	...	...	...	|	...	...	...	|	|	...	...	|	1815	|	|	...	2154	|
Pisa Centrale a.	1259	...	1339	1453	...	...	...	1653	...	...	...	1733	1739	...	...	1900	1911	1953	2120	...	2240	2250
Pisa Centrale d.	1302	...	1342	1456	...	...	...	1656	...	...	...	1736	1742	...	...	1903	1914	1956	2123	...	2243	2253
Viareggio d.	1317	...	1402	1512	...	...	...	1712	...	...	...	1753	1802	...	...	1919	|	2012	2140	...	|	2310
Massa Centro d.	1330	...	1414	1525	...	...	...	1725	...	...	...	1814	1814	...	...	1935	|	2025	2154	...	|	2323
Carrara-Avenza d.	1339	...	|	|	...	...	...	|	...	...	...	1821	|	...	...	|	|	|	|	...	|	2331
Sarzana d.	|	...	|	|	...	...	...	|	...	...	...	|	|	...	...	|	|	|	|	...	|	2340
La Spezia Centrale d.	1405	...	1438	1546	...	...	1638	1746	...	...	...	1838	1838	...	...	2003	1958	2046	2216	...	2327	0008
Monterosso d.	|	...	1455	|	...	...	1655	|	...	...	...	1855	1855	...	...	|	|	|	|	...	|	0024
Levanto d.	|	...	1502	|	...	...	1702	|	...	...	...	1902	1902	...	...	|	|	|	|	...	|	0031
Sestri Levante d.	1444	...	1524	|	...	...	1725	|	...	...	...	1925	1925	...	...	2030	|	|	|	...	|	0049
Chiavari d.	1451	...	1532	1616	...	...	1732	1816	...	...	...	1932	1932	...	...	2038	|	|	2246	...	|	...
Rapallo d.	1500	...	1541	1625	...	...	1741	|	...	...	...	1941	1941	...	...	2046	2035	2123	|	...	|	...
S. Margherita-Portofino d.	|	...	1546	|	...	...	1746	|	...	...	...	1946	1946	...	...	|	|	|	|	...	|	...
Genova Brignole d.	1529	...	1608	1651s	...	A	1809	1845	A	...	A	2010	2010	A	...	2129	2108s	2143s	2313s	...	0022s	...
Genova Piazza Principe a.	1535	...	1614	1658	...	|	1815	1850	|	...	|	2016	2016	|	...	2134	2117	2150	2320	...	0030	...
Genova Piazza Principe d.	1538	1612	1619	...	...	1719	1818	1852	1922	...	1922	2019	2019	2157	...	|	...	...	...	...	...	...
Tortona d.	|	1653	1700	...	...	|	1900	|	2000	...	2000	|	|	|	...	A	...	...	...	...	...	...
Voghera d.	|	|	|	...	...	1808	|	|	|	...	|	2108	2108	2249	...	...	...	...	...	...	...	...
Pavia d.	|	1719	1725	...	...	1825	1925	2006	2025	...	2025	2125	2125	2306	...	...	...	...	...	...	...	...
Milano Centrale a.	|	1740r	1753	...	...	1855	1957	2040	2057	...	2057	2153	2153	2340	...	...	...	...	...	...	...	...
Novi Ligure d.	|	...	...	...	...	...	...	...	...	...	...	...	...	...	...	...	...	...	...	...	...	...
Alessandria d.	1636	...	...	...	...	...	...	...	...	...	...	...	...	...	...	...	...	...	...	...	...	...
Asti d.	1700	...	...	...	...	...	...	...	...	...	...	...	...	...	...	...	...	...	...	...	...	...
Torino Porta Nuova a.	1740	...	...	...	...	...	...	...	...	...	...	...	...	...	...	...	...	...	...	...	...	...

FOR FOOTNOTES SEE PREVIOUS PAGE.

611 TORINO and MILANO - GENOVA - PISA - ROMA

2nd class

Regional trains. For long distance trains see Table **610**.

TORINO - GENOVA

km										
0	**Torino** Porta Nuova d.	0530	0630	0730	0830	and	1730	1830	1930	2130
56	Asti d.	0607	0707	0807	0907	hourly	1807	1907	2007	2207
91	Alessandria d.	0631	0731	0831	0931	hour	1831	1931	2031	2231
112	Novi Ligure d.	0644	0744	0844	0944	until	1844	1944	2044	2244
166	**Genova** Piazza Principe a.	0733	0830	0933	1033	◧	1933	2030	2130	2330

Genova Piazza Principe d.	0527	0627	0727	0827	and	1727	1827	2027	2127
Novi Ligure d.	0614	0714	0814	0914	hourly	1814	1914	2114	2214
Alessandria d.	0631	0731	0831	0931	hour	1831	1931	2131	2231
Asti d.	0654	0754	0854	0954	until	1854	1954	2154	2254
Torino Porta Nuova a.	0730	0830	0930	1030	◧	1930	2030	2230	2335

MILANO - GENOVA

km		⚒		⚒			Ⓐ	Ⓒ			
0	**Milano** Centrale d.	0625	0725	0830	1225	1425	1625	1625	1825	2025	...
10	**Milano** Rogoredo d.	0638	0738	0844	1238	1438	1638	1638	1840	2038	...
39	Pavia d.	0659	0759	0905	1259	1459	1659	1659	1903	2059	...
65	Voghera d.	0716	0816	0923	1316	1516	1716	1716	1918	2116	...
82	Tortona d.	0726	0826	0935	1326	1526	1726	1726	1929	2126	...
154	**Genova** Piazza Principe a.	0818	0908	1025	1418	1618	1818	1814	2021	2218	...
157	**Genova** Brignole a.	0826	0920	...	1427	...	1827	...	2030	...	...

			Ⓐ	Ⓒ	Ⓐ	Ⓒ	Ⓐ		⚒	Ⓑ
Genova Brignole d.	0536	...	1336	...	...	...	...	1936	...	...
Genova Piazza Principe d.	0544	0750	1344	1344	1544	1546	1744	1944	2035	2144
Tortona d.	0632	0832	1432	1432	1632	1632	1832	2032	2123	2232
Voghera d.	0643	0843	1443	1443	1643	1643	1843	2043	2134	2243
Pavia d.	0701	0901	1501	1501	1701	1701	1901	2101	2151	2301
Milano Rogoredo a.	0720	0918	1520	1520	1720	1720	1920	2120	2210	2320
Milano Centrale a.	0735	0935	1535	1535	1735	1735	1935	2135	2225	2335

◧ – No train from Torino at 0930, 1630; no train from Genova at 1127, 1527. Some trains continue to / from Genova Brignole. Timings may vary by 2–3 minutes.

2nd class TORINO and MILANO - GENOVA - PISA - ROMA 611

Regional trains. For long distance trains see Table **610**.

GENOVA - SESTRI LEVANTE - LA SPEZIA

km				⚒		†				Ⓐ		Ⓐ			Ⓐ			Ⓐ		Ⓐ		Ⓒ		
0	**Genova** Brignole d.	0500	0606	0720	...	0720	1045	1245	...	1322	1445	1620	...	1645	1738	1840	...	1819	1930	2045	...	2045	2256	...
25	S. Margherita-Portofino d.	0528	0637	0757	...	0759	1115	1315	...	1403	1515	1702	...	1715	1809	1917	...	1903	2009	2112	...	2112	2332	...
27	Rapallo d.	0532	0641	0801	...	0803	1119	1319	...	1408	1519	1708	...	1719	1814	1921	...	1908	2014	2116	...	2116	2336	...
36	Chiavari d.	0540	0650	0811	...	0811	1127	1327	...	1418	1527	1716	...	1727	1823	1929	...	1918	2023	2125	...	2125	2344	...
43	**Sestri Levante** a.	0548	0659	0819	...	0819	1134	1334	...	1428	1534	1728	...	1734	1832	1936	...	1932	2031	2132	...	2134	2354	...
43	**Sestri Levante** d.	0549	0700	0820	...	0820	1135	1335	...	1429	1535	1740	...	1735	1840	1937	...	1941	2032	2133	...	2135	2355	...
66	Levanto d.	0615	0725	0853	...	0847	1150	1350	...	1511	1550	1814	...	1750	1914	1953	...	2015	2052	2148	...	2150	0017	...
71	Monterosso d.	0620	0730	0858	...	0853	|	1355	...	1517	1555	1819	...	1755	1919	1958	...	2020	2057	2153	...	2155	0022	...
80	Riomaggiore d.	0635	|	0908	...	0909	1203	|	...	1533	1604	1834	...	|	1935	2008	...	2035	2106	2202	...	2203	0037	...
87	**La Spezia** Centrale a.	0645	0745	0914	...	0917	1210	1410	...	1540	1610	1845	...	1810	1942	2017	...	2045	2112	2210	...	2210	0048	...

			Ⓐ		Ⓐ	†		Ⓐ														Ⓒ		
	La Spezia Centrale d.	0508	0532	...	0540	0600	...	0625	0706	...	0750	...	0950	1150	...	1350	1550	...	1750	1945	...	2145	2310	...
	Riomaggiore d.	0517	0540	...	0549	0608	...	|	0714	...	|	...	|	|	...	1358	1558	...	1758	1953	...	2153	2319	...
	Monterosso d.	0533	0558	...	0604	0623	...	|	0729	...	|	...	|	|	...	1406	1606	...	|	2005	...	2201	2335	...
	Levanto d.	0538	0603	...	0609	0628	...	0641	0734	...	0811	...	1011	1211	...	1411	1611	...	1811	2011	...	2206	2340	...
	Sestri Levante a.	0604	0627	...	0635	0655	...	0655	0759	...	0825	...	1025	1225	...	1425	1625	...	1825	2035	...	2223	0004	...
	Sestri Levante d.	0605	0628	...	0656	0657	...	0657	0800	...	0826	...	1026	1226	...	1426	1626	...	1826	2036	...	2224	0005	...
	Chiavari d.	0617	0636	...	0645	0707	...	0706	0808	...	0833	...	1033	1234	...	1434	1634	...	1834	2044	...	2231	0014	...
	Rapallo d.	0628	0647	...	0656	0716	...	|	0816	...	0841	...	1041	1242	...	1442	1642	...	1842	2055	...	2239	0025	...
	S. Margherita-Portofino d.	0632	0651	...	0700	0720	...	|	0820	...	0845	...	1045	1246	...	1446	1646	...	1846	2059	...	2243	0029	...
	Genova Brignole a.	0709	0733	...	0753	0753	...	0740	0856	...	0915	...	1115	1315	...	1515	1715	...	1915	2139	...	2309	0123	...

LA SPEZIA - PISA

km			⚒	⚒	†	⚒	⚒		†	⚒		⚒			†	Ⓐ			Ⓐ			⚒		
0	**La Spezia** Centrale d.	0512	0600	0653	0712	0715	0740	0821	0915	0916	1020	1215	1319	1414	1440	1515	1540	1624	1710	1740	1821	1909	2016	2226
16	Sarzana d.	0530	0615	0714	0733	0736	0800	0837	0932	0931	1035	1228	1335	1429	1500	1531	1600	1637	1725	1800	1837	1927	2031	2241
26	Carrara-Avenza d.	0538	0623	0722	0743	0746	0807	0845	0940	0939	1043	1236	1343	1439	1508	1538	1608	1645	1733	1808	1845	1936	2039	2249
33	Massa Centro d.	0544	0630	0729	0749	0753	0814	0851	0946	0946	1049	1242	1349	1445	1514	1544	1614	1651	1739	1814	1850	1942	2045	2256
54	Viareggio d.	0604	0653	0755	0810	0813	0825	0911	1007	1010	1109	1259	1406	1502	1533	1603	1633	1708	1758	1833	1907	2011	2105	2316
75	**Pisa** Centrale a.	0624	0721	0818	0827	0834	0849	0934	1038	1043	1139	1322	1427	1526	1552	1625	1652	1727	1820	1852	1927	2032	2127	2339

		⚒	⚒	d		⚒	†e		⚒		⚒				Ⓑ			Ⓐ	Ⓒ	†		⚒		⚒
	Pisa Centrale d.	0526	0622	0702	0736	0819	0840	1106	1134	1234	1306	1334	1433	1506	1538	1634	1706	1736	1743	1806	1834	1935	2034	2136
	Viareggio d.	0546	0641	0724	0756	0837	0900	1123	1155	1254	1323	1357	1452	1523	1558	1655	1723	1757	1804	1823	1855	1955	2055	2156
	Massa Centro d.	0608	0701	0745	0817	0858	0923	1144	1215	1312	1344	1415	1510	1544	1615	1712	1744	1817	1822	1844	1913	2012	2113	2216
	Carrara-Avenza d.	0616	0707	0751	0823	0905	0930	1150	1221	1318	1350	1421	1516	1548	1621	1718	1750	1823	1828	1850	1919	2019	2119	2228
	Sarzana d.	0623	0715	0802	0831	0913	0939	1158	1229	1326	1358	1430	1525	1558	1628	1726	1758	1830	1836	1858	1928	2028	2128	2236
	La Spezia Centrale a.	0650	0731	0826	0851	0933	0957	1220	1257	1341	1420	1454	1539	1620	1645	1739	1820	1854	1854	1920	1943	2050	2143	2254

d – Daily until Apr. 10; ⚒ from Apr. 11.

e – From Apr. 17.

PISA - ROMA

km		⚒	Ⓒ							
0	**Pisa** Centrale d.	...	...	0545	0745	1145	1343	1545	1745	1945
20	**Livorno** Centrale d.	...	...	0603	0803	1203	1400	1603	1803	2003
43	Rosignano d.	...	...	0620	0820	1220	1416	1620	1820	2020
54	Cecina d.	...	...	0629	0829	1229	1424	1629	1829	2029
89	Campiglia Marittima d.	...	...	0650	0851	1251	1445	1651	1851	2051
106	Follonica d.	...	...	0700	0902	1302	1455	1702	1902	2102
148	Grosseto d.	0523	0615	0728	0930	1330	1530	1730	1930	2130
186	Orbetello-Monte Argentario d.	0549	0643	0751	0953	1353	1553	1753	1953	2153
225	Tarquinia d.	0622	0716	0827	1029	1429	1629	1829	2029	2229
255	Civitavecchia d.	0636	0730	0842	1044	1444	1644	1844	2044	2244
264	S. Marinella d.	0643	0737	0849	1051	1451	1651	1851	2051	2251
286	Ladispoli-Cerveteri d.	0700	0754	0904	1105	1505	1705	1905	2105	2305
329	**Roma** Ostiense a.	0739	0837	0936	1139	1536	1736	1936	2136	2336
336	**Roma** Termini a.	0750	0850	0948	1150	1548	1747	1948	2148	2348

	⚒								
Roma Termini d.	...	0612	1012	1212	1412	1612	1812	2012	2112
Roma Ostiense d.	...	0623	1023	1223	1423	1623	1823	2023	2121
Ladispoli-Cerveteri d.	...	0651	1051	1251	1451	1651	1855	2052	2155
S. Marinella d.	...	0707	1107	1307	1507	1707	1911	2107	2211
Civitavecchia d.	...	0715	1115	1315	1515	1715	1924	2115	2220
Tarquinia d.	...	0728	1128	1328	1528	1728	1936	2128	2233
Orbetello-Monte Argentario d.	0602	0800	1201	1401	1601	1801	2009	2201	2306
Grosseto d.	0628	0823	1226	1426	1626	1826	2033	2226	2330
Follonica d.	0652	0845	1250	1450	1650	1850	2057	2250	...
Campiglia Marittima d.	0704	0855	1301	1501	1701	1901	2108	2301	...
Cecina d.	0729	0916	1324	1524	1724	1924	2128	2324	...
Rosignano d.	0737	0927	1332	1532	1732	1932	2136	2333	...
Livorno Centrale a.	0753	0952	1355	1555	1755	1955	2155	2355	...
Pisa Centrale a.	0811	1018	1415	1615	1815	2015	2215	0015	...

CAMPIGLIA - PIOMBINO

km		⚒	⑥	⚒			f		g	†h
0	**Campiglia** Marittima d.	0556	1003	1336	1533	1645	1736	1804	1839	2055
14	**Piombino** a.	0608	1019	1352	1547	1700	1752	1816	1851	2111
16	**Piombino** Marittima a.	0624	1032	1405	1600	1713	1802	1831	1904	2124

	⚒		j	†k	⚒			f	
Piombino Marittima d.	0632	0920	1053	1140	1519	1608	1724	1812	1845
Piombino d.	0643	0931	1104	1151	1531	1619	1735	1820	1856
Campiglia Marittima a.	0659	0947	1120	1207	1552	1635	1753	1838	1909

f – Ⓐ (also † from Apr. 17).

g – † Apr. 17 - May 15; Ⓒ from May 21.

h – From May 15.

j – Ⓒ until Apr. 10; ⑥ Apr. 16 - May 14.

k – From Apr. 17.

2nd class PARMA - LA SPEZIA 612

For other trains Pontremoli - S. Stefano di Magra and v.v. see next page.

km		⚒						⚒			⚒			⚒			⚒			⚒			†
0	**Parma** d.	...	0514	...	0627	0745	...	...	...	...	1226	1344	...	...	1553	...	...	1748	...	1944	2057	...	2240
23	Fornovo d.	...	0532	...	0650	0812	...	...	...	...	1247	1407	...	...	1621	...	...	1815	...	2014	2124	...	2306
61	Borgo Val di Taro d.	...	0605	...	0731	0846	...	...	...	...	1323	1444	...	...	1655	...	...	1850	...	2045	2202	...	2340
79	Pontremoli d.	0544	0627	...	0749	0904	...	0942	1320	...	1342	1503	...	1542	1713	...	1741	1908	...	2103	2220	...	2359
100	Aulla Lunigiana d.	0607	0652	...	0819	0922	...	1010	1348	...	1410	1523	...	1610	1738	...	1810	1926	...	2124	2239	...	0021
108	S. Stefano di Magra d.	0614	0659	...	0826	0930	...	1016	1355	...	1416	1532	...	1616	1745	...	1817	1933	...	2131	2246	...	0028
120	**La Spezia** Centrale a.	0631	0722	...	0844	0944	...	1033	1410	...	1435	1556	...	1633	1803	...	1832	1954	...	2154	2306	...	0045

					⚒	⚒								⚒			⚒			⚒			
	La Spezia Centrale d.	0540	0614	...	0810	0927	...	1015	1226	...	1325	1416	...	1527	1604	...	1727	1809	...	1927	2009	...	2214
	S. Stefano di Magra d.	0551	0632	...	0827	0945	...	1032	1242	...	1343	1431	...	1545	1623	...	1745	1826	...	1945	2028	...	2125
	Aulla Lunigiana d.	0558	0638	...	0835	0952	...	1038	1249	...	1351	1439	...	1552	1632	...	1852	1835	...	1952	2037	...	2132
	Pontremoli d.	0626	0658	...	0856	1015	...	1058	1308	...	1413	1456	...	1613	1654	...	1815	1855	...	2015	2057	...	2151
	Borgo Val di Taro d.	0645	0717	...	0915	...	...	1116	1326	...	...	1515	...	...	1713	...	...	1913	...	...	2116	...	2210
	Fornovo d.	0720	0751	...	0952	...	...	1150	1404	...	...	1552	...	...	1746	...	...	1947	...	...	2148	...	2244
	Parma a.	0742	0813	...	1016	...	...	1209	1431	...	...	1614	...	...	1809	...	...	2010	...	...	2214	...	2310

612 MILANO - PISA - FIRENZE

2nd class

For other trains Pontremoli - S. Stefano di Magra and v.v. see previous page.

km					⚒	Ⓐ	⑥		Ⓑ	
0	**Milano** Centrale d.	...	0645	...	...	...	...	...	1641r	...
10	**Milano** Rogoredo d.	...	0701	...	...	...	...	...	1715	...
72	Piacenza d.	...	0759	...	...	...	...	...	1805	...
107	Fidenza d.	...	0824	...	...	...	...	...	1830	...
132	Fornovo d.	...	0842	...	...	...	...	...	1848	...
170	Borgo Val di Taro d.	0541	0933	...	...	...	...	...	1932	...
188	Pontremoli d.	0601	0954	1221	1421	1621	1621	1821	1954	...
209	Aulla Lunigiana d.	0623	1021	1243	1443	1643	1643	1843	2026	...
217	S. Stefano di Magra d.	0631	1028	1251	1451	1651	1651	1851	2034	...
225	Sarzana a.	0638	1043	1300	1500	1700	1700	1900	2043	...
235	Carrara-Avenza d.	0647	1052	1308	1508	1708	1708	1908	2051	...
242	Massa Centro d.	0653	1100	1314	1514	1714	1714	1914	2057	...
263	Viareggio d.	0714	1124	1333	1533	1733	1733	1933	2118	...
284	**Pisa** Centrale 613 d.	0744	1145	1354	1554	1754	1754	1954	2140	...
304	**Livorno** Centrale a.	|	...	|	|	|	|	|	2155	...
331	Empoli 613 d.	0815	...	1432	1532	1832	1836	2032	...	...
	Firenze Rifredi 613 a.	0839	...	1459	1705	1859	1912	2059	...	...
365	**Firenze** SMN 613 a.	0848	...	1508	1714	1908	1919	2108	...	...

		†	⚒	⚒	⚒	⚒			
Firenze SMN 613 d.	...	0850	1053	1253	1453	1653	...	1853	...
Firenze Rifredi 613 d.	...	0856	1059	1259	1459	1659	...	1859	...
Empoli 613 d.	...	0925	1128	1327	1527	1727	...	1927	...
Livorno Centrale d.	0552	|	|	|	|	|	...	|	...
Pisa Centrale 613 d.	0610	1006	1206	1406	1606	1806	1907	2006	...
Viareggio d.	0628	1023	1223	1423	1623	1823	1926	2023	...
Massa Centro d.	0645	1044	1244	1444	1644	1844	1946	2044	...
Carrara-Avenza d.	0651	1050	1250	1450	1650	1850	1952	2050	...
Sarzana d.	0700	1058	1258	1458	1658	1858	1959	2058	...
S. Stefano di Magra d.	0711	1109	1310	1509	1709	1909	2015	2109	...
Aulla Lunigiana d.	0718	1116	1317	1516	1716	1916	2025	2116	...
Pontremoli d.	0742	1140	1340	1540	1740	1940	2042	2140	...
Borgo Val di Taro d.	0803	...	...	...	...	...	2104	...	...
Fornovo d.	0844	...	...	...	...	...	2136	...	...
Fidenza d.	0905	...	...	...	...	...	2158	...	...
Piacenza d.	0930	...	...	...	...	...	2225	...	...
Milano Rogoredo a.	1015	...	...	...	...	...	2310	...	...
Milano Centrale a.	1040r	...	...	...	...	...	2322	...	...

r – Milano **Porta Garibaldi**.

613 FIRENZE - SIENA, PISA and LIVORNO

2nd class

km			⚒	†					⚒		⚒									⚒	⚒	⚒	†	
0	**Firenze** SMN 614 d.	0535	0620	0620	0653	0728	0810	0828	0910	0928	1010	1028	1100	...	1110	1128	1138	1210	1228	1300	1310	1328	1338	1410
	Firenze Rifredi 614 d.	0540	0626	0626	0659	0734	0816	0834	0916	0934	1016	1034	|	...	1116	1134	1144	1216	1234	|	1316	1334	1344	1416
34	Empoli d.	0601	0650	0650	0730	0758	0840	0858	0940	0958	1040	1058	1123	...	1140	1157	1213	1240	1258	1323	1340	1358	1413	1440
72	Poggibonsi-S. Gimignano d.	|	0729	0724	|	|	0915	|	1015	|	1115	|	|	...	1215	|	|	1315	|	|	1415	|	|	1514
97	**Siena** a.	|	0755	0747	|	|	0938	|	1040	|	1140	|	|	...	1238	|	|	1340	|	|	1440	|	|	1537
81	**Pisa** Centrale 614 d.	0637	...	...	0809	0837	...	0932	...	1032	...	1132	1154	...	...	1227	1302	...	1332	1354	...	1432	1509	...
101	**Livorno** Centrale a.	0651	...	...	0826	0851	...	0948	...	1048	...	1148	1211	...	...	1244	1320	...	1348	1411	...	1448	1526	...

			⚒		⚒	⚒	⚒									⑥			†	⚒	⚒		
Firenze SMN 614 d.	1428	1500	1510	1528	1610	1628	1700	1710	1728	1738	1810	1828	...	1910	1928	1953	2010	2053	2128	2128	2138	2200	2307
Firenze Rifredi 614 d.	1434	|	1516	1534	1616	1634	|	1716	1734	1744	1816	1834	...	1916	1934	1959	2016	2059	2134	2134	2144	2206	2313
Empoli d.	1458	1523	1640	1558	1640	1658	1723	1740	1758	1813	1840	1858	...	1940	1958	2027	2040	2127	2200	2200	2208	2236	2343
Poggibonsi-S. Gimignano d.	|	|	1615	|	1715	|	|	1815	|	|	1915	|	...	2015	|	|	2115	|	|	|	2246	|	|
Siena a.	|	|	1640	|	1738	|	|	1840	|	|	1938	|	...	2040	|	|	2137	|	|	|	2316	|	|
Pisa Centrale 614 d.	1532	1554	...	1632	...	1732	1754	...	1832	1858	...	1932	...	...	2032	2106	...	2206	2232	2239	...	2327	0032
Livorno Centrale a.	1548	1611	...	1648	...	1748	1811	...	1846	1912	...	1948	...	...	2048	2124	...	2224	2248	2257	...	2344	0050

	⚒		⚒		⚒	†	⚒	⚒	⚒	†	Ⓒ					⚒	†	⚒	⚒		⚒		
Livorno Centrale d.	0500	0519	...	0612	...	...	...	0716	...	...	0730	0743	0812	...	0849	0912	0912	...	1012	1110	...	1212	...
Pisa Centrale 614 d.	0519	0539	...	0629	...	...	...	0738	...	...	0754	0803	0832	...	0909	0932	0932	...	1032	1130	...	1232	...
Siena d.	|	|	0543	|	0613	0636	0636	|	0702	0715	|	|	|	0818	|	|	|	0918	|	|	1118	|	1218
Poggibonsi-S. Gimignano d.	|	|	0606	|	0648	0658	0659	|	0728	0742	|	|	|	0842	|	|	|	0942	|	|	1142	|	1242
Empoli d.	0602	0618	0645	0659	0723	0735	0750	0808	0820	0820	0832	0847	0904	0921	0937	1004	1017	1021	1104	1202	1221	1304	1322
Firenze Rifredi 614 a.	0631	0645	0713	0720	0744	0753	0822	0829	0850	0850	0859	0915	0926	0943	|	1025	1038	1043	1125	1226	1243	1325	1344
Firenze SMN 614 a.	0639	0653	0723	0728	0754	0804	0832	0838	0859	0859	0908	0923	0933	0952	1001	1033	1047	1052	1133	1233	1252	1333	1352

		Ⓑ				⚒	⚒	⚒		Ⓑ		⚒							⚒				
Livorno Centrale d.	1249	1312	...	1343	1412	...	1449	1512	...	1540	1612	...	1649	1712	...	1812	...	1849	...	2012	...	2112	...
Pisa Centrale 614 d.	1309	1332	...	1401	1432	...	1509	1532	...	1601	1632	...	1709	1732	...	1832	...	1909	...	2032	...	2132	...
Siena d.	|	|	1318	|	|	1418	|	|	1518	|	|	1618	|	|	1718	|	1818	|	1918	|	2018	|	2140
Poggibonsi-S. Gimignano d.	|	|	1342	|	|	1442	|	|	1542	|	|	1642	|	|	1742	|	1842	|	1942	|	2042	|	2207
Empoli d.	1337	1404	1421	1447	1504	1521	1537	1604	1621	1647	1704	1721	1737	1804	1821	1904	1921	1937	2021	2107	2121	2204	2241
Firenze Rifredi 614 a.	|	1425	1443	1516	1525	1543	|	1625	1643	1716	1725	1743	|	1825	1843	1925	1943	|	2043	2129	2143	2225	2306
Firenze SMN 614 a.	1401	1433	1452	1525	1533	1552	1601	1633	1652	1725	1733	1752	1801	1833	1852	1933	1952	2001	2052	2139	2152	2233	2315

614 FIRENZE - PRATO - BOLOGNA, VIAREGGIO and PISA

2nd class

km		⚒	⚒				†	⚒	⚒			⚒			⚒	†		Ⓐ			†			⚒
0	**Firenze** SMN 613 d.	0510	...	...	...	0709	...	...	...	0809	...	...	0909	...	...	1009	...	...	1209	...	...	1309	...	...
	Firenze Rifredi 613 d.	0516	...	...	...	0715	...	...	...	0815	...	...	0915	...	...	1015	...	...	1215	...	...	1315	...	...
17	Prato Centrale d.	0533	...	...	0615	0728	...	...	0738	0830	...	0908	0930	...	0940	1030	1040	...	1230	...	1240	1330	...	1340
	Bologna Centrale a.	|	...	...	0727	|	...	...	0850	|	...	1020	|	...	1052	|	1152	...	|	...	1352	|	...	1456
34	Pistoia d.	0551	...	...	...	0745	...	...	...	0844	...	...	0944	...	...	1044	...	...	1244	...	...	1344	...	...
47	Montecatini Centro d.	0604	...	...	...	0801	...	...	...	0901	...	...	1001	...	...	1101	...	...	1301	...	...	1401	...	...
78	Lucca d.	0646	0652	0755	...	0830	0842	0849	...	0930	0942	...	1033	1042	...	1130	...	1242	1330	1340	...	1430	1442	...
101	**Viareggio** a.	0707	|	|	...	0850	|	|	...	0950	|	...	1056	|	...	1150	...	|	1350	|	...	1450	|	...
102	**Pisa** Centrale 613 a.	...	0717	0825	...	...	0913	0916	...	...	1013	...	...	1111	...	...	...	1313	...	1413	...	...	1513	...

				Ⓑ	⚒					⚒			†	⚒	⚒			⚒		Ⓐ	⚒		
Firenze SMN 613 d.	1409	...	1509	...	...	1609	...	...	1709	...	...	1809	...	...	...	1909	...	...	2009	...	2109	2209	...
Firenze Rifredi 613 d.	1415	...	1515	...	...	1615	...	...	1715	...	...	1815	...	...	...	1915	...	...	2015	...	2115	2215	...
Prato Centrale d.	1430	...	1530	...	1540	1630	...	1640	1730	...	1740	1830	...	...	1910	1930	...	2008	2030	...	2130	2230	2249
Bologna Centrale a.	|	...	|	...	1656	|	...	1752	|	...	1852	|	...	...	2022	|	...	2120	|	...	|	|	2350
Pistoia d.	1444	...	1544	...	...	1644	...	...	1744	...	...	1844	...	...	...	1944	...	...	2044	...	2144	2246	...
Montecatini Centro d.	1501	...	1601	...	...	1701	...	...	1801	...	...	1901	...	...	...	2001	...	...	2101	...	2200	2301	...
Lucca d.	1530	1542	1630	1642	...	1730	1742	...	1830	1842	...	1930	1941	1945	...	2030	2042	...	2130	2142	2249	2330	...
Viareggio a.	1550	|	1650	|	...	1750	|	...	1850	|	...	1950	|	|	...	2050	|	...	2150	|	2309	2350	...
Pisa Centrale 613 a.	...	1613	...	1713	...	...	1813	...	...	1917	...	...	2013	2015	...	...	2113	...	...	2213	...	...	...

	⚒		⚒	⚒		⚒		⚒					⚒			⚒	⚒				⚒		
Pisa Centrale 613 d.	...	0525	...	0613	...	...	...	...	0750	...	0850	...	...	0950	...	...	1020	...	1250	...	...	1343	...
Viareggio d.	...	|	0545	|	0628	...	0710	...	|	0810	|	0910	...	|	1010	...	|	1207	|	1310	...	|	1410
Lucca d.	...	0559	0609	0640	0648	...	0727	...	0823	0831	0920	0931	...	1018	1031	...	1048	1231	1317	1331	...	1409	1431
Montecatini Centro d.	...	...	0641	...	0715	...	0753	...	...	0857	▬	0957	...	...	1057	...	...	1257	▬	1357	...	...	1457
Pistoia d.	...	...	0709	...	0732	...	0813	...	...	0913	...	1013	...	...	1113	...	...	1313	...	1413	...	...	1513
Bologna Centrale d.	0608	...	|	...	|	0708	|	0808	...	|	0908	|	1008	...	|	1208	...	|	1308	|	1408	...	|
Prato Centrale d.	0720	...	0728	...	0747	0820	0830	0920	...	0930	1024	1030	1120	...	1130	1320	...	1330	1420	1430	1520	...	1530
Firenze Rifredi 613 a.	...	...	0746	...	0801	...	0846	...	...	0946	...	1046	...	...	1146	...	...	1346	...	1446	...	...	1546
Firenze SMN 613 a.	...	...	0752	...	0807	...	0852	...	...	0952	...	1052	...	...	1152	...	...	1352	...	1452	...	...	1552

							⚒													⚒	⚒		
Pisa Centrale 613 d.	...	1450	...	...	1550	...	...	1650	...	...	1750	...	...	1850	...	1950	...	...	2050	...	...	2150	...
Viareggio d.	...	|	1510	...	|	1610	...	|	1710	...	|	1810	...	|	1910	|	2010	...	|	2110	...	|	2210
Lucca d.	...	1517	1531	...	1617	1631	...	1717	1731	...	1817	1831	...	1917	1931	2017	2031	...	2118	2131	...	2217	2231
Montecatini Centro d.	...	...	1557	...	...	1657	...	...	1757	...	...	1857	...	...	1957	...	2057	...	...	2157	...	...	2257
Pistoia d.	...	...	1613	...	...	1713	...	...	1813	...	...	1913	...	...	2013	...	2113	...	...	2213	...	...	2313
Bologna Centrale d.	1508	...	|	1608	...	|	1708	...	|	1808	...	|	1908	...	|	...	|	2038	...	|	2208	...	|
Prato Centrale d.	1620	...	1630	1724	...	1730	1824	...	1830	1924	...	1930	2020	...	2030	...	2130	2151	...	2230	2320	...	2330
Firenze Rifredi 613 a.	...	...	1646	...	...	1746	...	...	1846	...	...	1946	...	...	2046	...	2146	2202	...	2246	...	...	2344
Firenze SMN 613 a.	...	...	1652	...	...	1752	...	...	1852	...	...	1952	...	...	2052	...	2152	2210	...	2252	...	...	2350

🍷 on *FA*, *FB*, *FR* and *ITA* trains

MILANO, BOLOGNA, RIMINI, ANCONA and ROMA - BARI - LECCE 615

High-speed and long-distance trains. For local trains Milano - Bologna see Table **620**. For other local trains see page 303.

km			*ITA* 8141	*FA* 8303	*IC* 703	*FR* 9511	*FR* 9803	*FA* 8801	*IC* 603	*FR* 8803	*ITA* 9915	*IC* 605	*FA* 8311		*FR* 8807	*IC* 607	*FA* 8315	*FR* 8809	*IC* 1545	*FA* 8317	*FA* 8317	*FR* 8811	*IC* 609	*EC* 307
					B			V			T		Ⓑ						⑥	⑤⑦	⑤			A
0	**Milano** Centrale **600 620**	d.	...	...	...	0610	0705	...	...	0805	0740	0705	...	...	1105	...	...	1205	1000	...	...	1305	...	...
10	**Milano** Rogoredo △ **600 620**	d.	...	...	...	0620	|	...	...	|	|	0716	...	...	|	...	...	|	1013	...	...	|	...	1232
72	Piacenza **620**	d.	...	...	...	|	|	...	...	|	|	0808	...	...	|	...	...	|	1048	...	...	|	...	1314
107	Fidenza **620**	d.	...	...	...	|	|	...	...	|	|	0827	...	...	|	...	...	|	1105	...	...	|	...	|
129	Parma **620**	d.	...	...	...	◧	◧	...	...	0854	◧	0840	...	...	1154	...	...	1254	1118	...	...	1354	...	1346
157	Reggio Emilia **620**	d.	...	...	...	|	|	...	...	0908	|	0855	...	...	1208	...	...	1308	1133	...	...	1408	...	1400
	Reggio Emilia AV **600**	d.	...	...	...	0656	|	...	...	|	0828	|	...	...	|	...	...	|	|	...	...	|	...	|
182	Modena **620**	d.	...	...	...	|	|	...	...	0921	|	0926	...	...	1221	...	...	1321	1149	...	...	1421	...	1414
219	**Bologna** Centrale **600 620**	a.	...	...	...	0724	0812	...	...	0942	0854	0954	...	...	1242	...	...	1342	1219	...	...	1442	...	1435
219	**Bologna** Centrale	d.	...	...	...	0727	0815	0845	0800	0945	0857	0958	...	...	1245	1200	...	1345	1225	...	...	1445	1400	...
269	Faenza	d.	...	...	...	|	|	|	0828	|	|	1028	...	...	|	1228	...	|	1256	...	...	|	1428	...
284	Forlì	d.	...	...	...	|	|	|	0838	|	|	1038	...	...	|	1238	...	1416	1306	...	...	|	1438	...
302	Cesena	d.	...	...	...	|	|	|	0851	|	|	1052	...	...	1324	1251	...	|	1319	...	...	|	1451	...
331	**Rimini** ●	a.	...	...	...	|	0915	0938	0911	1038	|	1113	...	...	1341	1313	...	1441	1348	...	...	1541	1513	...
331	**Rimini** ●	d.	...	...	...	|	0917	0940	0919	1040	|	1115	...	...	1343	1315	...	1443	1352	...	...	1543	1515	...
340	Riccione	d.	...	...	...	|	0925	0947	0930	1047	|	1124	...	...	|	1324	...	|	1400	...	...	|	1524	...
364	Pesaro	d.	...	...	...	◧	0942	1002	0947	1102	◧	1142	...	...	1405	1342	...	1502	1418	...	...	1602	1542	...
376	Fano	d.	...	...	...	|	|	|	0956	|	|	1151	...	...	|	1351	...	|	1427	...	...	|	1551	...
398	Senigallia	d.	...	...	...	|	|	|	1010	|	|	1203	...	...	|	1403	...	1518	1439	...	...	|	1603	...
423	**Ancona**	a.	...	...	...	|	1013	1031	1036	1131	|	1223	...	...	1434	1423	...	1534	1458	...	...	1631	1623	...
423	**Ancona**	d.	...	...	...	|	...	1034	1039	1134	|	1226	...	...	1437	1426	...	1537	1500	...	...	1634	1626	...
466	Civitanova Marche-Montegranaro	d.	...	...	...	|	...	|	1101	1157	|	1252	...	...	|	1452	...	|	1523	...	...	|	1652	...
508	S. Benedetto del Tronto	d.	...	...	...	|	...	|	1126	|	|	1323	...	...	1516	1523	...	1616	1548	...	...	|	1723	...
569	**Pescara** Centrale	a.	...	...	...	|	...	1144	1201	1244	|	1359	...	...	1547	1559	...	1647	1631	...	...	1747	1759	...
569	**Pescara** Centrale	d.	...	...	...	|	...	1147	1203	1247	|	1401	...	...	1550	1601	...	1650	1635	...	...	1750	1801	...
659	Termoli	d.	...	...	...	|	...	1236	1254	1339	|	1452	...	...	1639	1652	...	1737	1750	...	...	1837	1852	...
	Roma Termini	d.	0745	0805	0728	1000	...	|	|	|	1145	|	1305	...	|	|	1505	|	|	1605	1605	|	|	...
	Caserta	d.	0855	0914	1008	1108	...	|	|	|	1253	|	1414	...	|	|	1614	|	|	1714	1714	|	|	...
	Benevento	d.	0946	1002	1104	1152	...	|	|	|	1337	|	1503	...	|	|	1702	|	|	1804	1804	|	|	...
746	**Foggia**	a.	1045	1105	1225	1254	...	1319	1349	1421	1445	1549	1606	...	1721	1741	1755	1821	1848	1902	1902	1921	1949	...
746	**Foggia**	d.	1054	1114	1236	1303	...	1322	1352	1424	1454	1552	1615	...	1724	1744	1804	1824	1851	1911	1911	1924	1952	...
814	Barletta	d.	1123	1143	1306	1333	...	1354	1421	1453	1522	1621	1644	...	1753	1819	1834	1853	1927	1943	1943	1953	2021	...
869	**Bari** Centrale	a.	1205	1211	1354	1410	...	1431	1505	1530	1610	1705	1714	...	1830	1858	1905	1930	2016	2020	2020	2030	2105	...
869	**Bari** Centrale	d.	...	1215	...	1418	...	1435	1509	...	...	1717	...	...	1840	1902	1909	1934	2020	...	2024	2034	2109	...
923	Gioia del Colle	d.	...	|	...	|	...	|	|	...	...	1751	...	...	1912	|	|	|	|	...	|	|	|	...
984	**Taranto**	a.	...	|	...	|	...	|	|	...	...	1826	...	...	1946	|	|	|	|	...	|	|	|	...
890	Monopoli	d.	...	1239	...	|	...	1501	1537	...	...	|	...	...	...	1927	1931	1956	2042	...	|	|	2137	...
904	Fasano	d.	...	|	...	|	...	1511	1549	...	...	|	...	...	...	1937	|	|	2054	...	|	|	2148	...
924	Ostuni	d.	...	1257	...	|	...	1524	1604	...	...	|	...	...	...	1954	|	2015	2113	...	|	|	2201	...
960	**Brindisi**	d.	...	1319	...	1527	...	1544	1627	...	...	1936	...	...	...	2018	2007	2036	2139	...	2119	2129	2225	...
999	**Lecce**	a.	...	1342	...	1550	...	1608	1651	...	...	1955	...	...	...	2040	2029	2100	2201	...	2145	2153	2249	...

		FA 8319	*FR* 8813	*ITA* 9939	*ITA* 8139	*IC* 705	*FA* 8323	*FR* 9547	*FA* 8325	*FB* 8815	*FR* 9809	*IC* 611	*IC* 613		*FR* 8819	*FR* 9811	*FA* 8823	*FA* 8825	*FA* 8829	*ICN* 789	*ICN* 755	*ICN* 765	*ICN* 757
		Ⓑ		Ⓐ T	Ⓒ T	⑤				V										⑤ ✤	✤	✤	T ✤
Milano Centrale **600 620**	d.	...	1405	1340	1340	...	...	1510	...	...	1535	...	1505	...	1605	1730	1750	1850	2005	...	2115	2150	...
Milano Rogoredo △ **600 620**	d.	...	|	|	|	...	...	1520	...	...	|	...	1516	...	|	|	|	|	|	...	|	|	...
Piacenza **620**	d.	...	|	|	|	...	...	|	...	...	|	...	1608	...	|	|	1820	1920	|	...	2205	2235	...
Fidenza **620**	d.	...	|	|	|	...	...	|	...	...	|	...	1627	...	|	|	|	|	|	...	|	|	...
Parma **620**	d.	...	1454	◧	◧	...	...	◧	...	...	◧	...	1642	...	1654	◧	1846	1954	2054	...	2236	2306	...
Reggio Emilia **620**	d.	...	1508	|	|	...	...	|	...	...	|	...	1659	...	1708	|	1903	2008	2108	...	2254	2324	...
Reggio Emilia AV **600**	d.	...	|	1428	1428	...	...	1556	...	...	1621	...	|	...	|	1814	|	|	|	...	|	|	...
Modena **620**	d.	...	1521	|	|	...	...	|	...	...	|	...	1716	...	1721	|	1919	2021	2121	...	2310	2340	...
Bologna Centrale **600 620**	a.	...	1542	1454	1454	...	...	1624	...	...	1650	...	1750	...	1742	1842	1942	2042	2142	...	2335	0006	...
Bologna Centrale	d.	...	1545	1457	1457	...	...	1627	...	1645	1655	1600	1758	...	1745	1845	1945	2045	2145	...	2339	0010	0027
Faenza	d.	...	|	|	|	...	...	|	...	|	|	1628	1828	...	1808	|	2008	2108	|	...	0009	0041	|
Forlì	d.	...	|	|	|	...	...	|	...	|	|	1638	1838	...	1817	1916	2017	2117	2216	...	0027	0055	|
Cesena	d.	...	1624	|	|	...	...	|	...	|	|	1651	1851	...	1829	|	2029	2129	|	...	0041	0109	|
Rimini ●	a.	...	1641	|	|	...	...	|	...	1741	1754	1713	1913	...	1849	1941	2049	2149	2241	...	0109	0140	0148
Rimini ●	d.	...	1643	|	|	...	...	|	...	1743	1756	1715	1915	...	1851	1943	2051	2151	2243	...	0119	0155	0201
Riccione	d.	...	1650	|	|	...	...	|	...	|	1804	1724	1924	...	|	|	2058	|	|	...	|	|	|
Pesaro	d.	...	1706	◧	◧	...	...	◧	...	1802	|	1742	1942	...	1910	2002	2113	2210	2302	...	0158	|	|
Fano	d.	...	|	|	|	...	...	|	...	|	|	1751	1951	...	|	|	|	|	|	...	|	|	|
Senigallia	d.	...	|	|	|	...	...	|	...	|	|	1803	2003	...	|	|	|	|	|	...	|	|	|
Ancona	a.	...	1734	|	|	...	...	|	...	1833	1847	1823	2023	...	1939	2031	2142	2242	2333	...	0242	0247	0252
Ancona	d.	...	1737	|	|	...	...	|	...	1836	1850	1826	2026	...	1942	2034	2145	...	...	...	0245	0251	0256
Civitanova Marche-Montegranaro	d.	...	|	|	|	...	...	|	...	|	|	1852	2052	...	|	|	|	...	...	...	|	|	|
S. Benedetto del Tronto	d.	...	1816	|	|	...	...	|	...	|	|	1928	2129	...	2022	2115	2225	...	...	...	|	|	|
Pescara Centrale	a.	...	1847	|	|	...	...	|	...	1944	1957	2008	2205	...	2054	2148	2305	...	...	...	0404	0411	0426
Pescara Centrale	d.	...	1850	|	|	...	...	|	...	1947	2000	2010	...	...	2057	...	...	...	...	...	0406	0413	0428
Termoli	d.	...	1939	|	|	...	...	|	...	2036	2048	2102	...	...	2145	...	...	...	...	...	|	|	|
Roma Termini	d.	1705	|	1743	1743	1601	1805	1900	1905	|	|	|	...	...	|	...	...	...	...	2358	|	|	|
Caserta	d.	1819	|	1857	1857	1754	1917	|	2014	|	|	|	...	...	|	...	...	...	...	0236	|	|	|
Benevento	d.	1900	|	1942	1942	1905	2002	|	2103	|	|	|	...	...	|	...	...	...	...	0324	|	|	|
Foggia	a.	2005	2021	2045	2045	2037	2102	|	...	2119	2129	2151	...	...	2228	...	...	...	...	0449	0546	0606	0617
Foggia	d.	2014	2024	2054	2054	2049	2111	|	...	2122	2132	2156	...	...	2231	...	...	...	...	0504	0549	0609	0638
Barletta	d.	2044	2053	2122	2122	2120	2139	|	...	2151	|	2227	...	...	2300	...	...	...	...	0537	0624	0650	0721
Bari Centrale	a.	2114	2130	2205	2217	2202	2210	|	...	2222	2232	2308	...	...	2336	...	...	...	...	0627	0658	0739	0810
Bari Centrale	d.	2118	2134	...	...	2224	2214	|	...	2226	...	...	...	...	...	...	...	...	...	0631	0702	0752	0814
Gioia del Colle	d.	|	|	...	...	2301	|	|	...	|	...	...	...	...	...	...	...	...	...	|	|	0827	|
Taranto	a.	|	|	...	...	2335	|	0007	...	|	...	...	...	...	...	...	...	...	...	|	|	0901	|
Monopoli	d.	|	|	...	...	...	|	...	...	|	...	...	...	...	...	...	...	...	...	0656	0734	|	0852
Fasano	d.	|	|	...	...	...	|	...	...	|	...	...	...	...	...	...	...	...	...	0707	0746	|	0904
Ostuni	d.	|	|	...	...	...	|	...	...	|	...	...	...	...	...	...	...	...	...	0720	0800	|	0919
Brindisi	d.	2243	2234	...	...	...	2315	...	...	2321	...	...	...	...	...	...	...	...	...	0742	0825	1008	0945
Lecce	a.	2306	2256	...	...	...	2338	...	...	2345	...	...	...	...	...	...	...	...	...	0810	0850	1037	1010

A – 🚃12 ✕ Zürich - Milano - Bologna and v.v. Ⓡ inclusive of supplement. Also available to passengers without reservation.
B – Also calls at Cassino (d. 0912) and Vairano-Caianello (d. 0935).
C – Also calls at Vairano-Caianello (d. 2029) and Cassino (d. 2049).
T – To / from Torino (*ITA* trains Table **600**; *ICN* trains Table **610**).
V – To / from Venezia (Table **600**).

d – Runs 5 – 7 minutes later Bologna - Parma on Ⓒ from May 28.
g – Milano **Porta Garibaldi**.
h – Also Aug. 22 – 25; not Aug. 20, 21.

◧ – Via Table **600**.
△ – Most trains call here to pick up only.
▽ – Most trains call here to set down only.
● – For 🚌 service to **San Marino** see next page.
✤ – 🛏 1, 2 cl., 🛌 2 cl. (4 berth). Running days, timings and numbers of *ICN* trains may vary - please check your reservation.
For confirmed timings please consult the *Trenitalia* journey planner at www.trenitalia.com.

615 LECCE - BARI - ROMA, ANCONA, RIMINI, BOLOGNA and MILANO

🍷 on *FA*, *FB*, *FR* and *ITA* trains

High-speed and long-distance trains. For local trains Bologna - Milano see Table **620**. For other local trains see page 303.

km		*FA* 8802	*FR* 9802	*FA* 8804	*FA* 8806	*FR* 8300 ①–⑥	*ITA* 9972	*IC* 604	*FR* 8810	*FA* 8348 ①–⑥	*FR* 9806 ⑤–⑦ h	*IC* 606	*FR* 8814	*FR* 9514 T	*ITA* 9928 T	*FA* 8302	*FA* 8816 V	*IC* 608	*FA* 8306 ①–⑥	*FR* 8818	*FR* 8820	*IC* 610
0	**Lecce** d.	...	...	...	...	...	...	...	...	...	...	...	0555	...	...	0605	0700	0623	0710	0804	...	0820
39	**Brindisi** d.	...	...	...	...	...	...	...	...	...	...	...	0617	...	...	0628	0723	0647	0734	0827	...	0842
75	Ostuni d.	...	...	...	...	...	...	...	...	...	...	...	|	...	...	|	|	0710	|	|	...	0904
95	Fasano d.	...	...	...	...	...	...	...	...	...	...	...	|	...	...	|	|	0723	|	|	...	0916
109	Monopoli d.	...	...	...	...	...	...	...	...	...	...	...	|	...	...	0702	|	0733	|	|	...	0928
	Taranto d.	...	...	...	...	...	...	...	...	...	...	...	|	0527	...	|	|	|	|	|	0916	|
	Gioia del Colle d.	...	...	...	...	...	...	...	...	...	...	...	|	|	...	|	|	|	|	|	0948	|
130	**Bari** Centrale a.	...	...	...	...	...	...	...	...	...	...	...	0726	|	...	0732	0826	0802	0834	0924	1020	0951
130	**Bari** Centrale d.	...	...	...	...	...	...	...	0530	0610	0630	0555	0730	|	0650	0746	0830	0806	0846	0928	1030	0955
185	Barletta d.	...	...	...	...	...	...	...	0606	0644	|	0634	0805	|	0737	0815	0906	0851	0915	1005	1106	1038
253	**Foggia** a.	...	...	...	...	...	...	...	0633	0711	0736	0707	0831	|	0806	0844	0933	0918	0944	1031	1133	1107
253	**Foggia** d.	...	...	...	...	...	...	...	0636	0720	0739	0710	0834	|	0815	0853	0936	0921	0953	1034	1136	1110
354	Benevento d.	...	...	...	...	0554	...	...	|	0818	|	|	|	|	0922	1000	|	|	1107	|	|	|
417	Caserta d.	...	...	...	...	0632	0645	...	|	0856	|	|	|	|	1006	1048	|	|	1147	|	|	|
633	**Roma** Termini a.	...	...	...	...	0745	0750	...	|	1003	|	|	|	1055	1115	1155	|	|	1255	|	|	|
	Termoli d.	...	...	...	...	...	|	...	0720	...	0824	0805	0919	|	|	...	1020	1009	...	1119	1220	1205
	Pescara Centrale a.	...	...	...	...	...	|	...	0807	...	0909	0900	1008	|	|	...	1107	1100	...	1205	1307	1300
	Pescara Centrale d.	...	0500	...	0600	...	|	0702	0810	...	0912	0902	1011	|	|	...	1110	1102	...	1208	1310	1302
	S. Benedetto del Tronto d.	...	0532	...	0636	...	|	0736	0841	...	|	0936	|	|	|	...	|	1148	...	1242	1341	1348
	Civitanova d.	...	|	...	|	...	|	0809	|	...	|	1009	1058	|	|	...	|	1213	...	|	|	1413
	Ancona a.	...	0612	...	0717	...	|	0835	0922	...	1025	1035	1123	|	|	...	1222	1235	...	1323	1422	1435
	Ancona d.	0520	0615	0620	0720	...	◧	0838	0925	...	1028	1038	1126	◧	◧	...	1225	1238	...	1326	1425	1438
	Senigallia d.	|	|	|	|	...	|	0856	|	...	|	1056	|	|	|	...	|	1256	...	|	|	1456
	Fano d.	|	|	|	|	...	|	0909	|	...	|	1109	|	|	|	...	|	1309	...	|	|	1509
	Pesaro d.	0547	0641	0647	0749	...	|	0919	0952	...	|	1119	1154	|	|	...	1252	1317	...	1354	1452	1517
	Riccione d.	|	|	|	0804	...	|	0938	1006	...	1111	1138	|	|	|	...	|	1338	...	|	|	1538
	Rimini ● a.	0608	0701	0708	0810	...	|	0945	1015	...	1118	1145	1214	|	|	...	1313	1345	...	1414	1515	1545
	Rimini ● d.	0610	0703	0710	0812	...	|	0947	1017	...	1120	1147	1216	|	|	...	1315	1347	...	1416	1517	1547
	Cesena d.	0627	|	0727	0828	...	|	1009	|	...	|	1207	|	|	|	...	|	1407	...	|	1534	1607
	Forlì d.	0640	0733	0739	0840	...	|	1021	1042	...	|	1219	|	|	|	...	|	1419	...	1442	|	1619
	Faenza d.	0649	|	0749	0849	...	|	1031	|	...	|	1229	|	|	|	...	|	1429	...	|	|	1629
	Bologna Centrale a.	0715	0810	0815	0915	...	1008	1101	1115	...	1215	1300	1315	1333	1403	...	1415	1500	...	1515	1615	1700
	Bologna Centrale 600 620 d.	0718	0813	0818	0918	...	1011	1105	1118	...	1218	...	1318	1336	1406	...	...	...	...	1518	1618	...
	Modena 620 d.	0737	|	0837	0937	...	|	1133	1137	...	|	...	1337	|	|	...	...	...	...	1537	1637	...
	Reggio Emilia AV 600 d.	|	0844	|	|	...	|	|	|	...	1242	...	|	1400	1435	...	...	...	...	|	|	...
	Reggio Emilia 620 d.	0752	|	0852	0952	...	|	1204	1152	...	|	...	1352	|	|	...	...	...	...	1552	1652	...
	Parma 620 d.	0807	|	0907	1007	...	◧	1220	1207	...	◧	...	1407	◧	◧	...	...	...	...	1607	1707	...
	Fidenza 620 d.	|	|	|	|	...	|	1232	|	...	|	...	|	|	|	...	...	...	...	|	|	...
	Piacenza 620 d.	0833	|	|	|	...	|	1252	|	...	|	...	|	|	|	...	...	...	...	|	|	...
	Milano Rogoredo ▽ 600 620 a.	0904	|	|	|	...	|	|	|	...	|	...	|	1438	|	...	...	...	...	|	|	...
	Milano Centrale 600 620 a.	0915	0935	0954	1054	...	1115	1340	1254	...	1325	...	1505	1450	1520	...	...	...	...	1654	1754	...

	FA 8312 ①	*FA* 8312 ⑥	*FR* 8824	*EC* 326 A	*IC* 1546 ⑦	*IC* 612	*FA* 8314	*ITA* 9952 T	*FA* 8828 V	*IC* 614	*FR* 9810	*FR* 9560	*IC* 704 C	*FR* 8830	*IC* 710 ⑦	*ITA* 8140	*FA* 8326	*ICN* 752 ✣	*ICN* 758 ✣	*ICN* 754 ①–⑥ T ✣	*ICN* 754 ⑦ T ✣	*ICN* 788 ⑦ ✣
Lecce d.	...	0941	0958	...	0935	0835	1115	...	1257	1154	...	1310	...	...	...	...	1708	1935	1831	2025	2025	2230
Brindisi d.	...	1004	1019	...	0956	0900	1138	...	1318	1214	...	1331	...	...	...	...	1731	2003	1901	2053	2053	2255
Ostuni d.	...	|	1040	...	1018	|	|	...	1339	1235	...	|	...	...	...	...	1751	2027	|	2116	2116	2317
Fasano d.	...	|	|	...	1030	|	|	...	1352	1247	...	|	...	...	...	...	|	2042	|	2131	2131	2330
Monopoli d.	...	|	1059	...	1040	|	|	...	1401	1257	...	|	...	...	...	...	1811	2053	|	2140	2140	2341
Taranto d.	...	|	|	...	|	1032	|	...	|	|	...	|	...	...	1540	...	|	|	2001	|	|	|
Gioia del Colle d.	...	|	|	...	|	1109	|	...	|	|	...	|	...	...	1612	...	|	|	2034	|	|	|
Bari Centrale a.	1101	1101	1124	...	1105	1143	1242	...	1426	1344	...	1444	...	...	1649	...	1842	2121	2115	2206	2206	0010
Bari Centrale d.	1105	1105	1128	...	1108	1155	1246	1300	1430	1355	...	1455	1605	1630	1700	1750	1846	2125	2145	2210	2210	0015
Barletta d.	1134	1134	1205	...	1151	1238	1315	1337	1506	1438	...	1527	1648	1706	1734	1837	1915	2213	2238	2246	2256	0103
Foggia a.	1206	1206	1231	...	1221	1307	1344	1406	1533	1507	...	1554	1728	1733	1809	1906	1944	2249	2315	2321	2328	0145
Foggia d.	1215	1215	1234	...	1223	1310	1353	1415	1536	1510	...	1603	1741	1736	1820	1915	1953	2304	2318	2325	2331	0200
Benevento d.	1316	1316	|	...	|	|	1500	1522	|	|	...	1702	1855	|	1953	2028	2100	|	|	|	|	0321
Caserta d.	1404	1404	|	...	|	|	1545	1609	|	|	...	1746	1958	|	2049	2109	2145	|	|	|	|	0407
Roma Termini a.	1515	1515	|	...	|	|	1655	1715	|	|	...	1855	2220	|	2300	2215	2255	|	|	|	|	0610
Termoli d.	...	...	1319	...	1332	1405	...	|	1620	1605	...	|	...	1820	...	...	...	|	|	|	0021	...
Pescara Centrale a.	...	...	1405	...	1430	1500	...	|	1707	1700	...	|	...	1907	...	...	...	0105	0114	0122	0122	...
Pescara Centrale d.	...	...	1408	...	1432	1502	...	|	1710	1702	...	|	...	1910	...	...	...	0108	0117	0126	0126	...
S. Benedetto del Tronto d.	...	...	1439	...	1512	1536	...	|	|	1748	...	|	...	|	...	...	...	0153	|	|	|	...
Civitanova d.	...	...	|	...	1539	1609	...	|	|	1813	...	|	...	|	...	...	...	|	|	|	|	...
Ancona a.	...	...	1520	...	1610	1635	...	|	1822	1835	...	|	...	2022	...	...	...	0256	0303	0309	0309	...
Ancona d.	...	...	1523	...	1614	1638	...	◧	1825	1838	1910	◧	...	2025	...	...	...	0306	0312	0317	0317	...
Senigallia d.	...	...	|	...	1630	1656	...	|	|	1856	|	|	...	|	...	...	...	|	|	|	|	...
Fano d.	...	...	|	...	1643	1709	...	|	|	1909	|	|	...	|	...	...	...	|	|	|	|	...
Pesaro d.	...	...	1554	...	1655	1717	...	|	1852	1917	1946	|	...	2052	...	...	...	|	|	0351	|	...
Riccione d.	...	...	|	...	1718	1738	...	|	1906	1938	2004	|	...	2107	...	...	...	|	|	|	|	...
Rimini ● a.	...	...	1614	...	1727	1745	...	|	1915	1945	2012	|	...	2115	...	...	...	0357	0407	0417	0417	...
Rimini ● d.	...	...	1616	...	1729	1747	...	|	1917	1947	2014	|	...	2117	...	...	...	0359	0409	0419	0419	...
Cesena d.	...	...	|	...	1746	1807	...	|	|	2007	|	|	...	|	...	...	...	|	|	0440	|	...
Forlì d.	...	...	1642	...	1758	1819	...	|	|	2019	|	|	...	|	...	...	...	|	|	0453	|	...
Faenza d.	...	...	|	...	1808	1829	...	|	|	2029	|	|	...	|	...	...	...	|	|	0503	|	...
Bologna Centrale a.	...	...	1715	...	1840	1901	...	2003	2015	2100	2115	2133	...	2215	...	...	...	0452	0502	0530	0530	...
Bologna Centrale 600 620 d.	...	...	1718	1726	1845	1905	...	2006	...	2104	2118	2136	...	2218	...	...	...	0456	0505	...	...	...
Modena 620 d.	...	...	1737	1749	1913	1936	...	|	...	2135	|	|	...	2237	...	...	...	0516	|	...	...	...
Reggio Emilia AV 600 d.	...	...	|	|	|	|	...	2030	...	|	2142	2200	...	|	...	...	...	|	|	...	...	...
Reggio Emilia 620 d.	...	...	1752	1805	1926	1956	...	|	...	2151	|	|	...	2252	...	...	...	0532	|	...	...	...
Parma 620 d.	...	...	1807	1825	1941	2013	...	◧	...	2210	◧	◧	...	2307	...	...	...	0548	|	...	...	...
Fidenza 620 d.	...	...	|	|	1954	2025	...	|	...	2224	|	|	...	|	...	...	...	|	|	...	...	...
Piacenza 620 d.	...	...	|	1859	2019	2046	...	|	...	2243	|	|	...	|	...	...	...	0622	|	...	...	...
Milano Rogoredo ▽ 600 620 a.	...	...	|	1935	2104	2126	...	|	...	2328	|	2238	...	|	...	...	...	|	|	...	...	...
Milano Centrale 600 620 a.	...	...	1855	...	2115	2140	...	2120	...	2340	2225	2250	...	2355	...	...	...	0705	0712	...	...	...

🚌 service **RIMINI - SAN MARINO**. *27 km*, journey 50 – 55 minutes. Operator: BonelliBus s.a.s. ✆ +39 0541 662 069. www.bonellibus.it
From Rimini (FS railway station) at 0810 ⚒, 1015 ⚒, 1700 ⚒, 1915 ⚒. **From San Marino** (Piazzale Calcigni) at 0810 ⚒, 1015 ⚒, 1700 ⚒, 1915 ⚒.

FOR FOOTNOTES SEE PREVIOUS PAGE.

PIACENZA - BOLOGNA - ANCONA - PESCARA and BARI - TARANTO - LECCE 615

Local trains. For high-speed and long-distance trains see previous two pages.

km				⚒					©	Ⓐ			A												
0	**Piacenza**	d.	...	...	...	0530	0649	0749	0849	0849	0949	1049	1149	...	1249	1345	1449	1549	1649	1749	1849	1909	1949	2055	2148
35	Fidenza	d.	...	...	...	0558	0714	0814	0914	0914	1014	1114	1214	...	1314	1412	1514	1614	1714	1814	1914	1937	2014	2118	2213
57	Parma	d.	...	...	...	0615	0727	0827	0927	0927	1027	1127	1227	...	1327	1427	1527	1627	1727	1827	1927	2000	2027	2133	2226
85	Reggio Emilia	d.	...	...	...	0642	0744	0844	0944	0944	1044	1144	1244	...	1344	1444	1544	1644	1744	1844	1944	2018	2044	2149	2243
110	Modena	d.	...	...	...	0707	0758	0858	0958	0958	1058	1158	1258	...	1358	1458	1558	1658	1801	1858	1958	2035	2058	2204	2257
147	**Bologna** Centrale	a.	...	...	...	0729	0825	0925	1025	1025	1125	1225	1325	...	1425	1525	1625	1725	1825	1925	2025	2108	2125	2233	2328
147	**Bologna** Centrale	d.	0500	0555	0634	0734	0834	0934	1034	1034	1134	1234	1334	...	1434	1534	1634	1734	1834	1934	2034	2112	2134	...	...
182	Imola	d.	0527	0622	0655	0802	0855	0955	1058	1058	1155	1255	1355	...	1455	1555	1655	1756	1855	1955	2055	2133	2155	...	...
189	Castelbolognese-Riolo Terme	d.	0533	0628	0702	0808	0902	1002	1104	1104	1202	1302	1402	...	1502	1602	1702	1802	1902	2002	2102	2140	2202	...	...
195	Faenza	d.	0539	0635	0717	0817	0917	1017	1117	1120	1217	1317	1417	...	1517	1617	1717	1817	1917	2017	2119	|	2217	...	...
210	Forlì	d.	0548	0644	0728	0828	0928	1033	1128	1138	1228	1328	1428	...	1528	1628	1734	1828	1928	2029	2130	|	2228	...	...
228	Cesena	d.	0603	0659	0742	0842	0942	1059	1142	1202	1244	1342	1442	...	1542	1642	1748	1844	1942	2046	2143	|	2245	...	...
257	**Rimini**	a.	0630	0725	0803	0903	1003	1120	1203	1225	1309	1403	1501	...	1603	1703	1805	1902	2003	2112	2203	2318	2322	...	...
257	**Rimini**	d.	...	...	0805	0905	1005	...	1205	1227	1319	1405	1503	...	1605	1705	1807	1904	2005	...	2205	...	...	...	...
266	Riccione	d.	...	...	0814	0914	1014	...	1214	1236	1331	1414	1511	...	1614	1715	1815	1911	2014	...	2214	...	...	...	...
275	Cattolica-Gabicce	d.	...	...	0822	0922	1022	...	1222	1244	1341	1422	1520	...	1622	1724	1823	1920	2022	...	2222	...	...	...	...
290	Pesaro	d.	...	...	0832	0932	1032	...	1232	1255	1352	1432	1532	...	1632	1735	1834	1932	2032	...	2232	...	...	...	...
302	Fano	d.	...	...	0840	0939	1049	...	1239	1304	1402	1439	1541	...	1639	...	1842	1940	2039	...	2239	...	...	...	...
324	Senigallia	d.	...	...	0854	0954	1054	...	1254	1323	1425	1454	1556	...	1654	...	1857	1953	2054	...	2253	...	...	...	...
341	Falconara Marittima	d.	...	...	0906	1011	1104	...	1304	1341	1439	1504	1607	...	1704	...	1911	2007	2104	...	2306	...	...	...	...
349	**Ancona**	a.	...	...	0920	1022	1116	...	1316	1353	1450	1516	1620	...	1716	...	1922	2020	2116	...	2318	...	...	...	...

																B	C			B	C		
Ancona	d.	...	...	0445	...	0545	0645	0745	0845	...	1045	1145	...	1245	...	1445	...	...	...	1645	...	...	...	1845
Falconara Marittima	d.	...	...	0454	...	0555	0655	0756	0854	...	1054	1154	...	1256	...	1455	...	...	...	1654	...	...	...	1855
Senigallia	d.	...	...	0505	...	0605	0707	0808	0904	...	1104	1204	...	1305	...	1505	...	...	...	1704	...	...	...	1905
Fano	d.	...	...	0519	...	0620	0720	0822	0919	...	1119	1219	...	1319	...	1518	...	...	...	1719	...	...	...	1918
Pesaro	d.	...	...	0527	...	0628	0728	0830	0927	...	1127	1227	...	1327	...	1526	...	1613	...	1727	...	1737	1823	1926
Cattolica-Gabicce	d.	...	...	0538	...	0639	0739	0841	0938	...	1138	1238	...	1338	...	1536	...	1624	...	1738	...	1748	1834	1936
Riccione	d.	...	...	0546	...	0645	0748	0847	0946	...	1146	1246	...	1347	...	1544	...	1633	...	1746	...	1756	1842	1944
Rimini	a.	...	...	0556	...	0652	0759	0856	0956	...	1156	1256	...	1356	...	1556	...	1644	...	1756	...	1805	1853	1956
Rimini	d.	...	...	0558	...	0654	0801	0858	0958	1041	1158	1258	...	1358	1441	1558	1640	1646	...	1758	...	1807	1854	1958
Cesena	d.	...	...	0618	...	0709	0819	0919	1019	1110	1219	1319	...	1419	1510	1619	1707	1711	...	1819	...	1830	1919	2019
Forlì	d.	...	...	0631	...	0720	0831	0931	1033	1127	1231	1331	...	1431	1528	1631	1724	1726	...	1831	...	1853	1933	2031
Faenza	d.	...	...	0641	...	0730	0841	0941	1043	1140	1241	1341	...	1441	1540	1641	1734	1735	...	1841	...	1903	1943	2041
Castelbolognese-Riolo Terme	d.	...	...	0647	...	0743	0847	0947	1049	1147	1247	1347	...	1447	1548	1647	1746	1748	...	1847	...	1909	1949	2047
Imola	d.	...	...	0700	...	0800	0900	1000	1100	1200	1300	1400	...	1500	1600	1700	1756	1756	...	1900	...	1916	2000	2100
Bologna Centrale	a.	...	...	0726	...	0826	0926	1026	1126	1226	1326	1426	...	1526	1626	1726	1826	1826	...	1926	...	1948	2026	2126
Bologna Centrale	d.	0500	0633	0733	0750	0833	0933	1033	1133	1233	1333	1433	...	1533	1633	1733	1833	1833	1850	1933	1950	1957	2033	2133
Modena	d.	0528	0702	0802	0824	0902	1002	1102	1202	1302	1402	1502	...	1602	1702	1802	1902	1902	1924	2002	2024	2029	2102	2202
Reggio Emilia	d.	0544	0719	0817	0842	0917	1017	1117	1217	1317	1417	1517	...	1617	1717	1817	1917	1917	1942	2017	2042	2047	2117	2217
Parma	d.	0600	0734	0833	0903	0933	1033	1133	1233	1333	1433	1533	...	1633	1733	1833	1933	1933	2003	2033	2103	2110	2133	2233
Fidenza	d.	0620	0746	0845	0926	0947	1045	1145	1245	1345	1445	1545	...	1645	1745	1845	1945	1945	2017	2045	2126	2126	2145	2245
Piacenza	a.	0635	0807	0910	0948	1013	1110	1210	1310	1410	1510	1610	...	1707	1810	1912	2010	2010	2051	2110	2150	2150	2210	2310

km			⚒	⚒		⚒	†							⑥		Ⓑ			Ⓐ		⚒				
0	**Ancona**	d.	0515	0625	...	0733	0810	...	1145	...	1345	...	...	1440	...	1445	...	1645	1745	...	1841	1945	...	...	...
43	Civitanova ◧	d.	0549	0700	...	0808	0845	...	1221	...	1421	...	...	1516	...	1521	...	1722	1821	...	1922	2020	...	...	...
85	S. Benedetto del Tronto	d.	0621	0732	...	0840	0919	...	1253	...	1454	...	...	1554	...	1554	...	1756	1854	...	1954	2053	...	...	...
146	**Pescara** Centrale	a.	0718	0824	...	0917	1010	...	1350	...	1540	...	...	1656	...	1656	...	1856	1940	...	2050	2145	...	...	...

		⚒			⚒	†		⚒	†		⚒	⚒		†	⚒					†	⚒			
Pescara Centrale	d.	0505	0550	...	0653	0915	...	1015	1158	...	1202	1417	...	1520	1602	...	1720	1820	...	1913	1920	...	...	...
S. Benedetto del Tronto	d.	0556	0649	...	0750	1007	...	1102	1256	...	1256	1506	...	1612	1700	...	1812	1908	...	2007	2007	...	...	...
Civitanova ◧	d.	0626	0723	...	0823	1039	...	1135	1330	...	1330	1539	...	1644	1732	...	1847	1939	...	2040	2040	...	...	...
Ancona	a.	0705	0802	...	0905	1115	...	1217	1410	...	1410	1615	...	1730	1809	...	1928	2010	...	2120	2120	...	...	...

km			⚒	⚒	⚒		†	⚒	⚒		⚒	⚒			⚒	†	⚒		⚒		⚒			Ⓐ	⑥
0	**Bari**	d.	0530	0623	0720	...	0815	0950	1050	...	1305	1335	1437	...	1524	1600	1625	...	1730	1820	1945	...	2050	2239	2350
54	Gioia del Colle	d.	0612	0706	0802	...	0858	1033	1132	...	1349	1418	1520	...	1606	1641	1707	...	1812	1900	2027	...	2133	2321	0033
115	**Taranto**	a.	0652	0745	0842	...	0937	1112	1212	...	1422	1457	1559	...	1646	1722	1747	...	1852	1940	2107	...	2212	2359	0112

		⚒	⚒			⚒	⚒	⚒		†	⚒	⚒			⚒	⚒			⚒	†		⚒	⚒	⚒
Taranto	d.	0440	0542	0620	...	0705	0756	0955	...	1040	1135	1300	...	1350	1432	1535	...	1650	1805	1910	...	1930	2015	2100
Gioia del Colle	d.	0514	0621	0659	...	0744	0836	1027	...	1119	1211	1340	...	1430	1512	1615	...	1730	1838	1950	...	2005	2055	2140
Bari	a.	0554	0704	0742	...	0827	0918	1103	...	1202	1252	1420	...	1512	1554	1657	...	1810	1922	2032	...	2047	2137	2222

km			⚒	⚒	⚒	⚒	⚒	⚒	⚒	⚒	
0	**Taranto**	d.	0535	0608	0845	1244	1402	1523	1652	1849	...
34	Francavilla Fontana	d.	0602	0637	0913	1312	1429	1551	1722	1915	...
70	**Brindisi**	a.	0635	0719	0954	1350	1506	1634	1759	2001	...

		⚒	⚒	⚒	⚒	⚒	⚒	⚒	⚒	
Brindisi	d.	0645	0754	1100	1401	1519	1644	1809	2018	...
Francavilla Fontana	d.	0722	0833	1138	1440	1554	1719	1846	2051	...
Taranto	a.	0750	0907	1206	1513	1625	1755	1922	2123	...

km			Ⓐ	©	Ⓐ		Ⓐ	⑥	Ⓐ		Ⓐ	†	⑥		Ⓐ	©	Ⓐ		©	©	Ⓐ		Ⓐ	Ⓐ	⑥
0	**Bari** Centrale	d.	0502	0520	0602	...	0632	0708	0732	...	0802	0802	0815	...	0902	0902	1002	...	1035	1220	1232	...	1302	1332	1335
41	Monopoli	d.	0537	0555	0629	...	0659	0745	0802	...	0830	0838	0851	...	0930	0939	1029	...	1112	1257	1259	...	1329	1359	1412
55	Fasano	d.	0546	0604	0637	...	0707	0754	0811	...	0838	0847	0900	...	0938	0948	1037	...	1121	1306	1307	...	1337	1407	1421
75	Ostuni	d.	0559	0618	0651	...	0718	0808	0825	...	0852	0901	0914	...	0952	1001	1048	...	1136	1321	1318	...	1351	1418	1436
111	**Brindisi**	d.	0622	0642	0714	...	0744	0831	0845	...	0916	0924	0940	...	1016	1026	1113	...	1158	1343	1344	...	1413	1444	1458
150	**Lecce**	a.	0655	0712	0743	...	0813	0901	0915	...	0945	0956	1009	...	1045	1058	1143	...	1228	1413	1413	...	1443	1513	1528

		Ⓐ	©	Ⓐ		⑥	Ⓐ	Ⓐ		©	Ⓐ	⑥		Ⓐ	©	Ⓐ		©	Ⓐ	©		Ⓐ		
Bari Centrale	d.	1402	1440	1502	...	1535	1602	1632	...	1635	1702	1735	...	1802	1818	1832	...	1950	2040	2040	...	2102	...	2302
Monopoli	d.	1429	1517	1529	...	1612	1629	1659	...	1712	1729	1812	...	1829	1854	1859	...	2026	2111	2117	...	2129	...	2339
Fasano	d.	1437	1526	1537	...	1621	1637	1707	...	1721	1737	1821	...	1837	1902	1907	...	2034	2120	2125	...	2137	...	2347
Ostuni	d.	1451	1541	1551	...	1636	1651	1720	...	1736	1748	1835	...	1851	1917	1918	...	2049	2133	2139	...	2151	...	0001
Brindisi	d.	1515	1603	1615	...	1658	1715	1744	...	1758	1812	1858	...	1915	1942	1944	...	2113	2157	2203	...	2215	...	0025
Lecce	a.	1543	1633	1645	...	1728	1743	1813	...	1828	1845	1928	...	1943	2013	2013	...	2144	2225	2234	...	2243	...	0055

			Ⓐ	©		Ⓐ	Ⓐ	©		Ⓐ		⑥		Ⓐ	©	Ⓐ		Ⓐ	©	Ⓐ		⑥		Ⓐ
Lecce	d.	0447	0611	0628	...	0640	0717	0722	...	0753	...	0847	...	1017	1017	1120	...	1217	1217	1317	...	1317	...	1347
Brindisi	d.	0515	0639	0658	...	0706	0746	0753	...	0820	...	0918	...	1045	1048	1147	...	1246	1248	1345	...	1348	...	1416
Ostuni	d.	0539	0659	0720	...	0728	0808	0816	...	0840	...	0941	...	1107	1111	1209	...	1307	1311	1407	...	1411	...	1439
Fasano	d.	0554	0713	0734	...	0740	0820	0830	...	0900	...	0955	...	1121	1125	1223	...	1321	1325	1421	...	1425	...	1451
Monopoli	d.	0602	0722	0743	...	0749	0830	0838	...	0910	...	1003	...	1130	1133	1231	...	1330	1333	1430	...	1433	...	1500
Bari Centrale	a.	0641	0759	0821	...	0822	0900	0918	...	0944	...	1041	...	1158	1211	1300	...	1358	1411	1458	...	1511	...	1528

		Ⓐ	©	Ⓐ		©		Ⓐ		©	Ⓐ	Ⓐ		©		©		Ⓐ	⚒	©		Ⓐ		⚒
Lecce	d.	1417	1417	1517	...	1517	...	1547	...	1605	1617	1720	...	1729	...	1800	...	1817	1905	2000	...	2017	...	2117
Brindisi	d.	1445	1448	1545	...	1548	...	1615	...	1635	1645	1747	...	1756	...	1832	...	1845	1933	2032	...	2045	...	2146
Ostuni	d.	1507	1511	1607	...	1611	...	1637	...	1658	1707	1809	...	1819	...	1855	...	1907	1956	2055	...	2107	...	2207
Fasano	d.	1521	1525	1621	...	1625	...	1651	...	1712	1721	1823	...	1835	...	1909	...	1921	2010	2109	...	2121	...	2218
Monopoli	d.	1529	1533	1630	...	1633	...	1700	...	1720	1730	1831	...	1843	...	1917	...	1929	2019	2117	...	2130	...	2227
Bari Centrale	a.	1558	1611	1658	...	1711	...	1728	...	1758	1758	1900	...	1922	...	1954	...	1958	2058	2154	...	2158	...	2311

A – By connecting trains on † (change at Bologna).
B – Daily until May 27; Ⓐ from May 30.
C – © from May 28.
◧ – Full name is Civitanova Marche-Montegranaro.

616 ROVIGO - CHIOGGIA

Sistemi Territoriali

km			⚒	†	⚒		†	⚒	Ⓐ		†	⑥	†		⚒	⚒	†		⚒	Ⓑ	Ⓐ			Ⓑ
0	**Rovigo**	d.	0609	...	0709	...	0715	0809	0909	...	0915	...	1115	...	1309	1409	1515	...	1609	1715	1815	...	1915	2055
25	Adria	d.	0636	0642	0736	...	0742	0836	0936	...	0942	1136	1142	...	1336	1436	1542	...	1636	1742	1842	...	1942	2121
57	**Chioggia**	a.	0719	0725	0819	...	0825	0919	1019	...	1025	1219	1225	...	1419	1519	1625	...	1719	1825	1925	...	2025	...

			⚒	†	⚒	⚒	†	⚒	⑥	Ⓐ	†	†	⚒	†	⚒	⑥	Ⓐ	†	Ⓐ		Ⓐ	Ⓑ	Ⓑ	⑥
	Chioggia	d.	0529	...	0629	0729	0735	0829	0929	0929	0935	1035	1229	1335	1429	1529	1529	...	...	1735	1835	1935	2035	2035
	Adria	d.	0608	0614	0708	0808	0814	0907	1007	1008	1014	1113	1308	1414	1508	1607	1608	1614	1714	1814	1914	2014	2113	2114
	Rovigo	a.	0639	0645	0739	0839	0845	...	...	1039	1045	...	1339	1445	1539	...	1639	1645	1745	1845	1945	2045	...	2145

619 SIENA - GROSSETO and CHIUSI

2nd class

km			⚒	†		⚒	†		⚒	†		⚒	⚒		†	†		⚒			†	⚒		
0	**Siena**	d.	0545	0748	...	0810	0943	...	1209	1243	...	1320	1542	...	1544	1738	...	1743	1846	...	1943	1943	...	...
29	Buonconvento	d.	0623	0819	...	0845	1012	...	1238	1312	...	1349	1610	...	1613	1815	...	1816	1934	...	2013	2013	...	...
102	**Grosseto**	a.	0735	0920	...	0948	1123	...	1342	1419	...	1502	1724	...	1715	1923	...	1924	2045	...	2116	2118	...	...

			⚒ 🚌	†		⚒			⚒	†		†	⚒		⚒	†		⚒						
	Grosseto	d.	0500	0500	...	0601	0716	...	0958	1004	...	1323	1330	...	1500	1617	...	1632	1755	...	1952	...	...	...
	Buonconvento	d.	|	0559	...	0718	0818	...	1102	1107	...	1435	1441	...	1611	1732	...	1732	1906	...	2100	...	...	...
	Siena	a.	0620	0629	...	0748	0846	...	1140	1137	...	1508	1513	...	1643	1805	...	1810	1940	...	2130	...	...	...

km			⚒	†	†	⚒		†	⚒	⚒	⚒		†	⚒		⚒		⚒	†	⚒	⚒		†	⚒
0	**Siena**	d.	0554	0600	0802	0813	...	1002	1215	1325	1352	...	1402	1443	1602	1648	...	1743	1802	1816	1926	...	2002	2023
89	**Chiusi-Chianciano Terme**	a.	0717	0721	0927	0936	...	1127	1336	1448	1525	...	1523	1610	1727	1813	...	1904	1927	1944	2055	...	2127	2147

			⚒	†	⚒	⚒		†	⚒	†	⚒		†	⚒	⚒	†		⚒	†	⚒	⚒		†	⚒
	Chiusi-Chianciano Terme	d.	0602	0627	0647	0710	...	0830	0900	1030	1046	...	1230	1348	1511	1630	...	1713	1830	1835	1955	...	2030	2153
	Siena	a.	0725	0746	0756	0835	...	0950	1027	1150	1201	...	1350	1522	1636	1750	...	1841	1950	2006	2125	...	2150	2310

620 VENEZIA and MILANO - BOLOGNA - FIRENZE - ROMA

Long-distance trains. For high-speed trains see Table **600**. For other long-distance trains Milano - Bologna see Table **615**. For other local trains see next page.

km			*IC* **581** ①–⑥	*FR* **9503** ①–⑥	2	2	*IC* **583**	2	*IC* **1589** ⑥ A		*IC* **584**	2	2	*IC* **594**	2	*IC* **597**		2	*ICN* **795** B ❖	*FR* **9329** Ⓑ C	2	*IC* **599** D	*ICN* **770** E ❖	*ICN* **797** F ❖
	Trieste Centrale **601**	d.	...	...	...	...	...	...	...	...	0721	...	...	1227	...	...	...	...	...	...	...	...	1950	...
0	**Venezia** Santa Lucia	d.	...	...	...	...	...	...	...	...	|	...	...	|	...	...	...	...	...	...	...	...	2305	...
9	**Venezia** Mestre	d.	...	...	...	...	...	...	...	...	0934	...	...	1434	...	...	...	...	...	...	...	...	2317	...
37	Padova	d.	...	...	...	...	...	...	...	...	0950	...	...	1450	...	...	...	...	...	...	...	...	2338	...
81	Rovigo	d.	...	...	...	...	...	...	...	...	1023	...	...	1530	...	...	...	...	...	...	...	...	0013	...
113	Ferrara	d.	...	...	...	...	...	...	...	...	1042	...	...	1548	...	...	...	...	...	...	...	...	0032	...
	Milano Centrale	d.	...	...	...	...	0650	...	0655	...	|	...	...	|	...	1448	...	...	1535g	1750	...	1740	|	2213g
	Milano Rogoredo △	d.	...	...	...	...	0700	...	0705	...	|	...	...	|	...	1458	...	...	|	|	...	1755	|	|
	Piacenza	d.	...	...	...	...	0738	...	0744	...	|	...	...	|	...	1545	...	...	1630	|	...	1836	|	2319
	Fidenza	d.	...	...	...	...	0758	...	0805	...	|	...	...	|	...	1603	...	...	|	|	...	1852	|	|
	Parma	d.	...	...	...	...	0811	...	0819	...	|	...	...	|	...	1616	...	...	1707	|	...	1904	|	2352
	Reggio Emilia	d.	...	...	...	...	0830	...	0835	...	|	...	...	|	...	1633	...	...	1726	1942v	...	1920	|	|
	Modena	d.	...	...	...	...	0848	...	0853	...	|	...	...	|	...	1650	...	...	1744	|	...	1936	|	|
160	**Bologna** Centrale	a.	...	...	...	...	0914	...	0933	...	1112	...	...	1614	...	1714	...	...	1814	2009	...	2000	0109	|
160	**Bologna** Centrale	d.	...	...	...	...	0918	...	0937	...	1118	...	...	1618	...	1718	...	...	1818	2012	...	2004	0151	|
241	Prato Centrale	d.	...	...	...	...	1006	...	1057	...	1210	...	...	1710	...	1810	...	...	1910	|	...	2105	|	|
	Firenze Rifredi	d.	...	...	...	...	1018	...	1116	...	1230	...	...	1730	...	1828	...	...	1934f	|	...	|	|	|
257	**Firenze** SMN	d.	0545	0600	0640	0904	|	1114	|	...	|	1314	1514	|	1714	|	...	1914	|	2059	2114	2152	|	|
345	Arezzo	d.	0625	0633	0743	1007	1113	1217	|	...	1311	1417	1617	1811	1817	1907	...	2017	|	2133	2217	2230	0425	|
363	Castiglion Fiorentino	d.	|	|	0755	1020	|	1228	|	...	|	1428	1628	|	1828	|	...	2028	|	|	2228	|	|	|
379	Terontola-Cortona	d.	0645	|	0808	1035	1134	1241	|	...	1330	1441	1641	1835	1842	1929	...	2042	|	2154	2241	2251	0445	|
422	**Perugia**	d.	|	|	|	|	|	|	|	...	|	|	|	|	|	|	...	|	|	2230	|	2317	|	|
390	Castiglione del Lago	d.	|	◧	0815	1042	|	1248	|	...	|	1448	1648	|	1849	|	...	2049	|	...	2248	...	|	|
408	Chiusi-Chianciano Terme	d.	0704	|	0831	1054	1152	1301	1230	...	1349	1500	1700	1856	1900	1950	...	2102	|	...	2259	...	0507	|
458	Orvieto	d.	0725	|	0857	1120	1217	1327	|	...	1413	1527	1727	1921	*1943*	2015	...	2129	|	...	2325	...	|	0448
490	Orte	d.	|	|	0938	1155	1249	1401	|	...	1449	1611	1811	1952	*2021*	2051	...	2211	|	...	2358	...	|	0520
568	**Roma** Tiburtina	a.	|	0739	1049	1231	1327	1430	1336	...	|	1648	1848	|	*2118*	2123	...	2243	2321	...	0105	...	|	0553
573	**Roma** Termini	a.	0820	0749	...	1245	|	1448	|	...	1535	1705	1900	2040	*2130*	|	...	2300	...	...	0114	...	0635	|
	Napoli Centrale **640**	a.	...	0913	...	...	1529	...	1609	...	...	...	...	...	...	2359	...	...	...	...	...	...	...	0846

km			*FR* **9300** ①–⑥ C	*IC* **580** D	*ICN* **794** B ❖	2	2	2	*IC* **588**	2	*IC* **590**	2 ⚒	2 †	2	*IC* **592**	*IC* **596**	*IC* **1588** ⑦ A	2	*IC* **598** Ⓑ	*FR* **9432**	2	*FR* **9568** Ⓑ	*ICN* **774** E ❖	*ICN* **798** F ❖
	Napoli Centrale **640**	d.	...	...	...	...	...	...	...	...	1031	...	...	...	...	1420	1446	...	...	1704	...	1940	...	2135
0	**Roma** Termini	d.	...	...	...	0606	0702	0902	1022	...	|	1302	1302	1502	1530	|	|	1720	1815	1835	2002	2110	2235	|
5	**Roma** Tiburtina	d.	...	...	0609	0615	0713	0912	|	1111	1240	1313	1313	1513	|	1635	1712	1730	|	1845	2012	2120	|	2355
83	Orte	d.	...	...	|	0650	0747	0952	1102	1149	1314	1346	1346	1552	1613	1705	|	1804	1854	|	2047	|	|	0027
115	Orvieto	d.	...	...	|	0724	0820	1029	1139	1229	1345	1419	1421	1626	1648	1743	1814	1837	1923	|	2121	|	|	0103
165	Chiusi-Chianciano Terme	d.	...	...	|	0758	0848	1058	1210	1258	1410	1514	1511	1658	1717	1814	1842	1906	1946	|	2149	|	0007	|
183	Castiglione del Lago	d.	...	...	|	0809	0900	1109	|	1310	|	1531	1529	1709	|	|	|	1918	|	◧	2200	◧	|	|
	Perugia	d.	0524	0638	|	|	|	|	|	|	|	|	|	|	|	|	|	|	|	|	|	|	|	|
194	Terontola-Cortona	d.	0556	0710	|	0819	0908	1119	1230	1319	1427	1540	1536	1719	1737	1836	1901	1927	2004	|	2207	|	0025	|
210	Castiglion Fiorentino	d.	|	|	|	0831	0923	1131	|	1332	|	...	1549	1731	|	|	|	1939	|	|	2220	|	|	|
228	Arezzo	d.	0625	0732	|	0844	0943	1145	1252	1345	1452	...	1603	1744	1802	1901	1927	1952	2026	1959	2233	2225	0047	|
316	**Firenze** SMN	d.	0710	0821	|	0952	1048	1250	|	1448	|	...	...	1848	|	|	|	2055	2125	2041	2342	2258	|	|
	Firenze Rifredi	d.	|	|	1007f	...	...	...	1333	...	1533	...	...	...	1845	1941	2016	...	...	|	...	...	0203f	|
332	Prato Centrale	d.	|	0833	1030	...	...	...	1352	...	1552	...	...	...	1901	1952	2038	...	...	|	...	...	|	|
413	**Bologna** Centrale	a.	0748	0942	1138	...	...	...	1442	...	1642	...	...	...	1956	2042	2130	...	...	2118	...	...	0328	|
413	**Bologna** Centrale	d.	0751	0946	1145	...	...	...	1446	...	1646	...	...	...	2000	2046	2139	...	...	2121	...	...	0333	|
450	Modena	d.	|	1010	1213	...	...	...	|	...	1708	...	...	...	|	2110	2209	...	...	|	...	...	|	|
475	Reggio Emilia	d.	0813v	1024	1231	...	...	...	|	...	1724	...	...	...	|	2124	2225	...	...	|	...	...	|	|
503	Parma	d.	|	1039	1250	...	...	...	|	...	1741	...	...	...	|	2140	2243	...	...	|	...	...	|	0524
525	Fidenza	d.	|	1054	|	...	...	...	|	...	1755	...	...	...	|	2154	2304	...	...	|	...	...	|	|
560	Piacenza	d.	|	1119	1328	...	...	...	|	...	1819	...	...	...	|	2219	2322	...	...	|	...	...	|	0556
622	**Milano** Rogoredo ▽	a.	|	1204	|	...	...	...	|	...	1904	...	...	...	|	2304	0001	...	...	|	...	...	|	|
632	**Milano** Centrale	a.	0858	1215	1425g	...	...	...	|	...	1917	...	...	...	|	2317	0015	...	...	|	...	...	|	0655g
	Ferrara	d.	...	...	...	...	...	...	1513	...	...	...	...	...	2034	...	...	...	...	2152	...	...	0402	...
	Rovigo	d.	...	...	...	...	...	...	1530	...	...	...	...	...	2053	...	...	...	...	|	...	...	0424	...
	Padova	d.	...	...	...	...	...	...	1600	...	...	...	...	...	2122	...	...	...	...	2229	...	...	0459	...
	Venezia Mestre	a.	...	...	...	...	...	...	1616	...	...	...	...	...	2136	...	...	...	...	2242s	...	...	0523	...
	Venezia Santa Lucia	a.	...	...	...	...	...	...	|	...	...	...	...	...	|	...	...	...	...	2255	...	...	0534	...
	Trieste Centrale **601**	a.	...	...	...	...	...	...	1837	...	...	...	...	...	2347	...	...	...	...	...	...	...	0901	...

A – (12) Milano - Reggio di Calabria and v.v.
B – 1, 2 cl., 2 cl. (4 berth) Torino - Reggio di Calabria and v.v.
C – (12) Torino - Perugia and v.v.
D – (12) Milano - Terni and v.v.
E – 1, 2 cl., 2 cl. (4 berth) (2) Trieste - Udine - Venezia - Roma and v.v.
F – 1, 2 cl., 2 cl. (4 berth) Torino - Salerno and v.v.

f – Firenze **Campo di Marte**.
g – Milano **Porta Garibaldi**.

v – Reggio Emilia **AV**.
s – Calls to set down only.

◧ – Via Table **600**.
△ – Trains call here to pick up only.
▽ – Trains call here to set down only.
❖ – Running days, timings and numbers of *ICN* trains may vary - please check your reservation. For confirmed timings please consult the *Trenitalia* journey planner at www.trenitalia.com.

2nd class VENEZIA - BOLOGNA and FIRENZE - PERUGIA - FOLIGNO 620

Local trains. For long-distance trains see previous page.

km				⚒																				
0	**Venezia** Santa Lucia	d.	...	0534	0640	...	0740	0840	0940	...	1040	1140	1240	...	1340	1440	1540	...	1640	1740	1840	...	1940	2140
9	**Venezia** Mestre	d.	...	0553	0653	...	0753	0853	0953	...	1053	1153	1253	...	1353	1453	1553	...	1653	1753	1853	...	1953	2153
37	Padova	d.	...	0612	0709	...	0809	0909	1009	...	1109	1209	1309	...	1409	1509	1609	...	1709	1809	1909	...	2009	2210
81	Rovigo	d.	0555	0647	0758	...	0844	0958	1044	...	1144	1244	1344	...	1444	1558	1644	...	1746	1858	1946	...	2046	2248
113	Ferrara	d.	0614	0711	0818	...	0905	1018	1105	...	1205	1305	1405	...	1505	1618	1705	...	1805	1918	2014	...	2111	...
160	**Bologna** Centrale	a.	0655	0746	0855	...	0946	1048	1146	...	1246	1346	1446	...	1546	1650	1746	...	1846	1948	2046	...	2146	...

		Ⓐ	†	⚒																			
Bologna Centrale	d.	...	...	0612	...	0712	0812	0912	...	1012	1112	1212	...	1312	1425	1512	...	1612	1712	1812	...	1912	2112
Ferrara	d.	0615	...	0648	...	0748	0844	0948	...	1044	1144	1244	...	1344	1500	1544	...	1644	1744	1844	...	1944	2144
Rovigo	d.	0634	0634	0708	...	0808	0903	1008	...	1103	1203	1303	...	1403	1518	1603	...	1703	1803	1903	...	2003	2203
Padova	d.	0721	0721	0753	...	0853	0953	1053	...	1153	1253	1353	...	1453	1553	1653	...	1753	1853	1953	...	2053	2253
Venezia Mestre	a.	0756	0756	0807	...	0907	1007	1107	...	1207	1307	1407	...	1507	1607	1707	...	1807	1907	2007	...	2107	2307
Venezia Santa Lucia	a.	0809	0809	0820	...	0920	1020	1120	...	1220	1320	1420	...	1520	1620	1720	...	1820	1920	2020	...	2120	2320

km				①		⑥⑦																		
0	**Milano** Centrale	d.	0515	0615	...	0630	0720	...	0920	1120	...	1320	1520	...	1720	1815	...	1920	2120	...	2205**g**	...	...	...
10	**Milano** Rogoredo	d.	0527	0627	...	|	0732	...	0932	1132	...	1332	1532	...	1732	1827	...	1932	2133	...	2227	...	...	...
72	Piacenza	d.	0609	0715	...	0727	0814	...	1014	1214	...	1414	1614	...	1814	1909	...	2014	2214	...	2305	...	...	...
107	Fidenza	d.	0632	0742	...	0751	0845	...	1037	1245	...	1437	1637	...	1840	1937	...	2037	2240	...	|	...	...	...
129	Parma	d.	0647	0755	...	0806	0900	...	1100	1300	...	1500	1700	...	1906	2000	...	2108	2257	...	2334	...	...	...
157	Reggio Emilia	d.	0706	0814	...	0821	0920	...	1120	1320	...	1520	1719	...	1927	2018	...	2118	...	...	2349	...	...	...
182	Modena	d.	0724	0834	...	0840	0938	...	1138	1338	...	1538	1738	...	1946	2035	...	2143	...	...	0005	...	...	...
219	**Bologna** Centrale	a.	0805	0910	...	0904	1010	...	1209	1410	...	1610	1810	...	2016	2108	...	2214	...	...	0033	...	...	...

			⚒															⑤		d			
Bologna Centrale	d.	0528	0540	...	0550	0658	...	0750	0950	...	1150	1350	...	1550	1750	...	1833	1850	...	1950	*2033*	...	...
Modena	d.	0555	0607	...	0624	0731	...	0824	1024	...	1224	1424	...	1624	1824	...	1902	1924	...	2024	*2102*	...	...
Reggio Emilia	d.	0610	0622	...	0642	0800	...	0842	1042	...	1242	1442	...	1642	1842	...	1917	1942	...	2042	*2117*	...	...
Parma	d.	0627	0640	...	0703	0818	...	0903	1103	...	1305	1503	...	1703	1903	...	1933	2003	...	2103	*2133*	...	...
Fidenza	d.	0639	0656	...	0726	0830	...	0926	1126	...	1326	1524	...	1726	1926	...	1945	2017	...	2126	2158	...	...
Piacenza	d.	0706	0725	...	0755	0853	...	0950	1150	...	1350	1550	...	1750	1950	...	2012	2053	...	2150	2225	...	...
Milano Rogoredo	a.	0747	0803	...	0836	0936	...	1033	1233	...	1433	1633	...	1833	2033	...	2046	2133	...	2233	2312	...	...
Milano Centrale	a.	0800	0837**g**	...	0850	0950	...	1045	1245	...	1445	1645	...	1845	2045	...	2110**g**	2145	...	2245	2322	...	...

km			⚒	⚒			⚒		⚒				Ⓐ			Ⓐ			⑥		Ⓑ			
0	**Firenze** SMN	d.	...	...	...	0802	*0948*	...	...	1214	...	1414	...	...	1614	...	...	1814	2014	...	2014	...	...	...
88	Arezzo	d.	...	...	...	0913	*1049*	...	...	1317	...	1517	...	...	1717	...	...	1917	2117	...	2117	...	...	...
106	Castiglion Fiorentino	d.	...	...	...	0924	*1102*	...	...	1328	...	1528	...	...	1728	...	...	1928	2128	...	2128	...	...	...
122	Terontola-Cortona	d.	0625	0710	...	0941	1139	...	1226	1341	...	1541	1620	...	1741	1850	...	1941	2141	...	2200	...	...	...
134	Passignano sul Trasimeno	d.	0639	0721	...	0950	1149	...	1235	1350	...	1550	1629	...	1750	1900	...	1950	2151	...	2209	...	...	...
165	**Perugia** **625**	d.	0718	0805	...	1022	1227	...	1316	1427	...	1623	1700	...	1828	1941	...	2024	2221	...	2239	...	...	...
176	**Perugia** Ponte San Giovanni **625**	d.	0727	0814	...	1032	1236	...	1327	1436	...	1632	1714	...	1839	1950	...	2035	2230	...	2248	...	...	...
189	Assisi **625**	d.	0739	0828	...	1045	1247	...	1343	1448	...	1645	1728	...	1852	2001	...	2047	2242	...	2259	...	...	...
200	Spello **625**	d.	0749	0840	...	1054	1255	...	1354	1456	...	1654	1737	...	1906	2009	...	2056	2251	...	2307	...	...	...
205	**Foligno** **625**	a.	0758	0850	...	1100	1301	...	1402	1501	...	1703	1744	...	1915	2016	...	2112	2257	...	2315	...	...	...

		⚒	⚒		⚒				⚒			⚒			Ⓐ			Ⓐ			⑥		
Foligno **625**	d.	0530	0636	...	0722	0912	...	1108	1150	...	1303	1345	...	1503	1533	...	1706	1810	...	1903	2053	...	...
Spello **625**	d.	0536	0641	...	0728	0917	...	1114	1156	...	1309	1351	...	1509	1538	...	1711	1816	...	1909	2059	...	...
Assisi **625**	d.	0545	0649	...	0742	0925	...	1122	1205	...	1317	1404	...	1517	1549	...	1721	1824	...	1917	2110	...	...
Perugia Ponte San Giovanni **625**	d.	0600	0708	...	0753	0938	...	1134	1216	...	1330	1417	...	1530	1603	...	1733	1842	...	1929	2124	...	...
Perugia **625**	d.	0615	0718	...	0804	0952	...	1144	1227	...	1341	1427	...	1540	1627	...	1744	1853	...	1941	2137	...	...
Passignano sul Trasimeno	d.	0642	0756	...	0838	1020	...	1212	1256	...	1409	1459	...	1609	1658	...	1812	1922	...	2009	2207	...	...
Terontola-Cortona	d.	0656	0808	...	0853	1036	...	1221	1309	...	1419	1511	...	1619	1714	...	1825	1933	...	2019	2220	...	...
Castiglion Fiorentino	d.	0710	...	...	...	|	...	1234	...	...	1431	...	...	1631	...	...	1837	...	...	2031	...	...	...
Arezzo	d.	0725	...	...	...	1100	...	1245	...	...	1444	...	...	1644	...	...	1849	...	...	2044	...	...	...
Firenze SMN	a.	0835	...	...	...	1155	...	1351	...	...	1548	...	...	1757	...	...	1954	...	...	2150	...	...	...

2nd class FERRARA and BOLOGNA - RAVENNA - RIMINI 621

km							⚒		⚒		†	⚒	⚒		†	⚒	†d		c	†e	Ⓒf	⚒		†
0	**Ferrara**	d.	...	0520	...	0546	0610	...	...	...	...	0709	...	...	0827	0827	...	...	...	...	...	0917	...	1005
	Bologna Centrale	d.	...	|	...	|	|	...	0650	...	...	|	...	0806	|	|	...	...	0906	...	0906	|	1006	|
	Imola	d.	...	|	...	|	|	...	0712	...	...	|	...	0827	|	|	...	...	0927	...	0927	|	1027	|
	Castelbolognese-Riolo Terme	d.	...	|	...	|	|	...	0719	...	...	|	...	0834	|	|	...	...	0934	...	0934	|	1034	|
	Lugo	d.	...	|	...	|	|	...	0734	...	...	|	...	0848	|	|	...	...	0948	...	0948	|	1048	|
74	**Ravenna**	a.	...	0622	...	0702	0733	...	0805	...	...	0833	...	0915	0942	0943	...	...	1016	...	1016	1027	1115	1113
74	**Ravenna**	d.	0533	...	0628	...	...	0747	...	...	0819	...	0847	0919	...	0947	0947	...	...	1019	1019	...	...	1119
95	Cervia-Milano Marittima	d.	0551	...	0646	...	...	0808	...	...	0838	...	0908	0938	...	1008	1008	...	...	1038	1038	...	...	1138
103	Cesenatico	d.	0559	...	0652	...	...	0816	...	...	0846	...	0916	0946	...	1016	1016	...	...	1046	1046	...	...	1146
124	**Rimini**	a.	0630	...	0723	...	...	0842	...	...	0912	...	0942	1017	...	1042	1042	...	...	1117	1117	...	...	1217

			⚒				⚒								⚒								
Ferrara	d.	...	1137	...	1235	...	1335	...	...	1435	...	...	1637	...	1737	...	...	1835	...	...	2037	...	...
Bologna Centrale	d.	1106	|	1206	|	1306	|	1406	...	|	1506	1606	|	1706	|	1806	...	|	1906	2006	|	2112	2206
Imola	d.	1127	|	1227	|	1327	|	1427	...	|	1527	1627	|	1727	|	1827	...	|	1927	2027	|	2133	2239
Castelbolognese-Riolo Terme	d.	1134	|	1234	|	1334	|	1434	...	|	1534	1634	|	1734	|	1834	...	|	1934	2034	|	2146	2245
Lugo	d.	1148	|	1248	|	1348	|	1448	...	|	1548	1648	|	1748	|	1848	...	|	1948	2048	|	2154	2301
Ravenna	a.	1216	1248	1316	1348	1416	1448	1516	...	1548	1616	1716	1748	1816	1848	1916	...	1950	2016	2116	2150	2220	2330
Ravenna	d.	1219	...	1319	...	1419	...	1519	...	...	1619	1719	...	1819	...	1919	...	...	2019	2119	...	2224	...
Cervia-Milano Marittima	d.	1238	...	1338	...	1438	...	1538	...	...	1638	1738	...	1838	...	1938	...	...	2038	2137	...	2241	...
Cesenatico	d.	1246	...	1346	...	1446	...	1546	...	...	1646	1746	...	1846	...	1946	...	...	2046	2143	...	2247	...
Rimini	a.	1317	...	1417	...	1517	...	1617	...	...	1717	1817	...	1917	...	2017	...	...	2117	2217	...	2318	...

c – Daily until May 22; Ⓐ from May 23.
d – From May 29.
e – Until May 22.
f – From May 28.

FOR RETURN SERVICE SEE NEXT PAGE →

621 RIMINI - RAVENNA - BOLOGNA and FERRARA

2nd class

km																							
				⚒				⚒		⚒	⚒			†		⚒			†		†	⚒	c
	Rimini d.	...	0520	...	0606	...	0654	...	...	0735	...	...	0843	...	0918	...	...	...	1043	...	...	...	...
	Cesenatico d.	...	0544	...	0636	...	0721	...	...	0800	...	...	0916	...	0946	...	...	...	1116	...	...	...	...
	Cervia-Milano Marittima d.	...	0551	...	0647	...	0727	...	...	0809	...	...	0922	...	0952	...	...	...	1122	...	...	...	...
	Ravenna a.	...	0612	...	0707	...	0746	...	...	0831	...	...	0941	...	1014	...	...	...	1140	...	...	...	...
0	**Ravenna** d.	0503	0627	0626	...	0712	0755	0757	...	...	0843	0844	0944	0955	...	1040	...	1045	...	1144	1147	1210	1244
28	Lugo d.	0528	0657	|	...	|	0815	|	...	...	|	0912	1012	|	...	|	...	1112	...	1212	|	|	1312
42	C'bolognese-Riolo Terme d.	0546	0714	|	...	|	|	|	...	...	|	0928	1028	|	...	|	...	1128	...	1228	|	|	1328
50	Imola d.	0555	0721	|	...	|	|	|	...	...	|	0934	1034	|	...	|	...	1134	...	1234	|	|	1334
84	**Bologna** Centrale a.	0626	0743	|	...	|	0854	|	...	...	|	0954	1054	|	...	|	...	1154	...	1254	|	|	1354
	Ferrara a.	...	...	0740	...	0824	...	0904	...	...	0955	...	...	1107	...	1200	...	...	...	...	1259	1324	...

	Ⓒ f					⚒							⚒								
Rimini d.	1143	...	1243	...	1343	...	1443	...	1520	1543	...	1643	...	1743	1843	...	...	1943	2043	...	2143	2243
Cesenatico d.	1216	...	1316	...	1416	...	1516	...	1546	1616	...	1716	...	1816	1916	...	...	2016	2116	...	2217	2315
Cervia-Milano Marittima d.	1222	...	1322	...	1422	...	1522	...	1552	1622	...	1722	...	1822	1922	...	...	2022	2122	...	2223	2321
Ravenna a.	1241	...	1341	...	1441	...	1541	...	1612	1641	...	1741	...	1841	1941	...	...	2041	2141	...	2245	2340
Ravenna d.	1244	1310	1344	1425	1444	1512	1544	...	1616	1645	1712	1744	1812	1844	1944	...	2012	2044	2145	2212	...	...
Lugo d.	1312	|	1412	|	1512	|	1612	...	|	1712	|	1812	|	1912	2012	...	|	2112	2220	|	...	...
Castelbolognese-Riolo Terme d.	1328	|	1428	|	1528	|	1628	...	|	1728	|	1828	|	1928	2028	...	|	2128	2234	|	...	...
Imola d.	1334	|	1434	|	1534	|	1634	...	|	1734	|	1834	|	1934	2034	...	|	2134	2240	|	...	...
Bologna Centrale a.	1354	|	1454	|	1554	|	1654	...	|	1754	|	1854	|	1954	2054	...	|	2154	2300	|	...	...
Ferrara a.	...	1424	...	1546	...	1624	...	...	1724	...	1824	...	1924	...	...	...	2124	...	...	2322	...	...

FOR RETURN SERVICE AND FOOTNOTES SEE PREVIOUS PAGE.

622 ROMA AIRPORTS ✈

ROMA FIUMICINO AIRPORT ✈. *Leonardo Express* rail service Roma Termini - Roma Fiumicino ✈ and v.v. *31 km* Journey time: 35 minutes. Special fare payable.

From **Roma** Termini: 0520, 0535, 0550, 0605, 0620, 0635, 0650, 0705, 0735, 0750, 0805, 0820, 0835, 0850, 0905, 0920, 0935, 1020, 1035, 1050, 1105, 1120, 1135, 1205, 1220, 1250, 1320, 1350, 1405, 1420, 1435, 1450, 1505, 1520, 1535, 1550, 1605, 1620, 1635, 1650, 1705, 1720, 1735, 1750, 1805, 1820, 1835, 1850, 1920, 1935, 1950, 2005, 2020, 2035, 2050, 2105, 2120, 2135, 2150, 2205, 2220, 2235.

From **Roma Fiumicino**: 0608, 0623, 0638, 0653, 0708, 0723, 0738, 0753, 0823, 0838, 0853, 0908, 0923, 0938, 0953, 1008, 1023, 1108, 1123, 1138, 1153, 1208, 1223, 1253, 1308, 1323, 1338, 1408, 1438, 1453, 1508, 1523, 1538, 1553, 1608, 1623, 1638, 1653, 1708, 1723, 1738, 1753, 1808, 1823, 1838, 1953, 1908, 1923, 1938, 2008, 2023, 2038, 2053, 2108, 2123, 2138, 2153, 2208, 2223, 2238, 2253, 2308, 2323.

Additional rail services operate Roma Tiburtina - Roma Ostiense - Roma Fiumicino ✈. *39 km* Journey times: Tiburtina - ✈ ± 45 minutes; Ostiense - ✈ ± 30 minutes.
From Roma Tiburtina approximately every 15 mins. Ⓐ / 30 mins. Ⓒ 0500 – 2200; from Roma Fiumicino ✈ approximately every 15 mins. Ⓐ / 30 mins. Ⓒ 0600 – 2200.

ROMA CIAMPINO AIRPORT ✈. Rail service Roma Termini - Ciampino and v.v. (Table **623**). A 🚌 connects Ciampino station and the airport. Overall journey time approximately 60 minutes.

623 ROMA - ALBANO LAZIALE and ANZIO

2nd class

km																								
		⚒			⚒			⚒	†	⚒		⚒	†	⚒		Ⓐ	⑥	†	⚒		⚒	†	⚒	⚒
0	**Roma** Termini d.	0542	0721	0821	0900	...	1221	1321	1421	1421	...	1521	1621	1621	...	1721	1721	1821	1821	...	1921	2021	2021	2121
14	Ciampino d.	0558	0740	0837	0918	...	1237	1337	1437	1437	...	1537	1637	1637	...	1737	1742	1837	1837	...	1937	2037	2037	2137
23	Marino Laziale d.	0614	0801	0857	0936	...	1257	1400	1456	1500	...	1600	1656	1700	...	1800	1802	1856	1900	...	2000	2056	2100	2157
26	Castel Gandolfo d.	0621	0807	0904	0942	...	1303	1406	1503	1507	...	1606	1703	1706	...	1806	1809	1903	1906	...	2007	2102	2106	2204
29	**Albano Laziale** a.	0627	0815	0912	0951	...	1312	1415	1511	1515	...	1615	1711	1715	...	1815	1817	1911	1915	...	2015	2111	2115	2213

	⚒	⚒	⚒				⚒				⚒		⚒		⑥		Ⓑ	⚒			⚒	⚒	†
Roma Termini d.	0629	0700	0743	0838	...	1023	1144	...	1343	...	1443	1543	1643	...	1743	...	1743	1843	...	1943	2043	2140	2145
Ciampino d.	0636	0707	0750	0845	...	1030	1151	...	1351	...	1451	1551	1651	...	1751	...	1751	1851	...	1951	2051	2148	2152
Marino Laziale d.	0643	0720	0802	0858	...	1036	1157	...	1359	...	1459	1559	1659	...	1803	...	1759	1859	...	1959	2059	2158	2158
Castel Gandolfo d.	0703	0739	0823	0917	...	1057	1218	...	1419	...	1519	1619	1719	...	1823	...	1819	1919	...	2019	2119	2219	2219
Roma Termini a.	0720	0754	0841	0934	...	1113	1234	...	1434	...	1534	1634	1734	...	1838	...	1834	1934	...	2034	2134	2234	2234

ROMA - ANZIO *57 km* Journey 56 – 68 minutes. All services continue to Nettuno (*3 km* and 4 – 6 minutes from Anzio). Subject to alteration on and around public holidays.

From **Roma** Termini: 0506 ⚒, 0640, 0742 ⚒, 0812, 0942, 1042 ⚒, 1142, 1242 ⚒, 1342, 1412 Ⓐ, 1442, 1542 ⚒, 1642, 1742 ⚒, 1812 Ⓐ, 1842, 1912 Ⓐ, 1942, 2042 ⚒, 2142.

From **Anzio**: 0559 ⚒, 0635, 0703 Ⓐ, 0731 †, 0733 ⚒, 0816 ⚒, 0912, 1012, 1112 ⚒, 1212 ⚒, 1310, 1412 ⚒, 1510, 1612 ⚒, 1630 Ⓐ, 1705 †, 1712 ⚒, 1810, 1912 ⚒, 2010, 2112 Ⓐ, 2201.

624 ROMA - PESCARA

2nd class

km																									
			†	⚒	⚒		⚒			⚒			⚒	†	†	⑥	Ⓑ		⚒		⚒		⚒		⚒
0	**Roma** Termini d.	...	...	0715	...	0903	...	...	...	...	...	1310	1420	...	...	...	...	1640	...	...	...	1847	...	...	...
	Roma Tiburtina ◧ d.	...	0710	|	0810	|	...	...	1110	...	...	|	|	...	...	1510	1515	|	...	...	1715	|	1915	2010	2050
40	Tivoli d.	...	0811	0828	0901	0951	...	...	1211	...	...	1359	1457	...	...	1604	1604	1720	...	...	1800	1922	2000	2101	2136
108	Avezzano d.	0630	0920	0947	1023	1106	1247	...	1319	1349	...	1405	1601	1615	...	1740	1740	1818	1845	...	1914	2020	2110	2215	2246
172	Sulmona ⊖ d.	0740	1020	...	...	...	1357	1402	...	1512	1557	...	1652	1730	1750	...	...	1908	1956	2001	...	2111	...	...	...
226	Chieti a.	0849	1059	...	...	...	...	1457	...	...	1647	...	1737	...	1843	...	...	1951	...	2054	...	2154	...	...	...
240	**Pescara** Centrale a.	0905	1117	...	...	...	...	1521	...	...	1712	...	1750	...	1900	...	...	2006	...	2112	...	2207	...	...	...

	⚒		⚒	⚒	†		⚒	†		⚒	⚒		⚒	⚒		†	⚒		⚒	†	⚒	⚒	⚒ 🚌	
Pescara Centrale d.	...	...	...	0523	...	0730	0925	...	...	...	1119	...	1215	...	...	1438	1510	...	...	1627	1715	1821	...	...
Chieti d.	...	...	...	0536	...	0744	0937	...	...	...	1138	...	1241	...	...	1458	1532	...	...	1648	1738	1842	...	...
Sulmona ⊖ d.	...	...	...	0619	0619	0826	1019	...	...	...	1232	...	1340	1410	...	1542	1626	1700	...	1736	1845	1943	1950	...
Avezzano d.	0508	0545	0626	0712	0711	0919	1112	1112	1145	1320	1339	1345	...	1530	1604	1637	...	1815	1835	1839	2010	...	2050	2112
Tivoli d.	0610	0700	0736	0812	0810	1023	1211	1210	1300	1437	...	1532	...	1642	1721	1750	...	...	2001	1951	...	...	...	2232
Roma Tiburtina ◧ a.	0700	0806	0833	|	|	1055	|	|	|	1536	...	|	...	1736	|	|	...	...	2053	2035	...	...	...	|
Roma Termini a.	...	...	...	0845	0845	...	1250	1250	1350	...	...	1624	...	...	1826	1825	...	...	...	...	...	...	...	2315

◧ – Roma **Tiburtina Piazzale Est**.

⊖ – For 🚌 service Sulmona - Castel di Sangro see Table **627**.

625 ROMA - PERUGIA, RAVENNA and ANCONA

km																									
			IC						*IC*								*IC*		*FB*					*IC*	
		2	**580**	2	2	2		2	**534**					2			**540**		**8852**					**546**	
		⚒	**A**	†	⚒	⚒		Ⓐ		⚒	†	⚒	†	⚒						Ⓑ	⚒	†	⚒	Ⓑ	
0	**Roma** Termini 620 d.	...	...	...	...	...	0547	...	0750	0802	0815	0928	1005	*1202*	1322	1428	1525	1558	1725	1802	1831	1855	1902	1955	*2102*
5	**Roma** Tiburtina 620 d.	...	...	...	...	...	0557	...	0758u	0813	0824	0938	1013	*1213*	1331	1436	|	1609	|	1812	1840	1906	1912	2006u	*2112*
83	Orte 620 d.	...	...	...	...	...	0634	...	0830	0847	0859	1013	1047	*1245*	1405	1509	1601	1645	|	1846	1917	1940	1946	2037	*2148*
112	Terni d.	...	0505	...	...	0620	0654	0733	0852	0908	0921	1037	1107	*1310*	1428	1529	1622	1708	1829	1910	1938	2001	2008	2056	*2212*
141	Spoleto d.	...	0537	...	...	0656	0717	0814	0917	0935	0953	1101	1139	*1334*	1458	1556	1647	1735	1852	1941	2005	2028	2032	2129	*2237*
167	**Foligno** a.	...	0557	...	...	0720	0740	0835	0933	0953	1010	1126	1154	*1355*	1518	1612	1704	1753	1907	1958	2023	2046	2051	2144	*2256*
167	**Foligno** 620 d.	0545	0559	0615	0640	0722	0742	0837	0935	0955	1012	1128	1156	1416	1520	1614	1706	1755	1909	2000	2025	2048	2053	2146	2303
172	Spello d.	|	|	|	|	0728	|	0843	|	|	|	|	|	|	|	1620	|	|	|	2006	|	|	2059	|	|
183	Assisi 620 d.	|	0615	|	|	0742	|	0853	|	1011	1027	|	1210	|	|	1630	|	|	|	2016	|	|	2110	2200	|
196	**Perugia** Ponte SG ⊡ d.	|	0626	|	|	0753	|	0906	|	1029	1046	|	1220	|	|	1644	|	|	|	2032	|	|	2124	2209s	|
207	**Perugia** 620 a.	|	0636	|	|	0802	|	0915	|	1044	1055	|	1230	|	|	1658	|	|	|	2046	|	|	2135	2222	|
224	Fabriano d.	0647	...	0714	0736	...	0837	...	1031	...	...	1226	...	1523	1614	...	1755	1846	1950	...	2123	2139	...	...	2357
268	Jesi d.	0733	...	0756	0821	...	0914	...	1101	...	...	1310	...	1606	1706	...	1828	1922	2020	...	2200	2213	...	...	0033
286	Falconara Marittima d.	0751	...	0813	0839	...	0927	...	1115	...	...	1328	...	1626	1727	...	1852	1940	2042	...	2213	2232	...	...	0048
	Pesaro d.	|	...	|	|	...	|	...	|	...	...	|	...	|	|	...	|	|	2105	...	|	|	...	...	|
	Rimini d.	|	...	|	|	...	|	...	|	...	...	|	...	|	|	...	|	|	2129	...	|	|	...	...	|
	Ravenna a.	|	...	|	|	...	|	...	|	...	...	|	...	|	|	...	|	|	2205	...	|	|	...	...	|
295	**Ancona** a.	0805	...	0828	0855	...	0940	...	1125	...	...	1340	...	1637	1740	...	1905	1956	...	...	2225	2245	...	...	0100f

A – 🚆12 Terni - Milano and v.v.

f – ⑤⑥ only.

s – Calls to set down only.

u – Calls to pick up only.

⊡ – Full name is Perugia Ponte San Giovanni.

FOR RETURN SERVICE SEE NEXT PAGE →

ANCONA, RAVENNA and PERUGIA - ROMA 625

					IC		IC	IC		FB									IC					IC
				2	531	2	533	533		8851									541				2	599
		⚒	⚒	⚒	①–⑥	⚒	†	⚒	†				⚒	†	⚒	⚒		⚒						A
Ancona d.	0333	...	...	0505	...	...	0550	0550	...	...	0905	...	...	...	1250	...	1350	...	1555	...	1850	1950	2130	...
Ravenna d.	|	...	...	|	...	...	|	|	...	0615	|	...	...	...	|	...	|	...	|	...	|	|	|	...
Rimini d.	|	...	...	|	...	...	|	|	...	0652	|	...	...	...	|	...	|	...	|	...	|	|	|	...
Pesaro d.	|	...	...	|	...	...	|	|	...	0716	|	...	...	...	|	...	|	...	|	...	|	|	|	...
Falconara Marittima d.	0346	...	...	0513	...	...	0600	0600	...	0750	0914	...	...	...	1305	...	1403	...	1604	...	1900	2001	2139	...
Jesi d.	0400	...	...	0526	...	...	0614	0614	...	0807	0928	...	...	...	1323	...	1417	...	1616	...	1914	2016	2153	...
Fabriano d.	0434	...	...	0605	...	...	0651	0651	...	0838	1007	...	...	...	1412	...	1457	...	1652	...	1955	2052	2235	...
Perugia 620 d.	|	...	0552	|	0640	0652	|	|	0723	|	|	1105	1350	1402	|	...	|	1555	|	1815	|	|	|	2319
Perugia Ponte SG ⊡ d.	|	...	0603	|	0651u	0705	|	|	0732	|	|	1115	1359	1412	|	...	|	1606	|	1825	|	|	|	2329
Assisi 620 d.	|	...	0616	|	0703	0720	|	|	0745	|	|	1130	1417	1423	|	...	|	1627	|	1838	|	|	|	2339
Spello d.	|	...	0626	|	|	0730	|	|	0754	|	|	1138	1430	|	|	...	|	1637	|	1848	|	|	|	|
Foligno 620 a.	0520	...	0633	0705	0715	0735	0740	0740	0800	0918	1102	1148	1436	1436	1509	...	1553	1643	1752	1854	2045	2145	2327	2350
Foligno d.	0522	0555	0636	...	0717	0737	0750	0750	0802	0920	1105	1150	1438	1438	...	1515	1555	1645	1754	1856	2047	2147	...	2354
Spoleto d.	0540	0616	0659	...	0737	0759	0814	0814	0824	0938	1124	1214	1501	1501	...	1537	1616	1704	1813	1912	2101	2206	...	0013
Terni d.	0610	0648	0740	...	0801	0828	0842	0842	0849	1002	1149	1247	1527	1527	...	1609	1647	1735	1853	1938	2126	2238	...	0040
Orte 620 d.	0633	|	0805	...	0818	...	0901	0901	0908	|	1214	1313	1555	1555	...	1632	1710	1756	1914	2001	2147	2259	...	...
Roma Tiburtina 620 a.	0708	0743	0840	...	0845s	...	|	|	0936	1048s	1248	1345	1629	1629	...	...	1748	1830	|	2039	2221	2329	...	...
Roma Termini 620 a.	0718	0800	0852	...	0855	...	0935	0940	0955	1057	1300	1355	1643	1643	...	...	1800	1845	1950	2050	2232	2342	...	...

FOR RETURN SERVICE AND FOOTNOTES SEE PREVIOUS PAGE.

ROMA and NAPOLI - CAMPOBASSO - TERMOLI 627

2nd class

km				⚒	⑤†	†	⚒	⚒	†	Ⓐ	⑥
0	**Roma** Termini d.	0615	0907	1307	1435	1740	1732t	1935	2014	2035	2042
138	Cassino d.	0742	1033	1445	1603	|	|	|	|	|	|
162	Venafro d.	0808	1056	1502	1625	1931	1933	2128	2205	2219	2226
169	Rocca Ravindola d.	|	1105	|	|	|	1941	|	|	|	|
187	Isernia d.	0829	1130*	1524	1700*	2005*	2005*	2200*	2235*	2250*	2257*
246	**Campobasso** Centro a.	0935*	1235*	1635*	1800*	2110*	2110*	2300*	2335*	2350*	2355*

			⚒		⚒		Ⓐ			
Campobasso Centro d.	0535*	...	1215*	...	1350*	...	1640*	...	1920*	...
Isernia d.	0620*	...	1315*	...	1503	...	1800	...	2032	...
Rocca Ravindola d.	0655	...	|	...	|	...	|	...	|	...
Venafro d.	0704	...	1358	...	1531	...	1822	...	2055	...
Cassino a.	0723	...	1416	...	1549	...	1840	...	2116	...
Roma Termini a.	0853	...	1553t	...	1727	...	2025	...	2254	...

km		⚒	†	⑥	Ⓐ	†	⚒	Ⓒ	Ⓐ	†	⚒
0	**Napoli** Centrale d.	...	...	1206	1206	1400	1400	1706	1706	1930	1930
34	Caserta d.	0805	0845	1241	1241	1440	1440	1739	1739	2005	2003
80	Vairano-Caianello d.	0850	0929	1322	1322	1516	1516	1824	1824	2044	2044
101	Venafro d.	0910	0948	1342	1342	1538	1538	1843	1843	2104	2104
108	Rocca Ravindola d.	|	0956	1348	1349	1546	|	1850	1850	2112	|
126	Isernia d.	0950*	1015	1420*	1407	1610*	1601	1915*	1906	2135*	2127
185	**Campobasso** Centro a.	1050*	1125*	1530*	1530*	1715*	1715*	2020*	2020*	2235*	2235*

	⚒	⚒	†	†	†	⑥	Ⓐ	⚒	†	⚒
Campobasso Centro d.	0450*	0605*	0705*	1205*	1230*	1235*	1245*	...	1720*	1745*
Isernia d.	0550*	0705*	0805*	1328	1345*	1350*	1411	...	1835*	1909
Rocca Ravindola d.	|	|	0845	|	1405*	1427	1427	...	1900*	1925
Venafro d.	0628	0750	0854	1352	1434	1434	1434	1713	1930	1932
Vairano-Caianello d.	0646	0809	0913	1411	1455	1455	1455	1731	1954	1954
Caserta a.	0716	0847	0944	1449	1529	1529	1529	1811	2030	2030
Napoli Centrale a.	0754	0929	1020	...	1609	1609	1609	...	2106	2106

km				🚌		⚒🚌				🚌	
0	**Campobasso** d.	0515	...	1000	...	1414	...	1825	...	2100	...
87	**Termoli** a.	0716	...	1145	...	1600	...	2018	...	2245	...

					⚒🚌		🚌		🚌	
Termoli d.	0558	...	1200	...	1410	...	1750	...	2100	...
Campobasso a.	0750	...	1355	...	1555	...	1935	...	2245	...

ROMA - CASSINO

	⚒		†	⚒	⚒	†		†	⚒	⚒	⚒				⚒	†	Ⓐ	⚒	†			⚒		Ⓐ	⑥	
Roma Termini d.	0535	0615	0707	0742	0800	0800	0907	1014	1014	1235	1307	1342	1435	1542	1642	1655	1707	1742	1745	1807	1842	1907	1942	2042	2049	2128
Cassino a.	0736	0742	0857	0942	0947	1014	1033	1227	1245	1406	1445	1544	1603	1742	1858	1857	1844	1940	1940	1946	2040	2045	2142	2248	2305	2340

		⚒		⚒	†	⚒			⚒	†		⚒	†	⚒			†	⚒	⑥	†	Ⓐ	†	⚒	Ⓑ		Ⓐ
Cassino d.	0608	0618	0724	0807	0850	0913	1018	1025	1218	1231	1318	1422	1458	1518	1550	1620	1715	1720	1758	1805	1808	1822	1841	1932	2018	2120
Roma Termini a.	0748	0820	0853	0954	1107	1107	1147	1227	1448	1448	1520	1620	1720	1720	1727	1820	1920	1920	2020	1934	2020	2020	2026	2148	2241	2334

CASSINO - NAPOLI

km		⚒	⚒	⚒	†	⚒	⚒	Ⓐ		Ⓐ
0	Cassino d.	0548	0703	0838	1305	1433	1514	1708	1857	2100
32	Vairano-Caianello d.	0621	0736	0911	1338	1506	1605	1741	1954	2126
78	Caserta d.	0705	0820	0955	1422	1550	1650	1826	2031	2209
112	Napoli Centrale a.	0746	0905	1040	1506	1635	1735	1910	2106	2252

	⚒	⚒		⚒	⚒	†	Ⓐ	⚒	Ⓐ
Napoli Centrale d.	0510	0612	0755	1154	1412	1550	1712	1755	1955
Caserta d.	0551	0653	0838	1235	1453	1631	1754	1838	2038
Vairano-Caianello d.	0638	0807	0920	1317	1618	1713	1836	1920	2120
Cassino a.	0710	0835	0957	1355	1656	1750	1913	1957	2157

Other 🚌 services:

Campobasso - Benevento and v.v.: from Campobasso Centro at 0620 ⚒, 1305 ⚒, 1416 ⚒, 1750 ⚒; from Benevento at 0640 ⚒, 0740 ⚒, 1420 ⚒, 1740 ⚒. Journey 75 minutes.

Sulmona - Castel di Sangro and v.v.: from Sulmona at 1030, 1950 ⚒; from Castel di Sangro at 0555 ⚒, 1615 †, 1640 ⚒. Journey 70 minutes.

t – Roma **Tiburtina**.

* – Connection by 🚌.

SARDINIA 629

2nd class

CAGLIARI - CARBONIA and IGLESIAS

km		⚒	⚒	Ⓐ					⚒	⚒	Ⓑ	Ⓑ	⚒	⚒	Ⓑ	Ⓑ	⚒	⚒			⚒	⚒b	⚒	⚒			Ⓑ
0	**Cagliari** d.	0526	0545	0614	0644	...	0744	...	0844	...	0944	...	1044	...	1145	...	1244	...	1344	...	1418	...	1444	...	1544	...	1644
7	Elmas Aeroporto ✈ d.	0532	0551	0620	0650	...	0750	...	0850	...	0950	...	1050	...	1150	...	1250	...	1350	...	1424	...	1450	...	1550	...	1650
17	Decimomannu d.	0541	0604	0635	0704	...	0804	...	0903	...	1003	...	1103	...	1203	...	1304	...	1403	...	1432	...	1503	...	1603	...	1703
46	Villamassargia a.	0603	0635	0703	0731	0734	0831	0834	0931	0934	1031	1034	1131	1134	1231	1234	1331	1334	1431	1434	1500	1504	1531	1534	1631	1634	1731
69	**Carbonia** Serbariu a.	|	0651	|	|	0751	0847	|	|	0951	1047	|	|	1150	1247	|	|	1350	1447	|	|	1527	|	1550	1647	|	|
55	**Iglesias** a.	0611	...	0712	0741	...	...	0843	0940	...	...	1043	1140	...	...	1243	1340	...	...	1443	1509	...	1540	...	...	1643	1740

	Ⓑ			Ⓐ	Ⓐb	Ⓐ	Ⓐ				b
Cagliari d.	...	1744	...	1810	...	1844	...	1944	...	2044	...
Elmas Aeroporto ✈ d.	...	1750	...	1816	...	1850	...	1950	...	2050	...
Decimomannu d.	...	1803	...	1830	...	1903	...	2004	...	2103	...
Villamassargia a.	1734	1831	1834	1858	1901	1931	1934	2031	2034	2130	2135
Carbonia Serbariu a.	1750	1847	|	|	1924	|	1950	2047	|	|	2158
Iglesias a.	...	...	1843	1906	...	1940	...	...	2043	2140	...

	Ⓐb	⚒	⚒	⚒	†	⚒b	⚒			Ⓐ	
Iglesias d.	...	0553	0623	...	0627	...	0653	...	0721	0754	0818
Carbonia Serbariu d.	0532	|	|	0613	|	0632	|	0710	|	|	|
Villamassargia d.	0558	0603	0630	0635	0636	0658	0703	0726	0731	0803	0826
Decimomannu d.	...	0633	...	0702	0703	...	0732	...	0756	0831	...
Elmas Aeroporto ✈ d.	...	0645	...	0717	0716	...	0744	...	0807	0844	...
Cagliari a.	...	0652	...	0724	0723	...	0750	...	0815	0850	...

		⚒	⚒	Ⓑ	Ⓑ	⚒	⚒	Ⓑ	Ⓑ	⚒	⚒		†	⚒	⚒	⚒	⚒			Ⓑ	Ⓑ			Ⓐ	Ⓐ		
Iglesias d.	...	...	0921	1018	...	...	1121	1218	...	...	1321	1418	...	...	...	1521	1552	1618	...	...	1721	1818	...	...	1921	2018	...
Carbonia Serbariu d.	0810	0910	|	|	1010	1110	|	|	1210	1310	|	|	1410	1410	1510	|	|	|	1610	1710	|	|	1810	1910	|	|	2010
Villamassargia d.	0831	0926	0931	1026	1031	1126	1131	1226	1231	1326	1331	1426	1431	1431	1526	1531	1601	1626	1631	1726	1731	1826	1831	1926	1931	2026	2031
Decimomannu d.	0856	...	0956	...	1057	...	1156	...	1257	...	1356	...	1456	1500	...	1556	1631	...	1656	...	1756	...	1857	...	1956	...	2059
Elmas Aeroporto ✈ d.	0909	...	1009	...	1009	...	1208	...	1310	...	1409	...	1509	1515	...	1607	1639	...	1711	...	1807	...	1911	...	2009	...	2113
Cagliari a.	0915	...	1015	...	1117	...	1215	...	1317	...	1415	...	1516	1522	...	1614	1645	...	1717	...	1814	...	1917	...	2015	...	2120

Narrow gauge services on Sardinia are operated by ARST (www.arst.sardegna.it). Regular services operate on the following routes: Alghero - Sassari, Sassari - Sorso, Macomer - Nuoro and Monserrato Gottardo - Isili. Tram connections are available Monserrato Gottardo - Cagliari Repubblica and v.v. *Trenino Verde della Sardegna* operates tourist trains (www.treninoverde.com).

b – By 🚌.

629 SARDINIA — 2nd class

CAGLIARI - SASSARI - GOLFO ARANCI

km																											
		⚒		⚒	Ⓐ	⚒	†	†	†	⚒	⚒	†	⚒	†	†	⚒	⚒	⚒	†	†	⚒	⚒	⚒	†	⚒	†	⚒
0	**Cagliari** d.	...	...	...	...	...	...	...	0624	0630	...	...	0722	...	...	0835	...	0925	0933	1014	...	1040	...	1110	1112	1222	1222
7	Elmas Aeroporto ✈ d.	...	...	...	...	...	...	...	0630	|	...	...	0729	...	...	0842	...	0931	0939	1020	...	1046	...	1116	1117	1229	1229
17	Decimomannu d.	...	...	...	...	...	...	...	0638	0641	...	...	0737	...	...	|	...	0939	0947	1032	...	|	...	1129	1131	1237	1237
95	**Oristano** d.	...	...	...	...	...	...	...	0730	0730	...	...	0830	...	...	0931	...	1048	1046	1136	...	1134	...	1225	1232	1330	1330
154	Macomer d.	...	...	...	...	...	...	...	0821	0824	...	...	▬	...	...	1024	...	1144	1142	▬	...	1227	...	▬	▬	1431	1431
214	Ozieri-Chilivani a.	...	...	...	...	...	...	...	0904	0903	...	...	...	...	...	1104	...	▬	...	⚒	...	|	...	...	⚒	1516	1516
214	Ozieri-Chilivani d.	...	...	0644	...	0645	0745	0748	0914	0906	0910	0912	...	1105	1105	1109	1109	...	...	1212	...	|	...	...	1441	1521	1524
261	**Sassari** d.	...	0650	|	...	0742	0835	|	0952	|	0950	|	...	1146	|	|	1149	...	...	|	...	1339	1345	...	1525	|	|
280	Porto Torres a.	...	0704	|	...	0801	0848	|	...	|	▬	|	...	...	|	|	...	...	...	|	...	...	1400	...	...	|	|
281	Porto Torres Marittima a.	...	0707	|	...	0804	0852	|	...	|	Ⓐ	|	Ⓐ	...	|	|	...	...	...	|	...	...	1404	⚒	...	|	|
285	Olbia a.	0640	...	0747	0752	...	...	0852	...	1002	1010	1015	1119	...	1211	1206	...	1227	...	1316	1340	...	...	1450	...	1623	1634
306	**Golfo Aranci** a.	0704	...	...	0816	...	...	...	...	...	1034	...	1143	...	...	...	...	1251	...	...	1404	...	...	1514	...	...	...

		⚒		⚒	†	†	⚒	⚒	Ⓐ	⚒	⚒	⚒	†	†	†	⚒	†	⚒	⚒	†	⚒	⚒b	⚒	†		b
Cagliari d.	...	...	...	1325	1413	...	1430	...	...	1522	1630	...	1640	...	1713	1720	1820	1830	...	1915	1920	...	2035	2040	2200	...
Elmas Aeroporto ✈ d.	...	...	...	1332	1419	...	1437	...	...	1529	1636	...	1647	...	1719	1726	1826	1836	...	1921	1926	...	2041	2046	2208	...
Decimomannu d.	...	...	...	1341	1428	...	|	...	...	1537	|	...	|	...	1732	1739	1834	|	...	1934	1940	...	2050	2055	2226	2231
Oristano d.	...	...	...	1438	1531	...	1534	...	...	1632	1731	...	1742	...	1829	1841	1928	1836	...	2034	2050	2056	2154	2201	...	0021
Macomer d.	...	...	...	1535	1629	...	1631	...	...	▬	1819	...	1830	...	...	...	2028	2024	2036	▬	...	2216	...	...	...	...
Ozieri-Chilivani a.	...	...	...	...	1712	...	1709	...	...	...	1858	...	1908	...	...	...	2117	|	2123	...	...	...	...	...	...	...
Ozieri-Chilivani d.	...	...	1521	...	1719	1718	1717	1714	...	...	1901	1903	1915	1913	...	...	2125	|	2125	2128	...	...	...	...	...	...
Sassari d.	...	1530	1601	...	1800	|	1759	|	...	...	|	1947	1954	|	...	...	|	2134	|	2210	...	...	...	...	...	...
Porto Torres a.	...	1545	...	...	1812	|	1811	|	...	...	|	...	...	|	...	...	|	...	|	...	...	...	...	...	...	...
Porto Torres Marittima a.	...	1549	...	...	1816	|	1816	|	...	Ⓒb	|	...	...	|	...	...	|	...	|	...	...	...	...	...	...	...
Olbia a.	1650	...	...	...	...	1823	...	1825	1830	1830	1959	...	...	2016	...	...	2224	...	2228	...	...	...	...	...	...	...
Golfo Aranci a.	1714	...	...	...	...	...	...	...	1854	1902	...	...	...	...	...	...	...	...	...	...	...	...	...	...	...	...

	⚒	⚒b	⚒	⚒	⚒b		⚒	⚒	†	†		⚒	†	⚒	†	⚒	Ⓐ	⚒	†	†	⚒	⚒	Ⓐ	Ⓐ		⚒
Golfo Aranci d.	...	...	...	...	...	...	...	...	...	...	...	...	...	0715	...	...	0827	...	...	...	...	...	1045	1153	1301	...
Olbia d.	...	...	...	...	...	...	0537	...	0632	...	...	...	...	0739	0757	0803	0851	...	0946	...	1005	...	1109	1217	1325	...
Porto Torres Marittima d.	...	...	...	...	...	...	|	...	|	...	0718	...	...	...	|	|	▬	0952	|	1005	|	...	▬	▬	▬	...
Porto Torres d.	...	...	...	...	...	...	|	...	|	...	0721	...	...	...	|	|	†	0955	|	1008	|	...	⚒	...	...	...
Sassari d.	...	...	...	0600	...	...	|	0630	|	0704	0736	0820	0826	...	|	|	0924	1010	|	1022	|	1023	1120	...	...	...
Ozieri-Chilivani a.	...	...	...	0639	...	...	0640	|	0740	0742	▬	0859	0905	...	0909	0902	1013	...	1101	1100	1106	1100	1210	...	...	...
Ozieri-Chilivani d.	...	...	...	...	...	...	0644	|	...	0750	...	...	...	...	0911	0905	...	...	...	1108	...	1107	...	...	...	...
Macomer d.	...	0510	...	...	0605	...	0731	0743	...	0839	⚒	...	...	...	0956	0945	...	...	...	1151	...	1146	...	⚒	†	1341
Oristano d.	0530	0620	0630	...	0725	0730	...	0831	...	0925	0930	...	...	...	1046	1031	...	...	...	1237	...	1233	...	1330	1430	1437
Decimomannu d.	0629	...	0721	...	...	0821	...	|	...	1015	1027	...	...	...	1144	|	...	...	...	1343	...	|	...	1422	1530	1538
Elmas Aeroporto ✈ d.	0637	...	0729	...	...	0830	...	0921	...	1022	1041	...	...	...	1152	1118	...	...	...	1351	...	1320	...	1430	1545	1546
Cagliari a.	0643	...	0737	...	...	0843	...	0928	...	1029	1048	...	...	...	1159	1125	...	...	...	1358	...	1327	...	1438	1552	1554

	⚒	†	†	†	⚒	⚒	⚒	⚒	⚒	⚒	⚒	⚒	†	†	⚒	⚒	⚒	†	⚒	†	†	Ⓐ	Ⓒb	†	⚒	†
Golfo Aranci d.	...	...	...	...	...	...	...	1415	1525	...	...	...	...	...	1725	...	...	...	...	...	...	1905	1905	...	...	...
Olbia d.	1330	...	1410	...	...	1415	...	1439	1549	...	...	1608	1554	...	1749	1757	...	...	...	...	1838	1929	1937	...	2015	2018
Porto Torres Marittima d.	|	...	|	...	1415	|	...	▬	...	1605	...	|	|	...	...	|	1830	1840	...	...	|	▬	...	...	|	|
Porto Torres d.	|	...	|	...	1418	|	...	...	...	1608	...	|	|	...	...	|	1833	1843	...	...	|	⚒	...	...	|	|
Sassari d.	|	...	|	1433	1433	|	1439	...	...	1623	1628	|	|	1630	...	|	1848	1858	1900	1904	|	2031	...	2032	|	|
Ozieri-Chilivani a.	1439	...	1514	1511	...	1520	1518	...	...	▬	1708	1707	1712	1712	...	1856	...	...	|	1949	1949	2120	...	2113	2123	2124
Ozieri-Chilivani d.	...	...	...	1519	...	...	1525	⚒	...	†	...	1713	▬	▬	...	1900	...	...	|	1956	...	...	...	...	...	...
Macomer d.	...	...	...	1558	...	...	1605	1632	...	1729	...	1752	†	⚒	...	1940	...	...	2024	2048	...	...	...	...	...	...
Oristano d.	...	1530	...	1654	...	...	1649	1732	...	1842	...	1848	1930	1936	...	2032	...	...	2116	2137	...	...	...	...	...	...
Decimomannu d.	...	1624	...	1745	...	...	|	1833	...	1936	...	|	2029	2036	...	|	...	...	2216	2235	...	...	...	...	...	...
Elmas Aeroporto ✈ d.	...	1639	...	1752	...	...	1737	1847	...	1944	...	1936	2043	2043	...	2121	...	...	2225	2242	...	...	...	...	...	...
Cagliari a.	...	1646	...	1800	...	...	1744	1853	...	1951	...	1943	2050	2049	...	2128	...	...	2232	2249	...	...	...	...	...	...

FOR FOOTNOTES AND CAGLIARI - CARBONIA / IGLESIAS SERVICE SEE PREVIOUS PAGE.

632 FOGGIA - POTENZA — 2nd class

km																								
				⚒		⚒	†			†	†	⚒		⚒		⚒			⚒			🚌		
0	**Foggia** d.	0506	0534	0620	...	0645	0645	0842	...	1029	1137	1120*	...	1300*	1424	1630*	...	1752	1830	2057	...	2250	...	...
67	Melfi d.	0555	0633	0723	...	0757	0748	0942	...	1124	1232	1238	...	1420	1534	1729	...	1849	1930	2156	...	2340	...	...
119	**Potenza** Centrale a.	0705	0758	0837	...	0917	0919	1101	...	1237	1347	1347	...	1530	1644	1850	...	2000	2051	2256	...	0053	...	...

		⚒	†		⚒	⚒	†		⚒		⚒		⚒	†							🚌		
Potenza Centrale d.	0528	0618	0715	...	0715	0840	0842	...	0936	1128	1234	...	1330	1330	1704	...	1816	2010	2111	...	2240	...	...
Melfi d.	0636	0726	0826	...	0847	0945	0945	...	1055	1229	1350	...	1448	1452	1815	...	1933	2119	2224	...	2350	...	...
Foggia a.	0746	0823	0935	...	0946*	1040	1040	...	1200*	1329	1500*	...	1558	1558	1931	...	2032	2222	2321	...	...	...	...

* – Connection by 🚌.

633 PAOLA - COSENZA - SIBARI — 2nd class

Service valid March 14 - June 11. For *FA* train Bolzano - Roma - Sibari see Tables **600** and **640**.

km																									
		⚒	⚒	⚒			Ⓒ	Ⓐ		Ⓒ	Ⓐ	⚒	⚒	Ⓑ	Ⓐ		⚒	†	†	⚒	†	⚒	†A		
	Napoli Centrale **640** d.	...	...	...	...	...	0650	...	0850	...	...	...	...	...	...	1250	...	...	...	...	...	...	...	...	1914
0	**Paola 640** d.	0515	0657	0727	0836	0956	1026	1108	1219	1312	1327	1406	1427	1527	1557	1627	1727	1741	1827	1847	1927	2008	2029	2159	2256
21	Castiglione Cosentino d.	0530	0711	0742	0850	1010	1040	1122	1233	1327	1342	1422	1442	1542	1612	1641	1743	1756	1843	1903	1941	2023	2046	2213	2311
26	**Cosenza** a.	0537	0719	0750	0857	1018	1049	1130	1242	1335	1350	1430	1450	1550	1620	1649	1753	1803	1850	1908	1949	2031	2053	2221	2318

	⚒		⚒		A	Ⓐ		†	⚒	⚒	Ⓒ			⚒			⚒	⚒	Ⓐ	Ⓐ	†		⚒	†
Cosenza d.	0536	0558	0615	0626	0737	0844	1002	1053	1120	1236	1320	1336	...	1436	1505	1635	1700	1736	1803	1823	1835	1857	2036	2055
Castiglione Cosentino d.	0543	0604	0621	0633	0744	0851	1009	1059	1126	1243	1326	1343	...	1443	1511	1642	1706	1743	1809	1830	1844	1903	2045	2101
Paola 640 a.	0559	0620	0637	0649	0759	0907	1023	1116	1141	1259	1342	1359	...	1459	1526	1657	1722	1759	1825	1845	1858	1919	2058	2116
Napoli Centrale **640** a.	...	1010	...	...	...	...	...	...	...	...	1738	...	...	...	1908	...	...	...	...	...	...	2258	...	...

km											
			⚒		Ⓐ	Ⓐ	†	⚒	⚒	†A	
0	**Cosenza** d.	0550	0727	1400	1443	1750	1845	1912	2102	2103	...
5	Castiglione Cosentino d.	0559	0733	1406	1449	1756	1851	1918	2108	2108	...
70	**Sibari** a.	0705	0820	1455	1534	1845	1946	2015	2150	2150	...

	⚒	A		Ⓐ		Ⓐ		Ⓐ	†
Sibari d.	0545	0615	0843	1243	...	1545	1643	1915	1920
Castiglione Cosentino d.	0632	0702	0932	1332	...	1632	1731	2002	2010
Cosenza a.	0640	0710	0938	1338	...	1638	1738	2010	2016

A – (2) Paola - Cosenza - Sibari and v.v.

634 CATANZARO - LAMEZIA TERME — 2nd class

km																								
		⚒	†		⚒	⚒		e	d			†		⚒	⚒		⚒	†		⚒	†		⚒	f
0	**Catanzaro** Lido d.	0547	0633	...	0635	0747	...	0820	0820	...	0950	1040	...	1235	1340	...	1438	1450	...	1547	1633	...	1856	2243
9	Catanzaro d.	0555	0641	...	0643	0755	...	0835	0835	...	0958	1048	...	1243	1348	...	1446	1458	...	1555	1647	...	1905	2254
47	**Lamezia Terme** Centrale a.	0632	0720	...	0724	0832	...	0915	0926	...	1034	1130	...	1332	1429	...	1523	1533	...	1630	1722	...	1940	2340

	⚒	⚒d	⚒e		†	⚒d	⚒e			†	⚒		†	⚒	⚒		⚒	†	⚒		†	⚒	⚒
Lamezia Terme Centrale d.	0647	0746	0750	...	0755	0900	0918	...	1105	1150	1250	...	1403	1403	1454	...	1551	1604	1712	...	1753	1910	1913
Catanzaro d.	0723	0835	0835	...	0836	0936	0959	...	1141	1225	1327	...	1440	1447	1534	...	1636	1646	1747	...	1829	1946	1955
Catanzaro Lido a.	0732	0843	0843	...	0844	0943	1009	...	1150	1232	1335	...	1448	1457	1542	...	1644	1655	1754	...	1837	1953	2003

d – From Mar. 14. e – Until Mar. 13. f – Until Mar. 31. By 🚌.

SUD EST SERVICES 635

Line 1 : BARI - TARANTO No service on †.

km																								
		⚒	⚒	⚒	⚒	⚒	⚒	⚒		⚒	⚒	⚒	⚒	⚒	⚒	⚒		⚒	⚒🚌	⚒	⚒	⚒	⚒	⚒
0	Bari Centrale d.	...	...	...	...	...	0521	...	...	0621	...	0721	...	0821	...	0921	...	...	...	1021	1121	...	...	1221
1	Bari Sud Est d.	...	...	...	...	...	0525	...	...	0625	...	0725	...	0825	...	0925	...	...	...	1025	1125	...	...	1225
4	Mungivacca d.	...	...	...	...	...	0535	...	...	0635	...	0735	...	0835	...	0935	...	...	...	1035	1135	...	...	1235
	Casamassima d.	...	...	...	...	...	0608	...	...	0708	...	0808	...	0908	...	1008	...	...	...	1108	1208	...	...	1308
43	Putignano a.	...	0501	...	0630	...	0639	0709	...	0739	0744	0839	0936	0939	1007	1039	...	1042	...	1139	1239	1248	...	1339
78	Martina Franca **2** d.	0530	0603	0637	0737	0750	...	0808	...	...	0848	...	1038	...	1109	...	...	1141	1210	...	...	1352	1400	...
113	Taranto a.	0625	...	0733	...	0848	...	...	...	...	...	...	...	...	...	...	...	...	1305	...	...	...	1456	...

km																								
		⚒	⚒	⚒	⚒	⚒		⚒	⚒	⚒	⚒	⚒		⚒	⚒	⚒	⚒	⚒		⚒	⚒	⚒	⚒	⚒
	Bari Centrale d.	...	...	1321	...	1421	...	...	...	...	...	1521	...	...	1621	1721	...	1821	...	...	1921	...	2021	2051
	Bari Sud Est d.	...	...	1325	...	1425	...	...	...	...	...	1525	...	...	1625	1725	...	1825	...	...	1925	...	2025	2055
0	Mungivacca d.	...	...	1335	...	1435	...	...	...	...	...	1535	...	...	1635	1735	...	1835	...	...	1935	...	2035	2105
20	Casamassima d.	...	...	1408	...	1508	...	...	...	...	...	1608	...	...	1708	1808	...	1908	...	...	2008	...	2058	2138
44	Putignano a.	1349	...	1439	1515	1539	...	1555	...	1625	...	1639	...	1730	1739	1839	1855	1939	...	1955	2039	2101	2139	2209
	Martina Franca **2** d.	1450	1500	...	1619	...	...	1655	1705	1723	1755	...	...	1828	...	...	1958	...	...	2058	...	2200	...	...
	Taranto a.	...	1556	...	...	...	...	...	1801	...	1851	...	...	...	...	...	...	...	...	...	...	...	...	...

	⚒	⚒	⚒	⚒	⚒		⚒	⚒	⚒	⚒	⚒		⚒	⚒	⚒	⚒	⚒		⚒	⚒	⚒	⚒	⚒
Taranto d.	...	...	...	...	...	...	...	...	...	...	...	...	0635	...	...	0740	...	...	...	...	0855	...	...
Martina Franca **2** d.	...	0442	...	0511	...	...	...	0611	...	0708	...	...	0735	0820	...	0836	0947	...	...	...	0947	1146	...
Putignano d.	0518	0533	0554	0605	0613	...	0654	0704	0754	0816	0854	...	...	0910	0954	...	1037	...	1054	1154	...	1238	1254
Casamassima d.	0547	...	0628	...	0646	...	0728	...	0828	...	0928	...	...	...	1028	...	...	...	1128	1228	...	...	1328
Mungivacca d.	0634	...	0704	...	0734	...	0804	...	0904	...	1004	...	...	...	1104	...	...	...	1204	1304	...	...	1404
Bari Sud Est a.	0640	...	0710	...	0740	...	0810	...	0910	...	1010	...	...	...	1110	...	...	...	1210	1310	...	...	1410
Bari Centrale a.	0644	...	0714	...	0744	...	0814	...	0914	...	1014	...	...	...	1114	...	...	...	1214	1314	...	...	1414

	⚒	⚒	⚒	⚒	⚒		⚒	⚒	⚒	⚒	⚒		⚒	⚒	⚒	⚒	⚒		⚒	⚒	⚒	⚒	⚒
Taranto d.	...	...	...	...	...	...	...	...	...	1515	...	...	...	1602	...	...	...	...	...	1812	1900	...	...
Martina Franca **2** d.	1223	...	1325	1400	...	...	1456	...	...	1617	1625	...	...	1658	1735	...	1835	...	...	1912	1956	2005	2131
Putignano d.	1320	1354	1421	1451	1454	...	1549	1554	1654	...	1726	...	1754	...	1830	1854	1927	...	1954	...	...	2055	2228
Casamassima d.	...	1428	...	...	1528	...	...	1628	1728	...	...	...	1828	...	...	1928	...	...	2028	...	...	...	...
Mungivacca d.	...	1504	...	...	1604	...	...	1704	1804	...	...	...	1904	...	...	2004	...	...	2104	...	...	...	...
Bari Sud Est a.	...	1510	...	...	1610	...	...	1710	1810	...	...	...	1910	...	...	2010	...	...	2110	...	...	...	...
Bari Centrale a.	...	1514	...	...	1614	...	...	1714	1814	...	...	...	1914	...	...	2014	...	...	2114	...	...	...	...

Line 2 : MARTINA FRANCA - LECCE No service on †.

km																									
		⚒		⚒		⚒		⚒		⚒		⚒		⚒		⚒		⚒		⚒					
0	Martina Franca **1** d.	0457	...	0540	...	0713	...	0854	...	1155	...	1308	...	...	...	1519	...	1740	...	1833	...	...	...	...	...
41	Francavilla Fontana d.	0556	...	0646	...	0819	...	0954	...	1254	...	1408	...	1413	...	1621	...	1838	...	1934	...	...	...	...	...
92	Novoli **3** d.	0720	...	0809	...	0937	...	1133	...	1418	...	...	...	1537	...	1750	...	1957	...	2054	...	...	...	...	...
103	Lecce **5** a.	0737	...	0825	...	0952	...	1149	...	1434	...	...	...	1552	...	1805	...	2012	...	2110	...	...	...	...	...

	⚒		⚒		⚒		⚒		⚒		⚒		⚒		⚒		⚒		⚒				
Lecce **5** d.	0417	...	0551	...	0704	...	0905	...	1230	...	...	...	1347	...	1440	...	1655	...	1832	...	...	...	...
Novoli **3** d.	0433	...	0606	...	0719	...	0921	...	1246	...	...	...	1402	...	1455	...	1710	...	1848	...	...	...	...
Francavilla Fontana d.	0557	...	0730	...	0903	...	1047	...	1405	...	1411	...	1527	...	1620	...	1839	...	2017	...	...	...	...
Martina Franca **1** a.	0655	...	0835	...	1012	...	1152	...	...	...	1511	...	1637	...	1728	...	1955	...	2121	...	...	...	...

Line 3 : NOVOLI - GAGLIANO No service on †.

km												
		⚒	⚒	⚒	⚒	⚒		⚒	⚒	⚒	⚒	⚒
0	Lecce **5** d.	0520	...	0833	1007	1118	...	1305	1500	1611	1925	2035
11	Novoli **2** d.	0540	0726	0853	1027	1138	...	1325	1529	1631	1945	2101
36	Nardò Centrale **5** d.	0623	0813	0941	1110	1224	...	1409	1616	1718	2033	2150
60	Casarano **4** d.	0717	0856	1026	1157	1311	...	1451	1703	1803	2116	...
85	Gagliano Leuca **6** a.	0759	0937	1108	1239	1353	...	1532	1746	1855	2157	...

	⚒	⚒	⚒	⚒	⚒	⚒	⚒	⚒	⚒	⚒	
Gagliano Leuca **6** d.	...	0634	0811	0943	1114	1248	1406	1543	1752	1906	...
Casarano **4** d.	0554	0716	0857	1025	1156	1335	1452	1625	1834	1948	...
Nardò Centrale **5** d.	0636	0800	0940	1111	1238	1421	1535	1717	1917	2034	2155
Novoli **2** d.	0718	0848	1028	1200	1327	1515	1627	1811	2013	2123	2234
Lecce **5**	...	0903	1044	1216	1342	1532	1643	1826	2028	2139	2250

Line 4 : CASARANO - GALLIPOLI No service on †.

km												
		⚒	⚒		⚒	⚒		⚒	⚒		⚒	
0	Casarano **3** d.	0725	0920	...	1325	1455	...	1625	1755	...	1925	...
22	Gallipoli **5** a.	0801	0956	...	1401	1531	...	1701	1831	...	2001	...

	⚒	⚒		⚒	⚒		⚒	⚒		⚒	⚒
Gallipoli **5** d.	0510	0635	...	0810	1225	...	1410	1540	...	1710	1840
Casarano **3** a.	0546	0711	...	0846	1301	...	1446	1616	...	1746	1916

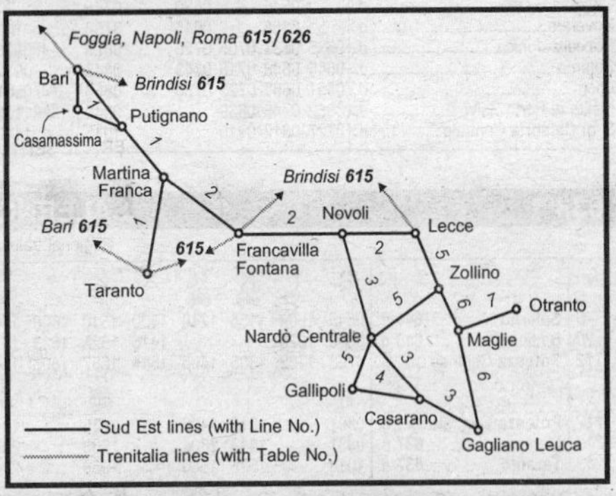

Foggia, Napoli, Roma **615/626**
Bari
Brindisi **615**
Putignano
Casamassima
Martina Franca
Brindisi **615**
Novoli
Lecce
Bari **615**
615
Francavilla Fontana
Zollino
Taranto
Otranto
Nardò Centrale
Maglie
Gallipoli
Casarano
Gagliano Leuca
Sud Est lines (with Line No.)
Trenitalia lines (with Table No.)

Line 5 : LECCE - GALLIPOLI No service on †.

km																									
		⚒	⚒		⚒	⚒		⚒	⚒		⚒	⚒		⚒	⚒		⚒	⚒		⚒					
0	Lecce **2** d.	0600	0700	...	0827	0931	...	1057	1254	...	1400	1433	...	1555	1702	...	1803	1925	...	2107	...	...	...	...	...
19	Zollino **6** d.	0635	0736	...	0907	1006	...	1137	1339	...	1439	1508	...	1642	1744	...	1844	2000	...	2142	...	...	...	...	...
36	Nardò Centrale **3** d.	0703	0810	...	0934	1041	...	1205	1408	...	1508	1536	...	1715	1820	...	1919	2037	...	2210	...	...	...	...	...
53	Gallipoli **4** a.	0732	0841	...	1004	1111	...	1234	1437	...	1537	1620	...	1755	1851	...	1948	2107	...	2239	...	...	...	...	...

	⚒	⚒		⚒	⚒		⚒	⚒		⚒	⚒		⚒	⚒		⚒	⚒		⚒				
Gallipoli **4** d.	0600	0630	...	0738	0900	...	1010	1130	...	1240	1334	...	1459	1543	...	1717	1813	...	2006	...	...	...	...	...
Nardò Centrale **3** d.	0631	0704	...	0809	0935	...	1040	1206	...	1310	1409	...	1537	1613	...	1747	1848	...	2036	...	...	...	...	...
Zollino **6** d.	0703	0737	...	0836	1007	...	1108	1234	...	1338	1438	...	1607	1641	...	1816	1931	...	2106	...	...	...	...	...
Lecce **2** a.	0743	0813	...	0916	1043	...	1143	1314	...	1420	1518	...	1642	1722	...	1851	2015	...	2152	...	...	...	...	...

Line 6 : ZOLLINO - GAGLIANO No service on †.

km																									
		⚒	⚒		⚒	⚒		⚒	⚒		⚒	⚒		⚒	⚒		⚒	⚒		⚒	⚒				
0	Lecce **2** d.	0530	0700	...	...	0855	...	0955	1057	...	...	1325	...	1400	...	...	1520	1725	...	1855	1955	...	...	...	...
19	Zollino **5** d.	0605	0735	...	0738	0935	...	1036	1136	...	1140	1405	...	1435	1451	...	1554	1809	...	1930	2030	...	...	...	...
29	Maglie **7** d.	0624	...	...	0757	0956	...	1054	...	...	1157	1434	...	...	1513	...	1613	1825	...	1949	2049	...	...	...	...
66	Gagliano Leuca **3** a.	0750	...	...	0907	1101	...	1202	...	...	1301	1541	...	...	1626	...	1722	1934	...	2100	2200	...	...	...	...

	⚒	⚒		⚒	⚒		⚒	⚒		⚒	⚒		⚒	⚒		⚒	⚒		⚒	⚒			
Gagliano Leuca **3** d.	0515	0607	...	...	0644	...	0827	...	...	0957	1122	...	1223	1308	...	...	1550	...	1730	1955	...	...	...	...
Maglie **7** d.	0625	0713	...	...	0758	...	0938	...	...	1113	1238	...	1337	1414	...	...	1652	...	1843	2110	...	...	...	...
Zollino **5** d.	0642	0731	...	0737	0815	...	0955	1007	...	1138	1256	...	1406	1433	...	1438	1708	...	1902	2142	...	...	...	...
Lecce **2** a.	0720	...	...	0813	0849	...	...	1043	...	1213	1345	...	1452	...	...	1518	1747	...	1946	2217	...	...	...	...

Line 7 : MAGLIE - OTRANTO No service on †.

km											
		⚒	⚒	⚒	⚒	⚒	⚒	⚒	⚒	⚒	⚒
0	Maglie **6** d.	0647	0801	1001	1202	1322	1437	1547	1657	1807	1917
18	Otranto a.	0716	0830	1030	1231	1351	1506	1616	1726	1836	1946

	⚒	⚒	⚒	⚒	⚒	⚒	⚒	⚒	⚒	⚒
Otranto d.	0722	0902	1036	1238	1358	1512	1622	1732	1842	1952
Maglie **6** a.	0751	0931	1105	1307	1427	1541	1651	1801	1911	2021

636 BARI - MATERA
2nd class FAL

km																											
		⚒	⚒	⚒	⚒		⚒	⚒	⚒	⚒		⚒	⚒	⚒	⚒		⚒	⚒	⚒	⚒		⚒	⚒	⚒	⚒		
0	**Bari** Centrale d.	0510	...	0616	0749	...	...	0957	1047	1132	...	1237	1339	1402	1446	...	1539	1653	1740	1806	...	1916	2001	2052	2126	...	...
48	Altamura a.	0619	...	0728	0859	...	...	1107	1159	1241	...	1346	1452	1510	1555	...	1652	1804	1851	1917	...	2028	2112	2202	2237	...	...
		⚒		⚒	⚒			⚒	⚒	⚒		⚒		⚒	⚒		⚒	⚒		⚒		⚒	⚒	⚒			
48	Altamura d.	0626	0703	0737	0913	...	1030	1116	1205	1243	...	1354	...	1511	1600	...	1658	1808	...	1924	...	2032	2116	2205	...	...	...
76	**Matera** Centrale a.	0655	0735	0806	0941	...	1058	1146	1236	1311	...	1425	...	1540	1631	...	1729	1836	...	1955	...	2103	2145	2235	...	...	...
		⚒	⚒	⚒	⚒		⚒	⚒	⚒	⚒		⚒	⚒	⚒	⚒		⚒	⚒	⚒	⚒		⚒	⚒	⚒	⚒		
	Matera Centrale d.	...	0555	0619	0706	...	...	0753	0832	...	...	1001	1109	1208	1320	...	1357	1527	1603	1718	...	1824	1920	2035	2132	...	...
	Altamura a.	...	0622	0650	0734	...	...	0822	0901	...	...	1028	1139	1237	1347	...	1428	1556	1633	1745	...	1854	1950	2104	2201	...	...
			⚒	⚒	⚒			⚒	⚒			⚒	⚒	⚒	⚒		⚒	⚒	⚒	⚒		⚒	⚒	⚒	⚒		
	Altamura d.	0602	0624	0654	0738	...	0805	0826	0903	0947	...	1031	1141	1242	1349	...	1432	1557	1635	1747	...	1900	1955	2113	2204	...	...
	Bari Centrale a.	0711	0731	0801	0847	...	0913	0933	1009	1057	...	1142	1249	1350	1458	...	1549	1705	1752	1901	...	2012	2105	2224	2312	...	...

Operator: Ferrovie Appulo Lucane. ✆ (+39) 800 050 500. www.ferrovieappulolucane.it

637 REGGIO DI CALABRIA - SIBARI - TARANTO
2nd class

km																											
									IC **564/5**								*IC* **562/3**										
		⚒	⚒	⚒		†	⚒			Ⓐ	†	⚒	Ⓑ	⚒	†			⚒	⚒	⚒	⚒	⚒		⚒	⚒	†	⚒
0	**R di Calabria** Centrale d.	...	...	0500	...	...	0545	0718	0735	...	0918	0918	1010	...	...	1155	1318	1408	...	1518	...	1620	1718	1802	1918	2006	2020
30	Melito di Porto Salvo d.	...	...	0524	...	...	0613	0745	0759	...	0943	0945	1042	...	...	1219	1343	1440	...	1543	...	1653	1743	1834	1944	2040	2044
96	Locri d.	...	...	0614	0635	...	0723	0835	0854	...	1035	1048	1153	1210	...	1317	1435	1551	...	1639	1709	1805	1837	1944	2039	2149	2146
101	Siderno d.	...	...	0619	0646	...	0729	0843	0901	...	1044	1054	1201	1216	...	1323	1442	1557	...	1645	1716	1810	1843	1950	2046	2155	2153
112	Roccella Jonica d.	...	...	0632	0658	...	0742	0856	0918	...	1056	1112	1215	1228	...	1340	1453	1610	...	1657	1727	1824	1858	2002	2102	2208	2207
160	Soverato d.	...	...	0714	0758	...	0827	0927	0959	...	1127	1147	...	1306	...	1425	1527	...	...	1730	1820	...	1930	...	2134	...	...
178	Catanzaro Lido a.	...	...	0731	0816	...	0842	0942	1011	...	1142	1201	...	1333	...	1439	1542	...	...	1745	1838	...	1945	...	2150	...	...
178	Catanzaro Lido d.	0515	0641	...	...	0848	...	...	1013	1054	...	*1230*	...	*1342*	1351	1441	*1555*	...	1715	...	*1900*	...	...	...	...	...	...
238	**Crotone** d.	0613	0730	...	...	0940	...	...	1110	1145	...	*1322*	...	*1436*	1439	1545	*1646*	...	1806	...	*1948*	...	...	...	...	...	...
325	Rossano d.	0733	0849	...	...	1054	...	...	1212	1303	...	*1432*	...	*1554*	1600	1704	*1801*	...	1923	...	*2103*	...	...	...	...	...	...
336	Corigliano Calabro d.	0741	0858	...	...	1109	...	...	1223	1319	...	*1447*	...	*1603*	1608	1717	*1815*	...	1936	...	*2112*	...	...	...	...	...	...
351	**Sibari** a.	0755	0910	...	...	1125	...	...	1239	1333	...	*1458*	...	*1615*	1620	1730	*1829*	...	1950	...	*2125*	...	...	...	...	...	...
351	**Sibari** d.	...	...	...	...	...	...	...	1242	...	...	...	...	...	...	1732	...	...	...	...	...	...	...	...	...	...	...
366	Trebisacce d.	...	...	...	...	...	...	...	1255	...	...	...	...	...	...	1744	...	...	...	...	...	...	...	...	...	...	...
430	Metaponto **638** d.	...	...	...	...	...	...	...	1339	...	...	...	...	...	...	1835	...	...	...	...	...	...	...	...	...	...	...
473	**Taranto** **638** a.	...	...	...	...	...	...	...	1410	...	...	...	...	...	...	1908	...	...	...	...	...	...	...	...	...	...	...

												IC **558/9**						*IC* **566/7**							
	⚒	⚒		⚒	⚒		⚒	⚒			⚒	⚒			Ⓐ	⚒		⚒		⚒	†	⚒	⚒	Ⓐ	†	
Taranto **638** d.	...	...	...	...	...	...	...	...	...	...	...	...	0923	...	...	...	...	...	1307	...	...	...	...	...	...	...
Metaponto **638** d.	...	...	...	...	...	...	...	...	...	...	...	...	0958	...	...	...	...	...	1339	...	...	...	...	...	...	...
Trebisacce d.	...	...	...	...	...	...	...	...	...	...	...	...	1040	...	...	...	...	...	1423	...	...	...	...	...	...	...
Sibari a.	...	...	...	...	...	...	...	...	...	...	...	...	1052	...	...	...	...	...	1432	...	...	...	...	...	...	...
Sibari d.	...	...	...	...	0505	...	0620	...	...	0726	...	...	1054	...	...	*1305*	...	...	1434	*1502*	*1538*	1617	*1703*	1758	1920	2241
Corigliano Calabro d.	...	...	...	...	0516	...	0630	...	...	0742	...	...	1108	...	...	*1318*	...	...	1446	*1513*	*1550*	1629	*1715*	1814	1935	2254
Rossano d.	...	...	...	...	0525	...	0638	...	...	0750	...	...	1118	...	...	*1326*	...	...	1456	*1521*	*1559*	1637	*1723*	1824	1944	2302
Crotone d.	...	...	...	...	0642	...	0752	...	...	0859	...	...	1226	...	...	*1453*	...	...	1606	*1645*	*1718*	1708	*1848*	1950	2104	2358
Catanzaro Lido a.	...	...	...	...	0730	...	0845	...	...	0945	...	...	1314	...	...	*1538*	...	...	1710	*1735*	*1800*	1850	*1941*	2045	2155	...
Catanzaro Lido d.	...	0545	...	0630	...	0745	...	...	0944	...	1015	...	1316	1344	...	1555	...	1654	1712	1805	1810	...	2010	...	...	...
Soverato d.	...	0558	...	0645	...	0758	...	...	0958	...	1033	...	1331	1357	...	1609	...	1713	1731	1819	1823	...	2026	...	...	...
Roccella Jonica d.	0535	0634	0705	0726	...	0829	...	0920	1028	...	1111	1320	1414	1429	1505	1642	1659	1805	1825	1858	1900	...	2104	...	...	...
Siderno d.	0546	0646	0716	0743	...	0843	...	0932	1039	...	1124	1337	1426	1443	1518	1657	1717	1822	1843	1912	1914	...	2116	...	...	...
Locri d.	0551	0651	0725	0750	...	0853	...	0937	1048	...	1131	1342	1434	1449	1524	1702	1725	1827	1852	1919	1920	...	2122	...	...	...
Melito di Porto Salvo d.	0652	0745	0839	...	...	0940	...	1105	1140	...	...	1504	1522	1540	1640	1805	1856	...	1941	2020	2018	...	2221	...	...	...
R di Calabria Centrale a.	0727	0812	0915	...	...	1015	...	1140	1210	...	...	1535	1550	1610	1715	1835	1930	...	2005	2046	2045	...	2255	...	...	...

638 SALERNO - POTENZA - TARANTO

Regional trains. For long-distance trains see Table **640**.

km											
		⚒	†	⚒ 🚌	⚒ 🚌	⚒	⚒		A	⚒	†
0	**Salerno** **640** d.	0545	1009	1135	1240	1400	1510	1608	1703	1954	2008
20	Battipaglia **640** d.	0600	1025	|	|	1415	1525	1623	1717	2010	2022
112	**Potenza** Centrale a.	0753	1202	1305	1405	1544	1657	1806	1846	2139	2153
		◧		|	⚒		⚒ 🚌		|		
112	**Potenza** Centrale d.	0801	...	1310	1428	...	1735	...	1848	...	...
219	Metaponto **637** d.	0931	...	1443	1604	...	1908	...	2007	...	...
263	**Taranto** **637** a.	1013	...	1523	1640	...	1950	...	2045	...	...

	⚒	†	⚒ 🚌	A	⚒	⚒ 🚌	⚒ 🚌	⚒	†	
Taranto **637** d.	...	...	0535	1010	1101	...	1230	...	...	1823
Metaponto **637** d.	...	...	0615	1047	1136	...	1310	...	...	1903
Potenza Centrale a.	...	...	0748	1215	1315	...	1445	...	...	2048
			|	|	◧		⚒			
Potenza Centrale d.	0625	0658	0800	1217	1325	1420	1729	1858	1928	...
Battipaglia **640** d.	0804	0845	|	1345	1502	1541	1913	2028	2115	...
Salerno **640** a.	0821	0903	0930	1358	1520	1620	1930	2045	2134	...

A – To/from Napoli Centrale (Table **640**).

◧ – Runs daily.

639 NAPOLI - SORRENTO, BAIANO and SARNO
2nd class Circumvesuviana Ferrovia

km																											
				A																							
	Napoli Porta Nolana d.	0648	0800	0818	0906	1018	1106	1154	1218	1242	1306	1336	1354	1418	1442	1512	1554	1618	1706	1736	1818	1906	1930	1954	2018	2042	2130
0	**Napoli** P. Garibaldi d.	0650	0802	0821	0909	1021	1109	1157	1221	1245	1309	1338	1357	1421	1445	1514	1557	1621	1709	1738	1821	1909	1933	1957	2021	2045	2133
10	Ercolano Scavi d.	0704	0816	0837	0925	1037	1125	1213	1237	1301	1325	1352	1413	1437	1501	1528	1613	1637	1725	1752	1837	1925	1949	2013	2037	2101	2149
23	Pompei S. Villa Misteri d.	0723	0835	0859	0947	1059	1147	1235	1259	1347	1347	1411	1435	1459	1523	1547	1635	1659	1747	1811	1859	1947	2011	2035	2059	2123	2211
29	Castellammare d.	0736	0848	0912	1000	1112	1200	1248	1312	1400	1400	1424	1448	1512	1536	1600	1648	1712	1800	1824	1912	2000	2024	2048	2112	2136	2224
42	**Sorrento** a.	0758	0910	0934	1022	1134	1222	1310	1334	1422	1422	1446	1510	1534	1558	1622	1710	1734	1822	1846	1934	2022	2046	2110	2134	2158	2246
		B																									
	Sorrento d.	0712	0800	0848	0936	1000	1048	1112	1136	1248	1336	1400	1448	1512	1536	1600	1624	1648	1736	1800	1824	1912	2000	2024	2048	2112	2136
	Castellammare d.	0735	0823	0911	0959	1023	1111	1135	1159	1311	1359	1423	1511	1535	1559	1623	1647	1711	1759	1823	1847	1935	2023	2047	2111	2135	2159
	Pompei S. Villa Misteri d.	0748	0836	0924	1012	1036	1124	1148	1212	1324	1412	1436	1524	1548	1612	1636	1700	1724	1812	1836	1900	1948	2036	2100	2124	2148	2212
	Ercolano Scavi d.	0809	0855	0943	1031	1057	1145	1207	1233	1343	1433	1455	1545	1609	1631	1657	1721	1745	1833	1855	1921	2007	2057	2121	2145	2209	2233
	Napoli P. Garibaldi a.	0826	0908	0956	1044	1114	1202	1220	1250	1356	1450	1508	1602	1626	1644	1714	1738	1802	1850	1908	1938	2020	2114	2138	2202	2226	2250
	Napoli Porta Nolana a.	0827	0910	0958	1046	1115	1203	1222	1251	1358	1451	1510	1603	1627	1646	1715	1739	1803	1851	1910	1939	2022	2115	2139	2203	2227	2251

NAPOLI - BAIANO and v.v. Journey 60 minutes.

From **Napoli** Porta Nolana*: 0626, 0650 ⚒, 0714, 0802, 0850, 0938, 1026, 1114, 1202, 1226, 1250, 1338, 1402, 1426, 1514, 1602, 1714 ⚒, 1738, 1826, 1850, 1914 ⚒, 1938.

From **Baiano**: 0608, 0632 ⚒, 0656, 0720 ⚒, 0744, 0808, 0832 ⚒, 0856, 0944, 1032, 1120, 1208, 1256, 1344, 1408, 1432, 1520, 1544, 1608, 1656, 1744, 1920, 2008.

NAPOLI - SARNO and v.v. Journey 65 minutes. All services call at Poggiomarino (52 minutes from Napoli, 14 minutes from Sarno).

From **Napoli** Porta Nolana*: 0628, 0652 ⚒, 0716, 0740, 0828, 0916, 1052, 1140, 1204 ⚒, 1228, 1316 ⚒, 1404, 1452, 1540, 1628, 1716, 1740 ⚒, 1804, 1828, 1852, 1940, 2004 **p**.

From **Sarno**: 0610, 0634 ⚒, 0658, 0722, 0810, 0834 ⚒, 0858, 0922, 1010, 1058, 1234, 1322, 1346 ⚒, 1410, 1458 ⚒, 1546, 1634, 1722, 1810, 1858, 1946, 2012.

A – Also at 0554, 0618, 0706, 0730, 0930, 1042.
B – Also at 0600, 0624, 0824, 0912, 1224, 1424.
p – To/from Poggiomarino only.
* – Trains call at Napoli Porta Garibaldi 2 – 3 minutes later.

Operator: Circumvesuviana Ferrovia. www.eavsrl.it.

SITA operates 🚌 services operate along the Amalfi Coast between Sorrento and Salerno. Change of buses at Amalfi is necessary. (www.sitasudtrasporti.it).

🍷 on all *FA*, *FR* and *ITA* services.

ROMA - NAPOLI - TARANTO and REGGIO DI CALABRIA 640

Subject to alteration until March 13.

km		*ICN* 1963	*ICN* 1965	*ICN* 799	*ICN* 797	*ITA* 8193	*IC* 701	*FR* 9501	*IC* 721	*IC* 723	*ITA* 9903	*FA* 8333	🚌	*IC* 551	*FA* 8863	*IC* 501	*ITA* 8113	*IC* 727	*IC* 729	*IC* 553	*FR* 9583	*IC* 583	2	*IC* 1589
								①–⑥					⚒											⑥
		❖	❖	❖	❖											A								
	Torino Porta Nuova **600 610** d.	...	...	2155	2030	...	...	...	...	...	...	...	...	...	...	...	...	...	...	...	0800	...	...	...
	Milano Centrale **600 620** d.	2010	2010	|	2213g	...	...	...	...	...	...	...	...	...	...	...	0640	...	...	...	0910	0650	...	0655
	Bologna Centrale **600 620** d.	|	|	|	|	...	...	...	...	...	...	...	...	...	...	...	0757	...	...	...	1027	0918	...	0937
0	**Roma** Termini **600** d.	|	|	0546o	0558t	0600	0626	0700	0726	0726	0740	0858	...	0926	1010	1018o	1030	1126	1126	1226	1300	1329t	...	1346t
62	Latina d.	|	|	0637	|	|	0700	|	0800	0800	|	|	...	1000	|	1057	|	1200	1200	1300	|	1400	...	1428
129	Formia-Gaeta d.	|	|	0717	|	|	0735	|	0835	0835	|	|	...	1035	|	1134	|	1235	1235	1335	|	1435	...	1507
195	Aversa d.	|	|	0758	|	|	0811	|	0911	0911	|	|	...	1111	|	1209	|	1311	1311	1411	|	1511	...	1545
	Napoli Afragola **600** a.	|	|	|	|	|	|	0756s	|	|	0839	0959	...	|	1113	|	|	|	|	|	1356	|	...	|
	Napoli Afragola **600** d.	|	|	|	|	|	|	0758s	|	|	0841	1001	...	|	1115	|	|	|	|	|	1358	|	...	|
214	**Napoli** Centrale **600** a.	|	|	0817	0846	0712	0829	0812	0929	0929	0854	|	...	1129	|	1229	1143	1329	1329	1429	1413	1529	...	1609
214	**Napoli** Centrale **600** d.	|	|	0835	0905	0725	0845	...	0950	0950	...	|	...	1145	|	...	1200	1345	1345	1445	1425	...	1614	1630
268	**Salerno** **600** a.	0613	0613	0911	0945	0802	0923	...	1037	1037	...	1028	...	1219	1141	...	1242	1421	1421	1524	1504	...	1658	1715
268	**Salerno** **638** d.	0616	0616	...	...	0805	0925	...	1039	1039	...	1031	1135	1222	1144	...	1245	1424	1424	1526	1507	...	1703	1718
288	Battipaglia **638** d.	0630	0630	...	...	|	0939	...	|	|	...	|	|	1235	1156	...	|	|	|	1538	|	...	1717	|
380	Potenza Centrale **638** d.	|	|	...	...	|	1102	...	|	|	...	|	1310	|	|	...	|	|	|	|	|	...	1848	|
487	Metaponto **638** d.	|	|	...	...	|	1223	...	|	|	...	|	1443	|	|	...	|	|	|	|	|	...	2007	|
531	**Taranto** **638** a.	|	|	...	...	|	1255	...	|	|	...	|	1523	|	|	...	|	|	|	|	|	...	2045	|
318	Agropoli-Castellabate d.	0650	0650	...	...	0830	...	...	|	|	...	|	...	1255	1211	...	1310	|	|	1606	|	...	...	|
395	Sapri d.	0745	0745	...	...	0916	...	...	1147	1147	...	|	...	1344	1255	...	1355	1533	1533	1709	|	...	...	1836
489	Paola d.	0846	0846	...	...	1003	...	...	1234	1234	...	1225	...	1458	1348	...	1445	1630	1630	1808	1702	...	...	1929
546	**Lamezia Terme** Centrale a.	0929	0929	...	...	1030	...	...	1300	1300	...	1252	...	1528	1418	...	1512	1656	1656	1839	1728	...	...	2004
546	**Lamezia Terme** Centrale d.	0932	0932	...	...	1033	...	...	1302	1302	...	1304	...	1530	1421	...	1515	1659	1659	1842	1730	...	...	2007
606	Rosarno d.	1006	1000	...	...	1107	...	...	|	|	...	1323	...	1701	1457	...	1551	|	|	1915	1758	...	...	2142
616	Gioia Tauro d.	1014	1014	...	...	|	...	...	1341	1341	...	|	...	1710	1505	...	|	1735	1735	1923	|	...	...	2151
652	Villa S. Giovanni a.	1040	1040	...	...	1135	...	...	1410	1410	...	1350	...	1734	1530	...	1619	1805	1805	1947	1828	...	...	2214
652	Villa S. Giovanni d.	1105	1105	...	...	1138	...	...	1430	1430	...	1353	...	1737	1533	...	1622	1825	1825	1950	1830	...	...	2217
667	**Reggio di Calabria** Centrale a.	|	|	...	...	1200	...	...	|	|	...	1406	...	1754	1548	...	1639	|	|	2007	1848	...	...	2235
	Siracusa **641** a.	1548	|	...	...	...	...	...	1833	|	...	...	...	...	...	...	...	2253	|	...	...	...	...	...
	Palermo Centrale **641** a.	...	1655	...	...	...	...	...	...	1925	...	...	...	...	...	...	...	...	2305	...	...	...	...	...

	FA 8867	*IC* 555	*FR* 9587	*IC* 707	*IC* 561	*FR* 8419	*IC* 591	*FR* 9639	*FA* 8519	*IC* 511	*ITA* 8143	*FR* 9547	*FR* 9551	*ICN* 1955	*ICN* 1957	*IC* 597	*ICN* 1955	*ICN* 1957	*ICN* 1955	*ICN* 1957	*ICN* 1959	*ICN* 1961	*ICN* 795
														①–④	①–④		⑤	⑤	⑥⑦	⑥⑦			
						B			C					❖	❖		❖	❖	❖	❖	❖	❖	❖
Torino Porta Nuova **600 610** d.	...	...	1000	...	...	...	...	...	...	1040	1320	...	...	...	...	...	...	...	...	...	...	...	1335
Milano Centrale **600 620** d.	...	...	1110	...	...	...	...	1430	...	|	1440	1510	1610	...	...	1448	...	...	...	...	...	...	1535g
Bologna Centrale **600 620** d.	...	...	1227	...	...	1402	...	1537	1547	|	1557	1627	1727	...	...	1718	...	...	...	...	...	...	1818
Roma Termini **600** d.	1405	1426	1500	1526	1626	1635	1726	1753	1820	1826	1830	1900	2000	2031	2031	2126t	2106	2106	2131	2131	2300	2300	2324t
Latina d.	|	1500	|	1557	1700	|	1800	|	|	1900	|	|	|	2107	2107	2200	2140	2140	2207	2207	|	|	|
Formia-Gaeta d.	|	1535	|	1635	1735	|	1835	|	|	1935	|	|	|	2144	2144	2235	2220	2220	2244	2244	|	|	|
Aversa d.	|	1611	|	1711	1811	|	1911	|	|	2011	|	|	|	|	|	2319	|	|	|	|	|	|	|
Napoli Afragola **600** a.	1507	|	1556	|	|	1736	|	1848	1921	|	1928	1956	2056	|	|	|	|	|	|	|	|	|	|
Napoli Afragola **600** d.	1509	|	1558	|	|	1738	|	1850	1923	|	1930	1958	2058	|	|	|	|	|	|	|	|	|	|
Napoli Centrale **600** a.	|	1629	1612	1729	1829	|	1929	|	|	2029	|	2010	2113	2308	2308	2359	2350	0006	0006	0006	|	|	|
Napoli Centrale **600** d.	|	1645	1625	1745	1855	|	1945	|	|	2045	|	2020	2125	2324	2324	...	0006	0022	0022	0022	|	|	|
Salerno **600** a.	1538	1726	1706	1823	1932	1809	2030	1919	1948	2124	2011	2057	2205	0001	0001	...	0053	0053	0053	0053	|	|	0227
Salerno **638** d.	1541	1729	1709	1826	1934	1811	...	1921	1950	...	2014	2059	2211	0004	0004	...	0055	0055	0055	0055	|	|	0231
Battipaglia **638** d.	1553	1743	|	1840	1948	|	...	|	|	...	|	|	2225	|	|	...	|	|	|	|	|	|	|
Potenza Centrale **638** d.	|	|	|	2008	|	|	...	|	|	...	|	2224	...	|	|	...	|	|	|	|	|	|	|
Metaponto **638** d.	|	|	|	2128	|	|	...	|	|	...	|	2338	...	|	|	...	|	|	|	|	|	|	|
Taranto **638** a.	|	|	|	2200	|	|	...	|	|	...	|	0007	...	|	|	...	|	|	|	|	|	|	|
Agropoli-Castellabate d.	|	1806	1736	...	|	|	...	|	|	...	2040	...	...	|	|	...	|	|	|	|	|	|	|
Sapri d.	1649	1906	1823	...	2102	|	...	|	|	...	2125	...	...	|	|	...	|	|	|	|	|	|	0353
Paola d.	1736	2014	1917	...	2202	1955	...	2115	2140	...	2218	...	...	|	|	...	|	|	|	|	|	|	0451
Lamezia Terme Centrale a.	1804	2044	1945	...	2233	2021	...	2142	...	...	2244	...	...	|	|	...	|	|	|	|	0459	0459	0530
Lamezia Terme Centrale d.	1807	2047	1948	...	2236	2024	...	2145	...	...	2247	...	...	|	|	...	|	|	|	|	0502	0502	0533
Rosarno d.	1838	2122	2020	...	2308	2054	...	2215	...	...	2317	...	...	|	|	...	|	|	|	|	|	|	0652
Gioia Tauro d.	1846	2130	|	...	2316	|	...	|	...	...	|	...	...	|	|	...	|	|	|	|	|	|	0701
Villa S. Giovanni a.	1910	2154	2051	...	2338	2122	...	2244	...	...	2346	...	...	0330	0330	...	0425	0425	0425	0425	0610	0610	0731
Villa S. Giovanni d.	1913	2157	2054	...	2341	2125	...	2247	...	...	2349	...	...	0350	0350	...	0445	0445	0445	0445	0635	0635	0734
Reggio di Calabria Centrale a.	1928	2214	2110	...	2357	2140	...	2305	...	...	0003	...	...	|	|	...	|	|	|	|	|	|	0757
Siracusa **641** a.	...	...	...	...	...	...	...	...	...	...	...	...	...	0857	|	...	0936	|	0936	|	1129	|	...
Palermo Centrale **641** a.	...	...	...	...	...	...	...	...	...	...	...	...	...	...	0924	...	...	1007	...	1007	...	1157	...

REGIONAL TRAINS

2nd class

km																							
			⚒	†	⚒	†	⚒	†	⚒	†	Ⓐ	⑥	⚒	†	⚒	†	⚒	†	⚒	†	⚒		⚒
0	**Roma** Termini d.	0531	0656	0736	0736	1036	1036	1136	1156	1238	1256	1256	1453	1536	1556	1636	1656	1736	1756	1836	1856	1956	2056
62	Latina d.	0608	0731	0818	0818	1118	1118	1218	1233	1323	1331	1331	1530	1618	1631	1718	1731	1818	1832	1918	1931	2032	2128
129	Formia-Gaeta d.	0657	0821	0906	0912	1207	1212	1311	1321	1413	1421	1421	1610	1707	1721	1807	1821	1907	1921	2007	2021	2110	2215
195	Aversa d.	0750	0914	1006	1013	1302	1314	1402	1414	1507	1514	|	|	1806	1814	1902	1914	2006	2014	2102	2114	|	|
216	**Caserta** **626** d.	|	|	|	|	|	|	|	|	|	|	1515	1716	|	|	|	|	|	|	|	|	2208	2323
214	**Napoli** Centrale **626** a.	0812	0950	1038	1036	1323	1340	1423	1440	1535	1548	1551	...	1843	1840	1923	1940	2043	2040	2123	2140	2252	2355

km																							
				Ⓐ	Ⓒ					⚒	†				Ⓐ	⚒	Ⓐ	⚒					Ⓑ
0	**Napoli** Centrale **638** d.	...	0540	0650	0650	0735	0750	...	0850	...	1150	1250	...	1350	...	1514	...	...	1714	1814	1914	2025	2116
54	Salerno **638** d.	0551	0637	0733	0733	0818	0833	...	0933	...	1232	1333	...	1433	...	1601	...	...	1803	1903	2003	2108	2203
74	Battipaglia **638** d.	0610	0652	0749	0749	0835	0849	...	0947	...	1247	1348	...	1448	...	1616	...	...	1827	1918	2017	2126	2221
104	Agropoli-Castellabate d.	0632	0715	0810	0810	0857	0911	...	1009	...	1317	1410	...	1510	...	1639	...	...	1850	1946	2046	2150	2241
135	Ascea d.	0656	0741	0834	0834	0921	0935	...	1033	...	1341	1434	...	1538	...	1705	...	...	1914	2011	2110	2214	2303
181	Sapri d.	0737	0825	0907	0907	1002	1020	1040	1109	1240	1422	1510	...	1625	1631	1745	1810	1852	1954	2049	2146	2249	2340
193	Maratea d.	0746	...	0916	0916	...	...	1052	1119	1252	1432	1520	...	...	1642	...	1820	1902	...	...	2156	...	...
241	Belvedere Marittimo d.	0831	...	0957	0957	...	...	1132	1154	1338	1509	1556	...	...	1729	...	1905	1943	...	...	2227	...	...
275	Paola **633** d.	0905	...	1024	1026	...	...	1200	1219	1407	1539	1627	...	...	1800	...	1935	2020	...	...	2256	...	...
301	**Cosenza** **633** a.	...	...	...	1049	...	...	...	1242	1430	...	1649	...	...	...	...	...	...	...	...	2318	...	...

km																							
		⚒	⚒		⚒	⚒					Ⓐ			⚒	⚒		Ⓐ	⚒		Ⓐ	†		
0	**Cosenza** **633** d.	...	...	...	...	0536	...	0626	1002	...	1236	1336	...	1436	1635	...	1758	1736	...	1823	1835	...	...
26	Paola **633** d.	...	...	...	0513	0609	...	0704	1033	...	1309	1409	...	1509	1707	...	|	1816	...	1855	1908	...	...
83	**Lamezia Terme** Centrale d.	0505	0540	...	0555	0651	...	0744	1117	...	1350	1456	...	1600	1749	...	1859	1905	...	1940	1949	...	...
143	Rosarno d.	0634	0612	...	0629	0721	...	0820	1149	...	1420	1526	...	1634	1823	...	1931	1937	...	2012	2021	...	...
153	Gioia Tauro d.	0643	0620	...	0636	0728	...	0827	1157	...	1427	1533	...	1641	1830	...	1938	1944	...	2021	2037	...	...
189	Villa S. Giovanni d.	0717	0654	...	0707	0801	...	0902	1229	...	1502	1607	...	1713	1904	...	2006	2015	...	2054	2111	...	...
204	**Reggio di Calabria** Centrale a.	0745	0712	...	0732	0819	...	0919	1246	...	1519	1624	...	1731	1921	...	2025	2033	...	2110	2127	...	...

A – [12] Sestri Levante - Napoli and v.v.
B – [12] 🍷 Venezia - Reggio di Calabria and v.v.
C – [12] 🍷 Bolzano - Sibari (a. 2231 / d. 0627) and v.v.

g – Milano Porta Garibaldi.
o – Roma Ostiense.
s – Calls to set down only.
t – Roma Tiburtina.

❖ – 1, 2 cl., 2 cl. (4 berth). Running days, timings and numbers of *ICN* trains may vary - please check your reservation. For confirmed timings please consult the *Trenitalia* journey planner at www.trenitalia.com.

640 REGGIO DI CALABRIA and TARANTO - NAPOLI - ROMA

🍸 on all *FA*, *FR* and *ITA* services

Subject to alteration until March 13.

	IC 582	*FR* 9516	*IC* 510	*FR* 9514	*FA* 8509	*FR* 8418	*IC* 590	*IC* 550	*FR* 9584	*ITA* 8134		*IC* 700	*IC* 552	*FA* 8862	*IC* 596	*IC* 1588	*FR* 9588	2	*IC* 556	*IC* 728	*IC* 722	*FR* 9658
					C	B										⑦						
Palermo Centrale **641** d.	...	...	...	...	...	...	...	...	...	...	...	...	...	...	...	...	...	...	...	0650	...	...
Siracusa **641** d.	...	...	...	...	...	...	...	...	...	...	...	...	...	...	...	...	...	...	...	|	0732	...
Reggio di Calabria Centrale d.	...	...	...	...	...	0612	...	0617	0644	0724	...	...	0756	0900	...	0847	1011	...	1000	|	|	1230
Villa S. Giovanni a.	...	...	...	...	...	0627	...	0635	0658	0739	...	...	0811	0914	...	0903	1026	...	1016	1120	1120	1244
Villa S. Giovanni d.	...	...	...	...	...	0630	...	0637	0701	0742	...	...	0813	0917	...	0905	1029	...	1018	1150	1150	1247
Gioia Tauro d.	...	...	...	...	...	|	...	0701	|	|	...	...	0836	0943	...	0930	|	...	1052	1217	1217	|
Rosarno d.	...	...	...	...	...	0657	...	0709	0730	0814	...	...	0844	0952	...	0942	1059	...	1105	|	|	1317
Lamezia Terme Centrale a.	...	...	...	...	...	0730	...	0741	0802	0848	...	...	0919	1022	...	1101	1129	...	1138	1251	1251	1349
Lamezia Terme Centrale d.	...	...	...	...	...	0733	...	0744	0805	0850	...	...	0922	1025	...	1103	1132	...	1141	1254	1254	1352
Paola d.	...	...	...	...	0723	0804	...	0817	0835	0922	...	...	0958	1057	...	1135	1201	...	1214	1333	1333	1423
Sapri d.	...	...	...	...	|	|	...	0916	0934	1010	...	...	1058	1143	...	1227	|	...	1310	1422	1422	|
Agropoli-Castellabate d.	...	...	...	...	|	|	...	|	1023	1055	...	...	1144	|	...	|	|	...	1404	|	|	|
Taranto **638** d.	...	...	...	0527	|	|	...	|	|	|	...	0801	|	|	...	|	|	1010	|	|	|	|
Metaponto **638** d.	...	...	...	0600	|	|	...	|	|	|	...	0835	|	|	...	|	|	1047	|	|	|	|
Potenza Centrale **638** d.	...	...	...	0717	|	|	...	|	|	|	...	0956	|	|	...	|	|	1217	|	|	|	|
Battipaglia **638** d.	...	0530	...	|	|	|	...	1020	|	|	...	1127	1208	1244	...	|	|	1345	1424	|	|	|
Salerno **638** a.	...	0545	...	0844	0910	0951	...	1034	1048	1119	...	1138	1220	1256	...	1334	1351	1358	1434	1534	1534	1614
Salerno **600** d.	0528	0550	0626	0846	0913	0954	...	1037	1051	1122	...	1140	1223	1258	...	1337	1354	1401	1437	1537	1537	1617
Napoli Centrale **600** a.	0606	0628	0705	0928	|	|	...	1117	1127	1158	...	1217	1305	|	...	1418	1428	1438	1517	1617	1617	|
Napoli Centrale **600** d.	0631	0640	0731	0940	|	|	1031	1131	1140	1215	...	1231	1331	|	1420	1446	1440	...	1531	1631	1631	|
Napoli Afragola **600** a.	|	0656	|	0956	0939	1018	|	|	1156	1228	...	|	|	1322	|	|	1456	...	|	|	|	1639
Napoli Afragola **600** d.	|	0658	|	0958	0941	1020	|	|	1158	1230	...	|	|	1324	|	|	1458	...	|	|	|	1641
Aversa d.	0648	|	0749	|	|	|	1049	1149	|	|	...	1249	1349	|	1438	1506	|	...	1549	1649	1649	|
Formia-Gaeta d.	0722	|	0822	|	|	|	1122	1222	|	|	...	1322	1422	|	1513	1545	|	...	1622	1722	1722	|
Latina d.	0800	|	0900	|	|	|	1200	1300	|	|	...	1400	1500	|	1551	1625	|	...	1700	1800	1800	|
Roma Termini **600** a.	0834	0755	0934	1055	1040	1125	1237**t**	1332	1300	1330	...	1434	1534	1425	1633**t**	1705**t**	1555	...	1734	1834	1834	1740
Bologna Centrale **600 620** a.	...	1033	|	1333	1313	1358	1642	...	1533	1603	...	...	...	...	2042	2130	1833	...	...	...	...	1953
Milano Centrale **600 620** a.	...	1150	|	1450	...	...	1917	...	1650	1720	...	...	...	...	2317	0015	1950	...	...	...	...	2100
Torino Porta Nuova **600 610** a.	...	1300	1740	1600	...	...	...	...	1800	1835	...	...	...	...	...	...	2100	...	...	...	...	...

	🚌 ⚒	*IC* 522	*ITA* 8158	*IC* 702	*FA* 8868	*IC* 730	*IC* 724	*IC* 560	*FA* 8332	*ICN* 798		*ICN* 796	*ICN* 796	*ICN* 796	*ITA* 8192	*ICN* 1964	*ICN* 1962	*ICN* 794	*ICN* 1954	*ICN* 1956	*ICN* 1958	*ICN* 1960
		A								❖		⑥⑦ ❖	①② ❖	③–⑤ ❖		❖	❖	①–⑤ ❖	❖	❖	❖	❖
Palermo Centrale **641** d.	...	...	...	...	...	1000	...	...	...	...	...	...	...	...	...	1235	...	...	1848	...	2055	...
Siracusa **641** d.	...	...	...	...	...	|	1010	...	...	...	...	...	...	...	...	|	1335	...	|	1910	|	2145
Reggio di Calabria Centrale d.	...	...	1328	...	1347	|	|	1510	1520	...	...	...	...	...	1734	|	|	2143	|	|	|	|
Villa S. Giovanni a.	...	...	1344	...	1403	1403	1420	1525	1535	...	...	...	...	...	1750	1815	1815	2200	2335	2335	|	|
Villa S. Giovanni d.	...	...	1347	...	1406	1406	1450	1528	1538	...	...	...	...	...	1753	1845	1845	2203	0005	0005	|	|
Gioia Tauro d.	...	...	|	...	1431	1431	1515	1601	|	...	...	...	...	...	|	1914	1914	2237	|	|	|	|
Rosarno d.	...	...	1416	...	1440	1440	|	1611	1606	...	...	...	...	...	1821	1922	1922	2247	|	|	|	|
Lamezia Terme Centrale a.	...	...	1448	...	1513	1513	1559	1642	1631	...	...	...	...	...	1854	1957	1957	0007	0105	0105	|	|
Lamezia Terme Centrale d.	...	...	1450	...	1516	1516	1601	1644	1634	...	...	...	...	...	1856	2000	2000	0010	0108	0108	|	|
Paola d.	...	...	1521	...	1547	1547	1639	1717	1705	...	...	...	...	...	1927	2052	2052	0054	|	|	|	|
Sapri d.	...	...	1610	...	1635	1635	1729	1812	|	...	...	...	...	...	2013	2156	2156	0153	|	|	|	|
Agropoli-Castellabate d.	...	...	1655	...	|	|	|	1901	|	...	...	...	...	...	2058	2254	2254	|	|	|	|	|
Taranto **638** d.	1230	...	|	1356	|	|	|	|	|	...	...	...	...	...	|	|	|	|	|	|	|	|
Metaponto **638** d.	1310	...	|	1430	|	|	|	|	|	...	...	...	...	...	|	|	|	|	|	|	|	|
Potenza Centrale **638** d.	1450	...	|	1548	|	|	|	|	|	...	...	...	...	...	|	|	|	|	|	|	|	|
Battipaglia **638** d.	|	...	|	1717	1731	1731	|	1922	|	...	...	...	...	...	|	2315	2315	|	|	|	|	|
Salerno **638** a.	|	...	1719	1730	1743	1743	1837	1934	1852	...	...	...	...	...	2125	2330	2330	0307	|	|	0642	0642
Salerno **600** d.	|	...	1722	1733	1745	1745	1839	1937	1854	2038	...	2052	2052	2052	2128	2333	2333	0310	|	|	0645	0645
Napoli Centrale **600** a.	1700	...	1758	1817	|	|	1917	2017	|	2120	...	2128	2128	2128	2208	|	|	|	|	|	0722	0722
Napoli Centrale **600** d.	...	1731	1820	1831	|	|	1931	2031	|	2135	...	2146	2146	2146	2218	|	|	|	|	|	0741	0741
Napoli Afragola **600** a.	...	|	|	|	1810	1810	|	|	1920	|	...	|	|	|	|	|	|	|	|	|	|	|
Napoli Afragola **600** d.	...	|	|	|	1812	1812	|	|	1922	|	...	|	|	|	|	|	|	|	|	|	|	|
Aversa d.	...	1749	|	1849	|	|	1949	2049	|	|	...	2205	2205	2205	|	|	|	|	|	|	|	|
Formia-Gaeta d.	...	1822	|	1922	|	|	2028	2122	|	|	...	2243	2243	2243	|	|	|	0454	0551	0551	0833	0833
Latina d.	...	1900	|	2000	|	|	2105	2200	|	|	...	2321	2321	2321	|	|	|	0530	0631	0631	0912	0912
Roma Termini **600** a.	...	1941**o**	1930	2034	1915	1915	2138	2234	2025	2349**t**	...	0008**o**	0015**o**	0008**o**	2330	|	|	0606**t**	0718	0718	0951	0951
Bologna Centrale **600 620** a.	...	...	2203	...	...	...	...	...	...	|	...	|	|	|	...	|	|	1138	...	...	...	...
Milano Centrale **600 620** a.	...	...	2320	...	...	...	...	...	...	0655**g**	...	|	|	|	...	1120	1120	1425**g**	...	...	...	...
Torino Porta Nuova **600 610** a.	...	...	...	...	...	...	...	...	...	0920	...	0810	0910	0910	...	...	...	1625	...	...	...	...

REGIONAL TRAINS

2nd class

	⚒	Ⓐ	⚒				⚒		⚒	Ⓐ	⚒		†	Ⓐ			Ⓐ		⚒		⚒	
Reggio di Calabria Centrale d.	0510	0552	0616	...	0725	0935	...	...	1200	1258	1415	...	1518	1618	1711	...	1803	1810	1915	...	2015	...
Villa S. Giovanni d.	0527	0609	0637	...	0744	1003	...	...	1217	1316	1432	...	1537	1635	1730	...	1820	1828	1936	...	2032	...
Gioia Tauro d.	0559	0633	0706	...	0816	1036	...	...	1249	1347	1503	...	1609	1707	1800	...	1845	1858	2006	...	2104	...
Rosarno d.	0605	0640	0712	...	0824	1044	1107	...	1256	1353	1511	...	1617	1713	1807	...	1852	1905	2012	...	2111	...
Lamezia Terme Centrale d.	0640	0716	0746	...	0902	...	1223	...	1328	1429	1543	...	1648	1752	1841	...	1926	1942	2047	...	2148	...
Paola **633** a.	0721	|	0826	...	0944	...	...	...	1416	1513	1622	...	1731	1837	1920	...	|	2019	2125	...	...	...
Cosenza **633** a.	0753	0818	0857	...	1018	...	...	...	1450	1550	...	...	1803	1908	...	...	2022	2053	...	...	...	...

	①–⑥						⚒			Ⓐ	Ⓒ	Ⓐ			Ⓐ	⚒	†	⚒	⚒			⚒
Cosenza **633** d.	...	...	...	...	0558	...	...	...	...	...	1320	...	1505	...	...	1700	...	...	...	...	1857	2035
Paola **633** d.	...	...	...	...	0622	*0838*	0940	...	1245	1344	1344	1450	1528	...	1642	1724	1725	...	1847	...	1930	2059
Belvedere Marittimo d.	...	...	...	...	0648	*0908*	1006	...	1311	1415	1415	1521	1556	...	1710	1753	1753	...	1914	...	1956	2126
Maratea d.	...	...	...	...	0721	*0947*	1039	...	1349	1452	1452	1609	1637	...	1751	1835	1836	...	1953	...	2028	2159
Sapri d.	0421	0540	0600	0642	0731	1012	1050	1256	1400	1511	1511	1621	1648	1715	1801	1845	1848	1848	2006	2016	2039	2211
Ascea d.	0457	0617	0638	0718	0808	1051	▬	1348	1445	1550	1550	...	1721	1802	...	...	1923	1923	...	2055	2112	...
Agropoli-Castellabate d.	0523	0643	0704	0744	0833	1113	⚒	1412	1515	1616	1616	...	1746	1836	...	...	1947	1947	...	2120	2136	...
Battipaglia **638** d.	0544	0706	0729	0810	0910	1135	1140	1440	1540	1641	1641	...	1809	1901	...	...	2011	2011	...	2144	2159	...
Salerno **638** d.	0604	0728	0750	0831	0931	1155	1201	1501	1601	1701	1701	...	1831	1920	...	...	2031	2031	...	2201	2217	...
Napoli Centrale **638** a.	0642	0807	0827	0908	1010	...	1238	1538	1638	1738	1738	...	1908	1958	...	...	2108	2108	...	2238	2258	...

	⚒	†	⚒	⚒	†	⚒	†	†	⚒	⚒	⚒	†	⚒	†	⚒	†	†	⚒	⚒	†	⚒	
Napoli Centrale **626** d.	0500	0510	...	0620	0637	0820	0830	1117	1120	1220	1325	1345	1425	1430	1520	1540	1617	1620	1720	1817	1820	2045
Caserta **626** d.	|	|	0609	|	|	|	|	|	|	|	|	|	|	|	|	|	|	|	|	|	|	|
Aversa d.	0525	0528	|	0638	0659	0838	0856	1145	1138	1238	1345	1403	1445	1456	1538	1559	1645	1638	1738	1845	1838	2109
Formia-Gaeta d.	0611	0614	0705	0738	0752	0938	0949	1249	1238	1340	1443	1454	1540	1553	1638	1652	1752	1738	1838	1952	1938	2209
Latina d.	0655	0710	0743	0828	0842	1028	1041	1338	1337	1438	1528	1542	1628	1640	1728	1742	1842	1828	1937	2042	2028	2257
Roma Termini a.	0734	0754	0827	0904	0924	1104	1124	1422	1422	1524	1604	1624	1712	1724	1804	1824	1924	1904	2024	2131	2112	2340

FOR FOOTNOTES AND RETURN SERVICES SEE PREVIOUS PAGE.

2nd class (unless otherwise noted) VILLA SAN GIOVANNI - MESSINA - SIRACUSA and PALERMO 641

km																								
			ICN 1955	*ICN* 1955		*ICN* 1959					*ICN* 1963					*IC* 721						*IC* 727		
		⚒	②–⑤	⑥–①	⚒			⚒	⚒	⚒		⚒	⚒	†	⚒				⚒		⚒			
			❖	❖		❖	Z				❖					R				Z		R		
0	**Villa S. Giovanni** ▲ d.	...	0350	0445	...	0635	...	...	...	...	1105	...	...	...	...	1430	...	...	...	...	...	1830	...	...
9	**Messina** Centrale ▲ a.	...	0515	0610	...	0805	...	...	...	...	1245	...	...	...	...	1535	...	...	...	...	...	1935	...	...
9	**Messina** Centrale ⊡ d.	0513	0545	0645	0726	0845	*0915*	1025	1115	1200	1315	1320	1415	*1435*	*1435*	1605	1618	1715	1745	*1825*	1927	2015	2018	2134
56	Taormina-Giardini ⊡ d.	0552	0631	0731	0806	0932	*1001*	1123	1156	1310	1356	1405	1505	*1547*	*1547*	1642	1723	1758	1850	*1932*	2028	2058	2127	2238
74	Giarre-Riposto ⊡ d.	0610	0654	0748	0820	0948	*1016*	1141	1216	1331	1410	1422	1534	*1609*	*1609*	1658	1741	1813	1909	*1950*	2052	2115	2144	2256
104	**Catania** Centrale ⊡ a.	0630	0724	0817	0840	1010	*1035*	1214	1236	1403	1432	1443	1609	*1639*	*1639*	1725	1820	1832	1934	*2022*	2117	2137	2218	2329
104	**Catania** Centrale d.	0635	0734	0820	0845	1016	1050	...	1240	...	1435	1455	...	1648	1653	1728	...	1837	...	2059	...	2140	...	...
110	**Catania** Fontanarossa ✈ ● d.	0646	|	|	0854	|	1058	...	1249	...	|	1504	...	1657	1701	|	...	1845	...	2108	...	|	...	...
160	Augusta d.	0730	0835	0913	0933	1109	1145	...	1333	...	1526	1551	...	1743	1748	1814	...	1931	...	2143	...	2226	...	...
191	**Siracusa** a.	0755	0857	0936	0955	1129	1210	...	1400	...	1548	1610	...	1805	1808	1833	...	2000	...	2210	...	2253	...	...

					IC 722		*IC* 724					*ICN* 1962									*ICN* 1956		*ICN* 1960
	⚒	⚒		⚒				⚒	⚒	⚒			⚒		⚒		†	⚒	⚒			⚒	
			Z		R		R					❖				Z					❖		❖
Siracusa d.	...	0506	0552	0640	0732	0844	1010	...	...	1253	...	1335	1418	...	...	1601	...	...	1712	1820	1910	1925	2145
Augusta d.	...	0525	0613	0706	0753	0912	1031	...	...	1316	...	1400	1437	...	...	1622	...	...	1733	1841	1932	1957	2206
Catania Fontanarossa ✈ ● d.	...	0604	0651	0758	|	1004	|	...	...	1356	...	|	1522	...	...	1701	...	1735	1820	1921	|	2035	|
Catania Centrale a.	...	0612	0705	0804	0838	1010	1115	...	...	1406	...	1451	1528	...	...	1708	...	1745	1829	1930	2019	2044	2255
Catania Centrale ⊡ d.	0501	0617	...	0806	0841	1020	1118	1244	1327	1410	1424	1454	1531	1540	1624	*1719*	1745	1747	1836	1935	2026	*2109*	2258
Giarre-Riposto ⊡ d.	0530	0640	...	0829	0904	1042	1142	1317	1400	1432	1457	1522	1552	1613	1656	*1741*	1818	1824	1900	1955	2051	*2134*	2320
Taormina-Giardini ⊡ d.	0552	0659	...	0848	0918	1103	1156	1341	1428	1448	1522	1539	1610	1643	1723	*1758*	1840	1850	1919	2011	2112	*2153*	2335
Messina Centrale ⊡ a.	0703	0751	...	0942	0953	1202	1245	1506	1536	1549	1622	1625	1655	1759	1807	*1840*	1943	1953	2000	2108	2150	*2240*	0015
Messina Centrale ▲ d.	...	...	...	...	1010	...	1310	...	...	...	...	1640	...	...	...	...	...	...	...	...	2210	...	0035
Villa S. Giovanni ▲ a.	...	...	...	...	1120	...	1420	...	...	...	...	1815	...	...	...	...	...	...	...	...	2335	...	◧

km																								
			ICN 1957			*ICN* 1957					*ICN* 1961				*ICN* 1965			*IC* 723						*IC* 729
		⚒	②–⑤		⚒	⑥–①		†	⚒			⚒		⚒						†	⚒		†	
		e	❖			❖					❖				❖			R						R
0	**Villa S. Giovanni** ▲ d.	...	0350	...	...	0445	...	...	...	...	0635	...	...	...	1105	...	...	1430	...	...	...	...	...	1830
9	**Messina** Centrale ▲ a.	...	0515	...	...	0610	...	...	...	...	0805	...	...	...	1245	...	...	1535	...	...	...	...	...	1935
9	**Messina** Centrale d.	0450	0555	...	0633	0655	...	0745	0753	...	0837	1043	...	1227	1320	...	1437	1615	...	1708	1714	...	1857	2005
45	Milazzo d.	0508	0617	...	0657	0719	...	0804	0812	...	0859	1101	...	1246	1343	...	1453	1637	...	1725	1731	...	1915	2026
174	Cefalù d.	0658	0827	...	0843	0917	...	1014	1000	...	1100	1242	...	1437	1557	...	1638	1835	...	1905	1920	...	2118	2214
204	Termini Imerese **645 647** d.	0720	0854	...	0902	0937	...	1031	1022	...	1120	1303	...	1500	1618	...	1700	1856	...	1925	1936	...	2136	2238
241	**Palermo** Centrale **645 647** a.	0747	0924	...	0929	1007	...	1104	1103	...	1157	1332	...	1529	1655	...	1729	1925	...	1955	2005	...	2205	2305

					IC 728			*IC* 730				*ICN* 1964							*ICN* 1954				*ICN* 1958
	⚒		⚒							⚒					⚒								
					R			R		h		❖							❖				❖
Palermo Centrale **645 647** d.	0507	...	0618	...	0650	0832	...	1000	...	1138	...	1235	...	1430	1628	...	1833	...	1848	...	2033	...	2055
Termini Imerese **645 647** d.	0532	...	0646	...	0715	0858	...	1035	...	1206	...	1305	...	1458	1653	...	1858	...	1917	...	2058	...	2122
Cefalù d.	0548	...	0707	...	0735	0918	...	1059	...	1242	...	1335	...	1526	1714	...	1919	...	1936	...	2116	...	2143
Milazzo d.	0735	...	0856	...	0917	1057	...	1234	...	1521	...	1558	...	1712	1900	...	2054	...	2125	...	2300	...	2350
Messina Centrale a.	0805	...	0920	...	0940	1117	...	1255	...	1553	...	1620	...	1732	1920	...	2116	...	2155	...	2322	...	0020
Messina Centrale ▲ d.	...	...	...	...	1010	...	...	1310	...	...	...	1640	...	...	...	...	...	...	2210	...	...	...	0035
Villa S. Giovanni ▲ a.	...	...	...	...	1120	...	...	1420	...	...	...	1815	...	...	...	...	...	...	2335	...	...	...	◧

R – To/from Roma (Table **640**).
Z – To / from Palermo (Table **645**).
e – From Jan. 31.
h – Change at S. Agata di Militello.
◧ – To Salerno (Table **640**), arrives 0642.
▲ – Through trains are conveyed by ⛴ Villa S. Giovanni - Messina and v.v. See Table **2695** for other sailings.

⊡ – Other trains Messina - Catania and v.v.: from Messina Centrale at 0539 ⚒, 0650 ⚒, 0652 †, 0755, 1335 ⚒; from Catania Centrale at 0529 ⚒, 0626, 1104 ⚒, 1123 †, 1939.
● – For additional trains Catania Centrale - Catania Fontanarossa ✈ and v.v. see also Table **645**.
❖ – 🛏 1, 2 cl., 🛏 2 cl. (4 berth). For origin see Table **640**. Running days, timings and numbers of *ICN* trains may vary - please check your reservation. For confirmed timings please consult the *Trenitalia* journey planner at www.trenitalia.com.

Ferrovia Circumetnea CATANIA - RANDAZZO - RIPOSTO 644

km		⚒	⚒	⚒	⚒	⚒	⚒	⚒	⚒	⚒	⚒
0	**Catania** Borgo ⊙ d.	...	0646	0805	1005	...	1220	1350	...	1530	1623
20	Paternò ⊙ d.	...	0722	0841	1040	...	1256	1426	...	1608	1658
36	Adrano Nord d.	...	0752	0909	...	...	1325	1453	...	1636	...
52	Bronte d.	...	0816	0936	...	...	1352	...	...	1703	...
71	**Randazzo** a.	...	0843	1003	...	...	1419	...	...	1730	...
71	**Randazzo** d.	0632	...	...	...	1210	...	...	1506	...	...
109	Giarre a.	0739	...	...	...	1323	...	...	1614	...	...
111	**Riposto** a.	0744	...	...	...	1327	...	...	1618	...	...

	⚒	⚒	⚒	⚒	⚒	⚒	⚒	⚒	⚒	⚒
Riposto d.	...	...	...	0855	...	...	...	1350	...	...
Giarre d.	...	...	...	0859	...	...	...	1354	...	...
Randazzo a.	...	...	...	1004	...	...	...	1459	...	...
Randazzo d.	0557	0715	...	...	1058	1230	...	...	1501	...
Bronte d.	0626	0744	...	...	1127	1259	...	...	1530	...
Adrano Nord d.	0651	0809	...	...	1152	1324	1508	...	1555	...
Paternò ⊙ d.	0723	0840	1008	...	1223	1353	1536	...	1626	1713
Catania Borgo ⊙ a.	0759	0915	1045	...	1300	1430	1611	...	1703	1750

Metropolitana di Catania operates a metro service Nesima - San Nullo - Milo - Catania Borgo - Giuffrida - Galatea - Giovanni XXIII - Stesicoro and v.v. (*8.8 km*).
From Nesima every 10 - 15 minutes 0640 ⚒/0830 † - 2030 †/2040 ⚒; **from Stesicoro** every 10 - 15 minutes 0700 ⚒/0855 † - 2100.

⊙ – Other trains: Catania Borgo - Paternò at 0607 ⚒, 0835 ⚒, 0920 ⚒, 1050 ⚒, 1135 ⚒, 1305 ⚒, 1435 ⚒; Paternò - Catania Borgo at 0650 ⚒, 0923 ⚒, 1053 ⚒, 1138 ⚒, 1308 ⚒, 1438 ⚒.

645 PALERMO and AGRIGENTO - CATANIA

2nd class

km		⚒	⚒	⚒	†	⚒	⚒	A	⚒	†	⚒	⚒	⚒	⚒	⚒	⚒	†	⚒		†	†A	⚒A	⚒	⚒	⚒
0	**Palermo** Centrale d.	...	...	...	...	...	...	0731	0931	...	...	...	1320	...	...	...	1531	1531	...	...	1731	1731	...	...	1945
37	Termini Imerese d.	...	...	...	...	...	...	0756	0956	...	...	...	1346	...	...	...	1555	1555	...	...	1755	1755	...	...	2012
70	Roccapalumba-Alia d.	...	...	0620	...	...	0730	|	|	...	...	...	1415	...	1519	1553	|	1617	...	...	|	1817	...	1954	2036
	Agrigento Centrale d.	...	...	|	...	...	|	|	|	...	...	1250	|	1350	|	|	|	|	...	1700	|	|	1912	|	|
	Aragona-Caldare d.	...	...	|	...	...	|	|	|	...	...	1306	|	1406	|	|	|	|	...	1716	|	|	1928	|	|
	Canicattì d.	...	...	|	...	...	|	|	|	...	...	1347	|	1443	|	|	|	|	...	1758	|	|	2007	|	|
	Caltanissetta Xirbi a.	...	...	0718	...	...	0821	0900	1100	...	...	|	1500	|	1616	1643	1700	1700	...	|	1900	1900	|	2044	2119
	Caltanissetta Centrale d.	0533	0607	0737	0800	0800	0838	|	|	...	1357	1415	|	1512	1634	...	|	|	1757	1828	|	|	2037	2100	|
127	Caltanissetta Xirbi d.	0543	0617	...	0808	0808	...	0904	1106	...	1405	...	1501	...	...	...	1701	1701	1805	...	1901	1901	...	...	2120
154	Enna d.	0616	0641	...	0832	0832	...	0926	1128	...	1438	...	1524	...	...	...	1724	1724	1838	...	1924	1924	...	...	2141
237	**Catania** Fontanarossa ✈ 641 d.	0735	0751	...	0950	0956	...	1032	1230	1356	1600	...	1640	...	...	...	1826	1827	1953	...	2042	2042	...	...	2242
243	**Catania** Centrale 641 a.	0749	0758	...	1001	1005	...	1040	1236	1407	1611	...	1646	...	...	...	1835	1835	2003	...	2049	2049	...	...	2249

km		⚒	⚒	⚒	⚒	A	⚒	†	⚒	⚒	⚒	⚒	⚒	⚒	†	⚒	⚒	⚒	⚒A	†A	†	⚒	†	⚒	⚒
	Catania Centrale 641 d.	...	...	0444	...	0720	0855	0855	0915	...	...	...	1325	1439	1520	1530	...	1648	1718	1720	...	...	1842	1843	1945
	Catania Fontanarossa ✈ 641 d.	...	...	0452	...	0730	0903	0903	0924	...	...	...	1332	1447	1527	1538	...	1656	1726	1727	...	...	1852	1852	1953
	Enna d.	...	...	0555	...	0833	1018	1035	1044	...	...	...	1437	1613	1637	1637	...	1811	1837	1837	...	...	2012	2013	2057
0	Caltanissetta Xirbi a.	...	...	0616	...	0903	1041	1058	1105	...	...	...	1500	1636	1700	1700	...	1835	1900	1900	...	...	2046	2039	2120
6	Caltanissetta Centrale d.	0502	0558	|	0645	|	1049	1106	|	1256	1405	1523	|	1645	|	|	1806	1842	|	|	1923	1935	2055	2049	2128
	Caltanissetta Xirbi d.	0517	|	0617	|	0904	...	...	1106	1311	1423	|	1501	...	1701	1701	1822	...	1901	1901	|	|	...	...	...
35	Canicattì d.	|	0635	|	0720	|	...	...	|	|	|	1605	|	...	|	|	|	...	|	|	2005	2015	...	...	...
65	Aragona-Caldare d.	|	0705	|	0753	|	...	...	|	|	|	1643	|	...	|	|	|	...	|	|	2043	2052	...	...	...
78	**Agrigento** Centrale a.	|	0730	|	0810	|	...	...	|	|	|	1659	|	...	|	|	|	...	|	|	2059	2109	...	...	...
	Roccapalumba-Alia d.	0609	...	0709	...	|	...	...	|	1405	1533	...	|	...	1743	|	1928	...	|	1946	...	...	...	...	...
	Termini Imerese d.	...	...	0732	...	1005	...	...	1208	...	...	...	1605	...	1807	1805	...	...	2012	2012	...	...	...	...	...
	Palermo Centrale a.	...	...	0759	...	1029	...	...	1232	...	...	...	1629	...	1831	1829	...	...	2037	2037	...	...	...	...	...

DIRECT TRAINS PALERMO - AGRIGENTO

km		⚒	⚒		Ⓐ	⚒	Ⓐ				Ⓐ	⚒			
0	**Palermo** Centrale d.	0543	0743	0843	1043	1143	1243	1343	...	1443	1543	1643	1743	1843	2043
37	Termini Imerese d.	0612	0812	0912	1112	1212	1312	1412	...	1512	1612	1712	1812	1912	2112
70	Roccapalumba-Alia d.	0643	0843	0943	1146	1243	1343	1443	...	1543	1643	1743	1843	1943	2143
125	Aragona-Caldare d.	0732	0932	1032	1232	1332	1432	1532	...	1632	1732	1832	1932	2032	2232
139	**Agrigento** Centrale a.	0747	0947	1047	1247	1347	1447	1547	...	1647	1747	1847	1947	2047	2247

	⚒	⚒	⚒	Ⓐ			Ⓐ	⚒	⚒	Ⓐ	†			⚒
Agrigento Centrale d.	0454	0522	0615	0715	0815	1015	1215	1315	1415	1515	1615	1715	1815	2015
Aragona-Caldare d.	0508	0536	0632	0732	0832	1032	1232	1332	1432	1532	1632	1732	1832	2032
Roccapalumba-Alia d.	0552	0617	0717	0817	0917	1117	1317	1417	1517	1617	1717	1817	1917	2117
Termini Imerese d.	0623	0651	0754	0849	0949	1149	1349	1449	1549	1649	1749	1849	1949	2149
Palermo Centrale a.	0655	0717	0823	0917	1017	1217	1417	1517	1617	1717	1817	1917	2017	2217

PALERMO - CATANIA - MESSINA

	FB **8638** 🍷 R		*FB* **8635** 🍷 R
Palermo Centrale d.	0708	**Messina** Centrale d.	1510
Caltanissetta Xirbi d.	0837	**Catania** Centrale a.	1613
Enna d.	0901	**Catania** Centrale d.	1615
Catania Centrale a.	1015	Enna d,	1723
Catania Centrale d.	1017	Caltanissetta Xirbi d.	1748
Messina Centrale a.	1123	**Palermo** Centrale a.	1930

TABLE 645 NOTES:

A – To / from Siracusa (Table **641**).

646 PALERMO - TRAPANI

2nd class

km		⚒	†	†		⚒	⚒	†		†	⚒	⚒		⚒	†	⚒			†	†		⚒	⚒		
0	**Palermo** Centrale d.	...	0808	...	...	1011	...	1108	...	...	1411	...	...	...	1708	1711	...	...	2008	...	...	2011	...	...	...
32	Piraineto d.	...	0859	0930	...	1112	1116	1159	...	1231	1512	1527	...	...	1759	1812	...	1833	2059	2122	...	2112	2135	...	...
73	Castellammare del Golfo d.	0722	...	1013	...	...	1156	...	...	1311	...	1610	...	...	...	...	...	1915	...	2201	...	...	2214	...	...
79	Alcamo Diramazione d.	0730	...	1021	...	...	1204	...	...	1318	...	1618	...	...	...	...	...	1923	...	2208	...	...	2221	...	...
121	Castelvetrano d.	0824	...	1112	...	...	1250	...	...	1407	...	1710	...	1735	...	...	...	2016	...	2258	...	...	2310	...	...
144	Mazara del Vallo d.	0846	...	1134	...	...	1318	...	...	...	...	...	...	1801	...	...	...	2039	...	...	...	...	...	...	...
165	Marsala d.	0913	...	1203	...	...	1349	...	...	...	...	...	...	1824	...	...	...	2103	...	...	...	...	...	...	...
196	**Trapani** a.	0941	...	1238	...	...	1422	...	...	...	...	...	...	1900	...	...	...	2140	...	...	...	...	...	...	...

	⚒f	†	†		⚒	⚒	†		†	⚒	⚒		⚒	⚒	†		†		†		⚒			
Trapani d.	...	0555	...	...	0652	...	0910	...	...	1153	...	...	1438	...	1520	...	...	1809	...	...	...	...	...	...
Marsala d.	...	0629	...	...	0726	...	0945	...	...	1225	...	...	1515	...	1553	...	...	1844	...	...	...	...	...	...
Mazara del Vallo d.	...	0652	...	...	0756	...	1007	...	...	1246	...	...	1537	...	1615	...	...	1905	...	...	...	...	...	...
Castelvetrano d.	0455	0718	...	...	0823	...	1029	...	...	1314	...	...	1606	...	1642	...	...	1933	...	...	...	...	...	...
Alcamo Diramazione d.	0545	0804	...	...	0909	...	1117	...	...	1401	...	...	1651	...	1729	...	...	2017	...	...	...	...	...	...
Castellammare del Golfo d.	0553	0811	...	...	0916	...	1125	...	...	1409	...	...	1658	...	1736	...	...	2024	...	...	...	...	...	...
Piraineto d.	0644	0856	0925	...	1001	1046	1211	...	1225	1452	1546	...	1741	1746	1820	...	1825	2111	2125	...	2146	...	...	...
Palermo Centrale a.	0747	...	1017	...	...	1147	...	...	1317	...	1647	...	...	1847	...	...	1917	...	2217	...	2247	...	...	...

f – Change trains at Cinisi-Terrasini (a. 0630 / d. 0635).

648 SIRACUSA - GELA - CALTANISSETTA

2nd class

km		⚒	⚒		P	Ⓐ		⚒	⚒		⚒	⚒		⚒	P		⚒	⚒						
0	**Siracusa** d.	...	0533	...	0552	...	...	...	1030	...	...	1410	...	1535	1601	...	1741	2019	...	...	...	...	...	...
62	Pozzallo d.	...	0646	...	|	...	...	...	1135	...	...	1527	...	1653	|	...	1850	2133	...	...	...	...	...	...
92	Modica d.	0531	0720	...	|	0738	...	0920	1211	...	1342	1601	...	1733	|	...	1926	2209	...	...	...	...	...	...
112	Ragusa d.	0553	0744	...	|	0800	...	0942	1232	...	1406	1627	...	1755	|	...	1955	...	...	...	...	...	...	...
153	Vittoria d.	0633	...	...	|	0842	...	1025	1319	...	1445	1718	...	1837	|	...	...	...	...	...	...	...	...	...
183	**Gela** d.	0657	...	...	|	0907	...	1053	1350	...	1508	1743	...	...	|	...	...	...	...	...	...	...	...	...
218	Licata d.	0725	...	...	|	0934	...	...	...	...	1534	...	...	...	|	...	...	...	...	...	...	...	...	...
264	Canicattì 645 d.	0806	...	...	|	1013	...	...	...	...	1615	...	...	...	|	...	...	...	...	...	...	...	...	...
293	**Caltanissetta** Centrale 645 a.	0836	...	...	|	1040	...	...	...	...	1642	...	...	...	|	...	...	...	...	...	...	...	...	...
299	**Caltanissetta** Xirbi 645 a.	0850	...	...	0900	1058	...	...	...	...	1655	...	...	...	1900	...	...	...	...	...	...	...	...	...

	⚒	⚒		⚒	⚒		⚒	P		⚒	⚒		⚒	Ⓐ		P	⑥		Ⓐ	⚒			
Caltanissetta Xirbi 645 d.	...	...	...	...	...	...	...	0904	...	...	...	...	...	1710	...	1901	...	...	...	1910	...	...	...
Caltanissetta Centrale 645 d.	...	...	...	0510	...	...	...	|	...	...	...	...	...	1721	...	|	...	...	...	1921	...	...	...
Canicattì 645 d.	...	...	...	0537	...	...	...	|	...	...	...	...	...	1746	...	|	...	...	...	1947	...	...	...
Licata d.	...	...	...	0615	...	...	...	|	...	...	...	...	...	1822	...	|	...	...	...	2025	...	...	...
Gela d.	...	...	...	0645	...	...	0727	|	...	1248	1513	...	1812	1849	...	|	...	...	...	2052	...	...	...
Vittoria d.	...	...	...	...	...	...	0751	|	...	1318	1542	...	1843	1912	...	|	1927	...	1933	2116	...	...	...
Ragusa d.	...	...	...	...	0805	...	0844	|	...	1407	1626	...	1930	1959	...	|	2015	...	2021	2158	...	...	...
Modica d.	0500	0547	...	...	0826	...	0907	|	...	1433	1647	...	1954	2020	...	|	2036	...	2042	2220	...	...	...
Pozzallo d.	0534	0620	...	...	0857	...	...	|	...	1506	1720	...	2025	...	...	|	...	...	...	...	...	...	...
Siracusa a.	0650	0737	...	...	1003	...	...	1210	...	1618	1836	...	2130	...	...	2210	...	...	...	...	...	...	...

P – To / from Palermo (Table **645**).

MALTA

Bus services on Malta and Gozo are operated by Malta Public Transport www.publictransport.com.mt. Travellers will also find useful information on the unofficial website www.maltabybus.com.

649 PRINCIPAL BUS SERVICES

Routes from Valletta: **X4** Airport - Hal Far, **1** L'Isla (Senglea), **2/4** Birgu (Vittoriosa), **3** Birgu - Smart City - Rinella - Kalkara, **13-15** Sliema - San Giljan (St Julian's), **13** Bahar ic-Caghaq, **31/45/48** Mosta - Bugibba (**45** via Qawra seafront), **31/43/45** Naxxar, **41/42** Mosta - St Paul's Bay - Mellieha - Ghadira - Cirkewwa (for Gozo ferry), **44** Ghajn Tuffieha (Golden Bay), **49** Armier Bay (summer), **51-53** Rabat / Mdina, **52/56** Dingli, **61** Zebbug, **62** Siggiewi, **71/73** Zurrieq, **72** Qrendi, **74** Hagar Qim - Blue Grotto, **80/82/X4** Birzebbuga, **81/85** Marsaxlokk, **91-93** Marsaskala, **94** Xghajra.

Other routes: **X1** Airport - Cirkewwa, **X2** Airport - Sliema, **X3** Airport - Rabat - Bugibba, **186** Bugibba - Ta' Qali - Rabat, **202** Sliema - Naxxar - Mosta - Rabat, **203** Sliema - Naxxar - Mosta - Bugibba, **212** Sliema - San Giljan - Bugibba, **221** Bugibba - Mellieha - Cirkewwa, **222** Sliema - St Paul's Bay - Mellieha - Cirkewwa, **223** Bugibba - Ghajn Tuffieha, **225** Sliema - St Paul's Bay - Ghajn Tuffieha.

Gozo: routes from Rabat (Victoria): **301/303** Mgarr (for Cirkewwa ferry), **302** Ramla, **305** Sannat, **306/330** Xlendi, **307** Xaghra, **308** Ta' Pinu - Ghasri, **309** Zebbug, **310** Marsalforn, **311** Dwejra.

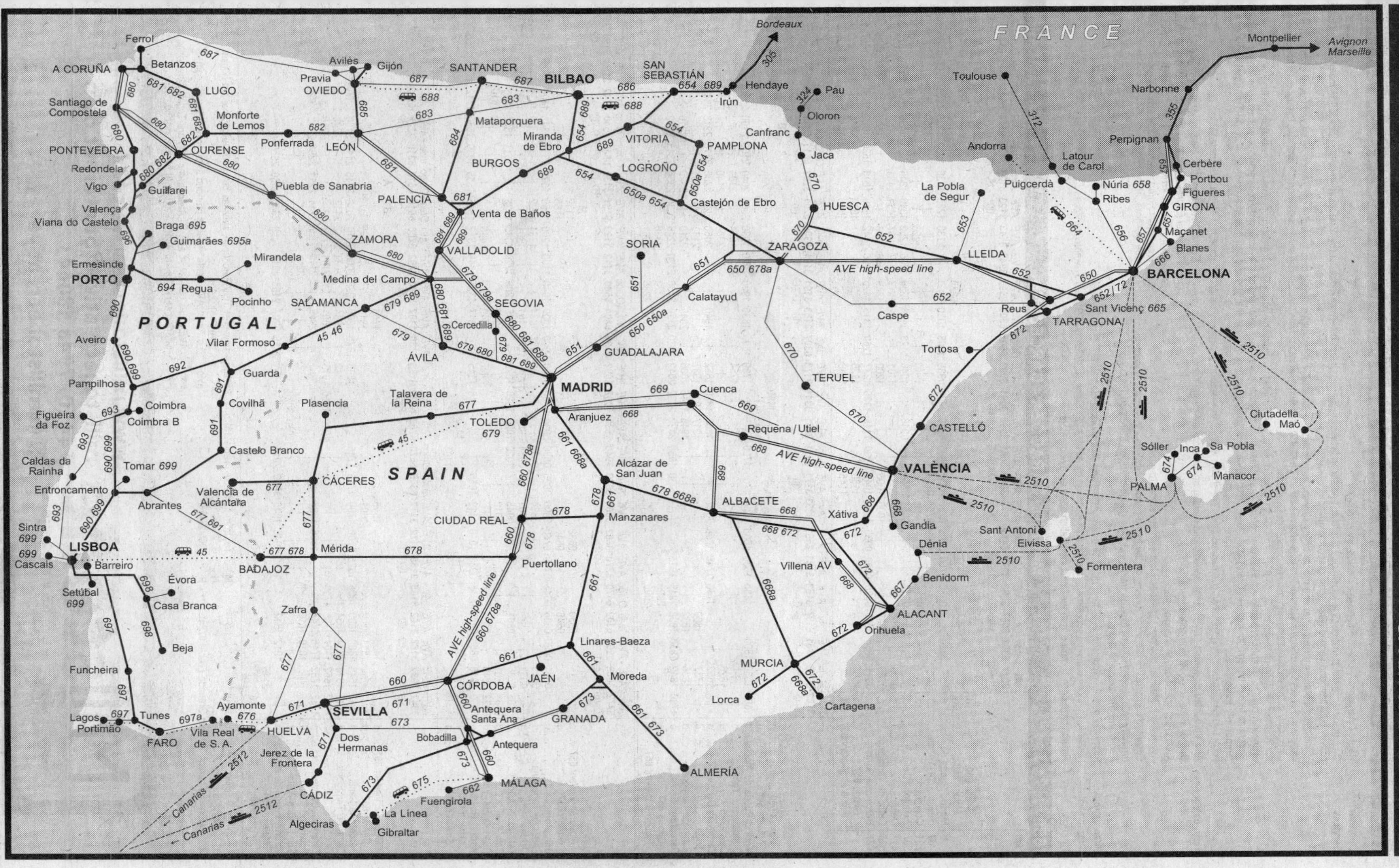
FRANCE
SPAIN
PORTUGAL
Bordeaux
Montpellier
Avignon
Marseille
Ferrol
A CORUÑA
Betanzos
LUGO
Santiago de Compostela
Monforte de Lemos
PONTEVEDRA
OURENSE
Ponferrada
LEÓN
Redondela
Vigo
Guillarei
Valença
Viana do Castelo
Braga 695
Guimarães 695a
Mirandela
Ermesinde
PORTO
694 Regua
Pocinho
Aveiro
Pampilhosa
Coimbra
Coimbra B
Figueira da Foz
Caldas da Rainha
Tomar 699
Entroncamento
Abrantes
Sintra 699
699 Cascais
LISBOA
Barreiro
Setúbal 699
Évora
Casa Branca
Beja
Funcheira
Lagos
Portimão
Tunes
FARO
Vila Real de S. A.
Ayamonte
HUELVA
Avilés
Gijón
Pravia
OVIEDO
SANTANDER
Mataporquera
BILBAO
SAN SEBASTIÁN
Irún
Hendaye
Pau
Oloron
Canfranc
Jaca
HUESCA
Miranda de Ebro
VITORIA
PAMPLONA
BURGOS
LOGROÑO
Castejón de Ebro
Puebla de Sanabria
PALENCIA
Venta de Baños
VALLADOLID
ZAMORA
Medina del Campo
SALAMANCA
SEGOVIA
Cercedilla
ÁVILA
Vilar Formoso
Guarda
Covilhã
Castelo Branco
Valencia de Alcántara
Plasencia
Talavera de la Reina
CÁCERES
MADRID
TOLEDO 679
Aranjuez
GUADALAJARA
Calatayud
SORIA
ZARAGOZA
AVE high-speed line
LLEIDA
La Pobla de Segur
Caspe
Reus
TARRAGONA
Sant Vicenç 665
BARCELONA
Toulouse
Andorra
Latour de Carol
Puigcerdà
Núria 658
Ribes
Perpignan
Narbonne
Cerbère
Portbou
Figueres
GIRONA
Maçanet
Blanes
Tortosa
TERUEL
Cuenca
Requena / Utiel
CASTELLÓ
VALÈNCIA
Alcázar de San Juan
CIUDAD REAL
Manzanares
ALBACETE
Xàtiva
Gandia
Dénia
Benidorm
Villena AV
ALACANT
Orihuela
MURCIA
Lorca
Cartagena
BADAJOZ
Mérida
Puertollano
Zafra
Linares-Baeza
JAÉN
Moreda
CÓRDOBA
Antequera Santa Ana
Antequera
GRANADA
ALMERÍA
SEVILLA
Dos Hermanas
Bobadilla
Jerez de la Frontera
CÁDIZ
MÁLAGA
Fuengirola
Algeciras
La Línea
Gibraltar
Canarias
Ciutadella
Maó
Sóller
Inca
Sa Pobla
Manacor
PALMA
Sant Antoni
Eivissa
Formentera

SPAIN

Operator: **Renfe Operadora** – unless otherwise indicated. www.renfe.es

Services: On long-distance trains first class is known as *Preferente* and second class as *Turista*. Unless otherwise indicated (by '2' in the train column or [2] in the notes), all trains convey both first- and second-class seating accommodation.

🍸 indicates a buffet car (*cafetería*) or a mobile trolley service. ✗ indicates the availability of hot meals served from the buffet car. Meals are served free of extra charge, on Mondays to Fridays and Sundays, to holders of *Preferente* tickets on all *AVE* and *Euromed* trains. Note that catering services may not be available throughout a train's journey particularly in the case of trains with multiple origins / destinations.

🛏 indicates sleeping-cars with single, double, and 4-berth compartments. The *Turista* fare is payable plus a sleeping-car supplement corresponding to the type and standard of accommodation. ***Trenhotel*** services additionally convey *Gran Clase* accommodation: *de luxe* single- and double-occupancy compartments with *en suite* shower and toilet. *Preferente* fare is payable for travel in *Gran Clase* plus a sleeping-car supplement corresponding to the type and standard of accommodation. **All Trenhotel services are temporarily suspended.**

Local (*Media Distancia*) and suburban (*Cercanías*) trains are shown without an indication of category except for some fast ***Media Distancia*** (*MD*).

Train categories: ***Alta Velocidad Española*** (*AVE*): High-speed trains running on the standard-gauge lines.
Ouigo, avlo: Low-cost high-speed trains.
Alvia: High-speed gauge-changing trains.
Avant (*Av*): Medium-distance high-speed trains on the standard-gauge lines.
Euromed (*Em*): *AVE*-like trains running on the broad-gauge Barcelona - València - Alacant route.
Intercity (*IC*): Long distance express trains, including gauge-changing trains and Talgo stock. Also certain medium and short distance trains.
Media Distancia (*MD*): Medium distance regional trains.
Regional Exprés (*RE*): Medium distance regional trains.
Train à Grande Vitesse (*TGV*): French High-speed trains.
Trenhotel (*Hotel*): Quality night express trains (see Services, above).

Reservations: Reservations are compulsory in all long distance trains, ***Avant*** and ***Media Distancia*** trains.

Supplements: Higher fares, incorporating a supplement, are payable for travel by *Alvia*, *AVE*, *Euromed*, *Intercity*, *TGV* and *Trenhotel* services.

Timings: Timings have been compiled from the latest information supplied by operators.

650 MADRID - ZARAGOZA - BARCELONA — High-speed services

km		*Av* 8077	*avlo* 6301	*Av* 8087	*AVE* 3063	*AVE* 3071	*Ouigo* 6471	*AVE* 3073	*AVE* 3073	*AVE* 3081	*AVE* 3083	*AVE* 3091	*AVE* 3093	*Ouigo* 6501	*avlo* 6303	*AVE* 3993	*AVE* 3943	*AVE* 3113	*AVE* 3123	*AVE* 3123	*AVE* 3131	*AVE* 9724	*Ouigo* 6541	*Ouigo* 6541	*Ouigo* 6541	*AVE* 3143
		①–⑤			①–⑤	①–④		①–⑤	⑥⑦	①–⑤	N	①–⑤					G		Ⓑ	⑥	①②③④⑦	M	①②③④⑥⑦ B	⑤ B	A	Ⓑ
	Sevilla **660** d.	...	...	...	...	...	...	...	...	...	...	...	...	...	...	...	0850	...	...	...	...	...	...	...	...	...
	Málaga **660** d.	...	...	...	...	...	...	...	...	...	...	...	...	...	...	0835	|	...	...	...	...	...	...	...	...	...
0	**Madrid** Puerta de Atocha d.	...	0620	...	0630	0700	0705	0730	0730	0800	0830	0900	0930	1005	1030	|	|	1130	1230	1230	1300	1325	1405	1405	1405	1430
64	Guadalajara - Yebes d.	...	|	...	|	|	|	0754	0754	|	|	|	|	|	|	|	|	|	|	|	|	1350	|	|	|	|
221	Calatayud d.	...	|	...	0726	|	|	|	|	|	|	|	|	|	|	|	|	1226	|	|	|	|	|	|	|	1525
307	**Zaragoza** Delicias d.	...	|	...	0752	|	|	0852	0852	|	0946	|	1046	1123	1146	1236	1236	1252	1346	1346	|	1450	1523	1523	1523	1552
447	Lleida d.	0705	|	0805	|	|	|	0937	0937	|	|	|	1131	|	|	1317	1317	1337	1431	1431	|	|	|	|	|	|
526	Camp de Tarragona d.	0735	|	0837	|	|	|	1006	1006	|	|	|	1200	|	|	1346	1346	1406	|	|	|	1546	|	1621	1621	|
621	**Barcelona** Sants a.	0811	0850	0913	0920	0930	0935	1042	1042	1030	1115	1130	1237	1250	1315	1420	1420	1442	1540	1540	1530	1622	1650	1657	1657	1721
	Girona **657** a.	...	...	...	...	...	...	...	1130	...	...	...	1325	...	...	...	...	...	1630	...	...	1714	...	...	...	...
	Figueres Vilafant **657** a.	...	...	...	...	...	...	...	1145	...	...	...	1340	...	...	...	...	...	1645	...	...	1731	...	...	...	...

	AVE 3151	*AVE* 3153	*AVE* 3161	*Av* 8187	*AVE* 3163	*AVE* 3163	*AVE* 3553	*Av* 10553	*AVE* 3171	*Ouigo* 6571	*AVE* 3991	*AVE* 3941	*AVE* 3173	*avlo* 6307	*AVE* 3183	*AVE* 3191	*AVE* 3191	*avlo* 6309	*AVE* 3201	*AVE* 3203	*Ouigo* 6611	*Ouigo* 6611	*Av* 10593			
	①–⑤	⑤⑥	①–⑤		①–⑤	⑦	⑤	④⑦	Ⓑ						Ⓑ	①②③④⑦	⑤		Ⓑ		A	B	Ⓑ			
Sevilla **660** d.	...	...	...	...	...	...	...	...	...	...	...	1450	...	...	...	...	...	...	...	...	...	...	...	...	...	...
Málaga **660** d.	...	...	...	...	...	...	...	...	...	...	1432	|	...	...	...	...	...	...	...	...	...	...	...	...	...	...
Madrid Puerta de Atocha d.	1500	1530	1600	...	1630	1630	1635	1635	1700	1720	|	|	1730	1800	1830	1900	1900	1930	2000	2040	2100	2100	2130	...	...	...
Guadalajara - Yebes d.	|	|	|	...	|	|	|	|	|	|	|	|	1754	|	|	|	|	1954	|	2104	|	|	2157	...	...	...
Calatayud d.	|	1626	|	...	|	|	|	|	|	|	|	|	|	|	|	|	|	2030	|	2140	|	|	2244	...	...	...
Zaragoza Delicias d.	|	1652	|	...	1746	1746	1756	1805	|	|	1830	1830	1852	|	1946	|	|	2056	|	2206	2218	2218	2310	...	...	...
Lleida d.	|	1737	|	1800	|	|	...	...	|	|	1917	1917	1937	|	|	|	|	2141	|	2251	|	|	...	...	...	...
Camp de Tarragona d.	|	1806	|	1832	|	|	...	...	|	|	1946	1946	2006	|	2045	|	|	2210	|	2320	|	2316	...	...	...	...
Barcelona Sants a.	1730	1842	1830	1908	1915	1915	...	...	1930	1950	2022	2022	2042	2030	2120	2130	2130	2246	2230	2356	2345	2352	...	...	...	...
Girona **657** a.	...	...	...	...	2005	...	...	...	...	...	...	...	...	...	...	2220	...	2336	...	...	...	...	...	...	...	...
Figueres Vilafant **657** a.	...	...	...	...	2020	...	...	...	...	...	...	...	...	...	...	2235	...	2351	...	...	...	...	...	...	...	...

	AVE 3772	*AVE* 3062	*AVE* 3260	*avlo* 6302	*Ouigo* 6470	*AVE* 3270	*AVE* 3662	*AVE* 3082	*AVE* 3080	*AVE* 3940	*AVE* 3990	*AVE* 3092	*AVE* 3092	*Av* 8096	*avlo* 6304	*Ouigo* 6500	*AVE* 3112	*AVE* 3122	*AVE* 9731	*AVE* 3130	*Ouigo* 6540	*Ouigo* 6540	*AVE* 3142	*AVE* 3152	*AVE* 3150	*Av* 3562
	①–⑥	①–⑥	①–④			①–④	①–⑤		①–⑤	G		①–⑥	⑦						M	①–⑤	⑦	①–⑥			①–⑤	⑤⑦
Figueres Vilafant **657** d.	...	...	...	0530	...	...	0630	...	...	...	...	0755	...	...	...	...	...	...	1139	...	...	...	...	...	...	...
Girona **657** d.	...	...	...	0546	...	...	0646	...	...	...	...	0811	...	...	...	...	...	...	1156	...	...	...	...	...	...	...
Barcelona Sants d.	...	0551	0620	0635	0645	0700	0740	0800	0825	0830	0830	0900	0900	0920	1000	1040	1100	1200	1250	1325	1338	1345	1400	1500	1525	1515
Camp de Tarragona d.	...	0625	|	|	|	|	|	0834	|	0905	0905	|	|	0957	1034	|	|	1234	1322	|	1412	|	1434	|	|	1548
Lleida d.	...	0652	|	|	|	|	|	0901	|	0934	0934	|	|	1028	1101	|	|	1301	|	|	|	|	1501	|	|	1614
Zaragoza Delicias d.	0705	0736	|	0801	|	|	|	0945	|	1020	1020	1026	1026	...	1145	1206	1226	1345	1425	|	1511	1511	1545	1626	|	1655
Calatayud d.	0736	0801	|	|	|	|	|	1010	|	|	|	|	|	...	1210	|	|	|	|	|	|	|	1610	|	|	...
Guadalajara - Yebes d.	0822	0840	|	|	|	|	|	|	|	|	|	|	|	...	1249	|	|	1445	|	|	|	|	|	|	|	...
Madrid Puerta de Atocha a.	0850	0910	0850	0920	0915	0930	1010	1112	1055	|	|	1145	1145	...	1317	1325	1345	1512	1545	1555	1630	1630	1712	1745	1755	...
Málaga **660** a.	...	...	...	...	...	...	...	...	...	|	1430	...	...	...	...	...	...	...	...	...	...	...	...	...	...	...
Sevilla **660** a.	...	...	...	...	...	...	...	...	...	1404	...	...	...	...	...	...	...	...	...	...	...	...	...	...	...	...

	AVE 3942	*AVE* 3992	*AVE* 3162	*AVE* 3162	*Av* 8166	*AVE* 3160	*AVE* 3172	*AVE* 3172	*avlo* 6308	*Ouigo* 6570	*AVE* 3782	*Av* 10782	*Av* 8186	*AVE* 3180	*AVE* 3192	*AVE* 3190	*AVE* 3202	*Av* 8206	*Ouigo* 6610	*Ouigo* 6610	*avlo* 6310	*AVE* 3222	*Av* 10222			
			①–⑥	⑦	Ⓑ	Ⓑ	①–⑤	⑦			⑤	④⑦		Ⓑ		Ⓑ			B	A		⑦	①–⑥			
Figueres Vilafant **657** d.	...	...	1455	...	...	...	...	1545	...	...	...	...	...	...	1755	...	...	...	...	...	...	...	...	...	...	...
Girona **657** d.	...	...	1511	...	...	...	...	1601	...	...	...	...	...	...	1811	...	...	...	...	...	...	...	...	...	...	...
Barcelona Sants d.	1545	1545	1600	1600	1605	1625	1700	1700	1725	1745	...	...	1805	1825	1900	1925	2000	2010	2038	2045	2110	2150	2200	...	...	...
Camp de Tarragona d.	1618	1618	1634	1634	1642	|	|	|	|	|	...	...	1842	|	1934	|	2034	2047	2112	|	|	2223	2237	...	...	...
Lleida d.	1652	1652	1701	1701	1713	|	|	|	|	|	1900	1900	1913	|	2001	|	2101	2118	|	|	|	2250	2307	...	...	...
Zaragoza Delicias d.	1732	1732	1745	1745	...	|	1826	1826	|	|	|	|	...	|	2045	|	2145	...	2211	2211	2238	2335	2354	...	...	...
Calatayud d.	|	|	1810	1810	...	|	|	|	|	|	|	|	...	|	|	|	2211	...	|	|	|	...	...	...	...	...
Guadalajara - Yebes d.	|	|	|	|	...	|	|	|	|	|	2020	2030	...	|	|	|	2249	...	|	|	|	...	...	...	...	...
Madrid Puerta de Atocha a.	|	|	1912	1912	...	1855	1945	1945	1955	2015	...	...	...	2055	2207	2155	2317	...	2330	2330	2355	...	...	...	...	...
Málaga **660** a.	|	2146	...	...	...	...	...	...	...	...	...	...	...	...	...	...	...	...	...	...	...	...	...	...	...	...
Sevilla **660** a.	2118	...	...	...	...	...	...	...	...	...	...	...	...	...	...	...	...	...	...	...	...	...	...	...	...	...

A – Apr. 1 - May 25. Oct. 3 - Dec. 10.
B – May 26 - Oct. 2.
G – Conveys portion to / from Granada (Table **678a**).
M – To / from Marseille (Table **13**).
N – ①②③④⑥⑦.
P – ①②③④⑥.
Ouigo – Low-cost ***TGV*** Euroduplex services branded **Ouigo**, internet booking only: www.ouigo.com
avlo – Low-cost ***AVE*** Renfe services branded **avlo**: www.avlorenfe.com
☛ *AVE* trains convey ✗ and 🍸. *Avant* trains (*Av*) are *Turista* class only.
☛ **Shaded services are suspended until further notice.**

MADRID – LOGROÑO, PAMPLONA / IRUÑA, HUESCA – BARCELONA 650a

	Hotel 921 🍷 A	IC 635 ①–⑤	IC 10655 ⑥ y	Alvia 533 K	Alvia 433 F	Alvia 601 ①–⑤	IC 631 ①–⑥ B	Alvia 705 ⑥⑦	Alvia 603 ⑥	Alvia 605 Ⓑ	IC 633 ⑦ B	Alvia 661 ①–⑥ G	AVE 3363 ⑤⑦	IC 10657 ⑦ b	Alvia 621 625 J	Alvia 537 K	Alvia 437 Ⓑ F	Alvia 609 Ⓑ	Alvia 613 ①–④	Alvia 701	AVE 3393	Alvia 801 Ⓑ	
Madrid Puerta de Atocha d.	...	...	...	...	...	0735	...	0805	0935	1135	...	...	1605	...	...	...	...	1505	1735	1815	1905	1935	...
Guadalajara - Yebes d.	...	...	...	...	...	|	...	0831	1002	1201	...	...	|	...	...	...	...	1531	|	1840	1928	|	...
Calatayud d.	...	...	...	...	...	|	...	0917	1106	1248	...	...	|	...	...	...	...	1619	|	1934	2006	|	...
Logroño **654** a.	0403	...	...	...	0904	|	1021	1132	|	|	1434	...	|	...	...	...	1753	|	|	2142	|	|	...
Pamplona / Iruña **654** a.	|	0625	0812	0913	|	1042	|	...	1303	1452	|	1508	|	1625	1732	1754	|	1828	2043	...	|	2240	...
Zaragoza Delicias d.	0632	0810	1003	1113	1113	...	1215	...	...	...	1628	1701	1727	1811	1922	1952	1952	...	...	...	2033	...	...
Huesca **670** a.	|	|	|	|	|	...	|	...	...	...	|	|	1810	|	|	|	|	...	...	...	2118	...	...
Lleida d.	0730	0900	1056	1203	1203	...	1313	...	...	...	1722	1754	...	|	2016	2051	2051	...	...	...	...	...	...
Camp de Tarragona d.	0804	0930	1127	1238	1238	...	1343	...	...	...	1753	1827	...	1924	2054	2128	2128	...	...	...	...	...	...
Barcelona Sants a.	0849	1010	1205	1320	1320	...	1420	...	...	...	1835	1903	...	2000	2135	2209	2209	...	...	...	...	...	...

	Alvia 802 ①–⑤	AVE 3272	Alvia 702	Alvia 800 ②–⑤	Alvia 600 ⑥	Alvia 534 K	Alvia 434 ①–⑥ F	Alvia 602 Ⓑ	Alvia 622 626 J	IC 10560 ⑥ b	Alvia 606	Alvia 664 G	IC 632 B	Alvia 530 K	Alvia 430 F	AVE 3592 ⑤⑦	Alvia 706 ⑥⑦	Alvia 610 Ⓑ	IC 562 ①–⑤ w	IC 562 ⑦	Hotel 922 🍷 A		
Barcelona Sants d.	...	...	...	...	...	0730	0730	...	0930	1005	...	1210	1410	1530	1530	...	...	...	1840	1930	2020	...	...
Camp de Tarragona d.	...	...	...	...	...	0808	0808	...	1007	1043	...	1248	1447	1608	1608	...	...	...	1918	2008	2103	...	...
Lleida d.	...	...	...	...	...	0844	0844	...	1037	1115	...	1322	1517	1639	1639	...	...	...	1950	2041	2142	...	...
Huesca **670** d.	...	0815	...	...	...	|	|	...	|	|	...	|	|	|	|	1935	...	...	|	|	|	...	...
Zaragoza Delicias d.	...	0900	...	...	...	0934	0934	...	1139	1204	...	1414	1608	1729	1729	2020	...	...	2102	2134	2250	...	...
Pamplona / Iruña **654** d.	0640	|	...	0810	0900	1117	|	1130	1321	1354	1537	1606	|	1922	|	|	...	1935	2244	2328	|	...	...
Logroño **654** d.	|	|	0730	|	|	...	1123	|	...	...	|	...	1750	...	1936	|	1845	|	...	...	0102	...	...
Calatayud d.	|	0925	0936	|	1113	...	...	1324	...	...	|	...	...	...	...	|	2055	2131	...	...	...	...	...
Guadalajara - Yebes d.	|	1005	1022	|	1202	...	...	1412	...	...	|	...	...	...	...	|	2157	2221	...	...	...	...	...
Madrid Puerta de Atocha a.	0945	1035	1050	1124	1230	...	...	1440	...	...	1845	...	...	...	...	2140	2225	2250	...	...	...	...	...

A – Ⓑ (daily June 17 - Sept. 16): GALICIA *Trenhotel* – 🛏, (1) (reclining) Barcelona - Logroño - A Coruña and Vigo and v.v.
B – (12) Salamanca - Valladolid - Barcelona and v.v. (Tables **654, 689**).
F – (12) Bilbao - Barcelona and v.v. (Table **654**).
G – (12) Gijón - Barcelona and v.v. (Table **685**).
J – (12) Vigo / A Coruña - Barcelona and v.v. (Table **680**).
K – (12) Irún - Barcelona and v.v. (Table **654**).
b – To Irún (Table **654**).
w – To Vitoria / Gasteiz on ⑤ (Table **654**).
y – From Vitoria / Gasteiz (Table **654**).

Shaded services are suspended until further notice.

MADRID - SORIA and ZARAGOZA 651

km	For high-speed trains see Tables **650** and **650a**	2 Ⓐ		2 Ⓒ		2 Ⓐ H	2 Ⓐ	2 Ⓒ	2 Ⓒ		2 Ⓐ		2 ⑤		2 ⑤	2 w		2 ⑦	2	2 ⑦	2 Ⓐ	2 ⑦	
0	**Madrid**-Chamartín-Clara Campoamor d.	...	...	...	...	0715	0747	0814	0915	...	...	...	1432	...	1543	1547	...	...	1900	1907	1952	2002	...
55	Guadalajara d.	...	...	...	...	0757	0826	0854	0959	...	...	...	1509	...	1628	1642	...	...	1939	2038	2050	2038	...
138	Sigüenza d.	...	...	...	...	0859	0920	0944	1102	...	...	...	1612	...	1717	1743	...	...	2031	2142	2153	2142	...
248	**Soria** a.	...	...	...	...	|	1047	1110	|	...	...	...	...	...	1840	|	...	...	2154	...	...	...	...
178	Arcos de Jalón d.	0650	...	0850	...	0936	...	...	1140	...	...	...	...	...	...	1815	...	...	...	...	...	...	...
241	Calatayud d.	0736	...	0936	...	1016	...	...	1221	...	1321	...	...	...	...	1859	...	2023	...	...	...	...	...
339	**Zaragoza** Delicias ♣ a.	0855	...	1101	...	1114	...	...	1325	...	1438	...	...	...	...	2011	...	2149	...	...	...	...	...

For high-speed trains see Tables **650** and **650a**	2 Ⓐ		2 Ⓐ		2 Ⓒ		2		2 H	2 ⑤	2 Ⓑ	2 ⑦		2		2 ⑦		2					
Zaragoza Delicias ♥ d.	...	...	...	...	...	...	0857	...	1407	...	1620	...	...	...	...	...	...	2036	...	...	...	...	...
Calatayud d.	...	...	...	...	...	...	1018	...	1506	...	1742	...	...	...	...	...	...	2157	...	...	...	...	...
Arcos de Jalón d.	...	...	...	...	...	...	1104	...	1543	...	...	...	...	...	...	...	...	2244	...	...	...	...	...
Soria d.	...	...	0702	...	0843	...	|	...	|	...	...	1657	...	1910	...	...	...	...	...	...	...	...	...
Sigüenza d.	0648	...	0826	...	1007	...	1140	...	1619	1700	...	1817	...	2033	...	2150	...	...	...	...	...	...	...
Guadalajara d.	0754	...	0923	...	1055	...	1244	...	1723	1758	...	1908	...	2126	...	2248	...	...	...	...	...	...	...
Madrid-Chamartín-Clara Campoamor a.	0913	...	1006	...	1136	...	1329	...	1807	1837	...	1950	...	2206	...	2327	...	...	...	...	...	...	...

H – To / from Barcelona (Table **652**).
w – To Lleida on Ⓑ (Table **652**).
♥ – All services call 7 – 8 minutes earlier at Zaragoza **Goya** and 5 minutes earlier at Zaragoza **Portillo**.
♣ – All services call 4 – 5 minutes later at Zaragoza **Portillo** and 6 – 8 minutes later at Zaragoza **Goya**.

Shaded services are suspended until further notice.

ZARAGOZA - BARCELONA 652

km	For high-speed trains see Tables **650** and **650a**	2 ⚒	2	2	2 ⚒	2	Hotel 921¶ G 🍷	2	2	2	2	2	2 ⑥	2 ⑦	2	2 Ⓐ	2 Ⓒ	2	2	2 Ⓐ	2 ⚒	2 †	2	2 Ⓑ	2
	Madrid Chamartín ‡ **651** d.	...	...	...	...	...	...	...	...	...	...	...	...	...	...	0715	...	...	...	...	...	...	...	1547	...
0	**Zaragoza** Delicias ♣ d.	...	...	...	...	...	0632	...	...	...	...	...	0857	1027	...	1116	1116	...	...	1515	...	...	1630	2012	2015
114	Caspe d.	...	...	...	...	...	|	0705	...	...	...	...	|	|	...	1252	1252	...	...	|	...	...	1800	|	2152
★	Lleida d.	...	...	...	0623	0715	0730	|	...	...	...	...	1121	1237	1310	|	|	1545	...	1727	1748	1748	|	2240	▬
239	Reus d.	0537	0641	0733	0743	|	|	0906	...	1107	1139	1308	...	...	1437	1454	1454	1714	1836	...	|	|	2005	...	2122
257	Tarragona **672** d.	0555	0659	0749	0800	|	0804t	0926	1021	1125	1158	1326	...	...	1455	1512	1512	1730	1858	...	|	|	2027	...	2140
282	Sant Vicenç de Calders **672** d.	0616	0719	0810	0831	0847	|	0948	1043	1145	1218	1347	...	...	1517	1536	1536	1750	1919	...	1913	1923	2046	...	2200
342	**Barcelona** Sants **672** a.	0720	0809	0909	0934	0939	0849	1040	1138	1240	1309	1440	...	...	1610	1637	1640	1840	2013	...	2010	2019	2139	...	2304
345	Barcelona Pass. de Gràcia a.	0725	0814	0914	0939	0944	...	1045	1143	1245	1314	1445	...	...	1615	1644	1645	1845	2018	...	2015	2024	2144	...	2309
350	**Barcelona** França a.	0735	0824	0925	0949	0954	...	1055	1155	1255	1325	1455	...	...	1625	1655	1655	1855	2028	...	2025	2034	2154	...	2319

For high-speed trains see Tables **650** and **650a**	2 Ⓐ	2 Ⓐ	2	2 Ⓒ	2	2	2	2	2	2	2	2 ⑦	2 Ⓐ	2	2	2	2	2	2	2 Ⓑ	Hotel 922¶ G 🍷	2			
Barcelona França d.	...	...	0613	...	0647	0713	0843	0913	1143	1313	1343	...	1513	1543	1643	1713	1843	1847	1940	2010	...	2113	...	...	...
Barcelona Pass. de Gràcia d.	...	...	0624	...	0659	0724	0854	0924	1154	1324	1354	...	1524	1554	1654	1724	1854	1858	1952	2021	...	2124	...	...	...
Barcelona Sants **672** d.	...	...	0630	...	0706	0730	0903	0930	1203	1330	1403	...	1533	1603	1703	1730	1903	1904	1957	2027	2020	2130	...	...	...
Sant Vicenç de Calders **672** d.	...	...	0724	...	0807	0822	0950	1017	1248	1420	1449	...	1619	1649	1747	1820	1948	2005	2046	2115	|	2222	...	...	...
Tarragona **672** d.	...	...	0746	...	|	0844	1011	1042	1308	1441	1511	...	1640	1710	1809	1841	|	2037	2107	2136	2103t	2243	...	...	...
Reus d.	...	...	0803	...	|	0900	1028	1048	1326	1458	1531	...	1656	1727	1827	1855	|	2052	2124	2152	|	2259	...	...	...
Lleida d.	...	0625	...	...	0956	...	|	...	1455	...	1650	1515	...	|	1955	|	2112	...	...	...	2142	...	...	...	...
Caspe d.	0653	|	...	1039	...	...	1229	...	...	...	...	|	...	1944	...	2108	...	...	...	...	|	...	...	...	...
Zaragoza Delicias ♥ a.	0825	0856	...	1212	...	...	1405	...	...	...	...	1731	...	2114	...	...	...	...	...	...	2238	...	...	...	...
Madrid Chamartín ‡ **651** a.	...	1329	...	...	...	...	1807	...	...	...	...	...	...	...	...	...	...	...	...	...	...	...	...	...	...

G – Ⓑ: GALICIA *Trenhotel* – 🛏, (1) (reclining) Barcelona - A Coruña and Vigo and v.v.
t – **Camp** de Tarragona.
‡ – Full name is Madrid-Chamartín-Clara Campoamor.
¶ – Via high speed line.
★ – Leida - Reus: *90 km.* Zaragoza - Lleida: *189 km.* Lleida - Sant Vicenç: *106 km.*
♥ – All trains (except *Hotel* **922**) call 5 – 8 minutes earlier at Zaragoza **Goya** and 3 – 5 minutes earlier at Zaragoza **Portillo**.
♣ – All trains (except *Hotel* **921**) call 4 – 5 minutes later at Zaragoza **Portillo** and 6 – 8 minutes later at Zaragoza **Goya**.

Shaded services are suspended until further notice.

LLEIDA - LA POBLA DE SEGUR 653

FGC 2nd class

km						A	Ⓑ		†	①–④		
0	**Lleida** d.	...	0620	0747	0905	1040	1047	1330	1705	1730	...	...
27	Balaguer d.	...	0646	0815	0931	1110	1115	1356	1731	1756	...	...
77	Tremp d.	...	...	0909	...	|	1209	...	1825	1850	...	...
90	**La Pobla de Segur** a.	...	...	0922	...	1235	1222	...	1838	1903	...	...

	Ⓐ	Ⓑ	Ⓑ	⑦	⑥	①–⑤	A	Ⓒ	①–④	B	
La Pobla de Segur d.	0708	1008	...	1515	...	1530	1700	1900	1930	...	...
Tremp d.	0719	1019	...	1526	...	1541	|	1911	1941	...	...
Balaguer d.	0815	1115	1408	1622	1623	1637	1830f	2007	2037	2202	...
Lleida a.	0841	1141	1434	1648	1649	1703	1900	2033	2103	2228	...

A – Tren dels Llacs: ⑥ Apr. 23 - Oct. 29.
B – Runs 19 minutes earlier on ⑥.
f – Arrive 1815.

654 ZARAGOZA - IRÚN and BILBAO

km		18071	16071	Alvia 601	Alvia 534	Alvia 434	Alvia 603	Alvia 622 632	Alvia 605	IC 10560	18021	IC 282	Alvia 664	18073	16015	IC 632	Alvia 609	18023	Alvia 530	16017	Alvia 430	Alvia 613	Alvia 611	18075
		2	2								2			2	2			2	②④	2	①③			2
		①–⑥	①–⑤	①–⑤		B	⑥	J	Ⓑ	⑥			A			C	Ⓑ	⑤	⑥⑦	①–⑥	⑤	①–③	④	
	Barcelona Sants **652** d.	...	...	...	0730	0730	...	0930	...	1005	...	...	1210	...	...	1410	...	...	1530	...	1530	...	...	...
	Madrid PA ‡ **650a** d.	...	...	0735	|	|	0935	|	1135	|	...	...	|	...	...	|	1505	...	|	...	|	1735	1735	...
0	**Zaragoza** Delicias d.	0625	...	|	0934	0934	|	1139	|	1204	1309	...	1414	1435	...	1608	|	1652	1729	...	1729	|	|	1742
94	Castejón de Ebro ★ d.	0729	0730	0944	1028	1031	1210	1231	|	1259	1417	...	|	1540	...	1702	|	1748	1833	...	1845	|	|	1849
182	**Pamplona / Iruña** d.	0837	|	1042	1119	|	1303	1323	1452	1356	1526	...	1608	|	1642	|	1828	1859	1924	1958	|	2043	2044	|
234	Altsasu **689** d.	0918t	|	...	1150	|	...	|	...	|	...	...	|	|	1718t	|	...	...	1953	2034t	|	...	|	|
275	Vitoria / Gasteiz **689** d.	0950	|	...	|	|	...	1416	...	|	...	1645	1702	|	1753	|	...	...	|	2107	|	...	|	|
321	San Seb / Don ❖ d.	|	|	...	1303	|	...	|	...	1550	...	1821	|	|	|	|	...	...	2110	...	|	...	2226	|
337	**Irún** **689** a.	|	|	...	...	|	...	|	...	...	...	1844	|	|	|	|	...	...	...	...	|	...	...	|
171	**Logroño 650a** d.	|	0829	...	...	1125	...	|	...	...	...	...	|	1635	|	1751	...	...	...	...	1938	...	...	1945
242	Miranda de Ebro **689** d.	1016	...	...	...	1225	...	1437	...	...	...	...	1722	...	1820	1851	...	...	...	...	2032	...	...	...
347	**Bilbao** Abando **689** a.	...	...	...	...	1404	...	...	...	...	...	...	...	...	...	...	...	...	...	...	2209	...	...	...

	16027	18077	IC 562	IC 562	Alvia 701	Alvia 801	18079	IC 562	Hotel 922
	2	2					2		G 🍸
	⑦		①–④	⑤	Ⓑ	Ⓑ	⑤⑥⑦	⑦	¶
Barcelona Sants **652** d.	...	...	1840	1840	...	...	...	1930	2020
Madrid PA ‡ **650a** d.	...	...	|	|	1815	1935	...	|	|
Zaragoza Delicias d.	...	1921	2102	2102	|	|	2109	2134	2250
Castejón de Ebro ★ d.	1852	2031	|	|	|	|	2215	|	0014
Pamplona / Iruña d.	2005	2138	2244	2246	|	2240	|	2328	|
Altsasu **689** d.	2046t	...	...	|	|	...	|	...	|
Vitoria / Gasteiz **689** d.	2118	...	...	2337	|	...	|	...	|
San Seb / Don ❖ d.	|	...	...	...	|	...	|	...	|
Irún **689** a.	|	...	...	...	|	...	|	...	|
Logroño 650a d.	|	...	...	...	2136	...	2312	...	0102
Miranda de Ebro **689** d.	2143	...	...	...	...	...	...	...	...
Bilbao Abando **689** a.	...	...	...	...	...	...	...	...	...

	18068	IC 635	18072	Alvia 802	Alvia 702	18074	Alvia 800	IC 10655	Alvia 600	
	2		2			2				
	①–⑤	①–⑤	①–⑤	②–⑤	①–⑥		②–⑤	⑥	⑥	
Bilbao Abando **689** d.	...	...	...	...	...	...	...	...	...	...
Miranda de Ebro **689** d.	...	...	...	...	...	...	...	...	...	...
Logroño 650a d.	...	...	0615	...	0735	...	...	...	...	...
Irún **689** d.	...	...	|	...	|	...	...	...	...	...
San Seb / Don ❖ d.	...	...	|	...	|	...	...	...	...	...
Vitoria / Gasteiz **689** d.	...	...	|	...	|	...	...	0718	...	...
Altsasu **689** d.	...	...	|	...	|	...	...	|	...	...
Pamplona / Iruña d.	...	0625	|	0640	|	0743z	0810	0812	0900	...
Castejón de Ebro d.	0605	0717	0720e	0730	|	0850	|	|	0952	...
Zaragoza Delicias a.	0715	0807	0836	|	|	0956	|	1000	|	...
Madrid PA ‡ **650a** a.	...	|	...	0950	1050	...	1124	|	1230	...
Barcelona Sants **652** a.	...	1010	...	...	...	...	...	1205	...	...

	Alvia 533	Alvia 433	16019	Alvia 602	IC 631		18076	IC 633	IC 281	Alvia 661	Alvia 606	IC 10657	18070	18029	Alvia 621 625	Alvia 537	Alvia 437	Alvia 612	Alvia 608	Alvia 610	16111	16011	18078	Hotel 921
	①③	②④	2 b		①–⑥		2	⑦		A			2	2							2	2	2	G 🍸
	⑤⑦	⑥	①–⑥	Ⓑ	C			C		①–⑥		⑦	⑤⑥⑦	b	J		P	⑦	⑤	Ⓑ	①–⑥	⑦		¶
Bilbao Abando **689** d.	...	0630	...	...	...	...	...	...	...	...	...	...	...	...	...	...	1520	...	...	...	...	...	...	...
Miranda de Ebro **689** d.	...	0805	0925	...	0921	...	...	1337	...	1347	...	...	...	1501	1613	...	1652	...	...	...	...	...	...	...
Logroño 650a d.	...	0904	|	...	1021	...	1415	1434	...	|	...	...	1642	|	|	...	1753	...	...	...	...	...	2023	0403
Irún **689** d.	...	|	|	...	|	...	|	|	1205	|	...	...	|	|	|	...	|	...	...	...	...	...	|	|
San Seb / Don ❖ d.	0728	|	|	...	|	...	|	|	1221	|	...	1437	|	|	|	1610	|	...	1640	...	...	...	|	|
Vitoria / Gasteiz **689** d.	|	|	0952	...	|	...	|	|	1358	1411	...	|	|	1530	1635	|	|	...	|	...	1900	1921	|	|
Altsasu **689** d.	0842	|	1025t	...	|	...	|	|	...	|	...	|	|	1601t	|	1722	|	...	|	...	1931t	1952t	|	|
Pamplona / Iruña d.	0913	|	1057	1130	|	...	|	|	...	1508	1537	1625	|	1638	1732	1754	|	1807	1828	1935	2015	2026	|	|
Castejón de Ebro d.	1010	1010	...	|	1114	...	1510	1527	...	1602	|	|	1741	1744	1826	1854	1854	|	|	|	2111	2123	2127	0456
Zaragoza Delicias a.	1110	1110	...	|	1212	...	1611	1628	...	1659	|	1808	...	1851	1919	1950	1950	|	|	|	...	2217	2235	0629
Madrid PA ‡ **650a** a.	|	|	...	1440	|	...	...	|	...	|	1845	|	...	...	|	|	|	2125	2135	2250	...	...	...	|
Barcelona Sants **652** a.	1320	1320	...	...	1420	...	...	1835	...	1903	...	2000	...	...	2135	2209	2209	...	...	...	...	...	...	0849

A – 12 Barcelona - Gijón and v.v. (Table **685**).
B – ①–⑥ (daily June 18 - Sept. 9).
C – 12 Barcelona - Valladolid - Salamanca and v.v. (Tables **650a**, **689**).
G – Ⓑ: GALICIA *Trenhotel* – 1 (reclining) Barcelona - A Coruña and Vigo and v.v.
J – 12 🍸 Barcelona - Vigo / A Coruña and v.v. (Table **680**).
P – Ⓑ (daily June 17 - Sept. 8).

b – From Burgos Rosa Manzano on ①–⑥ (Table **689**).
e – Arrive 0709.
t – Altsasu Pueblo (*230 km*).
z – ①–⑤.

¶ – Via high speed line.
★ – Calatayud - Castejón: *140 km*.
‡ – Full name is Madrid Puerta de Atocha.
❖ – Full name is San Sebastián / Donostia.

Shaded services are suspended until further notice.

656 BARCELONA - PUIGCERDÀ - LATOUR DE CAROL

2nd class

km																								
		Ⓐ													Ⓐ	Ⓒ								
0	**Barcelona** Sants d.	0501	0531	0601	0701	0731	0801	0831	0931	1031	1131	1201	1231	1301	1331	1331	1431	1501	1531	1631	1701	1731	1801	1831
	La Sagrera-Meridiana d.	0515	0545	0615	0715	0745	0815	0845	0945	1045	1145	1215	1245	1315	1345	1345	1445	1515	1545	1645	1715	1745	1815	1845
	Sant Andreu Arenal d.	0518	0548	0618	0718	0748	0818	0848	0948	1048	1148	1218	1248	1318	1348	1348	1448	1518	1548	1648	1718	1748	1848	1848
33	Granollers - Canovelles d.	0545	0615	0645	0745	0815	0845	0915	1015	1115	1215	1245	1315	1345	1415	1415	1515	1545	1615	1715	1745	1815	1845	1915
74	Vic d.	0622	0652	0723	0823	0852	0922	0953	1053	1153	1253	1322	1353	1422	1453	1453	1553	1622	1653	1753	1822	1853	1923	1952
90	Torelló d.	...	...	0738	0838	...	...	1008	1108	1208	1308	...	1408	...	1508	1508	1608	...	1708	1808	...	1908	1938	...
110	Ripoll d.	...	...	0805	0906	...	...	1035	1137	1237	1335	...	1437	...	1536	1536	1635	...	1737	1835	...	1942	2005	...
124	Ribes de Freser **658** a.	...	...	0826	0921	...	...	1056	...	...	1356	...	...	...	...	1551	1656	...	...	1856	...	...	2026	...
145	La Molina a.	...	...	0853	...	...	...	1126	...	...	1426	...	...	...	...	...	1726	...	...	1923	...	...	2053	...
159	Puigcerdà a.	...	...	0912	...	...	...	1145	...	...	1445	...	...	...	...	...	1745	...	...	1941	...	...	2111	...
163	**Latour de Carol** 🏛 **312** a.	...	...	0918	...	...	...	1151	...	...	1451	...	...	...	...	...	1751	...	...	...	...	...	...	...

	Ⓐ								
Barcelona Sants d.	1852	1901	1931	2001	2031	2101	2131	2231	...
La Sagrera-Meridiana d.	1906	1915	1945	2015	2045	2115	2145	2245	...
Sant Andreu Arenal d.	1908	1918	1948	2018	2048	2118	2148	2248	...
Granollers - Canovelles d.	1930	1946	2015	2045	2115	2145	2215	2315	...
Vic d.	2009	2022	2052	2123	2152	2223	2252	2352	...
Torelló d.	2021	...	...	2138	...	2238	...	...	...
Ripoll d.	2047	...	...	2207	...	2307	...	...	...
Ribes de Freser **658** a.	2104	...	...	...	...	...	...	...	...
La Molina a.	2131	...	...	...	...	...	...	...	...
Puigcerdà a.	2150	...	...	...	...	...	...	...	...
Latour de Carol 🏛 **312** a.	...	...	...	...	...	...	...	...	...

	Ⓐ				Ⓐ				
Latour de Carol 🏛 **312** d.	...	...	...	...	...	...	...	...	...
Puigcerdà d.	...	...	...	...	0524	...	...	...	0703
La Molina d.	...	...	...	...	0544	...	...	...	0723
Ribes de Freser **658** d.	...	...	...	...	0611	...	...	...	0750
Ripoll d.	...	...	0539	...	0629	...	0710	...	0809
Torelló d.	...	...	0606	...	0650	...	0737	...	0837
Vic d.	0524	0554	0623	0654	0705	0724	0754	0824	0854
Granollers - Canovelles d.	0601	0631	0701	0731	0745	0801	0831	0901	0931
Sant Andreu Arenal a.	0629	0659	0729	0759	0808	0829	0859	0929	0959
La Sagrera-Meridiana a.	0632	0702	0732	0802	0811	0832	0902	0932	1002
Barcelona Sants a.	0646	0716	0746	0816	0825	0846	0916	0946	1016

												Ⓒ	Ⓐ											
Latour de Carol 🏛 **312** d.	...	0825	...	1025	...	...	...	...	1325	...	...	...	...	...	1625	...	...	...	1855	...	...	...	...	...
Puigcerdà d.	...	0832	...	1032	...	...	...	...	1332	...	...	...	...	...	1632	...	...	...	1902	...	...	...	...	...
La Molina d.	...	0852	...	1052	...	...	...	...	1352	...	...	...	...	...	1652	...	...	...	1922	...	...	...	...	...
Ribes de Freser **658** d.	...	0919	1021	1121	...	...	...	...	1421	...	...	1621	...	...	1721	...	...	...	1949	...	...	...	...	...
Ripoll d.	...	0941	1039	1140	...	1239	...	1339	1440	...	1539	1639	1639	...	1740	...	1907	...	2008	...	2109	...	...	...
Torelló d.	...	1007	1107	1207	...	1307	...	1407	1507	...	1607	1707	1707	...	1807	...	1937	...	2038	...	2137	...	...	...
Vic d.	0954	1024	1124	1224	1254	1324	1354	1424	1524	1554	1624	1724	1724	1754	1824	1854	1954	2024	2054	2124	2154	2224	...	...
Granollers - Canovelles d.	1031	1101	1201	1301	1331	1401	1431	1501	1601	1631	1701	1801	1801	1831	1901	1931	2031	2101	2131	2201	2231	2301	...	...
Sant Andreu Arenal a.	1059	1129	1229	1329	1359	1429	1459	1529	1629	1659	1729	1829	1829	1859	1929	1959	2059	2129	2159	2229	2259	2329	...	...
La Sagrera-Meridiana a.	1102	1132	1232	1332	1402	1432	1502	1532	1632	1702	1732	1832	1832	1902	1932	2002	2102	2132	2202	2232	2302	2332	...	...
Barcelona Sants a.	1116	1146	1246	1346	1416	1446	1516	1546	1646	1716	1746	846	1846	1916	1946	2016	2116	2146	2216	2246	2316	2346	...	...

BARCELONA - GIRONA - FIGUERES - PORTBOU / PERPIGNAN 657

Reservations are not compulsory on *Media Distancia* (*MD*) services on the Barcelona - Girona - Portbou - Cebère route. All stopping services convey 2nd class only.

km	km		*MD*		*MD*		*Av*		*MD*	*AVE*	*MD*			*AVE*	*TGV*	*MD*	*MD*		*AVE*		*MD*	*MD*	*AVE*	*MD*		
							34609*			**9736**				**9708**	**9702**				**3073**				**3093**			
			Ⓐ	Ⓐ	Ⓐ	⑥		Ⓐ	Ⓒ	**34737***	Ⓐ	Ⓒ	Ⓐ	**34709***	**34703***	Ⓒ	Ⓐ	Ⓒ	**34073***	Ⓐ	Ⓐ	Ⓒ	**34093***	Ⓐ	Ⓒ	Ⓐ
										L				**PB**	**PT**				⑥⑦							
		Madrid ⊠ **660** d.	...	...	...	...	...	...	...	...	...	...	...	...	...	...	...	...	0730	...	...	...	0930	...	...	...
0	0	**Barcelona** Sants **666** d.	0556	0616	0646	0646	0705	0716	0746	0815	0816	0846	0916	0910	1000	0946	1016	1046	1050	1116	1146	1146	1245	1246	1246	1316
3		Barcelona P de G ¶ d.	0601	0621	0651	0651	|	0721	0751	|	0821	0851	0921	|	|	0951	1021	1051	|	1121	1151	1151	|	1251	1251	1321
31		Granollers Centre d.	|	0648	|	0718	|	0753	|	|	|	0918	0948	|	|	|	|	1118	|	1148	|	|	|	|	1318	1348
72		Maçanet - Massanes **666** d.	0659	0726	0752	0751	|	0831	0844	|	0914	0951	1021	|	|	1045	1114	1151	|	1221	1244	1244	|	1344	1351	1421
86		Caldes de Malavella d.	0719	0752	0804	0803	|	0843	0856	|	0925	1003	1033	|	|	1057	1126	1203	|	1233	1256	1256	|	1356	1403	1433
102	95	**Girona** d.	0731	0807	0816	0818	0746	0858	0907	0856	0937	1018	1048	0951	1041	1108	1137	1218	1130	1248	1307	1307	1325	1407	1418	1448
118		Flaçà d.	0744	0822	0832	0833	|	0913	0920	|	0950	1033	1103	|	|	1121	1150	1233	|	1303	1320	1320	|	1420	1433	1503
143		Figueres § d.	0801	0846	0849	0857	|	0935	0937	|	1007	1057	1127	|	|	1138	1207	1257	|	1327	1337	1337	|	1442	1457	1527
	129	Figueres Vilafant § d.	...	|	...	|	0800	|	|	0913	|	|	|	1008	1058	|	|	|	1145	|	...	|	1340	...	|	|
162		Llançà d.	...	0900	...	0911	...	0949	0951	|	1021	1111	1141	|	|	1152	1221	1311	...	1341	...	1351	...	...	1511	1541
169		**Portbou** 🏛 **355** a.	...	0911	...	0922	...	1000	0959	|	1029	1122	1152	|	|	1200	1229	1322	...	1352	...	1359	...	...	1522	1552
171		**Cerbère** 🏛 **355** a.	...	0915	...	0926	...	1004	...	|	...	1126	1156	|	|	...	...	1326	...	1356	...	...	...	...	1526	1556
	177	**Perpignan** **355** a.	...	...	...	...	...	...	...	0937	...	...	...	1034	1123	...	...	...	...	...	...	...	...	...	...	...

	MD	*TGV*	*MD*	*MD*	*MD*		*AVE*	*MD*		*AVE*	*AVE*	*Av*	*MD*	*MD*	*MD*	*AVE*	*MD*		*AVE*	*MD*	*MD*	*MD*	*AVE*	*MD*		
		9704					**3123**			**34725***	**9724**	**34143***				**34153***			**3163**				**3191**			
	†	**34705***	Ⓐ	⑥	†		**34123***			①–⑤	**34725***	⑦	Ⓐ	Ⓐ	Ⓒ	①–④	Ⓐ		**34163***	Ⓐ	Ⓒ	Ⓑ	**34191***			
		AP					Ⓑ				**MR**					⑦			①–⑤				**S**			
Madrid ⊠ **660** d.	...	...	...	...	...	...	1230	...	...	...	1325	...	...	...	...	...	...	...	1630	...	...	...	1900	...	...	...
Barcelona Sants **666** d.	1346	1400	1416	1416	1446	1516	1550	1616	1716	1636	1636	1737	1746	1816	1819	1830	1846	1916	1925	1946	2016	2046	2140	2146	...	...
Barcelona P de G ¶ d.	1351	|	1421	1421	1451	1521	|	1621	1721	|	|	|	1751	1821	1824	|	1851	1921	|	1951	2021	2051	|	2151	...	...
Granollers Centre d.	|	|	|	|	|	1548	|	|	1748	|	|	|	|	|	|	|	|	1948	|	|	|	|	|	|	...	...
Maçanet - Massanes **666** d.	1444	|	1514	1514	1544	1621	|	1714	1821	|	|	|	1844	1914	1921	|	1944	2021	|	2044	2114	2150	|	2250	...	...
Caldes de Malavella d.	1456	|	1526	1526	1556	1633	|	1726	1833	|	|	|	1856	1926	1933	|	1956	2033	|	2056	2126	2206	|	2306	...	...
Girona d.	1507	1441	1537	1537	1607	1648	1630	1737	1848	1717	1717	1817	1907	1937	1944	1911	2007	2048	2005	2107	2137	2217	2220	2315	...	...
Flaçà d.	1520	|	1550	1550	1620	1703	|	1750	1903	|	|	|	1920	1950	1957	|	2020	2103	|	2120	2150	2230	|	...	...	...
Figueres § d.	1537	|	1607	1607	1637	1727	|	1807	1927	|	|	|	1937	2007	2014	|	2040	2127	|	2137	2210	2247	|	...	...	...
Figueres Vilafant § d.	|	1458	...	|	|	|	1645	...	|	1731	1734	1832	|	...	...	1925	...	|	2020	...	...	...	2235	...	...	...
Llançà d.	1551	|	...	1621	1651	1741	...	...	1941	...	|	...	1951	...	...	...	...	2141	...	...	...	...	...	...	...	...
Portbou 🏛 **355** a.	1559	|	...	1629	1659	1752	...	...	1952	...	|	...	1959	...	...	...	...	2151	...	...	...	...	...	...	...	...
Cerbère 🏛 **355** a.	...	|	...	...	...	1756	...	...	...	...	|	...	...	...	...	...	...	...	...	...	...	...	...	...	...	...
Perpignan **355** a.	...	1523	...	...	...	...	...	...	...	...	1758	...	...	...	...	...	...	...	...	...	...	...	...	...	...	...

	MD	*MD*	*AVE*	*Em/Av*	*MD*	*MD*		*AVE*	*MD*	*MD*	*Em/Av*		*MD*		*AVE*	*MD*		*MD*	*AVE*	*MD*		*AVE*	*TGV*	*MD*	*MD*	
			3662	**1081**				**3092**			**1101**				**9731**				**3162**			**3172**	**9713**			
	Ⓐ	⚒	**34662***	**34082***		Ⓐ	⚒	**34092***	†	⚒	**34102***				**34730***				**34262***	Ⓐ		**34172***	**34712***	Ⓐ	Ⓒ	Ⓑ
			①–⑤	①–⑤				①–⑥							**MQ**				①–⑥			⑦	**P**			
Perpignan **355** d.	...	...	...	...	...	...	...	...	...	...	...	...	...	...	1112	...	...	...	...	...	...	...	1533	...	...	...
Cerbère 🏛 **355** d.	...	...	...	...	...	...	...	...	...	...	...	...	...	...	|	...	...	...	...	...	...	...	|	...	...	...
Portbou 🏛 **355** d.	...	...	...	...	...	...	0705	...	...	...	...	0835	...	1035	|	1124	1235	1324	...	...	1435	...	|	...	1524	1605
Llançà d.	...	...	...	...	...	...	0714	...	...	...	...	0844	...	1044	|	1132	1244	1332	...	...	1444	...	|	...	1532	1614
Figueres Vilafant § d.	...	...	0630	0710	...	...	|	0755	...	...	0910	|	...	|	1139	|	|	|	1455	...	|	1545	1559	...	|	|
Figueres § d.	...	0544	|	|	0636	0708	0729	|	0746	0816	|	0859	0946	1059	|	1146	1259	1346	|	1416	1459	|	|	1546	1546	1629
Flaçà d.	...	0604	|	|	0655	0728	0752	|	0805	0835	|	0922	1005	1122	|	1205	1322	1405	|	1435	1522	|	|	1605	1605	1652
Girona d.	0604	0619	0646	0726	0709	0744	0809	0811	0819	0849	0926	0939	1019	1139	1156	1219	1339	1419	1511	1449	1539	1601	1616	1619	1619	1709
Caldes de Malavella d.	0615	0631	|	|	0720	0755	0824	|	0830	0900	|	0954	1030	1154	|	1230	1354	1430	|	1500	1554	|	|	1630	1630	1724
Maçanet - Massanes **666** d.	0630	0647	|	|	0735	0806	0835	|	0841	0911	|	1005	1041	1205	|	1241	1405	1441	|	1511	1605	|	|	1641	1641	1735
Granollers Centre d.	|	|	|	|	|	|	0908	|	|	|	|	1038	|	1238	|	|	1438	|	|	|	1638	|	|	|	|	1808
Barcelona P de G ¶ a.	0735	0750	|	|	0835	0905	0935	|	0935	1005	|	1105	1135	1305	|	1335	1505	1535	|	1605	1705	|	|	1735	1735	1835
Barcelona Sants **666** a.	0739	0755	0725	0805	0840	0910	0940	0850	0940	1010	1005	1110	1140	1310	1234	1340	1510	1540	1550	1910	1710	1640	1654	1740	1739	1840
Madrid ⊠ **660** a.	...	...	1010	...	...	...	...	1145	...	...	...	...	...	...	1545	...	...	...	1912	...	...	1945	...	...	...	...

		MD	*AVE*	*MD*		*MD*	*AVE*	*MD*		*AVE*	*TGV*			*MD*		
			3192				**9743**			**34292***	**9715**					
	⑥	Ⓐ	**34192***	Ⓒ	Ⓐ	⑦	**34742***		⑦	⑦	**34714***	Ⓐ	Ⓒ	Ⓐ	Ⓐ	Ⓒ
							L				**CP**					
Perpignan **355** d.	...	...	...	...	...	...	1810	...	...	...	2033	...	...	...	...	...
Cerbère 🏛 **355** d.	...	...	...	...	...	...	|	...	...	...	|	...	...	...	...	...
Portbou 🏛 **355** d.	1635	...	...	1724	1735	1754	|	...	1839	...	|	1905	1945	...	2024	2025
Llançà d.	1644	...	...	1732	1744	1802	|	...	1848	...	|	1914	1954	...	2032	2034
Figueres Vilafant § d.	|	...	1755	|	|	|	1837	...	|	1939	2056	|	|	...	|	|
Figueres § d.	1659	1716	|	1746	1759	1816	|	1846	1903	|	|	1929	2009	2026	2046	2049
Flaçà d.	1722	1735	|	1805	1822	1835	|	1905	1926	|	|	1952	2032	2045	2105	2108
Girona d.	1739	1749	1811	1819	1839	1849	1854	1919	1943	1956	2113	2009	2049	2059	2119	2123
Caldes de Malavella d.	1754	1800	|	1830	1854	1900	|	1930	1958	|	|	2024	2104	2110	2130	2137
Maçanet - Massanes **666** d.	1805	1811	|	1841	1905	1911	|	1941	2009	|	|	2035	2115	2121	2141	2148
Granollers Centre d.	1838	|	|	|	1938	|	|	|	|	|	|	2108	2148	|	|	2221
Barcelona P de G ¶ a.	1905	1905	|	1935	2005	2005	|	2035	2105	|	|	2135	2215	2215	2235	2247
Barcelona Sants **666** a.	1910	1910	1850	1940	2010	2010	1932	2040	2110	2034	2154	2140	2220	2220	2239	2252
Madrid ⊠ **660** a.	...	...	2207	...	...	...	...	...	...	...	...	...	...	...	...	...

			⚒			Ⓑ					
Portbou 🏛 d.	...	...	1204	...	...	1404	...	...	1604	...	...
Cerbère 🏛 a.	...	...	1222	...	...	1410	...	...	1610	...	...

									⚒			Ⓑ		
Cerbère 🏛 d.	...	...	1239	...	...	1440	...	...	1541	...	...	1741	...	...
Portbou 🏛 a.	...	...	1245	...	...	1445	...	...	1545	...	...	1745	...	...

A – June 15 - Oct. 1.
B – Dec. 12 - July 1, Aug. 29 - Dec. 10.
C – June 14 - Sept. 30.
L – To/from Lyon (Table **13**).
M – To/from Marseille (Table **13**).
P – To/from Paris (Table **13**).
Q – Apr. 9 - Dec. 10.
R – Apr. 8 - Dec. 10.
S – ①②③④⑦.
T – July 2 - Aug. 28.
⊠ – Madrid Puerta de Atocha.
* – Train number for *Turista class (classified Av)*.
¶ – Barcelona Passeig de Gràcia.

§ – **FIGUERES VILAFANT** - **FIGUERES BUS STATION (150m from Figueres)**. *5 km*. By 🚌. Journey time: 15–20 minutes.

From **Figueres Vilafant**: 0810, 0915, 1115, 1155 Ⓒ, 1345, 1605, 1655 Ⓑ, 1845, 1935 ①②③④⑦, 2030 Ⓐ, 2245 ①②③④⑦, 2355.

From **Figueres Bus Station**: 0510, 0605 Ⓐ, 0645 Ⓐ, 0725 ⚒, 0840, 1030, 1425 ⚒, 1520, 1725, 1810.

2nd class VALL DE NÚRIA 658

Ribes Enllaç - **Ribes** Vila - **Queralbs** - **Núria** rack railway

HIGH SEASON:

⑥⑦ from June 4 (also June 24, July 30 - Sept. 4, also Oct. 31, Nov. 1):

From **Ribes** Enllaç: 0730 **v**, 0930, 1020, 1110, 1205, 1250, 1340, 1435, 1540, 1625, 1720, 1930 ⑤.
From **Núria**: 0820, 1020, 1110, 1205, 1250, 1340, 1435, 1540, 1625, 1710, 1830, 2015 ⑤.

LOW SEASON:

①–⑤ from June 1 (not June 24, July 30 - Sept. 4, Oct. 31, Nov. 1):

From **Ribes** Enllaç: 0730 **v**, 0930, 1110, 1250, 1435, 1625.
From **Núria**: 0820, 1020, 1205, 1340, 1540, 1710.

Journey times **Ribes** – **Queralbs** (*6 km*) 24 minutes, **Ribes** – **Núria** (*12 km*) 44 minutes.
Ferrocarrils de la Generalitat de Catalunya (FGC) ✆ +34 972 732 020. www.valldenuria.cat

v – From Ribes Vila.

2nd class AEROPORT BARCELONA 659

Local rail service *Cercanías* (suburban) line **R2 Nord**. *14km*

Aeroport - **Barcelona Sants** – **Barcelona Passeig de Gràcia**

Journey time: 19 minutes Sants, 26 minutes Passeig de Gràcia

From Aeroport del Prat:

0542, 0608, 0638, 0708, 0738 and every 30 minutes until 2208, 2238, 2308, 2338.

From Barcelona Sants:

0513, 0535, 0609, 0639, 0709 and every 30 minutes until 2139, 2209, 2239, 2314.

660 MADRID - CÓRDOBA - SEVILLA and MÁLAGA — High-speed services

km		Av 2260 ①–⑤ ⩚	AVE 2070	Alvia 2074	AVE 2072 ①–⑤	AVE 2076	AVE 2072 ⑥⑦	AVE 2080 ①–⑤	AVE 2082 ①–④	IC 9366	AVE 2090 ①–④	AVE 3982 ①–⑥ V	AVE 2092	Alvia 2394 ⑥ H	IC 2494 B	AVE 2100 A		AVE 2110	AVE 3990	AVE 3940	AVE 2112	AVE 3930	AVE 2310	AVE 2122	AVE 2130 Ⓑ	Alvia 2134	AVE 2140		
	Barcelona Sants **650** . d.	...	...	...	...	...	...	...	...	...	...	...	...	...	...	...	...	...	0830	0830	...	0830	...	...	...	...	...	...	...
0	**Madrid** Puerta de Atocha d.	0620	0700	0705	0735	0735	0735	0800	0825	0835	0905	...	0935	0945	0945	1000	...	1100	|	|	1135	|	1150	1235	1300	1305	1400	...	...
171	Ciudad Real d.	0720	0751	0759	|	|	|	|	|	0937	|	1021	1026	|	|	|	...	|	1212	1212	|	1212	1241	|	1351	1356	|	...	...
210	Puertollano d.	0738	0807	0816	|	|	|	|	|	0953	|	1037	1044	|	|	|	...	|	1228	1228	|	1228	1257	|	1407	1410	|	...	...
345	**Córdoba** d.	0830	0856	0906	0919	0919	0917	0947	|	1039	|	1121	1129	1134	1136	1147	...	1245	1330	1316	1321	1330	1346	1419	1452	1454	1547	...	...
470	**Sevilla** a.	0916	0940	0955	|	|	|	1034	|	|	1128	1205	|	|	1220	1234	...	1332	|	1404	|	|	1430	|	1540	1542	1634	...	...
	Cádiz **671** a.	...	...	1129	|	|	|	...	|	|	...	...	|	|	|	...	...	...	|	...	|	|	...	|	...	1717	...	...	...
	Huelva **671** a.	...	...	...	|	|	|	...	|	|	...	...	|	1331	1402	...	...	...	|	...	|	|	...	|	...	...	...	...	...
419	Puente Genil - Herrera ¶ a.	...	...	...	0940	0940	0940	...	|	|	...	...	|	...	...	...	...	...	1351	...	|	|	...	1440	...	...	...	...	...
455	Antequera - Santa Ana § a.	...	...	...	0956	0956	0956	...	|	1117	...	...	1200	...	...	...	...	...	1405	...	|	1401	...	1456	...	...	...	...	...
	Algeciras **673** a.	...	...	...	|	|	|	...	|	1348	...	...	|	...	...	...	...	...	|	...	|	|	...	|	...	...	...	...	...
	Granada **673, 678a** a.	...	...	...	|	1054	|	...	|	...	...	...	|	...	...	...	...	...	|	...	|	1452	...	|	...	...	...	...	...
513	**Málaga** María Zambrano a.	...	...	...	1025	...	1025	...	1051	...	...	...	1226	...	...	...	...	...	1430	...	1410	...	...	1525	...	...	...	...	...

	AVE 2142	AVE 2146	AVE 2150 Ⓑ	IC 9330 ◐	AVE 2152 G	AVE 2160	Alvia 2164	AVE 2360 Ⓑ G	AVE 2162	AVE 2170 Ⓑ	AVE 2172	AVE 2180 Ⓑ	Alvia 2384 Ⓑ J	AVE 2182 Ⓑ	AVE 3942	AVE 3992	AVE 3974 ①⑤⑦ E	AVE 2380 ④⑤⑦	AVE 2190	AVE 2196	AVE 2192	AVE 2196	AVE 2202 ⑦	AVE 2210	Av 2410 ⩚	AVE 2212 ⑤⑦			
Barcelona Sants **650** .. d.	...	...	...	...	...	...	...	...	...	...	...	...	...	...	1545	1545	...	...	...	...	...	...	...	...	...	...	...	...	...
Madrid Puerta de Atocha d.	1435	1435	1500	1505	1535	1600	1610	1630	1635	1700	1735	1800	1805	1830	|	|	...	1835	1900	1910	1935	1935	2030	2100	2125	2120	...	...	...
Ciudad Real d.	|	|	|	|	|	|	|	|	1726	|	|	|	|	|	1932	1932	1942	|	1951	2001	2026	2026	|	2150	2219	|	...	...	...
Puertollano d.	|	|	|	|	|	|	|	|	1742	|	|	|	|	|	|	|	1957	|	2007	2017	2042	2044	|	2207	2234	|	...	...	...
Córdoba d.	1621	1621	1647	1710	|	1747	|	|	1827	1847	1921	1947	2000	|	2029	2043	2045	|	2056	2106	2131	2127	2214	2256	2324	|	...	...	...
Sevilla a.	|	|	1734	|	|	1834	|	1853	|	1934	|	2034	|	|	2118	|	|	2109	2140	|	|	|	|	2340	0010	|	...	...	...
Cádiz **671** a.	|	|	...	|	|	...	2019	...	|	...	|	...	|	|	...	|	|	...	...	|	|	|	|	...	...	|	...	...	...
Huelva **671** a.	|	|	...	|	|	...	...	...	|	...	|	...	2154	|	...	|	|	...	...	|	|	|	|	...	...	|	...	...	...
Puente Genil - Herrera ¶ . a.	|	|	...	|	|	...	...	...	1848	...	|	...	...	|	...	2106	2110	...	...	|	|	|	2235	...	...	|	...	...	...
Antequera - Santa Ana § . a.	1654	1654	...	1755	|	...	...	...	1901	...	|	...	...	|	...	2121	2125	...	...	2136	2201	2156	2248	...	...	|	...	...	...
Algeciras **673** a.	|	|	...	2032	|	...	...	...	|	...	|	...	...	|	...	|	|	...	...	|	|	|	|	...	...	|	...	...	...
Granada **673, 678a** a.	|	1752	...	...	|	...	...	...	|	...	|	...	...	|	...	|	|	...	...	2232	|	2254	|	...	...	|	...	...	...
Málaga María Zambrano . a.	1723	...	...	...	1808	...	...	...	1927	...	2010	...	...	2058	...	2146	2151	...	...	...	2230	...	2314	...	...	2345	...	...	...

	Av 2261 ①–⑤ ★	AVE 2063 ①–⑤	AVE 2061 ①–④	AVE 2073 ①–④	AVE 2071	AVE 2273	AVE 2075	AVE 2077	AVE 2083 ①–④	AVE 2081 ①–⑤	AVE 3931	AVE 3943	AVE 3993	Alvia 2285 ①–⑤	AVE 2093	AVE 2091 ①–⑥	AVE 3971 ⑤⑥ U	AVE 2103	AVE 2101	IC 9367	Alvia 2205 ⑥	AVE 2111 A	IC 2417 ⑦	AVE 2123	AVE 2121 Ⓑ	AVE 2131	Alvia 2135		
Málaga María Zambrano . d.	...	0628	...	0710	...	0705	...	...	0808	...	...	...	0835	...	0858	...	0945	1028	...	...	...	...	...	1158	...	...	...	...	...
Granada **673, 678a** d.	...	|	...	|	...	|	...	0712	|	...	0815	...	|	...	|	...	|	|	...	...	...	...	1055	|	...	...	...	...	...
Algeciras **673** d.	...	|	...	|	...	|	...	|	|	...	|	...	|	...	|	...	|	|	...	0843	...	...	|	|	...	...	...	...	...
Antequera - Santa Ana § . d.	...	|	...	|	...	0729	...	0806	|	...	0906	...	0858	...	0924	...	1008	|	...	|	...	...	1150	|	...	...	...	...	...
Puente Genil - Herrera ¶ . d.	...	|	...	|	...	0742	...	|	|	...	|	...	0913	...	0938	...	1021	|	...	|	...	...	|	|	...	...	...	...	...
Huelva **671** d.	...	|	...	|	...	|	...	|	|	...	|	...	|	0800	|	...	|	|	...	|	1025	...	|	|	...	...	...	...	...
Cádiz **671** d.	...	|	...	|	...	|	0640	|	|	...	|	...	|	|	|	...	|	|	...	|	|	...	|	|	...	...	1220	...	...
Sevilla d.	0610	|	0643	|	0708	|	0815	|	|	0843	|	0850	|	|	|	0945	|	|	1043	|	|	1143	|	|	1245	1340	1345	...	...
Córdoba d.	0653	0722	0727	|	0754	0807	0906	0838	|	0927	0943	0943	0943	0950	1003	1028	1051	1122	1127	1202	1218	1227	1227	1249	1328	|	1441	...	...
Puertollano d.	0744	|	|	|	0841	|	0957	0923	|	|	|	|	|	|	1047	1111	1135	|	|	|	|	|	1310	|	1411	|	1526	...	...
Ciudad Real d.	0759	|	|	|	0857	|	1015	0939	|	|	1041	1041	1039	|	1103	1126	1148	|	|	|	|	|	1329	|	1426	|	1541	...	...
Madrid Puerta de Atocha a.	0858	0910	0915	0938	0952	0952	1109	1032	1038	1115	|	|	|	1143	1156	1223	...	1309	1316	1405	1410	1417	1424	1435	1523	1610	1636	...	...
Barcelona Sants **650** .. a.	...	...	...	...	...	...	...	...	...	...	1420	1420	1425	...	...	...	...	...	...	...	...	...	...	...	...	...	...	...	...

	AVE 2143	AVE 2141	AVE 3991	AVE 3941	AVE 2153 G	AVE 2151 Ⓑ	AVE 2161 Ⓑ G	AVE 2167	AVE 2163	AVE 2361 Ⓑ	AVE 3973 ⑦ F	AVE 2173	Alvia 2365 ⑦	AVE 2171	IC 9331 ★	AVE 2371 ④⑤⑦	AVE 2183 Ⓑ	AVE 3981 Ⓑ V	AVE 2181 Ⓑ	AVE 2193	IC 2375 ★ B	AVE 2191	Alvia 2175	AVE 2391 ④⑤⑦	AVE 2197	AVE 2203 ⑦	AVE 2211		
Málaga María Zambrano . d.	1358	...	1432	...	1458	...	...	...	1613	...	1638	1658	...	...	...	...	1800	...	...	1858	...	...	...	...	...	2000	...	...	...
Granada **673, 678a** d.	|	...	|	...	|	...	...	1540	|	...	|	|	...	...	...	...	|	...	...	|	...	...	...	...	1925	|	...	...	...
Algeciras **673** d.	|	...	|	...	|	...	...	|	|	...	|	|	...	...	1503	...	|	...	...	|	...	...	...	...	|	|	...	...	...
Antequera - Santa Ana § . d.	1423	...	1457	...	|	...	...	1643	1643	...	1701	1722	...	...	1738	...	|	...	...	|	...	...	...	...	2025	2025	...	...	...
Puente Genil - Herrera ¶ . d.	1437	...	1510	...	|	...	...	|	|	...	1714	1735	...	...	|	...	|	...	...	|	...	...	...	...	2046	2046	...	...	...
Huelva **671** d.	|	...	|	...	|	...	...	|	|	...	|	|	1615	...	|	...	|	...	...	|	1750	...	...	...	|	|	...	...	...
Cádiz **671** d.	|	...	|	...	|	...	...	|	|	...	|	|	|	...	|	...	|	...	...	|	|	...	1810	...	|	|	...	...	...
Sevilla d.	|	1443	|	1450	|	1543	1613	|	|	1643	|	|	|	1728	|	1743	|	1825	1843	|	1924	1943	|	2015	|	|	2058	...	...
Córdoba d.	1502	1527	1540	1540	|	1627	|	1719	1719	1727	1743	1800	1808	1813	1820	1827	1854	1909	1927	1952	2014	2027	|	|	2111	2111	2143	...	...
Puertollano d.	1546	|	1624	1624	|	|	|	|	|	|	1827	|	|	1900	1920	|	|	1952	|	2036	|	|	|	|	|	|	2230	...	...
Ciudad Real d.	1602	|	1640	1640	|	|	|	|	|	|	1843	|	|	1915	1937	|	|	2005	|	2052	|	|	|	|	|	|	2247	...	...
Madrid Puerta de Atocha a.	1655	1715	|	|	1742	1815	1840	1911	1911	1917	...	1945	2003	2010	2040	2017	2043	...	2117	2144	2212	2217	2222	2236	2300	2300	2342	...	...
Barcelona Sants **650** .. a.	...	...	2022	2022	...	...	...	...	...	...	...	...	...	...	...	...	...	...	...	...	...	...	...	...	...	...	...	...	...

A – ①–④ (daily from July 15).
B – June 13 - Sept. 11.
E – ①⑤⑦ (Ⓑ July 14 - Sept. 10). From València (Table **668**).
F – ⑦. To València (Table **668**).
G – From July 15.
H – Sept. 12 - Dec. 10.
J – Ⓑ (daily June 13 - Sept. 11).

U – ⑤⑥ (②③④⑤⑥ July 14 - Sept. 15). To València (Table **668**).
V – From / to València (Table **668**).

f – Arrive 23 minutes earlier.
j – 15 minutes earlier on ⑥.

‡ – Antequera - Ciudad.
§ – ± *17 km* from Antequera.

¶ – ± *8 km* from Puente Genil.
★ – Also calls at Villanueva de CLP (⊠), 23 – 25 mins. after departing Córdoba.
◐ – Also calls at Villanueva de CLP (⊠), 100 mins. after departing Madrid.
⩚ – Also calls at Villanueva de CLP (⊠), 25 – 28 mins. after departing Puertollano.
⊠ – Full name: Villanueva de Córdoba-Los Pedroches.

☛ All trains convey 🍷. *AVE* trains also convey ✕.

☛ **Shaded services are suspended until further notice.**

Avant high-speed shuttle services — Málaga – Córdoba – Sevilla — *Turista* class; 🍷

	8654 Ⓐ	8664 Ⓐ	8664 Ⓒ	8694	8714 Ⓐ	8744	8764 Ⓐ	8784	8704
Málaga María Zambrano d.	...	0643	...	0910	...	1415	1615	1818	2013
Antequera - Santa Ana § d.	...	0709	...	0936	...	1441	1641	1842	2039
Puente Genil - Herrera ¶ d.	...	0723	...	0950	...	1455	1655	1856	2053
Córdoba a.	...	0748	...	1015	...	1520	1720	1920	2118
Córdoba d.	0650	0753	0753	1020	1300	1525	1725	1928	2123
Sevilla a.	0735	0838	0838	1105	1345	1610	1810	2013	2208

	8075 Ⓐ	8085	8095 Ⓐ	8125	8155	8175 Ⓐ	8195	8215		
Sevilla d.	0650	0800	0920	1252	1530	1755	1935	2135	...	...
Córdoba a.	0735	0845	1005	1336	1612	1840	2020	2220	...	...
Córdoba d.	0740	0855	...	1341	1617	1845	2025	...	...	...
Puente Genil - Herrera ¶ d.	0803	0913	...	1407	1650	1908	2050	...	...	...
Antequera - Santa Ana § d.	0817	0927	...	1428	1704	1922	2104	...	...	...
Málaga María Zambrano a.	0845	0955	...	1456	1730	1950	2132	...	...	...

§ – ± *17 km* from Antequera. ¶ – ± *8 km* from Puente Genil.

☛ **Shaded services are suspended until further notice.**

Avant high-speed shuttle services — Madrid – Puertollano — *Turista* class; 🍷

		8260 Ⓐ		8080 Ⓐ		8100		8130	8140 Ⓐ		8150		8170	8180 Ⓐ	8190	8200 Ⓑ	8220							
Madrid Puerta de Atocha d.	...	0640	...	0805	...	1035	...	1315	1415	...	1545	...	1720	1815	1915	2015	2215	...	...	...	...	...	...	...
Ciudad Real d.	...	0736	...	0901	...	1131	...	1411	1511	...	1641	...	1817	1911	2011	2110	2311	...	...	...	...	...	...	...
Puertollano a.	...	0758	...	0918	...	1148	...	1428	1528	...	1658	...	1833	1928	2028	2128	2328	...	...	...	...	...	...	...

		8261 Ⓐ		8271 Ⓐ	8471 Ⓐ	8081 Ⓐ	8081 Ⓒ		8101		8111			8151 ⚒	8161 Ⓐ	8171	8181 ⑦	8191		8211 Ⓑ				
Puertollano d.	...	0625	...	0700	0725	0815	0820	...	1015	...	1120	...	...	1515	1615	1715	1828	1915	...	2120	...	...	...	...
Ciudad Real d.	...	0642	...	0717	0742	0832	0840	...	1032	...	1137	...	...	1532	1632	1732	1845	1932	...	2137	...	...	...	...
Madrid Puerta de Atocha a.	...	0742	...	0813	0838	0928	0944	...	1131	...	1236	...	...	1628	1728	1828	1940	2028	...	2233	...	...	...	...

MADRID - ALMERÍA and JAÉN — 661

For other trains Madrid – Córdoba – Granada / Málaga and v.v. via the AVE high-speed line, see Table **660**

km		MD 17008	MD 13331	MD 13079	IC 276	MD 18030	MD 18170	MD 13083	MD 13035	IC 697	IC 278	MD 18032	MD 18034	MD 18036	MD 17000
		2	2	2		2	2	2	2	🍷	🍷	2	2	2	2
		①–⑤	①–⑤									Ⓐ	Ⓑ		
				E			C	E	E	T			A		
0	**Madrid** Chamartín ‡ 668a 669 d.	...	...	...	0800	0916	...	...	...	...	1456	1545	1720	1918	2114
8	**Madrid** Atocha Cercanías 668a 669 d.	0713	...	...	0819	0929	1310	...	...	...	1513	1559	1734	1932	2128
57	Aranjuez 668a 669 d.	0751	...	...	|	1004	1343	...	...	...	|	1634	|	2010	2207
	Barcelona Sants **672** d.	|	...	...	|	|	|	...	...	0913	|	|	|	|	|
	València Nord **668** d.	|	...	...	|	|	|	...	...	1225	|	|	|	|	|
157	Alcázar de San Juan 678 d.	0840	...	...	0936	1058	1440	...	...	1532	1634	1723	1856	2101	2301
206	Manzanares 678 d.	...	...	...	|	1122	1505	...	...	1555	1657	1747	1921	2124	...
323	Linares - Baeza a.	...	...	...	1119	1246	...	...	...	1712	1811	1912	2044	2241	...
323	Linares - Baeza d.	...	...	...	1121	1247	...	...	...	1714	1813	1913	2045	2242	...
441	Moreda d.	...	...	...	|	|	...	...	...	|	1951	|	|	|	...
466	Guadix 673 d.	...	...	...	1314	|	...	...	...	|	2013	|	|	|	...
565	**Almería** 673 a.	...	...	...	1427	|	...	...	...	|	2129	|	|	|	...
¶	**Jaén** d.	...	0540	0639	...	1328	...	1432	1652	|	...	1954	2126	2323	...
371	Andújar d.	...	0621	0720	...	...	...	1514	1737	1754	...	...	...	...	...
450	**Córdoba** a.	...	0712	0810	...	...	...	1610	1828	1848	...	...	...	...	...

	MD 18047	MD 18031	MD 18033	IC 277	MD 13337	MD 13001	IC 694	MD 18171	MD 13003	MD 17041	MD 18035	MD 13009	MD 18037	MD 13011	IC 279	MD 13017
	2	2	2		2	2	🍷	2	2	2	2	2	2	2	🍷	🍷
	①–⑤	Ⓐ			①–⑤	①–⑤			⑥⑦							
						E	T		E	C		E		N		E
Córdoba d.	...	...	...	...	0732	0906	1013	...	1002	...	...	1451	...	1626	...	2105
Andújar d.	...	...	...	...	0836	0959	1107	...	1056	...	...	1544	...	1720	...	2157
Jaén d.	...	0612	0832	...	0928	1047	|	...	1143	...	1522	1627	1720	1811	...	2243
Almería 673 d.	...	|	|	0732	...	...	|	...	...	...	|	...	|	...	1605	...
Guadix 673 d.	...	|	|	0849	...	...	|	...	...	...	|	...	|	...	1719	...
Moreda d.	...	|	|	0910	...	...	|	...	...	...	|	...	|	...	|	...
Linares - Baeza a.	...	0650	0912	1041	...	...	1140	...	...	...	1602	...	1800	...	1914	...
Linares - Baeza d.	...	0651	0913	1043	...	...	1143	...	...	...	1603	...	1801	...	1916	...
Manzanares 678 d.	...	0807	1032	|	...	...	1258	...	...	1501	1723	...	1921	...	2035	...
Alcázar de San Juan 678 d.	0527	0832	1055	1223	...	...	1325	1355	...	1527	1745	...	1946	...	2059	...
València Nord **668** a.	|	|	|	|	...	...	1602	|	...	|	|	...	|	...	|	...
Barcelona Sants **672** a.	|	|	|	|	...	...	1938	|	...	|	|	...	|	...	|	...
Aranjuez 668a 669 d.	0621	0918	1143	|	...	...	...	1447	...	1624	1830	...	2032	...	|	...
Madrid Atocha Cercanías 668a 669 a.	0656	0959	1213	1343	...	...	...	1526	...	1704	1905	...	2109	...	2219	...
Madrid Chamartín ‡ 668a 669 a.	...	1013	1227	1358	...	...	...	1541	...	1718	1919	...	2122	...	2233	...

C – To / from Ciudad Real (Table **678**).
E – To / from Cádiz (Table **671**).
N – Daily from Sevilla. From Cádiz on ①–⑤. Table **671**.
T – TORRE DEL ORO – 12 🍷 Barcelona - València - Córdoba - Sevilla - Cádiz and v.v. (Table **672a**).
¶ – Linares - Jaen: *59 km.* Jaen - Andújar: *54 km.*
‡ – Full name is Madrid-Chamartín-Clara Campoamor.

☛ **Shaded services are suspended until further notice.**

MÁLAGA - TORREMOLINOS - FUENGIROLA — 662

2nd class

km					❦								
0	**Málaga** María Zambrano d.	0523	0558	0633	0653	and	2133	2203	2233	2303	2333	...
8	Málaga Aeropuerto ✈ d.	0532	0607	0642	0702	every	2142	2212	2242	2312	2342	...
16	**Torremolinos** d.	0543	0618	0653	0713	20	2153	2223	2253	2323	2353	...
20	Benalmádena d.	0554	0629	0704	0724	mins.	2204	2234	2304	2334	0004	...
31	**Fuengirola** a.	0606	0641	0716	0736	until	2216	2246	2316	2346	0016	...

				❦							
Fuengirola d.	0610	0645	0720	0740	and	2220	2250	2320	2350	0020	...
Benalmádena d.	0624	0659	0734	0754	every	2234	2304	2334	0004	0034	...
Torremolinos d.	0633	0708	0743	0803	20	2243	2313	2343	0013	0043	...
Málaga Aeropuerto ✈ d.	0644	0719	0754	0814	mins.	2254	2324	2354	0024	0054	...
Málaga María Zambrano a.	0652	0727	0802	0822	until	2302	2332	0002	0032	0102	...

❦ – 0653, 0733, 0813 from Málaga and 0740, 0820, 0900 from Fuengirola do not run on ⑥⑦.

🚌 BARCELONA - ANDORRA — 664

From **Barcelona** Nord bus station: 0630*, 0700, 0730*, 1030, 1500, 1700*, 1900.
From **Andorra la Vella** bus station: 0600, 0815*, 1100, 1500, 1700*, 1915.
Journey 3 hr 15 min (* 4 hours). Operator: Alsina Graells, Barcelona (ALSA) ✆ (+34) 91 327 05 40.

From **Barcelona Airport** ✈ (T1 and T2): 0730, 0930, 1100, 1300, 1500, 1730, 2000, 2130, 2300.
From **Barcelona** Sants railway station: 0615, 0815, 1015, 1145, 1345, 1545, 1815, 2045, 2215, 2345.
From **Andorra la Vella** bus station: 0330, 0615, 0815, 1115, 1315, 1515, 1630, 1815, 2015, 2215.
Journey 3 hours (3 hrs 30 mins to / from Barcelona ✈). Operator: Autocars Nadal ✆ +376 805 151.

BARCELONA - SITGES - SANT V de CALDERS — 665

2nd class

Local rail service **Barcelona** - **Sitges** - **Sant Vicenç de Calders**.
From Barcelona Sants: 0606, 0636 and every 30 minutes until 2206; then 2306.
From Sant Vicenç: 0601, 0616 ⚒, 0631 Ⓐ, 0659, 0729, 0751, 0831, 0902, 0932 and every 30 minutes until 2102, 2132 Ⓐ, then 2200.

Additional trains operate **Barcelona** - **Sitges** and v.v.
Journey times: **Barcelona** – **Sitges** (*34 km*) 30 minutes,
Barcelona – **Sant Vicenç** (*60 km*) 57 minutes.

BARCELONA - MATARÓ, BLANES and MAÇANET — 666

2nd class

Cercanías (suburban) line **R1**. For faster services Barcelona - Maçanet via Granollers, see Table **657**.
Approximate journey times (in mins) to / from **Barcelona** Sants: Mataró (46), Arenys de Mar (57), Calella (69), Pineda de Mar (73), Malgrat de Mar (79), Blanes (84), Maçanet-Massanes (97).

Barcelona Sants – **Mataró** and v.v. *35 km*
Ⓐ: 4–6 trains per hour.
From Barcelona 0555 – 2318; from Mataró 0501 – 2301.
Ⓒ: 2–4 trains per hour.
From Barcelona 0555 – 2318; from Mataró 0501 – 2231.

Barcelona Sants – **Blanes** *67 km*
0555, 0625 and every 30 mins. until 2155 Ⓒ, 2255 Ⓐ.
Blanes - **Barcelona** Sants
Daily: 0603, 0623 and every 30 mins. until 2153.

Barcelona Sants – Blanes – **Maçanet - Massanes** *82 km*
Daily: 0555, 0655 and every 30 mins. until 2155.
Maçanet - Massanes – Blanes – **Barcelona** Sants
Ⓐ: 0609, 0639 and every 30 mins until 1109 then hourly until 1909, 1939, 2009, 2039, 2109, 2139.
Ⓒ: 0609, 0639, 0709 and hourly until 1909, 2009, 2139.

ALACANT - BENIDORM - DÉNIA — 667

2nd class

◐ *By tram (route L1)*		①–⑤							
Alacant Luceros ⊙ d.	...	0541	0611	0711	every	1911	2011	2111	2211
El Campello d.	...	0609	0639	0739	30 mins.	1939	2039	2139	2239
La Vila Joiosa d.	0612	0635	0705	0805	◐	2005	2105	2205	2305
Benidorm a.	0630	0653	0723	0823	until	2023	2123	2223	2323

✣ *By tram (route L1)*	①–⑤								
Benidorm d.	0635	0705	0805	every	1905	2005	2105	2205	2235
La Vila Joiosa d.	0653	0723	0823	30 mins.	1923	2023	2123	2223	2253
El Campello d.	0723	0753	0853	✣	1953	2053	2153	2253	...
Alacant Luceros ⊙ a.	0751	0821	0921	until	2021	2121	2221	2321	...

By train (route L9)									
Benidorm d.	0520	0606	0706		1906	2006	2106	2206	...
Altea d.	0536	0622	0722	every	1922	2022	2122	2222	...
Calpe d.	0558	0644	0744	hour	1944	2044	2144	...	...
Teulada 🚌 d.	*0629*	*0715*	*0815*	◐	*2015*	*2115*	*2210*	...	...
Gata 🚌 d.	*0641*	*0727*	*0827*	until	*2027*	*2127*	*2222*	...	...
Dénia 🚌 a.	*0708*	*0754*	*0854*		*2054*	*2154*	*2249*	...	...

By train (route L9)									
Dénia 🚌 d.	0532	0632	0732		1932	2032	...	2120	...
Gata 🚌 d.	0559	0659	0759	every	1959	2059	...	2147	...
Teulada 🚌 a.	0611	0711	0811	hour	2011	2111	...	2159	...
Calpe d.	0645	0745	0845	◐	2045	2145	...	2229	...
Altea d.	0706	0806	0906	until	2106	2206	2230	2250	...
Benidorm a.	0722	0822	0922		2122	2222	2246	2306	...

◐ – Alacant - Benidorm runs every 30 minutes 0641 - 2141 (also 0025, 0155 night of ⑤⑥ June 30 - Aug. 26).
✣ – Benidorm - Alacant runs every 30 minutes 0635 - 2205 (also 0211, 0441 night of ⑤⑥ June 30 - Aug. 26).
⊙ – ± 400 m from Alacant Renfe station.
Operator: Tram Metropolitano / FGV ✆ 900 72 04 72 www.fgvalicante.com

668 MADRID - ALBACETE, ALACANT and VALÈNCIA

km		avlo	AVE		AVE		AVE	AVE	AVE	AVE	AVE	AVE	AVE	MD	AVE	MD	AVE	AVE	Alvia	AVE	avlo	IC	AVE	Alvia	AVE	IC
		6502	5270	18024	5066	18018	5072	5070	5080	5290	5092	5098	5100	14404	5102	18081	5110	5122	4072	3971	6506	694	5140	4092	5142	5750
			①-⑤	①-⑤	①-⑥	⑥⑦	①-⑥	①-④		①-⑤			Ⓑ	①-⑥		2	①-⑤	⑥⑦	①-⑤	⑤⑥		🍷		⑥⑦	①-⑤	⑤
				B		J									L	h			S	M		T		S		Z
0	**Madrid** Puerta de Atocha .. d.	0630	0645	...	0650	...	0745	0740	0845	0910	0930	0940	1040	...	1045	...	1140	1145	1211	...	1240	...	1405	1410	1445	1455
189	Cuenca Fernando Zóbel .... d.	0725	0740	...	0747	...	0842	|	0940	1006	1026	|	1135	...	1142	...	1236	|	1321	1319	1435	...	1500	1516	1542	1603
321	Requena / Utiel .... d.	0759	0814	...	|	...	|	|	1014	|	|	|	1209	...	|	...	|	|	|	|	1409	...	1534	|	|	|
322*	**Albacete** .... d.	|	|	0806	0822	0918	0918	|	|	|	1102	|	|	1100	1218	1229	|	1311	1401	|	|	1424	|	1555	1618	|
436	Villena AV .... d.	|	|	|	0856	|	0953	|	|	|	1138	|	|	|	1253	|	|	1346	1440	|	|	|	|	1634	1653	|
486	**Alacant** Terminal .... d.	|	|	|	0922	|	1014	|	|	|	1159	|	|	|	1314	1400	|	1407	1502	|	|	|	|	1656	1714	|
	Elche AV .... d.	|	|	|	0949	|	...	|	|	|	...	|	|	|	...	...	|	...	...	|	|	|	|	...	...	|
	Orihuela .... a.	|	|	|	1003	|	...	|	|	|	...	|	|	|	...	...	|	...	...	|	|	|	|	...	...	|
477	Xàtiva .... d.	|	|	0931	...	1042	...	|	|	|	...	|	|	1206	...	...	|	...	...	|	|	1524	|	...	...	|
391	**València** Joaquín Sorolla .. § a.	0823	0838	|	...	|	...	0920	1038	1059	...	1125	1233	|	...	...	1328	...	...	1418	1433	|	1558	...	...	1704
	València Nord △ .... § a.	...	...	1014	...	1118	...	...	...	...	...	|	...	1245	...	...	...	...	...	...	...	1602	...	...	...	|
	Sagunt .... a.	...	...	...	...	...	...	...	...	...	...	|	...	...	...	...	...	...	...	...	...	|	...	...	...	1740
	Castelló de la Plana **672** a.	...	...	...	...	...	...	...	...	...	...	*1245*x	...	...	...	...	...	...	...	...	...	1705	...	...	...	1809

	AVE	MD	Alvia	AVE	AVE	Alvia	MD	AVE	AVE	AVE	IC	avlo	AVE	AVE	AVE	AVE	Alvia	AVE	AVE	AVE	AVE					
	5150	14406	4584	5552	5162	4110	18181	5370	5170	5172	5036	6510	3973	5192	5198	5196	4140	3981	5200	5212	5410					
			⑥		Ⓑ		2	Ⓑ		⑤⑥⑦	Ⓑ		⑦	①-⑥		Ⓑ		Ⓑ	Ⓑ	Ⓑ						
			W			G	h						K				G	P								
Madrid Puerta de Atocha ... d.	1540	...	1555	1605	1640	1552	...	1710	1740	1745	1748	1840	...	1905	1940	1950	2010	...	2040	2115	2110	...	...	...	...	...
Cuenca Fernando Zóbel ..... d.	|	...	1701	1705	1737	1654	...	|	|	|	|	|	2012	|	2036	|	2117	2125	|	2212	2205	...	...	...	...	...
Requena / Utiel .... d.	|	...	|	|	|	|	...	|	|	|	|	|	|	|	|	|	|	|	|	|	2239	...	...	...	...	...
Albacete .... d.	|	1650	1741	1740	1813	|	1849	|	|	1911	2014	|	|	2031	|	|	2156	|	|	2248	|	...	...	...	...	...
Villena AV .... d.	|	|	1828	1813	1848	|	|	|	|	|	|	|	|	|	|	|	2239	|	|	2323	|	...	...	...	...	...
Alacant Terminal .... a.	|	|	1850	1834	1909	|	2031	|	|	2001	|	|	|	2121	|	|	2301	|	|	2344	|	...	...	...	...	...
Elche AV .... d.	|	|	...	1905	...	|	...	|	|	...	|	|	|	...	|	2200	...	|	|	...	|	...	...	...	...	...
Orihuela .... a.	|	|	...	1920	...	|	...	|	|	...	|	|	|	...	|	2215	...	|	|	...	|	...	...	...	...	...
Xàtiva .... d.	|	1800	...	...	...	|	...	|	|	...	2119	|	|	...	|	...	...	|	|	...	|	...	...	...	...	...
València Joaquín Sorolla ... § a.	1722	|	...	...	...	1757	...	1852	1920	...	|	2020	2118	...	2129	...	...	2219	2230	...	2303	...	...	...	...	...
València Nord △ .... § a.	...	1840	...	...	...	|	...	...	...	...	2158	...	...	...	|	...	...	...	...	...	...	...	...	...	...	...
Sagunt .... a.	...	...	...	...	...	1839	...	...	...	...	...	...	...	...	|	...	...	...	...	...	...	...	...	...	...	...
Castelló de la Plana **672** .. a.	...	...	...	...	...	1911	...	..	...	...	...	...	...	...	2226	...	...	...	...	...	...	...	...	...	...	...

	AVE	AVE	AVE	AVE	IC	AVE	AVE	AVE	AVE	AVE	AVE	AVE	avlo	AVE	AVE	AVE	IC	MD	Alvia	Alvia	Alvia	AVE	AVE	IC	MD	AVE
	5061	5063	5067	5367	5035	5069	5071	5079	5081	3982	5273	5281	6503	5083	5093	5301	5801	18183	4345	4143	4111	5321	5543	697	14405	5141
	①-④	①-⑤	①-⑤	⑥	①-⑤	①-⑤	①-④	⑥⑦		①-⑥	①⑥	①-④			①-⑤	①-⑤	①-⑥	2	⑦					🍷		
										P							D	h	F	S	G			T		
Castelló de la Plana **672** .. d.	...	...	...	...	...	0615	...	0640	...	...	...	...	...	...	...	...	...	...	...	...	1102	...	...	1130	...	...
Sagunt .... d.	...	...	...	...	...	|	...	|	...	...	...	...	...	...	...	...	...	...	...	...	1139	...	...	|	...	...
València Nord △ .... § d.	...	...	...	...	...	|	...	|	...	...	...	...	...	...	...	...	...	...	...	...	|	...	...	1225	1345	...
València Joaquín Sorolla ... § d.	0630	...	...	...	0620	0710	0740	0740	0755	0807	...	0840	0928	...	...	1040	1040	...	...	...	1221	1240	...	|	|	1410
Xàtiva .... d.	|	...	...	...	0659	|	|	|	|	|	...	|	|	...	...	|	|	...	...	...	|	|	...	1309	1426	|
Orihuela .... d.	|	...	0628	0636	|	|	|	|	|	|	...	|	|	...	...	|	|	...	...	...	|	|	1152	|	|	|
Elche AV .... d.	|	...	0640	0648	|	|	|	|	|	|	...	|	|	...	...	|	|	...	...	...	|	|	1204	|	|	|
Alacant Terminal .... d.	|	0605	|	|	|	|	|	|	|	|	0710	|	|	0840	0950	|	|	1012	1020	1035	|	|	1232	|	|	|
Villena AV .... d.	|	0626	|	|	|	|	|	|	|	|	0731	|	|	0901	1011	|	|	|	1043	1057	|	|	1252	|	|	|
Albacete .... d.	|	0702	|	0738	0803	|	|	|	|	|	0807	|	|	0937	1047	|	|	1150	1125	1135	|	|	1329	1412	1537	|
Requena / Utiel .... d.	0653	|	|	|	|	|	|	|	0819	|	|	|	0951	|	|	1103	1111	...	|	|	1249	|	|	...	...	|
Cuenca Fernando Zóbel ..... d.	0728	0738	|	0813	|	0806	|	0834	0854	0902	0843	|	1026	1013	|	1138	1151	...	1204	1213	1327	|	1404	...	...	|
Madrid Puerta de Atocha ..... a.	0822	0834	0849	0910	1020	0900	0920	0932	0947	...	0940	1020	1120	1110	1215	1232	1305	...	1310	1320	1429	1421	1503	...	...	1548

	Alvia	AVE	AVE	avlo	AVE	AVE	AVE	MD		AVE	AVE	AVE	AVE	AVE	IC	AVE	IC	AVE	AVE	avlo	AVE	MD	AVE			
	4181 4381	5143	5149	6507	5153	5171	3974	18083	18027	5181	5183	5191	5391	5193	5701	5201	5811	5203	5603	6511	5221	14407	5213			
							①⑤⑦	2		Ⓑ			⑤⑦	⑤⑦	⑦				Ⓑ		⑦	Ⓑ	⑦			
	G						C	h	A			N			Q											
Castelló de la Plana **672** .. d.	...	...	*1345*x	...	...	...	...	...	...	...	...	...	...	...	1905	...	2007	...	...	...	...	...	...	...	...	...
Sagunt .... d.	...	...	|	...	...	...	...	...	...	...	...	...	...	...	1928	...	|	...	...	...	...	...	...	...	...	...
València Nord △ .... § d.	...	...	|	...	...	...	...	...	1730	...	...	...	...	...	|	...	|	...	...	...	...	2050	...	...	...	...
València Joaquín Sorolla ... § d.	...	...	1510	1615	...	1705	1712	...	|	1805	...	1910	1940	...	2015	2015	2105	...	...	2110	2205	|	...	...	...	...
Xàtiva .... d.	...	...	|	|	...	|	|	...	1806	|	...	|	|	...	|	|	|	...	...	|	|	2129	...	...	...	...
Orihuela .... d.	...	...	|	|	...	|	|	...	|	|	...	|	|	...	|	|	|	...	1945	|	|	|	...	...	...	...
Elche AV .... d.	...	...	|	|	...	|	|	...	|	|	...	|	|	...	|	|	|	...	1957	|	|	|	...	...	...	...
Alacant Terminal .... d.	1445	1445	|	|	1550	|	|	1700	|	|	1810	|	|	1910	|	|	|	2015	2025	|	|	2237	2118	...	...	...
Villena AV .... d.	1508	1506	|	|	1611	|	|	|	|	|	|	|	|	|	|	|	|	2036	2045	|	|	...	|	...	...	...
Albacete .... d.	1553	1542	|	|	1647	|	|	1838	1927	|	1900	|	|	2000	|	|	|	2112	2122	|	|	...	|	...	...	...
Requena / Utiel .... d.	|	|	1533	|	|	|	|	...	...	1828	|	|	|	|	2042	|	2137	|	|	2133	|	...	|	...	...	...
Cuenca Fernando Zóbel ..... d.	1630	1618	1607	|	1723	|	1812	...	...	1903	|	|	|	|	2122	|	2217	2148	2157	2208	|	...	|	...	...	...
Madrid Puerta de Atocha ..... a.	1735	1711	1703	1755	1820	1845	...	...	...	1957	2025	2050	2124	2125	2237	2156	2332	2247	2254	2304	2352	...	2334	...	...	...

A – To Alcázar de San Juan on Ⓑ (a. 2050). To Ciudad Real on ⑥ (Table **678**).
B – From Alcázar de San Juan on ①–⑤ (d. 0645). From Ciudad Real on ① (Table **678**).
C – ①⑤⑦ (Ⓑ July 14 - Sept. 10). To Málaga (Table **660**).
D – June 11 - Sept. 5. From Gandia.
E – ①–⑥ (daily July 4 - Sept. 10).
F – To Ferrol (Table **682**).
G – From / to Gijón (Table **685**).
J – From Alcázar de San Juan, dep. 0800.
K – ⑦. From Málaga (Table **660**).
L – ①②③④⑥⑦.
M – ⑤⑥. From Málaga (Table **660**).
N – ①②③④⑥⑦.
P – From / to Sevilla (Table **660**).
Q – ⑦. From Vinaròs (Table **672**).
R – ⑤⑦ (⑥ June 19 - Sept. 10).
S – From / to Santander (Table **684**).
T – TORRE DEL ORO – (12) 🍷 Barcelona - Cádiz and v.v. (Table **672a**).
U – ①–⑤ (daily June 1 - Sept. 30).
W – From Pontevedra (Table **680**).
Z – ⑤. To Vinaròs (Table **672**).
h – From / to Ciudad Real (Table **678**).
x – By 🚌.
avlo – Low-cost ***AVE*** Renfe services branded **avlo**: www.avlorenfe.com
§ – Free 🚌 between València Joaquín Sorolla and València Nord, 0615 - 2330, every ± 10 minutes.
* – Albacete - Xàtiva - València: *203 km*.

Shaded services are suspended until further notice.

△ – *Cercanías* (suburban) line **C1**: **València** - **Gandia** and v.v. *62 km* 2nd class. Journey time: 54 - 60 minutes.

From **València** Nord
Ⓐ: 0611, 0641 and every 30 minutes until 1941; then 1956, 2033, 2041, 2111, 2141, 2211, 2241.
Ⓒ: 0641, 0741 and hourly until 2241.

From **Gandia**
Ⓐ: 0605, 0640, 0655, 0710, 0725, 0740, 0755, 0825, 0840, 0855, 0915, 0925, 0955 and every 30 minutes until 2225.
Ⓒ: 0655, 0755 and hourly until 2055; then 2225.

668a MADRID - CARTAGENA

km		AVE	IC	IC		MD	MD	AVE	IC	IC	MD
		5092	11092	11092		18040	18044	5172	11172	11172	18042
							⑤				Ⓑ
				🚌						🚌	
0	**Madrid** Chamartín ¶ . ‡ d.	...	...	...	...	1419	1643	...	...	...	1818
8	**Madrid** Atocha C ◧ .. ‡ d.	0930	...	...	...	1432	1657	1745	...	...	1832
57	Aranjuez .... ‡ d.	|	...	...	...	1509	1731	|	...	...	1908
157	Alcázar de San Juan ‡ d.	|	...	...	...	1604	1828	|	...	...	2000
288	**Albacete** .... d.	1100	1120	...	...	1715	1941	1909	1929	...	2106
354	Hellín .... d.	...	1202	...	...	...	...	...	2011	...	...
	Archena-Fortuna .... d.	...	1245	1300	...	...	...	...	2054	2110	...
450	Murcia .... **672** ⁞ d.	...	...	1335	...	...	...	...	...	2142	...
	Lorca Sutullena ... ⁞ a.	...	...	|	...	...	...	...	...	|	...
562	Aguilas .... ⁞ a.	...	...	|	...	...	...	...	...	|	...
515	**Cartagena** .... **672** ⁞ a.	...	...	1500	...	...	...	...	...	2307	...

	MD	MD	MD	IC	IC	AVE		MD	IC	IC	AVE	
	18041	18049	18049	11093	11093	5093		18043	11183	11183	5183	
	Ⓐ	⑥	⑦									
				🚌					🚌			
Cartagena .... **672** ⁞ d.	...	...	...	0640	...	...	...	...	1450	...	...	...
Aguilas .... ⁞ d.	...	...	...	|	...	...	...	...	|	...	...	...
Lorca Sutullena . ⁞ d.	...	...	...	|	...	...	...	...	|	...	...	...
Murcia .... **672** ⁞ d.	...	...	...	0810	...	...	...	...	1620	...	...	...
Archena-Fortuna .... d.	...	...	...	0840	0857	...	...	...	1650	1705	...	...
Hellín .... d.	...	...	...	...	0945	...	...	...	...	1753	...	...
Albacete .... d.	0605	0730	...	...	1027	1047	...	1740	...	1835	1900	...
Alcázar de San Juan ‡ d.	0711	0837	0837	...	...	|	...	1851	...	...	|	...
Aranjuez .... ‡ d.	0807	0933	0933	...	...	|	...	1948	...	...	|	...
Madrid Atocha C ◧ ‡ a.	0844	1008	1008	...	...	1215	...	2022	...	...	2025	...
Madrid Chamartín ¶ ‡ a.	0858	1022	1022	...	...	...	...	2036	...	...	...	...

‡ – See also Table **661**. ◧ – Madrid **Atocha Cercanías**. ¶ – Full name is Madrid-Chamartín-Clara Campoamor. ⁞ – Additional local trains operate between these stations.

MADRID - CUENCA - VALÈNCIA 669

2nd class

We understand a proposal to close this route is being considered

km		18160 Ⓐ	18160 ⑦	18160 Ⓒ	18168 Ⓑ	18162 ⑦	14162 ⑦	18164 ①-④	18164 ⑤⑥⑦	18768 ⑤
0	**Madrid** Chamartín ‡ d.	...	...	...	...	...	...	...	...	...
8	**Madrid** Atocha Cercanías d.	*0608*	0620	0730	...	1242	...	*1520*	1552	1754
16	Villaverde Bajo d.	*0615*	0630	0738	...	1250	...	*1527*	1602	1803
57	Aranjuez **661 668a** a.	*0652*	0700	0810	...	1318	...	*1628*	1628	1832
	change trains on certain services	|	|			|		|	|	|
57	Aranjuez **661 668a** d.	0702	0702	0811	...	1322	...	1631	1631	1833
209	**Cuenca** d.	*0940*	0918	*1040*	1455	1455	1740	*1921*	*1921*	2055
335	Requena d.	*1225*	1152	*1323*	1756	1756	2010	*2145*	*2145*	...
407	**València** Nord a.	1413	1317	1451	1925	1925	2143	2307	2307	...

	18161 ①-⑤	18161 Ⓒ	18163 ⑤⑦	18163	18765 ⑦	18165 ⑤	18165 ①-④	18165 ⑥⑦	14163 ⑤
València Nord d.	0638	0714	0950	1107	...	1450	1450	1450	1641
Requena d.	0818	0856	1126	1253	...	*1639*	*1639*	*1639*	1814
Cuenca d.	1045	1140	1405	1530	1745	*1920*	*1920*	*1908*	2045
Aranjuez **661 668a** a.	1310	1405	1618	...	1954	2145	2123	2126	...
change trains on certain services	|	|	|		|	|	|	|	
Aranjuez **661 668a** d.	1321	1405	1619	...	1955	2147	*2142*	2132	...
Villaverde Bajo a.	1358	1444	1649	...	2027	2217	*2224*	2205	...
Madrid Atocha Cercanías a.	1406	1453	1657	...	2035	2225	2235	2215	...
Madrid Chamartín ‡ a.	1420	...	...	...	...	...	...	...	...

‡ – Full name is Madrid-Chamartín-Clara Campoamor.

🚌 – Cuenca – Requena and v.v.

☛ **Shaded services are suspended until further notice.**

VALÈNCIA - TERUEL - ZARAGOZA - HUESCA - CANFRANC 670

2nd class (except *AVE* trains)

km		Ⓐ			🚌	*MD* 18502		*MD* 18504 A		*AVE* 3393	*MD* 18506		
0	**València** Nord d.	...	...	...	...	0935	...	1213	...	...	1622	...	...
34	Sagunt d.	...	...	...	...	1005	...	1248	...	...	1654	...	...
65	Segorbe d.	...	...	...	...	1033	...	1317	...	...	1721	...	...
171	**Teruel** d.	...	0640	...	...	1215	...	1451	...	...	1850	...	...
242	Calamocha d.	...	0727	...	...	1304	...	1535	...	...	1939	...	...
305	Cariñena d.	...	0817	...	...	1355	...	1625	...	...	2041	...	...
	Madrid ◇ **650** d.	...	|	...	...	|	...	|	...	1905	|	...	...
359	**Zaragoza** Delicias d.	0624	0901	...	1400	1432	1542	1702	1902	2033	2119	2139	...
361	**Zaragoza** Portillo d.	0627	0911	...	|	1436	1546	1705	1905	|	2123	2142	...
363	**Zaragoza** Goya d.	0629	0913	...	|	1439	1549	1707	1907	|	2125	2144	...
417	Tardienta d.	0709	...	...	|	1512	1629	...	1948	2103	...	2223	...
439	**Huesca** d.	0724	...	...	|	1528	1650	...	2003	2118	...	2238	...
474	Ayerbe d.	...	...	...	|	...	1730	...	...	...	...	...	...
533	Sabiñánigo d.	...	...	...	1610	...	1837	...	...	...	...	...	...
549	Jaca d.	...	...	...	1630	...	1858	...	...	...	...	...	...
574	**Canfranc 324** a.	...	...	...	...	...	1937	...	...	...	...	...	...

	Ⓐ	*MD* 18511	Ⓐ	*AVE* 3272	Ⓒ	Ⓐ	*MD* 18523		🚌	*MD* 18515		
Canfranc 324 d.	...	...	...	...	...	0605	...	...	...	...	...	1750
Jaca d.	...	...	...	...	...	0640	...	...	1300	...	...	1825
Sabiñánigo d.	...	...	...	...	...	0655	...	...	1320	...	...	1840
Ayerbe d.	...	...	...	...	...	0802	...	...	|	...	...	1951
Huesca d.	0640	...	0738	0815	0833	0850	...	...	|	1602	1838	2037
Tardienta d.	0656	...	0753	0827	0850	0905	...	...	|	1618	1856	2053
Zaragoza Goya d.	0737	0808	0831	|	0932	0949	1109	...	|	1702	1941	2138
Zaragoza Portillo d.	0740	0811	0833	|	0935	0952	1112	...	|	1705	1943	2142
Zaragoza Delicias d.	0743	0815	0836	0900	0938	0955	1120	...	1520	1725	1948	2147
Madrid ◇ **650** a.	...	|	...	1035	...	...	|	...	...	|	|	...
Cariñena d.	...	0859	...	...	...	...	1201	...	...	1813	2036	...
Calamocha d.	...	0959	...	...	...	...	1250	...	...	1910	2132	...
Teruel d.	...	1049	...	...	...	...	1337	...	...	2000	2221	...
Segorbe d.	...	1220	...	...	...	...	1511	...	...	2132	...	...
Sagunt d.	...	1250	...	...	...	...	1543	...	...	2203	...	...
València Nord a.	...	1323	...	...	...	...	1614	...	...	2232	...	...

A – From Cartagena on ①–⑤.
From Murcia on ⑥ (Table **672**).

◇ – Madrid Puerta de Atocha.

🚌 Jaca - Canfranc (- Astun). See Table **324** for 🚌 Canfranc - Bedous for connections to / from Pau.

CÓRDOBA - SEVILLA - HUELVA and CÁDIZ 671

km		*MD* 13000 2 ①–⑤	*MD* 13002 2 ①–⑥	*MD* 13030 2 ①–⑤	*MD* 13030 2 ⑥⑦	*MD* 13099 2 ⑥⑦	*Alvia* 2074	*MD* 13079 2 J	*MD* 13037 2 ①–⑤	*MD* 13020 2		*Alvia* 2394 C ⑥	*IC* 2494 B	*MD* 13008 2 ①–⑤		*MD* 13010 2	*MD* 13032 2 ⑥⑦	*MD* 13032 2 ①–⑤	*Alvia* 2134	*MD* 13014 2	*MD* 13039 2	*MD* 13083 2 J	*Alvia* 2164		*MD* 13035 2 J
	Madrid PA ✣ **660** d.	...	...	...	...	...	0705	...	...	...	...	0945	0945	...	...	...	...	...	1305	...	...	...	1610	...	...
0	**Córdoba 660** d.	...	...	0700	...	...	0906	0812	...	0908	...	1134	1136	...	...	...	1400	1400	1454	...	...	1612	|	...	1830
51	Palma del Río d.	...	...	0729	...	...	|	0845	...	0940	...	|	|	...	...	...	1431	1431	|	...	...	1643	|	...	1905
129	**Sevilla 660** a.	...	...	0821	...	...	0955	0937	...	1029	...	|	1220	...	...	...	1520	1520	1542	...	...	1730	|	...	1956
129	**Sevilla 673** § d.	0640	0745	0830	0830	0845	0957	0945	1000	1045	...	|	1240	1245	...	1445	...	1545	1545	1645	1700	1745	|	...	2010
204	La Palma del Condado d.	|	|	|	|	0949	|	|	1108	|	...	1302	1335	|	...	|	...	|	|	|	1758	|	|	...	|
244	**Huelva** a.	|	|	|	|	1020	|	|	1138	|	...	1331	1402	|	...	|	...	|	|	|	1834	|	|	...	|
145	Dos Hermanas **673** § d.	0654	0758	0843	0843	...	|	0958	...	1058	...	...	...	1258	...	1500	...	1559	|	1658	...	1758	|	...	2023
162	Utrera § d.	0705	|	0854	0854	...	|	|	...	1108	...	...	...	1308	...	|	...	1609	|	|	...	1808	|	...	|
224	Aeropuerto de Jerez ▲ d.	0739	|	0929	0929	...	|	|	...	1143	...	...	...	1345	...	1540	...	|	|	1741	...	1844	|	...	|
236	Jerez de la Frontera ▲ d.	0746	0846	0936	0936	...	1053	1045	...	1151	...	...	...	1353	...	1548	...	1651	1642	1749	...	1852	1942	...	2113
251	Puerto de Santa María d.	0756	0855	0946	0946	...	1103	1056	...	1200	...	...	...	1402	...	1558	...	1700	1651	1758	...	1901	1952	...	2122
270	San Fernando - Bahía Sur d.	0809	0911	1002	1002	...	1118	1112	...	1214	...	...	...	1418	...	1615	...	1714	1706	1813	...	1917	2007	...	2137
285	**Cádiz** a.	0826	0923	1013	1013	...	1129	1126	...	1226	...		...	1430	...	1627	...	1726	1717	1825	...	1930	2019	...	2150

	IC 697 A	*MD* 13394 2	*Alvia* 2384 D Ⓑ	*MD* 13095 2	*MD* 13073 2 J						
Madrid PA ✣ **660** d.	...	...	1805	...	...	...	...	...	...	...	...
Córdoba 660 d.	1853	...	2000	...	2010	...	...	...	...	...	...
Palma del Río d.	|	...	|	...	2042	...	...	...	...	...	...
Sevilla 660 a.	1940	...	|	...	2128	...	...	...	...	...	...
Sevilla 673 § d.	1942	2045	|	2050	2150	...	...	...	...	...	...
La Palma del Condado d.	|	|	2128	2149	|	...	...	...	...	...	...
Huelva a.	|	|	2154	2218	|	...	...	...	...	...	...
Dos Hermanas **673** § d.	|	2058	...	...	2203	...	...	...	...	...	...
Utrera § d.	|	2109	...	...	2213	...	...	...	...	...	...
Aeropuerto de Jerez ▲ d.	|	|	...	...	2248	...	...	...	...	...	...
Jerez de la Frontera ▲ d.	2034	2148	...	...	2256	...	...	...	...	...	...
Puerto de Santa María d.	2044	2157	...	...	2305	...	...	...	...	...	...
San Fernando - Bahía Sur d.	2059	2212	...	...	2321	...	...	...	...	...	...
Cádiz a.	2110	2223	...	...	2335	...	...	...	...	...	...

	MD 13001 2J ①–⑤	*MD* 13041 2	*MD* 13003 2 M	*Alvia* 2075	*Alvia* 2285 ①–⑤	*IC* 694 A	*MD* 13005 2	*MD* 13007 2 ①–⑤	
Cádiz d.	0540	...	0630	0640	...	0755	0840	0940	...
San Fernando - Bahía Sur d.	0553	...	0641	0652	...	0808	0851	0951	...
Puerto de Santa María d.	0608	...	0656	0705	...	0824	0905	1006	...
Jerez de la Frontera ▲ d.	0617	...	0705	0715	...	0834	0914	1015	...
Aeropuerto de Jerez ▲ d.	0624	...	0713	|	...	|	|	1023	...
Utrera § d.	0702	...	0751	|	...	|	|	|	...
Dos Hermanas **673** § d.	0712	...	0801	|	...	|	1005	1107	...
Huelva d.	|	0655	|	|	0800	|	|	|	...
La Palma del Condado d.	|	0725	|	|	0824	|	|	|	...
Sevilla 673 § a.	0728	0825	0816	0812	|	0923	1020	1120	...
Sevilla 660 d.	0740	...	0838	0815	|	0925	...	...	...
Palma del Río d.	0828	...	0926	|	|	|	...	...	...
Córdoba 660 a.	0904	...	1000	0904	0948	1008	...	...	...
Madrid PA ✣ **660** a.	...	...	...	1109	1143	...	...	...	...

	Alvia 2205	*MD* 13009 2 J	*Alvia* 2135	*MD* 13011 2J ①–⑤	*MD* 13011 2J ⑥⑦	*MD* 13393 2	*MD* 13013 2 ①–⑤	*MD* 13043 2	*Alvia* 2365 ⑦	*MD* 13015 2		*IC* 2375 B	*MD* 13017 2 J	*Alvia* 2175	*MD* 13031 2	*MD* 13049 2	*MD* 13019 2	*MD* 13021 2							
Cádiz d.	...	1140	1220	1240	...	1412	1440	...	...	1540	...	...	1740	1810	1840	...	1940	2040	...	...	...	...	...	...	...
San Fernando - Bahía Sur d.	...	1151	1231	1251	...	1423	1451	...	...	1551	...	...	1751	1822	1851	...	1951	2052	...	...	...	...	...	...	...
Puerto de Santa María d.	...	1206	1244	1306	...	1436	1506	...	...	1606	...	...	1805	1836	1905	...	2006	2106	...	...	...	...	...	...	...
Jerez de la Frontera ▲ d.	...	1215	1253	1315	...	1445	1515	...	...	1615	...	...	1814	1847	1914	...	2015	2115	...	...	...	...	...	...	...
Aeropuerto de Jerez ▲ d.	...	1223	|	|	...	|	1523	...	...	1623	...	...	1822	|	1921	...	|	|	...	...	...	...	...	...	...
Utrera § d.	...	|	|	1356	...	1525	|	...	...	1700	...	...	|	|	|	...	2102	2156	...	...	...	...	...	...	...
Dos Hermanas **673** § d.	...	1306	|	1406	...	1535	1606	...	...	1710	...	...	1906	|	2005	...	2112	2206	...	...	...	...	...	...	...
Huelva d.	1025	|	|	|	...	|	|	1500	1615	|	...	1750	|	|	|	1900	|	|	...	...	...	...	...	...	...
La Palma del Condado d.	1047	|	|	|	...	|	|	1530	1642	|	...	1817	|	|	|	1930	|	|	...	...	...	...	...	...	...
Sevilla 673 § a.	|	1320	1343	1420	...	1549	1620	1627	|	1725	...	1914	1920	|	2017	2030	2128	2220	...	...	...	...	...	...	...
Sevilla 660 d.	|	1330	1345	1503	1503	...	...	...	|	1735	...	1924	1940	|	2030	...	...	...	...	...	...	...	...	...	...
Palma del Río d.	|	1415	|	1551	1551	...	...	...	|	1824	...	|	2027	|	2117	...	...	...	...	...	...	...	...	...	...
Córdoba 660 a.	1216	1449	1439	1624	1624	...	...	...	1806	1857	...	2012	2102	|	2148	...	...	...	...	...	...	...	...	...	...
Madrid PA ✣ **660** a.	1410	...	1636	...	...	...	...	...	2003	...	...	2212	...	2222	...	...	...	...	...	...	...	...	...	...	...

A – TORRE DEL ORO – (12) 🍷 Barcelona - València - Córdoba - Sevilla - Cádiz and v.v. (Table **672a**).

B – June 13 - Sept. 11.

C – Sept. 12 - Dec. 10.

D – Ⓑ (daily June 13 - Sept. 11).

J – From / to Jaén (Table **661**).

M – To Jaén on ⑥⑦ (Table **661**).

t – ①–⑤.

✣ – Madrid Puerta de Atocha.

§ – Frequent suburban services operate Sevilla - Utrera and v.v.

▲ – Additional suburban services operate Jerez de la Frontera - Aeropuerto de Jerez and v.v.: depart Aeropuerto 0720 Ⓐ, 0820 Ⓒ, 1325, 1920; depart Jerez 0657 Ⓐ, 0757 Ⓒ, 1257, 1857.

☛ **Shaded services are suspended until further notice.**

672 BARCELONA - VALÈNCIA - ALACANT - CARTAGENA

km			MD 14123 2	AVE 5069 ①-⑤	Alvia 4111 ①-⑥ G	Ⓐ 2	⑥ 2	⚒ 2	Alvia 1071 ①-⑤	Em 1081 ①-⑤	Em 1081 ⑥	2	IC 697 A	Em 1101	2	IC 1311	Ⓑ 2	AVE 5149	Ⓐ 2	Ⓒ 2	IC 463 ♀	2	IC 1131 ⑤⑥⑦
	Figueres Vilafant	d.								0710				0910									
	Girona	d.								0726				0926									
0	**Barcelona** França	d.						0543				0743			0943				1043	1043			
5	Barcelona Passeig de Gràcia	d.						0554				0754			0956				1054	1054			
8	**Barcelona** Sants 652	d.						0600	0715	0815	0815	0803	0913	1015	1000	1100			1103	1103	1200		1300
68	Sant Vicenç de Calders 652	d.						0650				0848			1049					1148			
82	Altafulla - Tamarit	d.						0702				0901			1102					1200			
	Camp de Tarragona	d.							0751	0851	0851		0951	1051									
93	Tarragona 652	d.						0712				0912			1112	1159			1202	1210	1259		1359
103	Vila-Seca ¶	d.						0722				0922			1122				1212	1220			
105	Cambrils-AV	d.						0733				0934	1012		1134	1219			1224	1231	1318		1418
	Tortosa	d.				0635	0758															1335	
163	L'Aldea - Amposta	d.				0648	0811	0815				1014	1034		1212	1240			1301	1311	1340	1350	1439
176	Tortosa	a.						0826				1025			1223				1312	1322			
202	Vinaròs	d.				0710	0833						1052		1308	1255					1356	1412	1454
208	Benicarló - Peñíscola	d.				0716	0839						1058		1314	1302					1402	1418	1500
268	Benicàssim	d.			0722	0754	0924								1351	1328					1427	1455	1528
280	Castelló de la Plana	d.		0615	0732	0805	0935		0912	1012	1012		1130	1212	1400	1337		1415			1436	1504	1537
353	**València** Nord	a.				0905	1038						1220		1508	1429					1523	1608	1635
353	**València** Nord 668	d.	0708										1225			1439	1445				1535		
	València Joaquín Sorolla	a.		0703	0830				0955	1055	1055			1255				1500					
	València Joaquín Sorolla 668	d.		0710	0845					1103	1103			1305				1510					
409	Xàtiva 668	d.	0744										1309			1518	1522				1616		
	Madrid P de Atocha 668	a.		0900	1045													1703					
	Cádiz 671	a.											2110										
495	Elda - Petrer	d.	0840													1606	1620				1656		
536	**Alacant**	a.	0909							1252	1252			1449		1640	1653				1728		
536	**Alacant**	d.	0916																		1745		
614	Murcia 668a	a.	1043																		1900		
677	**Lorca** Sutullena	a.																					
679	**Cartagena** 668a	a.																					

		2	⑤ 2	Em 1141 Ⓑ	IC 165	2	IC 1351 ⑤	Em 1161	Ⓐ 2	Ⓒ 2	⑤ 2	IC 5701 ⑦	IC 1371 ⑤	IC 5811	2	Em 1171 Ⓑ	Em 1181	2	Av 31166	IC 1391	2	Em 1201 Ⓑ	2
Figueres Vilafant	d.			1310																			
Girona	d.			1326																			
Barcelona França	d.	1243				1443			1540	1540								1743			1943		2043
Barcelona Passeig de Gràcia	d.	1256				1454			1551	1551								1755			1955		2054
Barcelona Sants 652	d.	1303		1415	1500	1503	1530	1610	1557	1557			1700			1715	1815	1800	1830	1930	2000	2015	2103
Sant Vicenç de Calders 652	d.	1349				1547				1643								1847			2049		2148
Altafulla - Tamarit	d.	1401				1559				1656								1859			2102		2201
Camp de Tarragona	d.			1451				1648								1751	1851		1907			2051	
Tarragona 652	d.	1411			1558	1609	1630		1657	1706			1800					1910		2030	2111		2212
Vila-Seca ¶	d.	1421				1618			1706	1716								1920			2119		2222
Cambrils-AV	d.	1433			1615	1629			1716	1728			1818					1932	1927	2047	2130		2234
Tortosa	d.														1902								
L'Aldea - Amposta	d.	1513			1637	1712			1751	1806			1839		1919			2015	1955	2110	2210		2315
Tortosa	a.	1524				1725			1802	1821								2026	2005		2225		2326
Vinaròs	d.				1654							1820	1854		1942					2126	2305		
Benicarló - Peñíscola	d.				1700							1825	1900		1947					2132			
Benicàssim	d.	MD			1726							1855	1927		2026					2158			
Castelló de la Plana	d.	18523		1612	1736			1807				1905	1937	2007	2036	1912	2012			2217		2212	
València Nord	a.	2			1828		1848						2026		2155					2315			
València Nord 668	d.	1628	1705		1840		1858				1944		2038										
València Joaquín Sorolla	a.			1655				1850				2000		2055		1955	2102					2301	
València Joaquín Sorolla 668	d.							1900				2015		2105			2112						
Xàtiva 668	d.	1711	1741		1922		1948				2028		2123										
Madrid P de Atocha 668	a.											2237		2332									
Cádiz 671	a.																						
Elda - Petrer	d.	1753	1831		2001						2119		2207										
Alacant	a.	1825	1911		2027		2055	2037			2150		2235				2249						
Alacant	d.	1831			2039																		
Murcia 668a	a.	1945			2204																		
Lorca Sutullena	a.																						
Cartagena 668a	a.	2047			2308																		

		Ⓐ 2	⑥ 2	Av 31167	IC 1262 ①-⑥	Em 1072 ①-⑤	2	Em 1082 ①-⑥	2	Em 1092	2	2	IC 1102	Em 1112	AVE 5098	Ⓒ 2	Ⓐ 2	MD 18504 ①-⑥ 2f	IC 460 ♀	2	IC 5710	IC 1342 ⑦	2
Cartagena 668a	d.																	0732z					
Lorca Sutullena	d.																						
Murcia 668a	d.												0630					0841	0930				
Alacant	a.												0744					0955	1052				
Alacant	d.									0725			0800	0925				1003	1108				
Elda - Petrer	d.												0828					1034	1135				
Cádiz 671	d.																						
Madrid P de Atocha 668	d.														0940								
Xàtiva 668	d.												0917					1122	1216		1110		
València Joaquín Sorolla 668	a.									0858				1058	1124						1325		
València Joaquín Sorolla	d.					0705		0815		0915				1115	1130						1331		
València Nord 668	a.												0954					1158	1253				
València Nord	d.				0620						0755		1005						1305			1400	1417
Castelló de la Plana	d.				0711	0745		0855		0955	0907		1052	1155	1212				1350		1431	1452	1526
Benicàssim	d.				0719						0920		1100						1359			1500	1535
Benicarló - Peñíscola	d.				0747						0957		1129						1426			1528	1617
Vinaròs	d.				0752		0653				1003		1135						1432			1533	1622
Tortosa	d.	0600	0605	0620			0740		0936			1145				1346	1403			1545			
L'Aldea - Amposta	d.	0612	0619	0632	0810		0751		0950		1029	1156	1151			1357	1413		1448	1556		1551	1641
Tortosa	a.										1040												1707
Cambrils-AV	d.	0648	0707	0701	0838		0832		1033			1236	1220			1439	1448		1517	1639		1619	
Vila-Seca ¶	d.	0659	0717				0843		1044			1247				1449	1457			1649			
Tarragona 652	d.	0710	0726		0900		0854		1056			1258	1238			1500	1508		1538	1659		1638	
Camp de Tarragona	d.			0720		0907		1018		1118				1318									
Altafulla - Tamarit	d.		0734				0902		1105			1306				1507				1707			
Sant Vicenç de Calders 652	d.		0747				0915		1119			1319				1520				1720			
Barcelona Sants 652	a.	0812	0837	0756	1010	0945	1009	1055	1211	1155		1412	1340	1355		1612	1612		1640	1810		1740	
Barcelona Passeig de Gràcia	a.	0817	0842				1014		1216			1417				1617	1617			1815			
Barcelona França	a.	0827	0852				1025		1227			1428				1627	1627			1825			
Girona	a.																						
Figueres Vilafant	a.																						

FOR NOTES SEE NEXT PAGE →

CARTAGENA - ALACANT - VALÈNCIA - BARCELONA 672

	Em 1152 Ⓑ	Alvia 1162 ①–⑤	2	IC 694 A	IC 264	IC 5750 ⑤	2	2	Em 1182 Ⓑ	Em 1182 ⑥	IC 1382 ⑦
Cartagena 668a ¦ d.	...	...	...	...	1231	...	...	...	...	...	...
Lorca Sutullena ¦ d.	...	...	...	...	|	...	...	...	...	...	...
Murcia 668a ¦ d.	...	...	...	...	1347	...	...	...	...	...	...
Alacant ¦ a.	...	...	...	...	1455	...	...	...	...	...	...
Alacant d.	1325	...	...	...	1510	...	...	...	...	1620	1645
Elda - Petrer d.	|	...	...	...	1540	...	...	...	...	|	|
Cádiz **671** d.	|	...	...	0755	|	...	...	...	...	|	|
Madrid P de Atocha **668** d.	|	...	...	|	|	1455	...	...	...	|	|
Xátiva **668** d.	|	...	...	1524	1620	|	...	...	...	|	1804
València Joaquín Sorolla **668** a.	1500	...	...	|	|	1704	...	...	...	1758	|
València Joaquín Sorolla d.	1515	1613	...	|	|	1714	...	...	1815	1815	|
València Nord **668** a.	|	|	...	1602	1658	|	...	...	|	|	1848
València Nord ¦ d.	|	|	...	1612	1710	|	...	1638	|	|	1900
Castelló de la Plana ¦ d.	1555	1653	...	1707	1752	1809	...	1750	1855	1855	|
Benicàssim ¦ d.	|	|	...	|	1800	1817	...	1758	|	|	|
Benicarló - Peñíscola ¦ d.	|	|	...	1736	1826	1846	...	1837	|	|	|
Vinaròs ¦ d.	|	|	...	1743	1832	1852	...	1843	|	|	|
Tortosa d.	|	|	1644	|	|	...	1842	1938	|	|	|
L'Aldea - Amposta d.	|	|	1655	1800	1848	...	1855	1950	|	|	|
Tortosa a.	|	|	|	|	|	...	|	|	|	|	|
Cambrils-AV d.	|	|	1736	1827	1915	...	1937	2030	|	|	|
Vila–Seca ¶ d.	|	|	1747	|	|	...	1947	2042	|	|	|
Tarragona **652** d.	|	|	1758	|	1933	...	1958	2053	|	|	2105
Camp de Tarragona d.	1718	1817	|	1848	|	...	|	|	2018	2018	|
Altafulla - Tamarit d.	|	|	1807	|	|	...	2006	2102	|	|	|
Sant Vicenç de Calders **652** d.	|	|	1820	|	|	...	2019	2116	|	|	|
Barcelona Sants **652** a.	1755	1855	1912	1938	2040	...	2110	2210	2055	2055	2210
Barcelona Passeig de Gràcia a.	...	...	1917	...	...	...	2115	2215	...	...	...
Barcelona França a.	...	...	1927	...	...	...	2125	2225	...	...	...
Girona a.	...	...	...	...	...	...	...	...	...	...	...
Figueres Vilafant a.	...	...	...	...	...	...	...	...	...	...	...

	Em 1192	Alvia 4110 Ⓑ G	Em 1202 ⑤⑦	2	2	Ⓑ 2	IC 1402	MD 14202 2	①–⑤ 2	⑥ 2	AVE 5198
Cartagena 668a ¦ d.	...	...	...	...	...	...	...	1613	...	...	...
Lorca Sutullena ¦ d.	...	...	...	...	...	...	...	|	...	...	...
Murcia 668a ¦ d.	...	...	...	...	...	...	...	1716	...	...	...
Alacant ¦ a.	...	...	...	...	...	...	...	1849	...	...	...
Alacant d.	1730	...	1830	...	1755	...	...	1856	1928	1926	...
Elda - Petrer d.	|	...	|	...	1829	...	...	1928	2004	2003	...
Cádiz **671** d.	|	...	|	...	|	...	...	|	|	|	...
Madrid P de Atocha **668** d.	|	1612	|	...	|	...	...	|	|	|	1940
Xátiva **668** d.	|	|	|	...	1922	...	...	2032	2103	2101	|
València Joaquín Sorolla **668** a.	1905	1817	2005	...	|	...	...	|	|	|	2129
València Joaquín Sorolla d.	1915	1828	2015	...	|	...	...	|	|	|	2139
València Nord **668** a.	|	|	|	...	2002	...	...	2106	2143	2141	|
València Nord ¦ d.	|	|	|	...	...	2007	2031	...	...	...	|
Castelló de la Plana ¦ d.	1955	1931	2055	...	...	2109	2120	...	...	...	2226
Benicàssim ¦ d.	|	...	|	...	...	2122	2129	...	...	...	...
Benicarló - Peñíscola ¦ d.	|	...	|	...	...	2158	2159	...	...	...	...
Vinaròs ¦ d.	|	...	|	...	...	2204	2205	...	...	...	...
Tortosa d.	|	...	|	2052	...	|	|	...	...	...	...
L'Aldea - Amposta d.	|	...	|	2106	...	2225	2221	...	...	...	...
Tortosa a.	|	...	|	|	...	2246	|	...	...	...	...
Cambrils-AV d.	|	...	|	2147	...	...	2249	...	...	...	...
Vila–Seca ¶ d.	|	...	|	2159	...	...	|	...	...	...	...
Tarragona **652** d.	|	...	|	2210	...	...	2307	...	...	...	...
Camp de Tarragona d.	2118	...	2218	|	...	...	|	...	...	...	...
Altafulla - Tamarit d.	|	...	|	|	...	...	|	...	...	...	...
Sant Vicenç de Calders **652** d.	|	...	|	2230	...	...	|	...	...	...	...
Barcelona Sants **652** a.	2155	...	2255	2323	...	...	2359	...	...	...	...
Barcelona Passeig de Gràcia a.	...	...	...	2330	...	...	...	...	...	...	...
Barcelona França a.	...	...	...	2340	...	...	...	...	...	...	...
Girona a.	...	...	...	...	...	...	...	...	...	...	...
Figueres Vilafant a.	...	...	...	...	...	...	...	...	...	...	...

Orihuela – Murcia – Cartagena

	Ⓐ 2	⚒ 2	2	IC 11092 🚌	Ⓐ 2	Ⓐ 2	MD	2	IC 11172 🚌	IC 165	2	
Orihuela d.	...	...	...	...	...	...	1929	...	...	2146	...	...
Murcia d.	0720	1049	1215	1335	1440	1742	1953	2010	2142	2211	2303	...
Cartagena a.	0818	1151	1314	1500	1539	1842	2047	2105	2307	2308	2359	...

	⚒ 2	IC 11093 🚌	MD Ⓐ	⑥ 2	2	IC 264	IC 11183 🚌	MD	Ⓑ 2	Ⓐ 2	Ⓒ 2	
Cartagena d.	0440	0640	0732	...	1009	1231	1450	1613	1759	2115	2212	...
Murcia d.	0538	0808	0841	0841	1107	1347	1619	1716	1901	2221	2321	...
Orihuela a.	...	...	0858	0859	...	1405	...	1735	...	...	...	...

A – TORRE DEL ORO – ⟨12⟩ 🍷 Barcelona - València - Córdoba - Sevilla - Cádiz and v.v. (Table **672a**).

G – To / from Gijón (Tables **681**, **685**).

J – Ⓑ (daily July 31 - Aug. 31).

f – To Zaragoza (Table **670**).

z – ①–⑤.

¦ – Additional local trains operate between these stations.

¶ – Station for Port Aventura.

☛ **Shaded services are suspended until further notice.**

BARCELONA - SEVILLA - CADIZ 672a

	IC 697 A
Barcelona Sants d.	0913
Camp de Tarragona d.	0951
Cambrils-AV d.	1012
L'Aldea - Amposta d.	1034
Vinaròs d.	1052
Benicarló - Peñíscola d.	1058
Castelló de la Plana d.	1130
València Nord a.	1220
València Nord d.	1225
Xátiva d.	1309
Albacete d.	1427
Alcázar de San Juan d.	1532
Manzanares d.	1555
Linares - Baeza a.	1712
Linares - Baeza d.	1714
Andújar d.	1754
Córdoba a.	1848
Córdoba d.	1853
Sevilla a.	1940
Sevilla d.	1942
Jerez de la Frontera d.	2034
Puerto de Santa María d.	2044
San Fernando - Bahía Sur d.	2059
Cádiz a.	2110

	IC 694 A
Cádiz d.	0755
San Fernando - Bahía Sur d.	0808
Puerto de Santa María d.	0824
Jerez de la Frontera d.	0834
Sevilla a.	0923
Sevilla d.	0925
Córdoba a.	1008
Córdoba d.	1013
Andújar d.	1107
Linares - Baeza a.	1140
Linares - Baeza d.	1143
Manzanares d.	1258
Alcázar de San Juan d.	1325
Albacete d.	1424
Xátiva d.	1524
València Nord a.	1602
València Nord d.	1612
Castelló de la Plana d.	1707
Benicarló - Peñíscola d.	1736
Vinaròs d.	1743
L'Aldea - Amposta d.	1800
Cambrils-AV d.	1827
Camp de Tarragona d.	1848
Barcelona Sants a.	1938

A – TORRE DEL ORO – ⟨12⟩ 🍷 Barcelona - Cádiz and v.v. (Tables **661**, **668**, **671**, **672**, **678**).

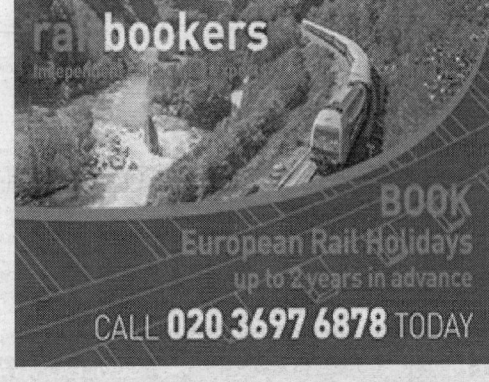

GRANADA - MÁLAGA / CÓRDOBA - SEVILLA 673

Avant high-speed shuttle services, *Turista* class

For trains **Sevilla** – **Málaga** and v.v. via **Córdoba**, see Table **660**. For trains **Sevilla** – **Granada** and v.v. via **Córdoba**, see Table **673** continued over page.

	8475	8795		8525		8575	8895		8505
Granada d.	0638	0740	...	1318	...	1720	1850	...	2028
Loja d.	0700	0802	...	1340	...	1750	1912	...	2051
Antequera - Ciudad d.	|	|	...	|	...	|	|	...	|
Málaga M. Zambrano a.	|	0850	...	|	...	|	2000	...	|
Antequera - Santa Ana § d.	0730	...	...	1411	...	1820	...	...	2124
Puente Genil - Herrera ¶ d.	0749	...	...	1430	...	1839	...	...	2143
Córdoba a.	0813	...	...	1455	...	1902	...	...	2215
Córdoba d.	0818	...	...	1500	...	1907	...	...	2220
Sevilla a.	0907	...	...	1545	...	1953	...	...	2305

	8275	8867		8295		8335		8287	8395	
Sevilla d.	0739	...	...	0913	...	1215	...	...	1920	...
Córdoba a.	0820	...	...	0956	...	1300	...	...	2005	...
Córdoba d.	0825	...	...	1001	...	1305	...	...	2010	...
Puente Genil - Herrera ¶ d.	0902	...	...	1032	...	1329	...	...	2039	...
Antequera - Santa Ana § d.	0920	...	...	1046	...	1343	...	...	2055	...
Málaga M. Zambrano d.	|	0925	...	|	...	|	...	2025	|	...
Antequera - Ciudad d.	|	|	...	|	...	|	...	|	|	...
Loja d.	1003	1016	...	1118	...	1425	...	2116	2132	...
Granada a.	1024	1037	...	1143	...	1445	...	2137	2152	...

§ – ± *17 km* from Antequera.

¶ – ± *8 km* from Puente Genil.

☛ **Shaded services are suspended until further notice.**

Table 673 continued over page →

673 SEVILLA and ALGECIRAS - MÁLAGA, GRANADA and ALMERÍA — 2nd class

For trains **Sevilla** – **Málaga** and v.v. via **Córdoba**, see Table **660**. For trains **Sevilla** – **Granada** and v.v. via **Córdoba**, see Table **673** continued on previous page.

km		*MD* 13063	*MD* 13900	*MD* 13940	*IC* 9367	*MD* 13902		*MD* 13065	*MD* 13942	*MD* 13904	*IC* 9331		*MD* 13906 ⑤⑦	*MD* 13944 ⑤⑦	*MD* 13944	*MD* 13077	*MD* 13908	*MD* 13946	*MD* 13910			
0	**Sevilla** d.	...	0724	...	...	0832	...	...	...	1149	...	...	1556	🚌	...	...	1858	...	1925	...	...	...
15	Dos Hermanas d.	...	0737	...	...	0847	...	...	...	1203	...	...	1612	...	...	...	1915	...	1941	...	...	...
	Algeciras d.	0620	|	...	0808	|	...	1030	...	|	1503	...	|	...	...	1722	|	...	|	...	...	...
	San Roque - La Línea d.	0635	|	...	0826	|	...	1046	...	|	1518	...	|	...	...	1738	|	...	|	...	...	...
	Ronda d.	0758	|	...	1009	|	...	1224	...	|	1631	...	|	...	...	1913	|	...	|	...	...	...
	Antequera - Santa Ana § d.	|	0901	...	|	1019	...	|	...	1329	|	...	1811	1823	...	|	2041	...	2147	...	...	...
167	Bobadilla d.	0851	0907	...	|	1025	...	1319	...	1335	|	...	1817	|	...	2001	2047	...	2154	...	...	...
236	**Málaga** M. Zambrano a.	|	1006	...	|	1117	...	|	...	1434	|	...	1917	|	...	|	2146	...	2249	...	...	...
	Antequera - Santa Ana § a.	0856	...	...	|	...	...	1325	...	...	1737	...	...	|	...	2006	...	...	...	...	...	...
	Madrid Pta de Atocha **660** a.	...	...	...	1405	...	...	...	...	...	2040	...	...	|	...	...	...	...	...	...	...	...
183	Antequera - Ciudad d.	...	...	...	...	...	...	...	...	...	...	...	...	|	...	...	...	...	...	...	...	...
290	**Granada** a.	...	...	1105	...	...	...	...	1458	...	...	...	...	1934	1938	...	...	2205	...	...	...	...
372	Guadix **661** d.	...	...	1209	...	...	...	...	1606	...	...	...	...	...	2055	...	...	2313	...	...	...	...
471	**Almería** **661** a.	...	...	1345	...	...	...	...	1737	...	...	...	...	...	2234	...	...	0032	...	...	...	...

km		*MD* 13901		*MD* 13951	*MD* 13903	*MD* 13062	*IC* 9366	*MD* 13953		*MD* 13905 ①–⑤	*MD* 13064		*MD* 13907	*IC* 9330	*MD* 13955	*MD* 13909		*MD* 13957	*MD* 13076	*MD* 13911		
0	**Almería** **661** d.	...	...	0550	...	...	...	1040	...	...	...	...	...	...	1358	...	...	1747	...	...	...	...
99	Guadix **661** d.	...	...	0740	...	...	...	1154	...	...	...	...	...	...	1544	...	...	1910	...	...	...	...
181	**Granada** d.	...	...	0850	...	...	...	1305	...	...	...	...	...	...	1657	...	...	2019	...	...	...	...
288	Antequera - Ciudad d.	...	...	|	...	...	...	...	...	...	...	...	...	...	...	...	...	...	...	...	...	...
	Madrid Pta de Atocha **660** d.	...	...	|	...	...	0835	...	...	...	...	...	...	1505	...	...	...	...	...	...	...	...
	Antequera - Santa Ana § d.	...	...	|	...	1009	1118	...	...	...	1433	...	...	1756	...	...	...	...	2015	...	...	...
	Málaga M. Zambrano d.	0644	...	|	0858	|	|	...	...	1322	|	...	1602	|	...	1719	...	...	|	2037	...	...
304	Bobadilla d.	0741	...	|	0954	1014	|	...	...	1419	1440	...	1706	|	...	1816	...	...	2022	2142	...	...
	Antequera - Santa Ana § d.	0747	...	1003	1000	|	|	...	...	1425	|	...	1719	|	...	1828	...	...	|	2148	...	...
376	Ronda d.	|	...	...	|	1108	1221	...	...	|	1534	...	|	1900	...	|	...	...	2122	|	...	...
468	San Roque - La Línea d.	|	...	...	|	1233	1409	...	...	|	1707	...	|	2018	...	|	...	...	2247	|	...	...
480	**Algeciras** a.	|	...	...	|	1248	1427	...	...	|	1726	...	|	2032	...	|	...	...	2302	|	...	...
456	Dos Hermanas a.	0921	...	...	1132	...	...	...	...	1631	...	...	1916	...	...	1958	...	...	...	2350	...	...
471	**Sevilla** a.	0938	...	...	1148	...	...	...	...	1646	...	...	1933	...	...	2012	...	...	...	0006	...	...

§ – ± *17 km* from Antequera.

Shaded services are suspended until further notice.

For Granada - Córdoba - Sevilla *Avant* services, see previous page.

674 PALMA DE MALLORCA - INCA - SA POBLA and MANACOR — SFM 2nd class

km			Ⓐ	Ⓐ	Ⓐ	Ⓐ	Ⓐ	Ⓐ	Ⓐ	Ⓐ	Ⓐ	and at the same	Ⓐ	Ⓐ	Ⓐ	Ⓐ	Ⓐ			Ⓒ	Ⓒ	and at the same	Ⓒ	Ⓒ	
0	**Palma** d.	Ⓐ	0546	0617	0632	0717	0732	0750	0817	0832	0850	minutes	2032	2050	2117	2132	2220	...	Ⓒ	0610	0640	minutes	2140	2210	...
7	Marratxi d.		0600	0625	0646	0725	0746	0804	0825	0846	0904	past	2046	2104	2125	2146	2235	...		0624	0654	past	2154	2224	...
29	**Inca** d.		0620	0645	0707	0745	0807	0824	0845	0907	0924	each	2107	2124	2145	2207	2255	...		0645	0715	each	2215	2245	...
***	sa Pobla a.		0637	|	0724	|	0824	...	|	0924	...	hour	2124	...	|	2224	|	...		|	0732	hour	2232	|	...
64	**Manacor** a.		...	0718	...	0816	...	...	0916	...	...	until	...	...	2216	...	2326	...		0715	...	until	...	2315	...

		Ⓐ	Ⓐ	Ⓐ	Ⓐ	Ⓐ	Ⓐ	Ⓐ	Ⓐ	Ⓐ	Ⓐ	and at the same	Ⓐ	Ⓐ	Ⓐ	Ⓐ			Ⓒ	Ⓒ	Ⓒ	and at the same	Ⓒ	Ⓒ	
Manacor d.	Ⓐ	...	0625	...	...	0725	...	...	0825	...	...	minutes	...	2125	...	2228	...	Ⓒ	0624	0724	...	minutes	...	2224	...
sa Pobla d.		0605	|	0700	...	|	0800	...	|	0900	...	past	...	|	2200	|	...		|	|	0807	past	2207	|	...
Inca d.		0621	0656	0716	0739	0756	0816	0839	0856	0916	0936	each	2136	2156	2216	2258	...		0655	0755	0823	each	2224	2255	...
Marratxi d.		0641	0716	0736	0759	0816	0836	0859	0916	0936	0956	hour	2156	2216	2236	2318	...		0715	0815	0844	hour	2244	2315	...
Palma a.		0655	0724	0750	0813	0824	0850	0913	0924	0950	1010	until	2210	2230	2250	2333	...		0729	0829	0858	until	2258	2329	...

*** – *19 km* Inca - sa Pobla.

Operator: Serveis Ferroviaris de Mallorca (SFM) ✆ +34 971 752 245.

PALMA DE MALLORCA - SÓLLER *28 km* Journey time: 55 minutes. **Operator**: Ferrocarril de Sóller (FS) ✆ +34 971 752 051.

Nov. - Mar.: 1000, 1250, 1510, 1800. Apr. - Oct.: 1000, 1040, 1730, 1830.

SÓLLER - PALMA DE MALLORCA

Nov. - Mar.: 0900, 1140, 1400, 1700. Apr. - Oct.: 0830, 0900, 1630, 1730.

A connecting tram service operates **Sóller - Port de Sóller**. *5 km*. Journey time: 15–20 minutes. Not all services shown.

From Sóller: 0800, 0900, 1000, 1100, 1200, 1300, 1330, 1400, 1430, 1500, 1530, 1600, 1700, 1800, 1900.
From Port de Sóller: 0830, 0930, 1030, 1130, 1230, 1330, 1430, 1500, 1530, 1630, 1700, 1730, 1830, 1930, 2000.

675 🚌 MÁLAGA and ALGECIRAS - LA LÍNEA (for Gibraltar)

There are no cross-border 🚌 services: passengers to / from Gibraltar must cross the frontier on foot (walking-time about 5 minutes) and transfer to / from Gibraltar local 🚌 services

🚌 **MÁLAGA** bus stn – **LA LÍNEA** bus station (for **Gibraltar**)

From Málaga: 0700, 1130▽, 1400, 1630, 1915⑦.

From La Línea: 0850, 1030, 1630▽, 1900, 2045⑦.

Journey time: 3 hours. Operator: Automóviles Portillo, Málaga ✆ (+34) 902 020 052.

▽ – Journey operated by Alsina Graells (see Table **664** for contact details).

🚌 **ALGECIRAS** bus station - **LA LÍNEA** bus station (for **Gibraltar**) Route M-120

From Algeciras: Ⓐ: 0700 and every 30 minutes until 2130, also 2230.
⑥: every 45 mins 0700 – 2115, also 2230. †: every 45 mins 0800 – 2130, also 2230.

From La Línea: Ⓐ: 0645, 0745 and every 30 minutes until 2215, also 2315.
⑥: every 45 mins 0700 – 2200, also 2315. †: 0700, 0845 then every 45 mins until 2215, also 2315.

Journey time: 45 mins. Operator: Transportes Generales Comes SA, Algeciras ✆ (+34) 902 450 550.

676 🚌 SEVILLA - AYAMONTE - FARO - LAGOS — DAMAS ☆

	Summer				⚒	⚒	†		Ⓐ			Winter		⚒		Ⓐ	⑥	⑦	Ⓐ		Ⓑ	⑥	†	⚒
Sevilla ⊖ d.	July 1 -	0730	0930	1130	...	1330	...	1530	...	1730	1930	Sept. 6 -	0730	0930	1130	...	1300	...	...	1530	...	1730	1900	1930
Huelva d.	Sept. 5	0900	1100	1300	1400	1500	1500	1700	1800	1900	2100	June 30,	0900	1100	1300	1400	1430	1430	1530	1700	1900	1900	2030	2100
Ayamonte a.	2021	1015	1215	1430	1500	1615	1615	1830	1905	2015	2230	2022	1015j	1215	1415f	1500	1545	1555	1630	1815z	2000x	2015	2145	2215

	Summer	⚒	⚒	Ⓐ						†		Winter	⚒	Ⓐ			Ⓐ	⑥	†	Ⓐ	⑥	⑥	Ⓑ	
Ayamonte d.	July 1 -	0640	0700	0815	0900	1100	1300	1500	1700	1800	1930	Sept. 6 -	0640	0830	0930	1145	1400	1500	1515	1545	1615	1715	1730	1930
Huelva d.	Sept. 5	0740	0815	0930	1030	1215	1430	1615	1815	1915	2100	June 30,	0740x	0930	1030j	1245j	1500	1600	1615	1645	1715	1830	1845	2045j
Sevilla ⊖ a.	2021	0910	1015	...	1215	1415	1615	1815	2015	2115	2230	2022	0910	...	1215	...	...	1715	1745	1815	1845	1945	...	2230

f – 15 minutes later on †. j – 15 minutes later on ©. x – 20–25 minutes later on ⑥. z – 15 minutes later on ⑥.

⛴ **Ayamonte - Vila Real de Santo António Guadiana** Journey time: 10 minutes. ✆ (+34) 959 470 617.
Sept. 16 - Apr. 30: hourly from Ayamonte 1000 - 1900 ⚒, 1100 - 1800 †. From Vila Real de Santo António Guadiana 0945 then hourly 1030 - 1730, 1900 ⚒, 1100 - 1800 †.

INTERNATIONAL 🚌 SERVICE Joint ALSA △ / REDE EXPRESSOS ☆ service *for international journeys only* No service Dec. 25, Jan. 1

	→ Summer July 1 - Sept. 12, 2021					→ Winter Sept. 13 - Mar. 31 2022		
Sevilla Santa Justa d.		0930	1130	1530	1800		0930	1530
Huelva, Estación de Autobuses d.		|	1315	|	|		|	|
Ayamonte 🏛 ES d.		|	|	|	|		|	|
Vila Real de Santo António 🏛 PT a.		|	|	|	|		|	|
Faro, Aeroporto a.		1115	1400	1730	2000		1115	1730
Albufeira, Terminal Rodoviário a.		1215	1500	1830	2100		1215	1830
Portimão, Av. Guanaré a.		1245	1530	1900	2130		1245	1900
Lagos, Terminal Rodoviário a.		1315	1600	1930	2200		1315	1930

	→ Summer July 1 - Sept. 12, 2021					→ Winter Sept. 13 - Mar. 31 2022		
Lagos, Terminal Rodoviário d.		0800	1030	1530	1700		0620	1515
Portimão, Av. Guanaré d.		0830	1100	1600	1730		0645	1540
Albufeira, Terminal Rodoviário d.		0900	1130	1630	1800		0720	1610
Faro, Aeroporto d.		0945	1230	1715	1900		0805	1655
Vila Real de Santo António 🏛 PT d.		|	|	|	|		0935	|
Ayamonte 🏛 ES a.		|	|	|	|		|	1950
Huelva, Estación de Autobuses a.		|	|	|	2200		1125	2105
Sevilla Santa Justa a.		1345	1645	2115	2345		1240	2220

☆ – REDE EXPRESSOS ✆ +707 22 33 44. www.rede-expressos.pt
△ – ALSA, ✆ +34 919 914 030. www.alsa.com

ES – Spain (Central European Time).
PT – Portugal (West European Time).

Huelva bus station is ± 1.7 km from the rail station.
Ayamonte bus station is ± 1.5 km from the ferry terminal.

MADRID - CÁCERES - BADAJOZ 677

km		13084					17905	17014	17016	MD 17900	MD 17902	17028		5500	4432	AP 126	17702			MD 17012	MD 18330	IC 194	17018	17706
		2	2	2	2	2	2	2	2	2	2	2	2	2	2		2	2	2	2	2		2	2
		①–⑥	Ⓐ	Ⓐ	Ⓒ	⑥	Ⓐ	Ⓐ	⑥	⑤⑥⑦		T				Ⓑ		Ⓑ	①⑤	⑤			Ⓑ	⑤⑦
0	**Madrid** Chamartín ‡ d.	...	...	...	...	...	...	...	...	...	...	...	...	...	...	...	...	...	...	...	...	1618	...	...
8	**Madrid** Atocha Cercanias d.	...	...	...	...	...	...	0804	0837	1018	1018	...	...	...	...	...	1232	...	...	1448	...	1638	1847	2053
146	Talavera de la Reina d.	...	...	...	...	...	...	0936	1012	1146	1148	...	...	...	...	...	1408	...	...	1614	...	1805	2019	2222
	Navalmoral de La Mata d.	...	...	...	...	...	...	1016	1048	1221	1223	...	...	...	...	...	...	...	...	1654	...	1840	2100	...
278	Plasencia a.	...	...	...	...	...	...	|	|	1301	1303	...	...	...	...	...	...	...	...	1746	...	|	2143	...
278	Plasencia d.	...	...	...	...	...	0704	|	|	1304	1306	...	...	...	...	...	...	...	...	1749	...	|	2146	...
343*	**Cáceres** d.	...	0654	...	0815	...	0822	1149	1224	1415	1415	1430	...	...	...	...	...	1658	1658	1852	...	2005	2254	...
	San Vicente de Alcántara d.	...	|	...	|	...	|	|	|	|	|	1541	...	...	...	...	...	|	|	...	...	|	...	...
430	Valencia de Alcántara d.	...	|	...	|	...	|	|	|	|	|	1555	...	...	...	...	...	|	|	...	...	|	...	...
409	Mérida a.	...	0746	...	0905	...	0924	1240	1315	1510	1510	...	...	...	...	...	...	1750	1750	...	...	2057	...	...
409	Mérida 678 d.	...	0756	0755	0916	0911	...	1248	1323	1522	1522	...	1525	⋙	...	...	...	...	1801	...	2026	2107	...	...
469	**Badajoz** 🏛 678 ES a.	...	|	0841	|	1000	...	1326	1401	|	|	...	1605	1624	...	...	...	...	|	...	2116	2146	...	...
	Elvas 🏛 PT a.	...	|	...	|	...	...	...	...	|	|	...	⋙	1540	...	...	...	...	|	...	...	...	...	...
	Abrantes 691 a.	...	|	...	|	...	...	...	...	|	|	...	...	1736	...	...	...	...	|	...	...	...	...	...
	Entroncamento 691 a.	...	|	...	|	...	...	...	...	|	|	...	...	1814	1844	1942	...	...	|	...	...	...	...	...
	Lisboa Oriente 691 a.	...	|	...	|	...	...	...	...	|	|	...	...	...	2013	2032	...	...	|	...	...	...	...	...
742	**Lisboa** S Apolónia 691 a.	...	|	...	|	...	...	...	...	|	|	...	...	...	2020	2040	...	...	|	...	...	...	...	...
475	Zafra d.	...	0845	...	1008	...	...	...	...	1617	1614	...	...	...	...	...	...	...	1853	...	...	...	...	...
649	Sevilla a.	...	1127	...	1248	...	...	...	...	|	1857	...	...	...	...	...	...	...	...	...	...	...	...	...
521	Fregenal de la Sierra d.	...	...	...	...	...	...	...	...	1656	...	...	...	...	...	...	...	...	...	...	...	...	...	...
	Jabugo-Galaroza d.	0735	...	...	...	...	...	...	...	1737	...	...	...	...	...	...	...	...	...	...	...	...	...	...
660	Huelva a.	0932	...	...	...	...	...	...	...	1930	...	...	...	...	...	...	...	...	...	...	...	...	...	...

	17703	17705	17021	MD 18331		IC 197		IC 199	17707		17026	17709	4407	IC 541	5501		MD 17901	MD 17907		17029	MD 17025			13089
	2	2	2	2	2		2		2	2	2	2	2		2	2	2	2		2	2	2	2	2
	Ⓐ	⑥	Ⓐ		Ⓐ	Ⓐ	⑥	Ⓒ	Ⓐ	Ⓐ	⑦	Ⓒ					⑤⑥⑦			T	Ⓑ			Ⓑ
Huelva d.	...	...	...	...	...	...	...	...	...	...	...	...	...	...	...	...	1100	...	...	...	...	...	...	1940
Jabugo-Galaroza d.	...	...	...	...	...	...	...	...	...	...	...	...	...	...	...	...	1256	...	...	...	...	...	...	2133
Fregenal de la Sierra d.	...	...	...	...	...	...	...	...	...	...	...	...	...	...	...	...	1339	...	...	...	...	...	...	...
Sevilla d.	...	...	...	...	...	...	...	...	...	...	...	...	...	...	...	...	|	1155	...	...	...	...	1730	...
Zafra d.	...	...	...	...	0655	...	0815	...	...	...	...	...	...	...	...	...	1425	1425	...	...	...	...	2015	...
Lisboa S Apolónia 691 d.	...	...	...	...	|	...	|	...	...	...	...	...	0745	0815	...	...	|	|	...	...	...	...	|	...
Lisboa Oriente 691 d.	...	...	...	...	|	...	|	...	...	...	...	...	0753	0823	...	...	|	|	...	...	...	...	|	...
Entroncamento 691 d.	...	...	...	...	|	...	|	...	...	...	...	...	0919	0923	1024	...	|	|	...	...	...	...	|	...
Abrantes 691 d.	...	...	...	...	|	...	|	...	...	...	...	...	...	...	1058	...	|	|	...	...	...	...	|	...
Elvas 🏛 PT d.	...	...	...	...	|	...	|	...	...	...	...	...	...	...	1300	⋙	|	|	...	...	...	...	|	...
Badajoz 🏛 678 ES d.	...	...	...	0656	|	0717	|	0845	...	1230	...	...	...	...	1414	1430	|	|	...	...	1645	2007	|	...
Mérida 678 a.	...	...	...	0741	0742	0753	0902	0923	...	1316	...	...	...	...	⋙	1514	1513	1513	...	...	1721	2052	2102	...
Mérida d.	...	...	...	...	...	0803	...	0933	...	...	...	...	...	...	...	...	1520	1520	...	...	1729	...	2107	...
Valencia de Alcántara d.	...	...	...	...	...	|	...	|	...	...	...	...	...	...	...	...	|	|	...	1640	|	...	|	...
San Vicente de Alcántara d.	...	...	...	...	...	|	...	|	...	...	...	...	...	...	...	...	|	|	...	1655	|	...	|	...
Cáceres d.	...	...	0712	...	...	0857	...	1027	...	...	1420	...	...	...	...	...	1611	1611	...	1808	1821	...	2205	...
Plasencia a.	...	...	0820	...	...	|	...	|	...	...	1532	...	...	...	...	...	1711	1711	...	...	|	...	...	...
Plasencia d.	...	...	0824	...	...	|	...	|	...	...	1536	...	...	...	...	...	1714	1714	...	...	|	...	...	...
Navalmoral de La Mata d.	...	...	0906	...	...	1018	...	1149	...	...	1621	...	...	...	...	...	1759	1759	...	...	1952	...	...	...
Talavera de la Reina d.	0623	0840	0939	...	...	1054	...	1229	1520	...	1702	1815	...	...	...	...	1845	1845	...	...	2025	...	...	...
Madrid Atocha Cercanías a.	0751	1017	1106	...	...	1226	...	1347	1647	...	1843	1938	...	...	...	...	2010	2010	...	...	2146	...	...	...
Madrid Chamartín ‡ a.	...	...	...	...	...	1240	...	1407	...	...	...	...	...	...	...	...	...	...	...	...	...	...	...	...

T – ③⑤⑦.

⋙ – Connection not guaranteed.

* – Madrid - Cáceres via Plasencia *363 km*.

‡ – Full name is Madrid-Chamartín-Clara Campoamor.

Shaded services are suspended until further notice.

ES – Spain (Central European Time).

PT – Portugal (West European Time).

ALCÁZAR DE SAN JUAN - BADAJOZ 678

km		MD 17042	MD 17044				MD 18183	IC 697	MD 18330	MD 18083	18027	
		2	2	2	2	2	2		2	2	A	
		Ⓐ	Ⓒ	Ⓐ	⑥		w	T		w	2	
	Madrid AC § **661 668** d.	...	...	...	...	...	...	...	...	...	...	
	Albacete **668a** d.	...	...	...	...	...	1150	1427	...	1838	1929	...
0	**Alcázar de San Juan** 661 d.	0715	0845	...	...	...	1302	1532	1535	1950	2053	...
50	Manzanares 661 d.	0740	0910	...	...	...	1327	1554	1559	2017	2120	...
114	Ciudad Real 660 d.	0820	0950	...	...	...	1408	...	1647	2058	2200	...
153	Puertollano 660 d.	...	...	...	...	1200	...	...	1711	...	...	...
265	Cabeza del Buey d.	...	...	0617	0735	1346	...	...	1854	...	...	...
392	Mérida 677 d.	...	...	0755	0911	1525	...	...	2026	...	...	...
451	**Badajoz** 677 a.	...	...	0841	1000	1605	...	...	2116	...	...	...

	18024	MD 18081	IC 694	MD 18331	MD 18181				
	B								
	2	2		2	2	2		2	
	Ⓐ	w	T		w				
Badajoz 677 d.	...	...	...	0656	...	1430	...	2007	...
Mérida 677 d.	...	...	...	0750	...	1530	...	2105	...
Cabeza del Buey d.	...	...	...	0920	...	1707	...	2241	...
Puertollano 660 d.	...	...	...	1105	...	1902	...	...	...
Ciudad Real 660 d.	0536	1012	...	1135	1624	...	...	...	...
Manzanares 661 d.	0614	1052	1258	1224	1710	...	...	...	...
Alcázar de San Juan 661 a.	0642	1117	1320	1252	1733	...	...	...	...
Albacete **668a** a.	0806	1227	1422	...	1847	...	...	...	...
Madrid AC § **661 668** a.	...	...	...	...	...	...	...	...	...

A – [2] València - Albacete - Ciudad Real (Table **668**).

B – [2] Ciudad Real - Albacete - València (Table **668**).

T – TORRE DEL ORO – [12] 🍸 Barcelona - València - Córdoba - Sevilla - Cádiz and v.v. (Table **672a**).

w – From/to Alacant (Table **668**).

§ – Madrid Atocha Cercanías.

BARCELONA / MADRID - GRANADA 678a

train type		AVE		AVE		AVE		AVE	
train number		2076		3930		2146		2196	
notes									
Barcelona Sants d.	...	...	...	0830	...	...	...	...	...
Madrid Puerta de Atocha d.	...	0735	...	|	...	1435	...	1910	...
Córdoba a.	...	0917	...	1311	...	1619	...	2104	...
Puente Genil - Herrera ¶ a.	...	0940	...	|	...	|	...	|	...
Antequera - Santa Ana § a.	...	0956	...	1401	...	1654	...	2136	...
Granada a.	...	1054	...	1452	...	1752	...	2232	...

train type	AVE		AVE		IC	AVE		AVE	
train number	2077		3931		2417	2167		2197	
notes					⑦				
Granada d.	0712	...	0815	...	1055	1540	...	1925	...
Antequera - Santa Ana § d.	0806	...	0906	...	1150	1643	...	2025	...
Puente Genil - Herrera ¶ d.	|	...	|	...	|	|	...	2046	...
Córdoba d.	0838	...	0943	...	1227	1719	...	2111	...
Madrid Puerta de Atocha a.	1032	...	|	...	1424	1911	...	2300	...
Barcelona Sants a.	...	...	1420	...	...	...	...	...	...

¶ – ± *8 km* from Puente Genil.

§ – ± *17 km* from Antequera.

679 MADRID - TOLEDO, SEGOVIA, VALLADOLID, SALAMANCA and EL ESCORIAL

2nd class

km		Av 8062 Ⓐ	Av 8072 Ⓐ	Av 8082	Av 8292	Av 8102	Av 8312	Av 8322		Av 8132	Av 8142 Ⓐ	Av 8152	Av 8162 Ⓐ	Av 8172	Av 8182 Ⓐ	Av 8192	Av 8212					
0	**Madrid** Puerta de Atocha d.	0655	0750	0850	0920	1020	1120	1220	...	1350	1450	1550	1650	1750	1850	1945	2050	...	...	...	...	...
75	**Toledo** a.	0728	0823	0923	0953	1052	1153	1253	...	1423	1523	1623	1723	1823	1923	2018	2123	...	...	...	...	...

	Av 8063 Ⓐ	Av 8273 Ⓐ	Av 8073 Ⓐ	Av 8283 Ⓐ		Av 8093	Av 8103		Av 8123	Av 8133		Av 8153	Av 8163 Ⓐ	Av 8173	Av 8183	Av 8193	Av 8203	Av 8213					
Toledo d.	0625	0650	0725	0755	...	0925	1025	...	1225	1325	...	1525	1613	1725	1825	1920	2025	2130	...	...	...	...	...
Madrid Puerta de Atocha a.	0658	0723	0758	0828	...	0959	1059	...	1258	1358	...	1558	1646	1759	1858	1954	2058	2203	...	...	...	...	...

km	km		Av 8069 Ⓐ	Av 31071 Ⓐ	Av 8079 Ⓐ	Alvia 4899	Av 8109		Av 8129	Alvia 4929 ①–⑤	Av 8139 ⑤	Av 34149 Ⓑ	Av 8159 ⑤	Av 8359	Alvia 4969	Av 31267	Av 8169 Ⓐ	Av 8179	Av 8389 Ⓑ	Av 8189 A	Av 8199 Ⓐ	Av 8209	Av 34209 Ⓑ	Alvia 4909	Av 8219
0	0	**Madrid** Chamartín ‡ d.	0640	0708	0752	0850	1015	...	1205	1240	1340	1440	1510	1540	1555	1610	1626	1700	1810	1845	1925	2000	2025	2040	2130
68	68	**Segovia** Guiomar d.	0708	|	0820	0918	1043	...	1233	1308	1408	1508	1548	1608	1623	1640	1654	1728	1838	1913	1954	2028	|	2108	2158
		Medina del Campo AV d.	|	|	|	0947	|	...	|	1336	|	|	|	|	|	|	|	|	|	|	|	|	|	2137	|
180		**Valladolid** ⊠ a.	0748	0807	0857	|	1120	...	1310	|	1445	1539	1615	1645	|	1726	1731	1805	1915	1950	2031	2105	2118	|	2235
	230	**Salamanca** a.	...	...	...	1031	...	...	...	1421	...	...	...	...	1731	...	...	...	...	...	...	...	...	2221	...

	Av 8058 Ⓐ	Av 8068 Ⓐ	Alvia 4868 Ⓐ	Av 8078 Ⓐ	Av 8278	Av 34078 Ⓐ	Av 8088 Ⓐ	Alvia 4898 Ⓒ	Av 8098 Ⓒ	Alvia 4918 ①–⑤	Av 8118 Ⓐ	Av 8148 Ⓐ	Av 8158	Alvia 4958	Av 8168 ⑤⑦	Av 8178	Av 34178 Ⓑ	Alvia 4988	Av 8198	Av 8208					
Salamanca d.	...	...	0625	...	...	...	...	0820	...	1050	...	...	...	1530	...	...	...	1820	...	...	...	...	...	...	...
Valladolid ⊠ d.	0623	0645	|	0715	0755	0816	0845	|	0950	|	1130	1405	1520	|	1622	1750	1836	|	1946	2035	...	...	...	...	...
Medina del Campo AV d.	|	|	0708	|	|	|	|	0904	|	|	|	|	|	1614	|	|	|	1903	|	|	...	...	...	...	...
Segovia Guiomar d.	0700	0722	0738	0752	0832	|	0922	0934	1027	1159	1207	1442	1557	1644	1659	1827	1911	1933	2023	2112	...	...	...	...	...
Madrid Chamartín ‡ a.	0728	0750	0805	0820	0900	0908	0950	1000	1055	1226	1235	1510	1625	1711	1727	1855	1937	2000	2051	2140	...	...	...	...	...

km		Ⓐ	Ⓒ	Ⓒ	Ⓐ	Ⓒ		⑤	Ⓒ	Ⓐ	Ⓒ
0	**Madrid** Chamartín ‡ d.	...	0845	*1015*	*1116*	*1216*	...	*1547*	*1616*	*1846*	*1916*
58	Cercedilla d.	0700	0950	1132	1230	1332	...	1700	1732	1930	2032
100	**Segovia** a.	0737	1032	1208	1312	1409	...	1736	1813	2014	2110

	Ⓐ	Ⓒ	Ⓒ	Ⓐ		⑤	Ⓒ	Ⓐ	Ⓒ	
Segovia d.	0750	1042	1250	1442	...	1750	1843	2046	2120	...
Cercedilla a.	0828	1126	1326	1524	...	1826	1924	2128	2157	...
Madrid Chamartín ‡ a.	*0935*	*1234*	*1435*	*1635*	...	*1935*	*2036*	*2235*	2254	...

km		MD 18001 Ⓐ	MD 18901 Ⓐ	MD 18921 Ⓒ	MD 18903	MD 18905 Ⓐ	MD 18907	MD 18913	MD 18909		
0	**Madrid** Principe Pio ◧ d.	0643	0740	0828	1110	1340	1525	1754	1937	2153q	...
122	Ávila ◧ d.	0822	0908	0955	1239	1510	1711	1936	2112	2341	...
233	**Salamanca** a.	...	1040	1123	1353	1619	1828	2046	2221	...	...

	Ⓐ	Ⓐ	MD 18900	MD 18912	MD 18902	MD 18004 Ⓐ	MD 18904	MD 18006	MD 18906 Ⓐ	MD 18908
Salamanca d.	...	...	0732	0941	1228	...	1644	...	1802	1958
Ávila ◧ d.	0555	0630	0840	1058	1339	1547	1812	1900	1912	2106
Madrid Principe Pio ◧ a.	0742	0813	1011	1233	1512	1731	1948	2048	2056	2244

MADRID ATOCHA CERCANÍAS - VILLALBA - EL ESCORIAL. *45 km*. Line C8. Journey time: Villalba, 53 minutes; El Escorial, 66-67 minutes. Depart 14 minutes later from Madrid Chamartín; arrive 15 minutes earlier at Madrid Charmartín. Additional services operate.

From **Madrid Atocha Cercanías**: 0621 Ⓐ, 0635 Ⓒ, 0651 Ⓐ, 0709 Ⓐ, 0723 Ⓐ, 0737 Ⓒ, 0750 Ⓐ, 0835 Ⓒ, 0839 Ⓐ; 0935 Ⓒ, 0941 Ⓐ, 1036, 1135, 1235, 1335, 1407 Ⓐ, 1436 Ⓒ, 1450 Ⓐ, 1521 Ⓐ, 1536 Ⓒ, 1547 Ⓐ, 1635, 1715 Ⓐ, 1736 Ⓒ, 1745 Ⓐ, 1827 Ⓐ, 1836 Ⓒ, 1847 Ⓐ, 1920, 1936, Ⓒ, 1944 Ⓐ, 2036 Ⓐ, 2042 Ⓒ, 2139, 2236, 2334.

From **El Escorial**: 0548, 0616 Ⓒ, 0631 Ⓐ, 0658 Ⓐ, 0706 Ⓐ, 0716 Ⓒ, 0736 Ⓐ, 0802 Ⓐ, 0817 Ⓒ, 0831 Ⓐ, 0915, 1015, 1115, 1215, 1315, 1414, 1515, 1601 Ⓐ, 1615 Ⓒ, 1624 Ⓐ, 1713, 1815, 1858 Ⓐ, 1912 Ⓐ, 1915 Ⓒ, 1930 Ⓐ, 1959 Ⓐ, 2013 Ⓒ, 2029 Ⓐ, 2115, 2215.

A – ①②③④⑥.

q – Madrid-Chamartín-Clara Campoamor.

MD – Medium Distance Plus.

Av – ***Avant*** high-speed services. Single class.

◧ – See also Tables **680**, **681**, **689**.

⊠ – Full name is Valladolid Campo Grande.

‡ – Full name is Madrid-Chamartín-Clara Campoamor.

☛ **Shaded services are suspended until further notice.**

679a MADRID - VALLADOLID

High-speed services. For Avant high-speed services, see Table **679**.

km			*Alvia* 4071 ①–⑥	*Alvia* 4073 ①–⑥	*Alvia* 4087	*Alvia* 4187 ①–⑥	*AVE* 4099 4299 L		*Alvia* 4143	*AVE* 4149 Ⓑ L	*IC* 4153 ⑤ 2	*Alvia* 4111 V	*Alvia* 4167	*Alvia* 4267 Ⓑ	*IC* 4177 ⑤ 2	*Alvia* 4377 ⑦ 2	*Alvia* 4181 Ⓑ	*IC* 4581 ⑥	*Alvia* 4193 Ⓑ	*Alvia* 4197 ①–④ T	*AVE* 4209 L				
	Alacant Terminal **668** d.	...	...	...	...	...	...	...	1035	...	...	...	...	...	...	...	...	...	...	...	...	...	...	...	...
0	**Madrid** Chamartín ‡ d.	...	0708	0745	0810	0810	0935	...	1410	1440	1525	1528	1610	1610	1738	1740	1835	1835	1908	1915	2025	...	...	...	...
68	Segovia Guiomar d.	...	|	|	0840	0840	1003	...	1441	1508	|	1558	1640	1640	|	|	|	|	|	|	|	...	...	...	...
180	**Valladolid** ⊠ a.	...	0809	0843	0926	0926	1038	...	1516	1541	1626	1636	1726	1726	1846	1848	1936	1936	2005	2023	2118	...	...	...	...
	Gijón Sanz Crespo **681** a.	...	1227	|	|	|	...	...	|	...	|	2046	|	|	|	|	2343	2343	|	...	...	...	...	...	...
	Santander **681** a.	...	...	1150	|	|	...	...	1815	...	1947	...	|	|	|	|	...	...	2312	...	...	...	...	...	...
	Bilbao Abando **689** a.	...	...	...	|	1317	...	...	...	...	...	...	|	2116	|	|	...	...	...	...	...	...	...	...	...
	Irún **689** a.	...	...	...	1418	...	...	...	...	...	...	...	2213	...	2311	2321	...	...	...	...	...	...	...	...	...

	AVE 4078 ①–⑤ L	*Alvia* 4076 ①–⑤ T	*AVE* 4288 ⑥⑦ L	*Alvia* 4072 ①–⑤	*Alvia* 4270 ①–⑥	*Alvia* 4092 ⑥⑦	*Alvia* 4086	*Alvia* 4186 ①–⑥	*AVE* 4128 ①–⑤ 2 L	*Alvia* 4110 V		*Alvia* 4142	*Alvia* 4140	*AVE* 4178 Ⓑ L	*AVE* 4188 ⑥ 2 L	*IC* 4176 ⑦ 2	*IC* 4162 ⑦ 2	*AVE* 4198 ⑥ L	*Alvia* 4166	*Alvia* 4266 Ⓑ	*AVE* 4398 ⑦ L	*Alvia* 4180 Ⓑ	*Alvia* 4192 Ⓑ		
Irún **689** d.	...	...	...	...	...	...	0823	...	...	...	...	...	...	...	...	1450	...	...	1535	...	...	...	...	...	...
Bilbao Abando **689** d.	...	...	...	...	...	...	|	0920	...	...	...	...	...	...	...	|	...	...	|	1700	...	...	...	...	...
Santander **681** d.	...	...	...	0705	...	0910	|	|	...	...	...	1400	...	...	...	|	1610	...	|	|	...	...	1900	...	...
Gijón Sanz Crespo **681** d.	...	...	...	|	0700	|	|	|	...	1010	...	|	1412	...	...	|	|	...	|	|	...	1800	|	...	...
Valladolid ⊠ d.	0816	0916	0941	1007	1107	1212	1311	1311	1331	1412	...	1700	1813	1836	1901	1914	1930	2005	2050	2050	2106	2157	2202	...	...
Segovia Guiomar d.	|	|	|	1046	|	1251	1359	1359	1414	1451	...	|	|	1911	1941	|	|	2042	2137	2137	2145	|	|	...	...
Madrid Chamartín ‡ a.	0908	1030	1037	1115	1207	1320	1428	1428	1441	1520	...	1800	1921	1937	2008	2033	2040	2110	2206	2206	2214	2300	2307	...	...
Alacant Terminal **668** a.	...	...	...	1502	...	1656	...	...	...	...	...	...	2301	...	...	...	...	...	...	...	...	...	...	...	...

L – To/from Leon (Table **681**).

T – To and from Vitoria/Gasteiz (Table **689**).

V – From/to Castelló de la Plana and València (Table **668**).

⊠ – Full name is Valladolid Campo Grande.

‡ – Full name is Madrid-Chamartín-Clara Campoamor.

☛ All trains convey 🍸. *AVE* trains also convey ✕.

☛ **Shaded services are suspended until further notice.**

MADRID - ZAMORA - VIGO, PONTEVEDRA and A CORUÑA 680

For services to / from A Coruña via León, see Table **682**

Additional connections between Vigo and Ourense can be made by changing trains at Santiago de Compostela

km		12512	MD 9072	Av 9480	MD 9082	Alvia 4254	12526	MD 9112	12623	12528	Alvia 4275	Av 9090	MD 9132	Alvia 4095	AVE 4105	Av 9120	Alvia 4115	Av 9140	Av 9550	12538	Alvia 4325	Av 9160	MD 9162	Alvia 4145	Alvia 4184
		[R]	[R]		[R]		[R]	[R]	[R]	[R]			[R]			2				[R]		[R]	[R]		
		2	2	2	2	Z	2	2	2	2	X	2	2	b			X	2	2	2	q	2	2		Z
		①–⑤									①–⑤	①–⑤		①–⑥			①–⑥		①–⑤					Ⓑ	Ⓑ
0	**Madrid** Chamartín ‡ **681 689** d.	...	...	...	...	...	...	...	...	...	0620	...	...	0800	1000	...	1120	...	...	...	1315	...	...	1430	...
68	Segovia Guiomar **679 679a** d.	...	...	...	...	...	...	...	...	...	0650	...	...	|	|	...	|	...	...	...	1346	...	...	|	...
	Irún **689** d.	...	...	...	...	...	...	...	...	...	|	...	...	|	|	...	|	...	...	...	|	...	...	|	...
	Barcelona Sants **650a** d.	...	...	...	...	...	...	...	...	...	|	...	...	|	|	...	|	...	...	...	|	...	...	|	...
	Miranda de Ebro **681 689** d.	...	...	...	...	...	...	...	...	...	|	...	...	|	|	...	|	...	...	...	|	...	...	|	...
207*	Medina AV **681 689** d.	...	...	...	...	...	...	...	...	...	0719	...	...	|	|	...	|	...	...	...	1415	...	...	|	...
297	**Zamora** d.	...	...	...	...	...	...	...	...	...	0747	...	...	0914	1106	...	1234	...	...	...	1442	...	...	1544	...
404	Sanabria AV a.	...	...	...	...	...	...	...	...	...	0825	...	...	|	|	...	|	...	...	...	1516	...	...	|	...
547	**Ourense** d.	...	...	0755	...	...	...	...	1005	...	0930	0940	...	1038	1215	1225	1401	1415	1535	...	1620	1635	...	1708	...
641	Guillarei d.	...	...	|	...	...	...	...	1127	...	|	|	...	|	...	|	|	|	|	...	...	|	...	|	...
	Vigo Urzáiz d.	0505c	0640	|	0800	0920	0913c	1100	|	1230c	1100	|	1340	|	...	|	1538	|	|	1502c	...	|	1635	|	1708
666	Redondela AV d.	0518r	0648	|	|	|	0926r	|	1150r	1243r	|	|	1348	|	...	|	|	|	|	1513r	...	|	|	|	|
678	**Vigo** Guixar a.	|	|	|	|	|	|	|	1205	|	|	|	|	|	...	|	|	|	|	|	...	|	|	|	|
684	**Pontevedra** d.	0536	0659	|	0815	0936	0945	1115	...	1302	1044	|	1401	|	...	|	1522	|	|	1534	...	|	1650	|	1724
717	Vilagarcía de Arousa d.	0553	0716	|	0830	0953	1003	1130	...	1320	...	|	1418	|	...	|	...	|	|	1552	...	|	1705	|	1742
677§	Santiago de Compostela d.	0637	0742	0835	0852	1020	1050	1152	...	1405	...	1020	1444	1122	...	1305	...	1455	1615	1636	...	1715	1727	1749	...
751§	**A Coruña** a.	0716	0813	0903	0920	...	1126	1220	...	1442	...	1048	1512	1202	...	1333	...	1523	1643	1713	...	1743	1755	1818	...

	MD 9172	MD 9182	12488	Alvia 4165	Av 9590	IC 283	MD 9192	Alvia 4175	12554		Alvia 622	Alvia 626	RE 18322	MD 9212	Alvia 4185	12560	AVE 4205	Av 31456		Hotel 922					
	[R]	[R]	[R]			🍸	[R]		[R]		🍸	🍸		[R]						🍸					
	2	2	2	X	2	2	2	b	2	2	P	Q	2	2	Z	2		2		G					
		Ⓑ				A					❖	❖	J				Ⓑ	Ⓑ							
Madrid Chamartín ‡ **681 689** d.	...	...	...	1600	...	...	...	1745	...	...	...	...	...	...	1915	...	2035	...	...	...	...	...	...	...	...
Segovia Guiomar .. **679 679a** d.	...	...	...	|	...	...	...	1815	...	...	...	...	...	...	|	...	|	...	...	...	...	...	...	...	...
Irún **689** d.	...	...	...	|	...	0910	...	|	...	...	...	...	...	...	|	...	|	...	...	...	...	...	...	...	...
Barcelona Sants **650a** d.	...	...	...	|	...	|	...	|	...	...	0930	0930	...	...	|	...	|	...	...	2020	...	...	...	...	...
Miranda de Ebro **681 689** .. d.	...	...	...	|	...	1140	...	|	...	...	1438	1438	...	...	|	...	|	...	...	|	...	...	...	...	...
Medina AV **681 689** d.	...	...	...	|	...	|	...	1844	...	...	|	|	1759x	...	|	...	|	...	...	|	...	...	...	...	...
Zamora d.	...	...	...	1714	...	|	...	1910	...	...	|	|	1852	...	2029	...	2141	...	...	|	...	...	...	...	...
Sanabria AV a.	...	...	...	|	...	|	...	1944	...	...	|	|	2014p	...	2103	...	|	...	...	|	...	...	...	...	...
Ourense d.	...	...	...	1839	1900	1908	...	2048	...	2102	2131	2131	...	...	2208	...	2250	2258	...	0938	...	...	...	...	...
Guillarei d.	...	...	...	|	|	|	...	|	...	2229	|	|	...	...	|	...	...	|	...	1109	...	...	...	...	...
Vigo Urzáiz d.	1730	1815	1820c	2012	|	|	1925	|	2025c	|	|	|	...	2135	|	...	...	|	...	|	...	...	...	...	...
Redondela AV d.	|	|	1833r	|	|	|	|	|	2038r	2257r	2301r	|	...	2143	|	...	...	|	...	1130	...	...	...	...	...
Vigo Guixar a.	|	|	|	|	|	|	|	|	|	2309	2312	|	...	|	|	...	...	|	...	1141	...	...	...	...	...
Pontevedra d.	1745	1830	1852	1956	|	|	1940	|	2057	...	...	|	...	2156	2331	...	...	|	...	...	...	...	...	...	...
Vilagarcía de Arousa d.	1800	1845	1914	...	|	|	1955	|	2116	...	...	|	...	2213	|	...	...	|	...	...	...	...	...	...	...
Santiago de Compostela d.	1822	1907	1956	...	1940	2001	2017	2131	2200	...	...	2211	...	2239	2251	2305	...	2337	...	...	...	...	...	...	...
A Coruña a.	1850	1935	...	...	2008	2033	2045	2209	2236	...	...	2241	...	2307	...	2338	...	0005	...	...	...	...	...	...	...

km		Av 31455	AVE 4054	RE 18321	RE 18321	Av 9061	Alvia 4484	12411	MD 9073	MD 9083	Alvia 621	Alvia 625	Alvia 4064	MD 9093	Av 9581	Alvia 4254	IC 280	12421	MD 9113	Av 9111	Alvia 4114	MD 9123	12453	Av 9131	Alvia 4354
				2	2			[R]	[R]	[R]	🍸	🍸		[R]			🍸	[R]	[R]			[R]			
		2		J	J	2	X	2	2	2	R	S	b	2	2	Z	2	2	2	2	q	2	2	2	X
		①–⑥	①–⑥	Ⓐ	Ⓒ	①–⑤	①–⑤	①–⑤			❖	❖	①–⑥		⑥⑦		A		①–⑤					①–⑤	
0	**A Coruña** d.	0508	...	...	...	0555	...	0535	0700	0800	...	0805	0838	0900	0920	...	0930	0930	1100	1130	...	1200	1240	1330	...
74	Santiago de Compostela d.	0538	...	...	...	0625	...	0614	0730	0830	...	0834	0909	0930	0949	1020	1006	1012	1130	1200	...	1230	1322	1400	...
116	Vilagarcía de Arousa d.	|	...	...	...	|	...	0651	0756	0850	...	|	|	0950	|	|	|	1050	1150	|	...	1250	1405	|	...
149	**Pontevedra** d.	|	...	...	...	|	0606	0711	0813	0906	...	|	|	1006	|	0936	|	1108	1206	|	...	1306	1423	|	1336
	Vigo Guixar d.	|	...	...	...	|	|	|	|	|	0742	|	|	|	|	|	|	|	|	|	...	|	|	|	|
167	Redondela AV d.	|	...	...	...	|	|	0730r	0825	|	0753r	|	|	|	|	|	|	1127r	|	|	...	|	1441r	|	|
179	**Vigo** Urzáiz d.	|	...	...	...	|	0550	0741c	0833	0920	|	|	|	1020	|	|	|	1140c	1220	|	...	1320	1454c	|	1320
192	Guillarei d.	|	...	...	...	|	|	...	...	...	0810	|	|	...	|	|	|	...	...	|	...	...	...	|	|
	Ourense d.	0616	0630	...	...	0703	0718	...	...	...	0916	0916	0949	...	1026	1102	1110	...	...	1238	1258	...	...	1438	1450
	Sanabria AV d.	...	|	0702p	0730p	...	0821	...	...	...	|	|	1054	...	...	|	|	...	...	...	1403	...	...	...	|
	Zamora d.	...	0741	0826	0854	...	0902	...	...	...	|	|	1130	...	...	1230	|	...	...	...	1439	...	...	...	1620
	Medina AV **681 689** d.	...	|	0919x	0947x	...	|	...	...	...	|	|	1158	...	...	|	|	...	...	...	1507	...	...	...	|
	Miranda de Ebro **681 689** a.	...	|	...	...	...	|	...	...	...	1611	1611	|	...	...	|	1842	...	...	...	|	...	...	...	|
	Barcelona Sants **650a** a.	...	|	...	...	...	|	...	...	...	2135	2135	|	...	...	|	|	...	...	...	|	...	...	...	|
	Hendaye **689** a.	...	|	...	...	...	|	...	...	...	...	...	|	...	...	|	2122	...	...	...	|	...	...	...	|
	Segovia Guiomar **679 679a** d.	...	|	...	...	...	|	...	...	...	...	...	1228	...	...	|	...	...	...	...	1537	...	...	...	|
	Madrid Chamartín ‡ **681 689** a.	...	0845	...	...	...	1020	...	...	...	...	...	1258	...	...	1342	...	...	...	...	1606	...	...	...	1736

		MD 9133	Alvia 4115	MD 9153	Av 9351	AVE 4164	MD 12431	Alvia 4134	12967	MD 9173	Av 9171	Alvia 4184	Hotel 921	MD 9183	12441	Alvia 4204	Av 9201	12459	MD 9213	12461	12561	Alvia 4185			
		[R]		[R]			[R]		[R]	[R]	2		🍸	[R]	[R]		2	[R]	[R]	[R]					
	2	2	X	2	2		2	b	2	2		X	G	2	2			2	2	2	2	Z			
	h		①–⑥									Ⓑ		Ⓑ		Ⓑ									
A Coruña d.	...	1400	...	1500	1510	...	1550	1626	...	1700	1720	...	...	1800	1908	1935	1950	...	2115	...	2210	...	...	...	...
Santiago de Compostela d.	...	1430	...	1530	1540	...	1632	1656	1725	1730	1750	...	...	1830	1950	2006	2020	2025	2147	2200	2243	2251	...	...	...
Vilagarcía de Arousa d.	...	1455	1504	1550	|	...	1709	|	|	1750	|	...	...	1850	2033	|	|	2105	2213	2241	...	2314	...	...	...
Pontevedra d.	...	1512	1522	1606	|	...	1727	|	|	1806	|	1724	...	1906	2054	|	|	2123	2231	2259	...	2331	...	...	...
Vigo Guixar d.	1410	|	|	|	|	...	|	|	|	|	|	|	1755	|	|	|	|	|	|	|	...	|	...	...	...
Redondela AV d.	1423r	1522	|	|	|	...	1745r	|	|	|	|	|	1805	|	2115r	|	|	2143r	2243	2319r	...	|	...	...	...
Vigo Urzáiz d.	|	1529	1538	1620	|	...	1759c	|	|	1820	|	1708	|	1920	2126c	|	|	2156c	2251	2332c	...	2346	...	...	...
Guillarei d.	1444	...	...	...	|	...	...	|	|	...	|	|	1825	...	...	|	|	...	...	...	...	...	...	...	...
Ourense d.	1610	...	...	...	1618	1625	...	1733	1906	...	1828	1844	1933	...	...	2047	2058	...	...	...	...	...	...	...	...
Sanabria AV d.	...	...	...	...	...	|	...	|	...	...	...	1947	|	...	...	|	...	...	...	...	...	...	...	...	...
Zamora d.	...	...	...	...	...	1736	...	1903	...	...	...	2024	|	...	...	2213	...	...	...	...	...	...	...	...	...
Medina AV **681 689** d.	...	...	...	...	...	|	...	|	...	...	...	2052	|	...	...	|	...	...	...	...	...	...	...	...	...
Miranda de Ebro **681 689** a.	...	...	...	...	...	|	...	|	...	...	...	|	|	...	...	|	...	...	...	...	...	...	...	...	...
Barcelona Sants **650a** a.	...	...	...	...	...	|	...	|	...	...	...	|	0849	...	...	|	...	...	...	...	...	...	...	...	...
Hendaye **689** a.	...	...	...	...	...	|	...	|	...	...	...	|	...	...	...	|	...	...	...	...	...	...	...	...	...
Segovia Guiomar .. **679 679a** d.	...	...	...	...	...	|	...	|	...	...	...	2123	...	...	...	|	...	...	...	...	...	...	...	...	...
Madrid Chamartín ‡ **681 689** a.	...	...	...	...	...	1840	...	2018	...	...	...	2152	...	...	...	2329	...	...	...	...	...	...	...	...	...

A – CAMINO DE SANTIAGO – 2 🍸 Irún / Hendaye - Miranda de Ebro - A Coruña and v.v.
G – Ⓑ (daily June 17 - Sept. 16): GALICIA *Trenhotel* – sleeper, 1 (reclining) Barcelona - Vigo and v.v.
J – 2 Valladolid - Medina del Campo - Puebla de Sanabria and v.v. (Table **689**).
P – ③⑤⑦ 12 🍸 Barcelona - Ourense - Vigo ❖.
Q – ①②④⑥ 12 🍸 Barcelona - Ourense - A Coruña ❖.
R – ①④⑥ 12 🍸 Vigo - Ourense - Barcelona ❖.
S – ②③⑤⑦ 12 🍸 A Coruña - Ourense - Barcelona ❖.
X – Routeing is Madrid - Ourense - Pontevedra - Vigo and v.v.
Z – Routeing is Madrid - Ourense - Santiago de Compostela - Pontevedra - Vigo and v.v. See opposite direction for further stops.

b – To / from Ferrol (Table **682**).
c – Vigo **Guixar**.
h – To Ponferrada (Table **682**).
p – Puebla de Sanabria
q – To / from Lugo (Table **682**).
r – Redondela **de Galica**.
x – Medina del Campo.

◐ – Via Lugo (Table **682**).
‡ – Full name is Madrid-Chamartín-Clara Campoamor.

* – *153 km* Madrid - Medina del Campo via high-speed line.
§ – *636 km* Madrid - Santiago de Compostela via high-speed line. *697 km* Madrid - A Coruña via high-speed line.
❖ – On days of indirect service, connections are available between Ourense and Vigo / A Coruña and v.v. in similar timings.

☛ **Shaded services are suspended until further notice.**

681 MADRID - LEÓN

km	km via HSL		Ⓐ 2	Ⓒ 2	18701 2 S	Alvia 4071 ①-⑥	Alvia 4073 ①-⑥	18101 2 T	AVE 4099 4299	IC 283 2🍷 B	Alvia 4143 E	Alvia 622 626 L	AVE 4149 Ⓑ	Alvia 4541 ⑥	Alvia 4141 Ⓑ	IC 4153 ⑤ 2	Alvia 4111 P	Alvia 664	MD 18003 2	IC 4171 ⑤ 2	Alvia 4181 Ⓑ	MD 18005 2	Alvia 4193 Ⓑ	AVE 4209	Hotel 922 G
0	0	**Madrid** Chamartín ¶ ... 680 689 d.	...	...	...	0708	0745	...	0935	...	1410	...	1440	1440	1450	1525	1528	...	1628p	1720	1835	1827p	1908	2025	...
121		Ávila ... 680 689 d.	...	...	...	|	|	...	|	...	|	...	|	|	|	|	|	...	1759	|	|	2009	|	|	...
207		Medina del Campo ... 680 689 d.	...	...	...	|	|	...	|	...	|	...	|	|	|	|	|	...	1845	|	|	2054	|	|	...
249	180	**Valladolid** C. Grande ... 689 d.	0700	0718	0750	0809	0845	0955	1040	...	1518	...	1541	1541	1551	1628	1636	...	1913	|	1936	2120	2007	2120	...
286		Venta de Baños ... 689 d.	0733	0751	0816	|	|	1027	|	...	|	...	|	|	|	|	|	...	1938	|	|	2147	|	|	...
		Barcelona Sants 652 ... d.	|	|	|	|	|	|	|	...	|	0930	|	|	|	|	|	1210	|	|	|	|	|	|	2020
		Irún 689 ... d.	|	|	|	|	|	|	|	0910	|	|	|	|	|	|	|	|	|	|	|	|	|	|	|
		Miranda de Ebro ... 689 d.	|	|	|	|	|	|	|	1140	|	1438	|	|	|	|	|	1723	|	|	|	|	|	|	|
		Burgos Rosa Manzano 689 d.	|	|	|	|	|	|	|	1234	|	1534	|	|	|	|	|	1816	|	|	|	|	|	|	0249
		Palencia ... 689 d.	0747	0805	0827	0835	0917	1038	1107	1323	1550	1627	1606	|	|	1706	1703	1906	1949	|	2002	2158	2039	2146	0342
297	233	*Santander* 684 ... a.	|	|	1125	|	1150	1344	|	|	1815	|	|	|	|	1947	|	|	|	|	|	|	2312	|	|
		León ... a.	0923	0927	...	0920	...	...	1150	1428	...	1735	1641	1655	|	...	1746	2014	2102	1930	2046	2307	...	2221	0450
420	345	*Gijón Sanz Crespo* 685 ... a.	1246	1246	...	1227	...	...	...	|	...	|	...	1943	1939	...	2046	2312x	...	2240	2343	...	...	...	|
		Ponferrada 682 ... a.	...	...	...	...	...	...	...	1614	...	1906	...	...	...	...	...	...	...	...	...	...	...	...	0649
		Vigo Guixar 682 ... a.	...	...	...	...	...	...	...	|	...	2312	...	...	...	...	...	...	...	...	...	...	...	...	1141
		A Coruña 682 ... a.	...	...	...	...	...	...	...	2033	...	2241	...	...	...	...	...	...	...	...	...	...	...	...	1114
		Ferrol 682 ... a.	...	...	...	...	...	...	...	...	...	...	...	...	...	...	...	...	...	...	...	...	...	...	...

	MD 18002 2 w	AVE 4078 ①-⑤	Alvia 4072 ①-⑤ E	AVE 4288 ⑥⑦	Alvia 4270 ①-⑥	Alvia 4092 ⑥⑦ E	Alvia 661	AVE 4128 ①-⑤	Alvia 4110 P	Alvia 625 621 L	IC 280 2🍷 B	Alvia 4142	MD 18006 2	IC 4540 ⑦ 2	Alvia 4140	AVE 4178 Ⓑ	18104 2	IC 4162 ⑦ 2	AVE 4198 ⑥	† 2	⚒ 2	IC 4160 ⑦ 2	Alvia 4180 Ⓑ	Alvia 4192 Ⓑ	Hotel 921 G
Ferrol 682 ... d.	...	...	...	...	...	...	...	...	...	...	...	...	...	...	...	...	...	...	...	...	...	...	...	...	...
A Coruña 682 ... d.	...	...	...	...	...	...	...	...	...	0805	0930	...	...	...	...	...	...	...	...	...	...	...	...	...	1749
Vigo Guixar 682 ... d.	...	...	...	...	...	...	...	...	...	0742	|	...	...	...	...	...	...	...	...	...	...	...	...	...	1755
Ponferrada 682 ... d.	...	...	...	...	...	...	...	...	...	1128	1344	...	...	...	...	...	...	...	...	1620	...	...	...	...	2222
Gijón Sanz Crespo 685 ... d.	...	...	...	...	0700	...	0757	...	0950	|	|	...	...	1403	1412	...	...	...	...	|	1515	1602	1800	...	|
León ... d.	0640	0715	...	0840	0948	...	1044	1220	1239	1304	1544	...	1542	1656	1659	1735	...	...	1850	1841	1843	1856	2047	...	0012
Santander 684 ... d.	|	|	0705	|	|	0910	|	|	|	|	|	1400	|	|	|	|	1538	1610	|	|	|	|	|	1900	|
Palencia ... 689 d.	0750	0751	0935	0916	1035	1140	1157	1304	1325	1416	1655	1628	1654	1746	1743	1811	1844	1856	1935	2007	2005	|	2131	2131	0124
Burgos Rosa Manzano 689 d.	|	|	|	|	|	|	1252	|	|	1511	1746	|	|	|	|	|	|	|	|	|	|	|	|	|	0217
Miranda de Ebro ... 689 a.	|	|	|	|	|	|	1345	|	|	1611	1842	|	|	|	|	|	|	|	|	|	|	|	|	|	|
Hendaye 689 ... a.	|	|	|	|	|	|	|	|	|	|	2122	|	|	|	|	|	|	|	|	|	|	|	|	|	|
Barcelona Sants 652 ... a.	|	|	|	|	|	|	1903	|	|	2135	...	|	|	|	|	|	|	|	|	|	|	|	|	|	0849
Venta de Baños ... 689 d.	0803	|	|	|	|	|	...	|	|	...	...	|	1706	|	|	|	1855	|	|	2023	2018	|	|	|	...
Valladolid C. Grande ... 689 d.	0833	0816	1007	0941	1107	1212	...	1331	1352	...	...	1700	1742	1813	1813	1836	1927	1930	2005	2057	2054	|	2157	2202	...
Medina del Campo ... 680 689 a.	0859	|	|	|	|	|	...	|	|	...	...	|	1807	|	|	|	...	|	|	...	...	|	|	|	...
Ávila ... 680 689 a.	0943	|	|	|	|	|	...	|	|	...	...	|	1852	|	|	|	...	|	|	...	...	|	|	|	...
Madrid Chamartín ¶ ... 680 689 a.	1126p	0908	1115	1037	1207	1320	...	1441	1500	...	...	1800	2041p	1917	1921	1937	...	2040	2110	...	...	2113	2300	2307	...

☛ **FOR NOTES**, SEE TABLE **682** BELOW.

682 LEÓN - VIGO, FERROL and A CORUÑA

km		MD 37064 2 ①-⑥	MD 12681 2	MD 12641 2	2	2	2	Alvia 4095 ①-⑥ A	MD 12695 2 J	IC 283 2 B	MD 12687 2	Alvia 4325 M		Alvia 4175 Ⓑ A	2	Alvia 626 L	Alvia 622 L	2 ⑤	MD 12646 2 H	2	IC 560 Ⓑ 2J		Hotel 922 G	Hotel 922 G
	Madrid Chamartín ¶ ‡ d.	...	...	...	...	...	...	0800	...	...	...	1315	...	1745	...	...	...	...	...	...	...	...	...	...
	Barcelona Sants ... ‡ d.	...	...	...	...	...	...	|	...	...	...	|	...	|	...	0930	0930	...	...	...	...	...	2020	2020
	Irún ... ‡ d.	...	...	...	...	...	...	|	...	0910	...	|	...	|	...	|	|	...	...	...	...	...	|	|
	Bilbao Abando ... ‡ d.	...	...	...	...	...	...	|	...	|	...	|	...	|	...	|	|	...	...	...	...	...	|	|
0	**León** ... d.	...	...	...	...	...	0705	|	...	1443	...	|	...	|	1700	1737	1737	1805	...	2235	...	...	0500	0500
52	Astorga ... d.	...	...	...	...	...	0752	|	...	1515	...	|	...	|	1733	1810	1810	1851	...	2322	...	...	0535	0535
128	**Ponferrada** ... d.	...	...	...	0615	...	0901	|	...	1616	...	|	...	|	1834	1907	1907	2008	...	0031	...	...	0644	0644
238	Monforte de Lemos ... a.	...	...	...	0801	...	...	|	...	1753	...	1700	...	|	2016	2037	2037	...	...	...	...	...	0822	0822
238	Monforte de Lemos ... d.	...	...	0730	0806	...	...	|	1321	1809	...	1702	...	|	2021	2042	2042	...	2042	...	2342	...	0835	0842
285	Ourense ... 680 d.	...	...	|	0857	1005	...	1038	1235	1908	...	1620	...	2048	2100	2131	2131	...	1955	...	2300	...	|	0938
416	**Vigo** Guixar ... 680 a.	...	...	|	...	1205	...	|	|	|	...	|	...	|	2249	|	2312	...	|	...	|	...	|	1141
309	Lugo ... d.	...	...	0825	...	...	...	|	1413	|	...	1755	...	|	...	|	...	...	2133	...	0035	...	0935	...
445	**Ferrol** ... d.	0720	0840	|	...	...	...	|	...	▲	1915	...	...	|	...	▲	...	...	|	...	...	...	|	...
402	Betanzos - Infesta ... d.	0806	0929	0946	...	...	...	1232	...	|	2006	...	...	2238	...	|	...	...	2247	...	...	...	1052	...
428	**A Coruña** ... 680 a.	0828	0954	1012	...	...	...	1202	...	2033	2037	...	...	2209	...	2241	...	...	2315	...	...	...	1114	...
445	**Ferrol** ... a.	...	...	...	...	...	...	1312	...	...	...	...	...	2323	...	...	...	...	...	...	...	...	...	...

	2 Ⓐ	2 Ⓒ	Alvia 4064 ①-⑥ A	2	MD 12644 2 H	MD 12680 2	Alvia 621 L	Alvia 625 L		Alvia 4114 M	IC 280 2 B	MD 12698 2 J	2	2 †y	2	Alvia 4134 A	MD 12696 2	Hotel 921 G	Hotel 921 G	IC 558 Ⓑ 2J	MD 12642 2	MD 37145 2		
Ferrol ... d.	...	...	0720	...	...	...	...	...	...	...	...	...	...	...	...	1510	...	...	...	...	...	...	...	...
A Coruña ... 680 d.	...	...	0836	...	0705	0645	...	0805	...	...	0930	...	...	...	...	1626	1720	...	1749	...	1935	2209	...	...
Betanzos - Infesta ... d.	...	...	0806	...	0733	0716	...	|	...	...	|	...	...	...	...	1553	1751	...	1811	...	2004	2238	...	...
Ferrol ... a.	...	...	|	...	|	0803	...	▲	...	...	▲	...	...	...	...	|	1838	...	|	...	|	2323	...	...
Lugo ... d.	...	...	|	...	0852	...	...	|	...	1120	|	1441	...	...	...	|	...	...	1924	1845	2127	...	...	...
Vigo Guixar ... 680 d.	...	...	|	0705	|	...	0742	|	...	|	|	|	...	...	1410	|	...	1755	|	|	|	...	...	...
Ourense ... 680 d.	...	...	0949	0858	1036	...	0916	0916	...	1258	1110	1615	...	...	1630	1733	...	1933	|	2030	|	...	...	...
Monforte de Lemos ... a.	...	...	|	0946	0941	...	0953	0953	...	1211	1148	1532	...	...	1720	|	...	2013	2021	1948	2220	...	...	...
Monforte de Lemos ... d.	...	...	|	0951	...	...	0958	0958	...	1213	1208	...	...	...	1725	|	...	2041	2041	...	...	...	...	...
Ponferrada ... d.	0515	0645	|	1144	...	...	1128	1128	...	|	1344	...	1515	1620	1920	|	...	2222	2222	...	...	...	...	...
Astorga ... d.	0619	0749	|	...	...	...	1228	1228	...	|	1453	...	1630	1740	...	|	...	2325	2325	...	...	...	...	...
León ... a.	0656	0828	|	...	...	...	1302	1302	...	|	1528	...	1710	1836	...	|	...	2357	2357	...	...	...	...	...
Bilbao Abando ... ‡ a.	...	...	|	...	...	...	|	|	...	|	|	...	...	...	...	|	...	|	|	...	...	...	...	...
Hendaye ... ‡ a.	...	...	|	...	...	...	|	|	...	|	2122	...	...	...	...	|	...	|	|	...	...	...	...	...
Barcelona Sants ... ‡ a.	...	...	|	...	...	...	2135	2135	...	|	...	...	...	...	...	|	...	0849	0849	...	...	...	...	...
Madrid Chamartín ¶ ‡ a.	...	...	1258	...	...	...	...	...	...	1606	...	...	...	...	...	2018	...	...	...	...	...	...	...	...

A – 12 Madrid - Zamora - Ourense - A Coruña - Betanzos - Ferrol and v.v. (Table **680**).
B – CAMINO DE SANTIAGO – 2 🍷 Irún / Hendaye - Monforte de Lemos - Santiago - A Coruña and v.v.
E – 12 Alacant - Madrid - Santander and v.v.
G – Ⓑ (daily June 17 - Sept. 16): GALICIA *Trenhotel* – 🛏, 1 (reclining) Barcelona - A Coruña and Vigo and v.v.
H – Routeing is A Coruña - Lugo - Monforte de Lemos - Ourense and v.v., with connections at Ourense to and from Madrid (Table **680**).
J – Routeing is Ourense - Monforte de Lemos - Lugo and v.v.
L – 12 🍷 Barcelona - A Coruña and Vigo and v.v. For days of running see Table **680**.
M – 12 Madrid - Zamora - Ourense - Monforte de Lemos - Lugo and v.v. (Table **680**).
P – From / to Castelló de la Plana and València (Table **668**).

S – ⑥⑦ July 3 - Aug. 29.
T – Not ⑥⑦ July 3 - Aug.

p – Madrid **Principe Pio**.
w – Runs 10 minutes later on Ⓒ.
x – Not ⑥.
y – To Valladolid (Table **681**).

▲ – Via Santiago (Table **680**).
‡ – See Table **681**.
¶ – Full name is Madrid-Chamartín-Clara Campoamor.
☛ **Shaded services are suspended until further notice.**

683 LEÓN - BILBAO

FEVE narrow-gauge

1350 ❖ →	1410 →	1445 →	1535 →	1636 →	1715 →	1801 →	1935 →	2044 →	2134
León	San Feliz	La Vecilla	Cistierna	Guardo	Vado Cervera	Mataporquera	Espinosa	Balmaseda	**Bilbao** Concordia
2203 ❖	← 2138	← 2059	← 2018	← 1921	← 1841	← 1800	← 1623	← 1520	← 1430

❖ – Journey may be by 🚌 between León and Asunción-Universidad y León, due to construction of a new tunnel.

PALENCIA - SANTANDER — 684

km		Alvia 4073			Alvia 4143	IC 4153			Alvia 4193	
		①–⑥	2			⑤	①–⑥	⑦		
					A	2	2	2		
	Madrid CCC ¶ **681 689** ..... d.	0745	...	...	1410	1525	...	...	1908	...
	Valladolid C G **681 689** ..... d.	0845	0955	...	1518	1628	1829	1829	2007	...
0	**Palencia** ..... d.	0917	1038	...	1550	1706	1915	1915	2039	...
98	Aguilar de Campoo ..... d.	1012	1152	...	|	1805	2028	2028	2132	...
110	Mataporquera **683** ‡ ..... d.	|	1201	...	|	1815	2042	2042	|	...
129	Reinosa ..... § d.	1035	1216	...	|	1831	2058	2058	2157	...
188	Torrelavega ..... § d.	1124	1315	...	1751	1921	2153	2157	2246	...
218	**Santander** ..... § a.	1150	1344	...	1815	1947	2222	2226	2312	...

		Alvia 4072	Alvia 4092		Alvia 4142		IC 4162	Alvia 4192	
	⑥⑦	①–⑤	⑥⑦	①–⑤			⑦	Ⓑ	
	2	A	A	2		2	2		
Santander ..... § d.	0700	0705	0910	0919	1400	1538	1610	1900	...
Torrelavega ..... § d.	0729	0729	0934	0953	1424	1609	1633	1923	...
Reinosa ..... § d.	0823	0816	1021	1056	|	1702	1729	2010	...
Mataporquera **683** ‡ ..... d.	0839	|	|	1112	|	1723	1745	|	...
Aguilar de Campoo ..... d.	0849	0838	1047	1122	|	1733	1754	2032	...
Palencia ..... a.	1004	0933	1138	1234	1626	1844	1854	2129	...
Valladolid C G **681 689** ..... a.	1050	1005	1210	1320	1658	1930	1928	2200	...
Madrid CCC ¶ **681 689** ..... a.	...	1115	1320	...	1800	...	2040	2307	...

A – From / to Alacant (Table **668**).
‡ – Narrow gauge station is 600 metres.
§ – Additional local services operate between these stations.
¶ – Full name is Madrid-Chamartín-Clara Campoamor.

LEÓN - OVIEDO - GIJÓN — 685

km				Alvia 4071	Alvia 4541	Alvia 4141	Alvia 4111	IC 4171	Alvia 664	Alvia 4181	IC 4581
		Ⓐ	Ⓒ	①–⑥	⑥	Ⓑ		⑤		Ⓑ	⑥
		2	2								
		A	A		U	S	V	2			
	Barcelona Sants **681** d.	...	...	...	...	...	...	...	1210	...	...
	Madrid CCC ¶ **681** .. d.	...	...	0708	1440	1450	1528	1720	|	1835	1835
0	**León** ..... d.	0925	0929	0922	1700	|	1748	1932	2019	2048	|
109	Pola de Lena ..... § a.	1138	1138	|	|	|	1944	|	2202x	|	|
140	**Oviedo** ▽ ..... § a.	1217	1217	1154	1910	1905	2013	2207	2236x	2312	2213
172	**Gijón** Sanz Crespo .. § a.	1246	1246	1227	1943	1939	2046	2240	2312x	2343	2343

	Alvia 4270	Alvia 661	Alvia 4110	Alvia 4140	2	IC 4160	Alvia 4180			
	①–⑥				⚒	⑦	Ⓑ	R	⑦	
			V	C	A	2		2	2	
Gijón Sanz Crespo § d.	0700	0757	0950	1412	1515	1602	1800	2025	2025	...
Oviedo ▽ ..... § d.	0730	0826	1019	1441	1544	1632	1830	2055	2055	...
Pola de Lena ..... § d.	|	0855	1050	1510	1622	|	|	2127	2130	...
León ..... a.	0946	1039	1237	1654	1841	1854	2045	2400	2352	...
Madrid CCC ¶ **681** . a.	1207	|	1500	1921	...	2113	2300	...	...	...
Barcelona Sants **681** a.	...	1903	...	...	...	...	...	...	...	...

A – From / to Valladolid (Table **681**).
C – From / to Alacant (Table **668**).
R – ①–⑥ July 3 - Aug. 29.
S – Ⓑ (⑤⑦ July 30 - Aug. 23).
U – ⑥ (①②③④⑥ July 30 - Aug. 23).
V – To / from Castelló de la Plana and València (Table **668**).
x – Not ⑥.
¶ – Full name is Madrid-Chamartín-Clara Campoamor.
☛ **Shaded services are suspended until further notice.**

▽ – **OVIEDO – AVILÉS** and v.v. ***Renfe Cercanías*** (suburban) service. *31 km.* Journey time: ± 38 minutes. **Additional services on Ⓐ.**
From Oviedo: Approximately 1 train each hour 0550 Ⓐ, 0616 Ⓐ, then 0716 until 2216. **From Avilés**: Approximately 1 train each hour 0641 Ⓐ, 0741 Ⓐ, then 0841 until 2311.

§ – **GIJÓN – OVIEDO – POLA de LENA** and v.v. ***Renfe Cercanías*** (suburban) service. *63 km.* Journey time: ± 78 minutes.
From Pola de Lena: Approximately 1–2 trains each hour from 0630 until 2200. **From Gijón**: Approximately 1–2 trains each hour from 0600 until 2230.

SAN SEBASTIÁN - BILBAO — 686

Euskotren (narrow gauge)

	Ⓐ	Ⓐ	Ⓒ					
San Sebastián ⊡ Amara ..... d.	0550	0650	0650	0750	0850		1950	2050
Zarautz ..... d.	0620	0720	0720	0820	0920		2020	2120
Zumaia ..... d.	0629	0729	0729	0829	0929	and	2029	2129
Eibar ..... d.	0711	0811	...	0911	1011	hourly	2111	2211
Durango ..... d.	0741	0841	...	0941	1041	until	2141	2241
Bilbao Casco Viejo § ⊖ ..... a.	0821	0921	...	1021	1121		2221	2321z
Bilbao Matiko ..... a.	0825	0925	...	1024	1124		2225	2325z

	Ⓐ	Ⓐ	Ⓒ					
Bilbao Matiko ..... d.	...	0555	...	0655x	0755x		1855x	1955x
Bilbao Casco Viejo § ⊖ ..... d.	...	0558	...	0658x	0758x		1858x	1958x
Durango ..... d.	0539	0639	...	0739	0839	and	1939	2039
Eibar ..... d.	0614	0714	...	0814	0914	hourly	2014	2114
Zumaia ..... d.	0700	0800	0800	0900	1000	until	2100	2200
Zarautz ..... d.	0708	0808	0808	0908	1008		2108	2208
San Sebastián ⊡ Amara ..... a.	0738	0838	0838	0938	1038		2138	2238

x – 3 mins. earlier on Ⓒ.
z – Ⓒ.
⊡ – San Sebastián / Donostia.
⊖ – Metro interchange.
§ – Bilbao Casco Viejo ⇆ Bilbao Abando (*Renfe*): ± *400 m.* Linked by tram approx every 3 - 5 minutes, journey 2 minutes.
Operator: Euskotren. 2nd class, narrow gauge. Distance: San Sebastian - Bilbao *108* km.

BILBAO - SANTANDER - OVIEDO - FERROL — 687

FEVE (narrow gauge)

			Ⓐ		Ⓐ					
Bilbao Concordia § ..... d.	...	...	...	0800	...	...	1300	...	1934	...
Marrón ..... d.	...	...	0710	0942	...	...	1439	...	2115	...
Treto ..... d.	...	...	0721	0953	...	...	1450	...	2126	...
Santander ..... a.	...	...	0830	1056	...	...	1556	...	2230	...
Santander ..... ▽ d.	...	0829	...	...	...	1528	...	...	...	...
Torrelavega ..... ▽ d.	...	0900	...	...	...	1559	...	...	...	...
Cabezón de la Sal ..... ▽ d.	...	0941	...	...	...	1634	...	...	...	...
Unquera ..... d.	...	1023	...	...	...	1718	...	...	...	...
Llanes ..... d.	0710	1101	...	...	1427	1758	...	...	...	...
Ribadesella ..... d.	0749	1138	...	...	1506	1837	...	...	...	...
Oviedo ..... a.	1022	1356	...	...	1731	2101	...	...	...	...

					Ⓐ			Ⓐ		
Oviedo ..... d.	...	...	0757	...	1110	...	1444	...	1839	...
Ribadesella ..... d.	...	...	1021	...	1337	...	1712	...	2105	...
Llanes ..... d.	...	...	1104	...	1416	...	1754	...	2144	...
Unquera ..... d.	...	...	1134	...	...	...	1824	...	...	...
Cabezón de la Sal ..... ▽ d.	...	...	1221	...	...	...	1909	...	...	...
Torrelavega ..... ▽ d.	...	...	1302	...	...	...	1947	...	...	...
Santander ..... ▽ a.	...	...	1334	...	...	...	2019	...	...	...
Santander ..... d.	0754	...	...	1400	...	1900	...	2037	...	...
Treto ..... d.	0858	...	...	1507	...	2003	...	2144	...	...
Marrón ..... d.	0910	...	...	1519	...	2014	...	2155	...	...
Bilbao Concordia § ..... a.	1108	...	...	1659	...	2205	...	...	...	...

Oviedo ..... △ d.	...	...	0719	...	...	...	...	...	1418	...
Gijón Sanz Crespo . △ d.	...	0701	|	0931	...	1131	...	1421	|	1831
Avilés ..... △ d.	...	0740	|	1018	...	1218	...	1500	|	1918
Pravia ..... △ d.	...	0812	0839	1048	...	1248	...	1529	1540	1948
Luarca ..... d.	...	...	1003	...	...	...	...	...	1708	...
Navia ..... d.	...	...	1033	...	...	...	...	...	1739	...
Ribadeo ..... d.	0655	...	1134	...	1500	...	...	...	1840	...
Viveiro ..... d.	0803	...	1244	...	1609	...	...	...	1949	...
Ortigueira ..... d.	0843	...	1324	...	1650	...	1840	...	2028	...
Ferrol ..... a.	1000	...	1444	...	1810	...	1957	...	2144	...

Ferrol ..... d.	...	...	0820	...	1045	...	1445	1530	...	1905
Ortigueira ..... d.	...	...	0938	...	1204	...	1601	1649	...	2027
Viveiro ..... d.	...	...	1018	...	1245	...	...	1729	...	2106
Ribadeo ..... d.	...	...	1130	...	1353	...	...	1842	...	2218
Navia ..... d.	...	...	1225	...	...	...	...	1940	...	...
Luarca ..... d.	...	...	1256	...	...	...	...	2012	...	...
Pravia ..... △ d.	0848	1148	1428	1448	...	1648	...	2152	2155	...
Avilés ..... △ d.	0926	1226	|	1526	...	1726	...	|	2229	...
Gijón Sanz Crespo ... △ a.	1008	1308	|	1608	...	1808	...	|	2309	...
Oviedo ..... △ a.	...	...	1542	...	...	...	...	2305	...	...

▽ – Additional trains run Santander - Cabezón de al Sal and v.v.
△ – Additional trains run Oviedo / Gijón - Pravia and v.v.
§ – Bilbao Concordia is adjacent to Bilbao Abando (*Renfe*).
Operator: FEVE. 2nd class, narrow gauge.

IRÚN - BILBAO - SANTANDER - GIJÓN — 688

ALSA ★

🚌	▽			♡	♡						♡			♡		♡						⊖			
	①–⑥			Ⓑ	⑥	①–⑥	⑦				Ⓑ	⑥		Ⓑ			⑤⑦					⑤⑦		⑦	
Irún RENFE rail station ..... d.	...	...	...	0645	...	0745	...	...	0845	...	...	...	1100	...	1345	1445	...	...	1615	...	1830	...	2045	2115	2355
San Sebastián / Donostia ..... d.	...	...	...	0710	...	0810	...	...	0910	...	...	...	1125	...	1410	1510	...	...	1640	...	1855	...	2110	2140	0020
Bilbao TermiBus ..... d.	0600	...	0700	0830	0830	0930	0930	1000	1030	1130	1230	1230	1330	1430	1530	1630	1730	1730	1800	1845	2030	2115	2230	2300	0145
Santander ..... d.	0715	0830	0830	0950	0950	1100	1115	1130	1215	1300	1350	1400	1530	1550	1700	1750	1900	1900	1930	2015	2200	2235	2350	0020	0330
Oviedo ..... a.	1000*	1145	...	1205	1205	...	...	...	1530	...	1605	...	1845	1805	...	2005	2145	...	2230	2230	...	0050	...	...	0600
Gijón ..... a.	0930	1215	...	1230	1230	...	...	...	1600	...	1635	...	1915	1835	...	2030	2215	...	2300	2300	...	0120	...	...	0700

🚌						♡	♡				♡			♡				♡				▽		▽	▽
		①–⑥			①–⑥		①–⑥	⑤	⑦	①–⑥	①–⑥		⑤⑦				⑥	Ⓑ				Ⓑ	⑤⑦	⑤	⑦
Gijón ..... d.	0014	...	...	...	...	0715	...	...	0815	0815	0915	1130	...	1315	...	1515	1545	1630	...	1715	...	1915	2015	2115	2115
Oviedo ..... d.	0100	...	...	...	...	0745	...	...	0845	0845	0945	|	...	1345	...	|	1615	1700	...	1745	...	1945	2045	2145	2145
Santander ..... d.	0345	0600	0700	0800	0930	1005	1200	...	1200	1230	1200	1400	1545	1605	1700	1900	1900	1920	...	2030	2100	2205	2340	0005	2359
Bilbao TermiBus ..... d.	0515	0730	0840	0930	1100	1120	1315	1400	1400	1415	1315	1530	1745	1720	1830	2045	2030	2035	2045	2200	2230	2320	...	0120	0115
San Sebastián / Donostia ..... a.	0640	0845	1000	...	1210	1230	...	1510	1600	1615	...	...	1855	1830z	1940	2155	...	2145r	2155	2310	...	...	...	...	0225
Irún RENFE rail station ..... a.	0700	0915	1030	...	1240	1305	...	1545	1630	1645	...	...	1925	1905z	2010	2225	...	2220r	2225	2340	...	...	...	...	0300

♡ – *Clase Supra+* luxury coach.
▽ – *Clase Supra Economy* luxury coach.
⊖ – *Supra+ on* ⑤, *Supra Economy* on ⑦.
r – ①–④ only.
z – ⑥ only.
* – Calls after Gijon.
★ – ALSA: ✆ +34 913 270 540 www.alsa.es
Frequent services operate Bilbao - Santander and Oviedo - Gijon.

689 MADRID and SALAMANCA - BILBAO and IRÚN

km △		RE	RE	Hotel	IC	RE			RE	Alvia	Alvia		MD	RE	RE	RE	IC	Alvia	MD			MD	
		16207	16001	310	631	16019	17227	17201	18302	4087	4187		18001	18321	17203	18321	633	661	18061	18029		18011	
		2	2	✕		2	2	2	2				2	Y 2	2	Y 2		A	2	2	2	2	
		Ⓐ		B	⚒	N	Ⓐ	Ⓐ			⚒		Ⓐ	Ⓐ	Ⓒ	Ⓒ	⑦	⚒		Z		Ⓒ	
0	**Madrid** Chamartín ‡ 680 681 d.	...	...	...	...	...	...	...	...	0810	0810	...	0643p	...	...	...	...	...	0907p	...	...	0940p	...
121	Ávila 680 681 d.	...	...	...	...	...	...	0645	...	|	|	...	0823	...	0833	...	...	...	1038	...	...	1118	...
	Salamanca d.	...	...	0456	0605	...	...	|	0712	|	|	...	|	...	|	...	1015	...	|	...	...	|	...
207	Medina del Campo 680 681 d.	...	...	0600	0645	...	0655	0733	0800	|	|	...	0911	0920	0923	0948	1057	...	1125	...	...	1206	...
250	**Valladolid** Campo Grande 681 d.	...	...	0635	0716	...	0730	0807	0828	0928	0928	...	0939	0955	0959	1025	1123	...	1150	...	1225	1235	...
286	Venta de Baños 681 d.	...	...	|	|	...	...	...	...	|	|	...	...	...	...	...	|	...	1215	...	1300	...	...
298	Palencia 681 d.	...	...	|	|	...	...	...	...	|	|	...	...	...	...	...	|	1157	1229	...	1313	...	...
371	**Burgos** Rosa Manzano 681 d.	...	...	0748	0821	0823	...	...	...	1038	1038	...	...	...	...	...	1231	1252	1320	...	...	...	...
460	Miranda de Ebro 654 d.	0720	0825	0848	0921	0925	...	...	...	1138	1148	...	...	...	...	...	1337	1347	1419	1501	...	...	...
565	**Bilbao** Abando 654 a.	|	|	|	|	|	...	...	...	|	1317	...	...	...	...	...	|	|	|	|	...	...	...
494	Vitoria / Gasteiz 654 d.	0747	0857	0912	|	0952	...	...	...	1201	...	...	...	...	...	...	|	1411	1442	1530	...	...	...
	Barcelona Sants **653** a.	...	|	|	1420	|	...	...	...	|	...	...	...	...	...	...	1835	1903	|	|	...	...	...
537	Altsasu 654 d.	...	0926	|	...	1025n	...	...	...	|	...	...	...	...	...	...	...	...	1511	1601n	...	...	...
624	**San Sebastián / Donostia** ▲ 654 d.	...	1048	1055	...	...	...	...	...	1351	...	...	...	...	...	...	...	...	1708	...	...	...	...
641	**Irún** ▲ 654 a.	...	...	1122	...	...	...	...	...	1418	...	...	...	...	...	...	...	...	1735	...	...	...	...
643	Hendaye ▲ 654 a.	...	...	1133	...	...	...	...	...	...	...	...	...	...	...	...	...	...	...	...	...	...	...

	Alvia	Alvia	IC	IC	MD	MD	MD	IC	MD	RE	MD		RE	Alvia	Alvia	IC	Alvia	MD	RE	MD	Hotel		
	631	621 625	280	282	18063	18063	18306	280	18905	17221	18314	16111	18009	4167	4267	4177	4197	18065	18312	18007	921		
					2	2	2	2	2	2	2	2	2			2		2	2	2	🍸		
		Q			Ⓑ	⑥	Ⓐ	D	Ⓐ			Z	⑤		Ⓑ	⑤	①–④	Ⓑ		Ⓑ	G		
Madrid Chamartín ‡ 680 681 d.	...	...	...	...	1226p	1226p	...	...	1340p	...	...	...	1455p	1610	1610	1738	1915	1712p	...	2028p	...	...	...
Ávila 680 681 d.	...	...	...	...	1405	1405	...	...	1510	1535	...	...	1641	|	|	|	|	1850	...	2209	...	...	...
Salamanca d.	1248	...	...	...	|	|	1400	...	1619	|	1604	...	|	|	|	|	|	|	2053	|	...	...	...
Medina del Campo 680 681 d.	1327	...	...	...	1452	1452	1504	...	...	1624	1644	...	1734	|	|	|	|	1938	2148	2256	...	...	...
Valladolid Campo Grande 681 d.	1353	...	...	...	1517	1517	1528	...	...	1657	1712	...	1806	1728	1728	1848	2025	2006	2223	2321	...	...	...
Venta de Baños 681 d.	|	...	...	...	1542	1542	1605	...	...	...	...	...	1834	|	|	|	|	2031	...	2347	...	...	...
Palencia 681 d.	|	1416	...	...	1557	1557	1617	1655	...	...	...	...	|	|	|	|	|	2050	...	2358	0124	...	...
Burgos Rosa Manzano 681 d.	1511	1511	...	...	1645	1652	...	1746	...	...	...	...	1927	1838	1838	1957	2134	2143	...	...	0217	...	...
Miranda de Ebro 654 d.	1613	1613	1623	...	1741	1759	...	1850	...	...	...	...	2027	1940	1948	2052	2230	2239	...	...	|	...	...
Bilbao Abando 654 a.	|	|	1812	...	|	|	...	|	...	...	...	...	|	|	2116	|	|	|	...	...	|	...	...
Vitoria / Gasteiz 654 d.	1635	1635	...	1645	1802	1819	...	1911	...	...	...	1900	2050	2001	...	2115	2252	2300	...	...	|	...	...
Barcelona Sants **654** a.	2135	2135	...	|	|	|	...	|	...	...	...	|	...	|	...	|	...	...	...	...	0849	...	...
Altsasu 654 d.	...	...	...	1706	1829	1848	...	1934	...	...	...	1931n	...	|	...	|	...	...	...	...	...	...	...
San Sebastián / Donostia ▲ 654 d.	...	...	...	1821	2001	2046	...	2051	...	...	...	...	...	2146	...	2250	...	...	...	...	...	...	...
Irún ▲ 654 a.	...	...	...	1844	2028	2113	...	2116	...	...	...	...	...	2213	...	2311	...	...	...	...	...	...	...
Hendaye ▲ 654 a.	...	...	...	...	...	...	...	2122	...	...	...	...	...	...	...	...	...	...	...	...	...	...	...

km		MD	MD	Alvia	Alvia	MD		MD	RE	RE	RE	Alvia	Alvia	IC	MD	MD	MD	MD	IC	IC	Alvia	Alvia	RE
		18066	18300	4056	4076	18304		18010	17218	16000	18071	4086	4186	283	18308	18004	18012	18012	281	283	622 626	632	16204
		2	2			2	2	2	2	2	Z 2			2	2	2	2	2		2			2
		⚒	Ⓐ	①	②–⑤			①–⑥		⚒	⚒		⚒	D		Ⓐ	⚒	†			Q		Ⓐ
0	**Irún** ▲ 654 d.	...	...	...	...	...	...	...	...	...	...	0823	...	0910	...	...	1023	1023	1154	...	...	...	...
17	**San Sebastián / Donostia** ▲ 654 d.	...	...	0510	...	...	...	...	...	0618	...	0857	...	0933	...	...	1122	1114	1221	...	...	...	...
104	Altsasu 654 d.	...	...	|	...	...	...	...	...	0736	0918n	|	...	1046	...	...	1245	1237	1336	...	...	...	...
	Barcelona Sants **653** d.	...	...	|	...	...	...	...	...	|	|	|	...	|	...	...	|	|	|	...	0930	0930	...
147	Vitoria / Gasteiz 654 d.	...	...	0645	0645	...	...	0740	...	0808	0950	1033	...	1108	...	...	1315	1307	1358	...	1416	1416	1430
	Bilbao Abando 654 d.	...	...	|	|	...	...	|	...	...	|	|	0920	|	...	...	|	|	...	1232	|	|	|
180	Miranda de Ebro 654 d.	...	...	0706	0706	...	0716	0801	...	...	1016	1058	1058	1140	...	...	1335	1327	...	1416	1438	1438	1457
270	**Burgos** Rosa Manzano 681 d.	...	...	0800	0800	...	0816	0900	...	...	...	1156	1156	1233	...	...	1432	1435	...	...	1534	1549	...
353	Palencia 681 d.	0545	...	|	|	...	...	0959	...	...	...	|	|	1321	1335	...	1524	1533	...	...	1625	|	...
355	Venta de Baños 681 d.	0558	...	|	|	...	...	1011	...	...	...	|	|	...	1348	...	1535	1544	...	...	...	|	...
391	**Valladolid** Campo Grande 681 d.	0626	0735	0916	0916	0940	...	1038	1300	...	...	1311	1311	...	1419	1424	1602	1610	...	...	...	1658	...
434	Medina del Campo 680 681 d.	0652	0814	|	|	1007	...	1105	1338	...	...	|	|	...	1448	1500	1628	1635	...	...	...	1727	...
511	**Salamanca** a.	|	0911	|	|	1046	...	|	|	...	...	|	|	...	1548	|	|	|	...	...	...	1806	...
	Ávila 680 681 d.	0740	...	|	|	...	...	1155	1429	...	...	|	|	...	...	1547	1718	1721	...	...	...	...	...
	Madrid Chamartín ‡ 680 681 a.	0928p	...	1030	1030	...	...	1325p	...	...	...	1428	1428	...	...	1731p	1855p	1909p	...	...	...	...	...

		RE	MD	RE	IC	Alvia	RE	RE		Alvia	Alvia		Hotel			RE	RE	Hotel					
		18322	18014	18318	4176	664	17200	18008	16015	4166	4266	17226	313	16017	16027	16004	16004	922					
	2	2	2	2	2		2	2	2			2	✕	2 N	2 b	2	2	G					
		Y			†	A		†	N		Ⓑ	Ⓐ	C	⚒	†	Ⓑ	⑥	🍸					
Irún ▲ 654 d.	...	...	1258	...	1450	...	...	...	...	1535	...	...	1845	...	...	...	...	...	...	...	...	...	...
San Sebastián / Donostia ▲ 654 d.	...	...	1404	...	1509	...	...	...	...	1633	...	...	1910	...	...	1957	2040	...	...	...	...	...	...
Altsasu 654 d.	...	...	1527	...	|	...	...	...	1715n	|	...	...	|	2034n	2047n	2116	2200	...	...	...	...	...	...
Barcelona Sants **653** d.	...	...	|	...	|	1210	...	...	|	|	...	...	|	|	|	|	|	2020	...	...	...	...	...
Vitoria / Gasteiz 654 d.	...	...	1557	...	1644	1702	...	1720	1750	1809	...	...	2046	2107	2119	2150	2234	|	...	...	...	...	...
Bilbao Abando 654 d.	...	...	|	...	|	|	...	|	|	|	1700	...	|	...	|	|	|	|	...	...	...	...	...
Miranda de Ebro 654 d.	...	...	1617	...	1705	1723	...	1744	1817	1835	1835	...	2108	...	2144	2215	2259	|	...	...	...	...	...
Burgos Rosa Manzano 681 d.	...	...	1716	...	1759	1816	...	1843	...	1933	1933	...	2200	...	...	...	...	0249	...	...	...	...	...
Palencia 681 d.	1633	...	1805	...	|	1904	...	|	...	|	|	...	|	...	...	...	...	0339	...	...	...	...	...
Venta de Baños 681 d.	1646	...	1817	...	|	...	...	1933	...	|	|	...	|	...	...	...	...	...	...	...	...	...	...
Valladolid Campo Grande 681 d.	1720	1734	1845	1856	1914	...	1948	2005	...	2050	2050	2240	2310	...	...	...	...	...	...	...	...	...	...
Medina del Campo 680 681 d.	...	1758	1916	1934	|	...	2025	2040	...	|	|	2314	0011	...	...	...	...	...	...	...	...	...	...
Salamanca a.	...	...	|	2027	|	...	|	|	...	|	|	...	0057	...	...	...	...	...	...	...	...	...	...
Ávila 680 681 d.	...	...	2003	...	|	...	2115	2137	...	|	|	...	...	...	...	...	...	...	...	...	...	...	...
Madrid Chamartín ‡ 680 681 a.	...	...	2142p	...	2033	...	...	2340p	...	2206	2206	...	...	...	...	...	...	...	...	...	...	...	...

A – 12 Gijón - Barcelona and v.v. (Table **685**).

B – SUD EXPRESSO / SUREX *Trenhotel* – 🛏 *Gran Clase / Gran Classe* (1, 2 berths), 🛏 *Preferente* (1, 2 berths), 🛏 *Turista* (4 berths), 2 ✕ Lisboa (**310**) - Vilar Formoso (**311**) - Salamanca - Hendaye (Table **45**).

C – SUREX / SUD EXPRESSO *Trenhotel* – 🛏 *Gran Clase / Gran Classe* (1, 2 berths), 🛏 *Preferente* (1, 2 berths), 🛏 *Turista* (4 berths), 2 ✕ Hendaye (**312**) - Salamanca - Vilar Formoso (**313**) - Lisboa (Table **45**).

D – CAMINO DE SANTIAGO – 2 A Coruña - Palencia - Miranda de Ebro - Irún / Hendaye and v.v.

G – Ⓑ GALICIA *Trenhotel* – 🛏, 1 (reclining) 🍸 Barcelona - A Coruña and Vigo and v.v.

N – To / from Pamplona (Table **654**).

Q – 12 Vigo / A Coruña - Palencia - Barcelona and v.v. (Table **680**).

Y – 2 Puebla de Sanabria - Medina del Campo - Valladolid and v.v. (Table **680**).

Z – To / from Pamplona and Zaragoza (Table **654**).

b – From / to Castejón de Ebro and Pamplona / Iruña (Table **654**)

n – Altsasu Pueblo.

p – Madrid **Principe Pio**.

△ – Km's via Ávila.

‡ – Full name is Madrid-Chamartín-Clara Campoamor.

☛ **Shaded services are suspended until further notice.**

▲ – **SAN SEBASTIÁN - IRÚN** and v.v. ***Renfe Cercanías*** (suburban) service. Additional journeys can be made by changing trains at Pasaia. *17 km.* Journey time: ± 27 minutes.

From San Sebastián: 0626⑦, 0701⚒, 0726Ⓒ, 0751Ⓐ, 0816⑥, 0838Ⓐ, 0946⑦, 0951⚒, 1036⚒, 1100⑦, 1116⑥, 1126⑦, 1146Ⓐ, 1218⑦, 1226⚒, 1346, 1421⚒, 1516⚒, 1546, 1639Ⓑ, 1648⑥, 1743, 1816⑦, 1931⚒, 1954⑦, 2001⚒, 2046⚒, 2144.

From Irún: 0648⚒, 0738Ⓐ, 0810⑥, 0828Ⓑ, 0928Ⓑ, 1028⚒, 1042⑦, 1128Ⓐ, 1158Ⓒ, 1218Ⓐ, 1258Ⓒ, 1333, 1453, 1535⑦, 1618, 1713⑦, 1723⑥, 1727Ⓐ, 1733⑦, 1813⑥, 1858Ⓑ, 1918, 2033, 2128, 2215.

▲ – **SAN SEBASTIÁN / DONOSTIA** (Amara) - **IRÚN** (Colón, near Renfe station) - **HENDAYE** (SNCF station) and v.v. ***EuskoTren*** (narrow-gauge) service. *22 km.* Journey time: ± 37 mins.

From San Sebastián: 0615Ⓐ, 0645Ⓐ, 0715, 0745 and every 30 mins until 2215, 2245. **From Hendaye** (⊙): 0533Ⓐ, 0603Ⓐ, 0633Ⓐ, 0703, 0733 and every 30 mins until 2233.

⊙ – 4 minutes later from Irún.

PORTUGAL

SEE MAP PAGE 315

Operator: CP – Comboios de Portugal (www.cp.pt).

Train categories: *Alfa Pendular – AP* – high-quality tilting express trains. *Intercidades – IC* – high-quality express trains linking the main cities. *Interregional – IR* – 'semi-fast' links usually calling at principal stations only. *Celta* – International services between Porto and Vigo. *Regional* and *Suburbano* – local stopping trains (shown without train numbers). Higher fares are payable for travel by *AP* and *IC* trains, and there is an additional supplement for travel by *AP* trains.

Services: All services shown with a train number convey first and second class accommodation (on *Alfa Pendular* trains termed, respectively, *Conforto* and *Turística*) unless otherwise indicated. *Regional* and *Suburbano* trains convey second-class seating only. *AP*, *IC*, *IR* and international trains convey a buffet car (*carruagem-bar*) and there is an at-seat service of meals to passengers in 1st class on *AP* and certain *IC* trains.

Reservations: Reservations are **compulsory** for travel by *AP*, *IC* and international trains. Seat reservation is not normally available on other services.

Timings: Timings are the latest received. Amendments to timetables may come into effect at short notice, especially during the Christmas and New Year period.

LISBOA - COIMBRA - PORTO — 690

Subject to alteration on and around public holidays (see page 4). Reservations are compulsory on *AP* and *IC* trains. Local trains Aveiro - Porto run approx hourly.

km		*IR* 831	*IC* 521	*AP* 131	*AP* 121	*AP* 123	*IC* 721	*AP* 182	*IC* 621	*AP* 125	*AP* 133	*IR* 821	*IC* 523	*AP* 135	*IC* 525	*AP* 127	*IC* 527	*IC* 731	*AP* 137	*AP* 186	*IC* 723	*AP* 141		*IC* 529
			①–⑥			Ⓐ				⚒		⑤		Ⓑ	⑤		⑥	Ⓑ				Ⓑ	Ⓑ	
		⊡		△			△	♧	☆		△			△				⊡	△	♧	△	☆		
0	**Lisboa** S Apolónia ▷ d.	...	0630	0700	0800	0900	0930	...	1130	1200	1400	...	1530	1600	1630	1700	1730	1730	1800	...	1930	2000	...	2200
7	**Lisboa** Oriente ▷ d.	...	0639	0709	0809	0909	0939	1009	1139	1209	1409	...	1539	1609	1639	1709	1739	1739	1809	1909	1939	2009	...	2209
31	Vila Franca de Xira ▷ d.	...	0652	|	|	|	0952	|	1152	|	|	...	1552	|	1652	|	1752	1752	|	|	1952	|	...	2222
75	Santarém ▷ d.	...	0713	|	0839	|	1013	|	1213	|	|	...	1613	|	1713	|	1813	1813	|	|	2013	2039	...	2243
107	**Entroncamento** ▷ d.	...	0730	|	0855	|	1030	|	1230	|	|	1405	1630	|	1730	|	1830	1830	|	|	2030	2055	2127	2300
140	Caxarias ▷ d.	...	|	|	|	|	1048	|	|	|	|	1428	|	|	1748	|	1848	1848	|	|	|	|	2157	2318
171	Pombal ▷ d.	...	0802	|	0924	|	1105	|	1303	|	|	1448	1703	|	1805	|	1905	1905	|	|	2102	2124	2220	2335
199	Alfarelos ▷ d.	...	|	|	|	|	|	|	1317	|	|	1505	1717	|	|	|	|	|	|	|	|	|	2243	|
218	**Coimbra** B ▷ d.	0725	0827	0841	0947	1041	1129	1141	1330	1341	1541	1519	1730	1741	1829	1841	1929	1929	1941	2041	2127	2147	2307	2359
232	Pampilhosa ▷ d.	0736	|	|	|	|	|	|	1341	|	|	1530	1741	|	|	|	|	|	|	|	|	|	2319	|
273	Aveiro ▷ d.	0803	0900	0910	1015	1110	1200	1210	1402	1410	1610	1603	1802	1810	1900	1910	2000	2000	2010	2110	2200	2215	2352	0030
318	Espinho d.	0831	0924	|	1037	|	1224	|	1424	|	|	1640	1824	|	1924	|	2024	2024	|	|	2224	2237	0021	0054
334	Vila Nova de Gaia d.	0849	0940	0947	1052	1146	1241	1246	1441	1446	1647	1659	1840	1847	1940	1946	2040	2041	2047	2145	2241	2253	0040	0110
337	**Porto** Campanhã a.	0900	0953	1000	1105	1158	1255	1258	1455	1458	1700	1711	1852	1900	1953	1958	2053	2053	2100	2158	2255	2307	0052	0123
			AP 180	*AP* 130	*IC* 520	*AP* 140	*IC* 522	*IC* 730	*AP* 120	*IC* 720	*AP* 122	*IC* 524	*AP* 132	*AP* 184	*IC* 722	*AP* 124	*IC* 526	*AP* 126	*IC* 620	*AP* 134	*IC* 528	*IR* 820	*IR* 830	*AP* 136
		①–⑥			①–⑥	①–⑥	⑦	①–⑥	⚒		Ⓑ						⑦	Ⓑ				⑦		Ⓑ
			♧	△		☆		⊡		△			△	♧	△				☆	△			⊡	△
	Porto Campanhã d.	0100	0532	0632	0637	0732	0837	0837	0932	1038	1132	1237	1332	1432	1438	1632	1637	1732	1737	1832	1937	1944	2015	2032
	Vila Nova de Gaia d.	0106	0537	0637	0642	0737	0842	0842	0937	1043	1137	1242	1337	1437	1443	1637	1642	1737	1742	1837	1942	1949	2021	2037
	Espinho d.	0135	|	|	0702	0756	0902	0902	|	1103	|	1302	|	|	1503	|	1702	1756	1802	|	2002	2010	2041	|
	Aveiro ▷ d.	0218	0621	0721	0732	0822	0932	0932	1021	1131	1221	1332	1421	1521	1531	1721	1732	1822	1832	1921	2032	2044	2126	2121
	Pampilhosa ▷ d.	0249	|	|	|	|	|	|	|	1150	|	|	|	|	1550	|	|	|	|	|	|	2111	2154	|
	Coimbra B ▷ d.	0300	0648	0748	0804	0849	1001	1001	1048	1202	1248	1401	1448	1548	1602	1748	1801	1849	1901	1948	2101	2121	2205	2148
	Alfarelos ▷ d.	0313	|	|	|	|	|	|	|	1214	|	|	|	|	1614	|	|	|	|	|	|	2133	...	|
	Pombal ▷ d.	0332	|	|	0829	0912	1026	1026	|	1228	|	1426	|	|	1628	|	1826	1912	1926	|	2126	2150	...	|
	Caxarias ▷ d.	0352	|	|	|	|	1042	1042	|	|	|	1442	|	|	|	|	1842	|	1942	|	2142	|	...	|
	Entroncamento ▷ d.	0417	|	|	0901	0942	1101	1101	|	1301	|	1501	|	|	1701	|	1901	1942	2001	|	2201	2239	...	|
	Santarém ▷ d.	0441	|	|	0919	0958	1119	1119	|	1319	|	1519	|	|	1719	|	1919	1958	2019	|	2219	2258	...	|
	Vila Franca de Xira ▷ d.	0524	|	|	0939	|	1139	1139	|	1339	|	1539	|	|	1739	|	1939	|	2039	|	2239	2326	...	|
	Lisboa Oriente ▷ a.	0551	0823	0922	0952	1032	1152	1152	1222	1352	1422	1552	1622	1723	1752	1922	1952	2032	2052	2122	2252	2343	...	2322
	Lisboa S Apolónia ▷ a.	0559	...	0930	1000	1040	1200	1200	1230	1400	1430	1600	1630	...	1800	1930	2000	2040	2100	2130	2300	2350	...	2330

△ – Lisboa - Porto - Braga and v.v. (Table **695**).
☆ – Lisboa - Porto - Guimarães and v.v. (Table **695a**).
⊡ – To/from Valença (Table **696**).
♧ – Faro - Lisboa - Porto and v.v. (Table **697**).
▷ – See also Tables **691**, **692**, **699**.

LISBOA - ENTRONCAMENTO - COVILHÃ - GUARDA — 691

Linha da Beira Baixa

Subject to alteration on and around public holidays (see page 4). Reservations are compulsory on *IC* trains.

km					*IC* 541		*IC* 543			*IC* 545	
		Ⓐ									
0	**Lisboa** Sta Apolónia ▷ d.	0550	...	...	0815	*0945*	1315	1615	*1745*	1915	*1945*
7	**Lisboa** Oriente ▷ d.	0558	...	...	0823	*0953*	1323	1623	*1753*	1923	*1953*
31	Vila Franca de Xira ▷ d.	0616	...	...	0838	*1011*	1338	1639	*1811*	1938	*2011*
75	Santarém ▷ d.	0655	...	...	0904	*1055*	1404	1706	*1855*	2004	*2055*
107	**Entroncamento** ▷ a.	0718	...	...	0923	*1119*	1423	1725	*1919*	2023	*2119*
107	**Entroncamento** d.	...	...	0746	0924	1128	1424	1726	1933	2024	2154
135	Abrantes d.	...	...	0817	0946	1204	1446	1802	2008	2046	2230
199	Ródão d.	...	...	0921	1043	1304	1536	1901	2111	2143	...
229	Castelo Branco a.	...	...	0949	1106	1332	1605	1935	2140	2206	...
229	Castelo Branco d.	...	0644	0954	1107	1439	1606	1945	...	2207	...
283	Fundaõ d.	...	0732	1042	1142	1533	1641	2033	...	2242	...
301	**Covilhã** a.	...	0748	1058	1155	1549	1655	2049	...	2255	...
301	**Covilhã** d.	...	0800	...	1203	1550	1656	...	...	2256	...
347	**Guarda** a.	...	0844	...	1257	1634	1742	...	...	2342	...

					IC 540			*IC* 542			*IC* 544
		①	Ⓐ	①–⑥							
	Guarda d.	...	...	...	0707	...	1159	1407	...	1743	1807
	Covilhã a.	...	...	...	0752	...	1242	1452	...	1826	1852
	Covilhã d.	0450	...	...	0753	0850	1256	1453	...	1827	1853
	Fundaõ d.	0506	...	...	0807	0906	1312	1507	...	1843	1907
	Castelo Branco a.	0553	...	...	0842	0953	1401	1542	...	1931	1942
	Castelo Branco d.	...	...	0556	0843	1010	1403	1543	1814	...	1943
	Ródão d.	...	...	0624	0907	1043	1431	1607	1843	...	2007
	Abrantes d.	...	0540	0721	1002	1141	1535	1702	1948	...	2102
	Entroncamento a.	...	0613	0800	1023	1217	1606	1723	2019	...	2123
	Entroncamento ▷ d.	...	*0626*	0808	1024	*1237*	*1639*	1724	*2044*	...	2124
	Santarém ▷ d.	...	*0645*	0827	1041	*1301*	*1703*	1741	*2107*	...	2141
	Vila Franca de Xira ▷ d.	...	*0717*	0856	1101	*1353*	*1747*	1801	*2147*	...	2201
	Lisboa Oriente ▷ a.	...	*0734*	0912	1113	*1413*	*1806*	1813	*2206*	...	2213
	Lisboa Sta Apolónia ▷ a.	...	*0741*	0920	1120	*1420*	*1813*	1820	*2213*	...	2220

km				
0	**Entroncamento** d.	...	1024	...
28	Abrantes d.	...	1058	...
110	Portalegre d.	...	1216	...
159	Elvas 🏛 d.	...	1300	...
169	**Badajoz** 🏛 ⊙ a.	...	1414	...

Badajoz 🏛 ⊙ d.	...	1624	...
Elvas 🏛 d.	...	1540	...
Portalegre d.	...	1624	...
Abrantes d.	...	1736	...
Entroncamento a.	...	1814	...

⊙ – Spanish time (one hour ahead of Portugal).
▷ – See also Tables **690**, **692**, **699**.

LISBOA - COIMBRA - GUARDA - VILAR FORMOSO — 692

Linha da Beira Alta

Subject to alteration on and around public holidays (see page 4). Reservations are compulsory on *IC* trains. Local trains run Coimbra B - Coimbra and v.v.

km		*IC* 511	🚌	🚌	🚌	*IC* 513	🚌	🚌	🚌	🚌	*IC* 515
				⚒			Ⓐ	Ⓑ			
	Lisboa S Apolónia ▷ d.	0730	...	...	...	1230	...	...	...	...	1830
	Lisboa Oriente ▷ d.	0739	...	...	...	1239	...	...	...	...	1839
	Vila Franca de Xira ▷ d.	0752	...	...	...	1252	...	...	...	...	1852
	Santarém ▷ d.	0813	...	...	...	1313	...	...	...	...	1913
	Entroncamento ▷ d.	0830	...	...	...	1330	...	...	...	...	1930
	Fátima ✣ d.	0844	...	...	...	1344	...	...	...	...	1944
	Caxarias d.	0851	...	...	...	1351	...	...	...	...	1951
	Pombal d.	0907	...	...	...	1407	...	...	...	...	2007
	Alfarelos d.	0921	...	...	...	1421	...	...	...	...	2021
0	**Coimbra** d.	|	...	1216	1216	|	1615	1615	1826	1826	|
2	**Coimbra** B d.	0933	...	1225	1225	1433	|	1625	1835	1835	2033
16	Pampilhosa d.	|	...	|	1245	|	1625	1645	|	1855	|
51	Santa Comba Dão d.	*1030**	...	1325	1340	*1530**	1725	1740	1935	1950	*2130**
83	Nelas d.	*1055**	...	1400	1425	*1555**	1800	1830	2010	2040	*2155**
95	Mangualde d.	*1115**	...	1420	1445	*1615**	1820	1850	2030	2100	*2215**
171	**Guarda** ● a.	*1215**	1300	1520	1600	*1715**	1920	2005	2130	2230	*2315**
218	Vilar Formoso 🏛 ● a.	...	1420	...	...	...	...	...	...	...	...

	🚌	🚌	🚌	*IC* 510	🚌	*IC* 512	🚌	🚌		*IC* 514
	⚒		⚒				①–⑥	⑦	⑦	
Vilar Formoso 🏛 ● d.	...	...	0515	...	...	...	...	...	...	...
Guarda ● d.	0415	0600	0635	*0640**	0900	*1210**	1530	1515	*1545**	*1740**
Mangualde d.	0530	0715	...	*0740**	1030	*1310**	1645	1645	*1655**	*1840**
Nelas d.	0550	0735	...	*0800**	1050	*1330**	1705	1705	*1715**	*1900**
Santa Comba Dão d.	0640	0810	...	*0825**	1140	*1355**	1750	1750	*1750**	*1925**
Pampilhosa d.	0735	|	...	|	1235	|	1845	1845	|	|
Coimbra B d.	0750	0910	...	0923	1250	1453	1900	1900	1914	2022
Coimbra a.	0800	...	...	|	1300	|	1910	...	|	|
Alfarelos d.	...	...	...	0937	...	1506	...	...	1928	2037
Pombal d.	...	...	...	0952	...	1521	...	...	1945	2052
Caxarias d.	...	...	...	1009	...	1538	...	...	2006	2109
Fátima ✣ d.	...	...	...	1017	...	1546	...	...	2014	2117
Entroncamento ▷ d.	...	...	...	1031	...	1600	...	...	2039	2131
Santarém ▷ d.	...	...	...	1048	...	1618	...	...	2059	2148
Vila Franca de Xira ▷ d.	...	...	...	1109	...	1639	...	...	2126	2209
Lisboa Oriente ▷ a.	...	...	...	1122	...	1652	...	...	2143	2222
Lisboa S Apolónia ▷ a.	...	...	...	1130	...	1700	...	...	2150	2230

● – Also from Guarda at 1805 🚌; also from Vilar Formoso at 0735 † 🚌, 1615 🚌.
▷ – See also Tables **690**, **691**, **699**.
✣ – Chão de Maças - Fátima (*20 km* from Fátima).
* – By 🚌.

693 LISBOA - CALDAS DA RAINHA - FIGUEIRA DA FOZ and COIMBRA *Linha do Oeste*

For connecting suburban services Lisboa - Mira Sintra - Meleças see Table **699**.

km											
								IR **811** Ⓐ	*IR* **813** Ⓒ		
	Lisboa Santa Apolónia ... d.	0535	...	...	1150	...	...	1653	1653	...	...
0	Entrecampos ... d.	0545	...	...	1201	...	...	1703	1703	...	...
2	Sete Rios ... d.	0549	...	...	1204	...	...	1707	1707	...	...
15	Agualva - Cacém ... d.	0604	...	...	1221	...	...	1725	1725	...	...
19	Mira Sintra - Meleças ... d.	0609	0735	0927	1227	...	1408	1730	1730	1833	1930
65	Torres Vedras ... d.	0720	0836	1027	1327	1415	1511	1821	1821	1935	2031
88	Bombarral ... d.	0746	0859	1049	1354	1438	1533	1843	1843	2002	2053
107	**Caldas da Rainha** ... a.	0808	0921	1111	1416	1459	1555	1859	1859	2023	2115

		IR **810**								
Caldas da Rainha ... d.	0520	0621	0725	1116	1230	...	1316	1616	1735	1923
Bombarral ... d.	0541	0638	0747	1138	1252	...	1337	1638	1756	1945
Torres Vedras ... d.	0603	0700	0809	1200	1313	...	1400	1700	1820	2009
Mira Sintra - Meleças ... d.	0703	0754	0916	1302	...	...	1502	1803	1923	2111
Agualva - Cacém ... d.	...	0758	...	...	...	...	1507	...	...	2115
Sete Rios ... a.	...	0813	...	...	...	...	1523	...	...	2130
Entrecampos ... a.	...	0816	...	...	...	...	1527	...	...	2133
Lisboa S Apolónia ... a.	...	0830	...	...	...	...	1541	...	...	2143

km											
		IR **801** ①–⑥			*IR* **803**			⊡	*IR* **805**		
0	**Caldas da Rainha** ... d.	0613	...	0830	1115	...	1420	...	1612	...	1906
12	São Martinho do Porto ... d.	0621	...	0841	1123	...	1430	...	1620	...	1916
46	Marinha Grande ... d.	0650	...	0920	1152	...	1503	...	1649	...	1949
56	Leiria ... d.	0658	...	0928	1200	...	1511	...	1657	...	1957
109	Verride ... a.	0743	...	...	1245	...	|	...	1743	...	2042
109	Verride ... d.	0744	0752	...	1248	1348	|	1624	1748	1748	2046
123	Bifurcação de Lares ... a.	|	0759	...	|	1355	1553	1615	|	1755	|
129	**Figueira da Foz** ... a.	|	0811	...	|	1409	1601	|	|	1809	|
117	Alfarelos ... d.	0752	...	...	1257	...	...	1634	1756	...	2056
136	**Coimbra** B ... a.	0805	...	...	1310	...	...	1701	1812	...	2113

			IR **800**			*IR* **802**	Ⓐ ⊡			*IC* **804** Ⓑ
Coimbra B ... d.	0515	...	0852	...	...	1352	1606	...	...	1941
Alfarelos ... d.	0530	...	0907	...	...	1407	1635	...	...	1955
Figueira da Foz ... d.	|	0858	|	...	1358	|	|	1717	1858	|
Bifurcação de Lares ... d.	|	0911	|	...	1411	|	1655	1726	1911	|
Verride ... a.	0537	0918	0915	...	1418	1415	1646	|	1918	2002
Verride ... d.	0537	...	0921	...	...	1421	...	|	...	2003
Leiria ... d.	0623	...	1009	1213	...	1510	...	1813	...	2053
Marinha Grande ... d.	0634	...	1019	1224	...	1519	...	1823	...	2103
São Martinho do Porto ... d.	0711	...	1046	1256	...	1547	...	1854	...	2129
Caldas da Rainha ... a.	0723	...	1055	1308	...	1557	...	1905	...	2138

LOCAL TRAINS **FIGUEiRA DA FOZ - COIMBRA**

km																									
		⚒	Ⓐ	A	⚒		Ⓐ																		
0	**Figueira da Foz** ... d.	0602	0630	0647	0658	...	0736	0858	0958	1058	...	1158	1258	1358	1458	...	1602	1658	1758	1858	...	1958	2158	...
8	Bifurcação de Lares ... d.	0615	0639	|	0711	...	0746	0911	1014	1111	...	1211	1311	1411	1511	...	1615	1711	1811	1911	...	2011	2211	...
20	Verride ... d.	0623	0648	|	0720	...	0753	0920	1022	1120	...	1220	1320	1420	1520	...	1624	1722	1820	1920	...	2020	2220	...
28	Alfarelos ... **699** d.	0633	0658	0707	0733	...	0803	0937	1033	1133	...	1233	1333	1433	1533	...	1634	1733	1833	1933	...	2033	2233	...
47	**Coimbra** B ... **699** a.	0700	0716	0720	0800	...	0820	1003	1100	1200	...	1300	1400	1500	1600	...	1701	1800	1900	2000	...	2100	2300	...
49	**Coimbra** ... **699** a.	0709	0725	...	0811	...	0834	1013	1109	1209	...	1309	1409	1509	1609	...	1710	1809	1913	2009	...	2109	2313	...

		⚒			Ⓐ									Ⓐ			Ⓑ	Ⓐ			A		
Coimbra ... **699** d.	0016	0552	0654	...	0757	0856	0955	...	1158	1258	1358	...	1455	1558	1658	...	1758	1904	1954	...	...	2238	...
Coimbra B ... **699** d.	0025	0600	0702	...	0806	0904	1003	...	1206	1306	1406	...	1503	1606	1706	...	1806	1913	2002	...	2206	2246	...
Alfarelos ... **699** d.	0055	0634	0731	...	0834	0938	1036	...	1235	1335	1435	...	1536	1635	1735	...	1835	1933	2032	...	2226	2315	...
Verride ... d.	0106	0647	0752	...	0849	0951	1049	...	1248	1348	1448	...	1551	1648	1748	...	1848	1942	2046	...	|	2326	...
Bifurcação de Lares ... d.	0114	0655	0759	...	0856	0959	1056	...	1255	1355	1455	...	1559	1655	1755	...	1855	|	2054	...	|	2333	...
Figueira da Foz ... a.	0126	0709	0811	...	0909	1013	1109	...	1309	1409	1509	...	1613	1709	1809	...	1909	1956	2106	...	2245	2345	...

A – (2) Valença - Porto - Figueira da Foz and v.v. (trains *IR* **830**/**831**).

⊡ – Calling order is Bifurcação de Lares - Verride - Alfarelos - Coimbra B and v.v.

694 PORTO - RÉGUA - TUA - POCINHO *Linha do Douro*

km																								
		⚒	⚒	*IR* **861**	*IR* **21861** ⊖		*IR* **865**			*IR* **867**		*IR* **869**	H				*IR* **871**	*IR* **873**	*IR* **875**				*IR* **877**	
0	**Porto** São Bento ... ◧ d.	0630	...	...	0820	...	0920	0930	...	...	...	1320	...	1330	...	...	1520	...	...	...	1830	...	1920	2220
3	**Porto** Campanhã ... ◧ d.	0635	...	0725	0825	...	0925	0935	...	1125	...	1325	...	1335	...	...	1525	...	1725	...	1835	...	1925	2225
12	Ermesinde ... ◧ d.	0647	...	0736	0836	...	0936	0947	...	1136	...	1336	...	1347	...	...	1536	...	1736	...	1847	...	1936	2238
50	Caíde ... ◧ d.	0721	...	0812	0911	...	1009	1023	...	1212	...	1409	...	1422	...	...	1609	...	1815	...	1922	...	2008	2317
59	Livração ... ◧ d.	0734	...	0822	0920	...	1019	1036	...	1222	...	1419	...	1434	...	...	1619	...	1825	...	1936	...	2016	2326
64	Marco de Canaveses ... ◧ d.	0739	0743	0828	0926	...	1025	1041	1050	1228	...	1425	...	1440	...	1450	1625	...	1831	...	1942	1950	2022	2332
107	**Régua** ... a.	...	0836	0916	1019	...	1111	...	1150	1316	...	1514	...	...	...	1548	1711	...	1923	...	...	2045	2107	0026
107	**Régua** ... d.	...	...	0918	1020	...	1112	...	...	...	...	1516	1528	...	...	1554	...	1717	1927	...	...	...	...	...
130	Pinhão ... d.	...	...	0946	1047	...	1138	...	...	...	...	1543	1615	...	...	1621	...	1743	1954	...	...	...	...	...
143	Tua ... d.	...	...	1001	1103	...	1155	...	...	...	...	1559	1635	...	...	...	...	1759	2010	...	...	...	...	...
175	**Pocinho** ... a.	...	...	1044	1150	...	1238	...	...	...	...	1641	...	...	...	...	...	1841	2053	...	...	...	...	...

		IR **860**	*IR* **862**	⚒			*IR* **864**	*IR* **866**				*IR* **868**	*IR* **21860** ⊖		*IR* **874**			H		*IR* **876**			
Pocinho ... d.	...	...	0708	...	...	...	...	1108	...	...	...	1308	1512	...	...	...	...	...	...	1714	1926	...	...
Tua ... d.	...	...	0750	...	...	...	...	1153	...	...	...	1350	1557	...	...	...	...	1706	...	1758	2009	...	...
Pinhão ... d.	...	...	0806	...	...	...	...	1209	...	...	...	1406	1621	...	1641	...	...	1750	...	1814	2024	...	...
Régua ... a.	...	...	0833	...	...	...	...	1235	...	...	...	1433	1648	...	1708	...	...	1826	...	1840	2050	...	...
Régua ... d.	0530	0648	0837	0917	...	...	1049	1236	1317	...	...	1434	1649	...	1712	1808	...	...	...	1841	...	2108	...
Marco de Canaveses ... ◧ d.	0625	0739	0925	1013	...	1014	1139	1325	1412	...	1414	1524	1739	...	1759	1906	1914	...	...	1928	...	2204	2208
Livração ... ◧ d.	0633	0745	0935	...	...	1020	1145	1335	...	...	1420	1535	1745	...	1805	...	1920	...	...	1935	...	...	2215
Caíde ... ◧ d.	0646	0755	0947	...	...	1036	1155	1347	...	...	1435	1547	1756	...	1815	...	1934	...	...	1945	...	...	2227
Ermesinde ... ◧ d.	0725	0829	1021	...	...	1114	1226	1421	...	...	1514	1626	1836	...	1849	...	2009	...	...	2017	...	...	2314
Porto Campanhã ... ◧ a.	0735	0839	1030	...	...	1125	1234	1430	...	...	1525	1635	1845	...	1900	...	2020	...	...	2025	...	...	2325
Porto São Bento ... ◧ a.	...	0845	...	...	...	1130	1240	...	...	...	1530	...	1850	...	1905	...	2025	...	...	2030	...	...	2330

H – COMBOIO HISTORICO – ⑥ June 4 - Oct. 29 (also ⑦ July 3 - Oct. 9). Steam-hauled tourist train. [R]. Special fare payable.

⊖ – May 15 - October 16.

◧ – Local trains run hourly Porto São Bento - Marco de Canaveses and v.v.

695 PORTO - BRAGA

Subject to alteration on and around public holidays (see page 4). Reservations are compulsory on *AP* and *IC* trains. Additional local trains run on Ⓐ.

km																										
						AP **131**				*IC* **721**					*AP* **133**			Ⓐ	*AP* **135** Ⓑ				*AP* **137**		*IC* **723**	
	Lisboa Sta Ap. **690**. d.	...	...	...	...	0700	...	...	...	0930	...	...	...	...	1400	...	...	...	1600	...	...	...	1800	...	1930	...
0	**Porto** São Bento **696** d.	0050	0645	0745	0845	|	1000	1045	1145	|	1240	1345	1455	1545	|	1645	1740	1815	|	1840	1915	1945	|	2105	|	2305
3	**Porto** Campanhã **696** d.	0055	0650	0750	0850	1000	1005	1050	1150	1255	1245	1350	1500	1550	1700	1650	1745	1820	1900	1845	1920	1950	2100	2110	2255	2310
12	Ermesinde ... **696** d.	0107	0702	0802	0902	|	1018	1102	1202	|	1304	1402	1512	1602	|	1709	1757	1832	|	1857	1932	2002	|	2122	|	2323
26	Trofa ... **696** d.	0120	0716	0816	0916	|	1032	1116	1216	|	1320	1416	1526	1616	|	1725	1811	1844	|	1908	1946	2016	|	2136	|	2337
35	Famalicão ... **696** d.	0128	0727	0827	0927	1021	1043	1127	1227	1317	1331	1427	1537	1627	1721	1736	1822	1852	1921	1923	1957	2027	2121	2147	2317	2348
42	Nine ... **696** d.	0133	0735	0835	0935	1026	1051	1135	1235	1323	1339	1435	1545	1635	1726	1744	1830	1857	1926	1932	2002	2035	2126	2155	2323	2356
57	**Braga** ... a.	0153	0756	0856	0956	1037	1112	1156	1257	1333	1359	1456	1606	1656	1737	1804	1851	1909	1937	1953	2014	2056	2137	2216	2333	0017

		AP **130**		Ⓐ	Ⓒ				*IC* **720**				*AP* **132**		*IC* **722**					*AP* **134**			*AP* **136** Ⓑ		
Braga ... d.	0434	0554	0629	0721	0734	0804	0834	0937	0959	1039	1134	1229	1254	1337	1359	1439	1534	1644	1735	1754	1834	1935	1954	2039	2332
Nine ... **696** d.	0454	0604	0649	0733	0754	0824	0854	0957	1010	1059	1154	1248	1304	1357	1410	1459	1554	1704	1755	1804	1854	1955	2004	2059	2352
Famalicão ... **696** d.	0502	0609	0657	0738	0802	0832	0902	1005	1015	1107	1202	1257	1309	1405	1415	1507	1602	1712	1811	1809	1902	2011	2009	2107	2357
Trofa ... **696** d.	0513	|	0708	0746	0813	0844	0913	1016	|	1118	1213	1308	|	1416	|	1518	1613	1723	1823	|	1913	2023	|	2118	0005
Ermesinde ... **696** d.	0529	|	0729	0759	0834	0859	0929	1039	|	1134	1229	1329	|	1439	|	1533	1629	1739	1839	|	1929	2039	|	2133	0019
Porto Campanhã ... **696** a.	0541	0632	0741	0811	0846	0911	0941	1051	1038	1146	1241	1341	1332	1451	1438	1545	1641	1751	1851	1832	1941	2051	2032	2145	0031
Porto São Bento ... **696** a.	0545	|	0745	0815	0850	0915	0945	1055	|	1150	1245	1345	|	1455	|	1550	1645	1755	1855	|	1945	2055	|	2150	0035
Lisboa Sta Ap. **690** ... a.	...	0930	...	...	...	...	...	...	1400	...	...	...	1630	...	1800	...	...	...	...	2130	...	...	2330	...	...

PORTO - GUIMARÃES 695a

60 km

							IC 621					AP 141
			Ⓐ							Ⓐ		Ⓑ
Lisboa Sta Ap. **690** d.	...	...	...	...	...	...	1130	...	...	...	...	2000
Porto São Bento ▷ d.	0725	0825	0925	1025	1225	1420	|	1620	1825	1910	2020	|
Porto Campanhã ▷ d.	0730	0830	0930	1030	1230	1425	1455	1625	1830	1915	2025	2307
Ermesinde ▷ d.	0742	0842	0940	1042	1242	1437	|	1637	1842	1925	2037	|
Trofa ▷ d.	0757	0857	0951	1057	1257	1452	1514	1652	1857	1936	2052	2326
Guimarães a.	0837	0941	1027	1138	1341	1532	1549	1744	1943	2009	2138	0001

		AP 140							IC 620			
	Ⓐ	①–⑥	Ⓐ							Ⓐ	Ⓐ	
Guimarães d.	0553	0639	0702	0853	0953	1153	1353	1553	1641	1813	2020	2148
Trofa ▷ d.	0633	0713	0739	0933	1036	1233	1433	1633	1716	1900	2105	2229
Ermesinde ▷ d.	0649	|	0751	0949	1053	1249	1449	1649	|	1918	2122	2247
Porto Campanhã ▷ a.	0701	0732	0801	1001	1106	1301	1501	1701	1737	1931	2136	2301
Porto São Bento ▷ a.	0705	|	0805	1005	1110	1305	1505	1705	|	1935	2140	2305
Lisboa Sta Ap. **690** a.	...	1040	...	...	...	...	...	...	2100	...	...	...

Also: **Porto - Guimarães** 0620Ⓐ, 1125Ⓐ, 1725Ⓐ, 1925Ⓐ, 2120Ⓒ, 2225Ⓐ, 2320; **Guimarães - Porto** 0653Ⓒ, 0802Ⓐ, 1253Ⓐ, 1707Ⓐ, 1758Ⓒ, 1921Ⓐ, 1953Ⓒ, 2247. ▷ – **695**, **696**.

PORTO - VIANA DO CASTELO - VALENÇA - VIGO 696

Linha do Minho

km		IR 851					421		IR 831		IR 853			IR 855				IR 857	423				IC 731	
			Ⓐ		①–⑥		C		D			Ⓐ							C				Ⓑ	
	Lisboa Sta Apolónia **690** d.	...	...	...	...	...	...	...	...	...	...	...	...	...	...	...	...	...	...	...	...	...	1730	...
	Coimbra B **690** d.	...	...	...	...	...	...	...	0725	...	...	...	...	...	...	...	...	...	...	...	...	...	1929	...
0	**Porto** São Bento **695** d.	...	0615	...	0645	...	...	...	|	1000	1305	1345	1455	...	1645	...	...	...	...	1915	...	...	|	...
3	**Porto** Campanhã **695** d.	0605	0620	...	0650	...	0813	...	0901	1005	1310	1350	1500	1610	1650	...	...	1815	1910	1920	...	...	2103	2210
15	Ermesinde **695** d.	0614	0632	...	0702	...	|	...	0910	1018	1321	1402	1512	1621	1709	...	...	1825	|	1932	...	...	|	2220
26	Trofa **695** d.	0624	0644	...	0716	...	|	...	0924	1032	1332	1416	1526	1631	1725	...	...	1835	|	1946	...	...	2122	2231
35	Famalicão **695** d.	0631	0652	...	0727	...	|	...	0935	1043	1340	1427	1537	1638	1736	...	...	1842	|	1957	...	...	2129	2238
42	**Nine** **695** a.	0636	0656	...	0735	...	0842	...	0944	1051	1345	1435	1545	1643	1743	...	...	1848	1939	2002	...	...	2134	2243
42	**Nine** d.	0637	...	0659	...	0746	0842	...	0952	*1054*	1346	*1503*	*1558*	1644	*1746*	...	...	1849	1940	...	2006	...	2135	2244
54	Barcelos d.	0646	...	0711	...	0804	|	...	1002	*1106*	1355	*1515*	*1610*	1653	*1758*	...	...	1858	|	...	2017	...	2145	2300
85	**Viana do Castelo** d.	0725	...	0804	...	0850	0916	...	1038	*1145*	1427	*1556*	*1650*	1723	*1840*	...	...	1932	2014	...	2058	2131	2216	2336
119	Vila Nova de Cerveira d.	0752	...	0847	...	...	|	...	1107	*1223*	1500	...	*1727*	1751	*1917*	...	...	2004	|	...	...	2208	2241	...
133	**Valença** 🏛 PT d.	0802	...	0900	...	...	0957	1005	1116	*1236*	1510	...	*1740*	1800	*1930*	1944	...	2014	2050	...	...	2221	2250	...
137	Tui 🏛 ES d.	...	...	...	...	...	|	1112	...	...	...	...	...	...	...	2051	...	...	|	...	...	...	...	...
165	Redondela **680** d.	...	...	...	...	...	|	1144	...	...	...	...	...	...	...	2124	...	...	|	...	...	...	...	...
177	**Vigo** Guixar **680** a.	...	...	...	...	...	1135	1155	...	...	...	...	...	...	...	2135	...	...	2234	...	...	...	...	...

						IC 730	IR 850	420			IR 852					IR 854			IR 830			422	IR 856
		Ⓐ		①–⑥		①–⑥		C				⊖		Ⓐ			⊖		D			C	
Vigo Guixar **680** d.	...	...	...	...	...	...	...	0858	0920	...	...	...	...	...	...	...	...	...	...	1812	...	1956	...
Redondela **680** d.	...	...	...	...	...	...	...	|	0931	...	...	...	...	...	...	...	...	...	...	1824	...	|	...
Tui 🏛 ES d.	...	...	...	...	...	...	...	|	1003	...	...	...	...	...	...	...	...	...	...	1858	...	|	...
Valença 🏛 PT d.	...	...	...	...	0549	0650	0721	0836	0911	...	0926	1140	1245	...	...	1425	1448	...	1802	1806	1834	1933	2023
Vila Nova de Cerveira d.	...	...	...	...	0602	0070	0731	|	...	...	0939	1153	1258	...	...	1435	1502	...	1812	...	1847	|	2038
Viana do Castelo d.	0511	...	...	0559	0642	0726	0803	0917	...	0941	1009	1236	1337	1348	...	1508	1608	1755	1848	...	1931	2014	2109
Barcelos d.	0548	...	...	0634	0733	0754	0832	|	...	1021	1038	1314	...	1429	...	1538	1654	1834	1929	...	...	|	2145
Nine a.	0600	...	...	0652	0744	0802	0840	0950	...	1033	1046	1326	...	1441	...	1547	1707	1846	1937	...	...	2048	2155
Nine **695** d.	...	0633	0649	...	0745	0803	0841	0951	...	*1059*	1047	*1357*	...	...	1459	1548	*1755*	*1854*	1938	...	...	2048	2156
Famalicão **695** d.	...	0638	0657	...	0751	0810	0847	|	...	*1107*	1053	*1405*	...	...	1507	1554	*1811*	*1902*	1944	...	...	|	2203
Trofa **695** d.	...	0646	0708	...	0758	0817	0854	|	...	*1118*	1100	*1416*	...	...	1518	1601	*1823*	*1913*	1951	...	...	|	2210
Ermesinde **695** d.	...	0659	0729	...	0810	|	0906	|	...	*1134*	1112	*1439*	...	...	1533	1612	*1839*	*1929*	2002	...	...	|	2220
Porto Campanhã **695** a.	...	0710	0740	...	0820	0834	0915	1020	...	*1145*	1120	*1450*	...	...	1544	1620	*1850*	*1940*	2010	...	...	2118	2230
Porto São Bento **695** a.	...	0715	0745	...	0825	|	...	...	...	*1150*	1125	*1455*	...	...	1550	...	*1855*	*1945*	|	...	...	...	...
Coimbra B **690** a.	...	...	...	...	...	0959	...	...	...	...	...	...	...	...	...	...	...	...	2205	...	...	...	...
Lisboa Sta Apolónia **690** a.	...	...	...	...	...	1200	...	...	...	...	...	...	...	...	...	...	...	...	...	...	...	...	...

C – *Celta*. 2 🅁.
D – 2 Valença - Porto - Figueira da Foz and v.v.

⊖ – Faster connection Nine - Porto available on Ⓐ.

ES – Spain (Central European Time).
PT – Portugal (West European Time).

LISBOA - PINHAL NOVO - TUNES - FARO 697

km			AP 180		IC 570	IC 572		AP 184	IC 574	
	Porto Campanhã **690** d.	...	0532	...	...	...	...	1432	...	...
	Coimbra B **690** d.	...	0648	...	...	...	...	1548	...	...
0	**Lisboa** Oriente ⊙ d.	...	0823	...	1002	1402	...	1723	1832	...
7	Entrecampos ⊙ d.	...	0831	...	1010	1410	...	1731	1840	...
9	Sete Rios ⊙ d.	...	|	...	1014	1414	...	|	1844	...
18	Pragal ⊙ d.	...	|	...	1026	1426	...	|	1855	...
47	Pinhal Novo ⊙ d.	...	0906	...	1048	1448	...	1806	1918	...
118	Grândola d.	...	|	...	1119	1516	...	|	1946	...
180	Funcheira d.	...	|	...	1155	1552	...	|	2022	...
264	**Tunes** ▷ d.	...	1054	...	1302	1707	...	1955	2134	...
269	Albufeira ▷ d.	...	1101	...	1307	1712	...	2002	2139	...
286	Loulé ▷ d.	...	1113	...	1319	1724	...	2014	2151	...
302	**Faro** ▷ a.	...	1123	...	1330	1735	...	2023	2202	...

		AP 182		IC 670	IC 672		AP 186		IC 674
Faro ▷ d.	...	0700	...	0822	1415	...	1600	...	1815
Loulé ▷ d.	...	0710	...	0833	1426	...	1611	...	1825
Albufeira ▷ d.	...	0723	...	0845	1438	...	1624	...	1837
Tunes ▷ d.	...	0729	...	0851	1444	...	1630	...	1844
Funcheira d.	...	0823	...	1000	1552	...	|	...	1954
Grândola d.	...	0854	...	1037	1638	...	|	...	2033
Pinhal Novo ⊙ d.	...	0923	...	1107	1707	...	1823	...	2105
Pragal ⊙ a.	...	|	...	1130	1734	...	|	...	2134
Sete Rios ⊙ a.	...	|	...	1143	1744	...	|	...	2144
Entrecampos ⊙ a.	...	0957	...	1146	1747	...	1857	...	2147
Lisboa Oriente ⊙ a.	...	1005	...	1156	1756	...	1905	...	2156
Coimbra B **690** a.	...	1141	...	...	...	...	2041	...	...
Porto Campanhã **690** a.	...	1258	...	...	...	...	2158	...	...

LOCAL TRAINS **LAGOS - TUNES - FARO**

km			⚒		Ⓐ					Ⓐ	
0	**Lagos** d.	0614	0658	0752	0903	1114	1326	1513	1721	1815	2015
18	Portimão d.	0634	0717	0809	0922	1133	1350	1532	1745	1834	2034
29	Silves d.	0650	0733	0825	...	1150	1405	1549	1802	1851	2051
42	Algoz d.	0705	0748	0841	...	1206	1421	1605	1819	1908	2106
46	**Tunes** ▷ d.	0711	0754	0851	...	1212	1427	1611	1825	1914	2112
52	Albufeira ▷ d.	0722	0800	0858	...	1218	1438	1623	1837	1921	2123
69	Loulé ▷ d.	0743	0815	0919	...	1242	1453	1638	1859	1940	2138
85	**Faro** ▷ a.	0759	0835	0934	...	1257	1508	1654	1916	1956	2154

	⚒	Ⓐ						Ⓐ		
Faro ▷ d.	0711	...	0902	1023	1225	1617	1741	1825	1922	2050
Loulé ▷ d.	0728	...	0919	1039	1242	1638	1758	1842	1940	2107
Albufeira ▷ d.	0743	...	0935	1100	1307	1655	1814	1900	2001	2123
Tunes ▷ d.	0754	...	0942	1106	1313	1708	1825	1914	2007	2133
Algoz d.	0800	...	0947	1112	1319	1714	1831	1919	2013	2138
Silves d.	0825	...	1003	1130	1335	1730	1851	1935	2030	2151
Portimão d.	0839	0931	1018	1150	1350	1745	1906	1950	2051	2205
Lagos a.	0858	0950	1036	1208	1408	1803	1925	2008	2110	2222

▷ – Also see other section of table above or below.

⊙ – See Table **698** for other fast trains, Table **699** for local services, including connections Barreiro - Pinhal Novo.

FARO - VILA REAL DE SANTO ANTÓNIO 697a

km			Ⓐ			Ⓐ						
0	**Faro** d.	0720	0857	0955	1130	1300	1515	1713	1753	1927	2030	2216
10	Olhão d.	0735	0908	1006	1141	1311	1531	1729	1804	1939	2040	2227
32	Tavira d.	0806	0939	1033	1208	1342	1558	1756	1831	2010	2106	2254
56	**Vila Real** § a.	0834	1008	1102	1237	1412	1627	1825	1900	2039	2135	2319

										Ⓐ	
Vila Real § d.	0548	0639	0706	0840	1108	1243	1430	1633	1753	1910	2107
Tavira d.	0617	0708	0735	0909	1135	1312	1504	1702	1831	1940	2138
Olhão d.	0644	0735	0802	0936	1204	1339	1531	1729	1901	2006	2201
Faro a.	0654	0746	0813	0946	1214	1349	1542	1739	1912	2017	2211

§ – ± 1500 metres from bus station / ferry terminal.

ADDITIONAL JOURNEYS: Faro - Villa Real at 1355, 1826 Ⓐ; Villa Real - Faro at 1524 Ⓐ.

LISBOA - PINHAL NOVO - ÉVORA and BEJA 698

Linha do Alentejo

km		IC 590	IC 592	IC 594	IC 790	IC 596	IC 598			
		Ⓐ	Ⓐ	Ⓒ	Ⓐ					
0	**Lisboa** Oriente ▷ d.	0702	0902	0952	1332	1702	1902	...	...	...
7	Entrecampos ▷ d.	0710	0910	1000	1340	1710	1910	...	...	...
9	Sete Rios ▷ d.	0714	0914	1004	1344	1714	1914	...	...	...
18	Pragal ▷ d.	0726	0926	1015	1356	1726	1926	...	...	...
47	**Pinhal Novo** ▷ d.	0748	0948	1032	1418	1748	1948	...	...	...
88	Vendas Novas d.	0818	1010	1102	1440	1810	2010	...	...	...
122	Casa Branca d.	0832	1024	1116	1454	1824	2024	...	...	...
148	**Évora** a.	0842	1035	1126	1505	1835	2035	...	...	...
185	**Beja** a.	*0926**	*1118**	*1210**	*1551**	*1920**	*2116**	...	...	...

	IC 690	IC 692	IC 698	IC 694	IC 696				
	Ⓐ		Ⓐ						
Beja d.	*0623**	*0822**	*1045**	*1611**	*1815**	...	...	...	...
Évora d.	0706	0906	1135	1657	1906	...	...	...	...
Casa Branca d.	0717	0917	1146	1708	1917	...	...	...	...
Vendas Novas d.	0731	0931	1200	1722	1931	...	...	...	...
Pinhal Novo ▷ d.	0753	0953	1223	1751	1953	...	...	...	...
Pragal ▷ a.	0814	1014	1244	1814	2014	...	...	...	...
Sete Rios ▷ a.	0824	1024	1254	1824	2024	...	...	...	...
Entrecampos ▷ a.	0828	1028	1258	1828	2028	...	...	...	...
Lisboa Oriente ▷ a.	0836	1036	1306	1836	2036	...	...	...	...

▷ – See Table **697** for other fast trains and Table **699** for local services, including connections Barreiro - Pinhal Novo.

* – Change at Casa Branca. *IC* train. 🅁.

699 OTHER LOCAL SERVICES

LISBOA - ESTORIL - CASCAIS

km		Ⓐ																Ⓒ						
0	**Lisboa** Cais do Sodre .d.	0530	every	0700	every	1000	every	1700	every	2024	2030	every	2130	2200	every	0130		0530	every	0800	every	1900	every	0130
24	Estoril .d.	0606	30	0729	12	1036	20	1729	12	2053	2106	20	2206	2236	30	0206		0606	30	0836	20	1936	30	0206
26	**Cascais** .a.	0610	mins	0733	mins	1040	mins	1733	mins	2057	2110	mins	2210	2240	mins	0210		0610	mins	0840	mins	1940	mins	0210

	Ⓐ											Ⓒ ⊡										
Cascais .d.	0530	0600	0630	0652	every	2016	2028	2040	2100	every	0130	0600	0630	0704	every	1904	1934	every	2104	2130	every	0130
Estoril .d.	0534	0604	0634	0656	12-20 ◧	2020	2032	2044	2104	30	0134	0604	0634	0708	20	1908	1938	30	2108	2134	30	0134
Lisboa Cais do Sodre .a.	0610	0640	0710	0725	mins	2049	2108	2120	2140	mins	0210	0640	0710	0744	mins	1944	2014	mins	2144	2210	mins	0210

◧ – Every 12 minutes 0704 - 1004, every 20 minutes 1004 - 1704, every 12 minutes 1704 - 2016.

⊡ – Also at 0530.

LISBOA ORIENTE - SINTRA

	Ⓐ				Ⓒ			
	Ⓐ		Ⓐ		Ⓒ		Ⓒ	
Lisboa Oriente .d.	0558		0108		0608		0108	
Roma Areeiro .d.	0605	See	0115		0615	every	0115	
Entrecampos .d.	0607	note	0117		0617	30	0117	
Sete Rios .d.	0610	△	0120		0620	mins	0120	
Monte Abraão .d.	0625		0135		0635	until	0135	
Agualva - Cacém .d.	0631		0141		0641		0141	
Sintra .a.	0645		0155		0655		0155	

	Ⓐ			Ⓒ		
	Ⓐ		Ⓐ	Ⓒ		Ⓒ
Sintra .d.	0506		0006	0506		0006
Agualva - Cacém .d.	0519	See	0019	0519	every	0019
Monte Abraão .d.	0524	note	0024	0524	30	0024
Sete Rios .d.	0539	▽	0039	0539	mins	0039
Entrecampos .d.	0542		0042	0542	until	0042
Roma Areeiro .d.	0544		0044	0544		0044
Lisboa Oriente .a.	0552		0052	0552		0052

△ – 0558, 0618, 0638, 0648 and at least every 30 mins until 2338, 0008, 0038, 0108.

▽ – 0506, 0536, 0606, 0616 and at least every 30 mins. until 2236, 2306, 2336, 0006.

LISBOA ROSSIO - SINTRA and MIRA SINTRA-MELEÇAS

	Ⓐ	Ⓒ			n		n
Lisboa Rossio .d.	0541	0601		0101	0621	and	2021
Monte Abraão .d.	0601	0621	See	0121	0641	hourly	2041
Agualva - Cacém .d.	0607	0627	note	0127	0647	until	2047
Mira Sintra - Meleças .a.	|	|	△	|	0650	⊡	2050
Sintra .a.	0621	0641		0141	...		...

Sintra .d.	0520		0020	...		...	...
Mira Sintra - Meleças .d.	|	See	|	0730	and	2030	...
Agualva - Cacém .d.	0533	note	0033	0733	hourly	2033	...
Monte Abraão .d.	0539	▽	0039	0739	until	2039	...
Lisboa Rossio .a.	0559		0059	0759	⊡	2059	...

n – Certain jnys 5 mins later. On Ⓒ runs 10 mins later.

△ – Ⓐ: every 30 mins 0541 - 2041 (◧) and 2101 - 0101.
Ⓒ: hourly 0601 - 2001, every 30 mins 2101 - 0101.

▽ – Ⓐ: every 30 mins 0520 - 0620, 0640 - 2010 (◐), 2050 - 0020.
Ⓒ: every 30 mins 0520 - 0650, hourly 0650 - 2050, every 30 mins 2050 - 0020.

⊡ – Additional services operate during peak hours on Ⓐ.

◧ – Between 0941Ⓐ and 1641Ⓐ runs at xx41, xx01.

◐ – Between 0940Ⓐ and 1640Ⓐ runs at xx40, xx00.

LISBOA - PINHAL NOVO - SETÚBAL

Operator: Fertagus. CP tickets not valid.

	Ⓐ					Ⓒ		
Roma-Areeiro .d.	0043	0543		2243	2358	0643		2343
Entrecampos .d.	0045	0545	and	2245	0000	0645	and	2345
Sete Rios .d.	0049	0549	every	2249	0004	0649	every	2349
Pragal .d.	0100	0600	hour	2300	0015	0700	hour	0000
Pinhal Novo .d.	0128	0628	until	2328	0043	0728	until	0028
Setúbal .a.	0141	0641		2341	0056	0741		0041

	Ⓐ								Ⓒ		
Setúbal .d.	0548	0658		1858	1928	2018		0018	0558		2258
Pinhal Novo .d.	0602	0712	and	1912	1942	2032	and	0032	0612	and	2312
Pragal .d.	0629	0739	every	1939	2009	2059	every	0059	0639	every	2339
Sete Rios .d.	0640	0750	hour	1950	2020	2110	hour	0110	0650	hour	2350
Entrecampos .d.	0644	0754	until	1954	2024	2114	until	0114	0654	until	2354
Roma-Areeiro .a.	0646	0756		1956	2026	2116		0116	0656		2356

Additional journeys on Ⓐ: from Roma Areeiro 1813, 1913, 2013, from Setúbal 0628, 0728, 0828. Trains run every 10 – 20 minutes (every 30 mins evenings and Ⓒ) Roma-Areeiro - Pragal - Coina.

Catamaran LISBOA - BARREIRO

Transtejo Soflusa — *Certain Ⓐ peak journeys do not run in July / August*

From Lisboa Terreiro do Paço: By ⛴ journey time 20 - 25 minutes. *10* km

Ⓐ: 0530, 0550, 0620, 0640, 0700 and every 5 - 15 minutes until 0920, 0940, 0955 and every 30 minutes until 1455, 1520, 1535, 1600, 1625, 1640 and every 5 - 15 minutes until 2035, 2100, 2125, 2155, 2230, 2255, 2330, 0000, 0030, 0100, 0200.

Ⓒ: 0545, 0615, 0647, 0715, 0755, 0825⑥, 0855, 0925⑥, 0955, 1025⑥, 1055, 1155, 1255, 1355, 1455, 1525, 1555, 1625, 1655, 1725, 1755, 1825, 1855, 1925, 1955, 2055, 2125, 2155, 2255, 0000, 0030, 0100, 0200.

From Barreiro Barcos: By ⛴ journey time 20 - 25 minutes. *10* km

Ⓐ: 0505, 0520, 0555, 0615, 0635 and every 5 - 15 minutes until 0910, 0925, 0940, 0955, 1025 and every 30 minutes until 1455, 1510, 1535, 1600 and every 5 - 15 minutes until 2010, 2035, 2100, 2125, 2200, 2225, 2300, 2330, 0005, 0030, 0130.

Ⓒ: 0515, 0545, 0622, 0650, 0725, 0755⑥, 0825, 0855⑥, 0925, 0955⑥, 1025, 1125, 1225, 1325, 1425, 1455, 1525, 1555, 1625, 1655, 1725, 1755, 1825, 1855, 1925, 2025, 2055, 2125, 2225, 2330, 0005, 0030, 0130.

BARREIRO - SETÚBAL

km		Ⓐ						
0	**Barreiro** .d.	0555	0625	every 30 mins	2125	2232	2325	0029
15	Pinhal Novo .d.	0614	0644	(hourly on Ⓒ)	2144	2251	2344	0048
28	**Setúbal** .a.	0626	0656	until	2156	2303	2356	0100

	Ⓐ	Ⓒ	Ⓐ				Ⓐ			
Setúbal .d.	0508	0548	0618	0648	every 30 mins	2048	2122	2151	2248	2348
Pinhal Novo .d.	0520	0600	0630	0700	(hourly on Ⓒ)	2100	2136	2202	2300	0000
Barreiro .a.	0538	0618	0648	0718	until	2118	2154	2220	2318	0018

Most journeys continue to / from Praias do Sado A (8 minutes from Setúbal).

LISBOA - ENTRONCAMENTO - TOMAR

km			Ⓐ	⚒		Ⓐ		Ⓐ		Ⓐ		Ⓐ		Ⓐ			Ⓐ§			Ⓐ§				Ⓐ	
0	**Lisboa** Santa Apolónia ... ▷ d.	0015	0550	0645	0745	0845	0945	1045	...	1145	1245	1345	1445	1545	1615	1645	1715	...	1745	1815	1845	1945	2045	2145	2245
7	**Lisboa** Oriente ▷ d.	0025	0558	0653	0753	0853	0953	1053	...	1153	1253	1353	1453	1553	1623	1653	1723	...	1753	1823	1853	1953	2053	2153	2253
31	Vila Franca de Xira .d.	0051	0616	0711	0811	0911	1011	1111	...	1211	1311	1411	1511	1611	1639	1711	1739	...	1811	1838	1911	2011	2111	2211	2311
75	Santarém .d.	0135	0655	0755	0855	0957	1055	1148	...	1255	1348	1455	1549	1655	1706	1756	1806	...	1855	1907	1955	2055	2149	2259	2349
107	Entroncamento .a.	0159	0718	0819	0919	1021	1119	1212	...	1319	1412	1519	1615	1719	1725	1820	1825	...	1919	1926	2019	2119	2214	2322	0012
130	**Tomar** .a.	...	0751	0847	0947	...	1151	1242	...	...	1440	1551	1647	1751	...	1853	1900	...	1951	2000	2051	2149	2251	2349	0040

	①–⑥	Ⓐ	Ⓐ§		Ⓐ§		①–⑥		Ⓐ					Ⓐ					Ⓐ	⑦d		Ⓐ	⑦d§	
Tomar .d.	...	0510	0605	0615r	0650	0711r	...	0802	...	1011	1111r	...	1315	...	1511	1606	1711	1811	1910	...	2011	...	...	2211
Entroncamento .d.	0417	0544	0626	0644	0711	0744	0808	0839	0944	1039	1144	1237	1344	1439	1544	1639	1744	1844	1944	2039	2044	2145	2239	2244
Santarém .d.	0441	0607	0645	0707	0731	0807	0827	0903	1008	1103	1207	1301	1408	1503	1607	1703	1807	1907	2009	2059	2107	2205	2258	2307
Vila Franca de Xira .d.	0524	0647	0717	0747	0800	0847	0856	0947	1047	1147	1247	1347	1447	1547	1654	1747	1847	1955	2055	2126	2147	2247	2326	2344
Lisboa Oriente ▷ d.	0551	0706	0734	0806	0819	0906	0912	1006	1106	1206	1306	1406	1506	1606	1713	1806	1906	2013	2113	2143	2206	2306	2343	0003
Lisboa Santa Apolónia ▷ a.	0559	0713	0741	0813	0828	0913	0920	1013	1113	1213	1313	1413	1513	1613	1720	1813	1913	2020	2120	2150	2213	2313	2350	0010

▷ – Additional local trains are available.

d – If ⑦ is a public holiday runs next day instead.

r – ⚒ only.

§ – *IR* train.

ENTRONCAMENTO - COIMBRA

Local trains — For fast trains see Table **690**

km		†	Ⓐ		Ⓐ						Ⓐ		Ⓑ
0	**Entroncamento** .d.	...	0555	0640	0738	0840	1038	1238	1532	1738	1838	1938	2127
24	Fátima ⊙ .d.	...	0616	0700	0804	0907	1104	1304	1553	1804	1904	2004	2148
64	Pombal .d.	...	0649	0733	0838	0940	1137	1338	1626	1838	1938	2037	2220
91	Alfarelos .d.	0712	0713	0756	0901	1004	1200	1401	1650	1901	2001	2100	2243
111	**Coimbra B** .a.	0733	0733	0816	0922	1024	1220	1422	1711	1922	2022	2121	2307
111	**Coimbra B** .d.	0738	0742	0826	0927	1029	1225	1427	1716	1931	2028	2129	...
113	**Coimbra** .a.	0743	0747	0830	0931	1034	1229	1431	1720	1935	2032	2133	...

	①–⑥	Ⓐ					Ⓐ			Ⓑ
Coimbra .d.	0608	0710	0812	1023	1324	1620	1721	1810	1918	2015
Coimbra B .a.	0611	0713	0815	1026	1327	1624	1724	1813	1921	2018
Coimbra B .d.	0616	0718	0820	1031	1332	1631	1730	1818	1929	2024
Alfarelos .d.	0639	0740	0842	1101	1355	1653	1802	1841	2001	2046
Pombal .d.	0703	0804	0906	1126	1419	1717	1827	1905	2026	2109
Fátima ⊙ .d.	0744	0854	0947	1159	1501	1750	1900	1955	2058	2141
Entroncamento .a.	0805	0915	1008	1221	1521	1810	1920	2015	2119	2209

r – Ⓐ only.

⊙ – Station is *20 km* from Fátima (full name of station is Chão de Maçãs - Fátima).

AVEIRO - COIMBRA

Local trains — For fast trains see Table **690**

km					Ⓐ		Ⓐ		Ⓐ				
0	**Aveiro** .d.	0645	0749	0949	1049	1135	1224	1349	1449	1535	1749	1949	2152
41	Pampilhosa .d.	0723	0826	1026	1126	1213	1302	1426	1526	1613	1826	2027	2231
55	**Coimbra B** .a.	0739	0841	1041	1141	1229	1317	1441	1541	1628	1841	2046	2245
57	**Coimbra** .a.	0754	0855	1047	1147	1234	1322	1447	1556	1634	1854	2051	2254

		⚒								
Coimbra .d.	0638	0738	0839	1053	1343	1449	1640	1832	1949	2208
Coimbra B .d.	0643	0742	0849	1057	1348	1454	1644	1843	1954	2213
Pampilhosa .d.	0659	0759	0909	1114	1404	1512	1700	1900	2015	2230
Aveiro .a.	0738	0838	0948	1153	1444	1551	1739	1939	2054	2309

Additional trains: **Aveiro - Coimbra**: 0545⚒, 0735Ⓐ, 0849Ⓐ, 1649Ⓐ, 1849Ⓐ, 2049Ⓐ. **Coimbra - Aveiro**: 0538Ⓐ, 1004Ⓐ, 1138Ⓐ, 1238Ⓐ, 1532Ⓐ, 1732Ⓐ, 2042Ⓐ.

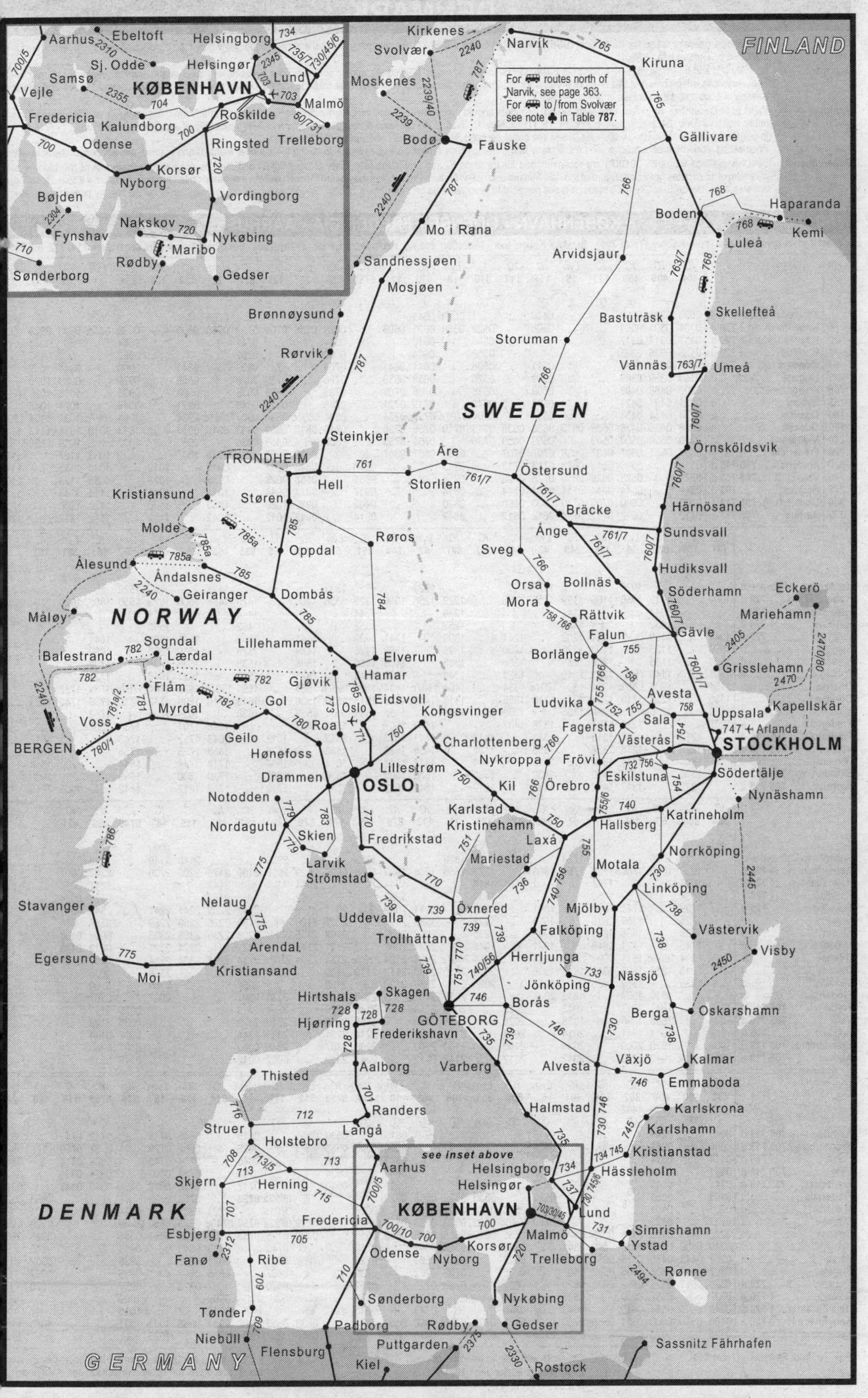

For routes north of Narvik, see page 363.
For to/from Svolvær see note ♣ in Table 787.
FINLAND
SWEDEN
NORWAY
DENMARK
GERMANY
KØBENHAVN
see inset above
STOCKHOLM
OSLO
GÖTEBORG
TRONDHEIM
BERGEN
Kirkenes
Narvik
Kiruna
Svolvær
Moskenes
Bodø
Fauske
Gällivare
Mo i Rana
Boden
Haparanda
Kemi
Luleå
Arvidsjaur
Sandnessjøen
Mosjøen
Brønnøysund
Storuman
Bastuträsk
Skellefteå
Rørvik
Vännäs
Umeå
Steinkjer
Örnsköldsvik
Hell
Storlien
Åre
Östersund
Kristiansund
Støren
Bräcke
Härnösand
Ånge
Sundsvall
Molde
Oppdal
Røros
Sveg
Ålesund
Åndalsnes
Hudiksvall
Geiranger
Dombås
Orsa
Bollnäs
Mora
Söderhamn
Eckerö
Måløy
Rättvik
Mariehamn
Falun
Gävle
Sogndal
Lillehammer
Balestrand
Lærdal
Elverum
Borlänge
Grisslehamn
Hamar
Flåm
Gjøvik
Avesta
Eidsvoll
Gol
Ludvika
Sala
Kapellskär
Voss
Myrdal
Oslo
Uppsala
Roa
Kongsvinger
Fagersta
Västerås
Arlanda
Geilo
Hønefoss
Charlottenberg
Nykroppa
Frövi
Lillestrøm
Eskilstuna
Södertälje
Drammen
Kil
Örebro
Nynäshamn
Notodden
Karlstad
Hallsberg
Katrineholm
Kristinehamn
Nordagutu
Laxå
Skien
Fredrikstad
Norrköping
Mariestad
Larvik
Strömstad
Motala
Linköping
Öxnered
Mjölby
Nelaug
Uddevalla
Stavanger
Trollhättan
Falköping
Västervik
Arendal
Herrljunga
Visby
Egersund
Kristiansand
Moi
Jönköping
Nässjö
Skagen
Hirtshals
Borås
Berga
Oskarshamn
Hjørring
Frederikshavn
Kalmar
Aalborg
Varberg
Alvesta
Växjö
Thisted
Emmaboda
Randers
Halmstad
Karlskrona
Struer
Langå
Karlshamn
Holstebro
Kristianstad
Aarhus
Helsingborg
Hässleholm
Skjern
Herning
Helsingør
Lund
Fredericia
Simrishamn
Esbjerg
Malmö
Ystad
Fanø
Ribe
Odense
Nyborg
Korsør
Trelleborg
Rønne
Sønderborg
Nykøbing
Tønder
Padborg
Rødby
Gedser
Niebüll
Flensburg
Puttgarden
Sassnitz Fährhafen
Kiel
Rostock
Ebeltoft
Sj. Odde
Samsø
Vejle
Kalundborg
Roskilde
Ringsted
Bøjden
Fynshav
Vordingborg
Nakskov
Maribo

DENMARK

Operators: The principal operator is Danske Statsbaner (*DSB*): www.dsb.dk. Arriva Tog (*AT*) operate many local services in Jutland: www.arriva.dk. Local trains over the Øresund bridge a marketed as Øresundståg (*Øtåg*).

Services: InterCity (*IC*) and InterCityLyn (*Lyn*) trains offer *Business* (1st class), *Standard* (2nd class), and on some services *Hvilepladser* ('quiet' seats) and *Familiepladser* ('family' seats These services often consist of two or more portions for different destinations and care should be taken to join the correct portion. Other trains convey 1st and 2nd (standar classes of accommodation unless otherwise shown.

Timings: **Valid until December 10** (unless otherwise stated). Readers should note, however, that minor amendments may be made at any time, especially on and around the dates o public holidays (Dec. 24, 25, 26, Jan. 1, Apr. 14, 15, 17, 18, May 1, 13, 26, June 5, 6) and during the Summer mid June - mid August when fewer trains run.
In our Danish tables Ⓐ = ①–⑤, Ⓒ = ⑥⑦. See the panel on page 343 for service provision on holiday dates.
Engineering work often affects schedules (particularly late evening/early morning services and also during the summer months) and readers are advised to check locally.

Reservations: Seat reservations (currently 30 DKK) are recommended for travel on *IC* and *Lyn* trains (especially at peak times) and may be purchased a maximum of two months and minimum of 15 minutes before departure of the train from its *originating* station. Passengers may board the train without a reservation but are not guaranteed a seat. Reservation are also available on EuroCity (*EC*) trains. It is not possible to reserve seats on other types of train. Special reservation rules may apply during holiday periods.

700 KØBENHAVN - ODENSE - FREDERICIA - AARHUS

Most Aarhus services run to/from Aalborg (Table **701**). Services København - Middelfart and v.v. run to/from Esbjerg (Table **705**). For other through cars see Tables **710**, **712** and **715**.

km		*IC* 401	*IC* 409	*IC* 409	*IC* 113	*Lyn* 15	*IC* 117	*IC* 117	*IC* 819	*Lyn* 19	*IC* 421	*IC* 121	*IC* 5750	*IC* 823	*Lyn* 23	*IC* 125	*IC* 827	*Lyn* 27	*IC* 129	*IC* 131	*IC* 831	*Lyn* 31	*IC* 133	*IC* 835	*Lyn* 35
				Ⓐ	Ⓐ	Ⓐ	Ⓐ		Ⓐ	Ⓐ	Ⓒ	Ⓐ	Fj	Ⓐ											
	København Lufthavn ✈ d.	0036	0236	0236	...	...	0440	...	...	0528	0541	...	...	...	0628	...	...	0728	...	...	...	0828	...	...	0928
0	**København** H ... § **720** d.	0101	0301	0301	...	...	0506	...	0529	0556	0601	0606	...	0629	0656	0706	0729	0756	0806	...	0829	0856	0906	0929	0956
20	Høje Taastrup .... § **720** d.	0117	0317	0317	...	...	|	...	0544	|	0616	|	...	0644	|	|	0744	|	|	...	0844	|	|	0944	|
31	Roskilde .... § **720** d.	0125	0325	0325	...	...	|	...	0552	|	0624	|	...	0652	|	|	0752	|	|	...	0852	|	|	0952	|
64	Ringsted .... **720** d.	0141	0341	0341	...	...	0541	...	0608	|	0641	0641	...	0709	|	0741	0809	|	0841	...	0909	|	0941	1009	|
93	Slagelse .... d.	0159	0359	0359	...	...	0559	...	0626	|	0658	0659	...	0726	|	0759	0826	|	0859	...	0926	|	0959	1026	|
108	Korsør .... d.	0208	0408	0408	...	...	0608	...	0635	|	0706	0708	...	0735	|	0808	0835	|	0908	...	0935	|	1008	1035	|
132	Nyborg .... d.	0221	0421	0421	...	...	0621	...	0648	|	0719	0721	...	0748	|	0821	0848	|	0921	...	0948	|	1021	1048	|
160	**Odense** .... a.	0234	0434	0434	...	...	0634	...	0704	0707**c**	0728	0734	...	0804	0807**c**	0834	0904	0907**c**	0934	...	1004	1007**c**	1034	1104	1107
160	**Odense** .... d.	0236	0436	0436	0536	0610	0636	0636	0713	0710	0735	0736	...	0813	0810	0836	0913	0910	0936	...	1013	1010	1036	1113	1110
210	Middelfart .... d.	0300	0500	0500	0559	|	0659	0659	0736	|	0759	0759	...	0836	|	0859	0936	|	0959	...	1036	|	1059	1136	|
220	**Fredericia** .... a.	0307	0507	0507	0607	0638	0707	0707	...	0738	0807	0807	...	...	0838	0907	...	0938	1007	...	...	1038	1107	...	1138
220	**Fredericia** .... **705 715** d.	0313	...	0513	0613	0643	0713	0713	...	0743	...	...	0816	...	0843	0913	...	0943	...	1012	...	1043	1113	...	1143
246	Vejle .... **705 715** d.	0328	...	0528	0628	0658	0728	0728	...	0758	...	...	0831	...	0858	0928	...	0958	...	1028	...	1058	1128	...	1158
277	Horsens .... **705** d.	0344	...	0544	0644	0714	0744	0744	...	0814	...	...	0847	...	0914	0944	...	1014	...	1044	...	1114	1144	...	1214
306	Skanderborg . **705 713** d.	0400	...	0600	0700	0730	0800	0800	...	0830	...	...	0902	...	0930	1000	...	1030	...	1100	...	1130	1200	...	1230
329	**Aarhus** .... **705 713** a.	0412	...	0612	0712	0744	0812	0812	...	0842	...	...	0914	...	0942	1012	...	1042	...	1112	...	1142	1212	...	1242

	IC 137	*IC* 139	*IC* 839	*Lyn* 39	*IC* 141	*IC* 843	*Lyn* 43	*IC* 145	*IC* 147	*IC* 847	*Lyn* 47	*IC* 149	*IC* 851	*Lyn* 51	*IC* 153	*IC* 155	*IC* 855	*Lyn* 55	*IC* 157	*IC* 859	*Lyn* 59	*IC* 161	*Lyn* 361	*IC* 163	
																							Ⓑn		
København Lufthavn ✈ d.	...	...	...	1028	...	...	1128	...	...	...	1228	...	...	1332	...	...	...	1428	...	...	1528	...	...	...	...
København H ... § **720** d.	1006	...	1029	1056	1106	1129	1156	1206	...	1229	1256	1306	1329	1356	1406	...	1429	1456	1506	1529	1556	1606	1626	...	...
Høje Taastrup .... § **720** d.	|	...	1044	|	|	1144	|	|	...	1244	|	|	1344	|	|	...	1444	|	|	1544	|	|	|	...	...
Roskilde .... § **720** d.	|	...	1052	|	|	1152	|	|	...	1252	|	|	1352	|	|	...	1452	|	|	1552	|	|	|	...	...
Ringsted .... **720** d.	1041	...	1109	|	1141	1209	|	1241	...	1309	|	1341	1409	|	1441	...	1509	|	1541	1609	|	1641	|	...	...
Slagelse .... d.	1059	...	1126	|	1159	1226	|	1259	...	1326	|	1359	1426	|	1459	...	1526	|	1559	1626	|	1659	|	...	...
Korsør .... d.	1108	...	1135	|	1208	1235	|	1308	...	1335	|	1408	1435	|	1508	...	1535	|	1608	1635	|	1708	|	...	...
Nyborg .... d.	1121	...	1148	|	1221	1248	|	1321	...	1348	|	1421	1448	|	1521	...	1548	|	1621	1648	|	1721	|	...	...
Odense .... a.	1134	...	1204	1207**c**	1234	1304	1307**c**	1334	...	1404	1407**c**	1434	1504	1507**c**	1534	...	1604	1607**c**	1634	1704	1707**c**	1734	1737	...	...
Odense .... d.	1136	...	1213	1210	1236	1313	1310	1336	...	1413	1410	1436	1513	1510	1536	...	1613	1610	1636	1713	1710	1736	1740	...	...
Middelfart .... d.	1159	...	1236	|	1259	1336	|	1359	...	1436	|	1459	1536	|	1559	...	1636	|	1659	1736	|	1759	|	...	...
Fredericia .... a.	1207	...	...	1238	1307	...	1338	1407	...	...	1438	1507	...	1538	1607	...	...	1638	1707	...	1738	1807	|	...	...
Fredericia ..... **705 715** d.	...	1212	...	1243	1313	...	1343	...	1412	...	1443	1513	...	1543	...	1612	...	1643	1713	...	1743	...	|	1812	...
Vejle .... **705 715** d.	...	1228	...	1258	1328	...	1358	...	1428	...	1458	1528	...	1558	...	1628	...	1658	1728	...	1758	...	|	1828	...
Horsens .... **705** d.	...	1244	...	1314	1344	...	1414	...	1444	...	1514	1544	...	1614	...	1644	...	1714	1744	...	1814	...	|	1844	...
Skanderborg .. **705 713** d.	...	1300	...	1330	1400	...	1430	...	1500	...	1530	1600	...	1630	...	1700	...	1730	1800	...	1830	...	|	1900	...
Aarhus .... **705 713** a.	...	1312	...	1342	1412	...	1442	...	1512	...	1542	1612	...	1642	...	1712	...	1742	1812	...	1842	...	1905	1912	...

	IC 384	*IC* 863	*Lyn* 63	*IC* 165	*IC* 867	*Lyn* 67	*IC* 169	*IC* 171	*IC* 871	*Lyn* 71	*IC* 173	*IC* 875	*Lyn* 75	*IC* 177	*IC* 879	*Lyn* 79	*IC* 181	*IC* 883	*IC* 185	*IC* 185	*IC* 5745	*IC* 489	*IC* 491		
	H																			⑤⑥	F				
København Lufthavn ✈ d.	...	...	1628	...	...	1728	...	...	...	1828	...	...	1928	...	...	2028	...	...	2140	2140	...	2240	2332	...	...
København H ... § **720** d.	...	1629	1656	1706	1729	1756	1806	...	1829	1856	1906	1929	1956	2006	2029	2056	2106	2129	2206	2206	...	2301	0001	...	...
Høje Taastrup .... § **720** d.	...	1644	|	|	1744	|	|	...	1844	|	|	1944	|	|	2044	|	|	2144	|	|	...	2317	0016	...	...
Roskilde .... § **720** d.	...	1652	|	|	1752	|	|	...	1852	|	|	1952	|	|	2052	|	|	2152	|	|	...	2325	0024	...	...
Ringsted .... **720** d.	...	1709	|	1741	1809	|	1841	...	1909	|	1941	2009	|	2041	2109	|	2141	2209	2241	2241	...	2341	0041	...	...
Slagelse .... d.	...	1726	|	1759	1826	|	1859	...	1926	|	1959	2026	|	2059	2126	|	2159	2226	2259	2259	...	2358	0058	...	...
Korsør .... d.	...	1735	|	1808	1835	|	1908	...	1935	|	2008	2035	|	2108	2135	|	2208	2235	2308	2308	...	0006	0106	...	...
Nyborg .... d.	...	1748	|	1821	1848	|	1921	...	1948	|	2021	2048	|	2121	2148	|	2221	2248	2321	2321	...	0019	0119	...	...
Odense .... a.	...	1804	1807**c**	1834	1904	1907**c**	1934	...	2004	2007**c**	2034	2104	2107**c**	2134	2204	2207**c**	2234	2304	2334	2334	...	0035	0135	...	...
Odense .... d.	...	1813	1810	1836	1913	1910	1936	...	2013	2010	2036	2113	2110	2136	...	2210	2236	...	...	2336	...	0036	...	...	...
Middelfart .... d.	...	1836	|	1859	1936	|	1959	...	2036	|	2059	2136	|	2159	...	|	2259	...	...	2359	...	0100	...	...	...
Fredericia .... a.	...	...	1838	1907	...	1938	2007	...	...	2038	2107	...	2138	2207	...	2238	2307	...	...	0007	...	0107	...	...	...
Fredericia ..... **705 715** d.	1819	...	1843	1913	...	1943	...	2012	...	2043	2113	...	2143	2220	...	2250	2313	...	...	...	0020	0113	...	...	...
Vejle .... **705 715** d.	1834	...	1858	1928	...	1958	...	2028	...	2058	2128	...	2158	2235	...	2310	2328	...	...	...	0035	0128	...	...	...
Horsens .... **705** d.	1850	...	1914	1944	...	2014	...	2044	...	2114	2144	...	2214	2251	...	2330	2344	...	...	...	0052	0144	...	...	...
Skanderborg .. **705 713** d.	1906	...	1930	2000	...	2030	...	2100	...	2130	2200	...	2230	2307	...	2345	0000	...	...	...	0107	0200	...	...	...
Aarhus .... **705 713** a.	1920	...	1942	2012	...	2042	...	2112	...	2142	2212	...	2243	2319	...	0002	0012	...	...	...	0119	0212	...	...	...

	IC 488	*IC* 100	*IC* 400	*IC* 802 4402	*IC* 104	*IC* 404	*Lyn* 6	*IC* 806	*Lyn* 308	*IC* 108	*IC* 408	*Lyn* 10	*IC* 810	*IC* 5753	*Lyn* 312	*IC* 112	*Lyn* 14	*IC* 814	*IC* 116	*Lyn* 18	*IC* 818	*IC* 5755	*IC* 118	*IC* 120	*Lyn* 22
		Ⓐ	Ⓒ	Ⓐ	Ⓐ	Ⓒ	Ⓐ	Ⓐ	Ⓐn	Ⓐ	Ⓒ	Ⓐ	Ⓐ	ⒶF	Ⓐ							ⒸF			
Aarhus .... **705 713** d.	0045	...	0245	...	...	...	0415	...	...	...	...	0515	...	0539	0555	...	0615	...	0645	0715	...	0739	0745	...	0815
Skanderborg .. **705 713** d.	0059	...	0259	...	...	...	0429	...	...	...	...	0529	...	0553	|	...	0629	...	0659	0729	...	0753	0759	...	0829
Horsens .... **705** d.	0114	...	0314	...	...	...	0445	...	...	...	...	0545	...	0608	|	...	0645	...	0714	0745	...	0808	0814	...	0845
Vejle .... **705 715** d.	0131	...	0331	...	...	...	0502	...	...	...	...	0602	...	0624	|	...	0702	...	0731	0802	...	0824	0831	...	0902
Fredericia ..... **705 715** a.	0145	...	0345	...	...	...	0517	...	...	...	...	0617	...	0640	|	...	0717	...	0745	0817	...	0840	0845	...	0917
Fredericia .... d.	0153	...	0353	...	...	...	0523	...	0530	0553	0553	0623	...	...	|	0653**a**	0723	...	0753	0823	...	...	...	0853	0923
Middelfart .... d.	0201	...	0401	...	...	...	|	0524	0538	0601	0601	|	0624	...	|	0701**a**	|	0724	0801	|	0824	...	...	0901	|
Odense .... a.	0223	...	0423	...	...	...	0550	0548**c**	0620	0623	0623	0650	0648**c**	...	0719	0723**a**	0750	0748**c**	0823	0850	0848**c**	...	...	0923	0950
Odense .... d.	0225	0416	0425	0456	0525	0525	0553	0556	0622	0625	0625	0653	0656	...	0722	0725	0753	0756	0825	0853	0856	...	...	0925	0953
Nyborg .... d.	0240	0430	0440	0513	0540	0541	|	0613	|	0640	0641	|	0713	...	|	0740	|	0813	0840	|	0913	...	...	0940	|
Korsør .... d.	0252	0443	0453	0525	0552	0553	|	0625	|	0652	0653	|	0725	...	|	0752	|	0825	0852	|	0925	...	...	0952	|
Slagelse .... d.	0302	0452	0503	0535	0602	0602	|	0635	|	0702	0702	|	0735	...	|	0802	|	0835	0902	|	0935	...	...	1002	|
Ringsted .... **720** d.	0320	0511	0521	0552	0620	0620	|	0652	|	0720	0720	|	0752	...	|	0820	|	0852	0920	|	0952	...	...	1020	|
Roskilde .... § **720** a.	0337	|	0537	0609	|	0637	|	0709	|	|	0737	|	0809	...	|	|	|	0909	|	|	1009	...	...	|	|
Høje Taastrup .... § **720** a.	0343	|	0544	0615	|	0643	|	0715	|	|	0743	|	0815	...	|	|	|	0915	|	|	1015	...	...	|	|
København H ... § **720** a.	0400	0546	0600	0631	0655	0700	0703	0731	0733	0755	0800	0803	0831	...	0833	0855	0903	0931	0955	1003	1031	...	...	1055	1103
København Lufthavn ✈ a.	0425	...	0625	...	...	0725	0725	...	0756	...	0825	0825	...	...	0856	...	0925	...	...	1025	...	...	...	...	1125

F – To/from Flensburg (Table **710**).

a – Ⓐ only.

c – Connects with train in previous column.

j – 2–4 minutes earlier June 18 - Aug. 20.

n – Not July 3 - Aug. 7.

§ – *IC* and *Lyn* trains are not available for local journeys. Frequent local trains run between Roskilde and København.

AARHUS - FREDERICIA - ODENSE - KØBENHAVN 700

Most services from Aarhus start from Aalborg (Table **701**). Services Middelfart - København start from Esbjerg (Table **705**). For other through cars see Tables **710**, **712** and **715**.

	IC 822	*IC* 124	*Lyn* 26	*IC* 826	*IC* 383	*IC* 126	*IC* 128	*Lyn* 30	*IC* 830	*IC* 132	*Lyn* 34	*IC* 834	*IC* 134	*IC* 136	*Lyn* 38	*IC* 838	*IC* 140	*Lyn* 42	*IC* 842	*IC* 385	*IC* 142	*IC* 144	*Lyn* 344	*Lyn* 46	*IC* 846
					H															H			Ⓑ n		
Aarhus .... **705 713** d.	...	0845	0915	...	0939	0945	...	1015	...	1045	1115	...	1145	...	1215	...	1245	1315	...	1339	1345	...	1355	1415	...
Skanderborg .. **705 713** d.	...	0859	0929	...	0953	0959	...	1029	...	1059	1129	...	1159	...	1229	...	1259	1329	...	1353	1359	...	|	1429	...
Horsens .... **705** d.	...	0914	0945	...	1008	1014	...	1045	...	1114	1145	...	1214	...	1245	...	1314	1345	...	1408	1414	...	|	1445	...
Vejle .... **705 715** d.	...	0931	1002	...	1024	1031	...	1102	...	1131	1202	...	1231	...	1302	...	1331	1402	...	1424	1431	...	|	1502	...
Fredericia ..... **705 715** a.	...	0945	1017	...	1040	1045	...	1117	...	1145	1217	...	1245	...	1317	...	1345	1417	...	1440	1445	...	|	1517	...
Fredericia .... d.	...	0953	1023	...	...	...	1053	1123	...	1153	1223	...	...	1253	1323	...	1353	1423	...	...	...	1453	|	1523	...
Middelfart .... d.	0924	1001	|	1024	...	...	1101	|	1124	1201	|	1224	...	1301	|	1324	1401	|	1424	...	...	1501	|	|	1524
Odense .... a.	0948c	1023	1050	1048c	...	...	1123	1150	1148c	1223	1250	1248c	...	1323	1350	1348c	1423	1450	1448c	...	...	1523	1519	1550	1548c
Odense .... d.	0956	1025	1053	1056	...	...	1125	1153	1156	1225	1253	1256	...	1325	1353	1356	1425	1453	1456	...	...	1525	1522	1553	1556
Nyborg .... d.	1013	1040	|	1113	...	...	1140	|	1213	1240	|	1313	...	1340	|	1413	1440	|	1513	...	...	1540	|	|	1613
Korsør .... d.	1025	1052	|	1125	...	...	1152	|	1225	1252	|	1325	...	1352	|	1425	1452	|	1525	...	...	1552	|	|	1625
Slagelse .... d.	1035	1102	|	1135	...	...	1202	|	1235	1302	|	1335	...	1402	|	1435	1502	|	1535	...	...	1602	|	|	1635
Ringsted .... **720** d.	1052	1120	|	1152	...	...	1220	|	1252	1320	|	1352	...	1420	|	1452	1520	|	1552	...	...	1620	|	|	1652
Roskilde .... § **720** a.	1109	|	|	1209	...	...	|	|	1309	|	|	1409	...	|	|	1509	|	|	1609	...	...	|	|	|	1709
Høje Taastrup.... § **720** a.	1115	|	|	1215	...	...	|	|	1315	|	|	1415	...	|	|	1515	|	|	1615	...	...	|	|	|	1715
København H ... § **720** a.	1131	1155	1203	1231	...	...	1255	1303	1331	1355	1403	1431	...	1455	1503	1531	1555	1603	1631	...	...	1655	1633	1703	1731
København Lufthavn ✈ a.	...	...	1225	...	...	...	...	1325	...	...	1425	...	...	...	1525	...	...	1625	...	...	...	...	1656	1725	...

	IC 148	*Lyn* 50	*IC* 850	*IC* 150	*IC* 152	*Lyn* 54	*IC* 854	*IC* 156	*Lyn* 58	*IC* 858	*IC* 5765	*IC* 160	*Lyn* 62	*IC* 862	*IC* 164	*Lyn* 66	*IC* 866	*IC* 168	*Lyn* 70	*IC* 472	*IC* 476	*IC* 480	*IC* 480		
											F											⑤⑥		2	
Aarhus .... **705 713** d.	1445	1515	...	1545	...	1615	...	1645	1715	...	1739	1745	1815	...	1845	1915	...	1945	2015	2045	2145	2245	2245	2345	...
Skanderborg .. **705 713** d.	1459	1529	...	1559	...	1629	...	1659	1729	...	1753	1759	1829	...	1859	1929	...	1959	2029	2059	2159	2259	2259	0002	...
Horsens .... **705** d.	1514	1545	...	1614	...	1645	...	1714	1745	...	1808	1814	1845	...	1914	1945	...	2014	2045	2014	2214	2314	2314	0017	...
Vejle .... **705 715** d.	1531	1602	...	1631	...	1702	...	1731	1802	...	1824	1831	1902	...	1931	2002	...	2031	2102	2131	2231	2331	2331	0037	...
Fredericia ..... **705 715** a.	1545	1617	...	1645	...	1717	...	1745	1817	...	1840	1845	1917	...	1945	2017	...	2045	2117	2145	2245	2345	2345	0056	...
Fredericia .... d.	1553	1623	...	...	1653	1723	...	1753	1823	...	...	1853	1923	...	1953	2023	...	2053	2123	2153	2253	2353	2353	...	...
Middelfart .... d.	1601	|	1624	...	1701	|	1724	1801	|	1824	...	1901	|	1924	2001	|	2024	2101	|	2201	2301	0001	0001	...	...
Odense .... a.	1623	1650	1648c	...	1723	1750	1748c	1823	1850	1848c	...	1923	1950	1948c	2023	2050	2048c	2123	2150	2223	2323	0023	0023	...	...
Odense .... d.	1625	1653	1656	...	1725	1753	1756	1825	1853	1856	...	1925	1953	1956	2025	2053	2056	2125	2153	2225	2325	0025	...	...	...
Nyborg .... d.	1640	|	1713	...	1740	|	1813	1840	|	1913	...	1940	|	2013	2040	|	2113	2141	|	2241	2341	0041	...	...	...
Korsør .... d.	1652	|	1725	...	1752	|	1825	1852	|	1925	...	1952	|	2025	2052	|	2125	2154	|	2254	2354	0054	...	...	...
Slagelse .... d.	1702	|	1735	...	1802	|	1835	1902	|	1935	...	2002	|	2035	2102	|	2135	2202	|	2302	0002	0102	...	...	...
Ringsted .... **720** d.	1720	|	1752	...	1820	|	1852	1920	|	1952	...	2020	|	2052	2120	|	2152	2220	|	2320	0020	0120	...	...	...
Roskilde .... § **720** a.	|	|	1809	...	|	|	1909	|	|	2009	...	|	|	2109	|	|	2209	|	|	2337	0037	0137	...	...	...
Høje Taastrup.... § **720** a.	|	|	1815	...	|	|	1915	|	|	2015	...	|	|	2115	|	|	2215	|	|	2343	0043	0143	...	...	...
København H ... § **720** a.	1755	1803	1831	...	1855	1903	1931	1955	2003	2031	...	2055	2103	2131	2155	2203	2231	2255	2303	2400	0100	0200	...	...	...
København Lufthavn ✈ a.	...	1825	...	...	...	1925	...	...	2025	...	...	...	2125	...	...	2225	...	...	2325	0025	0125	0225	...	...	...

F – To Flensburg (Table **710**).
H – (12) 🍸 Aarhus - Hamburg (Table **710**).
c – Connects with train in previous column.
n – Not July 3 - Aug. 7.
§ – *IC* and *Lyn* trains are not available for local journeys. Frequent local trains run between Roskilde and København.

AARHUS - AALBORG 701

km		*IC* 401		*IC* 4105	*Lyn* 4007	*IC* 4109	*Lyn* 4011	*IC* 113	*IC* 4113	*Lyn* 15	*IC* 117	*IC* 117	*Lyn* 19	*Lyn* 4019	*IC* 4123	*Lyn* 23	*IC* 125	*Lyn* 27	*IC* 131	*Lyn* 31	*IC* 133	*Lyn* 35	*IC* 139
				Ⓐ	Ⓐ		Ⓐ	Ⓐ		Ⓐ	Ⓐ		Ⓐ										
	København H **700** ......d.	0101	...	...	...	...	...	...	...	...	0506	...	0556	...	...	0656	0706	0756	...	0856	0906	0956	...
	Odense **700** ....d.	0236	...	...	...	...	...	0536	...	0610	0636	0636	0710	...	...	0810	0836	0910	...	1010	1036	1110	...
	Fredericia **700** ....d.	0313	...	...	...	...	...	0613	...	0643	0713	0713	0743	...	...	0843	0913	0943	1012	1043	1113	1143	1212
0	**Aarhus** .... **712** d.	0420	...	0520	0549	0620	0649	0720	0720	0750	0820	0820	0850	0850	0920	0950	1020	1050	1120	1150	1220	1250	1320
46	Langå .... **712** d.	0446	...	0546	|	0646	|	0746	0746	|	0846	0846	|	|	0946	|	1046	|	1146	|	1246	|	1346
59	Randers ....d.	0456	...	0556	0620	0656	0720	0756	0756	0821	0856	0856	0921	0921	0956	1021	1056	1121	1156	1221	1256	1321	1356
91	Hobro ....d.	0512	...	0612	0636	0712	0736	0812	0812	0837	0912	0912	0937	0937	1012	1037	1112	1137	1212	1237	1312	1337	1412
140	**Aalborg** ....a.	0551	...	0651	0706	0751	0806	0851	0851	0906	0951	0951	1006	1006	1051	1106	1151	1206	1251	1306	1351	1406	1451

	Lyn 39	*IC* 141	*Lyn* 43	*IC* 147	*Lyn* 47	*IC* 149	*Lyn* 51	*IC* 155	*Lyn* 55	*IC* 157	*Lyn* 59	*IC* 163	*Lyn* 63	*IC* 165	*Lyn* 67	*IC* 171		*IC* 173		*IC* 177	*IC* 181		*IC* 489
																					⑤⑥		⑤⑥
København H **700** ......d.	1056	1106	1156	...	1256	1306	1356	...	1456	1506	1556	...	1656	1706	1756	...	...	1906	...	2006	2106	...	2301
Odense **700** ....d.	1210	1236	1310	...	1410	1436	1510	...	1610	1636	1710	...	1810	1836	1910	...	...	2036	...	2136	2236	...	0036
Fredericia **700** ....d.	1243	1313	1343	1412	1443	1513	1543	1612	1643	1713	1743	1812	1843	1913	1943	2012	...	2113	...	2220	2313	...	0113
Aarhus .... **712** d.	1350	1420	1450	1520	1550	1620	1650	1720	1750	1820	1850	1920	1950	2020	2050	2120	...	2220	...	2325	0020	...	0222
Langå .... **712** d.	|	1446	|	1546	|	1646	|	1746	|	1846	|	1946	|	2046	|	2146	...	2246	...	2351	0046	...	0249
Randers ....d.	1421	1456	1521	1556	1621	1656	1721	1756	1821	1856	1921	1956	2021	2056	2121	2156	...	2256	...	0001	0056	...	0258
Hobro ....d.	1437	1512	1537	1612	1637	1712	1737	1812	1837	1912	1937	2012	2037	2112	2137	2212	...	2312	...	0017	0112	...	0314
Aalborg ....a.	1506	1551	1606	1651	1706	1751	1806	1851	1906	1951	2006	2051	2106	2151	2206	2251	...	2351	...	0056	0151	...	0353

	IC 4192		*IC* 400		*Lyn* 14	*IC* 116	*Lyn* 18	*IC* 118		*Lyn* 22	*IC* 124		*Lyn* 26	*IC* 126	*Lyn* 30	*IC* 132	*Lyn* 34	*IC* 134	*Lyn* 38	*IC* 140	*Lyn* 42	*IC* 142	*Lyn* 46
			A		Ⓐ	Ⓐ	Ⓐ																
Aalborg ....d.	0005	...	0105	...	0450	0505	0550	0605	...	0650	0705	...	0750	0805	0850	0905	0950	1005	1050	1105	1150	1205	1250
Hobro ....d.	0044	...	0144	...	0519	0544	0619	0644	...	0719	0744	...	0819	0841	0919	0944	1019	1044	1119	1141	1219	1244	1319
Randers ....d.	0101	...	0201	...	0535	0601	0635	0701	...	0735	0801	...	0835	0901	0935	1001	1035	1101	1135	1201	1235	1301	1335
Langå .... **712** d.	0109	...	0209	...	|	0609	|	0709	...	|	0809	...	|	0909	|	1009	|	1109	|	1209	|	1309	|
Aarhus .... **712** a.	0138	...	0238	...	0608	0638	0708	0738	...	0808	0838	...	0908	0938	1008	1038	1108	1138	1208	1238	1308	1338	1408
Fredericia **700** ....a.	...	...	0345	...	0717	0745	0817	0845	...	0917	0945	...	1017	1045	1117	1145	1217	1245	1317	1345	1417	1445	1517
Odense **700** ....a.	...	...	0423	...	0750	0823	0850	0923	...	0950	1023	...	1050	...	1150	1223	1250	...	1350	1423	1450	...	1550
København H **700** ......a.	...	...	0600	...	0903	0955	1003	1055	...	1103	1155	...	1203	...	1303	1355	1403	...	1503	1555	1603	...	1703

	IC 148	*Lyn* 50	*IC* 150	*Lyn* 54	*IC* 156	*Lyn* 58	*IC* 160	*Lyn* 62	*IC* 164	*Lyn* 66	*IC* 168	*Lyn* 70	*IC* 472		*Lyn* 4074	*IC* 476		*IC* 480	*IC* 180		*IC* 4184		*IC* 488
																			⑤⑥				
Aalborg ....d.	1305	1350	1405	1450	1505	1550	1605	1650	1705	1750	1805	1850	1905	...	1950	2005	...	2105	2105	...	2205	...	2305
Hobro ....d.	1344	1419	1444	1519	1544	1619	1644	1719	1744	1819	1844	1919	1944	...	2019	2044	...	2144	2144	...	2244	...	2344
Randers ....d.	1401	1435	1501	1535	1601	1635	1701	1735	1801	1835	1901	1935	2001	...	2035	2101	...	2201	2201	...	2301	...	0001
Langå .... **712** d.	1409	|	1509	|	1609	|	1709	|	1809	|	1909	|	2009	...	|	2109	...	2209	2209	...	2309	...	0009
Aarhus .... **712** a.	1438	1508	1538	1608	1638	1708	1738	1808	1838	1908	1938	2008	2038	...	2108	2138	...	2238	2238	...	2338	...	0038
Fredericia **700** ....a.	1545	1617	1645	1717	1745	1817	1845	1917	1945	2017	2045	2117	2145	...	...	2245	...	2345	2345	...	0056	...	0145
Odense **700** ....a.	1623	1650	...	1750	1823	1850	1923	1950	2023	2050	2123	2150	2223	...	...	2323	...	0023	0023	...	...	...	0223
København H **700** ......a.	1755	1803	...	1903	1955	2003	2055	2103	2155	2203	2255	2303	2400	...	...	0100	...	...	0200	...	...	...	0400

703 HELSINGØR - KØBENHAVN - KØBENHAVN LUFTHAVN ✈ - MALMÖ

EASTBOUND

Services operate every 20 minutes (less frequent 0000 - 0400 hours) **Helsingør** - Østerport - København H - København Lufthavn ✈ - **Malmö C**.

Journey times:
- Helsingør - København H: 47 minutes;
- København H - København Lufthavn ✈: 13 minutes;
- København Lufthavn ✈ - Malmö C: 26 minutes.

København H - København Lufthavn ✈ services operate every 10 minutes.

WESTBOUND

Services operate every 20 minutes (less frequent 0000 - 0400 hours) **Malmö C** - Københav Lufthavn ✈ - København H - Østerport - **Helsingør**.

Journey times:
- Malmö C - København Lufthavn ✈: 21 minutes;
- København Lufthavn ✈ - København H: 13 minutes;
- København H - Helsingør: 46 minutes.

København Lufthavn ✈ - København H services operate every 10 minutes.

704 KØBENHAVN - KALUNDBORG

km			Ⓐ	Ⓐ	Ⓐ	Ⓐ	Ⓒ	Ⓐ	Ⓐ	Ⓒ	Ⓐ	Ⓐ	Ⓒ		Ⓐ	Ⓒ		Ⓒ						
0	**København H** .... ▷ d.	0034	0534	0544	0614	0634	0634	0714	0734	0734	0814	0834	0848	and at	2034	2048	2134	2148	2234	2334	...	...	...	...
20	Høje Taastrup........ ▷ d.	0049	0547	0600	0630	0647	0649	0730	0747	0749	0830	0847	0901	the same	2047	2101	2149	2201	2249	2349	...	...	...	...
31	**Roskilde** .... ▷ d.	0057	0555	0608	0638	0656	0657	0738	0755	0757	0838	0855	0909	minutes	2056	2109	2157	2209	2257	2357	...	...	...	...
67	Holbæk.................. ▷ a.	0125	0613	0638	0708	0713	0725	0808	0813	0825	0908	0913	0929	past each	2113	2129	2225	2229	2325	0025	...	...	...	...
67	Holbæk.....................d.	0127c	0615	...	...	0715	0731	...	0815	...	...	0915	0931	hour until	2115	2131	2232a	2232	2327	0027	...	...	...	...
111	**Kalundborg** ....a.	0206c	0654	...	...	0754	0812	...	0854	...	...	0954	1012		2154	2212	2312a	2312	0007	0106	...	...	...	...

	Ⓐ	Ⓒ	Ⓐ	Ⓐn	Ⓒ	Ⓐ	Ⓐn	Ⓒ	Ⓐ	Ⓐn	Ⓒ	Ⓐ	Ⓒ	Ⓐ		Ⓒ	Ⓐ	Ⓐ	Ⓒ					
Kalundborg ....d.	...	...	0508	0531	0554	0602	0628	0654	0702	0728	0749	0802	0849	0902	and at	2049	2102	...	2149	2155a	2244	...	...	...
Holbæk.........................a.	...	...	0548	0606	0631	0643	0705	0731	0743	0805	0828	0843	0928	0943	the same	2128	2143	...	2228	2232a	2326	...	...	...
Holbæk.................. ▷ d.	0521	0533	0551	0611	0633	0645	0711	0733	0745	0811	0830	0845	0930	0945	minutes	2130	2145	2151	2230	2233	2333	...	...	...
Roskilde .... ▷ d.	0552	0602	0622	0634	0702	0704	0734	0802	0804	0834	0852	0904	0952	1004	past each	2152	2204	2222	2252	2302	0002	...	...	...
Høje Taastrup......... ▷ d.	0600	0610	0630	0642	0710	0713	0742	0810	0812	0842	0900	0912	1000	1012	hour until	2200	2212	2230	2300	2310	0010	...	...	...
København H .... ▷ a.	0616	0625	0646	0655	0725	0725	0755	0825	0825	0855	0913	0925	1013	1025		2213	2225	2246	2313	2325	0025	...	...	...

a – ①-⑤ only. c – ⑥⑦ only. n – Not July 4 - Aug. 5. ▷ – Additional trains run København - Holbæk and v.v.

705 AARHUS - FREDERICIA - ESBJERG

km						*IC*		*IC*		*IC*		*IC*		*IC*		*IC*		*IC*		*IC*		*IC*		*IC*		*IC*
		2		815		819		823		827		831		835		839		843		847		851		855		859
		Ⓐ	2	Ⓐ	2	Ⓐ	2	Ⓐ	2		2		2		2		2		2		2		2		2	
	Aarhus ....**700 713** d.	...	...	...	0558a	...	0658	...	0757	...	0858	...	0958	...	1058	...	1158	...	1258	...	1358	...	1458	...	1558	...
	Skanderborg **700 713** d.	...	...	...	0614a	...	0714	...	0814	...	0914	...	1014	...	1114	...	1214	...	1314	...	1414	...	1514	...	1614	...
	Horsens .... **700** d.	...	...	...	0629a	...	0729	...	0829	...	0929	...	1029	...	1129	...	1229	...	1329	...	1429	...	1529	...	1629	...
	Vejle ....**700 715** d.	...	...	...	0649a	...	0749	...	0849	...	0949	...	1049	...	1149	...	1249	...	1349	...	1449	...	1549	...	1649	...
	København H **700**.. d.	...	...	...	|	0529	|	0629	|	0729	|	0829	|	0929	|	1029	|	1129	|	1229	|	1329	|	1429	|	1529
	Odense.......... **700** d.	...	...	0613	|	0713	|	0813	|	0913	|	1013	|	1113	|	1213	|	1313	|	1413	|	1513	|	1613	|	1713
0	Middelfart .... **700** d.	...	...	0636	|	0736	|	0836	|	0936	|	1036	|	1136	|	1236	|	1336	|	1436	|	1536	|	1636	|	1736
	Fredericia 700 710/5 d.	0513	0613	|	0713	|	0813	|	0913	|	1013	|	1113	|	1213	|	1313	|	1413	|	1513	|	1613	|	1713	|
23	Kolding .... **710** d.	0528	0628	0652	0728	0752	0828	0852	0928	0952	1028	1052	1128	1152	1228	1252	1328	1352	1428	1452	1528	1552	1628	1652	1728	1752
36	Lunderskov .... **710** d.	0536	0636	0659	0736	0800	0836	0900	0936	1000	1036	1100	1136	1200	1236	1300	1336	1400	1436	1500	1536	1600	1636	1700	1736	1800
47	Vejen .... d.	0544	0644	0707	0744	0808	0844	0908	0944	1008	1044	1108	1144	1208	1244	1308	1344	1408	1444	1508	1544	1608	1644	1708	1744	1808
75	Bramming .... **709** d.	0607	0707	0729	0807	0822	0907	0922	1007	1022	1107	1122	1207	1222	1307	1322	1407	1422	1507	1522	1607	1622	1707	1722	1807	1822
91	**Esbjerg** .... **709** a.	0618	0718	0739	0818	0832	0918	0932	1018	1032	1118	1132	1218	1232	1318	1332	1418	1432	1518	1532	1618	1632	1718	1732	1818	1832

		IC		*IC*		*IC*		*IC*		
		863		867		871		875		
	2		2		2		2		2	2
Aarhus.........**700 713** d.	1658	...	1758	...	1858	...	1958	...	2058	2158
Skanderborg .**700 713** d.	1714	...	1814	...	1914	...	2014	...	2114	2214
Horsens..............**700** d.	1729	...	1829	...	1929	...	2029	...	2129	2229
Vejle............**700 715** d.	1749	...	1849	...	1949	...	2049	...	2149	2249
København H **700** .. d.	|	1629	|	1729	|	1829	|	1929	|	b
Odense...........**700** d.	|	1813	|	1913	|	2013	|	2113	|	|
Middelfart.........**700** d.	|	1836	|	1936	|	2036	|	2136	|	|
Fredericia . **700 710/5** d.	1813	|	1913	|	2013	|	2113	|	2213	2323
Kolding ....**710** d.	1828	1852	1928	1952	2028	2052	2128	2152	2228	2338
Lunderskov..........**710** d.	1836	1900	1936	2000	2036	2100	2136	2200	2236	2346
Vejen........................ d.	1844	1908	1944	2008	2044	2108	2144	2208	2244	2354
Bramming............**709** d.	1907	1922	2007	2022	2107	2122	2207	2222	2307	0017
Esbjerg...............**709** a.	1918	1932	2018	2032	2118	2132	2218	2232	2318	0028

	IC		*IC*		*IC*		*IC*		*IC*		*IC*
	806		810	2	814	d	818		822		826
	Ⓐ	Ⓐ	Ⓐ	Ⓐ		2		2		2	
Esbjerg.....................**709** d.	...	...	0526	0541	0626a	0641	0727	0741	0827	0841	0927
Bramming...................**709** d.	...	...	0538	0552	0638a	0652	0738	0752	0838	0852	0938
Vejen.............................. d.	...	...	0551	0614	0652a	0714	0751	0814	0851	0914	0951
Lunderskov...................**710** d.	...	...	0559	0622	0659a	0722	0759	0822	0859	0922	0959
Kolding ....**710** d.	0509	...	0609	0631	0709	0731	0809	0831	0909	0931	1009
Fredericia ... **700 710 715** d.	|	0620	|	0650	|	0750	|	0850	|	0950	|
Middelfart ....**700** d.	0524	|	0624	|	0724	|	0824	|	0924	|	1024
Odense ....**700** a.	0548	|	0648	|	0748	|	0848	|	0948	|	1048
København H **700** .... a.	0731	|	0831	|	0931	|	1031	|	1131	|	1231
Vejle...................**700 715** d.	...	0640	...	0710	...	0810	...	0910	...	1010	...
Horsens.......................**700** d.	...	0700	...	0730	...	0830	...	0930	...	1030	...
Skanderborg.......**700 713** d.	...	0715	...	0745	...	0845	...	0945	...	1045	...
Aarhus................**700 713** a.	...	0730	...	0801	...	0902	...	1002	...	1102	...

		IC		*IC*		*IC*		*IC*		*IC*		*IC*		*IC*		*IC*		*IC*		*IC*		*IC*				
		830		834		838		842		846		850		854		858		862		866		870				
	2		2		2		2		2		2		2		2		2		2		2		2	2	2	2
Esbjerg..............**709** d.	0941	1027	1041	1127	1141	1227	1241	1327	1341	1427	1441	1527	1541	1627	1641	1727	1741	1827	1841	1927	1941	2027	*2041*	*2141*	2241	2341
Bramming............**709** d.	0952	1038	1052	1138	1152	1238	1252	1338	1352	1438	1452	1538	1552	1638	1652	1738	1752	1838	1852	1938	1952	2038	*2052*	*2152*	2252	2352
Vejen........................ d.	1014	1051	1114	1151	1214	1251	1314	1351	1414	1451	1514	1551	1614	1651	1714	1751	1814	1851	1914	1951	2014	2051	*2114*	*2214*	2314	0014
Lunderskov..........**710** d.	1022	1059	1122	1159	1222	1259	1322	1359	1422	1459	1522	1559	1622	1659	1722	1759	1822	1859	1922	1959	2022	2059	*2122*	*2222*	2322	0022
Kolding ....**710** d.	1031	1109	1131	1209	1231	1309	1331	1409	1431	1509	1531	1609	1631	1709	1731	1809	1831	1909	1931	2009	2031	2109	*2131*	*2231*	2331	0031
Fredericia . **700 710/5** d.	1050	|	1150	|	1250	|	1350	|	1450	|	1550	|	1650	|	1750	|	1850	|	1950	|	2050	|	2150	2250	2348	0048
Middelfart.........**700** d.	|	1124	|	1224	|	1324	|	1424	|	1524	|	1624	|	1724	|	1824	|	1924	|	2024	|	2124	|	|	...	...
Odense...........**700** d.	|	1148	|	1248	|	1348	|	1448	|	1548	|	1648	|	1748	|	1848	|	1948	|	2048	|	2148	|	|	...	...
København H **700** .. a.	|	1331	|	1431	|	1531	|	1631	|	1731	|	1831	|	1931	|	2031	|	2131	|	2231	|	*0007*e	|	|	...	...
Vejle...........**700 715** d.	1110	...	1210	...	1310	...	1410	...	1510	...	1610	...	1710	...	1810	...	1910	...	2010	...	2110	...	2210	2310	...	...
Horsens..............**700** d.	1130	...	1230	...	1330	...	1430	...	1530	...	1630	...	1730	...	1830	...	1930	...	2030	...	2130	...	2230	2330	...	...
Skanderborg .**700 713** d.	1145	...	1245	...	1345	...	1445	...	1545	...	1645	...	1745	...	1845	...	1945	...	2045	...	2145	...	2245	2345	...	...
Aarhus.........**700 713** a.	1202	...	1302	...	1402	...	1502	...	1602	...	1702	...	1802	...	1902	...	2002	...	2102	...	2202	...	2302	0002	...	...

a – ①-⑤ only.
b – Connecting train from København (to Fredericia) departs at 2106 (Table **700**).
d – Change trains at Fredericia on ⑥⑦.
e – Connecting train departs Odense at 2225 (arrives København 2400 on ⑤⑥).

707 ESBJERG - SKJERN

Operator: *AT*; 2nd class only

km			Ⓐ	Ⓐ	Ⓐ	Ⓐ	Ⓐ		Ⓐ	Ⓐ	Ⓐ	Ⓐ	Ⓐ	Ⓐ	Ⓐ			⑥	⑦	⑥	Ⓒ		Ⓒ	Ⓒ	Ⓒ
0	**Esbjerg**............... ▷ d.	Ⓐ	0442	0537	0641	0802	0903	and	1603	1641	...	1839	2039	2239	2330	...	Ⓒ	...	...	0617	0817		2017	2217	2317
17	Varde .... ▷ d.		0501	0555	0702	0829	0929	hourly	1629	1700	1729	1857	2057	2257	2349	...		0437	0637	0637	0837	and every	2037	2237	2336
60	**Skjern**.......................a.		0538	0633	0739	0910	1010	until	1710	...	1810	1934	2134	2334	...	...		0513	0713	0713	0913	**two** hours	2113	2313	2134
	Herning **713** ....a.		0623	0723	0823	0956	1056		1756	...	...	2014	2214	0023	...	...		...	...	0755	0955	until	2155	2355	
	Aarhus **713** ....a.		...	...	...	1136	1236		1936	...	...	2139	2239	...	...	...		...	...	0930	1130		2330	...	...

		Ⓐ	Ⓐ	Ⓐ	Ⓐ	Ⓐ		Ⓐ	Ⓐ	Ⓐ	Ⓐ	Ⓐ	Ⓐ				⑥	⑥	⑦	Ⓒ		Ⓒ	Ⓒ		
Aarhus **713**........... d.	Ⓐ	...	...	...	0622	0726		1326	1426	1526	1726	1918	...	...	...	Ⓒ	...	0530	0730	0930		1930	...	...	...
Herning **713** .... d.		...	0556	0656	0756	0902		1502	1602	1702	1902	2102	...	...	...		0502	0702	0902	1102	and every	2102	...	...	...
Skjern .... d.		0602	0650	0742	0842	0942	and	1542	1642	1742	1942	2142	2342	...	...		0543	0743	0943	1143	**two** hours	2143	2343	...	...
Varde ....▷ d.		0645	0740	0822	0922	1022	hourly	1622	1720	1820	2019	2219	0018	...	...		0620	0820	1020	1220	until	2220	0019	...	...
Esbjerg...............▷ a.		0703	0801	0839	0940	1040	until	1640	1738	1838	2037	2237	...	...	...		0638	0838	1038	1238		2238	...	...	...

▷ – Additional services operate Esbjerg - Varde and v.v.

SKJERN - HOLSTEBRO 708

Operator: *MIDTTRAFIK* 2nd class only

km			Ⓐ	Ⓐ	Ⓐ	Ⓐ	Ⓐ	Ⓐ	Ⓐ		Ⓐ	Ⓐ	Ⓐ	Ⓐ	Ⓐ	Ⓐ				Ⓒ		Ⓒ	Ⓒ
0	**Skjern** d.	Ⓐ	0504	0619	0719	0801	0906	1044	1138	and	1638	1740	1911	2011	2139	2345	...	...	Ⓒ	0715	and every	2315	2347
23	Ringkøbing d.		0523	0639	0740	0822	0924	1102	1156	hourly	1656	1758	1930	2030	2156	0002	...	...		0735	**two** hours	2335	0004
71	**Holstebro** a.		0605	0720	0818	0857	1007	1140	1240	until	1735	1838	2008	2109	2234	...	...	...		0814	until	0014	...

		Ⓐ	Ⓐ	Ⓐ	Ⓐ	Ⓐ	Ⓐ	Ⓐ	Ⓐ		Ⓐ	Ⓐ	Ⓐ	Ⓐ	Ⓐ	Ⓐ				Ⓒ	Ⓒ		Ⓒ
olstebro d.	Ⓐ	0445	0534	0638	0737	0936	1021	1108	1208	and	1608	1808	1852	2025	2235	...	...	Ⓒ	...	0637	and every	2237
ingkøbing d.		0524	0620	0716	0819	1015	1102	1157	1257	hourly	1657	1848	1931	2107	2316	...	...		0648	0716	**two** hours	2316
kjern a.		0542	0637	0734	0837	1032	1120	1214	1314	until	1714	1906	1948	2125	2334	...	...		0706	0733	until	2333

ESBJERG - TØNDER - NIEBÜLL 709

Operator: *AT* 2nd class only

ESBJERG - TØNDER

km			Ⓐ	Ⓐ	Ⓐ	Ⓐ		Ⓐ	Ⓐ	Ⓐ	Ⓐ	Ⓐ				⑦	⑥	Ⓒ		Ⓒ	Ⓒ	Ⓒ	Ⓒ
0	**Esbjerg** ▷ d.	Ⓐ	0425	0531	0631	0756	and	1756	1956	2046	2156	2256	...	...	Ⓒ	...	0557	0757	and every	1957	2055	2157	2255
16	Bramming ▷ d.		0440	0546	0646	0812	hourly	1812	2012	2101	2212	2312	...	...		...	0612	0812	**two** hours	2012	2110	2212	2310
33	Ribe ▷ d.		0458	0603	0705	0831	until	1831	2031	2118	2231	2328	...	...		0635	0635	0835	until	2035	2127	2235	2327
80	**Tønder** a.		0546	0651	0754	0922		1922	2122	...	2319	...	...	...		0722	0722	0922		2122	...	2322	...

		Ⓐ	Ⓐ	Ⓐ		Ⓐ	Ⓐ	Ⓐ	Ⓐ	Ⓐ					⑥	Ⓒ		Ⓒ	Ⓒ	Ⓒ		
ønder d.	Ⓐ	0554	0657	0827	and	1927	...	2127	...	2327	...	...	...	Ⓒ	0527	0727	and every	2127	...	2327	...	...
ibe ▷ d.		0645	0750	0914	hourly	2014	2124	2214	2333	0013	...	...	...		0614	0814	**two** hours	2214	2332	0013	...	...
ramming ▷ d.		0712	0812	0932	until	2032	2142	2232	2351	...	...	...	...		0632	0832	until	2231	2351	...	...	...
sbjerg ▷ a.		0726	0826	0947		2047	2157	2247	0006	...	...	...	...		0647	0847		2247	0006	...	...	...

TØNDER - NIEBÜLL ★

7 km. Journey time: 17 – 19 minutes. Operated by Norddeutsche Eisenbahn.

rom Tønder: On ①–⑤ at 0706, 0832, 1032, 1232, 1345, 1432, 1532, 1632, 1832, 1932 and 2132; on ⑥ at 0732 and every **two** hours until 2132; on ⑦ at 0932 and every **two** hours until 2132.

rom Niebüll: On ①–⑤ at 0636, 0733, 1007, 1207, 1323, 1407, 1507, 1607, 1807, 1907 and 2107; on ⑥ at 0707 and every **two** hours until 2107; on ⑦ at 0907 and every **two** hours until 2107.

▷ – Additional services operate Esbjerg - Ribe and v.v. See Table **705** for other services Esbjerg - Bramming and v.v.

★ – Danish public holiday dates apply.

FREDERICIA - SØNDERBORG and FLENSBURG 710

See Table **705** for other *IC* services København - Odense - Kolding - Lunderskov and v.v. **Warning!** Timings of international services at København may vary by up to 9 minutes until Oct. 2.

km		*IC* 5751 Ⓐ		*Lyn* 911 Ⓐ	*Lyn* 6 Ⓐ	*IC* 5753	*IC* 5753 Ⓐ	*IC* 1191 j R	*Lyn* 919 Ⓒ	*Lyn* 19 919 Ⓐ	*Lyn* 116 919		*IC* 1183 5755 Ⓐ	*IC* 1183 5755 Ⓒ	*IC* 393 n R	*Lyn* 27 927	*Lyn* 124 927	*IC* 383 n R	*IC* 1193 j R	*Lyn* 35 935	*Lyn* 132 935		*IC* 34 5759	*IC* 395 R
	København H **700** d.	...	...	...	...	...	...	0526	...	0556	...	...	...	...	0726	0756	...	...	0926	0956	...	...	...	1126
	Odense **700** d.	...	...	0513	...	...	...	0640	0653	0710	...	...	...	...	0840	0910	...	...	1040	1110	...	...	...	1240
	Aarhus **700** d.	...	...	|	0415	...	0539	|	|	|	0645	...	0732	0739	|	|	0845	0939	|	|	1045	...	1115	|
0	**Fredericia** **705** d.	0445	...	0550	0550	0645	0645	|	0750	0750	0750	...	0845	0845	|	0950	0950	1045	|	1150	1150	...	1245	|
20	Kolding **705** d.	0458	...	0603	0603	0658	0658	0718	0803	0803	0803	...	0858	0858	0918	1003	1003	1058	1118	1203	1203	...	1258	1318
33	Lunderskov **705** d.	0506	...	0611	0611	0706	0706	|	0811	0811	0811	...	0906	0906	|	1011	1011	1106	|	1211	1211	...	1306	|
60	Vojens d.	0523	...	0628	0628	0723	0723	|	0828	0828	0828	...	0923	0923	|	1028	1028	1123	|	1228	1228	...	1323	|
95	Tinglev d.	0544	...	0649	0649	0744	0744	|	0849	0849	0849	...	0944	0944	|	1049	1049	1144	|	1249	1249	...	1344	|
136	**Sønderborg** a.	|	...	0722	0722	|	|	|	0922	0922	0922	...	|	|	|	1122	1122	|	|	1322	1322	...	|	|
110	Padborg 🏛 a.	0553	...	...	...	0753	0753	0759	...	...	...	...	0953	0953	0959	...	...	1153	1159	...	...	...	1353	1359
122	**Flensburg** 🏛 a.	0607	...	...	...	0807	0807	|	...	...	...	...	1007	1007	|	...	...	1207	|	...	...	...	1407	|
302	*Hamburg Hbf* **823** a.	...	...	...	...	...	...	1005	...	...	...	...	1206j	1206j	1204	...	...	1407	1407	...	...	...	...	1602

	Lyn 43 943	*Lyn* 140 943	*IC* 385 5761 R	*IC* 1197 j R	*Lyn* 51 951	*Lyn* 148 951	*IC* 1187 5763	*IC* 1187 j R	*IC* 397 n R	*Lyn* 59 959	*Lyn* 156 959	*IC* 5765	*IC* 1199 j R	*Lyn* 67 967	*Lyn* 164 967	*IC* 66 5767	*Lyn* 75 975	*Lyn* 472 975	*IC* 177 3374	*IC* 181 3390	*Lyn* 983	*IC* 399 m R	*IC* 399 k R
København H **700** d.	1156	...	...	1326	1356	...	...	...	1526	1556	...	...	1726	1756	...	...	1956	...	2006	2106	...	0001	0001
Odense **700** d.	1310	...	...	1440	1510	...	...	...	1640	1710	...	...	1840	1910	...	...	2110	...	2136	2236	...	0137	0137
Aarhus **700** d.	|	1245	1339	|	|	1445	...	1539	|	|	1645	1739	|	|	1845	1915	|	2045	|	|	...	|	|
redericia **705** d.	1350	1350	1445	|	1550	1550	1645	1645	|	1750	1750	1845	|	1950	1950	2045	2150	2150	2213	2323	2358	0221	0221
olding **705** d.	1403	1403	1458	1518	1603	1603	1658	1658	1718	1803	1803	1858	1918	2003	2003	2058	2203	2203	2228	2338	0011	|	|
underskov **705** d.	1411	1411	1506	|	1611	1611	1706	1706	|	1811	1811	1906	|	2011	2011	2106	2211	2211	2236	2346	0019	|	|
ojens d.	1428	1428	1523	|	1628	1628	1723	1723	|	1828	1828	1923	|	2028	2028	2123	2228	2228	...	...	0036	|	|
inglev d.	1449	1449	1544	|	1649	1649	1744	1744	|	1849	1849	1944	|	2049	2049	2144	2249	2249	...	...	0057	|	|
Sønderborg a.	1522	1522	|	|	1722	1722	|	|	|	1922	1922	|	|	2122	2122	|	2322	2322	...	...	0130	|	|
adborg 🏛 a.	...	...	1553	1559	...	...	1753	1753	1759	...	...	1953	1959	...	...	2153	...	...	...	...	...	0325	0325
lensburg 🏛 a.	...	...	1607	|	...	...	1807	1807	|	...	...	2007	|	...	...	2207	...	...	...	...	...	0340	0340
Hamburg Hbf **823** a.	...	...	1802n	1802	...	...	...	2002	2002	...	...	...	2158	...	...	...	...	...	...	...	...	0615h	0624

	Lyn 910 10	*Lyn* 910 113 Ⓐ	*Lyn* 914 14	*Lyn* 914 117 Ⓐ	*IC* 3321 116 Ⓒ	*IC* 5750 ⚒	*IC* 5750 ⑦		*Lyn* 922 22	*Lyn* 922 125	*IC* 1198 j R	*IC* 5752 31	*Lyn* 930 30	*Lyn* 930 133	*IC* 396 n R	*IC* 1186 j R	*IC* 5754 39 n	*Lyn* 938 38	*Lyn* 938 141	*IC* 1196 j R	*IC* 386 n R	*Lyn* 946 46	*Lyn* 946 149
Hamburg Hbf **823** d.	...	...	...	...	...	...	...	...	...	...	0652h	...	...	...	0856	0856	...	...	...	1053	1053	...	...
lensburg 🏛 ★ d.	...	...	...	...	...	0648	...	...	...	...	|	0848	...	...	|	1050	1048	...	...	|	1250	...	...
adborg 🏛 d.	...	...	...	...	...	0706	...	...	...	...	0859	0906	...	...	1059	1106	1106	...	...	1259	1306	...	...
Sønderborg d.	0435	0435	0535	0535	...	|	...	...	0735	0735	|	|	0935	0935	|	|	|	1135	1135	|	|	1335	1335
inglev d.	0510	0510	0610	0610	...	0716	0716	...	0810	0810	|	0916	1010	1010	|	1116	1116	1210	1210	|	1316	1410	1410
ojens d.	0529	0529	0629	0629	...	0736	0736	...	0829	0829	|	0936	1029	1029	|	1136	1136	1229	1229	|	1336	1429	1429
underskov **705** d.	0545	0545	0645	0645	0722	0753	0753	...	0845	0845	|	0953	1045	1045	|	1153	1153	1245	1245	|	1353	1445	1445
olding **705** d.	0555	0555	0655	0655	0731	0802	0802	...	0855	0855	0943	1002	1055	1055	1143	1202	1202	1255	1255	1343	1402	1455	1455
redericia **705** a.	0607	0607	0723	0723	0748	0814	0814	...	0907	0907	|	1014	1107	1107	|	1214	1214	1307	1307	|	1414	1507	1507
Aarhus **700** a.	|	0712	|	0812	|	0914	0914	...	|	1012	|	1142	|	1212	|	1318	1342	|	1412	|	1520	|	1612
Odense **700** a.	0650	...	0750	...	0823	...	...	...	0950	...	1019	...	1150	...	1219	...	...	1350	...	1340	...	1550	...
København H **700** a.	0803	...	0903	...	0955	...	...	...	1103	...	1133	...	1303	...	1333	...	...	1503	...	1533	...	1703	...

	IC 394 R	*IC* 5758 55	*Lyn* 954 54	*Lyn* 954 157		*IC* 1192 j R	*IC* 384 n R	*Lyn* 962 62	*Lyn* 962 165	*IC* 392 n R	*IC* 1182 j R	*IC* 5762 Ⓒn	*IC* 5762 71 Ⓐn	*Lyn* 970 70	*Lyn* 970 173	*IC* 3375 472	*IC* 1190 j R	*IC* 5764 177	*IC* 3379 476	*Lyn* 978	*Lyn* 978 181	*IC* 5766	*IC* 398 390 b R
Hamburg Hbf **823** d.	1253	...	...	...	...	1453	1452	...	...	1654	1652	...	...	...	...	...	1853	...	...	...	...	...	2356
lensburg 🏛 ★ d.	|	1448	...	...	...	|	1650	...	...	|	1850	1848	1848	...	...	...	|	2048	...	...	...	2248	0250
adborg 🏛 d.	1459	1506	...	...	...	1659	1706	...	...	1859	1906	1906	1906	...	...	...	2059	2106	...	...	...	2306	0340
Sønderborg d.	|	|	1535	1535	...	|	|	1734	1734	|	|	|	|	1935	1935	...	|	|	...	2135	2135	|	|
inglev d.	|	1516	1610	1610	...	|	1716	1810	1810	|	1916	1916	1916	2010	2010	...	|	2116	...	2210	2210	2316	|
ojens d.	|	1536	1629	1629	...	|	1736	1829	1829	|	1936	1936	1936	2029	2029	...	|	2136	...	2229	2229	2336	|
underskov **705** d.	|	1553	1645	1645	...	|	1753	1845	1845	|	1953	1953	1953	2045	2045	2122	|	2153	2222	2245	2245	2353	|
olding **705** d.	1543	1602	1655	1655	...	1743	1802	1855	1855	1943	2002	2002	2002	2055	2055	2131	2143	2202	2231	2255	2255	0002	|
redericia **705** a.	|	1614	1707	1707	...	|	1814	1923	1923	|	2014	2014	2014	2107	2107	2148	|	2214	2248	2307	2307	0014	0439
Aarhus **700** a.	|	1742	|	1812	...	|	1920	|	2012	|	2120	2120	2142	|	2212	|	|	2319	|	|	0012	0119	|
Odense **700** a.	1619	...	1750	...	...	1819	...	1950	...	2019	...	...	...	2150	...	2223	2219	...	2323	2348	...	...	0516
København H **700** a.	1733	...	1903	...	...	1933	...	2103	...	2133	...	...	...	2303	...	2400	2333	...	0100	...	...	...	0655a

R – 🅁 for international journeys.

a – 0700 on ⑥⑦.

b – June 17 - Sept. 11 (from Hamburg; following day from Flensburg).

h – Hamburg **Altona**.

j – June 18 - Aug. 21.

k – Aug. 21 - Sept. 11.

m – June 17 - Aug. 20.

n – Not June 18 - Aug. 21.

★ – Danish public holiday dates apply.

712 AARHUS - VIBORG - STRUER

Operator: AT 2nd class only

km	Ⓐ	Ⓐ	Ⓐ	Ⓐ	Ⓐ	Ⓐ	Ⓐ	Ⓐ	Ⓐ	Ⓐ	Ⓐ	Ⓐ	Ⓐ	Ⓐ	Ⓐ	Ⓐ	Ⓐ	Ⓐ	Ⓐ	Ⓐ	Ⓐ			
0	**Aarhus** 701 ▷ d.	0439	0523	0623	0654	0755	0854	0954	1054	1154	1254	1354	1454	1554	1654	1754	1854	1954	2054	2154	2329	...	...	...
46	Langå 701 ▷ a.	0509	0553	0653	0724	0825	0924	1024	1124	1224	1324	1424	1524	1624	1724	1824	1924	2024	2124	2224	2359	...	...	...
46	Langå ▷ d.	0514	0558	0658	0730	0830	0930	1030	1130	1230	1330	1430	1530	1630	1730	1830	1930	2030	2130	2230	0004	...	...	...
86	Viborg ▷ d.	0547	0648j	0730	0804	0904	1004	1104	1204	1304	1404	1504	1604	1704	1804	1904	2004	2104	2204	2304	0034	...	...	...
116	Skive d.	0613	0715	0753	0826	0926	1026	1126	1226	1326	1426	1526	1626	1726	1826	1926	2026	2125	2226	2326	...	...	...	...
148	**Struer** a.	0635	0737	0815	0852	0952	1052	1152	1252	1352	1452	1552	1652	1752	1852	1952	2052	...	2252	2352	...	...	...	...

Ⓒ	⑥	⑥	Ⓒ	Ⓒ	Ⓒ	Ⓒ	⑦	⑥	Ⓒ	Ⓒ	Ⓒ	Ⓒ	Ⓒ	Ⓒ	Ⓒ	⑥	⑦	Ⓒ	Ⓒ	Ⓒ	Ⓒ			
Aarhus 701 ▷ d.	0455	0555	0655	0755	0855	0955	1055	1055	1155	1255	1355	1455	1555	1655	1755	1855	1855	1955	2055	2155	2301	...	...	...
Langå 701 ▷ a.	0525	0625	0725	0825	0925	1025	1125	1125	1225	1325	1425	1525	1625	1725	1825	1925	1925	2025	2125	2225	2331	...	...	...
Langå ▷ d.	0530	0630	0730	0830	0930	1030	1130	1130	1230	1330	1430	1530	1630	1730	1830	1930	1930	2030	2130	2230	2336	...	...	...
Viborg ▷ d.	0610	0710	0810	0910	1010	1110	1210	1210	1310	1410	1510	1610	1710	1810	1910	2010	2010	2110	2210	2310	0006	...	...	...
Skive d.	0631	0734	0834	0934	1034	1134	1231	1234	1334	1434	1534	1634	1734	1834	1934	2031	2034	2134	2234	2332	...	...	...	...
Struer a.	...	0757	0857	0957	1057	1157	...	1257	1357	1457	1557	1657	1757	1857	1957	...	2057	2157	2257	2358	...	...	...	...

Ⓐ	Ⓐ	Ⓐ	Ⓐ	Ⓐ	Ⓐ	Ⓐ	Ⓐ	Ⓐ	Ⓐ	Ⓐ	Ⓐ	Ⓐ	Ⓐ	Ⓐ	Ⓐ	Ⓐ	Ⓐ	Ⓐ	Ⓐ	Ⓐ	Ⓐ			
Struer d.	...	0447	0514	0549	0641	0715	0816	0916	1016	1116	1216	1316	1416	1516	1616	1716	1816	1916	2016	...	2216	...	...	...
Skive d.	...	0509	0536	0612	0703	0740	0839	0939	1039	1139	1239	1339	1439	1539	1639	1739	1839	1940	2039	2140	2239	...	...	...
Viborg ▷ d.	0437	0533	0607	0637	0739k	0809	0909	1009	1109	1209	1309	1409	1509	1609	1709	1809	1909	2009	2109	2209	2309	...	...	...
Langå ▷ a.	0506	0610	0640	0710	0813	0843	0943	1043	1143	1243	1343	1442	1543	1643	1743	1843	1943	2043	2143	2243	2338	...	...	...
Langå 701 ▷ d.	0511	0615	0646	0715	0818	0848	0948	1048	1148	1248	1348	1448	1548	1648	1748	1848	1948	2048	2148	2248	2343	...	...	...
Aarhus 701 ▷ a.	0542	0647	0718	0746	0849	0919	1019	1119	1219	1319	1419	1519	1619	1719	1819	1919	2019	2119	2219	2319	0014	...	...	...

Ⓒ	⑥	⑥	⑥	Ⓒ	Ⓒ	Ⓒ	Ⓒ	Ⓒ	⑥	⑦	Ⓒ	Ⓒ	Ⓒ	Ⓒ	Ⓒ	Ⓒ	Ⓒ	⑥	⑦	Ⓒ	⑥	⑦	Ⓒ	
Struer d.	...	0520	...	0720	0820	0920	1020	1120	1220	...	1320	1420	1520	1620	1720	1820	1920	...	2020	2120	...	2220	2323	...
Skive d.	...	0546	0646	0746	0846	0946	1046	1146	1246	1246	1346	1446	1546	1646	1746	1846	1946	2046	2046	2146	2246	2246	2346	...
Viborg ▷ d.	0511	0611	0711	0811	0911	1011	1111	1211	1311	1311	1411	1511	1611	1711	1811	1911	2011	2111	2111	2211	2311	2311	0008	...
Langå ▷ a.	0543	0643	0743	0843	0943	1043	1144	1243	1343	1343	1443	1543	1643	1743	1843	1943	2043	2143	2143	2243	2348	2348	...	...
Langå 701 ▷ d.	0548	0648	0748	0848	0948	1048	1148	1248	1348	1348	1448	1548	1648	1748	1848	1948	2048	2148	2148	2248	2353	2353	...	...
Aarhus 701 ▷ a.	0619	0719	0819	0919	1019	1119	1219	1319	1419	1419	1519	1619	1719	1819	1919	2019	2119	2219	2219	2319	0024	0024	...	...

j – Arrives 0628. k – Arrives 0726. ▷ – Additional services operate Aarhus - Viborg and v.v.

713 AARHUS - HERNING - SKJERN and STRUER

Operator: AT; 2nd class only

km	Ⓐ	Ⓐ	Ⓐ	Ⓐ	Ⓐ	Ⓐ	Ⓐ	Ⓐ	Ⓐ	Ⓐ		Ⓐ	Ⓐ	Ⓐ	Ⓐ	Ⓐ	Ⓐ	Ⓐ	Ⓐ	Ⓐ	Ⓐ	Ⓐ	
0	**Aarhus** 700 705 d.	...	...	0453	...	0545	0622	0702	0726	0802	and at	1502	1526	1602	1702	1726	1802	1918	2018	2118	2218	2331	...
23	Skanderborg 700 705 d.	...	...	0512	...	0604	0641	0723	0745	0821	the same	1521	1545	1621	1721	1745	1821	1937	2037	2137	2237	2350	...
53	Silkeborg d.	...	...	0541	...	0641	0712	0745	0814	0849	minutes	1549	1614	1649	1749	1814	1853	2011	2111	2211	2311	0017	...
94	**Herning** a.	...	...	0624	...	0725	0754	0825	0854	0925	past each	1625	1654	1725	1825	1854	1925	2052	2152	2252	2349	0053	...
94	**Herning** 715 d.	0458	0556	0627	0656	0727	0756	0827	0902	0927	hour until	1627	1702	1727	1827	1902	...	2102	...	2302	...	...	...
	Holstebro 715 d.	|	|	0705	|	0805	|	0905	|	1005		1705	|	1805	1905	|	...	|	...	|	...	...	...
	Struer 715 a.	|	|	0718	|	0831	|	0918	|	1018		1718	|	1818	1918	|	...	|	...	|	...	...	...
136	**Skjern** a.	0535	0630	...	0730	...	0830	...	0936	...		...	1736	...	...	1936	...	2136	...	2336	...	...	...
	Esbjerg 707 a.	...	0801	...	0839	...	0940	...	1040	...		...	1838	...	...	2037	...	2237	...	...	...	...	...

Ⓒ	⑥	⑥	⑦	⑥	Ⓒ	Ⓒ	Ⓒ	Ⓒ	Ⓒ	Ⓒ	Ⓒ	Ⓒ	Ⓒ	Ⓒ	Ⓒ	Ⓒ	Ⓒ	Ⓒ	Ⓒ	Ⓒ	Ⓒ			
Aarhus 700 705 d.	...	0530	...	0630	0730	0830	0930	1030	1130	1230	1330	1430	1530	1630	1730	1830	1930	2030	2130	2230	2336	...	...	...
Skanderborg 700 705 d.	...	0550	...	0650	0750	0850	0950	1050	1150	1250	1350	1450	1550	1650	1750	1850	1950	2050	2150	2250	2355	...	...	...
Silkeborg d.	...	0617	...	0717	0817	0917	1017	1117	1217	1317	1417	1517	1617	1717	1817	1917	2017	2117	2217	2317	0026	...	...	...
Herning a.	...	0653	...	0753	0853	0953	1053	1153	1253	1353	1453	1553	1653	1753	1853	1953	2053	2153	2253	2353	0102	...	...	...
Herning 715 d.	0502	0702	0702	...	0902	...	1102	...	1302	...	1502	...	1702	...	1902	...	2102	...	2302	...	...	...	...	...
Holstebro 715 d.	|	|	|	...	|	...	|	...	|	...	|	...	|	...	|	...	|	...	|	...	...	...	...	...
Struer 715 a.	|	|	|	...	|	...	|	...	|	...	|	...	|	...	|	...	|	...	|	...	...	...	...	...
Skjern a.	0543	0737	0737	...	0937	...	1137	...	1337	...	1537	...	1737	...	1937	...	2137	...	2337	...	...	...	...	...
Esbjerg 707 a.	0638	0838	0838	...	1038	...	1238	...	1438	...	1638	...	1838	...	2038	...	2238	...	...	...	...	...	...	...

Ⓐ	Ⓐ	Ⓐ	Ⓐ	Ⓐ	Ⓐ	Ⓐ	Ⓐ	Ⓐ	Ⓐ	Ⓐ	Ⓐ	Ⓐ	Ⓐ	Ⓐ	Ⓐ		Ⓐ	Ⓐ	Ⓐ	Ⓐ	Ⓐ	Ⓐ	Ⓐ
Esbjerg 707 d.	...	...	0442	...	...	0537	...	...	0641	...	...	...	0802	...	0903	and at	...	1503	...	1603	...	1839	...
Skjern d.	...	0519	0545	...	...	0645	...	...	0745	...	...	...	0918	...	1018	the same	...	1618	...	1718	...	1939	...
Struer 715 d.	...	|	|	0532	...	|	0632	...	|	0723	...	0832	|	0932	|	minutes	1532	|	1632	|	...	|	...
Holstebro 715 d.	...	|	|	0548	...	|	0648	...	|	0748	...	0848	|	0948	|	past each	1548	|	1648	|	...	|	...
Herning 715 a.	...	0554	0623	0623	...	0723	0725	...	0823	0825	...	0926	0956	1025	1056	hour until	1625	1656	1725	1756	...	2014	...
Herning d.	0538	0600	...	0625	0702	...	0731	0802	...	0831	0902	0931	1002	1031	1102		1631	1702	1731	1802	1902	2015	2115
Silkeborg d.	0612	0637	...	0658	0747	...	0812	0847	...	0912	0947	1012	1047	1112	1147		1712	1747	1812	1847	1944	2053	2153
Skanderborg 700 705 d.	0637	0705	...	0721	0816	...	0838	0916	...	0938	1016	1038	1116	1138	1216		1738	1816	1838	1816	2011	2120	2220
Aarhus 700 705 a.	0658	0725	...	0740	0836	...	0857	0936	...	0957	1036	1057	1136	1157	1236		1757	1836	1857	1936	2031	2139	2239

	Ⓐ	Ⓐ	Ⓐ	Ⓒ	⑥	⑥	Ⓒ	⑥	⑦	Ⓒ	Ⓒ	Ⓒ	Ⓒ	Ⓒ	Ⓒ	Ⓒ	Ⓒ	Ⓒ	Ⓒ	Ⓒ	Ⓒ	Ⓒ	Ⓒ	Ⓒ	Ⓒ
Esbjerg 707 d.	2039	...	2239		...	...	...	0617	...	...	0817	...	1017	...	1217	...	1417	...	1617	...	1817	...	2017	...	2217
Skjern d.	2139	...	2345		...	0518	...	0718	0718	...	0918	...	1118	...	1318	...	1518	...	1718	...	1918	...	2118	...	2318
Struer 715 d.	|	...	|		...	|	...	|	|	...	|	...	|	...	|	...	|	...	|	...	|	...	|	...	|
Holstebro 715 d.	|	...	|		...	|	...	|	|	...	|	...	|	...	|	...	|	...	|	...	|	...	|	...	|
Herning 715 a.	2214	...	0023		...	0555	...	0755	0755	...	0955	...	1155	...	1355	...	1555	...	1755	...	1955	...	2155	...	2355
Herning d.	2215	2325	...		0502	0602	0702	0802	0802	0902	1002	1102	1202	1302	1402	1502	1602	1702	1802	1902	2002	2102	2202	2314	...
Silkeborg d.	2253	0002	...		0542	0642	0742	0842	0842	0942	1042	1142	1242	1342	1442	1542	1642	1742	1842	1942	2042	2142	2242	2353	...
Skanderborg 700 705 d.	2320	0031	...		0611	0711	0811	0911	0911	1011	1111	1211	1311	1411	1511	1611	1711	1811	1911	2011	2111	2211	2311	0020	...
Aarhus 700 705 a.	2339	0050	...		0630	0730	0830	0930	0930	1030	1130	1230	1330	1430	1530	1630	1730	1830	1930	2030	2139	2230	2330	0039	...

715 VEJLE - HERNING - STRUER

Operators: AT (2nd class only), DSB

km		2	2	2	2	2	*Lyn* 23 **723** 2	2	*Lyn* 31 **731** 2	2	2	2	*Lyn* 47 **747** 2	2	2	2	*Lyn* 63 **763** 2	2	2	2	2			
	København-H 700 d.	...	...	...	...	...	0656	...	0856	...	...	...	1256	...	...	...	1656	...	...	...	...	...	...	...
	Odense 700 d.	...	...	...	...	...	0810	...	1010	...	...	...	1410	...	...	...	1810	...	...	...	...	...	...	...
	Fredericia 700 d.	...	...	...	...	...	0846	...	1046	...	...	...	1446	...	...	...	1846	...	...	...	...	...	...	...
0	**Velje** d.	...	0503	0603	0703	0803	0904	1003	1104	1203	1303	1403	1504	1603	1703	1803	1904	2003	2103	2203	2303	...	...	...
73	Herning a.	...	0557	0657	0757	0857	0957	1057	1157	1257	1357	1457	1557	1657	1757	1857	1957	2057	2157	2257	2357	...	...	...
73	Herning 713 d.	0459	0559	0659	0759	0859	0959	1059	1159	1259	1359	1459	1559	1659	1759	1859	1959	2059	2159	2259	...	...	...	...
114	Holstebro 708 713 d.	0534	0634	0738	0834	0935	1034	1134	1234	1334	1434	1534	1634	1734	1834	1934	2034	2134	2234	2334	...	...	...	...
129	**Struer** 708 713 a.	0547	0647	0747	0847	0947	1047	1147	1247	1347	1447	1547	1647	1747	1847	1947	2047	2147	2247	2347	...	...	...	...

	2	2	2	*Lyn* **726** 26	2	2	2	*Lyn* **742** 42	2	*Lyn* **750** 50	2	2	2	*Lyn* **766** 66	2	2	2	2	2			
Struer 708 713 d.	0504	0604	0704	0804	0904	1004	1104	1204	1304	1404	1504	1604	1704	1804	1904	2004	2104	2204	2304	...	...	...
Holstebro 708 713 d.	0518	0618	0718	0818	0918	1018	1118	1218	1318	1418	1518	1618	1718	1818	1918	2018	2118	2218	2318	...	...	...
Herning 713 a.	0552	0652	0752	0852	0952	1052	1152	1252	1352	1452	1552	1652	1752	1852	1952	2052	2152	2252	2352	...	...	...
Herning d.	0558	0658	0758	0858	0958	1058	1158	1258	1358	1458	1558	1658	1758	1858	1958	2058	2158	2258	...	...	...	...
Vejle a.	0655	0755	0855	0955	1055	1155	1255	1355	1455	1555	1655	1755	1855	1955	2055	2155	2255	2356	...	...	...	...
Fredericia 700 a.	...	...	...	1017	...	...	...	1417	...	1617	...	...	...	2017	...	...	...	...	...	...	...	...
Odense 700 a.	...	...	...	1050	...	...	...	1450	...	1650	...	...	...	2050	...	...	...	...	...	...	...	...
København H 700 a.	...	...	...	1203	...	...	...	1603	...	1803	...	...	...	2203	...	...	...	...	...	...	...	...

STRUER - THISTED 716

Operator: *AT* 2nd class only

km			Ⓐ	Ⓐ	Ⓐ	Ⓐ		Ⓐ	Ⓐ	Ⓐ	Ⓐ	Ⓐ	Ⓐ	Ⓐ	Ⓐ	Ⓐ			⑥	Ⓒ		Ⓒ	Ⓒ	
0	**Struer** d.	Ⓐ	0415	0514	0606	0708	...	1007	1207	1307	1407	1507	1607	1807	2007	2207	...	Ⓒ	0509	0704	and every	2104	2220	...
74	**Thisted** a.		0532	0634	0737	0839	...	1124	1324	1424	1524	1624	1724	1924	2124	2324	...		0625	0821	**two** hours until	2221	2340	...

		Ⓐ	Ⓐ	Ⓐ	Ⓐ		Ⓐ	Ⓐ	Ⓐ	Ⓐ	Ⓐ	Ⓐ	Ⓐ	Ⓐ	Ⓐ			⑥	Ⓒ		Ⓒ	Ⓒ	Ⓒ
Thisted d.	Ⓐ	0537	0639	0742	0844	...	1134	1329	1429	1529	1629	1735	1935	2135	2329	...	Ⓒ	0631	0830	and every	2030	2229	2346
Struer a.		0653	0755	0858	1000	...	1254	1454	1554	1654	1745	1854	2054	2254	0045	...		0751	0951	**two** hours until	2151	2346	0102

KØBENHAVN - NYKØBING 720

km			Ⓒ	Ⓐ	Ⓐ	Ⓐ	Ⓐ	Ⓒ	Ⓐ	Ⓐ	Ⓒ		Ⓐ		Ⓐ								
0	**København** H ...... 700 704 ▷ d.	0023	0422	0507	...	0607	...	0622	0637	0643	...	0707	0743	0807	0843	0907	0943	1007	1043	1107	1143	1207	1243
20	Høje Taastrup ...... 700 704 ▷ d.	0037	0436	0521	...	0621	...	0636	0651	|	...	0721	|	0821	|	0921	|	1021	|	1121	|	1221	|
31	Roskilde ...... 700 704 ▷ d.	0050	0449	0532	...	0632	...	0649	0702	|	...	0732	|	0832	|	0932	|	1032	|	1132	|	1232	|
64	Ringsted ...... 700 ▷ d.	0110	0509	0554	...	0654	...	0709	0724	0717	...	0754	0817	0854	0917	0954	1017	1054	1117	1154	1217	1254	1317
91	Næstved ...... ▷ d.	0125	0524	0610	0614	0710	0714	0724	0740	0731	0732	0810	0831	0910	0931	1010	1031	1110	1131	1210	1231	1310	1331
118	Vordingborg ...... d.	...	...	...	0630	...	0730	...	...	0745	0748	...	0845	...	0945	...	1045	...	1145	...	1245	...	1345
147	**Nykøbing** (Falster) ...... ⊙ a.	...	...	...	0652	...	0752	...	...	0801	0810	...	0901	...	1001	...	1101	...	1201	...	1301	...	1401

						Ⓐ			Ⓐ			Ⓐ			Ⓐ								
København H ...... 700 704 ▷ d.	1307	1343	1407	1443	1507	1537	1543	1607	1637	1643	1707	1737	1743	1807	1837	1843	1907	1943	2007	2043	2143	2243	2343
Høje Taastrup ...... 700 704 ▷ d.	1321	|	1421	|	1521	1551	|	1621	1751	|	1721	1751	|	1821	1851	|	1921	|	2021	|	|	|	|
Roskilde ...... 700 704 ▷ d.	1332	|	1432	|	1532	1602	|	1632	1802	|	1732	1802	|	1832	1902	|	1932	|	2032	|	|	|	|
Ringsted ...... 700 ▷ d.	1354	1417	1454	1517	1554	1624	1617	1654	1824	1717	1754	1824	1817	1854	1924	1917	1954	2017	2054	2115	2217	2317	0017
Næstved ...... ▷ d.	1410	1431	1510	1531	1610	1640	1631	1710	1840	1731	1810	1840	1831	1910	1940	1931	2010	2031	2110	2129	2234	2334	0034
Vordingborg ...... d.	...	1445	...	1545	...	...	1645	...	...	1745	...	...	1845	...	...	1945	...	2045	...	2141	2250	2350	0050
Nykøbing (Falster) ...... ⊙ a.	...	1501	...	1601	...	...	1701	...	...	1801	...	...	1901	...	...	2001	...	2101	...	2159	2311	0011	0111

	Ⓐ	Ⓐ	Ⓐ	Ⓒ	Ⓒ	Ⓐ	Ⓐ		Ⓐ	Ⓒ	Ⓐ	Ⓒ	Ⓐ	Ⓐ	Ⓐ								
Nykøbing (Falster) ...... ⊙ d.	...	0438	...	0448	...	0508	...	0538	...	0548	0601	...	...	0701	0801	...	0901	...	1001	...	1101	...	1201
Vordingborg ...... d.	...	0459	...	0509	...	0529	...	0559	...	0609	0617	...	...	0717	0817	...	0917	...	1017	...	1117	...	1217
Næstved ...... ▷ d.	0432	0515	0519	0525	0533	0545	0549	0615	0619	0625	0631	0633	0649	0731	0831	0849	0931	0949	1031	1049	1131	1149	1231
Ringsted ...... 700 ▷ d.	0448	...	0535	...	0548	...	0605	...	0635	...	0645	0648	0705	0745	0845	0905	0945	1005	1045	1105	1145	1205	1245
Roskilde ...... 700 704 ▷ d.	0510	...	0557	...	0610	...	0627	...	0657	...	|	0710	0727	|	|	0927	|	1027	|	1127	|	1227	|
Høje Taastrup ...... 700 704 ▷ d.	0521	...	0606	...	0621	...	0636	...	0706	...	|	0721	0736	|	|	0936	|	1036	|	1136	|	1236	|
København H ...... 700 704 ▷ a.	0537	...	0622	...	0637	...	0652	...	0722	...	0718	0737	0752	0818	0918	0952	1018	1052	1118	1152	1218	1252	1318

						Ⓐ			Ⓐ			Ⓐ											
Nykøbing (Falster) ...... ⊙ d.	...	1301	...	1401	...	...	1501	...	...	1601	...	...	1701	...	1801	...	1901	...	2001	...	2049	2149	2320
Vordingborg ...... d.	...	1317	...	1417	...	...	1517	...	...	1617	...	...	1717	...	1817	...	1917	...	2017	...	2110	2211	2343
Næstved ...... ▷ d.	1249	1331	1349	1431	1449	1519	1531	1549	1619	1631	1649	1719	1731	1749	1831	1849	1931	1949	2031	2049	2128	2229	0001
Ringsted ...... 700 ▷ d.	1305	1345	1405	1445	1505	1535	1545	1605	1635	1645	1705	1735	1745	1805	1845	1905	1945	2005	2045	2105	2145	2245	0017
Roskilde ...... 700 704 ▷ d.	1327	|	1427	|	1527	1557	|	1627	1657	|	1727	1757	|	1827	|	1927	|	2027	|	2127	|	|	|
Høje Taastrup ...... 700 704 ▷ d.	1336	|	1436	|	1536	1606	|	1636	1706	|	1736	1806	|	1836	|	1936	|	2036	|	2136	|	|	|
København H ...... 700 704 ▷ a.	1352	1418	1452	1518	1552	1622	1618	1652	1722	1718	1752	1822	1818	1852	1918	1952	2018	2052	2118	2152	2218	2318	0049

▷ – Additional trains run København - Næstved and v.v.

⊙ – **NYKØBING - NAKSKOV** and v.v. Journey time: 46–47 minutes. Operator: Lokaltog A/S.
All trains call at Maribo (25 minutes from Nykøbing / 22 minutes from Nakskov). Local 🚌 720R operates Maribo - Rødby Færge (for ferry services to / from Puttgarden in Table **2375**); operates every 30 minutes on Ⓐ, hourly on Ⓒ, connecting with most rail services listed below (journey time: 40 minutes).
From Nykøbing on Ⓐ at 0506, 0536 and every 30 minutes until 1906, 1936; then 2007, 2107, 2207, 2317 and 0017.
From Nykøbing on Ⓒ at 0706, 0806 and hourly until 2206; then 2317 and 0017.
From Nakskov on Ⓐ at 0410, 0438, 0508 and every 30 minutes until 1838, 1908; then 2008, 2055, 2224 and 2319.
From Nakskov on Ⓒ at 0608, 0708 and hourly until 2008; then 2055, 2224 and 2319.

AALBORG - SKAGEN and HIRTSHALS 728

Nordjyske Jernbaner (2nd class only)

km			Ⓐ	Ⓐ	Ⓐ	Ⓐ	Ⓐ	Ⓐ	Ⓐ		Ⓐ	Ⓐ	Ⓐ	Ⓐ	Ⓐ	Ⓐ	Ⓐ	Ⓐ	Ⓐ	Ⓐ	Ⓐ	Ⓐ	Ⓐ	Ⓐ
0	**Aalborg** d.	Ⓐ	...	...	0404	...	...	0514	0544	★♥	1614	1644	1714	...	1814	...	1914	...	2014	...	2114	...	2214	...
48	Hjørring a.		...	...	0439	...	...	0549	0619	and at	1649	1719	1749	...	1849	...	1949	...	2049	...	2149	...	2249	...
48	Hjørring d.		...	...	0454	0455	0524	0554	0627	the same	1654	1727	1754	1755	1854	1902	1957	2002	2057	2102	2157	2202	2257	2302
66	**Hirtshals** a.		...	...	|	0517	|	|	0649	minutes	|	1750	|	1819	|	1924	|	2024	|	2124	|	2224	|	2324
85	**Frederikshavn** a.		...	...	0526	...	0556	0626	...	past each	1726	...	1826	...	1925	...	2025	...	2125	...	2225	...	2325	...
85	**Frederikshavn** d.		0435	0505	0535	...	0605	0635	...	hour until	1735	...	1838	...	1938	...	2038	...	2138	...	2238	...	2338	...
125	**Skagen** a.		0512	0542	0612	...	0642	0712	...		1812	...	1915	...	2015	...	2115	...	2215	...	2315	...	0015	...

		Ⓒ	Ⓒ	⑥	Ⓒ	Ⓒ		Ⓒ	Ⓒ
Aalborg d.	Ⓒ	0414	...	...	0614	...		2214	...
Hjørring a.		0449	...	...	0649	...	and at	2249	...
Hjørring d.		0457	0557	0602	0657	0702	the same	2257	2302
Hirtshals a.		|	|	0624	|	0724	minutes	|	2324
Frederikshavn a.		0525	0625	...	0725	...	past each	2325	...
Frederikshavn d.		0538	0638	...	0738	...	hour until	2338	...
Skagen a.		0615	0715	...	0815	...		0015	...

		Ⓐ	Ⓐ	Ⓐ	Ⓐ		Ⓐ	Ⓐ	Ⓐ	Ⓐ
Skagen d.	Ⓐ	...	...	...	0520	♣	...	1720	...	1750
Frederikshavn a.		...	...	...	0600	and at	...	1800	...	1830
Frederikshavn d.		...	0512	...	0612	the same	...	1812	...	1842
Hirtshals d.		0518	|	0549	|	minutes	1750	|	1829	|
Hjørring a.		0543	0545	0613	0645	past each	1813	1845	1851	1915
Hjørring d.		...	0549	0619	0649	hour until	1819	1849	...	1919
Aalborg a.		...	0627	0657	0727		1857	1927	...	1957

	Ⓐ	Ⓐ	Ⓐ	Ⓐ	Ⓐ	Ⓐ	Ⓐ	Ⓐ	Ⓐ	Ⓐ	Ⓐ	Ⓐ	
Skagen d.	...	1842	...	1942	...	2042	...	2142	...	2242	...	2342	...
Frederikshavn a.	...	1919	...	2019	...	2119	...	2219	...	2319	...	0019	...
Frederikshavn d.	...	1927	...	2027	...	2127	...	2227	...	2327	...	0027	...
Hirtshals d.	1929	|	2029	|	2129	|	2229	|	2329	|	0029	|	...
Hjørring a.	1951	1955	2051	2055	2151	2155	2251	2255	2351	2355	0051	0055	...
Hjørring d.	...	2002	...	2102	...	2202	...	2302	...	0002	...	...	...
Aalborg a.	...	2042	...	2142	...	2242	...	2342	...	0042	...	...	...

		Ⓒ	⑥	Ⓒ	Ⓒ	Ⓒ		Ⓒ	Ⓒ	Ⓒ	Ⓒ
Skagen d.	Ⓒ	...	...	...	...	0642		...	2242	...	2342
Frederikshavn a.		...	...	...	...	0719	and at	...	2319	...	0019
Frederikshavn d.		0527	...	0627	...	0727	the same	...	2327	...	0027
Hirtshals d.		|	0629	|	0729	|	minutes	2329	|	0029	|
Hjørring a.		0555	0651	0655	0851	0755	past each	2351	2355	0051	0055
Hjørring d.		0602	...	0702	...	0802	hour until	...	0002	...	...
Aalborg a.		0642	...	0742	...	0842		...	0042	...	...

★ – Hjørring d. 0857 / 0957 / 1057 / 1157 / 1257 (not 0854 / 0954 / 1054 / 1154 / 1254).

♥ – Additional trains on Ⓐ: Hjørring - Frederikshavn - Skagen at 0624, 0724, 1324, 1424, 1524 and 1624 (departing Frederikshaven at 0705, 0805, 1405, 1505, 1605 and 1705); Frederikshavn - Skagen at 1305; Hjørring - Hirtshals at 0002, 0427, 0527, 0555, 0655, 0755, 1355, 1455, 1555 and 1655.

♣ – Additional trains on Ⓐ: Skagen - Frederikshavn - Hjørring at 0550, 0650, 1350, 1450, 1550 and 1650 (departing Frederikshavn at 0642, 0742, 1442, 1542, 1642 and 1742); Skagen - Frederikshavn at 0042, 0750 and 0850; Hirtshals - Hjørring at 0618, 0718, 0818, 1419, 1519, 1619, 1719 and 1819.

TRAIN SERVICES IN DENMARK ON AND AROUND PUBLIC HOLIDAYS

On the following dates the service provided is as per the day of the week indicated

Date	DSB	Arriva	Date	DSB	Arriva	Date	DSB	Arriva
Dec. 23	⑤	⑤	Apr. 13	⑤	⑦	May 12	⑤	⑤
Dec. 24	⑥	⑦	Apr. 14	⑦	⑦	May 13	⑦	⑦
Dec. 25	⑦	⑦	Apr. 15	⑦	⑥	May 25	⑤	⑦
Dec. 26	⑦	⑦	Apr. 16	⑥	⑦	May 26	⑦	⑦
Dec. 31	⑥	⑦	Apr. 17	⑦	⑦	June 5	⑦	⑥
Jan. 1	⑦	⑦	Apr. 18	⑦	⑦	June 6	⑦	⑦

ICELAND

There are no railways in Iceland but bus services serve most major settlements. Principal services along road number 1 around the country and some other important routes are shown below. Buses have scheduled stops in all settlements (often at N1 filling stations) but stops at other points along the route are possible with prior agreement with the operator. For comprehensive information on all bus routes, including local services and ferries, see www.publictransport.is and the websites of operators (see bottom of page). Confirm all timings with operators as schedules may change at short notice. Buses may be cancelled, delayed, advanced or diverted owing to adverse weather conditions, particularly in winter. For current coronavirus regulations, see www.covid.is.

Scheduled public bus services (*STR*, *SVF*, *FAS*) and buses to Keflavík airport run all year, though there are no long-distance *STR* services on Dec. 24, 25, 31, Jan. 1. Tickets can be purchased from the driver or obtained beforehand. Travelling a full circle around the country by bus is only possible in summer and involves use of local buses in the east.

Scheduled touristic buses operated by private companies (*RE*, *TRX* and *SCA*) run only in summer, serving a few popular tourist destinations in the highlands. These have to be pre-booked, although tickets can also be obtained from the driver if there is space available. Tourist excursions and day tours to other destinations are available all year.

Public holidays in 2022: Jan. 1, Apr. 14, 15, 17, 18, 21, May 1, 26, June 5, 6, 17, Aug. 1, Dec. 25, 26.
No services on Dec. 25, Jan. 1. Only a limited service runs on Dec. 24, 31.

729 PRINCIPAL BUS SERVICES

REYKJAVÍK - AKUREYRI - EGILSSTADIR

km	*STR Route 57*		④‡	x	⑥‡	⑥‡	†		Ⓑ
0	Reykjavík (BSÍ terminal) ■ ▷ d.	...	*0832*c	*0832*c	*0832*c	...	0840	...	*1658*c
7	Reykjavík (Mjódd) ■ ▷ d.	...	0900	0900	0900	...	0900	...	1730
89	Borgarnes (N1) ▷ a.	...	1023	1023	1023b	...	1023	...	1853
89	Borgarnes (N1) d.	...	...	1028	...	1028	1028	...	1858
426	Akureyri (Hof) a.	...	...	1529	...	1529	1529	...	2359
	STR Route 56 ⊙	v							
426	Akureyri (Hof) d.	0800	...	...	...	...	...	...	...
513	Reykjahlíd (Mývatn) N1 d.	0915	...	...	...	...	...	...	...
676	Egilsstadir (Campsite) d.	1122	...	...	...	...	...	...	...

STR Route 56 ⊙				v				
Egilsstadir (Campsite) d.	...	...	...	1230	...	...	...	...
Reykjahlíd (Mývatn) N1 d.	...	...	...	1436	...	...	...	...
Akureyri (Hof) a.	...	...	...	1551b	...	...	...	...
STR Route 57	Ⓑ		④‡		y			
Akureyri (Hof) d.	1015	...	...	...	1620	...	...	...
Borgarnes (N1) a.	1518	...	...	...	2123	...	...	...
Borgarnes (N1) ▷ d.	1523	...	2128	...	2128	...	...	...
Reykjavík (Mjódd) ■ ▷ a.	1644	...	2249	...	2249	...	...	...
Reykjavík (BSÍ terminal) ■ ▷ a.	*1702*c	...	*2301*c	...	*2301*c	...	...	...

EGILSSTADIR - HÖFN

No winter service Breiddalsvík - Djúpivogur and v.v.

km	*STR Route 91*	Ⓐ	Ⓒ					Ⓐ	
0	Egilsstadir (Campsite) d.	0902	1012	...	...	...	...	1617	...
36	Reydarfjördur (Molinn) a.	0935	1045	...	...	...	...	1655	...
	STR Route 92	▬	▬		zE		Ⓐ		
36	Reydarfjördur (Molinn) d.	...	...	...	1200	...	1624	...	...
56	Fáskrúdsfjördur (Kirkjugardur) d.	...	...	...	1225f	...	1640	...	...
105	Breiddalsvík (Kaupfjelagid) a.	...	...	...	1305b	...	1730	...	...
	STR Route 94	wR	④R	†R		zA			†A
105	Breiddalsvík (Kaupfjelagid) d.	...	...	...	...	1325	...	...	1800
166	Djúpivogur (Hótel Framtíd) d.	0810	1245	1330	...	1430	...	...	1900
269	Höfn í Hornafirdi ★ a.	0930	1405	1445	...	1545	...	...	2020

STR Route 94			wR	zA		④R	†R	†A
Höfn í Hornafirdi ★ d.	...	...	1012t	1012	...	1442t	1525t	1520
Djúpivogur (Hótel Framtíd) d.	...	...	1130	1230	...	1557	1634	1700
Breiddalsvík (Kaupfjelagid) a.	...	...	▬	1325b	...	▬	...	1800
STR Route 92	Ⓐ				zE			
Breiddalsvík (Kaupfjelagid) d.	0620	...	...	...	1330	...	...	...
Fáskrúdsfjördur (Kirkjugardur) d.	0707	...	...	...	1410f	...	...	...
Reydarfjördur (Molinn) a.	0726b	...	...	...	1436b	...	...	...
STR Route 91		Ⓐ	Ⓒ			Ⓐ		
Reydarfjördur (Molinn) d.	...	0733	0843	...	...	1453	...	...
Egilsstadir (Campsite) a.	...	0806	0916	...	...	1526	...	...

Additional services, operated by *SVF*, run on Ⓐ Reydarfjördur - Fáskrúdsfjördur and v.v. (route 1): From Reydarfjördur at 0757, 1506, 1624, 1744 and 1917; from Fáskrúdsfjördur at 0717, 0820, 1430, 1550, 1720 and 1810. Additional services, operated by *SVF*, run on Ⓐ Fáskrúdsfjördur - Breiddalsvík and v.v. (route 2): From Fáskrúdsfjördur at 0715, 1645 and 1815 **g**; from Breiddalsvík at 0630, 1600 **g** and 1730 **g**.

HÖFN - REYKJAVÍK

km	*operator*	*RE*	*STR*	*STR*	*STR*	*STR*	*STR*	*STR*	*RE*
	route number	HB03	51	51	51	51	51	51	HB03
		B 🅁	†	Ⓒ	Ⓒ	u	Ⓐ	Ⓐ	B 🅁
0	Höfn í Hornafirdi ★ d.	...	1025	...	...	1155	...	...	...
79	Jökulsárlón glacier lagoon d.	...	1125	...	...	1255	...	...	...
135	Skaftafell (Service centre) d.	...	1220	...	...	1350	...	...	...
274	Vík í Mýrdal (N1) a.	...	1415b	...	...	1545b	...	...	...
274	Vík í Mýrdal (N1) d.	...	...	1442	...	...	1600	...	...
308	Skógar (Waterfall) ● d.	1015	...	1507	...	...	1625	...	...
357	Hvolsvöllur (N1) ● ▷ d.	1115r	...	1547	...	...	1705	...	1750
405	Selfoss (N1) ▷ d.	...	...	1627b	1629	...	1745b	1750	1830
458	Reykjavík (Mjódd) ■ ▷ a.	...	...	...	1724	...	...	1845	|
465	Reykjavík (BSÍ) ■ ▷ a.	...	...	...	*1802*c	...	...	*1902*c	1930

operator	*RE*	*STR*	*STR*	*STR*	*STR*	*STR*	*STR*	
route number	HB03	51	51	51	51	51	51	
	B 🅁	Ⓒ	Ⓒ	†	Ⓐ	Ⓐ	u	
Reykjavík (BSÍ) ■ ▷ d.	0700	*1102*c	...	...	*1232*c	...	...	...
Reykjavík (Mjódd) ■ ▷ d.	|	130	...	...	1300	...	...	...
Selfoss (N1) ▷ d.	0740	1224b	1227	...	1354b	1357	...	...
Hvolsvöllur (N1) ● ▷ d.	0900	...	1307	...	...	1437	...	...
Skógar (Waterfall) ● d.	0945	...	1342	...	...	1512	...	...
Vík í Mýrdal (N1) a.	...	...	1412b	...	...	1542b	...	...
Vík í Mýrdal (N1) d.	...	...	...	1445	...	...	1615	...
Skaftafell (Service centre) d.	...	...	...	1650	...	...	1820	...
Jökulsárlón glacier lagoon d.	...	...	...	1735	...	...	1905	...
Höfn í Hornafirdi ★ a.	...	...	...	1835	...	...	2005	...

OTHER SERVICES

Reykjavík - Keflavík Airport: *50 km*, journey ±50 minutes. From BSÍ terminal ■: *flybus*, operator *RE*, connecting with all flights. From Klettagardar 4: *Grayline*, operator *GL*.
From Reykjavík Terminal, Skógarhlíd 10: *Airport Direct Economy*, operator *AD*. All operators offer connecting shuttle services to / from hotels and other places in the Reykjavík area.
Additional stopping services: *STR* route 55, BSÍ (Vatnsmýrarvegur ■) - KEF Airport and v.v. on Ⓐ peak hours only. During off-peak hours and on Ⓒ route 55 only operates Hafnarfjördur (Fjördur) – KEF Airport and v.v. From Reykjavík, use *STR* city route 1 from Hlemmur via Gamla Hringbraut ■ direction Hfj. Vellir and change to route 55 at Hafnarfjördur (Fjördur). 7 – 13 services per day with a total journey time of 75 – 90 minutes.

Reykjavík - Blue Lagoon: 48 *km*, journey ±45 minutes. From BSÍ terminal ■: operator *RE*, daily, 🅁. From Reykjavík Terminal (Skógarhlíd 10) ■: 'Destination Blue Lagoon', operator *BL*, daily, 🅁. Both operators also provide infrequent services KEF Airport - Blue Laggon and v.v.

Egilsstadir - Seydisfjördur: 27 *km*, journey ±40 minutes, *STR* route 93, operated by *FAS*. Services connect with Smyril Line ferry (Table **2285**). Confirm departure point with operator.
Summer (June 10 - Aug. 19, 2021◇): From **Egilsstadir** (Campsite) 0900Ⓐ, 1005⑥, 1050④, 1640Ⓐ. From **Seydisfjördur** (Herdubreid, Austurvegur 4) 0745Ⓐ, 0905⑥, 1000④ **s**, 1430Ⓐ.
Winter (Aug. 20, 2021 - May 31, 2022): From **Egilsstadir** (Campsite) 0900Ⓐ, 1010⑥, 1105② **D**, 1615Ⓐ. From **Seydisfjördur** (Herdubreid, Austurvegur 4) 0745Ⓐ, 0920⑥, 1015② **D s**, 1515Ⓐ.

LAUGAVEGUR HIKING TRAIL. **Reykjavík - Landmannalaugar** (*215 km*, journey ± 4 h 15 m): *RE Highland Bus* daily June 15 - Sept. 11, 2022; *TRX Highland Bus* daily June 17 - Sept. 7, 2022.
Reykjavík - Thórsmörk (*158 km*, journey ± 4 h 30 m): *RE Highland Bus* daily June 3 - Sept. 15, 2022; *TRX Highland Bus* daily June 17 - Sept. 10, 2022. **Hvolsvöllur - Thórsmörk - Skógar**: *SCA* daily May 1 - Oct. 31, 2022. 🅁 on all routes with operation dependent on weather and highland road conditions (*RE* services are cancelled if no bookings received 24 hours before departure).

A – May 15 - ca. Aug. 15, 2022.
B – June 15 - Sept. 11, 2022 (service cancelled if no bookings received 24 hours before departure).
D – ② Aug. 24 - Sept. 28, 2021; ② Apr. 5 - May 31, 2022.
E – June 15 - Aug. 15, 2021. Awaiting confirmation of 2022 service
R – Aug. 16, 2021 - May 14, 2022.

b – Passengers connecting with onward services should inform operator / bus driver.
c – Connection with *STR* city route 3 from/to Gamla Hringbraut (next to BSÍ), change at Mjódd (see ■).
f – Fáskrúdsfjördur Búdavegur.
g – Runs on demand only. ✆ +354 892 0955 at least six hours before departure.
r – Continues to Reykjavík at 1750 (see later column).
s – Seydisfjördur Smyril Line terminal.

t – Höfn campsite (450 m north of swimming pool).
u – ①②④⑤ (not holidays)
v – ①②⑤†.
w – ①③⑤.
x – ①②③⑤ (not holidays).
y – ①②③⑤⑥⑦ (also holidays).
z – ①③④⑤.

‡ – Not holidays.
★ – Höfn swimming pool.
● – Additional *SCA* services operate.
▷ – Additional *STR* services operate.
◇ – Awaiting confirmation of 2022 service.
⊙ – Operated by *SBA*.

N1 – Bus stop is at N1 filling station.

■ – Reykjavík terminals

BSÍ / Umferdarmidstödin (city centre, south side)
- ○ BSÍ terminal (*RE*, also certain *STR* services on route 57)
- ○ bus stop "BSÍ" 50 m north of BSÍ at Vatnsmýrarvegur (STR route 55)
- ○ bus stop "Gamla Hringbraut" 100 m north of BSÍ (STR city buses)

Hlemmur (*STR* city services; city centre, east side)

Mjódd bus terminal (7 km southeast of city centre)
- ○ *STR* long-distance routes 51, 52, 27 and *STR* city services 3, 11, 12, 17.

Connections city centre - BSÍ - Mjódd: City service 3 runs every 30 minutes from Hlemmur to Sel/Fell via Gamla Hringbraut (at BSÍ) and Mjódd. Journey to Mjódd 25 – 32 minutes from Hlemmur, 14 – 21 minutes from Gamla Hringbraut. Connections Mjódd - city centre: *STR* city service 3 (direction Hlemmur), departs at xx21 and xx51 past each hour. Note: no city services on ⑦ and public holiday mornings before 0950.

Operators:

AD Airport Direct ✆ +354 497 8000 www.airportdirect.is
BL Destination Blue Lagoon ✆ +354 420 8800 www.destinationbluelagoon.is
FAS Ferdathjónusta Austurlands ✆ +354 472 1515 www.straeto.is
GL Gray Line Iceland ✆ +354 540 1313 www.grayline.is
RE Reykjavik Excursions ✆ +354 580 5400 www.re.is or www.ioyo.is
SBA SBA - Nordurleid ✆ +354 550 0700 www.sba.is
SCA Southcoast Adventure ✆ +354 867 3535 www.southadventure.is
STR Straetó ✆ +354 540 2700 www.straeto.is
SVF Straetisvagnar Fjardabyggdar ✆ +354 892 0955 www.fjardabyggd.is
TRX TREX ✆ +354 587 6000 www.trex.is

SWEDEN

SEE MAP PAGE 337

Operators: Most services are operated by Swedish State Railways (SJ): www.sj.se. There are, however, a number of other operators that run services and these are indicated by their initials in the relevant table heading, or at the top of each train column where more than one operator runs services on the same route.

AEX – Arlanda Express | *FLX* – FlixTrain | *IB* – Inlandsbanan AB | *MTR* – MTRX
NT – Norrtåg | *Øtåg* – Øresundståg | *ST* – Snälltåget | *Tågab* – Tågåkeriet i Bergslagen AB
Vy – Vy Tåg AB

The Regional Public Transport Authority is responsible for many local services, known collectively as Länstrafik (*LT*). Those shown within these pages are abbreviated as follows:

Krösa – Krösatågen | *M* – Mälartåg | Skåne – Skånetrafiken | *V* – Västtågen
VTAB – Värmlandstrafik | *XT* – X-Trafik

Services: Trains convey first and second classes of accommodation, unless otherwise shown. The fastest SJ trains are classified *Snabbtåg (Sn)* and *InterCity (IC)*. On overnight trains, sleeping cars (🛏) offer the following accommodation: First-class compartments (one or two berths) with shower and WC. These can only be booked as a private compartment and include breakfast in either the bistro car or at a nearby hotel at your destination. Second-class compartments (three berths) have shared shower and WC facilities in each coach. These can be booked as a private compartment for one, two or three persons, or as a single berth in a shared compartment (male or female). Couchette cars (▬) have six berths which can be booked as a single berth in a shared compartment or as a private compartment when four or more passengers are travelling together.

Timings: **Valid June 12 - December 10, 2022** (unless otherwise stated). Services may be amended on and around the dates of public holidays. On June 23 most services run as on ⑤. On June 24 most services run as on ⑥. On June 25 most services run as on ⑦. On Nov. 5 services may run as on ⑥ or ⑦ depending on the region (please check locally).

Catering: Most long-distance services convey a bistro-car (🍷) serving drinks, snacks and light meals. First-class tickets on *Sn* services includes access to complimentary tea, coffee and snacks with breakfast also served on departures before 0900. First-class tickets on *MTR* services include a complimentary meal and drinks.

Tickets: Travellers should ensure they are in possession of a valid ticket before joining a train as penalties can be severe. Local operators issue tickets on board the train where stations have no ticket machines.

Reservations: Seat reservation is compulsory on all *Snabbtåg*, *InterCity*, *MTRX*, *Snälltåget* and overnight trains. Reserved seats are not labelled and, if occupied, should be claimed by presenting the seat ticket on the train.

STOCKHOLM - MALMÖ - KØBENHAVN 730

For other regional and *IC* services Stockholm - Norrköping - Linköping, see next page. **Warning!** Subject to alteration Sept. 18 – 28.
Trains in this table are not available for local journeys Stockholm - Södertälje Syd and v.v. or København Lufthavn ✈ - København H and v.v.

km	All trains Ⓡ	*Sn*	*Sn*	*Sn*	*Sn*	*ST*	*Sn*	*ST*	*Sn*	*Sn*	*Sn*	*Sn*	*ST*	*Sn*	*Sn*	*Sn*	*Sn*	*Sn*	*Sn*	*Sn*	*ST*	*Sn*	*Sn*	*Sn*	*Sn*
		517	**519**	**521**	**523**	**3993**	**525**	**3941**	**527**	**529**	**531**	**533**	**3931**	**535**	**537**	**537**	**539**	**539**	**541**	**541**	**301**	**513**	**505**	**543**	**543**
		🍷	🍷	🍷	🍷	✕	🍷	✕	🍷	🍷	🍷	🍷	✕	🍷	🍷	🍷	🍷	🍷	🍷	🍷	✕	🍷	🍷	🍷	🍷
		①	①–⑤	①–⑥	Ⓑ	⑥															Y	Ⓑ	Ⓑ	Ⓑ	Ⓑ
		n	n			w					K		G	Q	n	R	R	n	n	R	★	n	n	R	n
0	**Stockholm** Central ... d.	0422	0519f	0617	0720	0725	0821	0900	0922	1022	1121	1220	1224	1321	1422	1422	1522	1522	1612	1612	1615	1636	1659	1718	1718
36	Södertälje Syd ... d.	0441	|	0636	|	0745	|	0920	0941	|	1141	|	|	1340	|	|	|	|	1632	1632	1635	1656	|	|	|
162	**Norrköping** ... 754 d.	0539	0633	0734	0833	0852	0935	1027	1039	1135	1239	1334	1350	1438	1535	1535	1635	1635	1732	1732	1740	1802	|	1836	1836
209	Linköping ... 754 d.	0603	0657	0758	0857	0918	0959	1053	1103	1159	1303	1358	1419	1502	1559	1559	1659	1659	1758	1758	1806	1828	|	1900	1900
241	**Mjölby** ... d.	|	|	0814	|	|	1015	|	|	1215	|	1414	|	|	1615	1615	|	|	1814	1814	|	1849	|	|	|
277	Tranås ... d.	|	|	|	0925	|	|	|	|	|	|	|	|	|	|	|	|	|	|	|	|	1908	|	|	|
329	**Nässjö** ... 733 d.	0654	0750	0854	0953	1016	1054	1149	1154	1254	1354	1454	1518	1554	1654	1654	1751	1751	1853	1853	1906	1941j	|	1951	1951
	Jönköping ... 733 a.	|	|	|	|	|	|	|	|	|	|	|	|	|	|	|	|	|	|	|	|	2013	|	|	|
416	Alvesta ... 746 d.	0727	0823	0927	1026	1056	1127	1224	1230	1327	1427	1527	1601	1627	1727	1727	1824	1824	1926	1926	1945	...	1955	2024	2024
463	Älmhult ... 746 d.	|	0842	|	|	|	|	|	|	|	|	|	|	|	|	|	1843	1843	|	|	|	...	|	|	|
514	Hässleholm ... 745 746 a.	0804	0904	1004	1104	1153	1204	1305s	1308	1404	1504	1604	1648s	1704	1805	1805	1905	1905	2003	2003	2025	...	2032	2103	2103
581	Lund ... 745 746 ● a.	0834s	0934s	1034	1134	1226s	1234	1340s	1341s	1434	1534s	1634	1725s	1734s	1834	1834s	1934	1934s	2034	2034s	2100	...	2105s	2133	2133s
597	**Malmö** C ... ● a.	0848	0948	1048	1148	1240	1248	1355	1357	1448	1548	1648	1740	1748	1848	1848	1948	1948	2048	2048	2115	...	2120	2148	2148
626	København Lufthavn ✈ ... ● a.	...	...	1110	1210	...	1310	...	...	1510	...	1710	...	...	1910	...	2010	...	2110	...	...	...	...	2210	...
638	**København** H ... ● a.	...	...	1124	1224	...	1325	...	...	1524	...	1724	...	...	1924	...	2025	...	2125	...	...	...	...	2224	...

All trains Ⓡ	*ST*	*Sn*	*Sn*	*Sn*	*Sn*				*ST*	*ST*
	3935	**545**	**547**	**549**	**10549**		**3**	**1**	**3901**	**3901**
	✕	🍷	🍷	🍷	🍷					
			Ⓑ	④⑤	⑦		P	N	⑥	④⑤⑦
	H		n	n	n		A	A	C	C
Stockholm Central ... d.	1812	1822	1921r	2022	2022	...	2309	2309	2351	2350
Södertälje Syd ... d.	|	|	1941r	|	|	...	|	|	|	|
Norrköping ... 754 d.	1941	1935	2039	2135	2135	...	0052	0052	0142s	0145s
Linköping ... 754 d.	2008	1959	2103	2159	2159	...	0122	0122	|	|
Mjölby ... d.	|	2015	|	2214	2214	...	|	|	|	|
Tranås ... d.	|	|	|	|	|	...	|	|	|	|
Nässjö ... 733 d.	2106	2054	2154	2253	2253	...	0229	0229	0334s	0400s
Jönköping ... 733 a.	|	|	|	|	|	...	|	|	|	|
Alvesta ... 746 d.	2146	2127	2227	2325	2325	...	0318	0318	0459s	0500s
Älmhult ... 746 d.	|	|	|	|	|	...	|	|	|	|
Hässleholm ... 745 746 a.	2230s	2204	2304	0002	0003	...	0409s	0409s	0605s	0605s
Lund ... 745 746 ● a.	2310s	2234s	2334s	0033s	0033s	...	0523s	0545s	0654s	0655s
Malmö C ... ● a.	2325	2248	2348	0048	0055	...	0538	0602	0714	0715
København Lufthavn ✈ ... ● a.	...	...	...	...	...	...	...	...	...	...
København H ... ● a.	...	...	...	...	...	...	...	...	...	...

All trains Ⓡ	*Sn*	*Sn*	*Sn*	*Sn*	*Sn*	*Sn*	*ST*	*Sn*	*Sn*
	520	**512**	**522**	**516**	**524**	**526**	**3932**	**528**	**530**
	🍷	🍷	🍷	🍷	🍷	🍷	✕	🍷	🍷
	①–⑤	①–⑤	①–⑤	⑥	①–⑤		⑥		
	n	n		n	n		w		
København H ... ● d.	...	...	...	...	...	...	...	...	0819
København Lufthavn ✈ ... ● d.	...	...	...	...	...	...	...	...	0835
Malmö C ... ● d.	0339	...	0504	...	0604	0704	0719	0804	0904
Lund ... 745 746 ● d.	0353u	...	0518u	...	0618u	0718u	0731u	0818u	0918
Hässleholm ... 745 746 d.	0422	...	0548	...	0648	0748	0807	0848	0948
Älmhult ... 746 d.	0443	...	|	...	0708	|	|	|	|
Alvesta ... 746 d.	0507	...	0627	...	0729	0827	0851	0927	1027
Jönköping ... 733 d.	|	0600	|	0657	|	|	|	|	|
Nässjö ... 733 d.	0544	0636	0701	0733	0803	0901	0931	1001	1101
Tranås ... d.	0610	0702	|	0759	|	|	|	|	|
Mjölby ... a.	|	|	0741	|	|	0940	|	|	1140
Linköping ... 754 a.	0650	0735	0757	0832	0856	0956	1033	1053	1156
Norrköping ... 754 a.	0716	0802	0821	0858	0920	1020	1100	1117	1220
Södertälje Syd ... a.	|	0910	0920	1004	|	|	1207	1217	|
Stockholm Central ... a.	0830	0929	0941	1023	1034	1137	1231	1236	1334

All trains Ⓡ	*ST*	*ST*	*Sn*	*Sn*	*Sn*	*Sn*	*ST*	*Sn*	*Sn*	*Sn*	*Sn*	*Sn*	*ST*	*Sn*		*Sn*	*Sn*	*ST*	*Sn*		*Sn*	*Sn*			
	3942	**300**	**532**	**534**	**502**	**536**	**3930**	**538**	**540**	**540**	**542**	**544**	**3942**	**546**		**548**	**506**	**3934**	**550**		**508**	**10508**		**2**	**10030**
	✕	✕	🍷	🍷	🍷	🍷	✕	🍷	🍷	🍷	🍷	🍷	✕	🍷		🍷	🍷	✕	🍷		🍷	🍷			⑤
		X			⑦				Ⓑ	⑥						⑤⑦	⑦		Ⓑ			⑦		D	E
		★			n		G			R			d			n	n	H			M	L		A	A
København H ... ● d.	...	...	...	1019	...	...	...	1219	1319	...	1419	...	...	1619	...	...	...	...	1819	...	...	...	...	...	...
København Lufthavn ✈ ... ● d.	...	...	...	1035	...	...	...	1235	1334	...	1435	...	...	1635	...	...	...	...	1835	...	...	...	...	...	...
Malmö C ... ● d.	0919	0919	1004	1104	1118	1204	1219	1304	1404	1404	1504	1604	1610	1704	...	1804	1810	1820	1904	...	2018	2018	...	2235	2235
Lund ... 745 746 ● d.	0931	0931	1018u	1118	1131u	1218u	1231u	1318	1418	1418u	1518	1618u	1625u	1718	...	1817u	1824u	1832u	1918	...	2032u	2032u	...	2250u	2250u
Hässleholm ... 745 746 d.	1006	1006	1048	1148	1202	1248	1307u	1348	1448	1448	1548	1648	1657u	1748	...	1848	1854	1908u	1948	...	2102	2102	...	0030	0030
Älmhult ... 746 d.	|	|	|	|	|	|	|	|	|	|	|	1708	|	|	...	|	|	|	|	...	|	|	...	|	|
Alvesta ... 746 d.	1045	1045	1127	1227	1239	1327	1351	1427	1527	1527	1627	1729	1736	1827	...	1927	1931	1952	2027	...	2140	2140	...	0124	0124
Jönköping ... 733 d.	|	|	|	|	|	|	|	|	|	|	|	|	|	|	...	|	|	|	|	...	|	|	...	|	|
Nässjö ... 733 d.	1122	1122	1201	1301	1312	1401	1433	1501	1601	1601	1701	1804	1815	1901	...	2002	2014	2032	2102	...	2214	2214	...	0213	0213
Tranås ... d.	|	|	|	|	|	|	|	|	1627	1627	|	|	|	|	...	|	|	|	2128	...	|	|	...	|	|
Mjölby ... a.	|	|	|	1340	|	|	|	1540	|	|	1740	|	|	1940	...	|	|	|	|	...	|	|	...	|	|
Linköping ... 754 a.	1221	1221	1252	1356	1403	1452	1533	1557	1657	1657	1756	1855	1922	1956	...	2054	2107	2129	2158	...	2306	2306	...	0321	0321
Norrköping ... 754 a.	1247	1247	1316	1420	1427	1516	1601	1621	1721	1721	1820	1919	1947	2020	...	2118	2131	2156	2222	...	2330	2330	...	0353	0353
Södertälje Syd ... a.	1354	1354	1415	|	|	1615	1708	|	1820	1820	|	|	2055	2119	...	2217	|	2303	2322	...	0029	0034	...	|	|
Stockholm Central ... a.	1415	1415	1434	1534	1541	1634	1731	1737	1840	1840	1937	2034	2115	2138	...	2237	2248	2325	2341	...	0048	0053	...	0546	0553

A – Conveys 🛏, ▬ and [2].
C – June 30 - Sept. 18.
D – ①②③④⑥⑦ to Aug. 18 (not June 18, 23, July 2); ①②③④⑦ from Aug. 21. Runs with train number **4** June 14 - Aug. 6.
E – ⑤ (also June 23; not June 24). Runs with train number **10004** June 17 - Aug. 5.
G – Daily to Aug. 15 (not June 14, 15, 18, 24, 25); ①④⑤⑦ Aug. 18 - Oct. 24; daily Oct. 27 - Nov. 7; ①④⑤⑦ from Nov. 10.
H – ①④⑤⑦ to June 17; daily June 19 – 26; ①④⑤⑦ from Aug. 15 (also Oct. 29, Nov. 5).
K – ⑤–⑦ to June 26; daily July 1 - Aug. 14; ⑤–⑦ from Aug. 19.
L – ⑦ from Aug. 14 (also June 19; not Oct. 30).
M – ④⑤⑦ to July 1 (not June 19); ④⑤ from Aug. 18 (also Oct. 30).
N – Ⓑ from Aug. 7 (also June 12, 13, Aug. 6, 13).
P – Daily June 14 - Aug. 5 (not June 18, 24, July 2).
Q – Ⓑ (daily July 3 - Aug. 19).
R – July 3 - Aug. 13 only.
X – Until Sept. 24.
Y – Until Sept. 23.

d – Not June 24.
f – 0514 on ①.
j – Arrives 1934.
n – Not July 3 - Aug. 13.
r – 6 minutes **earlier** on ①–⑤ Aug. 15 - Nov. 25.
s – Calls to set down only.
u – Calls to pick up only.
w – Not June 25 - Aug. 13, Oct. 29, Nov. 5.

★ – From / to Berlin and Hamburg (Table **50**).
● – See also Tables **735, 737, 745** and **746** for other trains Lund - Malmö - København and v.v.

☛ **First-class tickets:** On *Sn* services includes complimentary tea, coffee and snacks with breakfast served on departures before 0900

730 STOCKHOLM - MALMÖ - KØBENHAVN

Other regional and *IC* services STOCKHOLM - NORRKÖPING - LINKÖPING. *IC* train numbers may vary on certain dates.

	◇	*IC* 257	*IC* 259	◇	*IC* 261	*IC* 263	◇	*IC* 265	*IC* 267	◇	*IC* 269	*IC* 271	◇	*IC* 273	*IC* 275	◇	*IC* 277	*IC* 279	◇	*IC* 281	◇	*IC* 283	◇	*IC* 297	*IC* 287	◇
	①-⑤	◐	①-⑤		①-⑥	①-⑤			①-⑤			①-⑤			①-⑤			①-⑤		⑥⑦	①-⑤	①-⑤	Ⓑ	①-⑤	⑦	Ⓑ
	2	🅁	n🅁	2	🅁	n🅁	2	C🅁	n🅁	2	🅁	🅁	2	🅁	n🅁	2	🅁	🅁	2	🅁	2	🅁	2	n🅁	△🅁	⊖2
Gävle C **761** d.	...	...	0603	...	0704	0803	...	0904	1004	...	1104	1204	...	1304	1404	...	1504	1602	...	1704	...	1803	...	...	2004	...
Stockholm Central d.	0543	0637	0739	0743	0836	0936	0943	1036	1139	1143	1236	1335	1344	1435	1532	1539	1639	1737	1741	1838	1842	1936	1942	2146	2154	2143
Flemingsberg d.	0555	0649	0751	0755	0848	0948	0955	1048	1151	1155	1248	1347	1356	1447	1544	1551	1651	1749	1753	1850	1854	1948	1954	2158	2205	2155
Södertälje Syd d.	0604	0659	0801	0804	0858	0958	1004	1058	1201	1204	1258	1357	1405	1457	1554	1604	1701	1759	1802	1900	1903	1958	2003	2208	2215	2204
Nyköping d.	0645	|	|	0845	|	|	1045	|	|	1245	|	|	1445	|	|	1645	|	|	1845	|	1945	|	2045	|	|	2245
Norrköping **754** a.	0724	0807	0906	0926	1002	1102	1126	1202	1306	1326	1403	1502	1526	1602	1658	1734f	1806	1904	1926	2005	2026	2102	2126	2312	2325	2324
Linköping **754** a.	...	0833	0934	...	1029	1128	...	1232	1333	...	1429	1535	...	1635	1724	...	1832	1930	...	2031	...	2128	...	2338	2351	...

	IC 262	◇	*IC* 264	*IC* 20266	◇	*IC* 266	◇	◇	*IC* 270	◇	*IC* 272	*IC* 274	◇	*IC* 278	◇	*IC* 280	*IC* 282	◇	◇	*IC* 284	*IC* 286	◇	*IC* 288	*IC* 290	◇	◇
	①-⑤	①-⑤	①-⑤	⑦		①-⑥		①-⑤			①-⑤					①-⑤		⑥⑦	①-⑤	①-⑤			①-⑤	⑦		①-⑤
	n🅁	2	🅁	🅁	2	🅁	2	2	🅁	2	n🅁	🅁	2	🅁	2	n🅁	🅁	2	2	🅁	🅁	2	n🅁	🅁	2	2
Linköping **754** d.	0528	...	0624	0645	...	0721e	...	...	0929	...	1024	1131	...	1329	...	1429	1526	...	...	1625	1726	...	1824	1928	...	...
Norrköping **754** d.	0555	0633	0653	0712	0734j	0748e	0834	0934	0956	1034	1051	1157	1234	1356	1434	1456	1556	1634	1634	1652	1754	1834	1850	1954	2033	2134
Nyköping d.	|	0714	|	|	0814	|	0914	1014	|	1114	|	|	1314	|	1514	|	|	1714	1714	|	|	1914	|	|	2114	2214
Södertälje Syd d.	0700	0751	0759	0823	0851	0855e	0953	1050	1105	1154	1158	1302	1351	1501	1556	1601	1701	1752	1800	1757	1903	1951	1957	2059	2151	2255r
Flemingsberg d.	0710	0801	0809	0833	0901	0912	1003	1100	1115	1204	1208	1312	1400	1511	1606	1611	1711	1802	1810	1807	1913	2001	2009	2109	2201	2305r
Stockholm Central a.	0721	0812	0820	0844	0912	0923	1014	1111	1126	1215	1219	1323	1411	1522	1617	1622	1722	1813	1821	1818	1924	2012	2020	2120	2214	2316r
Gävle C **761** a.	0856	...	0956	1056k	...	1056	...	...	1256	...	1356	1456	...	1656	...	1756	1856	...	...	1958	2056	...	2156	2256	...	...

C – ⑥⑦ (daily July 2 - Aug. 14). Runs up to 5 minutes later Stockholm - Norrköping on ②④⑥.

e – 7–9 minutes later on ⑥.
f – 1725 on ⑦.
j – 0718 on ⑦.
k – 1032 July 3 - Aug. 7.

n – Not July 3 - Aug. 13.
r – 4 minutes earlier on July 8, 15, 22, Aug. 19.

◐ – Runs 15–18 minutes later on ⑦ (as train **10257**).
⊖ – Runs 5–6 minutes **earlier** on ⑦ from July 3 (also on June 19).
△ – Runs 14–15 minutes **earlier** Stockholm - Linköping on June 12, 26.
◇ – Operated by Mälartåg.

☛ Additional trains (◇) Stockholm - Norrköping and v.v.: **From Stockholm** Central at 0644 ①-⑤, 0843 ①-⑤, 1043 ①-⑤, 1243 ①-⑤, 1443 ①-⑤, 1642 ①-⑤ and 2044 ①②③④⑥. **From Norrköping** at 0534 ①-⑤, 0604 ①-⑤, 1134 ①-⑤, 1334 ①-⑤, 1534 ①-⑤, 1733 ①-⑤ and 1934 ①-⑤.

731 MALMÖ - YSTAD - SIMRISHAMN and TRELLEBORG

Operator: *Skåne*

km		Ⓐ	Ⓐ	⚒	Ⓐ		Ⓐ		⚒							⚒		⚒		⚒	⚒		⚒		
0	**Malmö C** d.	...	0507	...	0537	0607	0637	0707	0737	0807	0837	and at the same	1907	1937	2007	2037	2107	2137	2207	2207	2237	2307	2307	...	2342f
70	Ystad d.	0458	0558	0558	0626	0658	0726	0758	0826	0858	0926	minutes past	1958	2026	2058	2126	2158	2226	2256	2258	2326	2356	2358	...	0026
116	**Simrishamn** a.	0538	0638	0638	...	0738	...	0838	...	0938	...	each hour until	2038	...	2138	...	2238	...	...	2338	...	...	0038	...	...

	Ⓐ	Ⓐ		Ⓐ	Ⓐ		Ⓐ	⚒		Ⓐ							⚒		⚒		⚒		⚒	⚒	⑤⑥r
Simrishamn d.	...	...	...	...	0547	...	...	0647	...	...	0747	...	and at the same	1847	...	1947	...	2047	...	2147	...	2247	2247	2347	2347
Ystad d.	0430	0500	0530	0600	0630	0630	0700	0730	0730	0800	0830	0900	minutes past	1930	2000	2030	2100	2130	2200	2230	2300	2326	2330	0026	0030
Malmö C a.	0520	0550	0620	0650	0720	0720	0750	0820	0820	0850	0920	0950	each hour until	2020	2050	2120	2150	2220	2250	2315j	2350	...	0020	...	0120

km																		
0	**Malmö C** d.	0547	0620	0647	and at the same minutes past	2220	2247	2327f	2352f	...	**Trelleborg C** d.	0507	0540	and at the same minutes past	2107	2140	2207	2240	2307	2340
44	**Trelleborg C** a.	0619	0652	0719	each hour until	2252	2319	2352	0019	...	**Malmö C** a.	0539	0612	each hour until	2139	2212	2239	2305j	2332j	0005t

f – 5–7 minutes **earlier** on ⑤⑥ (not June 25, Nov. 5).
j – 5–7 minutes later on ⑤⑥ (not June 25, Nov. 5).

r – Not June 25, Nov. 5.
t – 0012 on the mornings of ⑥⑦ (not June 26, Nov. 6).

☛ **Warning!** Subject to alteration Sept. 19–28.

732 STOCKHOLM - ESKILSTUNA - ARBOGA - ÖREBRO

Operator: *Mälartåg* (2nd class only)

km		Ⓐ	Ⓐ	Ⓒ	Ⓐ	Ⓐ		Ⓐ	⑥		Ⓐ		Ⓐv		Ⓐe		Ⓐe	Ⓒ	z	Ⓐe	Ⓐ		Ⓐ		Ⓐ	Ⓐw
0	**Stockholm** Central d.	...	0555	0642	0655	0755	0855	0956k	0957	1055	1155	1255	1355k	1455	1510	1548	1609	1653	1653	1713	1755	1855	1955	2055	2155	2256
36	Södertälje Syd d.	...	0616	0703	0716	0816	0916	1017	1018	1116	1216	1316	1416	1516	|	1613	|	1716	1716	|	1816	1916	2016	2116	2216	2317
67	Läggesta ● d.	...	0633	0720	0733	0833	0933	1034	1035	1133	1233	1333	1433	1533	|	1633	|	1733	1733	|	1833	1933	2033	2133	2233	2334
83	Strängnäs d.	...	0641	0730	0741	0841	0941	1042	1043	1141	1241	1341	1441	1541	|	1641	|	1741	1741	|	1841	1941	2041	2141	2241	2342
115	Eskilstuna a.	...	0656	0744	0756	0856	0956	1057	1058	1156	1256	1356	1456	1556	1601	1656	1700	1756	1756	1802	1856	1956	2056	2156	2256	2357
115	Eskilstuna d.	0602	0702	0759	0759	0859	0959	1059	...	1159	1259	1359	1459	1559c	1602	1703z	1703	1759	1804	1804	1859	1959	2059	2159	2259	0000
141	Kungsör d.	0617	0717	0815	0815	0915	1015	1115	...	1215	1315	1415	1515	1615c	1618	1718z	1718	1815	1819	1819	1915	2015	2115	2215	2315	0015
159	Arboga **756** a.	0628	0728	0825	0825	0925	1025	1125	...	1225	1325	1425	1525	1625c	1629	1729z	1729	1825	1830	1830	1925	2025	2125	2225	2325	0024
205	**Örebro C** **756** a.	0649	0749	*0902*	0845	*1004*n	*1102*	*1204*n	...	*1302*	*1402*n	*1502*	1545	*1702*c	1650	1749z	1749	*1902*	1850	1850	1945	2045j	2145	2246a	2345	0046

	Ⓐ	Ⓐe	Ⓐ	Ⓐe		Ⓐe		Ⓒ	⑥	Ⓐ		⑥	Ⓐ		Ⓐv		Ⓐ	Ⓐ	Ⓒ	Ⓐw	Ⓒ	Ⓐ	Ⓐ		Ⓐ	
Örebro C **756** d.	0413	0510	0510z	0608	0608z	0704	0704z	...	...	0813	*0857*	...	*0957*n	*1057*	*1157*n	*1257*	*1357*n	1513	*1457*	1608	*1657*	1708	1808	1913t	2014	2113t
Arboga **756** d.	0434	0531	0531z	0629	0629z	0729	0729z	0734	...	0834	0934	...	1034	1134	1234	1334	1434	1534	1534	1629	1734	1729	1829	1934	2034	2134
Kungsör d.	0445	0542	0542z	0640	0640z	0740	0740z	0745	...	0845	0945	...	1045	1145	1245	1345	1445	1545	1545	1640	1745	1740	1840	1945	2045	2145
Eskilstuna a.	0500	0557	0557z	0655	0655z	0755	0755z	0800	...	0900	1000	...	1100	1200	1300	1400	1500	1600	1600	1655	1800	1755	1855	2000	2100	2200
Eskilstuna d.	0504	0600	0604	0700	0704	0800	0804	0804	0904	0904	1004	1104	1104	1204	1304	1404	1504	1602	1604	1702	1804	1804	1904	2004	2104	2204
Strängnäs d.	0518	|	0618	|	0718	|	0818	0818	0918	0918	1018	1118	1118	1218	1318	1418	1518	1616	1618	1716	1818	1818	1918	2018	2118	2218
Läggesta ● d.	0527	|	0627	|	0727	|	0827	0827	0927	0927	1027	1127	1127	1227	1327	1427	1527	1625	1627	1725	1827	1827	1927	2027	2127	2227
Södertälje Syd d.	0544	|	0644	|	0744	|	0844	0844	0945	0945	1045	1144	1144	1244	1344	1444	1544	1644	1644	1744	1844	1846	1944	2044	2144	2244
Stockholm Central a.	0605	0648	0705	0748	0805	0852	0905	0905	1006	1006	1106	1205	1205	1305	1407	1505	1607	1705	1705	1805	1905	1907	2005	2105	2206	2305

a – Ⓐ only.
c – Ⓒ only.
e – Not June 24 - Aug. 5.
j – Not July 3, 10, 17, 24, 31, Aug. 7. Arrives *2102* on ⑥⑦ (change trains at Arboga).

k – 3–4 minutes **earlier** on ①-⑤ Aug. 8 - Nov. 25.
n – Not July 4 - Aug. 12.
t – On Ⓒ depart 16 minutes **earlier** and change trains at Arboga.
v – Runs daily Stockholm - Eskilstuna and v.v.
w – Also runs on ⑦ Stockholm - Eskilstuna and v.v.

z – ①-⑤ June 27 - Aug. 5.

● – Narrow gauge service operates Mariefred - Läggesta (nedre) - Taxinge-Näsby. Summer only. Operator: Östra Södermanlands Järnväg, Box 53, SE-647 22 Mariefred. ✆ +46 (0) 159 210 00.

733 SKÖVDE - JÖNKÖPING - NÄSSJÖ

Operator: Västtågen; 2nd class only

See Table **730** for through *Sn* trains Jönköping - Nässjö - Stockholm and v.v.

km		Ⓐ	Ⓐ	Ⓐ	⑥	Ⓐ		⚒a		Ⓐr				Ⓑ	⑥k	Ⓒd	Ⓐr	Ⓐ	†	Ⓑm	⑥p	s	Ⓐr	†	Ⓐ	⑥
0	**Skövde** **740** d.	0444	0551	0654	0658	0802	0857	*0951*r	1057e	*1125*z	1258x	*1336*g	1457	*1552*r	1557	1648	1654	*1731*t	*1754*	1849	1852	1854	1958	2050	2101r	2159
30	Falköping **740** d.	0502	0612	0717	0717	0821	0916	1016	1117	1216	1316	1415	1515	1616	1616	1715f	1713	1805	1818	1916	1917	1916	2015	2121f	2121	2219
100	Jönköping a.	0544	0656	0800	0800	0902	1001	1100	1201	1301	1400	1459	1559	1703	1702	1803	1804	1850	1902	2000	2001	2000	2100	2203	2203	2303
100	Jönköping d.	0546	0704	0807	0807	0905	1004	1106	1205	1303	1406	1507	1607	1709	1709	1808	1808	1856	1909	2002	2003	2002	2106	2209	2209	2310
143	**Nässjö** a.	0617	0738	0840	0840	0940	1038h	1137	1241	1337	1439	1542	1640	1740	1740	1841	1841	1931	1940	2037	2037	2037	2140	2241	2241	2341

	Ⓐr	ⒶD	Ⓐ	⑥	Ⓐ	⚒		Ⓐ		Ⓐr	⑥		†	Ⓐr	⑥w	†u	Ⓐ	⑥k	Ⓑ		Ⓑ	Ⓑ	⑥	Ⓐr	B	A
Nässjö d.	0428	0438	0554	0711	0715	0819	0916	1017b	1117	1218	1218	1316	1416	1416	1515	1515	1528	1619	1619	1719	1820	1918	1918	2022	2120	2120
Jönköping a.	0459	0511	0626	0747	0749	0851	0954	1050	1152	1251	1251	1349	1447	1447	1548	1548	1602	1652	1652	1753	1853	1955	1956	2057	2151	2151
Jönköping d.	0501	0516	0628	0800	0800	0902	1001	1100	1201	1301	1301	1401	1459	1459	1604	1604	1604	1702	1704	1804	1902	2002	2002	2100	2204	2204
Falköping **740** a.	0544	0602	0713	0845	0845	0945	1046	1145	1245	1344	1344	1443	1544	1544	1647	1647	1647	1745	1745	1846	1945	2045	2045	2146	2247	2258
Skövde **740** a.	0605	0621	0738	0912	0912v	*1036*c	1110	*1233*r	1305e	1402	*1434*	1506j	1608	*1612*	1705	1711	1711	1804	*1819*y	1904	*2012*n	2103	*2125*	*2223*	2305	2325

A – ①-⑤ to July 8.
B – ⑥⑦ to July 3; daily from July 9.
D – June 27 - Aug. 12.

a – Not ①-⑤ June 27 - Aug. 12.
b – 1009 July 11 - Aug. 12.
c – *1013* on ⑥; *1023* on ①-⑤ June 27 - Aug. 12.
d – Runs daily June 24 - Aug. 14.
e – 2–3 minutes later on ⑥⑦ to June 26 / from Aug. 27.

f – Arrives 11–14 minutes earlier.
g – *1325* on ⑥ to July 2 / from Aug. 20; *1330* on ⑥ July 9 - Aug. 13; *1335* on Ⓑ June 27 - Aug. 14.
h – 1042 on ①④ July 11 - Aug. 11.
j – 1501 on ⑦ (also on ⑥ to June 25 / from Aug. 27).
k – Not June 25 - Aug. 13.
m – Not June 27 - Aug. 12, Aug. 15–21.
n – *2019* on ⑤ to June 17 / from Aug. 19.
p – Not July 2 - Aug. 20.

r – Ⓐ (not June 24 - Aug. 12).
s – June 27 - Aug. 13 and Aug. 15–21.
t – *1722* July 4 - Aug. 16.
u – Also July 2, 9, 16, 23, Aug. 20.
v – 0903 on ④⑤ to June 10 / from Aug. 19.
w – Not June 25 - July 23, Aug. 20.
x – 1249 on ①-④ June 27 - July 21 (also Aug. 17, 18).
y – *1839* on ⑦ July 3 - Aug. 14.
z – *1121* on Aug. 15.

KRISTIANSTAD - HÄSSLEHOLM - HELSINGBORG 734

Operator: *Skåne*

km		⑥⑦j	Ⓐ	Ⓐ	Ⓐ	Ⓐ	⚒	Ⓐ		Ⓐ		Ⓐ				Ⓐ			Ⓐ						
0	**Kristianstad** 745 d.	...	...	...	...	0540	...	0640	...	0740	...	0840	...	and at	...	1440	...	and at	1740	...	...	...	...	...	...
30	Hässleholm 745 a.	...	...	...	...	0600	...	0700	...	0800	...	0900	...	the same	...	1500	...	the same	1800	...	...	...	...	...	...
30	Hässleholm d.	0030	...	0501	0530	0601	0630	0701	0730	0801	0830	0901	0930	minutes	1430	1501	1530	minutes	1801	1830	1930	2030	2130	2230	2330
83	Åstorp d.	0110	0511	0541	0610	0641	0710	0741	0810	0841	0910	0941	1010	past each	1510	1541	1610	past each	1841	1910	2010	2110	2210	2310	0010
107	**Helsingborg** a.	0135	0535	0605	0635	0705	0735	0805	0835	0905	0935	1005	1035	hour until	1535	1605	1635	hour until	1905	1935	2035	2135	2235	2335	0035

	⑥⑦j	Ⓐ	Ⓐ	Ⓐ	⚒	Ⓐ		Ⓐ		Ⓐ				Ⓐ			Ⓐ							⚒
Helsingborg d.	0016	...	0416	0446	0516	0546	0616	0646	0716	0746	0816	and at	1316	1346	1416	and at	1646	1716	1816	1916	2016	2116	2216	2316
Åstorp d.	0039	...	0439	0510	0539	0610	0639	0710	0739	0810	0839	the same	1339	1410	1439	the same	1710	1739	1839	1939	2039	2139	2239	2339
Hässleholm a.	0118	...	0518	0549	0618	0649	0718	0749	0818	0849	0918	minutes	1418	1449	1518	minutes	1749	1818	1918	2018	2118	2218	2318	0018
Hässleholm 745 d.	...	0452	...	0551	...	0651	...	0751	...	0851	...	past each	...	1451	...	past each	1751	...	...	...	...	...	...	...
Kristianstad 745 a.	...	0514	...	0614	...	0714	...	0814	...	0914	...	hour until	...	1514	...	hour until	1814	...	...	...	...	...	...	...

j – Not June 24, 26, Sept. 24, Nov. 6.

☛ **Warning!** Subject to alteration Sept. 19–23, 26–28.

GÖTEBORG - MALMÖ - KØBENHAVN 735

Operator: *Øtåg* (except *Sn* trains)

WARNING! From June 13 to August 5 all services are diverted Ängelholm - Lund and v.v. (not calling at Helsingborg or Landskrona); train numbers and timings of *Sn* services may also vary. **Services are subject to further alteration June 30 - July 3** (please check locally for journeys during this period).

km		Ⓐ	Ⓐ	Ⓐ	⑥	*Sn* 481 Ⓐn 🅁🍷	*Sn* 469 B 🅁🍷		*Sn* 483 ⑥n 🅁🍷		*Sn* 485 A¶ 🅁🍷			*Sn* 487 n 🅁🍷	*Sn* 473 v 🅁🍷			*Sn* 475 v 🅁🍷		*Sn* 491 n 🅁🍷		*Sn* 477 v 🅁🍷		*Sn* 493 n 🅁🍷		*Sn* 479 v 🅁🍷
0	**Göteborg** C d.	...	...	0540	...	0624	0624	0640	0724	0740	0824	0840	0940	1024	1024	1040	1140	1224	1240	1324	1340	1424	1440	1524	1540	1624
28	Kungsbacka d.	...	...	0559	...	|	|	0659	|	0759	|	0859	0959	|	|	1059	1159	|	1259	|	1359	|	1459	|	1559	|
76	Varberg d.	...	...	0628	...	|	0705	0728	|	0828	0905v	0928	1028	|	1105	1128	1228	1305	1328	|	1428	1505	1528	|	1628	1705
106	Falkenberg d.	...	...	0644	...	|	|	0744	|	0844	|	0944	1044	|	|	1144	1244	|	1344	|	1444	|	1544	|	1644	|
150	**Halmstad** d.	0504	0604	0704	0704	0736	0736	0804	0836	0904	0936	1004	1104	1136	1136	1204	1304	1336	1404	1436	1504	1536	1604	1636	1704	1736
173	Laholm d.	0516	0616	0716	0716	|	|	0816	|	0916	|	1016	1116	|	|	1216	1316	|	1416	|	1516	|	1616	|	1716	|
185	Båstad d.	0522	0622	0722	0722	|	|	0822	|	0922	|	1022	1122	|	|	1222	1322	|	1422	|	1522	|	1622	|	1722	|
210	Ängelholm d.	0534	0634	0734	0734	|	|	0834	|	0934	|	1034	1134	|	|	1234	1334	|	1434	|	1534	|	1634	|	1734	|
237	**Helsingborg** a.	0608	0708	0808	0808	0818	0818	0908	0918	1008	1018	1108	1208	1218	1218	1308	1408	1418	1508	1518	1604	1618	1708	1718	1808	1818
237	**Helsingborg** 737 d.	0610	0710	0810	0810	0819	0819	0910	0919	1010	1019	1110	1210	1219	1219	1310	1410	1419	1510	1519	1610	1619	1710	1719	1810	1819
259	Landskrona 737 d.	0621	0721	0821	0821	|	|	0921	|	1021	|	1121	1221	|	|	1321	1421	|	1521	|	1621	|	1721	|	1821	|
290	Lund ● d.	0639	0739	0839	0839	0846s	0847	0939	0943s	1039	1043s	1139	1239	1243s	1247	1339	1439	1443s	1539	1546s	1639	1646s	1739	1746s	1839	1843s
306	**Malmö** C ● a.	0651	0751	0851	0851	0900	0900	0951	0957	1051	1100	1151	1251	1300	1300	1351	1451	1500	1551	1600	1651	1700	1751	1800	1851	1900
306	**Malmö** C ● d.	0653	0753	0853	0853	...	0902	0953	...	1053	...	1153	1253	...	1302	1353	1453	...	1553	...	1653	...	1753	...	1853	...
335	København Lufthavn ✈ ● a.	0714	0814	0914	0914	...	0919	1014	...	1114	...	1214	1314	...	1319	1414	1514	...	1614	...	1714	...	1814	...	1914	...
347	**København** H ● a.	0729	0829	0929	0929	...	0933	1029	...	1129	...	1229	1329	...	1333	1429	1529	...	1629	...	1729	...	1829	...	1929	...

		Sn 495 n 🅁🍷		*Sn* 499 v 🅁🍷		*Sn* 405 Ⓑz 🅁🍷					
Göteborg C d.	1640	1724	1740	1824	1840	1923	1940	2040	2140	2240	2340
Kungsbacka d.	1659	|	1759	|	1859	|	1959	2101	2159	2259	2359
Varberg d.	1728	|	1828	1905	1928	|	2028	2128	2228	2329	0028
Falkenberg d.	1744	|	1844	|	1944	|	2044	2144	2246	2346	0046
Halmstad d.	1804	1836	1904	1936	2004	2036	2104	2204	2309	0008	0108
Laholm d.	1816	|	1916	|	2016	|	2116	2216	2321	...	...
Båstad d.	1822	|	1922	|	2022	|	2122	2222	2327	...	...
Ängelholm d.	1834	|	1934	|	2034	|	2134	2234	2342	...	...
Helsingborg a.	1908	1918	2008	2018	2108	2118	2204	2308	0004	...	...
Helsingborg 737 d.	1910	1919	2010	2019	2110	2119	2210	2310	...	...	...
Landskrona 737 d.	1921	|	2021	|	2121	|	2221	2321	...	...	...
Lund ● d.	1939	1946s	2039	2047	2139	2144s	2239	2339	...	...	...
Malmö C ● a.	1951	2000	2051	2100	2151	2200	2251	2351	...	...	...
Malmö C ● d.	1953	...	2053	2102	2153	...	2253	...	...	...	...
København Lufthavn ✈ ● a.	2014	...	2114	2119	2214	...	2314	...	...	...	...
København H ● a.	2029	...	2129	2133	2229	...	2329	...	...	...	...

	Ⓐ	Ⓐ	Ⓐ D	*Sn* 426 Ⓐ‡ 🅁🍷	①-⑥ D	*Sn* 418 ⑥n 🅁🍷	*Sn* 482 Ⓐn 🅁🍷	*Sn* 470 B 🅁🍷		
København H ● d.	...	...	...	...	0527	...	...	0619	0627	0727
København Lufthavn ✈ ● d.	...	...	...	...	0542	...	...	0634	0642	0742
Malmö C ● a.	...	...	...	...	0606	...	...	0700	0706	0806
Malmö C ● d.	...	...	0508	0510	0608	0618	0658	0701	0708	0808
Lund ● d.	...	...	0522	0524u	0622	0633u	0712u	0715	0722	0822
Landskrona 737 d.	...	...	0536	|	0636	|	|	|	0736	0836
Helsingborg 737 a.	...	...	0549	0555	0649	0657	0740	0740	0749	0849
Helsingborg d.	...	0456	0554	0603	0654	0702	0741	0741	0753	0854
Ängelholm d.	...	0524	0618	|	0718	|	|	|	0824	0924
Båstad d.	...	0536	0630	|	0730	|	|	|	0836	0936
Laholm d.	...	0542	0636	|	0736	|	|	|	0842	0942
Halmstad d.	0446	0556	0656	0652	0756	0752	0822	0822	0856	0956
Falkenberg d.	0503	0613	0713	|	0813	|	|	|	0913	1013
Varberg d.	0521	0633	0733	|	0833	|	|	0855	0933	1033
Kungsbacka d.	0544	0659	0759	|	0859	|	|	|	0959	1059
Göteborg C a.	0605	0720	0820	0805	0920	0905	0935	0935	1020	1120

	Sn 472 v 🅁🍷		*Sn* 486 n 🅁🍷		*Sn* 474 v 🅁🍷		*Sn* 488 n 🅁🍷		*Sn* 476 v 🅁🍷		*Sn* 490 n 🅁🍷		*Sn* 478 v 🅁🍷			*Sn* 492 n 🅁🍷	*Sn* 480 v 🅁🍷			*Sn* 494 Ⓑn 🅁🍷	*Sn* 468 ⑥v 🅁🍷				*Sn* 498 Ⓑv 🅁🍷	
København H ● d.	...	0827	...	0927	...	1027	...	1127	...	1227	...	1327	1359	1427	1527	...	...	1627	1727	...	1819	1827	1927	2027	2119	2227
København Lufthavn ✈ ● d.	...	0842	...	0942	...	1042	...	1142	...	1242	...	1342	1413u	1442	1542	...	...	1642	1742	...	1835u	1842	1942	2042	2135u	2242
Malmö C ● a.	...	0906	...	1006	...	1106	...	1206	...	1306	...	1406	1443	1506	1606	...	...	1706	1806	...	1900	1906	2006	2106	2200	2306
Malmö C ● d.	0858	0908	1001	1008	1101	1108	1201	1208	1301	1308	1401	1408	1501	1508	1608	1658	1658	1708	1808	1901	1901	1908	2008	2108	2201	2308
Lund ● d.	0912u	0922	1015u	1022	1115u	1122	1215u	1222	1315u	1322	1415u	1422	1515	1522	1622	1712u	1712u	1722	1822	1915u	1915	1922	2022	2122	2216	2322
Landskrona 737 d.	|	0936	|	1036	|	1136	|	1236	|	1336	|	1436	|	1536	1636	|	|	1736	1836	|	|	1936	2036	2136	|	2336
Helsingborg 737 a.	0940	0949	1040	1049	1140	1149	1240	1249	1340	1349	1440	1449	1540	1549	1649	1740	1740	1749	1849	1940	1940	1949	2049	2149	2240	2349
Helsingborg d.	0941	0954	1041	1054	1141	1154	1241	1254	1341	1354	1441	1454	1541	1554	1654	1741	1741	1754	1854	1941	1941	1954	2054	2154	2241	2354
Ängelholm d.	|	1024	|	1124	|	1224	|	1324	|	1424	|	1524	|	1624	1724	|	|	1824	1924	|	|	2024	2124	2214	|	0014
Båstad d.	|	1036	|	1136	|	1236	|	1336	|	1436	|	1536	|	1636	1736	|	|	1836	1936	|	|	2036	2136	2226	|	0026
Laholm d.	|	1042	|	1142	|	1242	|	1342	|	1442	|	1542	|	1642	1742	|	|	1842	1942	|	|	2042	2142	2232	|	0032
Halmstad d.	1022	1056	1122	1156	1222	1256	1322	1356	1422	1456	1522	1556	1622	1656	1756	1822	1822	1856	1956	2022	2022	2056	2156	2246	2322	0044
Falkenberg d.	|	1113	|	1213	|	1313	|	1413	|	1513	|	1613	|	1713	1813	|	|	1913	2013	|	|	2113	2213	2303	|	...
Varberg d.	1055	1133	|	1233	1255	1333	|	1433	1455	1533	|	1633	1655	1733	1833	|	1855	1933	2033	|	2055	2133	2233	2321	2354	...
Kungsbacka d.	|	1159	|	1259	|	1359	|	1459	|	1559	|	1659	|	1759	1859	|	|	1959	2059	|	|	2159	2259	2343	|	...
Göteborg C a.	1135	1220	1235	1320	1335	1420	1435	1520	1535	1620	1635	1720	1735	1820	1920	1935	1935	2020	2120	2135	2135	2220	2320	0005	0035	...

A – ①-⑤ (daily July 4 - Aug. 13).
B – ①-⑥ July 4 - Aug. 13.
D – Runs daily Halmstad - Göteborg.
n – Not July 4 - Aug. 13.
s – Stops to set down only.
u – Stops to pick up only.
v – July 4 - Aug. 13 only.
z – Not June 29 - Aug. 12.
¶ – A different train number applies July 4 - Aug. 13.
‡ – Not July 4 - Aug. 12, Sept. 19–28. Train number may vary.
● – See also Tables **737**, **745** and **746**.

ÖREBRO - HALLSBERG - HERRLJUNGA - GÖTEBORG 736

Operator: *Västtågen* (2nd class only)

km		Ⓐz	Ⓐk	Ⓐ	⑥	Ⓐ	Ⓐm	⑥⑦	Ⓐ	⑥z	⑦	Ⓐ	⑥	Ⓐ	⑦	⑦	⑥	Ⓐz	⑥k	⑥z	Ⓐw	⑦	⑥z	Ⓐ	⑥z	⑦	Ⓐz
	Örebro C 755 756 d.	...	...	...	...	...	...	...	0746	...	...	...	...	...	...	...	...	...	...	...	...	...	...	1637	...	...	...
0	**Hallsberg** 740 755 756 d.	...	...	...	...	...	...	...	0814	...	...	...	1114e	...	1253	...	...	...	...	1519	...	...	...	1658	...	1848	1955
30	Laxå 756 d.	...	...	...	...	...	...	...	0830	...	...	...	1130e	1202	1309	...	...	...	...	1538	...	...	...	1713	...	1904	2013
92	Mariestad d.	...	...	0523	...	0656	0755	0820t	0923j	...	...	1113	1219	1256j	1355	1407	1408	1444	1622	1623	1626	1705	1820	1835r	...	1953	2059
146	Lidköping a.	...	...	0604	...	0746	0850	0904	1010	...	...	1159	1306	1342	...	1449	1452	1530	1710	1710	1713	1751	1906	1930	...	2039	2144
146	Lidköping d.	0522	0542	0616	0716	0751	0903	0907	1022	1113	1150	1210z	1327	1351	...	1452	1456	1533	1717	...	1719	1754	1912	2010	2105	...	2207
201	**Herrljunga** 740 756 a.	0608	0628	0701	0802	0836	0952	0950	1108	1159	1237	1256z	1415	1438	...	1536	1541	1623	1804	...	1806	1838	1956	2056	2151	...	2253
	Göteborg C 740 756 a.	...	...	0755	...	0925	...	1040	1200	...	1330	...	1505	1525	...	1630	1630	...	1900	...	...	1930	...	...	...	...	...

	Ⓐz	Ⓐ	Ⓐ	⑥	†	Ⓐ	⑥	Ⓐm	Ⓐz	⑥⑦	Ⓐk	Ⓐz	⑥z	Ⓐk	Ⓐz	⑦	⑥	Ⓐz	Ⓐ	⑦	⑥z	Ⓐ	⑥z	⑥k	⑦	Ⓐ	⑥
Göteborg C 740 756 d.	...	...	...	...	...	0830	...	...	1030	1130	...	...	...	1330	1350	1430	1530	...	1655	1730	1735	...	...	1950	1950	...	...
Herrljunga 740 756 d.	...	...	0701	...	...	0920	0956	1034	1119	1218	...	1302	1400	1419	1440	1517	1620	1632	1751	1819	1820	1902	2001	2038	2044	2103	2200
Lidköping a.	...	...	0749	...	...	1007	1044	1122	1204	1307	...	1347	1446	1508	1527	1606	1707	1717	1832	1904	1904	1947	2047	2122	2128	2149	2246
Lidköping d.	0438	0607	0755	0810	1013	1012	1046	...	1206	1308	1351	1356	1454	1521	1531	1608	1712	1721	1837	1907	1908	1950z	...	2125	...	...	...
Mariestad d.	0547f	0650	0843	0905	1103	1105	1132	...	1249	1352	1451h	1455h	1540	1609	1620	1657	1757	1820h	1920	1951	1951	2037z	...	2207	...	...	...
Laxå 756 d.	0629	...	...	0949	1146	1149	...	...	...	*1446*y	1535	1538	...	...	...	*1751*	...	1908	...	...	...	...	...	...	...	...	...
Hallsberg 740 755 756 a.	0648	...	...	1006	1203	*1218*	...	...	...	*1502*y	1553	1556	...	...	...	*1808*	...	1925	...	...	...	...	...	...	...	...	...
Örebro C 755 756 a.	0713	...	...	...	...	...	...	...	...	...	1619	1619	...	...	...	...	...	...	...	...	...	...	...	...	...	...	...

e – 3 minutes later July 2 - Aug. 13.
f – Arrives 0521.
h – Arrives 13–14 minutes earlier.
j – Arrives 8–10 minutes earlier.
k – June 27 - Aug. 13 only.
m – From Aug. 15.
r – Arrives 1756.
t – 0822 on ⑦.
w – Runs 14–20 minutes earlier July 25 - Aug. 12.
y – ⑥ only.
z – Not June 25 - Aug. 13.

☛ **Warning!** Journeys to/from Göteborg and Herrljunga are subject to alteration July 25 - August 16 and on ⑤-⑦ Oct. 14 - Nov. 6.

737 KØBENHAVN - MALMÖ - HELSINGBORG

Operators: *Skåne; Øtåg*

Local trains between Malmö and Helsingborg are 2nd class only. For other trains see Tables **735**, **745** and **746**.
Warnings! Subject to alteration Sept. 19 – 28. Journeys to / from Landskrona and Helsingborg are also subject to alteration June 13 - Aug. 5 (SEE NOTE ✣).

	ØⒶ	Ⓐb		Ø	Ⓐ	ØⒶ		Ø	Ⓐ	ØA		ØA	Ø	Ⓐ	ØA		ØA	Ø	Ⓐ		Ø	Ⓐ		Ø		Ø
København H d.	...	...	...	0527	...	...	...	0627	...	0656	...	0716	0727	...	0756	...	0816	0827	...	...	0927	...	...	1027	...	1127
København Lufthavn ✈ d.	...	...	...	0542	...	...	...	0642	...	0711	...	0731	0742	...	0811	...	0831	0842	...	...	0942	...	...	1042	...	1142
Malmö C d.	0508	0511	0541	0608	0614	0638	0641	0708	0714	0738	0741	0802	0808	0814	0838	0841	0902	0908	0914	0941	1008	1014	1041	1108	1141	1208
Lund d.	0522	0527	0557	0622	0630	0653	0657	0722	0730	0753	0757	0816	0822	0830	0853	0857	0916	0922	0930	0957	1022	1030	1057	1122	1157	1222
Landskrona d.	0536	0549	0620	0636	0652	0707	0720	0736	0752	0807	0820	0831	0836	0852	0907	0920	0931	0936	0952	1020	1036	1052	1120	1136	1220	1236
Helsingborg a.	0549	0607	0638	0649	0710	0722	0738	0749	0810	0822	0838	0845	0849	0910	0922	0938	0945	0949	1010	1038	1049	1110	1138	1149	1238	1249

		Ø		Ø	Ⓐ		Ø	Ⓐ	ØⒶ		ØⒶ	Ø	Ⓐ	ØⒶ		ØⒶ	Ø	Ⓐ	ØⒶ		ØⒶ	Ø	Ⓐ		Ø	Ⓐ
København H d.	...	1227	...	1327	...	...	1427	...	1456	...	1516	1527	...	1556	...	1616	1627	...	1656	...	1716	1727	...	...	1827	...
København Lufthavn ✈ d.	...	1242	...	1342	...	...	1442	...	1511	...	1531	1542	...	1611	...	1631	1642	...	1711	...	1731	1742	...	...	1842	...
Malmö C d.	1241	1308	1341	1408	1414	1441	1508	1514	1538	1541	1602	1608	1614	1638	1641	1702	1708	1714	1738	1741	1802	1808	1814	1841	1908	1914
Lund d.	1257	1322	1357	1422	1430	1457	1522	1530	1553	1557	1616	1622	1630	1653	1657	1716	1722	1730	1753	1757	1816	1822	1830	1857	1922	1930
Landskrona d.	1320	1336	1420	1436	1452	1520	1536	1552	1607	1620	1631	1636	1652	1707	1720	1731	1736	1752	1807	1820	1831	1836	1852	1920	1936	1952
Helsingborg a.	1338	1349	1438	1449	1510	1538	1549	1610	1622	1638	1645	1649	1710	1722	1738	1745	1749	1810	1822	1838	1845	1849	1910	1938	1949	2010

		Ø		Ø		Ø		Ø	⚒	Ø
København H d.	...	1927	...	2027	...	2127	...	2227	...	2327
København Lufthavn ✈ d.	...	1942	...	2042	...	2142	...	2242	...	2342
Malmö C d.	1941	2008	2041	2108	2141	2208	2241	2308	2341	0008
Lund d.	1957	2022	2057	2122	2157	2222	2257	2322	2357	0022
Landskrona d.	2020	2036	2120	2136	2220	2236	2320	2336	0020	0036
Helsingborg a.	2038	2049	2138	2149	2238	2249	2338	2349	0038	0049

	Ⓐ	ØⒶ	Ⓐ	Ⓐ	Ø		Ø	ØA	Ⓐ	ØA	
Helsingborg d.	0450	0510	0523	0538	...	0550	0610	0613	0623	0635	0650
Landskrona d.	0505	0521	0538	0551	...	0605	0621	0625	0638	0647	0705
Lund d.	0531	0539	0604	|	0619	0631	0639	0645	0704	0709	0731
Malmö C d.	0545	0553	0618	0624	0633	0645	0653	0701	0718	0723	0745
København Lufthavn ✈ a.	...	0614	...	...	0654	...	0714	0722	...	0744	...
København H a.	...	0629	...	...	0709	...	0729	0737	...	0759	...

	Ø	ØA	Ⓐ	ØA		Ø	Ⓐ		Ø	Ⓐ		Ø	Ⓐ		Ø		Ø		Ø		Ø	Ⓐ	ØⒶ		Ø	ØⒶ
Helsingborg d.	0710	0713	0723	0735	0750	0810	0823	0850	0910	0923	0950	1010	1023	1050	1110	1150	1210	1250	1310	1350	1410	1423	1435	1450	1510	1513
Landskrona d.	0721	0725	0738	0747	0805	0821	0838	0905	0921	0938	1005	1021	1038	1105	1121	1205	1221	1305	1321	1405	1421	1438	1447	1505	1521	1525
Lund d.	0739	0745	0804	0809	0831	0839	0904	0931	0939	1004	1031	1039	1104	1131	1139	1231	1239	1331	1339	1431	1439	1504	1509	1531	1539	1545
Malmö C d.	0753	0801	0818	0823	0845	0853	0918	0945	0953	1018	1045	1053	1118	1145	1153	1245	1253	1345	1353	1445	1453	1518	1523	1545	1553	1601
København Lufthavn ✈ a.	0814	0822	...	0844	...	0914	...	...	1014	...	...	1114	...	...	1214	...	1314	...	1414	...	1514	...	1544	...	1614	1622
København H a.	0829	0837	...	0859	...	0929	...	...	1029	...	...	1129	...	...	1229	...	1329	...	1429	...	1529	...	1559	...	1629	1637

	Ⓐ	ØⒶ		Ø	ØⒶ	Ⓐ	ØⒶ		Ø	Ⓐ	ØⒶ		Ø	Ⓐ		Ø	Ⓐ		Ø		Ø		Ø		Ø	
Helsingborg d.	1523	1535	1550	1610	1613	1623	1635	1650	1710	1723	1735	1750	1810	1823	1850	1910	1923	1950	2010	2050	2110	2150	2210	2250	2310	2350
Landskrona d.	1538	1547	1605	1621	1625	1638	1647	1705	1721	1738	1747	1805	1821	1838	1905	1921	1938	2005	2021	2105	2121	2205	2221	2305	2321	0005
Lund d.	1604	1609	1631	1639	1645	1704	1709	1731	1739	1804	1809	1831	1839	1904	1931	1939	2004	2031	2039	2131	2139	2231	2239	2331	2338	0031
Malmö C d.	1618	1623	1645	1653	1701	1718	1723	1745	1753	1818	1823	1845	1853	1918	1945	1953	2018	2045	2053	2145	2153	2245	2253	2345	2351	0045
København Lufthavn ✈ a.	...	1644	...	1714	1722	...	1744	...	1814	...	1844	...	1914	...	...	2014	...	...	2114	...	2214	...	2314	...	...	...
København H a.	...	1659	...	1729	1737	...	1759	...	1829	...	1859	...	1929	...	...	2029	...	...	2129	...	2229	...	2329	...	...	...

A – ①–⑤ (not July 4 - Aug. 5).
b – 3 minutes later until Aug. 12.

✣ – June 13 - Aug. 5 certain services (mainly xx27 from København / xx10 from Helsingborg) require a change of trains at Kävlinge (between Lund and Landskrona); journey time extended by up to 8 minutes (earlier departures / later arrivals at Landskrona and Helsingborg).

738 South-eastern SECONDARY LINES

Operator: *Krösatågen*

km		Ⓐ								Ⓑ	
0	**Västervik** d.	0541	0735	...	1007	1207	1407	1605	1807	2007	...
77	Åtvidaberg d.	0647	0841	...	1114	1314	1514	1714	1915	2114	...
116	**Linköping** a.	0727	0920	...	1151	1351	1551	1751	1951	2151	...

	Ⓐ										Ⓑ
Linköping d.	0539	...	0756	...	1007	1207	1408	1608	1808	...	2008
Åtvidaberg d.	0615	...	0841	...	1044	1243	1444	1644	1847	...	2042
Västervik a.	0725	...	0947	...	1151	1350	1550	1750	1952	...	2150

km		Ⓐ	Ⓐ	⑥						Ⓑ	Ⓑc
0	**Linköping** d.	...	0525	...	0818	1019	1219	1423	1622	1820	2020
41	Rimforsa d.	...	0601	...	0901	1102	1302	1502	1702	1902	2102
123	Hultsfred d.	0610	0707	0708	1004	1204	1404	1604	1804	2004	2204
159	Berga ▷ a.	0635	0733	0733	1030	1230	1430	1630	1830	2030	...
159	Berga ▷ d.	0640	0738	0738	1035	1235	1435	1634	1835	2035	...
235	**Kalmar** a.	0738	0837	0837	1138	1338	1538	1738	1938	2137	...

	Ⓐ	Ⓐ	⑥							Ⓑ	Ⓑc
Kalmar d.	...	0538	...	...	0829	1035	1235	1435	1635	1835	2035
Berga ▷ a.	...	0637	...	...	0934	1134	1334	1534	1734	1934	2134
Berga ▷ d.	...	0642	...	...	0939	1139	1339	1539	1739	1939	2139
Hultsfred d.	0534	0706	0707	...	1005	1205	1405	1605	1805	2005	2202
Rimforsa d.	0636	0806	0806	...	1103	1303	1503	1703	1903	2103	...
Linköping a.	0720	0843	0842	...	1140	1339	1540	1740	1941	2138	...

c – Not June 25.
d – Also ①–⑤ June 20 - Aug. 19, Sept. 19, Oct. 31 - Nov. 4.
e – Not June 20 - Aug. 19, Sept. 19, Oct. 31 - Nov. 4.

▷ – Connecting 🚌 services **Berga - Oskarshamn** and v.v. (operated by Länsbuss). *29 km.* Journey 31 – 40 minutes.
From Berga at 0640 Ⓐ, 0739 Ⓐ, 0740 ⑥, 1035 Ⓒ, 1235 Ⓒ, 1435, 1635, 1835 and 2035 Ⓑ.
From Oskarshamn at 0555 Ⓐ, 0855 Ⓒ, 1055, 1255, 1430 Ⓐ **e**, 1455 Ⓒ **d**, 1655, 1855 Ⓑ and 2055 Ⓑ.

739 VARBERG - UDDEVALLA

Operator: *Västtågen* (2nd class only).

SERVICE FROM AUGUST 17. Please check locally for amended service until August 16.

km		*Sn* **462** Ⓐ¶	Ⓐ	Ⓐ	*Sn* **460** ⑥¶	Ⓐ	Ⓒ	Ⓐ	Ⓐ	Ⓒ	Ⓐ	Ⓒ	Ⓒ	Ⓐ	Ⓐ	⚒⊙	⑦	Ⓐ	Ⓐ	⑦	⑥	Ⓐ	⑦	Ⓐ	⑥	Ⓑ△
0	**Varberg** d.	...	...	...	...	0607	...	0710**k**	0812	0843**r**	0915	1040	...	...	1343	1440	1442	...	*1540*f	1639	1639	1743	1840	1849	1942	2140
84	Borås a.	...	...	...	...	0729	...	0834**k**	0939	1000**r**	1056	1200	...	...	1459	1602	1600	...	*1701*f	1800	1800	1910	2000	2020	2100	2259
84	Borås d.	0548	0558	0657	0728	0731	0758	0918	...	1002	1134	1203	1400	1402	1502	1618	1612	1646	1733	1802	1803	1933	2003	...	...	...
127	**Herrljunga** a.	0622	0633	0735	0759	0809	0833	0956	...	1040	1211	1238	1438	1437	1540	1653	1647	1724	1813	1840	1841	2016	2038	...	...	...
127	**Herrljunga** d.	0632	0641	0755	0807	0814	0931		...	1125	...	1330	1543	1530	1608	...	1731	1732	1856	1858	1919	...	2119	...	...	...
	Stockholm C 740 a.	0918	|	|	1051	|	|	...	...	|	...	|	|	|	|	...	|	|	|	|	|	...	|	...	...	...
191	Vänersborg d.	...	0732	0852	...	0922	1021	...	...	1214	...	1416	1630	1621	1658	...	1818	1826	1943	1945	2014	...	2209	...	...	...
195	Öxnered d.	...	0739	0858	...	0929	1027	...	...	1221	...	1423	1636	1630	1704	...	1824	1833	1949	1951	2020	...	2219	...	...	...
217	**Uddevalla C** a.	...	0754	0914	...	0944	1042	...	...	1237	...	1439	1652	1650	1721	...	1839	1850	2003	2005	2035	...	2234	...	...	...

	Ⓐ	Ⓐ	Ⓐ	⑥	Ⓐ	Ⓐ	⑦	⑥	Ⓐ	Ⓐ	Ⓒ	Ⓐ	Ⓒ	Ⓐ	Ⓒ	Ⓐ	Ⓐ	Ⓒ	Ⓐ	Ⓐ	*Sn* **467** Ⓑ¶	Ⓐ	⑥	⑦	Ⓐ	⑦
Uddevalla C d.	...	...	0517	...	0630	0659	0729	0729	0817	...	0920	1120	1139	1315	1315	...	1515	1530	...	1611	...	...	...	1718	...	1935
Öxnered d.	...	...	0533	...	0646	0715	0746	0746	0833	...	0936	1136	1156	1322	1331	...	1531	1546	...	1629	...	...	...	1734	...	1951
Vänersborg d.	...	...	0538	...	0652	0721	0752	0752	0840	...	0942	1142	1202	1339	1339	...	1537	1552	...	1732	...	...	...	1740	...	1957
Stockholm C 740 d.	...	...	|	...	|	|	|	|	|	...	|	|	|	|	|	...	|	|	...	...	1607	...	...	|	...	|
Herrljunga a.	...	...	0624	...	0740	0811	0838	0838	0936	...	1029	1231	1252	1431	1429	...	1628	1638	...	...	1847	...	...	1833	...	2043
Herrljunga d.	...	0548	0644	...	0752	0835	0922	0922	1025	1125	1124	1321	1320	1523	1524	...	1636	1727	1755	...	1847	1920	1921	1922	2105	2119
Borås a.	...	0623	0722	...	0831	0911	1000	1000	1103	1200	1202	1356	1355	1601	1602	...	1711	1802	1835	...	1925	2000j	1956	1957	2140	2154
Borås d.	0428	0631	0731	0800	0839	0858**h**	1003	1057	...	1203	...	1359	1358	1604	1604	1702	...	1804	...	...	...	2023j	...	2002	...	...
Varberg a.	0550	0749	0852	0920	0957	1118**h**	1119	1251	...	1337	...	1521	1521	1720	1719	1821	...	1920	...	...	...	2145j	...	2119	...	...

GÖTEBORG - UDDEVALLA - STRÖMSTAD

km		⑥	Ⓐ		Ⓐ	⑦	Ⓐ	Ⓒ	⑦	Ⓐ	⑥	Ⓑ
0	**Göteborg C** ▲ d.	0710	0840	1040	1240	1240	1440	1440	1640	1645	1840	1840
89	Uddevalla C ▲ a.	0826	0953	1153	1353	1353	1553	1553	1753	1741	1953	1953
89	Uddevalla C d.	0828	1007	1208	1408	1413	1558	1608	1808	1748	2001	2012
173	Skee d.	0935	1123	1319	1524	1529	1714	1717	1924	1904	2113	2120
180	**Strömstad** a.	0941	1129	1325	1530	1535	1719	1723	1930	1909	2119	2126

	Ⓐ	⚒	Ⓒ	Ⓐ	Ⓐ	Ⓒ		Ⓐ	⑦	⑥
Strömstad d.	0526	0642	1041	1228	1434	1440	1623	1818	1834	1842
Skee d.	0532	0649	1048	1235	1440	1446	1630	1824	1841	1849
Uddevalla C a.	0645	0800	1200	1351	1554	1556	1748	1936	1951	1959
Uddevalla C ▲ d.	0648	0807	1207	1407	1607	1607	1807	1954	2007	2007
Göteborg C ▲ a.	0745	0920	1320	1520	1720	1720	1920	2110	2120	2120

f – ⑤ only.
h – ①② only.
j – On ② Borås a. 1958, d. 2000, Varberg a. 2122.
k – Not ③.
r – ⑥ only.

⊙ – On ⑥ Varberg d. 1442, Borås a. 1600, d. 1612, Herrljunga a. 1647.
△ – On ①–⑤ Varberg d. 2200, Borås a. 2321.
¶ – Conveys [12] and 🍸. [R].

▲ – **Warning!** Journeys from / to Göteborg are subject to alteration daily until Sept. 4, on ⑤–⑦ Oct. 14 - Nov. 6 and daily Dec. 2 – 7. Please check locally.
Other services Göteborg - Uddevalla and v.v.:
From Göteborg C at 0525 Ⓐ, 0640 Ⓐ, 0740 Ⓐ, 0840 Ⓒ, 0940 ⚒, 1140, 1240 ⑥, 1340, 1540, 1640 ⚒, 1710 Ⓐ, 1740, 1940, 2040, 2140 ⑥, 2240 ⑤⑥ and 2340 ⑦–④.
From Uddevalla C at 0507 Ⓐ, 0534 Ⓐ, 0607 Ⓐ, 0637 Ⓐ, 0707 ⚒, 0807 †, 0907 ⚒, 1007, 1107, 1207 Ⓐ, 1307, 1407 Ⓒ, 1507, 1707, 1907, 2107 and 2207.

STOCKHOLM - GÖTEBORG 740

SERVICE UNTIL JULY 24 AND FROM AUGUST 17. See Table **756** for slower regional services via Västerås and Örebro.
Warning! Subject to alteration July 25 - August 16 and on ⑤–⑦ October 14 - November 6. Note that *MTR* train numbers may vary until July 24.

km	All trains 🅁	*Sn*	*Sn*	*MTR*	*Sn*	*MTR*	*FLX*	*Sn*	*MTR*	*Sn*	*MTR*	*Sn*	*MTR*	*Sn*	*Sn*	*MTR*	*Sn*	*Sn*	*Sn*	*MTR*	*Sn*	*FLX*		*Sn*	*Sn*
		419	**401**	**2021**	**421**	**2023**	**23001**	**423**	**2025**	**425**	**2015**	**427**	**2027**	**429**	**10429**	**2029**	**10431**	**431**	**403**	**2033**	**433**	**23003**		**435**	**415**
		🍷	🍷	🍷	🍷	🍷	⊠	🍷	🍷	🍷	🍷	🍷	🍷	🍷	🍷	🍷	🍷	🍷	🍷	🍷	🍷	⊠		🍷	🍷
		①–⑤	①–⑤	①–⑤	①–⑥	①–③		①–⑤	④–⑥		⑦		⑥						⑤⑦					①–⑤	⑦
		n	n	A		r			u					n	L	◐	L	n	n					n	d
0	**Stockholm** C ... 750/6 d.	0529	0602	0607	0624	0708	0718	0733	0811	0833	0846	0929	0948	1028	1028	1049	1117	1133	1207	1210	1233	1230	...	1329	1329
36	Södertälje Syd △. 750 d.	0548	|	|	|	|	0740	|	|	|	|	0948	1007	|	|	1107	|	|	|	|	|	1253	...	1348	1348
131	Katrineholm .... 750 d.	0626	|	0706	0718	0806	|	0826	0910	0926	|	1026	|	1121	1121	|	1215	1226	|	1309	1326	|	...	1426	1426
197	**Hallsberg**..... 750 756 d.	|	|	|	0744	|	0852	|	|	|	|	|	|	|	|	|	|	|	|	|	|	1402	...	|	|
272	Töreboda .... 756 d.	|	|	|	|	|	|	|	|	|	|	|	|	|	|	|	|	|	|	|	|	|	...	|	|
311	**Skövde** .... 756 d.	0730	|	0814	0826	0914	0937	0930	1018	1030	1051	1130	1152	1225	1225	1252	1324	1330	|	1417	1430	1448	...	|	1530
341	Falköping............ 756 d.	|	|	0829	|	|	|	|	|	|	1106	|	1207	|	|	|	|	|	|	1432	|	1505	...	|	|
375	Herrljunga........... 756 d.	|	0817	|	|	|	|	|	|	|	|	|	|	1252	|	1319	|	|	|	|	|	|	...	1553	|
410	Alingsås ▽ .... 756 a.	|	|	0903	0907	0956	|	|	1100	|	1137	|	1237	|	1306	|	|	|	|	1502	|	|	...	|	|
455	**Göteborg** C .... 756 a.	0835	0900	0930	0935	1025	1045	1035	1130	1135	1204	1235	1307	1335	1335	1405	1435	1435	1505	1530	1535	1605	...	1635	1635

All trains 🅁	*IC*	*MTR*	*IC*	*Sn*	*MTR*	*Sn*	*Sn*	*MTR*	*Sn*	*Sn*	*Sn*	*Sn*	*Sn*	*MTR*	*MTR*	*Sn*	*Sn*	*Sn*	*FLX*	*IC*	*MTR*	*IC*	*Sn*	*Sn*	*Sn*
	105	**2035**	**105**	**437**	**2037**	**459**	**439**	**2009**	**405**	**10467**	**467**	**411**	**441**	**2041**	**2041**	**407**	**413**	**443**	**23005**	**109**	**2003**	**109**	**10409**	**409**	**445**
	🍷	🍷	🍷	🍷	🍷	🍷	🍷	🍷	🍷	🍷	🍷	🍷	🍷	🍷	🍷	🍷	🍷	🍷	⊠	🍷	🍷	🍷	🍷	🍷	🍷
	①–⑤	Ⓑ	①–⑤		⑥		Ⓑ	Ⓑ	Ⓑ	Ⓑ	Ⓑ	⑥	Ⓑ	⑥⑦	①–⑤	Ⓑ	⑥	Ⓑ		⑦	Ⓑ	⑦	①④	②③	Ⓑ
					m	L	n	t‡	¶	K	N			r	r	n♥	◇				◧		nb	nc	
Stockholm C .... 750/6 d.	1341	1350	...	1432	1449	1525	1526	1545	1551	1607	1607	1629	1633	1645	1647	1716	1712	1723	1727	1729	1746	...	1808	1812	1829
Södertälje Syd △.. 750 d.	1401	1408	...	|	1507	1544	|	|	1612	|	|	|	|	1704	1707	|	1731	1743	1747	1749	1805	...	|	|	|
Katrineholm .... 750 d.	|	|	←	1527	|	1622	1620	1641	|	|	|	1722	1726	1747	1747	|	1814	1821	|	|	1846	...	|	|	1922
Hallsberg...... 750 756 d.	1511	|	1517	|	|	|	|	|	1715	|	|	|	|	|	|	|	|	|	1856	1901	|	...	|	|	|
Töreboda .... 756 d.	→	|	|	|	|	|	|	|	|	1801	1801	|	|	|	|	|	|	|	|	|	|	←	|	|	|
Skövde .... 756 d.	...	1555	1607	1632	1652	1726	1724	1749	1756	1816	1816	1826	1831	1855	1855	|	1923	1925	1943	1950	1953	1959	|	|	2026
Falköping.............. 756 d.	...	|	|	|	1707	|	|	1804	|	1832	1832	|	|	|	|	|	|	|	2000	→	2008	|	|	|	|
Herrljunga...... 739 756 d.	...	|	1640	|	|	|	|	1819	|	1848	1847	1853	|	|	|	|	|	|	|	...	|	2028	|	|	2053
Borås .... 739 a.	...	|	|	|	|	|	|	|	|	|	1925	|	|	|	|	|	|	|	|	...	|	|	|	|	|
Alingsås ▽ .... 756 a.	...	|	|	|	1739	|	|	1837	1843	|	...	|	|	1936	1936	|	|	|	|	...	2038	|	|	|	|
Göteborg C.......... 756 a.	...	1705	1740	1735	1810	1830	1830	1905	1910	1940	...	1935	1935	2005	2005	2010	2035	2035	2100	...	2105	2115	2110	2110	2135

All trains 🅁	*Sn*	*MTR*	*Sn*	*Sn*	*MTR*	*MTR*	*Sn*	*MTR*	*Sn*	*Sn*	
	455	**2045**	**417**	**447**	**2047**	**2047**	**449**	**2051**	**451**	**453**	
	🍷	🍷	🍷	🍷	🍷	🍷	🍷	🍷	🍷	🍷	
	⑥	⑥	①–⑤		④⑤⑦	①–③			⑤⑦	⑦	
			G	H		e	B	J	n	n	
Stockholm C .... 750/6 d.	1829	1848	1918	1925	1948	1951	2028	2121	2133	2233	...
Södertälje Syd △.. 750 d.	|	1906	1938	1945	2006	|	|	|	|	|	...
Katrineholm .... 750 d.	1922	|	2019	2023	|	|	2121	2217	2226	2326	...
Hallsberg...... 750 756 d.	|	|	|	|	|	|	|	|	|	|	...
Töreboda .... 756 d.	|	|	|	|	|	|	|	|	|	|	...
Skövde .... 756 d.	2026	2051	2127	2127	2151	2151	2225	2325	2330	0030	...
Falköping.............. 756 d.	|	2106	|	|	2206	2206	|	|	|	|	...
Herrljunga............ 756 d.	|	|	|	|	|	|	|	|	|	|	...
Borås .... 739 a.	|	|	|	|	|	|	|	|	|	|	...
Alingsås ▽ .... 756 a.	2108	2137	|	|	2236	2236	|	0007	|	|	...
Göteborg C.......... 756 a.	2135	2205	2235	2235	2305	2305	2330	0035	0040	0135	...

All trains 🅁	*Sn*	*Sn*	*Sn*	*MTR*	*Sn*	*Sn*	*MTR*	*Sn*	*Sn*
	420	**400**	**402**	**2000**	**462**	**462**	**2022**	**422**	**404**
	🍷	🍷	🍷	🍷	🍷	🍷	🍷	🍷	🍷
	①–⑤	①–④	①–⑤	①–③	①–⑤	①–⑤		①–⑥	①–⑤
	n	n	n	r	n	N	D	j	n★
Göteborg C................ 756 d.	0459	0539	0544	0550	...	...	0555	0624	0650
Alingsås △ .... 756 d.	0525	|	|	|	...	...	0620	0649	|
Borås .... 739 d.	|	|	|	|	...	0548	|	|	|
Herrljunga.................. 756 d.	0543	|	|	|	0632	0632	0638	|	|
Falköping.................. 756 d.	0558	|	|	|	0648	0648	0653	|	|
Skövde.................... 756 d.	0613	|	|	0652	0703	0703	0707	0729	|
Töreboda .... 756 d.	0629	|	|	|	|	|	|	|	|
Hallsberg .... 750 756 d.	0701	|	|	|	0754	0754	|	|	|
Katrineholm................. 750 d.	0728	|	|	|	|	|	|	0836	|
Södertälje Syd ▽........ 750 a.	0806	|	|	|	|	|	0858	0914	|
Stockholm C........... 750/6 a.	0825	0836	0842	0857	0918	0918	0920	0935	0944

All trains 🅁	*MTR*	*Sn*	*Sn*	*Sn*	*FLX*	*MTR*	*MTR*	*Sn*	*Sn*	*MTR*	*Sn*	*Sn*	*Sn*	*Sn*	*MTR*	*MTR*	*Sn*	*Sn*	*MTR*	*Sn*	*Sn*	*FLX*	*Sn*	*MTR*	*Sn*
	2024	**424**	**460**	**10460**	**23000**	**2026**	**2026**	**82426**	**416**	**2008**	**418**	**428**	**430**	**410**	**2032**	**2062**	**432**	**406**	**2034**	**434**	**414**	**23002**	**412**	**2036**	**436**
	🍷	🍷	🍷	🍷	⊠	🍷	🍷	🍷	🍷	🍷	🍷	🍷	🍷	🍷	🍷	🍷	🍷	🍷	🍷	🍷	🍷	⊠	🍷	🍷	🍷
	①–④	①–⑥	⑥	⑥		④⑤	⑥	①–⑤	⑥⑦	⑤–⑦	⑥⑦	①–⑤		⑦		①–⑤		⑤	⑦	①–⑤	⑥⑦		⑤⑦		Ⓑ
			N	Y		X	a	n⊖	♣	v				n	P	Q		n	g	n	d		n	y	t
Göteborg C.......... 756 d.	0654	0724	...	0729	0745	0754	0754	0824	0824	0854	0924	0924	1024	1049	1054	1054	1124	1149	1154	1224	1224	1230	1249	1254	1324
Alingsås △ .... 756 d.	0720	|	...	|	|	0820	0820	|	|	0920	0949	|	|	|	|	|	|	|	1220	|	|	|	|	1321	|
Borås .... 739 d.	|	|	0728	|	|	|	|	|	|	|	|	|	|	|	|	|	|	|	|	|	|	|	|	|	|
Herrljunga............ 756 d.	|	|	0807	0814	|	0838	0838	|	0904	|	|	1004	|	|	1135	1135	|	|	|	1304	1304	|	|	|	|
Falköping.............. 756 d.	|	|	0823	0830	0843	|	|	|	|	0950	|	|	|	|	1151	1151	|	|	|	|	|	1326	|	1351	|
Skövde .... 756 d.	0802	0825	0838	0845	0858	0906	0905	0925	0930	1004	1029	|	1125	1151	1205	1205	1225	|	1301	|	1330	1342	1355	1405	1425
Töreboda .... 756 d.	|	|	|	|	|	|	|	|	|	|	|	|	|	|	|	|	|	|	|	|	|	|	|	|	|
Hallsberg...... 750 756 d.	|	|	0924	0931	0945	|	|	1010	|	|	|	|	|	1239	|	|	|	|	|	|	|	1428	1439	|	|
Katrineholm .... 750 d.	|	0933	|	|	|	1017	1018	1038	1038	|	|	1133	1233	|	1314	1314	1333	|	|	1433	1438	|	|	1515	1533
Södertälje Syd ▽.. 750 a.	0950	|	1033	1039	1055	1058	1100	|	|	|	|	|	|	|	1357	1357	1411	|	|	|	|	1538	|	|	1611
Stockholm C .... 750/6 a.	1009	1027	1051	1100	1114	1117	1120	1134	1134	1209	1228	1228	1327	1358	1417	1425	1430	1447	1508	1527	1532	1556	1601	1612	1630

All trains 🅁	*MTR*	*Sn*	*MTR*	*Sn*	*Sn*	*Sn*	*MTR*	*MTR*	*IC*	*Sn*	*Sn*	*MTR*	*MTR*	*Sn*	*Sn*	*FLX*	*Sn*	*MTR*	*MTR*	*Sn*	*MTR*	*MTR*	*Sn*	*MTR*	*Sn*
	2038	**438**	**2010**	**440**	**20454**	**454**	**2040**	**2092**	**104**	**442**	**408**	**2064**	**2044**	**444**	**456**	**23004**	**446**	**2046**	**2096**	**448**	**2050**	**2090**	**450**	**2052**	**452**
	🍷	🍷	🍷	🍷	🍷	🍷	🍷	🍷	🍷	🍷	🍷	🍷	🍷	🍷	🍷	⊠	🍷	🍷	🍷	🍷	🍷	🍷	🍷	🍷	🍷
	⑥		⑥	Ⓑ	⑥	⑥		⑥	Ⓑ		Ⓑ	⑦		Ⓑ						Ⓑ					⑦
	M		y		N	Y	F	M			n§		T	n	L			E	R	n	W	S	Z	J	n
Göteborg C.......... 756 d.	1354	1424	1454	1524	1519	1524	1529	1549	1554	1624	1649	1654	1659	1724	1724	1755	1824	1829	1849	1924	1954	1954	2024	2054	2124
Alingsås △ .... 756 d.	1420	|	1520	|	1548	1551	1555	1617	|	|	|	1722	1725	1749	1751	|	|	1855	1917	|	2020	2020	|	2120	|
Herrljunga............ 756 d.	|	|	|	|	|	|	|	1635	|	1704	|	1741	1743	|	|	|	|	|	|	|	|	|	|	|	|
Falköping.............. 756 d.	|	|	|	|	|	|	|	1650	|	|	|	1757	1758	|	|	1853	|	|	|	|	2051	2051	|	|	|
Skövde .... 756 d.	1459	1525	1602	1625	1631	1634	1636	1704	1706	1730	|	1812	1812	1829	1834	1909	1925	1935	1958	2025	2106	2106	2125	2201	2225
Töreboda .... 756 d.	|	|	|	|	|	|	|	|	|	|	|	|	|	|	|	|	|	|	|	|	|	|	|	|	|
Hallsberg...... 750 756 d.	|	|	|	|	|	|	|	|	1758	|	|	|	|	1913	|	1955	|	|	|	|	|	|	2210	|	|
Katrineholm .... 750 d.	1611	1633	|	1733	|	|	1747	1813	|	1838	|	1922	1922	1945	|	|	2033	2047	2108	2133	|	2215	2237	|	2334
Södertälje Syd ▽.. 750 a.	1656	|	|	1811	1823	1826	|	|	1909	|	|	|	|	|	2028	2105	2112	|	|	|	|	|	|	|	|
Stockholm C .... 750/6 a.	1716	1727	1809	1831	1842	1845	1849	1919	1929	1932	1949	2024	2024	2039	2047	2123	2132	2149	2221	2228	2313	2316	2331	0009	0028

A – ①–⑤ to June 16; ① June 27 - July 18; ①–⑤ from Aug. 22.
B – Ⓑ to July 3; ⑦ July 10 – 24; Ⓑ from Aug. 17 (not Oct. 13, 20, 27, Nov. 3).
D – ①–⑤ to June 23; ① June 27 - July 18; ①–⑤ from Aug. 22.
E – Daily to June 26 (also June 30); ⑤–⑦ July 1 – 24; daily from Aug. 19.
F – Ⓑ to June 26; ⑤⑦ July 1 – 24; Ⓑ from Aug. 19.
G – Ⓐ Aug. 17 - Nov. 25.
H – Ⓑ to July 1; ⑦ Aug. 21 - Nov. 20; Ⓑ from Nov. 27.
J – ④⑤⑦ (not June 30 - Aug. 21).
K – Ⓑ to July 1 (not June 24).
L – July 3 – 24 only.
M – ⑥ July 2 – 23 (also Aug. 20).
N – From Aug. 17.
P – ⑥⑦ (daily to July 24 and from Nov. 26).
Q – Aug. 17 - Nov. 25.
R – ①–④ June 27 - July 21 (also Aug. 17, 18; not June 30).
S – ⑤⑦ July 8 – 24 (also Aug. 19, 21).
T – ①–⑥ to June 30; ①–④ July 4 – 21 (also Aug. 17, 18); ①–⑥ from Aug. 22.
W – Ⓑ to July 3 (not June 27); ②–④ July 5 – 21 (also Aug. 17, 18); Ⓑ from Aug. 22.

X – From Aug. 19.
Y – Until July 2.
Z – Ⓑ to July 3; ⑦ July 10 – 24; Ⓑ from Aug. 17.

a – Also June 16, 17, 23, 24, July 1, 8, 15, 22.
b – Not June 27, 28, Sept. 19, 22, 26.
c – Also June 27, 28, Sept. 19, 22, 26.
d – Also July 4 – 8, 11 – 15, 18 – 22.
e – Not June 27, July 4, 11, 18.
g – Not July 3 - Aug. 21.
j – Not July 9, 16, 23.
m – Not July 2 - Aug. 13.
n – Not July 3 - Aug. 16.
r – Not June 27 - Aug. 19.
t – Also July 2, 9, 16, 23.
u – Also June 27 – 29, July 4 – 6, 11 – 13, 18 – 20, Aug. 17.
v – Also June 27 – 30, July 4 – 7, 11 – 14, 18 – 21, Aug. 17, 18.
y – Not July 2, 9, 16, 23, Aug. 20.

⊠ – FlixTrain service. Internet bookings only (www.flixtrain.com).
◇ – On July 9, 16, 23 runs with train number **10413** and is retimed as follows: Stockholm d. 1716, Södertälje Syd d. 1735, Katrineholm d. 1813, Skövde d. 1917, Göteborg a. 2029.
¶ – Not July 3 - Aug. 16. Train number **10405** on June 27, 28; **20407** Sept. 19 – 28.
‡ – Train number **2039** on ⑦ (daily June 27 - July 24, Aug. 17 – 19).
§ – Train number **10408** on ①–⑤ Aug. 17 - Nov. 25.
◧ – Train number **2043** on ⑦ (also on ①–⑤ June 27 - July 22).
⊖ – Train number **10426** until June 29 (**426** on June 30, July 1).
◐ – On ①–④ July 4 – 21 (also June 27 – 29) runs with train number **2099** and calls additionally at Katrineholm (d. 1148).
♥ – Continues to Trollhättan (a. 2048) and Uddevalla (a. 2107).
★ – From Uddevalla (d. 0549) and Trollhättan (d. 0609).
♣ – ⑥⑦ (also July 4 – 8, 11 – 15, 18 – 22). On ⑥ until July 2 / from Aug. 20 from Uddevalla (d. 0718) and Trollhättan (d. 0738).
△ – Trains call to pick up only.
▽ – Trains call to set down only.

☛ **First-class tickets**: On *Sn* services includes complimentary tea, coffee and snacks with breakfast served on departures before 0900. On *MTR* services includes a complimentary meal and drinks.

745 KØBENHAVN - MALMÖ - KRISTIANSTAD - KARLSKRONA

Operators: *Øtåg*; *Skåne*

Subject to alteration Sept. 19 – 28. For other trains København - Lund, see Tables **735** and **737**. For other trains København - Hässleholm, see Tables **730** and **746**.

km		②–⑦		Ⓐ	Ⓐ	Ⓐ	Ⓐ	⚒																		
0	**København** H d.	z	...	...	...	...	0447	0547	0547	0647	0747	0847	0947	1047	1147	1247	1347	1447	1547	1647	1747	1847	1947	2047	2147	2247
12	København Lufthavn ✈ d.	...	...	...	...	...	0502	0602	0602	0702	0802	0902	1002	1102	1202	1302	1402	1502	1602	1702	1802	1902	2002	2102	2202	2302
47	**Malmö** C a.	...	...	...	...	...	0526	0626	0626	0726	0826	0926	1026	1126	1226	1326	1426	1526	1626	1726	1826	1926	2026	2126	2226	2326
47	**Malmö** C d.	0052	...	...	...	0429	0528	0628	0628	0728	0828	0928	1028	1128	1228	1328	1428	1528	1628	1728	1828	1928	2028	2128	2228	2328
63	Lund d.	0107	...	...	...	0445	0542	0642	0642	0742	0842	0942	1042	1142	1242	1342	1442	1542	1642	1742	1842	1942	2042	2142	2242	2342
130	Hässleholm **734** d.	0154	...	...	0511	0532	0611	0711	0711	0811	0911	1011	1111	1211	1311	1411	1511	1611	1711	1811	1911	2011	2111	2211	2312	0012
160	**Kristianstad** **734** a.	0214	...	...	0531	0554	0631	0731	0731	0831	0931	1031	1131	1231	1331	1431	1531	1631	1731	1831	1931	2031	2131	2231	2331	0032
160	**Kristianstad** d.	...	...	0507	0537	*0602*	0637	0737	...	0837	0937	1037	1137	1237	1337	1437	1537	1637	1737	1837	1937	2037	2137	2237	...	...
191	Sölvesborg d.	...	...	0528	0558	*0625*	0658	0758	...	0858	0958	1058	1158	1258	1358	1458	1558	1658	1758	1858	1958	2058	2158	2258	...	...
222	**Karlshamn** d.	...	...	0549	0620	*0650*	0720	0820	...	0920	1020	1120	1220	1320	1420	1520	1620	1720	1820	1920	2020	2120	2220	2320	...	...
260	Ronneby d.	...	...	...	0646	...	0746	0846	...	0946	1046	1146	1246	1346	1446	1546	1646	1746	1846	1946	2046	2146	2246	2346	...	...
290	**Karlskrona** a.	...	...	...	0712	...	0812	0912	...	1012	1112	1212	1312	1412	1512	1612	1712	1812	1912	2012	2112	2212	2312	0012	...	...

	②–⑦		Ⓐ				Ⓐ		⚒		⚒															m
Karlskrona d.	z	...	...	...	...	...	0447	...	0547	...	0647	0747	0847	0947	1047	1147	1247	1347	1447	1547	1647	1747	1847	1947	2047	2147
Ronneby d.	...	...	...	...	...	...	0507	...	0607	...	0707	0807	0907	1007	1107	1207	1307	1407	1507	1607	1707	1807	1907	2007	2107	2207
Karlshamn d.	...	...	...	...	...	...	0535	...	0635	...	0735	0835	0935	1035	1135	1235	1335	1435	1535	1635	1735	1835	1935	2035	2135	2235
Sölvesborg d.	...	...	...	...	...	...	0557	...	0657	...	0757	0857	0957	1057	1157	1257	1357	1457	1557	1657	1757	1857	1957	2057	2157	2257
Kristianstad a.	...	...	...	...	...	...	0619	...	0719	...	0819	0919	1019	1119	1219	1319	1419	1519	1619	1719	1819	1919	2019	2119	2219	2319
Kristianstad **734** d.	0001	...	0401	...	0524	0624	0624	0724	0724	0824	0824	0924	1024	1124	1224	1324	1424	1524	1624	1724	1824	1924	2024	2124	2224	2324
Hässleholm **734** d.	0028	...	0428	0505	0544	0644	0644	0744	0744	0844	0844	0944	1044	1144	1244	1344	1444	1544	1644	1744	1844	1944	2044	2144	2244	2344
Lund d.	0115	...	0515	0552	0619	0719	0719	0819	0819	0919	0919	1019	1119	1219	1319	1419	1519	1619	1719	1819	1919	2019	2119	2219	2319	0019
Malmö C a.	0127	...	0527	0605	0631	0731	0731	0831	0831	0931	0931	1031	1131	1231	1331	1431	1531	1631	1731	1831	1931	2031	2131	2231	2331	0031
Malmö C d.	...	...	...	...	0633	0733	0733	0833	0833	0933	0933	1033	1133	1233	1333	1433	1533	1633	1733	1833	1933	2033	2133	2233	2333	0033
København Lufthavn ✈ a.	...	...	...	...	0654	0754	0754	0854	0854	0954	0954	1054	1154	1254	1354	1454	1554	1654	1754	1854	1954	2054	2154	2254	2354	0054
København H a.	...	...	...	...	0709	0809	0809	0909	0909	1009	1009	1109	1209	1309	1409	1509	1609	1709	1809	1909	2009	2109	2209	2309	0009	0109

m – Terminates at Lund on Sept. 18.

z – Not June 26, Nov. 6.

746 KØBENHAVN, MALMÖ and GÖTEBORG - KALMAR

Subject to alteration Sept. 19 – 28. Services from / to Göteborg are subject to alteration until July 10 and on Aug. 15, 16 (please check locally). Other trains: København - Lund see Tables **735** and **737**; København - Lund - Hässleholm see Table **745**; København - Lund - Hässleholm - Alvesta see Table **730**.

km		*Øtåg* Ⓐ	*Øtåg* Ⓐ	*Øtåg* Ⓐ	Ⓐ	*Øtåg*	*Øtåg* Ⓐ	Ⓐ	*Øtåg*	⑥	*Øtåg*	*Øtåg* Ⓐ	*Øtåg* n	⑥	Ⓐ	*Øtåg*	*Øtåg* Ⓐ	*Øtåg*	*Øtåg*	*Øtåg* ⑦	*Øtåg* Ⓐ	⑦	*Øtåg*	*Øtåg*	*Øtåg* Ⓐ	*Øtåg*	*Øtåg*
0	**København** H d.	...	...	0507	...	0607	0607	...	0707	...	0807	0807	0907	...	...	1007	1007	1107	1207	1207	1207	...	1307	1407	1407	1507	1607
12	København Lufthavn ✈ d.	...	...	0522	...	0622	0622	...	0722	...	0822	0822	0922	...	...	1022	1022	1122	1222	1222	1222	...	1322	1422	1422	1522	1622
47	**Malmö** C a.	...	...	0546	...	0646	0646	...	0746	...	0846	0846	0946	...	...	1046	1046	1146	1246	1246	1246	...	1346	1446	1446	1546	1646
47	**Malmö** C d.	...	...	0548	...	0648	0648	0718	0748	...	0848	0848	0948	...	...	1048	1048	1148	1249	1249	1248	...	1348	1449	1448	1548	1648
63	Lund d.	...	...	0602	...	0702	0702	0732	0802	...	0902	0902	1002	...	...	1102	1102	1202	1302	1302	1302	...	1402	1502	1502	1602	1702
80	Eslöv d.	...	...	0611	...	0711	0711	0741	0811	...	0911	0911	1011	...	...	1111	1111	1211	1311	1311	1311	...	1411	1511	1511	1611	1711
130	Hässleholm d.	...	...	0638	...	0735	0738	0807	0839	...	0935	0938	1038	...	...	1135	1138	1238	1335	1338	1338	...	1438	1538	1538	1639	1735
181	Älmhult d.	...	...	0702	...	...	0802	0829	0902	...	...	1002	1102	...	...	...	1202	1302	...	1402	1402	...	1502	1602	1602	1702	...
	Göteborg C d.	...	...	|	0524r	...	|	|	|	0729r	...	|	|	0919r	0929r	...	|	|	...	|	|	1119r	|	|	|	|	...
	Borås d.	...	...	|	0659	...	|	|	|	0900	...	|	|	1059	1059	...	|	|	...	|	|	1255	|	|	|	|	...
	Limmared d.	...	...	|	0728	...	|	|	|	0929	...	|	|	1129	1129	...	|	|	...	|	|	1325	|	|	|	|	...
	Värnamo d.	...	...	|	0808	...	|	|	|	1011	...	|	|	1210	1210	...	|	|	...	|	|	1411	|	|	|	|	...
228	Alvesta a.	...	...	0723	0834	...	0823	0851	0923	1036	...	1023	1123	1235	1235	...	1223	1323	...	1423	1423	1436	1523	1623	1623	1723	...
228	Alvesta d.	...	0631	0735	0836	...	0843	...	0935	1036	...	1035	1135	1235	1235	...	1243	1337	...	1436	1437	1438	1537	1637	1637	1735	...
245	**Växjö** d.	0549	0648	0749	0850	...	0855	...	0949	1050	...	1049	1149	1250	1250	...	1255	1349	...	1447	1449	1452	1549	1648	1649	1749	...
302	Emmaboda ▽ a.	0625	0724	0825	0926	...	...	...	1025	1126	...	1125	1225	1327	1327	...	...	1425	...	...	1525	1527	1625	...	1725	1825	...
302	Emmaboda ▽ d.	0630	0730	0829	0928	...	...	...	1029	1128	...	1129	1229	1329	1329	...	...	1429	...	...	1529	1532	1629	...	1730	1830	...
330	Nybro d.	0644	0743	0843	0943	...	...	...	1043	1143	...	1143	1243	1345	1345	...	...	1443	...	...	1543	1546	1643	...	1743	1843	...
359	**Kalmar** a.	0659	0758	0859	1000	...	...	...	1059	1200	...	1159	1259	1404	1404	...	...	1459	...	...	1559	1602	1659	...	1759	1859	...

	Øtåg Ⓑ		*Øtåg*	*Øtåg*	*Øtåg* Ⓑ	⑦	Ⓐ	*Øtåg*	*Øtåg*	*Øtåg* Ⓑ	*Øtåg*
København H d.	1607	...	1707	1807	1807	...	...	1907	2007	2007	2107
København Lufthavn ✈ d.	1622	...	1722	1822	1822	...	...	1922	2022	2022	2122
Malmö C a.	1646	...	1746	1846	1846	...	...	1946	2046	2046	2146
Malmö C d.	1648	...	1748	1848	1848	...	...	1948	2048	2048	2148
Lund d.	1702	...	1802	1902	1902	...	...	2002	2102	2102	2202
Eslöv d.	1711	...	1811	1911	1911	...	...	2011	2111	2111	2211
Hässleholm d.	1739	...	1839	1935	1939	...	...	2038	2135	2139	2245j
Älmhult d.	1802	...	1902	...	2002	...	...	2102	...	2202	2308
Göteborg C d.	|	1519z	|	...	|	1719r	1729r	|	...	|	|
Borås d.	|	1706	|	...	|	1853	1900	|	...	|	|
Limmared d.	|	1735	|	...	|	1927	1934	|	...	|	|
Värnamo d.	|	1817	|	...	|	2013	2013	|	...	|	|
Alvesta a.	1823	1842	1923	...	2023	2038	2038	2123	...	2223	2329
Alvesta d.	1836	1851	1938	...	2045	2041	2041	2135	...	2236	2336
Växjö d.	1847	1907	1949	...	2057	2054	2054	2147	...	2247	2347
Emmaboda ▽ a.	...	1944	2025	...	...	2129	2129	2224	...	...	...
Emmaboda ▽ d.	...	1945	2030	...	...	2130	2130	2227	...	...	...
Nybro d.	...	2000	2043	...	...	2146	2146	2240	...	...	...
Kalmar a.	...	2018	2059	...	...	2202	2202	2256	...	...	...

km		*Øtåg* Ⓐ	Ⓐ	*Øtåg* Ⓐ	*Øtåg* Ⓐ	*Øtåg* ⚒	*Øtåg*	*Øtåg*	⑥	*Øtåg* Ⓐ	*Øtåg* ⑥	*Øtåg*
	Kalmar d.	...	0454	...	0600	...	...	0700	0754	0800	...	...
	Nybro d.	...	0511	...	0615	...	...	0715	0811	0815	...	...
	Emmaboda ▽ a.	...	0526	...	0629	...	...	0729	0826	0829	...	...
	Emmaboda ▽ d.	...	0528	...	0631	...	...	0731	0830	0831	...	...
	Växjö d.	0517	0606	0617	0710	0710	...	0807	0906	0906	0910	...
	Alvesta a.	0529	0618	0629	0721	0721	...	0817	0918	0917	0921	...
0	Alvesta d.	0532	0619	0632	0732	0732	...	0832	0919	0932	0932	...
49	Värnamo d.	|	0645	|	|	|	...	|	0945	|	|	...
110	Limmared d.	|	0727	|	|	|	...	|	1028	|	|	...
149	Borås d.	|	0757	|	|	|	...	|	1059	|	|	...
222	**Göteborg** C a.	|	0940t	|	|	|	...	|	1230t	|	|	...
	Älmhult d.	0552	...	0652	0752	0752	...	0852	...	0952	0952	...
	Hässleholm d.	0623	...	0723	0823	0823	0823	0923	...	1023	1023	1023
	Eslöv d.	0646	...	0746	0846	0846	0846	0946	...	1046	1046	1046
	Lund d.	0659	...	0759	0859	0859	0859	0959	...	1059	1059	1059
	Malmö C a.	0711	...	0811	0911	0911	0911	1011	...	1111	1111	1111
	Malmö C d.	0713	...	0813	0913	0913	0913	1013	...	1113	1113	1113
	København Lufthavn ✈ a.	0734	...	0834	0934	0934	0934	1034	...	1134	1134	1134
	København H a.	0749	...	0849	0949	0949	0949	1049	...	1149	1149	1149

	Øtåg		*Øtåg* ⚒	*Øtåg*	*Øtåg*	Ⓑ	*Øtåg* Ⓐ	*Øtåg*	*Øtåg*	*Øtåg* Ⓐ	*Øtåg* Ⓑ	*Øtåg*	Ⓐ	*Øtåg*	⚒	*Øtåg* Ⓐ	*Øtåg*	*Øtåg*	⑦	*Øtåg* Ⓐ	*Øtåg* ⑦	*Øtåg*	*Øtåg*	*Øtåg* ⑦	*Øtåg* Ⓐ	*Øtåg*	*Øtåg* Ⓐ
Kalmar d.	0900	0954	...	...	1100	1154	...	...	1300	1400	...	...	...	1500	1554	...	...	1700	1754	1800	...	...	1900	...	2000	...	2100
Nybro d.	0915	1012	...	...	1115	1211	...	...	1315	1415	...	...	...	1515	1611	...	...	1715	1811	1815	...	...	1915	...	2015	...	2115
Emmaboda ▽ a.	0929	1027	...	...	1129	1226	...	...	1329	1429	...	...	...	1529	1626	...	...	1729	1826	1829	...	...	1929	...	2029	...	2129
Emmaboda ▽ d.	0931	1030	...	...	1131	1230	...	...	1331	1431	...	...	...	1531	1630	...	...	1731	1830	1831	...	...	1931	...	2033	...	2131
Växjö d.	1006	1106	1110	...	1206	1306	1312	...	1410	1510	1510	...	...	1611	1706	1712	...	1810	1906	1906	1910	...	2006	2107	2109	...	2204
Alvesta a.	1017	1118	1122	...	1217	1318	1324	...	1422	1521	1521	...	...	1622	1718	1724	...	1821	1918	1918	1921	...	2017	2117	2120	...	...
Alvesta d.	1032	1119	1132	...	1232	1319	1332	...	1432	1532	1532	...	1607	1632	1719	1732	...	1833	1919	1933	1933	...	2033	2132	2132	...	...
Värnamo d.	|	1146	|	...	|	1346	|	...	|	|	|	...	|	|	1747	|	...	|	1946	|	|	...	|	|	|	...	...
Limmared d.	|	1228	|	...	|	1426	|	...	|	|	|	...	|	|	1832	|	...	|	2027	|	|	...	|	|	|	...	...
Borås d.	|	1258	|	...	|	1456	|	...	|	|	|	...	|	|	1902	|	...	|	2057	|	|	...	|	|	|	...	...
Göteborg C a.	|	1440v	|	...	|	1640t	|	...	|	|	|	...	|	|	2040t	|	...	|	2230t	|	|	...	|	|	|	...	...
Älmhult d.	1052	...	1152	...	1252	...	1352	...	1452	1552	1552	...	1627	1652	...	1752	...	1852	...	1952	1952	...	2052	2152	2152	...	...
Hässleholm d.	1123	...	1223	1223	1323	...	1423	1423	1523	1623	1623	1623	1653	1723	...	1823	1823	1923	...	2023	2023	2023	2123	2223	2223	2223	...
Eslöv d.	1146	...	1246	1246	1346	...	1446	1446	1546	1646	1646	1646	1716	1746	...	1846	1846	1946	...	2046	2046	2046	2146	2246	2246	2246	...
Lund d.	1159	...	1259	1259	1359	...	1459	1459	1559	1659	1659	1659	1729	1759	...	1859	1859	1959	...	2059	2059	2059	2159	2259	2259	2259	...
Malmö C a.	1211	...	1311	1311	1411	...	1511	1511	1611	1711	1711	1711	1741	1811	...	1911	1911	2011	...	2111	2111	2111	2211	2311	2311	2311	...
Malmö C d.	1213	...	1313	1313	1413	...	1513	1513	1613	1713	1713	1713	...	1813	...	1913	1913	2013	...	2113	2113	2113	2213	2313	2313	2313	...
København Lufthavn ✈ a.	1234	...	1334	1334	1434	...	1534	1534	1634	1734	1734	1734	...	1834	...	1934	1934	2034	...	2134	2134	2134	2234	2334	2334	2334	...
København H a.	1249	...	1349	1349	1449	...	1549	1549	1649	1749	1749	1749	...	1849	...	1949	1949	2049	...	2149	2149	2149	2249	2349	2349	2349	...

EMMABODA - KARLSKRONA (2nd class only) — Operator: *Krösatågen*

km		Ⓐ	⚒	⚒	⚒		⚒				Ⓑ		Ⓑ		Ⓑ		Ⓑ
0	Emmaboda d.	0634	0734	0834	0934	1034	1134	1234	1334	1434	1534	1634	1734	1834	1949	2034	2134
57	Karlskrona a.	0716	0816	0916	1016	1116	1216	1316	1416	1516	1616	1716	1816	1916	2032	2116	2216

	Ⓐ	⚒	⚒	⚒		⚒				Ⓑ		Ⓑ		Ⓑ		Ⓑ
Karlskrona a.	0541	0641	0741	0841	0941	1041	1141	1241	1341	1441	1541	1641	1741	1841	1938	2041
Emmaboda d.	0625	0725	0825	0925	1025	1125	1225	1325	1424	1525	1625	1725	1825	1925	2021	2125

j – Arrives 2238.

n – Not Sept. 29.

r – 25 – 45 minutes later until Aug. 14.

t – 25 – 45 minutes earlier until Aug. 14.

v – ⑥⑦ (daily until Aug. 16). See also note **t**.

z – ⑥⑦ (daily until Aug. 16); departs up to 10 minutes later on certain dates from Aug. 20. See also note **r**.

▽ – See panel below main table for connecting trains Emmaboda - Karlskrona and v.v.

STOCKHOLM - STOCKHOLM ARLANDA ✈ 747

Operator: A-Train AB (*AEX*) Arlanda Express

Journey time: 18 minutes. All services stop at Arlanda Södra (17 minutes from Stockholm, 2 minutes from Arlanda Norra). Södra serves terminals 2, 3 and 4; Norra serves terminal 5.

From **Stockholm** Central: 0420, 0435, 0450, 0505, 0520, 0535, 0550 and every 15 minutes until 2335; then 0005 and 0035.

From **Arlanda** Norra: 0450, 0505, 0520, 0535, 0550 and every 15 minutes until 2350; then 0005, 0035 and 0105.

STOCKHOLM - HALLSBERG - KARLSTAD - OSLO 750

Service until August 8

km		*VTAB*	*VTAB*	*VTAB*	*VTAB*	*VTAB*	*VTAB*	*VTAB*	*IC* 611	*VTAB*	*VTAB*	*IC* 615	*Sn* 627	*VTAB*	*VTAB*	*IC* 10631	*VTAB*	*VTAB*	*VTAB*	*VTAB*	*VTAB*	*IC* 665	*IC* 635	*VTAB*	*IC* 659	*IC* 679	*IC* 669
		Ⓐz	⑥	Ⓐ	⑦	Ⓐ	⑥	⑦	⚒¶	Ⓐ	⑥	⑦	⚒	⑥	Ⓐ	⑦	⑦	Ⓐ	⑥	Ⓐz	Ⓐ	⑥	Ⓑ	⑦	Ⓐ¶	⑦	⑥
		2	2	2	2	2	2	2	🅁🍷	2	2	🅁🍷	🅁🍷	2	2	🅁🍷	2	2	2	2	2	🅁🍷	🅁🍷	2	🅁🍷	🅁🍷	🅁🍷
0	**Stockholm** C ......△ d.	...	...	...	...	...	...	...	0630	...	...	0726	0933	...	...	1136	...	...	...	...	...	1332	1332	...	1529	1529	1531
36	Södertälje Syd.....△ d.	...	...	...	...	...	...	...	0650**u**	...	...	0746**u**	0953**u**	...	...	1156**u**	...	...	...	...	...	1352**u**	1352**u**	...	|	|	1551**u**
131	Katrineholm.........△ d.	...	...	...	...	...	...	...	0734	...	...	0830	1031	...	...	1240	...	...	...	...	...	1436	1436	...	1631	1631	1635
197	**Hallsberg**...........△ d.	...	...	...	...	...	...	...	0805	...	...	0901	1057	...	...	1311	...	...	...	...	...	1507	1507	...	1701	1701	1711
261	Degerfors.................d.	...	...	...	...	...	...	...	0837	...	...	0936	1124	...	...	1341	...	...	...	...	...	1538	1538	...	1739	1738	1742
287	Kristinehamn.............d.	...	...	...	...	...	...	...	0904	...	...	1004	1137**r**	...	...	1403	...	...	...	...	...	1615	1553**r**	...	1814**j**	1817**j**	1757
327	**Karlstad** ....a.	...	...	...	...	...	...	...	|	...	...	|	...	...	...	...	...	...	...	...	...	|	...	...	|	|	...
327	**Karlstad** ....**751** d.	0531	0710	0749**z**	0847	0928**z**	0934	1017	|	1032**z**	1121	|	...	1359	1433**z**	...	1518	1523**z**	1623	1630	1705**z**	|	...	1734	|	|	...
347	Kil.........................**751** d.	0545	0723	0818**t**	0902	0951	0948	1031	1034	1045	1137	1130	...	1412	1447	...	1530	1541	1637	1644	1720	1749	...	1749	1955	1943	...
395	Arvika.........................d.	0622	0759	0853	0938	1026	1024	1108	1103	1122	1211	1157	...	1448	1522	...	1605	1615	1715	1719	1819	1817	...	1823	2024	2022	...
430	Charlottenberg 🏛.....a.	0649	0824	0916	1003	1051	1049	1132	|	1151	1236	|	...	1513	1548	...	1628	1641	1740	...	1848	|	...	1849	|	|	...
472	Kongsvinger..............a.	0723	0850	...	...	...	...	1200	1149	...	...	1250	...	1539	...	...	1654	...	...	...	...	1922	...	...	2113	2126	...
572	**Oslo** Sentral.............a.	...	1008	...	...	...	...	1314	1309	...	...	1409	...	1709	...	...	1823	...	...	...	...	2022	...	...	2304	2304	...

	VTAB	*VTAB*	*VTAB*	*Sn* 643		*Sn* 645	*VTAB*	*VTAB*	*VTAB*	*IC* 647	
	⑦	Ⓐ	⑦	Ⓑ		⑥	⑥	⑦	Ⓐ	Ⓑz	
	2	2	2	🅁🍷		🅁🍷	2	2	2	🅁🍷	
Stockholm C ....△ d.	...	...	...	1702	...	1832	...	...	...	1932	...
Södertälje Syd......△ d.	...	...	...	1720**u**	...	1851**u**	...	...	...	1952**u**	...
Katrineholm..........△ d.	...	...	...	1800**u**	...	1929	...	...	...	2036	...
Hallsberg............△ d.	...	...	...	1826	...	1957	...	...	...	2111	...
Degerfors.................d.	...	...	...	1855	...	2030	...	...	...	2141	...
Kristinehamn.............d.	...	...	...	1908**r**	...	2043	...	...	...	2157	...
Karlstad ....a.	...	...	...	...	...	...	...	...	...	...	...
Karlstad .... **751** d.	1909	1955**z**	2003	...	...	...	2116	2143	2141**z**	...	...
Kil...................... **751** d.	1922	2014	2015	...	...	...	2130	2156	2156	...	...
Arvika......................d.	2000	2051	2050	...	...	...	2206	2232	2232	...	...
Charlottenberg 🏛 .....a.	2025	2117	...	...	...	...	2231	2257	2300	...	...
Kongsvinger..............a.	...	...	...	...	...	...	...	...	...	...	...
Oslo Sentral.............a.	...	...	...	...	...	...	...	...	...	...	...

	Sn 660	*Sn* 620	*VTAB*	*Sn* 622	*IC* 624	*VTAB*	*VTAB*	*VTAB*	*VTAB*	*IC* 626	*IC* 676	*IC* 616
	Ⓐy	Ⓐe	Ⓐz	⑥	Ⓐd	Ⓐ	Ⓐ	⑦	⑥	B	⑦	Ⓐr
	🅁🍷	🅁🍷	2	🅁🍷	🅁🍷	2	2	2	2	🅁🍷	🅁🍷	🅁🍷
Oslo Sentral.........d.	...	...	...	...	...	...	...	...	...	...	...	0556
Kongsvinger.............d.	...	...	...	...	...	...	...	...	...	...	...	0706
Charlottenberg 🏛 . d.	...	...	...	...	...	0629	0658	0707	0803	...	...	|
Arvika......................d.	...	...	0558	...	...	0653	0721	0730	0828	...	...	0749
Kil.....................**751** d.	...	...	0634	...	...	0735	0759	0806	0907	...	...	0819
Karlstad.........**751** a.	...	...	0646	...	...	0749**z**	0812**z**	0823	0920	...	...	|
Karlstad...............d.	...	...	...	...	...	...	...	...	...	...	...	|
Kristinehamn.........d.	0624	0648**r**	...	0739	0753	...	...	...	...	...	0904	1023
Degerfors ....d.	0638	0703	...	0753	0808	...	...	...	...	0912	0920	1042
Hallsberg..........△ d.	0707	|	...	0822	0852	...	...	...	...	0955	0955	1116
Katrineholm.......△ a.	0733	|	...	0848	0923	...	...	...	...	1026	1026	1147
Södertälje Syd ..△ a.	0820**s**	|	...	0927**s**	1008**s**	...	...	...	...	1111**s**	1111**s**	1232**s**
Stockholm C ...△ a.	0839	0849	...	0946	1031	...	...	...	...	1131	1131	1252

	IC 628	*IC* 678	*VTAB*	*VTAB*	*VTAB*	*VTAB*	*Sn* 634	*VTAB*	*VTAB*	*VTAB*		*IC* 670	*VTAB*	*VTAB*	*IC* 644	*VTAB*	*IC* 666	*IC* 646	*IC* 648	*IC* 658	*VTAB*	*VTAB*	*VTAB*	*VTAB*		*VTAB*	*VTAB*
	⑥	⑦	Ⓐ	Ⓐ	⑥	⑦		⑥	Ⓐ	⑥		Ⓒ	Ⓐ	⑦	Ⓑ	Ⓐ	⑥	Ⓐr	B	⑦	Ⓐ	⑥	⑦	⑥		Ⓐ	⑦
	🅁🍷	🅁🍷	2	2	2	2	🅁🍷	2	2	2		🅁🍷	2	2	🅁🍷	2	🅁🍷	🅁🍷	🅁🍷	🅁🍷	2	2	2	2		2	2
Oslo Sentral.............d.	0636	0649	...	...	...	...	...	1051	...	...	...	...	...	1346	...	...	1451	1516	...	1536	...	...	...	1756	...	...	1936
Kongsvinger..............d.	0755	0809	0828	...	...	...	...	1211	...	...	...	...	...	1457	...	...	1611	1636	...	1655	...	...	...	1906	...	...	2058
Charlottenberg 🏛 .....d.	|	|	0852	1030	1104	1112	...	1235	1341	1343	...	...	1500	1521	...	1622	|	|	...	|	1744	1756	1915	1931	...	2058	2122
Arvika......................d.	0844	0851	0917	1101	1130	1140	...	1259	1403	1407	...	...	1523	1545	...	1655	1653	1721	...	1736	1805	1819	1940	1955	...	2122	2146
Kil........................ **751** d.	0913	0928	0953	1140	1208	1229	...	1336	1440	1447	...	...	1608	1624	...	1750	1748	1754	...	1815	1840	1856	2016	2033	...	2156	2224
Karlstad............ **751** a.	|	|	1006**z**	1153**z**	1224	1242	...	1349	1453**z**	1500	...	...	1624**z**	1637	...	1803**z**	|	|	...	|	1857**z**	1909	2029	2046	...	2209**z**	2240
Karlstad..................d.	|	|	...	...	...	...	...	...	...	...	...	...	...	...	...	...	|	|	...	|	...	...	...	...	...	...	...
Kristinehamn.............d.	1116	1124	...	...	...	...	1346**r**	...	...	...	...	1555	...	...	1743**r**	...	1925**t**	1945**c**	...	2018**c**	...	...	...	...	...	...	...
Degerfors..................d.	1140	1142	...	...	...	...	1401	...	...	...	...	1609	...	...	1758	...	1942	2001	2015	2040	...	...	...	...	...	...	...
Hallsberg............△ d.	1215	1215	...	...	...	...	1431	...	...	...	...	1645	...	...	1839	...	2013	2034	2046	2121	...	...	...	...	...	...	...
Katrineholm ....△ a.	1245	1245	...	...	...	...	1459	...	...	...	...	1720	...	...	1909	...	2043	2104	2116	2151	...	...	...	...	...	...	...
Södertälje Syd ......△ a.	1330**s**	1330**s**	...	...	...	...	1539**s**	...	...	...	...	1805**s**	...	...	1954**s**	...	2140**s**	2155**s**	2203**s**	2244**s**	...	...	...	...	...	...	...
Stockholm C ....△ a.	1350	1350	...	...	...	...	1558	...	...	...	...	1825	...	...	2014	...	2200	2215	2223	2308	...	...	...	...	...	...	...

Mälartåg; 2nd class ★	Ⓐ	⑥	Ⓐ	⑦	Ⓐ	Ⓒ	Ⓐ	Ⓐ	Ⓑ	⑥	Ⓐ	Ⓐ	Ⓐ		⑤	⑦–④
									n	p	k		w	♥		
Stockholm C ....d.	0633	0758	0759	0903	1058	1140	1258	1504	1558	1601	1650	1750	1904	1958	2058	2158
Flemingsberg..............d.	0645	0810	0811	0915	1110	1151	1310	1516	1609	1613	1702	1802	1916	2010	2110	2210
Södertälje Syd............d.	0654	0819	0820	0924	1119	1200	1319	1525	1619	1623	1711	1811	1925	2019	2119	2219
Flen....................**754** d.	0729	0854	0855	0959	1154	1235	1354	1559	1653	1657	1756	1847	1959	2054	2154	2254
Katrineholm ....**754** d.	0741	0906	0914	1016	1206	1247	1406	1611	1710	1709	1810	1858	2011	2106	2206	2306
Hallsberg..................a.	0811	0942	0944	1046	1236	1317	1436**v**	1641	1740	1739	1842	1933	2044	2136	2236	2336

Mälartåg; 2nd class ★	Ⓐ	Ⓐ	⑥	Ⓐ	⑥		⑥	Ⓐ	Ⓒ	Ⓐ	Ⓐ		Ⓐ	⑦	Ⓐ	Ⓑ
					E	D	●								w	
Hallsberg..................d.	0522	0622	0752	0819	0911	0917	1022	1217	1322	1415	1522	1616	1724	1821	1821	2023**b**
Katrineholm ....d.	0554	0654	0824	0855	0943	0949	1054	1249	1354	1446	1554	1648	1756	1858	1858	2055**b**
Flen....................**754** d.	0605	0705	0835	0907	0954	1000	1105	1300	1405	1457	1605	1659	1807	1909	1909	2105
Södertälje Syd ... **754** d.	0641	0741	0911	0942	1030	1036	1141	1336	1441	1533	1641	1735	1843	1945	1947	2142
Flemingsberg.............a.	0651	0751	0921	0952	1040	1046	1151	1346	1451	1543	1651	1745	1853	1955	1957	2161
Stockholm C ....a.	0702	0802	0932	1003	1054	1057	1202	1357	1502	1554	1702	1756	1904	2006	2008	2202

B – Runs on June 14 only. **D** – ⑥⑦ to Aug. 14; ⑦ from Aug. 21. **E** – From Aug. 20.

b – 11 minutes earlier July 3 - Aug. 12 (also June 27 – 29, Aug. 15 – 18).
c – Arrives 23 minutes earlier.
d – Not June 14, 15.
e – June 13 - July 1.
j – Arrives 1758.
k – Timings vary by up to 6 minutes July 11 - Aug. 12.
n – Not ①–⑤ July 2 - Aug. 12.
p – Also ①–⑤ July 2 - Aug. 12.
r – Not June 14.
s – Calls to set down only.
t – Arrives 11 – 13 minutes earlier.
u – Calls to pick up only.
v – 1441 on ⑤.
w – Not June 27 - Aug. 5.
y – July 4 - Aug. 8.
z – Not July 13, 14.
★ – Valid until Dec. 10.

♥ – Daily except ⑤ (runs 2 – 3 minutes later on ⑦).
● – 26 – 29 minutes later on July 30, Aug. 6.
¶ – On June 14 runs Stockholm - Degerfors only (with a different train number).
△ – For other regional services see panel below main table. For other fast services see Table **740**.

KARLSTAD - GÖTEBORG 751

Warning! Services on this route are subject to alteration July 13, 14, Aug. 13, 15, Sept. 6 - Oct. 8 and on ⑤–⑦ Oct. 14 - Nov. 6; please check locally before travelling.

km					*Tågab*			*Tågab*		*Tågab*		*Tågab*	△
		Ⓐ		⚒	⑥G			⑤G	Ⓑ	⑦H		⑦G	⑦–④
0	**Karlstad**.. **750** d.	0613	0812	1015	1050	1213	1415	1531	1612	1700	1813	2119	2229
19	Kil .... **750** d.	0626	0827	1028	1107	1227	1428	1549	1625	1711	1830	2133	2242
70	Säffle..............d.	0658	0900	1100	1139	1258	1501	1618	1659	1747	1901	2209	2314
87	Åmål ....d.	0708	0910	1110	1150	1310	1513	1629	1709	1758	1912	2218	2324
128	Mellerud ....d.	0733	0935	1135	1213	1336	1537	|	1737	1822	1938	|	2348
169	Öxnered ....a.	0753	0956	1155	1239	1356	1557	1727	1757	|	1958	|	0008
179	Trollhättan ......a.	0805	1005	1205	1245	1404	1606	1733	1805	1845	2004	2305	0014
251	**Göteborg** C ...a.	0845	1040	1240	1330	1440	1645	1815	1845	1920	2040	2340	0045

		Tågab			*Tågab*		*Tågab*			*Tågab*		
	Ⓐ	⑥G	Ⓐ		①M	⚒	⑦G			⑥H	Ⓑ	
Göteborg C .... d.	0514	0635	0714	0914	1035	1114	1140	1314	1514	1640	1714	1914
Trollhättan .... d.	0548	0708	0753	0953	1109	1151	1215	1345	1553	1715	1752	1945
Öxnered .... d.	0555	|	0759	1000	|	1158	1222	1355	1559	1721	1758	1957
Mellerud .... d.	0617	0732	0819	1020	1132	1219	1242	1415	1620	1745	1820	2017
Åmål................ d.	0641	0756	0844	1044	1159	1244	1305	1439	1643	1819	1844	2041
Säffle................ d.	0659	0806	0859	1059	1208	1257	1318	1459	1659	1829	1859	2053
Kil............. **750** a.	0729	0841	0930	1132	1253	1329	1346	1530	1730	|	1932	2124
Karlstad.... **750** a.	0744	0854	0945	1148	1306	1344	1400	1543**r**	1746	1922	1947	2139

G – From Aug. 12. **M** – Aug. 15 - Sept. 5 and from Nov. 7. **r** – 1546 on ⑥ to June 24 / from Aug. 20. △ – Subject to alteration on Aug. 14, Oct. 13, 20, 27, Nov. 3.
H – From Aug. 20.

VÄSTERÅS - LUDVIKA 752

2nd class only

km		Ⓐ	Ⓐ	⑥	Ⓐ	Ⓐn	Ⓒ	Ⓐ	Ⓐn	Ⓒ	Ⓐn	Ⓐ	Ⓒ	Ⓐn	Ⓐ	⑦	Ⓐ	⑥	Ⓐ	⑦	Ⓐn	Ⓐ	Ⓒ	Ⓐn	Ⓐ	Ⓐ
0	**Västerås** ....d.	0533	0651	0724	0741	0841	0927	0944	1044	1127	1144	1244	1327	1344	1444	1527	1548	1627	1648	1726	1748	1849	1927	1949	2047	2221
80	Fagersta C ....d.	0636	0751	0826	0839	0940	1027	1042	1141	1227	1241	1342	1427	1441	1542	1627	1645	1729	1746	1826	1847	1947	2027	2046	2145	2318
129	**Ludvika**............a.	0719	...	0914	0923	...	1114	1125	...	1314	...	1425	1514	...	1625	1714	...	1813	1828	1910	...	2030	2111	...	2228	...

	Ⓐ	Ⓐn	Ⓐ	Ⓐn	⑥	Ⓐ	Ⓐn	Ⓒ	Ⓐ	Ⓐn	Ⓒ	Ⓐn	Ⓐ	Ⓒ	Ⓐ	Ⓐ	Ⓒ	Ⓐn	Ⓐ	Ⓒ	Ⓐn	Ⓐ	⑦	Ⓐ	Ⓐn	Ⓐt
Ludvika.............d.	...	0525	0552**t**	...	0654	0729	...	0845	0932	...	1045	...	1231	1245	...	1432	1445	...	1636	1645	...	1837	1837	...	*2052*	2055
Fagersta C ....d.	0539	0611	0641	0712	0740	0815	0917	0931	1018	1117	1131	1217	1317	1331	1417	1518	1531	1622	1722	1731	1822	1923	1931	2021	2143	2143
Västerås ....a.	0636	0708	0738	0811	0840	0912	1014	1031	1115	1214	1231	1314	1414	1431	1514	1617	1631	1719	1819	1830	1919	2020	2031	2118	2240	2240

n – Not July 4 - Aug. 12. **t** – July 4 - Aug. 12 only.

754 LINKÖPING - NORRKÖPING - VÄSTERÅS - SALA

Operator: *Mälartåg* (2nd class only)

km		Ⓐ	Ⓐ		ⒶD		ⒶD		ⒶD		ⒶD		ⒶD	Ⓐ		ⒶD		Ⓐ		Ⓐz
	Linköping .... 730 d.	...	...	0611f	0709	0809	0911	1009	...	1209	1311	1411	1511	...	1611	1711	1811	1911	2011	...
0	**Norrköping** .... 730 d.	...	0538	0638f	0738	0838	0938	1038	1138	1238	1338	1438	1538	1608z	1638	1738	1838	1938	2037	2138
48	Katrineholm........ 750 d.	...	0604	0703f	0804	0904	1004	1104	1204	1304r	1404	1504	1604	1637z	1704	1804	1904	2004	2102	2204
71	Flen .... 750 d.	...	0615	0715f	0815	0915	1015	1115	1215	1315r	1415	1517	1615	1648z	1715	1815	1915	2015	2115	2215
112	Eskilstuna .... d.	0528	0652	0752	0852	0952	1052	1152	1252	1352	1452	1552	1652	1722	1751r	1852	1952	2052	2152	2252
160	**Västerås**.................. d.	0608	0726	0826	0926	1026	1126	1226	1326	1426	1526	1626	1726	1756	1826	1926	2026	2126	2226	2326
199	Sala .... a.	0646	0754	0854	0953	1054	1156t	1254	1354	1453	1556t	1654	1756t	1825	1854	1955	2053	2158	...	...

	Ⓐ	Ⓐ		ⒶD		ⒶD		ⒶD		ⒶD		Ⓐ	ⒶD	Ⓐ	Ⓒ	ⒶD		ⒶD		Ⓐ
Sala........................ d.	...	0603	0703r	0803r	0903r	1003r	1103r	1203r	1303r	1403r	1503r	1537	1603r	1703	1705	1803r	1903r	2005	2105	2206
Västerås .... d.	0529	0634	0734	0834	0934	1034	1134	1234	1334	1434	1534	1604	1634	1734	1734	1834	1934	2034	2134	2234
Eskilstuna.................. d.	0608j	0708	0808	0908	1008	1107	1208	1308	1408	1508	1608	1638	1709	1808	1808	1908	2008	2108	2207	2307
Flen...................750 d.	0646	0742	0845	0943	1042	1143	1243	1345	1443	1545	1643	1717z	1744	1841	1843	1942	2044	2142	...	...
Katrineholm ....750 d.	0701	0757	0859	0957	1057	1157	1257	1401	1457	1559	1656	1730z	1757	1857	1856	1954	2058	2158	...	...
Norrköping.........730 a.	0727	0822	0923	1021	1122	1221	1321	1427	1522	1624	1721	1755z	1822	1922	1921	2020	2123	2222	...	...
Linköping...........730 a.	0753	0849	0950r	...	1149	1249	1349	1453	1549	1650	1754	...	1849	1949	1948	2049	2149	...	...	...

D – Also runs Eskilstuna - Sala and v.v. on ⑥⑦ to June 24 / from Aug. 13.
f – Ⓐ only.
j – Arrives 0601.
r – 2 minutes later on ⑥⑦.
t – 3 minutes earlier on ⑥⑦.
z – Not June 27 - Aug. 5.

755 MJÖLBY - HALLSBERG - ÖREBRO - GÄVLE

2nd class only

Warning! Services Mjölby - Hallsberg - Borlänge and v.v. are subject to alteration July 10 - August 13 (services do not run Mjölby - Hallsberg and may be retimed Hallsberg - Borlänge).

km		Ⓐ	Ⓐ	Ⓐ	Ⓐ	⑥	Ⓐr	Ⓐ	⑥	①–⑥	Ⓐr	①–⑥	⑦	Ⓐr		Ⓐr	⑥	Ⓐ	⊖	Ⓐr		Ⓐr	Ⓑ¶	△	Ⓑ	⑦	Ⓐ	Ⓑr
0	**Mjölby** .... d.	...	...	...	...	...	...	...	...	◧	...	0801	...	...	1001	...	...	...	1201	...	1401	...	...	1601	1801	...	...	2001
27	Motala .... d.	...	...	...	...	...	...	...	...	...	...	0819	...	...	1019	...	...	...	1219	...	1419	...	...	1619	1819	...	...	2019
96	**Hallsberg**......... a.	...	...	...	...	...	...	...	...	...	...	0907	...	...	1107	...	...	...	1307	...	1507	...	...	1700	1907	...	...	2107
	Hallsberg.. 756 d.	...	...	...	0515	0524r	0618	0730	0740r	0820	0832	0916	0937r	1020	1116	1220	1220	1242	1316	1431	1518	1620	1641t	1711	1924	1949	1949	2116
121	**Örebro** C .. 756 a.	...	...	...	0535	0544r	0638	0750	0800r	0841	0852	0936	0957r	1041	1136	1241	1241	1302	1336	1451	1538	1641	1701t	1731	1944	2009	2009	2136
	Örebro C .... d.	...	...	...	0549	0546r	0650	0751	0801r	0848	0853	0952	0959r	1053	1152	1253	1253	1305	1352	1453	1552	1653	1704	1740	1951	2010	2010	2153
146	Frövi................. d.	...	...	...	0604	0601r	0705	0807	0816r	0903	0908	1007	1014r	1108	1207	1308	1308	1320	1407	1508	1607	1708	1719	1755	2006	2027	2027	2208
204	Kopparberg ...... d.	...	...	...	0648	0645r	0748	0853	0859r	|	0954	1052	1056r	1156	1255	1357	|	|	1450	1554	1654	1758	|	1839	2049	|	|	2250
232	Grängesberg .... d.	...	...	...	0711	0706r	0812	0924	0921r	|	1015	1124	1124r	1217	1323	1418	|	|	1516	1619	1721	1825	|	1900	2111	|	|	2317
247	Ludvika .... d.	...	...	0631	0724	0718r	0829	0935	0933r	|	1026	1137	1137r	1230	1338e	1438	|	|	1528	1632	1733	1837	|	1912	2123	|	|	2327
295	**Borlänge** .... a.	...	...	0659	0752	0746r	0905	1007	1000r	|	1103	1204	1204r	1257	1406	1509	|	|	1556	1700	1804	1905	|	1940	2152	|	|	2357
	Borlänge .. 758 d.	0530	...	0700	0800	0804	0907	1008	1008	|	1104	1205	1205	1304	1407	1511	|	|	1606	1701	1807	1913	|	2010	...	|	|	...
317	Falun......... 758 d.	0552	...	0719	0822	0822	0925	1026	1026	|	1122	1225	1225	1329f	1427	1529	|	|	1629	1718	1827	1931	|	2027	...	|	|	...
	Fagersta .... d.	|	0602	|	|	|	|	|	|	0949	|	|	|	|	|	|	1353	1409	|	|	|	|	1808	|	...	2112	2124	...
	Avesta Krylbo d.	|	0628	|	|	|	|	|	|	1016	|	|	|	|	|	|	1419	1435	|	|	|	|	1834	|	...	2139	2151	...
371	Storvik.............. d.	0628	0707	0759	0903	0903	1005	1105	1105	1054	1202	1305	1305	1405	1506	1605	1457	1513	1705	1803	1905	2007	1912	2105b	...	2216	2236	...
385	Sandviken .... d.	0639	0717	0810	0914	0914	1016	1116	1116	1106	1213	1316	1316	1416	1516	1615	1508	1524	1716	1816	1916	2017	1924	2116b	...	2226	2246	...
408	**Gävle**.............. a.	0655	0737	0826	0930	0930	1036	1136	1132	1122	1229	1336	1332	1436	1536e	1636	1524	1544	1736	1836	1932	2035	1942	2132b	...	2242	2302	...

km		Ⓐ	Ⓐ	Ⓐ	⑥	Ⓐr	v	①–⑥	Ⓐr	Ⓐ	Ⓒ	Ⓐr	⑦	①–⑥	⑦	Ⓐ	Ⓐr		Ⓐr		Ⓐr	⊗	Ⓐ	⑦		⑦	Ⓐ	Ⓑ
0	**Gävle**.............. d.	...	0415	0407r	...	0510	0607t	0817	0714	0823	0823k	0923	1025	1021	1033	1211	1121	1223	1321	1421	1521	1621	1628	1633	1821	1827	1906	2017
23	Sandviken .... d.	...	0431	0423r	...	0525	0623t	0833	0731	0839	0839k	0939	1041	1037	1048	1233	1137	1239	1337	1437	1537	1637	1644	1649	1838	1843	1927	2037
37	Storvik.............. d.	...	0441	0433r	...	0535	0638t	0843	0743	0849	0849k	0949	1051	1047	1058	1243	1147	1249	1347	1447	1547	1647	1654	1659	1848	1853	1937	2046
95	Avesta Krylbo d.	...	0521	|	...	|	|	0924	|	|	|	|	1131	|	|	1324	|	|	|	|	|	|	1735	1740	|	1933	2018	|
130	Fagersta .... d.	...	0548	|	...	|	|	0950	|	|	|	|	1155	|	|	1349	|	|	|	|	|	|	1806	1806	|	1959	2043	|
	Falun......... 758 d.	...	|	0514r	...	0620	0721t	|	0823	0926	0926k	1030	|	1141f	1135	|	1231	1331	1427	1530	1636f	1729	|	|	1930	...	...	2130
	Borlänge .. 758 a.	...	|	0531r	...	0641	0738t	|	0840	0943	0943k	1047	|	1158	1153	|	1248	1348	1444	1547	1653	1746	|	|	1950	...	...	2147
	Borlänge .... d.	...	|	0548	0602	0642	0759	|	0848	0954	0959	1049	|	1203	1203	|	1256	1349	1446	1600	1700	1751	|	|	2011b	...	...	...
	Ludvika .... d.	...	|	0617	0631	0720	0828	|	0920	1025	1027	1119	|	1232	1232	|	1324	1424	1525	1630	1729	1821	|	|	2040b	...	...	...
	Grängesberg .... d.	...	|	0628	0642	0732	0839	|	0934	1037	1038	1134	|	1243	1243	|	1335	1435	1537	1641	1741	1836	|	|	2053b	...	...	...
	Kopparberg ...... d.	...	|	0649	0708	0752	0900	|	0955	1057	1058	1155	|	1303	1303	|	1356	1455	1558	1701	1802	1901	|	|	2119b	...	...	...
202	Frövi................. d.	...	0642	0741	0752	0839	0944	1034	1041	1141	1142	1241	1240	1346	1346	1433	1441	1542e	1642	1749	1851	1947	1854	1850	2205b	...	...	...
228	**Örebro** C .... a.	...	0658	0757	0811	0855	1000	1050	1057	1157	1202	1257	1256	1406	1406	1449	1457	1558e	1658	1806	1906	2006	1912	1906	2221b	...	...	...
	Örebro C .. 756 d.	0617	0659	0817	0817	0856	1017	1051t	1110	1217	1217	1310	1310	1417	1417	1450	...	1622	1714	1817	1919	2017h	1912	1910	2222b	...	...	...
252	**Hallsberg**.. 756 a.	0637	0719	0837	0837	0916	1037	1111t	1131	1237	1237	1331	1331	1437	1437	1510	...	1642	1735	1837	1940	2037h	1932	1930	2242b	...	...	...
	Hallsberg......... d.	0646	...	0846	0846	...	1046	...	...	1246	1246	...	...	1446	1446	...	...	1644	...	1846b	...	2046b	...	...	...	...	...	...
	Motala............... d.	0728	...	0928	0928	...	1128	...	...	1328	1328	...	...	1528	1528	...	...	1728	...	1928b	...	2128b	...	...	...	...	...	...
	Mjölby .... a.	0744	...	0944	0944	...	1144	...	...	1344	1344	...	...	1544	1544	...	...	1745	...	1944b	...	2144b	...	...	...	...	...	...

b – Not ⑥.
e – 3–5 minutes earlier on Ⓒ.
f – Arrives 8–10 minutes earlier.
h – 8 minutes earlier on ⑥.
k – ⑥ only.
r – Not July 3 - Aug. 13.
t – ①–⑤ only.
v – Not ⑦ July 10 - Aug. 7.
⊗ – Does not run Borlänge - Hallsberg on ⑥ July 9 - Aug. 13.
◧ – 2–5 minutes later Örebro - Gävle on ⑥.
⊖ – Change trains at Borlänge on ①–⑥.
¶ – On ⑦ Örebro d. 1708, Frövi d. 1723, Fagersta d. 1808, Avestra d. 1835, Storvik d. 1918, Sandviken d. 1928, Gävle a. 1944.
△ – On ⑦ Kopparberg d. 1837, Grängesberg d. 1859, Ludvika d. 1918, Borlänge a. 1946, d. 2011, Falun d. 2029 and then as shown.

756 STOCKHOLM - VÄSTERÅS - ÖREBRO - HALLSBERG - GÖTEBORG

See Table **740** for fast services Stockholm - Hallsberg - Skövde - Göteborg and v.v. See Table **732** for Stockholm - Örebro via Eskilstuna.

Warning! Journeys from / to Stockholm are subject to alteration July 2–31. Journeys to / from Göteborg are subject to alteration July 25 - Aug. 16 and ⑤–⑦ Oct. 14 - Nov. 6.

km		①–⑤ w	①–⑥	①–⑥	①–⑤ v2◇	⑦	⑥	Ⓐ	①–⑥ w		w		w			Ⓑ	⑥	d	①–⑤ w		Ⓑ	e	⑦	①–⑥	Ⓑ
0	**Stockholm C** .... ‡ d.	...	...	0614	...	...	0714	0714	0814	0914	1014	1114	1214	1314	1414	1514	1514	1614	1636	1714	1814	1914	2006	2014	2214
72	Enköping .... ‡ d.	...	...	0655	...	...	0755	0755	0855	0955	1055	1155	1255	1355	1455	1555	1555	1655	1721	1755	1855	1955	2050	2055	2255
107	**Västerås** .... ‡ d.	0512	0612	0712	...	0812	0812	0812	0912	1012	1112	1212	1312	1412	1512	1612	1612	1712	1740	1812	1912	2012	2109	2112	2312
141	Köping........................d.	0529	0629	0729	...	0829	0829	0829	0929	1029	1129	1229	1329	1429	1529	1629	1629	1729	1804	1829	1929	2029	2128	2129	2329
159	Arboga........................d.	0542	0641	0741	...	0841	0841	0841	0941	1041	1141	1241	1341	1441	1541	1641	1641	1741	1817	1841	1941	2041	2139	2141	2340
205	**Örebro** C ....a.	0603	0702	0802	...	0902	0902	0902	1004	1102	1204r	1302	1402	1502	1602	1702	1702	1802	1846	1902	2002	2102	2202	2202	0002
205	**Örebro** C .... 755 d.	0609	0725	0803	0813	0914	0914	0914	1005	1110	1205r	1310	1403	1512	1603	1714	1727	1803	1848	1919	2003	2103	2203	2203	0003
230	**Hallsberg**..... 736 755 d.	0632	0749	0824	0834	0939	0939	0939	1026	1133	1226r	1339	1424	1535	1624	1737	1750	1824	1911	1950j	2024	2124	2224	2224	0024
260	Laxå .... 736 d.	0647	0804	...	0849	0954	0954	0954	...	1148	...	1353	...	1550	...	1752	1805	...	...	2005	...	...	...	...	...
305	Töreboda......................d.	0706	0823	...	0908	1023	1023	1023	...	1219	...	1421	...	1609	...	1823	1824	...	...	2024	...	...	...	...	...
344	**Skövde** ....d.	0723	0840	...	0925	1039	1039	1041	...	1239	...	1439	...	1639	...	1840	1840	...	...	2040	...	...	...	...	...
374	Falköping......................a.	0739	0855	...	0941	1054	1054	1056	...	1254	...	1454	...	1654	...	1855	1855	...	...	2055	...	...	...	...	...
408	Herrljunga........... 736 a.	0803	0911	...	1012	1110	1110	1112	...	1310	...	1510	...	1710	...	1911	1911	...	...	2111	...	...	...	...	...
443	Alingsås.......................a.	0825	0932	...	1034	1132	1132	1134	...	1332	...	1532	...	1732	...	1932	1932	...	...	2132	...	...	...	...	...
488	**Göteborg** C ....a.	0905	1000t	...	1103	1200	1200	1205	...	1400	...	1600	...	1800	...	2000	2000	...	...	2200	...	...	...	...	...

	①–⑤	①–⑤ w	①–⑥ s		⑥	Ⓑ	①–⑥	⑦	b		w		w		z		d		Ⓑ w			①–④ w	⑦ w		Ⓑ
Göteborg C................d.	...	...	...	...	...	...	0559	...	...	0759	...	0959	...	1159	...	1359	...	1559	...	1759	...	1855	1859	...	...
Alingsås......................d.	...	...	...	...	...	...	0627	...	...	0826	...	1026	...	1226	...	1426	...	1626	...	1826	...	1921	1926	...	...
Herrljunga............736 d.	...	...	...	...	...	...	0649	...	...	0849	...	1049	...	1249	...	1449	...	1649	...	1849	...	1942	1947	...	...
Falköping.....................d.	...	...	...	...	...	...	0705	...	...	0905	...	1105	...	1305	...	1505	...	1706	...	1905	...	2002	2014	...	...
Skövde ....d.	...	...	...	...	...	...	0720	...	...	0920	...	1120	...	1320	...	1520	...	1721	...	1920	...	2020	2033	...	...
Töreboda......................d.	...	...	...	...	...	...	0736	...	...	0936	...	1136	...	1336	...	1536	...	1736	...	1936	...	2036	2048	...	...
Laxå ....736 d.	...	...	...	...	...	...	0756	...	...	0955k	...	1202	...	1355k	...	1603	...	1755	...	2003	...	2103	2107	...	...
Hallsberg...... 736 755 d.	0534	0554	0634	...	0732	0734	0820	0834	0934	1020	1134	1220	1334	1420	1534	1620	1734	1820	1934	2020	...	2120	2123	...	2220
Örebro C.............755 a.	0555	0615	0655	...	0753	0755	0841	0855	0955	1041	1155	1241	1355	1441	1555	1641	1755	1841	1955	2041	...	2141	2144	...	2241
Örebro C....................d.	0557	0616	0657	...	0755	0757	0857	0857	0957	1057	1157	1257	1357	1457	1557	1657	1757	1857	1957	2057	...	2157	2157	...	2243
Arboga........................d.	0618	0642	0718	...	0818	0818	0918	0918	1018	1118	1218	1318	1418	1518	1618	1718	1818	1918	2018	2118	...	2218	2218	...	2304
Köping........................d.	0629	0658	0729	...	0829	0829	0929	0929	1029	1129	1229	1329	1429	1529	1629	1729	1829	1929	2029	2129	...	2229	2229	...	2315
Västerås .... ‡ d.	0648	0719	0748	...	0849	0848	0948	0948	1048	1148	1248	1348	1448	1548	1648	1748	1848	1948	2048	2148	...	2248	2248	...	2337
Enköping .... ‡ d.	0703	0736	0803	...	0906	0903	1003	1003	1103	1203	1303	1403	1503	1603	1703	1803	1903	2003	2103	2203	...	2303	2303	...	...
Stockholm C .... ‡ a.	0744	0821	0844	...	0951	0944	1044	1044	1144	1244	1344	1444	1544	1644	1744	1844	1944	2044	2144	2244	...	2344	2344	...	...

b – ①–⑥ to July 2; ⑥ July 9 - Aug. 6; ①–⑥ from Aug. 13.
d – Daily to July 1; ①–⑤ July 4 - Aug. 12; daily from Aug. 14.
e – Daily to July 2; ⑥ July 9 - Aug. 6; daily from Aug. 13.
j – Arrives 1940.
k – 7–8 minutes later on ①–⑤ to July 1 / from Aug. 15.
r – 2 minutes later on ⑥.
s – Also ⑦ July 3 - Aug. 7
t – 1005 on ①–⑤ from Aug. 17.
v – Not June 27 - Aug. 12.
w – Not July 2 - Aug. 13.
z – Not ⑥ July 2 - Aug. 13.
◇ – Operated by Västtågen.
‡ – Additional trains operate Stockholm - Västerås and v.v.

STOCKHOLM - BORLÄNGE - FALUN and MORA 758

Warning! From July 2 to August 7 trains may depart Stockholm up to 3 minutes earlier (train numbers may also vary during this period).

km			IC	IC	IC	IC		IC	IC		IC	IC	IC	IC		IC	IC	IC				IC		
			12	**32**	**10014**	**14**		**42**	**16**		**36**	**18**	**20**	**46**		**22¶**	**54‡**	**48/58**				**26**		**8202**
		①–⑤	①–⑤	①–⑥	⑥	①–⑤				①–⑤			①–⑥	⑦			⑧		①–⑥	⑦		⑧		①–⑤
		n	z	A	n	n		n	A	n	A	n					n					b		n
		⊖2	R 🍷	R 🍷	R 🍷	R 🍷		R 🍷	R 🍷	2	R 🍷	R 🍷	R 🍷	R 🍷		R 🍷	R 🍷	R 🍷	2	2		R 🍷		2
0	**Stockholm** C ♠ d.	...	0614	0744	0744	0747	...	0944	0944	...	1144	1144	1344	1344	...	1546	1646	1744	...	...	...	1944	...	2221
39	Arlanda C ✈ ♠ d.	...	0635	0806	0804	0807	...	1006	1006	...	1206	1206	1406	1406	...	1606	1706u	1806	...	...	...	2006	...	2242
69	Uppsala ♠ d.	...	0655	0825	0825	0825	...	1025	1025	...	1225	1225	1425	1425	...	1625	1725u	1825	...	...	...	2025	...	2301
131	Sala d.	0604	0740	0900	0900	0900	...	1100	1100	...	1300	1300	1500	1500	...	1700	1803	1900	...	...	...	2100	...	2338
164	Avesta Krylbo d.	0635	0758	0920	0920	0920	...	1120	1120	...	1320	1320	1520	1520	...	1719	1822	1920	...	...	...	2120	...	2358
229	**Borlänge** 755 ▽ d.	0722	0841	1014	1010	1010	...	1212	1209	1304	1412	1409	1609	1612	...	1810	1858	2004	2010	2011	...	2203	...	0042
253	**Falun** 755 a.	0744	0858	|	1029	1029	...	|	1227	1321	|	1428	1629	|	...	1827	1920	|	2026	2028	...	2220	...	0100
	Leksand ▽ d.	...	...	1051	...	...	...	1249	...	...	1449	...	...	1649	...	...	...	2041	...	...	...	...	...	...
	Rättvik ▽ d.	...	...	1109	...	...	...	1307	...	...	1507	...	...	1707	...	...	...	2059	...	...	...	...	...	...
	Mora ▽ a.	...	...	1134	...	...	...	1331	...	...	1531	...	...	1731	...	...	...	2124	...	...	...	...	...	...

	IC	IC	IC		IC	IC		IC	IC		IC	IC		IC	IC		IC	IC			IC	IC	IC	IC
	13	**53**	**51**		**41**	**15**		**43**	**17**		**55**	**19**		**31**	**21**		**23**	**47**	**8201**		**25**	**39**	**49**	**27**
	①–⑤	⑥	①–⑤	①–⑤	①–⑤	⑥	①–⑥	⑥	⑧		⑦								①–⑤				⑦	①–⑤
	c	n	n								n	D		A	n		A	n	n		n	A		n
	R 🍷	R 🍷	R 🍷	2	R 🍷	R 🍷	2	R 🍷	R 🍷		R 🍷	R 🍷	2	R 🍷	R 🍷	2	R 🍷	R 🍷	2	2	R 🍷	R 🍷	R 🍷	R 🍷
Mora ▽ d.	...	...	...	...	0628	...	...	0827	...	...	1030	...	...	1233	...	...	...	1432	...	...	...	1622	1822	...
Rättvik ▽ d.	...	...	...	...	0652	...	...	0851	...	...	1054	...	...	1257	...	...	...	1456	...	...	...	1646	1846	...
Leksand ▽ d.	...	...	...	...	0710	...	...	0909	...	...	1112	...	...	1315	...	...	...	1514	...	...	...	1706	1906	...
Falun 755 d.	0528	0612	0612	0721	|	0736	0926	|	0935	...	|	1136	1331	|	1336	1530	1535	|	1629	1729	1734	|	|	1929
Borlänge 755 ▽ d.	0550	0630	0631	0738	0751	0755	0943	0954	0954	...	1154	1154	1348	1354	1354	1547	1554	1554	1648	1746	1753	1753	1948	1948
Avesta Krylbo d.	0634	0710	0708	...	0839	0838	...	1036	1036	...	1236	1236	...	1436	1436	...	1636	1637	1741	...	1839	1835	2035	2035
Sala d.	0655	0728	|	...	0900	0900	...	1100	1100	...	1300	1300	...	1458	1458	...	1700	1700	1805	...	1900	1900	2100	2100
Uppsala ♠ d.	0732	0804s	0802s	...	0935	0935	...	1135	1135	...	1335	1335	...	1535	1535	...	1735	1735	1902	...	1934	1934	2137	2137
Arlanda C ✈ ♠ a.	0751	0821s	0824s	...	0952	0952	...	1152	1152	...	1352	1352	...	1552	1552	...	1752	1752	1922	...	1951	1951	2154	2154
Stockholm C ♠ a.	0813	0844	0843	...	1015	1015	...	1215	1215	...	1415	1415	...	1615	1615	...	1815	1815	1944	...	2014	2015	2217	2217

Other local services **BORLÄNGE - MORA** (2nd class only)

km											
		①–⑤		⑦	①–⑥			①–⑥		Ⓐ	⑧
			D	n	n	A	n			n	
0	**Borlänge** d.	0634	0852	1020	1024	1223	1422	1620	1818	2128	2214
43	Leksand d.	0707	0926	1053	1059	1256	1455	1651	1851	2205	2247
63	Rättvik d.	0725	0941	1111	1114	1314	1513	1707	1906	2220	2302
103	**Mora** ♣ a.	0748	1004	1134	1137	1337	1537	1729	1929	2243	2325
104	Morastrand ♣ a.	0752	1008	1138	1141	1341	1541	1733	1933	2247	2329

	①–⑤	①–⑤	⑥	⑧					①–⑥	⑧
		n		◧	D	n	A	n		
Morastrand ♣ d.	0503	0556	0626	0823	1020	1218	1418	1618	1818	2027
Mora ♣ d.	0508	0601	0631	0828	1025	1223	1423	1623	1823	2032
Rättvik d.	0532	0625	0655	0852	1049	1247	1447	1647	1847	2056
Leksand d.	0547	0640	0710	0908	1113	1305	1505	1705	1905	2114
Borlänge a.	0618	0714	0741	0944	1144	1336	1536	1740	1936	2145

A – July 3 - Aug. 13 only.
D – ①–⑥ (daily June 27 - Aug. 13).
b – Not July 18–22, 25–29, Aug. 1–5, 8–12.
c – Not July 19–22, 25–29, Aug. 1–5, 8–12.
n – Not July 3 - Aug. 13.

s – Calls to set down only.
u – Calls to pick up only.
z – Not July 5 - Aug. 12.
◧ – Departure times are 3–4 minutes later on ⑦.
⊖ – From Västerås (d. 0535).

¶ – **10052** on ⑥⑦ to June 26 / from Aug. 13 (also June 27 - July 1, Aug. 8–12).
‡ – **10054** on ⑦ (also June 27 - July 1).
▽ – See also panel below main table.
♠ – Frequent local services operate Stockholm - Uppsala and v.v.
♣ – Local journeys are not permitted Mora - Morastrand and v.v.

STOCKHOLM - SUNDSVALL - UMEÅ 760

Warning! From July 2 to August 7 trains may depart Stockholm up to 3 minutes earlier (train numbers may also vary during this period).
Connecting services Sundsvall - Umeå and v.v. are operated by *NT*. For additional services Stockholm - Gävle and v.v. see Table **761**. For sleeper services see Table **767**.

km		*NT*	*NT*	*Sn*	*NT*	*NT*	*Sn*	*NT*	*NT*	*Sn*	*Sn*	*NT*	*Sn*	*Sn*	*NT*	*Sn*	*Sn*	*IC*	*NT*	*Sn*	*NT*	*Sn*	*Sn*	*Sn*	*Sn*	*Sn*	*Sn*
				590			**560**			**562**	**564**		**566**	**568**		**570**	**572**	**6/8/10**		**576**		**578**	**20580**	**580**	**582**	**584**	**588**
		2	2	R 🍷	2	2	R 🍷	2	2	R 🍷	R 🍷	2	R 🍷	R 🍷	2	R 🍷	R 🍷	R 🍷	2	R 🍷	2	R 🍷	R 🍷	R 🍷	R 🍷	R 🍷	R 🍷
		①–⑤	①–⑤	①–⑤	①–⑥	⑦	①–⑥	①–⑤	⑥	①–⑤	⑥⑦		⑧	⑥		⑧			①–⑤		⑥⑦	⑧	⑥	⑧	⑧		⑦
		f		n			v					f△	w	m	△	w		⊙				n	d	n¶	w‡		n
0	**Stockholm** C. d.	...	...	0350	...	...	0621	...	...	0721	0821	...	0921	1021	...	1121	1221	1311	...	1421	...	1521	1621	1621	1721	1821	2021
39	Arlanda C ✈ ◧ d.	...	...	0410	...	...	0642	...	...	0742	0842	...	0942	1042	...	1142	1242	1334	...	1442	...	1542	1641	1641	1742	1842	2042
69	Uppsala ◧ d.	...	...	0428	...	...	0700	...	...	0801	0900	...	1000	1100	...	1200	1300	1355	...	1500	...	1600	1700	1700	1800	1900	2100
182	**Gävle** C d.	...	...	0512	...	...	0745	...	...	0845	0945	...	1045	1145	...	1245	1345	1447	...	1545	...	1645	1745	1745	1845	1945	2145
260	Söderhamn d.	...	...	0556	...	...	0830	...	...	0930	1030	...	1131	1230	...	1330	1430	1530	...	1630	...	1728	1830	1830	1930	2028	2227
314	Hudiksvall d.	...	...	0631	...	...	0858	...	...	0958	1058	...	1158	1258	...	1358	1458	1600	...	1658	...	1758	1858	1858	1958	2056	2255
402	**Sundsvall** C a.	...	...	0738	...	...	0953	...	...	1055	1156	...	1256	1353	...	1456	1553	1706	...	1756	...	1853	1953	1953	2053	2151	2350
402	**Sundsvall** C d.	0513	0713	...	0808c	0906	0957	1013	1113	...	1200e	1213	...	...	1413	*1513*	1557	...	1714	...	1813	1858	1957	...	2058z	...	...
470	Härnösand d.	0605	0805	...	0905	1000	1045	1106	1204	...	1248e	1306	...	...	1504	*1605*	1645	...	1811	...	1904	1950	2045	...	2149z	...	...
516	Kramfors d.	0633	0832	...	0931	1025	1109	1132	1232	...	1312e	1331	...	...	1529	*1630*	1709	...	1836	...	1929	2014	2109	...	2213z	...	...
603	Örnsköldsvik C d.	0718	0918	...	1015	1113	1144	1216	1312	...	1347e	1412	...	...	1615	*1712*g	1744	...	1916	...	2012	2049	2144	...	2248z	...	...
713	**Umeå** Östra ◐ a.	0817	1018	...	1118	1211	1228	1318	1418	...	1433e	1522	...	...	1721	*1818*	1828	...	2018	...	2115	2134	2228	...	2332z	...	...
715	**Umeå** C a.	0825	1022	...	1122	1215	1232	1322	1422	...	1437e	1526	...	...	1725	*1822*	1832	...	2022	...	2123	2138	2232	...	2336z	...	...

	Sn	*Sn*	*Sn*	*NT*	*Sn*	*Sn*	*Sn*	*Sn*	*NT*	*Sn*	*Sn*	*NT*	*Sn*	*Sn*	*IC*	*NT*	*NT*	*Sn*	*Sn*	*Sn*	*NT*	*NT*	*Sn*	*NT*	*NT*	*NT*	*Sn*
	561	**563**	**565**		**567**	**569**	**571**	**573**		**575**	**575**		**577**	**579**	**11**			**583**	**585**	**587**			**589**				**599**
	R 🍷	R 🍷	R 🍷	2	R 🍷	R 🍷	R 🍷	R 🍷	2	R 🍷	R 🍷		R 🍷	R 🍷	R 🍷	2	2	R 🍷	R 🍷	R 🍷	2	2	R 🍷	2	2	2	R 🍷
	①–⑤	①–⑥	①–⑤	①–⑤		①–⑤	⑥⑦	⑧	⑥	①–⑤	⑥⑦	⑦	⑦			⑥	⑧		⑧	⑥	⑦	①–⑤	⑧	⑥	①–⑤	⑧	⑦
	n	v	n										n		⊙			v	w◇	v		f	k				n
Umeå C d.	...	...	0422	0436	...	0622	0720	0819j	0836	*0836*f	0913	0936	...	*1036*	...	1236	1236	...	1422	1513	1536	1536	1614e	1636	1636	1736	...
Umeå Östra ◧ d.	...	...	0426	0438	...	0626	0724	0823j	0838	*0838*f	0917	0938	...	*1038*	...	1238	1238	...	1426	1517	1538	1538	1618e	1638	1638	1738	...
Örnsköldsvik C d.	...	...	0508	0538	...	0708	0806	0908j	0936	*0937*f	0959	1036	...	*1142*	...	1336	1335	...	1508	1559	1635	1635	1700e	1742	1734	1836	...
Kramfors d.	...	...	0544	0623	...	0744	0842	0944j	1020	*1022*f	1036	1120	...	*1222*	...	1417	1417	...	1544	1635	1719	1730	1741e	1823	1817	1917r	...
Härnösand d.	...	...	0607	0649	...	0807	0905	1007j	1045	*1046*f	1104	1145	...	*1248*	...	1443	1441	...	1607	1704	1744	1754	1804e	1848	1844	1948	...
Sundsvall C a.	...	...	0659	0748	...	0859	0957	1101j	1148	*1144*f	1200	1248	...	*1344*	...	1538	1548	...	1701	1757	1848	1848	1859e	1943	1949	2048	...
Sundsvall C d.	0509	0605	0702	...	0806	0903	1006	1105	...	1206	1206	...	1303	1406	1455	...	...	1606	1706	1802	...	...	1903	...	...	...	2054
Hudiksvall d.	0603	0700	0756	...	0900	1000	1100	1200	...	1300	1300	...	1400	1500	1557	...	...	1700	1800	1858	...	...	2000	...	...	...	2157
Söderhamn d.	0631	0728	0828	...	0928	1029	1128	1228	...	1328	1328	...	1428	1528	1629	...	...	1728	1828	1926	...	...	2028	...	...	...	2225
Gävle C d.	0716	0816	0915	...	1016	1116	1216	1316	...	1416	1416	...	1516	1616	1727	...	...	1816	1916	2016	...	...	2116	...	...	...	2310
Uppsala ◐ a.	0759	0859	0959	...	1059	1159	1259	1359	...	1459	1459	...	1559	1659	1819	...	...	1859	1959	2059	...	...	2201	...	...	...	2356
Arlanda C ✈ ◐ a.	0819	0917	1017	...	1117	1217	1317	1417	...	1517	1517	...	1616	1717	1838	...	...	1917	2022t	2117	...	...	2217	...	...	...	0017
Stockholm C a.	0838	0938	1038	...	1138	1238	1338	1438	...	1538	1538	...	1638	1738	1902	...	...	1938	2043t	2138	...	...	2238	...	...	...	0038

Other local services **GÄVLE - SUNDSVALL** (operated by *XT*, 2nd class only)

	①–⑤	⑦	⑥	①–⑤	①–⑤	⑥	①–⑤	⑦	①–⑤	⊖	⑦	①–⑥
Gävle C d.	0612	0744	0850	0921	1141	1259	1310	1506	1611	1707	2112	2115
Söderhamn d.	0704	0828	0941	1007	1227	1346	1402	1555	1700	1756	2158	2158
Hudiksvall d.	0736	0859	1012	1038	1259	1414	1431	1637	1742	1828	2234	2227
Sundsvall C a.	0842	0957	1118	1143	1358	1519	1545	1743	1842	1935	2332	2325

	①–⑤	⑥⑦	①–⑤	⑦	①–⑤	⑥	⑧w§	⑥	①–⑤	⑦	⊡	①–⑤
Sundsvall C d.	0531	0841	0931	1030	1232	1305	1424	1530	1616	1755	1953	2134
Hudiksvall d.	0634	0941	1036	1131	1332	1412	1531	1634	1716	1856	2057	2244
Söderhamn d.	0703	1010	1105	1202	1404	1446	1602	1703	1745	1928	2126	2313
Gävle C a.	0746	1109	1149	1248	1448	1534	1652	1746	1837	2027	2214	2400

c – 0813 on ⑥.
d – Runs daily July 2 - Aug. 13.
e – ⑥⑦ July 3 - Aug. 13.
f – Not ①–⑤ June 27 - Aug. 12.
g – *1719* on ⑦.
j – Not ⑦.
k – Also July 9, 16, 23, 30, Aug. 6, 13.
m – Also July 3, 10, 17, 24, 31, Aug. 7.
n – Not July 3 - Aug. 13.
r – 1924 on ①–⑤.

t – 5 minutes earlier on ①–⑤ (except on July 1, ②④ July 5 - Aug. 4).
v – Not July 9, 16, 23, 30, Aug. 6, 13.
w – Not July 3, 10, 17, 24, 31, Aug. 7.
z – Not ①–⑤ July 4 - Aug. 12.

◧ – Trains call to pick up only.
◐ – Trains call to set down only.
§ – Runs 12–16 minutes later on ⑦.
¶ – Train number **20580** on ⑦ (also June 27 - July 1).
‡ – Train number **20582** on ⑦ (also June 27 - July 1).

◇ – Train number **10585** on ⑦ (also July 1 and ②④ July 5 - Aug. 4).
△ – Timings may vary by up to 4 minutes (earliest departures shown).
⊙ – To / from Duved (Table **761**).
⊡ – Sunsvall d. 1959 on ⑥. Runs 14–22 minutes later on ⑦.
⊖ – On ⑥ Gävle d. 1657, Söderhamn d. 1757, Hudiksvall d. 1826, Sundsvall a. 1928. On ⑦ Sundsvall a. 1928.

☛ Additional *NT* trains run Umeå - Sundsvall as follows:
From Umeå C at 0636 ①–⑤, 1336 ⑥, 1436 ①–⑤ and 1836 ⑦.

761 STOCKHOLM and SUNDSVALL - ÖSTERSUND - TRONDHEIM

Warning! From July 2 to August 7 trains may depart Stockholm up to 3 minutes earlier (train numbers may also vary during this period). See Table **760** for other fast services Stockholm - Gävle - Sundsvall and v.v. For sleeper services see Table **767**.

km		NT	NT			NT	NT	NT	NT	NT	IC 80	IC 82	NT	NT	NT	IC 266	NT	NT	NT	IC 10	IC 6	IC 8	NT	NT	Sn 598	NT	IC 286
		⑥⑦	①-⑤			⑥	①-⑤	①-⑤	①-⑤		A	C	⑥⑦	⑥		‡	⑦	⑥	①-⑤	①-⑤	⑦	⑥	①-⑤	⑦		①-⑤	
		2	2	2	2	2	n2	2	2	2	R 🍸	R 🍸	2	2	2	R	2	2	2	R 🍸	R 🍸	R 🍸	2	2	R 🍸	2	R
0	**Stockholm C** ◇ d.	...	...	...	...	...	...	...	...	...	0748	0756	...	...	...	0931	...	...	...	1311	1311	1311	...	...	1659	...	1931
39	Arlanda C ✈ ◇ d.	...	...	...	...	...	...	...	...	...	0811	0821	...	...	...	0952	...	...	...	1334	1334	1334	...	...	1720u	...	1951
69	Uppsala ◇ d.	...	...	...	...	...	...	...	...	...	0831	0839	...	...	...	1010	...	...	...	1355	1355	1355	...	...	1738u	...	2007
182	**Gävle C** ◇ d.	...	...	...	...	...	...	...	...	...	0928	0932	...	...	...	1056	...	...	...	1447	1447	1447	...	...	1827	...	2056
281	Bollnäs d.	...	...	...	...	...	...	...	...	...	1032	1032	...	...	...	▬	...	...	...	|	|	|	...	...	1917	...	...
344	Ljusdal d.	...	...	...	...	...	...	...	...	...	1113	1113	...	...	...	...	...	...	...	|	|	|	...	...	1952	...	...
	Sundsvall d.	...	0455	...	...	0609	0607	0812	1009	1009	|	|	1207	1207	1410	...	1603	1607	1637	1710	1711	1710	1810	1910	|	2010	...
450	Ånge d.	...	0609	...	...	0722	0723	0925	1124	1124	1213	1213	1323	1323	1524	...	1714	1722	1757	1820	1820	1820	1927	2022	2051	2123	...
480	Bräcke d.	...	0627	...	...	0740	0741	0943	1142	1142	1233	1233	1341	1341	1542	...	1731	1740	1819	1843	1843	1843	1945	2040	2109	2141	...
551	**Östersund C** a.	...	0722	...	...	0832	0836	1036	1237	1237	1316	1316	1431	1431	1632	...	1821	1840	1915	1927	1927	1933	2036	2143	2202	2234	...
551	**Östersund C** d.	0720	0722	...	...	0840	...	1040n	1240	...	1323	1323	...	1431	1632	...	1821	...	...	1930	1930	1935	2036	...	...	...	...
656	Åre d.	0831	0834	...	...	0956	...	1157n	1358	...	1441	1441	...	1545	1744	2	1938	...	...	2047	2047	2052	2149	...	...	...	...
665	Duved d.	0839	0842	...	...	1004	...	...	1406	...	1454	1454	...	1553	1752		1946	...	...	2100	2100	2105	2157	...	...	...	...
713	Storlien 🏛 a.	0912	0916	0929	1441	...	...	...	...	...	...	...	...	...	1825	1849	...	...	...	...	...	...	...	...	...	...	...
819	**Trondheim** a.	...	...	1104	1628	...	...	...	...	...	...	...	...	...	...	2028	...	...	...	...	...	...	...	...	...	...	...

km		NT	Sn 591	NT	Sn 597	Sn 595	NT	NT	NT		NT	IC 11	NT	NT	NT	NT	NT	NT	IC 285		IC 85	IC 293	NT	NT		NT	NT
		①-⑤	①-⑤	①-⑤	⑥	⑦	⑥	⑦	①-⑤	2			⑥	⑥⑦	①-⑤	⑥	①-⑤	⑦	⊖	2		①-⑤	⑥	①-⑤	2	⑧	⑥
		2	R 🍸	2	R ✕	R ✕	2	2	n2		2	R 🍸	2	2	2	2	2	2	R		R 🍸	R	2	2		2	2
	Trondheim d.	...	...	...	...	...	...	...	...	0731	...	...	...	...	...	...	...	...	...	1245	...	...	...	...	1648	...	...
	Storlien 🏛 d.	...	...	...	...	...	...	...	...	0909	0929	...	...	...	...	...	...	...	...	1427	...	...	...	...	1827	1839	1840
	Duved d.	...	...	0600	...	...	0802	...	...	▬	1003	1030	1204	...	...	...	1510	...	...	▬	1532	...	1613	...	...	1913	1914
	Åre d.	...	...	0607	...	...	0809	...	...	...	1010	1048	1211	...	1213n	...	1517	...	...	...	1550	...	1620	...	...	1920	1921
	Östersund C a.	...	...	0720	...	...	0924	...	...	...	1125	1213	1325	...	1325n	...	1630	...	...	...	1716	...	1736	...	...	2034	2039
	Östersund C d.	0513	0604	0727	0733	0922	0926	0928	0930	...	1128	1217	1327	1327	1325	1525	1630	1632	...	...	1720	...	1736	1927	...	2034	...
	Bräcke d.	0602	0646	0818	0816	1003	1017	1017	1020	...	1219	1305	1418	1418	1418	1616	1720	1719	...	...	1804	...	1827	2018	...	2125	...
0	Ånge d.	0622	0704	0837	0834	1020	1034	1034	1039	*IC*	1236	1325	1435	1435	1435	1635	1737	1737	...	*IC*	1824	...	1844	2035	...	2142	...
94	**Sundsvall** a.	0739	|	0954	|	|	1151	1151	1156	**279**	1354	1449	1553	1553	1553	1752	1853	1821	...	**287**	|	...	1958	2153	...	2257	...
	Ljusdal a.	...	0802	...	0932	1126	...	...	...	①-⑤	...	|	...	...	...	...	...	...	...	⑧	1924	...	...	...	...	...	...
	Bollnäs a.	...	0836	...	1007	1201	...	...	...	R	...	|	...	...	...	...	...	...	...	R	2010	...	...	...	...	...	...
	Gävle C ◇ a.	...	0928	...	1108	1258	...	...	...	1602	...	1722	...	...	...	...	...	...	1903	2004	2106	2303	...	...	...	...	...
	Uppsala ◇ a.	...	1016s	...	1159s	1347s	...	...	...	1650	...	1819	...	...	...	...	...	...	1950	2050	2158	2350	...	...	...	...	...
	Arlanda C ✈ ◇ a.	...	1033s	...	1217s	|	...	...	...	1708	...	1838	...	...	...	...	...	...	2007	2108	2223	0007	...	...	...	...	...
	Stockholm C ◇ a.	...	1058	...	1238	1428	...	...	...	1728	...	1902	...	...	...	...	...	...	2029	2128	2246	0028	...	...	...	...	...

Other *IC* services **STOCKHOLM - GÄVLE**

km	All R	IC 262	IC 264	IC 268	IC 270	IC 272	IC 274	IC 278	IC 280	IC 282	IC 284	IC 288	IC 290
		¶	Ⓐ	Ⓐ		Ⓐr			Ⓐ		Ⓐ	Ⓐr	⑦
0	**Stockholm C** d.	0730	0830	1031	1131	1231	1331	1531	1631	1730	1829	2031	2131
39	Arlanda C ✈ d.	0752	0852	1052	1151	1251	1352	1552	1652	1751	1852	2051	2151
69	Uppsala d.	0810	0910	1110	1210	1310	1410	1610	1710	1809	1910	2109	2210
182	**Gävle C** a.	0856	0956	1156	1256	1356	1456	1656	1756	1856	1958	2156	2256

All R	IC 259	IC 261	IC 263	IC 267	IC 269	IC 271	IC 273	IC 275	IC 277	IC 281	IC 283
	Ⓐr	①-⑥	Ⓐr	Ⓐr		Ⓐ		Ⓐr		⑥⑦	
Gävle C d.	0603	0704	0803	1004	1104	1204	1304	1404	1504	1704	1803
Uppsala d.	0651	0751	0851	1051	1151	1251	1351	1451	1551	1751	1851
Arlanda C ✈ a.	0708	0808	0908	1108	1208	1308	1408	1508	1608	1808	1908
Stockholm C a.	0728	0828	0928	1128	1228	1328	1428	1528	1628	1828	1928

A – ①-⑤ to June 23; daily July 2 - Aug. 7; ①-⑤ from Aug. 15.
C – ⑥⑦ to June 26 (also June 27 - July 1, Aug. 8–12); ⑥⑦ from Aug. 13.
n – Not June 27 - Aug. 12.
r – Not July 4 - Aug. 12.
s – Calls to set down only.
u – Calls to pick up only.
¶ – Not ①-⑤ July 4 - Aug. 12. Train number **20262** on ⑥⑦.
‡ – Not ⑦ July 3 - Aug. 7. Train number **276** on ⑥, **20266** on ⑦.
⊖ – On ⑦ (also July 1 and ②④⑥⑦ July 2 - Aug. 7) runs with train number **10285** (arrives Arlanda 2017, Stockholm 2038).
◇ – For other *IC* trains Stockholm - Gävle and v.v. see panel below main table.

763 UMEÅ - LULEÅ

Operator: *NT (2nd class only)*

km		①-⑥	⑥⑦	①-⑤	⑦	
0	**Umeå** Östra ♣ d.	0812	1318	1328	1827	...
2	**Umeå** C ♣ d.	0814	1321	1331	1829	...
33	Vännäs ♣ d.	|	1352	|	1900	...
142	Bastuträsk d.	0948	1502	1502	2013	...
269	Älvsbyn d.	1108	1615	1614	2125	...
315	Boden 765 a.	1136	1641	1641	2156	...
351	**Luleå** 765 a.	1219	1727	1727	2231	...

	①-⑥	⑦	①-⑥	⑦
Luleå 765 d.	0835	1031	1334	1851
Boden 765 d.	0914	1106	1409	1928
Älvsbyn d.	0937	1137	1439	1954
Bastuträsk d.	1048	1245	1559	2108
Vännäs ♣ d.	|	1404	|	2231
Umeå C ♣ a.	1220	1427	1735	2255
Umeå Östra ♣ a.	1226	1432	1741	2300

♣ – Other local journeys Umeå Östra - Umeå C - Vännäs and v.v.:
From Umeå Östra at 0520 ①-⑤ **n**, 0640 ①-⑤, 0704 ⑥, 0750 ①-⑤, 1006 ⑦, 1040 ①-⑤, 1133 ⑥, 1214 ①-⑤, 1217 ⑦, 1433 ①-⑤ **n**, 1607 ①-⑤, 1629 ⑥⑦, 1729 ①-⑤, 1845 ①-⑤ **n** and 2138 ①-⑤.
From Vännäs at 0603 ①-⑤ **n**, 0716 ①-⑤, 0842 ⑥, 0956 ①-⑤, 1139 ①-⑤, 1201 ⑦, 1328 ⑥, 1354 ①-⑤, 1530 ①-⑤ **n**, 1551 ⑦, 1647 ①-⑤, 1806 ①-⑤, 1822 ⑥, 1952 ①-⑤ **n**, 2020 ⑦, 2028 ①-⑤ and 2318 ①-⑤.

n – Not June 27 - Aug. 12.

765 LULEÅ - NARVIK

km		Vy 94	Vy 94	NT		Vy 96	NT		NT	
		R ✕	R ✕			R 🍸				
		c	c	①-⑥			⑧		b	
		⊙	◐	2			2		2	
0	**Luleå** 763 d.	...	0513	0602	...	0943	1116	...	1628	...
36	Boden 763 d.	0606	0606k	0626	...	1016v	1142	...	1655	...
204	Gällivare d.	0806	0806	0843	...	1259h	1353	...	1859	...
304	**Kiruna** a.	0915	0915	0950	...	1427	1511	...	2022	...
304	**Kiruna** d.	0932	0932	...	...	1444	...	...	...	...
397	Abisko Östra d.	1102	1102	...	...	1556	...	...	...	...
406	Björkliden d.	1118	1118	...	...	1610	...	...	...	...
426	Vassijaure d.	|	|	...	...	1638	...	...	...	...
433	Riksgränsen 🏛 d.	1146	1146	...	...	1650	...	...	...	...
473	**Narvik** a.	1248	1248	...	...	1742	...	...	...	...

	NT	NT		NT		Vy 95	NT	Vy 93	Vy 93
						R 🍸		R ✕	R ✕
	①-⑥	⑦		①-⑥			⑧	b	b
	2	2		2			2	⊙	◧
Narvik d.	...	...	...	...	...	1029	...	1510	1510
Riksgränsen 🏛 d.	...	...	...	...	...	1123	...	1559	1559
Vassijaure d.	...	...	...	...	...	1137	...	|	|
Björkliden d.	...	...	...	...	...	1222	...	1631	1631
Abisko Östra d.	...	...	...	...	...	1237	...	1647	1647
Kiruna a.	...	...	...	...	...	1348	...	1754	1754
Kiruna d.	0552	0745	...	1045	...	1405	1605	1828	1828
Gällivare d.	0710	0903	...	1156	...	1531	1718	1957	1957
Boden 763 a.	0909	1111	...	1355	...	1740r	1924	2149	2149r
Luleå 763 a.	0935	1142	...	1425	...	1823	2009	...	2223

b – Not June 24.
c – Not June 25.
h – Arrives 1241.
k – Arrives 0537.
r – Departs 8 minutes later.
v – Arrives 1007.
◐ – Train number **3964** Luleå - Boden.
◧ – Train number **3963** Boden - Luleå.
⊙ – Overnight service from / to Stockholm (see Table **767**).

766 KRISTINEHAMN - MORA - ÖSTERSUND - GÄLLIVARE

INLANDSBANAN

km		⊡ H	⊡ L	⊡ M	C
	Göteborg d.	0710	0715	...	...
0	**Kristinehamn 750** d.	|	|	0920	...
131	Grängesberg d.	|	|	1104	...
146	Ludvika d.	1130	1126	1118	...
192	Borlänge d.	1207	1212	1210j	...
296	**Mora 758** d.	1320	1320	1320j	1340
310	Orsa d.	...	...	...	1354
433	Sveg d.	...	...	...	1621
617	**Östersund C 761** a.	...	...	...	2030

	C	⊡ K	⊡ J	⊡ M◇
Östersund C 761 d.	0723	...	...	...
Sveg d.	1013	...	...	...
Orsa d.	1212	...	...	...
Mora 758 d.	1229	1402	1402	1405f
Borlänge d.	...	1518	1518	1517
Ludvika d.	...	1556	1556	1551
Grängesberg d.	...	1606	1606	|
Kristinehamn 750 a.	...	1844	|	|
Göteborg a.	...	...	2010	2005f

km		D	
0	**Östersund C 761** d.	0756	...
115	Ulriksfors d.	0940	...
244	Vilhelmina d.	1217v	...
312	Storuman d.	1319	...
384	Sorsele d.	1441	...
420	Slagnäs d.	1515	...
473	Arvidsjaur d.	1703t	...
646	Jokkmokk d.	1957	...
746	**Gällivare 765** a.	2147	...

	E	
Gällivare 765 d.	0730	...
Jokkmokk d.	0921	...
Arvidsjaur d.	1244z	...
Slagnäs d.	1337	...
Sorsele d.	1426	...
Storuman d.	1537	...
Vilhelmina d.	1713r	...
Ulriksfors d.	1907	...
Östersund C 761 a.	2052	...

C – June 20 - Aug. 28.
D – June 20 - Aug. 27.
E – June 21 - Aug. 28.
H – ①④⑤ July 4 - Aug. 8.
J – ④⑤ July 7 - Aug. 5.
K – ①⑥ July 4 - Aug. 8.
L – ⑥ July 9 - Aug. 6.
M – ⑦ June 26 - Aug. 7.
f – On June 26 Mora d. 1400, Göteborg a. 2040.
j – 10 minutes earlier on June 26.
r – Arrives 1643.
t – Arrives 1608.
v – Also calls at Vilhelmina norra (a. 1138, d. 1217).
z – Arrives 1159.
⊡ – Operated by *Tågab*.

Operator: Inlandsbanan AB, Box 561, 831 27 Östersund ✆ +46 (0) 771 53 53 53.

LONG DISTANCE SLEEPER TRAINS 767

All services 🅁	*Vy*	*Vy*	*Vy*	*SJ*	*SJ*	*SJ*	*SJ*	*SJ*	*SJ*	*SJ*
	94	**94** **3965**	**92**	**70*/74** **84*/74**	**86**	**74**	**70***	**74/70**	**84***	**74/84**
	r	r	r	d	J	d	M	N	⑤	⑤d
	A	**B**	**D**	**G**	**G**	**F**	**E**	**H**	**E**	**H**
Göteborg d.	...	...	...	...	...	1929	...	1929	...	1929
Herrljunga △ d.	...	...	...	...	...	2015	...	2015	...	2015
Skövde △ d.	...	...	...	...	...	2047	...	2047	...	2047
Hallsberg △ d.	...	...	...	...	...	2140	...	2140	...	2140
Örebro C △ d.	...	...	...	...	...	2200	...	2200	...	2200
Stockholm C d.	1811	1811	2157	2239**e**	2308**f**	|	2239**h**	|	2239**h**	|
Arlanda C ✈ △ d.	1835	1835	2221	2303	2335	|	2303	|	2303	|
Uppsala △ d.	1902	1902	2243	2324	2356	|	2324	|	2324	|
Gävle △ d.	2001	2001	2352	0027	0057	|	0027	|	0027	|
Söderhamn d.	2056	2056	0042	0120	0145	|	0120	|	0120	|
Hudiksvall d.	2135	2135	0123	0212	0226	|	0212	|	0212	|
Sundsvall a.	2233	2233	0224	0314	0330	0330	0314	0330	0314	0330
Sundsvall d.	2245	2245	0236	0356	0415	0415	0356	0356	0356	0356
Härnösand d.	2340	2340	0331	0514	0514	0514	|	|	|	|
Kramfors d.	0010	0010	0407	0554	0554	0554	|	|	|	|
Ånge a.	|	|	|	|	|	|	0514	0514	0514	0514
Bräcke a.	|	|	|	|	|	|	0539	0539	0539	0539
Östersund C a.	|	|	|	|	|	|	0645	0645	0645	0645
Åre a.	|	|	|	|	|	|	0858	0858	0916	0916
Duved a.	|	|	|	|	|	|	0917	0917	0935	0935
Örnsköldsvik d.	0056	0056	0455	0644	0644	0644	...	...	...	...
Umeå C a.	0200	0200	0614	0818	0818	0818	...	...	...	...
Umeå C d.	0212	0212	0619	...	...	...	...	...	...	...
Bastuträsk d.	0343	0343	0813	...	...	...	...	...	...	...
Älvsbyn d.	0513	0513	0933	...	...	...	...	...	...	...
Boden a.	0542	0542	1003	...	...	...	...	...	...	...
Luleå a.	|	0631	1055	...	...	...	...	...	...	...
Narvik **765** a.	1248	...	...	...	...	...	...	...	...	...

All services 🅁	*SJ*	*SJ*	*SJ*	*SJ*	*SJ*		*Vy*		*Vy*	*Vy*
	87	**77/71‡** **77/81‡** **77/83‡**	**77**	**71‡** **81‡** **83‡**	**71‡/77** **81‡/77** **83‡/77**		**91**		**3962** **93**	**93**
	L	b	b		b		r		r	r
	G	**G**	**F**	**E**	**H**		**D**		**C**	**A**
Narvik **765** d.	...	...	...	...	...	...	...	...	...	1510
Luleå d.	...	...	...	...	...	...	1702	...	2111	|
Boden d.	...	...	...	...	...	...	1752	...	2213	2213
Älvsbyn d.	...	...	...	...	...	...	1820	...	2241	2241
Bastuträsk d.	...	...	...	...	...	...	1938	...	0008	0008
Umeå C a.	...	...	...	...	...	...	2111	...	0140	0140
Umeå C d.	1940	1940	1940	...	...	...	2114	...	0145	0145
Örnsköldsvik d.	2052	2052	2052	...	...	...	2234	...	0242	0242
Duved d.	|	|	|	1902	1902	...	|	...	|	|
Åre d.	|	|	|	1933	1933	...	|	...	|	|
Östersund C d.	|	|	|	2122	2122	...	|	...	|	|
Bräcke d.	|	|	|	2214	2214	...	|	...	|	|
Ånge d.	|	|	|	2236	2236	...	|	...	|	|
Kramfors d.	2140	2140	2140	|	|	...	2327	...	0330	0330
Härnösand d.	2210	2210	2210	|	|	...	0007	...	0401	0401
Sundsvall a.	2308	2308	2308	2343	2343	...	0102	...	0457	0457
Sundsvall d.	0014	0023	0014	0023	0014	...	0117	...	0512	0512
Hudiksvall d.	0111	0126	|	0126	|	...	0248	...	0610	0610
Söderhamn d.	0144	0200	|	0200	|	...	0322	...	0644	0644
Gävle ▽ a.	0230	0251	|	0251	|	...	0410	...	0729	0729
Uppsala ▽ a.	0340	0412	|	0412	|	...	0525	...	0832	0832
Arlanda C ✈ ▽ a.	|	0447	|	0447	|	...	0555	...	0856	0856
Stockholm C a.	0423	0516	|	0516	|	...	0627	...	0925	0925
Örebro C ▽ a.	...	...	0512	...	0512	...	...	...	...	...
Hallsberg ▽ a.	...	...	0533	...	0533	...	...	...	...	...
Skövde ▽ a.	...	...	0642	...	0642	...	...	...	...	...
Herrljunga ▽ a.	...	...	0715	...	0715	...	...	...	...	...
Göteborg a.	...	...	0815	...	0815	...	...	...	...	...

A – 🛏, 🛏, (2) and ✕ Stockholm - Boden - Narvik and v.v.
B – 🛏, 🛏, (2) and ✕ Stockholm (**94**) - Boden (**3965**) - Luleå.
C – 🛏, 🛏, (2) and ✕ Luleå (**3962**) - Boden (**93**) - Stockholm.
D – 🛏, 🛏, (2) and ✕ Stockholm - Boden - Luleå and v.v.
E – 🛏, 🛏, (2) and ✕ Stockholm - Sundsvall - Duved and v.v.
F – 🛏, 🛏, (2) and ✕ Göteborg - Sundsvall - Umeå and v.v.
G – 🛏, 🛏, (2) and ✕ Stockholm - Sundsvall - Umeå and v.v.
H – 🛏, 🛏, (2) and ✕ Göteborg - Sundsvall - Duved and v.v.
J – July 25 - Aug. 16 only.
L – July 24 - Aug. 15 only.
M – ①②③④⑥⑦.
N – ①②③④⑥⑦ (not July 25 - Aug. 16).

b – Not July 24 - Aug. 15.
d – Not July 25 - Aug. 16.
e – 2236 July 2 – 24.
f – 2311 Aug. 8 – 16.
h – 2236 July 2 - Aug. 7.
r – Not June 24.

* – Train number varies July 2 - Aug. 7 and Aug. 14 - Oct. 15.
‡ – **73/10081/10083** Aug. 15 - Oct. 16.
△ – Trains call to pick up only.
▽ – Trains call to set down only.

UMEÅ - LULEÅ - HAPARANDA-TORNIO - KEMI 768

Rail service **LULEÅ - BODEN - HAPARANDA** (operated by Norrtåg).

km		①–⑤	⑥	⑦	①–⑤	⑥	⑦	⑥	①–⑤	⑦	
0	**Luleå** 763 765 d.	0529	*0835*	*1031*	1124	1319	1552	*1628*	1636	2135	...
36	**Boden** 763 765 a.	0554	*0859*	*1056*	1149	1344	1617	*1655*	1709	2159	...
	Boden d.	0554	0915	1119	1149	1344	1617	1707	1709	2159	...
195	**Haparanda** a.	0724	1039	1243	1316	1514	1743	1831	1835	2325	

	①–⑤	⑥	①–⑤	⑦	⑥		⑦	①–⑤	⑥	⑦
Haparanda d.	0554	0729	0734	0930	1049	...	1307	1428	1524	1754
Boden a.	0719	0854	0858	1057	1214	...	1432	1553	1649	1919
Boden 763 765 d.	0724	*0909*	0858	*1111*	1214	...	1434	1553	*1657*	1919
Luleå 763 765 a.	0755	*0935*	0924	*1142*	1241	...	1502	1620	*1727*	2000

🚌 UMEÅ - LULEÅ - HAPARANDA-TORNIO ⊠

Länstrafiken Norrbotten, routes 20 / Express 100

	Ⓐ **20**		**100**	Ⓐ **20**	Ⓐ **20**	Ⓒ **20**		Ⓐ **20**	Ⓒ **20**	Ⓐ **20**	† **20**	⚒ **20**	Ⓐ **20**	Ⓐ **100**	Ⓒ **100**	Ⓒ **100**	† **20**	Ⓐ **20**	Ⓒ **100**	Ⓐ **100**	Ⓐ **20**		Ⓒ **100**	Ⓐ **100**	**100**
Umeå d.	...	...	...	...	0505	0545	...	0720	0730	0850	0900	...	...	1315	1315	1430	...	1525	1630	1630	1725	...	1930	2000	2100
Skellefteå d.	...	...	0535	0635	0740	0800	...	0955	0950	1125	1115	...	...	1530	1520	1635	...	1805	1835	1845	1955	...	2135	2215	2300
Piteå d.	...	...	0700	0805	0910	0925	...	1125	1115	1250	1240	...	...	1645	1635	1750	...	1935	1950	2000	2120	...	2250	2330	...
Luleå a.	...	...	0800	0905	1010	1025	...	1220	1210	1345	1335	...	...	1735	1725	1840	...	2025	2040	2050	2225	...	2340	0020	...
Luleå d.	0515	...	0820	0950	1050	1050	...	1245	1230	1400	1350	1510	1635	1745	1735	...	1855	...	2050	2100	...	...	...	...	...
Haparanda-Tornio 🏛 § d.	0800	...	1040	1220	1325	1315	...	1525	1500	1650	1635	1750**v**	1850	2005	1950	...	2110	...	2305	2320	...	...	...	...	...

	100		Ⓐ **100**	**100**		Ⓐ **20**	⑥ **20**	Ⓐ **100**	Ⓒ **100**	Ⓐ **20**	Ⓒ **100**		Ⓐ **100**	Ⓒ **100**	† **20**	Ⓐ **20**	Ⓒ **20**		Ⓐ **20**	Ⓐ **20**	Ⓐ **20**	Ⓒ **20**	Ⓐ **20**	† **20**	Ⓐ **20**
Haparanda-Tornio 🏛 § d.	...	...	0525	...	...	0640	0725	0805	0810	0950	1050	...	1225	1230	...	1335	1345	...	1510	...	1605	1710	1715	1810	2015
Luleå a.	...	...	0750	...	...	0940	0950	1030	1030	1235	1310	...	1450	1450	...	1605	1610	...	1755	...	1845	1945	1955	2045	2235
Luleå d.	0540	...	0800	0800	...	0955	...	1040	1040	1300	1320	...	1500	1500	...	1635	1635	...	1810	...	1910	2005	2010	2055	...
Piteå d.	0635	...	0855	0855	...	1100	...	1135	1135	1405	1415	...	1555	1555	...	1750	1750	...	1915	...	2010	2105	2110	2150	...
Skellefteå d.	0750	...	1015	1015	...	1225	...	1250	1250	1535	1530	...	1715	1715	1830	1925	1925	...	2025	2030	2130	2225	2230	2300	...
Umeå a.	0955**t**	...	1220	1210	...	1445	...	1455	1445	1750	1725	...	1920	1910	2035	2140	2130	...	...	2245	2350	0030	...	...	...

🚌 HAPARANDA-TORNIO - KEMI ⊠ *Subject to confirmation*

	ESK Ⓐ		*RO* Ⓐ **s**		*RO* Ⓐ **b s**		*EJK* Ⓐ **s**		*ORA* ⑦		*NET* ⑦ **b**		*ORA* Ⓐ		*EJK* Ⓐ **s**		*NET* ⑦ **b**		*PII* Ⓐ		*PII* ⑦		*ORA* ⚒ **b**		*ESK* ⑦ **b**
Haparanda-Tornio 🏛 § ⊡ d.	0645	...	0752	...	0945	...	1200	...	1205	...	1210	...	1310	...	1400	...	1410	...	1500	...	1540	...	1623	...	1755
Kemi ⊡ a.	0715	...	0830	...	1015	...	1240	...	1230	...	1245	...	1340	...	1435	...	1445	...	1530	...	1605	...	1650	...	1820

	EJK Ⓐ **s**		*EJK* Ⓐ **s**		*RO* Ⓐ **s**		*ORA* ⑥		*ORA* ②–⑤		*NET* ⑦ **a**		*RO* Ⓐ **c**		*ESK* Ⓐ **a**		*NET* ⑦		*NET* ⑦ **a**		*ORA* ①–④ **a**		*ORA* ⑦		*PII* ⑦
Kemi ⊡ d.	0705	...	0810	...	0900	...	1105	...	1200	...	1300	...	1339	...	1410	...	1500	...	1630	...	1740	...	1832	...	2015
Haparanda-Tornio 🏛 § ⊡ a.	0740	...	0845	...	0940	...	1130	...	1235	...	1335	...	1420	...	1445	...	1535	...	1705	...	1810	...	1857	...	2045

a – Calls at Kemi railway station 1 minute later.
b – Calls at Kemi railway station upon request.
c – Calls at Kemi railway station at 1335.
s – On school days.
t – 0945 on ⑥⑦.
v – 1745 on ⑥.

⊠ – All stops refer to bus stations except where shown otherwise.
⊡ – Finnish time, one hour later than Swedish time.
§ – Swedish name: Haparanda-Tornio. Finnish name: Tornio-Haaparanta.
☛ Haparanda-Tornio bus station is located on the Swedish side of the border (distance to border approximately 200 metres). See www.matkahuolto.fi for all Finnish long-distance bus services, including extra services on the Haparanda-Tornio - Kemi route.

Operators:
EJK – E. Jusila Ky: www.jussilanbussilla.fi
ESK – J. M. Eskelisen Lapin Linjat: www.eskelisen.fi
KTO – Kemin Takispalvelu Oy: www.kemintaksi.fi
NET – NET-Matkat: www.netmatkat.com
ORA – Orajärven Bussit: www.orajarvenbussit.fi
PII – Liikenne P. Piirainen Oy
RO – Rajalinjat Oy: ✆ 040 565 5711

NORWAY

SEE MAP PAGE 337

Operator: The principal and national operator is Vy (www.vy.no). Long distance services (and connecting local trains) between Oslo and Stavanger are operated by GoAhead Nordic (www.go-aheadnordic.no). Services Oslo - Åndalsnes / Trondheim, Hamar - Røros - Trondheim and Trondheim - Bodø are operated by SJ NORD (www.sj.no).

Services: All trains convey second class seating accommodation. Many services, as identified in the notes, also convey *Komfort* accommodation (see below). Sleeping-cars (🛏) have one and two-berth compartments; the sleeper supplement is 950 NOK per compartment (for two people travelling together, or sole use for single travellers). Most long distance express trains convey a bistro car (✕) serving hot and cold meals, drinks and snacks. 🍸 indicates that drinks and light refreshments are available from automatic vending machines.

Timings: **Valid until December 10**, 2022 (unless otherwise shown). Dec. 25, 26, Jan. 1, Apr. 14, 15, 17, 18, May 1, 17, 26, June 5, 6 are Norwegian public holidays and services are subject to alteration on and around these dates. Alterations to internal Norwegian services during holiday periods are not usually shown in the tables and readers are advised to confirm timings before travelling (✆ +47 61 05 19 10).

Reservations: Seat reservation is highly recommended on long-distance routes Oslo - Kristiansand - Stavanger (Table **775**), Oslo - Bergen (Table **780**), Oslo - Trondheim / Åndalsnes (Table **785**) and Trondheim - Bodø (Table **787**).

Komfort class: *Vy Komfort / Go Ahead Komfort / SJ NORD Premium* is a dedicated area provided on many trains with complimentary tea / coffee and newspapers; a supplement of 100 NOK is payable per single journey.

770 OSLO - HALDEN - GÖTEBORG

All trains convey *Vy Komfort* and 🍸

From June 25 to August 7 buses replace trains Oslo - Rygge and v.v. with earlier departures / later arrivals at Oslo (please confirm timings locally).

km	Norwegian train number	103	105	107	107	109	111	111	113	115	117	119	121	141	123	143	125	145	127	129	131	133	135	137	139
	Swedish train number	391			393		395					397							399						
		Ⓐ	⚒	Ⓑ	⑥	⚒	Ⓑ	⑥	⚒					Ⓐ		Ⓐ		Ⓐ		Ⓑ		Ⓑ		Ⓑ	
0	**Oslo** Sentral d.	0601	0701	0801	0801	0901	1001	1001	1101	1201	1301	1401	1501	1528	1601	1628	1702	1728	1801	1901	2001	2101	2201	2301	0001
60	Moss d.	0644	0746	0844	0844	0946	1044	1044	1146	1244	1346	1444	1546	1613	1646	1714	1746	1814	1844	1946	2044	2146	2244	2346	0052
69	Rygge ✈ d.	0651	0753	0851	0851	0953	1051	1051	1159	1251	1353	1451	1553	1620	1653	1721	1753	1821	1851	1953	2051	2155	2251	2353	0059
94	Fredrikstad d.	0710	0819	0911	0911	1014	1111	1111	1214	1311	1414	1511	1614	1642	1715	1742	1814	1842	1911	2014	2111	2214	2311	0014	0119
109	Sarpsborg d.	0724	0832	0925	0925	1029	1125	1125	1229	1325	1432	1526	1632	1657	1733	1756	1829	1855	1926	2029	2125	2229	2324	0027	0132
137	**Halden** ★ d.	0747	0851	0944	0947	1048	1147	1144	1248	1344	1451	1547	1651	1721	1752	1821	1848	1919	1947	2048	2144	2248	2342	0046	0151
268	Öxnered **751** d.	0904	...	...	1103	...	1303	...	...	...	...	1702	...	...	...	...	...	...	2103	...	...	...	...	...	...
278	Trollhättan **751** d.	0910	...	...	1109	...	1308	...	...	...	...	1708	...	...	...	...	...	...	2109	...	...	...	...	...	...
350	**Göteborg 751** a.	0945	...	...	1145	...	1345	...	...	...	...	1740	...	...	...	...	...	...	2145	...	...	...	...	...	...

Swedish train number										390			392		394				396				398		
Norwegian train number	102	154	104	142	156	106	144	108	146	110	112	114	114	116	118	120	122	124	126	128	130	132	134	136	138
	Ⓐ	⑥	Ⓐ	Ⓐ	⑦	⚒	Ⓐ	⚒	Ⓐ		⚒	Ⓑ	⑥	⚒								Ⓑ		Ⓑ	
Göteborg 751 d.	...	...	...	...	...	...	...	...	...	0610a	...	...	0755	...	1015b	...	...	...	1415	...	...	...	1810	...	...
Trollhättan **751** d.	...	...	...	...	...	...	...	...	...	0645a	...	...	0824	...	1044b	...	...	...	1444	...	...	...	1844	...	...
Öxnered **751** d.	...	...	...	...	...	...	...	...	...	0651a	...	...	0832	...	1050b	...	...	...	1450	...	...	...	1850	...	...
Halden ★ d.	0401	0500	0506	0531	0600	0602	0632	0701	0723	0811	0902	1011	1011	1102	1211	1302	1410	1502	1611	1704	1810	1902	2011	2102	2210
Sarpsborg d.	0422	0520	0527	0552	0620	0623	0653	0723	0748	0831	0924	1031	1031	1124	1231	1324	1431	1524	1630	1725	1831	1924	2031	2124	2231
Fredrikstad d.	0436	0534	0541	0607	0634	0637	0709	0737	0804	0844	0939	1044	1044	1139	1244	1339	1444	1539	1643	1740	1844	1939	2044	2139	2244
Rygge ✈ d.	0454	0552	0559	0626	0652	0655	0728	0758	0824	0903	0958	1103	1103	1158	1303	1358	1503	1558	1701	1758	1857	1958	2103	2158	2303
Moss d.	0503	0601	0608	0636	0701	0708	0737	0808	0836	0912	1008	1112	1112	1208	1312	1408	1512	1611	1712	1812	1912	2008	2112	2208	2312
Oslo Sentral a.	0552	0651	0651	0722	0751	0751	0822	0851	0922	0951	1052	1152	1152	1251	1351	1451	1551	1651	1751	1852	1952	2051	2151	2251	2352

a – ①–⑤.

b – Not ⑥.

★ – 🛃 at Kornsjø (*km169*).

771 OSLO - OSLO LUFTHAVN GARDERMOEN ✈

See also Tables 783 and 785

Operated by Flytoget AS.
Special fares apply.
✆ +47 23 15 90 00
www.flytoget.no

Daily services (journey time: 19 – 22 minutes)
Trains call at Lillestrøm 10 minutes from Oslo.
From Oslo Sentral Services every 20 minutes 0440 - 2400.
From Gardermoen Services every 20 minutes 0530 - 2350 (also at 0010, 0030, 0050).

773 OSLO - GJØVIK

All trains convey 🍸

km		b					Ⓐ				Ⓐ△	
0	**Oslo** Sentral d.	0702	0902	1102	1302	1502	1612	1702	1902	2102	2302	0002
56	Roa d.	0800	1001	1158	1358	1600	1705	1803	1959	2158	0003	0103
70	Jaren d.	0816	1017	1214	1414	1616	1722	1819	2015	2214	0019	0119
99	Eina d.	0840	1041	1238	1437	1639	1750	1842	2039	2238	0042	0142x
110	Raufoss d.	0850	1051	1248	1447	1649	1801	1852	2049	2248	0052	0152
122	**Gjøvik** a.	0900	1101	1258	1457	1659	1811	1902	2059	2258	0102	0202

	Ⓐ	Ⓒb	Ⓐ⊡	Ⓐ⊖								
Gjøvik d.	0430	0528	0541	0629	0733	0930	1131	1327	1530	1729	1932	2131
Raufoss d.	0441	0539	0552	0639	0744	0941	1142	1338	1541	1740	1943	2142
Eina d.	0451x	0549	0602	0649	0754	0951	1152	1348	1551	1751	1953	2152
Jaren d.	0514	0612	0625	0713	0817	1015	1215	1412	1615	1818	2016	2215
Roa d.	0530	0628	0643	0730	0833	1031	1231	1429	1631	1834	2032	2231
Oslo Sentral a.	0628	0728	0744	0830	0930	1128	1330	1530	1730	1930	2130	2328

b – Not ⑥⑦ July 2 - Aug. 7.
x – Request stop.
△ – Runs 29 – 36 minutes **earlier** June 27 - Aug. 5.

⊡ – Retimed June 27 - Aug. 5: Gjøvik d. 0547, Raufoss d. 0558, Eina d. 0608, Jaren d. 0639, Roa d. 0656, Oslo a. 0804.
⊖ – Retimed June 27 - Aug. 5: Gjøvik d. 0639, Raufoss d. 0649, Eina d. 0658, Jaren d. 0721, Roa d. 0738, Oslo a. 0848.
☛ Additional train on Ⓐ (not June 27 - Aug. 5): Gjøvik d. 0815, Raufoss d. 0826, Eina d. 0840, Jaren d. 0907, Roa d. 0923, Oslo a. 1028.

775 OSLO - KRISTIANSAND - STAVANGER

Long distance services are not available for local journeys Oslo - Drammen and v.v. or Sandnes - Stavanger and v.v.
Operated by GoAhead Nordic (except for local trains Oslo - Kongsberg shown in notes § and ‡).

km		701	705	705	707	709	711	713	715	719	721	725
		Ⓐ	Ⓒ	Ⓐ			Ⓑ	⚒			⑦	Ⓑ
		⊡	✕⊡	✕⊡	✕⊡	✕⊡	✕⊡	✕⊡	✕⊡	✕⊡	✕⊡	♣✕
0	**Oslo** Sentral § d.	...	...	0419	0725	0925	1125	1325	1525	1825	2125	2225
41	Drammen § d.	...	...	0454	0800	1000	1200	1400	1600	1900	2200	2300
87	Kongsberg § d.	...	...	0530	0836	1036	1236	1436	1648	1947	2247	2343
134	Nordagutu d.	...	...	0604	0909	|	1312	1513	1730	2020	2326	0020x
151	Bø d.	...	...	0619	0923	1124	1326	1527	1744	2034	2340	0036
209	Neslandsvatn d.	...	...	0711x	1006x	1209x	1409x	1609x	1826x	2117x	0023x	0124x
270	Nelaug d.	...	...	0756	1052	1255	1455	1656	1911	2215	0111	0215x
353	**Kristiansand** a.	...	...	0853	1151	1358	1554	1753	2008	2312	0207	0327
353	**Kristiansand** d.	0502	0905	0905	1200	1414	1608	1801	2016	...	...	0346
457	Sira d.	0622	1025	1025	1324	1543	1728	1921	2136	...	...	0512x
465	Moi d.	0629x	1032x	1032x	1331x	1551x	1735x	1928x	2143x	...	...	0520x
514	Egersund ◇ d.	0705	1107	1107	1406	1635	1814	2007	2217	...	...	0607
573	Sandnes S ◇ a.	0752	1152	1152	1452	1734	1904	2102	2300	...	...	0704
587	**Stavanger** ◇ a.	0805	1205	1205	1505	1749	1919	2115	2313	...	...	0720

	702	704	706	708	710	712	714	716	716	720	726
	Ⓐ	A	B				⑦	Ⓑ	⑥	Ⓐ	Ⓑ
	⊡	✕⊡	✕⊡	✕⊡	✕⊡	✕⊡	✕⊡	✕⊡	✕⊡	✕⊡	♣✕
Stavanger ◐ d.	...	0431	0647	0847	1016	1247	1447	1647	1647	1936	2235
Sandnes S ◐ d.	...	0445	0701	0901	1031	1301	1500	1700	1700	1950	2250
Egersund ◐ d.	...	0535	0744	0942	1118	1342	1547	1754	1754	2032	2334
Moi d.	...	0616x	0819x	1018x	1158x	1423x	1630x	1831x	1831x	2110x	0014x
Sira d.	...	0623	0826	1026	1206	1430	1637	1837	1837	2117	0023x
Kristiansand a.	...	0742	0942	1143	1331	1545	1802	1953	1953	2240	0152
Kristiansand d.	0448	0751	0954	1156	1347	1556	1812	2001	...	...	0222
Nelaug d.	0546	0854	1054	1254	1456	1655	1910	2058	...	...	0328x
Neslandsvatn d.	0630x	0938x	1140x	1341x	|	1740x	|	2141x	...	...	0418x
Bø d.	0713	1022	1225	1426	1628	1828	2034	2223	...	...	0507
Nordagutu d.	0727	1036	1239	1440	1642	1842	2050	2239	...	...	0522x
Kongsberg ‡ d.	0802	1117	1317	1517	1718	1917	2126	2317	...	...	0610
Drammen ‡ a.	0851	1151	1351	1551	1751	1951	2207	2355	...	...	0650
Oslo S ‡ a.	0925	1225	1425	1625	1825	2025	2245	0031	...	...	0726

Nelaug - Arendal

km		Ⓐ	⚒									
0	Nelaug d.	0700	0900	1100	...	1300	1500	1700	...	1915	2220	...
36	Arendal a.	0737	0937	1137	...	1337	1537	1737	...	1952	2257	...

	Ⓐ	⚒							Ⓑ	⑥	
Arendal d.	0503	0810	1010	...	1210	1410	1610	1825	2010	2120	...
Nelaug a.	0540	0847	1047	...	1247	1447	1647	1902	2047	2157	...

A – Stavanger - Kristiansand on Ⓐ; Kristiansand - Oslo on ⚒.
B – Stavanger - Kristiansand on ⚒; Kristiansand - Oslo daily.

x – Request stop.

♣ – Conveys 🛏 and [2]. Reservation recommended.
⊡ – Reservation recommended. Conveys *Go Ahead Komfort*.

§ – Other local trains (operated by Vy) **Oslo** S - **Drammen** (35 minutes) - **Kongsberg** (75 – 81 minutes): 0009, 0609 Ⓐ, 0709, 0809, 0909, 1009, 1109, 1209, 1309, 1409, 1509, 1549 Ⓐ, 1609, 1709, 1809, 1909, 2009, 2109, 2209 and 2309.

‡ – Other local trains (operated by Vy) **Kongsberg** - **Drammen** (43 – 44 minutes) - **Oslo** S (77 – 78 minutes): 0334 Ⓐ, 0434 Ⓐ, 0534, 0634, 0734, 0834, 0934, 1034, 1134, 1234, 1334, 1434, 1534, 1633, 1734, 1834, 1934 2034, 2134 and 2234.

◇ – Other local trains **Egersund** - **Sandnes** S (51 – 58 minutes) - **Stavanger** (67 – 71 minutes): 0453 Ⓐ, 0522 Ⓐ, 0551 Ⓐ, 0621 ⚒, 0650 Ⓐ, 0717 ⚒, 0818 ⚒, 0916, 1019, 1119, 1221, 1316, 1419, 1450 Ⓐ, 1520, 1550 Ⓐ, 1620, 1650 Ⓐ, 1721, 1819, 1920, 2018, 2122, 2221 and 2320.

◐ – Other local trains **Stavanger** - **Sandnes** S (16 minutes) - **Egersund** (67 – 71 minutes): 0449 Ⓐ, 0524 Ⓐ, 0554 ⚒, 0654 ⚒, 0754 ⚒, 0854, 0954, 1054, 1154, 1254, 1324 Ⓐ, 1354, 1424 Ⓐ, 1454, 1524 Ⓐ, 1554, 1624 Ⓐ, 1654, 1754, 1854, 1954, 2054, 2154, 2254 and 2354.

PORSGRUNN - NOTODDEN 779

km		Ⓐ	Ⓐn	Ⓐ	Ⓐ	Ⓐn	Ⓐ	Ⓐn	Ⓐ
0	**Porsgrunn** 783 d.	...	0639	0749	1151	1307	1441	1605	1751
9	Skien 783 d.	0527	0649	0759	1201	1321	1455	1618	1801
43	Nordagutu a.	0557	0719	0829	1231	1351	1528	1649	1831
43	Nordagutu d.	0606	0720	0830	1232	1352	1529	1650	1832
62	**Notodden** a.	0626	0740	0850	1252	1412	1549	1710	1852

	Ⓐ	Ⓐn	Ⓐ	Ⓐ	Ⓐn	Ⓐ	Ⓐn	Ⓐ
Notodden d.	0636	0807	0907	1309	1448	1606	1809	2009
Nordagutu a.	0655	0826	0926	1328	1507	1625	1828	2028
Nordagutu d.	0656	0829	0927	1329	1509	1626	1831	2029
Skien 783 a.	0730	0859	0957	1403	1539	1700	1901	2059
Porsgrunn 783 a.	0739	0908	1006	1412	1552	1709	1910	...

n – Not June 27 - Aug. 5.

☞ No service on ©.

OSLO - BERGEN 780

July 2 – 31 services are diverted Oslo - Hønefoss and v.v. (not calling at Drammen) with amended timings at Oslo; a rail replacement 🚌 operates Drammen - Hønefoss and v.v.

km		1815 B	61 A ✕⊡	63 ✕⊡	1825 A	601 ✕⊡	1833 A	65 E ✕⊡	67 ✕⊡		605 Ⓑ ♥✕
0	**Oslo** Sentral 783 d.	...	0625	0825	...	1025	...	1425	1625	...	2303
41	Drammen 783 d.	...	0700u	0900u	...	1100u	...	1500u	1700u	...	2338u
112	Hønefoss d.	...	0759	0955	...	1155	...	1600	1757	...	0040
208	Nesbyen d.	...	0907	1103	...	1309	...	1707	1911	...	0150
225	Gol d.	0623	0920	1116	...	1322	...	1720	1931	...	0202
250	Ål d.	0642	0939	1135	...	1341	...	1741	1950	...	0225
275	Geilo d.	0703	1001	1156	1308	1402	1548	1802	2011	...	0246
286	Ustaoset d.	0714	1012	1208	1319	1413	1602	1813	2022	...	0257
324	Finse d.	0745	1052	1239	1347	1440	1635	1845	2053	...	0327
354	**Myrdal** 781 a.	0812	1118	1305	1412	1504	1700	1910	2117	...	0355
403	**Voss** 781 a.	0805	1203	1349	1506	1550	1758	1956	2206	...	0438
443	Dale 781 a.	0950	|	|	1543	1629	1843	2029	2236	...	0506s
480	Arna 781 a.	1028	1300s	1453s	1619	1658s	1917	2108s	2309s	...	0536s
489	**Bergen** 781 a.	1036	1310	1505	1629	1710	1927	2118	2318	...	0548

	60 A ✕⊡	62 ✕⊡	1810 A	1814 A	602 ✕⊡	1820 D	64 ✕⊡	66 E ✕⊡		606 Ⓑ ♥✕
Bergen 781 d.	0619	0815	0928	1130	1349	1426	1544	1745	...	2318
Arna 781 d.	0628u	0824u	0936	1138	1358u	1434	1554u	1754u	...	2327u
Dale 781 d.	|	|	1009	1215	1437	1509	|	|	...	2358
Voss 781 d.	0728	0923	1103	1304	1506	1605	1700	1858	...	0033
Myrdal 781 d.	0812	1005	1154	1418v	1553	1709	1742	1948	...	0120
Finse d.	0838	1033	1222	1451	1620	1739	1808	2018	...	0200
Ustaoset d.	0903	1059	1251	1517	1645	|	1837	2047	...	0231
Geilo d.	0916	1112	1301	1526	1658	1827	1850	2101	...	0247
Ål d.	0939	1135	...	...	1721	1845	1910	2121	...	0307
Gol d.	0958	1154	...	...	1745	...	1930	2141	...	0325
Nesbyen d.	1010	1206	...	...	1757	...	1943	|	...	0338
Hønefoss d.	1129	1317	...	...	1913	...	2058	2301	...	0453
Drammen 783 a.	1228s	1427s	...	...	2007s	...	2151s	2350s	...	0549s
Oslo Sentral 783 a.	1305	1505	...	...	2045	...	2227	0027	...	0625

A – Until Sept. 30.
B – June 26 - Aug. 14.
D – June 25 - Aug. 13.
E – Daily until Oct. 14 (not Oct. 8); ⑤⑦ from Oct. 16.

s – Calls to set down only.
u – Calls to pick up only.
v – Arrives 1351.

♥ – Conveys 🛏 and 🛋2. Reservation recommended.
⊡ – Reservation recommended. Conveys *Vy Komfort*.

MYRDAL - VOSS - BERGEN and FLÅM 781

km		605 ⚒ ✕◇			Ⓐ		Ⓐ	L			61 A ✕◇		63 ✕◇		G	601 ✕◇	Ⓐ			G		65 E ✕◇	Ⓑ		67 ✕◇	Ⓑ
	Oslo Sentral 780 d.	2303p	...	...	...	...	...	...	...	...	0625	...	0825	...	...	1025	...	...	...	...	...	1425	...	...	1625	...
0	**Myrdal** d.	0356	...	...	...	...	...	0817g	...	1003h	1121	1153	1307	1314	1414h	1507	...	1556	...	1708h	1818	1914	...	2026h	2120	...
18	Mjølfjell d.	|	...	...	...	0720j	...	|	...	|	|	1212x	|	1336	|	|	1537h	1614x	...	|	1840	|	...	|	|	...
49	**Voss** a.	0438	...	...	...	0758j	...	0905g	...	1055h	1203	1254	1349	1403	1506h	1550	1604h	1652	...	1758h	1928	1956	...	2115h	2206	...
49	**Voss** d.	0439	0513	0613	0654	0801	0837	0907	1007	1058	1205	1256	1352	1405	1509	1555	1610	1701	...	1808	1933	1959	2033	2135	2209	2302
89	Dale d.	0506s	0545	0645	0729	0836	0915	0950	1041	1135	|	1330	1412	1438	1543	1629	1645	1737	...	1843	2011	2029	2110	2204	2236	2340
104	Vaksdal d.	|	0601	0703	0747	0858	0934	1009	1102	1156	|	1352	|	1455	1559	|	1701	1757	...	1859	2031	|	2125	2221	|	2400
126	Arna ‡ d.	0536s	0622	0724	0807	0919	0956	1028	1121	1215	1300s	1418	1453s	1518	1619	1658s	1723	1817	...	1917	2052	2108s	2144	2244	2309s	0019
135	**Bergen** ‡ a.	0548	0633	0734	0815	0927	1006	1036	1129	1223	1310	1426	1505	1528	1629	1710	1731	1825	...	1927	2100	2118	2152	2252	2318	0029

	Ⓐ	60 A ✕◇		62 ✕◇		G		G		Ⓐ	Ⓒk	602 ✕◇	M			64 ✕◇		Ⓐ	66 E ✕◇		Ⓐ		Ⓐ		606 Ⓑ ✕◇	
Bergen ‡ d.	0530	0619	0721	0815	0829	0928	1036	1130	1230	1322	...	1349	1426	...	1529	1544	1629	1731	1745	1830	1928	2025	2136	2236	2318	0015
Arna ‡ d.	0541	0628u	0729	0824u	0837	0936	1044	1138	1238	1330	...	1358u	1434	...	1537	1554u	1637	1739	1754u	1838	1936	2033	2147	2247	2327u	0024
Vaksdal d.	0601	|	0748	|	0858	0954	1102	1157	1300	1348	...	|	1454	...	1558	|	1700	1757	|	1859	1957	2051	2205	2309	|	0047
Dale d.	0616	|	0805	|	0913	1009	1117	1215	1315	1402	...	|	1509	...	1612	|	1715	1812	|	1914	2012	2110	2220	2324	2358	0105
Voss a.	0647	0726	0837	0921	0944	1041	1151	1249	1347	1438	...	1503	1543	...	1646	1658	1751	1843	1856	1948	2047	2146	2254	2356	0030	0136
Voss d.	0649j	0728	0839h	0923	0952	1103h	1203	1304h	1417h	1444	1444	1506	1605h	...	1707	1700	1822h	...	1858	...	...	...	...	...	0033	...
Mjølfjell d.	0715j	|	|	|	1026x	1136h	1238x	|	|	1522j	1522	|	|	...	1745x	|	|	...	|	...	...	...	...	...	|	...
Myrdal a.	...	0810	0921h	1003	1044	1152h	1256	1351h	1507h	1536k	1536	1551	1646h	...	1804	1740	1914h	...	1943	...	...	...	...	...	0116	...
Oslo Sentral 780 a.	...	1305	...	1505	...	...	...	...	...	...	...	2045	...	...	...	2227	...	...	0027	...	...	...	...	...	0625	...

MYRDAL - FLÅM

Service to October 31

km						A	H	J	J	H	A	
0	Myrdal d.	1007	1128	1243	1358	1521	1541	1634	1749	1918	1920	...
20	Flåm a.	1105	1226	1341	1501	1618	1629	1731	1847	2005	2017	...

						J	A	H	J		
Flåm d.	0900	1015	1135	1250	1410	1525	1640	1655	1755	...	...
Myrdal a.	0955	1110	1231	1346	1509	1622	1735	1736	1852	...	...

A – Until Sept. 30.
E – Daily until Oct. 14 (not Oct. 8); ⑤⑦ from Oct. 16.
G – From/to Geilo until Sept. 30 (Table **780**).
H – Oct. 1 – 31.
J – Until Aug. 31.
L – From Gol June 26 - Aug. 14 (Table **780**).

M – To Ål June 25 - Aug. 13 (Table **780**).

g – June 26 - Aug. 14.
h – June 1 - Sept. 30.
j – Not June 20 - Aug. 12.
k – From Oct. 1.

p – Previous day.
s – Calls to set down only.
u – Calls to pick up only.
x – Request stop.

◇ – Reservation recommended.
‡ – Additional local services operate.
⚒ – **Operator**: Flåm Utvikling AS. www.norwaysbest.com ✆ + 47 57 63 14 00. 30% discount for rail pass holders.

Service until October 31 ⛴ FLÅM - GUDVANGEN and 🚌 GUDVANGEN - VOSS 781a

	⛴	🚌	⛴	🚌
Flåm d.	0930	...	1520	...
Gudvangen ferjekai a.	1130	...	1720	...
Gudvangen ferjekai d.	...	1140	...	1725
Voss a.	...	1255	...	1855

	🚌	⛴	🚌	⛴
Voss d.	1010	...	1610	...
Gudvangen ferjekai a.	1105a	...	1710	...
Gudvangen ferjekai d.	...	1200	...	1750
Flåm a.	...	1400	...	1950

a – ⑥⑦ arrives 1135.

🚌 operators: Skyss ✆ +47 55 55 90 70.
⛴ operator: Fjord1 ✆ +47 57 75 70 00.

Service until September 30 ⛴ / 🚌 LILLEHAMMER and GOL - FLÅM - BALESTRAND - BERGEN 782

	🚌 Ⓐ	⛴ ⚒	🚌 Ⓐ	🚌 ⑦	🚌 ⚒	🚌 Ⓐ	⛴	🚌	🚌	🚌	🚌	🚌 ⑦
Lillehammer skysst. d.	...	...	...	...	0915	...	...	...	...	...	...	1305
Gjøvik skysstasjon d.	...	...	...	...	1000	...	...	...	...	...	...	1350
Sogndal ⊕ d.	0630	...	...	1130	|	...	...	...	1430	...	...	|
Kaupangsenteret d.	0645	...	...	1145	|	...	...	...	1445	...	...	|
Gol Skysstasjon d.	|	...	...	|	|	...	...	1320	|	...	1845	|
Lærdal Rådhus d.	0725	...	...	1225	|	...	...	1522	1525	...	2050	|
Kaupangsenteret d.	|	...	...	|	|	...	...	1600	|	...	2125	|
Sogndal ⊕ a.	|	...	...	|	|	...	...	1615	|	...	2140	|
Sogndal ⊕ d.	|	0705	0855	|	|	1450	...	...	|	1620	...	|
Flåm d.	0810	|	|	1310	1510	|	1530	...	1610	|	...	1900
Leikanger Kai d.	|	0730	0920	|	|	1515	1630	...	|	1645	...	|
Balestrand Kai d.	|	0750	1010	|	|	1605	1650	...	|	1735	...	|
Voss 781 a.	0915	|	...	1415	1618	...	|	...	1715	...	...	2010
Bergen ⊡ 781 a.	1100	1150	...	1605	1800	...	2045	...	1900	...	...	2150

	🚌 Ⓑ	🚌	⛴	🚌	🚌	🚌 ⚒	🚌	🚌 Ⓐ	🚌 Ⓐ	⛴ Ⓑ	🚌 ⑦
Bergen ⊡ 781 d.	...	...	0800	0830	0910	...	...	...	1520	1630	1715
Voss 781 d.	...	...	|	1016	1050	...	...	...	1715	|	1900
Balestrand Kai d.	1005	...	1155	|	|	1310	...	1540	|	2030	|
Leikanger Kai d.	1050	...	1220	|	|	1350	...	1625	|	2050	|
Flåm a.	|	...	1340j	1131	1200	|	...	|	1830	|	2020
Sogndal ⊕ a.	1120	...	...	|	|	1420	...	1650	|	2120	|
Sogndal ⊕ d.	...	1130	...	|	|	...	1430	...	|	...	|
Kaupangsenteret d.	...	1145	...	|	|	...	1445	...	|	...	|
Lærdal Rådhus a.	...	1222	...	1221	|	...	1522	...	1920	...	2105
Gol skysstasjon a.	...	1415	...	|	|	...	1715	...	|	...	|
Kaupangsenteret a.	...	...	...	1302	|	...	...	...	2000	...	2140
Sogndal ⊕ a.	...	...	...	1330	|	...	...	...	2025	...	2205
Gjøvik skysstasjon a.	...	...	...	...	1710	...	...	...	...	...	...
Lillehammer skysst. a.	...	...	...	...	1755	...	...	...	...	...	...

j – ⑥⑦ arrives 1325.
⊕ – 🚌: Sogndal skysstasjon. ⛴: Sogndal kai.
⊡ – 🚌: Bus station. ⛴: Strandkaiterminal.

🚌 operators: Vy Buss AS ✆ +47 4070 5070.
Nor-way Bussekspress ✆ +47 815 44 444.
⛴ operator: Norled AS ✆ +47 5186 8700.

783 EIDSVOLL - OSLO - SKIEN

All trains convey Vy Komfort and 🍷

km		Ⓐ	⚒		⚒		⚒				Ⓐ		Ⓐ	Ⓐ		Ⓐ	Ⓐ			Ⓑ		Ⓑ		Ⓑ	
0	**Eidsvoll** 785 d.	0500	0600	0700	0756	0900	1000	1100	1200	1300	...	1400	...	...	1500	...	...	1600	1700	1800	1900	2000	2100	2200	2300
16	Oslo Lufthavn ✈ ¶ 785 d.	0513	0613	0713	0813	0913	1013	1113	1213	1313	...	1413	...	...	1513	...	...	1613	1713	1813	1913	2013	2113	2213	2313
47	Lillestrøm 785 d.	0526	0626	0726	0826	0926	1026	1126	1226	1326	...	1426	...	...	1526	...	...	1626	1726	1826	1926	2026	2126	2226	2326
68	**Oslo** S 785 a.	0536	0636	0736	0836	0936	1036	1136	1236	1336	...	1436	...	...	1536	...	...	1636	1736	1836	1936	2036	2136	2236	2336
68	**Oslo** S 785 d.	0539	0639	0739	0839	0939	1039	1139	1239	1339	1405	1439	1505	1533	1539	1605	1633	1639	1739	1839	1939	2039	2139	2239	2339
108	Drammen 785 d.	0614	0714	0814	0914	1014	1114	1214	1314	1414	1445	1514	1545	|	1614	1645	|	1714	1814	1914	2014	2114	2214	2314	0014
142	Holmestrand d.	0638	0733	0833	0933	1033	1133	1233	1333	1433	1506	1533	1606	|	1633	1706	|	1733	1833	1933	2033	2133	2233	2333	0033
156	Skoppum d.	0650	0741	0841	0941	1041	1141	1241	1341	1441	1518	1541	1618	|	1641	1718	|	1741	1841	1941	2041	2141	2241	2341	0041
172	Tønsberg d.	0706	0752	0852	0952	1052	1152	1252	1352	1452	1529	1552	1629	1643z	1652	1729	1743z	1752	1852	1952	2052	2152	2252	2352	0052
191	Torp ✈ d.	0721	0812	0912	1012	1112	1212	1312	1412	1512	|	1612	|	|	1712	|	|	1812	1912	2012	2112	2212	2312	0011	|
196	**Sandefjord** d.	0729	0818	0918	1018	1118	1218	1318	1418	1518	1548	1618	1648	1705	1718	1748	1805	1818	1918	2018	2118	2218	2318	0016	0111
215	Larvik d.	0746	0833	0933	1033	1133	1233	1333	1433	1533	1602	1633	1702	1719	1733	1802	1819	1833	1933	2033	2133	2233	2333	0030	0125
240	Porsgrunn 779 d.	0758	0845	0945	1045	1145	1245	1345	1445	1545	1618	1645	1718	1731	1745	1818	1831	1845	1945	2045	2145	2245	2345	0042	0137
249	**Skien** 779 a.	0806	0853	0953	1053	1153	1253	1353	1453	1553	1626	1653	1726	1739	1753	1826	1839	1853	1953	2053	2153	2253	2353	0050	0145

	Ⓐ	Ⓐ	⚒	Ⓐ	Ⓐ		Ⓐ	Ⓐ	⚒		⚒										Ⓑ		Ⓑ	
Skien 779 d.	0410	0427	0511	0525	0544	0610	0620	0627	0709	0809	0909	1009	1109	1209	1309	1409	1509	1607	1707	1807	1909	2009	2109	2209
Porsgrunn 779 d.	0418	0435	0519	0533	0552	0618	0628	0635	0717	0817	0917	1017	1117	1217	1317	1417	1517	1617	1717	1817	1917	2017	2117	2217
Larvik d.	0431	0449	0532	0547	0605	0631	0642	0649	0732	0832	0932	1032	1132	1232	1332	1432	1532	1632	1732	1832	1932	2032	2132	2232
Sandefjord d.	0446	0504	0547	0602	0620	0647	0657	0704	0747	0847	0947	1047	1147	1247	1347	1447	1547	1647	1747	1847	1947	2047	2147	2247
Torp ✈ d.	0450	0508	0551	0606	|	0651	|	0708	0751	0851	0951	1051	1151	1251	1351	1451	1551	1651	1751	1851	1951	2051	2151	2251
Tønsberg d.	0508	0528	0608	0626	0640	0708	0719	0728	0808	0908	1008	1108	1208	1308	1408	1508	1608	1708	1808	1908	2008	2108	2208	2308
Skoppum d.	0518	0538	0618	0636	|	0718	|	0740	0818	0918	1018	1118	1218	1318	1418	1518	1618	1718	1818	1918	2018	2118	2218	2318
Holmestrand d.	0526	0547	0626	0645	|	0726	|	0749	0826	0926	1026	1126	1226	1326	1426	1526	1626	1726	1826	1926	2026	2126	2226	2326
Drammen 785 d.	0547	0609	0647	0710	|	0747	|	0812	0847	0947	1047	1147	1247	1347	1447	1547	1647	1747	1847	1947	2047	2147	2247	2347
Oslo S 785 a.	0621	0645	0721	0745	0749	0821	0825	0845	0921	1021	1121	1221	1321	1421	1521	1621	1721	1821	1921	2021	2121	2221	2321	0021
Oslo S 785 d.	0624	...	0724	...	0752	0824	...	...	0924	1024	1124	1224	1324	1424	1524	1624	1724	1824	1924	2024	2124	2224	2324	0024
Lillestrøm 785 d.	0635	...	0735	...	0802	0835	...	...	0935	1035	1135	1235	1335	1435	1535	1635	1735	1835	1935	2035	2135	2235	2335	0035
Oslo Lufthavn ✈ ¶ 785 d.	0649	...	0749	...	...	0849	...	...	0949	1049	1149	1249	1349	1449	1549	1649	1749	1849	1949	2049	2149	2249	2349	0049
Eidsvoll 785 a.	0700	...	0804	...	...	0900	...	...	1000	1100	1200	1300	1400	1500	1600	1700	1800	1900	2000	2100	2200	2300	2400	0100

z – Arrives 5–6 minutes earlier.

¶ – Oslo Lufthavn Gardermoen ✈.

784 HAMAR - RØROS - TRONDHEIM

Operated by SJ NORD

km		⑥	Ⓐ	⚒n	Ⓐ	⑦	⑥	Ⓐ		Ⓐn	⑦	Ⓑ
0	**Hamar** d.	...	0809	1009	1209	1209	...	1409	1609	1809	1809	2009
32	Elverum d.	...	0834	1034	1234	1234	...	1434	1634	1834	1834	2034
64	Rena d.	...	0859	1059	1259	1259	...	1459	1659	1901	1859	2059
120	Koppang d.	...	0940	1140	1340	1340	...	1540	1742	1944	1944	2139
273	**Røros** a.	...	1135	1335	1535	1535	...	1736	1935	2137	2137	2332
273	**Røros** d.	0702	...	...	1550	1605	1630	...	1953	...	...	...
384	Støren 785 d.	0838	...	...	1727	1740	1803	...	2129	...	...	...
435	**Trondheim** S 785 a.	0938	...	...	1826	1843	1855	...	2227	...	...	...

	Ⓐ	Ⓐn	Ⓐ	Ⓐ		Ⓐn		⑦	Ⓐ	⑦	
Trondheim S 785 d.	...	...	0537	...	0922	...	...	1330	1621	2019	...
Støren 785 d.	...	...	0640	...	1019	...	...	1428	1724	2127	...
Røros a.	...	...	0814	...	1153	...	...	1603	1859	2302	...
Røros d.	0418	0623	0821	1018	1218	1418	1619	1619	...	...	...
Koppang d.	0612	0817	1019	1219	1419	1619	1820	1820	...	...	...
Rena d.	0654	0900	1100	1300	1500	1700	1902	1902	...	...	...
Elverum d.	0716	0922	1122	1322	1522	1722	1924	1924	...	...	...
Hamar a.	0740	0946	1146	1346	1546	1746	1947	1947	...	...	...

n – Not ①–⑤ June 20 - Aug. 12.

785 OSLO - LILLEHAMMER - ÅNDALSNES and TRONDHEIM

Services to / from Trondheim and Åndalsnes are operated by SJ NORD. Local services Drammen - Oslo - Lillehammer are operated by Vy.

km		407		43	2343	311	2345	47	2347	49	2349	51	331	405	
		Ⓐ					Ⓐ			Ⓑ	Ⓑ	Ⓑ	Ⓑ	Ⓑ	
		n		R	R	◇	R	R	R	R	R	R	◇	RN	
				✕⊙	🍷	🍷⊡	🍷	✕⊙	🍷	✕⊙	🍷	✕⊙	🍷⊡	✕	
0	Oslo Sentral ★ d.	...	...	0802	...	0934	...	1402	...	1602	...	1802	1934	2250	...
21	Lillestrøm ★ d.	...	...	0813u	...	0945	...	1413u	...	1613u	...	1812u	1945	2320u	...
52	Oslo ✈ ⊖ ★ d.	...	...	0828u	...	0959	...	1429u	...	1629u	...	1828u	1959	2338u	...
127	**Hamar** ★ d.	...	...	0921	...	1052	...	1522	...	1722	...	1923	2052	0032	...
185	**Lillehammer** ★ d.	...	...	1009	...	1140	1211	1613	...	1811	...	2020	2149	0125	...
243	Ringebu d.	...	...	1051	...	...	1309	1655	...	1853	...	2102	2233	0207	...
267	Vinstra d.	...	...	1108	...	...	1326	1717	...	1914	...	2119	2248	0223	...
298	Otta d.	...	...	1132	...	...	1356	1740	...	1938	...	2144	2312	0259	...
344	Dombås d.	...	...	1204	1208	...	1435	1813	1816	2011	2016	2222	2341	0333	...
458	**Åndalsnes** ♥ a.	...	...	|	1328	...	1603	|	1936	|	2136	|	...	|	...
430	Oppdal ♥ d.	0634	...	1301	...	...	...	1910	...	2116	...	2319	...	0434	...
502	Støren 784 d.	0723	...	1351	...	...	...	2007	...	2209	...	0011	...	0534	...
553	**Trondheim** S 784 a.	0828	...	1439	...	...	...	2053	...	2254	...	0100	...	0628	...

N – Conveys 🛏 and [2].
R – Reservation recommended.

n – Not June 20 - Aug. 12.
s – Stops to set down only.
u – Stops to pick up only.

◇ – Operated by Vy.
⊡ – Conveys *Vy Komfort*.
⊙ – Conveys *SJ NORD Premium*.
⊖ – Oslo Lufthavn Gardermoen.
★ – See also panel below main table.
♥ – See Table **785a** for connecting 🚌 services to / from Molde, Ålesund and Kristiansund.

	308		2340	316	2342	42	44		2346	46	2348	48		406	
	⚒		Ⓐ				Ⓑ		Ⓑ	Ⓑ				Ⓑ	
	◇		Rn	◇	R	R	R		R	R	R	R		RN	
	🍷⊡		🍷	🍷⊡	🍷	✕⊙	✕⊙		🍷	✕⊙	🍷	✕⊙		✕	
Trondheim S 784 d.	...	...	...	...	...	0819	1018	...	...	1318	...	1523	...	2317	...
Støren 784 d.	...	...	...	...	...	0905	1108	...	...	1413	...	1615	...	0010	...
Oppdal ♥ d.	...	...	...	...	...	0959	1205	...	...	1506	...	1710	...	0106	...
Åndalsnes ♥ d.	...	...	0710	...	0925	|	|	...	1431	|	1630	|	...	|	...
Dombås d.	0517	...	0838	...	1050	1057	1308	...	1556	1603	1755	1810	...	0226	...
Otta d.	0549	...	0912	...	...	1130	1339	...	...	1634	...	1840	...	0306	...
Vinstra d.	0613	...	0936	...	...	1153	1403	...	...	1657	...	1902	...	0335	...
Ringebu d.	0629	...	0953	...	...	1210	1421	...	...	1715	...	1918	...	0352	...
Lillehammer ★ d.	0714	...	1038	1114	...	1254	1504	...	...	1807	...	2001	...	0435	...
Hamar ★ d.	0807	...	...	1207	...	1346	1550	...	...	1853	...	2051	...	0530	...
Oslo ✈ ⊖ ★ a.	0903	...	...	1303	...	1435s	1635s	...	...	1952s	...	2135s	...	0620s	...
Lillestrøm ★ a.	0916	...	...	1316	...	1458s	1658s	...	...	2012s	...	2152s	...	0638s	...
Oslo Sentral ★ a.	0926	...	...	1326	...	1508	1708	...	...	2024	...	2202	...	0650	...

Local services Drammen - Oslo - Lillehammer (operated by Vy).

	Ⓐ	Ⓐ		⚒		⚒		⚒			Ⓐ			Ⓐ		Ⓑ		Ⓑ		Ⓑ			①-④	⑦	
Drammen 783 d.	...	0557	0657	0757	0857	0957	1057	1157	1257	1357	...	1457	1557	...	1657	1757	1857	1957	2057	2157	2257	...	2347	2347	...
Oslo Sentral ... 771 783 d.	...	0634	0734	0834	0934	1034	1134	1234	1334	1434	1502	1534	1634	1702	1734	1834	1934	2034	2134	2234	2334	...	0024	0024	...
Lillestrøm 783 d.	...	0645	0745	0845	0945	1045	1145	1245	1345	1445	1513	1545	1645	1713	1745	1845	1945	2045	2145	2245	2345	...	0035	0035	...
Oslo ✈ ⊖ ... 771 783 d.	...	0659	0759	0859	0959	1059	1159	1259	1359	1459	1529	1559	1659	1729	1759	1859	1959	2059	2159	2259	2359	...	0049	0049	...
Eidsvoll 783 d.	...	0710	0810	0910	1010	1110	1210	1310	1410	1510	1540	1610	1710	1740	1810	1910	2010	2110	2210	2310	0010	...	0102	0102	...
Hamar a.	...	0750	0850	0950	1050	1150	1250	1346	1450	1550	1625	1650	1750	1820	1847	1950	2051	2150	2250	2354	0049	...	0142	0142	...
Hamar d.	0652	0752	0852	0952	1052	1152	1252	1348	1452	1552	...	1652	1752	...	1853	1952	2052	2152	2252	2356	0051	...	0144	...	...
Lillehammer a.	0740	0840	0937	1041	1140	1245	1340	1442	1537	1644	...	1737	1841	...	1940	2043	2141	2237	2340	0040	0137	...	0232	...	...

	Ⓐ	Ⓐ		Ⓐ	⚒	Ⓐ		⚒		⚒								Ⓑ		Ⓑ					
Lillehammer d.	0333	0414	0521	...	0614	...	0714	0814	0907	1014	1114	1215	1309	1411	1509	1614	1707	1812	1908	2017	2110	...	...	...	...
Hamar a.	0419	0500	0607	...	0706	...	0805	0905	1005	1105	1205	1305	1405	1505	1605	1705	1805	1905	2005	2106	2205	...	...	...	...
Hamar d.	0421	0502	0609	0631	0708	0728	0807	0907	1007	1107	1207	1307	1407	1507	1607	1707	1809	1908	2008	2108	2208	...	...	...	...
Eidsvoll 783 d.	0500	0540	0651	0711	0751	0811	0851	0951	1051	1151	1251	1351	1451	1551	1651	1751	1851	1951	2051	2151	2251	...	...	...	...
Oslo ✈ ⊖ ... 771 783 d.	0513	0603	0703	0723	0803	0823	0903	1003	1103	1203	1303	1403	1503	1603	1703	1803	1903	2003	2103	2203	2303	...	...	...	...
Lillestrøm 783 d.	0526	0616	0716	0738	0816	0838	0916	1016	1116	1216	1316	1416	1516	1616	1716	1816	1916	2016	2116	2216	2316	...	...	...	...
Oslo Sentral ... 771 783 a.	0536	0626	0726	0748	0826	0848	0926	1026	1126	1226	1326	1426	1526	1626	1726	1826	1926	2026	2126	2226	2326	...	...	...	...
Drammen 783 a.	0612	0702	0802	...	0902	...	1002	1102	1202	1302	1402	1502	1602	1702	1802	1902	2002	2102	2202	2302	0002	...	...	...	...

🚌 ÅNDALSNES - MOLDE and ÅLESUND; 🚌 OPPDAL - KRISTIANSUND 785a

ÅNDALSNES - MOLDE and ÅLESUND

🚌	Ⓐ	⑦	Ⓐ				Ⓐ		Ⓐ		⑥⑦		⑥	Ⓐ		⑦	Ⓐ					Ⓐ	⑦	
Åndalsnes d.	0610	0625	0725	...	1000	...	1140	...	1340	1340	1400	...	1600	1620	...	1800	1815	...	2000	2015	...	2200	2220	...
Molde a.	0740	0740	0855	...	1125	...	1305	...	1510	|	1525	...	1720	1745	...	1925	1935	...	|	2137	...	2320	2335	...
Ålesund a.	...	...	...	...	...	...	...	...	...	1545	...	...	...	...	...	...	...	...	2205	...	...	...	...	...

🚌				⚒		⑦	Ⓐ	⑦		Ⓐ	⑥⑦	Ⓐ	⑥		Ⓐ	Ⓐ		⑥⑦		Ⓐ	Ⓑ			
Ålesund d.	...	0710	...	...	...	...	...	1155	...	...	...	1400	1410	...	...	...	...	...	...	...	...	...	...	...
Molde d.	0750	|	...	0955	...	1235	1255	|	...	1430	1435	|	|	...	1545	1630	...	1755	...	1945	2015	...	2200	...
Åndalsnes a.	0913	0915	...	1113	...	1353	1413	1414	...	1553	1553	1605	1615	...	1713	1753	...	1910	...	2103	2133	...	2315	...

OPPDAL - KRISTIANSUND

🚌	Ⓐ	⑥		Ⓐ		Ⓑ		⑤⑦		Ⓑ		
Oppdal skysstasjon d.	0515	0530	...	1050	...	1315	...	1810	...	2120	...	...
Kristiansund a.	0855	0845	...	1425	...	1635	...	2125	...	0025	...	...

🚌	Ⓐ		Ⓐ	⑥		Ⓑ		⑤⑦		Ⓑ
Kristiansund d.	0630	...	1045	1125	...	1330	...	1640	...	2125
Oppdal skysstasjon a.	0940	...	1445	1445	...	1645	...	2005	...	0035

SOUTHWEST NORWAY 🚌 LINKS 786

BERGEN - TRONDHEIM (❖) Operator: NOR-WAY Bussekspress ✆ +47 2231 3150.
Bergen ⊡ d. 1630 → Otta ⊕ a. 0159 → Oppdal ⊕ a. 0440 → Trondheim a. 0642.
①②③④⑦: Trondheim d. 2000 → Oppdal ⊕ d. 2205 → Otta ⊕ d. 0045 → Bergen ⊡ a. 0940. ⑤⑥: Trondheim d. 2230 → Oppdal ⊕ d. 0032 → Otta ⊕ d. 0305 → Bergen ⊡ a. 1210.

BERGEN - ÅLESUND (❖) Operator: Nettbuss express ✆ +47 4070 5070. Bergen ⊡ d. 0800 → Ålesund a. 1715⑥/1745Ⓑ. Ålesund d. 1110 → Bergen ⊡ a. 2025Ⓑ/2015⑥.

BERGEN - STAVANGER (❖) Operator: NOR-WAY Bussekspress ✆ +47 2231 3150. *Journey time: 4½ – 5½ hours.*
From Bergen ⊡ at 0715Ⓐ, 0925Ⓑ, 0930Ⓑ, 0945⑥, 1105⑦ 1125Ⓐ, 1130Ⓑ 1215⑥, 1325Ⓐ, 1420Ⓐ, 1425⑦, 1535⑥ 1550Ⓐ, 1620Ⓐ, 1625⑦, 1730⑦.
From Stavanger ⊙ at 0745Ⓐ, 0900Ⓐ, 0915⑦, 0945Ⓐ, 0955⑥, 1045⑦, 1100Ⓐ, 1145Ⓑ, 1200⑦, 1215⑥, 1345Ⓐ, 1445⑦, 1500Ⓑ, 1545⑦, 1555⑥, 1700⑦.

⊡ – Bus station. ⊙ – Stavanger Byterminalen. ⊕ – Skysstasjon. ❖ – Subject to alteration / cancellation owing to coronavirus restrictions (please check with operator).

Operated by SJ NORD TRONDHEIM - BODØ and NARVIK 787

km		1795		1781	1783	475		1797	1785	483	473		1787	1789		471	481		1793		479	477			
		⑥⑦		Ⓐ	Ⓐ	NR	🚌	Ⓐ	Ⓐ	⑥R	ⒶR		Ⓐ	Ⓐ		ⒶR	ⒸR	🚌	Ⓐ		ⒷR	ⒷR			
						✕	◇	m	n				n	n		✕⊙	✕⊙	◇			n				
0	**Trondheim** S d.	...	...	...	...	2305	...	...	...	...	...	...	...	...	...	0749	0758	...	...	...	...	1603	...	...	...
33	Trondheim ✈ ‡ d.	...	...	...	...	2337	...	...	...	...	...	...	...	...	...	0824	0824	...	...	...	...	1636u	...	...	...
34	Stjørdal d.	...	...	...	...	2341	...	...	...	...	...	...	...	...	...	0828	0828	...	...	...	...	1641u	...	...	...
126	Steinkjer d.	...	...	...	...	0055	...	...	...	...	...	...	...	...	...	0951	0951	...	...	...	...	1807u	...	...	...
220	Grong d.	...	...	...	...	0205	...	...	...	...	...	...	...	...	...	1100	1100	...	...	...	...	1916	...	...	...
406	Mosjøen d.	...	...	...	...	0444	...	...	...	0638	0638	...	...	...	...	1320	1320	...	...	...	1657	2143z	...	...	...
498	Mo i Rana d.	...	...	...	...	0554	...	...	...	0747	0747	...	...	...	...	1437	1437	...	...	...	1801	2248	...	...	...
648	Rognan d.	0205	...	0535	0631	0750	...	0855	...	0933	0940	...	1124	...	...	1631	1624	...	1801	...	2001	...	...	...	...
	Bodø ⊖ d.	|	...	|	|	|	0722	|	...	|	|	...	|	...	...	|	|	1642	|	...	|	...	...	...	...
674	Fauske d.	0225	...	0555	0651	0819	0850	0915	0915	0954	1007	...	1144	1424	...	1659	1649	1809	1830	...	2020	...	...	...	...
	Narvik ⊡ ♣ a.	|	...	|	|	|	1340	|	|	|	|	...	|	|	...	|	|	2310	|	...	|	...	...	...	...
729	**Bodø** a.	0306	...	0636	0732	0905	...	1004	1004	1035	1054	...	1225	1505	...	1744	1734	...	1910	...	2101	...	...	...	...

	1794		478		470	1798	1782		1784			472	1786		1788		474			476	1792			
	⑥⑦		R		ⒶR	Ⓐ	Ⓐ		Ⓐ		🚌	R	Ⓐ		Ⓐ		R		🚌	NR	M			
					n	m	n		n		◇	✕⊙	n						◇	✕				
Bodø d.	0055	...	...	...	0734	0734	0816	...	1012	...	...	1227	1335	...	1513	...	1746	...	...	2110	2355	...	...	...
Narvik ⊡ ♣ d.	|	...	...	...	|	|	|	...	|	...	0705	|	|	...	|	...	|	...	1610	|	|	...	...	...
Fauske d.	0137	...	...	...	0817	0817	0905	...	1056	...	1210	1316	1416	...	1555	...	1828	...	2125	2202	0037	...	...	...
Bodø ⊖ a.	|	...	...	...	|	|	...	...	|	...	1320	|	...	...	...	...	|	...	2225	|	|	...	...	...
Rognan d.	0156	...	...	...	0835	0835	...	...	1115	...	...	1336	...	...	...	...	1852	...	...	2222	0056	...	...	...
Mo i Rana d.	...	...	0703	...	1020	...	...	...	...	...	...	1543	...	...	...	...	2035	...	...	0024	...	...	...	...
Mosjøen d.	...	...	0808	...	1123	...	...	...	...	...	...	1653	...	...	...	...	2138	...	...	0140	...	...	...	...
Grong d.	...	...	1015	...	...	...	...	...	...	...	...	1914	...	...	...	...	...	...	...	0406	...	...	...	...
Steinkjer a.	...	...	1131x	...	...	...	...	...	...	...	...	2024	...	...	...	...	...	...	...	0517	...	...	...	...
Stjørdal a.	...	...	1242x	...	...	...	...	...	...	...	...	2145	...	...	...	...	...	...	...	0640	...	...	...	...
Trondheim ✈ ‡ a.	...	...	1244x	...	...	...	...	...	...	...	...	2148	...	...	...	...	...	...	...	0643	...	...	...	...
Trondheim a.	...	...	1311	...	...	...	...	...	...	...	...	2213	...	...	...	...	...	...	...	0714	...	...	...	...

Local services Trondheim - Steinkjer and v.v.

km		Ⓐn	Ⓐ	⚒	Ⓐ	⚒	Ⓐ	⚒	Ⓐ	⚒	Ⓐn	Ⓐn	Ⓑ	Ⓐr	Ⓐ	Ⓑ	Ⓐ	Ⓑ	Ⓐn	Ⓑ	Ⓑ				
0	**Trondheim** S d.	0511	0616	0715	0817	0917	1017	1117	1217	1317	1417	1442	1517	1542	1617	1717	1817	1917	2017	2117	2317	...	...	...	...
31	Hell ● d.	0543	0650	0750	0850	0950	1050	1150	1250	1350	1450	1520	1550	1620	1650	1750	1850	1950	2051	2150	2350	...	...	...	...
33	Trondheim ✈ ‡ d.	0546	0653	0753	0853	0953	1053	1153	1253	1353	1453	1523	1553	1623	1653	1753	1853	1953	2054	2153	2353	...	...	...	...
34	Stjørdal d.	0552	0657	0759	0900	1000	1100	1200	1300	1400	1500	1528	1600	1628	1700	1800	1900	2000	2101	2200	2356	...	...	...	...
126	**Steinkjer** a.	0722	0821	0922	1024	1124	1225	1324	1424	1524	1624	1651	1724	1751	1824	1924	2024	2124	2226	2320	0115	...	...	...	...

	Ⓐ	Ⓐr	⚒	Ⓐn	Ⓐ	⚒	Ⓐ	⚒	Ⓐ	⚒n	Ⓐ	Ⓑ	Ⓐ	Ⓑ	Ⓐ	Ⓑ	Ⓐ	Ⓑ	Ⓐn					
Steinkjer d.	0431	0506	0534	0602	0632	0734	0833	0930	1037	1138	1237	1337	1437	1537	1632	1732	1837	1932	2037	2134	...	...	...	...
Stjørdal d.	0552	0623	0657	0724	0759	0900	1000	1100	1200	1300	1400	1500	1600	1700	1800	1900	2000	2101	2200	2300	...	...	...	...
Trondheim ✈ ‡ d.	0554	0626	0700	0727	0802	0903	1003	1103	1203	1303	1403	1503	1603	1703	1803	1903	2003	2104	2203	2303	...	...	...	...
Hell ● d.	0557	0629	0703	0730	0805	0906	1006	1106	1206	1306	1406	1506	1606	1706	1806	1906	2009	2107	2206	2306	...	...	...	...
Trondheim S a.	0629	0703	0741	0803	0841	0941	1041	1141	1241	1341	1441	1541	1641	1741	1841	1941	2043	2141	2241	2341	...	...	...	...

M – ②③④⑦ only.
N – Conveys 🛏, (2) and ✕.
R – Reservation recommended.

m – June 20 - Aug. 12 only.
n – Not ①–⑤ June 20 - Aug. 12.
r – Not June 27 - June 29.
u – Calls to pick up only.
x – Calls on request.
z – Arrives 2127.

⊙ – Conveys *SJ NORD Premium*.
● – Trains call at Hell on request.
‡ – Trondheim Lufthavn (station for Trondheim Værnes Airport).
☛ – Most trains have automatic vending machines on board.
⊡ – Bus station.
⊖ – Bodø Sentrumsterminalen buss.
◇ – Operator: Nordlandsbuss.
♣ – 🚌 **Narvik - Svolvær** (Lofoten) *253 km.*
From Narvik bussterminal at 0955 and 1550.
From Svolvær sentrum at 0940 and 1515.

FINLAND

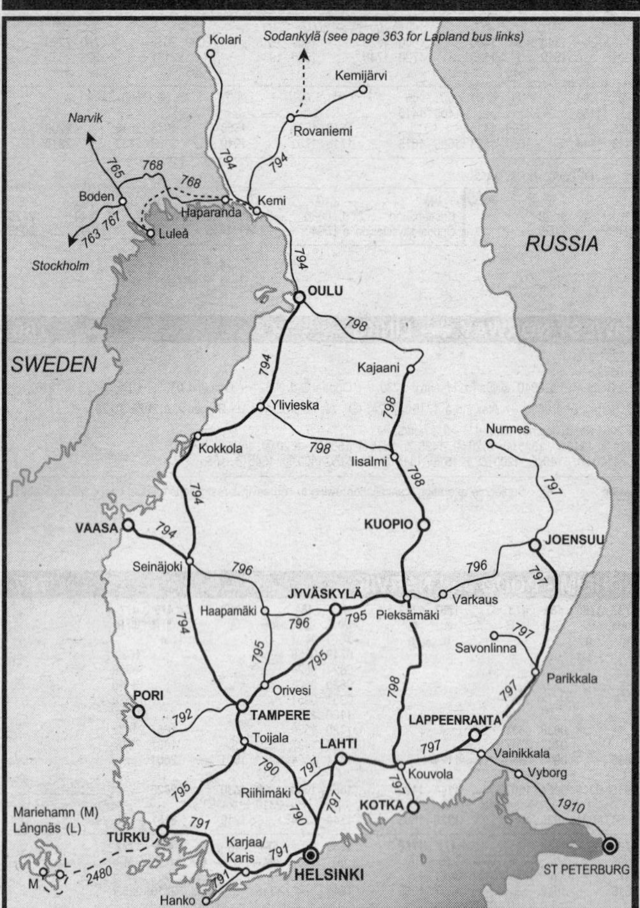

Operator: VR – VR-Yhtymä Oy www.vr.fi

Tickets and train types: Travel classes in Finland are referred to as *Extra* (1st) and *Eco* (2nd). For all except purely local journeys, tickets are always sold for travel by a specific train or combination of trains with seat reservations included. Standard *Eco* fares are referred to as 'Basic', whilst cheaper advance puchase 'Saver' fares are also available in limited numbers. In both cases tickets can be changed to a different date / departure time for a €5 fee (plus any price difference). Both ticket types can be upgraded to a seat in *Extra* class for a variable fee (€4 – 17, dependent on the length of journey). Tickets may be purchased on board long-distance trains (also regional trains outside of the Helsinki area), although an additional charge of €3 (for short journeys up to 76km) or €6 (for journeys over 76km) will be added to the 'Basic' fare. Please note that cash is no longer accepted for on board ticket purchase (only debit / credit cards are accepted). On board ticket purchase is **not** permitted on local trains (shown as 2nd class only in tables) Helsinki - Riihimäki - Tampere (Table **790**), Helsinki - Lahti - Kouvola - Kotka (Table **797**) and Riihimäki - Lahti (Table **797**).

- **S Pendolino** (e.g. *S* **123**) – high-speed tilting trains, with *Extra* and *Eco* class seats, all reservable.
- **InterCity** (e.g. *IC* **124**) – quality fast trains between major centres, with *Eco* class seats (most also convey *Extra* class seats), all reservable.
- **Express**, *pikajunat* (train number only shown, e.g. **128**) – other fast trains, with *Eco* class seats, all reservable. Night expresses convey sleeping-cars and *Eco* class seats only (marked ★ in the tables).
- **Regional**, *taajamajunat* (no train number shown) – stopping-trains, normally with *Eco* class seats only. Regional fares apply.

Rail tickets are **not** valid on 🚌 services (except Seinäjoki - Vaasa).

Services: ✕ indicates a train with a restaurant car. Trains marked 🍸 convey a *MiniBistro* trolley. A variable supplement is payable for travel in sleeping-cars (🛏) in addition to the relevant *Eco* class fare – the price to be paid depends on the date of travel and the type of accommodation required. A higher supplement is charged for occupancy of a single-berth cabin.

Timings: Valid **June 20 - August 14**, 2022.

In these tables Ⓐ = ①–⑤, ⚒ = ①–⑥, Ⓑ = ①–⑤ and ⑦.

Changes to the normal service pattern are likely to occur on and around the dates of public holidays (see page 4).

790 HELSINKI - TAMPERE

See next page for other regional services Helsinki - Riihimäki

For through journeys to / from **Oulu** and **Rovaniemi**, see Table **794**. For through journeys to / from **Jyväskylä** and **Pieksämäki**, see Table **795**.

km		S35	IC21	IC155	S155	IC41		S165	IC165	IC23	IC93	S93	IC43		S143	IC143	IC45		S171	IC171	IC25	IC145	IC37		S87	S175	IC87
		⚒ ✕	⚒ ✕	Ⓑ ✕	⑥ ✕	⚒◇ ◐✕	⚒ 2	①–④ ✕n	⑤P ✕	✕	◇ ✕	⑥ ✕	◇ ✕	2	Ⓐp ✕	⑥⑦ ✕	✕	2	⑤q ✕	⑦ ✕	✕	✕	✕	2	Ⓐ ✕	⑥P ✕	⑦ ✕
0	**Helsinki** d.	0503	0623	0703	0703	0723	0710	0803	0803	0824	0903	0903	0924	0910	1024	1024	1103	1110	1203	1230	1224	1303	1324	1310	1403	1403	1403
3	Pasila d.	0509	0629	0709	0709	0729	0715	0809	0809	0830	0909	0909	0930	0915	1030	1030	1109	1115	1209	1209	1230	1309	1330	1315	1409	1409	1409
16	Tikkurila d.	0519	0639	0719	0719	0739	0724	0819	0819	0841	0919	0919	0941	0924	1041	1041	1119	1124	1219	1219	1241	1319	1341	1324	1419	1419	1419
71	Riihimäki d.	0552	|	0752	0752	|	0815j	0852	0852	|	0952	0952	|	1012j	|	|	1152	1215j	1252	1252	|	1352	|	1415j	1452	1452	1452
108	Hämeenlinna d.	0611	|	0811	0811	|	0838	0911	0911	|	1011	1011	|	1035	|	|	1211	1238	1311	1311	|	1411	|	1438	1511	1511	1511
147	Toijala d.	0631	|	0831	0831	|	0901	0931	0931	|	1031	1031	|	1101	|	|	1231	1301	1331	1331	|	1431	|	1501	1531	1531	1531
187	**Tampere** a.	0653	0758	0853	0853	0858	0925	0953	0953	0958	1053	1053	1058	1125	1158	1158	1253	1325	1353	1353	1358	1453	1458	1525	1553	1553	1553

	IC27	IC151	IC47		IC147	IC51	S59	S59	IC59	IC177	S177	IC49		S89	IC89	IC29	IC149	S149		IC265	S183	S53	269		IC187		IC273
	◇ ✕	Ⓑ◇ ✕	Ⓑ ✕	2	✕	✕	⑦ ✕	①–④ ✕	⑤ ✕	Ⓑ ✕	⑥⊡ ✕	◇ ✕	2	Ⓑ ✕	⑥ ✕	⊠ ◐✕	Ⓑ❦ ✕	⑥ ✕	2	★	⑤ ✕	⑦ ✕	★	2	✕	2	★
Helsinki d.	1424	1503	1524	1510	1603	1624	1630	1640	1640	1703	1703	1724	1710	1803	1803	1824	1903	1903	1910	1929	2003	2024	2029	2110	2203	2240	2313
Pasila d.	1430	1509	1530	1515	1609	1630	1636	1646	1646	1709	1709	1730	1715	1809	1809	1830	1909	1909	1915	1937	2009	2030	2036	2115	2209	2245	2320
Tikkurila d.	1441	1519	1541	1524	1619	1641	|	|	|	1719	1719	1741	1724	1819	1819	1841	1919	1919	1924	2030	2019	2041	2114	2124	2219	2354	0001
Riihimäki d.	|	1552	|	1615j	1652	|	1725j	1725	1725	1752	1752	|	1815j	1852	1852	|	1952	1952	2015j	2116	2052	|	2158	2215j	2251	2345j	0044
Hämeenlinna d.	|	1611	|	1638	1711	|	1745	1745	1745	1811	1811	|	1838	1911	1911	|	2011	2011	2038	2140	2111	|	2224	2238	2311	0008	0106
Toijala d.	|	1631	|	1701	1731	|	|	|	|	1831	1831	|	1901	1931	1931	|	2031	2031	2101	|	2131	|	|	2301	2331	0031	0130
Tampere a.	1558	1653	1658	1725	1753	1758	1821	1821	1821	1853	1853	1858	1925	1953	1953	1958	2053	2053	2125	2231	2153	2158	2313	2325	2353	0055	0155

	IC266		IC160	IC162	S162	IC166	IC274		IC40	IC80	276	IC42	S140	IC140		IC150	S44	IC20		IC36	IC142	IC22	S94		S46	IC46	IC38
	★		Ⓐ ✕	Ⓐ ✕	⑥ ✕	Ⓐ ✕	★	2	Ⓐ ✕	⊕ ✕	★	⚒△ ✕	Ⓐ ✕	⑦ ✕	2	⚒△ ✕	⚒⊡ ✕	⚒⊡ ✕	2	⚒△ ✕	✕	✕	p ✕	2	Ⓐp ✕	⑥⑦ ✕	✕
Tampere d.	0345	...	0504	0545	0545	0622	0608	0635	0700	0704	0734	0800	0804	0804	0835	0900	0904	1000	1035	1100	1104	1200	1204	1235	1300	1300	1400
Toijala d.	0412	...	0526	0607	0607	|	0642j	0700	|	0726	0802	|	0826	0826	0900	|	0926	|	1100	|	1126	|	1226	1300	|	|	|
Hämeenlinna d.	0438	...	0547	0629	0629	0700	0708	0722	|	0747	0850k	|	0847	0847	0924	|	0947	|	1122	|	1147	|	1247	1322	|	|	|
Riihimäki d.	0503	...	0608	0650	0650	0720	0739	0755j	|	0808	0917	|	0908	0908	0955j	|	1008	|	1155j	|	1208	|	1308	1355j	|	|	|
Tikkurila d.	0547	...	0640	0721	0721	0755	0831	0835	0821	0840	1001	0921	0940	0940	1035	1021	1040	1121	1235	1221	1240	1321	1340	1435	1421	1421	1521
Pasila d.	0621	...	0649	0730	0730	0804	0909	0844	0830	0849	1040	0930	0949	0949	1044	1030	1049	1130	1244	1230	1249	1330	1349	1444	1430	1430	1530
Helsinki a.	0627	...	0654	0735	0735	0810	0915	0849	0835	0854	1045	0935	0954	0954	1049	1035	1054	1135	1249	1235	1254	1335	1354	1449	1435	1435	1535

	IC178	S178		IC48	IC144	S144	IC24	IC86		IC50	IC180	IC26	S146	IC146		IC54	S88	S186	IC88		S56	IC56	IC28		S58		
	ⒶP ✕	⑦P ❦✕	2	◇ ✕	Ⓑ ✕	⑥ ✕	Ⓑ ✕	◇ ✕	2	◇ ✕	⑤–⑦ ✕	✕	⚒ ✕	⑦ ✕	2	✕	Ⓐ ✕	⑥P ✕	⑦ ✕	2	Ⓑ ✕	⑥ ✕	✕	2	⑤⑦ ✕		
Tampere d.	1404	1404	1435	1500	1504	1504	1600	1604	1635	1700	1704	1800	1804	1804	1835	1900	2004	2004	2004	2035	2100	2100	2200	2235	2300	...	...
Toijala d.	1426	1426	1500	|	1526	1526	|	1628	1700	|	1728	|	1826	1826	1848	|	2026	2026	2026	2100	|	|	|	2300	|	...	...
Hämeenlinna d.	1447	1447	1522	|	1547	1547	|	1649	1722	|	1749	|	1847	1847	1922	|	2047	2047	2047	2122	|	|	|	2322	|	...	...
Riihimäki d.	1508	1508	1555j	|	1608	1608	|	1708	1755j	|	1808	|	1908	1908	1955j	|	2108	2108	2108	2155j	|	|	|	2355j	|	...	...
Tikkurila d.	1540	1540	1635	1621	1640	1640	1721	1740	1835	1821	1840	1921	1940	1940	1935	2021	2140	2140	2140	2235	2221	2221	2321	0035	0021	...	...
Pasila d.	1549	1549	1644	1630	1649	1649	1730	1749	1844	1830	1849	1930	1949	1949	1944	2030	2149	2149	2149	2244	2230	2230	2330	0044	0030	...	...
Helsinki a.	1554	1554	1649	1635	1654	1654	1735	1754	1849	1835	1854	1935	1954	1954	2049	2035	2154	2154	2154	2249	2235	2235	2335	0049	0035	...	...

FOR NOTES AND OTHER REGIONAL SERVICES, SEE TOP OF NEXT PAGE →

HELSINKI - TAMPERE 790

Other selected regional trains HELSINKI - RIIHIMÄKI (2nd class only)

km													
0	**Helsinki** d.	0610	0710	0810	1040		1940	2010	2140	2240	2340	...	...
3	Pasila d.	0615	0715	0815	1045	and	1945	2015	2145	2245	2345	...	...
16	Tikkurila d.	0624	0724	0824	1054	hourly	1954	2024	2154	2254	2354	...	...
37	Järvenpää d.	0640	0740	0840	1110	until	2010	2040	2210	2310	0010	...	...
59	Hyvinkää d.	0656	0756	0856	1126		2026	2056	2226	2326	0026	...	...
71	**Riihimäki** a.	0705	0805	0905	1135		2035	2105	2235	2335	0035	...	...

	Ⓐ	Ⓐ									
Riihimäki d.	0525	0620	0655	0755	0925		1925	2125	...	...	...
Hyvinkää d.	0533	0630	0703	0803	0933	and	1933	2133	...	...	...
Järvenpää d.	0548	0648	0718	0818	0948	hourly	1948	2148	...	...	...
Tikkurila d.	0605	0705	0735	0835	1005	until	2005	2215	...	...	...
Pasila d.	0614	0715	0744	0844	1014		2014	2214	...	...	...
Helsinki a.	0619	0720	0749	0849	1019		2019	2219	...	...	...

P – To / from Pori (Table **792**).

j – Arrives 7 – 10 minutes earlier.
k – Arrives 0827.
n – Not Aug. 8 – 11.
p – Not Aug. 8 – 12.
q – Not Aug. 12.

⊕ – Subject to cancellation on ①–⑤.
◇ – Subject to cancellation on ①–④.
⊖ – Subject to cancellation on ①–③.
‡ – Subject to cancellation on ②–④.
△ – Subject to cancellation on ②–⑤.
▽ – Subject to cancellation on ⑥⑦.
⊠ – Subject to cancellation on ⑤.

⊡ – Subject to cancellation on ⑥.
❦ – Subject to cancellation.
◐ – Train classification *S* on ⑥.
◧ – Train classification *IC* on ⑤.
★ – Overnight train to / from northern Finland.
For through cars and days of running see Table **794**.

HELSINKI - KARJAA - TURKU and KARJAA - HANKO 791

km		*S* 941	*IC* 943	*IC* 979	*S* 945	*IC* 945	*S* 947	*IC* 947	*S* 949	*IC* 949	*IC* 951	*S* 951	*IC* 953	*S* 955	*IC* 955	*IC* 957	*S* 957	*IC* 959	*S* 959	*IC* 924	*IC* 961	*IC* 963	*IC* 965	*IC* 971	*S* 967	*IC* 967
		Ⓐ	Ⓐ	Ⓐ	⑦	⚒	⑦	Ⓐ	⑤⑥	①–④	⑦–④	⑤⑥	⑤	⑦–④	⑤⑥	⑦–④	⑤	⚒	⑦	⑤⑦	Ⓑ		Ⓑ	⑥	①–④	⑤–⑦
		✕	🍷	◇🍷	✕	🍷	❦✕	❦🍷	❦✕	◇🍷	🍷	✕	🍷	✕	⊡🍷	🍷	✕	🍷	✕		🍷	🍷	🍷	❦🍷	✕	🍷
0	**Helsinki** d.	0528	0628	0736	0833	0836	0933	0936	1036	1036	1136	1136	1236	1336	1336	1436	1436	1536	1536	...	1636	1736	1836	1936	2036	2036
3	Pasila d.	0534	0634	0742	0839	0842	0939	0942	1042	1042	1142	1142	1242	1342	1342	1442	1442	1542	1542	...	1642	1742	1842	1942	2042	2042
87	Karjaa / Karis d.	0632	0726	0832	0932	0932	1032	1032	1132	1132	1232	1232	1332	1432	1432	1532	1532	1632	1632	...	1732	1832	1932	2032	2132	2132
138	Salo d.	0701	0803	0902	1001	1001	1101	1101	1201	1201	1301	1301	1401	1501	1501	1601	1601	1701	1701	...	1801	1901	2001	2101	2201	2201
194	**Turku** a.	0738	0834	0934	1031	1031	1134	1134	1234	1234	1334	1334	1434	1534	1534	1634	1634	1734	1734	1804	1834	1931	2036	2131	2231	2231
197	Turku satama a.	0747	...	...	...	...	...	...	...	...	...	...	...	...	...	...	...	...	...	1811	...	1940	...	...	...	...

	S 942	*IC* 944	*IC* 946	*S* 948	*IC* 950	*IC* 954	*IC* 956	*S* 956	*IC* 958	*IC* 960	*S* 960	*IC* 962	*S* 962	*S* 964	*IC* 964	*IC* 964	*S* 964	*IC* 966	*S* 966	*IC* 966	*IC* 968	*S* 968	*IC* 972	*IC* 974	
	Ⓐ	Ⓐ	Ⓐ		⚒		⚒	⑦		Ⓑ	⑥	Ⓑ	⑥	①–④	⑤	⑥⑦	⑦	①–④	⑤⑥	⑦	Ⓐ	⑦		⑦	
	⊠✕	🍷	🍷	✕	🍷	⊗🍷	⊕🍷	❦✕	◇🍷	◇🍷	❦✕	🍷	✕	✕	🍷	⊡🍷	✕	🍷	✕	🍷	🍷	✕	🍷	🍷	
Turku satama d.	...	...	...	0810	...	...	...	...	...	...	...	...	...	...	...	...	...	...	...	...	...	...	2018	...	...
Turku d.	0525	0623	0729	0825	0925	1125	1225	1225	1325	1425	1425	1525	1525	1625	1625	1625	1625	1718	1718e	1725	1825	1825	2027	2122	...
Salo d.	0556	0656	0802	0901	0959	1159	1259	1259	1359	1459	1459	1559	1559	1659	1657	1659	1659	1759	1759	1759	1859	1859	2059	2159	...
Karjaa / Karis d.	0628	0728	0831	0928	1028	1228	1328	1328	1428	1528	1528	1628	1628	1731	1731	1728	1728	1828	1828	1828	1928	1928	2128	2228	...
Pasila d.	0718	0818	0920	1018	1118	1318	1418	1418	1518	1618	1618	1718	1718	1821	1821	1818	1818	1921	1921	1921	2018	2018	2221	2321	...
Helsinki a.	0723	0823	0925	1023	1123	1323	1423	1423	1523	1623	1623	1723	1723	1826	1826	1823	1823	1926	1926	1926	2023	2023	2226	2326	...

KARJAA / KARIS - HANKO *All services are currently operated by* 🚌.

km		🚌	🚌		🚌	🚌	🚌		🚌		🚌	
		Ⓐ										
0	**Karjaa / Karis** d.	0731	0936	...	1236	1436	1636	...	1836	...	2136	...
16	Tammisaari d.	0750	0955	...	1255	1455	1655	...	1855	...	2155	...
49	**Hanko** a.	0825	1030	...	1330	1530	1730	...	1930	...	2230	...

	🚌	🚌		🚌	🚌	🚌		🚌		🚌	
	Ⓐ										
Hanko d.	0625	0825	...	1120	1320	1520	...	1720	...	2020	...
Tammisaari d.	0655	0855	...	1155	1355	1555	...	1755	...	2050	...
Karjaa / Karis a.	0720	0920	...	1220	1420	1620	...	1820	...	2120	...

e – 1725 on ⑥.

⊕ – Subject to cancellation on ①–⑤.
◇ – Subject to cancellation on ①–④.
⊠ – Subject to cancellation on ⑤.

⊗ – Subject to cancellation on ⑦.
⊡ – Subject to cancellation on ⑥.
❦ – Subject to cancellation.

TAMPERE - PORI 792

Most trains convey ✕

km		*IC* 477	*IC* 461	*IC* 165	*S* 165	*IC* 465	*IC* 467	*S* 469	*S* 175	*IC* 471	*S* 473	*IC* 475
		Ⓐ	⚒	⑤	C			Ⓑ	⑥		Ⓑ	
	Helsinki **790** d.	...	...	0803	0803	...	...	...	1403	...	...	...
0	**Tampere** d.	0557	0806	1009	1009	1209	1409	1609	1609	1809	2009	2209
17	Nokia d.	0614	0824	1027	1027	1227	1427	1627	1627	1827	2027	2228
59	Vammala d.	0658	0854	1102	1102	1258	1458	1658	1658	1858	2059	2257
135	**Pori** a.	0747	0940	1148	1148	1344	1544	1744	1744	1944	2145	2343

	S 460	*IC* 462	*IC* 466	*IC* 476	*IC* 464	*S* 474	*IC* 178	*IC* 468	*IC* 470	*S* 472	*S* 186
	⚒	⚒		Ⓐ		C	⑤d			Ⓑ	⑥
Pori d.	0517	0612	0717	0804	1003	1212	1212	1412	1612	1812	1812
Vammala d.	0604	0659	0804	0853	1050	1259	1259	1459	1659	1859	1859
Nokia d.	0633	0728	0838	0922	1119	1328	1328	1528	1728	1928	1928
Tampere a.	0650	0745	0855	0939	1136	1345	1345	1545	1745	1945	1945
Helsinki **790** a.	...	...	...	...	...	...	1554	...	...	...	2154

C – ①–④ (not Aug. 8 – 11).

d – Also Aug. 8 – 11.

☛ Frequent 🚌 services operate Turku - Rauma - Pori and v.v. See www.matkahuolto.fi.

TAMPERE - VAASA, OULU, KOLARI and ROVANIEMI 794

km		*S* 35	*S* 55	*S* 55	*IC* 21	*IC* 711	*IC* 41	*IC* 23	*IC* 43	*IC* 45	*IC* 25	*IC* 413	*IC* 37	*IC* 37	*S* 445	*IC* 27	*IC* 37	*IC* 415	*IC* 47	*IC* 51	*S* 447	*S* 59	*IC* 49	*IC* 29	*S* 53	*IC* 265	269	*IC* 273
		Ⓐ	⚒	Ⓐ	⚒		⚒◇		◇			Ⓑ		Ⓑ		◇	Ⓑ	⑥	Ⓑ		⊡	Ⓑ	◇	D	⑦	a	g	b
		✕	✕	✕	✕	K✕	◐✕	✕	✕	✕	✕	🍷	✕	✕	✕	✕	✕	🍷	✕	✕	✕	◧✕	✕	◐✕	✕	★	★	★
	Helsinki **790** d.	0503	0503	...	0623	...	0723	0824	0924	1103	1224	...	1324	1324	...	1424	...	...	1524	1624	...	1640h	1724	1824	2024	1929	2029	2313
0	**Tampere** d.	0702	0702	...	0802	...	0902	1002	1102	1302	1402	...	1502	1502	...	1602	...	...	1702	1802	...	1825	1902	2002	2202	2305	2359	0230
75	Parkano d.	0744	0744	...	|	...	|	|	1144	|	|	...	1545	1545	...	|	...	...	1735	|	...	1858	|	2035	2235	0001	|	0323
159	Seinäjoki a.	0827	0827	...	0918	...	1007	1105	1229	1416	1509	...	1625	1625	...	1713	...	...	1810	1905	...	1933	2013	2117	2307	0056	0138	0411
159	Seinäjoki d.	0839	...	0843	0922	...	1011	1109	1241	1420	1513	...	1637	1637	1632	1725	...	...	1814	1909	1927	1937	2016	2129	2310	0107	0155	0415
233	**Vaasa** a.	|	...	0933	|	...	1107	|	1338	1517	|	...	|	|	1728	|	...	...	1910	|	2017	|	2106	|	2359	|	|	|
292	Kokkola d.	0951	...	...	1040	...	...	1229	...	...	1616	...	1750	1750	...	1828	...	...	...	2014	...	2057	...	2233	...	0238	0334	0551
371	Ylivieska d.	1032	...	...	1120	...	...	1309	...	...	1653	...	1830	1830	...	1905	...	...	...	2055	...	...	...	2310	...	0326	0424	0642
493	**Oulu** a.	1144	...	...	1216	...	...	1422	...	...	1748	...	1951	1951	...	2012	←	...	...	2215	...	...	...	0016	...	0439	0542	0806
493	**Oulu** d.	...	...	...	...	1223	...	1427	...	...	...	1800	...	→	...	...	2020	2020	...	...	...	...	...	...	...	0449	0617	0836
599	Kemi d.	...	...	...	...	1326	...	1531	...	...	...	1909	...	...	...	...	2126	2126	...	...	...	...	...	...	...	0556	0744	0946
808	**Kolari** a.	...	...	...	...	|	...	|	...	...	...	|	...	...	...	...	|	|	...	...	...	...	...	...	...	|	1043	|
713	**Rovaniemi** a.	...	...	...	...	1445	...	1646	...	...	...	2023	...	...	...	...	2245	2245	...	...	...	...	...	...	...	0729	...	1113
796	Kemijärvi a.	...	...	...	...	...	...	...	...	...	...	...	...	...	...	...	...	...	...	...	...	...	...	...	...	0850	...	...

	IC 40	*S* 52	*IC* 42	*S* 44	*IC* 20	*IC* 36	*IC* 22	*IC* 22	*S* 46	*IC* 46	*S* 444	*IC* 38	*IC* 48	*IC* 24	*IC* 824	*IC* 50	*IC* 26	*IC* 54	*IC* 416	*S* 442	*S* 56	*IC* 710	*IC* 28	*S* 58	*IC* 266	*IC* 274	276	
	Ⓐ	Ⓐ	⚒△	⚒⊡	⚒⊡	⚒△		⚒	Ⓐ	⑥⑦	⑥		◇	d	e	◇					Ⓑ			⑤⑦	Ⓑb	c	f	
	✕	✕	✕	✕	✕	✕	✕	✕	✕	✕	✕	✕	✕	✕	✕	✕	✕	✕	🍷	✕	✕	K✕	✕	✕	★	★	★	
Kemijärvi d.	...	...	...	...	...	...	...	...	...	...	...	...	...	...	...	...	...	...	...	...	...	...	...	...	...	1915	...	...
Rovaniemi d.	...	...	...	...	...	...	...	0527	...	...	...	...	...	0932	0932	...	...	...	1310	...	...	1535	...	...	1745	2057	...	...
Kolari d.	...	...	...	...	...	...	...	|	...	...	...	...	...	|	|	...	...	...	|	...	...	|	...	...	|	|	1942	...
Kemi d.	...	...	...	...	...	...	...	0647	...	...	...	...	...	1050	1050	...	...	...	1432	...	...	1659	...	...	1917	2228	2250	...
Oulu a.	...	...	...	...	...	...	...	0745	...	...	...	...	...	1150	1150	...	...	...	1543	...	...	1800	...	...	2020	2349	0010	...
Oulu d.	...	...	...	...	0521	...	0749	0749	...	...	...	0916	...	1155	...	...	1333	...	...	...	1611	...	1808	...	2055	2353	0057	...
Ylivieska d.	...	...	...	...	0643	...	0848	0848	...	...	...	1030	...	1259	...	...	1441	...	...	...	1725	...	1904	...	2231	0109	0244	...
Kokkola d.	...	0517	...	...	0727	0815	0927	0927	...	...	...	1117	...	1338	...	...	1521	...	...	...	1806	...	1941	...	2331	0157	0335	...
Vaasa d.	0444	|	0544	0644	|	|	|	|	1035	1035	1137	|	1235	|	...	1445	|	1625	...	1807	|	...	|	2031	|	|	|	...
Seinäjoki a.	0533	0626	0633	0733	0833	0922	1031	1031	1124	1124	1232	1227	1324	1434	...	1534	1623	1714	...	1857	1921	...	2041	2124	0058	0345	0509	...
Seinäjoki d.	0537	...	0637	0737	0838	0926	1035	1035	1128	1128	...	1239	1328	1438	...	1538	1628	1724	...	...	1928	...	2044	2130	0115	0356	0519	...
Parkano d.	0612	...	0712	0812	|	|	|	|	1204	1204	...	1313	|	|	...	1612	1709	|	...	...	2008	...	|	|	0209	|	|	...
Tampere a.	0656	...	0751	0850	0951	1051	1151	1151	1251	1251	...	1351	1451	1551	...	1651	1751	1856	...	...	2051	...	2151	2249	0259	0535	0713	...
Helsinki **790** a.	0835	...	0935	1054	1135	1235	1335	1335	1435	1435	...	1535	1635	1735	...	1835	1935	2035	...	...	2235	...	2335	0035	0627	0915	1045	...

D – Daily except ⑤.
K – From / to Kuopio (Table **798**).

a – Not June 24, 25, July 19, Aug. 2.
b – Not June 24, 25.
c – Not June 24, 25, July 20, Aug. 2.

d – ⑤⑥⑦ (also June 20 – 23).
e – ①②③④ June 27 - Aug. 11.
f – ②④⑥⑦ (not June 25, Aug. 2).
g – ①③⑤⑥ (also June 23; not June 24, 25).
h – 1630 on ⑦.

◐ – Train classification *S* on ⑥.
◧ – Train classification *IC* on ⑤.
◇ – Subject to cancellation on ①–④.
△ – Subject to cancellation on ②–⑤.
⊡ – Subject to cancellation on ⑥.
★ – Conveys 🛏, 🛋 and ✕.

795 TURKU - TAMPERE - PIEKSÄMÄKI

km		S81		IC905	IC155		IC909	IC93		S143	IC143	IC917	IC145	S87		S921	IC151	IC923	IC147	IC927	S89	S149	IC931		IC933
		Ⓐ	⚒	⚒⊡				◇		Ⓐ	⑥⑦			Ⓑ		⑤⑦	Ⓑ◇			◇	Ⓑ	⑥	⊙		
		✕	2	🍷	◐✕	2	🍷	◐✕	2	n✕	✕	⊖🍷	✕	♤✕	2	♤🍷	✕	🍷	K🍷	🍷	✕	✕	🍷	2	🍷
	Turku satama d.	...	...	...	...	...	*0810*	...	...	...	...	...	...	...	...	...	...	...	...	...	...	...	1945	...	*2018*
0	**Turku** d.	...	...	0654	...	...	0905	...	...	...	...	1305	...	...	...	1505	...	1605	...	1805	...	...	2005	...	2100
66	Loimaa d.	...	...	0740	...	...	0944	...	...	...	...	1344	...	...	...	1544	...	1644	...	1844	...	...	2044	...	2142
86	Humppila d.	...	...	0753	...	...	0959	...	...	...	...	1357	...	...	...	1559	...	1659	...	1859	...	...	2057	...	2159
	Helsinki **790** d.	...	...	|	0703	...	|	0903	...	1024	1024	|	1303	1403	...	|	1503	|	1603	|	1803	1903	|	...	|
128	Toijala **790** d.	...	...	0819	0831	...	1025	1031	...	|	|	1425	1431	1531	...	1625	1631	1725	1731	1925	1931	2031	2123	...	2225
168	**Tampere** **790** a.	...	...	0842	0853	...	1047	1053	...	1158	1158	1447	1453	1553	...	1647	1653	1747	1753	1947	1953	2053	2145	...	2247
168	**Tampere** d.	0707	0806	...	0907	...	...	1107	1206	1212	1212	...	1507	1607	1616	...	1706	...	1807	...	2007	2107	...	2207	...
210	Orivesi d.	0731	0832	...	0932	...	...	1132	1232	1237	1237	...	1532	1632	1642	...	1730	...	1832	...	2032	2132	...	2233	...
	Vilppula d.	|	0907	...	|	...	...	|	1307	|	|	...	|	|	1717	...	|	...	|	...	|	|	...	2308	...
	Haapamäki a.	|	0925	...	|	1103	...	|	1325	|	|	...	|	|	1735	...	|	...	|	...	|	|	...	2326	...
266	Jämsä d.	0813	...	...	1012	|	...	1207	...	1312	1312	...	1607	1714	...	...	1805	...	1912	...	2108	2213	...	|	...
323	Jyväskylä **796** d.	0843	...	...	1041	1208	...	1240	...	1343	1343	...	1640	1744	...	...	1833	...	1941	...	2135	2243	...	0039	...
403	**Pieksämäki** **796** a.	...	...	...	1128	...	...	...	...	1430	1430	...	1729	...	...	...	...	...	2034	...	...	...	...	...	...

km		IC904	IC80		S140	IC140	IC150	IC910		IC142		S94	IC916	IC144	IC922		IC86	IC924	S146	IC928	S88	S930		IC148	IC934
			Ⓐ❦	⚒	Ⓐ	⑥❦	⚒△		⑦		⚒						◇	⊙			Ⓑ	⑤⑦			⑦
		🍷	✕	2	✕	✕	✕	⊖🍷	2	K✕	2	n✕	🍷	◐✕	🍷	2	◐🍷	🍷	♤✕	⊖🍷	♤✕	♤🍷	2	✕	🍷
	Pieksämäki **796** d.	...	...	...	...	...	...	...	...	0830	...	...	...	1220	...	...	...	...	1523	...	...	...	...	1811	...
	Jyväskylä **796** d.	...	0524	0505	0617	0617	0719	...	0805	0919	...	1015	...	1315	...	...	1420	...	1612	...	1810	...	...	1915	...
	Jämsä d.	...	0555	|	0648	0648	0748	...	|	0948	...	1051	...	1352	...	...	1451	...	1650	...	1848	...	...	1951	...
0	**Haapamäki** d.	...	|	0619	|	|	|	...	0919	|	1019	|	...	|	...	1419	|	...	|	...	|	...	1831	|	...
25	Vilppula d.	...	|	0640	|	|	|	...	0940	|	1040	|	...	|	...	1440	|	...	|	...	|	...	1852	|	...
72	Orivesi d.	...	0630	0715	0725	0725	0825	...	1015	1023	1115	1126	...	1427	...	1515	1526	...	1725	...	1923	...	1927	2026	...
114	**Tampere** a.	...	0654	0740	0749	0749	0849	...	1040	1049	1140	1150	...	1451	...	1540	1550	...	1749	...	1949	...	1955	2050	...
	Tampere **790** d.	0550	0704	...	0804	0804	0900	0910	...	1104	...	1204	1210	1504	1510	...	1604	1610	1804	1810	2004	1910	...	...	2112
	Toijala **790** d.	0614	0726	...	0826	0826	|	0935	...	1126	...	1226	1235	1526	1535	...	1628	1635	1826	1835	2026	1935	...	...	2135
	Helsinki **790** a.	|	0901	...	1001	1001	1042	|	...	1301	...	1401	|	1701	|	...	1801	|	2001	|	2201	|	...	...	|
	Humppila d.	0641	...	...	...	...	...	1000	...	...	...	...	1300	...	1600	...	...	1700	...	1900	...	2000	...	...	2200
	Loimaa d.	0655	...	...	...	...	...	1013	...	...	...	...	1313	...	1613	...	...	1713	...	1915	...	2013	...	...	2213
	Turku a.	0733	...	...	...	...	...	1050	...	...	...	...	1355	...	1655	...	...	1750	...	1955	...	2055	...	...	2250
	Turku satama a.	0752	...	...	...	...	...	...	...	...	...	...	...	...	...	...	...	1811	...	2007	...	...	...	...	...

K – To / from Kuopio (Table **798**).

n – Not Aug. 8–12.

◐ – Train classification *S* on ⑥.

⊖ – Train classification *S* on ⑦.

♤ – Train classification *IC* on ⑦.

⊙ – Subject to cancellation on ①②③④⑥.

◇ – Subject to cancellation on ①–④.

△ – Subject to cancellation on ②–⑤.

⊡ – Subject to cancellation on ⑥.

❦ – Subject to cancellation.

796 JOENSUU - PIEKSÄMÄKI - JYVÄSKYLÄ - SEINÄJOKI

km						IC142			IC148		
		2Ⓐ	2⚒	2⑦	2	✕	2	2	✕	2	
0	**Joensuu** d.	...	...	...	0608	...	...	1540	...	...	...
134	Varkaus d.	...	...	...	0745	...	...	1717	...	...	...
183	**Pieksämäki** **795** d.	...	...	...	0820	0830	...	1752	1811	...	...
263	**Jyväskylä** **795** d.	...	0505	0805	...	0919	1223	...	1915	1947	...
	Tampere **795** a.	...	|	|	...	1049	|	...	2050	|	...
341	Haapamäki d.	...	0611	0911	...	...	1330	...	...	2054	...
414	Alavus d.	0657	...	...	...	...	1430	...	...	2155	...
459	**Seinäjoki** d.	0729	...	...	...	...	1502	...	...	2227	...

		IC155			S143	IC145			IC147			
	2Ⓐ	◐✕	2	2	♤n	◐✕	2⑥	2	✕	2Ⓑ		
Seinäjoki d.	0525	...	...	0930	...	...	...	1652	...	...	...	...
Alavus d.	0557	...	...	1001	...	...	...	1724	...	...	...	...
Haapamäki d.	...	...	...	1103	...	...	...	1827	...	...	...	...
Tampere **795** d.	...	0907	...	|	1212	1507	...	|	1807	...	...	...
Jyväskylä **795** d.	...	1041	...	1208	1343	1640	...	1932	1941	...	...	...
Pieksämäki **795** d.	...	1128	1142	...	1430	1729	1807	...	2034	2039	...	...
Varkaus d.	...	...	1219	...	...	...	1844	...	...	2114	...	...
Joensuu a.	...	...	1353	...	...	...	2018	...	...	2249	...	...

n – Not Aug. 8–12.

◐ – Train classification *S* on ⑥.

♤ – Train classification *IC* on ⑥⑦.

797 HELSINKI - KOUVOLA - JOENSUU - NURMES

km			IC1			IC63	IC3		IC65	IC5			S67	S7		IC9	S9			IC111	IC11		IC73	IC115		
		⚒	⚒											Ⓑ◇		Ⓑ	⑥	Ⓑ	Ⓐ	Ⓑ			⊡	❦		
		2	✕	2	2	K✕	✕	2	K✕	✕	2	2	K✕	✕	2	✕	✕	2	2	✕	✕	2	K✕	◐🍷		2
0	**Helsinki** ▷ d.	...	0657	...	...	0819	1019	...	1119	1319	...	...	1419	1519	1530	1619	1619	...	1635	1719	1829	...	1919	2019	...	0010
3	Pasila ▷ d.	...	0703	...	...	0825	1025	...	1125	1325	...	...	1425	1525	1536	1625	1625	...	1641	1725	1835	...	1925	2025	...	0016
16	Tikkurila ▷ d.	...	0714	...	...	0836	1036	...	1136	1336	...	...	1436	1536	1545	1636	1636	...	1650	1736	1845	...	1936	2036	...	0025
104	**Lahti** ▷ d.	...	0751	...	...	0913	1113	...	1216	1413	...	...	1513	1613	1650	1713	1713	...	1750	1813	1923	...	2013	2113	...	0121
166	**Kouvola** a.	...	0819	...	...	0941	1141	...	1245	1441	...	...	1541	1641	1733	1741	1741	...	1833	1841	1951	...	2041	2141	...	0202
166	**Kouvola** d.	...	0823	...	...	...	1143	...	...	1443	...	...	...	1645	...	1744	1744	...	...	1844	2000	...	...	...	...	...
252	Lappeenranta d.	...	0909	...	...	...	1223	...	...	1523	...	...	...	1723	...	1827	1827	...	...	1927	2046	...	...	...	...	...
288	Imatra d.	...	0940	...	...	...	1254	...	...	1554	...	...	...	1750	...	1858	1855	...	...	1955	2116	...	...	...	...	...
352	Parikkala d.	0730	1022	1026	...	...	1333	1337	...	1633	1637	...	...	|	...	1940	...	1944	...	...	2157	2202	...	...	...	...
411	Savonlinna a.	0823	|	1119	...	...	|	1430	...	|	1730	...	...	|	...	|	...	2037	...	...	|	2255	...	...	...	...
482	**Joensuu** d.	...	1141	...	1154	...	1451	...	...	1751	...	1800	...	1936	...	2056	...	...	...	...	2315	...	...	...	...	...
586	Lieksa d.	...	...	...	1315	...	...	...	...	...	...	1921	...	...	...	...	...	...	...	...	...	...	...	...	...	...
642	**Nurmes** a.	...	...	...	1400	...	...	...	...	...	...	2006	...	...	...	...	...	...	...	...	...	...	...	...	...	...

			IC102	IC104		S2	IC62		IC4	S100	S64	IC64			IC6	S66		IC8	IC68		IC10		IC70		IC12	
	Ⓐ	Ⓐ	⚒❦	⚒	①⑥	⚒△	⚒	②–⑤	⚒	⑦	⚒•	⑦❦						⊡								Ⓑ
	2	2	✕	✕	2	✕	K✕	2	✕	✕	K✕	K✕	2	2	✕	K✕	2	✕	K✕	2	✕	2	K✕	2	✕	2
Nurmes d.	...	...	...	...	...	...	...	...	...	...	...	...	0635	...	...	...	...	...	...	...	...	1540	...	...	...	...
Lieksa d.	...	...	...	...	...	...	...	...	...	...	...	...	0722	...	...	...	...	...	...	...	...	1626	...	...	...	...
Joensuu d.	...	...	...	...	...	0458	...	...	0558	...	...	...	0850	...	0900	...	...	1211	...	...	1511	1745	...	...	1813	...
Savonlinna d.	...	...	...	...	0513	|	...	0622	|	...	...	...	...	0919	|	...	1230	|	...	1530	|	...	...	1837	|	2058
Parikkala d.	...	...	...	...	0606	0612	...	0715	0721	...	...	...	...	1012	1020	...	1323	1331	...	1623	1631	...	...	1930	1938	2151
Imatra d.	...	...	0502	0602	...	0656	...	...	0802	0802	...	...	...	...	1102	...	...	1409	...	...	1709	...	...	...	2020	...
Lappeenranta d.	...	...	0531	0631	...	0721	...	...	0831	0831	...	...	...	...	1131	...	...	1436	...	...	1744	...	...	...	2048	...
Kouvola a.	...	...	0615	0715	...	0805	...	...	0915	0915	...	...	...	...	1215	...	...	1515	...	...	1858	...	...	...	2127	...
Kouvola d.	0450	0527	0619	0719	...	0809	0819	...	0919	0919	1119	1119	...	...	1219	1419	...	1519	1719	...	1824	...	2015	...	2129	...
Lahti ▷ d.	0529	0613	0649	0749	...	0840	0849	...	0949	0949	1149	1149	...	...	1249	1449	...	1549	1749	...	1854	...	2047	...	2210	...
Tikkurila ▷ a.	0619	0709	0725	0825	...	0915	0925	...	1025	1025	1225	1225	...	...	1325	1525	...	1625	1825	...	1930	...	2130	...	2247	...
Pasila ▷ a.	0628	0719	0734	0834	...	0924	0934	...	1034	1034	1234	1234	...	...	1334	1534	...	1634	1834	...	1939	...	2139	...	2257	...
Helsinki ▷ a.	0634	0725	0740	0840	...	0930	0940	...	1040	1040	1240	1240	...	...	1340	1540	...	1640	1840	...	1945	...	2145	...	2303	...

Local trains **LAHTI - KOUVOLA - KOTKA** and v.v. 2nd class only.

km		⚒			Ⓐ	⑥⑦						Ⓐ	⑥⑦			
	Lahti d.	...	...	...	0711	...	...	...	...	...	...	1500	...	...	...	1930
0	**Kouvola** d.	0600	0653	...	0800	0800	0900	...	1200	...	1527	1618	1618	1718	...	2037
51	**Kotka** a.	0644	0737	...	0844	0844	0944	...	1244	...	1611	1702	1702	1802	...	2121
52	**Kotka** satama a.	0647	0740	...	0847	0847	0947	...	1247	...	1614	1705	1705	1805	...	2124

	⚒						Ⓐ	⑥⑦				Ⓐ	⑥⑦			
Kotka satama d.	0654	0752	0855	...	...	1200	...	...	...	1513	1621	1712	1712	...	2033	2215
Kotka d.	0657	0755	0858	...	...	1203	...	...	...	1516	1624	1715	1715	...	2036	2218
Kouvola a.	0742	0840	0943	1030	...	1248	1317	1330	...	1601	1709	1800	1800	...	2121	2303
Lahti a.	0834	...	...	1113	...	...	1400	1417	...	1652	...	1845	...	...	...	...

Local trains **RIIHIMÄKI - LAHTI** and v.v. 2nd class only.
59 km. Journey time: 42–43 minutes.

From Riihimäki at 0435 Ⓐ, 0513 ⑥, 0613 ⚒, 0613 ⑦, 0701 Ⓐ, 0713 ⑥, 0813 and hourly until 2213.

From Lahti at 0535 ⚒, 0704 ⚒, 0804 and hourly until 2004; then 2204.

K – To / from stations in Table **798**.

◐ – Train classification *S* on ⑥.

❦ – Subject to cancellation.

• – Subject to cancellation on ②–⑥.

◇ – Subject to cancellation on ①–④.

△ – Subject to cancellation on ②–⑤.

⊡ – Subject to cancellation on ⑥.

▷ – Other local journeys Helsinki - Lahti and v.v. (2nd class only, journey 63–72 minutes):
From Helsinki at 0130 ⑥⑦, 0510 ⚒, 0635 Ⓐ, 0640 ⑥⑦, 0735 ⚒, 0835 ⚒, 0935 and hourly until 2135; then 2310.
From Lahti at 0024, 0614 ⑥⑦, 0713 Ⓐ, 0714 ⑥⑦, 0757 Ⓐ, 0814 ⑦, 0819 ⑥, 0915 and hourly until 2219; then 2314.

KOUVOLA - KUOPIO - OULU 798

km		IC711		IC63	IC713		IC65		S67	S67		S69	IC147		IC73	IC73	
										Ⓑ		Ⓑ ⊕			⊡	Ⓑ	
		✕		✕	🍷		✕		✕	✕		✕	✕		✕	✕	
	Helsinki **797** d.	...	...	0819	...	...	1119	...	1419	1419	...	*1619*	1603	...	1919	1919	...
0	**Kouvola** d.	...	...	0948	...	...	1303	...	1550	1550	...	1748	|	...	2051	2051	...
113	Mikkeli d.	...	...	1054	...	...	1406	...	1656	1656	...	1853	|	...	2154	2154	...
	Tampere **795** d.	...	...	|	...	...	|	...	|	|	...	|	1807	...	|	|	...
184	Pieksämäki d.	...	...	1134	...	...	1445	...	1737	1737	...	1932	2036	...	2233	2233	...
273	**Kuopio** a.	...	...	1229	...	...	1535	...	1830	1830	...	2024	2128	...	2325	2325	...
273	**Kuopio** d.	0719	...	...	1239	...	1539	...	1838	1838	...	2029	...	...	...	2329	...
358	Iisalmi d.	0823	...	...	1340	...	1642	...	1937	1937	...	2128	...	...	...	0033	...
441	**Kajaani** a.	0911	...	...	1428	...	1732	...	2032	2032	...	2219	...	...	...	0122	...
441	**Kajaani** d.	0917	...	...	1432	...	1736	...	...	2108	...	...	...	...	...	...	...
484	Paltamo d.	0952	...	...	1501	...	1807	...	...	2144	...	...	...	...	...	...	...
633	**Oulu** a.	1136	...	...	1639	...	1956	...	...	2321	...	...	...	...	...	...	...
	Rovaniemi **794** a.	1445	...	...	...	...	...	...	...	...	...	...	...	...	...	...	...

	IC62		IC142	S64	IC64		S66	S66		IC716	IC68		IC70		IC710		
	⚒			⚒ ■	⑦ ❦		⚒										
	✕		✕	✕	✕		✕	✕		🍷	✕		✕		✕		
Rovaniemi **794** d.	...	...	...	...	...	...	...	...	...	...	...	...	...	...	1535	...	...
Oulu d.	...	...	...	...	...	...	0710	...	...	1003	...	...	1224	...	1812	...	...
Paltamo d.	...	...	...	...	...	...	0847	...	...	1140	...	...	1357	...	1959	...	...
Kajaani a.	...	...	...	...	...	...	0917	...	...	1210	...	...	1430	...	2031	...	...
Kajaani d.	0340	...	...	0633	...	...	0923	0923	...	1217	...	...	1433	...	2037	...	...
Iisalmi d.	0432	...	...	0725	...	...	1014	1014	...	1308	...	...	1535	...	2128	...	...
Kuopio a.	0528	...	...	0821	...	...	1111	1111	...	1407	...	...	1642	...	2224	...	...
Kuopio d.	0532	...	0738	0826	0826	...	1118	1118	...	...	1420	...	1700	...	...	...	...
Pieksämäki d.	0628	...	0830	0920	0920	...	1213	1213	...	...	1520	...	1804	...	...	...	...
Tampere **795** a.	|	...	1049	|	|	...	|	|	...	...	|	...	|	...	...	...	...
Mikkeli d.	0709	...	|	1000	1000	...	1253	1253	...	...	1600	...	1851	...	...	...	...
Kouvola a.	0811	...	|	1106	1106	...	1403	1403	...	...	1711	...	1952	...	...	...	...
Helsinki **797** a.	0940	...	1254	1240	1240	...	1540	1540	...	...	1840	...	2145	...	...	...	...

IISALMI - YLIVIESKA

km		①–④	⑤⑥	⑤–⑦	①–④
		🚌	2	2	🚌
0	**Iisalmi** d.	0740	0830	1645	1645
99	Haapajärvi d.	0925	0937	1748	1830
154	**Ylivieska** a.	1015	1013	1824	1920

	①–④	⑤–⑦	⑤⑦	①–④
	🚌	2	2	🚌
Ylivieska d.	1240	1337	1912	2000
Haapajärvi d.	1330	1413	1948	2050
Iisalmi a.	1515	1518	2055	2235

⊕ – Subject to cancellation on ①–⑤.
⊡ – Subject to cancellation on ⑥.
■ – Subject to cancellation on ②–⑥.
❦ – Subject to cancellation.

LAPLAND 🚌 LINKS 799

Subject to alteration on and around public holiday dates

Narvik – Tromsø – Alta

Operator: Torghatten www.tromskortet.no

km		①–⑤	⑥	①–⑤	Ⓑ		Ⓑ			⑦	⑦
0	**Narvik** bus station d.	0535	...	...	...	1310	...	...	1545	...	1900
181	Nordkjosbotn balsfjord d.	0825	0825	1030	1320	1620	1620	...	1845	2035	2200
252	**Tromsø** Prostneset d.	0930	0930	1130	1425	1725	|	1600	1950	|	2306
241	Lyngseidet ferjekai d.	...	...	...	...	...	1730	1740	...	2145	...
465	**Alta** sentrum a.	...	...	...	...	...	...	2220	...	...	...

km		①–⑤		⑤	①–⑥	Ⓑ □		⑦	⑦	⑦
0	**Alta** sentrum d.	...	...	...	1055	...	...	1415	...	...
224	Lyngseidet ferjekai d.	...	...	...	1555	1550	...	1925	1925	...
293	**Tromsø** Prostneset d.	0620	1030	1240	1730	|	1600	2100	|	1930
	Nordkjosbotn balsfjord d.	0725	1135	1342	...	1657	1705	...	2032	2035
	Narvik bus station a.	1010	1420	...	...	...	1950	...	...	2320

Alta – Hammerfest – Karasjok – Kirkenes

Operator: Snelandia www.snelandia.no

km		①–⑤	①–⑤	⑦	⑦	①–⑤	①–⑤	Ⓑ		⑤⑦	①–⑤ ◧	⑦
0	**Alta** sentrum d.	0640	...	0900	...	...	1145	...	1430	1550	1700	1745
	Hammerfest d.	|	0700	|	1140	1225	|	1515	|	|	|	|
87	Skaidi d.	0819	0820	1045	1300	1325	1330	1615	1615	|	1830	1915
144	Hammerfest a.	|	|	|	|	|	|	|	|	|	1930	2015
112	Olderfjord d.	0845	0845	1115	1325	1400	1400	1655	1655	|	...	...
212	Honningsvåg ★ a.	1045	|	1315	|	|	1545	|	1835	|	...	...
	Nordkapp a.	1120**d**	|	1350**d**	|	|	...	|	...	|	...	...
174	Lakselv d.	...	0945	...	1440	1515	...	1755	...	|	...	...
248	Karasjok d.	...	|	...	|	1620	...	1900	...	1915	...	...
429	Tana bru d.	...	1400	...	1845	...	...	...	...	...	...	...
571	**Kirkenes** AMFI ♠ a.	...	1646	...	2103	...	...	...	...	...	...	...

	①–⑤	①–⑤		⑦	①–⑤	①–⑤	①–⑤	⑦	Ⓑ	Ⓑ	⑦	⑤⑦
Kirkenes AMFI ♠ d.	...	...	...	...	...	0605	...	...	...	...	1120	...
Tana bru d.	...	...	...	...	...	0920	...	...	...	...	1415	...
Karasjok d.	...	0615	...	...	...	|	...	...	...	1430	|	1930
Lakselv d.	...	0730	...	...	...	1305	...	...	...	1545	1755	|
Nordkapp d.	...	|	...	...	...	|	...	...	1420**d**	|	|	|
Honningsvåg ★ d.	0655	|	...	0920	...	|	1220	..	1510	|	|	|
Olderfjord d.	0845	0845	...	1115	...	1400	1400	...	1655	1655	1855	|
Hammerfest d.	|	|	...	|	1100	|	|	1340	|	|	|	|
Skaidi d.	0910	0915	...	1145	1220	1425	1430	1500	1725	1725	1915	|
Hammerfest a.	|	1015	...	|	|	1525	|	|	|	1825	2015	|
Alta sentrum a.	1037	...	...	1312	1340	...	1557	1620	1852	...	...	2245

Rovaniemi – Muonio – Tromsø

www.matkahuolto.fi

km	Operator:	G	E	G
0	**Rovaniemi** bus station d.	0805	1140	1710
	Rovaniemi rail station d.	0820	1125*	1720
153	Kittilä d.	1030	1335	1925
232	Muonio d.	1300**g**	1505	2030
319	Karesuvanto d.	1435	1625**n**	...
428	Kilpisjärvi ⊡ FI d.	1625	1810**n**	...
535	Nordkjosbotn ⊕ NO d.	...	1820**n**	...
608	**Tromsø** Prostneset a.	...	1925**n**	...

	G	E	G
Tromsø Prostneset d.	...	0725**p**	...
Nordkjosbotn ⊕ NO d.	...	0820**p**	...
Kilpisjärvi ⊡ FI d.	...	1100**p**	1315
Karesuvanto d.	...	1240**p**	1515
Muonio d.	0855	1400	1700**k**
Kittilä d.	1010	1525	1825
Rovaniemi rail station a.	1210**x**	1720	2025**x**
Rovaniemi bus station a.	1215	1725	2030

Rovaniemi – Karasjok, Nordkapp and Tana bru

www.matkahuolto.fi

km	Operator:	G		E		J		E		L	
						①–⑤				⑦–④	
0	**Rovaniemi** bus station d.	0805	...	1145	...	1315	...	1720	...	2035	...
	Rovaniemi rail station d.	0820	...	1125*	...	|	...	1705*	...	2045	...
130	Sodankylä d.	1020	...	1345	...	1505	...	1905	...	2230	...
305	Ivalo, MH FI d.	1245	...	1630**j**	...	...	...	2115	...	0030	...
346	Inari, K-market FI d.	...	...	1710	...	...	...	2150	...	...	...
461	Karasjok ⊖ NO a.	...	...	1845	...	...	...	...	...	...	...
536	Lakselv, Circle K a.	...	...	...	...	...	...	...	...	...	...
	Honningsvåg ◇ a.	...	...	...	...	...	...	...	...	...	...
735	**Nordkapp** a.	...	...	...	...	...	...	...	...	...	...
	Tana bru ⊙ NO a.	...	...	...	...	...	...	...	...	...	...

Operator:	J		E		L		E		G	
	①–⑤				①–⑤					
Tana bru ⊙ NO d.	...	...	...	...	...	...	...	...	...	...
Nordkapp d.	...	...	...	...	...	...	...	...	...	...
Honningsvåg ◇ d.	...	...	...	...	...	...	...	...	...	...
Lakselv, Circle K d.	...	...	...	...	...	...	...	...	...	...
Karasjok ⊖ NO d.	...	...	...	...	...	...	0915	...	...	...
Inari, K-market FI d.	...	...	0720	...	...	...	1210	...	...	...
Ivalo, MH FI d.	...	...	0810	...	1145	...	1315**e**	...	1600	...
Sodankylä d.	0910	...	1030	...	1445**h**	...	1540	...	1830	...
Rovaniemi rail station a.	1105**x**	...	1210	...	1640•	...	1715	...	2015	...
Rovaniemi bus station a.	1110	...	1215	...	1635	...	1725	...	2020	...

Operator codes:

E – J M Eskelisen Lapin Linjat Oy.
G – OnniBus FLEX / Gold Line.
L – Liikenne O. Niemelä Oy.
J – Jbus Oy.

Time Zones:

FI – Finland (East European Time).
NO – Norway (Central European Time).
RU – Russia (Moskva Time).

Nordkapp
Honningsvåg
Hammerfest
Tana bru
Skaidi
Ol.
Kirkenes
Alta
La.
Murmansk
Tromsø
Ly.
Karasjok
Nordkjosbotn
Inari
Ivalo
St Peterburg 1905
Svolvær 787
Narvik
Muonio
Boden, Stockholm 761 / 767
Sodankylä
Fauske 787
Rovaniemi
Trondheim, Oslo 787
Oulu, Helsinki 793

d – May 1 - Sept. 30.
e – Arrives at 1245.
g – Arrives at 1200.
h – Arrives at 1415.
j – Arrives at 1600.
k – Arrives at 1625.
n – June 1 - Sept. 17.
p – June 2 - Sept. 18.
x – Stops on request.
* – Serves Rovaniemi rail station before bus station.
• – Serves Rovaniemi rail station after bus station.
◧ – Runs 45 minutes later on ⑦.
□ – Runs 50 minutes earlier on ⑦.
◇ – Honningsvåg, Scandic Hotel.
⊙ – Tanabru, Elva hotell og camping.
⊕ – Nordkjosbotn Gjestgiveri.
⊡ – Trekking centre (Retkeilykeskus).
⊖ – Karasjok, Scandic Hotel.

★ – Honningsvåg Nordkapphuset. **Honningsvåg - Nordkapp** and v.v. *34 km*. Journey time: 35 minutes. Operates May 1 - Sept. 30. **From Honningsvåg** at 1145¶. **From Nordkapp** at 1430¶.

¶ – Service operated by North Cape Tours (from Honningsvåg tourist information office). Timings may vary. Special fares apply. www.northcapetours.com

♠ – **Kirkenes - Murmansk** (RU) and v.v. Journey time: 4 hours. Operated by Pasvikturist AS. www.pasvikturist.no Please check visa requirements. From Kirkenes at 1500 (1400 during winter time). From Murmansk at 0700. **Service currently suspended**.

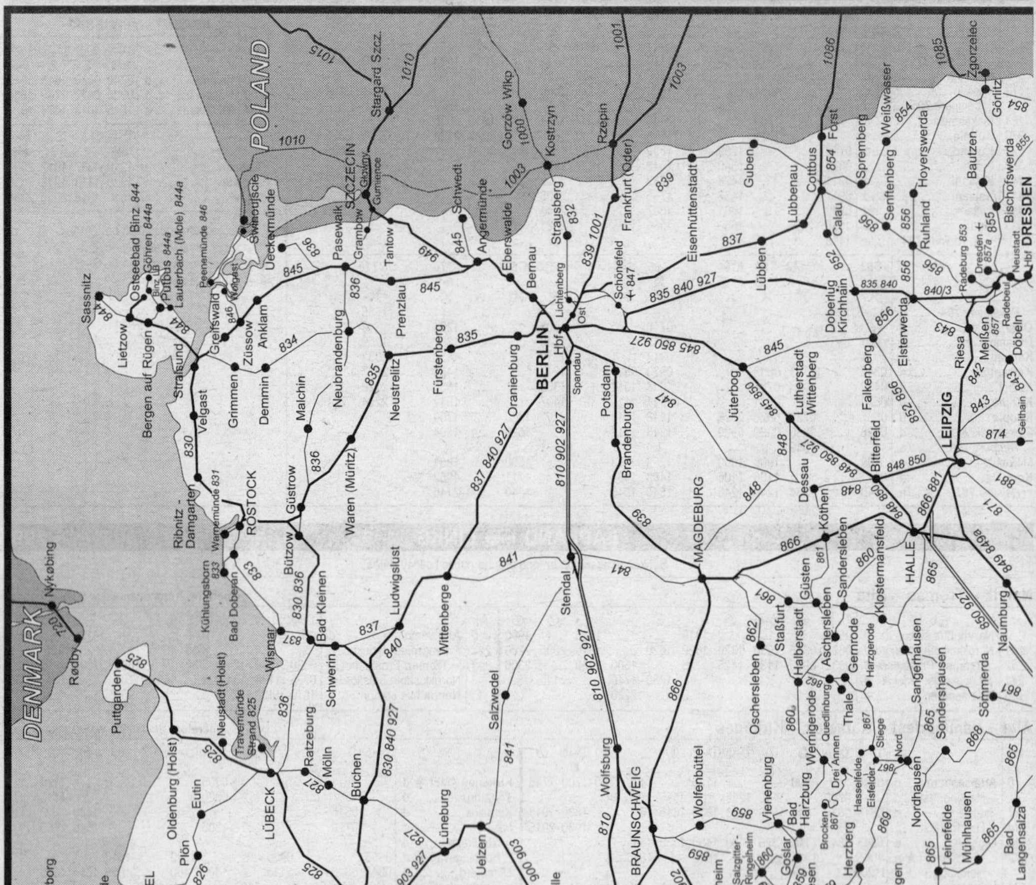
Table 800 shows long-distance trains which pass through the Ruhr area below (Table 927 for FlixTrain services). Regional services are shown in Table 802.
For more detail of the Ruhr area see inset
DENMARK
POLAND
NETHERLANDS
BERLIN
HAMBURG
HANNOVER
BREMEN
LEIPZIG
DRESDEN
MAGDEBURG
HALLE
ROSTOCK
KIEL
LÜBECK
SZCZECIN
BRAUNSCHWEIG
BIELEFELD
KASSEL
MÜNSTER (Westf)
DORTMUND
BOCHUM
ESSEN
DUISBURG
DÜSSELDORF
WUPPERTAL
HAGEN
KÖLN
AACHEN
MÖNCHENGLADBACH
OBERHAUSEN
GELSENKIRCHEN
KREFELD
BONN

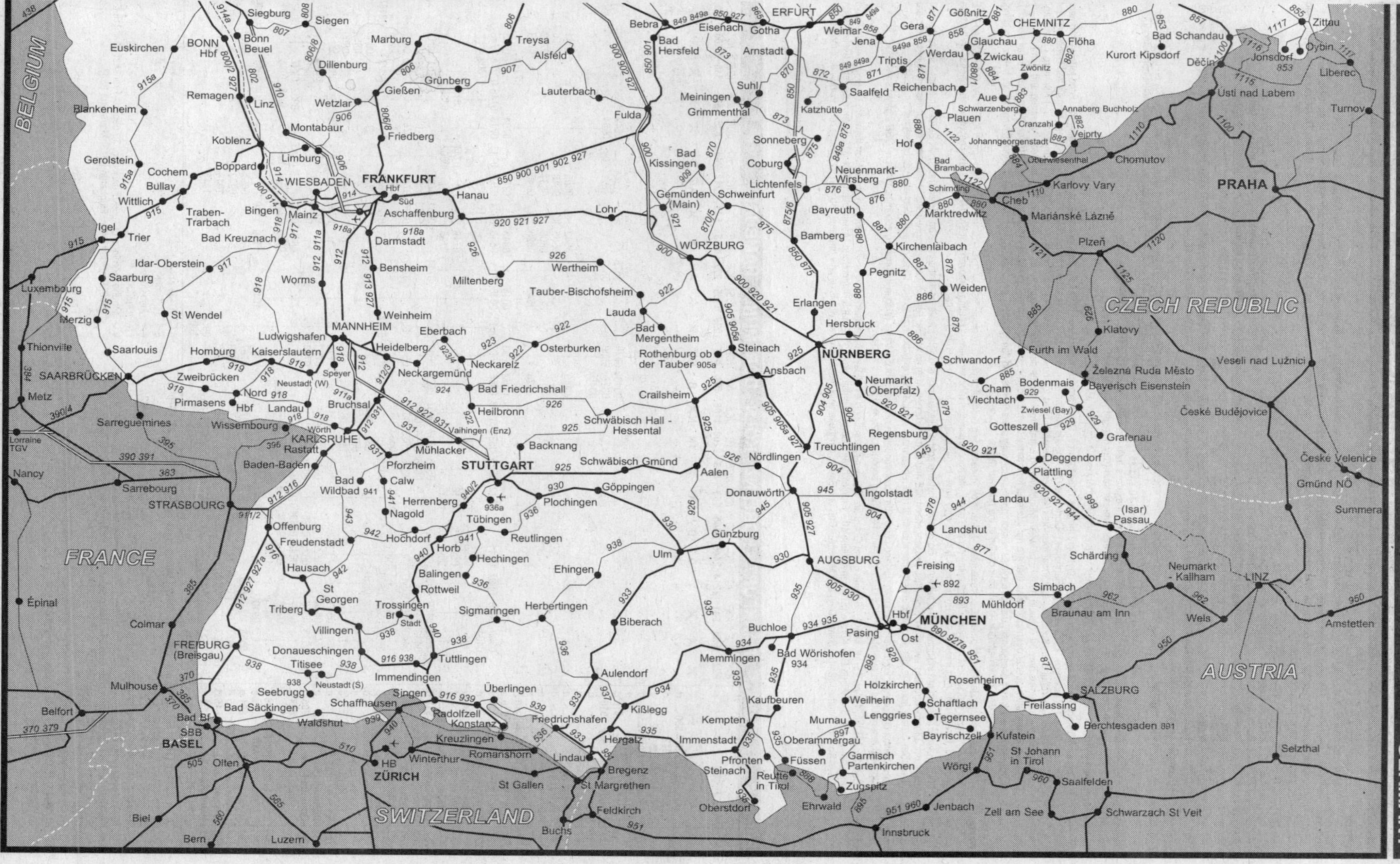
BELGIUM
FRANCE
SWITZERLAND
CZECH REPUBLIC
AUSTRIA
FRANKFURT
WIESBADEN
MANNHEIM
KARLSRUHE
STUTTGART
STRASBOURG
SAARBRÜCKEN
BASEL
ZÜRICH
WÜRZBURG
NÜRNBERG
AUGSBURG
MÜNCHEN
ERFURT
CHEMNITZ
PRAHA
LINZ
SALZBURG
BONN Hbf
Koblenz
Mainz
Trier
Luxembourg
Heidelberg
Freiburg (Breisgau)
Ulm
Regensburg
Ingolstadt
Passau
Innsbruck
Plzeň
Cheb
Lindau
Konstanz
Bregenz

GERMANY

SEE MAP ON PAGES 364/5

Operator: Principal operator is Deutsche Bahn AG (DB) www.bahn.de
Many regional services are run by private operators – these are specified in the table heading (or by footnotes for individual trains).

Services: Trains convey first- and second-class seating accommodation unless otherwise shown (by '2' in the column heading, a footnote or a general note in the table heading). Overnight sleeping car (🛏) and couchette (▬) trains do not necessarily convey seating accommodation - refer to individual footnotes for details. Descriptions of sleeping and couchette cars appear on page 10.

There are various categories of trains in Germany. The type of train is indicated by the following letter codes above each column (or by a general note in the table heading):

ICE	**InterCity Express**	German high-speed (230–320 km/h) train.
EC / ECE	**EuroCity**	International express train.
IC	**InterCity**	Internal express train.
ALX	**alex**	Regional express train operated by *Vogtlandbahn*.
FLX	**Flixtrain**	Independent long-distance operator – see special table below.
RJ / RJX	**Railjet**	Austrian express train. Conveys first and economy (2nd) class. *Business class* also available to first class ticket holders (supplement payable).
TGV	**Train à Grande Vitesse**	French high-speed (320 km/h) train. Reservation compulsory for all international journeys.
IRE	**InterRegio Express**	Regional express train.
RE	**Regional Express**	Regional semi-fast train.
RB	**Regional Bahn**	Regional stopping train.
S-Bahn		Suburban stopping train.

Overnight services:

NJ	**ÖBB nightjet**	Quality overnight express train operated by Austrian Railways. All services convey *Deluxe* sleeping cars (1/2/3 berth) with en-suite shower and WC, standard sleeping cars (1/2/3 berth), couchettes (4/6 berth) and 2nd class seats (in a compartment). Reservation compulsory. For further details see pages 10 and 35.
EN	**EuroNight**	Other international overnight express train. See also pages 10 and 35.
D	**Durchgangszug**	Or **Schnellzug** – other express train (day or night); rarely used nowadays.

Timings: **Valid JUNE 12 - SEPTEMBER 22, 2022** (except where shown otherwise).

Many long distance trains operate on selected days only for part of the journey. These are often indicated in the train composition footnote by showing the dated journey segment within brackets. For example '🚃12 Leipzig - Hannover (- Dortmund ⑦)' means that the train runs daily (or as shown in the column heading) between Leipzig and Hannover, but only continues to Dortmund on Sundays. Additional footnotes/symbols are often used to show more complex running dates, e.g. '🚃12 (München ⊡ -) Nürnberg - Hamburg' means that the train runs only on dates in note ⊡ between München and Nürnberg, but runs daily (or as shown in the column heading) between Nürnberg and Hamburg. Please note that international overnight trains that are not intended for internal German journeys are not usually shown in the German section (refer to the International section).

Engineering work may occasionally disrupt services at short notice (especially at weekends and during holiday periods), so it is advisable to check timings locally before travelling. Information regarding known alterations will be included in the relevant tables.

Tickets: There are three standard levels of fares, corresponding to travel by (in ascending order of price): ○ Regional trains. ○ *IC/EC* trains. ○ High-speed *ICE*, *TGV*, *RJ/RJX* and *ECE* trains. A variable supplement is payable for sleeping car and couchette accommodation (and sometimes seating) on overnight *EN/NJ* trains, the cost of which depends on the type required. Please note that Interrail and Eurail pass holders may have to pay a special fare on overnight trains.

Catering: Two types of catering are indicated in the tables: 🍷 Bordbistro – hot and cold drinks, snacks and light meals (at-seat service on certain trains); ✕ Bordrestaurant – full restaurant car service (bordbistro also available). First class passengers on *ICE* and *IC* trains benefit from an at-seat service. On overnight trains 🍷 indicates that drinks and light snacks are available, usually from the sleeping or couchette car attendant (the refreshment service may only be available to sleeping and couchette car passengers).

Reservations: Reservation compulsory for travel in sleeping car and couchette accommodation on overnight *EN* trains (also in the seating accommodation of *ÖBB nightjet* services). Optional reservations are available on *ICE/EC/IC* trains (€4,50 in second class, €5,90 in first class).

Holidays: Dec. 25, 26, Jan. 1, Apr. 15, 18, May 1, 26, June 6 and Oct. 3 are German national public holidays (trains marked ⚒ or Ⓐ do not run). In addition there are other regional holidays as follows: Jan. 6 – Heilige Drei Könige (Epiphany), June 16 – Fronleichnam (Corpus Christi), Aug. 15 – Mariä Himmelfahrt (Assumption), Oct. 31 – Reformationstag (Reformation Day), Nov. 1 – Allerheiligen (All Saints Day) and Nov. 16 – Buß und Bettag. On these days the regional service is usually that applicable on ⑦ (please refer to individual footnotes).

800 FRANKFURT - KOBLENZ - KÖLN - DORTMUND - HAMBURG

km		*ICE* 922	*ICE* 1028	*ICE* 541	*IC* 2214	*IC* 2445	*IC* 2445	*ICE* 853	*ICE* 843	*IC* 2208	*ICE* 1108	*NJ* 402	*ICE* 618	*ICE* 1038	*ICE* 1155	*ICE* 222	*ICE* 553	*ICE* 543	*IC* 2212	*IC* 2443	*ICE* 826	*ICE* 855	*ICE* 845	*IC* 2206	*ICE* 1545
		①–⑥ ✕	Ⓑ ✕	①–⑥ ✕	W 🍷	①–⑥ D🍷	D🍷	①–⑥ ✕	✕	④⑤ fN	⑥ N✕	B	K✕	✕	✕	A✕	✕	✕	R🍷	D🍷	✕	✕	✕	N	①–⑥ G🍷
	München Hbf **904 930** d.	...	...	...	...	...	...	...	...	...	...	...	0001	...	...	...	...	...	...	...	...	...	...	...	...
	Stuttgart Hbf **912** d.	...	...	...	...	...	...	...	...	...	...	...	0222	...	...	...	...	...	...	...	...	...	...	...	...
	Basel SBB 🏛 **912** d.	...	...	...	...	...	...	...	...	...	...	2313	|	...	...	...	...	...	...	...	...	...	...	...	...
	Karlsruhe Hbf **912** d.	...	...	...	...	...	...	...	...	...	...	0120	|	...	...	...	...	...	...	...	...	...	...	...	...
	Nürnberg Hbf **920** d.	...	...	...	...	...	...	...	...	...	...	|	|	...	...	...	...	...	...	...	...	...	...	...	...
0	**Frankfurt** (Main) Hbf **910** d.	...	...	...	...	...	...	...	...	...	...	0313v	0446	...	...	0528	...	...	...	...	0540	...	...	...	...
11	**Frankfurt** Flugh. ✈ § **910** d.	...	...	...	...	...	...	...	...	...	...	0329v	0500	...	...	0542	...	...	...	...	0554	...	...	...	...
37	**Mainz** Hbf d.	...	...	...	...	...	...	...	...	...	...	0348v	|	...	...	|	...	...	...	...	|	...	...	...	...
67	Bingen (Rhein) Hbf d.	...	...	...	...	...	...	...	...	...	...	|	|	...	...	|	...	...	...	...	|	...	...	...	...
128	**Koblenz** Hbf d.	...	...	...	...	...	...	...	...	...	...	0443	|	...	...	|	0542	...	0605	...	|	...	...	0641	...
146	Andernach d.	...	...	...	...	...	...	...	...	...	...	|	|	...	...	|	0555	...	0618	...	|	...	...	0656	...
167	Remagen d.	...	...	...	...	...	...	...	...	...	...	|	|	...	...	|	0608	...	0631	...	|	...	...	0708	...
187	**Bonn** Hbf d.	...	...	...	...	...	...	...	...	...	...	0526	|	...	0549	|	0623	...	0645	...	|	...	...	0723	...
	Köln/Bonn Flugh. ✈ **910** d.	...	...	...	...	...	...	...	...	...	...	|	|	...	|	|	|	...	|	...	|	...	0714a	|	...
221	**Köln** Hbf **910** a.	...	...	...	...	...	...	...	...	...	...	0553	0603	...	0615	|	0643	...	0705	...	0704	...	|	0743	...
221	**Köln** Hbf **910** d.	...	0359	0426	0507	0511	...	0542	0525	0539	0539	0556	0609	0612	0618	|	0648	0624	0709	0713	0713	0748	0727c	0746	...
222	**Köln** Messe/Deutz d.	...	0404	|	|	|	...	|	|	|	|	|	|	|	|	0645	|	|	|	|	|	|	0730a	|	...
	Solingen Hbf d.	...	|	|	|	0530	...	0603	|	|	|	|	|	|	|	|	|	|	|	0730	|	|	|	|	...
	Wuppertal Hbf d.	...	|	|	|	0544	...	0616	|	|	|	|	|	|	|	|	0716	|	|	0744	|	0816	|	|	...
	Hagen Hbf d.	...	|	|	|	0602	...	0635	|	|	|	|	|	|	|	|	0735	|	|	0802	|	0835	|	|	...
261	**Düsseldorf** Hbf **910** d.	...	0425	0450	0533	|	...	|	0549	0607	0607	0625	0633	0638	|	0711	|	0651	0734	|	0738	|	0751	0812	...
268	Düsseldorf Flughafen ✈ d.	...	0433	0458	|	|	...	|	0556	0614	0614	|	|	|	|	|	|	0659	|	|	|	|	0759	|	...
285	**Duisburg** Hbf d.	...	0443	0509	0547	|	...	|	0606	0625	0625	0640	0647	0651	|	0727	|	0710	0749	|	0753	|	0810	0827	0835
293	Oberhausen Hbf d.	...	|	|	|	|	...	|	|	0633	0633	...	|	|	|	0733	|	|	|	|	|	|	|	0834	|
304	**Essen** Hbf d.	...	0500	0522	0600	|	...	|	0619	|	|	...	0700	0704	|	...	|	0723	0802	|	0805	|	0823	|	0848
	Gelsenkirchen Hbf d.	...	|	|	0610	|	...	|	|	0643	0643	...	|	|	|	...	|	|	0812	|	...	|	|	0844	|
	Wanne-Eickel Hbf d.	...	|	|	|	|	...	|	|	0650	0650	...	|	|	|	...	|	|	|	|	...	|	|	0852	|
	Recklinghausen Hbf d.	...	|	|	|	|	...	|	|	0657	0657	...	|	|	|	...	|	|	|	|	...	|	|	0859	|
320	Bochum Hbf d.	...	0510	0532	|	|	...	|	0629	|	|	...	0710	|	|	...	|	0733	|	|	...	|	0833	|	|
338	**Dortmund** Hbf a.	...	0522	0544	|	0622	...	|	0641	|	|	...	0722	|	|	...	|	0746	|	0821	...	|	0846	|	0907
338	**Dortmund** Hbf **805** d.	...	0525	0546	|	0625	0625	|	0643	|	|	...	0724	|	|	...	|	0748	|	0825	...	|	0848	|	0909
	Hamm (Westf) **805** a.	...	|	0602	|	0643	0643	0702	0707	|	|	...	|	|	|	...	0802	0807	|	0843	...	0902	0907	|	0932
	Hannover Hbf **810** a.	...	|	0728	|	0818	0818	0828	0828	|	|	...	|	|	|	...	0928	0928	|	1018	...	1028	1028	|	1101
	Leipzig Hbf **849a 866** a.	...	|	|	|	1117	1117	|	|	|	|	...	|	|	|	...	|	|	|	1317	...	|	|	|	|
	Berlin Hbf **810** a.	...	|	0910	|	...	...	1014	1014	|	|	...	|	|	1012	...	1110	1110	|	...	...	1214	1214	|	1255t
394	Münster (Westf) Hbf **801** d.	...	0556	...	0657	...	...	...	...	0726	0726	...	0757	|	...	...	...	...	0857	...	...	...	...	0928	...
444	Osnabrück Hbf **801 815** d.	...	0623	...	0723	...	...	...	...	...	...	...	0823	|	...	...	...	...	0923	...	...	...	...	...	...
566	**Bremen** Hbf **801 815** d.	0718	0727	...	0818	...	...	...	...	...	...	...	0918	|	...	...	...	...	1018	...	...	...	...	...	...
681	**Hamburg** Hbf **801** a.	0814	0833	...	0914	...	...	...	...	...	...	...	1014	0950	...	...	...	...	1113	...	...	...	...	...	...
688	**Hamburg** Altona a.	0829	0849	...	...	...	...	...	...	...	...	...	...	1005	...	...	...	...	...	...	...	...	...	...	...

A – To Amsterdam (Table **28**). Diversions/retimings are scheduled June 11, 12, 18, 19, Aug. 27 - Sept. 9 (different train numbers may apply).
B – 🛏 1, 2 cl. and ▬ 2 cl. (Ⓡ) Zürich - Basel - Utrecht - Amsterdam. Also conveys 🚃2 (*IC* **60402**). Subject to alteration on the mornings June 11, 12, 18, 19, Aug. 27 - Sept. 9.
D – To Dresden (Table **842**).
G – KAROLINGER – From Aachen Hbf (d. 0708), Herzogenrath (d. 0723), Rheydt Hbf (d. 0752), Mönchengladbach Hbf (d. 0758), Viersen (d. 0806) and Krefeld Hbf (d. 0818).
K – To Kiel (Table **820**).
N – To Norddeich Mole (Table **812**).
R – RÜGEN – To Ostseebad Binz (Tables **830** and **844**).
W – To Westerland (Table **821**).

a – ①–⑤ only.
c – ⑥⑦ only.
f – Also June 15.
t – Until July 16.
v – On the mornings of ①②⑦ until Aug. 30 departs Frankfurt (Main) Hbf 0300, Frankfurt (Main) Flughafen 0313, Mainz Hbf 0333.

§ – Frankfurt Flughafen Fernbahnhof.

FRANKFURT - KOBLENZ - KÖLN - DORTMUND - HAMBURG 800

	IC 2306	ICE 1626	ICE 616	ICE 555	ICE 545	ICE 220	ICE 757	ICE 757	IC 2310	IC 2441	ICE 822	IC 2155	ICE 857	ICE 847	IC 2204	IC 5107	ICE 759	IC 2408	ICE 1022	ICE 614	ICE 820	ICE 557	ICE 547	ICE 128	ICE 1012
	⑥						m	R													①–⑥				Y
	E	🍴	🍴	🍴	🍴	A 🍴	B 🍴	🍴	🍷♦	D 🍷	🍴	♦	🍴	🍴	E	X	🍴♦	L 🍷	🍴	🍴	e 🍴	🍴	🍴	A 🍴	🍴
München Hbf **904 930** d.	...	...	0324	...	...	...	...	...	...	...	0427e	...	...	...	...	...	...	...	...	0533	0522	...	...	...	...
Stuttgart Hbf **912** d.	...	...	0551	...	...	...	...	...	...	...	|	...	...	...	...	...	...	...	...	0751	|	...	...	...	0837v
Basel SBB 🏛 **912** d.	...	...	|	...	...	...	...	...	...	...	|	...	...	...	...	...	...	...	...	|	|	...	...	...	|
Karlsruhe Hbf **912** d.	...	...	|	...	...	...	...	...	...	...	|	...	...	...	...	...	...	...	...	|	|	...	...	...	0854n
Nürnberg Hbf **920** d.	...	...	|	...	...	...	...	...	...	...	0536e	...	...	...	...	...	...	...	0510	|	0634	...	...	...	|
Frankfurt (Main) Hbf **910** d.	...	0542	|	...	...	0728	...	...	0643	...	0809	...	...	...	...	...	...	...	0742	|	0909	...	...	0926	|
Frankfurt Flughafen ✈ § **910** d.	...	0558	0708	...	...	0742	...	...	0657	...	0824	...	...	...	...	...	...	...	0758	0909	0922	...	...	0942	0953
Mainz Hbf d.	...	0617	|	...	...	|	...	...	0717	...	|	...	...	...	...	...	...	...	0820	|	|	...	...	|	|
Bingen (Rhein) Hbf d.	...	0634	|	...	...	|	...	...	|	...	|	...	...	...	...	...	...	...	|	|	|	...	...	|	|
Koblenz Hbf d.	...	0713	|	...	...	|	...	...	0813	...	|	...	...	...	...	0841	...	...	0913	|	|	...	...	|	|
Andernach d.	...	|	|	...	...	|	...	...	|	...	|	...	...	...	...	0856	...	...	|	|	|	...	...	|	|
Remagen d.	...	|	|	...	...	|	...	...	|	...	|	...	...	...	...	0908	...	...	|	|	|	...	...	|	|
Bonn Hbf d.	...	0745	|	0822	...	|	...	...	0845	...	|	...	...	...	...	0923	...	...	0945	|	|	...	...	|	|
Köln/Bonn Flugh. ✈ **910** d.	...	|	|	|	...	|	...	...	|	...	|	...	...	...	...	|	...	...	|	|	|	...	...	|	|
Köln Hbf **910** a.	...	0805	0805	0844	...	|	...	...	0905	...	|	...	...	...	...	0943	...	...	1005	1004	|	...	...	|	|
Köln Hbf **910** d.	0801	0809	0811	0848	0828	|	0842	0842	0909	0913	|	0916	0948	0924	0938	0946	0934	1004	1009	1011	|	1048	...	|	|
Köln Messe/Deutz d.	|	|	|	|	|	0836	|	|	|	|	0917	|	|	|	|	|	|	|	|	|	1027	|	...	1036	1045
Solingen Hbf d.	|	0828	|	|	|	|	|	|	|	0930	|	|	|	|	|	|	|	|	1028	|	|	|	...	|	|
Wuppertal Hbf d.	|	0843	|	0916	|	|	|	|	|	0944	|	|	1016	|	|	|	|	|	1043	|	|	1116	...	|	|
Hagen Hbf d.	|	0901	|	0935	|	|	|	|	|	1002	|	|	1035	|	|	|	|	|	1101	|	|	1135	...	|	|
Düsseldorf Hbf **910** d.	0829	|	0834	|	0852	0908	0915	0915	0933	|	0938	0943	|	0952	1011	1012	1016j	1029	|	1034	1048	|	1052	1108	1113
Düsseldorf Flughafen ✈ d.	|	|	|	|	0900	|	|	|	|	|	|	0950	|	1000	|	...	|	|	|	|	|	|	1059	|	|
Duisburg Hbf d.	0846	|	0848	|	0910	0926	0931	0930	0947	|	0955	1003	|	1011	1026	...	1031	1043	|	1048	1103	|	1110	1126	1128
Oberhausen Hbf d.	0853	|	|	|	|	0932	|	|	|	|	|	|	|	|	1034	...	|	|	|	|	|	|	|	1132	|
Essen Hbf d.	|	|	0901	|	0923	...	|	0946	1002	|	1006	1017	|	1024	|	...	1044	1058	|	1100	1114	|	1123	...	1141
Gelsenkirchen Hbf d.	0904	|	|	|	|	...	0946	|	1011	|	...	|	|	|	1044	...	|	|	|	|	...	|	|	...	|
Wanne-Eickel Hbf d.	0911	|	|	|	|	...	|	|	|	|	...	|	|	|	1052	...	|	|	|	|	...	|	|	...	|
Recklinghausen Hbf d.	0918	|	|	|	|	...	0957	|	|	|	...	|	|	|	1059	...	|	|	|	|	...	|	|	...	|
Bochum Hbf d.	|	|	0910	|	0934	...	|	0957	|	|	...	1030	|	1034	|	...	1055	|	|	1110	...	|	1134	...	1153
Dortmund Hbf a.	|	0921	0923	|	0946	...	|	1008	|	1021	...	1042	|	1046	|	...	1108	|	1121	1123	...	|	1146	...	1205
Dortmund Hbf **805** d.	|	...	0925	|	0948	...	|	1010	|	1025	...	1044	|	1048	|	...	1110	|	...	1125	...	|	1148	...	...
Hamm (Westf) **805** a.	|	...	|	1002	1007	...	|	1032	|	1043	...	1101	1102	1107	|	...	1132	|	...	|	...	1202	1207	...	...
Hannover Hbf **810** a.	|	...	|	1128	1128	...	|	1201	|	1218	...	...	1228	1228	|	...	1302	|	...	|	...	1328	1328	...	...
Leipzig Hbf **849a 866** a.	|	...	|	|	|	...	|	|	|	1517	...	...	|	|	|	...	|	|	...	|	...	|	|	...	...
Berlin Hbf **810** a.	|	...	|	1310	1310	...	|	1354t	|	...	...	...	1414	1414	|	...	1452t	|	...	|	...	1510	1510	...	...
Münster (Westf) Hbf **801** d.	0952	...	0956	...	...	...	1028	...	1057	...	...	...	...	...	1128	...	...	1147	...	1157	...	...	...	...	...
Osnabrück Hbf **801 815** d.	...	...	1023	...	...	...	1051	...	1123	...	...	...	...	...	...	...	...	|	...	1223	...	...	...	...	...
Bremen Hbf **801 815** d.	...	...	1118	...	...	...	...	...	1218	...	...	...	...	...	...	...	...	|	...	1318	...	...	...	...	...
Hamburg Hbf **801** a.	...	...	1214	...	...	...	...	...	1314	...	...	...	...	...	...	...	...	1349	...	1414	...	...	...	...	...
Hamburg Altona a.	...	...	1229	...	...	...	...	...	...	...	...	...	...	...	...	...	...	...	...	1429	...	...	...	...	...

	IC 1959	ICE 1110	IC 2010	IC 2010	IC 2216	IC 2049	ICE 728	ICE 859	ICE 849	IC 2202	IC 2202	ICE 1020	ICE 612	ICE 1157	ICE 726	ICE 559	ICE 549	ICE 126	ICE 126	ICE 1010	ICE 714	IC 2047	ICE 724	ICE 951	ICE 941
	⑤⑦	⑥	⑤ f	Ⓐ p							①–⑤							①–⑥	⑦	①–⑥					
	q	N 🍴	♠ 🍷	♠ 🍷	🍷♦	D 🍷	🍴	🍴	🍴	H	H	🍴♦	K 🍴	🍴	🍴	🍴	🍴	A 🍴	A 🍴	🍴	🍴	D 🍷	🍴	🍴	🍴
München Hbf **904 930** d.	...	...	...	...	...	...	0621	...	...	...	...	...	0728	...	0726	...	...	...	...	...	...	...	0815	...	...
Stuttgart Hbf **912** d.	...	0714	0714	0714	0736c	...	|	...	...	...	...	...	0951	...	|	...	...	...	...	1037v	0937v	...	|	...	...
Basel SBB 🏛 **912** d.	...	|	|	|	|	...	|	...	...	...	...	...	|	...	|	...	...	...	...	|	|	...	|	...	...
Karlsruhe Hbf **912** d.	...	|	|	|	0748r	...	|	...	...	...	...	...	|	...	|	...	...	...	...	1054n	0946n	...	|	...	...
Nürnberg Hbf **920** d.	...	|	|	|	|	...	0735	...	...	...	...	0727	|	...	0835	...	...	...	...	|	|	...	0926	...	...
Frankfurt (Main) Hbf **910** d.	...	|	|	|	*0842**	...	1009	...	...	...	...	0947•	|	...	1109	...	...	1126	1126	|	*1042**	...	1209	...	...
Frankfurt Flugh. ✈ § **910** d.	...	|	|	|	*0858**	...	1024	...	...	...	...	0958	1109	...	1122	...	...	1142	1142	1153	*1058**	...	1224	...	...
Mainz Hbf d.	...	0849	0849	0849	0920	...	|	...	...	...	...	1020	|	...	|	...	...	|	|	|	1120	...	|	...	...
Bingen (Rhein) Hbf d.	...	0907	0907	0907	|	...	|	...	...	...	...	|	|	...	|	...	...	|	|	|	|	...	|	...	...
Koblenz Hbf d.	...	0944	0944	0944	1013	...	|	...	...	...	1044	1113	|	...	|	...	...	|	|	|	1213	...	|	...	...
Andernach d.	...	0956	0956	0956	|	...	|	...	...	...	1056	|	|	...	|	...	...	|	|	|	|	...	|	...	...
Remagen d.	...	1008	1008	1008	|	...	|	...	...	...	1108	|	|	...	|	...	...	|	|	|	|	...	|	...	...
Bonn Hbf d.	...	1022	1023	1023	1045	...	|	...	...	...	1123	1145	|	1149	|	1220	...	|	|	|	1245	...	|	...	...
Köln/Bonn Flugh. ✈ **910** d.	...	|	|	|	|	...	|	...	...	...	|	|	|	|	|	|	...	|	|	|	|	...	|	...	...
Köln Hbf **910** a.	...	1043	1043	1043	1105	...	|	...	...	...	1143	1205	1205	1214	|	1243	...	|	|	|	1305	...	|	...	...
Köln Hbf **910** d.	1036	1046	1046	...	1109	1113	|	1148	...	1146	1146	1210	1211	1217	|	1248	...	|	|	|	1309	1313	|	1348	...
Köln Messe/Deutz d.	|	|	|	...	|	|	1117	|	...	|	|	|	|	|	1227	|	...	1233	1237	1246	|	|	1317	|	...
Solingen Hbf d.	1107	|	|	...	|	1130	|	|	...	|	|	|	1230	|	|	|	...	|	|	|	|	1330	|	|	...
Wuppertal Hbf d.	1123	|	|	...	|	1144	|	1216	...	|	|	|	1243	|	|	1316	...	|	|	|	|	1344	|	1416	...
Hagen Hbf d.	1142	|	|	...	|	1202	|	1235	...	|	|	|	1301	|	|	1335	...	|	|	|	|	1402	|	1435	...
Düsseldorf Hbf **910** d.	|	1117	1118	...	1133	|	1138	|	1153	1212	1212	1233	|	|	1248	|	1252	1308j	1308	1314	1333	|	1338	|	1351
Düsseldorf Flughafen ✈ d.	|	|	|	...	|	|	|	|	|	|	|	|	|	|	|	|	|	|	|	|	|	|	|	|	1359u
Duisburg Hbf d.	|	1132y	1133	...	1147	|	1155	|	1208	1227	1227	1247	|	|	1302	|	1310	1326	1326	1328	1347	|	1352	|	1410
Oberhausen Hbf d.	|	|	|	...	|	|	|	|	|	1234	1234	|	|	|	|	|	|	1332	1332	|	|	|	|	|	|
Essen Hbf d.	|	|	1146	...	1202	|	1206	|	1223	|	|	1300	|	|	1313	|	1323	...	...	1341	1402	|	1403	|	1423
Gelsenkirchen Hbf d.	|	1147	|	...	1211	|	...	|	|	1244	1244	|	|	|	...	|	|	...	...	|	1412	|	...	|	|
Wanne-Eickel Hbf d.	|	|	|	...	|	|	...	|	|	1251	1251	|	|	|	...	|	|	...	...	|	|	|	...	|	|
Recklinghausen Hbf d.	|	1158	|	...	|	|	...	|	|	1258	1258	|	|	|	...	|	|	...	...	|	|	|	...	|	|
Bochum Hbf d.	|	|	1157	...	|	|	...	|	1233	|	|	|	|	|	...	|	1334	...	...	1353	|	|	...	|	1434
Dortmund Hbf a.	|	|	1208	...	|	1221	...	|	1246	|	|	|	1321	|	...	|	1346	...	...	1404	|	1421	...	|	1446
Dortmund Hbf **805** d.	|	|	1210	...	|	1225	...	|	1248	|	|	|	1324	|	...	|	1348	...	...	...	|	1425	...	|	1448
Hamm (Westf) **805** a.	1213	|	1231	...	|	1243	...	1302	1307	|	|	|	|	|	...	1402	1407	...	...	...	|	1443	...	1502	1507
Hannover Hbf **810** a.	|	|	1401	...	|	1418	...	1428	1428	|	|	|	|	|	...	1528	1528	...	...	...	|	1618	...	1628	1628
Leipzig Hbf **849a 866** a.	1722	|	|	...	|	1717	...	|	|	|	|	|	|	|	...	|	|	...	...	...	|	1917	...	|	|
Berlin Hbf **810** a.	...	|	1554t	...	|	...	...	1614	1614	|	|	|	|	1613	...	1710	1710	...	...	...	|	...	...	1810	1810
Münster (Westf) Hbf **801** d.	...	1228	...	...	1257	...	...	...	...	1330	1330	1347	1357	...	...	...	...	...	...	...	1457	...	...	...	...
Osnabrück Hbf **801 815** d.	...	...	...	...	1323	...	...	...	...	1356	1356	|	1423	...	...	...	...	...	...	...	1523	...	...	...	...
Bremen Hbf **801 815** d.	...	...	...	...	1418	...	...	...	...	1457	1457	|	1518	...	...	...	...	...	...	...	1618	...	...	...	...
Hamburg Hbf **801** a.	...	...	...	...	1512	...	...	...	...	...	...	1550	1614	...	...	...	...	...	...	...	1714	...	...	...	...
Hamburg Altona a.	...	...	...	...	...	...	...	...	...	...	...	1605	...	...	...	...	...	...	...	...	1729	...	...	...	...

♦ – **NOTES** (LISTED BY TRAIN NUMBER)

759 – [12] 🍴 Köln - Hannover - Berlin - Stralsund - Ostseebad Binz. **Terminates at Hannover from July 18.**
1020 – [12] 🍴 (Passau ⑤⑥ **d** -) (Regensburg ①–⑥ -) Nürnberg - Frankfurt - Köln - Hamburg.
2155 – [12] Köln - Paderborn - Kassel - Weimar - Gera.
2216 – GREIFSWALDER BODDEN – [12] 🍷 Stuttgart / Karlsruhe - Köln - Hamburg - Stralsund (- Greifswald Ⓑ).
2310 – NORDFRIESLAND – To Westerland (Table **821**). Also calls at Boppard Hbf (d. 0758).

A – To Amsterdam (Table **28**). Diversions / retimings are scheduled June 11, 12, 18, 19, Aug. 27 - Sept. 9 (different train numbers may apply).
B – To Berlin (Table **810**).
D – To Dresden (Table **842**).
E – To Emden (Table **812**).
H – OSTFRIESLAND – To Bremerhaven (Table **815**).
K – To Kiel (Table **820**).
L – To Lübeck Hbf (a. 1442).
N – To Norddeich Mole (Table **812**).
R – June 24 - Aug. 5.
X – From Luxembourg (Table **915**).
Y – ①②③④⑥ (not June 15).

c – Not July 31, Aug. 7, 14, 21, 28, Sept. 4, 11.
d – Also June 15, 16; not June 17, 18.
e – Not ⑦.
f – Also June 15; not June 17.
j – Arrives 10 – 12 minutes earlier.
m – Not June 24 - Aug. 5.
n – July 30 - Sept. 11 only.
p – Not June 16, 17.
q – Also June 15.
r – ⑦ July 31 - Sept. 11.
t – Until July 17.
u – Calls to pick up only.
v – Not July 30 - Sept. 11.
y – Until July 30.
z – 1237 on ⑦.

* – Connecting *ICE* train (change trains at Mainz).
♠ – LORELEY. From Tübingen (Table **930**).
• – Frankfurt (Main) **Süd** (not Hbf).
§ – Frankfurt Flughafen Fernbahnhof.

800 FRANKFURT - KOBLENZ - KÖLN - DORTMUND - HAMBURG

	IC 2200	*ICE* 1116	*IC* 1916	*ICE* 732	*ICE* 928	*ICE* 610	*ICE* 722	*ICE* 651	*ICE* 641	*ICE* 1059	*ICE* 1059	*ICE* 124	*ICE* 918	*IC* 2312	*IC* 2045	*ICE* 720	*IC* 2157	*ICE* 953	*ICE* 943	*IC* 2006	*IC* 2004	*IC* 2014	*ICE* 1151	*ICE* 228	*ICE* 518
		⑦	⑤	⑤⑦						m⊖	R⊖									⑥	⑦–④	⑤	t		
	N	◧✕	⊙🍷	✕	P✕	✕	✕	✕	✕	B✕	✕	A✕	✕	🍷	D🍷	✕	♦	✕	✕	🍷♦	🍷♦	🍷♦	✕	E✕	✕
München Hbf **904 930** d.	...	...	...	...	...	0928	0923	...	...	...	...	...	...	...	...	1016	...	...	...	...	...	...	...	...	1128
Stuttgart Hbf **912** d.	...	1008	1008	...	...	1151	|	...	...	...	...	...	1237v	1137	...	|	...	...	...	...	...	1208	...	...	1351
Basel SBB 🚉 **912** d.	...	|	|	...	...	|	|	...	...	...	...	...	|	|	...	|	...	...	...	...	...	|	...	...	|
Karlsruhe Hbf **912** d.	...	|	|	...	...	|	|	...	...	...	...	...	1254n	|	...	|	...	...	...	1221	1222z	|	...	...	|
Nürnberg Hbf **920** d.	...	|	|	...	0930	|	1035	...	...	...	...	...	|	|	...	1124	...	...	...	|	|	|	...	1130	|
Frankfurt (Main) Hbf **910** d.	...	|	|	...	1147•	|	1309	...	...	...	...	1326	|	*1242**	...	1409	...	...	...	|	|	|	...	1347•	|
Frankfurt Flugh. ✈ § **910** d.	...	|	|	...	1158	1309	1324	...	...	...	...	1342	1353	*1258**	...	1424	...	...	...	|	|	|	...	1358	1509
Mainz Hbf d.	...	1144	1144	...	1220	|	|	...	...	...	...	|	|	1320	...	|	...	...	...	1344	1344z	1344	...	1420	|
Bingen (Rhein) Hbf d.	...	1207	1207	...	|	|	|	...	...	...	...	|	|	|	...	|	...	...	...	1407	1407z	1407	...	|	|
Koblenz Hbf d.	...	1244	1244	...	1313	|	|	...	...	...	...	|	|	1413	...	|	...	...	...	1444	1444	1444	...	1513	|
Andernach d.	...	1256	1256	...	|	|	|	...	...	...	...	|	|	|	...	|	...	...	...	1456	1456	1456	...	|	|
Remagen d.	...	1308	1308	...	|	|	|	...	...	...	...	|	|	|	...	|	...	...	...	1508	1508	1508	...	|	|
Bonn Hbf d.	...	1323	1323	...	1345	|	|	1420	...	...	...	|	|	1445	...	|	...	...	...	1523	1523	1523	...	1545	|
Köln/Bonn Flugh. ✈ **910** d.	...	|	|	...	|	|	|	|	...	...	...	|	|	|	...	|	...	...	...	|	|	|	...	|	|
Köln Hbf **910** a.	...	1343	1343	...	1405	1405	|	1443	...	...	...	|	|	1505	...	|	...	...	...	1543	1543	1543	...	1605	1605
Köln Hbf **910** d.	1343‡	1346	1346	1404	1409	1411	|	1448	...	1436	1436	|	|	1509	1513	|	1519	1548	...	1546	1546	1546	1537	1609	1611
Köln Messe/Deutz d.	|	|	|	|	|	|	1420	|	...	|	|	1433	1449	|	|	1517	|	|	...	|	|	|	|	|	|
Solingen Hbf d.	|	|	|	|	1428	|	|	|	...	|	|	|	|	|	1530	|	|	|	...	|	|	|	|	1628	|
Wuppertal Hbf d.	|	|	|	|	1443	|	|	1516	...	|	|	|	|	|	1544	|	|	1616	...	|	|	|	|	1643	|
Hagen Hbf d.	|	|	|	|	1501	|	|	1535	...	|	|	|	|	|	1602	|	|	1635	...	|	|	|	|	1701	|
Düsseldorf Hbf **910** d.	1412‡	1414	1414	1429	|	1434	1443	|	1451	1509	1509	1512c	1517	1533	|	1538	1543	|	1551	1612	1612	1612	1616	|	1634
Düsseldorf Flughafen ✈ d.	|	|	|	|	|	|	|	|	1459u	|	|	|	|	|	|	|	1550	|	1559u	|	|	|	|	|	|
Duisburg Hbf d.	1427	1429	1429	1443	|	1448	1501	|	1510	1523	1523	1527	1530	1547	|	1552	1602	|	1610	1627	1627	1627	1631	|	1648
Oberhausen Hbf d.	1434	|	|	|	|	|	|	|	|	|	|	1533	|	|	|	|	|	|	|	1634	1634	1634	|	|	|
Essen Hbf d.	|	1445	1445	1457	|	1500	1513	|	1523	1535	1536	...	1543	1602	|	1603	1616	|	1623	|	|	|	1644	|	1701
Gelsenkirchen Hbf d.	1444	|	|	1508	|	|	...	|	|	1546	|	...	|	1613	|	...	|	|	|	1644	1645	1645	|	|	|
Wanne-Eickel Hbf d.	1452	|	|	|	|	|	...	|	|	|	|	...	|	|	|	...	|	|	|	1652	1652	1652	|	|	|
Recklinghausen Hbf d.	1459	|	|	|	|	|	...	|	|	1558	|	...	|	|	|	...	|	|	|	|	1659	1659	|	|	|
Bochum Hbf d.	|	1456	1456	|	|	1510	...	|	1534	|	1550	...	1555	|	|	...	1628	|	1634	|	|	|	1655	|	1710
Dortmund Hbf a.	|	1508	1508	|	1521	1522	...	|	1546	|	1602	...	1606	|	1621	...	1639	|	1646	1708	|	|	1708	1721	1722
Dortmund Hbf **805** d.	|	1510	1510	|	...	1525	...	|	1548	|	1606	...	...	|	1625	...	1641	|	1648	...	|	|	1710	...	1725
Hamm (Westf) **805** a.	|	1531	1531	|	...	|	...	1602	1607	|	1632	...	...	|	1643	...	1701	1702	1707	...	|	|	1732	...	|
Hannover Hbf **810** a.	|	1701	1701	|	...	|	...	1728	1728	|	1802	...	...	|	1818	...	...	1828	1828	...	|	|	1901	...	|
Leipzig Hbf **849a 866** a.	|	|	|	|	...	|	...	|	|	|	|	...	...	|	2117	...	...	|	|	...	|	|	|	...	|
Berlin Hbf **810** a.	|	1855t	1855t	|	...	|	...	1908	1908	|	1955t	...	...	|	...	...	...	2014	2014	...	|	|	2055	...	|
Münster (Westf) Hbf **801** d.	1528	...	...	1547	...	1557	...	...	...	1630	...	...	...	1657	...	...	...	...	...	...	1728	1728	...	...	1757
Osnabrück Hbf **801 815** d.	...	...	...	|	...	1623	...	...	...	1654	...	...	...	1723	...	...	...	...	...	...	...	...	...	...	1823
Bremen Hbf **801 815** d.	...	...	...	|	...	1718	...	...	...	...	...	...	...	1818	...	...	...	...	...	...	...	...	...	...	1918
Hamburg Hbf **801** a.	...	...	...	1750	...	1814	...	...	...	...	...	...	...	1914	...	...	...	...	...	...	...	...	...	...	2014
Hamburg Altona a.	...	...	...	1804	...	1829	...	...	...	...	...	...	...	1929	...	...	...	...	...	...	...	...	...	...	2029

	ICE 628	*ICE* 653	*ICE* 643	*IC* 2012	*EC* 8	*IC* 2043	*ICE* 626	*ICE* 122	*ICE* 955	*ICE* 945	*IC* 2002	*ICE* 730	*ICE* 28	*ICE* 516	*ICE* 1159	*ICE* 624	*ICE* 655	*ICE* 645	*ICE* 914	*IC* 118	*EC* 6	*ICE* 204	*ICE* 104	*IC* 2041	*ICE* 622
										Ⓑ												Ⓐ		⑦	
	✕	✕	✕	🍷♦	✕♦	🍷♦	✕	A✕	✕	✕	M	✕	E✕	✕	✕	✕	✕	✕	✕	♦	✕♦	✕	A✕	🍷	✕
München Hbf **904 930** d.	1119	...	...	...	...	...	1216	...	...	...	...	...	...	1328	...	1319	...	...	...	...	...	...	...	...	1418
Stuttgart Hbf **912** d.	|	...	...	1311	...	...	|	...	...	...	...	...	...	1551	...	|	...	...	1634v	1512	...	...	...	...	|
Basel SBB 🚉 **912** d.	|	...	...	|	1220	...	|	...	...	...	...	...	...	|	...	|	...	...	|	|	1427	1513	1513	...	|
Karlsruhe Hbf **912** d.	|	...	...	|	1412	...	|	...	...	...	...	...	...	|	...	|	...	...	|	|	1613	1700	1700	...	|
Nürnberg Hbf **920** d.	1235	...	...	|	|	...	1326	...	...	...	...	...	1330	|	...	1434	...	...	|	|	|	|	|	...	1526
Frankfurt (Main) Hbf **910** d.	1509	...	...	|	*1442**	...	1609	1628	...	...	...	...	1547•	|	...	1709	...	...	|	|	*1642**	|	|	...	1809
Frankfurt Flugh. ✈ § **910** d.	1524	...	...	|	*1458**	...	1624	1642	...	...	...	...	1558	1709	...	1724	...	...	1753	|	*1658**	1809	1809	...	1824
Mainz Hbf d.	|	...	...	1449	1520	...	|	|	...	...	...	...	1620	|	...	|	...	...	|	1649	1720	|	|	...	|
Bingen (Rhein) Hbf d.	|	...	...	1507	|	...	|	|	...	...	...	...	|	|	...	|	...	...	|	1707	|	|	|	...	|
Koblenz Hbf d.	|	...	...	1544	1613	...	|	|	...	...	...	...	1713	|	...	|	...	...	|	1744	1813	|	|	...	|
Andernach d.	|	...	...	1556	|	...	|	|	...	...	...	...	|	|	...	|	...	...	|	1756	|	|	|	...	|
Remagen d.	|	...	...	1608	|	...	|	|	...	...	...	...	|	|	...	|	...	...	|	1808	|	|	|	...	|
Bonn Hbf d.	|	...	...	1623	1645	...	|	|	...	...	...	...	1745	|	1748	|	1825j	...	|	1823	1845	|	|	...	|
Köln/Bonn Flugh. ✈ **910** d.	|	...	...	|	|	...	|	|	...	...	...	...	|	|	|	|	|	...	|	|	|	|	|	...	|
Köln Hbf **910** a.	|	...	...	1643	1705	...	|	1736	...	...	...	...	1805	1805	1814	|	1845j	...	|	1842	1905	1904	1904	...	|
Köln Hbf **910** d.	|	1648	...	1646	1709	1713	|	1746	1748	...	1741	1804	1811	1811	1817	|	1848	...	|	1846	1909	1911	1914	1913	|
Köln Messe/Deutz d.	1619	|	...	|	|	|	1717	|	|	...	|	|	|	|	|	1820	|	...	1843	|	|	|	|	|	1923
Solingen Hbf d.	|	|	...	|	|	1730	|	|	|	...	|	|	|	1830	|	|	|	...	|	|	|	1930	|	1930	|
Wuppertal Hbf d.	|	1716	...	|	|	1744	|	|	1816	...	|	|	|	1843	|	|	1916	...	|	|	|	1943	|	1944	|
Hagen Hbf d.	|	1735	...	|	|	1802	|	|	1835	...	|	|	|	1901	|	|	1935	...	|	|	|	2001	|	2002	|
Düsseldorf Hbf **910** d.	1642	|	1651	1714	1733	|	1738	1812	|	1751	1815f	1829	1834	|	|	1842	|	1851	1907	1913	1933	|	1938	|	1946
Düsseldorf Flughafen ✈ d.	|	|	1659u	|	|	|	|	|	|	1759u	|	|	|	|	|	|	|	1859u	|	|	|	|	|	|	|
Duisburg Hbf d.	1656	|	1710	1732	1747	|	1753	1826	|	1810	1829	1844	1848	|	|	1900	|	1909	1923	1931	1947	|	1951	|	2003
Oberhausen Hbf d.	|	|	|	|	|	|	|	1832	|	|	1836	|	|	|	|	|	|	|	|	|	|	|	1957	|	|
Essen Hbf d.	1707	|	1723	1745	1802	|	1816f	...	|	1823	|	1857	1900	|	|	1917	|	1922	1936	1945	2002	|	...	|	2017
Gelsenkirchen Hbf d.	...	|	|	|	1811	|	|	...	|	|	1846	|	|	|	|	|	|	|	|	|	2013	|	...	|	|
Wanne-Eickel Hbf d.	...	|	|	|	|	|	|	...	|	|	|	|	|	|	|	|	|	|	|	|	|	|	...	|	|
Recklinghausen Hbf d.	...	|	|	|	|	|	|	...	|	|	1858	|	|	|	|	|	|	|	|	|	|	|	...	|	|
Bochum Hbf d.	...	|	1734	1756	|	|	1828	...	|	1834	|	|	1910	|	|	|	|	1933	1950	1956	|	|	...	|	2029
Dortmund Hbf a.	...	|	1746	...	|	1821	1841	...	|	1846	|	|	1922	1921	|	1939	|	1946	2001	2007	|	2021	...	2021	2042
Dortmund Hbf **805** d.	...	|	1748	...	|	1825	...	...	|	1848	|	|	...	1924	|	...	|	1948	...	...	|	...	...	2028	...
Hamm (Westf) **805** a.	...	1802	1807	...	|	1843	...	...	1902	1907	|	|	...	|	|	...	2002	2007	...	...	|	...	...	2043	...
Hannover Hbf **810** a.	...	1928	1928	...	|	2018	...	...	2028	2028	|	|	...	|	|	...	2128	2128	...	...	|	...	...	2218	...
Leipzig Hbf **849a 866** a.	...	|	|	...	|	2317h	...	...	|	|	|	|	...	|	|	...	|	|	...	...	|	...	...	...	...
Berlin Hbf **810** a.	...	2109	2109	...	|	...	...	...	2223	2223	|	|	...	|	2219	...	2310	2310	...	...	|	...	...	...	...
Münster (Westf) Hbf **801** d.	...	...	...	...	1857	...	...	...	...	...	1928	1947	...	1956	...	...	...	...	...	...	2057	...	...	...	...
Osnabrück Hbf **801 815** d.	...	...	...	...	1923	...	...	...	...	...	...	|	...	2023	...	...	...	...	...	...	2123	...	...	...	...
Bremen Hbf **801 815** d.	...	...	...	...	2018	...	...	...	...	...	...	|	...	2118	...	...	...	...	...	...	2220	...	...	...	...
Hamburg Hbf **801** a.	...	...	...	...	2114	...	...	...	...	...	...	2150	...	2214	...	...	...	...	...	...	2316	...	...	...	...
Hamburg Altona a.	...	...	...	...	2129	...	...	...	...	...	...	2203	...	2229	...	...	...	...	...	...	2331	...	...	...	...

♦ – **NOTES** (LISTED BY TRAIN NUMBER)

6 – 🚃12 ✕ Interlaken - Bern - Basel - Hamburg.
8 – 🚃12 ✕ Zürich - Basel - Hamburg.
118 – BODENSEE – 🚃12 Innsbruck - Lindau - Ulm - Stuttgart - Dortmund.
2004 – ⑦–④ (not June 15). SCHWARZWALD – 🚃12 🍷 (Konstanz - Karlsruhe ⑦ -) Koblenz - Emden.
2006 – SCHWARZWALD – 🚃12 🍷 Konstanz - Karlsruhe - Dortmund.
2012 – ALLGÄU – 🚃12 🍷 Oberstdorf - Ulm - Stuttgart - Bochum.
2014 – ⑤ (also June 15). 🚃12 🍷 Stuttgart - Mannheim - Münster - Emden.
2043 – 🚃12 Köln - Hannover (- Magdeburg Ⓑ) (- Leipzig ⑤⑦).
2157 – 🚃12 Köln - Paderborn - Kassel - Erfurt (- Gera Ⓑ).

A – To Amsterdam (Table **28**). Diversions / retimings are scheduled June 11, 12, 18, 19, Aug. 27 - Sept. 9 (different train numbers may apply).
B – To Berlin (Table **810**).
D – To Dresden (Table **842**).
E – From Wien (Tables **950/920**).
M – To Emden (Table **812**).
N – To Norddeich Mole (Table **812**).
P – From Passau (Table **920**).
R – June 24 - Aug. 5.

c – Arrives 1456.
f – Arrives 10 – 13 minutes earlier.
h – ⑤⑦ only.
j – ①②③④⑥ only.
m – Not June 24 - Aug. 5.
n – July 30 - Sept. 11 only.
t – Until July 17.
u – Calls to pick up only.
v – Not July 30 - Sept. 11.
z – ⑦ only.

* – Connecting *ICE* train (change trains at Mainz).
⊖ – Train number **1069** from July 18.
◧ – Train number **1118** from July 24.
⊙ – ⑤ (also June 15; not June 17). Train number **2016** from July 22.
‡ – On ⑤⑦ (also June 15) Köln Hbf d. 1337, Düsseldorf Hbf d. 1409.
• – Frankfurt (Main) **Süd** (not Hbf).
§ – Frankfurt Flughafen Fernbahnhof.

FRANKFURT - KOBLENZ - KÖLN - DORTMUND - HAMBURG 800

	ICE	ICE	EC	ICE	ICE	ICE	ICE	ICE	ICE	ICE	ICE	IC	ICE	ICE	ICE	ICE	IC	IC	IC	ICE	ICE	ICE	ICE		ICE
	957	**947**	**114**	**812**	**26**	**514**	**620**	**120**	**912**	**657**	**1518**	**2341**	**528**	**90**	**512**	**526**	**1910**	**1910**	**2210**	**100**	**949**	**524**	**22**		**920**
	⑤⑦			①-④				Ⓑ△	Ⓑ	⑤⑦	¶						⑦**M**	⑦**Q**	Ⓑ**b**				⊠		
	✕	✕	🍷♦	✕	E✕	✕	✕	A✕	✕	L✕	🍷		✕	E✕	✕	G✕	🍷	🍷	⊡🍷	✕			E✕		⊖
München Hbf ***904 930*** d.	...	...	1347	...	...	1528	1525			...	...	...	1614	...	1725	1719	1617	1617	...	...	...	1816	...	...	...
Stuttgart Hbf ***912*** d.	...	...	1607	...	...	1751		...	1837**v**	...	1737**h**	...		...	1951		1914	1914	1915**j**	...	...		...	...	...
Basel SBB 🚌 ***912*** d.	...	...		...	...			...		...		...		...						1913	...		...	...	...
Karlsruhe Hbf ***912*** d.	...	...		...	...			...	1854**n**	...	1745**k**	...		...					1948**n**	2101	...		...	...	...
Nürnberg Hbf ***920*** d.	...	...		...	1531		1636	...		...		...	1726	1729		1831					...	1926	1930	...	...
Frankfurt (Main) Hbf **910** d.	...	...		1816	1747•		1909	1928		...	*1842**	...	2009	1947•		2109			*2042**		...	2209	2147•	...	2324
Frankfurt Flugh. ✈ § **910** d.	...	...		1831	1758	1909	1922	1942	1953	...	*1858**	...	2025	1958	2108	2124			*2058**	2209	...	2223	2159	...	2339
Mainz Hbf d.	...	...	1744		1820					...	1920	...		2020			2049	2052	2120		...		2220	...	0001
Bingen (Rhein) Hbf d.	...	...	1807							...		...					2107				...			...	0018
Koblenz Hbf d.	...	...	1844		1913					...	2013	...		2113			2144	2205	2213		...		2313	...	0058
Andernach d.	...	...	1856							...		...					2156	2217			...			...	
Remagen d.	...	...	1908							...		...					2208	2231			...			...	0122
Bonn Hbf d.	...	...	1923		1945					...	2045	...		2145			2223	2245	2245		2248		2345	...	0138
Köln/Bonn Flugh. ✈ **910** d.	...	...		1939						...		...										2327		...	
Köln Hbf **910** a.	...	...	1943		2005	2005				...	2105	...		2205	2205		2243	2305	2305	2304	2309		0005	...	0205
Köln Hbf **910** d.	1948	1927**q**	1946		2009	2011				2048	2109	2113		2209	2211		2246	2309	2309	2311	2315		0010	...	0210
Köln Messe/Deutz d.				1951			2026	2033	2047				2116			2217						2338		...	
Solingen Hbf d.					2028							2130		2228				2328	2328					...	
Wuppertal Hbf d.	2016			2017	2043					2116		2144		2243				2343	2343					...	
Hagen Hbf d.	2035			2036						2135		2202		2301				0001	0001					...	
Düsseldorf Hbf **910** d.		1951	2010			2034	2048	2108**c**	2113		2133		2137		2234	2238	2309			2334	2338	2359	0033	...	0233
Düsseldorf Flughafen ✈ d.		1959																			2346			...	0240
Duisburg Hbf d.		2010	2027			2048	2103	2126	2128		2147		2151		2248	2252	2323			2348	2357	0013	0046	...	0251
Oberhausen Hbf d.								2132																...	
Essen Hbf d.		2023	2043			2100	2116	...	2141		2202		2204		2309**c**	2304**p**	2340			0000	0009	0026	0059	...	0306
Gelsenkirchen Hbf d.								...			2211				2320									...	
Wanne-Eickel Hbf d.								...																...	
Recklinghausen Hbf d.								...							2333									...	
Bochum Hbf d.		2034	2051			2110	2128	...	2152				2213			2314	2350			0009	0019	0035	0109	...	0316
Dortmund Hbf a.		2046	...	2107	2121	2122	2140	...	2204			2221	2227	2321		2326	0002	0021	0021	0023	0032	0048	0122	...	0328
Dortmund Hbf **805** d.		2048	...	...	...	2125	...	...	...			2225	...	...		...	...	...	...	...	0034	...	...	...	0332
Hamm (Westf) **805** a.	2102	2107	...	...	...		...	...	...	2202		2244	...	...		...	...	...	...	...	0049	...	...	...	0350
Hannover Hbf **810** a.	2228	2228	...	...	...		...	...	...	2328		0018	...	...		...	...	...	...	...	0223	...	...	...	
Leipzig Hbf **849a 866** a.			...	...	...		...	...	...			...	...	...		...	...	...	...	...		...	...	...	
Berlin Hbf **810** a.	0013	0013	...	...	...		...	...	...	0114		...	...	...		...	...	...	...	...	0536	...	...	...	
Münster (Westf) Hbf **801** d.	...	...	...	...	...	2157	...	...	...	...	2254	...	...	...	0001	...	...	...	...	...	...	...	...	...	0415
Osnabrück Hbf **801 815** d.	...	...	...	...	...	2223	...	...	...	...	...	...	...	...	...	...	...	...	...	...	...	...	...	...	0450
Bremen Hbf **801 815** d.	...	...	...	...	...	2318	...	...	...	...	...	...	...	...	...	...	...	...	...	...	...	...	...	...	0554
Hamburg Hbf **801** a.	...	...	...	...	...	0014	...	...	...	...	...	...	...	...	...	...	...	...	...	...	...	...	...	...	0650
Hamburg Altona a.	...	...	...	...	...	0029	...	...	...	...	...	...	...	...	...	...	...	...	...	...	...	...	...	...	0706

km	SEE NOTE ❖	ICE	ICE	ICE	ICE	ICE	ICE	ICE	IC	ICE	ICE	ICE	ICE	EC		ICE	IC	EC	ICE	ICE	IC	ICE	ICE	ICE	ICE
		523	**23**	**525**	**101**	**1519**	**948**	**913**	**2003**	**813**	**527**	**91**	**513**	**115**		**529**	**2040**	**7**	**121**	**915**	**119**	**646**	**656**	**621**	**1158**
		①-⑥			①-⑥	①-⑥		①-⑥	Ⓐ	①-⑤									①-⑥			①-⑥	①-⑥		
		✕	E✕	✕	✕	🍷		✕		✕	G✕	E✕	✕	🍷♦		✕	🍷	✕♦	A✕	✕	♦	✕	✕	✕	✕
	Hamburg Altona d.	...	...	...	...	...	...	...	...	...	...	...	...	...	...	...	...	0421	...	...	...	...	...	...	...
	Hamburg Hbf **801** d.	...	...	...	...	...	...	...	...	...	...	...	...	...	...	...	...	0437	...	...	...	...	...	...	...
	Bremen Hbf **801 815** d.	...	...	...	...	...	...	...	...	...	...	...	...	...	...	...	...	0540	...	...	...	...	...	...	...
	Osnabrück Hbf **801 815** d.	...	...	...	...	...	...	...	...	...	...	...	...	...	...	...	...	0636	...	...	...	...	...	...	...
	Münster (Westf) Hbf **801** d.	...	...	...	...	0503	...	...	...	...	...	...	0603	0631	...	...	...	0703	...	0731	...	...	...	...	...
	Berlin Hbf **810** d.	...	...	...	...		0021	...	...	...	...	...			...	...	...		...		...	0430	0430	...	0533
	Leipzig Hbf **849a 866** d.	...	...	...	...			...	...	...	...	...			...	...	...		...		...			...	
	Hannover Hbf **810** d.	...	...	...	...		0340	...	...	...	...	...			...	...	0540		...		...	0621	0621	...	
0	Hamm (Westf) **805** d.	...	...	...	...		0512	...	...	...	...	...			...	...	0716		...		...	0751	0754	...	
	Dortmund Hbf **805** a.	...	...	...	...	0534		...	...	...	...	...	0633		...	...	0734		...		...	0810		...	
	Dortmund Hbf d.	0401	0431	0522	0528	0536		0547	0549	0558	0622	0627	0636		...	0722	0736		...		0751	0812		...	
	Bochum Hbf d.	0415	0444	0535		0548		0603			0636		0648		...	0736			...			0824		...	
	Recklinghausen Hbf d.													0701	...				...	0800				...	
	Wanne-Eickel Hbf d.								0609					0709	...				...	0808				...	
	Gelsenkirchen Hbf d.								0614					0715	...			0744	...	0814				...	
	Essen Hbf d.	0427	0457	0549		0600		0615			0651		0700		...	0750		0757	...	0825**y**		0837		0839	
	Oberhausen Hbf d.								0626					0726	...				0829						
	Duisburg Hbf d.	0440	0510	0602		0613**y**		0628	0634		0704		0713**y**	0734	...	0803		0810	0838	0833		0850		0855	
	Düsseldorf Flughafen ✈ d.														...										
	Düsseldorf Hbf **910** d.	0455	0524	0617		0624		0645	0649		0718		0724	0750	...	0818		0824	0854	0847		0903		0910	
48	**Hagen** Hbf d.				0557		0550			0621		0657			...		0758				0815	...	0823		
75	Wuppertal Hbf d.				0615		0609			0638		0714			...		0814				0834	...	0840		
93	Solingen Hbf d.				0626					0650		0727			...		0826					...			
120	**Köln** Messe/Deutz a.	0518		0642				0709		0717	0742				...	0842			0922	0911		...		0933	
121	**Köln** Hbf **910** a.		0550		0646	0650	0657		0715			0746	0749	0815	...		0846	0850			0912	...	0909		0940
	Köln Hbf **910** d.		0553		0654	0653	...		0717			0753	0755	0818	...		...	0853			0917	...	...		0945
	Köln/Bonn Flugh. ✈ **910** a.	0529					...								...		...					...	...		
	Bonn Hbf d.		0614			0714	...		0738			0814		0838	...		...	0914			0938	...	...		1016
	Remagen d.						...		0751					0852	...		...				0952	...	...		...
	Andernach d.						...		0804					0904	...		...				1004	...	...		...
	Koblenz Hbf d.		0648			0748	...		0816			0848		0918	...		...	0948			1018	...	...		...
	Bingen (Rhein) Hbf d.						...		...					0952	...		...				1052	...	...		...
	Mainz Hbf a.		0738			0839	...		...			0939		1015	...		...	1039			1111	...	...		...
	Frankfurt Flugh. ✈ § **910** a.	0634	0759	0733	0749	*0859**	...	0807	...	0826	0833	0959	0850		...	0933	...	*1059**	1017	1007		...	...	1035	...
	Frankfurt (Main) Hbf **910** a.	0648	0809•	0748		*0913**	...		...	0841	0848	1009•			...	0948	...	*1113**	1031			...	...	1048	...
	Nürnberg Hbf **920** a.	0921	1028	1020			...		...	...	1120	1228			...	1220	...		...			...	...	1320	...
	Karlsruhe Hbf **912** a.		...		0858		...	0906**n**	...	...		...			...		...	1147	...	1117**n**		...	...		...
	Basel SBB 🚌 **912** a.		...		1047		...		...	...		...			...		...	1333	...			...	...		...
	Stuttgart Hbf **912** a.		...		...	1024	...	0924**v**	...	...		...	1008	1153	...		...	...	...	1122**v**	1246	...	...		...
	München Hbf **904 930** a.	1033	...	1130	...	...	...	...	...	...	1233	...	1227	1411**z**	...	1334	...	...	...	...	...	...	...	1432	...

♦ – **NOTES** (LISTED BY TRAIN NUMBER)

7 – [12] ✕ Hamburg - Basel - Bern - Interlaken.
114 – WÖRTHERSEE – [12] 🍷 Klagenfurt - Salzburg - München - Bochum.
115 – WÖRTHERSEE – [12] 🍷 Münster - München - Salzburg - Klagenfurt.
119 – BODENSEE – [12] Dortmund - Stuttgart - Ulm - Lindau - Innsbruck.

A – To / from Amsterdam (Table 28). Diversions / retimings are scheduled June 11, 12, 18, 19, Aug. 27 - Sept. 9 (different train numbers may apply).
E – From / to Wien (Tables **950**/**920**).
G – From / to Garmisch on ⑥ (Table **895**).
L – From Aachen Hbf (d. 1959) and Düren (d. 2027).
M – From Sept. 4.
Q – Until Aug. 28.

c – Arrives 10 – 12 minutes earlier.
h – Not July 30, Aug. 6, 13, 20, 27, Sept. 3, 10.
j – Not July 31 - Sept. 11; departs 1936 on ⑤⑦ (also June 15; not June 17).
k – ⑥ July 30 - Sept. 10.
n – July 30 - Sept. 11 only.

p – Connects at Essen with train **512** (in previous column).
q – ①②③④⑥.
v – Not July 30 - Sept. 11.
y – Until June 24.
z – Until July 13 calls at München **Ost** (a. 1424; not München Hbf).

¶ – Runs as *IC* **2318** on ⑥
△ – Terminates at Düsseldorf June 10, 12, 17, 19, Aug. 26 - Sept. 8.
⊡ – Runs 16 – 30 minutes later Koblenz - Dortmund on ①⑦ until Aug. 29.
⊠ – Runs 19 – 36 minutes later Koblenz - Dortmund on ①⑥⑦ until Aug. 29.
⊖ – On ①⑥⑦ until Aug. 29 (departing Frankfurt) runs 2 – 26 minutes later Mainz - Osnabrück and does not call at Bingen.
❖ – Timings Dortmund / Gelsenkirchen / Oberhausen - Düsseldorf - Köln may vary by up to 6 minutes until June 24. Berlin departures may be up to 4 minutes earlier until July 8.
* – Connecting *ICE* train (change trains at Mainz).
• – Frankfurt (Main) **Süd** (not Hbf).
§ – Frankfurt Flughafen Fernbahnhof.

800 HAMBURG - DORTMUND - KÖLN - KOBLENZ - FRANKFURT

SEE NOTE ✣	*ICE* 1031	*ICE* 27	*ICE* 515	*IC* 2005	*ICE* 946	*ICE* 956	*ICE* 623	*ICE* 105	*IC* 2042	*EC* 9	*IC* 2013	*ICE* 644	*ICE* 654	*ICE* 625	*ICE* 517	*ICE* 29	*ICE* 1152	*IC* 2009	*ICE* 944	*ICE* 954	*IC* 2156	*ICE* 627	*IC* 2044	*ICE* 713	*IC* 1915
	①–⑤			①–⑥	①–⑥		⑥⑦					①–⑥					t								⑦
	✕	E✕	✕	🍷♦	✕	✕	✕	A✕	🍷♦	✕♦	🍷♦	✕	✕	✕	✕	E✕	✕	M	✕	✕	♦	✕	D🍷	✕	🍷
Hamburg Altona d.	0554	...	0529	...	...	...	...	...	...	0629	...	...	...	...	0729	...	...	...	...	...	...	...	...	0829	...
Hamburg Hbf 801 d.	0611	...	0546	...	...	...	...	...	...	0646	...	...	...	...	0746	...	...	...	...	...	...	...	...	0846	...
Bremen Hbf 801 815 d.	|	...	0644	...	...	...	...	...	...	0744	...	...	...	...	0844	...	...	...	...	...	...	...	...	0944	...
Osnabrück Hbf 801 815 d.	|	...	0737	...	...	...	...	...	...	0836	...	...	...	...	0937	...	...	...	...	...	...	...	...	1037	...
Münster (Westf) Hbf 801 d.	|	...	0803	0832	...	...	...	...	...	0903	...	...	...	...	1003	...	...	1032	...	...	...	...	...	1103	...
Berlin Hbf 810 d.	|	...	|	|	0529	0529	...	...	...	|	...	0646	0646	...	|	...	0700	|	0746	0746	...	...	...	|	...
Leipzig Hbf 849a 866 d.	|	...	|	|	|	|	...	...	0443g	|	...	|	|	...	|	...	|	|	|	|	...	...	0638	|	...
Hannover Hbf 810 d.	|	...	|	|	0731	0731	...	...	0740	|	...	0831	0831	...	|	...	0856	|	0931	0931	...	...	0940	|	...
Hamm (Westf) 805 d.	|	...	|	|	0851	0854	...	...	0916	|	...	0951	0954	...	|	...	1026	|	1051	1054	1056	...	1116	|	...
Dortmund Hbf 805 a.	|	...	0833	|	0910	|	...	...	0933	|	...	1010	|	...	1033	...	1048	|	1110	|	1114	...	1133	|	...
Dortmund Hbf d.	|	0827	0836	|	0912	|	0942w	...	0936	|	0949	1012	|	...	1036	1027	1050	|	1112	|	1116	1122w	1136	|	1149
Bochum Hbf d.	|	|	0847	|	0924	|	0926w	...	|	|	1004	1024	|	...	1047	|	1102	|	1124	|	1130	1137w	|	|	1203
Recklinghausen Hbf d.	|	|	|	0900	|	|	|	...	|	|	|	|	|	...	|	|	|	1100	|	|	|	|	|	|	|
Wanne-Eickel Hbf d.	|	|	|	0909	|	|	|	...	|	|	|	|	|	...	|	|	|	1109	|	|	|	|	|	|	|
Gelsenkirchen Hbf d.	|	|	|	0914	|	|	|	...	|	0942	|	|	|	...	|	|	|	1114	|	|	|	|	|	1143	|
Essen Hbf d.	0856	|	0900	|	0937	|	0941	...	|	0957	1016	1041	|	1036	1100	|	1114	|	1137	|	1142	1150	|	1157	1214
Oberhausen Hbf d.	|	|	|	0926	|	|	|	0958	|	|	|	|	|	|	|	|	|	1126	|	|	|	|	|	|	|
Duisburg Hbf d.	0909y	|	0913y	0933	0950	|	0955	1007y	|	1010	1030	1055	|	1051	1113y	|	1130	1134	1150	|	1155	1203	|	1210	1229
Düsseldorf Flughafen ✈ d.	|	|	|	|	0958p	|	|	|	|	|	|	1103s	|	|	|	|	|	|	|	|	|	|	|	|	|
Düsseldorf Hbf 910 d.	0920	|	0924	0947	1007q	|	1009	1019	|	1024	1044	1112	|	1105	1124	|	1144	1149	1202	|	1211	1217	|	1224	1244
Hagen Hbf d.	|	0857	|	|	...	0923	|	|	0958	|	|	...	1023	|	|	1057	|	|	...	1123	|	|	1158	|	|
Wuppertal Hbf d.	|	0914	|	|	...	0940	|	|	1014	|	|	...	1040	|	|	1114	|	|	...	1140	|	|	1214	|	|
Solingen Hbf d.	|	0926	|	|	...	|	|	|	1026	|	|	...	|	|	|	1127	|	|	...	|	|	|	1226	|	|
Köln Messe/Deutz a.	|	|	|	|	...	|	1032	|	|	|	|	...	1128	|	|	|	|	|	...	|	|	1242	|	|	|
Köln Hbf 910 a.	0946	0946	0949	1013	...	1009	|	1045	1046	1050	1112	...	1109	|	1149	1146	1212	1215	...	1209	1239	|	1246	1250	1312
Köln Hbf 910 d.	...	0953	0955	1017	...	...	|	1054	...	1053	1117	...	...	|	1155	1153	...	...	...	...	...	|	...	1253	1317
Köln/Bonn Flugh. ✈ 910 a.	...	|	|	|	...	...	1043	|	...	|	|	...	...	|	|	|	...	...	...	...	...	|	...	|	|
Bonn Hbf d.	...	1014	|	1038	...	...	|	|	...	1114	1138	...	...	|	|	1214	...	...	...	...	...	|	...	1314	1338
Remagen d.	...	|	|	1051	...	...	|	|	...	|	1152	...	...	|	|	|	...	...	...	...	...	|	...	|	1352
Andernach d.	...	|	|	1104	...	...	|	|	...	|	1204	...	...	|	|	|	...	...	...	...	...	|	...	|	1404
Koblenz Hbf d.	...	1048	|	1118	...	...	|	|	...	1148	1218	...	...	|	|	1248	...	...	...	...	...	|	...	1348	1418
Bingen (Rhein) Hbf d.	...	|	|	1153h	...	...	|	|	...	|	1252	...	...	|	|	|	...	...	...	...	...	|	...	|	1452
Mainz Hbf a.	...	1139	|	1215h	...	...	|	|	...	1239	1311	...	...	|	|	1339	...	...	...	...	...	|	...	1439	1511
Frankfurt Flugh. ✈ § 910 a.	...	1159	1050	|	...	...	1133	1149	...	*1259**	|	...	...	1235	1250	1359	...	...	...	...	...	1333	...	*1459**	|
Frankfurt (Main) Hbf 910 a.	...	1209•	|	|	...	...	1148	|	...	*1313**	|	...	...	1248	|	1409•	...	...	...	...	...	1348	...	*1513**	|
Nürnberg Hbf 920 a.	...	1427	|	|	...	...	1420	|	...	|	|	...	...	1520	|	1629	...	...	...	...	...	1621	...	|	|
Karlsruhe Hbf 912 a.	...	...	|	1334h	...	...	|	1258	...	1347	|	...	...	|	|	...	...	...	...	...	...	|	...	1612c	|
Basel SBB ⊞ 912 a.	...	...	|	...	...	...	|	1447	...	1536	|	...	...	|	|	...	...	...	...	...	...	|	...	|	|
Stuttgart Hbf 912 a.	...	...	1208	...	...	...	|	...	...	...	1446	...	...	|	1408	...	...	...	...	...	...	|	...	1622z	1656
München Hbf 904 930 a.	...	...	1427	...	...	...	1529	...	...	...	...	...	...	1637	1627	...	...	...	...	...	...	1738	...	...	...

SEE NOTE ✣	*IC* 2015	*ICE* 123	*ICE* 1150	*ICE* 642	*ICE* 652	*ICE* 629	*ICE* 229	*ICE* 519	*ICE* 817	*IC* 5106	*IC* 2201	*ICE* 942	*ICE* 952	*ICE* 721	*IC* 2046	*IC* 2217	*IC* 2011	*IC* 2011	*ICE* 1011	*ICE* 640	*ICE* 650	*ICE* 125	*ICE* 723	*ICE* 1156	*ICE* 611
	⑤f																①–④	⑤⑦	Y						
	🍷	A✕	B✕	✕	✕	✕	E✕	✕	✕	L	H	✕	✕	✕	D🍷	🍷♦	T🍷	¶	✕	✕	✕	A✕	✕	✕	✕
Hamburg Altona d.	...	...	...	...	...	...	...	0929	...	...	...	...	...	...	...	...	...	...	...	...	...	...	...	...	1129
Hamburg Hbf 801 d.	...	...	...	...	...	...	...	0946	...	...	...	...	...	...	...	1046	...	...	...	...	...	...	...	...	1146
Bremen Hbf 801 815 d.	...	...	...	...	...	...	...	1044	...	...	1054	...	...	...	...	1144	...	...	...	...	...	...	...	...	1244
Osnabrück Hbf 801 815 d.	...	...	1106	...	...	...	...	1137	...	...	1157	...	...	...	...	1237	...	...	...	...	...	...	...	...	1337
Münster (Westf) Hbf 801 d.	...	...	1132	...	...	...	...	1203	...	...	1232	...	...	...	...	1303	...	...	...	...	...	...	...	...	1403
Berlin Hbf 810 d.	...	...	|	0846	0846	...	...	|	...	...	|	0946	0946	...	...	|	...	1000r	...	1046	1046	...	...	1141	|
Leipzig Hbf 849a 866 d.	...	...	|	|	|	...	...	|	...	...	|	|	|	...	0838	|	...	|	...	|	|	...	...	|	|
Hannover Hbf 810 d.	...	...	|	1031	1031	...	...	|	...	...	|	1131	1131	...	1140	|	...	1156	...	1231	1231	...	...	|	|
Hamm (Westf) 805 d.	...	...	|	1151	1154	...	...	|	...	...	|	1251	1254	...	1316	|	...	1326	...	1351	1354	...	...	|	|
Dortmund Hbf 805 a.	...	...	|	1210	|	...	...	1233	...	...	|	1310	|	...	1333	|	...	1349	...	1410	|	...	...	|	1433
Dortmund Hbf d.	1149	...	|	1212	|	...	1227	1236	...	...	|	1312	|	...	1336	|	...	1351	1349	1412	|	...	...	|	1435
Bochum Hbf d.	1204	...	|	1224	|	...	|	1247	...	...	|	1324	|	...	|	|	...	1404	1404	1424	|	...	...	|	|
Recklinghausen Hbf d.	|	...	1203	|	|	...	|	|	...	...	1300	|	|	...	|	|	...	|	|	|	|	...	...	|	|
Wanne-Eickel Hbf d.	|	...	|	|	|	...	|	|	...	...	1309	|	|	...	|	|	...	|	|	|	|	...	...	|	|
Gelsenkirchen Hbf d.	|	...	|	|	|	...	|	|	...	...	1314	|	|	...	|	1342	...	|	|	|	|	...	...	|	|
Essen Hbf d.	1215	...	1225	1241	|	1236	|	1300	1305	...	|	1337	|	1351	|	1355	...	1415	1415	1437	|	...	1439	|	|
Oberhausen Hbf d.	|	1226	|	|	|	|	|	|	|	...	1326	|	|	|	|	|	...	|	|	|	|	1426	|	|	|
Duisburg Hbf d.	1231	1234	1237	1255	|	1251	|	1313y	1318	...	1334	1350	|	1404	|	1409	...	1431	1428	1450	|	1438	1454	|	|
Düsseldorf Flughafen ✈ d.	|	|	|	1303s	|	|	|	|	|	...	|	1358s	|	|	|	|	...	|	|	|	|	|	|	|	|
Düsseldorf Hbf 910 d.	1244	1248	1252	1312	|	1305	|	1324	1333	1345	1351	1407	|	1418	|	1423	...	1445	1449	1502	|	1454	1508	|	|
Hagen Hbf d.	|	|	|	...	1223	|	1257	|	|	|	|	...	1323	|	1358	|	...	|	|	...	1423	|	|	|	1457
Wuppertal Hbf d.	|	|	|	...	1240	|	1315	|	|	|	|	...	1340	|	1414	|	...	|	|	...	1440	|	|	|	1514
Solingen Hbf d.	|	|	|	...	|	|	1327	|	|	|	|	...	|	|	1426	|	...	|	|	...	|	|	|	|	1527
Köln Messe/Deutz a.	|	1312	|	...	|	1329	|	|	1357	|	|	...	|	1442	|	|	...	|	1513	...	|	1519	1532	|	|
Köln Hbf 910 a.	1312	|	1319	...	1309	|	1346	1349	|	1414	1418	...	1409	|	1446	1450	...	1512	|	...	1509	|	|	1541	1546
Köln Hbf 910 d.	1317	|	...	...	1312	|	1353	1355	|	1417	...	...	...	|	...	1453	1517	1517	|	...	...	|	|	1543	1555
Köln/Bonn Flugh. ✈ 910 a.	|	|	...	...	|	|	|	|	|	|	...	...	...	|	...	|	|	|	|	...	...	|	|	|	|
Bonn Hbf d.	1338	|	...	...	1333	|	1414	|	|	1438	...	...	...	|	...	1514	1538	1538	|	...	...	|	|	1615	|
Remagen d.	1352	|	...	...	...	|	|	|	|	1451	...	...	...	|	...	|	1552	1552	|	...	...	|	|	...	|
Andernach d.	1404	|	...	...	...	|	|	|	|	1503	...	...	...	|	...	|	1604	1604	|	...	...	|	|	...	|
Koblenz Hbf d.	1418	|	...	...	...	|	1448	|	|	1516	...	...	...	|	...	1548	1618	1618	|	...	...	|	|	...	|
Bingen (Rhein) Hbf d.	1452	|	...	...	...	|	|	|	|	...	...	...	...	|	...	|	1652	1652	|	...	...	|	|	...	|
Mainz Hbf a.	1511	|	...	...	...	|	1539	|	|	...	...	...	...	|	...	1639	1711	1711	|	...	...	|	|	...	|
Frankfurt Flugh. ✈ § 910 a.	|	1412	...	...	...	1436	1559	1450	1508	...	...	...	...	1533	...	*1659**	|	|	1607	...	...	1617	1633	...	1650
Frankfurt (Main) Hbf 910 a.	|	1426	...	...	...	1448	1609•	|	1524	...	...	...	...	1548	...	*1713**	|	|	...	...	...	1631	1648	...	|
Nürnberg Hbf 920 a.	|	...	...	...	...	1720	1828	|	...	...	...	...	...	1820	...	|	|	|	...	...	...	...	1920	...	|
Karlsruhe Hbf 912 a.	|	...	...	...	...	|	...	|	...	...	...	...	...	|	...	1813b	|	|	1714n	...	...	...	...	...	|
Basel SBB ⊞ 912 a.	|	...	...	...	...	|	...	|	...	...	...	...	...	|	...	|	|	|	|	...	...	...	...	...	|
Stuttgart Hbf 912 a.	1646	...	...	...	...	|	...	1608	...	...	...	...	...	|	...	1827e	1846	1847	1720v	...	...	...	...	...	1808
München Hbf 904 930 a.	...	...	...	...	...	1833	...	1827	...	...	...	...	...	1941	...	...	...	...	...	...	...	...	2029	...	2028

♦ – **NOTES** (LISTED BY TRAIN NUMBER)

9 – [12] ✕ Hamburg - Basel - Zürich.
2005 – SCHWARZWALD – [12] 🍷 Emden - Münster - Köln - Koblenz (- Karlsruhe - Konstanz ⑤⑥).
2013 – ALLGÄU – [12] 🍷 Dortmund - Mainz - Mannheim - Stuttgart - Oberstdorf.
2042 – [12] 🍷 (Leipzig ① -) (Magdeburg ①–⑥ -) Hannover - Köln.
2156 – [12] 🍷 (Gera ①–⑥ -) Erfurt - Kassel - Paderborn - Köln.
2217 – GREIFSWALDER BODDEN – [12] 🍷 (Greifswald ⑤ -) Stralsund - Hamburg - Stuttgart / Karlsruhe.

A – From Amsterdam (Table **28**). Diversions / retimings are scheduled June 11, 12, 18, 19, Aug. 27 - Sept. 9 (different train numbers may apply).
B – Until June 23. From Berlin (Table **810**).
D – From Dresden (Table **842**).
E – To Wien (Tables **920**/**950**).
H – OSTFRIESLAND – From Bremerhaven (Table **815**).
L – To Luxembourg (Table **915**).
M – From Emden (Table **812**).

T – ①–④ (not June 15, 16). To Tübingen (Table **930**).
Y – ①②③④⑥ (not June 15).

b – ⑥ July 31 - Sept. 11.
c – ⑥⑦ July 30 - Sept. 11.
e – Daily to July 30; ⑥ Aug. 6 - Sept. 10; daily from Sept. 12.
f – Also June 15; not June 17.
g – ① only.
h – ⑤⑥ only.
n – July 30 - Sept. 11 only.
p – Not ⑥. Calls to set down only.
q – 1002 on ⑥.
r – ⑦ until July 17.
s – Calls to set down only.
t – Until July 17.

v – Not July 30 - Sept. 11.
w – ⑦ only.
y – Until June 24.
z – Not ⑥⑦ July 30 - Sept. 11.

¶ – Runs as *ICE* **1611** on ⑤. Conveys 🍷 on ⑦. Train number **2411** on ⑦ July 31 - Sept. 11.
✣ – Timings Dortmund / Gelsenkirchen / Oberhausen - Düsseldorf - Köln may vary by up to 6 minutes until June 24. Berlin departures may be up to 4 minutes earlier until July 8.
* – Connecting *ICE* train (change trains at Mainz Hbf).
• – Frankfurt (Main) **Süd** (not Hbf).
§ – Frankfurt Flughafen Fernbahnhof.

HAMBURG - DORTMUND - KÖLN - KOBLENZ - FRANKFURT 800

SEE NOTE ✣	ICE 927	ICE 1103	IC 2203	ICE 940	ICE 950	ICE 725	IC 2048	IC 2311	ICE 1013	ICE 717	IC 1917	ICE 127	IC 2305	ICE 548	ICE 558	ICE 727	ICE 929	ICE 613	ICE 735	IC 2205	ICE 1050	ICE 848	ICE 858	IC 2152	ICE 729
		⑥	Ⓑ						Ⓑ	⑤f	⑦		⑥						⑤⑦						
	P✕	✕N	N	✕	✕	✕	D🍷	🍷◆	✕	¶✕	U🍷	A✕	E	✕	✕	✕	✕◆	K✕	✕	N	✕	✕	✕	◆	✕
Hamburg Altona ... d.	1137	...	...	...	...	...	...	...	...	...	...	...	...	...	...	...	...	...	1339	...	...	...	...	...	...
Hamburg Hbf ... **801** d.	1153	...	...	...	...	...	...	1246	...	...	...	...	...	...	...	...	...	1346	1353	...	...	...	...	...	...
Bremen Hbf ... **801 815** d.	1252	...	...	...	...	...	...	1344	...	...	...	...	...	...	...	...	...	1444	1452	...	...	...	...	...	...
Osnabrück Hbf ... **801 815** d.	|	...	...	...	...	...	...	1437	...	...	...	...	...	...	...	...	...	1537	|	...	...	...	...	...	...
Münster (Westf) Hbf ... **801** d.	1409	1431	1432	...	...	...	...	1503	...	...	...	...	1530	...	...	...	...	1603	|	1632	...	...	...	...	...
Berlin Hbf **810** ... d.	|	|	|	1146	1146	...	...	|	...	1201t	1201t	...	|	1246	1246	...	...	|	|	|	1306t	1346	1346	...	...
Leipzig Hbf **849a 866** d.	|	|	|	|	|	...	1038	|	...	|	|	...	|	|	|	...	...	|	|	|	|	|	|	...	...
Hannover Hbf **810** ... d.	|	|	|	1331	1331	...	1340	|	...	1356	1356	...	|	1431	1431	...	...	|	|	|	1456	1531	1531	...	...
Hamm (Westf) ... **805** d.	|	|	|	1451	1454	...	1516	|	...	1533	1533	...	|	1551	1554	...	...	|	|	|	1626	1651	1654	1656	...
Dortmund Hbf ... **805** a.	|	|	|	1510	|	...	1533	|	...	|	|	...	|	1610	|	...	...	1633	|	|	1649	1710	|	1714	...
Dortmund Hbf ... d.	|	|	|	1512	|	...	1536	|	1549	|	|	...	|	1612	|	...	1627	1636	|	|	1651	1712	|	1716	...
Bochum Hbf ... d.	|	|	|	1524	|	...	|	|	1604	|	|	...	|	1624	|	...	|	1648	|	|	1703	1724	|	1730	...
Recklinghausen Hbf ... d.	1438	1500	1500	|	|	...	|	|	|	|	|	...	1559	|	|	...	|	|	1638	1700	|	|	|	|	...
Wanne-Eickel Hbf ... d.	|	1509	1509	|	|	...	|	|	|	|	|	...	1609	|	|	...	|	|	|	1709	|	|	|	|	...
Gelsenkirchen Hbf ... d.	|	1514	1514	|	|	...	|	1543	|	|	|	...	1614	|	|	...	|	|	|	1714	|	|	|	|	...
Essen Hbf ... d.	1500y	|	|	1536	|	1549	|	1557	1615	|	|	...	1626	1637	|	1649	|	1700	1704	|	1715	1737	|	1740	1749
Oberhausen Hbf ... d.	1503j	1526	1526	|	|	|	|	|	|	|	|	1626	|	|	|	|	|	|	|	1726	|	|	|	|	|
Duisburg Hbf ... d.	1511	1534y	1534y	1550	|	1604	|	1610	1628	|	|	1634	1638	1650	|	1704	|	1713y	1718	1734y	1734	1750	|	1755	1804
Düsseldorf Flughafen ✈ ... d.	|	|	|	|	|	|	|	|	|	|	|	|	|	1658s	|	|	|	|	|	|	|	|	|	1806	|
Düsseldorf Hbf ... **910** d.	1524	1545	1545	1603	|	1618	|	1624	1644	|	|	1651r	1654	1707	|	1718	|	1724	1732	1745	1749	1806	|	1811	1818
Hagen Hbf ... d.	|	|	|	...	1523	|	1558	|	|	1609	1609	|	|	...	1623	|	1657	|	|	|	|	|	1723	...	|
Wuppertal Hbf ... d.	|	|	|	...	1540	|	1614	|	|	1630	1630	|	|	...	1640	|	1714	|	|	|	|	|	1740	...	|
Solingen Hbf ... d.	|	|	|	...	|	|	1626	|	|	|	|	|	|	...	|	|	1727	|	|	|	|	|	|	...	|
Köln Messe/Deutz ... a.	|	|	|	...	|	1642	|	|	1708	|	|	1716r	|	...	|	1742	|	|	|	|	|	|	|	...	1842
Köln Hbf ... **910** a.	1550	1613	1613	...	1609	|	1646	1650	|	1712	1712	|	1719	...	1709	|	1746	1749	1800	1813	1819	1832z	1809	...	|
Köln Hbf ... **910** d.	1553	1617	...	...	...	|	...	1653	|	1717	1717	|	...	...	1716q	|	1753	1755	▽	1817	...	...	...	...	|
Köln/Bonn Flugh. ✈ .. **910** a.	|	|	...	...	...	|	...	|	|	|	|	|	...	...	|	|	|	|	...	|	...	...	...	...	|
Bonn Hbf ... d.	1614	1637	...	...	...	|	...	1714	|	1738	1738	|	...	...	1736q	|	1814	|	...	1838	...	...	...	...	|
Remagen ... d.	|	1651	...	...	...	|	...	|	|	1752	1752	|	...	...	...	|	|	|	...	1851	...	...	...	...	|
Andernach ... d.	|	1704	...	...	...	|	...	|	|	1804	1804	|	...	...	...	|	|	|	...	1904	...	...	...	...	|
Koblenz Hbf ... d.	1648	1718	...	...	...	|	...	1748	|	1818	1818	|	...	...	...	|	1848	|	...	1916	...	...	...	...	|
Bingen (Rhein) Hbf ... d.	|	1753	...	...	...	|	...	|	|	1852	1852	|	...	...	...	|	|	|	...	...	...	...	...	...	|
Mainz Hbf ... a.	1739	1815	...	...	...	|	...	1839	|	1911	1911	|	...	...	...	|	1939	|	...	...	...	...	...	...	|
Frankfurt Flugh. ✈ § ... **910** a.	1759	|	...	...	...	1733	...	*1859**	1807	|	|	1817	...	...	...	1833	1959	1850	...	...	...	...	...	...	1933
Frankfurt (Main) Hbf ... **910** a.	1809•	|	...	...	...	1748	...	*1913**	|	|	|	1831	...	...	...	1848	2009•	|	...	...	...	...	...	...	1948
Nürnberg Hbf **920** ... a.	2028	|	...	...	...	2020	...	|	|	|	|	...	...	...	...	2120	2229	|	...	...	...	...	...	...	2220
Karlsruhe Hbf **912** ... a.	...	|	...	...	...	|	...	2016n	1913n	|	|	...	...	...	...	|	...	|	...	...	...	...	...	...	|
Basel SBB 🏛 **912** ... a.	...	|	...	...	...	|	...	|	|	|	|	...	...	...	...	|	...	|	...	...	...	...	...	...	|
Stuttgart Hbf **912** ... a.	...	1946	...	...	...	|	...	2023v	1922v	2046	2046	...	...	...	...	|	...	2008	...	...	...	...	...	...	|
München Hbf **904 930** ... a.	...	...	...	...	...	2132	...	...	...	...	...	...	...	...	...	2233	...	2226	...	...	...	...	...	...	2336

SEE NOTE ✣	IC 2440	IC 2213	ICE 1659	ICE 1548	ICE 129	ICE 1015	ICE 821	ICE 546	ICE 556	ICE 556	ICE 615	ICE 1021	ICE 1021		IC 2207	ICE 846	ICE 856	ICE 823	IC 2215	IC 2442	ICE 221	ICE 544	ICE 554	ICE 1154	ICE 1627
			Ⓑ	Ⓑ		Ⓑ				①–⑥		⑥⑦	①–⑤		E										
	D🍷	🍷◆	Q	G🍷	A✕	✕	✕	✕	✕	✕	✕	F✕	✕			H✕	✕	✕	W🍷	D🍷	A✕	✕	✕	✕	✕
Hamburg Altona ... d.	...	...	...	...	...	...	...	...	...	...	1529	...	1555	...	...	...	...	...	...	...	...	...	...	...	...
Hamburg Hbf ... **801** d.	...	1446	...	...	...	...	...	...	...	...	1546	1609	1610	...	...	...	...	...	1646	...	...	...	...	...	...
Bremen Hbf ... **801 815** d.	...	1544	...	...	...	...	...	...	...	...	1644	|	|	...	...	...	...	...	1744	...	...	...	...	...	...
Osnabrück Hbf ... **801 815** d.	...	1637	...	...	...	...	...	...	...	...	1737	|	|	...	...	...	...	...	1837	...	...	...	...	...	...
Münster (Westf) Hbf ... **801** d.	...	1703	...	...	...	...	...	...	...	...	1803	|	|	...	1832	...	...	...	1903	...	...	...	...	...	...
Berlin Hbf **810** ... d.	...	|	...	1358t	...	...	...	1446	1446	1446	|	|	|	...	|	1546	1546	...	|	...	...	1647	1647	1741	...
Leipzig Hbf **849a 866** d.	1238	|	...	|	...	...	...	|	|	|	|	|	|	...	|	|	|	...	|	1438	...	|	|	|	...
Hannover Hbf **810** ... d.	1540	|	...	1556	...	...	...	1631	1631	1631	|	|	|	...	|	1731	1731	...	|	1740	...	1831	1831	|	...
Hamm (Westf) ... **805** d.	1716	|	...	1726	...	...	...	1751	1754	1754	|	|	|	...	|	1851	1854	...	|	1916	...	1951	1954	|	...
Dortmund Hbf ... **805** a.	1733	|	...	|	...	...	...	1810	|	|	1833	|	|	...	|	1910	|	...	|	1933	...	2010	|	|	...
Dortmund Hbf ... d.	1736	|	...	|	...	1750	...	1812	|	|	1835	|	|	...	|	1912	|	...	|	1936	...	2012	|	|	2027
Bochum Hbf ... d.	|	|	...	|	...	1806	...	1824	|	|	|	|	|	...	|	1924	|	...	|	|	...	2024	|	|	|
Recklinghausen Hbf ... d.	|	|	...	|	...	|	...	|	|	|	|	|	|	...	1900	|	|	...	|	|	...	|	|	|	|
Wanne-Eickel Hbf ... d.	|	|	...	|	...	|	...	|	|	|	|	|	|	...	1909	|	|	...	|	|	...	|	|	|	|
Gelsenkirchen Hbf ... d.	|	1742	...	1813	...	|	...	|	|	|	|	|	|	...	1914	|	|	...	1943	|	...	|	|	|	|
Essen Hbf ... d.	|	1757	...	|	...	1824	1837	1842	|	|	|	1854	1854	...	|	1937	|	1941	1957	|	...	2037	|	|	|
Oberhausen Hbf ... d.	|	|	...	|	1826	|	|	|	|	|	|	|	|	...	1926	|	|	|	|	|	2026	|	|	|	|
Duisburg Hbf ... d.	|	1810	...	1827	1834	1837	1851	1855	|	|	|	1908	1908	...	1933	1951	|	1954	2010	|	2034	2050	|	|	|
Düsseldorf Flughafen ✈ ... d.	|	|	...	...	|	|	|	|	|	|	|	|	|	...	|	|	|	|	|	|	|	|	|	|	|
Düsseldorf Hbf ... **910** d.	|	1824	...	...	1848	1852	1905	1907	|	|	|	1923	1923	...	1948	2015	|	2008	2024	|	2050	2104	|	|	|
Hagen Hbf ... d.	1758	|	...	...	|	|	|	...	1823	1823	1857	|	|	...	|	...	1923	|	|	1958	|	|	2023	|	2057
Wuppertal Hbf ... d.	1814	|	...	...	|	|	|	...	1840	1840	1914	|	|	...	|	...	1940	|	|	2014	|	|	2040	|	2114
Solingen Hbf ... d.	1826	|	...	...	|	|	|	...	|	|	1927	|	|	...	|	...	|	|	|	2026	|	|	|	|	2127
Köln Messe/Deutz ... a.	|	|	...	...	1913	1920	1928	...	|	|	|	|	|	...	|	...	|	2031	|	|	2116	|	|	|	|
Köln Hbf ... **910** a.	1846	1850	...	...	|	|	|	...	1909	1909	1947	1950	1950	...	2015	...	2009	|	2050	2046	|	2132	2111	2141	2146
Köln Hbf ... **910** d.	...	1853	...	...	|	|	|	...	1912	1912	1955	1953	1953	...	...	...	...	|	2053	...	|	...	2117	2143e	2153
Köln/Bonn Flugh. ✈ .. **910** a.	...	|	...	...	|	|	|	...	|	|	|	|	|	...	...	...	...	|	|	...	|	...	|	|	|
Bonn Hbf ... d.	...	1914	...	...	|	|	|	...	1935	1937	|	2014	2014	...	...	...	...	|	2114	...	|	...	2142	2209	2214
Remagen ... d.	...	|	...	...	|	|	|	...	...	1951	|	|	|	...	...	...	...	|	|	...	|	...	...	...	|
Andernach ... d.	...	|	...	...	|	|	|	...	...	2004	|	|	|	...	...	...	...	|	|	...	|	...	...	...	|
Koblenz Hbf ... d.	...	1948	...	...	|	|	|	...	...	2016	|	2048	2048	...	...	...	...	|	2148	...	|	...	...	...	2248
Bingen (Rhein) Hbf ... d.	...	|	...	...	|	|	|	...	...	...	|	2123c	2123	...	...	...	...	|	|	...	|	...	...	...	|
Mainz Hbf ... a.	...	2039	2043	...	|	|	|	...	...	...	|	2142c	2142	...	...	...	...	|	2239b	...	|	...	...	...	2339b
Frankfurt Flugh. ✈ § ... **910** a.	...	|	2059	...	2015	2008	2035	...	...	...	2050	2159c	2159	...	...	...	...	2135	2259b	...	2217	...	...	...	2359b
Frankfurt (Main) Hbf ... **910** a.	...	|	2113	...	2030	|	2048	...	...	...	|	2213c	2213	...	...	...	...	2148	2312b	...	2231	...	...	...	0013b
Nürnberg Hbf **920** ... a.	...	|	...	...	...	|	2320	...	...	...	|	0042c	0042	...	...	...	...	...	...	...	...	...	...	...	...
Karlsruhe Hbf **912** ... a.	...	2206g	...	...	...	|	|	...	...	...	|	...	...	...	...	...	...	...	...	...	...	...	...	...	...
Basel SBB 🏛 **912** ... a.	...	|	...	...	...	|	|	...	...	...	|	...	...	...	...	...	...	...	...	...	...	...	...	...	...
Stuttgart Hbf **912** ... a.	...	2223h	...	...	...	2123	|	...	...	...	2208	...	...	...	...	...	...	...	...	...	...	...	...	...	...
München Hbf **904 930** ... a.	...	...	...	...	...	...	0039	...	...	...	0027	...	...	...	...	...	...	...	...	...	...	...	...	...	...

◆ – **NOTES** (LISTED BY TRAIN NUMBER)

929 – [12] ✕ Dortmund - Frankfurt - Nürnberg (- Regensburg - Passau ♣).
2152 – [12] Gera - Weimar - Kassel - Paderborn - Düsseldorf.
2213 – RÜGEN – [12] 🍷 Ostseebad Binz - Stralsund - Hamburg - Köln - Stuttgart / Karlsruhe.
2311 – NORDFRIESLAND – From Westerland (Table **821**).

A – From Amsterdam (Table **28**). Diversions / retimings are scheduled June 11, 12, 18, 19, Aug. 27 - Sept. 9 (different train numbers may apply).
D – From Dresden (Table **842**).
E – From Emden (Table **812**).
F – From Stralsund (Table **830**), also Ostseebad Binz on ⑥ (Table **844**).
G – KAROLINGER – To Krefeld Hbf (a. 1841), Viersen (a. 1853), Mönchengladbach Hbf (a. 1901), Rheydt Hbf (a. 1907), Herzogenrath (a. 1937) and Aachen Hbf (a. 1952).
H – Continues to Neuss Hbf (a. 2028) and Mönchengladbach Hbf (a. 2043); on ⑦ continues further to Aachen Hbf (a. 2144).
K – From Kiel (Table **820**).
N – From Norddeich Mole (Table **812**).
P – To Passau (Table **920**).

Q – To Erfurt (Table **850**).
U – To Tübingen (Table **930**). Train number **2017** from July 24.
W – From Westerland (Table **821**).

b – 16 – 20 minutes later on ①⑥⑦ until Aug. 29.
c – On ①⑥⑦ until Aug. 29 does not call at Bingen and runs 11 – 14 minutes later Mainz - Nürnberg.
e – 2145 on ⑦.
f – Also June 15.
g – ①②③④⑥ July 30 - Sept. 10.
h – Daily to July 29; ⑤⑦ July 31 - Sept. 9; daily from Sept. 11.
j – From June 25.
n – July 30 - Sept. 11 only.
q – ①②③④⑥ only.
r – On ⑥ departs Düsseldorf Hbf 1649, arrives Köln Messe/Deutz 1712.

s – Calls to set down only.
t – Until July 17.
v – Not July 30 - Sept. 11.
y – Until June 24.
z – ①②③④⑥.

¶ – Train number **1117** from July 22.
✣ – Timings Dortmund / Gelsenkirchen / Oberhausen - Düsseldorf - Köln may vary by up to 7 minutes until June 24. Berlin departures may be up to 4 minutes earlier until July 8.
* – Connecting *ICE* train (change trains at Mainz).
• – Frankfurt (Main) **Süd** (not Hbf).
▽ – To Düren (a. 1823) and Aachen Hbf (a. 1847).
♣ – See Table **920** for running dates to Regensburg and Passau.
§ – Frankfurt Flughafen ✈ Fernbahnhof.

800 HAMBURG - DORTMUND - KÖLN - KOBLENZ - FRANKFURT

	ICE	*IC*	*IC*	*IC*	*ICE*	*ICE*	*ICE*	*IC*	*IC*	*ICE*	*IC*	*ICE*	*ICE*	*ICE*	*NJ*	*ICE*		*ICE*	*ICE*		*IC*	*ICE*		*ICE*	*ICE*
SEE NOTE ✣	**617**	**2409**	**2409**	**2209**	**1107**	**844**	**854**	**2444**	**2307**	**750**	**1952**	**542**	**552**	**552**	**403**	**619**		**842**	**852**		**2446**	**919**		**840**	**921**
		⑦	①–⑥	E	⑥			Ⓑ		⑦	⑤⑦			⑦					⑦		⑤⑦			⑤–⑦	
	✕	L🍷	L🍷	N	N✕	✕	✕	D🍷	🍷	S✕	J	✕	✕	✕	C	K✕		✕	✕		D	✕			
Hamburg Altona d.	1729	...	...	...	...	...	...	...	1828	...	...	...	...	...	...	...	...	...	...	...	...	2029	...	...	2230
Hamburg Hbf **801** d.	1746	1808	1808	...	...	...	...	...	1846	...	...	...	...	...	...	1946	...	...	...	...	...	2046	...	...	2246
Bremen Hbf **801 815** d.	1844	│	│	...	...	...	...	...	1944	...	...	...	...	...	...	2044	...	...	...	...	...	2144	...	...	2344
Osnabrück Hbf **801 815** d.	1937	│	│	...	...	...	...	...	2037	...	...	...	...	...	...	2137	...	...	...	...	...	2237	...	...	0037
Münster (Westf) Hbf **801** d.	2003	│	│	2032	2031	...	...	...	2103	...	...	...	...	...	...	2203	...	...	...	...	...	2304	...	...	0104
Berlin Hbf **810** d.	│	│	│	│	│	1746	1746	...	│	1809●	...	1846	1846	1846	...	│	...	1946	1946	...	...	│	...	2120	│
Leipzig Hbf **849a 866** d.	│	│	│	│	│	│	│	1638	│	│	1635	│	│	│	...	│	...	│	│	...	1838	│	...	│	│
Hannover Hbf **810** d.	│	│	│	│	│	1931	1931	1940	│	1956	│	2031	2031	2031	...	│	...	2131	2131	...	2140	│	...	2331	│
Hamm (Westf) **805** d.	│	│	│	│	│	2051	2054	2116	│	2126	2140	2151	2154	2154	...	│	...	2251	2254	...	2316	│	...	0101	0124
Dortmund Hbf **805** a.	2033	│	│	│	│	2110	│	2133	│	2149	2157	2210	│	│	...	2233	...	2310	│	...	2333	│	...	0119	0143
Dortmund Hbf d.	2036	│	│	│	│	2112	│	2136	│	2151	2159	2212	│	│	...	2236	...	2312	│	...	2336	│	...	0121	0145
Bochum Hbf d.	2047	│	│	│	│	2124	│	│	│	2203	2211	2224	│	│	...	2248	...	2324	│	...	│	│	...	0133	0158
Recklinghausen Hbf d.	│	│	│	2100	2100	│	│	│	│	│	│	│	│	│	...	│	...	│	│	...	│	│	...	│	│
Wanne-Eickel Hbf d.	│	│	│	2109	2109	│	│	│	│	│	│	│	│	│	...	│	...	│	│	...	│	│	...	│	│
Gelsenkirchen Hbf d.	│	│	│	2114	2114	│	│	│	2143	│	│	│	│	│	...	│	...	│	│	...	│	2343	...	│	│
Essen Hbf d.	2100	2056	2054	│	│	2137	│	│	2157	2215	2225	2237	│	│	...	2301	...	2337	│	...	│	0000	...	0146	0209
Oberhausen Hbf d.	│	│	│	2127	2127	│	│	│	│	│	│	│	│	│	...	│	...	│	│	...	│	│	...	│	│
Duisburg Hbf d.	2113y	2109y	2114	2134	2134	2150	│	│	2210	2231	2240	2250	│	│	2301	2314y	...	2350	│	...	│	0013	...	0159	0221
Düsseldorf Flughafen ✈ d.	│	│	│	│	│	│	│	│	│	│	2250	│	│	│	│	│	...	0000	│	...	│	│	...	0209	0230
Düsseldorf Hbf **910** d.	2123	2119	2128	2149	2149	2205	│	│	2224	2245	2259	2305	│	│	2316	2324	...	0008	│	...	│	0027	...	0218	0239
Hagen Hbf d.	│	│	│	│	│	│	2123	2158	│	│	│	│	2223	2223	│	│	...	│	2323	...	2358	│	...	│	│
Wuppertal Hbf d.	│	│	│	│	│	│	2139	2214	│	│	│	│	2240	2240	│	│	...	│	2340	...	0014	│	...	│	│
Solingen Hbf d.	│	│	│	│	│	│	│	2226	│	│	│	│	2253	2253	│	│	...	│	│	...	0026	│	...	│	│
Köln Messe/Deutz a.	│	│	│	│	│	│	│	│	│	│	│	│	│	│	│	│	...	│	│	...	│	│	...	│	│
Köln Hbf **910** a.	2149	2145	2157	2215	2216	2232	2209	2245	2250	2316	2326	2331	2313	2313	2345	2349	...	0034	0011	...	0046	0053	...	0244	0307
Köln Hbf **910** d.	2155	...	...	...	...	...	...	...	2253	...	...	...	2320b	2320	2353	2355	...	...	...	...	...	...	...	...	0349
Köln/Bonn Flugh. ✈ **910** a.	│	...	...	...	...	...	...	...	│	...	...	...	│	│	│	│	...	...	...	...	...	...	...	...	│
Bonn Hbf d.	│	...	...	...	...	...	...	...	2315	...	...	...	2344b	2346	0014	│	...	...	...	...	...	...	...	...	0414
Remagen d.	│	...	...	...	...	...	...	...	2329	...	...	...	...	0004	│	│	...	...	...	...	...	...	...	...	0430
Andernach d.	│	...	...	...	...	...	...	...	2342	...	...	...	...	0018	│	│	...	...	...	...	...	...	...	...	│
Koblenz Hbf d.	│	...	...	...	...	...	...	...	2355	...	...	...	...	0031	0049	│	...	...	...	...	...	...	...	...	0530r
Bingen (Rhein) Hbf d.	│	...	...	...	...	...	...	...	...	...	...	...	...	...	│	│	...	...	...	...	...	...	...	...	0609
Mainz Hbf a.	│	...	...	...	...	...	...	...	...	...	...	...	...	...	0140z	│	...	...	...	...	...	...	...	...	0627
Frankfurt Flugh. ✈ § **910** a.	2254	...	...	...	...	...	...	...	...	...	...	...	...	...	0206z	0054	...	...	...	...	...	...	...	...	0646
Frankfurt (Main) Hbf **910** a.	│	...	...	...	...	...	...	...	...	...	...	...	...	...	0222z	0110	...	...	...	...	...	...	...	...	0702
Nürnberg Hbf **920** a.	│	...	...	...	...	...	...	...	...	...	...	...	...	...	│	│	...	...	...	...	...	...	...	...	...
Karlsruhe Hbf **912** a.	│	...	...	...	...	...	...	...	...	...	...	...	...	...	0401	│	...	...	...	...	...	...	...	...	...
Basel SBB 🏛 **912** a.	│	...	...	...	...	...	...	...	...	...	...	...	...	...	0620	│	...	...	...	...	...	...	...	...	...
Stuttgart Hbf **912** a.	0008	...	...	...	...	...	...	...	...	...	...	...	...	...	...	0334	...	...	...	...	...	...	...	...	...
München Hbf **904 930** a.	...	...	...	...	...	...	...	...	...	...	...	...	...	...	...	0603	...	...	...	...	...	...	...	...	...

C – 🛏 1, 2 cl. and 🛌 2 cl. (Ⓡ) Amsterdam - Zürich. Also conveys 🚗 (*IC* **60403**). Subject to alteration June 11, 12, 18, 19, Aug. 27 - Sept. 9.
D – From Dresden (Table **842**).
E – ③④⑤⑦ (also June 14).
J – ⑤⑦ (also June 15). 🚃12 Leipzig - Kassel - Paderborn - Köln.
K – From Kiel (Table **820**). ✕ Kiel - Köln.
L – From Lübeck Hbf (d. 1718).
N – From Norddeich Mole (Table **912**).

S – From Stralsund until July 17 (Table **845**). From July 24 runs as *ICE* **1130** and starts from Hannover Hbf (d. 1959).

b – Not ⑥.
r – Arrives 0458.
y – Until June 23.
z – 9–16 minutes later on the mornings of ①②⑦ until Aug. 30.

✣ – Timings Dortmund / Gelsenkirchen / Oberhausen - Düsseldorf - Köln may vary by up to 6 minutes until June 24. Berlin departures may be up to 4 minutes earlier until July 8.
● – Until July 17. Berlin **Spandau**.
§ – Frankfurt Flughafen Fernbahnhof.

801 Local services BREMEN - HAMBURG

See Table **800** for fast trains

BREMEN - HAMBURG and v.v. Operated by *metronom*. Journey time: 70–90 minutes. Trains call at **Rotenburg** (Wümme), 21–30 minutes from Bremen, 47–56 minutes from Hamburg. On Oct. 31 services run as on ⑦.

From Bremen Hbf at 0015 Ⓒ, 0115 Ⓒ, 0315 Ⓒ, 0432 Ⓐ, 0458, 0528 Ⓐ, 0558, 0626 Ⓐ, 0633 Ⓒ, 0658, 0733, 0758, 0833, 0858, 0933, 0958, 1033, 1058, 1133, 1159, 1233 1258 and at 33 and 58 minutes past each hour until 2033, 2058; then 2133 ⑤⑥ (also Oct. 2, 30), 2158 and 2312.

From Hamburg Hbf at 0057 Ⓒ, 0256 Ⓒ, 0457, 0537, 0558 Ⓐ, 0615 Ⓒ, 0637, 0715, 0737, 0815, 0837 and at 15 and 37 minutes past each hour until 2115, 2137; then 2237 and 2337.

802 RHEIN – RUHR LOCAL SERVICES

RE / *RB* services

SERVICE FROM JUNE 25. Services in this table (pages 372–375) are shown route by route. Sub-headings indicate the route number and principal stations served.

RE1 / *RE11* **Aachen - Köln - Düsseldorf - Dortmund - Hamm (- Paderborn - Kassel ⊕) ♣ ⊡** *RE6* **Köln - Düsseldorf - Bielefeld (- Minden) ♣ ⊡**

km		m	Ⓐtk		Ⓐt		k	m		k	m		k			m									
0	**Aachen** Hbf **807** d.	...	...	...	m	0451t	...	...	0551	...	...	0651	...	▲	...	...	1951	...	...	2053	...	2151	...	2251	2351
31	Düren **807** d.	...	...	...	...	0517t	...	...	0617	...	...	0717	...		...	...	2017	...	...	2117	...	2217	...	2317	0017
	Köln/Bonn Flug ✈ d.	...	...	0448	0448	│	...	0548	│	...	...	│	...		...	...	│	...	...	│	...	│	...	│	│
70	**Köln** Hbf **807** a.	...	...	0501	0501	0544t	...	0601	0644	...	...	0744	...		...	...	2043	...	...	2144	...	2244	...	2344	0044
70	**Köln** Hbf d.	...	...	0507	0507	0549	...	0607	0649	...	0707	0749	...	and at	...	2007	2049	...	2107	2149	2207	2249	2307	2349	0049
71	**Köln** Messe/Deutz d.	...	...	│	│	0552	...	│	0653	...	│	0752	...		...	│	2052	...	│	2152	│	2252	│	2353	0053
83	Leverkusen Mitte d.	...	...	│	│	0604	...	│	0704	...	│	0804	...	the same	...	│	2104	...	│	2204	│	2304	│	0004	0104
	Neuss Hbf d.	...	...	0536	0536	│	...	0636	│	...	0736	│	...		...	2036	│	...	2136	│	2236	│	2336	│	│
110	**Düsseldorf** Hbf a.	...	...	0549	0549	0619	...	0647	0719	...	0747	0819	...	minutes	...	2047	2119	...	2147	2219	2247	2319	2347	0019	0119
110	**Düsseldorf** Hbf d.	...	0536	▬	0554	0622	0636	0654	0722	0736	0754	0822	0836		2036	2054	2122	2136	2154	2222	2254	2322	2354	0022	0122
117	Düsseldorf Flug ✈ d.	...	0542	...	0602	0628	0642	0702	0728	0742	0802	0828	0842	past each	2042	2102	2128	2142	2202	2228	2302	2328	0002	0028	0128
134	**Duisburg** Hbf d.	...	0557	...	0615	0638	0657	0717	0738	0758	0815	0838	0857		2057	2115	2138	2156	2215	2238	2315	2338	0017	0038	0138
144	Mülheim (Ruhr) Hbf d.	...	0604	...	0621	0644	0704	0723	0745	0804	0821	0844	0904	hour until	2104	2121	2144	2203	2221	2244	2321	2344	0023	0044	0144
153	**Essen** Hbf d.	...	0613	Ⓒz	0629	0653	0713	0731	0752	0813	0829	0853	0913		2113	2129	2153	2213	2229	2253	2329	2353	0031	0053	0153
169	Bochum Hbf d.	...	0624	m	0642	0704	0724	0743	0803	0824	0842	0904	0924		2124	2142	2204	2226	2242	2304	2342	0004	0043	0104	0204
187	**Dortmund** Hbf d.	0555	0644‡	0655	0656	0717	0744‡	0755	0817	0844‡	0855	0917	0944‡		2144‡	2155	2217	2238	2255	2317	2354	0017	0055	0117	0217
218	**Hamm** (Westf) **810** d.	0615	...	0715	0715	0741	...	0815	0841	...	0915	0939	...		...	2215	2241	...	2315	2343	...	0042	...	0141z	0242
268	Gütersloh Hbf **810** d.	0649	...	0749	0749	...	...	0849	...	...	0949	...	...		...	2249	...	...	2349	...	...	...	...	...	...
285	**Bielefeld** Hbf **810** a.	0658	...	0758	0758	...	...	0858	...	...	0958	...	...		...	2258	...	...	0001	...	...	...	...	...	...

					Ⓐt¶		⚒r¶		m	Ⓒz	Ⓐtk		m	k			m	k		m		m		⑤⑥f	m
Bielefeld Hbf **810** d.	...	...	...	...	...	...	0459	...	0559	...	...	...	0659	...	▲	...	1959	...	...	2059	...	2159	...	...	2259
Gütersloh Hbf **810** d.	...	...	...	...	...	...	0508	...	0608	...	...	...	0708	...		...	2011	...	...	2108	...	2208	...	...	2308
Hamm (Westf) **810** d.	0018z	...	0318	0418	...	0518	0544	0618c	0644	0645	...	0720	0744	...		2020	2047	...	2120	2144	2218	2244	2319	2319	2344
Dortmund Hbf d.	0046	...	0346	0446	0507	0546	0607	0646	0707	0710‡	0711‡	0746	0807	0811‡		2046	2107	2111‡	2146	2207	2246	2307	2346	2346	0007
Bochum Hbf d.	0057	...	0357	0457	0519	0557	0619	0657	0719	0736	0736	0757	0819	0833	and at	2057	2119	2133	2157	2219	2257	2319	2357	2357	0019
Essen Hbf d.	0110	...	0410	0510	0532	0610	0632	0710	0732	0749	0749	0810	0832	0847		2110	2132	2147	2210	2232	2310	2332	0010	0010	0032
Mülheim (Ruhr) Hbf d.	0116	...	0416	0516	0538	0616	0638	0716	0738	0756	0756	0816	0838	0853	the same	2116	2138	2153	2216	2238	2316	2338	0016	0016	0038
Duisburg Hbf d.	0123	...	0423	0523	0548	0623	0648	0723	0748	0807	0807	0823	0848	0907		2123	2148	2207	2223	2248	2323	2348	0023	0023	0048
Düsseldorf Flug ✈ d.	0132	...	0432	0532	0557	0632	0657	0732	0757	0816	0816	0832	0857	0916	minutes	2132	2157	2216	2232	2257	2332	2357	0032	0032	0057
Düsseldorf Hbf a.	0137	...	0437	0537	0605	0637	0705	0737	0805	0824	0824	0837	0905	0924		2137	2205	2224	2237	2305	2337	0005	0037	0037	0105
Düsseldorf Hbf d.	0139	0413	0439	0539	0613	0640	0713	0740	0813	...	...	0840	0913	...	past each	2140	2213	...	2239	2313	2339	...	...	0039	...
Neuss Hbf d.	│	0425	│	│	0624	│	0724	│	0824	...	...	│	0924	...		│	2224	...	│	2324	│	...	...	│	...
Leverkusen Mitte d.	0155	│	0455	0555	│	0655	│	0755	│	...	...	0855	│	...	hour until	2155	│	...	2255	│	2355	...	...	0055	...
Köln Messe/Deutz d.	0209	│	0509	0609	│	0708	│	0809	│	...	...	0909	│	...		2208	│	...	2308	│	0009	...	...	0109	...
Köln Hbf a.	0212	0455	0512	0612	0652	0712	0751	0812	0852	...	...	0912	0952	...		2212	2253	...	2312	2352	0012	...	...	0112	...
Köln Hbf **807** d.	0215z	0458	0515t	0615	...	0715	...	0815	...	...	...	0915	...	...		2215	...	...	2315	...	0015	...	...	0115	...
Köln/Bonn Flug ✈ a.	│	0511	│	│	...	│	...	│	...	...	...	│	...	...		│	...	...	│	...	│	...	...	│	...
Düren **807** d.	0239z	...	0539t	0639	...	0739	...	0839	...	...	...	0939	...	...		2239	...	...	2341	...	0039	...	...	0140	...
Aachen Hbf **807** a.	0307z	...	0607t	0707	...	0807	...	0907	...	...	...	1007	...	...		2307	...	...	0009	...	0108	...	...	0207	...

FOR NOTES SEE NEXT PAGE →

RE / RB services **RHEIN–RUHR LOCAL SERVICES** **802**

Services in this table (pages 372–375) are shown route by route. Sub-headings indicate the route number and principal stations served.

RE2 Düsseldorf - Essen - Gelsenkirchen - Münster ⊡ *RE42* Mönchengladbach - Essen - Münster

km			⚒r	⚒r	⚒r																	◇		
0	**Düsseldorf** Hbf d.	0006	...	0506	...	0606r	...	0706	...	0806	...	0906	●	...	1906	...	2006	...	2106	...	2206	...	...	2306
7	Düsseldorf Flughafen ✈ d.	0013	...	0513	...	0613r	...	0713	...	0813	...	0913		...	1913	...	2013	...	2113	...	2213	...	...	2313
	Mönchengladbach d.	│	...	│	0522	│	0622	│	0722	│	0822	│		1822	│	1922	│	2022	│	2122	│	...	2222	│
	Viersen d.	│	...	│	0531	│	0631	│	0731	│	0831	│	and at	1831	│	1931	│	2031	│	2131	│	...	2231	│
	Krefeld Hbf d.	│	...	│	0541	│	0641	│	0741	│	0841	│		1841	│	1941	│	2041	│	2141	│	...	2241	│
24	**Duisburg** Hbf d.	0024	...	0524	0602	0624r	0702	0724	0802	0824	0902	0924	the same	1902	1926	2002	2024	2102	2124	2202	2224	...	2302	2324j
34	Mülheim (Ruhr) Hbf d.	0030	...	0530	0609	0630r	0709	0730	0809	0830	0909	0930	minutes	1909	1933	2009	2030	2109	2130	2209	2230	...	2309	2330j
43	**Essen** Hbf d.	0046	0446	0541	0617	0641	0717	0741	0817	0841	0917	0941	past each	1917	1941	2017	2041	2117	2141	2217	2241	...	2317	2346
53	Gelsenkirchen Hbf d.	0054	0455	0550	0626	0650	0726	0750	0826	0850	0926	0950	hour until	1926	1950	2026	2050	2126	2150	2226	2250	...	2326	2354
58	Wanne-Eickel Hbf d.	0100	0500	0556	0631	0656	0731	0756	0831	0856	0931	0956		1931	1956	2031	2056	2131	2156	2231	2256	...	2331	0000
68	Recklinghausen Hbf d.	0109	0509	0604	0639	0704	0739	0804	0839	0904	0939	1004		1939	2004	2039	2104	2139	2204	2239	2304	...	2339	0009
84	Haltern am See d.	0120	0519	0613	0650	0713	0750	0813	0850	0913	0950	1013		1950	2013	2050	2113	2151	2213	2251	2313	...	2351	0020
97	Dülmen d.	0129	0528	0620	0659	0720	0759	0820	0859	0920	0959	1020		1959	2020	2059	2120	...	2220	...	2320	...	...	0029
126	**Münster** (Westf) Hbf ★ d.	0153	0550	0637	0722	0737	0822	0837	0922	0937	1022	1037		2022	2037	2122	2137	...	2237	...	2335	0003	...	0053
176	**Osnabrück** Hbf ★ a.	...	...	0711	...	0819	...	0910	...	1015	...	1111		...	2110	...	2215	...	2310e	...	...	0039	...	...

		Ⓐt	⚒r	⚒r	⚒r																	⑤⑥f	
Osnabrück Hbf ★ d.	...	...	...	...	...	...	0545y	...	0648	...	0748	...	0849	♥	...	1948	...	2049	...	...	2145	...	...	...
Münster (Westf) Hbf ★ d.	0209	...	0425	...	0525	0536t	0625	0636r	0725	0736r	0825	0836	0925		1936	2025	2036	2125	...	2209	2222	2309	2309	0007
Dülmen d.	0232	...	0439	...	0539	0558t	0639	0658r	0739	0758r	0839	0858	0939		1958	2039	2058	2139	...	2232	...	2332	2332	0029
Haltern am See d.	0242	...	0446	0507	0546	0607	0646	0707	0746	0807	0846	0907	0946		2007	2046	2107	2146	2207	2242	...	2342	2342	0039
Recklinghausen Hbf d.	0255	...	0455	0519	0555	0619	0655	0719	0755	0819	0855	0919	0955	and at	2019	2055	2119	2155	2219	2255	...	2355	2355	0050
Wanne-Eickel Hbf d.	0304	...	0503	0528	0603	0628	0703	0728	0803	0828	0903	0928	1003	the same	2028	2103	2128	2203	2228	2304	...	0004	0004	0059
Gelsenkirchen Hbf d.	0309	...	0509	0533	0609	0633	0709	0733	0809	0833	0909	0933	1009	minutes	2033	2109	2133	2209	2233	2309	...	0009	0009	0104
Essen Hbf d.	0321	...	0521	0545	0621	0645	0721	0745	0821	0845	0921	0945	1021	past each	2045	2121	2145	2221	2245	2321	...	0019	0021	0114
Mülheim (Ruhr) Hbf d.	0327	...	0527	0552	0627	0652	0727	0752	0827	0852	0927	0952	1027	hour until	2052	2127	2152	2227	2252	2327	...	...	0027	...
Duisburg Hbf d.	0336	0505	0536	0601	0636	0701	0736	0801	0836	0901	0936	1001	1036		2101	2136	2201	2236	2301	2336	...	...	0036	...
Krefeld Hbf d.	│	0530	│	0618	│	0718	│	0818	│	0918	│	1018	│		2118	│	2218	│	2318	│	...	...	│	...
Viersen d.	│	0543	│	0633	│	0733	│	0833	│	0933	│	1033	│		2133	│	2233	│	2333	│	...	...	│	...
Mönchengladbach a.	│	0551	│	0642	│	0742	│	0842	│	0942	│	1042	│		2142	│	2242	│	2342	│	...	...	│	...
Düsseldorf Flughafen ✈ d.	0346	...	0546	...	0646	...	0746	...	0846	...	0946	...	1046		...	2146	...	2246	...	2346	...	...	0046	...
Düsseldorf Hbf a.	0353	...	0553	...	0653	...	0753	...	0853	...	0953	...	1053		...	2153	...	2253	...	2353	...	...	0053	...

RE3 Düsseldorf - Duisburg - Gelsenkirchen - Dortmund - Hamm ⊡ ◇

km											
0	**Düsseldorf** Hbf d.	0445	0545	0645	❖	1845	1945	2045	2145	2245	2345
7	Düsseldorf Flughafen ✈ d.	0453	0553	0653		1853	1953	2053	2153	2253	2353
24	**Duisburg** Hbf d.	0510	0610	0710	and	1910	2010	2110	2210	2310	0010
32	Oberhausen Hbf d.	0516	0616	0716	hourly	1916	2016	2116	2216	2316	0016
48	Gelsenkirchen Hbf d.	0529	0629	0729	until	1929	2029	2129	2229	2329	0029
53	Wanne-Eickel Hbf d.	0534	0634	0734		1934	2034	2134	2234	2334	0034
57	Herne d.	0538	0638	0738		1938	2038	2138	2238	2338	0038
78	**Dortmund** Hbf a.	0557	0702	0757		1957	2057	2157	2257	2357	0057
109	**Hamm** (Westf) a.	0629t	0729r	0829		2029	...	...	...	...	...

Hamm (Westf) d.	...	0530t	0630t	0730r	0830		2030	...	...
Dortmund Hbf d.	0503	0603	0703	0803	0903		2103	2203	2303
Herne d.	0519	0619	0719	0819	0919	and	2119	2219	2319
Wanne-Eickel Hbf d.	0524	0624	0724	0824	0924	hourly	2124	2224	2324
Gelsenkirchen Hbf d.	0529	0629	0729	0829	0929	until	2129	2229	2329
Oberhausen Hbf d.	0543	0643	0743	0843	0943		2143	2243	2343
Duisburg Hbf d.	0553	0653	0753	0853	0953		2153	2253	2353
Düsseldorf Flughafen d.	0604	0704	0804	0904	1004		2204	2304	0004
Düsseldorf Hbf a.	0612	0712	0812	0912	1012		2212	2312	0012

RE4 Aachen - Mönchengladbach - Düsseldorf - Wuppertal - Dortmund ⊡ *RE13* Venlo - Mönchengladbach - Düsseldorf - Wuppertal - Hamm ◇ ⊡

km	SEE NOTE ❦		Ⓐt	⚒r	Ⓐt	⚒r	⚒r		⚒r															
0	**Aachen** Hbf 473 d.	0253	0422	0422	...	...	0522	0522	...	0622	...		1722	...	1822	...	1922	...	2022	...	2122	...	2237	2337
14	Herzogenrath 473 d.	0307	0438	0438	...	...	0538	0538	...	0638	...	⊖	1738	...	1838	...	1938	...	2038	...	2138	...	2253	2352
58	Rheydt Hbf d.	0343	0508	0508	...	...	0608	0608	...	0708	...		1808	...	1908	...	2008	...	2108	...	2208	...	2332	0032
	Venlo 🏛 d.	│	│	│	0505	0505	│	│	0605	│	0705	and at	│	1805	│	1905	│	2005	│	2105	│	2205	│	│
	Kaldenkirchen d.	│	│	│	0510	0510	│	│	0610	│	0710		│	1810	│	1910	│	2010	│	2110	│	2210	│	│
	Viersen d.	│	│	│	0527	0527	│	│	0627	│	0727	the same	│	1827	│	1927	│	2027	│	2127	│	2227	│	│
62	**Mönchengladbach** Hbf a.	0348	0512	0512	0536	0536	0612	0612	0636	0712	0736		1812	1836	1912	1936	2012	2036	2112	2136	2212	2236	2337	0037
62	**Mönchengladbach** Hbf d.	0350	0513	0513	0545	0545	0613	0613	0645	0713	0745	minutes	1813	1845	1913	1945	2013	2045	2113	2145	2213	...	...	...
79	Neuss Hbf d.	0403	0528	0528	0557	0557	0628	0628	0657	0728	0757		1828	1857	1928	1957	2028	2057	2128	2157	2228	...	...	...
90	**Düsseldorf** Hbf a.	0413	0539	0539	0609	0609	0639	0639	0709	0739	0809	past each	1839	1909	1939	2009	2039	2109	2139	2209	2239	...	...	...
90	**Düsseldorf** Hbf ❦ d.	d	0542	...	0612	...	0642	...	0712	0742	0812		1842	1912	1942	2012	2042	...	2142	...	2242	...	...	...
117	**Wuppertal** Hbf ❦ d.	...	0602	...	0632	...	0702	...	0732	0802	0832	hour until	1902	1932	2002	2032	2102	...	2202	...	2302	...	...	...
144	**Hagen** Hbf 804 d.	...	0627	...	0701	...	0727	...	0758	0827	0858		1927	1958	2027	2055	2127	...	2227	...	2327	...	...	...
159	Witten Hbf d.	...	0641	...	│	...	0741	...	│	0841	│		1941	│	2041	...	2141	...	2241	...	2341	...	...	...
175	**Dortmund** Hbf d.	...	0650	...	│	...	0750	...	│	0850	│		1950	│	2050	...	2150	...	2250	...	2350	...	...	...
	Schwerte 804 d.	...	...	...	0711	...	...	...	0808	...	0908		...	2008	...	...	...	...	...	...	...	...	...	...
	Unna d.	...	...	...	0722	...	...	...	0820	...	0920		...	2020	...	...	...	...	...	...	...	...	...	...
	Hamm (Westf) a.	...	...	...	0734	...	...	...	0834	...	0934		...	2036	...	...	...	...	...	...	...	...	...	...

km	SEE NOTE ❦	⚒r	Ⓐt	⚒r	⚒r		Ⓒz	Ⓐt	⚒r			⚒r											
0	**Hamm** (Westf) d.	...	...	...	...	...	...	...	0625	...	...	0725	...	...	0822b	...	0925		...	1925	...	...	...	...
19	Unna d.	...	...	...	...	...	...	...	0637	...	...	0737	...	...	0834b	...	0937	⊗	...	1937	...	...	...	...
35	Schwerte 804 d.	...	...	...	...	...	...	...	0649	...	...	0749	...	...	0850b	...	0949		...	1949	...	...	...	...
	Dortmund Hbf d.	...	...	...	...	...	...	0610	│	...	0710r	│	...	0810	│	0910	│	and at	1910	│	2010	...	2110	2210
	Witten Hbf d.	...	...	...	...	...	...	0620	│	...	0720r	│	...	0820	│	0920	│		1920	│	2020	...	2120	2220
48	**Hagen** Hbf 804 d.	...	...	...	...	0602t	...	0634	0702	...	0734r	0802	0802	0834	0902	0934	1002	the same	1934	2002	2034	...	2134	2234
75	**Wuppertal** Hbf ❦ d.	...	...	...	...	0625t	...	0658	0725	...	0758r	0825	0825	0858	0925	0958	1025		1958	2025	2058	...	2158	2258
102	**Düsseldorf** Hbf ❦ a.	...	...	...	...	0646t	...	0718	0746	...	0818r	0846	0846	0918	0946	1018	1046	minutes	2018	2046	2118	...	2218	2318
102	**Düsseldorf** Hbf d.	...	0521	0548	0621	0648r	0721	0721	0748	0748	0821	0848	0848	0921	0948	1021	1048		2022	2048	2121	2148	2221	2321
113	Neuss Hbf d.	...	0536	0601	0636	0701r	0736	0736	0801	0801	0836	0901	0901	0936	1001	1036	1101	past each	2038	2101	2136	2201	2236	2336
130	**Mönchengladbach** Hbf a.	...	0548	0611	0648	0711r	0748	0748	0811	0811	0848	0911	0911	0948	1011	1048	1111		2048	2111	2148	2211	2248	2348
130	**Mönchengladbach** Hbf d.	0525	0550	0625	0650	0725	0750	0750	0825	0825	0850	0925	0925	0950	1025	1050	1125	hour until	2050	2125	2150	2225	2250	2350
139	Viersen d.	0533	│	0633	│	0733	│	│	0833	0833	│	0933	0933	│	1033	│	1133		│	2133	│	2233	│	│
157	Kaldenkirchen d.	0551	│	0651	│	0751	│	│	0851	0851	│	0951	0951	│	1051	│	1151		│	2151	│	2251	│	│
167	**Venlo** 🏛 a.	0556	│	0656	│	0756	│	│	0856	0856	│	0956	0956	│	1056	│	1156		│	2156	│	2256	│	│
	Rheydt Hbf d.	...	0554	...	0654	...	0754	0754	...	...	0854	...	...	0954	...	1054	...		2054	...	2154	...	2254	2354
	Herzogenrath 473 d.	...	0623	...	0723	...	0823	0823	...	...	0923	...	...	1023	...	1123	...		2123	...	2223	...	2323	0023
	Aachen Hbf 473 a.	...	0643	...	0743p	...	0837	0843	...	...	0943h	...	...	1043h	...	1143	...		2142	...	2243n	...	2337	0037

b – On Oct. 2, 30 Hamm d. 0825, Unna d. 0837, Schwerte d. 0849.
c – 0620 on Ⓐ (not June 16, Nov. 1).
d – To Düsseldorf Flughafen Terminal (a. 0425).
e – ⑤⑥ (also June 15, Oct. 2, 30, 31).
f – ⑤⑥ (also June 15, Oct. 2, 31).
h – 6 minutes earlier on Ⓒ (also June 16, Nov. 1).
j – On ⑦ (also Oct. 3, Nov. 1; not Oct. 2, 30) Duisburg d. 2329, Mülheim d. 2336.
k – To / from stations in Table **805**.
m – To / from Minden (Table **811**).
n – 2237 on Ⓐ (not June 16, Nov. 1).
p – 0737 on ⑥.
r – ⚒ (not June 16, Nov. 1).
t – Ⓐ (not June 16, Nov. 1).
y – ⚒ only.
z – Ⓒ (also June 16, Nov. 1).

‡ – Dortmund **Hörde**.
¶ – Runs daily Düsseldorf - Köln.
▲ – Timings may vary by up to 3 minutes (earlier departures possible).

● – Certain Duisburg and Mülheim timings vary by up to 3 minutes. Osnabrück arrivals vary – subsequent arrivals are at 1219, 1310, 1419, 1510, 1615 (1619 on ⑤†), 1711, 1819, 1910 and 2019.
♥ – Osnabrück departures vary – subsequent departures are at 0947, 1047, 1145, 1249, 1347, 1449, 1547, 1649, 1747 and 1849.
⊖ – Timings of the 1105 and 1705 from Venlo vary by 1–2 minutes between Hagen and Hamm except on Oct. 2, 30 when the regular pattern is followed.
⊗ – Hamm d. 1422 (not 1425) / Unna d. 1434 (not 1437) except on Oct. 2, 30 when the regular pattern is followed.
❖ – The 0945, 1345 and 1745 from Düsseldorf arrive Dortmund Hbf 5 minutes later.
❦ – The direct rail service Düsseldorf - Wuppertal and v.v. is suspended June 25 - Aug. 5 (normal timings apply either side of the blockade).
◇ – Operated by *eurobahn*.
♣ – Operated by National Express.
⊕ – See Table **805** for timings to / from Paderborn and Kassel.
⊡ – See shaded panel on page 375 for a summary of the principal Rhein-Ruhr *RE* routes.
★ – Additional trains (◇) Münster - Osnabrück and v.v. (journey time 36 minutes):
From Münster at 0503 Ⓐ, 0603 ⚒, 0703 and hourly until 2303.
From Osnabrück at 0519 Ⓐ, 0619 ⚒, 0719 and hourly until 2119; then 2217 and 2319.

802 RHEIN – RUHR LOCAL SERVICES *RE / RB services*

RE5 Koblenz - Bonn - Köln - Düsseldorf - Duisburg - Wesel ♣ ⊡ *RE19* Düsseldorf - Emmerich - Arnhem ⊙

km				⚒r◐	⚒r	Ⓐt		◐		⚒r									h	⑤⑥f				◐
0	**Koblenz** Hbf d.	...	...	0426	...	0516	...	0526	...	0616	...	0716	...		1916	...	2016	...	2116	2116	...	2216	...	2326c
18	Andernach d.	...	...	0444	...	0528	...	0544	...	0628	...	0728	...		1928	...	2028	...	2128	2128	...	2228	...	2344
29	Bad Breisig d.	...	...	0454	...	0534	...	0554	...	0634	...	0734	...	and at	1934	...	2034	...	2134	2134	...	2234	...	2354
39	Remagen d.	...	...	0511j	...	0544	...	0611j	...	0644	...	0744	...		1944	...	2044	...	2144	2144	...	2244	...	0011j
59	**Bonn** Hbf d.	...	...	0533	...	0604	...	0633	...	0704	...	0804	...	the same	2004	...	2104	...	2204	2204	...	2304	...	0033
93	**Köln** Hbf d.	...	...	0602a	0631	0631	...	0702a	0731	0731	...	0831	...		2031	...	2131	...	2228a	2231	...	2328a	2349	0102a
94	**Köln** Messe/Deutz d.	...	...	0608	0634	0634	...	0710	0734	0734	...	0834	...	minutes	2034	...	2134	...	2233	2234	...	2334	2353	0108
106	Leverkusen Mitte d.	...	...	...	0645	0645	...	...	0745	0745	...	0845	...		2045	...	2145	...	...	2245	...	...	0004	▬
133	**Düsseldorf** Hbf d.	...	0626	...	0703	0703	0726	...	0803	0803	0826	0903	0926	past each	2103	2126	2203	2226	...	2303	2326	...	0022	...
140	Düsseldorf Flughafen ✈ d.	...	0633	...	0709	0709	0733	...	0809	0809	0833	0909	0933		2109	2133	2209	2233	...	2309	2333	...	0028	...
157	**Duisburg** Hbf d.	0544	0646	...	0720	0720	0744	...	0820	0820	0843	0920	0944	hour until	2120	2144	2220	2244	...	2318	2344	...	0036	0044
165	Oberhausen Hbf d.	0550	0652	...	0727	0727	0752	...	0827	0827	0850	0927	0950		2127	2150	2227	2250	...	...	2350	...	...	0050
192	Wesel d.	0616	0716	...	0756	0756	0816	...	0853	0853	0916	0955	1016		2155	2216	2254	2316	...	...	0016	...	...	0116
226	**Emmerich** 🏛 d.	0646b	0746	...	...	...	0846	...	...	...	0946	...	1046		...	2246	2316h	2346	...	...	0045	...	...	0145
256	**Arnhem** Centraal a.	0713b	0813	...	...	...	0913	...	...	...	1013	...	1113		...	2313	...	0013	...	...	...	...	...	...

	Ⓐt	◐		⚒r	◐			⚒r						▽						◐				
Arnhem Centraal d.	...	...	...	...	...	...	...	...	0545r	...	0645	...	0745	...		1845	...	1945	...	...	2045	2145	...	2245
Emmerich 🏛 d.	...	...	0409	...	...	0509	...	0539t	0609	...	0709	...	0809	...		1909	...	2008	...	...	2109	2209	...	2309
Wesel d.	...	...	0443	0506t	...	0543	...	0606	0643	0706	0743	0811	0843	0906	and at	1943	2011	2043	2111	...	2143	2243	...	2343
Oberhausen Hbf d.	...	...	0508	0533t	...	0608	...	0633	0708	0733	0808	0833	0908	0933		2008	2033	2108	2133	...	2208	2308	...	0008
Duisburg Hbf d.	...	...	0516	0542	...	0616	...	0642	0716	0742	0816	0842	0916	0942	the same	2016	2042	2116	2142	...	2216	2315	2323	0015
Düsseldorf Flughafen ✈ d.	...	...	0525	0550	...	0625	...	0650	0725	0750	0825	0850	0925	0950		2025	2050	2125	2150	...	2225	▬	2332	...
Düsseldorf Hbf d.	...	...	0533	0558	...	0633	...	0658	0733	0758	0833	0858	0933	0958	minutes	2033	2058	2133	2158	...	2233	...	2339	...
Leverkusen Mitte d.	...	...	...	0614	...	...	...	0714	...	0814	...	0915	...	1014		...	2115	...	2215	...	...	◐	2355	...
Köln Messe/Deutz d.	0526	0542	...	0626	0650	...	0726	0726	...	0826	...	0926	...	1026	past each	...	2126	...	2226	2250	...	2350	0009	...
Köln Hbf d.	0532	0556	...	0632	0656	...	0732	0732	...	0832	...	0932	...	1032		...	2132	...	2232	2256	...	2356	0012	...
Bonn Hbf d.	0556	0627	...	0656	0727	...	0756	0756	...	0856	...	0956	...	1056	hour until	...	2156	...	2256	2327	...	0027	...	...
Remagen d.	0615	0654j	...	0716	0754j	...	0816	0816	...	0916	...	1016	...	1116		...	2216	...	2316	2354j	...	0054j	...	...
Bad Breisig d.	0622	0702	...	0723	0802	...	0823	0823	...	0923	...	1023	...	1123		...	2223	...	2323	0002	...	0102	...	...
Andernach d.	0629	0712	...	0730	0813	...	0830	0830	...	0930	...	1030	...	1130		...	2230	...	2330	0012	...	0112	...	...
Koblenz Hbf a.	0642	0727	...	0742	0828	...	0842	0842	...	0942	...	1042	...	1142		...	2242	...	2342	0032	...	0132	...	...

RE7 Krefeld - Köln - Wuppertal - Hagen - Hamm - Münster (- Rheine: Table 812) ♣ ⊡

km		Ⓐt								⑤⑥f	
0	**Krefeld** Hbf d.	...	...	0535r	0635		2035	2135	2235	2235	...
18	Neuss Hbf d.	...	...	0553r	0653		2053	2153	2253	2253	...
54	**Köln** Hbf d.	...	0521t	0621r	0721	and	2121	2221	2318	2321	2352
55	**Köln** Messe/Deutz d.	...	0524t	0625r	0724		2124	2224	...	2324	2355
82	Solingen Hbf d.	...	0543t	0643r	0743	hourly	2143	2243	...	2343	0020
100	**Wuppertal** Hbf d.	...	0556t	0656r	0756		2156	2256	...	2356	0036
127	**Hagen** Hbf d.	0522	0622	0722	0822	until	2222	2322	...	0022	...
140	Schwerte (Ruhr) 808 d.	0533	0633	0733	0833		2233	2333	...	0033	...
156	Unna 808 d.	0544	0644	0744	0844		2244	2344	...	0044	...
175	**Hamm** (Westf) 805/8 d.	0559	0659	0759	0859		2259	2357	...	0057	...
211	**Münster** Hbf 805/8 a.	0622	0722	0822	0922		2322	...	...	...	...

	Ⓐt	⚒e						⑤⑥f		⑤⑥f
Münster Hbf 805/8 d.	...	...	0529t	0634		2034	2134	2134	2234	2234
Hamm (Westf) 805/8 d.	...	0500	0600	0700		2100	2200	2200	2300	2300
Unna 808 d.	...	0513	0613	0713	and	2113	2213	2213	2313	2313
Schwerte (Ruhr) 808 d.	...	0525	0625	0725		2125	2225	2225	2325	2325
Hagen Hbf d.	0439	0539	0639	0739	hourly	2139	2236	2239	2336	2339
Wuppertal Hbf d.	0504	0604	0704	0804		2204	▬	2304	...	0002
Solingen Hbf d.	0515	0615	0715	0815	until	2215	...	2315	...	...
Köln Messe/Deutz d.	0535	0635	0735	0835		2233	...	2335	...	...
Köln Hbf d.	0542	0642	0742	0842	✣	2242	2342	2342	...	...
Neuss Hbf d.	0607	0707	0807	0907		2307	0007	0007	...	...
Krefeld Hbf a.	0624	0724	0824	0924		2324	0024	0024	...	...

Düsseldorf - Krefeld - Kleve ⊖

km		Ⓐt	⚒r	Ⓐt		Ⓐt			♥	
0	**Düsseldorf** Hbf d.	0538	0608	0638	0708	0738	0808	0908		2308
27	**Krefeld** Hbf d.	0606	0636	0706	0736	0806	0836	0936	and	2336
57	Geldern d.	0632	0702	0732	0802	0832	0902	1002		0002
66	Kevelaer d.	0638	0708	0738	0808	0838	0908	1008	hourly	0008
72	Weeze d.	0647	0717	0747	0817	0847	0917	1017		0017
79	Goch d.	0653	0723	0753	0823	0853	0923	1023	until	0023
92	**Kleve** a.	0705	0735	0805	0835	0905	0935	1035		0035

	Ⓐt	⚒r	Ⓐt		Ⓐt				⑤⑥f
Kleve d.	0426	0525	0551	0625	0651	0721		2221	2351
Goch d.	0439	0538	0608	0638	0708	0738	and	2238	0008
Weeze d.	0445	0545	0615	0645	0715	0745		2245	0015
Kevelaer d.	0451	0551	0621	0651	0721	0751	hourly	2251	0021
Geldern d.	0458	0558	0628	0658	0728	0758		2258	0028
Krefeld Hbf d.	0526	0626	0656	0726	0756	0826	until	2326	0056
Düsseldorf Hbf a.	0553	0653	0723	0753	0823	0853		2353	0123

RE8 / RB27 Mönchengladbach - Köln - Königswinter - Koblenz

km		⚒d	⑥	Ⓐt		Ⓒz	Ⓐt		Ⓒz	Ⓐt		†z	⚒r			†z	⚒r					⑤⑥f		⑤⑥f
0	**Mönchengladbach** Hbf d.	0441	...	0507	0541	0607k	0607	0641	0707k	0707	0741	...	0807	0841	⊠	...	2007	2041	...	2141	2241	2241	2341	2341
3	Rheydt Hbf d.	0446	...	0512	0546	0612k	0612	0646	0712k	0712	0746	...	0812	0846		...	2012	2046	...	2146	2246	2246	2346	2346
22	Grevenbroich d.	0503	...	0529	0603	0629k	0629	0703	0729k	0729	0803	...	0829	0903	and at	...	2029	2103	...	2203	2303	2303	0003	0003
56	**Köln** Hbf a.	0535	...	0600	0635	0700k	0700	0735	0800k	0800	0835	...	0900	0935		...	2100	2135	...	2234	2335	2335	0035	0035
56	**Köln** Hbf 807 d.	0538	0602	0603	0638	0702	0703	0738	0802	0803	0838	0902	0903	0938	the same	2102	2103	2138	2201	2237	2338	2338	0038	0038
57	**Köln** Messe/Deutz d.	0542	0606	0607	0642	0705	0707	0742	0806	0807	0842	0906	0907	0942		2106	2107	2142	2205	2241	2342	2342	0042	0042
71	Köln/Bonn Flughafen ✈ d.	0551	|	|	0651	|	|	0751	|	|	0851	|	|	0951	minutes	|	|	2151	|	2251	2351	2351	0051	0051
83	Troisdorf 807 d.	0600	0623	0623	0700	0721	0723	0800	0821	0823	0900	0921	0923	1000		2121	2123	2200	2223	2300	0000	0000	0100	0100
92	**Bonn** Beuel d.	0611	0635	0635	0711	0735	0735	0811	0835	0835	0911	0935	0935	1011	past each	2135	2135	2211	2235	2311	0011	0011	0111	0111
100	Königswinter d.	0621	0644	0644	0721	0744	0744	0821	0844	0844	0921	0944	0944	1021		2144	2144	2221	2244	2321	0021	0021	0121	0121
105	Bad Honnef d.	0626	0651	0651	0726	0751	0751	0826	0851	0851	0926	0951	0951	1026	hour until	2151	2151	2226	2251	2326	0026	0026	0126	0126
115	Linz (Rhein) d.	0637	0701	0701	0737	0801	0801	0837	0901	0901	0939	1001	1001	1037		2201	2201	2237	2301	2337	0036	0037	0136	0137
122	Bad Hönningen d.	0644	0706	0706	0744	0806	0806	0844	0906	0906	0945	1006	1006	1044		2206	2206	2244	2306	2344	...	0044	...	0144
138	Neuwied 914 d.	0658	0719	0719	0758	0819	0819	0858	0919	0919	0959	1019	1019	1058		2219	2219	2258	2319	2358	...	0058	...	0158
153*	**Koblenz** Hbf 914 a.	0712	0737	0737	0812	0837	0837	0912	0937	0937	1012	1037	1037	1112		2237	2237	2312	2337	0012	...	0112	...	0212

	⚒r		⚒r	⚒r		Ⓐt	⑥	Ⓒz																⑤⑥f
Koblenz Hbf 914 d.	...	...	0447t	0519t	0547r	0619	0619	...	0647	0719	≋	1747	1819	1847	1919	1947	2019	2047	2119	2147	2219	2247	2347	2347
Neuwied 914 d.	...	...	0501t	0535t	0601r	0635	0635	...	0701	0735		1801	1835	1901	1935	2001	2035	2101	2135	2201	2235	2301	0001	0001
Bad Hönningen d.	...	...	0514t	0547t	0614r	0646	0647	...	0714	0747	and at	1814	1847	1914	1947	2014	2047	2114	2147	2214	2247	2314	0014	0014
Linz (Rhein) d.	...	...	0522	0553	0622	0652	0653	0653	0722	0753		1822	1853	1922	1953	2022	2053	2122	2153	2222	2253	2322	0022	0022
Bad Honnef d.	...	...	0532	0602	0632	0701	0702	0702	0732	0802	the same	1832	1902	1932	2002	2032	2102	2132	2202	2232	2302	2332	0032	0032
Königswinter d.	...	...	0538	0608	0638	0707	0708	0708	0738	0808		1838	1908	1938	2008	2038	2108	2138	2208	2238	2308	2338	0038	0038
Bonn Beuel d.	...	...	0547	0617	0647	0716	0717	0717	0747	0817	minutes	1847	1917	1947	2017	2047	2117	2147	2217	2247	2317	2347	0047	0047
Troisdorf 807 d.	...	...	0559	0628	0659	0728	0728	0728	0759	0828		1859	1928	1959	2028	2059	2128	2159	2228	2259	2328	2359	0059	0059
Köln/Bonn Flughafen ✈ d.	...	...	0609	|	0709	|	|	|	0809	|	past each	1909	|	2009	|	2109	|	2209	|	2309	|	0009	0109	0109
Köln Messe/Deutz d.	0512	0619	0619	0650	0719	0750	0750	0750	0819	0850		1919	1950	2019	2050	2119	2150	2219	2250	2319	2350	0019	0119	0119
Köln Hbf 807 a.	0516	0622	0622	0653	0722	0753	0753	0753	0822	0853	hour until	1922	1953	2022	2053	2122	2153	2222	2253	2322	2353	0022	0122	0122
Köln Hbf d.	0525	0625	0625	0659	0725	0759	0759	...	0825	0859r		1925	1959r	2025	...	2125	...	2225	...	2325	...	0025	...	0125
Grevenbroich d.	0555	0655	0655	0729	0755	0829	0829	...	0855	0929r		1955	2029r	2055	...	2155	...	2256	...	2355	...	0055	...	0155
Rheydt Hbf d.	0612	0712	0712	0746	0812	0846	0846	...	0912	0946r		2012	2046r	2115	...	2212	...	2313	...	0012	...	0112	...	0212
Mönchengladbach Hbf a.	0617	0719	0719	0751	0819	0851	0851	...	0919	0951r		2019	2051r	2121	...	2219	...	2319	...	0019	...	0119	...	0219

- **a** – Arrival time.
- **b** – On ⑦ (also June 16, Oct. 3, Nov. 1) Emmerich a. 0644, d. 0707, Arnhem a. 0729.
- **c** – 2321 on ①⑥⑦ until Aug. 29.
- **d** – ⚒ (not June 16, Nov. 1); runs daily Linz (Rhein) - Koblenz.
- **e** – ⚒ (not June 16, Nov. 1); runs daily Köln Messe/Deutz - Krefeld.
- **f** – Also June 15, Oct. 2, 31.
- **h** – ⑦–④ (not June 15, Oct. 2, 31).
- **j** – Arrives 8 minutes earlier.
- **k** – ⑥ only.
- **r** – ⚒ (not June 16, Nov. 1).
- **t** – Ⓐ (not June 16, Nov. 1).
- **z** – Also June 16, Nov. 1.

- ▽ – Wesel d. 1211 / 1411 / 1611 / 1811 (not xx06).
- ✣ – Köln Hbf d. 1741 / 1941 / 2141 (not xx42).
- ♥ – Düsseldorf Hbf d. 1907 (not 1908).
- ≋ – Koblenz Hbf d. 0940 (not 0947), Neuwied d. 1000 (not 1001) then follows regular pattern.
- ⊠ – On June 18 and Aug. 27 - Sept. 9 the 1007 from Mönchengladbach is retimed to depart Mönchengladbach 0956, Rheydt 1000 (other timings follow the regular pattern).
- ⊙ – *RE19* operated by VIAS.
- ◐ – Operated by Mittelrheinbahn.
- ♣ – Operated by National Express.
- ⊖ – Operated by NordWestBahn (additional services run on Ⓐ).
- ⊡ – See shaded panel on page 375 for a summary of the principal Rhein-Ruhr *RE* routes.
- * – Via Koblenz-Lützel (*159 km* via Ehrenbreitstein).

RHEIN – RUHR LOCAL SERVICES — 802

RE / RB services

S-Bahn 19 Köln - Köln/Bonn Flughafen ✈ - Troisdorf

		Ⓐt	Ⓐt		Ⓐt		⑥		⑥	⑥		⑥		†z		†z	D			
Köln Hbf d.	Ⓐ	0401	0421	and every	2041	⑥	0411	and every	0811	0821	and every	2041	†	0411	and every	2041	A	2111	and every	0341
Köln Messe/Deutz d.		0404	0423	20 minutes	2043		0413	30 minutes	0813	0823	20 minutes	2043		0413	30 minutes	2043	I	2113	30 minutes	0343
Köln/Bonn Flughafen ✈ d.		0416	0436	until	2056		0426	until	0826	0836	until	2056		0426	until	2056	L	2126	until	0356
Troisdorf a.		0427	0447		2107		0437		0837	0847		2107		0437		2107	Y	2137		0407

		Ⓐt	Ⓐt		Ⓐt		⑥		⑥	⑥		⑥		†z		†z	D			
Troisdorf d.	Ⓐ	0433	0453	and every	2113	⑥	0443	and every	0713	0753	and every	2113	†	0443	and every	2113	A	2143	and every	0413
Köln/Bonn Flughafen ✈ d.		0444	0504	20 minutes	2124		0454	30 minutes	0724	0804	20 minutes	2124		0454	30 minutes	2124	I	2154	30 minutes	0424
Köln Messe/Deutz a.		0456	0516	until	2137		0506	until	0736	0816	until	2137		0506	until	2137	L	2206	until	0436
Köln Hbf a.		0459	0519		2139		0509		0739	0819		2139		0509		2139	Y	2209		0439

Dortmund - Unna - Soest ◇

km			Ⓒ		⚒t	⚒t	Ⓐt		Ⓐt		Ⓐt		Ⓐt		⚒t			⚒t					
0	**Dortmund** Hbf 805 d.	0004	0104	...	0504	0604	0645	0704	0745	0804	0845	0904	0945	1004	1045	and at the same	1904	1945	2004	...	2104	2204	2304
8	**Dortmund** Hörde d.	0015	0115	...	0515	0615	0653	0715	0753	0815	0853	0915	0953	1015	1053	minutes past	1915	1953	2015	...	2115	2215	2315
23	Unna d.	0032	0132	...	0532	0632	0707	0732	0807	0832	0907	0932	1007	1032	1107	each hour until	1932	2007	2032	...	2132	2232	2332
53	**Soest** 805 a.	0054	0154	...	0554	0654	0729	0754	0829	0854	0929	0954	1029	1054	1129		1954	2029	2054	...	2154	2254	2354

		Ⓒ		⚒t	Ⓐt	⚒t	Ⓐt		Ⓐt		Ⓐt		⚒t			⚒t						
Soest 805 d.	0003	0103	...	0503	0543	0603	0643	0703	0743	0803	0843	0903	0943	and at the same	1803	1843	1903	...	2003	2103	2203	2303
Unna d.	0027	0127	...	0527	0607	0627	0707	0727	0807	0827	0907	0927	1007	minutes past	1826	1907	1927	...	2027	2127	2227	2327
Dortmund Hörde d.	0043	0143	...	0543	0622	0643	0722	0743	0822	0843	0922	0943	1022	each hour until	1843	1922	1943	...	2043	2143	2243	2343
Dortmund Hbf 805 a.	0051	0151	...	0551	0630	0651	0730	0751	0830	0851	0930	0951	1030		1851	1930	1951	...	2051	2151	2251	2351

RB 53 Dortmund - Schwerte - Iserlohn

km		Ⓒz	Ⓒz	Ⓐt	Ⓐt		⚒t		⊡	
0	**Dortmund** Hbf d.	0023	0123	0523	0553	0623	0623	0723	and	2323
8	**Dortmund** Hörde d.	0032	0132	0532	0602	0632	0632	0732	hourly	2332
18	Schwerte (Ruhr) d.	0045	0145	0545	0615	0642	0645	0745	until	2345
38	**Iserlohn** a.	0109	0209	0609	0639	...	0709	0809		0009

	Ⓒz	Ⓐt	Ⓐt		⚒t		⊙		⑤⑥f
Iserlohn d.	0051	0521	0621	...	0651	0751	and	2251	2351
Schwerte (Ruhr) d.	0120	0550	0650	0720	0720	0820	hourly	2320	0020
Dortmund Hörde d.	0130	0600	0700	0730	0730	0730	until	2330	0030
Dortmund Hbf a.	0138	0608	0708	0738	0738	0838		2338	0038

Summary of principal Rhein - Ruhr *RE* routes

	RE1	*RE2*	*RE3*	*RE4*	*RE5*	*RE6*	*RE7*	*RE11*	*RE13*	*RE42*
Aachen Hbf	●	...	...	●	...	...	...	...	...	...
Köln Hbf	●	...	...	|	●	●	●	...	...	...
Mönchengladbach Hbf	|	...	...	●	|	|	|	...	●	●
Düsseldorf Hbf	●	●	●	●	●	●	|	●	●	|
Duisburg Hbf	●	●	●	|	●	●	|	●	|	●
Essen Hbf	●	●	|	|	...	●	|	●	|	●
via Gelsenkirchen	|	●	●	|	...	|	|	|	|	●
via Wuppertal and Hagen	|	|	|	●	...	|	●	|	●	|
Dortmund Hbf	●	|	●	●	...	●	|	●	|	|
Hamm (Westf)	●	|	●	...	...	●	●	●	●	|
Münster (Westf) Hbf	...	●	...	...	...	...	●	...	...	●

OTHER S-BAHN LINKS

Services operate every 20 – 30 minutes

Service	*Route (journey time in minutes)*
S 1	Solingen Hbf - Düsseldorf Hbf (22) - Düsseldorf Flughafen ✈ (35) - Duisburg Hbf (53) - Essen Hbf (72) - Bochum Hbf (90) - Dortmund Hbf (113).
S 3	Oberhausen Hbf - Mülheim Hbf (8) - Essen Hbf (17).
S 9	Essen Hbf - Wuppertal Hbf (46).
S11	Düsseldorf Flughafen Terminal ✈ - Düsseldorf Hbf (12) - Neuss Hbf (31) - Köln Hbf (82).

f – Also June 15, Oct. 2, 31.
t – Not June 16, Nov. 1.
z – Also June 16, Nov. 1.

◇ – Operated by *eurobahn* (2nd class only).
⊡ – On Ⓐ (not June 16, Nov. 1) trains run every 30 minutes 0653 - 1723.
⊙ – On Ⓐ (not June 16, Nov. 1) trains run every 30 minutes 0721 - 1751.

DORTMUND and MÜNSTER - ENSCHEDE — 803

2nd class only; German holiday dates apply

km		Ⓐt	⚒r		⚒r					
0	**Dortmund** Hbf d.	0552	0652	...	0752	0852		2052	2152	2252
44	Dülmen d.	0640	0740	...	0840	0940	and	2140	2240	2340
61	Coesfeld (Westf) a.	0653	0753	...	0853	0953		2153	2253	2353
61	Coesfeld (Westf) d.	0705	0800	0900	0900	1000	hourly	2200	...	...
96	Gronau (Westf) a.	0738	0833	0933	0933	1033		2233	...	...
96	Gronau (Westf) 🚌 d.	0745	0845	0945	0945	1045	until	2245	...	...
103	**Enschede** a.	0756	0856	0956	0956	1056		2256	...	...

	Ⓐt	⚒r	⚒r		Ⓐt	⑥			
Enschede d.	...	...	0556t	...	0656	0702	0802		2102
Gronau (Westf) 🚌 a.	...	...	0607t	...	0707	0713	0813	and	2113
Gronau (Westf) d.	...	0524t	0620	...	0708	0720	0820		2120
Coesfeld (Westf) a.	...	0557t	0657	...	0757	0757	0857	hourly	2157
Coesfeld (Westf) d.	0506	0603	0703	0803	0803	0803	0903		2203
Dülmen d.	0520	0617	0717	0817	0817	0817	0917	until	2217
Dortmund Hbf a.	0607	0707	0807	0907	0907	0907	1007		2307

km			Ⓒz		Ⓐt	Ⓐt	⚒r			
0	**Münster** (Westf) Hbf d.	0008	0008	...	0508	0608	0708	0808	and	2308
56	Gronau (Westf) a.	0105	0105	...	0605	0705	0805	0905	hourly	0005
56	Gronau (Westf) 🚌 d.	...	0115	...	0609	0715	0815	0915	until	0015
63	**Enschede** a.	...	0126	...	0620	0726	0826	0926		0026

	Ⓐt	⚒r	⚒r						⑤⑥f
Enschede d.	...	...	0626	0732r	0832	and	2232	2332	2332
Gronau (Westf) 🚌 a.	...	...	0637	0743r	0843	hourly	2243	2343	2343
Gronau (Westf) d.	0445	0545	0645	0745	0845	until	2245	...	2345
Münster (Westf) Hbf a.	0544	0644	0744	0844	0944		2344	...	0044

f – Also June 15, Oct. 2, 31.
r – ⚒ (not June 16, Nov. 1).
t – Ⓐ (not June 16, Nov. 1).
z – Also June 16, Nov. 1.

HAGEN - KASSEL — 804

RE services

km		Ⓐt	⑥		⚒t																			
0	**Hagen** Hbf 802 d.	0503	...	...	0603	...	0717	0817	0917	1017	1117	1215	1317	1417	1517	1615	1717	1817	1917	...	2017	*2122*	*2222*	*2322*
14	Schwerte (Ruhr) 802 d.	0513	...	...	0613	...	0728	0828	0928	1028	1128	1228	1328	1428	1528	1628	1728	1828	1928	...	2028	2149	2249	2349
57	Arnsberg (Westf) d.	0542	...	...	0642	...	0758	0858	0958	1058	1158	1258	1358	1458	1558	1658	1758	1858	1958	2025	2058	2221	2321	0021
77	Meschede d.	0600	0609	...	0700	...	0816	0916	1016	1116	1216	1316	1416	1516	1616	1716	1816	1916	2016	2042	2116	2239	2339	0039
85	Bestwig d.	0608	0616	...	0708	...	0823	0923	1023	1123	1223	1323	1423	1523	1623	1723	1823	1923	2022	2054	2123	2245	2345	0045
100	Brilon Wald d.	0622	0629	...	0732j	...	0837	0937	1037	1137	1237	1337	1437	1537	1637	1737	1837	1937	...	2106	2137	...	...	...
126	Marsberg d.	0650	0700	...	0800	...	0900	1000	1100	1200	1300	1400	1500	1600	1700	1800	1900	2000	...	...	2200	...	...	...
151	Warburg (Westf) 805 d.	0721h	0721	...	0819	...	0921	1019	1119	1219	1321	1419	1521	1619	1721	1819	1921	2019	...	...	2219	...	...	...
177	Hofgeismar 805 d.	0737	0737	...	...	...	0937	...	...	...	1337	...	1537	...	1737	...	1937	...	...	...	...	...	...	...
202	**Kassel** Wilhelmshöhe 805 a.	0755	0755	...	...	...	0956	...	...	...	1356	...	1556	...	1755	...	1955	...	...	...	...	...	...	...

	⚒t	⚒t	⚒t		Ⓐt	⑥																		
Kassel Wilhelmshöhe 805 d.	...	...	...	...	...	...	...	...	0803	...	1003	...	1203	...	...	...	1603	...	1803	...	...	2003	...	...
Hofgeismar 805 d.	...	...	...	...	...	...	...	...	0820	...	1020	...	1220	...	...	...	1620	...	1820	...	...	2020	...	...
Warburg (Westf) 805 d.	...	...	0535	...	0630	0635	...	0738	0838	0938	1038	1138	1238	1338	1438	1538	1638	1738	1838	1938	...	2038	...	2138
Marsberg d.	...	...	0555	...	0651	0655	...	0758	0859	0958	1059	1158	1259	1358	1459	1558	1659	1758	1859	1958	...	2059	...	2159
Brilon Wald d.	...	...	0621	...	0719	0721	...	0821	0921	1021	1121	1221	1321	1421	1521	1621	1721	1821	1921	2021	...	2125	2149	2225
Bestwig d.	0434	0534	0634	0634	0734	0734	0734	0834	0934	1034	1134	1234	1334	1434	1534	1634	1734	1834	1934	2034	...	2138	2210	2238
Meschede d.	0441	0541	0641	0641	0741	0741	0741	0841	0941	1041	1141	1241	1341	1441	1541	1641	1741	1841	1941	2041	...	2145	2217	2245
Arnsberg (Westf) d.	0459	0559	0659	0659	0759	0759	0759	0859	0959	1059	1159	1259	1359	1459	1559	1659	1759	1859	1959	2059	...	...	2234	...
Schwerte (Ruhr) 802 a.	0528	0628	0728	0728	0828	0828	0828	0928	1028	1128	1228	1328	1428	1528	1628	1728	1828	1928	2028	2128	...	...	2303	...
Hagen Hbf 802 a.	0542	0642	0742	0742	0842	0842	0842	0942	1042	1142	1242	1342	1442	1542	1642	1742	1842	1942	2042	2142	...	...	2313	...

h – Arrives 0709.
j – Arrives 0722.
t – Not June 16, Nov. 1.

805 DORTMUND and MÜNSTER - PADERBORN - KASSEL

km																						*IC*				*IC*
		◇		⊙	◇	◇	⊙	⊙	⊙	◇	◇	⊙	◇	◇	⊙	◇	◇	⊙	◇	⊙	**2155**	◇	⊙	⊙	**1959**
		Ⓒ		Ⓐ	⚒			Ⓒ	Ⓐ	Ⓐ															⑤⑦
				t	r			z	t	t	⊗			⊖							**G**				**L**
	Köln Hbf **800 802** d.	...	...	...	...	...	...	...	...	...	...	...	...	...	...	...	...	...	...	...	0916	...	...	...	1036
	Düsseldorf Hbf **800 802** d.	...	...	...	...	...	...	...	0536	...	...	0636	...	...	0736	...	...	0836	...	...	0943	...	1036	...	|
0	**Dortmund** Hbf **802** d.	...	...	0433	...	...	...	0635	0645**h**	...	...	0745**h**	...	...	0845**h**	...	...	0945**h**	...	...	1044	...	1145**h**	...	|
	Münster (Westf) Hbf **802** d.	0010	...	|	0510	0608	0634	|	|	0640	0710	|	0740**t**	0810	|	0840**t**	0910	|	1010	1034	|	1110	|	1134	|
31	Hamm (Westf) **802** a.	0037	...	0453	0537	0634	0657	0656	|	0707	0737	|	0807**t**	0837	|	0907**t**	0937	|	1037	1057	1101	1137	|	1157	1213
31	Hamm (Westf) d.	0109	...	0501	0546	0646	...	0707	|	0717	0746	|	0817	0846	|	0917	0946	|	1046	...	1107	1146	|	...	1233
57	Soest **802** d.	0126	...	0516	0603	0703	...	0722	0722	0734	0803	0822	0834	0903	0921	0934	1003	1026	1103	...	1122	1203	1221	...	1249
77	Lippstadt d.	0138	...	0526	0615	0715	...	0732	0732	0745	0815	0832	0846	0915	0932	0946	1015	1037	1115	...	1132	1215	1232	...	1301
109	**Paderborn** Hbf **809 811** d.	0203	...	0543	0642	0740	...	0748	0748	0810	0842	0847	0910	0940	0948	1010	1042	1054	1140	...	1148	1242	1247	...	1317
126	Altenbeken **809 811** d.	...	...	0556	0654	...	...	0802	0802	...	0854	...	...	...	1002	...	1054	...	...	...	1204	1254	...	...	1330
163	Warburg (Westf) **804** d.	...	...	0618	0716	...	...	0824	0824	...	0916	...	...	...	1024	...	1116	...	...	...	1226	1316	...	...	|
189	Hofgeismar **804** d.	...	...	0634	...	...	...	0839	0839	...	...	...	...	...	1039	...	...	...	...	...	|	...	...	...	|
214	**Kassel** Wilhelmshöhe **804** a.	...	...	0652	...	...	...	0856	0856	...	...	...	...	...	1056	...	...	...	...	...	1255	...	...	...	1417

											IC														
	◇	⊙	◇	⊙	◇	⊙	◇	⊙	◇	⊙	**2157**	◇	⊙	◇	◇	⊙	◇	◇	⊙	◇	⊙	◇	◇	◇	◇
																								⑤⑥	
					◧						**G**												x	v	
Köln Hbf **800 802** d.	...	...	...	...	...	...	...	...	...	...	1519	...	...	...	...	...	...	...	...	...	...	...	...	...	...
Düsseldorf Hbf **800 802** d.	...	1136	...	1236	...	1336	...	1436	...	...	1543	...	1636	...	...	1736	...	...	1836	...	1936	...	...	...	...
Dortmund Hbf **802** d.	...	1245**h**	...	1345**h**	...	1445**h**	...	1545**h**	...	...	1641	...	1745**h**	...	...	1845**h**	...	...	1945**h**	...	2045**h**	...	...	...	...
Münster (Westf) Hbf **802** d.	1210	|	1310	|	1410	|	1510	|	1610	1634	|	1710	|	1740**t**	1810	|	1840**t**	1910	|	2010	|	*2134*	*2234*	*2234*	2310
Hamm (Westf) **802** a.	1237	|	1337	|	1435	|	1537	|	1637	1657	1701	1737	|	1807**t**	1835	|	1907**t**	1937	|	2037	|	*2157*	*2257*	*2257*	2337
Hamm (Westf) d.	1246	|	1346	|	1446	|	1546	|	1646	...	1707	1746	|	1817	1846	|	1917	1946	|	2046	|	2209	2309	2309	0009
Soest **802** d.	1303	1322	1403	1421	1503	1522	1603	1621	1703	...	1722	1803	1821	1834	1903	1922	1934	2003	2021	2103	2122	2226	2326	2326	0026
Lippstadt d.	1315	1332	1415	1432	1515	1532	1615	1632	1715	...	1732	1815	1832	1846	1915	1932	1946	2015	2032	2115	2132	2238	2338	2338	0038
Paderborn Hbf **809 811** d.	1340	1348	1442	1447	1540	1548	1642	1647	1740	...	1748	1842	1847	1910	1940	1948	2010	2040	2047	2140	2148	2303	0001	0002	0103
Altenbeken **809 811** d.	...	1402	1455	...	...	1602	1654	...	...	...	1804	1854	...	...	...	2002	...	...	...	...	2202	...	...	0014	...
Warburg (Westf) **804** d.	...	1424	1516	...	...	1624	1716	...	...	...	1826	1916	...	...	...	2024	...	...	...	...	2224	...	...	0036	...
Hofgeismar **804** d.	...	1439	...	...	...	1639	...	...	...	...	|	...	...	...	...	2038	...	...	...	...	2239	...	...	...	...
Kassel Wilhelmshöhe **804** a.	...	1456	...	...	...	1656	...	...	...	...	1857	...	...	...	...	2054	...	...	...	...	2257	...	...	...	...

																IC									
	◇	◇	⊙	◇	◇	⊙	⊙	◇	◇	⊙	◇	◇	⊙	◇	◇	**2156**	⊙	◇	⊙	◇	⊙	◇	⊙	◇	⊙
	Ⓐ	⚒	Ⓐ		Ⓐ	Ⓐ																			
	t	r	t		t	t								⊖		**G**		⊗							
Kassel Wilhelmshöhe **804** d.	...	...	...	...	...	0555	...	...	...	0703	...	...	...	...	...	0902	...	...	...	...	1103	...	...	...	1303
Hofgeismar **804** d.	...	...	...	...	...	0611	...	...	...	0720	...	...	...	...	...	|	...	...	...	...	1120	...	...	...	1320
Warburg (Westf) **804** d.	...	...	0535	...	...	0635	...	...	...	0735	...	...	...	0839	...	0934	...	...	...	1039	1135	...	...	1239	1335
Altenbeken **809 811** d.	...	...	0558	...	...	0658	...	...	...	0758	...	...	...	0902	...	0956	...	...	...	1102	1158	...	...	1302	1358
Paderborn Hbf **809 811** d.	0451	0521	0609	0621	0651	0709	0709	0721	0751	0809	0821	0851	0909	0921**j**	0951	1010	...	1021	1109	1121**j**	1209	1221	1309	1321**j**	1409
Lippstadt d.	0514	0544	0625	0644	0714	0725	0725	0744	0814	0825	0844	0914	0925	0944	1014	1026	...	1044	1125	1144	1225	1244	1325	1344	1425
Soest **802** d.	0526	0556	0635	0656	0726	0735	0735	0756	0826	0835	0856	0926	0935	0956	1026	1037	...	1056	1135	1156	1235	1256	1335	1356	1435
Hamm (Westf) a.	0544	0614	|	0714	0744	|	|	0814	0844	|	0914	0944	|	1014	1044	1050	...	1114	|	1214	|	1314	|	1414	|
Hamm (Westf) **802** d.	0550	0620	|	0722	0750	|	|	0820	0850**t**	|	*0920*	0950**t**	|	1020	1050**t**	1056	1059	1122	|	1220	|	1320	|	1420	|
Münster (Westf) Hbf **802** a.	0617	0647	|	0748	0816	|	|	0847	0917**t**	|	*0947*	1017**t**	|	1047	1117**t**	|	1122	1148	|	1247	|	1347	|	1447	|
Dortmund Hbf **802** a.	...	...	0710**h**	...	...	0810**h**	0810**h**	...	...	0910**h**	...	...	1010**h**	...	...	1114	...	...	1210**h**	...	1310**h**	...	1410**h**	...	1510**h**
Düsseldorf Hbf **800 802** a.	...	...	0824	...	...	0924	0924	...	...	1024	...	...	1124	...	...	1208	...	...	1324	...	1424	...	1524	...	1624
Köln Hbf **800 802** a.	...	...	...	...	...	...	...	...	...	...	...	...	...	...	...	1239	...	...	...	...	...	...	...	...	...

					IC														*IC*						
	◇	⊙	◇	◇	**2152**	⊙	◇	◇	⊙	◇	◇	⊙	◇	◇	⊙	◇	⊙	◇	**1952**	⊙	◇	⊙	◇	◇	◇
																			⑤⑦						
					G		⊖												**L**						
Kassel Wilhelmshöhe **804** d.	...	...	...	...	1502	...	...	...	...	...	...	1703	...	...	...	...	1903	...	1944	...	...	2103	...	...	...
Hofgeismar **804** d.	...	...	...	...	|	...	...	...	...	...	...	1720	...	...	...	...	1920	...	|	...	...	2120	...	...	...
Warburg (Westf) **804** d.	...	...	1438	...	1534	...	...	...	...	1639	...	1735	...	...	...	1839	1935	...	2018	...	2039	2135	...	...	...
Altenbeken **809 811** d.	...	...	1502	...	1556	...	...	...	...	1702	...	1758	...	...	...	1902	1958	...	2040	...	2102	2158	...	...	...
Paderborn Hbf **809 811** d.	1421	1504	1521**j**	1551	1610	...	1621	1651	1709	1721**j**	1751	1809	1821	1851	1909	1921**j**	2009	2015	2053	...	2115	2209	2215	2315	0012
Lippstadt d.	1445	1520	1544	1614	1626	...	1644	1714	1725	1744	1814	1825	1844	1914	1925	1944	2025	2038	2109	...	2138	2225	2238	2338	0035
Soest **802** d.	1458	1530	1556	1626	1637	...	1656	1726	1735	1756	1826	1835	1856	1926	1935	1956	2036	2050	2121	...	2150	2236	2250	2350	0050
Hamm (Westf) a.	1514	|	1614	1644	1650	...	1714	1744	|	1814	1844	|	1914	1944	|	2014	|	2108	2135	...	2208	|	2308	0008	0108
Hamm (Westf) **802** d.	1520	|	1620	1650	1656	1659	1720	1750**t**	|	1820	1850**t**	|	1922	*1959*	|	2020	|	2120	2140	2159	2220	|	2320	0010	0110
Münster (Westf) Hbf **802** a.	1547	|	1647	1717	|	1722	1747	1817**t**	|	1847	1917**t**	|	1947	*2022*	|	2047	|	2147	|	2222	2247	|	2347	0040	0140
Dortmund Hbf **802** a.	...	1610**h**	...	...	1714	...	...	...	1810**h**	...	...	1910**h**	...	...	2010**h**	...	2110**h**	...	2157	...	...	2317	...	...	...
Düsseldorf Hbf **800 802** a.	...	1724	...	...	1811	...	...	...	1923	...	...	2023	...	...	2124	...	2224	...	2256	...	...	...	...	...	...
Köln Hbf **800 802** a.	...	...	...	...	...	...	...	...	...	...	...	...	...	...	...	...	...	...	2326	...	...	...	...	...	...

G – To / from Gera via Weimar (Table **849a**).
L – ⑤⑦ (also June 15). To / from Leipzig (Table **849a**).

h – Dortmund **Hörde**. See Table **802** (Dortmund - Soest / Iserlohn panels) on page 375 for connections from / to Dortmund Hbf.
j – Arrives 5 – 6 minutes earlier.

r – Not June 16, Nov. 1.
t – Ⓐ (not June 16, Nov. 1).
v – Also Oct. 2.
x – Not June 15, Oct. 31.
z – Also June 16, Nov. 1.

⊗ – Change trains at Hamm on Ⓑ.
⊖ – Change trains at Hamm on Ⓐ (also Oct. 2; not June 16, Nov. 1).
◧ – Change trains at Hamm on Ⓐ (not June 16, Nov. 1).
◇ – Operated by *eurobahn* (2nd class only).
⊙ – Operated by National Express.

806 FRANKFURT - GIESSEN - KASSEL and SIEGEN

ICE / IC trains **KARLSRUHE - FRANKFURT - GIESSEN - KASSEL - HAMBURG - STRALSUND** (see next page for regional services).

ICE / IC trains	*ICE* **1676**	*IC* **1674**	*IC* **1672**	*IC* **2374**	*ICE* **1578**	*ICE* **1576**	*ICE* **2184**	*ICE* **1572**	*ICE* **1570**	*ICE* **1570**
	①								Ⓑ	⑦
		🍷	🍷	🍷	✕	✕	✕	✕	✕	✕
Karlsruhe Hbf **912** d.	...	...	0702	0910	1110	1310	1510	1710	1910	1910
Heidelberg Hbf **912** d.	...	...	0746	0946	1146	1346	1546	1746	1946	1946
Frankfurt (Main) Hbf d.	0344	0649	0851‡	1051‡	1251‡	1448‡	1648‡	1848‡	2051‡	2051‡
Friedberg (Hess) d.	0424	0716	0917	1117	1317	1517	1717	1917	2117	2117
Gießen d.	0443	0734	0934	1134	1334	1534	1734	1934	2134	2134
Marburg (Lahn) d.	0459	0750	0950	1151	1350	1550	1750	1950	2150	2150
Treysa d.	0527	0815	1015	1215	1415	1615	1815	2017	2215	2215
Wabern d.	0544	0833	1033	1233	|	1633	1833	2034	|	|
Kassel Wilhelmshöhe a.	0610	0854	1054	1254	1454	1654	1854	2054	2254	2254
Hannover Hbf **900** a.	0756	0957	1156	1356	1556	1756	1956	2156**b**	...	0010
Bremen Hbf **813** a.	0913	1113	1313	1515	1713	1916	...	|	...	...
Hamburg Hbf **900** a.	...	...	...	...	...	...	...	2332**w**	...	...
Stralsund Hbf **830** a.	...	...	...	...	...	...	...	...	...	...

ICE / IC trains	*ICE* **1571**	*ICE* **1573**	*ICE* **2185**	*ICE* **1577**	*ICE* **1579**	*IC* **1671**	*IC* **2375**	*IC* **1999**	*IC* **1675**	*ICE* **1677**
	①–⑤	①–⑥						⑦		⑤⑦
	✕	✕	O✕	O✕	O✕	🍷	🍷	S🍷	🍷	✕
Stralsund Hbf **830** d.	...	...	...	...	...	...	...	...	...	...
Hamburg Hbf **900** d.	...	...	...	...	...	...	...	...	...	...
Bremen Hbf **813** d.	...	...	0638**e**	0835	1034	1238	1437	...	1637	1837
Hannover Hbf **900** d.	...	0557**b**	0801**e**	1001	1201	1401	1601	1702**h**	1801	2001
Kassel Wilhelmshöhe d.	0459	0700	0903	1104	1303	1503	1703	1809	1903	2103
Wabern d.	0519	0719	|	1123	|	1522	1722	|	1922	2122
Treysa d.	0536	0736	0937	1140	1337	1539	1739	|	1939	2139
Marburg (Lahn) d.	0604	0804	1004	1205	1404	1604	1805	1906	2004	2204
Gießen d.	0622	0823	1023	1223	1423	1623	1823	1925	2023	2223
Friedberg (Hess) d.	0642	0842	1042	1242	1442	1642	1843	|	2043	2243
Frankfurt (Main) Hbf a.	0709§	0910§	1110§	1309§	1509§	1709§	1909§	2008**f**	2109	2309
Heidelberg Hbf **912** a.	0812	1013	1213	1413	1613	1813	2013	2112	...	...
Karlsruhe Hbf **912** a.	0851	1050	1250	1451	1650	1852	2054	...	...	...

O – From Oldenburg on dates in Table **813**.
S – From Berlin (Table **810**). To Ulm via Stuttgart (Tables **912** and **930**). Runs as *IC* **1991** from July 24.

b – Not ⑥.
e – Not ⑦.

h – Until July 17.
f – Frankfurt (Main) **West** (not Hbf).
w – ⑦ only.

‡ – Until Aug. 26 calls at Frankfurt (Main) **West** (not Hbf), departing 5 – 8 minutes later.
§ – Until Aug. 26 calls at Frankfurt (Main) **West** (not Hbf), arriving 3 – 6 minutes earlier.

FRANKFURT - GIESSEN - KASSEL and SIEGEN 806

Regional trains **FRANKFURT - GIESSEN - KASSEL / SIEGEN** (see previous page for *ICE / IC* services). See Table **808** for other *IC* services Frankfurt - Wetzlar - Siegen and v.v.

km				◇		◇	◇	◇	◇		◇		◇	◇		◇		◇	◇		◇		◇	◇		◇
		†z	⚒r	⚒r	Ⓐt	Ⓐt	Ⓐt	Ⓒz	Ⓒz		⚒r	⚒r					⚒r									
0	**Frankfurt (Main)** Hbf .. d.	0508	0521	...	0551	...	0616	0621	...	0717	...	0745	0814**n**	0814**k**	0919	...	0951	1021	1021	1119	...	1151	1221	1221	1319	...
34	Friedberg (Hess) .... d.	0533	0545	...	0615	...	0645	0645	...	0745	...	0815	0845	0845**r**	0945	...	1015	1045	1045	1145	...	1215	1245	1245	1345	...
39	Bad Nauheim .... d.	0537	|	...	0619	...	|	|	...	|	...	0819	|	|	|	...	1020	|	|	|	...	1220	|	|	|	...
66	**Gießen** .... a.	0603	0603	...	0635	...	0702	0702	...	0803	...	0835	0902	0902**r**	1003	...	1035	1102	1102	1203	...	1235	1302	1302	1403	...
66	**Gießen** .... **906** d.	0604	0604	0609	0640	0652	0703	0705	0709	0804	0815	0840	0905	0909	1004	1015	1040	1105	1109	1204	1215	1240	1305	1309	1404	1415
79	Wetzlar .... **906** d.	|	|	0624	0650	0703	|	|	0718	|	0824	0850	|	0918	|	1024	1050	|	1118	|	1224	1250	|	1318	|	1424
101	Herborn .... d.	|	|	0637	0712	0730	|	|	0733	|	0837	0912	|	0933	|	1037	1112	|	1133	|	1237	1312	|	1333	|	1437
107	Dillenburg .... d.	|	|	0643	0722	0738	|	|	0738	|	0843	0922	|	0938	|	1043	1122	|	1138	|	1243	1322	|	1338	|	1443
139	**Siegen** Hbf .... a.	|	|	0711	...	0805	|	|	0805	|	0912	...	|	1005	|	1111	...	|	1205	|	1311	...	|	1405	|	1511
96	Marburg (Lahn) .... d.	0620	0620	...	...	...	0720	0720	...	0820	...	...	0920	...	1020	...	...	1120	...	1220	...	...	1320	...	1420	...
118	Stadtallendorf .... d.	0634	0634	...	...	...	0737	0737	...	0834	...	...	0937	...	1034	...	...	1137	...	1234	...	...	1337	...	1434	...
138	Treysa .... d.	0649	0649	...	...	...	0755	0755	...	0849	...	...	0955	...	1049	...	...	1155	...	1249	...	...	1355	...	1449	...
166	Wabern .... d.	0707	0707	...	...	...	0818	0818	...	0907	...	...	1018	...	1107	...	...	1218	...	1307	...	...	1418	...	1507	...
196	**Kassel** Wilhelmshöhe a.	0726	0726	...	...	...	0846	0846	...	0926	...	...	1046	...	1126	...	...	1246	...	1326	...	...	1446	...	1526	...
200	**Kassel** Hbf .... a.	0734	0734	...	...	...	0855	0855	...	0934	...	...	1056	...	1134	...	...	1254	...	1334	...	...	1454	...	1534	...

		◇	◇		◇		◇	◇		◇	◇		◇	◇		◇		◇	◇		◇		◇	◇		◇
										Ⓒz	Ⓐt														D	
Frankfurt (Main) Hbf ... d.	1351	1421	1421	1519	...	1551	1620	1620	1719	...	1731	1751	1820	1820	1919	...	1951	2021	2021	2121	...	2151	2221	2221	2321	...
Friedberg (Hess) .... d.	1415	1445	1445	1545	...	1615	1645	1645	1745	...	|	1815	1845	1845	1945	...	2015	2045	2045	2145	...	2215	2245	2245	2345	...
Bad Nauheim .... d.	1420	|	|	|	...	1620	|	|	|	...	1800	1820	|	|	|	...	2020	|	|	|	...	2219	|	|	|	...
Gießen .... a.	1435	1502	1502	1603	...	1635	1702	1702	1803	...	|	1835	1902	1902	2003	...	2035	2102	2102	2203	...	2235	2302	2302	0005	...
Gießen .... **906** d.	1440	1505	1509	1604	1615	1640	1705	1709	1804	1815	|	1840	1905	1909	2004	2015	2040	2105	2109	2204	2209	2240	2305	2309	0007	0011
Wetzlar .... **906** d.	1450	|	1518	|	1624	1650	|	1718	|	1824	1824	1850	|	1918	|	2024	2050	|	2118	|	2218	2250	|	2318	|	0021
Herborn .... d.	1512	|	1533	|	1637	1712	|	1733	|	1838	1838	1912	|	1933	|	2037	2112	|	2133	|	2233	2312	|	2333	|	0043
Dillenburg .... d.	1522	|	1538	|	1643	1722	|	1738	|	1843	1843	1922	|	1938	|	2043	2122	|	2138	|	2238	2322	|	2338	|	0050
Siegen Hbf .... a.	...	|	1605	|	1712	...	|	1805	|	1912	1912	...	|	2005	|	2111	...	|	2205	|	2305	...	|	0005	|	0120
Marburg (Lahn) .... d.	...	1520	...	1620	...	...	1720	...	1820	...	...	...	1920	...	2020	...	...	2120	...	2220	...	...	2320	...	0031	...
Stadtallendorf .... d.	...	1537	...	1634	...	...	1737	...	1834	...	...	...	1937	...	2034	...	...	2137	...	2234	...	...	2339	...	0048	...
Treysa .... d.	...	1555	...	1649	...	...	1755	...	1849	...	...	...	1955	...	2049	...	...	2155	...	2249	...	...	2355	...	0104	...
Wabern .... d.	...	1618	...	1707	...	...	1818	...	1907	...	...	...	2018	...	2107	...	...	2218	...	2307	...	...	0018	...	0122	...
Kassel Wilhelmshöhe . a.	...	1646	...	1726	...	...	1846	...	1926	...	...	...	2048	...	2126	...	...	2245	...	2326	...	...	0048	...	0143	...
Kassel Hbf .... a.	...	1656	...	1734	...	...	1856	...	1934	...	...	...	2054	...	2134	...	...	2251	...	2334	...	...	0055	...	0150	...

			◇	◇	◇		◇		◇			◇	◇	◇	◇		◇		◇	◇		◇		◇	◇	
	Ⓐt	Ⓒz	Ⓐt	⑥	Ⓒz	Ⓐt	Ⓐt	⚒r	⑥	Ⓐt	Ⓒz	ⒶtA		†z	⚒r											
Kassel Hbf .... d.	0400	0423	...	...	...	...	...	...	...	0608	0615	...	...	...	0705	...	...	0823	...	0905	...	...	1023	...	1105	...
Kassel Wilhelmshöhe d.	0405	0429	...	...	...	...	...	...	...	0613	0620	...	...	...	0710	...	...	0829	...	0910	...	...	1029	...	1110	...
Wabern .... d.	0423	0448	...	...	...	...	...	...	...	0639	0645	...	...	...	0738	...	...	0848	...	0938	...	...	1048	...	1138	...
Treysa .... d.	0441	0506	...	...	0559	0600	...	...	...	0700	0703	...	...	0753	0805**j**	...	...	0906	...	1005	...	...	1106	...	1205	...
Stadtallendorf .... d.	0455	0519	...	...	0614	0615	...	...	...	0716	0718	...	...	0808	0819**j**	...	...	0919	...	1019	...	...	1119	...	1219	...
Marburg (Lahn) .... d.	0512	0535	...	...	0635	0634	...	...	...	0734	0734	...	...	0835	0835	...	...	0935	...	1035	...	...	1135	...	1235	...
Siegen Hbf .... d.	|	|	0457	0554	|	|	0600	...	0645	|	|	0645	0754**p**	|	|	...	0845	|	0954	|	...	1045	|	1154	|	...
Dillenburg .... d.	|	|	0525	0617	|	|	0626	0633	0717	|	|	0717	0817	|	|	0833**r**	0917	|	1017	|	1033**r**	1117	|	1217	|	1233
Herborn .... d.	|	|	0530	0622	|	|	0631	0640	0722	|	|	0736**y**	0822	|	|	0840**r**	0922	|	1022	|	1040**r**	1122	|	1222	|	1240
Wetzlar .... **906** d.	|	|	0547	0637	|	|	0649	0702	0737	|	|	0752	0837	|	|	0902	0937	|	1037	|	1102	1137	|	1237	|	1302
Gießen .... **906** a.	0534	0551	|	0646	0651	0651	0659	0714	0746	0751	0751	0801	0846	0851	0851	0914	0946	0951	1046	1051	1114	1146	1151	1246	1251	1314
Gießen .... d.	0536	0553	|	0655	0655	0652	0709	0722	...	0753	0753	*0808*	0855	0855	0855	0922	...	0953	1055	1055	1122	...	1153	1255	1255	1322
Bad Nauheim .... d.	0555	|	0611	|	|	|	0728	0739	...	|	|	*0826*	|	|	|	0939	...	|	|	|	1139	...	|	|	|	1339
Friedberg (Hess) .... d.	0559	0612	|	0713	0713	0712	0733	0743	...	0812	0812	*0830*	0913	0913	0913	0943	...	1012	1113	1113	1143	...	1212	1313	1313	1343
Frankfurt (Main) Hbf .. a.	0627	0635	0642	0738	0738	0742	0802§	0809	...	0840	0837.	*0857*	0939	0939	0939	1009	...	1040	1138	1138	1209	...	1240	1338	1338	1409

	◇		◇	◇		◇		◇	◇		◇		◇	◇		◇		◇	◇		◇		◇	◇	◇	
Kassel Hbf .... d.	...	1223	...	1305	...	...	1423	...	1505	...	...	1623	...	1705	...	...	1823	...	1905	...	...	2023	2105	...	...	2223
Kassel Wilhelmshöhe d.	...	1229	...	1310	...	...	1429	...	1510	...	...	1629	...	1710	...	...	1829	...	1910	...	...	2029	2110	...	...	2229
Wabern .... d.	...	1248	...	1338	...	...	1448	...	1538	...	...	1648	...	1738	...	...	1848	...	1938	...	...	2049	2138	...	...	2252
Treysa .... d.	...	1306	...	1405	...	...	1506	...	1605	...	...	1706	...	1805	...	...	1906	...	2005	...	...	2107	2205	...	...	2310
Stadtallendorf .... d.	...	1319	...	1419	...	...	1519	...	1619	...	...	1719	...	1819	...	...	1919	...	2019	...	...	2120	2219	...	...	2324
Marburg (Lahn) .... d.	...	1335	...	1435	...	...	1535	...	1635	...	...	1735	...	1835	...	...	1935	...	2035	...	...	2135	2235	...	...	2340
Siegen Hbf .... d.	1245	|	1354	|	...	1445	|	1554	|	...	1645	|	1754	|	...	1845	|	1954	|	...	2052	|	|	2154	2310	|
Dillenburg .... d.	1317	|	1417	|	1433	1517	|	1617	|	1633	1717	|	1817	|	1833	1917	|	2017	|	2033	2117	|	|	2217	2334	|
Herborn .... d.	1322	|	1422	|	1440	1522	|	1622	|	1640	1722	|	1822	|	1840	1922	|	2022	|	2040	2122	|	|	2222	2339	|
Wetzlar .... **906** d.	1337	|	1437	|	1502	1537	|	1637	|	1702	1737	|	1837	|	1902	1937	|	2037	|	2102	2137	|	|	2237	2352	|
Gießen .... **906** a.	1346	1351	1446	1451	1514	1546	1551	1646	1651	1714	1746	1751	1846	1851	1914	1946	1951	2046	2051	2114	2147	2151	2250	2246	0001	0005
Gießen .... d.	...	1353	1455	1455	1522	...	1553	1655	1655	1722	...	1753	1855	1855	1922	...	1953	2054	2054	2122	...	2153	...	2255	...	0008
Bad Nauheim .... d.	...	|	|	|	1539	...	|	|	|	1739	...	|	|	|	1939	...	|	|	|	2139	...	|	...	|	...	0031
Friedberg (Hess) .... d.	...	1412	1513	1513	1543	...	1612	1713	1713	1743	...	1812	1913	1913	1943	...	2012	2113	2113	2143	...	2212	...	2313	...	0036
Frankfurt (Main) Hbf .. a.	...	1440	1538	1538	1615	...	1642	1738	1738	1815	...	1842	1938	1938	2009	...	2040	2137	2137	2208	...	2237	...	2338	...	0110

A – From Au (Table **807**).
D – ⑤–⑦ (also June 15, 16, Oct. 3); runs daily Frankfurt - Treysa.
j – On ⑥ Treysa d. 0800, Stadtallendorf d. 0815.
k – ⑥ to Aug. 20; ⚒ from Aug. 27. Departs 0821 on ⑥.
n – Ⓒ to Aug. 21 (also June 16); daily from Aug. 27. Departs 0821 on Ⓒ **z**.
p – 0751 on † (also June 16).
r – ⚒ (not June 16).
t – Not June 16.
y – Arrives 0723.
z – Also June 16.
§ – Until Aug. 26 terminates at Frankfurt **West** (not Hbf), a. 0756.
◇ – Operated by Hessische Landesbahn.

RE / S-Bahn services AACHEN - KÖLN - SIEGEN 807

km		Ⓒz	Ⓐt2	Ⓐg	⑥	Ⓐt	⑥		Ⓒz	Ⓐt	⚒r	†z														
0	**Aachen** Hbf . **802 910** d.	...	...	...	...	0518	...	0618**t**	...	0718	0818	*0818*	0918	1018	1118	1218	1318	1418	1518	1618	1718	1817	1918	2018	2118	...
31	Düren .... **802** d.	...	...	...	...	0545	...	0645**t**	...	0745	0845	*0845*	0945	1045	1145	1245	1347	1445	1545	1645	1745	1845	1945	2045	2144	...
70	**Köln** Hbf ...... **802 910** a.	...	...	...	...	0612	...	0712**t**	...	0813	0912	*0912*	1012	1112	1212	1312	1412	1512	1622	1712	1813	1912	2012	2112	2211	...
70	**Köln** Hbf ...... **802 910** d.	0023	0431	...	...	0622	0623	0722	0820	0821	0921	0922	1021	1123	1222	1321	1419	1522	1624	1723	1823	1921	2021	2123	2222	2323
71	**Köln** M/D ⊡ **802 910** d.	0026	0433	...	...	0626	0626	0725	|	|	0924	|	1025	|	1225	1324	1424	1525	1627	1726	1826	1925	2024	2126	2226	2326
91	Troisdorf .... **802** d.	0041	0454	...	...	0641	0641	0741	0841	0841	0941	0941	1041	1141	1241	1341	1441	1541	1641	1741	1841	1941	2042	2141	2241	2341
95	Siegburg/Bonn ... **910** d.	0046	0500	...	...	0646	0646	0746	0846	0846	0946	0946	1046	1146	1246	1346	1446	1546	1646	1746	1846	1946	2047	2147	2246	2346
102	Hennef (Sieg) .... d.	0050	0506	...	...	0650	0650	0750	0850	0850	0950	0950	1050	1150	1250	1350	1450	1550	1650	1750	1850	1950	2052	2151	2251	2350
114	Eitorf .... d.	0059	0518	...	...	0659	0659	0759	0859	0859	0959	0959	1059	1159	1259	1359	1459	1559	1659	1759	1859	1959	2100	2200	2259	2359
136	Au (Sieg) .... d.	0116	0541	0556	0605	0716	0717	0816	0916	0916	1016	1016	1116	1216	1316	1416	1516	1616	1716	1816	1916	2016	2118	2217	2316	0016
142	Wissen (Sieg) .... d.	0124	...	0603	0612	0721	0722	0821	0921	0921	1021	1021	1121	1221	1321	1421	1521	1621	1721	1821	1921	2021	2123	2224	2324	0024
154	Betzdorf (Sieg) .... d.	0138	...	0618	0626	0730	0731	0830	0931	0930	1030	1031	1130	1230	1330	1430	1530	1631	1730	1830	1930	2030	2132	2238	2338	0038
171	**Siegen** Hbf .... a.	0200	...	0643	0649	0750	0750	0850	0950	0950	1050	1050	1150	1250	1350	1450	1550	1650	1750	1850	1950	2048	2150	2300	2400	0100

	⚒r2	Ⓐt	⑥	Ⓐt	Ⓐt	Ⓒz	⚒r																	2	2	
Siegen Hbf .... d.	...	...	0454	0454	0604	0610	0710	0710	0810	0910	1010	1110	1210	1310	1410	1510	1610	1710	1810	1910	2010	2110	2210	...	...	2311
Betzdorf (Sieg) .... d.	...	...	0515	0515	0624	0628	0728	0728	0828	0928	1028	1128	1228	1328	1428	1528	1628	1728	1828	1928	2028	2128	2228	...	...	2335
Wissen (Sieg) .... d.	...	...	0528	0528	0636	0637	0737	0737	0837	0937	1037	1137	1237	1337	1437	1537	1637	1737	1837	1937	2037	2137	2237	...	...	2347
Au (Sieg) .... d.	0420	...	0536	0537	0643	0642	0743	0743	0843	0943	1043	1143	1243	1343	1443	1543	1643	1743	1843	1943	2043	2143	2243	2320	...	2355
Eitorf .... d.	0439	...	0557	0557	0700	0700	0800	0800	0900	1000	1100	1200	1300	1400	1500	1600	1700	1800	1900	2000	2100	2200	2300	2339	...	...
Hennef (Sieg) .... d.	0453	...	0610	0609	0709	0709	0809	0809	0909	1009	1109	1209	1309	1409	1509	1609	1709	1809	1909	2009	2109	2209	2309	2353	0002	...
Siegburg/Bonn ..... **910** d.	0457	...	0614	0614	0714	0714	0814	0814	0914	1014	1114	1214	1314	1414	1514	1614	1714	1814	1914	2014	2114	2214	2314	2357	0007	...
Troisdorf .... **802** d.	0503	...	0619	0618	0718	0718	0818	0818	0918	1018	1118	1218	1318	1418	1518	1618	1718	1818	1918	2019	2118	2218	2318	0003	0013	...
Köln M/D ⊡ ... **802 910** d.	0527	0534	0634	0634	0734	0734	0837	0837	0934	1034	1134	1234	1334	1434	1534	1634	1737	1834	1934	2036	2134	2235	2334	0027	0037	...
Köln Hbf .... **802 910** a.	0529	0537	0637	0638	0737	0737	0839	0839	0937	1036	1138	1237	1337	1438	1537	1637	1739	1836	1937	2038	2137	2238	2336	0029	0039	...
Köln Hbf .... **802 910** d.	...	0547	...	0648	0747	...	0847	...	0947	1047	1147	1247	1346	1447	1547	1647	1745	1848	1946	2047	2147	*2247*	2348	...	0040	...
Düren .... **802** d.	...	0614	...	0714	0814	...	0914	...	1014	1114	1214	1314	1414	1514	1614	1714	1814	1914	2014	2114	2214	*2314*	0013	...	0118	...
Aachen Hbf .... **802 910** a.	...	0642	...	0742	0844	...	0942	...	1043	1143	1243	1343	1443	1543	1643	1743	1843	1944	2044	2144	2243	*2346*	0043	...	0145	...

g – Ⓐ (not June 16). To Gießen (Table **806**).
r – Not June 16, Nov. 1.
t – Ⓐ (not June 16, Nov. 1).
z – Also June 16, Nov. 1.
⊡ – Köln Messe/Deutz.

808 MÜNSTER - DORTMUND - SIEGEN - FRANKFURT and ESSEN - HAGEN - SIEGEN

IC services	*IC* 2221 Ⓐ h	*IC* 2223 ⚒	*IC* 2223 Ⓐ	*IC* 2225	*IC* 2225 ⚒	*IC* 2227	*IC* 2229	*IC* 2321 N	*IC* 2323	*IC* 2325	*IC* 2327
Münster (W) Hbf **802** d.	...	...	...	...	0619a	0829	...	1231	1419	...	1819
Hamm (Westf) **802** d.	...	...	...	...	0641a	0907	...	1307	1441	...	1841
Unna **802** d.	...	...	...	...	│	0917	...	1317	│	...	│
Schwerte (Ruhr) **802** d.	...	...	...	...	│	0930	...	1330	│	...	│
Dortmund Hbf **802** d.	...	...	0503	...	0703	│	1103	│	1503	1703	1903
Witten Hbf **802** d.	...	...	0514	...	0714	│	1114	│	1514	1714	1914
Letmathe d.	...	...	0539	...	0739	0949	1139	1349	1539	1739	1939
Altena (Westf) d.	...	...	0548	...	0748	│	1148	│	1548	1748	1948
Werdohl d.	...	...	0557	...	0757	│	1157	│	1557	1757	1957
Finnentrop d.	...	...	0615	...	0815	│	1215	│	1615	1815	2015
Lennestadt ♥ d.	...	...	0628	...	0828	1028	1228	1428	1628	1828	2028
Kreuztal d.	...	...	0645	...	0845	│	1245	│	1645	1845	2045
Siegen Hbf a.	...	...	0655	...	0855	1055	1255	1455	1655	1855	2055
Siegen Hbf **806** d.	0519	0701	0701	0901	0901	1101	1301	1501	1701	1901	...
Dillenburg **806** d.	0546	0725	0725	0925	0925	1125	1325	1525	1725	1925	...
Wetzlar **806** d.	0607	0742	0742	0942	0942	1142	1342	1542	1742	1942	...
Bad Nauheim d.	0629	0804	0804	1004	1004	1204	1404	1604	1804	2004	...
Frankfurt (M) Hbf **806** a.	0702	0835	0835	1035	1035	1235	1435	1635	1835	2035	...

IC services	*IC* 2328 Ⓐ	*IC* 2326 ⚒	*IC* 2326 Ⓐ S	*IC* 2324	*IC* 2322 N	*IC* 2320	*IC* 2228	*IC* 2226	*IC* 2224	*IC* 2222
Frankfurt (Main) Hbf **806** d.	...	...	0526	0726k	0926	1126	1326	1526	1726	1926
Bad Nauheim d.	...	...	0556	0756k	0956	1156	1356	1556	1756	1956
Wetzlar **806** d.	...	...	0618	0818k	1018	1218	1418	1618	1818	2018
Dillenburg **806** d.	...	...	0636	0836k	1036	1236	1436	1636	1836	2036
Siegen Hbf **806** a.	...	...	0658	0858k	1058	1258	1458	1658	1858	2101
Siegen Hbf d.	0501	0704	0704	0904	1104	1304	1504	1704	1904	...
Kreuztal d.	0512	0715	0715	0915	│	1315	│	1715	1915	...
Lennestadt ♥ d.	0532	0733	0733	0933	1132	1333	1532	1733	1933	...
Finnentrop d.	0544	0746	0746	0946	│	1346	│	1746	1946	...
Werdohl d.	0602	0804	0804	1004	│	1404	│	1804	2004	...
Altena (Westf) d.	0611	0813	0813	1013	│	1413	│	1813	2013	...
Letmathe d.	0622	0823	0823	1023	1213	1423	1613	1823	2023	...
Witten Hbf **802** d.	0647	0848	0848	1048	│	1448	│	1848	2048	...
Dortmund Hbf **802** a.	0659	0857	0857	1057	│	1458	│	1857	2057	...
Schwerte (Ruhr) **802** a.	│	...	...	│	1228	...	1628	│	...	...
Unna **802** a.	│	...	...	│	1238	...	1638	│	...	...
Hamm (Westf) **802** a.	0717	...	...	1117	1255	...	1655	1917	...	...
Münster (Westf) Hbf **802** a.	0738	...	...	1138	1328	...	1728	1939	...	...

Regional services. *See lower panel for other services Essen - Hagen and v.v. See note ⊠ for additional services Hagen - Siegen and v.v.*

km		Ⓐt	Ⓒz	Ⓐt	†z	⚒r						⚒r						⚒r			⚒r			⚒r			
0	**Essen** Hbf d.	...	...	...	...	...	0734t	...	0834r	0934	...	...	1134	...	1234	1334	...	...	1534	...	...	1734	...	...	1934	...	...
16	Bochum Hbf d.	...	...	...	...	...	0747t	...	0847r	0947	...	...	1146	...	1247	1347	...	...	1546	...	...	1747	...	...	1947	...	...
30	Witten Hbf d.	...	...	...	...	...	0757t	...	0857r	0957	...	...	1156	...	1257	1357	...	...	1556	...	...	1757	...	...	1957	...	...
45	**Hagen** Hbf a.	...	...	...	...	...	0809t	...	0909r	1009	...	...	1209	...	1309	1409	...	...	1608	...	...	1809	...	...	2009	...	...
45	**Hagen** Hbf d.	0610	0615	0640	0715	0740	0815	0840	0915	1015	1040	1140	1214	1240	1315	1415	1440	1540	1613	1640	1740	1815	1840	1940	2015	2115	2215
66	Letmathe d.	0628	0632	0657	0732	0757	0832	0857	0932	1032	1057	1157	1232	1257	1332	1432	1457	1557	1632	1657	1757	1832	1857	1957	2032	2132	2232
75	Altena (Westf) d.	0636	0640	0705	0740	0805	0840	0905	0940	1040	1105	1205	1240	1305	1340	1440	1505	1605	1640	1705	1805	1840	1905	2005	2040	2140	2240
84	Werdohl d.	0645	0649	0714	0749	0814	0849	0914	0949	1049	1114	1214	1248	1314	1349	1449	1514	1614	1649	1714	1814	1849	1914	2014	2049	2149	2249
106	Finnentrop d.	0703	0707	0731	0807	0831	0907	0931	1007	1107	1131	1231	1306	1331	1407	1507	1531	1631	1707	1731	1831	1907	1931	2031	2107	2207	2307
119	Lennestadt ♥ d.	0715	0718	0743	0818	0843	0918	0943	1018	1118	1143	1243	1318	1343	1418	1518	1543	1643	1718	1743	1843	1918	1943	2043	2119	2219	2319
141	Kreuztal d.	0738	0737	0806	0837	0906	0937	1006	1037	1137	1206	1306	1337	1406	1437	1537	1606	1706	1737	1806	1906	1937	2006	2106	2142	2242	2342
152	**Siegen** Hbf a.	0750	0748	0819	0849	0919	0948	1019	1049	1148	1219	1319	1347	1419	1449	1548	1619	1719	1748	1819	1919	1948	2020	2121	2154	2254	2354

	Ⓐt	⑥	Ⓐt		Ⓐt	†z	⚒r			⚒r						⚒r						⚒r					
Siegen Hbf d.	0402	0504	0543	0612	0635	0712	0743	0812	0843	0943	1012	1043	1112	1212	1243	1342	1412	1443	1512	1612	1643	1744	1812	1843	2011	2111	2211
Kreuztal d.	0413	0516	0554	0622	0647	0722	0754	0822	0854	0954	1022	1054	1122	1222	1254	1354	1422	1454	1522	1622	1654	1755	1822	1855	2022	2122	2222
Lennestadt ♥ d.	0436	0539	0617	0641	0710	0741	0817	0841	0917	1017	1041	1117	1141	1241	1317	1417	1441	1518	1541	1641	1717	1818	1841	1918	2045	2145	2245
Finnentrop d.	0453	0553	0630	0653	0730	0754	0830	0853	0930	1030	1053	1130	1153	1253	1330	1430	1453	1531	1553	1653	1730	1831	1853	1931	2058	2158	2258
Werdohl d.	0510	0610	0647	0710	0747	0812	0847	0910	0947	1047	1110	1147	1210	1310	1347	1447	1510	1547	1610	1710	1747	1848	1910	1947	2115	2215	2315
Altena (Westf) d.	0518	0619	0655	0718	0755	0820	0855	0918	0955	1055	1118	1156	1218	1318	1355	1455	1518	1556	1618	1718	1755	1856	1918	1956	2124	2223	2323
Letmathe d.	0530	0630	0708	0730	0808	0830	0908	0930	1008	1108	1130	1208	1230	1330	1408	1508	1530	1608	1630	1730	1808	1908	1930	2008	2136	2236	2336
Hagen Hbf a.	0546	0646	0724	0746	0824	0846	0924	0946	1024	1124	1146	1224	1246	1346	1424	1524	1546	1624	1646	1746	1824	1924	1946	2024	2152	2252	2352
Hagen Hbf d.	...	...	...	0751t	...	...	...	0951	...	...	1151	...	1251	1351	...	...	1551	...	1651	1751	...	...	1951	...	...	...	...
Witten Hbf d.	...	...	...	0802t	...	...	...	1002	...	...	1202	...	1302	1402	...	...	1602	...	1702	1802	...	...	2002	...	...	...	...
Bochum Hbf d.	...	...	...	0814t	...	...	...	1014	...	...	1214	...	1314	1414	...	...	1615	...	1714	1814	...	...	2014	...	...	...	...
Essen Hbf a.	...	...	...	0829t	...	...	...	1029	...	...	1229	...	1329	1429	...	...	1629	...	1729	1829	...	...	2029	...	...	...	...

Other services ESSEN - HAGEN

						Ⓐt					
Essen Hbf d.	0507		2307	0012	A	0634	1034	1434	1634	1834	...
Bochum Hbf d.	0521	and	2321	0026	L	0647	1047	1447	1647	1847	...
Witten Hbf d.	0533	hourly	2333	0038	S	0657	1057	1457	1657	1857	...
Hagen Hbf d.	0547	until	2347	0052	O	0715	1115	1515	1715	1915	...
Letmathe a.	...		...	...		0730	1130	1530	1730	1930	...

							Ⓐt	⚒r			
Letmathe d.	...		...	...	...	A	0630	0830	1030	1430	1830
Hagen Hbf d.	0516	and	2216	2316	0016	L	0651	0851	1051	1451	1851
Witten Hbf d.	0531	hourly	2231	2331	0031	S	0702	0903	1102	1502	1902
Bochum Hbf d.	0543	until	2243	2343	0043	O	0714	0915	1114	1514	1914
Essen Hbf a.	0558		2258	2358	0058		0729	0929	1129	1529	1929

N – From/to Norddeich Mole (Table **812**).
S – From Stuttgart (Table **912**).
a – Ⓐ only.

h – Also calls at Herborn (d. 0552).
k – ⚒ only.
r – ⚒ (not June 16, Nov. 1).
t – Ⓐ (not June 16, Nov. 1).

z – Also June 16, Nov. 1.
♥ – Lennestadt - Altenhundem.

⊠ – Additional services Hagen - Siegen and v.v.:
From Hagen at 0540 Ⓐt, 0940 ⚒r, 1340 ⚒r and 2315.
From Siegen at 1143 ⚒r and 1543 ⚒r.

809 PADERBORN - HAMELN - HANNOVER - HANNOVER FLUGHAFEN ✈ *S-Bahn 5*

SERVICE UNTIL JULY 1. See page 566 for service July 2 - October 25.

km		Ⓐ	⚒		⚒	⚒	Ⓐ	⑥		⚒	Ⓐ	⚒	†	⚒	Ⓐ		⚒		⚒		⚒		⚒		⚒
0	**Paderborn** Hbf **805 811** d.	...	...	...	...	...	0512	...	...	...	...	0615	...	...	...	0715	...	0815	...	0915	...	1015	...	1115	...
17	Altenbeken **805 811** d.	...	...	...	...	...	0524	...	...	...	...	0627	...	...	...	0727	...	0827	...	0927	...	1027	...	1127	...
56	Bad Pyrmont d.	...	...	...	0505	...	0602	0605	...	...	0635	0702	0705	...	0735	0802	...	0902	...	1002	...	1102	...	1202	...
75	Hameln a.	...	...	...	0519	...	0616	0618	...	...	0649	0716	0718	...	0749	0816	...	0916	...	1016	...	1116	...	1216	...
75	Hameln d.	0420	0450	0520	0520	0550	0620	0620	0620	0650	0650	0720	0720	0750	0750	0820	0850	0920	0950	1020	1050	1120	1150	1220	1250
133	**Hannover** Hbf a.	0509	0540	0610	0610	0640	0710	0710	0710	0740	0740	0810	0805	0840	0840	0910	0939	1010	1040	1110	1140	1210	1240	1310	1340

		⚒	Ⓐ		⚒					Ⓐ			Ⓐ			Ⓐ				Ⓐ				⑤⑥f	A
Paderborn Hbf **805 811** d.	1215	...	...	1314	...	1415	...	1515	...	...	1615	...	...	1715	...	...	1815	...	1915	...	2015	2115	2215	2310	...
Altenbeken **805 811** d.	1227	...	...	1327	...	1427	...	1527	...	...	1627	...	...	1727	...	...	1827	...	1927	...	2027	2127	2227	2322	...
Bad Pyrmont d.	1302	...	1335	1402	...	1502	...	1602	...	1635	1702	...	1735	1802	...	1835	1902	...	2002	...	2102	2202	2302	0002	0005
Hameln a.	1316	...	1349	1416	...	1516	...	1616	...	1649	1716	...	1749	1816	...	1849	1916	...	2016	...	2116	2216	2316	0016	0019
Hameln d.	1320	1350	1350	1420	1450	1520	1550	1620	1650	1650	1720	1750	1750	1820	1850	1850	1920	1950	2020	2050	2120	2220	2320	0020	0020
Hannover Hbf a.	1410	1440	1440	1510	1540	1610	1640	1710	1740	1740	1810	1840	1840	1910	1940	1940	2010	2040	2110	2140	2210	2310	0010	0110	0105

	Ⓐ		⚒	Ⓐ	⚒	Ⓐ	⚒		⚒		⚒		⚒		⚒		⚒		Ⓐ	⚒		⚒		⚒	
Hannover Hbf d.	0051	...	0451	0521	0551	0621	0621	0651	0721	0751	0821	0851	0921	0951	1021	1051	1121	1151	1221	1221	1251	1321	1351	1421	1451
Hameln a.	0143	...	0540	0610	0640	0710	0710	0740	0810	0840	0910	0940	1010	1040	1110	1140	1210	1240	1310	1310	1340	1410	1440	1510	1540
Hameln d.	...	...	0544	0611	0644	0711	...	0744	...	0844	...	0944	...	1044	...	1144	...	1244	1311	...	1344	...	1444	...	1544
Bad Pyrmont d.	...	...	0600	0625	0700	0725	...	0800	...	0900	...	1000	...	1100	...	1200	...	1300	1325	...	1400	...	1500	...	1600
Altenbeken **805 811** d.	...	...	0633	...	0733	...	...	0833	...	0933	...	1033	...	1133	...	1233	...	1333	...	...	1433	...	1533	...	1633
Paderborn Hbf **805 811** a.	...	...	0646	...	0746	...	...	0846	...	0946	...	1046	...	1146	...	1246	...	1346	...	...	1446	...	1546	...	1646

	Ⓐ			Ⓐ			Ⓐ							⚒		Ⓐ			⑤⑥f	B		⑤⑥			
Hannover Hbf d.	1521	1521	1551	1621	1621	1651	1721	1721	1751	1821	1851	1921	1951	2021	2051	2121	2151	...	2251	2255	...	2351	2351	...	...
Hameln a.	1610	1610	1640	1710	1710	1740	1810	1810	1840	1910	1940	2010	2040	2110	2140	2210	2240	...	2340	2340	...	0040	0040	...	...
Hameln d.	1611	...	1644	1711	...	1744	1811	...	1844	...	1944	...	2044	...	2144	...	2244	...	2344	2344	...	0042	...	...	...
Bad Pyrmont d.	1625	...	1700	1725	...	1800	1825	...	1900	...	2000	...	2100	...	2200	...	2300	...	0000	2358	...	0056	...	...	...
Altenbeken **805 811** d.	...	...	1733	...	...	1833	...	...	1933	...	2033	...	2133	...	2233	...	2333	...	0033	...	...	...	...	...	...
Paderborn Hbf **805 811** a.	...	...	1746	...	...	1846	...	...	1946	...	2046	...	2146	...	2246	...	2346	...	0046	...	...	...	...	...	...

SHUTTLE SERVICE HANNOVER HBF - HANNOVER FLUGHAFEN ✈ (*15 km*, journey 12 – 15 minutes)

From Hannover Hbf at 0001, 0122, 0611, 0657, 0808, 0903, 1010, 1110, 1209, 1311, 1408, 1510, 1609, 1704, 1809, 1857, 1954, 2104, 2210 and 2310.

From Hannover Flughafen at 0149, 0538, 0638, 0738, 0838, 0938, 1038, 1134, 1238, 1338, 1436, 1538, 1638, 1738, 1836, 1934, 2038, 2138, 2237 and 2341.

A – Mornings of ①–⑤ (not June 16).
B – ⑦–④ (not June 15).
f – Also June 15.

HAMM and BAD BENTHEIM - HANNOVER - BERLIN 810

Independent operator **FlixTrain** also run services Köln - Berlin (see Table **927**).

km		ICE 649		IC 2447	ICE 841	ICE 753	IC 2241	ICE 541	ICE 1041	IC 2445	ICE 843	ICE 853	ICE 1155	IC 245	IC 245	ICE 543	ICE 553	IC 2443	ICE 845	ICE 845	ICE 855	ICE 1545	IC 141	ICE 545	ICE 555
		①–⑤		①	①–⑥	①–⑤	①–⑥	①–⑥	⑦			①–⑥		⑦	①–⑥				①–⑤	⑥⑦		①–⑥			
		✕		D🍷	O✕	✕	🍷	✕	✕	D🍷	✕	✕	A✕	‡🍷	✱🍷	✕	K✕	D🍷	✕	✕	✕	T🍷	✱🍷	✕	A✕
	Köln Hbf **800** d.	...	...	...	...	...	...	0426	...	0511e	0525	0542	0618	...	...	0624	0648	0713	...	0727	0748	...	...	0828	0848
	Wuppertal Hbf **800** d.	...	...	...	...	...	...	|	...	0544e	|	0616	|	...	...	|	0716	0744	⊙	|	0816	...	...	|	0916
	Düsseldorf Hbf **800** d.	...	...	...	...	...	...	0450	...	|	0549	|	|	...	...	0651	|	|	0751	0751	|	...	...	0852	|
	Dortmund Hbf **800** d.	...	...	...	...	...	...	0546	...	0625	0643	|	|	...	...	0748	|	0825	0848	0848	|	0909	...	0948	|
0	**Hamm** (Westf) **802** d.	...	...	...	...	...	...	0604	...	0645	0711	0711	|	...	...	0811	0811	0845	0911	0911	0911	0934	...	1011	1011
50	Gütersloh Hbf **802** d.	...	...	...	...	...	...	0628	...	0708	|	|	|	...	...	|	|	0908	|	|	|	0955	...	|	|
67	**Bielefeld** Hbf **802 811** d.	...	...	0519	...	...	...	0640	...	0719	0738	0738	|	...	...	0838	0838	0919	0938	0938	0938	1006	...	1038	1038
81	Herford **811** d.	...	...	0528	...	...	...	|	...	0729	|	|	|	...	...	|	|	0929	|	|	|	1016	...	|	|
	Amsterdam C **22** d.	...	...	|	...	...	...	|	...	|	|	|	|	...	0502z	|	|	|	|	|	|	|	0700	|	|
	Bad Bentheim 🏛 **811** d.	...	...	|	...	...	...	|	...	|	|	|	|	...	0721	|	|	|	|	|	|	|	0928	|	|
	Rheine **811** d.	...	...	|	...	...	...	|	...	|	|	|	|	...	0735	|	|	|	|	|	|	|	0942	|	|
	Münster (Westf) Hbf. **800** d.	...	...	|	...	...	0533	|	...	|	|	|	|	0733	|	|	|	|	|	|	|	|	|	|	|
	Osnabrück Hbf . **800 811** d.	...	...	|	...	...	0604	|	...	|	|	|	|	0804	0805	|	|	|	|	|	|	|	1008	|	|
	Bünde (Westf) **811** d.	...	...	|	...	...	0627	|	...	|	|	|	|	0826	0826	|	|	|	|	|	|	|	|	|	|
97	Bad Oeynhausen **811** d.	...	...	|	...	...	0638	|	...	|	|	|	|	0839	0839	|	|	|	|	|	|	|	1037	|	|
112	Minden (Westf) **811** d.	...	...	0546	...	...	0647	|	...	0746	|	|	|	0848	0848	|	|	0946	|	|	|	|	1047	|	|
177	**Hannover** Hbf **811** a.	...	...	0618	...	...	0718	0728	...	0818	0828	0828	|	0918	0918	0928	0928	1018	1028	1028	1028	1101	1118	1128	1128
177	**Hannover** Hbf d.	0527	...	0636	0631	0703	0722	0731	0731	0836	0831	0831	|	0922	0922	0931	0931	1036	1031	1031	1031	1104t	1122	1131	1131
	Magdeburg Hbf **866** a.	▽	...	0754	|	|	|	|	|	0954	|	|	|	|	|	|	|	1154	|	|	|	|	|	|	|
	Leipzig Hbf **866** a.	|	...	0917	|	|	|	|	|	1117	|	|	|	|	|	|	|	1317	|	|	|	|	|	|	|
252	Wolfsburg **902** d.	0620	...	...	0704	0737	0754	|	0803	...	0904	0904	|	0954	0954	|	|	...	1104	1104	1104	1136t	1154	|	|
327	Stendal Hbf **838** d.	0646	...	...	0732	0804	0825	|	0833	...	|	|	|	1026	1026	|	|	...	|	|	|	|	1226	|	|
419	**Berlin** Spandau **838 902** a.	0722	...	...	0811	0838	0906	0854	0906	...	0959	0959	1002	1104	1104	1054	1054	...	1159	1159	1159	1238t	1304	1254	1254
435	**Berlin** Hbf **838 902** a.	0740	...	...	0825	0854	0922	0910	0923	...	1014	1014	1012	1122	1122	1110	1110	...	1214	1214	1214	1255t	1322	1310	1310
440	**Berlin** Ostbahnhof **838 902** a.	0750	...	...	0835	0904	0934	0920	0934	...	1025	1025	...	1134	1134	1120	1120	...	1225	1225	1225	1305t	1334	1321	1321

	ICE 757	ICE 757	IC 2441	ICE 847	ICE 857	ICE 759	IC 143	ICE 547	ICE 557	IC 2010	IC 2049	ICE 849	ICE 859	ICE 1157	IC 145	ICE 549	ICE 559	IC 2047	ICE 941	ICE 951	IC 1916	ICE 1116	IC 147	ICE 641	ICE 651
	m	R								⑤f											⑤f¶	⑦§			
	✕	✕	D🍷	✕	✕	Y✕	✱🍷	✕	✕	S🍷	D🍷	✕	✕	A✕	✱🍷	✕	A✕	D🍷	✕	✕	S🍷	S✕	✱🍷	✕	A✕
Köln Hbf **800** d.	0842	0842	0913	0924	0948	0934	...	...	1048	1046	1113	...	1148	1217	...	...	1248	1313	...	1348	1346	1346	...	...	1448
Wuppertal Hbf **800** d.	|	|	0944	|	1016	|	...	...	1116	|	1144	...	1216	|	...	...	1316	1344	...	1416	|	|	...	...	1516
Düsseldorf Hbf **800** d.	0915	0915	|	0952	|	1016	...	1052	|	1118	|	1153	|	|	...	1252	|	|	1351	|	1414	1414	...	1451	|
Dortmund Hbf **800** d.	|	1010	1025	1048	|	1110	...	1148	|	1210	1225	1248	|	|	...	1348	|	1425	1448	|	1510	1510	...	1548	|
Hamm (Westf) **802** d.	|	1034	1045	1111	1111	1134	...	1211	1211	1233	1245	1311	1311	|	...	1411	1411	1445	1511	1511	1533	1533	...	1611	1611
Gütersloh Hbf **802** d.	|	1055	1108	|	|	1155	...	|	|	1255	1308	|	|	|	...	|	|	1508	|	|	1555	1555	...	|	|
Bielefeld Hbf **802 811** d.	|	1106	1119	1138	1138	1206	...	1238	1238	1306	1319	1338	1338	|	...	1438	1438	1519	1538	1538	1606	1606	...	1638	1638
Herford **811** d.	◧	1116	1129	|	|	1216	...	|	|	1316	1329	|	|	|	...	|	|	1529	|	|	1616	1616	...	|	|
Amsterdam C **22** d.	|	|	|	|	|	|	0910	|	|	|	|	|	|	|	1100	|	|	|	|	|	|	|	1300	|	|
Bad Bentheim 🏛 **811** d.	|	|	|	|	|	|	1128	|	|	|	|	|	|	|	1328	|	|	|	|	|	|	|	1528	|	|
Rheine **811** d.	|	|	|	|	|	|	1142	|	|	|	|	|	|	|	1342	|	|	|	|	|	|	|	1542	|	|
Münster (Westf) Hbf **800** d.	1028	|	|	|	|	|	|	|	|	|	|	|	|	|	|	|	|	|	|	|	|	|	|	|	|
Osnabrück Hbf **800 811** d.	1053	|	|	|	|	|	1208	|	|	|	|	|	|	|	1408	|	|	|	|	|	|	|	1608	|	|
Bünde (Westf) **811** d.	|	|	|	|	|	|	1228	|	|	|	|	|	|	|	|	|	|	|	|	|	|	|	1628	|	|
Bad Oeynhausen **811** d.	|	|	|	|	|	|	|	|	|	|	|	|	|	|	1437	|	|	|	|	|	|	|	|	|	|
Minden (Westf) **811** d.	|	|	1146	|	|	|	1247	|	|	|	1346	|	|	|	1447	|	|	1546	|	|	|	|	1647	|	|
Hannover Hbf **811** a.	1201	1201	1218	1228	1228	1302	1318	1328	1328	1401	1418	1428	1428	|	1518	1528	1528	1618	1628	1628	1701	1701	1718	1728	1728
Hannover Hbf d.	1204j	1204t	1236	1231	1231	1304t	1322	1331	1331	1404t	1436	1431	1431	|	1522	1531	1531	1636	1631	1631	1704t	1704t	1722	1731	1731
Magdeburg Hbf **866** a.	|	|	1354	|	|	|	|	|	|	|	1554	|	|	|	|	|	|	1754	|	|	|	|	|	|	|
Leipzig Hbf **866** a.	|	|	1517	|	|	|	|	|	|	|	1717	|	|	|	|	|	|	1917	|	|	|	|	|	|	|
Wolfsburg **902** d.	1236j	1236t	...	1305	1305	1336t	1354	|	|	1438t	...	1504	1504	|	1554	|	|	...	1704	1704	1736t	1739t	1754	|	|
Stendal Hbf **838** d.	|	|	...	|	|	|	1426	|	|	|	...	|	|	|	1626	|	|	...	|	|	|	|	1826	|	|
Berlin Spandau **838 902** a.	1339j	1339t	...	1359	1359	1438t	1504	1454	1454	1539t	...	1559	1559	1602	1704	1654	1654	...	1800	1800	1838t	1838t	1904	1854	1854
Berlin Hbf **838 902** a.	1354j	1354t	...	1414	1414	1452t	1522	1510	1510	1554t	...	1614	1614	1613	1722	1710	1710	...	1810	1810	1855t	1855t	1922	1908	1908
Berlin Ostbahnhof **838 902** a.	1404j	1404t	...	1425	1425	...	1534	1520	1520	1605t	...	1625	1625	...	1734	1720	1720	...	...	...	1906t	1906t	1934	1921	1921

	ICE 1059	ICE 1059	IC 2045	ICE 943	ICE 953	ICE 1151	IC 149	ICE 643	ICE 653	ICE 1159	IC 2043	IC 2043	ICE 945	ICE 955	IC 241	IC 241	ICE 645	ICE 655	IC 2041	ICE 947	ICE 957	IC 243	ICE 657	IC 2341	ICE 949
	m⊖	R⊖				t				◇		⑧	⑧		B	⑦			⑦		⑤⑦	⑦	⑤⑦		
	✕	✕	D🍷	✕	✕	✕	✱🍷	✕	✕	A✕	🍷	🍷	✕	✕	✱🍷	✱🍷	✕	A✕	🍷	✕	✕	✱🍷	N✕		A♥
Köln Hbf **800** d.	1436	1436	1513	...	1548	1537	...	...	1648	1817	1713	1713	...	1748	...	...	...	1848	1913	1927q	1948	...	2048	2113	2315
Wuppertal Hbf **800** d.	|	|	1544	...	1616	|	...	...	1716	|	1744	1744	...	1816	...	...	...	1916	1944	|	2016	...	2116	2144	|
Düsseldorf Hbf **800** d.	1509	1509	|	1551	|	1616	...	1651	|	|	|	|	1751	|	...	...	1851	|	|	1951	|	...	|	|	2338
Dortmund Hbf **800** d.	|	1606	1625	1648	|	1710	...	1748	|	|	1825	1825	1848	|	...	...	1948	|	2028	2048	|	...	|	2225	0034
Hamm (Westf) **802** d.	|	1634	1645	1711	1711	1734	...	1811	1811	|	1845	1845	1911	1911	...	...	2011	2011	2045	2111	2111	...	2211	2246	0051
Gütersloh Hbf **802** d.	|	1655	1708	|	|	1755	...	|	|	|	1908	1908	|	|	...	...	|	|	2108	|	|	...	|	2309	0111
Bielefeld Hbf **802 811** d.	|	1706	1719	1738	1738	1806	...	1838	1838	|	1919	1919	1938	1938	...	...	2038	2038	2119	2138	2138	...	2238	2320	0126
Herford **811** d.	◧	1716	1729	|	|	|	...	|	|	|	1929	1929	|	|	...	...	|	|	2129	|	|	...	|	2330	|
Amsterdam C **22** d.	|	|	|	|	|	|	1500	|	|	|	|	|	|	|	1710	1710	|	|	|	|	|	1900	|	|	|
Bad Bentheim 🏛 **811** d.	|	|	|	|	|	|	1728	|	|	|	|	|	|	|	1928	1928	|	|	|	|	|	2128	|	|	|
Rheine **811** d.	|	|	|	|	|	|	1742	|	|	|	|	|	|	|	1942	1942	|	|	|	|	|	2142	|	|	|
Münster (Westf) Hbf **800** d.	1630	|	|	|	|	|	|	|	|	|	|	|	|	|	|	|	|	|	|	|	|	|	|	|	|
Osnabrück Hbf **800 811** d.	1656	|	|	|	|	|	1808	|	|	|	|	|	|	|	2008	2008	|	|	|	|	|	2208	|	|	|
Bünde (Westf) **811** d.	|	|	|	|	|	|	|	|	|	|	|	|	|	|	2028	2028	|	|	|	|	|	|	|	|	|
Bad Oeynhausen **811** d.	|	|	|	|	|	1824	1837	|	|	|	|	|	|	|	|	|	|	|	|	|	|	2237	|	|	|
Minden (Westf) **811** d.	|	|	1746	|	|	|	1847	|	|	|	1946	1946	|	|	2047	2047	|	|	2146	|	|	2247	|	2347	0151
Hannover Hbf **811** a.	1802	1802	1818	1828	1828	1901	1918	1928	1928	|	2018	2018	2028	2028	2118	2118	2128	2128	2218	2228	2228	2321	2328	0018	0223
Hannover Hbf d.	1805j	1805t	1836	1831	1831	1904	1922	1931	1931	|	...	2036	2031	2031	...	2122	2131	2131	...	2231	2231	...	2331	...	0240
Magdeburg Hbf **866** a.	|	|	1954	|	|	|	|	|	|	|	...	2154	|	|	...	|	|	|	...	|	|	...	|	...	0402
Leipzig Hbf **866** a.	|	|	2117	|	|	|	|	|	|	|	...	2317r	|	|	...	|	|	|	...	|	|	...	|	...	|
Wolfsburg **902** d.	1836j	1836t	...	1904	1904	1936	1954	|	|	|	...	...	2103	2103	...	2154	|	|	...	2304	2304	...	0003	...	|
Stendal Hbf **838** d.	|	|	...	|	|	|	2026	|	|	|	...	...	2131	2131	...	2226	|	|	...	|	|	...	|	...	|
Berlin Spandau **838 902** a.	1939j	1939t	...	1959	1959	2038	2104	2054	2054	2202	...	...	2207	2207	...	2304	2254	2254	...	2359	2359	...	0100	...	|
Berlin Hbf **838 902** a.	1955j	1955t	...	2014	2014	2055	2123	2109	2109	2219	...	...	2223	2223	...	2322	2310	2310	...	0013	0013	...	0114	...	0536
Berlin Ostbahnhof **838 902** a.	2005j	2005t	...	2025	2025	2106	2135	2120	2120	2231	...	...	2234	2234	...	2334	2320v	2320v	...	...	...	...	0125	...	0547

A – From Bonn (Table **800**).
B – Daily to Sept. 9; ⑧ from Sept. 11.
D – To Dresden (Table **842**).
K – From Koblenz (Table **800**).
N – From Aachen Hbf (d. 1959) and Düren (d. 2027).
O – From Oldenburg via Bremen (Table **813**) on ①–⑤.
R – June 24 - Aug. 5.
S – From Stuttgart (Tables **800** and **912**).
T – KAROLINGER - From Aachen Hbf (d. 0708), Herzogenrath (d. 0723), Rheydt Hbf (d. 0752), Mönchengladbach Hbf (d. 0758), Viersen (d. 0806) and Krefeld Hbf (d. 0818).
Y – To Ostseebad Binz until July 17 (Tables **844** and **845**).

e – ①–⑥.
f – Also June 15; not June 17.
j – Until June 23.
m – Not June 24 - Aug. 5.
q – ①②③④⑥ only.

r – ⑤⑦ only.
t – Until July 17.
v – ③–⑦ only.
z – Until Sept. 3.

‡ – Train number **2245** June 26 - July 31.
¶ – Train number **2016** from July 22.
§ – Train number **1118** from July 24.
⊖ – Train number **1069** from July 18.
♥ – Also calls at Braunschweig Hbf (a. 0314), Brandenburg Hbf (a. 0445), Potsdam Hbf (a. 0504), Berlin Wannsee (a. 0513) and Berlin Zoo (a. 0529).
⊙ – From Köln/Bonn Flughafen (Table **800**).
◇ – Also calls at Berlin Zoo (a. 2212).
◧ – Via Recklinghausen (Table **800**).
▽ – Via Braunschweig Hbf (d. 0601).
✱ – Service is retimed June 25 - Aug. 4. See special table on page 566.

810 BERLIN - HANNOVER - HAMM and BAD BENTHEIM

Berlin departures may be up to 4 minutes earlier until July 8. Independent operator **FlixTrain** also run services Berlin - Köln (see Table **927**).

km		ICE 948	IC 2040	ICE 656	ICE 646	IC 242	ICE 1158	ICE 956	ICE 946	IC 2042	ICE 654	ICE 644	IC 240	IC 240	ICE 1152	ICE 954	ICE 944	IC 2044	ICE 1150	ICE 652	ICE 642	IC 148	ICE 952	ICE 942
				①–⑥	①–⑥	①–⑥	◇		①–⑥			①–⑥	E	①–⑥	t				H					
		♥	🍷	✕	✕	≋🍷	A✕	✕	✕	🍷	✕	✕	≋🍷	≋🍷	✕	✕	✕	D🍷	✕	A✕	✕	≋🍷	✕	✕
0	**Berlin** Ostbahnhof . **838 902** d.	0010	...	...	...	...	0521	0518	0518	...	0635	0635	...	0622	0649	0735	0735	...	0747	0835	0835	0822	0935	0935
5	**Berlin** Hbf .... **838 902** d.	0021	...	0430	0430	...	0533	0529	0529	...	0646	0646	...	0634	0700	0746	0746	...	0758	0846	0846	0834	0946	0946
21	**Berlin** Spandau ...... **838 902** d.	|	...	0441	0441	...	0551	0545	0545	...	0702	0702	...	0651	0716	0800	0800	...	0813	0902	0902	0851	1000	1000
113	Stendal Hbf .... **838** d.	|	...	0514	0514	...	|	0624	0624	...	|	|	...	0731	|	|	|	...	|	|	|	0931	|	|
188	Wolfsburg .... **902** d.	|	...	0547	0547	...	|	0653	0653	...	0753	0753	...	0801	|	0853	0853	...	0920	|	|	1001	1053	1053
	Leipzig Hbf **866** .... d.	|	...	|	|	...	|	|	|	0443g	|	|	...	|	|	|	|	0638	|	|	|	|	|	|
	Magdeburg Hbf **866** .... d.	0149	...	|	|	...	|	|	|	0603e	|	|	...	|	|	|	|	0803	|	|	|	|	|	|
263	**Hannover** Hbf .... a.	0309	...	0618	0618	...	|	0728	0728	0723e	0828	0828	...	0836	0853	0928	0928	0923	0953	1028	1028	1036	1128	1128
263	**Hannover** Hbf .... **811** d.	0340	0540	0621	0621	0640	|	0731	0731	0740	0831	0831	0840	0840	0856	0931	0931	0940	0956	1031	1031	1040	1131	1131
328	Minden (Westf) .... **811** d.	0411	0612	0650	0650	0712	|	|	|	0813	|	|	0911	0911	|	|	|	1013	|	|	|	1111	|	|
343	Bad Oeynhausen .... **811** d.	|	|	|	|	0722	|	|	|	|	|	|	|	|	|	|	|	|	|	|	|	1122	|	|
359	Bünde (Westf) .... **811** d.	|	|	|	|	|	|	|	|	|	|	|	0932	0932	|	|	|	|	|	|	|	|	|	|
396	**Osnabrück** Hbf... **800 811** d.	|	|	|	|	0753	|	|	|	|	|	|	0953	0953	|	|	|	|	1106	|	|	1153	|	|
	Münster (Westf) Hbf .. **800** a.	|	|	|	|	|	|	|	|	|	|	|	|	|	|	|	|	|	1130	|	|	|	|	|
444	Rheine .... **811** d.	|	|	|	|	0820	|	|	|	|	|	|	1020	1020	|	|	|	|	|	|	|	1220	|	|
465	Bad Bentheim 🏛 .... **811** a.	|	|	|	|	0834	|	|	|	|	|	|	1034	1034	|	|	|	|	|	|	|	1234	|	|
647	*Amsterdam C* **22** .... a.	|	|	|	|	1100	|	|	|	|	|	|	1300	1300	|	|	|	|	|	|	|	1500h	|	|
	Herford .... **811** d.	|	0632	0711	0711	...	|	|	|	0832	|	|	...	...	0943	|	|	1032	◧	|	|	...	|	|
	Bielefeld Hbf......... **802 811** d.	0436	0640	0721	0721	...	|	0822	0822	0840	0922	0922	...	...	0953	1022	1022	1040	|	1122	1122	...	1222	1222
	Gütersloh Hbf .... **802** d.	0446	0652	|	|	...	|	|	|	0852	|	|	...	...	1003	|	|	1052	|	|	|	...	|	|
	Hamm (Westf) .... **802** a.	0510	0714	0747	0747	...	|	0848	0848	0914	0948	0948	...	...	1024	1048	1048	1114	|	1148	1148	...	1248	1248
	Dortmund Hbf **800** .... a.	|	0734	|	0810	...	|	|	0910	0933	|	1010	...	...	1048	|	1110	1133	|	|	1210	...	|	1310
	Düsseldorf Hbf **800** .... ▷ a.	|	|	|	0903	...	|	|	1007z	|	|	1112	...	...	1142	|	1202	|	1250	|	1312	...	|	1407
	Wuppertal Hbf **800** .... a.	0607	0812	0838	...	...	|	0938	...	1012	1038	...	...	...	|	1138	...	1212	|	1238	...	...	1338	...
	Köln Hbf **800** .... a.	0657	0846	0909	...	...	0940	1009	...	1046	1109	...	...	...	1212	1209	...	1246	1319	1309	...	...	1409	...

	IC 2046	IC 2011	ICE 1611	ICE 650	ICE 640	IC 146	ICE 1156	ICE 950	ICE 940	IC 2048	ICE 717	IC 1917	ICE 558	ICE 548	IC 144	ICE 1050	ICE 858	ICE 848	IC 2440	ICE 1548	ICE 556	ICE 546	IC 142	IC 1999
		⑦⊡	⑤								⑤f¶	⑦●								Ⓑ				⑦
	D🍷	S🍷	S	✕	✕	≋🍷	A✕	✕	✕	D🍷	S✕	S🍷	A✕	✕	≋🍷	✕	✕	✕	D🍷	K🍷	T✕	✕	≋🍷	U🍷
Berlin Ostbahnhof .. **838 902** d.	...	0949t	...	1035	1035	1022	...	1135	1135	...	1150t	1150t	1235	1235	1222	...	1335	1335	...	1346t	1435	1435	1422	1449
Berlin Hbf .... **838 902** d.	...	1000t	...	1046	1046	1034	1141	1146	1146	...	1201t	1201t	1246	1246	1234	1306t	1346	1346	...	1358t	1446	1446	1434	1500
Berlin Spandau .... **838 902** d.	...	1016t	...	1102	1102	1051	1151	1200	1200	...	1215t	1215t	1301	1301	1251	1316t	1400	1400	...	1412t	1502	1502	1451	1516
Stendal Hbf .... **838** d.	...	|	...	|	|	1131	|	|	|	...	|	|	|	|	1331	|	|	|	...	1446t	|	|	1531	|
Wolfsburg .... **902** d.	...	1120t	...	|	|	1201	|	1253	1253	...	1321t	1321t	|	|	1401	|	1453	1453	...	1520t	|	|	1601	1620
Leipzig Hbf **866** .... d.	0838	|	...	|	|	|	|	|	|	1038	|	|	|	|	|	|	|	|	1238	|	|	|	|	|
Magdeburg Hbf **866** .... d.	1003	|	...	|	|	|	|	|	|	1203	|	|	|	|	|	|	|	|	1403	|	|	|	|	|
Hannover Hbf .... a.	1123	1153t	...	1228	1228	1236	|	1328	1328	1323	1353t	1353t	1428	1428	1436	1453t	1528	1528	1523	1553t	1628	1628	1636	1652
Hannover Hbf .... **811** d.	1140	1156	1156	1231	1231	1240	|	1331	1331	1340	1356	1356	1431	1431	1440	1456	1531	1531	1540	1556	1631	1631	1640	...
Minden (Westf) .... **811** d.	1213	|	|	|	|	1311	|	|	|	1413	|	|	|	|	1511	|	|	|	1613	|	|	|	1711	...
Bad Oeynhausen .... **811** d.	|	|	|	|	|	|	|	|	|	|	|	|	|	|	1522	|	|	|	|	1634	|	|	|	...
Bünde (Westf) .... **811** d.	|	|	|	|	|	1332	|	|	|	|	|	|	|	|	|	|	|	|	|	|	|	|	1732	...
Osnabrück Hbf .... **811** d.	|	|	|	|	|	1353	|	|	|	|	|	|	|	|	1553	|	|	|	|	|	|	|	1753	...
Münster (Westf) Hbf .. **800** a.	|	|	|	|	|	|	|	|	|	|	|	|	|	|	|	|	|	|	|	|	|	|	|	...
Rheine .... **811** d.	|	|	|	|	|	1420	|	|	|	|	|	|	|	|	1620	|	|	|	|	|	|	|	1820	...
Bad Bentheim 🏛 .... **811** a.	|	|	|	|	|	1434	|	|	|	|	|	|	|	|	1634	|	|	|	|	|	|	|	1834	...
Amsterdam C **22** .... a.	|	|	|	|	|	1650	|	|	|	|	|	|	|	|	1900	|	|	|	|	|	|	|	2100	...
Herford .... **811** d.	1232	1244	1244	|	|	...	|	|	|	1432	1444	1444	|	|	...	1543	|	|	1632	1644	|	|	...	...
Bielefeld Hbf .... **802 811** d.	1240	1253	1254	1322	1322	...	|	1422	1422	1440	1453	1453	1522	1522	...	1553	1622	1622	1640	1653	1722	1722	...	...
Gütersloh Hbf .... **802** d.	1252	1303	1304	|	|	...	|	|	|	1452	1503	1503	|	|	...	1603	|	|	1652	1703	|	|	...	...
Hamm (Westf) .... **802** a.	1314	1324	1324	1348	1348	...	|	1448	1448	1514	1525	1525	1547	1547	...	1624	1648	1648	1714	1724	1748	1748	...	...
Dortmund Hbf **800** .... a.	1333	1349	1349	|	1410	...	|	|	1510	1533	|	|	|	1610	...	1649	|	1710	1733	...	|	1810	...	...
Düsseldorf Hbf **800** .... ▷ a.	|	1443	1443	|	1502	...	|	|	1603	|	|	|	|	1707	...	1747	|	1804	|	...	|	1907	...	...
Wuppertal Hbf **800** .... a.	1412	|	|	1438	...	...	|	1538	...	1612	1628	1628	1638	...	...	|	1738	|	1812	...	1838	...	...	...
Köln Hbf **800** .... a.	1446	1512	1512	1509	...	...	1541	1609	...	1646	1712	1712	1709	...	...	1819	1809	1832p	1846	...	1909	...	...	...

	ICE 856	ICE 846	IC 2442	ICE 554	ICE 544	IC 140	ICE 1154	ICE 854	ICE 844	IC 2444	ICE 750	ICE 552	ICE 542	IC 2242	ICE 852	ICE 842	ICE 832	IC 2446	ICE 1132	IC 2240	ICE 540	ICE 830	ICE 840	ICE 840
										Ⓑ	⑦				⑦		①–④	⑤⑦	⑦t	⑦	⑦	⑦		⑤–⑦
	✕	Y✕	D🍷	A✕	✕	≋🍷	A✕	✕	✕	D🍷	L✕	T✕	✕	🍷	✕	✕	O✕	D🍷	R	🍷	✕	O✕		
Berlin Ostbahnhof .. **838 902** d.	1535	1535	...	1635	1635	1622	...	1734	1734	...	...	1835	1835	1822	1935	1935	1935	...	...	2022	2035	2109	2109	2109
Berlin Hbf .... **838 902** d.	1546	1546	...	1647	1647	1634	1741	1746	1746	...	...	1846	1846	1834	1946	1946	1946	...	...	2034	2046	2120	2120	2120
Berlin Spandau .... **838 902** d.	1600	1600	...	1701	1701	1651	1751	1800	1800	...	1809	1900	1900	1851	2000	2000	2000	...	1954	2051	2102	2135	2135	2135
Stendal Hbf .... **838** d.	|	|	...	|	|	1731	|	|	|	...	1845	|	|	1931	|	|	|	...	2029	2131	2139	2218	2218	2218
Wolfsburg .... **902** d.	1653	1653	...	|	|	1801	|	1853	1853	...	1920	|	|	2001	2053	2053	2053	...	2105	2201	2208	2248	2248	2248
Leipzig Hbf **866** .... d.	|	|	1438	|	|	|	|	|	|	1638	|	|	|	|	|	|	|	1838	|	|	|	|	|	|
Magdeburg Hbf **866** .... d.	|	|	1603	|	|	|	|	|	|	1803	|	|	|	|	|	|	|	2003	|	|	|	|	|	|
Hannover Hbf .... a.	1728	1728	1723	1828	1828	1836	|	1928	1928	1923	1953	2028	2028	2036	2128	2128	2128	2123	2140	2236	2242	2322	2322	2322
Hannover Hbf .... **811** d.	1731	1731	1740	1831	1831	1840	|	1931	1931	1940	1956	2031	2031	2040	2131	2131	...	2140	...	2240	...	...	...	2331
Minden (Westf) .... **811** d.	|	|	1813	|	|	1911	|	|	|	2013	|	|	|	2111	|	|	...	2213	...	2311	...	...	...	|
Bad Oeynhausen .... **811** d.	|	|	|	|	|	1922	|	|	|	|	|	|	|	2122	|	|	...	|	...	2322	...	...	...	|
Bünde (Westf) .... **811** d.	|	|	|	|	|	|	|	|	|	|	|	|	|	2135	|	|	...	|	...	2335	...	...	...	|
Osnabrück Hbf .... **811** d.	|	|	|	|	|	1953	|	|	|	|	|	|	|	2201	|	|	...	|	...	2359	...	...	...	|
Münster (Westf) Hbf .. **800** a.	|	|	|	|	|	|	|	|	|	|	|	|	|	2225	|	|	...	|	...	0025	...	...	...	|
Rheine .... **811** d.	|	|	|	|	|	2020	|	|	|	|	|	|	|	...	|	|	...	|	...	...	...	...	...	|
Bad Bentheim 🏛 .... **811** a.	|	|	|	|	|	2034	|	|	|	|	|	|	|	...	|	|	...	|	...	...	...	...	...	|
Amsterdam C **22** .... a.	|	|	|	|	|	2300	|	|	|	|	|	|	|	...	|	|	...	|	...	...	...	...	...	|
Herford .... **811** d.	|	|	1832	|	|	...	|	|	|	2032	2043	|	|	...	|	|	...	2232	...	...	...	...	...	0016
Bielefeld Hbf .... **802 811** d.	1822	1822	1840	1922	1922	...	|	2022	2022	2040	2053	2122	2122	...	2222	2222	...	2240	...	...	...	...	...	0027
Gütersloh Hbf .... **802** d.	|	|	1852	|	|	...	|	|	|	2052	2103	|	|	...	|	|	...	2252	...	...	...	...	...	0038
Hamm (Westf) .... **802** a.	1847	1847	1914	1948	1948	...	|	2047	2047	2114	2124	2148	2148	...	2248	2248	...	2314	...	...	...	...	...	0059
Dortmund Hbf **800** .... a.	|	1910	1933	|	2010	...	|	|	2110	2133	2149	|	2210	...	|	2310	...	2333	...	...	...	...	...	0119
Düsseldorf Hbf **800** .... ▷ a.	|	2015	|	|	2102	...	|	|	2203	|	2243	|	2302	...	|	0006	...	|	...	...	...	...	...	0216
Wuppertal Hbf **800** .... a.	1938	...	2012	2038	|	...	|	2137	|	2212	|	2238	|	...	2338	|	...	0012	...	...	...	...	...	|
Köln Hbf **800** .... a.	2009	...	2046	2111	2132	...	2141	2209	2232	2245	2316	2313	2331	...	0011	0034	...	0046	...	...	...	...	...	0244

A – To Bonn (Table **800**).
D – From Dresden (Table **842**).
E – Daily to Sept. 10; ①–⑥ from Sept. 12.
H – Until June 23.
K – KAROLINGER – To Duisburg Hbf (a. 1827), Krefeld Hbf (a. 1841), Viersen (a. 1853), Mönchengladbach Hbf (a. 1901), Rheydt Hbf (a. 1907), Herzogenrath (a. 1937) and Aachen Hbf (a. 1952).
L – From Stralsund (Table **845**). From July 24 change trains at Hannover Hbf (train from Hannover runs as *ICE* **1130** and departs Hannover Hbf at 1959).
O – To Oldenburg via Bremen (Table **813**).
R – ⑫ Stralsund - Hannover - Bremen - Oldenburg.
S – To Stuttgart (Tables **800** and **912**).
T – To Bonn / Koblenz on days in Table **800**.
U – To Ulm via Gießen, Frankfurt and Stuttgart (Tables **806**, **912** and **930**). From July 24 runs as *IC* **1991**, departs Berlin Ostbahnhof 1351, Berlin Hbf 1402 and is diverted, not calling at Berlin Spandau, Wolfsburg or Hannover.
Y – Continues to Neuss Hbf (a. 2028) and Mönchengladbach Hbf (a. 2043). On ⑦ continues to Aachen Hbf (a. 2144).

e – ①–⑥.
f – Also June 15.
g – ① only.
h – 1450 June 12 - Sept. 4.
p – ①②③④⑥.
t – Until July 17.
z – 1002 on ⑥.

◇ – Also calls at Berlin Zoo (d. 0540).
◧ – Via Recklinghausen (Table **800**).
♥ – Also calls at Berlin Zoo (d. 0027), Berlin Wannsee (d. 0039), Potsdam Hbf (d. 0048), Brandenburg Hbf (d. 0108) and Braunschweig Hbf (d. 0236).
¶ – Train number **1117** from July 22.
● – Train number **2017** from July 24.
⊡ – Train number **2411** July 31 - Sept. 11.
▷ – Düsseldorf Hbf arrivals may vary by up to 5 minutes until June 24.
≋ – Service is retimed June 25 - Aug. 4. See special table on page 566.

Regional services BIELEFELD and HENGELO - HANNOVER and PADERBORN 811

See Table **22** for international *IC* services Amsterdam - Hengelo - Bad Bentheim - Hannover and v.v. See Table **810** for fast *ICE* / *IC* services Bielefeld / Bad Bentheim - Hannover and v.v.

km		¶	⚒‡	⚒¶	⚒‡	¶	⚒v§	‡	Ⓐ‡	¶	§	‡	⚒‡	¶	A§	A‡	B¶	A§	A‡	B¶		§	‡	¶
0	**Hengelo** ▷ d.	...	...	...	...	...	...	...	0534	...	...	...	0634	...	...	0734	...	...	0834	...	⊠	...	1834	...
26	Bad Bentheim 🚌 d.	...	...	...	...	...	...	...	0556	...	...	...	0656	...	...	0756	...	...	0856	...		...	1856	...
47	**Rheine** ❦ d.	...	...	...	0514	...	...	...	0614	0638	...	...	0714	...	...	0814	0838	...	0914	...		...	1914	...
69	Ibbenbüren ❦ d.	...	...	...	0528	...	...	...	0628	0654	...	...	0728	...	...	0828	0854	...	0928	...	and in	...	1928	...
95	**Osnabrück** Hbf ❦ d.	...	0447	0517	0547	...	...	0647	0647	0717	...	0747	0747	...	...	0847	0917	...	0947	...	the same	...	1947	...
132	Bünde (Westf) d.	...	0512	0539	0612	...	D	0712	0712	0739	K	0812	0812	...	K	0912	0939	K	1012	...	pattern	K	2012	...
	Bielefeld Hbf d.	0424	|	|	|	0624	0700	|	|	|	0800	|	|	0824	0900	|	|	1000	|	1023	every	2000	|	2024
146	Herford a.	0431	0527	|	0627	0631	0707	0727	0727	|	0807	0827	0827	0831	0907	0927	|	1007	1027	1031	**two** hours	2007	2027	2031
146	Herford d.	0433	0537	|	0637	0633	0708	0737	0737	|	0808	0837	0837	0833	0908	0937	|	1008	1037	1033	until	2008	2037	2033
160	**Bielefeld** Hbf a.	|	0548	|	0648	|	|	0748	0748		|	0848	0848	|	|	0948	|	|	1048	|		|	2048	|
	Löhne d.	0440	...	0551	▬	0640	0714	...	...	0751	0814	...	...	0840	0914	...	0951	1014	...	1040		2014	...	2040
	Bad Oeynhausen d.	0445	...	0557	...	0645	0719	...	...	0757	0819	...	...	0845	0919	...	0957	1019	...	1045		2019	...	2045
	Minden (Westf) a.	0457	...	0607	...	0657	0730	...	...	0807	0830	...	...	0857	0930	...	1007	1030	...	1057		2030	...	2057
	Minden (Westf) d.	0507	...	0608	0608	0707	*0735*	...	...	0808	*0835*	...	...	0904	*0935*	...	1008	*1035*	...	1104		*2035*	...	2104
	Hannover Hbf ● a.	0550	...	0650	0650	0750	*0830*	...	...	0852	*0930*	...	...	0950	*1030*	...	1050	*1130*	...	1150		*2130*	...	2150
	Hannover Hbf 866 d.	0555	...	0655	0655	0755	...	...	...	0855	...	...	...	0955	...	...	1055	...	...	1155		...	...	2155
	Peine 866 d.	0624	...	0724	0724	0824	...	...	...	0925	...	...	...	1024	...	...	1124	...	...	1224		...	...	2224
	Braunschweig Hbf 866 a.	0641	...	0741	0741	0841	...	...	...	0941	...	...	...	1041	...	...	1140	...	...	1241		...	...	2241

	§	‡	¶	§	‡	¶	§	‡	¶	‡
Hengelo ▷ d.	...	1934	...	...	2034	...	...	2134	...	2234
Bad Bentheim 🚌 d.	...	1956	...	...	2056	...	...	2156	...	2256
Rheine ❦ d.	...	2014	2038	...	2114	...	...	2214	2238	2314
Ibbenbüren ❦ d.	...	2028	2054	...	2128	...	...	2228	2254	2328
Osnabrück Hbf ❦ d.	...	2047	2117	...	2147	...	...	2247	2317	2344
Bünde (Westf) d.	K	2112	2139	K	2212	...	K	2312	2339	...
Bielefeld Hbf d.	2100	|	|	2200	|	2224	2300	|	|	...
Herford a.	2107	2127	|	2207	2227	2231	2307	2327	|	...
Herford d.	2108	2137	|	2208	2237	2233e	2308	2337	|	...
Bielefeld Hbf a.	|	2148	|	|	2248	|	|	2348	|	...
Löhne d.	2114	...	2151	2214	...	2240e	2315	▬	2351	...
Bad Oeynhausen d.	2119	...	2157	2219	...	2245e	2320	...	2357	...
Minden (Westf) a.	2130	...	2207	2230	...	2257e	2330	...	0007	...
Minden (Westf) d.	*2135*	...	2208	*2235*	...	2307	*2335*	...	...	...
Hannover Hbf ● a.	*2230*	...	2250	*2330*	...	2350	*0030*	...	...	...
Hannover Hbf 866 d.	...	...	2255	...	...	0014	...	0114	...	...
Peine 866 d.	...	...	2324	...	...	0040	...	0140	...	...
Braunschweig Hbf 866 a.	...	...	2341	...	...	0059	...	0159	...	...

km		Ⓐ‡	⚒‡	Ⓐv§	⚒¶	¶	⚒‡	§	¶	‡
0	**Braunschweig** Hbf 866 d.	...	...	...	0420c	...	...	...	0520	...
26	Peine 866 d.	...	...	...	0438c	...	...	...	0538	...
61	**Hannover** Hbf 866 a.	...	...	...	0505c	...	...	...	0605	...
61	**Hannover** Hbf ● d.	...	...	...	0509c	...	...	*0528*r	0609	...
126	Minden (Westf) a.	...	...	...	0551c	...	...	*0623*r	0654	...
126	Minden (Westf) d.	...	...	0528	0552	...	...	0628	0702	...
141	Bad Oeynhausen d.	...	...	0539	0604	...	...	0639	0714	...
147	Löhne d.	...	...	0544	0609	...	...	0644	0719	...
	Bielefeld Hbf d.	...	0511	|	|	...	0611	|	|	0712
157	Herford a.	...	0521	0549	|	...	0621	0649	0725	0723
157	Herford d.	...	0532	0550	|	...	0632	0650	0727	0732
171	**Bielefeld** Hbf a.	...	|	0557	|	...	|	0657	0739n	|
	Bünde (Westf) d.	...	0546	K	0620	...	0646	K	...	0746
	Osnabrück Hbf ❦ d.	0512	0614	...	0646	0646	0714	▬	...	0814
	Ibbenbüren ❦ d.	0530	0630	...	0704	0704	0730	...	...	0830
	Rheine ❦ d.	0549	0649	...	0721	0721	0749	0749	...	0849
	Bad Bentheim 🚌 a.	0603	0703	...	...	...	0803	0803	...	0903
	Hengelo ▷ a.	0626	0726	...	...	...	0826	0826	...	0926

	⚒v§	B¶	‡	A§	B¶	A‡	A§	B¶	A‡	⊠ ✣		¶	‡	§	¶	‡	§	¶	‡	§	¶	‡	¶	¶
Braunschweig Hbf 866 d.	...	0620	...	...	0720	...	...	0820	...		...	1820	...	...	1920	...	...	2020	...	...	2120	...	2220	2320
Peine 866 d.	...	0638	...	...	0738	...	...	0838	...		...	1837	...	...	1938	...	...	2038	...	...	2138	...	2238	2338
Hannover Hbf 866 a.	...	0703	...	...	0805	...	...	0905	...		...	1903	...	...	2005	...	...	2105	...	...	2205	...	2305	0004
Hannover Hbf ● d.	*0628*	0708	...	*0728*	0809	...	*0828*	0909	...	and in	*1828*	1905	...	*1928*	2009	...	*2028*	2109	...	*2128*	2209	...	2309	0009
Minden (Westf) a.	*0723*	0752	...	*0823*	0853	...	*0923*	0951	...	the same	*1923*	1951	...	*2023*	2053	...	*2123*	2151	...	*2223*	2253	...	2351	0052
Minden (Westf) d.	0728	0753	...	0828	0902	...	0928	0952	...	pattern	1928	1952	...	2028	2102	...	2128	2152	...	2228	2302	...	2352	...
Bad Oeynhausen d.	0739	0804	...	0839	0914	...	0939	1004	...	every	1939	2003	...	2039	2114	...	2139	2204	...	2239	2314	...	0004	...
Löhne d.	0744	0809	...	0844	0919	...	0944	1009	...	**two** hours	1944	2008	...	2044	2119	...	2144	2209	...	2244	2319	...	0009	...
Bielefeld Hbf d.	|	|	0812	|	|	0912	|	|	1012	until	|	|	2012	|	|	2112	|	|	2209	|	|	2312	|	...
Herford a.	0749	|	0823	0849	0925	0923	0949	|	1023		1949	|	2023	2049	2125	2123	2149	|	2220	2249	2325	2323	|	...
Herford d.	0750	|	0832	0850	0927	0932	0950	|	1032		1950	|	2032	2050	2127	2132	2150	|	2232	2250	2327	2332	|	...
Bielefeld Hbf a.	0757	|	|	0857	0936	|	0957	|	|		1957	|	|	2057	2136	|	2157	|	|	2257	2336	|	|	...
Bünde (Westf) d.	K	0820	0846	K	...	0946	K	1020	1046		K	2020	2046	K	...	2146	E	2220	2246	E	...	2346	0020	...
Osnabrück Hbf ❦ d.	...	0846	0914	...	...	1014	...	1046	1114		...	2046	2114	...	...	2214	...	2246	2314	...	...	0012	0041	...
Ibbenbüren ❦ d.	...	0904	0930	...	...	1030	...	1104	1130		...	2104	2130	...	...	2230	...	2304	2330	...	...	...	...	...
Rheine ❦ d.	...	0921	0949	...	...	1049	...	1121	1149		...	2121	2149	...	...	2249	...	2321	2346	...	...	...	...	...
Bad Bentheim 🚌 a.	...	...	1003	...	...	1103	...	...	1203		...	...	2203	...	...	2303	...	...	...	...	...	...	...	...
Hengelo ▷ a.	...	...	1026	...	...	1126	...	...	1226		...	...	2226	...	...	2326	...	...	...	...	...	...	...	...

BIELEFELD - PADERBORN - HOLZMINDEN - KREIENSEN ⊖ and OTTBERGEN - GÖTTINGEN ★ ⊖

km				Ⓐv	⚒v	⚒v	⚒v																		
0	**Bielefeld** Hbf d.	...	...	0434	0534	0634	0734	0834	0934	1034	1134	1234	1334	1434	1534	...	1634	1734	1834	1934	...	2034	2134	2234	2334
44	**Paderborn** Hbf a.	...	...	0527	0627	0727	0827	0927	1027	1127	1227	1327	1427	1527	1627	...	1727	1827	1927	2027	...	2127	2227	2327	0027
	Change trains	⚒	Ⓐ	⚒	d	⚒	d								Ⓐ	Ⓒ					†b		⑤⑥†		
44	**Paderborn** Hbf 805 809 d.	0453	0453	0553	0653	0753	0853	0953	1053	1153	1253	1353	1453	1553	1653	1653	1753	1853	1953	2053	2053	2206	2315	...	...
61	Altenbeken 805 809 d.	0507	0507	0607	0707	0807	0907	1007	1107	1207	1307	1407	1507	1607	1707	1707	1807	1907	2007	2107	2107	2219	2329	...	...
92	Ottbergen ★ a.	0532	0532	0632	0732	0832	0932	1032	1132	1232	1332	1432	1532	1632	1732	1732	1832	1932	2032	2132	2132	2244	2354	...	...
92	Ottbergen d.	...	0536	0636	0736	0836	0936	1036	1136	1236	1336	1436	1536	1636	1736	1736	1836	1936	2036	2136	2136	2245	2355	...	...
102	Höxter Rathaus d.	...	0545	0645	0745	0845	0945	1045	1145	1245	1345	1445	1545	1645	1745	1745	1845	1945	2045	2145	2145	2254	0003	...	...
110	Holzminden a.	...	0554	0654	0754	0854	0954	1054	1154	1254	1354	1454	1553	1654	1754	1754	1854	1954	2054	2154	2154	2302	0012	...	...
110	Holzminden d.	...	*0629*	*0711*t	0758	...	0958	...	1158	...	1358	...	1558	1654t	1754	1758	...	1958	...	...	2158	...	...	...	...
154	**Kreiensen** a.	...	*0703*	*0745*t	0832	...	1032	...	1232	...	1432	...	1632	1728t	1828	1832	...	2032	...	...	2232	...	...	...	...

		Ⓐ	⚒	⚒	Ⓐ	⑥											Ⓐ	Ⓒ		Ⓐ					†b
Kreiensen d.	...	...	...	0627t	0709	0723	...	0754t	0923	...	1123	...	1323	...	1523	...	1652	1723	...	1828	...	1923	...	2127j	2241
Holzminden a.	...	...	...	0700t	0742	0756	...	0827t	0956	...	1156	...	1356	...	1556	...	1725	1756	...	1900	...	1956	...	2200j	2314
Holzminden d.	...	0501	0601	0701	0801	0801	0801	0901	1001	1101	1201	1301	1401	1501	1601	1701	...	1801	1801	1901	1901	2001	2101	2201	2316
Höxter Rathaus d.	...	0510	0610	0710	0810	0810	0810	0910	1010	1110	1210	1310	1410	1510	1610	1710	...	1810	1810	1910	1910	2010	2110	2210	2325
Ottbergen a.	...	0519	0619	0719	0819	0819	0819	0919	1019	1119	1219	1319	1419	1519	1619	1719	...	1819	1819	1919	1919	2019	2119	2219	2334
Ottbergen ★ d.	...	0526	0626	0726	0826	0826	0826	0926	1026	1126	1226	1326	1426	1526	1626	1726	...	1826	1826	1926	1926	2026	2126	2226	2335
Altenbeken 805 809 d.	...	0552	0652	0752	0852	0852	0852	0952	1052	1152	1252	1352	1452	1552	1652	1752	...	1852	1852	1952	1952	2052	2152	2252	0001
Paderborn Hbf 805 809 a.	...	0605	0705	0805	0905	0905	0905	1005	1105	1205	1305	1405	1505	1605	1705	1805	...	1905	1905	2005	2005	2105	2205	2305	0015
Change trains	⚒v	⚒v	⚒v	d																					
Paderborn Hbf d.	0513	0613	0713	0813	...	...	0913	1013	1113	1213	1313	1413	1513	1613	1713	1813	...	...	1913	...	2013	2113	2213	2313	...
Bielefeld Hbf a.	0607	0707	0807	0907	...	...	1007	1107	1207	1307	1407	1507	1607	1707	1807	1907	...	...	2007	...	2107	2207	2307	0007	...

HERFORD - PADERBORN ‡

km		Ⓐv	⚒v					L	⑤⑥	
0	**Herford** d.	0530	0633	0733	and	2133	2233	2233	2336	...
8	Bad Salzuflen d.	0537	0640	0740	hourly	2140	2240	2240	2343	...
19	Lage (Lippe) d.	0549	0652	0752	until	2152	2252	2252	2355	...
28	Detmold d.	0559	0702	0802		2202	2258	2302	0002	...
57	Altenbeken 805 809 d.	0624	0727	0827		2227	...	2327	0027	...
74	**Paderborn** Hbf 805 809 a.	0638	0741	0841		2241	...	2342	0041	...

	Ⓐv	⚒v						⑤⑥
Paderborn Hbf 805 809 d.	...	0518	...	0621	and	2121	...	2219
Altenbeken 805 809 d.	...	0530	...	0633	hourly	2133	...	2233
Detmold d.	0458	0558	...	0701	until	2201	...	2301
Lage (Lippe) d.	0506	0606	...	0709		2209	...	2309
Bad Salzuflen d.	0517	0617	...	0720		2220	...	2320
Herford a.	0524	0624	...	0727		2227	...	2327

A – Train runs hourly.
B – Train runs every **two** hours.
D – From Dortmund (Table **802**).
E – To Düsseldorf (Table **802**).
K – From / to Köln via Dortmund (Table **802**).
L – ⑤⑥† (also June 16, Nov. 1).
b – Also Oct. 31.
c – Not Oct. 31.
d – Daily.
e – 2 – 3 minutes later on ⑦–④.
j – 2 minutes earlier on †b.

n – 0736 on Ⓒ (also June 16, Nov. 1).
r – ⚒ only.
t – Ⓐ only.
v – Not June 16, Nov. 1.
§ – Operated by National Express.
¶ – Operated by WestfalenBahn.
‡ – Operated by eurobahn.
⊖ – Operated by NordWestBahn. 2nd class only.
⊠ – Timings may vary by 1 – 2 minutes.

✣ – The 1220 from Braunschweig is retimed at the following stations: Peine d. 1237, Hannover Hbf a. 1303, d. 1305, Bad Oeynhausen d. 1403, Löhne d. 1408 (other timings follow the regular pattern).
▷ – Trains from / to Hengelo also call at Oldenzaal (7 – 9 minutes from Hengelo). German holiday dates apply.
● – Hannover timings shown in italics vary by 3 minutes until Aug. 24 (later arrivals / earlier departures).
❦ – **Warning!** No rail services operate between Rheine and Ibbenbüren June 25 - Aug. 4 (also from late evening on June 24). Alternative regional rail connections Rheine - Osnabrück and v.v. are available via Münster (Tables **802**/**812**). Normal services run Hengelo - Rheine and Osnabrück - Bielefeld / Hannover.
★ – **OTTBERGEN - GÖTTINGEN** ⊖. *63 km.* Journey: 72 – 83 minutes (103 – 113 minutes for trains marked ◇). Most trains run from / to Paderborn, attached to Holzminden trains shown in the main table above. **From Ottbergen** at 0534 ⚒, 0634 ⚒, 0734, 0834 ⚒, 0934, 1034 ⚒, 1134, 1234 ⑥, 1234 Ⓐ◇, 1334 Ⓒ, 1534, 1634 Ⓐ, 1734, 1834 Ⓐ, 1934 and 2034. **From Göttingen** at 0601 ⚒, 0710, 0801 ⚒, 0910, 1001 ⚒, 1110, 1201 ⚒, 1310 Ⓒ, 1331 Ⓐ◇, 1401 ⑥, 1510, 1601 Ⓐ, 1710, 1801 Ⓐ, 1910, 2001 Ⓐ and 2110.

812 MÜNSTER - EMDEN - NORDDEICH

km		◇ ⚒	IC 2438 ①–⑥	◇ ⚒	⊡ Ⓐv	◇	⊡ Ⓐv	IC 2208 ④⑤ d	ICE 1108 ⑥ ✕	◇	⊡	◇	⊡ Ⓐv	IC 2206	IC 2306 ⑥	◇	⊡	◇	⊡ Ⓐv	IC 2204	◇ Ⓒz	◇ Ⓐt	⊡	ICE 1110 ⑥ S✕	H	◇
	Koblenz Hbf **800** d.	...	...	...	...	...	...	...	...	...	...	...	...	0641	...	...	...	...	...	...	...	...	...	0944	...	...
	Köln Hbf **800 802** d.	...	...	...	...	...	0521	0539	0539	...	0621n	...	0721	0746	0801	...	0821	...	0921	0938	...	...	1021	1046	...	...
	Düsseldorf Hbf **800** d.	...	...	...	...	...	|	0607	0607	...	|	...	|	0812	0829	...	|	...	|	1011	...	...	|	1117	...	...
	Hagen Hbf **802** d.	...	...	...	0522	...	0622	|	|	...	0722	...	0822	|	|	...	0922	...	1022	|	...	...	1122	|	...	...
0	**Münster** (Westf) Hbf d.	0502a	...	0602	0624	0702	0724	0729	0729	0805	0824	0905	0924	0931	0955	1005	1024	1105	1124	1131	1205	1205	1224	1230	...	1305
15	Greven d.	0513a	...	0613	0637	0713	0733	|	|	0814	0833	0914	0933	|	|	1014	1033	1114	1133	|	1214	1214	1233	|	...	1314
26	Emsdetten d.	0522a	...	0622	0646	0722	0740	|	|	0822	0840	0922	0940	|	|	1022	1040	1122	1140	|	1222	1222	1240	|	...	1322
39	**Rheine** d.	0534	...	0634	0658	0734	0751	0756	0756	0834	0851	0934	0951	0956	1025	1034	1051	1134	1151	1156	1234	1234	1251	1258	...	1334
70	Lingen (Ems) d.	0555	...	0655	▬	0755	...	0815	0815	0855	▬	0955	...	1015	|	1055	▬	1155	...	1215	1255	1255	...	|	...	1355
90	Meppen d.	0609	...	0709		0809	...	0829	0830	0909	...	1009	...	1029	|	1109	...	1209	...	1229	1309	1328k	...	|	...	1409
136	Papenburg (Ems) d.	0642	...	0742	H	0842	...	0856	0857	0942	H	1042	...	1056	|	1142	H	1242	...	1256	1342	1404	...	|	...	1442
153	Leer (Ostfriesl) 813 d.	0653	0715	0753	0824	0853	...	0912	0911	0953	1024	1053	...	1109	1128	1153	1224	1253	...	1309	1353	1417	...	|	1424	1453
180	**Emden** Hbf ◧ 813 a.	0709	0731	0809	0841	0909	...	0927	0927	1009	1041	1109	...	1125	1144	1209	1241	1309	...	1325	1409	1432	...	1415	1441	1509
180	**Emden** Hbf 813 d.	...	0742	...	0842	...	...	0944	0944	...	1042	...	...	1142	...	...	1242	...	...	*1342*	...	...	...	1421	1442	...
209	Norden 813 d.	...	0808	...	0906	...	...	1007	1008	...	1106	...	...	1205	...	...	1306	...	...	*1408*	...	...	...	1447	1506	...
215	**Norddeich** 813 a.	...	0814	...	0912	...	...	1013	1014	...	1112	...	...	1211	...	...	1312	...	...	*1414*	...	...	...	1453	1512	...
	Norddeich Mole ‡ 813 a.	...	0820	...	0916	...	...	1018	1019	...	1116	...	...	1216	...	...	1316	...	...	*1420*	...	...	...	1500	1516	...

	⊡ Ⓐv	IC 2322 F	◇	⊡	◇	⊡ Ⓐv	IC 2200	◇	⊡	◇	⊡ Ⓐv	IC 2014 ⑤ 🍷♦	IC 2004 ⑦–④ 🍷♦	IC 2036 Ⓑ	◇	⊡	◇	⊡ Ⓐv	IC 2002	◇	⊡	◇	◇	⊙	◇	⊙
Koblenz Hbf **800** d.	...	...	...	...	...	...	...	...	...	...	...	1444	1444	...	...	...	...	...	...	...	...	...	...	...	...	...
Köln Hbf **800 802** d.	1121	...	...	1221	...	1321	1343f	...	1421	...	1521	1546	1546	...	...	1621	...	1721	1741	...	1821	...	...	...	...	...
Düsseldorf Hbf **800** d.	|	...	...	|	...	|	1412f	...	|	...	|	1612	1612	...	...	|	...	|	1815	...	|	...	...	...	...	...
Hagen Hbf **802** d.	1222	...	...	1322	...	1422	|	...	1522	...	1622	|	|	...	...	1722	...	1822	|	...	1922	...	...	...	...	...
Münster (Westf) Hbf d.	1324	1331	1405	1424	1505	1524	1531	1605	1624	1705	1724	1731	1731	...	1805	1824	1905	1924	1931	2005	2024	2105	2211	2313	...	0013
Greven d.	1333	|	1414	1433	1514	1533	|	1614	1633	1714	1733	|	|	...	1814	1833	1914	1933	|	2014	2033	2114	2222	2325	...	0025
Emsdetten d.	1340	|	1422	1440	1522	1540	|	1622	1640	1722	1740	|	|	...	1822	1840	1922	1940	|	2022	2040	2122	2231	2333	...	0033
Rheine d.	1351	1356	1434	1451	1534	1551	1556	1634	1651	1734	1751	1756	1756	...	1834	1851	1934	1951	1956	2034	2051	2134	2252j	2346	2356	0046
Lingen (Ems) d.	...	1415	1455	▬	1555	...	1615	1655	▬	1755	...	1815	1815	...	1855	▬	1955	...	2015	2055	▬	2155	2313	...	0017	...
Meppen d.	...	1429	1509	...	1609	...	1629	1709	...	1809	...	1829	1829	...	1909	...	2009	...	2029	2109	...	2209	2327	...	0030	...
Papenburg (Ems) d.	...	1456	1542	H	1642	...	1656	1742	H	1842	...	1856	1856	...	1942	H	2042	...	2056	2142	H	2242	0000	...	...	...
Leer (Ostfriesl) 813 d.	...	1509	1553	1624	1653	...	1709	1753	1824	1853	...	1909	1909	1922	1953	2024	2053	...	2110	2153	2224	2253	0012	...	...	...
Emden Hbf ◧ 813 a.	...	1525	1609	1641	1709	...	1725	1809	1841	1909	...	1925	1925	1938	2009	2041	2109	...	2125	2209	2241	2309	0028	...	...	...
Emden Hbf 813 d.	...	1542	...	1642	...	...	1727	...	1842	...	...	...	...	1942	...	2042	...	...	*2142*	...	2242	...	...	...	...	...
Norden 813 d.	...	1605	...	1706	...	...	1750	...	1906	...	...	...	...	2008	...	2106	...	...	*2208*	...	2306	...	...	...	...	...
Norddeich 813 a.	...	1611	...	1712	...	...	1756	...	1912	...	...	...	...	2014	...	2112	...	...	*2214*	...	2312	...	...	...	...	...
Norddeich Mole ‡ 813 a.	...	1616	...	1716	...	...	1804	...	1916	...	...	...	...	2020	...	2116	...	...	...	...	...	...	...	...	...	...

	⊙ ⚒n	⊡ Ⓐv	◇ ⚒	⚒t H	◇	IC 2005 ①–⑥ 🍷♦	⊡ Ⓐv	◇ Ⓐt	◇ Ⓒz	H	◇	IC 2009	⊡ Ⓐv	◇	H	◇	IC 2321 F	⊡ Ⓐv	◇	H	◇	◇ Ⓐt	IC 2203 Ⓑ	ICE 1103 ⑥ S✕	⊡ Ⓐv	◇ Ⓐt
Norddeich Mole ‡ 813 d.	...	...	...	...	...	...	...	...	...	...	...	*0736*e	...	...	0839	...	0951	...	...	1039	...	...	1136	1136	...	...
Norddeich 813 d.	...	...	...	0445	...	*0536*	...	...	...	0641	...	*0739*e	...	...	0841	...	0957	...	...	1041	...	...	1139	1139	...	...
Norden 813 d.	...	...	...	0451	...	*0543*	...	...	...	0647	...	*0746*e	...	...	0847	...	1007	...	...	1047	...	...	1146	1146	...	...
Emden Hbf 813 a.	...	...	...	0517	...	*0607*	...	...	...	0717	...	*0814*e	...	...	0917	...	1029	...	...	1117	...	...	1214	1214	...	...
Emden Hbf ◧ 813 d.	...	...	0452	0517	0552r	0634	...	0642	0652	0717	0752	0833	...	0852	0917	0952	1034	...	1052	1117	1152	1224	1234	1234	...	...
Leer (Ostfriesland) 813 d.	...	...	0509	0534	0609r	0653	...	0659	0709	0734	0809	0853	...	0909	0934	1009	1053	...	1109	1134	1209	1241	1253	1253	...	...
Papenburg (Ems) d.	...	...	0519	▬	0619r	0704	...	0709	0719	▬	0819	0904	...	0919	▬	1019	1104	...	1119	▬	1219	1251	1304	1303	...	←
Meppen d.	...	...	0550	⊡	0650	0731	...	0750j	0750	⊡	0850	0931	...	0950	⊡	1050	1131	...	1150	⊡	1250	1325	1331	1330	...	1337
Lingen (Ems) d.	...	...	0604		0704	0744	...	0804	0804		0904	0944	...	1004		1104	1144	...	1204		1304	→	1344	1344	...	1351
Rheine d.	0453	0608	0628	0708	0729	0804	0808	0829	0829	0908	0929	1004	1008	1029	1108	1129	1204	1208	1229	1308	1327	...	1404	1404	1408	1429j
Emsdetten d.	0502	0616	0636	0716	0737	|	0816	0837	0837	0916	0937	|	1016	1037	1116	1137	|	1216	1237	1316	1336	...	|	|	1416	1437
Greven d.	0510	0623	0644	0723	0745	|	0823	0845	0845	0923	0945	|	1023	1045	1123	1145	|	1223	1245	1323	1345	...	|	|	1423	1445
Münster (Westf) Hbf a.	0524	0633	0654	0733	0756	0829	0833	0856	0856	0933	0956	1029	1033	1056	1133	1156	1229	1233	1256	1333	1356	...	1429	1429	1433	1456
Hagen Hbf **802** a.	...	0736	...	0836	...	|	0936	...	...	1036	...	|	1136	...	1236	...	...	1336	...	1436	...	...	|	|	1536	...
Düsseldorf Hbf **800** a.	...	|	...	|	...	0945	|	...	...	|	...	1147	|	...	|	...	...	|	...	|	...	...	1543	1543	|	...
Köln Hbf **800 802** a.	...	0838	...	0938	...	1013	1038	...	...	1138	...	1215	1239	...	1338	...	...	1438	...	1538	...	...	1613	1613	1638	...
Koblenz Hbf **800** a.	...	...	...	...	...	1116	...	...	...	...	...	...	...	...	...	...	...	...	...	...	...	...	...	1716	...	...

	◇ Ⓒz	H	IC 2305 ⑥	⊡	◇	IC 2205 ⑥	IC 2205 Ⓑ	⊡ Ⓐv	◇	H	◇	IC 2207	⊡ Ⓐv	◇	H	◇	IC 2209 C	ICE 1107 ⑥ ✕	⊡ Ⓐv	◇	H	◇	◇	H	◇	⊙
Norddeich Mole ‡ 813 d.	...	1239	...	...	...	1336	1351	...	...	1439	...	*1537*	...	...	1639	...	1758	1758	...	...	1839	...	...	2039	...	...
Norddeich 813 d.	...	1241	...	...	...	1339	1357	...	...	1441	...	*1540*	...	...	1641	...	1801	1801	...	...	1841	...	...	2041	...	...
Norden 813 d.	...	1247	...	...	...	1347	1407	...	...	1447	...	*1547*	...	...	1647	...	1808	1808	...	...	1847	...	...	2047	...	...
Emden Hbf 813 a.	...	1317	...	...	...	1413	1429	...	...	1517	...	*1614*	...	...	1717	...	1830	1830	...	...	1917	...	...	2117	...	...
Emden Hbf ◧ 813 d.	1252	1317	1341	...	1352	1434	1434	...	1452	1517	1552	1634	...	1652	1717	1752	1834	1834	...	1852	1917	1952	2052	2117	2214	...
Leer (Ostfriesland) 813 d.	1309	1334	|	...	1409	1453	1453	...	1509	1534	1609	1653	...	1709	1734	1809	1853	1853	...	1909	1934	2009	2109	2134	2231	...
Papenburg (Ems) d.	1319	...	|	...	1419	1504	1504	...	1519	▬	1619	1703	...	1719	▬	1819	1904	1903	...	1919	...	2019	2119	▬	2240	...
Meppen d.	1350	...	|	...	1450	1531	1531	...	1550	⊡	1650	1730	...	1750	⊡	1850	1931	1930	...	1950	...	2050	2150	⊙	2313	...
Lingen (Ems) d.	1404	...	|	...	1504	1544	1544	...	1604		1704	1744	...	1804		1904	1944	1944	...	2004	...	2104	2204		2327	...
Rheine d.	1429	...	1459	1508	1529	1604	1604	1608	1629	1708	1729	1804	1808	1829	1908	1929	2004	2004	2008	2029	...	2129	2229	2253	2349	2353
Emsdetten d.	1437	...	|	1516	1537	|	|	1616	1637	1716	1737	|	1816	1837	1916	1937	|	|	2016	2037	...	2137	2237	2302	...	0002
Greven d.	1445	...	|	1523	1545	|	|	1623	1645	1723	1745	|	1823	1845	1923	1945	|	|	2023	2046	...	2146	2245	2310	...	0010
Münster (Westf) Hbf a.	1456	...	1527	1533	1556	1629	1629	1633	1656	1733	1756	1829	1833	1856	1933	1956	2029	2029	2033	2056	...	2156	2256	2324	...	0024
Hagen Hbf **802** a.	...	...	|	1636	...	|	|	1736	...	1836	...	|	1936	...	2036	...	|	|	2136	...	...	...	...	...	...	...
Düsseldorf Hbf **800** a.	...	...	1651	|	...	1743	1743	|	...	|	...	1946	|	...	|	...	2147	2147	|	...	...	...	...	...	...	...
Köln Hbf **800 802** a.	...	...	1719	1738	...	1813	1813	1838	...	1938	...	2015	2038	...	2138	...	2215	2216	2237	...	...	...	...	...	...	...
Koblenz Hbf **800** a.	...	...	...	...	...	1916	1916	...	...	...	...	...	...	...	...	...	...	...	...	...	...	...	...	...	...	...

♦ – **NOTES** (LISTED BY TRAIN NUMBER)

2004 – ⑦–④ (not June 15). SCHWARZWALD – 🚃12 🍷 (Konstanz - Karlsruhe ⑦ -) Koblenz - Emden.
2005 – SCHWARZWALD – 🚃12 🍷 Emden - Koblenz (- Karlsruhe - Konstanz ⑤⑥).
2014 – ⑤ (also June 15). 🚃12 🍷 Stuttgart - Mannheim - Münster - Emden.

C – ③④⑤⑦ (also June 14).
F – To / from Frankfurt via Siegen (Table **808**).
H – From / to Hannover (Table **813**).
S – To / from Stuttgart (Table **912**).

a – Ⓐ only.
d – Also June 15.
e – ①–⑥.
f – On ⑤⑦ (also June 15) Köln d. 1337, Düsseldorf d. 1409.
j – Arrives 9–11 minutes earlier.
k – Arrives 1307.

n – ⚒ (not June 16, Nov. 1).
r – ⚒ only.
t – Not Oct. 31.
v – Not June 16, Nov. 1.
z – Also Oct. 31.

⊡ – Operated by National Express.
◇ – Operated by WestfalenBahn.
⊙ – Operated by *eurobahn*.
‡ – For ⛴ to / from Juist and Norderney. See www.reederei-frisia.de for latest timings.
◧ – For train / 🚗 / ⛴ connections to / from Borkum via Emden Außenhafen (certain Emden trains may be extended to / from Emden Außenhafen to connect with sailings). See www.ag-ems.de for latest timings.

SERVICE UNTIL SEPTEMBER 21 — NORDDEICH - EMDEN - BREMEN - HANNOVER — 813

km		RE 4441	ICE 841	RE 4443	RE 14045	♣	IC 2033	IC 2033	RE 4405	ICE 2185	ICE 1633	RE 4407	IC 2035	IC 2035	RE 4409	ICE 1577	ICE 1577	RE 4411	IC 2037	IC 2037	RE 4413	ICE 1579	ICE 1579	RE 4415	IC 2039
			①–⑤		Ⓐ	⚒	①–⑥			①–⑥	⑦		①–⑥			⑥⑦				①–⑥		⑦			
			✕					🍷	B	A✕			🍷	🍷	B	A✕	A✕		🍷	🍷	B	A✕	A✕		🍷
	Norddeich Mole ‡ **812** d.	...	...	...	...	...	...	...	...	...	...	...	...	...	...	...	...	...	...	•0736	...	...	...	0839	0936
0	**Norddeich** **812** d.	...	...	...	...	...	...	...	...	...	...	0445r	0536	...	...	...	...	0641	...	0739	...	...	...	0841	0939
6	Norden **812** d.	...	...	...	...	...	...	...	...	...	...	0451r	0543	...	...	...	...	0647	...	0746	...	...	...	0847	0946
35	**Emden** Hbf ◧ **812** d.	...	...	...	...	...	0416	...	...	...	...	0517	0609	...	...	...	...	0717	0816	0816	...	...	...	0917	1016
62	Leer (Ostfriesland) **812** a.	...	...	...	...	...	0433	...	...	...	...	0534	0626	...	...	...	...	0734	0833	0833	...	...	...	0934	1033
62	Leer (Ostfriesland) d.	...	...	...	...	...	0441	...	...	...	...	0541	0634	...	...	...	...	0741	0841	0841	...	...	...	0941	1041
101	Bad Zwischenahn d.	...	...	...	...	...	0513	...	...	...	...	0612	0712	...	...	...	...	0812	0913	0913	...	...	...	1012	1113
116	**Oldenburg** (Oldb) a.	...	...	...	...	...	0523	...	...	...	...	0623	0723	...	...	...	...	0823	0923	0923	...	...	...	1023	1123
116	**Oldenburg** (Oldb) d.	...	0440	...	...	0506	0535	...	...	0556	...	0635	0735	0735	...	0759	...	0835	0935	0935	...	1001	...	1035	1135
147	Delmenhorst d.	...	0458	...	...	0530	0554	...	...	0618	...	0654	0754	0754	...	0818	...	0854	0954	0954	...	1018	...	1054	1154
161	**Bremen** Hbf a.	...	0508	...	...	0544	0605	...	...	0631	...	0705	0805	0805	...	0831	...	0905	1005	1005	...	1031	...	1105	1205
161	**Bremen** Hbf d.	0408	0512	0517	0545	...	0609	0609	0617	0638	0644	0717	0809	0809	0817	0835	0835	0917	1009	1009	1017	1034	1034	1117	1209
196	Verden (Aller) d.	0441	0533	0541	0609	...	0630	0630	0641	|	|	0741	0830	0830	0841	|	|	0941	1030	1030	1041	|	|	1141	1230
227	Nienburg (Weser) d.	0503	|	0603	0633	...	0646	0646	0703	|	|	0803	0846	0846	0903	|	|	1003	1046	1046	1103	|	|	1203	1246
283	**Hannover** Hbf a.	0538	0614	0638	0708	...	0713	0713	0738	0758	0759	0838	0913	0913	0938	0958	0958	1038	1113	1113	1138	1158	1158	1238	1313
	Magdeburg Hbf **866** a.	...	|	...	...	...	0856	0856	...	...	...	...	1056	1056	...	...	...	...	1256	1256	...	...	...	...	1456
	Berlin Hbf **810** a.	...	0825	...	...	...	|	|	...	...	...	...	|	|	...	...	...	...	|	|	...	...	...	...	|
	Leipzig Hbf **866** a.	...	...	...	...	...	1015	1015	...	...	...	...	1216	1216	...	...	...	...	1415	1415	...	...	...	...	1615
	Nürnberg Hbf **900** a.	...	...	...	...	...	...	...	...	...	...	...	...	...	...	...	...	...	...	...	...	...	...	...	...
	München Hbf **900** a.	...	...	...	...	...	...	...	...	...	...	...	...	...	...	...	...	...	...	...	...	...	...	...	...

	RE 4417	IC 1671	ICE 1133	RE 4419	IC 2431	RE 4421	IC 2375	RE 4423	IC 2433	RE 4425	IC 1675	RE 4427	IC 2435	RE 4429	ICE 1677	RE 4431	IC 2437	IC 2437	RE 4433	RE 4435	IC 2439	RE 4437	RE 4439	RE 4445	♣
			⑤															Ⓑ							
	B	A🍷	✕		C🍷	B	A🍷		🍷	B	G🍷		🍷	B	G✕			🍷	B			B			
Norddeich Mole ‡ **812** d.	...	...	...	1039	...	...	...	1239	...	...	...	1439	1537	...	...	1639	...	...	...	1839	...	...	2039	...	...
Norddeich **812** d.	...	...	...	1041	...	...	...	1241	...	...	...	1441	1540	...	...	1641	...	...	...	1841	...	...	2041	...	...
Norden **812** d.	...	...	...	1047	...	...	...	1247	...	...	...	1447	1547	...	...	1647	...	...	...	1847	...	...	2047	...	...
Emden Hbf ◧ **812** d.	...	...	...	1117	1218	...	...	1317	1416	...	...	1517	1616	...	...	1717	1813	1813	...	1917	2016	...	2117	...	...
Leer (Ostfriesland) **812** a.	...	...	...	1134	1235	...	...	1334	1433	...	...	1534	1633	...	...	1734	1833	1833	...	1934	2033	...	2134	...	...
Leer (Ostfriesland) d.	...	...	...	1141	1241	...	...	1341	1441	...	...	1541	1641	...	...	1741	1841	1841	...	1941	2041	...	2141	...	...
Bad Zwischenahn d.	...	...	...	1212	1313	...	...	1412	1513	...	...	1612	1713	...	...	1812	1913	1913	...	2012	2113	...	2212	...	2345•
Oldenburg (Oldb) a.	...	...	...	1223	1323	...	...	1423	1523	...	...	1623	1723	...	...	1823	1923	1923	...	2023	2123	...	2223	...	2357•
Oldenburg (Oldb) d.	...	...	1229	1235	1335	...	...	1434	1535	...	...	1635	1735	...	...	1835	1935	1935	...	2035	2135	...	2235	...	0006
Delmenhorst d.	...	...	1247	1254	1354	...	...	1454	1554	...	...	1654	1754	...	...	1854	1954	1954	...	2054	2154	...	2254	...	0030
Bremen Hbf a.	...	...	1300	1305	1405	...	...	1505	1605	...	...	1705	1805	...	...	1905	2005	2005	...	2105	2205	...	2305	...	0044
Bremen Hbf d.	1217	1238	1305	1317	1409	1417	1437	1517	1609	1617	1637	1717	1809	1817	1837	1917	...	2009	2017	2117	...	2217	2313	0013	...
Verden (Aller) d.	1241	|	|	1341	1430	1441	|	1541	1630	1641	|	1741	1830	1841	|	1941	...	2030	2041	2141	...	2243	2346	0046	...
Nienburg (Weser) d.	1303	|	|	1403	1446	1503	|	1603	1646	1703	|	1803	1846	1903	|	2003	...	2046	2103	2203	...	2305	0008	0108	...
Hannover Hbf a.	1338	1358	1407	1438	1513	1538	1558	1638	1713	1738	1758	1838	1913	1938	1958	2038	...	2113	2138	2238	...	2338	0040	0140	...
Magdeburg Hbf **866** a.	...	...	1536	...	1658	...	...	...	1858	...	...	...	2056	...	...	...	...	2302	...	...	...	...	...	...	...
Berlin Hbf **810** a.	...	...	|	...	1823	...	...	...	|	...	...	...	|	...	...	...	...	...	...	...	...	...	...	...	...
Leipzig Hbf **866** a.	...	...	1659	...	...	...	...	...	2015	...	...	...	2215	...	...	...	...	...	...	...	...	...	...	...	...
Nürnberg Hbf **900** a.	...	...	...	...	...	...	...	...	...	...	...	...	...	...	...	...	...	...	...	...	...	...	...	...	...
München Hbf **900** a.	...	...	...	...	...	...	...	...	...	...	...	...	...	...	...	...	...	...	...	...	...	...	...	...	...

	♣	RE 4448	RE 4400	IC 2438	RE 4402	RE 4404	IC 2436	IC 2436	RE 4406	ICE 1676	RE 4408	IC 2434	RE 4410	IC 1674	RE 4412	IC 2432	RE 4414	IC 1672	RE 4416	IC 2430	RE 4418	IC 2374	RE 4420	IC 2038	RE 4422
	Ⓐ	Ⓒ	Ⓐ	①–⑥				①–⑥		①–⑤															
			B			B		🍷		G✕	B	🍷		G🍷	B	C🍷		A🍷	B	🍷		A🍷	B	🍷	
München Hbf **900** d.	...	...	...	...	...	...	...	...	...	...	...	...	...	...	...	...	...	...	...	...	...	...	...	...	...
Nürnberg Hbf **900** d.	...	...	...	...	...	...	...	...	...	...	...	...	...	...	...	...	...	...	...	...	...	...	...	...	...
Leipzig Hbf **866** d.	...	...	...	...	...	...	...	...	...	...	...	0542e	...	...	...	...	...	...	...	0942	...	...	...	1142	...
Berlin Hbf **810** d.	...	...	...	...	...	...	...	...	...	...	...	|	...	...	...	0730	...	...	...	|	...	...	...	|	...
Magdeburg Hbf **866** d.	...	...	...	...	...	...	...	0500g	...	...	...	0700e	...	...	...	0900	...	...	...	1100	...	...	...	1300	...
Hannover Hbf d.	...	0417	0420	...	0520	0618h	...	0645	0720	0759	0820	0845	0920	0959	1020	1045	1120	1159	1220	1245	1320	1359	1420	1445	1520
Nienburg (Weser) d.	...	0458	0454	...	0554	0654	...	0713	0754	|	0854	0913	0954	|	1054	1113	1154	|	1254	1313	1354	|	1454	1513	1554
Verden (Aller) d.	...	0518	0515	...	0615	0715	...	0730	0815	|	0915	0930	1015	|	1115	1130	1215	|	1315	1330	1415	|	1515	1530	1615
Bremen Hbf a.	...	0540	0539	...	0639	0739	...	0750	0840	0913	0939	0950	1039	1113	1139	1150	1239	1313	1339	1350	1439	1515	1539	1550	1639
Bremen Hbf d.	0415	▬	...	0553	0653	...	0753	0753	0853	...	...	0953	1053	...	...	1153	1253	...	...	1353	1453	...	...	1553	1653
Delmenhorst d.	0428	...	...	0604	0703	...	0804	0804	0903	...	...	1004	1103	...	...	1204	1303	...	...	1404	1503	...	...	1604	1703
Oldenburg (Oldb) a.	0453	⚒	...	0623	0723	...	0823	0823	0923	...	...	1023	1123	...	...	1223	1323	...	...	1423	1523	...	...	1623	1723
Oldenburg (Oldb) d.	0458k	0533	...	0626	0733	...	0833	0833	0933	...	...	1033	1133	...	...	1233	1333	...	...	1433	1533	...	...	1633	1733
Bad Zwischenahn d.	0510k	0544	...	0637	0744	...	0844	0844	0944	...	...	1044	1144	...	...	1244	1344	...	...	1444	1544	...	...	1644	1744
Leer (Ostfriesland) a.	...	0613	...	0707	0813	...	0914	0914	1013	...	...	1114	1213	...	...	1314	1413	...	...	1514	1613	...	...	1714	1813
Leer (Ostfriesland) **812** d.	...	0624	...	0715	0824	...	0922	0922	1024	...	...	1122	1224	...	...	1322	1424	...	...	1522	1624	...	...	1722	1824
Emden Hbf ◧ **812** d.	...	0642	...	0742t	0842	...	0938	0938	1042	...	...	1138	1242	...	...	1342	1442	...	...	1538	1642	...	...	1738	1842
Norden **812** d.	...	0706	...	0808	0906	...	...	...	1106	...	...	...	1306	...	...	1408	1506	...	...	...	1706	...	...	...	1906
Norddeich **812** a.	...	0712	...	0814	0912	...	...	...	1112	...	...	...	1312	...	...	1414	1512	...	...	...	1712	...	...	...	1912
Norddeich Mole ‡ **812** a.	...	0716	...	0820	0916	...	...	...	1116	...	...	...	1316	...	...	1420	1516	...	...	...	1716	...	...	...	1916

	ICE 1578	RE 4424	IC 2036	RE 4426	ICE 1576	RE 4428	IC 2034	IC 1934	RE 4430	ICE 776	RE 4430	RE 4432	IC 2032	IC 2032	RE 4434	ICE 832	ICE 1132	ICE 1632	RE 4434	RE 4434	RE 4442	ICE 532	RE 4444	ICE 830	RE 4440
								⑦		Ⓑ				Ⓑ		①–④	⑦	⑤⑥		⑥				⑦	
	A✕	B	🍷		A✕	B	🍷	D		F✕		B	🍷	🍷		✕	S								
München Hbf **900** d.	...	...	...	...	...	...	...	...	...	...	...	...	...	...	...	...	...	...	...	...	...	...	...	...	...
Nürnberg Hbf **900** d.	...	...	...	...	...	...	...	...	...	...	...	...	...	...	...	...	...	...	...	...	...	...	...	...	...
Leipzig Hbf **866** d.	...	...	1342	...	...	...	1542	1602	...	...	...	...	...	1742	...	...	...	...	...	...	...	...	...	...	...
Berlin Hbf **810** d.	...	...	|	...	...	...	|	|	...	...	...	...	...	|	...	1946	1954z	...	...	...	...	...	...	2120	...
Magdeburg Hbf **866** d.	...	...	1500	...	...	...	1700	1726	...	...	...	...	...	1900	...	|	|	...	...	...	...	...	...	|	...
Hannover Hbf d.	1559	1620	1645	1720	1802	1820	1845	1900	1920	1951	...	2020	2045	2045	2120	2143	2143	2143	...	...	2220	2245	2320	2349	0020
Nienburg (Weser) d.	|	1654	1713	1754	|	1854	1913	1929	1954	|	...	2055	2113	2113	2154	2211	2211	2211	...	...	2254	2315	2354	0016	0054
Verden (Aller) d.	|	1715	1730	1815	|	1915	1930	1948	2015	|	...	2116	2130	2130	2215	2229	2229	2229	...	...	2315	2332	0015	0035	0115
Bremen Hbf a.	1713	1739	1750	1839	1916	1939	1950	2009	2039	2047	←	2141	2150	2150	2239	2247	2247	2247	←	←	2347	2352	0047	0056	0147
Bremen Hbf d.	...	...	1753	1853	...	...	1953	2013	→	2050	2054	...	2153	2153	→	2249	2249	2249	2253	2253	...	2355	...	0059	...
Delmenhorst d.	...	...	1804	1903	...	...	2004	2024	...	|	2104	...	2204	2204	...	2300	2300	2300	2304	2304	...	0007	...	0110	...
Oldenburg (Oldb) a.	...	...	1823	1923	...	...	2023	2040	...	2117	2123	...	2223	2223	...	2317	2318	2317	2323	2323	...	0025	...	0128	...
Oldenburg (Oldb) d.	...	...	1833	1933	...	...	2033	2042	...	...	2133	...	...	2233	...	...	...	...	...	2333	...	...	...	...	...
Bad Zwischenahn d.	...	...	1844	1944	...	...	2044	2055	...	...	2144	...	...	2244	...	...	...	...	...	2344	...	...	...	...	...
Leer (Ostfriesland) a.	...	...	1914	2013	...	...	2114	2128	...	...	2213	...	...	2314	...	...	...	...	...	0013	...	...	...	...	...
Leer (Ostfriesland) **812** d.	...	...	1922	2024	...	...	2122	2136	...	...	2224	...	...	2322	...	...	...	...	...	0024	...	...	...	...	...
Emden Hbf ◧ **812** d.	...	...	1942	2042	...	...	2142	2152	...	...	2242	...	...	2338	...	...	...	...	...	0041	...	...	...	...	...
Norden **812** d.	...	...	2008b	2106	...	...	2208	...	...	...	2306	...	...	...	...	...	...	...	...	...	...	...	...	...	...
Norddeich **812** a.	...	...	2014b	2112	...	...	2214	...	...	...	2312	...	...	...	...	...	...	...	...	...	...	...	...	...	...
Norddeich Mole ‡ **812** a.	...	...	2020b	2116	...	...	...	...	...	...	...	...	...	...	...	...	...	...	...	...	...	...	...	...	...

A – To/from Karlsruhe via Kassel, Gießen and Frankfurt (Tables **806**, **900** and **912**).
B – To/from Bremerhaven (Table **815**).
C – To/from Cottbus on dates in Table **837**.
D – From/to Dresden (Table **842**).
F – From Frankfurt (Table **900**).
G – To/from Frankfurt via Gießen (Tables **900** and **806**).
S – From Stralsund until July 17 (Table **845**). July 24 - Sept. 25 runs Hannover - Oldenburg only as *ICE* **1136**.

b – Ⓑ.
e – ①–⑥.
g – Ⓐ only.
h – 0620 on †.
k – Not June 27 - Aug. 5.
r – ⚒ only.
t – Arrives 0731.
z – Berlin **Spandau**.

• – Not June 24, 25, 27, July 2, 4–9, 11–16, 18–23, 25–30, Aug. 1–4.
‡ – For sailings from/to Juist and Norderney (see www.reederei-frisia.de).
◧ – For train/bus/ship connections from/to Borkum via Emden Außenhafen (see www.ag-ems.de).
♣ – Operated by Nord West Bahn (2nd class only).

814 OSNABRÜCK - OLDENBURG - WILHELMSHAVEN

Nord West Bahn

km		⚒t	⚒t	Ⓐt					†z
0	**Osnabrück** Hbf d.	...	...	0459	0601		2201	2301	2301
20	Bramsche d.	...	...	0518	0618	and	2218	2318	2318
50	Quakenbrück d.	...	...	0540	0640		2240	2341	2341
72	Cloppenburg d.	...	...	0556	0656	hourly	2256	2357	2357
113	**Oldenburg** (Oldb) a.	...	...	0629	0729		2329	0029	0029
113	**Oldenburg** (Oldb) d.	0536	0636	0636	0736	until	2336	...	0036
143	Varel (Oldb) d.	0601	0701	0701	0801		0001	...	0101
165	**Wilhelmshaven** Hbf a.	0621	0721	0721	0821		0021	...	0121

	Ⓐt	⚒t		⚒t	Ⓐt		✣		⑤⑥f	
Wilhelmshaven Hbf d.	...	0440	...	0540	0610	0640		2140	2310	2310
Varel (Oldb) d.	...	0458	...	0558	0628	0658	and	2158	2328	2328
Oldenburg (Oldb) a.	...	0524	...	0624	0654	0724		2224	2354	2354
Oldenburg (Oldb) d.	0403	0529	0629	0629	0659	0729	hourly	2229	2359	...
Cloppenburg d.	0435	0605	0705	0705	0735	0805		2305	0033	...
Quakenbrück d.	0450	0621	0721	0721	0751	0821	until	2321	...	...
Bramsche d.	0513	0641	0741	0741	0811	0841		2341	...	...
Osnabrück Hbf a.	0531	0658	0758	0758	0829	0858		2358	...	...

t – Not Oct. 31.
z – Also Oct. 31.
✣ – On ⑥ Wilhelmshaven d. *1328* (not 1340) and change trains at Sande (a. *1335*, d. 1347).

815 OSNABRÜCK - BREMEN - BREMERHAVEN - CUXHAVEN

RE services

km		⚒t¶	⚒t	ⒶtH	⚒t	H		H		H		H		A	H		H		H		H		¶		¶	
0	**Osnabrück** Hbf 800 d.	...	0417	...	0529	*0629*	0729	*0829*	0929	*1029*	1129	*1229*	1329	1356	*1429*	1529	*1629*	1729	*1829*	1929	*2029*	2129	...	2229	...	2329
53	Diepholz d.	...	0450	...	0603	*0703*	0803	*0903*	1003	*1103*	1203	*1303*	1403	|	*1503*	1603	*1703*	1803	*1903*	2003	*2103*	2203	...	2303	...	0003
122	**Bremen** Hbf 800 a.	...	0546	...	0651	*0749*	0851	*0949*	1051	*1149*	1251	*1349*	1451	1457	*1549*	1651	*1749*	1851	*1949*	2051	*2151*	2251	...	2351	...	0051
122	**Bremen** Hbf d.	0540	...	0556	0656	0756	0856	0956	1056	1156	1256	1356	1456	1507	1556	1656	1756	1856	1956	2056	2156	...	2312	...	0012	...
143	Osterholz-Scharmbeck d.	0556	...	0610	0710	0810	0910	1010	1110	1210	1310	1410	1510	1524	1610	1710	1810	1910	2010	2110	2210	...	2328	...	0028	...
185	**Bremerhaven** Hbf a.	0625	...	0631	0731	0831	0931	1031	1131	1231	1331	1431	1531	1546	1631	1731	1831	1931	2031	2131	2231	...	2357	...	0057	...
188	**Bremerhaven-Lehe** a.	0630	...	0635	0735	0835	0935	1035	1135	1235	1335	1435	1535	1553	1635	1735	1835	1945j	2035	2135	2235	...	0002	...	0102	...

	⚒t	⚒t	⚒t¶	ⒶtH		⚒t		H		H	B		H		H		H		H		H		H	¶		¶
Bremerhaven-Lehe d.	...	...	0407	0523	...	0623	...	0723	0823	0923	1004	1023	1123	1223	1323	1423	1523	1623	1723	1823	1923	2023	2123	2158	...	2258
Bremerhaven Hbf d.	...	...	0412	0528	...	0628	...	0728	0828	0928	1011	1028	1128	1228	1328	1428	1528	1628	1728	1828	1928	2028	2128	2203	...	2303
Osterholz-Scharmbeck d.	...	...	0444	0550	...	0650	...	0750	0850	0950	1035	1050	1150	1250	1350	1450	1550	1650	1750	1850	1950	2050	2150	2233	...	2333
Bremen Hbf a.	...	...	0504	0603	...	0703	...	0803	0903	1003	1051	1103	1203	1303	1403	1503	1603	1703	1803	1903	2003	2103	2203	2253	...	2350
Bremen Hbf 800 d.	0407	0507	...	...	0607	0707	0707	*0807*	0907	*1007*	1054	1107	*1207*	1307	*1407*	1507	*1607*	1707	*1807*	1907	*2007*	2107	*2207*	...	2313	...
Diepholz d.	0454	0554	...	...	0654	0754	0754	*0854*	0954	*1054*	|	1154	*1254*	1354	*1454*	1554	*1654*	1754	*1854*	1954	*2054*	2154	*2255*	...	0002	...
Osnabrück Hbf 800 a.	0526	0626	...	...	0726	0826	0826	*0926*	1026	*1126*	1151	1226	*1326*	1426	*1526*	1626	*1726*	1826	*1926*	2026	*2126*	2226	*2327*	...	0034	...

BREMERHAVEN - CUXHAVEN

km	⊡	©z		Ⓐt	⚒t					
0	**Bremerhaven** Hbf d.	0003	...	0506	0636	0736	0836	and	2236	...
3	Bremerhaven-Lehe d.	0008	...	0511	0641	0741	0841	hourly	2241	...
43	**Cuxhaven** a.	0050	...	0557	0727	0827	0927	until	2327	...

⊡	Ⓐt		⚒t					
Cuxhaven d.	0509	...	0639	0739	0839	and	2239	...
Bremerhaven-Lehe d.	0549	...	0719	0819	0919	hourly	2319	...
Bremerhaven Hbf a.	0553	...	0723	0823	0923	until	2323	...

A – *IC* **2202**. OSTFRIESLAND – From Koblenz / Köln (Table **800**).
B – *IC* **2201**. OSTFRIESLAND – To Köln (Table **800**).
H – From / to Hannover (Table **813**).
j – 1935 on © (also Oct. 31).
t – Not Oct. 31.
z – Also Oct. 31.
⊡ – Operated by Elbe-Weser.
¶ – Operated by Nord West Bahn (2nd class only).

818 HAMBURG - CUXHAVEN and BREMERHAVEN

Regionalverkehre Start Deutschland; Elbe-Weser

On Oct. 31 services run as on ⑦.

km	✣	⑥	Ⓐ‡	Ⓐ	‡	⑥	Ⓐ	‡	†	⚒																
0	**Hamburg** Hbf ⊖ d.	...	0448	...	0528	...	*0558*	0628	...	0705	0806	0906	1006	1106	1206	1306	1405	1506	1606	1706	1806	1906	2006	2106	2206	2306
12	**Hamburg** Harburg ⊖ d.	...	0503	...	0543	...	0624	0643	...	0724	0824	0924	1024	1124	1224	1324	1424	1524	1624	1724	1824	1924	2024	2124	2224	2324
33	**Buxtehude** ⊖ d.	...	0527	...	0607	...	0641	0707	...	0741	0841	0941	1041	1141	1241	1341	1441	1541	1641	1741	1841	1941	2041	2141	2241	2341
54	Stade ⊖ d.	0540	0549	0553	0629	0640	0657	0729	0740	0757	0857	0957	1057	1157	1257	1357	1457	1557	1657	1757	1857	1957	2057	2157	2257	2357
102	Otterndorf d.	0622	...	0635	...	0722	0737	...	0822	0837	0937	1037	1137	1237	1337	1437	1537	1637	1737	1837	1937	2037	2137	2237	2337	0037
116	**Cuxhaven** a.	0635	...	0648	...	0735	0750	...	0835	0850	0950	1050	1150	1250	1350	1450	1550	1650	1750	1850	1950	2050	2150	2250	2350	0050

✣	Ⓐ	⚒	Ⓐ		Ⓐ	©																⑤⑥j	k	‡
Cuxhaven d.	0430	0509	0549	0609	0650	0709	...	0809	0909	1009	1109	1209	1309	1409	1509	1609	1709	1809	1909	2009	2109	...	2209	2237	...
Otterndorf d.	0442	0521	0601	0621	0701	0721	...	0821	0921	1021	1121	1221	1321	1421	1521	1621	1721	1821	1921	2021	2121	...	2221	2250	...
Stade ⊖ d.	0524	0603	0643	0703	0743	0803	...	0903	1003	1103	1203	1303	1403	1503	1603	1703	1803	1903	2003	2103	2203	...	2303	2332	2334
Buxtehude ⊖ d.	0541	0621	0701	0721	0801	0821	...	0921	1021	1121	1221	1321	1421	1521	1621	1721	1821	1921	2021	2121	2221	...	2321	...	2354
Hamburg Harburg ⊖ a.	0556	0638	0717	0738	0817	0838	...	0938	1038	1138	1238	1338	1438	1538	1638	1738	1838	1938	2038	2138	2237	...	2336	...	0020
Hamburg Hbf ⊖ a.	*0619*	0657	0733	0756	0841	0854	...	0959	1058	1156	1257	1356	1459r	1557r	1659	1759	1900	1956r	2057	2158	2257	...	2356	...	0035

km	△		Ⓐ	Ⓐ	Ⓐ	Ⓐ	Ⓐ		Ⓐ	Ⓐ		Ⓐ	Ⓐ	Ⓐ	Ⓐ		⑥	©	©	©	©		©		©	†
	Hamburg Hbf ¶ d.	Ⓐ	...	*0448*	*0548*	*0628*	*0748*		*1248*	*1408*		*1908*	*2008*	*2108*	*2208*	©	...	...	...	*0648*	*0758*		*1958*	...	*2058*	*2128*
0	**Buxtehude** d.		...	0537	0637	0717	0837	and	1337	1453	and	1953	2053	2153	2253		...	...	...	0745	0845	and	2045	...	2145	2245
39	Bremervörde a.		...	0619	0720	0819	0919	hourly	1419	1535	hourly	2035	2135	2235	2335		...	...	...	0827	0927	hourly	2127	...	2227	2327
39	Bremervörde d.		0538	0638	0738	0838	0938	until	1438	1538	until	2038	2138	...	...		0538	0638	0738	0838	0938	until	2138	...	...	...
78	**Bremerhaven** Hbf a.		0620	0720	0820	0920	1020		1520	1620		2120	2220	...	...		0620	0720	0820	0920	1020		2220	...	...	...

△		Ⓐ	Ⓐ		Ⓐ	Ⓐ		Ⓐ	Ⓐ	⑤	Ⓐ	Ⓐ	Ⓐ		©	⑥	©		©	†	©	⑥j	©	©	©
Bremerhaven Hbf d.	Ⓐ	...	0536		1236	1336		1936	2036	2136	2136	2236	2354	©	...	0636	0736		1936	2036	2036	2136	2136	2236	2354
Bremervörde a.		...	0619	and	1319	1419	and	2019	2119	2219	2219	2319	0035		...	0719	0819	and	2019	2119	2119	2219	2219	2319	0035
Bremervörde d.		0526	0626	hourly	1326	1438	hourly	2038	2138	2238	...	...	...		0733	0733	0833	hourly	2033	2133	...	2233	...	...	...
Buxtehude a.		0609	0709	until	1409	1526	until	2126	2226	2326	...	...	...		0816	0816	0916	until	2116	2216	...	2316	...	...	...
Hamburg Hbf ¶ a.		*0655*	*0755*		*1455*	*1615*		*2215*	*2315*	*0015*	...	...	...		*0905*	*0905*	*1005*		*2205*	*2305*	...	*0035*	...	...	...

j – Also Oct. 2, 30.
k – ⑦–④ (not Oct. 2, 30).
r – 2 – 3 minutes later June 11 - Sept. 22.
‡ – Hamburg S-Bahn (2nd class only).
⊖ – Additional S-Bahn trains operate.
¶ – Connections shown are Hamburg S-Bahn services.
✣ – Hamburg - Cuxhaven operated by Regionalverkehre Start Deutschland.
△ – Buxtehude - Bremerhaven operated by Elbe-Weser.

820 HAMBURG - KIEL

RE services except where shown

km		⚒t	†z		©z	Ⓐt	⚒t				and at									ICE 618 F	ICE 474 D	ICE 804 E	ICE 612 F	ICE 74 Z	EC 378 L‡	ICE 574 Ⓑ S
0	**Hamburg** Hbf 823 d.	0436	0443	0536	0636	0640	0719	0740k	0822	0843	the same	2022	2043	2122	2146	2222	2324	2343	A	1017	1157	1230	1617	1757	1915	2100
34	Elmshorn 823 d.	0504	0511	0604	0704	0709	0747	0809k	0847	0909	minutes	2047	2109	2147	2214	2248	2349	0012	L	|	|	|	|	|	|	|
78	Neumünster 823 d.	0532	0535	0632	0734	0734	0814	0834	0914	0934	past each	2114	2134	2214	2240	2318	0016	0040	S	1106	1251	1325	1705	1857	2002	2149
109	**Kiel** Hbf a.	0555	0558	0655	0757	0757	0834	0857	0934	0957	hour until	2134	2157	2234	2303	2338	0036	0103	O	1123	1310	1343	1722	1915	2020	2207

	©z	©z	Ⓐt		Ⓐ	©	⚒t			✣ and at							ICE 573 ①-⑥ S	ICE 73 ①-⑥ Z	EC 379 L¶	ICE 75 ⑦ Z		ICE 613 F	ICE 801 E	ICE 1171 D		IC 619 F
Kiel Hbf d.	0105	0305	0311	0403	0447	0502	0525	0602	0625	the same	2102	2125	2205	2305	0005	A	0546	0645	0742	0835	...	1237	1413	1439	...	1838
Neumünster 823 d.	0133	0330	0331	0430	0514	0528	0545	0628	0645	minutes	2128	2145	2233	2333	0033	L	0604	0704	0759	0853	...	1256	1432	1459	...	1857
Elmshorn 823 d.	0157	0354	0400	0456r	0536	0549	0612	0649	0712	past each	2149	2212	2258	2358	0058	S	|	|	|	|	...	|	|	|	...	|
Hamburg Hbf 823 a.	0223	0420	0429	0521	0601	0615	0637	0715	0737	hour until	2216	2237	2325	0025	0125	O	0658	0759	0848	0958	...	1342	1532	1558	...	1943

D – 🚃 ✕ Basel - Frankfurt - Hannover - Kiel and v.v.
E – 🚃 ✕ München - Nürnberg - Erfurt - Berlin - Kiel and v.v.
F – 🚃 ✕ München - Stuttgart - Köln - Kiel and v.v.
L – 🚃 ✕ Praha - Dresden - Berlin - Kiel and v.v.
S – 🚃 ✕ Kiel - Frankfurt - Stuttgart and v.v.
Z – 🚃 ✕ Kiel - Frankfurt - Basel - Zürich and v.v.

k – On † (also Oct. 31) Hamburg Hbf d. 0736, Elmshorn d. 0804.
r – 0454 on © (also Oct. 31).
t – Not Oct. 31.
z – Also Oct. 31.

‡ – On ① from June 27 runs as *IC* **1178** (and starts from Dresden).
¶ – On ① from June 27 runs as *IC* **1179** (and terminates at Dresden).
✣ – On ⑦ (not June 19, 26) the 0702 from Kiel runs 7 – 12 minutes later Neumünster - Hamburg.

HAMBURG - WESTERLAND 821

See Tables **820** and **823** for connecting *RE* services Hamburg Hbf - Elmshorn and v.v. Frequent S-Bahn services operate Hamburg Hbf - Altona and v.v.

km		A		⚒ r		A		Ⓐ r	Ⓒ z	Ⓐ r	Ⓒ Y		Ⓒ C		*IC*• 2214 E🍷	W	E	① M	*IC* 2074 🍷	Ⓒ C	T			*IC*• 2310 F🍷		⑤–⑦ Y
	Köln Hbf **800** .... d.	...	...	...	...	...	...	...	...	...	...	...	...	...	0507	...	...	...	...	...	...	...	...	0909	...	...
	Berlin Hbf **840** .... d.	...	...	...	...	...	...	...	...	...	...	...	...	...	|	...	...	...	...	...	...	...	...	|	...	...
	Hamburg Hbf. **820** d.	...	...	...	...	...	...	...	...	...	...	...	...	...	0919	...	...	...	...	...	...	...	...	1317	...	1402
0	**Hamburg** Altona .... d.	...	...	...	...	...	...	0529	0629	0640	0730	0740	0830	0840	|	0937	0937	1005	1023	1040	1040	1140	1240	|	1340	|
30	Elmshorn .... **820** d.	...	...	...	...	...	...	0549	0649	0701	|	0801	|	0901	|	1001	1001	1032u	|	1101	1101	1201	1301	|	1401	|
64	Itzehoe .... d.	...	...	0508	...	...	...	0612	0714	0724	|	0824	|	0924	1015t	1024	1024e	1056u	1113	1124	1124	1224	1324	1415t	1424	|
123	Heide (Holst) .... a.	...	...	0548	...	...	...	0656	0758	0758	|	0858	|	0958	1050	1058	1100	1129	1149	1158	1158	1258	1358	1450	1458	1530
123	Heide (Holst) .... d.	...	...	0549	...	...	...	0701	0801	0801	|	0901	|	1001	1052	1101	1101	1131	1151	1201	1201	1301	1401	1452	1501	1532
157	Husum .... d.	0458	0558	0614	0630	0658	0730	0730	0830	0830	0905	0930	1005	1030	1118	1130	1130	1201	1218	1230	1230	1330	1430	1518	1530	1559f
197	Niebüll .... a.	0527	0627	...	0659	0727	0759	0759	0859	0859	0929	0959	1029	1059	1145	1159	1206	1226	1244	1306	1306	1359	1459	1545	1606	1624
197	Niebüll .... 🚗 d.	0531	0631	...	0701	0731	0801	0801	0901	0901	0931	1001	1031	1101	1201	1201	1216v	1231	1300	1316	1331	1401	1501	1601	1616h	1631
237	**Westerland** (Sylt) 🚗 a.	0605	0705	...	0735	0805	0835	0835	0937	0937	1005	1035	1107	1135	1235	1235	1251v	1305	1337	1351	1405	1435	1535	1635	1651h	1705

			IC 2364 🍷								⑤⑥† z	⑤⑦
Köln Hbf **800** .... d.	...	...	...	...	...	...	...	...	...	...	...	...
Berlin Hbf **840** .... d.	...	...	...	...	...	...	...	...	...	...	...	...
Hamburg Hbf...**820** d.	...	...	...	...	...	...	...	...	...	...	...	...
Hamburg Altona........ d.	1440	1540	1609	1640	1740	1840	1940	2040	2140	2245	2345	2345
Elmshorn ....**820** d.	1501	1601	|	1701	1801	1901	2001	2101	2201	2306	0006	0006
Itzehoe .... d.	1524	1624	1655	1724	1824	1926	2026	2126	2226	2331	0031	0031
Heide (Holst) .... a.	1558	1658	1730	1758	1858	2000	2100	2200	2310	0015	0115	0115
Heide (Holst) .... d.	1601	1701	1732	1801	1901	2001	2101	2201	2311	0016	...	0116
Husum........................ d.	1630	1730	1801	1830	1930	2030	2130	2230	2340	0044	...	0144
Niebüll .... a.	1659	1759	1826	1859	1959	2059	2159	2259	0009	...	...	...
Niebüll .... 🚗 d.	1701	1801	1831	1901	2001	2101	2201	2301	0010	...	...	...
Westerland (Sylt). 🚗 a.	1735	1835	1904	1935	2035	2135	2235	2335	0050g	...	...	...

	Ⓐ r	Ⓐ r	Ⓒ z		† z	⚒ r				*IC*• 2311 H🍷
Westerland...... 🚗 d.	...	0419	...	0519	0619	0619	0719	0819	0907	0923
Niebüll.............. 🚗 a.	...	0453	...	0559	0659	0659	0759	0859	0944	0959
Niebüll..................... d.	...	0454	...	0601	0701	0701	0801	0901	1000	1013
Husum .... d.	0424	0524	0524j	0631	0729	0731	0831	0931	1031	1042
Heide (Holst)........... a.	0449	0549	0549j	0657	0752	0757	0857	0957	1057	1106
Heide (Holst)........... d.	0450	0550	0550	0658	0753	0802	0902	1002	1102	1108
Itzehoe .... d.	0534	0634	0634	0734	0837	0837	0937	1037	1137	1156t
Elmshorn......... **820** d.	0600	0700	0700	0800	0900	0900	1000	1100	1200	|
Hamburg Altona .... a.	0621	0721	0721	0821	0921	0921	1021	1121	1221	|
Hamburg Hbf **820** a.	...	...	...	...	...	...	...	...	...	1242
Berlin Hbf **840**...... a.	...	...	...	...	...	...	...	...	...	|
Köln Hbf **800**........ a.	...	...	...	...	...	...	...	...	...	1650

	⑤–⑦ Y		*IC* 2375 🍷		⑤ E		E	W	*IC*• 2215 E F🍷		*IC*• 2075 🍷			⑦ N		L		⑥ Y				⑤⑥ d	⑦–④ b	△		
Westerland (Sylt). 🚗 d.	0949	1019	1053	1119	1149	1219	1307	1319	1323	1349	1420	1519	1619	1649	1719	1749	1819	1849	1919	2019	2119	2119	...	...	2219	2319
Niebüll .... 🚗 a.	1029	1059	1129	1159	1229	1259	1344	1359	1359	1429	1500	1559	1659	1729	1759	1829	1859	1929	1959	2059	2159	2159	...	...	2259	2355
Niebüll .... d.	1034	1101	1131	1201	1234	1301	1355	1401	1413	1455	1513	1601	1701	1731	1801	1831	1901	1931	2001	2101	2201	2201	...	...	2301	0001
Husum........................ d.	1104f	1131	1158	1231	1301	1331	1431f	1431	1442	1531f	1545	1631	1731	1756	1831	1856	1931	1956	2031	2131	2229	2231	2248	...	2329	0029
Heide (Holst) .... a.	1126	1157	1221	1257	1323	1357	1457	1457	1506	1557	1606	1657	1757	|	1857	|	1957	|	2057	2157	...	2257	2313	...	...	...
Heide (Holst) .... d.	1128	1202	1223	1302	1325	1402	1502	1502	1508	1602	1608	1702	1802	|	1902	|	2002	|	2104	2204	...	2304	2314	...	...	...
Itzehoe .... d.	|	1237	1302	1337	1359s	1437	1537	1537	1555t	1637	1658t	1737	1837	|	1937	|	2037	|	2139	2248	...	2348	2354	*0002*	...	...
Elmshorn ....**820** d.	|	1300	|	1400	1427s	1500	1600	1600	|	1700	|	1800	1900	|	2000	|	2100	|	2202	2310	...	0010	...	0033	...	...
Hamburg Altona........ a.	|	1321	1354	1421	1503	1521	1621	1621	|	1721	|	1821	1921	1928	2021	2028	2121	2128	2223	2331	...	0031	...	0057	...	...
Hamburg Hbf...**820** a.	1302	...	...	...	...	...	...	...	1642	...	1748	...	...	...	...	...	...	...	...	...	...	...	...	...	...	...
Berlin Hbf **840** .... a.	...	...	...	...	...	...	...	...	|	...	1955	...	...	...	...	...	...	...	...	...	...	...	...	...	...	...
Köln Hbf **800** .... a.	...	...	...	...	...	...	...	...	2050	...	...	...	...	...	...	...	...	...	...	...	...	...	...	...	...	...

A – Daily to Nov. 4; ①–⑤ from Nov. 7.
C – Ⓒ until Oct. 30 (also Oct. 31).
E – Until Nov. 1.
F – To / from Frankfurt (Table **800**).
H – NORDFRIESLAND – To Stuttgart (Tables **800** and **912**).
L – ⑥⑦ until Oct. 2; ⑥ Oct. 8 – 29 (also Oct. 30).
M – ① until Oct. 24 (also Oct. 4; not Oct. 3).
N – ⑦ until Oct. 23 (also Oct. 3, 31; not Oct. 2).
T – Ⓐ to Oct. 28; daily from Nov. 1.
W – From Nov. 2.
Y – Until Sept. 25.

b – Not Oct. 2, 30.
d – Also Oct. 2, 30.
e – 1027 on ②–⑤ (not Oct. 4).
f – Arrives 5 – 7 minutes earlier.
g – 0043 on the mornings of ⑦ (also Oct. 3, 31).
h – 14 – 15 minutes later on ①–④ (also Nov. 4, 11, 18, 25, Dec. 2, 9; not Oct. 31).
j – On ⑦ Husum d. 0442, Heide a. 0542 (by 🚌).
r – Not Oct. 31.
s – Arrival time. Calls to set down only.
t – Arrives 12 – 19 minutes earlier.

u – Calls to pick up only.
v – On Ⓒ (also Oct. 31) Niebüll d. 1230, Westerland a. 1305.
z – Also Oct. 31.

• – Conveys [2] to / from Dagebüll Mole on dates in Table **822**.
△ – Operated by *nordbahn*.
🚗 – Regular car-carrying shuttle services also operate between Niebüll and Westerland (18 – 28 per day in summer, 12 – 14 in winter).

SCHLESWIG-HOLSTEIN BRANCH LINES 822

NEUMÜNSTER - HEIDE - BÜSUM (Operated by *nordbahn*)

km		⚒ r	⚒ r	† z	⚒ r	⑥	Ⓐ r																		
0	Neumünster ....d.	...	...	*0535*	...	0535	0535	...	0735	...	0935	...	1135	...	1335	...	1535	...	1735	...	1935	...	...	...	2135
63	Heide (Holst) ....a.	...	...	*0645*	...	0645	0710	...	0845	...	1045	...	1245	...	1445	...	1645	...	1845	...	2045	...	...	...	2245
63	Heide (Holst) ....d.	0449	0556	0652	0701	0701	...	0801	0901	1001	1101	1201	1301	1401	1501	1601	1701	1801	1901	2003	...	2103	2203	...	...
87	Büsum..........................a.	0515	0622	0718	0727	0727	...	0827	0927	1027	1127	1227	1327	1427	1527	1627	1727	1827	1927	2029	...	2129	2229	...	...

	⚒ r	⚒ r	⚒ r	⑥		† z	⚒ r																		
Büsum..........................d.	...	0519	0626	0626	...	0722	0731	0831	0931	1031	1131	1231	1331	1431	1531	1631	1731	1831	1931	2033	...	...	2133	...	2233
Heide (Holst) ....a.	...	0545	0652	0652	...	0748	0757	0857	0957	1057	1157	1257	1357	1457	1557	1657	1757	1856	1957	2059	...	...	2159	...	2259
Heide (Holst) ....d.	0517	...	...	0717	0717	...	...	0917	...	1117	...	1317	...	1517	...	1717	...	1917	...	...	2117	...	...	...	2317
Neumünster ....a.	0625	...	...	0825	0825	...	...	1025	...	1225	...	1425	...	1625	...	1825	...	2025	...	...	2225	...	...	...	0025

HUSUM - BAD ST PETER ORDING

km		Ⓐ r								
0	Husum.........................d.	0436	0536	0636	and	1836	1936	2036	2136	2236
21	Tönning ....d.	0501	0601	0701	hourly	1901	2001	2101	2201	2301
43	Bad St Peter Ording ...a.	0527	0627	0727	until	1927	2027	2127	2227	2327

	Ⓐ r								
Bad St Peter Ording.d.	0533	0633	0733	and	1933	2033	2133	2233	2333
Tönning ....d.	0604	0704	0804	hourly	2004	2104	2204	2304	0004
Husum.........................a.	0625	0725	0825	until	2025	2125	2225	2325	0025

NIEBÜLL - DAGEBÜLL MOLE *See note* ⊡

km	*Until Oct. 30* ♥					★		◧	★		◇	⊙
	Hamburg Hbf....a.	...	...	...	...	0919	...	...	1317t	...	...	...
	Niebüll ....a.	...	...	...	...	1145	...	...	1545t	...	...	...
0	Niebüll neg ....d.	0635	0735	0905	1010	1212	1310	1435	1605	1710	1815	1910
14	Dagebüll Mole...a.	0653	0753	0923	1028	1228	1328	1453	1623	1728	1832	1928

Until Oct. 30 ♥		★		k		★	★			⊙	⊙
Dagebüll Mole d.	0815	0930	1035	1148	1245	1340	1440	1635	1735	1835	1935
Niebüll neg.....a.	0833	0948	1053	1204	1303	1357	1457	1653	1753	1853	1953
Niebüll ....d.	...	1013	...	...	...	1413	1513	...	...	...	...
Hamburg Hbf .a.	...	1242	...	...	...	1642	1748	...	...	...	...

km	*From Oct. 31*		①–⑤		①–⑤		①–⑤					
0	Niebüll neg ....d.	0635	0735	0905	1010	1125	1235	1335	1440	1605	1815	1910
14	Dagebüll Mole...a.	0653	0753	0923	1028	1143	1253	1353	1458	1621	1832	1928

From Oct. 31		①–⑤		①–⑤		①–⑤					
Dagebüll Mole d.	0700	0815	0930	1035	1148	1305	1415	1505	1625	1835	1935
Niebüll neg.....a.	0718	0833	0948	1053	1206	1323	1433	1523	1643	1853	1953

k – Not June 18 - Sept. 11.
r – Not Oct. 31.
t – Not Oct. 30.
z – Also Oct. 31.

◧ – Runs 30 minutes later on ⑥⑦ June 18 - Sept. 11.
◇ – Runs 4 – 5 minutes **earlier** June 18 - Sept. 11.
⊙ – Runs 25 minutes later on ⑥⑦ June 18 - Sept. 11.
★ – Conveys [2] (*IC*) from / to Hamburg and beyond (Table **821**).

♥ – **Additional journeys until June 17 and Sept. 12 - Oct. 30**:
Niebüll neg → Dagebüll Mole at 1125 and 1335; Dagebüll Mole → Niebüll neg at 0700 and 1505.
Additional journeys June 18 - Sept. 11:
Niebüll neg → Dagebüll Mole at 1025 ⑤–⑦, 1105 ⑤, 1125 (not ⑤), 1335, 1415 ⑥⑦, 2010 ①–⑤ and 2035 ⑥⑦.
Dagebüll Mole → Niebüll neg at 0700 ①–⑤, 0705 ⑥⑦, 1055 ⑥⑦, 1105 ⑤, 1420 ⑥⑦, 1505 ①–⑤, 1530 ⑥⑦, 2035 ①–⑤ and 2100 ⑥⑦.

⊡ – **Operator**: Norddeutsche Eisenbahngesellschaft Niebüll GmbH. ✆ +49 (0) 4661 980 880.
Niebüll neg station is situated a short distance from the Niebüll DB station forecourt.
Dagebüll Mole is the station for ferries to / from the islands of Föhr and Amrum (see www.faehre.de).

823 HAMBURG - NEUMÜNSTER - FLENSBURG

RE / RB services except where shown

km																											
									IC 1186			*IC* 386					*IC* 384			*IC* 1182	*EC* 174						
			⚒ r	①-⑥ c		⚒ r	† z		R A			n A					n A			R A	P						
0	**Hamburg** Hbf.... 820 d.	...	...	...	0640j	0740	...	0843	0856	0943	1043	1053	1143	1243	1342	1443	1452	1542	1643	1652	1714	1743	1843	1943	2043	2146	2243
34	Elmshorn........... 820 d.	...	...	...	0709j	0809	...	0909	|	1010	1109	|	1209	1309	1409	1509	|	1609	1709	|	|	1809	1909	2009	2109	2214	2314
78	Neumünster....... 820 d.	0040	0534	0646	0732	0832	0833	0932	|	1032	1132	|	1232	1332	1432	1532	|	1632	1732	|	1806	1832	1932	2032	2132	2237	2336
117	Rendsburg .... 824 d.	0107	0601	0715	0759	0859	0900	0959	1013	1059	1159	1213	1259	1359	1459	1559	1617	1659	1759	1815	1831	1859	1959	2059	2159	2304	0003
141	Schleswig.......... 824 d.	0123	0617	0731	0815	0915	0916	1015	|	1115	1216	|	1315	1415	1515	1615	|	1716	1815	|	1847	1915	2015	2115	2215	2320	0021
179	**Flensburg**.............. a.	0148	0642	0756	0840	0940	0941	1040	1048	1140	1240	1248	1340	1440	1540	1640	1649	1740	1840	1848	1907	1940	2040	2140	2240	2345	0045

								EC 175		*IC* 1183			*IC* 383					*IC* 385			*IC* 1187					
	Ⓐ r	⑥	⚒ r	①-⑥ c	⑦ d			Q		R A			n A					n A			R A					
Flensburg............... d.	0400	0415	0515	0615	0623	0715	0815	0831	0915	1009	1015	1115	1209	1215	1315	1415	1515	1609	1615	1715	1809	1815	1915	2015	2115	2215	2315
Schleswig .... 824 d.	0424	0439	0539	0639	0647	0739	0839	0901	0939	|	1039	1139	|	1239	1339	1439	1539	|	1639	1739	|	1839	1939	2039	2139	2239	2339
Rendsburg .... 824 d.	0441	0456	0556	0656	0704	0756	0856	0917	0956	1043	1056	1156	1243	1256	1356	1456	1556	1643	1656	1756	1843	1856	1956	2056	2156	2256	2357
Neumünster .... 820 a.	0508	0522	0622	0722	0731	0822	0922	0953	1022	|	1122	1222	|	1322	1422	1522	1622	|	1722	1822	|	1922	2022	2122	2222	2322	0022
Elmshorn .... 820 a.	0535	...	0648	0748	0755	0848	0948	|	1048	|	1148	1248	|	1348	1448	1548	1648	|	1748	1848	|	1948	2048	2148b	...	...	...
Hamburg Hbf.... 820 a.	0601	...	0715	0815	0827	0915	1015	1048	1115	1206	1215	1315	1407	1415	1515	1615	1716	1802	1816	1916	2002	2016	2116	2216b	...	...	...

A – To / from Aarhus (Table **710**).
P – Daily to June 26; ②–⑦ from June 28. 🚃 ✕ Praha - Dresden - Berlin - Flensburg.
Q – Daily to June 27; ①③④⑤⑥⑦ from June 29. 🚃 ✕ Flensburg - Berlin - Dresden - Praha. Train number **1175** on ① from June 27 (terminates at Dresden).
R – June 18 - Aug. 21 only.
b – ⑦–④ (not Oct. 2, 30).
c – Also June 19, 26.
d – Not June 19, 26.
j – ⚒ (not Oct. 31). On ⑥ Hamburg d. 0636, Elmshorn d. 0704.
n – Not June 18 - Aug. 21.
r – Not Oct. 31.
z – Also Oct. 31.

824 KIEL - HUSUM and FLENSBURG

RE / RB services

KIEL - HUSUM

km		v		⚒r	w						
0	**Kiel** Hbf............d.	0003	...	0348	0403	0503h	0603h	0703	and hourly until	2203	2303
40	Rendsburg. 823 d.	0043	...	0435j	0435	0535	0635	0735		2235	2343
65	Schleswig .. 823 d.	0101	...	0453	0453	0553	0653	0753		2253	0001
102	**Husum**............a.	0133	...	0525	0525	0625	0724	0825		2325	0033

	⚒r								
Husum....................d.	0430	0535	...	0635	and hourly until	2035	2135	2235	2335
Schleswig .... 823 d.	0502	0607	...	0707		2107	2207	2307	0007
Rendsburg......... 823 d.	0521	0626	...	0726		2126	2226	2329	0031
Kiel Hbf....................a.	0557	0657e	...	0757		2157	2257	2400	0113v

KIEL - FLENSBURG

km		Ⓐr	⚒r								
0	**Kiel** Hbf............d.	0414	0541	0641	0743	and hourly until	2043	2143	2248	2348	...
29	Eckernförde ....d.	0449	0611	0711	0811		2111	2216	2321	0021	...
50	Süderbrarup.........d.	0507	0631	0731	0831		2131	2240	2340	0040	...
81	**Flensburg**........a.	0537	0657	0757	0857		2157	2306	0006	0106	...

	⚒r								
Flensburg....................d.	0504	0604	0704	0804	and hourly until	2004	2104	2213	2313
Süderbrarup....................d.	0530	0630	0730	0830		2030	2130	2240	2340
Eckernförde ....d.	0550	0650	0750	0850		2050	2155	2300	0000
Kiel Hbf....................a.	0617	0717	0817	0917		2117	2224	2330	0030

e – On ⑦ (not June 19, 26) arrives 0724 (by 🚌 from Rendsburg).
h – On ⑦ (not June 19, 26) departs 28 minutes **earlier** (by 🚌 to Rendsburg).
j – Arrives 0419.
r – Not Oct. 31.
v – Change trains at Rendsburg on the mornings of June 18, 19, 25, 26.
w – Runs on June 18, 25 only.

825 HAMBURG - LÜBECK - PUTTGARDEN and TRAVEMÜNDE

RB / RE services

HAMBURG - LÜBECK

km		©z	⚒r		Ⓐr		p							Ⓑ								K		H
0	**Hamburg** Hbf...d.	0255	0507	0607	0634	0707	0734	0807	0834	and at the same minutes past each hour until	1907	1934	2007	2034	2107	2207	2324	0024	0055	...	Also	1359	...	2136
40	Bad Oldesloe....d.	0336	0533	0633	0704	0733	0804	0833	0904		1933	2004	2033	2104	2133	2233	2349	0051	0136	...		|	...	|
63	**Lübeck** Hbf.......a.	0354	0551	0651	0722	0751	0822	0851	0922		1951	2022	2051	2122	2151	2251	0007	0110	0154	...		1442	...	2220

	©z		⚒r	Ⓐr		⚒r															L		
Lübeck Hbf..................d.	0218	0418	0510	0538	0610	0638	0710	0742	0810	0838	and at the same minutes past each hour until	1910	1938	2010	2110	2210	2310	0018	...	Also	1718	...	...
Bad Oldesloe..............d.	0235	0435	0527	0555	0627	0655	0727	0759	0827	0855		1927	1955	2027	2127	2227	2327	0035	...		|	...	...
Hamburg Hbf..............a.	0317	0517	0553	0625	0653	0725	0753	0826	0853	0925		1953	2025	2053	2153	2253	2353	0110	...		1801	...	...

LÜBECK - TRAVEMÜNDE STRAND ⊠

km		Ⓐr	⚒r								
0	**Lübeck** Hbf..........................d.	0503	0603	0703	0803j	and hourly until	2003j	2103c	2203	2303
18	Travemünde Skandinavienkai a.	0519	0619	0719	0819		2019	2119	2219	2319
21	**Travemünde** Strand..............a.	0525	0625	0725	0825		2025	2125	2225	2325

	Ⓐr	⚒r						
Travemünde Strand.....................d.	0534	0634	0734	0834	and hourly until	2234	...	2334
Travemünde Skandinavienkai.......d.	0539	0639	0739	0839		2239	...	2339
Lübeck Hbf.................................a.	0556	0656	0756	0856f		2256f	...	2356

HAMBURG - LÜBECK - PUTTGARDEN *SERVICE UNTIL AUGUST 31*

km				*IC* 2414					*IC* 2416							
		Ⓐ			Ⓐ	©				Ⓐ	©				v	v
0	**Hamburg** Hbf.............d.	...	...	0646n	...	0823	...	...	1220	...	1423	...	...	...	...	...
40	Bad Oldesloe.................d.	...	...	|	...	0853	...	...	|	...	1453	...	...	...	...	...
63	**Lübeck** Hbf..................d.	0510	0710	0739	0910	0911	1110	1308	1316	1510	1511	...	1710	1910	2110	2310
115	Oldenburg (Holst)........d.	0609	0811	0832	1011	1012	1211	1406	1416	1611	1612	...	1811	2011	2211	0017
144	Fehmarn-Burg ....a.	0637	0834	0856	1034	1037	1234	1429	1440	1634	1637	...	1834	2034	2234	0040
151	**Puttgarden** ....a.	0650	0849	...	1049	1053	1249	1444	...	1649	1653	...	1849	2049	2249	0055

				IC 2413					*IC* 2415					
		Ⓐ				©	Ⓐ				©	Ⓐ		
Puttgarden ....d.	0512	0613	0713	...	0913	1108	1113	1308	...	1513	1708	1713	...	1913	2113
Fehmarn-Burg..........................d.	0523	0626	0726	0910	0926	1123	1126	1321	1508	1526	1723	1726	...	1926	2126
Oldenburg (Holst)....................d.	0546	0649	0749	0934	0949	1148	1149	1344	1534	1549	1748	1749	...	1949	2149
Lübeck Hbf..............................a.	0650	0750	0850	1034	1050	1241	1250	1450	1635	1650	1841	1850	...	2050	2250
Bad Oldesloe............................a.	...	...	...	|	...	1300	...	...	|	...	1900	...	...	...	...
Hamburg Hbf..........................a.	...	...	...	1127	...	1332	...	...	1735	...	1933	...	...	...	...

LÜBECK - NEUSTADT (Holst).
Journey time 32–43 minutes.

From Lübeck Hbf at 0438 Ⓐ, 0510 Ⓐ, 0610, 0710, 0810, 0910 Ⓐ, 0915 ©, 1010, 1110, 1210, 1308, 1410, 1510 Ⓐ, 1515 ©, 1610, 1710, 1810, 1910, 2010, 2110, 2210 and 2310 v.

From Neustadt (Holst) at 0516 Ⓐ, 0616, 0648 Ⓐ, 0711 Ⓐ, 0716 ©, 0811, 0916, 1011, 1116, 1211 Ⓐ, 1216 ©, 1311, 1411, 1511, 1611, 1716, 1811 Ⓐ, 1816 ©, 1916, 2011, 2116, 2211 and 2316.

H – *ICE* **584**. From München (Table **900**).
K – *IC* **2408**. From Köln (Table **800**).
L – *IC* **2409**. To Köln (Table **800**).
c – 2101 on ⑥ until Oct. 29.
f – 2 minutes later on © until Oct. 30 (also Oct. 31).
j – 2 minutes **earlier** on © until Oct. 30 (also Oct. 31).
n – Departs 0655 on ⑦; departs 0659 on ⑥.
p – Not Oct. 2, 30.
r – Not Oct. 31.
v – Not Aug. 31.
z – Also Oct. 31.
⊠ – Evening services (from approx. 1930) are subject to alteration July 22–31.

826 KIEL - LÜBECK

RE / RB services

km		Ⓐr	©z	Ⓐr	Ⓐr	©z	Ⓐr	©z	Ⓐr											
0	**Kiel** Hbf...........d.	0443	0443	0513	0543	0543	0605	0643	0643	0705	0743	and at the same minutes past each hour until	1905	1943	2005	2043	2143	2243	...	2343
33	Plön......................d.	0514	0515	0545	0615	0615	0645	0714	0715	0745	0815		1945	2015	2045	2115	2215	2315	...	0015
47	Eutin.....................d.	0528	0530	0600	0630	0630	0700	0728	0730	0800	0830		2000	2030	2100	2131	2230	2330	...	0030
80	**Lübeck** Hbf.........a.	0553	0558	0632	0654	0658	0732	0753	0753	0832	0853		2032	2053	2132	2153	2258	2358	...	0058

	©w	Ⓐt	Ⓐr	©z	⑥	Ⓐr	Ⓐr	©z	Ⓐr	Ⓐr										
Lübeck Hbf.......d.	0018	0018	0352	0401	0501	0504	0528	0601	0604	0628	0704	0728	0806	0828	and at the same minutes past each hour until	2006	2028	2106	2201	2301
Eutin...................d.	0048	0048	0418	0430	0530	0530	0600	0630	0630	0700	0730	0800	0830	0900		2030	2100	2131	2230	2330
Plön....................d.	0103	0103	0432	0445	0545	0545	0615	0645	0645	0715	0745	0815	0845	0915		2045	2115	2145	2245	2345
Kiel Hbf.............a.	0134	0145	0506	0517	0617	0617	0656	0717	0717	0756	0817	0856	0917	0956		2117	2156	2217	2317	0017

r – Not Oct. 31.
t – Not June 20–27, Oct. 31.
w – Also June 20–24, 27, Oct. 31.
z – Also Oct. 31.

LÜBECK - BÜCHEN - LÜNEBURG — 827

RE services

km				Ⓐr	⑥	Ⓐr	Ⓒz	Ⓐr	Ⓒz																
0	**Lübeck** Hbf	d.	0011	...	0501	0509	0601	0609	0705	0709	0809	0909	1009	1109	1209	1309	1409	1509	1609	1709	1809	1909	2009	2109	2209	2306
9	Lübeck Flughafen ✈ ▷	d.	0021	...	0510	0519	0610	0619	0714	0719	0819	0919	1019	1119	1219	1319	1419	1519	1619	1719	1819	1919	2019	2119	2219	2315
22	Ratzeburg	d.	0030	...	0523	0530	0627	0630	0730	0730	0830	0930	1030	1130	1230	1330	1430	1530	1630	1730	1830	1930	2030	2130	2230	2324
31	Mölln (Lauenburg)	d.	0037	...	0530	0537	0634	0637	0737	0737	0837	0937	1037	1137	1237	1337	1437	1537	1637	1737	1837	1937	2037	2137	2237	2331
50	Büchen	a.	0049	...	0542	0549	0646	0649	0749	0749	0849	0949	1049	1149	1249	1349	1449	1549	1649	1749	1849	1949	2049	2149	2249	2347
50	Büchen	d.	...	...	0553	0550	0655	0655	0759	0750	0859	0950	1107	1150	1307	1350	1507	1550	1707	1750	1907	1950	2107	2202	2250	2350
79	**Lüneburg**	a.	...	...	0616	0615	0718	0718	0822	0815	0922	1015	1130	1215	1330	1415	1530	1615	1730	1815	1930	2015	2130	2225	2315	0015

				Ⓐr	Ⓐr	⑥	Ⓐr	Ⓒz																	⑤⑥f
Lüneburg	d.	...	...	0420	0524	0545	0628	0630	...	0742e	0830	0945	1030	1145	1230	1345	1430	1545	1630	1745	1830	1945	2030	2138	2245	2345
Büchen	a.	...	...	0442	0545	0608	0650	0652	...	0808	0852	1008	1052	1208	1252	1408	1452	1608	1652	1808	1852	2008	2052	2200	2310	0008
Büchen	d.	0112	...	0453	0553	0609	0657	0709	0709	0809	0909	1009	1109	1209	1309	1409	1509	1609	1709	1809	1909	2009	2109	2209	2334	0009
Mölln (Lauenburg)	d.	0124	...	0505	0605	0622	0709	0722	0722	0822	0922	1022	1122	1222	1322	1422	1522	1622	1722	1822	1922	2022	2122	2222	2346	0022
Ratzeburg	d.	0132	...	0512	0612	0632	0717	0732	0732	0832	0932	1032	1132	1232	1332	1432	1532	1632	1732	1832	1932	2032	2132	2232	2353	0032
Lübeck Flughafen ✈ . ▷	d.	0140	...	0521	0621	0640	0726	0740	0740	0840	0940	1040	1140	1240	1340	1440	1540	1640	1740	1840	1940	2040	2140	2240	0001	0040
Lübeck Hbf	a.	0152	...	0532	0632	0652	0736	0752	0752	0852	0952	1052	1152	1252	1352	1452	1552	1652	1752	1852	1952	2052	2152	2253	0012	0052

e – 0745 on Ⓒ (also Oct. 31). **f** – Also Oct. 2, 30. **r** – Not Oct. 31. **z** – Also Oct. 31. ▷ – Trains call at Lübeck Flughafen on request only.

HAMBURG - ROSTOCK - STRALSUND — 830

RE services except where shown

km										ICE 1678			ICE 636	IC 2238			IC 2212	IC 2212			ICE 632			IC 2216	ICE 1074	
				◇ Ⓐ S		◇ S	Ⓐ a	◇ Ⓐ		◇ S	①–⑥ ✕♦		◇ S	①–⑥ ✕	♦		◇ S	⑥ 🍷♦	Ⓑ 🍷♦		◇ S	M✕		◇ S	🍷♦	⑤ ✕	
0	**Hamburg** Hbf	d.	0035	...	...	...	...	...	0621	...	0741	0821	...	0943	...	1021	...	1117	1142	1221	...	1341	1421	...	1517	1543	1621
47	Büchen	d.	0107	...	0458a	...	...	...	0658t	...	|	0858t	...	|	...	1058t	...	|	|	1258t	...	|	1458t	...	|	|	1658t
123	**Schwerin** Hbf **837**	d.	0158	...	0549	...	0642	...	0749	...	0838	0949	...	1038	1114	1149	...	1239y	1239	1349	...	1438	1549	...	1613	1638	1749
140	Bad Kleinen . **836 837**	d.	▬	...	0603	...	0659	...	0803	...	|	1003	...	|	1125	1203	...	|	|	1403	...	|	1603	...	|	|	1803
181	Bützow **836**	d.	◇	...	0629	...	0723	...	0829	...	0910	1029	...	1110	1148	1229	...	1310	1310	1429	...	1510	1629	...	1645	1713	1829
211	**Rostock** Hbf	a.	S	...	0650	...	0750	...	0850	...	0932	1050	...	1132	1208	1252	...	1332	1332	1450	...	1532	1650	...	1705	1733	1850
211	**Rostock** Hbf	d.	0454	0553	...	0700	...	0811	...	0900	0938	...	1100	1138	...	...	1300	1338	1338	...	1500	1538	...	1700	1717	1745	...
240	Ribnitz-D'garten West	d.	0517	0616	...	0725	...	0849	...	0922	1002o	...	1122	|	...	...	1322	1400	1400	...	1522	|	...	1722	1739	|	...
265	Velgast	d.	0539	0638	...	0742	...	0903	...	0940	1016	...	1140	1215	...	...	1340	1416	1416	...	1540	1615	...	1740	1754	1827	...
283	**Stralsund** Hbf	a.	0555	0655	...	0758	...	0922	...	0957	1029	...	1157	1229	...	...	1357	1430	1430	...	1557	1630	...	1757	1812	1841	...
	Ostseebad Binz **844**	a.	...	...	...	...	...	...	...	...	1119	...	...	...	...	...	...	1528	1528	...	...	1721e	...	...	...	...	...

			ICE 538			ICE 976	ICE 536	ICE 536			ICE 874	
		◇ S	M✕		◇ S	⑤ ✕	⑦ M✕	⑦–④ M✕		◇ S	⑦ M	
Hamburg Hbf	d.	...	1741	1821	...	1943	1943	1943	2021	...	2143	2254
Büchen	d.	...	|	1858t	...	|	|	|	2058t	...	|	2328
Schwerin Hbf **837**	d.	...	1838	1949	...	2038	2038	2038	2149	...	2238	0020
Bad Kleinen **836 837**	d.	...	1850	2003	...	|	2050	2050	2203	...	2250	0030
Bützow **836**	d.	...	1913	2029	...	2110	2113	2113	2229	...	2313	0055
Rostock Hbf	a.	...	1933	2050	...	2132	2133	2133	2250	...	2333	0118
Rostock Hbf	d.	1900	1938	...	2100	2138	2138	...	...	2300	...	...
Ribnitz-Damgarten West	d.	1922	|	...	2122	|	|	...	...	2322	...	...
Velgast	d.	1940	2015	...	2140	2215	2215	...	...	2340	...	...
Stralsund Hbf	a.	1957	2030	...	2157	2229	2229	...	...	2357	...	...
Ostseebad Binz **844**	a.	...	...	...	...	...	...	...	...	...	...	...

					ICE 1599			ICE 535			IC 2217
		Ⓐ a	Ⓒ z	Ⓐ a	①–⑤ ✕		◇ Ⓐ S	①–⑥ M✕	◇ S		🍷♦
Ostseebad Binz **844**	d.	...	...	...	...	...	...	...	...	...	...
Stralsund Hbf	d.	...	...	...	...	...	0450	0521	0558	...	0727
Velgast	d.	...	...	...	...	...	0506	0536	0614	...	0741
Ribnitz-Damgarten West	d.	...	...	...	...	...	0525	|	0632	...	0756
Rostock Hbf	a.	...	...	...	...	...	0548	0616	0654	...	0816
Rostock Hbf	d.	...	...	...	0458	0508	...	0625	...	0708	0825
Bützow **836**	d.	...	...	...	0518	0529	...	0645	...	0729	0845
Bad Kleinen **836 837**	d.	...	...	...	0543	0558	...	0709	...	0758	|
Schwerin Hbf **837**	d.	0349	0442	0451	0555	0610	...	0719	...	0810	0920
Büchen	d.	0448	0540	0551	0634	0707t	...	|	...	0907t	|
Hamburg Hbf	a.	0518	0611	0626	0704	0738	...	0819	...	0938	1016

				ICE 639			IC 2213			IC 2239	ICE 1021	ICE 633			ICE 635						ICE 679						
		◇ S		M✕	◇ S		🍷♦	◇		♦	⑥⑦ ✕♦	M✕	◇ S		✕	Ⓐ a	◇ S		◇	E	⑦ H✕			◇ S		◇ S	
Ostseebad Binz **844**	d.	...	...	0826	...	...	1043	1102	...	...	1156k	1226	...	...	...	...	...	...	1603	...	...	1702	...	...	...	...	...
Stralsund Hbf	d.	0759	...	0926	0959	...	1136	1159	...	...	1304	1326	1359	...	1526	...	1559	...	1658	...	1726	1759	...	1959	...	2159	...
Velgast	d.	0815	...	0940	1015	...	1156	1215	...	...	1317	1340	1415	...	1540	...	1615	...	1711	...	1740	1815	...	2015	...	2215	...
Ribnitz-Damgarten West	d.	0833	...	|	1033	...	1215	1233	...	...	|	|	1433	...	|	...	1633	...	1738t	...	1800	1833	...	2033	...	2233	...
Rostock Hbf	a.	0855	...	1019	1055	...	1239	1255	...	...	1401	1419	1455	...	1619	...	1655	...	1801r	...	1820	1855	...	2055	...	2255	...
Rostock Hbf	d.	...	0908	1025	...	1108	1244	...	1308	1348	1408	1425	...	1508	1625	...	...	1708	...	1809	1825	...	1908	...	2108	...	2313
Bützow **836**	d.	...	0929	1045	...	1129	1304	...	1329	1409	1429	1445	...	1529	1645	...	...	1729	...	1830	1845	...	1929	...	2129	...	2335
Bad Kleinen **836 837**	d.	...	0958	|	...	1158	|	...	1358	1433	|	|	...	1558	|	...	...	1758	...	1903t	|	...	1958	...	2158	...	0001
Schwerin Hbf **837**	d.	...	1010	1119	...	1210	1337	...	1410	1441	1507	1519	...	1611	1719	1723	...	1810	...	1914	1919	...	2010	...	2210	...	0011
Büchen	d.	...	1107t	|	...	1307t	|	...	1507t	...	|	|	...	1707t	|	1822	...	1907t	...	...	|	...	2107t	...	2303	...	...
Hamburg Hbf	a.	...	1138	1216	...	1341	1432	...	1538	...	1603	1616	...	1738	1819	1854	...	1938	...	...	2019	...	2138	...	2337	...	...

♦ – **NOTES** (LISTED BY TRAIN NUMBER)

1021 – [12] ✕ Ostseebad Binz - Hamburg - Köln - Nürnberg.
1678 – [12] ✕ (Hannover ①–⑤ -) Hamburg - Ostseebad Binz.
2212 – RÜGEN – [12] 🍷 Koblenz - Köln - Hamburg - Ostseebad Binz.
2213 – RÜGEN – [12] 🍷 Ostseebad Binz - Hamburg - Köln - Stuttgart.
2216/7 – GREIFSWALDER BODDEN – [12] 🍷 Stuttgart - Koblenz - Köln - Hamburg - Stralsund (- Greifswald on dates in Table **845**) and v.v.
2238 – WARNOW – [12] Leipzig - Magdeburg - Stendal - Rostock - Warnemünde (a. 1228).
2239 – WARNOW – [12] Warnemünde (d. 1321) - Rostock - Stendal - Magdeburg - Leipzig.

E – ①②③④⑥ (not Oct. 3, 31).
H – To Hannover (Table **900**).
S – To / from Sassnitz (Table **844**).
M – To / from München (Table **900**).

a – Ⓐ (not Oct. 31).
e – Not ⑦.
k – ⑥ only.

o – Ribnitz-Damgarten **Ost**.
r – 1812 on ⑤.
t – Arrives 6–8 minutes earlier.
y – Arrives 1222.
z – Also Oct. 31.

◇ – Operator: Ostdeutsche Eisenbahn.

ROSTOCK - WARNEMÜNDE — 831

S-Bahn

ROSTOCK - WARNEMÜNDE and v.v. *13 km.* Journey time: 21 minutes. Additional services run at peak times on Ⓐ.

From Rostock Hbf at 0003, 0126 ①⑥⑦, 0433, 0448 Ⓐ, 0503, 0518 Ⓐ, 0533, 0548 Ⓐ, 0603, 0618 Ⓐ, 0633, 0648 Ⓐ, 0703, 0718 Ⓐ, 0733, 0748 Ⓐ, 0803, 0818, 0833, 0848, 0903, 0918, 0933, 0948 and at 03, 18, 33 and 48 minutes past each hour until 2103, 2118, 2133, 2148; then 2203, 2233, 2303 and 2333.

From Warnemünde at 0003, 0033 ①⑥⑦, 0403, 0430, 0448 Ⓐ, 0503, 0518 Ⓐ, 0533, 0548 Ⓐ, 0603, 0618 Ⓐ, 0633, 0648 Ⓐ, 0703, 0718 Ⓐ, 0733, 0748 Ⓐ, 0803, 0818 Ⓐ, 0833, 0848, 0903, 0918, 0933, 0948 and at 03, 18, 33 and 48 minutes past each hour until 2103, 2118, 2133, 2148; then 2203, 2233, 2303 and 2333.

BERLIN - KOSTRZYN — 832

Niederbarnimer Eisenbahn (2nd class only)

km																						
0	**Berlin** Lichtenberg	d.	0538b	0638b	0738b	0838	0938b	1038	1138b	1238	1338b	1438	1538b	1638	1738b	1838	1938b	2038	2138b	2238	2338b
26	Strausberg	d.	0558	0658	0758	0858	0958	1058	1158	1258	1358	1458	1558	1658	1758	1858	1958	2058	2158	2258	2358
44	Müncheberg (Mark) ¶	d.	0614	0714	0814	0914	1014	1114	1214	1314	1414	1514	1614	1714	1814	1914	2014	2114	2214	2314	0014
79	Küstrin-Kietz	a.	0648	0739	0848	0938	1048	1138	1248	1338	1448	1538	1648	1738	1848	1938	2048	2138	2248	2338	0048
83	**Kostrzyn** ⊞ ... ▲ 🚌	a.	*0702*	*0752*	*0902*	*0952*	*1102*	*1152*	*1302*	*1352*	*1502*	*1552*	*1702*	*1752*	*1902*	*1952*	*2102*	*2152*	*2302*	*2352*	*0102*

Kostrzyn ⊞ ... ▲ 🚌	d.	*0357*	*0457*	*0557*	*0654*	*0757*	*0904*	*0957*	*1104*	*1157*	*1304*	*1357*	*1504*	*1557*	*1704*	*1757*	*1904*	*1957*	*2104*	*2157*
Küstrin-Kietz	d.	0410	0511	0611	0708	0811	0918	1011	1118	1211	1318	1411	1518	1611	1718	1811	1918	2011	2118	2211
Müncheberg (Mark) ¶	d.	0445	0549	0649	0749	0849	0949	1049	1149	1249	1349	1449	1549	1649	1749	1849	1949	2049	2149	2249
Strausberg	d.	0505	0605	0705	0805	0905	1005	1105	1205	1305	1405	1505	1605	1705	1805	1905	2005	2105	2205	2305
Berlin Lichtenberg	a.	0524c	0624c	0724c	0824	0924c	1024	1124c	1224	1324c	1424	1524c	1624	1724c	1824	1924c	2024	2124c	2224	2324c

b – From Berlin Ostkreuz (departs 5 minutes earlier).
c – To Berlin Ostkreuz (arrives 4 minutes later).
¶ – Station for Buckower Kleinbahn (operates on Ⓒ Apr. 30 - Oct. 3).
▲ – Connecting services Küstrin-Kietz - Kostrzyn and v.v. are by 🚌.

833 WISMAR - ROSTOCK

RE services

km		⚒t	Ⓐt				
0	**Wismar** d.	0442	0542	0642	and	2042	2142
22	Neubukow d.	0511	0611	0711	hourly	2111	2211
41	Bad Doberan ▲ d.	0530	0630	0730	until	2130	2230
57	**Rostock** Hbf a.	0551	0651	0751		2151	2251

	Ⓐt		⚒t				
Rostock Hbf d.	0412	0506	0606	0706	and	2006	2106
Bad Doberan ▲ d.	0432	0532	0632	0732	hourly	2032	2132
Neubukow d.	0451	0551	0651	0751	until	2051	2151
Wismar a.	0515	0615	0715	0815		2115	2215

t – Not Oct. 31.

▲ – **BAD DOBERAN - OSTSEEBAD KÜHLUNGSBORN WEST**. All services worked by steam locomotive. Journey time: 39 – 47 minutes.
Operator: Mecklenburgische Bäderbahn Molli GmbH, Am Bahnhof, 18209 Bad Doberan. ✆ +49 (0) 38293 431331. www.molli-bahn.de **Service until October 31.**
From **Bad Doberan** at 0835 Ⓐ, 0936, 1036 and hourly until 1636; then 1745 and 1845. From **Kühlungsborn West** at 0640 Ⓐ, 0828, 0935, 1035 and hourly until 1735.

834 STRALSUND - NEUBRANDENBURG - NEUSTRELITZ

SERVICE FROM JULY 1 (until June 30 all services are operated by 🚌 Stralsund - Demmin and v.v. in amended timings; please check locally).

km			Ⓐt			Ⓐt									Ⓑ			Ⓑ			Ⓑ					⑤⑥d
0	**Stralsund** Hbf d.	...	0406	...	0502	0604	...	0702	0804r	0902	1004r	1102	1204r	1302	1404	...	1502	1604	...	1702	1804	...	1902	...	2106	2106
23	Grimmen d.	...	0427	...	0523	0624	...	0723	0824r	0923	1024r	1123	1224r	1323	1424	...	1523	1624	...	1723	1824	...	1923	...	2128	2128
47	Demmin d.	...	0445	...	0546	0646	...	0746	0846r	0946	1046r	1146	1246r	1346	1446	...	1546	1646	...	1746	1846	...	1946	...	2146	2146
89	**Neubrandenburg** a.	...	0528	...	0629	0729	...	0829	0929r	1029	1129r	1229	1329r	1429	1529	...	1629	1729	...	1829	1929	...	2029	...	2229	2229
89	**Neubrandenburg** d.	0429	0529	0529	0630	0731	0731	0830	0931	1030	1131	1230	1331	1430	1531	1531	1630	1731	1731	1830	1931	1931	2030	2131	2230	2230
124	**Neustrelitz** Hbf a.	0458	0557	0557	0659	0756	0756	0859	0956	1059	1156	1259	1356	1459	1556	1556	1659	1756	1756	1859	1956	1956	2059	2156	2259	2259
	Berlin Hbf **835** a.	0614	...	...	0815	...	...	1016	...	1216	...	1416	...	1616	...	...	1813	...	...	2014	...	...	2214	...	...	0014

	Ⓐt	Ⓐ		Ⓐt									Ⓑ			Ⓑ			Ⓑ							⑤⑥d
Berlin Hbf **835** d.	...	...	...	...	...	0543	...	0743	...	0943	...	1143	...	...	1343	...	...	1543	...	...	1743	...	1943	...	2143	2345
Neustrelitz Hbf d.	...	0501	...	0602	0602	0701	0803	0901	1003	1101	1203	1301	1403	1403	1501	1603	1603	1701	1803	1803	1901	2003	2101	2203	2301	0108
Neubrandenburg a.	...	0528	...	0629	0629	0729	0829	0929	1029	1129	1229	1329	1429	1429	1529	1629	1629	1729	1829	1829	1929	2029	2129	2229	2329	0136
Neubrandenburg d.	0431	0531	0531	0631	...	0731	0831r	0931	1031r	1131	1231r	1331	1431	...	1531	1631	...	1731	1831	...	1931	...	2131	...	...	...
Demmin d.	0510	0609	0609	0710	...	0810	0910r	1010	1110r	1210	1310r	1410	1510	...	1610	1710	...	1810	1910	...	2010	...	2210	...	...	...
Grimmen d.	0529	0629	0629	0729	...	0829	0929r	1029	1129r	1229	1329r	1429	1529	...	1629	1729	...	1829	1929	...	2029	...	2229	...	...	...
Stralsund Hbf a.	0550	0651	0651	0750	...	0851	0950r	1051	1150r	1251	1350r	1451	1550	...	1651	1750	...	1851	1950	...	2051	...	2251	...	...	...

d – Also Oct. 2. r – ⚒ (not Oct. 31). t – Not Oct. 31.

835 ROSTOCK - BERLIN - ELSTERWERDA

km		*RE* 3503	*RE* 4353	*RE* 4353	*RE* 3505	*IC* 2173	*RE* 4355	*RE* 3507	*IC* 2175	*RE* 4357	*RE* 3509	*IC* 2177	*ICE* 1630	*RE* 4359	*RE* 3511	*IC* 2179	*RE* 4361	*RE* 3513	*IC* 2271	*RE* 4363	*RE* 3515	*IC* 2273	*IC* 2273	*RE* 4365
			Ⓐ			🍷			🍷			🍷	⑥ B✕			🍷			C🍷			🍷	Ⓑ C🍷	
	Warnemünde 831 d.	...	...	...	...	...	...	...	0756	...	...	0956	1014	...	...	1156	...	...	1352	...	...	1552	1552	...
0	**Rostock** Hbf 831 d.	...	0434	...	...	0621	0634	...	0821	0834	...	1021	1037	1034	...	1221	1234	...	1421	1434	...	1621	1621	1634
34	Güstrow d.	...	0456	...	...	|	0656	...	|	0856	...	|	|	1056	...	|	1256	...	|	1456	...	|	|	1656
85‡	Waren (Müritz) d.	...	0530	...	...	0701	0730	...	0901	0930	...	1101	|	1130	...	1301	1330	...	1501	1530	...	1701	1701	1730
	Stralsund Hbf **834** ≋ d.	...	|	...	0502	|	|	0702	|	|	0902	|	|	|	1102	|	|	1302	|	|	1502	|	|	|
	Neubrandenburg **834** d.	0429	|	...	0630	|	|	0830	|	|	1030	|	|	|	1230	|	|	1430	|	|	1630	|	|	|
120	**Neustrelitz** Hbf a.	0458	0552	...	0659	0718	0752	0859	0918	0952	1059	1118	|	1152	1259	1318	1352	1459	1518	1552	1659	1718	1718	1752
120	**Neustrelitz** Hbf d.	0459	0600	0600	0700	0719	0800	0900	0919	1000	1100	1119	|	1200	1300	1319	1400	1500	1519	1600	1700	1719	1719	1800
141	Fürstenberg (Havel) d.	0511	0613	0613	0713	|	0814	0913	|	1013	1113	|	|	1213	1313	|	1413	1513	|	1614	1713	|	|	1813
162	Gransee d.	0525	0628	0628	0726	|	0829	0926	|	1028	1126	|	|	1228	1326	|	1428	1526	|	1629	1726	|	|	1828
191	Oranienburg d.	0544	0644	0644	0744	0756	0845	0944	0956	1044	1144	1156	|	1244	1344	1356	1444	1544	1556	1645	1744	1756	1756	1844
223	**Berlin** Gesundbrunnen d.	0610	0711	0711	0811	0819	0911	1012	1019	1110	1212	1219	1237	1310	1412	1419	1509	1612	1619	1710	1810	1819	1819	1910
227	**Berlin** Hbf a.	0614	0715	0715	0815	0823	0916	1016	1023	1114	1216	1223	1241	1315	1416	1423	1513	1616	1623	1716	1813	1823	1823	1914
227	**Berlin** Hbf 840 d.	0618	0718	0718	0818	0826	0918	1018	1026	1118	1218	1226	1304	1318	1418	1426	1518	1618	1626	1718	1818	...	1826	1918
233	**Berlin** Südkreuz 840 d.	0624	0726	0726	0824	0833	0926	1024	1033	1126	1224	1233	1309	1326	1424	1433	1526	1624	1633	1726	1824	...	1833	1926
	Flughafen Berlin ✈ ★ 840 a.	...	|	|	...	0853	|	...	1053	|	...	1253	...	|	...	1453	|	...	1653	|	...	...	1853	|
347	Doberlug-Kirchhain 840 d.	...	0906j	0906j	...	0950	1106j	...	1150	1306j	...	1350	...	1506j	...	1550	1706j	...	1745	1906j	...	...	1945	2106j
367	**Elsterwerda** 840 a.	...	0920j	0920j	...	0959	1120j	...	1159	1320j	...	1359	...	1520j	...	1559	1720j	...	1754	1920j	...	...	1954	2120j
	Dresden Hbf **840** a.	...	...	...	...	1035	...	...	1235	...	...	1435	...	...	...	1635	...	...	1827	...	...	...	2027	...

	RE 3517	*IC* 2275	*RE* 4367	*RE* 3519	*IC* 95	*IC* 1975	*RE* 4369	*RE* 3521	*RE* 3525	
		🍷			Ⓑ A	⑥ 🍷		⑤⑥ d		
Warnemünde 831 d.	...	1752	...	...	...	1956	...	...	...	...
Rostock Hbf 831 d.	...	1821	1834	...	2021	2021	2034	...	2334	...
Güstrow d.	...	|	1856	...	|	|	2056	...	2356	...
Waren (Müritz) d.	...	1901	1930	...	2101	2101	2130	...	0030	...
Stralsund Hbf **834** ≋ d.	1702	|	|	1902	|	|	|	2106	|	...
Neubrandenburg **834** d.	1830	|	|	2030	|	|	|	2230	|	...
Neustrelitz Hbf a.	1859	1918	1952	2059	2118	2118	2152	2259	0052	...
Neustrelitz Hbf d.	1900	1919	2000	2100	2119	2119	2200	2300	...	...
Fürstenberg (Havel) d.	1913	|	2013	2113	|	|	2213	2313	...	...
Gransee d.	1926	|	2028	2126	|	|	2228	2326	...	...
Oranienburg d.	1944	1956	2044	2144	2156	2156	2244	2344	...	...
Berlin Gesundbrunnen d.	2010	2019	2110	2211	2219	2218a	2311	0010	...	...
Berlin Hbf a.	2014	2023	2115	2214	2223	2224	2316	0014	...	...
Berlin Hbf 840 d.	2018	2026	2118	2218	2229	|	2318	...	...	...
Berlin Südkreuz 840 d.	2024	2033	2126	2224	2233	2232	2324	...	...	...
Flughafen Berlin ✈ ★ 840 a.	...	2053	|	...	...	...	...	...	...	...
Doberlug-Kirchhain 840 d.	...	2150	2306j	...	...	...	...	...	...	...
Elsterwerda 840 a.	...	2159	2320j	...	...	...	...	...	...	...
Dresden Hbf **840** a.	...	2235	...	...	...	...	...	...	...	...

	RE 4350		*ICE* 1696	*RE* 3504	*RE* 3504	*IC* 94	*RE* 4352	*IC* 2274	*IC* 2274
	Ⓐ		⑥ ✕		Ⓐ	①–⑥ A		🍷	①–⑥ 🍷
Dresden Hbf **840** d.	...	...	...	...	...	...	...	...	0519
Elsterwerda 840 d.	...	...	...	...	...	...	0440	...	0556
Doberlug-Kirchhain 840 d.	...	...	...	...	...	...	0456	...	0608
Flughafen Berlin ✈ ★ 840 d.	...	...	...	...	...	...	|	...	0705
Berlin Südkreuz 840 d.	...	...	0525	...	0534	0626	0633	0727	0727
Berlin Hbf 840 a.	...	...	|	...	0541	0631	0640	0732	0732
Berlin Hbf d.	0443	...	0535	0543	0543	0638	0642	0736	0736
Berlin Gesundbrunnen d.	0448	...	0541	0548	0548	0644	0648	0744	0744
Oranienburg d.	0511	...	0603	0611	0611	0704	0711	0804	0804
Gransee d.	0530	...	|	0630	0630	|	0730	|	|
Fürstenberg (Havel) d.	0546	...	|	0646	0646	|	0746	|	|
Neustrelitz Hbf a.	0558	...	0639	0659	0659	0741	0759	0841	0841
Neustrelitz Hbf d.	0607	...	0641	0701	0701	0742	0807	0842	0842
Neubrandenburg **834** a.	|	...	|	0729	0729	|	|	|	|
Stralsund Hbf **834** ≋ a.	|	...	|	0851	0851	|	|	|	|
Waren (Müritz) d.	0630	...	0659	...	...	0759	0830	0859	0859
Güstrow d.	0701	...	|	...	...	|	0901	|	|
Rostock Hbf 831 a.	0723	...	0738	...	...	0839	0923	0937	0937
Warnemünde 831 a.	...	...	0801	...	...	0859	...	1001	1001

	RE 3506	*RE* 4354	*IC* 2272	*RE* 3508	*RE* 4356	*IC* 2270	*RE* 3510	*IC* 1978	*RE* 4358	*IC* 2178	*RE* 3512	*RE* 4360	*IC* 2176	*RE* 3514	*RE* 4362	*IC* 2174	*RE* 3516	*RE* 4364	*IC* 2172	*RE* 3518	*RE* 4366	*RE* 3520	*RE* 4368	*RE* 3522
			C🍷			C🍷		⑥ 🍷		🍷			🍷			🍷			🍷					⑤⑥ d
Dresden Hbf **840** d.	...	...	0730	...	...	0930	...	...	...	1119	...	...	1319	...	...	1519	...	...	1719	...	...	...	...	...
Elsterwerda 840 d.	...	0640	0804	...	0840	1004	...	...	1040	1156	...	1240	1356	...	1440	1556	...	1640	1756	...	1840	...	2040	...
Doberlug-Kirchhain 840 d.	...	0656	0814	...	0856	1014	...	...	1056	1208	...	1256	1408	...	1456	1608	...	1656	1808	...	1856	...	2056	...
Flughafen Berlin ✈ ★ 840 d.	...	|	0905	...	|	1105	...	...	|	1305	...	|	1505	...	|	1705	...	|	1905	...	|	...	|	...
Berlin Südkreuz 840 d.	0734	0833	0927	0934	1033	1127	1135	1159	1233	1327	1334	1433	1527	1534	1633	1727	1734	1833	1928	1934	2033	2134	2233	2334
Berlin Hbf 840 a.	0741	0840	0932	0941	1040	1132	1141	|	1240	1332	1341	1440	1532	1541	1640	1732	1741	1840	1933	1941	2040	2141	2240	2341
Berlin Hbf d.	0743	0842	0936	0943	1042	1135	1143	1208	1242	1337	1343	1442	1537	1543	1642	1735	1743	1842	1938	1943	2042	2143	2242	2345
Berlin Gesundbrunnen d.	0748	0848	0944	0948	1048	1144	1149	1214	1248	1344	1348	1448	1544	1548	1648	1744	1748	1848	1944	1948	2048	2148	2248	2350
Oranienburg d.	0811	0911	1004	1011	1111	1204	1211	|	1311	1404	1411	1511	1604	1611	1711	1804	1811	1911	2004	2011	2111	2211	2311	0012
Gransee d.	0830	0930	|	1030	1130	|	1230	|	1330	|	1430	1530	|	1630	1730	|	1830	1930	|	2030	2130	2230	2328	0038
Fürstenberg (Havel) d.	0846	0946	|	1046	1146	|	1246	|	1346	|	1446	1546	|	1646	1746	|	1846	1946	|	2046	2146	2246	2343	0052
Neustrelitz Hbf a.	0859	0959	1041	1059	1159	1241	1259	|	1359	1441	1459	1559	1641	1659	1759	1841	1859	1959	2041	2059	2159	2259	2356	0106
Neustrelitz Hbf d.	0901	1007	1042	1101	1207	1242	1301	|	1407	1442	1501	1607	1642	1701	1807	1842	1901	2007	2042	2101	2207	2301	2357	0108
Neubrandenburg **834** a.	0929	|	|	1129	|	|	1329	|	|	|	1529	|	|	1729	|	|	1929	|	|	2129	|	2329	|	0136
Stralsund Hbf **834** ≋ a.	1051	|	|	1251	|	|	1451	|	|	|	1651	|	|	1851	|	|	2051	|	|	2251	|	...	|	...
Waren (Müritz) d.	...	1030	1059	...	1230	1259	...	|	1430	1459	...	1630	1659	...	1830	1859	...	2030	2059	...	2230	...	0018	...
Güstrow d.	...	1101	|	...	1301	|	...	|	1501	|	...	1701	|	...	1901	|	...	2101	|	...	2301	...	0049	...
Rostock Hbf 831 a.	...	1123	1137	...	1323	1337	...	1359	1523	1537	...	1723	1737	...	1923	1937	...	2123	2137	...	2323	...	0111	...
Warnemünde 831 a.	...	...	1201	...	...	1405	...	1420	...	1605	...	...	1805	...	...	2001	...	...	...	...	...	...	...	...

A – From / to Wien via Nürnberg (Tables **849a**, **850** and **920**).
B – To Frankfurt via Erfurt (Table **850**).
C – From / to Chemnitz (Table **880**).
a – Arrival time. Calls to set down only.
d – Also Oct. 2.
j – 2 minutes earlier from Oct. 15.
‡ – Rostock to Waren is 78 km direct.
★ – Flughafen Berlin Brandenburg (BER).
≋ – Stralsund timings are valid from July 1 (please check locally for amended timings until June 30).

RE services

LÜBECK - BAD KLEINEN - PASEWALK - SZCZECIN 836

km		Ⓐt	Ⓑ	Ⓐt																		T	⑤		
	Lübeck Hbf ★ d.	...	...	...	...	...	0602t	...	0802	...	1002	...	1202	...	1402	...	1602	...	1802	...	...	...	2002	...	2206
0	**Bad Kleinen** 830 d.	...	...	...	...	*0603*	0705	*0803*	0904	*1003*	1102	*1203*	1304	*1403*	1504	*1603*	1705	*1803*	1904	*2003*	*2003*	*2003*	2107	*2203*	2304
41	Bützow 830 d.	...	...	...	0533	0633	0733	0833	0933	1033	1137	1233	1333	1433	1533	1633	1733	1833	1933	2033	2033	2033	2134	2233	2333
55	Güstrow a.	...	...	...	0542	0642	0742	0842	0942	1042	1146	1242	1342	1442	1542	1642	1742	1842	1942	2042	2042	2042	2143	2242	2342
55	Güstrow d.	...	...	...	0604	0704	0804	0904	1004	1104	1204	1304	1404	1504	1604	1704	1804	1904	2004	2104	2104	2104	2204	2304	...
84	Teterow d.	...	...	...	0633	0733	0833	0933	1033	1133	1233	1333	1433	1533	1633	1733	1833	1933	2033	2133	2133	2133	2233	2328	...
98	Malchin d.	...	...	0529	0644	0744	0844	0944	1044	1144	1244	1344	1444	1544	1644	1744	1844	1944	2044	2144	2144	2144	2243	2338	...
142	**Neubrandenburg** a.	...	...	0601	0721	0821	0921	1021	1121	1221	1321	1421	1521	1621	1721	1821	1921	2021	2121	2221	2221	2221	2315	0010	...
142	**Neubrandenburg** d.	0513	...	0606	0733	0833r	0933	1033	1133	1233	1333	1433	1533	1633	1733	1833	1933	2033	2133	...	2233	2233	...	...	...
195	**Pasewalk** a.	0559	...	0654	0814	0914r	1014	1114	1214	1314	1414	1514	1614	1714	1814	1914	2014	2114	2214	...	2314	2314	...	...	...
195	**Pasewalk** ▷ d.	0615	0615	0700	0815	...	1015	...	1215	...	1415	1525t	1615	...	1815	...	2015	...	...	...	...	2315	...	...	...
	Ueckermünde S¶ ▷ a.	|	|	0731	|	...	|	...	|	...	|	1556t	|	...	|	...	|	...	...	...	...	|	...	...	...
222	Grambow d.	0638	0638	...	0838	...	1038	...	1238	...	1438	...	1638	...	1838	...	2038	...	...	...	...	2338	...	...	...
232	Szczecin Gumience 🏛 d.	0648	0648	...	0848	...	1048	...	1248	...	1448	...	1648	...	1848	...	2048	...	...	...	...	2348	...	...	...
237	**Szczecin** Główny a.	0655	0655	...	0855	...	1055	...	1255	...	1455	...	1655	...	1855	...	2055	...	...	...	...	2355	...	...	...

	①g				Ⓐt		Ⓐt			Ⓐt	⚒t												S		
Szczecin Główny d.	...	...	...	...	0501	...	...	...	0701	...	...	...	0901	...	1101	...	1301	...	1501	...	1701	...	1901	...	2101
Szczecin Gumience 🏛 d.	...	...	...	...	0507	...	...	...	0707	...	...	...	0907	...	1107	...	1307	...	1507	...	1707	...	1907	...	2107
Grambow d.	...	...	...	...	0518	...	...	...	0718	...	...	...	0918	...	1118	...	1318	...	1518	...	1718	...	1918	...	2119
Ueckermünde S ¶ ▷ d.	...	...	...	...	|	...	0600	...	|	0738	...	...	|	...	|	...	|	...	|	1601t	|	...	|	...	|
Pasewalk ⊙ ▷ a.	...	...	...	...	0539	...	0632	...	0739	0810	...	...	0939	...	1139	...	1339	...	1539	1632t	1739	...	1939	...	2139
Pasewalk ⊙ d.	0301	...	...	...	0541	0541	0638	...	0743	0843	0843	...	0943	1043	1143	1243	1343	1443	1543	1643	1743	1843	1943	2043	2143
Neubrandenburg a.	0339	...	...	...	0623	0623	0723	...	0826	0926	0926	...	1026	1126	1226	1326	1426	1526	1626	1726	1826	1926	2026	2126	2226
Neubrandenburg d.	0340	...	0447	0544	0641	0641	0741	0741	0841	0941	0941	0941	1041	1141	1241	1341	1441	1541	1641	1741	1841	1941	2041	2141	...
Malchin d.	0410	...	0531	0620	0713	0713	0813	0813	0913	1013	1013	1013	1113	1213	1313	1413	1513	1613	1713	1813	1913	2013	2113	2213	...
Teterow d.	0421	...	0541	0631	0730	0730	0830	0830	0930	1030	1030	1030	1130	1230	1330	1430	1530	1630	1730	1830	1930	2030	2130	2230	...
Güstrow a.	0439	...	0603	0653	0753	0753	0853	0853	0953	1053	1053	1053	1153	1253	1353	1453	1553	1653	1753	1853	1953	2053	2153	2253	...
Güstrow d.	0440	0501	0608	0708	0808	0808	0908	0908	1008	1108	1108	1108	1208	1308	1405	1508	1608	1708	1808	1908	2008	2108	2208	2308	...
Bützow 830 a.	0450	0511	0618	0718	0818	0818	0918	0918	1018	1118	1118	1118	1218	1318	1415	1518	1618	1718	1818	1918	2018	2118	2218	2318	...
Bad Kleinen 830 a.	0517	*0554*	0646	*0754*	0846	0846	*0954*	*0954*	1046	*1154*	*1154*	*1154*	1246	*1354*	1442	*1554*	1646	*1754*	1846	*1954*	2046-	*2154*	2246	*2400*	...
Lübeck Hbf ★ a.	0623	...	0756	...	0956	0956	...	...	1156	...	...	...	1356	...	1556	...	1756	...	1956	...	2156	...	...	...	...

km			Ⓐt																	
0	**Lübeck** Hbf d.	0502	0602	0703	0802	0903	1002	1103	1202	1303	1402	1503	1602	1703	1802	1903	2002	2103	2206	2307
39	Grevesmühlen d.	0537	0637	0737	0837	0937	1037	1137	1237	1337	1437	1537	1637	1737	1837	1937	2037	2137	2242	2340
62	**Bad Kleinen** a.	0552	0656	0752	0854	0952	1054	1152	1254	1352	1454	1552	1656	1752	1854	1952	2054	2152	2259	2354

	Ⓐt	Ⓐt																	
Bad Kleinen d.	0434	0518	0603	0700	0803	0900	1003	1100	1203	1300	1403	1500	1603	1700	1803	1900	2003	2100	2204
Grevesmühlen d.	0448	0539	0617	0716	0817	0916	1017	1116	1217	1316	1417	1516	1617	1716	1817	1916	2017	2116	2221
Lübeck Hbf a.	0525	0623	0656	0756	0856	0956	1056	1156	1256	1356	1456	1556	1656	1756	1856	1956	2056	2156	2300

S – To Schwerin Hbf (a. 2318).
T – ⑤–⑦ (also Oct. 3, 31).

g – Also Oct. 4, Nov. 1; not Oct. 3, 31.
r – ⚒ (not Oct. 31).
t – Ⓐ (not Oct. 31).

★ – See panel for full service Lübeck - Bad Kleinen and v.v.
¶ – Ueckermünde Stadthafen.

▷ – Full service **PASEWALK - UECKERMÜNDE**. *30 km.* Journey 31 – 35 minutes (45 minutes for train marked ‡).
From Pasewalk at 0518 Ⓐt, 0610 ⚒t, 0700 Ⓐt, 0822, 1022, 1222, 1422, 1525 Ⓐt, 1608‡, 1822 and 2022.
From Ueckermünde Stadthafen at 0600 Ⓐt, 0700 ⚒t, 0738 Ⓐt, 0900, 1100, 1300, 1500, 1601 Ⓐt, 1700, 1900 and 2100.

DB; Ostdeutsche Eisenbahn

WISMAR - BERLIN - COTTBUS 837

km																					2239			2431	
			⚒		Ⓐ		⚒														L			ⒷE	
0	**Wismar** d.	...	...	...	0417	...	0522	...	...	0624	0733	...	0824	0924	...	1024	1124	...	1224	1324	...	...	1424	...	1524
16	Bad Kleinen 830 d.	...	...	...	0431	...	0536	...	...	0639	0747	...	0839	0938	...	1039	1141	...	1239	1339	1433	...	1439	...	1539
32	**Schwerin** Hbf 830 a.	...	...	...	0443	...	0548	...	...	0651	0758	...	0851	0950	...	1051	1153	...	1251	1351	1441	...	1451	...	1551
32	**Schwerin** Hbf d.	...	...	...	0459	0459	0559	...	|	0700	0800	...	0859	0959	...	1059	1159	...	1259	1359	1443	...	1500	...	1559
72	Ludwigslust 840 d.	...	...	...	0534	0534	0634	...	...	0735	0835	...	0934	1034	...	1134	1234	...	1334	1434	1509	...	1534	...	1634
116	Wittenberge 840 d.	0406	0506	...	0606f	0606f	0703	0703	0806	...	0903	1006	...	1103	1206	...	1303	1406	...	1503	1529	1606	...	...	1703
207	Nauen d.	0501	0601	...	0701	0701	0801	0801	0901	...	1001	1101	...	1201	1301	...	1401	1501	...	1601	...	1701	...	...	1801
229	**Berlin** Spandau 840 d.	0517	0617	...	0720	0720	0820	0820	0920	...	1020	1120	...	1220	1320	...	1420	1520	...	1620	...	1720	...	...	1820
241	**Berlin** Zoo d.	0526	0626	0626	0730	0730	0830	0830	0930	...	1030	1130	...	1230	1330	...	1430	1530	...	1630	...	1730	...	...	1830
245	**Berlin** Hbf 840 d.	0532	0632	0632	0735	0735	0835	0835	0936	...	1035	1135	...	1235	1336	...	1435	1536	...	1635	...	1736	...	1832	1835
252	**Berlin** Ostkreuz d.	0546	0646	0646	0751	0751	0851	0851	0951	...	1051	1151	...	1251	1351	...	1451	1551	...	1651	...	1751	...	1845	1851
283	Königs Wusterhausen d.	0608	0708	0708	0811	0811	0911	0911	1011	...	1111	1211	...	1311	1411	...	1511	1611	...	1711	...	1811	...	1905	1911
330	Lübben (Spreewald) d.	0631	0731	0731	0834	0834	0934	0934	1034	...	1134	1234	...	1334	1434	...	1534	1634	...	1734	...	1834	...	1927	1934
341	Lübbenau (Spreew) d.	0638	0737	0737	0841	0841	0941	0941	1041	...	1141	1241	...	1341	1441	...	1541	1641	...	1741	...	1841	...	1935	1941
370	**Cottbus** Hbf a.	0700	0759	0759	0859	0859	0959	0959	1059	...	1159	1259	...	1359	1459	...	1559	1659	...	1759	...	1859	...	1950	1959

Wismar d.	...	1624	1724	...	1824	1924	...	2024	2125	2224
Bad Kleinen 830 d.	...	1639	1738	...	1839	1938	...	2039	2139	2239
Schwerin Hbf 830 a.	...	1651	1750	...	1851	1950	...	2051	2151	2251
Schwerin Hbf d.	...	1659	1800	...	1859	1959	...	2052p	2159	2259
Ludwigslust 840 d.	...	1734	1834	...	1934	2034	...	2127p	2234	2334
Wittenberge 840 d.	1806	...	1903	2006	...	2103	...	...	2307f	...
Nauen d.	1901	...	2001	2101	...	2201	...	...	0004	...
Berlin Spandau 840 d.	1920	...	2020	2120	...	2220	...	...	0020	...
Berlin Zoo d.	1930	...	2030	2130	...	2230	...	...	0030	...
Berlin Hbf 840 d.	1935	...	2035	2135	...	2235	2348o	...	0038	...
Berlin Ostkreuz d.	1951	...	2051	2151	...	2251	2351	...	0102	...
Königs Wusterhausen d.	2011	...	2111	2211	...	2314	0012	...	0122	...
Lübben (Spreewald) d.	2034	...	2134	2234	...	2349	0048	...	0158	...
Lübbenau (Spreew) d.	2041	...	2141	2241	...	2356	0055	...	0205	...
Cottbus Hbf a.	2059	...	2159	2300	...	0019	0117	...	0228	...

											2432
	Ⓐt			Ⓐt		⚒			⚒	†	⚒G
Cottbus Hbf d.	...	...	...	...	0356	0356	...	0457	0532	0556	0605
Lübbenau (Spreew) d.	...	...	...	...	0419	0419	...	0520	0556	0619	0621
Lübben (Spreewald) d.	...	...	...	...	0426	0426	...	0527	0602	0626	0629
Königs Wusterhausen d.	...	...	...	...	0450	0450	...	0551	0628	0650	0651
Berlin Ostkreuz d.	...	...	0406	...	0510	0510	...	0610	0648	0710	0712
Berlin Hbf 840 d.	...	...	0420	...	0525	0525	...	0625	0704	0725	0726
Berlin Zoo d.	...	...	0426	...	0531	0532	...	0631	0731v	0731	▬
Berlin Spandau 840 d.	...	...	0435	...	▬	0541	...	0640	0740	0740	...
Nauen d.	...	...	0459	...	...	0559	...	0656	0756	0756	...
Wittenberge 840 d.	...	...	0603f	...	...	0701	...	0757	0901	0901	M
Ludwigslust 840 d.	0457	...	0628	0645	...	0726	0825	...	0926	0926	1025
Schwerin Hbf a.	0530	...	0659	0718	Ⓑ	0758	0858	...	0958	0958	1058
Schwerin Hbf 830 d.	0539	0539	0700	0739	0739	0806	0904	...	1005	1005	1104
Bad Kleinen 830 d.	0601f	0601f	0712	0801f	0801f	0819	0917	...	1018	1018	1117
Wismar a.	0616	0616	0727	0816	0816	0837	0937	...	1037	1037	1137

			2238																						
	N		L																						
Cottbus Hbf d.	...	0701	...	0801	...	0901	1001	...	1101	1201	...	1301	1401	...	1501	1601	...	1701	1801	...	1901	2001	2101	2201	2301
Lübbenau (Spreew) d.	...	0719	...	0819	...	0919	1019	...	1119	1219	...	1319	1419	...	1519	1619	...	1719	1819	...	1919	2019	2119	2226	2324
Lübben (Spreewald) d.	...	0726	...	0826	...	0926	1026	...	1126	1226	...	1326	1426	...	1526	1626	...	1726	1826	...	1926	2026	2126	2232	2331
Königs Wusterhausen d.	...	0750	...	0850	...	0950	1050	...	1150	1250	...	1350	1450	...	1550	1650	...	1750	1850	...	1950	2050	2150	2258	0007
Berlin Ostkreuz d.	...	0810	...	0910	...	1010	1110	...	1210	1310	...	1410	1510	...	1610	1710	...	1810	1910	...	2010	2110	2210	2323	0029
Berlin Hbf 840 d.	...	0825	...	0925	...	1025	1125	...	1225	1325	...	1425	1525	...	1625	1725	...	1825	1925	...	2025	2125	2225	2326o	0046
Berlin Zoo d.	...	0831	...	0931	...	1031	1131	...	1231	1331	...	1431	1531	...	1631	1731	...	1831	1931	...	2031	2131	2231	▬	0052
Berlin Spandau 840 d.	...	0840	...	0940	...	1040	1140	...	1240	1340	...	1440	1540	...	1640	1740	...	1840	1940	...	2040	2140	2240	...	0059
Nauen d.	...	0856	...	0956	...	1056	1156	...	1256	1356	...	1456	1556	...	1656	1756	...	1856	1956	...	2056	2156	2256	...	...
Wittenberge 840 d.	...	0957	1011	1101	...	1157	1301	...	1357	1501	...	1557	1701	...	1757	1901	...	1957	2101	...	2157	2301	2357	...	...
Ludwigslust 840 d.	1036	...	1035	1126	1225	...	1326	1425	...	1526	1625	...	1726	1825	...	1926	2025	...	2126	2256	...	2326	...	2356	...
Schwerin Hbf a.	1108	...	1112	1158	1258	...	1358	1459	...	1558	1658	...	1758	1858	...	1958	2106j	...	2158	2331	...	2358	...	0029	...
Schwerin Hbf 830 d.	1109	...	1114	1205	1304	...	1405	1504	...	1605	1704	...	1805	1904	...	2005	2107	...	2205	...	...	0005	...	...	...
Bad Kleinen 830 d.	1122	...	1123	1218	1317	...	1418	1517	...	1618	1717	...	1818	1917	...	2018	2119	...	2218	...	...	0032z	...	...	...
Wismar a.	1138	...	...	1237	1337	...	1437	1537	...	1637	1737	...	1837	1937	...	2037	2138	...	2237	...	...	0046	...	...	...

E – *IC* **2431**. (12) Emden - Bremen - Hannover - Magdeburg - Berlin - Cottbus.
G – *IC* **2432**. (12) Cottbus - Berlin - Magdeburg - Hannover - Bremen - Norddeich.
L – *IC* train. (12) Leipzig - Rostock - Warnemünde and v.v.
M – Until Nov. 4.
N – From Nov. 5.

f – Arrives 8 – 10 minutes earlier.
j – 2058 on ⑥⑦ from Nov. 5; 2104 on ①–⑤ from Nov. 7.
o – Berlin **Ostbahnhof**.
p – From Nov. 5 Schwerin d. 2059, Ludwigslust a. 2134.
t – Not Oct. 31.
v – Arrives 0709.
z – Arrives 0017.

839 MAGDEBURG - BERLIN - FRANKFURT (ODER) - COTTBUS

RE services

km		Ⓒ												P				B	W♣						
0	**Magdeburg** Hbf .... d.	0042	...	...	0427a	...	0527	0607	...	0708		1608	...	1704	1708	...	1808	...	1856	1908	...	2008	2108	2208	2322
79	**Brandenburg** Hbf ..... d.	0138	0425	0500	0526	0600	0626	0700	0726	0800		1700	1726	1742	1800	1826	1900	1926	1946	2000	2026	2100	2158	2258	0019
114	Potsdam Hbf .... d.	0206	0455	0525	0555	0625	0655	0725	0755	0825	and at	1725	1755	1800	1825	1855	1925	1955	2009	2025	2055	2125	2225	2325	0047
123	Berlin Wannsee .... d.	0213	0502	0532	0602	0632	0702	0732	0802	0832	the same	1732	1802	1809	1832	1902	1932	2002	2019	2032	2102	2132	2232	2332	0054
138	**Berlin** Zoo .... d.	0226	0515	0545	0615	0645	0715	0745	0815	0845	minutes	1745	1815	|	1845	1915	1945	2015	2032	2045	2116	2145	2245	2345	0106
142	**Berlin** Hbf .... **1001** d.	0232	0521	0551	0621	0651	0721	0751	0821	0851		1751	1821	1832	1851	1921	1951	2021	2038	2051	2123	2151	2251	2351	...
147	**Berlin** Ostbahnhof .... d.	0245	0534	0604	0634	0704	0734	0804	0834	0904	past each	1804	1834	1840	1904	1934	2004	2034	2051	2104	2135	2204	2307	0004	...
149	**Berlin** Ostkreuz .... d.	0250	0539	0609	0639	0709	0739	0809	0839	0909	hour until	1809	1839	1843**b**	1909	1939	2009	2039	...	2109	2138	2209	2312	0009	...
194	Fürstenwalde (Spree) d.	0321	0609	0638	0709	0738	0809	0838	0909	0938		1838	1909	...	1938	2009	2038	2109	...	2140	...	2240	2342	0040	...
228	**Frankfurt** (Oder) **1001** a.	0348	0627	0704	0727	0804	0827	0904	0927	1004		1904	1927	...	2004	2027	2104	2127	...	2207	...	2307	0009	0107	...

		Ⓒ	Ⓒ				B		Ⓒ♣	N		D							⑦z			B		⑤⑥f
Frankfurt (Oder) **1001** d.	0028	0028	...	...	0356	...	0456	0534	0558	...	...	0634	0658	0734	0758		1834	1858	1934	♣	2034	2128	2230	2325	2325
Fürstenwalde (Spree). d.	0055	0055	...	...	0422	...	0522	0552	0625	...	...	0652	0725	0752	0825	and at	1852	1925	1952	...	2052	2155	2257	2352	2352
Berlin Ostkreuz .... d.	0126	0126	...	...	0454	0524	0554	0624	0654	...	0712e	0724	0754	0824	0854		1924	1954	2024	...	2124	2226	2329	0024	0024
Berlin Ostbahnhof ..... d.	0131	0131	...	...	0459	0529	0559	0629	0659	0709	0718	0729	0759	0829	0859	the same	1929	1959	2029	2117	2129	2231	2333	0029	0029
Berlin Hbf .... **1001** d.	0143	0143	0244	...	0511	0541	0611	0641	0711	0720	0730	0741	0811	0841	0911	minutes	1941	2011	2041	2130	2141	2243	2345	0041	0041
Berlin Zoo .... d.	0148	0149	0250	...	0517	0547	0617	0647	0717	0727	|	0747	0817	0847	0917		1947	2017	2047	2136	2147	2249	2351	0047	0047
Berlin Wannsee .... d.	...	0202	0303	...	0530	0600	0630	0700	0730	0739	0745	0800	0830	0900	0930	past each	2000	2030	2100	2147	2200	2302	0004	0100	0100
Potsdam Hbf .... d.	...	0210	0311	...	0538	0608	0638	0708	0738	0749	0755	0808	0838	0908	0938	hour until	2008	2038	2108	2155	2208	2310	0012	0108	0108
Brandenburg Hbf ...... d.	...	0239	0340	0420	0600	0637	0700	0737	0800	0807	0814	0837	0900	0937	1000		2037	2100	2138	2215	2237	2341	0041	0138	0140
Magdeburg Hbf .... a.	...	...	...	0517	0651	...	0751	...	0851	0859	0854	...	0951	...	1051		...	2151	2235	2304	...	0031	...	...	0230

km		Ⓐ		Ⓐ					B	
0	**Frankfurt (Oder)** .... d.	0409	0537	0602	0636	0737	and	2037	2130	2315
23	Eisenhüttenstadt .... d.	0430	0557	0619	0657	0757	hourly	2057	2151	2336
48	Guben .... d.	0451	0618	0635	0718	0818	until	2118	2211	2356
86	**Cottbus** Hbf .... a.	0531	0656	0700	0756	0856		2156	2247	0032

	⚒B		ⒶD						B	
Cottbus Hbf .... d.	0414	0506	0550	0606	0706	and	1906	2006	2109	2306
Guben .... d.	0450	0544	0614	0644	0744	hourly	1944	2044	2146	2344
Eisenhüttenstadt .... d.	0510	0605	0634	0705	0805	until	2005	2104	2205	0004
Frankfurt (Oder) .... a.	0532	0626	0655	0726	0826		2026	2124	2227	0024

B – [12] Brandenburg - Frankfurt (Oder) - Cottbus and v.v.
D – [12] Cottbus - Frankfurt (Oder) - Magdeburg.
N – *IC* **2432**. [12] (Cottbus ⚒ -) Berlin - Hannover - Norddeich.
P – *IC* **2431**. [12] Emden - Hannover - Berlin (- Cottbus Ⓑ **b**).
W – ⑤⑥† only.

a – Ⓐ only.
b – Ⓑ (not Oct. 2).
e – ⚒ only.
f – Also Oct. 2.
z – Also Oct. 3; not Oct. 2.

♣ – *HARZ-BERLIN-EXPRESS*. [2] Berlin - Halberstadt - Thale / Ilsenburg / Goslar and v.v. (Tables **860** / **862**). Not available for local journeys Berlin - Brandenburg and v.v. Operated by Abellio Rail Mitteldeutschland. **DB tickets not valid**.

840 HAMBURG - BERLIN - DRESDEN

See Table **927** for services operated by FlixTrain

km		*RJ* **253** Y P✕	*EC* **171** J P✕	*IC* **1971** ①●	*ICE* **701** ①–⑤ M✕	*ICE* **1003** M✕	*ICE* **505** ①–⑥ M✕	*IC* **2173** 🍷	*IC* **1073** ①●	*EC* **173** J ✕	*ICE* **703** M✕	*ICE* **93** G✕	*ICE* **507** M✕	*IC* **2175** 🍷	*EC* **379** J K✕	*IC* **1179** ①● T	*ICE* **705** M✕	*ICE* **1005** M✕	*ICE* **509** M✕	*IC* **2177** 🍷	*EC* **175** J ¶P✕	*IC* **1175** ①● ¶	*ICE* **707** M✕	*ICE* **1205** M✕	*ICE* **1601** M✕
0	**Hamburg** Altona .... d.	...	...	...	0511	0532	0618	...	0635	0635	0719	0749	0818	...	...	...	0919	0948	1017	...	...	...	1119	1151	1217
7	**Hamburg** Hbf .... **830** d.	...	...	...	0527	0552	0634	...	0648	0648	0736	0804	0834	...	0851	0851	0936	1005	1034	...	1051	1051	1136	1204	1234
54	Büchen .... **830** d.	...	...	...	|	|	|	...	0714	0714	|	|	|	...	0914	0914	|	|	|	...	1114	1114	|	|	|
122	Ludwigslust .... **837** d.	...	...	...	0613	|	|	...	0741	0741	|	|	|	...	0941	0941	|	|	|	...	1141	1141	|	|	|
167	Wittenberge .... **837** d.	...	...	...	0631	|	|	...	0801	0801	|	|	|	...	1001	1001	|	|	|	...	1201	1201	|	|	|
280	**Berlin** Spandau .... **837** d.	...	...	...	0712	0744	0810	...	0846	0846	0912	0944	1010	...	1046	1046	1112	1144	1210	...	1246	1246	1312	1344	1410
	Rostock Hbf **835** .... d.	...	...	...	|	|	|	0621	|	|	|	|	|	0821	|	|	|	|	|	1021	|	|	|	|	|
293	**Berlin** Hbf .... **837** a.	...	...	...	0722	0755	0820	0823	0855	0855	0922	0953	1020	1023	1055	1055	1122	1155	1220	1223	1255	1255	1322	1355	1420
293	**Berlin** Hbf .... **835** d.	0617	0716	0716	0737	0805	0830	0826	0859	0916	0937	1004	1030	1026	1116	1116	1137	1205	1230	1226	1316	1316	1337	1404	1430
299	**Berlin** Südkreuz .... **835** d.	0623	0723	0723	0742	0809	0835	0833	|	0923	0942	1009	1035	1033	1123	1123	1142	1209	1235	1233	1323	1323	1342	1409	1435
	Flughafen Berlin ✈ ★ ..... d.	|	|	|	...	...	...	0901	|	|	...	...	...	1101	|	|	...	...	...	1301	|	|	...	...	...
413	Doberlug-Kirchhain ...... **835** d.	0725	|	|	...	...	...	0950	|	|	...	...	...	1150	|	|	...	...	...	1350	|	|	...	...	...
433	Elsterwerda .... **843 835** d.	0736	|	|	...	...	...	1001	|	|	...	...	...	1201	|	|	...	...	...	1401	|	|	...	...	...
486	**Dresden** Neustadt .... a.	0801	0900	0900	...	...	...	1029	1044	1100	...	...	...	1229	1300	1300	...	...	...	1429	1500	1500	...	...	...
490	**Dresden** Hbf .... **843** a.	0807	0907	0907	...	...	...	1035	1050	1107	...	...	...	1235	1307	1307	...	...	...	1435	1507	1507	...	...	...

	IC **2179** 🍷	*EC* **177** P✕	*ICE* **709** M✕	*ICE* **1007** ✕M	*ICE* **1046** ⑥ O	*ICE* **603** M✕	*IC* **2271** X🍷	*ICE* **836** C✕	*EC* **179** P✕	*ICE* **801** B✕	*ICE* **1009** M✕	*ICE* **1605** M✕	*ICE* **1705** Ⓑ Q✕	*IC* **2273** Ⓑ X🍷	*ICE* **871** Ⓑ ✕	*ICE* **803** N✕	*IC* **2075** U🍷	*ICE* **1607** D✕	*IC* **2275** 🍷	*IC* **2073** ✕	*ICE* **1743** ⑤⑦ ✕	*ICE* **699** F✕	*ICE* **607** Ⓑ ✕	*ICE* **905** ✕	*ICE* **907** ⑤⑦ ✕
Hamburg Altona .... d.	...	1236	1319	1351	...	1418	...	1437	...	1518	1535	1616	1616	...	...	1719	...	1818	...	1835	...	1919	2017	2135	2236
Hamburg Hbf .... **830** d.	...	1251	1336	1404	...	1435	...	1451	...	1536	1550	1634	1634	...	...	1735	1751	1835	...	1851	...	1936	2034	2151	2251
Büchen .... **830** d.	...	1314	|	|	...	|	...	1514	...	|	|	|	|	...	...	|	|	|	...	1914	...	|	|	2215	2315
Ludwigslust .... **837** d.	...	1341	|	|	...	|	...	1541	...	|	1646	|	|	...	...	|	1843	|	...	1942	...	|	2118	2242	2342
Wittenberge .... **837** d.	...	1401	|	|	...	|	...	1601	...	|	|	|	|	...	...	1833	|	|	...	2001	...	|	|	2303	0002
Berlin Spandau .... **837** d.	...	1446	1512	1544	...	1610	...	1646	...	1712	1744	1810	1810	...	...	1912	1942s	2010	...	2044s	...	2112	2211s	2343s	0042s
Rostock Hbf **835** .... d.	1221	|	|	|	...	|	1421	|	...	|	|	|	|	1621	...	|	|	|	1821	|	...	|	|	|	|
Berlin Hbf .... **837** a.	1423	1455	1522	1555	...	1622	1623	1655	...	1722	1755	1820	1820	1823	...	1922	1955	2020	2023	2055	...	2122	2223	2354	0054
Berlin Hbf .... **835** d.	1426	1516	1537	1605	1614	1630	1626	1704	1716v	1736	1805	1830n	1830	1826	1916	1926	|	2030	2026	|	2116	2128	|	|	|
Berlin Südkreuz .... **835** d.	1433	1523	1542	1609	1623	1635	1633	1709	1723v	1741	1809	1835n	1835	1833	1923	1931	2019	2035	2033r	2104	2123	2133	2232	0002	0103
Flughafen Berlin ✈ ★ ...... d.	1501	|	...	...	|	...	1701	...	|	...	...	...	...	1901	|	...	...	...	2101	...	|	...	...	...	...
Doberlug-Kirchhain .... **835** d.	1550	|	...	...	|	...	1745	...	|	...	...	...	...	1945	|	...	...	...	2150	...	|	...	...	...	...
Elsterwerda .... **843 835** d.	1601	|	...	...	1735	...	1756	...	|	...	...	...	...	1956	|	...	...	...	2201	...	|	...	...	...	...
Dresden Neustadt .... a.	1629	1700	...	...	1805	...	1821	...	1900	...	...	...	...	2021	2100	...	...	...	2229	...	2300	...	...	...	...
Dresden Hbf .... **843** a.	1635	1707	...	...	1812	...	1827	...	1907	...	...	...	...	2027	2107	...	...	...	2235	...	2307	...	...	...	...

	ICE **4** ① Z	*IC* **908** ① ✕	*ICE* **608** ①–⑤ ✕	*ICE* **808** ①–⑥ ✕	*IC* **2274** ①–⑥	*ICE* **1606** L✕	*ICE* **806** E✕	*ICE* **870** ①–⑥ ✕	*ICE* **870** ⑦ ✕	*IC* **2272** X🍷	*ICE* **1604** N✕	*ICE* **1704** ①–⑤ Q✕	*ICE* **1008** M✕	*ICE* **804** A✕	*EC* **178** P✕	*ICE* **933** ①–⑤ H✕	*ICE* **1045** ⑥⑦ W	*IC* **2270** X🍷	*ICE* **602** M✕	*ICE* **1006** M✕	*ICE* **802** M✕	*EC* **176** J P✕	*IC* **1076** ①●	*IC* **2178** 🍷	*ICE* **1600** M✕
Dresden Hbf .... **843** d.	...	...	...	...	0519	...	...	0654	...	0730	...	...	...	...	0855	...	0912	0930	...	...	...	1055	1055	1119	...
Dresden Neustadt .... d.	...	...	...	...	0526	...	...	0702	...	0737	...	...	...	...	0902	...	0919	0937	...	...	...	1102	1102	1126	...
Elsterwerda .... **843 835** d.	...	...	...	...	0556	...	...	|	...	0804	...	...	...	...	|	...	0947	1004	...	...	...	|	|	1156	...
Doberlug-Kirchhain .... **835** d.	...	...	...	...	0608	...	...	|	...	0814	...	...	...	...	|	...	|	1014	...	...	...	|	|	1208	...
Flughafen Berlin ✈ ★ ...... a.	...	...	...	...	0657	...	...	|	...	0857	...	...	...	...	|	...	|	1057	...	...	...	|	|	1257	...
Berlin Südkreuz .... **835** d.	0344	0457	0519	0629	0727	0723	0827	0837	0856	0927	0923	0923	0946	1019t	1035s	1050	1137	1127	1123	1146	1219	1237	1237	1327	1323
Berlin Hbf .... **835** a.	0349	|	|	|	0732	0729	0832	0842	|	0932	0930	0930	0951	1025t	1042	1056	1142	1132	1129	1151	1225	1242	1242	1332	1329
Berlin Hbf .... **837** d.	0353	0506	0528	0638	0736	0738	0838	0906	0906	0936	0938	0938	1006	1038	...	1106	...	1135	1138	1206	1238	1303	1303	1337	1338
Rostock Hbf **835** .... a.	|	|	|	|	0937	|	|	|	|	1137	|	|	|	|	...	|	...	1337	|	|	|	|	|	1537	|
Berlin Spandau .... **837** d.	|	0517	0538	0648	...	0748	0848	0917	0917	...	0948	0948	1016	1048	...	1117	...	...	1148	1216	1248	1315	1315	...	1348
Wittenberge .... **837** d.	|	0600	0621	|	...	|	|	1001	1001	...	|	|	|	|	...	1201	...	...	|	|	|	1401	1401	...	|
Ludwigslust .... **837** d.	|	0618	0641	0742	...	|	|	1020	1020	...	|	|	|	|	...	1220	...	...	|	|	|	1420	1420	...	|
Büchen .... **830** d.	|	0649	|	|	...	|	|	1047	1047	...	|	|	|	|	...	1248	...	...	|	|	|	1449	1449	...	|
Hamburg Hbf .... **830** a.	0539	0712	0725	0825	...	0924	1021	1115	1115	...	1124	1124	1151	1221	...	1311	...	...	1324	|	1421	1512	1512	...	1524
Hamburg Altona .... a.	...	0726	0740	0840	...	0939	1038	1128	1128	...	1140	1140	1205	1239	...	1324	...	...	1339	1403	1438	1527	1527	...	1539

A – [12] ✕ (München Ⓐ -) Nürnberg - Erfurt - Halle/Leipzig - Berlin - Kiel.
B – [12] ✕ Kiel - Hamburg - Berlin - Halle - Erfurt - Nürnberg - München.
C – [12] ✕ Hamburg - Berlin - Erfurt - Frankfurt - Saarbrücken.
D – [12] ✕ Hamburg - Leipzig (- Erfurt Ⓑ) (- München ⑤).
E – [12] ✕ (Eisenach ①–⑤ -) Leipzig - Berlin - Hamburg.
F – [12] ✕ Hamburg - Berlin - Leipzig - Erfurt - Frankfurt - Stuttgart - München.
G – BEROLINA – [12] ✕ Hamburg - Halle - Erfurt - Nürnberg - Wien.
H – [12] ✕ Darmstadt - Frankfurt - Erfurt - Berlin - Hamburg.
J – Daily to June 26; ②–⑦ from June 28.
K – [12] ✕ Kiel - Hamburg - Dresden - Praha.
L – From Leipzig (Table **850**).
M – To / from München via Erfurt (Table **850**).

N – To / from Nürnberg via Erfurt (Table **850**).
O – From Ostseebad Binz (Tables **844** and **845**).
P – To / from Praha (Tables **60/1100**).
Q – From / to Jena (Table **849a**).
T – From / to Kiel (Table **820**).
U – UTHLANDE – From Westerland (Table **821**).
W – To Stralsund (also Ostseebad Binz on ⑥). See Tables **844** and **845**.
X – From / to Chemnitz (Table **880**).
Y – ⑤–① June 26 - Aug. 29; daily from Sept. 2. From Sept. 2 runs as *RJ* **259** and continues to Wien and Graz (Table **60**).

Z – From Zürich via Basel, Frankfurt and Leipzig (Tables **850**, **912**).
n – Not ⑥.
r – From Sept. 2.
s – Arrival time. Calls to set down only.
t – On ⑦ Berlin Südkreuz d. 1024, Berlin Hbf a. 1029.
v – Until Sept. 1 departs Berlin Hbf 1705, Berlin Südkreuz 1717.
¶ – From Flensburg on dates in Table **823**.
● – From June 27.
★ – Flughafen Berlin Brandenburg (BER).

HAMBURG - BERLIN - DRESDEN 840

See Table 927 for services operated by FlixTrain

	ICE 1706	*ICE* 800	*EC* 174	*IC* 1974	*IC* 2176	*ICE* 508	*ICE* 1004	*ICE* 708	*EC* 378	*IC* 1178	*IC* 2174	*ICE* 506	*ICE* 92	*ICE* 706	*EC* 172	*IC* 1072	*IC* 2172	*ICE* 504	*ICE* 1002	*ICE* 704	*EC* 170	*ICE* 502	*RJ* 252	*ICE* 902	*ICE* 1740
			J	①●					J	①●					J	①●							⊡		⑤⑦
	M✕	M✕	F✕		🍷	M✕	M✕	M✕	K✕	T	🍷	M✕	G✕	M✕	P✕		🍷	M✕	M✕	M✕	P✕	M✕	P✕	✕	L✕
Dresden Hbf 843 d.	...	...	1255	1255	1319	...	...	...	1455	1503	1519	...	...	...	1655	1655	1719	...	...	...	1855	...	1955	...	2054
Dresden Neustadt d.	...	...	1302	1302	1326	...	...	...	1502	1509	1526	...	...	...	1702	1702	1726	...	...	...	1902	...	2002	...	2102
Elsterwerda 843 835 d.	...	...	|	|	1356	...	...	...	|	|	1556	...	...	...	|	|	1756	...	...	...	|	...	2029	...	|
Doberlug-Kirchhain 835 d.	...	...	|	|	1408	...	...	...	|	|	1608	...	...	...	|	|	1808	...	...	...	|	...	2041	...	|
Flughafen Berlin ✈ ★ a.	...	...	|	|	1458	...	...	...	|	|	1659	...	...	...	|	|	1857	...	...	...	|	...	|	...	|
Berlin Südkreuz 835 d.	1349	1419	1437	1437	1527	1523	1546	1619	1637	1658	1727	1723	1753	1819	1837	1837	1928	1923	1949	2019	2035s	2123	|	2228	2235s
Berlin Hbf 835 a.	1355	1425	1442	1442	1532	1529	1551	1625	1642	1703	1732	1729	1758	1825	1842	1842	1933	1930	1954	2024	2042	2129	2159	|	2242
Berlin Hbf 837 d.	1403	1438	1506	1506	1537	1538	1603	1638	1706	1706	1735	1738	1805	1838	1906	1906	1938	1938	2006	2038	...	2138	...	2238	...
Rostock Hbf 835 a.	|	|	|	|	1737	|	|	|	|	|	1937	|	|	|	|	|	2137	|	|	|	...	|	...	|	...
Berlin Spandau 837 d.	1416	1448	1517	1517	...	1548	1615	1648	1717	1717	...	1748	1815	1848	1917	1917	...	1948	2016	2048	...	2148	...	2248	...
Wittenberge 837 d.	|	|	1601	1601	...	|	|	|	1801	1801	...	|	|	|	2001	2001	...	|	|	|	...	2229	...	2329	...
Ludwigslust 837 d.	|	|	1620	1620	...	|	1711	|	1820	1820	...	|	|	|	2020	2020	...	|	|	|	...	2249	...	2347	...
Büchen 830 d.	|	|	1649	1649	...	|	|	|	1849	1849	...	|	|	|	2049	2048	...	|	|	|	...	|	...	|	...
Hamburg Hbf 830 a.	1559	1621	1711	1711	...	1724	1812	1822	1912	1912	...	1924	1951	2023	2119	2119	...	2124	2156	2222	...	2333	...	0033	...
Hamburg Altona a.	1623	1638	...	1723	...	1740	1824	1838	...	...	...	1939	2013	2038	2135	2135	...	2140	2214	2238	...	2349	...	0049	...

F – From Praha (Tables **60**/**1100**). To Flensburg (Table **823**).
G – BEROLINA – [12] ✕ Wien - Nürnberg - Erfurt - Halle - Hamburg.
J – Daily to June 26; ②–⑦ from June 28.
K – [12] ✕ Praha - Dresden - Hamburg - Kiel.
L – From June 26.
M – From München via Erfurt (Table **850**).
P – From Praha (Tables **60**/**1100**).
R – ① from June 27.
T – To Kiel (Table **820**).
s – Arrival time. Calls to set down only.
⊡ – ④–⑦ June 26 - Aug. 28; daily from Sept. 1. Train number **258** from Sept. 1 and runs from Graz via Wien (Table **60**).
● – From June 27.

MAGDEBURG - STENDAL - UELZEN and WITTENBERGE 841

RE / *S-Bahn* services

km		Ⓐt	⚒	Ⓐt				Ⓐt	†			R														
0	**Magdeburg** Hbf d.	...	0351	...	0510	0552	0610	0640	0703	0710	0810	0853	0903	0910	1010	1103	1110	1210	1303	1310	1403	1410	1503	1510	1603	1610
58	Stendal Hbf a.	...	0436	...	0557	0632	0657	0726	0743	0757	0857	0926	0943	0957	1057	1143	1157	1257	1343	1357	1443	1457	1543	1557	1643	1657
58	Stendal Hbf d.	0408	0440	0508	0601	0633	0701t	0730	0744	0801	0901r	0932	0944	1001	1101t	1144	1201	1301t	1344	1401	1444	1501t	1544	1601	1644	1701t
113	**Wittenberge** a.	0451	|	0551	0644	|	0744t	|	|	0844	0944r	1009	|	1044	1144t	|	1244	1344t	|	1444	|	1544t	|	1644	|	1744t
116	Salzwedel d.	...	0519	...	...	0714	...	0808	0814	...	...	...	1014	...	...	1214	...	...	1414	...	1514	...	1614	...	1714	...
167	**Uelzen** a.	...	0550	...	...	0746	...	...	0846	...	...	...	1046	...	...	1246	...	...	1446	...	1546	...	1646	...	1746	...

							T				
Magdeburg Hbf d.	1703	1710	1810	1903	1910	2010	2103	2110	2141	2210	2310
Stendal Hbf a.	1743	1757	1857	1943	1957	2057	2143	2157	2220	2257	2357
Stendal Hbf d.	1744	1801	1901t	1944	2001	2101b	2144	2201	2232b	...	...
Wittenberge a.	|	1844	1944t	|	2044	2144b	|	2244	|	...	...
Salzwedel d.	1814	...	...	2014	...	...	2214	...	2310b	...	...
Uelzen a.	1846	...	...	2046	...	...	2246	...	...	...	...

		Ⓐ		⚒			⚒		⚒		†
Uelzen d.	...	...	...	...	...	...	0619	...	0700	...	0802
Salzwedel d.	...	0502	...	0525	0557	...	0652	...	0734	...	0835
Wittenberge d.	...	|	0500t	|	|	0610t	|	0710	|	0810t	|
Stendal Hbf a.	...	0539	0542t	0556	0634	0652t	0722	0752	0813	0852t	0907
Stendal Hbf d.	0457	0546	0557	0606	0641	0657	0727t	0757	...	0857	0910
Magdeburg Hbf a.	0544	0626	0644	0649	0723	0744	0814t	0844	...	0944	0950

												S												Ⓑ		T
Uelzen d.	...	0902	...	...	1102	...	...	1302	...	...	1502	...	...	1602	...	1702	...	1802	...	1902	...	...	2102	...	...	2302
Salzwedel d.	...	0935	...	...	1135	...	...	1335	...	...	1535	...	...	1635	...	1735	...	1835	...	1935	...	...	2135	...	...	2336
Wittenberge d.	0910	|	1010r	1110	|	1210t	1310	|	1410t	1510	|	1549	1610t	|	1710	|	1810t	|	1910	|	2010t	2110	|	2210	2307	|
Stendal Hbf a.	0952	1007	1052r	1152	1207	1252t	1352	1407	1452t	1552	1607	1622	1653t	1707	1752	1807	1852t	1911	1952	2007	2052t	2152	2211	2252	2347	0005
Stendal Hbf d.	0957	1010	1057	1157	1210	1257	1357	1410	1457	1557	1610	1626	1657	1710	1757	1810	1857c	1912	1957	2010	2057	2157	2223	...	2348	0007
Magdeburg Hbf a.	1044	1050	1144	1244	1250	1344	1444	1450	1544	1644	1651	1700	1744	1750	1844	1850	1944	1952	2044	2050	2144	2244	2303	...	0033	0046

R – *IC* **2238**. [12] Leipzig - Schwerin - Rostock - Warnemünde.
S – *IC* **2239**. [12] Warnemünde - Rostock - Schwerin - Leipzig.
T – ⑤–⑦ (also Oct. 3, 31).
b – Not ⑥.
c – 1859 from Oct. 15.
r – ⚒ (not Oct. 31).
t – Ⓐ (not Oct. 31).

LEIPZIG - DRESDEN 842

	IC 2249	*IC* 2449	*ICE* 1553	*IC* 2447	*ICE* 1555	*IC* 2445	*ICE* 1557	*IC* 2443	*ICE* 1559	*IC* 2441	*ICE* 1651	*IC* 2049	*ICE* 1653	*IC* 2047	*ICE* 1655	*IC* 2045	*ICE* 1657							
	①–⑥	Ⓐ	①–⑥					⑦								Ⓑ								
		M	E	B		K		K		K		K		K		K								
			✕	🍷	✕	🍷	✕	🍷	✕	🍷	✕	🍷	✕	🍷	✕	🍷								
Wiesbaden Hbf **911** d.	...	...	...	...	...	...	0826	...	1026	...	1226	...	1426	...	1626	...	1826	...	...	...	...	...	...	...
Frankfurt (Main) Hbf **850** d.	...	...	...	...	0716	...	0919	...	1119	...	1319	...	1519	...	1719	...	1919	...	...	...	...	...	...	...
Leipzig Hbf d.	0630	0730	0831	0930	1031	1130	1231	1330	1431	1530	1631	1730	1831	1930	2031	2130	2231	...	...	...	...	...	...	...
Riesa d.	0702	0802	0902	1003	1102	1202	1302	1402	1502	1602	1702	1802	1902	2002	2102	2202	2302	...	...	...	...	...	...	...
Dresden Neustadt a.	0728	0837	0930	1051	1130	1251	1330	1437	1530	1637	1730	1837	1930	2037	2130	2237	2330	...	...	...	...	...	...	...
Dresden Hbf a.	0735	0846	0937	1100	1137	1300	1337	1445	1537	1648	1737	1844	1937	2046	2137	2245	2337	...	...	...	...	...	...	...

	IC 2044	*ICE* 1654	*IC* 2046	*ICE* 1652	*IC* 2048	*ICE* 1650	*IC* 2440	*ICE* 1558	*IC* 2442	*ICE* 1556	*IC* 1934	*IC* 2444	*ICE* 1554	*IC* 2446	*ICE* 1552	*IC* 2448		*IC* 2248						
	Ⓐ		①–⑥						⑦		⑦					Ⓑ		Ⓑ						
	K		K		K		K		K		G	K		K		H								
	🍷	✕	🍷	✕	🍷	✕	🍷	✕	🍷	✕		🍷	✕	🍷	✕									
Dresden Hbf d.	0512	0612	0712	0812	0844	1012	1044	1212	1244	1412	1422	1512	1612	1712	1812	1844	...	2112	...	...	...	...	...	...
Dresden Neustadt d.	0519	0619	0719	0819	0850	1019	1050	1219	1250	1419	1429	1519	1619	1719	1819	1850	...	2119	...	...	...	...	...	...
Riesa d.	0547	0647	0747	0847	0947	1047	1147	1247	1347	1447	1519	1547	1647	1747	1847	1947	...	2147	...	...	...	...	...	...
Leipzig Hbf a.	0621	0723	0821	0923	1021	1123	1221	1323	1421	1523	1555	1621	1723	1821	1923	2021	...	2221	...	...	...	...	...	...
Frankfurt (Main) Hbf **850** a.	...	1036	...	1236	...	1436	...	1636	...	1836	...	...	2036	...	2236	...	...	...	...	...	...	...	...	...
Wiesbaden Hbf **911** a.	...	1133	...	1333	...	1533	...	1733	...	1933	...	...	2133	...	...	...	...	...	...	...	...	...	...	...

RE services

km		⚒v		⚒v		N	⑥P															
0	**Leipzig** Hbf d.	0400	0500	0600	0700	0800	0800	0900		2200	...	2307	...	...	...	...	...	...	...	...	...	...	...
26	Wurzen d.	0418	0518	0618	0718	0818	0818	0918	and	2218	...	2325	...	...	...	...	...	...	...	...	...	...	...
53	Oschatz d.	0436	0536	0636	0736	0836	0836	0936		2236	...	2343	...	...	...	...	...	...	...	...	...	...	...
66	Riesa a.	0444	0544	0644	0744	0844	0844	0944	hourly	2244	...	2352	...	...	...	...	...	...	...	...	...	...	...
66	Riesa d.	0455	0555	0655	0755	0855	0855	0955		2255	...	2355	...	...	...	...	...	...	...	...	...	...	...
102	Coswig 843 856 857 d.	0525	0625	0725	0825	0925	0925	1025	until	2325	...	0025	...	...	...	...	...	...	...	...	...	...	...
110	Radebeul Ost 857 d.	|	|	|	|	|	|	|		|	...	|	...	...	...	...	...	...	...	...	...	...	...
116	**Dresden** Neustadt 856/7 a.	0534	0634	0734	0834	0934	0935	1034		2334	...	0034	...	...	...	...	...	...	...	...	...	...	...
120	**Dresden** Hbf ⊡ 843 856 857 a.	0541	0641	0742	0841	0942	0944	1041		2341	...	0041	...	...	...	...	...	...	...	...	...	...	...

	⚒v		Ⓐv	⑥								Ⓐv	Ⓒz		Ⓐ	Ⓒ		Q					
Dresden Hbf 843 856 857 d.	0409	0506	0606	0606	0706	0806	0906	1006	1106	1206	1306	1406	1406	1506	1606	1606	1706	1806	1906	2006	2106	2206	2306
Dresden Neustadt 856/7 d.	0416	0513	0613	0613	0713	0813	0913	1013	1113	1213	1313	1413	1413	1513	1613	1613	1713	1813	1913	2013	2113	2213	2313
Radebeul Ost 857 d.	0422	|	|	|	|	|	|	|	|	|	|	|	|	|	|	|	|	|	|	|	|	|	|
Coswig 843 856 857 d.	0429	0524	0624	0629	0729	0829	0929	1029	1124	1229	1324	1424	1429	1524	1624	1629	1724	1829	1924	2029	2124	2229	2324
Riesa a.	0458	0554	0658	0658	0758	0858	0958	1058	1154	1258	1354	1454	1459	1554	1654	1658	1754	1858	1954	2058	2155	2259	2355
Riesa d.	0506	0606	0706	0706	0806	0906	1006	1106	1206	1306	1406	1506	1506	1606	1706	1706	1806	1906	2006	2106	2206	2306	0006
Oschatz d.	0514	0614	0714	0714	0814	0914	1014	1114	1214	1314	1414	1514	1514	1614	1714	1714	1814	1914	2014	2114	2214	2314	0014
Wurzen d.	0531	0631	0731	0731	0831	0931	1031	1131	1231	1331	1431	1531	1531	1631	1731	1731	1831	1931	2031	2131	2231	2331	0031
Leipzig Hbf a.	0550	0650	0750	0750	0850	0950	1050	1150	1250	1350	1450	1550	1550	1650	1750	1750	1850	1950	2050	2150	2250	2350	0050

B – [12] (Bielefeld ① -) (Hannover ①–⑥ -) Leipzig - Dresden.
E – From Eisenach (Table **850**) on ⑥.
G – [12] Dresden - Leipzig - Magdeburg - Hannover - Emden.
H – To Hannover (Table **866**).
K – [12] Köln - Hannover - Magdeburg - Dresden and v.v.
M – From Magdeburg (Table **866**).
N – Ⓑ to Oct. 28; daily from Oct. 30.
P – ⑥ until Oct. 29. To Bad Schandau (Table **857**).
Q – On ⑥ July 2 - Oct. 29 starts from Bad Schandau (Table **857**).
v – Not Oct. 31, Nov. 16.
z – Also Oct. 31, Nov. 16.

843 ELSTERWERDA - CHEMNITZ and DRESDEN; DÖBELN - LEIPZIG *RE / RB services*

ELSTERWERDA - CHEMNITZ *Operated by Mitteldeutsche Regiobahn*

km		Ⓐv	Ⓐt		Ⓐt		Ⓐt		Ⓐv		Ⓐv		Ⓐv		Ⓐt		Ⓐt			Ⓐt		†w	Ⓑ	⚒v	
0	**Elsterwerda** d.	...	0514	...	0614	...	0714	0814	...	1014	...	1214	...	1414	1514	1614	1714	...	1814	1914	2014	2127	...	2214	...
24	Riesa a.	...	0539	...	0639	...	0739	0839	...	1039	...	1239	...	1439	1539	1639	1739	...	1839	1939	2039	2152	...	2239	...
24	Riesa d.	0449	0549	0549	0649	0649	0749	0849	0949	1049	1149	1249	1349	1449	1549	1649	1749	1749	1849	1949	2049	2153	2153	2253	2253
50	Döbeln Hbf d.	0510	0610	0610	0710	0710	0810	0910	1010	1110	1210	1310	1410	1510	1610	1710	1810	1810	1910	2010	2110	2218	2218	2318	2318
91	**Chemnitz** Hbf a.	0546	0646	0646	0746	0746	0846	0946	1046	1146	1246	1346	1446	1546	1646	1746	1846	1846	1946	2046	2146	2258	2258	2358	2358

	Ⓐt		Ⓐt		Ⓐv		Ⓐv		Ⓐv		Ⓐt			Ⓐt		Ⓐt		Ⓑ		⑥		Ⓐt		
Chemnitz Hbf d.	0409	0509	0509	0609	0707	0809	0909	1009	1109	1209	1309	1409	1509	1509	1609	1709	1809	1909	2009	2009	...	2137	...	2237
Döbeln Hbf d.	0447	0547	0547	0647	0747	0847	0947	1047	1147	1247	1347	1447	1547	1547	1647	1747	1847	1947	2047	2047	...	2219	...	2319
Riesa a.	0509	0609	0609	0709	0809	0909	1009	1109	1209	1309	1409	1509	1609	1609	1709	1809	1909	2009	2109	2109	...	2240	...	2340
Riesa d.	0515	...	0615	0715	...	0915	...	1115	...	1315	1415	1515	...	1615	1715	1815	1915	2015	...	2115	...	2249	...	...
Elsterwerda a.	0536	...	0636	0736	...	0936	...	1136	...	1336	1436	1536	...	1636	1736	1836	1936	2036	...	2136	...	2311	...	...

ELSTERWERDA - DRESDEN

km		Ⓐ		Ⓐ				
0	**Elsterwerda-Biehla** d.	0439	0539a	0639	0739	and every	2139	2327
2	Elsterwerda d.	0443	0543	0643	0743	two hours	2143	2343
41	Coswig ▷ d.	0522	0622	0722	0822	until	2222	0022
59	**Dresden** Hbf ▷ a.	0543	0643	0743	0843		2243	0043

		Ⓐ	Ⓒ	Ⓐ			⊠				Ⓐ
Dresden Hbf ▷ d.	0508	0608	0658	0708	0858	1108	and every	1908	2108	2308	1608
Coswig ▷ d.	0531	0631	0721	0742j	0921	1131	two hours	1931	2131	2331	1631
Elsterwerda d.	0610	0710	0800	0833	1000	1210	until	2010	2209	0009	1710
Esterwerda-Biehla a.	0613	0713	0803	0837	1003	1213		2013	...	...	1713

DÖBELN - LEIPZIG *Operated by Mitteldeutsche Regiobahn*

km		Ⓐv	Ⓐv		Ⓐv			Ⓐv		
0	**Döbeln** Hbf d.	0450	0550	0650	0750	and hourly	1850	1950	2050	...
13	Leisnig d.	0502	0602	0702	0802	on Ⓐ,	1902	2002	2102	...
28	Großbothen d.	0517	0617	0717	0817	every two	1917	2017	2117	...
35	Grimma ob Bf d.	0526	0626	0726	0826	hours on	1926	2026	2126	2308
66	**Leipzig** Hbf a.	0600	0700	0800	0900	Ⓒ until	2000	2100	2200	2341

	Ⓐv		Ⓐv			Ⓐv			
Leipzig Hbf d.	0506	0606	0706	and hourly	1806	1906	2006	2106	2206
Grimma ob Bf d.	0541	0641	0741	on Ⓐ,	1841	1941	2041	2139	2241
Großbothen d.	0547	0647	0747	every two	1847	1947	2047	...	2247
Leisnig d.	0604	0704	0804	hours on	1904	2004	2104	...	2301
Döbeln Hbf a.	0617	0717	0817	Ⓒ until	1917	2017	2117	...	2314

a – Ⓐ only.
j – Arrives 0730.
t – Not Oct. 31.
v – Not Oct. 31, Nov. 16.
w – Also Oct. 31, Nov. 16.
⊠ – Additional service on Ⓐ from Dresden Hbf at 1608 (see later column).
▷ – See also Tables **842**, **856**, **857**.

844 STRALSUND - OSTSEEBAD BINZ / SASSNITZ *Ostdeutsche Eisenbahn (except ICE / IC services)*

km													*ICE* 1678	*ICE* 1049					*ICE* 1051	*ICE* 1714				
		Ⓐ		Ⓐ	Ⓐ	Ⓐ							①–⑥ ◆	⑥ B					⑥ B	⑥ ◆				
	Rostock Hbf **830** d.	...	0454	...	0553	...	0700	...	...	...	0900	...	0938	...	...	...	1100	...	...	...	...	...	1300	...
0	**Stralsund** Hbf d.	0459	0559	...	0659	...	0759	...	0859	...	0959	...	1031	1040	1059	...	1159	...	1210	1240	1259	...	1359	...
29	Bergen auf Rügen d.	0529	0629	...	0729	...	0829	...	0929	...	1029	...	1055	1108	1129	...	1229	...	1241	1305	1329	...	1429	...
39	Lietzow (Rügen) d.	0538	0638	0641	0738	0741	0838	0841	0937	0939	1038	1041	|	|	1137	1139	1238	1241	|	|	1337	1339	1438	1441
	Ostseebad Binz a.	|	|	0655	|	0755	|	0855	0951	|	|	1056	1119	1131	1151	|	|	1255	1300	1328	1351	|	|	1455
51	**Sassnitz** a.	0553	0653	...	0753	...	0853	...	...	0954	1053	...	...	...	...	1154	1253	...	...	...	...	1354	1453	...

	IC 2212	*ICE* 1045					*ICE* 632	*ICE* 1710					*ICE* 759											
	◆	⑥ ◆					①–⑥ N	M					◆	D	Ⓐ			Ⓐ	Ⓐ					Ⓑ n
Rostock Hbf **830** d.	1338	...	...	...	1500	...	1538	...	...	...	1700	...	...	...	...	1900	...	...	...	...	2100	...	...	2300
Stralsund Hbf d.	1439	1449	1459	...	1559	...	1632	1649	1659	...	1759	...	1815	1859	...	1959	...	2101	...	...	2159	...	...	2359
Bergen auf Rügen d.	1505	1516	1529	...	1629	...	1656	1715	1729	...	1829	...	1841	1929	...	2029	...	2130	...	...	2229	...	...	0029
Lietzow (Rügen) d.	|	|	1537	1539	1638	1641	|	|	1737	1739	1838	1841	|	1937	1939	2038	2041	2138	2140	...	2238	2241	...	0038
Ostseebad Binz a.	1528	1536	1551	|	|	1655	1721	1737	1751	|	|	1855	1900	1951	|	|	2055	2153	|	...	|	2255	...	|
Sassnitz a.	...	...	...	1554	1653	...	...	...	...	1754	1853	...	...	...	1954	2053	...	...	2155	...	2253	...	...	0053

km										*ICE* 1042	*ICE* 639					*ICE* 1711	*IC* 2213			*ICE* 1021			*ICE* 1046	*ICE* 1640
		Ⓐ		Ⓐ	⚒			Ⓐ	Ⓐ	B	N					M	◆			⑥ ◆			⑥ ◆	⑤⑦ B
	Sassnitz d.	0352	0502	...	0602	...	0702	0759	...	...	...	...	0902	0959	...	...	...	1100	...	...	1159	...	...	...
0	**Ostseebad Binz** d.	|	|	0600	|	0700	|	|	0803	0819	0826	0900	|	|	1003	1021	1043	|	1102	1156	|	1203	1218	1218
12	Lietzow (Rügen) d.	0407	0517	0614	0617	0714	0717	0814	0818	0843	0855	0914	0917	1014	1018	|	|	1116	1119	|	1214	1218	|	|
22	Bergen auf Rügen d.	0416	0526	...	0626	...	0726	...	0827	|	|	...	0926	...	1027	1042	1108	...	1128	1217	...	1227	1242	1242
51	**Stralsund** Hbf a.	0446	0556	...	0656	...	0756	...	0857	0906	0921	...	0956	...	1057	1109	1132	...	1158	1247	...	1257	1306	1306
	Rostock Hbf **830** a.	0548	0654	...	...	...	0855	...	...	...	1019	...	1055	...	...	...	1239	...	1255	1401	...	...	...	...

	ICE 633					*ICE* 1715									*ICE* 1048									
	N					⑥ M									⑥ B△			Ⓐ	Ⓐ				Ⓐ	D
Sassnitz d.	...	...	1302	1359	...	...	...	1502	1559	...	1659	...	1759	...	...	...	1902	1959	...	...	2102	...	2200	...
Ostseebad Binz d.	1226	1300	|	|	1403	1421	1500	|	|	1603	|	1702	|	1803	1824	1900	|	|	2003	2100	|	...	|	2205
Lietzow (Rügen) d.	|	1314	1317	1414	1418	|	1514	1517	1614	1618	1714	1719	1814	1818	|	1914	1917	2014	2018	2114	2117	...	2215	2220
Bergen auf Rügen d.	1255	...	1326	...	1427	1442	...	1526	...	1627	...	1727	...	1827	1850	...	1926	...	2027	...	2126	...	...	2229
Stralsund Hbf a.	1321	...	1356	...	1457	1506	...	1556	...	1657	...	1757	...	1857	1914	...	1956	...	2057	...	2157	...	...	2258
Rostock Hbf **830** a.	1419	...	1455	...	...	...	...	1655	...	1801r	...	1855	...	...	...	...	2055	...	...	...	2255	...	...	...

◆ – NOTES (LISTED BY TRAIN NUMBER)

759 – 🚃12 ✕ Köln - Hannover - Berlin - Ostseebad Binz. July 18 - Oct. 1 starts from Berlin and runs with train number **659**.
1021 – 🚃12 ✕ Ostseebad Binz - Hamburg - Köln - Nürnberg.
1045/6 – 🚃12 Dresden - Berlin - Ostseebad Binz and v.v.
1678 – 🚃12 ✕ (Hannover ①–⑤ -) Hamburg - Ostseebad Binz.
1714 – POMMERSCHE BUCHT – 🚃12 ✕ Jena - Leipzig - Berlin - Ostseebad Binz.
2212 – RÜGEN – 🚃12 🍸 Koblenz - Köln - Hamburg - Ostseebad Binz.
2213 – RÜGEN – 🚃12 🍸 Ostseebad Binz - Hamburg - Köln - Stuttgart.

B – From / to Berlin (Table **845**).
D – Daily June 13 - Sept. 3; Ⓐ from Sept. 5.
M – 🚃12 ✕ Ostseebad Binz - Berlin - Nürnberg - München and v.v.
N – 🚃12 ✕ München - Nürnberg - Hannover - Hamburg - Ostseebad Binz and v.v.
n – Not Oct. 2.
r – 1812 on ⑤.
△ – On July 23, Aug. 6, 20 Ostseebad Binz d. 1819, Bergen auf Rügen d. 1841, Stralsund a. 1905.

844a BERGEN AUF RÜGEN - PUTBUS - LAUTERBACH and RÜGENSCHE BÄDERBAHN *Preßnitztalbahn*

km		Ⓐt	Ⓐt	Ⓐt	Ⓒz						
0	**Bergen** auf Rügen d.	0640	0740	0840	0940	1040	1240	and	1840	...	2040
10	**Putbus** a.	0649	0749	0849	0949	1049	1249	hourly	1849	...	2049
12	**Lauterbach** Mole a.	0654	0754	0854	0954	1054	1254	until	1854	...	...

	Ⓐt	Ⓐt	Ⓐt		Ⓒz					
Lauterbach Mole d.	0600	0700	0800	0900	1000	1100	1300	1400	and	1900
Putbus d.	0611	0711	0811	0911	1011	1111	1311	1411	hourly	1911
Bergen auf Rügen a.	0620	0720	0820	0920	1020	1120	1320	1420	until	1920

RÜGENSCHE BÄDERBAHN **SERVICE MAY 7 - OCTOBER 9.** Steam train service. Please note that Binz Lokalbahn station is situated 2½ km from Ostseebad Binz DB station.

km											A
0	**Lauterbach** Mole d.	...	...	...	1122	1322	1522	...	1722	1922	...
2	**Putbus** a.	...	...	...	1129	1329	1529	...	1729	1929	...
2	**Putbus** d.	0808	...	1008	1208	1408	1608	...	1808	2008	...
14	Binz Lokalbahn ♥ d.	0840	0944	1040	1240	1440	1640	1744	1840	2040	2244
22	Sellin (Rügen) Ost ♥ d.	0909	1013	1109	1309	1509	1709	1813	1909	2109	2313
27	**Göhren** (Rügen) ♥ a.	0923	1027	1123	1323	1523	1723	1827	1923	2123	2327

										A
Göhren (Rügen) ♥ d.	0849	0953	1153	1353	1553	1649	1753	1849	1953	2149
Sellin (Rügen) Ost. ♥ d.	0907	1011	1211	1411	1611	1707	1811	1907	2011	2207
Binz Lokalbahn ♥ d.	0933	1040	1240	1440	1640	1733	1840	1936	2040	2233
Putbus a.	...	1106	1306	1506	1706	...	1906	2002	2106	...
Putbus d.	...	1111	1311	1511	1711	...	1911	...	...	...
Lauterbach Mole a.	...	1117	1317	1517	1717	...	1917	...	...	...

A – May 26 - Sept. 4 only.
t – Not Oct. 31.
z – Also Oct. 31.
♥ – Additional journeys Binz Lokalbahn - Göhren: **From Binz** at 1144, 1344 and 1544. **From Göhren** at 1049, 1249 and 1449.

RE services except where shown

LUTHERSTADT WITTENBERG - BERLIN - STRALSUND 845

Certain timings may vary by up to 3 minutes until July 16.

km			Ⓒ	*IC* 2217 ⚒ N					*ICE* 1049 ⑥ O✕	S	G	*ICE* 1051 ⑥ O✕		*ICE* 1714 ⑥ B✕			*ICE* 1045 ⑥ M	*ICE* 1045 ⑦ P	⚒	†		*ICE* 1710 J✕		S
0	**Lutherstadt Wittenberg** .. 850	d.	...	0025	...	...	...	0503	...	...	...	0700	...	...	0848	0900	...	...	...	1100	1100	...	1248	1300	...
	Falkenberg (Elster)	d.	...	|	...	...	...	|	0548	...	...	|	...	0753	|	|	0951	...	...	|	|	1151	|	|	...
32	Jüterbog	d.	...	0053	...	...	0430	0534	0627	...	...	0734	...	0832	|	0936	1033	...	...	1136	1136	1231	|	1336	...
45	Luckenwalde	d.	...	0101	...	...	0438	0542	0635	...	...	0742	...	0840	|	0944	1041	...	...	1143	1143	1238	|	1343	...
91	**Berlin** Südkreuz 850	d.	...	0147	...	...	0521	0619	0716	0737	...	0823	0908	0916	0923	1019	1118	1137	1137	1216	1216	1320	1323	1416	...
97	**Berlin** Hbf 850	a.	...	0153	...	...	0529	0626	0724	|	...	0830	|	0924	0930	1027	1125	1142	1142	1224	1224	1327	1329	1424	...
97	**Berlin** Hbf	d.	0100	*0158*	...	0421	0531	0632	0732	0746	...	0832	0917	0932	0946	1032	1131	1146	1146	1232	1232	1332	1346	1432	...
101	**Berlin** Gesundbrunnen	d.	0106	*0204*	...	0427	0537	0638	0740	0752	0803	0839	0925	0939	0953	1039	1139	1153	1153	1239	1239	1339	1352	1439	1453
122	Bernau (b. Berlin)	d.	0119	*0219*	...	0441	0552	0654	0755	|	0819	0854	|	0954	|	1054	1154	|	|	1254	1254	1354	|	1454	1511
144	Eberswalde Hbf	d.	0141	*0239*	...	0507	0607	0709	0810	0822	0837	0909	0955	1009	1023	1109	1209	1223	1223	1309	1309	1409	1419	1509	1527
170	Angermünde	a.	...	▬	...	0526	0626	0729	0829	0839	0852	0929	1010	1028	1038	1129	1228	1240	1240	1329	1329	1428	1434	1528	1543
170	Angermünde	d.	...	...	...	0533	0634	0733	0834	0841	...	0933	1012	1034	1040	1133	1234	1242	1242	1333	1333	1434	1436	1533	...
193	**Schwedt** (Oder)	a.	...	...	...	|	0657	|	0857	|	...	|	|	1057	|	|	1257	|	|	|	|	1457	|	|	...
	Prenzlau	d.	...	⚒	...	0601	...	0801	...	0904	...	1001	1036	...	1104	1201	...	1305	1305	1401	1401	...	1501	1601	...
	Pasewalk	d.	...	0418	...	0619	...	0818	...	0920	...	1018	1052	...	1120	1218	...	1321	1321	1418	1418	...	1517	1618	...
	Anklam	d.	...	0451	...	0651	...	0851	...	0947	...	1051	1121	...	1147	1251	...	1347	1347	1451	1451	...	1546	1652	...
	Züssow 846	d.	...	0505	...	0705	...	0905	...	0959	...	1105	1135	...	1159	1305	...	1359	1359	1505	1505	...	1558	1706	...
	Greifswald 846	d.	...	0521	0701	0721	...	0921	...	1012	...	1121	1148	...	1213	1321	...	1413	1438z	1521	1528j	...	1612	1722	...
	Stralsund Hbf 846	a.	...	0547	0725	0745	...	0945	...	1034	...	1145	1207	...	1235	1345	...	1436	1458	1545	1552	...	1638	1746	...

		ICE 759 K✕			Y S		*ICE* 1647 ⑤	*ICE* 1053 ⑥ ✕	*ICE* 1092 ⑦–④ L✕	*ICE* 1055 ⑤ ✕				⑤–⑦		⑤Y S	⑥	Ⓑ	⑦	⑤⑥		①–④		⑦w	
Lutherstadt Wittenberg ... 850	d.	...	...	1500	...	...	...	...	...	...	1700	...	1900	1900	...	...	...	...	2100	2100	2100	...	...	...	...
Falkenberg (Elster)	d.	...	1351	|	...	1551	...	...	...	...	|	1751	|	|	...	...	1951	*1951*	|	|	|	...	...	...	2151
Jüterbog	d.	...	1431	1536	...	1631	...	...	...	...	1736	1831	1936	1936	...	...	2031	*2031*	2136	2136	2136	...	...	...	2230
Luckenwalde	d.	...	1438	1543	...	1638	...	...	...	...	1743	1838	1943	1943	...	...	2038	*2038*	2143	2143	2143	...	...	...	2238
Berlin Südkreuz 850	d.	...	1520	1616	...	1720	...	...	1753	...	1816	1920	2016	2016	...	...	2120	*2120*	2216	2216	2216	...	...	...	2321
Berlin Hbf 850	a.	...	1528	1624	...	1728	...	...	1758	...	1824	1927	2024	2024	...	...	2127	*2127*	2224	2224	2224	...	...	...	2329
Berlin Hbf	d.	1514	1532	1632	...	1732	1739	1739	1802	1816	1831	1932	...	2032	2032	...	2132	2135	2232	2232	...	2234	...	...	2332
Berlin Gesundbrunnen	d.	1521	1539	1639	1720	1739	1752	1753	1822	1822	1839	1939	...	2039	2039	2044	2141	2141	2241	2241	...	2240	...	...	2338
Bernau (b. Berlin)	d.	1536	1554	1654	1737	1754	1807	1812	1837	1837	1854	1954	...	2054	2054	2103	2155	2155	2256	2256	...	2255	...	...	2352
Eberswalde Hbf	d.	1552	1609	1709	1752	1809	1823	|	1853	1853	1909	2009	...	2109	2109	2119	2215	2215	2315	2315	...	2315	...	...	0012
Angermünde	a.	1607	1628	1729	1806	1828	1840	1840	|	|	1929	2028	...	2129	2129	2138	2235	2235	2337	2337	...	2337	...	...	...
Angermünde	d.	1609	1634	1733	...	1834	1842	1842	|	|	1933	2034	...	2133	2133	...	2237	2237	2338h	...	...	2338	2340	2340	...
Schwedt (Oder)	a.	|	1657	|	...	1857	|	|	|	|	|	2057	...	|	|	...	2259	2259	2400h	...	...	2400	|	|	...
Prenzlau	d.	1632	...	1801	...	...	1905	1905	1934	1934	2001	...	...	2201	2201	...	...	...	...	...	...	...	0009	0009	...
Pasewalk	d.	1649	...	1818	...	...	1921	1921	1951	1951	2018	...	...	2218	2218	...	...	...	...	...	...	...	0024	0026	...
Anklam	d.	1716	...	1851	...	...	|	|	2017	2017	2051	...	...	2251	2251	...	...	...	...	...	...	...	...	0057	...
Züssow 846	d.	1729	...	1905	...	...	1958	1958	|	|	2105	...	...	2305	2305	...	...	...	...	...	...	...	...	0111	...
Greifswald 846	d.	1743	...	1921	...	...	2012	2012	2039	2039	2121	...	...	2321	2321	...	...	...	...	...	...	...	...	0126	...
Stralsund Hbf 846	a.	1808	...	1945	...	...	2031	2032	2058	2058	2145	...	...	2345	2345	...	...	...	...	...	...	...	...	0147	...

km			Ⓐ			①g	Ⓐ	⚒		S			*ICE* 1644 ①–④			S	*ICE* 1042 O✕			*ICE* 1711 ⊠ J✕			*ICE* 1046 ⑥ M	*ICE* 1640 ⑤⑦ O	
0	**Stralsund** Hbf 846	d.	...	...	...	0350	...	0413	...	...	...	0613	0724	...	0803	...	0924	...	1013	1124	...	1215	1323	1323	...
31	Greifswald 846	d.	...	...	...	0424r	...	0438	...	...	...	0638	0746	...	0837r	...	0946	...	1038	1146	...	1239	1345	1345	...
49	Züssow 846	d.	...	...	...	0438	...	0455	...	...	...	0655	0800	...	0855	...	1001	...	1055	1200	...	1255	1358	1358	...
66	Anklam	d.	...	...	...	0449	...	0508	...	...	...	0708	|	...	0908	...	|	...	1108	|	...	1308	1410	1410	...
109	**Pasewalk**	d.	...	...	...	0518	0518	0544j	0544	...	...	0744j	0837	...	0944j	...	1039	...	1144j	1238	...	1344j	1440	1440	...
133	Prenzlau	d.	...	...	...	0535	0535	0601	0601	...	...	0801	0853	...	1001	...	1055	...	1201	1254	...	1401	1457	1457	...
	Schwedt (Oder)	d.	...	...	0506	|	|	|	|	...	0706	|	|	0906	|	...	|	1106	|	|	1306	|	|	|	1506
170	Angermünde	a.	...	...	0528	0603	0603	0628	0628	...	0728	0828	0914	0928	1028	...	1117	1128	1228	1316	1328	1428	1518	1518	1528
170	Angermünde	d.	0427	...	0533	0605	0605	0633	0633	0706	0733	0833	0916	0933	1033	1106	1119	1133	1233	1318	1333	1433	1520	1520	1533
196	Eberswalde Hbf	d.	0448	0448	0553	0627	0627	0652	0652	0723	0753	0852	0933	0953	1052	1123	1136	1153	1252	1335	1353	1452	1837	1537	1553
218	Bernau (b. Berlin)	d.	0509	0509	0607	0644	0644	0707	0707	0739	0807	0907	|	1007	1107	1137	|	1207	1307	|	1407	1507	|	|	1607
239	**Berlin** Gesundbrunnen	d.	0525	0525	0625	0659	0659	0724	0724	0754	0825	0925	1002a	1025	1125	1154t	1202a	1225	1325	1407	1426	1525	1608	1604a	1625
243	**Berlin** Hbf	a.	0529	0529	0630	0704	0704	0729	0729	...	0830	0929	1012	1030	1129	...	1213	1230	1329	1412	1430	1529	1612	1613	1630
243	**Berlin** Hbf 850	d.	0531	0531	0632	0709	0709	0731	0731	...	0832	0931	|	1032	1131	...	|	1232	1331	1430	1432	1534	1614	|	1632
249	**Berlin** Südkreuz 850	d.	0544j	0544j	0641	0717	0717	0747	0747	...	0841	0947j	1020	1041	1147j	...	1220	1241	1347j	1437	1441	1547	1619	1628	1641
295	Luckenwalde	d.	0618	0618	0714	...	...	0821	0821	...	0912	1021	...	1112	1221	...	...	1312	1421	|	1512	1621	...	...	1712
308	Jüterbog	d.	0627	0627	0723	...	...	0831	0831	...	0921	1032	...	1121	1231	...	...	1321	1431	|	1521	1631	...	...	1721
357	**Falkenberg** (Elster)	a.	0706	0706	|	...	...	0910	0910	...	|	1110	...	|	1310	...	...	|	1510	|	|	1710	...	...	|
	Lutherstadt Wittenberg .. 850	a.	...	...	0755	...	...	...	...	...	0955	...	...	1155	...	...	...	1356	...	1510	1555	...	...	...	1755

			ICE 750 ⑦ D✕	*ICE* 1715 ⑥ J✕		⑤Y S		*ICE* 1132 ⑦b A	*ICE* 1132 ⑦ T	⊗		⑥		*IC* 2216 Ⓑ N	S	*ICE* 1048 ⑥ O✕	⊗	⑦–④ h	⑤⑥ d				①–⑥ v	⑤⑥ d	⑦ w
Stralsund Hbf 846	d.	1413	1505	1525	...	...	1613	1702	1702	...	1814	1814	...	1824	...	1924	...	2005	2013	...	...	...	2217	2217	2234
Greifswald 846	d.	1438	1528	1547	...	...	1639	1724	1724	...	1839	1839	...	1848	...	1946	...	2038j	2037	...	...	...	2242	2242	2258
Züssow 846	d.	1455	1551	1602	...	...	1655	|	|	...	1855	1855	...	...	...	1959	...	2055	2055	...	...	...	2259	2259	2314
Anklam	d.	1508	1603	1614	...	...	1708	1746	1746	...	1908	1908	...	...	...	2011	...	2108	2108	...	...	...	2311	2311	2327
Pasewalk	d.	1544j	1629	1640	...	...	1744j	1812	1812	...	1944j	1944j	...	...	...	2038	...	2144j	2144j	...	...	...	2341	2344	2357
Prenzlau	d.	1601	1645	1657	...	...	1801	1828	1828	...	2001	2001	...	...	...	2055	...	2201	2201	...	...	...	▬	0001	...
Schwedt (Oder)	d.	|	|	|	1706	...	|	|	|	1906	|	|	...	...	...	|	2106	|	|	...	2306	...	...	|	...
Angermünde	a.	1628	|	1719	1728	...	1828	|	|	1928	2028	2028	...	...	...	2118	2128	2228	2228	...	2328	...	...	0028	...
Angermünde	d.	1633	|	1721	1733	1809	1833	|	|	1933	2033	2033	...	...	2046	2120	2133	2233	2233	...	2333	...	...	0033	...
Eberswalde Hbf	d.	1652	1723	1738	1753	1826	1852	1906	1906	1953	2052	2052	...	...	2104	|	2153	2252	2252	...	2353	...	...	0052	...
Bernau (b. Berlin)	d.	1707	|	1754	1807	1841	1907	|	|	2007	2107	2107	...	...	2118	|	2207	2312	2312	...	0007	...	...	0112	...
Berlin Gesundbrunnen	d.	1724	1748	1813	1825	1855	1925	1933	1933a	2023	2123	2123	...	...	2134	2202a	2223	2329	2329	...	0023	...	Ⓒ	0129	...
Berlin Hbf	a.	1729	...	1817	1830	...	1929	...	1944	2027	2127	2127	...	...	...	2211	2227	2334	2334	...	0028	...	H	0134	...
Berlin Hbf 850	d.	1738	...	1830	1832	...	1932	...	...	2032	...	2135	2135	...	...	|	2233	...	...	2343	...	0042	0042	...	...
Berlin Südkreuz 850	d.	1747	...	1837	1841	...	1942	...	...	2041	...	2147	2147	...	...	2219	2242	...	...	2352	...	0051	0051	...	...
Luckenwalde	d.	1821	...	|	1912	...	2021	...	...	2112	...	2221	2221	...	...	...	2326	...	...	0031	...	0134	0134	...	...
Jüterbog	d.	1831	...	|	1921	...	2031	...	...	2121	...	2231	2231	...	...	...	2335	...	...	0038	...	0141	0142	...	...
Falkenberg (Elster)	a.	1910	...	|	|	...	2110	...	...	|	...	2310	2310	...	...	...	|	...	...	...	...	...	|	...	...
Lutherstadt Wittenberg .. 850	a.	...	...	1910	1956	...	...	...	...	2149	...	...	...	...	...	...	0002	...	...	...	...	...	0158	...	...

A – (12) Stralsund - Berlin - Hannover - Bremen - Oldenburg.
B – POMMERSCHE BUCHT – (12) ✕ Jena - Leipzig - Berlin - Ostseebad Binz.
D – To Hannover / Köln (Table **810**). Until July 10 calls additionally at Bernau (d. 1740), then Berlin Gesundbrunnen a. 1752.
G – From Halle on Ⓒ (Table **848**).
H – To Halle (Table **848**).
J – (12) ✕ Ostseebad Binz - Berlin - Leipzig - München and v.v.
K – (12) ✕ Köln - Hannover - Berlin - Stralsund - Ostseebad Binz. July 18 - Oct. 1 starts from Berlin and runs with train number **659**.
L – (12) ✕ München - Nürnberg - Halle - Berlin - Stralsund.
M – (12) Dresden - Berlin - Ostseebad Binz and v.v.
N – GREIFSWALDER BODDEN – (12) Greifswald - Hamburg - Köln - Stuttgart and v.v.

O – To / from Ostseebad Binz (Table **844**).
P – From Dresden (Table **840**).
S – To / from Szczecin (Table **949**).
T – July 24 - Sept. 25.
Y – Until July 16.

a – Arrival time. Calls to set down only.
b – Not July 24 - Sept. 25.
d – Also Oct. 2.
g – Also Oct. 4; not Oct. 3.
h – Not Oct. 2.
j – Arrives 6 – 9 minutes earlier.

r – Arrives 11 – 14 minutes earlier.
t – Until July 16. From July 17 diverted to Berlin **Lichtenberg** (a. 1204).
v – Also Oct. 2; not Oct. 3.
w – Also Oct. 3; not Oct. 2.
z – Arrives 1411.

⊗ – Change trains at Berlin Hbf on ①–④.
⊠ – On ⑥ from July 23 train *ICE* **1711** runs Ostseebad Binz - Berlin Hbf only (change at Berlin Hbf to train *ICE* **1601** for journeys to Lutherstadt Wittenberg and beyond in the same timings).

846 ZÜSSOW - ŚWINOUJŚCIE

2nd class only

km						⊗								①–⑥	⑦
0	**Züssow** d.	...	0508	and	1508	1608	1708	1808	...	1908	2008	...	2108	2208	2308	2320
18	Wolgast d.	0430	0530		1530	1630	1730	1830	...	1930	2030	...	2130	2230	2330	2338
28	Zinnowitz ▲ d.	0449	0549	hourly	1549	1649	1749	1849	...	1949	2049	...	2149	2249	2349	2355
55	Seebad Heringsdorf a.	0525	0625		1625	1725	1825	1925	1930	2025	2125	2130	2225	2325	0025	0028
57	Seebad Ahlbeck a.	0534	0634	until	1634	1734	1834	...	1934	2034	...	2134	2234	...	...	...
61	**Świnoujście** Centrum a.	0539	0639		1639	1739	1839	...	1939	2039	...	2139	2239	...	...	...

				Ⓐt	Ⓒz		✧								
Świnoujście Centrum d.	...	...	0518	0555	0618	0718		1918	2018	2118	2218	2318	...	...	...
Seebad Ahlbeck d.	...	...	0524	0601	0624	0724	and	1924	2024	2124	2224	2324	...	...	...
Seebad Heringsdorf d.	...	0433	0533	0610	0633	0733		1933	2033	2133	2233	2328	...	...	...
Zinnowitz ▲ d.	...	0511	0611	0650	0711	0811	hourly	2011	2111	2211	2311	...	...	...	...
Wolgast d.	0430	0530	0630	0730‡	0730	0830	until	2030	2130	2230	2325	...	...	...	...
Züssow a.	0448	0548	0648	0748	0748	0848		2048	2148	2248	...	...	...	...	...

t – Not Oct. 31. **z** – Also Oct. 31.
⊗ – Change trains at Seebad Heringsdorf until Oct. 3.
✧ – On ⑥ until Oct. 1 Wolgast d. 1126 (not 1130), Züssow a. 1143 (not 1148).
‡ – Arrives 0704.
▲ – **Zinnowitz - Peenemünde** and v.v. (*12 km* journey 14 minutes). **From Zinnowitz** at 0434 Ⓐ**t**, 0513 Ⓐ**t**, 0613, 0659 Ⓐ**t**, 0713 Ⓒ**z**, 0813, 0913 and hourly until 2113. **From Peenemünde** at 0453 Ⓐ**t**, 0532 Ⓐ**t**, 0632, 0718 Ⓐ**t**, 0732 Ⓒ**z**, 0832, 0932 and hourly until 2132.

847 BERLIN BRANDENBURG ✈ - BERLIN - DESSAU

RE services

km			Ⓐ								†		★											
0	**Flughafen Berlin** ✈ d.	0442	0542	0642	0742	and in	1842	1942	2042	2142	2142	2246	2246		0415	0434	0459		2215	2234	2258	2315	2334	0013
17	**Berlin** Ostkreuz d.	0459	0559	0659	0759		1859	1959	2059	2200	2200	2304	2304	A	0434	0452	0518	and at	2234	2252	2318	2334	2352	0034
19	**Berlin** Ostbahnhof d.	0504	0604	0704	0804	the same	1904	2004	2104	2204	2204	2308	2308	L	|	|	0525		|	|	2325	|	|	0039
	Berlin Gesund ⊡ a.	|	|	|	|	pattern	|	|	|	|	|	|	|	S	0443	0501	|	the same	2243	2301	|	2343	0001	|
24	**Berlin** Hbf d.	0515	0615	0715	0815		1915	2015	2115	2215	2215	2319	2319	O	0448	0506	0537	minutes	2248	2306	2337	2349	0006	0051
28	**Berlin** Zoo d.	0521	0621	0721	0821	every	1921	2021	2121	2221	2221	2324	2324		...	...	0543		...	...	2343	...	...	0055
	Berlin Spandau a.	|	|	|	|	**two** hours	|	|	|	|	|	|	|		...	...	0554	past each	...	...	2354	...	...	...
43	Berlin Wannsee d.	0534	0634	0734	0834		1934	2034	2134	2234	2234	2337	2337		...	...	...	hour until	...	...	...	...	...	...
95	Bad Belzig d.	0619	0719	0819	0919	until	2019	2119	2219	2317	2319	0019	0021		...	...	...		...	...	...	...	...	...
139	Roßlau (Elbe) **848** d.	0649	0748	0849	0948t		2049	2148t	2249	...	2348	...	0050		...	...	...		...	...	...	...	...	...
144	**Dessau** Hbf **848** a.	0654	0753	0854	0953t		2054	2153t	2253	...	2353	...	0055		...	...	...		...	...	...	...	...	...

												Ⓐ	Ⓒ					⊠						
Dessau Hbf **848** d.	...	0405t	0505v	0605t	0705	0805t	and in	1805t	1905	2005t	2105	2218	2318		...	...	...		...	...	...	...	...	...
Roßlau (Elbe) **848** d.	...	0410t	0510v	0610t	0710	0810t		1810t	1910	2010t	2110	2223	2323		...	...	...	and at	...	...	...	...	...	...
Bad Belzig d.	0341t	0441	0541	0641	0741	0841	the same	1841	1941	2041	2141	2254	2354		...	...	...		...	...	...	...	...	...
Berlin Wannsee d.	0427t	0527	0627	0727	0827	0927	pattern	1927	2027	2127	2227	2339	0039		...	...	...	the same	...	...	...	...	...	...
Berlin Spandau d.	|	|	|	|	|	|		|	|	|	|	|	|		0459	...	...		2059	...	...	...	...	...
Berlin Zoo d.	0440	0540	0640	0740	0840	0940	every	1940	2040	2140	2240	2352	0054	A	0511	...	...	minutes	2111					
Berlin Hbf d.	0446	0546	0646	0746	0846	0946	**two** hours	1946	2046	2146	2246	2358	0100	L	0517	0527	0557	past each	2117	2128	2157	2227	2257	2327
Berlin Gesund ⊡ d.	|	|	|	|	|	|		|	|	|	|	|	|	S	|	0532	0602		|	2133	2202	2232	2302	2332
Berlin Ostbahnhof d.	0457	0557	0657	0757	0857	0957	until	1957	2057	2158	2256	0007	0111	O	0528	|	|	hour until	2128	|	|	|	|	|
Berlin Ostkreuz d.	0502	0602	0702	0802	0902	1002		2002	2102	2202	...	...	0114		0532	0542	0612		2132	2142	2212	2242	2312	2342
Flughafen Berlin ✈ a.	0519	0619	0719	0819	0919	1019		2019	2119	2219	...	...	...		0548	0559	0627		2148	2159	2227	2259	2327	2359

t – Ⓐ only.
v – Not ⑦.
★ – ⑦–④ (not Oct. 2).
⊡ – Berlin Gesundbrunnen.
⊠ – Berlin Hbf d. 2025 (not 2027). Berlin Spandau d. 0955 / 1155 / 1355 / 1555 / 1955 (not xx59) – these five trains also depart Berlin Zoo and Berlin Hbf up to 5 minutes **earlier**.

848 MAGDEBURG - DESSAU - LEIPZIG and HALLE (SAALE)

RE / RB / S-Bahn services

km		ⒸB	Ⓒz		Ⓐt	Ⓒz	Ⓐt	Ⓐt	Ⓒz	Ⓐt	Ⓑ	⑥	Ⓐt	Ⓐt				Ⓐt	Ⓐt	Ⓐt					
0	**Magdeburg** Hbf d.	...	...	...	...	...	...	...	...	0432	...	...	...	...	0513	...	...	...	...	...	0613	...	...	0713	...
56	Roßlau (Elbe) **847** d.	...	...	...	...	...	0440	...	...	0515	...	...	...	0540	0604	...	...	0626	0644	...	0704	...	...	0804	...
61	**Dessau** Hbf **847** a.	...	...	...	...	...	0444	...	...	0519	...	...	...	0545	0609	...	...	0632	0647	...	0709	...	...	0809	...
61	**Dessau** Hbf d.	0224	...	0416	...	...	0449	...	0518	0523	...	...	...	0547	0611	0617	...	0636	0649	...	0711	0719	...	0811	...
	Lutherstadt W ⊡ d.	|	...	|	...	0413	|	0440	|	|	...	0503	0542	|	|	|	0603	|	|	...	|	|	0704	|	0803
87	Bitterfeld a.	0240	...	0439	...	0441	0511	0508	0541	0541	...	0540	0610	0610	0628	0640	0643	0659	0711	...	0728	0742	0740	0828	0843
87	Bitterfeld d.	0241	0247	0446	0442	0445	0512	0516	0545	0545	0546	0547	0613	0616	0631	0646	0645	0701	0712	0716	0731	0745	0747	0831	0845
	Halle (Saale) Hbf a.	0258	|	0507	|	|	|	0537	|	|	0607	0607	|	0637	|	0708	|	0718	|	0737	|	|	0807	|	|
120	**Leipzig** Hbf a.	...	0314	...	0513	0513	0543	...	0613	0613	...	...	0643	...	0656	...	0713	...	0743	...	0756	0813	...	0856	0913
127	Leipzig-Stötteritz ★ a.	...	0326	...	0527	0527	0557	...	0627	0627	...	...	0657	...	...	...	0727	...	0757	...	...	0827	...	...	0927

					✧																			
Magdeburg Hbf d.	...	0813	...	...	and in	1613	...	...	1713	...	...	1813	...	...	1913	...	...	2013	...	...	2104	...	2203	2313
Roßlau (Elbe) **847** d.	...	0904	...	...		1704	...	...	1804	...	...	1904	...	...	2004	...	...	2104	...	...	2152	...	2252	0004
Dessau Hbf **847** a.	...	0909	...	...	the same	1709	...	...	1809	...	...	1909	...	...	2009	...	...	2109	...	...	2157	...	2256	0009
Dessau Hbf d.	0819	0911	0919	...		1711	1719	...	1811	...	1819	1911	1919	...	2011	...	2019	2111	2119	...	2158	...	2258	—
Lutherstadt W ⊡ d.	|	|	|	0903	pattern	|	|	1704	|	1803	|	|	|	1904	|	2016	|	|	|	2103	|	2216	|	...
Bitterfeld a.	0842	0928	0942	0940	every	1728	1742	1740	1828	1843	1842	1928	1942	1940	2028	2043	2042	2128	2142	2140	2221	2244	2318	...
Bitterfeld d.	0847	0931	0945	0947	**two** hours	1731	1745	1747	1831	1845	1847	1931	1945	1947	2031	2045	2047	2131	2145	2147	2222	2247	2319	2324
Halle (Saale) Hbf a.	0907	|	|	1007		|	|	1807	|	|	1907	|	|	2007	|	|	2107	|	|	2207	|	2307	|	2345
Leipzig Hbf a.	...	0956	1013	...	until	1756	1813	...	1856	1913	...	1958	2013	...	2056	2113	...	2159	2213	...	2244	...	2346	...
Leipzig-Stötteritz ★ a.	...	...	1027	...		...	1827	...	...	1927	...	...	2027	...	...	2127	...	...	2227	...	...	...	2359	...

	Ⓒz	Ⓒz	Ⓐt		Ⓐt	Ⓐt				ⒸA	Ⓐt									◇				
Leipzig-Stötteritz ★ d.	...	0006	...	...	...	...	...	0434	...	...	...	0534	...	...	0634	...	...	0734	...	and in	...	...	1434	...
Leipzig Hbf d.	...	0020	...	...	...	...	...	0448	0502	...	...	0548	0603	...	0648	0704	...	0748	0804		1404	...	1448	1504
Halle (Saale) Hbf d.	0026	|	...	...	0355	0355	0452	|	|	0551	0553	|	|	0652	|	|	0752	|	|	the same	|	1452	|	|
Bitterfeld a.	0046	0046	...	...	0416	0416	0513	0515	0523	0614	0613	0615	0625	0713	0715	0725	0813	0815	0825		1425	1513	1515	1525
Bitterfeld d.	0051	0051	...	...	0418	0421	0518	0516	0527	0620	0620	0618	0627	0718	0716	0727	0820	0818	0827	pattern	1427	1518	1516	1527
Lutherstadt W ⊡ a.	0120	|	...	...	|	0450	|	0550	|	0658	0655	|	|	|	0757	|	0855	|	|	every	|	|	1556	|
Dessau Hbf a.	...	0114	...	...	0442	...	0542	...	0547	...	...	0642	0647	0742	...	0747	...	0842	0847	**two** hours	1447	1542	...	1547
Dessau Hbf **847** d.	...	...	0356	0449	0449	...	...	...	0549	...	...	...	0649	...	...	0749	...	...	0849		1449	...	...	1549
Roßlau (Elbe) **847** d.	...	...	0401	0454	0454	...	...	...	0554	...	...	...	0654	...	...	0754	...	...	0854	until	1454	...	...	1554
Magdeburg Hbf a.	...	...	0451	0544	0544	...	...	...	0644	...	...	...	0744	...	...	0844	...	...	0944		1544	...	...	1644

			†E	G	Ⓐt																				
Leipzig-Stötteritz ★ d.	...	1534	...	...	1604	...	1634	...	...	1734	...	...	1834	...	...	1934	...	...	2034	2104	...	2204	2204	...	2306
Leipzig Hbf d.	...	1548	1546	1604	1618	...	1648	1704	...	1748	1804	...	1848	1904	...	1948	2004	...	2048	2118	...	2218	2218	...	2320
Halle (Saale) Hbf d.	1552	|	|	|	|	1652	|	|	1752	|	|	1852	|	|	1952	|	|	2052	|	|	2202	|	|	2326	|
Bitterfeld a.	1613	1615	1608	1625	1647	1713	1715	1725	1813	1815	1825	1913	1915	1925	2013	2015	2025	2113	2115	2147	2225	2247	2247	2346	2346
Bitterfeld d.	1620	1618	1610	1627	1648	1718	1716	1727	1820	1818	1827	1918	1916	1927	2020	2018	2027	2118	2116	2149	...	2249	2252	2351	2351
Lutherstadt W ⊡ a.	1655	|	|	|	|	|	1756	|	1855	|	|	|	1957	|	2055	|	|	|	2157	|	...	|	2328	|	0020
Dessau Hbf a.	...	1642	1628	1647	1708	1742	...	1747	...	1842	1847	1942	...	1947	...	2042	2047	2142	...	2212	...	2312	...	0015	...
Dessau Hbf **847** d.	...	...	1650	1649	1710	...	...	1749	...	...	1849	...	...	1949	...	...	2049	...	...	2214	...	2314	...	...	...
Roßlau (Elbe) **847** d.	...	...	1654	1654	1714	...	...	1754	...	...	1854	...	...	1954	...	...	2054	...	...	2218	...	2318	...	...	...
Magdeburg Hbf a.	...	...	1744	1744	...	...	...	1844	...	...	1944	...	...	2044	...	...	2144	...	...	2300	...	0008	...	...	...

km		ⒸB	Ⓐt	Ⓐt	Ⓒz	Ⓐt	⚒t	Ⓐt				Ⓐt		D	⑤F		Ⓐt						
0	**Lutherstadt Wittenberg** d.	0159	0411	0502	0516	0557	0616	0652	0716	and	1416	1452	1516	1545	1552	1616	1652	1716	1816	1916	2016	...	2216
32	Roßlau (Elbe) d.	|	0440	0532	0544	0626	0644	0717	0744	hourly	1444	1517	1544	1610	1617	1644	1717	1744	1844	1944	2044	...	2244
37	**Dessau** Hbf a.	0223	0444	0536	0549	0632	0647	0721	0749	until	1449	1521	1549	1614	1621	1649	1721	1749	1849	1949	2049	...	2249

	Ⓐt	Ⓒz	Ⓐt		Ⓐt		⚒t				Ⓐt		Ⓐt		Ⓐt		Ⓐt					
Dessau Hbf d.	0423	0509	0521	...	0621	0710	0810	0910	and	1410	1432	1510	1532	1610	1632	1710	1732	1810	1910	2010	2110	...	2300
Roßlau (Elbe) d.	0428	0514	0526	...	0626	0714	0814	0914	hourly	1414	1437	1514	1537	1614	1637	1714	1737	1814	1914	2014	2114	...	2304
Lutherstadt Wittenberg a.	0456	0541	0555	...	0655	0742	0842	0942	until	1442	1502	1542	1602	1642	1702	1742	1802	1842	1942	2042	2142	...	2332

A – To Stralsund (Table **845**).
B – From Berlin (Table **847**).
D – ①–④ to Oct. 13 (not Oct. 3); Ⓐ from Oct. 17 (not Oct. 31).
E – Until Oct. 9.
F – Until Oct. 14.
G – ⚒ until Oct. 8; daily Oct. 10 – 30 and from Nov. 1.
t – Not Oct. 31.
z – Also Oct. 31.
⊡ – Lutherstadt Wittenberg.
◇ – On Ⓐ (not Oct. 31) Halle d. 1350 (not 1352).
✧ – Dessau Hbf d. 1417 (not 1419). On † until Oct. 9 the 1413 from Magdeburg arrives Leipzig 1559.
★ – Trains also call at City Tunnel stations Leipzig Markt, Wilhelm-Leuschner-Platz, Bayerischer Bahnhof and MDR.

Local services HALLE and LEIPZIG - EISENACH and SAALFELD 849

Operated by ABELLIO Rail Mitteldeutschland. See Tables **849a** and **850** for faster *ICE* and *IC* trains.

HALLE / LEIPZIG - ERFURT - EISENACH *See lower panel for other connecting services Halle - Naumburg and v.v.*

km																									
				Ⓐt		Ⓒz	Ⓐt															⊕		⑤⑥f	
0	**Halle** (Saale) Hbf .... d.	...	0057	0417	...	0419	0457	...	0557	...	...	...	0805	...	and in	...	1805	...	...	2005	...	...	...	...	...
	Leipzig Hbf .... d.	0021	|	|	...	|	|	0519	|	0619	0651t	0719	|	0819	the same	1719	|	1819	1919	|	2019	2119	2219	2219	2321
32	Weißenfels .... d.	0100	0127	0448	...	0449	0521	0558	0620	0658	0721t	0758	0828	0858	pattern	1758	1828	1858	1958	2028	2058	2158	2258	2258	0000
46	Naumburg (Saale) Hbf d.	0110	0138	0458	0503	0503	0532	0608	0640r	0708	0732	0808	0838	0908	every	1808	1838	1908	2008	2038	2108	2208	2308	2308	0010
72	Apolda .... d.	...	▬	▬	0525	0525	0552	0629	0700	0729	0753	0829	0857	0929	two hours	1829	1857	1929	2029	2057	2129	2229	2329	2329	0031
87	Weimar .... **858** d.	...	...	...	0537	0537	0603	0642	0713	0742	0804	0842	0909	0942	until	1842	1909	1942	2042	2109	2142	2242	2342	2342	0043
108	**Erfurt** Hbf .... **858** a.	...	Ⓐt	Ⓐt	0552	0552	0619	0656	0728	0758	0818	0858	0922	0958		1858	1922	1958	2058	2122	2158	2258	2358	2358	0059
108	**Erfurt** Hbf .... **865** d.	...	0423	0507	0553	0553	0625	0703	...	0800	...	0905	...	1000		1905	...	2000	2104	...	*2218*	2310	...	0008	...
136	Gotha .... **865** d.	...	0453	0535	0615	0615	0643	0727	...	0821	...	0927	...	1021		1927	...	2021	2126	...	*2240*	2333	...	0030	...
165	**Eisenach** .... a.	...	0519	0559	0636	0636	0706	0749	...	0843	...	0949	...	1043		1949	...	2043	2148	...	*2301*	2355	...	0052	...

			Ⓐt		Ⓐt				⚒v															
Eisenach .... d.	...	...	0410	...	...	0458	...	0606	0643	...	0713	...	0806	0913	...	and in	1606	1713	...	1806	1913	...	2006	2113	2217
Gotha .... **865** d.	...	...	0434	...	...	0522	...	0630	0705	...	0736	...	0830	0936	...	the same	1630	1736	...	1830	1936	...	2030	2136	2244
Erfurt Hbf .... **865** a.	...	...	0456	...	...	0546	...	0653	0728	...	0758	...	0853	0958	...	pattern	1653	1758	...	1853	1959	...	2053	2158	2306
Erfurt Hbf .... **858** d.	...	...	0458	0458	0530	0559	0630	0701	0736	0736	0801	0837	0901	1001	1037	every	1701	1801	1837	1901	2001	2036	2102	2201	2318
Weimar .... **858** d.	...	...	0517	0517	0545	0617	0643	0718	0752	0752	0818	0852	0918	1018	1052	two hours	1718	1818	1852	1918	2018	2052	2119	2218	2335
Apolda .... d.	...	...	0529	0529	0555	0629	0653	0729	0803	0803	0829	0902	0929	1029	1102	until	1729	1829	1902	1929	2029	2102	2130	2229	2346
Naumburg (Saale) Hbf d.	0446	0446	0552	0552	0615	0652	0713	0752	0822	0822	0852	0922	0952	1052	1122		1752	1852	1922	1952	2052	2122	2152	2252	0009
Weißenfels .... d.	0457	0457	0602	0602	0625	0702	0722	0802	0832	0832	0902	0932	1002	1102	1132		1802	1902	1932	2002	2102	2131	2202	2302	0020
Leipzig Hbf .... a.	|	0541	0639	0639	0702	0739	|	0839	|	|	0939	|	1039	1139	|		1839	1939	|	2039	2139	|	2239	2339	|
Halle (Saale) Hbf .... a.	0528	...	...	...	...	...	0748	...	0855	0855	...	0956	...	...	1156		...	...	1956	...	...	2155	...	...	0050

HALLE / LEIPZIG - JENA - SAALFELD *See upper panel for other connecting services Leipzig - Naumburg and v.v.*

km																									
		Ⓐ	Ⓒ																	B					⑤⑥
	Halle (Saale) Hbf .... d.	...	...	0523	...	0623	0705	0723	...	0823	and in	...	1623	1705	1723	...	1823	1905	1923	...	2023	2123	2223	2323	2323
0	**Leipzig** Hbf .... d.	...	...	|	0558	|	|	|	0809	|	the same	1609	|	|	|	1809	|	|	|	2009	|	|	|	|	|
40	Weißenfels .... d.	...	...	0552	0626	0652	0730	0752	0840	0852	pattern	1640	1652	1730	1752	1840	1852	1930	1952	2040	2052	2152	2252	2352	2352
56	Naumburg (Saale) Hbf a.	...	...	0603	0634	0703	0739	0803	0848	0903	every	1648	1703	1739	1803	1848	1903	1939	2003	2048	2103	2203	2303	0003	0003
56	Naumburg (Saale) Hbf d.	...	...	0613	0635	0713	0740	0813	0850	0913	two hours	1650	1713	1740	1813	1850	1913	1940	2013	2050	2113	2213	2313	0013	0013
95	**Jena** Paradies .... d.	0509	0616	0646	0708	0746	0808	0846	0917	0946	until	1717	1746	1808	1846	1917	1946	2008	2046	2117	2146	2246	2346	0045	0045
100	Jena-Göschwitz .... d.	0513	0621	0650	0713	0750	0814	0850	0922	0950		1722	1750	1814	1850	1922	1950	2014	2050	2122	2150	2250	2350	0050	0053
132	Rudolstadt (Thür) .... d.	0539	0642	0716	0740	0816	...	0916	0943	1016		1743	1816	...	1916	1943	2016	...	2116	2143	2216	2316	0016	...	0119
142	**Saalfeld** (Saale) .... a.	0548	0651	0725	0750	0825	...	0925	0951	1025		1751	1825	...	1925	1951	2025	...	2125	2151	2225	2325	0025	...	0128
	Nürnberg Hbf **875** .. a.	0848**k**	0919	...	1018	...	...	...	1219	...		2019	...	...	...	2220**c**	...	...	...	...	...	...	...	...	...

		Ⓐt										❖										⑤⑥f	A	⑤⑥
Nürnberg Hbf **875** ... d.	...	...	...	...	...	...	0529	...	...	...	0738	and in	...	1538	...	...	...	1740	...	...	...	1938	...	...	...
Saalfeld (Saale) .... d.	0430	...	0523	...	0633	0733	0810	0833	...	0933	1003	the same	1733	1803	1833	...	1933	2003	2033	...	2133	2207	2233	2233	2333
Rudolstadt (Thür) .... d.	0439	...	0531	...	0642	0742	0820	0842	...	0942	1012	pattern	1742	1812	1842	...	1942	2012	2042	...	2142	2216	2242	2242	2342
Jena-Göschwitz .... d.	0505	0547	0558	0606	0708	0808	0842	0908	0944	1008	1034	every	1808	1834	1908	1944	2008	2034	2108	2144	2208	2238	2308	2308	0008
Jena Paradies .... d.	0511	0553	0603	0614	0714	0814	0848	0914	0950	1014	1040	two hours	1814	1840	1914	1950	2014	2040	2114	2150	2214	2242	2314	2314	0012
Naumburg (Saale) Hbf a.	0542	0624	0629	0647	0747	0847	0914	0947	1016	1047	1106	until	1847	1906	1947	2016	2047	2106	2147	2216	2247	...	2346	2347	...
Naumburg (Saale) Hbf d.	0556	0625	0630	0656	0756	0856	0915	0956	1017	1056	1107		1856	1907	1956	2017	2056	2107	2156	2217	2256	...	2347	...	...
Weißenfels .... d.	0606	0635	0640	0706	0806	0906	0924	1006	1027	1106	1118		1906	1918	2006	2027	2106	2118	2206	2227	2306	...	2357	...	...
Leipzig Hbf .... a.	|	|	0709	|	|	|	0952	|	|	|	1152		|	1952	|	|	|	2152	|	|	|	...	0033	...	...
Halle (Saale) Hbf .... a.	0635	0658	...	0735	0835	0935	...	1035	1051	1135	...		1935	...	2035	2051	2135	...	2235	2251	2335	...	...	...	...

EISENACH - BEBRA *45km.* Journey time: 35 – 48 minutes. Operated by CANTUS Verkehrsgesellschaft (2nd class only).

From Eisenach at 0436 Ⓐ, 0530 Ⓐ, 0613 ⚒, 0713 ⚒, 0813, 0902 ⚒, 1013, 1113 Ⓐ, 1213, 1302 Ⓐ, 1413, 1502 Ⓐ, 1613, 1702 Ⓐ, 1813, 1902 Ⓐ, 2013, 2116 Ⓐ and 2213 Ⓒ.

From Bebra at 0504 Ⓐ, 0559 ⚒, 0704 Ⓒ, 0716 Ⓐ, 0804 ⚒, 0904, 1004 Ⓐ, 1104, 1204 Ⓐ, 1304 Ⓒ, 1315 Ⓐ, 1404 Ⓐ, 1507, 1604 Ⓐ, 1704, 1804 Ⓐ, 1904, 2004 Ⓐ and 2104.

A – ⑦–④ (not Oct. 2, 30).
B – To Bamberg (Table **875**).
c – Ⓒ (also June 16, Nov. 1).
f – Also Oct. 2, 30.

k – Not June 16, Nov. 1.
r – Arrives 0630.
t – Ⓐ (not Oct. 31).
v – Not Oct. 31.
z – Ⓒ (also Oct. 31).

⊕ – Change trains at Erfurt on ①–⑤.
❖ – The 1138 from Nürnberg is retimed as follows: Saalfeld d. 1411, Rudolstadt d. 1421, Jena-Göschwitz d. 1443, Jena Paradies d. 1448, Naumburg a. 1514, d. 1515, Weißenfels d. 1524, Leipzig a. 1552; passengers travelling on this service from Nürnberg must change trains at Kronach (a. 1305, d. 1309) on ⑤ (not June 17, Aug. 5, 12, 19, 26, Sept. 2, 9, Nov. 4).

LEIPZIG - NAUMBURG - WEIMAR - ERFURT - KASSEL and LEIPZIG - JENA - SAALFELD - NÜRNBERG 849a

	IC	*IC*	*IC*	*IC*	*IC*	*IC*	*IC*	*ICE*	*IC*
	2156	**2156**	**2068**	**2152**	**1956**	**1952**	**2150**	**1705**	**95**
	①–⑥	⑦	①–⑥		⑦	⑤⑦	Ⓑ	Ⓑ	
			L		**K** 🍸	**r**		**H** ✕	**T**
Berlin Hbf **850** .... d.	...	...	...	...	...	...	...	1830	2229
Leipzig Hbf .... **849 850** d.	...	...	0749	...	1349	1635	...	1952	0035
Halle (Saale) Hbf... **849 850** d.	...	...	|	...	|	|	...	|	0110
Weißenfels .... **849** d.	...	...	0822**p**	...	1419	1705	...	2021	|
Naumburg (Saale) Hbf ..... **849** d.	...	...	0833	...	1430	1717	...	2031	0143
Jena Paradies...... **849 875** d.	...	...	0900	...	|	|	...	2057	0215
Jena Göschwitz.... **849 875** d.	...	...	0906	...	|	|	...	...	0221
Saalfeld (Saale) .... **849 875** d.	...	...	0934	...	|	|	...	...	0249
Kronach .... **875** d.	...	...	1026	...	|	|	...	...	|
Lichtenfels.................. **875** d.	...	...	1040	...	|	|	...	...	0348
Bamberg .... **850 875** d.	...	...	1057	...	|	|	...	...	0421
Erlangen .... **850 875** d.	...	...	1118	...	|	|	...	...	0442
Nürnberg Hbf ...... **850 875** a.	...	...	1133	...	|	|	...	...	0502
Apolda .... **849** d.	...	...	...	...	1448	1736	...	...	...
Gera Hbf..................... **858** d.	0604	...	...	1204	|	|	1804	...	...
Jena Göschwitz.......... **858** d.	0639	...	...	1239	|	|	1839	...	...
Jena West .... **858** d.	0646	...	...	1246	|	|	1846	...	...
Weimar.................. **849 858** d.	0704	...	...	1304	1500	1747	1904	...	...
Erfurt Hbf......... **849 850 858** a.	0716	...	...	1316	1515	1759	1916	...	...
Erfurt Hbf.............. **849 850** d.	0718	0718	...	1318	1517	1801	1918	...	...
Gotha .... **849 850** a.	0735	0741	...	1335	1535	1814	1935	...	...
Gotha .... **849 850** d.	0748	0748	...	1348	1547	1816	1948	...	...
Eisenach................ **849 850** d.	0804	0804	...	1404	1604	1836	2004	...	...
Frankfurt (Main) Hbf **850**......a.	|	|	...	|	1753**z**	|	|	...	...
Bebra .... **849 901** d.	|	|	...	|	...	1902	2029	...	...
Kassel Wilhelmshöhe..... **901** a.	0900	0900	...	1500	...	1938	2106	...	...
Dortmund Hbf **800 805** ....a.	1114	1114	...	1714	...	2157	...	...	...
Düsseldorf Hbf **800**.............a.	1208	1208	...	1811	...	2256	...	...	...
Köln Hbf **800** ....a.	1239	1239	...	...	...	2326	...	...	...

	IC	*ICE*	*ICE*	*IC*	*IC*	*IC*	*IC*	*IC*	*IC*	*IC*
	94	**698**	**1704**	**2151**	**2155**	**1959**	**1957**	**2161**	**2157**	**2157**
			①–⑤	①–⑥		⑤⑦	⑤f	Ⓑ	⑥	Ⓑ
	U	**M** ✕	**H** ✕			**r**	🍸	**L**		
Köln Hbf **800** ....d.	...	...	...	...	0916	1036	...	...	1519	1519
Düsseldorf Hbf **800**.........d.	...	...	...	...	0943	|	...	...	1543	1543
Dortmund Hbf **800 805** ....d.	...	...	...	...	1044	|	...	...	1641	1641
Kassel Wilhelmshöhe . **901** d.	...	...	...	0649	1257	1419	...	...	1859	1859
Bebra.................... **849 901** d.	...	...	...	0728	|	1503	...	...	|	|
Frankfurt (Main) Hbf **850**..d.	...	0249	...	|	|	|	1538	...	|	|
Eisenach............. **849 850** d.	...	0447	...	0752	1356	1527	1754	...	1956	1956
Gotha .... **849 850** a.	...	0501	...	0807	1410	1540	1819	...	2010	2010
Gotha .... **849 850** d.	...	0503	...	0825	1425	1542	1821	...	2017	2025
Erfurt Hbf............ **849 850** a.	...	0519	...	0842	1442	1558	1837	...	2034	2042
Erfurt Hbf..... **849 850 858** d.	...	0522	...	0844	1444	1600	1841	...	...	2044
Weimar .... **849 858** d.	...	0537	...	0859	1459	1614	1857	...	...	2059
Jena West................ **858** a.	...	|	...	0913	1513	|	|	...	...	2113
Jena Göschwitz .... **858** a.	...	|	...	0919	1519	|	|	...	...	2119
Gera Hbf .... **858** a.	...	|	...	0955	1555	|	|	...	...	2155
Apolda .... **849** d.	...	|	...	▬	...	1625	1909	...	...	...
Nürnberg Hbf... **850 875** d.	0026	|	...	...	...	|	|	1824	...	...
Erlangen........... **850 875** d.	0043	|	...	...	...	|	|	1839	...	...
Bamberg........... **850 875** d.	0105	|	...	*ICE*	...	|	|	1900	...	...
Lichtenfels............... **875** d.	0126	|	...	**1714**	...	|	|	1917	...	...
Kronach.................. **875** d.	|	|	...	⑥	...	|	|	1933	...	...
Saalfeld (Saale). **849 875** d.	0236	|	...	**O**	...	|	|	2023	...	...
Jena Göschwitz **849 875** d.	0303	|	...	✕	...	|	|	2054	...	...
Jena Paradies .. **849 875** d.	0311	|	0659	0659	...	|	|	2100	...	...
Naumburg (Saale) Hbf . **849** d.	0339	0605	0726	0726	...	1643	1927	2127	...	...
Weißenfels.................. **849** d.	|	|	0735	0735	...	1653	1937	2137	...	...
Halle (Saale) Hbf **849 850** a.	0411	0638	|	|	...	|	|	|	...	...
Leipzig Hbf .... **849 850** a.	0450	|	0802	0802	...	1722	2005	2206	...	...
Berlin Hbf **850** ....a.	0631	0758	0930	0930	...	...	...	...	...	...

H – To / from Hamburg (Table **840**).
K – To Karlsruhe (Table **912**).
L – SAALETAL – To / from Karlsruhe via Stuttgart (Tables **925/931**).
M – From München via Stuttgart (Table **930**).
O – To Ostseebad Binz (Tables **844** and **845**).
T – From Rostock (Table **835**) on Ⓑ. To Wien via Passau (Tables **920** and **950**).
U – From Wien via Passau (Tables **920** and **950**). To Warnemünde (Table **835**) on ①–⑥.

f – Also June 15; not June 17.
p – Until Aug. 9.
r – Also June 15.
z – Frankfurt (Main) **Süd**.

850 BERLIN - HALLE / LEIPZIG - ERFURT - FRANKFURT / NÜRNBERG

See Table **902** for other services Berlin - Frankfurt via Braunschweig. See Table **927** for services operated by FlixTrain.

Other regional services: Table **845** Berlin - Lutherstadt Wittenberg. Table **848** Lutherstadt Wittenberg - Bitterfeld - Leipzig / Halle. Table **849** Leipzig / Halle - Weimar - Erfurt - Eisenach.

km		*IC* 1950	*IC* 1950		*ICE* 1658	*ICE* 1656	*ICE* 1501	*ICE* 501	*ICE* 593	*ICE* 1701	*ICE* 1001	*ICE* 938	*ICE* 1654	*ICE* 503	*ICE* 936	*ICE* 595	*ICE* 701	*ICE* 1003	*ICE* 1652	*ICE* 505	*ICE* 934	*ICE* 597	*ICE* 703
		①	Ⓐ d		①–⑤	①–⑥	Ⓐ t	①–⑥		①–⑤		①–⑤			①–⑤						⑥⑦		
		⊙△	△		✕	✕	L✕	✕	M✕	✕	✕	✕	✕	✕	✕	M✕	✕	✕	✕	✕	✕	M✕	✕
	Hamburg Hbf **840** d.	...	...	...	...	...	...	...	...	...	...	...	...	...	...	...	0527v	0552	...	0634e	...	...	0736
0	**Berlin** Hbf d.	0027	...	...	...	...	...	0430	0528	0534	0601	0601	...	0630	0704	0728	0737	0805	...	0830	0904	0928	0937
6	**Berlin** Südkreuz d.	0034	...	...	...	...	...	0437	0535	0541	0608	0608	...	0637	0711	0735	0744	0811	...	0837	0911	0935	0944
97	Lutherstadt Wittenberg d.	0112	...	...	...	...	...	0511	0610	|	|	|	...	0711	|	0810	|	|	...	0911	|	1010	|
134	Bitterfeld d.	0131	...	...	...	...	...	|	|	0633	|	|	...	|	|	|	0833	|	...	|	|	|	1033
	Halle (Saale) Hbf d.	0151	...	...	...	...	...	|	|	0652	0712	0712	...	|	0818	|	0852	0918	...	|	1018	|	1052
	Dresden Hbf **842** d.	|	...	...	...	...	...	|	|	|	|	|	0612	|	|	|	|	|	0812	|	|	|	|
167	**Leipzig** Hbf a.	0213	...	...	...	...	...	0542	0642	|	|	|	0723	0742	|	0842	|	|	0923	0942	|	1042	|
167	**Leipzig** Hbf d.	0234	...	...	...	0533	...	0548	0648	|	|	|	0733	0748	|	0848	|	|	0933	0948	|	1048	|
287	**Erfurt** Hbf a.	0350	...	...	...	0615	...	0629	0728	0724p	0740	0740	0815	0829	0848	0928	0924p	0945	1015	1029	1048	1128	1124p
287	**Erfurt** Hbf **849a** d.	0357	0357	...	0514	0617	...	0631	0730	0732	0745	0751	0817	0831	0850	0930	0932	0947	1017	1031	1050	1130	1132
	Coburg **875** d.	|	|	...	|	|	...	0704	|	|	|	|	|	|	|	|	|	|	|	|	|	|	|
	Bamberg **875** d.	|	|	...	|	|	0643	0728	|	0818	|	|	|	0917	|	|	1017	|	|	1117	|	|	1217
	Erlangen **875** d.	|	|	...	|	|	0708	0753	|	|	|	|	|	0937	|	|	|	|	|	1137	|	|	|
	Nürnberg Hbf **875** a.	|	|	...	|	|	0725	0808	|	0852	0856	|	|	0953	|	|	1052	1056	|	1153	|	|	1250
	München Hbf **904 905** a.	|	|	...	|	|	0841	0917	|	1042	1002	|	|	1102	|	|	1242	1201	|	1302	|	|	1404
315	Gotha **849a** d.	0416	0416	...	0530	0633	...	...	|	...	...	|	0833	...	|	|	...	...	1033	...	|	|	...
344	**Eisenach** **849a** d.	0432	0432	...	0547	0648	...	...	0755	...	...	|	0848	...	|	0956	...	...	1048	...	|	1155	...
401	Bad Hersfeld d.	0508	0508	...	0616	0716	...	...	|	...	...	|	0916	...	|	|	...	...	1116	...	|	|	...
443	Fulda **900/1/2** d.	0540	0540	...	0644	0743	...	...	0850	...	...	|	0943	...	|	1050	...	...	1143	...	|	1250	...
543	**Frankfurt** (Main) Süd **901** a.	|	|	...	0739	|	...	...	|	...	...	|	|	...	|	|	...	...	|	...	|	|	...
547	**Frankfurt** (Main) Hbf **900/1/2** ◇ a.	0640	0640	...	|	0836	...	...	0944	...	...	0956	1036	...	1056	1144	...	...	1236	...	1256	1344	...
558	**Frankfurt** Flughafen ✈ § ◇ a.	...	...	...	0751	0855	...	...	|	...	...	...	1055	...	...	|	...	...	1256	...	...	|	...
	Stuttgart Hbf **912** a.	...	...	...	...	|	...	...	1108	...	...	...	|	...	...	1308	...	...	|	...	...	1508	...
586	**Mainz** Hbf ◇ a.	...	...	...	...	0915	...	...	...	...	...	...	1115	...	...	...	...	...	1315	...	...	...	...
596	**Wiesbaden** Hbf ◇ a.	...	...	...	...	0933	...	...	...	...	...	...	1133	...	...	...	...	...	1333	...	...	...	...

	ICE 93	*ICE* 1093	*ICE* 1650	*ICE* 507	*ICE* 932	*ICE* 599	*ICE* 705	*ICE* 1005	*ICE* 1558	*ICE* 509	*ICE* 1630	*ICE* 930	*IC* 1956	*ICE* 691	*IC* 1956	*ICE* 707	*ICE* 1556	*ICE* 1505	*ICE* 1205	*ICE* 1601	*ICE* 1711	*ICE* 838	*ICE* 693
											⑥	Ⓑ	⑦		⑦			⑦–④			D		
	A✕	✕	✕	✕	✕	M✕	✕	✕	✕	✕	U✕	✕	G🍷	M✕	G🍷	✕	✕	✕	B✕	✕	O✕	✕	M✕
Hamburg Hbf **840** d.	0804	...	...	0834	...	...	0936	1005	...	1034	...	...	...	...	...	1136	...	1204	1204	1234	...	...	...
Berlin Hbf d.	1004	1004	...	1030	1104	1128	1137	1205	...	1230	1304	1304	...	1328	...	1337	...	1404	1404	1430	1430	1504	1528
Berlin Südkreuz d.	1011	1011	...	1037	1111	1135	1144	1211	...	1237	1311	1311	...	1335	...	1344	...	1411	1411	1437	1437	1511	1535
Lutherstadt Wittenberg d.	|	|	...	1111	|	1210	|	|	...	1311	|	|	...	1410	...	|	...	|	|	1511	1511	|	1610
Bitterfeld d.	|	|	...	|	|	|	1233	|	...	|	|	|	...	|	...	1433	...	|	|	|	|	|	|
Halle (Saale) Hbf d.	1118	1118	...	|	1218	|	1252	1318	...	|	1415	1418	...	|	...	1452	...	1518	1518	|	|	1618	|
Dresden Hbf **842** d.	|	|	1012	|	|	|	|	|	1212	|	|	|	...	|	...	|	1412	|	|	|	|	|	|
Leipzig Hbf a.	|	|	1123	1142	|	1242	|	|	1323	1342	|	|	...	1442	...	|	1523	|	|	1542	1542	|	1642
Leipzig Hbf d.	|	|	1133	1148	|	1248	|	|	1333	1348	|	|	1349	1448	...	|	1533	|	|	1548	1548	|	1648
Erfurt Hbf a.	1152	1152	1215	1229	1248	1328	1324p	1345	1415	1429	1448	1448	1515	1528	...	1524p	1615	1552	1552	1629	1629	1648	1728
Erfurt Hbf **849a** d.	1154	1154	1217	1231	1250	1330	1332	1347	1417	1431	1450	1450	1517	1530	...	1532	1617	1554	1554	1631	1631	1650	1730
Coburg **875** d.	1229	1229	|	|	|	|	|	|	|	|	|	|	|	|	...	|	|	1629	1629	|	|	|	|
Bamberg **875** d.	|	|	|	1317	|	|	1417	|	|	1516	|	|	|	|	...	1617	|	|	|	|	|	|	|
Erlangen **875** d.	|	|	|	1337	|	|	|	|	|	1537	|	|	|	|	...	|	|	|	|	1738	1738	|	|
Nürnberg Hbf **875** a.	1324	1324	|	1353	|	|	1452	1456	|	1552	|	|	|	|	...	1652	|	1724	1724	1753	1753	|	|
München Hbf **904 905** a.	...	1517	|	1501	|	|	1642	1602	|	1702	|	|	|	|	←	1803	|	1838	1916	1903	1903	|	|
Gotha **849a** d.	...	...	1233	...	|	|	...	...	1433	...	|	|	1535	|	1547	...	1633	...	...	...	...	|	|
Eisenach **849a** d.	...	...	1248	...	|	1356	...	...	1448	...	|	|	→	1555	1604	...	1648	...	...	...	...	|	1755
Bad Hersfeld d.	...	...	1316	...	|	|	...	...	1516	...	|	|	...	|	1631	...	1716	...	...	...	...	|	|
Fulda **900/1/2** d.	...	...	1343	...	|	1450	...	...	1543	...	|	|	...	1650	1700	...	1743	...	...	...	...	|	1850
Frankfurt (Main) Süd **901** a.	...	...	|	...	|	|	...	...	|	...	|	|	...	|	1753	...	|	...	...	...	...	|	|
Frankfurt (Main) Hbf **900/1/2** ◇ a.	...	...	1436	...	1456	1544	...	...	1636	...	1656	1656	...	1744	...	...	1836	...	...	...	...	1856	1944
Frankfurt Flughafen ✈ § ◇ a.	...	...	1456	...	...	|	...	...	1655	...	...	...	...	|	...	...	1856	...	...	...	...	...	|
Stuttgart Hbf **912** a.	...	...	|	...	...	1708	...	...	|	...	...	...	...	1908	...	...	|	...	...	...	...	...	2108
Mainz Hbf ◇ a.	...	...	1515	...	...	...	...	...	1715	...	...	...	...	...	...	...	1915	...	...	...	...	...	...
Wiesbaden Hbf ◇ a.	...	...	1533	...	...	...	...	...	1733	...	...	...	...	...	...	...	1933	...	...	...	...	...	...

	ICE 709	*ICE* 1007	*ICE* 1554	*ICE* 603	*ICE* 836	*ICE* 695	*ICE* 801	*ICE* 1009	*ICE* 1552	*ICE* 1715	*ICE* 1605	*ICE* 1705	*ICE* 834	*ICE* 887	*ICE* 887	*ICE* 803	*ICE* 1109	*ICE* 1550	*ICE* 1607	*ICE* 1607	*ICE* 1607	*ICE* 699	*IC* 95
										⑥	Ⓑ	Ⓑ		Ⓑ	⑥			Ⓑ		Ⓑ	⑤		
	✕	✕	✕	✕	S✕	M✕	K✕	✕	✕	O✕	✕	J✕	✕			✕	✕	‡✕	✕	✕	✕	M	T
Hamburg Hbf **840** d.	1336	1404	...	1435	1451	...	1536	1550	...	...	1634	1634	...	1928	1928	1735	...	...	1835	1835	1835	1936	...
Berlin Hbf d.	1537	1605	...	1630	1704	1728	1736	1805	...	1830	1830	1830	1904	|	|	1926	2005	...	2030	2030	2030	2128	2229
Berlin Südkreuz d.	1544	1611	...	1637	1711	1735	1743	1811	...	1837	1837	1837	1911	|	|	1933	2011	...	2037	2037	2037	2135	2235
Lutherstadt Wittenberg d.	|	|	...	1711	|	1810	|	|	...	1911	1911	1911	|	|	|	2007	|	...	2111	2111	2111	2210	2317
Bitterfeld d.	1633	|	...	|	|	|	1833	|	...	|	|	|	|	|	|	2024	|	...	|	|	|	2228	2334
Halle (Saale) Hbf d.	1652	1718	...	|	1818	|	1852	1918	...	|	|	|	2018	|	|	|	2118	...	|	|	|	|	0110z
Dresden Hbf **842** d.	|	|	1612	|	|	|	|	|	1812	|	|	|	|	|	|	|	|	...	|	|	|	|	|
Leipzig Hbf a.	|	|	1723	1742	|	1842	|	|	1923	1942	1942	1942	|	|	|	2043	|	...	2142	2142	2142	2247	2358
Leipzig Hbf d.	|	|	1733	1748	|	1848	|	|	1933	1948	1948	...	|	|	|	2050	|	2133	...	2148	2148	2255	0035
Erfurt Hbf a.	1724p	1745	1815	1829	1848	1928	1924	1945	2015	2029	2029	...	2048	◐	◐	2129	2145	2215	...	2229	2229	2335	|
Erfurt Hbf **849a** d.	1732	1747	1817	1831	1850	1930	1932	1947	2017	2031	2031	...	2050	|	|	2131	2147	2217	...	...	2235	2341	|
Coburg **875** d.	|	|	|	|	|	|	|	|	|	|	|	...	|	|	|	2206	|	|	...	...	|	|	|
Bamberg **875** d.	1817	|	|	1916	|	|	2017	|	|	|	|	...	|	|	|	2230	|	|	...	...	2321	|	0421
Erlangen **875** d.	|	|	|	1937	|	|	|	|	|	2137	2137	...	|	|	|	2252	|	|	...	...	2342	|	0442
Nürnberg Hbf **875** a.	1852	1856	|	1952	|	|	2052	2056	|	2152	2152	...	|	|	|	2308	2256	|	...	...	2357	|	0502
München Hbf **904 905** a.	2043	2002	|	2102	|	|	2244	2201	|	2303	2303	...	|	|	|	...	0001	|	...	...	0112	|	...
Gotha **849a** d.	...	...	1833	...	|	|	...	...	2033	...	...	...	|	|	|	...	...	2233	...	...	...	2356	...
Eisenach **849a** d.	...	...	1848	...	|	1956	...	...	2048	...	...	...	|	|	|	...	...	2248	...	...	...	0012	...
Bad Hersfeld d.	...	...	1916	...	|	|	...	...	2116	...	...	...	|	|	|	...	...	2316	...	...	...	|	...
Fulda **900/1/2** d.	...	...	1943	...	|	2050	...	...	2143	...	...	...	|	2256	2308	...	...	2343	...	...	...	|	...
Frankfurt (Main) Süd **901** a.	...	...	|	...	|	|	...	...	|	...	...	...	|	|	|	...	...	|	...	...	...	|	...
Frankfurt (Main) Hbf **900/1/2** ◇ a.	...	...	2036	...	2056	2144	...	...	2236	...	...	...	2256	2353	0007	...	...	0040	...	...	...	0211	...
Frankfurt Flughafen ✈ § ◇ a.	...	...	2056	...	...	|	...	...	...	...	...	...	|	0025	0025	...	...	...	...	...	...	0238	...
Stuttgart Hbf **912** a.	...	...	|	...	...	2308	...	...	...	...	...	...	0051	|	|	...	...	...	...	...	...	0443	...
Mainz Hbf ◇ a.	...	...	2115	...	...	...	...	...	...	...	...	...	...	0044	0044	...	...	...	...	...	...	...	...
Wiesbaden Hbf ◇ a.	...	...	2133	...	...	...	...	...	...	...	...	...	...	0058	0058	...	...	...	...	...	...	...	...

A – BEROLINA – To Wien via Passau (Tables **920** and **950**).
B – To Innsbruck via Garmisch (Table **895**) on ⑤.
D – Daily to July 22; Ⓑ from July 24.
G – To Karlsruhe (Table **912**). Runs via Weimar (Table **849a**).
J – To Jena (Table **849a**).
K – From Kiel (Table **820**).
L – From Lichtenfels (d. 0622).
M – To München via Ulm (Table **930**).
O – From Ostseebad Binz (Tables **844/845**).
S – To Saarbrücken (Table **919**).
T – From Rostock (Table **835**) on Ⓑ. To Wien via Jena and Passau (Tables **849a**, **920** and **950**).
U – From Warnemünde (Table **835**).

d – Not June 16.
e – ①–⑥ only.
p – Connects with train in previous column.
t – Not June 16, Aug. 15.
v – ①–⑤ only.
z – Arrives 0056 (calls after Leipzig).

⊙ – Also calls at Weimar (d. 0338).
△ – Also calls at Hanau Hbf (a. 0622).
‡ – Also calls at Hanau Hbf (a. 0020).
◐ – Via Hannover (Table **900**).
§ – Frankfurt Flughafen Fernbahnhof ✈.
◇ – See Tables **914**, **917** and **917a** for other local services.

FRANKFURT and NÜRNBERG - ERFURT - LEIPZIG / HALLE - BERLIN 850

See Table **902** for other services Frankfurt - Berlin via Braunschweig. See Table **927** for services operated by FlixTrain.

Other regional services: Table **845** Lutherstadt Wittenberg - Berlin. Table **848** Leipzig / Halle - Bitterfeld - Lutherstadt Wittenberg. Table **849** Eisenach - Erfurt - Weimar - Leipzig / Halle.

km		IC 94		ICE 1606	ICE 698	ICE 806	ICE 806	ICE 1731	ICE 1604	ICE 1604	ICE 1704	ICE 1714	ICE 1553	ICE 1008	ICE 672	ICE 696	ICE 804	ICE 804	ICE 933	ICE 602	ICE 1555	ICE 1006	ICE 802
							①–⑤	①–⑤	①–⑥		①–⑤	⑥	⑥			①–⑥	①–⑥	⑦	①–⑤				
		W		✕	E✕	✕	✕	✕	✕	✕	J✕	JO ✕	✕	✕		L✕	K✕	K✕	D✕	✕	✕	✕	✕
	Wiesbaden Hbf ◇ d.	...	...	...	...	...	...	...	...	...	...		...	...	0500	...	...	...	...	...	...	...	...
	Mainz Hbf ◇ d.	...	...	...	...	...	...	...	...	...	...	...	...	...	0512	...	...	...	...	...	...	...	...
	Stuttgart Hbf **912** d.	...	...	...	0012	...	...	...	...	...	...	...	...	...	|	...	...	...	...	...	...	...	...
	Frankfurt Flughafen ✈ § ◇ d.	...	...	...	0229	...	...	...	...	...	...	...	...	...	0533	...	...	...	...	...	...	...	...
	Frankfurt (Main) Hbf **900/1/2** ◇ d.	...	...	...	0249	...	...	...	...	...	...	...	...	...	0550	0614	...	...	0702	...	0716	...	...
	Frankfurt (Main) Süd **901** d.	...	...	...	|	...	...	...	...	...	...	...	...	...	|	|	...	...	|	...	|	...	...
	Fulda **900/1/2** d.	...	...	...	|	...	...	...	...	...	...	...	...	...	0647	0709	...	...	|	...	0814	...	...
	Bad Hersfeld d.	...	...	...	|	...	...	...	...	...	...	...	...	...	|	|	...	...	|	...	0840	...	...
	Eisenach **849a** d.	...	...	...	0447	...	0553	0638	...	...	...	...	0708	...	|	0801	...	...	|	...	0908	...	...
	Gotha **849a** d.	...	...	...	0503	...	0611u	0653	...	...	...	...	0722	...	|	|	...	...	|	...	0922	...	...
	München Hbf **904 905** d.	...	...	...	|	...	|	|	...	...	...	...	|	0556	|	|	0506t	...	|	0656	|	0755	0713
0	**Nürnberg** Hbf **875** d.	0026	...	...	|	...	|	|	0544	...	...	...	|	0701	|	|	0705	0705	|	0804	|	0902	0905
24	Erlangen **875** d.	0043	...	...	|	...	|	|	0559	...	...	...	|	|	|	|	|	|	|	0819	|	|	|
62	**Bamberg** **875** d.	0105	...	...	|	...	|	|	0622	...	...	...	|	|	|	|	0741	0741	|	0842	|	|	0941
	Coburg **875** d.	|	...	...	|	...	|	|	0644	...	...	...	|	|	|	|	|	|	|	|	|	|	|
190	**Erfurt** Hbf **849a** a.	|	...	...	0519	...	0626	0708	0724	...	...	...	0738	0809	◐	0826	0824p	0824	0907	0926	0938	1009	1024
190	**Erfurt** Hbf d.	|	...	...	0522	...	0628	0710	0727	...	...	...	0740	0811	|	0828	0832	0828	0909	0928	0940	1011	1032
	Leipzig Hbf a.	0450	...	...	|	...	0710	|	0810	...	...	...	0824	|	|	0910	|	0910	|	1010	1024	|	|
	Leipzig Hbf d.	0507	...	0616	◧	0716	0716	|	0818	0818	0818	0818	0831	|	|	0916	|	0917	|	1016	1031	|	|
	Dresden Hbf **842** a.	|	...	|	|	|	|	|	|	|	|	|	0937	|	|	|	|	|	|	|	1137	|	|
284	**Halle** (Saale) Hbf d.	0431n	...	|	0640	|	|	0744	|	|	|	|	...	0840	|	|	0906	|	0942	|	...	1040	1106
314	Bitterfeld d.	0528	...	|	0656	|	|	0801	|	|	|	|	...	|	|	|	0925	|	|	|	...	|	1123
351	Lutherstadt Wittenberg d.	0546	...	0648	|	0748	0748	|	0848	0848	0848	0848	...	|	|	0948	|	0948	|	1048	...	|	|
442	**Berlin** Südkreuz a.	0624	...	0721	0749	0825	0825	0851	0921	0921	0921	0921	...	0944	|	1022	1017	1022	1048	1121	...	1144	1217
448	**Berlin** Hbf a.	0631	...	0729	0758	0832	0832	0858	0930	0930	0930	0930	...	0951	|	1031	1025	1029	1056	1129	...	1151	1225
	Hamburg Hbf **840** a.	...	...	0924	...	1021	1021	...	1124	1124	1124	...	...	1151	0954	...	1221	1221	1311	1324	...	1403•	1421

	ICE 694	ICE 935	ICE 1600	ICE 1710	ICE 1557	ICE 1706	ICE 800	ICE 692	ICE 937	ICE 508	ICE 1559	ICE 1004	ICE 708	ICE 690	ICE 939	ICE 506	ICE 1651	ICE 1092	ICE 92	ICE 706	ICE 598	ICE 831	ICE 504
															¶			⊡					
	✕	S✕	✕	O✕	✕	✕	✕	M✕	✕	✕	✕	✕	✕	M✕	✕	✕	✕	✕	A✕	✕	M✕	✕	✕
Wiesbaden Hbf ◇ d.	...	...	...	...	0826	...	...	...	...	...	1026	...	...	...	...	...	1226	...	...	...	...	...	...
Mainz Hbf ◇ d.	...	...	...	...	0843	...	...	...	...	...	1043	...	...	...	...	...	1243	...	...	...	...	...	...
Stuttgart Hbf **912** d.	0650	...	...	...	|	...	...	0851	0903c	...	|	...	...	1051	...	...	|	...	...	...	1251	...	...
Frankfurt Flughafen ✈ § ◇ d.	|	...	...	...	0902	...	...	|	|	...	1102	...	...	|	...	...	1302	...	...	...	|	...	...
Frankfurt (Main) Hbf **900/1/2** ◇ d.	0814	0902	...	...	0919	...	...	1014	1102	...	1119	...	...	1214	1302	...	1319	...	...	...	1414	1502	...
Frankfurt (Main) Süd **901** d.	|	|	...	...	|	...	...	|	|	...	|	...	...	|	|	...	|	...	...	...	|	|	...
Fulda **900/1/2** d.	0909	|	...	...	1014	...	...	1109	|	...	1214	...	...	1309	|	...	1414	...	...	...	1509	|	...
Bad Hersfeld d.	|	|	...	...	1040	...	...	|	|	...	1240	...	...	|	|	...	1440	...	...	...	|	|	...
Eisenach **849a** d.	1001	|	...	...	1108	...	...	1201	|	...	1308	...	...	1401	|	...	1508	...	...	...	1601	|	...
Gotha **849a** d.	|	|	...	...	1122	...	...	|	|	...	1322	...	...	|	|	...	1522	...	...	...	|	|	...
München Hbf **904 905** d.	|	|	0855	0855	|	0839	0955	|	|	1055	|	1156	1114	|	|	1255	|	1240y	...	1354	|	|	1456
Nürnberg Hbf **875** d.	|	|	1005	1005	|	1036	1106	|	|	1204	|	1301	1305	|	|	1404	|	1437	1437	1505	|	|	1604
Erlangen **875** d.	|	|	1019	1019	|	|	|	|	|	1219	|	|	|	|	|	1419	|	|	|	|	|	|	1619
Bamberg **875** d.	|	|	|	|	|	|	1141	|	|	1242	|	|	1341	|	|	1442	|	|	|	1541	|	|	1642
Coburg **875** d.	|	|	|	|	|	1129	|	|	|	|	|	|	|	|	|	|	|	1529	1529	|	|	|	|
Erfurt Hbf **849a** a.	1026p	1107	1126	1126	1138	1203	1224	1226p	1307	1326	1338	1409	1424	1426p	1507	1526	1538	1602	1602	1624	1626p	1707	1726
Erfurt Hbf d.	1028	1109	1128	1128	1140	1205	1232	1228	1309	1328	1340	1411	1432	1428	1509	1528	1540	1605	1605	1632	1628	1709	1728
Leipzig Hbf a.	1110	|	1210	1210	1224	|	|	1310	|	1410	1424	|	|	1510	|	1610	1624	|	|	|	1710	|	1810
Leipzig Hbf d.	1116	|	1216	1216	1231	|	|	1316	|	1416	1431	|	|	1516	|	1616	1631	|	|	|	1716	|	1816
Dresden Hbf **842** a.	|	|	|	|	1337	|	|	|	|	|	1537	|	|	|	|	|	1737	|	|	|	|	|	|
Halle (Saale) Hbf d.	|	1142	|	|	...	1240	1306	|	1342	|	...	1440	1506	|	1542	|	...	1640	1640	1706	|	1742	|
Bitterfeld d.	|	|	|	|	...	|	1323	|	|	|	...	|	1523	|	|	|	...	|	|	1723	|	|	|
Lutherstadt Wittenberg d.	1148	|	1248	1248	...	|	|	1348	|	1448	...	|	|	1548	|	1648	...	|	|	|	1748	|	1848
Berlin Südkreuz a.	1222	1247	1321	1321	...	1347	1417	1422	1448	1521	...	1544	1617	1622	1650	1721	...	1751	1751	1817	1822	1850	1921
Berlin Hbf a.	1229	1254	1329	1329	...	1355	1425	1429	1456	1529	...	1551	1625	1629	1657	1729	...	1758	1758	1825	1829	1857	1930
Hamburg Hbf **840** a.	...	...	1524	...	...	1559	1621	...	...	1724	...	1812	1822	...	...	1924	...	...	1951	2023	...	...	2124

	ICE 1653	ICE 1002	ICE 704	IC 1957	ICE 596	IC 1957	EC 218	ICE 833	ICE 502	ICE 1655	ICE 1000	ICE 702	ICE 594	ICE 835	ICE 500	ICE 1657	ICE 592	ICE 1100	ICE 592	ICE 1500	ICE 1659	ICE 1659	ICE 4
				⑤f		⑤f	①–④							Ⓑ					⑤⑥	Ⓑ	Ⓑ	⑤⑦	⑦
	✕	✕	✕	🍷	M✕	◧🍷	G🍷	✕	✕	✕	✕	✕	M✕	✕	✕	✕	M✕	✕	M	✕	✕	✕	Z
Wiesbaden Hbf ◇ d.	1426	...	...	...	...	...	...	...	...	1626	...	...	...	...	...	1826	...	...	...	...	2026	2026	...
Mainz Hbf ◇ d.	1443	...	...	...	...	...	...	...	...	1643	...	...	...	...	...	1843	...	...	...	...	2043	2043	...
Stuttgart Hbf **912** d.	|	...	...	...	1451	...	1405	...	...	|	...	...	1651	...	...	|	1851	...	...	...	|	|	...
Frankfurt Flughafen ✈ § ◇ d.	1502	...	...	...	|	...	|	...	...	1702	...	...	|	...	...	1902	|	...	...	...	2102	2102	...
Frankfurt (Main) Hbf **900/1/2** ◇ d.	1519	...	...	1538	1613	...	1615	1702	...	1719	...	...	1814	1902	...	1919	2014	...	...	...	2119	2119	2314
Frankfurt (Main) Süd **901** d.	|	...	...	|	|	...	|	|	...	|	...	...	|	|	...	|	|	...	...	...	|	|	|
Fulda **900/1/2** d.	1614	...	...	1653	1709	...	1723	|	...	1814	...	...	1909	|	...	2014	2109	...	...	...	2214	2214	0016
Bad Hersfeld d.	1640	...	...	1722	|	...	1754	|	...	1840	...	...	|	|	...	2040	2136	...	...	...	2240	2240	|
Eisenach **849a** d.	1708	...	...	1754	1801	←	1826	|	...	1908	...	...	2001	|	...	2108	2206	...	...	...	2308	2308	|
Gotha **849a** d.	1722	...	...	1819	|	1821	1844	|	...	1922	...	...	|	|	...	2122	2221	...	...	...	2322	2322	|
München Hbf **904 905** d.	|	1556	1513	→	|	|	|	|	1655	|	1756	1705	|	|	1856	|	|	1956	...	1909	|	|	|
Nürnberg Hbf **875** d.	|	1701	1705	...	|	|	|	|	1804	|	1901	1906	|	|	2004	|	|	2101	...	2105	|	|	|
Erlangen **875** d.	|	|	|	...	|	|	|	|	1819	|	|	|	|	|	2019	|	|	|	...	2119	|	|	|
Bamberg **875** d.	|	|	1741	...	|	|	|	|	1842	|	|	1941	|	|	2042	|	|	|	...	2143	|	|	|
Coburg **875** d.	|	|	|	...	|	|	|	|	|	|	|	|	|	|	|	|	|	|	←	2206	|	|	|
Erfurt Hbf **849a** a.	1738	1809	1824	...	1826p	1837	1900	1907	1926	1938	2009	2024	2026p	2107	2126	2138	2236	2209	2236	2238	2338	2338	0139
Erfurt Hbf d.	1740	1811	1832	...	1828	1841	...	1909	1928	1940	2011	2032	2028	2109	2128	2140	→	2211	2238	2243	...	2343	0141
Leipzig Hbf a.	1824	|	|	...	1910	2005	...	|	2010	2024	|	|	2110	|	2210	2224	...	|	2322	2326	...	0028	0224
Leipzig Hbf d.	1831	|	|	...	1916	...	...	|	2016	2031	|	|	2116	|	2216	2231	...	|	...	...	...	...	0236
Dresden Hbf **842** a.	1937	|	|	...	|	...	...	|	|	2137	|	|	|	|	|	2337	...	|	...	...	...	...	|
Halle (Saale) Hbf d.	...	1840	1906	...	|	...	...	1942	|	...	2040	2106	|	2142	|	...	...	2242	...	...	...	...	|
Bitterfeld d.	...	|	1923	...	|	...	...	|	|	...	|	2123	|	|	2234	...	...	|	...	...	...	...	|
Lutherstadt Wittenberg d.	...	|	|	...	1948	...	...	|	2048	...	|	|	2148	|	2250	...	...	|	...	...	...	...	|
Berlin Südkreuz a.	...	1947	2017	...	2022	...	...	2048	2121	...	2144	2217	2222	2248	2326	...	...	2343	...	...	...	...	0342
Berlin Hbf a.	...	1954	2024	...	2029	...	...	2055	2129	...	2151	2224	2230	2255	2335	...	...	2350	...	...	...	...	0349
Hamburg Hbf **840** a.	...	2156	2222	...	...	...	...	...	2333	...	...	...	...	...	...	...	...	...	...	...	...	...	0539

A – BERLINA – From Wien via Passau (Tables **950** and **920**).
D – From Darmstadt Hbf (d. 0637).
E – [12] München - Stuttgart - Frankfurt - Berlin. ✕ Erfurt - Berlin.
G – CHIEMGAU – [12] 🍷 Graz - Salzburg - München - Stuttgart - Frankfurt - Erfurt. Until Aug. 1 starts from München and runs as *IC* **2398**.
J – From Jena (Table **849a**).
K – To Kiel (Table **820**).
L – From Karlsruhe (Table **912**) on ①.
M – From München via Ulm (Table **930**).
O – To Ostseebad Binz (Tables **844/845**).
S – From Saarbrücken (Table **919**).
W – From Wien via Passau and Jena (Tables **849a**, **920** and **950**). To Warnemünde (Table **835**) on ①–⑥.
Z – From Zürich (Table **912**).

c – ⑥⑦ only.
f – Also June 15; not June 17.
n – Arrives 0411 (calls before Leipzig).
p – Connects with train in previous column.
t – Ⓐ (not June 16, Aug. 15).
u – Calls to pick up only.
y – 1239 on ⑥.
¶ – Train number **839** on ⑥⑦.
• – Hamburg **Altona**.
◐ – Via Hannover (Table **900**).
◧ – Via Weimar (see Table **849a**).
⊡ – To Stralsund on ⑦–④ (Table **845**).
§ – Frankfurt Flughafen Fernbahnhof ✈.
◇ – See Tables **914**, **917** and **917a** for other local services.

852 COTTBUS - LEIPZIG

RE / RB services

km		⚒									
0	**Cottbus** Hbf d.	0502	0705	0905	1105	1305	1505	1705	1905	2105	2304
24	Calau (Niederl) d.	0519	0722	0922	1122	1322	1522	1722	1922	2122	2323
46	Finsterwalde d.	0532	0736	0936	1136	1336	1536	1736	1936	2136	2339
56	Doberlug-Kirchhain d.	0540	0743	0943	1143	1343	1543	1743	1943	2143	2348
79	Falkenberg 856 d.	0556	0759	0959	1159	1359	1559	1759	1959	2159	0015
97	Torgau 856 d.	0608	0812	1012	1212	1412	1612	1812	2012	2212	...
124	Eilenburg 856 d.	0629	0829	1029	1229	1429	1629	1829	2029	2229	...
149	**Leipzig** Hbf 856 a.	0649	0849	1049	1249	1449	1649	1849	2049	2249	...

		⚒								
Leipzig Hbf 856 d.	...	0712	0912	1112	1312	1512	1712	1912	2112	2333
Eilenburg 856 d.	...	0731	0931	1131	1331	1531	1731	1931	2131	2352
Torgau 856 d.	...	0750	0950	1150	1350	1550	1750	1950	2150	0013
Falkenberg 856 d.	0652	0803	1003	1203	1403	1603	1803	2003	2203	0027
Doberlug-Kirchhain d.	0715	0816	1016	1216	1416	1616	1816	2016	2216	0040
Finsterwalde d.	0722	0824	1024	1224	1424	1624	1824	2024	2224	0048
Calau (Niederl) d.	0737	0839	1039	1239	1439	1639	1839	2039	2239	0102
Cottbus Hbf a.	0755	0855	1055	1255	1455	1655	1855	2055	2255	0119

☛ Additional trains: **Cottbus - Falkenberg** at 0604 Ⓐ, 0804, 1204, 1404, 1604, 1804, 2004, 2204. **Falkenberg - Cottbus** at 0443, 0552 Ⓐ, 0852 Ⓒ, 0855 Ⓐ, 1255, 1452, 1652, 1852.

853 STEAM TRAINS IN SACHSEN

Lößnitzgrundbahn. SDG Sächsische Dampfeisenbahngesellschaft mbH, Am Bahnhof 1, 01468 Moritzburg. ✆ +49 (0) 35207 8929. SEE NOTE ⊠. www.loessnitzgrundbahn.de

km		Ⓐe								h	
0	Radebeul Ost **842 857** d.	0515	...	0826	0956	1256	1426	...	1726	1856	...
8	Moritzburg d.	0542	...	0854	1026	1324	1456	...	1754	1924	...
16	Radeburg a.	0605	...	...	1050	...	1520	...	...	...	...

	Ⓐe								h
Radeburg d.	0620	...	...	1106	...	1536	...	...	...
Moritzburg d.	0648	...	0903	1133	1333	1603	1803	...	1933
Radebeul Ost **842 857** a.	0715	...	0930	1200	1400	1630	1830	...	2000

Weißeritztalbahn. SDG Sächsische Dampfeisenbahngesellschaft mbH, Am Bahnhof 1, 01468 Moritzburg. ✆ +49 (0) 35207 89290. SEE NOTE ✣. www.weisseritztalbahn.com

km		△			△			△			
	Dresden Hbf d.	0906	...	...	1306	...	...	1637	...	...	...
0	Freital-Hainsberg d.	0919	0925	...	1319	1325	...	1649	1705	...	...
15	Dippoldiswalde d.	...	1018	...	...	1418	...	...	1750	...	...
26	Kurort Kipsdorf a.	...	1051	...	...	1451	...	...	...	...	...

		△			△			△	
Kurort Kipsdorf d.	1111	...	...	1511	...	...	...	...	...
Dippoldiswalde d.	1145	...	...	1545	...	...	1802	...	...
Freital-Hainsberg a.	1230	1238	...	1630	1638	...	1847	1908	...
Dresden Hbf a.	...	1252	...	...	1652	...	...	1921	...

Zittauer Schmalspurbahn. SEE NOTE ❦. SOEG - Sächisch Oberlausitzer Eisenbahngesellschaft mbH, Bahnhofstraße 41, 02763 Zittau. ✆ +49 (0) 3583 540540. www.soeg-zittau.de

km				🍷	Cd		🍷		Cd		🍷		Cd		🍷		Cd		Cd		🍷	🍷	🍷	🍷	🍷	🍷
0	Zittau d.	High	0847	0909	1020	...	1109	...	1220	...	1309	...	1420	...	1509	...	1620	...	...	Low	0907	...	...	1307	...	...
9	Bertsdorf d.	season	0946r	0946t	1053	1055	1146t	1146	1253	1255	1346t	1346	1453	1455	1546t	1546	1653	1655	1742	season	0938	1039	1135	1338	1439	1535
12	Kurort Oybin a.	♥	|	0956	|	1106	1156	|	|	1306	1356	|	|	1506	1556	|	|	1706	1754	♣	0949	|	1146	1349	|	1546
13	Kurort Jonsdorf a.	→	0959	...	1106	...	...	1159	1306	...	...	1359	1506	...	...	1559	1706	...	...	→	...	1051	...	...	1451	...

			🍷		Cd		🍷		Cd		🍷		Cd		🍷	Cd		Cd		🍷	🍷	🍷	🍷	🍷	🍷
Kurort Jonsdorf d.	High	1008	...	...	1117	1208	...	...	1317	1408	...	...	1517	1608	...	1717	...	...	Low	...	1101	...	...	1501	...
Kurort Oybin d.	season	|	1007	1115	|	|	1207	1315	|	|	1407	1515	|	|	1607	|	1728	1804	season	0959	|	1156	1359	|	1556
Bertsdorf d.	♥	1019	1020	1126	1129	1219	1220	1326	1329	1419	1420	1526	1529	1619	1620	1728	1740	1815	♣	1010	1112	1208	1410	1512	1608
Zittau a.	→	...	1049	...	1159	...	1249	...	1359	...	1449	...	1559	...	1649	...	1810	1845	→	...	...	1237	...	...	1637

C – Ⓒ until Oct. 30 (also Oct. 31).
d – Diesel train.
e – Not July 18 - Aug. 26, Oct. 17–31, Nov. 16.
h – Until Oct. 31.
r – Arrives 0916.
t – Arrives 6 minutes earlier.
♣ – Nov. 26 - Dec. 10 (no service Nov. 7–25).
♥ – July 1 - Nov. 6.
❦ – Service from July 1 (please check locally for amended service until June 30).
⊠ – A special timetable operates on Sept. 17, 18. No service Oct. 24–28 and Nov. 1–14.
✣ – No service Nov. 1–11.
△ – Suggested main-line connecting service.

854 FORST - COTTBUS - GÖRLITZ - ZITTAU

Ostdeutsche Eisenbahn (ODEG); 2nd class only

km		⑦w		Ⓐt	Ⓐe	⚒t	⚒e		⚒e							
0	**Cottbus** Hbf d.	0021	...	...	0504	...	0604	0704	0804	...	0904		2104	2204	2304	...
24	Spremberg d.	0039	...	...	0522	...	0622	0722	0822	...	0922	and	2122	2222	2322	...
42	Weißwasser d.	0054	...	0430	0535	...	0635	0735	0835	...	0935		2135	2235	2336	...
72	Horka d.	0115	...	0453	0600	...	0700	0800	0900	...	1000	hourly	2200	2300	2359	...
93	**Görlitz** a.	0130	...	0508	0615	...	0715	0815	0915	...	1015		2215	2315	0014	...
93	**Görlitz** d.	...	...	*0513*	0621n	0621	0721n	0821	0921	0921	1021	until	2221	...	...	...
127	**Zittau** a.	...	...	*0548*	0656n	0656	0756n	0856	0956	0956	1056		2256	...	...	...

	Ⓐe	⚒e		⚒t	⚒e	Ⓐt			⚒t				⑥v		Ⓑr	
Zittau d.	...	...	...	0455	...	0603	0703	...	0803	0903		2103	2203	2203	...	...
Görlitz a.	...	...	...	0532	...	0640	0740	...	0840	0940	and	2140	2240	2240	...	...
Görlitz d.	0344	0437	0544	0544	0644	0644	0744	0844	0844	0944		2144	2244	...	2244	...
Horka d.	0358	0453	0559	0559	0659	0659	0759	0859	0859	0959	hourly	2159	2259	...	2259	...
Weißwasser d.	0420	0520	0620	0620	0720	0720	0820	0920	0920	1020		2220	2320	...	2319	...
Spremberg d.	0434	0538	0638	0638	0738	0738	0838	0938	0938	1038	until	2238	2338	...	...	...
Cottbus Hbf a.	0452	0556	0656	0656	0756	0756	0856	0956	0956	1056		2256	2356	...	...	...

FORST (Lausitz) - **COTTBUS** and v.v. *22 km*.
Journey time: 18 minutes.
From Forst at 0431 Ⓐ **e**, 0533, 0633 and hourly until 2133.
From Cottbus Hbf at 0507 Ⓐ **e**, 0607, 0707 and hourly until 2107; then 2307.

e – Not Oct. 31.
n – Not Nov. 16.
r – Not Oct. 2, 30.
t – Not Oct. 31, Nov. 16.
v – Also Oct. 2, 30; not Oct. 1, 29.
w – Also Oct. 3, 31; not Oct. 2, 30.

855 DRESDEN - BISCHOFSWERDA - GÖRLITZ and ZITTAU

Trilex (2nd class only)

km		⚒r	Ⓐt			⚒r			⚒r⊙			⚒r		⊖		◇					⚒r⊙					
0	**Dresden** Hbf ● d.	0356	0526	0629	0656	0729	0829	0858	0929	1029	1058	*1129*	1229	1329	1429	1529	1629	1729	1829	1858	1929	2029	2058	2129	2229	*2327*
4	Dresden Neustadt ● d.	0402	0532	0635	0705j	0735	0835	0905	0935	1035	1105	*1135*	1235	1335	1435	1535	1635	1735	1835	1905	1935	2035	2105	2135	2235	*2333*
41	Bischofswerda ● d.	0438	0607	0705	0740	0808	0905	0940	1008	1105	1140	1208	1305	1408	1505	1608	1705	1808	1905	1940	2008	2105	2140	2208	2305	0015
60	Bautzen d.	0452	0619	0717	0755	0820	0917	0955	1020	1117	1155	1220	1317	1420	1517	1620	1717	1820	1917	1955	2020	2117	2155	2223	2317	0029
82	Löbau (Sachs) d.	0510	0632	0731	0813	0833	0931	1013	1033	1131	1213	1233	1331	1433	1531	1633	1731	1833	1931	2013	2033	2131	2213	2240	2331	0047
105	**Görlitz** 1085 a.	0530	0648	0746	0833	0848	0946	1033	1048	1146	1233	1248	1346	1448	1546	1648	1746	1848	1946	2033	2048	2146	2233	2300	2346	0106
106	Zgorzelec 🚍 1085 a.	...	0655	0754	...	...	...	...	...	1154	...	1254	1354	1454	1554	1654	...	1854	1954	...	...	...	...	...	...	...

	Ⓐt	Ⓒz	Ⓐt		Ⓐt																⚒r					
Zgorzelec 🚍 1085 d.	...	...	...	...	...	0712t	0800	...	...	...	1200	1300	...	1400	1500	...	1600	1700	...	...	1900	*1900*	2000	...	...	...
Görlitz 1085 d.	0350j	0526	0538	0611	0651	0721	0811	0925	1011	1125	1211	1309	1325	1411	1509	1525	1611	1709	1725	1811	1909	1925	2011	2120	2220	2320
Löbau (Sachs) d.	0411j	0546	0553	0626	0706	0741	0826	0945	1026	1145	1226	1324	1345	1426	1524	1545	1626	1724	1745	1826	1924	1945	2026	2140	2240	2338
Bautzen d.	0428j	0604	0607	0640	0720	0759	0840	1002	1040	1202	1240	1338	1402	1440	1538	1602	1640	1738	1802	1840	1938	2002	2040	2157	2257	2354
Bischofswerda d.	0444j	0619	0619	0654	0733	0819	0854	1019	1054	1219	1254	1350	1419	1454	1550	1619	1654	1750	1819	1854	1950	2019	2054	2212	2312	0014
Dresden Neustadt a.	0516	0652	0652	0723	0803	0852	0921	1052	1121	1252	1321	*1422*	1452	1521	*1622*	1652	1721	*1822*	1852	1921	*2022*	2052	2121	2245	2345	0047
Dresden Hbf a.	0523	0658	0658	0729	0811	0858	0927	1058	1127	1258	1327	*1428*	1458	1527	*1628*	1658	1727	*1828*	1858	1927	*2028*	2058	2127	2252	2352	0054

km			Ⓐt																							
0	**Dresden** Hbf ● d.	0356	...	...	0526	0556	0729	0756	0929	0956	1129	1156	1329	1356	1529	1556	1729	1756	1929	1956	2129	2208	...	2327	...	...
4	Dresden Neustadt ● d.	0402	...	...	0532	0602	0735	0802	0935	1002	1135	1202	1335	1402	1535	1602	1735	1802	1935	2002	2135	2215	...	2333	...	...
41	Bischofswerda ● d.	0436	0440	...	0601	0637	0805	0837	1005	1037	1205	1237	1405	1437	1605	1637	1805	1837	2005	2037	2205	2248	...	0012	...	...
79	Ebersbach (Sachs) d.	...	0522	...	0633	0725	0834	0925	1034	1125	1234	1325	1434	1525	1634	1725	1834	1925	2034	2127	2234	2327	...	0047	...	...
83	Neugersdorf d.	...	0526	...	0637	0729	0838	0929	1038	1129	1238	1329	1438	1529	1638	1729	1838	1929	2038	2131	2238	2331	...	0051	...	...
105	**Zittau** a.	...	0547	...	0655	0749	0856	0949	1056	1149	1256	1349	1456	1549	1656	1749	1856	1949	2056	2151	2256	2351	...	0112	...	...
	Liberec 🚍 **1117** a.	...	...	...	0754c	...	0929	...	1129	...	1329c	...	1529c	...	1729	...	1929	...	2131c	...	...	...	...	...	...	...

	Ⓐt		Ⓐt	⊕																					
Liberec 🚍 **1117** d.	...	...	...	...	...	0628	...	0828	...	1028	...	1228c	1332e	1428c	...	1628	...	1828	...	2028c	...	...	...	...	...
Zittau d.	0414	0459	0531	0606	...	0703	0806	0903	1006	1103	1206	1303	1406	1503	1606	1703	1806	1903	2006	2101	...	...	2301	...	...
Neugersdorf d.	0436	0517	0552	0628	...	0721	0828	0921	1028	1121	1228	1321	1428	1521	1628	1721	1828	1921	2028	2122	...	...	2322	...	...
Ebersbach (Sachs) d.	0440	0523	0557	0634	...	0725	0836	0925	1036	1125	1236	1325	1436	1525	1636	1725	1836	1925	2036	2126	...	...	2326	...	...
Bischofswerda d.	0519	0555	0633	0719	...	0755	0919	0955	1119	1155	1319	1355	1519	1555	1719	1755	1919	1955	2119	2201	2212	...	0001	0014	...
Dresden Neustadt a.	0552	0622	0704	0752	...	0822	0952	1022	1152	1222	1352	1422	1552	1622	1752	1822	1952	2022	2152	...	2245	...	...	0047	...
Dresden Hbf a.	0559	0628	0711	0758	...	0828	0958	1028	1158	1228	1358	1428	1558	1628	1758	1828	1958	2028	2158	...	2252	...	...	0054	...

c – ⑥⑦ (also July 5, 6, Sept. 28, Oct. 28, Nov. 17).
e – ①-⑤ (not July 5, 6, Sept. 28, Oct. 28, Nov. 17).
j – 2–3 minutes earlier from Aug. 28.
r – Not Oct. 31, Nov. 16.
t – Ⓐ (not Oct. 31, Nov. 16).
z – Also Oct. 31, Nov. 16.
⊕ – Change trains at Bischofswerda on Ⓐ (not Oct. 31, Nov. 16).
⊙ – Change trains at Bischofswerda on ⑥.
⊖ – Change trains at Bischofswerda on Ⓒ (also Oct. 31, Nov. 16).
◇ – Change trains at Bischofswerda on † (also Oct. 31, Nov. 16).
● – Certain trains between Dresden and Bischofswerda convey portions for two separate destinations. Please take care to join the correct portion for your destination.

856 DRESDEN and LEIPZIG - RUHLAND - COTTBUS and HOYERSWERDA

RE / RB services

See Tables **842**, **843** and **857** for other services Dresden - Coswig. See Table **852** for other direct services Leipzig - Falkenberg - Cottbus.

km																									
			Ⓐ	E	⚒r	Ⓐ	Ⓒ																	⑥	
0	**Dresden** Hbf .... d.	...	...	...	...	...	...	0551	0651	...	...	0751	0851	...	...	0951		1851	...	...	1951	2051	...	...	2151
4	**Dresden** Neustadt .... d.	...	...	...	...	...	...	0558	0658	...	...	0758	0858	...	...	0958		1858	...	...	1958	2058	...	...	2158
18	Coswig .... d.	...	...	...	...	...	...	0607	0707	...	...	0807	0907	...	...	1007		1907	...	...	2007	2107	...	...	2207
	Leipzig-Connewitz ¶ d.	...	...	...	...	...	...	|	|	0546	...	|	|	0746	...	|		|	1746	...	|	|	1946	...	|
	Leipzig Hbf .... d.	...	...	...	...	...	...	|	|	0558	...	|	|	0758	...	|	and in	|	1758	...	|	|	1958	...	|
	Eilenburg .... d.	...	...	...	...	...	...	|	|	0629	...	|	|	0829	...	|	the same	|	1829	...	|	|	2029	...	|
	Torgau .... d.	...	...	...	...	...	...	|	|	0650	...	|	|	0850	...	|		|	1850	...	|	|	2050	...	|
	Falkenberg (Elster). a.	...	...	...	...	...	...	|	|	0709	...	|	|	0909	...	|	pattern	|	1909	...	|	|	2109	...	|
	Falkenberg (Elster). d.	...	0416	...	...	0616	...	|	|	0716	0816	|	|	0916	1016	|	every **two**	|	1916	2016	|	|	2116	...	|
	Elsterwerda-Biehla. d.	...	0434	0521	...	0634	...	|	|	0734	0834	|	|	0934	1034	|		|	1934	2034	|	|	2134	...	|
73	Ruhland .... a.	...	0455	0555	...	0655	...	0656*	0756	0755*	0855	0856*	0956	0955*	1055	1056*	hours until	1956	1955*	2055	2056*	2156	2155*	...	2256
73	Ruhland .... d.	0459	0459	0559	*0604*e	0659	0701	0702	0800	0802	0859	0902	1000	1002	1059	1102		2000	2002	2059	2102	2200	2202	...	2302
	Hoyerswerda .... a.	|	|	|	*0627*e	|	|	0725	|	0825	|	0925	|	1025	|	1125		|	2025	|	2125	|	2225	...	2325
	Hoyerswerda .... ♥ d.	|	|	|	0632	|	|	*0732*e	|	*0832*	|	...	|	*1032*	|	...		|	*2032*	|	...	|	...	2232	...
	Görlitz .... ♥ a.	|	|	|	0725	|	|	*0825*e	|	*0925*	|	...	|	*1125*	|	...		|	*2125*	|	...	|	...	2325	...
86	Senftenberg .... d.	0510	0510	0610	...	0710	0711	...	0810	...	0910	...	1010	...	1110	...		2010	...	2110	...	2210	...	...	...
120	**Cottbus** Hbf .... a.	0542	0542	0642	...	0742	0742	...	0841	...	0942	...	1038	...	1141	...		2038	...	2141	...	2238	...	...	...

km																									
			Ⓐ				Ⓒ	Ⓐ			Ⓐe												D		
	Cottbus Hbf .... d.	...	0415	...	0518	...	0615	0615	...	0718	...	...	0815	...	0918	⊠	...	1814	...	1916	...	2015	2215	...	2315
	Senftenberg .... d.	...	0447	...	0546	...	0646	0647	...	0746	...	...	0847	...	0946		...	1847	...	1946	...	2047	2247	...	2346
0	Görlitz .... ♥ d.	...	|	...	|	*0535*e	|	|	*0633*r	|	0733	...	|	*0833*	|		...	|	*1833*	|	...	|	|	2033	▬
72	**Hoyerswerda** .... ♥ a.	...	|	...	|	*0627*e	|	|	*0725*r	|	0825	...	|	*0925*	|		...	|	*1925*	|	...	|	|	2125	...
72	**Hoyerswerda** .... d.	0433	|	0533	|	0633	|	|	0733	|	...	0833	|	0933	|	and in	1833	|	1933	|	2033	|	|	...	...
97	Ruhland .... a.	0455	0457*	0555	0556*	0655	0656*	0657*	0755	0756*	...	0855	0857*	0955	0956*	the same	1855	1857*	1955	1956*	2055	2057*	2257	...	...
97	Ruhland .... d.	0502	0505	0602	0602	0702	...	0705	0802	0802	...	0902	0905	1002	1002		1902	1905	2002	2002	2102	2105	2305	...	...
123	Elsterwerda-Biehla. d.	|	0527	0624	|	|	...	0727	0824	|	...	|	0927	1024	|	pattern	|	1927	2024	|	|	2127	2327	...	...
147	Falkenberg (Elster). a.	|	0546	0646	|	|	...	0746	0846	|	...	|	0946	1046	|	every **two**	|	1946	2046	|	|	2146	...	...	...
147	Falkenberg (Elster). d.	|	...	0657	|	|	...	...	0857	|	...	|	...	1057	|		|	...	2057	|	|	...	...	...	...
165	Torgau .... d.	|	...	0713	|	|	...	...	0913	|	...	|	...	1113	|	hours until	|	...	2113	|	|	...	...	...	2307
192	Eilenburg .... d.	|	...	0736	|	|	...	...	0936	|	...	|	...	1136	|		|	...	2136	|	|	...	...	...	2331
217	**Leipzig** Hbf .... a.	|	...	0803	|	|	...	...	1003	|	...	|	...	1203	|		|	...	2203	|	|	...	...	...	2358
224	Leipzig-Connewitz ¶ a.	|	...	0814	|	|	...	...	1014	|	...	|	...	1214	|		|	...	2214	|	|	...	...	...	0018
	Coswig .... d.	0547	...	...	0647	0747	...	...	...	0847	...	0947	...	...	1047		1947	...	...	2047	2147	...	...	...	...
	Dresden Neustadt .... a.	0555	...	...	0655	0755	...	...	...	0855	...	0955	...	...	1055		1955	...	...	2055	2155	...	...	...	...
	Dresden Hbf .... a.	0602	...	...	0702	0802	...	...	...	0902	...	1002	...	...	1102		2002	...	...	2102	2202	...	...	...	...

– To Elsterwerda (a. 2330).
– From Elsterwerda (d. 0517).
e – Ⓐ (not Oct. 31, Nov. 16).
r – ⚒ (not Oct. 31, Nov. 16).
* – Connects with train in preceding column.
♥ – Hoyerswerda - Görlitz and v.v. is operated by Ostdeutsche Eisenbahn. **Subject to alteration July 18 - Sept. 23.**
⊠ – Cottbus departure variations: 1414 (not 1415), 1516 (not 1518), 1614 (not 1615), 1716 (not 1718).
¶ – Trains also call City Tunnel stations Leipzig MDR, Bayerischer Bahnhof, Wilhelm-Leuschner-Platz and Markt.

857 BAD SCHANDAU - DRESDEN - MEISSEN

S-Bahn

SERVICE FROM JUNE 26. On Oct. 31, Nov. 16 services run as on ⑦.

km																						
				Ⓐ			⚒															⑥L
0	**Bad Schandau** ⊡ .... **1100** d.	...	...	0443	...	0509	0542	...	0609	0643		2109	2143	2209	2243	2315	...	0015	...	...		1715
23	Pirna .... d.	...	0434	0507	0507	0537	0607	0607	0637	0707	and at	2137	2207	2237	2307	2337	0007	0037	...	...	A	1738
40	**Dresden** Hbf ..... **842 843 856 1100** d.	0430	0456	0530	0530	0600	0630	0630	0700	0730	the same	2200	2230	2300	2330	0000	0028	0058	...	...	L	1806j
44	**Dresden** Neustadt .... **842 856** d.	0437	0503	0537	0537	0607	0637	0637	0707	0737	minutes	2207	2237	2307	2337	0007	...	...	...	...	S	1813
50	Radebeul Ost .... d.	0446	0512	0546	0546	0616	0646	0646	0716	0746	past each	2216	2246	2316	2346	0016	...	...	...	...	O	|
58	Coswig .... **842 843 856** d.	0456	0526	0556	0556	0626	0656	0656	0726	0756	hour until	2226	2256	2326	2356	0029	...	...	...	...		1823
68	**Meißen** .... a.	0504	0534	0604	0604	0634	0704	0704	0734	0804		2234	2304	2334	0005	0037	...	...	...	...		...

		Ⓐ			⚒			✣													⑥L
Meißen .... d.	...	...	0421	0451	0451	0521	0551		2021	2051	2121	2151	2221	2251	2321	...	0021	...	...	...		...
Coswig .... **842 843 856** d.	...	...	0430	0500	0500	0530	0600	and at	2030	2100	2130	2200	2230	2300	2330	...	0030	...	...	...	A	0925
Radebeul Ost .... d.	...	...	0440	0510	0510	0540	0610	the same	2040	2110	2140	2210	2240	2310	2340	...	0040	...	...	...	L	|
Dresden Neustadt .... **842 856** d.	...	...	0450	0520	0520	0550	0620	minutes	2050	2120	2150	2220	2250	2320	2350	...	0050	...	...	...	S	0937
Dresden Hbf ...... **842 843 856 1100** d.	0429	0429	0459	0529	0529	0559	0629	past each	2059	2129	2159	2229	2259	2329	0012f	...	0057	0100	...	...	O	0952
Pirna .... d.	0450	0452	0526	0550	0552	0626	0652	hour until	2126	2152	2226	2256	2321	2350	0034	...	...	0121	...	...		1003
Bad Schandau ⊡ .... **1100** a.	...	0514	0548	...	0614	0648	0714		2148	2214	2248	2320	2343	...	0056	...	...	...	...	...		1022

– ⑥ until Oct. 29. To / from Leipzig (Table **842**).
– Arrives 2357.
– Arrives 1749.
✣ – On Ⓒ until Oct. 31 the 0721, 0921 and 1721 from Meißen depart Pirna 2 – 3 minutes earlier and arrive Bad Schandau 4 – 5 minutes earlier.
⊡ – A frequent ferry services links the railway station with Bad Schandau town centre. **Operator**: Oberelbische Verkehrsgesellschaft Pirna - Sebnitz mbH. ✆ + 49 (0) 3501 7920. www.ovps.de

857a DRESDEN - DRESDEN FLUGHAFEN ✈

S-Bahn

km									
0	**Dresden** Hbf .... d.	0418	0448	and every	2218	2248	2318	...	...
4	**Dresden** Neustadt .... d.	0425	0455	30 minutes	2225	2255	2325	...	...
15	**Dresden** Flughafen ✈ .... a.	0439	0509	until	2239	2309	2339	...	...

Dresden Flughafen ✈ .... d.	0448	0518	and every	2248	2318	2348	...	...
Dresden Neustadt .... a.	0500	0530	30 minutes	2300	2330	2400	...	...
Dresden Hbf .... a.	0508	0538	until	2308	2338	0008	...	...

858 GLAUCHAU - GERA - ERFURT

RE services

km																										
		Ⓐt ◧	Ⓒz ◧	⚒		⚒ ★	†						★						⑥	Ⓑb ★				◧	◧	
0	**Glauchau** (Sachs) ..... d.	...	...	...	...	...	...	0607r	...	0807	...	1007	...	1207	...	1407	...	1607	...	...	1807	...	2007	...	...	...
16	Gößnitz .... a.	...	...	...	...	...	...	0621r	...	0821	...	1021	...	1221	...	1421	...	1621	...	...	1821	...	2021	...	...	...
16	Gößnitz .... d.	...	...	...	...	...	...	0630	...	0830	...	1030	...	1230	...	1430	...	1630	...	...	1830	...	2030	...	...	...
51	**Gera** Hbf .... a.	...	...	...	...	...	...	0659	...	0859	...	1059	...	1259	...	1459	...	1659	...	...	1859	...	2059	...	...	...
51	**Gera** Hbf .... d.	...	...	0503	0555	0604	0619	0705	0805	0905	1005	1105	1204	1305	1405	1505	1605	1705	1805	1804	1905	2005	2106	2213	2341	...
91	Jena-Göschwitz .... d.	0412	0416	0532	0623	0639	0647	0732	0832	0932	1032	1132	1239	1332	1432	1532	1632	1732	1832	1839	1932	2032	2133	2243	0014	...
96	**Jena** West .... d.	0418	0421	0538	0629	0646	0653	0738	0838	0938	1038	1138	1246	1338	1438	1538	1638	1738	1838	1846	1938	2038	2138	2248	0019	...
119	Weimar .... **849 850** d.	0438	0438	0554	0646	0704	0708	0754	0854	0954	1054	1154	1304	1354	1454	1554	1654	1754	1854	1904	1954	2054	2154	2305	0038	0043
140	**Erfurt** Hbf .... **849 850** a.	0455	0452	0607	0701	0716	0721	0807	0909	1007	1109	1207	1316	1407	1509	1607	1709	1807	1909	1916	2007	2109	2207	2318	...	0059
	Göttingen **865** .... a.	...	...	0751	...	...	...	0951	...	1151	...	1351	...	1551	...	1751	...	1951	...	...	2150	2250	...	...	...	...

	◧	†w	⚒t	Ⓐt				⚒ ★	†						★						Ⓑ	Ⓑb ★	⑥			◧
Göttingen **865** .... d.	...	...	...	...	...	...	0604	...	...	0808	...	1008	...	1208	...	1408	...	1608	...	1808	1808	...	...	2008	2108	...
Erfurt Hbf ..... **849 850** d.	0038	0437	0437	0544	...	0651	0752	0844	0850	0952	1050	1150	1250	1352	1444	1550	1650	1752	1850	1952	1952	2044	2050	2152	2301	2349
Weimar .... **849 850** d.	0055	0451	0451	0557	...	0706	0806	0859	0904	1006	1104	1204	1304	1406	1459	1604	1704	1806	1904	2006	2006	2059	2104	2206	2315	0004
Jena West .... d.	0114	0505	0505	0612	...	0722	0822	0915	0920	1022	1120	1220	1320	1422	1515	1620	1720	1822	1920	2022	2022	2115	2120	2222	2330	0023
Jena-Göschwitz .... d.	0120	0513	0516	0625	...	0727	0827	0921	0925	1027	1125	1225	1325	1427	1521	1625	1725	1827	1925	2027	2027	2121	2125	2227	2335	0029
Gera Hbf .... a.	0151z	0541	0544	0654	...	0755	0855	0955	0953	1055	1153	1253	1353	1455	1555	1653	1753	1855	1953	2055	2055	2155	2153	2255	0003	0101
Gera Hbf .... d.	...	0547k	...	0658	0658	...	0858	...	...	1058	...	1258	...	1458	...	1658	...	1858	...	...	2058	...	...	...	...	...
Gößnitz .... a.	...	0623k	...	0729	0729	...	0929	...	...	1129	...	1329	...	1529	...	1729	...	1929	...	...	2129	...	...	...	...	...
Gößnitz .... d.	...	...	...	0735	0735	...	0935	...	...	1135	...	1336	...	1535	...	1735	...	1935	...	...	2135	...	...	...	...	...
Glauchau (Sachs) ...... a.	...	...	...	0749	0749	...	0949	...	...	1149	...	1349	...	1549	...	1749	...	1949	...	...	2149	...	...	...	...	...

– Not Oct. 2.
– Not Sept. 20.
– ⚒ (not Oct. 31).
t – Not Sept. 20, Oct. 31.
w – Also Sept. 20, Oct. 31.
z – Ⓒ (also Sept. 20, Oct. 31).
★ – *IC* service (see Table **849a**). Regional tickets are valid Gera - Erfurt and v.v.
◧ – Operated by Erfurter Bahn.

859 BRAUNSCHWEIG - BAD HARZBURG, GOSLAR and HERZBERG

DB (*RB* services); *erixx*

BRAUNSCHWEIG - GOSLAR and BAD HARZBURG ⊠

km		⚒t	Ⓐt	⚒t	⚒t					
0	**Braunschweig** Hbf ..... d.	0524	0524	0624	0624	0724	0724	and	2324	2324
12	Wolfenbüttel ..... d.	0533	0533	0633	0633	0733	0733	hourly	2333	2333
39	Vienenburg ..... **860** d.	0601	0602	0700	0702	0800	0802		0000	0002
47	**Bad Harzburg** . **860** a.	|	0611	|	0711	|	0811	until	|	0011
52	**Goslar** ..... **860** a.	0616	...	0712	...	0812	...		0012	...

	⚒t	⚒t	⚒t	Ⓐt		Ⓒz					
Goslar ..... **860** d.	0445	...	0545	...	0645	...	...	0745	and	...	2245
Bad Harzburg 860 d.	|	0545	|	0626	|	0645	0745	|	hourly	2245	|
Vienenburg ..... **860** d.	0503	0603	0603	0635	0700e	0703	0803	0803		2303	2303
Wolfenbüttel ..... d.	0526	0626	0626	0659	0726	0726	0826	0826	until	2326	2326
Braunschweig Hbf .. a.	0535	0635	0635	0709	0735	0735	0835	0835		2335	2335

BRAUNSCHWEIG - HERZBERG

km		ⒸzB		Ⓐt		⚒t				D
0	**Braunschweig** Hbf ..... d.	0005	...	0505	0605	0605	0705	and	2205	2305
31	Salzgitter-Ringelheim .. d.	0029	...	0529	0629	0629	0729	hourly	2229	2329
52	Seesen ..... d.	0043	...	0544	0643	0644	0744		2244	2343
71	Osterode (Harz) Mitte .. d.	...	...	0606	...	0706	0806	until	2306	...
83	**Herzberg** (Harz) ..... a.	...	...	0620	...	0720	0820		2320	...

	L		ⒶtB	⑥B	Ⓐt			⚒t			
Herzberg (Harz) ..... d.	...	...	...	...	0534	...	...	0634	0734	and	2234
Osterode (Harz) Mitte d.	...	...	...	...	0548	...	...	0648	0748	hourly	2248
Seesen ..... d.	0011	...	0511	0611	0611	...	0711	0711	0811		2311
Salzgitter-Ringelheim d.	0028	...	0528	0628	0628	...	0728	0728	0828	until	2328
Braunschweig Hbf .. a.	0050	...	0550	0650	0650	...	0750	0750	0850		2350

BAD HARZBURG - KREIENSEN - GÖTTINGEN

km		ⒸzB	Ⓐt	⚒t	Ⓒz	Ⓐt			Ⓐt	Ⓒz															HB
0	**Bad Harzburg** ..... **860** d.	...	...	0548	...	0628	0735	0748	...	0822	0935	1022	1135	1222	1335	1422	1535	1622	1735	1822	1935	2022	2135	2222	...
11	Goslar ..... **860** d.	...	0544	0600	0636	0641	0757	0800	0836	0836	0957	1036	1157	1236	1357	1436	1557	1636	1757	1836	1957	2036	2157	2236	...
34	Seesen ..... d.	0044	0603	...	0655	0700	0816	...	0855	0855	1016	1055	1216	1255	1416	1455	1616	1655	1816	1855	2016	2055	2216	2255	2344
48	Bad Gandersheim ..... d.	0054	0613	...	0705	0711	0826	...	0905	0905	1026	1105	1226	1305	1426	1505	1626	1705	1826	1905	2026	2105	2226	2305	2354
54	**Kreiensen** ..... a.	0100	0618	...	0711	0716	0831	...	0911	0911	1031	1111	1231	1311	1431	1511	1631	1711	1831	1911	2031	2111	2231	2311	2400
54	**Kreiensen** ..... **903** d.	...	*0624*	...	*0719*	*0723*	0839	...	*0919*	*0919*	1039	*1119*	1239	*1319*	1439	*1519*	1639	*1719*	1839	*1919*	2039	*2119*	2239	*2322*	*0023*
73	Northeim (Han) ..... **903** d.	...	*0637*	...	*0733*	*0736*	0855	...	*0933*	*0933*	1055	*1133*	1255	*1333*	1455	*1533*	1655	*1733*	1855	*1933*	2055	*2133*	2255	*2336*	*0036*
93	**Göttingen** ..... **903** a.	...	*0650*	...	*0746*	*0749*	0909	...	*0946*	*0946*	1109	*1146*	1309	*1346*	1509	*1546*	1709	*1746*	1909	*1946*	2109	*2146*	2309	*2349*	*0049*

	ⒶtB	Ⓐt	⑥B		Ⓐt	Ⓒz	Ⓒz	Ⓐt																	
Göttingen ..... **903** d.	*0408*	*0504*	*0504*	0604	...	...	0648	0719	...	*0809*	0848	*1009*	1048	*1209*	1248	*1407*k	1448	*1609*	1648	*1809*	1848	*2009*	2048	*2209*	...
Northeim (Han) ..... **903** d.	*0421*	*0517*	*0517*	0617	...	...	0703	0734	...	*0823*	0902	*1023*	1102	*1223*	1302	*1421*k	1502	*1623*	1702	*1823*	1902	*2023*	2102	*2223*	...
Kreiensen ..... **903** a.	*0434*	*0530*	*0530*	0631	...	...	0718	0749	...	*0836*	0918	*1036*	1118	*1236*	1318	*1434*k	1518	*1636*	1718	*1836*	1918	*2036*	2118	*2236*	...
Kreiensen ..... d.	0456	0535	0556	...	0640	0642	0723	0750	...	0842	0923	1042	1123	1242	1323	1442	1523	1642	1723	1842	1923	2042	2123	2242	...
Bad Gandersheim ..... d.	0501	0540	0601	...	0645	0647	0729	0756	...	0847	0929	1047	1129	1247	1329	1447	1529	1647	1729	1847	1929	2047	2129	2247	...
Seesen ..... d.	0511	0551	0611	...	0656	0658	0739	0806	...	0858	0939	1058	1139	1258	1339	1458	1539	1658	1739	1858	1939	2058	2139	2258	...
Goslar ..... **860** d.	...	0610	...	...	0718	0718	0800	0826	0856	0918	1000	1118	1200	1318	1400	1518	1600	1718	1800	1918	2000	2118	2200	2316	2356
Bad Harzburg ..... **860** a.	...	0623	...	...	0730	0730	0814	...	0907	0930	1014	1130	1214	1330	1414	1530	1614	1730	1814	1930	2014	2130	2214	...	0007

B – 12 Braunschweig - Seesen - Kreiensen and v.v.
D – To Kreisensen on dates in note **H** (see lower panel).
H – ①–④ (not Oct. 3, 31).
L – ①⑥⑦ (also Oct. 4, Nov. 1).

e – 0703 on Ⓒ (also Oct. 31).
k – 2 minutes later on Ⓒ (also Oct. 31).
t – Not Oct. 31.
z – Also Oct. 31.

⊠ – Operated by *erixx*.

860 HANNOVER - BAD HARZBURG and GOSLAR - HALLE

erixx; *Abellio*

HANNOVER - BAD HARZBURG ⊠ (see also notes ▶ and ▷)

km		Ⓐt	⚒t							
0	**Hannover** Hbf ..... ▶ d.	0446	0546	0646	0746	0846		2246	2346	...
36	**Hildesheim** Hbf ..... d.	0515	0614	0714	0814	0914	and	2314	0015	...
70	Salzgitter-Ringelheim .. d.	0542	0641	0741	0841	0941	hourly	2341	0042	...
89	Goslar **859** ..... d.	0556	0656	0756	0856	0956	until	2356	0057	...
100	**Bad Harzburg 859** ..... a.	0607	0707	0807	0907	1007		0007	0108	...

	Ⓐt	Ⓐt	⚒t	⚒t		Ⓐt				A	B
Bad Harzburg 859 .. d.	...	0448	...	0548	...	...	0648		2148	2248	2248
Goslar **859** ..... d.	0403	0503	0503	0603	0603	0635	0703	and	2203	2303	2303
Salzgitter-Ringelheim d.	0416	0516	0516	0616	0616	0648	0716	hourly	2216	2316	2316
Hildesheim Hbf ..... d.	0444	0544	0544	0644	0644	0717	0744	until	2244	2344	2344
Hannover Hbf ..... ▷ a.	0513	0613	0613	0713	0713	0744	0813		2313	0010	0013

GOSLAR - HALBERSTADT - HALLE ◇

km				Ⓐt	Ⓒz	Ⓐt			Ⓒz	⑥	Ⓐt														
0	**Goslar 859** ..... d.	...	...	...	...	...	...	...	...	0606	0606	0705	...	0806	0904	...	1006	1105	...	1206	1305	...	1406	1505	...
13	Vienenburg **859** ..... d.	...	...	...	...	...	...	...	...	0616	0616	0715	...	0816	0915	...	1016	1115	...	1216	1315	...	1416	1515	...
29	Ilsenburg ..... d.	...	...	0411	...	...	0529	...	0629	0629	0629	0731	...	0831	0931	...	1031	1131	...	1231	1331	...	1431	1531	...
38	Wernigerode ..... d.	...	...	0422	...	...	0540	...	0640	0640	0640	0742	...	0840	0942	...	1040	1142	...	1240	1342	...	1440	1542	...
62	**Halberstadt** ..... a.	...	...	0438	...	...	0555	...	0656	0656	0656	0755	...	0856	0955	...	1056	1155	...	1256	1355	...	1456	1555	...
62	**Halberstadt** ..... d.	0339	...	0446	0446	0528	0602	0607	0657	0657	0701	0801	0802	0901	1001	1002	1101	1201	1202	1301	1401	1402	1501	1601	1602
	Magdeburg Hbf **862** .. a.	|	...	|	|	|	0646	|	|	|	|	0846	|	|	1046	|	|	1246	|	|	1446	|	|	1646	|
	Berlin Hbf **839** ..... a.	|	...	|	|	|	...	|	|	|	|	...	|	|	...	|	|	...	|	|	...	|	|	...	|
94	Aschersleben ..... d.	0404	...	0521	0521	0557	...	0641	0726	0726	0726	...	0824	0926	...	1024	1126	...	1224	1326	...	1424	1526	...	1624
105	Sandersleben (Anh) ..... d.	0419	...	0537	0537	0606	...	0656	0737	0737	0737	...	0837	0937	...	1037	1137	...	1237	1337	...	1437	1537	...	1637
122	Könnern ..... d.	0433	...	0550	0550	0620	...	0710	0750	0750	0750	...	0850	0950	...	1050	1150	...	1250	1350	...	1450	1550	...	1650
152	**Halle** (Saale) Hbf ..... a.	0459	...	0608	0619	0637	...	0737	0811	0811	0811	...	0911	1011	...	1111	1211	...	1311	1411	...	1511	1611	...	1711

			D¶									
Goslar 859 ..... d.	1606	1705	1705	...	1806	1905	...	2006	2105	2206	2305	...
Vienenburg **859** ..... d.	1616	1715	1715	...	1816	1915	...	2016	2115	2216	2315	...
Ilsenburg ..... d.	1631	1731	1731	...	1831	1931	...	2031	2131	2232	2331	...
Wernigerode ..... d.	1640	1742	1742	...	1840	1942	...	2040	2142	2243	2342	...
Halberstadt ..... a.	1656	1755	1755	...	1856	1955	...	2056	2155	2258	2355	...
Halberstadt ..... d.	1701	1801	1801	1802	1901	2001	2002	2101	2202	2305	...	...
Magdeburg Hbf **862** .. a.	|	1846	1846	|	|	2056	|	|	2257	|	...	...
Berlin Hbf **839** ..... a.	|	...	2038	|	|	...	|	|	...	|	...	...
Aschersleben ..... d.	1726	...	...	1824	1926	...	2024	2126	...	2333	...	...
Sandersleben (Anh) ..... d.	1737	...	...	1837	1937	...	2037	2137	...	2347	...	...
Könnern ..... d.	1750	...	...	1850	1950	...	2050	2150	...	0000	...	...
Halle (Saale) Hbf ..... a.	1811	...	...	1911	2011	...	2111	2208	...	0028	...	...

	⚒t	Ⓐt						
Halle (Saale) Hbf ..... d.	...	0345	...	...	0525	0638	...	0749
Könnern ..... d.	...	0405	...	...	0551	0710	...	0810
Sandersleben (Anh) ..... d.	...	0418	...	...	0606	0724	...	0823
Aschersleben ..... d.	...	0429	...	...	0627c	0737	...	0835
Berlin Hbf **839** ..... d.	...	|	...	...	|	|	...	|
Magdeburg Hbf **862** ..... d.	...	|	...	...	|	|	0707	|
Halberstadt ..... a.	...	0458	...	...	0657	0757	0758	0900
Halberstadt ..... d.	0459	0459	...	0559	0702	...	0804	0904
Wernigerode ..... d.	0516	0516	...	0616	0719	...	0818	0921
Ilsenburg ..... d.	0530	0530	...	0630	0730	...	0829	0930
Vienenburg **859** ..... d.	0541	0541	...	0643	0741	...	0842	0941
Goslar 859 ..... a.	0552	0552	...	0654	0752	...	0853	0952

			Ⓒ¶																				E	⑦j¶	
Halle (Saale) Hbf ..... d.	0849	...	...	0949	1049	...	1149	1249	...	1349	1449	...	1549	1649	...	1749	1849	...	1949	2049	...	2309	...	...	2325
Könnern ..... d.	0910	...	...	1010	1110	...	1210	1310	...	1410	1510	...	1610	1710	...	1810	1910	...	2010	2110	...	2329	...	...	2358
Sandersleben (Anh) ..... d.	0923	...	...	1023	1123	...	1223	1323	...	1423	1523	...	1623	1723	...	1823	1923	...	2023	2123	...	2347	...	...	|
Aschersleben ..... d.	0937	...	...	1035	1137	...	1235	1337	...	1435	1537	...	1635	1737	...	1835	1937	...	2035	2137	...	0001	...	...	0047
Berlin Hbf **839** ..... d.	|	...	0720	|	|	...	|	|	...	|	|	...	|	|	...	|	|	...	|	|	...	|	...	2130	|
Magdeburg Hbf **862** .. d.	|	0908	0908	|	|	1108	|	|	1308	|	|	1508	|	|	1707	|	|	1908	|	|	2108	|	2319	2319	|
Halberstadt ..... a.	0957	0958	0958	1100	1157	1158	1300	1357	1358	1500	1557	1558	1700	1757	1758	1900	1957	1958	2102	2158	2159	0028	0009	0009	0115
Halberstadt ..... d.	...	1004	1004	1104	...	1204	1304	...	1404	1504	...	1604	1704	...	1804	1904	...	2004	2105	...	2205	...	0035	0035	...
Wernigerode ..... d.	...	1018	1018	1121	...	1218	1321	...	1418	1521	...	1618	1721	...	1818	1921	...	2018	2121	...	2219	...	0051	0051	...
Ilsenburg ..... d.	...	1029	1029	1130	...	1229	1330	...	1429	1530	...	1629	1730	...	1829	1930	...	2029	2129	...	2230	...	0101	0101	...
Vienenburg **859** ..... d.	...	1042	1042	1141	...	1242	1341	...	1442	1541	...	1642	1741	...	1842	1941	...	2042	2141	...	2242	...	...	...	...
Goslar 859 ..... a.	...	1053	1053	1152	...	1253	1352	...	1453	1552	...	1653	1752	...	1853	1952	...	2053	2152	...	2253	...	...	...	...

A – ⚒ from Aug. 25 (not Oct. 31).
B – Daily to Aug. 24; † from Aug. 28 (also Oct. 31).
D – ⑤⑥† only.
E – ①–⑥ (also Oct. 2; not Oct. 3).

c – Arrives 0618.
j – Also Oct. 3; not Oct. 2.
t – Not Oct. 31.
z – Also Oct. 31.

⊠ – Operated by *erixx*.
◇ – Operated by Abellio Rail Mitteldeutschland.
¶ – *HARZ-BERLIN-EXPRESS*.
▶ – Hannover departures are 2 minutes later from Aug. 25.
▷ – Hannover arrivals are 3 minutes earlier from Aug. 25 (except the 0744 arrival).

MAGDEBURG - SANGERHAUSEN - ERFURT and DESSAU - ASCHERSLEBEN 861

Operated by Abellio Rail Mitteldeutschland

Magdeburg - Erfurt and Aschersleben

km		Ⓒz	Ⓐt	Ⓐt		Ⓐt	Ⓒz								Ⓐt	Ⓒz	Ⓐt		Ⓐt							
0	**Magdeburg** Hbf .... d.	0051	0437	0511	0608	0712	0712	0826	0911	1026	1111	1226	1311	1426	1457	1511	1529	1626	1711	1711	1826	1911	2026	2111	2226	2255
17	Schönebeck (Elbe) .... d.	0106	0450	0526	0623	0726	0726	0839	0926	1039	1126	1239	1326	1439	1509	1526	1542	1639	1726	1726	1839	1926	2039	2126	2239	2316
37	Staßfurt .... d.	0130	0509	0550	0650	0750	0747	0853	0950	1053	1150	1253	1350	1453	1534	1550	1608	1653	1750	1750	1853	1950	2053	2150	2253	2337
44	Güsten .... d.	0137	0514	0558	0658	0758	0754	0858	0958	1058	1158	1258	1358	1458	1541	1558	1615	1658	1803	1759	1858	1958	2058	2158	2258	2344
	Aschersleben .... a.	0149	|	0610	|	0810	*0816*	|	1010	|	1210	|	1410	|	|	1610	1627	|	|	1810	|	2010	|	2210	|	2355
60	Sandersleben .... d.	▬	0546k	▬	0712	...	▬	0912	▬	1112	▬	1312	▬	1512	1555	▬	▬	1712	1815	▬	1912	▬	2112	...	2312	...
66	Hettstedt .... d.	...	0554	...	0719	...	...	0919	...	1119	...	1319	...	1519	1602	...	...	1719	1822	...	1919	...	2119	...	2319	...
75	Klostermansfeld .... d.	...	0603	...	0728	...	...	0928	...	1128	...	1328	...	1528	1611	Ⓒ	Ⓐ	1728	1832	...	1928	...	2128	...	2328	...
97	**Sangerhausen** .... d.	0547	0623	0641	0748	...	0852	0948	1052	1148	1252	1348	1452	1548	1634	1652	1652	1748	1857	1905	1956j	2100	2159j	...	2347	...
142	Sömmerda .... d.	0633	0701	0731	0829	...	0931	1029	1131	1229	1331	1429	1531	1629	...	1731	1736	1829	...	1953	2037	2142	2244	...	...	...
167	**Erfurt** Hbf .... a.	0654	0720	0751	0850	...	0951	1050	1151	1250	1351	1451	1551	1650	...	1751	1756	1850	...	2014	2058	2202	2305	...	...	...

	Ⓐt	Ⓐt	Ⓒz	Ⓐt	Ⓐt			Ⓐt																	
Erfurt Hbf .... d.	...	...	...	...	...	0506	...	0613	0704	0809	0910	1009	1110	1209	1310	1409	1509	1609	1710	1809	1906	...	2018	2136	2327
Sömmerda .... d.	...	...	...	...	...	0523	...	0633	0730	0829	0932	1029	1132	1229	1332	1429	1532	1629	1732	1829	1928	...	2038	2155	2347
Sangerhausen .... d.	...	...	...	0509	...	0618j	...	0723	0818	0909	1018	1109	1218	1309	1418	1509	1618	1709	1818	1909	2018	...	2123	2243	0032
Klostermansfeld .... d.	...	...	...	0528	...	0637	...	...	0837	▬	1037	▬	1237	▬	1437	▬	1637	▬	1837	▬	2037	...	...	...	...
Hettstedt .... d.	...	...	...	0537	...	0647	...	...	0847	...	1047	...	1247	...	1447	...	1647	...	1847	...	2047	...	...	...	...
Sandersleben .... d.	...	...	...	0545	...	0654	...	...	0854	...	1054	...	1254	...	1454	...	1654	...	1854	...	2054	...	...	...	...
Aschersleben .... d.	0448	0530	0544	|	0623	|	0746	...	|	0946	|	1146	|	1346	|	1546	|	1746	|	1946	|	2146	...	...	...
Güsten .... d.	0501	0541	0556	0559	0635	0708	0758	...	0908	0958	1108	1158	1308	1358	1508	1558	1708	1758	1908	1958	2108	2159	...	...	...
Staßfurt .... d.	0509	0553	0604	0612	0644	0715	0808	...	0915	1008	1115	1208	1315	1408	1515	1608	1715	1808	1915	2008	2115	2208	...	...	...
Schönebeck (Elbe) .... d.	0529	0615	0626	0629	0704	0730	0829	...	0930	1029	1130	1229	1330	1429	1530	1629	1730	1829	1930	2029	2130	2230	...	...	...
Magdeburg Hbf .... a.	0543	0627	0641	0643	0717	0742	0842	...	0942	1042	1142	1242	1343	1442	1542	1642	1742	1842	1942	2042	2142	2249	...	...	...

Dessau - Aschersleben (- Halberstadt)

km		Ⓐt	Ⓒz	Ⓐt		Ⓐt	Ⓒz	Ⓐt								Ⓐt	Ⓒz									
0	**Dessau** Hbf .... d.	0427	0453	0515	0553v	0643	0711	0730	0802	0901	1002	1101	1202	1301	1402	1501	1501	1602	1701	1802	1901	2002	2101	2217	2328	...
21	Köthen .... a.	0448	0515	0536	0620	0708	0732	0754	0822	0922	1022	1122	1222	1322	1422	1522	1522	1622	1722	1822	1922	2022	2122	2239	2350	...
21	Köthen .... d.	0451	0517	0539	0632	0723	0733	0754	0832	0923	1032	1123	1232	1323	1432	1523	1523	1632	1723	1832	1923	2032	...	2240	2351	...
42	Bernburg Hbf .... d.	0512	0539	0558	0653	0743	0754	0813	0853	0942	1053	1142	1253	1342	1453	1542	1542	1653	1742	1853	1942	2053	...	2301	0012	0023
54	Güsten .... d.	0524	0550	0610	0704	0754	0805	0824	0904	0954	1104	1154	1304	1354	1504	1553	1554	1704	1754	1904	1954	2104	...	2312	...	0034
66	**Aschersleben** ... **860** a.	0535	0602	0621	0715	*0810*	0816	0832	0915	*1010*	1115	*1210*	1315	*1410*	1515	1604	*1610*	1715	*1810*	1915	*2010*	2115	...	2323	...	0046
	Halberstadt .... **860** a.	...	...	...	...	...	...	...	0951	...	...	...	1351	...	1551	...	...	1751	...	...	...	...	...	...	...	0115

		Ⓐt											Ⓐt	Ⓒz											
Halberstadt .... **860** d.	...	...	...	...	...	...	...	1011	...	...	...	1411	...	...	1611	...	...	...	...	...	...	...	...	...	...
Aschersleben .... **860** d.	0421	0516	0557	0649	*0746*	0849	*0946*	1049	*1146*	1249	*1346*	1449	1537	*1546*	1649	*1746*	1849	*1946*	...	2042	...	2146	...	...	...
Güsten .... d.	0433	0527	0607	0701	0801	0902	1001	1102	1201	1302	1401	1502	1549	1601	1702	1801	1902	2001	...	2111n	...	2202	...	...	...
Bernburg Hbf .... d.	0454j	0538	0617	0713	0813	0913	1013	1113	1213	1313	1413	1513	1600	1613	1713	1813	1913	2013	...	2122	...	2214	...	...	...
Köthen .... a.	0516	0600	0638	0735	0834	0935	1034	1135	1234	1335	1434	1535	1622	1634	1735	1834	1935	2034	...	2144	...	2236	...	...	...
Köthen .... d.	0517	0601	0639	0737	0834	0937	1034	1137	1234	1337	1434	1537	1634	1634	1737	1834	1937	2034	...	2145	2217	2241	...	...	...
Dessau Hbf .... a.	0542	0623	0700	0756	0855	0956	1055	1156	1255	1356	1455	1556	1655	1655	1756	1855	1956	2055	...	2206	2243	2302	...	...	...

j – Arrives 9–12 minutes earlier. k – Arrives 0529. n – Arrives 2053. t – Not Oct. 31. v – 0558 on Ⓒ (also Oct. 31). z – Also Oct. 31.

Abellio Rail Mitteldeutschland MAGDEBURG - HALBERSTADT - THALE 862

km			Ⓐ t		⊙	◧		◧	Ⓒ ▲		◧		◧		◧		◧			◧		◧		◐	⑦w ▲
	Berlin Hbf **839** .... d.	...	...	...	...	...	...	...	0720	...	...	...	...	...	...	...	...	...	...	...	...	...	...	...	2130
0	**Magdeburg** Hbf .... d.	...	0429	...	0544	0707	0807	0908	0908	1007	1108	1207	1308	1407	1508	1607	1707	1808	1846	1908	2007	2108	2208	2319	2319
39	Oschersleben (Bode) ... d.	...	0505	...	0624	0742	0842	0942	0942	1042	1142	1242	1342	1442	1542	1642	1742	1842	1924	1942	2045	2145	2247	2355	2355
59	**Halberstadt** .... a.	...	0520	...	0640	0758	0857	0958	0958	1057	1158	1257	1358	1457	1558	1657	1758	1857	1940	1958	2100	2159	2302	0009	0009
59	**Halberstadt** .... d.	0540	0540	0610	0708	0808	0908	1008	1008	1108	1208	1308	1408	1508	1608	1708	1808	1908	...	2008	2109	2202	...	0029	0029
77	Quedlinburg .... a.	0556	0556	0625	0723	0823	0923	1023	1023	1123	1223	1323	1423	1523	1623	1723	1823	1923	...	2023	2124	2217	...	0043	0043
77	Quedlinburg .... d.	0557	0557	0630	0730	0830	0930	1030	1030	1130	1230	1330	1430	1530	1630	1730	1830	1930	...	2030	2130	2218	...	0044	0044
87	**Thale** Hbf .... a.	0609	0609	0642	0742	0842	0942	1042	1042	1142	1242	1342	1442	1542	1642	1742	1842	1942	...	2042	2142	2228	...	0054	0054

	Ⓐ t			◐		◧		◧		◧		◧		◧		◧	⑤⑥† ▲		◧		⊙◧			
Thale Hbf .... d.	...	...	...	0520	0617	0717	0817	0917	1017	1117	1217	1317	1417	1517	1617	1717	1717	1817	1917	2017	2117	...	2230	2342
Quedlinburg .... a.	...	...	...	0531	0628	0728	0828	0928	1028	1128	1228	1328	1428	1528	1628	1728	1728	1828	1928	2028	2128	...	2240	2352
Quedlinburg .... d.	...	...	...	0533	0633	0733	0833	0932	1033	1133	1233	1336	1433	1532	1633	1733	1733	1833	1936	2033	2133	...	2241	2353
Halberstadt .... a.	...	...	...	0549	0649	0749	0849	0948	1049	1149	1249	1351	1449	1548	1649	1749	1749	1849	1951	2049	2149	...	2257	0009
Halberstadt .... d.	0329	...	0444	0602	0701	0801	0901	1001	1101	1201	1301	1401	1501	1601	1701	1801	1801	1901	2001	2103	2202	...	...	...
Oschersleben (Bode) .... d.	0344	...	0501	0617	0717	0817	0917	1017	1117	1217	1317	1417	1517	1617	1717	1817	1817	1917	2017	2119	2218	...	...	...
Magdeburg Hbf .... a.	0421	...	0537	0646	0746	0846	0946	1046	1146	1246	1347	1446	1546	1646	1746	1846	1846	1946	2056	2152	2257	...	...	...
Berlin Hbf **839** .... a.	...	...	...	...	...	...	...	...	...	...	...	...	...	...	...	...	2038	...	...	...	...	...	...	...

t – Not Oct. 31.
w – Also Oct. 3; not Oct. 2.

⊙ – Change trains at Halberstadt on Ⓐ (not Oct. 31).
◧ – Conveys (12) Magdeburg - Halberstadt - Goslar and v.v. (Table **860**).
◐ – Conveys (12) Magdeburg - Halberstadt - Ilsenburg and v.v. (Table **860**).

▲ – *HARZ-BERLIN-EXPRESS*. DB tickets not valid for journeys from / to Berlin. Conveys (2) Berlin - Halberstadt - Ilsenburg / Goslar and v.v. (Table **860**).

Regionalverkehre Start Deutschland ◇; enno ⊠ WOLFSBURG - HILDESHEIM - HAMELN - BÜNDE 863

km		Ⓐt	⚒v	⑥	Ⓒz	Ⓐt																			
0	**Hildesheim** Hbf .... d.	...	0537	0634	...	0637	0737	0834	0937	1034	1137	1234	1337	1434	1537	1634	1737	1834	1937	2034	2137	2234	...	...	...
18	Elze .... a.	...	0553	0650	...	0653	0753	0850	0953	1050	1153	1250	1353	1450	1553	1650	1753	1850	1953	2050	2153	2250	...	...	...
18	Elze .... d.	...	0602	0702	...	0702	0802	0902	1002	1102	1202	1302	1402	1502	1602	1702	1802	1902	2002	2102	2202	2307	...	...	...
47	**Hameln** .... d.	0529	0629	0729	0729	0729	0829	0929	1029	1129	1229	1329	1429	1529	1629	1729	1829	1929	2029	2129	2229	2332	...	...	...
71	Rinteln .... d.	0546	0646	0746	0746	0746	0846	0946	1046	1146	1246	1346	1446	1546	1646	1746	1846	1946	2046	2146	2246	...	...	...	...
88	Vlotho .... d.	0601	0701	0801	0801	0801	0901	1001	1101	1201	1301	1401	1501	1601	1701	1801	1901	2001	2101	2201	2301	...	...	...	...
100	Löhne (Westf) ...... **811** a.	0614	0714	0814	0814	0814	0914	1014	1114	1214	1314	1414	1514	1614	1714	1814	1914	2014	2114	2214	2314	...	...	...	...
110	**Bünde** (Westf) ..... **811** a.	0625	0725t	...	...	0825	...	1025t	...	1225t	1325t	1425t	...	1625t	1725t	1825t	...	...	...	...	...	...	...	...	...

	Ⓐt	⚒v	Ⓐt	⚒v	⚒v							Ⓒz	A	Ⓐe										⑤⑥
Bünde (Westf) .... **811** d.	...	...	...	...	0632t	...	0732t	0832t	...	1032t	...	...	1232	1232	1332t	1432t	...	1632t	1732t	1832t	...	...	...	...
Löhne (Westf) .... **811** d.	0445	...	0545	...	0645	...	0745	0845	0945	1045	1145	1245	1245	1245	1345	1445	1545	1645	1745	1845	1945	2045	2145	2245
Vlotho .... d.	0459	...	0559	...	0659	...	0759	0859	0959	1059	1159	1259	1259	1259	1359	1459	1559	1659	1759	1859	1959	2059	2159	2259
Rinteln .... d.	0510	...	0610	...	0710	...	0810	0910	1010	1110	1210	1310	1310	1310	1410	1510	1610	1710	1810	1910	2010	2110	2210	2310
Hameln .... d.	0528	0528	0628	0628	0728	0728	0828	0928	1028	1128	1228	1328	1328	1335r	1428	1528	1628	1728	1828	1928	2028	2128	2228	2326
Elze .... a.	0553	0553	0653	0653	0753	0753	0852	0953	1052	1153	1252	1353	1353	1400	1452	1552	1652	1753	1852	1953	2052	2153	2252	...
Elze .... d.	0602	0602	0702	0702	0802	0802	0907	1002	1107	1202	1307	1402	1402	1402	1507	1602	1707	1802	1907	2002	2107	2202	2307	...
Hildesheim Hbf .... a.	0620	0620	0720	0720	0820	0820	0925	1020	1125	1220	1325	1420	1420	1423	1525	1620	1725	1820	1925	2020	2125	2220	2324	...

Regional trains **WOLFSBURG - BRAUNSCHWEIG - HILDESHEIM** ⊠. **Warning!** Services Wolfsburg - Braunschweig and v.v. are subject to alteration from October 14.

km		Ⓐt	⚒v	Ⓐt					
0	**Wolfsburg** Hbf .... d.	0514	0614	0643	0714	and	2314	0014	...
32	**Braunschweig** Hbf ..... d.	0535	0635	0704	0735	hourly	2335	0033	...
75	**Hildesheim** Hbf .... a.	0602	0702	...	0802	until	0002	...	...

	Ⓐt	⚒v	Ⓐt	⚒v		Ⓐt		⊡		
Hildesheim Hbf .... d.	0455	...	...	0555	...	...	0655	and	2255	...
Braunschweig Hbf .. d.	0526	0526	0551	0626	0626	0656	0726	hourly	2326	0046
Wolfsburg Hbf .... a.	0545	0545	0612	0645	0645	0719	0745	until	2345	0107

A – ①–⑤ July 14 - Aug. 24; ①–⑤ Oct. 17 – 28.
e – Not July 14 - Aug. 24, Oct. 17 – 31.
r – Arrives 1326.

t – Ⓐ (not Oct. 31).
v – Not Oct. 31.
z – Also Oct. 31.

⊡ – Braunschweig d. 0925 / 1325 (not 0926 / 1326).
◇ – Bünde - Hildesheim operated by Regionalverkehre Start Deutschland.
⊠ – Wolfsburg - Hildesheim operated by *enno*. See Table **902** for *ICE* trains operated by DB.

864 GÖTTINGEN - KASSEL local services

CANTUS Verkehrsgesellschaft (2nd class only

km		Ⓒ	Ⓐ	⚒	⚒	Ⓒ	Ⓐ	Ⓐ						Ⓒ	Ⓐ			Ⓐ								
0	**Göttingen** .... **908** d.	0026	0414	0514	0614	0714	0718	0748	0814	0914	1014	1114	1214	1314	1325	1414	1514	1543	1614	1714	1814	1914	2014	2114	2214	2314
20	Eichenberg .... **908** a.	0040	0428	0528	0628	0728	0732	0802	0828	0928	1028	1128	1228	1329	1339	1428	1528	1557	1628	1728	1828	1928	2028	2128	2228	2328
20	Eichenberg .... **865** d.	0041	0433	0533	0633	0733	0733	0803	0833	0933	1033	1133	1233	1333	1342	1433	1533	1603	1633	1733	1833	1933	2033	2133	2233	2333
43	Hann Münden .... **865** d.	0101	0453	0553	0653	0753	0753	0823	0853	0953	1053	1153	1253	1353	1402	1453	1553	1623	1653	1753	1853	1953	2053	2153	2253	2353
67	**Kassel** Hbf ⊡ .... **865** a.	0121	0513	0613	0713	0813	0813	0843	0913	1013	1113	1213	1313	1413	1426	1513	1613	1643	1713	1813	1913	2013	2113	2213	2313	0013

	Ⓒ	Ⓐ	Ⓐ	⑥	Ⓐ								Ⓐ				Ⓐ		Ⓐ							
Kassel Hbf ⊡ ...... **865** d.	0115	0416	0518	0546	0616	0646	0746	0846	0946	1046	1146	1246	1316	1346	1446	1546	1616	1646	1716	1746	1846	1946	2046	2146	2246	2346
Hann Münden ...... **865** d.	0135	0436	0537	0606	0636	0706	0806	0906	1006	1106	1206	1306	1336	1406	1506	1606	1636	1706	1736	1806	1906	2006	2106	2206	2306	0006
Eichenberg .... **865** a.	0154	0456	0557	0626	0656	0726	0826	0926	1026	1126	1226	1326	1356	1426	1526	1626	1656	1726	1756	1826	1926	2026	2126	2225	2326	0026
Eichenberg .... **908** d.	0155	*0502*	0605	0631	0704	0731	0831	0931	1031	1131	1231	1331	1357	1431	1531	1631	1659	1731	1806	1831	1931	2031	2131	2229	2331	0027
Göttingen .... **908** a.	0209	*0515*	0619	0645	0717	0745	0845	0945	1045	1145	1245	1345	1411	1445	1545	1645	1713	1745	1820	1845	1945	2045	2145	2243	2345	0041

⊡ – See Tables **806** and **901** for connecting trains to / from Kassel Wilhelmshöhe.

865 ERFURT and HALLE - LEINEFELDE - KASSEL and GÖTTINGEN

DB (*RE* / *RB* services); Abellio

km		Ⓐ △	Ⓐw	Ⓐt △	Ⓐ		Ⓐt	△	G	Ⓐt △			△	A	⚒r △			△	A	△			△	A	△
0	**Erfurt** Hbf .... **849 850** d.	...	...	...	...	0423	0502	...	0611	...	0622	0707	...	0810	...	0833	0907	...	1010	...	1033	1107	...	1210	...
27	Gotha .... **849 850** d.	...	...	...	...	0458	◇	...	0635	...	|	◇	...	0835	...	|	◇	...	1035	...	|	◇	...	1235	...
48	Bad Langensalza .... d.	...	...	...	0446	0509	0555	...	0646	...	0710	0800	...	0847	...	0914	1000	...	1047	...	1114	1200	...	1247	...
67	Mühlhausen (Thür) .... d.	...	...	...	0503	0524	0611	...	0700	...	0726	0815	...	0900	...	0926	1015	...	1100	...	1126	1215	...	1300	...
	Halle (Saale) Hbf .... d.	...	...	...	|	|	|	0453	|	0527	|	|	0702	|	0802	|	|	0902	|	1002	|	|	1102	|	1202
	Röblingen am See .... d.	...	...	...	|	|	|	0517	|	0601	|	|	0724	|	0824	|	|	0924	|	1024	|	|	1124	|	1224
	Lutherstadt Eisleben .... d.	...	...	...	|	|	|	0526	|	0610	|	|	0734	|	0832	|	|	0934	|	1032	|	|	1134	|	1232
	Sangerhausen .... d.	...	...	0414	|	|	|	0545	|	0634	|	|	0753	|	0848	|	|	0953	|	1048	|	|	1153	|	1248
	Nordhausen .... d.	...	...	0449	|	|	|	0619	|	0707	|	|	0826	|	0917	|	|	1026	|	1117	|	|	1226	|	1317
94	**Leinefelde** .... a.	...	...	0529	0532	0542	0634	0651	0717	0747	0750	0840	0857	0917	0948	0951	1040	1057	1117	1148	1151	1240	1257	1317	1348
94	**Leinefelde** .... d.	0423	0502	...	0533	0544	...	0655	0718	...	0751	...	0858	0918	...	0953	...	1058	1118	...	1153	...	1258	1318	...
110	Heilbad Heiligenstadt .... d.	0438	0513	...	0547	0556	...	0705	0729	...	0801	...	0908	0929	...	1004	...	1108	1129	...	1204	...	1308	1329	...
144	**Göttingen** .... a.	|	0539	...	|	0625	...	|	0751	...	|	...	|	0951	...	|	...	|	1151	...	|	...	|	1351	...
125	Eichenberg .... **864** d.	0501j	...	...	0602	...	...	0719	...	...	0816	...	0919	...	...	1018	...	1119	...	...	1218	...	1319	...	...
148	Hann Münden .... **864** d.	0520	...	...	0622	...	...	0736	...	...	0833	...	0936	...	...	1035	...	1136	...	...	1235	...	1336	...	...
172	**Kassel** Hbf .... **864** a.	0540	...	...	0643	...	...	|	...	...	|	...	|	...	...	|	...	|	...	...	|	...	|	...	...
176	**Kassel** Wilhelmshöhe .... a.	...	...	...	0656	...	...	0754	...	...	0852	...	0956	...	...	1054	...	1153	...	...	1254	...	1356	...	...

			△	A	△			△	A	△			△	A	△			△	A		△	G		△	△
Erfurt Hbf .... **849 850** d.	1233	1307	...	1410	...	1433	1507	...	1610	...	1633	1707	...	1810	...	1833	1907	...	2010	2034	...	2113	2252	...	...
Gotha .... **849 850** d.	|	◇	...	1435	...	|	◇	...	1635	...	|	◇	...	1835	...	|	◇	...	2035	|	...	2136	2316	...	...
Bad Langensalza .... d.	1314	1400	...	1447	...	1514	1600	...	1647	...	1714	1800	...	1847	...	1914	2000	...	2047	2113	...	2147	2329	...	...
Mühlhausen (Thür) .... d.	1326	1415	...	1500	...	1526	1615	...	1700	...	1726	1815	...	1900	...	1926	2016	...	2100	2127	...	2158	2343	...	...
Halle (Saale) Hbf .... d.	|	|	1302	|	1402	|	|	1502	|	1602	|	|	1702	|	1802	|	...	1902	|	|	2002	|	|	2109	2320
Röblingen am See .... d.	|	|	1324	|	1424	|	|	1524	|	1624	|	|	1724	|	1824	|	...	1924	|	|	2024	|	|	2128	2340
Lutherstadt Eisleben .... d.	|	|	1334	|	1432	|	|	1534	|	1632	|	|	1734	|	1832	|	...	1934	|	|	2032	|	|	2137	2349
Sangerhausen .... d.	|	|	1353	|	1448	|	|	1553	|	1648	|	|	1753	|	1848	|	...	1953	|	|	2048	|	|	2156	0008
Nordhausen .... d.	|	|	1426	|	1517	|	|	1626	|	1717	|	|	1826	|	1917	|	...	2026	|	|	2123j	|	|	2228	0041
Leinefelde .... a.	1351	1440	1456	1517	1548	1551	1640	1657	1717	1748	1751	1840	1857	1917	1948	1951	...	2057	2117	2147	2204	2216	2400	...	...
Leinefelde .... d.	1353	...	1456	1518	...	1553	...	1658	1718	...	1753	...	1858	1918	...	1953	...	2058	2118	2148	▬	2217	...	...	...
Heilbad Heiligenstadt .... d.	1404	...	1507	1529	...	1604	...	1708	1729	...	1804	...	1908	1929	...	2004	...	2108	2129	2158	...	2228	...	...	...
Göttingen .... a.	|	...	|	1551	...	|	...	|	1751	...	|	...	|	1951	...	|	...	|	2150	|	...	2250	...	...	...
Eichenberg .... **864** d.	1418	...	1519	...	...	1618	...	1719	...	...	1818	...	1919	...	...	2018	...	2119	...	2212	2233	...	...	...	...
Hann Münden .... **864** d.	1435	...	1536	...	...	1635	...	1736	...	...	1835	...	1936	...	...	2035	...	2136	...	...	2253	...	...	...	...
Kassel Hbf .... **864** a.	|	...	|	...	...	|	...	|	...	...	|	...	|	...	...	|	...	2154	...	...	2313	...	...	...	...
Kassel Wilhelmshöhe .... a.	1454	...	1554	...	...	1655	...	1756	...	...	1854	...	1954	...	...	2054	...	...	...	...	...	...	...	...	...

km		△		Ⓐ¶ △	Ⓐt	⚒r △	A	Ⓐ △	Ⓒ △		Ⓐ	⑥⑦	△	A	△			△	A	△			△	A	△
0	**Kassel** Wilhelmshöhe .... d.	...	...	...	...	...	...	...	...	...	0706	...	...	...	0806	...	0906	...	...	1006	...	1106	...	...	1206
	Kassel Hbf .... **864** d.	...	...	0416	...	...	...	0546	0606	...	|	...	...	...	|	...	|	...	...	|	...	|	...	...	|
23	Hann Münden .... **864** d.	...	...	0436	...	...	...	0605	0623	...	0722	...	...	...	0823	...	0922	...	...	1023	...	1122	...	...	1223
46	Eichenberg .... **864** d.	...	...	0457	...	...	...	0633j	0640	...	0741	...	...	...	0840	...	0941	...	...	1040	...	1141	...	...	1240
	Göttingen .... d.	...	...	|	...	...	0604	|	|	...	|	...	...	0808	|	...	|	...	1008	|	...	|	...	1208	|
61	Heilbad Heiligenstadt .... d.	...	0444t	0510	...	...	0628	0647	0652	...	0755	...	...	0831	0852	...	0955	...	1031	1052	...	1155	...	1231	1252
77	**Leinefelde** .... a.	...	0459t	0523	...	...	0638	0701	0702	...	0805	...	...	0842	0902	...	1005	...	1042	1102	...	1205	...	1242	1302
77	**Leinefelde** .... d.	0440v	0502	0524	0547	0549p	0640	0703	0703	0719t	0807	0807	0810t	0843	0903	0919	1007	1009r	1043	1103	1119	1207	1209	1243	1303
119	**Nordhausen** .... d.	0532k	|	0558	|	0632	|	0735	0735	|	|	|	0843t	|	0935	|	|	1043r	|	1135	|	|	1243	|	1335
157	Sangerhausen .... d.	0610	|	0630	|	0709	|	0809	0809	|	|	|	0912	|	1009	|	|	1112	|	1209	|	|	1312	|	1409
179	Lutherstadt Eisleben .... d.	0629	|	0650	|	0727	|	0827	0827	|	|	|	0929	|	1027	|	|	1129	|	1227	|	|	1329	|	1427
190	Röblingen am See .... a.	0637	|	0659	|	0735	|	0835	0835	|	|	|	0937	|	1035	|	|	1137	|	1235	|	|	1337	|	1435
217	**Halle** (Saale) Hbf .... a.	0658	|	0734	|	0755	|	0855	0855	|	|	|	0957	|	1055	|	|	1157	|	1255	|	|	1357	|	1455
—	Mühlhausen (Thür) .... d.	...	0522	...	0612	...	0657	...	...	0742	0832	0832	...	0859	...	0942	1032	...	1059	...	1142	1232	...	1259	...
0	Bad Langensalza .... d.	...	0535	...	0630	...	0709	...	...	0759	0844	0844	...	0910	...	0959	1044	...	1110	...	1159	1244	...	1310	...
	Gotha .... **849 850** a.	...	0551	...	⊙	...	0720	...	...	⊙	|	|	...	0922	...	⊙	|	...	1122	...	⊙	|	...	1322	...
38	**Erfurt** Hbf .... **849 850** a.	...	0617	...	0720	...	0746	...	...	0846	0921	0921	...	0946	...	1046	1121	...	1146	...	1246	1321	...	1346	...

			△	A	△			△	A	△			△	A	△			△	G	△	G		△		
Kassel Wilhelmshöhe .... d.	...	1306	...	...	1406	...	1506	...	...	1606	...	1706	...	...	1805	...	1905	...	...	2005	...	2106	...	...	...
Kassel Hbf .... **864** d.	...	|	...	...	|	...	|	...	...	|	...	|	...	...	|	...	|	...	...	|	...	|	...	*2146*	...
Hann Münden .... **864** d.	...	1322	...	...	1423	...	1523	...	...	1623	...	1722	...	...	1823	...	1922	...	...	2023	...	2122	...	*2206*	...
Eichenberg .... **864** d.	...	1341	...	...	1440	...	1541	...	...	1640	...	1741	...	...	1840	...	1941	...	...	2040	...	2141	...	2242	...
Göttingen .... d.	...	|	...	1408	|	...	|	...	1608	|	...	|	...	1808	|	...	|	...	2008	|	2108	|	...	|	2308
Heilbad Heiligenstadt .... d.	...	1355	...	1431	1452	...	1555	...	1631	1652	...	1755	...	1831	1852	...	1955	...	2031	2052	2132	2155	...	2254	2331
Leinefelde .... a.	...	1405	...	1442	1502	...	1605	...	1642	1702	...	1805	...	1842	1902	...	2005	...	2042	2102	2142	2206	...	2304	2342
Leinefelde .... d.	1319	1407	1409	1443	1503	1519	1607	1609	1643	1703	1719	1807	1809	1843	1903	1919	2007	2013	2043	2103	2148	2220	2226	...	...
Nordhausen .... d.	|	|	1443	|	1535	|	|	1643	|	1735	|	|	1843	|	1935	|	|	2054	|	2137	|	|	2306	...	...
Sangerhausen .... d.	|	|	1512	|	1609	|	|	1712	|	1809	|	|	1912	|	2009	|	|	2130	|	2211	|	|	2339	...	...
Lutherstadt Eisleben .... d.	|	|	1529	|	1627	|	|	1729	|	1827	|	|	1929	|	2027	|	|	2150	|	2229	|	|	2358	...	...
Röblingen am See .... a.	|	|	1537	|	1635	|	|	1737	|	1835	|	|	1937	|	2035	|	|	2159	|	2237	|	|	0008	...	...
Halle (Saale) Hbf .... a.	|	|	1557	|	1655	|	|	1757	|	1855	|	|	1957	|	2055	|	|	2234	|	2257	|	|	0040	...	...
Mühlhausen (Thür) .... d.	1342	1432	...	1459	...	1542	1632	...	1659	...	1742	1832	...	1859	...	1942	2027	...	2059	...	2212	2239	...	...	...
Bad Langensalza .... d.	1359	1444	...	1510	...	1559	1644	...	1710	...	1759	1844	...	1910	...	1959	2043	...	2110	...	2223	2255	...	...	...
Gotha .... **849 850** a.	⊙	|	...	1522	...	⊙	|	...	1722	...	⊙	|	...	1922	...	⊙	|	...	2122	...	2235	|	...	...	...
Erfurt Hbf .... **849 850** a.	1446	1521	...	1546	...	1646	1721	...	1746	...	1846	1921	...	1946	...	2052	2121	...	2149	...	2258	2334	...	...	...

A – From / to Glauchau (Table **858**).
G – From / to Gera (Table **858**).

j – Arrives 7–9 minutes earlier.
k – Arrives 0520.
p – 0558 on ⑥.
r – ⚒ (not Oct. 31).
t – Ⓐ (not Oct. 31).
v – Ⓐ (not Sept. 20, Oct. 31).
w – Not Sept. 20.

¶ – On Oct. 31 does not run Nordhausen - Halle.
△ – Operated by Abellio Rail Mitteldeutschland.
◇ – Connecting trains Gotha - Bad Langensalza (journey time: 18–21 minutes). **From Gotha** at 0529 Ⓐ **t**, 0737, 0937, 1137, 1337, 1537, 1737 and 1937.
⊙ – Connecting trains Bad Langensalza - Gotha (journey time: 19 minutes). **From Bad Langensalza** at 0650 Ⓐ **t**, 0801, 1001, 1201, 1401, 1601, 1801 and 2001.

HANNOVER - MAGDEBURG - LEIPZIG 866

See panels below main table for regional trains Braunschweig - Magdeburg - Halle (Saale) and v.v. See Table **848** for other regional trains between Magdeburg and Leipzig via Dessau.

km		IC 2449 Ⓐ	IC 2031 Ⓐ	IC 2447 ①–⑥	IC 2033	IC 2445	IC 2035	IC 2443	IC 2037	IC 2441	IC 2039	ICE 1133 ⑤	IC 2049	IC 2431 C	IC 2239 A	IC 2047	IC 2433	IC 2045	IC 2435	IC 2043 Ⓑ	IC 2043 ⑤⑦	RE 16339		IC 2437 Ⓑ	RE 16341
			🍷	🍷	🍷	🍷	🍷	🍷	🍷	🍷	🍷	✕	🍷	🍷		🍷	🍷	🍷	🍷						
	Köln Hbf **800** d.	...	...	...	...	0511e	...	0713	...	0913	...	...	1113	...	...	1313	...	1513	...	1713	1713	...	...	...	...
	Dortmund Hbf **800** d.	...	...	...	...	0625	...	0825	...	1025	...	...	1225	...	...	1425	...	1625	...	1825	1825	...	...	...	...
	Bielefeld Hbf **810** d.	...	...	0519g	...	0719	...	0919	...	1119	...	...	1319	...	...	1519	...	1719	...	1919	1919	...	...	...	...
	Norddeich **813** d.	...	...	|	...	|	0536e	|	0739e	|	0939	...	|	...	...	|	...	|	1540	|	|	...	...	...	...
	Emden Hbf **813** d.	...	...	|	0416e	|	0609e	|	0816	|	1016	...	|	1218	...	|	1416	|	1616	|	|	...	...	1813	...
	Oldenburg (Oldb) **813** d.	...	...	|	0535e	|	0735	|	0935	|	1135	1229	|	1335	...	|	1535	|	1735	|	|	...	...	1935	...
	Bremen Hbf **813** d.	...	...	|	0609	|	0809	|	1009	|	1209	1305	|	1409	...	|	1609	|	1809	|	|	...	...	2009	...
0	**Hannover** Hbf **811** d.	...	0534	0636	0736	0836	0936	1036	1136	1236	1336	1411	1436	1536	...	1636	1736	1836	1936	2036	2036	...	...	2136	...
35	Peine **811** d.	...	0555	|	|	|	|	|	|	|	|	|	|	|	...	|	|	|	|	|	|	...	...	2157	...
61	**Braunschweig** Hbf **811** d.	...	0610	0710	0810	0910	1010	1110	1210	1310	1410	1448	1510	1610	...	1710	1810	1910	2010	2110	2110	...	...	2213	...
97	Helmstedt d.	...	0631	|	0831	|	1031	|	1231	|	1431	|	|	1631	...	|	1831	|	2031	|	|	...	...	2234	...
145	**Magdeburg** Hbf a.	...	0656	0754	0856	0954	1056	1154	1256	1354	1456	1536	1554	1658	...	1754	1858	1954	2056	2154	2154	...	...	2302	...
145	**Magdeburg** Hbf d.	0600	0704	0800	0904	1000	1104	1200	1304	1400	1504	1538	1600	1704	1704	1800	1904	2000	2104	...	2200	2208	...	...	2308
	Berlin Hbf **839** a.	|	|	|	|	|	|	|	|	|	|	|	|	1823	|	|	|	|	|	...	|	|	...	...	|
195	Köthen d.	0629	0733	0829	0933	1029	1133	1229	1333	1429	1533	|	1629	...	1733	1829	1933	2029	2133	...	2229	2246	...	...	2346
231	**Halle** (Saale) Hbf a.	0647	0753	0847	0953	1047	1153	1247	1353	1447	1553	◐	1647	...	1753	1847	1953	2047	2153	...	2247	2313	...	...	0013
231	**Halle** (Saale) Hbf ⊡ d.	0655	0755	0855	0955	1055	1157	1255	1355	1455	1555	|	1655	...	1755	1855	1955	2055	2155	...	2255	*2325*	...	...	*0025*
249	Leipzig/Halle Flughafen ✈ ⊡ a.	0705	|	0905	|	1105	|	1305	|	1505	|	|	1705	...	|	1905	|	2105	|	...	2305	|	...	...	|
268	**Leipzig** Hbf ⊡ a.	0717	0815	0917	1015	1117	1216	1317	1415	1517	1615	1659	1717	...	1815	1917	2015	2117	2215	...	2317	*0002*	...	...	*0102*
	Dresden Hbf **842** a.	0846	...	1100	...	1300	...	1445w	...	1648	...	...	1844	...	...	2046	...	2245b	...	...	...	...	...	...	...

	IC 2436 Ⓐ	RE 16302	RE 16302 Ⓐ	IC 2042 ①	IC 2042 ①–⑥	IC 2434 ①–⑥	IC 2044	IC 2238 A	IC 2432 C	IC 2046	IC 2430	IC 2048	IC 2038	IC 2440	IC 2036	IC 2442	IC 2034	IC 1934 ⑦	IC 2444	IC 2444 Ⓑ	IC 2032 Ⓑ	IC 2446	IC 2446 ⑤⑦	IC 2030 ⑤	IC 2448 Ⓑ
						🍷	🍷		🍷	🍷	🍷	🍷	🍷	🍷	🍷	🍷	🍷		🍷	🍷	🍷	🍷	🍷		🍷
Dresden Hbf **842** ▷ d.	...	...	...	...	...	...	0512t	...	...	0712e	...	0844	...	1044	...	1244w	...	1422	1512	1512	...	1712	1712	...	1844
Leipzig Hbf ⊡ d.	...	...	*0358*	0443	...	0542	0638	0742	...	0838	0942	1038	1142	1238	1342	1438	1542	1602	1638	1638	1742	1838	1838	1942	2038
Leipzig/Halle Flughafen ✈ ⊡ d.	...	...	*0412*	0455	...	|	0650	|	...	0850	|	1050	|	1250	|	1450	|	|	1650	1650	|	1850	1850	|	2050
Halle (Saale) Hbf ⊡ a.	...	...	*0422*	0506	...	0602	0701	0800	...	0901	1000	1101	1200	1301	1400	1501	1600	|	1701	1701	1800	1901	1901	2000	2101
Halle (Saale) Hbf d.	...	...	0442	0509	...	0606	0709	0806	...	0909	1006	1109	1206	1309	1406	1509	1606	◧	1709	1709	1806	1909	1909	2006	2109
Köthen d.	...	0510	0510	0527	...	0627	0727	0827	...	0927	1027	1127	1227	1327	1427	1527	1627	|	1727	1727	1827	1927	1927	2027	2127
Berlin Hbf **839** d.	...	|	|	|	...	|	|	|	0730	|	|	|	|	|	|	|	|	|	|	|	|	|	|	|	|
Magdeburg Hbf a.	...	0549	0549	0556	...	0653	0756	0851	0854	0956	1053	1156	1253	1356	1453	1556	1653	1724	1756	1756	1853	1956	1956	2053	2156
Magdeburg Hbf d.	0500	...	...	0603	0603	0700	0803	...	0900	1003	1100	1203	1300	1403	1500	1603	1700	1726	1803	1803	1900	2003	2003	2100	2203
Helmstedt d.	0526	...	...	0628	0628	0726	|	...	0926	|	1126	|	1326	|	1526	|	1726	|	|	|	1926	|	|	2126	|
Braunschweig Hbf **811** d.	0549	...	...	0649	0649	0749	0849	...	0949	1049	1149	1249	1349	1449	1549	1649	1749	1814	1849	1849	1949	2049	2049	2149	2250
Peine **811** d.	0606	...	...	|	|	|	|	...	|	|	|	|	|	|	|	|	|	|	|	|	|	|	|	|	|
Hannover Hbf **811** a.	0626	...	...	0723	0723	0823	0923	...	1023	1123	1223	1323	1423	1523	1623	1723	1823	1851	1923	1923	2023	2123	2123	2223	2326
Bremen Hbf **813** a.	0750	...	...	|	|	0950	|	...	1150	|	1350	|	1550	|	1750	|	1950	2009	...	|	2150	...	|	...	...
Oldenburg (Oldb) **813** a.	0823	...	...	|	|	1023	|	...	1223	|	1423	|	1623	|	1823	|	2023	2040	...	|	2223	...	|	...	...
Emden Hbf **813** a.	0938	...	...	|	|	1138	|	...	1338	|	1538	|	1738	|	1938	|	2138	2152	...	|	2338	...	|	...	...
Norddeich **813** a.	...	...	...	|	|	...	|	...	1414	|	...	|	...	|	2014b	|	2214	...	...	|	...	...	|	...	...
Bielefeld Hbf **810** a.	...	...	...	0839	0839	...	1039	...	...	1239	...	1439	...	1639	...	1839	...	...	...	2039	...	...	2239	...	...
Dortmund Hbf **800** a.	...	...	...	0933	0933	...	1133	...	...	1333	...	1533	...	1733	...	1933	...	...	...	2133	...	...	2333	...	...
Köln Hbf **800** a.	...	...	...	1046	1046	...	1246	...	...	1446	...	1646	...	1846	...	2046	...	...	...	2245	...	...	0046	...	...

Other regional stopping trains **BRAUNSCHWEIG - MAGDEBURG**

	†		Ⓐ	Ⓒ	⚒	Ⓐ		Ⓐ		Ⓐ		Ⓐ	Ⓒ	Ⓐ	Ⓐ		Ⓐ		Ⓐ			Ⓑ	⑥	Ⓑ	
Braunschweig Hbf d.	0107	...	...	0542	...	0617	0717	0817	0917	1017	1117	1217	1317	1320	1417	1517	1617	1717	1817	1917	2017	2117	2147	2217	2347
Helmstedt d.	0136	0435	0606	0610	0646	0646	0746	0846	0946	1046	1146	1246	1346	1348	1446	1546	1646	1746	1846	1946	2046	2146	2216	2246	0017
Magdeburg Hbf a.	0219	0518	0652	0652	0729	0729	0829	0929	1029	1129	1229	1329	1429	1429	1529	1629	1729	1829	1929	2029	2129	2229	2259	2329	...

	⑥	Ⓐ	Ⓒ	Ⓐ				Ⓐ			Ⓐ		Ⓐ		Ⓐ			Ⓐ			Ⓐ				
Magdeburg Hbf d.	0253	0433	0533	*0530*	0633	0733	...	0833	0933	...	1033	1133	1233	1333	1433	1533	...	1633	1733	...	1833	1933	2033	2205	2314
Helmstedt d.	0333	0513	0613	0615	0713	0813	0913	0913	1013	1113	1113	1213	1313	1413	1513	1613	1713	1713	1813	1913	1913	2013	2113	2245	2354
Braunschweig Hbf a.	0402	0541	0641	0645	0741	0841	0941	0941	1041	1141	1141	1241	1341	1441	1541	1641	1741	1741	1841	1941	1941	2041	2141	2313	...

Other regional trains **MAGDEBURG - HALLE**

		Ⓐ						
Magdeburg Hbf d.	0414	0501	0535	and hourly until	2035	...	2208	2308
Schönebeck (Elbe) d.	0423	0512	0546		2046	...	2219	2319
Köthen d.	0447	0536	0613		2113	...	2246	2346
Halle (Saale) Hbf a.	0514	0600	0642		2142	...	2313	0013

	Ⓐ			Ⓐ						
Halle (Saale) Hbf d.	0442	...	0542	0614	0714	and hourly until	2014	2124	2259	0008
Köthen d.	0510	0510	0610	0643	0742		2042	2152	2327	0036
Schönebeck (Elbe) d.	0537	0537	0637	0709	0809		2109	2219	2353	0102
Magdeburg Hbf a.	0549	0549	0649	0723	0822		2122	2230	0005	0114

A – To/from Warnemünde via Schwerin and Rostock (see Tables **830**, **837** and **841**).
C – To/from Cottbus on dates in Table **837**.

b – Ⓑ.
e – ①–⑥.
g – ① only.
t – Ⓐ only.
w – ⑦ only.

◧ – Via Bitterfeld (d. 1626) and Dessau Hbf (d. 1647).
◐ – Via Dessau Hbf (a. 1614) and Bitterfeld (a. 1632).
⊡ – See Table **881** for other S-Bahn services.

867 HARZER SCHMALSPURBAHNEN

2nd class only

Nordhausen - Wernigerode: *Die Harzquerbahn*; Eisfelder Talmühle - Stiege - Alexisbad - Quedlinburg: *Die Selketalbahn*; Drei Annen Hohne - Brocken: *Die Brockenbahn*

SUMMER SERVICE VALID APRIL 9 - NOVEMBER 6, 2022

km			🚂	🚂	🚂	🚂	🚂 B	◧	🚂	🚂 B	A 🚂	
0	**Wernigerode** § d.	0825	0855	0940	1025	1155	...	1325	1455	...	1625	1725
15	Drei Annen Hohne a.	0902	0932	1017	1102	1232	...	1402	1532	...	1702	1802
15	Drei Annen Hohne ◇ d.	0903	0945	1030	1115	1248	1246	1415	1552	1548	1716	1803
20	Schierke ◇ a.	|	0957	1042	1127	|	1258	1427	1604	|	1728	|
20	Schierke ◇ d.	|	1005	1050	1135	|	1313	1440	1621	|	1748	|
34	**Brocken** ◇ a.	|	1036	1121	1206	|	1344	1530	1652	|	1819	|
19	Elend d.	0915	...	...	...	1300	▬	▬	...	1600	...	1818
28	Sorge d.	0934	...	...	...	1319	...	...	...	1619	...	1837
31	Benneckenstein d.	0948	...	...	...	1328	...	...	...	1628	...	1846
44	Eisfelder Talmühle a.	1016	...	...	...	1356	...	⑥⑦	...	1657	...	1914
44	Eisfelder Talmühle d.	1017	...	...	...	...	1402	1544	...	1714	...	1915
50	Ilfeld d.	1032	...	...	...	...	1417	1559	...	1729	...	1929
61	**Nordhausen** Nord § a.	1053	...	...	...	...	1439‡	1622	...	1751	...	1952

		🚂 B	🚂	🚂		🚂	⑥⑦	🚂		◧	A 🚂
Nordhausen Nord § d.	0833	1033	...	...	1325	...	1454‡	...	1626	...	...
Ilfeld d.	0900	1059	...	...	1346	...	1516	...	1648	...	...
Eisfelder Talmühle a.	0914	1113	...	...	1400	...	1530	...	1702	...	...
Eisfelder Talmühle d.	0915	1120	...	...	▬	1411	▬	...	1712	...	...
Benneckenstein d.	0947	1150	...	...	...	1441	...	...	1742	...	...
Sorge d.	0955	1158	...	...	...	1449	...	...	1750	...	...
Elend d.	1014	1217	...	...	🚂 B	1508	🚂	...	1819	...	...
Brocken ◇ d.	|	|	1136	1314	1451	|	1622	1707	|	1749	1831
Schierke a.	|	|	1216	1354	1521	|	1702	1746	|	1829	1901
Schierke ◇ d.	|	|	1224	1355	1522	|	1703	1747	|	1830	1902
Drei Annen Hohne ◇ a.	1025	1228	1236	1407	1533	1519	1714	1759	1830	1841	1913
Drei Annen Hohne d.	1041	...	1253	1423	...	1553	1721	1808	1831	1853	1923
Wernigerode § a.	1121	...	1333	1503	...	1633	1803	1845	1908	1930	2000

km		🚂		🚂	🚂		🚂					🚂
0	**Quedlinburg** § ... ▷ d.	...	0830	1030	1256	1341	...	...	1530	...	1728	1941
8	**Gernrode** ▷ a.	...	0845	1045	1312	1357	...	...	1545	...	1743	1956
8	**Gernrode** d.	0736	0846	1046	▬	▬	1413	...	1546	...	1744	▬
18	Mägdesprung d.	0806	0919	1117	...	...	1443	...	1618	...	1815	...
	Harzgerode d.	|	|	|	1219	1450	|	...	|	1614	|	1843
23	Alexisbad a.	0820	0933	1131	1229	1500	1457	...	1632	1624	1829	1853
23	Alexisbad d.	0827	0940	*1136*	1237	...	1504	1504	▬	1637	1830	1857
26	**Harzgerode** a.	0837	|	*1145*	|	...	|	1514	...	|	1839	|
26	Silberhütte d.	...	0949	▬	1246	...	1513	▬	...	1646	▬	1907
30	Straßberg (Harz) d.	...	1001	...	1257	...	1525	...	...	1658	...	1918
35	Güntersberge d.	...	1010	...	1307	...	1535	🚂	...	1707	...	1927
	Hasselfelde d.	...	|	1013	|	...	|	1615	...	|	1758	|
44	Stiege a.	...	1026	1026	1323	...	1551	1628	...	1723	1811	1943
44	Stiege d.	...	1040	1040	1329	...	1552	1629	...	1726	1812	1944
48	**Hasselfelde** a.	...	|	|	|	...	1605	|	🚂 B	1739	|	|
53	Eisfelder Talmühle d.	...	1101	1115	1402r	...	...	1649	1714	...	1833	2013
59	Ilfeld d.	...	...	1130	1417	...	...	...	1729	...	1850	2028
70	**Nordhausen** Nord § a.	...	...	1153	1439‡	...	...	...	1751	...	1913	2049‡

		⊕		🚂 B							🚂
Nordhausen Nord § d.	...	0854‡	0933	1033	...	1225	1325	...	...	1626	...
Ilfeld d.	...	0917	1000	1059	...	1246	1346	...	...	1648	...
Eisfelder Talmühle d.	...	0932	1018	1113	1115	1301	1401	...	...	1702	1704
Hasselfelde d.	...	|	|	▬	|	|	|	1444	...	▬	|
Stiege a.	...	0952	1038	...	1135	1321	1421	1457	...	...	1724
Stiege d.	...	0953	1042	...	1136	1325	1422	1458	...	...	1734
Hasselfelde a.	...	1006	|	...	|	|	1435	|	...	...	|
Güntersberge d.	...	▬	1100	...	1154	1343	▬	1514	...	...	1750
Straßberg (Harz) d.	...	...	1109	...	1203	1352	...	1526	...	...	1759
Silberhütte d.	...	🚂	1121	...	1215	1404	...	1538	...	...	1810
Harzgerode d.	...	0847	|	...	|	|	1542	|	...	*1614*	|
Alexisbad a.	...	0857	1131	🚂	1224	1413	1552	1547	...	*1624*	1820
Alexisbad d.	...	0904	1136	1146	1231	1417	...	1602	1556	1658	1831
Harzgerode a.	...	|	1145	|	|	1426	...	|	1605	|	|
Mägdesprung d.	...	0918	...	1200	1245	▬	...	1618	...	1713	1845
Gernrode a.	...	0949	...	1230	1315	...	...	1648	...	1742	1915
Gernrode d.	0800	0959	...	1231	1316	1459	...	1659	...	1759	1916
Quedlinburg § a.	0815	1015	...	1246	1331	1515	...	1715	...	1815	1931

A – Apr. 29 - Oct. 29.
B – (2) Brocken - Nordhausen and v.v.

r – Arrives 1351.

‡ – Nordhausen **Bahnhofsplatz**.
§ – Adjacent to DB station.

🚂 – Steam train.
◧ – 🚂 on ③④. Diesel train on other dates.
⊕ – Change trains at Ilfeld on Ⓐ (through train on Ⓒ).
◇ – Additional journeys (🚂) Drei Annen Hohne - Brocken and v.v.: From Drei Annen Hohne at 1200, 1339, 1506 and 1647◧. From Brocken at 1051, 1221, 1359 and 1540◧.
▷ – Additional journey: Quedlinburg d. 1830 - Gernrode a. 1845.

Operator: Harzer Schmalspurbahnen GmbH. Friedrichstraße 151, 38855 Wernigerode. ✆ + 49 (0) 3943 558 0. Fax + 49 (0) 3943 558 148.

868 ERFURT - NORDHAUSEN

RE / *RB* services

km		Ⓐt																	
0	**Erfurt** Hbf d.	0448	0559	0700	0802	0902	1002	1102	1202	1302	1402	1502	1602	1702	1802	1902	2016	...	2213
27	Straußfurt d.	0514	0624	0724	0828	0924	1028	1124	1228	1324	1428	1524	1628	1724	1828	1924	2045	...	2245
60	Sondershausen d.	0547	0657	0757	0857	0957	1057	1157	1257	1357	1457	1557	1657	1757	1857	1957	2113	...	2317
80	**Nordhausen** a.	0610	0715	0820	0915	1020	1115	1220	1315	1420	1515	1620	1715	1820	1915	2020	2130	...	2339

	Ⓐt	Ⓐt																
Nordhausen d.	0420	0521	0623	0729	0834	0929	1034	1129	1234	1329	1434	1529	1634	1729	1834	1929	...	2137
Sondershausen d.	0443	0550	0640	0757	0857	0957	1057	1157	1257	1357	1457	1557	1657	1757	1857	1957	...	2158
Straußfurt d.	0515	0626	0709	0830	0924	1030	1124	1230	1324	1430	1524	1630	1724	1830	1924	2030	...	2230
Erfurt Hbf a.	0541	0651	0738	0856	0950	1056	1150	1256	1350	1456	1550	1656	1750	1856	1950	2056	...	2256

t – Not Sept. 20, Oct. 31.

869 NORDHAUSEN - GÖTTINGEN

RB services

km		Ⓐe	⚒e																	
0	**Nordhausen** d.	...	0539	0639	0739	0839	0939	1039	1139	1239	1339	1439	1539	1639	1739	1839	1939	2039	2139	...
20	Walkenried d.	0503	0603	0703	0803	0903	1003	1103	1203	1303	1403	1503	1603	1703	1803	1903	2003	2103	2203	...
23	Bad Sachsa d.	0508	0608	0708	0808	0908	1008	1108	1208	1308	1408	1508	1608	1708	1808	1908	2008	2108	2208	...
37	Bad Lauterberg ⊡ d.	0519	0619	0719	0819	0919	1019	1119	1219	1319	1419	1519	1619	1719	1819	1919	2019	2119	2219	...
43	Herzberg (Harz) d.	0526	0626	0726	0826	0926	1026	1126	1226	1326	1426	1526	1626	1726	1826	1926	2026	2126	2226	2326
70	Northeim 859 903 a.	0550	0650	0750	0850	0950	1050	1150	1250	1350	1450	1550	1650	1750	1850	1950	2050	2150	2250	2350
90	**Göttingen** 859 903 a.	0608	0710	0808	*0909*	1009	*1109*	1209	*1309*	1409	*1509*	1609	*1709*	1809	*1909*	2009	*2109*	2209	*2309*	0010

	Ⓐe	⚒e	Ⓒz	Ⓐe															⑤⑥f	
Göttingen 859 903 d.	*0408*	0549	*0648*	0649	0749	*0848*	0949	*1048*	1149	*1248*	1349	*1448*	1549	*1648*	1749	*1848*	1949	*2048*	2149	2249
Northeim 859 903 d.	0506	0606	0706	0706	0806	0906	1006	1106	1206	1306	1406	1506	1606	1706	1806	1906	2006	2106	2206	2306
Herzberg (Harz) d.	0530	0630	0730	0730	0830	0930	1030	1130	1230	1330	1430	1530	1631	1730	1830	1930	2030	2130	2230	2330
Bad Lauterberg ⊡ d.	0536	0636	0736	0736	0836	0936	1036	1136	1236	1336	1436	1536	1637	1736	1836	1936	2036	2136	2236	...
Bad Sachsa d.	0547	0647	0747	0747	0847	0947	1047	1147	1247	1347	1447	1547	1648	1747	1847	1947	2047	2147	2247	...
Walkenried d.	0551	0651	0751	0751	0851	0951	1051	1151	1251	1351	1451	1551	1652	1751	1852	1951	2051	2151	2251	...
Nordhausen a.	0615	0715	0815	0815	0915	1015	1115	1215	1315	1415	1515	1615	1715	1815	1915	2015	2115	2215	2315	...

e – Not Oct. 31.
f – ⑤⑥ (also Oct. 2, 30); runs daily Göttingen - Herzberg.
z – Also Oct. 31.

⊡ – Bad Lauterberg im Harz Barbis.

870 ERFURT - MEININGEN - SCHWEINFURT - WÜRZBURG

DB (*RE* services); *STB*; *EB*

km				▽	▽◇	▽		▽		▽		▽		▽		▽		▽	▽		▽	▽	◇	▽	▽
				Ⓐv	Ⓐv													Ⓐv			Ⓐv				
0	**Erfurt** Hbf 872 d.	...	0459	...	0603	0700	0735	0902	0935	1102	1135	1301	1335	1501	1535	1701	1735	1805	1902	1935	2006	2116	...	2259	0002
23	Arnstadt Hbf 872 d.	...	0516	...	0620	0719	0752	0919	0952	1119	1152	1319	1352	1519	1552	1719	1752	1823	1919	1952	2029	2138	...	2317	0024
31	Plaue (Thür) d.	...	0523	...	0628	0727	0759	0927	0959	1127	1159	1327	1359	1527	1559	1727	1759	1831	1927	1959	2036	2146	...	2326	0033
37	Gräfenroda d.	...	0528	...	0633	0732	|	0932	|	1132	|	1332	|	1532	|	1732	|	1836	1932	2004	2041	2155	...	2331	0038
58	Zella-Mehlis d.	...	0543	...	0652	0751	0816	0951	1016	1151	1216	1351	1416	1551	1616	1751	1816	1854	1951	2019	2100	2214	...	2348	0058
64	Suhl d.	...	0549	...	0658	0758	0822	0958	1022	1158	1222	1358	1422	1558	1622	1758	1822	1900	1958	2025	2106	2220	...	2354	0104
84	Grimmenthal 873 a.	...	0559	0603	0714	0813	0832	1013	1032	1213	1232	1413	1432	1613	1632	1813	1832	1912	2013	2035	2119	2236	2240	0006	0120
92	**Meiningen** 873 a.	...	|	0609	*0724*	0821	*0846*	1021	*1046*	1221	*1246*	1421	*1446*	1621	*1646*	1821	*1846*	1919	2021	*2046*	2131	2245	|	0013	0128
			|		|	▬	|	▬	|	▬	|	▬	|	▬	|	▬	|		▬	|	▬	▬	|	▬	
		◇	|	◇	|	◇	|	◇	|	◇	|	◇	|	◇	|	◇	|		◇	|	◇	▽	|		
			|	⚒r	|	Ⓒw	|		|		|		|		|					|			|		
	Meiningen 873 d.	0521	*0548*	0642t	*0710*	0719	*0822*	0924	*1022*	1124	*1222*	1324	*1422*	1539	*1622*	1724	*1822*	...	1924	*2022*	2124	2229	|	...	...
84	Grimmenthal 873 d.	|	0604	|	0726	|	0835	|	1035	|	1235	|	1435	|	1635	|	1835	...	|	2036	|	2236	2240	...	...
110	Mellrichstadt d.	0548	0623	0709	0747	0747	0849	0948	1049	1148	1249	1348	1449	1603	1649	1748	1849	...	1948	2049	2148	...	2258	...	...
124	Bad Neustadt (Saale) d.	0559	0633	0718	0759	0759	0857	0959	1057	1159	1257	1358	1457	1611	1657	1759	1857	...	1959	2057	2159	...	2306	...	...
134	Münnerstadt d.	0607	0642	0726	0807	0807	0903	1007	1103	1207	1304	1406	1504	1619	1703	1807	1903	...	2007	2103	2207	...	2315	...	...
149	Ebenhausen (Unterfr) a.	0618	0653	0736	0818	0818	0912	1018	1112	1218	1312	1417	1512	1630	1712	1818	1912	...	2018	2112	2218	...	2326	...	...
149	Ebenhausen (Unterfr) d.	0625	0657	0742	0826	0826	0917	1025	1117	1225	1317	1425	1517	1639	1717	1825	1917	...	2025	2117	2225	...	2329	...	...
163	**Schweinfurt** Hbf 875 a.	0637	0713	0753	0842	0842	0926	1042	1126	1241	1326	1440	1525	1651	1725	1841	1926	...	2042	2126	2236	...	2340	2345	...
206	**Würzburg** Hbf 875 a.	*0721*	0746	*0821*	*0920*	*0920*	0955	*1120*	1155	*1320*	1355	*1521*	1555	*1721*	1755	*1922*	1955	...	*2121*	2157	...	...	...	0016	...

r – Not June 16, Aug. 15, Nov. 1.
t – Ⓐ (not June 16, Aug. 15, Nov. 1).
v – Not Sept. 20, Oct. 31.
w – Also Sept. 20, Oct. 31.
▽ – Operated by Süd Thüringen Bahn (2nd class only).
◇ – Operated by Erfurter Bahn (2nd class only).

WÜRZBURG - SCHWEINFURT - MEININGEN - ERFURT 870

)B (*RE* services); *STB*; *EB*

				◇	◇	◇	◇		◇		◇		◇	◇		◇		◇		◇		◇	◇	◇	
		⚒t		⚒t	Ⓐt	Ⓐt	Ⓒz						Ⓐt	Ⓒz										⑤⑥f	
ürzburg Hbf ...... 876 d.	...	0454	...	...	...	*0622*	*0603*	0801	*0835*	1001	*1035*	1201	*1208*	*1235*	1401	*1435*	1601	*1637*	1801	*1836*	2001	*2035*	*2139*	*2139*	...
chweinfurt Hbf .... 876 d.	...	0524	0530	0611	0611	0701	0718	0830	0912	1030	1112	1230	1242	1312	1430	1512	1630	1712	1830	1912	2030	2113	2224	2224	...
benhausen (Unterf) .... a.	...	▬	0539	0622	0622	0712	0731	0838	0928	1038	1128	1238	1252	1328	1439	1528	1638	1728	1838	1928	2038	2128	2239	2239	...
benhausen (Unterf) .... d.	...	...	0541	0629	0629	0714	0738	0840	0932	1040	1132	1240	1252	1332	1441	1532	1640	1732	1840	1932	2040	2132	2242	2242	...
ünnerstadt .... d.	...	...	0550	0646	0646	0726	0749	0849	0944	1049	1144	1249	1308	1344	1450	1544	1649	1744	1849	1944	2049	2144	2253	2253	...
ad Neustadt (Saale) ... d.	...	...	0557	0654	0654	0737	0758	0857	0958	1057	1158	1257	1319	1358	1457	1553	1657	1758	1857	1958	2057	2157	2307	2307	...
ellrichstadt .... d.	...	...	0605	0703	0707	0746	0807	0906	1007	1106	1207	1306	1328	1407	1506	1607	1706	1807	1906	2007	2106	2206	2315	2315	...
rimmenthal .... 873 a.	...	...	0619	▬	|	|	|	0919	|	1119	|	1319	|	|	1519	|	1719	|	1919	|	2121	2224	2333f	|	...
Meiningen .... 873 a.	...	...	*0629*	...	0731k	0810	0831	*0934*	1031	*1134*	1231	*1334*	1358	1431	*1534*	1631	*1734*	1831	*1934*	2031	*2131*	*2245*	2340h	|	...
	▽	▽	|	▽	▽	▽			▽		▽		▽	▽		▽		▽		▽		▽			▽
	Ⓐv			⚒vE		Ⓐv								Ⓐv									...		⑤⑥f
Meiningen .... 873 d.	0504	0524	*0609*	0710	0735	0822	...	*0901*	0935	*1101*	1135	*1301*	1335	1422	*1501*	1535	*1701*	1735	*1901*	1935	*2108*	2132	...	|	2331
rimmenthal .... 873 d.	0511	0532	0621	0717	0741	0834	...	0919	0941	1119	1141	1319	1341	1434	1519	1541	1719	1741	1919	1941	2121	2142	...	2333	2337
uhl .... d.	0524	0549	0633	0730	0759	0847	...	0932	0959	1132	1159	1332	1359	1447	1532	1559	1732	1759	1932	1959	2133	2159	...	...	2356
ella-Mehlis .... d.	0531	0555	0639	0737	0805	0855	...	0938	1005	1138	1205	1338	1405	1455	1538	1605	1738	1805	1938	2005	2139	2214j	...	...	0002
räfenroda .... d.	0548	0613	0654	0753	0824	0912	...	|	1024	|	1224	|	1424	1512	|	1624	|	1824	|	2024	2153	2232	...	...	0018
'aue (Thür) .... d.	0553	0626j	0700	|	0829	0917	...	0957	1029	1157	1229	1357	1429	1517	1557	1629	1757	1829	1957	2029	2158	2245j	...	...	0029
rnstadt Hbf .... 872 d.	0601	0634	0707	0805	0836	0925	...	1004	1036	1204	1236	1404	1436	1525	1604	1636	1804	1836	2004	2036	2205	2253	...	...	0037
rfurt Hbf .... 872 a.	0621	0655	0723	0820	0853	0943	...	1021	1053	1221	1253	1421	1453	1543	1621	1653	1821	1853	2021	2053	2221	2313	...	...	0054

– From Eisenach (Table **873**).
– ⑤⑥ (also Sept. 19, Oct. 2, 30).
h – 2345 on ⑤⑥ (also Sept. 19, Oct. 2, 30).
j – Arrives 7 – 10 minutes earlier.
k – 0734 on Sept. 20, Oct. 31.
t – Not June 16, Aug. 15, Nov. 1.
v – Not Sept. 20, Oct. 31.
z – Also June 16, Aug. 15, Nov. 1.
▽ – Operated by Süd Thüringen Bahn (2nd class only).
◇ – Operated by Erfurter Bahn (2nd class only).

LEIPZIG - GERA - SAALFELD 871

Erfurter Bahn; 2nd class only

km		Ⓐv	Ⓐv	Ⓒw	Ⓐv	Ⓐv		⚒n◧	⑥	Ⓒw		◧		◧		◧		◧		◧						
0	**Leipzig** Hbf .... d.	...	...	...	0508	0609	0609	0655	0655	...	0755	0856	0955	1055	1155	1255	1355	1455	1555	1655	1755	1855	1957	2057	2157	2309
45	Zeitz .... d.	0427	...	...	0550	0654	0654	0735	0735	...	0835	0935	1035	1135	1235	1335	1435	1535	1635	1735	1835	1935	2037	2137	2236	2350
72	**Gera** Hbf .... a.	0451	...	...	0619	0723	0723	0800	0800	...	0858	0959	1058	1159	1258	1400	1458	1559	1658	1759	1858	1959	2101	2204	2300	0013
72	**Gera** Hbf .... d.	0452	0531	0553	0628	0730	...	0802	0802	0802	0902	1002	1102	1202	1302	1402	1502	1602	1702	1802	1902	2002	2103	*2209*	2308	...
84	Weida .... d.	0504	0543	0608	0640	0745	...	0813	0815	0815	0914	1015	1114	1215	1314	1415	1514	1615	1714	1815	1914	2015	2115	*2221*	2320	...
99	Triptis .... d.	0516	0556	0620	0654	0757	...	...	0827	0827	0930	1027	1130	1227	1330	1427	1531	1627	1730	1827	1930	2027	2129	...	2333	...
108	Neustadt (Orla) ... d.	0523	0602	0626	0700	0803	...	...	0833	0833	0936	1034	1136	1234	1336	1433	1537	1633	1736	1834	1936	2037	2135	...	2339	...
139	**Saalfeld** (Saale) . a.	0552	0635	0653	0727	0836	...	...	0900	0900	0958	1101	1158	1301	1358	1500	1559	1700	1759	1901	1958	2105	2202	...	0006	...

	Ⓐn		⚒n	Ⓐn	⚒n		Ⓐv		Ⓒw	Ⓐv		◧		◧		◧		◧		◧		◧				⑤⑥f
aalfeld (Saale) . d.	...	...	...	...	0515	...	0553	...	0651	0651	0758	0855	0958	1055	1158	1255	1358	1457	1557	1655	1758	1856	2009	2057	2211	2211
eustadt (Orla) ... d.	...	...	...	...	0548	...	0619	...	0718	0725	0819	0922	1019	1122	1219	1322	1419	1524	1620	1722	1819	1923	2036	2121	2237	2237
'iptis .... d.	...	...	...	...	0556	...	0626	...	0725	0732	0828	0929	1028	1129	1228	1329	1428	1530	1628	1729	1828	1929	2043	2128	2243	2243
'eida .... d.	...	...	...	0524v	0608	...	0641	...	0745	0745	0843	0946	1041	1146	1241	1346	1441	1546	1641	1746	1841	1946	2055	2140	2256	2256
era Hbf .... a.	...	...	...	0536v	0621	...	0653	...	0756	0756	0855	0957	1053	1157	1253	1357	1453	1557	1653	1757	1853	1957	2108	2150	2307	2307
era Hbf .... d.	0348	0453	0545	0545	0628	0628	0659	0659	0801	0801	0901	1001	1101	1201	1301	1400	1500	1601	1700	1801	1901	2001	...	2151	...	2311
eitz .... d.	0412	0519	0609	0609	0654	0654	0725	0725	0825	0825	0925	1025	1125	1225	1325	1425	1525	1625	1725	1825	1925	2025	...	2215	...	2338
eipzig Hbf .... a.	0452	0600	0649	0649	0733	0733	0805	0805	0905	0905	1005	1105	1205	1305	1405	1505	1605	1705	1805	1905	2009	2105	...	2253	...	0022

km			⚒n						
	Leipzig Hbf .... d.	...	0655	...	0856	1055	1255	1455	1655
0	**Gera** Hbf .... d.	0553	0802	0802	1002	1202	1402	1602	1802
12	Weida .... d.	0612	0817	0817	1017	1217	1417	1617	1817
84	**Hof** Hbf .... a.	0726	0926	0925	1126	1326	1526	1726	1926

Hof Hbf .... d.	0834	1034	1234	1434	1634	1834	2034
Weida .... a.	0943	1143	1343	1540	1743	1943	2137
Gera Hbf .... a.	0957	1157	1357	1557	1757	1957	2157
Leipzig Hbf a.	1105	1305	1505	1705	1905	2105	...

f – Also Oct. 2, 30.
n – Not Oct. 31.
v – Not Sept. 20, Oct. 31.
w – Also Sept. 20, Oct. 31.
◧ – Conveys (12) Leipzig - Weida - Hof and v.v. (see panel below main table).

ERFURT - SAALFELD and ROTTENBACH - KATZHÜTTE 872

)B; Erfurter Bahn; 2nd class only

km		Ⓐv	Ⓐv							
0	**Erfurt** Hbf .... 870 d.	0430	0524	0637		2037	2145	...	2259	...
23	Arnstadt Hbf .... 870 d.	0453	0547	0700	and	2100	2205	2209	2316	2320
38	Stadtilm .... d.	0506	0600	0713	hourly	2113	...	2222	...	2333
54	Rottenbach .... d.	0520	0613	0727	until	2127	...	2237	...	2347
62	Bad Blankenburg .... d.	0528	0622	0734		2134	...	2245	...	2354
70	**Saalfeld** (Saale) .... a.	0535	0630	0742		2142	...	2252	...	0002

	Ⓐv								
Saalfeld (Saale) .... d.	0504	0612	0712		2012	2112	...	...	2221
Bad Blankenburg .... d.	0511	0621	0719	and	2019	2119	...	...	2228
Rottenbach .... d.	0519	0628	0727	hourly	2027	2127	...	...	2237
Stadtilm .... d.	0533	0642	0740	until	2040	2140	...	...	2249
Arnstadt Hbf .... 870 d.	0550	0658	0756		2056	2153	2157	...	2308
Erfurt Hbf .... 870 a.	0610	0715	0816		2116	...	2217	...	2323

km		Ⓐv						⑤⑦h		
0	Rottenbach .... d.	0535	...	0641	and	1941	...	2041	...	...
15	Obstfelderschmiede .. a.	0558	...	0705	hourly	2005	...	2105	...	...
25	Katzhütte .... a.	0614	...	0722	until	2022	...	2122	...	...

	Ⓐv						⑤⑦h		
Katzhütte .... d.	0529	...	0636	and	1936	...	2036	...	...
Obstfelderschmiede .... d.	0546	...	0653	hourly	1953	...	2053	...	...
Rottenbach .... a.	0609	...	0716	until	2016	...	2116	...	...

– Also Oct. 3, 31; not Oct. 2, 30.
– Not Sept. 20, Oct. 31.

☛ **Oberweißbacher Bergbahn**. Obstfelderschmiede - Lichtenhain - Cursdorf. Journey: 28 – 44 minutes.
From Obstfelderschmiede at 0630, 0700, 0730 and every 30 minutes until 1730; then 1808, 1830, 1908, 1930.
From Cursdorf at 0614, 0640, 0706, 0734, 0814, 0844 and every 30 minutes until 1944.

EISENACH - MEININGEN - SONNEBERG 873

Süd Thüringen Bahn (2nd class)

km		Ⓐt	Ⓐt	Ⓐt		Ⓐt	E						Ⓒz	Ⓐt		Ⓒz	Ⓐt									
0	**Eisenach** .... d.	...	...	0418	...	0500	0603	...	0716	0816	0916	1016	1116	1116	1216	1316	1316	1416	1516	1616	1716	*1816*	1916	2016	*2121*	2216
27	Bad Salzungen .... d.	...	...	0444	...	0531	0632	...	0742	0842	0942	1042	1142	1142	1242	1342	1342	1442	1542	1642	1742	*1842*	1942	2042	*2152*	2242
41	Wernshausen .... d.	...	...	0500	...	0547	0649	...	0759	0859	0959	1059	1159	1159	1259	1359	1359	1459	1559	1659	1759	*1859*	1959	2059	*2209*	2308f
61	**Meiningen** .... a.	...	...	0517	...	0604	0706	...	0816	0916	1016	1116	1216	1216	1316	1416	1416	1516	1616	1716	1816	*1916*	2016	2116	*2225*	2324
61	**Meiningen** .... 870 d.	0403	0455	...	0609	0609	0710r	0725	0822	0920	1022	1120	1222	1222	1320	1422	1422	1520	1622	1720	1822	1920	2022	...	2229	...
68	Grimmenthal ...... 870 a.	0410	0502	...	0616	0616	0716r	0732	0829	0927	1029	1127	1229	1229	1327	1429	1429	1527	1629	1727	1829	1927	2029	...	2236	...
68	Grimmenthal .... d.	0412	0506	...	0623	0623	...	0733	0841	0930	1041	1130	1241	1241	1330	1441	1441	1530	1641	1730	1841	1930	2045	...	2240	...
82	Themar .... d.	0425	0519	...	0636	0636	...	0746	0859j	0943	1059j	1143	1259j	1259j	1343	1459j	1459j	1543	1659j	1743	1859j	1943	2058	...	2253	...
94	Hildburghausen .... d.	0437	0535	...	0652j	0652j	...	0801	0911	1001j	1111	1201j	1311	1320f	1401j	1511	1528k	1601j	1711	1801j	1911	2004f	2116j	...	2304	...
109	**Eisfeld** .... d.	0452	0550	...	0707	0707	...	0816	0926	1016	1126	1216	1326	1335	1416	1526	1543	1616	1726	1816	1926	2019	2131	...	2319	...
141	**Sonneberg** (Thür) Hbf a.	0536	0638	...	...	...	...	0900	...	1100	...	1300	...	...	1500	...	...	1700	...	1900	...	2103	...	...	...	...

	Ⓐt	Ⓐt		Ⓐt																
onneberg (Thür) Hbf d.	...	...	...	...	...	0546t	0702	...	0902	...	1102	...	1302	...	1502	...	1702	...	1902	2012
isfeld .... d.	...	0419	...	0518	...	0632	0746	0831	0946	1031	1146	1231	1346	1431	1546	1631	1746	1831	1949	2059
ldburghausen .... d.	...	0440j	...	0534	...	0649	0801	0846	1001	1046	1201	1246	1401	1446	1601	1646	1801	1846	2004	2114
emar .... d.	...	0452	...	0545	...	0659	0812	0857	1012	1057	1212	1257	1412	1457	1612	1657	1812	1857	2015	2126
immenthal .... a.	...	0504	...	0557	...	0711	0824	0909	1024	1109	1224	1309	1424	1509	1624	1709	1824	1909	2027	2138
immenthal .... 870 d.	...	0513	...	0603	0623	0718	0830	0928	1030	1128	1230	1328	1430	1528	1630	1728	1830	1928	2030	2140
einingen .... 870 a.	...	0521	...	0609	0629	0724	0836	0934	1036	1134	1236	1334	1436	1534	1636	1734	1836	1934	2036	2147
einingen .... d.	0441	0525	0525	...	0630	0739	0839	0939	1039	1139	1239	1339	1439	1539	1639	1739	1839	1939	2039	*2151*
'ernshausen .... d.	0500	0548j	0548j	...	0649	0758	0858	0958	1058	1158	1258	1358	1458	1558	1658	1758	1858	1958	2058	*2209*
ıd Salzungen .... d.	0514	0602	0602	...	0712f	0812	0912	1012	1112	1212	1312	1412	1512	1612	1712	1812	1912	2012	2112	*2224*
senach .... a.	0542	0628	0628	...	0743	0843	0943	1043	1143	1243	1343	1443	1543	1643	1743	1843	1943	2043	2138	*2255*

E – To Erfurt on ⚒**r** (Table **870**).
f – Arrives 10 – 12 minutes earlier.
j – Arrives 6 – 8 minutes earlier.
k – Arrives 1510.
r – ⚒ (not Sept. 20, Oct. 31).
t – Ⓐ (not Sept. 20, Oct. 31).
z – Also Sept. 20, Oct. 31.

LEIPZIG - CHEMNITZ 874

Mitteldeutsche Regiobahn

km			⚒b				
0	**Leipzig** Hbf .... d.	0518	0622*	0722*		2222*	2337
33	Bad Lausick .... d.	0547	0647	0747	and	2247	0000
44	Geithain .... d.	0556	0656	0756	hourly	2256	0009
66	Burgstädt .... d.	0613	0713	0813	until	2313	0026
81	**Chemnitz** Hbf .... a.	0625	0725	0825		2325	0039

		⚒b				
Chemnitz Hbf .... d.	0421	0531	0631		2131	2231
Burgstädt .... d.	0433	0543	0643	and	2143	2243
Geithain .... d.	0451	0600	0700	hourly	2200	2300
Bad Lausick .... d.	0500	0609	0709	until	2209	2309
Leipzig Hbf .... a.	0526	0631	0730		2230	2333

b – Not Oct. 31, Nov. 16.
* – 2 minutes **earlier** until July 9.

875 NÜRNBERG - BAMBERG - SONNEBERG, SAALFELD and WÜRZBURG *RE / RB services*

km				Ⓒz	Ⓐt				Ⓒz		Ⓐt			⊖		Ⓐt	Ⓐt	⊖				Ⓐt				
0	**Nürnberg** Hbf .... 850 d.	0607	...	0638c	*0710*	0810	0838	0938	1010	1040	1110	1210	1238	1410	1441	1510	...	1610	1640c	1810	1838	1910	1938	...	2139	2246
8	Fürth (Bay) Hbf .... d.	0613	...	0644	*0716*	0816	0844	0944	1016	1046	1116	1216	1244	1416	1447	1516	...	1616	1646c	1816	1844	1916	1944	...	2146	2252
24	Erlangen .... 850 d.	0623	...	0654	*0727*	0827	0854	0954	1027	1055	1127	1227	1254	1427	1457	1527	...	1627	1656	1828	1854	1927	1954	...	2155	2302
39	Forchheim (Oberfr) .... d.	0632	...	0703	*0735*	0835	0902	1002	1035	1103	1135	1235	1302	1435	1505	1535	...	1635	1704	1836	1902	1935	2002	...	2203	2311
62	**Bamberg** .... 850 a.	0652	...	0720	*0752*	0852	0920	1020	1052	1120	1152	1252	1320	1452	1520	1552	...	1652	1720	1852	1920	1952	2020	...	2222	2328
62	**Bamberg** .... 876 d.	0654	...	0723	0805	0854	0922	1022	1054	1122	1154	1255	1322	1455	1522	1554	1605	1654	1722	1854	1922	1954	2022	...	2238	2340
94	Lichtenfels .... 876 a.	|	...	0741	|	|	0940	1044	|	1140	|	|	1343	|	1540	1622	|	|	1742	|	1945	|	2044	...	2303	0004
94	Lichtenfels .... d.	|	0701	0757	|	|	0944	*1102*	|	1159	|	|	1401	|	1544	1624	|	|	1802	|	2001	|	*2049*	2103z	2316	0005
114	**Coburg** .... 850 a.	0720	0724	0822	0828	0920	1001	*1122*	1117	1224	1218	1317	1425	1519	1600	1646	1628	1720	1823	1918	2025	2018	*2108*	2121z	2335	0025
114	**Coburg** .... d.	0731z	0729t	0831	0831	0931	1031	*1134*t	1134	1231	...	1331	1433	1534	1633	1707	*1633*	1731	1831	1931	2031z	*2039*	...	2126	2336	...
135	**Sonneberg** (Thür) Hbf a.	0753z	0754t	0853	0853	0953	1053	*1155*t	1153	1253	...	1353	1455	1554	1655	1735	*1655*	1753	1853	1953	2053z	*2101*	...	2148	2358	...

		Ⓐt			Ⓐt	Ⓐt	Ⓒz	Ⓒz		Ⓐt				⊖			Ⓐt		⊖	Ⓐt		Ⓒz	Ⓐt		Ⓐt	Ⓒz
Sonneberg (Thür) Hbf d.	...	0445	0539	*0610*t	...	0706	0705	0806	*0806*t	0906	0906z	1006	1104	1203	1306	1406	...	1505	1603	...	1706	1806	*1806*	1906	*2005*	*2005*
Coburg .... a.	...	0507	0600	*0631*t	...	0727p	0726	0827	*0827*t	0927	0927z	1027	1125	1224	1327	1427	...	1526p	1624	...	1727p	1827	*1827*	1927	*2026*	*2026*
Coburg .... 850 d.	0446	0508	0611	*0635*t	*0732*	0728	0753	0838	*0832*r	0938	0954	1038	1154	1238	1332	1436	*1530*	1554	1638	1738	1731	1838	*1832*	1935	2029	*2029*
Lichtenfels .... a.	0506	0529	|	*0655*t	|	0759	0811	|	*0855*r	|	1011	|	1211	|	1355	|	|	1611	|	|	1753	|	*1855*	1953	2047	*2047*
Lichtenfels .... 876 d.	0509	0530	|	0709	|	0818	0818	|	0912	|	1018	|	1218	|	1418	|	|	1618	|	|	1818	|	1912	2018	2114	2112
Bamberg .... 876 a.	0535	0556	0634	0735	*0756*	0836	0836	0902	0935	1002	1036	1102	1236	1302	1436	1502	*1554*	1636	1702	1803	1836	1902	1935	2037	2138	2137
Bamberg .... 850 d.	0538	0604	0638	0739	0804	0838	0838	0904	0939	1004	1038	1104	1238	1304	1438	1504	1603	1638	1704	1805	1838	1904	1939	2038	2140	2141
Forchheim (Oberfr) ..... d.	0554	0620	0653	0754	0820	0853	0853	0920	0954	1020	1053	1119	1253	1320	1453	1519	1619	1653	1720	1821	1853	1920	1954	2053	2154	2155
Erlangen .... 850 d.	0603	0629	0702	0803	0829	0902	0902	0929	1003	1029	1102	1129	1302	1329	1502	1529	1629	1702	1729	1830	1902	1929	2003	2102	2203	2204
Fürth (Bay) Hbf .... d.	0612	0641	0713	0813	0841	0912	0912	0941	1012	1041	1112	1141	1312	1341	1512	1541	1643	1712	1743	1841	1912	1941	2013	2112	2214	2214
Nürnberg Hbf ...... 850 a.	0619	0648	0719	0819	0848	0919	0919	0948	1018	1048	1119	1148	1319	1348	1519	1548	1649	1719	1749	1848	1918	1948	2019	2119	2220	2220

km		Ⓐt	◧	Ⓐt	Ⓒz	Ⓐt	◧		◧		⊗◧	Ⓒz	Ⓐt	◧		◧		Ⓐt	◧		◧				2
0	**Nürnberg** Hbf ..... 849a 850 d.	...	0529	0629	0638c	0710	0738	0838	0938	1040	1138	1238	1238	1338	1441	1538	1640c	1710	1740	1838	1938	2038	2139	2346	0049
8	Fürth (Bay) Hbf .... d.	...	0537	0637	0644	0716	0744	0844	0944	1046	1144	1244	1244	1344	1447	1544	1646c	1716	1746	1844	1944	2044	2146	2352	0057
24	Erlangen .... 849a 850 d.	...	0547	0648	0654	0727	0754	0854	0954	1055	1154	1254	1254	1354	1457	1554	1656	1727	1756	1854	1954	2055	2155	0002	0114
39	Forchheim (Oberfr) .... d.	...	0557	0657	0703	0735	0803	0902	1002	1103	1203	1302	1302	1403	1505	1603	1704	1735	1804	1902	2002	2103	2203	0011	0129
62	**Bamberg** .... 849a 850 d.	0507	0627f	0723	0723	0754	0822	0922	1022	1122	1222	1322	1322	1422	1522	1622	1722	1804f	1822	1922	2022	2136j	2238j	0034	0149
94	Lichtenfels .... 849a d.	0535	0653	0741	0743	0820	0845	0942	1045	1142	1245	1343	1345	1445	1542	1645	1744	1830	1845	1947	2045	2203	2309	0100	...
118	Kronach .... 849a d.	0557	0713	0758	0757	...	0905	0957	1105	1157	1309	1357	1359	1505	1557	1705	1758	...	1905	2007	2107	2223	2329	...	...
181	**Saalfeld** (Saale) .... 849a a.	0654	0809	0852	0851	...	1002	1051	1202	1251	1410	1451	1454	1602	1651	1802	1853	...	2002	2103	2204	...	...	...	...
	Jena Paradies 849 .... a.	...	0846	...	...	...	1038	...	1238	...	1446	...	...	1638	...	1838	...	...	2038	...	2242	...	...	...	...
	Leipzig Hbf 849 .... a.	...	0952	...	...	...	1152	...	1352	...	1552	...	...	1752	...	1952	...	...	2152	...	...	...	...	...	...

	Ⓐv	Ⓐt	◧	Ⓐt	Ⓒz	Ⓐt	◧		◧		◧		◧	Ⓐt		◧		◧			Ⓒz◧	Ⓐt			2
Leipzig Hbf 849 .... d.	◇	...	...	...	...	...	0558	...	0809	...	1009	...	1209	...	...	1409	...	1609	...	1809	1809	...	...	2009	...
Jena Paradies 849 .... d.	...	...	...	0509	0616n	...	0708	...	0917	...	1117	...	1317	...	...	1517	...	1717	...	1917	1917	...	...	2117	...
Saalfeld (Saale) .... 849a d.	...	...	...	0610	0658	0701	0752	0905	0952	1105	1152	1305	1352	...	1505	1552	1705	1752	1905	1952	1952	...	...	2152	...
Kronach .... 849a d.	...	0610	0647	0715	0753	0757	0852	0959	1052	1159	1252	1359	1452	...	1559	1652	1759	1852	1959	2052	2052	...	...	2252	...
Lichtenfels .... 849a d.	0622	0635	0709	0735	0818	0818	0912	1018	1112	1218	1312	1418	1512	1532	1618	1712	1818	1912	2018	2111	2112	2114	2212	2316	...
Bamberg .... 849a 850 d.	0643	0706f	0739	0804	0838	0838	0939	1038	1139	1238	1339	1438	1539	1603	1638	1739	1838	1939	2038	...	2141	2140	2239	2342	0034
Forchheim (Oberfr) .... d.	|	0721	0754	0820	0853	0853	0954	1053	1154	1253	1354	1453	1554	1619	1653	1754	1853	1954	2053	...	2155	2154	2254	...	0054
Erlangen .... 849a 850 d.	0708	0730	0803	0829	0902	0902	1003	1102	1203	1302	1403	1502	1603	1629	1702	1803	1902	2003	2102	...	2204	2203	2303	...	0108
Fürth (Bay) Hbf .... d.	|	0742	0813	0841	0912	0912	1012	1112	1213	1312	1413	1512	1613	1643	1712	1813	1912	2013	2112	...	2214	2214	2313	...	0125
Nürnberg Hbf ...... 849a 850 a.	0725	0748	0819	0848	0919	0919	1018	1119	1219	1319	1419	1519	1619	1649	1719	1819	1918	2019	2119	...	2220	2220	2319	...	0133

km		Ⓐv	Ⓒw	Ⓐv		⊙			⊙			⊙		⊙		⊙		⊙		⊙					
	Nürnberg Hbf ⊡ .... d.	...	...	...	0529	...	0738	...	...	...	0938	...	1138	...	1338	...	1538	...	1740	...	1938	...	...	...	...
0	**Bamberg** .... d.	0445	0445	0526	0625	0726	0827	0841	0926	0941	1027	1126	1227	1326	1427	1526	1627	1726	1827	1926	2027	2042	2141	2304	0036
32	Haßfurt .... d.	0506	0506	0548	0641	0742	0843	0902	0942	1002	1043	1142	1243	1342	1443	1542	1643	1742	1843	1942	2043	2102	2202	2326	0058
57	Schweinfurt Hbf .... 870 d.	0526	0526	0610	0656	0756	0856	0919	0956	1019	1056	1156	1256	1356	1456	1556	1656	1756	1856	1956	2056	2119	2220	2345	0116
100	**Würzburg** Hbf .... 870 a.	0548	0557	0648	0721	0821	0920	0951	1021	1051	1120	1221	1320	1421	1521	1621	1721	1821	1922	2021	2121	2150	2251	0016	...

	⚒v		Ⓐv	⊙			⊙			⊙		⊙		⊙		⊙			⊙			⊙			
Würzburg Hbf .... 870 d.	0454	0603	0635	0739	0835	0907	0939	1008	1035	1139	1235	1339	1435	1539	1637	1739	1808	1836	1939	2008	2035	2139	2236	2307	0036
Schweinfurt Hbf .... 870 d.	0543j	0634	0701	0803	0901	0938	1003	1038	1101	1203	1301	1403	1501	1603	1701	1803	1838	1901	2003	2038	2101	2203	2301	2345	0106
Haßfurt .... d.	0600	0652	0714	0816	0914	0955	1016	1055	1114	1216	1314	1416	1514	1616	1714	1816	1855	1914	2016	2055	2114	2216	2314	0004	...
Bamberg .... a.	0621	0715	0733	0832	0930	1016	1032	1116	1130	1232	1330	1432	1530	1632	1730	1832	1916	1930	2032	2116	2130	2232	2332	0028	...
Nürnberg Hbf ⊡ .... a.	...	...	0819	...	1018	...	...	...	1219	...	1419	...	1619	...	1819	...	...	2019	...	...	2220z	...	...	...	...

c – 1–2 minutes earlier from Oct. 17.
f – Arrives 9–11 minutes earlier.
j – Arrives 16–19 minutes earlier.
n – Not June 16, Nov. 1.
p – Connects with train in previous column.
r – ⚒ (not June 16, Nov. 1).
t – Ⓐ (not June 16, Nov. 1).
v – Not June 16, Aug. 15, Nov. 1.
w – Also June 16, Aug. 15, Nov. 1.
z – Ⓒ (also June 16, Nov. 1).
⊙ – From / to Frankfurt (Table **921**).
⊖ – Change trains at Coburg on Ⓐ (not June 16, Nov. 1).
⊗ – Change trains at Kronach on ⑤ (not June 17, Aug. 5, 12, 19, 26, Sept. 2, 9, Nov. 4)
◧ – Conveys (12) Nürnberg - Bamberg - Würzburg and v.v. (see lower panel).
⊡ – See Nürnberg - Saalfeld panel for intermediate calling points.
◇ – *ICE* **1501**. To München (Table **904**).

876 BAMBERG - HOF and BAYREUTH *RE services*

km				Ⓒz		Ⓐt								N				N				N				N
0	**Bamberg** .... 875 d.	...	...	...	...	...	...	...	0838	0838	...	...	1046	1046	...	...	1246	1246	...	...	1446	1446	...	...	1646	1646
32	Lichtenfels .... 875 d.	0546z	0549t	0658	0658z	0659	0802k	0802k	0859	0859	1003	1003	1104	1104	1203	1203	1304	1304	1403	1403	1504	1504	1603	1603	1704	1704
62	Kulmbach .... d.	0608z	0613t	0717	0717z	0721	0822	0822	0917	0917	1022	1022	1123	1123	1222	1222	1323	1323	1422	1422	1523	1523	1622	1622	1723	1723
74	Neuenmarkt-Wirsberg a.	0620z	0624t	0727	0727z	0729p	0830	0830	0927	0927	1032	1032	1131	1131	1232	1232	1331	1331	1432	1432	1531	1531	1632	1632	1731	1731
74	Neuenmarkt-Wirsberg d.	0634	0625	0729	0732	0730	0832	0835	0929	0932	1033	1035	1132	1135	1233	1235	1332	1335	1433	1435	1532	1535	1633	1635	1732	1735
96	**Bayreuth** Hbf .... a.	0658	|	|	0757	|	|	0857	|	0956	|	1057	|	1156	|	1257	|	1356	|	1457	|	1557	|	1657	|	1757
103	Münchberg .... 880 d.	...	0649	0755	...	0755	0859	...	0955	...	1100	...	1155	...	1300	...	1356	...	1500	...	1556	...	1700	...	1755	...
116	Schwarzenbach .... d.	...	0704	0806	...	0806	0911	...	1007	...	1112	...	1206	...	1312	...	1406	...	1512	...	1606	...	1711	...	1806	...
127	**Hof** Hbf .... 880 a.	...	0716	0818	...	0818	0921	...	1019	...	1123	...	1217	...	1323	...	1417	...	1523	...	1617	...	1724	...	1817	...

				N					◐	B◐		T
Bamberg .... 875 d.	...	...	1846	1846	...	...	2046	2046	...	...	2242h	2242h
Lichtenfels .... 875 d.	1803	1803	1904	1904	2003	2003	2106	2106	2236	...	2313	2313
Kulmbach .... d.	1823	1823	1923	1923	2022	2022	2128	2128	2300	...	2337	2337
Neuenmarkt-Wirsberg a.	1833	1833	1931	1931	2032	2032	2138	2138	2311	...	2349	2349
Neuenmarkt-Wirsberg d.	1834	1837	1932	1935	2033	2036	2139	2141	2312	2314	2350	2350
Bayreuth Hbf .... a.	|	1857	|	1957	|	2058	|	2200	2332	|	0016	|
Münchberg .... 880 d.	1902	...	1955	...	2100	...	2206	...	...	2341	...	0038
Schwarzenbach .... d.	1916	...	2006	...	2112	...	2217	...	...	2354	...	0047
Hof Hbf .... 880 a.	1928	...	2019	...	2122	...	2230	...	...	0006	...	0058

		Ⓒz	Ⓐt			N			
Hof Hbf .... 880 d.	...	0523	0526	...	0635	...	0744	...	0835
Schwarzenbach .... d.	...	0534	0536	...	0645	...	0752	...	0845
Münchberg .... 880 d.	...	0545	0545	...	0657	...	0802	...	0856
Bayreuth Hbf .... d.	0545	|	|	0701	|	0802	|	0902	|
Neuenmarkt-Wirsberg .... a.	0608	0613	0615	0720	0725	0820	0824	0920	0925
Neuenmarkt-Wirsberg .... d.	0615z	0615	0616	0727	0727	0827	0827	0927	0927
Kulmbach .... d.	0625z	0625	0626	0737	0737	0835	0835	0937	0937
Lichtenfels .... 875 a.	0648z	0648	0647	0756	0756	0853	0853	0957	0957
Bamberg .... 875 a.	...	...	...	0820	0820	0912	0912	...	...

	N				N				N				N												R	
Hof Hbf .... 880 d.	...	0944	...	1036	...	1144	...	1236	...	1344	...	1436	...	1544	...	1636	...	1743	...	1836	1935	...	...	2035	2135	...
Schwarzenbach .... d.	...	0952	...	1045	...	1152	...	1245	...	1352	...	1445	...	1552	...	1645	...	1753	...	1845	|	...	...	2046	2143	...
Münchberg .... 880 d.	...	1002	...	1056	...	1202	...	1256	...	1402	...	1456	...	1602	...	1656	...	1804	...	1856	1954	...	...	2058	2154	...
Bayreuth Hbf .... d.	1002	|	1102	|	1202	|	1301	|	1402	|	1502	|	1602	|	1702	|	1803	|	1902	|	|	2003	2103	|	|	2205
Neuenmarkt-Wirsberg a.	1020	1024	1120	1125	1221	1225	1321	1325	1421	1425	1520	1525	1621	1625	1720	1725	1825	1830	1920	1925	2022	2026	2121	2126	2231	2231
Neuenmarkt-Wirsberg d.	1027	1027	1127	1127	1227	1227	1328	1328	1427	1427	1527	1527	1627	1627	1727	1727	1832	1832	1927	1927	...	2027	2128	2128	2232	2232
Kulmbach .... d.	1035	1035	1137	1137	1235	1235	1337	1337	1435	1435	1537	1537	1635	1635	1737	1737	1841	1841	1936	1936	...	2036	2138	2138	2244	2244
Lichtenfels .... 875 a.	1053	1053	1156	1156	1254	1254	1358	1358	1453	1453	1557	1557	1653	1653	1756	1756	1901	1901	1956	1956	...	2056	2200	2200	2307	2307
Bamberg .... 875 a.	1112	1112	...	...	1312	1312	...	...	1511	1511	...	...	1712	1712	...	...	1922	1922	...	...	...	2120h	...	...	...	...

B – From Bayreuth (d. 2250).
N – To / from Nürnberg via Pegnitz (Table **880**).
R – Change trains at Trebgast (a. 2215, d. 2225).
T – Change trains at Trebgast (a. 2355, d. 0011).
h – ⑤–⑦ only.
k – 0801 on † (also June 16, Nov. 1).
p – Connects with train in previous column.
t – Ⓐ (not June 16, Nov. 1).
z – Ⓒ (also June 16, Nov. 1).
◐ – Operated by *agilis* (2nd class only).

LANDSHUT - MÜHLDORF - SALZBURG — 877

RB services

km						◇					⊡
0	**Landshut** (Bay) Hbf... d.	0608f	0738	0837	0936	1037	1136	1237	⊠	2037	2137
55	Mühldorf (Oberbay).... a.	0712f	0825	0928	1025	1128	1225	1329	and	2128	2228
55	Mühldorf (Oberbay).... d.	0741	0843	0943	1044	1143	1243	1342	hourly	2146	2250
120	Freilassing ...... 890/1 a.	0834	0944	1044	1143	1243	1343	1443	until	2239	2344
126	**Salzburg** Hbf .. 890/1 a.	0854	0954	1054	1154	1254n	1354	1454		2254	0017

	⊙	⊙			⊖						
Salzburg Hbf **890/1** d.	0615	0742	0908	1008	1108	1208	1313	1408	1508	⊠	2108
Freilassing .... **890/1** d.	0628	0813	0924	1024	1124	1224	1324	1424	1524	and	2124
Mühldorf (Oberbay). a.	0723	0915	1015	1115	1215	1315	1415	1515	1615	hourly	2224
Mühldorf (Oberbay). d.	0730	0933	1030	1132	1230	1332	1430	1532	1630	until	2240
Landshut (Bay) Hbf a.	0821	1021	1121	1221	1321	1421	1521	1621	1721		2328

f – On Ⓒ (also June 16, Aug. 15, Nov. 1) Landshut d. 0637, Mühldorf a. 0726.
n – *1313* on Ⓐ (not June 16, Aug. 15, Nov. 1).
⊡ – Change trains at Mühldorf and Freilassing.
⊙ – Change trains at Freilassing and Mühldorf.
⊖ – Change trains at Mühldorf on †.
◇ – Change trains at Mühldorf and Freilassing on Ⓐ (not June 16, Aug. 15, Nov. 1).
⊠ – Timings may vary by up to 4 minutes. Certain services require a change of trains at Mühldorf.

MÜNCHEN - REGENSBURG — 878

DB (RE services); ALX

See Table **892** for services Regensburg - Landshut - Freising - München Flughafen ✈ and v.v.

km		ALX		ALX		ALX		ALX		ALX		ALX		ALX	ALX	ALX			ALX		ALX	ALX		ALX	ALX
		⚒rP	N	P	N	P	N	P	N	P	N	P	N	⑦w	R	P	Ⓐt	N		N		⑦w			
0	**München** Hbf...... **944** d.	0444	0544	0644	0744	0843	0944	1043	1144	1243	1344	1443	1544	1604	1604	1643	1659	1744	1843	1944	2043	2043	2144	2244	0004
42	Freising .... **944** d.	0508	0608	0708	0808	0908	1008	1108	1208	1308	1408	1508	1608	1628	1628	1708	1728	1808	1908	2008	2108	2108	2208	2308	0028
76	Landshut (Bay) Hbf **944** d.	0529	0631	0729	0830	0929	1030	1129	1230	1329	1430	1529	1630	1649	1649	1729	1754	1830	1929	2030	2129	2129	2230	2334	0050
99	Neufahrn (Niederbay) .. d.	0543	0648	0744	0848	0943	1048	1143	1248	1343	1448	1543	1648	|	|	1743	|	1848	1946	2048	2146	2146	2248	2351	0107
138	**Regensburg** Hbf........a.	0607	0717	0807	0916	1006	1115	1206	1315	1406	1515	1607	1715	1726	1726	1806	1838	1915	2009	2115	2208	2208	2320	0017	0131
	Schwandorf **879 885** a.	0646	...	0842	...	1042	...	1242	...	1442	...	1642	...	1758	1802	1842	...	...	2105	...	2250	2250	...	0109	...
	Hof Hbf **879** ....a.	...	...	1018	...	1217	...	1418	...	1618	...	1818	...	m	1933	2018	...	...	m	...	...	0028	...	...	...

	ALX		ALX		ALX	ALX		ALX		ALX		ALX		ALX		ALX		ALX		ALX		ALX	ALX	ALX	
	⚒r			Ⓐt	Ⓒz	Ⓐt	ⒶtN		N	P	N	P	N	P	N	P	N	P	N	P	QN	⑦w		P	N
Hof Hbf **879**.............d.	...	...	...	...	m	m	...	0531r	...	0739	...	0939	...	1139	...	1339	...	1539	...	1739	...	m	...	1940c	...
Schwandorf **879 885**.d.	0400t	...	0502r	...	0603	0609	...	0707	...	0917	...	1117	...	1317	...	1517	...	1717	...	1917	...	2013	...	2117	...
Regensburg Hbf.........d.	0442	...	0547	0622	0646	0649	0702	0753	0846	0953	1046	1153	1246	1353	1446	1553	1646	1753	1846	1953	2040	2053	2053	2157	2247
Neufahrn (Niederbay) ...d.	0508	...	0610	0650	0711	|	0728	0816	0912	1016	1112	1216	1312	1416	1512	1616	1712	1816	1912	2016	2108	2116	2116	2222	2313
Landshut (Bay) Hbf **944** d.	0527	...	0628	0709	0729	0733	0747	0832	0929	1032	1129	1232	1329	1432	1529	1632	1729	1832	1929	2032	2126	2132	2132	2237	2335
Freising .... **944** d.	0548	...	0649	0732	0751	|	0810	0852	0950	1051	1150	1251	1350	1451	1550	1651	1750	1851	1950	2051		2152	2152	2256	2356
München Hbf....... **944** a.	0616	...	0716	0757	0817	0821	0836	0919	1018	1118	1216	1318	1416	1518	1616	1718	1816	1918	2016	2118		2217	2217	2321	0020

NOTES FOR TABLES 878 and 879

N – To / from Nürnberg (Table **921**).
P – Conveys 🚃 – ZÁPADNÍ EXPRES: München - Schwandorf - Praha and v.v. See Tables **76** and **885**.
Q – ⑤⑥ (also June 15, Aug. 14, Oct. 2, 31).
R – ①-⑥ (also Aug. 14, Oct. 2; not Aug. 15, Oct. 3).
c – Change trains at Schwandorf on ①-⑤ (not June 15, Aug. 15, Oct. 3, 31).
d – Also Aug. 15, Oct. 3.
e – Not Aug. 15, Oct. 3.
j – Arrives 2154.
k – ①-⑥ (not Aug. 15, Oct. 3).
m – To / from Marktredwitz (Table **879**).
r – ⚒ (not June 16, Aug. 15, Nov. 1).
t – Ⓐ (not June 16, Aug. 15, Nov. 1).
v – ①-⑥.
w – Also Aug. 15, Oct. 3; not Aug. 14, Oct. 2.
z – Also June 16, Aug. 15, Nov. 1.
ALX – *alex* train. Operated by Die Länderbahn. Most convey 🍸.

REGENSBURG - HOF — 879

ALX; Oberpfalzbahn

km		2	ALX	ALX	2	ALX	2	ALX	2	ALX	2	ALX	2	ALX	2	ALX	ALX	ALX	2	2	ALX	2	ALX	ALX	2	2
		Ⓐt	⚒r	⚒r												⑦w	R							⑦w		
	München Hbf **878** .. d.	...	0444	...	...	0644	...	0843	...	1043	...	1243	...	1443	...	1604	1604	1643	...	...	1843	...	2043	2043	...	...
0	**Regensburg** Hbf **885** d.	0512	0615	...	0707	0815	0857	1014	1057	1214	1257	1414	1457	1615	1658	1734	1734	1814	1857	1957	2037	2138	2218	2218	...	2336
42	Schwandorf........ **885** a.	0539	0646	...	0734	0842	0925	1042	1125	1242	1325	1442	1525	1642	1727	1758	1802	1842	1925	2026	2105	2207	2250	2250	...	0006
42	Schwandorf................ d.	0552	...	0651	0735	0846	0926	1046	1126	1246	1326	1446	1526	1646	1728	1759	1803	1846	1926	2027	2107	2209	...	2255	2315	0007
86	Weiden (Oberpf)........ d.	0630	...	0718	0814	0914	1002	1114	1202	1314	1402	1514	1602	1714	1804	1825	1830	1916	2002	2102	2132	2248	...	2321	2350	0042
137	Marktredwitz...... **880** a.	0711	...	0753	0855	0949	1044	1149	1244	1350	1442	1549	1644	1749	1844	1859	1906	1950	2044	2143	2213	2327	...	2400	...	...
179	**Hof** Hbf.............. **880** a.	0754	...	0820	0924	1018	1115	1217	1315	1418	1515	1618	1715	1818	1915v	1924e	1933	2018	2126	...	2242	0004	...	0028	...	...

	ALX	ALX	ALX	ALX	ALX	2	2	ALX	2	ALX	2	ALX	2	ALX	2	ALX	2	2	2	ALX	2	ALX	ALX		2	2
	⚒r	⑥	Ⓒz	Ⓐt		Ⓒz	Ⓐt											⑦d				⑦w	c			
Hof Hbf ....**880** d.	...	...	...	0432	0531r	0629	0629	0739	0843	0939	1043	1139	1243	1339	1443	1539	...	1643	1643k	1739	...	1843	1940	2043	...	2237
Marktredwitz...........**880** d.	...	0502	...	0508	0559	0704	0704	0806	0915	1006	1115	1206	1315	1406	1515	1606	1615	1707	1715k	1806	1815	1912	2006	2104	2115	2335
Weiden (Oberpf)......... d.	0414t	0539	...	0545	0639	0742	0744	0841	0955	1041	1155	1241	1356	1441	1555	1641	1656	1744	1755	1841	1856	1946	2041	...	2222j	0014
Schwandorf................ a.	0451t	0602	...	0608	0703	0807	0809	0906	1031	1106	1230	1306	1431	1506	1630	1706	1731	1809	1830	1906	1931	2010	2106	...	2257	...
Schwandorf..........**885** d.	0502	0603	0603	0609	0707	0808	0810	0917	1032	1117	1232	1317	1432	1517	1632	1717	1732	1810	1832	1917	1932	2013	2117	...	*2313*	...
Regensburg Hbf.**885** a.	0537	0636	0636	0640	0741	0837	0837	0945	1104	1145	1304	1345	1504	1545	1704	1745	1804	1838	1904	1945	2004	2045	2149	...	*2341*	...
München Hbf **878** ... a.	0716	0817	0817	0821	0919	...	...	1118	...	1318	...	1518	...	1718	...	1918	...	...	...	2118	...	2217	2321	...	...	...

FOR NOTES SEE TABLE 878 ABOVE

NÜRNBERG - HOF - DRESDEN — 880

RE / RB services

NÜRNBERG - HOF

km				Ⓒz	Ⓒz	Ⓐt	Ⓐt	B			Ⓐt		B			Ⓐt			B			Ⓐt			B
0	**Nürnberg** Hbf................ ● d.	0535j	0535j	0631	0631	0637	0637	0656	0738	0738	0805	0837	0905	0938	0938	1005	1037	1037	1105	1138	1138	1205	1237	1237	1305
28	Hersbruck (r Pegnitz)....... ● d.	0556	0556	0652	0652	|	|	0715	0754	0754	0820	|	0920	|	|	1019	|	|	1120	|	|	1219	|	|	1320
67	Pegnitz .... ● a.	0617	0617	0713	0713	0714	0714	0738	0822	0822	0842	0914	0942	1015	1015	1042	1114	1114	1142	1215	1215	1242	1314	1314	1342
67	Pegnitz ....d.	0628	0619	0715	0720	0715	0720	0739	0824	0828	0842	0916	0943	1017	1021	1043	1116	1120	1143	1217	1221	1243	1316	1320	1343
	Bayreuth Hbf.................d.	|	0641	0732	|	0732	|	0758	0847	|	0857	0932	1000	1042	|	1058	1132	|	1200	1242	|	1257	1332	|	1400
	Münchberg .... **876** d.	|	▬	0805	|	0805	|	...	...	|	▬	1004	...	...	|	▬	1205	|	...	...	|	▬	1405	|	...
94	Kirchenlaibach ....d.	0643	⊖	|	0734	|	0734	...	...	0845	⊖	|	...	...	1035	⊖	|	1134	...	...	1235	⊖	|	1334	...
125	Marktredwitz .... **879** d.	0700	0712	|	0759r	|	0759r	...	...	0901	0908	|	...	...	1053	1108	|	1159r	...	...	1253	1308	|	1359r	...
	Cheb...............................a.	|	0737	|	0822	|	0822	...	...	|	0933	|	...	...	|	1133	|	1222	...	...	|	1333	|	1422	...
167	**Hof** Hbf.............. **876 879** a.	0723	...	0823	...	0823	...	...	...	0924	...	1022	...	...	1115	...	1222	...	...	...	1315	...	1422	...	...

			Ⓐt			B			Ⓐt						Ⓐt										
Nürnberg Hbf.................. ● d.	1338	1338	1405	1437	1437	1505	1537	1537	1605	1637	1637	1705	1738	1738	1805	1837	1837	1905	1938	1938	2055	2055	2206	2206	2257
Hersbruck (r Pegnitz)......... ● d.	|	|	1420	|	|	1520	|	|	1620	|	|	1720	|	|	1820	|	|	1920	1954	1954	2112	2112	2223	2223	2313
Pegnitz .... ● a.	1415	1415	1442	1514	1514	1542	1615	1615	1642	1714	1714	1742	1815	1815	1842	1914	1914	1942	2021	2021	2137	2137	2248	2248	2337
Pegnitz ....d.	1417	1421	1443	1516	1520	1543	1617	1621	1643	1716	1720	1743	1817	1821	1843	1916	1920	1943	2023	2027	2139	2144	2250	2255	2338
Bayreuth Hbf....................d.	1442	|	1458	1532	|	1600	1642	|	1658	1732	|	1800	1842	|	1858	1932	|	2000	2048	|	2158	|	2310	|	2357
Münchberg .... **876** d.	...	|	▬	1605	|	...	...	|	▬	1805	|	...	...	|	▬	2005	|	...	...	|	...	|	▬	|	0038
Kirchenlaibach ....d.	...	1435	⊖	|	1534	...	...	1635	⊖	|	1734	...	...	1835	⊖	|	1935	...	...	2044	...	2158	⊖	2309	|
Marktredwitz .... **879** d.	...	1453	1508	|	1559r	...	...	1653	1708	|	1759r	...	...	1853k	1911	|	2001	...	...	2101	...	2216	2218	2333	|
Cheb...................................a.	...	|	1533	|	1622	...	...	|	1733	|	1822	...	...	|	1936	|	...	...	...	|	...	|	2243	|	|
Hof Hbf ....**876 879** a.	...	1515	...	1622	...	...	...	1715	...	1823	...	...	...	1915k	...	2022	...	...	...	2126	...	2242	...	0004	0058

HOF - DRESDEN ⊠

km					⊡★					d★												◇		◇
0	**Hof** Hbf....................... **881** d.	...	...	0428	...	...	0528	...	0628	...	...	0728	...		1828	...	1937	...	2028	...	...	...	...	2248
48	Plauen (Vogtl) ob Bf ..... **881** d.	...	...	0500	...	...	0600	...	0700	...	...	0800	...	and at	1900	...	2009	...	2100	...	...	2159	...	2328
73	Reichenbach (Vogtl) ob Bf **881** d.	...	...	0517	...	...	0617	...	0717	...	...	0817	...	the same	1917	...	2026	...	2117	...	...	2221	...	2350
96	**Zwickau** (Sachs) Hbf.... **881** d.	...	0439	0532	...	0539	0632	0639	0732	...	0739	0832	0839	minutes	1932	1939	2042	...	2132	2139	2239	2251	2343	0015
112	Glauchau (Sachs)......... **858** d.	...	0455	0542	...	0555	0642	0655	0742	...	0755	0842	0855	past each	1942	1955	2051	2055	2142	2155	2255	...	2359	...
144	**Chemnitz** Hbf.............. **858** d.	0504	0530r	0604	0626	0630r	0704	0730r	0804	0826	0830r	0904	0930r	hour until	2004	2030r	2114	2130	2203	2230r	2330r	...	0029	...
157	Flöha ....d.	0514	0543	0614	|	0643	0714	0743	0814	|	0843	0914	0943		2014	2043	2123	2143	...	2243	2343	...	...	...
183	Freiberg (Sachs)...................d.	0531	0607	0631	0655	0707	0731	0807	0831	0855	0907	0931	1007		2031	2107	2141	2207	...	2307	0007	...	...	...
223	**Dresden** Hbf......................a.	0603	0652	0703	0725	0752	0803	0852	0903	0925	0952	1003	1052		2103	2152	2212	2252	...	2352	0050	...	...	...

B – To Bamberg (Table **876**).
d – Not June 13–16, 21–24, 27–30, July 1.
j – 0538 on Ⓐ (not June 16, 29, 30, July 1 - Sept. 9, Nov. 1).
k – On ⑦ Marktredwitz a. 1852, d. 1902, Hof a. 1924.
r – Arrives 5–6 minutes earlier.
t – Not June 16, Nov. 1.
z – Also June 16, Nov. 1.
⊡ – ⚒ (not June 27 - July 1).
★ – *IC* service to Warnemünde via Berlin and Rostock (Tables **835** and **840**). Operated by DB.
⊖ – Operated by Oberpfalzbahn.
◇ – Operated by Vogtlandbahn.
⊠ – Operated by Mitteldeutsche Regiobahn (2nd class only).
● – Certain trains between Nürnberg and Pegnitz convey portions for two separate destinations. Passengers should take care to join the correct portion for their destination.

880 DRESDEN - HOF - NÜRNBERG

RE / RB services

DRESDEN - HOF ⊠

	Ⓐv												c★					⊙★		◇				Ⓒw
Dresden Hbf ... d.	◇	...	...	0452	0506	0552	0606	0652		1706	1752	1806	1834	1852	1906	1952	2006	2034	2052	...	2106	2206	2306	...
Freiberg (Sachs) ... d.	...	...	...	0525	0551	0625	0651	0725	and at	1751	1825	1851	1906	1925	1951	2025	2051	2106	2125	...	2151	2251	2351	...
Flöha ... d.	...	...	...	0542	0614	0642	0714	0742	the same	1814	1842	1914	|	1942	2014	2042	2114	|	2142	...	2214	2314	0014	...
Chemnitz Hbf ... **858** d.	...	0409	...	0552	0631f	0652	0731f	0752	minutes	1831f	1852	1931f	1931	1952	2031f	2052	2131f	2131	2152	...	2231f	2331f	0025	0050
Glauchau (Sachs) ... **858** d.	...	0440	...	0616	0702	0716	0802	0816	past each	1902	1916	2002	...	2016	2102	2116	2202	...	2216	...	2302	0002	...	0121
Zwickau (Sachs) Hbf ... **881** d.	0344	0511e	...	0627	0718	0727	0818	0827	hour until	1918	1927	2018	...	2027	2118	2127	2218	...	2227	2248	2318	0018	...	0137
Reichenbach (Vogtl) ob Bf **881** d.	0410	0529	...	0642	...	0742	...	0842		...	1942	...	...	2042	...	2142	...	...	...	2314	...	...	...	...
Plauen (Vogtl) ob Bf ... **881** d.	0440	0547	...	0700	...	0800	...	0900		...	2000	...	...	2100	...	2200	...	...	...	2336	...	...	...	...
Hof Hbf ... **881** a.	0519	0619	...	0732	...	0832	...	0932		...	2032	...	...	2132	...	2232	...	...	...	...	...	...	...	...

HOF - NÜRNBERG

km			Ⓐt	Ⓐt	Ⓒz	Ⓒz	Ⓐt	Ⓐt	⊖				⚒t	⊖						⊖			B		⊖
0	**Hof** Hbf ... **876 879** d.	...	0420	...	...	*0518*k	*0531*	0526	...	0629	...	...	0735	...	0843	...	...	...	0935	...	1043	...	...	1135	...
	Cheb ... d.	...	|	...	...	|	|	|	0629	|	...	...	|	0829	|	...	...	0936	|	1025	|	...	...	|	1225
	Marktredwitz ... **879** d.	...	0442	...	...	0601	0601	|	0654	0657	...	...	|	0855	0905	...	...	1009r	|	1050	1105	...	...	|	1250
	Kirchenlaibach ... d.	...	0507	...	...	0616	0620	|	—	0713	...	...	|	—	0923	...	...	1024	|	—	1123	...	...	|	—
24	Münchberg ... **876** d.	...	|	...	...	|	|	0545	Ⓐt	|	...	...	0752	Ⓐt	|	...	...	|	0952	Ⓐt	|	...	...	1153	Ⓐt
72	**Bayreuth** Hbf ... d.	0500	|	0551	0605	|	|	0624	0703	|	0712	0800	0829	0903	|	0915	1001	|	1029	1103	|	1115	1201	1229	1303
99	Pegnitz ... a.	0521	0525	0611	0624	0631	0634	0639	0717	0731	0735	0817	0844	0918	0937	0941	1018	1038	1043	1118	1137	1141	1219	1244	1318
99	Pegnitz ... d.	0529j	0529	0612	0634	0634	0641	0641	0718	0738	0738	0818	0845	0919	0944	0944	1019	1046	1046	1119	1144	1144	1219	1245	1319
138	Hersbruck (r Pegnitz) ... d.	0552j	0552	0634	0657	0657	0702	0702	0742	0802	0802	0841	|	0939	|	|	1039	|	|	1139	|	|	1241	|	|
166	**Nürnberg** Hbf ... a.	0607j	0607	0651	0713	0713	0719	0719	0757	0819	0819	0857	0922	0955	1020	1020	1056	1122	1122	1155	1220	1220	1256	1322	1355

			B			⊖			B			⊖			B			⊖		B			⊖		
Hof Hbf ... **876 879** d.	1243	...	...	...	1335	...	1443	...	...	...	1535	...	1643	...	...	...	1735	...	1843	...	...	1935	...	2043	2135
Cheb ... d.	|	...	...	1336	|	1425	|	...	...	1536	|	1625	|	...	...	1736	|	1825	|	...	1937	|	2025	|	|
Marktredwitz ... **879** d.	1306	...	...	1409r	|	1450	1506	...	...	1609r	|	1650	1705	...	...	1809r	|	1850	1906	...	2009r	|	2050	2105	|
Kirchenlaibach ... d.	1323	...	...	1424	|	—	1523	...	...	1624	|	—	1723	...	...	1824	|	—	1923	...	2025	|	—	2122	|
Münchberg ... **876** d.	|	...	...	|	1352	Ⓐt	|	...	...	|	1552	Ⓐt	|	...	...	|	1754	...	|	...	|	1954	...	|	2154
Bayreuth Hbf ... d.	|	1315	1401	|	1429	1503	|	1515	1601	|	1629	1703	|	1715	1801	|	1830	1915	|	2001	|	2029	2113	|	2227
Pegnitz ... a.	1337	1341	1419	1438	1443	1518	1537	1541	1619	1638	1644	1718	1737	1741	1819	1838	1845	1941	1937	2019	2039	2044	2133	2137	2246
Pegnitz ... d.	1344	1344	1419	1446	1446	1519	1544	1544	1619	1646	1646	1719	1744	1744	1819	1846	1846	1944	1944	2019	2047	2047	2140	2140	2247
Hersbruck (r Pegnitz) ... d.	1405	1405	1440	|	|	1539	|	|	1640	|	|	1739	|	|	1840	|	|	2007	2007	2040	|	|	2206	2206	2314
Nürnberg Hbf ... a.	1420	1420	1456	1522	1522	1555	1620	1620	1656	1722	1722	1755	1820	1820	1856	1922	1922	2022	2022	2056	2122	2122	2222	2222	2329

B – From Bamberg (Table **876**).

c – Not June 27 - July 1.
e – Arrives 0456.
f – Arrives 6 minutes earlier.
j – 7–8 minutes **earlier** on Ⓒ (also June 16, Nov. 1).

k – *0531* on ⑥.
r – Arrives 10 minutes earlier.
t – Not June 16, Nov. 1
v – Not Oct. 31, Nov. 16.
w – Also Oct. 31, Nov. 16.
z – Also June 16, Nov. 1.

⊙ – Ⓑ (not June 27 - July 1, Oct. 2).
★ – *IC* service from Warnemünde via Rostock and Berlin (Tables **835** and **840**). Operated by DB.
⊖ – Operated by Oberpfalzbahn.
◇ – Operated by Vogtlandbahn.
⊠ – Operated by Mitteldeutsche Regiobahn (2nd class only).

881 ZWICKAU - LEIPZIG - HALLE

S-Bahn 5

km																						
0	**Zwickau** (Sachs) Hbf ... **858** d.	0350	...	0504t	0521	0604	...	0704t	0721	0804	...	0904	and in	1721	1804	...	1904	1921	2004	...	2104t	2121	2230
9	Werdau ... **858** d.	0401	...	0513t	0532	0613	...	0713t	0732	0813	...	0913	the same	1732	1813	...	1913	1932	2013	...	2113t	2132	2241
29	Gößnitz ... **858** d.	0419	...	0530t	0551	0630	...	0730t	0751	0830	...	0930	pattern	1751	1830	...	1930	1951	2030	...	2130t	2151	2300
44	Altenburg ... d.	0432	0504	0542	0604	0642	0704	0742	0804	0842	0904	0942	every	1804	1842	1904	1942	2004	2042	2104	2142	2204	2313
80	Leipzig-Connewitz ★ ... d.	0511	0541	0611	0641	0711	0741	0811	0841	0911	0941	1011	**two** hours	1841	1911	1941	2011	2041	2111	2141	2211	2243	2352
85	**Leipzig** Hbf ★ ... **866** d.	0523	0553	0623	0653	0723	0753	0823	0853	0923	0953	1023	until	1853	1923	1953	2023	2053	2123	2153	2223	2253	0002
104	Leipzig/Halle Flughafen ✈ ... **866** d.	0536	0606	0636	0706	0736	0806	0836	0906	0936	1006	1036		1906	1936	2006	2036	2106	2136	2205	2236	*2321*	*0026*
122	**Halle** (Saale) Hbf ... **866** a.	0545	0618t	0645	0718	0745	0818	0845	0918	0945	1018	1045		1918	1945	2018	2045	...	2145	...	2246	...	*0036*

	Ⓐd										⊠												
Halle (Saale) Hbf ... **866** d.	0410	...	0515	0540t	0615	0640t	0715	0740	0815	0840	and in	1915	1940	2015	2040	2115	...	2215	...	...	...	2359	0059
Leipzig/Halle Flughafen ✈ ... **866** d.	0421	0456	0526	0552	0626	0652	0726	0752	0826	0852	the same	1926	1952	2026	2052	2126	2152	2226	2244	2328	2344	0010	0110
Leipzig Hbf ★ ... **866** d.	0435	0510	0540	0610	0640	0710	0740	0810	0840	0910	pattern	1940	2010	2040	2110	2140	2210	2240	2307k	2341	2357	0028	0123
Leipzig-Connewitz ★ ... d.	0445	0520	0550	0620	0650	0720	0750	0820	0850	0920	every	1950	2020	2050	2120	2150	2220	2250	2317	2351	...	0038	...
Altenburg ... d.	0516	0554	0616	0652	0716	0754	0816	0852	0916	0954	**two** hours	2016	2052	2116	2154	2223	2252	...	2357	...	...	...	...
Gößnitz ... **858** d.	0531	0608	0631t	...	0732	0808	0831	...	0932	1008	until	2031	...	2132	2208	2234	...	...	0008	...	...	...	...
Werdau ... **858** d.	0548	0633	0648t	...	0748	0833	0848	...	0948	1033		2048	...	2148	2233	2249	...	...	0027	...	...	...	...
Zwickau (Sachs) Hbf ... **858** a.	0556	0645	0656t	...	0756	0845	0856	...	0956	1045		2056	...	2156	2245	2257	...	...	0039	...	...	...	...

PLAUEN - WERDAU ◇

km		Ⓐr	⚒r							
	Plauen (Vogt) ob Bf ... **880** d.	0433	0528	0633	0728	and in the	1928	2033	2159	2328
0	Reichenbach (Vogt) ¶ **880** d.	0455	0550	0655	0750	same pattern	1950	2055	2221	2350
17	**Werdau** ... a.	0507	0602	0707	0802	every **two**	2002	2107	2234	0002
	Zwickau (Sachs) Hbf **880** a.	0522	0615	0722	0815	hours until	2015	2122	2251	0015

	Ⓐr	⚒r						
Zwickau (Sachs) Hbf ... **880** d.	0544	0636	0744	0836	and in the	2036	2144	2248
Werdau ... d.	0557	0651	0757	0851	same pattern	2051	2157	2301
Reichenbach (Vogt) ¶ ... **880** d.	0610	0704	0810	0904	every **two**	2104	2210	2314
Plauen (Vogt) ob Bf ... **880** a.	0632	0726	0832	0926	hours until	2126	2232	2336

d – Ⓐ (not Oct. 31). Runs daily Halle - Leipzig-Connewitz.
k – Arrives 2256.
r – Not Oct. 31, Nov. 16.
t – Ⓐ (not Oct. 31).

¶ – Reichenbach (Vogtl) ob Bf.
⊠ – The 1840 from Halle departs Werdau 2037 (not 2033), arrives Zwickau 2050 (not 2045).
◇ – Operated by Vogtlandbahn (2nd class only). Certain services run from / to Cheb (see Table **1122**).
★ – All trains also call at Leipzig MDR, Bayerischer Bahnhof, Wilhelm-Leuschner-Platz and Markt.

882 CHEMNITZ - CRANZAHL - VEJPRTY - CHOMUTOV

DB (*RB* services)

km												
0	**Chemnitz** Hbf ... **880** d.	0636	0836	0936	1136	1236	1336	1436	1636	1836	2036	2236
13	Flöha ... **880** d.	0647	0847	0947	1147	1247	1347	1447	1647	1847	2047	2247
31	Zschopau ... d.	0708	0908	1008	1208	1309	1410	1509	1708	1910	2108	2308
57	Annaberg-Buchholz ¶ d.	0743	0943	1049	1243	1349	1445	1544	1743	1945	2143	2343
64	Cranzahl ⊖ ... a.	...	0955	1101	1255	1402	1501	1556z	1755	...	...	...
			C⊙			C⊙			D⊙			
64	Cranzahl ... d.	...	1007	...	...	1407	...	...	1807	...	...	...
75	Vejprty 🏛 ... d.	...	1026	...	...	1426	...	...	1826	...	...	...
133	**Chomutov** ... a.	...	1145	...	...	1545	...	...	1945	...	...	...

			D⊙			C⊙			C⊙	
Chomutov ... d.	...	...	0810	...	...	1210	...	...	1610	...
Vejprty 🏛 ... a.	...	...	0930	...	...	1330	...	...	1730	...
Cranzahl ... a.	...	...	0948	...	...	1358	...	...	1748	...
			d			d			d	
Cranzahl ⊖ ... d.	...	...	1001	1155	1301	1445	1558	1655z	1801	...
Annaberg-Buchholz ¶ d.	0607	0807	1013	1207	1313	1508	1610	1707	1813	2007
Zschopau ... d.	0644	0844	1047	1245	1347	1545	1645	1744	1847	2045
Flöha ... **880** a.	0708	0908	1108	1308	1408	1608	1708	1808	1908	2108
Chemnitz Hbf . **880** a.	0720	0920	1120	1320	1420	1620	1720	1820	1920	2120

⊖ – **Cranzahl - Kurort Oberwiesenthal** *Fichtelbergbahn* (17 km, narrow gauge steam). Journey: 57–64 minutes. **No service Nov. 1–24.** Operator: SDG Sächsische Dampfeisenbahngesellschaft GmbH, Bahnhofstraße 7, 09484 Kurort Oberwiesenthal. ✆ + 49 (0) 37348 151 0.
From Cranzahl at 0959, 1137, 1315, 1504, 1640 **E** and 1813. **From Kurort Oberwiesenthal** at 0835, 1014, 1152, 1330, 1519 **E** and 1655.

C – ⑥⑦ until Oct. 2 (also July 5, 6, Sept. 28, Oct. 3).
D – ⑥⑦ until Oct. 2 (also July 5, 6, Sept. 28).
E – Daily until Sept. 18; Ⓒ from Sept. 24 (also Oct. 31).

d – Daily.
z – Ⓒ (also Oct. 31, Nov. 16).

¶ – Annaberg-Buchholz unterer Bf.
⊙ – Jointly operated by CD/DB.

883 CHEMNITZ - AUE

City-Bahn Chemnitz

km		⚒r							
0	**Chemnitz** Hbf ... d.	0551	0651	and	2051	...	2202	...	...
27	Thalheim ... d.	0646	0746	hourly	2146	...	2302	...	...
36	Zwönitz ... d.	0658	0758	until	2158	...	2313	...	...
51	**Aue** (Sachs) ... a.	0716	0816		2216	...	2330	...	...

Aue (Sachs) ... d.	0439	and	2039	...	2221	...	...
Zwönitz ... d.	0458	hourly	2058	...	2239	...	...
Thalheim ... d.	0509	until	2109	...	2250	...	...
Chemnitz Hbf ... a.	0603		2203	...	2346	...	...

r – Not Oct. 31, Nov. 16.

ZWICKAU - JOHANNGEORGENSTADT - KARLOVY VARY 884

DB; ČD (2nd class only)

km		Ⓐe							⑤⑥	
0	**Zwickau** (Sachs) Hbf . d.	0508	...	0608	and	2008	2108	2208	2308	...
27	Aue (Sachs) d.	0540	0540	0640	hourly	2040	2140	2240	2340	...
37	Schwarzenberg (Erzg) . d.	0555	0555	0655	until	2055	2153	...	2353	...
56	**Johanngeorgenstadt**. a.	0620	0620	0720		2120	...	...	...	...

	Ⓐe	Ⓐe							⑤⑥
Johanngeorgenstadt d.	...	0429	...	0529	0629	and	2029	2129	2129
Schwarzenberg (Erzg) d.	0355	0455	0455	0555	0655	hourly	2055	2155	2155
Aue (Sachs) d.	0408	0508	0508	0608	0708	until	2108	2208	2208
Zwickau (Sachs) Hbf a.	0440	0540	0540	0640	0740		2140	...	2240

km	*SEE NOTE* ▶		Ⓐ	⊗						Ⓒ	
0	**Johanngeorgenstadt**. d.	...	...	0732	0935	1235	1451	1635	2052	2052	...
1	Potučky 🏛 d.	0441	0601	0734	0937	1237	1453	1637	2054	2054	...
28	Nejdek d.	0525	0700	0819	1019	1319	1541	1719	2134	2136	2226
44	**Karlovy Vary** a.	0548	0725	0842	1042	1342	1604	1742	...	2159	2250
47	**Karlovy Vary** dolní ... a.	0555	0734	0851	1051	1347	1609	1747	...	...	...

SEE NOTE ▶					Ⓐ	Ⓒ	Ⓐ	Ⓒ		
Karlovy Vary dolní d.	0545t	0750	0950	1306	1412	1440	1706	1812	2106	...
Karlovy Vary d.	0552	0755	0955	1317	1417	1450	1717	1817	2111	...
Nejdek d.	0619	0819	1019	1341	1441	1514	1741	1841	2135	2221
Potučky 🏛 d.	0707	0900	1100	1423	1523	1557	1823	1923	...	2303
Johanngeorgenstadt a.	0709	0902	1102	1425	1525	1559	1825	1925	...	...

e – Not Oct. 31, Nov. 16. t – Ⓐ only. ⊗ – Change trains at Nejdek on Ⓐ. ▶ – Czech holiday dates apply (see page 4).

REGENSBURG - SCHWANDORF - FURTH IM WALD - PLZEŇ 885

km				◇	◇	351	◇	353	◇	355	◇	357	◇	◇	359	◇	◇	361	◇		363	◇		◇
		Ⓒ	Ⓐ	Ⓐt		‡🍷		‡w🍷		‡🍷		‡🍷	Ⓒz		‡🍷			‡🍷		DN	‡🍷		N	
	München Hbf **878** d.	...	...	...	...	0444r	...	0644	...	0843	...	1043	...	...	1243	...	...	1443	...	...	1643	...	...	...
0	**Regensburg** Hbf **879** d.	...	...	...	...	0615	...	0815	...	1014	...	1214	...	...	1414	...	...	1615	...	...	1814	...	...	...
42	**Schwandorf** **879** d.	...	...	0544	0623r	0654	0801	0852	1001	1052	1202	1252	1309	1403	1452	1509	1601	1652	1709	1737	1852	2003	2110	2317
90	Cham (Oberpf) d.	...	...	0621	0707	0724	0839	0924	1040	1124	1237	1324	1346	1437	1524	1546	1641	1724	1743	1815	1924	2037	2143	2351
109	**Furth im Wald** 🏛 d.	...	...	0637	0724	0740	0900	0940	1056	1140	1254	1340	1402	1454	1540	1602	1658	1740	1800	1832	1940	2053	2201	0008
131	Domažlice ⊠ d.	0635	0651	...	...	0801	0922c	1001	...	1201	...	1401	...	...	1601	...	...	1801	1823c	...	2001	...	...	...
190	**Plzeň** hl.n. ⊠ a.	0740	0749	...	...	0847	...	1047	...	1247	...	1447	...	...	1647	...	...	1847	...	...	2047	...	...	...
	Praha hl.n. **1120** a.	...	...	...	...	1021	...	1221	...	1421	...	1621	...	...	1821	...	...	2021	...	...	2221	...	...	...

			◇	◇	362	◇	360	◇	◇	358	◇	◇	◇	356	◇	354	◇	◇	352		350	◇		
	ⒶjN	N			‡🍷		‡🍷		Ⓐt	‡🍷		Ⓒz	Ⓐt	‡🍷		‡🍷			‡🍷		‡y🍷			
Praha hl.n. **1120** d.	...	...	...	...	0538	...	0738	...	...	0938	...	...	...	1138	...	1338	...	...	1538	...	1738	...	...	...
Plzeň hl.n. ⊠ d.	...	...	...	...	0711	...	0911	...	...	1111	...	...	...	1311	...	1511	...	...	1711	...	1911	...	2120	2247
Domažlice ⊠ d.	...	...	...	...	0801	...	1001	1036c	...	1201	...	...	...	1401	...	1601	...	...	1801	1836c	2001	...	2222	2347
Furth im Wald 🏛 d.	0445	0558	0659	0753	0823	0904	1022	1104	1150	1222	1304	1350	1354	1422	1502	1622	1704	1748	1822	1904	2022	2103	...	...
Cham (Oberpf) d.	0501	0618	0724	0813	0837	0924	1037	1124	1213	1237	1324	1413	1413	1437	1524	1637	1724	1814	1837	1924	2037	2122	...	...
Schwandorf **879** a.	0533	0653	0756	0851	0904	0956	1104	1155	1250	1304	1356	1450	1450	1504	1556	1704	1756	1850	1904	1956	2105	2156	...	...
Regensburg Hbf **879** a.	...	...	...	...	0945	...	1145	...	...	1345	...	...	...	1545	...	1745	...	...	1945	...	2149	...	...	...
München Hbf **878** a.	...	...	...	...	1118	...	1318	...	...	1518	...	...	...	1718	...	1918	...	...	2118	...	2321	...	...	...

D – ①-④ (not June 16, Oct. 3, Nov. 1).
N – From / to Nürnberg (Table **886**).
c – ⑥⑦ only.
j – Not June 16, Nov. 1.
r – ⚒ (not June 16, Aug. 15, Nov. 1).
t – Not June 16, Aug. 15, Nov. 1.

w – Change trains at Schwandorf on † (also June 16, Aug. 15, Nov. 1).
y – Change trains at Schwandorf on ⑥ (also June 15, Aug. 14, Oct. 2, 31).
z – Also June 16, Aug. 15, Nov. 1.
◇ – Operated by Oberpfalzbahn (2nd class only).

‡ – ZÁPADNÍ EXPRES. *ALX* train in Germany (operated by Die Länderbahn).
⊠ – Other local trains Domažlice - Plzeň and v.v. (journey 60–78 minutes): **From Domažlice** at 0345, 0430 Ⓐ, 0530, 0612 Ⓐ, 0726 Ⓐ, 0835, 1035, 1235, 1326 Ⓐ, 1435, 1528 Ⓐ, 1634 Ⓒ, 1637 Ⓐ, 1738 Ⓐ, 1835 Ⓒ, 1925 Ⓐ and 2034 Ⓒ. **From Plzeň hl.n.** at 0505 Ⓐ, 0605 Ⓐ, 0620 Ⓒ, 0820, 1020, 1220, 1320 Ⓐ, 1418, 1518 Ⓐ, 1620, 1720 Ⓐ, 1820, 1920 Ⓐ and 2020 Ⓒ.

NÜRNBERG - SCHWANDORF and WEIDEN 886

RE services

km			Ⓐt		Ⓐt	Ⓒz	Ⓐt										ⒶtF		D		D		F			
0	**Nürnberg** Hbf ◧ d.	0022	0430	0535	0559	0631	0631	0738	0843	0943	1043	1143	1243	1343	1443	1543	1605	1643	1705	1743	1805	1843	1938	2055	2206	2257
28	Hersbruck (r Pegnitz) ◧ d.	0038	0445	0551	0621	0648	0648	0757	0858	0958	1058	1158	1258	1358	1458	1558	1625	1658	1725	1758	1825	1858	1958	2117	2227	2316
56	Sulzbach-Rosenberg . d.	0104	0508	0619	0647	0722	0726	0826	0925	1025	1126	1225	1326	1425	1525	1625	1649	1726	1751	1825	1852	1926	2026	2142	2251	2341
68	Amberg d.	0112	0519	0627	0704	0731	0735	0833	0935	1033	1133	1233	1333	1433	1533	1632	1701	1736	1803	1833	1901	1933	2036	2150	2259	2348
94	**Schwandorf** a.	0126z	0533	0643	0727	0744	0756	0847	0948	1046	1148	1246	1350	1446	1548	1647	1724	1751	1824	1846	1927	1947	2051	2204	2312	0002

		Ⓐt	Ⓐt	Ⓒz	Ⓐt	ⒶtF	Ⓒz	Ⓐt	F	Ⓐt															
Schwandorf d.	0010	0407	0458	0516	0544	0607	0609	0644	0707	0739	0808	0908	1007	1107	1207	1307	1407	1507	1607	1707	1807	1908	2007	2111	2212
Amberg d.	0026	0423	0526	0532	0559	0624	0626	0700	0725	0755	0822	0921	1021	1121	1221	1321	1421	1521	1621	1721	1821	1922	2021	2125	2226
Sulzbach-Rosenberg d.	0032z	0432	0535	0541	0607	0635	0634	0707	0732	0807	0829	0929	1029	1129	1229	1329	1429	1529	1629	1729	1829	1929	2029	2133	2234
Hersbruck (r pegnitz) d.	...	0503	0607	0607	|	0707	0707	|	0757	0841	0900	0959	1100	1159	1300	1359	1500	1600	1700	1759	1900	1959	2100	2206	2314
Nürnberg Hbf a.	...	0518	0621	0622	0651	0723	0723	0751	0814	0857	0915	1014	1115	1214	1315	1414	1515	1615	1715	1814	1916	2014	2116	2222	2329

km													
0	**Nürnberg** Hbf ◧ d.	0535	0631	0738	0843	and	1743	1843	1938	2055	2206	2257
28	Hersbruck (r Pegnitz) ◧ d.	0551	0648	0757	0858	hourly	1758	1858	1958	2117	2227	2316
97	**Weiden** (Oberpf) a.	0646	0749	0852	0950	until	1850	1952	2051	2214	2321	0008

Weiden (Oberpf) d.	0610	0657	0806	and	1604	1704	1804	1906	2003	2215
Hersbruck (r Pegnitz) a.	0706	0756	0859	hourly	1659	1758	1859	1958	2059	2306
Nürnberg Hbf a.	0723	0814	0915	until	1715	1814	1916	2014	2116	2329

D – ①-④ (not June 16, Oct. 3, Nov. 1).
F – To / from Furth im Wald (Table **885**).
t – Not June 16, Nov. 1.
z – Ⓒ (also June 16, Nov. 1).
◧ – Trains from Nürnberg and Hersbruck may convey portions for two separate destinations. Take care to join the correct portion for your destination.
☞ **Warning!** June 29 - Sept. 11 most trains do not call at Hersbruck and Nürnberg timings may vary by up to 16 minutes (earlier departures possible).

BAYREUTH - WEIDEN 887

Operated by *agilis* (2nd class only)

km				Ⓐt					Ⓒz	Ⓐt												
0	**Bayreuth** Hbf.. d.	0002	...	0442	0617	0718	0805	0901	1001	1004	1101	1201	1300	1401	1501	1601	1701	1801	1901	2005	2023	2203
19	Kirchenlaibach d.	0018	...	0504	0652b	0740	0826	0920	1020	1020	1120	1220	1320	1420	1520	1620	1720	1820	1920	2021	2048c	2224
59	**Weiden** a.	...	...	0532	0726	...	0855	0950	1050	1050	1150	1249	1352	1449	1549	1649	1749	1849	1948	...	2117	2252

	Ⓐt	Ⓐt			Ⓐt							Ⓒz	Ⓐt									
Weiden d.	...	0549	...	...	0638	*0734*	...	0907	1007	1107	1207	1307	1323	1407	1507	1607	1707	1807	1907	2007	2134	...
Kirchenlaibach d.	0509	0618	0657	0720	0720	0807	0840	0941	1042	1142	1241	1342	1355	1442	1542	1642	1742	1842	1941	2045	2204	2337
Bayreuth Hbf a.	0525	0634	0716	0735	0735	0823	0856	0957	1056	1157	1257	1357	1415	1457	1557	1657	1757	1856	1957	2100	2220	2353

b – Arrives 0638.
c – Arrives 2039.
t – Not June 16, Nov. 1.
z – Also June 16, Nov. 1.

KEMPTEN - VILS - REUTTE IN TIROL - GARMISCH-PARTENKIRCHEN 888

RB services

km		Ⓐe	Ⓒd		❖		Ⓒd	Ⓐe				
0	**Kempten** (Allgäu) Hbf d.	0614	0630	0731		1131	1231	1300	1335		2035	2258
18	Oy-Mittelberg d.	0700r	0658	0800	and	1200	1300	1331	1403	and	2103	2329
24	Nesselwang d.	0711	0709	0811	hourly	1211	1311	1348	1414	hourly	2114	2340
31	Pfronten-Ried d.	0721	0719	0821	until	1224	1321	1357	1424	until	2124	2350
33	**Pfronten-Steinach** ... a.	0725	0723	0825		1227	1325	1401	1428		2128	2354

Pfronten-Steinach d.	0634		1134	1234	1334	1436		1936	2136
Pfronten-Ried d.	0638	and	1138	1238	1338	1440	and	1940	2140
Nesselwang d.	0647	hourly	1147	1247	1347	1449	hourly	1949	2149
Oy-Mittelberg d.	0658	until	1159	1259	1403	1503	until	2003	2203
Kempten (Allgäu) Hbf a.	0725		1225	1329	1429	1529		2029	2229

km		v		a	⑥						⑥⑦d		h		h			
0	**Pfronten-Steinach** ... d.	...	0636	...	...	0837c	0936	1036	1133j	1236	1336	1436	1536	1636	1736	1836	2036	2136
5	**Vils** Stadt ‡ d.	...	0644	...	...	0845	0944	1044	1141j	1244	1344	1444	1544	1644	1744	1844	2044	2144
15	**Reutte in Tirol** ‡ d.	0526	0701	0750	0801	0901	0959	1101	1158j	1301	1401	1501	1601	1701	1801	1901	2105	2159
35	Lermoos ‡ d.	0550	0725	0825	0825	0925	...	1125	1225	1325	1425	1525	1625	1725	1825	1925	2129	...
38	Ehrwald Zugspitzbahn ‡ d.	0556	0731	0831	0831	0931	...	1131	1231	1331	1431	1531	1631	1731	1831	1931	2135	...
60	**Garmisch**-Partenk. ... a.	0623	0757	0857	0901	0957	...	1157	1257	1357	1457	1557	1657	1757	1857	1957	2201	...
	München Hbf **895** .. a.	...	0926z	1026*	1026	1126	...	1326z	1426	1526	1626	1726z	1826	1926	...	2126k	2326f	...

		v	c	a	•		a		c		h		⑥⑦d		h		Ⓑw	
München Hbf **895** ... d.	...	0453g	0532h	...	0632z	...	0732	0832	...	1032z	1132	1232	1332	1432z	1532	1632	1732	1832z
Garmisch-Partenk. .... d.	...	0637	0704	0722	0804	...	0904	1004	1104	1204	1304	1404	1504	1604	1704	1804	1904	2004
Ehrwald Zugspitzbahn ‡ d.	...	0702	0731	0752	0831	...	0931	1031	1131	1231	1331	1431	1531	1631	1731	1831	1931	2031
Lermoos ‡ d.	...	0706	0735	0756	0835	...	0935	1035	1135	1235	1335	1435	1535	1635	1735	1835	1935	2035
Reutte in Tirol ‡ d.	0602	0736	0802	0823	0902	1004	1004	1102	1202	1302	1402	1502	1602	1702	1802	1902	2002	2102
Vils Stadt ‡ d.	0617	...	0817	0838	0917	1019	1019	1117	1217	1317	1417	1517	1617	1717	1817	1917	2017	2117
Pfronten-Steinach .... a.	0625	...	0825	...	0925	1027	1027	1125	1225	1325	1425	1525	1625	1725	1825	1925	2025	2125

a – ①-⑤ (not June 16, Aug. 15, Oct. 26, Nov. 1, Dec. 8).
c – ⑥⑦ (also June 16, Aug. 15, Oct. 26, Nov. 1, Dec. 8).
d – Also June 16, Aug. 15, Nov. 1.
e – Not June 16, Aug. 15, Nov. 1.
f – ⑤ only.
g – ① (not Aug. 15, Oct. 3).
h – Not Oct. 26, Dec. 8.
j – 3 minutes later on ⑥⑦ (also June 16, Aug. 15, Oct. 26, Nov. 1, Dec. 8).
k – Not ⑤.
r – Arrives 0641.
v – ①-⑥ (not June 16, Aug. 15, Oct. 26, Nov. 1, Dec. 8).
w – Not June 15, Aug. 14, Oct. 25, 31, Dec. 7.
z – ⑥⑦ (also June 16, Aug. 15, Oct. 3, Nov. 1).
* – Change trains at Garmisch on Oct. 3.
❖ – The 0831 from Kempten runs 1–2 minutes earlier Oy-Mittelberg - Pfronten-Steinach.
‡ – In Austria.

890 MÜNCHEN - SALZBURG

Bayerische Oberlandbahn; DB

SERVICE FROM AUGUST 2. See page 567 for amended service until August 1.

km		◇	WB 961	◇	RJX 265	◇	RJX 61	WB 963	◇	RJ 111	◇	RJX 63	RJX 63	◇	EC 217	◇	RJX 65	WB 967	◇	EC 113	◇	RJX 67	WB 969	◇	IC 2083
		Ⓐt	①–⑥ t⊙🍷		✕		B✕	⊙ 🍷		h ✕◆		Ⓒ B✕	B✕		🍷◆		B✕	⊙ 🍷		✕◆		B✕	⊙ 🍷		🍷◆
	Frankfurt (Main) Hbf **912** d.	...	...	...	...	...	...	...	...	...	...	0517	...	...	...	...	...	...	...	0820x	...	...	...	...	...
	Stuttgart Hbf **930** d.	...	...	...	...	...	...	...	...	...	...	0658	...	...	0758	...	...	...	...	0958h	...	...	...	...	...
0	**München** Hbf **951** d.	...	0548	0555	0622	0655	0723	0748	0756	0817	0856	0929	0929	0955	1017	1055	1129	1148	1155	1217	1255	1329	1348	1355	...
10	München Ost **951** d.	...	0558	0603	0633	0704	|	0758	0804	0826	0904	|	|	1004	1026	1104	|	1158	1204	1226	1304	|	1358	1404	1413
65	Rosenheim **951** d.	0532	|	0639	0703	0735	0803	|	0835	0856	0935	|	|	1035	1056	1135	|	|	1235	1256	1335	|	|	1435	1442
82	Bad Endorf d.	0543	|	0650	|	0746	|	|	0846	|	0946	|	|	1046	|	1146	|	|	1246	|	1346	|	|	1446	1455
90	Prien am Chiemsee d.	0549	|	0657	|	0752	|	|	0852	0913	0952	|	|	1052	1113	1152	|	|	1252	1313	1352	|	|	1452	1503
118	Traunstein d.	0612	|	0720	|	0816	|	|	0916	0933	1016	|	|	1116	1133	1216	|	|	1316	1333	1416	|	|	1516	1525
147	Freilassing **891** d.	0633	|	0742	|	0835	|	|	0935	0952	1035	|	|	1135	1152	1235	|	|	1335	1352	1435	|	|	1535	1542
153	**Salzburg** Hbf ▣ **891** a.	0640	0721	0752	0758	0842	0858	0921	0942	0959	1042	1058	1058	1142	1159	1242	1258	1321	1342	1359	1442	1458	1521	1542	...
	Wien Hbf **950** a.	...	0950•	...	1030	...	1130	1150•	...	...	...	1330	1330	...	...	...	1530	1550•	...	...	...	1730	1750•	...	...

	EC 115	◇	RJX 69	WB 971	◇	EC 219	◇	◇	◇	RJX 261	WB 973	◇	EC 117	◇	IC 1299	◇	NJ 295	IC 1291	◇	◇	◇		EN 463	EN 50463	◇
	🍷◆		✕	⊙ 🍷		🍷◆	Ⓐt		Ⓐt	B✕	⊙ 🍷		🍷◆		Ⓑ K🍷		Ⓡ ◆	Ⓑ 🍷					Ⓡ 🍷◆	Ⓡ 🍷◆	
Frankfurt (Main) Hbf **912** d.	...	...	...	...	...	1220	...	...	...	...	...	...	1420	...	...	...	...	1620	...	...	...	...	...	...	...
Stuttgart Hbf **930** d.	1158	...	...	...	...	1358	...	...	...	...	...	...	1558	...	1654	...	...	1758	...	...	...	...	...	...	...
München Hbf **951** d.	1417	1455	1529	1548	1555	1617	1635	1655	1722	1730	1749	1755	1817	1855	1917	1955	2010	2017	2043	2143	2243	...	2320	2320	2350
München Ost **951** d.	1426	1504	|	1558	1604	1626	1644	1704	1735	|	1759	1804	1826	1904	1927	2004	2020u	2029	2052	2152	2252	...	2331u	2331u	0002
Rosenheim **951** d.	1456	1535	|	|	1635	1657	1714	1735	1814	|	|	1835	1856	1935	1957	2035	2050u	2058	2131	2231	2331	...	0003u	0003u	0038
Bad Endorf d.	|	1546	|	|	1646	|	1726	1746	1826	|	|	1846	|	1946	2009	2046	|	2110	2142	2242	2342	...	|	|	0049
Prien am Chiemsee d.	1513	1552	|	|	1652	1713	1732	1752	1832	|	|	1852	1913	1952	2016	2052	|	2117	2148	2248	2348	...	|	|	0055
Traunstein d.	1533	1616	|	|	1716	1733	1756	1816	1856	|	|	1916	1933	2016	2035	2116	|	2137	2211	2311	0011	...	|	|	0119
Freilassing **891** d.	1552	1635	|	|	1735	1752	...	1835	...	|	|	1935	1952	2035	2053	2135	|	2155	2230	2330	0030	...	|	|	0138
Salzburg Hbf ▣ **891** a.	1559	1642	1658	1721	1742	1759	...	1842	...	1858	1921	1942	1959	2042	2100	2142	2152	2202	2237	2336	0037	...	0106	0106	0145
Wien Hbf **950** a.	...	...	1930	1950•	...	...	...	...	...	2130	2150•	...	...	...	...	...	...	...	...	...	...	...	0634	...	...

	◇	EN 462	EN 498	◇	IC 1296	◇	◇	IC 1298	◇	NJ 294		◇	IC 1290	◇	WB 960	◇	RJX 260	◇	IC 2082	EC 218	◇	WB 962	RJX 262	◇	EC 114
	Ⓐt	Ⓡ 🍷◆	Ⓡ 🍷◆		①–⑥	Ⓐt		①–⑥ hK🍷	Ⓐt	Ⓡ ◆	①–⑤ t		h 🍷		①–⑥ t⊙🍷	Ⓐt	✕		h 🍷◆	🍷◆		⊙ 🍷	✕		🍷◆
Wien Hbf **950** d.	...	2327	...	...	...	...	...	...	...	...	...	...	...	...	0610•	...	0630	...	...	...	...	0810•	0830	...	...
Salzburg Hbf ▣ **891** d.	0356	0427	0427	0515	0543	0600	0615	0640	0646	0701	0704	0715z	0800	0815	0839	...	0900	0915	...	1000	1015	1039	1100	1115	1200
Freilassing **891** d.	0404	|	|	0524	0551	0608	0624	0648	0654	|	0714	0724	0808	0824	|	...	|	0924	0945	1008	1024	|	|	1124	1208
Traunstein d.	0422	|	|	0544	0609	0627	0644	0705	0722	|	...	0744	0825	0844	|	0905	|	0944	1004	1025	1044	|	|	1144	1225
Prien am Chiemsee d.	0444	|	|	0606	0627	0650	0706	0725	0744	|	...	0806	0844	0906	|	0927	|	1006	1025	1044	1106	|	|	1206	1244
Bad Endorf d.	0451	|	|	0613	0635	0656	0713	0733	0751	|	...	0813	|	0913	|	0933	|	1013	1033	|	1113	|	|	1213	|
Rosenheim **951** d.	0504	0542s	0542s	0629	0649	0711	0729	0749	0806	0836s	...	0829	0902	0929	|	0948	|	1029	1047	1102	1129	|	|	1229	1302
München Ost **951** a.	0531	0615s	0615s	0656	0717	0738	0756	0818	0840	|	...	0856	0931	0955	1000	1016	|	1056	1115	1131	1155	1200	|	1256	1331
München Hbf **951** a.	0541	0629	0629	0706	0730	0747	0806	0830	0850	0920	...	0906	0941	1006	1013	1025	1030	1106	...	1141	1206	1213	1230	1306	1341
Stuttgart Hbf **930** a.	...	...	...	...	0959	...	...	1105	...	...	...	...	1159	...	...	...	...	...	...	1359	...	...	...	...	1559
Frankfurt (Main) Hbf **912** a.	...	...	...	...	1140	...	...	...	...	...	...	...	1340	...	...	...	...	...	...	1555j	...	...	...	...	...

	◇	WB 964	RJX 60	◇	EC 112	◇	WB 966	RJX 62	◇	EC 216	◇	RJX 64	◇	◇	WB 970	RJX 66	RJX 66	◇	RJ 110	◇	WB 972	RJX 68	◇	◇	◇
		⊙ 🍷	B✕		✕◆		⊙ 🍷	B✕		🍷◆		B✕			⊙ 🍷	B✕	⑤⑥f B✕		✕◆		⊙ 🍷	B✕			
Wien Hbf **950** d.	...	1010•	1030	...	...	...	1210•	1230	...	...	...	1430	...	...	1610•	1630	1630	...	...	...	1810•	1830	...	...	...
Salzburg Hbf ▣ **891** d.	1215	1239	1300	1313	1400	1415	1439	1500	1515	1600	1615	1700	1715	1815	1839	1900	1900	1915	2000	2015	2039	2100	2115	2215	2300
Freilassing **891** d.	1224	|	|	1324	1408	1424	|	|	1524	1608	1624	|	1724	1824	|	|	|	1929	2008	2024	|	|	2129	2224	2310
Traunstein d.	1244	|	|	1344	1425	1444	|	|	1544	1625	1644	|	1744	1844	|	|	|	1949	2025	2044	|	|	2149	2244	2329
Prien am Chiemsee d.	1306	|	|	1406	1444	1506	|	|	1606	1644	1706	|	1806	1906	|	|	|	2011	2044	2106	|	|	2211	2306	2351
Bad Endorf d.	1313	|	|	1413	|	1513	|	|	1613	|	1713	|	1813	1913	|	|	|	2018	|	2113	|	|	2218	2313	2357
Rosenheim **951** d.	1329	|	|	1429	1502	1529	|	|	1629	1702	1729	|	1829	1929	|	|	|	2032	2102	2132	|	2155	2232	2332	0012
München Ost **951** a.	1355	1400	|	1456	1530	1556	1600	|	1656	1731	1756	|	1856	1956	2000	|	|	2105	2131	2206	2155	|	2305	0008	0046
München Hbf **951** a.	1405	1413	1432	1506	1541	1606	1613	1633	1706	1741	1806	1831	1906	2006	2013	2031	2031	2115	2141	2215	2207	2231	2315	0017	0058
Stuttgart Hbf **930** a.	...	...	...	...	1759	...	...	...	...	1959	...	...	...	...	...	...	2259	...	...	...	...	...	...	...	...
Frankfurt (Main) Hbf **912** a.	...	...	...	...	1940v	...	...	...	...	...	...	...	...	...	...	...	0041	...	...	...	...	...	...	...	...

◆ – **NOTES** (LISTED BY TRAIN NUMBER)

110/1 – HOHE TAUERN – [12] ✕ Klagenfurt - Villach - München and v.v.
112/3 – BLAUER ENZIAN – [12] ✕ Klagenfurt - Villach - München - Frankfurt and v.v.; [12] Zagreb (**212/3**) - Ljubljana - Jesenice ▣ - Villach - München - Frankfurt and v.v.
114 – WÖRTHERSEE – [12] 🍷 Klagenfurt - München - Mannheim - Bochum.
115 – WÖRTHERSEE – [12] 🍷 Münster - Köln - Mannheim - München - Klagenfurt.
117 – SALZACH – [12] 🍷 Frankfurt - Villach - Klagenfurt.
216/7 – DACHSTEIN – [12] 🍷 Graz - Salzburg - Mannheim - Saarbrücken and v.v.
218 – CHIEMGAU – [12] 🍷 Graz - Salzburg - Frankfurt (- Erfurt ①–④).
219 – CHIEMGAU – [12] 🍷 Frankfurt - Salzburg - Bischofshofen - Graz.
294/5 – 🛏 1, 2 cl., ▬ 2 cl. and [2] Roma - Firenze - Bologna - München and v.v.; 🛏 1, 2 cl., ▬ 2 cl. and [2] Milano (**40235/40295**) - Verona - München and v.v.
462/3 – KÁLMÁN IMRE – 🛏 1, 2 cl., ▬ 2 cl., [2] and 🍷 Budapest - München and v.v.
498 – LISINSKI – 🛏 1, 2 cl., ▬ 2 cl. and [2] Zagreb - Ljubljana - Jesenice ▣ - Villach - München; 🛏 1, 2 cl. and [2] (**480**) Rijeka - Ljubljana - München; 🛏 1, 2 cl., ▬ 2 cl. and [2] (*NJ* **40236**) Venezia - Villach - München.
2082/3 – KÖNIGSSEE – [12] 🍷 Berchtesgaden - Augsburg - Hannover and v.v.
50463 – LISINSKI – 🛏 1, 2 cl., ▬ 2 cl. and [2] München - Villach - Jesenice ▣ - Ljubljana - Zagreb; 🛏 1, 2 cl. and [2] (**60463**) München - Ljubljana - Rijeka; 🛏 1, 2 cl., ▬ 2 cl. and [2] (*NJ* **40463**) München - Villach - Venezia.

B – To / from Budapest (Table **1250**).
K – To / from Karlsruhe (Table **931**).

f – Also Oct. 2.
h – Not Aug. 2.
j – 1540 on ⑤–⑦ from Aug. 27; 1615 on Aug. 5, 12, 19, 26.
s – Calls to set down only.
t – Not Aug. 15.
u – Calls to pick up only.
v – 1944 on ⑤ until Aug. 26.
x – Not Aug. 2. On ①–⑤ Aug. 3 – 26 departs Frankfurt (Main) **Süd**, d. 0819 (not Hbf).
z – Ⓒ (also Aug. 15).

• – Wien **Westbahnhof**.
◇ – *Meridian* regional service (operated by Bayerische Regiobahn; German holiday dates apply).
⊙ – Operated by *Westbahn* (special fares).

891 SALZBURG - FREILASSING - BERCHTESGADEN

Berchtesgadener Land Bahn *

SERVICE FROM AUGUST 2. See page 567 for amended service until August 1.

km		h◇	Ⓐt	Ⓒz												A									
0	**Salzburg** Hbf **890** d.	0615	0704	0715	0815	0842	0915	0942	and at	1313	1342	1415	1442	1515	1542	...	1615	1642	1715	1742	1815	1915	2042	2142	2229
6	Freilassing **890** a.	0622	0714	0722	0822	0854	0922	0954	the same	1320	1354	1422	1454	1522	1554	...	1622	1654	1722	1754	1822	1922	2054	2154	2241
6	Freilassing d.	0634	0718	0740	0840	0859	0939	0958	minutes	1339	1358	1439	1458	1539	1558	1618	1639	1658	1739	1758	1839	1939	2100	2201	2246
21	Bad Reichenhall d.	0655	0741	0759	0901	0920	1001	1020	past each	1401	1420	1501	1520	1601	1620	1631	1701	1720	1801	1820	1901	2001	2122	2219	2306
39	**Berchtesgaden** Hbf a.	0726	0810	0826	0928	...	1028	...	hour until	1428	...	1528	...	1628	...	1707	1728	...	1828	...	1928	2028	2150	2247	2334

	Ⓐt	①b	Ⓐt			Ⓐt		hA											◇						
Berchtesgaden Hbf d.	...	0529	...	0621	0706	...	...	0827	...	...	0932	...	and at	1532	...	1632	...	1732	1750	...	1832	...	1932	2032	2210
Bad Reichenhall d.	0528	0559	0559	0654	0740	0800	0837	0900	...	0937	1000	1037	the same	1600	1637	1700	1737	1800	1826	1837	1900	1937	2000	2100	2245
Freilassing a.	0546	0616	0616	0712	0757	0821	0858	0920	...	0957	1018	1057	minutes	1618	1657	1718	1757	1818	1838	1857	1918	1957	2018	2118	2303
Freilassing **890** d.	0547	0618	0618	0722	0807	0835	0903	...	0935	1007	1035	1107	past each	1635	1707	1735	1807	1835	1845	1907	1935	2007	2035	2135	2307
Salzburg Hbf **890** a.	0558	0629	0629	0733	0817	0842	0913	...	0942	1017	1042	1117	hour until	1642	1717	1742	1817	1842	1854	1917	1942	2017	2042	2142	2317

A – *IC* **2082/3**: KÖNIGSSEE – [12] 🍷 Berchtesgaden - Hannover and v.v. Train category *RE* Berchtesgaden - Freilassing and v.v. Operated by DB.

b – Not Aug. 15, Oct. 3.

h – Not Aug. 2.
t – Not Aug. 15.
z – Also Aug. 15.

***** – Services to / from Bad Reichenhall or Berchtesgaden are operated by Berchtesgadener Land Bahn 2nd class only. Other trains are operated by either DB or ÖBB. German holiday dates apply.
◇ – Operated by DB.

MÜNCHEN FLUGHAFEN ✈ 892

S-Bahn services S1 and S8 from / to München (2nd class only). Services on both routes run approximately every 20 minutes.

S1 München Hbf (low level) - Freising - München Flughafen Terminal ✈ (41 km). **From München Hbf** 0503 to 2323. **From München Flughafen** 0551 to 0011. Journey: ± 45 minutes. **S1** trains from München Hbf are often combined with a Freising service - travel in the rear portion for the Airport.

S8 München Pasing - München Hbf (low level) - München Ost - München Flughafen Terminal ✈ (44 km). **From München Pasing** 0305 to 0005 (10 minutes later from München Hbf, 19 minutes later from München Ost). **From München Flughafen** 0404 to 0004. Journey: 50 minutes from / to Pasing, 40 minutes from / to Hbf, 31 minutes from / to Ost.

Direct *RE* services Regensburg - Landshut - Freising - München Flughafen

Regensburg Hbf .... **878** d.	0313	0417	0512	0613	0713	0815	and	2215
Landshut (Bay) Hbf .... **878** d.	0358	0459	0558	0659	0759	0859	hourly	2259
Freising .... **878** d.	0420	0520	0620	0720	0820	0920	until	2320
München Flughafen ⊡ ✈ ..... a.	0433	0532	0632	0732	0832	0932		2332

		Ⓒz	Ⓐt	Ⓐt	Ⓒz	Ⓐt	Ⓒz					
München Flughafen ⊡ ✈. d.	0428	0528	0528	0608	0628	0708	0728	0828	and	2228	2328	0028
Freising .... **878** d.	0439	0539	0539	0620	0639	0719	0739	0839	hourly	2239	2339	0039
Landshut (Bay) Hbf .... **878** d.	0506	0606f	0614f	0646	0702	0745	0802	0902	until	2302	0003	0103
Regensburg Hbf .... **878** a.	0554t	0650	0701	0734	0746	0833	0845	0945		2345	0048	0148

f – Arrives 0601. t – Ⓐ (not June 16, Aug. 15, Nov. 1). z – Also June 16, Aug. 15, Nov. 1. ⊡ – München Flughafen Terminal.

MÜNCHEN - MÜHLDORF - SIMBACH 893

On June 16, Aug. 15, Nov. 1 services run as on ⑦

km		Ⓒ	Ⓐ									Ⓐ		Ⓐ	Ⓒ	Ⓐ	Ⓒ¶	Ⓐ		Ⓐ		Ⓐ		⊗		
0	**München** Hbf .... d.	0603j	0606j	0706j	0807c	0907j	1007j	1107j	1207j	1307j	1406j	1427j	1506j	1521j	1607j	1627	1707j	1726	1807j	1831	1907j	1948j	2026j	2128j	2228j	2328j
10	**München** Ost .... d.	0617	0615	0716	0816	0917	1017	1117	1217	1317	1417	1439	1515	1533	1617	1638	1717	1738	1818	1840	1917	1957	2038	2138	2238	2337
85	**Mühldorf** (Oberbay) .. a.	0722	0721	0819	0919	1017	1117	1217	1317	1417	1517	1535	1619	1630	1717	1731	1816	1830	1919	1931	2020	2102	2140	2235	2335	0038
		|									Ⓒ	|	Ⓒ	|		d	Ⓒ	|		d				|		
85	**Mühldorf** (Oberbay) .. d.	0737	0737	0837	0937	1037	1137	1227‡	1337	1437	1538	1538	1637	1634	...	1737	1837	1834	...	1937	2037	...	2147	2247	2342	...
124	**Simbach** (Inn) .... **962** a.	0813	0813	0913	1013	1113	1213	1258‡	1413	1513	1613	1613	1713	1708	...	1813	1913	1907	...	2013	2113	...	2219	2319	0014	...

			Ⓐ	⑥	Ⓐ	Ⓐ	Ⓒ											Ⓐ	Ⓒ		Ⓐ	Ⓒ				
Simbach (Inn) ...... **962** d.	...	...	0507	0540	0554	0648	0648	0749	0849	0949	1049	1149	1249•	1349	1449	1549	...	1641	1649	1749	1841	1849	1949	2049	2154	2254
Mühldorf (Oberbay) ... a.	...	...	0540	0611	0628	0722	0722	0822	0922	1022	1122	1222	1322•	1422	1523	1622	...	1718	1722	1822	1917	1922	2022	2125	2229	2329
		⚒	Ⓐ	Ⓒ	|	|	Ⓒ									Ⓒ	Ⓐ		d			d		|	|	
Mühldorf (Oberbay) ... d.	0429	0519	0546	0623	0637	0732	0732	0832	0937	1030	1138	1231	1340	1430	1538	1630	1634	...	1737	1843	...	1940	2034	2146	2246	...
München Ost .... a.	0524	0623	0640	0724	0722	0822	0826	0926	1045	1128	1244	1326	1444	1525	1645	1726	1744	...	1844	1943	...	2044	2142	2246	2352	...
München Hbf .... a.	0533j	0633j	0650	0735j	0734j	0835	0837j	0936j	1055j	1138j	1254j	1337j	1454j	1536j	1654j	1737j	1755j	...	1855j	1955j	...	2055j	2153j	2300j	0003j	...

c – Ⓒ from July 16.
d – Daily from Mühldorf.
j – From July 14.
⊗ – Change trains at Mühldorf on †.
¶ – July 14 - Aug. 1 departs München Hbf 1703, München Ost 1715.
• – 10 minutes later on Ⓐ.
‡ – On Ⓒ Mühldorf d. 1237, Simbach a. 1313.

MÜNCHEN - GARMISCH - INNSBRUCK 895

DB; ÖBB (2nd class only in Austria)

km																		*ICE*	*ICE*							
		◧		◧	◧			◧		◧			◧		◧		◧	**527**	**529**	◧	◧		◧			◧
		Ⓐ		Ⓒ			Ⓒ		Ⓒ		Ⓒ							⑥L	⑥M						Ⓐ	
		t		z			z		z		z							D	D						t	
0	**München** Hbf .... d.	0453	...	0532	0632	...	0713	0732	0813	0832	0913	0932	1032	...	1132	...	1232	1243	1313	1332	1432	...	1532	...	1613	1632
7	München Pasing .... d.	0500	...	0538	0638	...	0720	0738	0820	0839	0920	0938	1038	...	1138	...	1238	|	|	1338	1438	...	1538	...	1620	1638
40	Tutzing .... d.	0528	...	0601	0701	...	|	0801	|	0901	|	1001	1101	...	1201	...	1301	|	1343	1401	1501	...	1601	...	|	1700
54	Weilheim (Oberbay) ... d.	0545	...	0612	0712	...	0748	0814	0848	0912	0948	1012	1112	...	1212	...	1312	1329	1400	1412	1512	...	1612	...	1648	1712
75	Murnau .... d.	0604	...	0628	0728	...	0801	0832	0901	0928	1001	1028	1128	...	1228	...	1328	1352	1415	1428	1528	...	1628	...	1701	1728
101	**Garmisch**-Partenk. ¶ a.	0630	...	0654	0754	...	0824	0856	0924	0954	1024	1054	1154	...	1254	...	1354	1417	1441	1454	1554	...	1654	...	1724	1754
101	**Garmisch**-Partenk. ¶ d.	0632	0632	...	━	0802	0828	0906	0926	1002	1026	1102	━	1202	1302	...	1402	━	━	1502	━	1602	1702	...	1726	1802
118	**Mittenwald** .... a.	0653	0653	...	...	0823	0854	0927	0953	1023	1053	1123	...	1223	1323	...	1423	...	...	1523	...	1623	1723	...	1753	1823
118	**Mittenwald** 🏛 .... d.	0655	0655	...	...	0826	...	0936	━	1026	...	1136c	...	1226	1336c	...	1426	...	...	1536	...	1626	1736c	...	...	1826
125	Scharnitz 🏛 .... ⊡ d.	0703	0703	...	0803	0834	...	0944	...	1034	...	1144c	1203a	1234	1344c	1403a	1434	1503	...	1544	...	1634	1744c	1803a	...	1834
135	Seefeld in Tirol ..... ⊡ d.	0716	0716	...	0816	0846	...	0956	1016	1046	...	1156c	1216	1246	1356c	1416	1446	1516	...	1556	1616	1646	1756c	1816	...	1846
160	**Innsbruck** Hbf ...... ⊡ a.	0753	0753	...	0853	0923	...	...	1053	1123	...	...	1253	1323	...	1453	1523	1553	...	...	1653	1723	...	1853	...	1923

						ICE						
		◧		◧		**1205**						
	Ⓐ		Ⓐ			⑤						Ⓒ
	t		t			H		◇				z
München Hbf .... d.	1710	1732	1813	1832	...	1923	1932	2032	2132	2232	2332	2332
München Pasing .... d.	1716	1738	1820	1838	...	|	1938	2038	2138	2238	2338	2338
Tutzing .... d.	|	1801	|	1901	...	2006	2001	2101	2201	2301	0001	0001
Weilheim (Oberbay) .... d.	1749	1812	1849	1912	...	2018	2012	2112	2212	2312	0012	0012
Murnau .... d.	1801	1828	1901	1928	...	2035	2028	2128	2228	2328	0028	0028
Garmisch-Partenk. . ¶ a.	1824	1854	1924	1954	...	2057	2054v	2154	2254	2354	0054	0054
Garmisch-Partenk. . ¶ d.	1826	1902	1926	...	2002	2058	2102v	2206	2302	0005	━	0102
Mittenwald .... a.	1853	1923	1953	...	2023	2118	2123v	2227	2323	0026	...	0123
Mittenwald 🏛 .... d.	...	1936	━	...	2026	2120	...	...	...	...	...	...
Scharnitz 🏛 .... ⊡ d.	...	1944	...	...	2034	|	...	...	...	...	2303	...
Seefeld in Tirol ...... ⊡ d.	...	1956	2016	...	2046	2150	...	...	...	...	2316	...
Innsbruck Hbf ...... ⊡ a.	...	...	2053	...	2123	2222	...	...	...	...	2353	...

										◧
	⚒	Ⓐ	Ⓒ	Ⓐ	Ⓐ	Ⓒ	Ⓐ			
	t	t	z	t	t	z	t			
Innsbruck Hbf ... ⊡ d.	...	...	...	...	...	...	...	0638	0708	...
Seefeld in Tirol ... ⊡ d.	...	...	...	...	...	...	...	0715	0745	...
Scharnitz 🏛 ...... ⊡ d.	...	...	...	...	...	...	...	0728	0757	...
Mittenwald 🏛 .... a.	...	...	...	...	...	...	...	0735	━	...
Mittenwald .... d.	...	0530	0536	0603	0634	0634	*0658*	0736	...	0836
Garmisch-P .... ¶ a.	...	0551	0557	0630	0700	0700	*0720*	0757	◧	0858e
Garmisch-P .... ¶ d.	0500	0559	0607	0635	0702	0707	0735	...	0805e	0905e
Murnau .... d.	0524	0626	0632	0654	0728	0732	0758	...	0832	0932
Weilheim (Oberbay) d.	0541	0646	0649	0711	0746	0749	0812	...	0849	0949
Tutzing .... d.	0553f	0700	0700	|	0800	0800	|	...	0900	1000
München Pasing .... a.	0611f	0719	0719	0741	0819	0819	0839	...	0919	1019
München Hbf .... a.	0618f	0726	0726	0748	0826	0826	0846	...	0926	1026

						ICE		*ICE*			*ICE*	*ICE*														
	◧				◧	**1204**	◧	**1214**		◧	**528**	**526**			◧		◧						◧			
						⑦L		⑦M			⑥M	⑥L				Ⓒ										
						A		A			D	D				z								N	P	
Innsbruck Hbf ...... ⊡ d.	0838	*0908*	1038	1108	...	1224	1238	1254	1308	...	...	...	1438	1508	...	...	1638	1708	...	1838	1908	...	2038	...	...	2308
Seefeld in Tirol ...... ⊡ d.	0915	1004	1115	1145	1204c	1304	1315	1333	1345	1404c	...	...	1515	1544	1604	...	1715	1745	1804c	1915	1944	2004	2115	...	...	2345
Scharnitz 🏛 .... ⊡ d.	0928	1016	1128	1157a	1216c	|	1328	|	1357a	1416c	...	...	1528	━	1616	...	1728	1757a	1816c	1928	━	2016	2128	...	...	2357
Mittenwald 🏛 .... a.	0935	1025	1135	━	1225c	1324	1335	1353	...	1425c	...	...	1535	...	1625	...	1735	...	1825c	1935	...	2025	2135	...	...	━
Mittenwald .... d.	0936	1036	1136	...	1236	1326	1336	1403	...	1436	...	...	1536	...	1636	1704	1736	...	1836	1936	...	2036	2136	2236	2236	...
Garmisch-Partenk. . ¶ a.	1000	1057	1157	◧	1300	1348	1400	1430	...	1500	...	...	1557	◧	1700	1732	1800	...	1900	1957	◧	2057	2157	2257	2257	...
Garmisch-Partenk. . ¶ d.	1005e	1107	...	1207	1307	1359	1407	1432	...	1507	1515	1540	...	1607	1705	1735	1805	...	1905h	...	2005	2107	2207	2307	2302	PJ
Murnau .... d.	1032	1132	...	1231	1332	1427	1432	1505	...	1532	1543	1608	...	1632	1732	1758	1832	...	1932	...	2031	2132	2232	2332	2326	2332
Weilheim (Oberbay) .... d.	1049	1149	...	1249	1349	1442	1449	1526	...	1549	1600	|	...	1649	1749	1812	1849	...	1949	...	2049	2149	2249	2349	...	2349
Tutzing .... d.	1100	1200	...	1300	1400	1453	1500	|	...	1600	1616	1637	...	1700	1800	|	1900	...	2000	...	2100	2200	2300	0000	...	0000
München Pasing .... a.	1119	1219	...	1318	1419	|	1519	|	...	1619	|	|	...	1719	1819	1840	1919	...	2019	...	2119	2219	2319	0019	...	0019
München Hbf .... a.	1126	1226	...	1326	1426	1542	1526	1610	...	1626	1643	1708	...	1726	1826	1847	1926	...	2026	...	2126	2226	2326	0026	...	0026

A – (12) ✕ Innsbruck - Garmisch - Nürnberg - Hannover.
D – (12) ✕ Garmisch - Nürnberg - Frankfurt - Dortmund and v.v.
H – (12) ✕ Hamburg - Berlin - Nürnberg - Garmisch - Innsbruck.
J – From Oberammergau (Table **897**). Runs 22–24 minutes later until Aug. 14.
L – Until Oct. 16.
M – From Oct. 22.
N – From Oct. 3.
P – Until Oct. 2

a – ①–⑤ (not June 16, Aug. 15, Oct. 26, Nov. 1, Dec. 8).
c – ⑥⑦ (also June 16, Aug. 15, Oct. 26, Nov. 1, Dec. 8).
e – 2 minutes later on Ⓐ (not June 16, Aug. 15, Nov. 1).
f – 3–5 minutes later on ⑥.
h – 1907 on Ⓒ (also June 16, Aug. 15, Nov. 1).
t – Not June 16, Aug. 15, Nov. 1.
v – On ⑤ Garmisch a. 2051, d. 2108, Mittenwald a. 2128.
z – Also June 16, Aug. 15, Nov. 1.
◧ – Conveys (12) to / from stations in Table **888**.

◇ – Change trains at Garmisch until Oct. 2.
⊡ – Other local trains Scharnitz - Innsbruck and v.v. **From Scharnitz** at 0633, 0733 ⚒, 0903, 1103 Ⓑ, 1303 ⚒, 1703, 1903, 2103, 2203 and 0003. **From Innsbruck** at 0808, 1008 Ⓑ, 1208 ⚒, 1408, 1608, 1808, 2008, 2108 and 2208.
¶ – Bayerische Zugspitzbahn (rack railway) operates Garmisch-Partenkirchen - Zugspitzplatt: departures at 0815 and hourly to 1415, returning from Zugspitzplatt at 0930 and hourly to 1630.

MURNAU - OBERAMMERGAU 897

RB services

km		Ⓐt	⑥	Ⓐt										A	B	B	C
0	**Murnau** .... d.	0512	0548	0600	0648	0742	and	1142	1234	1334	1442	and	2142	2231	2242	2334	0032
12	Bad Kohlgrub .... d.	0530	0606	0619	0706	0800	hourly	1200	1252	1352	1500	hourly	2200	2249	2300	2352	0050
24	**Oberammergau** .... ♥ a.	0550	0626	0638	0726	0819	until	1219	1312	1412	1519	until	2219	2308	2319	0012	0109

	Ⓐt	⑥	Ⓐt												A	BM	AM	B
Oberammergau .... ♥ d.	0507	0543	0556	0643	0738	0838	0938	1038	1138	1229	1329	1438	and	2138	2227	2238	2316	2329
Bad Kohlgrub .... d.	0529	0605	0618	0705	0800	0900	1000	1100	1200	1252	1352	1500	hourly	2200	2249	2300	2335	2352
Murnau .... a.	0547	0623	0636	0723	0819	0919	1019	1119	1219	1310	1410	1519	until	2219	2308	2320	2353	0010

A – Until Aug. 14.
B – From Aug. 15.
C – Until Aug. 15.
M – To München (Table **895**).
t – Not June 16, Aug. 15, Nov. 1.
♥ – Trains call at Unterammergau (*km* 20) 4–7 minutes from Oberammergau.

GERMANY

900 NÜRNBERG and FRANKFURT - HAMBURG

km		ICE 990 ①	ICE 1688	ICE 1678 ①–⑤ Q	NJ 40470 ♦		ICE 1686 ①–⑤ ✕	NJ 40420 [R] B	NJ 490 [R] ♦		ICE 1088 ①–⑥ ✕	ICE 1676 ①–⑤ ✕	ICE 1676 ① ✕		ICE 672 Y✕	ICE 888 ①–⑤ ✕		ICE 774 ✕	ICE 684 ✕	IC 1674 🍷		ICE 474 K✕	ICE 886 ✕
	Basel SBB **912** 🏛 d.	...	...	...	2113	...	...	...	...	...	...	...	...	...	...	...	...	...	...	...	...	0500	...
	Karlsruhe Hbf **912** d.	...	...	...	2306	...	...	...	...	...	...	...	...	...	...	...	...	...	...	...	...	0651	...
	Stuttgart Hbf **912** d.	2305p	...	...	|	...	...	...	...	...	...	...	...	...	...	...	...	0502	...	...	...	|	...
	Mannheim Hbf **912** d.	2351p	...	...	2342	...	...	...	...	...	...	...	...	...	...	...	...	0605	...	...	...	0716	...
	Frankfurt Flughafen Fernbf ✈ **912** d.	0030	...	...	|	...	...	...	...	...	...	...	...	...	0533	...	...	0641	...	...	...	|	...
	Frankfurt (Main) Hbf **850 901 902** d.	0056	...	...	0052	...	...	...	...	...	0506	...	0344	...	0550	...	...	0658	...	0649	...	0758	...
	Hanau Hbf **850 901 902** d.	0113	...	...	|	...	...	...	...	...	0521	...	|	...	0607	...	...	|	...	|	...	|	...
	München Hbf **904 905** d.	|	2300	...	|	...	...	2250	...	...	|	...	|	...	|	0312	...	|	0412	|	...	|	0516
	Augsburg Hbf **905** d.	|	|	...	|	...	...	2323	...	...	|	...	◧	...	|	|	...	|	|	◧	...	|	|
0	**Nürnberg** Hbf **905 920 921** d.	|	0016	...	|	...	...	0151	0151	...	|	...	|	...	|	0424	...	|	0532	|	...	|	0632
102	**Würzburg** Hbf **920 921** d.	|	0120	...	|	...	...	0250	0250	...	|	...	|	...	|	0519	...	|	0626	|	...	|	0728
195	Fulda **850 901 902** d.	0157	|	...	0149	...	...	|	|	...	0604	...	|	...	0647	0704	...	|	0803	|	...	|	0904
285	**Kassel** Wilhelmshöhe **901 902** d.	|	|	...	|	...	...	|	|	...	0636	0623	0623	...	0724	0736	...	0821	0836	0856	...	0921	0936
330	Göttingen **902 903** d.	0325	0405	...	0316	...	0546	0553	0553	...	0655	0645	0645	...	0744	0755	...	0840	0855	0917	...	0940	0955
430	**Hannover** Hbf **903** a.	0421	0506	...	0558	...	0657	0649	0649	...	0732	0756	0756	...	0818	0832	...	0917	0932	0957	...	1017	1032
430	**Hannover** Hbf **903** d.	0424	0514	0554	0600	...	0701	0653	0653	...	0736	0759	0759	...	0820	0836	...	0920	0936	0959	...	1020	1036
	Bremen Hbf **813** a.	|	|	|	|	...	|	|	|	...	|	0913	0913	...	|	|	...	|	|	1113	...	|	|
471	Celle **903** d.	|	|	0617	|	...	0720	|	|	...	0757	...	...	...	|	0857	...	|	0957	...	...	|	1057
523	Uelzen **903** d.	|	|	0642	|	...	0742	|	|	...	0821	...	...	...	|	0921	...	|	1021	...	...	|	1121
559	Lüneburg **903** d.	|	|	0659	|	...	0758	|	|	...	0838	...	...	...	|	0938	...	|	1038	...	...	|	1138
608	**Hamburg** Hbf **903** a.	0608	0658	0729	0754	...	0829	0847	0847	...	0929	...	...	...	0954	1029	...	1054	1129	...	...	1154	1229
615	**Hamburg** Altona a.	...	0710	...	0809	...	0845	0904	0904	...	0946	...	...	...	1011	1046	...	1110	1146	...	...	...	1246

	ICE 772 ✕	ICE 682 ✕	ICE 632 ✕♦	IC 1672 🍷		ICE 78 Z✕	ICE 882 ✕	ICE 1176 ⑥ ✕		ICE 770 ✕	ICE 680 ✕	IC 2374 🍷		ICE 76 Z✕	ICE 880 ✕		ICE 578 ✕	ICE 588 ✕	ICE 538 T✕	ICE 1578 ✕		ICE 74 ✕♦	ICE 788 ✕
Basel SBB **912** 🏛 d.	...	...	...	...	...	0706	...	...	...	...	...	...	...	0906	...	...	...	...	...	...	...	1106	...
Karlsruhe Hbf **912** d.	...	...	...	0702	...	0851	...	...	...	...	...	0910	...	1051	...	...	...	...	...	1110	...	1251	...
Stuttgart Hbf **912** d.	0725	...	...	|	...	|	...	...	...	0923	...	|	...	|	...	...	1123	...	...	|	...	|	...
Mannheim Hbf **912** d.	0805	...	...	|	...	0916	...	...	...	1005	...	|	...	1116	...	...	1205	...	...	|	...	1316	...
Frankfurt Flughafen Fernbf ✈ **912** d.	0841	...	...	|	...	|	...	...	...	1041	...	|	...	|	...	...	1241	...	...	|	...	|	...
Frankfurt (Main) Hbf **850 901 902** d.	0858	...	...	0851‡	...	0958	...	1018	...	1058	...	1051‡	...	1158	...	...	1258	...	...	1251‡	...	1358	...
Hanau Hbf **850 901 902** d.	|	...	...	|	...	|	...	1036	...	|	...	|	...	|	...	...	|	...	...	|	...	|	...
München Hbf **904 905** d.	|	0614	0614	|	...	|	0717	|	...	|	0820	|	...	|	0918	...	|	1021	1021	|	...	|	1116
Augsburg Hbf **905** d.	|	|	|	◧	...	|	|	|	...	|	|	◧	...	|	|	...	|	|	|	◧	...	|	|
Nürnberg Hbf **905 920 921** d.	|	0731	0731	|	...	|	0832	|	...	|	0933	|	...	|	1032	...	|	1133	1133	|	...	|	1232
Würzburg Hbf **920 921** d.	|	0828	0828	|	...	|	0928	|	...	|	1028	|	...	|	1128	...	|	1228	1228	|	...	|	1328
Fulda **850 901 902** d.	|	1004	1004	|	...	|	1104	1122	...	|	1203	|	...	|	1304	...	|	1404	1404	|	...	|	1504
Kassel Wilhelmshöhe **901 902** d.	1021	1036	1036	1056	...	1121	1136	1157	...	1221	1236	1256	...	1321	1336	...	1421	1436	1436	1456	...	1521	1536
Göttingen **902 903** d.	1040	1055	1055	1116	...	1140	1155	1219	...	1240	1255	1317	...	1340	1355	...	1440	1455	1455	1516	...	1540	1556
Hannover Hbf **903** a.	1117	1132	1132	1156	...	1217	1232	1258	...	1317	1332	1356	...	1417	1432	...	1517	1532	1532	1556	...	1617	1632
Hannover Hbf **903** d.	1120	1136	1136	1159	...	1220	1236	...	...	1320	1336	1359	...	1420	1436	...	1520	1536	1536	1559	...	1620	1636
Bremen Hbf **813** a.	|	|	|	1313	...	|	|	...	...	|	|	1515	...	|	|	...	|	|	|	1713	...	|	|
Celle **903** d.	|	1157	1157	...	...	|	1257	...	...	|	1357	...	...	|	1457	...	|	1557	1557	...	...	|	1657
Uelzen **903** d.	|	1221	1221	...	...	|	1321	...	...	|	1421	...	...	|	1521	...	|	1621	1621	...	...	|	1721
Lüneburg **903** d.	|	1238	1238	...	...	|	1338	...	...	|	1440	...	...	|	1538	...	|	1638	1638	...	...	|	1738
Hamburg Hbf **903** a.	1254	1329	1329	...	...	1354	1429	...	...	1454	1529	...	...	1555	1629	...	1654	1729	1729	...	...	1754	1829
Hamburg Altona a.	1310	1350	...	...	...	1409	1446	...	...	1510	1546	...	...	1610	1646	...	1710	1751	...	...	...	...	1846

	ICE 576 ✕	ICE 586 ✕	ICE 536 ⑦–④ J✕	IC 2082 E 🍷	IC 2082 D 🍷	ICE 1576 ✕		ICE 72 ✕♦	ICE 786 ✕		ICE 1594 ⑤⑦ ✕	ICE 574 ⑧ K✕	ICE 574 ⑥ ✕		ICE 584 L✕	ICE 874 ⑦ U✕	ICE 776 ⑧G N✕	ICE 776 ⑧H N✕	ICE 2184 ✕		ICE 70 ✕♦	ICE 784 ✕	ICE 572 ✕
Basel SBB **912** 🏛 d.	...	...	...	...	...	...	...	1306	...	...	...	...	...	...	...	...	...	...	...	...	1506	...	...
Karlsruhe Hbf **912** d.	...	...	...	...	...	1310	...	1451	...	...	...	...	...	...	...	...	...	...	1510	...	1651	...	...
Stuttgart Hbf **912** d.	1323	...	...	...	...	|	...	|	...	...	...	1523	1523	...	...	...	...	...	|	...	|	...	1723
Mannheim Hbf **912** d.	1405	...	...	...	...	|	...	1516	...	...	...	1605	1605	...	...	...	...	...	|	...	1717	...	1805
Frankfurt Flughafen Fernbf ✈ **912** d.	1441	...	...	...	...	|	...	|	...	...	...	1641	1641	...	...	...	...	1705	|	...	|	...	1841
Frankfurt (Main) Hbf **850 901 902** d.	1458	...	...	...	...	1448‡	...	1558	...	...	1614	1658	1658	...	...	...	1701	|	1648‡	...	1758	...	1858
Hanau Hbf **850 901 902** d.	|	...	...	...	...	|	...	|	...	...	1638	|	|	...	...	...	1737	1737	|	...	|	...	1914
München Hbf **904 905** d.	|	1221	1221	...	1117o	|	...	|	...	...	|	|	|	...	1421	1421	|	|	|	...	|	1518	|
Augsburg Hbf **905** d.	|	|	|	1230	1230	◧	...	|	...	...	|	|	|	...	|	|	|	|	◧	...	|	|	|
Nürnberg Hbf **905 920 921** d.	|	1333	1333	|	|	|	...	|	1429	...	|	|	|	...	1534	1534	|	|	|	...	|	1633	|
Würzburg Hbf **920 921** d.	|	1428	1428	1440	1440	|	...	|	1528	...	|	|	|	...	1628	1628	|	|	|	...	|	1728	|
Fulda **850 901 902** d.	|	1557	1557	1604	1604	|	...	|	1704	...	1724	|	|	...	1804	1804	1819	1819	|	...	|	1904	|
Kassel Wilhelmshöhe **901 902** d.	1621	1631	1631	1638	1639	1656	...	1721	1736	...	1801	1821	1821	...	1836	1836	1852	1852	1856	...	1921	1936	2025
Göttingen **902 903** d.	1640	1655	1655	1701	1701	1716	...	1740	1755	...	1823	1840	1840	...	1855	1855	1912	1912	1917	...	1940	1958	2046
Hannover Hbf **903** a.	1717	1732	1732	1750	1750	1756	...	1817	1832	...	1902	1917	1917	...	1932	1932	1948	1948	1956	...	2017	2033	2119
Hannover Hbf **903** d.	1720	1736	1736	...	...	1802	...	1820	1836	...	1915	1920	1920	...	1936	1936	1951	1951	...	...	2020	2036	2122
Bremen Hbf **813** a.	|	|	|	...	...	1916	...	|	|	...	|	|	|	...	|	|	2047	2047	...	...	|	|	|
Celle **903** d.	|	1757	1757	...	...	...	...	|	1857	...	|	|	|	...	1957	1957	...	...	...	...	|	2057	|
Uelzen **903** d.	|	1821	1821	...	...	...	...	|	1921	...	|	|	|	...	2021	2021	...	...	...	...	|	2121	|
Lüneburg **903** d.	|	1838	1838	...	...	...	...	|	1938	...	|	|	|	...	2038	2038	...	...	...	...	|	2138	|
Hamburg Hbf **903** a.	1853	1929	1929	...	...	...	...	1954	2029	...	2051	2057	2057	...	2129	2129	...	...	...	...	2154	2229	2254
Hamburg Altona a.	1909	1951	...	...	...	...	...	2010	2046	...	2108	...	2113	...	...	...	...	...	...	...	2211	2246	2310

♦ – **NOTES** (LISTED BY TRAIN NUMBER)

70/2 – [12] ✕ Chur - Zürich - Basel - Hamburg.
74 – [12] ✕ Zürich - Basel - Hamburg - Kiel.
490 – 🛏 1, 2 cl., ▬ 2 cl. and [2] Wien - Passau - Nürnberg - Hamburg.
632 – [12] ✕ München - Hamburg - Stralsund (- Ostseebad Binz ①–⑥).
40470 – 🛏 1, 2 cl. and ▬ 2 cl. Zürich (d. 1959) - Basel - Hamburg. Also conveys [2] (*IC* **60400**).

B – 🛏 1, 2 cl., ▬ 2 cl. and [2] Innsbruck - Hamburg (Table **53**).
D – From Aug. 3. KÖNIGSSEE – [12] 🍷 Berchtesgaden - München Ost - Hannover; [12] Oberstdorf (**2084**) - Augsburg (**2082**) - Hannover.
E – Until Aug. 2. KÖNIGSSEE. [12] 🍷 Oberstdorf - Augsburg - Hannover.
G – ⑧ from Aug. 28.
H – ⑧ until Aug. 26.
J – To Rostock (Table **830**); continues to Stralsund on ⑦.
K – To Kiel (Table **820**).
L – To Lübeck (Table **825**).
N – To Oldenburg (Table **813**).
Q – To Ostseebad Binz (Tables **830** and **844**).
T – To Stralsund (Table **830**).
U – To Rostock (Table **830**).
Y – From Wiesbaden (Table **850**).
Z – From Zürich (Table **510**).

o – München **Ost**.
p – Previous day.

‡ – Until Aug. 26 calls at Frankfurt (Main) **West** (not Hbf), departing 5 – 8 minutes later.
◧ – Via Gießen (Table **806**).

NÜRNBERG and FRANKFURT - HAMBURG 900

	ICE	*ICE*	*ICE*	*ICE*	*ICE*	*ICE*	*ICE*		*ICE*		*ICE*	*ICE*	*ICE*	*ICE*	*ICE*	*ICE*		*ICE*		*ICE*		*ICE*	*ICE*
	582	**582**	**1204**	**1572**	**1572**	**376**	**782**		**570**		**580**	**580**	**292**	**580**	**272**	**272**		**1570**		**780**		**590**	**926**
	⑦	①–⑥	⑦	⑦	Ⓑ	Ⓑ			⑦		①–⑤	⑦	⑦	⑦	⑥	①–⑤		⑦		⑦		⑥	⑦
	✕	✕	R✕	✕	✕	✕◆	✕		✕		✕	✕	✕◆		Z✕	Z✕				✕			
Basel SBB **912** d.	...	...	...	...	...	1707	...	...	...	...	...	...	1813	...	1813	1813	...	...	...	...	...	...	...
Karlsruhe Hbf **912** d.	...	...	...	1710	1710	1851	...	...	...	...	...	...	2000	...	2000	2000	...	1910	...	...	...	...	...
Stuttgart Hbf **912** d.	...	...	...	|	|	|	...	...	1923	...	...	...	|	...	|	|	...	|	...	...	...	2051	...
Mannheim Hbf **912** d.	...	...	...	|	|	1916	...	...	2005	...	...	...	2032	...	2032	2032	...	|	...	...	...	2132	...
Frankfurt Flughafen Fernbf ✈ **912** d.	...	...	...	|	|	|	...	...	2041	...	...	...	|	...	|	|	...	|	...	...	...	|	...
rankfurt (Main) Hbf **850 901 902** d.	...	...	...	1848‡	1848‡	1958	...	...	2058	...	...	...	2114	...	2114	2114	...	2051‡	...	...	...	2218	...
anau Hbf **850 901 902** d.	...	...	...	|	|	|	...	...	2114	...	...	...	2130	...	2130	2130	...	|	...	...	...	2235	...
München Hbf **904 905** d.	1618	1618	1556	|	|	|	...	...	|	...	1821	1821	|	...	|	|	...	|	...	1919	...	|	2154
Augsburg Hbf **905** d.	|	|	|	◧	◧	|	...	...	|	...	|	|	|	...	|	|	...	◧	...	|	...	|	|
Nürnberg Hbf **905 920 921** d.	1735	1735	1735	|	|	|	1832	...	|	...	1934	1934	|	...	|	|	...	|	...	2031	...	|	2304
Würzburg Hbf **920 921** d.	1828	1828	1840	|	|	|	1928	...	|	...	2028	2028	|	...	|	|	...	|	...	2128	...	|	2357
ulda **850 901 902** d.	1958	2004	2004	|	|	|	2104	...	|	...	2204	2204	2212	...	2212	2212	...	|	...	2304	...	2319	...
assel Wilhelmshöhe **901 902** d.	2031	2036	2037	2056	2056	2121	2137	...	2225	...	2234	2236	2245	←	2245	2245	...	2258	...	2336	...	0042	...
öttingen **902 903** d.	2052	2055	|	2117	2117	2140	2157	...	2245	...	...	2255	2303	2307	2306	2306	...	2318	...	...	...	...	...
annover Hbf **903** a.	2130	2132	2133	2156	2156	2217	2232	...	2318	...	...	→	...	2341	2341	0002	...	0010	...	...	...	...	...
annover Hbf **903** d.	2136	2136	...	2159	...	2220	2236	...	2321	...	...	...	...	2345	2344	0005	...	...	...	...	...	...	...
Bremen Hbf **813** a.	|	|	...	|	...	|	|	...	|	...	...	...	...	|	|	|	...	...	...	...	...	...	...
elle **903** d.	2157	2157	...	|	...	|	2256	...	|	...	...	...	...	|	|	|	...	...	...	...	...	...	...
elzen **903** d.	2221	2221	...	|	...	|	2318	...	|	...	...	...	...	|	|	|	...	...	...	...	...	...	...
üneburg **903** d.	2238	2238	...	|	...	|	2335	...	|	...	...	...	...	|	|	|	...	...	...	...	...	...	...
amburg Hbf **903** a.	2329	2329	...	2332	...	2358	0005	...	0056	...	...	...	...	0117	0124	0147	...	...	...	...	...	...	...
amburg Altona a.	2346	2346	...	2357	...	0013	0021	...	0112	...	...	...	...	0133	0140	0204	...	...	...	...	...	...	...

	ICE		*ICE*	*ICE*	*ICE*	*ICE*		*ICE*		*ICE*	*ICE*		*ICE*	*ICE*	*ICE*	*ICE*		*ICE*	*IC*	*IC*	*ICE*	*ICE*	*ICE*
	1271		**591**	**591**	**781**	**781**		**1573**		**581**	**571**		**1097**	**783**	**783**	**71**		**2185**	**2083**	**2083**	**583**	**573**	**573**
	①		①–⑥		①	①–⑥		①–⑤		①–⑥			①–⑤	①–⑤	⑥⑦			①–⑥	E	D		①–⑥	⑦
	C		✕	✕	✕	✕		✕		✕	✕		✕	✕	✕	C✕		O✕	🍷	🍷	✕	K✕	✕
amburg Altona d.	0006	...	0302	...	0323	...	...	...	...	0436	0431	...	...	0503	0537	0537y	...	...	...	...	0606	...	0644
amburg Hbf **903** d.	0025	...	0320	...	0339	...	...	...	...	0454	0450	...	...	0526	0554	0554y	...	...	...	...	0626	0701	0701
üneburg **903** d.	|	...	|	...	|	...	...	...	...	0526	|	...	...	0557	0624	|	...	...	...	...	0658	|	|
elzen **903** d.	|	...	|	...	|	...	...	...	...	0542	|	...	...	0614	0641	|	...	...	...	...	0715	|	|
elle **903** d.	|	...	|	...	|	...	...	...	...	0604	|	...	...	0653	0704	|	...	...	...	...	0753	|	|
Bremen Hbf **813** d.	|	...	|	...	|	...	...	...	...	|	|	...	...	|	|	|	...	0638	...	...	|	|	|
annover Hbf **903** a.	0207	...	0456	...	0520	...	...	...	...	0623	0634	...	...	0720	0723	0734	...	0758	...	...	0820	0834	0834
annover Hbf **903** d.	0210	...	0519	...	0526	...	...	0557	...	0626	0641	...	0722	0726	0726	0741	...	0801	0808	0808	0826	0841	0841
öttingen **902 903** d.	0307	...	0554	...	0602	...	...	0636	...	0702	0716	...	|	0802	0802	0816	...	0839	0855	0855	0902	0916	0916
assel Wilhelmshöhe **901 902** d.	|	...	0615	0615	0623	0623	...	0700	...	0723	0737	...	|	0823	0823	0837	...	0903	0920	0920	0926	0937	0937
ulda **850 901 902** d.	0431	...	0648	0648	0656	0656	...	|	...	0756	|	...	|	0856	0856	|	...	|	0955	0955	0959	|	|
Würzburg Hbf **920 921** d.	|	...	|	|	0831	0831	...	|	...	0927	|	...	|	1032	1032	|	...	|	1124	1124	1131	|	|
Nürnberg Hbf **905 920 921** a.	|	...	|	|	0925	0925	...	◧	...	1024	|	...	|	1125	1125	|	...	◧	|	|	1224	|	|
Augsburg Hbf **905** a.	|	...	|	|	|	|	...	|	...	|	|	...	|	...	...	|	...	|	1330	1330	|	|	|
München Hbf **904 905** a.	|	...	|	|	1038	1038	...	|	...	1138	|	...	|	...	...	|	...	|	...	1411o	1338t	|	|
anau Hbf **850 901 902** d.	0520	...	0728	0728	...	...	...	|	...	...	|	...	|	...	...	|	...	|	...	...	...	|	|
rankfurt (Main) Hbf **850 901 902** a.	0537	...	0744	0744	...	...	...	0910§	...	...	0900	...	0928	...	...	1000	...	1110§	...	...	...	1100	1100
Frankfurt Flughafen Fernbf ✈ **912** a.	|	...	|	|	...	...	...	|	...	...	0918	...	0951	...	...	|	...	|	...	...	...	1118	1118
Mannheim Hbf **912** a.	0625	...	0827	0827	...	...	...	|	...	...	0956	...	...	...	...	1044	...	|	...	...	...	1156	1156
Stuttgart Hbf **912** a.	|	...	0908	0908	...	...	...	|	...	...	1039	...	...	...	...	|	...	|	...	...	...	1238	1238
Karlsruhe Hbf **912** a.	0656	...	...	...	...	...	...	1050	...	...	...	...	...	...	...	1109	...	1250	...	...	...	...	...
Basel SBB **912** a.	0847	...	...	...	...	...	...	...	...	...	...	...	...	...	...	1255	...	...	...	...	...	...	...

	ICE	*ICE*	*ICE*		*ICE*	*ICE*	*ICE*		*ICE*		*ICE*	*ICE*	*ICE*		*ICE*	*ICE*	*ICE*	*ICE*		*ICE*	*ICE*		*IC*
	785	**73**	**73**		**1577**	**585**	**535**		**575**		**787**	**75**	**75**		**1579**	**587**	**577**	**1285**		**789**	**77**		**1671**
		①–⑥	⑦				①–⑥					①–⑥	⑦					⑤–⑦					
	✕	✕◆	✕◆		M✕	✕	T✕		✕		✕	C✕	B✕		M✕	✕	✕	✕		✕	✕		🍷
amburg Altona d.	0712	...	0745	...	...	0806	...	...	0844	...	0908	0944	...	...	...	1011	1044	...	...	1111	1145	...	...
amburg Hbf **903** d.	0729	0802	0802	...	...	0828	0828	...	0901	...	0925	1001	1001	...	...	1028	1101	...	...	1128	1201	...	...
üneburg **903** d.	0801	|	|	...	...	0859	0859	...	|	...	0958	|	|	...	...	1100	|	...	...	1159	|	...	...
elzen **903** d.	0817	|	|	...	...	0916	0916	...	|	...	1015	|	|	...	...	1116	|	...	...	1215	|	...	...
elle **903** d.	0840	|	|	...	...	0953	0953	...	|	...	1053	|	|	...	...	1153	|	...	...	1253	|	...	...
Bremen Hbf **813** d.	|	|	|	...	0835	|	|	...	|	...	|	|	|	...	1034	|	|	...	...	|	|	...	1238
annover Hbf **903** a.	0910	0934	0934	...	0958	1020	1020	...	1034	...	1120	1134	1134	...	1158	1220	1234	...	...	1320	1334	...	1358
annover Hbf **903** d.	0926	0941	0941	...	1001	1026	1026	...	1041	...	1126	1141	1141	...	1201	1226	1241	1255	...	1326	1341	...	1401
öttingen **902 903** d.	1003	1016	1016	...	1037	1102	1102	...	1116	...	1202	1216	1216	...	1239	1302	1316	1333	...	1402	1416	...	1439
assel Wilhelmshöhe **901 902** d.	1025	1037	1037	...	1104	1123	1123	...	1137	...	1223	1237	1237	...	1303	1323	1337	1354	...	1423	1437	...	1503
ulda **850 901 902** d.	1057	|	|	...	|	1156	1156	...	|	...	1256	|	|	...	|	1356	|	1432	...	1456	|	...	|
Würzburg Hbf **920 921** d.	1232	|	|	...	|	1331	1331	...	|	...	1431	|	|	...	|	1532	|	|	...	1632	|	...	|
Nürnberg Hbf **905 920 921** a.	1325	|	|	...	◧	1424	1424	...	|	...	1525	|	|	...	◧	1628	|	|	...	1729	|	...	◧
Augsburg Hbf **905** a.	|	|	|	...	|	|	|	...	|	...	|	|	|	...	|	...	|	|	...	|	|	...	|
München Hbf **904 905** a.	1444	|	|	...	|	1541v	1541	...	|	...	1644	|	|	...	|	...	|	|	...	1855	|	...	|
anau Hbf **850 901 902** d.	...	|	|	...	|	...	...	...	|	...	...	|	|	...	|	...	|	1515	...	...	|	...	|
rankfurt (Main) Hbf **850 901 902** a.	...	1200	1200	...	1309§	...	...	...	1300	...	...	1400	1400	...	1509§	...	1500	1543	...	...	1600	...	1709§
Frankfurt Flughafen Fernbf ✈ **912** a.	...	|	|	...	|	...	...	...	1318	...	...	|	|	...	|	...	1518	...	...	...	|	...	|
Mannheim Hbf **912** a.	...	1244	1244	...	|	...	...	...	1356	...	...	1444	1444	...	|	...	1556	...	...	...	1644	...	|
Stuttgart Hbf **912** a.	...	|	|	...	|	...	...	...	1439	...	...	|	|	...	|	...	1639	...	...	...	|	...	|
Karlsruhe Hbf **912** a.	...	1309	1309	...	1451	...	...	...	...	...	...	1509	1509	...	1650	...	...	...	...	...	1709	...	1852
Basel SBB **912** a.	...	1455	1455	...	...	...	...	...	...	...	...	1655	1655	...	...	...	...	...	...	...	1855	...	...

◆ – **NOTES** (LISTED BY TRAIN NUMBER)

3 – [12] ✕ (Kiel ①–⑥ -) Hamburg - Basel - Zürich.
92 – [12] ✕ Zürich - Basel - Berlin.
76 – [12] ✕ Interlaken - Bern - Basel - Hamburg.

– [12] Kiel - Hamburg - Basel - Zürich - Chur.
– [12] Hamburg - Basel - Zürich - Chur.
– From Aug. 2. KÖNIGSSEE – [12] 🍷 Hamburg - München Ost - Berchtesgaden; [12] Hamburg - Augsburg (**2085**) - Oberstdorf.
– Until Aug. 1. KÖNIGSSEE – [12] 🍷 Hannover - Augsburg - Oberstdorf.
– From Kiel (Table **820**).
– From Oldenburg on dates in Table **813**.
– From/to Innsbruck via Garmisch (Table **895**).
– From Stralsund (Table **830**).
– From Zürich (Table **510**).

o – München **Ost**.
t – 1341 on ⑥.
v – 1545 on ⑦.
y – 8 minutes later on ⑥⑦.

‡ – Until Aug. 26 calls at Frankfurt (Main) **West** (not Hbf), departing 5–8 minutes later.
§ – Until Aug. 26 calls at Frankfurt (Main) **West** (not Hbf), arriving 5–6 minutes earlier.
◧ – Via Gießen (Table **806**).

900 HAMBURG - FRANKFURT and NÜRNBERG

	ICE 639	ICE 689	ICE 579	ICE 1597		ICE 881	ICE 79	ICE 1091		IC 2375	ICE 681	ICE 771		IC 1999	ICE 1589		ICE 883	ICE 1171		IC 1675	ICE 633	ICE 683	ICE 773
				⑦w				⑦						⑦	⑤								
	O✕	✕	✕	✕		✕	Z✕	Y✕		🍷	✕	✕		B🍷	✕		✕	K✕		🍷	O✕	✕	✕
Hamburg Altona ... d.	...	1206	1244	...	...	1311	1344	...	...	...	1411	1444	...	...	...	...	1511	...	...	...	...	1605	1644
Hamburg Hbf ... 903 d.	1228	1228	1301	...	...	1328	1401	...	...	...	1428	1501	...	...	...	...	1528	1601	...	...	1628	1628	1701
Lüneburg ... 903 d.	1259	1259	|	...	...	1359	|	...	...	...	1459	|	...	...	...	...	1558	|	...	...	1659	1659	|
Uelzen ... 903 d.	1315	1315	|	...	...	1415	|	...	...	...	1515	|	...	...	...	...	1615	|	...	...	1715	1715	|
Celle ... 903 d.	1353	1353	|	...	...	1453	|	...	...	...	1553	|	...	...	...	...	1653	|	...	...	1753	1753	|
Bremen Hbf **813** ... d.	|	|	|	...	...	|	|	...	...	1437	|	|	...	...	...	...	|	|	...	1637	|	|	|
Hannover Hbf ... 903 a.	1420	1420	1434	...	...	1520	1538	...	...	1558	1620	1634	...	...	...	...	1720	1734	...	1758	1820	1820	1834
Hannover Hbf ... 903 d.	1426	1426	1441	1454	...	1526	1541	1551	...	1601	1626	1641	...	1702h	1707	...	1726	1741	...	1801	1826	1826	1841
Göttingen ... 902 903 d.	1502	1502	1516	1535	...	1602	1616	1631	...	1640	1702	1716	...	1743	1746	...	1802	1816	...	1839	1902	1902	1916
Kassel Wilhelmshöhe ... 901 902 d.	1523	1523	1537	1558	...	1623	1637	1654	...	1703	1723	1737	...	1809	1810	...	1823	1837	...	1903	1923	1923	1937
Fulda ... 850 901 902 d.	1556	1556	|	1635	...	1656	|	1729	...	|	1757	|	...	|	1843	...	1856	|	...	|	1956	1956	|
Würzburg Hbf ... 920 921 d.	1731	1731	|	|	...	1831	|	|	...	|	1931	|	...	|	|	...	2031	|	...	|	2131	2131	|
Nürnberg Hbf ... 905 920 921 a.	1824	1824	|	|	...	1925	|	|	...	◧	2024	|	...	◧	|	...	2125	|	...	◧	2225	2225	|
Augsburg Hbf ... 905 a.	|	|	|	|	...	|	|	|	...	|	|	|	...	|	|	...	|	|	...	|	|	|	|
München Hbf **904 905** ... a.	1945	1945	|	|	...	2041	|	|	...	|	2139	|	...	|	|	...	2239	|	...	|	2340	2340	|
Hanau Hbf ... 850 901 902 d.	...	...	|	|	...	...	|	1815	...	|	...	|	...	|	1933j	...	...	|	...	|	...	...	|
Frankfurt (Main) Hbf ... 850 901 902 a.	...	...	1700	1740	...	...	1800	1832	...	1909§	...	1900	...	2008f	1956	...	...	2000	...	2109	...	...	2100
Frankfurt Flughafen Fernbf ✈ **912** a.	...	...	1718	...	...	...	|	|	...	|	...	1918	...	|	|	...	...	|	...	...	...	...	2118
Mannheim Hbf **912** ... a.	...	...	1755	...	...	...	1844	1916	...	|	...	1955	...	|	|	...	...	2044	...	...	...	...	2155
Stuttgart Hbf **912** ... a.	...	...	1838	...	...	...	|	1958	...	|	...	2038	...	2155	2157	...	...	|	...	...	...	...	2251
Karlsruhe Hbf **912** ... a.	...	...	...	...	...	...	1909	...	...	2054	...	...	...	...	...	...	...	2109	...	...	...	...	...
Basel SBB **912** ... a.	...	...	...	...	...	...	2055	...	...	...	...	...	...	...	...	...	...	2304	...	...	...	...	...

	ICE 1687	ICE 1687	ICE 1687	ICE 885	ICE 273	ICE 273	ICE 1677	ICE 1677	ICE 685	ICE 685	ICE 775		ICE 887	ICE 887		ICE 679	ICE 1679	NJ 491	NJ 40491		NJ 401		ICE 1689
	①–⑤	①–④	⑦			⑤⑥	⑤⑦			⑤–⑦	Ⓑ		Ⓑ	⑥		⑦	⑦	Ⓡ	Ⓡ				
	✕	✕	✕	✕	✕	✕	✕	✕	✕	✕	✕		N✕	N✕		T✕		H	A		D		
Hamburg Altona ... d.	1652	1652	1652	1711	1744	1744	...	...	1810	1810	1844	...	1905	1905	...	...	...	2011	2011	...	2035	...	2154
Hamburg Hbf ... 903 d.	1708	1708	1711	1728	1801	1801	...	...	1828	1828	1901	...	1928	1928	...	2024	...	2029	2029	...	2050	...	2212
Lüneburg ... 903 d.	|	|	|	1758	|	|	...	...	1859	1859	|	...	1958	1958	...	|	...	|	|	...	|	...	|
Uelzen ... 903 d.	|	|	|	1819	|	|	...	...	1915	1915	|	...	2015	2015	...	|	...	|	|	...	|	...	|
Celle ... 903 d.	|	|	|	1853	|	|	...	...	1953	1953	|	...	2053	2053	...	|	...	|	|	...	|	...	|
Bremen Hbf **813** ... d.	|	|	|	|	|	|	1837	1837	|	|	|	...	|	|	...	|	...	|	|	...	2153	...	|
Hannover Hbf ... 903 a.	1905	1905	1905	1920	1934	1934	1958	1958	2020	2020	2034	...	2120	2120	...	2205	...	2154	2154	...	2313	...	2400
Hannover Hbf ... 903 d.	...	1909	1909	1926	1941	1941	2001	...	2026	2026	2041	...	2126	2137	...	...	2209	2157	2157	...	2319	...	0003
Göttingen ... 902 903 d.	...	1946	1946	2002	2016	2016	2040	...	2102	2102	2116	...	2202	2213	...	...	2247	2259	2259	...	0116	...	0113
Kassel Wilhelmshöhe ... 901 902 d.	...	2010	2010	2023	2037	2037	2103	...	2123	2123	2137	...	2223	2235	...	...	...	|	|	...	|	...	|
Fulda ... 850 901 902 d.	...	...	...	2056	|	|	|	...	2157	2157	|	...	2256	2308	...	...	...	|	|	...	0245	...	|
Würzburg Hbf ... 920 921 d.	...	...	...	2231	|	|	|	...	2331	2331	|	...	|	|	...	...	...	0135	0135	...	|	...	0354
Nürnberg Hbf ... 905 920 921 a.	...	...	...	2325	|	|	◧	...	0024	0024	|	...	|	|	...	...	...	0253	0253	...	|	...	0447
Augsburg Hbf ... 905 a.	...	...	...	|	|	|	|	...	...	|	|	...	|	|	...	...	...	...	0623	...	|	...	|
München Hbf **904 905** ... a.	...	...	...	0043	|	|	|	...	...	0138	|	...	|	|	...	...	...	...	0711	...	|	...	0604
Hanau Hbf ... 850 901 902 d.	...	...	...	...	|	|	|	...	...	...	|	...	2335	2347	...	...	...	...	...	...	|	...	...
Frankfurt (Main) Hbf ... 850 901 902 a.	...	...	...	...	2200	2200	2309	...	...	...	2300	...	2353	0007	...	...	...	...	...	...	0346	...	...
Frankfurt Flughafen Fernbf ✈ **912** a.	...	...	...	...	|	|	...	...	...	...	2318	...	0025	0025	...	...	...	...	...	...	|	...	...
Mannheim Hbf **912** ... a.	...	...	...	...	2244	2244	...	...	...	...	0004	...	...	...	...	...	...	...	...	...	0440	...	...
Stuttgart Hbf **912** ... a.	...	...	...	...	|	|	...	...	...	...	|	...	...	...	...	...	...	...	...	...	|	...	...
Karlsruhe Hbf **912** ... a.	...	...	...	...	2309	2309	...	...	...	...	0037	...	...	...	...	...	...	...	...	...	0508	...	...
Basel SBB **912** ... a.	...	...	...	...	...	0105	...	...	...	...	...	...	...	...	...	...	...	...	...	...	0720	...	...

A – 🛏 1, 2 cl., 🛏 2 cl. and (2) Hamburg - München - Innsbruck (Table **53**).
B – From Berlin (Table **810**). To Ulm (Table **930**). Train number **1991** from July 24.
D – 🛏 1, 2 cl. and 🛏 2 cl. (Ⓡ) Hamburg - Basel - Zürich (a. 0905). Also conveys (2) (*IC* **60401**).
H – 🛏 1, 2 cl., 🛏 2 cl. and (2) Hamburg - Passau - Wien.
K – From Kiel (Table **820**).
N – To Wiesbaden (Table **850**).
O – From Ostseebad Binz (Table **844**).
T – From Stralsund (Table **830**).
Y – From Berlin (Table **902**).
Z – To Zürich (Table **510**).

f – Frankfurt (Main) **West** (not Hbf).
h – Until July 17.
j – Arrives 1923.

§ – Until Aug. 26 calls at Frankfurt (Main) **West** (not Hbf), arriving 5 – 6 minutes earlier.
◧ – Via Gießen (Table **806**).

901 Local services FRANKFURT - FULDA - KASSEL

RE / RB services

Other *ICE / IC* services: Table **850** for Bebra - Kassel Wilhelmshöhe and v.v., also Frankfurt - Fulda - Bad Hersfeld and v.v. Tables **900 / 902** for Frankfurt - Fulda - Kassel Wilhelmshöhe and v.v

km		⚒t	†z					A	
0	**Frankfurt** (Main) Hbf ... 921 d.	0519	0524	0626	0726		2126	2226	2326
4	**Frankfurt** (Main) Süd ... 921 d.	0524	0529	0633	0733	and	2133	2233	2333
10	Offenbach (Main) Hbf ... 921 d.	0529	0534	0638	0738	hourly	2138	2238	2338
23	Hanau Hbf ... 921 d.	0540	0544	0648	0748	until	2148	2248	2348
104	**Fulda** ... a.	0640	0644	0749	0849		2249	2349	0049

		ⒶB	†z	⚒t	ⒶB		✣				
Fulda ... d.	0400	0437	0507	0515	0600	0607		2007	2106	2207	2311
Hanau Hbf ... 921 d.	0500	0539	0609	0616	0655	0709	and	2109	2207	2309	0012
Offenbach (Main) Hbf ... 921 d.	0509	0548	0617	0624	|	0717	hourly	2117	2216	2317	0020
Frankfurt Main) Süd ... 921 d.	0515	0553	0623	0630	0710	0723	until	2123	2221	2323	0026
Frankfurt (Main) Hbf ... 921 a.	0520	0558	0628	0636	0716	0728		2128	2228	2328	0031

FULDA - KASSEL. Operated by CANTUS Verkehrsgesellschaft (except trains marked with note **B** and **E**). 2nd class only. Additional trains run Bad Hersfeld - Kassel and v.v.

km		Ⓐt		Ⓐt		Ⓐt												D	⑤⑦r						E
0	**Fulda** ... d.	...	...	0548	0616	0644	0720	0820	0920	1020	1120	1220	1320	1420	1520	1620	1720	1820	1820	1920	2020	2122	2221	2301c	2356
42	Bad Hersfeld ... d.	0505	...	0615	0644	0713	0748	0848	0948	1048	1148	1248	1348	1448	1548	1648	1748	1848	1848	1948	2048	2149	2249	2328c	0027
56	Bebra ... a.	0515	...	0626	0654	0723	0758	0858	0958	1058	1158	1258	1358	1458	1558	1658	1758	1858	1858	1958	2058	2159	2258	2338c	0041
56	Bebra ... d.	0518	0559	0633	0659	0733	0759	0859	0959	1059	1159	1259	1359	1459	1559	1659	1759	1859	1906	1959	2059	2200	2302	2348	...
62	Rotenburg (Fulda) ... d.	0524	0605	0639	0705	0739	0805	0905	1005	1105	1205	1305	1405	1505	1605	1705	1805	1905	1912	2005	2105	2206	2308	2354	...
84	Melsungen ... d.	0543	0624	0658	0724	0758	0824	0924	1024	1124	1224	1324	1424	1524	1624	1724	1824	1924	1930	2024	2124	2224	2326	0012	...
110	**Kassel** Wilhelmshöhe 804/6 d.	0608	0643	0719	0743	0822	0843	0943	1043	1143	1243	1343	1443	1543	1643	1743	1843	1943	1948	2043	2144	2252	2352	0037	...
114	**Kassel** Hbf ... 804/6 a.	0616	0647	0724	0748	0828	0847	0947	1047	1148	1248	1347	1447	1547	1647	1747	1848	1948	1954	2048	2148	2256	2356	0041	...

		ⒶB	Ⓐt	ⒶB	⚒t◐	Ⓒz	Ⓐt																	⑤⑥	
Kassel Hbf ... 804/6 d.	...	...	0355	...	0506	0606	0611	0711	0811v	0911	1011	1111	1211	1311	1411	1511	1611	1710	1811	1911	2011	2111	2211	2211	2311
Kassel Wilhelmshöhe 804/6 d.	...	...	0359	...	0510	0615	0618	0715	0815	0915	1015	1115	1215	1315	1415	1515	1615	1715	1815	1915	2015	2115	2216	2216	2316
Melsungen ... d.	...	...	0418	...	0528	0634	0636	0734	0834	0934	1034	1134	1234	1334	1434	1534	1634	1734	1834	1934	2034	2134	2234	2234	2334
Rotenburg (Fulda) ... d.	...	...	0437	...	0547	0653	0654	0753	0853	0953	1053	1153	1253	1353	1453	1553	1653	1753	1853	1953	2053	2153	2253	2253	2353
Bebra ... a.	...	...	0443	...	0554	0658	0659	0758	0859	0958	1058	1158	1258	1358	1459	1558	1658	1758	1858	1958	2058	2158	2258	2258	2358
Bebra ... d.	0315	0359	0446	0522	0559	0659	0702	0759	0859	0959	1059	1159	1259	1359	1459	1559	1659	1759	1859	1959	2059	2159	2259	2259	2359
Bad Hersfeld ... d.	0325	0409	0456	0531	0609	0709	0725b	0809	0909	1009	1109	1209	1309	1409	1509	1609	1709	1809	1909	2009	2109	2209	2309	2310	0011
Fulda ... a.	0354	0436	...	0558	0637	0737	0753	0837	0937	1037	1137	1237	1337	1437	1537	1637	1737	1837	1937	2037	2137	2237	...	2338	...

A – Continues to Bebra on ①②③④⑦; see lower panel.
B – Ⓐ (not June 16). (12) Bebra - Fulda - Frankfurt.
D – ①②③④⑥ (not June 15, Oct. 3, Nov. 1).
E – Starts from Frankfurt on ①②③④⑦; see upper panel.

b – Arrives 0712.
c – 7 – 8 minutes later on † (also June 16).
r – Also June 15, Oct. 3, Nov. 1.
t – Not June 16.
v – 0806 on †.

z – Also June 16.

✣ – On Ⓐ the 0807 from Fulda runs 4 minutes later Offenbach - Frankfurt.
◐ – Runs daily Bebra - Fulda.

FRANKFURT - BRAUNSCHWEIG - BERLIN 902

See Table 850 for additional services Frankfurt - Berlin and v.v. Independent operator **FlixTrain** also run services Stuttgart - Berlin and v.v. (see Table 927).

km		*NJ* 470	*ICE* 649		*ICE* 1088	*ICE* 876	*ICE* 1598	*ICE* 998	*ICE* 270	*ICE* 1590	*ICE* 374	*ICE* 992	*ICE* 372	*ICE* 798	*ICE* 370	*ICE* 796	*ICE* 278	*ICE* 794	*ICE* 276	*ICE* 792	*ICE* 274	*ICE* 1690	*ICE* 292
			①-⑤		①-⑥		①-⑤	①								p						p	⑦
		N	✕		✕	✕	p✕	✕	✕	✕	✕	✕	T✕	✕	✕	✕	T✕	✕	✕	✕	✕	⊖✕	Z✕
	Basel SBB 912 d.	2113	...	...	...	...	...	...	0403g	...	0606	...	0813	...	1013	...	1213	...	1413	...	1613	...	1813
	Karlsruhe Hbf 912 d.	2306	...	...	...	...	...	...	0558	...	0800	...	1000	...	1200	...	1400	...	1601	...	1801	...	2000
	Stuttgart Hbf 912 d.	|	...	...	...	...	...	...	|	...	|	...	|	...	|	...	|	...	|	...	|	...	|
	Mannheim Hbf 912 d.	2342	...	...	...	...	...	...	0632	...	0832	...	1032	...	1232	...	1432	...	1632	...	1832	...	2032
	Frankfurt Flughafen Fernbf ✈ d.	|	...	...	...	...	...	...	|	0809	|	1009	|	1209	|	1409	|	1609	|	1809	|	...	|
0	**Frankfurt** (Main) Hbf 850 900 d.	0052	...	...	0506	...	0553	...	0714	|	0914	|	1114	|	1314	|	1514	|	1714	|	1914	2016	2114
4	**Frankfurt** (Main) Süd d.	|	...	...	|	...	|	...	|	0820	|	1020	|	1220	|	1420	|	1620	|	1820	|	|	|
23	Hanau Hbf 850 900 d.	|	...	...	0521	...	|	...	0730	|	0930	|	1130	|	1330	|	1530	|	1730	|	1930	2034	2130
104	Fulda 850 900 d.	0149	...	...	0604	...	|	...	0812	0915	1012	1116	1212	1316	1412	1516	1612	1716	1812	1916	2012	2116	2212
194	**Kassel** Wilhelmshöhe 900 d.	|	...	...	0636	0643	|	0748	0845	0948	1045	1149	1245	1349	1445	1549	1645	1749	1845	1949	2045	2150	2245
239	Göttingen 900 d.	0316	...	...	0654	0706	|	0809	0906	1008	1106	1209	1306	1409	1506	1609	1706	1809	1906	2009	2106	2210	2304
317	Hildesheim Hbf 863 d.	|	...	...	...	0736	|	0837	0936	1037	1136	1237	1336	1437	1536	1637	1736	1837	1936	2037	2136	2242	2334
360	**Braunschweig** Hbf 863 d.	0459	0601	...	...	0801	|	0901	1001	1102	1201	1302	1401	1502	1601	1702	1801	1902	2001	2102	2201	2304	0001
392	Wolfsburg 810 863 d.	|	0620	...	...	0818	|	0919	1018	|	1218	|	1418	|	1618	|	1818	|	2018	2120	2218	2323	0018
559	**Berlin** Spandau 810 a.	|	0722	...	...	0913	0939	1011	1113	1211p	1313	1411p	1513	1611p	1713	1811	1913	2011	2113	2214	2313	0028	0113
575	**Berlin** Hbf 850 810 a.	0738	0740	...	...	0927	0953	1026	1128	1226p	1327	1426p	1527	1625p	1727	1825	1927	2026	2127	2228	2327	0042	0127
580	**Berlin** Ostbahnhof 810 a.	...	0750	...	...	0939	1004	1036	1139	1236p	1339	1437p	1539	1635p	1739	1836	1939	2036	2139	2239	2339t	0054v	0139

	ICE 275		*ICE* 277	*ICE* 791	*ICE* 279	*ICE* 793	*ICE* 371	*ICE* 795	*ICE* 373	*ICE* 797	*ICE* 1091	*ICE* 375	*ICE* 1699	*ICE* 377	*ICE* 995	*ICE* 877	*ICE* 877	*ICE* 997	*ICE* 887	*ICE* 887	*ICE* 879		*NJ* 471
	①-⑤					p					⑦						⑥		Ⓑ	⑥	⑦		
	T✕		✕	✕	✕	✕	T✕	✕	T✕	✕	⊙✕	✕	✕	✕	✕	✕	✕	✕	S✕	S✕	✕		Q
Berlin Ostbahnhof 810 d.	0418	...	0618	0721	0818	0921	1018	1119p	1218	1321p	...	1418	1521p	1618	1720p	1818	1818	...	...	...	2018	...	...
Berlin Hbf 850 810 d.	0430	...	0630	0733	0830	0933	1030	1130p	1230	1333p	1406	1430	1533p	1630	1732p	1830	1830	1935	...	...	2030	...	2054
Berlin Spandau 810 d.	0445	...	0645	0747	0845	0947	1045	1145q	1245	1347p	1417	1445	1547p	1645	1746p	1845	1845	1946	...	...	2045	...	|
Wolfsburg 810 863 d.	0538	...	0738	|	0938	|	1138	|	1338	|	1510	1538	|	1738	|	1938	1938	|	...	...	2138	...	|
Braunschweig Hbf 863 d.	0557	...	0757	0859	0957	1059	1157	1259	1357	1459	|	1557	1659	1757	1859	1957	1957	2059	...	...	2157	...	2328
Hildesheim Hbf 863 d.	0619	...	0819	0921	1019	1121	1219	1321	1419	1521	|	1619	1721	1819	1921	2019	2019	2121	...	...	2219	...	|
Göttingen 900 d.	0652	...	0852	0952	1052	1152	1252	1352	1452	1552	1631	1652	1754	1852	1952	2052	2052	2152	2202	2213	2252	...	0116
Kassel Wilhelmshöhe 900 d.	0714	...	0914	1014	1114	1214	1314	1414	1514	1614	1654	1714	1816	1914	2015	2114	2114	2214	2223	2235	2314	...	|
Fulda 850 900 d.	0747	...	0947	1046	1147	1246	1347	1446	1547	1646	1729	1747	1847	1947	2047	2147	2147	...	2256	2308	2347	...	0245
Hanau Hbf 850 900 d.	0827	...	1027	|	1227	|	1427	|	1627	|	1815	1827	|	2027	|	2227	2227	...	2335	2347	0028	...	|
Frankfurt (Main) Süd a.	|	...	|	1139	|	1339	|	1539	|	1739	|	|	|	|	|	|	|	...	|	|	|	...	|
Frankfurt (Main) Hbf 850 900 a.	0844	...	1044	|	1244	|	1444	|	1644	|	1832	1844	1940	2044	2140	2244	2244	...	2353	0007	0044	...	0346
Frankfurt Flughafen Fernbf ✈ a.	|	...	|	1151	|	1351	|	1551	|	1751	|	|	|	|	|	|	2318	...	0025	0025	|	...	|
Mannheim Hbf 912 a.	0927	...	1127	...	1327	...	1527	...	1727	...	1916	1927	...	2127	...	...	0005	...	...	...	0127	...	0440
Stuttgart Hbf 912 a.	|	...	|	...	|	...	|	...	|	...	1958	|	...	|	...	...	|	...	...	...	|	...	|
Karlsruhe Hbf 912 a.	0958	...	1158	...	1358	...	1558	...	1758	...	...	1958	...	2158	...	...	0037	...	...	...	0154	...	0508
Basel SBB 912 a.	1147	...	1347	...	1547	...	1747	...	1947	...	...	2149	...	2355	...	...	...	...	...	...	...	...	0720

N – 🛏 1, 2 cl. and 🛋 2 cl. (R) Zürich (d. 1959) - Basel - Berlin. Also conveys 🚗 (*IC* **60470**). Also calls at Magdeburg Hbf (a. 0555), Brandenburg Hbf (a. 0640) and Berlin Südkreuz (a. 0718).
Q – 🛏 1, 2 cl. and 🛋 2 cl. (R) Berlin - Basel - Zürich (a. 0905). Also conveys 🚗 (*IC* **60471**). Also calls at Berlin Südkreuz (d. 2103), Brandenburg Hbf (d. 2159) and Magdeburg Hbf (d. 2241).
S – To Wiesbaden (Table **850**).
T – From / to Interlaken via Bern (Table **560**).
Z – From Zürich HB (d. 1659).

g – ① only.
p – Until July 17.
q – Daily to June 25; ①-⑥ June 27 - July 16.
t – ③-⑦.
v – Mornings of ①④⑤⑥⑦.

⊖ – Also calls at Stendal (a. 2351).
⊙ – Also calls at Hannover Hbf (d. 1551).

metronom

Local services GÖTTINGEN - HANNOVER - UELZEN - HAMBURG 903

Services below are operated by ***metronom*** (except trains **A**, **B** and **C**). For faster *ICE* and *IC* services see Table **900**.

km																											
			⚒ n		⊖	①-⑤ A✕		①-⑤ B✕	© z	Ⓐ n																	
0	**Göttingen** d.	...	0408	...	0504	0546	0604	0645	0704	0707	0809	0904	1009	1104	1209	1304	1407r	1504	1609	1704	1809	1904	...	2009	2104	2209	2311t
20	Northeim (Han) d.	...	0421	...	0517	0600	0617	0658	0717	0720	0823	0917	1023	1117	1223	1317	1421r	1517	1623	1717	1823	1917	...	2023	2117	2223	2324t
39	Kreiensen d.	...	0435	...	0531	0616	0631	0712	0731	0733	0837	0931	1037	1131	1237	1331	1437	1531	1637	1733q	1837	1931	...	2037	2131	2237	2338
58	Alfeld (Leine) d.	...	0448	...	0544	0629	0644	0725	0744	0746	0850	0944	1050	1144	1250	1344	1450	1544	1650	1746q	1850	1944	...	2050	2144	2250	2351
75	Elze (Han) d.	...	0503	...	0558	0640	0659	0736	0759	0759	0903	0959	1103	1159	1303	1359	1503	1559	1703	1759	1903	1959	...	2103	2159	2303	0003
108	**Hannover** Hbf. a.	...	0526	...	0624	0657	0723	0756	0823	0823	0926	1023	1126	1223	1326	1423	1526	1623	1726	1823	1926	2023	...	2126	2223	2326	0027
			▽		|	|	▽		|	|	▽	|	▽	|	▽	|	▽	|	▽	|	▽	|		▽	|	▽	|
			Ⓐ n	⑥																						⊙	
108	**Hannover** Hbf. d.	...	0540	0540	0640	0701	0740	...	0840	0840	0940	1040	1140	1240	1340	1440	1540	1640	1740	1840	1940	2040	...	2140	2248	2340	0040
149	Celle d.	...	0608	0608	0708	0720	0808	...	0908	0908	1008	1108	1208	1308	1408	1508	1608	1708	1808	1908	2008	2108	...	2208	2316	0008	0106
201	**Uelzen** a.	...	0639	0639	0739	0740	0839	...	0939	0939	1039	1139	1239	1339	1439	1539	1639	1738	1839	1939	2039	2139	...	2239	2347	0039	0138
			|	|	▬	|	▬		▬	▽	|	▽	|	▽	|	▽	|	▽	|	▽	|	▽		|	▽		
																						⚒n	†z		D		
201	**Uelzen** d.	0605	0647e	0704	0704	0742	0801	...	0901	1001	1101	1201	1301	1401	1501	1601	1701	1801	1901	2001	2101	2201	2201	2306	2356	...	...
214	Bad Bevensen d.	0614	0655e	0713	0713	|	0809	...	0910	1009	1109	1209	1309	1409	1509	1609	1709	1809	1909	2009	2109	2209	2209	2314	0004	...	...
237	Lüneburg d.	0629	0709e	0728	0728	0758	0828	...	0928	1028	1131j	1228	1328	1428	1528	1628	1728	1828	1928	2031j	2128	2228	2232j	2338k	0021	...	...
256	Winsen (Luhe) d.	0640	0720e	0740	0740	|	0839	...	0939	1039	1142	1239	1339	1439	1539	1639	1739	1839	1939	2042	2139	2239y	2248y	2354	0036	...	...
286	**Hamburg** Hbf. a.	0702	0741e	0803	0803	0829	0902	...	1003	1103	1206	1303	1403	1503	1603	1703	1803	1903	2003	2104	2203	2302y	2321y	0027	0109	...	...

					Ⓐ en	Ⓐ n	© z																		⑤⑥ f	e
Hamburg Hbf d.	...	...	...	...	0433	0542	0558	0651	0757	0857	0957	1057	1157	1257	1357	...	1457	1557	1657	1757	1857	1957	2057	2157	2233	2233	2333
Winsen (Luhe) d.	...	...	...	...	0506	0604	0623	0713	0820	0920	1020	1120	1220	1320	1420	...	1520	1620	1720	1820	1920	2020	2119	2223	2306	2306	0008
Lüneburg d.	...	...	...	...	0532j	0615	0634	0724	0834	0934	1034	1134	1234	1332	1434	...	1534	1634	1734	1834	1934	2034	2130	2234	2324	2324	0023
Bad Bevensen d.	...	...	...	...	0549	0630	0648	0742	0848	0948	1048	1148	1248	1348	1448b	...	1548	1648	1748	1848	1948	2048	2145	2249	2338	2338	0037
Uelzen a.	...	...	...	...	0559	0638	0656	0750	0856	0956	1056	1156	1256	1356	1456b	...	1556	1655	1756	1856	1956	2056	2153	2256	2346	2346	0045
					▽	▽	▽	|	▽	|	▽	|	▽	|	▽		|	▽	|	▽	|	▽	|	▽	▬	|	
		Ⓐ n	© z	Ⓐ n	d	Ⓐ n	© z																	⑤⑥ f			
Uelzen d.	...	0412	0513	0513	0609	0651	0709	0809	0909	1009	1109	1209	1309	1409	1509	...	1609	1709	1809	1909	2009	2114	2209	2309	2309	2351	...
Celle d.	...	0446	0547	0547	0647	0747v	0747	0848	0947	1048	1147	1247	1347	1447	1547	...	1647	1747	1847	1947	2048	2147	2247	2349	2349	0028	...
Hannover Hbf a.	...	0514	0615	0615	0715	0815	0815	0915	1015	1115	1215	1315	1415	1515	1615	...	1715	1815	1915	2015	2115	2215	2315	0017	0017	0057	...
		▽	|	|	▽	|	|	▽	|	▽	|	▽	|	▽	|		▽	|	▽	|	▽	|	▽	|			
	Ⓐ n	⚒ n														①-④ C✕	⊡										
Hannover Hbf d.	0432	0536	0633	0634	0736	0833	0833	0936	1033	1136	1233	1336	1433	1536	1633	1703	1736	1833	1936	2033	2136p	2236	2336	0038	...	...	...
Elze (Han) d.	0455	0558	0655	0658	0800	0855	0855	1000	1055	1200	1255	1400	1455	1600	1655	1722	1758	1855	2000	2055	2200	2258	2358	0100	...	...	...
Alfeld (Leine) d.	0507	0610	0706	0710	0812	0906	0906	1012	1106	1212	1306	1412	1506	1612	1706	1733	1810	1906	2012	2106	2212	2309	0010	0112	...	...	...
Kreiensen d.	0520	0624	0719	0723	0825	0919	0919	1025	1119	1225	1319	1425	1519	1625	1719	1746	1823	1919	2025	2119	2225	2322	0023	0125	...	...	...
Northeim (Han) d.	0533	0637	0733	0736	0838	0933	0933	1038	1133	1238	1333	1438	1533	1638	1733	1759	1836	1933	2038	2133	2238	2336	0036	0138	...	...	...
Göttingen a.	0546	0650	0746	0749	0851	0946	0946	1051	1146	1251	1346	1451	1546	1651	1746	1814	1849	1946	2051	2146	2251	2349	0049	0153	...	...	...

A – *ICE* **1686**. Operated by DB.
B – *ICE* **1676**. Operated by DB. 🚌**12** (Frankfurt ① -) Kassel - Hannover - Bremen.
C – *ICE* **1585**. Operated by DB.
D – ①-⑥ from Sept. 23 (also Oct. 2, 30; not Oct. 3, 31).

b – 3 minutes later on ⑤.
d – Daily.
e – From Sept. 23.

f – Also Oct. 2, 30.
j – Arrives 7–9 minutes earlier.
k – Arrives 2327.
n – Not Oct. 31.
p – 2134 on ⑥.
q – 2 minutes **earlier** on © (also Oct. 31).
r – 2 minutes later on © (also Oct. 31).
t – 2 minutes **earlier** on † (also Oct. 31).
v – Arrives 0728.

y – Lüneburg - Hamburg from Aug. 5.
z – Also Oct. 31.

⊖ – Runs 2–4 minutes later Göttingen - Elze on † (also Oct. 31).
⊡ – Runs 2 minutes later Elze - Göttingen on © (also Oct. 31).
⊙ – Runs 8 minutes later on © (also Oct. 31).
▽ – Change trains.

904 MÜNCHEN - INGOLSTADT - NÜRNBERG

km	Most *ICE* trains convey ✕	*ICE* 888		*ICE* 684	*ICE* 822	*ICE* 886	*ICE* 820	*ICE* 1008	*ICE* 682	*ICE* 728	*ICE* 602	*ICE* 882	*ICE* 726	*ICE* 1006	*ICE* 724	*ICE* 680	*ICE* 1600	*ICE* 880	*ICE* 722	*ICE* 800	*ICE* 720	*ICE* 588	*ICE* 508	*ICE* 788	*ICE* 628	*ICE* 1004	*ICE* 626
		①–⑤			①–⑥		①–⑥																				
					K		K			K			K		K				K		K				K		K
0	**München** Hbf ... d.	0312	...	0412	0427	0516	0522	0556	0614	0621	0656	0717	0726	0755	0815	0820	0855	0918	0923	0955	1016	1021	1055	1116	1119	1156	1216
81	**Ingolstadt** Hbf ... d.	0350	...	0451	0504	0554	|	|	0654	0700	|	0756	|	|	0853	0859	|	0957	|	1032	|	1100	|	1156	|	|	|
171	**Nürnberg** Hbf ... a.	0421	...	0523	0533	0625	0631	0658	0726	0732	0801	0827	0832	0858	0922	0930	1002	1029	1032	1103	1120	1130	1201	1228	1232	1258	1323
	Würzburg Hbf **900 920** . a.	0516	...	0623	0629	0725	0729	|	0823	0829	|	0924	0929	|	1029	1025	|	1124	1129	|	1229	1225	|	1325	1329	|	1429
	Frankfurt (Main) Hbf **920** a.	|	...	|	0804	|	0904	|	|	1004	|	|	1104	|	1204	|	|	|	1304	|	1404	|	|	|	1504	|	1604
	Leipzig Hbf **850** ... a.	|	...	|	...	|	...	|	|	...	1010	|	...	|	...	|	1210	|	...	|	...	|	1410	|	...	|	...
	Berlin Hbf **850** ... a.	|	...	|	...	|	...	0951	|	...	1129	|	...	1151	...	|	1329	|	...	1425	...	|	1529	|	...	1551	...
	Hamburg Hbf **840 900** .. a.	1029	...	1129	...	1229	...	1151	1329	...	1324	1429	...	1403•	...	1529	1524	1629	...	1621	...	1729	1724	1829	...	1812	...

Most *ICE* trains convey ✕	*ICE* 586	*ICE* 506	*ICE* 624	*ICE* 706	*ICE* 622	*ICE* 584	*ICE* 504	*ICE* 784	*ICE* 620	*ICE* 1002	*ICE* 1708	*ICE* 528	*ICE* 582	*ICE* 502	*ICE* 526	*ICE* 1000	*ICE* 524	*ICE* 580	*ICE* 580	*ICE* 500	*ICE* 780	*ICE* 522	*ICE* 1100	*ICE* 520	*ICE* 926		*ICE* 1688
											⑦							①–⑤	⑦		⑦				⑦		
			K		K	D			K		H	K			GK		K	S			S	K					
München Hbf ... d.	1221	1255	1319	1354	1418	1421	1456	1518	1525	1556	1556	1614	1618	1655	1719	1756	1816	1821	1821	1856	1919	1926	1956	2054	2154	...	2300
Ingolstadt Hbf ... d.	1300	|	1400	1431	|	1500	|	1556	|	|	|	|	1700	|	1757	|	|	1900	1900	|	1957	2003	|	2131	2233	...	2337
Nürnberg Hbf ... a.	1330	1401	1431	1502	1523	1531	1601	1628	1633	1658	1708	1723	1732	1801	1828	1858	1923	1931	1931	2001	2028	2032	2058	2200	2301	...	0011
Würzburg Hbf **900 920** .. a.	1425	|	1529	|	1629	1625	|	1724	1729	|	1833	1829	1824	|	1929	|	2029	2025	2025	|	2124	2129	|	2255	2357	...	0116
Frankfurt (Main) Hbf **920**. a.	|	|	1704	|	1804	|	|	|	1904	|	...	2004	|	|	2104	|	2204	...	|	|	...	2304	|	0026**x**	...	...	|
Leipzig Hbf **850** ... a.	|	1610	...	|	...	|	1810	|	...	|	...	...	|	2010	...	|	...	...	|	2210	...	...	|	...	...	...	|
Berlin Hbf **850** ... a.	|	1729	...	1825	...	|	1930	|	...	1954	...	...	|	2129	...	2151	...	...	|	2335	...	...	2350	...	...	...	|
Hamburg Hbf **840 900** ... a.	1929	1924	...	2023	...	2129	2124	2229	...	2214	...	...	2329	2333	...	...	...	...	0117	...	...	...	...	...	...	...	0658

Most *ICE* trains convey ✕	*ICE* 1689	*ICE* 825	*ICE* 985	*ICE* 827	*ICE* 1501	*ICE* 501	*ICE* 521	*ICE* 1001	*ICE* 523	*ICE* 781	*ICE* 503	*ICE* 525	*ICE* 581	*ICE* 1003	*ICE* 527	*ICE* 505	*ICE* 529	*ICE* 583	*ICE* 703	*ICE* 621	*ICE* 785	*ICE* 507	*ICE* 623	*ICE* 585	*ICE* 1005	*ICE* 625	*ICE* 787
		Ⓐt	Ⓐt	①–⑥	Ⓐt	①–⑥				①–⑥			①–⑥														
				K	E		K		K	N		K			KG		K			K			K			K	
Hamburg Hbf **840 900** ... d.	2212	...	...	...	...	...	...	...	...	0339**g**	...	...	0454	0552	...	0634**e**	...	0626	0736	...	0729	0834	...	0828	1005	...	0925
Berlin Hbf **850** ... d.	|	...	...	...	...	0430	...	0601	...	|	0630	...	|	0805	...	0830	...	|	0937	...	|	1030	...	|	1205	...	|
Leipzig Hbf **850** ... d.	|	...	...	...	...	0548	...	|	...	|	0748	...	|	|	...	0948	...	|	|	...	|	1148	...	|	|	...	|
Frankfurt (Main) Hbf **920**. d.	|	...	...	0454	...	|	0554	|	0654	|	|	0754	|	|	0854	|	0954	|	|	1054	|	|	1154	|	|	1254	|
Würzburg Hbf **900 920** .. d.	0354	...	...	0627	...	|	0730	|	0827	0831	|	0927	0931	|	1027	|	1127	1131	|	1227	1232	|	1327	1331	|	1427	1431
Nürnberg Hbf ... d.	0452	0556	0629	0723	0728	0812	0827	0859	0924	0928	0956	1023	1027	1059	1123	1156	1223	1227	1253	1323	1328	1356	1423	1427	1459	1523	1528
Ingolstadt Hbf ... d.	0525	0626	0703	0752	0802	|	0901	|	|	1001	|	|	1101	|	1155	|	|	1301	1324	|	1401	|	|	1501	|	|	1606
München Hbf ... a.	0604	0704	0741	0833	0841	0917	0939	1002	1033	1038	1102	1130	1138	1201	1233	1302	1334	1338**j**	1404	1432	1444	1501	1529	1541**f**	1602	1637	1644

Most *ICE* trains convey ✕	*ICE* 509	*ICE* 627	*ICE* 707	*ICE* 629	*ICE* 1505	*ICE* 789	*ICE* 1601	*ICE* 721	*ICE* 689	*ICE* 1007	*ICE* 723	*ICE* 881	*ICE* 603	*ICE* 725	*ICE* 681	*ICE* 1009	*ICE* 727	*ICE* 883	*ICE* 1605	*ICE* 1715	*ICE* 729	*ICE* 683	*ICE* 1109	*ICE* 821	*ICE* 885	*ICE* 1607	*ICE* 685
					⑦–④														Ⓑ	⑥						⑤	⑤–⑦
		K		K				K				K		K			K			O	K			K			
Hamburg Hbf **840 900** ... d.	1034	...	1136	...	1204	1128	1234	...	1228	1404	...	1328	1435	...	1428	1550	...	1528	1634	...	...	1628	...	...	1728	1835	1828
Berlin Hbf **850** ... d.	1230	...	1337	...	1404	|	1430	...	|	1605	...	|	1630	...	|	1805	...	|	1830	1830	...	|	2005	...	|	2030	|
Leipzig Hbf **850** ... d.	1348	...	|	...	|	|	1548	...	|	|	...	|	1748	...	|	|	...	|	1948	1948	...	|	|	...	|	2148	|
Frankfurt (Main) Hbf **920**. d.	|	1354	|	1454	|	|	|	1554	|	|	1654	|	|	1754	|	|	1854	|	|	|	1954	|	|	2054	|	|	|
Würzburg Hbf **900 920** .. d.	|	1527	|	1627	|	1632	|	1727	1731	|	1827	1831	|	1926	1931	|	2027	2031	|	|	2127	2131	|	2227	2231	|	2331
Nürnberg Hbf ... d.	1555	1624	1655	1723	1728	1732	1756	1823	1827	1859	1923	1928	1955	2023	2027	2059	2124	2128	2155	2155	2223	2228	2259	2323	2330	0001	0028
Ingolstadt Hbf ... d.	|	1701	1726	|	|	1814	|	1858	1905	|	|	2001	|	2053	2101	|	|	2201	|	|	2254	2301	|	2352	0004	0034	0101
München Hbf ... a.	1702	1738	1803	1833	1838	1855	1903	1941	1945	2002	2029	2041	2102	2132	2139	2201	2233	2239	2303	2303	2336	2340	0001	0039	0043	0112	0138

RE services via the high-speed line

km																												
		⚒t	†z	⚒t	Ⓐt			⑥		Ⓑ	⑥		⑤	T	†z		U	Ⓒz	⑤	U	Ⓒz	Ⓐt	Ⓒz	Ⓐt	Ⓒz	Ⓐt		
0	**München** Hbf ... d.	0501	0602	0705	0803	0904	1001	1001	1104	1200	1201	1304	1358	1358	1402	1503	1601	1602	1602	1622	1705	1711	1805	1804	1905	1905	2002	2105
50	Pfaffenhofen (Ilm) ... d.	0531	0629	0733	0830	0931	1028	1028	1132	1231	1229	1332	1423	1429	1429	1531	1631	1629	1630	1646	1733	1743	1829	1833	1932	1934	2029	2132
81	**Ingolstadt** Hbf ... a.	0550	0648	0752	0850	0950	1049	1049	1152	1251	1248	1352	1443	1451	1448	1551	1652	1648	1654	1705	1752	1802	1848	1853	1952	1954	2050	2151
81	**Ingolstadt** Hbf ... d.	0603	0704	0804	...	1004	...	1104	1204	...	...	1403	1504	...	1504	1604	...	1704	1704	1707	1803	1803	1904	...	2006	2006	...	2157
112	Kinding ... d.	0619	0720	0820	...	1020	...	1120	1220	...	...	1419	1520	...	1520	1620	...	1721	1721	1723	1823	1823	1920	...	2023	2023	...	2213
146	Allersberg ... d.	0634	0735	0835	...	1035	...	1135	1235	...	...	1434	1535	...	1535	1635	...	1735	1735	1738	1838	1838	1935	...	2038	2038	...	2228
171	**Nürnberg Hbf** ... a.	0647	0749	0849	...	1049	...	1149	1249	...	...	1448	1549	...	1549	1649	...	1749	1749	1752	1852	1852	1949	...	2052	2052	...	2241

	Ⓐt	Ⓐt	Ⓐt	Ⓐt	Ⓒz	Ⓐt	⑥	Ⓐt	Ⓐt	⑥		Ⓑ		†z	⑥	Ⓐt				⑤†z	T		Ⓒz	Ⓐt				⑤⑥n
Nürnberg Hbf ... d.	...	0508	...	0608	0609	...	...	0732	...	0816	0904	...	1103	...	1203	...	1304	...	1509	1609	...	1700	1803	...	1904	...	2105	2336
Allersberg ... d.	...	0521	...	0621	0623	...	...	0745	...	0829	0917	...	1117	...	1217	...	1317	...	1522	1623	...	1714	1817	...	1917	...	2118	2349
Kinding ... d.	...	0537	...	0636	0640	...	...	0801	...	0849	0933	...	1132	...	1232	...	1333	...	1538	1638	...	1729	1832	...	1933	...	2134	0004
Ingolstadt Hbf ... a.	...	0555	...	0654	0658	...	...	0817	...	0907	0951	...	1150	...	1250	...	1351	...	1556	1656	...	1748	1850	...	1951	...	2152	0021
Ingolstadt Hbf ... d.	0438	0600	0609	0656	0701	0708	0806	0819	0905	0909	1004	1105	1203	1305	1305	1305	1405	1505	1601	1705	1705	1802	1909	1912	2004	2105	2205	0023
Pfaffenhofen (Ilm) ... d.	0458	0619	0632	0711	0719	0731	0827	0837	0926	0927	1026	1126	1224	1325	1326	1326	1426	1527	1627	1726	1727	1823	1929	1933	2026	2127	2226	0041
München Hbf ... a.	0534	0646	0700	0738	0748	0802	0855	0901	0953	0952	1054	1154	1251	1353	1354	1357	1454	1557	1656	1753	1754	1851	1957	2007	2053	2159	2254	0108

RE services via EICHSTÄTT and TREUCHTLINGEN

km																												
		Ⓒz	⑥	Ⓐt		Ⓐt		Ⓐt	◇															⑥				
0	**München** Hbf ... d.	...	...	...	...	0508	...	0601	0626	0722	0825	0928	1027	1127	1227	1324	1426	1530	1627	1725	1827	1930	2022	2131	2224	2224	2330	0030
50	Pfaffenhofen (Ilm) ... d.	...	0500	0500	...	0554	...	0628	0701	0801	0900	1004	1102	1202	1302	1359	1501	1605	1702	1802	1902	2005	2101	2206	2302	2302	0005	0106
81	**Ingolstadt** Hbf ... a.	...	0521	0521	...	0617	...	0647	0726	0823	0921	1026	1125	1224	1325	1421	1523	1626	1723	1824	1924	2026	2125	2227	2324	2324	0026	0127
81	**Ingolstadt** Hbf ... d.	0524	0524	0523	...	0629	0629	0650	0731	0830	0930	1027	1129	1226	1326	1429	1526	1628	1730	1826	1926	2030	2131	2230	2325	...	...	...
108	Eichstätt Bahnhof ♥ d.	0556	0556	0556	...	0656	0656	0710	0758	0857	0957	1056	1157	1256	1356	1457	1557	1657	1757	1857	1956	2057	2157	2257	2352	...	...	...
137	Treuchtlingen ... a.	0620	0620	0620	...	0719	0719	...	0820	0919	1020	1119	1220	1319	1419	1519	1620	1720	1821	1919	2020	2119	2220	2319	0015	...	...	...
137	Treuchtlingen ... **905** d.	0626	0626	0636	...	0725	0725	...	0828	0925	*1028*	1125	*1228*c	1325	*1428*	1525	*1628*	1728	*1829*	1925	*2028*	2125	*2225*	2325	0018	...	...	...
146	Weißenburg ... **905** d.	0632	0632	0644	...	0731	0731	...	0834	0931	*1034*	1131	*1234*c	1331	*1434*	1531	*1635*	1734	*1835*	1931	*2034*	2131	*2231*	2331	0024	...	...	...
199	**Nürnberg** Hbf.. **905** a.	0715	0715	0724	...	0815	0815	...	0916	1015	*1116*	1215	*1316*c	1415	*1516*	1615	*1717*	1816	*1918*	2015	*2116*	2215	*2313*	0015	0105	...	...	...

	Ⓐt	Ⓒz	⊕	Ⓐt	Ⓒz	Ⓐt	Ⓐt	⚒t	†d					Ⓒz	Ⓐt									⊕		⑥		
Nürnberg Hbf ... **905** d.	...	...	0440	0526	0539	...	0630	*0636*k	0637	0738	*0839*	0939	*1039*	1139	1139	*1239*	1339	*1438*	1539	*1639*	1739	*1838*	1938	2039	2138	2245	2245	2344
Weißenburg ... **905** d.	...	...	0521	0608	0621	...	0712	*0718*k	0721	0821	*0921*	1021	*1121*	1221	1221	*1322*	1421	*1521*	1621	*1721*	1822	*1921*	2020	2121	2221	2327	2327	0025
Treuchtlingen ... **905** a.	...	...	0528	0616	0628	...	0720	*0723*k	0727	0827	*0930*	1027	*1130*	1227	1227	*1330*	1427	*1530*	1627	*1727*	1831	*1930*	2027	2130	2230	2334	2334	0032
Treuchtlingen ... d.	0443	...	0532	0632	0632	...	0735	0735	0735	0835	0935	1035	1135	1235	1240	1336	1435	1535	1635	1735	1835	1935	2035	2135	2235	2337	...	...
Eichstätt Bahnhof ♥ d.	0507	...	0556	0655	0655	0720	0759	0759	0759	0900	0959	1058	1159	1258	1303	1400	1458	1559	1658	1759	1858	1959	2058	2159	2258	2359	...	...
Ingolstadt Hbf ... a.	0532	...	0621	0721	0721	0745	0825	0825	0825	0930	1030	1130	1229	1328	1331	1430	1530	1629	1737	1837	1930	2029	2130	2224	2330	0026	...	...
Ingolstadt Hbf ... d.	0534	0538	0631	0730	0730	0747	0831	0831	0831	0932	1031	1132	1232	1334	1334	1431	1533	1631	1738	1838	1934	2031	2132	2234	2334	...	...	...
Pfaffenhofen (Ilm) ... d.	0555	0559	0654	0753	0753	0813	0900	0900	0854**y**	0953	1054	1153	1253	1357	1357	1455	1554	1654	1759	1901	1958	2051	2153	2257	2358	...	...	...
München Hbf ... a.	0630	0634	0731	0828	0828	0838	0935	0935	0935	1042	1135	1237	1330	1441	1441	1536	1633	1731	1843	1936	2038	2127	2229	2343	0035	...	...	...

D – To/from Lübeck (Table **825**).
E – From Lichtenfels (Tables **850** and **875**).
G – From/to Garmisch on ⑥ (Table **895**).
H – From Innsbruck via Garmisch (Table **895**). To Hannover (Table **900**).
K – To/from Köln, Essen or Dortmund (Table **910**).
N – From Kassel (also Hamburg on ①). See Table **900**.
O – From Ostseebad Binz (Tables **844** and **845**).
S – To Kassel (Table **900**).
T – ①②③④⑥ (not June 16, Aug. 15, Oct. 3).
U – ①–④ (not June 16, Aug. 15, Oct. 3).

c – On Ⓐ (not June 16, Aug. 15) Treuchtlingen d. 1238, Weißenburg d. 1245, Nürnberg a. 1329.
d – † (also June 16, Aug. 15). Change trains at Ingolstadt on June 16, Aug. 15.
e – Not ⑦.
f – 1545 on ⑦.
g – ① only.
j – 1341 on ⑥.
k – ⑥ only.
n – Also June 15, Aug. 14, Oct. 2.
t – Not June 16, Aug. 15.

x – 0035 on ① mornings.
y – 0900 on June 16, Aug. 15.
z – Also June 16, Aug. 15.

• – Hamburg **Altona**.
◇ – Change trains at Treuchtlingen on ⚒ (not June 16, Aug. 15).
⊕ – Change trains at Treuchtlingen on Ⓐ (not June 16, Aug. 15).
♥ – Connecting trains run Eichstätt Bahnhof - Eichstätt Stadt (*5 km*; operated by Bayerische Regiobahn).

See Table **905** for services via Augsburg

MÜNCHEN - AUGSBURG - NÜRNBERG and WÜRZBURG 905

ICE | *IC* services. See Table **904** for services via Ingolstadt. See Table **905a** for local trains Treuchtlingen - Würzburg.

	ICE **804** Ⓐ t ✕	*ICE* **802** ✕	*ICE* **1706** ✕	*ICE* **708** ✕	*IC* **2082** T A 🍷	*IC* **2082** U B 🍷	*ICE* **1092** ⑥ ✕	*ICE* **1092** Ⓑ ✕	*ICE* **704** ✕	*ICE* **1502** ①–④ m ✕	*ICE* **702** ✕	*ICE* **1500** Ⓑ L✕
München Ost d.	...	...	...	...	1117	...	...	...	...	...	...	...
München Hbf 930 d.	0506	0713	0839	1114	|	...	1239	1240	1513	1609	1705	1909
München Pasing 930 d.	0515	0722	0848	1123	1130	...	1247	|	1522	1618	1714	1918
Augsburg Hbf 900 930 d.	0538	0748	0913	1146	1230h	1230	1312	1312	1546	1643	1738	1942
Donauwörth d.	0602	0808	0934	1208	1251	1251	1331	1331	1608	1704	1804	2006
Treuchtlingen d.	0622	|	|	|	1312	1312	|	|	|	1725	1825	2025
Nürnberg Hbf 900 920 a.	0657	0858	1025	1258	|	|	1421	1421	1658	1759	1859	2058
Berlin Hbf **850** a.	1025	1225	1355	1625	|	|	1758	1758	2024	...	2224	...
Würzburg Hbf 900 920 a.	|	|	|	|	1438	1438	...	...	|	...	...	...
Hamburg Hbf **840 900** a.	1221	1421	1559	1822	...	...	...	...	2222	...	...	...

	ICE **981** Ⓐ t ✕	*RJ* **987** ①–⑤	*ICE* **989** Ⓐ t ✕	*ICE* **1701** ①–⑤ ✕	*ICE* **701** ✕	*IC* **2083** Y B 🍷	*IC* **2083** X A 🍷	*ICE* **1093** ✕	*ICE* **705** ✕	*ICE* **1205** E ✕	*ICE* **709** ✕	*ICE* **801** ✕
Hamburg Hbf **840 900** d.	...	...	...	...	0527v	...	...	...	0936	1204	1336	1536
Würzburg Hbf 900 920 d.	...	...	...	...	|	1124	1124	...	|	|	|	|
Berlin Hbf **850** d.	...	...	...	0534	0737	|	|	1004	1137	1404	1537	1736
Nürnberg Hbf 900 920 d.	...	...	0615	0900	1059	|	|	1330	1459	1732	1859	2100
Treuchtlingen d.	...	...	0651	|	|	1246	1246	|	|	|	|	|
Donauwörth d.	0557	0643	0711	0950	1150	1311	1311	1421	1550	1825	1950	2151
Augsburg Hbf 900 930 a.	0618	0705	0731	1009	1209	1330	1330	1443	1609	1845	2009	2210
München Pasing 930 a.	0645	0734	0756	1032	1232	...	1358	|	1632	|	2032	2233
München Hbf 930 a.	0655	0744	0806	1042	1242	...	|	1517	1642	1916	2043	2244
München Ost a.	...	...	...	...	...	...	1411	...	...	...	...	...

RE services. See Table **930** for other connecting trains München - Augsburg and v.v.

km		Ⓒ z		Ⓒ z	Ⓐ t		⚒ t		MH			Ⓒ z	Ⓐ t								MH			Ⓐ t			
0	**München** Hbf 930 d.	0007	...	*0158*	...	0529	...	0735	...	...	0937	...	...	1135	...	1335	...	1534	...	1734	...	...	1935	...	2100	2200	2300
7	München Pasing 930 d.	0016	...	*0205*	...	0536	...	0743	...	...	0944	...	...	1143	...	1343	...	1542	...	1742	...	...	1943	...	2107	2207	2307
62	**Augsburg** Hbf 930 a.	0056	...	*0246*	...	0619	...	0820	...	...	1019	...	...	1218	...	1419	...	1620	...	1820	...	...	2019	...	2148	2248	2348
62	**Augsburg** Hbf d.	0102	...	0319	0517	0628	0720	0828	0926	0927e	1028	1127	1127	1224	1325	1428	1526	1628	1726	1828	1919	1926	2029	2129	2154	2254	0001
103	Donauwörth d.	0139	...	0359	0555f	0659	0758	0859	0949	0958e	1059	1158	1158	1259	1358	1459	1559	1659	1758	1859	1942	1958	2059	2158	2233	2332	0040
137	Treuchtlingen a.	...	...	0417	0618	0720	0820	0920	1006	1021	1120	1220	1220	1320	1419	1520	1620	1720	1818	1920	2000	2019	2120	2220	2253	...	...
137	Treuchtlingen 904 d.	...	0418	0418	0626	*0725*	0828	*0925*	1008	1028	*1125*	1228	1238	*1325*	1428	*1525*	1628	*1728*	1829	*1925*	2001	2028	*2125*	2225	*2325*	...	...
146	Weißenburg (Bay) 904 d.	...	0424	0424	0633	*0731*	0834	*0931*	|	1034	*1131*	1234	1245	*1331*	1434	*1531*	1635	*1734*	1835	*1931*	|	2034	*2131*	2231	*2331*	...	...
199	**Nürnberg** Hbf 904 a.	...	0507	0507	0715	*0815*	0916	*1015*	1045	1116	*1215*	1316	1329	*1415*	1516	*1615*	1717	*1816*	1918	*2015*	2034	2116	*2215*	2313	*0015*	...	...

	Ⓒ z	Ⓐ t	Ⓒ z⊕	Ⓐ t	Ⓐ t		⑥	Ⓐ t	MH											MH				Ⓐ t	Ⓒ z	Ⓐ t	
Nürnberg Hbf 904 d.	0053	...	...	0440k	0526	*0539*z	0636	0649	0716	*0738*	0839	*0939*	1039	*1139*	1239	*1339*	1438	*1539*	1639	1713	*1739*	1838	*1938*	2039	*2138*	*2138*	...
Weißenburg (Bay) 904 d.	0132	...	...	0521	0608	*0621*z	0718	0724	|	*0821*	0921	*1021*	1121	*1221*	1322	*1421*	1521	*1621*	1721	|	*1822*	1921	*2020*	2121	*2221*	*2221*	...
Treuchtlingen 904 a.	0139	...	...	0527	0616	*0628*z	0723	0730	0748	*0827*	0930	*1027*	1130	*1227*	1330	*1427*	1530	*1627*	1727	1745	*1831*	1930	*2027*	2130	*2230*	*2230*	...
Treuchtlingen d.	0142	...	...	0528	...	0633	0725	0731	0749	0834	0935	1034	1135	1235	1335	1436	1536	1634	1735	1746	1834	1935	2034	2135	2235	2235	...
Donauwörth d.	0203	0505	0520	0604j	...	0658	0754f	0754	0807	0858	0958	1058	1158	1258	1358	1458	1558	1658	1758	1806	1858	1958	2058	2158	2258	2258	...
Augsburg Hbf a.	0226	0550	0558	0635	...	0728	0825	0825	0828	0928	1028	1128	1228	1328	1428	1528	1630	1728	1827	1829	1928	2028	2128	2228	2328	2336	...
Augsburg Hbf 930 d.	...	0554	0604	*0649*	...	0739	...	...	...	0939	...	1139	...	1339	...	1539	...	1739	...	...	1939	...	2139	...	▷	...	2342
München Pasing 930 a.	...	0635	0644	*0729*	...	0813	...	...	...	1013	...	1213	...	1413	...	1613	...	1813	...	...	2014	...	2223	...	...	...	0024
München Hbf 930 a.	...	0644	0652	*0738*	...	0822	...	...	...	1021	...	1221	...	1421	...	1622	...	1823	...	...	2022	...	2231	...	...	...	0032

A – KÖNIGSSEE – [12] 🍷 Berchtesgaden - München Ost - Augsburg - Hannover and v.v.; conveys [12] Oberstdorf (**2084/5**) - Augsburg - Hannover and v.v.
B – KÖNIGSSEE – [12] 🍷 Oberstdorf - Augsburg - Hannover and v.v.
E – To Innsbruck via Garmisch on ⑤ (Table **895**).
H – From / to Lindau and Oberstdorf (Table **935**).
L – To Leipzig (Table **850**).
M – From Oct. 17.
T – From Aug. 3.
U – Until Aug. 2.
X – From Aug. 2.
Y – Until Aug. 1.

e – From Oct. 17 departs Augsburg 0932, Donauwörth 1000.
f – Arrives 8 minutes earlier.
h – Arrives 1200.
j – Arrives 0550.
k – 0434 from Oct. 17.
m – Not June 15, 16.
t – Not June 16, Aug. 15, Nov. 1.
v – ①–⑤ only.
z – Ⓒ (also June 16, Aug. 15, Nov. 1).

⊕ – Change trains at Augsburg on ⑥.
▷ – On ⑥ continues to München (departs Augsburg 2342; see later column).

TREUCHTLINGEN - WÜRZBURG 905a

RB services (except train **A**)

km		⚒ r	Ⓒ z	Ⓐ t	Ⓐ t	Ⓐ t	Ⓒ z		⑥						A	Ⓐ t	Ⓒ z									b
0	**Treuchtlingen** d.	...	0502	0512	0535	0616*	0625	*0705*t	0725	0825	0925	1025	1125	1225	1312	1306	1325	1425	1525	1625	1730	1826	1925	2025	2125	2225
24	Gunzenhausen d.	...	0516	0526	0550	0630	0639	*0721*t	0739	0838	0939	1039	1139	1239	|	1327n	1339	1439	1539	1639	1743	1840	1939	2039	2139	2239
51	Ansbach a.	...	0536	0546	0611	0650	0658	*0742*t	0759	0859	0959	1059	1159	1259	1342	1348	1359f	1459	1559	1659	1801	1900	1959	2059	2200	2259
51	Ansbach d.	0440	0538	0606	0638	0659*	0711	0811	0811	0910	1010	1111	1211	1311	1344	1410	1410	1511	1610	1711	1810	1911	2011	2111	...	2311
83	Steinach (b. Rothenb) d.	0503	0601	0628	0701	0722*	0733	0833	0833	0932	1031	1133	1233	1333	1404	1431	1431	1533	1631	1733	1831	1933	2033	2133	...	2333
140	**Würzburg** Hbf a.	0547	0644	0715	0743j	0805*	0816	0917	0917	1017	1122c	1217	1317	1417	1438	1522c	1522c	1616	1717e	1822k	1922	2017	2116	2216	...	0016

	⚒ h	Ⓐ t	Ⓒ z	Ⓐ D	Ⓐ t	Ⓒ z					B	Ⓒ z	Ⓐ t											† s	⚒ r
Würzburg Hbf d.	0430	...	0532	0532	0633	0641	0741	0843	0941	1041	1124	1140k	1140k	1243	1341	1441	1541	1643	1741	1841	1941k	2041	2140	2241	2304
Steinach (b. Rothenburg) d.	0513	...	0614	0614	0717	0724	0824	0925	1024	1124	1157	1224	1224	1326	1424	1524	1624	1725	1824	1924	2024	2124	2224	2325	2347
Ansbach a.	0535	...	0636	0636	0738	0746	0845	0947	1045	1145	1216	1245	1245	1348	1445	1545	1645	1747	1845	1945	2045	2145	2245	2348	0009
Ansbach d.	0537	0608	0644	0710	0754	0754	0854	0954	1054	1154	1218	1254	1316	1354	1454	1554	1654	1754	1854	1954	2054	2154	2254	...	0010
Gunzenhausen d.	0556	0627	0705	0729	0815	0815	0915	1015	1115	1214	|	1315	1336	1415	1515	1615	1715	1815	1915	2014	2115	2215	2313	...	0029
Treuchtlingen a.	0609	0642	0720	0745	0830	0830	0930	1030	1130	1229	1244	1330	1351	1430	1530	1630	1730	1830	1930	2029	2130	2230	2328	...	0044

Local trains **STEINACH** (b. Rothenburg) - **ROTHENBURG OB DER TAUBER** and v.v. 2nd class only. *12 km*. Journey time: 15 minutes.
From Steinach at 0422 ⚒ r, 0517, 0616 Ⓒ **z**, 0631 Ⓐ **t**, 0726 Ⓐ **t**, 0736 Ⓒ **z**, 0836, 0936, 1036, 1136, 1236, 1336, 1436, 1536, 1636, 1737, 1836 Ⓒ **z**, 1845 Ⓐ **t**, 1936, 2036 and 2236.
From Rothenburg ob der Tauber at 0444 ⚒ r, 0540 Ⓒ **z**, 0555 Ⓐ **t**, 0658 Ⓐ **t**, 0705 Ⓒ **z**, 0805, 0905, 1005, 1105, 1205, 1309, 1405, 1505, 1605, 1705, 1805, 1905, 2005, 2205 and 2305.

A – *IC* **2082**. KÖNIGSSEE – [12] 🍷 (From Aug. 3: Berchtesgaden - München -) Augsburg - Hannover; [12] Oberstdorf (**2084** ‡) - Augsburg - Hannover.
B – *IC* **2083**. KÖNIGSSEE – [12] 🍷 Hannover - Augsburg (- München - Berchtesgaden from Aug. 2); [12] Hannover - Augsburg (**2085** §) - Oberstdorf.
D – Ⓐ until Nov. 25 (not June 16, Nov. 1).

b – Does not run Steinach - Würzburg Oct. 17 - Nov. 27.
c – 5 minutes earlier until Oct. 16.
e – 1722 Oct. 17 - Nov. 27.
f – 1403 until Oct. 16.
h – Not June 16, Oct. 18 - Nov. 28.
j – Not Oct. 17 - Nov. 25.

k – 5–9 minutes earlier from Oct. 17.
n – Arrives 1319.
r – ⚒ (not June 16, Nov. 1).
s – † (also June 16, Nov. 1).
t – Ⓐ (not June 16, Nov. 1).
z – Ⓒ (also June 16, Nov. 1).

* – Oct. 17 - Nov. 25 Treuchtlingen d. 0615, Ansbach d. 0711, Steinach d. 0733, Würzburg a. 0816.
‡ – Runs as train **2082** throughout until Aug. 2.
§ – Runs as train **2083** throughout until Aug. 1.

906 GIESSEN - KOBLENZ; LIMBURG - FRANKFURT and WIESBADEN

DB (RE services); HLB★

GIESSEN - KOBLENZ. Additional stopping trains operate. On June 16 services run as on ⑦.

km				⚒								
0	**Gießen** .... 807 d.	...	0618	0716	0916	1116	1316	1516	1716	1916	2116	2122	2222
13	Wetzlar .... 807 d.	...	0631	0726	0926	1126	1326	1526	1726	1926	2126	2136	2236
36	Weilburg .... d.	...	0655	0743	0943	1143	1343	1543	1743	1943	2143	2200	2300
65	**Limburg** (Lahn) .. a.	...	0733	0808	1008	1208	1408	1608	1808	2008	2208	2237	2337
			◧	|	|	|	|	|	|	|	|	◧	◧
				|	|	|	|	|	|	|			⑤⑥
65	**Limburg** (Lahn) .. d.	0646	0746	0809	1009	1209	1409	1609	1809	2009	2209	2246	2346
68	Diez .... d.	0651	0751	0813	1013	1213	1413	1613	1813	2013	2213	2251	2351
91	Nassau (Lahn) .... d.	0716	0816	0833	1033	1233	1433	1633	1833	2033	2233	2316	0016
99	Bad Ems .... d.	0725	0825	0840	1040	1240	1440	1640	1840	2040	2240	2325	0025
112	Niederlahnstein... d.	0742	0842	0853	1053	1253	1453	1653	1853	2053	2253	2342	0042
117	**Koblenz** Hbf ...... a.	0750	0850	0900	1100	1300	1500	1700	1900	2100	2300	2351	0050

	Ⓐ										
Koblenz Hbf .... d.	0509	0657	0857	1057	1257	1457	1657	1857	2009	2109	2209
Niederlahnstein .... d.	0516	0704	0904	1104	1304	1504	1704	1904	2016	2116	2216
Bad Ems .... d.	0532	0716	0916	1116	1316	1516	1716	1916	2032	2132	2232
Nassau (Lahn) ...... d.	0544	0726	0926	1126	1326	1526	1726	1926	2044	2144	2244
Diez .... d.	0610	0746	0946	1146	1346	1546	1746	1946	2110	2210	2310
Limburg (Lahn).... a.	0614	0750	0950	1150	1350	1550	1750	1950	2114	2214	2314
	◧	|	|	|	|	|	|	|	◧	◧	
	d	|	|	|	|	|	|	|			
Limburg (Lahn).... d.	0618	0751	0951	1151	1351	1551	1751	1951	2123	2223	...
Weilburg .... d.	0655	0816	1016	1216	1416	1616	1816	2016	2200	2300	...
Wetzlar .... 807 d.	0720	0832	1032	1232	1432	1632	1832	2032	2227	2327	...
Gießen .... 807 a.	0731	0842	1042	1242	1442	1642	1842	2042	2238	2338	...

LIMBURG - NIEDERNHAUSEN - FRANKFURT and WIESBADEN. On June 16 services run as on ⑦.

km		ⓒ			⚒v	Ⓐ	Ⓐv	Ⓐ	Ⓐv	⑥	Ⓐ	Ⓐv	Ⓐ	ⓒ	Ⓐ	ⓒv	Ⓐ	Ⓐ		v	Ⓐ	Ⓐv		v	
0	**Limburg** (Lahn) .... d.	0019	...	0419	...	0449	...	0519	...	0519	0556	...	0610	0619	0626	...	0640	0656	0719	...	0756	...	0819	...	and at
21	Bad Camberg .... d.	0043	...	0443	...	0513	...	0543	...	0543	0615	...	0634	0643	0645	...	0704	0715	0743	...	0815	...	0843	...	the same
30	Idstein .... d.	0052	...	0452	...	0522	...	0552	...	0553	0622	...	0645	0652	0652	...	0715	0722	0752	...	0822	...	0852	...	minutes
38	Niedernhausen .... ‡ d.	0059	...	0459	0505	0529	0535	0559	0605	0605	0629	0635	0653	0659	0659	0705	0723	0729	0759	0805	0829	0835	0859	0905	past each
58	**Wiesbaden** Hbf ..... a.	|	...	|	0526	|	0558	|	0628	0628v	|	0658	0715v	|	|	0728	0745v	|	|	0828	|	0858	|	0928	hour until
70	**Frankfurt** (Main) Hbf ‡ a.	0131	...	0531	...	0601	...	0631	...	...	0701	...	...	0731	0731	...	...	0759	0831	...	0859	...	0931	...	

		v	Ⓐ		v	Ⓐ	Ⓐv			v	Ⓐ	Ⓐv		v	Ⓐ		v		v				v		⑤⑥f
Limburg (Lahn) .... d.	1219	...	1249	1319	...	1356	...	and at	1719	...	1756	...	1819	...	1849	1919	...	2019	...	2119	...	2219	...	2319	2319
Bad Camberg .... d.	1243	...	1313	1343	...	1415	...	the same	1743	...	1815	...	1843	...	1913	1943	...	2043	...	2143	...	2243	...	2343	2343
Idstein .... d.	1252	...	1323	1352	...	1422	...	minutes	1752	...	1822	...	1852	...	1923	1952	...	2052	...	2153	...	2252	...	2353	2353
Niedernhausen .... ‡ d.	1259	1305	1335	1359	1405	1429	1435	past each	1759	1805	1829	1835	1859	1905	1935	1959	2005	2059	2105	2205k	2203	2259	2305	2400	0005
Wiesbaden Hbf...... a.	|	1328	1358v	|	1428	|	1458	hour until	|	1828	|	1858	|	1928	1958v	|	2028	|	2128	2228v	|	|	2328	...	0028
Frankfurt (Main) Hbf ‡ a.	1331	...	...	1431	...	1501	..		1831	...	1901	...	1931	...	...	2031	...	2131	...	...	2238	2331	...	...	...

	ⓒv			Ⓐv	Ⓐ	⑥v	ⓒ	Ⓐv	Ⓐ	Ⓐv	Ⓐ	ⓒ	Ⓐ	v			v		Ⓐv	Ⓐ	v		Ⓐv	Ⓐ	ⓒv
Frankfurt (Main) Hbf ‡ d.	...	0029	...	...	0559	...	0629	...	0659	...	0728	...	...	...	0829	and at	...	1329	...	1359	...	1429	...	1459	...
Wiesbaden Hbf...... d.	0036	|	0536r	0606	|	0636	|	0653	|	0723	|	0736v	0806v	0836	|	the same	1336	|	1406	|	1436	|	1506	|	1536
Niedernhausen .... ‡ d.	0058	0101	0601	0628	0631	0658	0701	0718	0731	0745	0801	0801	0831	0858	0901	minutes	1358	1401	1428	1431	1458	1501	1528	1531	1558
Idstein .... d.	...	0108	0608	...	0637	...	0707	...	0737	...	0807	0808	0838	...	0907	past each	...	1407	...	1437	...	1507	...	1537	...
Bad Camberg .... d.	...	0117	0617	...	0646	...	0716	...	0744	...	0816	0817	0847	...	0916	hour until	...	1416	...	1444	...	1516	...	1544	...
Limburg (Lahn) .... a.	...	0142	0641	...	0709	...	0739	...	0803	...	0841	0841	0911	...	0941		...	1441	...	1503	...	1541	...	1603	...

	ⓒ	Ⓐ	Ⓐv	Ⓐ	ⓒv	ⓒ	Ⓐ	Ⓐ	Ⓐv	Ⓐ	v	ⓒ	Ⓐ	Ⓐv	Ⓐ	v		Ⓐv	Ⓐ	v			v		
Frankfurt (Main) Hbf ‡ d.	1529	...	...	1559	...	1629	...	1643	...	1657	...	1729	1743	...	1759	...	1829	...	1859	...	1929	and at	...	2229	...
Wiesbaden Hbf...... d.	|	1536v	1606	|	1636	|	1636v	|	1706	|	1736	|	|	1806	|	1836	|	1906	|	1936	|	the same	2236	|	2336v
Niedernhausen .... ‡ d.	1601	1601	1628	1631	1658	1701	1701	1716	1728	1731	1758	1801	1816	1828	1831	1858	1901	1928	1931	1958	2001	minutes	2258	2301	0001
Idstein .... d.	1607	1608	...	1637	...	1707	1708	1722	...	1737	...	1807	1822	...	1837	...	1907	...	1937	...	2007	past each	...	2307	0008
Bad Camberg .... d.	1616	1617	...	1644	...	1716	1717	1731	...	1744	...	1816	1831	...	1844	...	1916	...	1944	...	2016	hour until	...	2316	0017
Limburg (Lahn) .... a.	1641	1641	...	1703	...	1741	1741	1755	...	1803	...	1841	1853	...	1903	...	1941	...	2003	...	2041		...	2341	0041

d – Daily. Runs 5–7 minutes later on ⓒ.
f – Also June 15, Oct. 2; not July 23 - Sept. 3.
k – Arrives 2200.
r – ⚒ (not July 23 - Sept. 3).

v – Not July 23 - Sept. 4.
◧ – Change trains at Limburg.
★ – Hessische Landesbahn.

‡ – **Additional S-Bahn *S2* services** Frankfurt - Niedernhausen and v.v. Journey: 35 minutes.
From Frankfurt (Main) Hbf: On ⚒ every 30 minutes 0452–2352; on † at 0442, 0521, 0552, 0621, 0652, 0721, 0752, 0822, 0852 and every 30 minutes 2352.
From Niedernhausen: On ⚒ every 30 minutes 0403–0033; on † at 0443, 0533, 0603, 0633 and every 30 minutes until 2333.

907 GIESSEN - FULDA

Hessische Landesbahn

On June 16 services run as on ⑦.

km		Ⓐ	Ⓐ	Ⓐ	⑥	Ⓐ	⑥	Ⓐ	ⓒ	Ⓐ					Ⓐ	ⓒ										
0	**Gießen** .... d.	...	...	0524	...	...	...	0617	0744	0747	0844	0947	1044	1147	1241	1244	1347	1444t	1547	1644t	1747	1844t	1947	2111	2211	2311
23	Grünberg (Oberhess). d.	...	...	0549	...	0615	...	0709j	0811	0816	0911	1013	1111	1213	1311	1311	1411v	1511	1611v	1711	1811v	1911	2015	2135	2239	2336
60	Alsfeld (Oberhess) ..... d.	0515	0555	0635j	0649	0723r	0749	0749	0849	0849	0949	1049	1149	1249	1350	1349	1449	1549	1649	1749	1849	1948	2056	2219j	2320	0011
79	Lauterbach (Hess) ..... d.	0529	0610	0649	0703	0738	0803	0803	0903	0903	1003	1103	1203	1303	1403	1403	1503	1603	1703	1803	1903	2007	2109	2238	...	...
106	**Fulda** .... a.	0602	0640	0719	0730	0804	0829	0830	0929	0930	1029	1130	1230	1330	1430	1429	1530	1630	1730	1830	1930	2039	2139	2302	...	...

	Ⓐ	Ⓐ	Ⓐ	⑥	Ⓐ	ⓒ	Ⓐ	Ⓐ	ⓒ	⑥															⑤⑥f	
Fulda .... d.	...	...	...	...	0535	...	0610	0653	...	0735	0834	0935	1035	1134	1234	1334	1434	1534	1634	1734	1834	2010	2101	2209	2209	2309
Lauterbach (Hess) ...... d.	...	...	...	...	0612j	...	0654j	0723	...	0805	0905	1005	1105	1205	1305	1405	1505	1605	1705	1805	1905	2037	2127	2236	2236	2336
Alsfeld (Oberhess) ...... d.	0419	0532	0556	0612	0631	0712	0719j	0757j	0819	0819	0919	1019	1119	1219	1319	1419	1519	1619	1719	1819	1919	2058j	2141	2250	2251	2350
Grünberg (Oberhess).. d.	0453	0614	0639	0647	0705	0747	0753	0838	0850	0850	0953	1050	1153	1250t	1353	1450t	1553	1650t	1753	1850t	1953	2137	2217	...	2337	...
Gießen .... a.	0518	0640	0704	0711	0729	0815	0818	0906	0915	0915	1018	1115	1218	1315	1416v	1515	1616v	1715	1816v	1915	2018	2201	2242	...	0002	...

f – Also June 15. j – Arrives 7–12 minutes earlier. r – Arrives 0703. t – 3 minutes later on Ⓐ. v – 2–3 minutes later on ⓒ.

908 GÖTTINGEN - BEBRA

CANTUS Verkehrsgesellschaft (2nd class only)

km		Ⓐ	⚒	⚒	Ⓐ	ⓒd					
0	**Göttingen** .... 864 d.	0414	0514	0614	0646	0714	0814		2114	2214	2314
20	Eichenberg .... 864 d.	0430	0530	0630	0701	0730	0830	and	2130	2230	2330
35	Bad Sooden-Allendorf . d.	0440	0540	0640	0710	0740	0840	hourly	2140	2240	2340
49	Eschwege .... a.	0451	0551	0651	0721	0751	0851	until	2151	2251	2351
49	Eschwege .... d.	0521	0621	0725	|	0821	0921		2221	2314	2357
87	**Bebra** .... a.	0550	0650	0754	*0754*e	0850	0950		2250	2343	0027

	Ⓐ	⚒						
Bebra .... d.	0400	0530	0631	0708		2008	2108	2208
Eschwege .... a.	0428	0558	0659	0737	and	2036	2136	2236
Eschwege .... d.	0434	0605	0705	0805	hourly	2105	2205	2305
Bad Sooden-Allendorf d.	0445	0616	0716	0816	until	2116	2216	2316
Eichenberg .... 864 d.	0502	0631	0731	0831		2131	2229	2331
Göttingen .... 864 a.	0515	0645	0745	0845		2145	2243	2345

d – Runs daily Eschwege - Bebra.
e – Change trains at Eschwege-Niederhone (a. 0718, d. *0728*).

909 WÜRZBURG - BAD KISSINGEN - GEMÜNDEN

DB (RE services); EB★

On June 16, Aug. 15, Nov. 1 services run as on ⑦.

km								ⓒ	Ⓐ		Ⓐ														
0	**Würzburg** Hbf .... 870 876 ‡ d.	...	...	0801	...	...	1001	...	...	1201	...	...	1401	...	...	1601	...	...	1801	...	...	2001	...	...	...
43	**Schweinfurt** Hbf. 870 876 ‡ d.	0611	0812	0830	0912	1012	1030	1205	1205	1230	1302	1412	1430	1512	1612	1630	1712	1812	1830	1912	2012	2030	2113	2224	2351
57	Ebenhausen (Unterf)... 870 ‡ d.	0624	0825	0843	0929	1025	1043	1223	1223	1243	1316	1425	1443	1529	1625	1643	1729	1825	1843	1929	2025	2043	2129	2240	0005
66	**Bad Kissingen** .... a.	0633	0834	0853	0938	1034	1053	1232	1232	1253	1325	1434	1453	1538	1634	1653	1738	1834	1853	1938	2034	2053	2138	2249	0014
66	**Bad Kissingen** .... d.	0637	0839	...	...	1039	...	1239	1239	...	1343	1439	...	1543t	1639	...	1743t	1839	...	1943	2043	...	2142	...	...
85	Hammelburg .... d.	0659	0908	...	...	1106	...	1306	1313	...	1406	1506	...	1606t	1706	...	1807t	1906	...	2006	2107	...	2208	...	...
113	**Gemünden** (Main) .... a.	0737	0941	...	...	1140	...	1340	1350	...	1441	1540	...	1641t	1741	...	1841t	1941	...	2039	2143	...	...	...	...

	Ⓐ		ⓒ	Ⓐ							ⓒ	Ⓐ	Ⓐ												
Gemünden (Main) .... d.	...	...	...	*0614*	0707r	...	0811	...	1011	...	1211	1211	1320	...	1411	1507t	...	1609	1708t	...	1809	1910t	...	2113	2211
Hammelburg .... d.	0545	*0612*t	0636	*0700*	0748r	...	0844	...	1044	...	1244	1244	1407	...	1444	1543t	...	1644	1743t	...	1845	1943t	...	2146	2248
Bad Kissingen .... a.	0607	*0636*t	0702	*0722*	0810r	...	0907	...	1107	...	1307	1307	1429	...	1507	1609t	...	1707	1808t	...	1907	2008t	...	2209	2309
Bad Kissingen .... d.	0612	0641	0706	0730	0814	0900	0918	1100	1118	1300	1318	1326	...	1500	1518	1614	1700	1718	1813	1900	1918	2013	2100	2213	2314
Ebenhausen (Unterf) ..... 870 a.	0621	0650	0715	0739	0823	0909	0927	1109	1127	1309	1327	1335	...	1509	1527	1623	1709	1727	1822	1909	1927	2022	2109	2222	2322
Schweinfurt Hbf .... 870 876 a.	0637	0713	0730	0753	0842	0926	0942	1126	1144	1326	1342	1356	...	1525	1542	1641	1725	1743	1841	1926	1942	2042	2126	2236	2340
Würzburg Hbf .... 870 876 a.	...	0746	...	...	...	0955	...	1155	...	1355	...	...	...	1555	...	...	1755	...	...	1955	...	...	2157	...	...

t – Ⓐ only.
r – ⚒ only.

★ – Erfurter Bahn (2nd class only).

‡ – Trains between Würzburg, Schweinfurt and Ebenhausen are often combined with a service to Meiningen or Erfurt. Passengers should take care to join the correct portion for their destination.

AACHEN - KÖLN - FRANKFURT via high-speed line 910

See Tables **800**/**911** for services via Bonn and Koblenz. See Table **20** for *Thalys* services Paris - Brussels - Aachen - Köln.

km	km	SEE NOTES ⊠ and ▷	ICE 827	ICE 827 ①–⑥		ICE 521	ICE 523 ①–⑥	ICE 511	ICE 811 Ⓑ	ICE 711 Ⓐt	ICE 525	ICE 101	ICE 101 ①–⑥	ICE 913 ①–⑥	ICE 813	ICE 813 ①–⑤	ICE 527	ICE 513	ICE 11	ICE 815 ①–⑥	ICE 529	ICE 103	ICE 915	ICE 121 ①–⑥
							✕	✕	✕	✕	✕	✕	✕	✕	✕	✕	G✕	M✕	✕	✕	✕	✕	M✕	⊠✕
		Dortmund Hbf **800** ▷ d.	...	...	...	...	0401	...	...	...	0522	...	0528	0547	...	0558	0622	0636	...	...	0722	...	...	...
		Essen Hbf **800** ▷ d.	...	...	...	...	0427	...	...	...	0549	...	|	0615	...	|	0651	0700	...	...	0750	...	0825g	...
		Amsterdam Centraal **28** ⊠ d.	...	...	...	...	|	...	...	...	|	...	|	|	...	|	|	|	...	...	|	...	|	0638
		Düsseldorf Hbf **800** ▷ d.	...	...	...	...	0454	...	0534	...	0617	...	◐	0645	...	◐	0718	0724	...	...	0818	...	0847	0854
		Brussels Midi/Zuid **21** d.	...	...	...	...	|	...	|	...	|	...	|	|	...	|	|	|	0625	...	|	...	|	|
		Aachen Hbf **802 807** d.	...	...	...	...	|	...	|	...	|	...	|	|	...	|	|	|	0739	...	|	...	|	|
		Köln Hbf **800 802 807** a.	...	...	...	...	|	...	|	...	|	...	0646	|	...	|	|	0749	0816	...	|	...	|	|
0	0	**Köln** Hbf **802 807** d.	0319	0319	...	0422	|	0548	|	0600f	|	0654	0654	|	...	|	|	0755	0823	...	|	0854	|	|
1	1	**Köln** Messe/Deutz **802** d.	|	|	...	|	0520	|	0602	|	0644	|	|	0711	0720	0720	0744	|	|	0811	0844	|	0917	0928
	15	Köln/Bonn Flughafen ✈ **802** d.	0332	0332	...	|	0531	|	|	|	|	|	|	|	|	|	|	|	|	0822	|	|	|	|
25	31	Siegburg/Bonn 🚋 **807** d.	0342	0342	...	0436	0541	0602	0615	0624	|	0709	0709	0725	0733	0733	|	|	|	0831	|	0909	|	|
88	94	Montabaur d.	0403	0403	...	0456	0602	|	0635	0644	|	|	|	|	0753	0753	|	|	|	0857	|	|	|	|
110	116	Limburg Süd d.	0414	0414	...	0507	0613	|	0646	0654	|	|	|	|	0804	0804	|	|	|	0907	|	|	|	|
	171	**Wiesbaden** Hbf a.	|	|	...	|	|	|	|	0720	|	|	|	|	|	|	|	|	|	|	|	|	|	|
	181	**Mainz** Hbf a.	|	|	...	|	|	|	|	0744	|	|	|	|	|	|	|	|	|	|	|	|	|	|
169		**Frankfurt** Flughafen Fernbf ✈ a.	0435	0435	...	0526	0634	0650	0708	|	0733	0749	0749	0807	0826	0826	0833	0850	0917	0926	0933	0949	1007	1017
180		**Frankfurt** (Main) Hbf a.	0448	0448	...	0540	0648	|	0724	|	0748	|	|	|	0841	0841	0848	|	0931	0941	0948	|	|	1031
		Nürnberg Hbf **920** a.	...	0720	...	0824	0921	|	...	|	1020	|	|	|	...	...	1120	|	...	...	1220	|	|	...
		Mannheim Hbf **912** a.	...	|	...	|	|	0723	...	0824	|	0823	0823	0839	...	...	|	0924	...	...	|	1023	1039	...
		Karlsruhe Hbf **912** a.	...	|	...	|	|	|	...	|	|	0858	0858	0906z	...	...	|	|	...	...	|	1058	1117z	...
		Basel SBB **912** a.	...	|	...	|	|	|	...	|	|	1047	1047	|	...	...	|	|	...	...	|	1247	|	...
		Stuttgart Hbf **912** a.	...	|	...	|	|	0808	...	0920	|	...	...	0924v	...	...	|	1008	...	...	|	...	1122v	...
		München Hbf **904 930** a.	...	0833	...	0939	1033	1027	...	...	1130	...	...	...	...	...	1233	1227	...	...	1334	...	...	...

SEE NOTES ⊠ and ▷	ICE 621	ICE 515	ICE 13	ICE 623	ICE 105 ⊠	ICE 917	ICE 625	ICE 517	ICE 15	ICE 627	ICE 107	ICE 123 ⊠	ICE 629	ICE 519	ICE 817	ICE 315	ICE 721	ICE 109	ICE 1011	ICE 125 ⊠	ICE 723	ICE 611	ICE 819	ICE 17
	✕	H✕	✕	✕	✕	✕	✕	H✕	✕	✕	✕	✕	✕	H✕	✕	✕	✕	✕	✕	✕	✕	H✕	✕	✕
Dortmund Hbf **800** ▷ d.	...	0836	...	0912w	...	...	...	1036	...	1122w	...	...	...	1236	...	...	...	...	1349q	...	...	1435	...	...
Essen Hbf **800** ▷ d.	0839	0900	...	0941c	...	...	1036	1100	...	1150	...	...	1236	1300	1305	...	1351	...	1415q	...	1439	|	...	...
Amsterdam Centraal **28** ⊠ d.	|	|	...	|	0808	...	|	|	...	|	...	1038	|	|	|	...	|	...	|	1238	|	|	...	...
Düsseldorf Hbf **800** ▷ d.	0910	0924	...	1009	1019	1051	1105	1124	...	1217	...	1248	1305	1324	1333	...	1418	...	1449	1454	1508	◐	...	...
Brussels Midi/Zuid **21** d.	|	|	0823h	|	|	|	|	|	1025	|	...	|	|	|	|	1225	|	...	|	|	|	|	...	1425
Aachen Hbf **802 807** d.	|	|	0939	|	|	|	|	|	1139	|	...	|	|	|	|	1339	|	...	|	|	|	|	...	1539
Köln Hbf **800 802 807** a.	|	0949	1015	|	1045	|	|	1149	1215	|	...	|	|	1349	|	1415	|	...	|	|	|	1546	...	1615
Köln Hbf **802 807** d.	|	0955	1018	|	1054	|	|	1155	1218j	|	1254	|	|	1355	|	1427	|	1454	|	|	|	1555	...	1620
Köln Messe/Deutz **802** d.	0935	|	|	1034	|	1116	1130	|	|	1244	|	1319	1332	|	1401	|	1444	|	1515	1521	1536	|	1601	|
Köln/Bonn Flughafen ✈ **802** d.	|	|	|	1045	|	|	|	|	|	|	|	|	|	|	|	|	|	|	|	|	|	|	|	|
Siegburg/Bonn 🚋 **807** d.	|	|	1032	|	1109	|	1143	|	1232j	|	1309	|	1346	|	1415	|	|	1509	|	|	1549	|	1615	|
Montabaur d.	1004	|	|	|	|	|	1204	|	|	|	|	|	1406	|	1435	|	|	|	|	|	|	|	1635	|
Limburg Süd d.	1015	|	|	|	|	|	1215	|	|	|	|	|	1417	|	1446	|	|	|	|	|	|	|	1646	|
Wiesbaden Hbf a.	|	|	|	|	|	|	|	|	|	|	|	|	|	|	|	|	|	|	|	|	|	|	|	|
Mainz Hbf a.	|	|	|	|	|	|	|	|	|	|	|	|	|	|	|	|	|	|	|	|	|	|	|	|
Frankfurt Flughafen Fernbf ✈ a.	1035	1050	1117	1133	1149	1207	1235	1250	1317	1333	1349	1412	1436	1450	1508	1517	1533	1549	1607	1617	1633	1650	1708	1715
Frankfurt (Main) Hbf a.	1048	|	1131	1148	|	|	1248	|	1331	1348	|	1426	1448	|	1524	1531	1548	|	|	1631	1648	|	1724	1731
Nürnberg Hbf **920** a.	1320	|	...	1420	|	|	1520	|	...	1621	|	...	1720	|	...	...	1820	|	|	...	1920	|	...	...
Mannheim Hbf **912** a.	|	1123	...	|	1223	1239	|	1323	...	|	1423	...	|	1523	...	...	|	1623	1639	...	|	1723	...	...
Karlsruhe Hbf **912** a.	|	|	...	|	1258	1306z	|	|	...	|	1458	...	|	|	...	...	|	1658	1714z	...	|	|	...	...
Basel SBB **912** a.	|	|	...	|	1447	|	|	|	...	|	1647	...	|	|	...	...	|	1847	|	...	|	|	...	...
Stuttgart Hbf **912** a.	|	1208	...	|	...	1322v	|	1408	...	|	...	...	|	1608	...	...	|	...	1720v	...	|	1808	...	...
München Hbf **904 930** a.	1432	1427	...	1529	...	...	1637	1627	...	1738	...	...	1833	1827	...	...	1941	...	...	...	2029	2028	...	...

SEE NOTES ⊠ and ▷	ICE 725	ICE 201	ICE 1013 Ⓑ	ICE 127 ⊠	ICE 1224 Ⓐt	ICE 727	ICE 613	ICE 911 ⑥⑦	ICE 911 ①–⑤	ICE 317	ICE 729	ICE 203	ICE 129 ⊠	ICE 1015 Ⓑ	ICE 821	ICE 615	ICE 19	ICE 823	ICE 205	ICE 221 ⊠	ICE 617	ICE 319 ⑦		ICE 619
	✕	✕	✕	✕	✕	✕	K✕	✕	✕	✕	✕	✕	✕	✕	✕	H✕	✕	✕	✕	✕	H✕	✕		K
Dortmund Hbf **800** ▷ d.	...	...	1549	...	...	...	1636	...	...	...	...	...	...	1750	...	1835	...	...	...	...	2036	...	...	2236
Essen Hbf **800** ▷ d.	1549	...	1615	...	...	1649	1700	...	...	...	1749	...	...	1824	1837	|	...	1941	...	...	2100	...	...	2301
Amsterdam Centraal **28** ⊠ d.	|	...	|	1438	...	|	|	...	...	...	|	...	1638	|	|	|	...	|	...	1838	|	...	...	|
Düsseldorf Hbf **800** ▷ d.	1618	...	1644	1651n	1702	1718	1724	...	...	...	1818	...	1848	1852	1905	◐	...	2008	2014a	2050	2123	...	...	2324
Brussels Midi/Zuid **21** d.	|	...	|	|	|	|	|	...	...	1622x	|	...	|	|	|	|	1825	|	|	|	|	2025	...	|
Aachen Hbf **802 807** d.	|	...	|	|	|	|	|	...	...	1739	|	...	|	|	|	|	1939	|	|	|	|	2139	...	|
Köln Hbf **800 802 807** a.	|	...	|	|	|	|	1749	...	...	1816	|	...	|	|	|	1947	2015	|	2041a	|	2149	2213	...	2349
Köln Hbf **802 807** d.	|	1654	|	|	|	|	1755	...	...	1819	|	1854	|	|	|	1955	2017j	|	2054	|	2155	...	...	2355
Köln Messe/Deutz **802** d.	1644	|	1710	1721	1733	1744	|	1800	1802	|	1844	|	1916	1922	1930	|	|	2033	|	2128	|	...	...	|
Köln/Bonn Flughafen ✈ **802** d.	|	|	|	|	|	|	|	|	|	|	|	|	|	|	|	|	|	|	|	|	|	...	...	|
Siegburg/Bonn 🚋 **807** d.	|	1709	1725	|	1746	|	|	1818	1818	1833	|	1909	1936	|	1943	|	2033j	|	2109	|	2209	...	...	0009
Montabaur d.	|	|	|	|	1805	|	|	1838	1838	|	|	|	|	|	2004	|	|	2104	|	|	|	...	...	|
Limburg Süd d.	|	|	|	|	1820	|	|	1849	1849	|	|	|	|	|	2015	|	|	2115	|	|	|	...	...	|
Wiesbaden Hbf a.	|	|	|	|	1840	|	|	|	|	|	|	|	|	|	|	|	|	|	|	|	|	...	...	|
Mainz Hbf a.	|	|	|	|	1855	|	|	|	|	|	|	|	|	|	|	|	|	|	|	|	|	...	...	|
Frankfurt Flughafen Fernbf ✈ a.	1733	1749	1807	1817	1924	1833	1850	1909	1909	1917	1933	1949	2015	2008	2035	2050	2115	2135	2149	2217	2254	...	...	0054
Frankfurt (Main) Hbf a.	1748	|	|	1831	1939	1848	|	1924	1924	1931	1948	|	2030	|	2048	|	2131	2148	|	2231	|	...	...	0110
Nürnberg Hbf **920** a.	2020	|	|	...	...	2120	|	...	...	...	2220	|	...	|	2320	|	...	...	|	...	|	...	...	|
Mannheim Hbf **912** a.	|	1823	1839	...	...	|	1923	...	...	...	|	2023	...	2039	|	2123	...	...	2223	...	2327	...	...	0202
Karlsruhe Hbf **912** a.	|	1858	1913z	...	...	|	|	...	...	...	|	2058	...	|	|	|	...	...	2259	...	|	...	...	|
Basel SBB **912** a.	|	2047	|	...	...	|	|	...	...	...	|	2255	...	|	|	|	...	...	0059	...	|	...	...	|
Stuttgart Hbf **912** a.	|	...	1922v	...	...	|	2008	...	...	...	|	...	...	2123	|	2208	...	...	...	...	0008	...	...	0334
München Hbf **904 930** a.	2132	...	...	...	...	2233	2226	...	...	...	2336	...	...	...	0039	0027	...	...	...	...	...	...	...	0603

G – To Garmisch on ⑥ (Table **895**).
H – From Hamburg (Table **800**).
K – From Kiel via Hamburg (Tables **820** and **800**).
M – From Münster (Table **800**).

a – ①–⑤ only.
c – ⑥⑦ only.
f – 0609 June 27 - Aug. 5.
g – Until June 24.
h – 0825 on ⑥⑦ (also July 21, Aug. 15).
j – On June 11, 12, 18, 19, Aug. 27 - Sept. 9 departs Köln Hbf 9–10 minutes later and does not call at Siegburg/Bonn.
n – 1649 on ⑥.
q – ①②③④⑥ (not June 15).
t – Not June 16.
v – Not July 30 - Sept. 11.
w – ⑦ only.
x – 1625 on ⑥⑦ (also July 21, Aug. 15).
y – On ⑦ departs Amsterdam 0907, Utrecht 0936, 's-Hertogenbosch 1004.
z – July 30 - Sept. 11 only.

◐ – Via Wuppertal (Table **800**).
▷ – Timings Dortmund - Essen - Düsseldorf may vary by up to 6 minutes until June 24.

🚋 – Frequent light-rail services operate from / to Bonn Hbf.
⊠ – Amsterdam services are subject to alteration June 11, 12, 18, 19, Aug. 27 - Sept. 9 (diversions and / or retimings are scheduled; different train numbers apply; see the panel below for a summary of the amended service). Amsterdam departure times are up to 31 minutes **earlier** Aug. 7 – 22.

Amended Amsterdam service June 11, 12, 18, 19, Aug. 27 - Sept. 9

	ICE 153	ICE 255 ①–⑤	ICE 255 ⑥⑦	ICE 155	ICE 157	ICE 159	ICE 251 Ⓑ	ICE 251 ⑥
Amsterdam Centraal d.	0908y	0738	0746	1208	1408	1708	1838	1838
Utrecht Centraal d.	0938y	0808	0816	1238	1438	1738	1908	1908
's-Hertogenbosch d.	1009y	0839	0845	1309	1509	1809	1939	1939
Mönchengladbach Hbf a.	1130	1003	1003	1430	1630	1930	2102	2102
Köln Ehrenfeld a.	|	|	|	1513	1713	|	|	|
Köln Hbf a.	1222	1049	1049	|	|	2022	2153	2153
Frankfurt Flughafen Fernbf ✈ a.	1317	1149	1149	1617	1817	2117	2308	...
Frankfurt (Main) Hbf a.	1331	|	|	1631	1831	2131	2324	...
Basel SBB **912** a.	...	1447	1447	...	...	...	...	...

910 FRANKFURT - KÖLN - AACHEN via high-speed line

See Tables **800**/**911** for services via Koblenz and Bonn. See Table **20** for *Thalys* services Köln - Aachen - Brussels - Paris.

SEE NOTE ⊠	ICE 618		ICE 222	ICE 826	ICE 18	ICE 712	ICE 616	ICE 824	ICE 1223	ICE 220	ICE 1014	ICE 206	ICE 822	ICE 822	ICE 316	ICE 614	ICE 820	ICE 128	ICE 1012	ICE 202	ICE 728	ICE 16	ICE 612	ICE 726
						Ⓐ t		①–⑥	Ⓐ t	⊠	①–⑥			①–⑥			①–⑥	⊠	①–⑥					
	K X		⊠ X	X	X		H X	A X	D X	X	X	X	X	X	X	H X	X	X	X	X	X	X	K X	X
München Hbf **904 930** d.	0001	...	...	...	...	...	0324	...	...	...	...	...	...	0427	...	0533	0522	...	...	...	0621	...	0728	0726
Stuttgart Hbf **912** d.	0222	...	...	...	...	...	0551	...	...	...	0637	...	...	|	...	0751	|	...	0837v	...	|	...	0951	|
Basel SBB **912** d.	|	...	...	...	...	...	|	...	...	...	|	0506	...	|	...	|	|	...	|	0713	|	...	|	|
Karlsruhe Hbf **912** d.	|	...	...	...	...	...	|	...	...	...	|	0701	...	|	...	|	|	...	0854z	0901	|	...	|	|
Mannheim Hbf **912** d.	0401	...	...	...	...	...	0636	...	...	...	0721	0736	...	|	...	0836	|	...	0921	0936	|	...	1036	|
Nürnberg Hbf **920** d.	|	...	...	...	...	...	|	...	...	...	|	|	...	0536	...	|	0634	...	|	|	0735	...	|	0835
Frankfurt (Main) Hbf d.	0446	...	0528	0540	0628	...	|	0709	...	0728	|	|	0809	0809	0816	|	0909	0926	|	|	1009	1026	|	1109
Frankfurt Flughafen Fernbf ✈ d.	0500	...	0542	0554	0642	...	0708	0724	0711	0742	0753	0809	0824	0824	0830	0909	0922	0942	0953	1009	1024	1042	1109	1122
Mainz Hbf d.	|	...	|	|	|	0607	|	|	|	|	|	|	|	|	|	|	|	|	|	|	|	|	|	|
Wiesbaden Hbf d.	|	...	|	|	|	0623	|	|	|	|	|	|	|	|	|	|	|	|	|	|	|	|	|	|
Limburg Süd d.	|	...	|	0613	|	0643	|	|	0731	|	|	|	|	|	0848	|	0940	|	|	|	|	|	|	1140
Montabaur d.	|	...	|	0624	|	0654	|	|	0747	|	|	|	|	|	0859	|	0951	|	|	|	|	|	|	1151
Siegburg/Bonn 🚊 **807** d.	0547	...	0622	0646	|	0721	|	|	0808	|	|	0848	0901	0901	|	|	1011	|	|	1048	1101	|	|	1211
Köln/Bonn Flughafen ✈ **802** a.	|	...	|	|	|	|	|	|	|	|	|	|	|	|	|	|	|	|	|	|	|	|	|	|
Köln Messe/Deutz **802** a.	|	...	0636	|	|	0736k	|	0814	0822	0830	0842	|	0915	0915	|	|	1025	1030	1042	|	1115	|	|	1225
Köln Hbf **802 807** a.	0603	...	|	0704	0732	0748r	0805	|	|	|	|	0904	|	|	0933	1004	|	|	|	1104	|	1133	1205	|
Köln Hbf **800 802 807** d.	0609	...	|	0713	0742	...	0811	|	|	|	|	...	|	|	0942	1011	|	|	|	...	|	1143	1211	|
Aachen Hbf **802 807** a.	|	...	|	|	0816	...	|	|	|	|	|	...	|	|	1015	|	|	|	|	...	|	1216	|	|
Brussels Midi/Zuid **21** a.	|	...	|	|	0935	...	|	|	|	|	|	...	|	|	1135	|	|	|	|	...	|	1335	|	|
Düsseldorf Hbf **800** a.	0631	...	0708	0735	...	...	0832	0840	0846	0906	0914	...	0936	0936	...	1032	1046	1104	1109	...	1136	...	◐	1246
Amsterdam Centraal **28** ⊠ a.	|	...	0929	|	...	...	|	...	...	1129	...	...	|	|	...	|	|	1329	|	...	|	...	|	|
Essen Hbf **800** a.	0658	...	...	0805	...	...	0858	...	...	...	...	...	1006	1006	...	1058	1114	...	1140q	...	1206	...	|	1313
Dortmund Hbf **800** a.	0722	...	...	...	...	...	0923	...	...	...	...	...	...	...	...	1123	...	...	1205q	...	...	...	1321	...

SEE NOTE ⊠	ICE 126	ICE 1010	ICE 200	ICE 724	ICE 818	ICE 314	ICE 610	ICE 722	ICE 124	ICE 918	ICE 108	ICE 720	ICE 14	ICE 518	ICE 628	ICE 816	ICE 106	ICE 626	ICE 828	ICE 12	ICE 122	ICE 710	ICE 516	ICE 624
	⊠								⊠										①–⑤			Ⓐ t		
	X	X	X	X	X	X	H X	X	X	X	X	X	X	H X	X	X	X	X	X	X	X	X	H X	X
München Hbf **904 930** d.	...	...	...	0815	...	...	0928	0923	...	...	...	1016	...	1128	1119	...	...	1216	...	...	...	...	1328	1319
Stuttgart Hbf **912** d.	...	1037v	...	|	...	...	1151	|	...	1237v	...	|	...	1351	|	...	...	|	...	...	...	1435	1551	|
Basel SBB **912** d.	...	|	0913	|	...	...	|	|	...	|	1113	|	...	|	|	...	1313	|	...	...	...	|	|	|
Karlsruhe Hbf **912** d.	...	1054z	1100	|	...	...	|	|	...	1254z	1300	|	...	|	|	...	1500	|	...	...	...	|	|	|
Mannheim Hbf **912** d.	...	1121	1136	|	...	...	1236	|	...	1321	1336	|	...	1436	|	...	1536	|	...	...	...	1533	1636	|
Nürnberg Hbf **920** d.	...	|	|	0926	...	...	|	1035	...	|	|	1124	...	|	1235	...	|	1326	...	...	...	|	|	1434
Frankfurt (Main) Hbf d.	1126	|	|	1209	1215	1228	|	1309	1326	|	|	1409	1426	|	1509	1516	|	1609	1616	1628	1628	|	|	1709
Frankfurt Flughafen Fernbf ✈ d.	1142	1153	1209	1224	1230	1242	1309	1324	1342	1353	1409	1424	1442	1509	1524	1529	1609	1624	1630	1642	1642	|	1709	1724
Mainz Hbf d.	|	|	|	|	|	|	|	|	|	|	|	|	|	|	|	|	|	|	|	|	|	1622	|	|
Wiesbaden Hbf d.	|	|	|	|	|	|	|	|	|	|	|	|	|	|	|	|	|	|	|	|	|	1645	|	|
Limburg Süd d.	|	|	|	|	1249	|	|	|	|	|	|	|	|	|	|	1547	|	|	1648	|	|	1708	|	|
Montabaur d.	|	|	|	|	1306	|	|	|	|	|	|	|	|	|	|	1557	|	|	1658	|	|	1718	|	|
Siegburg/Bonn 🚊 **807** d.	|	|	1248	1301	1327	|	|	1401	|	|	1448	1501	|	|	|	1620	1648	1701	1727f	|	|	1739	|	|
Köln/Bonn Flughafen ✈ **802** a.	|	|	|	|	|	|	|	|	|	|	|	|	|	|	|	|	|	|	|	|	|	1747h	|	|
Köln Messe/Deutz **802** a.	1230	1241	|	1315	1341	|	|	1415	1430	1441	|	1515	|	|	1615	1637	|	1715	1740	|	|	1806k	|	1813
Köln Hbf **802 807** a.	|	|	1305	|	...	1333	1405	|	|	|	1504	|	1533	1605	|	...	1704	|	...	1736	1736	1819r	1805	|
Köln Hbf **800 802 807** d.	|	|	...	|	...	1342	1411	|	|	|	...	|	1540	1611	|	...	...	|	...	1741	1746	...	1811	|
Aachen Hbf **802 807** a.	|	|	...	|	...	1416	|	|	|	|	...	|	1616	|	|	...	...	|	...	1816	|	...	|	|
Brussels Midi/Zuid **21** a.	|	|	...	|	...	1535	|	|	|	|	...	|	1735	|	|	...	...	|	...	1935	|	...	|	|
Düsseldorf Hbf **800** a.	1256n	1310	...	1336	...	...	1432	1441	1456	1514	...	1536	...	1632	1640	...	...	1736	...	...	1810	...	◐	1840
Amsterdam Centraal **28** ⊠ a.	1529	|	...	|	...	...	|	|	1729	|	...	|	...	|	|	...	...	|	...	...	2029	...	|	|
Essen Hbf **800** a.	...	1340e	...	1403	...	...	1458	1513	...	1542	...	1603	...	1659	1707	...	...	1803	...	...	...	...	|	1914
Dortmund Hbf **800** a.	...	1404e	...	...	...	...	1522	...	...	1606	...	...	...	1722	...	...	...	1841	...	...	...	...	1921	1939

SEE NOTE ⊠	ICE 814	ICE 914	ICE 204	ICE 104	ICE 622	ICE 812	ICE 812	ICE 10	ICE 514	ICE 620	ICE 120	ICE 912	ICE 102	ICE 528	ICE 318	ICE 810	ICE 512	ICE 526		ICE 100	ICE 524		ICE 510	ICE 522
			Ⓐ	⊠		①–④	⑤⑦				Ⓑ	Ⓑ			⑦	①–⑥								
	X	X	X	X	X	X	X	X	H X	X	⊠ X	X	X	X	X	X	M X	G X		X	X			
München Hbf **904 930** d.	...	...	...	...	1418	...	...	...	1528	1525	...	...	...	1614	...	...	1725	1719	...	...	1816	...	1928	1926
Stuttgart Hbf **912** d.	...	1634v	...	...	|	...	...	...	1751	|	...	1837v	...	|	...	...	1951	|	...	...	|	...	2151	|
Basel SBB **912** d.	...	|	1513	1513	|	...	...	...	|	|	...	|	1713	|	...	...	|	|	...	1913	|	...	|	|
Karlsruhe Hbf **912** d.	...	|	1700	1700	|	...	...	...	|	|	...	1854z	1900	|	...	...	|	|	...	2101	|	...	|	|
Mannheim Hbf **912** d.	...	1721	1736	1736	|	...	...	...	1836	|	...	1921	1936	|	...	...	2036	|	...	2136	|	...	2236	|
Nürnberg Hbf **920** d.	...	|	|	|	1526	...	...	...	|	1636	...	|	|	1726	...	...	|	1831	...	|	1926	...	|	2035
Frankfurt (Main) Hbf d.	1716	|	|	|	1809	1816	1816	1828	|	1909	1928	|	|	2009	2016	2031	|	2109	...	|	2209	...	|	2309
Frankfurt Flughafen Fernbf ✈ d.	1729	1753	1809	1809	1824	1831	1831	1842	1909	1922	1942	1953	2009	2025	2029	2050	2108	2124	...	2209	2223	...	2308	2323
Mainz Hbf d.	|	|	|	|	|	|	|	|	|	|	|	|	|	|	|	|	|	|	...	|	|	...	|	|
Wiesbaden Hbf d.	|	|	|	|	|	|	|	|	|	|	|	|	|	|	|	|	|	|	...	|	|	...	|	|
Limburg Süd d.	1747	|	|	|	|	1850	1850	|	|	1940	|	|	|	|	2048	2108	|	|	...	|	2241	...	|	2341
Montabaur d.	1757	|	|	|	|	1907	1907	|	|	1951	|	|	|	|	2105	2119	|	|	...	|	2252	...	|	2351
Siegburg/Bonn 🚊 **807** d.	1820	|	1848	1848	1901	1927	1927	|	|	2011	|	|	2047	|	|	2139	2150	|	...	2247	2313	...	2349	0011
Köln/Bonn Flughafen ✈ **802** a.	1831	|	|	|	|	1937	1937	|	|	|	|	|	|	|	|	|	|	|	...	|	2325	...	|	|
Köln Messe/Deutz **802** a.	1850	1841	|	|	1915	1949	1949	|	|	2024	2030	2042	|	2114	|	2153	|	2213	...	|	2336	...	|	|
Köln Hbf **802 807** a.	...	|	1904	1904	|	|	|	1933	2005	|	|	|	2105	|	2140	...	2205	|	...	2304	|	...	0006	0028
Köln Hbf **800 802 807** d.	...	|	1911	1914	|	|	|	1940	2011	|	|	|	...	|	2142	...	2211	|	...	2311	|	...	...	...
Aachen Hbf **802 807** a.	...	|	|	|	|	|	|	2016	|	|	|	|	...	|	2215	...	|	|	...	|	|	...	...	...
Brussels Midi/Zuid **21** a.	...	|	|	|	|	|	|	2135	|	|	|	|	...	|	2335	...	|	|	...	|	|	...	...	...
Düsseldorf Hbf **800** a.	...	1905	◐	1935	1944	◐	2024	...	2032	2046	2056	2110	...	2135	...	...	2232	2236	...	2332	2357	...	...	...
Amsterdam Centraal **28** ⊠ a.	...	|	|	2159	|	|	...	...	|	|	2329x	|	...	|	...	...	|	|	...	|	|	...	...	...
Essen Hbf **800** a.	...	1935	|	...	2015	|	...	...	2058	2114	...	2140	...	2202	...	...	2259	2302	...	2358	0024	...	...	...
Dortmund Hbf **800** a.	...	2001	2021	...	2042	2107	...	...	2122	2140	...	2204	...	2227	...	...	...	2326	...	0023	0048	...	...	...

A – From Würzburg (Table **920**) on Ⓐ (not June 16).
D – From Darmstadt Hbf (d. 0647).
G – From Garmisch on ⑥ (Table **895**).
H – To Hamburg (Table **800**).
K – To Kiel via Hamburg (Tables **800** and **820**).
M – To Münster (Table **800**).

e – ①–⑥ only.
f – Arrives 1717.
h – Not June 13 – 24, Aug. 8 - Sept. 16.
k – June 27 - Aug. 5 only.
n – 1305 on ⑦.
q – ①②③④⑥ (not June 15).
r – Not June 27 - Aug. 5.
t – Not June 16.
v – Not July 30 - Sept. 11.
x – Not June 10, 12, 17, 19, Aug. 26 - Sept. 8.
z – July 30 - Sept. 11 only.

◐ – Via Wuppertal (Table **800**).
🚊 – Frequent light-rail services operate from / to Bonn Hbf.

⊠ – Amsterdam services are subject to alteration June 11, 12, 18, 19, Aug. 27 - Sept. 9 (diversions and / or retimings are scheduled; different train numbers apply; see the panel below for a summary of the amended service). Amsterdam arrival times are up to 24 minutes later Aug. 7 – 22.

Amended Amsterdam service June 11, 12, 18, 19, Aug. 27 - Sept. 9

	ICE 250	ICE 250	ICE 158	ICE 156	ICE 154	ICE 152	ICE 152	ICE 254
	⑦	①–⑥				①–⑥	⑦	
Basel SBB **912** d.	...	...	...	...	...	...	...	1513
Frankfurt (Main) Hbf d.	...	0628	0816	1128	1326	1628	1628	|
Frankfurt Flughafen Fernbf ✈ d.	...	0642	0830	1142	1342	1642	1642	1809
Köln Hbf d.	0739	0739	0939	|	|	1748	1748	1910
Köln Ehrenfeld d.	|	|	|	1244	1443	|	|	|
Mönchengladbach Hbf d.	0830	0830	1031	1330	1530	1831	1831	2000
's-Hertogenbosch a.	0952	0952	1152	1452	1652	1946	1952	2137
Utrecht Centraal a.	1023	1023	1223	1523	1723	2015	2021	2204
Amsterdam Centraal a.	1053	1053	1253	1553	1753	2044	2053	2230

STRASBOURG - OFFENBURG — 911

Südwestdeutsche Landesverkehrs (2nd class only)

km			①–⑤		①–⑤	①–⑤		①–⑤					①–⑤		①–⑤		①–⑤			①–⑤	①–⑤						
0	**Strasbourg** d.	0620	0720	0750	0820	0850	0920	0950	1050	...	1250	1320	1420	1450	1520	1620	1650	1720	1750	1820	1850	1922	2020	2150	2250	...	0005
21	Kehl 🏛 d.	0633	0733	0803	0831	0903	0933	1003	1103	...	1303	1333	1433	1503	1533	1633	1703	1733	1803	1833	1903	1932	2033	2203	2303	...	0016
29	**Offenburg** a.	0652	0751	0822	0849	0922	0952	1022	1122	...	1322	1353	1452	1522	1552	1652	1722	1752	1822	1852	1922	1952	2052	2222	2322	...	0034

		①–⑤		①–⑤		①–⑤	①–⑤	⑥⑦	①–⑤	⑥⑦		①–⑤	①–⑤	⑥⑦	①–⑤			①–⑤		①–⑤	①–⑤		①–⑤				
Offenburg d.	0632	0705	0735	0805	0842	0905	0935	1005	1035	1205	1235	1305	1335	1405	1435	1505	1605	1635	1705	1733	1805	1835	1905	2005	2105	2205	2325
Kehl 🏛 d.	0654	0724	0754	0826	0900	0924	0954	1022	1054	1224	1254	1324	1354	1424	1454	1524	1624	1654	1724	1754	1824	1854	1924	2024	2124	2224	2346
Strasbourg a.	0706	0736	0806	0836	0910	0936	1006	1033	1106	1236	1306	1336	1406	1436	1506	1536	1636	1706	1735	1806	1836	1906	1936	2036	2136	2236	2358

☛ On Nov. 1 services run as on ⑦.

Local services MAINZ - MANNHEIM and MAINZ - SPEYER - KARLSUHE — 911a

RE / *S-Bahn* services

km		Ⓐv	⚒r	Ⓐv	Ⓐv		Ⓐt																	Ⓒw	Ⓐt	Ⓒz
	Frankfurt (Main) Hbf ‡ d.	...	...	...	...	...	0608	...	...	...	...	...	0838	...	...	1038	...	...	1238	...	...	1438	...	...	1538	1638
0	**Mainz** Hbf **912** ‡ d.	0456	0515	0545	...	0553v	0647	0622	0656	0722	0813	...	0913	1013	...	1117	1213	...	1317	1413	...	1517	1613	...	1617	1717
46	Worms Hbf a.	0540	0556	0614	...	0634v	0714	0706	0739	0806	0839	...	0940	1039	...	1144	1239	...	1344	1439	...	1544	1639	...	1652	1744
46	Worms Hbf d.	0541	0556	0615	...	0635	0715	0717	0746	0816	0840	0848	0941	1040	1048	1145	1240	1249	1345	1440	1448	1545	1640	1648	1653	1745
67	Ludwigshafen Hbf **918** d.	0600	0616	0637	0654	0653	0731	0735	0804	0836	0857	0909	|	1057	1109	|	1257	1309	|	1457	1509	|	1655	1709	1708	|
87	Speyer Hbf **918** d.	|	|	|	0713	|	|	|	|	|	0913	|	|	1113	|	|	1313	|	|	1513	|	|	1713	|	|	|
101	Germersheim **918** d.	|	|	|	0722	|	|	|	|	|	0923	|	|	1123	|	|	1323	|	|	1523	|	|	1723	|	|	|
138	**Karlsruhe** Hbf a.	|	|	|	0753	|	|	|	|	|	0954	|	|	1153	|	|	1353	|	|	1553	|	|	1753	|	|	|
68	Ludwigshafen Mitte d.	0602	0619	|	...	0655	0733	0738	0809	0838	...	0912	0958	...	1111	1204	...	1311	1402	...	1511	1603	...	1711	1711	1806
70	**Mannheim** Hbf **912** a.	0604	0621	0641	...	0658	0737	0741	0812	0841	...	0915	1001	...	1115	1207	...	1314	1405	...	1514	1606	...	1714	1715	1810

	Ⓐt											
Frankfurt (Main) Hbf ‡ d.	1638	...	...	...	1838	...	...	...	...	2038	...	...
Mainz Hbf **912** ‡ d.	1717	...	1813	...	1917	1925	2013	...	2052	2117	2206	2308
Worms Hbf a.	1744	...	1839	...	1944	2008	2039	...	2136	2155	2251	2351
Worms Hbf d.	1745	1749	1840	1848	1945	2018	2040	2048	2148	2156	2251	2351
Ludwigshafen Hbf **918** d.	1800	1809	1857	1909	|	2037	2057	2109	2208	2215	2309	0009
Speyer Hbf **918** d.	1819	|	1913	|	|	|	2113	|	|	|	|	|
Germersheim **918** d.	1828	|	1923	|	|	|	2123	|	|	|	|	|
Karlsruhe Hbf a.	...	|	1953	|	|	|	2153	|	|	|	|	|
Ludwigshafen Mitte d.	...	1811	...	1913	2005	2039	...	2111	2211	2218	2311	0012
Mannheim Hbf **912** a.	...	1814	...	1916	2007	2042	...	2114	2214	2221	2314	0014

		Ⓒw	⑥	Ⓐv	Ⓐt	⚒r	Ⓐt	Ⓐt	
Mannheim Hbf **912** d.	0018	0018	0424	0425	0459	0530	0540	...	0650
Ludwigshafen Mitte d.	0020	0020	0427	0428	0501	0533	0542	...	0653
Karlsruhe Hbf d.	|	|	|	|	|	|	|	...	|
Germersheim **918** d.	|	|	|	|	|	|	|	0619	|
Speyer Hbf **918** d.	|	|	|	|	|	|	|	0632	|
Ludwigshafen Hbf **918** d.	0023	0023	0433	0433	0504	0535	0546	0656	0659
Worms Hbf a.	0039	0039	0451	0451	0522	0553	0607	0712	0718
Worms Hbf d.	...	0040	0452	0452	0523	0555	0607	0713	0725
Mainz Hbf **912** ‡ a.	...	0122	0538	0538	0608	0638	0641	0747	0808
Frankfurt (Main) Hbf ‡ a.	...	...	...	...	...	...	0722	0822	...

	Ⓐt	Ⓒz	Ⓐv																							
Mannheim Hbf **912** d.	...	0751	0749	0844	...	0915	0958	1044	...	1152	1244	...	1352	1445	...	1549	1644	...	1752	1844	...	1951	2044	...	2144	2247
Ludwigshafen Mitte d.	...	0753	0751	0847	...	0917	1000	1047	...	1154	1248	...	1354	1448	...	1552	1646	...	1754	1847	...	1954	2047	...	2146	2250
Karlsruhe Hbf d.	0647	|	|	|	0808	|	|	|	1008	|	|	1208	|	|	1408	|	|	1608	|	|	1808	|	|	2008	|	|
Germersheim **918** d.	0722	|	|	|	0838	|	|	|	1038	|	|	1238	|	|	1438	|	|	1638	|	|	1838	|	|	2038	|	|
Speyer Hbf **918** d.	0732	|	|	|	0847	|	|	|	1047	|	|	1247	|	|	1447	|	|	1647	|	|	1847	|	|	2047	|	|
Ludwigshafen Hbf **918** d.	0751	|	0755	0850	0904	0920	|	1050	1104	|	1250	1304	|	1451	1504	|	1649	1704	|	1850	1904	|	2050	2104	2150	2252
Worms Hbf a.	0804	0816	0814	0914	0919	0938	1019	1111	1119	1216	1311	1319	1416	1514	1519	1616	1714	1719	1816	1913	1919	2016	2114	2119	2213	2312
Worms Hbf d.	0805	0817	0825	...	0920	0955	1020	...	1120	1217	...	1320	1417	...	1520	1617	...	1720	1817	...	1920	2017	...	2120	2218	2315
Mainz Hbf **912** a.	0836	0843	0908	...	0947	1036	1046	...	1147	1243	...	1347	1443	...	1547	1643	...	1747	1843	...	1947	2043	...	2147	2301	0001
Frankfurt (Main) Hbf ‡ a.	*0922*	0922	...	...	1022	...	1122	...	1222	1322	...	1422	1523	...	1623	...	...	...	1922j	...	2022	2122	...	2222	...	...

j – Change trains at Mainz on Ⓐ (not June 16).
r – Not June 16, Nov. 1.
t – Not June 16.
v – Ⓐ (not June 16, Nov. 1).
w – Also June 16, Nov. 1.
z – Also June 16.
‡ – See Tables **800**, **914**, **917** and **917a** for other services Frankfurt - Mainz and v.v.

FRANKFURT - BASEL and STUTTGART — 912

See Table **927** for services operated by FlixTrain

km	km		*ICE*	*ICE*	*ICE*	*ICE*	*NJ*	*NJ*	*ICE*	*ICE*	*ICE*	*RJX*	*IC*	*ICE*	*ICE*	*ICE*	*TGV*	*RJ*	*EC*	*ICE*	*ICE*	*ICE*	*ICE*	*ICE*
			879	**619**	**699**	**403**	**401**	**471**	**1561**	**3**	**993**	**63**	**2381**	**991**	**271**	**1271**	**9578**	**897**	**217**	**511**	**5**	**9568**	**1511**	**1571**
			①						① g	①–⑤	⑥⑦	Ⓒ	①–⑤	①–⑤	②–⑦	①	①–⑥				①–⑥	Ⓑ Q	Ⓐ	①–⑤
				K	♦	♦	♦	♦		§ ✕	C ✕	✕ ♦	⊙	W	H ✕	H ✕	♦ 🅁	✕ ♦	🍸 ♦	✕	✕	🅁 ✕	¶	Y ✕
		Hamburg Hbf **800 900** d.	...	1946	1936	...	2050	...	...	...	...	...	...	...	...	0025	...	...	...	...	...	...	...	...
		Berlin Hbf **810 850 902** d.	2030p	|	2128	...	|	2054	...	...	...	...	...	...	...	|	...	...	...	...	...	...	...	...
		Hannover Hbf **810 900** d.	|	|	|	...	2319	|	...	...	...	...	...	...	...	0210	...	...	...	...	...	...	...	...
		Dortmund Hbf **800** d.	|	2236	|	...	|	|	...	...	...	...	...	...	...	|	...	...	...	...	...	...	...	...
		Köln Hbf **800 910** d.	|	2355	|	2353	|	|	...	...	...	...	...	...	...	|	...	...	...	0548	...	...	...	...
		Koblenz Hbf **800** d.	|	|	|	0049	|	|	...	...	...	...	...	...	...	|	...	...	...	|	...	...	...	...
		Wiesbaden Hbf **917a 918a** d.	|	|	|	|	|	|	...	...	...	...	...	0526	...	|	...	...	...	|	...	...	...	...
		Mainz Hbf **917a 918a** d.	|	|	|	0142	|	|	...	...	...	...	...	0540	...	|	...	...	...	|	...	...	...	...
0	0	**Frankfurt** (Main) Hbf **913** d.	0050	0117	0225	0245	0400	0400	0404	...	0517	0517	0519	|	0550	0550	...	0554	...	|	0648	0656	0655r	0714‡
		Frankfurt Flughafen ✈ ◧ d.	|	0057*	0246	0211*	|	|	|	...	0539	0539	|	|	|	|	...	|	...	0652	|	|	|	|
78		**Mannheim** Hbf **913** a.	0127	0202	0324	0331	0440	0440	0445	...	0610	0610	|	0623	0625	0625	...	|	...	0723	0727	0736	0749	|
78		**Mannheim** Hbf **913** d.	0130	0204	0326	0333	0442	0442	0447	...	0612	0612	|	0629	0633	0633	...	|	0711	0731	0735	0738	0752	|
	28	Darmstadt Hbf **913 918a** d.	|	|	|	|	|	|	|	...	|	|	0536	|	|	|	...	0613	|	|	|	|	|	0731
	50	Bensheim **913** d.	|	|	|	|	|	|	|	...	|	|	0550	|	|	|	...	0625	|	|	|	|	|	0746
	64	Weinheim **913** d.	|	|	|	|	|	|	|	...	|	|	0600	|	|	|	...	0636	|	|	|	|	|	0758
	87	**Heidelberg** Hbf **913 931** d.	|	0219	|	|	|	|	0459	...	|	|	0615	|	|	|	...	0652	|	|	|	|	0805	0814
	120	Bruchsal **913 931** d.	|	|	|	|	|	|	|	...	|	|	|	|	|	|	...	|	|	|	|	|	|	0837
		Vaihingen (Enz) **931** d.	|	|	|	|	|	|	|	...	|	|	|	|	|	|	...	|	|	|	|	|	|	|
		Stuttgart Hbf **931** a.	|	0334	0443	|	|	|	0552	...	0651	0652	0702	0708	|	|	...	0737	0753	0808	|	|	0846	|
		München Hbf **930** a.	|	0603	0731	|	|	|	0841	...	0913	0913	...	0928	|	|	...	...	1011	1027	|	|	...	|
138	141	**Karlsruhe** Hbf **913 916** d.	0154	...	...	0403	0510	0510	...	0556	...	...	...	...	0658	0658	0732	...	...	...	0800	0806	...	0851
167	172	Baden-Baden **916** d.	...	...	...	0427	0529	0529	...	0614	...	...	...	...	0717	0717	|	...	...	...	|	|	...	...
207		Offenburg **911 916** ☆ d.	...	...	...	0451	0548	0548	...	0630	...	...	...	...	0732	0732	|	...	...	...	0830	|	...	...
	225	**Strasbourg** ⊖ **911** a.	...	...	...	|	|	|	...	|	...	...	...	...	|	|	0812	...	...	...	|	0847	...	...
270		**Freiburg** (Brsg) Hbf ☆ d.	...	...	...	0529	0620	0620	...	0702	...	...	...	...	0803	0803	...	...	...	...	0901	...	...	...
327		**Basel** Bad Bf 🏛 ☆ a.	...	...	...	0611	0658	0658	...	0736	...	...	...	...	0836	0836	...	...	...	...	0935	...	...	...
332		**Basel** SBB ☆ a.	...	...	...	0620	0720	0720	...	0747	...	...	...	...	0847	0847	...	...	...	...	0947	...	...	...
		Zürich HB **510** a.	...	...	...	0805	0905	0905	...	0900	...	...	...	...	1000	1000	...	...	...	...	...	...	...	...

♦ – **NOTES** (LISTED BY TRAIN NUMBER)

63 – Ⓒ from Aug. 6. [12] ✕ Frankfurt - Salzburg - Wien - Budapest.
217 – DACHSTEIN – [12] 🍸 Saarbrücken - München (- Salzburg - Graz ♥). Runs as *IC* **2397** until Aug. 1.
401 – 🛏 1, 2 cl. and ▬ 2 cl. (🅁) Hamburg - Basel - Zürich (a. 0905). Also conveys [2] (*IC* **60401**).
403 – 🛏 1, 2 cl. and ▬ 2 cl. (🅁) Amsterdam - Basel - Zürich. Also conveys [2] (*IC* **60403**). On the mornings of ①②⑦ until Aug. 30 departs Mainz 0157, Frankfurt Flughafen 0217.
471 – 🛏 1, 2 cl. and ▬ 2 cl. (🅁) Berlin - Braunschweig - Basel - Zürich. Also conveys [2] (*IC* **60471**).
699 – [12] Hamburg - Berlin - Leipzig - Erfurt - Frankfurt - München.
897 – [12] ✕ Frankfurt - Ulm - Lindau - Bregenz (**867**) - Innsbruck - Wien. Train category *IC* until Aug. 1
9578 – [12] 🍸 Stuttgart - Karlsruhe - Paris (Table **32**).

C – ⑥⑦ until July 31.
H – To Chur (Table **520**).
K – From Kiel (Table **820**).
Q – To Paris (Table **30**).
W – Also calls at Worms Hbf (d. 0608).
Y – From Kassel (Table **806**).

g – Also Aug. 16; not Aug. 15.
p – Previous day.
r – 0704 until Aug. 26.

♥ – From Aug. 2.
§ – Continues to Chur (Table **520**) on Aug. 1 only.
¶ – Ⓐ (not June 15–17). Runs as *IC* **1911** on ⑤.
‡ – Until Aug. 26 calls at Frankfurt (Main) **West** (not Hbf), departing 0708.
⊙ – Continues to Singen (Table **940**) until July 29 and from Sept. 12. Runs with train number **1993** Aug. 1 - Sept. 9.
* – Calls at Frankfurt Flughafen before Frankfurt (Main) Hbf.
☆ – See also panel on page 423.
⊖ – 🏛 is at Kehl (8 km from Strasbourg). See Table **911** for local journeys Offenburg - Strasbourg.
◧ – Frankfurt Flughafen Fernbahnhof.

*See Table **927** for services operated by FlixTrain*

912 FRANKFURT - BASEL and STUTTGART

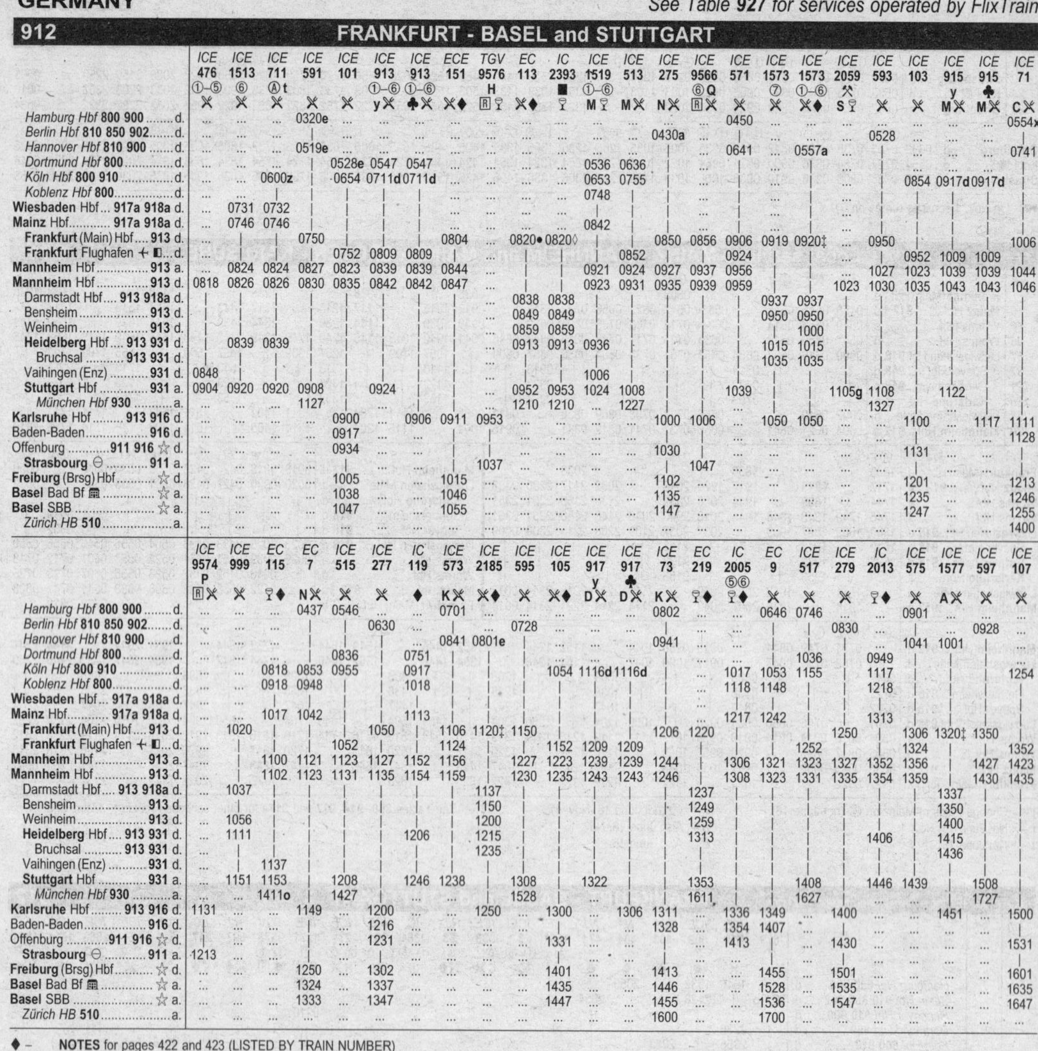

	ICE	*ICE*	*ICE*	*ICE*	*ICE*	*ICE*	*ICE*	*ECE*	*TGV*	*EC*	*IC*	*ICE*	*ICE*	*ICE*	*ICE*	*ICE*	*ICE*	*ICE*	*ICE*	*ICE*	*ICE*	*ICE*	*ICE*	*ICE*
	476	**1513**	**711**	**591**	**101**	**913**	**913**	**151**	**9576**	**113**	**2393**	**1519**	**513**	**275**	**9566**	**571**	**1573**	**1573**	**2059**	**593**	**103**	**915**	**915**	**71**
	①–⑤	⑥	Ⓐ t			①–⑥	①–⑥		H		■	①–⑥			⑥ Q		⑦	①–⑥	⚒			y	♣	
	✕	✕	✕	✕	✕	y ✕	♣ ✕	✕ ◆	🅁 🍷	✕ ◆	🍷	M 🍷	M ✕	N ✕	🅁 ✕	✕	✕	✕ ◆	S 🍷	✕	✕	M ✕	M ✕	C ✕
Hamburg Hbf **800 900** ....d.	...	...	...	0320**e**	...	...	...	...	...	...	...	...	...	...	...	0450	...	...	...	...	...	...	...	0554**x**
Berlin Hbf **810 850 902**.......d.	...	...	...	│	...	...	...	...	...	...	...	...	...	0430**a**	...	│	...	...	...	0528	...	...	...	│
Hannover Hbf **810 900** ....d.	...	...	...	0519**e**	...	...	...	...	...	...	...	...	...	│	...	0641	...	0557**a**	...	│	...	...	...	0741
Dortmund Hbf **800**..............d.	...	...	...	│	0528**e**	0547	0547	...	...	...	...	0536	0636	│	...	│	...	│	...	│	...	...	...	│
Köln Hbf **800 910** ....d.	...	...	0600**z**	│	0654	0711**d**	0711**d**	...	...	...	...	0653	0755	│	...	│	...	│	...	│	0854	0917**d**	0917**d**	│
Koblenz Hbf **800**.................d.	...	...	│	│	│	│	│	...	...	...	...	0748	│	│	...	│	...	│	...	│	│	│	│	│
Wiesbaden Hbf... **917a 918a** d.	...	0731	0732	│	│	│	│	...	...	...	...	│	│	│	...	│	...	│	...	│	│	│	│	│
Mainz Hbf........... **917a 918a** d.	...	0746	0746	│	│	│	│	...	...	...	...	0842	│	│	...	│	...	│	...	│	│	│	│	│
Frankfurt (Main) Hbf.... **913** d.	...	│	│	0750	│	│	│	0804	...	0820•	0820◊	│	│	0850	0856	0906	0919	0920‡	...	0950	│	│	│	1006
Frankfurt Flughafen ✈ ◧...d.	...	│	│	│	0752	0809	0809	│	...	│	│	│	0852	│	│	0924	│	│	...	│	0952	1009	1009	│
Mannheim Hbf.............. **913** a.	...	0824	0824	0827	0823	0839	0839	0844	...	│	│	0921	0924	0927	0937	0956	│	│	...	1027	1023	1039	1039	1044
Mannheim Hbf.............. **913** d.	0818	0826	0826	0830	0835	0842	0842	0847	...	│	│	0923	0931	0935	0939	0959	│	│	1023	1030	1035	1043	1043	1046
Darmstadt Hbf.... **913 918a** d.	│	│	│	│	│	│	│	│	...	0838	0838	│	│	│	│	│	0937	0937	│	│	│	│	│	│
Bensheim.................... **913** d.	│	│	│	│	│	│	│	│	...	0849	0849	│	│	│	│	│	0950	0950	│	│	│	│	│	│
Weinheim.................... **913** d.	│	│	│	│	│	│	│	│	...	0859	0859	│	│	│	│	│	│	1000	│	│	│	│	│	│
Heidelberg Hbf.... **913 931** d.	│	0839	0839	│	│	│	│	│	...	0913	0913	0936	│	│	│	│	1015	1015	│	│	│	│	│	│
Bruchsal .... **913 931** d.	│	│	│	│	│	│	│	│	...	│	│	│	│	│	│	│	1035	1035	│	│	│	│	│	│
Vaihingen (Enz) .... **931** d.	0848	│	│	│	│	│	│	│	...	│	│	1006	│	│	│	│	│	│	│	│	│	│	│	│
Stuttgart Hbf .... **931** a.	0904	0920	0920	0908	│	0924	│	│	...	0952	0953	1024	1008	│	│	1039	│	│	1105**g**	1108	│	1122	│	│
München Hbf **930** ....a.	...	...	...	1127	│	...	│	│	...	1210	1210	...	1227	│	│	...	│	│	...	1327	│	...	│	│
Karlsruhe Hbf......... **913 916** d.	...	...	...	...	0900	...	0906	0911	0953	...	...	...	...	1000	1006	...	1050	1050	...	...	1100	...	1117	1111
Baden-Baden................. **916** d.	...	...	...	...	0917	...	...	│	│	...	...	...	...	│	│	...	...	...	...	...	│	...	...	1128
Offenburg ....**911 916** ☆ d.	...	...	...	...	0934	...	...	│	│	...	...	...	...	1030	│	...	...	...	...	...	1131	...	...	│
Strasbourg ⊖ .... **911** a.	...	...	...	...	│	...	...	│	1037	...	...	...	...	│	1047	...	...	...	...	...	│	...	...	│
Freiburg (Brsg) Hbf.......... ☆ d.	...	...	...	...	1005	...	...	1015	...	...	...	...	...	1102	...	...	...	...	...	...	1201	...	...	1213
Basel Bad Bf 🏢 .... ☆ a.	...	...	...	...	1038	...	...	1046	...	...	...	...	...	1135	...	...	...	...	...	...	1235	...	...	1246
Basel SBB .... ☆ a.	...	...	...	...	1047	...	...	1055	...	...	...	...	...	1147	...	...	...	...	...	...	1247	...	...	1255
Zürich HB **510**....................a.	...	...	...	...	...	...	...	...	...	...	...	...	...	...	...	...	...	...	...	...	...	...	...	1400

	ICE	*ICE*	*EC*	*EC*	*ICE*	*ICE*	*IC*	*ICE*	*ICE*	*ICE*	*ICE*	*ICE*	*ICE*	*ICE*	*EC*	*IC*	*EC*	*ICE*	*ICE*	*IC*	*ICE*	*ICE*	*ICE*	*ICE*
	9574	**999**	**115**	**7**	**515**	**277**	**119**	**573**	**2185**	**595**	**105**	**917**	**917**	**73**	**219**	**2005**	**9**	**517**	**279**	**2013**	**575**	**1577**	**597**	**107**
	P											y	♣			⑤⑥								
	🅁 ✕	✕	🍷 ◆	N ✕	✕	✕	◆	K ✕	✕ ◆	✕	✕ ◆	D ✕	D ✕	K ✕	🍷 ◆	🍷 ◆	✕	✕	✕	🍷 ◆	✕	A ✕	✕	✕
Hamburg Hbf **800 900** ....d.	...	...	...	0437	0546	...	...	0701	...	...	...	...	...	0802	...	...	0646	0746	...	...	0901	...	...	...
Berlin Hbf **810 850 902**.......d.	...	...	...	│	│	0630	...	│	...	0728	...	...	...	│	...	...	│	│	0830	...	│	...	0928	...
Hannover Hbf **810 900** ....d.	...	...	...	│	│	│	...	0841	0801**e**	│	...	...	...	0941	...	...	│	│	│	...	1041	1001	│	...
Dortmund Hbf **800**..............d.	...	...	...	│	0836	│	0751	│	│	│	...	...	...	│	...	...	│	1036	│	0949	│	│	│	...
Köln Hbf **800 910** ....d.	...	...	0818	0853	0955	│	0917	│	│	│	1054	1116**d**	1116**d**	│	...	1017	1053	1155	│	1117	│	│	│	1254
Koblenz Hbf **800**.................d.	...	...	0918	0948	│	│	1018	│	│	│	│	│	│	│	...	1118	1148	│	│	1218	│	│	│	│
Wiesbaden Hbf... **917a 918a** d.	...	...	│	│	│	│	│	│	│	│	│	│	│	│	...	│	│	│	│	│	│	│	│	│
Mainz Hbf........... **917a 918a** d.	...	...	1017	1042	│	│	1113	│	│	│	│	│	│	│	...	1217	1242	│	│	1313	│	│	│	│
Frankfurt (Main) Hbf.... **913** d.	...	1020	│	│	│	1050	│	1106	1120‡	1150	│	│	│	1206	1220	│	│	│	1250	│	1306	1320‡	1350	│
Frankfurt Flughafen ✈ ◧...d.	...	│	│	│	1052	│	│	1124	│	│	1152	1209	1209	│	│	│	│	1252	│	│	1324	│	│	1352
Mannheim Hbf.............. **913** a.	...	│	1100	1121	1123	1127	1152	1156	│	1227	1223	1239	1239	1244	│	1306	1321	1323	1327	1352	1356	│	1427	1423
Mannheim Hbf.............. **913** d.	...	│	1102	1123	1131	1135	1154	1159	│	1230	1235	1243	1243	1246	│	1308	1323	1331	1335	1354	1359	│	1430	1435
Darmstadt Hbf.... **913 918a** d.	...	1037	│	│	│	│	│	│	1137	│	│	│	│	│	1237	│	│	│	│	│	│	1337	│	│
Bensheim.................... **913** d.	...	│	│	│	│	│	│	│	1150	│	│	│	│	│	1249	│	│	│	│	│	│	1350	│	│
Weinheim.................... **913** d.	...	1056	│	│	│	│	│	│	1200	│	│	│	│	│	1259	│	│	│	│	│	│	1400	│	│
Heidelberg Hbf.... **913 931** d.	...	1111	│	│	│	│	1206	│	1215	│	│	│	│	│	1313	│	│	│	│	1406	│	1415	│	│
Bruchsal .... **913 931** d.	...	│	│	│	│	│	│	│	1235	│	│	│	│	│	│	│	│	│	│	│	│	1436	│	│
Vaihingen (Enz) .... **931** d.	...	│	1137	│	│	│	│	│	│	│	│	│	│	│	│	│	│	│	│	│	│	│	│	│
Stuttgart Hbf .... **931** a.	...	1151	1153	│	1208	│	1246	1238	│	1308	│	1322	│	│	1353	│	│	1408	│	1446	1439	│	1508	│
München Hbf **930** ....a.	...	...	1411**o**	│	1427	│	...	...	│	1528	│	...	│	│	1611	│	│	1627	│	...	...	│	1727	│
Karlsruhe Hbf......... **913 916** d.	1131	...	...	1149	...	1200	...	...	1250	...	1300	...	1306	1311	...	1336	1349	...	1400	...	...	1451	...	1500
Baden-Baden................. **916** d.	│	...	...	│	...	1216	...	...	...	...	│	...	...	1328	...	1354	1407	...	│	...	...	...	...	│
Offenburg ....**911 916** ☆ d.	│	...	...	│	...	1231	...	...	...	...	1331	...	...	│	...	1413	│	...	1430	...	...	...	...	1531
Strasbourg ⊖ .... **911** a.	1213	...	...	│	...	│	...	...	...	...	│	...	...	│	...	...	│	...	│	...	...	...	...	│
Freiburg (Brsg) Hbf.......... ☆ d.	...	...	...	1250	...	1302	...	...	...	...	1401	...	...	1413	...	...	1455	...	1501	...	...	...	...	1601
Basel Bad Bf 🏢 .... ☆ a.	...	...	...	1324	...	1337	...	...	...	...	1435	...	...	1446	...	...	1528	...	1535	...	...	...	...	1635
Basel SBB .... ☆ a.	...	...	...	1333	...	1347	...	...	...	...	1447	...	...	1455	...	...	1536	...	1547	...	...	...	...	1647
Zürich HB **510**....................a.	...	...	...	...	...	...	...	...	...	...	...	...	...	1600	...	...	1700	...	...	...	...	...	...	...

◆ – **NOTES** for pages 422 and 423 (LISTED BY TRAIN NUMBER)

75 – [12] ✕ (Kiel ⑦ -) Hamburg - Zürich - Chur.
105 – [12] ✕ Amsterdam - Basel. Subject to alteration June 11, 12, 18, 19, Aug. 27 - Sept. 9.
113 – From Aug. 3. BLAUER ENZIAN – [12] ✕ Frankfurt - Salzburg - Villach - Klagenfurt; [12] Frankfurt - Villach (**213**) - Ljubljana - Zagreb.
115 – WÖRTHERSEE – [12] 🍷 Münster - München - Salzburg - Klagenfurt. Also calls at Worms Hbf (d. 1045).
117 – SALZACH – [12] 🍷 Frankfurt - München - Salzburg - Klagenfurt.
119 – BODENSEE – [12] Dortmund - Stuttgart - Ulm - Lindau - Bregenz - Innsbruck.
151 – [12] ✕ Frankfurt - Basel - Luzern - Chiasso - Milano.
219 – CHIEMGAU – [12] 🍷 Frankfurt - München - Salzburg - Bischofshofen - Graz. Until Aug. 1 runs as *IC* **2399** and terminates at München.
266 – BADEN-KURIER – [12] 🍷 München - Stuttgart - Basel.
1103 – NORDERNEY – [12] ✕ Norddeich Mole - Münster - Stuttgart. Also calls at Worms Hbf (d. 1845).
1291 – [12] 🍷 Frankfurt - München (- Salzburg ⊡).
1573 – [12] ✕ (Hannover ①–⑤ -) Kassel - Gießen - Frankfurt - Karlsruhe.
2005 – SCHWARZWALD – [12] 🍷 Emden - Münster - Karlsruhe - Konstanz. Also calls at Worms Hbf (d. 1245).
2013 – ALLGÄU – [12] 🍷 Dortmund - Stuttgart - Ulm - Oberstdorf.
2185 – [12] ✕ (Oldenburg - Bremen - Hannover ①–⑥ -) Kassel - Gießen - Frankfurt - Karlsruhe.
2213 – RÜGEN – [12] 🍷 Ostseebad Binz - Stralsund - Hamburg - Stuttgart (note **F**) / Karlsruhe (note **Y**).
2217 – GREIFSWALDER BODDEN – [12] 🍷 (Greifswald ⑤ -) Stralsund - Hamburg - Köln - Stuttgart ⊠/ Karlsruhe Ⓑ ♣.
9580 – [12] 🍷 Frankfurt - Strasbourg - Mulhouse - Lyon - Marseille.

A – [12] ✕ Bremen - Hannover - Kassel - Gießen - Frankfurt - Karlsruhe.
B – From Leipzig (Tables **849a**/**850**).
C – To Chur (Table **520**).
D – From Düsseldorf (Table **910**).
E – From Stuttgart (Table **931**).
F – Daily to July 29; ⑤⑦ July 31 - Sept. 9; daily from Sept. 11.
G – Runs as *TGV* **9592** on ⑥. *ICE* ✕, *TGV* 🍷.
H – [12] 🍷 München - Stuttgart - Paris (Table **32**).
J – From Westerland (Table **821**).
K – From Kiel (Table **820**).
L – ①②③④⑥.
M – From Münster (Table **800**).
N – To Interlaken via Bern (Table **560**).
P – [12] Stuttgart - Karlsruhe - Paris (Table **32**).
Q – To Paris (Table **30**).

R – To Ulm (Table **930**). From July 24 runs with train number **1991**, departs Berlin 1402 and does not call at Hannover.
S – From Saarbrücken (Table **919**).
U – To Tübingen (Table **930**).
Y – ①②③④⑥ July 30 - Sept. 10.

a – ①–⑤ only.
b – Not ⑥.
c – Not June 15, 16.
d – Köln **Messe/Deutz**.
e – ①–⑥ only.
f – ⑤ only.
g – 1119 July 30 - Sept. 10.
h – 1610 on ⑤ until Aug. 26.
j – Arrives 1815.
k – Also June 15; not June 17.
m – Also June 15.
n – Stuttgart - München on ⑥⑦ (arriving München on mornings of ①⑦).
o – Until July 13 calls at München **Ost** (a. 1424; not Hbf).
q – ①②③④⑥ (not June 15).
r – Not Aug. 1.
t – Not June 16.
v – Not ⑥⑦ July 30 - Sept. 11.
w – ⑦ until July 17.
x – 0602 on ⑥⑦.
y – Not July 30 - Sept. 11.
z – 0609 June 27 - Aug. 5.

* – On ⑥⑦ (also Aug. 1) arrives 6–7 minutes later (change trains at Basel Bad Bf).
❖ – Offenburg - Basel Bad Bf daily; Basel Bad Bf - Basel SBB on ①–⑤ (not Aug. 1).
⊕ – From July 22 runs with train number **1117** and starts from Hannover.
△ – From July 24 runs with train number **2017** and starts from Hannover.
⊙ – Runs as *ICE* **1611** on ⑤. Conveys 🍷 on ⑦. Train number **2411** on ⑦ July 31 - Sept. 11.
♣ – July 30 - Sept. 11 only.
■ – Until Aug. 2.
⊡ – Ⓑ from Aug. 2.
♠ – ①–④ from Aug. 29.
♥ – ①–④ until Aug. 25 (not June 15, 16).
▷ – Through trains from Karlsruhe also call at Baden-Baden 20–27 minutes after departing Karlsruhe Hbf.
⊠ – Daily to July 30; ⑥ Aug. 6 - Sept. 10; daily from Sept. 12.
¶ – Frankfurt (Main) **West** (not Hbf).
◊ – On ①–⑤ departs Frankfurt (Main) **Süd**, d. 0819 (not Hbf).
• – On ①–⑤ Aug. 3–26 departs from Frankfurt (Main) **Süd**, d. 0819 (not Hbf).
‡ – Until Aug. 26 calls at Frankfurt (Main) **West** (not Hbf), departing 6–14 minutes **earlier**.
⁝ – Frankfurt (Main) **Süd**.
☆ – See panel on page 423 for other local services.
⊖ – 🏢 is at Kehl (8 km from Strasbourg). See Table **911** for local journeys Offenburg - Strasbourg.
◧ – Frankfurt Flughafen Fernbahnhof.

FRANKFURT - BASEL and STUTTGART 912

	TGV 9580	*ICE* 75	*TGV* 9580	*ICE* 9572	*EC* 117	*ICE* 713	*ICE* 713	*ICE* 519	*ICE* 371	*IC* 2015	*IC* 1915	*ICE* 577	*ICE* 1579	*ICE* 599	*ICE* 109	*ICE* 1011	*ICE* 1011	*ICE* 77	*ICE* 713	*IC* 1291	*IC* 2217	*IC* 2217	*ICE* 611	*ICE* 373	*TGV* 9560
	[R]		[R]	G P		v	⑥⑦			⑤k	⑦					y	♣		①–⑤		⊠	Ⓑ♣			Q
	🍷♦	✕♦	🍷♦	[R]	🍷♦	✕	♣✕	✕	N✕	🍷	🍷	✕	A✕	✕	✕	✕	✕	✕	t E	🍷♦	🍷♦	🍷♦	✕	N✕	[R]🍷
Hamburg Hbf **800 900** d.	...	1001	...	...	...	0846	0846	0946	...	...	...	1101	...	...	...	...	...	1201	...	...	1046	1046	1146	...	...
Berlin Hbf **810 850 902** d.	...		...	...	...				1030	...	...		...	1128	...	...	...		...	...				1230	...
Hannover Hbf **810 900** d.	...	1141	...	...	...					...	...	1241	1201		...	...	...	1341	...	...					...
Dortmund Hbf **800** d.	...		...	...	...			1236		1149	1149				...	1349q	1349q		...	...			1435		...
Köln Hbf **800 910** d.	...		...	...	...	1253	1253	1355		1317	1317				1454	1515d	1515d		...	...	1453	1453	1555		...
Koblenz Hbf **800** d.	...		...	...	...	1348	1348			1418	1418								...	...	1548	1548			...
Wiesbaden Hbf **917a 918a** d.	...		...	...	...														...	...					...
Mainz Hbf **917a 918a** d.	...		...	...	...	1442	1442			1513	1513								...	...	1642	1642			...
Frankfurt (Main) Hbf **913** d.	1356	1406	...	...	1420				1450			1506	1520‡	1550				1606	...	1620h				1650	1656
Frankfurt Flughafen ✈ ◧ d.			...	...				1452				1524			1552	1609	1609		...				1652		
Mannheim Hbf **913** a.	1437	1444	...	...		1521	1521	1523	1527	1552	1552	1556		1627	1623	1639	1639	1644	...		1721	1721	1723	1727	1736
Mannheim Hbf **913** d.	1439	1446	...	...		1523	1523	1531	1535	1554	1554	1559		1630	1635	1642	1643	1646	...		1723	1723	1731	1735	1738
Darmstadt Hbf **913 918a** d.			...	...	1437								1537						...	1637					
Bensheim **913** d.			...	...	1449								1550						...	1649					
Weinheim **913** d.			...	...	1459								1600						...	1659					
Heidelberg Hbf **913 931** d.			...	...	1513	1536	1536			1606	1606		1615						...	1713	1736	1736			
Bruchsal **913 931** d.			...	...			1557						1636						...			1757			
Vaihingen (Enz) **931** d.			...	...		1604					1637								...		1810				
Stuttgart Hbf **931** a.			...	...	1553	1622		1608		1646	1656	1639		1708		1720			...	1753	1827		1808		
München Hbf **930** a.			←	...	1811	...		1827		...	...	...		1927		...			...	2011	...		2028		
Karlsruhe Hbf **913 916** d.	1505	1511	1512	1532	...	...	1612	...	1600	...	...	...	1650	...	1700	...	1714	1711	1733	...	...	1813	...	1800	1805
Baden-Baden **916** d.	→	1527	1535		...	...	...	...		...	...	...	...	...		...	...	1728	1754	...	...	...	...		
Offenburg **911 916** ☆ d.	...				...	...	...	...	1631	...	...	...	...	...	1731	...	...		1812	...	...	...	...	1830	
Strasbourg ⊖ **911** a.	...		1601	1612	...	...	...	...		...	...	...	...	...		...	...		...	...	...	...	...		1848
Freiburg (Brsg) Hbf ☆ d.	...	1613	...	...	...	...	...	...	1701	...	...	...	...	...	1801	...	...	1813	...	...	...	...	...	1901	...
Basel Bad Bf 🏛 ☆ a.	...	1646	...	...	...	...	...	...	1735	...	...	...	...	...	1835	...	...	1846	...	...	...	...	...	1935	...
Basel SBB ☆ a.	...	1655	...	...	...	...	...	...	1747	...	...	...	...	...	1847	...	...	1855	...	...	...	...	...	1947	...
Zürich HB **510** a.	...	1800	...	...	...	...	...	...	...	...	...	...	...	...	...	...	...	2000	...	...	...	...	...	...	...

	IC 1177	*ICE* 579	*IC* 2011	*IC* 2011	*IC* 1671	*IC* 2183	*ICE* 691	*ICE* 201	*ICE* 1013	*ICE* 1013	*ICE* 79	*TGV* 9570	*IC* 2183	*IC* 1956	*IC* 2297	*ICE* 1103	*ICE* 1091	*IC* 2311	*IC* 2311	*ICE* 613	*IC* 266	*ICE* 375	*ICE* 717	*IC* 1917	*ICE* 771
	⑤k		①–④	⑤⑦		①–④			Ⓑy	Ⓑ♣		P	①–④	⑦		⑥	⑦	y	♣		Ⓑ		⑤m	⑦△	
	🍷	✕	cU 🍷	⊙	A🍷	♠	✕	✕	✕	✕	✕	[R]🍷	♥	B🍷	🍷	✕♦	✕	J🍷	J🍷	K✕	🍷♦	✕	⊕✕	U🍷	✕
Hamburg Hbf **800 900** d.	...	1301		...	...	...	...	...	...	...	1401	...	...	...	...	...	...	1246	1246	1346	...	...	...	...	1501
Berlin Hbf **810 850 902** d.	...		...	1000w	...	...	1328	...	...	...		...	...	...	...	...	1406				...	1430	1201	1201	
Hannover Hbf **810 900** d.	...	1441	...	1156	1401	...		...	...	...	1541	...	...	...	...	...	1551				...		1356	1356	1641
Dortmund Hbf **800** d.	...		...	1351		...		...	1549	1549		...	...	...	...	...				1636	...				
Köln Hbf **800 910** d.	...		1517	1517		...		1654	1710d	1710d		...	...	...	...	1617		1653	1653	1755	...		1717	1717	
Koblenz Hbf **800** d.	...		1618	1618		...						...	...	...	...	1718		1748	1748		...		1818	1818	
Wiesbaden Hbf **917a 918a** d.	...					...						...	...	...	...						...				
Mainz Hbf **917a 918a** d.	...		1713	1713		...						...	...	...	...	1817		1842	1842		...		1913	1913	
Frankfurt (Main) Hbf **913** d.	1646	1706			1720‡	1746	1750				1806	...	1750	1755¦	1819		1838				...	1850			1906
Frankfurt Flughafen ✈ ◧ d.		1724						1752	1809	1809		...								1852	...				1924
Mannheim Hbf **913** a.		1755	1752	1752			1827	1823	1839	1839	1844	...				1901	1916	1921	1921	1923	...	1927	1952	1952	1955
Mannheim Hbf **913** d.		1759	1754	1754			1830	1835	1842	1843	1846	...				1903	1918	1923	1923	1931	...	1935	1954	1954	1959
Darmstadt Hbf **913 918a** d.	1704				1737	1803						...	1814	1813	1837						...				
Bensheim **913** d.					1750	1817						...	1827	1825	1849						...				
Weinheim **913** d.	1728				1800	1828						...	1838	1839	1859						...				
Heidelberg Hbf **913 931** d.	1744y		1806	1806	1815	1843						...	1853	1901	1913			1936	1936		...		2006	2006	
Bruchsal **913 931** d.					1835	1902						...		1924					1957		...				
Vaihingen (Enz) **931** d.												...						2005			...				
Stuttgart Hbf **931** a.		1838	1846	1847			1908		1922			...			1953	1946	1958	2023		2008	...		2046	2046	2038
München Hbf **930** a.		...	...	...			2127		...			...			2215b	...	...	...		2226	...	...	▬	...	2319f
Karlsruhe Hbf **913 916** d.	1827j	...	...	...	1852	1916	...	1900	...	1913	1911	1932	1937	1941	...	...	...	...	2016	...	1955	2000	*IC*	...	...
Baden-Baden **916** d.	1847	...	...	...	...	...	...		...	...	1928		...	...	...	...	...	...	...	...		2017	**266**	...	...
Offenburg **911 916** ☆ d.	1905	...	...	...	...	...	...	1931	...	...			...	...	...	...	...	...	...	...	2026	2035	Ⓑ♦	...	...
Strasbourg ⊖ **911** a.		...	...	...	...	...	...		...	...		2013	...	...	...	...	...	...	...	...			←	...	...
Freiburg (Brsg) Hbf ☆ d.	1942	...	...	...	...	...	...	2001	...	...	2013	...	...	...	...	...	...	...	...	...	2100	2107	2110	...	...
Basel Bad Bf 🏛 ☆ a.	2019	...	...	...	...	...	...	2035	...	...	2046	...	...	...	...	...	...	...	...	...	→	2140	2158	...	...
Basel SBB ☆ a.	2029	...	...	...	...	...	...	2047	...	...	2055	...	...	...	...	...	...	...	...	...	...	2149	2207	...	...
Zürich HB **510** a.	...	...	...	...	...	...	...	...	...	...	2200	...	...	...	...	...	...	...	...	...	...	...	...	...	...

	IC 2375	*ICE* 693	*ICE* 203	*ICE* 1015	*ICE* 1171	*IC* 1999	*ICE* 1589	*IC* 2299	*IC* 2213	*IC* 2213	*ICE* 615	*ICE* 377	*ICE* 773	*ICE* 695	*ICE* 205	*ICE* 205	*IC* 1997	*ICE* 273	*ICE* 273	*ICE* 205	*ICE* 617		*ICE* 877	*ICE* 775	*ICE* 834
				Ⓑ		⑦	⑤	L	F	Y					⑦–④	⑤⑥	⑦		⑤⑥	⑦–④			⑥	Ⓑ	
	A🍷	✕	✕	✕	K✕	R🍷	✕	✕	🍷♦	🍷♦	✕	✕	✕	✕	D✕	D ✕	🍷	✕	✕	D	✕				
Hamburg Hbf **800 900** d.	...	...	...	...	1601	...	...	...	1446	1446	1546	...	1701	...	...		...	1801	1801	...	1746	...	...	1901	...
Berlin Hbf **810 850 902** d.	...	1528	...	...		1500	...	...				1630		1728	...	...	...			...		...	1830		1904
Hannover Hbf **810 900** d.	1601		...	...	1741	1702	1707	...					1841		...	...	...	1941	1941	...		...		2041	
Dortmund Hbf **800** d.			...	1750				...			1835				...	...	...			...	2036	...			
Köln Hbf **800 910** d.			1854	1922d				...	1853	1853	1955				2054	2054	...			...	2155	...			
Koblenz Hbf **800** d.								...	1948	1948							...			...		...			
Wiesbaden Hbf **917a 918a** d.								...									...			...		...			
Mainz Hbf **917a 918a** d.								...	2042	2042							...			...		...			
Frankfurt (Main) Hbf **913** d.	1920‡	1950			2006	2009¶	2020	2020				2050	2106	2150			2155	2206	2206	...		...	2306	2306	2308
Frankfurt Flughafen ✈ ◧ d.			1952	2010							2052		2124		2152	2152				...	2256	...	2324	2324	
Mannheim Hbf **913** a.		2027	2023	2039	2044				2121	2121	2123	2127	2155	2227	2223	2223		2244	2244	...	2327	...	0005	0004	
Mannheim Hbf **913** d.		2030	2035	2043	2046				2123	2123	2131	2135	2158	2230	2235	2235		2246	2246	...	2330	...	0011	0011	
Darmstadt Hbf **913 918a** d.	1937					2037	2037	2037									2212			...		...			2326
Bensheim **913** d.	1950					2050	2050	2049									2224			...		...			2339
Weinheim **913** d.	2000					2100	2100	2059									2234			...		...			2350
Heidelberg Hbf **913 931** d.	2015					2114	2115	2114	2136	2136			2211				2249			...		...			0006
Bruchsal **913 931** d.	2035																			...		...			
Vaihingen (Enz) **931** d.									2205								2321			...		...			0034
Stuttgart Hbf **931** a.		2108		2123		2155	2157	2156	2223		2208		2251	2308			2337			...	0008	...			0051
München Hbf **930** a.		2329b		...		...	...	...	...		0027		...	0133n			...			←	...	...	...	...	...
Karlsruhe Hbf **913 916** d.	2054	...	2103	...	2112	...	...	...	...	2206	...	2200	...	...	2259	2302	...	2309	2312	2312	...	...	0037	0037	...
Baden-Baden **916** d.	...	...	2120	...	2129	...	...	...	...	...	...	2217	...	...	→	2320	...	...	2329	2330	...	...	...	...	...
Offenburg **911 916** ☆ d.	...	...	2138	...	2147	...	...	...	...	...	...	2235	...	...	...	2338	...	...	2347	2347	...	...	...	...	...
Strasbourg ⊖ **911** a.	...	...		...		...	...	...	...	...	...		...	...	...		...	...			...	...	...	...	...
Freiburg (Brsg) Hbf ☆ d.	...	...	2208	...	2217	...	...	...	...	...	...	2309	...	...	...	0014	...	...	0020	0017	...	...	...	...	...
Basel Bad Bf 🏛 ☆ a.	...	...	2242	...	2252	...	...	...	...	...	...	2346	...	...	...	0050	...	...	0055	0050	...	...	...	...	...
Basel SBB ☆ a.	...	...	2255	...	2304	...	...	...	...	...	...	2355	...	...	...	0059	...	...	0105	0059	...	...	...	...	...
Zürich HB **510** a.	...	...	...	...	...	...	...	...	...	...	...	...	...	...	...	...	...	...	...	...	...	...	...	...	...

Selected regional trains **OFFENBURG - BASEL** (German holiday dates apply). On June 16, Nov. 1 regional services between Offenburg and Basel Bad Bf run as on ⑦.

	Ⓒ	Ⓐ		Ⓐ	❖															❖	①–⑥				
Karlsruhe Hbf ▷ d.	...	...	...	...	...	...	...	0733	...	...	...	...	1239	...	1439	1539	1639	1739	1839	...	...	...	...	...	2308
Offenburg d.	0107	0423	...	0511	0552	0634	0742	0835	0946	1035	1147	1226	1347	1435	1547	1635	1747	1835	1936	2046	...	2141	2246	2317	0007
Freiburg (Brsg) Hbf a.	0150	0522	...	0607	0644	0716	0829	0914	1031	1115	1230	1315	1430	1515	1630	1715	1830	1915	2032	2130	...	2231	2336	0011	0051
Freiburg (Brsg) Hbf d.	0152	0536	0600	0627	0646	0718	0832	0918	1034	1118	1238	1317	1432	1518	1632	1718	1832	1918	2033	2132	...	2234	2343	0027	...
Müllheim (Baden) d.	0212	0558	0625	0649	0711	0737	0852	0937	1053	1137	1258	1338	1451	1537	1651	1737	1851	1937	2052	2151	...	2253	0008	0052	...
Basel Bad Bf 🏛 a.	0244	0629	0701	0721	0746	0803	0929	1002	1130	1201	1330	1402	1523	1602	1722	1803	1922	2001	2129	2223	2245	2323	0043	0128	...
Basel SBB a.	...	*0650*	*0725*	0730r	0801	*0825*	*0950*e	*1025*	*1150*e	1218*	*1350*e	*1425*	*1550*e	1619*	*1750*e	1819*	*1950*e	*2025*	*2150*e	2231	2250	...	...	...	...

← **FOR NOTES SEE PAGE 422**

912 BASEL and STUTTGART - FRANKFURT

km	km		ICE	IC	ICE	ICE	ICE	ICE	ICE	IC	IC	ICE	IC	ICE	ICE	ICE	ICE	IC	ICE	ICE	IC	ICE	IC	ICE
			618	2326	696	774	270	270	616	2372	2216	474	2298	1014	206	910	694	1672	476	772	2010	1110	267	374
				Ⓐ	①		①			Ⓐm	Ⓐ		ⒶY	①–⑥		Ⓐt			①–⑤		Ⓐ	⑥	①–⑥	
			K	◆	✕	✕	✕	✕	✕	🍷	F🍷	K✕	✕	D✕	✕		✕	A✕	✕	✕	🍷◆	✕◆	🍷◆	✕
		Zürich HB **510** d.	...	...	...	...	...	...	...	...	...	...	...	...	...	...	...	...	...	...	...	...	...	...
		Basel SBB ☆ d.	...	...	...	...	0403	...	...	...	...	0500	...	...	0506	...	...	...	0537	...	...	...	0551	0606
		Basel Bad Bf ☆ d.	...	...	...	...	0412	...	...	...	...	0508	...	...	0521	...	...	...	0546	...	...	...	0601	0616
		Freiburg (Brsg) Hbf ☆ d.	...	...	...	...	0446	...	...	...	...	0542	...	...	0552	...	...	...	0620	...	...	...	0646	0650
	0	**Strasbourg** ⊖ **911** d.	...	...	...	...	|	...	...	...	...	|	...	...	|	...	...	...	|	...	...	...	|	|
	29	Offenburg **911 916** ☆ d.	...	...	...	...	0519	...	...	...	0556	|	...	...	0626	...	...	...	0656	...	...	...	0730	0724
	—	Baden-Baden **916** d.	...	...	...	...	0535	...	...	...	0615	0632	...	...	0641	...	...	...	0714	...	...	...	0746	0740
		Karlsruhe Hbf **913 916** d.	...	0335	0500	...	0558	0558	...	0612	0635	0651	...	...	0701	...	...	0702	0736	...	...	...	0803	0800
		München Hbf **930** d.	0001	|	|	...	|	|	0324	|	...	|	...	...	|	...	...	|	|	...			...	
0	0	**Stuttgart** Hbf **931** d.	0222	0226	|	0502	|	|	0551	|	...	|	0602	0637	|	0624	0650	|	|	0725	0714	0714	...	
29	29	Vaihingen (Enz) **931** d.	|	|	|	0519	|	|	|	|	...	|	0625	|	|	0643	|	|	|	|	|	|	...	
		Bruchsal **913 931** d.	|	0347	|	|	|	|	|	0630	...	|	|	|	|	|	|	0723	|	|	|	|	...	
	92	**Heidelberg** Hbf **913 931** d.	0343	0410	|	0547	|	|	|	0655	...	|	0659	|	|	0720	|	0746	|	|	0755	0755	...	
		Weinheim **913** d.	|	|	|	|	|	|	|	|	...	|	0714	|	|	|	|	0800	|	|	|	|	...	
		Bensheim **913** d.	|	|	|	|	|	|	|	|	...	|	0728	|	|	|	|	0809	|	|	|	|	...	
		Darmstadt Hbf **913 918a** d.	|	|	|	|	|	|	|	|	...	|	0742	|	|	|	|	0824	|	|	|	|	...	
107	109	**Mannheim** Hbf **913** a.	0355	0420	0525	0559	0624	0624	0628	0707	...	0714	|	0718	0725	0732	0729	|	0800	0802	0806	0806	...	0823
107		**Mannheim** Hbf **913** d.	0401	0427	0528	0605	0632	0632	0636	0711	...	0716	|	0721	0736	0734	0732	|	...	0805	0808	0808	...	0832
179		**Frankfurt** Flughafen ✈ a.	0457§	0504	|	0635	|	|	0706	|	...	|	|	0751	0806	|	|	|	...	0835	|	|	...	|
		Frankfurt (Main) Hbf **913** a.	0439	0520	0608	0652	0708	0708	|	0756	...	0752	0800◊	|	|	|	0808	0840‡	...	0852	|	|	...	0908
		Mainz Hbf **917a 918a** a.	|	|	|	|	|	|	|	...	...	|	...	|	|	0815	|	|	...	|	0847	0847	...	|
		Wiesbaden Hbf **917a 918a** a.	|	|	|	|	|	|	|	...	...	|	...	|	|	0833	|	|	...	|	|	|	...	|
		Koblenz Hbf **800** a.	|	|	|	|	|	|	|	...	...	|	...	|	|	...	|	|	...	|	0942	0942	...	|
		Köln Hbf **800 910** a.	0603	|	|	|	|	|	0805	...	...	|	...	0842d	0904	...	|	|	...	|	1043	1043	...	|
		Dortmund Hbf **800** a.	0722	0857	|	|	|	|	0923	...	...	|	...	...	...	...	|	|	...	|	1208f	...	...	|
		Hannover Hbf **810 900** a.	|	...	|	0917	|	|	|	...	...	1017	...	...	...	...	|	1156	...	1117	1401f	...	...	|
		Berlin Hbf **810 850 902** a.	|	...	1031	|	1128	1128	|	...	...	|	...	...	...	...	1229	...	...	|	1554f	...	...	1327
		Hamburg Hbf **800 900** a.	1014	...	...	1054	...	...	1214	...	...	1154	...	...	...	...	...	...	...	1254	...	...	...	...

	ICE	IC	IC	IC	ICE	ICE	ICE	ICE	ICE	IC	ICE	ICE	ICE	TGV	ICE	ICE	ICE	ICE	IC	IC	ICE	ICE	ICE	ICE
	614	2216	2216	2296	78	1012	1012	202	692	2374	937	770	9571	9561	372	612	714	714	1296	1916	1116	76	1010	1010
		j	⑦T	①–⑥		①–⑥	①–⑥				⑥⑦		P	①–⑥			y	♣		⑤f	⑦		y	♣
	✕	🍷◆	🍷◆	🍷	✕	y✕	♣✕	✕	✕	A🍷	✕	✕	Ⓡ✕	QⓇ 🍷	N✕	K✕	✕	✕	G🍷	◐🍷	⊗✕	✕	✕	✕
Zürich HB **510** d.	...	...	...	...	0559	...	...	...	...	...	...	...	...	...	...	...	...	...	...	...	...	0759	...	...
Basel SBB ☆ d.	...	...	...	...	0706	...	...	0713	...	...	...	...	...	...	0813	...	...	...	...	...	...	0906	...	...
Basel Bad Bf ☆ d.	...	...	...	...	0714	...	...	0721	...	...	...	...	...	...	0823	...	...	...	...	...	...	0914	...	...
Freiburg (Brsg) Hbf ☆ d.	...	...	...	...	0748	...	...	0754	...	...	...	...	...	...	0856	...	...	...	...	...	...	0948	...	...
Strasbourg ⊖ **911** d.	...	...	...	...	|	...	...	|	...	...	...	...	0846	0912	|	...	...	...	...	...	...	|	...	...
Offenburg **911 916** ☆ d.	...	...	...	...	|	...	...	0826	...	...	...	...	|	|	0928	...	...	...	...	...	...	|	...	...
Baden-Baden **916** d.	...	...	...	...	0831	...	...	0841	...	...	...	...	|	|	|	...	...	...	...	...	...	1031	...	...
Karlsruhe Hbf **913 916** d.	...	...	0748	...	0851	...	0854	0901	...	0910	...	...	0926	0955	1000	...	...	0946	...	...	...	1051	...	1054
München Hbf **930** d.	0533	...	|	0540	|		|	|	0629	|	...	...	...	|	|	0728	...	|	0746	...	...	|	...	|
Stuttgart Hbf **931** d.	0751	0736	|	0805	|	0837	|	|	0851	|	0903	0923	...	|	|	0951	0937	|	1005	1008	1008	|	1037	|
Vaihingen (Enz) **931** d.	|	0755	|	|	|	|	|	|	|	|	0927	|	...	|	|	|	0954	|	|	|	|	|	|	|
Bruchsal **913 931** d.	|	|	0804	|	|	|	|	|	|	0923	|	|	...	|	|	|	|	1003	|	|	|	|	|	|
Heidelberg Hbf **913 931** d.	|	0825	0825	0846	|	|	|	|	|	0946	0956	|	...	|	|	|	1025	1025	1046	|	|	|	|	|
Weinheim **913** d.	|	|	|	0900	|	|	|	|	|	1000	1012	|	...	|	|	|	|	|	1100	|	|	|	|	|
Bensheim **913** d.	|	|	|	0909	|	|	|	|	|	1009	1022	|	...	|	|	|	|	|	1109	|	|	|	|	|
Darmstadt Hbf **913 918a** d.	|	|	|	0924	|	|	|	|	|	1024	1040	|	...	|	|	|	|	|	1124	|	|	|	|	|
Mannheim Hbf **913** a.	0828	0836	0836	|	0914	0918	0919	0925	0929	|	|	1002	...	1018	1024	1028	1037	1037	|	1050	1050	1114	1118	1119
Mannheim Hbf **913** d.	0836	0839	0839	|	0916	0921	0921	0936	0932	|	|	1005	...	1021	1032	1036	1039	1039	|	1052	1052	1116	1121	1121
Frankfurt Flughafen ✈ a.	0906	|	|	|	|	0951	0951	1006	|	|	|	1035	...	|	|	1106	|	|	|	|	|	|	1151	1151
Frankfurt (Main) Hbf **913** a.	|	|	|	0940	0952	|	|	|	1008	1040‡	1056	1052	...	1059	1108	|	|	|	1140	|	|	1152	|	|
Mainz Hbf **917a 918a** a.	|	0918	0918	...	|	|	|	|	|	|	|	|	...	...	|	|	1118	1118	...	1142	1142	|	|	|
Wiesbaden Hbf **917a 918a** a.	|	|	|	...	|	|	|	|	|	|	|	|	...	...	|	|	|	|	...	|	|	|	|	|
Koblenz Hbf **800** a.	|	1011	1011	...	|	|	|	|	|	|	|	|	...	...	|	|	1211	1211	...	1242	1242	|	|	|
Köln Hbf **800 910** a.	1004	1105	1105	...	|	1042d	1042d	1104	|	|	|	|	...	...	|	1205	1305	1305	...	1343	1343	|	1241d	1241d
Dortmund Hbf **800** a.	1123	|	|	...	|	1205q	1205q	...	|	|	|	|	...	...	|	1321	|	|	...	1508	1508	|	1404e	1404e
Hannover Hbf **810 900** a.	|	|	|	...	1217	...	...	...	|	1356	|	1317	...	...	|	|	|	|	...	1701	1701	1417	...	...
Berlin Hbf **810 850 902** a.	|	|	|	...	|	...	...	...	1429	...	1456	|	...	...	1527	|	|	|	...	1855	1855	|	...	...
Hamburg Hbf **800 900** a.	1414	1512	1512	...	1354	...	...	...	...	...	...	1454	...	...	...	1614	1714	1714	...	...	...	1555	...	...

	ICE	ICE	ICE	ICE	ICE	ICE	IC	IC	IC	IC	IC	ICE	ICE	ICE	ICE	ICE	ICE	IC	ICE	ICE	ICE	ICE	EC	EC
	200	690	1578	578	370	610	2312	1290	2006	2004	2014	74	918	918	108	598	1576	2012	576	9573	278	518	8	218
									⑥	⑦	⑤		y	♣						R				
	✕	✕	A✕	✕	✕	✕	🍷	G🍷	🍷◆	🍷◆	🍷◆	K✕	✕	✕	✕	✕	A✕	🍷◆	✕	PⓇ	N✕	✕	✕	🍷◆
Zürich HB **510** d.	...	...	...	...	...	...	...	...	...	...	...	0959	...	...	...	...	...	...	...	...	...	...	1059	...
Basel SBB ☆ d.	0913	...	...	...	1013	...	...	...	...	...	...	1106	...	...	1113	...	...	...	...	...	1213	...	1220	...
Basel Bad Bf ☆ d.	0923	...	...	...	1023	...	...	...	...	...	...	1114	...	...	1123	...	...	...	...	...	1223	...	1228	...
Freiburg (Brsg) Hbf ☆ d.	0956	...	...	...	1056	...	...	...	...	...	...	1148	...	...	1156	...	...	...	...	...	1256	...	1304	...
Strasbourg ⊖ **911** d.	|	...	...	...	|	...	...	...	...	...	...	|	...	...	|	...	...	...	...	1246	|	...	|	...
Offenburg **911 916** ☆ d.	1029	...	...	...	1128	...	...	...	1139	1139	...	|	...	...	1229	...	...	...	...	|	1328	...	|	...
Baden-Baden **916** d.	|	...	...	...	|	...	...	...	1202	1202	...	1231	...	...	|	...	...	...	...	|	|	...	1352	...
Karlsruhe Hbf **913 916** d.	1100	...	1110	...	1200	...	...	...	1221	1222	...	1251	...	1254	1300	...	1310	...	...	1326	1400	...	1412	...
München Hbf **930** d.	|	0827	|	...	|	0928	...	0947	|	|	...	|	...	|	|	1028	|	...	...	...	|	1128	|	1147
Stuttgart Hbf **931** d.	|	1051	|	1123	|	1151	1137	1204	|	|	1208	|	1237	|	|	1251	|	1311	1323	...	|	1351	|	1405
Vaihingen (Enz) **931** d.	|	|	|	|	|	|	1155	|	|	|	|	|	|	|	|	|	|	|	|	...	|	|	|	|
Bruchsal **913 931** d.	|	|	1122	|	|	|	|	|	|	|	|	|	|	|	|	|	1322	|	|	...	|	|	|	|
Heidelberg Hbf **913 931** d.	|	|	1146	|	|	|	1224	1246	|	|	|	|	|	|	|	|	1346	1355	|	...	|	|	|	1446
Weinheim **913** d.	|	|	1200	|	|	|	|	1300	|	|	|	|	|	|	|	|	1400	|	|	...	|	|	|	1500
Bensheim **913** d.	|	|	1209	|	|	|	|	1309	|	|	|	|	|	|	|	|	1409	|	|	...	|	|	|	1509
Darmstadt Hbf **913 918a** d.	|	|	1224	|	|	|	|	1324	|	|	|	|	|	|	|	|	1424	|	|	...	|	|	|	1524
Mannheim Hbf **913** a.	1124	1129	|	1202	1224	1228	1237	|	1250	1250	1256	1314	1318	1318	1324	1329	|	1406	1402	...	1424	1428	1437	|
Mannheim Hbf **913** d.	1136	1132	|	1205	1232	1236	1239	|	1258	1258	1258	1316	1321	1321	1336	1332	|	1408	1405	...	1432	1436	1439	|
Frankfurt Flughafen ✈ a.	1206	|	|	1235	|	1306	|	|	|	|	|	|	1351	1351	1406	|	|	|	1435	...	|	1506	|	|
Frankfurt (Main) Hbf **913** a.	|	1208	1240‡	1252	1308	|	|	1340	|	|	|	1352	|	|	|	1408	1440‡	|	1452	...	1508	|	|	1555n
Mainz Hbf **917a 918a** a.	|	|	|	|	|	|	1318	...	1342	1342	1342	|	|	|	|	|	|	1447	|	...	|	|	1518	...
Wiesbaden Hbf **917a 918a** a.	|	|	|	|	|	|	|	...	|	|	|	|	|	|	|	|	|	|	|	...	|	|	|	...
Koblenz Hbf **800** a.	|	|	|	|	|	|	1411	...	1442	1442	1442	|	|	|	|	|	|	1542	|	...	|	|	1611	...
Köln Hbf **800 910** a.	1305	|	|	|	|	1405	1505	...	1543	1543	1543	|	1441d	1441d	1504	|	|	1643	|	...	|	1605	1705	...
Dortmund Hbf **800** a.	...	|	|	|	|	1522	|	...	1708	...	...	|	1606	1606	...	|	|	...	|	...	|	1722	|	...
Hannover Hbf **810 900** a.	...	|	1556	1517	|	|	|	...	...	...	...	1617	...	...	...	|	1756	...	1717	...	|	|	|	...
Berlin Hbf **810 850 902** a.	...	1629	...	|	1727	|	|	...	...	...	...	|	...	...	...	1829	...	...	|	...	1927	|	|	...
Hamburg Hbf **800 900** a.	...	...	...	1654	...	1814	1914	...	...	...	...	1754	...	...	...	...	...	...	1853	...	...	2014	2114	...

Selected regional trains **BASEL - OFFENBURG** (German holiday dates apply). On June 16, Nov. 1 regional services between Basel Bad Bf and Offenburg run as on ⑦.

		⑥	Ⓐ		Ⓐ					⚒	†		❖				❖		❖				⑥⑦u	r	
Basel SBB d.	...	...	...	...	0501	0603e	0737c	0804e	0934	1004	...	1134	1225	1334	1404e	1534	1628	1734	1828	1934	2004e	2134	2240	2259	2342
Basel Bad Bf d.	0406	...	...	...	0537	0636	0758	0828	0958	1028	1028	1158	1233	1358	1427	1557	1638	1758	1838	1958	2028	2158	2308	2308	2353
Müllheim (Baden) d.	0444	...	...	...	0607	0705	0821	0904	1022	1104	1102	1222	1306	1422	1501	1620	1707	1822	1907	2021	2104	2222	2337	2337	0027
Freiburg (Brsg) Hbf a.	0510	...	...	...	0630	0724	0839	0924	1040	1124	1121	1240	1325	1440	1523	1638	1726	1840	1926	2040	2124	2240	2357	2357	0053
Freiburg (Brsg) Hbf d.	...	0517	0522	0626	...	0726	0843	0927	1042	1127	1129	1245	1327	1443	1527	1642	1729	1843	1929	2042	2127	2242	0010	0010	...
Offenburg a.	...	0609	0614	0712	...	0812	0924	1013	1121	1213	1214	1325	1412	1530	1613	1722	1814	1923	2014	2121	2213	2321	0106	0106	...
Karlsruhe Hbf ▷ a.	...	0712	0714	0821	...	...	...	...	...	...	...	1421	1522	1621	1721	1821	...	...	...	2221	...	0021	...	...	...

FOR NOTES SEE PAGE 425 →

BASEL and STUTTGART - FRANKFURT 912

	TGV 9583	ICE 72	TGV 9583	ICE 106	ICE 596	ICE 710	ICE 2184	IC 118	ICE 574	ICE 574	ICE 276	ICE 516	EC 6		ICE 994	EC 114	TGV 9575	ICE 70	ICE 914		ICE 104	ICE 204	ICE 594	ICE 1512	ICE 2058
	🅁		🅁			Ⓐt			Ⓑ	⑥							P					Ⓐ		Ⓑ	Ⓑ
	🍷♦	H✕	🍷♦	✕	✕	✕	✕	♦	K✕	✕	✕	✕	N✕		✕	🍷♦	🅁🍷	H✕	✕		✕♦	✕	✕	■	S🍷
Zürich HB **510** d.	...	1159	...	...	...	...	...	...	...	...	...	...	...	...	...	...	...	1359	...	...	...	...	...	...	...
Basel SBB ☆ d.	...	1306	...	1313	...	...	...	...	...	...	1413	...	1427	...	...	...	...	1506	...	...	1513	1513	...	...	...
Basel Bad Bf ☆ d.	...	1314	...	1323	...	...	...	...	...	...	1423	...	1435	...	...	...	...	1514	...	...	1523	1523	...	...	...
Freiburg (Brsg) Hbf ☆ d.	...	1348	...	1356	...	...	...	...	...	...	1454	...	1507	...	...	...	...	1548	...	...	1556	1556	...	...	...
Strasbourg ⊖ **911** d.	1355	|	...	|	...	...	...	...	...	...	|	...	|	...	...	...	1546	|	...	...	|	|	...	...	...
Offenburg **911 916** ☆ d.	|	|	...	1429	...	...	...	...	...	...	1525	...	|	...	...	...	|	|	...	...	1629	1629	...	...	...
Baden-Baden **916** d.	1425	1431	←	|	...	...	...	...	...	...	1541	...	|	...	...	...	|	1631	...	...	|	|	...	...	...
Karlsruhe Hbf **913 916** d.	1446	1451	1454	1500	...	...	1510	...	...	...	1601	...	1613	...	...	...	1625	1651	...	...	1700	1700	...	...	...
München Hbf **930** d.	→	|	|	|	1227	...	|	...	...	...	|	1328	|	...	...	1347	...	|	...	...	|	|	1427	...	...
Stuttgart Hbf **931** d.	...	|	|	|	1451	1435	|	1512	1523	1523	|	1551	|	...	1559	1607	...	|	1634y	...	|	|	1651	1622	1653
Vaihingen (Enz) **931** d.	...	|	|	|	|	1454	|	|	|	|	|	|	|	...	|	1625	...	|	|	...	|	|	|	|	|
Bruchsal **913 931** d.	...	|	|	|	|	|	1522	|	|	|	|	|	|	...	|	|	...	|	|	...	|	|	|	|	|
Heidelberg Hbf **913 931** d.	...	|	|	|	|	1520	1546	1555	|	|	|	|	|	...	1646	|	...	|	|	...	|	|	|	1720	|
Weinheim **913** d.	...	|	|	|	|	|	1600	|	|	|	|	|	|	...	1700	|	...	|	|	...	|	|	|	|	|
Bensheim **913** d.	...	|	|	|	|	|	1609	|	|	|	|	|	|	...	1709	|	...	|	|	...	|	|	|	|	|
Darmstadt Hbf **913 918a** d.	...	|	|	|	|	|	1624	|	|	|	|	|	|	...	1724	|	...	|	|	...	|	|	|	|	|
Mannheim Hbf **913** a.	...	1514	1518	1524	1529	1531	|	1606	1602	1602	1625	1628	1637	...	|	1655	...	1715	1718y	...	1724	1724	1729	1736	1746
Mannheim Hbf **913** d.	...	1516	1521	1536	1532	1533	|	1608	1605	1605	1632	1636	1639	...	|	1657	...	1717	1721	...	1736	1736	1732	1738	...
Frankfurt Flughafen ✈ ◧ a.	...	|	|	1606	|	|	|	|	1635	1635	|	1706	|	...	|	|	...	|	1751	...	1806	1806	|	|	...
Frankfurt (Main) Hbf **913** a.	...	1552	1559	|	1608	|	1640‡	|	1652	1652	1708	|	|	...	1740	|	...	1752	|	...	|	|	1808	|	...
Mainz Hbf **917a 918a** a.	...	|	...	|	|	1615	|	1647	|	|	|	|	1718	...	...	1740	...	|	|	...	|	|	|	1815	...
Wiesbaden Hbf **917a 918a** a.	...	|	...	|	|	1633	|	|	|	|	|	|	|	...	...	|	...	|	|	...	|	|	|	1833	...
Koblenz Hbf **800** a.	...	|	...	|	|	|	|	1742	|	|	|	|	1811	...	...	1842	...	|	|	...	|	|	|	...	...
Köln Hbf **800 910** a.	...	|	...	1704	|	1819•	|	1842	|	|	|	1805	1905	...	...	1943	...	|	1841d	...	1904	1904	|	...	...
Dortmund Hbf **800** a.	...	|	...	...	|	...	|	2007	|	|	|	1921	|	...	...	...	...	|	2001	...	...	2021	|	...	...
Hannover Hbf **810 900** a.	...	1817	...	...	|	...	1956	...	1917	1917	|	|	|	...	...	...	...	2017	...	...	...	...	|	...	...
Berlin Hbf **810 850 902** a.	...	|	...	...	2029	...	...	...	|	|	2127	|	|	...	...	...	...	|	...	...	...	...	2230	...	...
Hamburg Hbf **800 900** a.	...	1954	...	...	...	...	...	...	2057	2057	...	2214	2316	...	...	...	...	2154	...	...	...	...	...	...	...

	ICE 1572	ECE 52	ICE 572	ICE 9563	ICE 274	ICE 514	ICE 1518	IC 2318	EC 112	TGV 9577	ICE 376	ICE 376	ICE 912	ICE 912	ICE 102	ICE 592	ICE 1570	ICE 1570	ICE 570	ICE 570	IC 1910		ICE 272	ICE 272	ICE 292
				Q			¶	⑥♣		Ⓑ	Ⓑ	⑥	Ⓑy	Ⓑ♣			Ⓑ	⑦		⑦	⑦		⑥	①–⑤	⑦
	✕♦	✕♦	✕	🅁✕	✕	✕	M🍷	M🍷	✕♦	🅁♦ 🍷	N✕	N✕	✕	✕	✕	L✕	✕♦	✕♦	✕	✕	🍷		✕	✕	✕
Zürich HB **510** d.	...	...	...	...	...	...	...	...	...	...	...	...	...	...	...	...	...	...	...	...	...	...	1659	1659	1659
Basel SBB ☆ d.	...	1538	...	...	1613	...	...	...	...	...	1707	1707	...	...	1713	...	...	...	...	...	...	...	1813	1813	1813
Basel Bad Bf ☆ d.	...	1552	...	...	1623	...	...	...	...	...	1715	1715	...	...	1722	...	...	...	...	...	...	...	1823	1823	1823
Freiburg (Brsg) Hbf ☆ d.	...	1622	...	...	1654	...	...	...	...	...	1748	1748	...	...	1754	...	...	...	...	...	...	...	1856	1856	1856
Strasbourg ⊖ **911** d.	...	|	...	1713	|	...	...	...	...	1746	|	|	...	...	|	...	...	...	...	...	...	...	|	|	|
Offenburg **911 916** ☆ d.	...	|	...	|	1725	...	...	...	...	|	|	|	...	...	1825	...	...	...	...	...	...	...	1928	1928	1928
Baden-Baden **916** d.	...	|	...	|	1741	...	...	...	...	|	1831	1831	...	...	1841	...	...	...	...	...	...	...	|	|	|
Karlsruhe Hbf **913 916** d.	1710	1730	...	1755	1801	...	...	1745	...	1824	1851	1851	...	1854	1900	...	1910	1910	...	...	...	...	2000	2000	2000
München Hbf **930** d.	|	|	...	|	|	1528	...	|	1547	...	|	|	...	|	|	1627	|	|	...	...	1617	...	|	|	|
Stuttgart Hbf **931** d.	|	|	1723	|	|	1751	1737	|	1804	...	|	|	1837	|	|	1851	|	|	1923	1923	1914	...	|	|	|
Vaihingen (Enz) **931** d.	|	|	|	|	|	|	|	|	|	...	|	|	|	|	|	|	|	|	|	|	|	...	|	|	|
Bruchsal **913 931** d.	1722	|	|	|	|	|	|	1804	|	...	|	|	|	|	|	|	1922	1922	|	|	|	...	|	|	|
Heidelberg Hbf **913 931** d.	1746	|	|	|	|	|	1824	1824	1846	...	|	|	|	|	|	|	1946	1946	|	|	1955	...	|	|	|
Weinheim **913** d.	1800	|	|	|	|	|	|	|	1900	...	|	|	|	|	|	|	2000	2000	|	|	|	...	|	|	|
Bensheim **913** d.	1809	|	|	|	|	|	|	|	1909	...	|	|	|	|	|	|	2009	2009	|	|	|	...	|	|	|
Darmstadt Hbf **913 918a** d.	1824	|	|	|	|	|	|	|	1924	...	|	|	|	|	|	|	2024	2024	|	|	|	...	|	|	|
Mannheim Hbf **913** a.	|	1758	1802	1819	1825	1828	1837	1837	|	...	1914	1914	1918	1919	1924	1929	|	|	2002	2002	2006	...	2024	2024	2024
Mannheim Hbf **913** d.	|	1800	1805	1821	1832	1836	1839	1839	|	...	1916	1916	1921	1921	1936	1932	|	|	2005	2005	2008	...	2032	2032	2032
Frankfurt Flughafen ✈ ◧ a.	|	|	1835	|	|	1906	|	|	|	...	|	|	1951	1951	2006	|	|	|	2035	2035	|	...	|	|	|
Frankfurt (Main) Hbf **913** a.	1840‡	1844	1852	1859	1908	|	|	|	1940	...	1952	1954	|	|	|	2008	2040‡	2040‡	2052	2052	|	...	2108	2108	2108
Mainz Hbf **917a 918a** a.	|	...	|	...	|	|	1918	1918	...	...	|	...	|	|	|	...	...	|	...	|	2047	...	|	|	|
Wiesbaden Hbf **917a 918a** a.	|	...	|	...	|	|	|	|	...	...	|	...	|	|	|	...	...	|	...	|	|	...	|	|	|
Koblenz Hbf **800** a.	|	...	|	...	|	|	2011	2011	...	...	|	...	|	|	|	...	...	|	...	|	2142v	...	|	|	|
Köln Hbf **800 910** a.	|	...	|	...	|	2005	2105	2105	...	...	|	...	2042d	2042d	2105	...	...	|	...	|	2243v	...	|	|	|
Dortmund Hbf **800** a.	|	...	|	...	|	2122	...	...	...	...	|	...	2204	2204	...	...	...	|	...	|	0002v	...	|	|	|
Hannover Hbf **810 900** a.	2156b	...	2119	...	|	|	...	...	...	...	2217	...	...	...	...	...	...	0010	...	2318	...	...	2341	0002	|
Berlin Hbf **810 850 902** a.	|	...	|	...	2327	|	...	...	...	...	|	...	...	...	...	...	...	...	...	|	...	...	|	|	0127
Hamburg Hbf **800 900** a.	2332w	...	2254	...	...	0014	...	...	...	...	2358	...	...	...	...	...	...	...	...	0056	...	...	0124	0147	...

♦ – **NOTES** for pages 424 and 425 (LISTED BY TRAIN NUMBER)

52 – (12) ✕ Milano - Brig - Bern - Basel - Frankfurt.
104 – (12) ✕ Basel - Amsterdam. Subject to alteration June 11, 12, 18, 19, Aug. 27 - Sept. 9.
112 – BLAUER ENZIAN – (12) ✕ Klagenfurt - Villach - Salzburg - Frankfurt; (12) Zagreb (**212**) - Ljubljana - Villach (**112**) - Frankfurt. Until Aug. 1 does not run Klagenfurt - München and runs as *IC* **2392** (🍷) München - Frankfurt. Arrives Frankfurt 1944 on ⑤ until Aug. 26.
114 – WÖRTHERSEE – (12) 🍷 Klagenfurt - Salzburg - München - Bochum. Also calls at Worms Hbf (d. 1714).
118 – BODENSEE – (12) Innsbruck - Bregenz - Lindau - Ulm - Stuttgart - Bochum - Dortmund.
218 – CHIEMGAU – (12) 🍷 Graz - Bischofshofen - Salzburg - München - Frankfurt (- Erfurt ①–④). Until Aug. 1 starts from München and runs as *IC* **2398**. On ⑦ until Aug. 21 Darmstadt a. 1522, d. 1534.
267 – BADEN-KURIER – (12) 🍷 Basel - Stuttgart - München.
1110 – LORELEY – (12) ✕ Stuttgart - Köln - Münster - Norddeich Mole.
1570 – (12) ✕ Karlsruhe - Frankfurt - Gießen - Kassel (- Hannover ⑦).
1572 – (12) ✕ Karlsruhe - Frankfurt - Gießen - Kassel (- Hannover Ⓑ) (- Hamburg ⑦).
2004 – SCHWARZWALD – (12) 🍷 Konstanz - Karlsruhe - Münster - Emden. Also calls at Worms Hbf (d. 1315).
2006 – SCHWARZWALD – (12) 🍷 Konstanz - Karlsruhe - Dortmund. Also calls at Worms Hbf (d. 1315).
2010 – Ⓐ (not June 16, 17). LORELEY – (12) 🍷 Tübingen - Stuttgart - Köln (- Dortmund - Hannover - Berlin ⑤ f ●).
2012 – ALLGÄU – (12) 🍷 Oberstdorf - Ulm - Stuttgart - Bochum.
2014 – ⑤ (also June 15). (12) 🍷 Stuttgart - Münster - Emden. Also calls at Worms Hbf (d. 1315).
2216 – GREIFSWALDER BODDEN – (12) 🍷 Stuttgart (note **j**) / Karlsruhe (note **T**) - Hamburg - Rostock - Stralsund (- Greifswald Ⓑ).
2326 – (12) Stuttgart - Karlsruhe - Frankfurt - Siegen - Dortmund. See Table **808** for timings Frankfurt - Dortmund.
9577 – (12) 🍷 Paris - Strasbourg - Stuttgart - München.
9583 – (12) 🍷 Marseille - Lyon - Mulhouse - Strasbourg - Frankfurt.

A – (12) ✕ Karlsruhe - Frankfurt - Gießen - Hannover - Bremen.
D – To Düsseldorf (Table **910**).
F – Ⓐ (not June 16, 17). To Stuttgart (Table **931**). Also calls at Rastatt (d. 0623).
G – From Salzburg on dates in Table **890**.
H – From Chur (Table **520**).
K – To Kiel (Table **820**).
L – To Leipzig via Erfurt (Table **850**).
M – To Münster (Table **800**).
N – From Interlaken via Bern (Table **560**).
P – (12) Paris - Karlsruhe - Stuttgart (Table **32**).
Q – From Paris (Table **30**).
R – Runs as *TGV* **9593** on ⑥. *ICE* ✕, *TGV* 🍷.
S – To Saarbrücken (Table **919**).
T – ⑦ July 31 - Sept. 11.
Y – From Aug. 2.

b – Not ⑥.
c – *0734* (change trains at Basel Bad Bf) on ⑥⑦ (also Aug. 1).
d – Köln **Messe/Deutz**.
e – ①–⑥ only.
f – ⑤ (also June 15; not June 17).
j – Not July 31, Aug. 7, 14, 21, 28, Sept. 4, 11.
m – Not June 16, 17.
n – Not ⑤ June 17 - July 29. 1540 on ⑤–⑦ from Aug. 27; 1615 on Aug. 5, 12, 19, 26.
q – ①②③④⑥ (not June 15).
r – ①–⑤ (not Aug. 1).
t – Not June 16.
u – Also Aug. 1.
v – Until Aug. 28 arrives Koblenz 2203, Köln 2305, Dortmund 0021.
w – ⑦ only.
y – Not July 30 - Sept. 11.

♣ – July 30 - Sept. 11 only.
¶ – Not July 30, Aug. 6, 13, 20, 27, Sept. 3, 10. Runs as *IC* **2318** on ⑥.
✣ – Basel SBB - Basel Bad Bf on ①–⑤ (not Aug. 1); Basel Bad Bf - Offenburg daily.
■ – Ⓑ (not June 16). Runs as *ICE* **1114** on ⑤ (also June 15).
● – Terminates at Hannover from July 22.
◐ – From July 22 runs with train number **2016** and terminates at Hannover.
⊗ – From July 24 runs with train number **1118** and terminates at Hannover.
▷ – Through trains to Karlsruhe also call at Baden-Baden 19–21 minutes before arriving at Karlsruhe Hbf.
• – June 27 - Aug. 5 diverted to Köln **Messe/Deutz** (a. 1806).
‡ – Until Aug. 26 calls at Frankfurt (Main) **West** (not Hbf), arriving 14 minutes later.
◊ – Aug. 2–26 calls at Frankfurt (Main) **Süd** (not Hbf).
☆ – See panel on page 424 for other local services.
⊖ – 🏛 is at Kehl (8 km from Strasbourg). See Table **911** for local journeys Strasbourg - Offenburg.
§ – Calls at Frankfurt Flughafen after Frankfurt (Main) Hbf.
◧ – Frankfurt Flughafen Fernbahnhof.

912 BASEL and STUTTGART - FRANKFURT

*See Table **927** for services operated by FlixTrain*

	ICE 512	*IC* 2210	*IC* 2210	*IC* 2210	*EC* 216	*RJ* 890	*TGV* 9579	*ICE* 100	*ICE* 590		*ICE* 4	*ICE* 4	*ICE* 510	*ICE* 1596		*NJ* 40470	*NJ* 470		*ICE* 990	*ICE* 990	*RJX* 66	*IC* 1998		*ICE* 698	*NJ* 402
		①–④	⑤⑦	⑧			P		◇			⑦		⑤					⑦	Q	⑤⑥	⑤⑥			
	M ✕	A 🍷	B 🍷	C 🍷	🍷 ♦	✕ ♦	Ⓡ 🍷	✕	✕		✕	✕	✕	f		♦	♦		✕	✕	✕ ♦	k			♦
Zürich HB **510** d.	...	...	...	...	...	...	...	...	...	...	1859	1859	...	...	...	1959	1959	...	...	...	...	...	...	...	2159
Basel SBB ☆ d.	...	...	...	...	...	...	...	1913	...	...	2009	2009	...	...	...	2113	2113	...	...	...	...	...	...	...	2313
Basel Bad Bf 🏛 ☆ d.	...	...	...	...	...	...	...	1922	...	...	2018	2018	...	...	...	2122	2122	...	...	...	...	...	...	...	2323
Freiburg (Brsg) Hbf ☆ d.	...	...	...	...	...	...	...	1955	...	...	2054	2054	...	...	...	2158	2158	...	...	...	...	...	...	...	0005
Strasbourg ⊖ **911** d.	...	...	...	...	...	...	1946	|	...	...	|	|	...	...	...	|	|	...	...	...	...	...	...	...	|
Offenburg **911 916** ☆ d.	...	...	...	...	...	...	|	2026	...	...	2126	2126	...	...	...	2231	2231	...	...	...	...	...	...	...	0041
Baden-Baden **916** d.	...	...	...	...	...	...	|	2041	...	...	2142	2142	...	...	...	|	|	...	...	...	...	...	...	...	0102
Karlsruhe Hbf **913 916** d.	...	...	...	1948	...	...	2025	2101	...	...	2201	2201	...	...	...	2306	2306	...	...	...	...	...	...	...	0120
München Hbf **930** d.	1725	...	...	|	1747	...	...	|	1827	...	|	|	1928	...	...	|	|	...	2045	2045	2045	...	...	2151	|
Stuttgart Hbf **931** d.	1951	1915	1936	|	2004	2012n	...	|	2051	...	|	|	2151	2204	...	|	|	...	2305	2305	2305	2309	...	0012	|
Vaihingen (Enz) **931** d.	|	|	1955	|	|	|	...	|	|	...	|	|	|	|	...	|	|	...	|	|	|	2326	...	|	|
Bruchsal **913 931** d.	|	|	|	2004	|	|	...	|	|	...	|	|	|	|	...	|	|	...	|	|	|	|	...	|	|
Heidelberg Hbf **913 931** d.	|	2025t	2025	2025	|	2055	...	|	|	...	|	|	|	2247	...	|	|	...	|	|	|	0002	...	|	|
Weinheim **913** d.	|	|	|	|	|	2109	...	|	|	...	|	|	|	2302	...	|	|	...	|	|	|	0018	...	|	|
Bensheim **913** d.	|	|	|	|	|	2119	...	|	|	...	|	|	|	2313	...	|	|	...	|	|	|	0028	...	|	|
Darmstadt Hbf **913 918a** d.	|	|	|	|	|	2133	...	|	|	...	|	|	|	2327	...	|	|	...	|	|	|	0051	...	|	|
Mannheim Hbf **913** a.	2028	2037	2037	2037	2048	|	...	2125	2129	...	2224	2224	2228	|	...	2340	2340	...	2347	2347	2347	|	...	0140	0149
Mannheim Hbf **913** d.	2036	2039	2039	2039	...	|	...	2136	2132	...	2232	2232	2236	|	...	2342	2342	...	2351	2351	2351	|	...	0144	0152
Frankfurt Flughafen ✈ ◧ a.	2106	|	|	|	...	|	...	2206	|	...	|	|	2306	|	...	|	|	...	0022	0022	0022	|	...	0219	0326*
Frankfurt (Main) Hbf **913** a.	|	|	|	|	...	2152	...	|	2208	...	2308	2308	|	2343	...	0027	0027	...	0041	0041	0041	0106	...	0240	0245
Mainz Hbf **917a 918a** a.	|	2118	2118	2118	...	...	...	|	...	...	...	|	|	...	...	|	|	...	|	...	...	...	...	|	0346
Wiesbaden Hbf **917a 918a** a.	|	|	|	|	...	...	...	|	...	...	...	|	|	...	...	|	|	...	|	...	...	...	...	|	|
Koblenz Hbf **800** a.	|	2211z	2211z	2211z	...	...	...	|	...	...	...	|	|	...	...	|	|	...	|	...	...	...	...	|	0441
Köln Hbf **800 910** a.	2205	2305z	2305z	2305z	...	...	...	2304	...	...	...	|	0006	...	...	|	|	...	|	...	...	...	...	|	0553
Dortmund Hbf **800** a.	...	0020z	0020z	0020z	...	...	...	0023	...	...	...	|	...	...	...	|	|	...	|	...	...	...	...	|	...
Hannover Hbf **810 900** a.	...	...	...	...	...	...	...	...	...	...	...	|	...	...	...	0558	|	...	0421	...	...	...	...	|	...
Berlin Hbf **810 850 902** a.	...	...	...	...	...	...	...	...	...	...	...	0349	...	...	...	|	0738	...	|	...	...	...	...	0758	...
Hamburg Hbf **800 900** a.	...	...	...	...	...	...	...	...	...	...	...	0539	...	...	...	0754	...	...	0608	...	...	...	...	...	...

♦ – **NOTES** (LISTED BY TRAIN NUMBER)

66 – ⑤⑥ from Aug. 5. 🚃12 ✕ Budapest - Wien - Salzburg - Frankfurt.

216 – DACHSTEIN – 🚃12 🍷 (Graz - Bischofshofen - Salzburg ♥ -) München - Saarbrücken. Runs as *IC* **2396** until Aug. 1.

402 – 🛏 1, 2 cl. and 🛌 2 cl. (Ⓡ) Zürich - Basel - Amsterdam. Also conveys 🚃2 (*IC* **60402**). On the mornings of ①②⑦ until Aug. 30 arrives Frankfurt Flughafen 0311, Mainz 0331.

470 – 🛏 1, 2 cl. and 🛌 2 cl. (Ⓡ) Zürich - Basel - Braunschweig - Berlin. Also conveys 🚃2 (*IC* **60470**).

890 – 🚃12 ✕ Wien (**860**) - Innsbruck - Bregenz (**890**) - Lindau - Ulm - Frankfurt. Train category *IC* until Aug. 1.

40470 – 🛏 1, 2 cl. and 🛌 2 cl. (Ⓡ) Zürich - Basel - Hannover - Hamburg. Also conveys 🚃2 (*IC* **60400**).

A – ①–④ to July 28 (also June 17; not June 15); ①–④ from Sept. 12.
B – ⑤⑦ to July 29 (also June 15; not June 17); ⑤⑦ from Sept. 16.
C – ⑧ July 31 - Sept. 11.
M – To Münster (Table **800**).
P – 🚃12 🍷 Paris - Strasbourg - Stuttgart (- München ⑥).
Q – Daily to Aug. 4; ⑦–④ from Aug. 7.

f – Also June 15.
k – Not June 17.
n – Not July 30 - Sept. 11.
t – Arrives 2004.
z – On ①⑦ until Aug. 29 arrives Koblenz 2227, Köln 2332, Dortmund 0051.

* – Calls at Frankfurt Flughafen after Frankfurt (Main) Hbf.
♥ – From Aug. 2.
◇ – Continues to Kassel (Table **900**) on ⑥.
☆ – See panel on page 424 for other local services.
⊖ – 🏛 is at Kehl (8 km from Strasbourg). See Table **911** for local journeys Strasbourg - Offenburg.
◧ – Frankfurt Flughafen Fernbahnhof.

913 Local trains FRANKFURT - HEIDELBERG - KARLSRUHE

RE | RB | S-Bahn services

FRANKFURT - DARMSTADT - HEIDELBERG and MANNHEIM

			Ⓒw			Ⓐr			Ⓒw	Ⓐr		Ⓒw	Ⓐr		Ⓐr										
Frankfurt (Main) Hbf d.	0006b	...	0206	...	0406	0406	...	0506e	0506e	0533	0606e	0606e	0631	0706e	0736	...	0806	0834	0906e	0938	1006e	1034	1106e	1131	1206e
Darmstadt Hbf d.	0030	...	0226	...	0433	0433	...	0530	0530	0553	0630	0630	0653	0734	0758	...	0830	0853	0930	0956	1030	1053	1130	1150	1230
Bensheim d.	0055	...	0254	...	0458	0458	...	0557	0557	0610	0655	0655	0710	0758	0813	0832	0858	0910	0958	1011	1058	1110	1158	1211	1258
Weinheim (Bergstr) d.	0109	...	0307	...	0513	0513	...	0612	0612	0622	0710	0710	0722	0813	0826	0847	0913	0922	1013	1023	1113	1122	1212	1223	1313
Neu-Edingen / Friedrichsfeld a.	0123	...	0320	...	0525	0525	...	0625	0625	0631	0723	0723	0731	0825	0835	0858	0925	0932	1025	1032	1125	1132	1224	1233	1325
Mannheim Hbf a.	|	...	|	...	|	0546	...	|	0645	0646	|	0746	0743	|	0847	0913	|	0945	|	1046	|	1145	|	1246	|
Heidelberg Hbf a.	0134	...	0329	...	0539	...	...	0637	...	...	0736	...	...	0842	...	...	0939	...	1039	...	1139	...	1238	...	1339

											Ⓒw	Ⓐr												Ⓒw	
Frankfurt (Main) Hbf d.	1233	1306e	1331	1406e	1434	1506e	1534	1606	1634	1706e	1731	1734	1806e	1834	1906e	1906e	1931	2006e	2034	2106e	2106e	2206e	2206e	2234	2312c
Darmstadt Hbf d.	1253	1330	1350	1430	1453	1530	1553	1630	1653	1730	1750	1754	1830	1853	1930	1930	1951	2030	2053	2130	2130	2230	2230	2253	2333
Bensheim d.	1310	1358	1411	1458	1510	1558	1611	1658	1710	1758	1810	1831	1858	1910	1958	1958	2011	2058	2110	2155	2155	2255	2255	2310	2355
Weinheim (Bergstr) d.	1322	1413	1423	1513	1522	1613	1624	1713	1722	1813	1822	1843	1913	1922	2012	2012	2023	2113	2122	2210	2210	2310	2310	2322	0010
Neu-Edingen / Friedrichsfeld a.	1332	1425	1433	1525	1532	1625	1633	1725	1732	1825	1832	1853	1925	1932	2024	2024	2032	2125	2132	2222	2222	2322	2322	2330	0024
Mannheim Hbf a.	1344	|	1446	|	1545	|	1645	|	1745	|	1845	1905	|	1945	|	2041	2045	|	2142	|	2243	|	2345	2341	|
Heidelberg Hbf a.	...	1439	...	1539	...	1641	...	1739	...	1836	...	...	1939	...	2039	...	...	2141	...	2237	...	2337	...	...	0034

	Ⓒw	Ⓒw	Ⓒw		Ⓐr	Ⓐr			Ⓐr			Ⓐr	Ⓐr	Ⓒw	Ⓒw	Ⓐr									
Heidelberg Hbf d.	0022	...	0225	...	0423	...	...	0520	...	...	0622	...	...	...	0723	0724	...	0820	...	0920	...	1020	...	1120	...
Mannheim Hbf d.	|	0017	|	...	|	0450	0514	|	0606	0617	|	0650	0715	0715	|	|	0815	|	0915	|	1015	|	1115	|	1215
Neu-Edingen / Friedrichsfeld d.	0035	0035	0235	...	0433	0504	0535	0535	0616	0635	0635	0707	0728	0737	0737	0736	0828	0835	0925	0935	1028	1035	1128	1135	1228
Weinheim (Bergstr) d.	0049	0049	0253	...	0453	0518	0549	0549	0626	0648	0648	0720	0739	0749	0749	0748	0839	0848	0936	0948	1039	1048	1139	1148	1239
Bensheim d.	0104	0104	0307	...	0506	0534	0603	0603	0640	0702	0702	0735	0752	0802	0802	0802	0851	0901	0948	1001	1051	1101	1151	1201	1251
Darmstadt Hbf d.	0130	0130	0330	...	0530	0600	0630	0630	0658	0730	0730	0759	0809	0830	0830	0830	0907	0930	1005	1030	1107	1130	1207	1230	1307
Frankfurt (Main) Hbf a.	0148	0148	0348	...	0548v	0620	0648v	0648v	0716	0748	0748	0816	0832	0848v	0848v	0848v	0924	0948v	1024	1048v	1124	1148v	1224	1248v	1324

							Ⓒw	Ⓐr													Ⓒw	Ⓐr			
Heidelberg Hbf d.	1220	...	1320	...	1420	...	1520	1523	...	1620	...	1717	...	1820	...	1920	...	2020	...	2120	...	...	2220	...	2320
Mannheim Hbf d.	|	1315	|	1415	|	1515	|	|	1615	|	1715	|	1815	|	1915	|	2015	|	2117	|	2214	2216	|	2316	|
Neu-Edingen / Friedrichsfeld d.	1235	1326	1335	1428	1436	1528	1536	1536	1628	1635	1728	1735	1828	1835	1928	1935	2028	2035	2135	2135	2226	2235	2235	2335	2335
Weinheim (Bergstr) d.	1248	1337	1348	1439	1448	1539	1548	1548	1639	1648	1739	1748	1839	1848	1939	1948	2039	2048	2149	2149	2239	2248	2248	2349	2349
Bensheim d.	1301	1348	1401	1451	1501	1551	1601	1601	1651	1701	1751	1801	1851	1901	1951	2001	2051	2102	2203	2203	2251	2301	2301	0003	0003
Darmstadt Hbf d.	1330	1407	1430	1507	1530	1607	1630	1630	1707	1730	1807	1830	1907	1930	2007	2030	2107	2130	2230	2230	2307	2330	2330	0030	0030
Frankfurt (Main) Hbf a.	1348v	1424	1448v	1524	1548	1624	1648v	1648v	1724	1748v	1824	1848v	1924	1948v	2024	2048v	2124	2148v	2248v	2248v	2324	2348v	2348v	0048	0048

MANNHEIM - HEIDELBERG - KARLSUHE ⊠

S-Bahn ⊠		Ⓐt	Ⓒz	Ⓐt		Ⓐt	Ⓒz	Ⓐt				◇															
Mannheim Hbf ⊡ d.	0021	...	0436	0457	0535	0612	*0635*	0646	0729	0830	0930	and	1330	1429	1530	1559	1630	1700	1730	1759	1830	1930	2030	2137	2237	2304
Heidelberg Hbf ⊡ d.	0044	0407	0455	0515	0559	0632	0705	0707	0748	0847	0948	hourly	1349	1448	1548	1618	1648	1718	1748	1818	1848	1947	2053	2155	2255	2325
Bruchsal d.	0113	0435	0527	0544	0627	0701	0733	0734	0816	0918	1016	until	1416	1515	1616	1644	1716	1744	1816	1844	1915	2016	2121	2223	2333f	2353
Karlsruhe Hbf a.	0131	0452	0544	0559	0644	0718	0751	0751	0833	0936	1032		1432	1538	1632	1700	1737k	1801	1832	1859	1932	2032	2136	2238	2353	0013

S-Bahn ⊠		Ⓒz		Ⓐt	Ⓒz	Ⓐt	Ⓐt	Ⓒz	Ⓐt	Ⓒz	Ⓐt	Ⓐt	Ⓒz	Ⓐt			◇									
Karlsruhe Hbf d.	0011	0150	...	0420	0446	0446	0516	0520	0540	0607	0622	0648	0724	0728	0754	0828	and	1728	1757	1828	1858	1928	2028	2128	2228	2328
Bruchsal d.	0027	0205	...	0437	0503	0503	0533	0538	0556	0628	0644	0703	0741	0743	0814	0843	hourly	1743	1814	1843	1915	1943	2043	2143	2243	2343
Heidelberg Hbf ⊡ d.	0056	0234	...	0506	0533	0536	0602	0608	0631	0702	0712	0731	0814	0813	0843	0913	until	1813	1843	1913	1943	2013	2113	2214	2314	0014
Mannheim Hbf ⊡ a.	0114	0251	...	0522	0552	0552	0621	0626	0650	0719	0729	0748	0829	0829	0901	0929		1829	1901	1929	2001	2029	2129	2230	2330	0030

b – 0002 until Aug. 26.
c – 2302 until Aug. 26.
e – 3–5 minutes **earlier** until Aug. 26.
f – Arrives 2323.
k – 1732 on Ⓒ (also June 16, Nov. 1).
r – Not June 16.
t – Not June 16, Nov. 1.
v – 3–5 minutes later until Aug. 26.
w – Also June 16.
z – Also June 16, Nov. 1.
⊠ – Selected services.
◇ – Timings may vary by 1–2 minutes.
⊡ – See also Tables **918**, **919**, **923**, **924**.

Local trains KOBLENZ - FRANKFURT — 914

Koblenz - Bingen - Mainz - Frankfurt *(Linke Rheinstrecke)* ⊠

km				Ⓐt	Ⓐt	Ⓐt	Ⓒz	K		K		K		K		K		K		Y		⚒d			❦	❦	❦
0	**Koblenz** Hbf	d.	0507	0606	0617	0652	0707	0803	0904	1003	1104	1203	1304	1403	1504	1603	1704	1803	1902	2104		0552	0730		1930	2030	2152
19	Boppard Hbf	d.	0519	0618	0632	0704	0719	0815	0916	1015	1116	1215	1316	1415	1516	1615	1716	1815	1916	2116		0607	0744		1944	2044	2207
24	Boppard-Bad Salzig	d.	|	|	0636	|	|	|	|	|	|	|	|	|	|	|	|	|	|	|		0611	0748		1948	2048	2211
34	St Goar	d.	|	|	0645	|	|	|	|	|	|	|	|	|	|	|	|	|	|	|	A	0619	0756	and	1956	2056	2219
41	Oberwesel	d.	0533	0633	0651	0718	0733	0829	0930	1029	1130	1229	1330	1429	1530	1629	1730	1829	1930	2130	L	0625	0801		2001	2101	2225
47	Bacharach	d.	0537	|	0656	0723	0737	|	0936	|	1136	|	1336	|	1536	|	1736	|	1936	2136	S	0629	0806	hourly	2006	2106	2229
61	Bingen (Rhein) Hbf	a.	0546	0646	0709	0733	0746	0842	0946	1042	1146	1242	1346	1442	1546	1642	1746	1842	1946	2146	O	0643	0819		2019	2119	2243
61	Bingen (Rhein) Hbf	d.	0547	0647	0713	0734	0747	*0854*v	0947	*1056*v	1147	*1256*v	1347	*1456*v	1547	*1656*v	1747	*1856*v	1947	2147		0654	0824	until	2024	2127	2254
62	Bingen (Rhein) Stadt	d.	|	|	0716	|	|	*0857*v	|	*1059*v	|	*1259*v	|	*1459*v	|	*1659*v	|	*1859*v	|	|	⊡	0657	0827		2027	2129	2257
73	Ingelheim	d.	0556	0655	0722	0745	0755	*0907*v	0955	*1109*v	1155	*1309*v	1355	*1509*v	1555	*1709*v	1755	*1909*v	1955	2155		0707	0837		2037	2139	2307
91	**Mainz** Hbf	a.	0608	0708	0736	0757	0808	*0926*v	1008	*1126*v	1208	*1326*v	1408	*1526*v	1608	*1726*v	1808	*1926*v	2008	2208		0728	0900		2058	2156	2325
119	Frankfurt Flughafen ◧	a.	0634	0734	0805	0819	0834	...	1034	...	1234	...	1434	...	1634	...	1834	...	2034	...		...	...		...	...	...
130	**Frankfurt** (Main) Hbf	a.	0649	0749	0825	0836	0849	...	1049	...	1249	...	1449	...	1649	...	1851	...	2051	...		...	...		...	...	...

		Ⓐv		K		K		K		K		K	Ⓐt	S	ⒸzK	Ⓐt		Y		Ⓐv					❦	❦	❦
Frankfurt (Main) Hbf	d.	0456	0659	...	0908	...	1108	...	1308	...	1508	...	1626	1708	...	1826	1908	2108		...	...	...	...		...	...	...
Frankfurt Flughafen ◧	d.	0507	0708	...	0924	...	1123	...	1323	...	1524	...	1636	1724	...	1837	1923	2123e		...	...	...	...		...	...	...
Mainz Hbf	d.	0532	0732	*0832*v	0951	*1032*v	1151	...	1351	*1432*v	1551	*1632*v	1700	1751	...	1900	1951	2151		...	0547	0701	0803		2103	2203	2303
Ingelheim	d.	0547	0747	*0850*v	1002	*1050*v	1202	...	1402	*1450*v	1602	*1650*v	1711	1802	...	1911	2002	2202	A	...	0605	0719	0821	and	2121	2221	2321
Bingen (Rhein) Stadt	d.	|	|	*0900*v	|	*1100*v	|	...	|	*1500*v	|	*1700*v	|	|	...	|	|	|	L	...	0615	0734	0831		2131	2231	2331
Bingen (Rhein) Hbf	a.	0555	0755	*0903*v	1011	*1103*v	1211	...	1411	*1503*v	1611	*1703*v	1721	1811	...	1921	2011	2211	S	...	0618	0738	0834	hourly	2134	2234	2334
Bingen (Rhein) Hbf	d.	0556	0756	0913	1013	1113	1213	1313	1413	1513	1613	1713	1722	1813	1913	1922	2013	2216	O	0517	0626	0739	0839		2139	...	2335
Bacharach	d.	0604	0804	|	1021	|	1221	|	1421	|	1621	|	1734	1821	|	1930	2021	2228		0529	0638	0750	0850	until	2150	...	2346
Oberwesel	d.	0609	0809	0926	1026	1125	1226	1325	1426	1525	1626	1726	1739	1826	1925	1935	2026	2232	⊡	0533	0649	0754	0854		2154	...	2350
St Goar	d.	|	|	|	|	|	|	|	|	|	|	|	1745	|	|	|	|	2238		0539	0655	0800	0900		2200	...	2356
Boppard-Bad Salzig	d.	|	|	|	|	|	|	|	|	|	|	|	|	|	|	|	|	2247		0547	0703	0808	0908		2208	...	0004
Boppard Hbf	d.	0623	0823	0940	1040	1139	1240	1339	1440	1539	1640	1740	1754	1840	1939	1949	2040	2251		0551	0707	0812	0912		2212	...	0008
Koblenz Hbf	a.	0638	0838	0954	1054	1153	1254	1353	1454	1553	1654	1754	1809	1856	1953	2004	2054	2309		0610	0723	0827	0927		2227	...	0023

Neuwied - Koblenz - St Goarshausen - Wiesbaden - Frankfurt *(Rechte Rheinstrecke; operated by VIAS)*

km			Ⓐt	Ⓐt	Ⓐt	Ⓒz	Ⓐt	Ⓐt		Ⓐt					Ⓐt			Ⓐt		Ⓐt					⑤⑥f		⑤⑥f
0	**Neuwied** 802	d.	...	...	0437	...	...	0537	...	...	0637z	0737		1237	...	1337	1437	...	1537	...	1637		2037	2137	2137	2237	2237
15	**Koblenz** Hbf 802 906	d.	...	...	0452	...	...	0552	...	...	0652	0752		1252	1322	1352	1452	...	1552	1622	1652		2052	2152	2152	2252	2252
20	Niederlahnstein 906	d.	...	...	0459	...	...	0559	...	...	0659	0759		1259	1329	1359	1459	...	1559	1629	1659		2059	2159	2159	2259	2259
26	Braubach	d.	...	...	0506	...	...	0606	...	...	0706	0806	and	1306	1336	1406	1506	...	1606	1636	1706	and	2106	2206	2206	2306	2306
38	Kamp-Bornhofen	d.	...	...	0516	...	...	0616	...	...	0716	0816		1316	1346	1416	1516	...	1616	1646	1716		2116	2216	2216	2316	2316
50	St Goarshausen	d.	...	...	0527	...	...	0627	...	...	0727	0827	hourly	1327	1357	1427	1527	...	1627	1657	1727	hourly	2127	2227	2227	2327	2327
61	Kaub	d.	...	0506	0536	...	0606	0636	0636	0706	0736	0836		1336	1406	1436	1536	1606	1636	1706	1736		2136	2236	2236	2335	2336
67	Lorch (Rhein)	d.	...	0512	0542	...	0612	0642	0642	0712	0742	0842	until	1342	1412	1442	1542	1612	1642	1712	1742	until	2142	2242	2242	...	2342
79	Rüdesheim (Rhein)	d.	0453	0523	0553	0553h	0623	0653	0653	0723	0753	0853		1353	1423	1453	1553	1623	1653	1723	1753		2153	2253	2253	...	2353
109	**Wiesbaden** Hbf	a.	0525	0555	0625	0625h	0655	0725	0725	0755	0825	0925		1425	1455	1525	1625	1655	1725	1755	1825		2225	2325	2325	...	0025
109	**Wiesbaden** Hbf	d.	0532	0602	0632	0632	0702	0732	0732	0802	0832	0932		1432	1502	1532	1632	1702	1732	1802	1832		2232	...	2332	...	0032
117	**Mainz** Kastel	d.	0539	0609	0639	0639	0709	0739	0738	0809	0839	0939		1439	1509	1539	1639	1709	1739	1809	1839		2239	...	2339	...	0039
150	**Frankfurt** (Main) Hbf	a.	0605	0635	0705	0705	0735	0805	0805	0835	0905	1005		1505	1535	1605	1705	1735	1805	1835	1905		2305	...	0005	...	0105

		Ⓐt	Ⓐt		⚒r						Ⓐt		Ⓐt		Ⓐt		Ⓐt		Ⓐt		Ⓐt				⑤⑥f		T
Frankfurt (Main) Hbf	d.	...	...	...	0553t	0654	0754	0853		1353	1423	1453	1523	1553	1623	1654	1723	1754	1823	1853	1923	1953	2053	2153	2153	2253	2253
Mainz Kastel	d.	...	...	...	0619t	0719	0819	0919		1419	1449	1519	1549	1619	1649	1719	1749	1819	1849	1919	1949	2019	2119	2219	2219	2319	2319
Wiesbaden Hbf	a.	...	...	...	0628t	0728	0828	0928		1428	1458	1528	1558	1628	1658	1728	1758	1828	1858	1928	1958	2028	2128	2228	2228	2328	2328
Wiesbaden Hbf	d.	...	...	0533t	0633	0733	0833	0933	and	1433	1503	1533	1603	1633	1703	1733	1803	1833	1903	1933	2003	2033	2133	2233	2233	2333	2333
Rüdesheim (Rhein)	d.	...	0536	0606t	0706	0806	0906	1006		1506	1536	1606	1636	1706	1736	1806	1836	1906	1936	2006	2035	2106	2206	2306	2306	0005	0006
Lorch (Rhein)	d.	...	0545	0615t	0715	0815	0915	1015	hourly	1515	1546	1615	1646	1715	1745	1815	1845	1915	1945	2015	...	2115	2215	2315	2315	...	0015
Kaub	d.	0453	0553	0623	0723	0823	0923	1023		1523	1552	1623	1653	1723	1753	1823	1853	1923	1953	2023	...	2123	2223	2322	2323	...	0022
St Goarshausen	d.	0501	0601	0631	0731	0831	0931	1031	until	1531	...	1631	1701	1731	1801	1831	1901	1931	2001	2031	...	2131	2231	...	2331	...	...
Kamp-Bornhofen	d.	0512	0612	0642	0742	0842	0942	1042		1542	...	1642	1712	1742	1812	1842	1912	1942	2012	2042	...	2142	2242	...	2342	...	...
Braubach	d.	0523	0623	0653	0753	0853	0953	1053		1553	...	1653	1723	1753	1823	1853	1923	1953	2023	2053	...	2153	2253	...	2353	...	...
Niederlahnstein 906	d.	0529	0629	0659	0759	0859	0959	1059		1559	...	1659	1729	1759	1829	1859	1929	1959	2029	2059	...	2159	2259	...	2359	...	...
Koblenz Hbf 802 906	a.	0537	0636	0706	0806	0906	1006	1106		1606	...	1706	1736	1806	1836	1906	1936	2006	2036	2106	...	2206	2306	...	0006	...	...
Neuwied 802	a.	0556	...	0726	0826	0926	1026	1126		1626	...	1726	...	1826	...	1926	...	2026	...	2126	...	2226	2326	...	...	...	...

K – To/from Kaiserslautern (Table **918**).
S – To Saarbrücken (Table **915**).
T – ⑤⑥† (also June 15, 16).
Y – ②–⑤ to Aug. 26; daily from Aug. 30.

d – ⚒ (not June 16, Nov. 1); runs daily Bingen (Rhein) Hbf - Mainz.
e – Not Sept. 25.

f – Also June 15, Oct. 2.
h – ⑥ only.
r – Not June 16.
t – Ⓐ (not June 16).
v – Ⓐ (not June 16, Nov. 1).
z – Ⓒ (also June 16).

◧ – Frankfurt Flughafen Regionalbahnhof ✈.

⊡ – Stopping services (operated by Mittelrheinbahn).
❖ – Timings Bingen (Rhein) Hbf - Mainz may vary by up to 5 minutes.
❦ – The 1930, 2030, 2152 from Koblenz and 2103, 2203, 2303 from Mainz are subject to alteration on ①⑥⑦ until Aug. 29 (please check locally).
⊠ – See Table **800** for long-distance *ICE* / *IC* services. See Table **917** for other services Ingelheim - Mainz - Frankfurt and v.v. See Table **917a** for S-Bahn services Mainz - Frankfurt Flughafen ✈ - Frankfurt (Main) Hbf and v.v.

Köln Düsseldorfer Deutsche Rheinschiffahrt — KÖLN - KOBLENZ - MAINZ — *2022 service* — 914a

◐			A	A	B⛴	A	A	A	A	B⊠	B	C⊠	A
750	**Köln** (Rheingarten)	d.	...	...	...	...	...	...	...	...	0930	...	...
1600	**Bonn**	d.	...	...	...	...	...	...	...	1030	1230	1430	...
900	Königswinter Fähre	d.	...	...	...	...	...	...	...	1130	1330	1530	...
750	Bad Honnef (Rhein)	d.	...	...	...	...	...	...	...	1150	1350	1550	...
400	Remagen	d.	...	...	...	...	...	...	...	1220	1420	1620	...
750	Linz am Rhein	d.	...	...	...	...	...	...	...	1250	1450	1650	...
1500	Bad Breisig	d.	...	...	...	...	...	...	...	▬	...	...	...
400	Bad Hönningen	d.	...	...	...	...	...	...	...	...	...	...	...
1200	Andernach	d.	...	...	...	...	...	...	...	...	...	...	...
2200	**Koblenz** ⊙	d.	...	...	0900	...	...	1200	...	...	...	...	1750
150	Oberlahnstein	d.	...	...	0940	...	...	1240	...	...	...	...	1830
450	Braubach	d.	...	...	1005	...	...	1305	...	A	...	...	1855
400	**Boppard**	d.	...	1000	1100	...	1300	1400	...	1600	...	...	1945
400	Kamp-Bornhofen	d.	...	1010	1110	...	1310	1410	...	1610	...	...	...
300	Bad Salzig	d.	...	1025	1125	...	1325	1425	...	1625	...	...	...
450	**St Goarshausen** ★	d.	1045	|	1210	1310	|	|	1600	|	...	...	...
250	**St Goar** ★	d.	1055	1120	1220	1320	1420	1520	1610	1720	...	...	...
450	Oberwesel	d.	1125	...	1250	1350	...	...	1640	...	...	...	...
900	Kaub	d.	1140	...	1305	1405	...	...	1655	...	...	...	...
600	Bacharach	d.	1205	...	1330	1430	...	...	1720	...	...	...	...
400	**Bingen** (Rhein) ♥	d.	1335	...	1500	1600	...	...	1850	...	...	...	...
900	**Rüdesheim** ♥	d.	1350	...	1515	1620	...	...	1900	...	...	...	...
1500	Wiesbaden-Biebrich	d.	...	...	...	1800t	...	...	...	...	...	...	...
1600	**Mainz**	a.	...	...	...	1830t	...	...	...	...	...	...	...

		A	A	B⊠	A	A	A	A	A	A	B⛴
Mainz	d.	...	...	...	...	0915t	...	...	...	...	...
Wiesbaden-Biebrich	d.	...	...	...	...	0930t	...	...	...	...	...
Rüdesheim ♥	d.	0900	...	...	...	1100	...	...	1415	...	1615
Bingen (Rhein) ♥	d.	0915	...	...	...	1115	...	...	1430	...	1630
Bacharach	d.	1000	...	...	...	1200	...	...	1515	...	1715
Kaub	d.	1010	...	...	...	1210	...	...	1525	...	1725
Oberwesel	d.	1020	...	...	...	1220	...	...	1535	...	1735
St Goar ★	d.	|	...	...	1130	1240	1430	1530	|	1730	1755
St Goarshausen ★	d.	1045	...	...	1140	1250	1440	1540	1600	1740	1805
Bad Salzig	d.	...	...	...	1205	▬	1505	1605	...	1805	1830
Kamp-Bornhofen	d.	...	...	...	1215	...	1515	1615	...	1815	1840
Boppard	d.	...	1015	...	1230	...	1530	1630	...	1830	1850
Braubach	d.	...	1045	...	▬	...	▬	1700	...	...	1915
Oberlahnstein	d.	...	1100	...	...	...	...	1715	...	...	1930
Koblenz ⊙	d.	...	1145	...	...	...	...	1800	...	...	2000
Andernach	d.	...	...	...	...	...	...	...	...	...	...
Bad Hönningen	d.	...	...	...	...	...	...	...	...	...	...
Bad Breisig	d.	...	...	...	D	C	C⊠	...	...	...	...
Linz am Rhein	d.	...	...	1250	1450	1550	1650	...	...	...	...
Remagen	d.	...	...	1300	1500	1600	1700	...	...	...	...
Bad Honnef (Rhein)	d.	...	...	1325	1525	1625	1725	...	...	...	...
Königswinter Fähre	d.	...	...	1340	1540	1640	1740	...	...	...	...
Bonn	d.	...	...	1415	1615	1715	1815	...	...	...	...
Köln (Rheingarten)	a.	...	...	...	1800	1900	...	...	...	...	...

A – Apr. 9 - Oct. 23.
B – May 1 - Oct. 3.
C – ⑦–④ May 1 - Oct. 3.
D – ⑤⑥ May 6 - Oct. 1.

t – Not Apr. 9 – 30.

⊠ – Operated by Personenschifffahrt Siebengebirge.
⊙ – Koblenz (Konrad-Adenauer-Ufer).
◐ – Distance in metres from rail station to river landing stage.
⛴ – Operated by paddlesteamer *Goethe*.

★ – A frequent ferry service sails between St Goar and St Goarshausen operated by Rheinschifffahrt Goar. ✆ + 49 (0) 6771 26 20. www.faehre-loreley.de
♥ – A frequent ferry service sails between Bingen and Rüdesheim operated by Bingen-Rüdesheimer Fähr- und Schiffahrtsgesellschaft. ✆ + 49 (0) 6721 30808. www.bingen-ruedesheimer.de

Operator: Köln Düsseldorfer Deutsche Rheinschiffahrt, Frankenwerft 35, D-50667 Köln. ✆ +49 (0) 221 20 88 318. www.k-d.com

915 KOBLENZ - TRIER - LUXEMBOURG and SAARBRÜCKEN

RE services except where shown

Many Saarbrücken services continue to / start from stations in Table 919. **WARNING!** Journeys to / from Luxembourg are subject to alteration June 25 - Aug. 7, Sept. 17, 18, Oct. 1, 2.

km																								
		Ⓐ t	† w	Ⓐ t			†	⚒ r	⚒ r		⑥				⊠					D				
0	**Koblenz** Hbf d.	...	...	...	...	...	...	0603	0603	...	0706	0706	...	0806	0806	and at	1406	1406	1506	1506	1520	1606	1606	1706	1706
47	Cochem (Mosel) d.	...	...	0502	...	...	...	0638	0638	...	0741	0741	...	0841	0841		1441	1441	1541	1541	1555	1641	1641	1741	1741
59	Bullay d.	...	...	0513	...	...	...	0648	0648	...	0751	0751	...	0851	0851	the same	1451	1451	1551	1551	1603	1651	1651	1751	1751
76	Wittlich Hbf d.	...	...	0529	...	...	...	0700	0700	...	0803	0803	...	0903	0903		1503	1503	1603	1603	1616	1703	1703	1803	1803
112	**Trier** Hbf ● a.	...	...	0604	...	...	...	0731	0731	...	0830	0830	...	0930	0930	minutes	1530	1530	1630	1630	1642	1730	1730	1830	1830
112	**Trier** Hbf ● d.	0456	0533	...	0633	0637	0733	0733	0737	0737	0833	0837	0837	0933	0937		1533	1537	1633	1637	1646	1733	1737	1833	1837
163	**Luxembourg** a.	|	|	...	|	0724	|	|	0824	0824	|	0924	0924	|	1024	past each	|	1624	|	1724	1751	|	1824	|	1924
135	Saarburg d.	0514	0551	...	0651	...	0751	0751	...	...	0851	...	...	0951	...		1551	...	1651	...	...	1751	...	1851	...
161	Merzig (Saar) d.	0534	0610	...	0710	...	0810	0810	...	...	0910	...	...	1010	...		1610	...	1710	...	...	1810	...	1910	...
173	Dillingen (Saar) d.	0543	0619	...	0720	...	0820	0820	...	...	0920	...	...	1020	...	hour until	1620	...	1720	...	...	1820	...	1920	...
177	Saarlouis Hbf d.	0547	0623	...	0724	...	0824	0824	...	...	0924	...	...	1024	...		1624	...	1724	...	...	1824	...	1924	...
190	Völklingen d.	0557	0632	...	0732	...	0832	0832	...	...	0932	...	...	1032	...		1632	...	1732	...	...	1832	...	1932	...
200	**Saarbrücken** Hbf a.	0606	0641	...	0741	...	0841	0841	...	...	0941	...	...	1041	...		1641	...	1741	...	...	1841	...	1941	...

								Ⓒv				
			F		z			z			z	
Koblenz Hbf d.	1806	1806	1902b	1920	2020	2020	2119j	2119j	...	2220j	2220j	2321j
Cochem (Mosel) d.	1841	1841	1938	1955	2055	2055	2154	2154	...	2255	2255	2356
Bullay d.	1851	1851	1948	2003	2103	2103	2202	2202	...	2303	2303	0004
Wittlich Hbf d.	1903	1903	2001	2015	2115	2115	2214	2214	...	2315	2315	0016
Trier Hbf ● a.	1930	1930	2030	2041	2141	2141z	2240z	2240	...	2341z	2341	0042x
Trier Hbf ● d.	1933	1937	2033	2042	2143	2149z	2249z	2244	2244	2345z	2349	...
Luxembourg a.	|	2024	|	2131	2231	|	|	2331	2331	|	0035	...
Saarburg d.	1951	...	2051	...	...	2210	2310	...	...	0010	...	...
Merzig (Saar) d.	2010	...	2110	...	...	2230	2330	...	...	0034	...	...
Dillingen (Saar) d.	2020	...	2120	...	...	2240	2340	...	...	0046	...	...
Saarlouis Hbf d.	2024	...	2124	...	...	2244	2344	...	...	0050	...	...
Völklingen d.	2032	...	2132	...	...	2252	2352	...	...	0101	...	...
Saarbrücken Hbf a.	2041	...	2141	...	...	2301	0001	...	...	0114	...	...

	Ⓐ t		Ⓐ	Ⓒ w	† w	Ⓐ s	Ⓐ t	⚒ t		D
Saarbrücken Hbf d.	...	...	...	...	...	...	0458	...	0516	...
Völklingen d.	...	...	...	...	...	...	0506	...	0528	...
Saarlouis Hbf d.	...	...	...	...	...	...	0514	...	0539	...
Dillingen (Saar) d.	...	...	...	...	...	...	0518	...	0542	...
Merzig (Saar) d.	...	...	...	...	...	...	0527	...	0553	...
Saarburg d.	...	...	...	...	...	...	0547	...	0619	...
Luxembourg d.	...	...	...	...	...	0510	|	...	|	0613
Trier Hbf ● a.	...	...	...	...	...	0602	0606	...	0646	0707
Trier Hbf ● d.	0410x	...	0510	...	0525	0610	0610	0610	...	0710
Wittlich Hbf d.	0436	...	0536	...	0551	0636	0636	0636	...	0736
Bullay d.	0449	...	0549	...	0605	0649	0649	0649	...	0749
Cochem (Mosel) d.	0458	...	0558	0627	0627h	0658	0658	0658	...	0758
Koblenz Hbf a.	0536	...	0636	0718	0718	0736	0736	0736	...	0836

																		⑤	⑥					
				✣					⊕				z					z	z					
Saarbrücken Hbf d.	0619	...	0719		...	1619	...	1719	...	1819	...	1919	...	2019	...	2119	...	...	2222	2222	2232	...	...	2335	0034
Völklingen d.	0627	...	0727	and at	...	1627	...	1727	...	1827	...	1927	...	2027	...	2127	...	...	2231	2231	2244	...	...	2347	0045
Saarlouis Hbf d.	0636	...	0736		...	1636	...	1736	...	1836	...	1936	...	2036	...	2136	...	...	2239	2239	2255	...	...	2358	0056
Dillingen (Saar) d.	0640	...	0740	the same	...	1640	...	1740	...	1840	...	1940	...	2040	...	2140	...	...	2242	2242	2258	...	...	0001	0059
Merzig (Saar) d.	0648	...	0748		...	1648	...	1748	...	1848	...	1948	...	2048	...	2148	...	...	2250	2250	2309	...	...	0012	0111
Saarburg d.	0708	...	0808	minutes	...	1708	...	1808	...	1908	...	2008	...	2108	...	2208	...	...	2309	2309	2335	...	...	0038	...
Luxembourg d.	|	0733	|		1633	|	1733	|	1833	|	1933	|	2033	|	2133	|	2233	2233	|	|	|	2333	...	|	...
Trier Hbf ● a.	0727	0824	0827	past each	1724	1727	1824	1828	1924	1927	2024	2027	2124	2127z	2224	2227z	2324	2324	2328	2328	0001	0024	...	0105	...
Trier Hbf ● d.	0731	0831	0831		1731	1731	1831	1831	1931	1931	2031	2031	2131	2131z	...	2231z	...	2331	2331	...	...	...	...	...	...
Wittlich Hbf d.	0756	0856	0856	hour until	1756	1756	1856	1856	1956	1956	2056	2056	2156	2156	...	2256	...	2356	2356	...	...	...	...	...	...
Bullay d.	0809	0909	0909		1809	1809	1909	1909	2009	2009	2109	2109	2209	2209	...	2309	...	0009	0009	...	...	...	...	...	...
Cochem (Mosel) d.	0818	0918	0918		1818	1818	1918	1918	2018	2018	2118	2118	2218	2218	...	2318	...	0018	0018	...	...	...	...	...	...
Koblenz Hbf a.	0856	0956	0956		1856	1856	1956	1956	2056	2056	2156k	2156k	2256k	2256k	...	2356k	...	0056k	0056k	...	...	...	...	...	...

D – To / from Düsseldorf (Table **800**). Train classification is *IC* Koblenz - Düsseldorf and v.v.
F – From Frankfurt (Table **914**).

b – 1900 on ⑦.
h – Arrives 0614.
j – 24 – 26 minutes **earlier** Sept. 2 - Oct. 14, Oct. 29 - Nov. 13, Nov. 21 - Dec. 10 (by 🚌 to Kobern-Gondorf, then train).
k – 21 minutes later Sept. 2 - Oct. 14, Oct. 29 - Nov. 13, Nov. 21 - Dec. 10 (by train to Kobern-Gondorf, then by 🚌 to Koblenz).
r – Not June 16.
s – Not June 16, 23, Aug. 15, Nov. 1.
t – Not June 16, Nov. 1.
u – Also Nov. 1; not July 2 - Aug. 7.
v – Also June 16, Aug. 15, Nov. 1.
w – Also June 16, Nov. 1.
x – Not June 28 - Aug. 8.
z – Not June 27 - Aug. 7.

⊠ – The 0906 from Koblenz to Luxembourg requires a change of trains at Trier.
✣ – The 0833 from Luxembourg to Koblenz requires a change of trains at Trier on Aug. 15. The 1133 from Luxembourg to Koblenz requires a change of trains at Trier on June 16, Aug. 15, Oct. 3, Nov. 1. The 1333 from Luxembourg to Koblenz requires a change of trains at Trier on † (also June 16, Aug. 15, Nov. 1).
⊕ – Change trains at Trier on Ⓐ (not June 16, Aug. 15, Nov. 1).
● – Trier timings may vary by 1 – 2 minutes June 27 - Aug. 7 (the 1520 and 1920 from Koblenz terminate at Trier, arriving 7 – 8 minutes later).

BULLAY - TRABEN-TRARBACH

13 km Journey time: 18 minutes

Operated by Rhenus Veniro.

From Bullay at 0600 ⚒ t, 0658, 0838, 0938 and hourly until 2138.

From Traben-Trarbach at 0625 ⚒ t, 0741, 0901, 1001 and hourly until 2201.

TRIER - PERL - METZ

km		⑥⑦ u		⑥⑦ u			⑥⑦ u		⑥⑦ u	
0	**Trier** Hbf d.	1042	...	1942	...	**Metz** d.	0842	...	1742	...
49	Perl 🏛 d.	1120	...	2020	...	Thionville d.	0908	...	1808	...
70	Thionville a.	1153	...	2053	...	Perl 🏛 d.	0945	...	1845	...
100	**Metz** a.	1212	...	2120	...	**Trier** Hbf a.	1018	...	1918	...

Local *RB* services **Trier** - **Perl** and v.v. Journey time: 47 – 54 minutes.
Subject to alteration June 27 - Aug. 7. On June 16, Nov. 1 services run as on ⑦.
From Trier Hbf at 0506 Ⓐ, 0614 Ⓐ, 0706 ⚒, 0750, 0850, 0950, 1050, 1150, 1250, 1325 Ⓐ, 1350 Ⓒ, 1450, 1605, 1706, 1750, 1850, 1950, 2107, 2221 and 2322 ⑤⑥.
From Perl at 0505 Ⓐ, 0612 ⚒, 0649 Ⓐ, 0715 ⚒, 0815, 0915, 1015, 1115, 1215, 1317, 1415, 1515, 1613, 1715, 1815, 1915, 2015 and 2115.

915a KÖLN - EUSKIRCHEN - GEROLSTEIN - TRIER

Temporary service from June 12 until further notice. All services Kall - Gerolstein - Kyllburg and v.v. are operated by 🚌 owing to flood damage along the route. Services Köln - Kall and Kyllburg - Trier are by train. On June 16, Nov. 1 services run as on ⑦.

By Train	Ⓐ	⑥	Ⓐ	Ⓐ	⑥	Ⓐ		⚒														
Köln Hbf d.	...	...	...	0511	...	0546	0611	0646	0721	0746	and at the	1721	1745	1821	1847	1921	1943	2021	2046	2111	2148	2211	2246
Euskirchen d.	0430	0500	0530	0556	0600	0632	0658	0730	0800	0830	same minutes	1800	1830	1900	1930	2000	2030	2100	2130	2156	2230	2256	2330
Mechernich d.	0439	0509	0539	0608	0609	0642	0708	0742	0809	0842	past each	1809	1842	1909	1942	2009	2042	2109	2142	2208	2242	2308	2342
Kall a.	0447	0517	0547	0617	0617	0651	0717	0751	0817	0851	hour until	1817	1851	1917	1951	2017	2051	2117	2151	2217	2251	2317	2351

By Train		Ⓒ	Ⓐ	⚒	Ⓐ	Ⓐ	⚒	Ⓐ	⑥	Ⓐ	Ⓐ		⚒										
Kall d.	0005	0005	0505	0529	0559	0612	0642	0659	0705	0710	0727	0742	0805	0842	0905	and at the	2042	2105	2142	2205	2242	2305	2342
Mechernich d.	0014	0014	0514	0538	0608	0621	0649	0708	0714	0717	0736	0749	0814	0849	0914	same minutes	2049	2114	2149	2214	2249	2314	2349
Euskirchen d.	0026	0030	0530	0556	0626	0639	0703	0722	0730	0730	0750	0803	0830	0903	0930	past each	2103	2130	2203	2230	2303	2330	2359
Köln Hbf a.	...	0112	0612	0639	0712	0715	0739	0758	0812	0812	0834	0839	0912	0939	1012	hour until	2139	2212	2239	2315	2339	0012	...

By 🚌			⚒						Ⓐ	Ⓐ		Ⓐ											
Kall d.	0025	...	0525	0625	and	2325	...	A	0625	0825	and	2025	...	...	...	...	...	...	...	...	...	...	...
Blankenheim d.	0059	...	0544	0644	hourly	2344	...	L	|	|	every	|	...	...	...	...	...	...	...	...	...	...	...
Jünkerath d.	0130	...	0611	0711		0011	...	S	|	|	**two**	|	...	...	...	...	...	...	...	...	...	...	...
Gerolstein d.	0200	...	0641	0741	until	0041	...	O	|	|	hours	|	...	...	...	...	...	...	...	...	...	...	...
Trier Hbf a.	...	...	...	...		...	...		0820	1020	until	2220	...	...	...	...	...	...	...	...	...	...	...

By 🚌	Ⓐ	⚒							Ⓐ	Ⓐ		Ⓐ											
Trier Hbf d.	...	...	...	and	...	...	...	A	0539	0739	and	1939	...	...	...	...	...	...	...	...	...	...	...
Gerolstein d.	0406	0517	0617	hourly	2117	2159	...	L	|	|	every	|	...	...	...	...	...	...	...	...	...	...	...
Jünkerath d.	0436	0547	0647		2147	2229	...	S	|	|	**two**	|	...	...	...	...	...	...	...	...	...	...	...
Blankenheim d.	0503	0614	0714	until	2214	2300	...	O	|	|	hours	|	...	...	...	...	...	...	...	...	...	...	...
Kall d.	0523	0634	0734		2234	2334	...		0734	0934	until	2134	...	...	...	...	...	...	...	...	...	...	...

By train / 🚌					🚌	🚌			
Gerolstein d.	*0550**	and	*1850**	...	2113	2213	...	...	...
Kyllburg d.	0634	hourly	1934	...	2150	2250	...	...	...
Bitburg-Erdorf d.	0640	until	1940	...	2210	2310	...	...	...
Trier Hbf a.	0727		2027	...	0001	0101	...	...	...

By train / 🚌					🚌	🚌			
Trier Hbf d.	0535	and	1835	...	2100	2200	...	...	...
Bitburg-Erdorf d.	0619	hourly	1919	...	2251	2351	...	...	...
Kyllburg a.	0625	until	1925	...	2311	0011	...	...	...
Gerolstein a.	*0709**		*2009**	...	2348	0048	...	...	...

* – By 🚌.

KARLSRUHE - OFFENBURG - KONSTANZ 916

RE services except where shown

km		*IC* 60403	Ⓐ t	Ⓒ z									*IC* 2005 ⑤⑥ F 🍷									Ⓑ	⑥	Ⓑ H	G
0	**Karlsruhe** Hbf ...... **912 943** d.	0403	...	0456	0606	0702	0809g	0907	1007	1107	1207	1307	1336	1407	1507	1607	1707	1811	1907	2009	2116	2116	2209	2209	2308
21	Rastatt ...... **943** d.	|	...	0510	0619	0718	0824	0924	1025	1124	1224	1324	|	1422	1524	1624	1724	1825	1924	2024	2129	2129	2229	2229	2329
29	Baden-Baden ...... **912** d.	0427	...	0516	0625	0726	0831	0930	1031	1131	1231	1331	1354	1431	1531	1631	1731	1831	1931	2031	2136	2136	2236	2236	2335
69	**Offenburg** ...... **912 942** d.	0449	0523	0554n	0657	0759	0859	0959	1059	1159	1259	1359	1417	1459	1559	1659	1759	1859	1959	2059	2205	2205	2328h	2328h	0004
102	Hausach ...... **942** d.	▬	0548	0621	0722	0821	0922	1022	1122	1222	1322	1422	1439	1522	1622	1722	1822	1922	2022	2124	2229	2229	2352	2353	...
112	Hornberg (Schwarzw) ...... d.	...	0556	0629	0730	0829	0929	1029	1129	1229	1329	1429	1448	1529	1629	1729	1829	1929	2029	2132	2237	2237	...	0001	...
125	Triberg ...... d.	...	0609	0642	0743	0843	0943	1043	1143	1243	1343	1443	1503	1543	1643	1743	1843	1943	2043	2146	2250	2250	...	0015	...
140	St Georgen (Schwarzw) ...... d.	...	0625	0656	0757	0857	0957	1057	1157	1257	1357	1457	1520	1557	1657	1757	1857	1957	2057	2200	2305	2305	...	0029	...
155	Villingen (Schwarzw) ...... **938** d.	0551	0639	0705	0806	0906	1006	1106	1206	1306	1406	1506	1531	1606	1706	1806	1906	2006	2106	2209	2313	2314	...	0037	...
169	Donaueschingen ...... **938** d.	0602	0654k	0716	0816	0916	1016	1116	1216	1316	1416	1516	1542	1616	1716	1816	1916	2016	2116	2219	...	2323	...	...	...
188	Immendingen ...... **938** d.	0619	0706	0728	0828	0928	1028	1128	1228	1328	1428	1528	1554	1628	1728	1828	1928	2028	2128	2235	...	2336	...	...	...
204	Engen ...... **940** d.	0633	0719	0740	0840	0940	1040	1140	1240	1340	1440	1540	|	1640	1740	1840	1940	2040	2140	2247	...	|	...	...	...
218	**Singen** ...... **939 940** d.	0654j	0735	0752	0852	0952	1052	1152	1252	1352	1452	1552	1621	1652	1752	1852	1952	2052	2152	2303	...	2357	...	...	...
228	Radolfzell ...... **939** d.	0705	0746	0800	0900	1000	1100	1200	1259	1400	1500	1600	1630	1700	1759	1900	1959	2100	2200	2311	...	0004	...	...	...
248	**Konstanz** ...... a.	0727	0810	0816	0916	1016	1116	1216	1316	1416	1516	1616	1645	1716	1816	1916	2016	2116	2216	2330	...	0019	...	...	...

		Ⓐ t	⑥ s						*IC* 2006 ⑥ D 🍷	*IC* 2004 ⑦ E 🍷							Ⓒ z	Ⓐ t							
Konstanz ...... d.	...	0451	0502	...	0520	0640	0736	0839	0907	0907	0939	1039	1139	1239	1339	1439	1539	1539	1639	1739	1839	1939	2039	2158	2323
Radolfzell ...... **939** d.	...	0505	0516	...	0534	0656	0758	0856	0921	0921	0956	1056	1156	1256	1356	1456	1556	1556	1656	1756	1856	1956	2056	2222	2346
Singen ...... **939 940** d.	...	0512	0530	...	0546	0706	0807	0907	0930	0930	1007	1107	1207	1307	1407	1507	1607	1607	1707	1807	1907	2007	2106	2234	2358
Engen ...... **940** d.	...	0523	0539	...	0555	0715	0816	0916	|	|	1016	1116	1216	1316	1416	1516	1616	1616	1716	1816	1916	2016	2115	2250	0010
Immendingen ...... **938** d.	...	0536	0552	...	0612	0728	0830	0930	0951	0951	1030	1130	1230	1330	1430	1530	1630	1630	1730	1830	1930	2030	2128	2307	...
Donaueschingen ...... **938** d.	*0502*	0551	0603	...	0624	0740	0840	0940	1004	1004	1040	1140	1240	1340	1440	1540	1640	1640	1740	1840	1940	2040	2140	2319	...
Villingen (Schwarzw) ...... **938** d.	0535	0600	0612	...	0635	0750	0850	0950	1016	1016	1050	1150	1250	1350	1450	1550	1650	1650	1750	1850	1950	2050	2150	2328	...
St Georgen (Schwarzw) ...... d.	0544	0610	0621	...	0644	0759	0859	0959	1026	1026	1059	1159	1259	1359	1459	1559	1659	1659	1759	1859	1959	2059	2159	▬	...
Triberg ...... d.	0558	0625	0635	...	0659	0815	0914	1014	1041	1041	1114	1214	1314	1414	1514	1614	1714	1714	1814	1914	2014	2114	2213	...	...
Hornberg (Schwarzw) ...... d.	0612	0639	0649	...	0712	0826	0926	1026	1055	1056	1126	1226	1326	1426	1526	1626	1726	1726	1826	1926	2026	2128	2227	...	...
Hausach ...... **942** d.	0621	0649	0657	...	0720	0837	0937	1037	1104	1105	1137	1237	1337	1437	1537	1637	1737	1737	1837	1937	2037	2137	2235	...	...
Offenburg ...... **912 942** a.	0645	0721	0719	0734	0744	0859	0959	1059	1125	1126	1159	1259	1359	1459	1559	1659	1759	1759	1859	1959	2059	2159	2258	2302	...
Baden-Baden ...... **912** a.	0724	...	...	0800	0818	0927	1027	1127	1200	1200	1227	1327	1427	1527	1627	1727	1827	*1828*	1927	2027	2127	2227	...	2328	...
Rastatt ...... **943** a.	0731	...	...	0807	0825	0934	1034	1134	|	|	1234	1334	1434	1534	1634	1734	1834	*1835*	1934	2034	2134	2234	...	2334	...
Karlsruhe Hbf ...... **912 943** a.	0750	...	...	0821	0839	0949	1049	1149	1219	1220	1249	1349	1449	1548	1649	1749	1849	*1849*	1949	2049	2149	2249	...	2349	...

Through trains Stuttgart - Singen - Konstanz. **Warning!** Services in this panel do not run July 30 - September 11.

	Ⓒ z	*IC* 2389 Ⓐ	*IC* 2285 Ⓑ q	⑥
Stuttgart Hbf **940** ...... d.	0715	1516	2116	2117
Engen ...... d.	0913	1713	2313	2314
Singen ...... d.	0924	1727	2327	2328
Radolfzell ...... d.	0932	1736	2334	2336
Konstanz ...... a.	0948	1748	2346	2352

	⑦	*IC* 2284 ⚒	Ⓒ z	*IC* 2382 Ⓐ
Konstanz ...... d.	0603	0604	1648	1807
Radolfzell ...... d.	0620	0620	1704	1825
Singen ...... d.	0629	0629	1712	1835
Engen ...... a.	0637	0637	|	1843
Stuttgart Hbf **940** ...... a.	0843	0843	1916	2043

D – ⑥ (also Oct. 2, 31). SCHWARZWALD – [12] 🍷 Konstanz - Mannheim - Köln - Dortmund.
E – ⑦ (also Oct. 3, Nov. 1; not Oct. 2). SCHWARZWALD – [12] 🍷 Konstanz - Mannheim - Köln - Emden.
F – ⑤⑥ (also Oct. 2, 30, 31). SCHWARZWALD – [12] 🍷 Emden - Köln - Mannheim - Konstanz.

G – To Freiburg (Table **912**, panel on page 423).
H – Change trains at Offenburg on Ⓐ (not June 16, Nov. 1).

g – 0811 on † (also June 16, Nov. 1).
h – Arrives 2306.
j – Arrives 0645.
k – Arrives 0648.
n – Arrives 0540.
q – Not Oct. 2.
s – Also June 16, Oct. 3, Nov. 1.
t – Not June 16, Nov. 1.
z – Also June 16, Nov. 1.

FRANKFURT - MAINZ - IDAR OBERSTEIN - SAARBRÜCKEN 917

Vlexx

km			Ⓐ r		⚒ r												Ⓒ z	Ⓐ t		Ⓒ z	Ⓐ t	△	△	△
0	**Frankfurt** (Main) Hbf ...... **914** ‡ d.	...	...	...	...	0608t	0708	0808	...	1008	...	1202k	...	1408	...	1608	...	1726	1808	...	1924	2008	...	2208
11	Frankfurt Flughafen ✈ § **914** ‡ d.	...	...	...	...	0624t	0724	0824	...	1023	...	1223	...	1423	...	1624	...	1737	1824	...	1937	2023	...	2222
39	**Mainz** Hbf ...... **914** ‡ d.	...	...	...	0542	0655	0751	0852	0956	1053	1156	1254	1356	1453	1556	1652	1756	1800	1853	1956	2000	2053	2156	2253
57	Ingelheim ...... **914** d.	...	...	...	0555	0710	0805	0904	1010	1105	1210	1306	1410	1505	1610	1704	1810	1811	1905	2010	2011	2105	2210	2305
80	Bad Kreuznach ...... d.	...	0503	...	0611	0724	0822	0922	1024	1122	1224	1322	1424	1522	1624	1722	1824	1829	1922	2024	2026	2122	2224	2322
102	Bad Sobernheim ...... d.	...	0526	...	0634	0744	0843	0943	1045	1143	1244	1343	1444	1543	1644	1743	1844	1849	1943	2044	2046	2143	2244	2343
117	Kirn ...... d.	...	0540	...	0645	0754	0853	0953	1055	1153	1254	1353	1454	1553	1654	1753	1854	1859	1953	2054	2056	2153	2254	2353
131	Idar-Oberstein ...... d.	...	0602	...	0657	0805	0905	1005	1106	1205	1305	1405	1505	1605	1705	1805	1905	1910	2005	2105	2107	2205	2305	0005
170	St Wendel ...... d.	0557	0651	0659	0735	0836	0936	1036	1137	1236	1336	1436	1536	1636	1736	1836	1936	1941	2036	2136	2138	2236	2336	0036
179	Ottweiler (Saar) ...... d.	0606	0658	0708	0742	0842	0942	1042	1143	1242	1342	1442	1542	1642	1742	1842	1942	1947	2042	2142	2144	2242	2342	0042
184	Neunkirchen (Saar) ...... d.	0613	0705	0717	0751	0851	0951	1051	1151	1251	1351	1451	1551	1651	1751	1851	1951	1954	2051	2151	2151	2251	2351	0051
205	**Saarbrücken** Hbf ...... a.	0638	0723	0744	0810	0910	1010	1110	1210	1310	1410	1510	1610	1710	1810	1910	2010	2013	2110	2210	2210	2310	0010	0110

				Ⓐ t	Ⓒ z													△	△			△		
Saarbrücken Hbf ...... d.	0122	0342	0442	0545	0551	0651	0751	0851	0951	1051	1151	1251	1351	1451	1551	1651	1751	1851	1951	2035	2135	2151	2235	2351
Neunkirchen (Saar) ...... d.	0148	0400	0500	0603	0610	0711	0810	0911	1010	1111	1210	1311	1410	1511	1609	1711	1810	1911	2010	2100	2200	2214	2323e	0016
Ottweiler (Saar) ...... d.	0155	0406	0506	0609	0615	0716	0815	0916	1015	1116	1215	1316	1415	1516	1614	1716	1815	1916	2015	2107	2207	2219	2330	0023
St Wendel ...... d.	0204	0413	0513	0616	0622	0723	0822	0923	1022	1123	1222	1323	1422	1523	1621	1723	1822	1923	2022	2117	2217	2226	2339	0033
Idar-Oberstein ...... d.	...	0445	0545	0648	0652	0754	0852	0954	1052	1154	1252	1354	1453	1554	1653	1754	1852	1954	2052	...	...	2259	...	...
Kirn ...... d.	...	0456	0556	0659	0703	0806	0903	1006	1103	1206	1303	1406	1504	1606	1704	1806	1903	2006	2103	...	...	2310	...	...
Bad Sobernheim ...... d.	...	0506	0606	0709	0712	0816	0912	1016	1112	1216	1312	1416	1513	1616	1713	1816	1912	2016	2112	...	...	2319	...	...
Bad Kreuznach ...... d.	...	0527	0627	0737h	0733	0839	0933	1039	1133	1239	1331	1439	1533	1639	1733	1839	1933	2039	2133	...	...	2341	...	...
Ingelheim ...... **914** d.	...	0544	0644	0754	0747	0854	0947	1054	1147	1254	1347	1454	1547	1654	1747	1854	1947	2054	2147	...	...	0001	...	...
Mainz Hbf ...... **914** ‡ a.	...	0556	0656	0806	0759	0906	0959	1106	1159	1306	1359	1506	1557	1706	1757	1906	1959	2106	2159	...	...	0019	...	...
Frankfurt Flughafen ✈ § **914** ‡ a.	...	0619	0719	0833	...	0933	...	1133	...	1334	...	1534	1620t	1733	1820t	1933	...	2134	2236	...	...	...	...	...
Frankfurt (Main) Hbf ...... **914** ‡ a.	...	0633	0733	0849	...	0949	...	1149	...	1349	...	1549	1636t	1749	1836t	1949	...	2149	2249	...	...	...	...	...

e – Arrives 2259.
h – Arrives 0731.
k – 1208 on Ⓒ (also June 16).
r – Not June 16, Nov. 1.
t – Ⓐ (not June 16).
z – Also June 16.
‡ – See also Tables **800** and **917a**.
§ – Frankfurt Flughafen Regionalbahnhof.
△ – Timings Frankfurt - Mainz - Ingelheim and v.v. are subject to alteration on ①⑥⑦ June 12 - Aug. 29 (please check locally for amended timings).

FRANKFURT - FRANKFURT FLUGHAFEN ✈ - MAINZ - WIESBADEN 917a

S-Bahn 8/9

			v	w																					
Frankfurt (Main) Hbf .. d.	0002	0017	0047	0117	0217	0317	0417	0447	0502	0517	0532	0547	and at	2102	2117	2132	2147	2202	2217	2232	2247	2302	2317	2332	2347
Frankfurt Flughafen ★ d.	0015	0030	0100	0130	0230	0330	0430	0500	0515	0530	0545	0600	the same	2115	2130	2145	2200	2215	2230	2245	2300	2315	2330	2345	0000
Mainz Hbf ...... d.	|	0059	0129	0159	0259	0359	0459	0529	|	0559	|	0629	minutes	|	2159	|	2229	|	2259	|	2329	|	2359	|	0029
Mainz-Kastel ...... d.	0040	|	|	|	|	|	|	|	0540	|	0610	|	past each	2140	|	2210	|	2240	|	2310	|	2340	|	0010	|
Wiesbaden Hbf ...... a.	0049	0114	0144	0214	0314	0414	0514	0544	0549	0614	0619	0644	hour until	2149	2214	2219	2244	2249	2314	2319	2344	2349	0014	0019	0044

Wiesbaden Hbf ...... d.	0018	0048	0148	0248	0348	0409	0418	0439	0448	0509	0518	0539	0548	and at	2109	2118	2139	2148	2209	2218	2239	2248	2309	2318	2348
Mainz-Kastel ...... d.	|	|	|	|	|	0417	|	0447	|	0517	|	0547	|	the same	2117	|	2147	|	2217	|	2247	|	2317	|	|
Mainz Hbf ...... d.	0032	0102	0202	0302	0402	|	0432	|	0502	|	0532	|	0602	minutes	|	2132	|	2202	|	2232	|	2302	|	2332	0002
Frankfurt Flughafen ★ d.	0100	0130	0230	0330	0430	0445	0500	0515	0530	0545	0600	0615	0630	past each	2145	2200	2215	2230	2245	2300	2315	2330	2345	0000	0030
Frankfurt (Main) Hbf .. a.	0113z	0143	0243	0343	0443	0458	0513	0528	0543	0558	0613	0628	0643	hour until	2158	2213	2228	2243	2258	2313	2328	2343	2358	0013z	0043z

v – Runs 2–6 minutes later on ① (not Oct. 3).
w – Departure times are 2–4 minutes later on ① (not Oct. 3).
z – 3–7 minutes later on the mornings of ① (not Oct. 3).
★ – Frankfurt Flughafen Regionalbahnhof ✈.

918 RHEINLAND-PFALZ LOCAL SERVICES

RB / S-Bahn services

PIRMASENS - SAARBRÜCKEN

km		Ⓐt	⚒r	Ⓐt	⚒r					
0	**Pirmasens** Hbf d.	0515	0552	0622	*0732*	0832	and	1932	2032	...
7	Pirmasens Nord d.	0522	0559	0641	0743	0843	hourly	1943	2043	...
31	Zweibrücken Hbf d.	0552	0640	0713	0813	0913	until	2013	2113	...
67	**Saarbrücken** Hbf a.	0631	0723	0751	0851	0951		2051	2151	...

	⚒r	⑥	Ⓐt						
Saarbrücken Hbf d.	0602	...	0633	0705	0807	and	1907	2007	2107
Zweibrücken Hbf d.	0643	...	0713	0745	0845	hourly	1945	2045	2145
Pirmasens Nord a.	0715	0750	0741	0815	0915	until	2015	2115	2215
Pirmasens Hbf a.	*0728*t	0757	0753	0826	0926		2026	2126	2226

PIRMASENS - LANDAU (Pfalz)

km		Ⓐt	⑥	Ⓐt	Ⓐt					
0	**Pirmasens** Hbf d.	0438	0542	0544	*0622*	0702q	0802	and	2002	...
7	Pirmasens Nord d.	0450	0555	0609	0636	0718	0818	hourly	2018	...
55	**Landau** (Pfalz) Hbf a.	0546	0658	0708	0734	0818	0918	until	2118	...

	Ⓐt	Ⓐt	⑥						
Landau (Pfalz) Hbf d.	0527	0608	0641	...	0741	and	1841	1941	2041
Pirmasens Nord a.	0632	0715	0740	...	0840	hourly	1940	2040	2140
Pirmasens Hbf a.	0657	0728	0757	...	0857	until	1957	2057	2157

BINGEN - KAISERSLAUTERN - PIRMASENS

km			Ⓐt	⚒r						✣				Ⓒz	Ⓐt			m	Ⓑ	⑤⑥				
	Koblenz Hbf **914** d.	...	...	...	...	...	0803	...	...		...	1603	...	...	...	1803	...	...	...	...		1003	1203	1403
0	**Bingen** (Rhein) Hbf d.	...	...	0546t	0651r	0756	0843	0856	0956	and at	1556	1643	1656	1756	1756	1843	1856	1956	2056	2256	A	1043	1243	1443
16	Bad Kreuznach a.	...	...	0606t	0711r	0816	0855	0916	1016	the same	1616	1655	1716	1816	1816	1855	1916	2016	2116	2316	L	1055	1255	1455
16	Bad Kreuznach d.	...	0507	0607	0712	0827	0856	0927	1018	minutes	1618	1656	1727	1818	1834	1856	1927	2032	2127	2334	S	1056	1256	1456
43	Rockenhausen d.	...	0535	0635	0740	0856	0919	0956	1056	past each	1656	1719	1756	1856	1901	1929	1956	2059	2154	0001	O	1119	1319	1519
79	**Kaiserslautern** Hbf a.	...	0611	0712	0811	0926h	0952	1026	1126	hour until	1726	1752	1826	1926	1938	1959	2026	2130	2224	0033		1152	1352	1552
	Change trains	Ⓐt	⚒r	d										d					d	|				
79	**Kaiserslautern** Hbf d.	0516	0616	0735	0835	0935	...	1035	1135		1735	...	1835	1935	...	...	2035	...	2300	0053		...	...	...
108	Pirmasens Nord a.	0554	0702	0809	0909	1009	...	1109	1209		1809	...	1909	2009	...	...	2109	...	2332	0125		...	...	...
115	**Pirmasens** Hbf a.	0608	0719	0818	0918	1018	...	1118	1218		1818	...	1918	2018	...	...	2118	...	2341	0134		...	...	...

		Ⓐt	⊖				⊠																		
Pirmasens Hbf d.	...	0531	0637	...	0732f	0841		1341	1441	...	1541	...	1641	...	...	1741	...	1841	1941	2041		...	...	...
Pirmasens Nord d.	...	0538	0645	...	0750	0850	and at	1350	1450	...	1550	...	1650	...	...	1750	...	1850	1950	2050		...	...	...
Kaiserslautern Hbf a.	...	0610	0722	...	0826	0926	the same	1426	1526	...	1626	...	1726	...	...	1826	...	1926	2026	2126		...	...	...
Change trains	⚒r	⚒r					minutes				Ⓒz	Ⓐt	Ⓒz	Ⓐt		Ⓒz	Ⓐt							
Kaiserslautern Hbf d.	0520	0620	0736	0754	0832	0932	past each	1432	1532	1602	1632	1636	1732	1736	1802	1832	1836	1932	2032	2150j		1002	1202	1402
Rockenhausen d.	0551	0651	0805	0828	0901	1001	hour until	1501	1601	1628	1701	1710	1801	1805	1828	1901	1910	2001	2101	2223	A	1028	1228	1428
Bad Kreuznach a.	0620n	0720	0842	0851	0937	1031		1538	1631	1651	1738	1740	1829	1842	1851	1937	1940	2031	2137	2253	L	1051	1251	1451
Bad Kreuznach d.	0621n	0721	0843	0900	0941	1041		1541	1632p	1652p	1741	1741	1841	1843	1900	1941	1941	2041	2141	...	S	1100	1300	1501
Bingen (Rhein) Hbf a.	0642n	0742	0904	0912	1002	1102		1602	1653p	1704p	1802	1802	1902	1904	1912	2002	2002	2102	2202	...	O	1112	1312	1512
Koblenz Hbf **914** a.	...	...	...	0954	...	...		...	...	1754	...	...	...	...	1953c	...	...	...	...	...		1153	1353	1553

(KAISERSLAUTERN -) NEUSTADT - KARLSRUHE and WISSEMBOURG

km		Ⓐt	Ⓐt	Ⓐt	Ⓐt	⚒r	⚒r	Ⓐt	Ⓐt	†v	⑥		⑥	Ⓑ					D	†E		D	†E	
	Kaiserslautern Hbf **919** d.	...	...	...	...	...	...	...	0629	...	0629	...	...	...	...	0841v	...	0941	...	...	...	...	...	1141
0	**Neustadt** (Weinstr) Hbf **919** d.	0427	...	*0504*	...	0529	0608	0636	0659	0700	0709	0736	0805	0809	0836	0909	0936	1009	1036	1045	1109	1136	1145	1209
18	Landau (Pfalz) Hbf d.	0449	...	0535	...	0555	0634	0658	0713	0722	0722	0758	0822	0822	0858	0922	0958	1022	1058	1058	1122	1158	1158	1222
31	Winden (Pfalz) d.	0503	0505	0550	0555	0603	0650	0708	0722	0731	0731	0809	0831	0831	0909	0931	1009	1031	1109	1109	1131	1209	1209	1231
47	**Wissembourg** ▣ ◐ a.	|	0521	|	0615	|	|	0726	|	|	|	0827	|	|	0927	|	1028	|	1127	1127	|	1227	1227	|
44	Wörth (Rhein) d.	0520	...	0607	...	0617	0708	...	0735	0744	0744	...	0844	0844	...	0944	...	1044	...	...	1144	...	...	1244
58	**Karlsruhe** Hbf a.	0534	...	0619	...	0636	0725	...	0753	0754	0754	...	0854	0854	...	0954	...	1054	...	...	1154	...	...	1254

		Ⓐt	Ⓒz														†E							⑥
Kaiserslautern Hbf **919** d.	...	...	...	...	...	...	...	...	1541z	...	...	...	...	...	...	...	...	...	...	...	...	...	...	...
Neustadt (Weinstr) Hbf **919** d.	1236	1305	1309	1336	1409	1436	1509	1536	1609	1636	1709	1736	1809	1836	1909	1936	1952	2009	2104	2136	...	2230	2336	2336
Landau (Pfalz) Hbf d.	1258	1319	1322	1358	1422	1458	1522	1558	1622	1658	1722	1758	1822	1858	1922	1958	2008	2022	2122	2158	...	2252	2358	2359
Winden (Pfalz) d.	1309	1331	1331	1409	1431	1509	1531	1609	1631	1709	1731	1809	1831	1909	1931	2009	|	2031	2131	2213	2231	2306	...	0023e
Wissembourg ▣ ◐ a.	1327	|	|	1427	|	1527	|	1627	|	1727	|	1828	|	1927	|	2027	|	|	|	...	|	|	...	|
Wörth (Rhein) d.	...	1344	1344	...	1444	...	1544	...	1644	...	1744	...	1844	...	1944	...	2030	2044	2144	...	2244	2320	...	0038
Karlsruhe Hbf a.	...	1354	1354	...	1454	...	1554	...	1654	...	1754	...	1854	...	1954	...	2041	2054	2154	...	2254	2337	...	0049

	Ⓐt	Ⓐt	⑥	Ⓐt	Ⓐt	⑥	Ⓐt	Ⓒz	Ⓐt		Ⓐt	D	†E	Ⓑ	⑥									Ⓐt
Karlsruhe Hbf d.	0430	...	0528	0557	...	0611	0642	0705	0717	...	...	0805	0806	...	...	0905	...	1005	...	1105	...	1205	...	1305
Wörth (Rhein) d.	0447	...	0546	0617	...	0628	0652	0715	0736	...	...	0816	0816	...	...	0916	...	1016	...	1116	...	1216	...	1316
Wissembourg ▣ ◐ d.	|	0527	|	|	0626	|	|	|	|	...	0733	|	|	0832	0833	|	0933	|	1033	|	1133	|	1233	|
Winden (Pfalz) d.	0502	0547	0600	0631	0647	0641	0706	0727	0749	...	0758	0829	0829	0853	0853	0929	0953	1029	1053	1129	1153	1229	1253	1330
Landau (Pfalz) Hbf d.	0518	0601	0615	0645	0701	0703	0721	0736	0758	0807	0807	0838	0838	0903	0903	0938	1003	1038	1103	1138	1203	1238	1303	1339
Neustadt (Weinstr) Hbf **919** a.	0540	0622	0637	0704	0722	0724	0744	0751	0812	0826	0826	0851	0851	0924	0924	0951	1024	1051	1124	1151	1224	1251	1324	1351
Kaiserslautern Hbf **919** a.	...	...	...	...	...	...	0816	0816	...	...	...	...	...	...	...	1016	...	...	...	...	...	...	...	...

	Ⓒz						Ⓐt	Ⓒz	†E	D		†E	D							Ⓑ	⑥			
Karlsruhe Hbf d.	1306	...	1405	...	1505	...	1601	1605	...	...	1705	...	...	1805	...	1905	...	2005	...	...	...	2106	2206	2321
Wörth (Rhein) d.	1316	...	1416	...	1516	...	1616	1616	...	...	1716	...	...	1816	...	1916	...	2016	...	...	...	2116	2216	2331
Wissembourg ▣ ◐ d.	|	1333	|	1433	|	1533	|	|	1633	1633	|	1733	1733	|	1833	|	1933	|	...	2033	2103	|	|	|
Winden (Pfalz) d.	1329	1353	1429	1453	1529	1553	1629	1629	1653	1653	1729	1753	1753	1829	1853	1929	1953	2029	...	2053	2123	2131	2229	2344
Landau (Pfalz) Hbf d.	1338	1403	1438	1503	1538	1603	1638	1638	1701	1703	1738	1801	1803	1838	1903	1938	2003	2038	2103	2103	2131	2140	2238	2353
Neustadt (Weinstr) Hbf **919** a.	1351	1424	1451	1524	1551	1624	1651	1651	1712	1724	1751	1815	1824	1851	1924	1951	2024	2051	2124	2124	...	2201	2256	0012
Kaiserslautern Hbf **919** a.	1416	...	...	...	...	...	...	...	...	...	...	...	...	1919	...	...	...	...	...	...	...	2226b	...	...

GERMERSHEIM - SPEYER - MANNHEIM - HEIDELBERG

km		Ⓐt	Ⓒz	Ⓐt	⑥	Ⓐt	Ⓒz	Ⓐt				▲											
0	**Germersheim** **911a** d.	0409	0409	0559	0622	0704	0703	0727	0749	0812	0849		1912	1949	2014	2049	2114	2211	...	2257	2322	0006	...
14	Speyer Hbf **911a** d.	0423	0423	0613	0635	0713	0716	0740	0802	0825	0902	and at	1925	2002	2027	2102	2127	2224	...	2310	2335	0019	...
23	Schifferstadt **919** d.	0433	0433	0627	0647	|	0729	0801e	0811	0835	0911	the same	1935	2011	2046	2119	2148	2233	2238	2319	2351	0028	...
34	Ludwigshafen Hbf . **911a 919** d.	0451	0455	0640	0659	0726	0742	0814	0820	0847	0921	minutes	1948	2022	2057	2131	2201	...	2250	2330	0002	0040	0111
35	Ludwigshafen Mitte **919** d.	0453	0457	0643	0702	0729	0745	0816	0823	0850	0923	past each	1950	2024	2059	2133	2203	...	2254	2332	0006	...	0113
37	**Mannheim** Hbf **919** ⊡ a.	0456	0500	0645	0705	0732	0748	0819	0826	0853	0926	hour until	1953	2027	2102	2136	2205	...	2258	2335	0009	...	0116
54	**Heidelberg** Hbf **919** ⊡ a.	0515	*0552*	0704	0723	0753	*0816*	...	0844	0916	0945		2017	2046	2123	2154	2223	...	2322	2353	0037	...	0140

	Ⓐt	Ⓒz	Ⓐt	Ⓒz	Ⓐt	⚒r								▲									
Heidelberg Hbf **919** ⊡ d.	0506	*0533*	0602	*0608*	0643	0712t	0743t	0813	0843	0913	0943	1013	1043		1913	1943	2013	2033	2113	2144	2214	2244	2314
Mannheim Hbf **919** ⊡ d.	0526	*0554*	0622	0656	0705	0731	0804	0831	0904	0931	1004	1031	1104	and at	1931	2004	2031	2056	2137	2206	2243	2309	2338
Ludwigshafen Mitte **919** d.	0528	*0556*	0625	0658	0707	0733	0806	0833	0907	0933	1007	1033	1107	the same	1933	2007	2033	2058	2139	2209	2246	2311	2340
Ludwigshafen Hbf .. **911a 919** d.	0531	0610	0637e	0702	0710	0736	0810	0836	0910	0936	1010	1036	1110	minutes	1936	2009	2038	2103	2142	2214	2248	2315	2343
Schifferstadt **919** d.	0545	0623	0650	0717	0725	0752	0824	0847	0923	0947	1024	1047	1123	past each	1947	2023	2047	2120	2159	2234	2302	2326	2358
Speyer Hbf **911a** d.	0555	0632	0659	0726	0733	0802	0832	0856	0932	0956	1032	1056	1132	hour until	1956	2032	2056	2129	2208	2243	2311	2336	0007
Germersheim **911a** a.	0609	0645	0712	0740	0745	0817	0845	0909	0945	1009	1045	1109	1145		2009	2045	2109	2142	2221	2256	2323	2349	0020

D – ⚒ to Oct. 29 (not June 16, Nov. 1); daily from Oct. 31.
E – † to Oct. 30 (also June 16, Nov. 1).

b – Not ⑥.
c – Ⓒ (also June 16).
d – Daily.
e – Arrives 10 minutes earlier.
f – 0741 on † (also June 16, Nov. 1).
h – 0929 on † (also June 16, Nov. 1).

j – 2154 Aug. 7–11.
m – Change trains at Bad Kreuznach on Ⓐ (not June 16, Nov. 1).
n – On ⑥ Bad Kreuznach a. 0621, d. 0641, Bingen a. 0702.
p – 8–9 minutes later on Ⓒ (also June 16, Nov. 1).
q – Change trains at Pirmasens Nord on Ⓐ (not June 16, Nov. 1).
r – ⚒ (not June 16, Nov. 1).
t – Ⓐ (not June 16, Nov. 1).
v – † (also June 16, Nov. 1).
z – Ⓒ (also June 16, Nov. 1).

✣ – The 1056, 1256 and 1456 from Bingen depart Bad Kreuznach at 1127, 1327 and 1527 respectively (other timings follow the regular pattern).
⊠ – The 1032 and 1232 from Kaiserslautern arrive Bad Kreuznach 1137 and 1337 respectively (other timings follow the regular pattern).
⊖ – On † (also June 16, Nov. 1) Pirmasens Hbf d. 0641, Pirmasens Nord d. 0652, Kaiserslautern a. 0724.
▲ – Timings may vary by 1–2 minutes.
◐ – For Strasbourg connections see Table **396**.
⊡ – See also Tables **913**, **923** and **924**.

WIESBADEN - MAINZ - DARMSTADT - ASCHAFFENBURG — 918a

Hessische Landesbahn

km		©z		Ⓐt	⑥	⚒r								
0	**Wiesbaden** Hbf d.	0036	...	0436	...	0536	0536	0637	0736		2036	2136	2236	2336
10	**Mainz** Hbf a.	0048	...	0447	...	0548	0548	0648	0748	and	2048	2147	2248	2348
10	**Mainz** Hbf d.	0049	...	0449	...	0549	0549	0649	0749	hourly	2049	2149	2249	2349
43	Darmstadt Hbf a.	0121	...	0521	...	0621	0621	0721	0821	until	2121	2221	2321	0021
43	Darmstadt Hbf d.	...	...	0530	0532	0630	...	0731	0831		2131	2231	2331	...
87	**Aschaffenburg** Hbf a.	...	...	0615	0615	0712	...	0812	0912		2212	2312	0012	...

	Ⓐt		Ⓐt											⑤⑥f
Aschaffenburg Hbf d.	...	...	0443	0540r	0643r	0747		1747	1847	1947	2047	2147	2247	2347
Darmstadt Hbf a.	...	...	0527	0626r	0726r	0827	and	1827	1927	2027	2127	2227	2327	0027
Darmstadt Hbf d.	0438	0538	0538	0638	0738	0838	hourly	1838	1938	2038	2138	2238	2338	0038
Mainz Hbf a.	0510	0611	0611	0711	0812	0911	until	1911	2011	2111	2211	2312	0012	0111
Mainz Hbf d.	0512	0613	0613	0713	0814	0913		1913	2013	2113	2213	2313	0013	0113
Wiesbaden Hbf a.	0527	0625	0625	0727	0827	0927		1927	2028	2127	2227	2327	0027	0127

f – ⑤⑥ (also June 15, Oct. 2); runs daily Aschaffenburg - Darmstadt.
r – ⚒ (not June 16).
t – Not June 16.
z – Also June 16.

☛ Additional services run Wiesbaden - Darmstadt and v.v. on ⚒, Darmstadt - Aschaffenburg and v.v. on Ⓐ.

SAARBRÜCKEN - MANNHEIM - FRANKFURT and STUTTGART — 919

Additional S-Bahn services run Kaiserslautern - Mannheim - Heidelberg and v.v.

km						*EC* 217					*ICE* 935							*ICE* 2059				*TGV* 9551		
		©z	©z	Ⓐt	⚒r	‡ G🍸			Ⓐt		A✕	†z				Ⓐa	†	⚒ 🍸				P🍸		
	Trier Hbf **915** ● d.	...	...	...	...	...	...	...	0456	...	...	0533	...	0633	...	0733	0733	...	...	0833	...	...	...	1033
0	**Saarbrücken** Hbf d.	...	...	0444	...	0537	...	0550	0608	...	0628	0647	0700	0747	0801	0847	0847	0851	0902	0947	1002	1058	1102	1147
31	Homburg (Saar) Hbf d.	...	...	0505	0540	0558	...	0620	0632	...	0650	0709	0727	0809	0828	0909	0909	0916	0928	1009	1028	|	1128	1209
67	**Kaiserslautern** Hbf a.	...	...	0527	0609	0621	...	0650	0653	...	0712	0729	0754	0829	0854	0929	0936	0935	0954	1029	1054	1134	1154	1229
67	**Kaiserslautern** Hbf d.	0009	0511	0528	0611	0623	←	...	0654	0702	0714	0730	0758	0834	0858	...	0937	0937	0958	1034	1058	1136	1158	1234
100	Neustadt (Weinstr) Hbf d.	0042	0544	0551	0641	0647	0650	...	0717	0732	0740	0759	0830	0859	0930	...	1000	1001	1031j	1059	1130	|	1230j	1259
117	Schifferstadt **918** d.	0057	0559	|	→	|	0707	...	|	0747	|	|	0845	|	0945	...	|	|	1045	|	1145	|	1245	|
128	Ludwigshafen Hbf **918** d.	0111	0612	0609	...	0705	0719	...	0737	0800	|	|	0857	|	0957	...	|	|	1057	|	1158	|	1257	|
129	Ludwigshafen Mitte **918** d.	0113	0614	|	...	|	0722	...	|	0802	|	0817	0900	0917	1000	...	1017	|	1100	1117	1200	|	1300	1317
131	**Mannheim** Hbf **918** a.	0116	0617	0616	...	0709	0725	...	0745	0805	0800	0821	0903	0921	1003	...	1021	1021	1103	1121	1203	1217	1303	1321
131	**Mannheim** Hbf ... **912 918** ▽ d.	0121	0628	0629	...	0711	0729	...	0748	0807	0802	0830	0907	0930	1007	...	1030	1023	1107	1130	1206	1219	1308	1330
	Heidelberg Hbf ... **912 918** a.	0140	0645	0642	...	|	0744	...	0801	0823	|	0844	0923	0945	1023	...	1045	|	1123	1144	1223	|	1323	1345
	Stuttgart Hbf **912** a.	...	...	...	...	0753	...	...	...	...	|	...	...	...	...	...	...	1105b	...	...	...	|	...	...
	Bensheim ▽ a.	...	...	...	...	...	...	...	...	...	0825	...	...	...	...	...	...	...	...	...	...	|	...	...
191	Darmstadt Hbf ▽ a.	...	...	...	...	...	...	...	...	...	0838	...	...	...	...	...	...	...	...	...	...	|	...	...
219▲	**Frankfurt** (Main) Hbf ▽ a.	...	...	...	...	...	...	...	...	...	0856	...	...	...	...	...	...	...	...	...	...	1259	...	...

						ICE 9553									*ICE* 9555					*ICE* 9557				
						P✕								⑥	Ⓑ P✕				Ⓑ	⊡ P✕			†z	⚒r
Trier Hbf **915** ● d.	...	1133	...	1233	...	...	...	1433	...	1533	...	1633	...	1733	...	...	1833	...	1933	...	...	2033	...	...
Saarbrücken Hbf d.	1202	1247	1302	1347	1402	1459	1503	1547	1601	1647	1702	1747	1802	1847	1859	1903	1947	2002	2047	2059	...	2147	...	...
Homburg (Saar) Hbf d.	1228	1309	1328	1409	1428	|	1528	1609	1628	1709	1728	1809	1828	1909	|	1928	2009	2028	2109	|	...	2209	...	...
Kaiserslautern Hbf a.	1254	1329	1354	1429	1454	1535	1554	1629	1654	1729	1754	1829	1854	1929	1935	1954	2029	2054	2130	2135	...	2229	...	...
Kaiserslautern Hbf d.	1258	1334	1358	1434	1458	1537	1558	1634	1658	1734	1758	1834	1858	1934	1937	1958	2034	2058	▬	2136	2145	2230	2300	2301
Neustadt (Weinstr) Hbf d.	1330	1359	1430	1459	1530j	|	1630	1659	1730	1759	1830	1859	1930	1959	|	2030	2059	2130	...	|	2214	2302n	2332	2330
Schifferstadt **918** d.	1345	|	1445	|	1545	|	1645	|	1745	|	1845	|	1945	|	|	2046	|	2145	2148	|	2238k	2315	2351	2351
Ludwigshafen Hbf **918** d.	1357	|	1457	|	1557	|	1657	|	1757	|	1857	|	1957	|	|	2057	|	...	2201	|	2250	|	0002	0002
Ludwigshafen Mitte **918** d.	1400	1417	1500	1517	1600	|	1700	1717	1800	1817	1900	1917	2000	2017	|	2059	2117	...	2203	|	2254	2326	0006	0006
Mannheim Hbf **918** a.	1403	1421	1503	1521	1603	1617	1703	1721	1803	1821	1903	1921	2003	2021	2017	2102	2121	...	2205	2217	2258	2330	0009	0009
Mannheim Hbf .... **912 918** ▽ d.	1407	1429	1507	1530	1607	1619	1707	1730	1807	1830	1907	1930	2007	2030	2019	2107	2137	...	2207	2219	2304	2336	0021	0021
Heidelberg Hbf .... **912 918** a.	1423	1443	1523	1546	1623	|	1723	1745	1823	1845	1923	1945	2023	2046	|	2123	2154	...	2223	|	2322	2353	0037	0037
Stuttgart Hbf **912** a.	...	...	...	...	...	|	...	...	...	...	...	...	...	...	|	...	...	...	...	|	...	...	...	...
Frankfurt (Main) Hbf ▽ a.	...	...	...	...	...	1659	...	...	...	...	...	...	...	...	2059	...	...	...	...	2259	...	...	...	...

						ICE 9558						*ICE* 9586					*ICE* 9556						*ICE* 9554	
	⚒w	Ⓐa	©z	Ⓐt	Ⓐt	①–⑤ P✕	Ⓐt	⑥		Ⓑ	⑥	⑥ P✕	Ⓑ				①–⑤ P✕		⑥⑦				⑥⑦ P✕	Ⓐ
Frankfurt (Main) Hbf ▽ d.	...	...	...	...	...	0556	...	...	...	...	...	0656	...	...	...	...	0856	...	...	...	...	...	1056	...
Stuttgart Hbf **912** d.	...	...	...	...	...	|	...	...	...	...	...	|	...	...	...	...	|	...	...	...	...	...	|	...
Heidelberg Hbf .... **912 918** d.	...	...	0533	0536	0602	|	...	...	0631t	...	0656	|	0712v	0734	0817y	0834	|	...	0913	0933	1013	1033	|	1113
Mannheim Hbf .... **912 918** ▽ a.	...	...	0552	0552	0621	0639	...	...	0650t	...	0712	0738	0729v	0753	0836y	0851	0939	...	0929	0951	1029	1051	1140	1129
Mannheim Hbf **918** d.	...	...	0554	0554	0628	0640	...	...	0656	...	0718	0740	0736	0756	0839	0856	0940	...	0939	0954	1036	1056	1142	1139
Ludwigshafen Mitte **918** d.	...	...	0556	0556	0631	|	...	...	0658	...	0721	|	0739	0758	0842	0858	|	...	0942	0956	1040	1058	|	1142
Ludwigshafen Hbf **918** d.	...	...	0600	0600	|	|	...	...	0702	...	|	|	0743	0804	|	0903	|	...	|	1002	|	1103	|	|
Schifferstadt **918** d.	...	...	0613	0611	|	|	...	...	0713	...	|	|	|	0815	|	0915	|	...	|	1015	|	1115	|	|
Neustadt (Weinstr) Hbf d.	...	...	0632	0632	0648	|	←	...	0731	...	0739	|	0800	0832	0900	0932	|	...	1000	1032	1100	1132	|	1200
Kaiserslautern Hbf a.	...	...	0659	0659	0716	0721	0716	...	0759	...	0802	0822	0824	0859	0924	1000	1021	...	1024	1059	1124	1159	1223	1224
Kaiserslautern Hbf d.	0425	0623	...	...	→	0722	0731	0731	...	0803	0803	0823	0831	0903	0931	1003	1022	1031	1031	1103	1131	1203	1224	1231
Homburg (Saar) Hbf d.	0501	0653	...	...	...	|	0752	0752	...	0832	0831	|	0852	0930	0952	1030	|	1052	1052	1130	1152	1230	|	1252
Saarbrücken Hbf a.	0535	0716	...	...	...	0759	0816	0816	...	0858	0858	0902	0915	0956	1015	1056	1100	1115	1115	1156	1215	1256	1302	1315
Trier Hbf **915** ● a.	...	0827	...	...	...	...	0927	0927	...	...	1027	...	1027	...	1127	...	...	1227	1227	...	1327	...	...	1427

				TGV 9552									*ICE* 2058				*ICE* 9550			*EC* 216		*ICE* 836		
				P🍸									Ⓑ 🍸				Ⓑ P✕	⑥		¶ G🍸		B✕		
Frankfurt (Main) Hbf ▽ d.	...	...	...	1256	...	...	...	...	...	...	...	...	...	...	...	...	1856	...	...	...	...	2102	...	...
Darmstadt Hbf ▽ d.	...	...	...	|	...	...	...	...	...	...	...	...	...	...	...	...	|	...	...	...	...	2119	...	...
Bensheim ▽ d.	...	...	...	|	...	...	...	...	...	...	...	...	...	...	...	...	|	...	...	...	...	2132	...	...
Stuttgart Hbf **912** d.	...	...	...	|	...	...	...	...	...	...	...	...	1653	...	...	...	|	...	...	2004	...	|	...	...
Heidelberg Hbf .... **912 918** d.	1133	1213	1233	|	1335	1413	1433	1513	1533	1613	1632	1713	|	1733	1813	1833	|	1913	1933	|	2033	|	2214	2314
Mannheim Hbf .... **912 918** ▽ a.	1151	1229	1251	1338	1351	1429	1451	1529	1549	1629	1650	1729	1746	1751	1829	1851	1939	1929	1951	2048	2051	2155	2230	2330
Mannheim Hbf **918** d.	1156	1236	1256	1342	1356	1439	1456	1539	1556	1636	1656	1735	1748	1756	1836	1856	1940	1939	1956	2050	2056	2157	2239	2338
Ludwigshafen Mitte **918** d.	1158	1240	1258	|	1358	1442	1458	|	1558	|	1658	1739	|	1758	1840	1858	|	1942	1958	|	2058	|	2242	2340
Ludwigshafen Hbf **918** d.	1203	|	1303	|	1403	|	1503	1544	1603	1644	1703	|	|	1805	|	1903	|	|	2002	|	2103	|	|	2343
Schifferstadt **918** d.	1215	|	1315	|	1415	|	1515	|	1616	|	1715	|	|	1816	|	1915	|	|	2015	|	2115	|	|	0002
Neustadt (Weinstr) Hbf d.	1232	1300	1332	|	1432	1500	1532	1600	1632	1700	1732	1800	1811	1832	1900	1932	|	2000	2032	2111	2132	2219	2302	0019
Kaiserslautern Hbf a.	1259	1324	1359	1423	1459	1524	1559	1624	1659	1724	1759	1824	1833	1859	1924	1959	2021	2024	2059	2132	2159	2242	2327	0047
Kaiserslautern Hbf d.	1303	1331	1403	1424	1503	1531	1603	1631	1703	1731	1803	1830	1835	1903	1931	2003	2022	2031	2105	2134	2205	2244	2329	...
Homburg (Saar) Hbf d.	1330	1352	1430	|	1530	1552	1631	1652	1730	1752	1830	1850	1856	1930	1952	2030	|	2052	2133	2156	2233	2305	2356	...
Saarbrücken Hbf a.	1356	1415	1456	1502	1558	1615	1659	1715	1758	1815	1856	1912	1918	1956	2015	2056	2100	2115	2159	2218	2259	2329	0019	...
Trier Hbf **915** ● a.	...	1527	...	...	...	1727	...	1828	...	1927	...	2027	...	...	2127x	...	...	2227x	...	...	...	...	...	...

A – 🚃12 ✕ Saarbrücken - Frankfurt - Erfurt - Halle - Berlin.
B – 🚃12 ✕ Hamburg - Berlin - Halle - Erfurt - Frankfurt - Saarbrücken and v.v.
G – DACHSTEIN – 🚃12 🍸 (Graz - Salzburg ★ -) München - Stuttgart - Saarbrücken and v.v.
P – From / to Paris (Table 390). Ⓡ for international journeys.

a – Not June 16.
b – 1119 July 30 - Sept. 10.
j – Arrives 5–6 minutes earlier.

k – Arrives 2229.
n – 2300 on ⑦.
r – Not June 16, Nov. 1.
t – Ⓐ (not June 16, Nov. 1).
v – 10 minutes **earlier** on † (also June 16, Nov. 1).
w – Not June 16, Aug. 15, Nov. 1.
x – Not June 27 - Aug. 7.
y – On © (also June 16, Nov. 1) Heidelberg d. *0814*, Mannheim a. *0829*.
z – Also June 16, Nov. 1.

★ – From Aug. 2.
● – Trier timings may vary by 1–2 minutes June 27 - Aug. 7.
¶ – Runs as *IC* **2396** until Aug. 1.
‡ – Runs as *IC* **2397** until Aug. 1.
⊡ – On ⑥ runs as *TGV* **9559** (🍸).
▽ – See also Table **912** (*ICE* trains) and Table **913** (local trains).
▲ – *209 km* for trains running non-stop Mannheim - Frankfurt.

920 FRANKFURT - NÜRNBERG - PASSAU (- WIEN)

See Table **921** for other regional trains. See Table **927** for services operated by FlixTrain.

km		NJ	NJ	NJ	NJ						IC	RE	RE		ICE	ICE	ICE	ICE	ICE	ICE	ICE	ICE	ICE	ICE
		491	**40491**	**421**	**40421**						**95**	**59493**	**59275**		**827**	**521**	**21**	**523**	**523**	**525**	**23**	**527**	**529**	**91**
		🅁	🅁	🅁	🅁	⚒t	⚒t		Ⓐt	©z		Ⓐr	©H		①–⑥				①–⑥					
		N	NL	A△	J△	◐			◐	◐	R				✕	✕	✕	✕	✕	✕	✕	G✕	✕	✕
	Hamburg Hbf **800 900** d.	2029	2029	...	...	...	...	...	...	...	...	...	...	...	...	...	...	...	...	...	...	...	...	...
	Dortmund Hbf **800** ▷ d.	|	|	...	...	...	...	...	...	...	...	...	...	...	...	...	...	...	0401	0522	0431	0622	0722	0627
	Essen Hbf **800** ▷ d.	|	|	...	...	...	...	...	...	...	...	...	...	...	...	...	...	...	0427	0549	0457	0651	0750	|
	Düsseldorf Hbf **800** ▷ d.	|	|	2144	2144	...	...	...	...	...	...	...	...	...	...	...	...	...	0454	0617	0524	0718	0818	|
	Köln Hbf **800 910** d.	|	|	2216	2216	...	...	...	...	...	...	...	...	...	0319	0422	...	...	|	|	0553	|	|	0753
	Köln Messe/Deutz **910** d.	|	|	|	|	...	...	...	...	...	...	...	...	...	|	|	...	...	0520	0644	|	0744	0844	|
	Bonn Hbf **800** d.	|	|	2311	2311	...	...	...	...	...	...	...	...	...	|	|	...	...	|	|	0614	|	|	0814
	Koblenz Hbf **800** d.	|	|	2346	2346	...	...	...	...	...	...	...	...	...	|	|	...	...	|	|	0648	|	|	0848
	Mainz Hbf **800** d.	|	|	0041	0041	...	...	...	...	...	...	...	...	...	|	|	...	...	|	|	0740	|	|	0942
0	**Frankfurt** Flughafen ✈ § d.	|	|	0103	0103	...	...	...	...	...	...	...	...	...	0437	0529	...	...	0637	0736	0801	0836	0936	1001
11	**Frankfurt** (Main) Hbf d.	|	|	0117‡	0117‡	...	...	...	...	...	...	...	...	...	0454	0554	0604	0654	0654	0754	0812‡	0854	0954	1011‡
35	Hanau Hbf d.	|	|	|	|	...	...	...	...	...	...	...	...	...	|	0610	0620	|	|	|	|	|	|	|
57	Aschaffenburg Hbf d.	|	|	|	|	...	...	...	...	...	...	...	...	...	0523	0624	|	0723	0723	0823	|	0923	1023	|
136	**Würzburg** Hbf **900** d.	0135	0135	0241	0241	...	...	...	...	...	...	...	...	...	0627	0730	0735	0827	0827	0927	0934	1027	1127	1134
238	**Nürnberg** Hbf **900** a.	0253	0253	0336	0336	...	...	...	...	...	...	...	...	...	0720	0824	0827	0921	0921	1020	1028	1120	1220	1228
238	**Nürnberg** Hbf d.	0408	0435	0435	0408	...	...	...	*0501*	*0521*	0600	0615	0705	...	0723	0827	0831	0924	0924	1023	1031	1123	1223	1231
	München Hbf **904** a.	|	0711	0711	|	...	...	...	|	|	|	|	|	...	0833	0939	|	1033	1033	1130	|	1233	1334	|
271	Neumarkt (Oberpf) d.	|	...	...	|	0445	...	...	0549	0610	|	0638	0726	...	...	...	|	...	...	...	|	...	...	|
335	**Regensburg** Hbf d.	0507	...	...	0507	0540	...	...	0653d	0707	0717	0726	0818	...	...	...	0926	...	...	...	1126	...	...	1326
375	Straubing d.	|	...	...	|	0607	...	...	0722	0734	0740	...	0844	...	...	...	|	...	...	...	|	...	...	|
400	Plattling **944** d.	|	...	...	|	0623	0642	...	0738	0748	0753	...	0858	...	...	...	0958	...	...	...	1159	...	...	1359
452	**Passau** Hbf 🏛 **944** a.	0613	...	...	0613	...	0716	...	...	...	0822	...	0930	...	...	...	1023	...	...	...	1225	...	...	1425
	Linz Hbf **950** a.	0746	...	...	0746	...	...	...	...	...	0923	...	...	...	...	...	1124	...	...	...	1325	...	...	1525
	Wien Hbf **950** a.	0919	...	...	0919	...	...	...	...	...	1045	...	...	...	...	...	1245	...	...	...	1445	...	...	1645

	ICE	ICE	ICE	ICE	ICE	ICE	ICE	RE	ICE	ICE	ICE	ICE	ICE	ICE	ICE	ICE	ICE	ICE	ICE		RE	ICE		ICE
	621	**93**	**623**	**27**	**625**	**627**	**29**	**59495**	**629**	**721**	**229**	**723**	**725**	**927**	**727**	**729**	**929**	**929**	**929**		**59499**	**821**		**1021**
								Ⓐr										P	④⑤					
	✕	B✕	✕	✕	✕	✕	✕		✕	✕	✕	✕	✕	✕	✕	✕	✕	✕	q✕	◐		✕		⊡
Hamburg Hbf **800 900** d.	...	...	...	...	...	...	...	...	...	...	...	...	...	1153	...	...	...	...	...	...	...	...	...	1609
Dortmund Hbf **800** ▷ d.	...	...	0912v	0827	...	1122v	1027	...	...	...	1227	...	...	|	...	...	1627	1627	1627	...	...	...	...	|
Essen Hbf **800** ▷ d.	0839	...	0941c	|	1036	1150	|	...	1236	1351	|	1439	1549	1500y	1649	1749	|	|	|	...	...	1837	...	1854
Düsseldorf Hbf **800** ▷ d.	0910	...	1009	|	1105	1217	|	...	1305	1418	|	1508	1618	1524	1718	1818	|	|	|	...	...	1905	...	1923
Köln Hbf **800 910** d.	|	...	|	0953	|	|	1153	...	|	|	1353	|	|	1553	|	|	1753	1753	1753	...	...	|	...	1953
Köln Messe/Deutz **910** d.	0935	...	1034	|	1130	1244	|	...	1332	1444	|	1536	1644	|	1744	1844	|	|	|	...	...	1930	...	|
Bonn Hbf **800** d.	|	...	|	1014	|	|	1214	...	|	|	1414	|	|	1614	|	|	1814	1814	1814	...	...	|	...	2014
Koblenz Hbf **800** d.	|	...	|	1048	|	|	1248	...	|	|	1448	|	|	1648	|	|	1848	1848	1848	...	...	|	...	2048
Mainz Hbf **800** d.	|	...	|	1142	|	|	1342	...	|	|	1542	|	|	1742	|	|	1942	1942	1942	...	...	|	...	2144
Frankfurt Flughafen ✈ § d.	1037	...	1136	1201	1237	1336	1401	...	1438	1536	1601	1636	1736	1801	1836	1936	2001	2001	2001	...	...	2037	...	2202
Frankfurt (Main) Hbf d.	1054	...	1154	1212‡	1254	1354	1412‡	...	1454	1554	1612‡	1654	1754	1811‡	1854	1954	2012‡	2012‡	2012‡	...	...	2054	...	2222
Hanau Hbf d.	|	...	|	|	|	|	|	...	|	|	|	|	|	|	|	|	|	|	|	...	...	|	...	2238
Aschaffenburg Hbf d.	1123	...	1223	|	1323	1423	|	...	1523	1623	|	1723	1823	|	1923	2023	|	|	|	...	...	2123	...	2252
Würzburg Hbf **900** d.	1227	...	1327	1334	1427	1527	1535	...	1627	1727	1734	1827	1926	1934	2027	2127	2134	2134	2134	...	...	2227	...	2346
Nürnberg Hbf **900** a.	1320	...	1420	1427	1520	1621	1629	...	1720	1820	1828	1920	2020	2028	2120	2220	2229	2229	2229	...	...	2320	...	0042
Nürnberg Hbf d.	1323	1332	1423	1431	1523	1624	1632	1636	1723	1823	1831	1923	2023	2031	2124	2223	...	2237	2237	...	2316	2323	...	...
München Hbf **904** a.	1432	|	1529	|	1637	1738	|	|	1833	1941	|	2029	2132	|	2233	2336	...	|	|	...	|	0039	...	...
Neumarkt (Oberpf) d.	...	|	...	|	...	...	|	1657	...	...	|	...	...	|	...	...	...	|	|	...	2338	...	...	...
Regensburg Hbf d.	...	1426	...	1526	...	...	1726	1745	...	...	1926	...	...	2133	...	...	...	2338	2340	0009	0028	...	...	...
Straubing d.	...	1449	...	|	...	...	|	...	...	...	|	...	...	|	...	...	...	...	|	0036	...	...	...	...
Plattling **944** d.	...	|	...	1559	...	...	1759	...	...	...	1959	...	...	2208	...	...	...	...	0017	0051	...	...	...	...
Passau Hbf 🏛 **944** a.	...	1526	...	1625	...	...	1826	...	...	...	2026	...	...	2242	...	...	...	...	0050	*0130*	...	...	...	...
Linz Hbf **950** a.	...	1625	...	1725	...	...	1925	...	...	...	2133	...	...	...	...	...	...	...	...	...	...	...	...	...
Wien Hbf **950** a.	...	1745	...	1845	...	...	2045	...	...	...	2305	...	...	...	...	...	...	...	...	...	...	...	...	...

A – 🛏 1, 2 cl., ▬ 2 cl. and [2] Amsterdam - Innsbruck (see Table **53**). Also calls at Augsburg Hbf (a. 0623).
B – BEROLINA – From Berlin (Table **850**).
G – To Garmisch on ⑥ (Table **895**).
H – © until Oct. 16 (also June 16, Aug. 15). Departs Nürnberg 0659 on Aug. 15.
J – 🛏 1, 2 cl., ▬ 2 cl. and [2] Amsterdam - Wien (Table **53**); on ①③⑤ conveys 🛏 1, 2 cl., ▬ 2 cl. and [2] (*NJ* **50425**) Brussels - Bonn - Wien (Table **53**).
L – To Innsbruck (Table **53**). Also calls at Augsburg Hbf (a. 0623).
N – Conveys 🛏 1, 2 cl., ▬ 2 cl. and [2].
P – ④⑤⑦ (also June 14, 15; not June 16, 17).
R – From Rostock via Berlin and Jena (Tables **835**, **849a** and **850**).

c – ⑥⑦ only.
d – Arrives 0640.
q – Also June 14, 15; not June 16, 17.
r – Not June 16, Nov. 1.
t – Not June 16, Aug. 15, Nov. 1.
v – ⑦ only.
y – Until June 24.
z – Also June 16, Aug. 15, Nov. 1.
‡ – Frankfurt (Main) **Süd** (not Hbf).

△ – Subject to alteration Amsterdam - Köln June 11, 12, 18, 19, Aug. 27 - Sept. 9. On the mornings of ①②⑦ until Aug. 30 Mainz d. 0056, Frankfurt Flughafen d. 0120, Frankfurt Süd d. 0131.
▷ – Timings at Dortmund - Essen - Düsseldorf may vary by up to 7 minutes until June 24.
⊡ – Runs 11 – 13 minutes later Mainz - Nürnberg on ①⑥⑦ June 11 - Aug. 29.
§ – Frankfurt Flughafen Fernbahnhof.
◐ – Operated by *agilis*.

921 Regional trains FRANKFURT - WÜRZBURG - NÜRNBERG - REGENSBURG - PASSAU *RE* services

See Table **920** for faster *ICE* / *IC* trains. Neumarkt - Regensburg - Plattling trains are operated by *agilis*.

km			©w	Ⓐv										©w	Ⓐv			©w	Ⓐv						⑤⑥f	
0	**Frankfurt** (Main) Hbf d.	...	*0450*k	0524	0634	0730	0834	0930	1034	1130	1234	1330	1434	1530	1534	1634	1730	1734	1834	1930	2034	2130	2230	2330	2330	0030
4	**Frankfurt** (Main) Süd d.	...	*0458*k	0530	0640	0736	0840	0936	1040	1136	1240	1336	1440	1536	1540	1640	1736	1740	1840	1936	2040	2136	2236	2336	2336	0036
10	Offenbach (Main) Hbf d.	...	|	0535	0645	|	0845	|	1045	|	1245	|	1445	|	1545	1645	|	1745	1845	|	2045	|	|	|	|	|
24	Hanau Hbf d.	...	*0521*k	0545	0657	0758	0857	0958	1057	1158	1257	1358	1457	1558	1557	1657	1758	1757	1857	1958	2057	2158	2259	2359	2359	0059
46	Aschaffenburg Hbf d.	0501	0612	0612c	0716	0816	0916	1016	1116	1216	1316	1416	1516	1616	1616	1716	1816	1816	1916	2016	2116	2218	2322	0022	0022	0122
84	Lohr Bahnhof d.	0530	0640	0640	0741	0841	0941	1041	1141	1241	1341	1441	1541	1641	1641	1741	1841	1841	1941	2041	2141	2247	2350	0051	0051	...
96	Gemünden (Main) d.	0542	0654	0654	0752	0852	0952	1052	1152	1252	1356	1452	1552	1652	1652	1752	1852	1852	1952	2053	2152	2300	0002	0102	0103	...
109	Karlstadt (Main) d.	0554	0703	0703	0800	0900	1000	1100	1200	1300	1404	1500	1600	1700	1700	1800	1900	1900	2000	2101	2200	2309	0012	...	0112	...
134	**Würzburg** Hbf a.	0616	0721	0721	0821	0921	1021	1121	1221	1321	1421	1521	1621	1721	1721	1821	1921	1921	2021	2121	2221	2334	0027	...	0127	...
	Bamberg **875** a.	...	0832	0832	...	1032	...	1232	...	1432	...	1632	...	1832	1832	...	2032	2032	...	2232	...	...	...	...	...	...

km		Ⓐr		⚒r	©¶	Ⓐr										B	A					B	A			
0	**Würzburg** Hbf d.	0438	...	0536	...	0608	0636	0741	0841	0941	1041	1141	1241	1341	1441	1537	1541	1640	1741	1841	1941	2041	2041	2148	...	2304
23	Kitzingen d.	0456	...	0554	...	0623	0655	0801	0901	1001	1101	1201	1301	1401	1501	1556	1601	1701	1801	1901	2001	2101	2105	2208	...	2323
61	Neustadt (Aisch) Bf d.	0519	0544	0616	0641	0647	0718	0826	0926	1026	1126	1226	1324	1426	1526	1626	1626	1726	1826	1926	2026	2126	2127	2240	...	2346
94	Fürth (Bay) Hbf d.	0547	0613	0644	0711	0714y	0740	0847	0947	1047	1147	1247	1347	1447	1547	1647	1647	1747	1848	1947	2047	2147	2148	2309	...	0015
102	**Nürnberg** Hbf a.	0553	0621	0652	0718	0721y	0749	0853	0954	1054	1154	1254	1354	1454	1555	1654	1654	1754	1855	1954	2054	2154	2156	2316	...	0024

	Ⓐt	⊕				©D			⊕						⊕			⊕			⊕	◇				
Nürnberg Hbf d.	0551	...	0735	...	...	...	0934	...	...	1136	...	...	1336	...	...	1536	...	...	1736	...	...	1936	...	...	2134	...
Neumarkt (Oberpf) d.	0619	0706	0759	0810	*0910*	*0910*	0959	1010	1110	1159	1210	1310e	1359	1410	1510	1559	1610	1710	1759	1810	1910	1959	2010	2110	2159	2210
Regensburg Hbf a.	0700	0758	0840	0903	*1003*	*1003*	1038	1103	1203	1238	1303	1403e	1438	1503	1603	1639	1703	1803	1838	1903	2003	2039	2103	2203	2238	2303
Regensburg Hbf d.	0702	0809	0846	0909	1009	1009	1046	1109	1209	1246	1309	1409	1446	1509	1609	1646	1709	1809	1846	1909	2009	...	2109	2209	2247	2309
München Hbf **878** a.	0836	|	1018	|	|	|	1216	|	|	1416	|	|	1616	|	|	1816	|	|	2016	|	|	...	|	|	0020	|
Straubing d.	...	0836	...	0936	1036	1036	—	1136	1236	...	1336	1436	...	1536	1636	...	1736	1836	...	1936	2036	...	2136	2236	...	2336
Plattling a.	...	0851	...	0951	1051	1051	...	1151	1251	...	1351	1451	...	1551	1651	...	1751	1851	...	1951	2051	...	2151	2251	...	2351
Plattling **944** d.	...	*0902*	...	*1004*	...	1054	1102	*1204*	*1302*	...	*1404*	*1504*	...	*1604*	*1702*	...	*1804*	*1902*	...	*2004*	*2102*	...	*2202*	*2306*	...	...
Passau Hbf **944** a.	...	*0937*	...	*1039*	...	1129	1137	*1239*	*1337*	...	*1439*	*1539*	...	*1639*	*1737*	...	*1839*	*1937*	...	*2039*	*2137*	...	*2237*	*2341*	...	...

A – Until Oct. 16.
B – From Oct. 17.
D – © until Oct. 16 (also June 16, Aug. 15).

c – Arrives 0603.
e – On Ⓐ (not June 13 – 17, Aug. 1 - Sept. 12, Oct. 31 - Nov. 4) Neumarkt d. 1317, Regensburg a. 1408.
f – Also June 15, Oct. 2.
k – ⑥ only.
r – Not June 16, Nov. 1.
t – Not June 16, Aug. 15, Nov. 1.
v – Not June 16.
w – Also June 16.
y – Until Oct. 14 Fürth d. 0717, Nürnberg a. 0729.
¶ – Also June 16, Nov. 1. Runs 1 – 2 minutes later from Oct. 22.
◇ – To Landshut on dates in Table **878**.
⊕ – Change trains at Regensburg on Ⓐ (not June 16, Aug. 15, Nov. 1).

(WIEN -) PASSAU - NÜRNBERG - FRANKFURT — 920

See Table **921** for other regional trains. See Table **927** for services operated by FlixTrain.

	ICE 824 Ⓐv ✕	ICE 1022 ✕	ICE 822 ①–⑥ ✕		RE 59490 Ⓐr	ICE 820 ①–⑥ ✕	RE 59496 Ⓒs	RE 59492 Ⓐr	ICE 1020 ✕	ICE 1020 ①–⑥ ✕	ICE 1020 ⑤⑥ d✕	ICE 728 ✕	◐	RE 4850	ICE 726 ✕	ICE 928 ✕	ICE 724 ✕	ICE 722 ✕	ICE 228 ✕	ICE 720 ✕	IC 2022 ⑤f	ICE 628 ✕	ICE 28 ✕	ICE 626 ✕
Wien Hbf **950** d.	...	...	...	...	...	...	...	...	...	...	...	...	...	...	...	...	...	...	0651	...	...	...	0915	...
Linz Hbf **950** d.	...	...	...	...	...	...	...	...	...	...	...	...	...	...	...	...	...	...	0817	...	...	...	1035	...
Passau Hbf **944** d.	...	...	...	...	...	...	...	...	...	...	0511	...	0523	...	...	0717	...	...	0934	...	...	...	1134	...
Plattling **944** d.	...	...	...	...	...	...	...	...	...	...	0543	...	0609	...	...	0751	...	...	1001	...	...	...	1201	...
Straubing d.	...	...	...	...	...	...	...	...	...	...	0557	...	0625	...	...	0805	...	...	|	...	...	...	|	...
Regensburg Hbf d.	...	...	...	...	0421	...	0530	0530	...	0622	0622	...	0658	0719	...	0827	...	...	1032	...	...	...	1232	...
Neumarkt (Oberpf) d.	...	...	...	...	0520	...	0618	0620	...	|	|	...	0752	0800	...	|	...	...	|	...	...	...	|	...
München Hbf **904** d.	...	...	0427	...	|	0522	|	|	...	|	|	0621	...	|	0726	|	0815	0923	|	1016	...	1119	|	1216
Nürnberg Hbf a.	...	...	0533	...	0545	0631	0640	0642	...	0721	0721	0732	...	0823	0832	0926	0922	1032	1127	1120	...	1232	1327	1323
Nürnberg Hbf **900** d.	...	0510	0536	...	...	0634	...	...	0727	0727	0727	0735	...	...	0835	0930	0926	1035	1130	1124	1158	1235	1330	1326
Würzburg Hbf **900** d.	0523	0607	0632	...	...	0732	...	...	0824	0824	0824	0832	...	...	0932	1024	1032	1132	1224	1232	1258	1332	1424	1432
Aschaffenburg Hbf d.	0633	0705	0733	...	...	0833	...	...	|	|	|	0933	...	...	1033	|	1133	1233	|	1333	1404	1433	|	1533
Hanau Hbf d.	|	|	|	...	...	|	...	...	|	|	|	|	...	...	|	|	|	|	|	|	|	|	|	|
Frankfurt (Main) Hbf a.	0704	0736	0804	...	...	0904	...	...	0945‡	0945‡	0945‡	1004	...	...	1104	1145‡	1204	1304	1345‡	1404	1440	1504	1545‡	1604
Frankfurt Flughafen ✈ § a.	0722	0756	0821	...	...	0920	...	...	0956	0956	0956	1021	...	...	1120	1156	1221	1321	1356	1421	...	1521	1556	1621
Mainz Hbf **800** a.	|	0818	|	...	...	|	...	...	1018	1018	1018	|	...	...	|	1218	|	|	1418	|	...	|	1618	|
Koblenz Hbf **800** a.	|	0911	|	...	...	|	...	...	1111	1111	1111	|	...	...	|	1311	|	|	1511	|	...	|	1711	|
Bonn Hbf **800** a.	|	0943	|	...	...	|	...	...	1143	1143	1143	|	...	...	|	1343	|	|	1543	|	...	|	1743	|
Köln Messe/Deutz **910** a.	0814	|	0915	...	...	1025	...	...	|	|	|	1115	...	...	1225	|	1315	1415	|	1515	...	1615	|	1715
Köln Hbf **800 910** a.	|	1005	|	...	...	|	...	...	1205	1205	1205	|	...	...	|	1405	|	|	1605	|	...	|	1805	|
Düsseldorf Hbf **800** a.	0840	|	0936	...	...	1046	...	...	1231	1231	1231	1136	...	...	1246	|	1336	1441	|	1536	...	1640	1832	1736
Essen Hbf **800** a.	...	|	1006	...	...	1114	...	...	1258	1258	1258	1206	...	...	1313	|	1403	1513	|	1603	...	1707	1858	1803
Dortmund Hbf **800** a.	...	1121	...	...	...	...	...	...	|	|	|	...	...	...	...	1521	...	...	1721	...	...	...	1922	1841
Hamburg Hbf **800 900** a.	...	...	...	...	...	...	...	...	1550	1550	1550	...	...	...	...	...	...	...	...	...	...	...	...	...

	ICE 92 B✕	ICE 624 ✕	ICE 26 ✕	ICE 622 ✕	ICE 620 ✕	ICE 90 ✕	ICE 528 ✕	ICE 1128 ①–⑤ E✕	ICE 526 G✕	ICE 22 ◇✕	ICE 524 ✕	ICE 522 ✕		RE 59272 ⒸH	ICE 20 ✕	ICE 520		IC 94 R	RE 59494	◐	NJ 490 Ⓡ N	NJ 40420 Ⓡ NL	NJ 420 Ⓡ A△	NJ 40490 Ⓡ J△
Wien Hbf **950** d.	1015	...	1115	...	...	1315	...	...	...	1515	...	...	...	...	1715	...	...	1915	...	...	2013	...	...	2013
Linz Hbf **950** d.	1135	...	1235	...	...	1435	...	...	...	1635	...	...	...	...	1835	...	...	2037	...	...	2136	...	...	2136
Passau Hbf **944** d.	1233	...	1337	...	...	1537	...	...	...	1737	...	...	...	1820	1937	...	...	2147	...	...	2253	...	...	2253
Plattling **944** d.	|	...	1404	...	...	1604	...	...	...	1804	...	...	...	1900	2004	...	...	2217	...	2307	|	...	...	|
Straubing d.	1312	...	|	...	...	|	...	...	...	|	...	...	...	1913	|	...	...	2237	...	2323	|	...	...	|
Regensburg Hbf d.	1333	...	1435	...	...	1635	...	...	...	1835	...	...	...	1937	2035	...	...	2259	2328	2351	2356	...	...	2356
Neumarkt (Oberpf) d.	|	...	|	...	...	|	...	...	...	|	...	...	...	2021	|	...	...	|	0023	...	|	...	...	|
München Hbf **904** d.	|	1319	|	1418	1525	|	1614	1614	1719	|	1816	1926	...	|	|	2054	...	|	|	...	|	2250	2250	|
Nürnberg Hbf a.	1428	1431	1528	1523	1633	1726	1723	1723	1828	1927	1923	2032	...	2043	2128	2200	...	2400	0045	...	0056	0052	0052	0056
Nürnberg Hbf **900** d.	...	1434	1531	1526	1636	1729	1726	1726	1831	1930	1926	2035	...	...	2131	2204	...	...	...	...	0151	0151	0141	0141
Würzburg Hbf **900** d.	...	1532	1624	1632	1732	1824	1833	1833	1932	2024	2032	2132	...	...	2225	2258	...	...	...	...	0250	0250	|	|
Aschaffenburg Hbf d.	...	1633	|	1733	1833	|	1933	1933	2033	|	2133	2233	...	...	|	2357	...	...	...	...	|	|	|	|
Hanau Hbf d.	...	|	|	|	|	|	|	|	|	|	|	2247	...	...	2336	|	...	...	...	...	|	|	|	|
Frankfurt (Main) Hbf a.	...	1704	1745‡	1804	1904	1945‡	2004	2004	2104	2145‡	2204	2304	...	...	2356	0026j	...	...	...	...	|	|	0345‡	0345‡
Frankfurt Flughafen ✈ § a.	...	1721	1756	1821	1920	1956	2021	2021	2121	2156	2220	2321	...	...	...	...	...	...	...	...	|	|	0356	0356
Mainz Hbf **800** a.	...	|	1818	|	|	2018	|	2052	|	2218	|	|	...	...	...	...	...	...	...	...	|	|	0416	0416
Koblenz Hbf **800** a.	...	|	1911	|	|	2111	|	...	|	2311	|	|	...	...	...	...	...	...	...	...	|	|	0511	0511
Bonn Hbf **800** a.	...	|	1943	|	|	2143	|	...	|	2343	|	|	...	...	...	...	...	...	...	...	|	|	0558	0559
Köln Messe/Deutz **910** a.	...	1813	|	1915	2024	|	2114	...	2213	|	2336	|	...	...	...	...	...	...	...	...	|	|	|	|
Köln Hbf **800 910** a.	...	|	2005	|	|	2205	|	...	|	0005	|	0028	...	...	...	...	...	...	...	...	|	|	0651	0651
Düsseldorf Hbf **800** a.	...	1840	|	1944	2046	|	2135	...	2236	0031	2357	...	...	...	...	...	...	...	...	...	|	|	0723	0723
Essen Hbf **800** a.	...	1914	|	2015	2114	|	2202	...	2302	0057	0024	...	...	...	...	...	...	...	...	...	|	|	...	...
Dortmund Hbf **800** a.	...	1939	2121	2042	2140	2321	2227	...	2326	0122	0048	...	...	...	...	...	...	...	...	...	|	|	...	...
Hamburg Hbf **800 900** a.	...	...	...	...	...	...	...	...	...	...	...	...	...	...	...	...	...	...	...	...	0847	0847	...	...

A – 1, 2 cl., 2 cl. and (2) Innsbruck - Amsterdam (Table **53**). Also calls at Augsburg Hbf (d. 2323).
B – BEROLINA – To Berlin (Table **850**).
E – To Wiesbaden Hbf (a. 2105).
G – From Garmisch on ⑥ (Table **895**).
H – Ⓒ until Oct. 16 (also June 16, Aug. 15).
J – 1, 2 cl., 2 cl. and (2) Wien - Amsterdam (Table **53**); on ②④⑦ conveys 1, 2 cl., 2 cl. and (2) (*NJ* 50490) Wien - Bonn - Brussels (Table **53**).
L – From Innsbruck (Table **53**). Also calls at Augsburg Hbf (d. 2323).

N – Conveys 1, 2 cl., 2 cl. and (2).
R – To Warnemünde via Jena and Berlin (Tables **835**, **849a**, **850**).

d – Also June 15, 16; not June 17, 18.
f – Also June 15; not June 17.
j – 0035 on ① mornings.
r – Not June 16, Nov. 1.
s – Also June 16, Nov. 1.
v – Not June 16.

‡ – Frankfurt (Main) **Süd** (not Hbf).
△ – Subject to alteration Köln - Amsterdam on the mornings June 11, 12, 18, 19, Aug. 27 - Sept. 9.
◇ – Runs 18–36 minutes later Koblenz - Dortmund on ①⑥⑦ June 11 - Aug. 29.
§ – Frankfurt Flughafen Fernbahnhof.
◐ – Operated by *agilis*.

RE services — Regional trains PASSAU - REGENSBURG - NÜRNBERG - WÜRZBURG - FRANKFURT — 921

See Table **920** for faster *ICE* / *IC* trains. Plattling - Regensburg - Neumarkt trains are operated by *agilis*.

	Ⓐt	Ⓒz				⊕			⊕			⊕			⊕				ⒸD			⊕				
Passau Hbf **944** d.	0604	0627	...	0726	...	0826	0919	...	1026	1119	...	1219	1319	...	1426	1519	...	1626	1620	1719	...	1826	1919	...	2026	2126
Plattling **944** a.	0640	0701	...	0800	...	0900	0953	...	1100	1153	...	1253	1353	...	1500	1553	...	1700	1655	1753	...	1900	1953	...	2100	2200
Plattling d.	▬	...	0707	0809	...	0907	1009	...	1107	1209	...	1307	1409	...	1507	1609	...	1707	1707	1809	...	1907	2009	...	2107	2207
Straubing d.	...	...	0723	0823	...	0923	1023	...	1123	1223	...	1323	1423	...	1523	1623	...	1723	1723	1823	...	1923	2023	...	2123	2223
München Hbf **878** d.	0544	...	|	|	0744	|	|	0944	|	|	1144	|	|	1344	|	|	1544	|	|	|	1744	|	|	1944	|	|
Regensburg Hbf a.	0717	...	0750	0850	0916	0950	1050	1115	1150	1250	1315	1350	1450	1515	1550	1650	1715	1750	1750	1852	1915	1950	2051	2115	2152	2252
Regensburg Hbf d.	0719	...	0756	0856	0918	0957	1056	1118	1157	1256	1318	1357	1456	1518	1557	1656	1717	1757	1757	1856	1918	1957	2056	2118	2217	...
Neumarkt (Oberpf) d.	0800	...	0850	0950	1000	1051	1150	1200	1251	1350	1400	1451	1550	1600	1651	1750	1801	1851	1851	1950	2000	2051	2150	2200	2311	...
Nürnberg Hbf a.	0823	...	...	...	1023	...	...	1222	...	...	1423	...	...	1623	...	...	1824	...	...	...	2022	...	...	2223	...	...

			⚒r			Ⓐr	Ⓒs										ⒶB	ⒶA								
Nürnberg Hbf d.	0104	...	0428	...	0604	0703	0704	0805	0905	1005	1105	1205	1305	1405	1505	1604	1624	1624	1705	1804	1904	2005	2105	2206	2238	2335
Fürth (Bay) Hbf d.	0111	...	0436	...	0611	0711	0711	0811	0912	1011	1111	1211	1311	1411	1511	1612	1632	1632	1712	1811	1911	2011	2111	2212	2247	2344
Neustadt (Aisch) Bf d.	0140	...	0506	...	0634	0734	0734	0834y	0934	1034	1134	1234	1334	1434	1534	1634	1654	1700	1734	1834	1934	2034	2134	2234	2316	0013
Kitzingen d.	...	...	0528y	...	0657	0758	0758	0857y	0958	1057	1157	1257	1357	1457	1557	1657	1719	1725	1757	1857	1957	2057	2157	2257	...	0034
Würzburg Hbf a.	...	...	0548y	...	0715	0817	0817	0919	1016	1116	1216	1316	1416	1517	1616	1717	1748	1746	1817	1917	2016	2116	2219	2316	...	0053

		Ⓒz			Ⓐv	Ⓒw		Ⓐv	Ⓒw																	
Bamberg **875** d.	...	...	...	...	...	...	...	...	...	...	0726	...	0926	...	1126	...	1326	...	1526	...	1726	...	1926	...	...	...
Würzburg Hbf d.	0047	0047	...	...	0419	...	0515	0637	0637	0737	0837	0937	1037	1137	1237	1337	1437	1537	1637	1737	1837	1937	2037	2135	2236	2339
Karlstadt (Main) d.	0109	0109	...	...	0443	...	0538	0654	0654	0755	0855	0955	1055	1155	1255	1355	1455	1555	1655	1755	1855	1955	2055	2156	2258	0003
Gemünden (Main) d.	0121	0122	...	...	0453	...	0548	0705	0705	0805	0905	1005	1105	1205	1305	1405	1505	1605	1705	1805	1905	2005	2105	2207	2309	0013
Lohr Bahnhof d.	...	0131	...	...	0504	...	0559	0715	0715	0816	0915	1015	1115	1215	1315	1415	1515	1615	1715	1816	1915	2015	2115	2217	2319	0023
Aschaffenburg Hbf d.	...	0202	...	0428	0536	0536	0637j	0743	0743	0843	0943	1043	1143	1243	1343	1443	1543	1643	1743	1843	1943	2043	2143	2251	2352	0055
Hanau Hbf d.	...	...	...	0454	0600	0600	0702	0802	0803	0902	1003	1102	1203	1302	1403	1502	1603	1702	1803	1902	2003	2102	2209	2315	0017	...
Offenbach (Main) Hbf d.	...	...	...	|	0611	|	0712	0811	|	0912	|	1112	|	1312	|	1512	|	1712	|	1912	|	2112	|	|	|	...
Frankfurt (Main) Süd a.	...	...	...	0516	0615	0623	0716	0816	0825	0916	1025	1116	1225	1316	1425	1516	1625	1716	1825	1916	2025	2116	2231	2338	0040	...
Frankfurt (Main) Hbf a.	...	...	...	0524	0624	0632	0724	0827	0832	0924	1032	1124	1232	1324	1432	1524	1632	1724	1832b	1924	2032e	2124	2240	2346	0048	...

A – Ⓐ until Oct. 14 (not June 16).
B – Ⓐ from Oct. 17 (not Nov. 1).
D – Ⓒ until Oct. 16 (also June 16, Aug. 15).

b – 1840 on ⑦ (also Oct. 3; not Oct. 2).
e – 2040 on ⑤⑦ (also Oct. 3; not Oct. 2).
j – Arrives 0628.
r – Not June 16, Nov. 1.

s – Also June 16, Nov. 1.
t – Not June 16, Aug. 15, Nov. 1.
v – Not June 16.
w – Also June 16.

y – 3–6 minutes later from Oct. 17.
z – Also June 16, Aug. 15, Nov. 1.

⊕ – Change trains at Regensburg on Ⓐ**t**.

922 WÜRZBURG - HEILBRONN - STUTTGART

Operated by Go-Ahead / ABELLIO / DB

km		Ⓐt	Ⓐt	Ⓐt	Ⓒz	Ⓐt																				
0	**Würzburg** Hbf d.	...	...	...	...	0505	0630t	0737	0837	0937	1037	1137	1237	1338	1437	1538	1637	1738	1837	1937	2037	2137		...		...
43	Lauda d.	...	0458	...	0537	0609	0708	0809	0909	1009	1109	1209	1309	1409	1509	1609	1709	1809	1909	2009	2109	2209		...		...
78	Osterburken d.	0500	0526	0534	0605	0631	0730	0831	0931	1031	1131	1231	1331	1431	1531	1631	1731	1831	1931	2031	2131	2231		0836		2036
94	Möckmühl d.	0516	0540	0549	0621	0643	0743	0843	0943	1043	1143	1243	1343	1443	1543	1643	1743	1843	1943	2043	2143	2243	A	0851	and	2051
116	Bad Friedrichshall Hbf d.	0539	0558	0614	0644	0702	0801	0901	1001	1101	1201	1301	1401	1501	1601	1701	1801	1901	2001	2101	2201	2301	L	0916		2116
127	**Heilbronn** Hbf ★d.	0557	0612	0630	0657	0720	0814	0912	1012	1112	1212	1312	1412	1512	1612	1712	1812	1912	2012j	2112	2212	2312	S	0930	hourly	2130
140	Lauffen (Neckar) ★d.	0607	|	0640	0706	|	|	|	|	|	|	|	|	|	|	|	|	|	|	|	|	2322	O	0940		2140
157	Bietigheim-Bissingen ★d.	0626	0632	0657	0725	0740	0833	0932	1032	1132	1232	1332	1432	1532	1632	1732	1832	1932	2032	2132	2232	2339		0957	until	2157
180	**Stuttgart** Hbf ★a.	0643	0653f	0715	0742	0758	0853f	0957f	1053f	1157f	1253f	1350f	1453f	1550f	1653f	1757f	1853f	1950f	2053f	2153f	2253f	2359		1015		2216

	Ⓐt	Ⓐt	Ⓒz																							
Stuttgart Hbf ★d.	0448c	0546f	0605	0707f	0744	0808	0845	0908f	1011f	1106f	1211f	1308f	1408f	1505f	1611f	1711f	1808f	1907f	2008f	2115f	2143	2215f		0943		2042
Bietigheim-Bissingen ★d.	0505	0603	0622	0729	0801	0829	0902	0929	1029	1129	1229	1329	1429	1529	1629	1729	1829	1929	2029	2134	2200	2234		1000	and	2100
Lauffen (Neckar) ★d.	0520	0617	0637	|	0816	|	0917	|	|	|	|	|	|	|	|	|	|	|	|	2149	2216	2249	A	1016		2116
Heilbronn Hbf ★d.	0530	0629	0648	0748	0828	0848	0928	0948	1048	1148	1248	1348	1448	1548	1648	1748	1848	1948	2048	2202	2228	2302	L	1028	hourly	2128
Bad Friedrichshall Hbf d.	0543	0642	0658	0758	0843	0858	0943	0958	1058	1158	1258	1358	1458	1558	1658	1758	1858	1958	2058	2212	2243	2312	S	1043		2143
Möckmühl d.	0601	0705	0715	0815	0905	0915	1005	1015	1115	1215	1314	1415	1515	1615	1715	1815	1915	2015	2115	2229	2305	2335	O	1105	until	2205
Osterburken d.	0614	0727	0727	0827	0921	0927	1021	1027	1127	1227	1327	1427	1527	1627	1727	1827	1927	2027	2127	2242	2321	2351		1121		2221
Lauda d.	0639	0750	0750	0850	...	0950	...	1050	1150	1250	1350	1450	1550	1650	1750	1850	1950	2050	2150	2306	...	0020		...		...
Würzburg Hbf a.	0721	0820	0820	0921	...	1021	...	1120	1221	1320	1420	1520	1619	1720	1821	1919	2022	2119	2220	2334	...	...		...		...

	Ⓒz	Ⓒz	Ⓐt	Ⓐt	Ⓒz	Ⓐt	Ⓒz	Ⓒz	Ⓐt	Ⓐt		Ⓐt		⚒r	⚒r	⚒r	⚒r	⚒r	⚒r	⚒r	⚒r	⚒r	⚒r	⚒r		
Heilbronn Hbf d.	0111	0311	0429	0452	0455	0533	0557	0630	0637	0653	0730	0756	0830	0856	0956	1056	1156	1256	1356	1456	1556	1656	1756	1856	...	2229
Lauffen (Neckar) d.	0121	0321	0439	0502	0505	0542	0607	0640	0647	0703	0740	0806	0840	0906	1006	1106	1206	1306	1406	1506	1606	1706	1806	1906	...	2239
Bietigheim-Bissingen d.	0138	0337	0457	0519	0522	0559	0625	0657	0703	0719	0757	0825	0857	0925	1025	1125	1225	1325	1425	1525	1625	1725	1825	1925	...	2256
Stuttgart Hbf a.	0156	0355	0515	0539f	0540	0617	0643f	0715	0723	0740	0815	0842	0915	0942	1042	1142	1242	1342	1442	1543	1642	1742	1842	1942	...	2315

			Ⓒz		Ⓒz		Ⓐt		Ⓐt	Ⓐt	Ⓐt	⚒r	⚒r	⚒r	⚒r	⚒r	⚒r	⚒r	⚒r	⚒r	⚒r	⚒r	✝z			
Stuttgart Hbf d.	0019	...	0210	...	0410	...	0613	0644	0721	0816	0919	1016	1119	1219	1319	1420	1520	1619	1719	1819	1919	2016	2016f	...	2243	2319f
Bietigheim-Bissingen d.	0036	...	0227	...	0429	...	0630	0701	0738	0836	0936	1036	1136	1236	1336	1437	1537	1636	1736	1836	1939	2036	2036	...	2300	2336
Lauffen (Neckar) d.	0051	...	0242	...	0444	...	0645	0716	0753	0851	0951	1051	1151	1251	1351	1451	1552	1651	1751	1851	1953	2051	2051	...	2316	2351
Heilbronn Hbf a.	0101	...	0252	...	0454	...	0655	0726	0802	0901	1001	1101	1201	1301	1401	1501	1601	1701	1801	1901	2002	2101	2101	...	2326	0001

c – 0446 Aug. 1 - Sept. 9.
f – Not July 30 - Sept. 11. **See also note** △.
j – 2015 on ✝ (also June 16, Nov. 1).
r – Not June 16, Nov. 1.
t – Ⓐ (not June 16, Nov. 1).
z – Also June 16, Nov. 1.
★ – See also panel below main table.
△ – Local S-Bahn connections Bietigheim - Stuttgart and v.v. July 30 - Sept. 11 (journey: 28 minutes). From Bietigheim-Bissingen at 0537 ⚒, 0607, 0637 ⚒, 0707, 0737 and every 30 minutes until 2337. From Stuttgart Hbf at 0527, 0557 ⚒, 0627, 0657 ⚒, 0727, 0757 and every 30 minutes until 2357.

923 MANNHEIM - EBERBACH - OSTERBURKEN

S-Bahn

km		Ⓒz	Ⓐt		Ⓒz	Ⓐt	Ⓐt		Ⓐt				✣											
0	**Mannheim** Hbf 924 ▷ d.	0211	0419	0535	0628	0634	*0646*	0738	0807	0837	0907	0938	and at	1907	1938	2007	2038	2107	2143	...	2137	2207	2304	0021
17	**Heidelberg** Hbf 924 ▷ d.	0240	0442	0555	0655	0655	0727	0754	0825	0854	0925	0955	the same	1925	1955	2026	2055	2127	2157	...	2201c	2235e	2329c	0038
28	Neckargemünd 924 d.	0255	0456	0609	0709	0709	0741	0809	0839	0909	0939	1009	minutes	1939	2009	2040	2109	2141	2207	...	2216	2249	2343	0053
34	Neckarsteinach d.	0301	0502	0616	0715	0715	0747	0815	0845	0915	0945	1015	past each	1945	2015	2046	2115	2147	|	...	2222	2255	2349	0059
41	Hirschhorn (Neckar) d.	0308	0509	0622	0722	0722	0754	0822	0852	0922	0952	1022	hour until	1952	2022	2053	2122	2154	|	...	2229	2302	2356	0106
50	Eberbach 924 d.	0315	0516	0629	0729	0729	0801	0829	0859	0929	0959	1029		1959	2029	2100	2129	2201	2224	...	2235	2309	0002	0113
69	Mosbach-Neckarelz 924 d.	0333	0535	0648	0748	0748	0820	0848	0918	0948	1018	1048		2018	2048	2119	2148	2219	2237	2244	2254	2329	0021	0132
72	Mosbach (Baden) d.	0338	0540	0653	0753	0753	0824	0853	0923	0953	1023	1053		2023	2053	2123	2153	...	...	2249	...	2333	0026	0137
101	**Osterburken** a.	...	0610	0723	0823	0823	...	0923	...	1023	...	1123		...	2123	...	2223	...	...	2320	...	...	0056	...

	Ⓐt	Ⓒz	Ⓐt	Ⓐt	Ⓒz	Ⓐt	Ⓐt	①-⑤	Ⓒz		Ⓐt	Ⓐt	⚒r											
Osterburken d.	...	...	...	0508	0529	0534	0557	...	0636	...	0640	...	0702t	0733	...	0836	and at	...	1836	...	1938	2038	2138	2238
Mosbach (Baden) d.	0432	0454	0508	0537	0558	0603	0627	...	0705	0705	0718	...	0731t	0802	0835	0905	the same	1835	1905	1935	2007	2107	2207	2307
Mosbach-Neckarelz 924 d.	0437	0459	0521v	0546	0603	0608	0633	0638	0710	0710	0724	0728	0740	0810	0840	0910	minutes	1840	1910	1940	2012	2112	2212	2312
Eberbach 924 d.	0456	0518	0541	0605	0622	0627	0647	0656	0729	0729	...	0742	0759	0829	0859	0929	past each	1859	1929	1959	2031	2131	2231	2331
Hirschhorn (Neckar) d.	0503	0525	0548	0612	0629	0634	|	0703	0736	0736	...	|	0806	0836	0906	0936	hour until	1906	1936	2006	2038	2138	2238	2338
Neckarsteinach d.	0509	0532	0555	0618	0635	0640	0659	0711	0742	0742	...	|	0812	0842	0912	0942		1912	1942	2012	2045	2144	2244	2344
Neckargemünd 924 d.	0516	0538	0601	0625	0642	0647	0704	0717	0749	0749	...	0757	0819	0849	0919	0949		1919	1949	2019	2051	2151	2251	2351
Heidelberg Hbf 924 ▷ a.	0530	0551	0614	0639	0655	0701	0716	0733	0802	0802	...	0809	0832	0902	0932	1002		1932	2002	2032	2105	2205	2305	0005
Mannheim Hbf 924 ▷ a.	0552	0609	0635	0700	0712	0719	*0746*	0753	0819	0819	...	0824	0851	0920	0951	1019		1951	2020	2051	2129	2230	2330	0030

c – Arrives 7 minutes earlier.
e – Arrives 2223.
r – Not June 16, Nov. 1.
t – Ⓐ (not June 16, Nov. 1).
v – Arrives 0512.
z – Also June 16, Nov. 1.
✣ – Mannheim Hbf d. 1206 / 1308 (not 1207 / 1307).
▷ – See also Tables **913**, **918**, **919**.

924 MANNHEIM - HEIDELBERG - HEILBRONN

Additional S-Bahn trains run Heidelberg - Sinsheim - Heilbronn and Mosbach-Neckarelz - Heilbronn.
Mannheim - Heilbronn services are operated by ABELLIO Rail Baden-Württemberg. Local S-Bahn services operated by DB / Albtal-Verkehrs-Gesellschaft.

km		Ⓐt2	Ⓐt	Ⓒz2	Ⓐt	Ⓒz2	Ⓐt	Ⓒz	Ⓒz2	Ⓐt	Ⓒz2	Ⓐt2	Ⓐ	2	2									
0	**Mannheim** Hbf ▷ d.	...	...	...	...	...	0629	0635	...	...	*0707*	0719	0735	...	...	0834	0935	1035	1135	1235	1335	1435	1535	1635
17	**Heidelberg** Hbf 923 ▷ d.	...	...	...	...	...	0645	0649	...	...	0731	0731	0749	...	...	0847	0949	1049	1149	1249	1349	1449	1549	1649
28	Neckargemünd 923 d.	...	...	...	...	...	0655	0659	...	...	0745	0745	0759	...	...	0859	0959	1059	1159	1259	1359	1459	1559	1659
50	Eberbach 923 d.	...	...	...	...	...	|	|	...	...	|	|	0815	...	...	|	1015	|	1215	|	1415	|	1615	|
69	Mosbach-Neckarelz 923 d.	...	0619	...	0650	0650	|	|	0750	0752	|	|	0829	...	0850	|	1029	|	1229	|	1429	|	1629	|
	Sinsheim (Elsenz) Hbf d.	0540	|	0610	|	|	0710	0714	|	|	0808	0808	|	0811	|	0914	|	1114	|	1314	|	1514	|	1714
	Bad Rappenau d.	0603	|	0630	|	|	0727	0727	|	|	...	...	|	0830	|	0927	|	1127	|	1327	|	1527	|	1727
	Bad Wimpfen d.	0612	|	0638	|	|	0732	0732	|	|	...	...	|	0839	|	0932	|	1132	|	1332	|	1532	|	1732
87	Bad Friedrichshall Hbf 922 d.	0619	0637	0648	0708	0708	0741	0738	0808	0811	...	...	0843	0848	0908	0938	1042	1138	1242	1338	1442	1538	1642	1738
98	**Heilbronn** Hbf 922 a.	0648	0649	0717	0721	0737	0753	0749	0837	0822	...	...	0854	0917	0937	0949	1051	1149	1251	1349	1451	1549	1651	1749
	Stuttgart Hbf 922 a.	...	0740	...	0815	...	...	...	...	0915	...	...	...	...	...	...	...	...	...	...	...	...	...	...

								2
Mannheim Hbf ▷ d.	1735	1835	1935	2035	2143	2240	0013	*0021*
Heidelberg Hbf 923 ▷ d.	1749	1849	1949	2050	2157	2259	0025	0044
Neckargemünd 923 d.	1759	1859	1959	2100	2207	2309	0035	0057
Eberbach 923 d.	1815	|	2015	|	2224	|	0050	|
Mosbach-Neckarelz 923 d.	1829	|	2029	|	2238	|	0104	|
Sinsheim (Elsenz) Hbf d.	|	1914	|	2114	|	2325	|	0120
Bad Rappenau d.	|	1927	|	2127	|	2339	|	...
Bad Wimpfen d.	|	1932	|	2132	|	2344	|	...
Bad Friedrichshall Hbf 922 d.	1842	1938	2042	2138	2251	2350	0117	...
Heilbronn Hbf 922 a.	1851	1949	2051	2149	2300	2359	0126	...
Stuttgart Hbf 922 a.	...	...	...	...	...	...	...	...

km		Ⓐt2		Ⓐt	Ⓒz2	Ⓐt2	Ⓒz2	Ⓒz2	Ⓐt2	Ⓐt	Ⓒz
	Stuttgart Hbf 922 d.	...	...	...	...	...	...	...	...	0613	...
	Heilbronn Hbf 922 d.	...	0455	0542	...	0545	0618	0636	0638	0700	0706
0	Bad Friedrichshall Hbf 922 d.	...	0504	0553	...	0614	0648	0712	0710	0710	0716
3	Bad Wimpfen d.	...	|	0556	...	|	|	0718	0718	|	|
9	Bad Rappenau d.	...	|	0604	...	|	|	0728	0727	|	|
26	Sinsheim (Elsenz) Hbf d.	0449	|	0620	0649	|	|	0745	0745	|	|
	Mosbach-Neckarelz 923 d.	|	0517	|	|	0634	0707	...	...	0728	0728
	Eberbach 923 d.	|	0531	|	|	...	...	...	...	0742	0742
47	Neckargemünd 923 d.	0510	0547	0637	0712	...	...	...	...	0757	0757
58	**Heidelberg** Hbf 923 ▷ a.	0526	0558	0648	0728	...	...	...	...	0809	0809
75	**Mannheim** Hbf ▷ a.	*0552*	0615	0706	*0753*	...	...	...	...	0824	0824

	2											Ⓐt		Ⓐt		Ⓐt				2	2	2	2	2
Stuttgart Hbf 922 d.	...	...	...	...	...	...	...	...	...	...	...	1619	...	1719	...	1819	...	...	...	...	...	...	...	...
Heilbronn Hbf 922 d.	...	0806	0906	1006	1106	1206	1306	1406	1504	1604	1706	1709	1804	1812	1906	1912	2006	2106	2206	2218	2255	2318	2348	0018
Bad Friedrichshall Hbf 922 d.	...	0819	0916	1019	1116	1219	1316	1419	1516	1619	1716	1724	1819	1824	1916	1924	2019	2116	2219	2248	2325	2348	0017	0048
Bad Wimpfen d.	...	0823	|	1023	|	1223	|	1423	|	1623	|	|	1823	|	|	|	2023	|	2223	|	2330	|	0021	|
Bad Rappenau d.	...	0831	|	1031	|	1231	|	1431	|	1631	|	|	1831	|	|	|	2031	|	2231	|	2341	|	0032	|
Sinsheim (Elsenz) Hbf d.	0749	0843	|	1043	|	1243	|	1443	|	1643	|	|	1843	|	|	|	2043	|	2245	|	2400	|	0049	|
Mosbach-Neckarelz 923 d.	|	|	0929	|	1129	|	1329	|	1529	|	1729	1743	|	1843	1929	1943	|	2129	|	2307	...	0007	...	0107
Eberbach 923 d.	|	|	0942	|	1142	|	1342	|	1542	|	1742	...	|	...	1942	...	|	2142	|	...	...	...	...	...
Neckargemünd 923 d.	0812	0857	0957	1057	1157	1257	1357	1457	1557	1657	1757	...	1857	...	1957	...	2057	2157	2300	...	...	...	...	...
Heidelberg Hbf 923 ▷ a.	0828	0909	1009	1109	1209	1309	1409	1509	1609	1709	1809	...	1909	...	2009	...	2109	2209	2309	...	...	...	...	...
Mannheim Hbf ▷ a.	*0851*	0924	1024	1124	1224	1323	1424	1524	1624	1723	1824	...	1924	...	2024	...	2124	2224	2324	...	...	...	...	...

t – Ⓐ (not June 16, Nov. 1).
z – Also June 16, Nov. 1.
▷ – See also Tables **913**, **918**, **919** and **923**.

STUTTGART - BACKNANG / AALEN - NÜRNBERG 925

km																										
				IC 2061			*IC* 2063				*IC* 2065				*IC* 2067			*IC* 2069				*IC* 2161				*IC* 2163
			Ⓐt	Ⓐ																						
		◇	◇		◇	◇		◇	◇			◇	◇			◇	◇		◇	◇		A	◇	◇		
	Karlsruhe Hbf **931** .. d.	...	...	...	...	...	0706	...	...	...	0906	...	...	...	1106	...	...	1306	...	...	...	1506	...	...	...	1706
0	**Stuttgart** Hbf .... ‡ d.	0423	0554	0605	0620	0653	0808	0820	0857	0955	1009	1020	1057	1155	1209	1220	1300	1409	1420	1456	1555	1609	1620	1657	1755	1809
31	Backnang .... d.	0451	0622	|	|	0724	|	|	0924	1024	|	|	1124	1224	|	|	1324	|	|	1524	1624	|	|	1724	1825	|
73	Schwäbisch H-H ⊡ a.	0536	0656	|	|	0759	|	|	0959	1056	|	|	1158	1256	|	|	1358	|	|	1559	1656	|	|	1758	1857	|
73	Schwäbisch H-H ⊡ d.	0537	0657	|	|	0800	|	|	1000	*1100*	|	|	1200	*1300*	|	|	1400	|	|	1600	*1700*	|	|	1800	*1900*	|
	Schwäbisch Gmünd ‡ d.	|	|	0642	0702	|	0842	0902	|	|	1041	1102	|	|	1241	1302	|	1441	1502	|	|	1641	1702	|	|	1841
	Aalen Hbf .... ‡ a.	|	|	0658	0720	|	0857	0920	|	|	1057	1120	|	|	1257	1320	|	1457	1520	|	|	1657	1720	|	|	1857
	Aalen Hbf .... d.	|	|	0659	0728	|	0858	0928	|	|	1058	1128	|	|	1258	1328	|	1458	1528	|	|	1658	1728	|	|	1858
	Ellwangen .... d.	|	|	0710	0748	|	0910	0948	|	|	1109	1148	|	|	1309	1348	|	1509	1548	|	|	1709	1748	|	|	1909
100	Crailsheim .... d.	0610k	0715	0726	0812	0820	0926	1012	1020	*1120*	1125	1212	1220	*1320*	1325	1412	1420	1525	1612	1620	*1720*	1725	1812	1820	*1920*	1925
146	Ansbach .... d.	0641	0746	0751	...	0850	0951	...	1050	...	1150	...	1250	...	1351	...	1450	1550	...	1650	...	1750	...	1850	...	1950
190	**Nürnberg** Hbf .... a.	0717	...	0818	...	0920	1018	...	1120	...	1218	...	1320	...	1418	...	1520	1618	...	1720	...	1818	...	1920	...	2018

				IC 2165				*IC* 2167		
				Ⓑ				⑦		
	◇	◇		b	◇	◇	◇	w	◇	◇
Karlsruhe Hbf **931** .. d.	...	...	...	1906	...	...	...	2106	...	...
Stuttgart Hbf .... ‡ d.	1820	1857	1952c	2008	2020	2057	2157	2208	2220	2327
Backnang .... d.	|	1924	2025	|	|	2124	2224	|	|	2354
Schwäbisch H-H ⊡. a.	|	1958	2056	|	|	2159	2258	|	|	0028
Schwäbisch H-H ⊡. d.	|	2000	*2100*	|	|	2200	*2301*	|	|	0030
Schwäbisch Gmünd . ‡ d.	1902	|	|	2040	2102	|	|	2240	2302	|
Aalen Hbf .... ‡ a.	1920	|	|	2056	2120	|	|	2256	2320	|
Aalen Hbf .... d.	1928	|	|	2057	2133	|	|	2257	2333	|
Ellwangen .... d.	1948	|	|	2108	2151	|	|	2308	2351	|
Crailsheim .... d.	2012	2020	*2120*	2125	2211	2220	*2321*	2325	0008	0047
Ansbach .... d.	...	2050	...	2150	...	2250	...	2350	...	...
Nürnberg Hbf .... a.	...	2120	...	2218	...	2320	...	0018	...	...

km												
					IC 2164					*IC* 2162		
			Ⓐt	Ⓐt	Ⓐ							
		◇				◇	◇	◇	d◇			◇
0	**Nürnberg** Hbf .... d.	...	...	...	0538	...	...	0638	...	0741	...	0837
44	Ansbach .... d.	...	...	...	0603	...	...	0707	...	0807	...	0907
90	Crailsheim .... d.	0456	*0509*	0540	0631	0634	0648	0742	0752	0835	*0838*	0942
111	Ellwangen .... d.	|	*0527*	|	0647	|	0711	|	0811	0850	|	|
127	**Aalen** Hbf .... a.	|	*0544*	|	0658	|	0728	|	0828	0900	|	|
127	**Aalen** Hbf .... ‡ d.	|	0600	|	0700	|	0735	|	0837	0902	|	|
152	Schwäbisch Gmünd ‡ d.	|	0615	|	0718	|	0754	|	0856	0918	|	|
	Schwäbisch H-H ⊡ a.	0512	|	0556	|	0651	|	0758	|	|	*0859*	0958
	Schwäbisch H-H ⊡ d.	0520	|	0600	|	0700	|	0800	|	|	0903	1000
	Backnang .... d.	0605	|	0635	|	0737	|	0838	|	|	0937	1038
203	**Stuttgart** Hbf .... ‡ a.	0631	0650	0700	0752	0808	0840	0907	0939	0952	1004	1108
	Karlsruhe Hbf **931** . a.	...	...	...	0853	...	...	...	...	1053	...	...

		IC 2160				*IC* 2068				*IC* 2066				*IC* 2064				*IC* 2062				*IC* 2060				
																						Ⓑ				
	◇			◇	◇	A		◇	◇			◇	◇			◇	◇			◇	e◇	b	◇	◇	◇	◇
Nürnberg Hbf .... d.	...	0942	...	1038	...	1142	...	1238	...	1341	...	1438	...	1542	...	1638	...	1742	...	1838	...	1942	2038	...	...	2238
Ansbach .... d.	...	1007	...	1107	...	1207	...	1310	...	1407	...	1507	...	1607	...	1707	...	1807	...	1907	...	2007	2107	...	...	2307
Crailsheim .... d.	0952	1035	*1038*	1142	1152	1235	*1238*	1342	1352	1435	*1438*	1542	1552	1635	*1638*	1742	1752	1835	*1838*	1942	1952	2035	2142	2152	*2240*	2338
Ellwangen .... d.	1011	1050	|	|	1211	1250	|	|	1411	1450	|	|	1611	1650	|	|	1811	1850	|	|	2011	2050	|	2211	|	...
Aalen Hbf .... a.	1028	1100	|	|	1230	1300	|	|	1428	1500	|	|	1628	1700	|	|	1828	1900	|	|	2028	2100	|	2228	|	...
Aalen Hbf .... ‡ d.	1037	1102	|	|	1237	1302	|	|	1437	1502	|	|	1637	1702	|	|	1837	1902	|	|	2037	2102	|	2237	|	...
Schwäbisch Gmünd . ‡ d.	1056	1118	|	|	1256	1318	|	|	1456	1518	|	|	1656	1718	|	|	1856	1918	|	|	2056	2118	|	2256	|	...
Schwäbisch H-H ⊡. a.	|	|	*1059*	1158	|	|	*1259*	1358	|	|	*1459*	1558	|	|	*1659*	1758	|	|	*1859*	1958	|	|	2158	|	*2300*	...
Schwäbisch H-H ⊡. d.	|	|	1103	1200	|	|	1303	1400	|	|	1503	1600	|	|	1703	1800	|	|	1903	2000	|	|	2200	|	2312	...
Backnang .... d.	|	|	1137	1238	|	|	1337	1438	|	|	1537	1638	|	|	1737	1838	|	|	1937	2038	|	|	2238	|	2355	...
Stuttgart Hbf .... ‡ a.	1139	1152	1204	1307	1339	1352	1404	1507	1539	1552	1604	1702j	1739	1752	1803	1907	1939	1953	2004	2107	2139	2153	2305	2339	0023	...
Karlsruhe Hbf **931** .. a.	...	1253	...	...	...	1453	...	...	...	1653	...	...	...	1853	...	...	...	2054	...	...	...	2300	...	...	...	...

A – SAALETAL – To / from Leipzig on dates in Table 849a.
b – Not Oct. 2.
c – 1955 on Ⓒ (also June 16, Nov. 1).
d – Change trains at Aalen on Ⓐt.
e – On ⑤ Crailsheim d. 1951 and change trains at Aalen.

j – 1707 July 30 - Sept. 11.
k – Arrives 0555.
t – Ⓐ (not June 16, Nov. 1).
w – Also Oct. 3; not Oct. 2.
z – Also June 16, Nov. 1.

⊡ – Schwäbisch Hall-Hessental.
◇ – Operated by Go-Ahead.

‡ – Other regional services (◇) Stuttgart - Schwäbisch Gmünd - Aalen and v.v. (journey 60 – 65 minutes, except those marked * which are faster services taking just 48 – 49 minutes).
From Stuttgart Hbf at 0020, 0120 Ⓒ z, 0320 Ⓒ z, 0447 Ⓐ t, 0519 Ⓐ t, 0547 Ⓐ t, 0647 Ⓐ t, 0708 Ⓐ t*, 0720, 0747 Ⓐ t, 0847 Ⓐ t, 0908*, 0920, 0947, 1047, 1108*, 1120, 1147, 1247, 1308*, 1320, 1347, 1446, 1508*, 1520, 1547, 1647, 1708*, 1720, 1747, 1847, 1908*, 1920, 1947, 2108*, 2120, 2238* and 2320.
From Aalen at 0106 Ⓒ z, 0306 Ⓒ z, 0435 Ⓐ t, 0505 Ⓐ t, 0535, 0605 Ⓐ t, 0635, 0705 Ⓐ t, 0802*, 0806 Ⓐ t, 0907, 0937, 1002*, 1007, 1107, 1137, 1202*, 1207, 1307, 1337, 1402*, 1407, 1507, 1537, 1602*, 1607, 1707, 1737, 1801*, 1807, 1907, 1937, 2002*, 2007 Ⓐ t, 2137, 2202* and 2337.

RE / RB services HEILBRONN / ASCHAFFENBURG - CRAILSHEIM and AALEN - DONAUWÖRTH / ULM 926

ASCHAFFENBURG - LAUDA - CRAILSHEIM

2nd class only

km		Ⓒz	Ⓐt							Ⓒz‡	Ⓐt‡
0	**Aschaffenburg** Hbf .. d.	...	...	0721k	0926	1126	1326	1526	1726	1926	1926
38	Miltenberg .... d.	...	0551	0753k	1000	1200	1400	1600	1800	2000	2008
69	Wertheim .... d.	0626	0641	0834	1034	1234	1434	1634	1834	2034	2041
93	Tauberbischofsheim ..... d.	0652	0707	0900	1100	1300	1500	1700	1900	2100	2102
100	**Lauda** .... a.	0700	0714	0906	1106	1306	1506	1706	1906	2106	2108
100	**Lauda** .... d.	0717	0716	0912	1112	1312	1512	1712	1912	2112	2112
110	Bad Mergentheim .... d.	0730	0730	0922	1122	1322	1522	1722	1922	2122	2123
169	**Crailsheim** .... a.	0827	0827	1026	1226	1426	1626	1826	2026	2226	2226

	Ⓐt	Ⓒz	Ⓐt						Ⓒz	Ⓐt	¶
Crailsheim .... d.	...	...	0626	0733	0933	1133	1333	1533	1733	1733	1933
Bad Mergentheim ..... d.	0545	0629	0735	0837	1037	1237	1437	1637	1837	1837	2036
Lauda .... a.	0555	0639	0746	0846	1046	1246	1446	1646	1846	1846	2046
Lauda .... d.	0605	0640	0752	0852	1052	1252	1452	1652	1852	1852	2052
Tauberbischofsheim d.	0614	0700n	0800	0900	1100	1300	1500	1700	1900	1900	2106
Wertheim .... d.	0700r	0726	0827	0926	1126	1326	1526	1726	1926	1935n	2135
Miltenberg .... d.	0741	0800	0900	1000	1200	1359	1600	1800	2000	2006	2215
Aschaffenburg Hbf. a.	0835	0835	0935	1032	1232	1435	1632	1832	2032	*2104*	2259

HEILBRONN - CRAILSHEIM

2nd class only

km		Ⓐt		Ⓐt			Ⓐt		
0	**Heilbronn** Hbf .... d.	0702	0806	0906	and in the	1806	1906	2006	2206
27	Öhringen .... d.	0726	0828	0926	same pattern	1828	1926	2028	2228
54	Schwäbisch Hall .... d.	0749	0851	0949	every **two**	1851	1949	2051	2251
61	Schwäbisch H-H ⊡ ... a.	0756	0858	0956	hours until	1858	1956	2058	2258
88	**Crailsheim** .... a.	*0817*	0920	*1017*		1920	*2017*	2120	2321

	Ⓐt	Ⓐt	Ⓒz	Ⓐt			Ⓐt		
Crailsheim .... d.	0520	*0634*	*0634*	*0742*	0838	and in the	*1742*	1838	2038
Schwäbisch H-H ⊡ d.	0540	0655	0701	0803	0901	same pattern	1803	1901	2101
Schwäbisch Hall..... d.	0546	0701	0707	0809	0907	every **two**	1809	1907	2107
Öhringen .... d.	0610	0731	0731	0832	0931	hours until	1832	1931	2131
Heilbronn Hbf .... a.	0635	0752	0752	0852	0952		1852	1952	2152

AALEN - DONAUWÖRTH *See note* ⊠

km		Ⓐt	Ⓐt	Ⓒz	Ⓐt	Ⓐt	Ⓐt		Ⓐt		Ⓒz	Ⓐt	Ⓒz	Ⓐt	Ⓐt	Ⓐt	Ⓒz	Ⓐt	Ⓒz	Ⓐt	Ⓐt		Ⓐt	Ⓐt	Ⓒz		
0	**Aalen** Hbf .... d.	...	...	0531	...	0603	0625	0733	0833	0933	0933	1033	1135	1135	1233	1333	1333	1433	1533	1533	1635	1733	1833	1933	1933	2035	2237
39	Nördlingen ...... a.	...	...	0613	...	0638	0706	0813	0913	1013	1013	1112	1213	1219	1313	1413	1413	1513	1613	1613	1713	1813	1913	2013	2013	2113	2314
39	Nördlingen ...... d.	0518	0558	0622	0623	0639	0707	0821	0914	1015	1020	1114	1216	1221	1315	1414	1421	1514	1622	1621	1721	1821	1915	2015	2019	2116	...
68	**Donauwörth** ... a.	0546	0632	0650	0650	0706	0734	0853	0945	1046	1047	1145	1244	1253	1347	1445	1448	1545	1650	1653	1753	1856	1946	2047	2046	2148	...

		Ⓐt			Ⓐt	Ⓐt	Ⓒz	Ⓐt		Ⓐt	Ⓐt	Ⓒz	Ⓐt		Ⓐt		Ⓐt	Ⓐt		Ⓐt	Ⓐt	Ⓐt		Ⓐt		Ⓐt	Ⓒz
Donauwörth.....d.	...	...	...	...	0607	0706	0707	0811	0904	1005	1104	1107	1211	1305	1404	1504	1611	1625	1711	1735	1811	1837	1905	2005	2106	2205	2238
Nördlingen ....a.	...	...	...	...	0637	0739	0735	0839	0932	1033	1132	1134	1239	1333	1432	1532	1639	1657	1739	1809	1839	1909	1933	2033	2134	2233	2303
Nördlingen ....d.	0442	0531	...	0641	0641	0742	0742	0842	0942	1042	1144	1144	1242	1342	1442	1542	1644	...	1742	...	1842	...	1942	...	2134	...	...
Aalen Hbf.........a.	0524	0613	...	0721	0721	0824	0824	0924	1024	1124	1226	1226	1324	1424	1524	1624	1726	...	1824	...	1924	...	2024	...	2215	...	...

AALEN - ULM ◇

km		Ⓐt	Ⓒz2	Ⓐt	2	2		2	2		2	2		2	2		2	2		2	2		2	2		2	2
0	**Aalen** Hbf .... d.	0553	0630	0703	0734	0834	0907	0934	1034	1107	1134	1234	1307	1334	1434	1507	1534	1634	1707	1734	1834	1907	1934	2034	2107	2134	2234
23	Heidenheim..... d.	0612	0654	0726	0800	0900	0924	1000	1100	1124	1200	1300	1324	1400	1500	1524	1600	1700	1724	1800	1900	1924	2000	2100	2124	2156	2300
73	**Ulm** Hbf.......... a.	0658	0742	0758	0847	0947	0956	1047	1147	1156	1247	1347	1356	1447	1547	1556	1647	1747	1756	1847	1947	1956	2047	2144	2156	2251	2354

	Ⓐt	Ⓐt	2	Ⓐt2	Ⓒz2		2	2		2	2		2	2		2	2		2	2		2	2		2	2	2
Ulm Hbf............d.	0425	0538	0555c	0644	0705	0804	0811	0911	1002	1011	1111	1202	1211	1311	1402	1411	1511	1602	1611	1711	1802	1811	1911	2002	2011	2117	2217
Heidenheim ......d.	0516	0626	0658	0800	0800	0835	0900	1000	1034	1100	1200	1234	1300	1400	1434	1500	1600	1634	1700	1800	1834	1900	2000	2034	2100	2206	2302
Aalen Hbf.........a.	0545	0650	0724	0824	0824	0853	0924	1024	1051	1124	1224	1251	1324	1424	1451	1524	1624	1651	1724	1824	1851	1924	2024	2051	2124	2227	2324

c – 0606 on Ⓒ (also June 16, Nov. 1).
k – On Ⓒz: Aschaffenburg d. 0718, Miltenberg d. 0800.
n – Arrives 11 – 12 minutes earlier.
r – Arrives 0638.
t – Not June 16, Nov. 1.
z – Also June 16, Nov. 1.

‡ – Until Oct. 3 by 🚌 Wertheim - Gamburg (a. 2110; connecting train departs 2114, then runs 34 – 37 minutes later on Ⓒ / 12 – 22 minutes later on Ⓐ).
¶ – Until Oct. 3 Tauberbischofsheim d. 2058, Gamberg a. 2109, then by 🚌 Gamburg (d. 2111) - Wertheim (a. 2136), then train from Wertheim (d. 2140).

◇ – Operated by Hohenzollerische Landesbahn (trains shown as 2nd class only) or DB.
⊡ – Schwäbisch Hall-Hessental.
⊠ – From July 9 to November 13 journeys to / from Donauwörth are subject to alteration with partial 🚌 replacement and extended journey times (see amended table on page 568).

927 FLIXTRAIN service summary

Special fares (**DB tickets not valid**). Engineering work may affect timings; **subject to alteration on and around public holidays** (please check when booking). Website: www.flixtrain.de

Routes *FLX* 10/11/15¶		1243 ①⑤⑥	1240 ①	1240 ②–⑥	1245 ⑦	1242/6 ④–①		1244 A	1244 ⑦q	1806 ④–①	
Stuttgart Hbf	d.	...	0704	0717	0729	...	...	1516	1529	1554	...
Basel Bad Bf	d.	...				0854	...				...
Freiburg (Brsg) Hbf	d.	...				0952	...				...
Offenburg	d.	...				1043	...				...
Baden Baden	d.	...				1105	...				...
Karlsruhe Hbf	d.	...				1125	...				...
Heidelberg Hbf	d.	...	0807	0807	0850	1206	...	1606	1617	1706	...
Darmstadt Hbf	d.	...	0853	0853	0922	1252	...	1651	1651	1741	...
Wiesbaden Hbf	d.	0544					...				...
Mainz Hbf	d.	0555			0955		...				...
Frankfurt Flug ✈ ⊡	d.	0619					...				...
Frankfurt (Main) Süd	d.	0628	0912	0912	1028	1312	...	1713	1713	1809	...
Hanau Hbf	d.	0643			1043		...				...
Fulda	d.	0734	1007	1007p	1132	1407	...	1808	1808	1922	...
Bad Hersfeld	d.					1432	...				...
Eisenach	d.						...	1858	1858		...
Gotha	d.		1108	1108			...				...
Erfurt Hbf	d.		1122	1122		1522	...	1923	1923		...
Halle (Saale) Hbf	d.		1201	1201		1601	...	2001	2001		...
Kassel Wilhelmshöhe	d.	0811			1211		...			2001	...
Göttingen	d.	0832			1232		...			2022	...
Hannover Hbf	d.						...			2103	...
Hamburg Hbf	a.						...			2249	...
Hildesheim Hbf	d.	0905			1305		...			...	...
Braunschweig Hbf	d.	0929			1329		...			...	...
Wolfsburg Hbf	d.	0947			1347		...			...	...
Berlin Spandau	a.	1102			1502		...			...	...
Berlin Südkreuz	a.					1715	...			...	...
Berlin Hbf	a.	1111	1318	1318	1510	1720	...	2117	2117	...	...

Routes *FLX* 10/11/15¶		1241 ⑤–①	1805 ⑤–②		1243/7 ④–①		1240 ⑥	1245 ⑧		1242 ④⑤⑦	
Berlin Hbf	d.	0724	...	...	1124	...	1327	1523	...	1727	...
Berlin Südkreuz	d.		...	...	1132	...			...		...
Berlin Spandau	d.		...	...		...	1342		...	1736	...
Wolfsburg Hbf	d.		...	...		...	1450		...	1850	...
Braunschweig Hbf	d.		...	...		...	1511		...	1908	...
Hildesheim Hbf	d.		...	...		...	1534		...	1933	...
Hamburg Hbf	d.		0722	...		...			...		...
Hannover Hbf	d.		0945	...		...			...		...
Göttingen	d.		1026	...		...	1609		...	2009	...
Kassel Wilhelmshöhe	d.		1049	...		...	1630		...	2030	...
Halle (Saale) Hbf	d.	0844		...	1244	...		1644	...		...
Erfurt Hbf	d.	0920		...	1321	...		1720	...		...
Gotha	d.			...		...		1739	...		...
Eisenach	d.	0951		...		...			...		...
Bad Hersfeld	d.			...	1416	...			...		...
Fulda	d.	1042	1125	...	1443	...		1842	...		...
Hanau Hbf	d.			...		...			...	2151	...
Frankfurt (Main) Süd	d.	1135	1230	...	1532	...	1756	1935	...	2208	...
Frankfurt Flug ✈ ⊡	d.			...		...	1806		...	2228	...
Mainz Hbf	d.			...		...	1834		...	2254	...
Wiesbaden Hbf	a.			...		...			...	2305	...
Darmstadt Hbf	d.	1154	1257	...	1557	...	1900	1954	...	...	...
Heidelberg Hbf	d.	1246z	1345	...	1639	...	1950	2035	...	...	...
Karlsruhe Hbf	d.			...	1718	...			...	...	...
Baden Baden	d.			...	1747	...			...	...	...
Offenburg	d.			...	1804	...			...	...	...
Freiburg (Brsg) Hbf	d.			...	1839	...			...	...	...
Basel Bad Bf	a.			...	1928	...			...	...	...
Stuttgart Hbf	a.	1330	1429	...	...	...	2046	2119	...	...	...

Routes *FLX* 30/35§		1320 B	1320 ⑦	1230 ⑤–①	1340 ⑦	1340 ①–⑥	1342 ⑦	1236	1346 ①–⑥	1348 ⑦	
Leipzig Hbf	d.	0642	...	...	1042	...	...	1442k	...	...	...
Dresden Hbf	d.		...	0617h		...	...		...	...	...
Dresden Neustadt	d.		...	0622h		...	...		...	...	...
Berlin Südkreuz	d.	0755	...	0816	1151	...	...	1613v	...	...	...
Berlin Hbf	a.	0800	...	0821	1156	...	...	1618	...	...	...
Berlin Hbf	d.	0805	0805	0828	1201	1206t	1404	1624	1804	2000	...
Berlin Spandau	d.	0815		0837	1229	1229		1637			...
Wittenberge	d.										...
Ludwigslust	d.	0913	0913								...
Büchen	d.										...
Hamburg Hbf	a.	1004	1004		1451	1451	1655		2050	2306	...
Stendal Hbf	d.	...	...	0918	...	...	...	1719	...	...	...
Hannover Hbf	d.	...	...	1023	...	...	...	1823	...	...	...
Bielefeld Hbf	d.	...	...	1116	...	...	...	1916	...	...	...
Gütersloh Hbf	d.	...	...	1132	...	...	...	1932	...	...	...
Hamm (Westf)	d.	...	...	1206	...	...	...	2006	...	...	...
Dortmund Hbf	d.	...	...	1225	...	...	...	2025	...	...	...
Essen Hbf	d.	...	...	1251	...	...	...	2050	...	...	...
Duisburg Hbf	d.	...	...	1306	...	...	...	2105	...	...	...
Düsseldorf Hbf	d.	...	...	1320	...	...	...	2118	...	...	...
Köln Hbf	a.	...	...	1345	...	...	...	2145	...	...	...
Aachen Hbf	a.	...	...	1424f	...	...	...	...	...	...	...

Routes *FLX* 30/35§		76307 ①–⑥	1233 ①–⑥	1339 ⑦	1235 ⑦	1341 ⑥	1343 ①–⑤	76301 B	76301 ⑦	1239 ④–⑦	1349 ⑥	1349 ⑦
Aachen Hbf	d.	...	...	...	...	...	...	...	...	1526f	...	...
Köln Hbf	d.	...	0645	...	0814	...	...	...	...	1615	...	...
Düsseldorf Hbf	d.	...	0714	...	0838	...	...	...	...	1638	...	...
Duisburg Hbf	d.	...	0730	...	0851	...	...	...	...	1651	...	...
Essen Hbf	d.	...	0744	...	0904	...	...	...	...	1704	...	...
Dortmund Hbf	d.	...	0806	...	0931	...	...	...	...	1731	...	...
Hamm (Westf)	d.	...	0834	...	0952	...	...	...	...	1752	...	...
Gütersloh Hbf	d.	...	0855	...	1023	...	...	...	...	1823	...	...
Bielefeld Hbf	d.	...	0906	...	1042	...	...	...	...	1842	...	...
Hannover Hbf	d.	...	1007	...	1144	...	...	...	...	1944	...	...
Stendal Hbf	d.	...	1104	...	1243	...	...	...	...	2043	...	...
Hamburg Hbf	d.	0815r		0953		1150	1350	1651	1651		1951	1951
Büchen	d.							1715	1715		2016	2016
Ludwigslust	d.							1742	1742			
Wittenberge	d.							1802	1802			
Berlin Spandau	d.				1323			1846	1846	2123	2143	2143
Berlin Hbf	a.	1058	1152	1259	1333	1459	1658	1854	1904	2131	2153	2153
Berlin Hbf	d.	...	1157	...	1341	...	...	1900	...	2136	...	2159
Berlin Südkreuz	d.	...	1205	...	1346	...	...	1906	...	2144	...	2207
Dresden Neustadt	a.	...		...	...	...	...		...	2339e	...	
Dresden Hbf	a.	...		...	...	...	...		...	2346e	...	
Leipzig Hbf	a.	...	1318k	...	...	...	...	2017	...	...	...	2319

Route *FLX* 20		1355		1359 ①	1359 ④–⑦		1363 ⑧
Hamburg Hbf	d.	0850	...	1250	1250	...	1650
Bremen Hbf	d.	0949	...	1349	1349	...	1749
Osnabrück Hbf	d.	1044	...	1444	1444	...	1844
Münster (Westf) Hbf	d.	1109	...	1509	1509	...	1909
Gelsenkirchen Hbf	d.	1148	...	1549	1549	...	1949
Essen Hbf	d.	1201	...	1604	1604	...	2002
Duisburg Hbf	d.	1214	...	1617	1617	...	2015
Düsseldorf Hbf	d.	1230	...	1631	1631	...	2029
Köln Hbf	a.	1256	...	1657	1657	...	2057
Köln Hbf	d.	1301	...	...	1701	...	...
Bonn Hbf	d.	1323	...	...	1724	...	...
Remagen	d.		...	...	1737	...	...
Andernach	d.		...	...		...	...
Koblenz Hbf	d.	1355	...	...	1758	...	...
Mainz Hbf	d.	1454	...	...	1854	...	...
Frankfurt Flughafen	d.	1515	...	...	1921	...	...
Frankfurt (Main) Süd	d.	1530	...	...	1929	...	...
Aschaffenburg Hbf	d.	1558	...	...	...	...	...
Würzburg Hbf	d.	1710	...	...	...	...	...
Augsburg Hbf	d.	1933	...	...	...	...	...
München Hbf	a.	2007●	...	...	...	...	...

Route *FLX* 20		1350 ①–⑥		1354 ④	1354 ⑤–①		1358
München Hbf	d.	...	...	...	...	...	0748
Augsburg Hbf	d.	...	...	...	...	...	
Würzburg Hbf	d.	...	...	...	...	...	1040
Aschaffenburg Hbf	d.	...	...	...	...	...	1153
Frankfurt (Main) Süd	d.	...	...	...	0821	...	1219
Frankfurt Flughafen	d.	...	...	...		...	
Mainz Hbf	d.	...	...	...	0555	...	1251
Koblenz Hbf	d.	...	...	...	0948	...	1344
Andernach	d.	...	...	...	1002	...	1357
Remagen	d.	...	...	...		...	1409
Bonn Hbf	d.	...	...	...	1028	...	1427
Köln Hbf	a.	...	...	...	1054	...	1455
Köln Hbf	d.	0701	...	1059	1059	...	1501
Düsseldorf Hbf	d.	0729	...	1127	1127	...	1527
Duisburg Hbf	d.	0745	...	1142	1142	...	1542
Essen Hbf	d.	0759	...	1156	1156	...	1556
Gelsenkirchen Hbf	d.		...	1206	1206	...	1606
Münster (Westf) Hbf	d.	0848	...	1247	1247	...	1648
Osnabrück Hbf	d.	0914	...	1315	1315	...	1715
Bremen Hbf	d.	1010	...	1410	1410	...	1810
Hamburg Hbf	a.	1108	...	1508	1508	...	1907

A – ④–⑥ (also ⑦ July 31 - Sept. 11).
B – ①④⑤⑥.
e – ④⑤⑦.
f – ⑤⑦.
h – ①⑤⑥.
j – Not ⑦.
k – ①④⑤.
p – ②③④.
q – Not July 31 - Sept. 11.
r – 0753 on ⑥.
t – Not June 11, 18, 25, July 2. Departs 1153 on ①–⑤ June 10 - July 8.
v – Arrives 1550.
z – Arrives 1234.
¶ – Route FLX10 (Basel/Stuttgart - Erfurt - Berlin) is valid from June 23.
§ – Route FLX35 (Leipzig - Berlin - Hamburg) is valid until Sept. 11.
● – Also calls at München Pasing (a. 1957).
⊡ – Frankfurt Flughafen Fernbahnhof.

927a WESTERLAND (SYLT) - HAMBURG - SALZBURG and BASEL

ALPEN-SYLT *nachtexpress*. Operates **MAY 20 - OCTOBER 23**, 2022. Services convey 🛏 1, 2 cl., ▬ 2 cl. (6 berth ✣), 🚌 and 🍸. Website: www.nachtexpress.de

WESTERLAND - HAMBURG - SALZBURG

		NEX ⑥ h		
Westerland (Sylt)	d.	2000	...	...
Niebüll	d.	2030	...	...
Husum	d.	2100	...	...
Heide	d.	2120	...	...
Hamburg Hbf	d.	2300	...	...
Nürnberg	a.	0745	...	...
Augsburg Hbf	a.	0930	...	...
München Ost	a.	1020	...	...
Rosenheim	a.	1100	...	...
Prien am Chiemsee	a.	1120	...	...
Freilassing	a.	1200	...	...
Salzburg Hbf	a.	1220	...	...

		NEX ⑤ f		
Salzburg Hbf	d.	1800	...	...
Freilassing	d.	1815	...	...
Prien am Chiemsee	d.	1845	...	...
Rosenheim	d.	1900	...	...
München Ost	d.	1930	...	...
Augsburg Hbf	d.	2030	...	...
Nürnberg	d.	2215	...	...
Hamburg Hbf	a.	0800	...	...
Heide	a.	1020	...	...
Husum	a.	1045	...	...
Niebüll	a.	1130	...	...
Westerland (Sylt)	a.	1200	...	...

WESTERLAND - HAMBURG - BASEL

		NEX ⑥ h		
Westerland (Sylt)	d.	2000	...	...
Niebüll	d.	2030	...	...
Husum	d.	2100	...	...
Heide	d.	2120	...	...
Hamburg Hbf	d.	2300	...	...
Frankfurt (Main) Süd	a.	0600	...	...
Mannheim Hbf	a.	0650	...	...
Karlsruhe Hbf	a.	0730	...	...
Freiburg (Brsg) Hbf	a.	0900	...	...
Basel Bad Bf	a.	1000	...	...

		NEX ⑤ f		
Basel Bad Bf	d.	1830	...	...
Freiburg (Brsg) Hbf	d.	1930	...	...
Karlsruhe Hbf	d.	2130	...	...
Mannheim Hbf	d.	2220	...	...
Frankfurt (Main) Süd	d.	2320	...	...
Hamburg Hbf	a.	0800	...	...
Heide	a.	1020	...	...
Husum	a.	1045	...	...
Niebüll	a.	1130	...	...
Westerland (Sylt)	a.	1200	...	...

f – Also May 25. h – Also May 26. ✣ – All six berths must be reserved.

MÜNCHEN - BAYRISCHZELL, LENGGRIES and TEGERNSEE — 928

Bayerische Regiobahn

Most trains run with multiple portions from München (please make sure you join the correct portion for your journey). On June 16, Aug. 15, Nov. 1 services run as on ⑦.

km			Ⓐ		Ⓐ	Ⓐ	Ⓐ	Ⓐ		Ⓐ	Ⓐ	Ⓐ	Ⓐ	Ⓐ			Ⓒ		†	Ⓒ	⊡⊙	Ⓒ	Ⓒ	Ⓒ	†	Ⓒ	Ⓒ	Ⓒ
0	**München** Hbf. d.	Ⓐ	0010	...	0629	0703	0804	0904	and	1904	2004	2104	2204	2310	...	Ⓒ	0010	...	0530	0630	and	1830	1930	2003	2030	2103	2204	2310
37	Holzkirchen .... d.		0037	...	0701	0732	0832	0932	hourly	1932	2032	2132	2232	2337	...		0037	...	0600	0700	hourly	1900	2000	2030	2100	2130	2232	2337
61	Schliersee ...... d.		0106	...	0727	0802	0902	1001	until	2001	2102	2202	2302	0006	...		0106	...	0632	0732	until	1932	2026	2102	2126	2202	2302	0006
78	**Bayrischzell** .. a.		0130	...	...	0825	0925	1025		2025	2125	2225	2325	0030	...		0130	...	0656	0756		1956	...	2125	...	2225	2325	0030

km			Ⓐ		Ⓐ	Ⓐ	Ⓐ	Ⓐ	⊖	Ⓐ	Ⓐ			Ⓒ		Ⓒ	Ⓒ	Ⓒ	◇⊡	Ⓒ	Ⓒ	Ⓒ	†	Ⓒ	Ⓒ	Ⓒ
0	**München** Hbf. d.	Ⓐ	0010	...	0604	0629	0703	0804		2204	2310	...	Ⓒ	0010	...	0604	0704	0730		1904	1930	2003	2030	2103	2204	2310
37	Holzkirchen .... d.		0040	...	0635	0705	0735	0835	and	2235	2340	...		0040	...	0635	0735	0802	and at the	1935	2002	2035	2102	2135	2235	2340
47	Schaftlach ...... d.		0053	...	0648	0718	0748	0848	hourly	2248	2353	...		0053	...	0648	0748	0818	same minutes	1948	2018	2048	2118	2148	2248	2353
57	Bad Tölz .... d.		0105	...	0700	0730	0800	0900	until	2300	0005	...		0105	...	0700	0800	0830	past each	2000	2030	2100	2130	2200	2300	0005
67	**Lenggries**...... a.		0116	...	0711	0741	0811	0911		2311	0016	...		0116	...	0711	0811	0841	hour until	2011	2041	2111	2141	2211	2311	0016

km			Ⓐ		Ⓐ	Ⓐ	Ⓐ	Ⓐ	⊖	Ⓐ	Ⓐ			Ⓒ		Ⓒ	Ⓒ	Ⓒ	◇⊡	Ⓒ	Ⓒ	Ⓒ	†	Ⓒ	Ⓒ	Ⓒ
	München Hbf d.	Ⓐ	0010	...	0604	0629	0703	0804	and	2204	*2310*	...	Ⓒ	0010	..	0604	0704	0730	and at the same	1904	1930	2003	2030	2103	2204	2310
0	Schaftlach ...... d.		0053	...	0648	0718	0748	0848	hourly	2248	2353	...		0053	...	0648	0748	0818	minutes past	1948	2018	2048	2118	2148	2248	2353
12	**Tegernsee** ..... a.		0113	...	0709	0739	0809	0909	until	2309	0013	...		0113	...	0709	0809	0839	each hour until	2009	2039	2109	2139	2209	2309	0013

		Ⓐ	Ⓐ	Ⓐ	Ⓐ	Ⓐ	Ⓐ	Ⓐ	Ⓐ	Ⓐ	Ⓐ	Ⓐ	Ⓐ	Ⓐ	Ⓐ	Ⓐ	Ⓐ		Ⓐ			Ⓒ	Ⓒ		Ⓒ	Ⓒ	Ⓒ	Ⓒ
Bayrischzell.... d.	Ⓐ	0449	0532	0607	0634	0705	0732	0832	0932	1032	1132	1232	...	1432	1532	1632	1732	and	2232	...	Ⓒ	0503	0603	and	2003	2032	2132	2232
Schliersee........ d.		0516	0559	0635	0702	0734	0759	0900	0959	1059	1159	1304	1359	1459	1559	1704	1759	hourly	2259	...		0530	0630	hourly	2030	2059	2159	2259
Holzkirchen...... d.		0544	0629	0705	0732	0803	0831	0931	1030	1129	1231	1332	1429	1531	1631	1732	1829	until	2329	...		0604	0704	until	2104	2132	2231	2331
München Hbf .. a.		0612	0655	0735	0758	0832	0857	0957	1056	1155	1257	1359	1455	1557	1657	1758	1855		2355	...		0632	0732		2132	2158	2257	2357

		Ⓐ	Ⓐ	Ⓐ	Ⓐ	Ⓐ	Ⓐ	Ⓐ	Ⓐ	Ⓐ	△	Ⓐ			⑥	Ⓒ	Ⓒ	Ⓒ	⊗	Ⓒ	Ⓒ	Ⓒ	Ⓒ		Ⓒ	Ⓒ
Lenggries .... d.	Ⓐ	0506	0547	0617	0647	0717	0747	0817	0847	0947		2247	...	Ⓒ	0447	0517	0617	0647		1917	1947	2017	2047	...	2147	2247
Bad Tölz.......... d.		0518	0600	0630	0700	0730	0800	0830	0900	1000	and	2300	...		0500	0530	0630	0700	and at the	1930	2000	2030	2100	...	2200	2300
Schaftlach......... d.		0531	0617	0647	0717	0747	0817	0847	0917	1017	hourly	2317	...		0517	0549	0649	0717	same minutes	1949	2017	2049	2117	...	2217	2317
Holzkirchen...... d.		0544	0629	0701	0732	0803	0831	0903	0931	1030	until	2329	...		0531	0604	0704	0729	past each	2004	2029	2104	2132	...	2231	2331
München Hbf .. a.		0612	0655	0730	0758	0832	0857	0932	0957	1056		2355	...		0557	0632	0732	0755	hour until	2032	2055	2132	2158	...	2257	2357

		Ⓐ	Ⓐ	Ⓐ	Ⓐ	Ⓐ	Ⓐ	Ⓐ	Ⓐ	Ⓐ	△	Ⓐ			⑥	Ⓒ	Ⓒ	Ⓒ	⊗	Ⓒ	Ⓒ	Ⓒ	Ⓒ		Ⓒ	Ⓒ
Tegernsee ...... d.	Ⓐ	0505	0552	0622	0652	0722	0752	0822	0852	0952	and	2252	...	Ⓒ	0452	0522	0622	0652	and at the same	1922	1952	2022	2052	...	2152	2252
Schaftlach......... a.		0525	0613	0643	0713	0743	0813	0843	0913	1013	hourly	2313	...		0513	0543	0643	0713	minutes past	1943	2013	2043	2113	...	2213	2313
München Hbf a.		0612	0655	0730	0758	0832	0857	0932	0957	1056	until	2355	...		0557	0632	0732	0755	each hour until	2032	2055	2132	2158	...	2257	2357

⊡ – München Hbf d. 1528, 1628, 1728 (not 1530, 1630, 1730).
⊙ – Holzkirchen d. 1558, 1658, 1758 (not 1600, 1700, 1800).
◇ – München Hbf d. 0803, 0903, 1003 (not 0804, 0904, 1004). No service from München (to Lenggries / Tegernsee) at 1230 or 1330.

△ – Holzkirchen and München timings may vary by up to 3 minutes. Extra trains on Ⓐ: from Lenggries to München at 1217, 1317, 1517, 1617 and 1817; from Tegernsee to München at 1222, 1322, 1522, 1622 and 1822.

⊖ – Extra trains on Ⓐ from München (to Lenggries / Tegernsee) at 0926, 1140, 1229, 1526, 1627, 1726, 1826 and 1926.
⊗ – Timings may vary by 1 – 2 minutes. No service from Tegernsee (to München) at 1322 or 1422. No service from Lenggries (to München) at 1417.

PLATTLING - BAYERISCH EISENSTEIN - PLZEŇ — 929

Waldbahn ⊠; ČD; 2nd class only

km			753		755	757	759				761			763			767			771				775	
			◇¶	Ⓐ	◇	◇	◇	Ⓐt	Ⓐt		◇			◇			◇			◇		ⒸB		◇	
0	**Plattling** .... d.	0101	...	...	...	...	...	0519	0629	0659	...	0806	0906	...	1006	1106	...	1206	1306	...	1406	...	1506	...	1606
9	Deggendorf Hbf....... d.	0110	...	...	...	...	...	0531	0638	0709	...	0816	0916	...	1016	1116	...	1216	1316	...	1416	...	1516	...	1616
33	Gotteszell....... d.	0129	...	...	...	...	...	0554	0657	0733	...	0835	0935	...	1035	1135	...	1235	1335	...	1435	...	1535	...	1635
48	Regen....... d.	0143	...	...	...	...	...	0609	0711	0748	...	0848	0948	...	1048	1148	...	1248	1348	...	1448	...	1548	...	1648
58	Zwiesel (Bay)....... d.	0153	...	...	...	...	...	0623	0725	0800	...	0900	1000	...	1100	1200	...	1300	1400	...	1500	...	1600	...	1700
72	**Bayerisch Eisenstein** ☆ 🏛 a.	...	...	...	...	...	...	0636	0738	0813	...	0913	1013	...	1113	1213	...	1313	1413	...	1513	...	1613	...	1713
72	**Železná Ruda-Alžbětín** ☆ 🏛 d.	...	...	0417	...	...	*0617*	▬	...	...	*0816*	▬	...	1017	▬	...	*1217*	▬	...	*1416*	▬	1553	...	1617	▬
75	Železná Ruda centrum....... d.	...	...	0421	...	...	*0621*	...	...	...	*0820*	...	...	1021	...	...	*1221*	...	...	*1420*	...	1557	...	1621	...
79	Špičák....... d.	...	...	0429	...	...	*0629*	...	...	...	*0827*	...	...	1029	**765**	...	*1229*	**769**	...	*1427*	**773**	1606	...	1629	**777**
131	**Klatovy** .... a.	...	...	0517	...	...	*0716*	◇	...	...	*0916*	◇	...	1116	◇	...	*1316*	◇	...	*1516*	◇	1704	...	1716	◇
131	**Klatovy** .... d.	...	0428	...	0528	0630	0730	0828	...	...	0930	1028	...	1130	1228	...	1330	1428	...	1530	1628	1708	...	1730	1828
141	Švihov u Klatov....... d.	...	0437	...	0537	0639	0740	0837	...	...	0940	1037	...	1140	1237	...	1340	1437	...	1540	1637	|	...	1740	1837
170	**Plzeň** hl.n. .... a.	...	0519	...	0619	0719	0819	0919	...	...	1019	1119	...	1219	1319	...	1419	1519	...	1619	1719	1759	...	1819	1919
	Praha hl.n. **1120** .... a.	...	0651	...	0751	0851	0951	...	...	...	1151	...	...	1351	1451	...	1551	1651	...	1751	1851	...	...	1951	2051

			779							
	E		◇							
Plattling .... d.	...	1707	...	1806	...	1906	2006	2106	2213	2308
Deggendorf Hbf .... d.	...	1716	...	1816	...	1916	2016	2116	2222	2319
Gotteszell .... d.	...	1735	...	1835	...	1935	2035	2135	2241	2338
Regen....... d.	...	1748	...	1848	...	1948	2048	2148	2254	2350
Zwiesel (Bay) .... d.	...	1800	...	1900	...	2000	2100	2158	2304	0001
Bayerisch Eisenstein ☆ 🏛 . a.	...	1813	...	1913	...	2013	2113	...	...	...
Železná Ruda-Alžbětín ☆ 🏛 . d.	1740	...	*1817*	...	1953	...	...	...	...	...
Železná Ruda centrum....... d.	1744	...	*1821*	...	1957	...	...	...	...	...
Špičák .... d.	1752	...	*1829*	...	2005	...	...	...	...	...
Klatovy .... a.	1834	...	*1918*	...	2057	...	...	...	...	...
Klatovy .... d.	1845	...	1930	...	2059	...	...	...	...	...
Švihov u Klatov....... d.	|	...	1940	...	2110	...	...	...	...	...
Plzeň hl.n. .... a.	1933	...	2019	...	2154	...	...	...	...	...
Praha hl.n. **1120** .... a.	...	...	2151	...	...	...	...	...	...	...

								778	778
	Ⓐt	Ⓐt	Ⓒz	Ⓐt	Ⓒz	Ⓐt		◇	Ⓐ◇
Praha hl.n. **1120** .... d.	...	...	...	...	...	...	...	...	0508
Plzeň hl.n. .... d.	...	...	...	...	...	...	0540	0640	0640
Švihov u Klatov....... d.	...	...	...	...	...	...	0619	0719	0719
Klatovy .... a.	...	...	...	...	...	...	0629	0729	0729
Klatovy .... d.	...	...	...	...	...	...	*0640*	▬	▬
Špičák .... d.	...	...	...	...	...	...	*0728*	...	...
Železná Ruda centrum....... d.	...	...	...	...	...	...	*0734*	...	...
Železná Ruda-Alžbětín ☆ 🏛 .... a.	...	...	...	...	...	...	*0738*	Ⓐt	...
Bayerisch Eisenstein ☆ 🏛 .... d.	...	...	...	...	...	0705	...	0744	...
Zwiesel (Bay) .... d.	0414	0529	0559	0621	0652	0722	...	0759	0759
Regen....... d.	0424	0539	0609	0631	0702	0732	...	0809	0809
Gotteszell....... d.	0438	0555	0622	0644	0715	0751	...	0822	0822
Deggendorf Hbf....... d.	0459	0614	0645	0709	0738	0815	...	0845	0845
Plattling .... a.	0508	0623	0654	0718	0747	0825	...	0854	0854

			776		774	772			770			768	766			764		762	760		758	756		752	
		C	◇		◇	◇		◇	◇	D	◇	◇	◇	Ⓐ		◇		◇	◇		◇	◇		◇	
Praha hl.n. **1120** .... d.	...	...	0608	...	0708	0808	...	...	1008	...	...	1208	1308	...	...	1408	...	1508	1608	...	1708	1808	...	2108	...
Plzeň hl.n. .... d.	...	0700	0740	...	0840	0940	...	1040	1140	...	1240	1340	1440	...	...	1540	...	1640	1740	...	1840	1940	2111	2240	...
Švihov u Klatov....... d.	...	|	0818	...	0919	1018	...	1119	1218	...	1319	1418	1519	...	...	1618	...	1719	1818	...	1919	2019	2157	2319	...
Klatovy .... a.	...	0749	0827	...	0929	1027	...	1129	1227	...	1329	1427	1529	...	...	1627	...	1729	1827	...	1929	2029	2208	2329	...
Klatovy .... d.	...	0803	0840	...	▬	*1040*	...	▬	*1240*	...	▬	1440	▬	1535	...	*1640*	...	▬	*1840*	...	▬	*2035*	▬	▬	...
Špičák .... d.	...	0849	0929	...	...	*1128*	...	...	*1328*	...	...	1529	...	1629	...	*1728*	...	...	*1928*	...	...	*2122*	...	...	...
Železná Ruda centrum....... d.	...	0856	0936	...	...	*1134*	...	...	*1334*	...	...	1536	...	1636	...	*1734*	...	...	*1934*	...	...	*2129*	...	...	...
Železná Ruda-Alžbětín ☆ 🏛 . a.	...	0900	0940	...	...	*1138*	...	...	*1338*	...	...	1540	...	1640	...	*1738*	...	...	*1938*	...	...	*2133*	...	...	...
Bayerisch Eisenstein ☆ 🏛 . d.	0841	...	...	0944	1041	...	1144	1241	...	1344	1444	...	1544	...	1644	...	1744	1841	...	1944	2041	...	2141	...	...
Zwiesel (Bay) .... d.	0859	...	...	0959	1059	...	1159	1259	...	1359	1459	...	1559	...	1659	...	1759	1859	...	1959	2059	...	2204f	...	...
Regen....... d.	0909	...	...	1009	1109	...	1209	1309	...	1409	1509	...	1609	...	1709	...	1809	1909	...	2009	2109	...	2214	...	...
Gotteszell .... d.	0922	...	...	1022	1122	...	1222	1322	...	1422	1522	...	1622	...	1722	...	1822	1922	...	2022	2122	...	2228	...	...
Deggendorf Hbf .... d.	0945	...	...	1045	1145	...	1245	1345	...	1445	1545	...	1645	...	1745	...	1845	1946	...	2045	2145	...	2251	2329	0038
Plattling .... a.	0954	...	...	1054	1154	...	1254	1354	...	1454	1554	...	1654	...	1754	...	1854	1955	...	2054	2154	...	2300	2339	0049

BRANCH LINE SERVICES ⊠

ZWIESEL - GRAFENAU *32 km.* Journey time: 47 – 49 minutes.
From Zwiesel (Bay) at 0702 Ⓒ **z**, 0713 Ⓐ **t**, 0902, 1102, 1304, 1502, 1702 and 1902.
From Grafenau at 0805, 1000, 1200, 1400, 1600, 1800 and 2000.

ZWIESEL - BODENMAIS *15 km.* Journey time: 20 minutes.
From Zwiesel at 0624 Ⓐ **t**, 0802 Ⓐ **t**, 0902, 1002 and hourly until 2002; then 2202.
From Bodenmais at 0558 Ⓐ **t**, 0649 Ⓐ **t**, 0829, 0929 and hourly until 2029.

GOTTESZELL - VIECHTACH *25 km.* Journey time: 40 – 47 minutes.
From Gotteszell at 0132 Ⓒ **z**, 0450 Ⓐ **t**, 0601 Ⓐ **t**, 0658 Ⓐ **t**, 0739 ⑥, 0751 Ⓐ **t**, 0939, 1039 ⚒ **t**, 1139, 1239 ⚒ **t**, 1336 Ⓐ **t**, 1339 Ⓒ **z**, 1439, 1539 and hourly until 2039; then 2245.
From Viechtach at 0042 Ⓒ **z**, 0351 Ⓐ **t**, 0451 Ⓐ **t**, 0600 Ⓐ **t**, 0629 ⑥, 0656 Ⓐ **t**, 0837, 0937 ⚒ **t**, 1037, 1137 ⚒ **t**, 1237, 1328 Ⓐ **t**, 1337 Ⓒ **z**, 1437, 1537 and hourly until 1937; then 2137.

B – Ⓒ from Oct. 1 (also Oct. 26, 27).
C – Daily June 11 - Sept. 4; Ⓒ from Sept. 10 (also Oct. 26, 27).
D – Change trains at Zwiesel on Ⓐ (not June 16, Aug. 15, Nov. 1).
E – Daily June 11 - Sept. 4; Ⓒ Sept. 10 – 28.

f – Arrives 2154.
t – Not June 16, Aug. 15, Nov. 1.
z – Also June 16, Aug. 15, Nov. 1.

◇ – Also conveys [1].
¶ – Train number **743** on Ⓒ.
⊠ – *Waldbahn* services are operated by Die Länderbahn.
☆ – Bayerisch Eisenstein (German) / Železná Ruda-Alžbětín (Czech) is the same station.

930 STUTTGART - MÜNCHEN

km		ICE 619		ICE 699	◇	RE 4205	ICE 891	ICE 1561	ICE 1561	◇	ICE 993	RJX 63	RE 4207	ICE 991	RJ 897	EC 217	RE 4209	ICE 511	IC 267	RE 4211	ICE 591	EC 113	IC 2393	RE 4213
						Ⓐt	①–⑥	①–⑤	①		Y	Ⓒ		①–⑤									■	
		H		✕♦		L	✕	u✕	g✕		✕	✕♦	L	✕♦	✕♦	🍸♦	L	✕	🍸♦	L	✕♦	✕♦	🍸	L
	Dortmund Hbf **800** d.	2236	...	...	...	...	...	...	...	...	...	...	...	...	...	...	...	...	...	...	...	...	...	...
	Köln Hbf **800 910** d.	2355	...	...	...	...	...	...	...	...	...	...	...	...	...	...	...	0548	...	...	...	...	...	...
	Frankfurt (Main) Hbf **912** d.	0117	...	0225	...	...	...	...	0404	...	0517c	0517	...	...	0554	...	...	|	...	...	0750	0820•	0820§	...
	Frankfurt Flughafen ✈ **912** d.	0057*	...	0246	...	...	...	...	|	...	0539c	0539	...	...	|	...	...	0652	...	...	|	|	|	...
	Mannheim Hbf **912** d.	0204	...	0326	...	...	...	...	0447	...	0612c	0612	...	0629	|	0711	...	0731	...	...	0830	|	|	...
	Heidelberg Hbf **912** d.	0219	...	|	...	...	...	...	0459	...	|	|	...	|	0652	|	...	|	...	...	|	0913	0913	...
	Karlsruhe Hbf **931** d.	|	...	|	...	...	0453	...	|	...	|	|	...	|	|	|	...	|	0805	...	|	|	|	...
0	**Stuttgart** Hbf **936** d.	0340	...	0512	...	0541	0551	...	0558	0601	0657	0658	0700	0714	0744	0758	0801	0814	0854	0900	0914	0958	0958	1001
22	Plochingen **936** d.	|	...	|	0529	0559	|	...	0616	0621	|	|	0718	|	|	|	0818	|	0909	0918	|	|	|	1018
42	Göppingen d.	|	...	|	0548	0612	|	...	|	0639	|	|	0729	|	|	|	0829	|	0921	0929	|	|	|	1029
61	Geislingen (Steige) d.	|	...	|	0616	0626	|	...	|	0717y	|	|	0740	|	|	|	0840	|	|	0940	|	|	|	1040
94	**Ulm** Hbf **945** d.	0442	...	0612	0648	0702	0655	0713	0713	0749	0756	0756	0804	0812	0900	0856	0904	0912	0957	1004	1013	1056	1056	1104
118	Günzburg **945** d.	0458	...	0627	...	...	0710	0735	0735	...	0811	0811	...	|	...	0910	...	|	|	...	|	1110	1110	...
180	**Augsburg** Hbf **905** d.	0532	...	0659	...	...	0741	0807	0807	...	0842	0842	...	0855	...	0941	...	0955	1041	...	1055	1141	1141	...
235	München Pasing **905** a.	0553	...	0721	...	...	0807	0831	0831	...	0903	0903	...	0918	...	|	...	1018	1103	...	1118	|	|	...
242	**München** Hbf **905** a.	0603	...	0731	...	...	0817	0841	0841	...	0913	0913	...	0928	...	1011	...	1027	1112	...	1127	1210	1210	...
	Salzburg Hbf **890** a.	...	...	...	...	...	...	...	...	...	...	1058	...	...	...	1159h	...	...	...	...	...	1359	...	...

	ICE 513	ICE 1163	RE 4215	ICE 593	EC 115	RE 4217	ICE 515	RE 4219	IC 2265	IC 119	ICE 595	◇	EC 219	RE 4221	ICE 517	RE 4223	IC 2013	ICE 597	EC 117	RE 4225	ICE 519	IC 1299	RE 4227	ICE 599
	M✕	✕	L	B✕	🍸♦	L	H✕		🍸	♦	B✕		🍸♦	L	H✕	L	🍸♦	B✕	🍸♦	L	H✕	🍸	L	B✕
Dortmund Hbf **800** d.	0636	...	...	...	...	...	0836	...	...	0751	...	...	...	...	1036	...	0949	...	...	...	1236	...	...	...
Köln Hbf **800 910** d.	0755	...	...	...	0818	...	0955	...	...	0917	...	...	...	...	1155	...	1117	...	...	...	1355	...	...	...
Frankfurt (Main) Hbf **912** d.	|	...	...	0950	|	...	|	...	...	|	1150	...	1220	...	|	...	|	1350	1420	...	|	...	...	1550
Frankfurt Flughafen ✈ **912** d.	0852	...	...	|	|	...	1052	...	...	|	|	...	|	...	1252	...	|	|	|	...	1452	...	...	|
Mannheim Hbf **912** d.	0931	...	...	1030	1102	...	1131	...	...	1154	1230	...	|	...	1331	...	1354	1430	|	...	1531	...	...	1630
Heidelberg Hbf **912** d.	|	...	...	|	|	...	|	...	...	1206	|	...	1313	...	|	...	1406	|	1513	...	|	...	...	|
Karlsruhe Hbf **931** d.	|	0949z	...	|	|	...	|	...	1206	|	|	...	|	...	|	...	|	|	|	...	|	1606	...	|
Stuttgart Hbf **936** d.	1014	1054	1100	1114	1158	1201	1214	1240	1254	1257	1314	1303	1358	1401	1414	1452	1458	1514	1558	1601	1614	1654	1700	1714
Plochingen **936** d.	|	|	1118	|	|	1218	|	1259	1309	|	|	1329n	|	1418	|	1509	1514	|	|	1618	|	1709	1718	|
Göppingen d.	|	|	1129	|	|	1229	|	1312	1320	1325	|	1348	|	1429	|	1522	1528	|	|	1629	|	1720	1729	|
Geislingen (Steige) d.	|	|	1140	|	|	1240	|	1327	|	|	|	1416n	|	1440	|	1536	|	|	|	1640	|	|	1740	|
Ulm Hbf **945** d.	1112	1158	1204	1212	1256	1304	1312	1350	1358	1404	1412	1447	1456	1504	1512	1604	1614	1612	1656	1704	1712	1758	1804	1812
Günzburg **945** d.	|	|	...	|	1310	...	|	...	|	...	|	...	1510	...	|	...	...	|	1710	...	|	|	...	|
Augsburg Hbf **905** d.	1155	1241	...	1255	1341	...	1355	...	1441	...	1455	...	1541	...	1555	...	...	1655	1741	...	1755	1840	...	1855
München Pasing **905** a.	1217	1302	...	1318	|	...	1418	...	1503	...	1518	...	|	...	1618	...	...	1718	|	...	1818	1902	...	1918
München Hbf **905** a.	1227	1312	...	1327	1411o	...	1427	...	1512	...	1528	...	1611	...	1627	...	...	1727	1811	...	1827	1911	...	1927
Salzburg Hbf **890** a.	...	...	...	...	1559h	...	...	...	...	...	...	...	1759h	...	...	...	...	...	1959h	...	...	2100q	...	...

	IC 1291	RE 4229	ICE 611	IC 2011	IC 2269	RE 4231	ICE 691	TGV 9577	IC 2297	RE 4233	ICE 613	IC 1917	ICE 771	IC 2369	RE 4235	ICE 693	TGV 9579	◇	RE 4237	ICE 615	IC 1999	◇	ICE 695	RE 4239
				①–④				Ⓑ	Ⓑ			⑦	⑤	①–④		Ⓑ	⑥				⑦		⑥⑦	
	🍸	L	H✕	🍸♦	🍸	F	B✕	P🍸	🍸	L	H✕	🍸♦	G✕	m	L	B✕	P🍸			H	A🍸		B	
Dortmund Hbf **800** d.	...	...	1435	...	...	...	...	...	...	...	1636	...	...	...	...	...	...	...	...	1835	...	...	...	...
Köln Hbf **800 910** d.	...	...	1555	1517	...	...	...	...	...	...	1755	1717	...	...	...	...	...	...	...	1955	...	...	...	...
Frankfurt (Main) Hbf **912** d.	1620k	...	|	|	...	...	1750	...	1819	...	|	|	1906	...	...	1950	...	...	...	|	2009f	...	2150	...
Frankfurt Flughafen ✈ **912** d.	|	...	1652	|	...	...	|	...	|	...	1852	|	1924	...	...	|	...	...	...	2052	|	...	|	...
Mannheim Hbf **912** d.	|	...	1731	1754	...	...	1830	...	|	...	1931	1954	1959	...	...	2030	...	...	...	2131	|	...	2230	...
Heidelberg Hbf **912** d.	1713	...	|	1806	...	...	|	...	1913	...	|	2006	|	...	...	|	...	...	...	|	2114	...	|	...
Karlsruhe Hbf **931** d.	|	...	|	|	1806	...	|	1827	|	...	|	|	|	2006	...	|	2028	...	...	|	|	...	|	...
Stuttgart Hbf **936** d.	1758	1801	1814	1851	1854	1900	1914	1922	1958	2001	2014	2051	2054	2054	2101	2114	2114	2129	2201	2214	2211	2229	2314	2323
Plochingen **936** d.	|	1818	|	1904	1909	1918	|	|	|	2018	|	2104	|	2109	2118	|	|	2147	2218	|	|	2247	|	2341
Göppingen d.	|	1829	|	...	1920	1929	|	|	|	2029	|	...	|	2120	2129	|	|	2205	2229	|	2238	2305	|	2353
Geislingen (Steige) d.	|	1840	|	...	|	1940	|	|	|	2040	|	...	|	2134	2140	|	|	2229	2240	|	2253	2336n	|	0006
Ulm Hbf **945** d.	1856	1904	1912	...	1958	2004	2012	2020	2056	2104	2112	...	2200	2159	2204	2212	2212	2301	2305	2312	2319	0006	0014	0038
Günzburg **945** d.	1910	...	|	...	|	...	|	|	2111	...	|	...	2215	...	...	|	|	...	...	|	...	...	0030	...
Augsburg Hbf **905** d.	1941	...	1955	...	2041	...	2055	2106	2142	...	2155	...	2247	...	...	2255	2258	...	...	2355	...	...	0101	...
München Pasing **905** a.	|	...	2018	...	2103	...	2117	|	2206	...	2216	...	2309	...	...	2320	|	...	...	0018	...	...	0123	...
München Hbf **905** a.	2011	...	2028	...	2112	...	2127	2136	2215	...	2226	...	2319	...	...	2329	2329	...	...	0027	...	...	0133	...
Salzburg Hbf **890** a.	2202q	...	...	...	...	...	...	...	...	...	...	...	...	...	...	...	...	...	...	...	...	...	...	...

Regional trains ULM - MÜNCHEN

		Ⓐr		Ⓐr		Ⓐr															⊖			
Ulm Hbf d.	...	0446	0522	0545	0621	0643	0723	0823	0923	1023	1123	1223	1323	1423	1523	1623	1723	1824	1923	2023	2123	2223	...	2323
Günzburg d.	...	0504	0540	0606	0640	0702	0742	0842	0942	1042	1142	1242	1342	1442	1542	1642	1742	1843	1942	2042	2142	2242	...	2341
Augsburg Hbf a.	...	0559	0630	0658	0734	0802	0833	0933	1033	1133	1233	1333	1433	1533	1633	1733	1833	1933	2033	2133	2233	2333	...	...
Augsburg Hbf **905** d.	0539	0605	0639	0705	0739	0806	0839	0939	1039	1139	1239	1339	1439	1539	1639	1739	1839	1939	2039	2139	2239	2342	...	...
München Pasing **905** a.	0613	0641	0714	0745	0813	0846	0913	1013	1113	1213	1313	1413	1513	1613	1713	1813	1913	2014	2123	2223	2315	0024	...	...
München Hbf **905** a.	0621	0649	0721	0754	0822	0853	0921	1021	1121	1221	1321	1421	1521	1622	1723	1823	1921	2022	2132	2231	2324	0032	...	...

♦ – **NOTES** (LISTED BY TRAIN NUMBER)

63 – Ⓒ from Aug. 6. [12] ✕ Frankfurt - Wien - Budapest.
113 – From Aug. 3. BLAUER ENZIAN – [12] ✕ Frankfurt - Salzburg - Villach - Klagenfurt; [12] Frankfurt - Villach (**213**) - Ljubljana - Zagreb.
115 – WÖRTHERSEE – [12] 🍸 Münster - Köln - Koblenz - Salzburg ▲ - Villach - Klagenfurt.
117 – SALZACH – [12] 🍸 Frankfurt - Salzburg ▲ - Villach - Klagenfurt.
119 – BODENSEE – [12] Dortmund - Köln - Koblenz - Ulm - Lindau - Bregenz - Innsbruck.
217 – DACHSTEIN – [12] 🍸 Saarbrücken - München - Salzburg - Bischofshofen - Selzthal - Graz. Until Aug. 1 runs as *IC* **2397** and terminates at München.
219 – CHIEMGAU – [12] 🍸 Frankfurt - München - Salzburg - Bischofshofen - Selzthal - Graz. Until Aug. 1 runs as *IC* **2399** and terminates at München.
267 – BADEN-KURIER – [12] 🍸 (Basel ①–⑥ -) Karlsruhe - München.
591 – [12] ✕ (Hamburg ①–⑥ -) Kassel - Frankfurt - München.
699 – [12] Hamburg - Berlin - Leipzig - Erfurt - Frankfurt - München. ✕ Stuttgart - München.
897 – [12] ✕ Frankfurt - Ulm - Lindau - Bregenz (**867**) - Innsbruck - Wien. Train category *IC* until Aug. 1.
991 – [12] ✕ Wiesbaden - Mainz - München.
1917 – [12] 🍸 Berlin - Köln - Stuttgart - Nürtingen (a. 2116) - Reutlingen (a. 2136) - Tübingen Hbf (a. 2149).
2011 – ①–④ (not June 15, 16). LORELEY – [12] 🍸 Köln - Stuttgart - Plochingen - Nürtingen (a. 1916) - Reutlingen (a. 1936) - Tübingen Hbf (a. 1949).
2013 – ALLGÄU – [12] and 🍸 Dortmund - Köln - Koblenz - Ulm - Kempten - Oberstdorf.

A – From Berlin via Kassel and Gießen (Tables **806** and **810**). Train number **1991** from July 24.
B – From Berlin via Leipzig and Erfurt (Table **850**).
F – To Friedrichshafen (Table **933**).
G – From Hamburg (Table **900**).
H – From Hamburg (Table **800**).
L – To Lindau (Table **933**).
M – From Münster (Table **800**).
P – [12] and 🍸 Paris - Strasbourg - München. Ⓡ for international journeys.
Y – Daily until Aug. 5; ①–⑤ from Aug. 8.

c – ⑥⑦ until July 31.
f – Frankfurt (Main) **West** (not Hbf).
g – Also Aug. 16; not Aug. 15.
h – From Aug. 2.
k – 1610 on ⑤ until Aug. 26.
m – Not June 15.
n – Arrives 7 – 10 minutes earlier.
o – Until July 13 calls at München **Ost** (a. 1424; not Hbf).
q – Ⓑ from Aug. 2.
r – Not June 16, Aug. 15.
t – Not June 16.
u – Not June 16, 17, Aug. 15.
y – Arrives 0702.
z – ⑥⑦ (not July 30 - Sept. 11).

§ – On ①–⑤ departs Frankfurt (Main) **Süd**, d. 0819 (not Hbf).
• – On ①–⑤ Aug. 3 – 26 departs from Frankfurt (Main) **Süd**, d. 0819 (not Hbf).
* – Calls at Frankfurt Flughafen before Frankfurt (Main) Hbf.
‡ – Until Aug. 21 calls at Frankfurt (Main) **West** (not Hbf), departing 2010.
■ – Until Aug. 2.
▲ – Until Aug. 1 service is diverted and does not call at Salzburg.
⊖ – Change trains at Augsburg on ①②③④⑦.
◇ – Stopping service operated by Go-Ahead Baden-Württemberg.

MÜNCHEN - STUTTGART 930

		ICE				ICE		RE	IC	IC		RE	ICE	RE	IC			IC	ICE	RE	TGV	ICE	RE	IC
	◇	618		◇	◇	616	◇	4200	2368	2010	◇	4202	614	4204	2296	◇	◇	2366	692	4206	9576	612	4208	1296
	Ⓒz			Ⓐt	Ⓒz				Ⓐs	Ⓐ		Ⓐt			①–⑥	Ⓒz	Ⓐt	①–⑥						
		H				H		⊡		🍷♦			H✕	F	🍷			🍷	B✕	L	P🍷	H✕	L	🍷
Salzburg Hbf **890** d.	...	...	...	...	...	...	...	...	...	...	...	...	...	...	...	...	...	...	...	...	...	...	...	0543v
München Hbf **905** d.	...	0001	...	...	...	0324	...	...	...	...	...	...	0533	...	0540	...	...	0619	0629	...	0646	0728	...	0746
München Pasing **905** d.	...	0009	...	...	...	0332	...	...	...	...	...	...	0541	...	0549	...	...	0627	0638	...	|	0736	...	|
Augsburg Hbf **905** d.	...	0032	...	...	...	0357	...	...	...	...	...	...	0605	...	0612	...	...	0652	0704	...	0716	0803	...	0816
Günzburg **945** d.	...	0102	...	...	...	|	...	...	...	...	...	...	|	...	0643	...	...	0722	|	...	|	|	...	0848
Ulm Hbf **945** d.	0012	0116	...	...	...	0439	0449t	0520	0601	...	0545t	0617	0648	0654	0658	0702	0704	0738	0749	0754	0802	0848	0854	0903
Geislingen (Steige) d.	0046	|	...	0406	0425	|	0520	0549	0623	...	0616	0644	|	0717	0723	0731	0731	|	|	0817	|	|	0918	|
Göppingen d.	0107	|	...	0434	0448	|	0542	0604	0637	...	0644	0702	|	0730	|	0754	0754	0812	|	0829	|	|	0929	|
Plochingen **936** d.	0125	|	...	0454	0507	|	0601	0618	0650	0655	0702	0719	|	0741	0745	0812	0812	|	|	0840	|	|	0940	|
Stuttgart Hbf **936** a.	*0201*	0216	...	0511	0524	0535	0619	0636	0705	0709	0721	0736	0745	0756	0800	0829	0829	0837	0845	0856	0900	0945	0956	0959
Karlsruhe Hbf **931** a.	...	|	...	...	...	|	...	...	0753	|	...	...	|	...	|	...	...	0928	|	...	0951	|	...	|
Heidelberg Hbf **912** a.	...	0335	...	...	...	|	...	...	...	0753	...	...	|	...	0844	...	...	...	|	...	...	|	...	1044
Mannheim Hbf **912** a.	...	0355	...	...	...	0628	...	...	...	0806	...	...	0828	...	|	...	...	...	0929	...	...	1028	...	|
Frankfurt Flughafen ✈ **912** a.	...	0457*	...	...	...	0706	...	...	...	|	...	...	0906	...	|	...	...	...	|	...	...	1106	...	|
Frankfurt (Main) Hbf **912** a.	...	0439	...	...	...	|	...	...	...	|	...	...	|	...	0940	...	...	...	1008	...	...	|	...	1140
Köln Hbf **800 910** a.	...	0603	...	...	...	0805	...	...	...	1043	...	...	1004	...	...	...	...	...	...	...	...	1205	...	...
Dortmund Hbf **800** a.	...	0722	...	...	...	0923	...	...	...	1208f	...	...	1123	...	...	...	...	...	...	...	...	1321	...	...

	ICE	RE	IC	ICE	RE	IC	ICE	RE	IC	ICE	RE	EC	ICE	IC	IC	RE	ICE	RE	EC	ICE	RE	ICE	ICE	RE
	690	4210	1298	610	4212	1290	598	4214	2012	518	4216	218	596	118	2266	4218	516	4220	114	594	4222	1164	514	4224
	B✕	L	🍷	H✕	L	🍷	B✕	L	🍷♦	H✕	L	🍷♦	B✕	♦	🍷		H✕	L	🍷♦	B✕	L	✕	H✕	L
Salzburg Hbf **890** d.	...	...	0640k	...	...	0800g	...	...	...	...	...	1000h	...	...	...	...	...	...	1200h	...	...	...	...	...
München Hbf **905** d.	0827	...	0846	0928	...	0947	1028	...	...	1128	...	1147	1227	...	1247	...	1328	...	1347	1427	...	1447	1528	...
München Pasing **905** d.	0837	...	0853	0936	...	|	1037	...	...	1136	...	|	1237	...	1255	...	1336	...	|	1437	...	1455	1536	...
Augsburg Hbf **905** d.	0903	...	0921	1003	...	1016	1103	...	...	1203	...	1216	1302	...	1321	...	1403	...	1416	1503	...	1519	1603	...
Günzburg **945** d.	|	...	|	|	...	1048	|	...	...	|	...	1248	|	...	|	...	|	...	1448	|	...	|	|	...
Ulm Hbf **945** d.	0948	0954	1003	1048	1054	1103	1148	1154	1157	1248	1254	1303	1348	1356	1403	1407	1448	1454	1503	1548	1554	1603	1648	1654
Geislingen (Steige) d.	|	1019	|	|	1118	|	|	1217	|	|	1318	|	|	|	|	1432	|	1518	|	|	1619	|	|	1718
Göppingen d.	|	1031	1037	|	1129	|	|	1229	1235	|	1329	|	|	1433	|	1445	|	1529	|	|	1631	|	|	1729
Plochingen **936** d.	|	1042	1051	|	1140	|	|	1240	|	|	1340	|	|	|	1449	1458	|	1540	|	|	1642	|	|	1740
Stuttgart Hbf **936** a.	1045	1059	1105	1145	1156	1159	1245	1256	1303	1345	1356	1359	1445	1500	1504	1516	1545	1556	1559	1645	1658	1702	1745	1756
Karlsruhe Hbf **931** a.	|	...	1153	|	...	|	|	...	|	|	...	|	|	|	1552	...	|	...	|	|	...	1753	|	...
Heidelberg Hbf **912** a.	|	...	...	|	...	1244	|	...	1353	|	...	1444	|	1553	...	...	|	...	|	|	...	...	|	...
Mannheim Hbf **912** a.	1129	...	...	1228	...	|	1329	...	1406	1428	...	|	1529	1606	...	...	1628	...	1655	1729	...	...	1828	...
Frankfurt Flughafen ✈ **912** a.	|	...	...	1306	...	|	|	...	|	1506	...	|	|	|	...	...	1706	...	|	|	...	...	1906	...
Frankfurt (Main) Hbf **912** a.	1208	...	...	|	...	1340	1408	...	|	|	...	1555c	1608	|	...	...	|	...	|	1808	...	...	|	...
Köln Hbf **800 910** a.	...	...	...	1405	...	...	...	...	1643	1605	...	...	...	1842	...	...	1805	...	1943	...	...	...	2005	...
Dortmund Hbf **800** a.	...	...	...	1522	...	...	...	...	...	1722	...	...	...	2007	...	...	1921	...	...	...	...	...	2122	...

	EC	IC	ICE	IC	RE	IC	ICE	ICE	RE	EC	RJ	ICE	RE	ICE	ICE	RE	RE	ICE	RJX			ICE		
	112	1910	592	1910	4226 4240	266	1560	512	4228	216	890	590	4230	1160	510	4232	4234	990	66	◇	◇	698	◇	◇
		⑦		⑦			①–④							Ⓑ				Q	⑤⑥					
	✕♦	🍷	A✕	🍷	L	🍷♦	u✕	M✕	L	🍷♦	✕♦	✕♦	L	✕	✕	L	L	✕	✕♦			♦		
Salzburg Hbf **890** d.	1400	...	...	...	...	...	...	...	...	1600h	...	...	...	...	...	...	...	...	1900	...	...	...	...	...
München Hbf **905** d.	1547	1617	1627	...	...	1646	1715	1725	...	1747	...	1827	...	1841b	1928	...	...	2045	2045	...	...	2151	...	...
München Pasing **905** d.	|	1626	1637	...	...	1655	1725	1733	...	|	...	1837	...	1850b	1936	...	...	2054	2054	...	...	|	...	...
Augsburg Hbf **905** d.	1616	1656	1703	...	...	1721	1749	1759	...	1816	...	1902	...	1918	2003	...	...	2118	2118	...	...	2220	...	...
Günzburg **945** d.	1648	1728	|	...	...	|	1819	|	...	1848	...	|	...	1948	|	...	...	2148	2148	...	...	2252	...	...
Ulm Hbf **945** d.	1703	1742	1748	←	1754	1803	1836	1848	1854	1903	1909	1948	1954	2003	2048	2054	2153	2203	2203	...	2217	2308	...	*2312*
Geislingen (Steige) d.	|	1804	|	1813	1819	|	...	|	1918	|	|	|	2019	|	|	2119	2214	|	|	2232	2249	|	2335	2348
Göppingen d.	|	→	|	1827	1831	1838	...	|	1929	|	|	|	2031	|	|	2131	2227	|	|	2253	2310	|	2356	0009
Plochingen **936** d.	|	...	|	|	1842	1850	...	|	1940	|	|	|	2042	|	|	2142	2238	|	|	2311	2327	|	0014	0027
Stuttgart Hbf **936** a.	1759	...	1845	1856	1858	1904	...	1945	1956	1959	2005x	2045	2059	2104	2145	2159	2256	2259	2259	2328	*0005*	0006	0031	...
Karlsruhe Hbf **931** a.	|	...	|	|	...	1953	...	|	...	|	|	|	...	2153	|	...	...	|	|	...	...	|	...	...
Heidelberg Hbf **912** a.	1844	...	|	1953	...	...	...	|	...	|	2053	|	...	...	|	...	...	|	|	...	...	|	...	...
Mannheim Hbf **912** a.	|	...	1929	2006	...	...	...	2028	...	2048	|	2129	...	...	2228	...	...	2347	2347	...	...	0140	...	...
Frankfurt Flughafen ✈ **912** a.	|	...	|	|	...	...	...	2106	...	...	|	|	...	...	2306	...	...	0022	0022	...	...	0219	...	...
Frankfurt (Main) Hbf **912** a.	1940	...	2008	|	...	...	...	|	...	...	2152	2208	...	...	|	...	...	0041	0041	...	...	0240	...	...
Köln Hbf **800 910** a.	...	...	...	2243e	...	...	...	2205	...	...	...	...	...	...	0006	...	...	...	...	...	...	...	...	...
Dortmund Hbf **800** a.	...	...	...	0002e	...	...	...	...	...	...	...	...	...	...	...	...	...	...	...	...	...	...	...	...

Regional trains MÜNCHEN - ULM

		Ⓒw											Ⓐr	Ⓒw										
München Hbf d.	0007	0007	...	...	0529	0636	0735	0833	0937	1035	1135	1235	1335	1335	1435	1534	1635	1734	1835	1935	2035	2100	2200	2300
München Pasing d.	0016	0016	...	...	0536	0644	0743	0842	0944	1043	1143	1243	1343	1343	1443	1542	1643	1742	1843	1943	2043	2107	2207	2307
Augsburg Hbf a.	0056	0056	...	...	0619	0720	0820	0918	1019	1119	1218	1319	1419	1419	1519	1620	1719	1820	1918	2019	2122	2148	2248	2348
Augsburg Hbf d.	...	0059	...	0522	0623	0724	0825	0925	1025	1125	1222	1325	1424	1424	1525	1625	1725	1825	1928	2025	2125	2151	2251	2351
Günzburg d.	...	0150	...	0614	0714	0816	0920	1016	1116	1217	1319	1416	1515	1519	1616	1716	1822n	1916	2017	2116	2216	2242	2342	0042
Ulm Hbf a.	...	0208	...	0633	0733	0835	0939	1035	1135	1236	1337	1435	1534	1539	1635	1735	1840	1935	2037	2135	2235	2302	0002	0101

♦ – **NOTES** (LISTED BY TRAIN NUMBER)

66 – ⑤⑥ from Aug. 5. [12] ✕ Budapest - Wien - Frankfurt.

112 – BLAUER ENZIAN – [12] ✕ Klagenfurt - Villach - Salzburg - Frankfurt; [12] Zagreb (**212**) - Ljubljana - Villach (**112**) - Frankfurt. Until Aug. 1 does not run Klagenfurt - München and runs as *IC* **2392** (🍷) München - Frankfurt. Arrives Frankfurt 1944 on ⑤ Aug. 5 – 26.

114 – WÖRTHERSEE – [12] 🍷 Klagenfurt - Villach - Salzburg ▲ - Mannheim - Koblenz - Köln - Bochum.

118 – BODENSEE – [12] Innsbruck - Bregenz - Lindau - Ulm - Koblenz - Köln - Dortmund.

216 – DACHSTEIN – [12] 🍷 Graz - Selzthal - Bischofshofen - Salzburg - München - Saarbrücken. Until Aug. 1 starts from München and runs as *IC* **2396**.

218 – CHIEMGAU – [12] 🍷 Graz - Selzthal - Bischofshofen - Salzburg - München - Frankfurt (- Erfurt ①–④). Until Aug. 1 starts from München and runs as *IC* **2398**.

266 – BADEN-KURIER – [12] 🍷 München - Karlsruhe (- Basel Ⓑ).

590 – [12] München - Frankfurt (- Kassel ⑥).

698 – [12] München - Stuttgart - Frankfurt - Erfurt - Weimar - Halle - Berlin.

890 – [12] ✕ Wien (**860**) - Innsbruck - Bregenz (**890**) - Lindau - Ulm - Frankfurt. Train category *IC* until Aug. 1.

2010 – Ⓐ (not June 16, 17). LORELEY – [12] 🍷 Tübingen Hbf (d. 0611) - Reutlingen (d. 0623) - Nürtingen (d. 0642) - Plochingen - Köln (- Dortmund - Berlin ⑤**f**).

2012 – ALLGÄU – [12] and 🍷 Oberstdorf - Ulm - Köln - Bochum.

A – To Leipzig via Erfurt (Table **850**).
B – To Berlin via Erfurt and Leipzig (Table **850**).
F – From Friedrichshafen on Ⓐ**t** (Table **933**).
H – To Hamburg (Table **800**).
L – From Lindau (Table **933**).
M – To Münster (Table **800**).
P – [12] and 🍷 München - Strasbourg - Paris. Ⓡ for international journeys.
Q – Daily to Aug. 4; ⑦–④ from Aug. 7.

b – Until Aug. 1 departs München Hbf 1844, Pasing 1852.
c – 1540 on ⑤–⑦ from Aug. 27; 1615 on Aug. 5, 12, 19, 26. Terminates at Darmstadt (a. 1522) on ⑤ until July 29.
e – Until Aug. 28 arrives Köln 2305, Dortmund 0021.
f – ⑤ (also June 15; not June 17).
g – From Aug. 3.
h – From Aug. 2.
k – ①–⑥ from Aug. 3.
n – Arrives 1815.
r – Not June 16, Aug. 15.
s – Not June 16, 17.
t – Ⓐ (not June 16).
u – Not June 15, 16, Aug. 15.
v – Daily to Aug. 6; ①–⑥ from Aug. 8. Departs 0510 until July 13; departs 0537 July 14 - Aug. 1.
w – Also June 16, Aug. 15.
x – Not July 30 - Sept. 11.
z – Also June 16.

* – Calls at Frankfurt Flughafen after Frankfurt (Main) Hbf.
▲ – Until Aug. 1 service is diverted and does not call at Salzburg.
⊡ – Runs 1 – 2 minutes earlier July 30 - Sept. 11.
◇ – Operated by Go-Ahead Baden-Württemberg.

931 KARLSRUHE - STUTTGART and HEIDELBERG - MÜHLACKER

See Table **32** for full details of international *TGV* services from / to Paris. See Table **912** for fast trains Heidelberg - Stuttgart and v.v.

km ◧		*ICE* **891**	*ICE* **1061**	◇	*IC* **2216**	*ICE* **1063**	*IC* **2063**	◇	*IC* **1965**	*IC* **267**	◇	⊙	*IC* **2065**	◇	*ICE* **1163**	◇	⊙	◇	*IC* **2067**	*IC* **2265**	◇	⊙	◇	*IC* **2069**	◇	*ICE* **1967**
		①–⑥	⚒t		Ⓐv	Ⓐt			Ⓐv						⑥⑦											Ⓑ
			¶		O🍷		N			B🍷			N		u✕				N	🍷				N		
0	**Karlsruhe** Hbf .... d.	0453	0558	0601	0637	0658	0706	0733	0741	0805	0805	...	0906	0933	0949	1005	...	1033	1106	1206	1205	...	1233	1306	1405	1406
	Pforzheim .... d.	|	|	0624	|	|	0726	0754	|	|	0828	...	0927	0954	|	1028	...	1054	1127	|	1228	...	1254	1327	1428	|
	Heidelberg Hbf. **912** d.	|	|	|	|	|	|	|	|	|	|	0810	|	|	|	|	1010	|	|	|	|	1210	|	|	|	|
21	Bruchsal .... **912** d.	0510	0616	|	0655	0719	|	|	0757	0820	|	0830	|	|	1003	|	1030	|	|	1219	|	1230	|	|	|	1421
	Mühlacker .... d.	|	|	0633	|	|	0735	0802	|	|	0836	0854	0937	1002	|	1036	1054	1102	1137	|	1236	1254	1302	1337	1436	|
58	Vaihingen (Enz) ... **912** d.	0529	|	0639	|	|	0743	0808	|	|	0842	...	|	1011	|	1042	...	1108	1144	|	1242	...	1310**f**	|	1442	|
87	**Stuttgart** Hbf ...... **912** a.	0545	0649	0656	0726	0751	0802	0825	0829	0849	0900	...	1002	1028	1033	1100	...	1125	1202	1249	1300	...	1327**f**	1358	1500	1450
	München Hbf **930** .. a.	0817	...	...	...	...	...	...	...	1112	...	...	...	...	1312	...	...	...	...	1512	...	...	...	...	...	...

	⊙	◇	*IC* **2161**	*IC* **1299**	◇	⊙	◇	*IC* **2163**	*IC* **2269**	◇	*TGV* **9577**	⊙	◇	*IC* **2165**	*IC* **2369**	*IC* **2169**	◇	*TGV* **9579**	⊙	◇	*IC* **2167**	◇	◇	◇	⊙	◇
											Ⓑ				①–④	⑦		⑥								
			N	S🍷				N	🍷		P🍷			N	mH			P🍷			N					
Karlsruhe Hbf .... d.	...	1433	1506	1606	1605	...	1633	1706	1806	1805	1827	...	1833	1906	2006	2006	2005	2028	...	2033	2106	2133	2205	2233	...	2315
Pforzheim .... d.	...	1454	1527	|	1628	...	1654	1727	|	1828	|	...	1854	1927	|	|	2029	|	...	2054	2127	2154	2228	2254	...	2338
Heidelberg Hbf **912** d.	1410	|	|	|	|	1610	|	|	|	|	|	1810	|	|	|	|	|	|	2010	|	|	|	|	|	2243**h**	|
Bruchsal .... **912** d.	1430	|	|	1620	|	1630	|	|	1819	|	|	1830	|	|	2019	2019	|	|	2030	|	|	|	|	|	2303	|
Mühlacker .... d.	1454	1502	1537	|	1636	1654	1702	1737	|	1836	|	1855	1902	1937	|	|	2037	|	2054	2102	2137	2202	2236	2302	2327	2346
Vaihingen (Enz) .... **912** d.	...	1508	1544	|	1642	...	1708	1744	|	1842	|	...	1908	1945	|	|	2042	|	...	2110**f**	2145	2210	2245	2308	...	2352
Stuttgart Hbf .... **912** a.	...	1525	1602	1649	1700	...	1725	1803	1849	1859	1904	...	1925	2001	2049	2057	2059	2104	...	2126	2202	2225	2300	2325	...	0021
München Hbf **930** ... a.	...	...	...	1911	...	...	...	...	2112	...	2136	...	...	...	...	...	...	2329	...	...	...	...	...	...	...	...

km ◐		*IC* **2326**	*IC* **1964**	◇	⊙	◇	*IC* **2368**	◇	*IC* **2164**	*IC* **2366**	⊙	◇	*TGV* **9576**	◇	*IC* **2162**	◇	⊙	◇	*IC* **1298**	*IC* **2160**	◇	⊙	◇	*ICE* **1968**	*IC* **2068**	◇
		Ⓐ	Ⓐd	Ⓒz			Ⓐv																	①–⑥		
		D					H		N	🍷			P🍷		N				S🍷	N					N	
	München Hbf **930** .. d.	...	...	...	...	...	...	...	...	0619**e**	...	...	0646	...	...	...	...	...	0846	...	...	...	...	...	...	...
0	**Stuttgart** Hbf ...... **912** d.	0226	0602	0559	*0632*t	0659	0710	0732	0759	0842	...	0859	0910	0932	0958	1032	...	1059	1111	1159	1232	...	1259	1300	1358	1430
39	Vaihingen (Enz) ... **912** d.	|	|	0616	*0648*t	0716	|	0748	0816	|	...	0916	|	0948	1016	1048	...	1116	|	1216	1248	...	1316	|	1416	1446
47	Mühlacker .... d.	|	|	0622	0701	0722	|	0754	0824	|	0903	0922	|	0954	1023	1054	1103	1122	|	1223	1254	1303	1322	|	1423	1454
79	Bruchsal .... **912** d.	|	0631	|	0728	|	0739	|	|	0911	0930	|	|	|	|	|	1130	|	1140	|	|	1330	|	1338	|	|
112	**Heidelberg** Hbf **912** a.	|	|	|	0749	|	|	|	|	|	0952	|	|	|	|	|	1152	|	|	|	|	1352	|	|	|	|
60	Pforzheim .... d.	0306	|	0631	...	0731	|	0803	0834	|	...	0931	|	1003	1033	1103	...	1131	|	1233	1303	...	1331	|	1433	1503
86	**Karlsruhe** Hbf .... a.	0327	0648	0653	...	0753	0753	0825	0853	0928	...	0953	0951	1025	1053	1125	...	1153	1153	1253	1325	...	1353	1353	1453	1525

	⊙	◇	*IC* **2266**	*IC* **2066**	◇	*ICE* **713**	⊙	◇	*ICE* **1164**	*ICE* **1062**	*IC* **2064**	◇	⊙	◇	*IC* **266**	*IC* **2062**	◇	⊙	◇	*ICE* **1160**	◇	*IC* **2060**	◇	*IC* **1960**	◇	◇
						①–⑤				①–④										Ⓑ				⑦		
			🍷	N		rO✕			✕	m	N				B🍷	N				✕		N				
München Hbf **930** ... d.	...	...	1247	...	...	...	...	...	1447	...	...	...	...	...	1646	...	...	...	...	1841**k**	...	...	...	...	...	...
Stuttgart Hbf .... **912** d.	...	1459	1509	1558	1632	1640	...	1658	1708	1734	1759	1833	...	1859	1910	1959	2032	...	2059	2110	2132	2159	2232	2309	2313	0016
Vaihingen (Enz) .... **912** d.	...	1516	|	1616	1648	|	...	1716	|	|	1817	1848	...	1916	|	2016	2048	...	2116	|	2148	2216	2248	|	2331	0043
Mühlacker .... d.	1503	1522	|	1623	1654	|	1703	1722	|	|	1824	1854	1903	1922	|	2023	2054	2103	2122	|	2154	2224	2254	|	2340	0049
Bruchsal .... **912** d.	1530	|	1537	|	|	1712	1730	|	1736	1803	|	|	1930	|	1938	|	|	2130	|	2139	|	|	|	2339	|	|
Heidelberg Hbf **912** a.	1552	|	|	|	|	|	1752	|	|	|	|	|	1952	|	|	|	|	2152	|	|	|	|	|	|	|	|
Pforzheim .... d.	...	1531	|	1633	1703	|	...	1731	|	|	1834	1903	...	1931	|	2033	2103	...	2131	|	2203	2234	2303	|	2348	0057
Karlsruhe Hbf .... a.	...	1553	1552	1653	1725	1731	...	1753	1753	1820	1853	1925	...	1953	1953	2054	2125	...	2153	2153	2225	2300	2325	2358	0011	0119

B – From / to Basel on dates in Table **912**.
D – To Dortmund via Frankfurt and Siegen (Tables **808** and **912**).
H – From / to Ulm (Table **930**).
N – To / from Nürnberg on dates in Table **925**.
O – To / from Offenburg (Table **912**).
P – [12] and 🍷 München - Stuttgart - Paris and v.v. [R] for international journeys.
S – From / to Salzburg on dates in Table **890**.

d – Not June 16, 17, Aug. 1 - Sept. 9.
e – ①–⑥.
f – 2–3 minutes earlier July 30 - Sept. 11.
h – 2237 on † (also June 16).
k – 1844 until Aug. 1.
m – Not June 15.
r – Not June 16.
t – Ⓐ (not June 16).
u – Not July 30 - Sept. 11.
v – Not June 16, 17.

z – Also June 16.

◧ – Distance via high-speed line.
◐ – Distance via classic route.
¶ – Runs as *IC* **1961** on ⑥.
⊙ – Regional service operated by Abellio Rail Baden-Württemberg.
◇ – Regional service operated by Go-Ahead Baden-Württemberg.
Additional trains run Karlsruhe - Stuttgart and v.v. on Ⓐ (not June 16, Nov. 1):
From Karlsruhe Hbf at 0533, 0633, 0832, 1133, 1333, 1533, 1733 and 1933.
From Stuttgart Hbf at 0529, 0632, 0831, 1132, 1332, 1531, 1731 and 1932.

933 ULM - FRIEDRICHSHAFEN - LINDAU

IRE / *RE* services

km		Ⓐt	Ⓒz	Ⓐt	Ⓐt						*RJ* 897 G		⊙				⊙					*IC* 119 D			⊙		⊡
	Stuttgart Hbf **930** ... d.	...	...	...	...	...	0541t	...	0700	...	0744	0801	...	0900	...	1001	...	1100	...	1201	...	1257	...	1401	...	1452	...
0	**Ulm** Hbf .... d.	0500	0530	0537	0607	0649	0719	0743	0819	0847	0902	0919	0947	1019	1047	1119	1147	1219	1246	1319	1347	1411	1447	1519	1547	1619	1647
37	Biberach (Riß) .... d.	0523	0557	0601	0631	0716	0741	0806	0841	0909	0925	0941	1009	1041	1109	1141	1209	1241	1311	1341	1409	1432	1509	1540	1609	1640	1709
62	Aulendorf .... d.	0543	0614	0620	0648	0735	0757	0822	0900	0925	|	1000	1025	1100	1125	1200	1225	1300	1327	1400	1425	1451	1525	1600	1625	1700	1725
84	Ravensburg .... d.	0558	0627	0633	0700	0748	0809	0836	0912	0938	0951	1012	1038	1112	1138	1212	1238	1312	1341	1412	1439	1505	1538	1612	1638	1712	1741
95	Meckenbeuren .... d.	0605	0634	0640	0706	|	0816	|	0918	|	|	1018	|	1118	|	1218	|	1318	|	1418	|	|	|	1618	|	1718	|
103	Friedrichshafen Stadt a.	0614	0643	0648	0715	0801	0823	0850	0925	0952	1002	1025	1052	1125	1152	1225	1252	1325	1355	1425	1454	1516	1552	1625	1652	1725	1755
103	Friedrichshafen Stadt d.	0624	0652	0654	0728	0805	0831	0907	0932	*0958*	1010	1032	1107	1132	*1206*	1232	1306	1332	1407	1432	1506	1533	1607	1632	1658	1732	1806
	Lindau Insel .... a.	0652	0722	0729	|	0843	|	0940	|	*1026*	|	|	1140	|	*1240*	|	1340	|	1440	|	1540	|	1640	|	1733	|	1840
127	**Lindau** Reutin .... a.	...	...	...	0755	...	0855	...	0955	...	1028	1055	...	1155	...	1255	...	1355	...	1455	...	1556	...	1655	...	1755	...

								⊙			
Stuttgart Hbf **930** ... d.	1601	...	1700	...	1801	...	1900	...	2001	2101	...
Ulm Hbf .... d.	1719	1747	1819	1847	1919	1947	2019	2047	2119	2219	2325
Biberach (Riß) .... d.	1740	1809	1841	1909	1941	2009	2041	2109	2141	2242	0006
Aulendorf .... d.	1800	1825	1900	1925	2000	2025	2100	2125	2202	2259	0027
Ravensburg .... d.	1812	1838	1912	1938	2012	2038	2112	2138	2214	2311	0040
Meckenbeuren .... d.	1818	|	1918	|	2018	|	2118	|	2220	2317	0047
Friedrichshafen Stadt. a.	1825	1852	1925	1952	2025	2052	2125	2152	2227	2324	0055
Friedrichshafen Stadt. d.	1832	1907	1932	2007	2032	...	*2130*	2158	2234	2331	...
Lindau Insel .... a.	|	1940	|	2040	|	...	|	|	|	|	...
Lindau Reutin .... a.	1855	...	1955	...	2055	...	*2157*	2224	2255	2358	...

		Ⓐt	Ⓐt	Ⓒz							
Lindau Reutin .... d.	...	...	0601	...	...	0702	...	0807	...	0904	...
Lindau Insel .... d.	0450t	...	|	*0602*	0617t	|	*0735*t	|	0822	|	*0920*
Friedrichshafen Stadt ...... a.	0517t	...	0623	*0627*	0644t	0727	*0807*t	0828	0851	0927	*0951*
Friedrichshafen Stadt ...... d.	0524	0543	0631	0631	0700	0735	0810	0835	0905	0935	1005
Meckenbeuren .... d.	0530	0549	0637	0637	|	0741	|	0841	|	0941	|
Ravensburg .... d.	0538	0556	0644	0644	0713	0748	0822	0848	0918	0948	1018
Aulendorf .... d.	0552	0612	0657	0657	0728	0802	0837	0902	0933	1002	1033
Biberach (Riß) .... d.	0609	0627	0715	0715	0742	0820	0851	0920	0948	1020	1048
Ulm Hbf .... a.	0640	0649	0739	0739	0808	0842	0914	0942	1011	1042	1111
Stuttgart Hbf **930** .... a.	...	0756	0856	0856	...	0956	...	1059	...	1156	...

				Ⓒz	Ⓐt	*IC* 118 D					⊙			Ⓒz	Ⓐt	⊡		*RJ* 890 G			⊙						2
Lindau Reutin .... d.	1003	...	1104	...	...	1200	...	1304	...	1404	...	1504	...	1604	1604	...	1704	1731	...	1804	...	1904	...	2004	2104	2202	...
Lindau Insel .... d.	|	1029	|	*1120*	*1120*	|	1220	|	1320	|	1420	|	1520	|	|	1620	|	|	1720	|	1820	|	1920	|	|	|	...
Friedrichshafen Stadt a.	1027	1058	1127	*1151*	*1151*	1219	1255	1326	1351	1427	1451	1527	1553	1627	1627	1651	1726	1754	1751	1826	1851	1927	1951	2027	2128	2231	...
Friedrichshafen Stadt d.	1035	1105	1135	1205	1205	1235	1301	1335	1405	1435	1507	1534	1605	1635	1635	1704	1735	1802	1809	1835	1905	1935	2005	2035	2135	2238	2337
Meckenbeuren .... d.	1041	|	1141	|	|	|	1307	1341	|	1441	|	1541	|	1641	1643	|	1741	|	|	1841	|	1941	|	2041	2141	2245	2344
Ravensburg .... d.	1048	1118	1148	1218	1218	1249	1314	1348	1418	1448	1520	1548	1618	1648	1650	1718	1748	1816	1821	1848	1918	1948	2018	2048	2148	2252	2351
Aulendorf .... d.	1102	1133	1202	1233	1232	1304	1329	1402	1433	1502	1534	1602	1633	1702	1703	1733	1802	1830	1836	1902	1933	2002	2033	2102	2202	2306	0009
Biberach (Riß) .... d.	1120	1148	1220	1248	1250	1321	1345	1420	1448	1520	1548	1618	1648	1720	1720	1748	1820	1845	1851	1920	1948	2020	2048	2120	2220	2322	0025
Ulm Hbf .... a.	1142	1211	1242	1311	1318	1347	1410	1442	1512	1542	1611	1644	1711	1742	1742	1811	1842	1907	1915	1942	2012	2042	2111	2143	2242	2351	0052
Stuttgart Hbf **930** ... a.	1256	...	1356	...	...	1500	...	1556	...	1658	...	1756	...	1858	1858	...	1956	2005**f**	...	2059	...	2159	...	2256	...	...	...

D – BODENSEE – [12] Innsbruck - Bregenz - Lindau - Dortmund and v.v.
G – [12] ✕ Wien - Innsbruck - Bregenz - Stuttgart - Frankfurt and v.v. Train category *IC* until Aug. 1.

f – Not July 30 - Sept. 11.
t – Ⓐ (not June 16, Nov. 1).

z – Also June 16, Nov. 1.

⊙ – Change trains at Friedrichshafen Stadt on Ⓐ (not June 16, Nov. 1).
⊡ – Change trains at Friedrichshafen Stadt on Ⓒ (also June 16, Nov. 1).

RE/RB services except where shown — MÜNCHEN and AUGSBURG - MEMMINGEN - LINDAU — 934

See Table **935** for services via Kempten (also for connecting services from/to Augsburg).

km		⊖ Ⓐt	Ⓐt	⊖ Ⓐt	Ⓐt	Ⓒz	⊖	⊖	*ECE* **198** ✕				⊖	⊖	*ECE* **196** ✕				⊖	⊖				⊖	⊖	*ECE* **192** ✕	
0	**München** Hbf ⊡ d.	...	0439	...	...	...	...	0621	0655	0720	...	...	0754	0820	0855	0920	...	...	0954	1020	1120	...	...	1154	1220	1255	1320
7	München Pasing d.	...	0447	...	...	...	...	0627	|	0727	...	...	0801	0827	|	0927	...	...	1001	1027	1127	...	...	1201	1227	|	1327
42	Geltendorf d.	...	0507	...	...	...	...	0648	|	0748	...	...	|	0849	|	0948	...	...	|	1048	1148	...	...	|	1248	|	1348
56	Kaufering d.	...	0515	...	...	...	...	0656	|	0757	...	...	|	0857	|	0956	...	...	|	1056	1157	...	...	|	1256	|	1357
	Augsburg Hbf d.	...	|	...	0522	0532	...	|	|	|	0741	0741	|	|	|	|	0941	0941	|	|	|	1141	1141	|	|	|	|
68	Buchloe a.	...	0522	...	0555	0603	...	0703	0734	0805	0804	0804	0832	0903	0934	1003	1004	1004	1032	1103	1205	1204	1204	1232	1303	1334	1405
68	Buchloe d.	...	▬	0543	0558	0606	...	0712	0736	▬	0809	0809	0833	0912	0936	▬	1009	1009	1033	1112	▬	1209	1209	1233	1312	1336	▬
76	Türkheim (Bay) ♠ d.	...	...	0549	0616j	0620f	...	0720	|	...	0817	0820	0839	0920	|	...	1017	1020	1039	1120	...	1217	1220	1239	1320	|	...
81	Bad Wörishofen ♠ a.	...	...	|	|	|	...	|	|	...	0823	|	|	|	|	...	1023	|	|	|	...	1223	|	|	|	|	...
87	Mindelheim d.	...	⊖	0559	0630	0630	...	0729	|	⊖	...	0831	0846	0929	|	⊖	...	1031	1046	1129	⊖	...	1233	1246	1329	|	⊖
114	**Memmingen** a.	...	Ⓒz	0621	0657	0651	...	0748	0758		...	0851	0859	0948	0958		...	1051	1059	1148		...	1252	1259	1348	1358	
114	**Memmingen** d.	0455	0606	0624	...	...	0706	...	0801	0806	...	...	0901	...	1001	1006	...	...	1101	...	1206	...	...	1301	...	1401	1406
146	Leutkirch **937** d.	0523	0636f	0707	...	...	0736f	...	|	0836f	...	...	0923	...	|	1036f	...	...	1123	...	1236f	...	...	1323	...	|	1436f
157	Kißlegg **937** a.	0531	0643	0715	...	...	0743	...	|	0843	...	...	0931	...	|	1043	...	...	1131	...	1243	...	...	1331	...	|	1443
157	Kißlegg **937** d.	0544	0644	0718	...	...	0744	...	|	0844	...	...	0938	...	|	1044	...	...	1138	...	1244	...	...	1338	...	|	1444
170	Wangen (Allgäu) **937** d.	0553	0653	0729	...	...	0753	...	|	0853	...	...	0953f	...	|	1053	...	...	1153f	...	1253	...	...	1353f	...	|	1453
176	Hergatz d.	0558	0658	0735	...	...	0759	...	|	0859	...	...	0959	...	|	1059	...	...	1159	...	1259	...	...	1359	...	|	1459
199	**Lindau** Insel a.	0614	0715	0751	...	...	0816	...	|	0916	...	...	1015	...	|	1116	...	...	1216	...	1316	...	...	1416	...	|	1516
	Lindau Reutin a.	*0624*	*0728*	*0757*	...	...	*0827*	...	0850	*0928*	...	...	*1024*	...	1050	*1127*	...	...	*1226*	...	*1328*	...	...	*1426*	...	1450	*1528*
	Zürich HB **75** a.	...	...	...	...	...	...	...	1027	...	...	...	...	...	1227	...	...	...	...	...	...	...	...	...	...	1627	...

			⊖	⊖	*ECE* **190** ✕				⊖	⊖	*ECE* **98** ✕				⊖	⊖	*ECE* **96** ✕				⊖	⊖			⊖		
München Hbf ⊡ d.	...	...	1354	1420	1455	1520	...	...	1552	1620	1652	1720	...	...	1751e	1820	1852	1919	...	...	1954	2020	...	2120	2220	2319	...
München Pasing d.	...	...	1401	1427	|	1527	...	...	1559	1627	|	1727	...	...	1759e	1827	|	1927	...	...	2001	2027	...	2127	2227	2327	...
Geltendorf d.	...	...	|	1448	|	1548	...	...	|	1648	|	1748	...	...	|	1848	|	1948	...	...	|	2048	...	2148	2248	2348	...
Kaufering d.	...	...	|	1456	|	1557	...	...	|	1656	|	1757	...	...	|	1856	|	1957	...	...	|	2056	...	2157	2256	2357	...
Augsburg Hbf d.	1341	1341	|	|	|	|	1541	1541	|	|	|	|	1741	1741	|	|	|	|	1941	1941	|	|	2132	|	|	|	2334
Buchloe a.	1404	1404	1432	1503	1534	1605	1603	1603	1632	1703	1733	1805	1804	1804	1832	1903	1934	2005	2004	2004	2032	2103	2204	2205c	2304	0004	0004
Buchloe d.	1409	1409	1433	1512	1536	▬	1609	1609	1633	1712	1736	▬	1809	1809	1833	1912	1936	▬	2009	2009	2033	2112	2209	▬	2312	...	0009
Türkheim (Bay) ♠ d.	1417	1420	1439	1520	|	...	1617	1620	1639	1720	|	...	1817	1820	1839	1920	|	...	2017	2020	2039	2120	2220f	...	2320	...	0020
Bad Wörishofen ♠ a.	1423	|	|	|	|	...	1623	|	|	|	|	...	1823	|	|	|	|	...	2023	|	|	|	|	...	|	...	|
Mindelheim d.	...	1431	1446	1529	|	⊖	...	1631	1646	1729	|	⊖	...	1831	1846	1929	|	⊖	...	2031	2046	2129	2231	⊖	2329	...	0031
Memmingen a.	...	1452	1459	1548	1558		...	1652	1659	1748	1758		...	1852	1859	1948	1958		...	2052	2059	2148	2251		2348	...	0053
Memmingen d.	...	...	1501	...	1601	1606	...	...	1701	...	1801	1806	...	...	1901	...	2001	2006	...	...	2101	*2206*	...	2306	...	...	...
Leutkirch **937** d.	...	...	1523	...	|	1636f	...	...	1723	...	|	1836f	...	...	1923	...	|	2036f	...	...	2123	*2236*	...	2329	...	...	...
Kißlegg **937** a.	...	...	1531	...	|	1643	...	...	1731	...	|	1843	...	...	1931	...	|	2043	...	...	2131	*2243*	...	2336	...	...	...
Kißlegg **937** d.	...	...	1538	...	|	1644	...	...	1738	...	|	1844	...	...	1938	...	|	2044	...	...	2138	*2244*	...	2339	...	...	...
Wangen (Allgäu). **937** d.	...	...	1553f	...	|	1653	...	...	1753f	...	|	1853	...	...	1953f	...	|	2053	...	...	2153f	*2253*	...	2349	...	...	...
Hergatz d.	...	...	1559	...	|	1659	...	...	1759	...	|	1859	...	...	1959	...	|	2059	...	...	2159	...	...	2354	...	...	...
Lindau Insel a.	...	...	1616	...	|	1716	...	...	1816	...	|	1916	...	...	2016	...	|	2116	...	...	2216	...	...	0012	...	...	...
Lindau Reutin a.	...	...	*1628*	...	1650	*1725*	...	...	*1826*	...	1850	*1928*	...	...	*2029*	...	2050	*2130*	...	...	*2228*	...	...	...	...	...	...
Zürich HB **75** a.	...	...	...	...	1827	...	...	...	...	...	2027	...	...	...	...	...	2227	...	...	...	...	...	...	...	...	...	...

	⊖ Ⓐt	⚒r	⊖ Ⓐt	⊖	⊖ Ⓐt	⊖ Ⓐt				⊖ Ⓐt	⊖	⊖			⊖	*ECE* **97** ✕	⊖	⊖			⊖	*ECE* **99** ✕	⊖	⊖			⊖
Zürich HB **75** d.	...	...	...	...	...	...	...	...	...	...	...	...	...	...	...	0733	...	...	...	...	...	0933	...	...	...	...	...
Lindau Reutin d.	...	...	...	...	...	...	...	...	...	...	...	*0729*	...	...	*0829*	0910	...	*0930*	...	...	*1029*	1110	...	*1127*	...	...	*1229*
Lindau Insel d.	...	...	...	...	...	0551	...	...	...	0646	0646z	0746	...	...	0835	|	...	0946	...	...	1035	|	...	1146	...	...	1235
Hergatz d.	...	...	...	...	...	0607	...	...	...	0703	0703z	0804	...	...	0900f	|	...	1004	...	...	1100f	|	...	1204	...	...	1300f
Wangen (Allgäu). **937** d.	...	...	...	0526t	...	0613	*0608*z	...	...	0707	0707z	0808	...	...	0904	|	...	1008	...	...	1104	|	...	1208	...	...	1304
Kißlegg **937** a.	...	...	...	0535t	...	0622	*0618*z	...	...	0716	0716z	0818	...	...	0913	|	...	1018	...	...	1113	|	...	1218	...	...	1313
Kißlegg **937** d.	...	...	0501	0536t	...	0623	*0628*z	...	...	0723	0723z	0828	...	...	0914	|	...	1028	...	...	1114	|	...	1228	...	...	1314
Leutkirch **937** d.	...	...	0509	0544t	...	0630	*0635*z	...	...	0731	0731z	0835	...	...	0928f	|	...	1035	...	...	1128f	|	...	1235	...	...	1328f
Memmingen a.	...	...	0533	0607t	...	0657	*0658*z	...	...	0753	0753z	0858	...	...	0954	0959	...	1058	...	...	1153	1159	...	1258	...	...	1354
Memmingen d.	0450	0504	0541	0611	0641	...	0708	...	...	0800	0811	0900	0908	...	▬	1001	1011	1100	1108	...	▬	1201	1208	1300	1308	...	▬
Mindelheim d.	0508	0524	0558	0630	0658	...	0729	...	...	0813	0831	0913	0930	...	...	|	1031	1113	1130	...	...	|	1231	1313	1330	...	...
Bad Wörishofen ♠ d.	|	|	|	|	|	...	|	0734	...	|	|	|	|	0935	...	|	|	|	|	1135	...	|	|	|	|	1335	...
Türkheim (Bay) ♠ d.	0515	0535	0605	0641	0705	...	0743	0743	...	0820	0841	0920	0944	0944	...	|	1041	1120	1144	1144	...	|	1241	1320	1344	1344	...
Buchloe a.	0520	0542	0611	0649	0711	...	0749	0749	...	0826	0847	0926	0950	0950	...	1022	1047	1126	1150	1150	...	1222	1247	1326	1350	1350	...
Buchloe d.	0523	0552	0616	0656	0716	...	0756	0756	0755	0827	0856	0927	0956	0956	0955	1025	1056	1127	1156	1156	1155	1225	1256	1327	1356	1356	1355
Augsburg Hbf a.	|	0625	|	|	|	...	0820	0820	|	|	|	|	1020	1020	|	|	|	|	1220	1220	|	|	|	|	1421	1421	|
Kaufering d.	0530	...	0623	0703	0723	...	...	...	0802	|	0903	|	...	...	1002	|	1103	|	...	...	1202	|	1303	|	...	...	1402
Geltendorf d.	0538	...	0631	0711	0731	...	...	...	0810	|	0911	|	...	...	1010	|	1111	|	...	...	1210	|	1311	|	...	...	1410
München Pasing a.	0558	...	0652	0735	0757	...	...	...	0833	0857	0933	0957	...	...	1033	|	1133	1157	...	...	1233	|	1333	1357	...	...	1432
München Hbf ⊡ a.	0606	...	0659	0742	0804	...	...	...	0840	0904	0942	1004	...	...	1042	1104	1144	1204	...	...	1241	1304	1339	1405	...	...	1439

	ECE **191** ✕	⊖	⊖			⊖	*ECE* **193** ✕	⊖	⊖			⊖	⊖	⊖			⊖	*ECE* **197** ✕	⊖	⊖	⊖ †v		⊖	*ECE* **199** ✕	⊖	⊖	
Zürich HB **75** d.	1133	...	...	...	...	...	1333	...	...	...	...	...	...	...	...	...	...	1733	...	...	...	...	...	1933	...	...	...
Lindau Reutin d.	1310	...	*1330*	...	...	*1429*	1510	...	*1530*	...	...	*1629*	...	*1726*	...	...	*1829*	1910	...	*1930*	*1930*	...	*2029*	2110	...	*2131*	...
Lindau Insel d.	|	...	1346	...	...	1435	|	...	1546	...	...	1635	...	1746	...	...	1835	|	...	1946	1946	...	2035	|	...	2146	...
Hergatz d.	|	...	1404	...	...	1500f	|	...	1604	...	...	1700f	...	1804	...	...	1900f	|	...	2004	2004	...	2100f	|	...	2204	...
Wangen (Allgäu). **937** d.	|	...	1408	...	...	1504	|	...	1608	...	...	1704	...	1808	...	...	1904	|	...	2008	2008	...	2104	|	...	2208	...
Kißlegg **937** a.	|	...	1418	...	...	1513	|	...	1618	...	...	1713	...	1818	...	...	1913	|	...	2018	2018	...	2113	|	...	2218	...
Kißlegg **937** d.	|	...	1428	...	...	1514	|	...	1628	...	...	1714	...	1828	...	...	1914	|	...	2028	2028	...	2114	|	...	2228	...
Leutkirch **937** d.	|	...	1435	...	...	1528f	|	...	1635	...	...	1728f	...	1835	...	...	1928f	|	...	2035	2035	...	2128f	|	...	2235	...
Memmingen a.	1359	...	1458	...	...	1554	1558	...	1658	...	...	1754	...	1858	...	...	1954	1959	...	2058	2058	...	2154	2159	...	2258	...
Memmingen d.	1401	1411	1500	1508	...	▬	1601	1611	1700	1708	...	▬	1811	1900	1908	...	▬	2001	2011	...	2100	2108	▬	2201	2211	▬	2308
Mindelheim d.	|	1430	1513	1530	...	...	|	1631	1713	1730	...	...	1831	1913	1930	...	...	|	2031	...	2113	2130	...	|	2231	...	2330
Bad Wörishofen ♠ d.	|	|	|	|	1535	...	|	|	|	|	1735	...	|	|	|	1935	...	|	|	...	|	|	...	|	|	...	|
Türkheim (Bay) ♠ d.	|	1441	1520	1544	1544	...	|	1641	1720	1744	1744	...	1841	1920	1944	1944	...	|	2041	...	2120	2144	...	|	2241	...	2344
Buchloe a.	1423	1447	1526	1550	1550	...	1622	1647	1726	1750	1750	...	1847	1926	1950	1950	...	2022	2047	...	2126	2150	...	2222	2247	...	2350c
Buchloe d.	1425	1456	1527	1556	1556	1555	1625	1656	1727	1756	1756	1755	1856	1927	1956	1956	1955	2025	2056	...	2127	2158	2155	2225	2256	2354	0010
Augsburg Hbf a.	|	|	|	1619	1619	|	|	|	|	1818	1818	|	|	|	2019	2019	|	|	|	...	|	2227	|	|	|	|	0046
Kaufering d.	|	1503	|	...	...	1602	|	1703	|	...	...	1802	1903	|	...	...	2002	|	2103	...	|	...	2202	|	2303	0001	...
Geltendorf d.	|	1511	|	...	...	1610	|	1711	|	...	...	1810	1911	|	...	...	2010	|	2111	...	|	...	2210	|	2311	0010	...
München Pasing a.	|	1533	1557	...	...	1632	|	1733	1757	...	...	1833	1934	1957	...	...	2032	|	2133	...	2156	...	2233	|	2333	0032	...
München Hbf ⊡ a.	1504	1542	1604	...	...	1639	1704	1742	1804	...	...	1841	1942	2004	...	...	2041	2104	2142	...	2204	...	2241	2304	2342	0041	...

c – Connects with train in previous column.
e – On Ⓒ (also June 16, Aug. 15, Nov. 1) departs München Hbf 1754, München Pasing 1801.
f – Arrives 6 – 8 minutes earlier.
j – Arrives 0605.
r – Not June 16, Aug. 15, Nov. 1.
t – Ⓐ (not June 16, Aug. 15, Nov. 1).
v – Also June 16, Aug. 15, Nov. 1.
z – Ⓒ (also June 16, Aug. 15, Nov. 1).

⊖ – Operated by Go Ahead Bayern.
⊡ – Most trains in Table **934** use platforms 27 – 36 at München Hbf (minimum connecting time with other services is 10 minutes).

♠ – Other journeys Türkheim - Bad Wörishofen and v.v. (journey time 6 – 7 minutes).
From Türkheim at 0435 Ⓐ t¶, 0510 Ⓐ t, 0515 ⑥ ¶, 0543 ⚒ r, 0549 † v ¶, 0617, 0643, 0722, 0747 Ⓐ t ‡, 0843, 0922, 1043, 1122, 1243, 1322, 1443, 1522, 1643, 1722, 1843, 1922, 2043, 2122, 2217, 2247, 2322 and 0018.
From Bad Wörishofen at 0448 Ⓐ t, 0525 Ⓐ t, 0530 ⑥, 0555 Ⓐ t, 0602 Ⓒ z, 0629, 0655 Ⓐ t, 0702 Ⓒ z, 0806 Ⓐ t §, 0829, 0906, 1029, 1106, 1229, 1306, 1429, 1506, 1629, 1706, 1829, 1906, 2029, 2106, 2135, 2229, 2301, 2335 and 0030 ◧.
¶ – From Buchloe (departs 6 – 8 minutes earlier).
‡ – From Buchloe (d. 0732).
§ – To Buchloe (a. 0822).
◧ – To Buchloe (a. 0044).

GERMANY

935 MÜNCHEN, AUGSBURG and ULM - KEMPTEN - LINDAU

RE/RB services except where shown

See Table **934** for other services München - Buchloe - Memmingen - Lindau.

km																											
		⚒r	Ⓐt	Ⓐt	◇ Ⓐt	Ⓐt	Ⓒz	⚒r	◇ Ⓒz			◇ Ⓐt	⊖		⊗	◇ Ⓒz	◇ Ⓐt		Ⓒw	Ⓐt	Ⓒz				◇		
0	**München** Hbf ⊡ d.	...	0439	...	...	...	...	0519	...	0539	...	...	0621	...	...	...	...	0639	...	...	...	...	0720	0736h	...	...	...
7	München Pasing d.	...	0447	...	...	...	...	0527	...	0547	...	...	0627	...	...	...	...	0647	...	...	...	...	0727	0742h	...	...	...
42	Geltendorf d.	...	0507	...	...	...	...	0548	...	0607	...	...	0648	...	...	...	...	0707	...	...	...	...	0748	0807	...	...	...
56	Kaufering d.	...	0515	...	...	...	...	0556	...	0615	...	...	0656	...	...	...	...	0715	...	...	...	...	0757	0815	...	...	...
	Nürnberg Hbf **905** d.	...	|	...	...	...	...	|	...	|	...	...	|	...	...	...	...	|	...	...	...	...	|	|	...	...	...
	Augsburg Hbf d.	...	|	0450	...	0522	0532	|	...	|	0611t	0618	|	0632	0632	...	...	|	...	0711	...	0741	|	|	0748	0811	...
68	Buchloe a.	...	0522	0522	...	0555	0603	0603	...	0622	0637t	0651	0703	0658p	0658p	...	...	0722	...	0738	...	0804	0805	0822	0820	0839	...
68	Buchloe d.	...	▬	0529	0557	▬	▬	0606	...	▬	0640	0655	▬	0706	0706	...	←	▬	...	0739	0739	▬	0807	▬	0831	0840	...
88	Kaufbeuren d.	...	...	0546	0612	...	...	0616	0621	...	0652	0708	...	0717	0717	0721	0728	...	...	0751	0751	...	0818	...	0845	0852	...
94	Biessenhofen d.	...	...	0550	0618	...	...	|	0626	...	0656	→	...	|	|	0727	0734	...	...	0756	0756	...	|	...	0850	0856	...
100	Marktoberdorf d.	...	...	|	0639k	...	...	|	0635	...	|	▬	...	|	|	0736	0746	...	...	|	|	...	|	...	0859	|	...
131	**Füssen** a.	...	...	|	0721	...	Ⓒz	|	0716	...	|	Ⓐt	Ⓒw	|	|	0816	0837	Ⓐt	...	|	|	...	|	...	0939	|	...
	Ulm Hbf d.	...	...	|	...	...	0510	|	▬	...	|	0548	0614	|	|	...	...	0658	0721	|	|	Ⓐt	|	...	...	|	0817
	Memmingen a.	...	...	|	...	Ⓐt	0553	|	...	...	|	0641	0701	|	|	...	...	0743	0751	|	|	←	|	...	...	|	0855
	Memmingen d.	...	...	|	...	0555	0601	|	...	...	|	0645	0703	|	|	...	...	0804	0758	|	|	0804	|	...	...	|	0900
131	**Kempten** Hbf a.	...	⚒r	0616	...	0620	0625	0640	...	...	0722	0713	0727	0742	0742	...	...	→	0817	0822	0822	0825	0841	...	...	0922	0925
131	**Kempten** Hbf d.	0543	0543	...	...	0627	...	0641	0641	...	...	0730	0730	0744	0744	...	...	...	0818	...	0830	0830	0843	...	...	...	0930
152	Immenstadt a.	0555	0555	...	...	0643	...	0655	0655	◐	...	0745	0745	0756	0756	...	...	...	0832	...	0845	0845	0855	◀	...	...	0945
152	Immenstadt d.	0557	0612	...	...	0649	...	0657	0657	0710	...	0751	0751	0758	0812	...	...	...	0838	...	0851	0851	0857	0912	...	...	0951
	Sonthofen d.	|	0621	...	...	0659	...	|	|	0719	...	0801	0801	|	0824	...	...	...	0848	...	0900	0900	|	0923	...	...	1000
	Oberstdorf a.	|	0639	...	...	0723	...	|	|	0739	...	0819	0819	|	0840	...	...	...	0912	...	0919	0919	|	0940	...	...	1022
197	Hergatz d.	0629	...	...	...	...	...	0729	0729	...	...	...	...	0829	...	...	...	...	...	...	...	...	0929	...	...	...	...
220	**Lindau** Insel a.	|	...	...	...	...	...	|	|	...	...	...	...	|	...	...	...	...	...	...	...	...	|	...	...	...	...
	Lindau Reutin a.	0645	...	...	...	...	...	0745	0745	...	...	...	...	0845	...	...	...	...	...	...	...	...	0945	...	...	...	...

	◇ Ⓒz	⊖			◇				◇	◇		⊖			◇						◇		⊖			◇	
München Hbf ⊡ d.	0807	0820	...	0840	...	...	...	0920	...	0936	...	1020	...	1039	...	...	...	...	1120	1139	...	...	1220	...	1239	...	...
München Pasing d.	0815	0827	...	0847	...	...	...	0927	...	0947	...	1027	...	1047	...	...	...	...	1127	1147	...	...	1227	...	1247	...	...
Geltendorf d.	|	0849	...	0907	...	...	...	0948	...	1007	...	1048	...	1107	...	...	...	...	1148	1207	...	...	1248	...	1307	...	...
Kaufering d.	|	0857	...	0915	...	...	...	0956	...	1015	...	1056	...	1115	...	...	...	...	1157	1215	...	...	1256	...	1315	...	...
Nürnberg Hbf **905** d.	|	|	0716e	|	...	...	...	|	...	|	...	|	...	|	...	...	...	...	|	|	...	...	|	...	|	...	...
Augsburg Hbf d.	|	|	0842	|	0848	0912t	0941	|	0948	|	1012	|	1042	|	1048	1111t	...	1141	|	|	1148	1212	|	1242	|	1248	...
Buchloe a.	0853	0903	0905	0922	0921	0939t	1004	1003	1020	1022	1039	1103	1105	1122	1121	1137t	...	1204	1205	1222	1222	1239	1303	1305	1322	1321	...
Buchloe d.	0858	...	0907	▬	0931	0940	▬	1007	▬	1029	1040	▬	1107	▬	1129	1140	...	▬	1207	▬	1229	1240	▬	1307	▬	1329	1339
Kaufbeuren d.	0910	...	0920	...	0945	0952	...	1020	...	1045	1052	...	1120	...	1145	1152	...	...	1220	...	1245	1252	...	1320	...	1345	1351
Biessenhofen d.	|	...	|	...	0950	0956	...	|	...	1051	1056	...	|	...	1150	1157	...	...	|	...	1251	1256	...	|	...	1350	1356
Marktoberdorf d.	0927	...	|	...	0959	|	...	|	...	1101	|	...	|	...	1200	|	...	...	|	...	1302	|	...	|	...	1406f	|
Füssen a.	1007	...	|	...	1041	|	...	|	...	1141	|	...	|	...	1241	|	...	Ⓐt	|	...	1343	|	...	|	...	1445	|
Ulm Hbf d.	...	...	|	...	...	|	0917	|	...	...	|	1017	|	...	...	|	1117	1117	|	...	▬	|	1217	|	...	...	|
Memmingen a.	...	...	|	...	...	|	0955	|	...	...	|	1055	|	...	...	|	1200	1200	|	...	...	|	1255	|	...	...	|
Memmingen d.	...	...	|	...	...	|	1004	|	...	...	|	1100	|	...	...	|	1204	1204	|	...	...	|	1300	|	...	...	|
Kempten Hbf a.	...	...	0941	...	...	1022	1025	1041	...	...	1122	1127	1141	...	...	1222	1225	1225	1242	...	...	1322	1325	1341	...	...	1422
Kempten Hbf d.	...	...	0943	...	...	...	1030	1043	...	...	...	1130	1143	...	...	...	...	1230	1243	Ⓒz	Ⓐt	...	1329	1343	...	...	...
Immenstadt a.	...	...	0955	◀	...	...	1045	1055	◀	...	...	1145	1155	◀	...	...	...	1245	1255	◀	◀	...	1345	1355	◀	...	...
Immenstadt d.	...	...	0957	1021	...	...	1051	1057	1112	...	...	1151	1157	1212	...	...	...	1251	1257	1312	1315	...	1351	1357	1412	...	...
Sonthofen d.	...	...	|	1030	...	...	1100	|	1121q	...	...	1200	|	1221	...	...	...	1300	|	1321	1327	...	1400	|	1421	...	...
Oberstdorf a.	...	...	|	1059	...	...	1118	|	1140	...	...	1219	|	1242	...	...	...	1319	|	1340	1351	...	1418	|	1440	...	...
Hergatz d.	...	...	1029	...	...	...	...	1129	...	...	...	...	1229	...	...	...	...	...	1329	...	...	...	...	1429	...	...	...
Lindau Insel a.	...	...	|	...	...	...	...	|	...	...	...	...	|	...	...	...	...	...	|	...	...	...	...	|	...	...	...
Lindau Reutin a.	...	...	1045	...	...	...	...	1145	...	...	...	...	1245	...	...	...	...	...	1345	...	...	...	...	1445	...	...	...

					IC 2085 H		◇		⊖		◇	◇					*RE* 2013 A 🍷		◇		Ⓐt	⊖			◇		
München Hbf ⊡ d.	...	...	1320	1320	...	1340	...	...	1420	...	...	1440	...	...	1520	1520	...	1536	...	...	...	1620	...	1640	...	...	...
München Pasing d.	...	...	1327	1327	...	1347	...	...	1427	...	...	1447	...	...	1527	1527	...	1543q	...	...	...	1627	...	1647	...	...	...
Geltendorf d.	...	...	1348	1348	...	1407	...	...	1448	...	...	1507	...	...	1548	1548	...	1607	...	...	...	1648	...	1707	...	...	...
Kaufering d.	...	...	1357	1357	...	1415	...	...	1456	...	...	1515	...	...	1557	1557	...	1615	...	...	...	1656	...	1715	...	...	...
Nürnberg Hbf **905** d.	...	...	|	|	...	|	...	...	|	...	...	|	...	...	|	|	...	|	...	...	...	|	...	|	...	...	...
Augsburg Hbf d.	...	1341	|	|	1357	|	1348	1414	|	1444	1448	|	...	1541	|	|	...	|	1548	1612	1612	|	1641	|	1646	1712t	1741
Buchloe a.	...	1404	1405	1405	1423	1422	1430	1439	1503	1505	1520	1522	...	1603	1605	1605	...	1622	1624	1638	1638	1703	1705	1722	1722	1739t	1804
Buchloe d.	...	▬	1407	1407	1424	...	1431	1440	▬	1507	▬	1529	1539	▬	1607	1607	...	...	1627	1639	1639	▬	1707	▬	1731	1740	▬
Kaufbeuren d.	...	...	1420	1420	1439	...	1445	1452	...	1520	...	1545	1551	...	1620	1620	...	...	1645	1651	1651	...	1720	...	1745	1752	...
Biessenhofen d.	...	...	|	|	|	...	1450	1456	...	|	...	1551	1556	...	|	|	...	...	1650	1656	1656	...	|	...	1750	1756	...
Marktoberdorf d.	...	...	|	|	|	...	1506f	|	...	|	...	1607f	|	...	|	|	...	...	1712n	|	|	...	|	...	1759	|	...
Füssen a.	...	Ⓐt	|	|	|	...	1546	|	...	|	...	1645	|	...	|	|	...	...	1754	|	|	Ⓒz	|	...	1841	|	...
Ulm Hbf d.	1317	1317	|	|	|	...	...	|	1417	|	...	...	|	1517	|	|	1616	...	...	|	|	1621	|	...	...	|	1717
Memmingen a.	1355	1355	|	|	|	...	...	|	1455	|	...	...	|	1554	|	|	1644	...	...	|	|	1703	|	...	...	|	1755
Memmingen d.	1404	1404	|	|	|	...	...	|	1500	|	...	...	|	1604	|	|	1645	...	...	|	|	1704	|	...	...	|	1804
Kempten Hbf a.	1425	1425	1442	1442	1509	...	...	1522	1525	1541	...	...	1622	1625	1641	1641	1708	...	...	1721	1721	1729	1741	...	...	1822	1825
Kempten Hbf d.	...	1429	1443	1443	1510	...	...	...	1529	1543	...	...	...	1629	1643	1643	1709	...	...	...	1730	1730	1743	...	...	...	1829
Immenstadt a.	...	1445	1455	1455	1527	...	...	...	1545	1555	◀	...	...	1645	1655	1655	1725	...	...	...	1745	1745	1755	◀	...	...	1845
Immenstadt d.	...	1451	1457	1512	1542	...	...	...	1551	1557	1612	...	...	1651	1657	1712	1743	...	...	...	1751	1751	1757	1812	...	...	1851
Sonthofen d.	...	1500	|	1523	1552	...	...	...	1601	|	1621	...	...	1701	|	1721	1752	...	...	...	1801	1801	|	1821	...	...	1900
Oberstdorf a.	...	1519	|	1539p	1611	...	...	...	1619	|	1640	...	...	1724	|	1738	1811	...	...	...	1819	1819	|	1840	...	...	1919
Hergatz d.	...	...	1529	...	...	...	...	...	...	1629	...	...	...	...	1729	...	...	...	...	...	...	...	1829	...	...	...	...
Lindau Insel a.	...	...	|	...	...	...	...	...	...	|	...	...	...	...	|	...	...	...	...	...	...	...	|	...	...	...	...
Lindau Reutin a.	...	...	1545	...	...	...	...	...	...	1645	...	...	...	...	1745	...	...	...	...	...	...	...	1845	...	...	...	...

			◇		⊖			◇				◇	◇		⊖		⊗	◇				◇	⊖		◇		
München Hbf ⊡ d.	1720	1736j	...	...	1820	...	1839	...	...	...	1919	...	1936	*1954*	2020	...	...	...	2039	...	2120	...	2220	...	...	...	2319
München Pasing d.	1727	1743j	...	...	1827	...	1847	...	...	...	1927	...	1947	*2001*	2027	...	...	...	2047	...	2127	...	2227	...	...	...	2327
Geltendorf d.	1748	1807	...	...	1848	...	1907	...	...	...	1948	...	2007	|	2048	...	...	...	2107	...	2148	...	2248	...	...	...	2348
Kaufering d.	1757	1815	...	...	1856	...	1915	...	...	...	1957	...	2015	|	2056	...	...	...	2115	...	2157	...	2256	...	...	...	2357
Nürnberg Hbf **905** d.	|	|	...	...	|	1713e	|	...	...	...	|	...	|	|	|	...	...	...	|	...	|	...	|	...	...	...	|
Augsburg Hbf d.	|	|	1748	1812	|	1844	|	1848	1912t	1941	|	1948	|	|	|	2033	2033	...	|	2132	|	...	|	2233	...	2334	|
Buchloe a.	1805	1822	1821	1839	1903	1905	1922	1921	1939t	2004	2005	2019	2022	*2032*	2103	2105	2105	...	2122	2204	2205	...	2304	2304	...	0004	0004
Buchloe d.	1807	▬	1828	1840	▬	1907	▬	1929	1940	▬	2007	▬	2027	2039	▬	2107	2107	...	...	▬	2207	...	▬	2307	...	▬	0007
Kaufbeuren d.	1818	...	1845	1852	...	1920	...	1945	1952	...	2020	...	2045f	2051	...	2118	2118	2122	...	...	2218	2226	...	2318	2330	...	0018
Biessenhofen d.	|	...	1850	1856	...	|	...	1950	1956	...	|	...	2050	2056	...	2122	2122	2127	...	...	2222	2231	...	2323	2339	...	0023
Marktoberdorf d.	|	...	1900	|	...	|	...	2006f	|	...	|	...	2105f	|	...	|	|	2136	...	...	|	2240	...	|	2349	...	|
Füssen a.	|	...	1942	|	...	|	...	2045	|	...	|	...	2147	|	...	|	|	2218	...	...	|	2321	...	|	0029	...	|
Ulm Hbf d.	|	...	▬	|	1817	|	...	...	|	1917	|	...	...	|	2017	|	|	...	...	2117	|	▬	2217	|	▬	2318	|
Memmingen a.	|	...	...	|	1855	|	...	...	|	1953	|	...	...	|	2055	|	|	...	...	2154	|	...	2257	|	...	2400	|
Memmingen d.	|	...	...	|	1900	|	...	...	|	2004	|	...	...	|	2100	|	|	...	...	2204	|	...	2301	|	...	0001	|
Kempten Hbf a.	1841	...	Ⓐt	1922	1925	1941	...	...	2023	2030	2041	...	...	2121	2125	2143	2143	...	...	2229	2243	...	2326	2344	...	0026	0045
Kempten Hbf d.	1843	...	1916	...	1929	1943	...	...	...	...	2043	...	...	...	...	2145	2145	...	...	...	2245	...	...	2346	...	...	...
Immenstadt a.	1855	◀	1931	...	1945	1955	◀	...	...	...	2056	◀	...	...	...	2201	2201	...	...	...	2300	...	...	0001	...	...	...
Immenstadt d.	1857	1912	1932	...	1951	1957	2012	...	...	...	2058	2112	...	...	...	2202	2212	...	...	...	2302	2312	...	0003	0012	...	...
Sonthofen d.	|	1921	|	...	2001	|	2021	...	...	...	|	2121	...	...	...	|	2221	...	...	...	|	2321	...	|	0021	...	...
Oberstdorf a.	|	1940	|	...	2019	|	2043	...	...	...	|	2143	...	...	...	|	2243	...	...	...	|	2343	...	|	0040	...	...
Hergatz d.	1929	...	2012	...	...	2029	...	...	...	...	2129	...	...	...	...	2233	...	...	...	...	2333	...	...	0035	...	...	...
Lindau Insel a.	|	...	2029	...	...	|	...	...	...	...	|	...	...	...	...	|	...	...	...	...	2350	...	...	0050	...	...	...
Lindau Reutin a.	1945	...	...	...	...	2045	...	...	...	...	2145	...	...	...	...	2250	...	...	...	...	...	...	...	...	...	...	...

FOR NOTES SEE NEXT PAGE →

RE / RB services except where shown

LINDAU - KEMPTEN - ULM, AUGSBURG and MÜNCHEN 935

See Table 934 for other services Lindau - Memmingen - Buchloe - München.

km		Ⓐt	⊖ Ⓐt	Ⓐt	⑥	Ⓐt		Ⓐt	◇	Ⓐt	Ⓐt	Ⓒz	⊖	◇ Ⓐt	Ⓒz	Ⓐt	Ⓐt	◇ Ⓒz	⚒r	⚒r				◇ Ⓐt	Ⓐt	Ⓒz	
	Lindau Reutin d.	...	...	...	...	...	...	...	...	...	...	...	...	...	...	...	...	...	...	...	...	...	...	...	...	...	0715
	Lindau Insel d.	...	...	...	...	...	0413t	...	...	...	0505	...	...	...	...	...	...	...	...	0608	...	...	...	...	...	...	|
	Hergatz d.	...	...	...	...	...	0430t	...	...	...	0519	...	...	...	...	...	...	...	...	0623	...	...	...	...	...	...	0730
0	**Oberstdorf** d.	...	...	...	...	0439	|	...	...	0523	|	...	...	...	...	0537	...	...	0617	|	...	0640t	...	...	0703	0719	|
13	Sonthofen d.	...	...	...	...	0456	|	...	...	0541	|	...	...	...	...	0555	...	...	0639	|	...	0658t	...	...	0728	0741	|
21	Immenstadt a.	...	...	...	...	0505	0507t	...	...	0550	0554	...	...	...	...	0604	...	...	0648	0658	...	0707t	...	...	0737	0750	0803
21	Immenstadt d.	...	...	...	...	▬	0508t	...	...	▬	0557	...	...	...	...	0610	...	...	▶	0701	...	0713t	...	...	▶	▶	0806
42	**Kempten** Hbf a.	...	...	...	...	...	0524t	...	...	...	0611	...	...	...	...	0626	...	...	▬	0714	...	0727t	...	...	▬	▬	0818
42	**Kempten** Hbf d.	0433	...	0507	0512	...	0529	0533	...	...	0616	0616	...	...	0631	0631	0633	...	...	0718	0718	0732	0737	...	...	...	0819
77	Memmingen a.	|	...	|	|	...	0554	|	...	...	|	|	...	...	0656	0705	|	...	...	|	|	0757	|	...	...	...	|
77	Memmingen d.	|	...	|	|	◇	0555	|	...	...	|	|	...	...	0704	0708	|	...	...	|	|	0803	|	...	◇	...	|
129	**Ulm** Hbf a.	|	...	|	|	Ⓐt	0642	|	...	...	|	|	...	...	0741	0743	|	...	...	|	|	0838	|	...	Ⓒz	...	|
—	**Füssen** d.	|	...	|	|	0450	▬	|	0517z	...	|	|	...	0550	...	▬	|	0623	...	|	|	...	|	0659	0726	...	|
	Marktoberdorf d.	|	...	|	|	0532	...	|	0600	...	|	|	...	0632	...	...	|	0707	...	|	|	...	|	0801g	0808	...	|
	Biessenhofen d.	0457	...	0531	0535	0540	...	0557	0607	...	|	|	...	0640	...	...	0657	0715	...	|	|	...	0801	0809	0816	...	|
	Kaufbeuren d.	0502	...	0538	0540	0548	⊖	0602	0619	...	0640	0640	...	0648	...	⊖	0702	0720	...	0743	0743	...	0806	0819	0821	◇	0842
	Buchloe a.	0513	...	0549	0551	0601	Ⓐt	0613c	0631	...	0650	0652	...	0700	...	Ⓐt	0713c	0731	Ⓒz	0753	0753	...	0818	0831	0831		0853
0	Buchloe d.	0523	0523	0555	0555	0606	0616	0623	0638	0636	0652	0653	0656	0706	...	0716	0723	0738	0736	0755	0755	...	0823t	0835	0835	0838	0855
40	**Augsburg** Hbf a.	0557	|	|	|	0640	|	0649	0711	|	0717	0717	|	0739	...	|	0750	0811	|	|	|	...	0851t	|	|	0911	0914
	Nürnberg Hbf **905** a.	...	|	|	|	...	|	...	...	|	...	...	|	...	...	|	...	...	|	|	|	...	...	|	|	...	1045e
	Kaufering d.	...	0530	0602	0602	...	0623	...	...	0644	...	...	0703	...	...	0723	...	...	0744	0802	0802	...	...	0844	0844	...	...
	Geltendorf d.	...	0538	0610	0610	...	0631	...	...	0651	...	...	0711	...	...	0731	...	...	0751	0810	0810	...	...	0852	0852	...	...
	München Pasing a.	...	0558	0633	0634	...	0652	...	...	0712	...	...	0735	...	...	0757	...	...	0812	0833	0833	...	...	0912	0912	...	...
	München Hbf ⊡ a.	...	0606	0641	0642	...	0659	...	...	0719	...	...	0742	...	...	0804	...	...	0819	0840	0840	...	...	0919	0919	...	...

			Ⓐt	Ⓒz				◇					*IC* **2084** **N**	◇	*IC* **2012** **B**					◇					◇		
Lindau Reutin d.	...	...	...	...	0815	...	...	...	...	0915	...	...	...	...	...	...	1015	...	...	...	...	1115	...	...	...	...	1215
Lindau Insel d.	...	...	...	...	|	...	...	...	...	|	...	...	...	...	...	...	|	...	...	...	...	|	...	...	...	...	|
Hergatz d.	...	...	...	...	0830	...	...	...	...	0930	...	...	...	...	...	...	1030	...	...	...	...	1130	...	...	...	...	1230
Oberstdorf d.	0741	...	0820	0826	|	0841	...	...	0859v	|	...	...	0941	...	0951	1023	|	1041	...	...	1120	|	1141	...	...	1220q	|
Sonthofen d.	0801	...	0840	0848	|	0901	...	...	0931	|	...	...	1003	...	1011	1041	|	1101	...	...	1140	|	1201	...	...	1241	|
Immenstadt a.	0811	...	0850	0900	0903	0911	...	...	0940	1003	...	...	1012	...	1020	1050	1103	1111	...	...	1150	1203	1211	...	...	1251	1303
Immenstadt d.	0817	...	▶	▶	0906	0917	...	...	▶	1006	...	...	1027	...	1038	1106	1106	1117	...	...	▶	1206	1217	...	...	▶	1306
Kempten Hbf a.	0832	...	▬	▬	0918	0932	...	...	▬	1018	...	...	1043	...	1052	1118	1118	1132	...	...	▬	1218	1232	...	...	▬	1318
Kempten Hbf d.	0834	0837	...	...	0919	0934	0937	...	...	1019	1032	1037	1044	...	1054	1119	1119	1135	1137	...	...	1219	1234	1237	...	...	1319
Memmingen a.	0859	|	...	...	|	0959	|	...	...	|	1058	|	|	...	1121	|	|	1156	|	...	...	|	1259	|	...	...	|
Memmingen d.	0904	|	◇	...	|	1004	|	...	...	|	1101	|	|	...	1124	|	|	1204	|	...	...	|	1304	|	...	...	|
Ulm Hbf a.	0938	|	...	...	|	1038	|	...	...	|	1143	|	|	...	1155	|	|	1238	|	...	...	|	1340	|	...	...	|
Füssen d.	▬	|	0815	...	|	...	|	0915	...	|	▬	|	|	1016	▬	|	|	...	|	1116	...	|	▬	|	1217	...	|
Marktoberdorf d.	...	|	0901	...	|	...	|	1001	...	|	...	|	|	1104f	...	|	|	...	|	1202f	...	|	...	|	1304	...	|
Biessenhofen d.	...	0901	0909	...	|	...	1001	1009	...	|	...	1101	|	1113	...	|	|	...	1201	1210	...	|	...	1301	1312	...	|
Kaufbeuren d.	⊖	0906	0919	...	0942	...	1006	1019	...	1042	⊖	1106	1114	1121	...	1142	1142	...	1206	1219	...	1242	⊖	1306	1320	◇	1342
Buchloe a.		0918	0931	...	0953	...	1018	1030	...	1053		1118	1129	1132	...	1153	1153	...	1218	1231	...	1253		1318	1331		1353
Buchloe d.	0856	0923	0938	0936	0955	...	1023t	1038	1036	1055	1056	1123	1134	1142	1137	1155	1155	...	...	1238	1236	1256	1256	1323	1335	1338	1355
Augsburg Hbf a.	|	0951	1011	|	|	...	1051t	1111	|	1116	|	1151	1200	1211	|	|	|	...	...	1311	|	1316	|	1350	|	1411	|
Nürnberg Hbf **905** a.	|	...	...	|	|	...	...	...	|	...	|	...	...	...	|	|	|	...	...	...	|	...	|	...	|	...	|
Kaufering d.	0903	...	...	0944	1003	...	...	...	1044	...	1103	...	...	...	1144	1203	1203	...	...	...	1244	...	1303	...	1344	...	1403
Geltendorf d.	0911	...	...	0951	1011	...	...	...	1051	...	1111	...	...	...	1151	1211	1211	...	...	...	1251	...	1311	...	1352	...	1411
München Pasing a.	0933	...	...	1012	1033	...	...	...	1112	...	1133	...	...	...	1212	1233	1233	...	...	...	1312	...	1333	...	1413	...	1432
München Hbf ⊡ a.	0942	...	...	1019	1042	...	...	...	1119	...	1144	...	...	...	1220	1241	1241	...	...	...	1319	...	1339	...	1420	...	1439

			◇					◇		⊗				◇			Ⓒz	Ⓐt		◇					◇		
Lindau Reutin d.	...	...	...	...	1315	...	...	...	...	...	1414	...	...	...	...	1515	...	...	...	...	...	1615	...	...	...	...	1715
Lindau Insel d.	...	...	...	...	|	...	...	...	...	...	|	...	...	...	...	|	...	...	...	...	...	|	...	...	...	...	|
Hergatz d.	...	...	...	...	1330	...	...	...	...	...	1429	...	...	...	...	1530	...	...	...	...	...	1630	...	...	...	...	1730
Oberstdorf d.	1241t	...	...	1319	|	1337q	...	...	...	1419	|	1441	...	...	1505	|	1531	1540	...	...	1623	|	1641t	...	...	1705	|
Sonthofen d.	1301t	...	...	1341	|	1401	...	...	...	1441	|	1501	...	...	1531	|	1601	1601	...	...	1641	|	1701t	...	...	1731	|
Immenstadt a.	1311t	...	...	1350	1403	1411	...	...	...	1450	1502	1511	...	...	1540	1603	1611	1611	...	...	1650	1703	1711t	...	...	1740	1803
Immenstadt d.	1317t	...	...	▶	1406	1417	...	...	...	1505	1505	1517	...	...	▶	1606	1617	1617	...	...	▶	1706	1717t	...	...	▶	1806
Kempten Hbf a.	1331t	...	...	▬	1418	1432	...	...	...	1518	1518	1532	...	...	▬	1618	1632	1632	...	...	▬	1718	1732t	...	...	▬	1818
Kempten Hbf d.	1334	1337	...	...	1419	1434	1437	...	...	1519	1519	1535	1537	...	...	1619	1635	1635	1637	...	...	1719	1735	1737	...	...	1819
Memmingen a.	1359	|	...	...	|	1459	|	...	...	|	|	1557	|	...	...	|	1704	1704	|	...	...	|	1758	|	...	...	|
Memmingen d.	1404	|	...	...	|	1504	|	...	...	|	|	1603	|	...	...	|	1706	1706	|	...	...	|	1804	|	...	...	|
Ulm Hbf a.	1439	|	...	...	|	1539	|	...	...	|	|	1641	|	...	...	|	1739	1739	|	...	...	|	1839	|	...	...	|
Füssen d.	...	|	1320	...	|	▬	|	1422	...	|	|	...	|	1523	...	|	▬	...	|	1623	...	|	...	|	1705	...	|
Marktoberdorf d.	...	|	1404	...	|	...	|	1504	...	|	|	...	|	1605	...	|	...	...	|	1704	...	|	...	|	1801b	...	|
Biessenhofen d.	...	1401	1412	...	|	...	1501	1512	...	|	|	...	1601	1613	...	|	...	...	1701	1712	...	|	...	1801	1810	...	|
Kaufbeuren d.	...	1406	1419	...	1442	⊖	1506	1519	...	1542	1542	...	1606	1619	...	1642	⊖	...	1706	1719	...	1742	...	1806	1819	◇	1842
Buchloe a.	...	1418	1431	...	1453		1518	1531	...	1552	1552	...	1618	1630	...	1653		...	1718	1731	...	1753	...	1818	1830		1853
Buchloe d.	...	...	1438	1436	1455	1456	1523	1538	1536	1555	1555	...	1623t	1638	1636	1656	1656	...	1723	1738	1736	1755	...	1823t	1835	1838	1856
Augsburg Hbf a.	...	...	1511	|	1517	|	1550	1612	|	|	|	...	1649t	1711	|	1716	|	...	1751	1811	|	|	...	1849t	|	1911	1916
Nürnberg Hbf **905** a.	...	...	...	|	...	|	...	...	|	|	|	...	...	...	|	...	|	...	...	...	|	|	...	...	|	...	2034e
Kaufering d.	...	...	...	1444	...	1503	...	...	1544	1603	1603	...	...	...	1644	...	1703	...	...	...	1744	1803	...	...	1844	...	...
Geltendorf d.	...	...	...	1451	...	1511	...	...	1551	1611	1611	...	...	...	1651	...	1711	...	...	...	1751	1811	...	...	1852	...	...
München Pasing a.	...	...	...	1511	...	1533	...	...	1612	1632	1632	...	...	...	1712	...	1733	...	...	...	1812	1833	...	...	1912	...	...
München Hbf ⊡ a.	...	...	...	1519	...	1542	...	...	1619	1639	1639	...	...	...	1719	...	1742	...	...	...	1819	1841	...	...	1919	...	...

NOTES for pages 442 and 443

A – ALLGÄU – (12) ꝗ Dortmund (*IC* **2013**) - Köln - Stuttgart - Ulm (*RE* **2013**) - Oberstdorf.
B – ALLGÄU – (12) ꝗ Oberstdorf - Ulm - Stuttgart - Bochum.
H – NEBELHORN – (12) Hannover (**2083**) - Augsburg (**2085**) - Oberstdorf. Runs as train **2083** throughout until Aug. 1.
N – NEBELHORN – (12) Oberstdorf - Augsburg (**2082**) - Hannover. Runs as train **2082** throughout until Aug. 2.

b – Arrives 1746.
c – Connects with train in previous column.
e – From Oct. 17.
f – Arrives 6–9 minutes earlier.
g – Arrives 0739.
h – On Ⓒ (also June 16, Aug. 15, Nov. 1) departs München Hbf 0739, München Pasing 0747.
j – On Ⓒ (also June 16, Aug. 15, Nov. 1) departs München Hbf 1739, München Pasing 1747.
k – Arrives 0625.
n – Arrives 1657.
p – 5–6 minutes later on Ⓒ (also June 16, Aug. 15, Nov. 1).
q – 3–4 minutes later on Ⓒ (also June 16, Aug. 15, Nov. 1).
r – Not June 16, Aug. 15, Nov. 1.
t – Ⓐ (not June 16, Aug. 15, Nov. 1).
v – 0905 on Ⓐ (not June 16, Aug. 15, Nov. 1).
w – Also June 16, Nov. 1.
z – Ⓒ (also June 16, Aug. 15, Nov. 1).

⊗ – Change trains at Immenstadt on Ⓒ (also June 16, Aug. 15, Nov. 1).
◐ – Runs 1–2 minutes later on Ⓒ (also June 16, Aug. 15, Nov. 1). Detached from train in preceding column on Ⓒ (also June 16, Aug. 15, Nov. 1).
◀ – Detached from train in preceding column.
▶ – Attached to train in following column.
◇ – Operated by Bayerische Regiobahn.
⊖ – Operated by Go Ahead Bayern.
⊡ – Most trains in Table **935** use platforms 27–36 at München Hbf (minimum connecting time with other services is 10 minutes).

935 LINDAU and OBERSTDORF - ULM, AUGSBURG and MÜNCHEN

RE / RB services except where shown

See Table **934** for other services Lindau - Memmingen - Buchloe - München.

			◇			©z	Ⓐt	©z		©z	Ⓐt	◇ ©z				◇										
Lindau Reutin d.	...	...	...	...	1815	...	...	...	...	...	...	...	...	1915	...	...	...	2011	...	...	2115	...	...	2206	...	2311
Lindau Insel d.	...	...	...	...	│	...	...	...	...	...	...	...	...	│	...	...	...	│	...	...	│	...	...	│	...	│
Hergatz d.	...	...	...	...	1830	...	...	...	...	...	...	...	...	1930	...	...	...	2026	...	...	2130	...	...	2221	...	2326
Oberstdorf d.	1739	...	...	1823	│	...	1841	1841	...	1847	...	...	1923	│	...	...	2023	│	...	2123	│	...	2223	│	2323	│
Sonthofen d.	1801	...	...	1841	│	...	1901	1901	...	1909	...	...	1941	│	...	...	2041	│	...	2141	│	...	2241	│	2341	│
Immenstadt a.	1811	...	...	1850	1903	...	1911	1911	...	1922	...	...	1950	2003	...	...	2050	2059	...	2150	2203	...	2250	2255	2350	2400
Immenstadt d.	1817	...	...	▶	1906	...	1917	1917	...	1928	...	...	▶	2006	...	...	▶	2104	...	▬	2208	...	▬	2300	▬	0001
Kempten Hbf a.	1832	...	...	▬	1918	...	1933	1933	...	1942	...	...	▬	2018	...	...	▬	2117	...	...	2222	...	...	2313	...	0015
Kempten Hbf d.	1835	1837	...	...	1919	...	1935	1937	1937	1943	...	...	...	2019	2034	...	...	2118	2132	...	2222	2236	...	2317	2335	...
Memmingen a.	1900	│	...	...	│	...	1957	│	│	2003	...	...	...	│	2059	...	...	│	2158	...	│	2301	...	│	2400	...
Memmingen d.	1904	│	...	...	│	...	2004	│	│	2004	...	...	...	│	2102	...	◇	│	2204	◇	│	2304	◇	│	0007	...
Ulm Hbf a.	1939	│	...	...	│	...	2038	│	│	2038	...	...	...	│	2140	...	©z	│	2239		│	2353		│	0047	...
Füssen d.	▬	│	1817	...	│	1853	...	│	│	▬	1920	1920	...	│	▬	2023	2023	│	...	2126	│	...	2230	│	▬	...
Marktoberdorf d.	...	│	1902f	...	│	1936f	...	│	│	...	2004	2004	...	│	...	2103	2103	│	...	2208	│	...	2312	│	...	...
Biessenhofen d.	...	1901	1910	...	│	│	...	2002	2002	...	2011	2011	...	│	...	2111	2111	2138	...	2216	│	...	2320	2338	...	...
Kaufbeuren d.	⊖	1906	1919	...	1942	1948	...	2007	2007	...	2019	2019	◇	2042	⊖	2116	2119	2142	...	2221	2246	...	2325	2342	...	...
Buchloe a.		1918	1931	...	1953	1958	...	2020	2020	©z	2030	2030	Ⓐt	2053		...	2131	2154	...	...	2259	...	...	2353	...	...
Buchloe d.	1856	1923	1938	1936	1955	2001	...	...	...	2036	2036	2038	2038	2054	2056	...	2138	2155	...	...	2259	...	...	2354	0010	...
Augsburg Hbf a.	│	1951	2011	│	│	│	...	...	...	│	│	2111	2111	2125	│	...	2211	│	...	...	2327	...	...	│	0046	...
Nürnberg Hbf **905** a.	│	...	...	│	│	│	...	...	...	│	│	...	...	...	│	...	...	│	...	...	...	...	...	│	...	...
Kaufering d.	1903	...	...	1944	2002	│	...	...	...	2044	2044	...	...	...	2103	...	...	2202	...	...	...	...	...	0001	...	...
Geltendorf d.	1911	...	...	1951	2010	│	...	...	...	2051	2052	...	...	...	2111	...	...	2210	...	...	...	...	...	0010	...	...
München Pasing a.	1934	...	...	2012	2032	2037	...	...	...	2112	2113	...	...	...	2133	...	...	2233	...	...	...	...	...	0032	...	...
München Hbf ⊡ a.	1942	...	...	2020	2041	2045	...	...	...	2120	2120	...	...	...	2142	...	...	2241	...	...	...	...	...	0041	...	...

f – Arrives 6 minutes earlier.
t – Not June 16, Aug. 15, Nov. 1.
z – Also June 16, Aug. 15, Nov. 1.
▶ – Attached to train in following column.
◇ – Operated by Bayerische Regiobahn.
⊖ – Operated by Go Ahead Bayern.
⊡ – Most trains in Table **935** use platforms 27 – 36 at München Hbf (minimum connecting time with other services is 10 minutes).

936 STUTTGART - TÜBINGEN - AULENDORF

IRE / RB services

Operated by DB except local services Stuttgart - Tübingen (Abellio) and local services Tübingen - Sigmaringen (HzL ◇).

km																											
		Ⓐt2	2		2	2		2	2		2	2	s	2	2		2	2		2	2		2	2		2	⊙
0	**Stuttgart** Hbf ☆ d.	...	...	0610e	...	...	0815e	...	...	1015e	...	...	1215e	...	...	1415e	...	...	1615e	...	...	1815e	...	...	2015e	...	2215e
57	Reutlingen ☆ d.	...	...	0648	...	...	0850	...	...	1050	...	...	1250	...	...	1450	...	...	1650	...	...	1850	...	...	2050	...	2250
71	**Tübingen** Hbf ☆ d.	...	...	0658	...	0729	0900	...	0929	1100	...	1129	1300	...	1329	1500	...	1529	1700	...	1729	1900	...	1929	2100	...	2310
96	Hechingen d.	...	...	0719	...	0801	0920	...	1000	1120	...	1200	1320	...	1400	1520	...	1600	1720	...	1800	1920	...	2000	2120	...	2329
113	Balingen (Württ) d.	...	...	0734	...	0823	0936	...	1023f	1136	...	1223f	1336	...	1423f	1536	...	1623f	1736	...	1823f	1936	...	2023f	2136	...	2342
131	Albstadt-Ebingen d.	...	0625r	0747	...	0845	0948	...	1045	1148	...	1245	1348	...	1445	1548	...	1645	1748	...	1845	1948	...	2045	2149	...	2355
158	**Sigmaringen** **938** d.	0559	0655	0813	0906	0914	1013	1106	1114	1213	1306	1314	1413	1506	1514	1613	1706	1714	1813	1906	1914	2013	2106	2114	2212	2311	0017
175	Herbertingen **938** d.	0619	0714	0831	0931	...	1031	1131	...	1231	1331	...	1431	1531	...	1631	1731	...	1831	1931	...	2031	2131	...	2231	2335	...
184	Bad Saulgau d.	0629	0730f	0840	0940	...	1040	1140	...	1240	1340	...	1440	1540	...	1640	1740	...	1840	1940	...	2040	2140	...	2240	2344	...
203	**Aulendorf** a.	0644	0745	0855	0955	...	1055	1155	...	1255	1355	...	1455	1555	...	1655	1755	...	1855	1955	...	2055	2155	...	2255	2400	...

	Ⓐt	©z	Ⓐt2		2	2		2	2		2	2		2	2		2	2		2	2		2	2	2	2	2
Aulendorf d.	...	...	0544	0704	...	0806	0906	...	1006	1106	...	1206	1306	...	1406	1506	...	1606	1706	...	1806	1906	...	2006	2106	2206	2309
Bad Saulgau d.	...	...	0559	0723	...	0821	0921	...	1021	1121	...	1221	1321	...	1421	1521	...	1621	1721	...	1821	1921	...	2021	2121	2221	2325
Herbertingen **938** d.	...	...	0608	0732	...	0829	0929	...	1029	1129	...	1229	1329	...	1429	1529	...	1629	1729	...	1829	1929	...	2029	2129	2229	2334
Sigmaringen **938** d.	0538	0548	0622	0750	0847	0850	0950	1047	1050	1150	1247	1250	1350	1447	1450	1550	1647	1650	1750	1847	1850	1950	2047	2050	2144	2251	2349
Albstadt-Ebingen d.	0601	0612	...	0811	0915	...	1010	1115	...	1210	1315	...	1410	1515	...	1610	1715	...	1810	1915	...	2010	2115	...	2214	2315	...
Balingen (Württ) d.	0615	0625	...	0825	0943f	...	1025	1143f	...	1225	1343f	...	1425	1543f	...	1625	1743f	...	1825	1943f	...	2025	2143f	...	2231	...	...
Hechingen d.	0631	0639	...	0839	1001	...	1039	1201	...	1239	1401	...	1439	1601	...	1639	1801	...	1839	2001	...	2039	2201	...	2243	...	...
Tübingen Hbf ☆ a.	0652	0657	...	0857	1028	...	1057	1228	...	1257	1428	...	1457	1628	...	1657	1828	...	1857	2028	...	2057	2227	...	2302	...	...
Reutlingen ☆ a.	0707	0708	...	0908	...	...	1108	...	...	1308	...	...	1508	...	...	1708	...	...	1908	...	...	2108	...	...	...	...	...
Stuttgart Hbf ☆ a.	0743e	0743e	...	0943e	...	...	1143e	...	...	1343e	...	...	1543e	...	...	1742e	...	...	1943e	...	...	2143e	...	...	...	...	...

OTHER SERVICES STUTTGART - TÜBINGEN

km		Ⓐt		Ⓐt	Ⓐt						
0	**Stuttgart** Hbf **930** d.	0528	0545j	0626	0650	0723	and hourly until	2223	2315	2323	0048
22	Plochingen **930** d.	0547	0606	0643	0713	0741		2241	│	2341	0106
35	Nürtingen d.	0600	0620	0654	0725	0754		2254	│	2354	0120
57	Reutlingen Hbf d.	0617	0638	0710	0741	0811		2311	2351	0011	0137
71	**Tübingen** Hbf a.	0626	0648	0721	0751	0821		2321	0002	0021	0148

	Ⓐt	e		Ⓐt		Ⓐt				
Tübingen Hbf d.	0414	0456	0531	0551	0635	0703	0733	and hourly until	2233	2333
Reutlingen Hbf d.	0426	0508	0546	0601	0646	0717	0743		2243	2343
Nürtingen d.	0445	│	0604	0616	0704	0734	0759		2259	2359
Plochingen **930** d.	0500	│	0618	0628	0718	0749	0817		2317	0016
Stuttgart Hbf **930** a.	0518	0543	0637	0644	0737	0807	0835		2335	0035

e – Not July 30 - Sept. 11.
f – Arrives 8 minutes earlier.
j – 0547 on © (also June 16, Nov. 1).
r – 0630 on © (also June 16, Nov. 1).
s – Not July 31, Aug. 7, 14, 21, 28, Sept. 4, 11.
t – Not June 16, Nov. 1
z – Also June 16, Nov. 1.
⊙ – Change trains at Tübingen on Ⓐ (not June 16, Nov. 1).
☆ – See panel below main table for other selected services.
◇ – Hohenzollerische Landesbahn.

936a STUTTGART - STUTTGART FLUGHAFEN / MESSE ✈

S-Bahn 2/3

20 km. Journey time: 27 minutes. **SERVICE TO JULY 29 AND FROM SEPT. 11.** On June 16, Nov. 1 services run as on ⑦.

Warning! *Timings of late evening services (2200 to 0100 the following morning) may vary on June 20, 27, July 4, 25, Sept. 12, 19, Oct. 10, 17, 24, Nov. 7, 21, Dec. 5.*

From Stuttgart Hbf: On Ⓐ at 0025, 0055, 0430, 0455, 0515, 0525, 0540, 0555, 0610, 0625, 0640, 0655 and every 15 minutes until 2010, 2025, 2040, 2055; then 2115, 2125, 2145, 2155, 2215, 2225, 2245, 2255, 2315, 2325, 2355. On © at 0025, 0055, 0125, 0225, 0325, 0345, 0425, 0525, 0545 †, 0555 ⑥, 0625, 0645 †, 0655 ⑥, 0725, 0745, 0755, 0815, 0825, 0845, 0855 and at 15, 25, 45 and 55 minutes past each hour until 1815, 1825, 1845, 1855; then 1925, 1955 and every 30 minutes until 2325, 2355.

From Stuttgart Flughafen ✈: On Ⓐ at 0008, 0038, 0508, 0518, 0538, 0548, 0608, 0623, 0638, 0653 and every 15 minutes until 1953, 2008, 2023, 2038; then 2048, 2108, 2138, 2148, 2208, 2218, 2238, 2248, 2308, 2318, 2338, 2348. On © at 0008, 0038, 0108, 0208, 0308, 0408, 0508, 0538 ⑥, 0548 †, 0608, 0638 ⑥, 0648 †, 0708, 0738 ⑥, 0748 †, 0808, 0818, 0838, 0848 and at 08, 18, 38 and 48 minutes past each hour until 1808, 1818, 1838, 1848; then 1908, 1918, 1938, 2008, 2038 and every 30 minutes until 2308, 2338.

AMENDED SERVICE JULY 30 - SEPT. 10

From Stuttgart Hbf: 0155 ⑥⑦, 0255 ⑥⑦, 0355 ⑥⑦, 0435 ①–⑤, 0455, 0525, 0555 and every 30 minutes until 0025, 0055.
From Stuttgart Flughafen ✈: 0138 ⑥⑦, 0238 ⑥⑦, 0338 ⑥⑦, 0438 ⑥⑦, 0508, 0538 and every 30 minutes until 0008, 0038.

937 AULENDORF - KISSLEGG - LEUTKIRCH and WANGEN

RB services; 2nd class only

km		Ⓐt	Ⓐt																					
0	**Aulendorf** d.	0459	0554	0650	...	0803	0907	1003	1107	1203	1307	1403	1507	1603	1707	1803	1907	2003	2107	2205	...	2310	...	...
10	Bad Waldsee d.	0506	0602	0657	...	0811	0915	1011	1115	1211	1315	1411	1515	1611	1715	1811	1915	2011	2115	2213	...	2318	...	...
30	Kißlegg a.	0528	0619	0714	...	0825	0932	1025	1132	1225	1332	1425	1532	1625	1732	1825	1932	2025	2132	2227	...	2335	...	...
	Kißlegg **934** d.	...	0625v	...	...	0832	0943	1032	1143	1232	1343	1532	1543	1632	1743	1832	1943	2032	2143	...	...	2343	...	...
	Wangen (Allgäu) **934** a.	...	0635v	...	...	0842	│	1042	│	1242	│	1442	│	1642	│	1842	│	2042	│	...	...	│	...	...
	Leutkirch **934** a.	...	...	...	...	...	0951	...	1151	...	1351	...	1551	...	1751	...	1951	...	2151	...	...	2351	...	...

	Ⓐt	Ⓐt			©z		Ⓐt																	
Leutkirch **934** d.	0453	...	...	...	0711	...	0806	...	...	1006	...	1206	...	1406	...	1606	...	1806	...	2006	...	2206	...	
Wangen (Allgäu) **934** d.	│	...	...	...	│	...	│	...	0915	│	1115	│	1315	│	1515	│	1715	│	1915	│	2115	│	...	...
Kißlegg **934** a.	0500	...	...	...	0719	...	0814	...	0925	1014	1125	1214	1325	1414	1525	1614	1725	1814	1925	2014	2125	2214	...	...
Kißlegg d.	0505	0542	...	0720	0720	0827	0827	...	0934	1027	1134	1227	1334	1427	1534	1627	1734	1827	1934	2027	2134	2228	...	2339
Bad Waldsee d.	0525	0602	...	0736	0736	0846	0846	...	0948	1046	1148	1246	1348	1446	1548	1646	1748	1843	1948	2043	2149	2245	...	2355
Aulendorf a.	0532	0609	...	0744	0744	0853	0853	...	0955	1053	1155	1253	1355	1453	1555	1653	1755	1851	1955	2051	2157	2252	...	0003

t – Not June 16, Nov. 1.
v – Not Aug. 15.
z – Also June 16, Nov. 1.

DB (*RE / S-Bahn* services)

ULM and ROTTWEIL - DONAUESCHINGEN - NEUSTADT - FREIBURG 938

ULM - DONAUESCHINGEN - VILLINGEN *On June 16, Nov. 1 services run as on ⑦.*

km		Ⓐ	Ⓒ	Ⓐ			Ⓐ					Ⓐ			Ⓐ						◇2				
0	**Ulm** Hbf d.	0602	0602	0702	0817	0917	0917	1017	1117	1217	1317	1317	1417	1517	1517	1617	1717	1817	1917	2017	2036	2117	2217	...	2326
16	Blaubeuren d.	0614	0618	0714	0829	0929	0929	1029	1129	1229	1329	1329	1429	1529	1529	1629	1729	1829	1929	2029	2054	2133	2234	...	2344
34	Ehingen (Donau) d.	0636	0636	0736	0842	0942	0942	1042	1142	1242	1342	1342	1442	1542	1542	1642	1742	1842	1942	2042	2111	2145	2248	...	0001
76	Herbertingen 937 d.	0712	0713	0814	0915	1015	1015	1116	1215	1316	1415	1415	1515	1615	1615	1716	1815	1916	2015	2116	2151	2215	2320	...	0032
93	**Sigmaringen** 937 d.	0730	0728	0829	0932	1029	1032	1132	1229	1332	1429	1432	1532	1629	1632	1732	1832	1932	2030	2135	2205	2230	2335	...	0046
135	Tuttlingen d.	0813	0813	...	1013	...	1113	1213	...	1413	...	1513	1613	...	1713	1813	1913	2013	...	2216	...	...	...	...	...
145	Immendingen 916 d.	0821	0821	...	1021	...	1121	1221	...	1421	...	1521	1621	...	1721	1821	1921	2021	...	2224	...	...	...	...	...
164	**Donaueschingen** 916 a.	0835	0835	...	1035	...	1135	1235	...	1435	...	1535	1635	...	1735	1835	1935	2035	...	2237	...	...	...	...	...
178	**Villingen** (Schwarwz) 916 a.	...	...	...	...	...	...	...	...	...	...	...	...	...	...	...	1945	2045	...	2305	...	...	...	...	...

	Ⓐ	Ⓐ	Ⓒ	Ⓐ			Ⓐ	Ⓒ								Ⓐ			Ⓐ	Ⓐ	Ⓒ		Ⓐ		
Villingen (Schwarzw) 916 d.	...	...	...	0504	...	...	0705	0711	0812	...	...	...	...	...	...	...	...	...	...	...	...	...	...	...	2059
Donaueschingen 916 d.	...	...	...	0514	...	...	0717	0721	0821	0921	...	1121	...	1321	...	1421	1521	...	1604	1721	1722	...	1821	1921	2121
Immendingen 916 d.	...	...	...	0528	...	...	0733	0735	0835	0935	...	1135	...	1335	...	1435	1535	...	1621	1735	1735	...	1835	1935	2135
Tuttlingen d.	...	...	...	0536	...	...	0750j	0746	0844	0944	...	1144	...	1344	...	1444	1544	...	1637f	1744	1744	...	1844	1944	2147
Sigmaringen 937 d.	0432	0521	0522	0618	0623	0728	0830	0830f	0931	1030	1131	1230	1331	1430	1531	1531	1630	1731	1731	1830	1830	1931	1931	2031	2232
Herbertingen 937 d.	0444	0535	0536	...	0640	0742	0843	0843	0944	1043	1144	1243	1344	1443	1544	1544	1643	1744	1744	1843	1843	1944	1944	2045	2244
Ehingen (Donau) d.	0520	0606	0605	...	0713	0813	0913	0913	1013	1113	1213	1313	1413	1513	1613	1613	1713	1813	1813	1913	1913	2013	2013	2116	2318
Blaubeuren d.	0534	0625	0621	...	0730	0830	0929	0929	1029	1129	1229	1329	1429	1529	1629	1629	1729	1829	1829	1929	1929	2029	2029	2133	2332
Ulm Hbf a.	0549	0637	0638	...	0741	0841	0941	0941	1041	1141	1241	1341	1441	1541	1641	1641	1741	1841	1841	1941	1941	2041	2041	2144	2351

VILLINGEN / SEEBRUGG - FREIBURG (BREISGAU) *On June 16, Nov. 1 services run as on ⑦.*

km		⚒	⚒	⚒	⚒	⚒	⚒	⚒	⚒	⚒	⚒	⚒	⚒	⚒		⚒	⚒	⚒	⚒	⚒	⚒	⚒	⚒	⚒	⚒
	Villingen (Schwarzw) d.		...	...	0521	...	...	0618	...	...	0737	...	...	0837	and at the same minutes past each hour until	...	...	1837	...	...	1937	...	2037	2137	2237
	Donaueschingen d.		...	...	0540	*0612*t	...	0639	...	...	0748	...	...	0848		...	...	1848	...	...	1948	...	2048	2148	2248
0	**Neustadt** (Schwarzw) d.		0550	...	0623	0656	...	0728	...	0758	0828	...	0858	0928		...	1858	1928	...	1958	2028	...	2128	2228	2328
	Seebrugg ⊡ d.		|	0600	|	|	0702	|	0731	|	|	0831	|	|		1831	|	|	1931	|	|	2104	|	|	|
5	Titisee ⊡ a.		0556	0626	0629	0702	0728	0734	0757	0804	0834	0857	0904	0934		1857	1904	1934	1957	2004	2034	2131	2134	2234	2334
	Titisee d.		0559	...	0633	0705	0737k	0737	0808	0808	0838	0908	0908	0938		1908	1908	1938	2008	2008	2038	...	2138	2238	2338
36	**Freiburg** (Brsg) Hbf a.		0638	...	0715	0743	0818k	0818	0848	0848	0918	0948	0948	1018		1948	1948	2018	2048	2048	2118	...	2218	2318	0018

	†	†	†	†	†	†	†	†	†	†	†		†	†	†	†	†	†	†	†	†	†	†	†	†
Villingen (Schwarzw). d.		...	...	...	...	...	...	0737	...	...	0837	and at the same minutes past each hour until	...	...	1737	...	1837	...	...	1937	...	...	2037	2137	2237
Donaueschingen d.		...	...	...	...	...	...	0748	...	...	0848		...	...	1748	...	1848	...	...	1948	...	...	2048	2148	2248
Neustadt (Schwarzw). d.		0623	...	0728	...	0758	...	0836j	...	0916	0936j		...	1816	1836j	...	1928	...	1958	2028	...	2059	2128	2228	2328
Seebrugg ⊡ d.		|	0600	|	0728	|	0809	|	0832r	|	|		1731	|	|	1831	|	1931	|	|	2036	|	|	|	|
Titisee ⊡ a.		0629	0626	0734	0755	0804	0838	0842	0858	0921	0942		1756	1821	1842	1857	1934	1957	2004	2034	2102	2105	2134	2234	2334
Titisee d.		0633	0633	0736	0807	0807	0845	0845	0905	0925	0945		1805	1825	1845	1905	1938	2008	2008	2038	2108	2108	2138	2238	2338
Freiburg (Brsg) Hbf... a.		0713	0713	0815	0843	0843	0924	0924	0944	1004	1024		1844	1911	1931	1944	2015	2045	2045	2115	2145	2145	2215	2315	0018

km		⚒	⚒	⚒	Ⓐ	⚒	⚒	Ⓐ	Ⓐ	⚒	⚒	⚒		⚒	⚒	⚒	⚒	🚌	⚒	⚒	🚌	⚒	🚌	⚒	⚒
0	**Freiburg** (Brsg) Hbf d.		0536	...	0608	...	0642	0713	0713	0740	0810	0810	and at the same minutes past each hour until	1840	1910	1910	1940	...	2010	2040	...	2140	...	2240	2340
31	Titisee a.		0610	...	0643	...	0715	0746	0746	0819	0848	0848		1919	1948	1948	2019	...	2048	2119	...	2219	...	2319	0019
	Titisee ⊡ d.		0613	0631	0644	0649	0717	0750	0759	0820	0850	0859		1920	1950	1959	2020	2023	2050	2120	2123	2220	2223	2320	0020
50	**Seebrugg** ⊡ a.		|	0657	|	0721	|	|	0825	|	|	0925		|	|	2025	|	2057	|	|	2157	|	2257	|	|
	Neustadt (Schwarzw) d.		0623	...	0650	...	0730f	0756	...	0830	0856	...		1930	1956	...	2030	...	2056	2130	...	2230	...	2330	0026
	Donaueschingen d.		0703	...	*0736*	...	0810	...	...	0910	...	...		2010	...	...	2110	...	...	2210	...	2310	...	0010	...
	Villingen (Schwarzw) a.		0717	...	...	...	0820	...	...	0920	...	...		2020	...	...	2120	...	...	2220	...	2320	...	0020	...

	†	†	†	†	†	†	†	†		†	†	†	†	†	†	†	†	🚌	†	†	🚌	†	🚌	†	†
Freiburg (Brsg) Hbf d.		0643	...	0745	0817	0837	0857	0917	and at the same minutes past each hour until	1737	1757	1817	1817	1846	1905	1905	1940	...	2016	2046	...	2146	...	2246	2346
Titisee a.		0715	...	0818	0855	0915	0935	0955		1815	1835	1855	1855	1918	1948	1948	2019	...	2048	2118	...	2218	...	2318	0018
Titisee ⊡ d.		0717	0719	0819	0859	0923	0944	0958		1823	1844	1858	1905	1920	1950	1958	2020	2023	2050	2119	2123	2220	2223	2320	0020
Seebrugg ⊡ a.		|	0745	|	0926	|	|	1025		|	|	1925	|	|	|	2025	|	2057	|	|	2157	|	2257	|	|
Neustadt (Schwarzw). d.		0730f	...	0830	...	0930	0950	...		1830	1850	...	1910	1930	1956	...	2030	...	2056	2130	...	2226	...	2330	0026
Donaueschingen d.		0810	...	0910	...	1010	...	...		1910	...	...	...	2010	...	...	2110	...	...	2210	...	...	...	0010	...
Villingen (Schwarzw). a.		0820	...	0920	...	1020	...	...		1920	...	...	...	2020	...	...	2120	...	...	2220	...	...	...	0025	...

ROTTWEIL - DONAUESCHINGEN ◇ *On June 16, Nov. 1 services run as on ⑦.*

km		Ⓐ				⊠				
0	**Rottweil** d.	0514	...	0643	0749	and	1949	2049	2149	2249
12	Trossingen Bf ▲ d.	0529	...	0655	0800	hourly	2000	2100	2200	2300
27	Villingen (Schwarzw) d.	0548	0551	0720f	0823	until	2023	2123	2223	2318
41	**Donaueschingen** a.	...	0601	0738	0840		2040	2140	2240	*2340*

		Ⓐ		Ⓐ		Ⓒ				n	
Donaueschingen d.	0502	0537	*0624*	*0703*	...	0714	0816	and	2016	2116	*2319*
Villingen (Schwarzw) d.	0525	0606j	0638	0722	...	0735	0840	hourly	2040	2140	2333
Trossingen Bf ▲ d.	0547	0625	0656	0739	0801	0801	0901	until	2101	2201	2346
Rottweil a.	0558	0635	0707	...	0811	0811	0911		2111	2212	2355

f – Arrives 7–8 minutes earlier.
j – Arrives 9–11 minutes earlier.
k – ⑥ only.
n – Change trains at Villingen on Ⓑ.
r – Subsequent departures are at 0932, 1031 and then at xx31.
t – Ⓐ only.

◇ – Operated by Hohenzollerische Landesbahn.
⊠ – The 1449 from Rottweil departs Villingen 1522, arrives Donaueschingen 1537.
⊡ – Other daily 🚌 connections Seebrugg - Titisee and v.v. (journey 32–34 minutes): **From Seebrugg** at 2159 and 2259. **From Titisee** at 2323 and 0023.
▲ – Connecting services run to / from Trossingen Stadt (operated by Hohenzollerische Landesbahn). Journey time: 5 minutes.

IRE / RB services (some 2nd class only)

FRIEDRICHSHAFEN - SINGEN - BASEL 939

km			①–⑤	Ⓐt	Ⓒz	Ⓐt	Ⓒz	Ⓒz	Ⓐt	Ⓒz															
0	**Friedrichshafen** Stadt d.	...	0425v	0528	0541	0632	0648	0657	0720	0807	0844	0901	1044	1101	1244	1301	1444	1501	1644	1701	1844	1901	2045	2105	2238	2331
34	Überlingen d.	...	0504v	0559	0620	0703	0714	0736	0808	0841	0909	0941	1109	1141	1309	1341	1509	1541	1709	1742	1909	1941	2109	2143	2315	0010
59	Radolfzell a.	...	0527v	0633	0648	0731	0733	0809	0839	0909	0930	1009	1130	1209	1330	1409	1530	1609	1730	1809	1930	2009	2130	2209	2341	0033
59	Radolfzell 916 d.	...	0529v	*0637*	*0656*	0732	0734	*0816*	*0846*	*0914*	0932	*1016*	1132	*1216*	1332	*1416*	1532	*1616*	1732	*1816*	1932	*2016*t	2132	*2222*	*2346*	0034
69	**Singen** 916 a.	...	0538v	*0647*	*0703*	0740	0742	*0826*	*0856*	*0924*	0940	*1026*	1140	*1226*	1340	*1426*	1540	*1626*	1740	*1826*	1940	*2026*t	2140	*2233*	*2356*	0042
			|		d	|	|	d	d		|		|		|		|		|		|		|			
69	**Singen** ▦ 940 d.	...	0545	0645	0706	0745	0745	0845	0906	...	0945	1045	1145	1245	1345	1445	1545	1645	1745	1845	1945	2045	2145	2236	0006	...
88	**Schaffhausen** ▦ 940 d.	...	0600	0700	0724	0800	0800	0900	0924	...	1000	1100	1200	1300	1400	1500	1600	1700	1800	1900	2000	2100	2200	2254	0024	...
107	Erzingen (Baden) ▦ d.	...	0613	0713	...	0815	0815	0915	...	...	1015	1115	1215	1314	1415	1515	1615	1715	1815	1915	2015	2115	2215	...	...	...
127	Waldshut d.	0611	0636f	0731	...	0831	0831	0934	...	...	1034	1134	1234	1334	1434	1534	1634	1734	1834	1934	2034	2131	2231	...	...	...
150	Bad Säckingen d.	0633	0653	0750	...	0849	0849	0949	...	...	1049	1149	1249	1349	1449	1549	1649	1749	1849	1949	2049	2153	2254	...	...	...
167	Rheinfelden (Baden) d.	0648	0705	0801	...	0901	0901	1001	...	...	1101	1201	1301	1401	1501	1601	1701	1801	1901	2001	2101	2209	2304	...	...	...
182	**Basel** Bad Bf a.	0703	0715	0812	...	0912	0912	1012	...	...	1112	1212	1312	1412	1512	1612	1712	1812	1912	2012	2112	2224	2316	...	...	...

					①–⑤		Ⓐt	Ⓒz	Ⓐt																	
Basel Bad Bf d.	...	...	...	...	0458	...	0534	0633	0638	0749	0849	0949	1049	1149	1249	1349	1449	1549	1649	1749	1849	1949	...	2049	...	2152
Rheinfelden (Baden) d.	...	...	...	...	0513	...	0549	0648	0649	0759	0859	0959	1059	1159	1259	1359	1459	1559	1659	1759	1859	1959	...	2059	...	2206
Bad Säckingen d.	...	...	...	...	0529	...	0605	0704	0701	0809	0909	1009	1109	1209	1309	1409	1509	1609	1709	1809	1909	2009	...	2109	...	2223
Waldshut d.	...	...	...	...	0553	...	0629	0729	0729	0829	0929	1029	1129	1229	1329	1429	1529	1629	1729	1829	1929	2029	...	2129	...	2246
Erzingen (Baden) ▦ d.	...	...	...	...	0614	...	0644	0744	0744	0844	0944	1044	1144	1244	1344	1444	1544	1644	1744	1844	1944	2044	...	2144	...	2303
Schaffhausen ▦ 940 d.	...	...	0528	...	0628	0632	0700	0800	0800	0900	1000	1100	1200	1300	1400	1500	1600	1700	1800	1900	2000	2100	2137	2200	2307	2318
Singen ▦ 940 a.	...	...	0547	...	0641	0651	0719	0814	0814	0914	1014	1114	1214	1314	1414	1514	1614	1714	1814	1914	2014	2114	2155	2214	2325	2332
	Ⓐt	Ⓒz	Ⓐt	Ⓒz	Ⓐt	Ⓒz	|	Ⓒz	d	|		|		|		|		|		|		|			
Singen 916 d.	*0510*	0534	0603	*0557*r	*0654*	0701	0721	*0726*	*0832*	0916	*1032*	1116	*1232*	1316	*1432*	1516	*1632*	1716	*1832*	1916	*2032*t	2116	*2202*	...	*2334*	...
Radolfzell 916 a.	*0519*	0541	0610	*0606*r	*0704*	0709	0729	*0735*	*0841*	0923	*1041*	1123	*1241*	1323	*1441*	1523	*1641*	1723	*1841*	1923	*2041*t	2123	*2211*	...	*2343*	...
Radolfzell d.	0522	0542	0611	0625	0707	0710	0731	0747	0847	0925	1047	1125	1247	1325	1447	1525	1647	1725	1847	1925	2047	2125	2225	...	2347	...
Überlingen d.	0545	0605	0638	0649	0735	0741	0753	0814	0914	0947	1114	1147	1314	1347	1514	1547	1714	1747	1914	1947	2114	2149	2248	...	0015	...
Friedrichshafen Stadt. a.	0618	0644	0718	0728	0806	0806	0828	0855	0954	1012	1154	1212	1354	1412	1554	1612	1754	1812	1954	2012	2151	2221	2324	...	0051	...

d – Daily. f – Arrives 0628. r – 3 minutes later on †z. v – Not June 16, Oct. 3, Nov. 1. t – Ⓐ (not June 16, Nov. 1). z – Also June 16, Nov. 1.

940 STUTTGART - SINGEN - ZÜRICH

Regional tickets are valid on *IC* trains in this table

WARNING! Subject to alteration July 30 - September 11.

km		RE 17611 Ⓐt	IC 1081 Ⓒ	IC 181 Ⓐ	IC 181	IC 2381 ⒶtF	RE 4775 ⒸzK	IC 183 ⚒s	IC 183	IC 2383	IC 185	IC 2385	IC 187	IC 2387	IC 189	IC 2389 K	IC 281	IC 2281	IC 283	IC 2289	IC 285 Ⓑb	IC 2285 ⒷqK	RE 4779 ⑥K	RB 17677	IRE 4777 ⑦v	IC 2287 ¶
0	**Stuttgart** Hbf ..... **942** d.	0458	0616	0617	...	0716	0715	0826	...	0916	1029	1116	1229	1316	1429	1516	1624	1713	1826	1916	2028	2116	2117	2217	2316	2326
26	Böblingen .... **942** d.	0522	0638	0638	...	0738	0738	0850	...	0938	1050	1138	1250	1338	1450	1538	1650	1738	1850	1938	2048	2138	2139	2239	2339	2347
42	Herrenberg .... **942** d.	0535	0647	0648	...	0747	0747	|	...	0947	|	1147	|	1347	|	1547	|	1747	|	1947	|	2147	2148	2248	2349	2356
51	Bondorf .... **942** d.	0542	0655	0656	...	0755	0755	|	...	0955	|	1155	|	1355	|	1555	|	1755	|	1955	|	2155	2156	2256	|	0004
67	Horb .... d.	0557	0710	0710	...	0807	0806	0914	...	1007	1114	1207	1314	1407	1514	1607	1714	1807	1914	2007	2113	2207	2208	2320	0006	0023
110	Rottweil .... d.	0640	0743	0743	...	0842	0842	0944	...	1042	1144	1242	1344	1442	1544	1642	1744	1842	1944	2042	2145	2242	2243	2353v	0034	0056e
138	Tuttlingen .... d.	0719	0800	0801	...	0859	0859	1001	...	1059	1201	1259	1401	1459	1601	1659	1801	1859	2001	2059	2203	2259	2300	...	0051	...
157	Engen .... **916** d.	0740	|	|	...	0913	0913	|	...	1113	|	1313	|	1513	|	1713	|	1913	|	2113	|	2313	2314	...	0105	...
172	**Singen** .... **916** a.	0751	0825	0825	...	0925	0922	1025	...	1125	1225	1325	1425	1525	1625	1725	1825	1925	2025	2125	2225	2325	2326	...	0114	...
172	**Singen** .... **939** d.	...	...	0832	0832	0932	0932	1032	1032	1132	1232	1332	1432	1532	1632	1732	1832	1932	2032	2132	2232	...	...	...	...	...
191	**Schaffhausen** ▦ **939** a.	...	...	0845	0845	0945	0945	1045	1045	1145	1245	1345	1445	1545	1645	1745	1845	1945	2045	2145	2245	...	...	...	...	...
239	**Zürich** HB .... a.	...	...	0923	0923	1023	1023	1123	1123	1223	1323	1423	1523	1623	1723	1823	1923	2023	2123	2223	2323	...	...	...	...	...

	RE 17604 Ⓐt	RE 17608	IC 2286 Ⓐt	RE 17618 ⚒r	RE 17620 †z	IC 1086 Ⓐs	IC 2284 ⚒K	RE 4774 ⑦K	IC 284 ⚒w	IC 2288	IC 282	IC 2280	IC 280	IC 2388	IC 188	IC 2386	IC 186	IC 2384	RE 4778 ⒸzK	IC 184	IC 2382 K	IRE 4776 ⑤	IC 182 Ⓑq	IC 182	IC 2380	IC 180
Zürich HB .... d.	...	...	...	...	...	...	...	...	0637	0737	0837	0937	1037	1137	1237	1337	1437	1537	...	1637	1737	...	1837	1837	1937	2037
Schaffhausen ▦ **939** d.	...	...	...	...	...	...	...	...	0716	0816	0916	1016	1116	1216	1316	1416	1516	1616	...	1716	1816	1837	1916	1916	2016	2116
Singen ....**939** a.	...	...	...	...	...	...	...	...	0730	0830	0930	1030	1130	1230	1330	1430	1530	1630	...	1730	1830	1855	1930	1930	2030	2130
Singen ....**916** d.	...	...	...	...	...	0551	0629	0629	0737	0835	0937	1035	1137	1235	1337	1435	1537	1635	1712	1737	1835	1903	1937	...	2035	...
Engen ....**916** d.	...	...	...	...	...	0600	0638	0638	|	0844	|	1044	|	1244	|	1444	|	1644	|	|	1844	|	|	...	2044	...
Tuttlingen .... △ d.	...	...	...	...	...	0615	0652	0652	0800	0859	1000	1059	1200	1259	1400	1459	1600	1659	1735	1800	1859	1926	2000	...	2059	...
Rottweil .... d.	...	0511t	0537v	0604	0614	0639	0711	0711	0816	0917	1016	1117	1216	1317	1416	1517	1616	1717	1756	1816	1917	1945	2017	...	2117	...
Horb .... d.	0447	0547	0610	0638	0645	0710	0751	0751	0845	0951	1045	1151	1245	1351	1445	1551	1645	1751	1828	1845	1951	2027	2046	...	2151	...
Bondorf ....**942** d.	0502	0602	0630	.0702	0702	|	0802	0803	|	1003	|	1203	|	1403	|	1603	|	1803	|	|	2003	|	|	...	2203	...
Herrenberg ....**942** d.	0511	0611	0640	0711	0711	0725	0810	0811	|	1011	|	1211	|	1411	|	1611	|	1811	1843	|	2011	2043	|	...	2211	...
Böblingen ....**942** d.	0521	0621	0650	0721	0721	0736	0821	0822	0911	1022	1111	1222	1311	1422	1511	1622	1711	1822	1853	1911	2022	2053	2111	...	2222	...
Stuttgart Hbf ....**942** a.	0545	0642	0711	0742	0742	0759	0843	0843	0932	1043	1132	1243	1332	1443	1536	1643	1732	1843	1916	1932	2043	2118	2132	...	2243	...

km									
0	**Schaffhausen** .... d.	0547	0617	and at the same	2117	2147	2157	2247	2327
28	Bülach .... d.	|	0637	minutes past	2137	|	2228	|	2358
48	**Zürich** HB .... a.	0623	0655	each hour until	2155	2223	2253	2323	0023

Zürich HB .... d.	0507	0605	0637	and at the same	2037	2105	2205	2305	0005
Bülach .... d.	0532	0623	|	minutes past	|	2123	2223	2323	0023
Schaffhausen .... a.	0604	0643	0713	each hour until	2113	2143	2244	2344	0044

F – From Frankfurt (Table **912**).
K – To/from Konstanz (Table **916**).
b – Also Nov. 26, Dec. 3, 10; not Oct. 2.
e – Does not run Horb - Rottweil on mornings until Sept. 12.
q – Not Oct. 2.
r – Not June 16, Nov. 1.
s – Not Nov. 1.
t – Ⓐ (not June 16, Nov. 1).
v – From Sept. 12.
w – Also Nov. 27, Dec. 4.
z – Also June 16, Nov. 1.
¶ – Runs as *RE* **17685** on ⑤⑥ (also June 15, Oct. 2, 31).

941 TÜBINGEN - HORB - PFORZHEIM - BAD WILDBAD

On June 16, Nov. 1 services run as on ⑦

km		Ⓐ	Ⓐ	⑥	Ⓐ	Ⓐ	Ⓒ	Ⓒ	Ⓐ				Ⓐ							Ⓒ	Ⓐ				
0	**Horb** .... d.	0424	...	0557	0616	0647	0649	0756	0804	0853	1004	1056	1125	1204	1256	1404	1456	1604	...	1656	1725	1804	1856	2007	2208
15	Hochdorf (b. Horb) .... d.	0437	0602	0610	0627	0659	0701	0820c	0820	0917c	1020	1117c	1149c	1220	1317c	1420	1517c	1620	1717	1717c	1749c	1820	1917c	2020	2220
25	Nagold .... d.	0455c	0614	0621	0638	0712	0712	0832	0832	0931	1031	1131	1202	1231	1331	1431	1531	1631	1731	1731	1802	1831	1931	2031	2231
34	Wildberg (Württ) .... d.	0503	0621	0629	0646	0720	0720	0841	0841	0939	1039	1139	1209	1239	1339	1439	1539	1639	1739	1739	1809	1839	1939	2039	2239
45	Calw .... d.	0518	0631	0639	0657	0730	0730	0851	0851	0950	1050	1150	1220	1250	1350	1450	1550	1650	1750	1750	1820	1850	1950	2050	2250
52	Bad Liebenzell .... d.	0526	0639	0647	0705	0738	0738	0900	0900	1001	1101	1201	1228	1301	1401	1501	1601	1701	1801	1801	1828	1901	2001	2101	2308c
71	**Pforzheim** Hbf .... a.	0548	0659	0708	0726	0759	0759	0922	0922	1022	1122	1222	1248	1322	1422	1522	1622	1722	1822	1822	1848	1922	2022	2122	2329

	Ⓐ		Ⓐ	Ⓒ	Ⓐ	⚒									Ⓐ		Ⓐ			Ⓐ					⑤⑥f
Pforzheim Hbf .... d.	0439	...	0618	0638	0641	0741	0836	0936	1036	1136	1236	1334	1436	1534	1606	1636	1706	1734	1836	1906	1934	2036	...	2246	2352
Bad Liebenzell .... d.	0459	...	0641	0702	0710	0805	0900	1000	1100	1200	1300	1400	1500	1600	1630	1700	1730	1800	1900	1930	2000	2100	...	2307	0012
Calw .... d.	0506	...	0648	0709	0716	0812	0907	1007	1107	1207	1307	1407	1507	1607	1637	1707	1737	1807	1907	1937	2007	2107	...	2314	0019
Wildberg (Württ) .... d.	0516	...	0703	0721	0731	0822	0921	1021	1121	1221	1321	1421	1521	1621	1651	1721	1751	1821	1921	1951	2021	2117	...	2324	0029
Nagold .... d.	0523	...	0714	0728	0739	0832	0929	1032	1129	1232	1329	1432	1529	1632	1701	1729	1801	1832	1929	2001	2032	2125	...	2332	0035
Hochdorf (b. Horb) .... d.	0535	...	0726	0740	0750	0851c	0940	1052c	1140	1252c	1340	1452c	1540	1652c	1712	1740	1821c	1850c	1940	2021c	2052c	2136	...	2344	...
Horb .... a.	...	...	0739	0753	.0801	0904	0956	1105	1156	1305	1356	1505	1553	1705	...	1756	1834	1903	1953	2033	2105	2150	...	2358	...

km		Ⓐ	Ⓐ	Ⓐ	Ⓒ	Ⓐ	†m						Ⓐ					Ⓐ							n
0	**Tübingen** Hbf .... d.	0524	0600	0628	0723	0725	0806	0834	0929	1034	1129	1234	1303	1330	1433	1530	1634	1703	1728	1834	1928	2034	2129	...	2232
32	**Horb** .... a.	0553	0633	0705	0752	0755	0838	0910	0957	1110	1157	1310	1336	1358	1510	1558	1710	1736	1757	1910	1957	2110	2157	...	2312

	n	Ⓐ	Ⓐ	Ⓒ	Ⓐ		Ⓒ						Ⓐ				Ⓐ		Ⓐ		†m				
Horb .... d.	0452	0613	0644	0652	0725	0759	0852	0959	1052	1159	1252	1400	1415	1452	1600	1652	1716	1801	1820	1852	1918	1959	2052	2159	2252
Tübingen Hbf .... a.	0522	0651	0724	0723	0801	0829	0923	1029	1123	1229	1323	1429	1454	1523	1629	1723	1752	1829	1854	1923	1952	2029	2124	2229	2326

km	*SEE NOTE* ▶	Ⓐ	⚒	Ⓐ	†	⚒	Ⓐ		⊠	
0	**Pforzheim** Hbf .... d.	0507	0607	0645	0707	0717	0747	0817	and	0017
23	**Bad Wildbad** Bf .... a.	0537	0637	0717	0737	0748	0818	0848	hourly	0048
25	**Bad Wildbad** Kurpark .. a.	0540	0640	0720	0740	0752	0822	0852	until	0052

SEE NOTE ▶	Ⓐ	⑥	Ⓐ	†	⚒		⊠	
Bad Wildbad Kurpark .... d.	0559	0647	0705	0747	0805	0905	and	0005
Bad Wildbad Bf .... d.	0602	0651	0708	0751	0809	0909	hourly	0009
Pforzheim Hbf .... a.	0633	0722	0740	0822	0840	0940	until	0040

c – Arrives 8 – 12 minutes earlier.
f – Also June 15, Oct. 2, 31.
m – Until Oct. 16.
n – From July 30.
⊠ – The 1217 from Pforzheim and 1205 from Bad Wildbad Kurpark run only on Ⓒ.
▶ – S-Bahn route **S6**. Additional journeys on Ⓐ: **From Pforzheim** Hbf at 1224, 1247, 1347, 1547, 1647, 1747 and 1847. **From Bad Wildbad** Kurpark at 0459, 0525, 0635, 0735, 1216, 1335, 1535, 1635 and 1735.

942 STUTTGART - FREUDENSTADT - OFFENBURG

On June 16, Nov. 1 services run as on ⑦

km			Ⓐ2	Ⓒ	Ⓐ		2	†	†	⚒	2		2		2		2		2		2		2		
0	**Stuttgart** Hbf ▲ .. **940** d.	0535•	...	0616	0617	...	...	0818	...	0818	...	1018	...	1217	...	1418	...	1616	...	1816	...	2018	...	2217	...
26	Böblingen .... **940** d.	0559	...	0638	0638	...	...	0838	...	0839	...	1039	...	1239	...	1439	...	1639	...	1839	...	2039	...	2239	...
42	Herrenberg .... **940** d.	0614	0618	0647	0648	...	...	0847	...	0848	...	1048	...	1248	...	1448	...	1648	...	1848	...	2048	...	2248	...
51	Bondorf .... **940** d.	...	0626	0655	0656	...	0802	0854	...	0856	1002	1056	1202	1256	1402	1456	1602	1656	1802	1856	2002	2056	2202	2256	...
57	Eutingen im Gäu .... d.	...	0633	0701	0700	0708	0809	0900	0908	0908	1009	1108	1209	1308	1409	1508	1609	1708	1809	1908	2009	2108	2209	2303	2309
62	Hochdorf (b. Horb) ...... d.	...	0641	...	...	0713	0814	...	0913	0913	1014	1113	1214	1313	1414	1513	1614	1713	1814	1913	2014	2113	2214	...	2315
87	**Freudenstadt** Hbf ...... a.	...	0709	...	...	0744	0843	...	0944	0944	1043	1144	1243	1344	1443	1543	1643	1744	1843	1944	2043	2144	2243	...	2343

	Ⓐ2		⚒	†	2	⚒	†	2		2		2		2		2	⚒	†	2	⚒	†	2		¶	2
Freudenstadt Hbf .... d.	0512	...	0611	0615	0715	0813	0813	0915	1013	1115	1213	1315	1413	1515	1615	1715	1813	1813	1915	2013	2013	2115	2215	...	...
Hochdorf (b. Horb) .... d.	0539	...	0641	0647	0745	0845	0845	0945	1045	1145	1245	1345	1445	1545	1646	1745	1845	1845	1945	2045	2045	2145	2245	...	...
Eutingen im Gäu .... d.	0548	0556	0656	0656	0751	0856	0856	0951	1056	1151	1256	1351	1456	1551	1656	1751	1856	1856	1951	2056	2056	2151	2251	2256	...
Bondorf .... **940** a.	0555	0602	0702	0702	0757	0902	0902	0957	1102	1157	1302	1357	1502	1557	1702	1757	1902	1902	1957	2102	2102	2157	...	2303	...
Herrenberg .... **940** a.	0604	0610	0710	0710	...	0910	0910	...	1110	...	1310	...	1510	...	1710	...	1910	1910	...	2110	2110	...	...	2311	2316
Böblingen .... **940** a.	...	0620	0720	0720	...	0920	0920	...	1120	...	1320	...	1520	...	1720	...	1920	1920	...	2120	2120	...	...	...	2330
Stuttgart Hbf ▲ ... **940** a.	...	0642	0742	0742	...	0942	0942	...	1142	...	1342	...	1543	...	1742	...	1942	1942	...	2142	2142	...	...	...	2355•

FREUDENSTADT - OFFENBURG (operated by Südwestdeutsche Landesverkehrs; 2nd class only). ***SERVICE FROM OCTOBER 9*** *(see page 568 for amended service until October 8).*

km		Ⓐ	⚒				✣		
0	**Freudenstadt** Hbf ...... d.	0531	0636	0720	0821	0900	and	2100	2200
16	Alpirsbach .... d.	0553	0659	0736	0838	0916	hourly	2116	2216
25	Schiltach .... d.	0604	0710	0750	0850	0930	until	2130	2230
35	Wolfach .... d.	0615	0720	0801	0902	0941		2141	2241
39	Hausach .... **916** a.	0619	0725	0805	0906	0945		2145	2245
72	**Offenburg** .... **916** a.	0659	0755	0834	0935	1014		2214	2314

	Ⓐ	⑥	Ⓐ							
Offenburg .... **916** d.	0453	0554	0558	0702	0740	0841	0941	and	2041	2241
Hausach .... **916** d.	0522	0626	0626	0730	0810	0910	1010	hourly	2110	2310
Wolfach .... d.	0527	0631	0631	0734	0815	0915	1016	until	2116	2316
Schiltach .... d.	0537	0642	0642	0749	0826	0929	1029		2129	2329
Alpirsbach .... d.	0551	0654	0654	0800	0840	0940	1040		2140	2340
Freudenstadt Hbf .... a.	0607	0710	0710	0816	0856	0956	1056		2156	2356

▲ – **Warning!** Journeys from/to Stuttgart are subject to alteration July 30 - Sept. 11.
✣ – The 1200 from Freudenstadt runs on Ⓒ only. On Ⓐ service is retimed: Freudenstadt d. 1221, Alpirsbach d. 1242, Schiltach d. 1255, Wolfach d. 1307, Hausach a. 1311, Offenburg a. 1342.
¶ – Not June 15, Oct. 2, 31.
• – Underground platforms.

KARLSRUHE - FREUDENSTADT 943

S-Bahn (2nd class only)

km		Ⓐt	Ⓐt	⑥	Ⓐt	Ⓒz		†w									⑤⑥f						
	Karlsruhe Bahnhofsvorplatz d.	0431	0505	0511	...	0611	0711z	...	0806j	0911	1011	1111		2011	2111	2211	2311		...	...	...	...	...
0	**Karlsruhe** Hbf .... **916** d.	│	│	│	0610	│	0707t	0806	│	│	│	│		│	│	│	│		1010	1210	1410	1610	1810
24	Rastatt .... **916** d.	0503	0533	0538	0633	0638	0738	0829	0838	0938	1038	1138	and	2038	2138	2238	2338	also	1029	1229	1429	1629	1829
40	Gernsbach Bf .... d.	0525	0556	0600	0656	0700	0800	0844	0900	1000	1100	1200		2100	2200	2300	0000	faster	1044	1244	1444	1644	1844
51	Forbach (Schwarzw) .... d.	0544	0613	0618	0717	0717	0817	0859	0917	1017	1117	1217	hourly	2117	2217	2317	0017		1059	1259	1459	1659	1859
61	Schönmünzach .... d.	0556	0624	0631	0729	0729	0829	0910	0929	1029	1129	1229		2129	2229	2329	0029	trains	1110	1310	1510	1710	1910
74	Baiersbronn Bf .... d.	0612	0642	0649	0750	0749	0849	0923	0949	1049	1149	1249	until	2149	2249	2346	0046		1123	1323	1523	1723	1923
79	**Freudenstadt** Stadt .... a.	0620	0650	0657	0758	0757	0857	0930	0957	1057	1157	1257		2157	2257	2354	0054	at	1130	1330	1530	1730	1930
82	**Freudenstadt** Hbf .... a.	0625	0705	0707	0807	0807	0907	0937	1007	1112k	1210n	1307		2207	2307	2400	0100		1137	1337	1537	1737p	1937

	Ⓒz	Ⓐt	Ⓐt	⑥	Ⓐt	Ⓐt	Ⓒz	Ⓐt	Ⓐt	Ⓒz	⚒r												Ⓒz
Freudenstadt Hbf .... d.	0015	0440	0524	0555	0614	0648	0653	0720	0748	0753	0823	0853		1953	2053	2153	2253		1023y	1223	1423	1623	1823
Freudenstadt Stadt .... d.	0025	0446	0530	0607	0620	0654	0703	0729	0803	0803	0829	0903		2003	2103	2203	2303	also	1029	1229	1429	1629	1829
Baiersbronn Bf .... d.	0032	0458	0539	0616	0628	0702	0711	0737	0811	0811	0837	0911	and	2011	2111	2211	2311		1037	1237	1437	1637	1837
Schönmünzach .... d.	0049	0513	0555	0631	0645	0728	0728	0748	0828	0828	0848	0928		2028	2128	2228	2328	faster	1048	1248	1448	1648	1848
Forbach (Schwarzw) .... d.	0100	0525	0612	0643	0701	0742	0742	0801	0842	0842	0901	0942	hourly	2042	2153v	2254v	2341	trains	1101	1301	1501	1701	1901
Gernsbach Bf .... d.	0117	0541	0631	0659	0728	0800	0800	0815	0900	0900	0915	1000		2100	2211	2311	0000		1115	1315	1515	1715	1915
Rastatt .... **916** d.	0140	0557	0706v	0722	0754	0822	0822	0830	0922	0922	0931	1022	until	2122	2232	2332	0022	at	1130	1330	1530	1730	1930
Karlsruhe Hbf .... **916** a.	│	0614	0728	│	0816	│	│	0849	│	│	0950	│		│	│	│	│		1149	1350	1550	1750	1948
Karlsruhe Bahnhofsvorplatz a.	0205	...	...	0747	...	0847	0847	...	0947	0947	...	1047		2147	2300	2400	0047		...	...	...	...	...

f – Also June 15, Oct. 2, 31.
j – 0811 on Ⓒ (also June 16, Nov. 1).
k – 1107 on Ⓒ (also June 16, Nov. 1).
n – 1207 on Ⓒ (also June 16, Nov. 1).
p – 1739 on Ⓒ (also June 16, Nov. 1).
r – Not June 16, Nov. 1.
t – Ⓐ (not June 16, Nov. 1).
v – Arrives 13 – 15 minutes earlier.
w – Also June 16, Nov. 1.
y – 1021 on Ⓒ (also June 16, Nov. 1).
z – Ⓒ (also June 16, Nov. 1).

MÜNCHEN - PASSAU 944

RE services

km		Ⓐt	⚒t	⚒t	Ⓐt	Ⓐt	Ⓒz																	
0	**München** Hbf .... **878** d.	...	0444	...	0524	0604	0624	0724	0824	0924	1024	1124	1224	1324	1424	1524	1623	1724	1824	1924	2024	2124	...	2324
42	Freising .... **878** d.	...	0508	...	0549	0628	0649	0749	0849	0949	1049	1149	1249	1349	1449	1549	1650	1749	1849	1949	2049	2149	...	2349
76	Landshut (Bay) Hbf .... **878** d.	...	0527	0543	0614	0651	0715	0815	0915	1015	1115	1215	1315	1416	1515	1615	1715	1815	1915	2015	2115	2215	...	0013
121	Landau (Isar) .... d.	...	...	0625	0701v	0737n	0748	0848	0948	1048	1148	1248	1348	1448	1548	1648	1748	1848	1948	2048	2148	2248	...	0042
139	Plattling .... a.	...	...	0640	0714	0750	0800	0900	1000	1100	1200	1300	1400	1500	1600	1700	1800	1900	2000	•2100	2200	2300	...	0054
139	Plattling .... **920** d.	0559	...	0642	0725	0800	0802	0902	1004	1102	1204	1302	1404	1504	1604	1702	1804	1902	2004	2102	2202	2306	...	0055
191	**Passau** Hbf .... **920** a.	0634	...	0716	0800	0835	0837	0937	1039	1137	1239	1337	1439	1539	1639	1737	1839	1937	2039	2137	2237	2341	...	0130

	⚒t		Ⓐt	Ⓒz	Ⓐt																			
Passau Hbf .... **920** d.	0440	0523	0604	0627	0646	0726	0826	0919	1026	1119	1219	1319	1426	1519	1626	1719	1826	1919	2026	2126	...	2319	...	...
Plattling .... **920** a.	0513	0558	0640	0701	0720	0800	0900	0953	1100	1153	1253	1353	1500	1553	1700	1753	1900	1953	2100	2200	...	2353	...	...
Plattling .... d.	0520	0600	0642	0702	0722	0802	0902	1002	1102	1202	1302	1402	1502	1602	1702	1802	1902	2002	2102	2202	...	2357	...	...
Landau (Isar) .... d.	0532	0613	0656	0714	0734	0814	0914	1014	1114	1214	1314	1414	1514	1614	1714	1814	1914	2014	2114	2214	...	0008	...	...
Landshut (Bay) Hbf .... **878** d.	0608	0644	0728	0747	0806	0848	0948	1048	1148	1248	1348	1448	1548	1648	1748	1848	1948	2048	2148	2248	...	0038	...	...
Freising .... **878** d.	0629	0709	0749	0810	0829	0910	1010	1110	1210	1310	1410	1510	1610	1710	1810	1910	2010	2110	2210	2310	...	...	...	...
München Hbf .... **878** a.	0656	0736	0817	0836	0856	0937	1036	1137	1236	1337	1436	1537	1637	1737	1836	1937	2036	2137	2237	2337	...	...	...	...

n – Arrives 0729.
t – Not June 16, Aug. 15, Nov. 1.
v – Arrives 0649.
z – Also June 16, Aug. 15, Nov. 1.

REGENSBURG - INGOLSTADT - DONAUWÖRTH - ULM 945

agilis

SERVICE FROM AUGUST 15. See page 568 for service until August 14. On Aug. 15, Nov. 1 services run as on ⑦.

km			Ⓐ	Ⓐ	Ⓐ	Ⓐ	Ⓐ	Ⓐ	Ⓐ	Ⓐ	Ⓐ	Ⓐ	Ⓐ	Ⓐ	Ⓐ	Ⓐ	Ⓐ	Ⓐ	Ⓐ	Ⓐ	Ⓐ	Ⓐ	Ⓐ	Ⓐ	Ⓐ
0	**Regensburg** Hbf .... d.	Ⓐ	...	*0357c*	*0452*	0508	0534	0608	...	0713	*0741*	0846	*0952*	1046	*1152*	*1246*	*1352*	*1446*	*1552*	1614	*1646*	1728	*1752*	*1846*	*1952*
46	Neustadt (Donau) .... d.		...	*0434c*	*0534*	0556	0626	0654	...	0803	*0831*	0927	*1029*	1128	*1229*	*1323*	*1429*	*1528*	*1629*	1703	*1731*	1811	*1829*	*1928*	*2028*
74	**Ingolstadt** Hbf .... a.		...	*0454c*	*0554*	0622	0654	0720	...	0826	*0851*	0953	*1050*	1154	*1250*	*1349*	*1449*	*1548*	*1650*	1734	*1755*	1835	*1852*	*1950*	*2051*
74	**Ingolstadt** Hbf .... d.		...	0507	0607	0631	0702	...	0807	...	0908	1008	1108	1209	1307	1406	1509	1608	1709	1740	1808	1841	1908	2003	2102
95	Neuburg (Donau) .... d.		...	0523	0627	0648	0729	...	0828	...	0926	1028	1129	1228	1329	1428	1529	1628	1725	1802	1829	1856	1929	2026	2127
127	**Donauwörth** .... a.		...	0549	0653	0724	0753	...	0852	...	0951	1053	1154	1253	1353	1454	1554	1653	1753	1838	1853	1920	1953	2053	2200
127	**Donauwörth** .... d.		0452	0603	0702	0728	0803	...	0901	...	1002	1101	1202	1302	1401	1503	1601	1702	1801	...	1901	1938	2010	2101	...
153	Dillingen (Donau) .... d.		0513	0632	0724	0749	0823	...	0925	...	1023	1121	1223	1330	1423	1525	1623	1725	1823	...	1922	1958	2032	2124	...
176	Günzburg .... **930** a.		0534	0649	0741	0807	0839	...	0940	...	1039	1140	1240	1347	1439	1540	1639	1740	1839	...	1939	2022	2048	2140	...
200	**Ulm** Hbf .... **930** a.		0554	0710	0808	0830	0857	...	0958	...	1057	1158	1258	1410	1457	1558	1657	1758	1857	...	1957	...	2108	2209	...

	Ⓐ	Ⓐ	Ⓐ		Ⓒ	Ⓒ	⑥	Ⓒ	Ⓒ	Ⓒ	Ⓒ	Ⓒ	Ⓒ	Ⓒ	Ⓒ	Ⓒ	Ⓒ	Ⓒ	Ⓒ	Ⓒ	Ⓒ	Ⓒ	Ⓒ	Ⓒ	Ⓒ
Regensburg Hbf .... d.	2015	2112	2222	Ⓒ	0024	...	...	...	0557	0649	0800	0845	1000	1045	1200	1245	1400	1445	1600	1645	1800	1845	2000	2045	2222
Neustadt (Donau) .... d.	2102	2204	2302		0106	...	...	...	0638	0733	0838	0933	1038	1133	1238	1333	1438	1533	1638	1733	1838	1933	2038	2133	2302
Ingolstadt Hbf .... a.	2123	2227	2322		0128	...	...	...	0655	0754	0855	0954	1054	1154	1254	1354	1454	1553	1654	1754	1854	1954	2054	2153	2322
Ingolstadt Hbf .... d.	2143	2240	2355		...	...	...	0607	0708	0808	0908	1008	1107	1208	1308	1408	1508	1608	1708	1808	1908	2008	2108	2208	2355
Neuburg (Donau) .... d.	2203	2257	0017		...	...	...	0627	0722	0824	0923	1024	1122	1224	1322	1424	1522	1624	1722	1824	1922	2024	2133	2228	0017
Donauwörth .... a.	2228	2323	0043		...	...	...	0653	0746	0853	0945	1053	1146	1253	1346	1453	1545	1653	1746	1853	1945	2053	2159	2253	0043
Donauwörth .... d.	2238	2338	...		...	0452	0607	0703	0750	0901	0950	1101	1150	1303	1350	1503	1550	1702	1750	1901	1950	2101	2201	2338	...
Dillingen (Donau) .... d.	2302	2358	...		...	0513	0633	0723	0807	0922	1006	1121	1206	1324	1406	1525	1606	1725	1806	1922	2007	2122	2222	2358	...
Günzburg .... **930** a.	2319	0014	...		...	0534	0650	0739	0824	0937	1022	1140	1222	1340	1422	1540	1622	1740	1825	1939	2024	2140	2245	0014	...
Ulm Hbf .... **930** a.	2337	0033	...		...	0554	0710	0758	0840	0958	1040	1158	1240	1358	1440	1558	1640	1758	1844	1957	2041	2209	2316	0033	...

		Ⓐ	Ⓐ	Ⓐ	Ⓐ	Ⓐ	Ⓐ	Ⓐ	Ⓐ	Ⓐ	Ⓐ	Ⓐ	Ⓐ	Ⓐ	Ⓐ	Ⓐ	Ⓐ	Ⓐ	Ⓐ	Ⓐ	Ⓐ	Ⓐ	Ⓐ	Ⓐ	Ⓐ
Ulm Hbf .... **930** d.	Ⓐ	...	...	...	0450	0527	...	0625	...	0745	0848	0948	1048	1148	1248	1348	...	1448	1548	1648	1742	1831	...	1942	2038
Günzburg .... **930** d.		...	...	...	0509	0545	...	0645	0652	0804	0913	1006	1116	1206	1314	1406	...	1513	1606	1713	1803	1851	...	2003	2058
Dillingen (Donau) .... d.		...	...	...	0524	0608	0634	0701	0727	0828	0933	1025	1132	1223	1331	1423	...	1533	1623	1733	1826	1907	...	2019	2114
Donauwörth .... a.		...	...	...	0545	0629	0657	0725	0754	0849	0953	1049	1153	1246	1352	1445	...	1553	1646	1753	1847	1932	...	2042	2136
Donauwörth .... d.		...	0456	...	0554	0631	0701	0731	0801	0859	1004	1101	1201	1302	1401	1502	...	1601	1703	1802	1901	1942	2009	2101	2138
Neuburg (Donau) .... d.		...	0524	...	0627	0705	0730	0804	0830	0930	1028	1128	1230	1328	1430	1530	...	1629	1735	1828	1930	2007	2038	2125	2205
Ingolstadt Hbf .... a.		...	0544	...	0650	0723	0747	0831	0847	0947	1046	1147	1246	1346	1448	1547	...	1647	1750	1848	1947	2023	2055	2143	2223
Ingolstadt Hbf .... d.		0521	0600	0628	*0705*	0730	*0805*	...	*0906*	1005	*1105*	1205	*1318*	*1405*	*1505*	*1605*	1624	*1705*	*1805*	*1905*	*2007*	2030	*2108*	*2206*	2236
Neustadt (Donau) .... d.		0545	0621	0655	*0729*	0752	*0828*	...	*0927*	1028	*1127*	1228	*1339*	*1428*	*1527*	*1628*	1651	*1727*	*1829*	*1927*	*2028*	2048	*2133*	*2227*	2302
Regensburg Hbf .... a.		0625	0706	0741	*0807*	0836	*0911*	...	*1007*	1111	*1207*	1310	*1430*	*1510*	*1607*	*1710*	1734	*1807*	*1910*	*2007*	*2110*	2129	*2210*	*2312*	2340

	Ⓐ	Ⓐ	Ⓐ		Ⓒ	Ⓒ	Ⓒ	Ⓒ	Ⓒ	Ⓒ	Ⓒ	Ⓒ	Ⓒ	Ⓒ	Ⓒ	Ⓒ	Ⓒ	Ⓒ	Ⓒ	Ⓒ	Ⓒ	Ⓒ	Ⓒ	Ⓒ	Ⓒ
Ulm Hbf .... **930** d.	*2123*	2219	2255	Ⓒ	...	...	0555	0718	0745	0918	0948	1118	1148	1318	1348	1518	1550	1718	1742	1918	1942	2100	...	2148	2255
Günzburg .... **930** d.	2147	2245	2318		...	...	0616	0736	0804	0936	1013	1136	1213	1336	1413	1536	1613	1736	1813	1936	2003	2120	...	2210	2318
Dillingen (Donau) .... d.	2203	2301	2335		...	...	0631	0752	0828	0952	1032	1152	1231	1352	1431	1552	1632	1752	1831	1952	2029	2140	...	2232	2335
Donauwörth .... a.	2223	2323	0002		...	...	0653	0812	0849	1013	1053	1212	1252	1412	1452	1612	1652	1812	1851	2012	2051	2200	...	2253	0002
Donauwörth .... d.	2238	2339	...		0501	...	0701	0815	0905	1014	1101	1214	1302	1413	1502	1614	1702	1813	1901	2014	2104	2203	...	2339	...
Neuburg (Donau) .... d.	2308	0006	...		0526	...	0732	0838	0932	1037	1132	1237	1332	1437	1533	1637	1733	1837	1933	2037	2132	2228	...	0006	...
Ingolstadt Hbf .... a.	2326	0023	...		0546	...	0748	0851	0949	1051	1148	1251	1349	1451	1549	1651	1749	1852	1949	2051	2148	2244	...	0023	...
Ingolstadt Hbf .... d.	2359	...	...		0604	0655	0805	0905	1005	1105	1205	1305	1405	1505	1605	1705	1805	1905	2005	2105	2205	...	2359	...	...
Neustadt (Donau) .... d.	0019	...	...		0627	0718	0828	0922	1027	1122	1227	1322	1427	1522	1627	1722	1827	1922	2027	2122	2226	...	0019	...	...
Regensburg Hbf .... a.	0104	...	...		0708	0807	0911	0956	1111	1156	1311	1356	1511	1556	1711	1756	1911	1957	2111	2156	2312	...	0104	...	...

c – 8 minutes later from Oct. 17.

ANGERMÜNDE - SZCZECIN 949

German holiday dates apply

km		⚒					B	A			⑤A
	Berlin Gesundbr. **845** .... d.	...	0803	...	...	1453	...	1720	...	...	2044
0	**Angermünde** .... d.	0544	0855	1056	1340	1545	1802	1808	1933	2140	2140
40	Tantow .... d.	0625	0929	1135	1419	1625	1858	1858	2014	2220	2220
59	Szczecin Gumience 🚌 .... d.	0638	0943	1149	1433	1636	1910	1909	2025	2234	2234
64	**Szczecin** Głowny .... a.	0646	0949	1155	1439	1644	1918	1917	2033	2240	2240

	⚒						⑤A	B	D	
Szczecin Głowny .... d.	0428	0603	0807	1006	1213	1457	1709	1709	1719	1951
Szczecin Gumience 🚌 .... d.	0435	0610	0813	1013	1220	1504	1716	1716	1726	1958
Tantow .... d.	0448	0624	0827	1026	1234	1538	1730	1730	1740	2012
Angermünde .... a.	0527	0704	0906	1104	1313	1622	1807	1809	1819	2044
Berlin Gesundbr. **845** .... a.	...	0754	...	1154t	...	...	1855	...	...	2134

A – Until July 16.
B – From July 17.
D – ①②③④⑥⑦ until July 16.
t – Until July 16. From July 17 diverted to Berlin Lichtenberg (a. 1204).

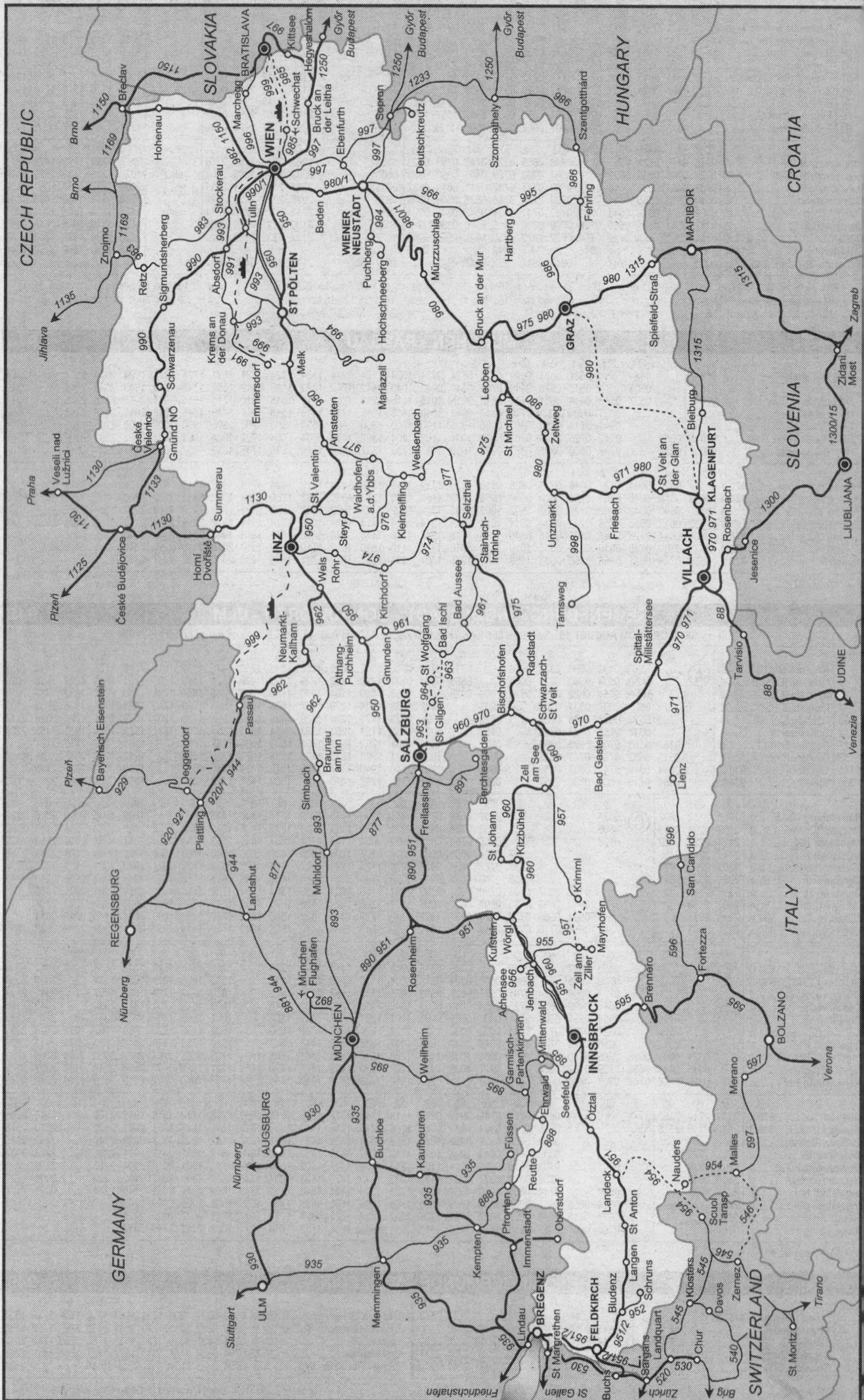

A list of scenic rail routes will be found on page 40

AUSTRIA

Operator: Except where otherwise stated, rail services are operated by Österreichische Bundesbahnen (**ÖBB**) www.oebb.at

Timings: Valid **until December 10, 2022** unless stated otherwise in individual tables. See page 4 for public holiday dates.

Services: Trains convey both first and second class seating unless footnotes show otherwise or there is a '2' in the train column. Overnight sleeping car (🛏) or couchette (🛏) trains do not necessarily convey seating accommodation - refer to individual footnotes for details. Descriptions of sleeping and couchette cars appear on page 10.

Train categories:

RJX or *RJ*	**Railjet xpress** **Railjet**	Austrian high-speed train. Conveys first and economy (2nd) class. *Business class* also available to first class ticket holders (supplement payable).
ICE	**InterCity Express**	German high-speed train.
EC	**EuroCity**	International express train.
IC	**InterCity**	Internal or international express train.
D	**Schnellzug**	Ordinary fast train.
NJ	**ÖBB nightjet**	Quality overnight express train - see page 10.
EN	**EuroNight**	Other international overnight express train - see page 10.
WB	**Westbahn**	Wien - Salzburg private operator (special fares payable).
REX	**Regional Express**	Semi-fast regional train (train number not usually shown).
CJX	**Cityjet xpress**	Similar to *REX* but using dedicated modern rolling stock.
	Regional / S-Bahn	Local stopping trains – no category or train number shown.

Reservations: Seats may be reserved on all long-distance express trains (*RJX, RJ, ICE, EC, IC, NJ, D*).

Catering: Three types of catering are indicated in the tables: ✕ – Restaurant car; ⊗ – Bordbistro; 🍸 – At seat trolley service.

WIEN - LINZ - SALZBURG 950

km	SEE NOTE ❖	RJ 848 Ⓐ♠ ✕	RJX 368 ✕	RJ 540 ✕	RJX 660 ✕	RJX 260 ✕	ICE 228 R✕	RJ 542 ✕	RJX 160 L✕	RJX 560 e F✕	RJ 544 ✕	RJX 662 ✕	RJX 262 ✕	IC 1018 Ⓒ S		RJX 1262 ⑥h G✕	RJ 596 K✕	ICE 28 R✕	RJX 162 B✕	RJX 562 F✕	RJ 860 V✕	ICE 92 P✕	RJX 60 B✕	RJ 640 ✕	ICE 26 R✕	RJX 564 ✕
0	**Flughafen Wien** ✈ d.	...	...	...	...	...	...	...	...	0703	0733	0803	...	...	...	...	0833	...	...	0903	...	...	...	1033	...	1103
17	**Wien** Hbf d.	0455	0530	0555	0630	0630	0651	0655	0730	0730	0755	0830	0830	0842	...	0846	0855	0915	0930	0930	0955	1015	1030	1055	1115	1130
21	**Wien** Meidling d.	0502	0537	0602	0637	0637	0658	0702	0737	0737	0802	0837	0837	0849	...	0853	0902	0922	0937	0937	1002	1022	1037	1102	1122	1137
52	Tullnerfeld **993** d.	0516	|	0616	|	|	|	0716	|	|	0816	|	|	|	...	|	0916	|	|	|	1016	|	|	1116	|	|
82	**St Pölten** Hbf **993** d.	0530	0600	0630	0700	0700	0723	0730	0800	0800	0830	0900	0900	0915	...	0920	0930	0946	1000	1000	1030	1046	1100	1130	1146	1200
142	Amstetten d.	0601p	|	0656	|	|	0749	0756	|	|	0856	|	|	|	...	|	1001p	|	|	|	1056	|	|	1201p	|	|
179	St Valentin **976** d.	0616	|	0715	|	|	|	0815	|	|	0915	|	|	|	...	|	1016	|	|	|	1115	|	|	1215	|	|
204	**Linz** Hbf **976** a.	0629	0644	0729	0744	0744	0815	0829	0844	0844	0929	0944	0944	1000	...	1014	1029	1033	1044	1044	1129	1133	1144	1229	1233	1244
204	**Linz** Hbf **962** d.	0631	0646	0731	0746	0746	0817	0831	0846	0846	0931	0946	0946	1002	...	1017	1031	1035	1046	1046	1131	1135	1146	1231	1235	1246
229	**Wels** Hbf **962** d.	0645	0700	0745	|	|	0833	0845	|	|	0945	|	|	|	...	|	1045	|	|	|	1145	|	|	1245	|	|
	Passau Hbf **962** a.	|	|	|	|	|	0922	|	|	|	|	|	|	|	...	|	|	1131	|	|	|	1231	|	|	1331	|
259	Attnang-Puchheim d.	0700	|	0800	|	|	...	0900	|	|	1000	|	|	1034	...	|	1100	...	|	|	1200	...	|	1300	...	|
264	Vöcklabruck d.	0706	|	0806	|	|	...	0906	|	|	1006	|	|	...	...	|	1106	...	|	|	1206	...	|	1306	...	|
329	**Salzburg** Hbf a.	0748	0754	0848	0852	0852	...	0948	0952	0952	1048	1052	1052	...	...	1130	1148	...	1152	1152	1248	...	1252	1348	...	1352
	München Hbf **890** a.	...	|	...	|	1030c	...	...	|	|	...	|	1230c	...	...	...	...	...	|	|	|	...	1432c	...	...	|
	Innsbruck Hbf **951** a.	...	0944	...	1044	...	...	...	1144	1144	...	1244	...	...	...	...	...	...	1344	1344	1444	...	...	...	...	1544
	Zürich HB **520** a.	...	1320	...	|	...	...	...	1520	...	...	|	...	...	...	...	...	...	1720	...	|	...	...	...	...	...
	Bregenz **951** a.	...	...	...	1317	...	...	...	...	...	...	1517	...	...	...	...	...	...	...	...	1717	...	...	...	...	...

SEE NOTE ❖	RJ 642 ✕	RJX 62 B✕	RJX 862 ✕	RJ 644 ✕	ICE 90 E✕	RJX 166 ✕	RJX 566 F✕	RJ 646 ✕	RJX 64 B✕	RJX 864 ✕	RJ 698 K✕	ICE 22 R✕	RJX 168 Y✕	RJ 740 ✕	RJX 66 N✕	RJX 866 ✕	RJ 742 ✕	ICE 20 Q✕	RJX 760 ✕	RJX 1260 ⑤★ G✕	RJ 744 ✕	RJX 68 B✕	RJX 868 ✕	RJ 746 ✕	IC 94 U🍸	RJX 762 ✕
Flughafen Wien ✈ d.	...	...	1203	1233	...	...	1303	...	...	1403	1433	...	1503	1533	...	1603	1633	...	1703	...	...	...	1803	1833	...	1903
Wien Hbf d.	1155	1230	1230	1255	1315	1330	1330	1355	1430	1430	1455	1515	1530	1555	1630	1630	1655	1715	1730	1730	1755	1830	1830	1855	1915	1930
Wien Meidling d.	1202	1237	1237	1302	1322	1337	1337	1402	1437	1437	1502	1522	1537	1602	1637	1637	1702	1722	1737	1737	1802	1837	1837	1902	1922	1937
Tullnerfeld **993** d.	1216	|	|	1316	|	|	|	1416	|	|	1516	|	|	1616	|	|	1716	|	|	|	1816	|	|	1916	|	|
St Pölten Hbf **993** d.	1230	1300	1300	1330	1346	1400	1400	1430	1500	1500	1530	1546	1600	1630	1700	1700	1730	1746	1800	1800	1830	1900	1900	1930	1947	2000
Amstetten d.	1256	|	|	1401p	|	|	|	1456	|	|	1556	|	|	1656	|	|	1756	|	|	|	1856	|	|	1956	|	|
St Valentin **976** d.	1315	|	|	1416	|	|	|	1515	|	|	1615	|	|	1715	|	|	1815	|	|	|	1915	|	|	2015	|	|
Linz Hbf **976** a.	1329	1344	1344	1429	1433	1444	1444	1529	1544	1544	1629	1633	1644	1729	1744	1744	1829	1833	1844	1844	1929	1944	1944	2029	2034	2044
Linz Hbf **962** d.	1331	1346	1346	1431	1435	1446	1446	1531	1546	1546	1631	1635	1646	1731	1746	1746	1831	1835	1846	1846	1931	1946	1946	2031	2036	2046
Wels Hbf **962** d.	1345	|	|	1445	|	|	|	1545	|	|	1645	|	|	1745	|	|	1845	1850	|	|	1945	|	|	2045	2050	|
Passau Hbf **962** a.	|	|	|	|	1531	|	|	|	|	|	|	1731	|	|	|	|	|	1934	|	|	|	|	|	|	2137	|
Attnang-Puchheim d.	1400	|	|	1500	...	|	|	1600	|	|	1700	...	|	1800	|	|	1900	...	|	|	2000	|	|	2100	...	|
Vöcklabruck d.	1406	|	|	1506	...	|	|	1606	|	|	1706	...	|	1806	|	|	1906	...	|	|	2006	|	|	2106	...	|
Salzburg Hbf a.	1448	1452	1452	1548	...	1552	1552	1648	1652	1652	1748	...	1752	1848	1852	1852	1948	...	1952	1952	2048	2052	2052	2148	...	2152
München Hbf **890** a.	...	1633c	|	...	...	|	|	...	1830c	|	...	...	|	...	2032c	|	...	...	|	...	...	2231c	|	...	...	|
Innsbruck Hbf **951** a.	...	...	1644	...	...	1744	1744	...	...	1844	...	...	1944	...	...	2044	...	...	2144	...	...	...	2248	...	...	2348
Zürich HB **520** a.	...	...	|	...	...	2120	...	...	...	|	...	...	2320	...	...	|	...	...	|	...	...	...	...	...	...	...
Bregenz **951** a.	...	...	1917	...	...	...	...	...	...	2117	...	...	...	...	...	2317	...	...	0017	...	...	...	...	...	...	...

SEE NOTE ❖	RJ 748 ✕	NJ 490 H♣	RJX 42 B✕	RJ 840 ✕	NJ 466 A	RJ 820 ✕	RJX 764 ✕	NJ 446 ♥	EN 70462 D♣	EN 40462 ⊙
Flughafen Wien ✈ d.	1933	...	...	2033	...	2133	2203	2233	...	...
Wien Hbf d.	1955	2013	2030	2055	2127	2155	2230	2255	2327	2327
Wien Meidling d.	2002	2021	2037	2102	2135	2202	2237	2303	2335	2335
Tullnerfeld **993** d.	2016	|	|	2116	|	2216	|	2321	|	|
St Pölten Hbf **993** d.	2030	2047	2100	2130	2201	2230	2300	2338	0001	0001
Amstetten d.	2056	|	|	2201p	2227	2301	|	0007	|	|
St Valentin **976** d.	2115	|	|	2216	|	2316	|	0026	|	|
Linz Hbf **976** a.	2129	2134	2144	2229	2254	2329	2344	0040	0048	0048
Linz Hbf **962** d.	2131	2136	2146	2231	2256	...	2346	0042	0059	0059
Wels Hbf **962** d.	2145	2150	2200	2245	2313	...	0000	0058	0114	0114
Passau Hbf **962** a.	|	2235	|	|	|	...	|	|	|	|
Attnang-Puchheim d.	2200	...	|	2300	2331	...	0015	0116	|	|
Vöcklabruck d.	2206	...	|	2306	|	...	|	0122	|	|
Salzburg Hbf a.	2248	...	2254	2348	0013	...	0056	0200	0210	0210
München Hbf **890** a.	...	...	...	...	|	...	...	|	0610c	|
Innsbruck Hbf **951** a.	...	...	...	...	0423	...	...	0519	...	0423
Zürich HB **520** a.	...	...	...	...	0820	...	...	|	...	0820
Bregenz **951** a.	...	...	...	...	...	...	...	0829	...	...

SEE NOTE ❖	RJ 825 ⚒ ✕	NJ 447 ♥	EN 40467 ⊖	EN 463 D	RJ 821 ✕	RJ 823 Ⓐ ✕	NJ 467 A	RJ 541 ✕	RJX 761 ✕	RJ 543 ✕	NJ 491 H♣
Bregenz **951** d.	...	2140	...	...	...	...	...	...	...	...	...
Zürich HB **520** d.	...	|	2140	...	...	...	2140	...	...	...	...
Innsbruck Hbf **951** d.	...	0044	0128	...	...	...	0128	...	...	...	...
München Hbf **890** d.	...	|	|	2320c	...	...	|	...	...	...	...
Salzburg Hbf d.	...	0321	0345	0345	...	...	0442	0512	0602	0612	...
Vöcklabruck d.	...	0402	|	|	...	...	|	0554	|	0654	...
Attnang-Puchheim d.	...	0408	|	|	...	...	0530	0600	0647	0700	...
Passau Hbf **962** d.	...	|	|	|	...	...	|	|	|	|	0615
Wels Hbf **962** d.	0354a	0427	|	|	...	0554a	0548	0616	0702	0716	0717
Linz Hbf **962** a.	0408a	0444	0452	0452	...	0608a	0604	0629	0714	0729	0746
Linz Hbf **976** d.	0410	0504	0510	0510	0531	0610	0614	0631	0716	0731	0748
St Valentin **976** d.	|	0525p	|	|	0545	|	|	0645	|	0748	|
Amstetten d.	0435	0545	|	|	0606p	0635	0643	0706	|	0806	0817
St Pölten Hbf **993** d.	0502	0620	0602	0602	0632	0702	0718j	0732	0802	0832	0844
Tullnerfeld **993** a.	0514	|	|	|	0643	|	|	0743	|	0843	|
Wien Meidling a.	0532	0649	0626	0626	0658	0723	0751	0758	0823	0858	0911
Wien Hbf a.	0539	0658	0634	0634	0705	0730	0758	0805	0830	0905	0919
Flughafen Wien ✈ a.	0557	...	...	...	0727	0757	...	0827	0857	0927	...

SEE NOTE ❖	RJX 269 B ✕	RJ 545 ✕	RJX 763 ✕	RJX 265 ✕	IC 95 U🍸	RJ 547 ✕	RJX 861 ✕	RJX 61 B✕	RJ 549 ✕	RJX 765 ✕	ICE 21 Q✕	RJ 691 K✕	RJX 863 ✕	RJ 63 M✕	RJ 643 ✕	RJX 161 X✕	ICE 23 R✕	RJ 645 ✕	RJX 1265 ⊕ G✕	RJ 65 B✕	RJ 865 ✕	RJX 563 ✕	ICE 91 E✕	RJ 649 ✕	RJX 897 W✕	RJX 67 B✕
Bregenz **951** d.		...	...	...	...	...	0437a	...	...	0548	...	...	0639	...	...	...	...	...	...	...	0840	...	...	...	1040	...
Zürich HB **520** d.	...	...	...	...	...	...	|	...	...	|	...	...	|	...	...	0640	...	...	...	...	|	...	...	...	|	...
Innsbruck Hbf **951** d.	0510	...	0610	...	...	...	0713	...	...	0817	...	...	0914	...	...	1017	...	...	...	...	1114	1217	...	...	1314	...
München Hbf **890** d.	|	...	|	0622c	...	...	|	0723c	...	|	...	...	|	0929c	...	|	...	...	...	1129c	|	|	...	...	|	1329c
Salzburg Hbf d.	0708	0712	0808	0808	...	0812	0908	0908	0912	1008	...	1012	1108	1108	1112	1208	...	1212	1308	1308	1312	1408	...	1412	1508	1508
Vöcklabruck d.	|	0754	|	|	...	0854	|	|	0954	|	...	1054	|	|	1154	|	...	1254	|	|	1354	|	...	1454	|	|
Attnang-Puchheim d.	|	0800	|	|	...	0900	|	|	1000	|	...	1100	|	|	1200	|	...	1300	|	|	1400	|	...	1500	|	|
Passau Hbf **962** d.	|	|	|	|	0824	|	|	|	|	|	1026	|	|	|	|	|	1229	|	|	|	|	|	1429	|	|	|
Wels Hbf **962** d.	|	0816	|	|	0911	0916	|	|	1016	|	1112	1116	|	|	1216	|	|	1316	|	|	1416	|	|	1516	|	|
Linz Hbf **962** a.	0814	0829	0914	0914	0923	0929	1014	1014	1029	1114	1125	1129	1214	1214	1229	1314	1325	1329	1414	1414	1429	1514	1525	1529	1614	1614
Linz Hbf **976** d.	0816	0831	0916	0916	0925	0931	1016	1016	1031	1116	1127	1131	1216	1216	1231	1316	1327	1331	1416	1416	1431	1516	1527	1531	1616	1616
St Valentin **976** d.	|	0848	|	|	|	0948	|	|	1048	|	|	1145	|	|	1248	|	|	1345	|	|	1448	|	|	1545	|	|
Amstetten d.	|	0906	|	|	|	1006	|	|	1106	|	|	1206p	|	|	1306	|	|	1406p	|	|	1506	|	|	1606p	|	|
St Pölten Hbf **993** d.	0902	0932	1002	1002	1014	1032	1102	1102	1132	1202	1216	1232	1302	1302	1332	1402	1416	1432	1502	1502	1532	1602	1616	1632	1702	1702
Tullnerfeld **993** a.	|	0943	|	|	|	1043	|	|	1143	|	|	1243	|	|	1343	|	|	1443	|	|	1543	|	|	1643	|	|
Wien Meidling a.	0923	0958	1023	1023	1038	1058	1123	1123	1158	1223	1238	1258	1323	1323	1358	1423	1438	1458	1523	1523	1558	1623	1638	1658	1723	1723
Wien Hbf a.	0930	1005	1030	1030	1045	1105	1130	1130	1205	1230	1245	1305	1330	1330	1405	1430	1445	1505	1530	1530	1605	1630	1645	1705	1730	1730
Flughafen Wien ✈ a.	...	*1027*	1057	...	...	1127	1157	...	*1227*	1257	...	1327	1357	...	1427	1457	...	1527	1557	...	*1627*	1657	...	1727	1757	...

☛ See page 450 for regional trains Wien Westbf - St Pölten - Melk - Amstetten - Linz, also services Wien - Linz - Salzburg operated by *Westbahn*.

FOR NOTES SEE PAGE 450 →

950 SALZBURG - LINZ - WIEN

SEE NOTE ❖	ICE 93	RJ 741	RJX 565	RJX 165	ICE 27	RJ 743	RJX 869	RJX 69	RJ 745	RJX 167	RJX 567	ICE 29	RJ 797	RJ 1267	IC 1019	RJX 661	RJX 1261	RJX 261	RJ 769	RJX 169	RJ 841	ICE 229	RJX 663	RJ 843	RJX 367	RJ 845
											⑧			⑦k	Ⓒ	⑦k	⑥		¶							
	P✕	✕	F✕	B✕	R✕	✕	✕	✕	✕	L✕	F✕	R✕	K✕	G✕	S	✕	G✕	B✕	✕	✕	✕	R✕	✕	✕	✕	✕
Bregenz 951 d.	...	...	...	...	...	...	1240	...	...	...	...	...	...	...	...	1440	...	...	1440f	...	...	...	...	...	...	...
Zürich HB 520 d.	...	...	...	1040	...	...	|	...	...	1240	...	...	...	...	...	|	...	...	|	1440	...	...	...	...	1640	...
Innsbruck Hbf 951 d.	...	...	1417	1417	...	...	1514	...	...	1617	1617	...	...	...	...	1714	...	...	1714f	1817	...	...	1914	...	2017	...
München Hbf 890 d.	...	...	|	|	...	...	|	1529c	...	|	|	...	...	...	...	|	...	1730c	|	|	...	...	|	...	|	...
Salzburg Hbf d.	...	1512	1608	1608	...	1612	1708	1708	1712	1808	1808	...	1812	1830	...	1908	1908	1908	1912	2008	2012	...	2108	2112	2208	2212
Vöcklabruck d.	...	1554	|	|	...	1654	|	|	1754	|	|	...	1854	|	...	|	|	|	1954	|	2054	...	|	2154	|	2254
Attnang-Puchheim d.	...	1600	|	|	...	1700	|	|	1800	|	|	...	1900	|	1925	|	|	|	2000	|	2100	...	|	2200	|	2300
Passau Hbf 962 🏛 d.	1529	|	|	|	1629	|	|	|	|	|	|	1829	|	|	|	|	|	|	|	|	|	2031	|	|	|	|
Wels Hbf 962 d.	|	1616	|	|	|	1716	|	|	1816	|	|	|	1916	|	|	|	|	|	2016	|	2116	2120	|	2216	2305	2316
Linz Hbf 962 a.	1625	1629	1714	1714	1725	1729	1814	1814	1829	1914	1914	1925	1929	1944	1958	2014	2014	2014	2029	2114	2129	2133	2214	2229	2317	2329
Linz Hbf 976 d.	1627	1631	1716	1716	1727	1731	1816	1816	1831	1916	1916	1927	1931	1946	2000	2016	2016	2016	2031	2116	...	2135	2216	2231	2319	...
St Valentin 976 d.	|	1645	|	|	|	1748	|	|	1848	|	|	|	1948	|	|	|	|	|	2048	|	...	|	|	2245	|	...
Amstetten d.	|	1701	|	|	|	1806	|	|	1906	|	|	|	2006	|	|	|	|	|	2106	|	...	2206p	|	2306p	|	...
St Pölten Hbf 993 d.	1716	1732	1802	1802	1816	1832	1902	1902	1932	2002	2002	2016	2032	2038	2047	2102	2102	2102	2132	2202	...	2232	2302	2332	0005	...
Tullnerfeld 993 a.	|	1743	|	|	|	1843	|	|	1943	|	|	|	2043	|	|	|	|	|	2143	|	...	2243	|	2343	|	...
Wien Meidling a.	1738	1758	1823	1823	1838	1858	1923	1923	1958	2023	2023	2038	2058	2104	2111	2123	2123	2123	2158	2223	...	2258	2323	2358	0026	...
Wien Hbf a.	1745	1805	1830	1830	1845	1905	1930	1930	2005	2030	2030	2045	2105	2111	2118	2130	2130	2130	2205	2230	...	2305	2330	0005	0033	...
Flughafen Wien ✈ ❦ a.	...	*1827*	1857	...	...	1927	1957	...	*2027*	...	2057	...	2127	...	...	2157	...	...	2227	...	...	...	...	...	...	...

Regional ÖBB trains **WIEN - MELK - AMSTETTEN - ST VALENTIN** (2nd class only; most from / to Wien are classified *CJX*)

km ‡																								
		⚒	ⒶT		Ⓐ	T						T	Ⓐ	◧	Ⓐ		Ⓐ	◇	Ⓐ	T					
0	**Wien** Westbahnhof d.	...	0424	0520	0550	0620	0720	0750a	0820		1420	1520	1550	1620	1650	1720	1750	1820	1850	1920	2020	2120	2220	2320	0020
6	**Wien** Hütteldorf d.	...	0431	0527	0557	0627	0727	0757a	0827		1427	1527	1557	1627	1657	1727	1757	1827	1857	1927	2027	2127	2227	2327	0027
	Tullnerfeld d.	...	|	0540	0610	0640	0740	0810a	0840	and	1440	1540	1610	1640	1710	1740	1810	1840	1910	1940	2040	2140	2240	2340	0040
61	**St Pölten** Hbf a.	...	0525	0554	0624	0654	0754	0824a	0854		1454	1554	1624	1654	1724	1754	1824	1854	1924	1954	2054	2154	2254	2354	0054
61	**St Pölten** Hbf d.	0447	0527	0603	0626	0703	0803	0835	0903	hourly	1503	1603	1625	1703	1725	1803	1825	1903	1925	2003	2103	2205	2305	0005	0105
85	Melk d.	0506	0549	0619	0650	0719	0819	0857	0919		1519	1619	1642	1719	1742	1819	1842	1919	1942	2019	2119	2221	2321	0021	0121
94	Pöchlarn d.	0512	0556	0628	0656	0728	0828	0904	0928	until	1528	1628	1650	1728	1750	1828	1850	1928	1950	2028	2128	2228	2328	0028	0128
107	Ybbs an der Donau d.	0523	0607	0637	0707	0737	0837	...	0937		1537	1637	1658	1737	1758	1837	1858	1937	1958	2037	2137	2237	2337	0037	0137
124	Amstetten a.	0536	0619	0651	0720	0751	0851	...	0951		1551	1651	1713	1751	1813	1851	1913	1951	2013	2051	2151	2251	2351	0051	0151
124	Amstetten d.	0537	*0622*	*0707*	...	*0807*	*0907*	...	*1007*		*1607*	*1707*	...	1807	...	1907	...	2007	...	*2107*	*2207*	2307	*0013*	...	*0431*
163	**St Valentin** a.	0606	*0639*	*0736*	...	*0836*	*0936*	...	*1036*		*1636*	*1736*	...	1836	...	1936	...	2036	...	*2136*	*2236*	2336	*0042*	...	*0500*

		Ⓐ	T	Ⓐ	ⒶT	Ⓐ	T	Ⓐ	T	Ⓐ			T				Ⓐ		T		T			Ⓒ
St Valentin d.	...	0359	...	0429	...	0453	*0524*	...	...	0559	*0624*	...	*0724*	*0824*		*1624*	...	*1724*	1824	*1923*	*2024*	*2124*	...	2224	2224
Amstetten a.	...	0428	...	0458	...	0522	*0553*	...	...	0628	*0653*	...	*0753*	*0853*		*1653*	...	*1753*	1853	*1953*	*2053*	*2153*	...	2253	2253
Amstetten d.	0409	0447	0503	0517	0531	0547	0604	0617	0631	0646	0709	0731a	0809	0909	and	1709	1746	1809	1909	2009	2109	2209	...	2309	2309
Ybbs an der Donau d.	0422	0500	0515	0527	0544	0557	0617	0627	0644	0657	0722	0744a	0822	0922		1722	1759	1822	1922	2022	2122	2222	...	2322	2322
Pöchlarn d.	0433	0510	0528	0535	0556	0605	0628	0635	0656	0705	0733	0756	0833	0933	hourly	1732	1810	1833	1933	2033	2133	2233	...	2333	2333
Melk d.	0439	0516	0532	0541	0602	0611	0634	0641	0702	0711	0739	0802	0839	0939		1739	1816	1839	1939	2039	2139	2239	...	2339	2339
St Pölten Hbf a.	0459	0533	0554	0558	0624	0628	0653	0658	0724	0728	0757	0822	0857	0957	until	1757	1834	1857	1957	2057	2157	2257	...	2357	2357
St Pölten Hbf d.	0506	0536	0606	*0606*	0636	*0636*	0706	*0706*	0736	*0736*	0806	0836a	0906	1006		1806	1836	1906	2006	2106	2206	2306	...	...	0008
Tullnerfeld a.	0519	0549	0619	*0619*	0649	*0649*	0719	*0719*	0749	*0749*	0819	0849a	0919	1019		1819	1849	1919	2019	2119	2219	2319	...	...	0021
Wien Hütteldorf a.	0533	0603	0633	*0633*	0703	*0703*	0733	*0733*	0803	*0803*	0833	0903a	0933	1033		1833	1903	1933	2033	2133	2233	2333	...	...	0035
Wien Westbahnhof a.	0540	0610	0640	*0640*	0710	*0710*	0740	*0740*	0810	*0810*	0840	0910a	0940	1040		1840	1910	1940	2040	2140	2240	2340	...	...	0042

Services operated by *WESTbahn* **WIEN - LINZ - SALZBURG**. Special fares payable (ÖBB tickets not valid). All trains convey 🍸. **Warning!** Subject to alteration.

km		WB 900	WB 960	WB 902	WB 980	WB 904	WB 962	WB 906	WB 908	WB 964	WB 910	WB 912	WB 966	WB 914	WB 916	WB 968	WB 918	WB 988	WB 920	WB 970	WB 922	WB 990	WB 924	WB 972	WB 926	WB 992	WB 928	WB 930
		⚒	⚒																									
0	**Wien** Westbahnhof d.	0540	0610	0640	0710	0740	0810	0840	0940	1010	1040	1140	1210	1240	1340	1410	1440	1510	1540	1610	1640	1710	1740	1810	1840	1910	1940	2040
6	**Wien** Hütteldorf d.	0547	0617	0647	0717	0747	0817	0847	0947	1017	1047	1147	1217	1247	1347	1417	1447	1517	1547	1617	1647	1717	1747	1817	1847	1917	1947	2047
60	**St Pölten** Hbf d.	0608	0638	0708	0738	0808	0838	0908	1008	1038	1108	1208	1238	1308	1408	1438	1508	1538	1608	1638	1708	1738	1808	1838	1908	1938	2008	2108
120	Amstetten d.	0631	0701	0731	0801	0831	0901	0931	1031	1101	1131	1231	1301	1331	1431	1501	1531	1601	1631	1701	1731	1801	1831	1901	1931	2001	2031	2131
182	**Linz** Hbf d.	0657	0727	0757	0827	0857	0927	0957	1057	1127	1157	1257	1327	1357	1457	1527	1557	1627	1657	1727	1757	1827	1857	1927	1957	2027	2057	2157
207	Wels Hbf d.	0710	0740	0810	0840	0910	0940	1010	1110	1140	1210	1310	1340	1410	1510	1540	1610	1640	1710	1740	1810	1840	1910	1940	2010	2040	2110	2210
237	Attnang-Puchheim d.	0725	0755	0825	0855	0925	0955	1025	1125	1155	1225	1325	1355	1425	1525	1555	1625	1655	1725	1755	1825	1855	1925	1955	2025	2055	2125	2224
242	Vöcklabruck d.	0730	0800	0830	0900	0930	1000	1030	1130	1200	1230	1330	1400	1430	1530	1600	1630	1700	1730	1800	1830	1900	1930	2000	2030	2100r	2130	...
307	**Salzburg** Hbf a.	0814	0838	0908	0938	1008	1038	1108	1208	1238	1308	1408	1438	1508	1608	1638	1708	1738	1808	1838	1908	1938	2008	2038	2108	2138r	2208	...
	München Hbf 890 a.	...	1013v	...	...	...	1213	...	...	1413	...	...	1613v	...	...	...	...	...	...	2013	...	...	...	2207z	...	...	...	...

	WB 901	WB 959	WB 903	WB 979	WB 905	WB 961	WB 907	WB 981	WB 909	WB 963	WB 911	WB 913	WB 965	WB 915	WB 917	WB 967	WB 919	WB 921	WB 969	WB 923	WB 989	WB 925	WB 917	WB 927	WB 991	WB 929	WB 973	WB 931
	⚒	⚒																										
München Hbf 890 d.	...	...	...	...	...	0548t	...	...	...	0748	...	...	...	...	...	1148v	...	...	1348	...	...	...	1548	...	...	...	1749v	...
Salzburg Hbf d.	...	...	0552t	0622t	0652	0722	0752	0822	0852	0922	0952	1052	1122	1152	1252	1322	1352	1452	1522	1546	1622	1646	1722	1746	1822	1852	1922	1952
Vöcklabruck d.	...	...	0631t	0701t	0731	0801	0831	0901	0931	1001	1031	1131	1201	1231	1331	1401	1431	1531	1601	1631	1701	1731	1801	1831	1901	1931	2001	2031
Attnang-Puchheim d.	...	0606	0636t	0706	0736	0806	0836	0906	0936	1006	1036	1136	1206	1236	1336	1406	1436	1536	1606	1636	1706	1736	1806	1836	1906	1936	2006	2036
Wels Hbf d.	...	0620	0650t	0720	0750	0820	0850	0920	0950	1020	1050	1150	1220	1250	1350	1420	1450	1550	1620	1650	1720	1750	1820	1850	1920	1950	2020	2050
Linz Hbf d.	0605	0635	0705	0735	0805	0835	0905	0935	1005	1035	1105	1205	1235	1305	1405	1435	1505	1605	1635	1705	1735	1805	1835	1905	1935	2005	2035	2105
Amstetten d.	0630	0700	0730	0800	0830	0900	0930	1000	1030	1100	1130	1230	1300	1330	1430	1500	1530	1630	1700	1730	1800	1830	1900	1930	2000	2030	2100	2130
St Pölten Hbf d.	0653	0723	0753	0823	0853	0923	0953	1023	1053	1123	1153	1253	1323	1353	1453	1523	1553	1653	1723	1753	1823	1853	1923	1953	2023	2053	2123	2153
Wien Hütteldorf a.	0713	0743	0813	0843	0913	0943	1013	1043	1113	1143	1213	1313	1343	1413	1513	1543	1613	1713	1743	1813	1843	1913	1943	2013	2043	2113	2143	2213
Wien Westbf a.	0720	0750	0820	0850	0920	0950	1020	1050	1120	1150	1220	1320	1350	1420	1520	1550	1620	1720	1750	1820	1850	1920	1950	2020	2050	2120	2150	2220

A – 🛏 1, 2 cl., 🛌 2 cl. and 🚃2 Wien - Zürich and v.v.; conveys 🛏 1, 2 cl., 🛌 2 cl. and 🚃2 (*NJ* **40466** / *NJ* **236**) Wien - Salzburg - Villach - Tarvisio 🏛 - Venezia and v.v.
B – From / to Budapest (Table **1250**).
D – KÁLMÁN IMRE – 🛏 1, 2 cl., 🛌 2 cl. and 🚃2 Budapest - Wien - Salzburg and v.v.
E – 🚃12 and ✕ Hamburg - Hannover - Nürnberg - Regensburg - Passau - Wien and v.v.
F – To / from Feldkirch on dates in Table **951**.
G – To / from Wörgl via Zell am See (Table **960**).
H – 🛏 1, 2 cl., 🛌 2 cl. and 🚃2 Wien - Hannover - Hamburg and v.v.; 🛏 1, 2 cl., 🛌 2 cl. and 🚃2 (**40490** / **50490**) Wien - Köln - Brussels / Amsterdam and v.v. (see Table **53**).
K – To / from Klagenfurt (Table **970**).
L – From / to Bratislava (Table **86**).
M – 🚃12 and ✕ (Frankfurt ⑥⑦ -) München - Wien - Budapest.
N – 🚃12 and ✕ Budapest - Wien - München (- Frankfurt ⑤⑥ **b**).
P – 🚃12 and ✕ Hamburg - Berlin - Erfurt - Nürnberg - Regensburg - Passau 🏛 - Wien and v.v.
Q – 🚃12 and ✕ Frankfurt - Nürnberg - Regensburg - Passau 🏛 - Wien and v.v.
R – 🚃12 and ✕ Dortmund - Frankfurt - Nürnberg - Regensburg - Passau 🏛 - Wien and v.v.
S – SALZKAMMERGUT – 🚃12 Wien - Attnang-Puchheim - Stainach-Irdning and v.v. (Table **961**).
T – To / from stations in Table **977**.
U – 🚃12 Wien - Nürnberg - Leipzig - Berlin - Rostock and v.v.
V – Conveys 🚃12 Wien - Bregenz (*RJ* **890**) - Ulm - Stuttgart - Frankfurt (Tables **912** and **933**).
W – Conveys 🚃12 Frankfurt - Stuttgart - Ulm - Bregenz (*RJ* **867**) - Wien (Tables **912** and **933**).
X – Conveys 🚃12 (*RJX* **184**) Bolzano - Innsbruck - Wien Hbf and v.v. (Tables **86**/**595**).
Y – Conveys 🚃12 (*RJX* **185**) Wien Hbf - Innsbruck - Bolzano and v.v. (Tables **86**/**595**).

a – Ⓐ only.
b – ⚒ from June 12.
c – For timings until Aug. 1 please see Table **890** on page 567.
e – Not Aug. 15, Nov. 1.
f – ①–⑥ (also June 5, Aug. 14, Oct. 30; not June 6, Aug. 15, Nov. 1).
h – ⑥ July 2 - Sep. 10.
j – Arrives 0709.
k – ⑦ (also June 6, Aug. 15, Nov. 1; not June 5, Aug. 14, Oct. 30).
p – Arrives 7 minutes earlier.
r – ⑤⑥.
t – ⚒ only.
v – From Aug. 2.
z – ⑧ (daily from Aug. 2).

★ – ⑤ from June 24 (also June 15, Dec. 7; not Dec. 9).
⊕ – ⑤⑥ from June 18 (also June 15, 16, Dec. 7; not Dec. 9) .
♠ – Runs daily Linz - Salzburg.
◧ – Change trains at Amstetten on Ⓐ.
◇ – Change trains at Amstetten on Ⓒ.
¶ – Train number **749** on ⑦.
⊙ – 🛏 1, 2 cl., 🛌 2 cl. and 🚃2 Budapest (**462**) - Salzburg (**466**) - Zürich.
⊖ – 🛏 1, 2 cl., 🛌 2 cl. and 🚃2 Zürich (**467**) - Salzburg (**463**) - Budapest.
♥ – Conveys 🛏 1, 2 cl., 🛌 2 cl. and 🚃2 .
❦ – See Table **985** for full service from / to Wien Flughafen ✈.
♣ – Ⓡ for journeys to / from Germany.
❖ – For timings of trains to / from Zürich, Bregenz and Innsbruck until Aug. 1 please see special version of Table **951** on pages 561 and 562.
‡ – Distance via the classic route. Trains calling at Tullnerfeld use the high-speed line between Wien and St Pölten.

SALZBURG and MÜNCHEN - INNSBRUCK - FELDKIRCH - BREGENZ - LINDAU 951

km	SEE NOTE ❖	NJ 466	EN 40462		NJ 464		NJ 446		RJ 666		RJX 366	RJ 668	IC 118	NJ 421	EC 81	RJX 368		RJX 660		EC 83	RJX 160		RJ 662		EC 85	RJX 162
										⚒				Ⓡ	⊕						D					U
		N	⊙	2	♦	2	N	2	✕	2	✕	✕	🍷♦	♦	A✕	✕	2	✕	2	A✕	R✕	2	F✕	2	A✕	B✕
	Wien Hbf **950** d.	2127	2327	...	...	...	2255	...	...	...	...	...	...	...	...	0530	...	0630	...	...	0730	...	0830	...	...	0930
	Linz Hbf **950** d.	2256	0100	...	...	...	0042	...	...	...	...	...	...	...	...	0646	...	0746	...	...	0846	...	0946	...	...	1046
0	**Salzburg** Hbf d.	0230	0230	...	...	...	0306	...	...	...	0556	0656	...	...	...	0756	...	0856	...	...	0956	...	1056	...	...	1156
	München Hbf **890** ‡ d.	|	|	...	...	...	|	...	...	...	|	|	...	0728	0734	|	...	|	...	0934	|	...	|	...	1134	|
	München Ost **890** ‡ d.	|	|	...	...	...	|	...	...	...	|	|	...	|	0744	|	...	|	...	0944	|	...	|	...	1144	|
⊖	Rosenheim .. **890** ‡ d.	|	|	...	...	...	|	...	...	...	|	|	...	0805	0813	|	...	|	...	1013	|	...	|	...	1213	|
120	Kufstein 🏛 ‡ d.	|	|	...	...	...	|	0539	...	0636	0709	|	...	0828	0836	0909	...	|	...	1036	1109	...	|	...	1236	1309
134	Wörgl Hbf **960** d.	|	|	...	...	...	|	0553	...	0649	0719	0817	...	0839	0846	0919	...	1015	...	1046	1119	...	1215	...	1246	1319
159	Jenbach **960** d.	|	|	...	...	...	|	0613	...	0709	|	0831	...	0855	0901	|	...	1029	...	1101	|	...	1229	...	1301	|
193	**Innsbruck** Hbf **960** a.	0423	0423	...	...	...	0519	0639	...	0740	0744	0846	...	0914	0918	0944	...	1044	...	1118	1144	...	1244	...	1318	1344
193	**Innsbruck** Hbf d.	0431	0431	...	0453	...	0523	...	0641	...	0747	▬	0854	...	...	0947	0952	1047	1052	...	1147	1152	1247	1252	...	1347
239	Ötztal d.	|	|	...	|	...	0551	...	0706	...	0812	...	0928	...	...	1012	1030	|	1127	...	1212	1230	|	1327	...	1412
248	Imst-Pitztal d.	|	|	...	|	...	0602	...	0716	...	|	...	0939	...	...	|	1041	1119	1139	...	|	1241	1319	1339	...	|
265	Landeck-Zams d.	0520	0520	...	0545	...	0622	...	0730	...	0833	...	0954	...	...	1033	1056	1133	1154	...	1233	1256	1333	1354	...	1433
293	St Anton am Arlberg d.	|	|	...	0616	...	0648	...	0754	...	0857	...	1022	...	...	1057	▬	|	...	...	1257	▬	|	...	...	1457
304	Langen am Arlberg d.	|	|	...	0626	...	0659	...	0804	...	|	...	1032	...	...	|	...	1204	...	...	|	...	1404	...	...	|
329	Bludenz **952** d.	0625	0625	0630	0706	...	0735	...	0831	...	0931	...	1102	...	...	1131	...	1231	...	...	1331	...	1431	...	...	1531
350	**Feldkirch** **952** a.	0637	0637	0645	0721	...	0749	...	0842	...	0942	2	1113	...	...	1142	2	1242	...	...	1342	2	1442	...	...	1542
350	**Feldkirch** **952** d.	0640	0640	0647	0738	0747	0754	...	0847	...	0944	0947	1115	...	...	1148	1147	1247	...	...	1348	1347	1447	...	...	1548
369	**Buchs** 🏛 **952** a.	0656	0656	|	0753	|	|	...	|	...	0959	|	|	...	...	1206	|	|	...	...	1406	|	|	...	...	1606
	Zürich HB **520** a.	0820	0820	|	0920	|	|	...	|	...	1120	|	|	...	...	1320	|	|	...	...	1520	|	|	...	...	1720
375	Dornbirn **952** d.	...	...	0709	...	0809	0821	...	0909	...	...	1009	1142	...	...	...	1209	1309	...	...	...	1409	1509	...	...	...
387	**Bregenz** 🏛 **952** a.	...	...	0718	...	0818	0829	...	0917	...	...	1018	1149	...	...	...	1218	1317	...	...	...	1418	1517	...	...	...
	Lindau Reutin 🏛 **952** a.	...	...	0728	...	0828	*0858*	...	*0929*	...	...	1028	1157	...	...	...	1228	*1329*	...	...	...	1428	*1529*	...	...	...
397	**Lindau**-Insel 🏛 **952** a.	...	...	0732	...	0832	*0903*	...	*0934*	...	...	1032	...	...	...	...	1232	*1334*	...	...	...	1432	*1534*	...	...	...

SEE NOTE ❖		RJX 860		EC 87	RJX 564	EC 164		RJ 1287	RJX 862	RJ 1287	ICE 1283	EC 89	RJX 166		RJX 864		EC 287	RJX 168		RJX 866	EC 289	RJX 760		RJX 868	RJX 762	
		T						⑥E		⑥E	⑥C		V					F								
	2◧	✕	2	A✕	F✕	✕♦	2	✕	F✕	✕	✕S	A✕	✕	2	F✕	2	✕	Y✕	2	F✕	✕	F✕	2	F✕	F✕	2
Wien Hbf **950** d.	...	0955	...	...	1130	...	...	...	1230	...	...	...	1330	...	1430	...	...	1530	...	1630	...	1730	...	1830	1930	...
Linz Hbf **950** d.	...	1131	...	...	1246	...	...	...	1346	...	...	...	1446	...	1546	...	...	1646	...	1746	...	1846	...	1946	2046	...
Salzburg Hbf d.	...	1256	...	...	1356	...	...	...	1456	...	...	...	1556	...	1656	...	...	1756	...	1856	...	1956	...	2056	2156	...
München Hbf **890** ‡ d.	...	|	...	1334	|	...	...	1427	|	...	1520	1534	|	...	|	...	1734	|	...	|	1934	|	...	|	|	...
München Ost **890** ‡ d.	...	|	...	1344	|	...	...	1437	|	...	|	1544	|	...	|	...	1744	|	...	|	1944	|	...	|	|	...
Rosenheim **890** ‡ d.	...	|	...	1413	|	...	...	1507	|	...	1601	1613	|	...	|	...	1813	|	...	|	2013	|	...	|	|	...
Kufstein 🏛 ‡ d.	...	|	...	1436	1509	...	...	1528	|	...	1622	1636	1709	...	|	...	1836	1909	...	|	2036	2109	2136	2209	2309	...
Wörgl Hbf **960** d.	...	1415	...	1446	1519	1502	...	1539	1615	...	1630	1646	1719	...	1815	...	1846	1919	...	2015	2046	2119	2154	2219	2319	...
Jenbach **960** d.	...	1429	...	1501	|	1518	...	1555	1629	...	▬	1701	|	...	1829	...	1901	|	...	2029	2101	|	2214	2233	2333	...
Innsbruck Hbf **960** a.	...	1444	...	1518	1544	1540	...	1615	1644	...	2	1718	1744	...	1844	...	1918	1944	...	2044	2118	2144	2240	2248	2348	...
Innsbruck Hbf d.	1352	1447	1452	...	...	1547	1552	1620	1647	...	1652	...	1747	1752	1847	1852	...	1947	...	2047	...	2147	...	...	...	0005
Ötztal d.	1430	|	1527	...	...	1612	1630	1652	|	...	1727	...	1812	1830	|	1927	...	2012	...	|	...	2212	...	...	...	0057
Imst-Pitztal d.	1441	1519	1539	...	...	|	1641	1702	1719	←	1739	...	|	1841	1919	1939	...	2022	...	2119	...	2222	...	...	...	0107
Landeck-Zams d.	1456	1533	1554	...	...	1633	1656	1715	1733	1738	1754	...	1833	1856	1933	1954	...	2036	...	2133	...	2236	...	...	...	0122
St Anton am Arlberg d.	▬	|	...	...	...	1657	▬	→	|	1806	...	...	1857	▬	|	...	...	2100	...	|	...	2300	...	...	...	...
Langen am Arlberg d.	...	1604	...	...	...	|	...	...	1804	1816	...	...	|	...	2004	...	...	|	...	2204	...	2310	...	...	...	...
Bludenz **952** d.	...	1631	...	...	...	1731	...	...	1831	1854	...	...	1931	...	2031	...	...	2134	...	2231	...	2337	...	...	...	...
Feldkirch **952** a.	2	1642	...	...	...	1742	2	...	1842	1805	...	...	1942	2	2042	...	...	2145	...	2242	...	2348	...	...	...	...
Feldkirch **952** d.	1547	1647	...	...	...	1744	1747	...	1847	...	...	...	1948	1947	2047	...	...	2148	2150	2247	...	2350	...	...	...	...
Buchs 🏛 **952** a.	|	|	...	...	...	1759	|	...	|	...	...	...	2006	|	|	...	...	2203	|	|	...	|	...	...	...	...
Zürich HB **520** a.	|	|	...	...	...	1920	|	...	|	...	...	...	2120	|	|	...	...	2320	|	|	...	|	...	...	...	...
Dornbirn **952** d.	1609	1709	...	...	...	...	1809	...	1909	...	...	...	...	2009	2109	...	...	...	2212	2309	...	0009	...	...	...	...
Bregenz 🏛 **952** a.	1618	1717	...	...	...	...	1818	...	1917	...	...	...	...	2018	2117	...	...	...	2221	2317	...	0017	...	...	...	...
Lindau Reutin 🏛 **952** a.	1628	1728	...	...	...	...	1828	...	*1929*	...	...	...	...	2028	*2129*	...	...	...	2231	*2329*	...	...	...	...	...	...
Lindau-Insel 🏛 **952** a.	1632	...	...	...	...	...	1832	...	*1934*	...	...	...	...	2032	*2134*	...	...	...	2236	*2332*	...	...	...	...	...	...

SEE NOTE ❖	RJX 269		RJX 763	RJX 861	RJX 861	EC 288	RJX 765	RJX 863	ICE 1282		RJX 161	EC 286		RJ 1286	RJ 865	RJ 1286			EC 163	RJX 563	EC 88		RJX 867		RJX 165	EC 86
				Ⓐ					⑥C		F			⑥E		⑥E							Z		W	
	✕B	2	F✕	F✕	F✕	✕	F✕	F✕	S✕	2	X✕	✕	2	✕	✕	✕		2	✕♦	F✕	A✕	2	F✕	2	B✕	A✕
Lindau-Insel 🏛 **952** d.	...	...	...	...	...	...	...	*0622*	...	0725	...	...	...	...	*0823*	...	...	0925	...	...	...	...	*1021*	1124	...	...
Lindau Reutin 🏛 **952** d.	...	...	...	...	...	...	...	*0626*	...	0729	...	...	...	...	*0827*	...	...	0929	...	...	...	...	1031	1129	...	...
Bregenz 🏛 **952** d.	...	...	...	0437	...	...	0548	0639	...	0740	...	...	...	...	0840	...	...	0940	...	...	...	...	1040	1140	...	...
Dornbirn **952** d.	...	...	...	0446	...	...	0557	0652	...	0751	...	...	...	...	0851	...	...	0951	...	...	...	...	1051	1151	...	...
Zürich HB **520** d.	...	...	...	|	...	...	|	|	...	|	0640	...	...	...	|	...	...	|	0840	...	...	...	|	|	1040	...
Buchs 🏛 **952** d.	...	...	...	|	...	...	|	|	...	|	0754	...	...	...	|	...	...	|	1000	...	...	...	|	|	1154	...
Feldkirch **952** a.	...	...	...	0500	...	...	0611	0712	...	0812	0809	...	...	...	0912	...	...	1012	1015	...	...	...	1112	1212	1209	...
Feldkirch **952** d.	...	...	...	0502	...	...	0613	0717	...	▬	0817	...	...	0850	0917	...	...	▬	1017	...	...	...	1117	▬	1217	...
Bludenz **952** d.	...	...	...	0515	...	...	0626	0730	...	...	0830	...	...	0905	0930	...	...	...	1030	...	...	...	1130	...	1230	...
Langen am Arlberg d.	...	...	...	|	...	...	0652	0756	...	...	|	...	...	0937	0956	...	...	...	|	...	...	...	1156	...	|	...
St Anton am Arlberg d.	...	...	...	0548	...	...	0703	|	...	2	0903	...	...	0948	|	...	...	2	1103	...	...	...	|	2	1303	...
Landeck-Zams d.	...	0430	...	0613	...	...	0727	0827	...	0901	0927	...	1001	1017	1027	←	...	1101	1127	...	...	1201	1227	1301	1327	...
Imst-Pitztal d.	...	0445	...	0627	...	...	0740	0840	...	0917	|	...	1020	1033	1040	1048	...	1118	|	...	...	1220	1240	1318	|	...
Ötztal d.	...	0504	...	0638	...	...	0751	|	...	0931	0948	...	1031	→	|	1107	...	1131	1148	...	...	1231	|	1331	1348	...
Innsbruck Hbf a.	...	0553	...	0706	...	...	0814	0911	...	1006	1011	...	1106	...	1111	1136	...	1206	1211	...	...	1306	1311	1406	1411	...
Innsbruck Hbf **960** d.	0510	0558	0610	0713	0713	0717	0817	0914	...	...	1017	1040	...	...	1114	1146	...	...	1221	1217	1240	...	1314	...	1417	1440
Jenbach **960** d.	0527	0631	0627	0730	0730	0735	|	0931	...	...	|	1101	...	...	1131	1206	...	...	1244	|	1301	...	1331	...	|	1501
Wörgl Hbf **960** d.	0541	...	0641	0745	0745	0749	0843	0945	1025	...	1043	1116	...	...	1145	1222	...	...	1257	1243	1316	...	1345	...	1443	1516
Kufstein 🏛 ‡ d.	0551	...	0651	|	|	0759	0853	|	1037	...	1053	1126	...	...	|	1232	...	...	...	1253	1326	...	|	...	1453	1526
Rosenheim **890** ‡ a.	|	...	|	|	|	0818	|	|	1057	...	|	1145	...	...	|	|	...	...	...	|	1345	...	|	...	|	1545
München Ost. **890** ‡ a.	|	...	|	|	|	0849	|	|	|	...	|	1215	...	...	|	1322	...	...	...	|	1416	...	|	...	|	1616
München Hbf. **890** ‡ a.	|	...	|	|	|	0902	|	|	1134	...	|	1226	...	...	|	1333	...	...	...	|	1427	...	|	...	|	1627
Salzburg Hbf a.	0702	...	0802	0902	0902	...	1003	1102	...	...	1203	...	...	...	1302	...	...	...	...	1403	...	...	1502	...	1603	...
Linz Hbf **950** a.	0814	...	0914	1014	1014	...	1114	1214	...	...	1314	...	...	...	1429	...	...	...	...	1514	...	...	1614	...	1714	...
Wien Hbf **950** a.	0930	...	1030	1130	1130	...	1230	1330	...	...	1430	...	...	...	1605	...	...	...	...	1630	...	...	1730	...	1830	...

♦ – **NOTES** (LISTED BY TRAIN NUMBER)

118 – BODENSEE – [12] Innsbruck - Lindau - Stuttgart - Köln - Dortmund.

163/4 – TRANSALPIN – [12] and ✕ Zürich - Kitzbühel - Schwarzach - Graz and v.v.

421 – 🛏 1, 2 cl., ▬ 2 cl. and [2] Amsterdam / Brussels / Düsseldorf - Innsbruck; 🛏 1, 2 cl., ▬ 2 cl. and [2] (**40491**) Hamburg - Innsbruck.

464 – 🛏 1, 2 cl., ▬ 2 cl. and [2] Graz - Schwarzach - Zürich; 🛏 1, 2 cl., ▬ 2 cl. and [2] (*EN* **40414**) Zagreb - Ljubljana - Villach - Schwarzach - Zürich.

A – To Verona, Bologna or Venezia via Brennero (Table **70**).
B – From / to Budapest (Table **1250**).
C – ⑥ July 16 - Oct. 15.
D – On ①–⑥ (not Aug. 15, Nov. 1) conveys [12] (*RJ* **560**) Flughafen Wien - Wien Hbf - Innsbruck (- Feldkirch ⑤⑥ **v**).
E – ⑥ July 16 - Sep. 10.
F – From / to Flughafen Wien ✈ (Table **950**).
N – Conveys 🛏 1, 2 cl., ▬ 2 cl. and [2].
R – From Bratislava (Table **86**).
S – To / from Schwarzach (Table **960**).

T – Conveys [12] Wien - Bregenz (*RJ* **890**) - Ulm - Stuttgart - Frankfurt (Tables **912** and **933**).
U – Conveys [12] (*RJX* **562**) Flughafen Wien - Wien Hbf - Innsbruck (- Feldkirch ⑤–⑦ **z**).
V – Conveys [12] (*RJX* **566**) Flughafen Wien - Wien Hbf - Innsbruck (- Feldkirch ⑧ **t**).
W – Conveys [12] (*RJX* **565**) (Feldkirch ⑥⑦ **r** -) Innsbruck - Wien Hbf - Flughafen Wien.
X – Conveys [12] (*RJX* **184**) Bolzano - Innsbruck - Wien Hbf (Tables **86**/**595**).
Y – Conveys [12] (*RJX* **185**) Wien Hbf - Innsbruck - Bolzano (Tables **86**/**595**).
Z – Conveys [12] Frankfurt - Stuttgart - Ulm - Bregenz (*RJ* **867**) - Wien (Tables **912** and **933**).

r – Also June 6, 16; not June 5, Aug. 14.
t – Not June 14, Aug. 14, Dec. 7.
v – Also June 5, 6, 12, 15, 16, 19, 26, 29, Dec. 7; not June 17, Dec. 9.
z – Also June 6, 15, 16, Aug. 15, Nov. 1, Dec. 7; not June 17, Aug. 14, Oct. 30, Dec. 9.

⊕ – Train number **1281** on ⑥⑦.
⊙ – 🛏 1, 2 cl., ▬ 2 cl. and [2] Budapest (**462**) - Salzburg (**466**) - Zürich. Also conveys through cars from Praha (see Table **52**).
⊖ – Rosenheim - Kufstein is *34 km*.
❖ – For amended service until Aug. 1 please see page 561.
‡ – See note on page 452 for other regional services Kufstein - München and v.v.

951 LINDAU - BREGENZ - FELDKIRCH - INNSBRUCK - MÜNCHEN and SALZBURG

SEE NOTE ❖		RJX 869		RJX 167 E	EC 84		RJX 661 ⑦	RJ 769 ①–⑥		RJX 169	EC 86	IC 119	RJX 663		RJX 367	EC 80 ⊕	NJ 420 Ⓡ	RJX 667		RJX 369		NJ 447	NJ 465		EN 40467	NJ 467
	2	F✕	2	R✕	A✕	2	t✕	w✕	2	✕	A✕	🍷♦	✕	2	✕	A✕	♦	✕	2	✕	2	N	♦	2	⊙	N
Lidau-Insel 🏛 .....952 d.	...	1223	1325	...	...	...	1423	1423	1525	...	...	...	...	1722	...	...	...	1823	1925	...	...	2056	...	2225	...	...
Lindau Reutin 🏛 .952 d.	...	1227	1329	...	...	...	1427	1427	1529	...	...	1558	...	1729	...	...	...	1827	1929	...	...	2103	...	2229	...	...
Bregenz 🏛 ....952 d.	...	1240	1340	...	...	...	1440	1440	1540	...	...	1606	...	1740	...	...	...	1840	1940	...	...	2140	...	2240	...	...
Dornbirn ....952 d.	...	1251	1351	...	...	...	1451	1451	1551	...	...	1617	...	1751	...	...	...	1851	1951	...	...	2151	...	2251	...	...
Zürich HB 520 .... d.	...	|	|	1240	...	...	|	|	|	1440	...	|	...	|	1640	...	...	|	|	1840	...	|	2040	|	2140	2140
Buchs 🏛 ....952 d.	...	|	|	1354	...	...	|	|	|	1554	...	|	...	|	1800	...	...	|	|	1954	...	|	2205	|	2305	2305
Feldkirch ....952 a.	...	1312	1412	1409	...	...	1512	1512	1612	1609	...	1634	...	1812	1815	...	...	1912	2012	2009	...	2216	2220	2314	2321	2321
Feldkirch ....952 d.	...	1317	▬	1417	...	...	1517	1517	▬	1617	...	1637	...	▬	1817	...	...	1917	▬	2017	...	2227	2245	2329	2324	2324
Bludenz ....952 d.	...	1330	...	1430	...	...	1530	1530	...	1630	...	1656	...	...	1830	...	...	1930	...	2030	...	2242	2301	...	2340	2340
Langen am Arlberg .... d.	...	1356	...	|	...	...	1556	1556	...	|	...	1728	...	...	|	...	...	1956	...	|	...	2310	2335	...	|	|
St Anton am Arlberg .. d.	...	|	2	1503	...	...	|	|	2	1703	...	1738	...	2 ©	1903	...	...	2007	...	2103	...	2320	2345	...	|	|
Landeck - Zams .... d.	1401	1427	1501	1527	...	1601	1627	1627	1701	1727	...	1805	...	1901	1927	...	...	2031	...	2127	...	2348	0009	...	0036	0036
Imst-Pitztal .... d.	1420	1440	1518	|	...	1620	1640	1640	1718	|	...	1821	...	1918	1940	...	...	2044	...	2140	...	0002	|	...	|	|
Ötztal .... d.	1431	|	1531	1548	...	1631	|	|	1731	1748	...	1835	...	1931	1951	...	...	2055	...	2151	...	0013	|	...	|	|
Innsbruck Hbf .... a.	1506	1511	1606	1611	...	1706	1711	1711	1806	1811	...	1905	...	2006	2014	...	...	2118	2	2214	...	0039	0054	...	0120	0120
Innsbruck Hbf.....960 d.	...	1514	...	1617	1640	...	1714	1714	...	1817	1840	...	1914	...	2017	2040	2044	...	2135	2217	2235	0044	...	...	0128	0128
Jenbach ....960 d.	...	1531	...	|	1701	...	1731	1731	...	|	1901	...	1931	...	|	2101	2106	...	2209	|	2309	|	...	...	|	|
Wörgl Hbf ....960 d.	...	1545	...	1643	1716	...	1745	1745	...	1843	1916	...	1945	...	2043	2116	2123	...	2235	2243	2335	|	...	...	|	|
Kufstein 🏛 ....‡ d.	...	|	...	1653	1726	...	|	|	...	1853	1926	...	|	...	2053	2126	2135	...	2248	2253	2348	|	...	...	|	|
Rosenheim .... 890 ‡ a.	...	|	...	|	1745	...	|	|	...	|	1945	...	|	...	|	2145	2156	...	...	|	...	|	...	...	|	|
München Ost 890 ‡ a.	...	|	...	|	1816	...	|	|	...	|	2014	...	|	...	|	2215	|	...	...	|	...	|	...	...	|	|
München Hbf 890 ‡ a.	...	|	...	|	1827	...	|	|	...	|	2026	...	|	...	|	2227	2238	...	...	|	...	|	...	...	|	|
Salzburg Hbf .... a.	...	1702	...	1802	...	...	1902	1902	...	2003	...	...	2104	...	2206	...	...	...	...	0003	...	0255	...	...	0322	0322
Linz Hbf 950 .... a.	...	1814	...	1914	...	...	2014	2029	...	2114	...	...	2214	...	2317	...	...	...	...	...	...	0444	...	...	0452	0604
Wien Hbf 950 .... a.	...	1930	...	2030	...	...	2130	2205	...	2230	...	...	2330	...	0033	...	...	...	...	...	...	0658	...	...	0634	0758

♦ – **NOTES** (LISTED BY TRAIN NUMBER)

119 – BODENSEE – (12) Dortmund - Köln - Stuttgart - Lindau - Innsbruck.

420 – 🛏 1,2 cl., ▬ 2 cl. and (2) Innsbruck - Frankfurt - Düsseldorf - Amsterdam; 🛏 1,2 cl., ▬ 2 cl. and (2) (**40420**) Innsbruck - Hamburg.

465 – 🛏 1,2 cl., ▬ 2 cl. and (2) Zürich - Schwarzach - Graz; ▬ 1,2 cl., ▬ 2 cl. and (2) (*EN* **40465**) Zürich - Schwarzach - Villach - Ljubljana - Zagreb.

A – From Verona or Venezia via Brennero (Table **70**).

E – On ①②③④⑦ conveys (12) (*RJX* **567**) (Feldkirch ⑦ **v** -) Innsbruck - Wien Hbf - Flughafen Wien.

F – To Flughafen Wien ✈ (Table **950**).

N – Conveys 🛏 1,2 cl., ▬ 2 cl. and (2).

R – To Bratislava (Table **86**).

t – Also Nov. 1; not Aug. 14, Oct. 30.

v – Also June 3, 4, 6, 16, Nov. 1; not Aug. 14, Oct. 30.

w – Also Aug. 14, Oct. 30; not Aug. 10, 15, Nov.1.

⊕ – Train number **1280** on ⑥⑦.

⊙ – 🛏 1,2 cl., ▬ 2 cl. and (2) Zürich (**467**) - Salzburg (**463**) - Budapest. Also conveys through cars to Praha (see Table **52**).

❖ – For service until Aug. 1 please see page 562.

‡ – Additional local services run München - Rosenheim - Kufstein and v.v. (branded *Meridian*, operated by Bayerische Oberlandbahn). Journey: 73–80 minutes.
From München at 0640, 0743, 0843 and hourly until 2043 (also Rosenheim to Kufstein at 0039, 2235 and 2335).
From Kufstein at 0600, 0702, 0801 and hourly until 1902 (also Kufstein to Rosenheim at 1959, 2058, 2158 and 2258).

952 VORARLBERG LOCAL SERVICES

2nd class only (except where shown)

BLUDENZ - BREGENZ - LINDAU ⊖ △

Bludenz ....d.	0439	0600	0656	0730	0800	0809	0900	1000	1009	1200	1209	1300	1400	1409	1500	1600	1609	1700	1800	1809	1900	2000	2039	2139	2209	2309	0039
Feldkirch ....d.	0500	0617	0715	0747	0817	0830	0917	1017	1030	1217	1230	1317	1417	1430	1517	1617	1630	1717	1817	1830	1917	2017	2100	2200	2230	2330	0100
Dornbirn ....d.	0529	0639	0739	0809	0839	0859	0939	1039	1059	1239	1259	1339	1439	1459	1539	1639	1659	1739	1839	1859	1939	2039	2129	2229	2259	2359	0129
Bregenz 🏛.......d.	0545	0649	0748	0819	0849	0920c	0949	1049	1115	1249	1320c	1349	1449	1520c	1549	1649	1715	1749	1849	1920c	1949	2049	2145	2245	2320c	0014	0144
Lindau Reutin 🏛 a.	0554	0658	...	0828	0858	0929	0958	1058	1125	1258	1329	1358	1458	1529	1558	1658	1724	1758	1858	1929	1958	2058	2154f	2254	2329	...	...
Lindau Insel 🏛 a.	0559	0703	...	0832	0903	0934	1003	1103	1131	1303	1334	1403	1503	1534	1604	1703	1730	1803	1903	1934	2003	2104	2204	2259	2332	...	...

Lindau Insel 🏛 d.	0552	0621	0655	0754	0823	0855	0955	1021	1055	1154	1223	1255	1355	1423	1455	1556	1625	1655	1755	1823	1855	1955	2026	2127	2225	2259	2329
Lindau Reutin 🏛 d.	0559	0626	0659	0759	0827	0859	0959	1024	1059	1159	1227	1259	1359	1427	1459	1603	1629	1659	1759	1827	1859	1959	2033	2133	2229	2303	2333
Bregenz 🏛.......d.	0611	0644e	0711	0811	0844e	0911	1011	1044e	1111	1211	1244e	1311	1411	1444e	1511	1614	1640	1711	1811	1844e	1911	2011	2044	2144	2240	2314	2344
Dornbirn ....d.	0621	0700	0721	0821	0900	0921	1021	1100	1121	1221	1300	1321	1421	1500	1521	1630	1651	1721	1821	1900	1921	2021	2100	2200	2251	2330	0000
Feldkirch ....d.	0644	0731	0744	0844	0931	0944	1044	1131	1144	1244	1331	1344	1444	1531	1544	1701	1714	1744	1844	1931	1944	2044	2131	2231	2314	0001	0031
Bludenz ....a.	0659	0751	0759	0859	0951	0959	1059	1151	1159	1259	1351	1359	1459	1551	1559	1721	1729	1802	1859	1951	1959	2059	2151	2251	2329	0021	0051

ST MARGRETHEN - BREGENZ - LINDAU △

km							EC 97				EC 99				EC 191				EC 193							
					Ⓐ		♥		Ⓐ		♥		Ⓐ		♥		Ⓐ		♥		Ⓐ		Ⓐ		Ⓐ	
0	St Margrethen 🏛 ...... d.	0550	0625	0655	0725	0755	0851	0855	0925	0955	1051	1055	1125	1155	1251	1255	1325	1355	1451	1455	1525	1555	1625	1655	1725	1755
12	Bregenz 🏛 .... a.	0610	0640	0710	0740	0810	0900	0910	0940	1010	1102	1110	1140	1210	1300	1310	1340	1410	1500	1510	1540	1610	1640	1710	1740	1810
20	Lindau Reutin 🏛 .... a.	0624	0658	0728	0754	0828	0908	0929	0958	1028	1108	1125	...	1228	1308	1329	1358	1428	1508	1529	1558	1628	1658	1724	1758	1828
22	Lindau Insel 🏛 .... a.	0629	0703	0732	0802	0832	0924	0934	1003	1032	1124	1131	...	1232	1324	1334	1403	1432	1524	1534	1604	1632	1703	1730	1803	1832

		EC 197				EC 199					
	Ⓐ	♥		Ⓐ		♥					
St Margrethen 🏛 .... d.	1825	1851	1855	1925	1955	2051	2055	2155	2255	2355	0025
Bregenz 🏛 .... a.	1840	1902	1910	1940	2010	2100	2110	2210	2310	0010	0040
Lindau Reutin 🏛 .... a.	1858	1908	1929	1958	2028	2108	2129	2231	2329	...	...
Lindau Insel 🏛 .... a.	1903	1924	1934	2003	2032	2124	2134	2236	2332	...	...

									EC 198		
					Ⓐ		Ⓐ		♥		Ⓐ
Lindau Insel 🏛 ...... d.	...	...	0552	0621	0655	0725	0754	0824	0837	0925	0955
Lindau Reutin 🏛 .... d.	...	...	0559	0626	0659	0729	0759	0827	0852	0929	0959
Bregenz 🏛 .... d.	0517	0542	0617	0647	0717	0747	0817	0847	0900	0947	1017
St Margrethen 🏛 ... a.	0534	0559	0634	0704	0734	0804	0834	0904	0909	1004	1034

		EC 196								EC 192			EC 190						EC 98				EC 96			
		♥		Ⓐ		Ⓐ		Ⓐ		♥		Ⓐ		♥	Ⓐ		Ⓐ		♥	Ⓐ			♥			
Lindau Insel 🏛 .... d.	1021	1037	1124	1154	1223	1255	1325	1355	1423	1437	1525	1556	1625	1637	1655	1722	1755	1823	1837	1855	1925	2026	2037	2127	2225	2329
Lindau Reutin 🏛 .... d.	1024	1052	1129	1159	1227	1259	1329	1359	1427	1452	1529	1603	1629	1652	1659	1729	1759	1827	1852	1859	1929	2033	2052	2133	2229	2333
Bregenz 🏛 .... d.	1047	1100	1147	1217	1247	1317	1347	1417	1447	1500	1547	1617	1647	1700	1717	1747	1817	1847	1900	1917	1947	2047	2100	2147	2247	2347
St Margrethen 🏛 .... a.	1104	1109	1204	1234	1304	1334	1404	1434	1504	1509	1604	1634	1704	1709	1734	1804	1834	1904	1909	1934	2004	2104	2109	2204	2304	0004

FELDKIRCH - BUCHS ⊖

km		A	A	AB	A	A		A	A	A	A	
0	Feldkirch .... d.	0533	0649	0714	0745	0849	...	1612	1645	1715	1815	...
16	Schaan-Vaduz d.	0552	0708	0733	0806	0908	...	1634	1704	1734	1834	...
19	Buchs 🏛 .... a.	0555	0711	0736	0809	0911	...	1637	1707	1737	1837	...

	A	A	A		A		A	A	A	A	A
Buchs 🏛 .... d.	0617	0716	0819	...	1234	...	1619	1649	1719	1819	1849
Schaan-Vaduz .... d.	0620	0719	0822	...	1237	...	1622	1652	1722	1822	1852
Feldkirch .... a.	0639	0737	0841	...	1256	...	1641	1711	1741	1841	1911

BLUDENZ - SCHRUNS ⊡

Operated by Montafonerbahn.

km		©	Ⓐ																		
0	Bludenz ....d.	0053	0535	...	0602	...	0632	...	0702	0735	0805	and at the same	1805	1835	1935	...	2035	2135	...	2245	2353
6	St. Anton im Montafon ....d.	0102	0544	...	0611	...	0641	...	0711	0744	0814	minutes past	1814	1844	1944	...	2044	2144	...	2254	0002
12	Schruns ....a.	0112	0554	...	0621	...	0651	...	0721	0754	0824	each hour until	1824	1854	1954	...	2054	2154	...	2304	0012

	©		Ⓐ																	
Schruns ....d.	0018	...	0504	...	0534	0601	...	0631	0701	0734	0804	and at the same	1834	1904	2004	...	2104	...	2204	...	2312
St. Anton im Montafon ....d.	0028	...	0514	...	0544	0611	...	0641	0711	0744	0814	minutes past	1844	1914	2014	...	2114	...	2214	...	2322x
Bludenz ....a.	0037	...	0523	...	0553	0620	...	0650	0720	0753	0823	each hour until	1853	1923	2023	...	2123	...	2223	...	2331

A – ①–⑤ (not Oct. 26).

B – From Bludenz (d. 0647).

c – Arrives 6 minutes earlier.

e – Arrives 7–8 minutes earlier.

f – Departs 6 minutes later.

x – Calls on request.

♥ – (12) and ✕ Zürich - München and v.v. See Table **75**.

⊖ – Selected local trains. See also Table **951**.

△ – Austrian holiday dates apply.

⊡ – Certain services run as through trains from / to Bregenz or Lindau.

LANDECK - NAUDERS - SCUOL and MALLES — 954

Landeck - Nauders and Martina

Route 210												Ⓐ					
Landeck - Zams Bahnhof d.	0655	0805	0858	1005	1058	1217	1258	1405	1458	1605	1652	1707	1810	1910	...	...	...
Ried im Oberinntal (Gemeindeamt) d.	0718	0828	0923	1028	1123	1240	1323	1428	1523	1628	1715	1730	1833	1933	...	...	...
Martina cunfin 🏛 a.	|	|	0956	|	1156	|	1356	|	1556	|	1756	|	|	|	...	...	...
Nauders Mühle a.	0800	0910	...	1110	...	1322	...	1510	...	1710	...	1812	1915	2015	...	...	...
Nauders Mühle d.	0607	0644	...	0847	...	1047	...	1247	...	1447	...	1647	...	1847	...	...	...
Martina cunfin 🏛 d.	|	|	...	|	1000	|	1200	|	1400	|	1600	|	1800	|	...	...	...
Ried im Oberinntal (Gemeindeamt) d.	0647	0727	...	0927	1032	1127	1232	1327	1432	1527	1632	1727	1832	1927	...	...	...
Landeck - Zams Bahnhof a.	0707	0747	...	0947	1052	1147	1252	1347	1452	1547	1652	1747	1852	1947	...	...	...

Scuol Tarasp - Nauders - Malles

Routes 273/921												
Scuol Tarasp Staziun d.	0630	...	0730	...	and at	1730	...	1830	...	2030	...	...
Martina cunfin 🏛 d.	0655	0705	0755	0805	the same	1755	1805	1855	1910	2101	2010	2110
Nauders Mühle 🏛 d.	...	0716	...	0816	minutes	...	1816	...	1921	...	2021	2121
Reschenpass/Passo di Resia 🏛 d.	...	0720	...	0820	past each	...	1820	...	1925	...	2025	2125
Resia d.	...	0723	...	0823	hour until	...	1823	...	1928	...	2028	2128
Malles Stazione **597** a.	...	0753	...	0853		...	1853	...	1958	...	2058	2158
Malles Stazione **597** d.	0601	...	0701	...	and at	1801	...	1901	...	2001	...	...
Resia d.	0631	...	0731	...	the same	1831	...	1931	...	2031	...	...
Passo di Resia/Reschenpass 🏛 d.	0634	...	0734	...	minutes	1834	...	1934	...	2034	...	...
Nauders Mühle 🏛 d.	0638	...	0738	...	past each	1838	...	1938	...	2038	...	...
Martina cunfin 🏛 d.	0649	0701	0749	0801	hour until	1849	1901	1949	...	2049	2101	...
Scuol Tarasp Staziun a.	...	0727	...	0827		...	1927	...	...	...	2133	...

Operators

Landeck - Nauders: Tioler Linien Bus GmbH, Nauders. ✆ +43 (0)664 384 1360.

Scuol Tarasp - Martina: Auto Da Posta, Svizra. CH-7550 Scuol. ✆ +41 (0)58 453 28 28.

Martina - Nauders - Malles: Servizi Autobus Dolomiti (SAD). Corso Italia 13N, I-39100 Bolzano. ✆ +39 0471 450 111.

2nd class only Narrow gauge Zillertalbahn * JENBACH - MAYRHOFEN — 955

km																	🚂 A
0	**Jenbach** Zillertalbahnhof § d.	0630	0652	0748	0811	0841	0911	0941	and at	1711	1741	1811	1841	1858	2007		0944
11	Fügen-Hart d.	0646	0709	0806	0826	0856	0926	0956	the same	1726	1756	1826	1856	1913	2022		1014
17	Kaltenbach-Stumm d.	0656	0720	0817	0837	0907	0937	1007	minutes	1737	1807	1837	1907	1924	2033	also	1031
21	Aschau im Zillertal d.	0703	0727	0823	0843	0913	0943	1013	past each	1743	1813	1843	1913	1930	2039		1046
25	**Zell am Ziller** d.	0710	0735	0830	0850	0920	0950	1020	hour until	1750	1820	1850	1920	1937	2046		1057
32	**Mayrhofen** a.	0722	0747	0841	0901	0931	1001	1031		1801	1831	1901	1931	1948	2057		1116

	Ⓒ	Ⓐ															🚂 A
Mayrhofen d.	0546	0552	0610	0635	0734	0819	0849	and at	1619	1649	1719	1749	1819	1909	1949		1205
Zell am Ziller d.	0557	0601x	0621	0647	0744	0831	0901	the same	1631	1701	1731	1801	1831	1921	2001		1222
Aschau im Zillertal d.	0603	0606x	0627	0653	0750	0837	0907	minutes	1637	1707	1737	1807	1837	1926	2006	also	1239
Kaltenbach-Stumm d.	0610	0611x	0634	0659	0757	0843	0913	past each	1643	1713	1743	1813	1843	1933	2013		1249
Fügen-Hart d.	0620	0621x	0646	0710	0807	0854	0925	hour until	1654	1725	1754	1825	1854	1944	2023		1311
Jenbach Zillertalbahnhof § a.	0637	0636	0704	0727	0823	0910	0940		1710	1740	1810	1840	1910	1959	2038		1334

A – June 4–5; ②–⑥ June 7 - Aug. 31; ②–⑦ Sept. 1 - Oct. 2.

x – Trains call on request.

🚂 – Steam train. Special fares apply.

§ – Adjacent to ÖBB station.

* – Zillertaler Vehrkehrsbetriebe, Austraße 1, A-6200 Jenbach. ✆ +43 (0)5244 606 0.

2nd class only Achenseebahn JENBACH - ACHENSEE — 956

Narrow gauge rack railway operated by steam locomotives (special fares apply). *7 km.* Journey time 42–50 minutes. **Service April 30 - October 30, 2022**

Operator: Achenseebahn AG, A-6200 Jenbach: ✆ +43 (0)5244 62243, Fax +43 (0)5244 622435. Jenbach Achensee Bf is adjacent to the ÖBB station.

⑥⑦ Apr. 30 - June 5 (also May 26, 27, June 6, 7); daily except ② June 9–24; daily except ② Sept. 19 - Oct. 3; Ⓒ Oct. 8–30:
From Jenbach Achensee Bf at 1100, 1315, 1530. **From Achnsee Seespitz Bahnstation** at: 1210, 1425, 1635.

Daily except ② June 25 - Sept. 18:
From Jenbach Achensee Bf at 0955, 1053, 1210, 1410, 1529. **From Achnsee Seespitz Bahnstation** at: 1113, 1308, 1430, 1549, 1638.

2nd class only ZELL AM SEE - KRIMML and 🚌 KRIMML - MAYRHOFEN — 957

ZELL AM SEE - KRIMML ⊡

km						Ⓐ				Ⓐ	Ⓒ			T 🚂		
0	**Zell am See** Lokalbahn d.	0630	0800	and	1600	1650	1700	1800	1900	2000	2050	...		0918	...	...
29	Mittersill d.	0723	0848	hourly	1648	1727	1748	1848	1948	2048	2134	...	also	1108j	...	...
39	Bramberg d.	0737	0903	until	1703	1739	1803	1903	2003	2103	2147	...		1131	...	...
53	**Krimml** a.	0756	0923		1723	1756	1823	1923	2023	2123	2205	...		1202	...	...

		Ⓐ	Ⓐ										T 🚂		
Krimml d.	0533	0603	0628	0640	0733	and	1533	1633	1733	1833	...		1355	...	...
Bramberg d.	0552	0622	0644	0658	0752	hourly	1552	1652	1752	1852	...	also	1420	...	...
Mittersill d.	0608	0638	0656	0720	0808	until	1608	1708	1808	1908	...		1520k	...	...
Zell am See Lokalbahn a.	0655	0725	0738	0807	0855		1655	1755	1855	1955	...		1637	...	...

🚌 Krimml Bahnhof - Krimml Wasserfälle and v.v. Route 670. *3 km.* Journey time: 5–8 minutes.

From Krimml Bahnhof at 0830, 0929 and hourly until 1829, 1930Ⓐ, 2200Ⓐ.

From Krimml Wasserfälle at 0537 Ⓐ, 0620, 0823, 0900 Ⓐ, 1010, 1023 and hourly until 1823.

Additional buses also run at irregular intervals.

🚌 routes **673** and **4094**: KRIMML - KÖNIGSLEITEN - MAYRHOFEN *Winter service December 12, 2021 - April 18, 2022.*

km											
0	**Krimml** Bahnhof d.	...	...	...	...	...	...	...	...	...	...
3	Krimml Wasserfälle d.	...	...	...	...	...	...	...	...	...	...
16	Königsleiten Almdorf d.	...	1000	...	1120	1303	...	1428	...	1523	1703
25	**Gerlos** Gasthaus Oberwirt d.	...	1011	...	1141	1321	...	1446	...	1541	1721
45	Zell am Ziller Bahnhof **955** a.	...	1047	...	1217	1357	...	1522	...	1617	1757
53	**Mayrhofen** Bahnhof **955** a.	...	...	...	...	1408	...	...	...	...	1806

Mayrhofen Bahnhof **955** d.	0845	...	0945	...	...	...	...	...	...	...
Zell am Ziller Bahnhof **955** d.	0900	...	1000	...	1105	...	...	...	1600	...
Gerlos Gasthaus Oberwirt d.	0931	...	1031	...	1141	...	...	...	1636	...
Königsleiten Almdorf d.	0951	...	1051	...	1201	...	...	...	1647	...
Krimml Wasserfälle a.	...	...	...	...	...	...	...	...	...	...
Krimml Bahnhof a.	...	...	...	...	...	...	...	...	...	...

T – ④ May 20 - Sept. 23 (also Sept. 11).

j – Arrives 1038.
k – Arrives 1440.

🚂 – Steam train with special fares. A Christmas and New Year service also operates.
⊡ – Narrow gauge railway. **Operator**: Pinzgauer Lokalbahn. Trains call at Mittersill and Bramberg on request only. **Warning!** Following flood damage, rail services are replaced by 🚌 Niedernsill (km15) - Krimml and v.v. until further notice (in similar timings).

960 SALZBURG - SCHWARZACH - INNSBRUCK

km		NJ 464 A	2	Ⓐ 2	⚒ 2	⚒ 2	2	Ⓒ 2	⑥ 2	Ⓒ 2	Ⓐ 2	Ⓐ 2	IC 894 ✕⊖	2	2	ICE 1282 ⑥K ✕	2	IC 898 ⊖	2	2	2	RJ 111 ✕⊖	2	2	2
	Wien Hbf **950** d.	...	...	...	...	...	...	...	...	...	...	...	...	...	...	...	...	...	...	...	...	...	...	...	...
0	**Salzburg** Hbf. **951 970 975** ‡ d.	...	...	...	...	...	...	0411	...	...	0430	...	0612	...	...	...	0708	0812	...	...	0908	1012	...	...	1108
29	Golling-Abtenau **970** ‡ d.	...	...	...	...	...	...	0449	...	...	0454	...	0633	...	...	...	0734	0833	...	...	0934	1033	...	...	1134
53	**Bischofshofen** **970 975** ‡ d.	0158	...	...	...	...	...	0513	...	...	0518	...	0654	...	...	...	0756	0854	...	...	0956	1054	...	...	1156
61	St Johann im Pongau **970** ‡ d.	|	...	...	...	...	...	0523	...	...	0528	...	0703	...	...	...	0804	0903	...	...	1004	1103	...	...	1204
67	**Schwarzach - St Veit** **970** ‡ a.	0211	...	...	...	...	...	0529	...	...	0534	...	0709	...	...	...	0810	0909	...	...	1010	1109	...	...	1210
67	**Schwarzach - St Veit** d.	0232	...	...	...	...	...	0531	...	...	0536	...	▬	0712	...	0800	0812	▬	0912	...	1012	▬	1112	...	1212
99	**Zell am See** d.	|	...	...	...	...	...	0607	...	...	0612	...	2	0745	...	0832	0845	...	0945	...	1045	...	1145	...	1245
113	Saalfelden d.	|	0401	0451	0516	...	0536	0619	0625	...	0625	0644	0716c	0755	...	0843	0855	2	0955	...	1055	2	1155	...	1255
131	Hochfilzen d.	|	0418	0509	0533	...	0554	▬	0643	0643	0643	0702	0734c	0813	0834	0859	0913	0934	1013	1034	1113	1134	1213	1234	1313
148	St Johann in Tirol d.	|	0434	0527	0549	...	0612	...	0700	0700	0700	0720	0752	0828	0852	0917	0928	0956	1028	1052	1128	1152	1228	1252	1328
157	**Kitzbühel** d.	|	0442	0536	0557	...	0621	...	0708	0708	0708	0729	0801	0835	0901	0926	0935	1001	1035	1101	1135	1201	1235	1301	1335
166	Kirchberg in Tirol d.	|	0451	0546	0607	...	0631	...	0717	0717	0717	0739	0811	0844	0911	0938	0943	1011	1044	1111	1143	1211	1244	1311	1343
192	Wörgl Hbf a.	|	0518	0615	0633	...	0700	2Ⓐ	0742	0742	0742	0808	0840	0909	0940	1002	1008	1040	1109	1140	1208	1240	1309	1340	1408
192	Wörgl Hbf **951** d.	|	0519	0617	0640a	0649	0719	0709	0747	0747	0747	0817	0846	0919	0947	1025	1015	1046	1119	1147	1215	1246	1319	1347	1415
	München Hbf **951** a.	|	|	|	|	|	|	|	|	|	|	|	|	|	|	1134t	|	|	|	|	|	|	|	|	|
217	Jenbach **951** a.	|	0538	0638	0657a	0708	|	0727	0759	0759	0759	0829	0859	|	0959	...	1027	1059	|	1159	1227	1259	|	1359	1427
251	**Innsbruck** Hbf **951** a.	0449	0607	0713	0717a	0740	0744	0748	0820	0820	0820	0846	0918	0944	1020	...	1044	1118	1144	1220	1244	1318	1344	1420	1444

	2	RJX 1262 ⑥H ✕	RJ 596 ✕⊖	EC 164 Z ✕	2	2	EC 113 ✕⊖	2	2	2	EC 115 ⊗⊖	IC 518 G 2	2	2	2	Ⓐ 2	RJ 698 ✕⊖	2	2	2	2	EC 117 ⊗⊖	2	RJ 1260 ⑤J ✕	2
Wien Hbf **950** d.	...	0846	0855	...	...	...	...	...	...	...	...	...	...	...	...	...	1455	...	...	...	...	...	...	1730	...
Salzburg Hbf **951 970 975** ‡ d.	...	1144	1212	...	...	1308	1412	...	...	1508	1612	...	...	1708	...	1743	1812	...	...	1908	...	2012	...	2016	2215
Golling-Abtenau **970** ‡ d.	...	1209	1233	...	...	1334	1433	...	...	1534	1633	...	...	1734	...	1812	1833	...	...	1934	...	2033	...	2040	2242
Bischofshofen **970 975** ‡ d.	...	1230	1254	1250	...	1356	1454	...	...	1556	1654	1650	...	1756	...	1837	1854	...	...	1956	...	2054	...	2101	2305
St Johann im Pongau **970** ‡ d.	...	1240	1303	1259	...	1404	1503	...	...	1604	1703	1659	...	1804	...	1847	1903	...	...	2004	...	2103	...	2111	2314
Schwarzach - St Veit **970** ‡ a.	...	1246	1309	1305	...	1410	1509	...	...	1610	1709	1705	...	1810	...	1852	1909	...	...	2010	...	2109	...	2117	2319
Schwarzach - St Veit d.	...	1252	▬	1313	...	1412	▬	1512	...	1612	▬	1713	...	1813	...	1853	...	1912	...	2012	...	▬	2112	2123	2321
Zell am See d.	...	1324	...	1344	...	1445	...	1545	...	1645	...	1744	...	1846	...	1929	...	1946	...	2046	...	2	2148	2155	2356
Saalfelden d.	...	1335	...	1354	1416a	1455	2	1555	...	1655	2	1754	...	1856	...	1941	...	1957	...	2057	...	2148	2200	2207	0005
Hochfilzen d.	1334	|	...	|	1434	1513	1534	1613	1634	1713	1734	|	1834	1914	1934	...	...	2016	2034	2116	2134	2206	...	|	...
St Johann in Tirol d.	1352	1406	...	1422	1452	1528	1552	1628	1652	1728	1752	1822	1852	1929	1952	...	...	2030	2052	2130	2152	2224	...	2239	...
Kitzbühel d.	1401	1415	...	1430	1501	1535	1601	1635	1701	1735	1801	1830	1901	1936	2001	...	...	2038	2101	2138	2201	2233	...	2248	...
Kirchberg in Tirol d.	1411	1424	Ⓐ	1438	1511	1543	1611	1644	1711	1743	1811	1838	1911	1944	2011	...	...	2047	2111	2147	2211	2243	...	2257	...
Wörgl Hbf a.	1440	1448	2	1500	1540	1608	1640	1709	1740	1808	1840	1900	1940	2009	2040	...	...	2112	2140	2212	2240	2312	...	2321	...
Wörgl Hbf **951** d.	1446	...	1449	1502	1547	1615	1646	1719	1747	1815	1846	1902	1947	2015	2046	...	...	2119	2154	2219	...	2319	...	2329	...
München Hbf **951** a.	|	...	|	|	|	|	|	|	|	|	|	|	|	|	|	...	...	|	|	|	...	|	...	|	...
Jenbach **951** a.	1459	...	1508	1516	1559	1627	1659	|	1759	1827	1859	1916	1959	2027	2059	...	...	|	2213	2231	...	2331	...	2350	...
Innsbruck Hbf **951** a.	1518	...	1535	1540	1620	1644	1718	1744	1820	1844	1918	1940	2020	2044	2118	...	...	2144	2240	2248	...	2348	...	0025	...

	NJ 465 A	⚒ 2	2	2	⚒ 2	2	2	2	RJ 691 ✕⊖	2	2	2	IC 515 G	EC 114 ⊗⊖	RJX 1265 ⑥H ✕	2	2	2	EC 112 ✕⊖	2	2	2	EC 163 Z ✕	IC 793 ⊖	2
Innsbruck Hbf **951** d.	0056	...	...	...	0510	0514a	...	0610	...	0620r	0717	0721	0821	...	0850	0914	0940	1017	...	1040	1114	1140	1221	...	1240
Jenbach **951** d.	|	...	...	...	0527	0541a	...	0627	...	0649r	0735	0750	0844	...	0917	0931	1001	|	...	1101	1131	1201	1244	...	1301
München Hbf **951** d.	|	...	...	...	|	|	...	|	...	|	|	|	|	...	|	|	|	|	...	|	|	|	|	...	|
Wörgl Hbf **951** a.	|	...	...	...	0539	0600a	...	0639	...	0708r	0747	0809	0857	...	0936	0943	1013	1041	...	1114	1143	1213	1257	...	1314
Wörgl Hbf d.	|	...	...	...	0542	0605	...	0649	...	0722	0750	0822	0859	...	0941	0952	1022	1050	...	1122	1152	1222	1259	...	1322
Kirchberg in Tirol d.	|	...	...	...	0609	0634	...	0714	...	0751	0816	0851	0920	...	1007	1017	1051	1116	...	1151	1217	1251	1320	...	1351
Kitzbühel d.	|	...	...	...	0620	0645	...	0725	...	0802	0825	0902	0929	...	1016	1025	1102	1125	...	1202	1225	1302	1329	...	1402
St Johann in Tirol d.	|	...	...	...	0629	0654	...	0732	...	0811	0832	0911	0937	...	1025	1032	1111	1132	...	1211	1232	1311	1337	...	1411
Hochfilzen d.	|	...	...	...	0646	0714	...	0747	...	0828	0847	0928	|	...	|	1047	1128	1147	...	1228	1247	1328	|	...	1429
Saalfelden d.	|	0458	0551	0705	0705	0731b	0734r	0805	...	...	0905	...	1005	...	1057	1105	...	1205	...	...	1305	...	1405	...	1446a
Zell am See d.	|	0508	0602	0715	0715	...	0747r	0815	...	...	0915	...	1016	...	1109	1115	...	1215	...	...	1315	...	1416	...	...
Schwarzach - St Veit a.	0317	0541	0637	0748	0748	...	0822r	0848	...	...	0948	...	1046	...	1139	1148	...	1248	...	...	1348	...	1446	...	...
Schwarzach - St Veit **970** ‡ d.	0324	0542	0639	0749	0749	...	0824	...	0852	...	0949	...	1056	1052	1143	1149	...	...	1252	...	1349	...	1456	1452	...
St Johann im Pongau **970** ‡ d.	|	0548	0646	0755	0755	...	0829	...	0858	...	0955	...	1102	1058	1150	1155	...	...	1258	...	1355	...	1502	1458	...
Bischofshofen **970 975** ‡ d.	0336	0558	0655	0804	0804	...	0840	...	0907	...	1004	...	1110	1107	1200	1204	...	...	1307	...	1404	...	1510	1507	...
Golling-Abtenau **970** ‡ d.	...	0620	0718	0825	0825	...	0904	...	0928	...	1025	...	...	1128	1221	1225	...	...	1328	...	1425	...	...	1528	...
Salzburg Hbf **951 970 975** ‡ a.	...	0645	0744	0851	0851	...	0940	...	0948	...	1051	...	...	1148	1245	1251	...	...	1348	...	1451	...	...	1548	...
Wien Hbf **950** a.	...	...	...	...	...	...	...	...	1305	...	...	...	...	...	1530	...	...	...	...	...	...	...	...	...	...

	2	2	2	RJ 797 ✕⊖	RJ 1267 ⑦L ✕	2	2	2	ICE 1283 ⑥M ✕	2	RJ 110 ✕⊖	2	2	2	2	IC 895 ✕⊖	2	2	2	Ⓐ 2	Ⓒ 2	2	2	2	2
Innsbruck Hbf **951** d.	1314	1320	1417	...	...	1440	1514	1540	...	1600a	...	1640	1714	1740	1817	...	1840	1914	1920	2017	2017	2121	2135	2335	0105
Jenbach **951** d.	1331	1347	|	...	...	1501	1531	1601	...	1625a	...	1701	1731	1801	|	...	1901	1931	1947	|	|	2148	2209	0009	0139
München Hbf **951** d.	|	|	|	...	...	|	|	|	1520v	|	...	|	|	|	|	...	|	|	|	|	|	|	|	|	|
Wörgl Hbf **951** a.	1343	1406	1441	...	...	1514	1543	1613	1635	1647a	...	1714	1743	1813	1841	...	1914	1943	2006	2041	2041	2207	2231	0031	0204
Wörgl Hbf d.	1352	1422	1450	...	1516	1522	1552	1622	1638	1650	...	1722	1752	1822	1850	...	1922	1952	2022	2052	2052	2222	▬	0037	0210
Kirchberg in Tirol d.	1417	1451	1516	...	1542	1551	1617	1651	1704	1716	...	1751	1817	1851	1916	...	1951	2017	2051	2117	2121	2251	...	0106	0239
Kitzbühel d.	1425	1502	1525	...	1551	1602	1625	1702	1716	1725	...	1802	1825	1902	1925	...	2002	2026	2102	2125	2132	2302	...	0117	0250
St Johann in Tirol d.	1432	1511	1532	...	1600	1611	1632	1711	1725	1732	...	1811	1832	1911	1932	...	2011	2034	2111	2132	2141	2311	...	0126	0259
Hochfilzen d.	1447	1528	1547	...	|	1628	1647	1728	1742	1747	...	1828	1847	1928	1947	...	2029	2050	2128	2147	2159	2329	D	0144	0317
Saalfelden d.	1505	...	1605	...	1632	...	1705	...	1759	1805	...	...	1905	...	2005	...	...	2107	...	2205	2217	2346	**899**	0201	0334
Zell am See d.	1515	...	1615	...	1644	...	1715	...	1810	1815	...	...	1915	...	2015	...	...	...	...	2215	2229	...	...	...	...
Schwarzach - St Veit a.	1548	...	1648	...	1714	...	1748	...	1840	1848	...	...	1948	...	2048	...	...	...	...	2248	...	...	2	...	...
Schwarzach - St Veit **970** ‡ d.	1549	...	...	1652	1717	...	1749	...	...	...	1852	...	1949	...	...	2052	...	...	...	...	...	...	2252	...	...
St Johann im Pongau **970** ‡ d.	1555	...	...	1658	1724	...	1755	...	...	...	1858	...	1955	...	...	2058	...	...	...	...	...	...	2258	...	...
Bischofshofen **970 975** ‡ d.	1604	...	...	1707	1734	...	1804	...	...	...	1907	...	2004	...	...	2107	...	...	...	...	...	...	2307	...	...
Golling-Abtenau **970** ‡ d.	1625	...	...	1728	1756	...	1825	...	...	...	1928	...	2025	...	...	2128	...	...	...	...	...	...	2328	...	...
Salzburg Hbf **951 970 975** ‡ a.	1651	...	...	1748	1817	...	1851	...	...	...	1948	...	2051	...	...	2148	...	...	...	...	...	...	2348	...	...
Wien Hbf **950** a.	...	...	...	2105	2111	...	...	...	...	...	...	...	...	...	...	...	...	...	...	...	...	...	...	...	...

A – 🛏 1, 2 cl., 🛏 2 cl. and (2) Graz - Feldkirch - Buchs 🏛 - Zürich and v.v. Conveys from/to Schwarzach 🛏 1, 2 cl., 🛏 2 cl. and (2) (*EN* **40414/40465**) Zagreb - Ljubljana - Villach - Zürich and v.v.
G – From/to Graz (Table **975**).
H – ⑥ July 2 - Sept. 10.
J – ⑤ July 1 - Sept. 9.
K – ⑥ June 18 - Oct. 15.
L – ⑦ July 3 - Sept. 11 (not Aug. 14).
M – ⑥ June 11 - Oct. 15.
Z – TRANSALPIN – (12) and ✕ Graz - Bischofshofen - Innsbruck - Buchs 🏛 - Zürich and v.v.

a – Ⓐ only.
b – Ⓑ only.
c – Ⓒ only.
r – ⚒ only.
t – 1201 until July 9.
v – 1450 until July 9.

⊖ – See Table **970** for further details.
‡ – See panel below main table for additional S-Bahn services (calling at all stations).

Freilassing **890** d.	0607		2307
Salzburg Hbf **890** d.	0621	and	2321
Golling-Abtenau d.	0659	hourly	2359
Bischofshofen d.	0724	until	0024
St Johann im Pongau d.	0734		0034
Schwarzach - St Veit a.	0739		0039

Schwarzach - St Veit d.	0524		2224
St Johann im Pongau d.	0529	and	2229
Bischofshofen d.	0540	hourly	2240
Golling-Abtenau d.	0604	until	2304
Salzburg Hbf **890** a.	0640		2340
Freilassing **890** a.	0653		2354

ATTNANG-PUCHHEIM - STAINACH-IRDNING 961

2nd class only (except trains **A** and **B**)

km																								
			⚒	Ⓐ								©A			⑤E									
	Wien Hbf **950**	d.	...	...	...	...	...	...	...	...	...	0842	...	...	...	...	...	...	...	...	...	...	...	...
0	**Attnang-Puchheim**	d.	...	0446	...	0603	0716	0807	...	0907	1007	1037	1107	1207	1237	1307	1407	1507	1607	1707	1807	1907	2007	2107
12	**Gmunden**	d.	...	0502	...	0621	0736	0823	...	0924	1023	1052	1124	1223	1251	1324	1423	1524	1623	1724	1823	1924	2023	2124
17	Altmünster am Traunsee	d.	...	0509	...	0626	0742	0830	...	0930	1030	1059	1130	1230	1257	1330	1430	1530	1630	1730	1830	1930	2030	2130
22	Traunkirchen	d.	...	0515	...	0633	0748	0836	...	0937	1036	|	1137	1236	1303	1337	1436	1537	1636	1737	1836	1937	2036	2137
27	Ebensee Landungsplatz	d.	...	0521	...	0640	0756	0843	...	0945	1043	|	1145	1243	1309	1345	1443	1545	1643	1745	1843	1945	2043	2145
28	Ebensee	d.	...	0523	...	0643	0759	0846	...	0948	1046	1112	1148	1246	1312	1348	1446	1548	1646	1748	1846	1948	2046	2148
44	**Bad Ischl**	d.	...	0539	...	0705	0819	0903	...	1011	1103	1128	1211	1303	1330	1411	1503	1630	1703	1830	1903	2030	2103	2208
54	Bad Goisern	d.	...	...	...	0717	0832	0913	...	1026	1113	1142	1226	1313	...	1426	1513	1626	1713	1826	1913	2026	2116	...
64	Hallstatt ⊡	d.	...	...	...	0730	0848	0925	...	1048	1125	1156	1248	1325	...	1448	1525	1648	1725	1848	1925	|	|	...
67	Obertraun-Dachsteinhöhlen	d.	...	...	...	0734	0851	0928	...	1051	1128	1201	1251	1328	...	1451	1528	1651	1728	1851	1928	2051	2132	...
78	**Bad Aussee**	d.	0503	...	0632	0749	...	0942	...	...	1142	1216	...	1342	...	...	1542	...	1742	...	1942	2104	2144	...
93	Bad Mitterndorf	d.	0521	...	0650	0804	...	0959	...	...	1159	1235	...	1359	...	...	1559	...	1759	...	1959	...	...	...
108	**Stainach-Irdning**	a.	0538	...	0707	0818	...	1015	...	...	1215	1251	...	1415	...	...	1615	...	1815	...	2015	...	...	...

				Ⓐ	⚒	⚒								E					©B				©	
Stainach-Irdning	d.	...	...	...	...	0609	...	0713	...	0940	...	1140	...	...	1340	...	1540	...	1704	1740	...	1940	1940	2140
Bad Mitterndorf	d.	...	...	...	...	0627	...	0730	...	0959	...	1159	...	...	1359	...	1559	...	1725	1759	...	1959	1959	2159
Bad Aussee	d.	...	0459	...	0612	0654	0651	0810f	...	1016	...	1216	...	...	1416	...	1616	...	1755	1816	...	2015	2016	2215
Obertraun-Dachsteinhöhlen	d.	...	0511	...	0624	0703	0703	0823	0903	1028	1103	1228	1303	...	1428	1503	1628	1703	1729	1828	1903	...	2028	...
Hallstatt ⊡	d.	...	|	...	|	0707	0707	0828	0907	1032	1107	1232	1307	...	1432	1507	1632	1707	1800	1832	|	...	|	...
Bad Goisern	d.	...	0526	...	0639	0725	0725	0843	0933	1043	1133	1243	1333	...	1443	1533	1643	1733	1814	1843	1933	...	2043	...
Bad Ischl	d.	0436	0540	0554	0652	0740	0740	0853	0950	1053	1150	1253	1350	1428	1453	1550	1653	1750	1831	1853	1950	...	2053	...
Ebensee	d.	0453	0559	0611	0712	0800	0800	0912	1011	1112	1211	1312	1411	1445	1512	1511	1712	1811	1847	1912	2011	...	2112	...
Ebensee Landungsplatz	d.	0456	0601	0613	0714	0803	0803	0914	1014	1114	1214	1314	1414	1448	1514	1614	1714	1814	|	1914	2014	...	2114	...
Traunkirchen	d.	0503	0609	0620	0722	0811	0811	0922	1022	1122	1222	1322	1422	1454	1522	1622	1722	1822	|	1922	2022	...	2122	...
Altmünster am Traunsee	d.	0509	0614	0630	0727	0817	0817	0930	1030	1130	1230	1330	1430	1501	1530	1630	1730	1830	1859	1930	2030	...	2130	...
Gmunden	d.	0516	0621	0636	0736	0836r	0836r	0937	1036	1137	1236	1337	1436	1506	1537	1636	1737	1836	1906	1937	2036	...	2137	...
Attnang-Puchheim	a.	0531	0638	0653	0753	0853	0853	0953	1053	1153	1253	1353	1453	1523	1553	1653	1753	1853	1922	1953	2053	...	2153	...
Wien Hbf **950**	a.	...	...	...	...	...	...	...	...	...	...	...	...	...	...	...	...	...	2118	...	...	...	...	...

A – *IC* **1018**. SALZKAMMERGUT – (12) Wien - Attnang-Puchheim - Stainach-Irdning.
B – *IC* **1019**. SALZKAMMERGUT – (12) Stainach-Irdning - Attnang-Puchheim - Wien.
E – ⑤ until July 1; ⑤ from Sept. 16 (not Oct. 28).

d – Runs daily until Oct. 29
f – Arrives 0748.
r – Arrives 0822.

⊡ – ⛴ services operate Hallstatt Bahnhof - Hallstatt Markt. Journey: 8 minutes.
Operator: Hallstättersee-Schifffahrt Hemetsberger KG ✆ +43 (0) 6134 8228.
From Hallstatt Bahnhof at 0707⚒, 0735⚒, 0830⚒**d**, 0900, 0930, 1035, 1100, 1130©, 1156©, 1235, 1300, 1330, 1435, 1500, 1530, 1635, 1700, 1730 and 1850.
From Hallstatt Markt at 0650⚒, 0715⚒, 0810⚒**d**, 0845, 0915, 1015, 1045, 1215, 1245, 1415, 1445, 1615, 1645, 1715 and 1815.

LINZ - PASSAU and SIMBACH 962

km																										
										ICE						*ICE*			*ICE*			*ICE*				*ICE*
										228						**28**			**92**			**26**				**90**
			Ⓐ		⚒									Ⓐ							⚒					⚒	
			2	2	2	**G**2	2	2	2	✕	2	2	2	2	**D**✕	2	2	**B**✕	2	2	**D**✕	2	2	2	2	**H**✕
	Wien Hbf **950**	d.	...	...	...	...	...	...	...	0651	...	...	...	...	0915	...	...	1015	...	...	1115	...	...	...	...	1315
0	**Linz** Hbf **950**	d.	...	...	0452	0540	0558	0650	...	0817	0850	...	0950	...	1035	1050	...	1135	1150	...	1235	1250	...	1350	...	1435
25	**Wels** Hbf **950**	d.	0444	...	0516	0613j	0620	0709	...	0833	0909	...	1009	...	|	1109	...	|	1209	...	|	1309	...	1409	...	|
54	Neumarkt-Kallham	d.	0508	...	0543	0641	0646	0736	0740	|	0936	0940	1032	1040	|	1140t	1140	|	1232	1240	|	1336	1340	1432	1440	|
	Ried im Innkreis	d.	0529	...	|	|	0710	|	0801	|	|	1001	|	1101	|	1201	|	|	|	1301	|	|	1401	|	1501	|
	Braunau am Inn	a.	0604	0641	|	|	0740	|	0841	|	|	1041	|	1141	|	1241	|	|	|	1341	|	|	1441	|	1541	|
	Simbach (Inn) 🏛 **893**	a.	...	0644	|	|	0745	|	0845	|	|	1045	|	1145	|	1245	|	|	|	1345	|	|	1445	|	1545	|
92	Schärding	d.	...	...	0615	0714	...	0809	...	0911	1009	...	1057	...	|	...	1211	|	1257	...	|	1409	...	1457	...	|
106	**Passau** Hbf	a.	...	...	0628	0727	...	0822	...	0922	1022	...	1112	...	1131	...	1224	1231	1312	...	1331	1422	...	1512	...	1531
	Nürnberg Hbf **920**	a.	...	...	...	...	...	...	...	1127	...	...	...	...	1327	...	...	1428	...	...	1528	...	...	...	...	1729
	Frankfurt (Main) Hbf **920**	a.	...	...	...	...	...	...	...	1336	...	...	...	...	1536	...	...	...	...	...	1736	...	...	...	...	...

								ICE							*ICE*					*IC*		*NJ*	*RJX*		*RJ*	
								22							**20**					**94**		**490**	**42**		**840**	
				Ⓐ		⚒	Ⓐ		Ⓐ			Ⓐ	Ⓐ				Ⓐ									
		2	2	2	2	2	2	**D**✕	2	2	2	2	2	2	✕	2	2	2	2	**W**🍷	2	⊡	✕	2	✕	2
Wien Hbf **950**	d.	...	...	...	...	...	...	1515	...	...	...	...	...	...	1715	...	...	...	...	1915	...	2013	2030	...	2055	...
Linz Hbf **950**	d.	1450	...	*1525*	1550	...	1614	1635	1640	1650	...	1714	1750	1750	1835	1850	...	1950	...	2036	2050	2136	2146	...	2231	...
Wels Hbf **950**	d.	1509	...	*1550*	1609	...	1631	|	1655	1709	...	1731	1809	1814k	1850	1909	...	2009	...	2050	2109	2150	2158	2209	2243	2249
Neumarkt-Kallham	d.	1540t	1540	1620	1632	1640	1652	|	1720	1736	1740	1758	1835	1840	|	1936	1940	2036	2040	|	2136	|	...	2237	...	2316
Ried im Innkreis	d.	1601	|	1637	|	1701	|	|	1737	|	1801	|	|	1901	|	|	2001	|	2101	|	|	|	...	2257	...	|
Braunau am Inn	a.	1641	|	1707	|	1741	|	|	1808	|	1841	|	|	1941	|	|	2041	|	2141	|	|	|	...	2331	...	|
Simbach (Inn) 🏛 **893**	a.	1645	|	1711	|	1745	|	|	...	|	1845c	|	|	1945	|	|	2045	|	2145	|	|	|	...	...	...	|
Schärding	d.	...	1611	...	1657	...	1717	|	...	1809	...	1831	1900	...	|	2009	...	2109	...	2125	2209	|	...	...	...	2348
Passau Hbf	a.	...	1624	...	1712	...	...	1731	...	1822	...	1844	1913	...	1934	2022	...	2122	...	2137	2222	2235	...	...	...	...
Nürnberg Hbf **920**	a.	...	...	...	...	...	...	1928	...	...	...	...	...	...	2128	...	...	...	...	2400	...	0056	...	...	...	...
Frankfurt (Main) Hbf **920**	a.	...	...	...	...	...	...	2136	...	...	...	...	...	...	2339	...	...	...	...	...	...	...	...	...	...	...

km																										
										NJ							*IC*			*ICE*					*ICE*	
										491							**95**			**21**					**23**	
			⚒	Ⓐ		⚒	†		⚒		Ⓐ	Ⓐ									Ⓐ					⚒
			2	2	2	2	2	2	2	⊡	2	2	2	2	2	2	**W**🍷	2	2	✕	2	2	2	2	**D**✕	2
	Frankfurt (Main) Hbf **920**	d.	...	...	...	...	...	...	...	...	...	...	...	...	...	...	...	...	...	0621	...	...	...	...	0822	...
	Nürnberg Hbf **920**	d.	...	...	...	...	...	...	...	0408	...	...	...	...	...	...	0600	...	...	0831	...	...	...	...	1031	...
	Passau Hbf	d.	...	0411	0420c	...	...	0539	0604	0615	...	0625	...	0650	0740	...	0824	0840	...	1026	...	1048	...	1140	1229	...
	Schärding	d.	0358	0423	0432	...	...	0552	0616	|	...	0637	...	0703	0752	...	|	0852	...	|	...	1102	...	1152	|	...
0	**Simbach** (Inn) 🏛 **893**	d.	|	|	|	...	...	|	|	|	...	|	...	|	|	0718	|	|	0918	|	1018	|	1118	|	|	1218a
2	**Braunau** am Inn	d.	|	|	|	0514	0526	|	|	|	0610	|	0629	|	|	0723	|	|	0924	|	1024	|	1124	|	|	1224
39	Ried im Innkreis	d.	|	|	|	0552	0601	|	|	|	0643	|	0710	|	|	0801	|	|	1001	|	1101	|	1201	|	|	1301
61	Neumarkt-Kallham	d.	0429	0451	0504	0613	0619	0624	0642	|	0709r	0706	0728	0736	0820	0824	|	0924	1024t	|	1119	1128	1219	1224	|	1319
90	**Wels** Hbf **950**	d.	0456	0515	0531	0637	...	0652	0712	0717	0737	0728	...	0807	...	0853	0911	0953	1053	1112	...	1153	...	1253	|	...
115	**Linz** Hbf **950**	a.	0519	0532	0554	0652	...	0708	0744	0746	...	0748	...	0824	...	0910	0923	1010	1110	1125	...	1210	...	1310	1325	...
	Wien Hbf **950**	a.	...	...	...	...	...	...	...	0919	...	...	...	...	...	...	1045	...	...	1245	...	...	...	...	1445	...

					ICE				*ICE*		*ICE*					*ICE*			*RJ*		*ICE*			*RJ*		*RJX*
					91				**93**		**27**					**29**			**749**		**229**			**843**		**367**
																			769							
						⚒						⚒										Ⓐ				
		2	2	2	**H**✕	2	2	2	**B**✕	2	**D**✕	2	2	2	2	**D**✕	2	2	✕	2	**D**✕	2	2	✕	2	✕
Frankfurt (Main) Hbf **920**	d.	...	...	...	...	...	...	...	...	...	1222	...	...	...	...	1422	...	...	...	...	1621	...	...	...	...	...
Nürnberg Hbf **920**	d.	...	...	...	1231	...	...	...	1333	...	1431	...	...	...	...	1631	...	...	...	...	1831	...	...	...	...	...
Passau Hbf	d.	1248	1336	...	1429	...	1448	...	1529	1540	1629	...	1648	1736	...	1829	...	1840	...	...	2031	...	2040	...	...	...
Schärding	d.	1302	1349	...	|	...	1502	...	|	1552	|	...	1702	1749	...	|	...	1852	...	...	2043	...	2052	...	...	...
Simbach (Inn) 🏛 **893**	d.	|	|	1318	|	1418	|	1518	|	|	|	1618	|	|	1718	|	1818	|	...	1918	|	*2018*	|	...	2118	...
Braunau am Inn	d.	|	|	1324	|	1424	|	1524	|	|	|	1624	|	|	1724	|	1824	|	...	1924	|	2024	|	...	2124	...
Ried im Innkreis	d.	|	|	1401	|	1501	|	1601	|	|	|	1701	|	|	1801	|	1901	|	...	2001	|	2101	|	...	2201	...
Neumarkt-Kallham	d.	1328	1420	1424t	|	1519	1528	1619	|	1624	|	1719	1728	1821	1824t	|	1919	1924	...	2024t	|	2119	2124	...	2224	...
Wels Hbf **950**	d.	1353	...	1453	|	...	1553	...	|	1653	|	...	1753	1841	1853	|	...	1953	2016	2053	2120	...	2151	2216	2251	2305
Linz Hbf **950**	a.	1410	...	1510	1525	...	1610	...	1625	1710	1725	...	1810	...	1910	1925	...	2010c	2029	2110	2133	...	...	2228	...	2317
Wien Hbf **950**	a.	...	...	...	1645	...	...	...	1745	...	1845	...	...	...	...	2045	...	...	2205	...	2305	...	...	0005	...	0033

B – To / from Berlin and Hamburg (Table **850**).
D – To / from Dortmund (Table **800**).
G – From Garsten (Table **976**).
H – To / from Hamburg (Table **900**).
W – To / from Warnemünde via Berlin (Tables **835** and **849a**).

a – Ⓐ only.
c – © only.
j – Arrives 0603.
k – 1819 on Ⓐ.
r – Arrives 0702.

t – Arrives 5 minutes earlier.

⊡ – 🛏 1, 2 cl., 🛌 2 cl. and (2) Wien - Nürnberg - Hamburg and v.v.;
🛏 1, 2 cl., 🛌 2 cl. and (2) (**40490**/**40421**/**50490**/**50425**) Wien - Frankfurt - Köln - Amsterdam / Brussels and v.v. Ⓡ for journeys to / from Germany.

963 🚌 SALZBURG and ST WOLFGANG - STROBL - BAD ISCHL

Routes 150, 546

km	*Route* **150**	⚒	Ⓐ	Ⓒ		Ⓐ								Ⓑ		Ⓑ	Ⓑ	Ⓑ	†	†			⚒	
0	**Salzburg** Hbf △ d.	0526	0556	0615	...	0615	0645	0715	0745	and every	1615	1645	1715	1745	...	1815	1845	1915	1945	2015	...	2115	2215	2315
32	St Gilgen (Busbahnhof) d.	0610	0645	0659	...	0704	0738	0808	0838	30 minutes	1708	1738	1808	1834	...	1904	1934	2004	2029	2059	...	2159	2259	2359
45	Strobl (Busbahnhof) d.	0624	0702	0713	...	0721	0756	0826	0856	until	1726	1756	1826	1851	...	1921	1951	2021	2043	2113	...	2213	2313	0013
57	**Bad Ischl** Bahnhof a.	0640	0719	0729	...	0738	0815	0845	0915		1745	1815	1845	1908	...	1938	2008	2038	2059	2129	...	2229	2329	0029

Route **150**	⚒	Ⓐ	⑥	Ⓐ	Ⓐ	Ⓒ	Ⓐ	⑥	Ⓑ	⚒	Ⓑ						†	†	†	†			Ⓒ	
Bad Ischl Bahnhof d.	0457	0525	0541	0541	0611	0624	0646	0654	0724	0754	0824	0854	0924	and every	1654	1724	1754	1824	1854	1924	1954	2024	2054	2124
Strobl (Busbahnhof) d.	0513	0542	0557	0600	0630	0640	0705	0715	0745	0815	0845	0915	0945	30 minutes	1715	1745	1811	1841	1911	1941	2010	2040	2110	2140
St Gilgen (Busbahnhof) d.	0528	0558	0612	0615	0645	0655	0721	0734	0804	0834	0904	0934	1004	until	1734	1804	1827	1857	1927	1957	2025	2055	2125	2155
Salzburg Hbf △ a.	0613	0645	0657	0700	0737j	0740	0812	0826	0856	0926	0956	1026	1056		1826	1856	1914	1944	2014	2044	2110	2140	2210	2240

km	*Route* **546**	Ⓐ	⚒	⚒	Ⓒ	Ⓐ	Ⓐ	Ⓐ			Ⓐ	Ⓒ		Ⓒ	Ⓐ			Ⓐ			Ⓐ		Ⓒ		
0	**St Wolfgang** ⊡ ‡ d.	0500	0600	0649	0732	0740	0813	0900	0913	1013	1100	1113	1213	1313	1323	1413	1513	1513	1613	1713	1713	1813	1828	1908	1956
7	Strobl (Busbahnhof) d.	0512	0613	0702	0745	|	0824	|	0924	1026	|	1124	1226	1324	1336	1426	1526	1526	1626	1724	1726	1826	1839	1919	2007
19	**Bad Ischl** Bahnhof a.	0531	0639	0728	0811	0811	...	0931	...	1047	1131	...	1247	...	1402	1447	...	1552	1647	...	1752	1847	...	...	...

Route **546**	Ⓐ	⚒	Ⓐ				Ⓒ	Ⓐ		Ⓑ	⚒	Ⓒ	Ⓐ	k	Ⓐn				Ⓐ		Ⓒ	Ⓐ			
Bad Ischl Bahnhof d.	0606	0642	...	0823	0913	...	...	1023	1113	...	1223	1323	1336	...	1423	...	1513	...	1623	1713	...	1823	...	1913	...
Strobl (Busbahnhof) d.	0630	0706	0825	0845	0935	...	1045	1045	1135	1245	1245	1345	1358	1445	1445	...	1535	1645	1645	1735	1845	1845	1925	|	2045
St Wolfgang ⊡ ‡ a.	0642	0718	0837	0857	0947	...	1057	1057	1147	1257	1257	1357	1410	1457	1457	...	1547	1657	1657	1747	1857	1857	1937	1940	2057

j – 0730 on school days.
k – Daily to July 10 (not June 17); Ⓒ July 16 - Sept. 4; daily from Sept. 10 (not Oct. 27, 28, Oct. 31, Nov. 2).
n – Not June 17, July 11 - Sept. 9, Oct. 26 - Nov. 2.

△ – All services also call at Mirabellplatz.
⊡ – St Wolfgang Schafbergbahnhof. All services also call at St Wolfgang Markt.
‡ – **Schafbergbahn** narrow-gauge steam rack railway operates St Wolfgang - Schafbergspitze (*6 km*). Services operate subject to demand and weather conditions **April 24 - Nov. 1**, 2022. 2nd class only. Special fares payable. Journey time: 35 minutes each way. ✆ +43 (0) 6138 2232 0.

964 ⛴ STROBL - ST GILGEN (WOLFGANGSEE)

Service June 16 - Sept. 11

			🚢			🚢			🚢			🚢					
Strobl Schiffstation ⊡ d.	...	0845	...	0925	1025	...	1125	1225	...	1325	1425	...	1525	1625	1725	1820	1920
St Wolfgang Markt d.	...	|	...	|	|	1135	1200	1300	1335	1400	1500	1535	1600	1700	1800	1832s	1932s
St Wolfgang Schafbergbahnhof ‡ d.	0830	0910	0935	0955	1055	1145	1208	1308	1345	1408	1508	1545	1608	1708	1808	1840	1940
St Wolfgang Markt d.	|	0918	0945	1005	1105	|	|	|	|	|	|	|	|	|	|	...	...
St Gilgen Schiffstation ● a.	0855	0955	1015	1045	1145	1215	1245	1345	1415	1445	1545	1625	1645	1745	1845	...	...

					🚢			🚢			🚢			🚢			
St Gilgen Schiffstation ● d.	...	...	0900	1000	1030	1100	1200	1230	1300	1400	1430	1500	1600	1630	1700	1800	1850
St Wolfgang Markt d.	...	...	|	|	|	|	|	|	|	|	|	|	|	|	|	|	1920s
St Wolfgang Schafbergbahnhof ‡ d.	0825	0855	0937	1037	1100	1137	1237	1300	1337	1437	1500	1537	1637	1700	1737	1837	1928
St Wolfgang Markt d.	|	0905	0950	1050	1110	1150	1250	1310	1350	1450	1510	1550	1650	1710	1750	1850	...
Strobl Schiffstation ⊡ a.	0840	0920	1015	1115	...	1215	1315	...	1415	1515	...	1615	1715	...	1815	1915	...

s – Set down only.
‡ – See note under Table **963**.
⊡ – Approximately 400 metres from Strobl Busbahnhof.
● – Approximately 500 metres from St Gilgen Busbahnhof.
🚢 – July 2 - Aug. 28 (subject to weather conditions). Operated by paddle-steamer *Kaiser Franz Josef I*. Small supplement payable.

969 TAUERN TUNNEL CAR-CARRYING TRAINS

BÖCKSTEIN - MALLNITZ-OBERVELLACH *11 km.* Transit time: 11 minutes. Passengers without cars are also conveyed. ✆ 05-1717. E-mail: autoschleuse.tauernbahn@pv.oebb.at
From Böckstein at 0620, 0720 and hourly until 2320. **From Mallnitz-Obervellach** at 0550, 0650 and hourly until 2250.

970 SALZBURG - VILLACH - KLAGENFURT

SERVICE FROM AUGUST 2. See page 562 for services until August 1.

km		*NJ* **40463** R B	*NJ* **40466** R ♦	*NJ* **40294** 2	⚒ 2		*EN* **40465** R ♦	2	⚒ 2	2	*IC* **894** ✕	*IC* **898**	*RJ* **111** ✕	*RJ* **596** ✕	*EC* **113** ✕♦		*EC* **115** ⊗♦	Ⓐ 2	2	*RJ* **698** ✕	*EC* **117** ⊗♦	*IC* **794** Ⓑ	*NJ* **295** R ♦
	Wien Hbf **950** d.	...	2127	...	...	...	...	...	...	...	...	...	...	0855	...	...	...	...	...	1455	...	...	...
	München Hbf **890** d.	2320	|	...	...	...	...	...	...	...	...	...	0817	|	1217	...	1417	...	...	|	1817	...	2010
0	**Salzburg** Hbf **960 975** d.	0140	0140	...	...	...	...	...	...	...	0612	0812	1012	1212	1412	...	1612	...	...	1812	2012	2112	2202
29	Golling-Abtenau **960** d.	|	|	...	...	...	...	...	...	...	0633	0833	1033	1233	1433	...	1633	...	...	1833	2033	2138	|
53	**Bischofshofen** **960 975** d.	|	|	...	...	...	...	...	...	...	0654	0854	1054	1254	1454	...	1654	...	...	1854	2054	2200	|
61	St Johann im Pongau **960** d.	|	|	...	...	...	...	...	...	...	0703	0903	1103	1303	1503	...	1703	...	...	1903	2103	2209	|
67	**Schwarzach - St Veit** **960** d.	0232	0232	...	...	...	0425	...	...	...	0711	0911	1111	1311	1511	...	1711	...	...	1911	2111	2216	2254
86	Bad Hofgastein d.	|	|	...	...	...	0440	...	...	...	0729	0929	1129	1329	1529	...	1729	...	...	1929	2129	2233	|
97	Bad Gastein d.	|	|	...	...	...	0500	...	...	...	0742	0942	1142	1342	1542	...	1742	...	...	1942	2142	2245	|
113	Mallnitz-Obervellach d.	|	|	...	...	...	0515	...	0650	...	0756	0956	1156	1356	1556	...	1756	1800	...	1956	2156	2259	|
146	Spittal-Millstättersee **971** d.	|	|	...	...	...	0540	...	0717	0729	0820	1020	1220	1420	1620	...	1820	1827	1832	2020	2220	2322	|
182	**Villach** Hbf **971** a.	0357	0357	...	...	...	0604	...	...	0753	0843	1043	1243	1443	1643	...	1843	...	1904	2043	2243	2344	0019
182	**Villach** Hbf **971** d.	...	...	0417	0450	...	...	0620	...	0756	0847	1047	1247	1447	1648	...	1847	...	1920	2047	2247	2347	...
198	Velden am Wörthersee **971** d.	...	...	|	0505	...	...	0634	...	0806	0858	1058	1258	1458	1659	...	1858	...	1934	2058	2258	2358	...
207	Pörtschach am Wörthersee **971** d.	...	...	|	0513	...	...	0642	...	|	0904	1104	1304	1504	1705	...	1904	...	1942	2104	2304	0004	...
220	**Klagenfurt** Hbf **971** a.	...	...	0438	0529	...	...	0656	...	0822	0913	1113	1316	1513	1717	...	1916	...	1956	2116	2316	0013	...

	NJ **236** R ♦	*NJ* **40236** R A		*NJ* **294** R ♦	*IC* **597** ①–⑥	⚒ 2		*RJ* **691** ✕		*EC* **114** ⊗♦		*EC* **112** ✕♦	*IC* **793**	*RJ* **797** ✕	Ⓐ 2	Ⓐ 2	*RJ* **110** ✕	*IC* **895** ✕	*D* **899** 2		2		*EN* **40414** R ♦
Klagenfurt Hbf **971** d.	...	...	...	...	0442	...	...	0645	...	0842	...	1027	1245	1445	1532	...	1642	1845	2045	...	2232	...	...
Pörtschach am Wörthersee **971** d.	...	...	...	...	0455	...	...	0655	...	0855	...	1040	1255	1455	1547	...	1655	1855	2055	...	2247	...	...
Velden am Wörthersee **971** d.	...	...	...	...	0502	...	...	0702	...	0902	...	1047	1302	1502	1554	...	1702	1902	2102	...	2254	...	...
Villach Hbf **971** a.	...	...	...	...	0513	...	...	0713	...	0913	...	1058	1313	1513	1609	...	1713	1913	2113	...	2309	...	...
Villach Hbf **971** d.	0150	0150	...	0429	0516	0529	...	0716	...	0916	...	1116	1316	1516	1610	...	1716	1916	2116	...	...	...	2326
Spittal-Millstättersee **971** d.	|	|	...	|	0540	0605	...	0740	...	0940	...	1140	1340	1540	1634	1644	1740	1940	2140	...	...	...	2351
Mallnitz-Obervellach d.	|	|	...	|	0604	0633	...	0804	...	1004	...	1204	1404	1604	...	1712	1804	2004	2204	...	...	...	0014
Bad Gastein d.	|	|	...	|	0617	...	...	0817	...	1017	...	1217	1417	1617	...	...	1817	2017	2217	...	...	...	0030
Bad Hofgastein d.	|	|	...	|	0630	...	...	0830	...	1030	...	1230	1430	1630	...	...	1830	2030	2230	...	...	...	0042
Schwarzach - St Veit **960** d.	0315	0315	...	0549	0652	...	...	0852	...	1052	...	1252	1452	1652	...	...	1852	2052	2252	...	...	...	0058
St Johann im Pongau **960** a.	|	|	...	|	0657	...	...	0857	...	1057	...	1257	1457	1657	...	...	1857	2057	2257	...	...	...	...
Bischofshofen **960 975** a.	|	|	...	|	0705	...	...	0905	...	1105	...	1305	1505	1705	...	...	1905	2105	2305	...	...	...	...
Golling-Abtenau **960** a.	|	|	...	|	|	...	...	0927	...	1127	...	1327	1527	1727	...	...	1927	2127	2327	...	...	...	...
Salzburg Hbf **960 975** a.	0404	0404	...	0649	0748	...	...	0948	...	1148	...	1348	1548	1748	...	...	1948	2148	2348	...	...	...	...
München Hbf **890** a.	|	0629	...	0920	...	...	...	|	...	1341	...	1541	...	|	...	...	2141	...	...	...	...	...	...
Wien Hbf **950** a.	0758	...	...	...	...	...	...	1305	...	...	...	...	...	2105	...	...	...	...	...	...	...	...	...

♦ – **NOTES** (LISTED BY TRAIN NUMBER)

112 – BLAUER ENZIAN – (12) and ✕ Klagenfurt - München - Stuttgart - Frankfurt; also conveys (12) Zagreb (**212**) - Ljubljana - Villach (**112**) - Frankfurt.
113 – BLAUER ENZIAN – (12) and ✕ Frankfurt - Stuttgart - München - Klagenfurt; also conveys (12) Frankfurt - Villach (**213**) - Ljubljana - Zagreb.
114 – WÖRTHERSEE – (12) and ⊗ Klagenfurt - München - Stuttgart - Köln - Dortmund.
115 – WÖRTHERSEE – (12) and ⊗ Münster - Köln - Stuttgart - München - Klagenfurt.
117 – SALZACH – (12) and ⊗ Frankfurt - Stuttgart - München - Salzburg - Klagenfurt.
236 – 🛏 1, 2 cl., ▬ 2 cl. and (2) Venezia - Tarvisio 🏛 - Villach - Salzburg - Wien.
294/5 – 🛏 1, 2 cl., ▬ 2 cl. and (2) Roma - Firenze - Bologna - München and v.v.; 🛏 1, 2 cl., ▬ 2 cl. and (2) (**40235/40295**) Milano - Verona - München and v.v.
40414 – 🛏 1, 2 cl., ▬ 2 cl. and (2) Zagreb - Ljubljana - Villach - Schwarzach (**464**) - Innsbruck - Feldkirch - Zürich.
40465 – 🛏 1, 2 cl., ▬ 2 cl. and (2) Zürich (**465**) - Feldkirch - Innsbruck - Schwarzach (**40465**) - Villach - Ljubljana - Zagreb.

40466 – 🛏 1, 2 cl., ▬ 2 cl. and (2) Wien - Salzburg - Villach - Tarvisio 🏛 - Venezia.

A – 🛏 1, 2 cl., ▬ 2 cl. and (2) Venezia - Villach - München. Also conveys 🛏 1, 2 cl., ▬ 2 cl. and (2) (**498** – LISINSKI) Zagreb - Ljubljana - Jesenice 🏛 - Villach - München; also 🛏 1, 2 cl. and (2) (**480**) Rijeka - Ljubljana - München.
B – 🛏 1, 2 cl., ▬ 2 cl. and (2) München - Villach - Venezia. Also conveys 🛏 1, 2 cl., ▬ 2 cl. and (2) (**50463** – LISINSKI) München - Villach - Jesenice 🏛 - Ljubljana - Zagreb; also 🛏 1, 2 cl. and (2) (**60463**) München - Ljubljana - Rijeka.
C – ⑥⑦ June 5 - July 4; daily July 10 - Sept. 12.
R – 🅁 for international journeys.

v – Arrives 1646.

LIENZ - VILLACH - KLAGENFURT - FRIESACH (- WIEN) 971

km		NJ 235		RJ 530					RJ 532				IC 894		RJ 534			IC 898	RJ 536			RJ 111	RJ 132		D 730
		★	⚒																						⑦w
		2	2	✕	U 2	2	2	2	✕	2	2	2	◐✕	2	✕	2	2	◐	✕	2	2	◐✕	V✕	2	2
0	**Lienz** d.	...	...	...	...	...	...	0524	...	...	0629	...	...	0719	0753e	...	...	...	...	0924	1024	...	...	1124	...
68	Spittal-Millstättersee a.	...	...	...	...	...	...	0627	...	...	0726	...	...	0822	0842e	...	...	...	...	1022	1122	...	...	1222	...
68	Spittal-Millstättersee **970** d.	...	...	...	0448r	0530a	...	0630	...	0635a	0729	0732	0820	0832	0846e	...	0932	1020	...	1032	1132	1220	...	1232	...
104	**Villach** Hbf **970** a.	...	...	...	0520r	0558a	...	0656	...	0708a	0753	0804	0843	0904	0909e	←	1004	1043	...	1104p	1204	1243	...	1304p	...
104	**Villach** Hbf **970** d.	0417	0450	0525	0529	0604	0620	0659a	0714	0720	0756	0820	0847	0920	0914	0920	1020	1047	1114	1120	1220	1247	1314	1320	1413
120	Velden am Wörthersee **970** d.	|	0505	|	0543	|	0634	0711a	0725	0734	0806	0834	0858	→	|	0934	1034	1058	1125	1134	1234	1258	|	1334	1424
129	Pörtschach am W ⊡ **970** d.	|	0513	|	0551	|	0642	|	|	0742	|	0842	0904	...	0929	0942	1042	1104	|	1142	1242	1304	1329	1342	1430
135	Krumpendorf d.	|	0520	|	0557	|	0648	|	|	0748	|	0848	|	...	|	0948	1048	|	|	1148	1248	1310	|	1348	|
142	**Klagenfurt** Hbf **970** a.	0438	0529	0546	0605	0625	0656	0727a	0737	0756	0822	0856	0913	...	0937	0956	1056	1113	1137	1156	1256	1316	1337	1356	1438
142	**Klagenfurt** Hbf **980** d.	0440	...	0548	0607	0626	0704	...	0739	0804	0824	0904	...	...	0939	1004	1104	...	1139	1204	1304	...	1339	1404	1439
162	St Veit an der Glan **980** d.	|	...	0601	0627	0639	0724	...	0753	0824	0838	0924	...	...	0953	1024	1124	...	1153	1224	1324	...	1353	1424	1452
195	**Friesach** **980** a.	|	...	|	0658	0703	0756	...	|	0856	...	0956	...	...	1015	1056	1156	...	|	1256	1356	...	1415	1456	1516
	Wien Hbf **980** a.	0852	...	0935	...	...	...	...	1135	...	...	...	...	...	1335	...	...	...	1535	...	...	...	1735	...	1835

		RJ 596	RJ 630			IC 732		EC 113		IC 632				IC 734		EC 115	RJ 130			RJ 698			EC 117	IC 794	
						⑦w						Ⓐ		⑦w							◇			Ⓑ	
	2	◐✕	✕	2	2		2	◐✕	2	✕	2	2	2		2	◐⊗	V✕	2	2	◐✕	2	2	◐⊗	◐	2
Lienz d.	1224	...	...	1324	1424	1453	...	...	1524	1553	...	...	1624	1653	...	...	...	1724	1824	...	1924	2024	...	...	...
Spittal-Millstättersee a.	1322	...	...	1422	1522	1542	...	...	1622	1642	...	...	1722	1742	...	...	...	1822	1922	...	2022	2122	...	...	...
Spittal-Millstättersee **970** d.	1332	1420	...	1432	1532	1546	...	1620	1632	1646	...	...	1732	1746	...	1820	...	1832	1932	2020	2032	2132	2220	2322	...
Villach Hbf **970** a.	1404p	1443	...	1504p	1604	1609	←	1643	1704	1709	←	...	1804	1809	←	1843	...	1904p	2004	2043	2104	2204	2243	2344	...
Villach Hbf **970** d.	1420	1447	1514	1520	1620	1613	1620	1648	1720	1714	1720	1750	1820	1813	1820	1847	1914	1920	2020	2047	2120	2220	2247	2347	2350
Velden am Wörthersee **970** d.	1434	1458	1525	1534	→	1624	1634	1659	→	|	1734	1804	→	1824	1834	1858	1925	1934	2034	2058	2134	2234	2258	2358	0004
Pörtschach am W ⊡ **970** d.	1442	1504	|	1542	...	1630	1642	1705	...	1729	1742	1812	...	1830	1842	1904	|	1942	2042	2104	2142	2242	2304	0004	0012
Krumpendorf d.	1448	|	|	1548	...	|	1648	1711	...	|	1748	1818	...	|	1848	1910	|	1948	2048	2110	2148	2248	2310	|	0018
Klagenfurt Hbf **970** a.	1456	1513	1537	1556	...	1638	1656	1717	...	1737	1756	1826	...	1838	1856	1916	1937	1956	2056	2116	2156	2256	2316	0013	0026
Klagenfurt Hbf **980** d.	1504	...	1539	1604	...	1639	1704	...	...	1739	1804	1828	...	1839	1904	...	1939	2004	2104	...	2204	2304	...	...	0028
St Veit an der Glan **980** d.	1524	...	1553	1624	...	1652	1724	...	...	1753	1824	1847	...	1852	1924	...	1953	2024	2124	...	2224	2324	...	...	0047
Friesach **980** a.	1556	...	|	1656	...	1716	1756	...	...	1815	1856	...	...	1916	1956	...	|	2056	2156	...	2256	2356	...	...	...
Wien Hbf **980** a.	...	...	1935	...	...	2035	...	...	...	2135	...	...	...	2235	...	...	2335	...	...	...	...	...	...	...	...

	IC 597					RJ 691				RJ 639	EC 114			RJ 131	EC 112			IC 533		IC 793			RJ 535	RJ 797	
	①–⑥	⚒	⚒		⚒			⚒⊕	◇																
	◐	2	2	2	2	◐✕	2	U 2	2	G✕	◐⊗	2	2	V✕	◐✕	2	2	✕	2	◐	2	2	✕	◐✕	2
Wien Hbf **980** d.	...	...	...	...	...	...	...	...	...	...	...	...	...	0625	...	...	...	0825	...	...	...	...	1025	...	...
Friesach **980** d.	...	...	...	0508	0546	...	0608	0643	0708	0741	...	0808	0908	|	...	1008	1108	1144	...	...	1208	1308	|	...	1408
St Veit an der Glan **980** d.	...	...	0512	0542	0617	...	0642	0718	0742	0808	...	0842	0942	1008	...	1042	1142	1208	...	...	1242	1342	1408	...	1442
Klagenfurt Hbf **980** a.	...	...	0530	0600	0631	...	0700	0738	0800	0820	...	0900	1000	1020	...	1100	1200	1220	...	...	1300	1400	1420	...	1500
Klagenfurt Hbf **970** d.	0442	...	0532	0602	0633	0645	0702	0744	0802	0822	0842	0902	1002	1022	1027	1102	1202	1222	...	1245	1302	1402	1422	1445	1502
Krumpendorf d.	0448	...	0540	0610	0642	|	0710	0752	0810	|	0848	0910	1010	|	1033	1110	1210	|	...	|	1310	1410	|	|	1510
Pörtschach am W ⊡ **970** d.	0455	...	0547	0617	0647	0655	0717	0757	0817	0832	0855	0917	1017	|	1040	1117	1217	1232	...	1255	1317	1417	|	1455	1517
Velden am Wörthersee **970** d.	0502	...	0554	0624	0654	0702	0724	0804	0824	|	0902	0924	1024	1036	1047	1124	1224	|	...	1302	1324	1424	1436	1502	1524
Villach Hbf **970** a.	0513	...	0609	0639	0710	0713	0739	0820	0839	0846p	0913	0939	1039	1046p	1058	1139	1239	1246	←	1313	1339	1439	1446p	1513	1539
Villach Hbf **970** d.	0516	*0529*	0619a	0654	...	0716	0754	...	0854	...	0916	0954	1054	...	1116	1154	1254	1250	1254	1316	1354	1454	...	1516	1554
Spittal-Millstättersee **970** a.	0538	*0602*	0652a	0726	...	0738	0826	...	0926	...	0938	1026	1126	...	1138	1226	→	1314	1326	1338	1426	1526	...	1538	1626
Spittal-Millstättersee d.	...	0632	...	0737	...	...	0837	...	0937	...	...	1037	1137	...	...	1237	...	1316	1337	...	1437	1537	...	...	*1637*
Lienz a.	...	0732	...	0837	...	...	0937	...	1037	...	...	1137	1237	...	...	1337	...	1406	1437	...	1537	1637	...	...	*1647*

			RJ 133		RJ 110		IC 737				RJ 539		IC 895		IC 739			RJ 631	D 899			RJ 633		NJ 233	
	Ⓐ			Ⓐ			⑤y		Ⓐ						⑤y		⊖							★	
	2	2	V✕	2	◐✕	2		2	2	2	✕	2	◐✕	2		2	2	✕	◐2	2	2	✕	2.	2	2
Wien Hbf **980** d.	...	...	1225	...	...	...	1325	...	...	...	1425	...	...	...	1525	...	...	1625	...	...	...	1825	...	1923	...
Friesach **980** d.	...	1508	1544	...	...	1608	1642	...	...	1708	|	...	...	1808	1842	...	1908	1944	...	2008	2108	|	...	2302	...
St Veit an der Glan **980** d.	1512	1542	1608	1612	...	1642	1708	...	1712	1742	1808	...	...	1842	1908	...	1942	2008	...	2042	2142	2208	...	|	...
Klagenfurt Hbf **980** a.	1530	1600	1620	1630	...	1700	1719	...	1730	1800	1820	...	...	1900	1919	...	2000	2020	...	2100	2200	2220	←	2335	...
Klagenfurt Hbf **970** d.	1532	1602	1622	1632	1642	1702	1721	...	1732	1802	1822	...	1845	1902	1921	...	2002	2022	2045	2102	2232	2222	2232	2337	2340
Krumpendorf d.	1540	1610	|	1640	1648	1710	|	...	1740	1810	|	...	|	1910	|	...	2010	|	|	2110	→	|	2240	|	2349
Pörtschach am W ⊡ **970** d.	1547	1617	1632	1647	1655	1717	1731	...	1747	1817	|	...	1855	1917	1931	...	2017	2032	2055	2117	...	|	2247	|	2356
Velden am Wörthersee **970** d.	1554	1624	|	1654	1702	1724	1738	...	1754	1824	1836	...	1902	1924	1938	...	2024	|	2102	2124	...	2236	2254	|	0003
Villach Hbf **970** a.	1609	1639	1646p	1709	1713	1739	1748	←	1809	1839	1846	←	1913	1939	1948	←	2039	2046p	2113	2139	...	2246	2309	0001	0019
Villach Hbf **970** d.	1610	1654	...	1710	1716	1754	1750	1754	1810	1854	1850z	1854	1916	1954	1950	1954	2054	...	2116	2154	...	*2254*	...	...	...
Spittal-Millstättersee **970** a.	1634	1726	...	1734	1738	→	1814	1826	1834	→	1914z	1926	1938	→	2014	2026	2126	...	2138	2226	...	*2326*	...	...	...
Spittal-Millstättersee d.	1637	1737	...	...	...	...	1816	1837	...	...	1916z	1937	...	...	2016	*2037*	2143	...	...	...	...	...	...	...	...
Lienz a.	1737	1837	...	...	...	...	1906	1937	...	...	2006z	2037	...	...	2106	*2136*	2241	...	...	...	...	...	...	...	...

G – From Graz (Table **980**).
U – To / from Unzmarkt (Table **980**).
V – From / to Venezia (Table **88**).
a – Ⓐ only.
e – ①–⑤ only.

p – Connects with train in previous column.
r – ⚒ only.
w – Also June 6, Aug. 15, Nov.1; not June 5, Aug. 14, Oct. 30.
y – Also June 15, Dec. 7; not June 17, Dec 9.
z – ①②③④⑦ only.

⊕ – Change trains at Klagenfurt on Ⓐ.
◇ – Change trains at Spittal-Millstättersee on Ⓐ.
⊖ – Change trains at Spittal-Millstättersee on Ⓑ.
★ – See Table **980** for through cars to / from Roma and Milano.
◐ – See Table **970** for further details.
⊡ – Pörtschach am Wörthersee.

2nd class only (except *IC* trains) LINZ - SELZTHAL 974

km							IC 503													IC 603						
		⚒	⚒											Ⓐ			Ⓐ									
0	**Linz** Hbf d.	0457	0506	0536	0657	0736	0757	0836	1057	1136	1236	1257	1357	1406	1457	1536	1557	1657	1736	1757	1857	1936	2036	2136	2236	2336
28	Rohr - Bad Hall d.	0519	0540	0610	0719	0810	0819	0909	1119	1209	1309	1319	1419	1440	1519	1409	1619	1719	1810	1819	1919	2010	2110	2210	2310	0010
32	Kremsmünster d.	0524	0546	0616	0724	0816	0824	0915	1124	1215	1315	1324	1424	1446	1524	1415	1624	1724	1815	1824	1924	2015	2116	2215	2315	0015
51	Kirchdorf a. d. Krems d.	0537	0604	0633	0737	0833	0839	0933	1139	1233	1333	1339	1437	1503	1539	1433	1637	1739	1833	1839	1939	2033	2139	2233	2334	0033
68	Hinterstoder d.	0601	...	...	0801	...	0900	...	1201	...	...	1401	1501	...	1601	...	1659	1801	...	1900	2001	...	2201r	...	2355	...
82	Windischgarsten d.	0615	...	...	0815	...	0913	...	1215	...	...	1415	1515	...	1615	...	1713	1815	...	1913	2015	...	2215r	...	0010	...
87	Spital am Pyhrn d.	0621	...	...	0821	...	|	...	1221	...	...	1421	1520	...	1621	...	1719	1821	...	|	2021	...	2221r	...	0016	...
104	**Selzthal** a.	0641	...	...	0840	...	0933	...	1240	...	...	1440	...	...	1640	...	1734	1840	...	1933	2040	...	2240r	...	0032	...
	Liezen **975** a.	0700	...	...	0851a	...	|	...	1251a	...	...	1451a	...	...	1648a	...	...	...	...	|	...	...	...	...	...	...
	Graz Hbf **975** a.	...	...	...	...	...	1103	...	...	...	...	...	...	...	...	...	...	...	...	2103	...	...	...	...	...	...

												IC 500										IC 600			
		Ⓐ		⚒	⚒		Ⓐ	Ⓐ	Ⓒ											Ⓐ					
Graz Hbf **975** d.	...	...	...	...	...	...	...	...	...	...	...	0656	...	...	...	...	...	...	...	...	...	...	1656	...	...	...
Liezen **975** d.	...	...	...	...	...	...	...	...	...	0706a	...	|	...	0906a	...	...	1306a	...	1506a	...	...	...	|	...	...	...
Selzthal d.	...	0420	...	...	0520	...	...	0615	0615	0720	...	0826	...	0920	1120	...	1320	...	1520	...	...	...	1826	1920	...	2120
Spital am Pyhrn d.	...	0438	...	...	0538	...	...	0638	0638	0738	...	|	...	0938	1138	...	1338	...	1538	...	1637	...	|	1938	...	2138
Windischgarsten d.	...	0444	...	...	0544	...	...	0644	0644	0744	...	0846	...	0944	1144	...	1344	...	1544	...	1643	...	1846	1944	...	2144
Hinterstoder d.	...	0500	...	...	0600	...	...	0700	0700	0800	...	0900	...	1000	1200	...	1400	...	1600	...	1700	...	1900	2000	...	2200
Kirchdorf a. d. Krems d.	0425	0521	0525	0555	0621	0625	0649	0721	0725	0821	0825	0918	0925	1021	1221	1325	1421	1425	1621	1650	1725	1825	1918	2021	2125	2221
Kremsmünster d.	0445	0535	0545	0615	0635	0645	0703	0735	0745	0835	0845	0935	0945	1035	1235	1345	1435	1445	1635	1715	1745	1845	1935	2035	2145	2235
Rohr - Bad Hall d.	0449	0540	0549	0619	0640	0649	0709	0740	0749	0840	0849	0940	0949	1040	1240	1349	1440	1449	1640	1719	1749	1849	1940	2040	2149	2240
Linz Hbf a.	0524	0604	0624	0654	0704	0724	0738	0804	0824	0904	0924	1004	1024	1104	1304	1424	1504	1524	1704	1754	1824	1924	2004	2104	2224	2304

a – Ⓐ only.
r – ⚒ only.

☛ Additional trains run Linz - Kirchdorf and v.v.:
From **Linz** at 0636, 0936, 1036, 1336, 1436, 1636, 1836.
From **Kirchdorf** at 1025, 1125, 1225, 1525, 1625, 1925, 2025.

975 SALZBURG - BISCHOFSHOFEN - SELZTHAL - GRAZ

km			*NJ*		*D*			*IC*		*IC*			*IC*		*RJ*	*IC*		*IC*		*EC*			*EC*	*EC*		
			465		**619**			**719**		**503**			**513**		**111**	**515**		**507**		**217**			**113**	**163**		
		⚒		⚒	①–⑥	Ⓐ			Ⓐ			⚒					Ⓐ				Ⓐ				Ⓐ	
		2	**A**	2	**d**2	2	2	⊗	2	🍷	2	2	🍷	2		🍷	2**L**		2	**G**⊗	2**L**	2		**Z**✕	2	2
0	**Salzburg** Hbf ...... **960 970** d.	...	...	...	🍷	...	...	0616	...	...	...	*0621*	0816	...	1012	...	...	...	...	1216	...	...	1412	...	...	...
	Innsbruck Hbf **960** .... d.	...	0056	...	...	...	...	|	...	...	...	|	|	...	|	0821	...	...	...	|	...	...	|	1221	...	...
	Schwarzach ⊖. **960 970** d.	...	0324	...	0446	...	...	|	...	...	...	|	|	...	|	1056	...	...	...	|	...	...	|	1456	...	...
53	**Bischofshofen** ... **960 970** a.	...	0336	...	0500	...	...	0702	...	...	...	*0722*	0902	...	1052	1110	...	...	...	1302	...	...	1452	1510	...	...
53	**Bischofshofen** .... d.	...	0338	...	0502	...	...	0712	...	...	...	0741	0912	...	...	1112	...	...	...	1312	...	...	...	1512	...	...
77	Radstadt .... d.	...	|	...	0527	...	0610	0735	...	...	0809	0809	0935	...	...	1135	...	...	...	1335	...	...	...	1535	...	...
94	Schladming .... d.	...	0416	0500	0544	...	0629	0752	...	...	0831	0831	0952	1031	...	1152	...	...	1231	1352	...	1431	...	1552	...	1631
133	**Stainach-Irdning** .... d.	0415	0446	0541	0619	...	0710	0822	...	...	0912	0912	1022	1112	...	1222	...	...	1312	1422	...	1512	...	1622	...	1712
145	Liezen .... d.	0427	0457	0553	0629	...	0726	0832	0857	...	0926	0926	1032	1126	...	1232	1305	...	1326	1432	1505	1526	...	1632	1704	1726
	Linz Hbf **974** .... d.	|	|	|	|	...	|	|	|	0757	|	|	|	|	...	|	|	1157	|	|	|	|	...	|	|	|
152	**Selzthal** .... a.	0433	0504	0559	0636	...	0732	0839	0904	0933	0932	0932	1039	1132	...	1239	1312	1333	1332	1439	1512	1532	...	1639	1711	1732
152	**Selzthal** .... d.	0440	0513	0606	0644	0716	0739	0848	...	0935	0939	0939	1048	1139	...	1248	...	1335	1339	1446	...	1539	...	1648	...	1739
158	Stadt Rottenmann .... d.	0447	|	0613	0652	0722	0745	|	...	0942	0945	0945	|	1145	...	|	...	1342	1345	|	...	1545	...	|	...	1745
169	Trieben............................. d.	0455	|	0621	|	0729	0753	|	...	|	0953	0953	|	1153	...	|	...	|	1353	|	...	1553	...	|	...	1753
215	St Michael .... **980** a.	0530	0550	0655	0721	0802	0828	0921	...	|	1028	1028	1121	1228	...	1321	...	|	1428	1521	...	1628	...	1721	...	1828
225	Leoben Hbf .... **980** a.	0538	0557	0708	0728	0810	*0840*	0928	...	1017	*1040*	*1040*	1128	*1240*	...	1328	...	1417	*1440*	1528	...	*1640*	...	1728	...	*1840*
	Bruck a. d. Mur .... **980** a.	|	0610	|	|	0825	*0853*	|	...	|	*1053*	*1053*	|	*1253*	...	|	...	|	*1453*	|	...	*1653*	...	|	...	*1853*
293	**Graz** Hbf .... **980** a.	0634	0700	0801	0817**t**	*0925*	...	1014	...	1103	...	...	1214	...	...	1414	...	1503	...	1614	...	...	...	1814	...	...

	IC	*IC*			*EC*	*EC*		*D*		
	611	**603**			**219**	**117**		**615**		
				Ⓐ				⑦**e**	Ⓐ	†
	🍷	🍷	2	2	**F**⊗		2	2🍷	2	2
Salzburg Hbf.......... **960 970** d.	1616	...	...	*1643*	1816	2012	...	...	...	...
Innsbruck Hbf **960** .... d.	|	...	...	|	|	|	...	...	...	...
Schwarzach ⊖ ....**960 970** d.	|	...	...	|	|	|	...	2056	...	...
Bischofshofen.......**960 970** a.	1702	...	...	*1735*	1902	2052	...	2110	...	...
Bischofshofen.................... d.	1712	...	...	1741	1912	...	2057	2112	...	...
Radstadt............................. d.	1735	...	...	1810	1935	...	2127	2135	...	...
Schladming........................ d.	1752	...	1831	...	1952	...	2146	2152	2152	2210
Stainach-Irdning............... d.	1822	...	1912	...	2022	...	...	2222	2231	2249
Liezen................................ d.	1832	...	1926	...	2032	...	...	2232	...	...
Linz Hbf **974**..................... d.	|	1757	|	...	|	...	...	|	...	...
Selzthal............................. a.	1839	1933	1932	...	2039	...	...	2239	...	...
Selzthal............................. d.	1848	1935	1939	...	2048	...	...	2246	...	...
Stadt Rottenmann............... d.	|	1942	1945	...	|	...	...	2253	...	...
Trieben............................... d.	|	|	1953	...	|	...	...	|	...	...
St Michael .... **980** a.	1921	|	2028	...	2121	...	...	2321	...	...
Leoben Hbf.................. **980** a.	1928	2017	*2041*	...	2128	...	...	2328	...	...
Bruck a. d. Mur.......... **980** a.	|	|	*2054*	...	|	...	...	|	...	...
Graz Hbf .... **980** a.	2014	2103	...	...	2214	...	...	0014	...	...

					EC		*IC*		*IC*	
					218		**500**		**512**	
	⚒	⚒		Ⓐ				Ⓐ		
	2	2	2	2	**F**⊗	2	🍷	2**L**	🍷	2
Graz Hbf.................. **980** d.	...	...	...	...	0545	...	0656	...	0745	...
Bruck a. d. Mur...... **980** d.	...	...	...	*0536*	|	*0706*	|	...	|	*0906*
Leoben Hbf............... **980** d.	...	...	...	*0549*	0630	*0719*	0741	...	0831	*0919*
St Michael................ **980** d.	...	...	...	0600	0638	0731	|	...	0838	0931
Trieben .... d.	...	...	...	0636	|	0805	|	...	|	1005
Stadt Rottenmann .... d.	...	...	...	0644	0708	0812	0818	...	|	1012
Selzthal......................... a.	...	...	...	0650	0713	0818	0823	...	0911	1018
Selzthal......................... d.	...	0544	...	...	0719	0826	0826	0844	0919	1026
Linz Hbf **974**................ a.	...	|	...	...	|	|	1004	|	|	|
Liezen............................. d.	...	0552	...	...	0727	0832	...	0851	0927	1032
Stainach-Irdning............ d.	...	0604	...	...	0738	0845	...	...	0938	1045
Schladming...................... d.	0506	0647	0647	...	0810	0928	...	...	1010	1128
Radstadt.......................... d.	0526	0705	0705	...	0826	...	...	...	1026	...
Bischofshofen................ a.	0554	0734	0734	...	0848	...	...	...	1048	...
Bischofshofen...**960 970** d.	*0558*	*0740*	*0740*	...	0857	...	...	...	1057	...
Schwarzach ⊖ **960 970** a.	|	|	|	...	|	...	...	...	|	...
Innsbruck Hbf **960** .... a.	|	|	|	...	|	...	...	...	|	...
Salzburg Hbf......**960 970** a.	*0645*	*0840*	*0840*	...	0944	...	...	...	1144	...

	EC	*EC*			*EC*			*IC*	*RJ*				*IC*					*IC*		*IC*			*D*	*D*	*NJ*
	164	**112**			**216**			**518**	**797**				**610**					**600**		**718**			**614**	**899**	**464**
				Ⓐ			Ⓐ				Ⓐ	Ⓐ		Ⓐ	Ⓐ		Ⓑ		⚒			⑥			
	Z✕	✕	2	2**L**	**G**⊗	2	2**L**	🍷	✕	2	2**L**	2	🍷	2	2	2	2	🍷	2	⊗	2	2	2🍷	2	**A**
Graz Hbf .... **980** d.	0945	...	...	...	1145	...	...	1345	...	...	...	1501	1545	...	...	...	...	1656	1701**f**	1745	...	...	1945	...	2226
Bruck a. d. Mur.......... **980** d.	|	...	*1106*	...	|	*1306*	...	|	...	*1506*	...	|	|	...	...	*1706*	*1706*	|	|	|	*1906*	*1906*	|	...	2317
Leoben Hbf.................. **980** d.	1030	...	*1119*	...	1230	*1319*	...	1430	...	*1519*	...	1557	1630	...	...	*1719*	*1719*	1741	1801	1830	*1919*	*1919*	2030	...	2330
St Michael .... **980** d.	1038	...	1131	...	1238	1331	...	1438	...	1531	...	1608	1638	...	...	1731	1731	|	1810	1838	1931	1931	2038	...	2340
Trieben............................... d.	|	...	1205	...	|	1405	...	|	...	1605	...	1644	|	...	...	1805	1805	|	1846	|	2005	2005	|	...	|
Stadt Rottenmann............... d.	|	...	1212	...	|	1412	...	|	...	1612	...	1652	|	...	...	1812	1812	1818	1854	|	2012	2012	2108	...	|
Selzthal............................. a.	1111	...	1218	...	1311	1418	...	1511	...	1618	...	1658	1711	...	...	1818	1818	1823	1900	1911	2018	2018	2113	...	0017
Selzthal............................. d.	1119	...	1226	1244	1319	1426	1444	1519	...	1626	1641	...	1719	...	1746	1826	1826	1826	...	1919	2026	2026	2120	...	0028
Linz Hbf **974**..................... a.	|	...	|	|	|	|	|	|	...	|	|	...	|	...	|	|	|	2004	...	|	|	|	|	...	|
Liezen................................ d.	1127	...	1232	1251	1327	1432	1451	1527	...	1632	1648	...	1727	...	1753	1832	1832	...	...	1927	2032	2032	2127	...	0036
Stainach-Irdning............... d.	1138	...	1245	...	1338	1445	...	1538	...	1645	...	...	1738	...	1806	1845	1845	...	...	1937	2045	2045	2137	...	0046
Schladming........................ d.	1210	...	1328	...	1410	1528	...	1610	...	1728	...	...	1810	...	1848	1928	1929	...	...	2010	2126	2134	2210	...	0118
Radstadt............................. d.	1226	...	...	...	1426	...	...	1626	...	...	...	...	1826	1920	...	...	1952	...	...	2026	...	2154	2226	...	|
Bischofshofen.................... a.	1248	...	...	...	1448	...	...	1648	...	...	...	...	1848	1950	...	...	...	...	...	2048	...	...	2251	...	0156
Bischofshofen.......**960 970** d.	1250	1307	...	...	1457	...	...	1650	1707	...	...	...	1857	*2004*	...	...	...	...	...	2057	...	...	2253	2307	0158
Schwarzach ⊖ ....**960 970** a.	1305	|	...	...	|	...	...	1705	|	...	...	...	|	|	...	...	...	...	...	|	...	...	2308	|	0211
Innsbruck Hbf **960** .... a.	1540	|	...	...	|	...	...	1940	|	...	...	...	|	|	...	...	...	...	...	|	...	...	...	|	0449
Salzburg Hbf..........**960 970** a.	...	1348	...	...	1544	...	...	...	1748	...	...	...	1944	*2051*	...	...	...	...	...	2144	...	...	...	2348	...

A – 🛏 1, 2 cl., 🛏 2 cl. and (2) Graz - Innsbruck - Buchs 🏛 - Zürich and v.v.
F – CHIEMGAU – (12) and ⊗ Graz - München - Stuttgart - Frankfurt and v.v.
G – DACHSTEIN – (12) Graz - München - Stuttgart - Saarbrücken and v.v.
L – To / from Linz (Table **974**).
Z – TRANSALPIN – (12) and ✕ Zürich - Graz and v.v.

d – Also June 5, Aug. 14, Oct. 30; not June 6, Aug. 15, Nov. 1.
e – Also June 6, Aug. 15, Nov. 1; not June 5, Aug. 14, Oct. 30.
f – On ⑥ change at Leoben.
t – 0823 on July 30, Aug. 1, 2, 6, 8, 9.

⊖ – Schwarzach-St Veit.

976 LINZ - STEYR - KLEINREIFLING - WEISSENBACH

2nd class only

km		⚒	Ⓐ		Ⓐ	Ⓒ		Ⓒ	Ⓐ			Ⓒ	Ⓐ			Ⓒ	Ⓐ		Ⓐ		Ⓒ	Ⓐ		Ⓐ		Ⓒ
0	**Linz** Hbf............. **950 992** d.	0425	0514	0619	0649	0649	0752	0752	0822	0852	0952	0952	*1030*	1052	1152	1152	1222	1252	1252	1352	1352	1422	1452	1522	1552	1552
17	Enns .... **992** d.	0442	0532	0637	0707	0707	0810	0810	0840	0910	1010	1010	|	1110	1210	1210	1240	1310	1310	1410	1410	1440	1510	1540	1610	1610
25	St Valentin .... **950** d.	0509**v**	0540	0649	0721**t**	0721**t**	0821	0821	0851	0921	1021	1021	1051	1121	1221	1221	1251	1321	1321	1421	1421	1451	1521	1551	1621	1621
45	**Steyr**............................. d.	0532	0605	0714	0754**t**	0754**t**	0846	0846	0912	0946	1046	1046	1112	1146	1246	1246	1312	1346	1346	1446	1446	1512	1546	1612	1646	1646
47	Garsten............................ d.	0536	0608	0717	0758	0758	0849	0850	0916	0949	1049	1050	1116	1149	1249	1250	1316	1349	1350	1449	1450	1516	1549	1616	1649	1650
67	Losenstein........................ d.	0601	...	...	0822	0822	...	0917	0937	...	...	1117	1137	...	...	1317	1337	...	1423	...	1517	1537	...	1640	...	1717
89	Kastenreith................ **977** a.	0628	...	...	0848	0852	...	0941	1004	...	...	1141	1204	...	...	1341	1404	...	1447	...	1541	1604	...	1704	...	1741
92	**Kleinreifling** .... **977** a.	0633	...	...	0852	0856	...	0946	1008	...	...	1146	1208	...	...	1346	1408	...	1451	...	1546	1608	...	1708	...	1746
106	Weißenbach ⊡ .... **977** a.	0648**a**	...	...	0907	*0916*	...	...	...	...	...	*1216*	...	...	...	*1416*	...	...	...	...	...	1623	...	1723	...	*1816*

	Ⓐ		Ⓐ		Ⓒ	Ⓐ					
Linz Hbf.......**950 992** d.	1622	1652	1722	1752	1752	1822	*1852*	1952	*2052*	2152	2252
Enns...................**992** d.	1640	1710	1740	1810	1810	1840	*1910*	2010	*2110*	2210	2310
St Valentin...........**950** d.	1651	1721	1751	1821	1821	1851	1921	2021	2121	2221	2321
Steyr......................... d.	1712	1746	1812	1846	1846	1912	1946	2045	2146	2246	2346
Garsten .... d.	1716	1749	1816	1849	1850	1916	1949	2048	2149	2249	2349
Losenstein .... d.	1737	...	1841	...	1917	1937	...	2111	...	...	...
Kastenreith ....**977** a.	1804	...	1905	...	1941	2005	...	2135	...	...	...
Kleinreifling........**977** a.	1808	...	1910	...	1946	2009	...	2139	...	...	...
Weißenbach ⊡....**977** a.	1823	...	1924	...	...	...	...	...	...	...	...

	P	Ⓐ	⚒		Ⓐ			Ⓐ	Ⓐ		Ⓒ
Weißenbach ⊡.**977** d.	...	...	...	...	...	0603**a**	...	0706	...	...	...
Kleinreifling....**977** d.	...	0437	0513	...	...	0618	...	0721	0754	...	0812
Kastenreith ......**977** d.	...	0441	0517	...	...	0622	...	0724	0758	...	0816
Losenstein .... d.	...	0505	0540	...	...	0647	...	...	0822	...	0843
Garsten.................... d.	0442	0527	0601	0609	0637	0709	0809	...	0843	0909	0909
Steyr .... d.	0446	0532	0606	0614	0642	0714	0814	...	0847	0914	0914
St Valentin.......**950** d.	0511	0556	0623	0641	0711	0741	0841	...	0907	0941	0941
Enns..................**992** d.	0518	0602	0628	0646	0718	0748	0848	...	|	0948	0948
Linz Hbf ...**950 992** a.	0536	0617	0640	0700	0738	0808	0908	...	*0930*	1008	1008

		Ⓐ		Ⓒ		Ⓐ		Ⓒ		Ⓐ		Ⓒ	Ⓐ		Ⓐ		Ⓒ	Ⓐ		Ⓐ	Ⓐ		Ⓒ			
Weißenbach ⊡....**977** d.	...	0940	...	...	...	...	...	*1144*	...	1338	...	*1341*	...	...	...	...	*1541*	...	...	1639	1738	...	*1744*	...	*1941*	...
Kleinreifling........**977** d.	...	0954	...	1015	...	1154	...	1215	...	1354	...	1415	...	...	1554	...	1615	...	...	1654	1753	...	1815	...	2021	...
Kastenreith ....**977** d.	...	0958	...	1019	...	1158	...	1219	...	1358	...	1419	...	...	1558	...	1619	...	...	1658	1757	...	1819	...	2025	...
Losenstein................. d.	...	1022	...	1044	...	1222	...	1244	...	1422	...	1444	...	...	1621	...	1644	...	...	1744**v**	1821	...	1844	...	2050	...
Garsten .... d.	1009	1043	1109	1109	1209	1243	1309	1309	1409	1443	1509	1509	1543	1609	1643	1709	1709	1743	1809	1809	1843	1909	1909	2009	2113	2209
Steyr .... d.	1014	1047	1114	1114	1214	1247	1314	1314	1414	1447	1514	1514	1547	1614	1647	1714	1714	1747	1814	1814	1847	1914	1914	2014	2116	2214
St Valentin...........**950** d.	1041	1111	1141	1141	1241	1311	1341	1341	1441	1511	1541	1541	1607	1641	1711	1741	1741	1807	1841	1841	1907	1941	1941	2041	2141	2241
Enns...................**992** d.	1048	1118	1148	1148	1248	1318	1348	1348	1448	1518	1548	1548	|	1648	1718	1748	1748	|	1848	1848	|	1948	1948	2048	2148	2248
Linz Hbf ....**950 992** a.	1108	1138	1208	1208	1308	1338	1408	1408	1508	1538	1608	1608	*1630*	1708	1738	1808	1808	*1830*	1908	1908	*1930*	2008	2008	2108	2206	2306

P – To Passau (Table **962**). **a** – Ⓐ only. **k** – ⑥ only. **t** – Arrives 8–9 minutes earlier. **v** – Arrives 19–20 minutes earlier. ⊡ – Weißenbach-St Gallen.

AMSTETTEN - KLEINREIFLING - SELZTHAL — 977

nd class only

km																								
		⚒	⚒		†		Ⓒ	Ⓒ	Ⓐ		Ⓒ	Ⓐ		Ⓐ	Ⓒ	Ⓐ	Ⓐ		Ⓒ	Ⓒ	Ⓐ		Ⓐ	†	⑥
	Wien Westbahnhof **950** d.	...	0424a	...	...	...	0620	...	...	...	...	...	...	...	1120	...	...	...	1220	...	...	...	...	1520	...
0	**Amstetten** d.	0451	0621	0704	0704	0804	0804	0904	0904	1004	1104	1104	1204	1204	1304	1304	1324	1404	1404	1504	1504	1604	1604	1704	1704
23	Waidhofen a. d. Ybbs d.	0548**h**	0710**j**	0730	0731	0830	0831	0931	0931	1030	1131	1131	1230	1231	1331	1331	1352	1431	1431	1531	1531	1630	1631	1731	1731
41	Weyer d.	0608	0729	...	0748	...	0852	0948	0948	...	1148	1148	...	1248	1348	1348	...	1448	1448	1548	1548	...	1648	1748	1748
44	Kastenreith **976** d.	0611	0733	...	0752	...	0856	0952	0952	...	1152	1152	...	1252	1352	1352	...	1452	1452	1552	1552	...	1652	1752	1752
47	**Kleinreifling** **976** a.	0615	0737	...	0756	...	0859	0956	*1008*	...	1156	*1208*	...	1256	1356	*1408*	...	1456	1456	1556	*1608*	...	*1708*	1756	1756
61	Weißenbach-St Gallen . **976** a.	*0648***a**	...	...	...	...	0916	...	...	...	1216	...	...	...	1416	...	...	...	1516	...	*1623*	...	*1723*	...	1816
19	**Selzthal** a.	...	...	...	...	...	1015	...	...	...	...	...	...	...	...	...	...	...	1615	...	...	...	...	...	...

	Ⓐ		Ⓐ	†			e				
Wien Westbahnhof **950** d.	...	...	...	...	...	...	...	1920**v**	...	...	...
nstetten d.	1704	1804	1804	1804	1904	2004	2004	2104	2204	2304	0010
aidhofen a. d. Ybbs d.	1731	1830	1831	1831	1931	2030	2034	2130	2230	2330	0036
eyer d.	1748	...	1848	1848	1948	...	2051	...	...	...	...
astenreith **976** d.	1752	...	1852	1852	1952	...	2056	...	...	...	...
einreifling **976** a.	*1808*	...	1956	1856	1956	...	2059	...	...	...	...
eißenbach-St Gallen ... **976** a.	*1823*	...	...	1911	...	...	...	...	...	...	...
elzthal a.	...	...	...	...	...	...	...	...	...	...	...

	⚒	Ⓐ		Ⓐ	Ⓐ		⚒		
Selzthal d.	...	...	...	...	...	...	...	...	...
Weißenbach-St Gallen .. **976** d.	...	...	...	...	...	...	*0603***a**	...	*0706***a**
Kleinreifling **976** d.	...	...	...	0504	...	0600	0623	...	0804
Kastenreith **976** d.	...	...	...	0508	...	0604	0632	...	0808
Weyer d.	...	...	...	0512	...	0610	0635	...	0812
Waidhofen a. d. Ybbs d.	0431	0459	0531	0531	0550	0629	0654	0735	0831
Amstetten a.	0456	0526	0556	0556	0615	0656	0720	0756	0856
Wien Westbahnhof **950** .. a.	0640**a**	0710	0740	0740	0810	...	...	0940	...

		Ⓐ	Ⓒ		Ⓐ	Ⓒ	Ⓒ	Ⓐ	Ⓐ	Ⓒ		Ⓐ	Ⓐ	Ⓒ		Ⓐ	Ⓐ	Ⓒ		†		Ⓐ	Ⓒ		
elzthal d.	...	...	...	...	...	1045	...	...	...	...	...	...	...	...	...	...	...	1645	...	...	...	...	...	...	...
eißenbach-St Gallen ... **976** d.	...	*0940*	...	...	...	1144	...	...	*1338*	1341	...	...	...	*1541*	...	*1639*	*1738*	1744	...	...	1941	...	...	...	...
leinreifling **976** d.	...	*0954*	1004	...	*1154*	1204	...	1304	*1354*	1404	...	1504	*1554*	1604	...	*1654*	*1753*	1804	...	1904	1955	2000	2004	...	...
astenreith **976** d.	...	1008	1008	...	1208	1208	...	1308	1408	1408	...	1508	1608	1608	...	1708	1808	1808	...	1908	...	2008	2008	...	...
eyer d.	...	1012	1012	...	1212	1212	...	1312	1412	1412	...	1512	1612	1612	...	1712	1812	1812	...	1912	...	2012	2012	...	...
aidhofen a. d. Ybbs d.	0931	1031	1031	1131	1231	1231	1331	1331	1431	1431	1531	1531	1631	1631	1731	1731	1831	1831	1931	1931	...	2031	2031	2131	2231
mstetten a.	0956	1056	1056	1156	1256	1256	1356	1356	1456	1456	1556	1556	1656	1656	1756	1756	1856	1856	1956	1956	...	2056	2056	2156	2256
Wien Westbahnhof **950** a.	...	...	...	...	...	1440	1540	...	...	...	...	...	...	...	...	...	...	2040	...	...	...	...	...	...	...

– Ⓐ only. **e** – ①②③④⑦. **h** – Arrives 0525. **j** – Arrives 0652. **v** – † only.

WIEN - GRAZ and KLAGENFURT — 980

km																										
				RJ **639**	*RJ* **72**				*RJ* **551**		*RJ* **131**		*RJ* **553**		*EC* **151**	*RJ* **558**	*IC* **533**	*RJ* **71**		*RJ* **559**		*RJ* **535**		*RJ* **73**		*RJ* **653**
		Ⓐ	⚒			†	⚒	†																		
		2	2	✕	✕	2	2	2	✕	2	V✕	2	✕	2	E✕	✕	L✕	P✕	2	✕	2	✕	2	P✕	2	✕
	Flughafen Wien ✈ ..... **985** d.	...	...	...	...	...	...	...	...	...	...	...	0633	...	...	...	...	...	...	0933	...	...	...	...	...	1133
0	**Wien** Hbf .... **981 985** d.	...	...	...	...	...	...	...	0558	...	0625	...	0658	...	0758	...	0825	0858	...	0958	...	1025	...	1058	...	1158
4	**Wien** Meidling .... **981** d.	...	...	...	...	...	...	...	0605	...	0632	...	0705	...	0805	...	0832	0905	...	1005	...	1032	...	1105	...	1205
49	**Wiener Neustadt** Hbf.. **981** a.	...	...	...	...	...	...	...	0628	...	0654	...	0728	...	0828	...	0854	0928	...	1028	...	1054	...	1128	...	1228
	Wiener Neustadt Hbf.. **981** d.	...	...	...	...	...	...	...	0632	...	0656	...	0732	...	0832	...	0856	0932	...	1032	...	1056	...	1132	...	1232
04	Semmering .... **981** d.	...	...	...	...	...	...	...	|	...	|	...	|	...	0914	...	|	1014	...	1114	...	|	...	|	...	1314
18	Mürzzuschlag .... **981** d.	...	0520	...	...	0620	0622	...	0729	...	|	...	0829	...	0929	...	|	1029	...	1129	...	|	...	1229	...	1329
	Graz Hbf............ **975** ▷ d.	...	|	0519	0626	|	|	0612	|	*0726*	|	...	|	*0826*	|	0926	|	|	*1026*	|	*1126*	|	...	|	*1226*	|
58	**Bruck** an der Mur............ a.	...	0601	0557	0701	0701	0703	0658	0756	*0801*	0813	...	0856	*0901*	0956	1001	1013	1056	*1101*	1156	*1201*	1213	...	1256	*1301*	1356
58	**Bruck** an der Mur... **975** ⊙ d.	0436	0608	0609	...	0708	0706	0706	0758	0806	0815	...	0858	0906	0958	...	1015	1058	1106	1158	1206	1215	...	1258	1306	1358
12	**Graz** Hbf.................. ⊙ a.	|	0655	|	...	0755	|	|	0833	|	|	...	0933	|	1033	...	|	1133	|	1233	|	|	...	1333	|	1433
74	Leoben Hbf .... **975** d.	0451	▬	0622	...	...	0721	0721	▬	0821	0827	...	...	0921	▬	...	1027	...	1121	▬	1221	1227	...	...	1321	▬
◧	St Michael .... **975** a.	0458	...	|	...	...	0728	0728	...	0828	|	←	...	0928	...	...	|	...	1128	...	1228	|	←	...	1328	...
◧	St Michael .... d.	0507	...	|	...	...	0734	0734	...	0834	|	0834	...	0934	...	...	|	...	1134	...	1234	|	1234	...	1334	...
05	Knittelfeld .... d.	0525	...	0642	...	...	0752	0752	...	→	0847	0852	...	0952	...	...	1047	...	1152	...	→	1247	1252	...	1352	...
13	Zeltweg .... d.	0531	⚒	|	...	...	0758	0758	...	...	|	0858	...	0958	...	...	|	...	1158	...	...	|	1258	...	1358	...
20	Judenburg .... d.	0539	2	0655	...	...	0806	0806	...	...	0859	0906	...	1006	...	...	1059	...	1206	...	...	1259	1306	...	1406	...
39	Unzmarkt........................... d.	0554	0608	0709	...	...	0822	0822	2L	...	0913	0921	...	1022	2L	...	1113	...	1222	2L	...	1313	1321	...	1422	2L
76	Friesach .... **971** a.	...	0642	0739	...	...	0855	0855	0908	...	|	...	...	1055	1108	...	1143	...	1255	1308	...	|	...	...	1455	1508
09	St Veit an der Glan...... **971** a.	...	0716	0806	...	...	...	...	0940	...	1006	...	...	...	1140	...	1206	...	...	1340	...	1406	...	...	...	1540
29	**Klagenfurt** Hbf....... **971** ▷ a.	...	0738	0820	...	...	...	...	1000	...	1020	...	...	...	1200	...	1220	...	...	1400	...	1420	...	...	...	1600
	Villach Hbf **971** .... a.	...	0820**t**	0846	...	...	...	...	1039	...	1046	...	...	...	1239	...	1246	...	...	1439	...	1446	...	...	...	1639

	RJ **656**	*RJ* **133**	*RJ* **75**		*IC* **737**		*RJ* **657**	*RJ* **750**	*RJ* **539**	*RJ* **257**		*IC* **739**			*EC* **159**		*RJ* **631**		*RJ* **79**			*D* **859**	*RJ* **755**		*RJ* **633**	
					⑤f		‡					⑤f	⚒		¶						Ⓐ	Ⓐ	§			
	✕	V✕	P✕	2	L	2L	✕	✕	L✕	N✕	2	L	2	2L	F✕	2	✕	2	P✕	2	2	2	✕	2	✕	2
ughafen Wien ✈ ......**985** d.	...	...	...	...	...	...	1333	...	...	...	...	...	...	...	...	...	...	...	...	...	...	...	1733	...	...	...
ien Hbf..............**981 985** d.	...	1225	1258	...	1325	...	1358	...	1425	1458	...	1525	...	...	1558	...	1625	...	1658	...	...	1725	1758	...	1825	...
ien Meidling...............**981** d.	...	1232	1305	...	1332	...	1405	...	1432	1505	...	1532	...	...	1605	...	1632	...	1705	...	...	1732	1805	...	1832	...
iener Neustadt Hbf...**981** a.	...	1254	1328	...	1354	...	1430	...	1454	1530	...	1554	...	...	1628	...	1654	...	1730	...	...	1755	1830	...	1854	...
iener Neustadt Hbf...**981** d.	...	1256	1332	...	1356	...	1432	...	1456	1532	...	1556	...	...	1632	...	1656	...	1732	...	...	1757	1832	...	1856	...
emmering....................**981** d.	...	|	|	...	|	...	|	...	|	1614	...	|	...	...	|	...	|	...	1814	...	...	1850	1914	...	|	...
ürzzuschlag.................**981** d.	...	|	1429	...	|	...	1529	...	|	1629	...	|	...	...	1729	...	|	...	1829	...	...	1905	1929	...	|	...
Graz Hbf.............**975** ▷ d.	1326	|	|	*1426*	|	...	|	1526	|	|	*1626*	|	1701	...	|	*1726*	|	...	|	*1826*	1901	|	|	*1926*	|	...
ruck an der Mur............ a.	1401	1413	1456	*1501*	1513	...	1556	1601	1613	1656	*1701*	1713	|	...	1756	*1801*	1813	...	1856	*1901*	|	0937	1956	*2001*	2013	...
ruck an der Mur.... **975** ⊙ d.	...	1415	1458	1506	1515	...	1558	...	1615	1658	1706	1715	|	...	1758	1806	1815	...	1858	1906	|	0945	1958	2006	2015	...
Graz Hbf.................... ⊙ a.	...	|	1533	|	|	...	1633	...	|	1733	|	|	|	...	1833	|	|	...	1933	|	|	|	2033	|	|	...
eoben Hbf...................**975** d.	...	1427	...	1521	1527	...	...	...	1627	...	1721	1727	1758	...	...	1821	1827	...	...	1921	1956	2000	...	2021	2027	...
St Michael..................**975** a.	...	|	...	1528	|	...	...	...	|	...	1728	|	|	...	...	1828	|	←	...	1928	2003	|	...	2028	|	←
St Michael........................ d.	...	|	...	1534	|	...	...	...	|	...	1734	|	|	...	...	1834	|	1834	...	1934	2009	|	...	2034	|	2034
iittelfeld............................ d.	...	1447	...	1552	1546	...	...	...	1647	...	1752	1746	1820	...	...	→	1847	1852	...	1952	2027	2020	...	→	2047	2052
eltweg................................ d.	...	|	...	1558	|	...	...	...	|	...	1758	|	1827	...	...	...	|	1858	...	1958	2034	|	...	...	|	2058
denburg .... d.	...	1459	...	1606	1559	...	...	...	1659	...	1806	1759	1834	...	...	...	1859	1906	...	2006	2041	2033	...	...	2059	2106
izmarkt.............................. d.	...	1513	...	1622	|	...	...	...	1713	...	1822	|	1850	...	...	...	1913	1921	...	2021	2057	2048	...	...	2113	2121
iesach ....**971** a.	...	1543	...	1655	1641	1708	...	...	|	...	1855	1841	...	1908	...	...	1943	...	...	...	...	2119	...	...	|	...
Veit an der Glan ....**971** a.	...	1606	...	...	1707	1740	...	...	1806	...	...	1907	...	1940	...	...	2006	...	...	...	...	2147	...	...	2206	...
agenfurt Hbf........ **971** ▷ a.	...	1620	...	...	1719	1800	...	...	1820	...	...	1919	...	2000	...	...	2020	...	...	...	...	2203	...	...	2220	...
Villach Hbf **971** .... a.	...	1646	...	...	1748	1839	...	...	1846	...	...	1948	...	2039	...	...	2046	...	...	...	...	2232	...	...	2246	...

– EMONA – [12] and ✕ Wien - Graz - Spielfeld-Straß 🏛 - Maribor - Ljubljana - Trieste (Table **91**).
– CROATIA – [12] and ✕ Wien - Graz - Spielfeld-Straß 🏛 - Maribor - Zagreb (Table **91**).
– To Lienz (Table **971**).
– [12] and ✕ Berlin ★ - Praha - Břeclav 🏛 - Wien - Graz (Table **60**).
– [12] and ✕ Praha - Břeclav 🏛 - Wien - Graz (Table **60**).
– [12] and ✕ Wien - Tarvisio 🏛 - Udine - Venezia (Table **88**).

– ⑤ (also June 15, Dec. 7; not June 17, Dec. 9).
– ⚒ only.
– Change trains at Klagenfurt on Ⓐ.

◧ – Leoben - St Michael is *10 km*. St Michael - Knittelfeld is *22 km*.
¶ – Train number **1259** on Ⓒ.
§ – Train number **1255** on Ⓒ.
‡ – Train number **1057** on ⑤ (also June 15, Dec. 7; not June 17, Dec. 9).
⊙ – For other local journeys see panel below main table on page 460.
▷ – For fast **ÖBB** *Intercitybus* services Graz - Klagenfurt and v.v., see panel below main table on page 460.

980 WIEN - GRAZ and KLAGENFURT

	RJ 371		*NJ* 233	*EC* 105		*NJ* 1237	*RJ* 373	*RJ* 853	*D* 855
						③⑤			Ⓐ
	P✕	2	AR	Q✕	2	DR	P✕	✕	b2
Flughafen Wien ✈ ...... **985** d.	...	...	...	...	...	...	...	...	...
Wien Hbf .... **981 985** d.	1858	...	1923	1958	...	2001	2058	2158	2258
Wien Meidling .... **981** d.	1905	...	1931	2005	...	2008	2105	2205	2305
Wiener Neustadt Hbf ... **981** a.	1930	...	1956	2028	...	2056	2128	2228	2330
Wiener Neustadt Hbf ... **981** d.	1932	...	1958	2032	...	2058	2132	2232	2332
Semmering .... **981** d.	|	...	|	|	...	|	2214	|	0014
Mürzzuschlag .... **981** d.	2029	...	|	2129	...	|	2229	2329	0029
Graz Hbf .... **975** ▷ d.	|	*2026*	|	|	*2126*	|	|	|	|
Bruck an der Mur .... a.	2056	*2101*	2125	2156	*2201*	2220	2256	2356	0056
Bruck an der Mur ..... **975** ⊙ d.	2058	2106	2127	2158	2206	2222	2258	2358	0058
Graz Hbf .... ⊙ a.	2133	|	|	2233	|	|	2333	0033	0133
Leoben Hbf .... **975** d.	...	2121	2142	...	2220	2235	...	...	...
St Michael .... **975** a.	...	2128	|	...	|	|	...	...	...
St Michael .... d.	...	2134	|	...	|	|	...	...	...
Knittelfeld .... d.	...	2152	2206	...	2243	|	...	...	...
Zeltweg .... d.	...	2158	|	...	2249	|	...	...	...
Judenburg .... d.	...	2206	|	...	2256	|	...	...	...
Unzmarkt .... d.	...	2221	|	...	2311	|	...	...	...
Friesach .... **971** a.	...	...	2300	...	...	|	...	...	...
St Veit an der Glan .... **971** a.	...	...	|	...	...	|	...	...	...
Klagenfurt Hbf .... **971** ▷ a.	...	...	2335	...	...	0019	...	...	...
Villach Hbf **971** .... a.	...	...	0001	...	...	0043	...	...	...

	D 858				*EC* 104	*NJ* 1234	*NJ* 235			*RJ* 72	
	Ⓐ	⚒	⚒	⚒		⑤⑦		Ⓐ	©		⚒
	2	2	2	2	Q✕	RB	AR	2	2	P✕	2
Villach Hbf **971** .... d.	...	...	...	...	...	0344	0417	...	...	...	...
Klagenfurt Hbf ..... **971** ▷ d.	...	...	...	...	...	0409	0440	...	...	...	...
St Veit an der Glan .... **971** d.	...	...	...	...	...	|	|	...	...	...	050
Friesach .... **971** d.	...	...	...	...	...	|	|	...	...	...	052
Unzmarkt .... d.	...	0438	...	...	...	|	|	0548	0548	...	060
Judenburg .... d.	...	0455	...	...	...	|	|	0605	0605	...	...
Zeltweg .... d.	...	0502	...	...	...	|	|	0612	0612	...	...
Knittelfeld .... d.	...	0509	...	...	...	|	|	0619	0619	...	...
St Michael .... a.	...	0526	...	←	...	|	|	|	|	...	...
St Michael .... **975** d.	...	0535	0531	0535	...	|	|	|	|	...	...
Leoben Hbf .... **975** d.	...	→	0539	0543	...	0608	0627	0641	0641	...	...
Graz Hbf .... ⊙ d.	0414	...	|	|	0526	|	|	|	|	0626	...
Bruck an der Mur . **975** ⊙ a.	0452	...	|	0557	0601	0620	0639	0655	0655	0701	...
Bruck an der Mur .... d.	0454	...	|	*0608*	0603	0624	0641	0708	0714	0703	...
Graz Hbf .... **975** ▷ a.	|	...	0634	*0655*	|	|	|	0755	|	|	...
Mürzzuschlag .... **981** d.	0525	...	...	...	0633	|	|	...	0755	0733	...
Semmering .... **981** d.	0538	...	...	...	|	|	|	...	...	0747	...
Wiener Neustadt Hbf .. **981** a.	0626	...	...	...	0728	0748	0801	...	...	0828	...
Wiener Neustadt Hbf .. **981** d.	0630	...	...	...	0730	0752	0804	...	...	0832	...
Wien Meidling .... **981** a.	0655	...	...	...	0755	0836	0845	...	...	0855	...
Wien Hbf .... **981 985** a.	0702	...	...	...	0802	0842	0852	...	...	0902	...
Flughafen Wien ✈ ... **985** a.	...	...	...	...	...	...	...	...	...	...	...

				RJ 530	*RJ* 551			*RJ* 74	*RJ* 532	*EC* 151			*RJ* 256	*RJ* 534	*RJ* 559	*EC* 158			*RJ* 78	*RJ* 536	*RJ* 653			*RJ* 370	*RJ* 132
	Ⓐ	⚒				†																			
	2	2	2	✕	✕	2	2	P✕	✕	✕	2	2	N✕	L✕	✕	F✕	2L	2	P✕	✕	✕	2L	2	P✕	V✕
Villach Hbf **971** .... d.	...	...	...	0525	...	0529	...	...	0714	...	0720	...	...	0914	...	...	0920	...	...	1114	...	1120	...	...	1314
Klagenfurt Hbf .... **971** ▷ d.	...	...	...	0548	...	0607	...	...	0739	...	0804	...	...	0939	...	...	1004	...	...	1139	...	1204	...	...	1339
St Veit an der Glan .... **971** d.	...	...	...	0601	...	0627	...	...	0753	...	0824	...	...	0953	...	...	1024	...	...	1153	...	1224	...	...	1353
Friesach .... **971** d.	...	...	...	|	...	0659	...	...	|	...	0856	0904	...	1016	...	...	1056	1104	...	|	...	1256	1304	...	1416
Unzmarkt .... d.	0608	...	0632	|	...	0733	0738	...	0848	...	▬	0938	...	1048	...	...	▬	1138	...	1248	...	▬	1338	...	1447
Judenburg .... d.	0624	...	0649	|	...	▬	0754	...	0902	...	...	0954	...	1102	...	...	...	1154	...	1302	...	...	1354	...	1501
Zeltweg .... d.	0632	...	0656	|	...	...	0802	...	|	...	...	1002	...	|	...	...	...	1202	...	|	...	...	1402	...	|
Knittelfeld .... d.	0638	...	0703	|	...	*RJ*	0808	...	0914	...	*RJ*	1008	...	1114	...	...	...	1208	...	1314	...	*RJ*	1405	...	1514
St Michael .... a.	0655	...	|	|	...	**554**	0825	...	|	...	**558**	1025	...	|	...	...	...	1225	...	|	...	**656**	1425	...	|
St Michael .... **975** d.	0705	0701	|	|	...		0832	...	|	...		1032	...	|	...	...	...	1232	...	|	...		1432	...	|
Leoben Hbf .... **975** d.	0713	0709	0725	0733	...	✕	0841	...	0933	...	✕	1041	...	1133	...	...	...	1241	...	1333	...	✕	1441	...	1534
Graz Hbf .... ⊙ d.	|	|	|	|	...	0726	|	0826	|	...	0926	|	1026	|	...	1126	...	|	1226	|	...	1326	|	1426	|
Bruck an der Mur ..... **975** ⊙ a.	0727	|	0736	0743	...	0801	0854	0901	0943	...	1001	1054	1101	1143	...	1201	...	1254	1301	1343	...	1401	1454	1501	1544
Bruck an der Mur .... d.	...	|	*0743*r	0745	0758	0803	*0858*	0903	0945	0958	1003	*1058*	1103	1145	1158	1203	...	*1258*	1303	1345	1358	1403	*1458*	1503	1546
Graz Hbf .... **975** ▷ a.	...	0801	*0829*r	|	0833	|	*0933*	|	|	1033	|	*1133*	|	|	1233	|	...	*1333*	|	|	1433	|	*1533*	|	|
Mürzzuschlag .... **981** d.	...	...	...	|	...	0833	...	0933	|	...	1033	...	1132	|	...	1233	...	...	1333	|	...	1433	...	1533	|
Semmering .... **981** d.	...	...	...	|	...	0847	...	0947	|	...	|	...	1147	|	...	|	...	...	1347	|	...	|	...	1547	|
Wiener Neustadt Hbf ... **981** a.	...	...	...	0903	...	0928	...	1028	1103	...	1128	...	1228	1303	...	1328	...	...	1428	1503	...	1528	...	1628	1703
Wiener Neustadt Hbf ... **981** d.	...	...	...	0905	...	0932	...	1032	1105	...	1132	...	1232	1305	...	1332	...	...	1432	1505	...	1532	...	1632	1705
Wien Meidling .... **981** a.	...	...	...	0928	...	0955	...	1055	1128	...	1155	...	1255	1328	...	1355	...	...	1455	1528	...	1555	...	1655	1728
Wien Hbf .... **981 985** a.	...	...	...	0935	...	1002	...	1102	1135	...	1202	...	1302	1335	...	1402	...	...	1502	1535	...	1602	...	1702	1735
Flughafen Wien ✈ ...... **985** a.	...	...	...	...	...	1027	...	...	...	...	1227	...	...	...	...	...	...	...	...	...	...	1627	...	...	...

	RJ 657 1057			*D* 730	*RJ* 372		*RJ* 630				*IC* 732	*RJ* 374		*IC* 632					*IC* 734	*RJ* 850	*RJ* 130	*EC* 105	*D* 852		
				⑦w							⑦w					⑦z			⑦w					⑤⑥†	⚒
	✕	2L	2	2🍷	P✕	2	✕	2	2L	2	L🍷	S✕	2	L✕	2	2	2L	2	L🍷	✕	V✕	✕	2	2	2
Villach Hbf **971** .... d.	...	1320	...	1413	...	...	1514	...	1520	...	1613	...	...	1714	...	...	1720	...	1813	...	1914	...	...	...	...
Klagenfurt Hbf .... **971** ▷ d.	...	1404	...	1439	...	...	1539	...	1604	...	1639	...	...	1739	...	...	1804	...	1839	...	1939	...	...	...	...
St Veit an der Glan .... **971** d.	...	1424	...	1552	...	...	1553	...	1624	...	1652	...	...	1753	...	...	1824	...	1852	...	1953	...	...	...	...
Friesach .... **971** d.	...	1456	1504	1518	...	...	|	...	1656	1704	1718	...	...	1816	...	...	1856	1904	1918	...	|	...	...	...	...
Unzmarkt .... d.	...	▬	1538	|	...	1638	1648	...	▬	1738	|	...	1838	1848	...	1857	▬	1938	|	...	2048	...	...	2138	...
Judenburg .... d.	...	...	1554	1602	...	1654	1702	...	...	1754	1802	...	1854	1902	...	1910	...	1954	2002	...	2102	...	...	2154	...
Zeltweg .... d.	...	...	1602	|	...	1702	|	...	...	1802	|	...	1902	|	...	1918	...	2002	|	...	|	...	...	2202	...
Knittelfeld .... d.	...	*RJ*	1608	1614	...	1708	1714	...	*RJ*	1808	1814	...	1908	1914	...	1924	*EC*	2008	2014	...	2114	...	...	2208	...
St Michael .... a.	...	**750**	1625	|	...	1725	|	←	**754**	1825	|	...	1925	|	←	|	**150**	2025	|	...	|	...	...	2225	...
St Michael .... **975** d.	...		1632	|	...	1732	|	1732		1832	|	...	1932	|	1932	|		2032	|	...	|	...	...	2232	...
Leoben Hbf .... **975** d.	...	✕	1641	1633	...	→	1733	1741	✕	1841	1833	...	→	1933	1941	1945	E✕	2041	2033	...	2133	...	...	2241	...
Graz Hbf .... ⊙ d.	...	1526	|	|	1626	...	|	|	1726	|	|	1826	...	|	|	|	1926	|	|	2026	|	...	2126	|	2205
Bruck an der Mur ..... **975** ⊙ a.	...	1601	1654	1643	1701	...	1743	1754	1801	1854	1843	1901	...	1943	1954	|	2001	2054	2043	2101	2143	...	2201	2254	2251
Bruck an der Mur .... d.	1558	1603	*1658*	1645	1703	...	1745	*1758*	1803	*1858*	1845	1903	...	1945	*1958*	|	2003	*2058*	2045	2103	2145	2158	2203	*2258*	2308
Graz Hbf .... **975** ▷ a.	1633	|	*1733*	|	|	...	|	*1833*	|	*1933*	|	|	...	|	*2033*	2029	|	*2133*	|	|	|	2233	|	*2333*	|
Mürzzuschlag .... **981** d.	...	1633	...	|	1733	...	|	...	1833	...	|	1933	...	|	...	...	2033	...	|	2133	|	...	2233	...	2348
Semmering .... **981** d.	...	1647	...	|	1747	...	|	...	1847	...	|	|	...	|	...	...	|	...	|	|	|	...	2247	...	...
Wiener Neustadt Hbf ... **981** a.	...	1728	...	1803	1828	...	1903	...	1928	...	2003	2028	...	2103	...	...	2128	...	2203	2228	2303	...	2328	...	...
Wiener Neustadt Hbf ... **981** d.	...	1732	...	1805	1832	...	1905	...	1932	...	2005	2032	...	2105	...	...	2132	...	2205	2232	2305	...	2332	...	...
Wien Meidling .... **981** a.	...	1755	...	1828	1855	...	1928	...	1955	...	2028	2055	...	2128	...	...	2155	...	2228	2255	2328	...	2355	...	...
Wien Hbf .... **981 985** a.	...	1802	...	1835	1902	...	1935	...	2002	...	2035	2102	...	2135	...	...	2202	...	2235	2302	2335	...	0002	...	...
Flughafen Wien ✈ ...... **985** a.	...	1827	...	...	...	...	...	...	2027	...	...	...	...	...	...	...	...	...	...	...	...	...	...	...	...

Local stopping trains **BRUCK AN DER MUR - GRAZ - SPIELFELD-STRASS** (for international services Graz - Spielfeld Straß - Maribor - Ljubljana / Zagreb see Table **1315**).

km			Ⓐ	Ⓐ							
	Bruck a. d. Mur .... d.	*0457*	0608	*0651*	*0708*	and	*1808*	*1908*	*2008*r	*2108*	*2208*
	Graz Hbf .... a.	*0544*	0655	*0730*	*0755*		*1855*	*1955*	*2055*r	*2155*	*2255*
0	**Graz** Hbf .... **1315** d.	0610	0710	0740	0808	hourly	1910	2010	2110	2210	2310
9	Flughafen Graz ✈ ..... d.	0621	0721	0751	0821	until	1921	2021	2121	2221	2321
35	Leibnitz .... d.	0649	0749	0819	0849		1949	2049	2149	2249	2349
47	**Spielfeld-Straß 1315** a.	0659	0759	0829	0859		1959	2059	2159	2259	2359

	Ⓐ			⚒	Ⓐ		❖				
Spielfeld-Straß 1315 d.	0400	0430	0500	0525	0614	0700	and	1854	2000	2100	2200
Leibnitz .... d.	0410	0440	0510	0535	0624	0710		1910	2010	2110	2210
Flughafen Graz ✈ .. d.	0438	0508	0538	0603	0651	0738	hourly	1938	2038	2138	2238
Graz Hbf .... **1315** a.	0450	0520	0550	0615	0703	0750	until	1950	2050	2150	2250
Graz Hbf .... d.	...	...	*0600*a	*0641*a	0709	*0805*		*2005*	*2105*r	*2205*	*2305*
Bruck a. d. Mur ...... a.	...	...	*0641*a	*0727*a	0755	*0851*		*2051*	*2151*r	*2251*	*2351*

ÖBB *Intercitybus* services **GRAZ - KLAGENFURT**. Rail tickets valid. 1st and 2nd class. 🍷 in 1st class. Number of seats limited so reservation is recommended.

	🚌	🚌	🚌		🚌	🚌		🚌	🚌	
Graz Hbf .... d.	0630	0805	1005	...	1230	1405	...	1630	1845	...
Klagenfurt Hbf .... a.	0830	1005	1205	...	1430	1605	...	1830	2045	...

	🚌	🚌	🚌		🚌	🚌		🚌	🚌		
Klagenfurt Hbf ...... d.	0720	0920	1120	...	1350	1520	...	1750	1950	...	...
Graz Hbf .... a.	0920	1120	1320	...	1550	1720	...	1950	2150	...	...

A – 🛏 1, 2 cl., ▬ 2 cl. and [2] Milano - Wien and v.v.; 🛏 1, 2 cl., ▬ 2 cl. and [2] (**40294/40233**) Roma - Bologna - Venezia - Wien and v.v.
B – ⑤⑦ until Oct. 10. Previous night from Livorno. 🛏 1, 2 cl., ▬ 2 cl. and [2] Livorno - Pisa - Firenze - Bologna - Wien.
D – ③⑤ from Apr. 6; also Apr. 17. 🛏 1, 2 cl., ▬ 2 cl. and [2] Wien - Bologna - Firenze - Pisa - Livorno.
E – EMONA – [12] and ✕ Trieste - Ljubljana - Maribor - Spielfeld-Straß 🏛 - Graz - Wien (Table **91**).
F – CROATIA – [12] and ✕ Zagreb - Maribor - Spielfeld-Straß 🏛 - Graz - Wien (Table **91**).
L – From Lienz (Table **971**).
N – [12] and ✕ Graz - Wien - Břeclav 🏛 - Praha - Berlin ★ (Table **60**).
P – [12] and ✕ Graz - Wien - Břeclav 🏛 - Praha and v.v. (Table **60**).
Q – PORTA MORAVICA – [12] and ✕ Przemyśl - Kraków - Katowice - Wien - Graz and v.v. (Table **99**).
R – Ⓡ for journeys from / to Italy.

S – [12] and ✕ Graz - Wien - Břeclav 🏛 - Brno (Table **60**).
V – [12] and ✕ Venezia - Udine - Tarvisio 🏛 - Wien (Table **88**).

a – Ⓐ only.
b – Also calls at Baden (d. 2318).
r – ⚒ only.
w – Also June 6, Aug. 15, Nov. 1; not June 5, Aug. 14, Oct. 30.
z – Also June 6, Aug. 15; not June 5, Aug. 14.

❖ – Spielfeld-Straß d. 1053 (not 1100).
⊙ – For other local journeys see panel below main table.
▷ – For fast ÖBB *Intercitybus* services Graz - Klagenfurt and v.v., see panel below main table.

2nd class only — Local trains WIEN - WIENER NEUSTADT - MÜRZZUSCHLAG — 981

WIEN - WIENER NEUSTADT ⊡

km		⚒	Ⓐ						
0	**Wien** Floridsdorf d.	0409	0439	0509	0539	and at	2309	2339	0009
5	**Wien** Praterstern d.	0418	0448	0518	0548	the same	2318	2348	0018
7	**Wien** Mitte d.	0422	0452	0522	0552	minutes	2322	2352	0022
10	**Wien** Hbf d.	0429	0459	0529	0559	past each	2329	2359	0029
14	**Wien** Meidling d.	0437	0507	0537	0607	hour until	2337	0007	0037
26	Mödling d.	0449	0519	0549	0619		2349	0019	0049
37	Baden d.	0457	0527	0557	0627		2357	0027	0057
59	**Wiener Neustadt** Hbf a.	0521	0548	0621	0648		0021	0048	0121

Wiener Neustadt Hbf d.	0503	and every	0733	0811	0838	and at	2211	2238	2311	0011
Baden d.	0523	30 minutes	0753	0833	0903	the same	2233	2303	2333	0033
Mödling d.	0530	until	0800	0840	0910	minutes	2240	2310	2340	0040
Wien Meidling a.	0542		0812	0853	0923	past each	2253	2323	2353	0053
Wien Hbf a.	0549		0819	0859	0929	hour until	2259	2329	2359	0059
Wien Mitte a.	0556		0826	0906	0936		2306	2336	0006	0106
Wien Praterstern a.	0600		0830	0910	0940		2310	2340	0010	0110
Wien Floridsdorf a.	0609		0839	0919	0949		2319	2349	0019	0119

(WIEN -) WIENER NEUSTADT - PAYERBACH-REICHENAU - MÜRZZUSCHLAG ⊡

km		Ⓒ	Ⓐ	⚒	ⒸB	Ⓐ	⚒						L	Ⓓ	Ⓐ	L	Ⓒ	Ⓐ		Ⓐ	Ⓒ	Ⓐ				Ⓒ
	Wien Hbf d.	0529	0538	...	0725	0708	...	0829	...	1029	...	1229	...	1429	1452	...	1629	1638	...	1725	1829	1852	...	2029	...	2258
	Wien Meidling d.	0537	0545	...	0732	0715	...	0837	...	1037	...	1237	...	1437	1500	...	1637	1645	...	1732	1837	1900	...	2037	...	2305
	Baden d.	0557	0606	...	|	0736	...	0857	...	1057	...	1257	...	1457	|	...	1657	1706	...	|	1857	|	...	2057	...	2318
	Wiener Neustadt Hbf a.	0621	0624	...	0755	0751	...	0921	...	1121	...	1321	...	1521	1527	...	1721	1724	...	1755	1921	1927	...	2121	...	2330
0	**Wiener Neustadt** Hbf d.	0635	0635	...	0758	0802	...	0935	...	1135	...	1335	...	1535	1535	...	1735	1735	...	1757	1935	1935	...	2135	...	2335
14	Neunkirchen NÖ d.	0646	0646	...	0808	0813	...	0947	...	1147	...	1347	...	1547	1547	...	1747	1747	...	|	1947	1947	...	2147	...	2347
27	Gloggnitz d.	0658	0658	...	0817	0825	...	0958	...	1158	...	1358	...	1558	1558	...	1758	1758	...	1815	1958	1958	...	2158	...	2358
34	Payerbach-Reichenau d.	0708	0708	0710	0826	0835	0838	1008	1011	1208	1211	1408	1411	1608	1608	1611	1808	1808	1811	1824	2008	2008	2011	2208	2211	0009
55	Semmering a.	...	...	0733	0850	...	0906	...	1040	...	1240	...	1440	...	...	1640	...	...	1840	1848	...	...	2040	...	2240	0033
69	**Mürzzuschlag** a.	...	...	...	0908	...	...	...	1055	...	1255	...	1455	...	...	1655	...	...	1855	1903	...	...	2055	...	2255	0048

	Ⓐ	Ⓐ	Ⓒ	G	G		⚒	⚒		†							Ⓐ	Ⓒ	ⒸB		Ⓐ	Ⓒ				
ürzzuschlag d.	0346	...	...	0525v	0606	...	...	...	...	0906	...	1106	...	1306	...	1506	...	...	1650	1706z	...	...	1906z	...	2106z	...
emmering d.	0401	...	...	0537	0622	...	0752	...	0922	0922	...	1122	...	1322	...	1522	...	...	1707	1722z	...	...	1922z	...	2122z	...
ayerbach-Reichenau d.	0428	0526	0526	0603	0651	0654	0821	0824	0951	0951	0954	1151	1154	1351	1354	1551	1554	1554	1735	1751	1754	1754	1951	1954	2151	2154
loggnitz d.	0436	0535	0535	0611	...	0703	...	0833	...	...	1003	...	1203	...	1403	...	1603	1603	1742	...	1803	1803	...	2003	...	2203
eunkirchen NÖ d.	0447	0547	0547	|	...	0714	...	0844	...	...	1014	...	1214	...	1414	...	1614	1614	1750	...	1814	1814	...	2014	...	2214
iener Neustadt Hbf a.	0458	0558	0558	0626	...	0725	...	0855	...	...	1025	...	1225	...	1425	...	1625	1625	1758	...	1825	1825	...	2025	...	2225
iener Neustadt Hbf d.	0500	0600	0603	0630	...	0733	...	0911	...	...	1038	...	1238	...	1438	...	1635	1638	1759	...	1835	1838	...	2035	...	2238
aden d.	|	0614	0623	|	...	0753	...	0933	...	...	1103	...	1303	...	1503	...	1653	1703	|	...	1853	1903	...	2053t	...	2303
ien Meidling a.	0529	0629	0642	0655	...	0812	...	0953	...	...	1123	...	1323	...	1523	...	1713	1723	1825	...	1913	1923	...	2113t	...	2323
ien Hbf a.	0536	0638	0649	0702	...	0819	...	0959	...	...	1129	...	1329	...	1529	...	1719	1729	1832	...	1919	1929	...	2119t	...	2329

– From/to Bratislava-Petržalka (Table **997**).
– From Graz on Ⓐ (Table **980**).
– Runs 6 minutes later on ⑤.
– 10 minutes later on †.
– 0522 on Ⓒ.

z – 5–6 minutes **earlier** on ⑦.

⊡ – Only selected services are shown Wien Floridsdorf - Wiener Neustadt - Payerbach-Reichenau and v.v. Additional journeys Wien Floridsdorf - Wiener Neustadt are shown in Tables **982** and **983**. See Table **980** for long-distance services.

2nd class only; Austrian Holiday dates apply — Local trains WIEN - BŘECLAV — 982

See Table **1150** for other fast international services

km		Ⓐ		Ⓐ		E		E		E	Ⓐ		E	Ⓐ		Ⓐ	E	Ⓐ		Ⓐ	E				
	Wiener Neustadt Hbf. **980/1** d.	...	0515a	0615	0715a	0811	0911	1011	1111	1211	1238	1311	1411	1438	1511	1538	1611	1638	1711	1738	1811	1911	2011	2111	2211
	Baden **981** d.	...	0538a	0638	0738a	0833	0933	1033	1133	1233	1303	1333	1433	1503	1533	1603	1633	1703	1733	1803	1833	1933	2033	2133	2233
0	**Wien** Meidling **980/1** d.	0457	0557	0700	0800	0854	0954	1054	1154	1254	1324	1354	1454	1524	1554	1624	1654	1724	1754	1824	1854	1954	2054	2154	2254
4	**Wien** Hbf **980/1** d.	0503	0603	0706	0806	0900	1000	1100	1200	1300	1330	1400	1500	1530	1600	1630	1700	1730	1800	1830	1900	2000	2100	2200	2300
7	**Wien** Mitte **981** d.	0510	0610	0713	0813	0907	1007	1107	1207	1307	1337	1407	1507	1537	1607	1637	1707	1737	1807	1837	1907	2007	2107	2207	2307
9	**Wien** Praterstern **981** d.	0514	0614	0717	0817	0911	1011	1111	1211	1311	1341	1411	1511	1541	1611	1641	1711	1741	1811	1841	1911	2011	2111	2211	2311
14	**Wien** Floridsdorf **981** d.	0523	0623	0726	0826	0920	1020	1120	1220	1320	1350	1420	1520	1550	1620	1650	1720	1750	1820	1850	1920	2020	2120	2220	2320
40	Gänserndorf d.	0545	0645	0748	0848	0942	1042	1142	1242	1342	1412	1442	1542	1612	1642	1712	1742	1812	1842	1913	1942	2042	2142	2242	2342
74	Hohenau 🏛 a.	0617	0718	0820	0920	1014	1114	1214	1314	1414	1444	1514	1614	1644	1714	1736	1814	1836	1914	1936	2014	2114	2214	2314	0014
92	**Břeclav** 🏛 a.	0632	0746	0835	0935	1029	1129	1229	1329	1429	...	1529	1629	...	1729	...	1829	...	1929	...	2029	2129	...	...	0029

	Ⓐ	Ⓐ		Ⓐ		Ⓒ	Ⓐ			D		D		D		Ⓐ	D		Ⓐ	D		D		Ⓐ	
řeclav 🏛 d.	0427	...	...	0557	...	0627	0657	0727	0827	0927	1027	1127	1227	1327	1427	...	1527	1627	...	1727	1827	1927	2027	2127	2227
ohenau 🏛 d.	0442	0503	0533	0612	0642	0642	0712	0742	0842	0942	1042	1142	1242	1342	1442	1512	1542	1642	1716	1742	1842	1942	2042	2142	2242
änserndorf d.	0515	0545	0615	0645	0715	0715	0745	0815	0915	1015	1115	1215	1315	1415	1515	1545	1615	1715	1741	1815	1915	2015	2115	2215	2315
ien Floridsdorf **981** a.	0538	0608	0638	0708	0738	0738	0808	0838	0938	1038	1138	1238	1338	1438	1538	1608	1638	1738	1808	1838	1938	2038	2138	2238	2338
ien Praterstern **981** a.	0546	0616	0646	0716	0746	0746	0816	0846	0946	1046	1146	1246	1346	1446	1546	1616	1646	1746	1816	1846	1946	2046	2146	2246	2346
ien Mitte **981** a.	0550	0620	0650	0720	0750	0750	0820	0850	0950	1050	1150	1250	1350	1450	1550	1620	1650	1750	1820	1850	1950	2050	2150	2250	2350
ien Hbf **980/1** a.	0559	0629	0659	0729	0759	0759	0829	0859	0959	1059	1159	1259	1359	1459	1559	1629	1659	1759	1829	1859	1959	2059	2159	2259	2359
ien Meidling **980/1** a.	0604	0634	0704	0734	0804	0804	0834	0904	1004	1104	1204	1304	1404	1504	1604	1634	1704	1804	1834	1904	2004	2104	2204	2304	0004
aden **981** a.	0627	0657	0727	0757	0827	0827	0857	0927	1027	1127	1227	1327	1427	1527	1627	1657	1727	1827	1857	1927	2027	2127	2227	2327	0027
iener Neustadt Hbf **980/1** a.	0649	0721	0749	0821	0849	0849	0921	0949	1049	1149	1249	1349	1449	1549	1649	1721	1749	1849	1921	1949	2049	2149	2249	2349	0049

D – Břeclav - Gänserndorf on Ⓐ only; Gänserndorf - Wiener Neustadt daily.
E – Wiener Neustadt - Gänserndorf daily; Gänserndorf - Břeclav on Ⓐ only.

a – Ⓐ only.

2nd class only; Austrian holiday dates apply — WIEN - RETZ - ZNOJMO — 983

km		⚒											Ⓐ		Ⓐ		Ⓐ		Ⓐ						
	Wiener Neustadt Hbf **980/1** d.	...	0503	0603	0703	0808r	0908a	...	...	...	...	...	...	1508a	1535	1608a	1635	1708a	1735	1808a	1908a	2008a	...	...	...
	Baden **981** d.	...	0523	0623	0723	0823r	0923a	...	...	...	...	...	...	1523a	1553	1623a	1653	1723a	1753	1823a	1923a	2023a	...	...	...
0	**Wien** Meidling **980/1** d.	...	0544	0644	0744	0844	0944	1044	1144	1244	1344	1444	1514	1544	1614	1644	1714	1744	1814	1844	1944	2044	2144	2244	2344
4	**Wien** Hbf **980/1** d.	...	0550	0650	0750	0850	0950	1050	1150	1250	1350	1450	1520	1550	1620	1650	1720	1750	1820	1850	1950	2050	2150	2250	2350
7	**Wien** Mitte **981** d.	...	0557	0657	0757	0857	0957	1057	1157	1257	1357	1457	1527	1557	1627	1657	1727	1757	1827	1857	1957	2057	2157	2257	2357
9	**Wien** Praterstern **981** d.	...	0601	0701	0801	0901	1001	1101	1201	1301	1401	1501	1531	1601	1631	1701	1731	1801	1831	1901	2001	2101	2201	2301	0001
14	**Wien** Floridsdorf **981** d.	...	0611	0711	0811	0911	1011	1111	1211	1311	1411	1511	1541	1611	1641	1711	1741	1811	1841	1911	2011	2111	2211	2311	0011
34	Stockerau d.	...	0628	0728	0828	0928	1028	1128	1228	1328	1428	1528	1601	1628	1701	1728	1801	1828	1901	1928	2028	2128	2228	2328	0028
60	Hollabrunn d.	...	0645	0745	0845	0945	1045	1145	1245	1345	1445	1545	1623	1645	1723	1745	1823	1845	1923	1945	2045	2145	2245	2354	0054
90	**Retz** a.	...	0712	0812	0912	1012	1112	1212	1312	1412	1512	1612	1652	1712	1752	1812	1852	1912	1952	2012	2112	2212	2312	0020	0120
90	**Retz** 🏛 d.	0620	...	0817	...	1017	...	1217	...	1417	...	1617	...	...	...	1817	...	...	...	2017	...	...	...	...	...
96	Šatov 🏛 d.	0628	...	0825	...	1025	...	1225	...	1425	...	1625	...	...	...	1825	...	...	...	2025	...	...	...	...	...
107	**Znojmo** a.	0638	...	0836	...	1036	...	1236	...	1436	...	1636	...	...	...	1836	...	...	...	2036	...	...	...	...	...

	Ⓐ	Ⓐ	Ⓐ	⚒	Ⓒ	Ⓐ	Ⓐ	Ⓒ		⚒															
nojmo d.	...	...	...	...	...	...	0555	...	...	0655	...	0857	...	1057	...	1257	...	1457	...	1657	...	1857	...	2057	...
atov 🏛 d.	...	...	...	...	...	...	0606	...	...	0706	...	0906	...	1106	...	1306	...	1506	...	1706	...	1906	...	2106	...
etz 🏛 a.	...	...	...	...	...	...	0614	...	...	0714	...	0914	...	1114	...	1314	...	1514	...	1714	...	1914	...	2114	...
etz d.	0402	0434	0510	0510	0514h	0530	0616	0616	0716	0716	0816	0916	1016	1116	1216	1316	1416	1516	1616	1716	1816	1916	2016	2116	2216
ollabrunn d.	0430	0502	0539	0539	0543	0558	0645	0645	0745	0745	0845	0945	1045	1145	1245	1345	1445	1545	1645	1745	1845	1945	2045	2145	2245
tockerau d.	0447	0527	0556	0556	0614	0625	0702	0702	0802	0802	0902	1002	1102	1202	1302	1402	1502	1602	1702	1802	1902	2002	2102	2202	2302
ien Floridsdorf **981** a.	0502	0547	0617	0617	0641	0647	0717	0717	0817	0817	0917	1017	1117	1217	1317	1417	1517	1617	1717	1817	1917	2017	2117	2217	2317
ien Praterstern **981** a.	0510	0556	0626	...	0649	0656	0726	0726	0826	0826	0926	1026	1126	1226	1326	1426	1526	1626	1726	1826	1926	2026	2126	2226	2326
ien Mitte **981** a.	0514	0600	0630	...	0653	0700	0730	0730	0830	0830	0930	1030	1130	1230	1330	1430	1530	1630	1730	1830	1930	2030	2130	2230	2330
ien Hbf **980/1** a.	0522	0607	0637	...	0701	0707	0737	0737	0837	0837	0937	1037	1137	1237	1337	1437	1537	1637	1737	1837	1937	2037	2137	2237	2337
ien Meidling **980/1** a.	0528	0614	0644	...	0707	0714	0744	0744	0844	0844	0944	1044	1144	1244	1344	1444	1544	1644	1744	1844	1944	2044	2144	2244	2344
aden **981** a.	|	0636	0706	...	...	0736	0806	0806k	...	...	...	...	...	...	...	1506a	1606a	1706a	1806a	1906a	2006a	...	...	...	...
iener Neustadt Hbf **980/1** a.	0559	0652	0724	...	...	0752	0824	0824k	...	...	...	...	...	...	...	1524a	1624a	1724a	1824a	1924a	2024a	...	...	...	...

– Ⓐ only. h – † only. r – ⚒ only. k – ⑥ only.

984 WIENER NEUSTADT - PUCHBERG am Schneeberg - HOCHSCHNEEBERG — 2nd class only

WIENER NEUSTADT - PUCHBERG am Schneeberg *28 km.* Journey time: 45–48 minutes.

From Wiener Neustadt at 0039 Ⓒ, 0637 Ⓒ, 0737, 0837 and hourly until 2237; then 2339 ⑦–④.

From Puchberg at 0406 Ⓐ, 0452 Ⓐ, 0522 Ⓐ, 0536 Ⓒ, 0552 Ⓐ, 0622 Ⓐ, 0636 Ⓒ, 0645 Ⓐ, 0736, 0836 and hourly until 2136.

PUCHBERG am Schneeberg - **HOCHSCHNEEBERG** *Schneebergbahn* (narrow-gauge rack railway). *9 km.* Journey time: ± 40 minutes.
Services operate April 30 - Nov. 1, **subject to demand and weather conditions.** Operator: **NÖ Schneebergbahn GmbH, Bahnhofplatz 1, A-2734 Puchberg.** ✆ +43 (0) 2636 3661 2
From Puchberg at 0900, 1030, 1200, 1430. **From Hochschneeberg** at 0945, 1115, 1345, 1515. Additional trains operate during July and August, also at other times when there is sufficie demand. A steam service operates on † July 3 - August 28: also Aug. 15. Departs Puchberg 1053, departs Hochschneeberg 1517 (extended journey time; special fares apply).

985 FLUGHAFEN WIEN ✈ Schwechat — *CAT ★*; S-Bahn (2nd class only)

km																						
0	**Wien** Floridsdorf d.	0406	0436	...	0506	...	0536	...	0606	...	0636	and at the same	...	2206	...	2236	...	2306	...	2336	0006	...	0036
5	**Wien** Praterstern d.	0415	0445	...	0515	...	0545	...	0615	...	0645	minutes past	...	2215	...	2245	...	2315	...	2345	0015	...	0045
7	**Wien** Mitte d.	0419	0449	...	0519	0537	0549	0607	0619	0637	0649	each hour until	2207	2219	2237	2249	2307	2319	...	2349	0019	...	0049
26	**Flughafen Wien** ✈ a.	0441	0511	...	0541	0553	0611	0623	0641	0653	0711		2223	2241	2253	2311	2323	2341	...	0011	0041	...	0111

Flughafen Wien ✈ d.	0449	0519	0549	0608	0619	0638	0646	0708	0719	0738	0746	0808	0819	0838	0849	and at the same	2238	2319	2308	2349	2338	0019	0049
Wien Mitte d.	0513	0543	0613	0624	0643	0654	0710	0724	0743	0754	0810	0824	0843	0854	0913	minutes past	2254	2343	2324	0013	2354	0043	0113
Wien Praterstern d.	0517	0547	0617	...	0647	...	0714	...	0747	...	0814	...	0847	...	0917	each hour until	...	2347	...	0017	...	0047	0117
Wien Floridsdorf a.	0525	0555	0625	...	0655	...	0722	...	0755	...	0822	...	0855	...	0925		...	2355	...	0025	...	0055	0125

★ – *City Airport Train (CAT).* Non-stop service with special fares.

RJ trains **Wien Hbf - Flughafen Wien** ✈ and v.v. Journey time: 15–17 minutes. Most trains run from / to Salzburg, Linz and St Pölten (Table **950**) or Graz (Table **980**).
From Wien Hbf at 0542, 0612, 0642, 0712, 0742, 0812, 0840, 0912, 0940, 1012, 1040, 1112, 1142, 1212, 1240, 1312, 1342, 1412, 1440, 1512, 1540, 1612, 1640, 1712, 1742, 1812, 1840, 1912, 1940, 2012, 2040, 2112, 2142 and 2212. **From Flughafen Wien** ✈ at 0633, 0703, 0733 and at 03 and 33 minutes past each hour until until 2203, 2233, 2303.

🚌 *Vienna Airport Lines*: Wien Westbahnhof (Europaplatz) – Flughafen Wien ✈ and v.v. Journey time: 40 minutes.
🚌 From **Wien Westbahnhof**: 0330 and hourly until 2230. 🚌 From **Flughafen Wien** ✈: 0615 and hourly until 2315.

🚌 Slovak Lines: **Bratislava**, AS Mlynské nivy (bus station) – **Flughafen Wien** ✈ and v.v. Journey time: 60 minutes.
Reservation recommended ✆ +43 (0) 810 222333-6 or +421 2 55422734. Please note that a much reduced service operates on Dec. 24, 25, 26, 31, Jan. 1.
🚌 From **Bratislava** AS Mlynské nivy at 0300, 0400, 0600, 0800 and hourly 1600, 1800, 1900, 2000, 2200.
🚌 From **Flughafen Wien** ✈ at 0355, 0630, 0830, 1030 and hourly until 1830, 2030, 2130, 2250, 2359.

986 GRAZ - SZENTGOTTHÁRD - SZOMBATHELY — ÖBB, GySEV •; 2nd class only

km			W		A ↯	W						⊖		Ⓐ		Ⓐ	N	Ⓐ ⊡				Ⓐ		⚒		⚒	
0	**Graz** Hbf d.	0608	0708	0808	0838	0908	1008	1108	1208	1308	1408	1438	1508	1538	1608	1638	1708	1738	1808	1838	1908	1938	2008	2108	2208	2308	000
29	Gleisdorf d.	0650	0749	0850	0914	0950	1050	1150	1250	1350	1450	1513	1550	1613	1650	1713	1750	1813	1850	1913	1950	2013	2050	2150	2249	2345	0045
53	Feldbach d.	0714	0814	0914	0929	1014	1114	1214	1314	1414	1514	1530	1614	1630	1714	1730	1814	1830	1914	1930	2014	2033	2114	2214	2310	0006	0106
62	Fehring d.	0727	0822	0924	0936	1022	1124	1227z	1326	1431t	1524	1538	1622	1637	1724	1737	1822	1842	1924	1942	2022	2042	2130t	2222	2318	0015	0115
82	**Szentgotthárd** ▦ a.	0748	...	0945	0955	...	1145	1248	1347	1452a	1545c	1556	...	*1702*	1745c	*1804*	...	1903	1945c	2003a	...	2103	2151	...	...	...	...

		Ⓐ	Ⓑ	Ⓐ	Ⓐ	⑥k	†	Ⓐ	⚒	Ⓐ H			N		N	⊖		Ⓐ	Ⓒ					Wg	B ↯	Ⓐ	
Szentgotthárd ▦ d.	...	*0450*	0450a	*0534*	...	...	0618	*0618*	0642k	...	...	0818	...	1018	...	1206	1304	1409	1418	*1509*a	1618	1718a	1818	...	2006	...	210
Fehring d.	0410	0514	0541	0558	0616	0618	0641	0644	0704	0733	0741	0841	0941	1041	1141	1225	1326v	1432	1441	1541	1641	1741	1841	1941	2025	2041	2141
Feldbach d.	0420	0523	0550	0606	0626	0627	0650	0654	0715	0741	0750	0850	0950	1050	1150	1234	1350	1450	1450	1550	1650	1750	1850	1950	2034	2050	2153
Gleisdorf d.	0443	0542	0613	0626	0650	0655	0713	0714	0738	0802	0813	0914	1013	1113	1213	1250	1413	1513	1513	1613	1713	1813	1913	2013	2050	2113	2213
Graz Hbf a.	0519	0615	0653	0703	0724	0734	0753	0748	0816	0836	0853	0953	1053	1153	1253	1321	1453	1553	1553	1653	1753	1853	1953	2053	2121	2153	2251

SZENTGOTTHÁRD - SZOMBATHELY •

km			⊖		Ⓐ				A ↯			Ⓐ		Ⓐ		Ⓐ	⊖	Ⓐ								
0	**Szentgotthárd** ▦ d.	0401	0501	0606	0636	0706	...	0806	1006	1206	1306	1336	1406	1436	1506	1536	1606	1636	1706	1806	1906	...	2006	2106	...	2236
28	Körmend d.	0425	0525	0630	0700	0730	...	0830	1030	1230	1330	1400	1430	1500	1600	1600	1630	1700	1730	1830	1930	...	2030	2130	...	2306
64	**Szombathely** a.	0448	0547	0653	0723	0753	...	0923	1053	1253	1353	1423	1453	1523	1553	1623	1653	1723	1753	1853	1953	...	2053	2153	...	2323
	Sopron **1233** a.	0556	...	...	...	...	...	0951	...	1351	1451	...	1551	...	1651	...	...	...	1851	1951	2051	...	2151	...	...	...

				Ⓐ				⊖	Ⓐ		Ⓐ		Ⓐ		Ⓐ			Ⓐ			B ↯			⊖		
Sopron **1233** d.	...	0408	0450	...	0556	...	0808	...	...	1208	...	1308	...	1408	...	...	1508	...	1608	1706	...	1906	...	...	...	...
Szombathely d.	0431	0501	0606	0636	0706	...	0906	1106	1236	1306	1336	1406	1436	1506	1536	...	1606	1636	1706	1806	1906	2006	2036	2106	...	2236
Körmend d.	0455	0525	0630	0700	0730	...	0930	1130	1300	1330	1400	1430	1500	1530	1600	...	1630	1700	1730	1830	1930	2030	2100	2130	...	2300
Szentgotthárd ▦ a.	0519	0549	0654	0724	0754	...	0954	1154	1324	1354	1424	1454	1524	1554	1624	...	1654	1724	1754	1854	1954	2054	2124	2154	...	2324

A – 🚃 Ljubljana (*IC* **311**) - Graz - Szentgotthárd - Budapest.
B – 🚃 Budapest (*IC* **310**) - Szentgotthárd - Graz - Ljubljana.
H – From Hartberg (Table **995**).
N – To / from Wiener Neustadt on dates shown in Table **995**.
W – To / from Wiener Neustadt (Table **995**).
a – Ⓐ only.
c – Ⓒ only.
g – ⑤⑥⑦.
k – ⑥ only.
t – Arrives 8–12 minutes earlier.
v – Arrives 1325; departs 1341 on Ⓒ.
z – Arrives 1222.
◇ – Change trains at Fehring on ⑤ (Fehring d. *1546*, Szentgotthárd a. *1607*)
⊡ – Change trains at Fehring on ①–④.
⊖ – *IC* train to / from Budapest (Tables **1250/2**). Ⓡ and supplement payable
↯ – Ⓡ and supplement payable in Hungary.
• – Szentgotthárd - Szombathely operated by Györ-Sopron-Ebenfurti Vasút.

990 WIEN - GMÜND - ČESKÉ VELENICE — 2nd class only

km										⑤			Ⓐ		Ⓒ	Ⓐ		Ⓐ		Ⓒ	Ⓐ				
0	**Wien** Franz-Josefs-Bf **991/3** d.	0620	0732	0828	0932	1028	1132	1228	1328	1400	1428	1528	1616	1628	1628	1658	1726	1816	1828	1828	1859	1928	2028	2128	2228
1	Wien Spittelau ● **991/3** d.	0624	0735	0831	0935	1031	1135	1231	1331	1403	1431	1531	1618	1631	1631	1701	1731	1818	1831	1831	1902	1931	2031	2131	2231
3	Wien Heiligenstadt △ **991/3** d.	0634	0738	0834	0938	1034	1138	1234	1334	1406	1434	1534	1621	1634	1634	1705	1735	1821	1834	1834	1906	1934	2034	2134	2234
33	Tulln a. d. Donau **991/3** d.	0657	0759	0857	0959	1057	1159	1257	1357	|	1457	1557	|	1657	1657	1728	1757	1844	1857	1857	1927	1957	2057	2157	2257
44	Absdorf-Hippersdorf **991** d.	0705	0808	0905	1008	1105	1208	1305	1405	|	1505	1605	|	1705	1705	|	1806	|	1905	1905	|	2006	2105	2205	2305
79	Eggenburg d.	0734	0838	0934	1038	1134	1238	1334	1438	1454	1534	1637	1715	1734	1734	1802	1837	1913	1934	1934	2002	2037	2134	2234	2334
89	Sigmundsherberg d.	0742	0846	0942	1046	1142	1246	1342	1446	1502	1542	1646	1723	1741	1742	1813	1846	1922	1941	1942	2014	2046	2142	2242	2342
121	Göpfritz an der Wild d.	0807	0907c	1007	...	1207	...	1407	...	1522	1607	1711a	1748	...	1806	1837	1911a	1947	...	2006	2037f	2110a	2207	2307a	0007
138	Schwarzenau d.	0820	0919c	1020	...	1220	...	1420	...	1536	1620	1729a	1801	...	1821	1849	1933a	2001	...	2021	2050f	2123a	2220	2321a	0020
162	**Gmünd** NÖ a.	0842	0938c	1042	...	1242	...	1442	...	1553	1642	1751a	1822	...	1842	1911	1956a	2022	...	2042	2112f	2145a	2242	2344a	0042
162	**Gmünd** NÖ ▦ ⊡ d.	0845	...	1045	...	1245	...	1445	...	...	1645	...	1825	...	1845	...	...	2025	...	2045	...	...	...	...	...
164	**České Velenice** ▦ ⊡ a.	0849	...	1049	...	1249	...	1449	...	...	1649	...	1829	...	1849	...	...	2029	...	2049	...	...	...	...	...

	Ⓐ	⚒		Ⓐ	Ⓐ		Ⓐ											Ⓐ	Ⓒ		Ⓒ	Ⓐ	Ⓒ		Ⓒ
České Velenice ▦ ⊡ d.	...	...	...	...	...	...	...	0602	0707	...	0907	...	1107	...	1307	...	1507	...	...	1701	...	...	...	1905	1955
Gmünd NÖ ▦ ⊡ a.	...	...	...	...	...	...	...	0606	0711	...	0911	...	1111	...	1311	...	1511	...	...	1705	...	...	...	1909	1959
Gmünd NÖ d.	...	0351	...	0430	...	0514	0546	0609	0714	...	0914	...	1114	...	1314	...	1514	...	...	1708	1802	...	...	1912	2002
Schwarzenau d.	...	0412	...	0450	...	0535	0605	0631	0735	...	0935	...	1135	...	1335	...	1535	...	...	1733	1821	...	...	1933	2021
Göpfritz an der Wild d.	...	0426	...	0502	...	0549	0617	0645	0749	...	0949	...	1149	...	1349	...	1549	...	...	1748	1834	...	...	1948	2034
Sigmundsherberg d.	0409	0449	0509	0522	0539	0614	0639	0710	0814	0909	1014	1109	1214	1309	1414	1509	1614	1655	1709	1813	1855	1855	1909	2014	2055
Eggenburg d.	0419	0457	0518	0530	0548	0622	0648	0718	0822	0918	1022	1118	1222	1318	1422	1518	1622	1718	1718	1822	1903	1918	1918	2022	2103
Absdorf-Hippersdorf **991** d.	0449	|	0546	|	0616	0651	0718	0748	0852	0948	1052	1148	1252	1348	1455	1548	1652	1748	1748	1852	|	1948	1948	2052	|
Tulln a. d. Donau **991/3** d.	0458	|	0554	|	0624	0659	0727	0757	0901	0958	1101	1158	1301	1358	1504	1558	1701	1758	1758	1901	|	1958	1958	2101	|
Wien Heiligenstadt △ **991/3** d.	0520	0554	0620	0624	0620	0724	0749	0820	0923	1020	1123	1220	1323	1420	1526	1620	1723	1820	1820	1923	1956	2020	2020	2123	2156
Wien Spittelau ● **991/3** d.	0523	0557	0623	0627	0653	0727	0753	0823	0926	1023	1126	1223	1326	1423	1529	1623	1726	1823	1823	1926	2000	2023	2023	2126	2200
Wien Franz-Josefs-Bf **991/3** a.	0525	0559	0625	0629	0655	0729	0755	0825	0928	1025	1128	1225	1328	1425	1531	1625	1728	1825	1825	1928	2002	2025	2025	2128	2203

a – Ⓐ only.
c – Ⓒ only.
f – Not ⑤.
r – ⑤⑥⑦ mornings.
⊡ – Additional trains Gmünd - České Velenice and v.v.: **From Gmünd** at 0522, 0635 and 1941 Ⓒ **S.** **From České Velenice** at 2037 Ⓐ and 2105 Ⓒ.
△ – S-Bahn (Line **S45**) trains run every 10–15 minutes from / to Wien Hütteldorf (journey: 21–23 minutes
● – Direct U-Bahn links: Line **U4** – Wien Mitte - Spittelau. Line **U6** – Wien Meidling - Westbahnhof - Spittelau - Floridsdorf.

2nd class only — WIEN - KREMS an der Donau - EMMERSDORF — 991

km				Ⓐ				⑤		Ⓐ		Ⓐ	Ⓐ	Ⓒ	Ⓐ		Ⓐ	Ⓐ	Ⓒ	Ⓐ		Ⓑb				
0	**Wien** Franz-Josefs-Bf **990/3** d.	0505	0601	0703	0805	and	1305	1333	1405	1433	1505	1533	1601	1605	1633	1705	1733	1801	1805	1833	1905	1933	2005	and	2305	0005
1	Wien Spittelau ● **990/3** d.	0507	0604	0706	0807		1307	1336	1407	1436	1507	1536	1604	1607	1636	1707	1736	1804	1807	1836	1907	1936	2007		2307	0007
3	Wien Heiligenstadt △ **990/3** d.	0510	0610	0710	0810	hourly	1310	1339	1410	1439	1510	1539	1608	1610	1639	1710	1739	1808	1810	1839	1910	1939	2010	hourly	2310	0010
33	Tulln a. d. Donau **990/3** d.	0533	0633	0733	0833		1333	1401	1433	1501	1533	1601	1633	1633	1701	1733	1801	1833	1833	1901	1933	2001	2033	until	2333	0033
44	Absdorf-Hippersdorf **990** d.	0541	0641	0741	0841	until	1341	1409	1441	1509	1541	1609	1641	1641	1709	1741	1809	1841	1841	1909	1941	2009	2041		2341	0041
76	**Krems** a. d. Donau a.	0614	0716	0814	0914		1414	1436	1514	1536	1614	1636	1714	1714	1736	1814	1836	1914	1914	1936	2014	2036	2114		0014	0114

	Ⓐ		Ⓐ		Ⓐ	Ⓐ		Ⓐ			Ⓐ							Ⓐc	Ⓒd	Ⓒ		Ⓒ				
rems a. d. Donau d.	0429	0451	0529	0551	0616	0629	0651	0729	0751	...	0829	0851	0951	1051	1151	1251	...	1343	1351	1451	1551	1651	1751	and	2151	2251
bsdorf-Hippersdorf **990** d.	0454	0523	0555	0625	0642	0655	0723	0754	0823	...	0856	0923	1023	1123	1223	1323	...	1423	1423	1523	1623	1723	1823		2223	2323
ulln a. d. Donau **990/3** d.	0503	0532	0603	0633	0653	0703	0734	0803	0831	...	0905	0931	1031	1131	1231	1331	...	1431	1431	1531	1631	1731	1831	hourly	2231	2331
Vien Heiligenstadt △ **990/3** d.	0524	0559	0628	0701	0720	0728	0756	0824	0852	...	0927	0952	1052	1152	1252	1352	...	1452	1452	1552	1654	1752	1852	until	2252	2352
Vien Spittelau ● **990/3** d.	0528	0604	0631	0706	0723	0734	0801	0828	0856	...	0930	0956	1056	1156	1256	1356	...	1456	1456	1556	1700	1756	1856		2256	2356
Vien Franz-Josefs-Bf **990/3** a.	0530	0606	0633	0708	0725	0736	0803	0830	0858	...	0932	0958	1058	1158	1258	1358	...	1458	1458	1558	1703	1758	1858		2258	2358

KREMS - EMMERSDORF ⊠

km		R		R		R		R		
0	**Krems** an der Donau d.	0920	...	1120	...	1320	...	1620	...	...
18	**Spitz** an der Donau d.	0951	...	1151	...	1351	...	1651	...	...
34	**Emmersdorf** an der Donau a.	1010	...	1210	...	1410	...	1705	...	...

	R		R		R		R		
Emmersdorf an der Donau d.	1020	...	1220	...	1450	...	1750	...	...
Spitz an der Donau d.	1040	...	1240	...	1510	...	1810	...	...
Krems an der Donau a.	1110	...	1310	...	1540	...	1840	...	...

– Daily until Oct. 2 (not Sept. 25); Ⓒ Oct. 8 - Nov. 1. **Special fares apply.**

b – Not June 5, Aug. 14.
c – Ⓐ until July 1; Ⓐ from Sept. 5.
d – Ⓒ (daily July 2 - Sept. 4).

● – Direct U-bahn links: Line **U4** – Wien Mitte - Spittelau. Line **U6** – Wien Meidling - Westbahnhof - Spittelau - Floridsdorf.
△ – S-Bahn trains run every 10 – 15 minutes from / to Wien Hütteldorf (journey: 21 – 23 minutes).
⊠ – Operated by NÖVOG (Wachaubahn). ✆ +43 (0) 2742 360 990-99. www.wachaubahn.at

2nd class only — ST PÖLTEN - KREMS and TULLN — 993

ST PÖLTEN - KREMS

km					Ⓐ		Ⓐ				Ⓐ		Ⓐ		Ⓐ		Ⓐ		Ⓐ		Ⓐ		Ⓐ			
0	**St Pölten** Hbf d.	0008	...	0505	0539	0605	0639	0705	and	1205	1239	1305	1339	1405	1439	1505	1539	1605	1639	1705	1739	1805	1839	1905	and	2305
10	Herzogenburg d.	0017	...	0514	0547	0614	0647	0714	hourly	1214	1248	1314	1348	1414	1448	1514	1548	1614	1648	1714	1748	1814	1848	1914	hourly	2314
30	**Krems** a. d. Donau a.	0044	...	0541	0627	0641	0727	0741	until	1241	1316	1341	1416	1442	1516	1541	1612	1641	1712	1741	1812	1841	1912	1941	until	2341

	Ⓐ	Ⓐ		⚒		Ⓐ		Ⓐ							Ⓐ	Ⓒ	Ⓐ									
rems a. d. Donau d.	0419	0446	0519	0546	0618	0646	0718	0746	0819	0919	1019	1119	1219	1319	1342	1419	1421	1519	1619	1719	1819	1919	2019	2119	2219	2319
erzogenburg d.	0447	0513	0547	0613	0647	0714	0747	0814	0847	0947	1047	1147	1247	1347	1413	1447	1447	1547	1647	1747	1847	1947	2047	2147	2247	2347
t Pölten Hbf a.	0455	0522	0555	0622	0655	0723	0755	0822	0855	0955	1055	1155	1255	1355	1423	1455	1455	1555	1655	1755	1855	1955	2055	2155	2255	2355

ST PÖLTEN - TULLN - WIEN

km		⚒	⚒		⚒			⚒																	
0	**St Pölten** Hbf **950** d.	0404	0445a	0512	0545a	...	0612	0656a	...	0713	0812	0912		1412	1512	...	1612	...	1712	...	1812	1912	2012	2112	2212
10	Herzogenburg d.	0417	0503a	0528	0602a	...	0629	0708a	...	0730	0833	0929		1429	1529	...	1629	...	1731	...	1829	1929	2029	2129	2229
40	Tullnerfeld **950** a.	0449	0538a	0607	0638a	...	0708	0737a	...	0811	0911	1011		1511	1611	...	1711	...	1811	...	1911	2011	2111	2211	2311
40	Tullnerfeld d.	0450	0554	0624	0654	0648	0724	0754	0751	0825	0925	1025	and	1525	1625	1648	1725	1748	1825	1848	1925	2025	2125	2225	2325
46	**Tulln** Stadt d.	0456	0600	0630	0700	0653	0730	0801	0756	0830	0930	1030		1530	1630	1653	1730	1753	1830	1853	1930	2030	2130	2230	2330
	Absdorf-Hippersdorf ▷ a.	|	|	|	|	0701	|	|	0803	|	|	|	hourly	|	|	1701	|	1801	|	1901	|	|	|	|	|
	Stockerau ▷ a.	|	|	|	|	0726	|	|	0826	|	|	|		|	|	1726	|	1826	|	1926	|	|	|	|	|
47	**Tulln** a. d. Donau **990/1** a.	0458	0602	0632	0702	...	0732	0802	...	0832	0932	1032	until	1532	1632	...	1732	...	1832	...	1932	2032	2132	2232	2332
77	Wien Heiligenstadt **990/1** a.	0547	0647	0717	0747	...	0817	0847	...	0917	1017	1117		1617	1717	...	1817	...	1917	...	2017	2117	2217	2317	0017

	Ⓐ			⚒			⚒																		
Vien Heiligenstadt **990/1** d.	...	...	...	0513	0543	...	0613	0643	...	0743	0843	0943	1043		1443	1543	...	1643	...	1743	1843	1943	2043	2143	2243
ulln a. d. Donau **990/1** d.	0441	0527	...	0557	0627	...	0658	0727	...	0827	0927	1027	1127	and	1527	1627	...	1727	...	1827	1927	2027	2127	2227	2327
Stockerau ▷ d.	|	|	0531	|	|	0631	|	|	0731	|	|	|	|		|	|	1631	|	1731	|	|	|	|	|	|
Absdorf-Hippersdorf ▷ d.	|	|	0558	|	|	0658	|	|	0758	|	|	|	|	hourly	|	|	1700	|	1800	|	|	|	|	|	|
ulln Stadt d.	0445	0530	0606	0600	0630	0706	0701	0730	0806	0830	0930	1030	1130		1530	1630	1708	1730	1808	1830	1930	2030	2130	2230	2330
ullnerfeld a.	0450	0535	0610	0605	0635	0710	0706	0735	0810	0835	0935	1035	1135	until	1535	1635	1713	1735	1813	1835	1935	2035	2135	2235	2335
ullnerfeld **950** d.	0451	0548	...	0617	0648	...	0718	0748	...	0848	0948	1048	1148		1548	1648	...	1748	...	1848	1948	2048	2148	2248	...
erzogenburg d.	0524	0630	...	0652	0730	...	0752	0830	...	0930	1030	1130	1230		1630	1732	...	1830	...	1930	2030	2130	2230	2330	...
t Pölten Hbf **950** a.	0537	0649	...	0704	0744	...	0804	0844	...	0944	1044	1144	1249		1649	1749	...	1849	...	1944	2044	2144	2244	2344	...

– Ⓐ only.

▷ – Additional local trains run Absdorf-Hippersdorf - Stockerau and v.v.

Narrow gauge 2nd class only — ST PÖLTEN - MARIAZELL — 994

km				★	CⓇ	SⓇ						
0	**St Pölten** Hbf d.	0635	0735	0837	0842	0902	0937	1037	1237	1437	1637	1837
12	Ober Grafendorf d.	0654	0754	0854	0904	0924	0954	1054	1254	1454	1654	1854
31	Kirchberg d.	0723	0823	0923	0938	1003	1023	1123	1323	1523	1723	1923
43	Frankenfels ⊗ d.	0741	0841	0941	0958	1030	1041	1141	1341	1541	1741	1941
48	Laubenbachmühle d.	0751	0851	0951	1011	1056	1051	1151	1351	1551	1751	1949
67	Gösing ⊗ d.	0819	0919t	1019	1047	1142	1119z	1219	1419	1619	1819	...
80	Mitterbach ⊗ d.	0846	0946t	1046	1116	1216	1146z	1246	1446	1646	1846	...
84	**Mariazell** a.	0854	0954t	1054	1124	1224	1154z	1254	1454	1654	1854	...

						CⓇ	SⓇ	★			
Mariazell d.	...	0905	1105	1305	1505	1520	1520	1605r	1705	1805z	1905
Mitterbach ⊗ d.	...	0911	1111	1311	1511	1526	1526	1611r	1711	1811z	1911
Gösing ⊗ d.	...	0938	1138	1338	1538	1558	1558	1638r	1738	1838z	1938
Laubenbachmühle d.	0609	1009	1209	1409	1609	1633	1649	1709	1809	1909	2009
Frankenfels ⊗ d.	0617	1017	1217	1417	1617	1642	1658	1717	1817	1917	2017
Kirchberg d.	0635	1036	1236	1436	1636	1702	1722	1736	1836	1936	2036
Ober Grafendorf d.	0704	1104	1304	1504	1704	1734	1754	1804	1904	2004	2104
St Pölten Hbf a.	0722	1122	1322	1522	1722	1757	1817	1822	1922	2022	2122

– ⑥⑦ June 4 - Oct. 30 (also Aug. 15, Oct. 26, Nov. 1, 19, 26, Dec. 3, 10; not June, 5, 12, 19, 26, July, 10, Aug. 14, Sept. 11, Oct. 9). ÖTSCHERBÄR – Traditional loco-hauled electric train. Conveys (12) and 🍸.
– Runs on June 12, July 10, Aug. 14, Sept. 11, Oct. 9, Nov. 20, 27, Dec. 4, 8. Steam train with special fares. Conveys (12) and 🍸.
– Not Nov. 2 – 18.

t – Daily until Nov. 1; ⑥⑦ Nov. 5 – 13; daily from Nov. 19.
z – Ⓒ (not Nov. 5 – 13).
★ – On Ⓒ May 1 - Nov. 1 (not Nov. 5 - 18 Nov) conveys first class panorama cars (Ⓡ and special fares payable for travel in the panorama car which includes drinks and meals served at your seat).
⊗ – Trains call on request only.

Operator: NÖVOG.
✆ +43 (0) 2742 360 990 99
www.noevog.at/mariazellerbahn

☛ Additional trains run between St Pölten and Laubenbachmühle.

2nd class only — (WIEN -) WIENER NEUSTADT - FEHRING — 995

km		⚒	Ⓐ			Ⓐ			B	Ⓐ		Ⓐ	Ⓐ		Ⓑ	Ⓐ			
	Wien Hbf **980/1** d.	...	...	0827c	...	...	...	...	...	...	...	...	...	...	...	...	...	...	...
0	**Wien** Meidling **980/1** d.	...	...	0834c	...	...	...	...	...	...	...	1735	...	...	...	...	...	...	...
44	**Wiener Neustadt** Hbf. **980/1** d.	...	0639	0903	1103	...	1303	1503	1503	1633	1703	1801	1833	1903	2003	2003	2103	2139	2239
99	Friedberg d.	...	0802	1002	1202	...	1402	1602	1602	1734	1802	1857	1932	2003	2057	2058	2158	2245	2345
126	Hartberg d.	0621	0836	1036	1235	1328	1436	1635	1636	1812	1836	1929	...	2038	...	2132	2232b	...	...
157	Fürstenfeld d.	0655	0910	1110	...	1359	1510	...	1710	...	1910	...	...	2110	...	...	...	...	...
177	**Fehring** a.	0722	0937	1137	...	1426	1537	...	1737	...	1937	...	...	2137	...	...	...	...	...
	Graz Hbf **986** a.	0836a	1053	1253	...	...	...	...	...	...	2053d	...	...	...	...	...	...	...	...

	Ⓐ	Ⓐ	Ⓐ	⚒	Ⓐ	Ⓑ						Ⓐ	Ⓒ			Ⓒ	B		
Graz Hbf **986** d.	...	...	...	...	...	...	...	...	0708	0908	...	...	...	...	...	...	...	...	1708a
ehring d.	...	...	...	...	0501	...	...	0627	0827	1027	...	1227	1427	1427	...	1627	1627	...	1827
ürstenfeld d.	...	...	...	...	0528	...	...	0654	0854	1054	...	1254	1454	1454	...	1654	1654	...	1854
artberg d.	...	...	0435	0533	0601	...	...	0727	0927	1127	1327	1327	1527	1527	1727	1727	1727	...	1930
riedberg d.	0347	0428	0509	0607	0636	0636	0700	0802	1002	1202	1402	1402	1602	1602	1802	1802	1802	...	2004
iener Neustadt Hbf **980/1** a.	0454	0529	0611	0711	0735	0735	0757	0857	1057	1257	1457	1457	1657	1657	1857	1857	1857	...	2057
ien Meidling **980/1** a.	...	0559	0643	0743a	...	...	...	...	...	...	...	...	1733	...	...	1933	...	...	...
ien Hbf **980/1** a.	...	0606	0651	...	...	...	...	...	...	...	...	...	1740	...	...	1940	...	...	...

B – ⑤⑥† (also June 15, Dec. 7; not June 17, Dec. 9).

a – Ⓐ only.
b – Not ⑥.
c – Ⓒ only.
d – ⑤⑥† only.

996 WIEN - BRATISLAVA via Marchegg

2nd class only; Austrian holiday dates apply

km														A	C
0	**Wien** Hbf d.	0516	0616	0716	0816	0916		2016	2116	2216	2316	0016	A	1442	2042
4	**Wien** Simmering ⊖ d.	0522	0622	0722	0822	0922	and	2022	2122	2222	2322	0022	L	|	|
47	Marchegg 🛃 d.	0603	0703	0803	0903	1003	hourly	2103	2200	2303	2400	0100	S	⊠	⊠
53	Devínska Nová Ves 🛃 d.	0610	|	|	|	1010	until	2110	...	2310	...	...	O	|	|
66	**Bratislava** hl. st. a.	0623	0723	0823	0923	1023		2123	...	2323	...	...		1558	2151

												D		B	
Bratislava hl. st. d.	...	0537	0637		2037	...	2237	...	...	A	0610	...	1208	...
Devínska Nová Ves 🛃 d.	...	0550	0650	and	2050	...	2250	...	...	L	|	...	|	...
Marchegg 🛃 d.	0500	0600	0700	hourly	2100	2200	2300	0000	...	S	⊠	...	⊠	...
Wien Simmering ⊖ a.	0537	0637	0737	until	2137	2237	2337	0037	...	O	|	...	|	...
Wien Hbf a.	0544	0644	0744		2144	2244	2344	0044	...		0718	...	1324	...

A – *IC* **45** – [12] ✕ Wien - Bratislava - Košice (Table **1180**). Ⓡ Bratislava - Košice.
B – *IC* **44** – [12] ✕ Košice - Bratislava - Wien (Table **1180**). Ⓡ Košice - Bratislava.
C – *RJX* **167** – [12] ✕ Zürich - Bratislava.
D – *RJX* **160** – [12] ✕ Bratislava - Zürich.

⊠ – Via Bratislava - Petržalka
⊖ – For U-Bahn connections (line U3) from / to Wien Mitte and Wien Westbahnhof.

997 BRATISLAVA - WIEN - SOPRON - DEUTSCHKREUTZ

2nd class only; Austrian holiday dates apply

km	△	Ⓐ			Ⓐ	ⒸM	Ⓐ		Ⓐ	♣		♣	Ⓐ	♣	Ⓐ	♣	Ⓐ	♣	♣	♣	♣	♣	Ⓒ	
0	**Bratislava**-Petržalka 🛃 ☆ d.	0415	0415	0515	0546	0611	0611	...	0646	0715		1415	...	1515	...	1615	...	1715	1815	1915	2015	2115	2215	2315
5	Kittsee 🛃 d.	0421	0421	0521	0552	0617	0617	...	0652	0721		1421	...	1521	...	1621	...	1721	1821	1921	2021	2121	2221	2321
33	Bruck an der Leitha d.	0446	0446	0546	0618	0646	0646	...	0718	0746	and	1446	...	1546	...	1646	...	1746	1846	1946	2046	2146	2246	2346
74	**Wien** Hbf a.	0516	0516	0615	0646	0715	0715	...	0746	0815		1515	...	1615	...	1715	...	1815	1915	2015	2115	2215	2315	0015
74	**Wien** Hbf d.	0517	...	*0617*	...	0725	...	0723	...	0823	hourly	1523	1546	1623	1646	1723	1746	1823	1923	2023	2123	2223	...	...
78	**Wien** Meidling d.	0524	...	*0624*	...	0730	...	0730	...	0830		1530	1553	1630	1653	1730	1753	1830	1930	2030	2130	2230	...	...
116	Ebenfurth d.	0602	...	*0702*	...	...	...	0802	...	0902	until	1602	1636	1702	1736	1802	1836	1902	2002	2102	2202	2302	...	...
148	**Sopron** 🛃 a.	0637	...	*0737*	...	...	...	0837	...	0937		1637	1710	1737	1810	1837	1910	1937	2037	2137	2237	2337	...	...
157	**Deutschkreutz** a.	0657	...	*0759*	...	...	...	0847	...	0947		1647	1722	1747	1822	1847	1922	1947	2047	2147	2247	2347	...	...

△				Ⓐ		Ⓐ	♣	Ⓐ	♣	Ⓐ	♣	Ⓐ	♣		♣			ⒸM	♣		♣	♣		
Deutschkreutz d.	...	...	...	0413	...	0435	0513	0535	0613	0635	0713	0735	0813		1613	1713	...	...	1813	...	1913	2013	...	...
Sopron 🛃 d.	...	...	...	0423	...	0446	0523	0546	0623	0646	0723	0746	0823		1623	1723	...	...	1823	...	1926	2023	...	...
Ebenfurth d.	...	...	...	0504	...	0526	0604	0626	0704	0726	0804	0826	0904	and	1704	1804	...	...	1904	...	2005	2104	...	...
Wien Meidling d.	...	...	...	0532	...	0557	0632	0657	0732	0757	0832	0857	0932		1732	1832	...	1827	1932	...	2032	2132	...	...
Wien Hbf a.	...	...	...	0537	...	0603	0637	0703	0737	0803	0837	0903	0937	hourly	1737	1837	...	1832	1937	...	2037	2137	...	...
Wien Hbf d.	0050	...	0445	...	0539	...	0645	...	0745	...	0845	...	0945		1745	...	1845	1845	1945	2042	2045	2145	2245	2345
Bruck an der Leitha d.	0129	...	0513	...	0607	...	0713	...	0813	...	0913	...	1013	until	1813	...	1913	1913	2013	|	2113	2213	2313	0013
Kittsee 🛃 a.	0153	...	0538	...	0634	...	0738	...	0838	...	0938	...	1038		1838	...	1938	1938	2038	|	2138	2238	2338	0038
Bratislava-Petržalka 🛃 ☆ a.	0159	...	0544	...	0641	...	0744	...	0844	...	0944	...	1044		1844	...	1944	1944	2044	2126	2144	2244	2344	0044

km	▽	Ⓐ							Ⓐ	Ⓐ	Ⓒ	Ⓐ	Ⓐ		Ⓐ	Ⓐ	Ⓒ	Ⓐ	Ⓐ	Ⓒ	Ⓐ	Ⓐ	Ⓒ	Ⓐ	Ⓐ
	Wien Meidling **980 981** d.	...	...	...	...	...		...	...	...	...	...	...	...	...	...	...	...	1600	...	...	1700	...	...	1800
0	**Wiener Neustadt** Hbf d.	0503	0603	0703	0739	0837	and	1237	1301	1331	1337	1401	1431	1437	1501	1531	1537	1601	1631	1637	1701	1731	1737	1801	1831
16	Mattersburg d.	0526	0626	0726	0803	0902	hourly	1302	1321	1344	1402	1421	1444	1502	1521	1544	1602	1621	1644	1702	1721	1744	1802	1821	1844
33	**Sopron** 🛃 a.	0541	0641	0741	0818	0917	until	1317	1336	1400	1417	1436	1500	1517	1536	1600	1617	1636	1700	1717	1736	1800	1817	1836	1900
42	**Deutschkreutz** a.	...	...	...	...	...		...	...	1410	...	...	1510	...	...	1610	...	...	1710	...	...	1810	...	...	1910

▽	Ⓒ	Ⓐ	Ⓐ					
Wien Meidling **980 981** d.	...	...	...	...	...	...	...	...
Wiener Neustadt Hbf d.	1837	1901	1931	1937	2037	2137	2237	2337
Mattersburg d.	1902	1921	1944	2002	2102	2202	2302	0002
Sopron 🛃 a.	1917	1936	2000	2017	2117	2217	2317	0017
Deutschkreutz a.	...	...	2010	...	...	...	...	...

▽	Ⓐ	⚒	Ⓐ		Ⓐ		⑥	Ⓐ				
Deutschkreutz d.	...	...	0459	...	0559	...	0635	0659	...	...		...
Sopron 🛃 d.	0418	0447	0509	0547	0609	0647	0647	0709	0747	0844	and	2244
Mattersburg d.	0434	0503	0527	0603	0627	0703	0703	0727	0803	0902	hourly	2302
Wiener Neustadt Hbf a.	0453	0525	0539	0625	0639	0725	0725	0739	0825	0925	until	2325
Wien Meidling **980 981** a.	...	...	0614	...	0714	...	...	0814	...	...		...

M – To / from Mürzzuschlag (Table **981**).
♣ – Change at Wien Hbf.
☆ – Bus 93 links Petržalka station with Bratislava hlavná every 5–10 minutes (journey time ±12 minutes).
△ – Operated by GySEV Győr-Sopron-Ebenfurti Vasút (in German Raab-Oedenburg-Ebenfurter Eisenbahn – ROeEE).
▽ – Operated by ÖBB.

998 UNZMARKT - TAMSWEG

2nd class only; narrow gauge

km		Ⓐ	H		④B 🚂	Ⓒ 🚌	Ⓐ	②A 🚂		⑦C 🚂	Ⓒ	Ⓐ	Ⓒ 🚌	Ⓐ	Ⓐ 🚌		🚌
0	**Unzmarkt** d.	0719	0719	0922	...	1118	1122	...	1322	...	*1518**	1522	1718	1722	...	1922	2125
27	Murau-Stolzalpe d.	0759	0800	1000	1015	1202	1200	1250	1400	1410	1600	1600	1800	1758	1805	2000	2200
34	St Lorenzen d.	...	0813	1013	1035	1212	1213	1310	1413	1430	1613	1613	1812	...	1816s	2013	2208s
44	Stadl an der Mur d.	...	0827	1027	1105	1225	1227	1343	1427	1450	1627	1627	1825	...	1827s	2027	2219s
65	**Tamsweg** a.	...	0857	1057	1153	1252	1257	1431	1457	...	1657	1657	1852	...	1855	2057	2240

	Ⓐ	Ⓐ	Ⓒ	Ⓐ	Ⓒ 🚌		Ⓒ 🚌	Ⓐ	④B 🚂	⑦C 🚂	Ⓒ	Ⓐ	②A 🚂		Ⓐ 🚌	Ⓐ 🚌	Ⓒ 🚌
Tamsweg d.	...	0650	0703	0903	0910	1103	1310	1303	1335	...	1503	1503	1615	1703	1820	...	1910
Stadl an der Mur d.	...	0718	0731	0931	0929	1131	1329	1331	1425	1515	1531	1531	1710	1731	1840	...	1929
St Lorenzen d.	...	0732	0745	0945	0943	1145	1343	1345	1446	1535	1545	1545	1732	1745	1853	...	1943
Murau-Stolzalpe d.	0631	0802	0802	1002	1000	1202	1400	1402	1500	1550	1559	1602	1745	1804	1905	2000	2000
Unzmarkt a.	0711	0840	0840	1040	1040	1240	1440	1440	...	...	*1640**	1640	...	1842	...	2040	2040

A – June 15 - Sept. 7.
B – June 17 - Sept. 23.
C – July 25 - Aug. 29.
s – Stops to set down only.
* – By 🚌.
🚂 – Steam train. Special fares payable.
2022 schedules not yet confirmed (2020 timings/running dates shown).
Operator: Steiermärkische Landesbahnen.

999 Danube shipping

2021 Service

Catamaran services. 🍸	W Ⓡ♠				W Ⓡ♠		W Ⓡ♠		
Wien Schwedenplatz ▲ d.	0830	...	...	...	1230	...	1630	...	...
Bratislava a.	0945	...	...	...	1345	...	1745	...	...

Catamaran services. 🍸	W Ⓡ♠		W Ⓡ♠					W Ⓡ♠	
Bratislava d.	1030	...	1430	...	...	...	...	1830	...
Wien Schwedenplatz ▲ a.	1200	...	1600	...	...	...	...	2000	...

All sailings convey ✕	C ⊡	B ◐		D ◐	⑦J ◐Ⓡ	D ⊡	D ◐	D ◐	
Wien Reichsbrücke ▲ d.	...	...	...	...	0830	...	...	...	...
Tulln d.	...	...	...	...	1120	...	...	...	...
Krems an der Donau d.	1005	1015	...	1310	1400	1540	1545	...	...
Dürnstein d.	1040	1050	...	1340	1430	1610	1620	...	...
Spitz an der Donau d.	1135	1145	...	1445	...	1700	1720	1730	...
Melk a.	1255	1320	...	1605	...	*1730**	...	1850	...

All sailings convey ✕	D ◐		C ⊡	B ◐		⑦J ◐Ⓡ	D ⊡	D ◐	D ◐
Melk d.	1100	...	1345	1350	...	...	...	1625	...
Spitz an der Donau d.	1200‡	...	1430	1440	...	...	1705	1710	1725
Dürnstein d.	1230	...	1500	1510	...	1640	1730	...	1750
Krems an der Donau d.	1250	...	1525	1530	...	1700	1755	...	1810
Tulln d.	...	...	...	...	...	1900	...	...	...
Wien Reichsbrücke ▲ a.	...	...	...	...	...	2100	...	...	...

All sailings convey ✕	⊖A	⊖F	
Linz Lentos d.	...	1420	...
Schlögen d.	...	1800	...
Engelhartszell d.	1530	1845	...
Passau Liegestelle 11 🛃 d.	1730	2050	...
Deggendorf a.	...	...	...

All sailings convey ✕	⊖F	⊖A	
Deggendorf d.	...	...	...
Passau Liegestelle 11 🛃 d.	0900	1000	...
Engelhartszell d.	1030	1130	...
Schlögen a.	1110	...	...
Linz Lentos a.	1410	...	...

A – Apr. 30 - Oct. 3.
B – Apr. 3 - Nov. 1.
C – May 22 - Oct. 26.
D – May 22 - Oct. 3.
F – ⑥⑦ Aug. 12 - Oct. 2.
J – ⑦ May 30 - Oct. 17 (not June 20).
W – May 5 - Oct. 2; ⑤⑥⑦† Oct. 3 - Nov. 11.

* – By 🚌 from Spitz.
‡ – Arrives 1140.

▲ – DDSG operates Wien sightseeing cruises Schwedenplatz - Reichsbrücke and v.v. Daily Mar. 27 - Nov. 1.
From Schwedenplatz (duration 1 h 55 m via Schleuse Freudenau) at 1030, 1400 (also 1130, 1500 Apr. 4 - Oct. 4).
From Reichsbrücke (duration 1 h 20 m via Schleuse Nussdorf) at 1230, 1600 (also 1330, 1700 Apr. 4 - Oct. 4).
Also shorter *City Cruise* available daily throughout the year from Schwedenplatz at 1100, 1300, 1430 and 1600 (duration 1 h 15 m).

Operators:
⊡ – Brandner Schiffahrt, Ufer 15, A-3313 Wallsee. ✆ +43 (0) 7433 25 90 21. www.brandner.at
◐ – DDSG Blue Danube Schiffahrt, Handelskai 265, A-1020 Wien. ✆ +43 (0)1 588 80. www.ddsg-blue-danube.at
⊖ – Wurm und Köck, Höllgasse 26, D-94032 Passau. ✆ +49 (0) 851 92 92 92. www.donauschiffahrt.de
♠ – *Twin City Liner*. DDSG Blue Danube, Handelskai 265, A-1020 Wien. Check-in 30 minutes before departure. Austrian holiday dates apply. ✆ +43 (0)1 904 88 80. Internet booking: www.twincityliner.com

POLAND

Operators: Express services are operated by PKP Intercity www.intercity.pl. Most local trains are operated by Przewozy Regionalne (PR) www.przewozyregionalne.pl. Certain local services are operated by regional companies owned by local government: e.g. Koleje Dolnośląskie, Koleje Mazowieckie, Koleje Śląskie and Koleje Wielkopolskie.

Services: **PKP InterCity** : Note reservation is compulsory (Ⓡ) on all services operated by PKP InterCity (*EC, EIC, EIP, EN, IC, MP, TLK*). *EC, EIC* and *EIP* trains are fast premium-rate trains on long-distance routes (*EC* or *EuroCity* trains run on international routes) - first and second class seats, higher rate of fares apply and a supplement is payable for pass holders. *EC, EIC* and *EIP* trains normally convey ✕ or 🍸 for at least part of the route. *IC* and *TLK* trains are lower-cost long distance trains with first and second class seats (also sleepers and couchettes on nights routes as shown in the tables). *TLK* is short for *Twoje Linie Kolejowe* (Your Railway Lines). *IRE* is an Interregio-Express. Certain trains convey 🍸 but it is not possible to identify these in the tables. *MP* is the classification (within Poland) for other international trains; *TLK* fares apply within Poland. *EN* trains are *EuroNight* services with 'global' fares which include the sleeping accommodation. Descriptions of sleeping (🛏) and couchette (▬) cars appear on page 10.

Przewozy Regionalne and other local operators : *IR (InterRegio)* and *RE* (*Regional Express*) trains are semi-fast trains operated by Przewozy Regionalne on longer distance routes, with second class seats. Fares are cheaper than *TLK* services but slightly higher than local *Regio* trains. All other trains are local *R* (*Regio*) trains, second class only, calling at all or most stations en route. No train category is shown in our tables for these trains. They are operated by Przewozy Regionalne unless otherwise shown in the table heading or by a footnote. Fares on *Regio* trains are the cheapest available.

Timings: Valid **until June 11, 2022** except where shown otherwise. *However, alterations and amendments are possible at any time (particularly on and around public holidays) and readers are advised to check specific dates locally before travelling.* Engineering work can often affect schedules; major changes are shown in the tables where possible but other changes may occur at short notice. A number of long-distance trains running only in high summer (particularly to coastal resorts) are not shown owing to lack of space. Note that train numbers often change en route by one or two digits. In station names, Gł. is short for Główny or Główna, meaning main station.

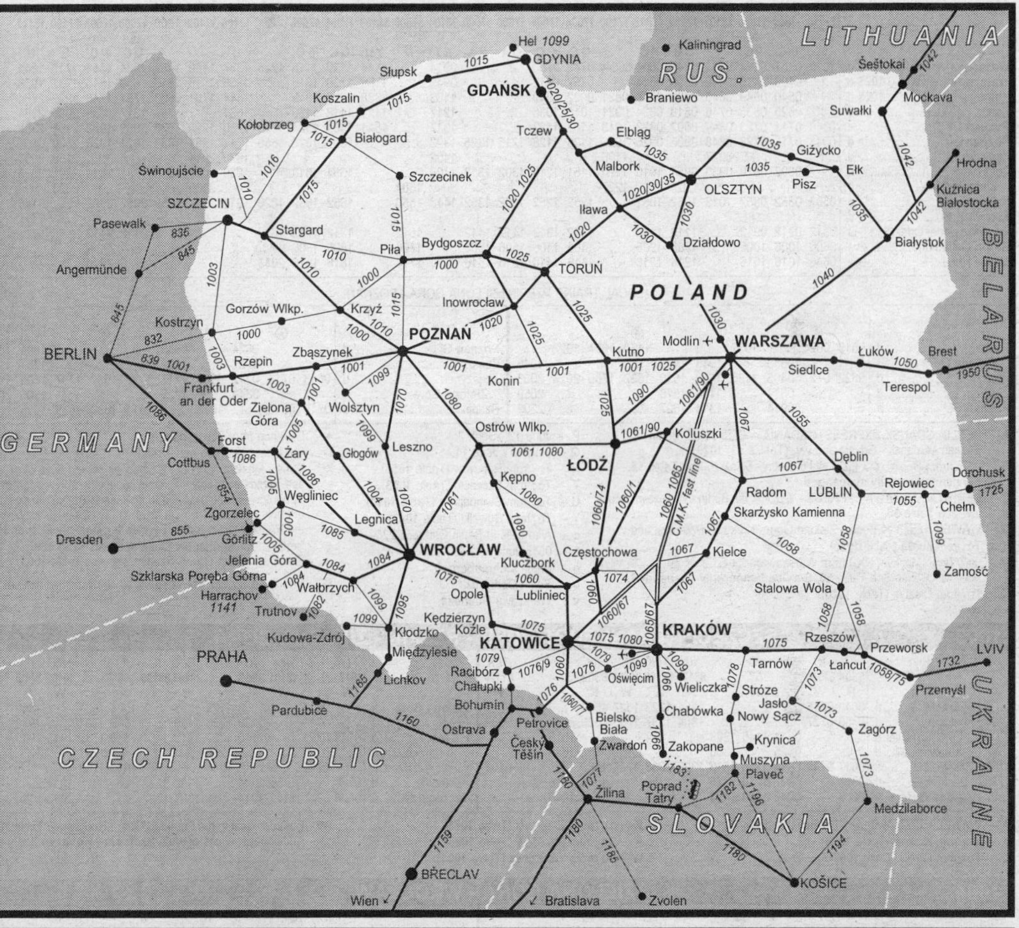

KOSTRZYN - KRZYŻ - POZNAŃ and BYDGOSZCZ 1000

Service subject to confirmation

km		IC 81112 W	Ⓐ	TLK 85112 2G					TLK 82104 B		⚒		Ⓑ	Ⓐ		TLK 82100 A			Ⓐ	TLK 85110 2G			Ⓐ			⚒	Ⓐ
0	**Kostrzyn** d.	...	...	...	...	0554	0651	...	...	0840	...	1006	...	1158	...	...	...	1349	1452	1509	1552	...	1635	1813	2035	...	2130
43	Gorzów Wlkp. d.	...	...	0520	...	0636	0728	...	...	0924	...	1048	...	1244	...	...	...	1426	1530	1550	1633	...	1712	1851	2112	...	2208
103	Krzyż **1010** a.	...	...	0612	...	0728	0819	...	...	1015	...	1136	...	1335	...	...	...	1523	1621	1640	1724	...	▬	1942	2203	...	...
103	Krzyż **1010** d.	...	0510	0614	0637	0733	...	0833	...	1018	1034	▬	1257	...	1341	...	1455	▬	...	1641	1727	1730	...	▬	...	2210	...
186	**Poznań** **1010** a.	...	|	|	|	0932	...	|	...	1215	|	...	|	...	|	...	|	Ⓑ	...	|	1857	|	...	...	...	|	...
163	Piła Gł. d.	0548	0603	0734r	0730	...	...	0930	1032	...	1129	1157	1352	...	1438	1514	1547	1615	...	1732	...	1823	1830	2007	...	2303	...
248	**Bydgoszcz** a.	0702	...	0850	...	...	...	...	1146	...	...	1331	...	...	...	1627	...	1744	...	...	...	...	2000	2135	...	...	...

	Ⓐ		Ⓑ	⚒					Ⓐ	TLK 58111 2G			TLK 28101 A	⚒	Ⓐ		Ⓑ	Ⓑ			TLK 28105 B				TLK 58113 2G	IC 18113 W	Ⓐ
Bydgoszcz d.	...	...	...	0553	...	0749	...	...	...	...	...	...	1212	...	...	...	1435	...	1605	...	1642	1759	...	...	1929	2106	...
Piła Gł. d.	...	...	0515	0717	0722	0913	0922	...	...	1139	1201	...	1321	1354	...	1455	1559	1612	1730	1735	1751	1923	2002	...	2107	2221	...
Poznań **1010** d.	...	...	|	▬	|	▬	|	0933	...	|	|	1230	...	|	...	|	▬	|	▬	|	...	...	|	1947	|	...	...
Krzyż **1010** a.	...	...	0607	...	0824	...	1028	1102	...	1238	1255	1401	...	1445	...	1548	...	1704	...	1826	...	...	2053	2132	2157	...	...
Krzyż **1010** d.	...	0523	...	0621	...	0829	...	1103	1209	1239	...	1402	...	...	1456	...	1621	...	1750	...	...	...	...	2133	2159	...	...
Gorzów Wlkp. d.	0552	0619	...	0724	...	0923	...	1156	1303	1353	...	1455	...	...	1551	...	1715	...	1845	...	...	...	...	2226	2252	...	2300
Kostrzyn a.	0630	0658	...	0802	...	0959	...	1232	1340	1429	...	1532	...	...	1628	...	1752	...	1929	...	...	...	...	2317	...	...	2337

– 🚃12 Szczecin - Piła - Bydgoszcz - Warszawa - Lublin and v.v.
B – To / from Lublin (Table **1055**).
G – To / from Gdynia (Table **1025**).
W – To / from Warszawa (Table **1025**).
r – Arrive 0705.

1001 BERLIN - POZNAŃ - WARSZAWA

km		TLK	IC	EIC	IC	EC	EC	IC	MP	IC	EC	EC	EC	IC	EC	EC	EC	EC	IC	EC	EC	IC	EC	EC	EC
		81170	71105	8100	72101	41	41	81106	453	81102	45	45	57	83100	59	59	49	49	71100	247	247	81100	249	249	44
		81171	71104	8101	72100	71008	71008	81107	❋	81103	71006	71006	73000	83101	75000	75000	71004	71004	71101	71002	71002	81101	71000	71000	710
				①–⑥		⚒	⚒		⊠														Ⓑ	Ⓑ	❋
		U			E	PC	QC	U		UY	PC	QC	D	TR	PA	QA	PC	QC		PC	QC	T	PC	QC	B
0	**Berlin** Hbf ⊖ d.	...	...	...	...	0543f	0543	...	0726	...	0938	0937	1039	...	1238	1237	1341	1342	...	1541	1543	...	1741	1743	20
5	**Berlin** Ostbahnhof ⊖ d.	...	...	...	...	0555o	0555o	...	0801g	...	0952	0951	1052	...	1252	1253	1353	1353	...	1555	1553	...	1753	1753	20
87	Frankfurt an der Oder 🏛 ⊖ d.	...	...	...	...	0645	0645	...	0855	...	1045	1045	1145	...	1345	1345	1445	1445	...	1645	1645	...	1845	1845	21
98	Kunowice 🏛 ⊖ d.	...	...	...	...	|	|	...	|	...	|	|	|	...	|	|	|	|	...	|	|	...	|	|	|
110	Rzepin ▷ d.	0102	...	0502	...	0707	0707	0848	0919	...	1107	1107	1210	1327	1407	1407	1507	1507	...	1707	1707	1757	1907	1907	21
•58	**Zielona Góra** ▷ d.	|	...	|	0512	|	|	|	|	...	|	|	1253	|	|	|	|	|	1509	|	|	|	|	|	|
185	Zbąszynek ▷ d.	0153	...	0545	0634	0746	0745	0931	|	...	1146	1143	...	1406	1446	1444	1546	1544	1631	1746	1744	1837	1946	1943	|
191	Zbąszyń ▷ d.	0201	...	|	0640	|	|	0938	|	...	|	|	...	1412	|	|	|	|	1638	|	|	1843	|	|	|
266	**Poznań** Gł. ▷ a.	0300	...	0624	0723	0831	0849	1017	1040	...	1231	1250	...	1452	1531	1541	1631	1639	1718	1831	1840	1928	2031	2039	23
266	**Poznań** Gł. d.	0305	0459	0627	0728	0841	0853	1024	1043	1220	1236	1254	...	1458	...	...	1642	1654	1730	1836	1854	1931	2036	2053	23
366	Konin d.	0412	0600	0712	0827	0932	0937	1125	|	1337	1324	1339	...	1557	...	...	1731	1739	1832	1924	1939	2030	2124	2138	|
445	Kutno **1025** d.	0508	0711	0802	0920	1019	1024	1214	|	1434	1416	1425	...	1702	...	...	1818	1824	1930	2009	2025	2131	2211	2226	|
572	**Warszawa** Centralna **1025** a.	0703	0848	0933	1105	1146	1150	1350	|	1611	1539	1553	...	1835	...	...	1941	1951	|	2132	2151	|	2335	2352	|
577	**Warszawa** Wschodnia **1025** a.	0716	0901	0946	1116	1156	1201	1401	1511	1626	1553	1604	...	1846	...	...	1952	2002	2112y	2143	2201	2311y	2346	0002	03

	EC ❋	EC	EC	IC	EC	EC	TLK	EC	EC	EC	EC	IC	EC	IC	EC	EC	MP	IC	IC	EIC	EC	EC	IC	TLK
	440	248	248	18101	246	246	17101	48	48	58	58	38100	56	18102	44	44	452	18107	17103	1801	40	40	27101	18170
	17010	17000	17000	18100	17002	17002	17100	17004	17004	57000	57000	38101	37000	18103	17006	17006	❋	18106	17102	1800	17008	17008	27100	18171
		⚒	⚒														⊠			Ⓑ	Ⓑ	Ⓑ		
	M	QC	PC	T	QC	PC		QC	PC	QA	PA	RT	D	YU	QC	PC		U			QC	PC	E	U
Warszawa Wschodnia. **1025** d.	2310	0357	0404	0434	0547	0604	0654y	0742	0753	...	...	0914	...	1144	1139	1155	1225	1337	1450	1459	1534	1554	1719	1944
Warszawa Centralna... **1025** d.	|	0406	0415	0448	0558	0614	|	0757	0812	...	...	0949	...	1159	1150	1215	|	1355	1515	1510	1556	1615	1732	1956
Kutno **1025** d.	|	0540	0549	0645	0733	0748	0831	0932	0949	...	...	1133	...	1338	1328	1349	|	1544	1701	1653	1731	1748	1922	2154
Konin d.	|	0626	0635	0746	0818	0834	0921	1018	1036	...	...	1217	...	1421	1418	1436	|	1631	|	1739	1817	1835	2008	2254
Poznań Gł. a.	0340	0711	0723	0844	0902	0922	1018	1102	1123	...	...	1317	...	1541	1501	1524	1655	1730	1920	1823	1905	1923	2104	2358
Poznań Gł. ▷ d.	0343	0715	0728	0848	0905	0925	1025	1105	1128	1215	1225	1322	...	...	1504	1528	1658	1744	1931	1830	1921	1928	2009	0003
Zbąszyń ▷ d.	|	|	|	0927	|	|	1105	|	|	|	|	1402	...	...	|	|	|	1830	2014	|	|	|	2150	0051
Zbąszynek ▷ d.	|	0802	0810	0933	0951	1010	1120	1151	1210	1302	1312	1408	...	...	1551	1610	|	1836	2029	1912	1951	2010	2206	0058
Zielona Góra ▷ a.	|	|	|	|	|	|	1227	|	|	|	|	|	1504	...	|	|	|	|	2136	|	|	|	2323	|
Rzepin ▷ d.	0503	0852	0852	1013	1052	1052	...	1252	1252	1352	1352	1448	1550	...	1652	1652	1820	1914	...	1958	2052	2052	...	0146
Kunowice 🏛 ⊖ d.	|	|	|	...	|	|	...	|	|	|	|	...	|	...	|	|	|	...	...	...	|	|	...	...
Frankfurt an der Oder 🏛 ⊖ a.	0512	0912	0912	...	1112	1112	...	1312	1312	1412	1412	...	1612	...	1712	1712	1842	...	...	...	2112	2112	...	...
Berlin Ostbahnhof ⊖ a.	0606	1006	1006	...	1206	1206	...	1406	1406	1506	1506	...	1706	...	1806	1806	1946g	...	...	...	2207c	2208c	...	...
Berlin Hbf ⊖ a.	0646	1016	1016	...	1216	1216	...	1416	1416	1516	1516	...	1716	...	1816	1816	2053	...	...	...	2216	2216	...	...

LOCAL TRAINS RZEPIN / ZIELONA GORA - POZNAŃ

		Ⓐ		⚒			Ⓐ			
Rzepin d.	0519	0624	...	1032	...	...	1430	1604	1922	...
Zielona Góra d.	|	|	0658	|	1045	1403	|	|	|	1946
Zbąszynek d.	0622	0727	0805	1135	1152	1510	1532	1700	2026	2053
Zbąszyń d.	...	...	0811	...	1158	1516	...	...	...	2059
Poznań Gł. a.	...	...	0914	...	1314	1627	...	...	...	2209

		Ⓐ		⚒			Ⓐ			
Poznań Gł. d.	...	...	0624	...	0959	...	...	...	1644	182
Zbąszyń d.	...	...	0727	...	1102	...	...	...	1751	193
Zbąszynek d.	0613	0714	0742	0909	1117	1420	1531	1737	1808	195
Zielona Góra a.	|	|	0844	|	1229	|	|	|	1905	204
Rzepin a.	0715	0817	...	1013	...	1514	1633	1839	...	...

A – BERLIN GDANSK EXPRESS / GEDANIA – 12 ✕ Ⓡ, Berlin - Poznań - Gdansk - Gdynia and v.v. (Tables **51**, **1020**).
B – ①⑥ (from Berlin): 🛏 1 ✕ Ⓡ Berlin - Moskva. See Table **56**. **Service temporarily suspended**.
C – BERLIN WARSZAWA EXPRESS – 12 ✕ Ⓡ, Berlin - Warszawa and v.v. See Table **56**.
D – WAWEL – 12 ✕ Berlin - Zielona Góra - Krakow - Przemyśl and v.v.
E – To / from Lublin (Table **1055**).
M – ⑤⑦ (from Moskva, ⑥① from Warszawa): 🛏 1 ✕ Ⓡ Moskva - Berlin. See Table **56**. **Service temporarily suspended**.
O – To / from Olsztyn (Table **1020**).

P – June 12 - Sept. 3.
Q – Mar. 13 - June 11.
R – To / from Rzeszów (Table **1058**).
T – To / from Szczecin (Table **1003**).
U – To / from Świnoujście (Table **1010**).
Y – To / from Suwałki (Table **1042**).
c – Also calls at Berlin Ostkreuz 2202.
f – 0515 June 13 - July 8.
g – Berlin **Lichtenberg**.
o – Berlin **Ostkreuz**.
y – Warszawa **Gdańska**.

• – Distance from Zbąszynek.
▷ – For local trains see panel below main table.
⊠ – Paris - Moskva service; for composition and days of runni see Tables **24 / 56 / 95**. Special conditions apply. Journeys within the European Union (e.g. Paris to Berlin) are possib but only bookable through agents of Russian Railways or the Russian rail website. **Service temporarily suspende**
⊖ – Berlin - Frankfurt an der Oder: see also Table **839**. Frankfurt an der Oder - Rzepin: see also Table **1003**.
❋ **Shaded services are suspended until further notice.**

1003 SZCZECIN \ FRANKFURT ODER - RZEPIN - ZIELONA GÓRA

km		IC	IC	IC			IC	TLK	IC	IC			TLK
		8304	81106	57			83100	82102	81100	8302			81170
		P	W	A			R	L	W	K			W
0	**Szczecin** Gł. d.	0640	0615	...	...	...	1154	1223	1627	1514	...	...	2329
104	Kostrzyn d.	0756	0727	...	...	...	1304	1337	1735	1629	...	...	0039
	Frankfurt / Oder d.	|	|	0814	1145	1258	|	|	|	|	1815	...	|
	Kunowice 🏛 d.	|	|	0825	|	1308	|	|	|	|	1825	...	|
136	Rzepin a.	0817	0749	0834	1206	1316	1325	1358	1756	1650	1833	...	0101
136	Rzepin d.	0823	...	0837	1210	1325	...	1359	...	1651	1846	...	...
207	**Zielona Góra** a.	0907	...	0940	1253	1423	...	1442	...	1734	1946	...	...

	TLK		IC	IC		TLK	IC	IC		IC	IC
	18171		18101	3803		28103	38100	56		18107	3805
	W		W	K		L	R	A		W	P
Zielona Góra d.	...	0617	...	1053	1125	1333	...	1504	1631	...	1848
Rzepin a.	...	0718	...	1138	1226	1418	...	1547	1731	...	1939
Rzepin d.	0155	0721	1014	1140	1227	1419	1451	1550	1732	1915	1940
Kunowice 🏛 d.	|	0730	|	|	1236	|	|	|	1741	|	|
Frankfurt / Oder a.	|	0742	|	|	1248	|	|	1612	1753	|	|
Kostrzyn d.	0226	...	1036	1204	...	1451	1512	...	...	1937	2003
Szczecin Gł. a.	0334	...	1141	1314	...	1607	1617	...	...	2043	2116

A – WAWEL – 12 ✕ Berlin - Przemyśl and v.v.
K – To / from Kraków (Table **1075**).
L – To / from Lublin (Table **1067**).
P – To / from Przemyśl (Table **1075**).
R – To / from Rzeszów (Table **1058**).
W – To / from Warszawa (Table **1001**).
☛ For additional trains Frankfurt/Oder - Rzepin see Table 10 Additional services operate **Szczecin - Kostrzyn** and v.v.

1004 ZIELONA GÓRA - WROCŁAW

km			TLK	IC		IC		IC	TLK		IC	IC		
		⚒	71106	83104		8304		57	82102		8302	86104		
			⚒W	SP		SP		A	SL		S	S		
0	**Zielona Góra** d.	0525	0612	0706	0744	0908	1124	1256	1444	1536	1736	1930	2016	...
23	Nowa Sól d.	0544	0628	0722	0803	0923	1143	|	1459	1555	1751	1945	2035	...
54	Glogów d.	0621	0700	0748	0839	0949	1214	1334	1527	1626	1817	2009	2110	...
154	**Wrocław** Gł a.	0810	0828	0911	1020	1116	1407	1457	1701	1836	1940	2141	2258	...
	Kraków **1075** a.	...	...	1305	...	1501	...	1801	...	...	2346	...	...	...

		IC	IC		IC	IC		IC		TLK	IC	
		68105	3803		28103	56		3805		17107	38105	
		S	S		LS	A		PS		ⒷW	PS	
Kraków **1075** d.	...	...	0458	...	...	1012	...	1248	...	...	1529	...
Wrocław Gł. d.	0535	0615	0842	1025	1125	1306	1442	1636	1658	1840	1957	2007
Glogów d.	0722	0735	1010	1203	1249	1424	1632	1803	1842	2001	2129	2145
Nowa Sól d.	0751	0805	1038	1233	1317	|	1705	1832	1912	2028	2157	2218
Zielona Góra a.	0815	0824	1052	1252	1331	1502	1724	1846	1949	2051	2211	2242

A – WAWEL – 12 ✕ Berlin - Wrocław - Przemyśl and v.v.
L – To / from Lublin (Table **1067**).
P – To / from Przemyśl (Table **1075**).
S – To / from Szczecin (Table **1003**).
W – To / from Warszawa (Table **106**

1005 ZIELONA GÓRA - WEGLINIEC - JELENIA GÓRA

km		⊖	IC		⊖		⊖			⊖		⊖
			16170									
			16190									
0	**Zielona Góra** d.	...	...	...	...	0738	...	1134	1338	...	1539	...
	Żagań **1086** d.	...	...	0521	...	|	...	|	|	...	|	...
54	Zary **1086** d.	...	...	0538	...	0840	...	1239	1437	...	1644	...
94	Wegliniec **1085** d.	...	0637	0642	...	0941	...	1358	1544	...	1744	...
118	Zgorzelec Miasto d.	...	|	0707	...	1006	...	1424	1609	...	1808	...
	Görlitz **1085** d.	0539	|	|	0939	|	1339	|	|	1739	|	1939
120	Zgorzelec **1085** d.	0544	|	0710	0944	1010	1344	1428	1613	1744	1813	1944
	Görlitz **1085** a.	|	|	...	|	1014	|	1432	1617	|	1817	|
144	Lubań Śląski d.	0613	0709	...	1017	...	1414	...	...	1815	...	2013
196	**Jelenia Góra** a.	0716	0812	...	1120	...	1516	...	...	1917	...	2123

	⊖			⊖		⊖		⊖		⊖	IC
											611
											611
Jelenia Góra d.	0546	...	...	0946	...	1346	...	1546	...	1946	20
Lubań Śląski d.	0654	...	...	1055	...	1454	...	1654	...	2054	21
Görlitz **1085** d.	|	0902	1103	|	1508	|	1708	|	1920	|	|
Zgorzelec **1085** d.	0726	0907	1108	1126	1513	1526	1713	1726	1939	2126	|
Görlitz **1085** a.	0730	|	|	1130	|	1530	|	1730	|	2130	|
Zgorzelec Miasto d.	...	0910	1111	...	1516	...	1715	...	1941	...	|
Wegliniec **1085** d.	...	0941	1147	...	1550	...	1747	...	2013	...	21
Zary **1086** d.	...	1033	1237	...	1642	...	1901	...	2116	...	...
Żagań **1086** a.	...	|	|	...	|	...	|	...	2129	...	...
Zielona Góra a.	...	1132	1336	...	1748	...	1959	...	...	...	...

⊖ – Operator: Koleje Dolnośląskie.

☛ 🚌 Görlitz Bahnhof - Zgorzelec Miasto and v.v. every 30 minutes (journey 22 minutes).

SZCZECIN - POZNAŃ 1010

km																							
			IC				*IC*										*IC*		*IC*				
			83102				**81103**										**81108**		**83173**				
							81102										**81109**		**83172**				
					⚒				Ⓐ	Ⓒ		Ⓒ	Ⓐ		⑦	Ⓐ							
							Y										**L**		**P**				
	Świnoujście d.	...	...	...	...	...	0616	0820	1013	...	...	1150	...	...	1356	...	...	...	1550	1627	...	...	...
0	**Szczecin** Gł. **1015** d.	...	0414	...	0537	...	0748	1020	1209	1209	...	1354	1354	...	1610	1610	1705	...	1815	1900	...	...	...
15	Szczecin Dąbie **1015** d.	...	0427	...	0550	...	0803	1038	1224	1224	...	1409	1409	...	1627	1627	1718	...	1832	1917	...	...	...
40	Stargard **1015** d.	...	0452	...	0621	...	0831	1104	1257	1257	...	1442	1442	...	1706	1706	1742	...	1903	1950	...	...	...
130	Krzyż **1000** d.	...	0652	0737	0820	...	1044	1304	1451	1451	...	1647	1647	...	1903	1903	1945	...	2055	2208	...	...	...
213	**Poznań** Gł. **1000** a.	...	0831	0932	0958	...	1207	1436	1648	1648	...	1816	1816	...	2050	2050	2146	...	2229	2338	...	...	...
	Warszawa Cent. **1001** a.	...	|	...	...	...	1611	...	...	...	...	...	...	...	...	...	...	...	|	...	...	...	...
	Katowice **1075 1080** a.	...	1306	...	...	...	...	...	...	...	...	...	...	...	...	...	...	...	0416	...	...	...	...
	Kraków Gł **1075 1080** a.	...	1433	...	...	...	...	...	...	...	...	...	...	...	...	...	...	...	0538	...	...	...	...

					IC		*IC*							*IC*				*IC*				
					38173		**18109**							**18103**				**38103**				
					38172		**18108**							**18102**				**38102**				
	Ⓐ	⑥	Ⓐ													⑤⑦						
					P		**L**							**Y**								
Kraków Gł. **1075 1080** d.	...	...	...	...	2241	...	...	...	...	...	...	...	...	...	...	...	...	1337	...	...	...	...
Katowice **1075 1080** d.	...	...	...	...	0003	...	...	...	...	...	...	...	...	...	...	...	...	1459	...	...	...	...
Warszawa Cent. **1001** d.	...	...	...	...	|	...	...	...	...	...	...	...	...	1155	...	...	...	|	...	...	...	...
Poznań Gł. **1000** d.	...	...	...	...	0554	0619	0729	...	1013	...	...	1320	1455	1603	...	1740	...	1938	...	2138	...	...
Krzyż **1000** d.	0431	0431	0540	...	0737	0827	0857	...	1145	...	...	1500	1640	1725	...	1940	...	2117	...	2314	...	...
Stargard **1015** d.	0627	0627	0737	...	0927	1015	1026	...	1338	...	...	1654	1820	1927	...	2129	...	2249	...	...	...	...
Szczecin Dąbie **1015** d.	0655	0655	0802	...	0954	1040	1049	...	1403	...	...	1722	1844	1949	...	2157	...	2312	...	...	...	...
Szczecin Gł. **1015** a.	0710	0710	0818	...	1008	1055	1112	...	1418	...	...	1736	1909	2006	...	2230	...	2325	...	...	...	...
Świnoujście a.	0916	...	...	...	1214	...	...	...	1616	...	...	1941t	...	2149	...	...	...	...	...	...	...	...

km		Ⓐ	Ⓒ	Ⓐ			Ⓒ	Ⓒ				Ⓑ
0	**Świnoujście** d.	0433	0539	0615	0820	1013	1150	1400	1621	...	1807	1958
99	Szczecin Dąbie a.	0603	0715	0746	0947	1140	1322	1538	1755	...	1947	2126
111	**Szczecin** Gł. a.	0617	0729	0801	1004	1155	1340	1553	1810	...	2002	2142

				Ⓒ				Ⓑ		
Szczecin Gł. d.	0526	0720	...	1110	...	1428	1546	1757	2032	...
Szczecin Dąbie d.	0541	0741	...	1126	...	1441	1601	1811	2047	...
Świnoujście a.	0718	0916	...	1255	...	1613	1735	1946	2224	...

km								**82100**				
								§M				
0	**Szczecin** Gł. d.	...	...	...	0752	...	1035	1133	...	...	...	...
12	Szczecin Dąbie d.	...	...	...	0807	...	1051	1150	...	...	...	...
37	Stargard d.	...	0449	...	0838	...	1120	1224	...	...	...	...
102	Kalisz Pomorski d.	...	0559	...	0959	...	1237	1333	...	1726	...	...
146	Wałcz d.	...	0643	...	1042	...	1320	1422	...	1812	...	...
176	**Piła** Główna a.	...	0714	...	1113	...	1350	1454	...	1848	...	...

					28101					
			A		**§M**					
Piła Główna d.	...	0725	1123	...	1342	...	1555	...	1940	...
Wałcz d.	...	0755	1153	...	1421	...	1626	...	2010	...
Kalisz Pomorski d.	...	0839	1236	...	1503	...	1709	...	2053	...
Stargard d.	...	0945	1351	...	1606	...	1816	...	2205	...
Szczecin Dąbie d.	...	1014	1416	...	1634	...	1848	...	2230	...
Szczecin Gł. a.	...	1030	1434	...	1656	...	1902	...	2253	...

A – Not Sept. 6 - Oct. 21.
L – To / from Łódź (Table **1055**).
M – To / from Lublin (Table **1061**).
P – To / from Przemyśl (Table **1075**).
Y – To / from Suwałki (Table **1042**).
t – Not ⑥.
§ – *TLK* service.

SZCZECIN - KOSZALIN - GDYNIA - GDAŃSK 1015

km																									
		EIP	*IC*	*IC*	*IC*			*TLK*		*IC*	*IC*		*IC*	*IC*		*IC*	*IC*			*TLK*	*IC*		*IC*	*TLK*	
		8300	**85108**	**78172**	**85106**			**81114**		**48101**	**81104**		**3807**	**85104**		**48103**	**85102**			**38107**	**85100**		**68103**	**83170**	
		8301	**85109**	**78173**	**85107**			**81115**		**48100**	**81105**			**85105**		**48102**	**85103**			**38106**			**68102**		
														Ⓑ											
		K	**O**		**O**			**L**		**S**	**Y**		**J**	**O**		**A**	**O**			**J**			**A**	**K**	
0	**Szczecin** Gł. **1010** d.	...	0509	...	0650	0703	...	...	...	...	1056	1151	...	1257	...	...	1457	1547	...	...	1805	...	...	...	1949
15	Szczecin Dąbie **1010** d.	...	0522	...	0703	0718	...	...	...	...	1109	1205	...	1310	...	...	1510	1605	...	...	1819	...	...	...	2003
40	Stargard **1010** d.	...	0545	...	0736	0744	...	...	...	...	1133	1231	...	1334	...	...	1533	1631	...	...	1844	...	...	...	2032
**231*	**Poznań** Gł. d.	...	|	0528	|	|	0542	...	0826	0939	|	|	1144	|	1242	1344	|	|	1440	1557	|	1655	1732	...	|
**135*	Piła Gł. d.	...	|	0642	|	|	0725	...	1010	1050	|	|	1256	|	1412	1453	|	|	1624	1742	|	1833	1851	...	|
**64*	Szczecinek d.	...	|	0736	|	|	0828	...	1120	1143	|	|	1350	|	1524	1546	|	|	1740	1842	|	1939	2012	...	|
151	Białogard a.	...	0700	0827	0850	0920	0935	...	1218	1238	1249	1405	1446	1455	1620	1641	1653	1758	1835	1939	2007	2044t	2106	...	2200
151	Białogard d.	...	0701	0830	0852	0921	0936	...	1222	1239	1251	1408	1447	1502	1620	1642	1654	1759	1835	1942	2010	2044t	2107	...	2201
187	Kołobrzeg a.	...	|	|	|	|	1011	...	1246	|	|	|	1520	|	|	|	|	|	1910	2015	|	|	|	...	|
***43*	Kołobrzeg d.	0612	|	|	|	|	...	1004	...	|	|	|	...	|	|	|	|	|	...	...	|	|	|	2043	|
175	**Koszalin** d.	0647	0716	0852	0911	0941	...	1046	...	1256	1317	1443	...	1524	1656	1700	1711	1815	...	...	2030	2059t	2122	2141	2217
242	Słupsk d.	0727	0759	0937	0955	1036	...	1134	...	1336	1408	1543t	...	1613	...	1739	1753	1905	...	...	2120	...	2203	2221	...
294	Lębork d.	0757	0832	...	1025	...	...	1214	...	...	1441	...	...	1647	...	...	1845	...	...	...	2153	...	...	2253	...
353	**Gdynia** Gł. a.	0834	0917	...	1108	...	...	1308	...	...	1522	...	...	1727	...	...	1928	...	...	...	2236	...	...	2336	...
353	**Gdynia** Gł. ▷ d.	0836	0920	...	1125	...	...	1333	...	...	1525	...	...	1737	...	...	1930	...	...	...	2237	...	...	2340	...
362	Sopot ▷ d.	0845	0928	...	1133	...	...	1343	...	...	1534	...	...	1746	...	...	1940	...	...	...	2246	...	...	2351	...
374	**Gdańsk** Gł. ▷ a.	0859	0942	...	1148	...	...	1359	...	...	1548	...	...	1800	...	...	1954	...	...	...	2300	...	...	0007	...
	Warszawa C. **1025/30** a.	1135	...	...	...	...	...	1730	...	...	...	...	...	...	...	...	...	...	...	...	...	...	...	0355	...

				IC	*IC*		*IC*	*TLK*		*IC*	*IC*		*TLK*	*IC*		*IC*	*IC*			*TLK*		*IC*	*IC*	*IC*	*EIP*
				86103	**58101**		**83106**	**38171**		**84103**	**58103**		**58105**	**8306**		**84101**	**18105**			**18115**		**87173**	**58107**	**58109**	**3801**
				86102			**83107**	**38170**		**84102**	**58102**					**84100**	**18104**			**18114**		**87172**	**58106**	**58108**	**3800**
									Ⓐ												Ⓑ				
				A			**J**	**K**		**A**	**O**		**O**	**J**		**S**	**Y**			**L**			**O**	**O**	**K**
Warszawa C. **1025/30** d.	...	...	...	...	...	...	...	0150f	...	...	...	...	...	...	...	...	...	...	...	1035	...	...	...	...	1625
Gdańsk Gł. ▷ d.	...	...	...	...	0518	...	...	0532	...	...	0831	...	1023	...	...	...	1223	...	...	1357	...	...	1546	1734	1857
Sopot ▷ d.	...	...	...	...	0532	...	...	0549	...	...	0845	...	1037	...	...	...	1239	...	...	1413	...	...	1600	1748	1912
Gdynia Gł. ▷ a.	...	...	...	...	0540	...	...	0558	...	...	0853	...	1045	...	...	...	1247	...	...	1422	...	...	1608	1755	1920
Gdynia Gł. d.	...	...	...	...	0542	...	...	0614	...	...	0857	...	1048	...	...	...	1300	...	...	1443	...	...	1641	1758	1923
Lębork d.	...	...	...	...	0627	...	...	0716	...	...	0954	...	1132	...	...	...	1346	...	...	1544	...	...	1754	1845	2000
Słupsk d.	...	...	0504k	0536	0659	...	...	0759	0858	0958	1038	1110	1214	...	...	1359	1430	1446t	...	1631	1753	1806	1827	1925	2031
Koszalin d.	0425	0455j	0553	0621	0758	...	...	0843	1001	1039	1125	1201	1255	...	1332	1443	1522	1548	...	1741	1847	1858	1910	2005	2111
Kołobrzeg a.	|	|	|	|	|	...	...	0922	|	|	|	|	|	...	|	|	|	|	...	1827	|	|	|	|	2145
Kołobrzeg d.	|	|	|	|	|	0718	0830	...	|	|	|	|	|	1243	|	|	|	|	1719	...	|	|	|	|	...
Białogard a.	0440	0514j	0610	0637	0813	0826	0859	...	1017	1054	1140	1220	1313	1314	1350	1459	1537	1607	1754	...	1903	1912	1925	2026	...
Białogard d.	0441	0517j	0615	0638	0820	0829	0900	...	1018	1056	1141	1223	1321	1316	1352	1500	1538	1609	1808	...	1905	1913	1927	2027	...
Szczecinek d.	|	0614	|	0737	|	0932	0956	...	|	1208	|	|	|	1419	1502	1614	|	|	1920	...	|	2011	|	|	...
Piła Gł. d.	|	0733	|	0911	|	1045	1114	...	|	1307	|	|	|	1521	1628	1711	|	|	2026	...	|	2103	|	|	...
Poznań Gł. a.	|	0917	|	1033	|	1213	1223	...	|	1432	|	|	|	1629	1810	1828	|	|	2202	...	|	2219	|	|	...
Stargard **1010** d.	0615	...	0800	...	0957	...	...	...	1150	...	1301	1402	1442	...	...	...	1705	1740	...	...	2031	...	2049	2145	...
Szczecin Dąbie **1010** a.	0641	...	0825	...	1021	...	...	...	1214	...	1325	1427	1506	...	...	...	1729	1806	...	...	2056	...	2113	2208	...
Szczecin Gł. **1010** a.	0656	...	0840	...	1034	...	...	...	1229	...	1343	1443	1519	...	...	...	1742	1822	...	...	2110	...	2127	2221	...

A – To / from Wrocław (Table **1070**).
J – To / from Kraków (Tables **1070**, **1075**).
K – To / from Kraków (Tables **1065**, **1067**).
L – To / from Łódź (Table **1090**).
O – To / from Olsztyn (Table **1035**).
S – To / from Katowice (Tables **1070**, **1075**).
Y – To / from Białystok (Table **1035**).
f – Warszawa **Wschodnia**.
j – Not ⑦.
k – Ⓐ.
t – Not ⑥.
* – Distance from Białogard.
** – Distance from Koszalin.
▷ – Frequent local trains run between Gdynia and Gdansk.

1016 SZCZECIN - KOŁOBRZEG

km										
		Ⓐ	Ⓒ			Ⓐ				⚒	
0	**Szczecin** Gł. d.	0558	0838	1045	...	1224	1408	1611	...	1829	2008
35	Goleniów ✈ d.	0638	0912	1121	...	1259	1453	1653	...	1905	2043
141	Kołobrzeg a.	0831	1106	1309	...	1442	1649	1833	...	2118	2225

	Ⓐ	⚒								⑦
Kołobrzeg d.	0330	0427	0626	...	0913	1316	...	1516	1713	1835
Goleniów ✈ d.	0513	0610	0833	...	1050	1501	...	1719	1901	2026
Szczecin Gł. a.	0550	0650	0906	...	1138	1536	...	1755	1944	2107

1020 GDYNIA - GDAŃSK - BYDGOSZCZ - POZNAŃ

km																										
		TLK/IC		*IC*		*IC*	*IC*		*IC*	*IC*		*IC*	*TLK*		*IC*		*IC*	*IC*		*IC*		*IC*	*IC*	*IC*	*TLK*	
		54150		**5600**		**56104**	**57108**		**5312**	**58**		**57100**	**53106**		**5602**		**56102**	**57104**		**5604**		**57102**	**57106**	**5700**	**54190**	
		53150		**5601**			**57109**		**5313**	**57000**		**57101**	**53107**		**5452**		**56103**	**57105**		**5605**		**57103**	**57107**	**5701**	**54170**	
			Ⓐ					Ⓐ										2			Ⓑ		Ⓑ			
		B					**F**		**J**	**C**		**F**	**J**				**Y**	**F**					2		**A**	
0	**Gdynia** Gł. ▷ d.	...	...	0503	...	...	0554	...	0752	0858	...	...	1004	...	1150	...	...	1357	...	1530	...	...	1737	1934	2135	...
9	Sopot ▷ d.	...	...	0512	...	...	0603	...	0801	0907	...	...	1013	...	1158	...	...	1406	...	1539	...	...	1746	1942	2146	...
21	**Gdańsk** Gł. ▷ d.	...	...	0529	...	...	0620	...	0819	0923	...	...	1030	...	1216	...	...	1422	...	1600	...	...	1803	2000	2210	...
53	Tczew ▷ d.	...	...	0547	...	...	0642	...	0838	0940	...	...	1048	...	1234	...	...	1442	...	1620	...	...	1823	2021	2231	...
181	**Bydgoszcz** Gł. ▷ a.	...	...	0704	...	...	0801	...	0952	1048	...	...	1203	...	1348	...	...	1600	...	1737	...	...	1943	2137	2326	...
181	**Bydgoszcz** Gł. d.	0443	0518	0707	...	...	0804	...	0955	1051	...	...	1206	...	1354	1450	...	1603	...	1742	...	...	1946	2140	0006	...
	Olsztyn Gł. d.	|	|	|	...	0555	|	...	|	|	...	0952	|	...	|	|	1350	|	...	|	...	1748	|	|	|	...
	Iława d.	|	|	|	...	0643	|	...	|	|	...	1039	|	...	|	|	1450	|	...	|	...	1835	|	|	|	...
	Toruń Gł. d.	|	|	|	0712	0801	|	0903	|	|	1102	1153	|	1255	|	|	1604	|	1709	|	1908	1950	|	|	|	...
227	Inowrocław d.	0518	0559	0741	0747	0826	0838	0940	1028	1118	1137	1218	1240	1329	1427	1535	1630	1638	1740	1818	1941	2015	2023	2212	0043	...
283	Gniezno d.	0554	0639	0814	0829	0900	0914	1027	1102	1151	1218	1254	1313	1412	1501	1616	1707	1713	1820	1853	2027	2050	2059	2243	0126	...
334	**Poznań** Gł. a.	0626	0728	0840	0916	0930	0943	1114	1129	1220	1304	1323	1340	1459	1528	1702	1736	1743	1906	1920	2114	2120	2129	2309	0213	...
	Wrocław **1070** a.	0831	...	1027	...	...	...	...	1319	...	...	...	1531	...	1721	...	1941	...	...	2120	...	...	...	...	0522	...

km																										
		TLK	*IC*		*IC*	*IC*		*IC*		*IC*	*IC*		*IC*		*TLK*	*IC*	*IC*		*IC*		*IC*	*IC*	*IC*		*TLK*	
		45191	**7501**		**75106**	**75103**		**6505**		**65103**	**75104**		**6503**		**35106**	**75101**	**59**		**3512**		**75108**	**65105**	**6501**		**45151**	
		45171	**7500**		**75107**	**75102**		**6504**		**65102**	**75105**		**4553**		**35106**	**75100**	**75000**		**3513**		**75109**	**65104**	**6500**		**35151**	
				⚒	①–⑥					2	2	Ⓐ														
		A			2					**Y**	**F**				**J**	**F**	**C**				**F**				**B**	
	Wrocław **1070** d.	2307	...	...	...	...	...	0625	...	0833	...	...	1030	...	1225	...	...	...	1428	...	...	1633	1737	...	1855	...
	Poznań Gł. d.	0207	0520	0554	0636	0643	0750	0827	0949	1033	1041	1149	1236	1345	1430	1440	1536	1550	1624	1759	1839	1848	1930	1948	2109	...
	Gniezno d.	0255	0547	0640	0707	0715	0837	0855	1036	1103	1111	1237	1304	1432	1458	1511	1605	1637	1652	1845	1910	1918	1958	2034	2139	...
0	Inowrocław d.	0332	0618	0723	0742	0749	0921	0930	1121	1138	1147	1320	1337	1521	1532	1545	1634	1726	1725	1930	1947	2002	2030	2118	2215	...
35	**Toruń** Gł. d.	|	|	0755	|	0815	0954	|	1154	1207	|	|	|	1554	|	1615	|	1758	|	|	|	2028	|	2150	|	...
129	Iława d.	|	|	...	|	0933	...	|	...	1321	|	|	|	...	|	1730	|	...	|	|	|	2143	|	...	|	...
198	**Olsztyn** Gł. a.	|	|	...	|	1019	...	|	...	1409	|	|	|	...	|	1817	|	...	|	|	|	2230	|	...	|	...
	Bydgoszcz Gł. a.	0402	0649	...	0816	...	...	1003	...	...	1219	1400	1406	...	1607	...	1700	...	1757	2010	2019	...	2102	...	2244	...
	Bydgoszcz Gł. ▷ d.	0420	0652	...	0820	...	...	1008	...	...	1224	...	1413	...	1617	...	1703	...	1800	...	2025	...	2105	...	...	...
	Tczew ▷ d.	0544	0808	...	0938	...	...	1129	...	...	1344	...	1529	...	1740	...	1812	...	1915	...	2153	...	2224	...	...	...
	Gdańsk Gł. ▷ a.	0605	0826	...	1002	...	...	1147	...	...	1404	...	1546	...	1758	...	1827	...	1932	...	2215	...	2243	...	...	...
	Sopot ▷ a.	0624	0842	...	1016	...	...	1205	...	...	1422	...	1604	...	1816	...	1845	...	1951	...	2233	...	2301	...	...	...
	Gdynia Gł. ▷ a.	0632	0852	...	1024	...	...	1213	...	...	1430	...	1612	...	1824	...	1853	...	1959	...	2241	...	2309	...	...	...

A – ROZEWIE – 🛏 1, 2 cl., (2) Gdynia - Katowice - Bielsko Biała and v.v.
B – To / from Bielsko Biała.
C – BERLIN GDANSK EXPRESS / GEDANIA – (12) ✕ Ⓡ Berlin - Poznań - Gdansk - Gdynia and v.v. (Table **51**).
F – To / from Zielona Góra (Table **1001**).
J – To / from Kraków (Table **1075**).
Y – To / from Białystok (Table **1035**).
▷ – See also Table **1025**. Frequent local services run between Gdynia and Gdansk (see Table **1035**).

1025 GDYNIA - GDAŃSK - BYDGOSZCZ - WARSZAWA / ŁODŹ

km																							
			IC	*IC*		*IC*	*IC*	*TLK*	*TLK*	*IC*		*TLK*	*IC*		*IC*	*IC*	*TLK*	*TLK*	*IC*	*TLK*			
			52100	**5130**		**81112**	**51106**	**54100**	**58110**	**5128**		**82104**	**5360**		**5126**	**5420**	**82100**	**58112**	**5124**	**51112**			
			52101	**5131**		**81113**	**51107**		**58111**	**5129**		**82105**	**5330**		**5127**	**5421**	**82101**	**58113**	**5125**	**51113**			
			2			2		2	2			2						2		2			
			B			**L**			**K**			**TD**					**TS**	**H**					
0	**Gdynia** Gł. ▷ d.	...	...	...	...	...	...	0657	0740	...	...	...	1108	...	...	1457	...	1653	...	...	...	...	...
9	Sopot ▷ d.	...	...	...	...	...	...	0706	0750	...	...	...	1117	...	...	1505	...	1701	...	...	...	...	...
21	**Gdańsk** Gł. ▷ d.	...	...	...	...	...	...	0722	0808	...	...	...	1134	...	...	1522	...	1718	...	...	...	...	...
53	Tczew ▷ d.	...	...	...	...	...	...	0744	0833	...	...	...	1155	...	...	1542	...	1744	...	...	...	...	...
181	**Bydgoszcz** Gł. ▷ a.	...	...	...	...	...	...	0902	...	...	...	...	1310	...	...	1656	...	1909	...	...	...	...	...
181	**Bydgoszcz** Gł. d.	...	0409	0531	...	0654	0828	0923	...	1026	...	1216	1321	...	1524	1709	1728	...	1921	1939	...	...	...
232	**Toruń** Gł. d.	...	0448	0611	...	0734	0908	1002	...	1109	...	1256	1359	...	1602	1747	1808	...	1959	2017	...	...	...
287	Włocławek d.	...	0523	0646	...	0808	0943	1038	...	|	...	1332	1434	...	|	1823	1843	...	|	2053	...	...	...
342	Kutno d.	...	0600	0722	...	0844	1029	1114	...	|	...	1411	1511	...	|	1901	1918	...	|	2129	...	...	...
	Warszawa Wschodnia a.	...	|	|		|	|	|	...	1422	...	|	|	...	1907	|	2054	...	2300	|	...	...	...
469	**Warszawa** Centralna a.	...	0735	0901	...	1036	1207	|	...	1430	...	1604	|	...	1915	|	2111	...	2310	|	...	...	...
474	**Warszawa** Wschodnia a.	...	0751	0910	...	1111	1221	|	...	...	...	1616	|	...		|		...	...	|	...	...	...
413	**Łódź** Widzew a.	...	...	...	...	...	...	1243	...	...	...	...	1639	...	...	2032	...	...	...	2305	...	...	...
	Katowice **1060** a.	...	...	...	...	...	...	1600	...	...	...	...	|	...	...	2322	...	...	...	...	...	...	...
	Kraków **1065** a.	...	...	...	...	...	...	...	...	...	...	...	1931	...	...	...	...	...	...	...	...	...	...

		TLK	*TLK*	*IC*		*IC*	*TLK*		*IC*	*IC*	*TLK*		*IC*	*IC*	*TLK*	*IC*	*TLK*	*IC*	*IC*				
		15113	**85112**	**1525**		**4521**	**28100**		**1527**	**3561**	**28104**		**15106**	**1529**	**45100**	**1530**	**85110**	**18113**	**25100**				
		15112	**85113**	**1524**		**4520**	**28101**		**1526**	**3560**	**28105**		**15107**	**1528**	**45101**	**1531**	**85111**	**18113**	**25101**				
		2	2								2				2		2	2	2				
			H				**ST**				**TD**						**K**	**L**	**B**				
Kraków **1065** d.	...	...	...	...	...	...	...	...	...	0923	...	...	...	...	...	...	...	...	...	...	...	...	...
Katowice **1060** d.	...	...	...	...	...	0455	...	...	...	|	...	...	...	...	1306	...	...	...	...	...	...	...	...
Łódź Widzew d.	...	0515	...	...	...	0747	...	...	...	1202	...	...	...	...	1624	...	...	...	...	...	...	...	...
Warszawa Wschodnia d.	...	|	...	...	...	|	0804	...	...	|	1209	...	1444	...	|	1614	...	1749	1904	...	...	...	...
Warszawa Centralna d.	...	|	...	0555	...	|	0826	...	1050	|	1241	...	1520	1450	|	1624	...	1800	1957	...	...	...	...
Warszawa Wschodnia d.	...	|	...	0609	...	|	|	...	1058	|	|		|	1458	|	|		|	|	...	...	...	...
Kutno d.	...	0642	...	|	...	0913	1025	...	|	1328	1428	...	1654	|	1752	1806	...	1940	2145	...	...	...	...
Włocławek d.	...	0718	...	|	...	0949	1100	...	|	1404	1503	...	1734	|	1827	1842	...	2015	2221	...	...	...	...
Toruń Gł. d.	...	0754	...	0910	...	1026	1135	...	1405	1444	1545	...	1815	1804	1904	1918	...	2051	2257	...	...	...	...
Bydgoszcz Gł. a.	...	0832	...	0948	...	1104	1213	...	1443	1522	1624	...	1852	1841	1941	1955	...	2129	2335	...	...	...	...
Bydgoszcz Gł. ▷ d.	...	...	0904	...	...	1119	...	...	...	1533	...	...	...	...	2001	...	...	...	...	...	...	...	...
Tczew ▷ d.	...	...	1032	...	...	1238	...	...	...	1648	...	...		...	2121	...	2025	...	...	...	...	...	...
Gdańsk Gł. ▷ a.	...	...	1051	...	...	1257	...	...	...	1707	...	...	...	...	2142	...	2053	...	...	...	...	...	...
Sopot ▷ a.	...	...	1109	...	...	1315	...	...	...	1723	...	...	...	...	2200	...	2109	...	...	...	...	...	...
Gdynia Gł. ▷ a.	...	...	1117	...	...	1323	...	...	...	1733	...	...		...	2208	...	2118	...	...	...	...	...	...

B – To / from Lublin (Table **1055**).
D – To / from Kołobrzeg (Table **1015**).
H – To / from Gorzów Wlkp (Table **1000**).
K – To / from Kostrzyn (Table **1000**).
L – To / from Piła (Table **1000**).
S – To / from Szczecin (Table **1010**).
T – To / from Lublin (Table **1067**).
▷ – See also Table **1020**. Frequent local services run between Gdynia and Gdansk.

GDYNIA - GDAŃSK - (OLSZTYN -) WARSZAWA 1030

km		IC	EIP	TLK	EIP	EIP	EIP	IC	TLK	EIP	EIC	IC	IC	EIP	IC	TLK	EIP	EIP	IC	EIP	EIP	IC	IC	EIP	EIC	IC	TLK	EIP	TLK
		5326	5400	53100	5300	5440	8300	5324	53104	5404	5310	5322	54000	5302	5320	81114	5406	5304	5422	5408	5306	5122	51100	5308	5110	5328	53170	5102	83170
		5327	5401	53101	5301	5402	8301	5325	53105	5405	5311	5323	107	5303	5321	81115	5407	5305	5423	5409	5307	5123		5309		5329	53171		83171
						⚒				⚒													Ⓐ						
		K	T	Z	K	T	K	K	P	T	K	K	X	K	K	L	T	R	B	B	K	L				K	Z		K
	Kołobrzeg **1015** ..d.	...	...	...	...	...	0612	...	...	...	...	...	...	...	...	1004	...	...	...	...	...	...	...	...	...	...	...	...	2043
0	**Gdynia** Gł. ▶ d.	...	0527	0540	0626	0726	0836	...	0900	0928	1022	...	1044	1221	...	1333	1325	1425	...	1522	1627	...	1717	1731	1814	...	1844	1947	2340
9	Sopot ▶ d.	...	0536	0549	0635	0735	0845	...	0910	0937	1032	...	1053	1230	...	1343	1334	1434	...	1531	1636	...	1726	1740	1823	...	1855	1956	2351
21	**Gdańsk** Gł. ▶ d.	...	0554	0606	0653	0753	0902	...	0930	0955	1050	...	1110	1248	...	1402	1352	1452	...	1549	1654	...	1743	1757	1840	...	1916	2014	0010
53	Tczew ▶ d.	...	0608	0624	0708	0808	|	...	0949	1009	1106	...	1128	1303	...	1422	1407	1507	...	1604	1709	...	1800	|	1858	...	1935	2029	0031
72	Malbork ▶ d.	...	0619	0637	0719	0819	|	...	1003	1020	1117	...	1141	1314	...	1435	1418	1518	...	1615	1720	...	1811	|	1910	...	1949	2040	0045
•	**Olsztyn** ▶ d.	0454	|	|	|	|	|	0952	|	|	|	1123	|	|	1401	|	|	|	1524	|	|	1821	|	|	|	1936	|	|	|
41	Iława Gł. ▶ d.	|	0653	0720	0753	0854	|	|	1045	1054	1152	|	1220	1347	|	1516	1452	1552	|	1649	1753	|	1857	|	1945	2027	2032	2114	0133
01	Działdowo d.	0556	|	0753	|	|	|	1056	1128	|	|	1233	1252	|	1501	1549	1523	|	1636	|	|	1925	1930	|	|	2059	2106	|	0209
51	Ciechanów d.	0622	|	0821	|	|	|	1121	1158	|	|	1258	|	|	1527	1622	|	|	1702	1739	|	1951	1956	|	2038	2125	2136	|	0241
05	Modlin ✈ d.	0650	|	|	|	|	|	|	|	|	|	|	|	|	1555	|	|	|	|	|	|	|	|	|	|	|	|	|	|
45	**Warszawa** Wsch. ..a.	0717	0822	0915	0923	1023	1128	1216	1251	1224	1321	1348	1403	1517	1621	1720	1626	1722	1753	1822	1922	2039	2045	2023	2124	2215	2231	2244	0345
50	**Warszawa** Cent. ...a.	0730	0830	0928	0930	1032	1135	1225	1300	1235	1330	1358y	1415	1530	1632	1730	1634	1730	1800	1830	1930	2047	2055	2030	2135	2225	2240	2258	0355

	TLK	EIP	IC	TLK	EIC	EIP	IC	IC	EIC	EIP	EIP	IC	EIP	TLK	EIP	IC	EIP	IC	IC	EIP	TLK	EIP	IC	EIP	EIP	EIP	TLK	EIP	IC
	38171	1503	1521	35170	1511	1501	15101	1522	4550	3508	4508	4522	3506	18115	4506	3520	3504	106	3522	3502	38154	4502	3524	3801	4500	3500	35100	4500	3526
	38170			35171				1523	4551	3509	4509	4523	3507	18114	4507	3521	3505	45000	3523	3503	35105	4503	3525	3800	4501	3501	35101	4501	3527
		⚒					Ⓐ		⑥																				
	K			Z				L	T	K	T	B	R	L	B	K	K	X	K	K	P	T	K	K	T	K	Z	T	K
arszawa Cent. ....d.	...	0514	0527	0540	0610	0720	0730	0740	0820	0830	0925	...	1035	1035	1135	1140	1230	1345	1403y	1430	1501	1535	1611	1625	1738	1830	1903	1940	2007y
arszawa Wsch. ...d.	0150	0523	0535	0548	0617	0730	0738	0748	0829	0838	0933	1050g	1043	1043	1142	1148	1238	1404	1412	1438	1508	1544	1619	1633	1749	1838	1912	1950	2017
odlin ✈ d.	|	|	|	|	|	|	|	|	|	|	|	|	|	|	|	|	|	|	|	|	|	|	1646	|	|	|	|	|	2044
echanów d.	0255	0607	0630	0646	|	|	0834	0843	|	|	|	1143	|	1217	1215	1239	|	|	1507	|	1607	|	1715	|	|	|	2006	|	2113
iałdowo d.	0330	|	|	0715	|	|	0902	0916	|	|	1035	1209	|	1300	|	1304	|	1516	1533	|	1647	|	1741	|	|	|	2035	|	2144
wa Gł. ▶ d.	0408	0657	0740	0749	0756	0902	0934	|	|	|	1106	|	1209	1335	1315	|	1409	1551	|	1609	1721	1709	|	|	1909	2009	2108	2122	|
Olsztyn ▶ a.	|	|	0830	|	|	|	|	1027	|	|	|	1310	|	|	|	1406	|	|	1633	|	|	|	1850	|	|	|	|	|	2244
albork ▶ d.	0451	0731	...	0839	|	0936	1010	...	|	|	1140	...	1243	1418	1349	...	1442	1628	...	1643	1800	1742	...	|	1942	2042	2149	2154	...
zew ▶ d.	0510	0742	...	0856	|	0947	1024	...	|	|	1151	...	1254	1432	1400	...	1453	1642	...	1654	1818	1753	...	|	1953	2053	2201	2207	...
dańsk Gł. ▶ a.	0529	0756	...	0913	0855	1002	1040	...	1116	1103	1206	...	1308	1354	1415	...	1508	1658	...	1709	1835	1807	...	1855	2007	2107	2217	2221	...
pot ▶ a.	0549	1813	...	0931	0914	1020	1058	...	1134	1120	1223	...	1326	1413	1432	...	1525	1715	...	1727	1853	1826	...	1912	2025	2124	2235	2240	...
dynia Gł. ▶ a.	0558	0822	...	0940	0922	1028	1107	...	1142	1130	1232	...	1334	1422	1441	...	1534	1723	...	1735	1901	1839	...	1920	2042	2133	2243	2249	...
Kołobrzeg **1015** ...a.	0922	...	...	...	...	...	...	...	...	...	...	...	...	1827	...	...	...	...	...	...	...	...	...	2145	...	...	...	...	...

– To/from Bielsko Biała (Table **1060**).
– To/from Kraków (Tables **1065/1067**).
– To/from Łódź (Table **1090**).
– To/from Przemyśl (Table **1075**).
– To/from Rzeszów (Table **1075**).
– To/from Katowice (Table **1060**).

X – SOBIESKI – 12 ✕ Gdynia - Warszawa - Katowice - Wien and v.v.
Z – To/from Zakopane (Table **1066**).

g – Warszawa **Gdańska**.
y – Warszawa **Śródmieście**.

• – Olsztyn - Działdowo: *84 km.*
▶ – For additional trains Gdynia - Gdańsk - Iława (- Olsztyn) see Table **1035**. Frequent local trains (every 10-30 mins.) run between Gdynia and Gdańsk operated by *SKM*.

GDYNIA - GDAŃSK - EŁBLAG - OLSZTYN - BIAŁYSTOK 1035

Olsztyn - Ełblag - Malbork and v.v. subject to alteration

km		IC	TLK	TLK	IC	IC	IC		IC	IC	IC	
		5620	50105	51102	85108	65103	85106		81104	85104	85102	
			50104	51103	85109	65102	85107		81105	85105	85103	
		C		A		C		Ⓑ		Ⓑ		
	Szczecin Gł. **1015**.. d.	...	...	...	0509	...	0650	...	1056	1257	1457	...
0	**Gdynia** Gł. ▶ d.	...	0443	0806	0920	...	1125	1449	1525	1737	1930	2132
9	Sopot ▶ d.	...	0452	0814	0928	...	1133	1457	1534	1746	1940	2141
21	**Gdańsk** Gł. ▶ d.	...	0509	0830	0945	...	1151	1511	1555	1802	1957	2154
53	Tczew ▶ d.	...	0529	0850	1005	...	1211	1544	1631	1821	2018	2230
72	Malbork ▶ d.	...	0549	0904	1024	...	1229	1602	1650	1834	2049	2248
01	**Ełblag** d.	...	0615	0927	1052	...	1301	1627	1715	|	2111	2313
	Iława Gł. ▶ a.	...	|	|	|	...	|	...	|	1916	|	...
	Iława Gł. d.	...	|	|	|	1256	|	...	|	1938	|	...
200	**Olsztyn** a.	...	0806	1058	1235	1348	1433	...	1856	2033	2236	...
200	**Olsztyn** d.	...	0834	1133	...	1413	...	...	1923	...	...	...
19	Giżycko d.	...	1019	|	...	1554	...	...	|	...	...	...
66	Ełk a.	...	...	1343	...	...	...	...	2151	...	...	...
66	Ełk d.	0610	...	1408	...	...	...	...	2216	...	...	...
70	**Białystok** a.	0742	...	1526	...	...	...	...	2333	...	...	...

			IC	IC	IC	IC	IC	IC	TLK	TLK	IC
			58103	58105	18105	56103	58107	58109	15103	55105	6521
			58102	58104	18104	56102	58106	58108	15102	55104	6520
		⚒		⚒		C			A		C
Białystok d.	...	...	...	...	0515	...	...	...	1234	...	2053
Ełk a.	...	...	...	...	0634	...	...	...	1351	...	2210
Ełk d.	...	...	...	...	0702	...	...	...	1416	...	...
Giżycko d.	...	...	...	...	|	1143	...	...	|	1644	...
Olsztyn a.	...	...	...	...	0911	1323	...	...	1632	1830	...
Olsztyn d.	...	...	0600	0748	0941	1349	1308	1503	1701	1859	...
Iława Gł. a.	...	...	|	0838	|	1441	|	|	|	|	...
Iława Gł. ▶ d.	...	...	|	0905	|	...	|	|	|	|	...
Ełblag d.	0428	0620	0735	|	1117	...	1451	1637	1831	2027	...
Malbork ▶ d.	0454	0649	0756	0947	1140	...	1512	1700	1851	2048	...
Tczew ▶ d.	0514	0710	0809	1002	1201	...	1525	1713	1904	2101	...
Gdańsk Gł. ▶ a.	0545	0735	0828	1020	1220	...	1543	1731	1923	2119	...
Sopot ▶ a.	0604	0750	0845	1037	1239	...	1600	1748	1940	2136	...
Gdynia Gł. ▶ a.	0613	0759	0853	1045	1247	...	1608	1755	1948	2144	...
Szczecin Gł. **1015** a.	...	...	1343	1519	1742	...	2127	2221	...	...	...

LOCAL SERVICES OLSZTYN - EŁK - BIAŁYSTOK

km														
		⚒	Ⓑ		🚌		🚌		Ⓑ	🚌	Ⓐ			P Ⓑ
0	**Olsztyn** d.	...	...	0925	0856	...	1329	1429	...	1635	1635	...	1827	2050
45	Szczytno d.	...	...	1005	|	...	|	1514	...	|	1715	...	1907	|
02	Pisz d.	...	...	1056	|	...	|	1604	...	|	1816	...	1958	|
	Giżycko d.	...	...	|	1054	...	1526	|	...	1832	|	...	|	2250
57	Ełk d.	0458	0724	1156	1208	1457	1640	1705	1708	1946	1915	...	2058	0004
61	**Białystok** a.	0634	0854	...	...	1632	...	...	1909	...	...	...	...	...

	P ⚒		Ⓐ	🚌			🚌	Ⓑ		🚌		Ⓐ	
Białystok d.	...	...	0530	...	1042	...	...	1456	...	...	1807	...	...
Ełk d.	0425	0430	0712	0728	1214	1242	1229	1640	1716	1602	1948	1953	...
Giżycko d.	0546	|	...	0839	...	|	1350	...	|	1723	...	|	...
Pisz d.	|	0529	...	|	...	1349	|	...	1815	|	...	2057	...
Szczytno d.	|	0620	...	|	...	1441	|	...	1908	|	...	2148	...
Olsztyn a.	0740	0702	...	1034	...	1521	1549	...	1957	1920	...	2229	...

– To/from Warszawa via Siedlce (Table **1040**).
– To/from Wrocław (Table **1020**).

P – 🚌.
* – *210 km* via Iława.

▶ – For additional trains Gdynia - Gdansk - Iława (- Warszawa) see Table **1030**. Frequent local trains run between Gdynia and Gdańsk operated by *SKM* (every 10–30 minutes).

WARSZAWA - BIAŁYSTOK 1040

km			TLK		TLK		IC		IC		IC		IC		IC		IC						
			31103		15103		61103		61105		4123		81103		6521		10103						
			31102		15102		61102		61104		4122		81102		6520								
			V		G		C		C		A		PT		CE								
0	**Warszawa** Cent d.	...	0750	...	...	...	0919g	...	1140	...	1400	...	1620	...	1757	...	2024	...	...	...	...	...	...
5	**Warszawa** Wsch d.	...	0759	...	0827	...	|	...	1151	...	1414	...	1629	...	1811	...	2040	...	...	...	...	...	...
95	Małkinia d.	...	0904	...	|	...	1038	...	1255	...	1513	...	1726	...	1910	...	2144	...	...	...	...	...	...
184	**Białystok** a.	...	1026	...	1201	...	1220	...	1420	...	16446	...	1854	...	2039	...	2308	...	...	...	...	...	...

		IC		IC		IC		IC		IC		TLK		TLK		IC							
		10112		5620		18102		16104		16102		51102		13102		1100							
				5621		18103		16105		16103		51103		13103									
				EC		PT		C		C		G		V		L							
ałystok d.	...	0453	...	0751	...	0924	...	1317	...	1536	...	1555	...	1739	...	1944	...	...	...	...	...	...	...
ałkinia d.	...	0617	...	0914	...	1048	...	1443	...	1717	...	|	...	1906	...	2114	...	...	...	...	...	...	...
arszawa Wsch a.	...	0720	...	1012	...	1146	...	1547	...	1823	...	1934	...	2007	...	2211	...	...	...	...	...	...	...
arszawa Cent a.	...	0730	...	1020	...	1155	...	1555	...	1830	...	...	...	2015	...	2225	...	...	...	...	...	...	...

– From/to Katowice (Table **1060**).
– To/from Wrocław (Table **1061**).
– To/from Ełk (Table **1035**).
– From/to Gdynia (Table **1035**).

L – To Łódź (Table **1090**).
P – To/from Suwałki (Table **1042**).
T – To/from Świnoujście (Table **1010**).

V – HAŃCZA – 12 Kraków - Warszawa - Białystok - Suwałki and v.v.
g – Warszawa **Gdańska**.

1042 BIAŁYSTOK - VILNIUS and HRODNA

PKP, BCh, LG

Service valid until Sept. 3

km					TLK				IC		IC
			143		31103			142	4123		81103
			⑥⑦		V	Ⓑ		B			S
0	*Warszawa Cent* **1040** d.	...	...	...	0750	...	...	...	1405	...	1621
5	*Warszawa Wsch* **1040** d.	...	...	...	0759	...	...	...	1418	...	1633
184	**Białystok** a.	...	...	...	1035	...	...	...	1647	...	1855
184	**Białystok** d.	0615	0755	...	1100	1158	1458	...	...	1806	1920
225	Sokółka d.	0652	0848	...	1134	1235	1542	...	...	1851	1954
324	**Suwałki** d.	|	1008	...	1247	|	1708	1743	...	|	2105
	Mockava ⊞ ◐ § a.	|	|	...	...	|	...	|	...	|	...
377	Šeštokai § a.	|	|	...	...	|	...	2054	...	|	...
471	**Kaunas** **1811** § a.	|	1357	1430	...	|	...	2220	...	|	...
575	**Vilnius** **1811** § a.	|	...	1549	...	|	...	...	...	|	...
241	Kuźnica Białostocka ⊞ a.	0709	...	...	...	1251	...	...	...	1908	...
241	Kuźnica Białostocka ⊞ d.	...	...	...	...	...	...	...	...	...	...
268	**Hrodna** ⊞ ‡ a.	...	...	...	...	...	...	...	...	...	...

			IC				TLK			
			18102		141		13102			146
			S		C		V			⑥⑦
Hrodna ⊞ ‡ d.	...	...	...	...	...	...	...	...	...	...
Kuźnica Białostocka ⊞ a.	...	...	...	...	...	...	...	...	...	...
Kuźnica Białostocka ⊞ d.	0505	0720	...	...	...	...	...	1922	...	...
Vilnius **1811** § d.	|	|	...	0602	...	...	...	|	1530	...
Kaunas **1811** § d.	|	|	...	0729	0910	...	...	|	1646	173
Šeštokai § d.	|	|	...	...	1034	...	...	|	...	|
Mockava ⊞ ◐ d.	|	|	...	...	|	...	...	|	...	|
Suwałki d.	|	|	0657	...	1037	1145	1521	|	...	190
Sokółka d.	0522	0736	0810	...	...	1330	1640	1938	...	201
Białystok a.	0602	0813	0846	...	...	1410	1715	2022	...	204
Białystok d.	...	...	0923	...	...	...	1740	...	...	...
Warszawa Wsch **1040** a.	...	...	1137	...	...	...	2012	...	...	...
Warszawa Cent **1040** a.	...	...	1145	...	...	...	2020	...	...	...

B – ⑤⑥ July 1 - Sept. 2: BALTI - [2] Suwałki - Kaunas. Lithuanian times to be confirmed.
C – ⑥⑦ July 2 - Sept. 3: BALTI - [2] Kaunas - Suwałki. Lithuanian times to be confirmed.
S – From / to Świnoujście (Table **1010**).
V – HAŃCZA – [12] Kraków - Warszawa - Suwałki and v.v.

§ – Lithuanian time.
‡ – Belarus time (one hour earlier from Mar. 27, 2022).
◐ – ⊞ = Trakiszki (Poland) / Mockava (Lithuania); ticketing point is Mockava.

☛ Shaded services are suspended until further notice.

1050 WARSZAWA - TERESPOL - BREST

km				IC			IC		IC		IC	IC
				11001			11003		11101		41004	11103
											130	
											B	Ⓑ
0	**Warszawa** Cent. d.	...	...	...	...	...	...	...	...	...	1934	...
5	**Warszawa** Wsch. d.	...	...	0746	...	...	1349	...	1621	...	1941	2047
93	Siedlce d.	...	...	0844	0926	1229	1444	1702	1727	...	2029	2144
121	Łuków d.	0539	...	0859	0954	1256	1459	1730	1743	...	2044	2159
173	Biała Podlaska d.	0625	...	0928	1040	1341	1527	1824	1815	...	2113	2227
210	Terespol ⊞ a.	0700	...	1001	1146	1417	1558	1900	1847	...	2141	2258
217	**Brest** Tsentralny ⊞ ‡ a.	...	...	...	...	...	...	...	...	...	...	...

	IC		IC		IC		IC				IC
	11112		131		11110		11010				1101
			14004								
	①–⑥		B					Ⓐ			
Brest Tsentralny ⊞ ‡ d.	...	...	...	...	...	...	...	...	...	...	...
Terespol ⊞ d.	0512	0534	0614	0810	0947	...	1401	1446	...	1906	192
Biała Podlaska d.	0545	0611	0645	0911	1020	...	1435	1523	...	1940	195
Łuków d.	0614	0718	0713	1005	1052	...	1505	1621	...	2022	202
Siedlce d.	0629	0745	0728	1032	1108	...	1520	1649	...	...	204
Warszawa Wsch. a.	0733	...	0816	...	1210	...	1617	...	...	...	213
Warszawa Cent. a.	...	...	0825	...	...	...	...	...	...	...	...

B – BÁTHORY – [12] ✕ Budapest - Warszawa - Terespol and v.v. The 🛏 1, 2 cl. Praha - Bohumín - Moskva cars are temporarily suspended (Table **95**).

¦ – 1 hour earlier from Mar. 27.
‡ – Belarus time.

☛ Shaded services are suspended until further notice.

TERESPOL - BREST and v.v. local services

Terespol d.	1026	1401	2027	Brest ‡ d.	0815¦	1300¦	1721¦
Brest ‡ a.	1147¦	1522¦	2148¦	Terespol a.	0736	1221	1643

1055 WARSZAWA - LUBLIN - CHEŁM - DOROHUSK

km						IC		IC	IC			IC		IC			TLK		IC	MP		TLK			TLK	
						12101		52100	6200			72101		12103			82104		6228	12011		83100			82100	
		Ⓐ			Ⓐ			52101	6201	Ⓐ		72100			Ⓐ		82105		6229	68LJ	Ⓑ	83101	Ⓐ		82101	
								2K	Ⓑ C			T					2JY		C	B	Z	SR			S	
0	**Warszawa** Cent d.	...	...	...	...	...	...	0745	0850	...	...	1110	...	1340	...	...	1610	...	1650	...	...	1830	...	...	2105	...
5	**Warszawa** Wsch d.	...	...	...	...	0653	...	0758	0858	...	...	1118	...	1356	...	...	1618	...	1658	1749	...	1839	...	...	2114	...
104	Dęblin d.	0400	0505	0557	0740	0802	...	0914	1015	...	1209	1229	1420	1515	1524	1652	1728	1758	1815	1900	...	1948	2018	...	2225	...
125	Puławy Miasto d.	0422	0527	0618	0802	0817	...	0928	1029	...	1229	1242	1441	1529	1547	1714	1742	1820	1829	1914	...	2002	2041	...	2239	...
175	**Lublin** a.	0509	0614	0706	0849	0853	...	1001	1103	...	1313	1323	1528	1603	1639	1807	1818	1916	1903	1948	...	2037	2134	...	2313	...
		⚒		Ⓐ		|	Z				Z				Z					|						
175	**Lublin** d.	0514	0620	0721	...	0856	0935	...	1110	1220	1332	...	1550	...	1659	...	1846	...	1938	2014	2045	...	2146	2240	...	...
228	Rejowiec d.	0605	0710	0810	...	0933	1026	...	1200	1315	1423	...	1639	...	1750	...	1940	...	2032	2057	2135	...	2240	2329	...	...
249	Chełm a.	0620	0725	0825	...	0948	...	...	1215	1331	...	...	1654	...	...	...	1957	...	2049	2114	...	...	2257	2344	...	...
270	**Dorohusk** ⊞ a.	...	...	...	...	...	...	...	...	...	...	...	...	...	...	...	...	...	...	2135	...	...	...	...	...	...

		TLK		MP				TLK	TLK			IC			IC			IC		IC		IC		IC		
		28100		67KJ				38101	28104			2102			27100			25100		2600		21100		21104		
	Ⓐ	28101		21010		⚒		38100	28105		⚒	2103			27101	Ⓐ		25101		2601						
		S		A		Z		RS	2JV	Z		Ⓑ		Z	T			2K		C	Z					
Dorohusk ⊞ d.	...	...	...	0615	...	...	...	...	...	...	...	...	...	...	...	...	...	...	...	...	...	...	...	...	...	...
Chełm d.	0355	...	0504	0637	0545	...	0642	...	...	...	1039	...	1203	...	...	1418	1526	...	1634	...	...	1845	1817	...	2005	...
Rejowiec d.	0410	...	0519	0656	0602	0626	0659	...	...	1000	1054	...	1220	1335	...	1435	1543	...	1649	...	1730	1900	1834	...	2021	...
Lublin a.	0500	...	0609	0739	0656	0718	0753	...	...	1052	1145	...	1314	1427	...	1529	1638	...	1740	...	1821	1937	1929	...	2116	...
	Ⓐ			|										Ⓐ								|			Ⓐ	
Lublin d.	0530	0555	0624	0802	...	0726	...	0758	0958	1059	...	1157	1337	1440	1510	1540	1643	1658	...	1757	...	1940	1939	1955	2240	...
Puławy Miasto d.	0617	0630	0711	0837	...	0817	...	0833	1032	1148	...	1232	1437	1528	1545	1628	1742	1733	...	1832	...	2015	2038	2031	2331	...
Dęblin d.	0637	0645	0732	0854	...	0840	...	0847	1046	1209	...	1246	1459	1549	1601	1649	1805	1747	...	1847	...	2029	2039	2046	2354	...
Warszawa Wsch a.	...	0800	...	1004	...	...	...	1000	1202	...	...	1359	...	...	1711	...	...	1859	...	2001	...	2139	...	2201	...	...
Warszawa Cent a.	...	0810	...	...	...	...	...	1010	1215	...	...	1415	...	...	1737	...	...	1910	...	2010	...	2203	...	2215	...	...

A – KYIV EKSPRES / KIEV EXPRESS – 🛏 1, 2 cl. Kyiv - Warszawa. (Table **1725**). International journeys only.
B – KIEV EXPRESS / KYIV EKSPRES – 🛏 1, 2 cl. Warszawa - Kyiv. (Table **1725**). International journeys only.
C – To / from Wrocław (Table **1061**).
J – To / from Kołobrzeg (Table **1015**).
K – To / from Bydgoszcz (Table **1025**).
R – To / from Rzeszów (Table **1058**).
S – To / from Szczecin (Table **1010**).
T – To / from Zielona Góra (Table **1001**).
V – From Zamość (depart 0734).
Y – To Zamość (arrive 2043).
Z – To / from Zamość (Table **1099**).

1058 LUBLIN - RZESZÓW - PRZEMYŚL

km				IC		IC		TLK		TLK		TLK
				26101		13105		24001		13107		83101
			Ⓐ		Ⓒ			310				83100
						2		C2		2		S
	Warszawa Cent. **1055** d.	...	...	...	...	0615	...	...	...	1715	...	1840
	Warszawa Wsch. **1055** d.	...	...	...	...	0623	...	...	...	1724	...	1849
0	**Lublin** d.	...	0536	0643	0745	◧	1246	1359	1655	◧	...	2113
103	Stalowa Wola Rozwadów d.	0454	0732	0827	0940	1057	1426	1525	1836	2159	...	|
132	Tanobrzeg d.	0550	0804	|	1012	|	1458	|	1909	|	...	2245
204	**Rzeszów** a.	0709	0918	1002	1126	|	1615	1657	2027	|	...	2335
204	**Rzeszów** **1075** d.	...	...	1033	1239	|	1715	1926	...	|	2234	...
178	Przeworsk **1075** d.	...	...	1106	1311	1202	1748	1958	...	2305	2311	...
193	Jarosław **1075** d.	...	...	1119	1323	1212	1759	2009	...	2315	2323	...
228	**Przemyśl** **1075** a.	...	...	1155	1329	1242	1836	2047	...	2345	0003	...

	TLK	TLK			TLK			IC		IC	
	38100	31106			42000			31104		62100	
	38101				311						
	S	2			C2			2			
Przemyśl **1075** d.	...	0413	...	0443	...	1052	1310	1415	1538	...	...
Jarosław **1075** d.	...	0446	...	0521	...	1130	1348	1448	1617	...	...
Przeworsk **1075** d.	...	0456	...	0531	...	1141	1358	1458	1628	...	...
Rzeszów **1075** a.	...	|	...	0604	...	1212	1431	|	1701	...	...
Rzeszów d.	0413	|	0534	...	0942	1230	...	|	...	1749	174
Tanobrzeg d.	0508	|	0647	...	|	1344	...	|	...	|	185
Stalowa Wola Rozwadów d.	|	0605	0737	...	1117	1430	...	1608	...	1937	194
Lublin a.	0645	◧	0919	...	1227	1611	...	◧	...	2053	213
Warszawa Wsch. **1055** a.	0910	1030	...	...	...	...	...	2030	...	...	...
Warszawa Cent. **1055** a.	0920	1040	...	...	...	...	...	2040	...	...	...

C – To / from Bohumín (Table **1076**).
S – To / from Szczecin (Tables **1001**).
◧ – Via Radom (Table **1067**).

WARSZAWA / ŁÓDŹ - KATOWICE and BIELSKO BIAŁA 1060

km		IC	IC	IC	IC	EIP	TLK	IC	TLK	EIP	EIP	TLK	IC	IC	IC	IC	EIP	IC	IC	EIP	IC	EIC	TLK	
		14000	14002	1420	1460	1400	14101	14004	56100	5400	5402	54101	14006	1422	54000	1410	5404	14008	5422	5406	5420	5450	53170	
		116	103	1421	1461	1401	14100	131	56101	5401	5403	54100	112	1423	107	1411	5405	110	5423	5407	5421	5451	53171	
				Ⓐ	Ⓒ		2					2				Ⓐ								
		Z	P	B	B			V	O	G	G	G	M		S		GB	Q	BO	G	GB	G	E	
0	**Warszawa** Wschodnia d.	0444	0554	0534	0534	0719	...	0819	1019	1029	1229	...	1254	1354	1404	1536	1630	1710	1819	1929	...	2027	2319	...
5	**Warszawa** Centralna d.	0455	0605	0549	0555	0730	...	0830	1040	1049	1240	...	1305	1405	1415	1550	1641	1720	1849	1941	...	2048	2330	...
	Łódź Widzew d.	|	|	|	|	|	0745	|	|	|	|	1235	|	|	|	|	|	|	|	|	2029	|	|	...
	Koluszki d.	|	|	0702	0702	|	|	|	1200	|	|	|	|	1517	|	|	|	|	2004	|	|	|	0054	...
	Piotrków Trybunalski d.	|	|	0728	0728	|	0833	|	1225	|	|	1314	|	1542	|	|	|	|	2029	|	2108	|	0123	...
	Częstochowa d.	|	|	0826	0826	|	0928	|	1323	|	|	1413	|	1638	|	|	|	|	2122	|	2202	|	0220	...
259	Zawiercie 1067 d.	0716	0824	0856	0856	|	0958	1042	1353	|	1435	1444	1521	1710	1625	1806	1837	1935	2152	|	2236	2258	...	...
294	Sosnowiec Gł. 1067 d.	|	0853	|	|	0957	|	1114	1432	1316	1503	|	1556	1746	1655	1840	1904	2009	2223	2209	2308	2330	...	...
302	**Katowice** 1067 a.	0806	0902	0941	0941	1012	1045	1124	1441	1325	1515	1533	1605	1755	1703	1855	1915	2018	2235	2218	2317	2344	...	...

km		IC	EIC	IC	EIP	IC	EIP	TLK	IC	IC	IC	EIP	TLK	TLK	EIP	IC	TLK	EIP	IC	IC	IC	IC	TLK	
		4520	4550	4110	4506	111	4504	45102	4122	106	113	4502	45100	65100	4500	130	41100	4100	4160	4120	102	117	35170	
		4521	4551	4111	4507	41008	4505	45103	4123	45000	41006	4503	45101	65101	4501	41004	41101	4101	4161	4121	41002	41000	35171	
			⑥	Ⓐ				2					2		Ⓑ		2		Ⓒ	Ⓐ				
		BG	G		G	Q	BG	G	L	S	M	G	G	O	G	V			B	B	P	Z	E	
	Katowice d.	0543	0531	0531	0641	0746	0900	0906	1013	1055	1147	1301	1319	1339	1500	1633	1737	1739	1757	1757	1857	1947	...	...
	Sosnowiec Gł. 1067 d.	0552	0540	0540	0651	0756	0909	0917	1023	1104	1157	1310	|	1348	1510	1643	|	1748	|	|	1906	1957	...	...
0	Zawiercie 1067 d.	0625	0611	0612	0719	0825	|	0949	1055	1133	1235	1337	1405	1418	|	1714	1825	|	1853	1853	1940	2027	...	...
43	**Częstochowa** d.	0657	|	|	|	|	|	1023	1125	|	|	|	1445	1451	|	|	1855	|	1923	1923	|	|	0132	...
129	Piotrków Trybunalski d.	0749	|	|	|	|	|	1114	1216	|	|	|	1536	1544	|	|	1946	|	2014	2014	|	|	0247	...
168	Koluszki d.	|	|	|	|	|	|	|	1242	|	|	|	|	1612	|	|	|	|	2040	2040	|	|	0324	...
	Łódź Widzew a.	0849	|	|	|	|	|	1152	|	|	|	|	1615	|	|	|	2024	|	|	|	|	|	|	...
273	**Warszawa** Centralna a.	...	0809	0815	0916	1038	1125	...	1345	1333	1443	1526	...	|	1734	1929	...	2015	2144	2144	2138	2235	0440	...
278	**Warszawa** Wschodnia a.	...	0826	0826	0926	1051	1136	...	1406	1401	1454	1541	...	1720j	1744	1940	...	2026	2156	2156	2149	2246	0451	...

km		IC	LE		IC	TLK	IC	IC	IC	IC	IC	IC		EIP	IC	TLK	IC	IC	EIP	IC	IC	IC	
		40001	412		14000	421	14002	1420	1460	14004	34000	34002		5402	14006	34004	54000	1422	5404	14008	5422	5420	
		101	🍷		116	54190	103	1421	1461	131	114	105		5403	112	300	107	1423	5405	110	5423	5421	
						54170		Ⓐ	Ⓒ														
		R	J		Z	N	P			V	H	C		G	M	K	S		G	Q	O	G	
0	**Katowice** 1075 d.	0455	0512	...	0812	0825	0905	0949	0949	1127	1145	1456	...	1518	1614	1615	1706	1801	1920	2021	2238	2325	...
	Tychy ▷ d.	|	0530	...	0827	0840	|	1003	1003	|	1200	|	...	|	1629	|	|	|	1935	2037	2254	2342	...
45	Rybnik ▷ a.	|	0608	...	0856	|	0948	|	|	|	1233	1539	...	|	1658	|	1750	|	|	2107	|	|	...
	Gliwice 1075 a.	0516	...	...	...	|	...	|	|	1148	...	...	...	1539	...	1636	...	1824	|	|	|	|	...
	Bielsko Biała ▷ a.	...	...	...	...	0919	...	1105	1105	...	...	...	...	...	...	...	...	...	2036	...	0003	0051	...

km		IC	EIP	IC	EIP	IC	IC	IC	TLK	IC		EIP	IC	IC	IC	IC	IC	TLK	IC		LE	IC
		4520	4506	111	4504	4122	106	113	301	104		4500	115	130	4120	4160	102	420	117		411	100
		4521	4507	41008	4505	4123	45000	41006	43004	43002		4501	43000	41004	4121	4161	41002	45170	41000		🍷	44000
												Ⓑ						45190				
		G	G	Q	G		S	M	K	C		G	H	V	Ⓐ	Ⓒ	P	N	Z		A	R
0	**Bielsko Biała** ▷ d.	0424	...	...	0745	...	...	...	...	...	...	...	...	...	1642	1642	...	1846	...	...	...	...
	Gliwice 1075 d.	|	0614	...	|	0938	...	...	1123	...	...	1431	...	1605	|	|	...	|	...	...	...	2240
	Rybnik ▷ d.	|	|	0653	|	|	1006	1056	|	1209	...	|	1526	|	|	|	1808	|	1900	...	2015	|
39	Tychy ▷ d.	0526	|	0722	0842	|	|	1129	|	|	...	|	1555	|	1738	1738	|	1921	1929	...	2057	|
55	**Katowice** 1075 a.	0540	0638	0735	0856	1003	1049	1144	1146	1254	...	1455	1611	1630	1751	1751	1850	1934	1943	...	2112	2303

A – ④⑤⑦: LEO EXPRESS – [12] 🍷 Praha - Bohumín - Katowice - Kraków.
B – To/from Bielsko Biała.
C – PORTA MORAVIA – [12] ✕ Przemyśl - Kraków - Katowice - Wien - Graz and v.v.
E – 🛏 1, 2 cl., [12] Gdynia Gł. - Warszawa - Kraków - Zakopane and v.v. (Tables **1030/1066**).
G – To/from Gdynia (Tables **1025/30**).
H – CRACOVIA – [12] 🍷 Przemyśl - Kraków - Katowice - Bohumín - Praha and v.v.
J – ①⑤⑥: LEO EXPRESS – [12] 🍷 Kraków - Katowice - Bohumín - Praha.
K – GALICJA – [12] Przemyśl - Kraków - Katowice - Ostrava and v.v.
L – To Białystok (Table **1040**).
M – [12] ✕ Warszawa - Praha and v.v.
N – ROZEWIE – [12] Gdynia - Katowice - Bielsko Biała - Zwardoń and v.v.
O – From Olsztyn (Table **1030**).
P – POLONIA – [12] ✕ Warszawa - Wien and v.v.
Q – SILESIA – [12] ✕ Warszawa - Ostrava and v.v.
R – MORAVIA – [12] ✕ Katowice - Ostrava - Wien and v.v.
S – SOBIESKI – [12] ✕ Gdynia - Warszawa - Wien and v.v.
T – To/from Przemyśl (Table **1075**).
V – BÁTHORY – [12] ✕ Terespol - Warszawa - Bohumín - Budapest and v.v.
Z – SILESIA – [12] ✕ Warszawa - Praha and v.v.

j – Warszawa **Gdańska**.

▷ – For local trains Katowice - Bielsko Biała and Rybnik – see Tables **1077/79**.
☛ **Shaded services are suspended until further notice.**

WARSZAWA - ŁÓDŹ / CZESTOCHOWA - WROCŁAW 1061

km		IC	IC	IC	EIP	IC	IC	EIP	IC	TLK	IC		TLK		EIP	IC	IC		IC		IC	IC		IC
		18109	1620	16150	1610	1622	1654	1611	5620	16152	1628		17106		1600	16104	1630		16102		2600	14104		16170
		18108	1621	16151	1611	1623	1624		5621	16153	1629		17107		1601	16105	1660		16103		2601	14125		16190
				Ⓒ	Ⓐ			Ⓒ		①⑥					Ⓑ						Ⓑ	Ⓑ		
		S					J		E	2			A			Y	YZ		Y		L			YJ
0	**Warszawa** Wschodnia d.	...	0504	0544	0544	0634	0744	0844	1014	1104	1149	...	1359	...	1544	1549	1604	...	1824	...	2004	2059	...	2259
4	**Warszawa** Centralna d.	...	0515	0555	0557	0648	0816	0905	1025	1115	1215	...	1420	...	1602	1626	1616	...	1835	...	2025	2121	...	2310
122	Koluszki d.	...	0619	|	|	0748	0916	|	1143	1223	1315	...	1529	...	|	1753	1711	...	2004	...	2125	2221	...	0013
160	Piotrków Trybunalski d.	...	|	|	|	|	0940	|	|	1247	1339	...	|	...	|	1819	1735	...	|	...	2149	2246	...	|
•	Częstochowa d.	...	|	|	|	|	1033	|	|	1339	1433	...	|	...	|	1920	1827	...	|	...	2245	2343	...	|
	Częstochowa Stradom d.	...	|	0803	0807	|	1038	1110	|	1344	1438	...	|	...	1806	1938	1832	...	|	...	2250		...	|
130	**Łódź** Widzew ▷ d.	0404	0632	|	|	0807	|	|	1159	|	|	...	1559	...	|	|	|	...	2022	...	|		...	0100
257	Kalisz ▷ d.	0544	0812	|	|	0949	|	|	1325	|	|	...	1743	...	|	|	|	...	2156	...	|		...	0240
281	Ostrów Wlkp ▷ d.	...	0832	|	|	1006	|	|	1344	|	|	...	1800	...	|	|	|	...	2214	...	|		...	0258
	Opole Gł. d.	...	|	0858	0904	|	1135	1204	|	1445	1545	...	|	...	1902	2043	1927	...	|	...	2349		...	|
	Brzeg d.	...	|	0918	|	|	1156	|	|	1509	1606	...	|	...	1922	2110	1947	...	|	...	0009		...	|
382*	**Wrocław** Gł. ▷ a.	...	0955	0942	0946	1128	1223	1245	1504	1545	1640	...	1926	...	1946	2139	2020	...	2335	...	0036		...	0439

	IC		IC	IC		EIP	IC		TLK		IC	IC	TLK	EIP	IC	IC		IC	IC		IC
	41104		6200	61103		6100	61104		71106		6228	6521	61153	6112	6154	6123		6121	81108		61170
	41105		6150	61102		6101	61105		71107		6229	6520	61152		6124	6122		6120	81109		61190
	①-⑥					①-⑥							⑤⑦								
			L	Y			Y		A		L	E	2		J				S		JY
Wrocław Gł. ▷ d.	...	...	0435	0407	...	0647	0650	...	0900	...	1204	1300	1400	1435	1535	1703	...	1921	...	...	2351
Brzeg d.	...	...	0502	|	...	0711	0725	...	0930	...	1238	|	1438	|	1607	|	...	|	...	...	|
Opole Gł. d.	...	...	0524	|	...	0734	0753	...	0956	...	1300	|	1504	1525	1630	|	...	|	...	...	|
Ostrów Wlkp. ▷ d.	...	...	|	0541	...	|	|	...	|	...	1431	|	|	|	|	1840	...	2045	...	...	0132
Kalisz ▷ d.	...	...	|	0559	...	|	|	...	|	...	1449	|	|	|	|	1857	...	2102	2237	...	0149
Łódź Widzew ▷ d.	...	...	|	0740	...	|	|	...	|	...	1626	|	|	|	|	2055	...	2245	0042f	...	0432
Częstochowa Stradom d.	...	...	0620	|	...	0828	0900	...	1058	...	1400	|	1609	1619	1725	|	...	|	...	...	|
Częstochowa d.	0435	...	0628	|	...	|	0907	...	1105	...	1407	|	1619	|	1733	|	...	|	...	...	|
Piotrków Trybunalski d.	0531	...	0719	|	...	|	0958	...	1157	...	1458	|	1712	|	1824	|	...	|	...	...	|
Koluszki d.	0557	...	0743	0759	...	|	1026	...	1221	...	1522	1643	1736	|	1848	2108	...	2300	...	...	0444
Warszawa Centralna a.	0708	...	0842	|	...	1028	1136	...	1330	...	1620	1749	1842	1825	1946	2208	...	0012	...	...	0545
Warszawa Wschodnia a.	0721	...	0856	0911j	...	1041	1146	...	1341	...	1656	1803	1851	1841	2011	2221	...	0021	...	...	0556

A – To/from Zielona Góra (Table **1086**).
E – To/from Ełk (Table **1035**).
J – To/from Jelenia Góra (Table **1084**).
L – To/from Lublin (Table **1055**).
S – To/from Szczecin (Table **1010**).
Y – To/from Białystok (Table **1040**).
Z – To/from Zgorzelec (Table **1085**).
f – Łódź **Fabryczna**.
j – Warszawa **Gdańska**.
▷ – For local trains see Table **1080**.
* – *406 km* via CMK.
• – Częstochowa - Opole Gł: *91 km*.

1065 WARSZAWA - KRAKÓW

km		IC		EIP	EIP	EIP	TLK	EIP		EIP		TLK	EIP	EIP	EIP	TLK	EIP	EIP		TLK		IC		
		13100		1300	1302	5300	53100	5302		8300		53104	5304	1304	5306	13110	5308	5310		13102		5328		
		13101		1301	1303	5301	53101	5303		8301		83154	5305	1305	5307	13111	5309	5311		13103		5329		
		P				G	GZ	G		S		G	G	Ⓑ	G	Ⓑ	GR	G		C		O		
0	**Warszawa** Wsch ... d.	0454	...	0603	0714	0829	0919	0929	...	1129	...	1324	1329	1434	1529	1639	1729	1829	...	2009	...	2249	...	...
4	**Warszawa** Cent ... d.	0514	...	0612	0725	0846	0933	0940	...	1155	...	1347	1340	1445	1540	1655	1740	1841	...	2032	...	2305	...	...
246	**Kraków** Gł ... a.	0819	...	0906	1017	1128	1343	1218	...	1442	...	1705	1632	1732	1830	2041	2019	2128	...	2343	...	0224	...	...

	TLK	EIP	EIP		EIP		EIP		TLK	EIP		EIP	TLK	EIP	EIP		EIP	EIP	IC	IC				
	31102	3510	3100		3508		3506		35104	3504		3800	35100	3104	3502		3500	3102	3128	31100				
	31103	3511	3101		3509		3507		38154	3505		3801	35101	3105	3503		3501	3103	3129	31101				
	C	G	⚒		RG		G		G	G		S	GZ		G		G			P				
Kraków Gł. ... d.	0413	0546	0650	...	0747	...	0954	...	1050	1145	...	1341	1440	1508	1548	...	1703	1856	1924	2031	...	...	...	...
Warszawa Centralna ... a.	0731	0825	0936	...	1019	...	1224	...	1400	1424	...	1612	1819	1740	1825	...	1934	2130	2221	2320	...	...	...	...
Warszawa Wschodnia ... a.	0756	0836	0946	...	1031	...	1236	...	1440	1435	...	1631	1841	1751	1836	...	1945	2140	2231	2331	...	...	...	...

C – HAŃCZA – 12 Kraków - Warszawa - Białystok - Suwałki and v.v. (Table **1042**).
G – From / to Gdynia (Table **1030**).
O – From Olsztyn (Table **1030**).
P – To / from Przemyśl (Table **1075**).
R – To / from Rzeszów (Table **1075**).
S – From / to Kołobrzeg (Table **1015**).
Z – To / from Zakopane (Table **1066**).

1066 KRAKÓW - ZAKOPANE

km			TLK		EIC	IC		TLK		IC
			53171		1351	13151		53100		5360
		🚌	✣	🚌			🚌	G	🚌	H
	Warszawa Cent. **1065** ... d.	...	2245	...	0642	0450	...	0933	...	...
0	**Kraków** Gł. ... d.	...	0433	0650	0915	0932	1214p	1403	1751	1949
62	Sucha Beskidzka Zamek ... d.	0517c	0552	0827c	|	1046	1409c	1527	1928c	2105
95	Chabówka ... a.	0615	0634	0926	1056	1121	1508	1614	2027	|
95	Chabówka ... d.	0622	0648	0933	1110	1135	1515	1629	2035	|
121	Nowy Targ ... d.	0713	0734	1024	1145	1229	1607	1723	2129	2236
142	**Zakopane** ... a.	0738	0757	1049	1212	1254	1632	1634	2155	2259

		IC		TLK	EIC	IC			TLK
		3560		35100	3140	31150			35170
	🚌	H	🚌	G			🚌	🚌	G
Zakopane ... d.	0405	0608	0834	1045	1321	1412	1407	1731	2031
Nowy Targ ... d.	0435	0632	0904	1213	1346	1439	1437	1801	2054
Chabówka ... a.	0520	0706	0949	1241	1425	1509	1522	1846	2126
Chabówka ... d.	0527	0707	0956	1302	1439	1530	1529	1853	2143
Sucha Beskidzka Zamek ... d.	0627c	0805	1056c	1338	|	1612	1629c	1953c	2220
Kraków Gł. ... a.	0811	0913	1252p	1420	1632	1730	1818	2137	2338t
Warszawa Cent. **1065** ... a.	...	...	...	1816	1911	2235	...	...	0530

G – To / from Gdynia (Tables **1030/1060**).
H – To / from Gdynia (Table **1025**).
c – Sucha Beskidzka.
p – Kraków Płaszów.
t – Depart 0028.
☛ **Shaded services are suspended until further notice.**

1067 WARSZAWA and LUBLIN - KIELCE - KATOWICE and KRAKÓW

km	*For fast trains to Kraków see Table* **1065**		TLK		TLK		IC	IC	IC		IC		IC		IC	IC	IC		TLK	IC		TLK		
			83170		28103		13105	24101	5326		26103		5324		5322	26105	5320		13107	23100		12111		
			83171		28102				5327				5325		5323	26104	5321			23101				
			Y	Ⓐ	S		2 P		O		W		O	Ⓐ	O	W	O		P			Ⓑ		
0	**Warszawa** Wschodnia ... d.	...	0317	...	...	...	0615	...	0724	...	...	...	1219	...	1351	...	1623	...	1718	...	...	1959	...	...
4	**Warszawa** Centralna ... d.	...	|	...	...	...	0649	...	0746	...	...	...	1232	...	1400y	...	1634	...	|	...	...	|	...	...
	Warszawa Wschodnia ... d.	...	|	...	...	...	|	...	|	...	...	...	|	...	|	...	|	...	|	...	...	|	...	...
	Lublin ... d.	...	|	...	0453	...	|	0738	|	...	1101	...	|	...	|	1615	|	...	|	1812	...	|	...	...
•	Dęblin ... d.	0357	|	0450	|	0653	|	|	|	1012	|	1231	|	1421	|	|	|	1729	1834	|	1912	2120	2127	...
107*	Radom ... d.	0449	0457	0550	0622	0758	0820	0902	0911	1103	1232	1324	1356	1512	1523	1747	1758	1821	1922	1938	2009	2204	2227	...
148	Skarżysko Kamienna ... d.	...	0525	...	0652	...	0853k	0926	0936	...	1258	...	1422	...	1550	1812	1823	...	2002k	2003	...	2229	...	...
192	Kielce ... d.	...	0614	...	0727	...	...	1022	1014	...	1402	...	1509	...	1632	1847	1858	...	...	2040	...	2303	...	...
	Zawiercie ... **1060** d.	...	|	...	...	...	...	|	|	...	1528	...	|	...	|	...	|	...	...	|	...	...	...	...
	Sosnowiec Gł. ... **1060** d.	...	|	...	...	...	...	|	|	...	1559	...	|	...	|	...	|	...	...	|	...	...	...	...
	Katowice ... **1060** a.	...	|	...	...	...	...	1234	|	...	1607	...	|	...	|	...	|	...	...	|	...	...	...	...
324	**Kraków** Gł. ... a.	...	0823	...	...	...	...	...	1204	...	...	...	1709	...	1824	...	2049	...	...	2225	...	...	...	...

km				TLK		TLK	IC	IC	IC		IC		IC		IC		IC	IC	IC	TLK		TLK		
				21110		31106	32100	3520	62104		3522		3524		62102		3526	31104	42100	82102		38170		
								3521			3523		3525				3527					38171		
			Ⓐ	①–⑥		P		O	W		O	Ⓐ	O		W	Ⓐ	O	2 P		S		Y		
	Kraków Gł. ... d.	...	...	...	...	...	0528	0705	...	...	0936	...	1132	...	...	...	1524	...	...	...	...	2027	...	...
0	**Katowice** ... **1060** d.	...	...	...	...	...	|	|	...	...	|	...	|	...	1208	...	|	...	1556	...	...	...	...	...
9	Sosnowiec Gł. ... **1060** d.	...	...	...	...	...	|	|	...	...	|	...	|	...	1217	...	|	...	|	...	...	...	...	...
44	Zawiercie ... **1060** d.	...	...	...	...	...	|	|	...	...	|	...	|	...	1250	...	|	...	|	...	...	|	...	...
161	Kielce ... d.	...	...	0418	...	...	0716	0858	1004	...	1125	...	1328	...	1433	...	1734	...	1837	2113	...	2239	...	...
	Skarżysko Kamienna ... d.	...	...	0454	...	0812k	0752	0934	1046	...	1202	...	1404	...	1514	...	1809	1932k	1913	2149	...	2316	...	...
	Radom ... d.	0355	0455	0523	0600	0859	0819	1002	1119	1200	1237	1341	1441	1448	1543	1553	1840	2015	1942	2219	2240	0006	...	...
	Dęblin ... d.	0456	0548	0605	0717	0944	|	|	|	1301	|	1441	|	1541	|	1658	|	|	|	|	2332	|	...	...
	Lublin ... a.	...	...	|	...	|	0943	|	1247	...	|	...	|	...	1709	...	|	|	2111	2346	...	|	...	...
	Warszawa Wschodnia ... a.	...	...	|	...	|	...	|	...	...	|	...	|	...	...	...	|	|	...	...	...	|	...	...
	Warszawa Centralna ... a.	...	...	|	...	|	...	1123	...	...	1401y	...	1606	...	...	...	2005y	2138	...	...	...	|	...	...
	Warszawa Wschodnia ... a.	...	...	0732	...	1100	...	1146	...	...	1410	...	1617	...	...	...	2013	2150	...	...	...	0252	...	...

O – To / from Olsztyn (Table **1030**).
P – To / from Przemyśl (Table **1058**).
S – To / from Szczecin (Table **1003**).
W – To / from Wrocław (Tables **1061/75**).
Y – To / from Kołobrzeg (Table **1030**).
k – Skarżysko Kościelne.
y – Warszawa **Śródmieście**.
• – Lublin - Radom: *121 km.*
* – *161 km* via Dęblin

1070 POZNAŃ - WROCŁAW

km			IC	TLK		IC		IC	IC		IC		TLK	IC	IC	IC		IC	IC		IC	IC	TLK	
			7300	54151		5601		56105	86102		5312		53106	84102	5603	8306		56103	84100		5605	83172	54072	
			7301	53151		5600		56104	86103		5313		53107	84103	5453			56102	84101		5604	83173	421	
																		2					❄	
			P	A	S	G		O	D		GH		GH	D	G	EH	K	Q	DB		G	UP	R	
0	**Poznań** Gł. ... d.	0509	0551	0634	0645	0843	0851	0940	1047	1054	1135	1241	1345	1417	1535	1630	1645	1741	1841	1846	1927	2305	0205	...
69	Leszno ... d.	0618	0635	0723	0753	0928	1004	1030	1136	1159	1219	1356	1431	1507	1620	1718	1800	1831	1928	1953	2015	2355	|	...
165	**Wrocław** Gł. ... a.	0754	0735	0831	0917	1027	1133	1138	1246	1338	1319	1514	1531	1614	1721	1826	1931	1941	2033	2115	2120	0107	0449	...

	IC			IC	IC	IC	IC		IC	TLK		IC		IC	IC		IC	TLK		IC	TLK	IC		
	6505			48101	65103	3806	6503		48103	35106		3512		68103	65105		6501	45151		3701	420	38172		
	6504			48100	65102	3807	4553		48102	35107		3513		68102	65104		6500	35151		3700	45072	38173		
																					❄			
	G		K	BD	Q	EH	G		D	HG		HG		D	O	T	G	A	W	P	R	PU		
Wrocław Gł ... d.	0625	0638	0705	0732	0833	0944	1030	1037	1138	1225	1230	1428	1440	1525	1633	1646	1737	1855	1946	2027	2320	0307	...	...
Leszno ... d.	0732	0802	0847	0838	0940	1050	1135	1202	1244	1329	1403	1531	1603	1633	1740	1816	1838	2006	2119	2137	|	0424	...	...
Poznań Gł ... a.	0821	0911	1002	0927	1028	1139	1222	1311	1332	1417	1525	1616	1713	1722	1830	1936	1925	2055	2245	2225	0205	0515	...	...

A – To / from Bydgoszcz (Table **1020**).
B – To / from Katowice (Table **1075**).
D – To / from Słupsk (Table **1015**).
E – To / from Kołobrzeg (Table **1015**).
G – To / from Gdynia (Tables **1015/20**).
H – To / from Kraków (Table **1075**).
K – To / from Kłodzko (Table **1095**).
O – To / from Olsztyn (Table **1030**).
P – To / from Przemyśl (Table **1075**).
Q – To / from Białystok (Table **1035**).
R – ROZEWIE **54072/45072** – 1, 2 cl., 2 cl., 2 Gdynia - Katowice - Žilina and v.v.
S – To Szklarska Poreba Górna (Table **1084**).
T – On Ⓐ from Szklarska Poreba Górna (Table **1084**).
U – To / from Świnoujście (Table **1010**).
W – On Ⓐ from Szklarska Poreba Górna (Table **1084**).
❄ – **Shaded services are suspended until further notice.**

RZESZÓW - JASŁO - ZAGÓRZ - MEDZILABORCE 1073

km												
					TLK							*TLK*
					30113							30111
					R			①–⑥	①–④	⑤		P
		Ⓐ			2	Ⓐ	Ⓐ					2
0	**Rzeszów** Gł	d.	...	0505	0725	...	1217	...	1440	1629	1629	1925	...
9	Boguchwała	d.	...	0521	0736	...	1229	...	1451	1641	1641	1936	...
48	Frysztak	d.	...	0616	0818	...	1313	...	1533	1725	1725	2020	...
52	Przybówka	d.	...	0620	0822	...	1317	...	1538	1729	1729	2025	...
70	**Jasło**	d.	0458	0640	0842	1238	1337	1348	1557	1751	1759	2045	2215
94	Krosno	d.	0529	...	...	1304	...	1419	...	...	1829	...	2246
133	Sanok	d.	0630	...	...	1402	...	1522	...	...	1924	...	2343
139	Nowy Zagórz	d.	...	...	...	|	...	...	...	...	...	...	|
140	**Zagórz**	d.	...	...	...	1413	...	...	...	...	...	...	2354
188	Łupków 🚌	a.	...	...	...	...	...	...	...	...	...	...	...
204	**Medzilaborce** mesto	a.	...	...	...	...	...	...	...	...	...	...	...
206	Medzilaborce	a.	...	...	...	...	...	...	...	...	...	...	...

				TLK				*TLK*				
				33110				33112				
		Ⓐ		Q	Ⓐ		Ⓐ	S	⑦	Ⓐ	①–⑥	
				2				2				
Medzilaborce	d.	...	...	...	...	...	...	...	...	...	...	...
Medzilaborce mesto	d.	...	...	...	...	...	...	...	...	...	...	...
Łupków 🚌	d.	...	...	...	...	...	...	...	...	...	...	...
Zagórz	d.	...	...	0500	...	...	...	1441	...	...	...	...
Nowy Zagórz	d.	...	...	|	...	...	...	|	...	...	...	...
Sanok	d.	...	...	0511	0638	...	...	1453	1515	1528	...	...
Krosno	d.	...	...	0610	0734	...	...	1551	1609	1623	...	...
Jasło	d.	0445	0551	0636	0805	0903	1433	1617	1655	1655	1708	2053
Przybówka	d.	0503	0609	...	...	0921	1452	...	1713	...	1732	2112
Frysztak	d.	0507	0613	...	...	0925	1456	...	1718	...	1736	2116
Boguchwała	d.	0556	0657	...	...	1007	1552	...	1759	...	1818	2200
Rzeszów Gł	a.	0608	0709	...	...	1019	1609	...	1811	...	1830	2213

P – From Kraków, depart 1922. **Q** – To Kraków, arrive 0930. **R** – From Kraków, depart 0944. **S** – To Kraków, arrive 1901.

ŁÓDŹ - CZESTOCHOWA - KRAKÓW / KATOWICE 1074

km												
			IC		*TLK*		*TLK*				*IC*
			13109		14101		54101				5421
					14100		54100				5420
							G				G
	Łódź Kaliska	d.	...	0448	...	...	...	1449	1616	1809	...
0	**Łódź** Fabryczna	d.	0535	0550	...	1056	...	1551	1703	1859	...
	Koluszki **1060**	d.	|	|	0726	|	1230	|	|	|	2020
15	**Łódź** Widzew **1060**	d.	0543	0558	0759	1103	1308	1558	1710	1906	2042
	Koluszki **1060**	d.	|	0627	|	1139	|	1627	1743	1940	|
67	Piotrków Trybunalski **1060**	d.	0617	0701	0834	1213	1343	1701	1817	2014	2116
153	**Częstochowa** **1060**	d.	0712	0815	0927	1326	1438	1814	1930	2128	2211
	Katowice **1060**	a.	|	...	1038	...	1600	...	...	...	2322
299*	**Kraków** Gł.	a.	0902	...	...	...	...	...	...	...	...

			IC			*TLK*		*TLK*		*IC*
			4520			45100		41100		31108
		Ⓐ	4521			45101		41101		
			G			G				
Kraków Gł.	d.	...	...	...	...	...	...	...	...	1904
Katowice **1060**	d.	...	0455	...	...	1306	...	1731	...	|
Częstochowa **1060**	d.	0502	0607	0642	1244	1440	1543	1858	1918	2040
Piotrków Trybunalski **1060**	d.	0616	0659	0755	1401	1531	1656	1949	2031	2135
Koluszki **1060**	d.	0658	|	0837	1443	|	1748	|	2113	|
Łódź Widzew **1060**	a.	0718	0731	0900	1506	1604	1811	2022	2136	2208
Koluszki **1060**	a.	|	0759	|	|	1637	|	2059	|	|
Łódź Fabryczna	a.	0725	...	0907	1513	...	1818	...	2143	2217
Łódź Kaliska	a.	0817	...	1011	1601	...	1907	...	2233	...

G – To/from Gdynia (Table **1025**). * – *274 km* via CMK.

WROCŁAW - KATOWICE - KRAKÓW - PRZEMYŚL 1075

For other trains Poznań - Katowice / Kraków see Tables **1080** (via Ostrów Wlkp) and **1025** (via Łódź)

km																												
			TLK		*TLK*	*IC*	*IC*	*IC*	*IC*	*TLK*	*IC*	*IC*	*IC*	*IC*	*IC*	*TLK*	*IC*	*IC*	*IC*	*TLK*	*EIP*	*IC*	*TLK*	*IC*	*IC*	*IC*	*IC*	
			30105		42000	13100	63104	6300	7300	301	83104	62102	104	8304	62100	53104	5312	115	73000	53106	5309	63000	82102	8306	8302	84100	83172	
			30104		311	13101	63105	6301	7301	43004	83105		43002	8305	62101	53105	5313	43000	57	53107	5308	51	82103	8307	8303	84101	83173	
				2	2		①–⑥					2				Ⓑ												
					UL	W			G	T	L	H	T	L	W	Q	S	B	Q	P	E	KL	M	T	X	T		
0	**Wrocław** Gł. **1061**	d.	...	...	...	...	0458	0635	0740	...	0912	0931	...	1130	1247	...	1330	...	1502	1557	...	1646	1652	1848	2002	2041	0118	...
42	Brzeg **1061**	d.	...	...	...	...	0535	|	0815	...	0945	1008	...	1206	|	...	1400	...	|	1635	...	1717	1722	|	2030	2111	0155	...
82	Opole Gł. **1061**	d.	...	...	...	...	0600	0728	0837	...	1012	1035	...	1229	1338	...	1422	...	1554	1701	...	1745	1748	1942	2052	2137	0223	...
162	Gliwice **1060**	d.	...	...	0542	...	0653	0817	0932	1121	|	1127	...	1321	1430	...	1523	...	1643	1751	...	1836	|	2031	2142	2241	0342	...
190	**Katowice** **1060**	a.	...	...	0605	...	0715	0839	0953	1146	|	1150	...	1343	1453	...	1546	...	1706	1815	...	1859	|	2053	2203	2305	0411	...
190	**Katowice**	d.	...	0557	0608	...	0720	0842	0956	1153	|	...	1301	1346	1456	...	1549	1613	1710	1819	...	1904	|	2056	2206	...	0416	...
•	Częstochowa Stradom	d.	...	|	|	...	|	|	|	|	1111	...	|	|	|	...	|	|	|	|	...	|	1844	|	|	...	|	...
268	**Kraków** Gł.	a.	...	0713	0709	...	0825	0945	1106	1253	1245	...	1354	1458	1553	...	1655	1706	1801	1922	...	2003	...	2155	2311	...	0531	...
268	**Kraków** Gł. **1078**	d.	0649	0718	0733	0845	...	1006	1126	...	1306	...	1401	1505	1606	1706	...	1707	1813	...	2021	2007	...	...	...	...	0555	...
273	Kraków Płaszów **1078**	d.	|	0725	|	|	...	|	|	...	|	...	1412	1515	1614	1714	...	1722	1810	...	2029	2016	...	...	...	...	|	...
346	Tarnów **1078**	d.	0801	0854	0844	0948	...	1111	1235	...	1416	...	1459	1604	1706	1808	...	1810	1908	...	2113	2111	...	...	...	...	0724	...
379	Dębica	d.	0820	0917	0903	1006	...	1127	1251	...	1433	...	1519	1621	1724	1827	...	1830	1926	...	2129	2129	...	...	...	...	0744	...
426	**Rzeszów** **1058**	d.	0856	1003	0938	1041	...	1152	1321	...	1507	...	1552	1653	1747	1902	...	1908	2001	...	2157	2155	...	...	...	...	0811	...
463	Przeworsk **1058**	d.	0921	...	...	1107	...	1218	1347	...	1533	...	1623	1719	...	1931	...	1938	2031	...	...	2223	...	...	...	...	0840	...
478	Jarosław **1058**	d.	0932	...	...	1117	...	1231	1357	...	1548	...	1635	1730	...	1945	...	1948	2041	...	...	2235	...	...	...	...	0852	...
513	**Przemyśl** **1058**	a.	1003	...	...	1145	...	1300	1428	...	1618	...	1703	1801	...	2017	...	2017	2105	...	...	2304	...	...	...	...	0920	...

		IC	*IC*	*IC*	*IC*	*TLK*	*TLK*	*EIP*	*IC*	*IC*	*IC*	*IC*	*TLK*	*IC*	*IC*		*IC*	*IC*	*TLK*	*IC*	*IC*	*IC*		*TLK*	*IC*	*IC*	*TLK*	*IC*
		48101	3802	3806	36000	28102	35106	3508	34000	37000	34000	3512	35104	26101	3804		105	26102	300	38104	3700	3600		24001	36104	31100	33104	38173
		48100	3803	3807	52	28103	35107	3509	114	56	114	3513	38155	26100	3805		34002	26103	34004	38105	3701	3601		310	36105	31101	33105	38172
																					•		2	2	Ⓑ			
		X	K	M	E	LK	Q	P	S	B	S	Q	Q	L	T		H	L	G	T				UL		W		T
Przemyśl **1058**	d.	...	...	...	0435	...	...	...	0710	0718	...	...	0802	...	0930	...	1021	...	...	1156	1400	1515	...	...	...	1704	1805	1858
Jarosław **1058**	d.	...	...	...	0510	...	...	...	0738	0742	...	...	0838	...	1005	...	1046	...	...	1230	1434	1547	...	...	...	1731	1839	1931
Przeworsk **1058**	d.	...	...	...	0521	...	...	...	0749	0753	...	...	0850	...	1015	...	1057	...	...	1240	1444	1557	...	...	...	1742	1849	1943
Rzeszów **1058**	d.	...	...	...	0551	...	...	0604	0819	0823	←	...	0918	1008	1042	...	1132	...	...	1311	1521	1624	1612	1657	...	1818	1922	2012
Dębica	d.	...	...	...	0617	...	...	0633	0859	0853	0900	...	0948	1032	1114	...	1204	...	...	1343	1551	1650	1657	1733	...	1854	1955	2039
Tarnów **1078**	d.	...	...	...	0636	...	...	0650	→	0910	0919	...	1005	1049	1132	...	1226	...	...	1401	1607	1706	1720	1752	...	1915	2014	2058
Kraków Płaszów **1078**	d.	...	...	...	0728	...	...	0733	...	|	|	...	|	|	|	...	|	...	...	1456	1657	1755	1830	|	...	2006	|	|
Kraków Gł. **1078**	a.	...	...	...	0735	...	...	0741	...	1005	1027	...	1117	1154	1240	...	1331	...	...	1503	1704	1803	1839	1856	...	2013	2126	2212
Kraków Gł.	d.	...	0505	0616	0741	...	0843	...	...	1012	1049	1106	...	1221	1304	...	1353	...	1500	1508	1709	1817	1849	1916	1953	...	...	2232
Częstochowa Stradom	d.	...	|	|	|	0918	|	...	...	|	|	|	...	|	|	...	|	...	|	1640	|	|	|	|	|	...	...	|
Katowice	a.	...	0609	0713	0840	|	0949	...	...	1106	1142	1213	...	1319	1408	...	1450	...	1607	|	1813	1913	2004	2016	2057	...	...	2350
Katowice **1060**	d.	0509	0616	0718	0850	|	0952	...	...	1109	...	1216	...	1329	1411	...	...	1607	1615	|	1821	1916	...	2019	2104	...	...	0009
Gliwice **1060**	d.	0534	0639	0743	0920	|	1015	...	...	1130	...	1239	...	1352	1434	...	...	1632	1637	|	1849	1939	...	2040	2129	...	...	0036
Opole Gł. **1061**	d.	0630	0734	0832	1013	1020	1105	...	...	1218	...	1334	...	1440	1525	...	...	1722	...	1736	1939	2028	...	...	2221	...	...	0155
Brzeg **1061**	d.	0655	0759	|	1034	1044	1127	...	...	|	...	1355	...	|	1547	...	...	1747	...	1757	1959	|	...	...	2247	...	...	0222
Wrocław Gł. **1061**	a.	0725	0829	0924	1102	1113	1200	...	...	1301	...	1422	...	1529	1621	...	...	1823	...	1830	2025	2116	...	...	2323	...	...	0255

ADDITIONAL SERVICES KATOWICE - KRAKÓW and v.v.

					TLK					*TLK*			*LE*
					83102					63102			413
					83103					J			C
										2			
Katowice	d.	0454	0647	1116	1246	1329	1501	1719	1838	1959	2045	2205	2121
Kraków Gł	a.	0611	0755	1231	1356	1453	1608	1844	1946	2110	2217	2319	2221

		LE			*TLK*					*TLK*			
		412			36102					38102			
		F			J					38103			
					2								
Kraków Gł.	d.	0405	0418	0608	0642	0800	0920	1054	1310	1353	1636	2028	2141
Katowice	a.	0502	0542	0726	0757	0926	1038	1231	1419	1457	1746	2136	2258

B – WAWEL – 12 ✕ Berlin - Wrocław - Krakow and v.v.

C – ④⑤⑦: LEO EXPRESS – 12 🍷 Praha - Katowice - Kraków.

E – 12 Wrocław - Przemyśl and v.v. The 🛏 2 cl., Wrocław - Przemyśl - Lviv cars are temporarily suspended.

F – ①⑤⑥: LEO EXPRESS – 12 🍷 Kraków - Katowice - Praha.

G – GALICJA – 12 Kraków - Katowice - Ostrava and v.v. (Table **99**).

H – PORTA MORAVIA / PORTA MORAVICA – 12 ✕ Przemyśl - Katowice - Wien - Graz and v.v.

J – To/from Jelenia Góra (Table **1084**).

K – To/from Szczecin (Table **1003**).

L – To/from Lublin (Table **1067**).

M – To/from Kołobrzeg (Table **1015**).

P – To/from Gdynia (Tables **1030**, **1065**).

Q – To/from Gdynia (Tables **1020**).

S – To/from Praha (Table **99**).

T – To/from Szczecin / Świnoujście (Tables **1010**, **1080**).

U – To/from Bohumín (Table **1076**).

W – To/from Warszawa (Table **1065**).

X – To/from Słupsk (Table **1015**).

• – Wrocław - Kraków Gł. via Częstochowa Stradom adds *47 km*.

1076 KATOWICE and KRAKÓW - BOHUMÍN - OSTRAVA

For night trains see Table 99

km	km		IC¶ 101	LE 412	IC¶ 116	IC¶ 103	IC¶ 131	IC¶ 114	IC¶ 105	EN 409	IC* 112	IC¶ 107	TLK 310
			✕✓	🍷	✕✓	✕✓	✕✓	✓	✓	✕✓	✕✓	✕✓	✓
			R	K	Y	P	D	C	E	A		S	G
		Warszawa Cen **1060** d.	...	...	0454	0602	0828	...	...	1238	1305	1405	...
	0	**Kraków** Gł. ▷ d.	...	0401	|	|	|	1047	1353	|	|	|	1910
0		**Katowice** d.	0455	0512	0813	0905	1124	1144	1451	|	1614	1703	2016
	65	Oświęcim ▷ d.	|	|	|	|	|	|	|	|	|	|	|
74	116	Zebrzydowice ▦ d.	|	|	|	|	|	|	|	|	|	|	|
45		Rybnik ▷ d.	|	0608	0858	0948	|	1234	1542	|	1700	1750	|
82		Racibórz ▷ d.	0607	|	|	|	1241	|	|	|	|	|	2138
102		Chałupki ▦ ▷ d.	0622	0711	0937	1024	1258	1310	1615	1717	1737	1824	2152
Δ94		Bohumín ▦ a.	0628	0717	0943	1030	1308	1316	1621	1723	1743	1830	2158
94		Bohumín ▦ **1160** d.	0642	0736	1000	1042	1342	1400	1642	1758	1800	1842	...
102		**Ostrava** hlavní **1160** a.	0649	0742	1007	1049	1349	1407	1649	|	1807	1849	...
		Praha hlavní **1160** a.	|	1137	1352	|	|	1752	|	|	2152	|	...
		Wien Hbf **1150** a.	0949	...	...	1349	|	...	1949	2117	...	2149	...
		Budapest Nyugati a.	...	...	...	...	1934	...	...	...	...	...	...

	TLK 311	IC¶ 106	EN 408	IC* 113	IC¶ 104	IC¶ 115	IC¶ 130	IC¶ 102	IC¶ 117	IC¶ 100	LE 411
	✓ 2	✕✓	✕✓	✕✓	✓	✓	✕✓	✕✓	✕✓	✕✓	🍷
	G	S	B		E	C	D	P	Y	R	J
Budapest Nyugati d.	...	...	...	...	...	...	0828	...	...	...	...
Wien Hbf **1150** d.	...	0610	0547	...	0810	...	|	1410	...	1810	...
Praha hlavní **1160** d.	...	|	|	0602	|	1002	|	|	1412	|	1528
Ostrava hlavní **1160** d.	...	0909	|	0950	1109	1350	1409	1709	1750	2109	1917
Bohumín ▦ **1160** a.	...	0916	0921	0957	1116	1357	1416	1716	1757	2116	1924
Bohumín ▦ d.	0426	0926	0951	1009	1128	1446	1454	1728	1809	2128	1936
Chałupki ▦ ▷ d.	0434	0933	0958	1022	1135	1453	1501	1735	1828	2135	1943
Racibórz ▷ d.	0449	|	|	|	|	|	1515	|	|	2151	|
Rybnik ▷ d.	|	1007	|	1055	1209	1526	|	1808	1902	|	2015
Zebrzydowice ▦ d.	|	|	|	|	|	|	|	|	|	|	|
Oświęcim ▷ a.	|	|	|	|	|	|	|	|	|	|	|
Katowice a.	0605	1050	|	1139	1254	1609	1630	1850	1949	2303	2112
Kraków Gł. ▷ a.	0707	|	|	|	1356	1704	|	|	|	...	2223
Warszawa Cen **1060** a.	...	1333	1424	1431	...	...	1929	2134	2305	...	...

A – ④ (⑤ from Warszawa): 🛏 1 cl. (lux), 🛏 1, 2 cl. Moskva - Nice. ✕ (PKP) Warszawa - Nice.
B – ⑦ (① from Wien): 🛏 1 cl. (lux), 🛏 1, 2 cl. Nice - Moskva. ✕ (PKP) Nice - Warszawa.
C – CRACOVIA – [12] 🍷 Przemyśl - Kraków - Bohumín - Praha and v.v.
D – BÁTHORY – [12] ✕ Terespol (depart 0616; arrive 2136) - Warszawa - Budapest and v.v.
E – PORTA MORAVIA / PORTA MORAVICA – [12] ✕ Przemyśl - Kraków - Katowice - Wien - Graz and v.v.
G – ROZTOCZE – [2] Lublin - Kraków - Bohumín and v.v.
J – ④⑤⑦: LEO EXPRESS – [12] 🍷 Praha - Bohumín - Kraków.
K – ①⑤⑥: LEO EXPRESS – [12] 🍷 Kraków - Bohumín - Praha.
P – POLONIA – [12] ✕ Warszawa - Wien and v.v.
R – MORAVIA – [12] ✕ Katowice - Wien and v.v.
S – SOBIESKI – [12] ✕ Gdynia - Warszawa - Wien and v.v.
Y – PRAHA – [12] ✕ Warszawa - Praha and v.v.

✓ – Supplement payable.
▷ – For local trains see Tables **1079/99**.
Δ – *106 km* via Chałupki.
¶ – Classified *EC* in Czech Republic.
* – Classified *Ex* in Czech Republic.
☛ **Shaded services are suspended until further notice.**

1077 KATOWICE - BIELSKO BIAŁA - ZWARDOŃ - ŽILINA

Koleje Śląskie, 2nd class

km				Ⓐ	Ⓒ					⊠	⊠	Ⓐ	⊠		
0	**Katowice** **1060** d.	0435	0536	0700	0749	0929	1133	1217	1330	1446	1533	1632	1740	1947	2136
17	Tychy d.	0453	0555	0719	0805	0948	1153	1236	1348	1504	1551	1651	1800	2005	2154
44	Czechowice-Dziedzice d.	0519	0621	0745	0827	1014	1222	1302	1414	1530	1624	1717	1826	2034	2220
55	**Bielsko Biała** Gł. **1060** d.	0537	0639	0813	0839	1034	1239	1326	1433	1546	1641	1742	1843	2051	2246
76	Zywiec a.	0614	0711	0840	0903	1101	1306	1353	1500	1613	1708	1811	1910	2123	2313
113	**Zwardoń** a.	...	0834	0948	1000	1201	1403	1450	1556t	1709f	1804	1913	2006	2220	0011

				⊠	Ⓐ	Ⓒ	Ⓐ	Ⓒ		Ⓐ	Ⓒ	Ⓐ	Ⓒ	⊠	
Zwardoń d.	...	0356	0458	0555	0629	0804	0858	1002	1210	1313	1332	1526	1611	1806	1957
Zywiec d.	0354	0452	0554	0652	0725	0905	0958	1106	1308	1425	1451	1644	1705	1914	2104
Bielsko Biała Gł. **1060** d.	0425	0524	0626	0723	0801	0938	1029	1137	1337	1454	1533	1723	1736	1945	2133
Czechowice-Dziedzice d.	0441	0540	0641	0739	0813	0954	1045	1152	1353	1509	1549	1738	1751	2000	2149
Tychy d.	0507	0605	0707	0809	0833	1020	1111	1219	1425	1535	1615	1804	1821	2027	2215
Katowice **1060** a.	0524	0623	0724	0826	0848	1037	1128	1236	1442	1554	1632	1822	1839	2044	2233

					Ⓒ	Ⓐ	Ⓐ
Katowice ❦ d.	...	...	...	...	...	...	...
Zebrzydowice d.	0707	0910	1332	1552	1739	1744	1940
Cieszyn ★ a.	0730	0932	1355	1615	1802	1807	2003

				Ⓐ	Ⓒ	Ⓐ	Ⓐ
Cieszyn ★ d.	0748	1202	1420	1622	1809	1818	2130
Zebrzydowice d.	0811	1225	1443	1645	1832	1841	2152
Katowice ❦ a.	...	...	...	...	...	...	...

f – Ⓐ.
t – Arrives 1609 on Ⓒ.

⊠ – Timings vary on Ⓒ.
★ – Cieszyn station (Poland) is situated ±1500 metres from Český Těšín station (Czech Republic).
❦ – **Shaded services are suspended until further notice.**

ZWARDÓN - ŽILINA

km					Ⓐ		
0	**Zwardoń** ▦ d.	0352	0652	1540	1647	1952	...
22	Čadca **1160** a.	0425	0726	1626	1726	2026	...
52	**Žilina** **1160** a.	0506	0813	1713	1813	2113	...

	Ⓒ		Ⓐ			
Žilina **1160** d.	0456	1347	1447	1759	2247	...
Čadca ▦ **1160** d.	0544	1437	1537	1839	2328	...
Zwardoń ▦ a.	0623	1510	1610	1910	2359	...

1078 KRAKÓW - NOWY SĄCZ - KRYNICA

km			TLK 30166 2	Ⓐ		□	TLK 30101 2X		TLK 30102 2	□	□	□
0	**Kraków** Gł. **1075** d.	...	0409	0410	0529	0739	0854	...	1332	1540	1645	2008
5	Kraków Płaszów **1075** d.	...	|	0417	|	|	0902	...	|	|	|	|
78	Tarnów **1075** a.	...	0511	0539	0647	0906	1001	...	1440	1650	1756	2131
78	Tarnów d.	0423	0512	0542	0648	0913	1002	1335	1447	1656	1801	2136
136	Stróze d.	0539	0624	0710	0753	1009	1057	1448	1544	1811	1904	2249
167	**Nowy Sącz** d.	0622	0659	0746	0826	1042	1131	1530	1618	1847	1944	2327
217	Muszyna d.	0731	0813	...	0939	1158	1250	1642	1731	...	2055	...
228	**Krynica Zdrój** a.	...	0827	...	0953	1212	1304	1657	1745	...	2109	...

	□	□	□		TLK 33102 2		□	TLK 33100 2X		Ⓐ	TLK 33166 2
Krynica Zdrój d.	...	...	0500	...	1026	1216	1346	1510	1713	...	1913
Muszyna d.	...	...	0532	0925	1055	1237	1408	1539	1735	...	1943
Nowy Sącz d.	0343	0431	0626	1030	1204	1342	1513	1653	1835	1956	2046
Stróze d.	0419	0507	0658	1107	1237	1418	1549	1726	1908	2031	2123
Tarnów a.	0524	0619	0806	1219	1339	1529	1654	1832	2006	2144	2219
Tarnów **1075** d.	0530	0625	0810	...	1341	...	1700	1834	2007	2155	2221
Kraków Płaszów **1075** a.	|	|	0918	...	|	...	|	|	2105	2314	|
Kraków Gł. **1075** a.	0648	0735	0926	...	1446	...	1810	1947	2113	2322	2326

X – ⑥⑦.
□ – Operator: Koleje Małopolskie.

1079 LOCAL SERVICES IN SILESIA

2nd class

KATOWICE - OŚWIĘCIM

Operator: Koleje Śląskie

km		Ⓐ		Ⓐ				Ⓐ		Ⓐ			
0	Katowice d.	0431	0529	0637	0741	0953	1123	1420	1537	1637	1742	1947	2158
33	Oświęcim d.	0526	0626	0730	0839	1041	1221	1524	1639	1732	1840	2051	2301

	Ⓐ							Ⓐ		Ⓐ		
Oświęcim d.	0439	0539	0641	0741	1110	1234	1433	1547	1649	1738	1843	2053
Katowice a.	0528	0635	0730	0840	1204	1341	1549	1646	1738	1858	1943	2207

KATOWICE - RYBNIK - RACIBÓRZ

Operator: Koleje Śląskie

km							Ⓐ			Ⓐ		
0	Katowice d.	0427	0638	0828	0940	1118	...	1335	1536	1641	1929	2144
45	Rybnik d.	0531	0743	0930	1045	1231	1346	1434	1631	1739	2023	2238
81	Racibórz a.	0620	0838	1018	1141	1318	1440	1535	1723	1826	2112	2326

				Ⓐ							
Racibórz d.	0432	0536	0727	0832	0955	1150	1331	1545	1739	2000	2154
Rybnik d.	0526	0640	0820	0923	1043	1240	1422	1635	1834	2053	2245
Katowice a.	0624	0741f	0921	...	1201	1335	1516	1735	1948	...	2347

RACIBÓRZ - BOHUMIN

Operator: Koleje Śląskie

km		Ⓐ	Ⓒ										Ⓑ	
0	Racibórz d.	0533	0625	...	0840	...	1019	...	1514	...	1831	...	1939	...
20	Chałupki d.	0552	0653	0659	0859	0910	1038	1216	1533	1607	1850	1918	1958	2117
25	Bohumín a.	...	...	0705	...	0916	...	1222	...	1613	...	1924	...	2123

								Ⓐ	Ⓒ		Ⓐ		
Bohumín d.	...	...	0848	...	1040	...	1240	...	...	1635	...	2013	2150
Chałupki d.	0504	0703	0851	0930	1046	1051	1246	1417	1445	1641	1711	2019	2156
Racibórz a.	0523	0722	...	0949	...	1110	...	1436	1504	...	1730	...	...

WROCŁAW - OPOLE - KEDZIERZYN-KOŹLE - RACIBÓRZ

Operator: Przewozy Regionalne

km		Ⓐ			Ⓒ	Ⓐ		Ⓐ		Ⓐ			
	Wrocław Gł d.	...	...	...	0757	0900	0954	1114	1152	...	1438	1612	1912
0	Opole Gł. d.	...	...	...	0910	1007	1113	1238	1312	1427	1555	1800	2021
42	Kedzierzyn-Koźle d.	0340	0431	0632	1005	1111	1206	1331	1406	1525	1710	1910	2113
74	Racibórz a.	0441	0528	0737	1059	1207	...	...	1501	1621	1816	2011	2208

	Ⓐ			Ⓐ	Ⓒ		Ⓐ			Ⓒ	Ⓐ	Ⓒ	Ⓐ
Racibórz d.	0453	0600	...	1041	1115	1311	...	1526	1849	2021	*2022*	2215	2215
Kedzierzyn-Koźle d.	0553	0650	0818	1140	1219	1411	1458	1621	2003	2123	2123	2305	2306
Opole Gł. d.	0647	0750	0915	1240	1312	1506	1618	1721	2057	2238	2238	...	2355
Wrocław Gł a.	0753	0855	1020	1354	1424	1612	1722	1824	2200	2353	2353	...	...

f – Ⓐ.

POZNAŃ - OSTRÓW - KATOWICE - KRAKÓW 1080

For other trains Poznań - Katowice - Kraków (via Wrocław) see Table **1075**

km			*IC*			*IC*		*IC*			*TLK*	*TLK*	
		⊗	**73102**	⊗	⊗	**83102**	⊗	**83106-**	⊗	⊗	**73100**	**74100**	⊗
			73103			**83103**		**83107**			2	2	
		🚌		🚌	🚌	**S**	🚌	**K**	🚌	🚌			🚌
0	**Poznań** Gł. d.	...	0546	...	...	0832	...	1239	...	...	1545	1746	...
67	Jarocin d.	...	0633	...	...	0921	...	1324	...	...	1633	1833	...
114	Ostrów Wlkp. d.	...	0703	...	...	0956	...	1355	...	...	1705	1904	...
160	Kępno d.	...	0735	...	...	1030	...	1429	...	...	1738	1936	...
201	Kluczbork d.	...	0806	...	...	1101	...	1459	...	...	|	2006	...
252	Lubliniec d.	0645	0842	0904	1107	1139	1531	1537	1731	1928	|	2042	2118
	Gliwice d.	|	|	|	|	1223	|	|	|	|	|	2127	|
302	Bytom d.	|	|	|	|	|	|	|	|	|	|	|	|
	Częstochowa ✣ d.	|	0914	|	|	|	|	1602	|	|	1920	|	|
*320**	**Katowice** a.	0817	|	1032	1235	1248	1710	|	1900	2056	|	2152	2242
398	**Kraków** Gł. a.	...	1058	...	...	1351	...	1744	...	...	2049	...	...

		TLK	*TLK*			*IC*		*IC*		*IC*		
	⊗	**47101**	**37101**	⊗	⊗	**38107**	⊗	**38103**	⊗	**37103**	⊗	⊗
		2	2			**38106**		**38102**		**37102**		
	🚌			🚌	🚌	**K**	🚌	**S**	🚌		🚌	🚌
Kraków Gł. d.	...	...	0647	...	...	1037	...	1417	...	1702	...	...
Katowice d.	0505	0614	|	0658	1102	|	1347	1526	1536	|	1917	2137
Częstochowa ✣ d.	|	|	0838	|	|	1224	|	|	|	1845	|	|
Bytom d.	|	|	|	|	|	|	|	|	|	|	|	|
Gliwice d.	|	0640	|	|	|	|	|	1551	|	|	|	|
Lubliniec d.	0629	0722	|	0829	1229	1251	1514	1630	1715	1914	2051	2300
Kluczbork d.	...	0758	|	...	...	1327	...	1708	...	1950	...	...
Kępno d.	...	0828	1026	...	...	1358	...	1744	...	2019	...	...
Ostrów Wlkp. d.	...	0858	1102	...	...	1433	...	1818	...	2051	...	...
Jarocin d.	...	0931	1132	...	...	1504	...	1849	...	2122	...	...
Poznań Gł. a.	...	1015	1216	...	...	1553	...	1933	...	2205	...	...

2nd class — LOCAL TRAINS POZNAŃ / WROCŁAW - OSTRÓW WLKP - ŁÓDŹ

		♣	♣		⑤⑦	Ⓐ			♣	A	
Poznań Gł. d.	...	0633	0800	...	1210	...	...	1910	2033	...	2150
Jarocin d.	...	0738	0855	...	1254	...	...	2003	2120	...	2247
Wrocław Gł. **1061** d.	...	|	|	0815	|	1150	1613	|	|	2026	|
Ostrów Wlkp. **1061** d.	0530	0814	0932	1018	1337	1411	1817	2039	|	2221	2325
Kalisz **1061** d.	0552	...	...	...	1401	...	...	...	2207	...	...
Łódź Kaliska **1061** a.	0726	...	...	...	1540f	...	...	...	2355f	...	...

			A	Ⓐ	♣			♣		⑤⑦	
Łódź Kaliska **1061** d.	...	...	0358f	...	...	...	...	...	...	1729f	...
Kalisz **1061** d.	...	...	0707	...	...	...	...	...	...	1912	...
Ostrów Wlkp. **1061** d.	0529	0526	|	0759	1059	1240	1641	1654	1846	1946	2042
Wrocław Gł. **1061** a.	0732	|	|	0942	|	1440	1848	|	2037	|	|
Jarocin d.	...	0604	0751	...	1139	...	...	1731	...	2015	2120
Poznań Gł. a.	...	0700	0841	...	1235	...	...	1829	...	2102	2218

A – *IC* **18108/81108** [12] ✕ Szczecin - Łódz and v.v.
K – To / from Kołobrzeg (Table **1015**).
S – To / from Szczecin / Świnoujście (Table **1010**).
f – Łódź **Fabryczna**.
t – Ⓐ.
✣ – Częstochowa **Stradom**.
* – *331 km* via Gliwice.
⊗ – Operator: Koleje Śląskie.
♣ – Operator: Koleje Wielkopolskie.

JELENIA GÓRA - TRUTNOV 1082

km		S		S		P		S		T		S
0	**Jelenia Góra** d.	...	...	...	...	...	...	...	...	...	...	...
27	Sędzisław d.	0700	...	1201	...	1504	...	1712	...	1915	...	2000
43	Lubawka 🏛 d.	0727	...	1227	...	1530	...	1739	...	1941	...	2027
48	Královec 🏛 d.	0734	...	1234	...	1537	...	1746	...	1948	...	2034
65	**Trutnov** hlavní a.	...	...	...	...	...	...	...	...	...	...	...

	S		S		P	P		P		T	S
Trutnov hlavní d.	...	...	...	...	...	...	...	...	...	...	...
Královec 🏛 d.	0614	...	0920	...	1120	1354	...	1620	...	1810	1920
Lubawka 🏛 d.	0621	...	0927	...	1127	1401	...	1627	...	1817	1927
Sędzisław d.	0645	...	0951	...	1153	1428	...	1654	...	1843	1953
Jelenia Góra a.	...	...	...	...	...	...	...	...	...	...	...

P – Mar. 14 - June 12. S – Apr. 24 - June 12. T – Mar. 14 - Apr. 23.
☛ Operated by Koleje Dolnośląskie (in Czech Republic by GW Train Regio).

SZKLARSKA POREBA - JELENIA GÓRA - WAŁBRZYCH - WROCŁAW 1084

km			*EIP*	*IC*			*IC*		*IC*			
		⊖	**6100**	**66100**	⊖	⊖	**6124**	⊖	**61150**	⊖	⊖	
			①-⑥				**6125**					
			B	2			A		Ⓒ			
0	**Jelenia Góra** d.	0351	0443	0718	0928	1131	1230	1521	1549	1750	1930	...
27	Sedzisław d.	0417	|	0746	0957	1200	1307	1549	1615	1818	2001	...
47	Wałbrzych Gł. d.	0439	0543r	0804	1019	1223	1327	1610	1644r	1839	2023	...
78	Jaworzyna Śląska d.	0516	|	0838	1056	1258	1411	1646	1707	1914	2057	...
127	**Wrocław** Gł. a.	0600	0634	0910	1138	1340	1445	1729	1740	1957	2140	...
	Warszawa C. △ a.	...	1025	...	...	...	1931	...	2223	...	...	...

				IC	*IC*				*IC*	*EIP*	
	⊖	⊖		**16151**	**1625**	⊖	⊖	⊖	**60101**	**1601**	⊖
			2		**1624**					Ⓑ	
			P	Ⓒ	A				2	C	
Warszawa C. △ d.	...	...	...	0640	0801	...	...	...	...	1640	...
Wrocław Gł. d.	0501	0712	0928	1107	1234	1312	1510	1742	1933	2028	2115
Jaworzyna Śląska d.	0542	0753	1007	1138	1305	1353	1557	1817	2008	|	2158
Wałbrzych Gł. d.	0625	0832	1044	1200r	1341	1429	1635	1839r	2047	2120r	2237
Sedzisław d.	0650	0853	1103	1230	1359	1458	1658	1912	2105	|	2259
Jelenia Góra a.	0721	0924	1131	1258	1429	1528	1732	1936	2132	2219	2326

km		⊖	⊖	⊖	P	‡Ⓒ	⊖	⊖	⊖	
0	Jelenia Góra d.	0533	0730	0927	1132	1302	1531	1733	1937	...
32	Szklarska Poreba Górna a.	0626	0823	1020	1224	1347	1623	1826	2026	...

	⊖	⊖	⊖	‡Ⓒ	⊖	⊖	⊖		
Szklarska Poreba Górna d.	0833	1031	1428	1456	1653	1836	2036	...	...
Jelenia Góra a.	0925	1130	1520	1546	1749	1929	2129	...	...

A – [12] Białystok - Warszawa - Jelenia Góra and v.v. (Tables **1040/1061**).
B – ①-⑥ Apr. 29 - June 12 (not May 3, June 4).
C – Ⓑ Apr. 29 - June 11 (not May 2, June 3).
P – From Poznań (Table **1070**).
r – Wałbrzych **Miasto**.
‡ – *IC* service.
⊖ – Operator: Koleje Dolnośląskie.
△ – **1060** via Katowice; **1070** via Poznań; **1061/1090** via Łódź.

GÖRLITZ - WROCŁAW 1085

km		*IC*	⊖	⊖	⊖	⊖	⊖	⊖	⊖	⊖	*IC*
		6130									**61171**
		P									**61170**
	Dresden Hbf **855** d.	...	0631	...	1231	...	1431	...	1831	...	...
0	**Görlitz** 🏛 **855** d.	...	0750	...	1350	...	1554	...	1950	...	...
1	Zgorzelec 🏛 **1005** d.	0508	0753	0807	1353	1404	1557	1616	1954	2007	...
3	Zgorzelec Miasto d.	0519	...	0810	...	1407	...	1620	...	2010	...
28	Węgliniec **1005** d.	0540	...	0828	...	1428	...	1640	...	2028	2159
	Zary a.	|	...	|	...	|	...	|	...	|	|
53	Bolesławiec d.	0555	...	0843	...	1446	...	1658	...	2043	2215
99	Legnica **1086** d.	0623	...	0907	...	1520	...	1732	...	2107	2243
164	**Wrocław** Gł. **1086** a.	0705	...	0944	...	1614	...	1825	...	2146	2330

	IC	⊖	⊖	⊖	⊖	⊖	⊖	⊖	⊖	*IC*
	16170									**1631**
	16171									**Q**
Wrocław Gł. **1086** d.	0501	0613	...	0950	...	1244	...	1818	...	2104
Legnica **1086** d.	0552	0653	...	1044	...	1345	...	1857	...	2151
Bolesławiec d.	0621	0722	...	1116	...	1416	...	1920	...	2218
Zary d.	|	|	...	|	...	|	...	|	...	|
Węgliniec **1005** d.	0637	0737	...	1134	...	1435	...	1937	...	2234
Zgorzelec Miasto d.	...	0753	...	1151	...	1452	...	1952	...	2251
Zgorzelec 🏛 **1005** d.	...	0755	0800	1155	1200	1455	1500	1955	2000	2255
Görlitz 🏛 **855** a.	...	...	0804	...	1204	...	1504	...	2004	...
Dresden Hbf **855** a.	...	...	0924	...	1327	...	1648	...	2125	...

P – ①-⑥. To / from Białystok (Tables **1040**, **1061**).
Q – Ⓑ. From Białystok (Tables **1040**, **1061**).
⊖ – Operator: Koleje Dolnośląskie.

COTTBUS - FORST - WROCŁAW 1086

km		⊖	⊖		⊖	*IC*	*IRE*	⊖	*IRE*	⊖	⊖		⊖
						76113	**5837**		**5839**				
			Ⓐ	Ⓐ	Ⓒ		⑥		⑤		Ⓐ	Ⓐ	Ⓒ
						Z	K		K				
	Berlin L ❦ d.	...	...	...	...	...	0826	...	1346	...	...	...	...
	Berlin O ✣ d.	...	...	...	...	...	0832	...	1352	...	...	...	...
0	**Cottbus** **854** d.	...	...	*0607*	*0707*	...	0952	...	1526	...	...	*1707*	*1807*
22	Forst 🏛 **854** a.	...	...	*0625*	*0725*	...	|	...	|	...	...	*1725*	*1825*
22	Forst d.	...	...	0658	0815	...	1020	...	1556	...	...	1738	1835
36	Tuplice d.	0514	...	0714	0831	...	|	...	|	1636	...	1754	1850
57	Záry **1005** d.	0538	0743	0758	0853	1013	1052s	1118	1627s	1703	1821	1836	1913
70	Zagań **1005** d.	0552	0755	0810	0905	1032	1104s	1131	1639s	1715	1834	1848	1925
144	Legnica **1085** d.	0705	0901	...	1015	1147	1206s	1237	1754s	1825	1939	...	2030
210	**Wrocław** Gł. **1085** a.	0751	...	...	1101	1240	1253s	...	1849s	1918c	...	...	2119

		⊖	⊖	⊖	⊖		⊖	⊖	*IC*	*IRE*	⊖	*IRE*
									67103	**5836**		**5838**
	Ⓐ	Ⓒ	Ⓐ			Ⓐ	Ⓒ	Ⓐ		⑦		⑤
									Z	K		K
Wrocław Gł. **1085** d.	...	0513	...	...	1337	...	1513	...	1537	1730	1930c	2010
Legnica **1085** d.	...	0612	0612	0951	1424	...	1557	1557	1630	1813	2018	2057
Zagań **1005** d.	0603	0723	0723	1102	1528	1641	1705	1705	1740	1912	2124	2156
Záry **1005** d.	0614	0734	0734	1112	1543	1651	1716	1716	1751	1929	2139	2207
Tuplice d.	0636	0754	...	...	1603	1713	1737	...	...	|	2159	|
Forst a.	0651	0809	...	...	...	1728	1754	...	...	2001	...	2240
Forst 🏛 **854** d.	*0733*	*0833*	...	...	...	*1733*	*1833*	...	...	|	...	|
Cottbus **854** a.	*0751*	*0851*	...	...	...	*1751*	*1851*	...	...	2028	...	2305
Berlin O ✣ a.	...	...	...	...	...	...	...	...	...	2203	...	0039
Berlin L ❦ a.	...	...	...	...	...	...	...	...	...	2212	...	0045

K – KULTURZUG / POCIAG DO KULTURY - [2] Berlin - Wrocław and v.v. For International journeys only. Special fares apply.
Z – To / from Zielona Góra (d. 0906), (a. 1854).
c – ⑤⑦.
s – Stops to set down only.
❦ – Full name: Berlin Lichtenberg.
✣ – Full name: Berlin Ostkreuz.
⊖ – Operator: Koleje Dolnośląskie.

1090 WARSZAWA - ŁÓDŹ

km		IC	IR	IC	IC	IR	IR	IC	IC	IR	♣	♣	IR	IC	♣	IR	TLK	IC	TLK	♣	IC	♣	IR	IC	TLK	IC	IR
		1620	**11120**	**1900**	**1622**	**99100**	**11124**	**1902**	**1904**	**11126**	**19100**	**19102**	**11128**	**1906**	**19104**	**11130**	**17106**	**2103**	**19132**	**19106**	**19100**	**19108**	**11134**	**1910**	**81114**	**1632**	**11136**
		1621	**11121**	**1901**	**1623**	**99101**	**11125**	**1903**	**1905**	**11127**	**19101**	**19103**	**11129**	**1907**	**19105**	**11131**	**17107**	**1909**	**19133**	**19107**	**19101**	**19109**	**11135**	**1911**	**81115**	**1633**	**11137**
			Ⓐ			Ⓐ	⑥	Ⓐ		Ⓐ	Ⓒ	Ⓒ	Ⓐ		Ⓒ	Ⓐ			Ⓐ	Ⓒ	Ⓐ	Ⓒ	Ⓐ				Ⓐ
		W			**W**												**W**								**E**	**YW**	
0	**Warszawa** Wsch d.	0504	0519	0559	0634	0709	0724	0754	0854	0939	0959	1124	1134	1224	1304	1334	1359	1409	1519	1519	1619	1659	...	1704	1709	1804	1844
4	**Warszawa** Cent. d.	0515	0530	0615	0648	0725	0747	0805	0910	0950	1010	1138	1144	1235	1315	1346	1420	1445	1528	1533	1628	1720	1709	1723	1747	1819	1856
70	Skierniewice d.	0559	0617	0655	0728	0813	0837	0845	0950	1039	1045	1215	1235	1315	1351	1435	1506	1527	1615	1612	1710	1755	1800	1805	1835	1859	1947
109	Koluszki d.	0619	0643	0715	0748	0839	0903	0905	1010	1105	1105	1236	1301	1335	1411	1501	1529	1547	1639	1633	1731	1815	1834	1825	1859	1919	2014
130	**Łódź** Widzew a.	0630	0657	0726	0759	0853	0917	0916	1021	1119	1116	1247	1315	1346	1421	1515	1542	1558	1653	1643	1743	1825	1848	1836	1911	1930	2028
145	**Łódź** Kaliska a.	...	|	|	...	|	|	|	|	|	|	|	|	|	|	|	...	|	|	|	|	|	|	|	|	...	|
135	**Łódź Fabryczna** a.	...	0705	0735	...	0901	0925	0925	1031	1127	1123	1254	1323	1355	1428	1523	...	1607	1704	1649	1753	1832	1856	1845	1922	...	2036

	♣	IR	♣	IC	IR	♣	♣	IC	IC	
	19110	**11138**	**19112**	**5122**	**11140**	**19114**	**19116**	**1912**	**1100**	
	19111	**11139**	**19113**	**5123**	**11141**	**19115**	**19117**	**1913**	**1101**	
	Ⓒ	Ⓐ	Ⓒ		Ⓐ	Ⓒ	Ⓒ	Ⓑ		
				O					**Y**	
Warszawa Wsch d.	1859	1939	1944	1954	2039	2044	2154	2214	2219	...
Warszawa Cent d.	1910	1952	2005	2014	2051	2108	2205	2225	2235	...
Skierniewice d.	1945	2041	2041	2055	2140	2145	2242	2307	2327	...
Koluszki d.	2004	2107	2101	2114	2206	2205	2302	2327	2346	...
Łódź Widzew a.	2015	2121	2112	2127	2221	2217	2314	2339	0001	...
Łódź Kaliska a.	|	|	|	|	|	|	|	|	|	...
Łódź Fabryczna a.	2022	2128	2121	2134	2228	2224	2321	2349	0009	...

	IR	IC	TLK	IR	IC	IC	IC	IR	IC	♣
	10135	**61191**	**91131**	**10131**	**18153**	**1523**	**9111**	**10151**	**6133**	**91103**
	10134	**61171**	**91133**	**10130**	**18152**	**1522**	**9110**	**10150**	**6132**	**91102**
	Ⓐ			Ⓐ	⑥			Ⓐ	⚒	Ⓒ
		JY				**O**			**WY**	
Łódź Fabryczna d.	0339	0424	0435	0501	0519	0623	0759	0811	...	0914
Łódź Kaliska d.	|	|	|	|	|	|	|	|	...	|
Łódź Widzew d.	0346	0432	0444	0508	0528	0632	0807	0818	0905	0924
Koluszki d.	0401	0444	0500	0523	0541	0644	0820	0834	0918	0936
Skierniewice d.	0427	0503	0524	0550	0603	0704	0840	0900	0937	0958
Warszawa Cent a.	0517	0545	0613	0642	0646	0745	0920	0948	1015	1032
Warszawa Wsch a.	0526	0556	0626	0651	0701	0756	0936	1001	1031	1051

km		TLK	IC	IC	IR	♣	IC	IR	♣	IC	IR	♣	♣	IC	IR	IR	♣	IC	♣	IC	♣	IC	IR	IC			
		18115	**9109**	**6161**	**10139**	**91105**	**9105**	**10141**	**91107**	**9107**	**10143**	**91109**	**91111**	**6127**	**10145**	**10147**	**91113**	**9103**	**91115**	**9101**	**91117**	**6123**	**10149**	**6121**			
		18114	**9108**	**6131**	**10138**	**91104**	**9104**	**10140**	**91106**	**9106**	**10142**	**91108**	**91110**	**6126**	**10144**	**10146**	**91112**	**9102**	**91114**	**9100**	**91116**	**6122**	**10148**	**6120**			
			Ⓐ		Ⓐ	Ⓒ		Ⓐ	Ⓒ		Ⓐ	Ⓒ	Ⓒ		Ⓐ	Ⓐ	Ⓒ		Ⓒ		Ⓒ		Ⓑ				
		E		**WY**										**WY**								**W**					
0	**Łódź Fabryczna** d.	0917	1019	...	1104	1109	1126	1317	1323	1427	1514	1520	1555	...	1601	1659	1711	1726	1850	1920	2017	...	2102	...	...	...	...
	Łódź Kaliska d.	|	|	...	|	|	|	|	|	|	|	|	|	...	|	|	|	|	|	|	|	...	|	...	...	...	...
5	**Łódź** Widzew d.	0928	1027	1031	1111	1116	1134	1324	1330	1435	1521	1527	1604	1614	1608	1706	1720	1734	1857	1928	2024	2055	2109	2245	...	...	...
26	Koluszki d.	0943	1039	1044	1126	1128	1146	1339	1342	1447	1536	1539	1616	1627	1630	1722	1732	1746	1909	1940	2036	2108	2124	2300	...	...	...
65	Skierniewice d.	1005	1058	1103	1152	1149	1206	1405	1403	1506	1602	1600	1637	1646	1656	1749	1753	1806	1930	1959	2057	2128	2150	2311	...	...	...
131	**Warszawa** Cent. a.	1049	1137	1142	1240	1230	1245	1453	1437	1546	1651	1637	1711	1725	1744	1837	1830	1847	2004	2038	2132	2208	2240	0009	...	...	...
135	**Warszawa** Wsch a.	1101	1151	1156	1251	1241	1256	1506	1446	1556	...	1651	1731	1801	1756	1846	1846	1856	2021	2051	2146	2221	2251	0021	...	...	...

E – To/from Kołobrzeg (Table **1015**).
J – To/from Jelenia Góra/Szklarska Poreba (Tables **1061/84**).
O – To/from Olsztyn (Table **1030**).
W – To/from Wrocław (Table **1061**).
Y – To/from Białystok (Table **1040**).
♣ – Operator: Łódźka Kolej Aglomeracyjna (ŁKA).

1095 WROCŁAW - KŁODZKO

Certain trains continue beyond Kłodzko – see Table **1165**

km		⊖	**1292**	TLK	⊖	⊖	⊖	⊖	**60151**		⊖	⊖	⊖	⊖	⊖	⊖	⊖				⊖		⊖	
		Ⓐ	**A**	**60161**		Ⓒ			Ⓒ				Ⓑ						**P**		Ⓑ			
0	**Wrocław** Gł. d.	0511	0601	0556	0614	0753	0821	1012	1030	...	1311	1401	1520	1552	1651	1743	1854	...	2006	...	2126	...	2255	...
72	Kamieniec Ząbkowicki d.	0630	0702	0702	0718	0901	0931	1117	1146	...	1419	1510	1632	1656	1801	1843	2011	...	2127	...	2238	...	0003	...
94	**Kłodzko** Gł. **1165** a.	0649	0721	0723	0740	0919	0951	1137	1207	...	1439	1532	1653	1713	1822	1902	2031	...	2149	...	2259	...	0024	...

	⊖	⊖		⊖	⊖	⊖		⊖	⊖		⊖		⊖	**66150**	⊖	⊖	⊖		⊖	TLK	⊖	**1293**	
	①–⑥		**P**	Ⓐ		①–⑥								Ⓒ			Ⓒ			**66160**		**A**	
Kłodzko Gł. **1165** d.	0328	0429	0525	0558	0641	0746	...	0934	1018	...	1254	...	1454	1555	1656	1744	1823	...	1919	2051	2139	2113	...
Kamieniec Ząbkowicki d.	0348	0449	0547	0616	0703	0807	...	0953	1045	...	1317	...	1517	1616	1719	1802	1844	...	1939	2112	2156	2134	...
Wrocław Gł. a.	0500	0600	0701	0737	0816	0918	...	1059	1159	...	1424	...	1628	1741	1822	1919	1946	...	2049	2218	2259	2243	...

A – ⑤⑥ from Praha, ⑥⑦ from Wrocław: LEO EXPRESS – 🛏 🍸 Praha - Lichkov - Wrocław and v.v. International journeys only.
P – To/from Poznań (Table **1070**).
⊖ – Operated by Koleje Dolnośląskie.
☛ **Shaded services are suspended until further notice.**

1099 OTHER LOCAL SERVICES

2nd class only

GDYNIA - HEL *77 km, journey 1 hr 50 mins - 2 hrs*

Gdynia Główna depart: 0511, 0710, 0839, 1040, 1238, 1422, 1539, 1650, 1907, 2032, 2155.
Hel depart: 0446, 0549, 0643, 0853, 1112, 1357, 1438, 1614, 1710, 1834, 2039.

KŁODZKO - KUDOWA-ZDRÓJ *44 km, journey 1 hr 10 mins*

Kłodzko Główne depart: 0458Ⓐ, 0732, 0920Ⓒ, 1229Ⓒ, 1415, 1544, 1907.
Kudowa-Zdrój depart: 0617, 0902, 1426Ⓒ, 1610, 1703Ⓒ, 1748, 2028.
Operator: Koleje Dolnośląskie.

KRAKÓW - LOTNISKO (for Kraków John Paul II Airport ✈)

Kraków Główny depart: 0404, 0444, 0514, 0546, 0612, 0646, 0714, 0744, 0814, 0846 and at the same minutes past each hour until 2246, 2314, 2350.
Kraków Lotnisko depart: 0449, 0523, 0547, 0623, 0649 and at the same minutes past each hour until 2223, 2249, 2315, 0005, 0039.
12 km, journey 17 mins. Timings may vary by up to ± 6 minutes.

KRAKÓW - OŚWIĘCIM (for Auschwitz-Birkenau Memorial and Museum)

VIA TRZEBINIA 65 km Journey 1 hr 45 mins - 1 hr 59 mins. Some journeys by 🚌.
Kraków Główny depart: 0623, 0821, 1323, 1424, 1535, 1822, 1923, 2245.
Oświęcim depart: 0346, 0408, 0457, 0559, 1033, 1358, 1510, 1724, 1906.

KRAKÓW - WADOWICE *62 km, journey 1 hr 45 mins*

Kraków Płaszów d.: 0353 🚌, 0602 🚌, 1008 🚌, 1313 🚌, 1507 🚌, 1644 🚌, 1829 🚌.
Wadowice d.: 0436 🚌, 0757 🚌, 1005 🚌, 1259 🚌, 1559 🚌, 1834 🚌, 2023 🚌.
Wadowice is the birthplace of Pope John Paul II.

KRAKÓW - WIELICZKA (for Salt Mine) *14 km, journey 25–30 mins*

Kraków Główny depart: 0510 🚌, 0545, 0610 🚌, 0645, 0710 🚌, 0743, 0810 🚌, 0845, 0910 🚌, 0945Ⓒ, 1045Ⓒ, 1145Ⓒ, 1245Ⓒ, 1345Ⓒ, 1445, 1510 🚌, 1546, 1610 🚌, 1647, 1710 🚌, 1745, 1810 🚌, 1845, 1910 🚌, 1945, 2015 🚌, 2049, 2115 🚌, 2148, 2215 🚌, 2250, 2320 🚌.
Wieliczka Rynek depart: 0440 🚌, 0518, 0540 🚌, 0618, 0640 🚌, 0717, 0740 🚌, 0818, 0840 🚌, 0918Ⓒ, 1018Ⓒ, 1118Ⓒ, 1218Ⓒ, 1318Ⓒ, 1418, 1445 🚌, 1520, 1545 🚌, 1620, 1645 🚌, 1719, 1745 🚌, 1818, 1845 🚌, 1919, 1945 🚌, 2018, 2045 🚌, 2122, 2145 🚌, 2219, 2245 🚌, 2322.

LESZNO - WOLSZTYN - ZBĄSZYNEK

		Ⓐ	Ⓐ	Ⓒ	Ⓐ	Ⓐ				
Leszno d.	0515	0605	0741	0749	1045	1335	1500	1746	1845	...
Wolsztyn d.	0617	0659	0905	0849	1151	1459	1555	1840	1939	...
Zbąszyń d.	0644	...	...	...	1217	...	1622	...	...	...
Zbąszynek a.	0650	...	...	...	1224	...	1628	...	...	...

	Ⓐ		Ⓐ	Ⓐ						
Zbąszynek d.	...	0704	...	1255	...	...	1653	...	...	...
Zbąszyń d.	...	0711	...	1302	...	...	1700	...	...	...
Wolsztyn d.	0534	0738	1141	1333	...	1556	1727	...	2035	...
Leszno a.	0651	0832	1253	1427	...	1650	1828	...	2129	...

Operator: Koleje Wielkopolskie.

POZNAN - WOLSZTYN *80 km, journey 1 hr 25 mins - 2 hrs 39 mins*

Poznan Główny depart: 0558, 0819, 1002Ⓐ, 1029⑥, 1153, 1352, 1503, 1555, 1656⚒, 1828, 1956, 2252.
Wolsztyn depart: 0344, 0441Ⓐ, 0554, 0645⑥, 0648Ⓑ, 1018, 1150⚒, 1343, 1406⑥, 1553, 1723Ⓐ, 1826, 2015.
Operator: Koleje Wielkopolskie.

REJOWIEC - ZAMOŚĆ *63 km, journey 1 hr 20 mins*

Rejowiec depart: 1032, 1429, 1756, 2143Ⓑ. All journeys to/from Lublin (Table **1055**).
Zamość depart: 0507①–⑥, 0834, 1208, 1604.

WAŁBRZYCH - KŁODZKO *51 km, journey 1 hr 25 mins*

Wałbrzych Główny depart: 0625, 0842, 1052, 1314, 1654, 2023.
Kłodzko Główne depart: 0553, 0802, 1015, 1451, 1724, 1910.
Operator: Koleje Dolnośląskie.

WARSZAWA - WARSZAWA MODLIN AIRPORT ✈ *40 km, journey 59 mins*

Warszawa Centralna depart: 0310, 0416, 0510, 0600, 0705, 0805, 0900, 1015, 1100, 1200, 1300, 1400, 1515, 1605, 1700, 1805, 1905, 2000, 2055, 2205, 2305.
Modlin ✈ depart: 0025**g**, 0424, 0508, 0605, 0715, 0759, 0921, 1015, 1121, 1217, 1313, 1424, 1515, 1610, 1706, 1818, 1914, 2016, 2115, 2221, 2315.

g – Warszawa **Gdánska**. Operator: Koleje Mazowieckie.

GłówneA 🚌 connects the rail station with the terminal. Additional slower trains run Modlin ✈ to Warszawa Gdánska, with metro connection to city centre.

NOTES FOR TABLE 1099 (ALL ROUTES): **g** – To Warszawa **Gdanska**.

CZECH REPUBLIC

ervices: Operator: České Dráhy (ČD), www.cd.cz. Railway infrastructure and timetables are the responsibility of Správa Železnic, www.spravazeleznic.cz. All daytime trains convey first and second classes of travel unless otherwise shown by '2' at the top of the column or by a note (which may be in the table heading).

imings: Valid **December 12, 2021 - December 10, 2022** with amendments as received. Certain trains are cancelled during the Christmas / New Year period, particularly the evening of Dec. 24, 31 and the morning of Dec. 25, 26, Jan. 1; passengers travelling during this period are advised to confirm train times before travel.

ckets: It is possible to reserve seats on most Express trains. SuperCity (*SC*) tilting trains have a compulsory reservation fee. *Business* class on Railjet (*RJ*) trains requires a first class ticket and a supplement. Note that ČD tickets, including day passes and Interrail / Eurail passes, are not valid on trains operated by GW Train Regio.

tation names: hlavní nádraží (hl. n.) = main station; západ = west; východ = east; horní = upper; dolní = lower; střed = centre, starý = old; město = town; předměstí = outskirts.

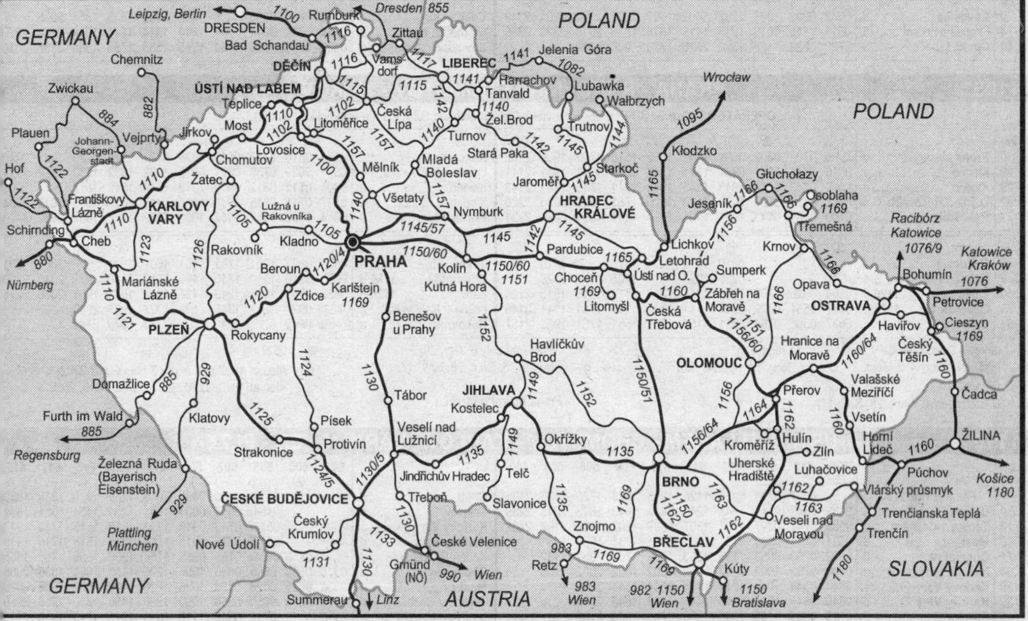

PRAHA - ÚSTÍ NAD LABEM - DĚČÍN - DRESDEN 1100

WARNING! *BERLINER* trains are subject to alteration on ① June 27 - August 29.

km		618	698 Ⓐ	*EC* 178 B	696	616	*EC* 176 B	692	614	*EC* 174 B	690	612	*EC* 378 B	688	610	686 Ⓐ	*EC* 172 B	684	608	682 Ⓐ	*EC* 170 B	680	606	*RJ* 258 Rm	*RJ* 252 Bs
0	**Praha** hlavní nádraží d.	0517	0546	0625	0646	0725	0825	0846	0925	1025	1046	1125	1225	1246	1325	1346	1425	1446	1525	1546	1625	1646	1725	...	1728
3	**Praha** Holešovice d.	0526	0556	0634	0656	0734	0834	0856	0934	1034	1056	1134	1234	1256	1334	1356	1434	1456	1534	1556	1634	1656	1734	1737	1737
27	Kralupy nad Vltavou d.	0548	0618	|	0718	|	|	0918	|	|	1118	|	|	1318	|	1418	|	1518	|	1618	|	1718	|	|	|
66	Roudnice nad Labem d.	0608	0644	|	0744	|	|	0944	|	|	1144	|	|	1344	|	1444	|	1544	|	1644	|	1744	|	|	|
84	Lovosice d.	0620	0659	|	0759	|	|	0959	|	|	1159	|	|	1359	|	1459	|	1559	|	1659	|	1759	|	|	|
106	**Ústí nad Labem** hl. n. a.	0637	0716	0737	0816	0837	0937	1016	1037	1137	1216	1237	1337	1416	1437	1516	1537	1616	1637	1716	1737	1816	1837	1843	1843
106	**Ústí nad Labem** hl. n. ▶ d.	0643	0716	0739	0816	0843	0939	1016	1043	1139	1216	1243	1339	1416	1443	1516	1539	1616	1643	...	1739	1816	1843	1845	1845
	Karlovy Vary **1110** ▷ a.	0844	|	|	|	1044	|	|	1244	|	|	1444	|	|	1644	|	|	|	1844	...	|	|	2044	|	|
129	**Děčín** ▶ a.	...	0734	0754	0834	...	0954	1034	...	1154	1234	...	1354	1434	...	1534	1554	1634	...	...	1754	1834	...	1900	1900
129	**Děčín** 🏛 ⊖ 1116 d.	...	...	0807	...	...	1007	...	...	1207	...	...	1407	...	...	...	1607	...	...	...	1807	...	...	1907	1907
151	Bad Schandau 🏛 ⊖ 1116 a.	...	...	0823	...	...	1023	...	...	1223	...	...	1423	...	...	...	1623	...	...	...	1823	...	...	1923	1923
191	**Dresden** Hbf 1116 a.	...	...	0851	...	...	1051	...	...	1251	...	...	1451	...	...	...	1651	...	...	...	1851	...	...	1952	1952

	678 Ⓐ	*RJ* 256 Rn	*IC* 578	676	604	674 Ⓐ	672	602	600 Ⓑd	670
raha hlavní nádraží d.	1746	...	1825	1846	1925	1946	2046	2135	2235	2326
raha Holešovice d.	1756	1806	1834	1856	1934	1956	2056	2144	2244	2336
ralupy nad Vltavou d.	1818	|	|	1918	|	2018	2118	|	|	2357
oudnice nad Labem d.	1844	|	|	1944	|	2044	2144	2223	2323	0022
ovosice d.	1859	|	|	1959	|	2059	2159	2234	2334	0037
stí nad Labem hl. n. a.	1916	1912	1937	2016	2037	2116	2216	2250	2350	0053
stí nad Labem hl. n. ▶ d.	1916	1914	1939	2016	2043	...	2216	2259	...	0053
Karlovy Vary **1110** ▷ a.	|	|	|	|	c	...	|	c	...	|
ěčín ▶ a.	1934	1929	1954	2034	...	...	2234	...	...	0110
ěčín 🏛 ⊖ 1116 d.	...	1937	...	...	...	...	...	...	...	...
ad Schandau 🏛 ⊖ 1116 a.	...	1953	...	...	...	...	...	...	...	...
resden Hbf 1116 a.	...	2020	...	...	...	...	...	...	...	...

	671 Ⓐ	601	673	603 e	675 Ⓐ	605	677	*IC* 579	*RJ* 257 Rn	679 Ⓐ
Dresden Hbf 1116 d.	...	...	...	...	...	...	...	...	0740	...
Bad Schandau 🏛 ⊖ 1116 d.	...	...	...	...	...	...	...	...	0803	...
Děčín 🏛 ⊖ 1116 a.	...	...	...	...	...	...	...	...	0826	...
Děčín ▶ d.	0421	...	0525	...	0625	...	0725	0802	0831	0825
Karlovy Vary **1110** ▷ d.	|	c	|	c	|	0515a	|	|	|	|
Ústí nad Labem hl. n. ▶ a.	0436	0515	0540	0615	0640	0715	0740	0818	0845	0840
Ústí nad Labem hl. n. d.	0442	0521	0542	0621	0642	0721	0742	0821	0848	0840
Lovosice d.	0459	0537	0559	|	0659	|	0759	|	|	0859
Roudnice nad Labem d.	0514	0547	0614	|	0714	|	0814	|	|	0914
Kralupy nad Vltavou d.	0540	|	0640	|	0740	|	0840	|	|	0940
Praha Holešovice a.	0601	0626	0701	0726	0801	0826	0901	0926	0948	1001
Praha hlavní nádraží a.	0612	0635	0712	0735	0812	0835	0912	0935	...	1012

	RJ 259 Rp	*RJ* 253 Br	607	681	*EC* 171 B	609	683	*EC* 173 B	611	685	*EC* 379 B	687 Ⓐ	613	689	*EC* 175 B	691 Ⓐ	615	693	*EC* 177 B	695 Ⓐ	617	697	*EC* 179 B	619	699
resden Hbf 1116 d.	0810	0810	...	...	0910	...	...	1110	...	...	1310	...	...	...	1510	...	...	...	1710	...	...	...	1910	...	...
ad Schandau 🏛 ⊖ 1116 d.	0837	0837	...	...	0937	...	...	1137	...	...	1337	...	...	...	1537	...	...	...	1737	...	...	...	1937	...	...
ěčín 🏛 ⊖ 1116 a.	0855	0855	...	...	0954	...	...	1154	...	...	1354	...	...	...	1554	...	...	...	1754	...	...	...	1954	...	...
ěčín ▶ d.	0900	0900	...	0925	1002	...	1125	1202	...	1325	1402	...	...	1525	1602	1625	...	1725	1802	...	...	1925	2002	...	2147
Karlovy Vary **1110** ▷ d.	|	|	0715	|	|	0915	|	|	1115	|	|	...	1315	|	|	|	1515	|	|	...	1715	|	|	1915	|
stí nad Labem hl. n. ▶ a.	0914	0914	0915	0940	1018	1115	1140	1218	1315	1340	1418	...	1515	1540	1618	1640	1715	1740	1818	...	1915	1940	2018	2115	2202
stí nad Labem hl. n. d.	0917	0917	0921	0942	1021	1121	1142	1221	1321	1342	1421	1442	1521	1542	1621	1642	1721	1742	1821	1842	1921	1942	2021	2121	2204
ovosice d.	|	|	|	0959	|	|	1159	|	|	1359	|	1459	|	1559	|	1659	|	1759	|	1859	|	1959	|	|	2220
oudnice nad Labem d.	|	|	|	1014	|	|	1214	|	|	1414	|	1514	|	1614	|	1714	|	1814	|	1914	|	2014	|	|	2234
ralupy nad Vltavou d.	|	|	|	1040	|	|	1240	|	|	1440	|	1540	|	1640	|	1740	|	1840	|	1940	|	2040	|	|	2300
raha Holešovice a.	1018	1018	1026	1101	1126	1226	1301	1326	1426	1501	1526	1601	1626	1701	1726	1801	1826	1901	1926	2001	2026	2101	2126	2226	2321
raha hlavní nádraží a.	...	1027	1035	1112	1135	1235	1312	1335	1435	1512	1535	1612	1635	...	1735	1812	1835	1912	1935	2012	2035	2112	2135	2235	2331

– BERLINER – 🚃12 ✕ Praha - Berlin and v.v. (Table **60**). Some extend to / from Hamburg or Kiel.
– VINDOBONA – 🚃12 ✕ Berlin - Praha and v.v. (Table **60**).
– Ⓐ only. From Chomutov on Ⓒ.
– To / from Chomutov or Teplice v Čechách (Table **1110**).
– Ⓑ (not July 5, Oct. 28).
– ①-⑥ (not July 6, Oct. 29).
– From Sept. 1.

n – Until June 25.
p – From Sept. 2.
r – ①⑤⑥⑦ June 26 - Aug. 29.
s – ④⑤⑥⑦ June 26 - Aug. 28.
▷ – Praha - Karlovy Vary trains continue to / from Cheb (Table **1110**).
▶ – Ústí nad Labem - Děčín: see also Table **1115** and foot of Table **1110**.
⊖ – Routeing point for international tickets: Schöna.

1102 MOST - LOVOSICE - LITOMĚŘICE - ČESKÁ LIPA — 2nd class

OPERATORS: AŽD Praha (Most - Litoměřice horní); ČD (Lovosice - Česká Lípa).

km			Ⓐ							
0	**Most** d.	0420	0523	0628	0828	and	1628	1828	2028	2231
44	Lovosice a.	0522	0625	0725	0925	every	1725	1925	2125	2326
44	Lovosice d.	0532	0632	0732	0932	two hours	1732	1932	2132	...
52	**Litoměřice** horní a.	0543	0643	0743	0943	until	1743	1943	2143	...

		Ⓐ							
Litoměřice horní d.	0409	0511	0614	0814	and	1614	1814	2014	2206
Lovosice a.	0420	0522	0625	0825	every	1625	1825	2025	2217
Lovosice d.	0425	0528	0632	0832	two hours	1632	1832	2032	2237
Most a.	0520	0623	0727	0927	until	1727	1927	2127	2332

WARNING ! 🚌 replace trains Lovosice - Blíževedly and v.v. until June 29. 🚌 call at Litoměřice Cihelna, **not** Litoměřice horní.

km											
0	**Lovosice** d.	0602	0802	1002	1202	1402	1602	1802	2002	2204	2349
8	Litoměřice horní d.	0615	0815	1015	1215	1415	1615	1815	2015	2220	2350
50	**Česká Lípa** a.	0720	0920	1120	1320	1520	1720	1920	2120	...	...

	Ⓐ									Ⓐ
Česká Lípa d.	0435	0635	0835	1035	1235	1435	1635	1835	2035	...
Litoměřice horní d.	0544	0744	0944	1144	1344	1544	1744	1944	2144	2259
Lovosice a.	0555	0755	0955	1155	1355	1555	1755	1955	2155	2310

1105 PRAHA - RAKOVNIK - CHOMUTOV - JIRKOV — 2nd class

OPERATORS: Arriva / ČD (Praha - Rakovník); Die Länderbahn CZ (Lužná u Rakovnika - Jirkov).

km				●				Ⓐ			⑦b
0	**Praha** Masarykovo d.	0516z	0702	0802	0902	1302	1502	1618	1702	1902	2102
29	Kladno a.	0616	0741	0841	0941	1341	1541	1708	1741	1941	2141
29	Kladno d.	0618	0743	*0846*	0943	1343	1543	1711	1743	1943	2143
62	Lužná u Rakovnika a.	0658	0820	*0927*	1020	1420	1620	1751	1820	2020	2220
71	**Rakovník** a.	0709	0831	*0943*	1031	1431	1631	1801	1831	2031	2231

	e			⊙						⑦b
Rakovník d.	0518	0618	0723	0810	0923	1323	1523	1723	1923	2210
Lužná u Rakovnika a.	0527	0629	0732	0821	0932	1332	1532	1732	1932	2221
Kladno a.	0604	0711	0812	0903	1012	1412	1612	1812	2012	2303
Kladno d.	0607	0715	0815	*0915*	1015	1415	1615	1815	2015	2304
Praha Masarykovo a.	0644	0752	0852	*0952*	1052	1452	1652	1852	2052	0003y

km		Ⓐ	⑥		Ⓒ						
0	**Rakovník** d.	...	...	...	*0810*	*1010*	...	*1410*	...	*1810*	...
9	Lužná u Rakovnika d.	0420x	...	...	0825	1025	...	1425	...	1825	...
50	Žatec 1126 d.	0504	0526	0705	0916	1116	1316	1516	1716	1916	2124
75	**Chomutov** 1126 a.	0527	0551	0729	0943	1141	1341	1541	1741	1941	2148
81	**Jirkov** a.	0537	0601	0751	0951	1151	1351	1551	1751	1951	2157

	⚒	Ⓒ					A	B		
Jirkov d.	0605	0801	1001	1201	1401	1601	1801	...	2001	2201
Chomutov 1126 d.	0613	0810	1010	1210	1410	1610	1810	...	2010	2210
Žatec 1126 d.	0638	0843	1036	1243	1436	1643	1843	1953	2036	2234
Lužná u Rakovnika a.	0723a	0927	...	1327	...	1727	1927	2037	...	...
Rakovník a.	0742a	*0943*	...	*1343*	...	*1743*	*1940*	*2142*	...	...

A – Jirkov - Žatec runs daily; Žatec - Lužná runs ⑦g.
B – ⑤⑥ (also July 4, 5, Sept. 27, Oct. 27, Nov. 16; not Oct. 28).
a – Ⓐ only.
b – ⑦ (also July 6, Sept. 28, Nov. 17).
e – ①-⑥ (not July 6, Oct. 29).
g – Also July 6, Sept. 28, Nov. 17.
x – ①
y – Praha **hlavní nádraží**.
z – 0527 on Ⓒ.
● – Also at 1002 and every 2 hours until 2202.
⊙ – Also at 1010, 1210, 1410, 1610, 1810, 2033.

1110 ÚSTI NAD LABEM - CHOMUTOV - KARLOVY VARY - CHEB - PLZEŇ

km		620 Ⓐ	618	616	614	612	610	608	606	604	602
	Praha hlavní 1100 d.	...	0517	0725	0925	1125	1325	1525	1725	1925	2135
0	**Ústí nad Labem** hl. n. d.	0439	0643	0843	1043	1243	1443	1643	1843	2043	2259
17	Teplice v Čechách d.	0505	0707	0907	1107	1307	1507	1707	1907	2107	2322
46	**Most** d.	0531	0731	0931	1131	1331	1531	1731	1931	2131	...
71	**Chomutov** d.	0553	0753	0953	1153	1353	1553	1753	1953	2152	...
84	Kadaň-Prunéřov ⊕ d.	0602	0802	1002	1202	1402	1602	1802	2002	*2206*	...
130	**Karlovy Vary** ⊗ a.	0644	0844	1044	1244	1444	1644	1844	2044	*2254*	...
130	**Karlovy Vary** ⊗ d.	0646	0846	1046	1246	1446	1646	1846	2046	...	...
156	Sokolov d.	0705	0905	1105	1305	1505	1705	1905	2105	...	...
184	**Cheb** a.	0729	0929	1129	1329	1529	1729	1929	2129	...	...

	601	603 Ⓐ	605	607	609	611	613	615	617	619
Cheb d.	...	...	0430a	0630	0830	1030	1230	1430	1630	1830
Sokolov d.	...	...	0454a	0654	0854	1054	1254	1454	1654	1854
Karlovy Vary ⊗ a.	...	...	0513a	0713	0913	1113	1313	1513	1713	1913
Karlovy Vary ⊗ d.	...	...	0515a	0715	0915	1115	1315	1515	1715	1915
Kadaň-Prunéřov ⊕ d.	...	0456	0556a	0756	0956	1156	1356	1556	1756	1956
Chomutov d.	*0316*	0506	0606	0806	1006	1206	1406	1606	1806	2006
Most d.	*0336*	0526	0626	0826	1026	1226	1426	1626	1826	2026
Teplice v Čechách d.	0450	0550	0650	0850	1050	1250	1450	1650	1850	2050
Ústí nad Labem hl. n. a.	0515	0615	0715	0915	1115	1315	1515	1715	1915	2115
Praha hlavní 1100 a.	0635	0735	0835	1035	1235	1435	1635	1835	2035	2235

km		e	IC 505 ▲						Ⓒ		Ⓐ
0	**Karlovy Vary** ⊗ d.	0427	0552	0627a	1027	1227	1427	1627	1912	...	*2126*
26	Sokolov d.	0448	0608	0648a	1048	1248	1448	1648	1933	...	*2151*
54	**Cheb** a.	0517	0630	0717a	1117	1317	1517	1717	2002	...	*2224*
54	**Cheb** ◧ d.	0519	0634	0719	1119	1319	1519	1719	2005	2005	2254
84	Mariánské Lázně ◧ d.	0544	0655	0745	1145	1345	1545	1745	2036	2036	2326
96	P u Marián. Lázni ◧ d.	0556	0705	0755	1155	1355	1555	1755	2046	2046	
127	Stříbro ◧ d.	0621	0727	0821	1221	1421	1621	1821	...	...	...
160	**Plzeň** hlavní n. ◧ a.	0649	0752	0849	1249	1449	1649	1849	...	...	...
	Praha hl. n. 1120 a.	...	0921	...	...	...	...	...	...	...	...

	e	Ⓒ		Ⓒ	Ⓐ					IC 504 ▲
Praha hl. n. 1120 d.	...	...	...	...	...	...	...	...	...	1838
Plzeň hlavní n. ◧ d.	...	...	0707	0907	1107	1307	1507	1707	1907d	2005
Stříbro ◧ d.	...	...	0737	0937	1137	1337	1537	1737	1937d	2031
P u Marián. Lázni ◧ d.	0546	0653f	0804	1003	1204	1404	1604	1804	2002d	2054
Mariánské Lázně ◧ d.	0556	0707f	0816	1014	1216	1416	1616	1816	2012	2107
Cheb ◧ a.	0622	0733f	0838	1038	1238	1438	1638	1838	2305	2127
Cheb d.	0635a	0742	0840	1040	1240	1440	1640	1840c	2040	2131
Sokolov d.	0704a	0810	0908	1108	1308	1508	1708	1908c	2108	2154
Karlovy Vary ⊗ a.	0726a	0832	0930	1130	1330	1530	1730	1930c	2130	2209

LOCAL TRAINS **DĚČÍN - ÚSTI NAD LABEM - CHOMUTOV** — 2nd class

Děčín d.	0427a	0530	0630	0730	and	1830	1930	2030	*2147*
Ústí nad Labem hl. n. d.	0458	0558	0658	0758	hourly	1858	1958	2120	2220
Teplice v Čechách d.	0524	0624	0724	0824	until	1924	2024	2146	2246
Most d.	0601	0701	0801	0901	⊖	2001	2101	2220	2320
Chomutov a.	0623	0723	0823	0923		2023	2123	2242	2342

Chomutov d.	0433a	0533	0633c	0733	and	1933	2033	2133	2235
Most d.	0501	0601	0701	0801	hourly	2001	2101	2201	2258
Teplice v Čechách d.	0532	0632	0732	0832	until	2032	2132	2232	*2356*
Ústí nad Labem hl. n. a.	0558	0658	0758	0858	⊖	2058	2157	2257	*0021*
Děčín a.	0624	0724	0824	0924		2124	*2234*	*2335*	

a – Ⓐ only.
c – Ⓒ only.
d – Ⓑ (not July 5, Oct. 28).
e – ①-⑥ (not July 6, Oct. 29).
f – ⑦ (also July 6, Oct. 29).
⊖ – Timings may vary by up to 5 minutes. Certain services continue to / from Kadaň-Prunéřov.
⊕ – Local trains run to Kadaň (5 km).
⊗ – Known locally as Karlovy Vary horní (upper).
▲ – PENDOLINO. To / from Praha and Ostrava (Table **1121**).
◧ – For other trains see Table **1121**.

1115 ÚSTÍ NAD LABEM - DĚČÍN - ČESKÁ LIPA - LIBEREC — 2nd class Arriva

km		1341 e	1343	C◇	1345	1347	1349	1351	1353	1355	1357
0	**Ústí nad Labem** hl. § d.	0527	0727		0927	1127	1327	1527	1727	1927	2123
23	**Děčín** § d.	0545	0745	0845	0945	1145	1345	1545	1745	1945	2141
54	Česká Lipa d.	0622	0822	0934	1022	1222	1422	1622	1822	2022	2222
113	**Liberec** a.	0728	0927	1053	1127	1327	1527	1727	1927	2127	2328

	1340 e	1342	D◇	1344	1346	1348	1350	1352	1354	1356
Liberec d.	0428	0628	0703	0828	1028	1228	1428	1628	1828	2028
Česká Lipa d.	0539	0737	0832	0937	1137	1337	1537	1737	1937	2134
Děčín § d.	0614	0812	0910	1012	1212	1412	1612	1812	2012	2208
Ústí nad Labem hl. § a.	0632	0832	...	1032	1232	1432	1632	1832	2032	2224

C – Also 0643, 1045 and every two hours until 2043 (note ◇ applies to all trains).
D – Also 0500, 0902 and every two hours until 2102 (note ◇ applies to all trains).
e – ①-⑥ (not July 6, Oct. 29).
§ – See also Table 1100 and foot of Table 1110.
◇ – Operated by ČD.

1116 DĚČÍN - RYBNIŠTĚ - RUMBURK / DĚČÍN - SEBNITZ - RUMBURK

km								Ⓐ			
0	**Děčín** d.	0634	0836	1036	1236	1436	1636	1736	1836	2036	2236
25	Česká Kamenice d.	0706	0906	1106	1306	1506	1706	1806	1906	2106	2306
50	Rybniště a.	0734	0934	1134	1334	1534	1734	1837	1934	2134	2333
61	**Rumburk** a.	0748	0948	1148	1348	1548	1748	1851	1948	2148	2350

	Ⓐ									E
Rumburk d.	0517	0607	0807	1006	1207	1406	1609	1805	2006	2107
Rybniště d.	0529	0620	0820	1019	1220	1419	1622	1818	2019	2121
Česká Kamenice d.	0555	0648	0848	1047	1248	1447	1649	1847	2047	2153
Děčín a.	0622	0719	0919	1119	1319	1519	1719	1919	2119	2222

km		w									
0	**Děčín** ◻ ▷ d.	0515	0641	0841	1041	1241	1441	1641	1841	2041	2241
22	Bad Schandau 🏛 ▷ a.	0553	0715	0915	1115	1315	1515	1715	1915	2115	2310
22	Bad Schandau d.	0554	0718	0918	1118	1318	1518	1718	1918	2118	...
37	Sebnitz d.	0627	0742	0942	1142	1342	1542	1742	1942	2142	...
38	Dolní Poustevna 🏛 d.	0631	0746	0946	1146	1346	1546	1746	1946	2146	...
65	**Rumburk** a.	0710	0830	1030	1230	1430	1630	1830	2030	2224	...

Rumburk d.	0533	0730	0930	1130	1330	1530	1730	1930	2039	
Dolní Poustevna 🏛 d.	0612	0812	1012	1212	1412	1612	1812	2012	2117	
Sebnitz d.	0618	0818	1018	1218	1418	1618	1818	2018	2120	
Bad Schandau a.	0639	0839	1039	1239	1439	1639	1839	2039	...	
Bad Schandau 🏛 ▷ d.	0641	0841	1041	1241	1441	1641	1841	2041	...	2350
Děčín ▷ a.	0716	0916	1116	1316	1516	1716	1916	2116	...	0012

E – ⑤⑥ (also July 4, 5, Sept. 27, Oct. 27, Nov. 16).
w – ①-⑤. A change of trains at Bad Schandau may be necessary on certain dates. Runs up to 10 minutes later Sebnitz - Rumburk on certain dates.
◻ – Most trains depart Děčín 5 minutes later and arrive Děčín 5 minutes earlier from June 26.
▷ – See also Table **1100**.

RYBNIŠTĚ - VARNSDORF - ZITTAU - LIBEREC 1117

2nd class

Subject to alteration on and around Czech and German hoilday dates (see page 4). **OPERATORS:** ČD (Rybniště - Varnsdorf), Die Länderbahn *Trilex* (Varnsdorf - LIberec - Dresden).

km																										
		①-⑤	⑥⑦	①-⑤	①-⑤	⑥⑦	①-⑤	①-⑤		①-⑤	⑥⑦	①-⑤	⑥⑦		①-⑤	①-⑤	⑥⑦	①-⑤	①-⑤	⑥⑦	⑥⑦	①-⑤			①-⑤	⑤⑥
																				A						
0	**Rybniště** ◇ d.	*0409*	*0508*	*0536*	*0644*	*0709*	...	0736	*0909*	*1036*	*1109*	*1244*	*1309*	...	*1336*	...	*1509*	*1536*	...	1644	*1709*	*1736*	*1909*	...	2136	...
11	Varnsdorf ▦ a.	*0423*	*0522*	*0550*	*0658*	*0723*	...	0750	*0923*	*1050*	*1123*	*1258*	*1323*	...	*1350*	...	*1523*	*1550*	...	1658	*1723*	*1750*	*1923*	...	2150	...
11	Varnsdorf ▦ d.	0425	0524	0553	0700	0724	0747	...	0924	1100	1124	1300	1328	...	1400	1500	1524	1556	1700	1700	1728	1810	1924	2136	...	2331
29	**Zittau** ▦ d.	0443	0542	0615	0718	0742	0810	...	0952	1118	1142	1318	1352	...	1418	1518	1542	1615	1718	1718	1752	1836	1942	2155	...	2357
56	**Liberec** a.	0518	0624	0650	0755	0819	0849	...	1024	1157	1224	1355	1424	...	1455	1555	1624	1649	1755	1755	1824	1909	2017	2229	...	0030

	①-⑤	⑥⑦	①-⑤	①-⑤	⑥⑦	⑥⑦	⑥⑦	①-⑤	⑥⑦	①-⑤	⑥⑦	①-⑤	①-⑤	⑥⑦	①-⑤	①-⑤	⑥⑦	①-⑤	①-⑤	⑥⑦	①-⑤			①-⑤	
							A																		
Liberec d.	0455	0529	0602	0702	...	0731	0758	0908	0932	1108	1131	1202	1302	1332	1402	1502	1531	1602	1708	1732	1800	1931	2140	...	2238
Zittau ▦ d.	0529	0610	0642	0742	...	0810	0826	0942	1015	1142	1210	1242	1342	1415	1442	1542	1610	1642	1742	1815	1836	2010	2220	...	2312
Varnsdorf ▦ a.	0546	0627	0659	0759	...	0833	0841	0959	1032	1159	1227	1259	1359	1432	1459	1606	1627	1659	1759	1832	1953	2027	2237	...	2329
Varnsdorf ▦ d.	*0604*	*0629*	*0702*	*0802*	0829	...	0842	*1002*	*1034*	*1202*	*1229*	*1302*	*1402*	*1434*	...	*1607*	*1629*	...	*1802*	*1834*	...	*2029*	...	2239	...
Rybniště ◇ a.	*0618*	*0643*	*0716*	*0816*	0843	...	0856	*1016*	*1048*	*1216*	*1243*	*1316*	*1416*	*1448*	...	*1621*	*1643*	...	*1816*	*1848*	...	*2043*	...	2253	...

	⑥⑦			⑥⑦		⑥⑦			⑥⑦	
Dresden **855** d.	0526	0729	0929	1129	...	1329	1529	1729	1929	...
Zittau ▦ d.	0715	0901	1101	1301	...	1501	1701	1901	2101	...
Liberec a.	0754	0929	1129	1329	...	1529	1729	1929	2131	...

				⑥⑦		⑥⑦			B	
Liberec d.	0628	0828	1028	1228	...	1428	1628	1828	2028	...
Zittau ▦ a.	0658	0856	1056	1256	...	1456	1659	1856	2056	...
Dresden Hbf **855** a.	0828	1028	1228	1428	...	1628	1828	2028	*2252*	...

A – ⑥⑦ Apr. 2 - Oct. 30.

B – ⑥⑦. For Dresden change at Bischofswerda (Table **855**).

◇ – For connections Rybniště - Děčín and v.v. see Table **1116**.

PRAHA - BEROUN - PLZEŇ 1120

🍸 on most *EC* and *IC* trains

km			*EC*		*IC*		*EC*		*IC*		*EC*		*IC*•		*EC*		*IC*		*EC*		*IC*		*EC*		*IC*
		778	**362**	**776**	**566**	**774**	**360**	**772**	**564**	**1706**	**358**	**770**	**512**	**1708**	**356**	**768**	**562**	**766**	**354**	**764**	**560**	**762**	**352**	**760**	**558**
		Ⓐ	C	z			C				C		D		C	z			C				C		
	Ostrava hl. n. **1160** d.	...	...	...	...	...	...	...	...	...	...	...	0707	...	...	...	...	...	...	...	...	...	...	...	...
0	**Praha** hlavní n. **1124** d.	0508	0538	0608	0638	0708	0738	0808	0838	...	0938	1008	1038	...	1138	1208	1238	1308	1338	1408	1438	1508	1538	1608	1638
4	**Praha** Smíchov **1124** d.	0515	0545	0615	0645	0715	0745	0815	0845	...	0945	1015	1045	...	1145	1215	1245	1315	1345	1415	1445	1515	1545	1615	1645
43	Beroun **1124** d.	0551	|	0651	|	0751	|	0851	|	...	|	1051	|	...	|	1251	|	1351	|	1451	|	1551	|	1651	|
52	Zdice **1124** d.	0558	|	0658	|	0758	|	0858	|	...	|	1058	|	...	|	1258	|	1358	|	1458	|	1558	|	1658	|
90	Rokycany d.	0627	|	0727	|	0827	|	0927	|	1026	|	1127	|	1226	|	1327	|	1427	|	1527	|	1627	|	1727	|
107	**Plzeň** hlavní n. a.	0637	0658	0737	0758	0837	0858	0937	0958	1038	1058	1137	1158	1238	1258	1337	1358	1437	1458	1537	1558	1637	1658	1737	1758
	Cheb **1121** a.	|	...	|	0926	|	...	|	1126	|	...	|	1326	|	...	|	1526	|	...	|	1726	|	...	|	1926
	Klatovy **929** a.	0729	...	0827	...	0929	...	1027	...	1129	...	1227	...	1329	...	1427	...	1529	...	1627	...	1729	...	1827	...

		EC		*IC*•		*IC*	*IC*		*IC*	
	758	**350**	**756**	**504**	**754**	**556**	**554**	**752**	**550**	**750**
		C		E					Ⓑd	
Ostrava hl. n. **1160** d.	...	...	...	1507	...	...	...	...	...	...
Praha hlavní n. **1124** d.	1708	1738	1808	1838	1908	1938	2038	2108	2240	2343
Praha Smíchov **1124** d.	1715	1745	1815	1845	1915	1945	2045	2115	2247	2350
Beroun **1124** d.	1751	|	1851	|	1951	|	|	2151	|	0026
Zdice **1124** d.	1758	|	1858	|	1958	|	|	2158	|	0033
Rokycany d.	1827	|	1927	|	2027	|	2152	2227	2346	0102
Plzeň hlavní n. a.	1837	1858	1937	1958	2037	2058	2201	2237	2355	0112
Cheb **1121** a.	|	...	|	2127	...	|	2323	|	...	...
Klatovy **929** a.	1929	...	2029	...	...	*2208*	...	2329	...	...

		IC		*IC*		*IC*		*IC*•		*EC*
	751	**551**	**753**	**553**	**755**	**555**	**757**	**505**	**759**	**351**
	Ⓐ	e						E		C‡
Klatovy **929** d.	...	...	0428	...	0528	...	0630	...	0730	...
Cheb **1121** d.	...	...	|	0432e	|	...	|	0634	|	...
Plzeň hlavní n. d.	0422	0457	0522	0600	0622	0700	0722	0800	0822	0900
Rokycany d.	0432	0509	0532	|	0632	|	0732	|	0832	|
Zdice **1124** d.	0458	|	0558	|	0658	|	0758	|	0858	|
Beroun **1124** d.	0506	|	0606	|	0706	|	0806	|	0906	|
Praha Smíchov **1124** a.	0543	0613	0643	0713	0743	0813	0843	0913	0943	1013
Praha hlavní n. **1124** a.	0551	0621	0651	0721	0751	0821	0851	0921	0951	1021
Ostrava hl. n. **1160** a.	...	...	...	...	...	...	...	1249	...	...

		IC		*EC*		*IC*		*EC*		*IC*		*EC*		*IC*•		*EC*		*IC*		*EC*		*IC*		*EC*	*IC*
	1701	**557**	**761**	**353**	**1703**	**559**	**763**	**355**	**765**	**561**	**767**	**357**	**769**	**515**	**771**	**359**	**773**	**563**	**775**	**361**	**777**	**565**	**779**	**363**	**567**
				C			z	C				C		D		C			z	C				C	
Klatovy **929** d.	0828	...	0930	...	1028	...	1130	...	1228	...	1330	...	1428	...	1530	...	1628	...	1730	...	1828	...	1930	...	*2059*y
Cheb **1121** d.	|	0833	|	...	|	1033	|	...	|	1233	|	...	|	1436	|	...	|	1633	|	...	|	1833	|	...	2033
Plzeň hlavní n. d.	0922	1000	1022	1100	1122	1200	1222	1300	1322	1400	1422	1500	1522	1600	1622	1700	1722	1800	1822	1900	1922	2000	2022	2100	2200
Rokycany d.	0935	|	1032	|	1135	|	1232	|	1332	|	1432	|	1532	|	1632	|	1732	|	1832	|	1932	|	2032	|	2212
Zdice **1124** d.	...	|	1058	|	...	|	1258	|	1358	|	1458	|	1558	|	1658	|	1758	|	1858	|	1958	|	2058	|	|
Beroun **1124** d.	...	|	1106	|	...	|	1306	|	1406	|	1506	|	1606	|	1706	|	1806	|	1906	|	2006	|	2106	|	|
Praha Smíchov **1124** a.	...	1113	1143	1213	...	1313	1343	1413	1443	1513	1543	1613	1643	1713	1743	1813	1843	1913	1943	2013	2043	2113	2143	2213	2316
Praha hlavní n. **1124** a.	...	1121	1151	1221	...	1321	1351	1421	1451	1521	1551	1621	1651	1721	1751	1821	1851	1921	1951	2021	2051	2121	2151	2221	2324
Ostrava hl. n. **1160** a.	...	...	...	...	...	...	...	...	...	...	...	...	...	2049	...	...	...	...	...	...	...	...	...	...	...

C – ZÁPADNI EXPRES – [12] 🍸 Praha - Plzeň - München and v.v. (Tables **76**, **885**).

D – [12] Bohumín - Ostrava - Praha - Plzeň - Cheb - Františkovy Lázně and v.v. (Table **1121**).

E – [12] Ostrava - Praha - Plzeň - Cheb - Karlovy Vary and v.v. (Table **1110**).

d – Ⓑ (not July 5, Oct. 28).

e – ①-⑥ (not July 6, Oct. 29).

y – Change at Plzeň. From Železná Ruda (Table **929**).

z – To / from Železná Ruda (Table **929**).

‡ – From Regensburg on ⑦ (Table **885**).

• – PENDOLINO – classified *SC* (with [R]) Bohumín / Ostrava - Praha and v.v.

PLZEŇ - MARIÁNSKÉ LÁZNĚ - CHEB 1121

🍸 on all *Ex* and *IC* trains

For Plzeň - Cheb - Karlovy Vary trains see Table **1110**. Additional local trains are available Mariánské Lázně - Cheb.

km		*IC*	*IC*	*IC*	*IC*•	*IC*	*IC*	*IC*	*IC*•	*IC*
		568	**566**	**564**	**512**	**562**	**560**	**558**	**504**	**554**
		e			D				E	
	Ostrava hl. n. **1160** d.	...	...	...	0707	...	...	...	1507	...
	Praha hl. n. **1120** d.	...	0638	0838	1038	1238	1438	1638	1838	2038
0	**Plzeň** hlavní n. d.	0605	0805	1005	1205	1405	1605	1805	2005	2205
33	Stříbro d.	0631	0831	1031	1231	1431	1631	1831	2031	2231
64	Planá u Marián. Lázni d.	0654	0854	1054	1254	1454	1654	1854	2054	2253
76	Mariánské Lázně d.	0707	0907	1107	1307	1507	1707	1907	2107	2303
106	**Cheb** a.	0728	0926	1126	1326	1526	1726	1926	2127	2323
	Františkovy Lázně a.	...	...	...	1335	...	...	...	...	...

	IC	*IC*•	*IC*	*IC*	*IC*	*IC*•	*IC*	*IC*	*IC*
	553	**505**	**557**	**559**	**561**	**515**	**563**	**565**	**567**
	e	E				D			
Františkovy Lázně d.	...	...	...	...	...	1427	...	...	...
Cheb d.	0432	0634	0833	1033	1233	1436	1633	1833	2033
Mariánské Lázně d.	0455	0655	0854	1054	1254	1455	1654	1854	2054
Planá u Marián. Lázni d.	0505	0705	0905	1105	1305	1505	1705	1905	2105
Stříbro d.	0527	0727	0927	1127	1327	1527	1727	1927	2127
Plzeň hlavní n. a.	0552	0752	0952	1152	1352	1552	1752	1952	2152
Praha hl. n. **1120** a.	0721	0921	1121	1321	1521	1721	1921	2121	2324
Ostrava hl. n. **1160** a.	...	1249	...	...	...	2049	...	...	...

D – [12] Bohumín - Ostrava - Praha - Plzeň - Cheb - Františkovy Lázně and v.v.

E – [12] Ostrava - Praha - Plzeň - Cheb - Karlovy Vary and v.v. (Table **1110**).

e – ①-⑥ (not July 6, Oct. 29).

• – PENDOLINO – classified *SC* (with [R]) Bohumín / Ostrava - Praha and v.v.

MARKTREDWITZ - CHEB - FRANTIŠKOVY LÁZNĚ - HOF / ZWICKAU 1122

2nd class

Subject to alteration on Czech and German public holiday dates (see page **4**). **OPERATORS**: Die Länderbahn *Oberpfalzbahn* and *Vogtlandbahn*.

km		⑥									r
0	**Marktredwitz** **880** d.	...	...	0712	0908	1108	1308	1508	1708	1911	2218
27	Cheb **880** d.	0522	0632	0738	0937	1137	1337	1537	1737	1937	2250
34	Františkovy Lázně d.	0530	0640	0745	0945	1145	1345	1545	1745	1945	2258
55	Aš ▦ d.	0601	0704	0808	1008	1208	1408	1608	1808	2008	2327
89	**Hof** a.	0640	...	0845	1048	1248	1448	1648	1848	2044	0001

	①-⑤	⑥								s
Hof d.	0508	0516	0709	0907	1107	1307	1508	1707	1907	...
Aš d.	0546	0554	0747	0947	1147	1347	1547	1747	1947	2047
Františkovy Lázně d.	0609	0617	0812	1012	1212	1412	1612	1812	2012	2112
Cheb **880** a.	0616	0624	0819	1019	1219	1419	1619	1819	2019	2119
Marktredwitz **880** a.	0654	...	0855	1050	1250	1450	1650	1850	2050	...

km		①-⑤	①-⑤	⑥⑦							
0	**Cheb** d.	0527	0547	0803	1003	1203	1603	1803	...	...	...
7	Františkovy Lázně d.	0534	0554	0812	1012	1212	1612	1812	...	...	...
24	Bad Brambach ▦ a.	...	0621	0835	1035	1235	1635	1835	...	...	...
73	Plauen a.	...	0727	0927	1127	1327	1727	1927	...	...	...
121	**Zwickau** Hbf a.	...	0815	1015	1215	1415	1815	2015	...	...	...
123	**Zwickau** Stadthalle a.	...	0820	1020	1220	1420	1820	2020	...	...	...

	①-⑤	①-⑤								
Zwickau Stadthalle d.	...	0540	0740	0940	1340	1540	1740	...	...	...
Zwickau Hbf d.	...	0544	0744	0944	1344	1544	1744	...	...	...
Plauen d.	...	0633	0833	1033	1433	1633	1833	...	...	...
Bad Brambach ▦ d.	...	0724	0925	1125	1525	1725	1925	...	...	...
Františkovy Lázně d.	0616	...	0947	1147	1547	1747	1947	...	...	...
Cheb a.	0624	...	0955	1155	1555	1755	1955	...	...	...

r – Change at Cheb and Aš on Ⓑ.

s – Also at 2218.

1123 KARLOVY VARY - MARIÁNSKÉ LÁZNĚ

2nd class GW Train Regio

ČD tickets and passes are not valid on GW Train Regio services.

km											
0	**Karlovy Vary** dolní ......d.	...	0620	0857	1056	1257	1457	1656	1928	2128	2234
33	Bečov nad Teplou ....d.	0442	0651	0926	1126	1326	1526	1726	1958	2158	2303
53	**Mariánské Lázně** ....a.	0526	0736	1011	1211	1411	1611	1811	2043	2243	...

Mariánské Lázně ....d.	...	0604	0826	1039	1226	1426	1639	1911	2111	2305
Bečov nad Teplou ....d.	0539	0651	0912	1126	1312	1512	1726	1959	2159	2350
Karlovy Vary dolní .....a.	0608	0720	0943	1155	1343	1543	1755	2028	2228	...

1124 PRAHA - PŘÍBRAM - ČESKÉ BUDĚJOVICE

2nd class Arriva

For direct trains Praha - České Budějovice see Table **1130**. ČD operates additional services Beroun - Březnice, Březnice - Protivín and Pisek - České Budějovice.

km		1162	1164		1166	1166	1168	1170	1172	1174	1174
				Ⓒz		Ⓒ	Ⓐ				⑦f
0	**Praha** hlavní n..... **1120** d.	...	0723	0817	0923	0923	...	1323	1523	1723	1723
4	Praha Smichov ... **1120** d.	...	0730	0830	0930	0930	...	1330	1530	1730	1730
43	Beroun............... **1120** d.	...	0813	0918	1013	1013	...	1413	1613	1813	1813
52	Zdice .... **1120** d.	...	0821	0933	1021	1021	...	1421	1621	1821	1821
82	Přibram........................d.	...	0859	1009	1059	1059	...	1459	1659	1859	1859
100	Březnice ....d.	...	0917	1031	1117	1117	...	1517	1717	1917	1917
142	Pisek ....d.	0759	0959	...	1157	1203	1359	1559	1759	1957	1959
155	Protivín ....d.	0812	1012	...	...	1216	1416	1612	1812	...	2012
192	**České Budějovice** ......a.	0841	1041	...	...	1246	1452	1641	1841	...	2041

	1161	1163	1165	1167	1169	1171		1173	1175	1177
	Ⓐ	Ⓐ	Ⓒ				Ⓒz			⑦f
České Budějovice .....d.	*0507*	0712	...	0912	1312	1512	...	1712	1912	2207
Protivín ....d.	*0542*	0743	0743y	0943	1343	1543	...	1743	1943	2238
Pisek ....d.	0557	0756	0758	0958	1358	1558	...	1758	1956	2251
Březnice.........................d.	0639	...	0839	1039	1439	1639	1723	1839	...	...
Přibram..........................d.	0701	...	0901	1101	1501	1701	1749	1901	...	...
Zdice .... **1120** d.	0733	...	0933	1133	1533	1733	1823	1933	...	...
Beroun.............. **1120** d.	0746	...	0946	1146	1546	1746	1845	1945	...	...
Praha Smichov .. **1120** a.	0825	...	1025	1223	1627	1827	1926	2023	...	...
Praha hlavní n.... **1120** a.	0835	...	1033	1231	1635	1835	1934	2035	...	...

f – ⑦ (also July 6, Oct. 29).
y – ⑥ (also July 5, Sept. 28, Oct. 28, Nov. 17; not Oct. 29).
z – Until Oct. 30. Operated by ČD.

1125 PLZEŇ - ČESKÉ BUDĚJOVICE

🍷 on most numbered trains. Different train numbers are used on Ⓒ.

km				661	663	665	667	669	655	657	659
		2Ⓒ	2Ⓐ								
0	**Plzeň** hlavní n. ....d.	...	...	0603	0803	1003	1203	1403	1603	1803	2003
34	Nepomuk ....d.	...	...	0631	0831	1031	1231	1431	1631	1831	2031
59	Horažďovice předměstí d.	...	...	0651	0851	1051	1251	1451	1651	1851	2051
76	Strakonice.....................d.	0549	0554	0706	0906	1106	1306	1506	1706	1906	2106
99	Protivín .... ⊖ d.	0612	0616	0725	0925	1125	1325	1525	1725	1925	2125
136	**České Budějovice** . ⊖ a.	0648	0652	0754	0954	1154	1354	1554	1754	1954	2154
	Jihlava **1135** ....a.	...	...	1018	1218	1418	1618	1818	2018	...	...
	Brno **1135** ....a.	...	...	1214	1414	1614	1814	2014	2211	...	...

		658	656	654	668	666	664	662	660	
	2Ⓐ									2
Brno **1135** ....d.	...	...	...	0541	0741	0944	1144	1344	1544	...
Jihlava **1135** ....d.	...	...	0540e	0740	0940	1140	1340	1540	1740	...
České Budějovice ⊖ d.	...	0604	0804	1004	1204	1404	1604	1804	2004	2252
Protivín .... ⊖ d.	...	0632	0832	1032	1232	1432	1632	1832	2032	2331
Strakonice......................d.	0547	0653	0853	1053	1253	1453	1653	1853	2053	2352
Horažďovice předměstí d.	0606	0709	0909	1109	1309	1509	1709	1909	2109	...
Nepomuk ....d.	0631	0729	0929	1129	1329	1529	1729	1929	2129	...
Plzeň hlavní n. ....a.	0702	0757	0957	1157	1357	1557	1757	1957	2157	...

e – ①–⑥ (not July 6, Oct. 29).
⊖ – See also Table **1124**.

1126 PLZEŇ - CHOMUTOV - MOST

GW Train Regio

ČD tickets and passes are not valid on GW Train Regio services.

km		1098	1080	1082	1084	1086	1088	1090	1092	1094
		Ⓐ		A						⑦x
0	**Plzeň** hlavní n......................d.	...	0604	0804	1004	1204	1404	1604	1804	2004
59	Blatno u Jesenice.................d.	0505	0707	0907	1107	1307	1507	1707	1907	2107
107	Žatec........................... **1105** d.	0601	0801	1001	1201	1401	1601	1801	2001	2201
130	Chomutov..................... **1110** d.	0629	0823	1023	1223	1423	1623	1823	2023	2223
155	**Most** .... **1110** a.	0656	0848	1048	1248	1448	1648	1848	2048	2248

	1081	1083	1085	1087	1089	1091	1093	1099	1095
	e			A				Ⓐ	⑦x
Most......................... **1110** d.	0505	0705	0905	1105	1305	1505	1705	1905	1905
Chomutov .... **1110** d.	0530	0730	0930	1130	1330	1530	1730	1930	1930
Žatec .... **1105** d.	0553	0753	0953	1153	1353	1553	1753	1953	1953
Blatno u Jesenice ....d.	0645	0845	1045	1245	1445	1645	1845	2046	2045
Plzeň hlavní n....................a.	0752	0952	1152	1352	1552	1752	1952	...	2152

A – Ⓒ (daily May 2 - Sept. 18).
e – ①–⑥ (not July 6, Oct. 29).
x – ⑦ (also July 6; not July 3).

1130 PRAHA - TÁBOR - ČESKÉ VELENICE and ČESKÉ BUDĚJOVICE

🍷 on most *EC* and *IC* trains

WARNING! Subject to alteration Praha - Tábor Apr. 2 - July 1.
Trains are replaced by 🚌 between Olbramovice and Chotoviny or Tabor. Trains will NOT call at Praha Holešovice and will depart Praha hlavní nádrazi up to 15 minutes earlier.

km								*EC*			*IC*			*IC*				*EC*				*IC*			
		2	2	701	2	703	2	331	705	707	531	2	709	533	711	711	2	333	713	715	2	535	2	717	719
				Ⓐ	w	e	v	B					e	C		Ⓐ		B						Ⓐ	
	Praha Holešovice...............d.	...	...	...	...	...	...	...	...	0707e	...	...	0807	0850	0907	0907	...	0950e	1007	1107	...	1150	...	1207	1307
0	**Praha** hlavní nádrazi..........d.	...	...	...	...	...	...	0604	0630	0730	0804	...	0830	0904	0930	0930	...	1004	1030	1130	...	1204	...	1230	1330
49	Benešov u Prahy ....d.	...	...	...	...	...	...	|	0712	0812	|	...	0912	|	1012	1012	...	|	1112	1212	...	|	...	1312	1412
103	**Tábor** ....d.	...	...	0601	...	0701	...	0719	0801	0901	0919	...	1001	1019	1101	1101	...	1119	1201	1301	...	1319	...	1401	1501
130	Veselí nad Lužnicí...............a.	...	...	0623	...	0722	...	|	0822	0922	|	...	1022	|	1122	1122	...	|	1222	1322	...	|	...	1422	1522
130	Veselí nad Lužnicí...... **1135** d.	...	0538	0625	0656	0724	0743	|	0824	0932	|	...	1024	|	...	1124	1143	|	1224	1332	1345	|	...	1424	...
151	Třeboň.............................d.	...	0602	|	0722	|	0809	|	|	0950	|	...	|	|	...	|	1209	|	|	1350	1410	|	...	|	...
185	**České Velenice** 🏛..........a.	...	0639	|	0811	|	0847	|	|	1023	|	...	|	|	...	|	1247	|	|	1423	1449	|	...	|	...
169	**České Budějovice** .... **1135** a.	...	...	0652	...	0751	...	0802	0851	...	1002	...	1051	1102	..	1151	...	1202	1251	...	...	1402	...	1451	...
169	**České Budějovice** ....d.	0600	...	...	...	...	...	0806	...	...	...	1003	...	...	...	...	...	1206	...	...	...	...	1403	...	...
219	Rybnik ....d.	0653	...	...	...	...	...	0853	...	...	...	1053	...	...	...	...	...	1253	...	...	...	...	1453	...	...
233	Summerau 🏛.......................a.	0708	...	...	...	...	...	0906	...	...	...	1107	...	...	...	...	...	1306	...	...	...	...	1507	...	...
242	Freistadt ....a.	0720	...	...	...	...	...	0916	...	...	...	1120	...	...	...	...	...	1316	...	...	...	...	1520	...	...
295	**Linz** Hbf ....a.	0824	...	...	...	...	...	1006	...	...	...	1224	...	...	...	...	...	1406	...	...	...	...	1624	...	...

			EC		*IC*		*IC*				*IC*		*EC*			*IC*			*IC*						
	719	2	335	721	537	723	539	2	725	2	541	727	337	729	2	543	2	731	545	2	733	2	2	735	737
	Ⓑn		B		Ⓐ						Ⓑd		E◧			⑦k		Ⓑd							
Praha Holešovice ....d.	1307	...	1350	1407	1450	1507	1550	...	1607	...	1650	1707	1750a	1807	...	1850	...	1907	1950	...	2007	...	...	...	...
Praha hlavní nádrazi.............d.	1330	...	1404	1430	1504	1530	1604	...	1630	...	1704	1730	1804	1830	...	1904	...	1930	2004	...	2030	...	...	2200	2340
Benešov u Prahy ....d.	1412	...	|	1512	|	1612	|	...	1712	...	|	1812	|	1912	...	|	...	2012	|	...	2112	...	...	2242	0022
Tábor ....d.	1501	...	1519	1601	1619	1701	1719	...	1801	...	1819	1901	1919	2001	...	2019	...	2056	2119	...	2158	...	...	2323	0104
Veselí nad Lužnicí ....a.	1522	...	|	1622	|	1722	|	...	1822	...	|	1922	|	2022	...	|	...	...	2135	...	2219	...	...	2342	...
Veselí nad Lužnicí .... **1135** d.	1524	1540	|	1624	|	1741	|	...	1824	1845	|	1932	|	2024	2039	|	...	...	2136	2142	2220	...	2240	2343	...
Třeboň ....d.	|	1604	|	|	|	1800	|	...	|	1907	|	1950	|	|	2102	|	...	...	|	2204	|	...	2305	|	...
České Velenice 🏛............a.	|	1646	|	|	|	1833	|	...	|	1949	|	2023	|	|	2143	|	...	...	|	2246	|	...	2342	|	...
České Budějovice ...... **1135** a.	1551	...	1602	1651	1702	...	1802	...	1851	...	1902	...	2002	2051	...	2102	...	...	2203	...	2247	...	...	0011	...
České Budějovice ....d.	...	...	1606	...	...	...	...	1803	...	...	...	...	2006	...	...	...	2107	...	...	...	...	2252	...	...	...
Rybnik ....d.	...	...	1653	...	...	...	...	1853	...	...	...	...	2053	...	...	...	2203	...	...	...	...	2343	...	...	...
Summerau 🏛 ....a.	...	...	1707	...	...	...	...	1907	...	...	...	...	2106	...	...	...	...	...	...	...	...	...	...	...	...
Freistadt ....a.	...	...	1716	...	...	...	...	1920	...	...	...	...	2116	...	...	...	...	...	...	...	...	...	...	...	...
Linz Hbf ....a.	...	...	1806	...	...	...	...	2024	...	...	...	...	2206	...	...	...	...	...	...	...	...	...	...	...	...

B – JIŽNÍ EXPRES – 🚃12 🍷 Praha - Linz and v.v.
C – JIŽNÍ EXPRES – 🚃12 🍷 Praha - České Budějovice - Český Krumlov (a. 1151).
D – JIŽNÍ EXPRES – 🚃12 🍷 Český Krumlov (d. 1407) - České Budějovice - Praha.
E – JIŽNÍ EXPRES – 🚃12 Praha - Linz and v.v.; 🛏 1,2 cl. Praha - Linz (**462/463**) - Salzburg (**466/467**) - Innsbruck - Zürich and v.v. (see note **K** and Table **52**).
F – From České Budějovice on Ⓐ, from Tábor on ①–⑥**e**.
G – From České Budějovice on Ⓐ, from Veselí nad Lužnicí on ①–⑥**e**.
H – Ⓒ (daily Apr. 30 - Sept. 28).
J – Ⓐ (daily Apr. 25 - Sept. 30).
K – Suspended Praha - Zürich July 1 - Aug. 21; Zürich - Praha July 2 - Aug. 22.

a – Ⓐ only.
d – Ⓑ (not July 5, Oct. 28).
e – ①–⑥ (not July 6, Oct. 29).
f – ⑦ (also July 6, Oct. 29).
k – ⑦ (also July 6, Sept. 28; not July 3).
n – Ⓑ (also Oct. 29; not July 5, Sept. 28, Oct. 28, Nov. 17).
t – Apr. 30 - Sept. 25.
v – ⑥⑦ (also July 1 - Aug. 30, Oct. 28, Nov. 26 – 28).
w – ①–⑤ (not July 1 - Aug. 30, Oct. 28, Nov. 26 – 28).

FOR RETURN SERVICE SEE NEXT PAGE →

ČESKÉ BUDĚJOVICE and ČESKÉ VELENICE - TABOR - PRAHA 1130

🍷 on most *EC* and *IC* trains

WARNING! Subject to alteration Praha - Tábor Apr. 2 - July 1.
Trains are replaced by 🚌 between Olbramovice and Chotoviny or Tabor. Trains will NOT call at Praha Holešovice and will depart Praha hlavní nádrazi up to 15 minutes earlier.

		IC			*IC*				*IC*				*IC*			*EC*						*IC*			
	734	**544**	**732**	2	**542**	**730**	**730**	2	**540**	2	**728**	2	**538**	2	**726**	**330**	**724**	2	2	**722**	**720**	**536**	**718**	2	**716**
	F	Ⓐ		Ⓐ		**e**			**e**							**E**◧	**e**				Ⓐ				
Linz Hbf d.	...	...	...	...	...	...	...	...	...	...	...	...	...	...	...	0652	...	...	0735	...	...	...	...	0935	...
Freistadt d.	...	...	...	...	...	...	...	...	...	...	...	...	...	...	...	0742	...	...	0839	...	...	...	...	1039	...
Summerau 🏛 d.	...	...	...	...	...	...	...	...	...	...	...	...	...	...	...	0753	...	...	0852	...	...	...	...	1051	...
Rybnik d.	...	...	...	0432	...	...	...	0535	...	...	...	0629	...	...	...	0806	...	...	0907	...	...	...	...	1107	...
České Budějovice a.	...	...	...	0525	...	...	...	0630	...	...	...	0728	...	...	...	0852	...	...	0958	...	...	...	...	1157	...
České Budějovice 1135 d.	0412	0457	0508	...	0557	...	...	...	0657	...	0708	...	0757	...	...	0857	0908	...	...	1008	1108	1157	...	...	1308
České Velenice 🏛 d.	|	|	|	...	|	0530	...	...	|	0548	|	...	|	0642	0736	|	|	0910	...	|	|	|	1136	...	|
Třeboň d.	|	|	|	...	|	0608	...	...	|	0629	|	...	|	0721	0808	|	|	0950	...	|	|	|	1208	...	|
Veselí nad Lužnicí 1135 a.	0438	|	0534	...	|	0625	...	...	|	0651	0734	...	|	0742	0825	|	0934	1012	...	1034	1134	|	1225	...	1334
Veselí nad Lužnicí d.	0439	|	0536	...	|	0636	0636	...	|	...	0736	...	|	...	0836	|	0936	...	...	1036	1136	|	1236	...	1336
Tábor d.	0505	0539	0601	...	0639	0701	0701	...	0739	...	0801	...	0839	...	0901	0939	1001	...	...	1101	1201	1239	1301	...	1401
Benešov u Prahy d.	0549	0619	0649	...	|	0749	0749	...	|	...	0849	...	|	...	0949	|	1049	...	...	1149	1249	|	1349	...	1449
Praha hlavní nádrazi a.	0630	0700	0730	...	0757	0830	0830	...	0857	...	0930	...	0957	...	1030	1057	1130	...	...	1230	1330	1357	1430	...	1530
Praha Holešovice a.	0645	...	0745	...	0811	0845	0845	...	0911	...	0945	...	1011	...	1045	1111	1145	...	...	1245	1341	1411	1449	...	1541

	EC					*IC*		*IC*						*IC*		*EC*							*EC*		
	332	2	**714**	**714**	**714**	**534**	**712**	**532**	2	2	**710**	**708**	2	**530**	**706**	**334**	2	**704**	**702**	2	2	**700**	**336**	2	2
	B			Ⓐ		**D**			Ⓒ	Ⓐ	⑦**f**	**G**		⑦**k**		**B**							**B**		Ⓐ
Linz Hbf d.	1154	...	...	...	...	...	...	...	...	...	...	...	1335	...	...	1554	...	...	...	...	1735	...	1854	...	...
Freistadt d.	1242	...	...	...	...	...	...	...	...	...	...	...	1439	...	...	1644	...	...	...	...	1839	...	1944	...	...
Summerau 🏛 d.	1252	...	...	...	...	...	...	...	...	...	...	...	1451	...	...	1653	...	...	...	...	1851	...	1953	...	...
Rybnik d.	1307	...	...	...	...	...	...	...	...	...	...	...	1508	...	...	1707	...	...	...	...	1908	...	2006	...	...
České Budějovice a.	1352	...	...	...	...	...	...	...	...	...	...	...	1558	...	...	1752	...	...	...	...	1957	...	2052	...	...
České Budějovice 1135 d.	1357	...	...	1408	...	1457	1508	1557	...	...	...	1608	...	1657	1708	1757	...	...	1908	...	...	2008	2057	...	...
České Velenice 🏛 d.	|	1310	...	|	...	|	|	|	1506	1524	1536	|	...	|	|	|	1701	1725	|	1910	...	|	|	2104	2206
Třeboň d.	|	1350	...	|	...	|	|	|	1544	1603	1608	|	...	|	|	|	1739	1808	|	1950	...	|	|	2143	2244
Veselí nad Lužnicí 1135 a.	|	1412	...	1434	...	|	1534	|	1609	1625	1625	1634	...	|	1734	|	1804	1825	1934	2013	...	2034	2123	2207	2306
Veselí nad Lužnicí d.	|	...	1436	1436	1436	|	1536	|	...	...	1636	1636	...	|	1736	|	...	1836	1936	...	...	2036	2129	...	...
Tábor d.	1439	...	1501	1501	1501	1539	1601	1639	...	...	1701	1701	...	1739	1801	1839	...	1901	2001	...	...	2101	2147	...	...
Benešov u Prahy d.	|	...	1549	1549	1549	|	1649	|	...	...	1749	1749	...	|	1849	|	...	1949	2049	...	...	2149	2225	...	...
Praha hlavní nádrazi a.	1557	...	1630	1630	1633	1657	1730	1757	...	...	1830	1830	...	1857	1930	1957	...	2030	2130	...	...	2230	2303	...	...
Praha Holešovice a.	1611**d**	...	1649	1649	1646	1723**a**	1749	1811	...	...	...	...	...	1911	1949	...	...	...	...	...	...	...	...	...	...

RYBNIK - LIPNO NAD VLTAVOU

km						**H**						**t**			**J**				**J**					
0	Rybnik d.	0623	0700	...	0904	1007	...	...	1105	1205	...	1305	1407	...	1512	1607	...	...	1705	1805	...	1912	2057	...	...
22	Lipno nad Vltavou a.	0704	0751	...	0945	1050	...	...	1147	1248	...	1348	1448	...	1553	1650	...	...	1746	1849	...	1955	2138	...	...

	Ⓐ							**H**			**J**			**t**				**J**						
Lipno nad Vltavou d.	0540	0714	...	0814	1013	...	...	1110	1211	...	1311	1411	...	1515	1613	...	...	1709	1812	...	1918	2008	...	...
Rybnik a.	0619	0759	...	0854	1055	...	...	1151	1254	...	1352	1455	...	1556	1654	...	...	1750	1854	...	1958	2048	...	...

FOR RETURN PRAHA - ČESKÉ VELENICE / LINZ SERVICE AND FOOTNOTES SEE PREVIOUS PAGE.

ČESKÉ BUDĚJOVICE - NOVÉ ÚDOLÍ 1131

GW Train Regio 2nd class

An express train operates Praha - Český Krumlov and v.v. (see Table **1130**). ČD tickets and passes are not valid on GW Train Regio services.

km			p	q	q	p					
0	**České Budějovice** ⊙ d.	0512	0743	0812	1018	1018	1211	1424	1611	1811	2011
31	Český Krumlov ⊙ d.	0605	0833	0901	1108	1108	1305	1512	1705	1904	2058
68	Horní Planá d.	0659	0836	0957	1203	1214	1400	1606	1803	1959	...
88	Černý Kříž a.	0726	1014	1023	1229	1245	1425	1631	1828	2024	...
96	**Nové Údolí** a.	0739	1043	1039	1243	1259	1439	1644	1841**r**	...	...

		Ⓐ								
Nové Údolí d.	...	...	...	...	0914	1120	1319	1524	1722	1918**r**
Černý Kříž d.	...	...	0443	0650	0927	1135	1332	1538	1736	1932**r**
Horní Planá d.	...	...	0510	0717	0955	1204	1400	1606	1803	1959**r**
Český Krumlov d.	0403	0444	0604	0812	1047	1258	1455	1700	1859	2059
České Budějovice a.	0450	0532	0651	0900	1134	1346	1542	1746	1945	2145

p – May 1 - Sept. 30.
q – Not May 1 - Sept. 30.
r – Ⓒ (daily Apr. 30 - Oct. 2).
⊙ – Also České Budějovice - Český Krumlov at 1522 Ⓐ, 2256.

ČESKÉ BUDĚJOVICE - ČESKÉ VELENICE 1133

For connections České Velenice - Wien see Table **990**.

km		Ⓐ	v	w							
0	České Budějovice ⊕ d.	0509	0610	0625	0810	1010	1210	1410	1610	1810	2010
50	České Velenice 🏛 ⊕ a.	0557	0658	0713	0857	1057	1257	1457	1657	1857	2057

	Ⓐ	v	w							
České Velenice 🏛 ⊗ d.	0502	0618	0704	0719	0903	1103	1303	1503	1703	1903
České Budějovice ⊗ a.	0549	0705	0750	0804	0950	1150	1350	1550	1750	1950

v – ⑥⑦ (also July 1 - Aug. 30, Oct. 28, Nov. 26–28).
w – ①–⑤ (not July 1 - Aug. 30, Oct. 28, Nov. 26–28).
⊕ – Also from Česke Budějovice at 1511 Ⓐ, 1710 Ⓐ, 2252.
⊗ – Also from Česke Velenice at 0405 Ⓐ, 1603 Ⓐ, 2103.

ČESKÉ BUDĚJOVICE - JIHLAVA - BRNO 1135

WARNING! 🚌 replace trains Trebíc - Jihlava until July 7 with extended journey times - please check locally. 🍷 on most numbered trains. Different train numbers are used on Ⓒ.

km			**651**	**653**	**661**	**663**	**665**	**667**	**669**	**655**
		Ⓐ								
	Plzeň **1125** d.	...	...	...	0603	0803	1003	1203	1403	1603
0	**České Budějovice** d.	...	0402**e**	0602	0802	1002	1202	1402	1602	1802
39	Veselí nad Lužnicí ▷ d.	...	0430**e**	0630	0830	1030	1230	1430	1630	1830
65	Jindřichův Hradec ▷ d.	...	0500**e**	0700	0900	1100	1300	1500	1700	1900
117	Kostelec u Jihlavy d.	...	|	|	|	|	|	|	|	|
132	**Jihlava** a.	...	0618**e**	0818	1018	1218	1418	1618	1818	2018
132	**Jihlava** d.	*0440*	0626	0826	1026	1226	1426	1626	1826	2026
161	Okříšky d.	*0515*	0653	0853	1053	1253	1453	1653	1853	2053
173	Trebíč d.	0606	0708	0908	1108	1308	1508	1708	1908	2108
236	**Brno** hlavní n. a.	0711	0809	1014	1214	1414	1614	1814	2014	2211

	656	**654**	**668**	**666**	**664**	**662**	**660**	**652**	**650**
	e								
Brno hlavní n. d.	...	0541	0741	0944	1144	1344	1544	1744	1944
Trebíč d.	...	0650	0850	1050	1250	1450	1650	1850	2050
Okříšky d.	...	0707	0907	1107	1307	1507	1707	1907	2107
Jihlava a.	...	0733	0933	1133	1333	1533	1733	1933	2133
Jihlava d.	0540	0740	0940	1140	1340	1540	1740	1940	...
Kostelec u Jihlavy d.	|	|	|	|	|	|	|	|	...
Jindřichův Hradec ▷ d.	0659	0859	1059	1259	1459	1659	1859	2059	...
Veselí nad Lužnicí ▷ d.	0728	0928	1128	1327	1528	1728	1928	2128	...
České Budějovice a.	0756	0956	1156	1356	1556	1756	1956	2156	...
Plzeň **1125** a.	0957	1157	1357	1557	1757	1957	2157	...	...

km		Ⓐ	**L**	Ⓐ		Ⓒ**t**	Ⓐ**u**				**v**		⑦**w**	**y**	⑦**h**		Ⓐ			Ⓐ	Ⓐ	⑤**b**		
0	Okříšky d.	...	0451	...	...	0702	0702	...	0902	1102	1302	...	1302	1502	1502	...	...	1702	...	1759	1912	...	...	...
32	Moravské Budějovice a.	0435	0539	0647	...	0739	0747	...	0939	1139	1339	...	1352	1539	1552	...	1639	1739	...	1830	1947	1953	...	...
70	Znojmo a.	0519	0622	0730	...	0822	0830	...	1022	1222	1422	...	1439	1622	1639	...	1722	1822	...	1906	...	2036	...	...

	Ⓐ	Ⓐ	Ⓐ		⑥**K**				⑥**s**	Ⓑ**x**		Ⓐ		Ⓐ			Ⓒ		Ⓐ		⑤**b**		
Znojmo d.	0453	0536	0658	...	0738	...	...	0938	1120	1138	1338	1438	1538	1638	...	1738	1738	...	...	1908	2108	...	...
Moravské Budějovice d.	0530	0623	0745	...	0823	0823	...	1023	1207	1223	1423	1522	1623	1722	...	1822	1823	...	1830	2013	2152	...	...
Okříšky a.	0558	0658	...	...	0858	0858	...	1058	1258	1258	1458	...	1658	...	...	...	1858	...	1903	2048	...	...	...

K – ⑥ (not Oct. 29). Also † Apr. 15 - Oct. 2 and ①–⑤ July 1 - Aug. 31.
L – From Okříšky on Ⓐ; from Moravské Budějovice on ①–⑥ (daily Apr. 11 - Oct. 8; not Oct. 29).
b – Also Sept. 27, Oct. 27, Nov. 16; not Oct. 28, Nov. 18.
e – ①–⑥ (not July 6, Oct. 29).
h – ⑦ (also July 6, Sept. 28, Nov. 17).
s – ⑥ (also July 5, Oct. 28; not Oct. 29).
t – Daily July 1 - Aug. 31.
u – Not July 1 - Aug. 31.
v – ①–⑥ (not July 6).
w – ⑦ (also July 6).
x – Ⓑ (also Oct. 29; not July 5, 6, Oct, 28).
y – ①–⑥ (not July 6, Sept. 28, Nov. 17).
▷ – Other trains Veselí nad Lužnicí - Jindřichův Hradec and v.v. Journey 36 mins.:
From Veselí nad Lužnicí at 0654, 0735 Ⓐ, 0745 Ⓒ, 0943, 1143, 1332 Ⓐ, 1343 Ⓒ, 1532 Ⓐ, 1543 Ⓒ, 1732 Ⓐ, 1743 Ⓒ, 2039, 2144 Ⓐ, 2235, 2347.
From Jindřichův Hradec at 0440 Ⓐ, 0500 Ⓒ, 0546 Ⓒ, 0555 Ⓐ, 0748 Ⓒ, 0755 Ⓐ, 0946, 1146, 1346 Ⓒ, 1544 Ⓐ, 1546 Ⓒ, 1744, 1943, 2142 Ⓐ, 2233.

1140 PRAHA - MLADÁ BOLESLAV - TURNOV - TANVALD

2nd class Arriva

km		1140	1275	1144	1148	1150	1152	1154	1156	1158
			G	A	B		C			Ⓑd
0	**Praha** hlavní nádrazi .... d.	0711	0858	0911	1111	1311	1511	1711	1911	2111
34	Neratovice .... d.	0757	0939	0957	1157	1357	1557	1757	1957	2157
40	Všetaty .... d.	0804	0950	1004	1204	1404	1604	1804	2004	2204
72	**Mladá Boleslav** .... a.	0831	1018	1031	1231	1431	1631	1831	2031	2231
72	**Mladá Boleslav** .... d.	0841	...	1041	1241	1441	1641	1841	2041	...
88	Mnichovo Hradiště .... d.	0858	...	1058	1258	1458	1658	1858	2058	...
102	**Turnov** .... a.	0910	...	1110	1310	1510	1710	1910	2110	...
102	**Turnov** .... d.	0917	...	1117	1317	1517	1717	1917	*2124*	...
116	Železný Brod .... a.	0933	...	1132	1332	1532	1732	1932	*2141*	...
116	Železný Brod .... △ d.	0934	...	1133	1333	1533	1733	1933	...	...
133	**Tanvald** .... △ a.	0958	...	1157	1357	1557	1757	1957	...	...

	1139	1141	1143	1145	1147	1159	1149	1151	1274	1155
	e	D			E	Ⓐn	F		G	
Tanvald .... ▽ d.	...	0558	0758	...	1158	1346	1358	1558	...	1758
Železný Brod .... ▽ a.	...	0620	0820	...	1220	1409	1420	1621	...	1821
Železný Brod .... d.	...	0622	0822	...	1222	1412	1422	1622	...	1822
Turnov .... a.	...	0636	0836	...	1236	1427	1436	1636	...	1836
Turnov .... d.	*0441*	0644	0844	1044	1244	...	1444	1644	...	1844
Mnichovo Hradiště .... d.	*0459*	0658	0858	1058	1258	...	1458	1658	...	1858
Mladá Boleslav .... a.	*0519*	0714	0914	1114	1314	...	1514	1714	...	1914
Mladá Boleslav .... d.	0522	0723	0923	1123	1323	...	1523	1723	1813	1923
Všetaty .... d.	0549	0750	0950	1150	1350	...	1550	1750	1842	1950
Neratovice .... d.	0558	0758	0958	1158	1358	...	1558	1758	1849	1958
Praha hlavní nádrazi ..... a.	0635	0835	1035	1235	1435	...	1635	1838	1946	2033

A – From Praha daily; from Turnov on Ⓒ **m**.
B – From Praha daily; from Železný Brod on Ⓒ (daily July 1 - Aug. 30).
C – From Praha daily; from Turnov on Ⓑ **d**.
D – From Tanvald on ①–⑥ **e**; from Turnov daily.
E – From Tanvald on Ⓒ **m**; from Turnov daily.
F – From Tanvald on Ⓒ (daily July 1 - Aug. 30); from Turnov daily.
G – Ⓒ Mar. 26 - Oct. 30. Heritage train operated by KŽC. To / from Mikulášovice.

d – Ⓑ (not July 5, Oct. 28).
e – ①–⑥ (not July 6, Oct. 29).
k – Ⓐ (daily Apr. 19 - Sept. 30).
m – Ⓒ (daily July 1 - Aug. 30. Also Oct. 27).
n – Not July 1 - Aug. 30.
△ – Also at 0700 and every two hours until 2100, 2300 Ⓐ **k**.
▽ – Also at 0627 and every two hours until 2027, 2227 Ⓐ **k**.

1141 LIBEREC - TANVALD - HARRACHOV - SZKLARSKA POREBA

2nd class

WARNING ! 🚌 replace trains Smržovka (not shown) - Tanvald and v.v. until July 3. There are alterations to some timings - please check departure times locally.

km																								
																					⑤r			
0	**Liberec** .... d.	0535	0635	0735	0835	...	0935	1035	1135	1235	...	1335	1435	1535	...	1635	1735	1835	1935	...	...	2035	2135	2235
12	Jablonec nad Nisou .... d.	0556	0656	0756	0856	...	0956	1056	1156	1256	...	1356	1456	1556	...	1656	1756	1856	1956	...	...	2056	2156	2256
27	**Tanvald** .... a.	0625	0725	0825	0925	...	1025	1125	1225	1225	...	1425	1525	1625	...	1725	1825	1925	2025	...	2027	2125	2225	2325
39	Harrachov .... a.	...	0754	0854	0954	...	1052	1154**p**	1252	1354	...	1454	1554	1654	...	1754	1854	1954**p**	...	...	2052	...	...	...
55	**Szklarska Poreba** Górna ‡... a.	...	0821	0921**p**	1021	...	1121**p**	1221**p**	...	1421	...	1521**q**	1621**p**	1721**q**	...	1821	...	2021**p**	...	...	...	...	...	...

						Ⓒ															H	J	
Szklarska Poreba Górna ‡ .... d.	...	...	...	...	...	...	0830	0930**p**	1030	...	1130**p**	1230**p**	...	...	1430	1530**q**	1630**p**	1730**q**	...	1830	...	2030	...
Harrachov .... d.	...	...	...	...	...	0757	0857	0957	1057	...	1157**p**	1257	1357	...	1457	1557	1657	1757	...	1900	1957	2057	...
Tanvald .... d.	0529	0629	0729	0829	...	0829	0929	1029	1129	...	1229	1329	1429	...	1529	1629	1729	1829	...	1929	2029	2129	2229
Jablonec nad Nisou .... d.	0557	0657	0757	0857	...	0857	0957	1057	1157	...	1257	1357	1457	...	1557	1657	1757	1857	...	1957	2057	2157	2257
Liberec .... a.	0618	0718	0817	0917	...	0917	1017	1117	1217	...	1318	1418	1518	...	1618	1718	1818	1917	...	2017	2117	2217	2317

H – From Harrachov on Ⓒ Apr. 23 - Aug. 28 (daily June 20 - Aug. 31); from Tanvald daily.
J – From Szklarska Poreba on dates in note **p**; from Harrachov on dates in note **p** and on ⑤ Mar. 25 - May 3 and Sept. 30 - Dec. 9 (also Oct. 27, Nov. 16; not Oct. 28, Nov. 18); from Tanvald daily.
p – ⑥⑦ until May 29 (also May 2, 3); daily June 4 - Sept. 28; ⑥⑦ Oct. 1 – 23 (also Oct. 28).

q – ⑥⑦ (also May 2, 3, June 16, 17, July 5, 6, Aug. 15, Sept. 28, Oct. 28, Nov. 1, 11, 17).
r – Also Sept. 27, Oct. 27, Nov. 16; not Oct. 28. Nov. 18.
‡ – 🛃 Czech Republic / Poland = Jakuszyce.

1142 LIBEREC - HRADEC KRÁLOVÉ - PARDUBICE

2nd class Arriva

WARNING ! 🚌 replace trains Hradec Králové - Pardubice and v.v. until July 15 with extended journey times - please check departure times locally.

km		1061	1063	1065	1067	1069	1071	1073	1075	1077
0	**Liberec** .... d.	0405	0605	0805	1005	1205	1405	1605	1805	2005
38	Turnov .... a.	0438	0639	0839	1040	1239	1439	1639	1839	2038
38	Turnov .... **1140** d.	0440	0640	0840	1041	1240	1440	1640	1840	2040
52	Železný Brod .... **1140** a.	0456	0656	0856	1056	1256	1456	1656	1856	2056
52	Železný Brod .... d.	0457	0657	0857	1057	1257	1457	1657	1857	2057
76	Stará Paka .... d.	0526	0731	0931	1131	1331	1531	1731	1931	2131
107	Dvůr Králové n. L .... d.	0603	0803	1003	1203	1403	1603	1803	2003	2157
122	Jaroměř .... d.	0619	0819	1019	1219	1419	1619	1819	2019	2209
139	**Hradec Králové** .... a.	0631	0833	1033	1233	1430	1633	1833	2035	2224
139	**Hradec Králové** .... ⊡ d.	0633	0837	1037	1237	1437	1637	1837	2037	2229
161	**Pardubice** .... ⊡ a.	0651	0855	1055	1255	1455	1655	1855	2055	2251

	1060	1062	1064	1066	1068	1070	1072	1074	1076
Pardubice .... ⊡ d.	0503	0703	0903	1103	1303	1503	1703	1903	2103
Hradec Králové .... ⊡ a.	0523	0723	0923	1123	1323	1523	1723	1923	2123
Hradec Králové .... d.	0526	0727	0926	1126	1326	1526	1726	1926	2126
Jaroměř .... d.	0542	0743	0943	1143	1343	1543	1743	1943	2144
Dvůr Králové n. L. .... d.	0558	0758	0958	1158	1358	1558	1758	1958	2158
Stará Paka .... d.	0630	0830	1030	1230	1430	1630	1830	2030	2230
Železný Brod .... a.	0656	0856	1056	1256	1456	1656	1856	2056	2256
Železný Brod .... **1140** d.	0657	0857	1057	1257	1457	1657	1857	2057	2257
Turnov .... **1140** a.	0716	0916	1116	1316	1516	1716	1916	2116	2316
Turnov .... d.	0721	0920	1120	1320	1520	1720	1920	2119	2323
Liberec .... a.	0754	0955	1153	1356	1553	1754	1953	2151	2357

e – ①–⑥ (not July 6, Oct. 29).
* – To / from Jaroměř.

⊡ – Additional trains Hradec Kralové - Pardubice and v.v. Operator: ČD. Journey 20 - 30 minutes:
From Hradec Kralove at 0532 **e** *, 0604, 0648 Ⓐ *, 0704, 0728 *, 0742 Ⓐ *, 0804, 0904, 0937 *, 1004, 1104, 1137 *, 1204, 1304, 1337 *, 1404, 1504, 1537 *, 1604, 1704, 1737 *, 1804, 1904, 1937 *, 2004, 2104, 2204.
From Pardubice at 0531, 0606 **e** *, 0630, 0644 Ⓐ, 0719 Ⓐ, 0740, 0806 *, 0835, 0933, 1006 *, 1033, 1133, 1206 *, 1233, 1333, 1406 *, 1434, 1534, 1607 *, 1633, 1733, 1806 *, 1833, 1933, 2006, 2033, 2135, 2259.

1144 STARKOČ - WAŁBRZYCH

2nd class

km										
		◧	S		◧	S				
0	**Starkoč** .... d.	0942	...	...	1742	...	...	...	...	...
9	Náchod .... d.	1000	...	...	1800	...	...	...	...	...
40	Meziměsti 🛃 .... d.	1038	1112	...	1838	1912	...	...	...	...
62	**Walbrzych** Gl. .... a.	...	1154	...	...	1954	...	...	...	...
	Wroclaw Gl. **1084** .... a.	...	1303	...	...	2103	...	...	...	...

	S	◧		S	◧				
Wroclaw Gl. **1084** .... d.	0750	...	...	1550	...	...	...	...	...
Walbrzych Gl. .... d.	0904	...	...	1701	...	...	...	...	...
Meziměsti 🛃 .... d.	0946	1019	...	1746	1819	...	...	...	...
Náchod .... a.	...	1103	...	...	1903	...	...	...	...
Starkoč .... a.	...	1117	...	...	1917	...	...	...	...

S – ⑥⑦ Apr. 16 - Sept. 25 (also May 3, June 16, July 5, 6, Aug. 15, Sept. 28). Operated by GW Train Regio (ČD tickets and passes not valid).

◧ – Starkoč - Meziměsti hourly 0642 - 2042; Meziměsti - Starkoč hourly 0619 - 1819, 2019.

1145 PRAHA - HRADEC KRÁLOVÉ - TRUTNOV

🍷 on most **9xx** trains

km		939	941		921	943		923	945		925		927	947		929	949		931	951		933	953		955		957
			Ⓐ	2Ⓒ			2			2		2			2			2			2			2		2	
0	**Praha** hlavní n. .... d.	...	0508	...	0608	0708	...	0808	0908	...	1008	...	1208	1308	...	1408	1508	...	1608	1708	...	1808	1908	...	2008	...	2208
55	Nymburk .... **1157** d.	...	0555	...	0655	0755	...	0855	0955	...	1055	...	1255	1355	...	1455	1555	...	1655	1755	...	1855	1955	...	2055	...	2255
66	Poděbrady .... **1157** d.	...	0602	...	0702	0802	...	0902	1002	...	1102	...	1302	1402	...	1502	1602	...	1702	1802	...	1902	2002	...	2102	...	2302
125	**Hradec Králové** .... a.	...	0650	...	0750	0850	...	0950	1050	...	1150	...	1350	1450	...	1550	1650	...	1750	1850	...	1950	2050	...	2150	...	2350
125	**Hradec Králové** .... d.	0604	...	0702	0804	...	0904	1004	...	1104	1204	1304	1404	...	1504	1604	...	1704	1804	...	1904	2004	...	2102	...	2204	...
142	Jaroměř .... d.	0619	...	0718	0819	...	0918	1019	...	1118	1219	1318	1419	...	1518	1619	...	1718	1819	...	1918	2019	...	2119	...	2224	...
160	Starkoč .... d.	0639	...	0739	0841	...	0939	1041	...	1139	1241	1339	1441	...	1539	1641	...	1739	1841	...	1939	2041	...	2138	...	2245	...
194	**Trutnov** hlavní n. ...... a.	0720	...	0819	0920	...	1018	1120	...	1218	1320	1418	1520	...	1618	1720	...	1818	1920	...	2018	2120	...	2217	...	2322	...

	954	952	934		950	932		948	930		928		946		926		944	924		942	922		940	920		
	Ⓐ			2			2			2		2				2			2			2				2
Trutnov hlavní n. .... d.	...	...	0440	0542	...	0642	0743	...	0842	0942	1042	1142	...	...	1242	1342	...	1442	1542	...	1642	1742	...	1842	...	2042
Starkoč .... d.	...	...	0520	0625	...	0722	0825	...	0922	1025	1122	1225	...	...	1322	1425	...	1522	1625	...	1722	1825	...	1922	...	2123
Jaroměř .... d.	...	...	0540	0643	...	0741	0843	...	0941	1043	1141	1243	...	...	1341	1444	...	1541	1643	...	1741	1843	...	1941	...	2142
Hradec Králové .... a.	...	...	0555	0658	...	0755	0857	...	0955	1057	1155	1257	...	...	1355	1457	...	1555	1657	...	1755	1857	...	1955	...	2158
Hradec Králové .... d.	0408	0508	0608	...	0708	0808	...	0908	1008	...	1208	...	1308	...	1408	...	1508	1608	...	1708	1808	...	1908	2008	...	...
Poděbrady .... **1157** a.	0452	0552	0652	...	0752	0852	...	0952	1052	...	1252	...	1352	...	1452	...	1552	1652	...	1752	1852	...	1952	2052	...	...
Nymburk .... **1157** a.	0500	0600	0700	...	0800	0900	...	1000	1100	...	1300	...	1400	...	1500	...	1600	1700	...	1800	1900	...	2000	2100	...	...
Praha hlavní n. .... a.	0549	0649	0749	...	0849	0949	...	1046	1146	...	1346	...	1449	...	1549	...	1649	1749	...	1849	1949	...	2046	2146	...	...

HRADEC KRÁLOVÉ - LETOHRAD Journey 80 – 85 mins
From Hradec Králové at 0505, 0705, 0905, 1105, 1303, 1403 Ⓐ, 1505, 1705, 1905, 2105 Ⓐ.
From Letohrad at 0530, 0633 Ⓐ, 0734, 0933, 1133, 1332, 1533, 1733, 1933.

HAVLÍČKŮV BROD - JIHLAVA - SLAVONICE 1149

2nd class

km																							
			Ⓐ					©	Ⓐ		©	Ⓐ		Ⓐ		Ⓐ					©		
0	**Havlíčkův Brod** △ d.	0602	0703	0803	1003	1203	...	1203	1255	1403	1403	...	...	1503	1603	1703	1803	1905	...	2003	2003	2105	2208
27	Jihlava △ d.	0622	0723	0823	1023	1223	...	1223	1323	1423	1423	...	...	1523	1623	1725	1823	1936	...	2023	2023	2136	2237
42	Kostelec u Jihlavy d.	0647	0747	0847	1047	1247	...	1247	1324	1447	1447	...	...	1547	1647	1749	1847	...	...	2047	2047	...	2300
65	Telč d.	0734	0831	0934	1134	1331	...	1334	1431	1531	1534	1534	...	1631	1734	1831	1934	...	...	2131	2134	...	2337
95	**Slavonice** a.	0826	...	1026	1226	...	...	1426	...	...	1626	1626	...	...	1826	...	2026	...	...	...	2226	...	...
		©	Ⓐ	Ⓐ	©			Ⓐ	©					©		Ⓐ	©	Ⓐ		Ⓐ			
	lavonice d.	...	...	0432	0538	...	...	...	0725	...	0925	1125	...	1325	...	...	1525	*1525*	...	...	1725	1925	...
	elč d.	0428	0434	0534	0636	0636	...	0736	0836	0836	1036	1236	...	1436	1436	1536	1636	1636	...	1736	1836	2036	...
	ostelec u Jihlavy d.	0508	0515	0615	0717	0717	...	0817	0917	0917	1117	1317	...	1517	1517	1617	1717	1717	...	1817	1917	2117	...
	ihlava ▽ d.	0527	0535	0637	0737	0737	...	0836	0937	0937	1137	1337	...	1537	1537	1637	1737	1737	...	1836	1937	2137	2237
	avlíčkův Brod ▽ a.	0555	0555	0657	0757	0757	...	...	0957	0957	1157	1357	...	1557	1557	1657	1757	1757	...	...	1957	2203	2308

△ – Also Havlíčkův Brod - Jihlava at 0705 ©, 0905, 1105, 1305 ©, 1505 ©, 1705 ©, 1905.

▽ – Also Jihlava - Havlíčkův Brod at 0822, 1022, 1222, 1422 ©, 1450 Ⓐ, 1822, 2022.

PRAHA - PARDUBICE - BRNO - BŘECLAV - WIEN and BRATISLAVA 1150

APRIL 23 - AUGUST 31. FAST TRAINS. For semi-fast trains Praha - Brno see Table **1151**.
EC trains **100 – 107** are subject to alteration July 3 – 14. Regiojet trains call additionally at Havlíčkův Brod and Žďár nad Sázavou - for timings see Table **1152**.

km																							
		EC	*RJ*	*RJ*	*EC*	*EC*	♥	♥		*RJ*	♥	♥	*EC*	*RJ*	♥		♥	*EC*	*EC*	*RJ*	♥	*EC*	*RJ*
		271	**71**	**71**	**273**	**101**	**1031**	**1031**		**73**	**1041**	**1041**	**275**	**75**	**1033**		**1033**	**277**	**103**	**257**	**1043**	**279**	**79**
		✕	✕	✕	✕	✕	🍷	🍷		✕	🍷	🍷	✕	✕	🍷		🍷	✕	✕	✕	🍷	✕	✕
				e		⊡	**k**	**m**			**k**	**m**			**k**		**m**		⊡	**A**			
0	**Praha** hlavní nádrazi 1160 d.	...	...	0412	0512	...	0520	0538	...	0553	0620	0638	0656	0753	0823	...	0838	0856	...	0957**h**	1038	1056	1156
62	Kolín 1160 d.	...	...	0501	0601	...	0622	0622	...	0644	0722	0722	0744	0844	0922	...	0922	0944	...	|	1122	1144	1244
104	**Pardubice** 1160 d.	...	...	|	|	...	|	|	...	|	|	|	|	|	|	...	|	|	...	|	|	|	|
164	Česká Třebová 1160 d.	...	...	|	|	...	|	|	...	|	|	|	|	|	|	...	|	|	...	|	|	|	|
255	**Brno** hlavní nádrazí d.	0622	0722	0722	0822	...	0848	0848	...	0920	0948	0948	1020	1120	1148	...	1148	1220	...	1320	1348	1420	1520
314	Břeclav a.	0652	0752	0752	0852	...	0918	0918	...	0952	1018	1018	1052	1152	1218	...	1218	1252	...	1352	1418	1452	1552
314	Břeclav 982 d.	0655	0755	0755	0855	0855	0920	0920	...	0955	1020	1020	1055	1155	1220	...	1220	1255	1255	1355	1420	1455	1555
402	**Wien** Hbf 982 a.	|	0849	0849	|	0949	1021	1021	...	1049	|	|	|	1249	1321	...	1321	|	1349	1449	|	|	1649
	Graz **980** a.	|	1133	1133	|	...	|	|	...	1333	|	|	|	1533	...	...	...	|	...	1733	|	|	1933
332	Kúty 🏛 a.	0711	...	...	0911	...	|	|	...	...	|	|	1111	...	...	...	...	1311	...	...	|	1511	...
396	**Bratislava** hl. st. a.	0754	...	...	0954	...	|	|	...	...	1128	1128	1154	...	...	...	...	1354	...	...	1522	1554	...
	Budapest Nyugati **1175** a.	1020	...	...	1220	...	|	|	...	...	...	...	1420	...	...	...	...	1620	...	...	...	1820	...
	Budapest Déli **1250** a.	...	...	...	...	...	1314	1314	...	...	...	...	...	...	...	...	...	...	...	...	...	...	...
		EC	♥	*EC*	*RJ*	♥		*EC*	*EC*	♥	*RJ*	♥		*EC*	*EC*	♥	*RJ*		*EC*	♥	*IC*	**575**	*NJ*
		131	**1035**	**287**	**371**	**1045**		**281**	**105**	**1037**	**373**	**1047**		**283**	**107**	**1049**	**375**		**285**	**1051**	**575**	**477**	**457**
		✕	🍷	🍷	✕	🍷		✕	✕	🍷	✕	🍷		✕	✕	🍷	✕		✕	🍷	✕		
		B				**C**			⊡			**D**		**E**	⊡							**F**	**G**§
	raha hlavní nádrazi 1160 d.	...	1238	1256	1356	1438	...	1456	...	1538	1556	1638	...	1656	...	1738	1756	...	1912	1938	2234	2234	...
	olín 1160 d.	...	1322	1344	1444	1522	...	1544	...	1622	1644	1722	...	1744	...	1822	1844	...	2001	2022	2322	2322	...
	ardubice 1160 d.	...	|	|	|	|	...	|	...	|	|	|	...	|	...	|	|	...	|	|	|	|	...
	eská Třebová 1160 d.	...	|	|	|	|	...	|	...	|	|	|	...	|	...	|	|	...	|	|	|	|	...
	rno hlavní nádrazí d.	...	1548	1620	1720	1748	...	1820	...	1848	1920	1948	...	2020	...	2046	2120	...	2222	2246	0141	0141	...
	řeclav a.	...	1618	1652	1752	1818	...	1852	...	1918	1952	2018	...	2052	...	...	2152	...	2252	...	0211	0211	...
	řeclav 982 d.	1555	1620	1655	1755	1820	...	1855	1855	1920	1955	2020	...	2055	2055	...	2155	...	2255	...	...	0455	0549
	Wien Hbf 982 a.	|	1721	|	1849	|	...	|	1949	2021	2049	|	...	|	2149	...	2249	...	|	...	...	|	0700
	Graz **980** a.	|	|	|	2133	|	...	|	2233	...	2333	|	...	|	...	...	...	...	|	...	...	|	...
	úty 🏛 a.	1611	|	1711	...	|	...	1911	...	...	...	|	...	2111	...	...	...	...	|	...	...	0511	...
	ratislava hl. st. a.	1702	|	1754	...	1928	...	1954	...	...	...	2128	...	2154	...	...	...	...	2354	...	...	0554	...
	Budapest Nyugati **1175** a.	1934	|	2020	...	...	...	2223	...	...	...	...	...	...	...	...	...	...	...	...	...	0820	...
	Budapest Déli **1250** a.	...	2014	...	...	...	...	...	...	...	...	...	...	...	...	...	...	...	...	...	...	...	...

	RJ	*NJ*	♥	*IC*	**476**	♥	*EC*	♥	♥	*EC*	*EC*	♥	♥	*RJ*	*EC*	*EC*	♥	♥	*RJ*	*EC*	♥	♥
	576	**456**	**1040**	**574**	**574**	**1042**	**284**	**1044**	**1044**	**106**	**282**	**1030**	**1030**	**70**	**104**	**280**	**1046**	**1046**	**72**	**286**	**1032**	**1032**
	✕		🍷	✕		🍷	✕	🍷	🍷	✕	✕	🍷	🍷	✕	✕	✕	🍷	🍷	✕	✕	🍷	🍷
	e	**G**§			**F**			**m**	**k**	⊡	**E**	**m**	**k**		⊡		**CDm**	**CDk**			**m**	**k**
Budapest Déli **1250** d.	...	...	...	...	...	...	...	...	...	...	...	...	...	...	...	...	...	...	...	...	0745	0745
Budapest Nyugati **1175** d.	...	...	...	...	1940	...	...	...	...	...	...	...	...	...	...	0540	...	...	...	0740	|	|
ratislava hl. st. d.	...	...	...	...	2206	...	0457	0532	0532	...	0606	...	...	...	...	0806	0832	0832	...	1006	|	|
úty 🏛 d.	...	...	...	...	2249	...	0545	|	|	...	0649	...	...	...	...	0849	|	|	...	1049	|	|
Graz **980** d.	...	...	...	...	|	...	|	|	|	...	|	...	...	...	0526	|	|	|	0626	|	|	|
Wien Hbf 982 d.	...	2210	...	...	|	...	|	|	|	0610	|	0639	0639	0710	0810	|	|	|	0910	|	1039	1039
řeclav 982 a.	...	2307	...	...	2304	...	0600	0636	0636	0704	0704	0736	0736	0804	0904	0904	0936	0936	1004	1104	1136	1136
řeclav d.	...	...	...	0507	0507	...	0607	0638	0638	...	0707	0738	0738	0807	...	0907	0938	0938	1007	1107	1138	1138
rno hlavní nádrazí d.	0410	...	0509	0538	0538	0609	0638	0709	0709	...	0738	0809	0809	0838	...	0938	1009	1009	1038	1138	1209	1209
eská Třebová 1160 d.	|	...	|	|	|	|	|	|	|	...	|	|	|	|	...	|	|	|	|	|	|	|
ardubice 1160 d.	|	...	|	|	|	|	|	|	|	...	|	|	|	|	...	|	|	|	|	|	|	|
olín 1160 d.	0630	...	0731	0757	0757	0831	0857	0931	0931	...	0957	1032	1032	1058	...	1157	1231	1231	1257	1357	1430	1430
raha hlavní nádrazi 1160 a.	0719	...	0819	0842	0842	0919	0942	1014	1030	...	1042	1114	1127	1151**z**	...	1242	1314	1330	1351**z**	1442	1519	1519
	EC	*RJ*	*EC*	♥	♥	*RJ*	*EC*	*EC*	♥	♥	*RJ*	♥	♥	*EC*	*RJ*	♥	♥	*EC*	*EC*	*RJ*	*EC*	*RJ*
	130	**74**	**278**	**1048**	**1048**	**256**	**102**	**276**	**1034**	**1034**	**78**	**1050**	**1050**	**274**	**370**	**1036**	**1036**	**100**	**272**	**372**	**270**	**374**
	✕	✕	✕	🍷	🍷	✕	✕	✕	🍷	🍷	✕	🍷	🍷	✕	✕	🍷	🍷		✕	✕	✕	✕
	B			**m**	**k**	**A**	⊡		**m**	**k**		**m**	**k**			**m**	**k**	⊡				
Budapest Déli **1250** d.	...	...	...	...	...	...	...	...	...	...	...	...	...	...	...	1445	1445	...	...	...	...	...
Budapest Nyugati **1175** d.	0828	...	0940	...	...	...	...	1140	...	...	...	...	...	1340	...	|	|	...	1540	...	1740	...
ratislava hl. st. d.	1057	...	1206	1232	1232	...	...	1406	...	...	...	1537	1537	1606	...	|	|	...	1806	...	2006	...
úty 🏛 d.	1148	...	1249	|	|	...	...	1449	...	...	...	|	|	1649	...	|	|	...	1849	...	2049	...
Graz **980** d.	|	0826	|	|	|	1026	...	|	...	...	1226	|	|	|	1426	|	|	...	|	1626	|	1826
Wien Hbf 982 d.	|	1110	|	|	|	1310	1410	|	1439	1439	1510	|	|	|	1710	1736	1736	1810	|	1910	|	2110
řeclav 982 a.	1204	1204	1304	1336	1336	1404	1504	1504	1536	1536	1604	1636	1636	1704	1804	1836	1836	1904	1904	2004	2104	2204
řeclav d.	...	1207	1307	1338	1338	1407	...	1507	1538	1538	1607	1638	1638	1707	1807	1838	1838	...	1907	2007	2107	2207
rno hlavní nádrazí d.	...	1238	1338	1409	1409	1438	...	1538	1609	1609	1638	1709	1709	1738	1838	1909	1909	...	1938	2038	2136	2236
eská Třebová 1160 d.	...	|	|	|	|	|	...	|	|	|	|	|	|	|	|	|	|	...	|	|	...	...
ardubice 1160 d.	...	|	|	|	|	|	...	|	|	|	|	|	|	|	|	|	|	...	|	|	...	...
olín 1160 d.	...	1457	1557	1631	1631	|	...	1758	1831	1831	1857	1931	1931	1957	2057	2131	2131	...	2157	2258	...	...
raha hlavní nádrazi 1160 a.	...	1553**z**	1642	1719	1719	1752**j**	...	1858**x**	1919	1919	1942	2014	2014	2042	2141	2214	2214	...	2241	2342	...	...

– VINDOBONA – [12] ✕ Berlin - Dresden - Praha - Brno - Břeclav - Wien - Graz. *Railjet* service (see *RJ* note).
– BATHORY – [12] ✕ Budapest - Bratislava - Břeclav - Ostrava - Bohumín - Katowice - Warszawa - Terespol and v.v.; [2] Terespol - Brest* and v.v. Ⓡ required for journeys to / from Poland.
– [12] 🍷 Praha - Bratislava - Žilina and v.v. (Table **1180**).
– Conveys ▬ 2 cl. (4 berth) [2] 🍷 Praha - Bratislava - Rijeka / Split and v.v. on dates in Table **83** (Trains **1221 / 1220**).
– METROPOLITAN SLOVENSKÁ STRELA – [12] ✕ Praha - Bratislava - Nové Zámky and v.v. Conveys on dates in Table **1170**: 🛏 1, 2 cl. Praha (**283/282**) - Bratislava - Nové Zámky (**801/800**) - Košice - Prešov and v.v.
– METROPOL – [12] ✕ Praha - Břeclav and v.v.; 🛏 1, 2 cl., ▬ 2 cl. Praha - Břeclav (**477/476**) - Bratislava - Budapest and v.v. For other cars Břeclav - Budapest and v.v. see Tables **60** (Berlin - Budapest) and **99** (Warszawa - Kraków - Budapest).
– NIGHTJET – 🛏 1, 2 cl., ▬ 2 cl., [2] Berlin - Wroclaw - Břeclav - Bohumín - Wien - Graz and v.v. (Table **77**); 🛏 1, 2 cl., [2] Warszawa - Kraków - Bohumín - Břeclav - Wien and v.v. (Table **99**).

e – ①–⑥ (not July 6, Oct. 29).
h – Praha **Holesovice**.
j – See notes **h** and **z**.
k – June 20 - July 19.
m – Until June 19 and from July 20.
x – 16 minutes earlier until July 20.
z – 9 minutes earlier from July 20.

♥ – Operated by REGIOJET. Separate fares apply.
⊡ – For origin / destination see Table **99** or **1164**.
§ – Ⓡ for international journeys.
* – Subject to confirmation.

RJ – Railjet train (operated by ÖBB and ČD). Conveys Business, First, Economy classes.

1151 PRAHA - OLOMOUC and BRNO

🍷 on most trains

SEMI-FAST TRAINS. For faster trains see Tables **1150** and **1160**. Most Přerov trains continue to / from destinations on Table **1162**.

km		861 Ⓐ	2Ⓐ	883 e	2Ⓐ	863	885	865	887	867	889	869	891	2Ⓐ	871	893	2Ⓐ	873	895	875	897	877	879	899	IC57
0	**Praha** hlavní nádrazi d.	...	...	0442	...	0542	0642	0742	0842	0942	1042	1142	1242	...	1342	1442	...	1542	1642	1742	1842	2011	2100	2300	2345
62	Kolín d.	...	...	0530	...	0630	0730	0830	0930	1030	1130	1230	1330	...	1430	1530	...	1630	1730	1830	1930	2058	2147	2347	0028
104	Pardubice d.	...	...	0557	...	0657	0757	0857	0957	1057	1157	1257	1357	...	1457	1557	...	1657	1757	1857	1957	2122	2208	0012	0050
139	Choceň d.	...	...	0618	...	0718	0818	0918	1018	1118	1218	1318	1418	...	1518	1618	1610	1718	1818	1918	2018	2142	2228	...	0110
154	Ústí nad Orlicí d.	...	...	0635	...	0735	0835	0935	1035	1135	1235	1335	1435	...	1535	1635	1630	1735	1835	1935	2035	2158	|	...	0126
164	Česká Třebová d.	0456	0542	0646	0648	0746	0846	0946	1046	1146	1246	1346	1446	1448	1546	1646	1648	1746	1846	1946	2046	2206	2251	...	0135
252	Olomouc d.	|	|	0731	|	|	0931	|	1131	|	1331	|	1531	|	|	1731	|	|	1931	|	2131	...	|	...	|
274	**Přerov** a.	|	|	0745	|	|	0945	|	1145	|	1345	|	1545	|	|	1745	|	|	1945	|	2145	...	|	...	|
181	Svitavy d.	0507	0555	...	0701	0802	...	1002	...	1202	...	1402	...	1502	1602	...	1702	1802	...	2002	...	...	2302	...	0146
208	Letovice d.	0526	0621	...	0727	0823	...	1023	...	1223	...	1423	...	1528	1623	...	1728	1823	...	2023	...	...	2319	...	|
233	Blansko d.	0549	0646	...	0747	0846	...	1046	...	1246	...	1446	...	1547	1646	...	1747	1846	...	2046	...	...	2335	...	0218
255	**Brno** hlavní nádrazí a.	*0632**	...	...	...	*0930**	...	*1130**	...	*1330**	...	*1530**	...	...	*1730**	...	...	*1930**	...	*2130**	...	...	*0018**	...	*0301*

	876	898	896 e	874 A	894	872	892		870	890	868	888	866	886	2Ⓐ	864		2Ⓐ	884	862	2Ⓐ	882	860	IC57 B
Brno hlavní nádrazi d.	*0245**	...	...	*0245**	...	*0625**	...	...	*0825**	...	*1025**	...	*1225**	...	...	*1425**	...	...	...	*1625**	...	...	*1825**	2142
Blansko d.	0330	...	...	0513	...	0713	...	...	0913	...	1113	...	1313	...	1413	1513	...	1613	...	1713	1813	...	1913	2228
Letovice d.	|	...	...	0534	...	0734	...	...	0934	...	1134	...	1334	...	1433	1534	...	1633	...	1734	1833	...	1934	2245
Svitavy d.	0402	...	...	0602	...	0802	...	...	1002	...	1202	...	1402	...	1500	1602	...	1700	...	1802	1900	...	2002	2302
Přerov d.	|	...	0447	|	0612	|	0812	...	|	1012	|	1212	|	1412	|	|	...	|	1612	|	|	1812	|	|
Olomouc d.	|	...	0503	|	0631	|	0831	...	|	1031	|	1231	|	1431	|	|	...	|	1631	|	|	1831	|	|
Česká Třebová d.	0415	...	0558	0615	0715	0815	0915	...	1015	1115	1215	1315	1415	1515	1524z	1615	...	1711	1715	1815	1911	1915	2015	2315
Ústí nad Orlicí d.	0425	...	0607	0625	0725	0825	0925	...	1025	1125	1225	1325	1425	1525	1537	1625	...	...	1725	1825	...	1925	2025	|
Choceň d.	0445	...	0625	0645	0745	0845	0945	...	1045	1135	1245	1345	1445	1545	1552	1645	...	...	1745	1845	...	1945	2045	|
Pardubice d.	0509	0609	0645	0710	0809	0809	1009	...	1109	1209	1309	1409	1509	1609	...	1709	...	...	1809	1909	...	2009	2109	0000
Kolín d.	0535	0635	0706	0735	0835	0935	1035	...	1135	1235	1335	1435	1535	1635	...	1735	...	...	1835	1935	...	2035	2135	0020
Praha hlavní nádrazi a.	0619	0722	0752	0822	0922	1019	1119	...	1222	1319	1419	1522	1622	1722	...	1819	...	...	1922	2019	...	2119	2219	0102

A – From Blansko on Ⓐ; from Česká Třebová daily.
B – By 🚌 Brno hlavní nádrazi - Blansko.
e – ①–⑥ (not July 6, Sept. 29).
z – Arrives 1511 (connects with train in previous column).
* – By 🚌. At Brno services call at Benešova tř., hotel Grand (approximately 5 minutes walk from hlavní nádrazi).

1152 PRAHA - HAVLIČKŮV BROD - BRNO

🍷 on most trains

APRIL 23 - AUGUST 31. Local trains operate Kolín - Ždár nad Sázavou and v.v. For other trains Praha - Kolín see Tables **1150**, **1151** and **1160**.

km		971 B	973	1031 ♥	96975	1041 ♥	96977	1033 ♥	961 ⑥m	96979	1043 ♥	96981	1035 ♥	96983	1045 ♥	96985 Ⓐ	1037 ♥	96987	1047 ♥	96989 Ⓑd	96989 ⑦g	1049 ♥	991	963 Ⓑd	1051 ♥	965	967
0	**Praha** hlavní nádrazi d.	...	...	0520f	0559	0620f	0759	0823f	0859	0959	1038	1159	1238	1359	1438	1459	1538	1559	1638	1659	1659	1738	1759	1859	1938	1959	2159
62	Kolín d.	...	...	0622	0647	0722	0847	0922	0947	1047	1122	1247	1322	1447	1522	1547	1622	1647	1722	1747	1747	1822	1847	1947	2022	2047	2246
73	Kutná Hora d.	...	...	|	0658	|	0858	|	0958	1058	|	1258	|	1458	|	1558	|	1658	|	1758	1758	|	1858	1958	|	2058	2256
82	Čáslav d.	...	...	|	0707	|	0907	|	1007	1107	|	1307	|	1507	|	1607	|	1707	|	1807	1807	|	1907	2007	|	2107	2305
136	**Havlíčkův Brod** a.	...	...	0721	0757	0821	0957	1021	1057	1157	1221	1357	1421	1557	1621	1657	1721	1757	1821	1857	1857	1921	1957	2057	2121	2157	...
136	**Havlíčkův Brod** d.	0502	0602	0722	0802	0822	1002	1022	*1102*	1202	1222	1402	1422	1602	1622	1702	1722	1802	1822	1902	1902	1922	2002	2102	2122	*2210*	...
169	Ždár nad Sázavou d.	0529	0629	0746	0829	0846	1029	1046	*1135*	1229	1246	1429	1446	1629	1646	1729	1746	1829	1846	1927	1929	1946	2029	2127	2146	*2241*	...
	Brno dolní nádrazi a.	|	|	|	0943	|	1143	|	...	1343	|	1543	|	1743	|	1843	|	1943	|	...	2043	|	|	...	|	...	...
246	**Brno** hlavní nádrazi a.	0640	0740	0846	...	0946	...	1146	...	...	1346	...	1546	...	1746	...	1846	...	1946	...	...	2046	2142	...	2246	...	...

	966 Ⓐ	964 e	962 C	1040 ♥	990 D	1042 ♥	988	1044 ♥	1030 ♥	96986	1046 ♥	96984	1032 ♥		96982	960 ⑦g	1048 ♥	96980	96978 Ⓑ	1034 ♥	96976	1050 ♥	96974 Ⓐ	96972	1036 ♥	9697
Brno hlavní nádrazi d.	...	...	...	0509	0520	0609	0620	0709	0809	...	1009	...	1209	...	...	...	1409	...	...	1609	...	1709	...	...	1909	...
Brno dolní nádrazi d.	...	...	...	|	|	|	|	|	|	0815	|	1017	|	...	1217	...	|	1417	1517	|	1617	|	1717	1817	|	2017
Ždár nad Sázavou d.	...	...	0530	0608	0630	0708	0730	0808	0908	0930	1108	1130	1308	...	1330	...	1508	1530	1630	1708	1730	1808	1830	1930	2008	2130
Havlíčkův Brod a.	...	...	0557	0631	0657	0731	0757	0831	0931	0957	1131	1157	1331	...	1357	...	1531	1557	1657	1731	1757	1831	1857	1957	2031	2157
Havlíčkův Brod d.	*0351*	0501	0601	0632	0701	0732	0801	0832	0932	1001	1132	1201	1332	...	1401	1501	1532	1601	1701	1732	1801	1832	*1904*	2001	2032	2232
Čáslav d.	0451	0551	0651	|	0751	|	0851	|	|	1051	|	1251	|	...	1451	1551	|	1651	1751	|	1851	|	*2001*	2051	|	*2329*
Kutná Hora d.	0500	0600	0700	|	0800	|	0900	|	|	1100	|	1300	|	...	1500	1600	|	1700	1800	|	1900	|	*2012*	2100	|	...
Kolín d.	0511	0611	0711	0731	0811	0831	0911	0931	1032	1111	1231	1311	1431	...	1511	1611	1631	1711	1811	1931	1911	1931	*2022*	2111	2131	...
Praha hlavní nádrazi a.	0557	0657	0758	0819	0858	0919	0958	1030f	1127f	1158	1330f	1358	1528f	...	1600	1700	1734f	1800	1858	1926f	2000	2027f	...	2158	2224f	...

B – From Havlíčkův Brod on Ⓐ; from Ždár nad Sázavou on ①–⑥ **e**.
C – From Ždár nad Sázavou on ①–⑥ **e**; from Havlíčkův Brod daily.
D – From Brno on ① **q**; from Ždár nad Sázavou on Ⓐ; from Čáslav on ①–⑥ **e**
d – Ⓑ (not July 5).
e – ①–⑥ (not July 6).
f – Time at Praha is altered until June 19 and from July 20 (see Table **1150**).
g – ⑦ (also July 6).
m – ⑥ (also July 5).
q – ① (also July 7).
♥ – Operated by REGIOJET. Separate fares apply. For origin / destination see Table **1150**.

1156 BRNO - OLOMOUC - ŠUMPERK and JESENÍK

km		901 e	903	905	907	909	911	913	2	915 E	917 ⑦g
0	**Brno** hlavní nádrazi d.	0522	0718	0918	1118	1318	1518	1718	...	1918	2119
45	Vyškov na Moravé d.	0559	0759	0959	1159	1359	1559	1759	...	1959	2159
61	Nezamyslice d.	0620	0820	1020	1220	1420	1620	1820	...	2020	2216
80	Prostějov d.	0635	0835	1035	1235	1435	1635	1835	...	2035	2235
100	**Olomouc** d.	0656	0856	1056	1256	1456	1656	1856	...	2056	2252
146	Zábřeh na Moravé a.	0722	0922	1122	1322	1522	1722	1924	...	2124	...
146	Zábřeh na Moravé d.	0726	0926	1126	1326	1526	1726	1926	...	2126	...
159	**Šumperk** a.	0741	0941	1141	1341	1541	1741	1943	2116	2141	...
176	Hanušovice a.	0759r	0959r	1159r	1359r	1559r	1759r	...	2153	...	...
208	Lipová Lázně a.	0850r	1050r	1250r	1449r	1651r	1851r	...	2248	...	...
212	**Jeseník** a.	0858r	1058r	1258r	1458r	1658r	1858r	...	2256	...	...

	916 Ⓐ	914 F	912	910	908	906	904	902	Ⓒ	900 p
Jeseník d.	...	...	0700s	0901s	1101s	1301s	1501s	1701s	1904	...
Lipová Lázně d.	...	...	0708s	0908s	1108s	1308s	1508s	1708s	1911	...
Hanušovice d.	...	...	0800s	1000s	1200s	1400s	1600s	1800s	2000	...
Šumperk d.	*0449*	0611	0809	1009	1209	1409	1609	1809	|	2015
Zábřeh na Moravé a.	*0506*	0630	0822	1022	1222	1422	1622	1822	2032	2031
Zábřeh na Moravé d.	*0515*	0631	0835	1035	1235	1435	1635	1835	...	2035
Olomouc d.	0558	0706	0906	1106	1306	1506	1706	1906	...	2106
Prostějov d.	0615	0723	0923	1123	1323	1523	1723	1923	...	2123
Nezamyslice a.	0635	0738	0938	1138	1338	1538	1738	1938	...	2138
Vyškov na Moravé a.	0655	0756	0956	1156	1356	1556	1756	1956	...	2157
Brno hlavní nádrazi a.	0743	0842	1042	1242	1443	1643	1843	2038	...	2237

E – Brno - Olomouc runs daily; Olomouc - Šumperk runs Ⓑ **d**. See note ⊡.
F – From Šumperk on ①–⑥ **e**; from Olomouc daily.
d – Ⓑ (not July 5, Oct. 28).
e – ①–⑥ (not July 6, Sept. 29).
g – ⑦ (also July 6, Sept. 28, Nov. 17).
p – ⑤⑦ (also July 4, 6, Sept. 27, 28, Oct. 27, Nov. 16, 17; not Oct. 28).
r – Jeseník portion detaches at Zabreh na Moravé (d. xx31). ◧.
s – Jeseník portion attaches at Zabreh na Moravé (a. xx25). ◧.
⊡ – Change trains at Olomouc on Ⓐ.
◧ – Different train numbers apply Zábřeh - Jeseník and v.v.

1157 DĚČÍN - ÚSTÍ NAD LABEM - MĚLNÍK - KOLÍN and RUMBURK - KOLÍN

Regiojet

km						
0	**Ústí n. L** hlavní n. d.	0440	0636		1636	1836
1	**Ústí n. L** západ d.	0446	0643		1643	1843
3	**Ústí n. L** Střekov d.	0452	0652		1652	1852
28	Litoměřice město d.	0512	0712	and	1712	1912
64	**Mělník** d.	0540	0740	every	1740	1940
74	Všetaty d.	0548	0748	**two**	1748	1948
86	Stará Boleslav d.	0558	0758	hours	1758	1958
97	Lysá n. Labem ▷ d.	0606	0806	until	1806	2006
112	Nymburk ▷ d.	0618	0818		1818	2018
119	Poděbrady ▷ d.	0625	0825		1825	2025
135	**Kolín** a.	0639	0839		1839	2039

Kolín d.	0714	0914		1914	2114
Poděbrady ▷ d.	0729	0929		1929	2129
Nymburk ▷ d.	0737	0937		1937	2137
Lysá n. Labem. ▷ d.	0748	0948	and	1948	2148
Stará Boleslav d.	0755	0955	every	1955	2155
Všetaty d.	0807	1007	**two**	2007	2206
Mělník d.	0816	1016	hours	2016	2214
Litoměřice město d.	0845	1045	until	2045	2243
Ústí n. L Střekov a.	0902	1102		2102	2300
Ústí n. L západ a.	0907	1107		2107	2304
Ústí n. L hlavní n. a.	0913	1113		2113	2310

km	⊖	n					
0	**Děčín** hl. n. d.	0802	1002	1202	1402	1602	1802
28	**Ústí n. L** Střekov a.	0843	1043	1243	1443	1643	1843

⊖	m					
Ústí n. L Střekov. d.	0912	1112	1312	1512	1712	1912
Děčín hl. n. a.	0953	1153	1353	1553	1753	1953

RUMBURK - ČESKA LIPÁ - KOLÍN ⊙

	G						
Rumburk d.	0523	0712	...	...	1312	1512t	1712
Česka Lipá d.	0624	0824	1024	1224	1424	1624	1824
Mladá Boleslav d.	0722	0922	1122	1322	1522	1722	1922
Nymburk ▷ d.	0748	0948	1148	1348	1548	1748	1948
Poděbrady ▷ d.	0756	0956	1156	1356	1556	1756	1956
Kolín a.	0809	1009	1209	1409	1609	1809	2009

Kolín d.	0745	0945	1145	1345	1545	1745	1945
Poděbrady ▷ d.	0759	0959	1159	1359	1559	1759	1959
Nymburk ▷ d.	0808	1008	1208	1408	1608	1808	2008
Mladá Boleslav d.	0837	1037	1237	1437	1637	1837	2037
Česka Lipá a.	0931	1131	1331	1531	1731	1931	2131
Rumburk a.	1037	*1324*	1437	1634t	1837	2037	*2319*

G – From Rumburk on Ⓐ; from Česka Lipá daily.
m – Also at 0519, 0654 Ⓐ, 0712 Ⓒ.
n – Also at 0448 Ⓐ, 0602.
t – ⑤⑥⑦ (also July 4 – 6, Sept. 27, 28, Oct. 27, 28, Nov. 16, 17).
▷ – See also Table **1145**.
⊖ – 2nd class only. For Dečín - Ústí nad Labem hl. n. see Table **1100**.
⊙ – Rumburk - Kolín trains are operated by Arriva.

PRAHA - PÚCHOV, OSTRAVA and ŽILINA 1160

SC and *IC* trains are not available for local travel Ostravá - Bohumín or v.v.
For additional fast trains Praha - Česká Třebová and v.v. see Table **1150**. For semi-fast trains Praha - Olomouc and v.v. see Table **1151**.

km							*EC*	*EC*	♥	♥	*SC*•	*EC*	*EC*		♥	♥	*LE*♠	*EC*	*SC*•	*LE*♠	*EC*	♥	*LE*♠	*EC*
			341	**641**	**641**	**343**	**121**	**113**	**1001**	**1001**	**241**	**123**	**141**		**1003**	**1003**	**1251**	**125**	**505**	**1241**	**115**	**1005**	**1233**	**127**
			🍷	2 ①–⑥	2 ①	🍷	🍷	🍷⊖	🍷 ⚒	🍷 ⚒	🍷[R]	🍷	🍷		🍷	🍷	🍷[R]	🍷	🍷[R]	🍷[R]	🍷⊖	🍷	🍷[R]	🍷
				e	k			§♦	f	g					f	g			⊕		§♦			
0	**Praha** hl. n.	d.	...	...	0402	...	0502	0550	0556	0618	0605	0650	0802	...	0756	0818	0828	0902	0925	0928	1002	1018	1028	1102
62	Kolín	d.	...	...	0449	...	0549	0649	|	|	0708	0749	0849	...	|	|	0913	0949	|	1013	1049	|	1113	1149
104	**Pardubice**	d.	...	...	0513	...	0613	0713	0724	0724	0729	0813	0913	...	0927	0927	0933	1013	1029	1033	1113	1127	1133	1213
139	Choceň	d.	...	...	|	...	0634	0734	|	|	|	0834	0934	...	|	|	|	1034	|	|	1134	|	|	1234
154	Ústí nad Orlici	d.	...	...	0550	...	|	|	|	|	|	|	|	...	|	|	|	|	|	|	|	|	|	|
155	Ústí nad Orlici městó	d.	...	...	|	...	|	0751	|	|	|	|	0951	...	|	|	|	|	|	|	1151	|	|	|
164	Česká Třebová	d.	...	...	0600	...	0700	0801	0808	0808	0811	0900	1001	...	1011	1011	|	1100	|	|	1201	1211	|	1300
206	Zábřeh na Moravé	d.	...	...	0622	...	0722	0822	0833	0833	|	0922	1022	...	1033	1033	1038	1122	|	1135	1222	1233	1238	1322
252	**Olomouc**	d.	...	0645	0645	...	0753	0845	0857	0857	0849	0953	1045	...	1057	1057	1104	1153	1149	1158	1245	1257	1304	1353
	Přerov	d.	...	|	|	...	|	|	|	|	|	|	|	...	|	|	1122	|	|	1220	|	|	1322	|
303	Hranice na Moravě	d.	...	0714	0714	...	0825	0913	0928	0928	|	1025	1113	...	1127	1127	1139	1225	|	1237	1313	1328	1339	1425
329	Valašské Meziříčí	d.	...	|	|	...	0846	|	|	|	|	1046	|	...	|	|	|	1246	|	|	|	|	|	1446
348	Vsetín	d.	...	|	|	...	0903	|	|	|	|	1103	|	...	|	|	|	1303	|	|	|	|	|	1503
366	Horní Lideč 🚌	d.	...	|	|	...	*0939***z**	|	|	|	|	*1139***z**	|	...	|	|	|	*1339***z**	|	|	|	|	|	*1539***z**
394	**Púchov**	a.	...	|	|	...	*1015***z**	|	|	|	|	*1215***z**	|	...	|	|	|	*1415***z**	|	|	|	|	|	*1615***z**
353	Ostrava Svinov	d.	0650	0748	0748	0850	...	0942	0957	0957	0946	...	1142	...	1157	1157	1211	...	1241	1307	1342	1357	1412	...
381	Opava východ	a.	|	|	|	|	...	|	|	|	|	...	|	...	|	|	|	...	|	|	|	|	|	...
358	**Ostrava** hl. n.	d.	0658	0754	0754	0858	...	0950	1005	1005	0955	...	1150	...	1205	1205	1217	...	1249	1313	1350	1405	1420	...
376	Havířov	d.	|	|	|	|	...	|	1023	1023	|	...	|	...	1224	1224	|	...	...	|	|	1423	|	...
366	Bohumín	a.	0704	0802	0802	0904	...	0957	...	...	|	...	1157	...	|	|	1225	...	...	1319	1357	...	1426	...
366	Bohumín	d.	0706	...	...	0906	...	1009	...	...	|	...	1206	...	|	|	...	...	...	...	1446	...	...	...
380	Petrovice u Karviné	a.	|	...	...	|	...	|	...	...	|	...	|	...	|	|	...	...	...	...	|	...	...	...
	Katowice **1076**	a.	|	...	...	|	...	1139	...	...	|	...	|	...	|	|	...	...	...	...	1606	...	...	...
	Kraków Glowny **1076**	a.	|	...	...	|	...	|	...	...	|	...	|	...	|	|	...	...	...	...	1659	...	...	...
	Warszawa Centralna **1060**	a.	|	...	...	|	...	1435	...	...	|	...	|	...	|	|	...	...	...	...	...	...	...	...
381	Karviná hl. n.	d.	0715	...	...	0915	...	...	...	...	|	...	1215	...	|	|	...	...	...	...	...	...	...	...
397	**Český Těšín**	d.	0732	...	...	0932	...	...	...	...	1023	...	1232	...	1242	1242	...	...	...	...	...	...	...	...
405	Trinec centrum	d.	0740	...	...	0940	...	...	...	...	|	...	1240	...	1250	1250	...	...	...	...	...	...	...	...
417	Návsi	d.	0748	...	...	0948	...	...	...	...	|	...	1248	...	|	|	...	...	...	...	...	...	...	...
435	Čadca 🚌	a.	0804	...	...	1004	...	...	...	...	1053	...	1304	...	1310	1310	...	...	...	...	...	...	...	...
Δ*466*	**Žilina**	a.	0833	...	...	1033	...	...	...	...	1117	...	1333	...	1343	1343	...	...	...	...	...	...	...	...
	Banská Bystrica **1185**	a.	1026	...	...	1226	...	...	...	...	|	...	...	...	|	|	...	...	...	...	...	...	...	...
	Zvolen **1185**	a.	...	...	...	...	...	...	...	...	|	...	...	...	|	|	...	...	...	...	...	...	...	...
	Poprad Tatry **1180**	a.	...	...	...	...	...	...	...	...	1310	...	...	...	1558	1558	...	...	...	...	...	...	...	...
	Prešov **1196**	a.	...	...	...	...	...	...	...	...	|	...	...	...	|	|	...	...	...	...	...	...	...	...
	Košice **1180**	a.	...	...	...	...	...	...	...	...	1418	...	...	...	1710	1710	...	...	...	...	...	...	...	...

		SC•		*EC*	♥	*LE*♠	*EC*	*SC*•			*EC*	♥	*IC*	*EC*	♥		*SC*•	*SC*•	*LE*♠	*LE*♠	*EC*	*EC*	♥
		507	**345**	**143**	**1007**	**1257**	**129**	**509**		**347**	**117**	**1009**	**511**	**221**	**1011**		**243**	**243**	**411**	**411**	**145**	**145**	**1013**
		🍷[R]	🍷	🍷	🍷	🍷[R]	🍷	🍷[R]		🍷	🍷⊖	🍷	🍷[R] Ⓐ	🍷	🍷		🍷[R]	🍷[R] ⑤	🍷[R]	🍷[R] ④⑤⑦	🍷	🍷 Ⓑ	🍷
											§♦							n				d	
Praha hl. n.	d.	1125	...	1202	1218	1228	1302	1325	...	...	1402	1418	1425	1502	1518	...	1525	1525	1528	1528	1602	1602	1618
Kolín	d.	|	...	1249	|	1313	1349	|	...	...	1449	|	|	1549	|	...	|	|	1613	1613	1649	1649	|
Pardubice	d.	1229	...	1313	1327	1333	1413	1429	...	...	1513	1524	1529	1613	1624	...	1629	1629	1633	1633	1713	1713	1724
Choceň	d.	|	...	1333	|	|	1434	|	...	...	1534	|	|	1634	|	...	|	|	|	|	1734	1734	|
Ústí nad Orlici	d.	|	...	|	|	|	|	|	...	...	|	|	|	|	|	...	|	|	|	|	|	|	|
Ústí nad Orlici městó	d.	|	...	1351	|	|	|	|	...	...	1551	|	|	|	|	...	|	|	|	|	1751	1751	|
Česká Třebová	d.	|	...	1401	1411	|	1500	|	...	...	1601	1608	|	1700	1712	...	|	|	|	|	1801	1801	1808
Zábřeh na Moravé	d.	|	...	1422	1433	1438	1522	|	...	...	1622	1633	|	1722	1733	...	|	|	1738	1738	1822	1822	1833
Olomouc	d.	1349	...	1445	1457	1504	1553	1549	...	...	1645	1657	1648	1753	1757	...	1749	1749	1800	1800	1845	1845	1857
Přerov	d.	|	...	|	|	1522	|	|	...	...	|	|	|	|	|	...	|	|	1820	1820	|	|	|
Hranice na Moravě	d.	|	...	1513	1527	1539	1625	|	...	...	1713	1727	|	1825	1827	...	|	|	1837	1837	1913	1913	1927
Valašské Meziříčí	d.	|	...	|	|	|	1646	|	...	...	|	|	|	1846	|	...	|	|	|	|	|	|	|
Vsetín	d.	|	...	|	|	|	1703	|	...	...	|	|	|	1903	|	...	|	|	|	|	|	|	|
Horní Lideč 🚌	d.	|	...	|	|	|	*1739***z**	|	...	...	|	|	|	*1939***z**	|	...	|	|	|	|	|	|	|
Púchov	a.	|	...	|	|	|	*1815***z**	|	...	...	|	|	|	*2015***z**	|	...	|	|	|	|	|	|	|
Ostrava Svinov	d.	1441	1450	1542	1557	1620	...	1641	...	1650	1742	1757	1744	...	1856	...	1843	1843	1909	1909	1942	1942	2022
Opava východ	a.	|	|	|	|	|	...	|	...	|	|	|	|	...	|	...	|	|	|	|	|	|	2030
Ostrava hl. n.	d.	1449	1458	1550	1605	1628	...	1649	...	1658	1750	1805	1753	...	1905	...	1851	1851	1917	1917	1950	1950	...
Havířov	d.	...	|	|	1623	|	...	...	...	|	|	1823	|	...	1927	...	|	|	|	|	|	|	...
Bohumín	a.	...	1504	1557	...	1634	...	...	...	1704	1757	...	1801	...	|	...	1857	1857	1923	1923	1957	1957	...
Bohumín	d.	...	1506	1606	...	1645	...	...	...	1706	1809	...	...	...	|	...	...	1858	...	1936	2006	2006	...
Petrovice u Karviné	a.	...	|	|	...	|	...	...	...	|	|	...	...	...	|	...	...	|	...	|	|	|	...
Katowice **1076**	a.	...	|	|	...	|	...	...	...	|	2002	...	...	...	|	...	...	|	...	2124	|	|	...
Kraków Glowny **1076**	a.	...	|	|	...	|	...	...	...	|	|	...	...	...	|	...	...	|	...	2223	|	|	...
Warszawa Centralna **1060**	a.	...	|	|	...	|	...	...	...	|	2257	...	...	...	|	...	...	|	...	...	|	|	...
Karviná hl. n.	d.	...	1515	1615	...	1655	...	...	...	1715	...	...	...	...	|	...	...	|	...	...	2015	2015	...
Český Těšín	d.	...	1532	1632	...	1711	...	...	...	1732	...	...	...	...	1949	...	...	1921	...	...	2032	2032	...
Trinec centrum	d.	...	1540	1640	...	1718	...	...	...	1740	...	...	...	...	1957	...	...	|	...	...	2040	2040	...
Návsi	d.	...	1548	1648	...	|	...	...	...	1748	...	...	...	...	|	...	...	|	...	...	2048	2048	...
Čadca 🚌	a.	...	1604	1704	...	1738	...	...	...	1804	...	...	...	...	2018	...	...	1944	...	...	...	2104	...
Žilina	a.	...	1633	1733	...	1818	...	...	...	1833	...	...	...	...	2046	...	...	2007	...	...	...	2133	...
Banská Bystrica **1185**	a.	...	1826	...	...	|	...	...	...	2026	...	...	...	...	|	...	...	|	...	...	...	...	...
Zvolen **1185**	a.	...	...	...	...	|	...	...	...	2056	...	...	...	...	|	...	...	|	...	...	...	...	...
Poprad Tatry **1180**	a.	...	...	...	...	2009	...	...	...	...	...	...	...	...	2253	...	...	2203	...	...	...	...	...
Prešov **1196**	a.	...	...	...	...	2132	...	...	...	...	...	...	...	...	|	...	...	|	...	...	...	...	...
Košice **1180**	a.	...	...	...	...	2211	...	...	...	...	...	...	...	...	0015	...	...	2311	...	...	...	...	...

♦ – **NOTES** (LISTED BY TRAIN NUMBER)

112/113 – SILESIA – [12] Warszawa - Katowice - Bohumín - Praha and v.v.
114/115 – CRACOVIA – [12] 🍷 Przemyśl - Kraków - Bohumín - Praha and v.v.;
[2] Brest ◧ (**131/130**) - Warszawa - Bohumín (**114/115**) - Praha and v.v. (Table **99**).
116/117 – SILESIA – [12] ✕ Warszawa - Katowice - Bohumín - Praha and v.v. and v.v.
406/407 – CHOPIN – [sleeper] 1, 2 cl., [couchette] 2 cl., [2] Praha (**443/442**) - Bohumín - Warszawa and v.v.
442/443 – SLOVAKIA – [sleeper] 1, 2 cl., [couchette] 2 cl., [2] Humenné - Košice - Bohumín - Praha and v.v.
1020/21 – [sleeper] (1, 2, 3 berth), [couchette] (6 berth), [12] Košice - Praha and v.v.
1022/23 – [sleeper] (1, 2, 3 berth), [couchette] (6 berth), [12] Przemyśl - Kraków - Praha and v.v. (see note ⊡).

A – ①②③④⑦.
d – Ⓑ (not July 5, Oct. 28).
e – ①–⑥ (not July 6, Oct. 29).
f – June 20 - July 19.
g – Until June 19 and from July 20.
j – ⑦ (also July 6, Sept. 28; not July 3).
k – ① (also July 7, Sept. 29; not July 4).
m – ⑥⑦ (also July 5, 6, Sept. 28, Oct. 28, Nov. 17).
n – ⑤ (also Sept. 27, Oct. 27, Nov. 16; not Oct. 28, Nov. 18).
p – ⑥ (also July 3, 5, Oct. 28, Nov. 17).
q – ⑥ (also Sept. 28, Oct. 28, Nov. 17; not Oct. 29, Nov. 19).
v – Warszawa **Wschodnia**.
z – Connection by 🚌.

♠ – Operated by LEO EXPRESS. Separate fare tariff applies.
♥ – Operated by REGIOJET. Separate fare tariff applies.
• – *SUPERCITY PENDOLINO* train, [R]; reservation fee.

⊗ – From / to Františkovy Lázně via Plzeň (Table **1120**).
⊕ – From / to Karlovy Vary via Cheb and Plzeň (Tables **1120, 1121** and **1110**).
⊖ – [R] for international journeys.
◧ – Subject to confirmation.
⊡ – A date for the introduction of this service has yet to be announced.
● – Timings may vary by up to 3 minutes.
Δ – *439 km* via Vsetin.
* – Classified *Ex* in Slovakia.
§ – [R] for journeys to / from Poland.

For local trains Ostrava - Český Těšín and v.v. see pages 486 and 487

1160 PRAHA - PÚCHOV, OSTRAVA and ŽILINA

SC and *IC* trains are not available for local travel Ostravá - Bohumín or v.v.
For additional fast trains Praha - Česká Třebová and v.v. see Table **1150**. For semi-fast trains Praha - Olomouc and v.v. see Table **1151**.

	IC	*IC*	♥	*SC*•	*LE*♠	*IC*	*IC*		♥	*LE*♠	*IC*	*SC*•	*LE*♠	♥		♥	*IC*	*EN*	443	♥	*IC*	*IC*
	513	**521**	**1015**	**515**	**413**	**549**	**549**		**1017**	**1259**	**523**	**517**	**1261**	**1019**		**1021**	**525**	**443**	**406**	**1023**	**519**	**571**
	🍷 R	🍷	🍷	R 🍷	🍷 R	🍷	🍷		🍷	🍷 R	🍷	R 🍷	🍷 R	🍷		🍷	🍷	R	R	🍷	🍷 R	🍷
							Ⓑ														⑥⑦	
				⊗			d									♦		♦	♦	⊡ ♦	m	
Praha hl. n. d.	1625	1702	1718	1725	1728	1802	1802	...	1818	1828	1902	1925	1928	2018	...	2137	2142	2205	2205	2254	2340	2345
Kolín d.	|	1749	|	|	1813	1849	1849	...	|	1913	1949	|	2013	|	...	|	2230	2254	2254	|	|	0028
Pardubice d.	1729	1813	1829	1829	1833	1913	1913	...	1927	1933	2013	2029	2033	2127	...	2240	2257	2321	2321	2355	0041	0050
Choceň d.	|	1834	|	|	|	1934	1934	...	|	|	2034	|	|	|	...	|	2317	|	|	|	|	0110
Ústí nad Orlici d.	|	|	|	|	|	|	|	...	|	|	|	|	|	|	...	|	2335	|	|	|	|	0126
Ústí nad Orlici město d.	|	|	|	|	|	1951	1951	...	|	|	|	|	|	|	...	|	|	|	|	|	|	|
Česká Třebová d.	|	1900	1912	|	|	2001	2001	...	2011	|	2100	|	|	2211	...	|	2346	0008	0008	|	|	0134
Zábřeh na Moravé d.	|	1922	1933	|	1937	2022	2022	...	2033	2038	2122	|	2137	2233	...	2342	0008	|	|	|	|	...
Olomouc d.	1849	1953	1957	1949	2000	2045	2045	...	2057	2104	2153	2149	2200	2257	...	0007	0031	0108	0108	0118	0158	...
Přerov d.	|	|	|	|	2020	|	|	...	|	2122	|	|	2220	|	...	|	0045	|	|	|	|	...
Hranice na Moravě d.	|	2034	2027	|	2037	2113	2113	...	2127	2139	2225	|	2237	2327	...	0037	...	|	|	|	|	...
Valašské Meziříčí d.	|	2054	|	|	|	|	|	...	|	|	2247	|	|	|	...	|	...	|	|	|	|	...
Vsetín d.	|	2110	|	|	|	|	|	...	|	|	2303	|	|	|	...	|	...	|	|	|	|	...
Horní Lideč 🏛 d.	|	...	|	|	|	|	|	...	|	|	...	|	|	|	...	|	...	|	|	|	|	...
Púchov a.	|	...	|	|	|	|	|	...	|	|	...	|	|	|	...	|	...	|	|	|	|	...
Ostrava Svinov d.	1947	...	2057	2041	2109	2147	2147	...	2157	2211	...	2241	2309	2357	...	0108	...	0213	0213	0221	0252	...
Opava východ a.	2008	...	|	|	|	|	|	...	|	|	...	|	|	|	...	|	...	|	|	|	|	...
Ostrava hl. n. d.	...	...	2105	2049	2117	2155	2155	...	2205	2219	...	2249	2317	0003	...	0115	...	0221	0221	0229	0300	...
Havířov d.	...	...	2125	|	|	|	|	...	2225	|	...	|	|	|	...	0134	...	|	|	|	|	...
Bohumín a.	...	...	|	2057	2123	2202	2202	...	|	2225	...	2257	2323	0012	...	|	...	0228	0228	0236	0308	...
Bohumín d.	...	...	|	...	...	...	2212	...	|	...	...	...	2325	...	...	|	...	0300	0318	0253	...	...
Petrovice u Karviné a.	...	...	|	...	...	...	|	...	|	...	...	...	|	...	...	|	...	|	|	|	...	...
Katowice **1076** a.	...	...	|	...	...	...	|	...	|	...	...	...	|	...	...	|	...	|	0440	0413	...	...
Kraków Glowny **1076** a.	...	...	|	...	...	...	|	...	|	...	...	...	|	...	...	|	...	|	0542	0507	...	...
Warszawa Centralna **1060** a.	...	...	|	...	...	...	|	...	|	...	...	...	|	...	...	|	...	|	0905v	...	...	...
Karviná hl. n. d.	...	...	|	...	...	...	2221	...	|	...	...	...	2335	...	...	|	...	|	...	...	...	...
Český Těšín d.	...	...	2143	...	...	...	2237	...	2243	...	...	...	2349	...	...	|	...	|	...	...	...	...
Trinec centrum d.	...	...	2151	...	...	...	2246	...	2251	...	...	...	2356	...	...	|	...	|	...	...	...	...
Návsi d.	...	...	2202	...	...	...	2254	...	2302	...	...	...	|	...	...	|	...	|	...	...	...	...
Čadca 🏛 a.	...	...	...	...	...	...	...	...	...	...	...	...	0015	...	...	0223	...	0350	...	...	...	...
Žilina a.	...	...	...	...	...	...	...	...	...	...	...	...	0039	...	...	0249	...	0417	...	...	...	...
Banská Bystrica **1185** a.	...	...	...	...	...	...	...	...	...	...	...	...	|	...	...	|	...	|	...	...	...	...
Zvolen **1185** a.	...	...	...	...	...	...	...	...	...	...	...	...	|	...	...	|	...	|	...	...	...	...
Poprad Tatry **1180** a.	...	...	...	...	...	...	...	...	...	...	...	...	0235	...	...	0450	...	0641	...	...	...	...
Prešov **1196** a.	...	...	...	...	...	...	...	...	...	...	...	...	0401	...	...	|	...	|	...	...	...	...
Košice **1180** a.	...	...	...	...	...	...	...	...	...	...	...	...	0428	...	...	0607	...	0829	...	...	...	...

	♥	♥	*IC*	407	*EN*	*LE*♠	*IC*	*LE*♠	*IC*	*SC*•	♥	*LE*♠	*IC*	*IC*	*IC*	♥	*IC*	*SC*•	♥	♥	*LE*♠	*LE*♠
	1020	**1022**	**524**	**442**	**442**	**1252**	**518**	**1254**	**522**	**516**	**1000**	**1230**	**514**	**548**	**548**	**1002**	**520**	**512**	**1024**	**1004**	**412**	**412**
	🍷	🍷	🍷	R	R	🍷 R	🍷 R	🍷 R	🍷	🍷 R	🍷	🍷 R	🍷 R	🍷	🍷	🍷	🍷	🍷 R	🍷	🍷	R 🍷	R 🍷
							Ⓐ				⚒				①–⑥				†	⚒		①⑤⑥
	♦	⊡ ♦		♦	♦										e			⊗				
Košice **1180** d.	2113	...	...	...	2157	2237	...	...	...	...	...	...	...	...	...	...	...	...	...	...	...	...
Prešov **1196** d.	|	...	...	...	|	2307	...	...	...	...	...	...	...	...	...	...	...	...	...	...	...	...
Poprad Tatry **1180** d.	2231	...	...	...	2333	0021	...	...	...	...	...	...	...	...	...	...	...	...	...	...	...	...
Zvolen **1185** d.	|	...	...	...	|	|	...	...	...	...	...	...	...	...	...	...	...	...	...	...	...	...
Banská Bystrica **1185** a.	|	...	...	...	|	|	...	...	...	...	...	...	...	...	...	...	...	...	...	...	...	...
Žilina d.	0041	...	...	...	0140	0218	...	...	...	...	...	...	...	...	...	...	...	...	...	...	...	...
Čadca 🏛 d.	0108	...	...	...	0208	0242	...	...	...	...	...	...	...	...	...	...	...	...	...	...	...	...
Návsi d.	|	...	...	...	|	|	...	...	...	...	...	...	...	...	0502	...	...	...	...	0610	...	...
Trinec centrum d.	|	...	...	...	|	0303	...	...	...	...	...	...	...	...	0509	...	...	...	...	0621	...	...
Český Těšín d.	|	...	...	...	|	0310	...	...	...	...	...	...	...	...	0519	...	...	...	...	0630	...	...
Karviná hl. n. d.	|	...	...	...	|	0324	...	...	...	...	...	...	...	...	0534	...	...	...	...	|	...	...
Warszawa Centralna **1060** a.	|	...	...	1955	|	|	...	...	...	...	...	...	...	...	|	...	...	...	...	|	...	...
Kraków Glowny **1076** d.	|	2359	...	2304	|	|	...	...	...	...	...	...	...	...	|	...	...	...	...	|	...	0401
Katowice **1076** d.	|	|	...	0007	|	|	...	...	...	...	...	...	...	...	|	...	...	...	...	|	...	0512
Petrovice u Karviné a.	|	|	...	|	|	|	...	...	...	...	...	...	...	...	|	...	...	...	...	|	...	|
Bohumín a.	|	0212	...	0128	0258	0333	...	...	...	...	...	...	...	...	0544	...	...	...	...	|	...	0717
Bohumín d.	|	0245	...	0328	0328	0336	0400	...	...	0459	0504	0513	...	0550	0550	...	...	0659	0703	|	0736	0736
Havířov d.	0158	|	...	|	|	|	|	...	...	|	|	|	...	|	|	...	...	|	|	0649	|	|
Ostrava hl. n. d.	0214	0254	...	0337	0337	0344	0408	...	...	0507	0512	0527	...	0559	0559	...	...	0707	0712	0712	0744	0744
Opava východ d.	|	|	...	|	|	|	|	...	...	|	|	|	0550	|	|	0557	...	|	|	|	|	|
Ostrava Svinov d.	0223	0302	...	0346	0346	0352	0415	...	...	0515	0520	0535	0615	0607	0607	0622	...	0715	0720	0720	0752	0752
Púchov d.	|	|	...	|	|	|	|	...	...	|	|	|	|	|	|	|	...	|	|	|	|	|
Horní Lideč 🏛 d.	|	|	...	|	|	|	|	...	...	|	|	|	|	|	|	|	...	|	|	|	|	|
Vsetín d.	|	|	...	|	|	|	|	...	0453	|	|	|	|	|	|	|	0647	|	|	|	|	|
Valašské Meziříčí d.	|	|	...	|	|	|	|	...	0511	|	|	|	|	|	|	|	0704	|	|	|	|	|
Hranice na Moravě d.	|	|	...	|	|	0423	0442	...	0531	|	0548	0610	|	0642	0642	0648	0731	|	0748	0748	0823	0823
Přerov d.	|	|	0357	|	|	0442	|	0544	|	|	|	0644	|	|	|	|	|	|	|	|	0844	0844
Olomouc d.	0320	0401	0413	0446	0446	0500	0510	0600	0603	0610	0618	0700	0710	0714	0714	0718	0803	0810	0818	0818	0900	0900
Zábřeh na Moravé d.	0346	|	0435	|	|	0522	|	0622	0636	|	0641	0725	|	0737	0737	0741	0836	|	0841	0841	0925	0925
Česká Třebová d.	|	|	0458	0536	0536	|	|	|	0700	|	0704	|	|	0759	0759	0804	0900	|	0904	0904	|	|
Ústí nad Orlicí město d.	|	|	|	|	|	|	|	|	|	|	|	|	|	0806	0806	|	|	|	|	|	|	|
Ústí nad Orlicí d.	|	|	0508	|	|	|	|	|	|	|	|	|	|	|	|	|	|	|	|	|	|	|
Choceň d.	|	|	0526	|	|	|	|	|	0725	|	|	|	|	0825	0825	|	0925	|	|	|	|	|
Pardubice d.	0455	0523	0548	0623	0623	0631	0627	0735	0745	0729	0749	0831	0827	0845	0845	0849	0945	0931	0949	0949	1032	1032
Kolín d.	|	|	0615	|	|	0651	|	0755	0806	|	|	0851	|	0906	0906	|	1006	|	|	|	1052	1052
Praha hl. n. a.	0600	0624	0700	0755	0755	0737	0732	0839	0852	0832	0855	0937	0932	0952	0952	0955	1052	1032	1055	1055	1137	1137

CONTINUED FROM PREVIOUS PAGE. FOR FOOTNOTES SEE PAGE 485. TABLE CONTINUES ON NEXT PAGE.

1160a OSTRAVA - ČESKÝ TĚŠÍN LOCAL TRAINS

	Ⓐ	Ⓐ	Ⓐ	Ⓐ	Ⓐ	Ⓐ	Ⓐ	Ⓐ	Ⓐ	Ⓐ			2	2	2		2	2	2	2	2
Opava východ d.	0514	0625	0711	0824	1024	1224	1424	1624	1824	2021	...		0631	0742	0842		1842	1942	2043	2142	2243
Ostrava Svinov a.	0541	0649	0734	0848	1048	1248	1448	1648	1848	2048	...	A	0701	0814	0914	and at the	1912	2020	2114	2216	2313
Ostrava Svinov d.	0552	0654	0741	0853	1053	1253	1454	1653	1853	2053	...	L	0724	0824	0924	same minutes	1924	2024	2124	...	...
Ostrava hl. n. d.	0600	0700	0800	0900	1000	1300	1500	1700	1900	2059	...	S	|	|	|	past each	|	|	|	...	...
Havířov d.	0621	0722	0820	0921	1121	1321	1522	1721	1921	...	...	O	0750	0850	0950	hour until	1951	2051	2151	...	...
Český Těšín a.	0641	0742	...	0941	1141	1341	1542	1741	1941	...	...		0811	0912	1012	●	2012	2112	2212	...	...

Ostrava Svinov d.	...	...	...	...	0834	0934	1034	...	1134	1234	1334	...	1434	1534	1634	...	1734	1833	1934	...	2034	...	2231
Ostrava hl. n. d.	...	...	...	...	0842	0942	1042	...	1142	1242	1342	...	1442	1542	1642	...	1742	1841	1942	...	2042	...	2240
Bohumín d.	0550	0649	0749	...	0849	0949	1049	...	1149	1249	1349	...	1449	1549	1649	...	1749	1847	1949	...	2049	2149	2300
Karviná hl. n. d.	0602	0702	0802	...	0902	1002	1102	...	1202	1302	1402	...	1502	1602	1702	...	1802	1900	2002	...	2102	2202	2313
Český Těšín d.	0620	0720	0820	...	0920	1026	1120	...	1220	1320	1420	...	1520	1620	1720	...	1820	1920	2020	...	2120	2220	2331
Trinec centrum d.	0632	0732	0832	...	0932	1037	1132	...	1232	1332	1432	...	1532	1632	1732	...	1832	1932	2032	...	2132	2232	2343
Návsi a.	0644	0744	0844	...	0944	1049	1144	...	1234	1344	1444	...	1544	1644	1744	...	1844	1944	2044	...	2144	2244	2355

ŽILINA, OSTRAVA and PÚCHOV - PRAHA — 1160

SC and *IC* trains are not available for local travel Ostravá - Bohumín or v.v.
For additional fast trains Praha - Česká Třebová and v.v. see Table **1150**. For semi-fast trains Praha - Olomouc and v.v. see Table **1151**.

	EC	*EC* *	♥	♥	*EC*		*SC*•	*SC*•	♥	*EC*	*LE*♠	*EC*	*IC*	♥	♥	*EC*	*LE*♠	*EC*		*SC*•	♥	♥
	144	**144**	**1006**	**1006**	**220**	**346**	**242**	**242**	**1008**	**116**	**1258**	**128**	**508**	**1010**	**1010**	**142**	**1260**	**126**	**344**	**506**	**1012**	**1012**
	🍷	🍷	🍷	🍷	🍷	🍷	🍷[R]	🍷[R]	🍷	🍷⊖	[R]🍷	🍷	🍷[R]	🍷	🍷	🍷	🍷[R]	🍷	🍷	🍷[R]	🍷	🍷
		①-⑥						⑥					⑥		†							
		e	**g**	**f**				**q**		§♦			**p**								**g**	**f**
Košice **1180** d.	...	...	...	...	...	...	...	0448	0350	...	0457	...	...	...	...	...	...	...	...	...	0750	0750
Prešov **1196** d.	...	...	...	...	...	...	...	|	|	...	0536	...	...	...	...	...	...	...	...	...	|	|
Poprad Tatry **1180** d.	...	...	...	...	...	...	...	0554	0506	...	0648	...	...	...	...	...	...	...	...	...	0900	0900
Zvolen **1185** d.	...	...	...	...	...	0502	...	|	|	...	|	...	...	...	...	...	...	...	...	...	|	|
Banská Bystrica **1185** a.	...	...	...	...	...	0534	...	|	|	...	|	...	...	...	...	...	...	...	0934	...	|	|
Žilina d.	...	0627	...	...	...	0727	...	0748	0705	...	0842	...	...	...	...	1022	...	...	1127	...	1105	1105
Čadca 🏛 d.	...	0656	...	...	...	0756	...	0813	0730	...	0918	...	...	...	...	1056	...	...	1156	...	1130	1130
Návsi d.	0711	0711	0703	0703	...	0811	...	|	0746	...	|	...	...	...	1010	1111	...	...	1211	...	|	|
Třinec centrum d.	0719	0719	0714	0714	...	0819	...	|	0757	...	0937	...	...	...	1021	1119	...	...	1219	...	1154	1154
Český Těšín d.	0727	0727	0723	0723	...	0827	...	0837	0806	...	0951	...	...	...	1030	1127	...	...	1227	...	1206	1206
Karviná hl. n. d.	0742	0742	|	|	...	0842	...	|	|	...	1006	...	...	...	|	1142	...	...	1242	...	|	|
Warszawa Centralna **1060** a.	|	|	|	|	...	|	...	|	|	0456	|	...	...	...	|	|	...	...	|	...	|	|
Kraków Glowny **1076** d.	|	|	|	|	...	|	...	|	|	|	|	...	...	...	|	|	...	...	|	...	|	|
Katowice **1076** d.	|	|	|	|	...	|	...	|	|	0801	|	...	...	...	|	|	...	...	|	...	|	|
Petrovice u Karviné a.	|	|	|	|	...	|	...	|	|	|	|	...	...	...	|	|	...	...	|	...	|	|
Bohumín a.	0752	0752	|	|	...	0852	...	0858	|	0943	1015	...	...	...	|	1152	...	...	1252	...	|	|
Bohumín d.	0800	0800	|	|	...	0853	0859	0859	|	1000	1036	...	1059	...	|	1200	1236	...	1253	...	|	|
Havířov d.	|	|	0749	0749	...	|	|	|	0849	|	|	...	|	1049	1049	|	|	...	|	...	1249	1249
Ostrava hl. n. d.	0809	0809	0812	0812	...	0859	0907	0907	0910	1009	1044	...	1107	1110	1110	1209	1244	...	1259	1307	1310	1310
Opava východ d.	|	|	|	|	...	|	|	|	|	|	|	...	|	|	|	|	|	...	|	|	|	|
Ostrava Svinov d.	0818	0818	0821	0821	...	0909	0915	0915	0918	1018	1052	...	1115	1118	1118	1218	1252	...	1309	1315	1318	1318
Púchov d.	|	|	|	|	*0743*z	...	|	|	|	|	|	*0943*z	|	|	|	|	|	*1143*z	...	|	|	|
Horní Lideč 🏛 d.	|	|	|	|	*0818*z	...	|	|	|	|	|	*1018*z	|	|	|	|	|	*1218*z	...	|	|	|
Vsetín d.	|	|	|	|	0853	...	|	|	|	|	|	1053	|	|	|	|	|	1253	...	|	|	|
Valašské Meziříčí d.	|	|	|	|	0911	...	|	|	|	|	|	1111	|	|	|	|	|	1311	...	|	|	|
Hranice na Moravě d.	0845	0845	0848	0848	0931	...	|	|	0948	1045	1123	1131	|	1148	1148	1245	1323	1331	...	|	1348	1348
Přerov d.	|	|	|	|	|	...	|	|	|	|	1144	|	|	|	|	|	1344	|	...	|	|	|
Olomouc d.	0914	0914	0918	0918	1003	...	1010	1010	1018	1114	1200	1203	1210	1218	1218	1314	1400	1403	...	1410	1418	1418
Zábřeh na Moravé d.	0937	0937	0941	0941	1036	...	|	|	1041	1137	1222	1236	|	1241	1241	1337	1422	1436	...	|	1441	1441
Česká Třebová d.	0959	0959	1004	1004	1100	...	|	|	1104	1159	|	1300	|	1304	1304	1359	|	1500	...	|	1504	1504
Ústí nad Orlicí město d.	1006	1006	|	|	|	...	|	|	|	1206	|	|	|	|	|	1406	|	|	...	|	|	|
Ústí nad Orlicí d.	|	|	|	|	|	...	|	|	|	|	|	|	|	|	|	|	|	|	...	|	|	|
Choceň d.	1025	1025	|	|	1125	...	|	|	|	1225	|	1325	|	|	|	1425	|	1525	...	|	|	|
Pardubice d.	1045	1045	1049	1049	1145	...	1131	1131	1149	1245	1335	1345	1331	1349	1349	1445	1535	1545	...	1531	1549	1549
Kolín d.	1106	1106	|	|	1206	...	|	|	|	1306	1355	1406	|	|	|	1506	1555	1606	...	|	|	|
Praha hl. n. a.	1152	1152	1155	1209	1252	...	1232	1232	1255	1352	1439	1452	1432	1455	1455	1552	1639	1652	...	1632	1655	1710

	LE♠	*EC*	*LE*♠	*EC*	*SC*•	♥	♥	*EC*	*IC*	*EC*		*SC*•	♥	*EC*	*SC*•	*EC*	♥				*LE*♠	*LE*♠
	1236	**114**	**1262**	**124**	**504**	**1014**	**1014**	**140**	**502**	**122**	**342**	**500**	**1016**	**112**	**240**	**120**	**1018**	**640**	**640**	**340**	**1266**	**1266**
	🍷[R]	🍷⊖	🍷[R]	🍷	🍷[R]	🍷	🍷	🍷	🍷[R]	🍷	🍷	🍷[R]	🍷	🍷⊖	🍷[R]	🍷	🍷	2	2		🍷[R]	🍷[R]
									⑦									Ⓑ	⑦			
		§♦			⊕	**g**	**f**		**j**					§♦				**d**	**j**		**A**	
Košice **1180** d.	...	...	...	...	...	...	...	...	...	...	...	...	...	...	1459	...	...	...	...	...	...	...
Prešov **1196** d.	...	...	...	...	...	...	...	...	...	...	...	...	...	...	|	...	...	...	...	...	...	...
Poprad Tatry **1180** d.	...	...	...	...	...	...	...	...	...	...	...	...	...	...	1606	...	...	...	...	...	...	...
Zvolen **1185** d.	...	...	...	...	...	...	...	...	...	...	...	...	...	...	|	...	...	...	...	...	...	...
Banská Bystrica **1185** a.	...	...	...	...	...	...	...	...	...	...	1334	...	...	...	|	...	...	...	...	1734	...	...
Žilina d.	...	...	...	...	...	...	...	1427	...	...	1527	...	...	...	1752	...	...	...	...	1927	...	...
Čadca 🏛 d.	...	...	...	...	...	...	...	1456	...	...	1556	...	...	...	1817	...	...	...	...	1956	...	...
Návsi d.	...	...	...	...	...	...	...	1511	...	...	1611	...	...	...	|	...	...	...	...	2011	...	...
Třinec centrum d.	...	...	...	...	...	...	...	1519	...	...	1619	...	...	...	|	...	...	...	...	2019	...	...
Český Těšín d.	...	...	...	...	...	...	...	1527	...	...	1627	...	...	...	1841	...	...	...	...	2027	...	...
Karviná hl. n. d.	...	...	...	...	...	...	...	1542	...	...	1642	...	...	...	|	...	...	...	...	2042	...	...
Warszawa Centralna **1060** a.	...	...	...	...	...	...	...	|	...	...	|	...	...	1338	|	...	...	...	...	|	...	...
Kraków Glowny **1076** d.	...	1055	...	...	...	...	...	|	...	...	|	...	...	|	|	...	...	...	...	|	...	...
Katowice **1076** d.	...	1150	...	...	...	...	...	|	...	...	|	...	...	1623	|	...	...	...	...	|	...	...
Petrovice u Karviné a.	...	|	...	...	...	...	...	|	...	...	|	...	...	|	|	...	...	...	...	|	...	...
Bohumín a.	...	1312	...	...	...	...	...	1552	...	...	1652	...	...	1743	|	...	...	...	...	2052	...	...
Bohumín d.	1328	1400	1436	...	...	...	...	1600	...	...	1653	...	...	1800	|	...	...	1958	1958	2054	2145	2145
Havířov d.	|	|	|	...	...	1449	1449	|	...	...	|	...	1649	|	|	...	1849	|	|	|	|	|
Ostrava hl. n. d.	1336	1409	1444	...	1507	1510	1510	1609	...	...	1659	1707	1710	1809	1907	...	1910	2007	2007	2100	2153	2153
Opava východ d.	|	|	|	...	|	|	|	|	1552	...	|	|	|	|	|	...	|	|	|	|	|	|
Ostrava Svinov d.	1350	1418	1452	...	1515	1518	1518	1618	1619	...	1709	1715	1718	1818	1915	...	1918	2015	2015	2108	2202	2202
Púchov d.	|	|	|	*1343*z	|	|	|	|	|	*1543*z	...	|	|	|	|	*1808*z	|	|	|	▬	|	|
Horní Lideč 🏛 d.	|	|	|	*1418*z	|	|	|	|	|	*1618*z	...	|	|	|	|	*1833*z	|	|	|	...	|	|
Vsetín d.	|	|	|	1453	|	|	|	|	|	1653	...	|	|	|	|	1853	|	|	|	...	|	|
Valašské Meziříčí d.	|	|	|	1511	|	|	|	|	|	1711	...	|	|	|	|	1911	|	|	|	...	|	|
Hranice na Moravě d.	1421	1445	1523	1531	|	1548	1548	1645	|	1731	...	|	1748	1845	|	1931	1948	2046	2046	...	2238	2238
Přerov d.	1444	|	1544	|	|	|	|	|	|	|	...	|	|	|	|	|	|	|	|	*IC*	2258	2258
Olomouc d.	1500	1514	1600	1603	1610	1618	1618	1714	1710	1803	...	1810	1818	1914	2009	2002	2018	2112	2114	**570**	2314	2314
Zábřeh na Moravé d.	1525	1537	1622	1636	|	1641	1641	1737	|	1836	...	|	1841	1937	|	2036	2041	...	2137		2342	...
Česká Třebová d.	|	1559	|	1700	|	1704	1704	1759	|	1900	...	|	1904	1959	2048	2100	2104	...	2200	2315	0017	...
Ústí nad Orlicí město d.	|	1606	|	|	|	|	|	1806	|	|	...	|	|	2006	|	|	|	...	|	|	...	...
Ústí nad Orlicí d.	|	|	|	|	|	|	|	|	|	|	...	|	|	|	|	2109	|	...	2209	|	...	...
Choceň d.	|	1625	|	1725	|	|	|	1825	|	1925	...	|	|	2025	|	2126	|	...	2226	|	...	...
Pardubice d.	1635	1645	1735	1745	1731	1749	1749	1845	1831	1945	...	1931	1949	2045	2131	2146	2150	...	2246	0000	...	...
Kolín d.	1655	1706	1755	1806	|	|	|	1906	|	2006	...	|	|	2106	2151	2155	|	...	2309	0020	...	...
Praha hl. n. a.	1739	1752	1839	1852	1832	1855	1855	1952	1932	2052	...	2032	2055	2152	2233	2254	2257	...	2354	0102	...	...

CONTINUED FROM PREVIOUS PAGES. FOR FOOTNOTES SEE PAGE 485.

ČESKÝ TĚŠÍN - OSTRAVA LOCAL TRAINS — 1160a

	Ⓐ	Ⓐ	Ⓐ	Ⓐ	Ⓐ		Ⓐ	Ⓐ	Ⓐ	Ⓐ											
													2	2	2		2	2	2	2	2
Český Těšín d.	0513	0614	0713	0814	1014	...	1214	1414	1614	1814	...		0443	0543	0643		1843	1943	2044	2144	2243
Havířov d.	0535	0636	0735	0836	1036	...	1236	1436	1636	1836	...	**A**	0506	0606	0706	and at the	1907	2006	2107	2207	2306
Ostrava hl. n. a.	0557	0657	0757	0857	1057	...	1257	1457	1657	1857	...	**L**	|	|	|	same minutes	|	|	|	|	|
Ostrava Svinov a.	...	0707	...	0906	1106	...	1306	1506	1706	1908	...	**S**	0533	0634	0734	past each	1935	2034	2135	2248	2334
Ostrava Svinov d.	...	0713	...	0913	1113	...	1313	1513	1713	1913	...	**O**	0534	0641	0741	hour until	1940	*2041*	*2158*	*2256*	*2338*
Opava východ a.	...	0736	...	0936	1136	...	1336	1536	1736	1936	...		0606	0720	0814	●	2020	*2118*	*2235*	*2332*	*0008*

		Ⓐ																					
Návsi d.	0453	0453	0615	0716	0816	...	0916	1016	1116	1216	1316	...	1416	1516	1616	1716	1814	...	1916	2016	2116	2216	...
Třinec centrum d.	0505	0505	0626	0727	0827	...	0927	1027	1127	1227	1327	...	1427	1527	1627	1727	1825	...	1927	2027	2127	2227	...
Český Těšín d.	0526	0526	0641	0741	0841	...	0941	1041	1141	1241	1341	...	1441	1541	1641	1741	1845	...	1941	2041	2141	2241	...
Karviná hl. n. d.	0544	0544	0659	0759	0859	...	0959	1059	1159	1259	1359	...	1459	1559	1659	1759	1903	...	1959	2059	2159	2259	...
Bohumín d.	0556	0557	0711	0811	0911	...	1011	1111	1211	1311	1411	...	1511	1611	1711	1811	1915	...	2011	2111	2211	2311	...
Ostrava hl. n. a.	...	0603	0718	0818	0918	...	1018	1118	1218	1319	1418	...	1518	1618	1718	1818	1922	...	2018	2118	...	...	...
Ostrava Svinov a.	...	0611	0727	0827	0927	...	1027	1127	1227	1327	1427	...	1527	1627	1727	1827	1930	...	2027	2127	...	...	...

1162 PRAHA - UHERSKÉ HRADIŠTĚ - BŘECLAV - BRATISLAVA, BRNO and WIEN

EC trains are subject to alteration July 3 – 14. For faster trains Praha - Bratislava and v.v. see Table **1150**.

km		457		828		826		824		881	814	*EC* 101	883		812		885		810	*EC* 103	887		808
			2	🍷	2		2	🍷 *		🍷	🍷		🍷	2	🍷		🍷	2	🍷		🍷	2	🍷
		A	Ⓐ	Ⓐ	Ⓐ			e		e		B §								C §			
	Praha hl. n. **1151 1160** d.	...	...	...	...	...	...	...	...	...	...	...	0442e	...	...	...	0642	...	...	...	0842	...	...
	Ostrava hl. n. **1164** d.	0224	...	...	...	...	...	...	...	...	...	0651	|	...	...	...	|	...	...	1051	|	...	...
0	**Olomouc** **1160** d.	|	...	...	...	...	...	...	...	0554	0708	|	0731	...	0908	...	0931	...	1108	|	1131	...	1308
22	Přerov **1160** d.	|	0357	...	0444	...	0540	...	...	0611	0724	0745	0748	0738	0924	...	0948	0941	1124	1145	1148	1138	1324
37	Hulín d.	|	0407	...	0500	...	0600	...	...	0622	0734	|	0758	0801	0934	...	0958	1001	1134	|	1158	1201	1334
50	Otrokovice ▷ d.	|	0417	...	0513	...	0613	...	...	0631	0743	0804	0809	0814	0943	...	1009	1014	1143	1204	1209	1214	1343
68	Staré Město U.H. ⊖ a.	|	0427	...	0532	...	0632	...	...	0645	0755	0817	0822	0833	0955	...	1022	1033	1155	1217	1222	1233	1355
68	Staré Město U.H. ⊖ **1163** d.	|	0434	...	0537	...	0637	...	...	0656	0802	0818	0833	0837	0957	...	1033	1037	1157	1218	1233	1237	1357
73	Uherské Hradiště **1163** a.	|	|	...	|	...	|	...	...	0702	|	|	0839	|	|	...	1039	|	|	|	1239	|	|
90	Uherský Brod **1163** a.	|	|	...	|	...	|	...	...	0722	|	|	0857	|	|	...	1057	|	|	|	1257	|	|
104	**Luhačovice** **1163** a.	|	|	...	|	...	|	...	...	0741	|	|	0922	|	|	...	1122	|	|	|	1322	|	|
102	Hodonin d.	|	0508	0524	0608	0619	0708	0724	...	...	0823	0834	...	0908	1023	...	...	1108	1223	1234	...	1308	1423
122	Břeclav a.	0410	0525	0536	0625	0634	0725	0736	...	...	0835	0845	...	0925	1035	...	...	1125	1235	1245	...	1325	1435
122	Břeclav **1150** d.	0549	...	0542	...	0642	...	0742	...	...	0844	0855	...	...	1044	...	...	...	1244	1255	...	...	1444
140	Kúty 🏛 **1150** a.	|	...	|	...	|	...	|	...	...	|	|	...	...	|	...	...	...	|	|	...	...	|
204	**Bratislava** hl. st. **1150** a.	|	...	|	...	|	...	|	...	...	|	|	...	...	|	...	...	...	|	|	...	...	|
181	**Brno** hlavní nádrazi **1150** a.	|	...	0622	...	0722	...	0822	...	...	0922	|	...	...	1122	...	...	...	1322	|	...	...	1522
210	**Wien** Hbf **1150** a.	0700	...	...	...	...	...	...	...	...	...	0949	...	...	...	...	...	...	...	1349	...	...	...

	889		822	*EC* 131	806	891			820	804	*EC* 105	893		802		*EC* 107	895		800	897		
	🍷	2	🍷		🍷	🍷	2		🍷	🍷		🍷	2	🍷			🍷	2		🍷	2	2
			Ⓐ	D §					Ⓐ		E §					F §			Ⓑ d			
Praha hl. n. **1160** d.	1042	...	...	...	...	1242	...	...	...	...	...	1442	...	...	...	...	1642	...	...	1842	...	...
Ostrava hl. n. **1164** d.	|	...	...	1352	...	|	...	...	...	...	1651	|	...	...	...	1851	|	...	...	|	...	...
Olomouc **1160** d.	1331	...	...	|	1508	1531	...	...	...	1708	|	1731	...	1908	...	|	1931	...	2108	2131	...	...
Přerov **1160** d.	1348	1341	...	1445	1524	1548	1541	...	...	1724	1745	1748	1738	1924	...	1945	1948	1908	2124	2148	...	2243
Hulín d.	1358	1401	...	|	1534	1558	1601	...	...	1734	|	1758	1801	1934	...	|	1958	1924	2134	2158	...	2259
Otrokovice ▷ d.	1409	1414	...	1504	1543	1609	1614	...	...	1743	1804	1809	1814	1943	...	2004	2009	2016	2143	2207	2213	2323
Staré Město U.H. ⊖ a.	1422	1433	...	1517	1555	1622	1633	...	...	1755	1817	1822	1833	1955	...	2017	2022	2035	2155	|	2232	2345
Staré Město U.H. ⊖ **1163** d.	1433	1437	...	1518	1557	1633	1637	...	...	1757	1818	1833	1837	1957	...	2018	2034	2037	2157	z	...	...
Uherské Hradiště **1163** a.	1439	|	...	|	|	1639	|	...	...	|	|	1839	|	|	...	|	2040	|	|	...	...	...
Uherský Brod **1163** a.	1457	|	...	|	|	1657	|	...	...	|	|	1902	|	|	...	|	|	|	|	...	...	...
Luhačovice **1163** a.	1522	|	...	|	|	1722	|	...	...	|	|	1922	|	|	...	|	v	|	|	...	...	...
Hodonin d.	...	1508	1524	1534	1623	...	1708	...	1724	1823	1834	...	1908	2023	...	2034	...	2108	2218	...	...	...
Břeclav a.	...	1525	1536	1545	1635	...	1725	...	1736	1835	1845	...	1925	2035	...	2045	...	2125	2230	...	...	...
Břeclav **1150** d.	...	...	1542	*1555*	1644	...	...	...	1742	1844	1855	...	...	2044	...	2055	...	...	...	...	...	...
Kúty 🏛 **1150** a.	...	...	|	|	|	...	...	...	|	|	|	...	...	|	...	|	...	...	...	...	...	...
Bratislava hl. st. **1150** a.	...	...	|	|	|	...	...	...	|	|	|	...	...	|	...	|	...	...	...	...	...	...
Brno hlavní nádrazi **1150** a.	...	...	1622	|	1722	...	...	...	1822	1922	|	...	...	2122	...	|	...	...	...	...	...	...
Wien Hbf **1150** a.	...	...	...	*1649*	...	...	...	...	...	...	1949	...	...	...	...	2149	...	...	...	...	...	...

	896	894	801			892	*EC* 106		803	890	890		*EC* 104		805	888		807	*EC* 130	886		809
			🍷	2	2			2	🍷	🍷	🍷			2	🍷	🍷	2	🍷		🍷	2	🍷
	e		e		Ⓐ		F				e		E §						D §			
Wien Hbf **1150** d.	...	...	...	...	...	...	0606	...	...	...	...	...	0810	...	...	...	...	...	*1110*	...	...	...
Brno hlavní nádrazi **1150** d.	...	...	...	...	...	...	|	...	0636	...	...	...	|	...	0836	...	...	1036	|	...	...	1236
Bratislava hl. st. **1150** d.	...	...	...	...	...	...	|	...	|	...	...	...	|	...	|	...	...	|	|	...	...	|
Kúty 🏛 **1150** d.	...	...	...	...	...	...	|	...	|	...	...	...	|	...	|	...	...	|	|	...	...	|
Břeclav **1150** a.	...	...	...	...	...	...	0704	...	0715	...	...	...	0904	...	0915	...	...	1115	*1204*	...	...	1315
Břeclav d.	...	...	0526	...	0535	...	0710	0635	0721	...	...	...	0910	0835	0921	...	1035	1121	1210	...	1235	1321
Hodonin d.	...	...	0538	...	0554	...	0722	0654	0738	...	...	...	0922	0854	0938	...	1054	1138	1222	...	1254	1338
Luhačovice **1163** d.	...	...	|	...	|	v	|	|	|	...	0831	...	|	|	|	1031	|	|	|	1231	|	|
Uherský Brod **1163** d.	...	...	|	...	|	|	|	|	|	...	0857	...	|	|	|	1057	|	|	|	1257	|	|
Uherské Hradiště **1163** d.	...	...	|	...	|	0714	|	|	|	...	0914	...	|	|	|	1114	|	|	|	1314	|	|
Staré Město U.H. ⊖ **1163** a.	...	y	0556	...	0624	0720	0737	0724	0756	...	0920	...	0937	0924	0956	1120	1124	1156	1237	1320	1324	1356
Staré Město U.H. ⊖ d.	0410	|	0558	0625	0625	0731	0738	0725	0800	0932	0932	...	0938	0925	0958	1132	1125	1158	1238	1332	1325	1358
Otrokovice ▷ d.	0422	0544	0611	0643	0643	0743	0751	0754	0811	0944	0944	...	0951	0946	1011	1144	1146	1211	1251	1344	1346	1411
Hulín d.	0433	0556	0622	0659	0659	0754	|	0809	0822	0956	0956	...	|	1004	1022	1156	1202	1222	|	1356	1402	1422
Přerov **1160** d.	0442	0612	0635	0713	0713	0812	0813	0823	0835	1012	1012	...	1013	1018	1035	1212	1216	1235	1313	1412	1416	1435
Olomouc **1160** a.	0456	0627	0649	...	...	0827	|	...	0849	1027	1027	...	|	...	1049	1227	...	1249	|	1427	...	1449
Ostrava hl. n. **1164** a.	|	|	...	...	...	|	0908	...	...	|	|	...	1108	...	...	|	...	...	1407	|	...	...
Praha hl. n. **1160** a.	0752	0922	...	...	...	1119	...	...	...	1319	1319	...	...	...	...	1522	...	...	...	1722	...	...

	884	823	*EC* 102		811	882	825			813	880	827	*EC* 100			815	858	829		831	833	456
	🍷	🍷		2	🍷	🍷	🍷		2	🍷	🍷			2		🍷		🍷	2			
		Ⓐ	C §				Ⓐ					Ⓐ	B §					Ⓑ d	w			A
Wien Hbf **1150** d.	...	...	1410	...	...	...	...	...	...	...	...	...	1810	...	...	...	...	...	...	...	...	2210
Brno hlavní nádrazi **1150** d.	...	1336	|	...	1436	...	1534	...	...	1636	...	1736	|	...	...	1836	...	1936	...	2036	2236	|
Bratislava hl. st. **1150** d.	...	|	|	...	|	...	|	...	...	|	...	|	|	...	...	|	...	|	...	|	|	|
Kúty 🏛 **1150** d.	...	|	|	...	|	...	|	...	...	|	...	|	|	...	...	|	...	|	...	|	|	|
Břeclav **1150** a.	...	1415	1504	...	1515	...	1615	...	...	1715	...	1815	1904	...	...	1915	...	2015	...	2118	2315	2307
Břeclav d.	...	1421	1510	1435	1521	...	1621	...	1635	1721	...	1821	1910	1835	...	1921	...	2021	2035	2125	2322	2350
Hodonin d.	...	1433	1522	1454	1538	...	1633	...	1654	1738	...	1833	1922	1854	...	1938	...	2033	2054	2140	2337	|
Luhačovice **1163** d.	1431	...	|	|	|	1631	...	...	|	|	1804	...	|	|	...	|	1945	...	|	|	...	|
Uherský Brod **1163** d.	1457	...	|	|	|	1657	...	...	|	|	1828	...	|	|	...	|	2005	...	|	|	...	|
Uherské Hradiště **1163** d.	1514	...	|	|	|	1714	...	...	|	|	1845	...	|	|	...	|	2021	...	|	|	...	|
Staré Město U.H. ⊖ **1163** a.	1520	...	1537	1524	1556	1720	...	...	1724	1756	1852	...	1937	1924	...	1956	2027	...	2124	*2217*	...	|
Staré Město U.H. ⊖ d.	1532	...	1538	1525	1558	1732	...	...	1725	1758	1903	...	1938	1925	...	1958	...	...	2125	*2218*	...	|
Otrokovice ▷ d.	1544	...	1551	1554	1611	1744	...	...	1746	1811	1915	...	1951	1944	...	2011	...	...	2141	*2241*	...	|
Hulín d.	1556	...	|	1609	1622	1756	...	...	1802	1822	1929	...	|	2003	...	2022	...	...	*2201*	*2258*	...	|
Přerov **1160** d.	1612	...	1613	1623	1635	1812	...	...	1816	1835	1948	...	2013	2017	...	2035	...	...	*2219*	*2314*	...	|
Olomouc **1160** a.	1627	...	|	...	1649	1827	...	...	...	1849	1958	...	|	...	...	2049	...	...	*2254*	...	...	|
Ostrava hl. n. **1164** a.	|	...	1708	...	...	|	...	...	...	...	...	...	2107	...	...	...	...	...	...	...	...	0131
Praha hl. n. **1160** a.	1922	...	...	...	...	2119	...	...	...	...	...	...	...	...	...	...	...	...	...	...	...	...

A – NIGHTJET – 🛏 1, 2 cl., ▬ 2 cl., (2) Berlin - Wroclaw - Bohumín - Břeclav - Wien - Graz and v.v. (Table **77**);
🛏 1, 2 cl., ▬ 2 cl., (2) Berlin (**457/6**) - Břeclav (**477/6**) - Bratislava - Budapest and v.v. (Table **77**);
🛏 1, 2 cl., ▬ 2 cl., (2) Warszawa (**407/6**) - Kraków - Bohumín (**457/6**) - Wien and v.v. (Table **99**);
🛏 1, 2 cl., ▬ 2 cl., (2) Warszawa (**407/6**) - Kraków - Bohumín (**457/6**) - Břeclav (**477/6**) - Bratislava - Budapest and v.v. (Table **99**). Ⓡ for international journeys.

B – MORAVIA – (12) ✕ Katowice - Bohumín - Břeclav - Wien and v.v.

C – POLONIA – (12) ✕ Warszawa - Katowice - Bohumín - Břeclav - Wien and v.v.

D – BATHORY – (12) ✕ Budapest - Bratislava - Břeclav - Ostrava - Bohumín - Katowice - Warszawa - Terespol and v.v.; (2) Terespol - Brest* and v.v.; (2) Ⓡ Budapest - Bratislava - Bohumín (**115/114**) - Przemyśl and v.v.

E – PORTA MORAVICA – (12) Przemyśl - Kraków - Katowice - Bohumín - Břeclav - Wien - Graz and v.v.; ✕ Graz - Bohumín and v.v.

F – SOBIESKI – (12) ✕ Gdynia - Warszawa - Katowice - Bohumín - Břeclav - Wien and v.v.

d – Ⓑ (not July 5, Oct. 28).

e – ①–⑥ (not July 6, Oct. 29).

v – To / from Veseli nad Moravou (Table **1163**).

w – Connecting train change at Otrokovice and Přerov.

y – From Zlín střed (d. 0519).

z – To Zlín střed (Otrokovice d. 2219, Zlín střed a. 2232).

⊖ – Full name: Staré Město u Uherské Hradiště.

▷ – Local trains Otrokovice - Zlín: 1 – 2 per hour (trolleybus every 10 mins).

§ – Ⓡ for international journeys to / from Poland.

* – Subject to confirmation.

2nd class

BRNO - UHERSKÉ HRADIŠTĚ - BYLNICE and LUHAČOVICE 1163

BRNO - STARÉ MĚSTO U UHERSKÉ HRADIŠTĚ (ČD)

km		k	Ⓐ														m							⑤⑥
0	Brno hlavní nádrazi d.	...	0512	0735	0812	...	0928	1015	1128	1215	...	1328	1414	1528	1614	...	1728	1815	1928	2015	...	2128	2225	2225
67	Kyjov d.	...	0638	0834	0938	...	1032	1138	1232	1338	...	1432	1538	1632	1738	...	1832	1938	2032	2138	...	2232	2346	2347
90	Veselí nad Moravou d.	0659	0706	0900	1006	...	1100	1206	1300	1406	...	1500	1606	1700	1806	...	1900	2006	2100	2204	...	2258	...	0013
106	Uherské Hradiště a.	0712	0725	0918	1027	...	1118	1227	1318	1427	...	1518	1627	1718	1827	...	1924	2027	2118	2225	...	...	...	...
111	Staré Město u Uh. H ⊖ a.	0720	0733	0926	...	...	1126	...	1326	...	...	1526	...	1726	1846	...	1932	...	2126	2232	...	...	...	...

	©	Ⓐ		n																	qr	k	
Staré Město u Uh. H ⊖ d.	*0433*	*0431*	...	...	...	...	0827	...	1027	...	...	1227	...	1427	...	...	1627	...	1827	...	1940	2034	...
Uherské Hradiště d.	*0440*	*0440*	0535	0630	...	0735	0837	0935	1037	...	1135	1237	1335	1437	...	1535	1637	1735	1836	...	1954	2045	2036
Veselí nad Moravou d.	0500	0525	0601	0701	...	0757	0901	0957	1101	...	1157	1301	1357	1501	...	1557	1701	1757	1901	...	2020	2058	2101
Kyjov d.	0526	0555	0628	0728	...	0825	0928	1025	1128	...	1225	1328	1425	1528	...	1625	1728	1825	1928	...	2045	...	2128
Brno hlavní nádrazi a.	0650	0720	0733	0833	...	0948	1033	1148	1233	...	1348	1433	1548	1633	...	1748	1833	1948	2033	...	2145	...	2233

STARÉ MĚSTO U UHERSKÉ HRADIŠTĚ - UHERSKÝ BROD - BYLNICE - VLÁRSKÝ PRŮSMYK (Arriva)

km			Ⓐ		©		◧			◧		◧		◧		◧								
0	Staré Město u Uh. H ⊖ . 1162 d.	0536	0536	0628	0628	0735	...	0935	...	...	1135	...	1339	...	1539	...	...	1739	...	...	2028	2129	2159	2236
5	Uherské Hradiště 1162 d.	0544	0544	0635	0635	0743	...	0943	...	...	1143	...	1346	...	1546	...	...	1746	1855	...	2039	2136	2206	2243
7	Kunovice d.	0547	0547	0638	0638	0749	...	0946	...	...	1146	...	1350	...	1550	...	...	1750	1858	...	2042	2139	2209	2246
22	Uherský Brod 1162 d.	0606	0606	0659	0659	0810	0900	1006	...	1100	1206	1300	1411	1500	1611	1700	...	1811	1920	...	2105	2158	2228	2305
26	Újezdec u Luhačovic d.	0611	0611	0703	0703	0814	0904	1010	...	1104	1210	1304	1415	1504	1615	1704	...	1815	1924	...	2110	2202	2232	2309
35	Bojkovice a.	0625	0625	0717	0717	0828	0918	1024	...	1118	1224	1318	1429	1518	1629	1718	...	1829	1938	2000	2124	2216	2246	2323
63	Bylnice a.	...	0709	...	0754	...	0954	...	...	1154	...	1354	...	1554	...	1754	...	...	...	2036	...	2252	...	...

			Ⓐ			©		◧		◧			◧		◧		◧						
Bylnice d.	...	...	0545	...	...	0600	...	0801	...	1001	...	...	1201	...	1401	...	1601	...	...	1805	...	2013	...
Bojkovice d.	0505	0625	0625	0640	...	0640	0734	0836	0931	1036	1131	...	1236	1336	1437	1536	1637	1731	...	1842	2023	2056	2203
Újezdec u Luhačovic d.	0518	0638	0638	0654	...	0654	0747	0850	0944	1050	1144	...	1250	1349	1450	1549	1650	1745	...	1856	2036	2110	2217
Uherský Brod 1162 d.	0523	0643	0643	0708	...	0708	0753	0854	0950	1054	1150	...	1254	1354	1454	1554	1654	1754	...	1902	2046	2120	2227
Kunovice d.	0541	0701	0701	0727	...	0727	0811	...	1009	...	1209	...	...	1413	...	1613	...	1813	...	1921	2105	2139	2246
Uherské Hradiště 1162 a.	0544	0704	0704	0730	...	0730	0814	...	1012	...	1212	...	...	1416	...	1616	...	1816	...	1924	2108	2142	2249
Staré Město u Uh. H ⊖ 1162 a.	0555	0713	0713	0752	...	0752	0826	...	1026	...	1223	...	...	1423	...	1623	...	1824	...	1932	2115	2151	...

km		Ⓐ	⑤s	⑤t	⑤t	⑦q	⑦q			
0	Staré Město u Uh. H ⊖ . 1162 d.	1359	1559	1559	...	1559	...	1759	...	...
5	Uherské Hradiště 1162 d.	1409	1609	1609	...	1609	...	1809	...	...
7	Kunovice d.	|	|	|	...	|	...	|	...	...
22	Uherský Brod 1162 d.	1425	1625	1625	...	1625	...	1825	...	...
26	Újezdec u Luhačovic d.	|	|	|	...	|	...	1829	...	...
35	Bojkovice a.	1437	1637	1637	...	1637	...	1839	...	...
63	Bylnice a.	1514	1714	1714	...	1714	...	1916	...	...
68	Vlárský průsmyk 🏛 a.	...	...	1721	1722	1721	1847	...	...	...
80	Trenčianska Teplá a.	...	...	...	1738	...	1904	...	...	...

	Ⓐ	v	⑤t	⑤t		⑦q	⑦q		
Trenčianska Teplá d.	...	...	1652	...	...	1826	...	...	...
Vlárský průsmyk 🏛 d.	...	...	1711	1730	...	1844	1850	...	...
Bylnice d.	0647	1640	...	1736	1805	...	1858	...	...
Bojkovice d.	0723	1718	...	...	1842	...	1931	...	...
Újezdec u Luhačovic d.	|	|	...	...	1856	...	1941	...	...
Uherský Brod 1162 d.	0736	1731	...	...	1902	...	1946	...	...
Kunovice d.	|	|	...	...	1921	...	1959	...	...
Uherské Hradiště 1162 a.	0751	1745	...	...	1924	...	*2005*	...	...
Staré Město ⊖ 1162 a.	0758	1752	...	...	1932	...	*2013*	...	...

ÚJEZDEC U LUHAČOVIC - LUHAČOVIC (Arriva)

km														w	q									
0	Újezdec u Luhačovic d.	0523	0613	...	0705	1012	...	1212	1416	...	1616	1746	...	1926	2004	...	2037	2112	...	2233	...	...	...	...
10	Luhačovice a.	0537	0627	...	0719	1026	...	1226	1430	...	1630	1800	...	1940	2018	...	2051	2126	...	2247	...	...	...	...

												w	q									
Luhačovice d.	0430	0554	...	0638	0928	...	1128	1332	...	1532	1729	...	1840	1924	...	2020	2054	...	2145	...	...	...	...
Újezdec u Luhačovic a.	0444	0608	...	0652	0942	...	1142	1346	...	1546	1743	...	1854	1938	...	2037	2108	...	2159	...	...	...	...

k – To / from Praha (Table **1162**).
m – Change at Kunovice (a. 1917 / d. 1921).
n – Change at Kunovice (a. 0633 / d. 0636).
q – ⑦ (not July 3 - Aug. 28).
r – Change at Kunovice (a. 1957 / d. 2000).
s – ⑤ (also Oct. 27; not Oct. 28).

t – ⑤ (also Oct. 27; not July 1 - Aug. 26, Oct. 28).
v – ⑤⑦ (also Oct. 27; not July 3, 10, 17, 24, 31, Aug. 7, 14, 21, 28, Oct. 28).
w – ①-⑥ (daily June 27 - Sept. 3).

◧ – Connects with Praha - Luhačovice and v.v. trains on Table **1162**.
⊖ – Full name is Staré Město u Uherské Hradiště.

BRNO - PŘEROV - OSTRAVA - BOHUMÍN 1164

EC trains are subject to alteration July 3 – 14. Brno - Přerov - Ostrava - Bohumín trains are operated by Regiojet (🍷 on most trains).

km		1101	1103	1105		1129	1131	1133	
		⚒					p		
0	**Brno** hlavní nádrazi 1156 d.	0502	0602	0702	and	1902	2002	2102	...
45	Vyškov na Moravě 1156 d.	0540	0640	0740	at the	1940	2040	2141	...
71	Kojetin d.	0606	0706	0806	same	2006	2106	2206	...
88	Přerov 1160 d.	0624	0724	0824	minutes	2024	2124	2224	...
117	Hranice na Moravě 1160 d.	0643	0743	0843	past	2043	2143	2243	...
167	**Ostrava** Svinov 1160 a.	0714	0814	0914	each	2115	2214	2314	...
172	**Ostrava** hl. n. 1160 a.	0722	0822	0922	hour	2122	2222	2323	...
180	**Bohumín** 1160 a.	0730	0830	0930	until	2130	2230	2330	...

	1100	1102	1104		1128	1130	1132	
	⚒					p		
Bohumín 1160 d.	0431	0531	0631	and	1831	1931	2031	...
Ostrava hl. n. 1160 d.	0439	0539	0639	at the	1839	1939	2039	...
Ostrava Svinov 1160 d.	0447	0547	0647	same	1847	1947	2047	...
Hranice na Moravě 1160 d.	0518	0618	0718	minutes	1918	2018	2118	...
Přerov 1160 d.	0537	0637	0737	past	1937	2037	2137	...
Kojetin d.	0553	0653	0753	each	1953	2052	2153	...
Vyškov na Moravě 1156 d.	0617	0717	0817	hour	2017	2117	2217	...
Brno hlavní nádrazi 1156 a.	0659	0759	0859	until	2055	2155	2253	...

km		*EC* 106 A	*EC* 104 B	*EC* 130 C	*EC* 102 D	*EC* 100 E	456 F			
							p			
	Wien Hbf **1150** d.	0606	0810	*1110*	1410	1810	2210	...	...	...
	Břeclav **1162** d.	0710	0910	1210	1510	1910	2350	...	...	...
0	**Přerov** 1160 d.	0813	1013	1313	1613	2013	|	...	...	...
29	Hranice na Moravě 1160 d.	0831	1031	1331	1631	2031	|	...	...	...
79	**Ostrava** Svinov 1160 a.	0858	1058	1359	1658	2058	|	...	...	...
84	**Ostrava** hl. n. 1160 a.	0908	1108	1407	1708	2107	0131	...	...	...
92	**Bohumín** 1160 a.	0916	1116	1416	1716	2116	0140	...	...	...

	457 F	*EC* 101 E	*EC* 103 D	*EC* 131 C	*EC* 105 B	*EC* 107 A			
	⚒								
Bohumín 1160 d.	0215	0642	1042	1342	1642	1842	...	...	...
Ostrava hl. n. 1160 d.	0224	0651	1051	1352	1651	1851	...	...	...
Ostrava Svinov 1160 d.	|	0659	1059	1401	1659	1859	...	...	...
Hranice na Moravě 1160 d.	|	0727	1123	1427	1727	1927	...	...	...
Přerov 1160 a.	|	0744	1144	1444	1744	1944	...	...	...
Břeclav **1162** a.	0410	0845	1245	1545	1845	2045	...	...	...
Wien Hbf **1150** a.	0700	0949	1349	*1649*	1949	2149	...	...	...

A – SOBIESKI – (12) ✕ Gdynia - Warszawa - Katowice - Bohumín - Břeclav - Wien and v.v.
B – PORTA MORAVICA – (12) Przemyśl - Kraków - Katowice - Bohumín - Břeclav - Wien - Graz and v.v.; ✕ Graz - Bohumín and v.v.
C – BATHORY – (12) ✕ Budapest - Bratislava - Břeclav - Ostrava - Bohumín - Katowice - Warszawa - Terespol and v.v.; (2) Terespol - Brest* and v.v.; (2) Ⓡ Budapest - Bratislava - Bohumín (**115/114**) - Przemyśl and v.v.
D – POLONIA – (12) ✕ Warszawa - Katowice - Bohumín - Břeclav - Wien and v.v.
E – MORAVIA – (12) ✕ Katowice - Bohumín - Břeclav - Wien and v.v.
F – NIGHTJET – 🛏 1, 2 cl., ▬ 2 cl., (2) Berlin - Wroclaw - Bohumín - Břeclav - Wien - Graz and v.v. (Table **77**); 🛏 1, 2 cl., ▬ 2 cl., (2) Berlin (**457/6**) - Břeclav (**477/6**) - Bratislava - Budapest and v.v. (Table **77**); 🛏 1, 2 cl., ▬ 2 cl., (2) Warszawa (**407/6**) - Kraków - Bohumín (**457/6**) - Wien and v.v. (Table **99**); 🛏 1, 2 cl., ▬ 2 cl., (2) Warszawa (**407/6**) - Kraków - Bohumín (**457/6**) - Břeclav (**477/6**) - Bratislava - Budapest and v.v. (Table **99**). Ⓡ for international journeys.

p – ④⑤⑦.
* – Subject to confirmation.

CZECH REPUBLIC

1165 PRAHA - ÚSTI NAD ORLICI - LICHKOV - KLODZKO (- WROCŁAW)

2nd class LEO Express

Subject to alteration on Czech and Polish holiday dates (see page 4).

km																							
		Ⓐ			Ⓒ			◨	Ⓒ	Ⓐ						Ⓒ	Ⓐ						
					m				m	k						m	k						
0	**Praha** hlavní n. **1151** d.	...	...	...	...	...	...	...	...	...	...	...	...	...	...	...	...	...	...	...	...	...	...
62	Kolín **1151** d.	...	...	...	...	...	...	...	...	...	...	...	...	...	...	...	...	...	...	...	...	...	...
104	Pardubice **1151** d.	...	...	...	...	...	...	...	...	...	...	...	...	...	...	...	...	...	...	...	...	...	...
139	Choceň **1151** d.	...	...	...	...	...	...	...	...	...	...	...	...	...	...	...	...	...	...	...	...	...	...
154	**Ústi nad Orlici** **1151** d.	0521	0740	...	0840	0940	...	1140	1240	1240	...	1340	1440	...	1540	1640	1640	1740	...	1840	...	2040	2206
168	Letohrad d.	0554	0803	...	0856	1001	...	1204	1256	1307	...	1401	1507	...	1601	1656	1707	1801	...	1907	...	2100	2231
189	Lichkov a.	0622	0826	...	0917	1026	...	1227	1317	1332	...	1426	1532	...	1626	1717	1732	1826	...	1932	...	2127	2256
189	Lichkov d.	...	...	0844	...	...	1145	...	...	...	1345	...	...	1553	...	...	...	...	1843	...	2043	...	...
198	Miedzylesie 🏛 a.	...	...	0853	...	...	1154	...	...	...	1354	...	...	1602	...	...	...	...	1852	...	2052	...	...
234	**Klodzko** Gl. ⊕ a.	...	...	0933	...	...	1303	...	...	...	1452	...	...	1652	...	...	...	...	1933	...	2133	...	...
	Wroclaw **1095** ⊕ a.	...	...	1100	...	...	1431	...	...	...	1628	...	...	1830	...	...	...	...	2105	...	...	...	...

	1290																					
	Ⓐ						Ⓒ				Ⓐ	Ⓒ				Ⓒ	Ⓐ		Ⓒ			
							m				k	m				m	k		m			
Wroclaw **1095** ⊕ d.	...	...	0618	...	...	0753	...	...	1010	...	...	...	1313	...	1410	...	...	...	...	1658	...	...
Klodzko Gl. ⊕ d.	...	...	0740	...	...	0930	...	...	1139	...	...	...	1438	...	1537	...	...	...	...	1829	...	...
Miedzylesie 🏛 d.	...	...	0820	...	...	1009	...	...	1220	...	...	...	1520	...	1624	...	...	...	...	1914	...	...
Lichkov a.	...	...	0829	...	...	1018	...	...	1229	...	...	...	1529	...	1633	...	...	...	...	1923	...	...
Lichkov d.	0605	0735	...	0831	0935	...	1040	1135	...	1335	1428	1440	...	1535	...	1628	1635	1735	1840	...	1935	2111
Letohrad d.	0632	0800	...	0900	1000	...	1103	1200	...	1400	1500	1503	...	1600	...	1700	1700	1800	1903	...	2000	2136
Ústí nad Orlicí **1151** d.	0651	0817	...	0917	1017	...	1117	1217	...	1417	1517	1517	...	1617	...	1717	1717	1817	1917	...	2017	2153
Choceň **1151** d.	0708	...	...	...	...	...	...	...	...	...	...	...	...	...	...	...	...	...	...	...	...	...
Pardubice **1151** d.	0733	...	...	...	...	...	...	...	...	...	...	...	...	...	...	...	...	...	...	...	...	...
Kolín **1151** d.	0755	...	...	...	...	...	...	...	...	...	...	...	...	...	...	...	...	...	...	...	...	...
Praha hlavní n. **1151** a.	0839	...	...	...	...	...	...	...	...	...	...	...	...	...	...	...	...	...	...	...	...	...

k – Not July 1 - Aug. 31.
m – Ⓒ (daily July 1 - Aug. 31).
◨ – Change trains at Letohrad on Ⓒ (daily July 1 - Aug. 31).
⊕ – Operator in Poland: Koleje Dolnoślaskie.

1166 OLOMOUC - KRNOV - OPAVA - OSTRAVA

2nd class

km																								
		Ⓐ			①–⑥																		Ⓐ	
					e																			
0	**Olomouc** d.	...	...	...	0705	...	...	0905	...	1105	...	1305	...	...	1505	...	1705	...	...	1905	...	...	...	...
64	Bruntál d.	0543	...	0708	0826	...	0908	1026	1108	1226	1308	1426	...	1508	1626	1708	1826	1908	...	2026	...	...	...	...
87	Krnov a.	0611	...	0738	0851	...	0938	1051	1138	1251	1338	1451	...	1538	1651	1738	1851	1938	...	2051	...	...	...	...
87	Krnov d.	0614	0706	0741	0906	0906	0941	1106	1141	1306	1341	1506	...	1541	1706	1741	1906	1939	...	...	2101	...	2209	...
116	**Opava** východ a.	0706	0733	0821	0932	0932	1021	1132	1221	1332	1421	1532	...	1621	1732	1821	1932	2017	...	...	2138	...	2239	...
116	**Opava** východ **1160a** d.	...	0737	...	0937	0937	...	1137	...	1337	...	1537	...	...	1737	...	1937	...	2043	...	...	2142	...	2243
144	**Ostrava** Svinov **1160a** a.	...	0757	...	0957	0957	...	1157	...	1358	...	1558	...	...	1758	...	2001	...	2114	...	...	2216	...	2313
149	**Ostrava** hl. n. a.	...	0808	...	...	...	...	1208	...	1410	...	1609	...	...	...	...	...	...	...	...	...	...	...	...

	①–⑥	Ⓐ														①–⑥	⑦				Ⓐ		
	e															n	j		p				
Ostrava hl. n. d.	...	...	...	...	...	...	0948	...	...	...	1349	...	1549	...	1749	...	...	...	...	...	...	...	...
Ostrava Svinov **1160a** d.	...	...	0550	...	0800	...	1000	...	1200	...	1400	...	1600	...	1800	...	...	1947	...	2041	...	2158	...
Opava východ **1160a** a.	...	...	0621	...	0822	...	1022	...	1222	...	1422	...	1622	...	1822	...	...	2008	...	2118	...	2235	...
Opava východ d.	*0427*	0527	0628	0739	0828	0939	1028	1139	1228	1339	1428	1539	1628	1739	1828	...	...	...	2023	...	2126	...	2246
Krnov a.	*0503*	0606	0656	0815	0856	1015	1056	1215	1256	1415	1456	1615	1656	1815	1856	...	...	...	2100	...	2205	...	2327
Krnov d.	0505	0615	0705	0816	0905	1016	1105	1216	1305	1416	1505	1616	1705	1816	...	1903	1903	...	2112	...	...	...	...
Bruntál d.	0534	0652	0734	0852	0934	1052	1134	1252	1334	1452	1534	1652	1734	1852	...	1931	1932	...	2137	...	...	...	...
Olomouc a.	0652	...	0852	...	1052	...	1252	...	1452	...	1652	...	1852	...	...	...	2057	...	2302	...	...	...	...

km										
0	**Jesenik** d.	0530	...	0930	...	1330	...	1730	...	...
22	Glucholazy (Poland) d.	0611	...	1011	...	1411	...	1811	...	...
43	Tremešná ve Slezsku d.	0639	0839	1039	1239	1439	1642	1839	2039	...
60	**Krnov** a.	0658	0900	1058	1300	1458	1702	1858	2059	...

Krnov d.	0705	0748	0908	1105	1308	1505	1713	1905	...
Tremešná ve Slezsku d.	0726	0808	0928	1126	1328	1526	1733	1926	...
Glucholazy (Poland) d.	0759	...	...	1159	...	1559	...	1959	...
Jesenik a.	0836	...	...	1236	...	1636	...	2036	...

e – ①–⑥ (not July 6, Oct. 29).
j – ⑦ (also July 6, Sept. 28; not July 3).
n – ①–⑥ (also July 3; not Sept. 28).
p – Change trains at Moravský Beroun (a. 2207 / d. 2210).

1169 OTHER LOCAL SERVICES

May vary on holidays 2nd class

BRNO - ZNOJMO *89 km* Journey 2 hours

From Brno: *No service currently available.*

From Znojmo: *No service currently available.*

ČESKÝ TĚŠÍN - CIESZYN (Poland) *3 km* Journey 5 mins

From Český Těšín: 0522 Ⓐ, 0548 Ⓒ, 0722 Ⓐ, 0748 Ⓒ, 0948, 1148, 1322 Ⓐ, 1348 Ⓒ, 1422 Ⓐ, 1548 Ⓒ, 1722 Ⓐ, 1748 Ⓒ, 1948, 2148.

From Cieszyn: 0533 Ⓐ, 0603 Ⓒ, 0805, 1003, 1205, 1333 Ⓐ, 1403 Ⓒ, 1433 Ⓐ; 1603 Ⓒ, 1733 Ⓐ, 1803 Ⓒ, 2003, 2203.

CHOCEŇ - LITOMYŠL *24 km* Journey 55 minutes

From Choceň: 0628 Ⓐ, 0637 Ⓒ, 0837, 1037, 1337 Ⓒ, 1428 Ⓐ, 1637 Ⓒ, 1737 Ⓐ, 1837 Ⓒ.

From Litomyšl: 0608 Ⓐ, 0718 Ⓐ **k**, 0736 Ⓒ **m**, 0936, 1236, 1536, 1736 Ⓒ, 1836 Ⓐ, 1936 Ⓒ.

JINDŘICHŮV HRADEC - NOVÁ BYSTŘICE *33 km* Narrow gauge, 80 mins

From Jindřichův Hradec: 0723 **t**, 0923, 1039 **A**, 1123, 1323, 1523, 1723 **t**.

From Nová Bystřice: 0907 **t**, 1107, 1307, 1507, 1518 **A**, 1707, 1907 **t**.

Operator: JHMD www.jhmd.cz

KOJETIN - KROMĚŘÍŽ *9 km* Journey 12 minutes

From Kojetin: 0623, 0723, 0809, 0921, 1021, 1121, 1221, 1321, 1421, 1521, 1621, 1721, 1821, 1921, 2009, 2114 ④⑤⑦, 2209, 2259 Ⓐ.

From Kroměříž: 0537, 0637, 0737, 0837, 0937, 1037, 1137, 1237, 1337, 1437, 1537, 1637, 1737, 1837, 1937, 2037 ④⑤⑦, 2137, 2237 Ⓐ.

KROMĚŘÍŽ - HULIN *8 km* Journey 8 minutes

From Hulin: 1 - 2 trains per hour connecting with trains in Table **1162**.

From Kroměříž: 1 - 2 trains per hour connecting with trains in Table **1162**.

PRAHA - KARLŠTEJN *33 km* Journey 42 minutes

From Praha hl. n.: 0421, 0451 Ⓐ, 0521, 0551 Ⓐ, 0621, 0651, 0719, 0821, 0851, 0919 0951 Ⓒ, 1021, 1051 Ⓒ, 1121, 1151 Ⓒ, 1221, 1251, 1319, 1351, 1421, 1451, 1519, 1551 1621, 1651, 1719, 1751, 1821, 1851, 1921, 1951 Ⓐ, 2021, 2121, 2221, 2321.

From Karlštejn: 0527, 0557, 0627 Ⓐ, 0657, 0727, 0757, 0857, 0927, 0957, 1027 Ⓒ, 1057 1127 Ⓒ, 1157, 1227 Ⓒ, 1257, 1327, 1357, 1427, 1457, 1527, 1557, 1627, 1657, 1727, 1757 1827, 1857, 1927, 1957, 2027 Ⓐ, 2057, 2157, 2257.

Trains continue to / from Beroun (journey 10 mins).

TŘEMEŠNÁ VE SLEZSKU - OSOBLAHA *20 km* Narrow gauge, 45 minutes

From Třemešná: 0727 ①–⑥ **e**, 1045 **B**, 1127, 1527, 1927.

From Osoblaha: 0546 ①–⑥ **e**, 0946, 1346, 1510 **B**, 1746.

ZNOJMO - BŘECLAV *69 km* Journey 80 minutes

From Znojmo: 0458 Ⓐ, 0558 ①–⑥ **e**, 0656, 0757 Ⓐ **k**, 0856, 1056, 1156 Ⓐ, 1256, 1356 Ⓐ 1456, 1556 Ⓑ **d**, 1656, 1756 Ⓐ, 1758 **s**, 1856.

From Břeclav: 0456 Ⓐ, 0556 ①–⑥ **e**, 0640 Ⓐ **k**, 0740, 0847 Ⓒ **q**, 0938, 1138, 1240 Ⓐ, 1336 1440 Ⓐ, 1537, 1642 **r**, 1737, 1937, 2136 Ⓑ **d**.

A – ⑥ May 7 - Sept. 24 (also ①③⑤⑦ June 26 - Aug. 31). Steam hauled train. 🍷. Special fares. 1039 arrives Nová Bystřice 1305; 1518 arrives Jindřichův Hradec 1712.
B – ⑥ June 4 - Sept. 17 (also † July 3 - Aug. 28). Steam hauled train. Special fares. Journey 80 – 90 minutes.
d – Ⓑ (not July 5, Oct. 28).
e – ①–⑥ (not July 6, Oct. 29).
k – Not July 1 - Aug. 31.
m – Ⓒ (daily July 1 - Aug. 31).
q – Until Oct. 2.
r – Ⓐ until Sept. 30 (not July 4); Ⓑ from Oct. 3 (not Oct. 28, Nov. 17).
s – ⑦ (Ⓒ Apr. 15 - Oct. 2).
t – June 25 - Aug. 31.

SLOVAKIA

Operator: National railway operator is Železničná spoločnosť Slovensko (ŽSSK), www.slovakrail.sk, which runs on the network of Železnice Slovenskej Republiky (ŽSR), www.zsr.sk.

Services: All trains convey first and second class seating, **except** where shown otherwise in footnotes or by '2' in the train column, or where the footnote shows sleeping and/or couchette cars only. Reservation of 1st class seats is compulsary on domestic trains. Descriptions of sleeping (🛏) and couchette (▬) cars appear on page 10.
Note: hl. st. = hlavná stanica = main station.

Timings: Valid **December 12, 2021 - December 10, 2022** with amendments as received. Certain trains may be cancelled during the period December 24 - January 1.

Supplements: A higher level of fares applies to travel by *EC* and *IC* trains. It is possible to reserve seats on most Express trains.

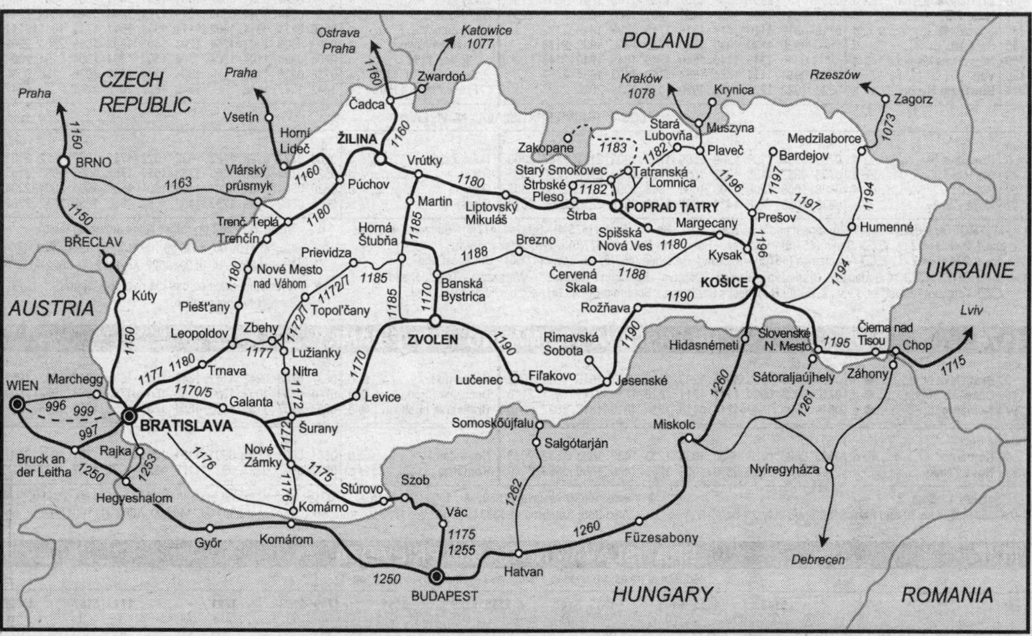

BRATISLAVA - LEVICE - ZVOLEN - BANSKÁ BYSTRICA — 1170

Service until October 18

km		831	833	835	837	839	15843	841	853	845	855	801		800	850	830	832	834	836	838	840	842	17840	844
							⑤e		Ⓐ		f	A		A	Ⓐ	g							⑦h	
0	**Bratislava** hl. st. ...... d.	0604	0804	1004	1204	1404	1504	1604	1655	1804	2004	2235	Nová Baňa .... d.	...	...	*0550**	*0750**	*0950**	*1150**	*1350**		*1750**	...	*1950**
49	Galanta .... d.	0637	0838	1038	1238	1438	1546	1638	1728	1838	2038	2313	**Šurany** .... d.	...	0608	0651	0851	1051	1251	1451	1651	1851	...	2051
60	Šal'a .... d.	0646	0847	1047	1247	1447	1556	1647	1736	1847	2047	2324	**Nové Zámky** .... d.	0442	|	|	|	|	|	|	|	|	1921	|
	Nové Zámky .... a.	|	|	|	|	|	1619	|	|	|	|	2347	Šal'a .... d.	0506	0633	0714	0914	1114	1314	1514	1714	1914	1944	2114
89	**Šurany** .... a.	0708	0908	1108	1308	1508	...	1708	1757	1908	2108	...	Galanta .... d.	0518	0642	0725	0925	1125	1325	1525	1724	1925	1954	2125
	Nová Baňa .... a.	*0805**	*1005**	*1205**	*1405**	*1605**	...	*1805**	...	*2005**	...	...	**Bratislava** hl. st. ...... a.	0558	0718	0758	0958	1158	1358	1558	1758	1958	2032	2158

km		801	861	11831	11833	11835		11837	11839	11841	15843	15845		800	11830	11832	11834	11836		11838	11840	17840	11842	11844
		A	g								⑤e			A	g							⑦h		
	Nové Zámky .... d.	0001	...	...	...	...	...	...	...	...	1627	...	**Banská Bystrica** ..... d.	...	0432	0632	0832	1032	...	1232	1432	1532	1632	1832
0	**Levice** .... d.	0136	0548	0748	0948	1148	...	1348	1548	1748	1756	1948	**Zvolen** osob. .... d.	...	0454	0654	0854	1054	...	1254	1454	1554	1654	1854
27	Nová Baňa .... d.	0207	0614	0814	1014	1214	...	1414	1614	1814	1824	2014	**Zvolen** osob. .... d.	0149	0457	0657	0857	1057	...	1257	1457	1605	1657	1857
55	Žiar nad Hronom ..... d.	0231	0640	0840	1040	1240	...	1440	1640	1840	1852	2040	Žiar nad Hronom ..... d.	0209	0517	0717	0917	1117	...	1317	1530	1626	1717	1917
77	**Zvolen** osob. .... a.	0249	0659	0859	1059	1259	...	1459	1659	1859	1912	2059	Nová Baňa .... d.	0234	0542	0742	0942	1142	...	1342	1542	1652	1742	1942
77	**Zvolen** osob. .... d.	...	0702	0902	1102	1302	...	1502	1702	1902	1915	2102	**Levice** .... a.	0303	0620	0820	1020	1220	...	1420	1620	1730	1820	2020
98	**Banská Bystrica** ..... a.	...	0727	0926	1126	1326	...	1526	1726	1926	1944	2126	**Nové Zámky** .... a.	0437	...	...	...	...	...	...	...	1920	...	...

OTHER TRAINS ZVOLEN - BANSKÁ BYSTRICA — 2nd class

km																								
		B			Ⓐ					j					Ⓒ		Ⓐ		k			B		
0	**Zvolen** osob. .... d.	0502	0602	0802	1002	1202	1402	1602	1802	2002	2121	2239	**Banská Bystrica** ..... d.	0532	0732	0932	1132	1332	1532	1732	1932	2033	2129	2229
21	**Banská Bystrica** ..... a.	0529	0626	0826	1026	1226	1426	1626	1826	2026	2155	2311	**Zvolen** osob. .... a.	0557	0757	0957	1157	1357	1557	1757	1957	2056	2159	2259

A – GEMERAN POL'ANA – From Bratislava and Prešov on ⑧ (not Aug. 28), from Zvolen next day: 🛏 1, 2 cl., ▬2▬ Bratislava - Zvolen - Košice - Prešov and v.v.; 🛏 1, 2 cl. Praha (**283/2**) - Bratislava - Nové Zámky (**801/0**) - Zvolen - Košice - Prešov and v.v.
B – ▬12▬ Ostrava - Žilina - Banská Bystrica - Zvolen and v.v. (Tables **1160** and **1185**).
e – ⑤ (also July 4, Aug. 31, Sept. 14, Oct. 31, Nov. 16).
f – ⑧ (not Aug. 28).
g – ①–⑥ (not Aug. 29).
h – ⑦ (also July 5, Aug. 29, Sept. 1, 15, Nov. 1, 17; not Aug. 28).
j – ①②③④⑥⑦ (also July 4, Aug. 31, Sept. 14, Oct. 31. Nov. 16).
k – ①–⑥ (also Aug. 28; not July 5, Aug. 29, Sept. 1, 15, Nov. 1, 17).
* – Connection by 🚌 from / to **Šal'a**.

NOVÉ ZAMKY - NITRA - TOPOL'ČANY - PRIEVIDZA — 1172

2nd class

km																									
			Ⓐ			Ⓐ		Ⓒ	Ⓐ			Ⓐ			Ⓐ		Ⓐ		Ⓒ	Ⓐ		Ⓐ	Ⓐ			
0	**Nové Zamky**	d.	...	0415	0521	...	0628	0715	0725	0915	1115	...	1315	...	1420	1515	1620	1715	1820	1820	1915	1915	...	2054	...	2303
10	Šurany	a.	...	0426	0532	...	0639	0726	0736	0926	1126	...	1326	...	1431	1526	1631	1726	1832	1832	1926	1926	...	2105	...	2313
10	Šurany	d.	...	0428	0533	...	0640	0728	0738	0928	1128	...	1328	...	1437	1528	1637	1728	1836	1836	1934	1934	...	2112	...	2314
36	**Nitra**	a.	...	0500	0605	...	0717	0800	0810	1000	1200	...	1400	...	1518	1600	1718	1800	1908	1922	2005	2005	...	2144	...	2346
36	**Nitra** **1177**	d.	0413	0536	0606	0634	...	0812	0812	1012	1212	...	1412	...	1525	1612	...	1812	...	...	...	2014	...	...	2240	...
40	Lužianky **1177**	d.	0424	0549	0616	0644	...	0823	0823	1023	1223	...	1423	...	1543	1623	...	1823	...	...	...	2026	...	...	2252	...
69	**Topol'čany** **1177**	a.	0505	0624	...	0719	...	0858	0858	1058	1258	...	1458	...	1618	1658	...	1858	...	...	...	2102	...	...	2329	...
69	**Topol'čany** **1177**	d.	0545	0644	...	...	...	0910	0910	1100	1300	1408	1500	...	...	1700	...	1908	...	...	...	...	2223	...	...	...
86	Partizánske **1177**	d.	0621	0733	...	...	...	0937	0937	1137	1337	1444	1537	...	...	1737	...	1946	...	...	...	...	2248	...	...	...
113	**Prievidza** **1177**	a.	0712	0818	...	...	...	1023	1023	1223	1423	1528	1623	...	...	1823	...	2029	...	...	...	...	2326	...	...	...
				Ⓐ			Ⓐ	Ⓒ	Ⓐ			Ⓐ		Ⓐ		Ⓐ		Ⓐ	Ⓐ	Ⓒ		Ⓒ	Ⓐ			Ⓐ
	Prievidza **1177**	d.	...	0402	...	0517	...	...	0615	0725	0937	...	1137	...	1337	...	1537	1627	...	...	1737	...	...	1937	...	2231
	Partizánske **1177**	d.	...	0439	...	0552	...	...	0651	0801	1015	...	1215	...	1415	...	1615	1709	...	...	1815	...	...	2015	...	2315
	Topol'čany **1177**	a.	...	0509	...	0618	...	...	0715	0825	1052	...	1252	...	1442	...	1652	1734	...	...	1852	...	...	2052	...	2339
	Topol'čany **1177**	d.	0419	0511	...	0632	...	...	0748	0904	1104	...	1304	...	1504	...	1704	1735	...	...	1904	...	...	2116	...	...
	Lužianky **1177**	d.	0454	0550	0619	0715	...	...	0844	0938	1138	...	1338	...	1538	...	1738	1825	1845	...	1938	...	...	2153	...	...
	Nitra **1177**	a.	0504	0600	0629	0726	...	...	0854	0948	1148	...	1348	...	1548	...	1748	1836	1855	...	1948	...	...	2204	...	...
	Nitra	d.	0519	...	0631	...	0747	0803	...	1003	1203	1255	1403	1455	1603	1655	1803	...	1858	1915	...	2032	2122	...	2238	...
	Šurany	a.	0554	...	0701	...	0829	0834	...	1034	1234	1326	1434	1526	1634	1726	1834	...	1928	1955	...	2103	2201	...	2311	...
	Šurany	d.	0600	...	0703	...	0835	0835	...	1035	1235	1330	1435	1530	1635	1730	1835	...	1929	2002	...	2111	2202	...	2315	...
	Nové Zamky	a.	0614	...	0714	...	0846	0846	...	1046	1246	1341	1446	1541	1646	1741	1846	...	1941	2013	...	2123	2213	...	2327	...

1175 BRATISLAVA - ŠTÚROVO - BUDAPEST

APRIL 23 - AUGUST 31. All *EC* trains convey ✕. For additional trains Bratislava - Šal'a see Table **1170**. For local trains Szob - Budapest and v.v. see Table **1255**.

km		575 477	*EC* 271	*EC* 273	*EC* 275	*EC* 277	*EC* 279	*EC* 131	*EC* 287	*EC* 281	*EC* 283
		🅁 A						B			
	Praha hlavní **1150** ..... d.	2134	...	0512	0656	0856	1056	...	1256	1456	1656
	Brno hlavní n. **1150** ... d.	0141	0622	0822	1020	1220	1420	...	1620	1820	2020
	Břeclav **1150** .... d.	0455	0655	0855	1055	1255	1455	1555	1655	1855	2055
0	**Bratislava** hlavná .... d.	0557	0757	0957	1157	1357	1557	1705	1757	1957	2157
91	Nové Zámky.................. d.	0651	0851	1051	1251	1451	1651	1800	1851	2054	2258
135	Štúrovo 🛃..................... d.	0719	0919	1119	1319	1519	1719	1829	1919	2122	...
150	Szob 🛃........................ d.	|	0930	1130	1330	1530	1730	1840	1930	2133	...
163	Nagymaros-Visegrád ¶.... d.	|	0940	1140	1340	1540	1740	1849	1940	2143	...
180	Vác.............................. d.	0753	0954	1154	1354	1554	1754	1903	1954	2157	...
214	**Budapest** Nyugati......... a.	0820	1020	1220	1420	1620	1820	1934	2020	2223	...

	EC 282	*EC* 280	*EC* 286	*EC* 130	*EC* 278	*EC* 276	*EC* 274	*EC* 272	*EC* 270	476 574
				B						🅁 A
Budapest Nyugati .... d.	...	0540	0740	0828	0940	1140	1340	1540	1740	1940
Vác .... d.	...	0606	0806	0856	1006	1206	1406	1606	1806	2006
Nagymaros-Visegrád ¶.... d.	...	0619	0819	0910	1019	1219	1419	1619	1819	|
Szob 🛃.......................... d.	...	0631	0831	0922	1031	1231	1431	1631	1831	|
Štúrovo 🛃....................... d.	...	0644	0844	0935	1044	1244	1444	1644	1844	2044
Nové Zámky .... d.	0500	0711	0911	1002	1111	1311	1511	1711	1911	2111
Bratislava hlavná.......... a.	0603	0803	1003	1054	1203	1403	1603	1803	2003	2203
Břeclav **1150** .... a.	0704	0904	1104	1204	1304	1504	1704	1904	2104	2304
Brno hlavní n. **1150**.... a.	0736	0936	1136	...	1336	1536	1736	1936	2136	0536
Praha hlavní **1150**...... a.	1042	1242	1442	...	1642	1858	2042	2241	...	0842

LOCAL TRAINS BRATISLAVA - NOVÉ ZÁMKY — 2nd class

km										d	
0	Bratislava hl .... △ d.	0709	0909	1109	1309	1509	1709	1909	2109	2157	2309
49	Galanta..................... △ d.	0758	0957	1158	1358	1558	1758	1958	2158	2230	2357
60	Šal'a .... △ d.	0808	1008	1208	1408	1608	1808	2008	2208	2239	0007
91	Nové Zámky............. △ a.	0838	1038	1238	1438	1638	1838	2038	2238	2258	0035

	d							Ⓐ		
Nové Zámky............. ▽ d.	0500	0722	0920	1122	1322	1522	1722	1822	1922	2122
Šal'a.......................... ▽ d.	0521	0753	0950	1153	1353	1553	1753	1853	1953	2153
Galanta .... ▽ d.	0530	0804	1001	1204	1404	1604	1804	1904	2004	2204
Bratislava hl.............. ▽ a.	0603	0852	1049	1252	1452	1652	1852	1952	2052	2252

A – METROPOL – (12) Břeclav - Budapest and v.v.; 🛏 1, 2 cl., 🛌 2 cl. Praha (**575/4**) - Břeclav (**477/6**) - Budapest and v.v.;
🛏 1, 2 cl., 🛌 2 cl., (2) Berlin (**457/6**) - Wroclaw - Bohumín - Břeclav (**477/6**) - Budapest and v.v.;
🛏 1, 2 cl., 🛌 2 cl., (2) Warszawa (**407/6**) - Kraków - Bohumín (**457/6**) - Břeclav (**477/6**) - Budapest and v.v.

B – BATHORY – (12) ✕ Budapest - Bratislava - Břeclav - Ostrava - Bohumín - Katowice - Warszawa - Terespol and v.v.;
(2) Terespol - Brest* and v.v.; (2) 🅁 Budapest - Bratislava - Bohumín (**115/114**) - Przemyśl and v.v.

d – Trains **283**/**282** (for other times see main table).
△ – Also at 1209 Ⓐ, 1409 Ⓐ, 1609 Ⓐ, 1809 Ⓐ, 2009 Ⓐ.
▽ – Also at 0530, 0618 Ⓐ, 0622 Ⓐ, 1422 Ⓐ, 1622 Ⓐ.
¶ – A ferry operates across the river to Visegrád.
* – Subject to confirmation.

1176 BRATISLAVA - KOMÁRNO - NOVÉ ZÁMKY

2nd class

km		Ⓒ	Ⓐ					Ⓒ	Ⓐ		
0	**Bratislava** hl. st......... ● d.	0603	0703	0803	1003	1203	1403	1603	1615	1803	2003
46	Dunajská Streda........ ● d.	0716	0824	0934	1111	1311	1510	1711	1711	1921	2110
94	**Komárno**................... ● a.	0819	0928	1040	1214	1413	1614	1813	1817	2027	2215

	Ⓐ					k	Ⓐ	Ⓒ	Ⓐ	
Komárno .... ● d.	0637	0748	0942	1142	1342	1543	1630	1742	1842	1952
Dunajská Streda .... ● d.	0744	0853	1053	1253	1453	1651	1753	1853	1950	2109
Bratislava hl. st. .... ● a.	0833	0957	1155	1355	1554	1755	1855	1954	*2054*	2219

km		Ⓐ		Ⓐ							
0	**Komárno**................. ⊙ d.	0533	0633	0733	0833	1033	1233	1433	1633	1833	2033
29	**Nové Zámky**............. ⊙ a.	0559	0659	0759	0859	1059	1259	1459	1659	1859	2059

	Ⓐ									
Nové Zámky .... ⊙ d.	0501	0601	0701	0901	1101	1301	1501	1701	1901	2101
Komárno .... ⊙ a.	0527	0627	0727	0927	1127	1327	1527	1727	1927	2127

j – Not July 1 - Sept. 2.
k – Daily until June 30 and from Sept. 3; Ⓒ July 2 - Sept. 1.
● – Also from Bratislava at 0503 Ⓐ, 1303 Ⓐ j, 1515 Ⓐ, 1703 Ⓐ; from Komárno at 0330 Ⓐ, 0422, 0544 Ⓐ, 1434 Ⓐ.
⊙ – Also from Komárno at 1333 Ⓐ, 1533 Ⓐ, 1733 Ⓐ; from Nové Zámky at 0801 Ⓐ, 1401 Ⓐ, 1601 Ⓐ, 1801 Ⓐ.

1177 BRATISLAVA - NITRA and PRIEVIDZA

2nd class

Additional trains are available Bratislava - Leopoldov and v.v. on Ⓒ.

km				5143		1711	5145		1713	5147		1715	5149		5151		1719	5153		1721			1723	5157		17725
			Ⓐ	Ⓐ	Ⓒ		Ⓐ			Ⓐ			Ⓐ		Ⓐ			Ⓐ		Ⓑe	Ⓐ		f	Ⓐ		⑦g
0	**Bratislava** hl.... **1180** d.	...	...	...	...	0633	...	...	0833	...	...	1033	...	...	...	...	1433	...	...	1633	...	...	1833	...	...	2033
46	Trnava .... **1180** d.	...	0624	0650	...	0720	0750	0850a	0920	0950	1050a	1120	1150	1250a	1350	1450a	1520	1550	1650a	1720	1750	1850a	1920	1950	2050a	2120
63	Leopoldov .... **1180** a.	...	0637	0704	...	0733	0804	0904a	0933	1004	1104a	1133	1204	1304a	1404	1504a	1533	1604	1704a	1733	1804	1904a	1933	2004	2104a	2133
63	Leopoldov .... d.	0535	0638	0705	0707	0737	0807	0907	0937	1007	1107	1137	1207	1307	1407	1507	1537	1607	1707	1737	1807	1907	1937	2007	2107	2137
87	Zbehy .... d.	0612	0710	|	0735	0801	|	0934	1001	|	1134	1201	|	1334	|	1534	1601	|	1734	1801	1839	1934	2001	|	2133	2201
91	Lužianky .... **1172** d.	0619	0722	|	0742	|	|	0945	|	|	1145	|	|	1345	|	1545	|	|	1745	|	1845	1945	|	|	2141	|
98	**Nitra**............ **1172** a.	0629	0734	0743	0753	|	0847	0956	|	1047	1156	|	1247	1356	1447	1556	|	1647	1756	|	1855	1956	|	2057	2151	|
114	Topol'čany .... **1172** d.	...	...	...	...	0830	...	...	1030	...	...	1230	...	...	...	...	1630	...	...	1830	...	...	2030	...	...	2230
131	Partizánske...... **1172** d.	...	...	...	...	0854	...	...	1054	...	...	1254	...	...	...	...	1654	...	...	1854	...	...	2054	...	...	2254
158	**Prievidza**........ **1172** a.	...	...	...	...	0928	...	...	1128	...	...	1328	...	...	...	...	1728	...	...	1928	...	...	2128	...	...	2328

			1710		5142	1712		5144		5146	1716			5148	1718		5150	1720		5152	17722		5154	1724	
		Ⓐ	h		Ⓐ			Ⓐ		Ⓐ				Ⓐ			Ⓐ	f		Ⓐ	⑦g		Ⓐ		
Prievidza.................. **1172** d.	...	...	0428	...	...	0628	...	...	...	...	1028	...	...	...	1228	...	...	1428	...	...	1628	...	...	1828	...
Partizánske................. **1172** d.	...	...	0503	...	...	0702	...	...	...	...	1108	...	...	...	1308	...	...	1501	...	...	1708	...	...	1908	...
Topol'čany.................. **1172** d.	...	...	0530	...	...	0730	...	...	...	...	1130	...	...	...	1330	...	...	1525	...	...	1730	...	...	1930	...
Nitra .... **1172** d.	0404	0509	|	0606	0655	|	0804	0858	1004	1058	|	1204	...	1258	|	1404	1458	|	1604	1658	|	1804	1859	|	2007
Lužianky..................... **1172** d.	0415	0519	|	0620	|	|	0814	|	1014	|	|	1214	...	|	|	1414	|	|	1614	|	|	1816	|	|	2017
Zbehy.............................. d.	0422	0526	0556	0627	|	0802	0821	|	1021	|	1202	1221	...	|	1402	1421	|	1602	1621	|	1802	1823	|	2002	2023
Leopoldov........................ a.	0449	0552	0619	0653	0734	0824	0852	0936	1052	1136	1224	1252	...	1336	1424	1452	1536	1624	1652	1736	1824	1849	1936	2024	2050
Leopoldov................. **1180** d.	0453a	0555	0629	0655a	0738	0829	0855a	0938	1055a	1138	1229	1255a	...	1338	1429	1455a	1538	1629	1655a	1738	1829	1855a	1938	2029	2055
Trnava...................... **1180** d.	0507a	0609	0645	0709a	0752	0845	0909a	0952	1109a	1152	1245	1309a	...	1352	1445	1509a	1552	1645	1709a	1752	1845	1909a	1952	2045	2109
Bratislava hl.............. **1180** a.	...	...	0727	...	...	0927	...	...	...	...	1327	...	...	...	1527	...	...	1727	...	...	1927	...	...	2127	...

a – Ⓐ only.
e – Not Aug. 28.
f – ①-⑥ (also Aug. 28; not July 5, Aug. 29, Sept. 1, 15, Nov. 1, 17).
g – Also July 5, Aug. 29, Sept. 1, 15, Nov. 1, 17; not Aug. 28.
h – ①-⑥ (not Aug. 29).

1180 BRATISLAVA - ŽILINA - POPRAD TATRY - KOŠICE

km			♥			*EN*			*IC*				*SC*					*IC*	♥						
		1761	1021	1763	1765	443	767	701	521	601	703	603	241		705	605	707	523	1023	1751	607	709	1733	1753	609
		2	🍷🅁	✕	2	⊖	✕		✕🅁	✕		✕	✕🅁			✕		✕🅁	🍷	2	✕		2	2	✕
		Ⓐ	⊡	Ⓐ	⚒	A		Ⓐ			Ⓐ		B				Ⓐ			Ⓐ		Ⓐ	Ⓐ	Ⓐ	
	Wien Hbf. **996** ....d.	...	...	...	...	...	...	...	...	...	...	...	...	...	...	...	...	...	...	...	...	...	...	...	...
0	**Bratislava** hlavná st... **1177** d.	...	...	...	...	...	...	0513	0555	0613	0713	0813	...	...	0913	1013	1113	1151	...	...	1213	1313	1335	...	1413
46	Trnava .... **1177** d.	...	...	...	...	...	...	0544	0620	0644	0744	0844	...	...	0944	1044	1144	1216	...	...	1244	1344	1415	...	1444
63	Leopoldov .... **1177** d.	...	...	...	...	...	...	0556	|	0656	0756	0856	...	...	0956	1056	1156	|	...	...	1256	1356	1428	...	1456
81	Piešťany..............................d.	...	...	...	...	...	...	0607	|	0707	0807	0907	...	...	1007	1107	1207	|	...	...	1307	1407	1441	...	1507
99	Nové Mesto nad Váhom......d.	...	...	...	...	...	...	0619	|	0719	0819	0919	...	...	1019	1119	1219	|	...	...	1319	1419	1457	...	1519
124	**Trenčín** ....d.	...	...	...	...	...	0526	0635	0653	0735	0835	0935	...	...	1035	1135	1235	1249	...	...	1335	1435	1513	...	1535
132	Trenčianska Teplá..............d.	...	...	...	...	...	0533	0643	|	0743	0843	0943	...	...	1043	1143	1242	|	...	...	1343	1443	...	...	1543
	Praha hl. n. **1160** ....d.	...	2137	...	...	2205	|	|	|	|	|	|	0625	...	|	|	|	|	0818d	...	|	|	...	...	|
159	**Púchov** .... **1161** d.	...	|	...	...	|	0600	0700	|	0800	0900	1000	|	...	1100	1200	1300	|	|	...	1400	1500	...	...	1600
171	Považská Bystrica...... **1161** d.	...	|	...	...	|	0610	0711	|	0812	0912	1012	|	...	1112	1212	1318	|	|	...	1412	1512	...	...	1612
203	**Žilina**......................... **1161** a.	...	0249	...	...	0417	0638	0735	0741	0836	0936	1036	1117	...	1136	1236	1342	1336	1343	...	1436	1536	...	...	1636
203	**Žilina**......................... **1185** d.	...	0250	...	...	0435	0641	...	0743	0842	...	1042	1119	...	...	1242	...	1338	1350	1357	1442	...	...	1542	1642
224	Vrútky .... **1185** d.	...	0315	...	...	0501	0706	...	0807	0907	...	1107	|	...	...	1307	...	1402	1417	1426	1507	...	...	1611	1707
242	Kral'ovany ....d.	...	|	...	...	0515	0721	...	|	0921	...	1121	|	...	...	1321	...	|	|	1446	1521	...	...	1628	1721
260	Ružomberok ....d.	...	0344	...	...	0533	0738	...	0836	0939	...	1139	1209	...	...	1339	...	1429	1450	1504	1539	...	...	1649	1739
286	Liptovský Mikuláš.................d.	...	0403	...	...	0552	0758	...	0854	0958	...	1158	1227	...	...	1358	...	1446	1511	1526	1558	...	...	1709	1758
325	Štrba.......................................d.	...	0432	...	...	0622	0827	...	|	1027	...	1227	1255	...	...	1427	...	|	1539	1604	1627	...	...	...	1827
344	**Poprad-Tatry**........................d.	0429	0453	0529	0623	0714	0850	...	0940	1050	...	1250	1312	...	...	1450	...	1532	1601	1625	1650	...	...	...	1850
370	Spišská Nová Ves..................d.	0449	0511	0550	0642	0734	0909	...	0957	1109	...	1309	|	...	...	1509	...	1549	1619	...	1709	...	...	...	1909
410	Margecany ....d.	0523	0537	0622	0714	0801	0936	...	|	1136	...	1336	|	...	...	1536	...	|	|	...	1736	...	...	...	1936
	Prešov..................................a.	|	|	|	|	|	|	...	|	|	...	|	|	...	...	|	...	|	|	...	|	...	...	...	|
429	Kysak .... **1196** d.	0539	0551	0639	0729	0816	0951	...	1036	1151	...	1351	1406	...	...	1551	...	1628	1658	...	1751	...	...	...	1951
445	**Košice**...................... **1196** a.	0551	0607	0651	0741	0829	1003	...	1048	1203	...	1403	1418	...	...	1603	...	1640	1710	...	1803	...	...	...	2003
	Humenné **1194** ....a.	...	...	...	...	1033	...	...	...	...	...	...	...	...	...	...	...	...	...	...	...	...	...	...	...

TABLE CONTINUES ON NEXT PAGE →

Continued from previous page

BRATISLAVA - ŽILINA - POPRAD TATRY - KOŠICE 1180

	711	15711	1735	*IC* 45	*LE*♠ 1257	611	713	15713	*IC* 525	1739	*SC* 243	613		♥ 1011	715	15715	17715	♥ 1045		717	717 443	719		*LE*♠ 1261	615
			2	✕🅁	🍷🅁	✕			✕🅁		✕🅁	✕		🍷					2	✕	🛏	✕	2	🍷🅁	2
	m	⑤n	Ⓐ				p	⑤n		Ⓐ	Bv				m	⑤n	⑦q	C			D				E
Wien Hbf. **996** d.	...	...	...	1437	...	...	...	...	...	...	...	...	...	...	...	...	...	...	...	...	...	...	...	...	...
Bratislava hlavná st. **1177** d.	1513	1513	1535	1606	...	1613	1713	1713	1752	1735	...	1813	...	...	1913	1913	1913	1933	...	2013	2013	2213	...	...	2257
Trnava **1177** d.	1544	1544	1615	1631	...	1644	1744	1744	1818	1822	...	1844	...	...	1943	1943	1943	1959	...	2044	2044	2244	...	...	2329
Leopoldov **1177** d.	1556	1556	1628	|	...	1656	1756	1756	|	1835	...	1856	...	...	1955	1955	1955	|	...	2056	2056	2256	...	...	2342
Piešťany d.	1607	1607	1651	|	...	1707	1807	1807	|	1847	...	1907	...	...	2007	2007	2007	2017	...	2107	2107	2307	...	...	2355
Nové Mesto nad Váhom d.	1619	1619	1706	|	...	1719	1819	1819	|	1902	...	1919	...	...	2019	2019	2019	2028	...	2119	2119	2319	...	...	0008
Trenčín d.	1635	1635	1722	|	...	1735	1835	1835	1852	1926	...	1935	...	...	2030	2037	2037	2042	...	2135	2135	2332	...	...	0025
Trenčianska Teplá d.	1643	1643	...	|	...	1743	1843	1843	|	...	...	1943	...	...	...	2044	2044	2049	...	2143	2143	...	...	...	0032
Praha hl. n. **1160** d.	|	|	...	|	1228	|	|	|	|	...	1525	|	...	1518	...	|	|	|	...	|	|	...	...	1928	|
Púchov **1161** d.	1700	1700	...	|	|	1800	1900	1900	|	...	|	2000	...	|	...	2100	2100	2106	...	2200	2200	...	2238	|	0052
Považská Bystrica **1161** d.	1712	1712	...	|	|	1812	1921	1921	|	...	|	2012	...	|	...	2111	2111	2116	...	2212	2212	...	2249	|	0102
Žilina **1161** a.	1736	1736	...	1749	1818	1836	1945	1945	1938	...	2007	2036	...	2046	...	2133	2133	2139	...	2236	2236	...	2324	0039	0129
Žilina **1185** d.	...	1742	...	1755	1820	1842	...	1951	1940	...	2011	2042	...	2050	...	...	...	...	2154	...	0435	...	...	0041	0131
Vrútky **1185** d.	...	1807	...	|	1842	1907	...	2016	2004	...	|	2107	...	2116	...	...	...	...	2222	...	0501	...	...	0105	0155
Kraľovany d.	...	1824	...	|	|	1921	...	2030	|	...	|	2121	...	|	...	...	...	...	2243	...	0515	...	...	|	0208
Ružomberok d.	...	1852	...	|	1910	1939	...	2045	2033	...	2059	2139	...	2146	...	...	...	...	2309	...	0533	...	...	0135	0224
Liptovský Mikuláš d.	...	1912	...	|	1927	1958	...	2104	2050	...	2117	2158	...	2205	...	...	...	...	2335	...	0552	...	...	0152	0243
Štrba d.	...	1940	...	|	1953	2027	...	2132	|	...	2145	2227	...	2235	...	...	...	...	...	...	0622	...	...	0219	|
Poprad-Tatry d.	...	2001	...	1946	2014	2050	...	2154	2138	...	2204	2250	...	2257	...	...	...	...	...	...	0714	...	...	0236	0330
Spišská Nová Ves d.	...	2021	...	|	2032	2109	...	2212	2156	...	|	2309	...	2317	...	...	...	...	...	...	0734	...	...	0254	0349
Margecany d.	...	2050	...	|	|	2136	...	2238	|	...	|	2336	...	|	...	...	...	...	...	...	0801	...	...	|	0416
Prešov a.	...	2120	...	|	2132	|	...	|	|	...	|	|	...	|	...	...	...	...	...	...	|	...	...	0344	|
Kysak **1196** d.	...	|	...	2040	2159	2151	...	2253	2236	...	2259	2351	...	0003	...	...	...	...	...	...	0816	...	...	0417	0431
Košice **1196** a.	...	|	...	2052	2211	2203	...	2305	2248	...	2311	0003	...	0015	...	...	...	...	...	...	0829	...	...	0428	0443
Humenné **1194** a.	...	2303	...	...	...	...	...	...	...	...	...	...	...	...	...	...	...	...	...	...	1033	...	...	...	0633

	1730	614	700	702	16702	704	1736	♥ 1046		706	1750	♥ 1008		600	*SC* 242	*LE*♠ 1258	*IC* 520	708	602	*IC* 44	710	♥ 1012	604	712	606
	2		✕	✕	✕	✕	2		2		2	🍷		✕	🅁✕	🍷🅁	✕🅁		✕	✕🅁		🍷	✕		✕
	Ⓐ	E	Ⓐ	Ⓐ	Ⓒ		Ⓐ	C	Ⓐ	r	Ⓐ				Bw			Ⓐ			Ⓐ			Ⓑs	
Humenné **1194** d.	...	2154	...	...	...	...	...	...	...	...	...	...	...	...	...	...	...	...	...	...	...	...	...	...	...
Košice **1196** d.	...	2345	...	...	...	...	...	...	...	...	...	0350	...	0357	0448	0457	0512	...	0557	0711	...	0750	0757	...	0957
Kysak **1196** d.	...	2359	...	...	...	...	...	...	...	...	...	0403	...	0411	0500	0510	0525	...	0611	0724	...	0803	0811	...	1011
Prešov d.	...	|	...	...	...	...	...	...	...	...	...	|	...	|	|	0536	|	...	|	|	...	|	|	...	|
Margecany d.	...	0014	...	...	...	...	...	...	...	...	...	|	...	0427	|	|	|	...	0627	|	...	|	0827	...	1027
Spišska Nová Ves d.	...	0041	...	...	...	...	...	...	...	...	...	0441	...	0454	|	0628	0602	...	0654	|	...	0841	0854	...	1054
Poprad-Tatry d.	...	0101	...	...	...	...	...	...	...	...	0415	0506	...	0514	0554	0648	0620	...	0715	0818	...	0900	0915	...	1115
Štrba d.	...	|	...	...	...	...	...	...	...	...	0438	0527	...	0534	0614	0707	|	...	0735	|	...	0921	0935	...	1135
Liptovský Mikuláš d.	...	0148	...	...	...	...	...	...	0429	...	0517	0556	...	0604	0640	0734	0705	...	0803	|	...	0949	1003	...	1203
Ružomberok d.	...	0206	...	...	...	...	...	...	0454	...	0539	0613	...	0623	0659	0751	0724	...	0823	|	...	1007	1023	...	1223
Kraľovany d.	...	0222	...	...	...	...	...	...	0519	...	0602	|	...	0640	|	|	|	...	0840	|	...	|	1040	...	1240
Vrútky **1185** d.	...	0237	...	...	...	...	...	...	0547	...	0618	0641	...	0654	|	0818	0754	...	0854	|	...	1035	1054	...	1254
Žilina **1185** a.	...	0301	...	...	...	...	...	...	0615	...	0644	0703	...	0718	0747	0839	0817	...	0918	1008	...	1057	1118	...	1318
Žilina **1161** d.	...	0310	...	0424	...	0524	...	0602	...	0624	...	0705	...	0724	0748	0842	0819	0825	0924	1010	1024	1105	1123	1224	1324
Považská Bystrica **1161** d.	...	0338	...	0450	...	0550	...	|	...	0650	...	|	...	0750	|	|	|	0850	0950	|	1050	|	1150	1250	1350
Púchov **1161** d.	...	0349	...	0502	...	0602	...	0634	...	0702	...	|	...	0802	|	|	|	0902	1002	|	1102	|	1202	1302	1402
Praha hl. n. **1160** a.	...	|	...	|	...	|	...	|	...	|	...	1255	...	|	1232	1439	|	|	|	|	|	1655e	|	|	|
Trenčianska Teplá d.	...	0407	...	0518	...	0618	...	0652	...	0718	...	...	...	0818	...	...	|	0918	1018	|	1118	...	1218	1318	1418
Trenčín d.	0348	0416	0437	0526	0526	0626	0634	0701	...	0726	...	...	...	0826	...	...	0905	0926	1026	|	1126	...	1226	1326	1426
Nové Mesto nad Váhom d.	0405	0435	0454	0541	0541	0641	0659	0714	...	0741	...	...	...	0841	...	...	|	0941	1041	|	1141	...	1241	1341	1441
Piešťany d.	0419	0449	0507	0552	0552	0652	0714	0726	...	0752	...	...	...	0852	...	...	|	0952	1052	|	1152	...	1252	1352	1452
Leopoldov **1177** d.	0433	0502	0522	0604	0604	0704	0727	|	...	0804	...	...	...	0904	...	...	|	1004	1104	|	1204	...	1304	1404	1504
Trnava **1177** d.	0446	0517	0538	0618	0618	0718	0742	0747	...	0818	...	...	...	0918	...	...	0939	1018	1118	1129	1218	...	1318	1418	1518
Bratislava hlavná st. **1177** a.	0525	0549	0607	0647	0647	0747	0825	0830	...	0847	...	...	...	0947	...	...	1005	1047	1147	1154	1247	...	1347	1447	1547
Wien Hbf. **996** a.	...	...	...	...	...	...	...	...	...	...	...	...	...	...	...	...	...	...	...	1326	...	...	...	...	...

	IC 522	714	608	1738	716	17716	17610	610	*SC* 240	1760	17718	17612	612	*IC* 524	17720	1762	764	17764			1764	♥ 1020	*EN* 442	442 704	*LE*♠ 1252
	✕🅁		✕			2		✕	✕🅁	2	2		✕	✕🅁		2	✕	✕	2	2	2	🍷	⊖	🛏	🍷🅁
		Ⓑs		Ⓐ	Ⓐ	⑦t	⑦t		B	Ⓐ	⑦q	⑦t			⑦q	Ⓐ	r	⑦t			⚒	⊡	A	F	
Humenné **1194** d.	...	...	...	...	...	...	...	...	...	...	...	1406	...	...	...	...	...	...	...	...	...	...	1930	...	...
Košice **1196** d.	1118	...	1157	...	...	...	1344	1357	1459	1504	...	|	1557	1704	...	1712	1757	1757	1917	...	2032	2113	2157	2157	2237
Kysak **1196** d.	1131	...	1211	...	...	...	1357	1411	1511	1517	...	|	1611	1717	...	1725	1811	1811	1935	...	2046	2126	2211	2211	2249
Prešov d.	|	...	|	...	...	...	|	|	|	|	...	1536	|	|	...	|	|	|	|	...	|	|	|	|	2307
Margecany d.	|	...	1227	...	...	...	1411	1427	|	1531	...	1607	1627	|	...	1741	1827	1827	1956	...	2101	2141	2226	2226	|
Spišska Nová Ves d.	1208	...	1254	...	...	...	1437	1454	|	1604	...	1636	1654	1754	...	1813	1854	1854	2038	...	2133	2208	2253	2253	0002
Poprad-Tatry d.	1226	...	1315	...	...	...	1458	1515	1606	1625	...	1655	1715	1814	...	1833	1915	1915	2106	...	2152	2231	2333	2333	0021
Štrba d.	|	...	1335	...	...	...	1517	1535	1622	...	...	1716	1735	|	...	...	1935	1935	...	...	...	2253	|	|	0041
Liptovský Mikuláš d.	1311	...	1403	...	...	...	1544	1603	1649	...	...	1745	1803	1859	...	...	2003	2003	...	...	...	2321	0019	0019	0108
Ružomberok d.	1330	...	1423	...	...	...	1603	1623	1707	...	...	1802	1823	1919	...	...	2023	2023	...	...	...	2340	0037	0037	0126
Kraľovany d.	|	...	1440	...	...	...	1619	1640	|	...	...	1819	1840	|	...	...	2040	2040	...	...	...	|	|	|	|
Vrútky **1185** d.	1359	...	1454	...	...	...	1633	1654	|	...	...	1833	1854	1950	...	...	2054	2054	...	...	...	0009	|	|	0153
Žilina **1185** a.	1422	...	1518	...	...	...	1657	1718	1751	...	...	1857	1918	2013	...	...	2118	2118	...	...	...	0033	0126	0126	0214
Žilina **1161** d.	1425	1418	1524	...	1624	1620	1709	1724	1752	...	1801	1900	1924	2015	2024	...	2121	2121	...	2252	...	0041	0140	0524	0218
Považská Bystrica **1161** d.	|	1451	1550	...	1650	1650	1735	1750	|	...	1831	|	1950	|	2050	...	2151	2151	...	2330	...	|	|	0550	|
Púchov **1161** d.	|	1502	1602	...	1702	1702	1746	1802	|	...	1842	|	2002	|	2102	...	2202	2202	...	2340	...	|	|	0602	|
Praha hl. n. **1160** a.	|	|	|	...	|	|	|	|	2233	...	|	|	|	|	|	...	|	|	...	...	...	0600	0755	|	0737
Trenčianska Teplá d.	|	1518	1618	...	1718	1727	1802	1818	...	...	1906	|	2018	|	2117	...	2224	2224	...	...	...	...	...	0618	...
Trenčín d.	1511	1526	1626	1644	1726	1735	1809	1826	...	...	1914	1948	2026	2101	2125	...	2230	2232	...	...	...	...	...	0626	...
Nové Mesto nad Váhom d.	|	1541	1641	1701	1741	1755	1825	1841	...	...	1935	|	2041	|	2138	...	...	2245	...	...	...	...	...	0641	...
Piešťany d.	|	1552	1652	1721	1752	1808	1836	1852	...	...	1947	|	2052	|	2149	...	...	2256	...	...	...	...	...	0652	...
Leopoldov **1177** d.	|	1604	1704	1734	1804	1822	1849	1904	...	...	2001	|	2104	|	2201	...	...	2309	...	...	...	...	...	0704	...
Trnava **1177** d.	1546	1618	1718	1748	1818	1837	1903	1918	...	...	2015	2024	2118	2135	2214	...	...	2321	...	...	...	...	...	0718	...
Bratislava hlavná st. **1177** a.	1612	1647	1747	1825	1847	1911	1932	1947	...	...	2050	2055	2147	2201	2241	...	...	2349	...	...	...	...	...	0747	...
Wien Hbf. **996** a.	...	...	...	...	...	...	...	...	...	...	...	...	...	...	...	...	...	...	...	...	...	...	...	...	...

A – SLOVAKIA – 🛏 1, 2 cl., ▬ 2 cl., (2) Humenné - Košice - Bohumín - Praha and v.v.
B – PENDOLINO KOŠIČAN – (12) ✕ Praha - Bohumín - Žilina - Košice and v.v.
C – (12) 🍷 Praha - Bratislava - Žilina and v.v. (Table **1150**).
D – 🛏 1, 2 cl. Bratislava (**717**) - Žilina (**443**) - Košice.
E – TATRAN ZEMPLÍN – 🛏 1, 2 cl., ▬ 2 cl., (2) Bratislava - Košice - Humenné and v.v. 🅁 required for (2) Poprad-Tatry - Trenčín and v.v.
F – 🛏 1, 2 cl. Košice (**442**) - Žilina (**704**) - Bratislava.

d – Departs 0756 June 20 - July 19.
e – Arrives 1710 June 20 - July 19.
m – ①-④ (not July 4, 5, Aug. 29, 31, Sept. 1, 14, 15, Oct. 31, Nov. 1, 16, 17).
n – ⑤ (also July 4, Aug. 31, Sept. 14, Oct. 31, Nov. 16).
p – ①②③④⑦ (not July 4, Aug. 28, 31, Sept. 14, Oct. 31, Nov. 16).

q – ⑦ (also Nov. 1; not July 3 - Aug. 28).
r – ①-⑥ (also Aug. 28; not July 5, Aug. 29, Sept. 1, 15, Nov. 1, 17).
s – Ⓑ (not Aug. 28).
t – ⑦ (also July 5, Aug. 29, Sept. 1, 15, Nov. 1, 17; not Aug. 28).
v – ⑤ (also Sept. 27, Oct. 27, Nov. 16; not Oct. 28, Nov. 18).
w – ⑥ (also 15, Sept. 28, Oct. 28, Nov. 17; not Oct. 29, Nov. 19).

♥ – Operated by REGIOJET. Separate fares.
♠ – Operated by LEO EXPRESS. Separate fares.
⊡ – 🛏 (1,2,3 berth), ▬ (6 berth), (12).
⊖ – 🅁 for international journeys.

1182 LOCAL LINES IN POPRAD TATRY AREA

2nd class

km				Ⓐ			A			Ⓐ			B	Ⓐ		A		C	Ⓐ			Ⓐ		D
0	**Poprad Tatry** d.	0402	0531	0531	0634	...	0732	0931	1131	1131	...	1331	1331	1431	...	1518	1536	...	1631	...	1731	1831	1931	2200
8	Studený Potok d.	0418	0547	0547	0652	...	0744	0943	1143	1143	...	1343	1343	1443	...	1531	1548	...	1643	...	1743	1843	1943	2212
14	Kežmarok d.	0436	0607	0607	0703	...	0754	1003	1203	1203	...	1403	1403	1454	...	1541	1601	...	1654	...	1803	1854	1956	2224
44	**Stará Lubovňa** a.	0519	...	0650	0746	...	0834	1046	...	1246	...	1450	1450	...	...	1623	1644	1700	...	...	1846	...	2039	2307
60	Plaveč 🏛 a.	...	...	...	...	...	0851	...	...	...	...	...	1509	...	...	1640	...	1719	...	...	...	...	...	...
75	**Muszyna** a.	...	...	...	...	...	0910	...	...	...	...	...	...	...	...	1701	...	...	...	...	...	...	...	...

				Ⓐ			Ⓐ	A			Ⓐ		Ⓐ			Ⓐ	B			Ⓐ	A	C	D
Muszyna d.	...	...	...	...	...	...	...	0959	...	...	...	...	...	...	...	...	...	...	...	...	1756	...	...
Plaveč 🏛 d.	...	...	...	...	...	...	...	1018	...	...	...	...	...	...	...	...	1635	...	...	...	1815	1840	...
Stará Lubovňa d.	...	0447	...	0546	...	0714	0917	1032	...	...	1117	1317	...	...	1511	...	1654	1717	...	...	1830	1906	2235
Kežmarok d.	0439	0534	0637	0637	...	0801	1001	1105	1201	...	1201	1401	1501	...	1602	1701	...	1801	...	1901	1904	1957	2321
Studený Potok d.	0451	0546	0651	0651	...	0813	1013	1117	1213	...	1213	1413	1513	...	1614	1713	...	1813	...	1913	1916	2009	2333
Poprad Tatry a.	0505	0600	0705	0705	...	0827	1027	1129	1227	...	1227	1427	1527	...	1628	1727	...	1827	...	1927	1929	2023	2347

Poprad Tatry - Starý Smokovec (25 mins, *13* km, narrow gauge): 0452, 0552, 0617 Ⓐ, 0717 **e**, 0817, 0917, 1017, 1117, 1217, 1317, 1417, 1517, 1617, 1717, 1817, 1917, 2017, 2117, 2217. Most trains continue to Štrbské Pleso (see below).

Starý Smokovec - Štrbské Pleso (42 mins, *16* km, narrow gauge): 0519, 0619, 0649 Ⓐ, 0749 **d**, 0849, 0949, 1049, 1149, 1249, 1349, 1449, 1549, 1649, 1749, 1849, 1949, 2049, 2149, 2249. Most trains start at Poprad Tatry (see above).

Starý Smokovec - Tatranská Lomnica (14 mins, *6* km, narrow gauge): 0416, 0544, 0648, 0752 **e**, 0828 **f**, 0852 **g**, 0904 **f**, 0952, 1052, 1152, 1252, 1352, 1452, 1552, 1652, 1752, 1852 **d**, 1952, 2052, 2152.

Štrbské Pleso - Štrba (18 mins): 0511, 0613, 0713, 0802, 0902, 1002, 1102, 1202, 1248, 1338, 1448, 1548, 1648, 1748, 1848, 2002, 2242.

Studený Potok - Tatranská Lomnica (11 mins, *9* km): 0419, 0548, 0652, 0820, 0950, 1150, 1350, 1620, 1820, 1950.

Starý Smokovec - Poprad Tatry (23 mins, *13* km, narrow gauge): 0443, 0543, 0643, 0723 Ⓐ, 0749, 0843, 0943, 1043, 1143, 1243, 1343, 1443, 1543, 1643, 1743, 1843 **e**, 1943, 2043, 2143, 2243. Most trains start at Štrbské Pleso (see below).

Štrbské Pleso - Starý Smokovec (39 mins, *16* km, narrow gauge): 0503, 0603, 0628 Ⓐ, 0711, 0800, 0900, 1000, 1100, 1200, 1300, 1400, 1500, 1602, 1700, 1800 **d**, 1900, 2000, 2100, 2200. Most trains continue to Poprad Tatry (see above).

Tatranská Lomnica - Starý Smokovec (14 mins, *6* km, narrow gauge): 0502, 0602, 0706 Ⓐ **d h**, 0724 Ⓒ **d j**, 0810 **f**, 0824 **g**, 0846 **f**, 0924, 1024, 1224, 1324, 1424, 1524, 1624, 1724, 1814 **e**, 1924, 2024, 2124, 2224.

Štrba - Štrbské Pleso (15 mins): 0447, 0547, 0655, 0740, 0840, 0940, 1040, 1140, 1230, 1320, 1430, 1520, 1630, 1720, 1830, 1940, 2040.

Tatranská Lomnica - Studený Potok (13 mins, *9* km): 0436, 0636, 0757, 0927, 1127, 1327, 1557, 1757, 1927, 2158 **D k**.

A – ⑥⑦ June 4 - Sept. 4.
B – ⑤ (also June 30, Sept. 14, Oct. 27, Nov. 16; not July 1 - Sept. 2, Oct. 28).
C – ⑦ (also Sept. 15, Nov. 1, 17; not July 3 - Aug. 28, Oct. 30).
D – Runs 8 minutes later on ⑤ (also Sept. 27, Oct. 27. Nov. 16; not Oct. 28, Nov. 18).

d – Štrbské Pleso - Starý Smokovec - Tatranská Lomnica and v.v.
e – Tatranská Lomnica - Starý Smokovec - Poprad Tatry and v.v.

f – July 1 - Sept. 4.
g – Not July 1 - Sept. 4.
h – Not July 1 - Sept. 2.
j – Daily July 1 - Sept. 2.
k – To Poprad Tatry (a. 2227).

1183 🚌 POPRAD TATRY - ZAKOPANE 🚌

Flixbus

	⑤–①				
Poprad Tatry (Bus Stn stand 4)* d.	1540	...	...	...	...
Starý Smokovec (Bus Station) d.	1555	...	...	...	...
Tatranská Lomnica (Bus Stn) d.	|	...	...	...	...
Zakopane (Bus Stn)* a.	1730	...	...	...	...
Zakopane (Bus Stn stand 11)* d.	1740	...	...	...	...
Kraków (MDA Terminal) ⊖ a.	2005	...	...	...	...

	⑤–①				
Kraków (MDA Terminal) ⊖ d.	1010	...	...	...	...
Zakopane (Bus Stn stand 11)* a.	1215	...	...	...	...
Zakopane (Bus Stn stand 11)* d.	1225	...	...	...	...
Tatranská Lomnica (Bus Stn) d.	|	...	...	...	...
Starý Smokovec (Bus Station) d.	1430	...	...	...	...
Poprad Tatry (Bus Station)* a.	1452	...	...	...	...

RAIL TICKETS NOT VALID

* – Adjacent to railway station
⊖ – adjacent to Kraków Gowny.

🏛 = Lysa Polana.

1185 ŽILINA - VRÚTKY - MARTIN - BANSKÁ BYSTRICA and ZVOLEN

2nd class ⊡

km		941			945		341		343			951			953	953			345			347			
				Ⓐ							Ⓐ		◧	Ⓐ		Ⓐ	◧	Ⓐ			Ⓐ	A		⑦	①–⑥
	Ostrava hl. n. **1160** d.	...	...	...	...	...	0658	...	0858	...	...	...	...	...	...	...	...	...	1458	...	...	1658	...	...	...
0	**Žilina** **1180** d.	...	...	...	...	...	0835	...	1035	...	...	...	...	...	...	1447	...	...	1635	...	...	1835	...	...	...
21	Vrútky **1180** a.	...	...	...	...	...	0859	...	1059	...	...	...	...	...	...	1511	...	...	1659	...	...	1859	...	...	...
21	Vrútky d.	0513	0524	0619	0713	0719	0913	0919	1113	1119	1219	1313	1319	1419	1513	1513	1519	1619	1713	1719	1819	1913	1919	2119	2225
28	**Martin** d.	0520	0531	0628	0720	0728	0920	0928	1120	1128	1228	1320	1328	1428	1520	1520	1528	1628	1720	1728	1828	1920	1928	2128	2234
51	Turčianske Teplice d.	0538	0559	0657	0738	0757	0938	0957	1138	1157	1257	1338	1357	1457	1538	1538	1557	1657	1738	1757	1857	1938	1957	2157	2302
	Horná Štubňa Obec d.	0546	|	|	0746	|	0946	|	1146	|	|	1346	|	|	1546	1546	|	|	1746	|	|	1946	|	|	|
97	**Banská Bystrica** a.	0626	|	|	0826	|	1026	|	1226	|	|	1426	|	|	1626	1626	|	|	1826	|	|	2026	|	|	|
60	Horná Štubňa a.	...	0607	0707	...	0807	...	1007	...	1207	1307	...	1407	1507	...	...	1607	1707	...	1807	1907	...	2007	2207	2312
60	Horná Štubňa d.	...	0617	...	...	0817	...	1017	...	1217	...	...	1417	...	...	...	1617	...	...	1817	...	...	2017	...	...
78	Handlová d.	...	0640	...	...	0840	...	1040	...	1240	...	...	1440	...	...	...	1640	...	...	1840	...	...	2040	...	...
97	**Prievidza** a.	...	0711	...	...	0911	...	1111	...	1311	...	...	1511	...	...	...	1711	...	...	1911	...	...	2111	...	...

		346		942		344		946			342				952			340		956			
		A	Ⓐ						Ⓐ				Ⓐ			Ⓐ			Ⓐ				
Prievidza d.	0438	...	...	0641	...	0841	...	1041	...	...	1241	...	...	...	1441	...	...	1641	...	...	...	1841	...	2141
Handlova d.	0521	...	...	0717	...	0917	...	1117	...	...	1317	...	...	...	1517	...	...	1717	...	...	...	1917	...	2221
Horná Štubňa a.	0544	...	...	0741	...	0941	...	1141	...	...	1341	...	...	...	1541	...	...	1741	...	...	...	1941	...	2244
Horná Štubňa d.	0553	...	0653	0753	...	0953	...	1153	...	1253	1353	...	...	1453	1553	...	1653	1753	...	1853	...	...	2019	...
Banská Bystrica d.	|	0534	|	|	0734	|	0934	|	1134	|	|	1334	...	|	|	1534	|	|	1734	|	1934	...	|	...
Horná Štubňa Obec d.	|	0615	|	|	0815	|	1015	|	1215	|	|	1415	...	|	|	1615	|	|	1815	|	2015	...	|	...
Turčianske Teplice d.	0603	0621	0703	0803	0821	1003	1021	1203	1221	1303	1403	1421	...	1503	1603	1621	1703	1803	1821	1903	2021	...	2028	...
Martin d.	0633	0640	0733	0833	0840	1033	1040	1233	1240	1333	1433	1440	...	1533	1633	1640	1733	1833	1840	1933	2040	...	2055	...
Vrútky a.	0641	0646	0741	0841	0846	1041	1046	1241	1246	1341	1441	1446	...	1541	1641	1646	1741	1841	1846	1941	2046	...	2102	...
Vrútky **1180** d.	...	0701	...	...	...	...	1103	...	...	...	...	1501	...	...	...	...	...	...	1901	...	...	...	...	...
Žilina **1180** a.	...	0725	...	...	...	...	1127	...	...	...	...	1525	...	...	...	...	...	...	1925	...	...	...	...	...
Ostrava hl. n. **1160** a.	...	0859	...	...	...	...	1259	...	...	...	...	1659	...	...	...	...	...	...	2100	...	...	...	...	...

km		Ⓐ	Ⓐ		Ⓒ				Ⓑ●	
0	**Horná Štubňa** d.	0410	0546	...	0612	1409	...	1609	1809	...
20	Kremnica d.	0436	0611	...	0637	1434	...	1634	1834	...
46	Hronská Dúbrava d.	0509	0644	...	0709	1509	...	1709	1907	...
57	**Zvolen** osob. a.	0518	0653	...	0718	1518	...	1718	1916	...

	Ⓐ	Ⓒ		Ⓐ			Ⓑ●		
Zvolen osob. d.	0420	0620	...	0633	1422	...	1622	1905	...
Hronská Dúbrava d.	0430	0630	...	0648	1432	...	1632	1914	...
Kremnica d.	0508	0709	...	0723	1504	...	1704	1947	...
Horná Štubňa a.	0533	0734	...	0748	1530	...	1730	2012	...

A – 🚃12 Ostrava - Žilina - Banská Bystrica - Zvolen and v.v. (Tables **1160** and **1185**).

● – Ⓑ (not Aug. 28).
◧ – Change trains at Horná Štubňa on Ⓐ.

⊡ – Trains with a number also have 1st class.

1188 BANSKÁ BYSTRICA - BREZNO - MARGECANY

2nd class

km						1781			1783	
		Ⓐ					Ⓐ	Ⓐ		
0	**Banská Bystrica** ▷ d.	...	...	...	...	0937	*1047*	*1237*	1547	...
43	Brezno ▷ d.	...	...	...	...	1036	1147	1406	1702	...
86	Červená Skala d.	...	...	...	...	1132	1246	1506	1755	...
94	Telgárt penzión d.	...	...	...	...	1140	—	—	1803	...
106	Dobšinká L'adová Jaskyňa d.	0453	...	...	...	1154	...	...	1816	1939
114	Dedinky d.	0502	...	...	...	1205	...	...	1826	1949
139	Nálepkovo d.	0535	0656	0839	1039	1235	1427	1635	1852	2024
171	Gelnica d.	0628	0737	0938	1138	1327	1521	1733	1935	2118
179	**Margecany** a.	0640	0749	0950	1150	1339	1533	1744	1947	2130

		1780				1782			
Margecany d.	0648	0808	1008	1228	1408	1608	1828	2018	2248
Gelnica d.	0707	0820	1020	1240	1429	1620	1840	2030	2259
Nálepkovo d.	0753	0903	1103	1335	1510	1702	1935	2112	2341
Dedinky d.	—	0930	—	—	1537	1735	...	2145	...
Dobšinká L'adová Jaskyňa d.	...	0940	...	...	1547	1745	...	2154	...
Telgárt penzión d.	Ⓐ ⊙	0952	Ⓐ	Ⓐ	1559	...	...	...	...
Červená Skala d.	0611	1000	1253	1516	1607	...	...	...	...
Brezno ▷ d.	0713	1118	1353	1615	1708	...	...	...	...
Banská Bystrica ▷ a.	*0816*	1220	*1526*	*1723*	1817	...	...	...	...

▷ – Also Banská Bystrica - Brezno at 0533 Ⓐ, 0613 Ⓐ, 0647 Ⓒ, 0747 Ⓐ, 0837, 1047, 1237, 1347 Ⓐ, 1437, 1634, 1747, 1837, 1947 Ⓐ, 2037, 2237.
Also Brezno - Banská Bystrica at 0501 Ⓐ, 0558 Ⓐ, 0608 Ⓒ, 0718 Ⓐ, 0818, 0918 Ⓐ, 1008, 1218, 1308 Ⓐ, 1418, 1508, 1618, 1818, 2018, 2218.

⊙ – Not July 1 - Sept. 2.

ZVOLEN - LUČENEC - KOŠICE 1190

2nd class (also 1st in **8xx 9xx**)

km		801	911			915	917	919		921	923	
		A										Ⓐ
	Bratislava **1170** d.	2235	...	...	...	...	...	...	...	...	...	...
0	**Zvolen** osob. d.	0315	0513	0615	0725	0913	1113	1313	1525	1713	1913	2125
54	Lučenec d.	0405	0600	0722	0835	1000	1200	1400	1635	1800	2000	2235
69	Fil'akovo d.	0419	0614	0739	0852	1014	1214	1414	1652	1814	2014	2253
98	Jesenské d.	0447	0641	*0841*	*0942*	1041	1241	1441	*1742*	1841	2041	...
162	Rožňava d.	0548	0740	...	...	1140	1340	1540	...	1940	2138	...
202	Moldava nad Bodvou d.	0625	0811	...	...	1211	1411	1611	...	2011	2208	...
233	**Košice** a.	0653	0838	...	...	1238	1438	1638	...	2038	2238	...
	Prešov **1196** a.	0742	...	...	...	...	...	...	...	...	...	...

			910	912	914		918	920	922		800
		Ⓐ								d	A
Prešov **1196** d.	...	...	...	...	...	...	...	...	...	...	2115
Košice d.	...	...	0523	0723	0923	...	1323	1523	1723	...	2205
Moldava nad Bodvou d.	...	...	0550	0748	0948	...	1348	1548	1748	...	2233
Rožňava d.	...	...	0620	0819	1019	...	1419	1619	1819	...	2310
Jesenské d.	...	...	0719	0919	1119	*1234*	1519	1719	1919	*1933*	0007
Fil'akovo d.	0504	0542	0746	0946	1146	1310	1546	1746	1946	*2016*	0035
Lučenec d.	0523	0602	0801	1001	1201	1328	1601	1801	2001	2236	0049
Zvolen osob. a.	0629	0716	0848	1048	1248	1440	1648	1848	2048	2344	0146
Bratislava **1170** a.	...	...	...	...	...	...	...	...	...	...	0558

km												
0	Fil'akovo d.	0552	...	*0806*	0855	1055	*1255*	1455	*1605*	1655	1855	...
29	Jesenské a.	0627	...	*0841*	0942	1142	*1336*	1542	*1641*	1742	1940	...
29	Jesenské ◧ d.	0642	0725	0844	0944	1144	1344	1544	1644	1744	1944	2044
40	Rimavská Sobota ◧ a.	0658	0739	0858	0958	1158	1358	1558	1658	1758	1958	2058

	Ⓐ										
Rimavská Sobota ◧ d.	0430	0601	0817	0901	1017	1217	1301	1417	1617	1901	2017
Jesenské ◧ a.	0444	0615	0832	0915	1031	1231	1315	1432	1631	1915	2031
Jesenské d.	0500	0619	0834	...	1034	1234	*1334*	1433	1634	*1933*	...
Fil'akovo a.	0534	0655	0908	...	1108	1308	*1408*	1508	1708	*2008*	...

A – GEMERAN POL'ANA – For days of running and cars see Table **1170**.
d – Change at Fil'akovo and Lučenec.
◧ – Also from Jesenské at 0506 Ⓐ, 1044, 1244, 1444, 1844. Also from Rimavská Sobota at 0701, 1101, 1501, 1701, 1817.

KOŠICE - HUMENNÉ - MEDZILABORCE 1194

2nd class

km		615	1901	443	1903	1905	1907	1909	1911	1913	1915	1917
		B		C				Ⓐ				e
	Bratislava **1180** d.	2257	...	...	...	...	...	...	...	...	...	...
0	**Košice** d.	0501	0701	0901	1101	1301	1501	1537	1701	1901	2101	2301
68	Trebišov d.	0550	0750	0947	1150	1350	1550	1629	1750	1950	2150	2350
88	Michalovce d.	0611	0811	1011	1211	1411	1611	1648	1811	2011	2218	0011
112	**Humenné** a.	0633	0833	1033	1233	1433	1633	1709	1833	2033	2240	0033

	1902	1904	1906	1908	1910	17912	1912	1914	1916	442	614
		Ⓐ				⑦	①–⑥			C	B
Humenné d.	0528	0612	0728	0928	1128	1319	1328	1528	1728	1930	2154
Michalovce d.	0551	0635	0751	0951	1151	1342	1351	1551	1751	1951	2216
Trebišov d.	0612	0656	0812	1012	1212	1403	1412	1612	1812	2013	2237
Košice a.	0659	0748	0859	1059	1259	1449	1459	1659	1859	2059	2325
Bratislava **1180** a.	...	...	...	...	...	...	...	...	...	...	0549

km					Ⓐ	Ⓐ		Ⓐ			Ⓐ	f
0	Humenné d.	0637	0837	1037	1237	1329	1437	1529	1637	1837	2037	2244
41	Medzilaborce a.	0746	0946	1146	1346	1423	1546	1623	1746	1946	2147	2341

		Ⓐ				⑦	①–⑥				
Medzilaborce d.	0427	0504	0628	0828	1028	1210	1228	1428	1628	1828	2028
Humenné a.	0524	0559	0724	0924	1124	1307	1324	1524	1724	1923	2124

B – TATRAN ZEMPLÍN – For details see Table **1180**.
C – SLOVAKIA – For details see Table **1180**.
e – Runs 14 minutes later on ⑤ (also July 4, Aug. 31, Sept. 14, 27, Oct. 27, 31, Nov. 16).
f – Runs 23 minutes later on ⑤ (also July 4, Aug. 31, Sept. 14, Oct. 31, Nov. 16).

KOŠICE - ČIERNA NAD TISOU - CHOP - MUKACHEVO 1195

2nd class

km					⊡		⊡				
0	**Košice** △ d.	0513	...	0713	0908	1013	1151	1213	1413	1513	1913
62	Slovenské N. Mesto △ d.	0617	...	0818	|	1118	|	1318	1518	1616	2023
95	Čierna nad Tisou △ a.	0653	...	0853	1020	1153	1303	1353	1553	1651	2058
95	Čierna nad Tisou ▦ d.	...	0700	...	1023	...	1314	...	...	1707	...
105	Chop ▦ ⊕ a.	...	0840	...	1200	...	1451	...	...	1847	...
105	Chop **1715** d.	...	...	...	1240	...	1532	...	...	...	...
146	**Mukachevo** **1715** a.	...	...	...	1400	...	1653	...	...	...	...
	Lviv **1715** a.	...	...	...	...	...	...	...	...	...	...
	Kyïv **1700** a.	...	...	...	...	...	...	...	...	...	...

						⊡			⊡	
Kyïv **1700** d.	...	...	...	...	...	...	...	...	...	...
Lviv **1715** d.	...	...	...	...	...	...	...	...	...	...
Mukachevo **1715** d.	...	...	...	...	...	1450	...	...	1816	...
Chop **1715** a.	...	...	...	...	...	1613	...	...	1926	...
Chop ▦ ⊕ d.	...	...	...	...	...	1650	...	...	2006	2100
Čierna nad Tisou a.	...	...	...	...	...	1649	...	...	2005	2100
Čierna nad Tisou ▽ d.	0554	0704	1004	1204	1404	1657	1815	1954	2017	...
Slovenské N. Mesto ▽ d.	0639	0746	1046	1246	1446	|	1858	2034	|	...
Košice ▽ a.	0730	0849	1149	1349	1549	1813	2005	2149	2133	...

e – Runs 14 minutes later on ⑤ (also July 4, Aug. 31, Sept. 14, 27, Oct. 27, 31, Nov. 16).
△ – Also Košice - Čierna nad Tisou at 0813 Ⓐ, 1613 Ⓒ, 1627 Ⓐ, 1713 Ⓐ, 2113, 2306 **e**.
▽ – Also Čierna nad Tisou - Košice at 0304, 0404, 0504, 0804 Ⓐ, 1504, 1604 Ⓐ.
⊡ – Ⓡ for domestic journeys within Slovakia.
⊕ – Ukraine time (one hour ahead of Slovakia).

KOŠICE - PREŠOV - LIPANY - PLAVEČ 1196

2nd class

km			Ⓐ	801			⑥	Ⓑ	Ⓐ		Ⓐ			⑤	⑦		1936							⑤
		⊖		A									⊙	g	h		Ⓐ	⊖					j	k
0	**Košice** **1180** d.	0536	0636	0703	0736	0836	*0917*	0936	1036	1136	1236	1336	1436	1436	...	1536	1608	1636	1736	1836	1936	*2127*	2213	2242
16	Kysak **1180** d.	0553	0653	0726	0753	0853	0953	0953	1053	1153	1253	1353	1453	1453	...	1553	1623	1653	1753	1853	1953	2152	2238	2302
33	**Prešov** **1180** a.	0618	0723	0742	0815	0915	1015	1015	1115	1215	1315	1415	1515	1515	...	1615	1640	1715	1815	1915	2015	2214	2300	2324
33	**Prešov** d.	0636	0729	...	0819	...	1019	1019	...	1219	1319	1419	1519	1519	...	1619	...	1719	1819	1919	2019	...	2301	2325
65	Lipany a.	0713	0806	...	0856	...	1056	1056	...	1256	1356	1456	1556	1556	1607	1656	...	1756	1856	1956	2056	...	2338	0001
88	**Plaveč** ● a.	...	...	...	...	...	...	...	...	...	...	...	...	1629	1638	...	...	...	...	...	...	...	...	...

			Ⓐ													1939			⑤⑦			800	
										⊖			⊙		⊖	Ⓐ	⊙		g h			A	
Plaveč ● d.	...	...	...	...	...	...	...	...	...	...	...	...	...	...	...	...	...	...	1717	...	...	...	...
Lipany d.	0420	0503	0557	...	0646	0903	...	...	1103	1203	1303	...	1403	1503	1603	...	1703	1803	1803	...	...	...	2029
Prešov a.	0457	0540	0634	...	0725	0940	...	...	1140	1240	1340	...	1440	1540	1640	...	1740	1840	1840	...	...	...	2107
Prešov **1180** d.	0459	0542	0642	...	0742	0942	1042	...	1142	1242	1342	...	1442	1542	1642	1717	1742	1842	1842	...	1942	2115	2141
Kysak **1180** a.	0523	0608	0708	...	0807	1008	1108	...	1208	1308	1412	...	1508	1608	1710	1737	1808	1908	1908	...	2006	2131	2205
Košice **1180** a.	0541	0624	0724	...	0824	1024	1124	...	1224	1324	1428	...	1524	1624	1727	1749	1824	1924	1924	...	*2047*	2143	2222

A – GEMERAN POL'ANA – For days of running and cars see Table **1170**.
g – ⑤ (also June 30, Sept. 14, Oct. 27, Nov. 16; not July 1 - Sept. 2, Oct. 28).
h – ⑦ (also Sept. 15, Nov. 1, 17; not July 3 - Aug. 28, Oct. 30).
j – ①②③④⑥⑦ (not July 4, Aug. 31, Sept. 14, 27, Oct. 27, 31, Nov. 16).
k – ⑤ (also July 4, Aug. 31, Sept. 14, 27, Oct. 27, 31, Nov. 16).
⊖ – Daily Košice - Prešov and v.v.; Ⓐ Prešov - Lipany and v.v.
⊙ – Daily Košice - Prešov and v.v.; Ⓑ Prešov - Lipany and v.v.
● – For connections to / from Muszyna see Table **1182**.

PREŠOV - BARDEJOV and HUMENNÉ 1197

2nd class

km					Ⓐ		Ⓒ			Ⓐ			Ⓐ	Ⓐ		⑦m	n							⑤p	q	r
0	**Prešov** d.	0415	0424	0504	0603	0610	0626	0824	0846	1024	1046	1224	1246	1344	1424	1432	1446	1624	1646	1824	1846	2110	...	2146	2303	2328
10	Kapušany pri Prešove d.	0428	0435	0526	0614	0622	0637	0835	0857	1035	1100	1235	1300	1355	1435	1452	1500	1635	1700	1835	1900	2121	2124	|	2324	2339
45	**Bardejov** a.	|	0534	|	0713	|	0736	0934	|	1134	|	1334	|	|	1534	|	|	1734	|	1934	|	|	2216	|	0017	0033
46	Vranov nad Toplou d.	0514	...	0614	...	0712	...	...	0943	...	1146	...	1346	1448	...	1546	1546	...	1746	...	1946	2207	...	2229	...	...
70	**Humenné** a.	0603	...	0646	...	0750	...	...	1020	...	1220	...	1420	1520	...	1620	1620	...	1820	...	2020	2252	...	2303	...	...

	①–⑥			Ⓐ	Ⓐ		Ⓒ				Ⓐ			⑦m	⑦m	n	⑦p	n							s
Humenné d.	...	0350	...	0440	...	0540	...	0754	...	0940	...	1140	...	...	1335	1340	1406	...	1540	...	1740	...	...	1940	...
Vranov nad Toplou d.	0340	0420	...	0518	...	0617	...	0824	...	1010	...	1210	...	...	1405	1410	1432	...	1610	...	1810	...	...	2010	...
Bardejov d.	|	|	0428	|	0607	|	0631	|	0828	|	1028	|	1228	1338	|	|	|	1428	|	1628	|	1828	1958	|	2223
Kapušany pri Prešove d.	0436	0516	0524	0622	0702	0711	0725	0916	0923	1058	1123	1258	1323	1436	1453	1458	|	1523	1658	1723	1858	1923	2052	2058	2322
Prešov a.	0447	0527	0535	0633	0713	0723	0736	0927	0934	1109	1134	1309	1334	1447	1504	1509	1519	1534	1709	1734	1909	1934	...	2109	2333

m – ⑦ (also July 5, Aug. 29, Sept. 1, 15, Nov. 1, 17; not Aug. 28).
n – ①–⑥ (also Aug. 28; not July 5, Aug. 29, Sept. 1, 15, Nov. 1, 17).
p – 12 Bratislava - Prešov - Humenné and v.v. For days of running see Table **1180**.
q – ⑥–④ (not July 4, Aug. 31, Sept. 14, 27, Oct. 27, 31, Nov. 16).
r – ⑤ (also July 4, Aug. 31, Sept. 14, 27, Oct. 27, 31, Nov. 16).
s – Runs 18–25 minutes later on ⑤ **r**.

HUNGARY

Operator: MÁV-START (www.mav-start.hu) running on the network of MÁV (www.mav.hu). Certain services in the west are operated by Győr - Sopron - Ebenfurthi Vásút (GySEV).

Services: All trains convey first and second class seating, except where shown otherwise in table headers, footnotes or train columns, or where the footnote shows sleeping or couchette cars only. Descriptions of sleeping (🛏) and couchette (▬) cars appear on page 10. Certain international services cannot be used for internal journeys.

Timings: Valid **December 12, 2021 - December 10, 2020** with amendments as received. Engineering work may affect travel - it is not always possible to show short-term changes.

Reservations: Most InterCity (*IC*) and Express (*Ex*) trains have **compulsory** reservation, as shown by 🅁 in the tables. *IC* trains also require a supplement; the amount depends on distance of the journey. Higher reservation fees apply at peak times (Friday and Sunday afternoons), and if purchased on day of travel. A supplement is required for **domestic** journeys on **international** *EC* / *IC* / *RJ* / *EN* trains (and seat reservation is compulsory where shown as 🅁 in tables). For **international** journeys on these trains the supplement does not apply but seat reservation is possible (and is **compulsory** where shown in the tables). If a seat reservation or supplement is not paid in advance, a higher supplement is payable on the train: 500 HUF for domestic journeys and 10 EUR (which can be paid in HUF) for international journeys.

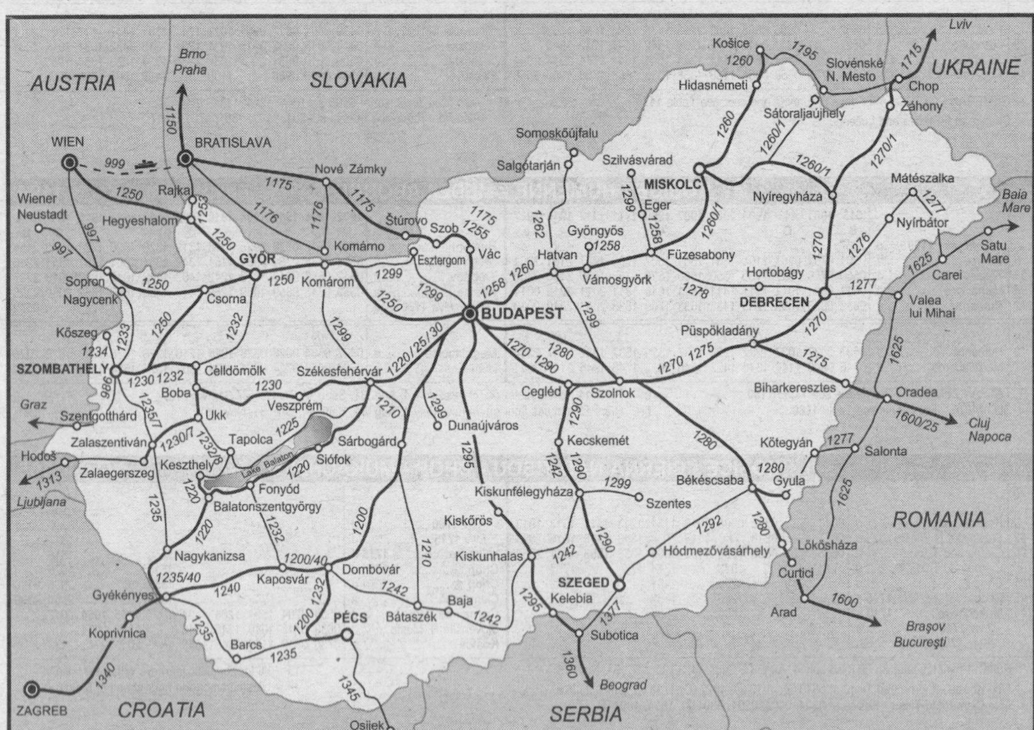

1200 BUDAPEST - DOMBÓVÁR - KAPOSVÁR and PÉCS

km		2 Ⓐ	2	2	2	*IC* **800** 🅁	2	*IC* **822** 🅁	2	*IC* **802** 🅁	2	2	*IC* **812** 🅁	2	2 ⑦	*IC* **804** 🅁	2	*IC* **824** 🅁	2	*IC* **814** 🅁	2	2	*IC* **806** 🅁	2
0	**Budapest** Keleti d.	...	...	...	...	0553	...	0630	...	0753	...	...	0953	...	...	1153	...	1230	...	1353	...	...	1553	...
	Budapest Déli d.	...	...	...	0450	|	...	|	0650	|	...	0850	|	...	1050	|	...	|	1250	|	...	1450	|	...
13	Kelenföld d.	...	...	...	0457	0609**u**	...	0653**u**	0657	0809**u**	...	0857	1009**u**	...	1057	1209**u**	...	1253**u**	1257	1409**u**	...	1457	1609**u**	...
	Pusztaszabolcs d.	...	...	...	0556	|	...	|	0804	|	...	1004	|	...	1157	|	...	|	1404	|	...	1604	|	...
93	Sárbogárd d.	...	0441	...	0629	0659	...	|	0829	0859	...	1029	1059	...	1219	1259	...	|	1429	1459	...	1629	1659	...
173	Dombóvár a.	...	0553	...	0742	0749	...	0856	0942	0949	...	1142	1149	...	...	1349	...	1456	1542	1549	...	1742	1749	...
173	Dombóvár **1240** d.	0513	...	0606	...	0750	0806	0857	...	0950	1006	...	1150	1206	...	1350	1406	1457	...	1550	1606	...	1750	1806
204	**Kaposvár** **1240** a.	|	...	|	...	|	|	0922	...	|	|	...	|	|	...	|	|	1522	...	|	|	...	|	|
218	Szentlőrinc d.	0605	...	0653	...	0828	0853	...	...	1028	1053	...	1228	1253	...	1428	1453	...	...	1628	1653	...	1828	1853
237	**Pécs** a.	0622	...	0714	...	0842	0914	...	...	1042	1114	...	1242	1314	...	1442	1514	...	...	1642	1714	...	1842	1914

	IC **826** 🅁	2	*IC* **808** 🅁	2	2 ⑥	2 Ⓑ	*IC* **818** 🅁	2
Budapest Keleti d.	1630	...	1753	...	...	...	1953	...
Budapest Déli d.	|	1650	|	...	1850	1915	|	2050
Kelenföld d.	1653**u**	1657	1809**u**	...	1857	1922	2009**u**	2057
Pusztaszabolcs d.	|	1804	|	...	2004	2004	|	2204
Sárbogárd d.	|	1829	1859	...	2029	2029	2059	2227
Dombóvár a.	1856	1942	1949	...	2142	2142	2149	...
Dombóvár **1240** d.	1857	...	1950	2006	...	...	2150	...
Kaposvár **1240** a.	1922	...	|	|	...	...	|	...
Szentlőrinc d.	**d**	...	2028	2053	...	...	2225	...
Pécs a.	...	...	2042	2114	...	...	2239	...

	2	2 Ⓐ	*IC* **809** 🅁	2	*IC* **829** 🅁	2	*IC* **807** 🅁	2
Pécs d.	0437	...	0518	...	...	0639	0719	...
Szentlőrinc d.	0458	...	0532	...	**d**	0705	0733	...
Kaposvár **1240** d.	|	...	|	...	0607	|	|	...
Dombóvár **1240** a.	0545	...	0606	...	0633	0750	0806	...
Dombóvár d.	...	...	0607	0610	0634	...	0807	0810
Sárbogárd d.	...	0623	0659	0727	|	...	0859	0928
Pusztaszabolcs d.	...	0705	|	0805	|	...	|	1005
Kelenföld a.	...	0801	0749**s**	0901**s**	0835**s**	...	0949**s**	1101
Budapest Déli a.	...	0809	|	0909	|	...	|	1109
Budapest Keleti a.	...	...	0805	...	0857	...	1005	...

	2	*IC* **817** 🅁	2	2	*IC* **805** 🅁	2 ⑦	*IC* **825** 🅁	2	*IC* **815** 🅁	2	2	*IC* **803** 🅁	2	*IC* **823** 🅁	2	*IC* **801** 🅁	2	2	*IC* **811** 🅁	2	2	2 Ⓑ	2 Ⓑ
Pécs d.	0848	0919	...	1048	1119	...	...	1248	1319	...	1448	1519	...	...	1648	1719	...	1848	1919	...	2048	2148	*2244*
Szentlőrinc d.	0905	0933	...	1105	1133	...	...	1305	1333	...	1505	1533	...	...	1705	1733	...	1905	1933	...	2105	2204	2305
Kaposvár **1240** d.	|	|	...	|	|	...	1207	|	|	...	|	|	...	1607	|	|	...	|	|	...	|	...	|
Dombóvár **1240** a.	0950	1006	...	1150	1206	...	1233	1350	1406	...	1550	1606	...	1633	1750	1806	...	1950	2006	...	2150	...	2350
Dombóvár d.	...	1007	1010	...	1207	...	1234	...	1407	1410	...	1607	1610	1634	...	1807	1810	...	2007	2010	...	...	...
Sárbogárd d.	...	1059	1128	...	1259	1327	|	...	1459	1528	...	1659	1727	|	...	1859	1928	...	2059	2128	...	...	...
Pusztaszabolcs d.	...	|	1205	...	|	1405	|	...	|	1605	...	|	1805	|	...	|	2005	...	|	2209	...	...	...
Kelenföld a.	...	1149**s**	1301	...	1349**s**	1501	1435**s**	...	1549**s**	1701	...	1749**s**	1901	1835**s**	...	1949**s**	2101	...	2149**s**	2301	...	...	...
Budapest Déli a.	...	|	1309	...	|	1509	|	...	|	1709	...	|	1909	|	...	|	2109	...	|	2309	...	...	...
Budapest Keleti a.	...	1205	...	...	1405	...	1457	...	1605	...	...	1805	...	1857	...	2005	...	...	2205	...	...	...	...

d – To / from Gyékényes (Table **1240**). **s** – Calls to set down only. **u** – Calls to pick up only.

2nd class SZÉKESFEHÉRVÁR - SZEKSZÁRD - BAJA 1210

km		*IR* 8302 Ⓐ	*IR* 18302 ⑥	*IR* 8392	*IR* 8304	*IR* 8394	*IR* 8306	*IR* 8396	*IR* 8308	*IR* 8398		*IR* 8399 Ⓐ	*IR* 8309	*IR* 8307	*IR* 8397 ⚒	*IR* 8305	*IR* 8395	*IR* 8303	*IR* 8393	*IR* 8301
0	**Székesfehérvár** d.	...	0602	0802	1002	1202	1402	1602	1802	2002	**Baja** **1242** d.	...	0514	0714	0914	1114	1314	1514	1714	1914
39	Sárbogárd ◧ a.	...	0653	0853	1053	1253	1453	1653	1853	2053	Bátaszék **1242** d.	...	0534	0734	0934	1134	1334	1534	1734	1934
39	Sárbogárd ◧ d.	0702	0702	0902	1102	1302	1502	1702	1902	2102	Szekszárd d.	...	0559	0759	0959	1159	1359	1559	1759	1959
104	Szekszárd a.	0800	0800	1000	1200	1400	1600	1800	2000	2200	Sárbogárd ◧ a.	...	0655	0855	1055	1255	1455	1655	1855	2055
123	Bátaszék **1242** a.	0818	0818	1018	1218	1418	1618	1818	2018	2218	Sárbogárd ◧ d.	0620	0701	0901	1101	1301	1501	1701	1901	2101
143	**Baja** **1242** a.	0839	0839	1039	1239	1439	1639	1839	2039	...	**Székesfehérvár** a.	0711	0752	0952	1152	1352	1552	1752	1952	2152

◧ – For connections from/to Budapest see Table **1200**.

2nd class BUDAPEST - SIÓFOK - FONYÓD - KESZTHELY and NAGYKANIZSA 1220

SERVICE FROM SEPTEMBER 12. For service June 18 - August 28 see page 569.
Additional slower trains and connections are available Budapest - Székesfehérvár - Siófok and v.v. Carriages without 🅁 are available on *IC* trains.

km		Ⓐ			Ⓐ		*IC* 860 🅁	*IC* 842 🅁	*IC* 862 🅁	Ⓒ	*IC* 852 🅁	*IC* 864 🅁	*IC* 844 🅁	*IC* 874 🅁	*IC* 854 🅁	*IC* 866 🅁	*IC* 204 🅁 A	*IC* 876 🅁	*IC* 856 🅁	*IC* 868 🅁	*IC* 848 🅁		
0	**Budapest** Déli **1225 1230** d.	...	...	...	0405	0505	0635	0735	0835	0805	0935	1035	1135	1235	1335	1435	1535	1635	1735	1835	1935	...	2140
4	Kelenföld **1225 1230** d.	...	...	...	0412	0512	0642	0742	0842	0812	0942	1042	1142	1242	1342	1442	1542	1642	1742	1842	1942	...	2147
67	**Székesfehérvár** **1225 1230** a.	...	...	...	0509	0550	0720	0820	0920	0851	1020	1120	1220	1320	1420	1520	1620	1720	1820	1920	2020	...	2244
67	**Székesfehérvár** d.	...	...	...	0513	0551	0721	0821	0921	0852	1021	1121	1221	1321	1421	1521	1621	1721	1821	1921	2021	...	2251
95	Lepsény d.	...	...	...	0536	0612	0740	0840	|	0919	1040	|	1240	|	1440	|	1640	|	1840	|	2040	...	2313
115	**Siófok** a.	...	...	...	0556	0632	0755	0855	0955	0944	1055	1155	1255	1355	1455	1555	1655	1755	1855	1955	2055	...	2333
115	**Siófok** d.	...	...	...	...	0633	0757	0857	0957	1004	1057	1157	1257	1357	1457	1557	1657	1757	1857	1957	2057	...	...
124	Zamárdi d.	...	...	...	...	0644	0804	0904	1004	1016	1104	1204	1304	1404	1504	1604	1704	1804	1904	2004	2104	...	...
130	Balatonföldvár d.	...	...	...	...	0653	0809	0909	1009	1024	1109	1209	1309	1409	1509	1609	1709	1809	1909	2009	2109	...	...
139	Balatonszemes d.	...	...	...	...	0702	0818	0918	1018	1034	1118	1218	1318	1418	1518	1618	1718	1818	1918	2018	2118	...	...
146	Balatonlelle d.	...	...	...	...	0708	0824	0924	1024	1042	1124	1224	1324	1424	1524	1624	1724	1824	1924	2024	2124	...	...
149	Balatonboglár d.	...	...	...	...	0712	0830	0930	1030	1047	1130	1230	1330	1430	1530	1630	1730	1830	1930	2030	2130	...	...
157	**Fonyód** a.	...	...	...	...	0715	0835	0935	1035	1056	1135	1235	1335	1435	1535	1635	1735	1835	1935	2035	2135	...	...
157	**Fonyód** **1232** d.	...	...	0625	...	0723	0837	0937	1037	...	1137	1237	1337	1437	1537	1637	1737	1837	1937	2037	2137	...	...
165	Balatonfenyves **1232** d.	...	...	0639	...	0730	0843	0943	1043	...	1143	1243	1343	1443	1543	1643	1743	1843	1943	2043	2143	...	...
181	Balatonszentgyörgy **1232** a.	...	...	0657	...	0744	0857	0956	1057	...	1156	1257	1356	1457	1556	1657	1756	1857	1956	2057	2156	...	...
181	Balatonszentgyörgy **1232** d.	0433	0601	0700	...	0801	0900	1001	1100	...	1201	1300	1401	1500	1601	1700	1801	1900	2001	2100	2201	2208	...
221	**Keszthely** **1232** a.	|	|	0711	...	|	0911	|	1111	...	|	1311	|	1511	|	1711	|	1911	|	2111	|	2220	...
221	**Nagykanizsa** a.	0513	0644	...	...	0841	...	1041	...	...	1241	...	1441	...	1641	...	1841	...	2041	...	2241	...	...
352	*Zagreb* **1340** a.	...	...	...	...	...	...	...	...	...	...	...	...	...	...	...	2152	...	...	...	...	...	...

			IC 849 🅁	Ⓐ	Ⓐ	*IC* 867 🅁	*IC* 847 🅁	*IC* 877 🅁	*IC* 857 🅁	*IC* 865 🅁	*IC* 845 🅁	*IC* 875 🅁	*IC* 855 🅁	*IC* 863 🅁	*IC* 843 🅁	*IC* 873 🅁	Ⓒ	*IC* 853 🅁	*IC* 861 🅁	*IC* 201 🅁 A		
Zagreb **1340** d.	...	...	...	...	...	...	...	...	...	...	...	...	...	...	...	...	...	...	...	1635	...	
Nagykanizsa d.	0345	...	0517	0557	...	...	0717	...	0917	...	1117	...	1317	...	1517	...	...	1717	...	1917	...	2115
Keszthely **1232** d.	|	0428	|	|	...	0648	|	0848	|	1048	|	1248	|	1448	|	1648	...	|	1848	|	2048	|
Balatonszentgyörgy **1232** a.	0425	0439	0557	0640	...	0659	0757	0859	0957	1059	1157	1259	1357	1459	1557	1659	...	1757	1859	1957	2059	2157
Balatonszentgyörgy **1232** d.	...	0440	0603	...	...	0702	0803	0902	1003	1102	1203	1302	1403	1502	1603	1702	...	1803	1902	2003	2102	...
Balatonfenyves **1232** d.	...	0458	0617	...	...	0717	0817	0917	1017	1117	1217	1317	1417	1517	1617	1717	...	1817	1917	2017	2118	...
Fonyód **1232** a.	...	0506	0622	...	...	0722	0822	0922	1022	1122	1222	1322	1422	1522	1622	1722	...	1822	1922	2022	2123	...
Fonyód d.	...	0507	0624	...	0641	0724	0824	0924	1024	1124	1224	1324	1424	1524	1624	1724	1702	1824	1924	2024	2124	...
Balatonboglár d.	...	0516	0630	...	0648	0730	0830	0930	1030	1130	1230	1330	1430	1530	1630	1730	1713	1830	1930	2030	2130	...
Balatonlelle d.	...	0520	0634	...	0653	0734	0834	0934	1034	1134	1234	1334	1434	1534	1634	1734	1717	1834	1934	2034	2134	...
Balatonszemes d.	...	0527	0640	...	0701	0740	0840	0940	1040	1140	1240	1340	1440	1540	1640	1740	1725	1840	1940	2040	2140	...
Balatonföldvár d.	...	0535	0649	...	0711	0749	0849	0949	1049	1149	1249	1349	1449	1549	1649	1749	1735	1849	1949	2049	2149	...
Zamárdi d.	...	0541	0654	...	0718	0754	0854	0954	1054	1154	1254	1354	1454	1554	1654	1754	1743	1854	1954	2054	2154	...
Siófok a.	...	0551	0701	...	0728	0801	0901	1001	1101	1201	1301	1401	1501	1601	1701	1801	1756	1901	2001	2101	2201	...
Siófok d.	...	0552	0703	...	...	0803	0903	1003	1103	1203	1303	1403	1503	1603	1703	1803	1815	1903	2003	2103	2202	...
Lepsény d.	...	0612	0717	...	...	|	0917	|	1117	|	1317	|	1517	|	1717	|	1840	1917	|	2117	2222	...
Székesfehérvár a.	...	0635	0736	...	...	0836	0936	1036	1136	1236	1336	1436	1536	1636	1736	1836	1905	1936	2036	2136	2242	...
Székesfehérvár **1225 1230** d.	...	0636	0737	...	...	0837	0937	1037	1137	1237	1337	1437	1537	1637	1737	1837	1906	1937	2037	2137	2248	...
Kelenföld **1225 1230** a.	...	0716	0816	...	...	0916	1016	1116	1216	1316	1416	1516	1616	1716	1816	1916	1946	2016	2116	2216	2345	...
Budapest Déli **1225 1230** a.	...	0724	0824	...	...	0924	1024	1124	1224	1324	1424	1524	1624	1724	1824	1924	1954	2024	2124	2224	2354	...

A – AGRAM-TOPART – 2nd class Budapest - Zagreb and v.v. **TRAIN NAMES:** Budapest - Nagykanizsa *IC* trains are named TOPART. Budapest - Keszthely *IC* trains are named BALATON.

2nd class BUDAPEST - SZÉKESFEHÉRVÁR - BALATONFÜRED - TAPOLCA 1225

SERVICE FROM SEPTEMBER 12. For service June 18 - August 28 see page 570.
Connecting trains Budapest - Székesfehérvár and v.v. may require 🅁.

km		Ⓐ		Ⓐ												Ⓒ							
0	**Budapest** Déli **1220 1230** d.	...	...	0405	...	*0510*	0705	*0735*	0905	*0935*	1105	*1135*	...	1305	*1335*	...	1505	*1535*	1705	*1735*	1905	*1935*	*2200*
4	Kelenföld **1220 1230** d.	...	...	0412	...	*0517*	0712	*0742*	0912	*0942*	1112	*1142*	...	1312	*1342*	...	1512	*1542*	1712	*1742*	1912	*1942*	*2207*
67	**Székesfehérvár** **1220 1230** a.	...	...	0509	...	*0609*	0750	*0820*	0950	*1020*	1150	*1220*	...	1350	*1420*	...	1550	*1620*	1750	*1820*	1950	*2020*	*2248*
67	**Székesfehérvár** d.	...	0420	...	0527	0627	0751	0830	0951	1030	1151	1230	...	1351	1430	...	1551	1630	1751	1830	1951	2030	2259
105	Balatonkenese d.	...	0504	...	0619	0712	0825	0913	1025	1113	1225	1313	...	1425	1513	...	1625	1713	1825	1913	2025	2113	2342
117	Balalatonalmádi d.	...	0521	...	0633	0732	0838	0932	1038	1132	1238	1332	...	1438	1532	...	1638	1732	1838	1932	2038	2132	2355
123	Alsóörs d.	...	0528	...	0640	0739	0845	0939	1045	1139	1245	1339	...	1445	1539	...	1645	1739	1845	1939	2045	2139	0002
132	**Balatonfüred** a.	...	0538	...	0651	0751	0855	0951	1055	1151	1255	1351	...	1455	1551	...	1655	1751	1855	1951	2055	2151	0013
132	**Balatonfüred** d.	0400	0600	...	0705	...	0905	...	1105	...	1305	...	...	1505	...	1600	1705	...	1905	...	2105	...	...
157	Révfülöp d.	0437	0640	...	0742	...	0942	...	1142	...	1342	...	...	1542	...	1636	1742	...	1942	...	2142	...	...
168	Badacsonytomaj d.	0455	0655	...	0759	...	0959	...	1159	...	1359	...	...	1559	...	1650	1759	...	1959	...	2159	...	...
170	Badacsony d.	0458	0658	...	0803	...	1003	...	1203	...	1403	...	...	1603	...	1653	1803	...	2003	...	2203	...	...
184	**Tapolca** a.	0516	0716	...	0822	...	1022	...	1222	...	1422	...	...	1622	...	1709	1822	...	2022	...	2222	...	...

			Ⓐ							Ⓒ												
Tapolca d.	...	...	...	0435	0551	...	0734	...	0934	1044	...	...	1134	...	1334	...	1534	...	1734	...	1934	2134
Badacsony d.	...	...	...	0452	0606	...	0753	...	0953	1059	...	...	1153	...	1353	...	1553	...	1753	...	1953	2153
Badacsonytomaj d.	...	...	...	0455	0609	...	0759	...	0959	1103	...	...	1159	...	1359	...	1559	...	1759	...	1959	2159
Révfülöp d.	...	...	...	0510	0621	...	0815	...	1015	1117	...	...	1215	...	1415	...	1615	...	1815	...	2015	2215
Balatonfüred a.	...	...	...	0544	0652	...	0852	...	1052	1156	...	...	1252	...	1452	...	1652	...	1852	...	2052	2252
Balatonfüred d.	0350	0450	...	0550	0702	0805	0902	1005	1102	...	1205	...	1302	1405	1502	1605	1702	1805	1902	2005	2113	...
Alsóörs d.	0400	0500	...	0600	0711	0815	0911	1015	1111	...	1215	...	1311	1415	1511	1615	1711	1815	1911	2015	2124	...
Balalatonalmádi d.	0407	0507	...	0607	0718	0822	0918	1022	1118	...	1222	...	1318	1422	1518	1622	1718	1822	1918	2022	2131	...
Balatonkenese d.	0419	0520	...	0619	0731	0842	0931	1042	1131	...	1242	...	1331	1442	1531	1642	1731	1842	1931	2042	2145	...
Székesfehérvár a.	0504	0603	...	0703	0806	0932	1006	1132	1206	...	1332	...	1406	1532	1606	1732	1806	1932	2006	2132	2228	...
Székesfehérvár **1220 1230** d.	*0514*	...	0607	*0712*	0807	*0937*	1007	*1137*	1207	...	*1337*	...	1407	*1537*	1607	*1737*	1807	*1937*	2007	*2137*	*2248*	...
Kelenföld **1220 1230** a.	*0612*	...	0651	*0751*	0846	*1016*	1046	*1216*	1246	...	*1416*	...	1446	*1616*	1646	*1816*	1846	*2016*	2046	*2216*	*2345*	...
Budapest Déli **1220 1230** a.	...	...	0659	*0759*	0854	*1024*	1054	*1224*	1254	...	*1424*	...	1454	*1624*	1654	*1824*	1854	*2024*	2054	*2224*	*2354*	...

1230 BUDAPEST - ZALAEGERSZEG and SZOMBATHELY 2nd class

🅁 is required for some carriages on *IC* trains. For faster trains Budapest - Györ - Szombathely see Table **1252**. For local trains Zalaegerszeg - Celldömölk / Szombathely see Table **1237**.

km					*IC* 950 ⚒	*IC* 900	*IC* 952	*IC* 902		*IC* 246 A	*IC* 904	*IC* 954	*IC* 9004		*IC* 964	*IC* 9006	*IC* 956	*IC* 906		*IC* 966	*IC* 908	*IC* 958		
				Ⓐ																				
0	**Budapest** Déli ..... 1220 1225 d.	...	...	...	0445	0600	0700	0800	...	0900	1000	1100	1200	...	1300	1400	1500	1600	...	1700	1800	1900	2035	2200
4	Kelenföld ..... 1220 1225 d.	...	...	...	0452	0607	0707	0807	...	0907	1007	1107	1207	...	1307	1407	1507	1607	...	1707	1807	1907	2042	2207
67	Székesfehérvár ..... 1220 1225 d.	...	...	...	0531	0646	0746	0846	...	0946	1046	1146	1246	...	1346	1446	1546	1646	...	1746	1846	1946	2121	2250
90	Várpalota ..... d.	...	...	...	0551	0706	0806	0906	...	1006	1106	1206	1306	...	1406	1506	1606	1706	...	1806	1906	2006	2138	2306
112	Veszprém ..... d.	0415	...	0530	0622	0734	0829	0934	0940	1029	1134	1229	1334	...	1429	1534	1629	1734	1740	1829	1934	2029	2204	2329
148	Ajka ..... d.	0450	0633	0633	0701	0806	0901	1006	1033	1101	1206	1301	1406	1433	1501	1606	1701	1806	1833	1901	2006	2101	2238	...
181	Boba ..... d.	0526	0710	0710	|	0831	|	1031	1110	|	1231	|	1431	1513	|	1631	|	1831	1913	|	2035	|	2312	...
199	Ukk ..... d.	|	|	|	0735	|	0935	|	|	1135	|	1335	|	|	1535	|	1735	|	|	1935	|	2135	|	...
230	Zalaszentiván ..... 1235 a.	|	|	|	0759	|	0959	|	|	1159	|	1359	|	|	1559	|	1759	|	|	1959	|	2159	|	...
239	**Zalaegerszeg** ..... 1235 a.	|	|	|	0808	|	1008	|	|	1208	|	1408	|	|	1608	|	1808	|	|	2008	|	2208	|	...
191	Celldömölk ..... ◧ a.	0536	0721	0721	...	0840	...	1040	1120	...	1240	...	1440	1523	...	1640	...	1840	1923	...	2044	...	2322	...
236	**Szombathely** ..... ◧ a.	*0620*	0820	0820	...	0917	...	1117	1220	...	1317	...	1517	1620	...	1717	...	1917	2020	...	2125	...	...	...

			Ⓐ	*IC* 959	*IC* 909	*IC* 957	*IC* 907	*IC* 967	*IC* 905	*IC* 955			*IC* 9005	*IC* 247 A		*IC* 9003	*IC* 953	*IC* 903	*IC* 963		*IC* 901	*IC* 951 Ⓑ	e
Szombathely ..... ◧ d.	...	0450	0450	...	0624	...	0842	...	1042	...	1140	...	1242	...	1340	1442	...	1642	...	1740	1842	...	1940
Celldömölk ..... ◧ d.	0435	0532	0532	...	0704	...	0916	...	1116	...	1238	...	1316	...	1438	1516	...	1716	...	1838	1916	...	2038
Zalaegerszeg ..... 1325 d.	|	|	|	0549	|	0749	|	0949	|	1149	|	...	|	1349	|	|	1549	|	1749	|	|	1949	|
Zalaszentiván ..... 1235 d.	|	|	|	0600	|	0800	|	1000	|	1200	|	...	|	1400	|	|	1600	|	1800	|	|	2000	|
Ukk ..... d.	|	|	|	0623	|	0823	|	1023	|	1223	|	...	|	1423	|	|	1623	|	1823	|	|	2023	|
Boba ..... d.	0444	0543	0543	|	0713	|	0925	|	1125	|	1248	...	1325	|	1448	1525	|	1725	|	1848	1925	|	2048
Ajka ..... d.	0524	0614	0615	0700	0751	0900	0951	1100	1151	1300	1322	...	1351	1500	1529	1551	1700	1751	1900	1929	1951	2100	2123
Veszprém ..... d.	0602	...	0650	0732	0832	0932	1032	1132	1232	1332	...	...	1432	1532	1612	1632	1732	1832	1932	2013	2032	2132	2158
Várpalota ..... d.	0625	...	...	0754	0854	0954	1054	1154	1254	1354	...	...	1454	1554	...	1654	1754	1854	1954	...	2054	2154	*2228*
Székesfehérvár ..... 1220 1225 d.	0641	...	...	0812	0912	1012	1112	1212	1312	1412	...	...	1512	1612	...	1712	1812	1912	2012	...	2112	2212	*2244*
Kelenföld ..... 1220 1225 a.	0722	...	...	0852	0952	1052	1152	1252	1352	1452	...	...	1552	1652	...	1752	1852	1952	2052	...	2152	2257	*2347*
Budapest Déli ..... 1220 1225 a.	0729	...	...	0859	0959	1059	1159	1259	1359	1459	...	...	1559	1659	...	1759	1859	1959	2059	...	2159	2304	*2354*

A – CITTADELLA – 🚃2 Budapest - Zalaegerszeg - Hodoš - Ljubljana and v.v.

e – Connecting train change at Veszprém and Székesfehérvár.

◧ – Local trains Celldömölk - Szombathely and v.v. (journey 41 minutes):
From Celldömölk at 0540 and every two hours until 1940, 2205.
From Szombathely at 0540 and every two hours until 1940, 2114, 2234.

1232 GYÖR - CELLDÖMÖLK - TAPOLCA - KESZTHELY - FONYÓD - PÉCS 2nd class

km		B		*IR* 9609	B	*IR* 9697	*IR* 19697 ⑤		C	*IR* 9607		*IR* 9605			*IR* 9695	*IR* 19695 ⑦D	*Ex* 18803 🅁E		*IR* 9603		*IR* 9693	*IR* 19693 ⑦F		*IR* 9601
0	**Györ** ..... d.	...	...	*0505*	...	0711	0711	...	...	0911	...	1111	...	...	1311	1311	...	...	1511	...	1711	1711	...	1911
47	Pápa ..... d.	...	...	*0559*	...	0802	0802	...	...	1002	...	1202	...	...	1402	1402	...	...	1602	...	1802	1802	...	2002
72	**Celldömölk** ..... a.	...	...	*0628*	...	0825	0825	...	...	1025	...	1225	...	...	1425	1425	...	...	1625	...	1825	1825	...	2025
72	**Celldömölk** ..... 1237 d.	...	...	0631	...	0833	0833	...	...	1033	...	1233	...	...	1433	1433	...	1448	1633	...	1833	1833	...	2033
82	Boba ..... 1237 d.	...	...	|	...	|	|	...	...	|	...	|	...	...	|	|	...	1458	|	...	|	|	...	|
100	Ukk ..... 1237 a.	...	...	|	...	|	|	...	...	|	...	|	...	...	|	|	...	1520	|	...	|	|	...	|
100	Ukk ..... d.	...	0515	|	0810	|	|	0940	1010	|	1140	|	1340	1426	|	|	...	1540	|	1747	|	|	1947	|
108	Sümeg ..... d.	...	0526	0701	0820	0901	0901	0951	1020	1101	1151	1301	1351	1437	1501	1501	...	1551	1701	1800	1901	1901	2000	2101
128	**Tapolca** ..... a.	...	0546	0718	0838	0918	0918	...	1038	1118	...	1318	...	...	1518	1518	...	1612	1718	1820	1918	1918	2020	2118
128	**Tapolca** ..... d.	0447	0557	0719	0843	0919	0919	...	1043	1119	...	1319	...	...	1519	1519	...	...	1719	...	1919	1919	...	2119
153	**Keszthely** ..... a.	0518	0629	0747	0914	0947	0947	...	1114	1147	...	1347	...	...	1547	1547	...	...	1747	...	1947	1947	...	2147
153	**Keszthely** ..... 1220 d.	0541	...	0748	...	0948	0948	...	...	1148	...	1348	...	...	1548	1548	1626	...	1748	...	1948	1948	...	2148
163	Balatonszentgyörgy ..... 1220 a.	0552	...	0759	...	0959	0959	...	...	1159	...	1359	...	...	1559	1559	1637	...	1759	...	1959	1959	...	2159
163	Balatonszentgyörgy ..... 1220 d.	...	...	0806	...	1006	1006	...	...	1206	...	1406	...	...	1606	1606	1638	...	1806	...	2006	2006	...	...
179	Balatonfenyves ..... 1220 d.	...	...	0825	...	1025	1025	...	...	1225	...	1425	...	...	1625	1625	1708	...	1825	...	2025	2025	...	...
187	**Fonyód** ..... 1220 a.	...	...	0836	...	1036	1036	...	...	1236	...	1436	...	...	1636	1636	1719	...	1836	...	2036	2036	...	...
187	**Fonyód** ..... ◀ d.	...	...	0846	...	1046	1046	...	...	1246	...	1446	...	...	1646	1646	1723	...	1841	...	2046	2046	...	...
240	Kaposvár ..... ◀ a.	...	...	0945	...	1145	1145	...	...	1345	...	1545	...	...	1745	1745	1809	...	1940	...	2140	2140	...	...
269	Dombóvár alsó ..... a.	...	...	...	...	...	|	...	...	...	...	...	...	...	...	|	1841	...	2004	...	...	|	...	...
316	Szentlörinc ..... a.	...	...	...	...	...	1257	...	...	...	...	...	...	...	...	1857	1923	...	2039	...	...	|	...	...
335	**Pécs** ..... a.	...	...	...	...	...	1331	...	...	...	...	...	...	...	...	1931	1948	...	2101	...	...	2257	...	...

	Ⓐ		*IR* 9600		*IR* 9690		*IR* 9602	*Ex* 18802 🅁E		*IR* 9604		*IR* 9694		*IR* 9606	G		*IR* 9696	*IR* 19696 ⑤	H	*IR* 9608	*IR* 8808 ⒶJ	*IR* 18808 K	
Pécs ..... d.	...	...	...	...	...	...	0634	0810	...	...	...	...	...	...	...	...	...	1427	...	...	...	...	...
Szentlörinc ..... d.	...	...	...	...	...	...	0655	0830	...	...	...	...	...	...	...	...	...	1454	...	...	...	...	...
Dombóvár alsó ..... d.	...	...	...	...	...	...	0732	0918	...	...	...	...	...	...	...	...	...	|	...	...	...	...	...
Kaposvár ..... ▶ d.	...	...	...	...	0617	...	0817	0955	...	1017	...	1217	...	1417	...	...	1617	1617	...	1812	1946	1946	...
Fonyód ..... ▶ a.	...	...	...	...	0715	...	0912	1040	...	1112	...	1312	...	1512	...	...	1712	1712	...	1907	2043	2043	...
Fonyód ..... 1220 d.	...	...	...	...	0726	...	0923	1042	...	1123	...	1323	...	1523	...	...	1723	1723	...	1923	▬	2103	...
Balatonfenyves ..... 1220 d.	...	...	...	...	0736	...	0933	1053	...	1133	...	1333	...	1533	...	...	1733	1733	...	1933	...	2122	...
Balatonszentgyörgy ..... 1220 a.	...	...	...	...	0757	...	0953	1123	...	1153	...	1353	...	1553	...	...	1753	1753	...	1953	...	2142	...
Balatonszentgyörgy ..... 1220 d.	...	...	0600	...	0800	...	1000	1124	...	1200	...	1400	...	1600	...	...	1800	1800	...	2000	...	...	2208
Keszthely ..... 1220 a.	...	...	0611	...	0811	...	1011	1135	...	1211	...	1411	...	1611	...	...	1811	1811	...	2011	K	...	2220
Keszthely ..... d.	0521	...	0612	0642	0812	...	1012	...	...	1212	...	1412	...	1612	1644	...	1812	1812	1844	2012	2127	...	2221
Tapolca ..... a.	0549	...	0640	0713	0840	...	1040	...	...	1240	...	1440	...	1640	1715	...	1840	1840	1915	2040	2200	...	2253
Tapolca ..... d.	0550	0550	0641	0740	0841	...	1041	...	...	1241	...	1441	...	1641	1720	1740	1841	1841	1920	2041	2225	...	...
Sümeg ..... d.	0609	0609	0701	0758	0901	0957	1101	...	1207	1301	1407	1501	1607	1701	1738	1800	1901	1901	1938	2101	2244	...	...
Ukk ..... a.	0620	0620	|	0808	|	1008	|	...	1218	|	1418	|	1618	|	1746	1812	|	|	1946	|	2254	...	...
Ukk ..... 1237 d.	0636	0636	|	...	|	...	|	...	...	|	...	|	...	|	...	...	|	|	...	|	2255	...	...
Boba ..... 1237 d.	0659	0659	|	...	|	...	|	...	...	|	...	|	...	|	...	...	|	|	...	|	2314	...	...
Celldömölk ..... 1237 a.	0709	0709	0729	...	0929	...	1129	...	...	1329	...	1529	...	1729	...	...	1929	1929	...	2129	2325	...	...
Celldömölk ..... d.	...	...	0737	...	0937	...	1137	...	...	1337	...	1537	...	1737	...	...	1937	1937	...	*2155*	...	...	...
Pápa ..... d.	...	...	0801	...	1001	...	1201	...	...	1401	...	1601	...	1801	...	...	2001	2001	...	*2226*	...	...	...
Györ ..... a.	...	...	0846	...	1046	...	1246	...	...	1446	...	1646	...	1846	...	...	2046	2046	...	*2318*	...	...	...

ADDITIONAL LOCAL TRAINS **GYÖR - CELLDÖMÖLK**

km																			
0	**Györ** ..... d.	0505	0610	0807	1007	and every	2007	2115	2241	**Celldömölk** ..... d.	0345	0444	0542	0630	and every	1630	1830	2155
47	Pápa ..... d.	0559	0702	0902	1102	**two** hours	2102	2227	2329	Pápa ..... d.	0410	0515	0615	0701	**two** hours	1701	1901	2226
72	**Celldömölk** ..... a.	0628	0732	0932	1132	until	2135	2256	2353	**Györ** ..... a.	0458	0603	0708	0749	until	1749	1949	2318

B – Until Sept. 11.

C – Ⓒ until June 12; daily June 18 - Aug. 28; Ⓒ Sept. 3 - Oct. 23.

D – Until May 15 and from Sept. 18.

E – May 16 - Sept. 11.

F – June 19 - Aug. 28.

G – Daily May 16 - Sept. 11; Ⓒ Sept. 17 - Oct. 23.

H – Ⓒ until June 12; daily June 18 - Aug. 28; Ⓒ Sept. 3 - 11.

J – Not June 20 - Aug. 26.

K – June 18 - Aug. 28.

L – Ⓒ (daily June 18 - Aug. 28).

◀ – Other trains Fonyód - Kaposvár at 0356 Ⓐ, 0607, 0648 Ⓐ **J**, 1205, 1801 **L**, 1940, 2140 Ⓒ **K**.

▶ – Other trains Kaposvár - Fonyód at 0400 Ⓐ, 0512 Ⓐ **J**, 0723 **L**, 0853 **K**, 1453, 1653, 2237.

SOPRON - SZOMBATHELY — 1233

GySEV 2nd class

km																								
															Ⓐ									
0	**Sopron** d.	0408	0450	0556	...	0644	0808	1008	...	1108	1208	1308	...	1408	1428	1508	...	1608	1706	1806	...	1906	2008	2245
38	Bük d.	0440	0523	0628	...	0717	0840	1040	...	1140	1240	1340	...	1440	1500	1540	...	1640	1740	1840	...	1940	2040	2317
62	**Szombathely** a.	0458	0541	0650	...	0735	0858	1058	...	1158	1258	1358	...	1458	1520	1558	...	1658	1758	1858	...	1958	2058	2334
	Szentgotthárd 🚌 **986** a.	0549	0654	0754	...	...	0954	...	...	...	1354	1454	...	1554	...	1654	...	1754	1854	...	...	2054	...	...

													Ⓐ										
Szentgotthárd 🚌 **986** d.	...	0401	...	...	...	0706	0806	...	...	1206	1306	...	...	1406	1506	...	...	1706	1806	...	1906	2006	...
Szombathely d.	0423	0506	0630	...	0700	0800	0900	...	1100	1300	1400	...	1435	1500	1600	...	1700	1800	1900	...	2000	2100	2237
Bük d.	0441	0524	0652	...	0718	0818	0918	...	1118	1318	1418	...	1459	1518	1618	...	1718	1818	1918	...	2018	2118	2255
Sopron a.	0513	0556	0727	...	0750	0851	0951	...	1151	1351	1451	...	1531	1551	1651	...	1751	1851	1951	...	2051	2151	2327

SZOMBATHELY - KÖSZEG — 1234

GySEV 2nd class

km																								
				Ⓐ				Ⓐ			Ⓐ			Ⓐ					Ⓐ					
0	**Szombathely** d.	0500	0606	0706	...	0806	0906	1006	...	1106	1206	1306	...	1406	1506	1606	...	1706	1806	1906	...	2109	2257	...
18	**Köszeg** a.	0523	0629	0729	...	0829	0929	1029	...	1129	1229	1329	...	1429	1529	1629	...	1729	1829	1929	...	2132	2320	...

					Ⓐ		Ⓐ			Ⓐ			Ⓐ					Ⓐ					
Köszeg d.	0432	0526	0632	...	0732	0832	0932	...	1032	1132	1232	...	1332	1432	1532	...	1632	1732	1832	...	2032	2205	...
Szombathely a.	0455	0549	0655	...	0755	0855	0955	...	1055	1155	1255	...	1355	1455	1555	...	1655	1755	1855	...	2055	2228	...

SZOMBATHELY - NAGYKANIZSA - PÉCS — 1235

2nd class

km			*IR* 8900	*IR* 8902	*IR* 8992	*IR* 8904	*IR* 8994	*IR* 8906	*IR* 8996	*IR* 9808
0	**Szombathely** **1237** d.	...	0509	0705	0912	1103	1310	1512	1710	1903
24	Vasvár **1237** d.	...	0533	0729	0933	1126	1333	1533	1733	1926
49	Zalaszentiván **1237** a.	...	0554	0757	0954	1154	1354	1554	1754	1954
49	Zalaszentiván d.	...	0558	0802	1002	1202	1402	1602	1802	2002
101	**Nagykanizsa** a.	...	0647	0851	1046	1251	1446	1651	1846	2051
101	**Nagykanizsa** **1240** d.	0417	0649	0853	1053	1253	1453	1653	1848	...
130	Gyékényes **1240** a.	0448	0715	0918	1120	1318	1520	1718	1925	...
130	Gyékényes d.	0449	0725	0930	1127	1330	1527	1730	1927	...
185	Barcs d.	0549	0827	1025	1225	1425	1625	1825	2025	...
215	Szigetvár d.	0626	0858	1058	1258	1458	1658	1858	2101	...
230	Szentlörinc d.	0650	0922	1122	1322	1522	1722	1922	2119	...
249	**Pécs** a.	0705	0942	1142	1342	1542	1742	1942	2134	...

		IR 9807	*IR* 8907	*IR* 8997	*IR* 8905	*IR* 8995	*IR* 8903	*IR* 8993	*IR* 8901
Pécs d.	...	...	0629	0817	1017	1217	1417	1617	1817
Szentlörinc d.	...	...	0647	0841	1041	1241	1441	1641	1841
Szigetvár d.	...	...	0703	0857	1057	1257	1457	1657	1857
Barcs d.	0518	...	0731	0925	1125	1325	1525	1725	1925
Gyékényes a.	0616	...	0823	1029	1226	1429	1626	1829	2029
Gyékényes **1240** d.	0627	...	0837	1032	1235	1432	1635	1835	2044
Nagykanizsa **1240** a.	0702	...	0906	1106	1306	1506	1706	1909	2108
Nagykanizsa d.	...	0708	0908	1113	1308	1513	1708	1913	2109
Zalaszentiván a.	...	0757	0957	1157	1357	1557	1757	1957	2158
Zalaszentiván **1237** d.	...	0802	1002	1202	1402	1602	1802	2002	2202
Vasvár **1237** d.	...	0827	1022	1227	1427	1627	1822	2027	2222
Szombathely **1237** a.	...	0852	1043	1252	1455	1652	1843	2052	2252

CELLDÖMÖLK and SZOMBATHELY - ZALAEGERSZEG — 1237

2nd Class

km																								
						d					Ⓐ	Ⓐ				Ⓐ					Ⓒ			
0	**Celldömölk** **1232** d.	0400	0445	0553	...	...	...	...	0753	1153	...	...	1448	1553	...	...	1753	...	...	2003	...	2206	...	
10	Boba **1232** d.	0409	0454	0603	...	...	...	...	0803	1203	...	...	1458	1603	...	...	1803	...	...	2013	...	2216	...	
28	Ukk **1232** a.	0424	0511	0621	...	...	...	...	0821	1221	...	...	1520	1621	...	...	1821	...	...	2034	...	2234	...	
28	Ukk d.	0425	0525	0625	...	...	...	...	0825	1225	...	...	...	1625	...	...	1825	...	...	2035	...	2235	...	
	Szombathely **1235** d.	|	|	|	0617	...	...	...	|	|	1405	1437	...	|	1602	1629	|	...	1808	|	2109	|	2233	
	Vasvár **1235** d.	|	|	|	0640	...	...	...	|	|	1428	1500	...	|	1627	1654	|	...	1832	|	2132	|	2256	
59	Zalaszentiván **1235** a.	0456	0556	0656	0702	...		...	0856	1256	1450	1522	...	1656	1650	1722	1856	...	1854	2105	2154	2305	2318	
59	Zalaszentiván d.	0458	0600	0700	...	0706	...	0800	0900	1300	...	1525	...	1700	1706	1725	1900	...	1906	2106	2205	2306	2322	
68	**Zalaegerszeg** a.	0506	0608	0709	...	0715	...	0809	0909	1309	...	1534	...	1709	1715	1734	1909	...	1915	2115	2214	2315	2330	

								†		Ⓐ			Ⓐ	e						⑦f			
Zalaegerszeg d.	0349	0430	0443	...	0543	0651	...	0743	1051	1251	1451	...	...	1639	1645	1651	1845	...	1851	1921	1949	2040	2149
Zalaszentiván a.	0357	0437	0451	...	0551	0659	...	0751	1059	1259	1459	...	...	1647	1653	1659	1853	...	1859	1929	1957	2048	2157
Zalaszentiván **1235** d.	0400	0438	0458	...	0603	0700	0706	...	1100	1300	1500	...	1505	...	1706	1700	1902	...	1900	1934	...	2049	2201
Vasvár **1235** d.	0423	|	0521	...	0629	|	0729	...	|	|	|	...	1532	...	1732	|	1925	...	|	1957	...	|	|
Szombathely **1235** a.	0445	|	0543	...	0654	|	0751	...	|	|	|	...	1554	...	1754	|	1947	...	|	2016	...	|	|
Ukk a.	...	0511	...	...	...	0731	...	...	1131	1331	1531	...	...	...	...	1731	...	...	1931	...	...	2121	2234
Ukk **1232** d.	...	0512	...	0636	...	0735	...	...	1135	1335	1535	...	...	...	...	1735	...	...	1935	...	...	2122	2235
Boba **1232** a.	...	0529	...	0658	...	0753	...	...	1153	1353	1553	...	...	...	...	1753	...	...	1953	...	...	2142	2251
Celldömölk **1232** a.	...	0539	...	0709	...	0803	...	...	1203	1403	1603	...	...	...	...	1803	...	...	2003	...	...	2153	2301

d – From Nagykanizsa (d. 0608). **e** – To Nagykanizsa (a. 1746). **f** – Not June 19 - Aug. 28.

DOMBÓVAR - KAPOSVÁR - NAGYKANIZSA — 1240

2nd class

km																								
							8907*		8997*		8905*		8995*						8993*		*IC* 826	8901*		
		⚒	⚒											Ⓐg		Ⓐ					ⓇA		Ⓑ	⑥
0	**Dombóvár** **1200** d.	...	0411	...	...	0635	...	0759	...	0959	...	1156	...	...	1359	...	1556	...	1759	1857	...	2003	2159	2159
	Dombóvár also **1232** d.	...	0415	...	...	0639	...	0803	...	1003	...	1200	...	...	1403	...	1600	...	1803	|	...	2007	2205	2205
31	**Kaposvár** **1200 1232** a.	...	0446	...	...	0710	...	0834	...	1028	...	1234	...	...	1434	...	1634	...	1829	1922	...	2038	2230	2230
31	**Kaposvár** d.	...	0447	0447	...	0712	...	0845	...	1045	...	1245	...	1349	1445	1548	1649	...	1840	1924	...	2108	2242	...
71	Somogyszob a.	...	0541	0541	...	0802	...	0939	...	1139	...	1339	...	1443	1539	1642	1739	...	1930	2010	...	2158	2332	...
71	Somogyszob d.	...	0548	0548	...	0803	...	0940	...	1140	...	1340	...	1444	1554	1643	1740	...	1941	2011	...	2209	2333	...
101	Gyékényes a.	...	0623	0623	...	0834	...	1011	...	1211	...	1411	...	1514	1624	1714	1811	...	2015	2040	...	2240	0004	...
101	Gyékényes **1235** d.	0427	...	...	0627	...	0837	...	1032	...	1235	...	1432	...	1640	...	...	1835	...	...	2044	...	...	...
130	**Nagykanizsa** **1235** a.	0459	...	...	0702	...	0906	...	1106	...	1306	...	1506	...	1721	...	...	1909	...	...	2108	...	...	...

					IC 829		8900*		8902*		8992*			8904*		8994*			8996*				
	⚒		Ⓐ		ⓇA																	Ⓑ	
Nagykanizsa **1235** d.	...	...	...	0417	...	0510	0649	...	0853	...	1053	...	...	1253	...	1453	...	1710	1848	...	2055	2055	...
Gyékényes **1235** a.	...	...	...	0448	...	0540	0715	...	0918	...	1120	...	...	1318	...	1520	...	1740	1925	...	2136	2136	...
Gyékényes d.	0345	...	0410	...	0451	0541	...	0718	...	0945	...	...	1145	...	1344	...	1523	1745	...	1933	2137	2137	...
Somogyszob a.	0416	...	0441	...	0519	0612	...	0749	...	1020	...	...	1220	...	1420	...	1553	1820	...	2004	2208	2208	
Somogyszob d.	0417	...	0447	...	0520	0613	...	0821	...	1021	...	...	1221	...	1421	...	1554	1828	...	2011	2212	2212	2308
Kaposvár a.	0511	...	0541	...	0606	0707	...	0911	...	1111	...	...	1311	...	1511	...	1644	1922	...	2101	2302	2306	0002
Kaposvár **1200 1232** d.	0515	0515	...	...	0607	0722	...	0929	...	1119	...	...	1329	...	1524	...	1722	1924	...	2116	...	2307	...
Dombóvár also **1232** a.	0546	0546	...	...	|	0753	...	0953	...	1150	...	...	1353	...	1555	...	1753	1955	...	2139	...	2337	...
Dombóvár **1200** a.	0550	0550	...	...	0633	0757	...	0957	...	1154	...	...	1357	...	1603	...	1757	1959	...	2143	...	2341	...

A – 12 Budapest - Kaposvár - Gyékényes and v.v. **g** – Not June 16 - Aug. 31. ***** – *IR* train - see Table **1235**.

DOMBÓVAR - BAJA - KISKUNFÉLEGYHÁZA - KECSKEMÉT — 1242

2nd class

km		Ⓐ		B						
0	**Dombóvár** d.	...	0620	1020	1420	1620	1820	...	...	...
60	Bátaszék a.	...	0727	1127	1527	1727	1927	...	...	...
60	Bátaszék **1210** d.	0534	0734	1134	1534	1734	1934	...	...	...
80	**Baja** **1210** a.	0555	0755	1155	1555	1755	1955	...	...	...

	⚒	Ⓐ	h	B					
Baja **1210** d.	0425	...	0615	0815	1415	1615	1815	...	...
Bátaszék **1210** a.	0443	...	0636	0839	1439	1639	1839	...	...
Bátaszék d.	...	0447	0641	0845	1441	1641	1841	...	...
Dombóvár a.	...	0553	0753	0953	1553	1753	1953	...	...

km										
0	**Baja** d.	0414	0614	0814	1014	1214	1414	1614	1814	...
76	Kiskunhalas a.	0520	0720	0920	1120	1320	1520	1720	1920	...
76	Kiskunhalas d.	0530	0730	0930	1130	1330	1530	1730	1930	...
122	Kiskunfélegyháza **1290** d.	0615	0815	1015	1215	1415	1615	1815	2014	...
147	**Kecskemét** **1290** a.	0637	0837	1037	1237	1437	1637	1837	...	...

Kecskemét **1290** d.	0510	0721	0921	1121	1321	1521	1721	1921	
Kiskunfélegyháza **1290** d.	0544	0744	0944	1144	1344	1544	1744	1944	...
Kiskunhalas a.	0625	0825	1025	1225	1425	1625	1825	2025	...
Kiskunhalas d.	0636	0836	1036	1236	1436	1636	1836	2036	...
Baja a.	0746	0946	1146	1346	1546	1746	1946	2141	...

B – Ⓒ (daily June 18 - Aug. 28). **h** – By connecting trains on Ⓐ.

1250 BUDAPEST - GYÖR - WIEN

For additional services Budapest - Kelenföld and v.v. see Tables **1200**, **1220**, **1225**, **1230**. An hourly local service operates Budapest Déli - Györ and v.v.

km			*IC*	*RJX*	*IC*		*RJX*	♥	*IC*	*EC*		*IC*	*RJX*	*IC*	*EC*		*IC*	*RJX*	*IC*	*EC*		*IC*	
		346	**912**	**162**	**932**		**60**	**1032**	**312**	**140**		**942**	**62**	**914**	**142**		**934**	**64**	**924**	**144**		**944**	
		✕ 🅁	🅁	✕ ⊖	🅁		✕ ⊖	🍸 🅁	🅁	⊖		🅁	✕ ⊖	🅁	⊖		🅁	✕ ⊖	🅁	⊖		🅁	
		A		**B**			**C**	**D**	**E**	**F**			**C**					**C**					
0	**Budapest** Keleti d.	0540	0615	0640	0715	...	0740	...	0815	0840	...	0915	0940	1015	1040	...	1115	1140	1215	1240	...	1315	...
	Budapest Déli d.	|	|	|	|	...	|	0745	|	|	...	|	|	|	|	...	|	|	|	|	...	|	...
13	Kelenföld d.	0555	0629	0655	0729	...	0755	0758	0829	0855	...	0929	0955	1029	1055	...	1129	1155	1229	1255	...	1329	...
75	Tatabánya d.	0626	0700	0726	0800	...	0826	|	0900	0926	...	1000	1026	1100	1126	...	1200	1226	1300	1326	...	1400	...
83	Tata d.	|	0707	|	0807	...	|	|	0907	|	...	1007	|	1107	|	...	1207	|	1307	|	...	1407	...
103	Komárom d.	|	0720	|	0820	...	|	|	0920	|	...	1020	|	1120	|	...	1220	|	1320	|	...	1420	...
140	**Györ** a.	0700	0737	0800	0837	...	0900	0905	0937	1000	...	1037	1100	1137	1200	...	1237	1300	1337	1400	...	1437	...
140	**Györ** d.	0702	0739	0802	0839	...	0902	0907	0939	1002	...	1039	1102	1139	1202	...	1239	1302	1339	1402	...	1439	...
171	Csorna d.	|	0759	|	0859	...	|	|	0959	|	...	1059	|	1159	|	...	1259	|	1359	|	...	1459	...
225	**Sopron** a.	|	|	|	0938	...	|	|	|	|	...	1138	|	|	|	...	1338	|	|	|	...	1538	...
243	**Szombathely** a.	|	0849	|	...	...	|	|	1049	|	...	...	|	1249	|	...	...	|	1449	|	...	...	...
176	Mosonmagyaróvár d.	0720	...	0820	...	...	0920	0925	...	1020	...	...	1120	...	1220	...	...	1320	...	1420	...	...	...
187	Hegyeshalom 🛃 a.	0729	...	0829	...	...	0929	0934	...	1029	...	...	1129	...	1229	...	...	1329	...	1429	...	...	...
256	**Wien** Hbf a.	0821	...	0918	...	...	1021	1032	...	1121	...	...	1221	...	1321	...	...	1421	...	1521	...	...	...

	RJX	*IC*	*EC*	♥		*IC*	*RJX*	*IC*	*EC*		*IC*	*RJX*	*IC*	*EC*		*IC*	*RJX*	*IC*	*EN*			
	66	**916**	**146**	**1036**		**936**	**68**	**310**	**148**		**946**	**42**	**918**	**340**		**938**	**264**	**928**	**462**			
	✕ ⊖	🅁	⊖	🍸 🅁		🅁	✕ ⊖	⊖	⊖		🅁	✕ ⊖	🅁	⊖		🅁	✕ ⊖	🅁	🅁		2	
	C d		**G**	**D**			**C**	**H**				**J**	**K**						**L**			
Budapest Keleti d.	1340	1415	1440	...	...	1515	1540	1615	1640	...	1715	1740	1815	1840	...	1915	1940	2015	2040	...	2140	...
Budapest Déli d.	|	|	|	1445	...	|	|	|	|	...	|	|	|	|	...	|	|	|	|	...	|	...
Kelenföld d.	1355	1429	1455	1458	...	1529	1555	1629	1655	...	1729	1755	1829	1855	...	1929	1955	2029	2055	...	2157	...
Tatabánya d.	1426	1500	1526	|	...	1600	1626	1700	1726	...	1800	1826	1900	1926	...	2000	2026	2100	2126	...	2235	...
Tata d.	|	1507	|	|	...	1607	|	1707	|	...	1807	|	1907	|	...	2007	|	2107	|	...	2244	...
Komárom d.	|	1520	|	|	...	1620	|	1720	|	...	1820	|	1920	|	...	2020	|	2120	|	...	2257	...
Györ a.	1500	1537	1600	1605	...	1637	1700	1737	1800	...	1837	1900	1937	2000	...	2037	2100	2137	2200	...	2323	...
Györ d.	1502	1539	1602	1607	...	1639	1702	1739	1802	...	1839	1902	1939	2002	...	2039	2102	2139	2202	...	...	...
Csorna d.	|	1559	|	|	...	1659	|	1759	|	...	1859	|	1959	|	...	2059	|	2159	|	...	...	...
Sopron a.	|	|	|	|	...	1738	|	|	|	...	1938	|	|	|	...	2138	|	|	|	...	...	...
Szombathely a.	|	1649	|	|	...	...	|	1849	|	...	...	|	2049	|	...	...	|	2249	|	...	...	...
Mosonmagyaróvár d.	1520	...	1620	1625	...	...	1720	...	1820	...	...	1920	...	2020	...	...	2120	...	2220	...	...	...
Hegyeshalom 🛃 a.	1529	...	1629	1634	...	...	1729	...	1829	...	...	1929	...	2029	...	...	2129	...	2229	...	...	...
Wien Hbf a.	1621	...	1721	1732	...	...	1821	...	1921	...	...	2021	...	2118	...	...	2221	...	2321	...	...	...

		IC		*IC*	*IC*		*EN*	*IC*	*RJX*	*IC*	*EC*		*IC*	*RJX*	*IC*	♥		*EC*	*IC*	*RJX*	*IC*	*EC*
		949		**919**	**937**		**463**	**917**	**41**	**947**	**141**		**927**	**269**	**935**	**1031**		**143**	**311**	**61**	**945**	**145**
	2	🅁	2	🅁	🅁		⊖	🅁	✕ ⊖	🅁	⊖		🅁	✕ ⊖	🅁	🍸 🅁		✕ ⊖	⊖	✕ ⊖	🅁	⊖
	Ⓐ		Ⓐ	**K**			**L**							**M**		**D**		**G**	**H**	**C**		
Wien Hbf d.	...	...	...	...	...	...	0640	...	0740	...	0842	...	...	0942	...	1027	...	1042	...	1140	...	1242
Hegyeshalom 🛃 d.	0457	...	0557	...	...	...	0728	...	0828	...	0928	...	...	1028	...	1122	...	1128	...	1228	...	1328
Mosonmagyaróvár d.	0506	...	0606	...	...	...	0736	...	0836	...	0936	...	...	1036	...	1131	...	1136	...	1236	...	1336
Szombathely d.	|	...	|	0552	...	...	|	0710	|	...	|	...	0910	|	...	|	...	|	1110	|	...	|
Sopron d.	|	...	|	|	0624	...	|	|	|	0821	|	...	|	|	1021	|	...	|	|	|	1221	|
Csorna d.	|	...	|	0640	0702	...	|	0759	|	0859	|	...	0959	|	1059	|	...	|	1159	|	1259	|
Györ a.	0533	...	0633	0701	0723	...	0753	0819	0853	0919	0953	...	1019	1053	1119	1148	...	1153	1219	1253	1319	1353
Györ d.	0535	0621	0635	0703	0726	...	0756	0821	0856	0921	0956	...	1021	1056	1121	1149	...	1156	1221	1256	1321	1356
Komárom d.	0600	0638	0700	|	0743	...	|	0838	|	0938	|	...	1038	|	1138	|	...	|	1238	|	1338	|
Tata d.	0619	0651	0719	|	0756	...	|	0851	|	0951	|	...	1051	|	1151	|	...	|	1251	|	1351	|
Tatabánya d.	0629	0658	0729	|	0803	...	0830	0858	0930	0958	1030	...	1058	1130	1158	|	...	1230	1258	1330	1358	1430
Kelenföld a.	0702	0728	0802	0807	0833	...	0902	0928	1002	1028	1102	...	1128	1202	1228	1258	...	1302	1328	1402	1428	1502
Budapest Déli a.	|	|	|	|	|	...	|	|	|	|	|	...	|	|	|	1314	...	|	|	|	|	|
Budapest Keleti a.	0719	0744	0819	0823	0849	...	0919	0944	1019	1044	1119	...	1144	1219	1244	...	...	1319	1344	1419	1444	1519

	IC	*RJX*	*IC*	*EC*		*IC*	*RJX*	*IC*	*EC*		*IC*	♥		*RJX*	*IC*	*RJX*	*IC*			*IR*	*EC*	*RJX*
	915	**63**	**933**	**147**		**913**	**65**	**943**	**149**		**313**	**1035**		**67**	**931**	**165**	**911**		**347**	**1941**	**341**	**261**
	🅁	✕ ⊖	🅁	⊖		🅁	✕ ⊖	🅁	⊖		🅁	🍸 🅁		✕ ⊖	🅁	✕ ⊖	🅁		✕ 🅁		⊖	✕ ⊖
		C d					**C**		**F**		**E**	**D**		**C**		**B**			**A**	⑦		**C**
Wien Hbf d.	...	1340	...	1437	...	...	1542	...	1642	...	...	1727	...	1740	...	1842	...	...	1942	...	2037	2140
Hegyeshalom 🛃 d.	...	1428	...	1528	...	...	1628	...	1728	...	...	1822	...	1828	...	1928	...	...	2028	...	2128	2228
Mosonmagyaróvár d.	...	1436	...	1536	...	...	1636	...	1736	...	...	1831	...	1836	...	1936	...	...	2036	...	2136	2236
Szombathely d.	1310	|	...	|	...	1510	|	...	|	...	1710	|	...	|	...	|	1910	...	|	...	|	|
Sopron d.	|	|	1421	|	...	|	|	1621	|	...	|	|	...	|	1821	|	|	...	|	2021	|	|
Csorna d.	1359	|	1459	|	...	1559	|	1659	|	...	1759	|	...	|	1859	|	1959	...	|	2058	|	|
Györ a.	1419	1453	1519	1553	...	1619	1653	1719	1753	...	1819	1848	...	1853	1919	1953	2019	...	2053	2118	2153	2253
Györ d.	1421	1456	1521	1556	...	1621	1656	1721	1756	...	1821	1849	...	1856	1921	1956	2021	...	2056	2121	2156	2256
Komárom d.	1438	|	1538	|	...	1638	|	1738	|	...	1838	|	...	|	1938	|	2038	...	|	2138	|	|
Tata d.	1451	|	1551	|	...	1651	|	1751	|	...	1851	|	...	|	1951	|	2051	...	|	2151	|	|
Tatabánya d.	1458	1530	1558	1630	...	1658	1730	1758	1830	...	1858	|	...	1930	1958	2030	2058	...	2130	2158	2230	2330
Kelenföld a.	1528	1602	1628	1702	...	1728	1802	1828	1902	...	1928	1958	...	2002	2028	2102	2128	...	2202	2228	2302	0002
Budapest Déli a.	|	|	|	|	...	|	|	|	|	...	|	2014	...	|	|	|	|	...	|	2239	|	|
Budapest Keleti a.	1544	1619	1644	1719	...	1744	1819	1844	1919	...	1944	...	...	2019	2044	2119	2144	...	2220	...	2319	0019

LOCAL TRAINS **GYÖR - SOPRON** (SEE NOTE ⊡)

km												
			Ⓐ									
0	**Györ** d.	0643	0751	0851	1051	1251	1451	1651	1851	1951	2051	2251
31	Csorna d.	0717	0821	0921	1121	1323	1520	1720	1920	2021	2121	2317
85	**Sopron** a.	0806	0906	1006	1206	1413	1613	1815	2013	2106	2204	2400

		Ⓐ									
Sopron d.	0558	0645	0744	0944	1144	1345	1545	1746	1846	1944	2228
Csorna d.	0646	0734	0834	1034	1234	1434	1634	1834	1934	2034	2316
Györ a.	0715	0806	0906	1106	1306	1506	1706	1906	2006	2106	2342

- **A** – DACIA-CORVIN – [12] ✕ Budapest - Wien and v.v.; 🛏 1, 2 cl., ▬ 2 cl., [2] Wien - Budapest - Szolnok (**405/4**) - Cluj Napoca and v.v.
- **B** – [12] ✕ Budapest - Wien - Salzburg - Innsbruck - Zürich and v.v. (Table **86**).
- **C** – [12] ✕ Budapest - Wien - Salzburg - München and v.v. (Table **65**).
- **D** – [12] 🍸 Praha - Wien - Budapest and v.v. 🅁. (Table **1150**).
- **E** – MURA – [12] Budapest - Szombathely - Graz and v.v. (Table **986**).
- **F** – HORTOBÁGY – [12] ✕ Záhony - Nyiregyháza - Debrecen - Budapest - Wien and v.v. Conveys 🛏 1, 2 cl. Kyïv - Lviv - Chop - Záhony - Budapest - Wien and v.v. (Table **96**).
- **G** – TRANSILVANIA-SZAMOS – [12] Cluj Napoca - Oradea - Budapest - Wien and v.v.; [12] Baia Mare - Püspökladány - Budapest - Wien and v.v.
- **H** – DRÁVA – [12] Budapest - Szombathely - Ljubljana and v.v. (Table **91**).
- **J** – [12] ✕ Budapest - Wien - Salzburg (Table **65**).
- **K** – [12] Budapest - Szombathely - Szentgotthárd and v.v. (Table **986**).
- **L** – KÁLMÁN IMRE / WIENER WALZER – 🛏 1, 2 cl., ▬ 2 cl., [2] Budapest - Wien - Salzburg - München and v.v.; 🛏 1, 2 cl., ▬ 2 cl., [2] Budapest - Wien - Salzburg (**466/7**) - Zürich and v.v.
- **M** – [12] ✕ Innsbruck - Salzburg - Wien - Budapest (Table **86**).
- **d** – Extended to / from Frankfurt on dates in Tables **912** / **930**.
- ♥ – Operated by REGIOJET. Separate fare tariff applies.
- ⊖ – Reservation compulsory for domestic journeys in Hungary.
- ⊡ – Also from Györ at 0519 Ⓐ, 0558, 1351 Ⓐ, 1551, 1751; from Sopron at 0455, 1446, 1646. Operator: GySEV.

RJX – Railjet Express. Conveys Business, 1st and economy class.

1253 GYÖR - RAJKA - BRATISLAVA

2nd class

km											
			f								
0	**Györ** 1250 d.	0546	...	0646	...	1246	...	1446	...	1646	...
36	Mosonmagyaróvár 1250 d.	0612	...	0712	...	1312	...	1512	...	1712	...
47	Hegyeshalom 1250 d.	0622	0633	0733	...	1322	1333	1522	1533	1722	1733
60	Rajka 🛃 a.	...	0645	0745	0749	...	1341	...	1541	...	1741
77	**Bratislava** Petržalka ☆ a.	...	0707	...	0807	...	1407	...	1607	...	1807

	f	Ⓐ								
Bratislava Petržalka ☆ d.	0726	...	0849	...	1449	...	1649	...	1849	...
Rajka 🛃 d.	0744	0752	0910	...	1510	...	1710	...	1910	...
Hegyeshalom 1250 d.	...	0805	0922	0935	1522	1535	1722	1735	1922	1935
Mosonmagyaróvár 1250 d.	...	0814	...	0944	...	1544	...	1744	...	1944
Györ 1250 a.	...	0841	...	1011	...	1611	...	1811	...	2011

- **f** – ①–⑥ (subject to alteration on and around Slovak and Hungarian public holiday dates).
- ☆ – Bus 93 links Petržalka station with Bratislava hlavná stanica (main station) every 5 - 12 minutes; journey approx 10 minutes.

GYÖR - BRUCK AN DER LEITHA — 1254

2nd class

km		Ⓐ	Ⓐ			d	Ⓐ	Ⓐ			d
0	**Györ** 1250 d.	0446	0546	0746	0946	1146	1346	1546	1746	1946	2146
36	Mosonmagyaróvár 1250 d.	0512	0612	0812	1012	1212	1412	1612	1812	2012	2212
47	Hegyeshalom ▦ 1250 a.	0522	0622	0822	1022	1222	1422	1622	1822	2022	2222
47	Hegyeshalom ▦ d.	0530	0630	0844	1044	...	1425	1644	1844	2044	...
79	**Bruck an der Leitha** a.	0555	0655	0909	1109	...	1454	1709	1909	2109	...

	Ⓐe	e	Ⓐ	Ⓐ				e		
Bruck an der Leitha d.	...	...	0748	0948	1148	1348	...	...	1948	2148
Hegyeshalom ▦ a.	...	...	0814	1014	1214	1414	...	...	2014	2214
Hegyeshalom ▦ 1250 d.	0705	0735	0835	1035	1235	1435	1635	1835	2035	2235
Mosonmagyaróvár 1250 d.	0714	0744	0844	1044	1244	1444	1644	1844	2044	2244
Györ 1250 a.	0741	0811	0911	1111	1311	1511	1711	1911	2111	2311

d – Also Györ - Hegyeshalom at 0446 and hourly until 2246.

e – Also Hegyeshalom - Györ at 0535 and hourly until 2235.

BUDAPEST - VÁC - SZOB — 1255

2nd class

Local trains. For *EC* trains every two hours (to / from Praha) see Table **1175**.

km										
0	**Budapest** Nyugati d.	0053	0453	0540	0608	and	2108	2208	2253	2353
34	Vác d.	0134	0534	0606	0634	hourly	2134	2234	2334	0034
51	Nagymaros-Visegrád ¶ d.	0149	0549	0619	0649	until	2149	2249	2349	0049
64	**Szob** a.	0205	0605	0630	0705	⊡	2205	2305	0005	0105

Szob d.	0456	0556	0656	0756	and	1956	2101	2201	2301
Nagymaros-Visegrád ¶ d.	0512	0612	0712	0812	hourly	2012	2117	2217	2317
Vác d.	0528	0628	0728	0828	until	2028	2134	2234	2334
Budapest Nyugati a.	0554	0654	0754	0854	⊡	2054	2214	2314	0014

⊡ – Also Budapest - Szob at 0153 Ⓒ, 0253 Ⓒ, 0353 Ⓒ; Szob - Budapest at 0331 Ⓐ, 0401.

¶ – A ferry operates across the river to Visegrád.

BUDAPEST - FÜZESABONY - EGER — 1258

2nd class

km										
0	**Budapest** Keleti d.	0500	0600	0700	0800		1800	1900	2000	2100
67	Hatvan d.	0553	0653	0753	0853	and	1853	1953	2053	2159
87	Vámosgyörk ⊙ d.	0609	0706	0806	0906	hourly	1906	2006	2106	2213
126	**Füzesabony** a.	0640	0729	0829	0929	until	1929	2036	2129	2243
126	**Füzesabony** d.	0650	0731	0831	0931		1931	2053	2131	...
143	**Eger** a.	0707	0748	0848	0948		1948	2110	2148	...

Eger d.	0500	0602	0706	0807		1707	1807	1902	2007
Füzesabony a.	0518	0620	0725	0825	and	1725	1825	1922	2025
Füzesabony d.	0520	0621	0727	0827	hourly	1727	1827	1923	2027
Vámosgyörk ⊕ d.	0551	0651	0751	0851	until	1751	1851	1953	2051
Hatvan d.	0605	0705	0805	0905		1805	1905	2009	2105
Budapest Keleti a.	0700	0800	0900	1000		1900	2000	2105	2200

⊙ – **Vámosgyörk - Gyöngyös** (journey 16 mins): at 0522, 0610, 0708, 0908, 1108, 1308, 1408 Ⓐ, 1508, 1608, 1708, 1908.

⊕ – **Gyöngyös - Vámosgyörk** (journey 16 mins): at 0546, 0633, 0732, 0932, 1132, 1332, 1432 Ⓐ, 1532, 1632, 1732, 1932.

BUDAPEST - MISKOLC - KOŠICE, SÁTORALJAÚJHELY and NYÍREGYHÁZA — 1260

Fast trains. For slower connecting trains via Füzesabony see Tables **1258** and **1261**.

km		*IC* 580 🅁	*IC* 582 🅁	*IC** 182 ⊖	*IC* 520 🅁	*IC* 560 🅁	*IC** 190 ⊖	*IC* 522 🅁	*IC* 562 🅁	*IC** 192 ⊖	*IC* 504 🅁	*IC* 564 🅁	*IC** 184 ⊖	*IC* 524 🅁	*IC* 566 🅁	*IC** 194 ⊖	*IC* 506 🅁	*IC* 568 🅁	*IC** 186 ⊖	*IC* 526 🅁	*IC* 516 🅁	*IC* 586 🅁	*IC** 188 ⊖	*IC* 528 🅁	*IC* 508 🅁	*IC* 518 🅁◧
0	**Budapest** Keleti d.	...	...	0630	0630	0730	0830	0830	0930	1030	1030	1130	1230	1230	1330	1430	1430	1530	1630	1630	1730	1730	1830	1830	1930	2030
126	Füzesabony d.	...	...	|	|	0851	|	|	1051	|	|	1251	|	|	1451	|	|	1651	|	|	1851	1851	|	|	2051	2152
139	Mezökövesd d.	...	...	0756	0756	|	0956	0956	|	1156	1156	|	1356	1356	|	1556	1556	|	1756	1756	|	|	1956	1956	2101	2202
183	**Miskolc** a.	...	...	0826	0826	0927	1026	1026	1127	1226	1226	1327	1426	1426	1527	1626	1626	1727	1826	1826	1927	1927	2026	2026	2129	2232
183	**Miskolc** d.	0630	0730	0830	0840	0930	1030	1040	1130	1230	1240	1330	1430	1440	1530	1630	1640	1730	1830	1840	1930	1930	2030	2040	...	...
244	Hidasnémeti ▦ a.	|	|	0927	|	|	1127	|	|	1327	|	|	1527	|	|	1727	|	|	1927	|	|	|	2127	|	...	...
270	**Košice** a.	|	|	0959	|	|	1159	|	|	1359	|	|	1559	|	|	1759	|	|	1959	|	|	|	2159	|	...	...
221	Szerencs a.	0654	0754	...	0905	0954	...	1105	1154	...	1305	1354	...	1505	1554	...	1705	1754	...	1905	1954	1954	...	2105	...	...
221	Szerencs d.	0655	0755	...	0906	0955	...	1106	1155	...	1306	1355	...	1506	1555	...	1706	1755	...	1906	1958	2007	...	2106	...	...
257	Sárospatak d.	|	|	...	0940	|	...	1140	|	...	1340	|	...	1540	|	...	1740	|	...	1940	2027	|	...	2140	...	...
267	**Sátoraljaújhely** a.	|	|	...	0949	|	...	1149	|	...	1349	|	...	1549	|	...	1749	|	...	1949	2036	|	...	2149	...	...
239	Tokaj d.	0708	0808	...	...	1008	...	...	1208	...	...	1408	...	...	1608	...	...	1808	...	...	...	2020	...	...	...	...
271	**Nyíregyháza** a.	0733	0831	...	...	1029	...	...	1229	...	...	1429	...	...	1629	...	...	1829	...	...	...	2041	...	...	...	...
	Debrecen **1270** a.	0805	0905	...	...	1105	...	...	1305	...	...	1505	...	...	1705	...	...	1905	...	...	...	2114	...	...	...	...

	IC 509 🅁◧	*IC* 529 🅁	*IC* 507 🅁	*IC** 189 ⊖	*IC* 682 🅁B	*IC* 527 🅁	*IC** 199 ⊖		*IC* 650 🅁	*IC* 525 🅁	*IC** 187 ⊖	*IC* 652 🅁	*IC* 523 🅁	*IC** 197 ⊖	*IC* 654 🅁	*IC* 503 🅁	*IC** 195 ⊖		*IC* 656 🅁	*IC* 521 🅁	*IC** 193 ⊖	*IC* 658 🅁	*IC* 501 🅁	*IC** 191 ⊖	*IC* 688 🅁
Debrecen **1270** d.	...	...	...	...	0653	...	...	...	0853	...	...	1053	...	...	1253	...	...	...	1453	...	...	1653	...	...	1853
Nyíregyháza d.	...	...	...	...	0726	...	...	...	0926	...	...	1126	...	...	1326	...	...	...	1526	...	...	1726	...	...	1926
Tokaj d.	...	...	...	...	0748	...	...	...	0948	...	...	1148	...	...	1348	...	...	...	1548	...	...	1748	...	...	1950
Sátoraljaújhely d.	...	0520	0604	...	|	0804	...	...	|	1004	...	|	1204	...	|	1404	...	...	|	1604	...	|	1804	...	|
Sárospatak d.	...	0532	0614	...	|	0814	...	...	|	1014	...	|	1214	...	|	1414	...	...	|	1614	...	|	1814	...	|
Szerencs a.	...	0600	0649		0801	0849	...	...	1001	1049	...	1201	1249	...	1401	1449	...	...	1601	1649	...	1801	1849	...	2003
Szerencs d.	...	0602	0650		0802	0850	...	...	1002	1050	...	1202	1250	...	1402	1450	...	...	1602	1650	...	1802	1850	...	2004
Košice d.	...	|	|	0601	|	|	0801	...	|	|	1001	|	|	1201	|	|	1401	...	|	|	1601	|	|	1801	|
Hidasnémeti ▦ d.	...	|	|	0626	|	|	0826	...	|	|	1026	|	|	1226	|	|	1426	...	|	|	1626	|	|	1826	|
Miskolc a.	...	0627	0715	0718	0827	0915	0919	...	1027	1115	1119	1227	1315	1319	1427	1515	1519	...	1627	1715	1719	1827	1915	1919	2029
Miskolc d.	0532	0630	0730	0730	0830	0930	0930	...	1030	1130	1130	1230	1330	1330	1430	1530	1530	...	1630	1730	1730	1830	1930	1930	...
Mezökövesd d.	0602	|	0756	0756	|	0956	0956	...	|	1156	1156	|	1356	1356	|	1556	1556	...	|	1756	1756	|	1956	1956	...
Füzesabony d.	0613	0704	|	|	0904	|	|	...	1104	|	|	1304	|	|	1504	|	|	...	1704	|	|	1904	|	|	...
Budapest Keleti a.	0740	0830	0930	0930	1030	1130	1130	...	1230	1330	1330	1430	1530	1530	1630	1730	1730	...	1830	1930	1930	2030	2130	2130	...

B – From Püspökladány (Table **1270**).

◧ – Via Hatvan (train **518** d. 2116; train **509** d. 0649).

⊖ – 🅁 for domestic journeys.

* – Classified *EC* in Slovakia.

FÜZESABONY - MISKOLC - SÁTORALJAÚJHELY and NYÍREGYHÁZA — 1261

2nd class

For fast trains Budapest - Miskolc - Sátoraljaújhely / Nyiregyháza see Table **1260**.

km							Ⓐ				Ⓐ			Ⓐ		C								
0	**Füzesabony** d.	...	...	...	...	0400	0430	...	...	0500	...		...	0534	...	0554	0625	...	...	0651	0734	0834	0934	...
13	Mezökövesd d.	...	...	...	...	0411	0441	...	...	0511	...		...	0545	...	0605	0638	...	...	0702	0745	0845	0945	...
57	**Miskolc** a.	...	...	...	...	0448	0518	...	...	0548	...		...	0622	...	0642	0719	...	...	0739	0822	0922	1022	...
57	**Miskolc** d.	...	...	0418	...	...	...	0526	...	...	0601	...	...	...	0637	...	...	...	0737	...	0837	0937	1037	...
95	Szerencs a.	...	...	0454	...	...	...	0602	...	...	0637	...	...	...	0715	...	...	...	0815	...	0915	1015	1115	...
95	Szerencs d.	0347	0410	0456	0516	...	...	0608	0604	...	...	0704	...	...	0716	...	...	0804	0816	...	...	1016	...	1204
131	Sárospatak d.	0425	|	0532	|	...	...	|	0640	...	...	0740	...	...	|	...	...	0840	|	...	...	|	...	1240
141	**Sátoraljaújhely** a.	0434	|	0541	|	...	...	|	0649	...	...	0749	...	...	|	...	...	0849	|	...	...	|	...	1249
113	Tokaj d.	...	0430	...	0534	...	...	0634	...	...	...	...	...	...	0734	...	...	...	0834	...	...	1034	...	...
145	**Nyíregyháza** a.	...	0505	...	0615	...	...	0715	...	...	...	...	...	...	0815	...	...	...	0915	...	...	1115	...	...

																					Ⓑ	D
Füzesabony d.	1034	1134	...	...	1234	1334	...	...	1434	1534	...	...	1634	1734	1834	...	1934	...	...	2055	...	...	2250
Mezökövesd d.	1045	1145	...	...	1245	1345	...	...	1445	1545	...	...	1645	1745	1845	...	1945	...	...	2106	...	...	2301
Miskolc a.	1122	1222	...	...	1322	1422	...	...	1522	1622	...	...	1722	1822	1922	...	2022	...	...	2143	...	...	2338
Miskolc d.	1137	...	1237	...	1337	1437	1507	...	1537	1637	...	...	1737	1837	1937	...	2037	2137	...	...	2310	2310	...
Szerencs a.	1215	...	1315	...	1415	1515	1549	...	1615	1715	...	...	1815	1915	2015	...	2115	2215	...	...	2346	2346	...
Szerencs d.	1216	...	1316	1404	1416	1516	...	1604	1616	1716	1804	...	1816	1916	2016	2021	2116	2216	2226	...	...	2348	...
Sárospatak d.	|	...	|	1440	|	|	...	1640	|	|	1840	...	|	|	|	2057	|	|	2302	...	...	|	...
Sátoraljaújhely a.	|	...	|	1449	|	|	...	1649	|	|	1849	...	|	|	|	2106	|	|	2311	...	...	|	...
Tokaj d.	1234	...	1334	...	1434	1534	...	...	1634	1734	...	...	1834	1934	2034	...	2134	2234	...	...	...	0006	...
Nyíregyháza a.	1315	...	1415	...	1515	1615	...	...	1715	1815	...	...	1915	2015	2116	...	2215	2315	...	...	...	0040	...

FOR RETURN SERVICE AND FOOTNOTES SEE NEXT PAGE →

1261 NYÍREGYHÁZA and SÁTORALJAÚJHELY - MISKOLC - FÜZESABONY

2nd class

For fast trains Nyiregyháza / Sátoraljaújhely - Miskolc - Budapest see Table **1260**.

		E		⚒					Ⓐ															
Nyíregyháza	d.	...	...	0301	...	...	0342	...	...	...	...	0440	0523	...	0538	...	0641	...	...	...	...	0838	...	1038
Tokaj	d.	...	...	0336	...	...	0418	...	...	...	...	0520	0546	...	0616	...	0720	...	...	...	...	0920	...	1120
Sátoraljaújhely	d.	...	...	|	...	...	|	0351	...	...	0456	|	|	...	|	...	|	0704	...	...	...	|	...	|
Sárospatak	d.	...	...	|	...	...	|	0401	...	...	0506	|	|	...	|	...	|	0714	...	...	...	|	...	|
Szerencs	a.	...	...	0353	...	...	0435	0437	...	...	0541	0539	0558	...	0633	...	0739	0752	...	...	...	0939	...	1139
Szerencs	d.	...	...	0354	0354	...	...	0438	0510	...	...	0546	0606	...	0636	...	0740	...	...	0840	...	0940	1034	1140
Miskolc	a.	...	...	0430	0430	...	...	0514	0546	...	...	0622	0644	...	0712	...	0816	...	...	0918	...	1016	1110	1216
Miskolc	d.	0323	0400	...	...	0502	...	0526	...	0556	...	...	...	0704	...	0733	...	...	0833	...	0933	1033	1133	1233
Mezökövesd	d.	0400	0437	...	...	0539	...	0609	...	0633	...	...	...	0741	...	0810	...	...	0910	...	1010	1110	1210	1310
Füzesabony	a.	0412	0449	...	...	0551	...	0619	...	0645	...	...	...	0753	...	0822	...	...	0922	...	1022	1122	1222	1322

				Ⓐ																				
Nyíregyháza	d.	...	1138	...	1238	...	...	1338	1438	...	1538	1638	...	1738	1838	...	...	1938	...	...	2042	...	...	2238
Tokaj	d.	...	1220	...	1320	...	...	1420	1520	...	1620	1720	...	1820	1920	...	...	2020	...	...	2120	...	...	2320
Sátoraljaújhely	d.	1104	|	...	|	...	1304	|	|	1504	|	|	1704	|	|	...	1904	|	1953	2128	|	...	2226	|
Sárospatak	d.	1114	|	...	|	...	1314	|	|	1514	|	|	1714	|	|	...	1914	|	2003	2140	|	...	2236	|
Szerencs	a.	1152	1239	...	1339	...	1352	1439	1539	1552	1639	1739	1752	1839	1939	...	1952	2039	2043	2218	2139	...	2314	2339
Szerencs	d.	...	1240	...	1340	...	...	1440	1540	...	1640	1740	...	1840	1940	...	...	...	2045	...	2220	...	...	...
Miskolc	a.	...	1318	...	1416	...	...	1518	1616	...	1718	1816	...	1918	2016	...	...	...	2121	...	2256	...	...	...
Miskolc	d.	...	1333	1356	...	1433	...	1533	1633	...	1733	1833	...	1933	...	2032	...	...	...	...	...	2300	...	...
Mezökövesd	d.	...	1410	1441	...	1510	...	1610	1710	...	1810	1910	...	2010	...	2109	...	...	...	...	...	2337	...	...
Füzesabony	a.	...	1422	1454	...	1522	...	1622	1722	...	1822	1922	...	2022	...	2121	...	...	...	...	...	2349	...	...

C – From Hatvan (d. 0505) and Vámosgyörk (d. 0520).
D – From Budapest Keleti (d. 2100), Hatvan (d. 2159) and Vámosgyörk (d. 2213).
E – To Vámosgyörk (a. 0448), Hatvan (a. 0505) and Budapest Keleti (a. 0620).

FOR RETURN SERVICE SEE PREVIOUS PAGE.

1262 HATVAN - SALGÓTARJÁN - SOMOSKÖÚJFALU

2nd class

km				Ⓐ			Ⓐ						Ⓐ			Ⓐ			Ⓐ			Ⓐ			
0	**Hatvan**	d.	0400	0510	...	0610	0710	...	0810	1010	...	1210	1310	...	1410	1510	...	1610	1710	...	1810	1910	...	2011	2210
59	Salgótarján	a.	0534	0634	...	0734	0834	...	0934	1134	...	1334	1434	...	1534	1634	...	1734	1834	...	1934	2034	...	2134	2334
65	**Somosköújfalu**	a.	0545	0645	...	0745	0845	...	0945	1145	...	1345	1445	...	1545	1645	...	1745	1845	...	1945	2045	...	2145	2345

					Ⓐ			Ⓐ						Ⓐ			Ⓐ							
Somosköújfalu	d.	0306	0412	...	0512	0612	...	0712	0812	...	1012	1212	...	1312	1412	...	1512	1612	...	1812	2012	...	2212	...
Salgótarján	d.	0318	0424	...	0524	0624	...	0724	0824	...	1024	1224	...	1324	1424	...	1524	1624	...	1824	2024	...	2224	...
Hatvan	a.	0438	0547	...	0647	0747	...	0847	0947	...	1147	1347	...	1447	1547	...	1647	1747	...	1947	2147	...	2347	...

1270 BUDAPEST - DEBRECEN - NYÍREGYHÁZA - ZÁHONY - CHOP

Ferihegy ✈ is served by 5-6 trains per hour. For local trains Nyíregyháza - Záhony - Chop - Mukachevo see Table **1271**.
The minimum connection time to / from Chop local trains at Záhony is 15 minutes.

km			*IC*	*IC*	*IC*	*IC*		*IC*	*IC*	*IC*	*IC*		*IC*	*IC*		*IC*	*IC*	*IC*	*IC*		*IC*	*IC*	*EC*	*IC*
			682	**600**	**650**	**34**		**652**	**602**	**654**	**604**		**656**	**614**		**658**	**606**	**688**	**626**		**608**	**618**	**149**	**628**
			[R]	[R]	[R]	F ⊖		[R]	[R]	[R]	[R]		[R]	[R]		[R]	G [R]	[R]	[R]		[R]	[R]	H ⊖	⑤ [R]
0	**Budapest** Nyugati	**1280 1290** d.	...	0523	0623	0723	...	0823	0923	1023	1123	...	1223	1323	...	1423	1523	1623	1723	...	1823	1923	1940**k**	2023
11	Köbánya Kispest	**1280 1290** d.	...	0537	0637	0737	...	0837	0937	1037	1137	...	1237	1337	...	1437	1537	1637	1737	...	1837	1937	|	2037
18	Ferihegy ✈	**1280 1290** d.	...	0543	0643	0743	...	0843	0943	1043	1143	...	1243	1343	...	1443	1543	1643	1743	...	1843	1943	|	2043
73	Cegléd	**1280 1290** d.	...	0618	0718	0818	...	0918	1018	1118	1218	...	1318	1418	...	1518	1618	1718	1818	...	1918	2018	|	2118
100	**Szolnok**	**1280 1290** d.	0510	0638	0738	0838	...	0938	1038	1138	1238	...	1338	1438	...	1538	1638	1738	1838	...	1938	2038	2104	2138
177	Püspökladány	d.	0611	0722	0822	0922	...	1022	1122	1222	1322	...	1422	1522	...	1622	1722	1822	1922	...	2022	2122	2202	2222
201	Hajdúszoboszló	d.	0630	0740	0837	0937	...	1037	1137	1237	1337	...	1437	1537	...	1637	1737	1837	1937	...	2037	2137	2219	2237
221	**Debrecen**	a.	0646	0756	0851	0951	...	1051	1151	1251	1351	...	1451	1551	...	1651	1751	1851	1951	...	2051	2151	2235	2251
221	**Debrecen**	d.	0653	0758	0853	0953	...	1053	1153	1253	1353	...	1453	1553	...	1653	1756	1853	1953	...	2053	2153	2237	2253
270	**Nyíregyháza**	a.	0724	0829	0924	1024	...	1124	1224	1324	1424	...	1524	1624	...	1724	1827	1924	2024	...	2124	2224	2308	2324
270	**Nyíregyháza**	**1271** d.	0726	...	0926	1031	...	1126	...	1326	...	...	1526	1631	...	1726	1831	1926	2031	...	...	...	2318	...
	Miskolc **1260**	a.	0827	...	1027	|	...	1227	...	1427	...	...	1627	|	...	1827	|	2029	|	...	...	...	|	...
313	Kisvárda	**1271** d.	...	...	...	1102	...	...	...	...	...	...	...	1702	...	...	1902	...	2102	...	...	...	2351	...
335	Záhony	**1271** a.	...	...	...	1121	...	...	...	...	...	...	...	1721	...	...	1921	...	2121	...	...	...	0010	...
335	Záhony 🛃	d.	...	...	...	1223	...	...	...	...	...	...	...	...	...	...	...	...	...	...	...	...	0110	...
341	**Chop** 🛃	⊡ **1715** a.	...	...	...	1340	...	...	...	...	...	...	...	...	...	...	...	...	...	...	...	...	0228	...
382	**Mukachevo**	⊡ **1715** a.	...	...	...	1530	...	...	...	...	...	...	...	...	...	...	...	...	...	...	...	...	0622	...

		EC	*IC*	*IC*	*IC*		*IC*	*IC*	*IC*	*IC*		*IC*	*IC*		*IC*	*IC*	*IC*	*IC*		*IC*	*IC*	*IC*	*IC*
		140	**609**	**619**	**580**		**582**	**617**	**560**	**605**		**562**	**615**		**564**	**33**	**566**	**603**		**603**	**568**	**601**	**586**
		H ⊖	[R]	G [R]	[R]		[R]	[R]	[R]	[R]		[R]	[R]		[R]	F ⊖	[R]	[R]		⑦ [R]	[R]	[R]	[R]
Mukachevo	⊡ **1715** d.	0048	...	...	...	...	...	...	...	...	...	...	...	...	...	1230	...	...	...	...	...	...	...
Chop 🛃	⊡ **1715** d.	0328	...	...	...	...	...	...	...	...	...	...	...	...	...	1410	...	...	...	...	...	...	...
Záhony 🛃	a.	0246	...	...	...	...	...	...	...	...	...	...	...	...	...	1327	...	...	...	...	...	...	...
Záhony	**1271** d.	0405	...	0535	...	...	...	0840	...	...	...	...	...	...	...	1440	...	...	...	1628	...	1840	...
Kisvárda	**1271** d.	0424	...	0554	...	...	...	0859	...	...	...	...	...	...	...	1459	...	...	...	1647	...	1859	...
Miskolc **1260**	d.	|	...	|	0630	...	0730	|	0930	...	...	1130	...	...	1330	|	1530	...	...	|	1730	|	1930
Nyíregyháza	**1271** a.	0456	...	0624	0733	...	0831	0930	1029	...	...	1229	...	...	1429	1530	1629	...	...	1718	1829	1930	2041
Nyíregyháza	d.	0458	0534	0626	0734	...	0834	0934	1034	1134	...	1234	1334	...	1434	1534	1634	1734	...	1734	1834	1934	2043
Debrecen	a.	0529	0605	0657	0805	...	0905	1005	1105	1205	...	1305	1405	...	1505	1605	1705	1805	...	1805	1905	2005	2114
Debrecen	d.	0531	0607	0707	0807	...	0907	1007	1107	1207	...	1307	1407	...	1507	1607	1707	1807	...	1807	1907	2007	...
Hajdúszoboszló	d.	0546	0622	0722	0822	...	0922	1022	1122	1222	...	1322	1422	...	1522	1622	1722	1822	...	1822	1922	2022	...
Püspökladány	d.	0602	0637	0737	0837	...	0937	1037	1137	1237	...	1337	1437	...	1537	1637	1737	1837	...	1837	1937	2037	...
Szolnok	**1280 1290** d.	0657	0721	0821	0921	...	1021	1121	1221	1321	...	1421	1521	...	1621	1721	1821	1921	...	1921	2021	2121	...
Cegléd	**1280 1290** d.	|	0743	0843	0943	...	1043	1143	1243	1343	...	1443	1543	...	1643	1743	1843	1943	...	1943	2043	2143	...
Ferihegy ✈	**1280 1290** d.	|	0815	0915	1015	...	1115	1215	1315	1415	...	1515	1615	...	1715	1815	1915	2015	...	2015	2115	2215	...
Köbánya Kispest	**1280 1290** d.	|	0821	0921	1021	...	1121	1221	1321	1421	...	1521	1621	...	1721	1821	1921	2021	...	2021	2121	2221	...
Budapest Nyugati	**1280 1290** a.	0820**k**	0837	0937	1037	...	1137	1237	1337	1437	...	1537	1637	...	1737	1837	1937	2037	...	2037	2137	2237	...

LOCAL TRAINS **BUDAPEST - NYÍREGYHÁZA**

							⚒	
Budapest Nyugati	**1280 1290** d.	0503	0628	0828		1828	2028	2128	2228
Köbánya Kispest	**1280 1290** d.	0518	0642	0842		1842	2042	2142	2242
Ferihegy ✈	**1280 1290** d.	0524	0648	0848	and	1848	2048	2148	2248
Cegléd	**1280 1290** d.	0621	0724	0924	every	1924	2124	2224	2328
Szolnok	**1280 1290** d.	0650	0750	0950	**two**	1950	2150	2250	2350
Püspökladány	d.	0751	0851	1051	hours	2051	2251	2352	0051
Hajdúszoboszló	d.	0810	0910	1110	until	2110	2310	0010	0110
Debrecen	a.	0826	0926	1126		2126	2326	0026	0126
Debrecen	d.	0837	0937	1137	●	2137	...	...	...
Nyíregyháza	a.	0919	1019	1219		2219	...	...	...

		Ⓐ							
Nyíregyháza	d.	0441	0545	0745	0945		1745	1845	1945
Debrecen	a.	0524	0628	0828	1028		1828	1928	2028
Debrecen	d.	0534	0634	0834	1034	and	1834	1934	2034
Hajdúszoboszló	d.	0551	0651	0851	1051	every	1851	1951	2051
Püspökladány	d.	0611	0711	0911	1111	**two**	1911	2011	2109
Szolnok	**1280 1290** d.	0715	0815	1015	1215	hours	2015	2115	...
Cegléd	**1280 1290** d.	0738	0838	1038	1238	until	2038	2148	...
Ferihegy ✈	**1280 1290** d.	0810	0910	1110	1310		2110	2240	...
Köbánya Kispest	**1280 1290** d.	0816	0916	1116	1316	●	2116	2249	...
Budapest Nyugati	**1280 1290** a.	0832	0932	1132	1332		2132	2305	...

F – LATORCA – 12 Budapest - Záhony and v.v.; 2 Budapest - Mukachevo (Table **1715**) and v.v.; 2 Záhony - Chop and v.v.
G – Conveys 2 [R] Budapest Nyugati - Debrecen (**638/639**) - Mátészalka and v.v. (Table **1276**).
H – HORTOBÁGY – 12 Wien - Budapest - Debrecen - Záhony and v.v.; Conveys 🛏 1, 2 cl. Wien - Budapest - Chop - Lviv - Kyïv and v.v. (Table **96**).

k – Budapest **Keleti**.
⊖ – [R] for domestic journeys within Hungary.
⊡ – Ukrainian (East European) time, one hour ahead of Hungarian time.
● – Additional local trains run Cegléd - Nyíregyháza and v.v..

NYÍREGYHÁZA - ZÁHONY - CHOP - MUKACHEVO 1271

Local trains. For long-distance trains see Table **1270**. The minimum connection time to / from Chop local trains at Záhony is 15 minutes.

km																								
										⚒		⚒	Ⓐd		Ⓐ				Ⓐ	⚒		e		
0	**Nyíregyháza** d.	0500	0546	0646	0746	0846	0946	1046	...	1146	1246	1346	1423	1446	1523	1546	...	1646	1723	1746	1846	1946	2046	2246
43	Kisvárda d.	0545	0631	0731	0831	0931	1031	1131	...	1231	1331	1431	1508	1531	1608	1631	...	1731	1808	1831	1931	2031	2131	2331
65	**Záhony** a.	0612	0657	0757	0857	0957	1057	1157	...	1257	1357	1457	1534	1557	1634	1657	...	1757	1834	1857	1957	2057	2157	2357

			⚒					⚒		⚒			Ⓐ	⑦f		Ⓐ	⑦f						
Záhony d.	0355	0457	0524	0551	0703	...	0803	0903	1003	1103	1203	...	1303	1303	1403	1503	1503	...	1603	1703	1803	1927	2003
Kisvárda d.	0421	0523	0549	0618	0729	...	0829	0929	1029	1129	1229	...	1329	1329	1429	1529	1529	...	1629	1729	1829	1953	2029
Nyíregyháza a.	0506	0608	0636	0704	0814	...	0914	1014	1114	1214	1314	...	1414	1414	1514	1614	1614	...	1714	1814	1914	2038	2114

km										
0	**Záhony** d.	0342	0634	...	0835	1424	...	1837	2041	...
6	Chop ⊡ **1715** a.	0500	0752	...	0953	1542	...	1955	2159	...
47	**Mukachevo** ⊡ **1715** a.	...	...	...	1133	...	...	...	...	...

Mukachevo ⊡ **1715** d.	...	...	...	...	...	1630	...	...	...
Chop ⊡ **1715** d.	0529	0822	...	1025	1612	1815	...	2025	2229
Záhony a.	0447	0740	...	0943	1530	1733	...	1943	2147

d – Not June 16 - Aug. 31.
e – ⚒ (daily June 18 - Aug. 28).
f – Not June 19 - Aug. 28.
⊡ – Ukrainian (East European) time, one hour ahead of Hungarian time.

(WIEN -) BUDAPEST - ORADEA (- BRASOV) 1275

June 18 - November 6

		IC 34	367	*IR* 367			143*	407*	
	🚌		🚌		🚌	🚌			🚌
	☆	[R]	[R]	B [R]	☆	☆	C [R]	D [R]	☆
Wien Hbf **1250** d.	...	...	...	...	...	...	1042	...	...
Budapest Keleti d.	...	0723n	...	...	...	...	1340	1740	...
Szolnok d.	...	0838	...	...	...	...	1503	1903	...
Püspökladány d.	0826	0922	0942	...	1216	1416	1602	1958	2130
Biharkeresztes 🏛 d.	0944	...	1055	...	1334	1444	|	|	2248
Debrecen d.	...	...	|	...	...	...	1705	2100	...
Nyirábrány a.	...	...	|	...	...	...	1751	2135	...
Nyirábrány 🏛 d.	...	...	|	...	...	...	1811	2200	...
Valea lui Mihai 🏛 ⊙ a.	...	...	|	...	...	...	1926	2315	...
Valea lui Mihai ⊙ d.	...	...	|	...	...	...	1946	2350	...
Episcopia Bihor 🏛 ⊙ d.	...	...	|	...	...	...	2101	0100	...
Oradea ⊙ d.	...	...	1302	1333	...	...	2117	0115	...
Cluj Napoca **1600** ⊙ a.	...	...	...	1609	...	...	2358	0348	...
Brasov **1600** ⊙ a.	...	...	...	0014	...	...	...	1124	...

		406*	146*			*IR* 366	366	*IC* 568	
	🚌			🚌	🚌		🚌		🚌
	☆	D [R]	C [R]	☆	☆	B [R]	[R]	[R]	☆
Brasov **1600** ⊙ d.	...	1921	...	...	...	0727	...	...	...
Cluj Napoca **1600** ⊙ d.	...	0248	0603	...	...	1455	...	...	...
Oradea ⊙ d.	...	0531	0835	...	...	1730	1740	...	...
Episcopia Bihor 🏛 ⊙ a.	...	0539	0843	...	...	...	|	...	...
Valea lui Mihai ⊙ a.	...	0652	1012	...	...	...	|	...	...
Valea lui Mihai 🏛 ⊙ d.	...	0712	1044	...	...	...	|	...	...
Nyirábrány 🏛 a.	...	0627	0959	...	...	...	|	...	...
Nyirábrány d.	...	0649	1019	...	...	...	|	...	...
Debrecen d.	...	0739	1113	...	...	...	|	...	...
Biharkeresztes 🏛 d.	0610	|	|	1125	1325	...	1800	...	1910
Püspökladány d.	0728	0817	1203	1243	1443	...	1906	1937	2028
Szolnok d.	...	0917	1257	...	...	...	...	2021	...
Budapest Keleti a.	...	1105	1420	...	...	...	...	2137n	...
Wien Hbf **1250** a.	...	...	1721	...	...	...	...	...	...

B – HARGITA – [12] Oradea - Cluj Napoca - Brasov and v.v.; conveys on dates in Table **1615** [2] Oradea - Cluj Napoca - Târgu Mures and v.v.
C – TRANSILVANIA-SZAMOS – [12] ✕ Wien - Budapest - Oradea - Cluj Napoca and v.v.; conveys [2] Wien (**143/144**) - Püspökladány (**686/687**) - Baia Mare and v.v. (Table **1277**).
D – CORONA – [couchette] 1, 2 cl., [sleeper] 2 cl., [2] ✕ Budapest - Cluj Napoca - Brasov and v.v.
n – Budapest **Nyugati**.
☆ – Also from Püspökladány at 0505, 0552 ⚒, 0616 Ⓐ, 0716, 1316, 1516, 1626, 1716, 1826, 1926, 2016; also from Biharkeresztes at 0325 ⚒, 0425, 0510, 0542 Ⓐ, 0700, 1010, 1225, 1510 ⑦, 1525 ①–⑥, 1610, 1710.
⊙ – Romanian (East European) time, one hour ahead of Hungary.
* – *IC* in Hungary; *IR* in Romania (trains **143/146** are *EC* in Hungary).

DEBRECEN - MÁTÉSZALKA 1276

2nd class

km									F		Ⓑ	h
0	**Debrecen** d.	0454	0716	0916	1116	1316	1516	1716	1809	1913	2017	2248
58	Nyírbátor d.	0625	0838	1038	1238	1438	1638	1838	1916	2031	2146	0006
78	**Mátészalka** a.	0650	0900	1100	1300	1500	1700	1900	1937	2053	2208	0028

		G						⑦			
Mátészalka d.	0446	0521	0704	0904	1104	1304	1504	1614	1704	1910	2122
Nyírbátor d.	0509	0541	0727	0927	1127	1327	1527	1639	1727	1938	2145
Debrecen a.	0632	0648	0845	1045	1245	1445	1645	1758	1852	2105	2258

F – [2] [R] Budapest Nyugati (**606**) - Debrecen (**638**) - Mátészalka.
G – [2] [R] Mátészalka (**639**) - Debrecen (**619**) - Budapest Nyugati.
h – Runs 12 minutes later on ⑤.

DEBRECEN - ORADEA and BAIA MARE and other cross-border services 1277

2nd class

km		6812	6822	686 H
	Püspökladány d.	...	...	1602
0	**Debrecen** d.	0657	0905	1705
30	Nyirábrány a.	0751	0945	1751
30	Nyirábrány 🏛 d.	...	1005	1811
39	Valea lui Mihai 🏛 ⊙ a.	...	1120	1926
39	Valea lui Mihai ⊙ d.	...	1136	1944
105	**Oradea** ⊙ a.	...	|	|
70	Carei **1625** ⊙ a.	...	1210	2009
106	Satu Mare **1625** ⊙ a.	...	1256	2043
165	**Baia Mare** **1625** ⊙ a.	...	...	2208

	687 H	6811	6821
Baia Mare **1625** ⊙ d.	0800	...	...
Satu Mare **1625** ⊙ d.	0927	...	1855
Carei **1625** ⊙ d.	0959	...	1940
Oradea ⊙ d.	|	...	|
Valea lui Mihai ⊙ a.	1024	...	2022
Valea lui Mihai 🏛 ⊙ d.	1044	...	2049
Nyirábrány 🏛 a.	0959	...	2004
Nyirábrány d.	1019	1819	2019
Debrecen a.	1059	1900	2059
Püspökladány a.	1142	...	...

km			
0	**Békéscsaba** **1280** d.	0642	1544
16	Gyula **1280** d.	0700	1600
36	Kötegyán a.	0725	1625
36	Kötegyán 🏛 d.	0740	1645
50	**Salonta** 🏛 ⊙ a.	0900	1805

Salonta 🏛 ⊙ d.	0940	1830
Kötegyán 🏛 a.	0900	1750
Kötegyán d.	0932	1832
Gyula **1280** d.	1000	1900
Békéscsaba **1280** a.	1015	1915

km			
0	**Mátészalka** d.	0905	1408
18	Tiborszállás a.	0936	1439
18	Tiborszállás 🏛 d.	...	...
33	**Carei** ⊙ a.	...	...

Carei ⊙ d.	...	...
Tiborszállás 🏛 a.	...	...
Tiborszállás d.	1150	1801
Mátészalka a.	1221	1832

H – SZAMOS – [2] Wien (**143/144**) - Püspökladány (**686/687**) - Baia Mare and v.v.
⊙ – Romanian (East European) time, one hour ahead of Hungary. For other trains within Romania see Table **1625**.

DEBRECEN - FÜZESABONY 1278

2nd class

km										Ⓑ	
0	**Debrecen** d.	*0435**	*0632**	*0832**	*1032**	*1232**	*1432**	*1632**	*1832**	*2000**	*2245**
42	Hortobágy d.	0535	0736	0936	1136	1336	1536	1736	1936	2100	2345
73	Tiszafüred d.	0611	0812	1012	1212	1412	1612	1812	2012	2135	0020
103	**Füzesabony** a.	0644	0845	1045	1245	1445	1645	1845	2045	...	...

			Ⓐ							
Füzesabony d.	0500	0701	...	0901	1101	1301	1501	1701	1901	2253
Tiszafüred d.	0534	0735	0826	0935	1135	1335	1535	1735	1935	2326
Hortobágy d.	0615	0816	0900	1016	1216	1416	1616	1816	2016	...
Debrecen a.	*0716**	*0916**	*1000**	*1116**	*1316**	*1516**	*1716**	*1916**	*2116**	...

* – By 🚌 Debrecen - Balmazújváros (not shown) and v.v.

BUDAPEST - BÉKÉSCSABA - LÖKÖSHÁZA - ARAD 1280

2nd class (except where noted)

km						*IC** 371	*IC* 7400	*IC** 73	*IC* 7402	*IC** 75	*IC* 742	*IC** 375	*IC* 7404	*IC** 377	*IC* 746	*IC** 79	*IC* 7406	*IC** 379	*IC* 748	*IC** 473	*IC* 7408	347	347
				Ⓐ		⊖	[R]	J ⊖	[R]	K ⊖	[R]	⊖	[R]	⊖	[R]	L ⊖	[R]	⊖	[R]	M [R]	[R]	N [R]	N [R]
0	**Budapest** Keleti **1270** d.	...	...	...	...	...	0610	0710	0810	0910	1010	1110	1210	1310	1410	1510	1610	1710	1810	1910	2010	2245	2245
100	Szolnok **1270** d.	...	...	0445	0545	0633	0733	0833	0933	1033	1133	1233	1333	1433	1533	1633	1733	1833	1933	2033	2133	0030	0030
141	Mezőtúr d.	0429	0529	0529	0629	0659	0759	0859	0959	1059	1159	1259	1359	1459	1559	1659	1759	1859	1959	2059	2159	|	|
159	Gyoma d.	0445	0545	0545	0645	0712	0812	0912	1012	1112	1212	1312	1412	1512	1612	1712	1812	1912	2012	2112	2212	|	|
196	**Békéscsaba** a.	0515	0615	0615	0715	0739	0839	0939	1039	1139	1239	1339	1439	1539	1639	1739	1839	1939	2039	2139	2239	0124	0124
196	**Békéscsaba** d.	0541	0635	0635	...	0741	...	0941	...	1141	...	1341	...	1541	...	1741	...	1941	...	2141	*2243*	0126	0126
225	Lökösháza a.	0610	0715	0715	...	0810	...	1010	...	1210	...	1410	...	1610	...	1810	...	2010	...	2210	*2312*	0159	0159
225	Lökösháza 🏛 d.	...	...	...	...	0845	...	1045	...	1245	...	1445	...	1645	...	1845	...	2045	...	2245	...	0239	0239
236	Curtici 🏛 ⊙ a.	...	...	...	...	0955	...	1155	...	1355	...	1555	...	1755	...	1955	...	2155	...	2355	...	0349	0349
236	Curtici ⊙ d.	...	...	...	...	1020	...	1225	...	1420	...	1620	...	1820	...	2032	...	2220	...	0037	...	0415	0415
253	**Arad** ⊙ a.	...	...	...	...	1035	...	1237	...	1433	...	1635	...	1835	...	2045	...	2235	...	0050	...	0428	0428
	Timisoara Nord **1625** ⊙ a.	...	...	...	...	...	...	1327	...	|	...	...	...	1930	...	2139	...	...	...	|	...	|	0552
	Brasov **1600** ⊙ a.	...	...	...	...	...	...	|	...	2323	...	...	...	...	...	|	...	...	...	0923	...	1326	|
	Bucuresti Nord **1600** ⊙ a.	...	...	...	...	...	...	2330	...	...	...	...	...	...	...	0806	...	...	...	1159	...	1547	1600

J – TRAIANUS – [2] Budapest - Arad - Timisoara - Craiova - Bucuresti and v.v.
K – FOGARAS – [2] Budapest - Arad - Sibiu - Brasov and v.v.
L – MUNTENIA – [sleeper] 2 cl., [2] Budapest - Arad - Timisoara - Craiova - Bucuresti and v.v.
M – ISTER – [couchette] 1, 2 cl., [sleeper] 2 cl., [2] Budapest - Arad - Sibiu - Brasov - Bucuresti and v.v.
N – DACIA – [couchette] 1, 2 cl., [sleeper] 2 cl., [2] Wien - Budapest - Arad - Brasov - Bucuresti and v.v.; [couchette] 1, 2 cl. Wien - Budapest - Arad - Timisoara - Bucuresti and v.v.

* – Classified *IR* in Romania.
△ – Timings may vary by up to 3 minutes.
⊙ – Romanian (East European) time, one hour ahead of Hungary.
⊖ – Reservation compulsory for domestic journeys in Hungary ([R] in Romania).

FOR RETURN SERVICE SEE NEXT PAGE →

1280 BUDAPEST - BÉKÉSCSABA - LÖKÖSHÁZA - ARAD

2nd class (except where noted)

		IC* 472	IC 759	IC* 378	IC 7407	IC* 78	IC 747	IC* 376	IC 745	IC* 374		IC 743	IC* 74	IC 741	IC* 72	IC 7401	IC* 370				346	346
		M R	R	⊖	R	L ⊖	R	⊖	R	⊖	Ⓐ	R	K ⊖	R	J ⊖	R	⊖				N R	N R
Bucuresti Nord **1600** ⊙ d.	...	1745	...	...	...	2202	...	...	...	...	...	...	...	...	0606	...	...	...	...	...	1345	1400
Brasov **1600** ⊙ d.	...	2022	...	...	...	|	...	...	...	...	...	...	0620	...	|	...	...	...	...	...	|	1621
Timisoara Nord **1625** ⊙ d.	...	|	...	0600	...	0810	...	...	...	...	...	...	|	...	1605	...	...	...	...	...	2356	|
Arad ⊙ d.	...	0452	...	0654	...	0902	...	1055	...	1255	...	...	1445	...	1656	...	1855	...	...	...	0120	0120
Curtici ⊙ a.	...	0505	...	0708	...	0914	...	1109	...	1309	...	...	1458	...	1708	...	1909	...	...	...	0133	0133
Curtici 🏛 ⊙ d.	...	0534	...	0734	...	0934	...	1134	...	1334	...	...	1534	...	1734	...	1934	...	...	...	0210	0210
Lökösháza 🏛 a.	...	0444	...	0644	...	0844	...	1044	...	1244	...	...	1444	...	1644	...	1844	...	...	...	0120	0120
Lökösháza d.	0446	0540	0640	0740	...	0940	...	1140	...	1340	...	...	1540	...	1740	...	1940	...	2048	...	0200	0200
Békéscsaba a.	0515	0613	0715	0813	...	1013	...	1213	...	1413	...	...	1613	...	1813	...	2013	...	2117	...	0233	0233
Békéscsaba d.	0532	0620	0720	0820	0920	1020	1120	1220	1320	1420	1441	1520	1620	1720	1820	1920	2020	2040	━	2240	0235	0235
Gyoma d.	0601	0646	0746	0846	0946	1046	1146	1246	1346	1446	1512	1546	1646	1746	1846	1946	2046	2111	...	2311	|	|
Mezőtúr d.	0616	0700	0800	0900	1000	1100	1200	1300	1400	1500	1541	1600	1700	1800	1900	2000	2100	2127	...	2326	|	|
Szolnok **1270** d.	0649	0727	0827	0927	1027	1127	1227	1327	1427	1527	1615	1627	1727	1827	1927	2027	2126	2201	2219	...	0353	0353
Budapest Keleti **1270** a.	0815	0850	0950	1050	1150	1250	1350	1350	1550	1650	...	1750	1850	1950	2050	2150	...	...	0015	...	0520	0520

km												
0	Békéscsaba d.	0528	0642	0742	0944	1144	and hourly	1842	1942	2042	2241
16	Gyula a.	0544	0659	0759	0959	1159	(△) until	1859	1959	2059	2258

		Ⓐ								
Gyula d.	0546	0623	0700	and hourly	1100	1300	1500	and hourly	2100
Békéscsaba a.	0604	0641	0715	(△) until	1115	1315	1515	(△) until	2118

FOR RETURN ARAD - BUDAPEST SERVICE AND FOOTNOTES SEE PREVIOUS PAGE.

1290 BUDAPEST - KECSKEMÉT - SZEGED

km			IC	IC		IC	IC	IC		IC	IC	IC		IC	IC	IC		IC	IC	IC		IC	IC	
		2	700	702		712	722	732		704	714	724		734	706	716		726	736	708		718	728	2
			R	R		R	R	R		R	R	R		R	R	R		R	R	R		R	d R	
0	**Budapest** Nyugati **1270** d.	0403	0553	0653	...	0753	0853	0953	...	1053	1153	1253	...	1353	1453	1553	...	1653	1753	1853	...	1953	2053	2203
11	Köbánya-Kispest **1270** d.	0418	0607	0707	...	0807	0907	1007	...	1107	1207	1307	...	1407	1507	1607	...	1707	1807	1907	...	2007	2107	2218
18	Ferihegy ✈ **1270** d.	0427	0613	0713	...	0813	0913	1013	...	1113	1213	1313	...	1413	1513	1613	...	1713	1813	1913	...	2013	2113	2224
73	Cegléd **1270** d.	0535	0648	0748	...	0848	0948	1048	...	1148	1248	1348	...	1448	1548	1648	...	1748	1848	1948	...	2048	2148	2313
106	**Kecskemét** d.	0605	0711	0811	...	0911	1011	1111	...	1211	1311	1411	...	1511	1611	1711	...	1811	1911	2011	...	2111	2211	2342
131	Kiskunfélegyháza d.	0630	0730	0830	...	0930	1030	1130	...	1230	1330	1430	...	1530	1630	1730	...	1830	1930	2030	...	2130	2230	...
191	**Szeged** a.	0715	0815	0915	...	1015	1115	1215	...	1315	1415	1515	...	1615	1715	1815	...	1915	2015	2115	...	2215	2315	...

			IC		IC	IC	IC		IC	IC	IC		IC	IC	IC		IC	IC	IC		IC	IC	IC
	2	2	709		707	717	727		737	705	715		725	735	703		713	723	733		701	711	721
Szeged d.	...	0434	0547	...	0645	0745	0845	...	0945	1045	1145	...	1245	1345	1445	...	1545	1645	1745	...	1845	1945	2045
Kiskunfélegyháza d.	...	0521	0631	...	0731	0831	0931	...	1031	1131	1231	...	1331	1431	1531	...	1631	1731	1831	...	1931	2031	2131
Kecskemét d.	0432	0538	0648	...	0748	0848	0948	...	1048	1148	1248	...	1348	1448	1548	...	1648	1748	1848	...	1948	2048	2148
Cegléd **1270** d.	0504	0604	0713	...	0813	0913	1013	...	1113	1213	1313	...	1413	1513	1613	...	1713	1813	1913	...	2013	2113	2214
Ferihegy ✈ **1270** a.	0539	0639	0744	...	0844	0944	1044	...	1144	1244	1344	...	1444	1544	1644	...	1744	1844	1944	...	2044	2144	2248
Köbánya Kispest **1270** a.	0545	0645	0750	...	0850	0950	1050	...	1150	1250	1350	...	1450	1550	1650	...	1750	1850	1950	...	2050	2150	2254
Budapest Nyugati **1270** a.	0602	0707	0807	...	0907	1007	1107	...	1207	1307	1407	...	1507	1607	1707	...	1807	1907	2007	...	2107	2207	2311

d – ⑤⑦ only.

☛ Carriages without R are available on *IC* trains.

1292 SZEGED - BÉKÉSCSABA

2nd class

km			Ⓐ					Ⓒ		Ⓒ		Ⓐ												
0	**Szeged** d.	...	...	0528	0628	0728	...	0828	0928	1028	1128	1228	...	1328	1428	1528	1628	1728	...	1828	1928	2028	2228	...
31	Hódmezővásárhely d.	...	...	0601	0705	0801	...	0905	1001	1105	1201	1305	...	1401	1505	1601	1705	1801	...	1905	2001	2054	2259	...
62	Orosháza d.	0430	0531	0631	0731	0831	...	0931	1031	1131	1231	1331	...	1431	1531	1631	1731	1831	...	1931	2031	2133	2327	...
97	**Békéscsaba** a.	0509	0612	0712	0810	0910	...	1010	1110	1210	1310	1410	...	1510	1610	1710	1810	1910	...	2010	2110	...	...	...

							Ⓒ		Ⓒ		Ⓐ										Ⓐ		
Békéscsaba d.	...	...	0547	0647	0747	...	0847	0947	1047	1147	1247	...	1347	1445	1547	1645	1747	...	1847	1947	2047	2245	...
Orosháza d.	0432	0528	0632	0732	0832	...	0932	1032	1132	1232	1332	...	1432	1532	1632	1732	1832	...	1932	2032	2127	2324	...
Hódmezővásárhely d.	0502	0602	0702	0802	0902	...	1002	1102	1202	1300	1402	...	1502	1602	1702	1802	1902	...	2002	2102	...	...	...
Szeged a.	0533	0633	0733	0833	0933	...	1033	1133	1233	1333	1433	...	1533	1633	1733	1833	1933	...	2033	2133	...	...	...

1295 BUDAPEST - KELEBIA - SUBOTICA

2nd class

Warning! Rail services Budapest - Kelebia are suspended due to engineering work. No rail replacement 🚌 service is available, other than between Szeged and Kelebia. Commercial services are operated by Volánbuz (routes **653**, **1115** and **5255**) - rail tickets not valid.

km		*IC* 700		349		*IC* 714		343		
		R	🚌			R	🚌			
0	**Budapest** Keleti d.	...	...	...	...	...	...	...	...	...
	Budapest Nyugati **1290** d.	0553	...	...	...	1153	...	...	...	...
	Szeged **1290** d.	0815	0822	...	...	1415	1422	...	...	...
7	Ferencváros d.	...	|	...	...	...	|	...	...	...
61	Kunszentmiklós-Tass d.	...	|	...	...	...	|	...	...	...
107	Kiskőrös d.	...	|	...	...	...	|	...	...	...
134	Kiskunhalas d.	...	|	...	...	...	|	...	...	...
163	**Kelebia** 🏛 d.	...	0917	0941	...	...	1517	1541	...	...
	Subotica a.	...	...	0955	...	...	...	1555	...	...

	348		*IC* 737		342		*IC* 713		
		🚌	R			🚌	R		
Subotica d.	0802	...	...	...	1402	...	...	...	...
Kelebia 🏛 d.	0816	0840	...	...	1416	1440	...	...	...
Kiskunhalas d.	...	|	...	...	...	|	...	...	...
Kiskőrös d.	...	|	...	...	...	|	...	...	...
Kunszentmiklós-Tass d.	...	|	...	...	...	|	...	...	...
Ferencváros d.	...	|	...	...	...	|	...	...	...
Szeged **1290** d.	...	0935	0945	...	...	1535	1545	...	...
Budapest Nyugati **1290** a.	...	...	1207	...	...	...	1807	...	...
Budapest Keleti a.	...	...	...	...	...	...	...	...	...

1299 OTHER LOCAL SERVICES

BUDAPEST - DUNAÚJVÁROS

80 km, journey 65 – 95 minutes

From **Budapest** Déli: 0450, 0550, 0650, 0750 Ⓐ, 0850, 1050, 1250, 1350 Ⓒ, 1415 Ⓐ, 1450 Ⓒ, 1515 Ⓐ, 1550 Ⓒ, 1615 Ⓐ, 1650 Ⓒ, 1715 Ⓐ, 1815 Ⓐ, 1850, 2050, 2250.

From **Dunaújváros**: 0336, 0442, 0532, 0632, 0732, 0837 Ⓐ, 0932, 1137, 1332, 1437, 1537, 1637, 1732, 1837, 1937 Ⓐ, 2032, 2242.

BUDAPEST - ESZTERGOM

53 km, journey 65 – 74 minutes

From **Budapest** Nyugati: 0025, 0225 Ⓒ, 0401, 0440 Ⓐ, 0510, 0540 Ⓐ, 0621, 0651 and every 30 minutes until 2121, 2215, 2315.

From **Esztergom**: 0356, 0422, 0453 Ⓒ, 0505 Ⓐ, 0535, 0605, 0635 and every 30 minutes until 2105, 2135, 2235, 2335.

Ⓒ Apr. 2 - Nov. 1: 0921, 1021, 1221 call at **Vasútmúzeum**, returning 1530, 1630, 1730.

BUDAPEST - SZENTENDRE

21 km, journey time 40 minutes

HÉV suburban trains (line H5) from Budapest Batthyány tér (on metro M2), every 12 – 30 mins.

EGER - SZILVÁSVÁRAD

34 km, journey time 65 minutes

From **Eger**: 0732 **Q**, 1002, 1302, 1602 **Q**.

From **Szilvásvárad**: 0847 **Q**, 1147, 1447, 1754 **Q**.

Via Szilvásvárad-Szalajkavölgy (for the forest railway), 5 minutes before Szilvásvárad.

Q – Until Nov. 1.

ESTERGOM - KOMÁROM - SZÉKESFEHÉRVÁR

km						Ⓒ				
0	Esztergom d.	0813	...	...	...	1443	...	1843	...	2013
53	Komárom d.	1002	...	1020	...	1615	...	2015	...	2155
135	Székesfehérvár a.	...	...	1141	...	...	...	...	...	...

	Ⓐ			Ⓒ					Ⓒ
Székesfehérvár d.	...	...	...	...	...	1157	...	...	...
Komárom d.	0442	0539	...	0654	...	1317	...	1340	1756
Esztergom a.	0616	0716	...	0846	...	...	...	1516	1946

HATVAN - SZOLNOK

68 km, journey 71 – 73 minutes

From **Hatvan**: 0406, 0508 Ⓐ, 0608, 0708 Ⓐ, 0808, 1008, 1208, 1308 Ⓐ, 1408, 1508 Ⓐ, 1608, 1708 Ⓐ, 1808, 1908 Ⓐ, 2008, 2108 Ⓐ, 2219.

From **Szolnok**: 0323, 0433, 0533 Ⓐ, 0633, 0733 Ⓐ, 0833, 1033, 1233, 1332 Ⓐ, 1432, 1532 Ⓐ, 1632, 1732 Ⓐ, 1833, 1933 Ⓐ, 2033, 2133.

KISKUNFÉLEGYHÁZA - SZENTES

39 km, journey time 51 minutes

Trains call at **Csongrád** 36 mins. after Kiskunfélegyháza / 17 mins. after Szentes.

From **Kiskunfélegyháza**: 0534 Ⓐ, 0734, 0934, 1134, 1334, 1534, 1734, 1934, 2134.

From **Szentes**: 0423 Ⓐ, 0634, 0834, 1034, 1234, 1434, 1634, 1834, 2034.

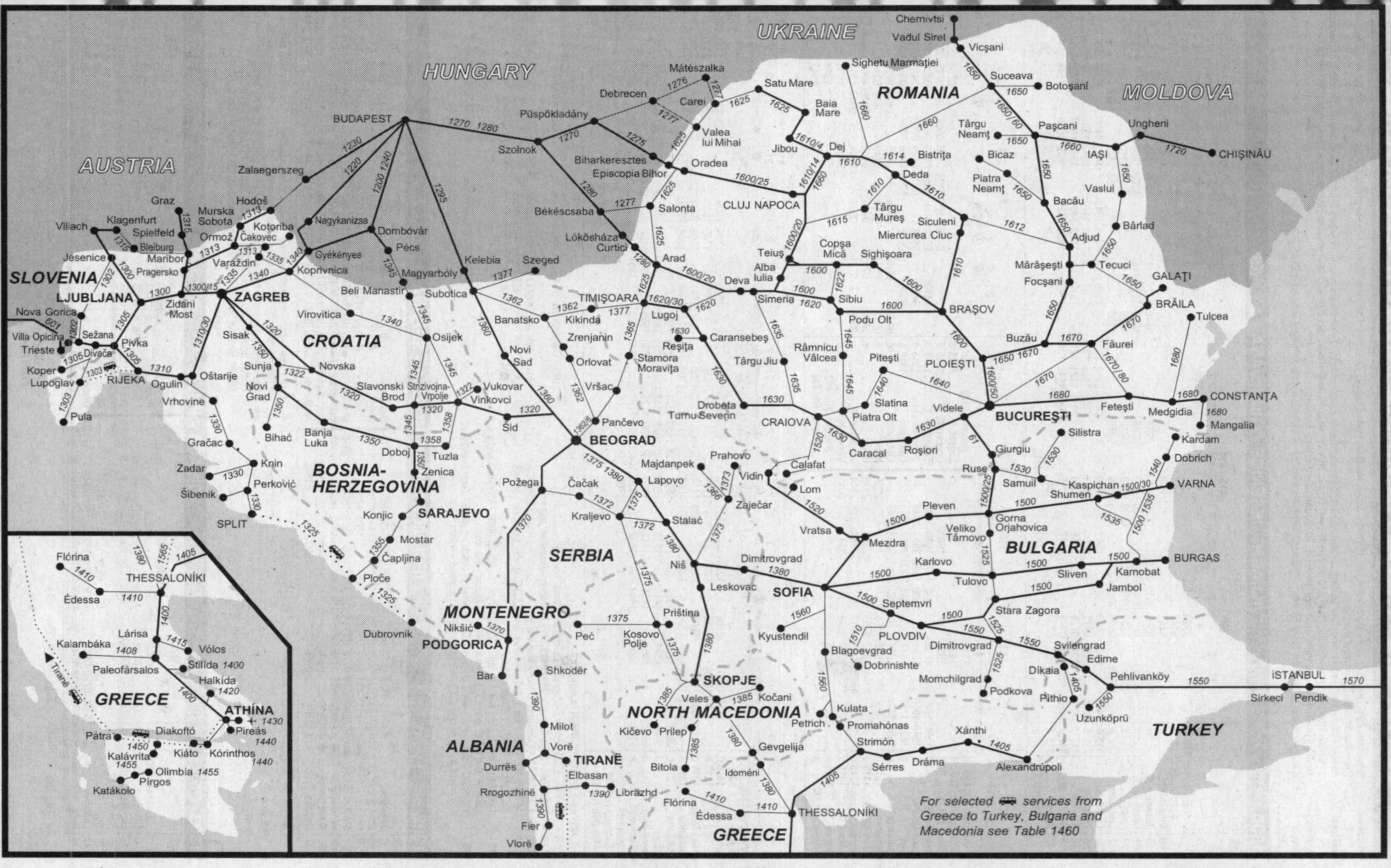
UKRAINE
HUNGARY
MOLDOVA
CHIŞINĂU
ROMANIA
BUCUREŞTI
BUDAPEST
AUSTRIA
SLOVENIA
LJUBLJANA
CROATIA
ZAGREB
BOSNIA-HERZEGOVINA
SARAJEVO
SERBIA
BEOGRAD
MONTENEGRO
PODGORICA
ALBANIA
TIRANË
NORTH MACEDONIA
SKOPJE
BULGARIA
SOFIA
GREECE
THESSALONÍKI
ATHÍNA
TURKEY
İSTANBUL
CONSTANŢA
VARNA
BURGAS
For selected services from Greece to Turkey, Bulgaria and Macedonia see Table 1460

SLOVENIA, CROATIA and BOSNIA-HERZEGOVINA

Operators: Slovenske Železnice (SŽ): www.slo-zeleznice.si; Hrvatske Željeznice (HŽ): www.hzpp.hr; Željeznice Federacije Bosne i Hercegovine (ŽFBH): www.zfbh.ba; and Željeznice Republike Srpske (ŽRS): www.zrs-rs.com

Services: All trains convey first and second class seating, **except** where shown otherwise in footnotes or by '2' in the train column, or where the footnote shows sleeping and/or couchette cars only. Descriptions of sleeping (🛏) and couchette (▬) cars appear on page 10. In Slovenia, travel by *ICS* train requires reservation and payment of a special fare.

Timings: **Timings in Slovenia are valid until September 4, 2022 (unless otherwise shown).**

Tickets: A supplement is payable for travel by internal express trains. Reservation of seats is possible on most express trains.

1300 VILLACH - JESENICE - LJUBLJANA - ZAGREB — SŽ, HŽ, ÖBB

km					499					415	415											211					
		2	2	2		2	2	2	2		2•	2	2	2	2	2	2	2	2	2	2		2	2	2	2	
		Ⓐ	Ⓐ		♦		Ⓐ		Ⓐ	♦	≋	Ⓐ	Ⓐ	Ⓐ		Ⓐ	Ⓐ			Ⓐ	Ⓐ	♦	Ⓐ			Ⓑ	
	München Hbf **890** d.	...	...	...	2320	...	...	...	...	...	...	...	...	...	...	...	...	...	...	...	...	...	...	...	...	...	...
	Salzburg Hbf **970** d.	...	...	...	0140	...	...	...	...	...	...	...	...	...	...	...	...	...	...	...	...	...	...	...	...	...	...
0	**Villach** Hbf. d.	...	...	...	0417	...	...	...	...	0628	...	...	...	...	...	...	...	...	...	...	...	1253	...	...	...	...	...
38	**Jesenice** ▦ d.	...	0422	...	0506	0535	0609	...	0626	0710	...	0734	...	...	...	0946	...	1113	...	...	1236	1339	...	1422	...	...	...
51	Lesce-Bled d.	...	0436	...	0518	0549	0623	...	0640	0722	...	0748	...	...	...	1003	...	1127	...	...	1250	1351	...	1436	...	...	...
74	Kranj d.	...	0500	...	0539	0613	0647	...	0708	0749	...	0812	...	...	...	1029	...	1151	...	...	1328	1410	...	1500	...	...	...
102	**Ljubljana** a.	...	0531	...	0600	0644	0721	...	0743	0809	...	0843	...	...	...	1100	...	1221	...	...	1353	1432	...	1532	...	...	...
102	**Ljubljana** **1315** d.	0450	...	0552	0620	...	...	0653	...	0830	...	...	0855	0955	*1055*	...	1155	...	*1255*	1345	...	1445	1450	...	1550	1655	...
166	Zidani Most **1315** d.	0605	...	0659	0711	...	...	0800	...	0921	...	...	1000	1103	1201	...	1301	...	1404	1442	...	1543	1602	...	1702	1800	...
182	Sevnica **1315** d.	0623	...	0717	0726	...	...	0818	...	0936	...	...	1018	1121	1219	...	1319	...	1422	1457	...	1558	1619	...	1720	1817	...
215	Dobova ▦ **1315** a.	0650	...	0744	0749	...	...	0847	...	1015	...	...	1045	1142	1247	...	1347	...	1450	1523	...	1622	1648	...	1749	1847	...
245	**Zagreb** **1315** a.	...	...	...	0832	...	...	...	...	1040	1104	...	...	...	...	...	...	...	...	...	...	1707	...	...	...	...	...
	Beograd **1320** a.	...	...	...	...	...	...	...	...	...	1812	...	...	...	...	...	...	...	...	...	...	...	...	...	...	...	...

				213				315		
	2	2	2		2	2	2		2	2
	Ⓐ	Ⓐ		♦			Ⓒ N	♦		Ⓐ
München Hbf **890** d.	...	...	...	1217	...	...	...	...	...	...
Salzburg Hbf **970** d.	...	...	...	1412	...	...	...	...	...	...
Villach Hbf. d.	...	...	...	1653	...	...	...	1853	...	...
Jesenice ▦ d.	1535	1627	...	1739	...	1806	1925	1939	2034	...
Lesce-Bled d.	1549	1650	...	1751	...	1820	1942	1953	2048	...
Kranj d.	1625	1717	...	1811	...	1847	2006	2012	2114	...
Ljubljana a.	1655	1749	...	1831	...	1921	2041	2033	2146	...
Ljubljana **1315** d.	...	...	1755	1838	1855	...	...	2105	...	2225
Zidani Most **1315** d.	...	...	1905	1929	1959	...	...	2202	...	2326
Sevnica **1315** d.	...	...	1923	1944	2017	...	...	2217	...	2344
Dobova ▦ **1315** a.	...	...	1952	2006	2046	...	...	2241	...	0011
Zagreb **1315** a.	...	...	...	2046	...	...	...	...	...	...
Beograd **1320** a.	...	...	...	...	...	...	...	...	...	...

							314			212		
	2	2	2	2	2	2		2	2		2	
	Ⓐ		Ⓐ	Ⓐ	Ⓒ N	Ⓐ	♦		Ⓐ	♦		
Beograd **1320** d.	...	...	...	...	...	...	...	...	...	...	...	...
Zagreb **1315** d.	...	...	...	...	...	...	...	...	...	0703	...	...
Dobova ▦ **1315** d.	...	...	...	0455	...	0525	0540	0604	...	0745	0713	...
Sevnica **1315** d.	...	0410	...	0524	...	0552	0605	0633	...	0809	0742	...
Zidani Most **1315** d.	...	0428	...	0543	...	0610	0621	0700	...	0825	0808	...
Ljubljana **1315** a.	...	0530	...	0636	...	0704	0716	0802	...	0916	0908	...
Ljubljana d.	0443	...	0610	...	0648	...	0725	...	0824	0923	...	...
Kranj d.	0516	...	0647	...	0719	...	0749	...	0856	0944	...	...
Lesce-Bled d.	0549	...	0711	...	0748	...	0813	...	0919	1003	...	...
Jesenice ▦ a.	0602	...	0726	...	0802	...	0824	...	0932	1014	...	...
Villach Hbf. a.	...	...	...	...	...	...	0908	...	...	1058	...	...
Salzburg Hbf **970** a.	...	...	...	...	...	...	...	...	...	1348	...	...
München Hbf **890** a.	...	...	...	...	...	...	...	...	...	1541	...	...

										210												414	414				498
	2	2	2	2	2	2	2	2	2		2	2	2	2	2	2	2	2	2	2	2	2◧		2	2	2	
			Ⓐ			Ⓐ	Ⓐ			♦		Ⓐ	Ⓐ		Ⓐ			Ⓑ	Ⓐ			≋	♦	Ⓑ			♦
Beograd **1320** d.	...	...	...	...	...	...	...	...	...	...	...	...	...	...	...	...	...	...	...	...	...	1005	...	...	...	...	...
Zagreb **1315** d.	...	...	...	...	...	...	...	...	...	1247	...	...	...	...	...	...	...	...	...	...	...	1813	1838	...	...	...	2127
Dobova ▦ **1315** d.	...	0910	1010	...	1106	...	1209	...	1311	1332	...	...	...	1510	...	...	1610	...	1711	1806	...	...	1925	2004	...	2111	2207
Sevnica **1315** d.	...	0939	1039	...	1135	...	1238	...	1340	1359	...	...	...	1539	...	...	1639	...	1740	1835	...	...	1950	2033	...	2140	2230
Zidani Most **1315** d.	...	1000	1058	...	1200	...	1257	...	1359	1416	...	...	...	1558	...	...	1701	...	1802	1900	...	...	2006	2052	...	2200	2248
Ljubljana **1315** a.	...	1102	1200	...	1302	...	1357	...	1501	1507	...	...	...	1700	...	...	1802	...	1904	2002	...	...	2054	2152	...	2302	2338
Ljubljana d.	0958	...	...	1250	...	1332	...	1447	...	1527	1533	1550	1623	...	1719	1753	...	1846	...	...	2042	...	2110	...	2228	...	2351
Kranj d.	1029	...	...	1321	...	1410	...	1518	...	1552	1605	1625	1657	...	1751	1826	...	1919	...	...	2114	...	2131	...	2316	...	0012
Lesce-Bled d.	1053	...	...	1351	...	1436	...	1549	...	1615	1629	1650	1721	...	1820	1850	...	1942	...	...	2138	...	2151	...	2324	...	0031
Jesenice ▦ a.	1106	...	...	1404	...	1449	...	1602	...	1626	1645	1703	1734	...	1833	1903	...	1957	...	...	2150	...	2202	...	2337	...	0042
Villach Hbf. a.	...	...	...	...	...	...	...	...	...	1708	...	...	...	...	...	...	...	...	...	...	...	...	2249	...	...	...	0126
Salzburg Hbf **970** a.	...	...	...	...	...	...	...	...	...	...	...	...	...	...	...	...	...	...	...	...	...	...	...	...	...	...	0404
München Hbf **890** a.	...	...	...	...	...	...	...	...	...	...	...	...	...	...	...	...	...	...	...	...	...	...	...	...	...	...	0629

♦ – **NOTES** (LISTED BY TRAIN NUMBER)

210/1 – SAVA – [12] Vinkovci - Zagreb - Ljubljana - Villach and v.v.
212/3 – MIMARA – [12] Zagreb - Villach (**112/3**) - München - Frankfurt and v.v.
314/5 – [12] Villach - Ljubljana - Dobova and v.v.
414/5 – ALPINE PEARLS – 🛏 1, 2 cl., ▬ 2 cl. and [2] Zagreb - Ljubljana - Villach - Schwarzach (**464/5**) - Zürich and v.v.
498 – LISINSKI – 🛏 1, 2 cl., ▬ 2 cl. and [2] Zagreb - Salzburg (**462**) - München and v.v.; conveys 🛏 1, 2 cl. and [2] Rijeka (**480**) - Ljubljana - München.
499 – LISINSKI – 🛏 1, 2 cl., ▬ 2 cl. and [2] München - Salzburg (**463**) - Zagreb and v.v.; conveys 🛏 1, 2 cl. and [2] München (**481**) - Ljubljana - Rijeka.

N – Conveys on Ⓒ: [2] Ljubljana - Jesenice - Nova Gorica and v.v.

◧ – Train number **412** Beograd - Zagreb.
• – Train number **413** Zagreb - Beograd.
≋ – Currently suspended.

1302 JESENICE - NOVA GORICA - SEŽANA — 2nd class only — SŽ

km		Ⓐ	Ⓒ	Ⓐ	Ⓐ	N			Ⓐ		Ⓑ	
0	**Jesenice** d.	0415	0415	0605	0827	0827	1115	...	1432	1651	...	1918
10	Bled Jezero d.	0431	0431	0621	0843	0843	1131	...	1448	1706	...	1934
28	Bohinjska B ⊡ 🚗 d.	0451	0451	0648	0903	0903	1151	...	1508	1726	...	1954
56	Most na Soči 🚗 d.	0526	0526	0724	0939	0939	1227	...	1553	1801	...	2036
89	Nova Gorica ♣ a.	0605	0605	0812	1016	1016	1304	...	1632	1838	...	2113
89	Nova Gorica ♣ d.	0608	...	0854	...	...	...	1444	...	...	1850	...
130	**Sežana** a.	0707	...	0950	...	...	...	1550	...	...	1946	...

	Ⓐ		Ⓐ	Ⓒ d	Ⓐ	Ⓒ	Ⓐ	Ⓐ		Ⓒ	N	
Sežana d.	...	...	0626	...	1010	...	...	1430	...	1624	...	...
Nova Gorica ♣ a.	...	...	0719	...	1103	...	...	1522	...	1716	...	...
Nova Gorica ♣ d.	0330	0529	0735	0735	1120	1120	1447	...	1555	...	1719	1956
Most na Soči 🚗 d.	0407	0607	0813	0813	1159	1159	1526	...	1634	...	1803	2035
Bohinjska B ⊡ 🚗 d.	0453	0646	0905	0905	1245	1245	1604	...	1727	...	1839	2114
Bled Jezero d.	0513	0707	0926	0926	1306	1306	1624	...	1747	...	1859	2133
Jesenice a.	0529	0722	0942	0942	1322	1322	1640	...	1803	...	1915	2149

N – Conveys on Ⓒ: [2] Ljubljana - Jesenice - Nova Gorica and v.v.

d – Not June 6 - Aug. 28.

⊡ – Bohinjska Bistrica.

♣ – Line **1** 🚌 service operates between Nova Gorica (bus stop 100 metres from station on Italian side) and Gorizia Centrale (Italy) stations. Total journey time ± 20 minutes.

🚗 – Car-carrying service exists between Bohinjska Bistrica and Most na Soči. Depart Bohinjska Bistrica 0913, 1325, 1648 also 2116 (Apr. 2 - Sept. 4). Depart Most na Soči 0745, 1038 and 1445 also 1843 (Apr. 2 - Sept. 4).

1303 DIVAČA - PULA — 2nd class only — HŽ, SŽ

km				1272								
		⚒	Ⓐ	L			Ⓐ	Ⓐ				
	Ljubljana **1305** d.	...	...	0603	...	...	...	...	...	...	...	...
0	**Divača** d.	...	...	0752	...	...	...	...	...	...	...	...
12	Hrpelje-Kozina d.	...	...	0804	...	...	...	...	...	...	...	...
30	Rakitovec ▦ d.	...	...	0838	...	...	...	...	...	...	...	...
36	Buzet ▦ d.	...	0706	0900	...	1109	1309	...	...	1707	...	...
43	Lupoglav ▲ d.	0535	0726	0918	...	1129	1329	1523	...	1734	...	2020
117	**Pula** a.	0712	0902	1042	...	1305	1513	1704	...	1910	...	2200

										1273	
	Ⓐ	Ⓐ			Ⓐ		Ⓐ		Ⓐ	L	
Pula d.	0449	0634	0905	...	1320	1438	1544	...	1719	1755	1940
Lupoglav ▲ d.	0635	0822	1042	...	1507	1631	1721	...	1901	1924	2122
Buzet ▦ d.	0653	0840	1100	...	...	1649	...	...	1919	1954	2140
Rakitovec ▦ d.	...	...	...	...	...	...	...	...	...	2015	...
Hrpelje-Kozina d.	...	...	...	...	...	...	...	...	...	2042	...
Divača a.	...	...	...	...	...	...	...	...	...	2054	...
Ljubljana **1305** a.	...	...	...	...	...	...	...	...	...	2203	...

L – Apr. 16 - Sept. 25. ISTRA – [2] Ljubljana - Pula and v.v.

▲ – 🚌 service **Lupoglav - Rijeka** and v.v. Journey 40 minutes.
From Lupoglav at 0634Ⓐ, 1100, 1630, 2121.
From Rijeka at 0550Ⓐ, 1015, 1425Ⓐ, 1545Ⓒ,1930.

SŽ, HŽ 2nd class only except where shown — LJUBLJANA - RIJEKA, KOPER, SEŽANA and TRIESTE — 1305

km		Ⓐ	Ⓐ		1605 ♦	1272 ♦	🚌	481 ♦		IC 503 ♦		Ⓐ	Ⓐ		EC 134 ♦			483 ♦	b	Ⓐ	IC 509 ♦		Ⓐ			
	Maribor **1315** d.	...	...	...	0323	...	...	...	...	...	...	...	...	...	1145	...	...	...	...	...	...	...	...	...	...	...
0	**Ljubljana** d.	0416	0520	0552	0603	0603	...	0630	0755	0905	...	1027	1210	1315	1409	1419	...	1511	1550	1650	1755	1849	1931	...	2112	...
67	Postojna d.	0534	0640	0654	0705	0705	...	0730	0916	1010	...	1149	1320	1432	1513	1529	...	1619	1702	1806	1907	1956	2052	...	2208	...
80	Pivka ▲ d.	0547	0654	0707	0718	0718	...	0745	0930	1021	...	1200	1334	1433	1526	1526	...	1634	1715	1819	1920	2009	2106	...	2231	...
	Ilirska Bistrica 🏛 ▲ d.	│	│	│	│	│	...	0815	│	│	...	│	│	│	│	│	...	1703	│	│	│	│	│	...	│	...
	Šapjane 🏛 d.	│	│	│	│	│	...	0844	│	│	...	│	│	│	│	│	...	1733	│	│	│	│	│	...	│	...
	Rijeka a.	│	│	│	│	│	...	0929	│	│	...	│	│	│	│	│	...	1822	│	│	│	│	│	...	│	...
104	Divača a.	0607	0715	0726	0738	0738	...	...	0950	1040	...	1221	1356	1509	1548	1604	...	...	1734	1839	1941	2033	2126	...	2251	...
104	Divača d.	0613	0716	0727	0745	0752	0757	...	0951	1042	1045	1222	1357	1509	1549	1605	1621	...	1738	1840	1947	2034	2127	2127	2252	...
116	Hrpelje-Kozina ⊡ d.	│	│	│	0759	0804	0816	...	│	1054	│	│	│	│	│	│	│	...	1757	│	1959	│	│	│	│	...
153	**Koper** ⊡ a.	│	│	│	0833	...	0836	...	│	1127	│	│	│	│	│	│	│	...	1817	│	2036	│	│	│	│	...
113	**Sežana** 🏛 a.	0621	0726	0736	...	...	...	...	1000	...	1055	1230	1407	1519	1558	1615	1631	...	...	1850	...	2044	2131	2136	2302	...
113	**Sežana** 🏛 d.	0622	...	0739	...	...	...	...	1001	...	...	1231	...	...	1559	1616	...	...	...	...	...	2045	2136	2137	...	...
120	Villa Opicina ¶ a.	0633	...	0750	...	...	...	...	1012	...	...	1242	...	...	1610	1627	...	...	...	...	...	2056	2148	2148	...	...
144	**Trieste** Centrale ¶ a.	...	...	0833	...	...	...	...	...	...	...	...	...	...	1652	...	...	...	...	...	...	...	...	...	...	...

km		Ⓐ	Ⓐ	Ⓐ	Ⓐ	IC 508 ♦	Ⓐ		Ⓐ			b	482 ♦	Ⓐ	EC 135 ♦	Ⓐ	IC 502 ♦	Ⓐ		Ⓑ		1273 ♦	1604 ♦	480 ♦	Ⓐ	
	Trieste Centrale ¶ d.	...	...	...	...	...	...	...	...	0903	...	...	...	...	1303	...	...	...	...	...	...	...	...	...	...	...
	Villa Opicina ¶ d.	...	...	...	...	...	...	0658	...	0945	1018	...	...	1330	1345	...	...	...	1741	1844	1945	...	...	...	2158	...
	Sežana 🏛 a.	...	...	...	...	...	...	0709	...	0956	1029	...	...	1341	1356	...	...	...	1752	1855	1956	...	...	...	2209	...
	Sežana 🏛 d.	...	0435	0503	0555	...	...	0710	0855	0958	1030	...	...	1342	1358	1440	...	1652	1753	1856	1958	...	...	...	...	...
	Koper ⊡ d.	...	│	│	│	0525	...	│	│	│	│	1004	...	│	│	│	1520	│	│	│	│	...	2015	...	...	...
	Hrpelje-Kozina ⊡ d.	...	│	│	│	0559	...	│	│	│	│	1024	...	│	│	│	1552	│	│	│	│	2050	2050	...	...	...
	Divača a.	...	0444	0512	0604	0611	...	0720	0904	1007	1040	1043	...	1352	1408	1449	1603	1701	1802	1906	2007	2102	2102	...	...	...
	Divača d.	...	0445	0513	...	0612	...	0721	0905	1008	...	1051	...	1353	1410	1450	1605	1702	1803	1907	2009	2104	2104	...	...	...
0	**Rijeka** d.	...	│	│	...	│	...	│	│	│	...	│	1150	│	│	│	│	│	│	│	│	│	│	2040	...	...
28	Šapjane 🏛 d.	...	│	│	...	│	...	│	│	│	...	│	1254	│	│	│	│	│	│	│	│	│	│	2140	...	...
40	Ilirska Bistrica 🏛 ▲ d.	...	│	│	...	│	0632	│	│	│	...	│	1323	│	│	│	│	│	│	│	│	│	│	2208	...	...
56	Pivka ▲ d.	...	0507	0535	...	0636	0648	0741	0926	1029	...	1112	1339	1415	1431	1515	1625	1726	1825	1928	2030	2125	2125	2224	...	...
	Postojna d.	0410	0520	0548	...	0649	0703	0756	0940	1041	...	1124	1352	1429	1443	1527	1636	1739	1838	1929	2042	2138	2138	2237	...	...
	Ljubljana a.	0527	0629	0656	...	0753	0823	0917	1100	1146	...	1245	1459	1548	1547	1644	1740	1848	1957	2101	2145	2241	2241	2335	...	...
	Maribor **1315** a.	...	...	...	...	...	...	...	...	...	...	...	...	...	1816	...	...	...	...	...	...	...	0123	...	...	...

♦ – **NOTES** (LISTED BY TRAIN NUMBER)

134/5 – (12) Wien (**150/1**) - Ljubljana - Trieste and v.v.

480/1 – OPATIJA – (12) Rijeka - Ljubljana and v.v.; (2) (also 🛏 1, 2 cl.) Rijeka - Ljubljana (**498/9**) - München and v.v.

482/3 – LJUBLJANA – (12) Ljubljana - Rijeka - and v.v.

502/3 – POHORJE – (12) Hodoš - Ljubljana - Koper and v.v.

508/9 – KOPER – (12) Ljubljana - Koper and v.v. Conveys (12) Budapest (**246/7**) - Ljubljana - Koper and v.v.

1272/3 – Apr. 16 - Sept. 25. ISTRA – (2) Ljubljana - Pula and v.v.

1604 – (2) Koper - Ljubljana - Maribor.

1605 – (2) Maribor - Ljubljana - Koper.

b – By 🚌 Divaca - Koper and v.v.

¶ – For frequent tram connections Villa Opicina - Trieste and v.v., see panel in Table **601**.

▲ – Local services **Pivka - Ilirska Bistrica** and v.v.: Journey 16 minutes.
From Pivka at 0553Ⓐ, 0934Ⓐ, 1203Ⓐ, 1342Ⓐ, 1530Ⓐ, 1736Ⓑ, 1830Ⓑ.
From Ilirska Bistrica at 0514Ⓐ, 0632Ⓐ, 1050Ⓐ, 1302Ⓐ, 1412Ⓐ, 1605Ⓐ, 1758Ⓑ, 1952Ⓑ.

⊡ – 🚌 service **Koper - Trieste** and v.v.: Journey 45 minutes.
From Koper at 0600⚒, 0642Ⓐ, 0700Ⓐ, 0730⚒, 1030⚒, 1115Ⓐ, 1215Ⓐ, 1400⚒, 1730⚒. **From Trieste** at 0700⚒, 0900⚒, 1000Ⓐ, 1115Ⓐ, 1230⚒, 1300⚒, 1400Ⓐ, 1530⚒, 1900⚒.
Service is subject to alteration. No service on ⑦, Slovenian and Italian holidays.
Operator: Arriva Slovenija, Meljska cesta 97, 2000 Maribor.

HŽ 2nd class only except where shown — RIJEKA - ZAGREB — 1310

km		Ⓡc	⚒				⚒	Ⓐ		Ⓐ	Ⓡd		
0	**Rijeka** d.	0135	...	0530	0735	...	...	1153	1358	1523	1730	...	1930
61	Delnice d.	0240	...	0642	0850	...	...	1311	1513	1637	1842	...	2046
90	Moravice d.	0311	0600	0716	0924	...	...	1345	1547	1714	1913	1952	2120
120	Ogulin **1330** d.	0341	0632	0743	0954	1039	1215	1418	1620	1744	1942	2023	2150
126	Oštarije **1330** d.	│	0642	...	...	1044	1220	...	1625	...	1948	2030	...
176	Karlovac **1330** d.	0450	0758	...	...	1147	1323	...	1737	...	2039	2131	...
229	**Zagreb** **1330** a.	0547	0858	...	...	1242	1418	...	1829	...	2123	2225	...
	Osijek **1340** a.	1136	...	...	...	...	...	...	...	...	...	...	...

	Ⓡb	Ⓐ			Ⓐ			Ⓐ			Ⓐ	
Osijek **1340** d.	2000	...	...	...	...	...	...	...	...	...	...	...
Zagreb **1330** d.	0110	...	0627	0807	...	1312	...	1422	1544	1720	1832	2146
Karlovac **1330** d.	0210	...	0727	0903	...	1411	...	1520	1645	1820	1927	2243
Oštarije **1330** d.	│	...	0829	1012	...	1514	...	1626	1753	1925	2029	2348
Ogulin **1330** d.	0308	0559	0833	1026	1405	1518	1602	1630	1758	1930	2033	2352
Moravice d.	0344	0633	...	1057	1435	...	1635	...	1828	...	...	...
Delnice d.	0414	0710	...	1131	1514	...	1709	...	...	...	...	...
Rijeka a.	0518	0824	...	1243	1628	...	1819	...	...	...	...	...

b – July 2 - Aug. 28: 🛏 2 cl. and (2) Vinkovci - Zagreb - Rijeka; 🛏 2 cl. and (2) Osijek (**1782**) - Zagreb (**1540**) - Rijeka.

c – July 3 - Aug. 29: 🛏 2 cl. and (2) Rijeka - Zagreb - Vinkovci; 🛏 2 cl. and (2) Rijeka (**1541**) - Zagreb (**1783**) - Osijek.

d – ⑦ to June 19 and from Oct. 2 (also May 30; not Feb. 20, Apr. 17, May 29, Oct. 30, Nov. 1).

SŽ, MÁV 2nd class only except where shown — MARIBOR - ČAKOVEC, MURSKA SOBOTA and ZALAEGERSZEG — 1313

km		1247 ♦	Ⓐ		Ⓐ	Ⓐ	Ⓐ		Ⓐ		IC 247 ♦		⚒	⑦g	Ⓐ	Ⓐ			Ⓐ				Ⓐ			IC 502 ♦	Ⓐ	Ⓐ
	Ljubljana **1315** d.	0030	...	...	...	...	...	...	...	...	0935	...	...	...	...	...	...	...	...	...	...	...	1515	...	...	1743	...	...
0	**Maribor** **1315** d.	│	...	...	...	...	...	0707	...	0918	│	...	...	...	1343	...	1440	...	...	1538	...	1620	│	...	...	│	1845	2210
19	Pragersko **1315** d.	0226	...	...	...	...	0610	│	...	0945	1135	...	1328	1328	1402	1419	1505	...	...	│	...	│	1701	...	...	1939	│	│
37	Ptuj d.	0238	...	...	...	...	0633	0745	...	0957	1146	...	1348	1348	...	1441	1525	...	...	1619	...	1657	1713	...	...	1952	1944	2251
59	Ormož d.	│	...	...	0447	0555	0657	0804	0811	1010	1200	1205	1407	1407	...	1504	1546	...	1550	1639	1647	1714	1726	...	1733	2004	2010	2315
	Središče 🏛 a.	│	...	...	0458	│	...	│	0822	│	│	1216	│	│	...	1515	│	...	1601	│	1658	...	│	...	1744	│	│	...
	Čakovec a.	│	...	...	...	│	...	│	0841	│	│	...	│	│	...	...	│	...	...	│	...	...	│	...	1803	│	│	...
98	**Murska Sobota** d.	0319	0330	...	...	0638	...	0840	...	1040	1230	...	1443	1443	...	...	1622	...	...	1718	...	...	1800	...	...	2029	2047	...
127	Hodoš a.	0338	0355	...	...	...	...	...	...	...	1248	...	...	...	...	...	...	...	...	...	...	...	1824	...	...	2046	2108	...
127	Hodoš 🏛 d.	0353	...	0613	...	...	...	...	...	...	1301	...	...	...	...	...	...	1651	...	...	...	...	...	1851	...	...	...	...
174	**Zalaegerszeg** a.	0431	...	0703	...	...	...	...	...	...	1337	...	...	...	...	...	...	1741	...	...	...	...	...	1941	...	...	...	...
	Budapest Déli **1230** a.	0859	...	...	...	...	...	...	...	...	1659	...	...	...	...	...	...	...	...	...	...	...	...	...	...	...	...	...

km		1246 ♦		Ⓐn	Ⓐ		IC 503 ♦	Ⓐn	Ⓒ	Ⓐ	Ⓐ	Ⓐ			IC 246 ♦	Ⓐ	⚒	g	Ⓐ	Ⓐ		Ⓐ	g	g				Ⓐ
	Budapest Déli **1230** d.	2035	...	...	...	...	...	...	...	...	...	...	...	...	0900	...	...	...	...	...	...	...	...	...	...	...	...	...
	Zalaegerszeg d.	0012	...	...	...	...	...	...	...	...	...	...	...	...	1222	...	...	...	...	...	1457	...	...	...	1657	...	1813	...
	Hodoš 🏛 a.	0048	...	...	...	0457	...	...	...	...	...	...	...	...	1259	...	...	...	...	...	1548	...	...	...	1751	...	1906	...
	Hodoš d.	0103	...	0425	...	0548	0551	0620	...	...	...	...	...	...	1315	...	...	...	...	...	▬	1615	1623	...	▬	...	...	1920
	Murska Sobota d.	0122	...	0452	...	▬	0610	0644	...	...	...	0933	1235	...	1335	...	1510	1510	...	...	...	1637	1646	1830	...	1855	...	1941
0	**Čakovec** d.	│	...	│	...	Ⓐ	│	│	...	0930	...	│	│	...	│	...	│	│	...	...	...	...	│	│	1811	│	...	...
12	Središče 🏛 d.	│	0433	│	0538	│	│	│	...	0949	...	│	│	1349	│	1528	│	│	1620	...	1710	...	│	│	1830	│	...	...
22	Ormož d.	│	0445	0522	0546	0549	0636	0724	0840	1000	1007	1010	1313	1400	1407	1539	1546	1546	1631	1700	1721	...	1724	1900	1841	1932	...	...
	Ptuj d.	0201	0509	0536	...	0608	0650	0745	0900	...	1029	1029	1334	...	1421	...	1604	1604	...	1726	...	...	1743	1913	...	1952	...	...
	Pragersko **1315** d.	0337t	0539	0547	...	0632	0702	│	│	...	1046	1046	│	...	1434	...	1632	1632	...	1749	...	...	1809	1927	...	2019	...	...
	Maribor **1315** a.	0226	0602	...	...	0651	│	0830	0935	...	...	...	1414	...	│	...	1650	1650	...	...	...	...	│	│	...	2039	...	...
	Ljubljana **1315** a.	0550	...	...	...	...	0856	...	...	...	...	...	...	...	1632	...	...	...	...	...	...	...	2005	2114	...	...	...	...

♦ – **NOTES** (LISTED BY TRAIN NUMBER)

246/7 – CITADELLA – (12) Budapest - Ljubljana and v.v: (12) Budapest - Ljubljana (**508/9**) - Koper and v.v.

502/3 – POHORJE – (12) Hodoš - Ljubljana - Koper and v.v.

1246 – June 17 - Aug. 29. ISTRA – 🛏 1, 2 cl. and (2) Budapest - Hodoš - Maribor (**1605**) Ljubljana - Koper.

1247 – June 19 - Aug. 31. ISTRA – 🛏 1, 2 cl. and (2) Koper - Ljubljana (**1604**) - Maribor - Hodoš - Budapest.

g – ⑦ to June 19 (also Feb. 8, Apr. 18, May 2; not Dec. 26, Apr. 17, May 1).

n – Not Feb. 18, Apr. 18, 27, May 2, Aug. 15.

t – Via Maribor.

1315 LJUBLJANA and ZAGREB - MARIBOR - GRAZ

SŽ, HŽ, ÖBB

km					IC		ICS	EC	IC				IC				ICS			EC	IC		IC			
				Ⓐ	512		14	158	247				518				20			150	502		526		604	1604
		2	2	2			🅁	✕🅁	🅁	2	2			2	2	2	🅁	2	2	✕🅁		2	🅁	2	2	2
		h	Ⓐ					♦	♦			Ⓐ			⚒	Ⓐ				♦	♦		2		♦	♦
	Koper **1305** d.	...	...	...	...	...	...	...	...	...	...	...	...	...	...	...	...	...	...	...	1520	...	...	...	...	2015
0	**Ljubljana** 1300 d.	0050	...	...	0536	...	0805	...	0935	1055	...	...	1315	1255	1350	...	1515	...	...	1605	1743	...	1950	2050	2300	2300
*	**Zagreb** 1300 d.	|	...	...	|	...	|	0725	|	|	...	...	|	|	|	...	|	...	...	|	|	...	|	|	|	|
	Dobova 🛃 1300 d.	|	...	0505	|	...	|	0812	|	|	...	...	|	|	|	...	|	...	...	|	|	...	|	|	|	|
	Sevnica 1300 d.	|	...	0533	|	...	|	0838	|	|	...	...	|	|	|	...	|	...	...	|	|	...	|	|	|	|
64	Zidani Most 1300 d.	0146	...	0603	0626	...	0850	|	1030	1200	...	...	1400	1403	1500	...	1600	1603	...	1701	1838	...	2035	2203	0006	0002
89	Celje d.	0208	...	0627	0647	...	0910	0917	1056	1224	...	...	1420	1427	1524	...	1620	1627	...	1725	1902	...	2055	2228	0031	0028
137	Pragersko 1313 d.	0248	...	0711	0721	...	0943	0954	1135	1308	...	...	1453	1511	1608	...	1653	1710	...	1800	1939	...	2128	2312	0110	0107
156	**Maribor** ▲ 1313 a.	0301	...	0729	0735	...	0955	1009	...	1327	...	...	1505	1529	1627	...	1705	1730	...	1816	...	...	2140	2331	0124	0123
156	**Maribor** d.	...	0500	...	...	0835	...	1019	...	...	1335	1501	...	...	...	1635	...	...	1736	1821	...	1950	...	...	...	...
172	Spielfeld-Straß 🛃 a.	...	0519	...	...	0854	...	1034	...	...	1354	1526	...	...	...	1654	...	...	1755	1836	...	2009	...	...	...	...
172	Spielfeld-Straß 🛃 980 d.	...	...	...	...	...	...	1046	...	...	...	...	...	...	...	...	...	...	...	1848	...	...	...	...	...	...
219	**Graz** Hbf 980 a.	...	...	...	...	...	...	1122	...	...	...	...	...	...	...	...	...	...	...	1922	...	...	...	...	...	...
	Wien Hbf **980** a.	...	...	...	...	...	...	1402	...	...	...	...	...	...	...	...	...	...	...	2202	...	...	...	...	...	...

				ICS		IC			IC	EC	IC		IC					IC						EC	IC	
		605	1605	11	Ⓐ	503		Ⓐ	517	151	246		519	Ⓐ		1611		521	1641	1615		2	1643	159	523	1613
	2	2	2	🅁	2		2	2	🅁	✕🅁	🅁	2	🅁	2	2	2🅁	2	2🅁	2	2	2	Ⓐ	2	✕🅁	🅁	2
	h	♦	♦			♦				♦	♦				Ⓐ	g	Ⓐ		g	g			g	♦		g
Wien Hbf **980** d.	...	...	...	...	...	...	...	...	...	0758	...	...	...	...	...	...	...	...	...	...	...	...	...	1558	...	...
Graz Hbf 980 d.	...	...	...	...	...	...	...	...	...	1038	...	...	...	...	...	...	...	...	...	...	...	...	...	1838	...	...
Spielfeld-Straß 980 a.	...	...	...	...	...	...	...	...	...	1113	...	...	...	...	...	...	...	...	...	...	...	...	...	1913	...	...
Spielfeld-Straß d.	...	...	...	...	0545	...	0904	...	...	1125	...	1404	...	1604	...	...	1717	...	...	...	1804	...	...	1926	...	...
Maribor a.	...	...	...	...	0604	...	0923	...	...	1140	...	1423	...	1623	...	...	1735	...	...	...	1820	...	...	1941	...	...
Maribor ▲ 1313 d.	0115	0323	0323	0550	...	...	...	0926	1050	1145	...	...	1520	...	1629	1635	...	1750	...	1812	...	1830	...	1950	2005	2010
Pragersko 1313 d.	0134	0338	0338	0602	...	0702	...	0945	1103	1200	1434	...	1533	...	1648	1651	...	1803	1809	1825	...	1848	1927	2005	2019	2025
Celje d.	0215	0422	0422	0637	...	0740	...	1029	1137	1239	1512	...	1607	...	1733	1730	...	1837	1848	1905	...	1932	2003	2044	2057	2106
Zidani Most 1300 d.	0237	0448	0448	0657	...	0804	...	1052	1157	1305	1538	...	1627	...	1755	1754	...	1857	1911	1929	...	1953	2025	|	2120	2130
Sevnica 1300 d.	|	|	|	|	...	|	...	...	|	|	|	...	|	...	...	|	...	|	|	|	...	...	|	2122	|	|
Dobova 🛃 1300 d.	|	|	|	|	...	|	...	...	|	|	|	...	|	...	...	|	...	|	|	|	...	...	|	2205	|	|
Zagreb 1300 a.	|	|	|	|	...	|	...	...	|	|	|	...	|	...	...	|	...	|	|	|	...	...	|	2228	|	|
Ljubljana 1300 a.	0332	0547	0547	0740	...	0856	...	...	1240	1400	1635	...	1710	...	...	1842	...	1940	2005	2022	...	...	2114	...	2208	2218
Koper **1305** a.	...	...	0833	...	...	1127	...	...	...	...	...	...	...	...	...	...	...	...	...	...	...	...	...	...	...	...

ADDITIONAL SERVICES MARIBOR - ZIDANI MOST and v.v.: 2nd class only

			Ⓐ	Ⓐ	Ⓐ		Ⓐ	Ⓐ			Ⓐ		Ⓑ
Maribor ▲ d.	0423	0517	0620	0725	0825	1021	1125	1220	1525	1720	1922	2020	2110
Pragersko d.	0442	0536	0639	0744	0844	1041	1144	1240	1544	1739	1941	2039	2129
Celje d.	0527	0622	0724	0829	0928	1127	1229	1327	1627	1823	2028	2123	2213
Zidani Most a.	0554	0645	0746	0851	0951	1149	1251	1349	1651	1844	2049	2144	2234

			Ⓐ	Ⓐ	Ⓐ	Ⓐ	Ⓐ		Ⓐ			Ⓐ	
Zidani Most d.	0457	0700	0802	0926	1001	1101	1300	1705	1803	1903	2008	2100	2203
Celje d.	0521	0724	0826	0950	1025	1125	1325	1728	1827	1926	2031	2123	2228
Pragersko d.	0605	0811	0910	1034	1109	1209	1417	1813	1910	2007	2112	2204	2312
Maribor ▲ a.	0624	0830	0929	1053	1128	1228	1437	1833	1930	2026	2131	2223	2331

♦ – **NOTES** (LISTED BY TRAIN NUMBER)

150/1 – EMONA – [12] ✕ Ljubljana - Wien and v.v. Also conveys [12] Ljubljana (**134/5**) - Trieste and v.v.
158/9 – CROATIA – [12] ✕ Zagreb - Wien and v.v.
246/7 – CITADELLA – [12] Budapest - Ljubljana and v.v.
502/3 – POHORJE – [12] Hodoš - Ljubljana - Koper and v.v.
604 – Dec. 15 - Apr. 15. [2] Ljubljana - Maribor.
605 – Dec. 15 - Apr. 15. [2] Maribor - Ljubljana.
1604 – Apr. 17 - Sept. 5. [2] Koper - Ljubljana - Maribor.
1605 – Apr. 16 - Sept. 4. [2] Maribor - Ljubljana - Koper.

a – Ⓐ only.
c – Not Dec. 25, Feb. 18, 27, Apr. 27, May 2, June 25, Aug. 15.
g – ⑦ (also Feb. 8, Apr. 18, May 2; not Apr. 17, May 1, June 26).
h – June 18 - Sept. 4.

* – Zagreb - Celje: *104 km*.
▲ – For Maribor - Bleiburg (- Klagenfurt) services see panel above.

MARIBOR - BLEIBURG - (KLAGENFURT)

km		Ⓐ	Ⓑ		Ⓐ	Ⓑ
0	Maribor d.	0520	1445	*Klagenfurt* d.	*0805*	*1636*
87	Bleiburg 🛃 a.	0730	1659	Bleiburg 🛃 d.	0854	1720
126	*Klagenfurt* a.	*0839*	*1755a*	Maribor a.	1055	*1928*

Other services are available Bleiburg - Klagenfurt and v.v.

1320 ZAGREB - VINKOVCI - BEOGRAD

SŽ, HŽ, ŽS

km		541	1541		413	543	545	211	547	411
			🅁§		≋ 2¶					≋
			♦	⚒	♦	⚒e		♦		♦
	Ljubljana **1300** d.	...	...	...	0830	...	...	1445	...	2105
0	**Zagreb** d.	0620	0620	0940	1104	1300	1516	1738	2135	2341
105	Novska d.	0830	0830	1215	1256	1504	1727	1940	2337	0130
191	Slavonski Brod d.	0936	0936	1335	1358	1614	1833	2044	0050	0229
224	Strizivojna-Vrpolje 1345 d.	0956	0956	1402	1418	1634	1853	2104	0115	0249
	Osijek 1345 a.	|	|	|	|	|	|	|	|	|
256	**Vinkovci** d.	1015	1015	1425	1444	1653	1912	2123	0139	0310
288	Šid 🛃 a.	...	...	...	1522	...	...	...	...	0348
407	**Beograd** Centar a.	...	...	...	1812	...	...	...	...	0610

	540	542		210	544	412	546	1540	410
	e	f				≋ 2¶		🅁§	≋
				♦		♦		♦	♦
Beograd Centar d.	...	...	...	...	...	1005	...	...	2100
Šid 🛃 d.	...	...	...	...	...	1335	...	...	0022
Vinkovci d.	0236	0540	0636	0853	1143	1440	1713	2049	0104
Osijek 1345 d.	|	|	|	|	|	|	|	|	|
Strizivojna-Vrpolje 1345 d.	0300	0600	0658	0912	1202	1500	1738	2109	0123
Slavonski Brod d.	0326	0621	0735	0933	1223	1521	1804	2130	0144
Novska d.	0439	0732	0913	1036	1328	1623	1916	2233	0242
Zagreb a.	0644	0936	1138	1239	1539	1813	2122	0051	0427
Ljubljana **1300** a.	...	...	...	1507	...	2056	...	...	0718

♦ – **NOTES** (LISTED BY TRAIN NUMBER)

210/1 – SAVA – [12] Vinkovci - Zagreb - Ljubljana - Villach and v.v.
410 – [12] Beograd - Dobova (**314**) - Ljubljana.
411 – [12] Ljubljana (**315**) - Dobova - Beograd.
412/3 – [12] Ljubljana - Dobova - Beograd and v.v.
1540 – July 1 - Aug. 27. 🛏 2 cl. [2] Vinkovci - Zagreb - Rijeka.
1541 – July 3 - Aug. 29. 🛏 2 cl. [2] Rijeka - Zagreb - Vinkovci.

e – Runs on Ⓐ only until further notice.
f – Does not run on ⑦ until further notice.

¶ – Also conveys [1] Zagreb - Vinkovci and v.v.
§ – Also conveys 🛏 2 cl. and [2] Vinkovci - Zagreb - Split and v.v.
≋ – Service currently suspended.

1322 LOCAL SERVICES in Croatia

2nd class only HŽ

ZAGREB - SISAK CAPRAG: Journey 60–75 minutes. All services call at Sisak (5 minutes from Sisak Caprag).
From Zagreb at 0634, 0733Ⓐ, 0900, 1113, 1218Ⓐ, 1349, 1451Ⓐ, 1548, 1655Ⓐ, 1758Ⓐ, 1909, 2021, 2125Ⓐ, 2251.
From Sisak Caprag at 0418⚒, 0525, 0602Ⓐ, 0618, 0701Ⓐ, 0752Ⓐ, 1030⚒, 1213, 1410Ⓐ, 1514, 1604Ⓐ, 1645, 1804Ⓐ, 1950, 2121.

SISAK CAPRAG - SUNJA: Journey 30 minutes.
From Sisak Caprag at 0737, 0955, 1214, 1446, 1644, 1853Ⓐ, 2007, 2346.
From Sunja at 0505⚒, 0558, 0641Ⓐ, 1153, 1254, 1621, 1930, 2101, 2201Ⓐ.

SUNJA - NOVSKA: Journey 70 minutes.
From Sunja at 0757, 1234, 2037Ⓑ.
From Novska at 0458, 0540Ⓐ, 1052, 1822Ⓑ.

VINKOVCI - VUKOVAR: Journey 40 minutes.
From Vinkovci at 0420Ⓐ, 1021Ⓐ, 1200Ⓐ, 1519, 1919Ⓐ.
From Vukovar at 0503Ⓐ, 1100Ⓐ, 1313Ⓐ, 1634, 2002Ⓐ.

1325 🚌 SPLIT - PLOČE - DUBROVNIK

Subject to confirmation

🚌 SPLIT - DUBROVNIK: Journey 4 hrs - 5 hrs 10 mins.
🚌 SPLIT - PLOČE: Journey 2 hrs - 2 hrs 50 mins.
🚌 PLOČE - DUBROVNIK: Journey 2 hrs - 2 hrs 20 mins.

Note: various operators run on these routes; tickets are not interchangeable.
Split and Ploče bus stations are situated adjacent to the railway stations.
Buses pass through Bosnia between Ploče and Dubrovnik (passports required).

ZAGREB - ZADAR, ŠIBENIK and SPLIT — 1330

HŽ, Regiojet 2nd class only except where shown

km	km																							
							IC						♥		ICN	ICN						ICN		
							1204		1782				1047		521	1521						523		
							R		R				R		R 🍷	R 🍷						R 🍷		
				Ⓐ	Ⓐ		♦		♦		Ⓐ		♦		c	♦	Ⓐ	Ⓐ					Ⓐ	Ⓐ
		Budapest Keleti **1220** d.	...	...	...	...	1845	...	...	...	...	...	0005**k**	...	...	...	...	...	...	...	...	...	...	...
0		**Zagreb** **1310** d.	...	...	...	...	|	...	0110	...	...	...	0523	...	0730	0735	...	...	...	...	...	1520	...	...
53		Karlovac **1310** d.	...	...	...	...	|	...	0155	...	...	...	|	...	0815	0815	...	...	...	...	...	1600	...	...
103		Oštarije **1310** d.	...	...	...	...	|	...	|	...	...	...	|	...	0903	0903	...	...	...	...	...	1645	...	...
109		**Ogulin** **1310** d.	...	...	...	...	|	...	|	...	...	...	0759	...	|	|	...	...	...	...	...	|	...	...
225		Gospić d.	...	...	...	...	|	...	0451	...	...	...	|	...	1041	1041	...	...	...	...	...	1819	...	...
269		Gračac d.	...	...	...	...	|	...	0527	...	...	...	1030	...	1114	1114	...	...	...	...	...	1853	...	...
333		Knin a.	...	...	...	...	0558	...	0631	...	...	...	|	...	1205	1205	...	...	...	...	...	1944	...	...
333	0	Knin ‡ d.	...	...	...	0514	0559	...	0632	...	0814	...	|	...	1216	1216	...	...	...	1515	...	1945	1957	...
	95	**Zadar** ‡ a.	...	...	...	|	|	...	|	...	|	...	|	...	|	|	...	...	...	|	...	|	|	...
387	—	Perković a.	...	...	...	0617	0654	...	0729	...	0922	...	|	...	1302	1302	...	...	...	1623	...	2040	2101	...
387	0	Perković d.	0525	0550	0620	0704	0705	...	0731	0927	0930	1222	|	...	1303	1303	1306	1520	...	1631	1635	2040	2102	2104
	22	**Šibenik** a.	|	0621	|	0735	|	...	|	|	1002	|	|	...	|	|	1337	1550	...	1702	|	|	2133	|
435		**Split** a.	0632	...	0725	...	0812	...	0842	1031	...	1326	1344	...	1353	1353	...	...	...	...	1737	2130	...	2204

						ICN						ICN	ICN				♥	IC				
						520						522	1522				1046	1205				1783
						R 🍷						R 🍷	R 🍷				R	R				R
	Ⓐ	Ⓐ				d	Ⓐ		Ⓐ	Ⓐ		e	♦	Ⓐ			♦	♦		Ⓐ		♦
plit d.	...	...	...	...	0742	0831	1036	...	...	...	...	1425	1425	...	...	1522	1551	1827	...	1945	...	2206
Šibenik d.	0453	0627	0813	...	|	|	|	...	1108	1427	...	|	|	1557	...	|	|	|	...	|	2028	|
erković a.	0523	0657	0843	...	0847	0924	1142	...	1138	1457	...	1517	1517	1627	...	1629	|	1937	...	2056	2058	2316
erković d.	...	0659	0851	...	...	0927	...	...	...	...	...	1518	1518	1632	...	...	|	1938	...	...	2103	2317
Zadar ‡ d.	...	|	|	...	...	|	...	...	...	...	...	|	|	|	...	...	|	|	...	...	|	|
nin ‡ a.	...	0804	0954	...	...	1012	...	...	...	...	...	1602	1602	1735	...	...	|	2046	...	...	2206	0013
nin d.	...	...	...	...	...	1013	...	...	...	...	...	1603	1603	...	...	...	|	2048	...	...	...	0014
račac d.	...	...	...	...	...	1117	...	...	...	...	...	1657	1657	...	...	...	1927	|	...	...	...	0127
ospić d.	...	...	...	...	...	1150	...	...	...	...	...	1731	1731	...	...	...	|	|	...	...	...	0204
gulin **1310** d.	...	...	...	...	...	|	...	...	...	...	...	|	|	...	...	...	2222	|	...	...	...	|
štarije **1310** d.	...	...	...	...	...	1326	...	...	...	...	...	1914	1914	...	...	...	|	|	...	...	...	|
arlovac **1310** d.	...	...	...	...	...	1415	...	...	...	...	...	2006	2006	...	...	...	|	|	...	...	...	0505
agreb **1310** a.	...	...	...	...	...	1454	...	...	...	...	...	2057	2057	...	...	...	0054	|	...	...	...	0557
Budapest Keleti **1220** a.	...	...	...	...	...	...	...	...	...	...	...	...	...	...	...	...	0555**k**	0935	...	...	...	...

– **NOTES** (LISTED BY TRAIN NUMBER):

046 – ①③⑥ May 28 - Sept. 30 (daily July 1 - Aug. 31). 🛏 2 cl. (4 berth), [2] Split - Zagreb - Budapest - Bratislava - Praha.
047 – ①③⑥ May 28 - Sept. 30 (daily July 1 - Aug. 31). 🛏 2 cl. (4 berth), [2] Praha - Bratislava - Budapest - Zagreb - Split (previous day from Praha).
204 – ADRIA – Budapest - Gyékényes - Split and v.v. For days of running see Table **1340**.
205 – ADRIA – Split - Gyékényes - Budapest and v.v. For days of running see Table **1340**.
521 – July 1 - Sept. 4. DIOKLECIJAN – [12] Čakovec - Varaždin - Zagreb - Split.
522 – July 2 - Sept. 5. DIOKLECIJAN – [12] Split - Zagreb - Varaždin - Čakovec.
782 – July 1 - Aug. 27. DALMACIJA – 🛌 2 cl., [2] Osijek - Zagreb - Split; conveys 🛌 2 cl., [2] Vinkovci (**1540**) - Slavonski Brod - Zagreb (**1782**) - Split.
783 – July 2 - Aug. 28. DALMACIJA – 🛌 2 cl. and [2] Split - Zagreb - Osijek; conveys 🛌 2 cl. and [2] Split - Zagreb (**1541**) - Slavonski Brod - Vinkovci.

c – ⚒ to June 30 and from Oct. 5 (also June 16, 19, 22, Oct. 30, Nov. 1); daily July 1 - Sept. 4.
d – ⚒ to June 30 and from Oct. 5 (also June 16, 19, 22, Oct. 30, Nov. 1; not May 30); daily July 1 - Sept. 4.
e – † to June 26 and from Sept. 11 (also June 15, 17, 18, 20 – 21, Oct. 28, 29, 31).
k – Budapest **Kelenföld**.
♥ – Operated by REGIOJET. Seperate fare tariff.
‡ – Services Knin - Zadar and v.v are currently suspended until further notce.

ZAGREB - VARAŽDIN - KOTORIBA and KOPRIVNICA — 1335

HŽ 2nd class only except where shown

km																												
																772										1522		
		⚒		Ⓐ	Ⓐ	Ⓐ				Ⓐ	Ⓐ	Ⓐ				R ♦	Ⓐ	Ⓐ			Ⓐ					R ♦		
0	**Zagreb** d.	...	...	...	0542	...	0732	...	1130	...	1317	...	1436	...	...	1534	1538	...	1646		...	...	2009	...	2137	2137	2232	...
38	Zabok d.	...	...	0548	0642	0703	0819	0848	1217	1228	1405	1414	1525	1530	...	**k**	1630	1635	1734	1751	...	...	2055	2107	2235	2235	2317	...
104	**Varaždin** d.	0529	0658	0751	...	0837	...	1023	...	1359	...	1553	...	1710	...	1728	...	1808	...	1937	2020	2149	...	2238	0009	0009	...	...
115	Čakovec d.	0542	0716	0806	...	0848	...	1037**d**	...	...	...	...	...	1723**d**	...	...	...	...	...	...	2033	2202	...	...	0020	0020	...	...
145	**Kotoriba** a.	0622	0752	0847	...	...	...	1118**d**	...	...	...	...	...	1800**d**	...	...	...	...	...	...	2109	2238	...	...	...	..	...	...

		1521		773																							
		R ♦	⚒	R ♦					Ⓐ	⚒		Ⓐ	Ⓐ		⚒	⚒	⚒	⚒			⑦		Ⓑ	Ⓑ			
otoriba d.	...	...	0425	...	0549	...	...	0815	...	...	...	1024	...	...	1155	...	...	1502	...	...	1607	1640	...	...	1821	...	2121
akovec d.	...	0420	0503	...	0629	...	...	0854	...	...	...	1103	...	...	1233	...	...	1546	...	...	1644	1724	...	...	1905	...	2203
araždin d.	0340	0433	0514	0524	0640	0650	...	0905	...	1043	...	1114	1215	...	1244	1410	...	1557	1603	...	1655	1735	1750	...	1919	...	2214
abok d.	0515	0630	...	**k**	...	0825	0848	...	1046	1219	1229	...	1351	...	...	1556	1604	...	1740	1748	...	...	1921	1930	2054	2105	...
agreb a.	0604	0719	...	0714	...	...	0935	...	1133	...	1316	...	...	...	...	...	1650	...	...	1839	...	...	...	2018	...	2153	...

VARAŽDIN - KOPRIVNICA

km												
			773									
		Ⓐ	Ⓐ		Ⓐ	⚒	⚒		Ⓐ	⚒		Ⓐ
0	Varaždin d.	0427	0524	0653	0755	1021	1310	1432	1600	1709	1922	2217
42	Koprivnica a.	0516	0600	0738	0841	1107	1400	1521	1645	1754	2008	2301

									772			
	Ⓐ	⚒	Ⓐ		⚒	Ⓐ	⚒		Ⓐ	⚒	Ⓐ	
Koprivnica d.	0433	0538	0816	0903	1150	1314	1437	1600	1654	1801	1922	2029
Varaždin a.	0518	0633	0910	0949	1236	1402	1523	1649	1728	1847	2012	2115

– **NOTES** (LISTED BY TRAIN NUMBER):

72 – [2] Zagreb (**771**) - Koprivnica - Varaždin.
73 – [2] Varaždin - Koprivnica (**770**) - Zagreb.
1521 – July 1 - Sept. 4. DIOKLECIJAN – [12] Čakovec - Varaždin - Zagreb - Split.
1522 – July 2 - Sept. 5. DIOKLECIJAN – [12] Split - Zagreb - Varaždin - Čakovec.
d – ⚒ only.
k – Via Koprivnica.

ZAGREB - KOPRIVNICA - NAGYKANIZSA and OSIJEK — 1340

HŽ, MÁV, Regiojet

km		783	1783	205	981	771	201	581	975	1046	1205
		R	R	R	R	R	R	R	R	♥ R	R
		n	♦	♦	Ⓒ	Ⓐ t	♦	♦	2	♦	♦
	Split **1330** d.	...	...	...	...	...	...	...	...	1551	1827
0	**Zagreb** d.	0648	0648	1005	1244	1534	1635	1635	1838	0113	|
57	Križevci d.	0744	|	1059	1353	1626	1729	1729	1940	|	|
88	Koprivnica d.	0813	|	1135	1443	1646	1758	1757	2010	|	|
103	Gyékényes ▦ d.	|	|	1229	|	...	1829	|	...	|	0549
132	**Nagykanizsa** a.	|	|	1251	|	...	1902	|	...	|	0614
	Budapest Déli **1220** a.	|	|	1624	|	...	2224	|	...	0555**k**	0935**e**
153	Virovitica d.	0936	0917	...	1600	...	...	1917	...	...	...
225	Našice d.	1056	1042	...	1737	...	...	2034	...	...	...
275	**Osijek** a.	1153	1136	...	1849	...	...	2129	...	...	...

	1047	970	770	580	200	782	204	1204	1782
	♥ R	R	R	R	R	R	R	R	R
	♦	Ⓐ 2	Ⓐ t	♦	♦	m	♦	♦	♦
Osijek d.	...	0102	...	0520	...	1610	...	...	2000
Našice d.	...	0159	...	0615	...	1707	...	...	2115
Virovitica d.	...	0321	...	0733	...	1830	...	...	2233
Budapest Déli **1220** d.	0005**k**	|	...	|	0635	|	1535	1845**e**	|
Nagykanizsa d.	|	|	...	|	0956	|	1842	2159	|
Gyékényes ▦ d.	|	|	...	|	1045	|	1935	2255	|
Koprivnica d.	|	0440	0604	0851	1112	1951	2022	|	|
Križevci d.	|	0517	0623	0911	1144	2011	2051	|	|
Zagreb a.	0517	0624	0714	1001	1255	2103	2203	|	0045
Split **1330** a.	1334	...	...	...	...	...	...	0812	...

– **NOTES** (LISTED BY TRAIN NUMBER):

00/5 – June 6 - Sept. 11. GRADEC – [12] Budapest - Gyékényes - Koprivnica - Zagreb and v.v.
01/4 – AGRAM – [12] Budapest - Gyékényes - Koprivnica - Zagreb and v.v.
80/1 – PODRAVKA – [12] Zagreb - Osijek and v.v.
046 – ①③⑥ May 28 - Sept. 30 (daily July 1 - Aug. 31). 🛏 2 cl. (4 berth) and [2] Split - Zagreb - Budapest - Bratislava - Praha.
047 – ①③⑥ May 28 - Sept. 30 (daily July 1 - Aug. 31). 🛏 2 cl. (4 berth) and [2] Praha - Bratislava - Budapest - Zagreb - Split (previous day from Praha).
204 – ADRIA – Budapest - Gyékényes - Split ②⑤ June 10 – 17, Aug. 30 - Sept. 23 (②⑤⑦ June 19 - Aug. 28).
205 – ADRIA – Split - Gyékényes - Budapest ③⑥ June 11 – 18, Aug. 31 - Sept. 24 (①③⑥ June 20 - Aug. 29).
782 – July 1 - Aug. 27. DALMACIJA – 🛌 2 cl. and [2] Osijek - Zagreb - Split.
783 – July 2 - Aug. 28. DALMACIJA – 🛌 2 cl. and [2] Split - Zagreb - Osijek.

e – Budapest **Keleti**.
k – Budapest **Kelenföld**.
m – Not July 1 - Aug. 27.
n – Not July 3 - Aug. 29.
t – To / from Varaždin (Table **1335**).
♥ – Operated by REGIOJET. Separate fare tariff.

1345 PÉCS - OSIJEK - DOBOJ

2nd class only except where shown — HŽ, MÁV, ŽRS

There is currently no service Strizivojna-Vrpolje - Slavonski Šamac - Šamac - Doboj and v.v.

km																												
		⚒	Ⓐ			⚒	Ⓐ	⚒	Ⓐ	⚒	Ⓐ			Ⓐ		Ⓐ			Ⓑ	⚒						Ⓑ	Ⓑ	
	Budapest Déli **1200** d.	...	...	...	...	...	...	...	...	...	...	...	...	...	...	...	...	...	...	...	...	...	...	...	...	...	...	...
0	**Pécs** d.	...	...	0508	...	...	...	...	...	...	...	0850	...	...	...	...	1250	...	...	...	...	...	1650	...	...	...	...	...
36	Villány d.	...	...	0555	...	...	...	...	...	...	...	0934	...	...	...	...	1334	...	...	...	...	...	1734	...	...	...	...	...
43	Magyarbóly 🏛 d.	...	...	0622	...	...	...	...	...	...	...	1001	...	...	...	...	1401	...	...	...	...	...	1801	...	...	...	...	...
54	Beli Manastir 🏛 d.	...	0549	0633	0700	...	...	0813	...	...	...	1012	1051	1222	...	...	1412	1425	...	...	1615	...	1812	1849	...	...	2005	...
82	**Osijek** a.	...	0618	...	0729	...	...	0842	...	...	...	...	1120	1251	...	...	...	1454	...	...	1644	...	...	1918	...	...	2034	...
82	**Osijek** d.	0417	...	...	...	0743	0814	...	0920	1056	1104	...	...	...	1337	1339	...	...	1553	1620	...	1814	...	...	2003	2043	...	2239
	Vinkovci a.	|	...	...	...	0826	|	...	1003	1139	|	...	...	...	1420	|	...	...	|	1703	...	1857	...	...	|	2126	...	2322
130	Strizivojna-Vrpolje d.	0507	...	...	...	...	0906	...	...	...	1156	...	...	...	...	1431	...	...	1644	...	...	...	...	...	2055	...	...	...
150	Slavonski Šamac 🏛 d.	...	...	...	...	...	...	...	...	...	...	...	...	...	...	...	...	...	...	...	...	...	...	...	...	...	...	...
154	Šamac 🏛 d.	...	...	...	...	...	...	...	...	...	...	...	...	...	...	...	...	...	...	...	...	...	...	...	...	...	...	...
226	**Doboj** a.	...	...	...	...	...	...	...	...	...	...	...	...	...	...	...	...	...	...	...	...	...	...	...	...	...	...	...

km																												
		Ⓐ	⚒	Ⓐ			⚒	⚒	⚒	⚒			Ⓐ	Ⓐ		Ⓐ				⚒	Ⓐ				Ⓑ		Ⓑ	Ⓑ
	Doboj d.	...	...	...	...	...	...	...	...	...	...	...	...	...	...	...	...	...	...	...	...	...	...	...	...	...	...	...
	Šamac 🏛 d.	...	...	...	...	...	...	...	...	...	...	...	...	...	...	...	...	...	...	...	...	...	...	...	...	...	...	...
	Slavonski Šamac 🏛 d.	...	...	...	...	...	...	...	...	...	...	...	...	...	...	...	...	...	...	...	...	...	...	...	...	...	...	...
	Strizivojna-Vrpolje d.	...	...	0526	...	...	0627	...	...	...	...	...	1005	...	...	1206	...	...	...	...	1650	...	...	...	...	...	1902	...
0	Vinkovci d.	...	0537	|	...	...	|	0638	...	0836	...	...	|	...	1203	|	...	...	...	1522	|	1722	...	...	...	1915	|	2127
35	**Osijek** a.	...	0620	0617	...	...	0718	0721	...	0919	...	...	1055	...	1246	1256	...	...	...	1605	1740	1805	...	...	...	1958	1951	2210
	Osijek d.	0510	...	...	0624	...	...	...	0735	...	1011	...	...	1144	...	...	1320	...	1524	...	...	...	1810	...	1925	...	...	...
	Beli Manastir 🏛 d.	0540	...	...	0654	0720	...	...	0805	...	1041	1143	...	1214	...	...	1350	1543	1554	...	...	...	1840	1917	1955	...	...	...
	Magyarbóly 🏛 d.	...	...	...	...	0814	...	...	...	...	...	1214	...	...	...	...	...	1614	...	...	...	...	...	1948	...	...	...	...
	Villány d.	...	...	...	...	0822	...	...	...	...	...	1222	...	...	...	...	...	1622	...	...	...	...	...	1956	...	...	...	...
	Pécs a.	...	...	...	...	0907	...	...	...	...	...	1307	...	...	...	...	...	1707	...	...	...	...	...	2037	...	...	...	...
	Budapest Déli **1200** a.	...	...	...	...	...	...	...	...	...	...	...	...	...	...	...	...	...	...	...	...	...	...	...	...	...	...	...

1350 ZAGREB - DOBOJ - SARAJEVO

2nd class only except where shown — HŽ, ŽFBH, ŽRS

There is currently no service Volinja - Dobrljin and v.v.

km																										
				711		715										713										
				🅁		🅁 ¥				¥						🅁 ¥			¥							
0	**Zagreb** d.	...	...	...	...	...	...	...	...	...	...	...	0900	...	...	...	...	1349	...	1548	...	...	1909	...	2251	...
72	Sunja d.	...	...	...	...	...	...	...	...	...	...	...	1015	...	...	...	...	1506	...	1704	...	...	2027	...	0006	...
92	Volinja 🏛 d.	...	...	...	...	...	...	...	...	...	...	...	1042	...	...	...	...	1533	...	1731	...	...	2054**a**	...	0033**c**	...
98	Dobrljin 🏛 d.	...	...	...	...	...	...	...	...	...	0631	...	...	...	...	...	1456	...	...	...	...	1842	...	...	...	...
	Bihać d.	...	...	...	...	0203	...	...	...	...	|	...	...	...	...	...	|	...	...	...	...	|	...	...	...	...
112	Novi Grad d.	...	...	...	...	0358	0429	...	...	...	0651	...	...	...	...	...	1515	...	...	...	...	1902	...	...	...	...
214	Banja Luka d.	...	...	...	0439	0531	0631	0726	...	...	0844	...	...	1526	...	1601	1709	...	...	...	1930	2102	...	...	...	...
324	**Doboj** a.	...	...	...	0638	0655	...	0921	...	...	...	...	...	1721	...	1735	...	...	...	...	2138	...	...	...	...	...
324	**Doboj** d.	...	...	...	...	0656	...	...	...	...	...	...	...	...	...	1737	...	...	...	...	...	...	...	...	...	...
347	Maglaj d.	...	0448	0601	...	0731	...	...	0926	...	...	...	...	...	1718	1812	...	...	...	...	...	...	...	...	...	...
370	Zavidovici d.	...	0520	0624	...	0754	...	...	0958	...	...	...	...	...	1750	1835	...	...	...	...	...	...	...	...	...	...
419	Zenica d.	0454	0621	0718	...	0850	...	...	1059	1107	...	1528	...	...	1851	1926	...	...	1941	...	...	...	...	...	...	...
447	Kakanj d.	0531	...	0747	...	0919	...	...	...	1148	...	1605	...	...	...	1955	...	...	2018	...	...	...	...	...	...	...
465	Visoko d.	0553	...	0804	...	0936	...	...	...	1214	...	1627	...	...	...	2012	...	...	2040	...	...	...	...	...	...	...
472	Podlugovi d.	0602	...	0812	...	0944	...	...	...	1223	...	1703	...	...	...	2020	...	...	2049	...	...	...	...	...	...	...
496	**Sarajevo** a.	0639	...	0843	...	1014	...	...	...	1259	...	1739	...	...	...	2050	...	...	2125	...	...	...	...	...	...	...

km																										
												712										710				
		⚒								¥		🅁 ¥					¥			Ⓐ		🅁			¥	
	Sarajevo d.	...	...	...	...	...	0441	...	...	0733	...	1018	...	...	...	...	1102	...	1538	...	...	1630	...	...	1924	...
	Podlugovi d.	...	...	...	...	...	0518	...	...	0814	...	1049	...	...	...	...	1139	...	1615	...	...	1701	...	...	2001	...
	Visoko d.	...	...	...	...	...	0527	...	...	0823	...	1057	...	...	...	...	1148	...	1629	...	...	1709	...	...	2014	...
	Kakanj d.	...	...	...	...	...	0553	...	...	0845	...	1114	...	...	...	...	1210	...	1651	...	...	1726	...	...	2040	...
	Zenica d.	...	...	...	...	...	0629	...	0715	0924	...	1144	...	...	...	...	1246	1533	1727	...	...	1801	...	1928	2116	...
	Zavidovici d.	...	...	...	...	...	...	...	0816	...	...	1233	...	...	...	...	...	1634	...	...	...	1850	...	2029	...	...
	Maglaj d.	...	...	...	...	...	...	...	0847	...	...	1256	...	...	...	...	...	1705	...	...	...	1912	...	2100	...	...
	Doboj a.	...	...	...	...	...	...	...	...	...	...	1328	...	...	...	...	...	...	...	...	...	...	...	...	...	...
	Doboj d.	...	...	0426	...	...	...	0727	...	...	...	1329	...	...	...	1528	...	...	...	...	...	...	1925	...	...	...
	Banja Luka d.	...	0410	0617	0724	...	...	0931	...	...	...	1451	...	1525	...	1730	...	...	...	...	1925	...	2119	...	...	...
0	Novi Grad d.	...	0602	...	0921	...	...	...	...	...	1345	...	...	1730	...	...	...	...	...	...	2118	...	...	...	...	...
78	Bihać a.	...	|	...	...	...	...	...	...	...	|	...	...	|	...	...	...	...	...	...	...	...	...	...	...	...
	Dobrljin 🏛 d.	...	0620	...	...	...	...	...	...	...	1404	...	...	1748	...	...	...	...	...	...	...	...	...	...	...	...
	Volinja 🏛 d.	0437	...	...	...	1115	...	...	...	...	...	...	1553	...	1902	...	...	...	...	2133	...	...	...	...	...	...
	Sunja d.	0505	...	...	...	1142	...	...	...	...	...	...	1621	...	1930	...	...	...	...	2200	...	...	...	...	...	...
	Zagreb a.	0621	...	...	...	...	...	...	...	...	...	...	1745	...	2054	...	...	...	...	...	...	...	...	...	...	...

a – Ⓐ only. c – ⚒ only. ¥ – Service currently suspended.

1355 SARAJEVO - PLOČE

Most services 2nd class only — HŽ, ŽFBH

There is currently no service Čapljina - Metković - Ploče and v.v.

km		723 🅁n		1391 🅁p		Ⓐ		721 🅁			
	Zagreb **1350** d.	...	...	...	...	...	...	...	...	...	...
0	**Sarajevo** d.	0715	...	0715	...	1548	...	1649	...	...	...
67	Konjic d.	0822	...	0822	...	1714	...	1800	...	...	...
129	Mostar d.	0912	...	0912	...	...	...	1850	...	...	...
149	Žitomislići d.	0925	...	0925	...	...	...	1903	...	...	...
163	Čapljina 🏛 d.	0937	...	0947	...	...	...	1915	...	...	...
173	Metković d.	...	...	|	...	...	...	...	...	...	...
194	**Ploče** a.	...	...	1036	...	...	...	...	...	...	...

	Ⓐ		720 🅁		722 🅁		1390 🅁p			
Ploče d.	...	...	...	...	...	...	1826	...	...	...
Metković d.	...	...	...	...	...	...	|	...	...	...
Čapljina 🏛 d.	...	...	0609	...	1642	...	1929	...	...	...
Žitomislići d.	...	...	0621	...	1654	...	1941	...	...	...
Mostar d.	...	...	0636	...	1709	...	1956	...	...	...
Konjic d.	0525	...	0725	...	1758	...	2045	...	...	...
Sarajevo a.	0651	...	0835	...	1904	...	2151	...	...	...
Zagreb **1350** a.	...	...	...	...	...	...	...	...	...	...

n – Not July 1 - Aug. 28.
p – July 1 - Aug. 28.

☛ Alternative 🚌 services are available Sarajevo - Mostar - Metković - Dubrovnik and v.v

1358 LOCAL SERVICES in Bosnia

2nd class only — HŽ, ŽFBH, ŽRS

VINKOVCI - TUZLA

There is currently no service Gunja - Brčko - Tuzla and v.v.; also no service Tuzla - Petrovo Novo and v.v.

km		Ⓐ		⚒				Ⓐ
0	Vinkovci d.	0325	...	0923	...	1459	...	1933
49	Gunja d.	0424	...	1022	...	1558	...	2032
53	Brčko 🏛 d.	...	...	...	...	...	...	...
127	Tuzla a.	...	...	...	...	...	...	...

	Ⓐ		⚒				Ⓐ
Tuzla d.	...	...	...	...	...	...	...
Brčko 🏛 d.	...	...	...	...	...	...	...
Gunja d.	0434	...	1032	...	1608	...	2042
Vinkovci a.	0533	...	1131	...	1707	...	2141

TUZLA - DOBOJ

km					Ⓐ			
0	Tuzla d.	...	...	...	...	...	...	...
32	Petrovo Novo d.	0536	1054	...	1412	...	1753	2039
60	Doboj a.	0631	1149	...	1505	...	1846	2132

				Ⓐ			
Doboj d.	0420	0730	...	1310	1526	...	1932
Petrovo Novo d.	0515	0825	...	1405	1620	...	2025
Tuzla a.	...	...	...	...	...	...	...

SERBIA, MONTENEGRO and NORTH MACEDONIA

MAP PAGE 505

Operators: Železnice Srbije (ŽS): www.srbvoz.rs; Železnice Crne Gore (ŽCG): www.zcg-prevoz.me; Makedonski Železnici (MŽ): www.mztransport.mk; Trainkos (KŽ/HK): www.trainkos.com

Services: All trains convey first- and second-class seating, except where shown otherwise in footnotes, by a '2' in the train column, or where the footnote shows that the train conveys sleeping- (🛏) and / or couchette (🛏) cars only. Descriptions of sleeping- and couchette cars are given on page 10.

Timings: Valid **until December 10, 2022.**
Services may be amended or cancelled at short notice and passengers are strongly advised to check locally before travelling.

Tickets: A supplement is payable for travel by internal express trains. Reservation of seats is possible on most express trains.

Visas: Most nationals do not require a visa to enter Serbia and Montenegro, but must obtain an entry stamp in their passport, sight of which will be required by officials on leaving the country. These must be obtained at a border crossing recognised by the authorities - this excludes Kosovo's external borders with Montenegro, North Macedonia and Albania. Note also that Serbia should not be entered from Kosovo unless initial travel into Kosovo was via Serbia. Visas are not required for entry into North Macedonia for most nationals.

Currency: Visitors must declare large amounts of foreign currency upon arrival; currently 2,000 EUR in Montenegro, and 10,000 EUR in Serbia and North Macedonia. It is reported, however, that North Macedonia may now be operating on a threshold of 2,000 EUR. A certificate issued by the customs officer must be presented on departure, otherwise any funds held may be confiscated.

Security: Following the declaration of independence by Kosovo (which has not been recognised by Serbia) caution should be exercised when travelling in southern Serbia and northern Kosovo. Caution is also advised in the northern and western border regions of North Macedonia.

ŽS (BUDAPEST) - KELEBIA - SUBOTICA - BEOGRAD 1360

Rail services are suspended between Subotica and Novi Sad until further notice.
Travellers must make their own way between these points using scheduled bus services. Selected bus services are shown in this table.
Note that bus services operate to / from Novi Sad and Subotica central bus stations (not the rail station). **Rail tickets are not valid on bus services.**

km			🚌	IC 541 R		IC 543 R		🚌	REx 741 R	IC 571 R	IC 545 R		349 ♥	🚌	REx 743 R	IC 573 R		IC 547 R	🚌	IC 551 R		IC 549 R	343 ♥	🚌		IC 553 R
	Budapest Nyugati **1295** d.	...	...	...	...	...	...	...	...	...	...	...	...	...	...	...	...	...	...	...	...	...	...	...	...	...
0	**Kelebia** 🛃 d.	...	...	...	...	...	...	...	...	...	...	...	0941	...	...	...	...	...	...	...	...	...	1541	...	...	...
10	**Subotica** 🛃 a.	...	...	...	...	...	...	...	...	...	...	...	0955	...	...	...	...	...	...	...	...	...	1555	...	...	...
10	**Subotica** d.	...	0430	...	...	...	...	0730	...	...	...	...	...	1115	...	...	...	...	1500	...	...	...	...	1800	...	...
108	Novi Sad a.	...	0605	...	...	...	...	0930	...	...	...	...	...	1305	...	...	...	...	1650	...	...	...	...	2000	...	...
108	Novi Sad d.	0528	...	0704	0746	0830	0902	...	1007	1056	1201	1300	...	...	1407	1500	1517	1604	...	1745	1916	2001	...	...	2101	2202
181	Novi Beograd d.	0622	...	0737	0840	0903	0956	...	1052	1129	1234	1354	...	...	1452	1533	1610	1637	...	1818	2010	2034	...	...	2155	2235
186	**Beograd** Centar a.	0625	...	0740	0843	0906	0959	...	1055	1132	1237	1357	...	...	1455	1536	1613	1640	...	1821	2013	2037	...	...	2158	2238

	IC 550 R			IC 540 R	348 ♥	🚌	REx 742 R		IC 570 R	🚌	342 ♥	IC 542 R		REx 744 R	IC 572 R	🚌	IC 544 R		🚌	IC 552 R		IC 554 R		IC 548 R	🚌	
Beograd Centar d.	0555	0600	0700	0734	...	...	0803	0903	0935	...	...	1005	1100	1203	1255	...	1405	1515	...	1630	1703	1803	1910	2005	...	2220
Novi Beograd d.	0559	0604	0704	0738	...	...	0807	0907	0939	...	...	1009	1104	1207	1259	...	1409	1519	...	1634	1707	1807	1914	2209	...	2224
Novi Sad a.	0631	0656	0756	0810	...	...	0852	0959	1011	...	...	1041	1156	1252	1331	...	1441	1612	...	1706	1800	1839	2007	2041	...	2317
Novi Sad d.	...	...	...	...	...	0825	...	...	...	1040	...	...	...	...	...	1440	...	...	1720	...	...	...	...	...	2115	...
Subotica a.	...	...	...	...	...	1015	...	...	...	1230	...	...	...	...	...	1630	...	...	1910	...	...	...	...	...	2300	...
Subotica 🛃 d.	...	...	...	...	0802	...	...	...	...	...	1402	...	...	...	...	...	...	...	...	...	...	...	...	...	...	...
Kelebia 🛃 a.	...	...	...	...	0816	...	...	...	...	...	1416	...	...	...	...	...	...	...	...	...	...	...	...	...	...	...
Budapest Nyugati **1295** a.	...	...	...	...	...	...	...	...	...	...	...	...	...	...	...	...	...	...	...	...	...	...	...	...	...	...

♥ – For journeys from / to Budapest see Table **1295**.

ŽS 2nd class only SUBOTICA and KIKINDA - ZRENJANIN - PANČEVO - BEOGRAD 1362

Services on the Zrenjanin - Pančevo - Beograd route are suspended until further notice.

km											
	Subotica d.	...	0650	...	...	...	1350	...	1705	...	1955
	Senta d.	...	0750	...	...	...	1450	...	1805	...	2040
	Banatsko Miloševo d.	...	0851	...	...	...	1555	...	1911	...	...
0	**Kikinda** d.	0505	|	...	1116	...	1614	1700	1930	...	...
19	Banatsko Miloševo d.	0525	|	...	1154	...	...	1720	...	...	...
71	**Zrenjanin** d.	0640	1006	...	1309	...	...	1835	...	...	...
96	Orlovat Stajalište d.	...	...	...	...	...	...	...	...	...	...
145	**Pančevo** Glavna **1365** d.	...	...	...	...	...	...	...	...	...	...
159	Pančevački Most **1365/6** d.	...	...	...	...	...	...	...	...	...	...
161	**Beograd** Centar **1365/6** a.	...	...	...	...	...	...	...	...	...	...

Beograd Centar **1365/6** d.	...	...	...	...	...	...	...	...	...	...
Pančevački Most **1365/6** d.	...	...	...	...	...	...	...	...	...	...
Pančevo Glavna **1365** d.	...	...	...	...	...	...	...	...	...	...
Orlovat Stajalište d.	...	...	...	...	...	...	...	...	...	...
Zrenjanin d.	...	0719	...	1027	...	1415	...	...	1945	...
Banatsko Miloševo a.	...	0834	...	|	...	1530	...	...	2101	...
Kikinda d.	0415	0912	...	|	...	1550	1617	...	2120	...
Banatsko Miloševo d.	0449	...	...	1143	...	...	1651	...	...	...
Senta d.	0555	...	...	1247	...	...	1757	...	...	2100
Subotica a.	0640	...	...	1332	...	...	1842	...	...	2145

ŽS, CFR 2nd class only BEOGRAD - VRŠAC - TIMIŞOARA 1365

There is currently no cross-border service Vršac - Stamora Moravița and v.v.

km							①–⑤ s			
0	**Beograd** Centar **1362/6** d.	...	0658	1000	...	1135	...	1530	1658	2054
2	Pančevački Most **1362/6** d.	...	0710	1012	...	1147	...	1542	1710	2106
16	Pančevo Glavna **1362** d.	...	0727	1029	...	1205	...	1600	1728	2124
83	Vršac a.	...	0844	1146	...	1317	...	1712	1840	2236
83	Vršac 🛃 d.	...	...	...	...	...	...	...	▬	...
103	Stamora Moravița 🛃 § a.	...	...	...	...	...	...	...	...	...
103	Stamora Moravița § d.	0534	...	...	1213	...	1639	...	2018	...
159	**Timişoara** Nord § a.	0650	...	...	1325	...	1753	...	2310	...

							①–⑤ s		
Timişoara Nord § d.	...	...	0746	...	...	...	1452	1640	1850
Stamora Moravița § a.	...	...	0901	...	...	...	1606	1803	2004
Stamora Moravița 🛃 § d.	...	...	...	...	...	...	...	▬	...
Vršac 🛃 a.	...	...	...	...	...	...	...	...	...
Vršac d.	0448	0618	...	0920	1205	1444	...	1850	...
Pančevo Glavna **1362** d.	0601	0731	...	1033	1331	1601	...	2003	...
Pančevački Most **1362/6** d.	0619	0749	...	1051	1349	1619	...	2021	...
Beograd Centar **1362/6** a.	0628	0758	...	1100	1358	1628	...	2030	...

s – ①–⑤ May 2 - June 10 (not June 1); ①–⑤ Sept. 12 - Dec. 9 (not Nov. 30, Dec. 1).

§ – Romanian (East European) time.

ŽS 2nd class only OVČA - BEOGRAD - BATAJNICA 1366

Ovča d.	0614	0714	0814	0959	1159	1259	1359	1544	1614	1644	1859
Pančevački Most **1362/5** d.	0630	0730	0830	1015	1215	1315	1415	1600	1630	1700	1915
Beograd Centar **1362/5** d.	0638	0738	0838	1023	1223	1323	1423	1608	1638	1708	1923
Novi Beograd d.	0643	0743	0843	1028	1228	1328	1428	1613	1643	1713	1928
Batajnica a.	0659	0759	0859	1044	1244	1344	1344	1629	1659	1729	1944

Batajnica d.	0600	0700	0800	1000	1200	1300	1400	1530	1600	1700	1900
Novi Beograd d.	0617	0717	0817	1017	1217	1317	1417	1547	1617	1717	1917
Beograd Centar **1362/5** d.	0622	0722	0822	1022	1222	1322	1422	1552	1622	1722	1922
Pančevački Most **1362/5** d.	0632	0732	0832	1032	1232	1332	1432	1602	1632	1732	1932
Ovča a.	0645	0745	0845	1045	1245	1345	1445	1615	1645	1745	1945

1370 BEOGRAD and NIKŠIĆ - PODGORICA - BAR — ŽCG, ŽS

km																										
																431							711		433	
												K				B		©							A	
																[R]									[R]	
0	**Beograd** Centar d.	...	...	...	...	...	...	...	...	...	...	...	...	0755	...	0900	...	1110	1240	...	...	1525	1705	1940	2020	...
93	Valjevo d.	...	...	...	...	...	...	...	...	...	...	...	...	0925	...	1015	...	1240	1408	...	...	1657	1821	2106	2135	...
159	Požega d.	...	...	...	...	...	...	...	...	...	...	0930	...	1110	...	1140	...	1429	1548	...	...	1857	1952	2242	2300	...
185	Užice d.	...	...	...	...	...	...	...	...	...	0715	1000	...	1135	...	1205	...	1457	1623	...	...	1929	2013	2310	2325	...
243	Štrpci 🏛 d.	...	...	...	...	...	...	...	...	...	0856	...	...	...	...	|	...	...	1804	...	...	2102	...	...	|	...
256	Priboj d.	...	...	...	...	...	...	...	...	...	0922	...	...	...	...	1354	...	...	1830	...	...	2128	...	...	0111	...
292	Prijepolje Teretna d.	...	...	...	...	...	...	...	...	...	1033	...	...	...	...	1526	...	...	1941	...	...	2239	...	...	0259a	...
328	Vrbnica 🏛 d.	...	...	...	...	...	...	...	...	...	...	...	...	...	...	1613	...	...	...	...	...	...	...	...	|	...
338	Bijelo Polje 🏛 d.	...	...	...	0629	...	0938	...	...	...	...	...	...	...	...	1655	...	...	...	...	1945	...	...	...	0420c	...
	Nikšić d.	...	0620	...	|	1040	|	...	1415	...	...	...	...	...	1700	|	...	...	...	2000	|	...	...	...	|	...
	Danilovgrad d.	...	0656	...	|	1116	|	...	1450	...	...	...	...	...	1736	|	...	...	...	2036	|	...	...	...	|	...
468	**Podgorica** a.	...	0723	...	0852	1143	1201	...	1517	...	...	...	...	...	1803	1852	...	...	...	2103	2207	...	...	...	0617	...
468	**Podgorica** d.	0510	...	0755	0912	...	1211	1255	...	1530	...	...	1636	...	...	1859	1913	...	...	...	2217	...	...	...	0625	...
	Sutomore d.	0555	...	0841	1007	...	1257	1341	...	1616	...	...	1721	...	...	1945	2001	...	...	...	2302	...	...	...	0709	...
524	**Bar** a.	0609	...	0855	1021	...	1311	1355	...	1630	...	...	1735	...	...	1959	2015	...	...	...	2316	...	...	...	0723	...

	710									430											432					
				K				©		C											A					
										[R]											[R]					
Bar d.	...	...	...	...	0511	0624	...	...	...	0900	0923	...	1132	...	1413	...	1530	1703	...	1756	1900	2038	...	...	...	...
Sutomore d.	...	...	...	...	0526	0639	...	...	...	0917	0938	...	1147	...	1428	...	1545	1722	...	1812	1918	2054	...	...	...	...
Podgorica a.	...	...	...	...	0614	0726	...	...	...	0954	1022	...	1235	...	1512	...	1634	1806	...	1856	1958	2138	...	...	...	...
Podgorica d.	...	...	...	...	0624	...	0800	...	...	1000	...	...	...	1250	...	1535	1648	...	1830	1910	2005	...	2145	...	...	...
Danilovgrad d.	...	...	...	...	|	...	0829	...	...	|	...	...	...	1319	...	1604	|	...	1859	|	|	...	2214	...	...	...
Nikšić a.	...	...	...	...	|	...	0903	...	...	|	...	...	...	1353	...	1638	|	...	1933	|	|	...	2248	...	...	...
Bijelo Polje 🏛 d.	...	...	...	...	0843	...	...	...	...	1225	...	...	...	...	...	...	1907	...	...	2133	2243b	...	...	...	...	...
Vrbnica 🏛 d.	...	...	...	...	...	...	...	...	...	1243	...	...	...	...	...	...	...	...	...	...	|	...	...	...	...	...
Prijepolje Teretna d.	...	0330	0645	...	...	...	...	...	1150	1350	...	...	...	...	...	...	...	...	...	...	0008d	...	...	...	...	...
Priboj d.	...	0442	0757	...	...	...	...	...	1301	1509	...	...	...	...	...	...	...	...	...	...	0116	...	...	...	...	...
Štrpci 🏛 d.	...	0508	0822	...	...	...	...	...	1326	|	...	...	...	...	...	...	...	...	...	...	|	...	...	...	...	...
Užice d.	0455	0648	1005	1035	...	...	...	1250	1513	1703	...	1755	...	...	...	...	...	...	...	...	0308	...	...	...	...	...
Požega d.	0518	0717	1034	1105	...	...	...	1319	1549	1724	...	1822	...	...	...	...	...	...	...	...	0330	...	...	...	...	...
Valjevo d.	0643	0858	1215	...	...	...	...	1510	1724	1849	...	2006	...	...	...	...	...	...	...	...	0455	...	...	...	...	...
Beograd Centar a.	0757	1030	1340	...	...	...	...	1634	1849	2002	...	2139	...	...	...	...	...	...	...	...	0608	...	...	...	...	...

A – LOVĆEN – 🛏 1, 2 cl., 🛏 2 cl., [2] Beograd - Bar and v.v.
B – June 17 - Sept. 18. TARA – [2] ✕ Beograd - Bar.
C – June 18 - Sept. 19. TARA – [2] ✕ Bar - Beograd.
K – To/from Kraljevo (Table **1372**).

a – Arrives 0224.
b – Arrives 2203.
c – Arrives 0349.
d – Arrives 2333.

1372 POŽEGA - KRALJEVO - STALAĆ — ŽS

tariff km										
		J 2		U			J 2			
0	**Požega** d.	...	...	0757	1143	1310	...	...	1730	2015
45	Čačak d.	...	0531	0846	1221	1348	...	...	1821	2053
83	**Kraljevo** d.	0500	0615	0930	1305	1432	1520	...	1905	2137
155	Stalać a.	0742	...	...	...	...	1802	...	...	...

			U		J 2				J 2
Stalać d.	...	...	...	...	0958	...	...	...	2008
Kraljevo d.	0430	0620	0755	1000	1241	1510	...	1730	2251
Čačak d.	0514	0705	0840	1045	...	1555	...	1815	...
Požega a.	...	0743	0918	1123	...	1633	...	1853	...

J – To/from Jagodina (Table **1380**).

U – To/from Užice (Table **1370**).

1373 MAJDANPEK and PRAHOVO - ZAJEČAR - NIŠ — 2nd class only ŽS

tariff km										
		⚒								
0	Majdanpek d.	0335	...	...	0955	...	...	...	1820	...
★	Prahovo Pristanište d.	|	...	0855	|	...	...	1800	|	...
87	**Zaječar** d.	0602	0647	1115	1222	1230	1720	2030	2048	...
130	Knjaževac d.	...	0856	...	...	1416	1925	...	...	...
195	**Niš** a.	...	1044	...	...	1604	2113	...	...	...

								Ⓑ	
Niš d.	...	...	0548	1105	...	...	1620	...	...
Knjaževac d.	...	...	0737	1254	...	...	1809	...	...
Zaječar d.	0620	0636	0922	1503	1510	1526	1954	2055	...
Prahovo Pristanište a.	0840	|	...	...	1740	|	...	|	...
Majdanpek d.	...	0902	...	...	...	1752	...	2321	...

★ – Prahovo - Zaječar: *81 km.*

1375 LAPOVO and PRIŠTINA - KOSOVO POLJE - SKOPJE — 2nd class only ŽS, KŽ, MŽ

km										
		Ⓐ								
	Beograd **1380** d.	...	...	...	...	...	...	...	...	...
0	**Lapovo** d.	...	...	...	...	0940	1125	...	...	1935
28	**Kragujevac** d.	...	...	...	...	1012	1158	...	...	2008
82	Kraljevo d.	0240	...	...	0650	...	1357	1450	...	2207
163	Raška d.	0417	...	...	0828	...	...	1628	...	
180	Lešak/Leshak d.	...	...	...	0900	...	...	1700	...	...
210	Zvečan/Zveçan d.	...	...	...	1017	...	...	1817	...	...
214	Kosovska Mitrovica Sever a.	...	...	...	1022	...	...	1822	...	...
			891							
214	Mitrovica/Mitrovicë ♣ d.	...	h ❦	...	...	...	...	...	...	...
	Priština/Prishtinë d.	...	0710	0750	...	...	...	...	1630	...
247	**Kosovo Polje/Fushë Kosovë** ♣ d.	...	0722	0804	...	...	...	...	1641	...
*	Peć/Pejë a.	...	|	0953	...	...	...	...	1829	...
276	Uroševac/Ferizaj d.	...	0802	...	...	...	...	...	...	...
304	Deneral Janković/Hani I Elezit 🏛 a.	...	0900	...	...	...	...	...	...	...
331	**Skopje** a.	...	0952	...	...	...	...	...	...	...

									892 h ❦
Skopje d.	...	...	...	...	...	...	...	...	1630
Deneral Janković/Hani I Elezit 🏛 d.	...	...	...	...	...	...	...	...	1735
Uroševac/Ferizaj d.	...	...	...	...	...	...	...	...	1816
Peć/Pejë d.	...	...	0532	...	...	...	1210	...	|
Kosovo Polje/Fushë Kosovë ♣ d.	...	...	0723	...	...	...	1359	...	1900
Priština/Prishtinë a.	...	...	0732	...	...	...	1410	...	1910
Mitrovica/Mitrovicë ♣ a.	...	...	...	...	...	...	...	...	...
	Ⓐ								
Kosovska Mitrovica Sever d.	...	...	...	...	1050	...	...	1840	...
Zvečan/Zveçan d.	...	...	...	...	1056	...	...	1846	...
Lešak/Leshak d.	...	...	...	...	1213	...	...	2003	...
Raška d.	0435	...	...	...	1246	...	...	2037	...
Kraljevo d.	0610	0655	...	...	1421	1505	...	2212	...
Kragujevac d.	...	0854	...	1035	...	1704	...	...	...
Lapovo a.	...	0926	...	1107	...	1736	...	...	...
Beograd **1380** a.	...	...	...	...	...	...	...	...	...

h – A change of train maybe necessary at Deneral Janković / Hani I Elezit (connection between trains is guaranteed).

❦ – Service currently suspended.
♣ – Currently no service Mitrovica/Mitrovicë - Kosovo Polje/Fushë Kosovë and v.v.
* – Kosovo Polje - Peć: *82 km.*

1377 MINOR BORDER CROSSINGS — 2nd class only ŽS, MÁV

SUBOTICA - SZEGED — *Service suspended*

km			
0	Subotica d.		Szeged d.
24	Horgoš 🏛 d.		Röszke 🏛 d.
31	Röszke 🏛 a.		Horgoš 🏛 d.
43	Szeged a.		Subotica a.

KIKINDA - JIMBOLIA - TIMISOARA — *Service run by Regio Călători.*

km														
0	Kikinda d.	...	...	...	...	...	...	Timisoara § d.	0706	0810	1345	1627	1934	2315
19	Jimbolia 🏛 § d.	0455	0600	0905	1245	1445	1740	Jimbolia 🏛 § d.	0747	0849	1426	1708	2015	2357
58	Timisoara § a.	0538	0642	0946	1326	1524	1821	Kikinda a.	...	...	...	...	...	...

§ – East European time, one hour ahead of Central European time.

BEOGRAD - NIŠ - SOFIA, SKOPJE and THESSALONÍKI — 1380

ŽS, MŽ, BDŽ

km		611	641		601			791		643	651	631	7991		1491		645						793	1335		
		2			2		2⚒		K2	2	2	2[R]	2		B❦	2	[R]		2	2	2	K2		H❦		
0	**Beograd** Centar d.	...	...	...	...	0353	...	0605	...	...	...	...	...	0725	0915	...	...	1305	...	...	1510	...	1755	1825	2010	...
110	Lapovo d.	...	...	0305	...	0630	...	0805	...	...	...	...	...	0955	1101	...	...	1535	...	...	1747	...	2005	2028	2236	...
135	Jagodina d.	...	...	0350	...	0715	...	0845	0900	...	...	...	...	1036	1141	...	...	1620	...	...	1832	1910	2045	2108	...	...
155	Paraćin d.	...	...	0407	...	0732	...	0901	0918	...	...	...	...	1053	1157	...	...	1637	...	...	1850	1928	2101	2124	...	...
176	Stalać d.	...	...	0441	...	0807	...	0936	0958	...	...	...	...	1129	1232	...	...	1712	...	...	1924	2008	2136	2159	...	...
244	**Niš** a.	...	...	0618	...	0945	...	1048	...	...	...	...	...	1306	1341	...	...	1852	...	...	2103	...	2248	2308	...	...
244	**Niš** d.	...	...	...	...	...	...	...	...	...	...	...	...	...	1407	...	...	...	...	...	...	...	...	2318	...	...
	Dimitrovgrad 🛂 d.	...	...	...	...	...	...	...	...	...	...	...	...	...	1718	...	...	...	...	...	...	...	...	|	...	...
	Dragoman 🛂 § d.	...	...	...	...	...	...	...	...	...	...	...	1357	...	1949	...	...	...	...	...	...	...	...	|	...	...
	Sofia § a.	...	...	...	...	...	...	...	...	...	...	...	1500	...	2037	...	...	...	...	...	...	...	...	|	...	...
288	Leskovac d.	...	...	...	...	...	...	...	...	...	...	...	...	...	...	...	...	...	...	...	...	...	...	0003	...	...
392	Preševo 🛂 d.	...	...	...	...	...	...	...	...	...	...	...	...	...	...	...	...	...	...	...	...	...	...	0307	...	...
401	Tabanovci 🛂 d.	0515	...	...	0800	...	...	...	...	...	...	...	...	...	...	1740	...	...	2115	...	...	...	...	0345	...	...
449	**Skopje** a.	0609	...	...	0854	...	...	...	...	...	...	...	...	...	...	1834	...	...	2209	...	...	...	...	0425	...	...
449	**Skopje** 1385 d.	0623	0653	...	0915	...	1320	...	...	1430	1523	1655	...	...	...	...	2005	...	...	2240	...	...	...	0445	...	...
513	Veles 1385 d.	0725	0749	...	1007	...	1412	...	...	1525	1621	1747	...	...	...	...	2057	...	...	2332	...	...	...	0526	...	...
626	Gevgelija a.	0911	...	...	...	...	...	...	...	...	...	1938	...	...	...	...	...	...	...	...	...	...	...	0650	...	...
626	Gevgelija 🛂 d.	...	...	...	...	...	...	...	...	...	...	...	...	...	...	...	...	...	...	...	...	...	...	0723	...	...
629	Idoméni 🛂 § a.	...	...	...	...	...	...	...	...	...	...	...	...	...	...	...	...	...	...	...	...	...	...	0828	...	...
629	Idoméni § d.	...	...	...	...	...	...	...	...	...	...	...	...	...	...	...	...	...	...	...	...	...	...	0856	...	...
705	**Thessaloníki** § a.	...	...	...	...	...	...	...	...	...	...	...	...	...	...	...	...	...	...	...	...	...	...	1033	...	...

km					790			600	640	630	650		1490	7990	2					642			632		644	1334
			2	K2			2	2	2	-2	2		B❦	2			2⚒	K2	792	2	2		2	2	2	H❦
	Thessaloníki § d.	...	...	...	...	...	...	...	...	...	...	...	...	...	...	...	...	...	...	...	...	...	...	...	...	1851
	Idoméni § a.	...	...	...	...	...	...	...	...	...	...	...	...	...	...	...	...	...	...	...	...	...	...	...	...	1936
	Idoméni 🛂 § d.	...	...	...	...	...	...	...	...	...	...	...	...	...	...	...	...	...	...	...	...	...	...	...	...	2011
	Gevgelija 🛂 a.	...	...	...	...	...	...	...	...	...	...	...	...	...	...	...	...	...	...	...	...	...	...	...	...	1916
	Gevgelija d.	...	...	...	...	...	...	...	...	0440	...	...	...	...	...	...	...	...	...	...	...	...	1655	...	...	1948
	Veles 1385 d.	...	...	...	...	...	...	0503	0546	0627	0726	...	...	...	1210	...	1424	...	...	1524	...	...	1840	...	2058	2113
	Skopje 1385 a.	...	...	...	...	...	...	0555	0637	0719	0822	...	...	...	1302	...	1520	...	...	1615	...	...	1931	...	2149	2154
	Skopje d.	...	...	...	...	...	0401	0645	...	...	...	...	...	...	...	...	...	...	...	...	1625	...	...	2000	...	2219
	Tabanovci 🛂 d.	...	...	...	...	...	0455	0739	...	...	...	...	...	...	...	...	...	...	...	...	1719	...	...	2054	...	2329
	Preševo 🛂 d.	...	...	...	...	...	...	...	...	...	...	...	...	...	...	...	...	...	...	...	...	...	...	...	...	0018
	Leskovac d.	...	...	...	...	...	...	...	...	...	...	...	...	...	...	...	...	...	...	...	...	...	...	...	...	0239
0	**Sofia** § d.	...	...	...	...	...	...	...	...	...	...	...	0915	0920	...	...	...	...	...	...	...	...	...	...	...	|
42	Dragoman 🛂 § d.	...	...	...	...	...	...	...	...	...	...	...	1005	1022	...	...	...	...	...	...	...	...	...	...	...	|
63	Dimitrovgrad 🛂 d.	...	...	...	...	...	...	...	...	...	...	...	1100	...	...	...	...	...	...	...	...	...	...	...	...	|
161	**Niš** a.	...	...	...	...	...	...	...	...	...	...	...	1336	...	...	...	...	...	...	...	...	...	...	...	...	0323
	Niš d.	...	0310	...	0530	0730	...	...	...	...	...	1225	1410	...	...	1552	...	...	1720	...	...	1955	...	...	...	0337
	Stalać d.	...	0445	0744	0646	0905	...	...	...	...	...	1402	1520	...	...	1728	...	1804	1836	...	...	2132	...	...	...	0447
	Paraćin d.	...	0510	0813	0707	0930	...	...	...	...	...	1427	1541	...	...	1752	...	1833	1857	...	...	2157	...	...	...	0508
	Jagodina d.	...	0528	0830	0723	0948	...	...	...	...	...	1445	1557	...	...	1809	...	1854	1913	...	...	2215	...	...	...	0524
	Lapovo d.	0350	0607	...	0757	1031	...	...	...	...	...	1528	1634	...	...	1852	...	...	1947	...	...	2248	...	...	...	0606
	Beograd Centar a.	0604	0831	...	1002	1250	...	...	...	...	...	1750	1829	...	...	2110	...	...	2151	...	...	...	...	...	...	0813

B – BALKAN – 2nd class Beograd - Sofia and v.v.
H – HELLAS – 🛏 2 cl., 2nd class Beograd - Skopje - Gevgelija - Thessaloniki and v.v.
K – To/from Kraljevo (Table **1372**).
§ – East European time.
❦ – Service currently suspended.

BRANCH LINES in North Macedonia — 1385

MŽ 2nd class only

SKOPJE - KOČANI and BITOLA

km		641		643	651		645
0	Skopje 1380 d.	0653	...	1430	1523	...	2005
64	Veles 1380 d.	0751	...	1525	1621	...	2100
★	Kočani a.	|	...	|	1813	...	|
134	Prilep d.	0936	...	1710	...	...	2245
178	Bitola a.	1020	...	1754	...	...	2329

	640	650		642		644
Bitola d.	0315	...	...	1251	...	1827
Prilep d.	0401	...	...	1336	...	1912
Kočani d.	|	0526	...	|	...	|
Veles 1380 d.	0546	0726	...	1524	...	2058
Skopje 1380 a.	0637	0822	...	1615	...	2149

★ – Veles - Kočani: *110 km.*

SKOPJE - KIČEVO

km				660
0	Skopje d.	...	...	1645
56	Tetovo d.	...	...	1748
79	Gostivar d.	...	...	1810
116	Kičevo a.	...	...	1849

	661		
Kičevo d.	0530	...	...
Gostivar d.	0607	...	...
Tetovo d.	0630	...	...
Skopje a.	0732	...	...

ALBANIA

SEE MAP PAGE 505

Operator: Hekurudha Shqiptarë (HSH). www.hsh.com.al
Services: Trains convey one class of accommodation only. Tickets are not sold in advance, only for the next available departure.
Timings: **Timings have been compiled from the latest information received (Febuary 22, 2022).**
Readers should be aware that timetable amendments usually come into effect at short notice.
Trains can also be cancelled at short notice, again readers are advised to check information locally before travelling.
Security: Most visits to Albania are reported to be trouble free, but travellers are advised to avoid the north-east of the country.

ALBANIAN RAILWAYS — 1390

HSH One class only

Kashar - central Tiranë and v.v. is operated by 🚌 *(approximately 7.5 km)*

km	km			🚌							
	0	**Shkodër** d.	...	...	...	...	...	...	...	...	...
	84	Vorë d.	...	...	...	...	...	...	...	...	...
	98	**Tiranë** 🚌 d.	...	...	...	...	...	...	...	...	...
0	→	Kashar 🚌 d.	...	0715	...	...	...	...	...	...	...
10		Vorë d.	...	|	...	...	...	...	...	...	...
32		**Durrës** a.	...	0820	...	...	...	...	...	...	...
—	0	**Durrës** d.	...	...	...	1355	...	...	...	...	...
0	35	Rrogozhinë d.	...	...	...	1509	...	...	...	...	...
	76	Elbasan a.	...	...	...	1638	...	...	...	...	...
	100	**Librazhd** a.	...	...	...	...	...	...	...	...	...
16		Lushnjë a.	...	...	...	...	...	...	...	...	...
47		Fier a.	...	...	...	...	...	...	...	...	...
81		**Vlorë** a.	...	...	...	...	...	...	...	...	...

				🚌					
Vlorë d.	...	...	...	...	...	...	...	...	...
Fier d.	...	...	...	...	...	...	...	...	...
Lushnjë d.	...	...	...	...	...	...	...	...	...
Librazhd d.	...	...	...	...	...	...	...	...	...
Elbasan d.	...	0630	...	...	...	...	...	...	...
Rrogozhinë d.	...	0800	...	...	...	...	...	...	...
Durrës a.	...	0912	...	...	...	...	...	...	...
Durrës d.	...	...	...	1450	...	...	...	...	...
Vorë d.	...	...	...	|	...	...	...	...	...
Kashar 🚌 a.	...	...	...	1600	...	...	...	...	...
Tiranë 🚌 a.	...	...	...	...	...	...	...	...	...
Vorë d.	...	...	...	...	...	...	...	...	...
Shkodër a.	...	...	...	...	...	...	...	...	...

GREECE

SEE MAP PAGE 505

Operator: TRAINOSE S.A., ΤΡΑΙΝΟΣΕ Α.Ε.: www.trainose.gr

Services: All trains convey first and second class seating except where shown otherwise in footnotes or by '2' in the train column, or where the footnote shows sleeping and/or couchette cars only. Descriptions of sleeping (🛏) and couchette (▬) cars appear on page 10. Services that convey catering may vary from day to day.

Timings: Timings have been compiled from the latest available information. Readers should be aware that timetable amendments may come into effect at short notice, and are advised to check information locally before travelling.

Tickets: Reservation of seats is possible (and recommended) on most express trains. *Icity and IcityE* trains carry a supplement which varies depending upon distance travelled. Break of journey is only permitted when tickets are so endorsed before travel with the station quoted.

1400 ATHÍNA - LÁRISA - THESSALONÍKI — OSE

km		*ICE* 50 ✕⚡		590	*IC* 882 🍷			*IC* 52 ✕⚡	1884 2		*IC* 54 ✕⚡			*IC* 56 ✕⚡	886 2		*IC* 58 ✕⚡		*ICE* 60 ✕⚡	888 2	2596		*IC* 62 ✕⚡		600 ≋
0	**Athína** Lárisa **1420/30/40** d.	0722	...	...	0757	...	...	0922	...	...	1122	...	...	1322	...	...	1522	...	1722	...	...	...	1922	...	2350
61	Inói **1420** d.	|	...	...	0850	...	...	1010	...	...	1210	...	...	1410	...	...	1610	...	|	...	...	...	2010	...	0038
89	Thíva d.	|	...	...	0907	...	...	1024	...	...	1224	...	...	1424	...	...	1624	...	|	...	...	...	2024	...	0057
129	Levadiá d.	|	...	...	0930	...	...	1042	...	...	1242	...	...	1442	...	...	1642	...	|	...	...	...	2042	...	0124
154	Tithoréa d.	|	...	...	0945	...	...	1055	...	...	1255	...	...	1455	...	...	1655	...	|	...	...	...	2055	...	0139
210	Lianokládi d.	|	...	...	1012	1058	...	1118	...	...	1318	1438	...	1518	...	...	1718	...	|	...	...	...	2118	...	0213
	Lamia d.	|	...	...	|	1109	...	|	...	...	|	1450	...	|	...	...	|	...	|	...	...	...	|	...	|
	Stilída a.	|	...	...	|	1145	...	|	...	...	|	1513	...	|	...	...	|	...	|	...	...	...	|	...	|
276	Domokos d.	|	...	...	1051	...	...	|	...	...	|	...	...	|	...	...	|	...	|	...	...	...	|	...	0245
291	Paleofársalos d.	|	...	1037	1102	...	...	1151	1205	...	1351	...	...	1551	1605	...	1751	...	|	1944	2020	...	2151	...	0255
	Kalambáka **1408** a.	|	...	|	1203	...	...	|	1303	...	|	...	...	|	1703	...	|	...	|	2042	|	...	|	...	|
333	**Lárisa** ▲ d.	1000	...	1100	...	...	...	1211	...	...	1411	...	...	1611	...	...	1811	...	2002	...	2042	...	2211	...	0333
417	Kateríni ▲ d.	|	...	1146	...	...	...	1253	...	...	1453	...	...	1653	...	...	1853	...	|	...	2130	...	2253	...	0425
465	Platí **1410** ▲ d.	|	...	1209	...	...	...	1313	...	...	1513	...	...	1713	...	...	1913	...	|	...	2154	...	2312	...	0452
502	**Thessaloníki** **1410** ▲ a.	1120	...	1236	...	...	...	1335	...	...	1535	...	...	1735	...	...	1935	...	2121	...	2219	...	2335	...	0520

km		1521		*ICE* 51 🍷⚡		1595	883 2	*IC* 53 ✕⚡		*IC* 55 ✕⚡		1883	*IC* 57 ✕⚡		*IC* 59 ✕⚡			591	*ICE* 61 ✕⚡		*IC* 887 🍷	595	*IC* 63 ✕⚡		601 ≋
	Thessaloníki **1410** ▲ d.	...	...	0708	...	0815	...	0856	...	1056	...	...	1256	...	1456	...	...	1612	1708	...	...	1740	1901	...	2350
	Platí **1410** ▲ d.	...	...	|	...	0841	...	0917	...	1117	...	...	1317	...	1517	...	...	1639	|	...	...	1807	1922	...	0018
	Kateríni ▲ d.	...	...	|	...	0905	...	0937	...	1137	...	...	1337	...	1537	...	...	1703	|	...	...	1830	1942	...	0046
	Lárisa ▲ d.	...	...	0827	...	0951	...	1017	...	1217	...	...	1417	...	1617	...	...	1748	1828	...	...	1916	2022	...	0140
	Kalambáka **1408** d.	...	...	|	...	|	0928	|	...	|	...	1322	|	...	|	...	...	|	|	...	1822	|	|	...	|
	Paleofársalos d.	...	...	|	...	1011	1025	1036	...	1236	...	1421	1436	...	1636	...	...	1808	|	...	1923	1936	2041	...	0204
	Domokos d.	...	...	|	...	...	...	|	...	|	...	...	|	...	|	...	...	...	|	...	1932	...	|	...	0214
0	Stilída d.	...	...	|	0745	...	...	|	...	|	...	...	|	...	|	...	1635	...	|	...	|	...	|	...	|
17	Lamia d.	...	...	|	0821	...	...	|	...	|	...	...	|	...	|	...	1659	...	|	...	|	...	|	...	|
23	Lianokládi d.	0657	...	|	0832	...	...	1107	...	1307	...	...	1507	...	1707	...	1710	...	|	...	2015	...	2113	...	0251
	Tithoréa d.	0802	...	|	...	...	...	1131	...	1331	...	...	1531	...	1731	...	...	...	|	...	2044	...	2136	...	0321
	Levadiá d.	0823	...	|	...	...	...	1142	...	1342	...	...	1542	...	1742	...	...	...	|	...	2057	...	2148	...	0336
	Thíva d.	0852	...	|	...	...	...	1200	...	1400	...	...	1600	...	1800	...	...	...	|	...	2121	...	2206	...	0402
	Inói **1420** d.	0909	...	|	...	...	...	1214	...	1414	...	...	1614	...	1814	...	...	...	|	...	2137	...	2219	...	0419
	Athína Lárisa **1420/30/40** a.	0958	...	1103	...	...	...	1303	...	1503	...	...	1703	...	1903	...	...	...	2104	...	2226	...	2306	...	0506

▲ – **Local service Thessaloníki - Litóhoro - Lárisa and v.v.:**

Thessaloníki d.	0530	0620	1013	1135	1340	1540	1719	2036	2223
Platí d.	0556	0646	1039	1201	1406	1606	1746	2102	2249
Kateríni d.	0620	0710	1103	1225	1430	1630	1809	2126	2313
Litóhoro △ d.	0628	0718	1111	1233	1438	1638	1818	2134	2321
Lárisa a.	0705	0754	1148	1310	1515	1715	1853	2211	2358

Lárisa d.	0625	0715	0915	1250	1520	1640	1854	2220	2254
Litóhoro △ d.	0705	0755	0954	1330	1600	1720	1933	2257	2334
Kateríni d.	0713	0803	1002	1338	1608	1728	1942	2306	2342
Platí d.	0737	0827	1026	1402	1632	1752	2005	2329	0006
Thessaloníki a.	0802	0852	1052	1427	1657	1817	2031	2355	0031

≋ – Service currently suspended. ⚡ – Ⓡ with supplement payable. *Icity and IcityE* train. △ – Station for Mount Ólimbos.

1405 THESSALONÍKI - ALEXANDRÚPOLI - DÍKAIA — OSE

km		600 ≋		1682		*IC* 90 ⚡≋		*IC* 1632		
0	**Thessaloníki** d.	0550	...	...	...	1508	...	1605	...	...
42	Kilkís d.	0626	...	...	...	1541	...	1639	...	...
97	Rodópolis d.	0721	...	...	...	1633	...	1732	...	...
130	Strimón d.	0812	...	...	...	|	...	1822	...	...
162	Sérres d.	0845	...	...	...	1753	...	1855	...	...
232	Dráma d.	1011	...	...	...	1912	...	2017	...	...
327	Xánthi d.	1248	...	...	...	2146	...	...	...	...
374	Komotiní d.	1321	...	...	...	2214	...	...	...	...
443	**Alexandrúpoli Port** a.	1419	...	...	...	2319	...	...	...	...
443	**Alexandrúpoli Port** d.	...	...	1510	...	...	...	...	...	...
556	Píthio d.	...	...	1645	...	...	...	...	...	...
574	Orestiáda d.	...	...	1703	...	...	...	...	...	...
611	**Díkaia** a.	...	...	1734	...	...	...	...	...	...

	IC 1631		*IC* 91 ⚡≋		3635		601 ≋		1683
Díkaia d.	...	...	...	...	...	...	...	...	1808
Orestiáda d.	...	...	...	...	...	...	...	...	1839
Píthio d.	...	...	...	...	...	...	...	...	1856
Alexandrúpoli Port d.	...	...	...	...	...	...	...	...	2033
Alexandrúpoli Port d.	...	...	0559	...	...	...	1450	...	...
Komotiní d.	...	...	0705	...	...	...	1558	...	...
Xánthi d.	...	...	0736	...	...	...	1633	...	...
Dráma d.	0615	...	1010	...	...	...	1913	...	...
Sérres d.	0738	...	1129	...	1140	...	2037	...	...
Strimón d.	0810	...	|	...	1211	...	2110	...	...
Rodópolis d.	0901	...	1249	...	1300	...	2201	...	...
Kilkís d.	0954	...	1341	...	1343	...	2256	...	...
Thessaloníki a.	1026	...	1412	...	1421	...	2330	...	...

≋ – Service currently suspended. ⚡ – Ⓡ with supplement payable. *Icity* train. △ – Station for Mount Ólimbos.

1408 LÁRISA - PALEOFÁRSALOS - KALAMBÁKA — OSE

km		1880 2		*IC* 882 🍷	1884 2		886 2		888 2
	Thessaloníki **1400** d.	...	...	...	...	...	...	...	...
	Athína **1400** d.	...	...	0757	...	...	...	...	...
	Lárisa **1400** d.	...	...	|	...	...	...	...	...
0	Paleofársalos **1400** d.	0825	...	1102	1205	...	1605	...	1944
31	Kardítsa d.	0844	...	1122	1226	...	1626	...	2005
60	Tríkala d.	0903	...	1144	1247	...	1647	...	2026
82	**Kalambáka** ⊡ a.	0919	...	1203	1303	...	1703	...	2042

	883 2		1883 2		1885 2	*IC* 887 🍷		1889 2
Kalambáka ⊡ d.	0928	...	1322	...	1720	1822	...	2046
Tríkala d.	0944	...	1340	...	1738	1840	...	2104
Kardítsa d.	1005	...	1401	...	1759	1902	...	2125
Paleofársalos **1400** a.	1025	...	1421	...	1819	1922	...	2145
Lárisa **1400** a.	...	...	...	...	...	|	...	...
Athína **1400** a.	...	...	...	...	...	2226	...	...
Thessaloníki **1400** a.	...	...	...	...	...	...	...	...

⊡ – An infrequent bus service operates Kalambáka - Igumenítsa and v.v. (approximately *250 km*).

THESSALONÍKI - ÉDESSA - FLÓRINA 1410

km		81		713		733		715		735	
		2 ✱		2		2 ✱		2		2 ✱	
0	**Thessaloníki** .... **1400** d.	0646	...	1305	...	1540	...	1845	...	2200	...
38	Platí .... **1400** d.	0714	...	1334	...	1608	...	1919	...	2228	...
69	Véria .... d.	0736	...	1402	...	1637	...	1948	...	2257	...
97	Skídra .... d.	0756	...	1425	...	1700	...	2010	...	2320	...
112	**Édessa** .... d.	0812	...	1440	...	1713	...	2025	...	2333	...
162	Amíndeo .... d.	0855	...	1524	...	...	...	2109	...	...	...
196	**Flórina** .... a.	0924	...	1553	...	...	...	2139	...	...	...

	730		710		84		714		734	
	2 ✱		2		2 ✱		2		2 ✱	
Flórina .... d.	...	...	0645	...	1020	...	1635	...	...	...
Amíndeo .... d.	...	...	0717	...	1051	...	1717	...	...	...
Édessa .... d.	0505	...	0801	...	1135	...	1751	...	2040	...
Skídra .... d.	0520	...	0815	...	1149	...	1805	...	2055	...
Véria .... d.	0542	...	0838	...	1209	...	1828	...	2117	...
Platí .... **1400** d.	0611	...	0907	...	1238	...	1857	...	2146	...
Thessaloníki ..... **1400** a.	0639	...	0934	...	1306	...	1924	...	2214	...

✱ – Service currently suspended.

LÁRISA - VÓLOS 1415

km												
0	Lárisa .... d.	0620	...	0827	...	1022	...	1420	1445	1620	1820	...	2230
61	Vólos .... a.	0712	...	0919	...	1114	...	1512	1533	1712	1912	...	2322

Vólos .... d.	0522	0717	...	0923	...	1315	1340	1516	...	1716	...	2110
Lárisa .... a.	0614	0809	...	1015	...	1407	1428	1608	...	1808	...	2202

PIREÁS - ATHÍNA - HALKÍDA 1420

km																							
				Ⓐ		❖			❖		Ⓐ												
0	**Pireás** ....**1430 1440** d.	...	...	...	0615	...	and at	1415	...	1515	...	1615	...	1715	1815	...	1915	2017	...	2117	...	2217	...
10	**Athína** Lárisa ▲ **1400/30/40** d.	...	0452	0552	0634	0652	the same	1434	1452	1634	1552	1634	1652	1734	1834	1852	1934	2034	2052	2134	2152	2234	...
17	SKA (Acharnon).................. d.	...	0505	0602	...	0702	minutes	...	1502	...	1602	...	1702	...	...	1902	...	...	2102	...	2203	...	...
71	Inói .... **1400** d.	0450	0548	0648	...	0748	past each	...	1548	...	1648	...	1748	...	...	1947	...	...	2149	...	2249	...	...
94	**Halkída** ....a.	0509	0610	0710	...	0810	hour until	...	1610	...	1710	...	1810	...	...	2010	...	...	2210	...	2310	...	...

						Ⓐ		❖			❖		Ⓐ									
alkída ....d.	...	0515	...	0615	...	0715	...	0815	and at	...	1615	...	1716	...	1816	...	...	2015	...	2224	2316	...	...
ói .... **1400** d.	...	0538	...	0638	...	0738	...	0838	the same	...	1638	...	1738	...	1838	...	...	2038	...	2247	2335	...	...
KA (Acharnon)..................... d.	...	0623	...	0723	...	0823	...	0923	minutes	...	1723	...	1824	...	1924	...	...	2123	...	2332	...	...	...
thína Lárisa . ▲ **1400/30/40** d.	0623	0648	0723	0748	0822	0848	0923	0948	past each	1723	1748	1822	1848	1920	1948	2022	2119	2148	2219	2341	...	...	...
ireás .... **1430 1440** a.	0639	...	0739	...	0839	...	0839	...	hour until	1739	...	1839	...	1937	...	2039	2137	...	2237	...	...	...	...

❖ – Every two hours.

▲ – See below Table **1440** for summary of Metro services.

PIREÁS - ATHÍNA - ATHÍNA AIRPORT ✈ 1430

km									
0	**Pireás** ....**1420 1440** d.	...	0445	0545	0645	and at	2045	...	...
10	**Athína** Lárisa ▲ **1400/20/40** d.	0416	0505	0605	0705	the same	2105	...	...
15	Káto Acharnai .... **1440** d.	0427	0515	0615	0715	minutes	2115	...	...
21	Neratziótissa.................... ▲ d.	0436	0524	0624	0724	past each	2124	...	...
46	**Athína Airport** ✈ .... ▲ a.	0500	0548	0648	0748	hour until	2148	...	...

Athína Airport ✈ .... ▲ d.	0607	0707	and at	2207	2308	...	...	...
Neratziótissa................. ▲ d.	0632	0732	the same	2232	2332	...	...	...
Káto Acharnai .... **1440** d.	0640	0740	minutes	2240	2340	...	...	...
Athína Lárisa▲**1400/20/40** d.	0652	0752	past each	2252	2353	...	...	...
Pireás .... **1420 1440** a.	0710	0810	hour until	2310	...	...	...	...

▲ – See below Table **1440** for summary of Metro services.

PIREÁS - ATHÍNA - KÓRINTHOS - KIÁTO 1440

km									
0	**Pireás** ....**1420 1430** d.	...	0615	and at	2117	2217	...	...	...
10	**Athína** Lárisa ▲ **1400/20/30** d.	0530	0635	the same	2136	2236	...	...	...
15	Káto Acharnai .... **1430** d.	0541	0645	minutes	2144	2244	...	...	...
90	**Kórinthos** ....d.	0637	0741	past each	2239	2339	...	...	...
111	**Kiáto 1450** ....a.	0652	0755	hour until	2255	2355	...	...	...

Kiáto 1450 ....d.	0456	0556	0656	0759	and at	2059	2159	...	...
Kórinthos..............................d.	0512	0612	0712	0815	the same	2114	2214	...	...
Káto Acharnai .... **1430** d.	0609	0709	0809	0909	minutes	2209	2308	...	...
Athína Lárisa▲**1400/20/30** a.	0620	0720	0820	0920	past each	2219	2317	...	...
Pireás .... **1420 1430** a.	0639	0739	0839	0937	hour until	2237	...	...	...

▲ – Frequent Metro services operate as follows:
Line 1 (green): Pireás - Monastiraki - Omónia - Attiki - Neratziótissa - Kifissia.
Line 2 (red): Elliniko - Syntagma - Omónia - Athína Lárisa (for **Athína** mainline station) - Attiki - Anthoupoli.
Line 3 (blue): Agia Marina - Monastiraki - Syntagma - Athína Airport ✈.
Operators: ISAP Line 1; Attiko Metro Lines 2 and 3.

KIÁTO - PÁTRA 🚌 services 1450

	🚌	🚌	🚌	🚌	🚌	🚌	🚌	🚌 Ⓑ	🚌	🚌
iáto 1440 ....d.	0805	1005	1205	1405	1605	1705	1805	1905	2005	2105
iakoftó 1455 ....d.	|	|	|	|	1650	|	1850	|	|	|
átra ....a.	0930	1130	1330	1530	1740	1830	1940	2040	2130	2230

	🚌	🚌	🚌	🚌	🚌	🚌	🚌	🚌	🚌	🚌
Pátra ....d.	0625	0815	1015	1225	1425	1525	1625	1725	1825	1925
Diakoftó **1455**......................d.	|	0905	1105	|	|	|	|	|	|	|
Kiáto 1440...........................a.	0750	0950	1150	1350	1550	1650	1750	1850	1950	2050

PELOPÓNNISOS narrow-gauge branches 1455

IAKOFTÓ – KALÁVRITA *Rack railway*

km						
0	Diakoftó ....d.	0952	...	1217	...	1507
23	Kalávrita ....a.	1059	...	1324	...	1618

Kalávrita .... d.	1104	...	1337	...	1645
Diakoftó.......... a.	1211	...	1448	...	1756

KATÁKOLO – PÍRGOS – OLIMBÍA

km											
		Ⓐ		Ⓐ		Ⓐ		Ⓐ			
0	**Katákolo** ..... d.	...	...	0840	...	...	...	1410	...	...	...
12	Pírgos .... d.	0700	...	0903	...	1235	...	1432	...	...	...
33	**Olimbía** .... a.	0729	...	0931	...	1303	...	...	...	...	...

	Ⓐ		Ⓐ		Ⓐ				
Olimbía .... d.	0735	...	0940	...	1310	...	...	...	...
Pírgos.................... d.	0805	...	1008	...	1339	...	...	...	...
Katákolo .... a.	0827	...	...	...	1402	...	...	...	...

🚌 INTERNATIONAL BUS SERVICES 1460

number of operators run long-distance 🚌 services to and from Greece, and selected services are listed below. Details should be checked with the relevant operator before travel. ail tickets and passes are not valid. Further details about travelling to Greece by bus can be found on www.europebyrail.eu

THÍNA - ISTANBUL: Depart Athína 1700. Depart Istanbul 1800. Journey 16 hours. Operator: Metro www.metroturizm.com.tr

HESSALONIKI - ISTANBUL: Depart Thessaloniki 1000. Depart Istanbul (Esenler Otogari) 0530. Journey 10 hours. Operator: Ozikizler Turizm www.ozikizlerturizm.com
Depart Thessaloniki 1000, 2200, 2330. Depart Istanbul 1000, 1800, 2200. Journey 10 - 11 hours. Operator: Metro www.metroturizm.com.tr

HESSALONIKI - SKOPJE: Depart Thessaloniki 0830, 1730. Depart Skopje 0600, 1700. Journey 3½ - 4 hours. Operator: Simeonidis Tours www.simeonidistours.gr

HESSALONIKI - SOFIA: Coach services are operated by Union Ivkoni (www.union-ivkoni.com) as follows:

Thessaloniki 1430 → Sofia 2045.
Thessaloniki 2330 → Sofia 0615.

Sofia 0730 → Thessaloniki 1300.
Sofia 1630 → Thessaloniki 2215.

BULGARIA and TURKEY IN EUROPE

SEE MAP PAGE 505

Operators: Bâlgarski Dârzhavni Zheleznitsi (BDZ Passenger Services) www.bdz.bg
Türkiye Cumhuryeti Devlet Demiryolları (TCDD) www.tcddtasimacilik.gov.tr

Services: Trains convey first- and second-class seating, except where shown otherwise in footnotes or by '2' in the train column, or where the footnote shows sleeping and/or couchette cars only. Descriptions of sleeping (🛏) and couchette (▬) cars appear on page 10. Seat reservation is possible on most long-distance trains (compulsory on express trains).

Timings: BDŽ schedules valid **until December 10, 2022. Timetable amendments are possible at short notice so it is advisable to confirm timings locally before travelling.** Subject to alteration on and around public holiday dates. Please refer to Tables **61**, **98** and **99** for international through cars to/from Burgas and Varna (summer only). TCDD schedules are the latest available. For services in Asian Turkey see pages 520–522.

1500 SOFIA - RUSE, BURGAS and VARNA

km	km			2655	8631	8601	3621	2601	460	462	2611	8651		8611	2613	3623	2615	3601	2641	8641	2663	493	9647	8657	2627	8627	3637
						⚡[R]		⚡[R]	[R]	[R]								⚡[R]	⚡[R]								
			2	v		🍷e			A	C		e	2	e					G			B	L	Z	Z	eZ	DZ
0	0	**Sofia** **1520** d.	...	...	...	0620	0705	0715	0715	0715	1015	1030	...	1305	1315	1325	1515	1615	1615	1630	1815	1830	2015	2125	2235	2240	2255
	103	Septemvri d.	...	...	...	0821	│	│	│	│	│	1229	...	1516	│	│	│	│	│	1829	│	2045	│	2328	│	0104	│
	119	Pazardzhik d.	...	...	...	0833	│	│	│	│	│	1241	...	1528	│	│	│	│	│	1841	│	2056	│	2340	│	0116	│
	156	**Plovdiv** a.	...	...	...	0855	│	│	│	│	│	1306	...	1555	│	│	│	│	│	1905	│	2121	│	0005	│	0131	│
	156	**Plovdiv** d.	...	...	0735	0905	│	│	│	│	│	1310	...	1600	│	│	│	│	│	1910	│	...	│	0010	│	0136	│
	262	Stara Zagora d.	...	...	0920	1048	│	│	│	│	│	1500	...	1753	│	│	│	│	│	2050	│	...	│	0240	│	0335	│
	340	Jambol d.	0600	...	1010	1135	│	│	│	│	│	1547	...	1845	│	│	│	│	│	...	│	...	│	0329	│	0425	│
		Karlovo d.	│	...	│	│	0933	│	│	│	│	│	...	│	│	1541	│	1834	│	...	│	...	│	│	│	│	0116
		Kazanlak d.	│	...	│	│	1034	│	│	│	│	│	...	│	│	1640	│	1930	│	...	│	...	│	│	│	│	0214
		Tulovo d.	│	...	│	│	1102	│	│	│	│	│	...	│	│	1654	│	1944	│	...	│	...	│	│	│	│	0245
		Sliven d.	│	...	│	│	1221	│	│	│	│	│	...	│	│	1820	│	2056	│	...	│	...	│	│	│	│	0400
	389	Karnobat ..... **1535** d.	0642	...	1048	1207	1301	│	│	│	│	1624	...	1921	│	1900	│	2134	│	...	│	...	│	0403	│	0503	0442
	450	**Burgas** **1535** a.	0747	...	│	1257	1350	│	│	│	│	│	...	2006	│	1945	│	2220	│	...	│	...	│	│	│	0555	│
88		Mezdra **1520** d.	▬	0524	│	...	...	0844	0844	0844	1144	│	...	...	1444	...	1644	▬	1744	...	1952	...	2157	│	0024	...	│
194		Pleven d.	...	0701	│	...	...	1001	1001	1001	1301	│	...	...	1601	...	1801	...	1901	...	2115	...	2315	│	0142	...	│
239		Levski d.	...	0732	│	...	...	1031	1031	1031	1331	│	...	...	1631	...	1831	**4640**	1931	...	...	...	2344	│	0214	...	│
294		Gorna Orjahovica a.	...	0810	│	...	...	1110	1110	1110	1410	│	...	...	1710	...	1910	T	2010	...	...	...	0022	│	0255	...	│
294		Gorna Orjahovica d.	...	0820	│	...	...	1115	1130	1130	1420	│	...	...	1720	...	1930	1933	...	...	...	...	0027	│	0300	...	│
405		**Ruse** 🏛 a.	2	│	│	...	...	│	1324	1324	│	│	...	...	│	...	│	2132	...	...	...	...	0228	│	│	...	│
435		Shumen **1530/5** d.	0720	1010	│	...	...	1305	...	...	1610	│	1710	...	1910	...	2120	...	...	...	...	...	...	│	0452	...	│
459		Kaspichan **1530/5** d.	0748	1030	│	...	...	1325	...	...	1630	│	1739	...	1930	...	2140	...	...	...	...	...	...	│	0513	...	│
518		Poveljanovo **1530/5** d.	0900	│	1242	...	...	1425	...	...	│	│	1851	...	2030	...	│	...	...	...	...	...	...	0556	0613	...	0646
543	546	**Varna** **1530/5** a.	0930	1155	1306	...	...	1450	...	...	1755	1840	1919	...	2055	...	2305	...	...	...	...	...	...	0620	0640	...	0710

km		2640	8640	3602	4641	2610	8610		2602	8650	2612	461	463	2614		3624	8602	2654	8632				8626	3636	9646	2626	8656
		⚡[R]		⚡[R]					⚡[R]			[R]	[R]				⚡[R]										
		G			T			2				A	C		2		🍷e	v		2	2	2	Z	DZ	N	Z	Z
	Varna **1530/5** d.	...	...	...	...	0440	...	0600	0730	0905	1030	...	...	1330	1430	...	...	1630	1700	...	1725	1940	...	2145	...	2155	2350
	Poveljanovo **1530/5** d.	...	...	...	...	│	...	0633	0755	│	1055	...	...	1355	1502	...	...	1655	1725	...	1757	2010	...	2239	...	2219	│
	Kaspichan **1530/5** d.	...	...	...	...	0604	...	0743	0854	│	1154	...	...	1454	1610	...	...	1754	│	...	1905	2118	...	│	...	2316	│
	Shumen **1530/5** d.	...	...	...	...	0624	...	0810	0914	│	1214	...	...	1514	1635	...	...	1814	│	...	1930	2145	...	│	...	2337	│
	Ruse 🏛 d.	...	...	...	0610	│	...	▬	│	│	│	1410	1410	│	▬	...	...	│	│	...	▬	...	...	│	2336	│	│
	Gorna Orjahovica a.	...	...	...	0814	0815	...	...	1105	│	1405	1610	1610	1705	...	...	...	2005	│	...	...	...	...	│	0131	0124	│
	Gorna Orjahovica d.	0515	...	...	...	0830	...	...	1115	│	1415	1615	1615	1715	...	...	...	2015	│	...	...	...	...	│	0149	0149	│
	Levski d.	0555	...	...	...	0910	...	...	1155	│	1455	1655	1655	1755	...	...	...	2055	│	...	...	...	...	│	0232	0232	│
	Pleven d.	0625	...	...	...	0940	...	**3622**	1225	│	1525	1725	1725	1825	...	...	...	2125	│	...	...	...	...	│	0303	0303	│
	Mezdra **1520** d.	0740	...	...	...	1055	...		1340	│	1640	1840	1840	1940	2	...	...	2246	│	...	2	...	...	│	0421	0421	│
0	**Burgas** **1535** d.	│	...	0535	...	│	0705	0830	│	│	│	│	│	│	1340	1420	1500	...	│	1850	1950	...	2145	│	│	│	│
61	Karnobat **1535** d.	│	...	0621	...	│	0751	0916	│	1136	│	│	│	│	1452	1506	1546	...	1925	1956	2056	...	2233	0045	│	│	0209
119	Sliven d.	│	...	0703	...	│	│	0956	│	│	│	│	│	│	│	1548	│	...	│	2043	│	...	│	0123	│	│	│
195	Tulovo d.	│	...	0810	...	│	│	1104	│	│	│	│	│	│	│	1712	│	...	│	...	│	...	│	0240	│	│	│
210	Kazanlak d.	│	...	0824	...	│	│	1118	│	│	│	│	│	│	│	1727	│	...	│	...	│	...	│	0255	│	│	│
269	Karlovo d.	│	...	0920	...	│	│	1218	│	│	│	│	│	│	│	1835	│	...	│	...	│	...	│	0350	│	│	│
	Jambol d.	│	...	│	...	│	0827	│	│	1212	│	│	│	│	1536	│	1620	...	1959	...	2140	...	2309	│	│	│	0253
	Stara Zagora d.	│	0615	│	...	│	0919	│	│	1302	│	│	│	│	...	│	1715	...	2043	...	...	...	0003	│	│	│	0343
	Plovdiv a.	│	0756	│	...	│	1108	│	│	1442	│	│	│	│	...	│	1849	...	2230	...	...	...	0235	│	│	│	0518
	Plovdiv d.	│	0800	│	...	│	1125	│	│	1450	│	│	│	│	...	│	1854	...	...	...	...	...	0245	│	│	│	0530
	Pazardzhik d.	│	0828	│	...	│	1152	│	│	1516	│	│	│	│	...	│	1916	...	...	...	...	...	0312	│	│	│	0556
	Septemvri d.	│	0839	│	...	│	1203	│	│	1527	│	│	│	│	...	│	1927	...	...	...	...	...	0323	│	│	│	0607
418	**Sofia** **1520** a.	0910	1045	1137	...	1225	1418	1448	1510	1742	1810	2010	2010	2110	...	2100	2135	...	...	...	...	...	0538	0637	0555	0555	0818

Other trains **SOFIA - PLOVDIV**

	1611	2640		1613			
	S	G	2	S	2		
Sofia d.	0825	0935	1140	1530	1725	...	...
Septemvri d.	1035	1133	1429	1738	1955	...	...
Pazardzhik d.	1047	1145	1448	1750	2014	...	...
Plovdiv a.	1114	1210	1525	1815	2054	...	...

		1622		2641	1626		1614
	2		2	G		2	S
Plovdiv d.	0420	0630	1148	1325	1545	1615	1750
Pazardzhik d.	0450	0658	1218	1350	1612	1654	1817
Septemvri d.	0505	0709	1256	1401	1623	1711	1830
Sofia a.	0747	0935	1528	1610	1846	1951	2045

Other local trains **GORNA ORJAHOVICA - RUSE**

	2		2		2
Gorna Orjahovica d.	0835	...	1425	...	1730
Ruse a.	1055	...	1725	...	1958

	2		2		2
Ruse d.	0739	...	1130	...	1800
Gorna Orjahovica a.	1001	...	1355	...	2025

A – June 3 - Oct. 3. To/from Bucureşti (Table **61**).
B – ISTANBUL - SOFYA EXPRESS – [12] Sofia - Svilengrad and v.v.; 🛏 and ▬ Sofia - Halkalı and v.v. (Table **1550**).
C – To June 2 and from Oct. 4.
D – Conveys 🛏 and [2] Sofia - Poveljanovo - Dobrich and v.v. (Table **1540**).
G – YANTRA – [12] Gorna Orjahovica - Sofia - Plovdiv and v.v.
L – ▬ and [2] Sofia - Ruse - Silistra (Table **1530**).
N – ▬ and [2] Silistra - Ruse - Gorna (**2626**) - Sofia.
S – To/from Svilengrad (Table **1550**).
T – To/from Stara Zagora (Table **1525**).
Z – Conveys 🛏 and [12].
e – Engineering work may affect this train; enquire locally.
v – To/from Vratsa (Table **1520**).
⚡ – Express train. Higher fare payable.

1510 SEPTEMVRI - DOBRINISHTE

Narrow gauge; 2nd class only

Timings may change at short notice.

km		2		2	2🍷	2	2	2		2
0	**Septemvri** d.	0220	...	...	0850	1050	1240	1540	...	1855
39	Velingrad d.	0406	...	...	1014	1227	1406	1740	...	2025
119	Bansko d.	0714	...	0930	1304	...	1728	2103	...	...
125	**Dobrinishte** a.	0726	...	1005	1315	...	1740	2115	...	...

	2	2	2		2		2🍷		2	
Dobrinishte d.	...	0625	0800	...	1025	...	1440	...	1805	...
Bansko d.	...	0640	0813	...	1038	...	1452	...	1820	...
Velingrad d.	0640	0942	...	...	1335	...	1732	...	2133	...
Septemvri a.	0805	1120	...	...	1504	...	1849	...	2253	...

1520 SOFIA - VIDIN - CRAIOVA

km			7620		7622				7624		7630	2654
		2		2		2	Ⓑn2	2		2	Ⓑ	v
0	**Sofia** **1500** d.	...	0735	...	1215	...	*1425*	...	1715	...	1915	...
88	Mezdra **1500** d.	0440	│	...	1358	...	1715	...	1900	...	2117	2251
106	Vratsa d.	0458	0919	...	1413	...	1724	...	1917	...	2132	2305
145	Bojchinovci d.	0542	0958	...	1451	...	1827	...	1955	...	2210	...
182	Brusarci ⊖ d.	0630	1039	1050	1531	1535	1913	1918	2038	2040	2252	...
204	Lom ⊖ a.	│	│	1117	│	1602	│	1945	│	2107	2320	...
269	**Vidin** a.	0820	1218	...	1706	...	2055	...	2215	...	...	...

	2655	7631		7621					7623				7625
	v	⚒	2		2	2	2⚒	2		Ⓑn2	Ⓑn2	2	
Vidin d.	...	...	...	0455	...	0605	...	...	1225	...	1600	...	1730
Lom ⊖ d.	...	0450	0545	│	0715	│	1130	1330	│	1705	│	1835	│
Brusarci ⊖ d.	...	0519	0610	0629	0740	0751	1155	1355	1408	1730	1745	1900	1913
Bojchinovci d.	...	0559	...	0710	...	0831	1234	...	1452	...	1825	...	1956
Vratsa d.	0500	0641	...	0757	...	0914	1317	...	1534	...	1911	...	2037
Mezdra **1500** a.	0514	0655	...	0811	...	0930	1335	...	│	...	1930	...	│
Sofia **1500** a.	...	0848	...	1000	...	*1200*	...	...	1717	...	...	...	2222

km			⚒		
	Vidin 🏛 d.	...	...	...	1245
0	**Calafat** d.	0315	0607	...	│
107	**Craiova** a.	0625	0925	...	1551

km					Ⓑ
0	**Craiova** d.	0815	...	1640	1925
	Calafat a.	│	...	1957	2233
119	**Vidin** 🏛 a.	1123	...	...	...

n – Not Apr. 22, 24, May 1, 6.
p – From Plovdiv (Table **1500**).
v – To/from Varna (Table **1500**).
⊖ – Other services Brusarci - Lom and v.v.: **From Brusarci** at 0633, 0755, 0915, 1220 Ⓑ, 1413 and 1751 Ⓑ **n**. **From Lom** at 0840, 0956, 1455 and 2000.

RUSE - STARA ZAGORA - DIMITROVGRAD - MOMCHILGRAD - PODKOVA 1525

km			4641					465		4657
		2		2	2	2		B2	2	
0	**Ruse** ... **1500** d.	...	0550	...	...	...	...	...	1755	2230
111	**Gorna Orjahovica** ... **1500** d.	0530	0830	...	1130	1430	...	1725	2030	0039
125	Veliko Târnovo ... d.	0549	0849	...	1150	1450	...	1745	2049	0055
226	Tulovo ... a.	0817	1114	...	1418	1707	...	1953	...	0249
226	Tulovo ... d.	0818	1116	...	1419	1708	...	1954	...	0251
253	Stara Zagora ... d.	0850	1150	1350	1453	1742	...	2026	...	0354
310	**Dimitrovgrad** ... a.	...	...	1510	...	...	...	2136	...	0500

	4656		464					4640	
		2	B2	2	2	2			2
Dimitrovgrad ... d.	0035	...	0600	...	0925	...	...	...	...
Stara Zagora ... d.	0200	...	0720	1017	1100	1312	...	1630	1905
Tulovo ... a.	0230	...	0752	1051	...	1346	...	1701	1938
Tulovo ... d.	0232	...	0753	1052	...	1401	...	1703	1957
Veliko Târnovo ... d.	0427	0724	1016	1316	...	1619	...	1910	2230
Gorna Orjahovica ... **1500** a.	0500	0745	1036	1335	...	1640	...	1925	2250
Ruse ... **1500** a.	0701	...	...	...	...	...	...	2131	...

km		2	2	2	2	2
0	**Dimitrovgrad** ... d.	...	0505	...	...	1550
23	Haskovo ... d.	...	0532	...	...	1618
87	Kârdzhali ... d.	...	0711	0730	1310	1811
101	**Momchilgrad** ... d.	0540	...	0751	1331	1832
119	**Podkova** ... a.	0605	...	0815	1355	1856

	2	2	2	2	2	2
Podkova ... d.	0615	...	0820	1410	...	1900
Momchilgrad . d.	0639	...	0844	1435	1740	1923
Kârdzhali ... d.	0658	0715	0903	...	1810	...
Haskovo ... d.	...	0852	...	...	1954	...
Dimitrovgrad . a.	...	0918	...	...	2020	...

B – ⌸2 Gorna Orjahovica - Dimitrovgrad and v.v.
See Table **61** for seasonal through cars Bucureşti - Ruse - Svilengrad - Kapıkule - Halkalı and v.v.

RUSE - SILISTRA and VARNA 1530

km		9647		9621	2655				9623		
		A	2			2	2			2	2
0	**Ruse** ... d.	0233	...	0600	...	...	...	...	1600	1830	...
5	Ruse Razpr ... d.	0252	...	0609	...	0735	...	...	1609	1839	...
71	Razgrad ... d.	0355	...	0713	...	0848	...	...	1711	1958	...
93	Samuil ... d.	0439f	0515	0734	...	0909	0930	...	1732	2018	2040
	Silistra ... a.	0723	|	|	...	|	1220	...	|	...	2325
142	Kaspichan ... **1500** d.	...	0622	0835	1030	1100f	...	...	1833	...	...
	Shumen ... **1500** a.	...	...	|	|	1125	...	...	|	...	...
201	Poveljanovo .. **1500** d.	...	...	0935	|	...	...	...	1935	...	...
226	**Varna** ... **1500** a.	...	...	1000	1155	...	...	...	2000	...	...

km				2610		9620				9622	9646
		2	2		2		2	2	2		D
	Varna ... **1500** d.	...	...	0440	...	0930	1430	...	...	1810	...
	Poveljanovo .. **1500** d.	...	...	|	...	0955	1502	...	...	1835	...
	Shumen ... **1500** d.	...	...	|	...	|	|	...	...	|	...
	Kaspichan ... **1500** d.	...	...	0604	0640	1053	1609	...	1640	1933	...
0	**Silistra** ... d.	...	0430	...	|	|	...	1435	|	|	1900
113	Samuil ... d.	0520	0718	...	0759	1155	...	1725	1756	2035	2159f
	Razgrad ... d.	0542	...	...	0820	1215	...	...	1816	2055	2219
	Ruse Razpr ... d.	0658	...	...	0937	1317	...	...	1933	2157	2321
	Ruse ... a.	...	...	...	0945	1325	...	...	1941	2205	2329

A – 🛏 and ⌸2 Sofia - Ruse - Silistra.
D – 🛏 and ⌸2 Silistra - Gorna Orjahovica (**2626**) - Sofia.
f – Arrives 15–45 minutes earlier.

VARNA and SHUMEN - BURGAS 1535

km				8650	8601							
		2	2	R	R	2	2	2	2	2	2	2
	Varna ... **1500** d.	...	0700	0905	...	1130	...	...	1345	...	1825	...
	Poveljanovo ... **1500** d.	...	0732	|	...	1202	...	...	1417	...	1857	...
0	**Shumen** ... d.	0455	|	|	...	|	...	1400	|	...	|	1935
50	Komunari ... d.	0553	0830	1012	...	1259	...	1500	1511	...	1949	2035
133	Karnobat ... **1500** d.	...	1051r	1136	1207	1440	1451	...	1655	1930	2126	...
194	**Burgas** ... **1500** a.	...	1156	...	1257	...	1556	...	...	2035	...	...

							8602	8651		
	2	2	2	2	2	2	R	R	2	2
Burgas ... **1500** d.	...	0630	0730	...	1345	...	1500	...	...	...
Karnobat ... **1500** d.	...	0755r	0835	...	1450	1520	1545	1619	1720	...
Komunari ... d.	0605	0947	...	1520	...	1659	...	1728	1907	2040
Shumen ... a.	0705	|	...	1620	...	|	...	|	|	2140
Poveljanovo .. **1500** d.	...	1047	...	...	...	1800	...	|	2004	...
Varna ... **1500** a.	...	1120	...	...	...	1830	...	1840	2035	...

– Arrives 20–25 minutes earlier.

VARNA - DOBRICH - KARDAM 1540

km		D	2637	2	2		2	2	2		2
0	**Varna** ... **1500** d.	...	0615	...	0715	...	1215	1530	...	...	2015
	Sofia **1500** ... d.	2255	|	...	|	...	|	|	...	...	|
25	Poveljanovo ... **1500** d.	0641	0705	...	0748	...	1246	1604	...	...	2048
93	**Dobrich** ... a.	...	0827	0835	0906	...	1405	1733	1740	...	2210
131	Kardam ... a.	...	...	0939	...	...	...	...	1844	...	...

	2		2	2	2		2	2	2636	E
Kardam ... d.	...	...	...	1100	...	...	...	1900	...	...
Dobrich ... d.	0505	...	0915	1204	1215	...	1515	2004	2040	...
Poveljanovo ... **1500** a.	0624	...	1034	...	1342	...	1633	...	2205	2239
Sofia **1500** ... a.	|	...	|	...	|	...	|	...	|	0637
Varna ... **1500** a.	0655	...	1105	...	1415	...	1703	...	2250	...

– 🛏 and ⌸2 Sofia (**3637**) - Poveljanovo (**2637**) - Dobrich.
E – 🛏 and ⌸2 Dobrich (**2636**) - Poveljanovo (**3636**) - Sofia.

(SOFIA) - PLOVDIV - SVILENGRAD - İSTANBUL 1550

BDŽ; TCDD

km	*Bulgarian train number*					1611		1613				493
	Turkish train number			12701					12703			12501
		2	2		2		2			2	2	A R
0	*Sofia* **1500** ... d.	...	...	...	...	0825	...	1530	...	...	...	1830
156	**Plovdiv** ... ▷ d.	0550	0728	...	0935	1120	1420	1820	...	1925	2100	2131
202	Parvomaj ... ▷ d.	0644	0820	...	1022	1200	1507	1903	...	2010	2147	2211
234	Dimitrovgrad ... ▷ a.	0711	0847	...	1048	1217	1543	1920	...	2045	2216	2228
234	Dimitrovgrad ... d.	0715	...	...	1049	1218	...	1921	...	...	...	2245
299	Svilengrad ... a.	0808	...	...	1140	1310	...	2013	...	...	...	2332
299	Svilengrad 🏛 ... d.	...	...	...	...	...	...	...	...	...	...	0017
318	**Kapıkule** 🏛 ... a.	...	...	...	...	...	...	...	...	...	...	0037
318	**Kapıkule** ... d.	...	...	0800	...	...	...	...	...	...	...	0145
338	Edirne ... d.	...	...	0817	...	...	...	...	...	...	...	0200
	Uzunköprü ... d.	...	...	|	...	...	...	...	1820	...	...	|
385	Pehlivanköy ... d.	...	...	0851	...	...	...	...	1838	...	...	|
406	Alpullu ... d.	...	...	0914	...	...	...	...	1901	...	...	0252
506	Çerkezköy ... d.	...	...	1044	...	...	...	...	2033	...	...	0408
593	Halkalı ... **1570** a.	...	...	1211	...	...	...	...	2205	...	...	0534
621	**İstanbul** Sirkeci ... a.	...	...	◇	...	...	...	...	◇	...	...	◇

Turkish train number				12704					12702		12502
Bulgarian train number							1614				492*
	2	2	2		2	2		2		2	A R
İstanbul Sirkeci ... d.	...	...	...	◇	...	...	...	...	◇	...	◇
Halkalı ... **1570** d.	...	...	...	1240	...	...	...	...	1810	...	2140
Çerkezköy ... d.	...	...	...	1411	...	...	...	...	1942	...	2307
Alpullu ... d.	...	...	...	1541	...	...	...	...	2113	...	0026
Pehlivanköy ... d.	...	...	...	1601	...	...	...	...	2133	...	|
Uzunköprü ... a.	...	...	...	1616	...	...	...	...	|	...	|
Edirne ... d.	...	...	...	...	...	...	...	...	2210	...	0115
Kapıkule ... a.	...	...	...	...	...	...	...	...	2225	...	0128
Kapıkule 🏛 ... d.	...	...	...	...	...	...	...	...	...	...	0220
Svilengrad 🏛 ... a.	...	...	...	...	...	...	...	...	...	...	0240
Svilengrad ... d.	...	0450	...	...	0820	1250	1550	1740	...	...	0325
Dimitrovgrad ... a.	...	0547	...	...	0913	1345	1642	1833	...	...	0417
Dimitrovgrad ... ▷ d.	0505	0550	0725	...	0930	1346	1643	1835	...	2025	0424
Parvomaj ... ▷ d.	0531	0619	0755	...	0957	1419	1702	1902	...	2056	|
Plovdiv ... ▷ a.	0612	0708	0842	...	1039	1506	1743	1950	...	2138	0513
Sofia **1500** ... a.	...	...	...	...	...	...	2045	...	...	...	0935

A – ISTANBUL - SOFYA EXPRESS – ⌸2 Sofia - Svilengrad and v.v. 🛏 and 🛏 Sofia - Halkalı and v.v. Seasonal through cars from / to Bucureşti are expected to start from June 3 (see Table **61**).
– Train number **1622** between Plovdiv and Sofia (see Table **1500**).
▷ – Additional trains Plovdiv - Dimitrovgrad and v.v.: **From Plovdiv** at 1320, 1610 and 1715. **From Dimitrovgrad** at 1100, 1523 and 1745.
◇ – Frequent Maramary suburban services (at least every 15 minutes) operate between Halkalı - central İstanbul - Gebze and v.v see Table **1570.**

SOFIA - KYUSTENDIL, PETRICH, KULATA and THESSALONÍKI 1560

Most trains 2nd class only

km				5621	6621		5623		361	5683	5611	6623	5625
										R			
0	**Sofia** ... d.	...	0605	0730	0830	1030	1230	1430	1530	1630	1730	...	1930
33	Pernik ... d.	...	0712	0829	0927	1120	1317	1528	1615	1710	1820	...	2021
48	Radomir ... d.	...	0732	0845	0946	1139	1333	1551	1631	1724	1839	1845	2037
102	**Kyustendil** ... a.	...	|	|	1115	|	|	|	|	|	|	2015	|
91	Dupnitsa ... d.	0625	0830	0931	▬	1244	1414	1640	1719	1802	1926	▬	2116
123	**Blagoevgrad** ... a.	0709	0910	0959	...	1320	1442	▬	1748	1830	2000	...	2145
123	**Blagoevgrad** ... d.	0710	▬	*1005*	...	...	*1450*	...	1749	▬	2001	...	...
186	Sandanski ... d.	0828	...	*1118*	...	...	*1611*	...	1844	...	2105	...	...
197	General Todorov. a.	0840	...	*1130*	...	...	*1624*	...	1854	...	2117	...	...
197	General Todorov. d.	0841	0845	*1132*	1135	...	*1626*	1630	1855	1900	2120	2125	...
207	**Petrich** ... a.	|	0858	|	1148	...	|	1643	|	1913	2133	|	...
210	Kulata ... a.	0856	...	*1145*	...	...	*1640*	...	1905	...	...	2138	...
210	Kulata 🏛 ⊗ ... d.	...	...	...	...	...	...	...	...	...	...	...	...
354	**Thessaloníki** ... a.	...	...	...	...	...	...	...	...	...	...	...	...

		5610			5682		360		5622		5624
					R						
Thessaloníki ... d.	...	...	...	...	...	...	...	...	...	...	...
Kulata 🏛 ⊗ ... a.	...	...	...	...	...	...	...	...	...	...	...
Kulata ... d.	...	0515	0610	...	...	...	1050	...	*1350*	...	*1735*
Petrich ... d.	0510	|	|	0615	...	1040	|	1345	|	1730	|
General Todorov .. a.	0524	0528	0623	0628	...	1054	1100	1400	*1404*	1744	*1748*
General Todorov .. d.	▬	0529	▬	0629	...	▬	1101	▬	*1406*	▬	*1750*
Sandanski ... d.	**5620**	0542	...	0642	...	...	1119	...	*1420*	...	*1803*
Blagoevgrad ... a.		0644	...	0751	...	...	1212	...	*1535*	...	*1920*
Blagoevgrad ... d.	0530	0645	**6620**	...	0800	1000	1213	1415	1545	**6622**	1935
Dupnitsa ... d.	0609	0715		...	0831	1039	1243	1456	1615		2013
Kyustendil ... d.	|	|	0700	...	|	|	|	|	|	1830	|
Radomir ... d.	0653	0757	0831	...	0908	1132	1322	1546	1654	2004	2058
Pernik ... d.	0720	0815	0851	...	0924	1153	1341	1606	1710	2020	2114
Sofia ... a.	0809	0910	0945	...	1003	1245	1420	1702	1805	2103	2207

☛ Additional journeys Radomir - Kyustendil and v.v.: **From Radomir** at 0706, 1145, 1355, 1635, and 2017. **From Kyustendil** at 0425, 0930, 1130, 1350 and 1620.
– The border between Bulgaria and Greece is currently closed due to the covid-19 pandemic.

TURKEY IN ASIA

Operator: Türkiye Cumhuryeti Devlet Demiryolları (TCDD).

Services: *YHT* (high-speed) trains convey first and second class seating. Long distance trains convey a single class of seating known locally as 'Pullman' (shown as [1] in footnotes) which are gender specific and may also convey sleeping and/or couchette cars. Local trains convey 2nd class seating, shown as '2' in the train column. Descriptions of sleeping (🛏) and couchette (🛏) cars appear on page 10. Reservation of seats (free of charge) is required for high-speed (*YHT*) and express trains.

Timings: Schedules are the latest available. Timetable amendments are possible at short notice, please confirm timings locally before travelling.

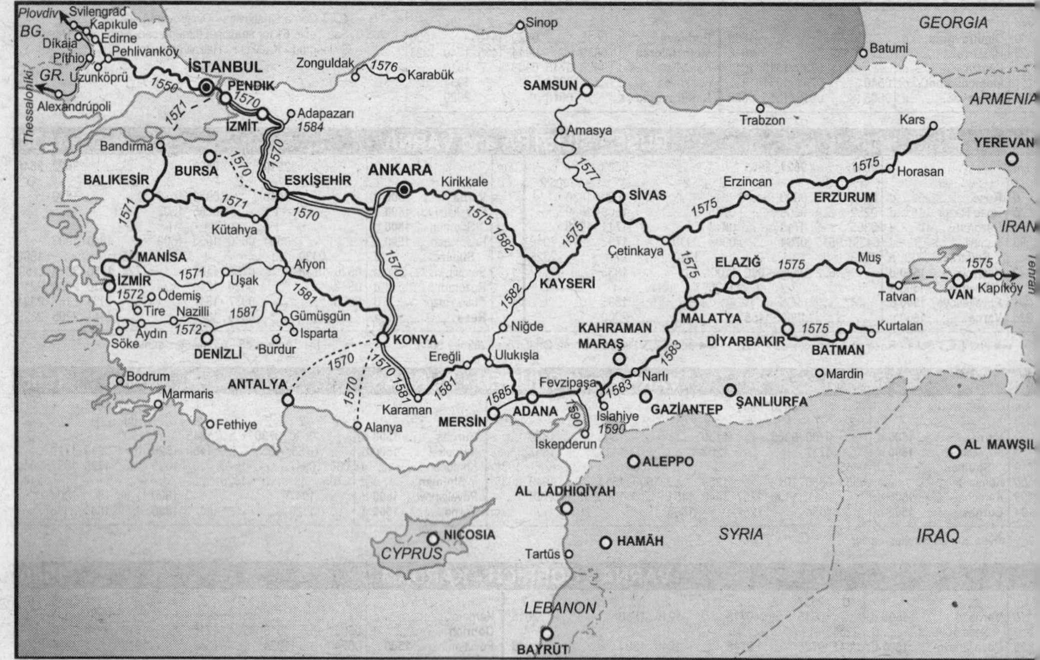

1570 İSTANBUL - ESKİŞEHİR - KONYA and ANKARA

km	*YHT* trains: 🅁 and 🍷	*YHT* 81102	*YHT* 81202	*YHT* 81002	*YHT* 81206	*YHT* 81302	*YHT* 81004	*YHT* 81208	*YHT* 81304	*YHT* 81008	*YHT* 81106	*YHT* 81010	*YHT* 81306	*YHT* 81012	*YHT* 81110	*YHT* 81214	*YHT* 81016	*YHT* 81218	*YHT* 81018	*YHT* 81020	*YHT* 81310	*YHT* 81022				1200 ● 🅁
	Halkalı .... **1550** d.	...	...	...	...	...	0635	...	0720	...	...	...	...	...	...	...	...	...	...	...	...	...	...	...	...	2200
	İstanbul Söğütlüçesme . d.	...	...	0605	...	0655	0725	...	0815	0935	...	1120	1205	1320	...	...	1515	...	1640	1710	1845	1915	...	...	...	2253
	İstanbul Pendik ... **1584** d.	...	...	0637	...	0727	0757	...	0849	1020	...	1203	1235	1359	...	...	1553	...	1728	1750	1919	1953	...	...	...	2324
	Gebze .... **1584** d.	...	...	|	...	0747	0819	...	0909	1044	...	|	1258	1422	...	...	|	...	1748	1811	1946	|	...	...	...	2350
	Izmit .... **1584** d.	...	...	|	...	0823	0852	...	0942	1117	...	1257	1331	1455	...	...	1648	...	1821	1844	2019	2048	...	...	...	0026
	Arifiye .... **1584** d.	...	...	|	...	0844	0913	...	1003	1138	...	1318	1352	1517	...	...	1709	...	1842	1905	2040	2109	...	...	...	0058
	Bilecik .... d.	...	...	|	...	0922	0951	...	1041	1216	...	|	1430	1556	...	...	|	...	1921	1947	2119	|	...	...	...	0230
	Bozüyük .... d.	...	...	|	...	0946	1015	...	1105	1240	...	|	1454	1620	...	...	|	...	1945	2012	2144	|	...	...	...	0303
0	**Eskişehir** .... d.	0615	...	0905	...	1006	1035	...	1125	1300	1350	1435	1514	1640	1740	...	1826	...	2005	2032	2204	2227	...	...	...	0344
	Konya .... **1581** a.	|	...	|	...	1152	|	...	1316j	|	|	|	1706	|	|	...	|	...	|	|	2350	|	...	...	...	|
	Karaman .... **1581** d.	|	...	|	...	...	|	1025	1418	|	|	|	...	|	|	...	|	1820	|	|	...	|	...	...	...	|
	Konya .... **1581** d.	|	0625	|	0910	...	|	1124	...	|	|	|	...	|	|	1740	|	1919	|	|	...	|	...	...	...	|
156	Polatli YHT .... d.	0703	0734	|	1019	...	1123	1234	...	1348	1438	|	...	1728	1828	1849	|	2029	2053	2120	...	|	...	...	...	0535
220	Eryaman YHT .... d.	0728	0759	|	1044	...	1148	1259	...	1413	1503	1545	...	1753	1853	1914	1936	2054	2118	2145	...	2337	...	...	...	|
245	**Ankara** .... a.	0744	0815	1030	1100	...	1204	1315	...	1429	1519	1601	...	1809	1909	1930	1952	2110	2134	2201	...	2353	...	...	...	0645

km	*YHT* trains: 🅁 and 🍷	*YHT* 81001	*YHT* 81301	*YHT* 81201	*YHT* 81003	*YHT* 81103	*YHT* 81205	*YHT* 81007	*YHT* 81009	*YHT* 81011	*YHT* 81013	*YHT* 81305	*YHT* 81211	*YHT* 81105	*YHT* 81015	*YHT* 81107	*YHT* 81307	*YHT* 81019	*YHT* 81215	*YHT* 81107	*YHT* 81309	*YHT* 81021	*YHT* 81219			1200 ● 🅁
0	**Ankara** .... d.	0600	...	0620	0715	0835	0855	0920	1045	1125	1300	...	1410	1430	1535	1650	...	1745	1805	1825	...	1915	2040	...	...	2200
21	Eryaman YHT .... d.	|	...	0638	0733	0853	0913	0938	1103	1143	1318	...	1428	1448	1553	1708	...	1803	1823	1843	...	1933	2058	...	...	|
89	Polatlı YHT .... d.	|	...	0701	0756	0916	0936	|	1126	1206	|	...	1451	1511	1616	1731	...	1826	1846	1906	...	|	2121	...	...	2316
309	**Konya** .... **1581** a.	|	...	0810j	|	|	1046	|	|	|	|	...	1600j	|	|	|	...	|	1956	|	...	|	2231	...	...	|
411	Karaman .... **1581** d.	|	...	0912	|	|	...	|	|	|	|	...	1657	|	|	|	1545	|	|	|	...	|	|	...	...	|
	Konya .... **1581** d.	|	0600	...	|	|	...	|	|	|	|	1255	...	|	|	|	1643	|	...	|	1825	|	...	...	...	|
245	**Eskişehir** .... d.	0726	0749	...	0846	1001	...	1048	1216	1256	1428	1448	...	1556	1706	1816	1838	1916	...	1951	2014	2043	...	...	...	0113
296	Bozüyük .... d.	|	0805	...	0902	...	...	|	1232	1312	|	1504	...	...	1722	...	1854	1932	...	...	2030	|	...	...	...	0147
330	Bilecik .... d.	|	0827	...	0924	...	...	|	1254	1334	|	1527	...	...	1744	...	1917	1954	...	...	2052	|	...	...	...	0226
	Arifiye .... **1584** d.	|	0904	...	1001	...	...	1158	1331	1411	|	1606	...	...	1821	...	1954	2031	...	...	2129	2157	...	...	...	0359
	Izmit .... **1584** d.	|	0927	...	1024	...	...	1221	1354	1434	1600	1629	...	...	1844	...	2017	2054	...	...	2152	2220	...	...	...	0426
487	Gebze .... **1584** d.	|	0959	...	1057	...	...	1259	1428	1506	|	1701	...	...	1916	...	2049	2127	...	...	2224	|	...	...	...	0458
506	**İstanbul** Pendik ... **1584** d.	0951	1020	...	1121	...	...	1322	1453	1528	1655	1722	...	...	1937	...	2112	2149	...	...	2245	2313	...	...	...	0519
529	**İstanbul** Söğütlüçesme . a.	1019	1050	...	1151	...	...	1353	1527	1559	1726	1801	...	...	2006	...	2143	2224	...	...	2320	2351	...	...	...	0540
563	Halkalı .... **1550** a.	...	...	...	...	...	...	...	...	...	...	...	...	...	...	...	2243	2309	...	...	...	...	...	...	...	0657

km	🚌										
0	Eskişehir .... d.	0855	...	1220	...	1455	...	1920	...	...	...
	Bursa .... a.	1105	...	1435	...	1705	...	2135	...	...	...

🚌										
Bursa .... d.	0345	...	0800	...	1200	...	1505	...	1800	...
Eskişehir .... a.	0600	...	1020	...	1420	...	1725	...	2020	...

km	🚌										
0	Konya .... d.	0920	...	1120	...	1325	...	1620	...	2020	...
	Alanya .... a.	|	...	|	...	|	...	2120	...	0120	...
	Antalya .... a.	1435	...	1635	...	1835	...	...	...	...	...

🚌										
Antalya .... d.	0100	...	...	...	...	...	1300	...	...	2359
Alanya .... d.	|	...	0800	...	1200	...	|	1400	...	|
Konya .... a.	0610	...	1240	...	1635	...	1900	1900	...	0515

j – Departs 5–10 minutes later.

● – ANKARA EKSPRESİ – Conveys 🛏, [1] and ✕

‡ – Departs from Polatli town station.

Suburban services run Halkalı - İstanbul - Gebze via the 1.4 km Marmaray Tunnel at least every 15 minutes 0600 - 2230. Route (with journey time): Halkalı (0) - Yenikapi (32) - Sirkeci (35) - Söğütlüçesme (46) - Pendik (80) - Gebze (108).

TCDD — ESKIŞEHIR, BANDIRMA and AFYON - IZMIR — 1571

km		32008 K	32602	32010 F❦	22006 B	32606	32002 C❦	32610	32004 D	72018 E	72610
	Ankara **1570** d.	...	...	...	2100	...	...	...	...	...	...
0	**Eskişehir** ♧ d.	...	...	...	0020	...	...	...	...	1210	...
77	Kütahya ♧ d.	...	...	...	0129	...	...	...	...	1330	1545
128	Tavşanlı ♧ d.	...	...	...	0217	...	...	...	...	1419	1635
‡	**Bandirma** Şehir d.	...	...	...	|	...	0800	...	1600	|	|
‡	**Bandirma** Gar d.	...	...	...	|	...	0806	...	|	|	|
331	Balikesir d.	...	...	0500	0609	...	0953	...	1743	1818	2013
386	Savaştepe d.	...	...	0555	0658	...	1047	...	1837	1914	...
413	Soma d.	...	...	0618	0724	...	1110	...	1901	1937	...
454	Akhisar d.	...	...	0652	0802	...	1145	...	1936	2015	...
◇	**Afyon** Ali Çetinkaya d.	2306	...	|	|	...	|	...	|	|	...
◇	Uşak d.	0141	...	|	|	0620	|	1615	|	|	...
◇	Alaşehir d.	0411	0530	|	|	0838	|	1830	|	|	...
506	Manisa d.	0556	0720	0741	0854	1027	1228	2041	2019	2107	...
572	**Izmir** Basmane a.	0726	0847	0901	1026	1202	1344	2214	2150	2237	...

	72609	32011 E	32601	32001 C	32603	32003 D❦	32607	32009 F❦	32005 B	32007 K
Izmir Basmane d.	...	0640	0740	0915	1055	1355	1505	1740	1905	1955
Manisa d.	...	0810	0924	1053	1227	1513	1642	1904	2042	2131
Alaşehir d.	...	|	1117	|	1414	|	1834	|	|	2316
Uşak d.	...	|	1326	|	...	|	2043	|	|	0148
Afyon Ali Çetinkaya a.	...	|	...	|	...	|	...	|	|	0417
Akhisar d.	...	0859	...	1136	...	1555	...	1949	2125	...
Soma d.	...	0938	...	1215	...	1630	...	2024	2200	...
Savaştepe d.	...	1001	...	1238	...	1652	...	2047	2223	...
Balikesir d.	0710	1122	...	1334	...	1747	...	2141	2340	...
Bandirma Gar a.	|	|	...	|	...	1921	...	...	|	...
Bandirma Şehir a.	|	|	...	1513	...	1926	...	...	|	...
Tavşanlı ♧ d.	1101	1453	...	...	...	...	...	...	0321	...
Kütahya ♧ d.	1145	1541	...	...	...	...	...	...	0408	...
Eskişehir ♧ a.	...	1652	...	...	...	...	...	...	0513	...
Ankara **1570** a.	...	...	...	...	...	...	...	...	0853	...

Istanbul - Bandirma

İstanbul Deniz Otobüsleri *

km						⑥					
0	**İstanbul** Yenikapi d.	0700	...	0905	...	1235	...	1330	...	1605	...
	Bandirma Şehir a.	0930	...	1130	...	1500	...	1600	...	1830	...

					⑥					
Bandirma Şehir d.	1015	...	1200	...	1530	...	1700	...	1900	...
İstanbul Yenikapi a.	1245	...	1455	...	1800	...	1930	...	2130	...

– IZMIR MAVI TRENİ – 🛏 [1] and ✕ Izmir - Ankara and v.v.
– 6 EYLÜL EKSPRESİ – [1] Izmir - Bandirma and v.v.
– 17 EYLÜL EKSPRESİ – [1] Izmir - Bandirma and v.v.
– EGE EKSPRESİ – [1] Izmir - Eskişehir and v.v.
– KARESI EKSPRESİ – [1] Izmir - Balikesir and v.v.
– KONYA MAVI TRENİ – 🛏 [1] and ✕ Izmir - Konya and v.v.

♧ – For local services see Table **1581**.
‡ – Bandirma Şehir - Bandirma Gar: *1 km*. Bandirma Şehir - Balıkesir *101 km*.
◇ – Afyon - Manisa: *355 km*. Uşak - Manisa: *220 km*. Alaşehir - Manisa: *103 km*.
* – İstanbul Deniz Otobüsleri ✆ +90 (212) 455 6900. www.ido.com.tr
❦ – Currently suspended.

TCDD 2nd class — IZMIR - TIRE, ÖDEMIŞ, SÖKE and DENIZLI — 1572

km		32759	32743	32721	32701		32723	32751	32705		32725	32707	32739	32745	32753	32755	32727	32711	32729	32761	32757	32731			32015 G
0	**Izmir** Basmane ⊡ d.	...	...	0630	0710	...	0900	1000	1045	...	1200	1230	1310	...	1415	1520	1530	1645	1700	...	1930	2040	...	...	2305
18	Adnan Menderes ⊡ d.	...	...	0656	0732	...	0919	1020	1108	...	1222	1256	1333	...	1444	1545	1558	1709	1723	...	1923	2109	...	...	2334
49	Torbalı ⊡ d.	...	...	0724	0803	...	0946	1053	1137	...	1250	1324	1403	...	1514	1617	1636	1737	1750	...	1950	2139	...	...	0004
86	Çatal d.	0555	...	0816	|	...	1032	1144	|	...	1340	|	|	...	1556	1658	1724	|	1840	1850	2042	2222	...	...	|
96	**Tire** a.	0610	...	|	|	...	|	1200	|	...	|	|	|	...	1611	1714	1752	|	|	1905	2057	|	...	...	|
111	**Ödemiş** Gar a.	...	...	0846	|	...	1059	...	|	...	1409	|	|	..	...	...	1757	|	1910	...	...	2249	...	...	|
112	**Ödemiş** Şehir a.	...	...	0851	|	...	1104	...	|	...	1414	|	|	...	...	...		|	1915	...	...	2254	...	...	|
77	Selçuk d.	...	...	...	0834	...	...	...	1208	...	...	1355	1437	...	...	...	...	1815	...	...	...	...	...	...	0038
	Söke d.	...	0632	...	|	...	...	...	|	...	...	|	|	1630	...	...	...	|	...	...	...	...	...	...	|
100	Ortaklar d.	...	0703	...	0908	...	...	...	1240	...	...	1428	1510	1659	...	...	...	1853	...	...	...	...	...	...	0112
130	Aydin d.	...	0734	...	0939	...	...	...	1315	...	...	1503	1636	1730	...	...	...	1929	...	...	...	...	...	...	0148
175	Nazilli d.	...	0831	...	1031	...	...	...	1411	...	...	1600	...	1823	...	...	...	2018	...	...	...	...	...	...	0237
260	**Denizli** a.	...	0958	...	1149	...	...	...	1529	...	...	1729	...	1943	...	...	...	2135	...	...	...	...	...	...	0353
	Isparta **1587** a.	...	...	...	...	...	...	...	...	...	...	...	...	...	...	...	...	...	...	...	...	...	...	...	0737

km		32760	32722	32752		32724	32754	32704		32726	32744		32706	32728	32756	32708		32730	32710	32758	32732	32746	32714		32016 G
	Isparta **1587** d.	...	...	...	...	...	...	...	...	...	...	...	...	...	...	...	...	...	...	...	...	...	...	...	2230
0	**Denizli** d.	...	...	...	...	...	...	0545	...	...	0640	...	0830	...	...	1045	...	...	1245	...	...	...	1630	...	0204
85	Nazilli d.	...	...	...	...	...	...	0707	...	...	0804	...	0952	...	...	1221	...	...	1409	...	...	1715	1755	...	0327
130	Aydin d.	...	...	...	...	...	...	0759	...	...	0857	...	1043	...	...	1314	...	...	1501	...	...	1818	1847	...	0420
160	Ortaklar d.	...	...	...	...	...	...	0830	...	...	0930	...	1114	...	...	1346	...	...	1531	...	...	1852	1918	...	0454
182	**Söke** a.	...	...	...	...	...	...	|	...	...	0956	...	|	...	...	|	...	...	|	...	...	1918	|	...	|
183	Selçuk d.	...	...	...	...	...	...	0901	...	...	...	...	1146	...	...	1422	...	...	1604	...	...	...	1949	...	0528
	Ödemiş Şehir d.	...	0520	...	...	0710	...	|	...	0935	...	...	|	1130	...	|	...	1500	|	...	1805	...	|	...	|
	Ödemiş Gar d.	...	0524	...	...	0714	...	|	...	0939	...	...	|	1134	...	|	...	1504	|	...	1809	...	|	...	|
	Tire d.	0535	|	0630	...	|	0800	|	...	|	...	...	|	|	1300	|	...	|	|	1640	|	...	|	...	|
	Çatal d.	0548	0556	0645	...	0744	0817	|	...	1008	...	...	|	1204	1317	|	...	1532	|	1657	1842	...	|	...	|
211	Torbalı ⊡ d.	...	0650	0725	...	0837	0904	0941	...	1054	...	...	1218	1251	1402	1454	...	1618	1635	1751	1939	...	2020	...	0605
242	Adnan Menderes ⊡ a.	...	0720	0756	...	0909	0935	1010	...	1122	...	...	1245	1322	1433	1523	...	1644	1702	1820	2009	...	2046	...	0634
260	**Izmir** Basmane ⊡ a.	...	0744	0820	...	0933	0957	1035	...	1145	...	...	1309	1345	1457	1545	...	1709	1726	1844	2033	...	2109	...	0657

– GÖLLER EKSPRESİ – [1]

⊡ – IZBAN suburban trains operate Izmir (Alsancak) - Adnan Menderes (Airport) - Torbalı and v.v. 0550 - 2359.

TCDD — ANKARA - SIVAS, KARS, KURTALAN, TATVAN and TEHRAN — 1575

km					22012 ②⑦	22014 △	22512 ③❦	22016 ●❦	22010	22018	21206 ❦
		2	2	2	B [R]	C [R]	G f [R]	H [R]	D [R]	E [R]	F
0	**Ankara** **1582** d.	...	...	...	1120	1120	1425	1555	1755	1855	2005
43	Elmadağ **1582** d.	...	...	...	1216	1216	|	|	1847	1946	2056
92	Kirikkale **1582** d.	...	...	...	1317	1317	|	|	1942	2045	2146
203	Yerköy **1582** d.	...	...	...	1513	1513	|	1936	2138	2233	2339
379	Kayseri d.	...	...	...	1857	1857	2109	2303	0115	0225	...
602	**Sivas** a.	...	...	...	2226	2226	|	0225	0445	0546	...
602	**Sivas** d.	...	0800	...	2253	2253	|	0258	0512	0600	...
710	Çetinkaya d.	...	0927	...	0037	0037	|	0443	0659	0737	...
779	Divriği d.	0510	1043	1545	|	|	|	0605	0831	|	...
935	Erzincan d.	0817	▬	1855	|	|	|	1223	1149	|	...
150	Erzurum d.	▬	...	▬	|	|	|	1943n	1606	|	...
235	Horasan d.	...	...	...	|	|	|	|	1730	|	...
307	Sarkamiş d.	...	...	...	|	|	|	2230	1908	|	...
365	**Kars** a.	...	...	...	|	|	|	2336	2010	|	...
854	Malatya d.			...	0332	0332	0434	...	...	1007	...
949	Yolçatı d.	2	2	...	0553	0553	|	...	...	...	...
107	Diyarbakir d.	0900	1750	...	|	0956	|	...	...	...	...
198	Batman d.	1128	2013	②⑤⑦	|	1217	|	...	...	...	...
267	**Kurtalan** a.	▬	...	2	|	1358	|	...	...	...	...
973	Elaziğ d.	...	...	0634	0634	...	0721	...	...	...	...
201	Muş d.	...	...	1106	1106	...	1154	...	...	...	...
295	**Tatvan** Gar a.	**51516**	...	1237	1237	...	1336	...	...	...	...
300	**Tatvan** Iskele a.	①❦	...	...	...	...	1426	...	...	...	...
0	**Van** Iskele d.	**d**	...	...	...	...	2125	...	...	...	...
3	**Van** Gar d.	2100	...	...	...	...	2152	...	...	...	...
114	Kapiköy 🏛 d.	2330	...	...	...	...	0120	...	...	...	...
120	Razi 🏛 d.	0125	...	...	...	...	0600	...	...	...	...
342	Tabriz a.	0505	...	...	...	...	0950	...	...	...	...
342	Tabriz **4630** d.	0530	...	...	...	...	1020	...	...	...	...
078	**Tehran** **4630** a.	1820	...	...	...	...	2320	...	...	...	...

	51515 ⑦❦		①③⑥		52019	42015 ●❦	21205 ❦	52511 ③❦	42009	52013 ▽	52011 ②④
	d	2	2	2	E [R]	H	F	G f	D [R]	C [R]	B [R]
Tehran **4630** d.	1300	...	...	...	...	...	...	2205	...	...	...
Tabriz **4630** a.	0130	...	...	...	...	...	...	1020	...	...	...
Tabriz d.	0200	...	...	...	...	...	...	1100	...	...	...
Razi 🏛 d.	0800	...	...	...	...	...	...	1745	...	...	...
Kapiköy 🏛 d.	0915	...	...	...	...	...	...	1830	...	...	...
Van Gar a.	1100	...	...	...	...	...	...	2000	...	...	...
Van Iskele a.	▬	...	...	...	...	...	...	2123	...	...	...
Tatvan Iskele d.	...	...	...	...	...	...	...	0550	...	...	...
Tatvan Gar d.	...	...	0940	...	...	...	...	0730	...	...	0840
Muş d.	...	...	1017	...	...	...	...	0906	...	...	1017
Elaziğ d.	...	...	1505	...	...	...	...	1413	...	...	1545
Kurtalan d.	2	...	▬	...	...	...	...	|	...	0810	|
Batman d.	0530	1500	...	...	...	...	...	|	...	0956	|
Diyarbakir d.	0752	1722	...	...	...	...	...	|	...	1230	|
Yolçatı d.	▬	▬	...	...	...	...	...	|	...	1625	1625
Malatya d.	...	...	...	...	1520	...	...	1657	...	1857	1857
Kars d.	...	...	...	...	|	2220	...	|	0800	|	|
Sarkamiş d.	...	...	...	...	|	2328	...	|	0907	|	|
Horasan d.	...	...	...	...	|	|	...	|	1033	|	|
Erzurum d.	...	2	...	...	|	0235	...	|	1210	|	|
Erzincan d.	2	0630	2	1500	|	0945p	...	|	1617	|	|
Divriği d.	0620	0936	1700	1806	|	1526r	...	|	1934	|	|
Çetinkaya d.	0745	...	1819	...	1749	1634	...	|	2057	2138	2138
Sivas a.	0911	...	1944	...	1919	1812	...	|	2228	2318	2318
Sivas d.	...	...	...	...	1935	2021	...	|	2303	2340	2340
Kayseri d.	...	...	...	...	2305	2348	...	0124	0239	0317	0317
Yerköy **1582** d.	...	...	...	...	0221	0315	0350	|	0608	0702	0702
Kirikkale **1582** d.	...	...	...	...	0408	|	0539	|	0801	0901	0901
Elmadağ **1582** a.	...	...	...	...	0510	|	0640	|	0915	1024	1024
Ankara **1582** a.	...	...	...	...	0557	0657	0735	0743	1008	1111	1111

– VANGÖLÜ EKSPRESİ – 🛏 🛌 (4 berth) [1] and ✕ Ankara - Tatvan and v.v.
– GÜNEY EKSPRESİ – 🛏 🛌 (4 berth) [1] and ✕ Ankara - Kurtalan and v.v.
– DOĞU EKSPRESİ – 🛌 (4 berth) and ✕ Ankara - Kars and v.v.
– 4 EYLÜL MAVI TRENİ – 🛌 (4 berth) and [1] ✕ Ankara - Malatya and v.v.
– CÜKUROVA MAVI TRENİ – 🛏 🛌 and [1] ✕ Ankara - Adana and v.v.
– TRANSASYA EKSPRESİ – 🛏 and ✕ Tehran (**718**/**719**) - Razi - Ankara and v.v.
– TURISTIK DOĞU EKSPRESİ – Conveys 🛏 and ✕ Ankara - Kars and v.v.

d – Conveys 🛏 and ✕.
f – By ⛴ Tatvan Iskele - Van Iskele and v.v.
n – Arrives 1627.
p – Arrives 0620.
r – Arrives 1243.

❦ – Service currently suspended.
● – Special fares apply.
△ – ①③④⑤⑥.
▽ – ①③⑤⑥⑦.

1576 KARABÜK - ZONGULDAK TCDD

km		22626	22630	22632	22636		22621	22625	22627	22633
0	**Karabük** d.	0710	1305	1605	1810	**Zonguldak** d.	0730	1130	1330	1830
59	Gökçebey d.	0830	1432	1730	1934	Filyos d.	0812	1212	1412	1925
75	Çaycuma d.	0854	1451	1749	1956	Çaykuma d.	0853	1245	1452	1958
96	Filyos d.	0926	1524	1822	2028	Gökçebey d.	0913	1305	1512	2018
120	**Zonguldak** a.	1006	1603	1903	2108	**Karabük** a.	1035	1426	1633	2140

Additional local trains run Zonguldak - Gökçebey and v.v.
From Zonguldak at 0930, 1630, 1735, 2030. **From Gökçebey** at 0540, 0630, 1225, 1830.

1577 SIVAS - AMASYA - SAMSUN TCDD

Service suspended until further notice

km								
0	**Sivas** d.	...	...	...	**Samsun** d.	...	...	...
53	Yildizeli d.	...	...	...	Havza d.	...	...	...
205	Turhal d.	...	...	...	Suluova d.	...	...	...
268	**Amasya** d.	...	...	...	**Amasya** d.	...	...	...
295	Suluova d.	...	...	...	Turhal d.	...	...	...
315	Havza d.	...	...	...	Yildizeli d.	...	...	...
401	**Samsun** a.	...	...	...	**Sivas** a.	...	...	...

1581 ESKIŞEHIR - AFYON - KONYA - ADANA TCDD

For YHT (high-speed) services between Eskişehir and Konya, see Table **1570**.

km		72007	72018	72602	72014	62006	72604	72608	72606		72006
		K	E	2	P	T	2		2		C
0	**Eskişehir** 1571 d.	...	0830	0910	1055	...	1420	1745	1945	...	0020
77	Kütahya 1571 d.	...	0946	1024	1207	...	1530	1910	2100	...	0129
127	Tavşanlı 1571 a.	...	1027	...	...	...	...	|	2143	...	0210
163	**Afyon** d.	0432	...	...	...	...	...	2051	...	...	...
261	Akşehir d.	0554	...	...	...	...	...	...	...	...	...
435	**Konya** 1570 d.	0828	...	...	...	1500	...	...	...	...	...
537	Karaman 1570 d.	...	...	...	...	1641	...	...	...	...	...
624	Ereğli d.	...	...	...	...	1820	...	...	...	...	...
672	Ulukışla 1582 d.	...	...	...	...	1928	...	...	...	...	...
781	Yenice 1582 d.	...	...	...	...	2130	...	...	...	...	...
804	**Adana** 1582 a.	...	...	...	...	2154	...	...	...	...	...

	72005	72601	72607	72603	62005	72011	72013	72605		72008
	C	2		2	T	E	P	2		K
Adana 1582 d.	...	...	...	...	0700	...	...	...	...	...
Yenice 1582 d.	...	...	...	...	0727	...	...	...	...	...
Ulukışla 1582 d.	...	...	...	...	0945	...	...	...	...	...
Ereğli d.	...	...	...	...	1034	...	...	...	...	...
Karaman 1570 d.	...	...	...	...	1200	...	...	...	...	...
Konya 1570 d.	...	...	...	...	1321	...	...	...	...	1900
Akşehir d.	...	...	...	...	...	...	...	...	...	2132
Afyon d.	...	...	0730	...	...	...	1504	...	...	2252
Tavşanlı d.	0321	0550	|	...	...	1453	|	...	...	...
Kütahya 1571 d.	0408	0637	0923	1220	...	1541	1706	1800	...	...
Eskişehir 1571 a.	0513	0745	1032	1334	...	1652	1815	1911	...	...

km											
0	Konya 1570 d.	0555	...	1120	...	1750	...	2010	...	...	...
102	Karaman d.	0711	...	1236	...	1906	...	2127	...	...	...

Karaman d.	0730	...	1605	...	1940	...	2200	...	...	...
Konya 1570 d.	0847	...	1722	...	2059	...	2317	...	...	...

C – IZMIR MAVI TRENİ – and ✕ Izmir - Eskişehir - Ankara and v.v.
E – EGE EKSPRESİ – Izmir - Eskişehir and v.v.
K – KONYA MAVI TRENİ – and ✕ Konya - Izmir and v.v.
P – PAMUKKALE EKSPRESİ – Eskişehir - Denizli and v.v.
T – TOROS EKSPRESİ – Adana - Konya and v.v.

1582 ANKARA - KAYSERI - ADANA TCDD

km		22002	22012	22014	22512	22016	62006	22010	22018	21206
		G	B	C	T	H	J	D	E	F
			△	▽	③✱	✱				✱
0	**Ankara** 1575 d.	...	1120	1120	1425	1555	...	1755	1855	2005
43	Elmadağ 1575 d.	...	1216	1216	|	|	...	1847	1946	2056
92	Kirikkale 1575 d.	...	1317	1317	|	|	...	1942	2045	2148
203	Yerköy 1575 d.	...	1513	1513	|	1936	...	2134	2233	2339
379	**Kayseri** 1575 d.	0730	1857	1857	2109	2303	...	0115	0225	|
479	Niğde d.	0951	...	...	...	...	...	...	...	0351
542	Ulukışla 1581 d.	1104	...	...	...	...	1928	...	...	0504
651	Yenice 1581 d.	1256	...	...	...	...	2130	...	...	0706
674	**Adana** 1581 d.	1320	...	...	...	...	2154	...	...	0725

	62005	62001	22019	22015	21205	22511	22009	22011	22013
	J	G	E	H	F	T	D	B	C
				✱	✱	⑥✱		△	▽
Adana 1581 d.	0700	1630	...	...	1930	...	...	...	...
Yenice 1581 d.	0727	1658	...	...	1951	...	...	...	...
Ulukışla 1581 d.	0945	1849	...	...	2220	...	...	...	...
Niğde d.	...	2003	...	...	2321	...	...	...	...
Kayseri 1575 d.	...	2222	2305	2348	|	0124	0239	0317	0317
Yerköy 1575 d.	...	...	0221	0315	0350	|	0608	0702	0702
Kirikkale 1575 d.	...	...	0408	|	0539	|	0801	0901	0901
Elmadağ 1575 a.	...	...	0510	|	0640	|	0915	1024	1024
Ankara 1575 a.	...	...	0557	0657	0735	0743	1008	1111	1111

B – VAN GÖLÜ EKSPRESİ – and ✕ Ankara - Tatvan and v.v.
C – GÜNEY EKSPRESİ – and ✕ Ankara - Kurtalan and v.v.
D – DOĞU EKSPRESİ – and ✕ Ankara - Kars and v.v.
E – 4 EYLÜL MAVI TRENİ – and ✕ Ankara - Malatya and v.v.
F – CÜKUROVA MAVI TRENİ – and ✕ Ankara - Adana and v.v.
G – ERCIYES EKSPRESİ – Kayseri - Adana and v.v.
H – TURISTIK DOĞU EKSPRESİ – and ✕ Ankara - Kars and v.v. Special fares apply.
J – TOROS EKSPRESİ – Adana - Konya and v.v.
T – TRANSASYA EKSPRESİ – and ✕ Ankara - Tehran and v.v.
△ – Runs on ②⑦ from Ankara. Runs on ②④ from Tatvan.
▽ – Runs on ①③④⑤⑥ from Ankara. Runs on ①③⑤⑥⑦ from Kurtalan.
✱ – Currently suspended.

1583 ADANA - MALATYA - ELAZIĞ TCDD

km		62004			52003	
		L			L	
0	**Adana** d.	0840	...	**Elazığ** d.	0830	...
78	Toprakkale d.	1000	...	Yolçatı d.	0859	...
141	Fevzipaşa d.	1141	...	**Malatya** d.	1114	...
210	Narlı d.	1247	...	Doğanşehir d.	1227	...
335	Doğanşehir d.	1522	...	Narlı d.	1503	...
392	**Malatya** d.	1645	...	Fevzipaşa d.	1624	...
487	Yolçatı d.	1850	...	Toprakkale d.	1740	...
511	**Elazığ** a.	1911	...	**Adana** a.	1859	...

L – FIRAT EKSPRESİ – Elaziğ - Adana and v.v.

1584 İSTANBUL - ARIFIYE - ADAPAZARI TCDD

ADA REGIONAL EKSPRES TRENİ – Conveys .

km		12602	12604	12606	12608	12610		12601	12603	12605	12607	12609
0	**İstanbul** Pendik d.	...	...	...	...	...	**Adapazarı** d.	0630	1005	1405	1730	1955
19	Gebze d.	0720	1125	1310	1725	2105	Arifiye d.	0643	1018	1418	1743	2009
66	Izmit d.	0802	1205	1350	1804	2145	Izmit d.	0716	1051	1451	1816	2042
107	Arifiye d.	0833	1236	1421	1835	2216	Gebze d.	0753	1128	1528	1853	2119
115	**Adapazarı** a.	0846	1249	1434	1848	2229	**İstanbul** Pendik a.	...	...	...	...	...

For other trains İstanbul - Gebze and v.v. see Table **1570**.

1585 MERSIN - ADANA TCDD

km				K									K						K		J						
0	**Mersin** d.	0545	0610	0630	0700	0730	0800	0830	0915	1000	1045	1145	1240	1320	1345	1430	1515	1600	1630	1715	1730	1800	1830	1900	1945	2130	2230
26	Tarsus d.	0615	0644	0706	0733	0800	0832	0900	0951	1033	1115	1215	1310	1352	1415	1500	1547	1630	1706	1745	1809	1836	1902	1938	2015	2206	2306
43	Yenice d.	0634	0703	0725	0752	0823	0851	0919	1007	1052	1134	1234	1330	1411	1434	1519	1607	1649	1726	1804	1828	1855	1922	1959	2034	2225	2325
68	**Adana** a.	0656	0727	0750	0816	0845	0915	0941	1028	1114	1156	1258	1354	1433	1458	1541	1631	1711	1750	1828	1852	1919	1943	2023	2056	2249	2349

								K	J						K									K			
Adana d.	0545	0615	0640	0705	0730	0815	0900	0953	1036	1100	1130	1200	1230	1315	1444	1500	1530	1615	1645	1720	1745	1815	1845	1948	2005	2130	2230
Yenice d.	0608	0641	0703	0728	0754	0838	0924	1017	1101	1123	1154	1224	1253	1339	1509	1527	1554	1639	1710	1743	1809	1838	1909	2012	2030	2153	2254
Tarsus d.	0627	0700	0722	0747	0813	0857	0943	1036	1121	1142	1213	1243	1312	1358	1529	1546	1613	1658	1729	1802	1828	1857	1928	2031	2049	2212	2313
Mersin a.	0656	0731	0755	0820	0841	0925	1012	1107	1157	1210	1241	1316	1342	1431	1557	1615	1641	1729	1802	1832	1901	1928	1956	2104	2118	2241	2346

J – Islahiye - Adana - Mersin and v.v.
K – Iskenderun - Adana - Mersin and v.v.

1587 AFYON - BURDUR, ISPARTA & DENIZLI TCDD

km		72014	(bus)	72016		72015	(bus)	72013
		P		G		G		P
	Eskişehir ◇ d.	1055	...	...	**Denizli** d.	0408	...	1015
0	**Afyon** d.	1400	...	...	Dinar d.	0617	...	1232
◧	Isparta d.	|	...	2230	Karakuyu d.	0638	...	1252
	Burdur d.	|	2220	|	Gümüşgün a.	0708	0710	|
◧	Gümüşgün a.	|	2245	2256	Burdur d.	|	0737	|
112	Karakuyu d.	1606	...	2330	Isparta d.	0737	...	|
126	Dinar d.	1625	...	2346	**Afyon** a.	...	...	1457
260	**Denizli** a.	1848	...	0149	*Eskişehir* ◇ a.	...	...	1815

G – GÖLLER EKSPRESİ – Izmir - Isparta/Burdur and v.v.
P – PAMUKKALE EKSPRESİ – Eskişehir - Denizli and v.v.
◧ – Distance from Karakuyu: Gümüşgün 33 km, Isparta 62 km.
◇ – See Table **1581**.

1590 ADANA - ISLAHIYE / ISKENDERUN TCDD

km		2 K	2 K	2 K	J		2 K	J	2 K	2 K
0	**Adana** d.	0754	1401	1756	1903	**Islahiye** d.	...	0730	...	...
78	Toprakkale d.	0912	1520	1915	2022	Fevzipaşa d.	...	0745	...	...
137	Iskenderun a.	1009	1633	2012	|	Iskenderun a.	0715	|	1200	1715
141	Fevzipaşa d.	...	...	...	2152	Toprakkale d.	0816	0910	1316	1819
150	**Islahiye** d.	...	...	...	2203	**Adana** a.	0942	1024	1432	1943

J – Islahiye - Adana - Mersin and v.v.
K – Iskenderun - Adana - Mersin and v.v.

ROMANIA

SEE MAP PAGE 50

Operator: Societatea Natională de Transport Feroviar de Călători (CFR Călători): www.cfrcalatori.ro. Certain services are operated by private companies as shown in relevant tables.

Services: Trains convey 1st- and 2nd-class seating accommodation unless otherwise indicated. Sleeping- (🛏) and couchette (▬) cars are described on page 10. Most long-distance trai are classified *IR* (Interregio), shown in our tables with just the train number.

Timings: Valid **until December 10, 2022**. Alterations to schedules are possible at any time.

Tickets: Reservation is obligatory for travel by all CFR Călători services for which a train number is shown in the tables, and passengers boarding without a prior reservation are surcharge CFR trains shown without numbers are slow stopping-services calling at all, or most, stations.

1600 BUCUREŞTI - BRAŞOV - CLUJ NAPOCA / ORADEA / SIBIU / ARAD (- BUDAPEST)

km		146 S■	2	74 F	72 T	366 H■	1735 4004	1880	1623 ✕	2	1645 Ln	346 D■	404 E	1738	406 C■	1635 2005 r	472 R	1741 ⊕	⊡ 1942 ⊕	1930 ⊕	1641 ⊗2	1639 1648 ⊗	78 M	1914 ⊕t	182 192 ⊕
	Mangalia **1680** d.	...	...	...	...	...	...	...	...	...	...	...	...	...	...	...	...	...	1514	1602	...	...	...	1815	1912
	Constanţa **1680** d.	...	...	...	...	...	...	0530	...	...	...	...	...	...	...	1400	...	...	1705	1750	...	...	...	2000	204
0	**Bucureşti** Nord ▷ d.	...	...	...	0606	...	0608	0806	0955	...	1229	1400	...	1400	...	1637	1745	1850	1938b	2006b	2105	2105	2202	2257	234
59	Ploieşti Vest ▷ d.	...	...	...	|	...	0644	0840	1037	...	1305	1437	...	1437	...	1713	1821	1925	2024	2051	2143	2143	|	|	|
121	Sinaia ▷ d.	...	...	...	|	...	0736	0925	1127	...	1351	1520	...	1520	...	1804	1908	2011	2111	2140	2233	2233	|	|	|
140	Predeal ▷ d.	...	...	...	|	...	0801	0950	1153	...	1415	1539	...	1539	...	1829	1932	2036	2137	2205	2259	2259	|	|	|
166	**Braşov** ▷ a.	...	...	...	|	...	0838	1028	1231	...	1454	1617	...	1617	...	1907	2010	2114	2215	2243	2337	2337	|	|	|
166	**Braşov** d.	...	...	0620	|	0727	0847	...	1251	1434	...	1621	...	1621	1921	1930	2022	2128	2227	2257	2352	2352	|	|	|
294	**Sighişoara** **1622** d.	...	0550	|	|	|	1201	...	|	|	...	1928	...	1928	|	|	|	0040	|	0223	|	|	|	|	|
330	Mediaş **1622** d.	...	0630	|	|	|	1231	...	|	|	...	1953	...	1953	|	|	|	0110	|	0254	|	|	|	|	|
340	Copşa Mică **1622** d.	...	0646	|	|	|	1240	...	|	|	...	|	...	|	|	|	|	0119	|	0303	|	|	|	|	|
370	Blaj d.	...	0732	|	◧	◐	1302	...	|	|	...	2018	...	2018	◐	|	|	0142	◐	0326	◐	◐	◧	△	▽
392	Teiuş **1620** d.	...	0820	|	|	|	1330	...	|	|	...	2046	...	2104	|	|	|	0212	|	0356	|	|	|	|	|
405	Aiud **1620** d.	...	0835	|	|	|	1345	...	|	|	...	2100	...	2118	|	|	|	0229	|	0412	|	|	|	|	|
425	Războieni **1620** d.	...	0908	|	|	|	1410	...	|	|	...	2124	...	2142	|	|	|	0306	|	0438	|	|	|	|	|
442	Câmpia Turzii **1620** d.	...	0927	|	|	|	1426	...	|	|	...	2139	...	2157	|	|	|	0323	|	0455	|	|	|	|	|
494	**Cluj Napoca** **1620** a.	...	1038	|	|	1432	1524	...	|	|	...	2237	...	2255	0238	|	|	0423	|	0553	|	0734	|	|	|
494	**Cluj Napoca** **1625** d.	0739	...	|	|	1455	1543	...	|	|	...	2251	2251	...	0248	|	|	0435	|	0608	|	...	|	|	|
543	Huedin **1625** d.	0828	...	|	|	1546	|	...	|	|	...	2343	2343	...	0340	|	|	0526	|	0704	|	...	|	|	|
646	**Oradea** **1625** a.	1011	...	|	|	1733	|	...	|	|	...	0129	0129	...	0521	|	|	0707	|	0920	|	...	|	|	|
	Baia Mare **1610/14** a.	|	...	|	|	|	2000	...	|	|	...	|	|	...	|	|	|	|	0755	...	0917	...	|	|	|
	Satu Mare **1610/25** a.	|	...	|	|	|	...	...	|	|	...	|	|	...	|	|	|	0917	0945	...	...	...	|	|	|
•65	Făgăraş d.	|	...	0739	|	|	...	...	1409	1610	...	|	|	...	|	2107	2139	...	...	...	...	...	|	|	|
•127	Podu Olt **1645** d.	|	...	|	|	|	...	...	1509	1740	...	|	|	...	|	|	|	...	...	...	...	...	|	0707	|
•149	**Sibiu** **1645** d.	|	...	0901	|	|	...	...	1541	1821	...	|	|	...	|	2240	2301	...	...	...	...	...	|	0738	|
•223	Sebeş Alba d.	|	...	1030	|	|	...	...	...	...	...	|	|	...	|	...	0030	...	...	...	...	...	|	...	|
	Alba Iulia d.	|	...	|	|	|	...	...	...	...	...	|	|	...	|	...	|	...	...	...	...	...	|	...	|
•232	Vinţu de Jos d.	|	...	1042	|	|	...	...	...	...	...	|	|	...	|	...	0042	...	...	...	...	...	|	...	|
•276	Simeria **1620** d.	|	...	1126	|	|	...	...	...	...	...	|	|	...	|	...	0129	...	...	...	...	...	|	...	081
•285	Deva **1620** d.	|	...	1137	|	|	...	...	...	...	...	|	|	...	|	...	0142	...	...	...	...	...	|	...	083
•433	**Arad** **1620** a.	|	...	1439	1605	|	...	...	...	...	...	|	|	...	|	...	0440	...	...	...	...	...	0859	...	113
	Budapest Keleti **1280** ‡ a.	1420	...	1850	2050	2120	...	...	...	...	...	0520	0520	...	0920	...	0850	...	...	...	...	...	1250	...	...

	73 T	1912 ⊕h	367 H■	75 F	⊡ 1941 ⊕h	1932 ⊕h	1642 ⊗2	1638 1649 ⊗	1822 1922* ⊕h	1742 ⊕	143 S■	79 M	2004 1630 r	407 C■	473 R	1634 2r	347 D■	405 E	1636	2	4006 1746	1734	1646 P	1624	173
Budapest Keleti **1280** ‡ d.	0710	...	0740	0910	...	...	...	...	...	...	1340	1510	...	1740	1910	...	2245	2245	...	...	...	...	...	...	...
Arad **1620** d.	1239	...	|	1435	...	...	...	...	1818	...	|	2050	...	|	0102	...	|	|	...	...	...	...	...	...	...
Deva **1620** d.	|	...	|	1735	...	...	...	...	2123	...	|	|	...	|	0347	...	|	|	...	...	...	...	...	...	...
Simeria **1620** d.	|	...	|	1757	...	...	...	...	2136	...	|	|	...	|	0408	...	|	|	...	...	...	...	...	...	...
Vinţu de Jos d.	|	...	|	1836	...	...	...	...	|	...	|	|	...	|	0446	...	|	|	...	...	...	...	...	...	...
Alba Iulia d.	|	...	|	|	...	...	...	...	|	...	|	|	...	|	|	...	|	|	...	...	...	...	...	...	...
Sebeş Alba d.	|	...	|	1849	...	...	...	...	|	...	|	|	...	|	0458	...	|	|	...	...	...	...	...	...	...
Sibiu **1645** d.	|	1838	|	2028	...	...	...	...	|	...	|	|	0355	|	0632	...	|	|	...	1151	...	...	...	1630	...
Podu Olt **1645** d.	|	1916	|	|	...	...	...	...	|	...	|	|	|	|	|	...	|	|	...	1237	...	...	...	1707	...
Făgăraş d.	|	|	|	2206	...	...	...	...	|	...	|	|	0539	|	0806	...	|	|	...	1410	...	...	...	1812	...
Satu Mare **1610/25** d.	|	|	|	|	1320	...	...	...	|	1700	|	|	|	|	|	...	|	|	...	|	...	...	...	|	...
Baia Mare **1610/14** d.	|	|	|	|	1501	...	1750	...	|	|	|	|	|	|	|	...	|	|	...	|	0540	...	...	|	...
Oradea **1625** d.	|	|	1333	|	|	1621	|	...	|	1926	1950	|	|	2330	|	...	0535	0535	...	|	|	...	...	|	...
Huedin **1625** d.	|	|	1518	|	|	1829	|	...	|	2109	2134	|	|	0110	|	...	0728	0728	...	|	|	...	...	|	...
Cluj Napoca **1625** a.	|	|	1609	|	|	1919	|	...	|	2200	2223	|	|	0159	|	...	0819	0819	...	|	0946	...	...	|	...
Cluj Napoca **1620** d.	|	|	1624	|	|	1933	|	1920	|	2212	...	|	|	0211	|	...	0834	...	...	|	1000	1000	...	|	134
Câmpia Turzii **1620** d.	|	|	|	|	|	2035	|	|	|	2318	...	|	|	|	|	...	0936	...	...	|	1102	1102	...	|	144
Războieni **1620** d.	|	|	|	|	|	2053	|	|	|	2347	...	|	|	|	|	...	0953	...	...	|	1119	1119	...	|	150
Aiud **1620** d.	|	|	|	|	|	2117	|	|	|	0011	...	|	|	|	|	...	|	...	...	|	1143	1143	...	|	152
Teiuş **1620** d.	|	|	|	|	|	2136	|	|	|	0031	...	|	|	|	|	...	1031	...	...	|	1202	1202	...	|	154
Blaj d.	◧	△	◐	|	◐	2200	◐	◐	▽	0056	...	◧	|	◐	|	...	1057	...	...	|	1226	1226	...	|	160
Copşa Mică **1622** d.	|	|	|	|	|	2220	|	|	|	0120	...	|	|	|	|	...	|	...	...	|	1245	1246	...	|	163
Mediaş **1622** d.	|	|	|	|	|	2229	|	|	|	0129	...	|	|	|	|	...	1122	...	...	|	1254	1254	...	|	164
Sighişoara **1622** d.	|	|	|	|	|	2256	|	|	|	0159	...	|	|	|	|	...	1147	...	...	|	1326	1326	...	|	171
Braşov a.	|	|	0014	2323	0056	0210	0343	0343	|	0507	...	|	0724	0942	0923	...	1451	...	...	1554	1643	1643	...	1929	202
Braşov ▷ d.	|	|	...	...	0108	0222	0355	0355	|	0519	...	|	0738	...	0936	1115	1456	...	1422	...	1656	1656	1948	1948	203
Predeal ▷ d.	|	|	...	...	0154	0308	0441	0441	|	0604	...	|	0814	...	1012	1151	1532	...	1458	...	1741	1741	2026	2026	210
Sinaia ▷ d.	|	|	...	...	0222	0333	0459	0459	|	0629	...	|	0841	...	1059	1218	1551	...	1526	...	1808	1808	2053	2053	213
Ploieşti Vest ▷ d.	|	|	...	...	0311	0421	0549	0549	|	0717	...	|	0932	...	1122	1313	1636	...	1620	...	1857	1857	2142	2142	222
Bucureşti Nord ▷ a.	2330	0258	...	...	0357b	0505b	0627	0627	0544	0757	...	0806	1009	...	1159	1350	1713	...	1657	...	1934	1934	2222	2222	225
Constanţa **1680** a.	...	0557	...	...	0629	0744	...	...	0848t	...	...	...	1256	...	...	...	...	...	...	...	...	...	...	...	...
Mangalia **1680** a.	...	0742	...	...	0818	0949	...	...	1043t	...	...	...	...	...	...	...	...	...	...	...	...	...	...	...	...

ADDITIONAL TRAINS BUCUREŞTI - BRAŞOV

	1631 2	◇ 2n	♥ c	1732	♥ c	♣	◇ 2	1633	2	♣	1882
Constanţa **1680** d.	...	...	...	...	...	...	...	...	...	...	1730
Bucureşti Nord d.	0708	0745	0910	g	1015	1105	1420	1515	1646	1816	1942
Ploieşti Vest d.	0743	0823	0946	1010	1050	1157	1458	1551	1753	1908	|
Sinaia d.	0828	0913	1035	1058	1138	1255	1548	1637	1903	2023	|
Predeal d.	0853	0940	1100	1124	1203	1323	1615	1659	1940	2051	2113
Braşov a.	0931	1018	1138	1202	1243	1404	1655	1737	2030	2132	2151

	♣	2	♣	1884	1632	◇ 2	♣	♥ c	1730	◇ 2	163 ⑦r
Braşov d.	0435	0600	0641	0712	0845	1040	1400	1550	1716	1725	180
Predeal d.	0514	0643	0719	|	0921	1119	1438	1626	1752	1804	183
Sinaia d.	0538	0708	0744	|	0945	1145	1504	1651	1820	1831	190
Ploieşti Vest d.	0638	0816	0854	|	1030	1232	1612	1740	1910	1918	195
Bucureşti Nord a.	0737	0935	0949	0916	1108	1311	1713	1817	g	1958	202
Constanţa **1680** a.	...	...	...	1126	...	...	...	...	...	...	...

C – CORONA – 🛏 1, 2 cl., ▬ 2 cl., (2) Braşov - Cluj Napoca - Budapest and v.v.
D – DACIA – 🛏 1, 2 cl., ▬ 2 cl., (2) Bucureşti - Arad - Budapest - Wien and v.v; (2) Bucureşti - Budapest and v.v.
E – CORVIN – 🛏 1, 2 cl., ▬ 2 cl., (2) Cluj Napoca - Szolnok - Budapest - Wien and v.v.
F – FĂGĂRAS – (2) Braşov - Arad - Budapest and v.v.
H – HARGHITA – (12) Braşov - Miercurea Ciuc - Cluj Napoca - Budapest and v.v. Conveys (2) Târgu Mures (**1748/9**) - Cluj Napoca - Budapest and v.v, on dates in Table **1615**.
L – (12) Bucureşti - Braşov - Târgu Mureş (Table **1610**).
M – MUNTENIA – 🛏 1, 2 cl., ▬ 2 cl., (12) Bucureşti - Timişoara - Arad - Budapest and v.v.
P – (12) Târgu Mureş (Table **1610**) - Braşov - Bucuresti.
R – ISTER – 🛏 1, 2 cl., ▬ 2 cl., (2) Bucureşti - Budapest and v.v.
S – TRANSILVANIA – (12) Cluj Napoca - Oradea - Budapest - Wien and v.v.
T – TRAIANUS – (2) Bucureşti - Craiova - Timişoara - Arad - Budapest and v.v.

b – Bucureşti **Băneasa**.
c – From / to Craiova (Table **1630**).
g – From / to Galaţi via Ploieşti Sud (Table **1670**).
h – June 10 - Sept. 10.
n – Not June 12.
r – Not June 11 - Sept. 11.
t – June 11 - Sept. 11.

◐ – Via Miercurea Ciuc (Table **1610**).
◧ – Via Craiova and Timişoara (Table **1630**).
▷ – For additional trains Bucureşti - Braşov and v.v. see panel below main table.
△ – Via Râmnicu Vâlcea (Table **1645**).
▽ – Via Craiova and Târgu Jiu (Tables **1630/35**).

⊡ – For portion Mangalia - Cluj Napoca and v.v. see Table **1610**.
♥ – Operated by Softrans.
♣ – Operated by Regio Călători.
◇ – Operated by Astra Trans Carpatic.
⊕ – 🛏 1, 2 cl., ▬ 2 cl., (12)
⊗ – 🛏 1, 2 cl., ▬ 2 cl., (2)
‡ – Table **1275** for trains via Oradea.
• – Distance from Braşov.
* – Train number applies when extende to / from Constanţa or Mangalia.
■ – Subject to alteration June 18 - Nov. check times locally before travellin

BRAŞOV - MIERCUREA CIUC - TÂRGU MUREŞ / CLUJ / BAIA MARE 1610

For other trains from Bucureşti and Braşov to Cluj Napoca and Baia Mare / Satu Mare, see Table **1600**.

km			366	1543		1645		406	1942	1641	1641
		2	H■	2c	2		2	C■	J	⊗	D
	Bucureşti N **1600** d.	...	...	...	...	1229	...	...	1938b	2105	2105
0	**Braşov** d.	0555	0727	1150	...	1513	1602	1921	2227	2352	2352
32	Sfântu Gheorghe d.	0634	0756	1221	...	1550	1649	1951	2257	0027	0027
95	**Miercurea Ciuc** d.	0758	0857	1335	1550	1654	1938d	2053	0002	0126	0126
03	Siculeni d.	0807	0906	1349	1603	1707	1953	2102	0015	0138	0138
50	Gheorghieni d.	...	0956	...	1718	1813	2112	2152	0109	0233	0233
84	Topliţa d.	...	1032	...	1808	1853	2205	2228	0148	0310	0310
28	Deda a.	...	1129	...	1939	1953	...	2335	0247	0407	0407
28	Deda ▷ d.	...	1130	...	2032	2012	...	2336	0301	0410	0410
50	Reghin ▷ d.	...	|	...	2102	2039	...	|	0337*	|	|
82	**Târgu Mureş** ▷ a.	...	|	...	2146	2114	...	|	0412*	|	|
75	Sărăţel d.	...	1222	...	...	...	...	0028	0357	0511	0520
86	Bistriţa Nord a.	...	|	...	...	...	...	|	|	|	0532
00	Beclean pe Someş d.	...	1246	...	...	...	...	0051	0429	0550	0543
24	Dej Călători **1614** d.	...	1323	...	...	...	...	0128	0513	0633	0626
83	**Cluj Napoca** a.	...	1455	...	...	...	...	0235	0650*	|	0734
	Budapest Kel. **1275** a.	...	2120	...	...	...	...	0920	|	|	...
01	Jibou **1614** a.	...	...	...	...	...	...	...	0643	0815	...
58	**Baia Mare** **1614** a.	...	...	...	...	...	...	...	0755	0917	...
	Satu Mare **1625** a.	...	...	...	...	...	...	...	0945	...	...

		407	1541		1646		367	1941	1642	1642
	2	C■	2c	2Ⓐ	n	2	H■	K	⊗	D
Satu Mare **1625** d.	...	...	...	...	...	...	...	1320	...	...
Baia Mare **1614** d.	...	...	...	...	...	...	...	1501	1750	...
Jibou **1614** d.	...	...	...	...	...	...	...	1614	1902	...
Budapest Kel. **1275** d.	...	1740	...	...	...	...	0740	|	|	...
Cluj Napoca d.	...	0211	...	...	...	...	1624	1630*	|	1920
Dej Călători **1614** d.	...	0322	...	...	...	...	1736	1821	2050	2050
Beclean pe Someş d.	...	0354	...	...	...	...	1808	1853	2140	2140
Bistriţa Nord d.	...	|	...	...	...	...	|	|	|	2145
Sărăţel d.	...	0418	...	...	...	...	1831	1917	2216	2216
Târgu Mureş ▷ d.	...	|	...	*1043*	1351	*1435*	|	1920*	|	|
Reghin ▷ d.	...	|	...	*1126*	1427	*1524*	|	2007*	|	|
Deda ▷ a.	...	0518	...	*1151*	1443	*1553*	1922	2007	2307	2307
Deda d.	...	0519	...	1301	1455	1629	1923	2025	2310	2310
Topliţa d.	0421	0616	...	1413	1551	1745	2031	2120	0007	0007
Gheorghieni d.	0506	0655	...	1458	1627	1857	2108	2206	0044	0044
Siculeni d.	0616	0747	1226	1607	1733	2021	2214	2302	0203	0203
Miercurea Ciuc d.	0736a	0757	1237	1620	1743	2033	2225	2315	0213	0213
Sfântu Gheorghe d.	0855	0912	1337	1755	1846	2200	2336	0026	0313	0313
Braşov a.	0934	0942	1407	1836	1916	2250	0014	0056	0343	0343
Bucureşti N **1600** a.	...	...	...	...	2222	...	...	0357b	0627	0627

– CORONA – 1,2 cl., 2 cl., (2) Braşov - Budapest and v.v.

– 1, 2 cl., 2 cl., (2) Bucureşti - Dej Călători (**4009/10**) - Cluj Napoca and v.v; 2 cl., (2) Bucureşti - Sărăţel (**4007/8**) - Bistriţa Nord and v.v; 2 cl., (2) Bucureşti - Beclean pe Someş (**4112/3**) - Sighetu Marmaţiei and v.v.

– HARGHITA – (12) Braşov - Cluj Napoca - Budapest and v.v.

– June 11 - Sept. 11. 1, 2 cl., 2 cl., (12) Mangalia - Constanţa - Bucureşti Băneasa - Târgu Mures / Cluj Napoca / Satu Mare.

– June 10 - Sept. 10. 1, 2 cl., 2 cl., (12) Satu Mare / Cluj Napoca / Târgu Mures - Bucureşti Băneasa - Constanţa - Mangalia.

a – Arrives at 0624.

b – Bucureşti **Băneasa**.

c – Braşov - Iasi and v.v (Tables **1610** and **1650**).

d – Arrives at 1810.

▷ – Additional trains: Deda - Târgu Mureş at 0421, 0523, 0852, 1211, 1727. Târgu Mures - Deda at 0246, 0731, 1545, 1920, 2214. Journey 1hr 20m.

⊗ – 1, 2 cl., 2 cl., (2).

■ – Subject to alteration June 18 - Nov. 6; check times locally before travelling.

* – Seperate portion of train.

ADJUD - COMĂNEŞTI - MIERCUREA CIUC 1612

2nd class

km				Ⓐn	c	Ⓐn					
0	**Adjud** d.	...	0457	0644	0935	1311	1510	1743	2000	2201	...
39	Oneşti d.	...	0552	0737	1015	1405	1601	1842	2054	2330	...
75	Comăneşti d.	0438	0650	0837	1057	1504	1657	1939	2203	0026	...
09	Ghimeş d.	0527	0739	0933	1137	1552	1749	2027	...	...	...
50	Siculeni d.	0628	0907	1036	1226	...	1846	2122	...	...	...
58	**Miercuria Ciuc** a.	0637	0917	1044	1235	...	1855	...	...	...	...

					Ⓑ	c	Ⓐn			
Miercuria Ciuc d.	...	...	0725	...	...	1335	...	1616	1930	...
Siculeni d.	...	0422	0734	...	...	1349	...	1625	1944	...
Ghimeş d.	...	0529	0831	...	...	1435	1615	1724	2052	...
Comăneşti d.	0433	0626	0918	1250	...	1520	1711	1820	2144	...
Oneşti d.	0528	0730	...	1408	1545	1559	1807	1930	2337	...
Adjud a.	0619	0819	...	1459	1636	1648	1858	2020	0017	...

OR NOTES SEE TABLE 1614 BELOW

CLUJ NAPOCA - DEJ - BAIA MARE / BISTRIŢA 1614

km							4004		Ⓐ	Ⓐ	
			2	2		2	b	2	2n	2n	2
0	**Cluj Napoca** ▷ d.	0530	0633	1110	1415	1530	1543	1630	1725	1830	1940
59	Dej Călători **1610** d.	0657	0757	1236	1524	1645	1705	1754	1850	1941	2121
36	Jibou **1610** d.	0842	...	|	1709	|	1851	...	...	2119	|
93	**Baia Mare** **1610** a.	...	...	|	1824	|	2000	...	...	2216	|
84	Beclean pe Someş ▷ d.	...	...	1319	...	1730	...	...	...	...	2202
09	Sărăţel d.	...	...	1351	...	1803	...	...	...	...	2234
19	**Bistriţa** Nord a.	...	...	1405	...	1817	...	...	...	...	2250

	Ⓐ	⚒			4006					
	2n	2	2	2	b	2	2	2	2	⑦
Bistriţa Nord d.	...	0300	...	0410	...	0739	...	1532	...	...
Sărăţel d.	...	0313	...	0424	...	0749	...	1547	...	...
Beclean pe Someş ▷ d.	...	0400	...	0517	...	0826	...	1619	...	...
Baia Mare **1610** d.	...	|	...	|	0540	|	0842	|	1525	1710
Jibou **1610** d.	...	|	...	|	0650	|	1001	|	1640	1818
Dej Călători **1610** d.	0350	0446	0522	0554	0836	0915	1132	1714	1835	1954
Cluj Napoca ▷ a.	0520	0615	0650	0725	0946	1044	1240	1843	2003	2101

– Also conveys From / to Bucureşti Nord (Table **1600**).

– Braşov - Iasi and v.v (Tables **1610** and **1650**).

n – Not June 1, 13, Aug. 15, Nov. 30, Dec. 1.

▷ – For additional trains Cluj Napoca - Dej Călători - Beclean pe Someş and v.v. see Table **1660**.

CLUJ NAPOCA - RĂZBOIENI - TÂRGU MURES 1615

m									Ⓐ			
				2	2		2		2n			2
0	**Cluj Napoca** **1620** d.	...	...	...	0747	...	...	...	1510	...	1640	...
51	Câmpia Turzii **1620** d.	...	...	...	0904	...	...	...	1630	...	1742	...
69	Războieni **1620** a.	...	...	...	0924	...	...	...	1651	...	1758	...
69	Războieni d.	0342	0505	0543	...	...	1206	...	...	1656	1820	2000
88	Luduş d.	0413	0531	0614	...	...	1239	...	...	1720	1839	2034
28	**Târgu Mures** a.	0527	0630	0723	...	...	1335	...	...	1817	1933	2134

							Ⓐ		Ⓐ		
	2		2	s			2n	2	2n		2
Târgu Mures d.	0310	...	0718	...	1128	...	1430	1522	...	1934	2220
Luduş d.	0414	...	0837	...	1216	...	1529	1618	...	2035	2339
Râzboieni a.	0441	...	0902	...	1233	...	1554	1641	...	2100	0007
Râzboieni **1620** d.	...	0522	...	0908	1255	...	...	...	2025	...	0008
Câmpia Turzii **1620** d.	...	0544	...	0926	1311	...	...	...	2044	...	t
Cluj Napoca **1620** a.	...	0659	...	1038	1410	...	...	...	2157	...	...

– Not June 1, 13, Aug. 15, Nov. 30, Dec. 1.

s – To / from Sighişoara (Table **1600**).

t – To Teiuş (arrive 0055).

CLUJ NAPOCA - SIMERIA - ARAD and TIMIŞOARA 1620

m						1836	1734		1736	Ⓐ		1763
		2	2	2	2	C	b	2	b	2n	2	⊗e
	Iaşi **1660** d.	...	...	...	...	...	...	...	...	...	...	1526
	Suceava **1660** d.	...	...	...	...	...	...	...	...	...	...	1732
0	**Cluj Napoca** **1615** d.	...	...	...	0521	0740	1000	1135	1340	1510	1645	0036
51	Câmpia Turzii **1615** d.	...	...	...	0642	0843	1102	1249	1442	1630	1807	0138
	Târgu Mures **1615** d.	...	0310	...	|	|	|	|	|	|	|	|
69	Războieni **1615** a.	...	0441	...	0701	0859	1118	1309	1458	1651	1828	0153
69	Războieni d.	...	0443	...	0703	0907	1119	1310	1500	1653	1829	0154
89	Aiud d.	...	0514	...	0734	0930	1143	1343	1524	1724	1858	0219
02	Teiuş d.	...	0544	...	0813	0948	1202	1359	1544	1740	1921	0238
21	**Alba Iulia** d.	...	0620	...	0853	1012		▬	...	▬	s	0305
•	**Sibiu** **1600** d.	...	|	...	|	|		...	...	...	...	|
31	Vinţu de Jos **1600** d.	...	0643	...	0905	1022	...	...	...	...	...	0316
•	**Sibiu** a.	...	0853	...	|	|	...	...	...	...	...	|
75	**Simeria** a.	...	...	...	1007	1058	...	2	...	2	...	0353
75	**Simeria** **1600** d.	0633	...	1014	...	...	...	1135	...	1705	...	0402
84	Deva **1600** d.	0644	...	1028	...	...	...	1152	...	1718	...	0414
32	**Arad** **1600** a.	1105	...	1410	...	...	...	1541	...	2205	...	0727
90	Lugoj d.	...	...	...	...	...	...	...	...	...	...	|
49	**Timişoara** Nord a.	...	...	...	...	...	...	...	...	...	...	0853

				1735			Ⓑ		1765	1738	1835
	2		2	b		2	2	2	⊗e	b	B
Timişoara Nord a.	...	...	...	...	...	...	1334	...	1418	...	...
Lugoj d.	...	...	...	...	...	...	|	...	|	...	...
Arad **1600** d.	0529	...	0756	...	...	...	1505	...	1535	...	...
Deva **1600** d.	1000	...	1151	...	...	...	1858	...	1833	...	...
Simeria **1600** a.	1013	...	1204	...	...	...	1911	...	1843	...	...
Simeria d.	▬	...	▬	...	...	1406	...	...	1847	...	0115
Sibiu d.	...	...	...	...	...	|	...	1549	|	...	|
Vinţu de Jos **1600** d.	...	...	...	...	...	1509	...	1812	1927	...	0157
Sibiu **1600** a.	...	...	Ⓐ	...	...	|	...	|	|	...	|
Alba Iulia d.	2	s	2n	...	2	1522	...	1829	1939	...	0208
Teiuş d.	0449	0820	1052	1330	1415	1600	...	1909	2009	2104	0245
Aiud d.	0505	0835	1108	1345	1431	1615	...	1924	2025	2118	0301
Războieni a.	0541	0906	1138	1409	1501	1645	...	1954	2050	2141	0325
Războieni **1615** d.	0543	0908	1139	1410	1502	1646	...	2000	2052	2142	0326
Târgu Mures **1615** a.	0723	|	|	|	|	|	...	2134	|	|	|
Câmpia Turzii **1615** d.	...	0927	1159	1426	1522	1706	...	...	2111	2157	0347
Cluj Napoca **1615** a.	...	1038	1309	1524	1635	1817	...	...	2209	2255	0500
Suceava **1660** a.	...	...	...	...	...	...	...	...	0520	...	...
Iaşi **1660** a.	...	...	...	...	...	...	...	...	0720	...	...

– Bucureşti - Teiuş (**3081**) - Cluj Napoca (via Târgu Jiu, Table **1635**).

– Cluj Napoca - Craiova (**9010**) - Bucureşti (via Târgu Jiu, Table **1635**).

– To / from Bucureşti (via Sighişoara, Table **1600**).

– Conveys (2) Botosani - Suceava - Timişoara and v.v. (Table **1660**).

n – Not June 12.

s – To / from Sighişoara (Table **1600** / **1615**).

⊗ – 1, 2 cl., 2 cl., (2).

• – Sibiu - Vintu de Jos = *83 km*.

SIGHIŞOARA - SIBIU 1622

m		2	⚒	⚒	2			2	2		
0	**Sighişoara** **1600** d.	...	...	0707	1001	...	...	1533	1835	...	
39	Mediaş **1600** d.	0416	0545	0746	1040	1219	...	1614	1913	2002	...
50	Copşa Mică **1600** d.	0433	0600	0801	...	1249	...	1641	1928	2018	...
95	**Sibiu** a.	0547	0713	0919	...	1409	...	1804	...	2136	...

	2	2				2				2Ⓑ
Sibiu d.	...	...	0725	1215	...	1603	1731	...	1943	2315
Copşa Mică **1600** d.	0602	0756	0844	1333	...	1725	1851	...	2101	0032
Mediaş **1600** d.	0616	0810	0858	1349	...	1740	1906	...	2114	0047
Sighişoara **1600** a.	0654	0849	...	1428	...	...	1945	...	...	...

1625 TIMIŞOARA - ARAD - ORADEA - CLUJ NAPOCA / BAIA MARE

For Timişoara - Cluj Napoca via Simeria and Teiuş see Table **1620**

km			⚒		1741		378	6822	1831			78			Ⓑ	6811	⚒		1765	1533	72		1537		
		2	2k	2	⊕		B	2	n	2	2	Me		2	2n	2m	2	♡	D	①-④	Te	2			2
0	**Timişoara** Nord d.	...	...	...	...	0450	0600	...	0642	...	0802	0810	...	...	1259	...	1331	...	1418	1552	1605	1623	1701	1802	195
57	**Arad** a.	...	...	...	...	0606	0651	...	0743	...	0930	0914	...	...	1412	...	1439	...	1509	1644	1654	1729	1750	1915	211
57	**Arad** d.	...	...	...	...	0615	...	...	0757	...	▬	▬	...	...	1427	...	▬	...	1535	1659	...	▬	1801	1920	...
139	Salonta d.	...	...	...	...	0815	...	...	0925	...	...	...	...	...	1606	...	...	...	|	1821	...	Ⓐ	1932	2113	...
178	**Oradea** a.	...	...	...	b	0915	...	...	1015	...	♡	♡	...	...	1710	...	...	...	◐	1916	...	2k	2023	2210	...
178	**Oradea** 1600 d.	0250	0248	...	0717	▬	...	...	1021	...	1249	1521	...	1518	...	1635	...	1720	|	1921	...	1945	2028	...	...
281	Huedin 1600 d.	0513	|	...	|	...	...	...	1205	...	1449	1734	...	|	...	|	**686**	1934	|	|	...	|	2231	...	...
330	**Cluj Napoca** 1600 a.	0624	|	...	|	...	...	d	1256	...	1551	1835	...	|	...	|	H	2037	2209	|	...	|	2320	...	...
244	Valea lui Mihai d.	▬	0436	...	0823	...	...	1136	u	1252	...	...	...	1701	...	1756	1944	...	...	2027	...	2129	...	...	...
275	Carei d.	...	0511	...	0848	2Ⓐ	...	1211	...	1326	...	...	...	1741	...	d	2010	...	...	2051	...	2203	...	...	...
311	**Satu Mare** a.	2⚒	0556	...	0917	k	...	1256	...	1411	...	...	...	1825	...	...	2043	...	...	2121	...	2247	...	...	...
311	**Satu Mare** d.	0456	...	0800	...	1130	...	...	...	...	...	...	1610	...	...	...	2047	...	...	...	...	...	...	...	...
370	**Baia Mare** a.	0625	...	0950	...	1305	...	...	...	...	...	...	1742	...	...	...	2208	...	...	...	...	...	...	...	...

	⚒	1532		1763	⚒	⚒	1539		73		6812		687	377	Ⓐ		79	1833		1742		Ⓑ	6821	Ⓐ	
	2			D	2k	2		♡	Te	2	2m	2	H	B	2k	♡	Me		2	⊕	2	2n	2	2k	2Ⓑ
Baia Mare d.	...	...	...	...	...	...	...	...	...	...	...	0725	0800	...	1225	...	...	...	...	...	1540	...	...	...	2015
Satu Mare a.	...	...	...	...	...	...	...	...	...	...	...	0856	0922	...	1408	...	...	...	...	...	1724	...	...	...	220
Satu Mare d.	...	0200	...	...	0330	...	...	...	...	0743	...	▬	0927	...	▬	...	...	...	1545	1700	▬	...	1855	1957	...
Carei d.	...	0233	...	...	0402	...	...	...	...	0849	d	...	0959	...	...	...	...	...	1628	1737	...	...	1940	2052	...
Valea lui Mihai d.	...	0258	...	...	0445	...	...	...	...	0925	0942	...	1044	...	...	...	...	u	1700	1805	♡	...	2049	2126	...
Cluj Napoca 1600 d.	...	|	...	0036	|	...	0550	0714	...	▬	|	...	▬	...	...	1358	...	1529	|	|	1614	...	d	|	...
Huedin 1600 d.	...	|	...	|	|	...	0638	0814	...	...	|	...	...	...	...	1459	...	1621	|	|	1714	...	...	|	...
Oradea 1600 a.	...	0406	...	|	0615	...	0826	1005	...	...	1104	...	...	...	...	1656	...	1815	1827	1913	1923	...	...	2249	...
Oradea d.	...	0412	0438	◐	...	0643	0831	...	...	...	...	...	...	...	1553	...	...	1832	...	b	...	2002	...	...	...
Salonta d.	...	0504	0539	|	...	0740	0926	...	...	...	...	...	...	...	1651	...	...	1933	...	...	...	2112	...	...	...
Arad a.	...	0628	0719	0727	...	0944	1048	...	...	2	...	2	2	...	1838	...	...	2106	...	...	...	2311	...	...	...
Arad d.	0550	0633	0724	0753	...	...	1053	...	1239	1332	...	1614	1755	1839	1845	...	2050	2118	...	...	...	2333	...	...	...
Timişoara Nord a.	0711	0736	0845	0853	...	...	1142	...	1327	1450	...	1742	1903	1930	1958	...	2139	2211	...	...	...	0044	...	...	...

B – BEGA – [2] Timişoara - Arad - Budapest and v.v.
D – ▬ 2 cl., [2] Timişoara - Arad - Cluj Napoca - Iaşi and v.v; [2] Timişoara - Arad - Cluj Napoca - Suceava (**5560/6**) - Botoşani and v.v.
H – SZAMOS – [2] Baia Mare - Püspökladány (**143/144**) - Budapest - Wien and v.v.
M – MUNTENIA – 🛏 1, 2 cl., ▬ 2 cl., [12] Bucureşti - Timişoara - Arad - Budapest and v.v.
T – TRAIANUS – [2] Bucureşti - Timişoara - Arad - Budapest and v.v.

b – From / to Bucureşti (Table **1600**).
d – From / to Debrecen (Table **1277**).
e – From / to Bucureşti (Table **1630**).
k – Not June 1, 13, Aug. 15, Nov. 30, Dec. 1.
m – Currently running within Hungary only.

n – Not June 12.
u – To / from Iaşi (Table **1660**).
◐ – Via Alba Iulia and Teius (Table **1620**
⊕ – 🛏 1, 2 cl., ▬ 2 cl., [12]
♡ – Operated by Trans Feroviar Călători

1630 BUCUREŞTI - CRAIOVA - TIMIŞOARA

km				72		1823		1521	1691		349	9015	1595	1835		♥	♥	1597	11501 ◇	11502 ◇	78	1821	1920	199
		2	2	T	2	n	2Ⓑ	n		2			Ⓐk			d	d	2	⊗p	⊗j	M	⊕q	⊕g	⊕h
	Mangalia 1680 d.	...	...	...	...	...	...	...	...	...	...	...	...	...	...	...	...	...	...	...	...	...	1912	195
	Constanţa 1680 d.	...	...	...	...	...	...	...	...	...	...	...	...	...	...	...	...	...	...	1715	...	...	2045	214
0	**Bucureşti** Nord d.	...	...	0606	...	0846	...	0928	1120	1135	1345	1445	1540	1636	...	1745	1835	1945	2018	2018	2202	2341	2341	0005
51	Videle d.	...	...	0656	...	0934	...	1013	1205	1240	1437	1530	1625	1722	...	1829	1919	2030	2106	2106	2252	0031	0031	005
100	Roşiori Nord d.	...	...	0745	...	1028	...	1058	1250	1341	1526	1616	1711	1807	...	1914	2004	2123	2157	2157	2340	0120	0120	014
155	Caracal d.	...	...	0842	...	1130	...	1157	1345	1450	1626	1712	1806	1904	...	2008	2056	2218	2253	2253	0037	0221	0221	024
209	**Craiova** a.	...	...	0927	...	1215	...	f	1430	1556	1716	1804	1851	1950	...	2054	2141	2303	2340	2340	0122	0308	0308	033
209	**Craiova** 1635 d.	...	...	0935	...	1220	1335	...	1438	...	1723	1810	...	1958	...	...	...	...	2348	2348	0130	0317	0317	034
245	Filiaşi 1635 d.	...	...	1002	...	1249	1418	...	1506	...	1750	1837	...	2026	...	...	...	...	0016	0016	0157	0345	0345	040
323	Drobeta Turnu Severin d.	...	...	1153	...	e	1623	...	1654	...	1939	e	...	c	...	...	...	...	0200	0200	0347	|	|	055
347	Orşova d.	...	...	1225	1340	...	...	...	1730	...	2011	...	...	...	...	...	...	...	0238	0238	0419	|	|	063
364	Băile Herculane d.	...	...	1250	1405	...	...	...	1757	...	2036	...	...	...	...	...	...	...	0303	0303	0445	◐	◐	065
435	Caransebeş ⊡ d.	0727	1313	1411	1558	...	...	...	1920	...	2157	...	...	...	...	...	...	...	0423	0423	0616	|	|	084
474	Lugoj d.	0823	1409	1456	1656	...	...	...	2002	...	2245	...	...	...	...	...	...	...	0504	0504	0657	|	|	093
533	**Timişoara** Nord a.	0943	1527	1555	1811	...	...	...	2103	...	2351	...	...	...	...	...	...	...	0604	0604	0757	|	|	103
	Arad 1625 a.	...	...	1654	...	...	...	...	...	...	0048	...	...	...	...	...	...	...	0656	0656	0914	1133	1133	...

	1594	1994	♥	♥	⚒	9016	1824		348		1596	1522	1836 9010	1590		73			1992	1822	1922	11500 ◇	11504 ◇	79
	2	g	d	d			n	2		2	2					T	2	2	⊕g	⊕t	⊕h	⊗m	⊗j	M
Arad 1625 d.	...	...	...	...	...	...	...	...	0500	...	...	...	...	...	...	1239	...	...	...	1818	1818	2036	2036	205
Timişoara Nord d.	...	...	...	...	...	...	...	...	0605	0743	...	...	...	...	...	1355	1615	...	1828	|	|	2130	2130	220
Lugoj d.	...	...	...	...	...	...	...	...	0712	0904	...	...	...	...	...	1457	1735	...	1930	|	|	2233	2233	230
Caransebeş ⊡ d.	...	...	...	...	...	...	...	0717	0754	0957	...	...	...	...	...	1539	1828	1956	2030	|	|	2314	2314	235
Băile Herculane d.	...	...	...	...	...	...	...	0902	0916	...	...	...	...	...	...	1705	...	2147	2201	◐	◐	0036	0036	012
Orşova d.	...	...	...	...	...	...	...	0926	0940	...	...	...	...	...	...	1729	...	2213	2226	|	|	0101	0101	014
Drobeta Turnu Severin d.	...	...	...	...	0418	e	e	...	1022	...	...	...	e	1515	...	1803	...	...	2301	|	|	0136	0136	022
Filiaşi 1635 d.	...	...	...	...	0621	0702	1036	...	1214	...	...	...	1602	1706	...	1945	...	...	0048	0158	0158	0328	0328	041
Craiova 1635 a.	...	...	...	...	0705	0730	1104	...	1242	...	...	...	1630	1734	...	2013	...	...	0117	0227	0227	0402	0402	043
Craiova d.	0430	0430	0605	0705	...	0735	1109	...	1250	...	1435	f	1645	1738	...	2021	...	...	0127	0237	0237	0407	0407	044
Caracal d.	0513	0513	0647	0747	...	0818	1152	...	1333	...	1518	1657	1756	1820	...	2110	...	...	0212	0323	0323	0454	0454	053
Roşiori Nord d.	0605	0605	0732	0832	...	0911	1243	...	1427	...	1607	1753	1915	1908	...	2158	...	...	0304	0415	0415	0545	0545	062
Videle d.	0657	0657	0817	0917	...	0955	1329	...	1512	...	1650	1844	2023	1952	...	2243	...	...	0347	0501	0501	0633	0633	071
Bucureşti Nord a.	0742	0742	0901	1000	...	1038	1416	...	1600	...	1733	1931	2113	2035	...	2330	...	...	0444b	0544	0544	0720	0720	080
Constanţa 1680 a.	...	1040	...	...	...	...	...	...	...	...	...	...	...	...	...	...	...	...	0708	...	0848	...	1021	...
Mangalia 1680 a.	...	1215	...	...	...	...	...	...	...	...	...	...	...	...	...	...	...	...	0852	...	1043	...	...	...

M – MUNTENIA – 🛏 1, 2 cl., ▬ 2 cl., [12] Bucureşti - Timişoara - Arad - Budapest and v.v.
T – TRAIANUS – [12] Bucureşti - Timişoara - Arad - Budapest and v.v (✕ from Timişoara).

b – Bucureşti **Băneasa**.
c – To Teiuş / Cluj Napoca via Târgu Jiu (Table **1635**).
d – From / to Braşov (Table **1600**).
e – To / from Deva or Târgu Jiu (Table **1635**).
f – To / from Călimăneşti (Table **1645**).

g – June 11 - Sept. 11.
h – June 10 - Sept. 10.
j – June 16 - Sept. 11.
k – Not June 1, 13, Aug. 15, Nov. 30, Dec. 1.
m – Not June 16 - Sept. 11.
n – Not June 12.
p – Not June 17 - Sept. 12.
q – Not June 11 - Sept. 11.
t – Not June 10 - Sept. 10.

⊕ – 🛏 1, 2 cl., ▬ 2 cl., [12]
⊗ – 🛏 1, 2 cl., ▬ 2 cl., [2]
♥ – Operated by Softrans.
◇ – Operated by Astra Trans Carpatic.
◐ – Via Târgu Jiu and Simeria (Table **1635**).

⊡ – **CARANSEBES - REŞIŢA SUD** (journey 64–73 minutes
From Caransebeş at 0359, 0705, 1332Ⓐ, 1637, 1935.
From **Reşiţa Sud** at 0540, 0844, 1303, 1519Ⓐ, 2220.

1635 CRAIOVA - TÂRGU JIU - DEVA

km					1823				9015	1835	1821
			2	①-④	n	Ⓑn	2			u	⊕s
	Bucureşti N 1630 d.	...	...	...	0846	...	...	...	1445	1636	2341
0	**Craiova** 1630 d.	0308	...	0815	1220	1412	...	1635	1810	1958	0317
36	Filiaşi 1630 d.	0413	...	0901	1249	1511	...	1735	1837	2026	0345
107	**Târgu Jiu** a.	0547	...	1053	1432	1653	...	1910	2018	2141	0458
107	**Târgu Jiu** d.	0554	...		1436	1655	...	1912	...	2143	0500
157	Petroşani a.	0726	...		1556	1825	...	2046	...	2300	0615
157	Petroşani d.	...	0741	...	1602	...	1905	...	...	2306	0620
237	Simeria 1620 d.	...	1014	...	1751	...	2120	...	...	0115	0817
246	**Deva** 1620 a.	...	1026	...	1804	...	...	...	...	|	0827
	Cluj Napoca 1620 a.	...	|	...	...	...	...	...	...	0500	|
	Arad 1600 a.	...	1410	...	...	...	...	...	...	...	1133

	9016		1824		①-④	1836	Ⓑ	Ⓐ		182
			n				2	2n		⊕s
Arad 1600 d.	...	...	...	...	...	...	...	...	...	181
Cluj Napoca 1620 d.	...	...	...	...	...	0740	...	...	...	|
Deva 1620 d.	...	...	0553	...	...	|	...	1544	...	212
Simeria 1620 d.	...	...	0607	...	...	1118	...	1558	...	213
Petroşani a.	...	...	0807	...	...	1315	...	1826	...	232
Petroşani d.	...	0440	0812	0820	...	1320	1435	...	...	232
Târgu Jiu a.	...	0615	0925	1000	...	1435	1616	...	...	004
Târgu Jiu d.	0520	0630	0927	1010	1404	1438	1624	...	1915	004
Filiaşi 1630 d.	0702	0825	1036	1146	1531	1602	1755	...	2120	015
Craiova 1630 a.	0730	0908	1104	1230	1615	1630	1839	...	2206	022
Bucureşti N 1630 a.	1038	...	1416	...	...	2113*	...	...	...	054

n – Not June 12.
s – Extended from / to Mangalia and Constanţa on dates in Table **1630** (numbered **1920/2**).
u – Train number **3081** from Teiuş.
⊕ – 🛏 1, 2 cl., ▬ 2 cl. and [12]
* – Train number **9010** from Craiova - Bucureşti.

BUCUREŞTI - PITESTI - CRAIOVA 1640

km		9033 Ⓑ	1781	1783	1785	9035	1787 Ⓐ	9037	1789	1891	1793	1795
0	**Bucureşti** Nord ‡ d.	0600	0734	0935	1135	1336	1429	1531	1627	1730	1926	2030
108	Piteşti ‡ d.	0800	0927	1111	1327	1533	1623	1752	1803	1933	2102	2219
189	Slatina d.	0934	...	...	...	1718	...	1925	...	2103	...	...
206	Piatra Olt 1645 d.	0952	...	...	...	1743	...	1945	...	2125	...	...
250	**Craiova** 1645 a.	1038	...	...	...	1844	...	2030	...	2210	...	...

	1782	1890	1784	9034	1786 Ⓐ	1788 Ⓐ	1790	9036 Ⓑ	1792	1794	9038
Craiova 1645 d.	...	0420	...	0708	...	...	...	1212	...	...	1612
Piatra Olt 1645 d.	...	0506	...	0753	...	...	...	1306	...	...	1700
Slatina d.	...	0524	...	0816	...	...	...	1323	...	...	1722
Piteşti ‡ d.	0607	0707	0807	1009	1118	1308	1400	1502	1600	1712	1904
Bucureşti Nord ‡ a.	0745	0849	0941	1144	1252	1444	1537	1642	1748	1859	2124

‡ – Bucureşti - Piteşti (and v.v) are 2nd class only.

SIBIU - RÂMNICU VÂLCEA - CRAIOVA / BUCUREŞTI 1645

km						1522	⚒			1912	
		n	2	Ⓑm	2m	n	2m		2m	K	
0	**Sibiu** 1600 d.	0220	0255	0639	0730	...	*1151*	1546	1610	1838	...
22	Podu Olt 1600 d.	|	0336	0715	0815	...	1252	1622	1655	1916	...
83	Călimăneşti d.	0442	0530	0900	1028	1435	1449	1805	1901	2104	...
99	**Râmnicu Vâlcea** d.	0505	0546	0920	1053	1455	1515	1828	1930	2124	...
186	Piatra Olt 1640 d.	0630	0812	1045	...	1622	1738	2008	2155	2315	...
230	**Craiova** 1640 a.	|	...	1136	...	|	...	2105	2255	|	...
•32	Caracal 1630 a.	0705	...	...	...	1655	...	...	...	|	...
•17	Slatina d.	...	...	...	...	|	...	...	...	2333	...
•98	Piteşti d.	...	...	...	...	△	...	...	...	0122	...
206	**Bucureşti** Nord 1630 a.	...	...	...	...	1931	...	...	...	0258	...
	Constanţa 1680 a.	...	...	...	...	...	...	...	...	0557	...
	Mangalia 1680 a.	...	...	...	...	...	...	...	...	0742	...

		1914	⚒				1521		Ⓑ	
	2m	J	2m		2m		n	2	m	n
Mangalia 1680 d.	...	1815	...	...	...	...	...	...	...	...
Constanţa 1680 d.	...	2000	...	...	...	...	...	...	...	...
Bucureşti N 1630 d.	...	2257	...	...	...	...	0928	...	...	...
Piteşti d.	...	0110	...	...	...	...	△	...	...	...
Slatina d.	...	0246	...	...	...	...	|	...	...	...
Caracal 1630 d.	...	|	...	...	...	...	1157	...	...	1825
Craiova 1640 d.	...	|	...	...	0520	0747	|	...	1510	|
Piatra Olt 1640 d.	...	0325	0348	...	0634	0901	1234	...	1620	1909
Râmnicu Vâlcea d.	0245	0504	0625	...	0900	1035	1358	1613	1750	2040
Călimăneşti d.	0311	0523	0652	...	0927	1055	1416	1639	1809	2058
Podu Olt 1600 d.	0530	0707	0859	0935	1127	1233	...	1853	2000	2238
Sibiu 1600 a.	0612	0738	...	1016	1210	1300	...	1935	2027	2305

– June 11 - Sept. 11.
– June 10 - Sept. 10.
m – Not June 1, 13, Aug. 15, Nov. 30, Dec. 1.
n – Not June 12.
△ – Via Rosiori Nord (Table **1630**).
• – Distance from Piatra Olt.

BUCUREŞTI - BUZĂU - BACĂU - IAŞI and SUCEAVA 1650

km ☆			1830	1661	1655	1751	1663	6004	1543	1753	1657	1665	1755	1755	1555		402	1653	1667	1862	1960	1954			
															Ⓑ		①③⑤								
			2	n	n			n	2		n	n	S	S			P	⊕	⊗	h	⊙f	⊙f			
0	**Bucureşti** Nord 1600/70 d.	...	...	0624	0707	1055	1207	...	...	1353	1459	1610	1722	1722	1858	...	1920	2232	2250	...	...	...	...	...	...
59	Ploieşti Sud 1600/70 d.	...	...	0703	0733	1133	1245	...	...	1431	1537	1648	1800	1800	1943	...	2014	2313	2328	...	...	...	...	...	...
	Mangalia 1680 d.	...	...	|	|	|	|	...	...	|	|	|	|	|	...	...	|	|	|	...	2030	2145	...	...	...
	Constanţa 1680 d.	...	...	|	|	|	|	...	...	|	|	|	|	|	...	...	|	|	|	2120	2221	2325	...	...	...
	Făurei 1670 d.	...	...	|	|	|	|	...	...	|	|	|	|	|	...	...	|	|	|	2347	|	0146	...	...	...
128	**Buzău** 1670 d.	...	...	0808	0841	1241	1352	...	...	1539	1646	1757	1904	1904	...	...	2120	0021	0055	0055	|	0235	...	...	...
161	Râmnicu Sărat d.	...	...	|	0907	1308	1419	...	...	1607	1714	1824	|	|	...	...	2148	0048	0122	0122	|	0303	...	...	...
199	Focşani d.	...	...	0905	0940	1342	1452	...	...	1641	1748	1857	2000	2000	...	...	2221	0121	0155	0155	△	0337	...	...	...
219	Mărăşeşti d.	0455	...	|	0959	1401	|	...	...	1701	1808	1927	|	|	...	...	2241	0140	|	|	|	0357	...	...	...
244	Adjud d.	0528	...	|	1021	1423	|	...	1708	1724	1830	|	|	|	...	...	2304	0202	|	|	|	0419	...	...	...
303	**Bacău** d.	0638	...	|	1059	1501	|	...	1746	1811	1906	|	2112	2112	...	...	2357	0240	|	|	|	0457	...	...	...
346	Roman d.	0725	...	|	1127	1531	|	...	1815	1841	...	|	|	|	...	...	0035	0310	|	|	|	0528	...	...	...
	Galaţi d.	|	0615	|	|	|	|	1632	|	|	...	|	|	|	...	...	|	|	|	|	|	|	...	...	...
238	Tecuci d.	|	0758	0954	|	|	1541	1809	|	|	...	1951t	|	|	...	...	|	|	0244	0244	0341	|	...	...	...
288	Bârlad d.	|	0844	1036	|	|	1623	1857	|	|	...	2031	|	|	...	...	|	|	0323	0323	0421	|	...	...	...
340	Vaslui d.	|	0928	1117	|	|	1708	1946	|	|	...	2115	|	|	...	...	|	|	0407	0407	0506	|	...	...	...
408	**Iaşi** a.	0952	1033	1219	|	|	1813	2052	1944	|	...	2221	|	2320‡	...	...	0211	|	0512	0512	0612	|	...	...	...
538	*Chişinău* 1720 MD a.	...	c	...	|	|	...	...	...	|	...	...	|	...	...	...	0815	|	...	...	...	|	...	...	...
387	Paşcani 1660 d.	...	...	...	|	1558	...	...	...	1908	...	...	2214	...	...	...	...	0338	...	...	...	0556	...	...	...
432	Vereşti 1660 d.	...	...	...	1223	1639	...	...	...	1942	...	...	|	...	...	...	...	0412	...	...	...	0631	...	...	...
476	Botoşani a.	...	...	...	|	1816v	...	...	...	|	...	...	|	...	...	...	...	|	...	...	...	|	...	...	...
448	**Suceava** 1660 a.	...	...	...	1255	1650	...	...	...	1953	...	...	2253	...	...	...	...	0423	...	...	...	0642	...	...	...
450	**Suceava** Nord a.	...	...	...	...	...	...	...	...	2000	...	...	...	...	...	...	...	d	...	...	...	0650	...	...	...
499	Vadul Siret 🛃 ▲ UA a.	...	...	...	...	...	...	...	...	...	...	...	...	...	...	...	...	...	...	...	...	...	...	...	...
539	**Chernivtsi** UA a.	...	...	...	...	...	...	...	...	...	...	...	...	...	...	...	...	...	...	...	...	...	...	...	...

	1552	1658	1750	1750	1541	1660	1752	6002		1754	1556	1662	1664			1832	1952	1962	1668	1861	401	1654			
	Ⓐ										Ⓐ										②④⑦				
		n	S	S	2b	n		n	2			2				2	⊙g	⊙g	⊕	h	P	⊕			
hernivtsi UA d.	...	...	...	...	...	...	...	...	...	...	...	...	...	...	...	...	...	...	...	...	...	...	...	...	...
adul Siret 🛃 ▲ UA d.	...	...	...	...	...	...	...	...	...	...	...	...	...	...	...	...	...	...	...	...	...	...	...	...	...
uceava Nord d.	...	...	...	...	...	...	0852	...	...	...	...	...	...	...	...	...	2031	...	...	...	...	d	...	...	...
uceava 1660 d.	...	...	0544	...	...	...	0859	...	...	1247	...	...	...	...	...	...	2038	...	...	...	...	2330	...	...	...
Botoşani d.	...	...	|	...	...	...	|	...	...	1117v	...	...	...	...	...	...	|	...	...	...	...	|	...	...	...
ereşti 1660 d.	...	...	|	...	...	...	0911	...	...	1310	...	...	...	...	...	...	2050	...	...	...	...	2342	...	...	...
aşcani 1660 d.	...	...	0634	...	...	...	0944	...	...	1343	...	...	...	...	...	...	2124	...	...	...	...	0016	...	...	...
Chişinău 1720 MD d.	...	...	|	...	...	...	|	...	...	|	...	...	...	...	...	c	|	...	...	...	1720	|	...	...	...
Iaşi d.	...	...	|	0514•	0630	0620	|	0804	0911	|	...	1426	1600	1633	...	1838	|	2125	2250	2250	2330	|	...	...	...
Vaslui d.	...	...	|	|	|	0726	|	0911	|	|	...	1532	1707	|	...	1944	|	2239	2358	2358	|	|	...	...	...
Bârlad d.	...	...	|	|	|	0816	|	1003	|	|	...	1622	1753	|	...	2033	|	2331	0050	0050	|	|	...	...	...
Tecuci d.	...	...	|	|	|	0908	|	1059	|	|	...	1712t	1833t	|	...	2114	|	0012	0140	0140	|	|	...	...	...
Galaţi a.	...	...	|	|	|	|	|	1234	|	|	...	|	|	|	...	2249	|	|	|	|	|	|	...	...	...
oman d.	...	...	|	|	0800	|	1009	...	1142	1409	...	|	|	1929	...	...	2150	|	|	|	0110	0041	...	...	...
acău d.	...	0433	0728	0728	0831	|	1050	...	1231	1440	...	|	|	2030	...	...	2221	|	|	|	0150	0122	...	...	...
djud d.	...	0511	|	|	0935	|	1127	...	...	1517	...	|	|	2135	...	...	2259	|	|	|	0235	0159	...	...	...
ărăşeşti d.	...	0534	|	|	...	|	1149	...	...	1539	...	|	1911	2204	...	...	2322	|	|	|	0258	0221	...	...	...
ocşani d.	...	0552	0838	0838	...	0947	1207	...	...	1558	...	1750	1930	...	...	...	2341	△	0218	0218	0318	0239	...	...	...
âmnicu Sărat d.	...	0625	|	|	...	1020	1240	...	...	1631	...	1823	|	...	...	...	0015	|	0251	0251	0351	0312	...	...	...
uzău 1670 d.	...	0652	0936	0936	...	1047	1306	...	...	1658	...	1850	2027	...	...	...	0100	|	0326	0345	0419	0339	...	...	...
Făurei 1670 a.	...	|	|	|	...	|	|	...	...	|	...	|	|	...	...	...	0127	|	|	0411	|	|	...	...	...
Constanţa 1680 a.	...	|	|	|	...	|	|	...	...	|	...	|	|	...	...	...	0335	0503	|	0634	|	|	...	...	...
Mangalia 1680 a.	...	|	|	|	...	|	|	...	...	|	...	|	|	...	...	...	0510	0644	|	...	|	|	...	...	...
oieşti Sud 1600/70 d.	0659	0800	1040	1040	...	1155	1413	...	...	1805	1932	1957	2131	...	...	...	...	...	0435	...	0526	0447	...	...	...
ucureşti Nord 1600/70 a.	0751	0838	1118	1118	...	1235	1452	...	...	1843	2020	2035	2210	...	...	...	...	...	0513	...	0617	0527	...	...	...

BACĂU - PIATRA NEAMŢ - BICAZ

km											
	Bucureşti Nord ⊡ d.	...	...	...	...	...	...	...	1353	...	1459
0	**Bacău** d.	0403	0509	0736	...	1443	...	1647	1826	...	1936
60	Piatra Neamţ a.	0535	0640	0907	...	1614	...	1823	2008	...	2056
86	**Bicaz** a.	0616	...	...	...	...	...	...	2049	...	...

			n							
Bicaz d.	...	0639	...	...	...	...	...	...	2112	...
Piatra Neamţ d.	0447	0719	0914	...	1426	1636	1851	...	2321	...
Bacău a.	0627	0854	1027	...	1601	1806	2021	...	0051	...
Bucureşti Nord ⊡ a.	...	...	1452	...	...	...	...	...	...	...

– PRIETENIA – 🛏 1, 2 cl., (2) Bucureşti - Ungheni (106/5) - Chişinău and v.v.
– STEFAN CEL MARE EXPRESS (12) Bucureşti - Paşcani - Suceava and v.v; (12) Paşcani (1750/5) - Iaşi and v.v.
– To / from Braşov via Comăneşti (Table **1610/1612**).
– To / from Cluj Napoca via Suceava (Table **1660**).
– To / from Vatra Dornei Băi (Table **1660**).
– June 11 - Sept. 11.
– June 10 - Sept. 10.
– Not June 11 - Sept. 11.
– Not June 1, 13, Aug. 15, Nov. 30, Dec. 1.
– Not June 12.

t – Tecuci **Nord**.
v – Portion attached / detached to main train at Vereşti.
• – Calls Paşcani at 0614 after Iaşi.
‡ – Calls Paşcani at 2220 before Iaşi.
⊕ – 🛏 1,2 cl., ▬ 2 cl.,
⊗ – 🛏 1,2 cl., ▬ 2 cl., (2)
⊙ – ▬ 2 cl., (12)
△ – Via Brăila.
⊡ – See main table.
☆ – Tecuci - Galaţi 85 km. Iaşi - Roman 114 km.
▲ – 🛃: Vicsani (RO) / Vadul Siret (UA).

MD Moldova. RO Romania. UA Ukraine.

PAŞCANI - TÂRGU NEAMŢ *31 km*, ± 45 mins
From Paşcani: 0412Ⓐ m, 0720, 1645, 1912.
From Târgu Neamţ: 0522Ⓐ m, 1011, 1755, 2019.

VEREŞTI - BOTOŞANI *44 km*, ± 75 mins
From Vereşti: 0644, 0849, 1429, 1708, 1900Ⓑ.
From Botoşani: 0905, 1117, 1505, 1918, 2049Ⓑ.

1660 IAŞI - SUCEAVA - DEJ - CLUJ NAPOCA

km		1653 ⊕	2n	1833 n	1830 g	Ⓐ 2m	4113 2¶	1763 ⊗B	Ⓑ 2	
0	**Iaşi** d.	c	...	0600	1056	...	...	1526	...	...
76	Paşcani **1650** d.	0338	...	0704	1201	...	...	1631	...	...
122	Vereşti **1650** d.	0412	...	0738	1234	...	...	1704	...	...
137	**Suceava** **1650** a.	0423	...	0750	1246	...	...	1716	...	...
137	**Suceava** d.	0433	...	0803	1248	...	...	1732	...	...
187	Gura Humorului Oraş d.	0520	...	0850	1335	...	...	1823	...	...
219	Câmpulung Moldovenesc d.	0602	...	0933	1417	...	...	1906	...	...
257	Vatra Dornei Băi d.	0708	...	1036	1520	...	...	2011	...	...
351	Năsăud d.	...	...	1235	1715	...	...	2208	...	...
	Sighetu Marmaţiei d.	...	0730	|	|	1425	1610	|	2330	...
	Vişeu de Jos d.	...	0958	|	|	1623	1813	|	0124	...
357	Salva d.	...	...	1243	1723	...	2008	2216	0305	...
379	Beclean pe Someş **1610/4** d.	...	...	1306	1745	...	2106	2239	0400	...
402	Dej Călători **1610/4** d.	...	...	1341	1824	...	2144	2316	0446	...
460	**Cluj Napoca** **1610/4** a.	...	...	1450	1932	...	2303	0024	0615	...
	Oradea **1600/25** a.	...	...	1815	...	...	...	|	...	...
	Timişoara N **1620/25** a.	...	...	2211	...	...	...	0853	...	...

	⚒ 2m	Ⓐ 2m	4110 2¶	1832 g	1831	⚒ 2	1654 ⊕	1765 ⊗B	
Timişoara N **1620/25** d.	...	...	...	...	0642	...	...	1418	...
Oradea **1600/25** d.	...	...	...	...	1021	...	...	|	...
Cluj Napoca **1610/4** d.	...	...	0325	0935	1311	1435	...	2209	...
Dej Călători **1610/4** d.	...	...	0454	1045	1419	1602	...	2341	...
Beclean pe Someş **1610/4** d.	...	...	0550	1118	1452	1641	...	0015	...
Salva d.	...	...	0624	1140	1515	1735	...	0037	...
Vişeu de Jos a.	0430	0522	0801	|	|	1931	...	|	...
Sighetu Marmaţiei a.	0628	0720	0956	|	|	2129	...	|	...
Năsăud d.	...	...	...	1148	1524	...	...	0046	...
Vatra Dornei Băi d.	...	...	...	1339	1726	...	2045	0239	...
Câmpulung Moldovenesc d.	...	...	...	1440	1827	...	2148	0342	...
Gura Humorului Oraş d.	...	...	...	1525	1921	...	2234	0427	...
Suceava a.	...	...	...	1610	2006	...	2319	0513	...
Suceava **1650** d.	...	...	...	1623	2008	...	2330	0520	...
Vereşti **1650** d.	...	...	...	1634	2019	...	2342	0532	...
Paşcani **1650** d.	...	...	...	1708	2053	...	0016	0617	...
Iaşi a.	...	...	...	1811	2156	...	c	0720	...

B – Conveys 🛏 1, 2 cl., ▬ 2 cl., [2] Botoşani - Suceava - Timişoara and v.v.
c – From/to Bucureşti (Table **1650**).
g – From/to Galaţi (Table **1650**).
m – Not June 1, 13, Aug. 15, Nov. 30.
n – Not June 12.
⊕ – 🛏 1, 2 cl., ▬ 2 cl., [12]
⊗ – 🛏 1, 2 cl., ▬ 2 cl., [2]
¶ – Conveys 🛏 2 cl. [2] to/from Bucureş

1670 BUCUREŞTI - GALAŢI

km		1571 Ⓑ		1573		1575		1577		1731 b	
0	**Bucureşti** Nord **1650** d.	0530	...	0816	...	1316	...	1800	...	...	...
	Ploieşti Sud **1650** d.	0607	...	0854	...	1354	...	1840	...	1918	...
**	Buzău **1650** d.	0715	...	1002	...	1502	...	1949	...	2026	...
71	Urziceni d.	|	...	|	...	|	...	|	...	|	...
Δ	Feteşti d.	|	...	|	...	|	...	|	...	|	...
138	Făurei d.	0740	...	1028	...	1528	...	2015	...	2110	...
198	Brăila d.	0830	...	1118	...	1618	...	2105	...	2200	...
229	**Galaţi** a.	0907	...	1155	...	1655	...	2142	...	2238	...

	1570	...	1732 b	...	1572		1574		1576	
Galaţi d.	0521	...	0650	...	0830	...	1447	...	1750	...
Brăila d.	0558	...	0727	...	0907	...	1524	...	1829	...
Făurei d.	0646	...	0825	...	0957	...	1613	...	1918	...
Feteşti a.	|	...	|	...	|	...	|	...	|	...
Urziceni d.	|	...	|	...	|	...	|	...	|	...
Buzău **1650** d.	0714	...	0853	...	1032	...	1641	...	1947	...
Ploieşti Sud **1650** d.	0821	...	1002	...	1141	...	1751	...	2056	...
Bucureşti Nord **1650** a.	0903	...	...	...	1221	...	1829	...	2134	...

b – From/to Braşov (Table **1600**). ** – Buzău - Făurei: *40 km.* Δ – Feteşti - Făurei: *89 km.*

1680 BUCUREŞTI - CONSTANTA - MANGALIA

km		1952 ⊙ C•	1962 ⊙ C•	1912 C•	2 N	1941 ⊕ C•	1861 ⊙ N•	2 N	1992 ⊕ C•	1932 ⊕ C•	1922 ⊕ C•	1970 D	2 N	1581 N	1981 D	2	1994 D	1583 N	1884 A	1585 N	1928 D	2 Q	Ⓐ	2 Q	
	From:	*Suc*	*Iasi*	*Ram*		*Sat*	*Ia/S*		*Tim*	*Ora*	*Tar*	*Gal*					*Cra*		*Bra*		*Sib*				
0	**Bucureşti** Nord d.	|	|	0322	...	0407**b**	|	...	0451**b**	0515**b**	0615	|	...	0720	0720	...	0830	0830	0930	1030	1030	...	1130	...	...
146	Feteşti d.	0240	0404	0454	...	0523	0535	...	0604	0637	0742	0812	...	0837	0837	...	0946	0946	|	1145	1145	...	1257	...	...
190	Medgidia d.	0312	0435	0526	...	0554	0608	...	0637	0710	0815	0843	...	0908	0917	0938	1017	1017	|	1216	1216	...	1328	...	...
334	**Tulcea** Oraş a.	|	|	|	...	|	|	...	|	|	|	|	...	|	|	1244	|	|	|	|	|	...	|	...	...
225	**Constanţa** a.	0335	0503	0557	...	0629	0634	...	0708	0744	0848	0906	...	0931	0941	...	1040	1040	1126	1239	1239	...	1351	...	...
225	**Constanţa** d.	0350	0518	0612	0614	0650	...	0735	0725	0811	0913	...	1000	...	1006	...	1058	...	...	...	...	1252	...	1359	...
239	Eforie Nord ▷ d.	0413	0540	0643	0644	0715	...	0756	0754	0839	0941	...	1018	...	1036	...	1120	...	...	...	...	1309	...	1419	...
268	**Mangalia** a.	0510	0644	0742	0726	0818	...	0842	0852	0949	1043	...	1101	...	1128	...	1215	...	...	...	...	1356	...	1510	...

		2 N	1983 D	1587 N	2 N	2		1589	2 P	1681	2		2 ⒷT	1734											
From:														*Bra*											
Bucureşti Nord d.	1230	...	1330	1430	...	...	1530	1630	...	1730	...	1830	...	2005	...	...	...	...	...	...	...	...	...	...	...
Feteşti d.	1357	...	1448	1548	...	...	1657	|	...	1848	...	1957	...	2126	...	...	...	...	...	...	...	...	...	...	...
Medgidia d.	1428	...	1519	1619	...	1623	1728	|	...	1919	...	2028	...	2157	...	...	...	...	...	...	...	...	...	...	...
Tulcea Oraş a.	|	...	|	|	...	1929	|	|	...	|	...	|	...	|	...	...	...	...	...	...	...	...	...	...	...
Constanţa a.	1451	...	1542	1642	...	...	1751	1826	...	1942	...	2051	...	2220	...	...	...	...	...	...	...	...	...	...	...
Constanţa d.	...	1504	...	...	1654	...	...	...	1820	...	2010	...	2110	...	...	...	...	...	...	...	...	...	...	...	...
Eforie Nord ▷ d.	...	1531	...	...	1715	...	...	...	1842	...	2042	...	2130	...	...	...	...	...	...	...	...	...	...	...	...
Mangalia a.	...	1621	...	...	1757	...	...	...	1926	...	2139	...	2213	...	...	...	...	...	...	...	...	...	...	...	...

	1880	2	1580	2	2 ⚒U	1582	2 N		N	2 Q	1584	1926 2 D	1586 Ⓐ S	1996 D	2 Q	2 Q	1588	1680	2 N	1942 ⊕ D	1882 A	1930 ⊕ D	2 N	2	
Mangalia d.	...	0544	...	...	0636	...	0748	...	...	1200	...	...	...	1243	1307	1420	...	...	1534	1514	...	1602	1710	...	...
Eforie Nord ▷ d.	...	0641	...	...	0726	...	0838	...	...	1242	...	...	...	1349	1356	1504	...	...	1615	1619	...	1705	1759	...	...
Constanţa a.	...	0705	...	...	0745	...	0900	...	...	1300	...	...	...	1414	1417	1525	...	...	1635	1643	...	1729	1817	...	...
Constanţa d.	0530	...	0740	...	...	0840	...	1030	1130	...	1330	1410	1440	1440	...	...	1540	1640	...	1705	1730	1750	...	...	...
Tulcea Oraş d.	|	...	|	0509	...	|	...	|	|	...	|	|	|	|	...	...	|	|	...	|	|	|	...	1508	...
Medgidia d.	0553	...	0803	0820	...	0903	...	1053	1153	...	|	1433	1503	1503	...	...	1603	1703	...	1731	|	1813	...	1825	...
Feteşti d.	0622	...	0833	...	...	0933	...	1124	1224	...	|	1503	1532	1532	...	...	1632	1732	...	1803	|	1851	...	...	...
Bucureşti Nord a.	0741	...	0949	...	...	1049	...	1250	1350	...	1526	1619	1648	1648	...	...	1748	1848	...	1929**b**	1926	1959**b**	...	...	...
To:	*Bra*											*Sib*		*Cra*						*Sat*	*Bra*	*Ora*			

	1982 D	1972 D	1682 D	1984 D	1914 D	2 P	N	1920 ⊙ D	1862 ⊙ N	1990 ⊕ D	2 N	1960 ⊙ D	1954 ⊙ D												
Mangalia d.	...	...	...	1720	1815	1835	...	1912	...	1955	1956	2030	2145	...	...	...	...	...	...	...	...	...	...	...	...
Eforie Nord ▷ d.	...	...	...	1834	1925	1926	...	2008	...	2101	2039	2140	2246	...	...	...	...	...	...	...	...	...	...	...	...
Constanţa a.	...	...	...	1857	1944	1948	...	2029	...	2126	2059	2201	2307	...	...	...	...	...	...	...	...	...	...	...	...
Constanţa d.	1815	1838	1830	1930	2000	...	2000	2045	2120	2145	...	2221	2325	...	...	...	...	...	...	...	...	...	...	...	...
Tulcea Oraş d.	|	|	|	|	|	...	|	|	|	|	...	|	|	...	...	...	...	...	...	...	...	...	...	...	...
Medgidia d.	1853	1901	1853	1953	2026	...	2023	2108	2145	2210	...	2246	2350	...	...	...	...	...	...	...	...	...	...	...	...
Feteşti d.	1923	1931	1923	2023	2058	...	2052	2140	2219	2242	...	2320	0021	...	...	...	...	...	...	...	...	...	...	...	...
Bucureşti Nord a.	2038	|	2038	2137	2232	...	2218	2302	|	2359**b**	...	|	|	...	...	...	...	...	...	...	...	...	...	...	...
To:		*Gal*			*Ram*			*Tar*	*Ia/S*	*Tim*		*Iasi*	*Suc*												

To/From:
Bra – Braşov (Table **1600**).
Cra – Craiova (Table **1630**).
Gal – Galaţi (Table **1670**).
Iasi – Iaşi (Table **1650**).
Ia/S – Iaşi and Suceava (Table **1650**).
Ora – Oradea via Cluj Napoca (Table **1600**).
Ram – Sibiu via Râmnicu Vâlcea (Table **1645**).
Sat – Satu Mare (Tables **1600/10**).
Sib – Sibiu via Braşov (Table **1600**).
Suc – Suceava (Table **1650**).
Tar – Arad via Târgu Jiu (Tables **1600/35**).
Tim – Timişoara via Craiova (Table **1630**).

A – TOMIS EXPRES – [12] Braşov - Bucureşti - Constanţa and v.v.
C – June 10 - Sept. 10.
D – June 11 - Sept. 11.
N – Not June 11 - Sept. 11.
P – Not June 11 - Sept. 18.
Q – Not June 1 - Sept. 18.
S – Not June 13 - Sept. 9.
T – Not June 12 - Sept. 11.
U – Not June 11 - Sept. 10.

b – Bucureşti **Băneasa**.
⊕ – 🛏 1, 2 cl., ▬ 2 cl., [12]
⊗ – 🛏 1, 2 cl., ▬ 2 cl., [2]
⊙ – ▬ 2 cl., [12]
• – Previous day from point of origin.
▷ – Trains also call at Eforie Sud (7–9 minutes south Eforie Nord) and Costineşti (25–35 minutes south Eforie Nord).

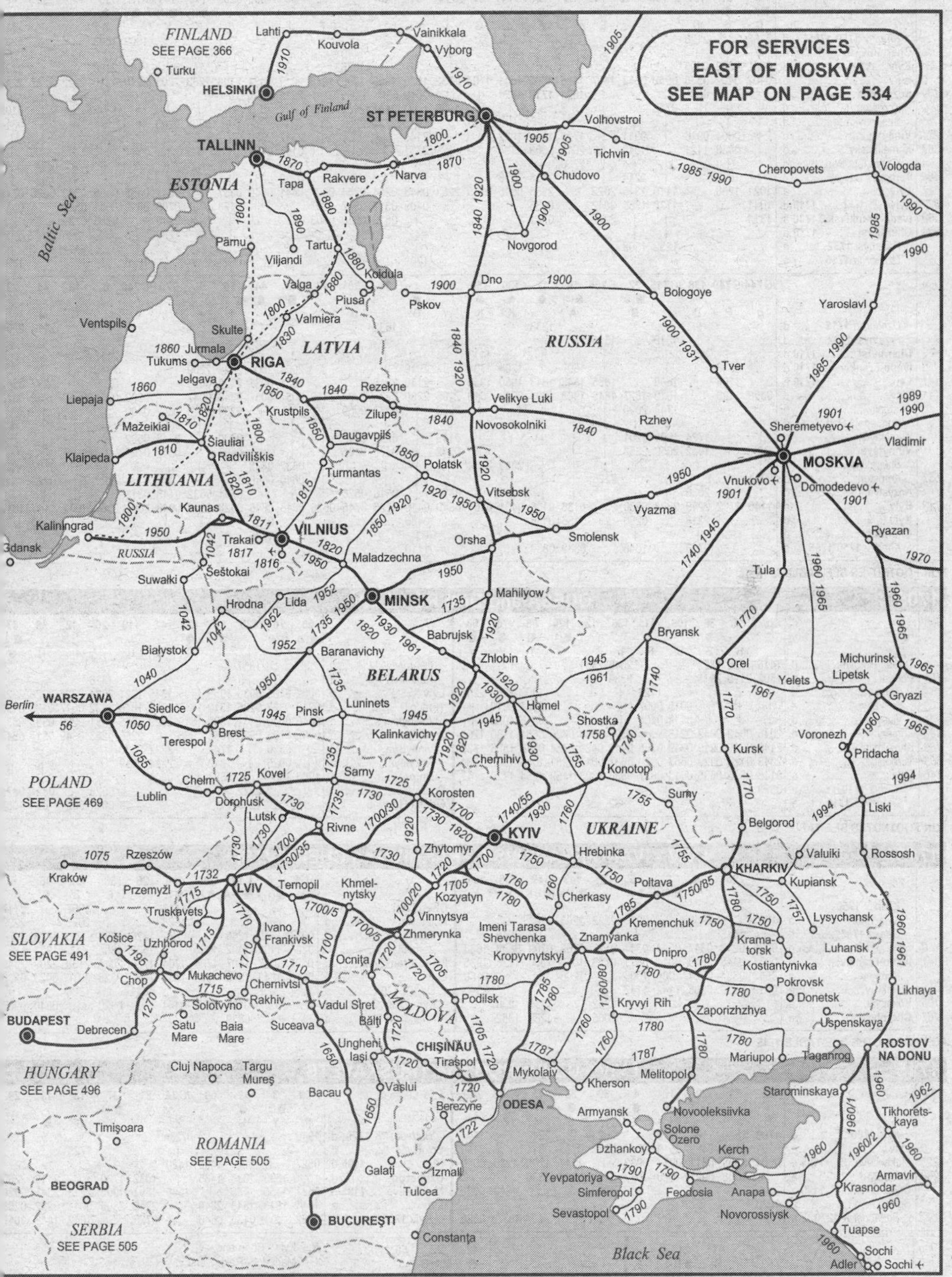

UKRAINE and MOLDOVA

perators: **UZ**: Ukrzaliznytsya, www.uz.gov.ua **CFM**: Calea Ferată din Moldova, www.railway.md Other operators as indicated in the table headings and notes.

rvices: Overnight trains convey sleeping and couchette cars and may not convey seating accommodation. Prior reservation is necessary except for travel by purely local trains. See also the panel on page 535. Trains shown as *IC* are fast day trains classified *Interciti* or *Interciti+* at premium fares.

mings: Timings shown are the latest received. Readers ae strongly recommended to check all times before travelling as there are a significant number of minor alterations which it has not been possible to show due to space constraints.

me zones: Local time is used throughout: East European Time for Ukraine and Moldova (UTC+2 winter, UTC+3 summer). Times within European Russia are in the Moskva time zone (UTC+3 all year) unless otherwise shown. As Russia and Belarus do not put their clocks forward in summer (daylight saving time), trains running between Ukraine or Moldova and Russia or Belarus change their timings by approximately one hour when clocks change (last Sunday in March and October) as shown in the tables.

1700 KYÏV - VINNYTSYA - LVIV - IVANO-FRANKIVSK — UZ, CFM

km		2	21	138	IC705	IC715	IC749	769	55	IC747	13	IC743	81	43	44	95	49	59	29	149	149	17	15	7	91	46
		■(3)	●											●	■					■(1)	■(1)	■	●			
		C	B	D			E		F	d	G	f				F	J	W		K	K		A			M
	Kharkiv **1750 1755** d.	2108	2015	2126	...	...	...	...	...	...	...	...	...	...	...	...	...	...	...	...	...	1509	1509	...	...	1236
	Chernihiv d.	|	|	|	...	...	...	...	...	...	...	...	...	...	1440	...	...	...	...	...	...	|	|	...	...	|
	Kyïv a.	0342	0342	0505	...	...	...	...	...	...	...	...	...	...	1836	...	...	...	...	...	...	2150	2150	...	...	2227
0	**Kyïv** d.	0402	0402	0535	0552	0650	1407	1425	1502	1641	1709	1732	1830	1906	1906	1948	2012	2021	2108	2203	2203	2210	2210	2222	2237	2247
159	Kozyatyn 1 d.	|	|	0806	|	|	|	1621	1710	1824	|	|	2046	|	|	|	2219	2227	|	|	|	|	|	|	|	|
	Korosten d.	|	|	|	0725	|	|	|	|	|	|	1906	|	2101	2101	2212	|	|	|	|	|	|	|	|	|	0105
	Shepetivka d.	|	|	|	|	|	|	|	|	|	2151	|	|	2321	2321	|	|	|	|	0205	0205	|	|	|	|	0314
221	**Vinnytsya** d.	|	0654	0916	|	0911	|	1720	1807	1912	|	|	2145	|	|	|	2317	2326	|	|	|	|	|	|	|	|
367	Khmelnytsky d.	|	0838	1121	|	1049	|	2017	2008	2104	|	|	2351	|	|	|	0107	0125	|	|	|	|	|	|	|	|
	Kamianets-Pod. d.	|	|	...	|	|	|	2256	|	|	|	|	|	|	|	|	|	|	|	|	|	|	|	|	|	|
486	Ternopil d.	|	1019	...	|	1214	|	...	2158	2256	|	|	0148	|	|	|	0252	0332	|	|	|	|	|	|	|	|
627	**Lviv** a.	1021	1208	...	1110	1345	2022	...	2358	0045	0135	2253	0343	0254	0254	0327	0441	0549	0357	0647	0647	0455	0455	0503	0625	0745
627	**Lviv** **1710** d.	1041	...	...	1120	1355	2042	...	0038	...	...	...	0409	0317	0317	0347	...	...	0423	0709	0709	0519	0541	0523	...	081
768	**Ivano-Frankivsk** **1710** a.	1313	...	...	|	|	2242	...	0311	...	...	...	|	0810	0810	0603	...	...	|	0940	0940	|	0756	0739	...	|
894	**Chernivtsi** **1710** a.	...	...	...	|	|	...	...	...	...	...	...	|	...	...	...	...	...	|	...	1230	|	...	1005	...	|
	Przemysl **1732** a.	...	...	...	1232	1503	...	...	...	...	...	...	|	...	...	...	...	...	|	...	...	|	...	...	...	|
	Uzhhorod **1715** a.	...	...	...	...	...	...	...	...	...	...	...	1008	...	...	...	...	...	0921	...	...	1020	...	...	...	1320

km		IC744	IC749	138	IC715	22	IC705	16	17	130	150	60	1	81	50	92	43	44	56	96	770	IC748	8	13	45	29
						■(3)		■(3)	●	●	●		●				■	●								
		g	P	D		B		A		K	K	W	C		J				F	F		e		G	M	
	Uzhhorod **1715** d.	...	...	...	...	...	...	...	1333	...	...	...	...	1632	...	...	...	...	...	...	...	...	...	...	2113	2200
	Przemysl **1732** d.	...	...	...	1310	...	1545	...	|	...	...	...	...	|	...	...	...	...	...	...	...	...	...	...	|	|
	Chernivtsi **1710** d.	...	...	...	|	...	|	...	|	...	1413	...	...	|	...	...	...	...	...	...	...	...	2117	...	|	|
0	**Ivano-Frankivsk** **1710** d.	...	0856	...	|	...	|	1607	|	1704	1704	...	1919	|	...	...	2004	2004	2044	2209	...	...	2349	...	|	|
141	**Lviv** **1710** a.	...	1106	...	1600	...	1835	1843	1843	1950	1950	...	2140	2215	...	...	0031	0031	2328	0023	...	...	0205	...	0232	0253
141	**Lviv** d.	0558	1126	...	1610	1827	1845	1903	1903	2010	2010	2105	2200	2235	2309	2319	0057	0057	2348	0047	...	0200	0225	0240	0252	0313
	Ternopil d.	|	|	...	1743	2020	|	|	|	|	|	2358	|	0037	0059	|	|	|	0200	|	...	0400	|	|	|	|
	Kamianets-Pod. d.	|	|	...	|	|	|	|	|	|	|	|	|	|	|	|	|	|	|	|	0053	|	|	|	|	|
	Khmelnytsky d.	|	|	1724	1909	2201	|	|	|	|	|	0149	|	0228	0242	|	|	|	0400	|	0345	0532	|	|	|	|
	Vinnytsya d.	|	|	1942	2050	2353	|	|	|	|	|	0342	|	0426	0435	|	|	|	0603	|	0647	0727	|	|	|	|
	Shepetivka d.	|	|	|	|	|	|	|	|	2359	2359	|	|	|	|	|	0432	0432	|	|	|	|	|	0630	0707	|
557	Korosten d.	0941	|	|	|	|	2226	|	|	|	|	|	|	|	|	|	0640	0640	|	|	|	|	|	|	0922	|
	Kozyatyn 1 d.	|	|	2036	|	|	|	|	|	|	|	0433	|	0518	0526	|	|	|	0701	0632	0745	0813	|	|	|	|
713	**Kyïv** a.	1140	1722	2249	2308	0230	2357	0136	0136	0401	0401	0640	0416	0725	0745	0626	0848	0848	0920	0840	0948	1003	0907	1042	1146	1017
	Kyïv d.	...	...	2318	...	0250	...	0156	0156	...	...	...	0436	...	...	...	...	0933	...	...	...	...	...	...	1206	...
	Chernihiv a.	...	...	|	...	|	...	|	|	...	...	...	|	...	...	...	...	1225	...	...	...	...	...	...	|	...
	Kharkiv **1750 1755** a.	...	...	0750	...	1048	...	0839	0839	...	...	...	1110	...	...	...	...	...	...	...	...	...	...	...	2210	...

FOR FOOTNOTES SEE TABLE 1715.

1705 ODESA and DNIPRO - LVIV — UZ

km		26	35	38	109	41	136	12	120	86	70	68
				●					■(1)	◧	●	■
			H	S	U	R	h		Q	T	V	V
0	**Odesa** Holovna d.	1415	1822	1822	...	...	2049	2131	...	...	...	...
186	Podilsk d.	1702	2115	2115	...	...	2336	|	...	...	...	...
	Dnipro d.	|	|	|	...	1426	|	|	...	1809	2253	2253
	Kozyatyn 1 d.	|	|	|	0015	0007	|	|	...	0443	0918	|
	Vinnytsya d.	|	|	|	0114	0105	|	|	...	0546	1023	|
387	Zhmerynka d.	2015	0042	0042	0218	|	0308	0300	0620	0651	1130	1205
486	Khmelnytsky d.	2149	0215	0215	0349	0355	0440	0429	0754	0846	1306	1339
605	Ternopil d.	2343	0423	0423	0553	0620	0632	0613	0951	1046	1512	1534
746	**Lviv** a.	0148	0635	0635	0813	0827	0836	0803	1159	1254	1720	1742
	Rakhiv **1710** a.	0829	...	...	...	...	|	...	...	...	...	...
	Chernivtsi **1710** a.	...	...	...	...	...	1352	...	...	...	...	...

	68	70	136	86	120	42	110	26	12	36	37
	■(2)	●(4)		◧	●						■(3)
	V	V	j	T	Q	R	U			H	S
Chernivtsi **1710** d.	...	...	1857	...	...	...	...	...	...	...	...
Rakhiv **1710** d.	...	...	|	...	...	...	...	1326	...	...	...
Lviv d.	0002	0105	0030	1055	1405	1546	1621	2031	2225	2328	2328
Ternopil d.	0213	0322	0235	1310	1617	1814	1843	2232	0017	0133	0133
Khmelnytsky d.	0410	0540	0431	1507	1819	2022	2045	0031	0208	0332	0332
Zhmerynka d.	0609	0733	0623	1656	1958	|	2246	0223	0349	0517	0517
Vinnytsya d.	|	0820	|	1743	...	2232	2330	|	|	|	|
Kozyatyn 1 a.	|	0925	|	1843	...	2324	0019	|	|	|	|
Dnipro a.	1950	1950	|	0537	...	0944	...	|	|	|	|
Podilsk d.	...	...	0922	...	...	...	...	0528	|	0821	0821
Odesa Holovna a.	...	...	1200	...	...	...	...	0811	0901	1054	1054

FOR FOOTNOTES SEE TABLE 1715.

1710 LVIV - IVANO-FRANKIVSK - RAKHIV and CHERNIVTSI — UZ

km		55	26	95	6	15	7	149	149	136	134
		F		F	■(3) X	● A		■(1) K	■(1) K	h	k
	Kharkiv **1750** d.	...	...	...	...	1509	...	...	...	...	...
	Kyïv **1700** d.	1502	...	1948	...	2210	2222	2203	2203	...	...
	Odesa **1705** d.	|	1415	|	...	|	|	|	|	2049	...
0	**Lviv** d.	0038	0213	0347	0541	0541	0523	0709	0709	0856	1638
141	**Ivano-Frankivsk** d.	0331	0448	0613	0811	0811	0759	1000	1000	1126	1935
	Vorokhta a.	0543	0654	0824	1006	1006	|	1206	|	|	2159
	Rakhiv a.	0719	0829	0955	1142	1142	|	...	|	|	2340
196	Kolomyia a.	...	...	...	...	...	0852	...	1113	1229	...
267	**Chernivtsi** a.	...	...	...	...	...	1005	...	1230	1352	...

	126	6	16	130	150	26	56	136	96	8
	k	●(4) X	■(3) A	● K	● K		F	j	F	
Chernivtsi d.	...	...	...	...	1413	...	...	1857	...	2117
Kolomyia d.	...	...	...	...	1528	...	...	2025	...	2229
Rakhiv d.	0037	1240	1240	...	|	1326	1630	|	1828	|
Vorokhta d.	0224	1402	1402	1430	|	1502	1805	|	1954	|
Ivano-Frankivsk d.	0502	1607	1607	1704	1704	1735	2044	2138	2209	2349
Lviv a.	0812	1843	1843	1950	1750	2011	2328	0010	0023	0205
Odesa **1705** a.	...	...	|	|	|	0811	|	1200	|	|
Kyïv **1700** a.	...	...	0136	0401	0401	...	0920	...	0840	0907
Kharkiv **1750** a.	...	...	0839	...	...	...	...	...	...	...

FOR FOOTNOTES SEE TABLE 1715.

1715 LVIV - UZHHOROD and TRUSKAVETS — UZ

km		13	81	29	17	4	59	38	46	IC33	749
					■	●		●			
		G			L	Y		S	M	Z	E
	Kyïv **1700** d.	1709	1830	2108	2210	...	2021	...	2247	...	1407
0	**Lviv** d.	0201	0409	0423	0519	0541	0615	0735	0811	...	2100
225	Mukachevo **1195** d.	0601	0853	0811	0911	0933	|	1147	1205	1230	0048
288	**Uzhhorod** a.	|	1008	0921	1020	1042	1157	1258	1320	|	|
	Chop ⊖ **1195** a.	|	...	...	...	...	1233	...	...	1340	0328
	Solotvyno 1 a.	1036	...	...	...	...	...	...	...	|	|
	Budapest K **1270** a.	...	...	...	...	...	...	...	...	1837n	0820

	149	3	17	60	IC34	81	37	13	45	29
		■(3)	●				■(3)			
	P	Y	L		Z		S	G	M	
Budapest K **1270** d.	1940	...	...	...	0723n	...	...	...	...	...
Solotvyno 1 d.	|	...	...	...	|	...	...	1725	...	...
Chop ⊖ **1195** d.	0527	...	...	1400	1420	...	...	|	...	...
Uzhhorod d.	|	1333	1333	1435	|	1632	1730	|	2113	2200
Mukachevo **1195** d.	0627	1455	1455	|	1530	1802	1902	2213	2245	2320
Lviv a.	1014	1843	1843	2040	...	2215	2300	0211	0232	0253
Kyïv **1700** a.	1722	...	0136	0640	...	0725	...	1042	1146	1017

km		49	41	21	
		J	R	● B	
	Kyïv **1700** d.	2012	...	0402	...
0	**Lviv** d.	0504	0848	1228	...
78	Sambir d.	0639	|	|	...
121	Drohobych a.	0748	1043	1416	...
133	**Truskavets** a.	0806	1101	1433	...

	42	22	50	
	R	■(3) B	J	
Truskavets d.	1315	1600	1942	...
Drohobych d.	1359	1640	2004	...
Sambir d.	|	|	2130	...
Lviv a.	1522	1807	2240	...
Kyïv a.	...	0230	0745	...

NOTES FOR TABLES 1700, 1705, 1710 and 1715.

A – Kharkiv - Rakhiv and v.v.
B – Kharkiv - Truskavets and v.v.
C – Kostiantynivka - Ivano-Frankivsk and v.v.
D – Lysychansk - Khmelnytsky and v.v. For days of running see Table **1757**.
E – 🛏 1, 2 cl. Kyiv (*IC*749) - Lviv (**145**) - Chop (**140**) - Záhony - Wien (Tables **65** and **96**).
F – Kyïv - Rakhiv and v.v.
G – Kyïv - Solotvyno and v.v.
H – Odesa - Lviv - Przemyśl and v.v.
J – Kyïv - Truskavets and v.v.
K – Poltava - Chernivtsi / Vorokhta and v.v.
L – Uzhhorod - Kharkiv and v.v.
M – Lysychansk - Uzhhorod and v.v.
P – 🛏 1, 2 cl. Wien (**149**) - Záhony - Chop (**145**) - Lviv (*IC*749) - Kyïv (Tables **65** and **96**).
Q – Zaporizhzhya - Lviv and v.v.
R – Dnipro - Truskavets and v.v.
S – Odesa - Uzhhorod and v.v.
T – Novooleksiivka - Lviv and v.v.
U – Kherson - Lviv and v.v. For days of running see Table **1760**.
V – Mariupol - Lviv and v.v.
W – Kyiv - Chop and v.v.
X – Mariupol - Rakhiv and v.v.
Y – Zaporizhzhya - Uzhhorod and v.v.
Z – LATORCA – [2] Budapest - Mukachevo and v.v.

d – ②③④⑤⑦ (daily Dec. 21 - Jan. 14 and from Apr. 1).
e – ①③④⑤⑥ (daily Dec. 21 - Jan. 14 and from Apr. 1).
f – ①④⑤⑦ until Dec. 19 and Jan. 16 - Mar. 31; ①③④⑤⑦ Dec. 20 - Jan. 14 and from Apr. 1.
g – ①②⑤⑥ until Dec. 18 and Jan. 15 - Mar. 29; ①②④⑤⑥ Dec. 20 - Jan. 14 and from Apr. 1.
h – Daily until Feb. 1; ● Feb. 2 - Mar. 26; daily from Mar. 28.
j – Daily until Jan. 31; ■(1) Feb. 1 - Mar. 25; daily from Mar. 27.
k – Rakhiv - Lviv - Mykolaiv and v.v. Not daily.
n – Budapest **Nyugati**.
◧ – For days of running see Table **1780**.
● – Even dates (see page 535).
■ – Uneven dates (see page 535).
⊖ – 🛃 for trains to / from Hungary, Slovakia.

KYÏV - ZHMERYNKA - ODESA and CHISINĂU 1720

UZ, CFM

Tiraspol and Bender (formerly Tighina) are located in the *de facto* autonomous region of Transnistria.

km		78	779		1064	6924		642	IC763		6826	803		402	145		105	1062		830			
		■(1)	⑥⑦		②④⑦	⑤⑥⑦		⑤⑥⑦				①–⑥		②④⑦									
		A	G						B					C	D								
	Moskva Kiyev. **1740** d.	...	...	...	...	...	...	...	...	...	...	...	...	...	...	...	...	...	...	...	...	...	...
	St P'burg Vit. **1920** d.	...	...	...	...	...	...	...	...	...	...	...	...	...	...	...	...	...	...	...	...	...	...
	Orsha Tsent. **1920** d.	...	...	...	...	...	...	...	...	...	...	...	...	...	...	...	...	...	...	...	...	...	...
	Minsk **1930** d.	...	...	...	...	...	...	...	...	...	...	...	...	...	...	...	...	...	...	...	...	...	...
0	**Kyïv** **1700** d.	...	0530	...	...	...	...	...	1630	...	...	...	...	...	1750	...	2115	...	...	...	...	...	...
157	Kozyatyn 1 **1700** d.	0210	1216	...	...	...	...	...	|	...	...	...	...	...	2008	...	|	...	...	...	...	...	...
221	**Vinnytsya** **1700** d.	0316	1311	...	...	...	...	...	1856	...	...	...	...	...	2108	...	0028	...	...	...	...	...	...
268	Zhmerynka **1700 1705** d.	0415	...	...	...	...	...	...	1931	...	...	...	...	...	2207	...	|	...	...	...	...	...	...
469	Podilsk **1705** d.	0723	...	...	...	...	...	...	2143	...	...	...	...	...	0118	...	0357	...	...	...	...	...	...
655	**Odesa** Holovna **1705** a.	0956	...	...	...	...	...	1831	2349	...	...	...	...	...	0349	...	0624	...	...	...	...	...	...
627	Tiraspol MD d.	...	...	...	...	...	...	2110	...	...	...	...	...	...	...	...	...	...	...	...	...	...	...
640	Bender d.	...	...	...	...	...	...	2127t	...	...	...	0505	...	...	...	...	...	...	...	...	...	...	...
422	Ocnita d.	...	...	...	...	1700	...	|	...	...	...	|	...	...	...	...	...	...	...	...	...	...	...
	Bălti Slobozia d.	...	...	...	...	1936	...	|	...	...	...	|	...	...	...	...	...	...	...	...	...	...	...
	Iasi RO d.	...	...	...	1833	...	...	|	...	...	...	|	...	0234	...	...	...	1307	...	...	...	...	...
598	Ungheni 🏛 a.	...	...	...	1959	...	...	|	...	...	...	|	...	0409	...	...	...	1443	...	...	...	...	...
598	Ungheni d.	...	...	...	...	...	...	|	...	...	0356	|	...	0610	...	...	...	...	...	1451	...	...	...
705	**Chisinău** a.	...	...	...	...	...	...	2233	...	...	0656	0705	...	0824	...	...	...	...	...	1738	...	...	...

		146	IC764		1061	642		825	6931		780	78		1063	401		6831	804		106			
					②④⑥	①⑥⑦			⑤⑥⑦		⑥⑦	●			②④⑦			⑧					
		D	E								G	A			C								
	hisinău d.	...	...	...	...	0727	...	0902	...	...	...	...	...	...	1720	...	1803	1813	...	...	...	...	...
	ngheni a.	...	...	...	...	|	...	1211	...	...	...	...	...	...	1931	...	2115	|	...	...	...	...	...
	ngheni 🏛 d.	...	...	...	0710	|	...	...	...	...	...	...	...	1614	2135	...	...	|	...	...	...	...	...
	Iasi RO a.	...	...	...	0842	|	...	...	...	...	...	...	...	1748	2305	...	...	|	...	...	...	...	...
	ălti Slobozia d.	...	...	...	...	|	...	...	0910	...	...	...	...	...	...	...	...	|	...	...	...	...	...
	cnita d.	...	...	...	...	|	...	...	1203	...	...	...	...	...	...	...	...	|	...	...	...	...	...
	Bender d.	...	...	...	...	0827t	...	...	...	...	...	...	...	...	...	...	...	2004	...	...	...	...	...
	Tiraspol MD d.	...	...	...	...	0845	...	...	...	...	...	...	...	...	...	...	...	...	...	...	...	...	...
	Odesa Holovna **1705** d.	0049	0525	...	...	1114	...	...	...	...	...	1813	...	...	...	...	...	...	...	2203	...	...	...
	Podilsk **1705** d.	0325	0736	...	...	...	...	...	...	...	...	2059	...	...	...	...	...	...	...	0035	...	...	...
	nmerynka **1700 1705** d.	0658	0957	...	...	...	...	...	...	...	...	0011	...	...	...	...	...	...	...	|	...	...	...
	innytsya **1700** d.	0745	1032	...	...	...	...	...	...	...	1346	0058	...	...	...	...	...	...	...	0354	...	...	...
	ozyatyn 1 **1700** d.	0842	|	...	...	...	...	...	...	...	1436	0155	...	...	...	...	...	...	...	|	...	...	...
	yïv **1700** a.	1052	1247	...	...	...	...	...	...	...	1647	...	...	...	...	...	...	...	...	0710	...	...	...
	Minsk **1930** a.	...	...	...	...	...	...	...	...	...	...	...	...	...	...	...	...	...	...	...	...	...	...
	Orsha Tsent. **1920** a.	...	...	...	...	...	...	...	...	...	...	...	...	...	...	...	...	...	...	...	...	...	...
	St P'burg Vit. **1920** a.	...	...	...	...	...	...	...	...	...	...	...	...	...	...	...	...	...	...	...	...	...	...
	Moskva Kiyev. **1740** a.	...	...	...	...	...	...	...	...	...	...	...	...	...	...	...	...	...	...	...	...	...	...

ODESA - BEREZYNE and IZMAÏL 1722

UZ

km		145			146	
	Kyïv **1720** d.	1750	...	**Izmaïl** d.	1844	...
0	**Odesa** Holovna d.	0424	...	**Berezyne** d.	|	...
85	Bilhorod-Dnistrovsky d.	0617	...	Artsyz d.	2058	...
175	Artsyz a.	0744	...	Bilhorod-Dnistrovsky a.	2241	...
210	**Berezyne** a.	|	...	**Odesa** Holovna a.	0014	...
282	**Izmaïl** a.	0955	...	*Kyïv* **1720** a.	1052	...

KYÏV - CHELM - WARSZAWA 1725

UZ, PKP

km		67 F 🄡			68 F 🄡	
0	**Kyïv** d.	1913e	...	*Warszawa W* **1055** d.	1749	...
510	Yahodyn 🏛 ⊡ a.	0250	...	*Lublin* **1055** d.	2015	...
510	Yahodyn 🏛 ⊡ d.	0450	...	**Chelm** d.	2118	...
542	**Chelm** a.	0640	...	Yahodyn 🏛 ⊡ a.	0059	...
	Lublin **1055** a.	0741	...	Yahodyn 🏛 ⊡ d.	0300	...
	Warszawa W **1055** a.	1008	...	**Kyïv** a.	1100	...

OTES FOR TABLES 1720, 1722 and 1725:

–. Kovel - Odesa and v.v. For days of running see Table **1730**.
– ①④⑤⑥⑦ (daily Dec. 20 - Jan. 14 and from Apr. 1).
– 🛏 🍷 Bucuresti - Iasi - Chisinău and v.v.
– Kyïv - Odesa - Izmaïl / Berezyne and v.v. (Table **1722**).
– ①②⑤⑥⑦ (daily Dec. 20 - Jan. 14 and from Apr. 1).
– KYÏV EKSPRES / KIEV EXPRESS – 🛏 1, 2 cl. Kyiv - Warszawa and v.v.
– Vinnytsya - Kyïv - Sumy (Table **1755**).
– Board train by 1848 for customs control.

t – Bender 2.
⊡ – 🏛 = Yahodyn (Ukraine) and Dorohusk (Poland). Ukraine is one hour ahead of Poland.
● – Even dates (see page 535).
■ – Uneven dates (see page 535).
* – Odessa - Tiraspol *120 km.* Chisinău via Tiraspol *698 km.*
MD – Moldova (UTC+2 in winter, UTC+3 in summer).
RO – Romania (UTC+2 in winter, UTC+3 in summer).
UA – Ukraine (UTC+2 in winter, UTC+3 in summer).

KYÏV and LVIV - RIVNE - KOVEL 1730

UZ

km		78		88		114		97				88		78		114		98		
		●		●								■(1)								
		G		H		J						H		G		J				
	Kharkiv **1750** d.	...	...	...	...	0411	...	...	...	...	**Lviv** **1735** d.	...	...	...	...	1000	...	...	...	...
0	**Kyïv** d.	...	...	...	...	1334	...	2122	...	...	Rivne **1735** d.	...	...	...	...	1408	...	...	...	...
156	Korosten d.	...	...	...	...	1825	...	2322	...	...	Kovel d.	1014	...	1814	...	1842	...	2010	...	...
311	Sarny d.	...	...	...	...	2150	...	|	...	...	Lutsk d.	1233	...	2033	...	|	...	2221	...	...
234	Kozyatyn 1 d.	0215	...	0511	...	|	...	|	...	...	Rivne d.	1349	...	2154	...	|	...	2355	...	...
	Shepetivka d.	0433	...	0739	...	|	...	0126	...	...	Shepetivka d.	1542	...	2337	...	|	...	0145	...	...
383	Rivne d.	0648	...	0950	...	|	...	0348	...	...	Kozyatyn 1 a.	1810	...	0148	...	|	...	|	...	...
461	Lutsk d.	0830	...	1132	...	|	...	0531	...	...	Sarny d.	...	...	...	...	2105	...	|	...	...
545	Kovel d.	1050	...	1334	...	0058	...	0723	...	...	Korosten d.	...	...	...	...	0055	...	0356	...	...
	Rivne **1735** d.	...	...	...	...	0442	...	...	...	...	**Kyïv** a.	...	...	...	...	0540	...	0551	...	...
744	**Lviv** **1735** a.	...	...	...	...	0846	...	...	...	...	*Kharkiv* **1750** a.	...	...	...	...	1410	...	...	...	...

– Kovel - Odesa and v.v. (Table **1720**). From Kovel on ■(1) until May 29, daily from June 1; from Odesa on ● until May 30, daily from June 1.
– Novooleksiivka - Kovel and v.v.
– Bakhmut - Kharkiv - Kyïv - Kovel - Lviv and v.v.

● – Even dates (see page 535).
■ – Uneven dates (see page 535).
* – Distance from Rivne.

PRZEMYSL - LVIV 1732

UZ, PKP

km		IC715	IC705	33025 36			35 33026	IC705	IC715	
	Wrocław **1075** d.	...	...	...	...	*Odesa* **1705** d.	1822	...	...	...
	Kraków Gł. **1075** d.	...	...	...	...	*Kyïv* **1700** d.	|	0552	0650	...
	Przemyśl **1075** a.	...	...	...	...	**Lviv** UA d.	0710	1120	1355	...
0	**Przemyśl** ⊖ PL d.	1310	1545	1859	...	**Przemyśl** ⊖ PL a.	0902	1232	1503	...
98	**Lviv** UA a.	1600	1835	2240	...	*Przemyśl* **1075** d.	...	...	...	...
	Kyïv **1700** a.	2308	2357	|	...	*Kraków Gł.* **1075** a.	...	...	...	...
	Odesa **1705** a.	...	...	1054	...	*Wrocław* **1075** a.	...	...	...	...

MINSK - LVIV 1735

km				
0	Mahilyow d.	...	**Lviv** **1730** d.	...
243	**Minsk** a.	...	Rivne **1730** d.	...
243	**Minsk** d.	...	Sarny ‡ UA d.	...
384	Baranavichy Pol. d.	...	Luninets BY d.	...
500	Luninets BY d.	...	Baranavichy Pol. d.	...
607	Sarny ‡ UA d.	...	**Minsk** a.	...
694	Rivne **1730** d.	...	**Minsk** d.	...
901	**Lviv** **1730** a.	...	Mahilyow a.	...

OTES FOR TABLES 1732 AND 1735

– 🏛 = Medyka / Mostiska II.
– 🏛 : Horyn (BY) / Udrytsk (UA).

BY – Belarus (UTC+3 all year).
PL – Poland (UTC+1 winter, UTC+2 summer).
UA – Ukraine (UTC+2 winter, UTC+3 summer).

1740 MOSKVA - KONOTOP - KYÏV

RZhD, U

km																					
0	**Moskva** Kiyevskaya ..... **1945** d.	...	...	...	...	...	...	...	...	...	*Lviv* **1700** ..... d.	...	...	...	...	...	...	...	...	...
387	Bryansk Orlovski ..... **1945** d.	...	...	...	...	...	...	...	...	...	*Chisinău* **1720** ..... d.	...	...	...	...	...	...	...	...	...
504	Suzemka ..... RU d.	...	...	...	...	...	...	...	...	...	*Odesa* **1720** ..... d.	...	...	...	...	...	...	...	...	...
519	Zernove ..... UA d.	...	...	...	...	...	...	...	...	...	**Kyïv** ..... d.	...	...	...	...	...	...	...	...	...
651	Konotop ..... d.	...	...	...	...	...	...	...	...	...	Konotop ..... d.	...	...	...	...	...	...	...	...	...
872	**Kyïv** ..... a.	...	...	...	...	...	...	...	...	...	Zernove ..... UA d.	...	...	...	...	...	...	...	...	...
	Odesa **1720** ..... a.	...	...	...	...	...	...	...	...	...	Suzemka ..... RU d.	...	...	...	...	...	...	...	...	...
	Chisinău **1720** ..... a.	...	...	...	...	...	...	...	...	...	Bryansk Orlovski ..... **1945** d.	...	...	...	...	...	...	...	...	...
	Lviv **1700** ..... a.	...	...	...	...	...	...	...	...	...	**Moskva** Kiyevskaya ..... **1945** a.	...	...	...	...	...	...	...	...	...

RU – Russia (Moskva Time UTC+3). UA – Ukraine (UTC+2 in winter, UTC+3 in summer).

1750 KYÏV - POLTAVA - KHARKIV and KOSTIANTYNIVKA

U

km		17	16	130	1	IC722	IC724	IC726	64	138
		●	■(3)	●	●				●(4)	
		A	B	F	C					D
	Lviv **1700** ..... d.	1903	1903	2010	2200	...	...	...	...	...
0	**Kyïv** ..... d.	0156	0156	0421	0436	0645	1320	1803	2312	2318
150	Hrebinka ..... d.	|	|	0626	|	|	|	|	|	0131
335	**Poltava** Kyivska ..... a.	0603	0603	1013	0833	0955	1632	2113	0319	0459
335	**Poltava** Kyivska ..... **1785** d.	0623	0623	...	0854	1000	1634	2115	0339	0519
493	**Kharkiv** ..... **1785** a.	0839	0839	...	1110	1136	1811	2251	0600	0750

	IC725	IC723	149	IC721	17	15	2	138	63
			■(1)		■	●	■(3)		■(
			F		A	B	C	D	
Kharkiv ..... **1785** d.	0711	1305	...	1836	1509	1509	2108	2126	23
Poltava Kyivska ..... **1785** a.	0851	1444	...	2016	1720	1720	2320	2344	01
Poltava Kyivska ..... d.	0853	1446	1603	2018	1740	1740	2340	0004	01
Hrebinka ..... d.	|	|	1929	|	|	|	|	0315	|
Kyïv ..... a.	1203	1756	2133	2329	2150	2150	0342	0505	06
Lviv **1700** ..... a.	...	...	0647	...	0455	0455	1021	...	

km		1	IC712	114	126
		●C	d	E	
	Lviv **1700/30** ..... d.	2200	...	1000	...
0	**Kyïv** ..... d.	0436	0610	0445	2220
150	Hrebinka ..... d.	|	|	0839	0025
335	**Poltava** Kyivska ..... d.	0854	0923	1158	0314
493	**Kharkiv** ..... d.	1133	|	1439	|
	Bakhmut ..... a.	|	|	1855	|
635	Slovyansk ..... a.	1451k	1212	...	0822
649	Kramatorsk ..... a.	1514	1224	...	0841
679	Kostiantynivka ..... a.	1550	1248	...	0919
744	**Donetsk** ◇ ..... a.	...	...	...	...

	IC712	2	126	114
	d	■(3) C		E
Donetsk ◇ ..... d.	...	...	...	...
Kostiantynivka ..... d.	1618	1631	2212	...
Kramatorsk ..... d.	1642	1704	2250	...
Slovyansk ..... d.	1654	1728k	2311	...
Bakhmut ..... d.	|	|	|	2325
Kharkiv ..... a.	|	2043	|	0346
Poltava Kyivska ..... d.	1945	2340	0427	0709
Hrebinka ..... d.	|	|	0727	1050
Kyïv ..... a.	2302	0342	0944	1309
Lviv **1700/30** ..... a.	...	1021	...	0846

A – Uzhhorod - Lviv - Kyïv - Kharkiv and v.v.
B – Kharkiv - Kyïv - Lviv - Rakhiv and v.v.
C – Kostiantynivka - Kharkiv - Kyïv - Lviv - Ivano-Frankivsk and v.v.
D – Lysychansk - Kharkiv - Kyïv - Khmelnytsky and v.v. For days of running see Table **1757**.
E – Bakhmut - Kharkiv - Kyïv - Kovel - Lviv and v.v.
F – Poltava - Kyïv - Lviv - Ivano-Frankivsk - Vorokhta and v.v.
d – ①③④⑤⑥⑦ (daily Dec. 20 - Jan. 14 and from Apr. 1).
k – Slovyansk **Kurort**.
◇ – Service suspended.
● – Even dates (see page 535).
■ – Uneven dates (see page 535).

1755 KYÏV - SUMY - KHARKIV

U

km		22		45		780		780		
		■(3)				①-⑤		⑥⑦		
		G		H				J		
	St Peterburg **1930** ..... d.	...	...	...	...	...	...	...	...	...
	Minsk **1930** ..... d.	...	...	...	...	...	...	...	...	...
	Homel **1930** ..... d.	...	...	...	...	...	...	...	...	...
	Lviv **1700** ..... d.	1827	...	0252	...	...	...	...	...	...
0	**Kyïv** ..... d.	0250	...	1206	...	1707	...	1707	...	...
221	Konotop ..... d.	0524	...	1522	...	1938	...	1938	...	...
350	Sumy ..... d.	0752	...	1830	...	2145	...	2145	...	...
552	**Kharkiv** ..... a.	1048	...	2210	...	...	...	...	...	...
	Lysychansk **1757** ..... a.	...	...	0415	...	...	...	...	...	...

	779		779		46		21		
			⑥⑦				●		
			J		H		G		
Lysychansk **1757** ..... d.	...	...	...	...	0653	...	...	...	...
Kharkiv ..... d.	...	...	...	...	1236	...	2015	...	...
Sumy ..... d.	0530	...	0530	...	1637	...	2305	...	...
Konotop ..... d.	0734	...	0734	...	1919	...	0112	...	...
Kyïv ..... a.	1000	...	1000	...	2227	...	0342	...	...
Lviv **1700** ..... a.	...	...	...	...	0745	...	1208	...	...
Homel **1930** ..... a.	...	...	...	...	...	...	...	...	...
Minsk **1930** ..... a.	...	...	...	...	...	...	...	...	...
St Peterburg **1930** ..... a.	...	...	...	...	...	...	...	...	...

G – Kharkiv - Kyïv - Truskavets and v.v.
H – Lysychansk - Kharkiv - Kyïv - Lviv - Uzhhorod and v.v.
J – Vinnytsya (Table **1720**) - Kyïv - Sumy.
● – Even dates (see page 535).
■ – Uneven dates (see page 535).

1757 KHARKIV - LYSYCHANSK

UZ

km		138	90	45		46	138	90
		Kf	Tf	L		L	Ke	Te
0	**Kharkiv** ..... d.	0820	0915	2240	**Luhansk** ◇ ..... d.	...	...	...
129	Kupiansk-Vuslov ..... d.	1101	1217	0130	Lysychansk ..... d.	0653	1510	1704
254	Lysychansk ..... a.	1350	1534	0415	Kupiansk-Vuslov ..... d.	0957	1817	2004
382	**Luhansk** ◇ ..... a.	...	...	...	**Kharkiv** ..... a.	1206	2035	2211

K – Lysychansk - Kharkiv - Kyïv - Khmelnytsky and v.v.
L – Lysychansk - Kharkiv - Kyïv - Lviv - Uzhhorod and v.v.
T – Lysychansk - Kharkiv - Odesa and v.v.
e – ● Dec., Feb. Mar., June; ■ Jan., Apr, May.
f – ■ Dec., Feb. Mar., June; ● Jan., Apr, May.

1758 KYÏV - SHOSTKA

U

km		786			786	
0	**Kyïv** ..... d.	0720	...	**Shostka** ..... d.	1212	...
197	Bakhmach Pas. ..... d.	0955	...	Konotop ..... d.	1323	...
221	Konotop ..... d.	1018	...	Bakhmach Pas. ..... d.	1347	...
302	**Shostka** ..... a.	1127	...	**Kyïv** ..... a.	1619	...

◇ – Service suspended.
● – Even dates (see page 535).
■ – Uneven dates (see page 535).

1760 LVIV and KYÏV - MYKOLAIV - KHERSON

U

km		126	139		102	52	110		752	148
			●							
		M ◧	S				N			P
	Lviv 1705 ..... d.	0832	...	...	...	...	1621	...	...	...
	Ternopil ..... d.	1032	...	...	...	...	1843	...	...	...
	Khmelnytsky ..... d.	1226	...	...	...	...	2045	...	...	...
	Zhmerynka ..... d.	1415	...	...	...	...	2246	...	...	...
	Vinnytsya ..... d.	1510	...	...	...	...	2330	...	...	...
	Kozyatyn 1 ..... d.	1609	...	...	...	...	0021	...	...	...
0	**Kyïv** ..... d.	|	...	...	2034	2340	|	...	1415	1555
	Konotop ..... d.	|	...	...	|	|	|	...	|	|
	Cherkasy ..... d.	|	...	...	|	|	|	...	|	2009
216	Im. T. Shevchenka ..... d.	2036	...	...	0006	|	0444	...	|	2055
308	Znamyanka ..... d.	|	...	...	|	|	|	...	|	...
448	Kryvyi Rih Hol. ..... d.	0057	0126	...	0450	|	|	...	|	...
651	**Mykolaiv** ..... a.	0553j	0643j	...	|	0642	1005	...	2133	...
706	**Kherson** ..... a.	0443	0545	...	0846	0737	1115	...	2227	...

	148	751		109	102		134	140	5
								■(1)	
	Q			R			M ◧	S	
Kherson ..... d.	...	0913	...	1315	1814	...	1936k	2107k	23
Mykolaiv ..... d.	...	1007	...	1419	|	...	1830	1946	00
Kryvyi Rih Hol. ..... d.	...	|	...	|	2212	...	2345	0121	|
Znamyanka ..... d.	...	|	...	|	|	...	|	...	|
Im. T. Shevchenka ..... d.	0407	|	...	2018	0229	...	0424	...	|
Cherkasy ..... d.	0457	|	...	|	|	...	|	...	|
Konotop ..... a.	|	|	...	|	|	...	|	...	|
Kyïv ..... a.	0924	1705	...	|	0519	...	|	...	07
Kozyatyn 1 ..... d.	...	...	...	0015	...	...	0850	...	...
Vinnytsya ..... d.	...	...	...	0114	...	...	0951	...	...
Zhmerynka ..... d.	...	...	...	0218	...	...	1055	...	...
Khmelnytsky ..... d.	...	...	...	0349	...	...	1226	...	...
Ternopil ..... d.	...	...	...	0553	...	...	1415	...	...
Lviv 1705 ..... a.	...	...	...	0813	...	...	1618	...	...

M – Rakhiv - Lviv - Mykolaiv and v.v.
N – ■(1) until May 29; daily from June 1.
P – To Odesa (a. 0458) via Voznesensk (d. 0157). From Kyiv on ● until May 26, daily from May 27.
Q – From Odesa (d. 2011) and Voznesensk (d. 2319). From Odesa on ■(1) until May 25, daily from May 26.
R – ● until May 30; daily from June 2.
S – Dnipro - Kryvyi Rih - Mykolaiv and v.v. (Table **1782**).
j – Calls after Kherson.
k – Calls after Mykolaiv.
◧ – Not daily.
● – Even dates (see page 535).
■ – Uneven dates (see page 535).

MOSKVA - OREL - BELGOROD - KHARKIV 1770

RZhD, UZ

km		81*AJ*	715	741	719	743	119*AJ*	721	99*MJ*	71*VJ*	141*VJ*		
			❖	❖	❖			❖	B				
	St Peterburg Gl. **1900** d.	2004	...	...	...	...	0012	...	...	...	...	...	...
0	**Moskva** Kurskaya d.	0459v	0848	1147	1418	1548	1007v	1635	1942v	2030v	2100v	...	...
194	Tula I d.	0734	1104	1401	1630	1759	1411	1852	2245	2331	0021	...	...
383	Orel d.	0930	1300	1551	1817	1946	1736	2044	0100	0136	0330	...	...
537	Kursk d.	1105	1442	1727	2004	2117	2050	2228	0257	0328	0947	...	...
697	Belgorod § RU d.	1319	...	1920	2148	2300	2338	...	0530	0610	...	...	...
781	**Kharkiv** § UA a.	...	...	...	...	...	...	...	...	...	...	...	...

	722	720	744	742	120*VJ*	716	82*VJ*	141*MJ*	72*VJ*	100*VJ*		
	❖	❖	❖	❖		❖				A		
harkiv § UA d.	...	...	...	...	...	...	...	...	...	...	...	...
elgorod § RU d.	...	0432	0729	1215	0938	...	1715	...	2210	2320	...	...
ursk d.	0540	0621	0914	1413	1228	1701	1931	1933	0045	0204	...	...
rel d.	0724	0759	1045	1550	1516	1844	2107	0143	0229	0349	...	...
ula I d.	0913	0951	1228	1738	1806	2038	2257	0423	0433	0556	...	...
loskva Kurskaya a.	1128	1210	1446	1958	2120v	2252	0136v	0734v	0803v	0909v	...	...
St Peterburg Gl. **1900** a.	...	...	...	...	0616x	...	1035	...	...	...	...	...

A – ● Dec., Feb., Mar., June; ■ Jan., Apr., May.
B – ■ Dec., Feb., Mar., June; ● Jan., Apr., May.

v – Moskva **Vostochny**.
x – St Peterburg **Ladozhski**.

● – Even dates (see page 535).
■ – Uneven dates (see page 535).
❖ – *Lastochka* (Swallow) fast day train.
§ – Krasny Khutor (RU) / Kozacha Lopan (UA).

RU – Russia (Moskva Time UTC + 3).
UA – Ukraine (UTC + 2 winter, UTC + 3 summer).

LVIV and KYÏV - DNIPRO - ZAPORIZHZHYA - MELITOPOL and MARIUPOL 1780

UZ

km		*IC*732	*IC*738	68	70	84	*IC*740	*IC*734	10	12	72	92	116	136	38	88	86	76	80	54	54	120	42	3	6
				■(2)	●(4)						●					■(1)						●		■(3)	●(4)
												Cf	A	Bd		D	N			h	h		F	E	L
	Lviv 1705 d.	...	...	0002	0105	...	...	...	...	...	...	...	...	...	...	...	1055	...	...	...	...	1405	1546	1920	1920
•	Kozyatyn 1 1705 d.	...	...	|	0927	...	...	...	...	...	...	...	...	...	...	1830	1845	...	...	...	...	|	2326	|	|
0	**Kyïv** d.	0708	1150	|	|	1632	1722	1735	1903	1925	1952	...	2001	2001	2107	|	|	2128	2305	...	...	|	|	|	|
216	Im. Tar. Shevchenka d.	0933	1444	1414	1414	1920	1948	2001	|	2218	2245	...	2257	2257	|	0027	0027	0102	|			|	0406	|	|
	Odesa Holovna d.	|	|	|	|	|	|	|	|	|	|	1714	|	|	|	|	|	|	|	2156	2156	|	|	|	|
	Kropyvnytskyi d.	|	|	|	|	|	|	|	|	|	|	2303	|	|	|	|	|	|	|	0338	0338	0359	|	|	|
308	Znamyanka d.	1046	|	1603	1603	2041	|	2113	|	2341	|	0015	0025	0025	|	0152	0152	0230	|	0453	0453	0502	0539	|	|
353	Oleksandria d.	1121	1634	1646	1646	2124	|	2248	|	0024	|	0059	0108	0108	|	0236	0236	0319	0402	0536	0536	0550	0630	|	|
490	**Kryvyi Rih** Hol. a.	|	|	|	|	|	2328	|	|	|	0255	|	|	|	|	|	|	0620	|	|	1049	0857	|	|	|
496	Kamianske d.	1253	|	1914	1914	2341	...	2321	|	0238	|	0320	0330	0330	0412	0500	0500	...	0615	0919	...	|	0902	0833	0833
534	**Dnipro** Hol. a.	1318	1902	1950	1950	0014	...	2346	0205	0310	|	0352	0402	0402	0445	0537	0537	...	0648	1001	...	|	0944	0912	0912
534	**Dnipro** Hol. d.	1328	1907	2010	2010	0034	...	2356	0215	0328	|	...	0429	0451	0500	0557	0557	...	...	...	...	|	...	0927	0927
735	Pokrovsk a.	|	|	|	|	|	...	0209	|	|	|	...	|	0746	|	|	|	...	...	...	...	|	...	|	|
658	**Zaporizhzhya** I a.	1447	2036	2211	2211	0215	...	...	0342	0509	0714	...	0609	...	0636	0754	0754	...	...	...	...	1405	...	1104	1104
658	**Zaporizhzhya** I 1782 d.	...	...	2226	2226	0219	...	...	0402	0517	...	...	...	...	...	0759	0759	...	...	...	...	...	...	...	1107
770	Melitopol 1782 a.	...	...	|	|	|	...	...	|	0656	...	...	...	...	...	0946	0946	...	...	...	...	...	...	...	|
861	Novooleksiivka 1782 a.	...	...	|	|	|	...	...	|	0805	...	...	...	...	...	1105	1105	...	...	...	...	...	...	...	|
033	**Mariupol** 1782 a.	...	...	0532	0532	0850	...	...	0910	...	...	...	...	...	...	...	...	...	...	...	...	...	...	...	1726

	116	135	*IC*739	*IC*733	*IC*738	41	*IC*732	120	4	6	86	88	53	564	76	92	79	72	70	68	38	10	12	84
								■(1)	●	■(3)		●						■(1)	●	■				
	A	Be				F			E	L	M	D	j	j		Cg								
ariupol 1782 d.	...	...	...	...	...	...	...	...	...	0808	...	...	...	...	...	...	...	...	1315	1315	...	1715	...	1750
Novooleksiivka 1782 d.	...	...	...	...	...	...	...	...	...	|	1308	1308	...	...	...	...	...	...	|	|	...	|	1910	|
Melitopol 1782 d.	...	...	...	...	...	...	...	...	...	|	1438	1438	...	...	...	...	...	...	|	|	...	|	2031	|
aporizhzhya I 1782 a.	...	...	...	...	...	...	...	...	...	1441	1600	1600	...	...	...	...	...	...	2017	2017	...	2237	2155	0018
aporizhzhya I d.	0005	...	...	...	0816	...	1533	1220	1445	1445	1605	1605	...	...	...	...	...	1947	2037	2037	2138	2257	2203	0023
Pokrovsk d.	|	2250	...	0438	|	...	|	|	|	|	|	|	...	...	...	...	...	|	|	|	|	|	|	|
nipro Hol. a.	0150	0200	...	0652	0949	...	1653	|	1634	1634	1749	1749	...	...	...	...	...	|	2233	2233	2311	0029	2338	0213
nipro Hol. d.	0242	0242	...	0702	0954	1426	1703	|	1639	1639	1809	1809	1910	...	...	2157	2230	|	2253	2253	2326	0034	2358	0233
amianske d.	0322	0322	...	0729	|	1501	1730	|	1711	1711	1847	1847	1948	...	...	2234	2305	|	2332	2332	2357	|	0032	0309
Kryvyi Rih Hol. d.	|	|	0605	|	|	|	|	1711	|	|	|	|	|	1810	2058	|	|	0014	|	|	|	|	|	|
leksandria d.	0556	0556	|	0903	|	1736	1903	2011	|	|	2152	2152	2253	2253	0004	0114	0124	|	0216	0216	|	|	0253	0531
namyanka d.	0642	0642	|	0937	|	1819	1937	2113	|	|	2237	2237	2357	2357	0054	0218	|	|	0310	0310	|	|	0346	0613
Kropyvnytskyi d.	|	|	|	|	|	|	|	2203	|	|	|	|	0043	0043	|	0306	|	|	|	|	|	|	|	|
Odesa Holovna a.	|	|	|	|	|	|	|	|	|	|	|	|	0615	0615	|	0910	|	|	|	|	|	|	|	|
n. Tar. Shevchenka d.	0804	0804	0939	1038	1401	1957	2038	|	|	|	0024	0044	...	...	0211	...	|	0417	0451	0451	|	|	0502	0729
yiv a.	1104	1104	1154	1252	1635	|	2253	|	|	|	|	|	...	...	0458	...	0552	0658	|	|	0609	0711	0808	1007
Kozyatyn 1 1705 a.	...	...	...	...	...	0005	...	|	|	|	0441	0449	...	...	...	...	...	...	0916	|	...	...	...	...
Lviv 1705 a.	...	...	...	...	...	0827	...	1159	0515	0515	1254	...	...	...	...	...	...	...	1720	1742	...	...	...	...

– Kyïv - Zaporizhzhya - Berdiansk (a. 1145 / d. 1850) and v.v.
– Kyïv - Dnipro - Pokrovsk - Avdiivka (a. 0920 / d. 2145) and v.v.
– Odesa - Dnipro - Kostiantynivka (a. 0856 / d. 1707) and v.v.
– Novooleksiivka - Kovel and v.v.
– Zaporizhzhya - Lviv - Uzhhorod and v.v.
– Dnipro - Lviv - Truskavets and v.v.
– Mariupol - Dnipro - Lviv - Rakhiv and v.v.

M – ● until Mar. 26; ■(3) Mar. 29 - May 27; daily from May 28.
N – ■(1) until Mar. 25; ● Mar. 28 - May 26; daily from May 27.

d – ● Dec., Feb., Mar., June; ■ Jan., Apr., May.
e – ■ Dec., Feb., Mar., June; ● Jan., Apr., May.
f – ■(1) until May 27; daily from May 28.
g – ● until May 28; daily from May 29.

h – ● until May 26; daily from May 27.
j – ■(1) until May 25; daily from May 26.
● – Even dates (see page 535).
■ – Uneven dates (see page 535).
• – Kozyatyn - Im. Tarasa Shevchenka *304 km*.

KHARKIV - ZAPORIZHZHYA - MELITOPOL and MARIUPOL 1782

km		793	77	139	795	81				
		⑤–⑦	●	●						
				P		j				
0	**Kharkiv** d.	0645	1623	1707	1927	2201	...	...	...	...
**	**Dnipro** Hol. a.	1031	|	2127	2321	|	...	...	...	...
	Dnipro Hol. d.	1051	|	2147	...	|	...	...	...	...
327	**Zaporizhzhya** I a.	|	2102	|	...	0229	...	...	...	...
327	**Zaporizhzhya** I 1780 d.	|	2107	|	...	0234	...	...	...	...
	Kamianske d.	1123	|	2223	...	|	...	...	...	...
512	**Kryvyi Rih** Hol. a.	1327	|	0046	...	|	...	...	...	...
439	Melitopol 1780 a.	...	|	...	...	0412	...	...	...	...
530	Novooleksiivka 1780 a.	...	|	...	...	0525	...	...	...	...
702	**Mariupol** 1780 a.	...	0425	...	...	...	...	...	...	...

	82	78	140	796	794				
		■(5)	■(1)		⑤–⑦				
	h		P						
Mariupol 1780 d.	...	2044	...	...	...	...	...	...	...
Novooleksiivka 1780 d.	2243	|	...	...	...	...	...	...	...
Melitopol 1780 d.	0010	|	...	...	...	...	...	...	...
Kryvyi Rih Hol. d.	|	|	0201	...	1536	...	...	...	...
Kamianske d.	|	|	0424	...	1741	...	...	...	...
Zaporizhzhya I 1780 a.	0139	0348	|	...	|	...	...	...	...
Zaporizhzhya I d.	0144	0353	|	...	|	...	...	...	...
Dnipro Hol. a.	|	|	0455	...	1813	...	...	...	...
Dnipro Hol. d.	|	|	0515	0623	1833	...	...	...	...
Kharkiv a.	0614	0824	0945	1007	2221	...	...	...	...

– Dnipro - Kryvyi Rih - Mykolaiv and v.v. (Table **1760**).
– Lysychansk - Kharkiv - Odesa and v.v.
– ● Dec., Feb., Mar., June; ■ Jan., Apr., May.
– ■ Dec., Feb., Mar., June; ● Jan., Apr., May.

h – ● until May 26; daily from May 27.
j – ■(1) until May 25; daily from May 26.
k – ● Apr., May; ■ June.
m – ■ Apr., May; ● June.

● – Even dates (see page 535).
■ – Uneven dates (see page 535).
** – Karkhiv - Dnipro Hol.: *300 km*.

KHARKIV - KREMENCHUK - ODESA 1785

UZ

km		7	59	90	791
			k	Qd	
0	**Kharkiv** d.	2143	2246	2246	...
140	Poltava Pivdenna d.	0002	0113	0113	...
259	**Kremenchuk** d.	0143	0318	0318	2349
353	Znamyanka a.	0320	0514	0514	0138
	Kyïv a.	|	|	|	0527
407	Kropyvnytskyi a.	0409	0557	0557	...
765	**Odesa** Holovna a.	0919	1147	1147	...

	90	60	8	792
	Qe	m		
Odesa Holovna d.	1920	1920	2225	...
Kropyvnytskyi d.	0107	0107	0321	...
Kyïv d.	|	|	|	1742
Znamyanka d.	0218	0218	0422	2156
Kremenchuk d.	0422	0422	0546	2314
Poltava Pivdenna d.	0623	0623	0747	...
Kharkiv a.	0828	0828	0945	...

OR FOOTNOTES SEE TABLE 1782.

ODESA - MARIUPOL 1787

UZ

km		142
		●
0	**Odesa** Hol. d.	1425
232	Mykolaiv d.	1853
287	Kherson d.	2012
643	**Zaporizh.** 1 a.	0247
643	**Zaporizh.** 1 d.	0254
1018	**Mariupol** a.	1009

	142
	■(1)
Mariupol d.	1626
Zaporizh. 1 a.	2321
Zaporizh. 1 d.	2329
Kherson d.	0651
Mykolaiv d.	0829
Odesa Hol. a.	1236

FOR FOOTNOTES SEE TABLE 1782.

1790 CRIMEAN PENINSULA

Subject to alteration UTC+3 Crimean Railwa

km										
0	Simferopol ...... d.	0755	0950	1405	1725	Sevastopol .... d.	0523	1007	1215	1732
78	Sevastopol ..... a.	0949	1145	1608	1927	Simferopol .... a.	0730	1207	1420	1925

km										
0	Simferopol ...... d.	0545	0955	1440	1750	Yevpatoriya ...... d.	0535	0825	1505	182
79	Yevpatoria ...... a.	0720	1135	1615	1920	Simferopol .... a.	0710	1010	1640	200

km												
0	Armyansk .... d.	...	...	...	...	...	0735	...	...	...	...	1535
78	Dzhankoy .... ● d.	...	0305	...	0600	...	0914	...	1405	...	...	1715
	Feodosia ..... ● d.	0305	|	...	|	...	|	1035	|	...	1555	|
179	Vladyslavivka .. ● d.	0343	0508	0659	0838	0855	1119	1127	1615	1630	1633	1909
196	Feodosia ..... ● a.	|	|	0730	|	0930	1150	|	|	1705	|	1940
270	Kerch .... a.	0540	0710	...	1100	...	...	1315	1840	...	1815	...

Kerch .... d.	...	...	0835	1155	...	1415	...	1620	...	2120	221
Feodosia ..... ● d.	0625	0810	|	|	1520	|	...	|	1750	|	|
Vladyslavivka .. ● d.	0702	0840	1118	1340	1555	1616	...	1813	1834	0018	003
Feodosia ..... ● a.	|	▬	|	1410	...	|	...	1840	|	|	010
Dzhankoy .... ● d.	0905	0955	1310	...	...	1810	1930	...	2045	0215	...
Armyansk .... a.	...	1120	...	...	...	...	2055	...	...	...	...

km												
	Feodosia .... ● d.	...	...	0555	...	...	...	1435	...	1720	...	2005
	Vladyslavivka .. ● d.	...	...	0622	...	...	...	1513	...	1748	...	2036
0	Solone Ozero .. d.	...	0600	|	0900	...	1505	|	...	|	2005	...
20	Dzhankoy .... ● d.	0520	0626	0812	0930	1210	1535	1710	1740	2000	2035	...
111	Simferopol .... a.	0700	0750	0940	1110	1350	1715	1830	1920	2120	2200	...

Simferopol .... d.	0605	0820	0930	1150	1230	1450	1740	1850	1955	2030	...
Dzhankoy .... ● d.	0805	1000	1115	1332	1416	1635	1916	2053	2135	2215	...
Solone Ozero .. a.	0830	|	...	|	1440	...	1940	2115	|	...	...
Vladyslavivka .. ● d.	...	1159	...	1514	...	...	...	...	2312	...	...
Feodosia .... ● a.	...	1230	...	1545	...	...	...	...	2340	...	...

● – For all trains see middle and lower panels.

☛ For through trains from Moskva and St Peterburg see Table **1960**.

LITHUANIA, LATVIA and ESTONIA

SEE MAP PAGE 52

Operators: Lithuania: **LTG Link** (Lietuvos Geležinkeliai), www.litrail.lt Latvia: **LDz** (Latvijas Dzelzcelš), www.ldz.lv Estonia: **Elron** www.elron.ee

Services: Trains convey first- and second-class seating unless indicated otherwise. International trains to and from Belarus, Russia and Ukraine are composed of Russian-style sleepir cars (for details of train types and classes of travel see the panel on page **535**).

Timings: Schedules are the latest available and may be subject to alteration at any time. Timings are expressed in local time at the station concerned (time comparison chart: page 4

Reservations: Reservation is compulsory for travel by international services to / from Russia.

1800 RIGA - TALLINN, ST PETERBURG, VILNIUS and KALININGRAD

Riga and Vilnius coach stations are close to the railway stations. Tallinn coach station is 3 km from the railway station (by tram).

RIGA - PÄRNU - TALLINN ⊡
Journey time: 4h 25m
From **Riga**: 0235, 0700, 1230, 1800.
From **Tallinn**: 0700, 1230, 1800, 2230.

TALLINN - ST PETERBURG ⊡
Journey time: 6h 15m - 8h 00m.
From Tallinn: 0700, 1015, 1545.
From St Peterburg: 0730, 1715, 2230.

RIGA - VILNIUS ⊡
Journey time: 4h 10m - 4h 30m
From Riga: 0255, 0930, 1630.
From Vilnius: 1000, 1730, 2230.

RIGA - KALININGRAD ⊙
Journey time: 7h 30m.
From Riga: 2330⑥.
From Kaliningrad: 2230⑦.

⊡ – Operator: Lux Express (www.luxexpress.eu).

⊙ – Operator: Ecolines (www.ecolines.net).

1810 VILNIUS - ŠIAULIAI - KLAIPEDA

LTG

km			①–⑤					④–⑦	①–⑥		⑦	
0	**Vilnius** .... **1811** d.	...	0555	0725	1101	1240	...	1435	...	1701	...	1815
67	Kaišiadorys ... **1811** d.	...	|	0809	|	1324	...	1519	...	|	...	1900
	Kaunas ..... **1811** d.	...	|	|	|	|	...	|	1650	|	1742	|
192	Radviliškis .... d.	0550	0804	0941	|	1455	1620	1652	1846	|	1926	2031
212	Šiauliai .... d.	0620	0821	0959	1318	1514	1653	1709	1905	1918	1943	2050
376	**Klaipeda** .... a.	0854	1010	1155	1500	1718	1942	...	...	2100	...	2248

	①–⑤	①–⑥			⑤–⑦			⑦			
Klaipeda .... d.	0525	...	0630	0745	...	1100	1250	...	1525	1657	180
Šiauliai .... d.	0721	0735	0830	1017	1105	1244	1452	1505	1807	1843	200
Radviliškis .... d.	0737	0804	0848	1050	1125	|	1510	1524	1840	|	202
Kaunas .... **1811** a.	|	1000	|	...	|	|	|	1715	...	|	|
Kaišiadorys .. **1811** d.	|	...	1029	...	1304	|	1644	...	...	|	215
Vilnius .... **1811** a.	0949	...	1111	...	1350	1506	1727	...	...	2104	224

km			①–⑤	⑥⑦			⑥⑦			①–⑥	⑦	
	Panevežys .... d.	...	0745	...	...	1110	1252	...	1515	...	...	1900
0	Radviliškis .... d.	0655	0834	0855	...	1201	1338	1520	1604	...	...	1949
20	Šiauliai .... d.	0731	0909	0927	1035	1236	1413	1542	1633	1935	2015	2024
98	**Mažeikiai** .... a.	0845	...	...	1149	...	...	1656	...	2049	2129	...

	①–⑤	①–⑥	⑦				Ⓑ	⑤–⑦			
Mažeikiai .... d.	...	0555	0555	...	0857	...	1325	...	...	1710	...
Šiauliai .... d.	0610	0707	0727	0930	1006	1300	1438	1520	1715	1823	205
Radviliškis .... d.	0644	...	0758	1004	...	1334	1503	1554	1749	1856	211
Panevežys .... a.	0732	...	...	1052	...	1422	...	1643	1840	...	...

☛ Trains not calling at Vilnius are 3rd class only. The ④–⑦ Vilnius - Šiauliai and ⑤–⑦ Šiauliai - Vilnius trains are 2nd class only.

1811 VILNIUS - KAUNAS

LTG

km		①–⑤														①–⑤									
0	**Vilnius** .... **1810** d.	0455	0602	0650	...	0800	0910	1010	...	1130	1230	1330	...	1442	1530	1620	...	1645	1730	1750	...	1855	2015	2125	...
67	Kaišiadorys .... **1810** d.	0548	0659	0745	...	0852	0957	1058	...	1228	1316	1418	...	1535	1618	1706	...	1738	1816	1850	...	1943	2110	2215	...
104	**Kaunas** .... a.	0618	0729	0816	...	0920	1020	1127	...	1258	1339	1446	...	1606	1646	1730	...	1806	1843	1921	...	2011	2138	2242	...

			①–⑤																①–⑤					
Kaunas .... d.	0510	0550	0630	...	0700	0800	0900	...	1001	1110	1220	...	1320	1430	1530	...	1700	1750	1810	...	1845	1943	2048	...
Kaišiadorys .... **1810** d.	0537	0621	0657	...	0733	0829	0929	...	1034	1137	1253	...	1346	1458	1559	...	1731	1817	1841	...	1914	2010	2119	...
Vilnius .... **1810** a.	0633	0724	0745	...	0831	0918	1020	...	1138	1230	1344	...	1446	1549	1652	...	1831	1903	1944	...	2008	2058	2216	...

1815 VILNIUS - TURMANTAS - DAUGAVPILS

3rd class LTG

km						①–⑤				
0	**Vilnius** .... d.	0545	0740	1100	1510	1628	1742	1950	2120	...
101	Ignalina .... d.	0727	0923	1243	1646	1805	1921	2125	2239	...
147	Turmantas 🏛 .... a.	0803	1004	1323	1725	...	1959	2201	...	...
174	**Daugavpils** .... a.	...	...	...	...	...	...	...	...	...

Daugavpils .... d.	...	...	...	...	...	...	...	...	...
Turmantas 🏛 .... d.	0435	0525	...	0920	1242	1605	1802	...	...
Ignalina .... d.	0511	0603	0640	1002	1321	1646	1838	...	...
Vilnius .... a.	0640	0737	0830	1138	1453	1822	2020	...	...

1816 VILNIUS AIRPORT

LTG

3rd class. Journey time 7-8 minutes. *4 km.* Some trains continue to / from Jašiunai.
From Vilnius: 0557, 1520, 1640, 1710, 1750①–⑥.
From Vilnius ✈: 0609①–⑤, 0719, 1305①–⑤, 1540, 1730, 1801, 1909①–⑤.

1817 VILNIUS - TRAKAI

LTG

2nd class. Journey time 33-36 minutes. *27 km.*
From Vilnius: 0613①–⑤, 0700, 0923, 1115, 1300, 1626, 1736, 1919.
From Trakai: 0655①–⑤, 0820, 1010, 1230, 1525, 1735, 1845, 2042.

1820 KYÏV - MINSK - VILNIUS - RIGA

Kyïv .... d.	...	...	...
Kalinkavichy .... d.	...	...	...
Zhlobin .... d.	...	...	...
Minsk .... a.	...	...	...
Minsk .... d.	...	...	...
Maladzechna .... d.	...	...	...
Vilnius .... d.	...	...	...
Siauliai .... d.	...	...	...
Riga .... a.	...	...	...

Riga .... d.	...	...	...
Siauliai .... d.	...	...	...
Vilnius .... d.	...	...	...
Maladzechna .... d.	...	...	...
Minsk .... a.	...	...	...
Minsk .... d.	...	...	...
Zhlobin .... d.	...	...	...
Kalinkavichy .... d.	...	...	...
Kyïv .... a.	...	...	...

🏛 at Slovechno (Ukraine / Belarus), Kena (Belarus / Lithuania), Yonishkis (Lithuania / Latvia).
For other trains: Kyïv - Minsk via Homel see Table **1930**, Minsk - Vilnius see Table **1950**.

RIGA - VALMIERA - VALGA 1830

Dz

km							Ⓐ			⑦	
0	**Riga** ⊙ d.	0646	1046	1246	1446	1544	1716	1816	1846	2116	2146
53	Sigulda ⊙ d.	0756	1154	1356	1556	1652	1804	1911	1954	2210	2256
93	Cesis d.	0838	1233	...	...	...	1833	1943	2031	2242	...
21	Valmiera d.	0906	1302	...	...	...	1859	2010	2104	2308	...
64	Lugaži LV a.	...	1336	...	...	...	...	2044	...	...	...
68	**Valga** EE a.	...	1342	...	...	...	...	2050	...	...	...

		Ⓐ						Ⓐ	Ⓒ	⑤
Valga EE d.	...	0513	...	...	...	...	...	1503	1653	...
Lugaži LV d.	...	0520	...	...	...	...	...	1510	1700	...
Valmiera d.	0457	0554	0631	...	1001	...	...	1544	1734	2016
Cesis d.	0528	0620	0659	...	1030	...	...	1612	1802	2045
Sigulda ⊙ d.	0609	0652	0727	0908	1112	1408	1610	1652	1842	2120
Riga ⊙ a.	0715	0745	0815	1015	1215	1515	1715	1745	1945	2215

– Additional trains available. EE – Estonia. LV – Latvia. For trains Valga - Tallinn see Table **1880**.

RIGA - REZEKNE - ST PETERBURG and MOSKVA 1840

Dz, RZhD

km		806	702		62AJ Sko ②④	64AJ Sko ⑦		816		
0	**Riga** 1850 d.	0931	1201	...	...	...	...	1701	...	...
51	Lielvarde 1850 d.	1022	|	...	...	...	...	1752	...	...
29	Krustpils ⊡ 1850 d.	1136	1341	...	...	...	...	1900	...	...
24	**Rezekne 2** d.	1307	1446	...	...	...	...	2031	...	...
79	Zilupe LV d.	1410	...	...	...	...	...	2134	...	...
06	Sebezh RU d.	...	...	...	...	...	...	...	...	...
47	Novosokolniki d.	...	...	...	...	...	...	...	...	...
93	Dno d.	...	...	...	...	...	...	...	...	...
38	**St Peterburg** Vitebski a.	...	...	...	...	...	...	...	...	...
46	**Velikiye Luki** d.	...	...	...	1955	1955	...	...	...	...
87	Rzhev d.	...	...	...	0113	0113	...	...	...	...
22	**Moskva** Belorusskaya a.	...	...	...	0718	0718	...	...	...	...

	815		61AJ Sko ①③	63AJ Sko ⑤		701	805		
Moskva Belorusskaya d.	...	...	2114	2114	...	...	...	...	...
Rzhev d.	...	...	0330	0330	...	...	...	...	...
Velikiye Luki d.	...	...	0750	0750	...	...	...	...	...
St Peterburg Vitebski d.	...	...	...	...	...	...	...	...	...
Dno d.	...	...	...	...	...	...	...	...	...
Novosokolniki d.	...	...	...	...	...	...	...	...	...
Sebezh RU d.	...	...	...	...	...	...	...	...	...
Zilupe LV d.	0324	...	...	...	...	...	1503	...	...
Rezekne 2 d.	0429	...	...	...	...	1516	1608	...	...
Krustpils ⊡ 1850 d.	0559	...	...	...	...	1624	1743	...	...
Lielvarde 1850 d.	0710	...	...	...	...	|	|	...	...
Riga 1850 a.	0800	...	...	...	...	1800	1930	...	...

⊡ – Station for Jekabpils. LV – Latvia (UTC+2 winter, UTC+3 summer). RU – Russia (Moskva Time UTC+3).

RIGA - DAUGAVPILS - MINSK 1850

Dz, BCh

km		802	806	702	808	814	704	816	818	824
0	**Riga** 1840 d.	0731	0931	1201	1301	1531	1631	1701	1801	2131
51	Lielvarde 1840 d.	0822	1022	|	1352	1628	|	1752	1848	2235
29	Krustpils ⊡ 1840 d.	0937	1136	1341	1503	1741	1811	1900	1959	2348
18	**Daugavpils** LV d.	1057	...	...	1633	...	1918	...	2119	...
79	Polatsk § BY d.	...	...	...	...	...	...	...	...	...
78	Maladzechna d.	...	...	...	...	...	...	...	...	...
55	**Minsk** a.	...	...	...	...	...	...	...	...	...

	821	815	703	817	801	701	805	813	807
Minsk d.	...	...	...	...	...	...	...	...	...
Maladzechna d.	...	...	...	...	...	...	...	...	...
Polatsk § BY d.	...	...	...	...	...	...	...	...	...
Daugavpils LV d.	...	...	0621	0739	1306	...	...	...	1737
Krustpils ⊡ 1840 d.	0441	0559	0724	0901	1428	1624	1743	1758	1900
Lielvarde 1840 d.	0555	0710	|	1012	1542	|	|	1911	2012
Riga 1840 a.	0700	0800	0900	1100	1630	1800	1930	2000	2100

⊡ – Station for Jekabpils. § – Border: Indra (LV) / Bihosava (BY). LV – Latvia (UTC+2 winter, UTC+3 summer). BY – Belarus (UTC+3 all year).

RIGA - LIEPAJA, JURMALA, TUKUMS and SAULKRASTI 1860

Dz

km		⑦	⑤		⑥	⑦
0	**Riga** § d.	1349	1825	**Liepaja** d.	0806	1730
43	Jelgava § d.	1427	1903	Saldus d.	0931	1850
125	Saldus d.	1550	2022	Jelgava § d.	1049	2008
223	**Liepaja** a.	1710	2142	**Riga** § a.	1125	2043

§ – Riga - Jelgava: 1 - 2 trains per hour.

RIGA - SLOKA ◧ - TUKUMS 1* *65 km* Journey 1h 25m

From **Riga**: 0530, 0730, 0930, 1130, 1300, 1430, 1600, 1700, 1745 Ⓐ, 1900, 2030, 2200, 2245, 2345.

From **Tukums 1**: 0444, 0538, 0612, 0709 Ⓐ, 0813, 0948, 1114, 1346, 1512, 1645, 1743, 1912 Ⓐ, 1944, 2117, 2213.

RIGA - SLOKA ◧ 1 - 2 trains per hour. Journey ± 50 mins.

RIGA - SAULKRASTI *48 km* Journey 1 hour

From **Riga**: 0537 Ⓐ, 0607, 0737, 0809, 1009, 1207, 1407, 1507, 1607, 1707, 1737, 1837, 1937, 2037, 2137, 2337.

From **Saulkrasti**: 0626, 0754, 0856, 0957, 1156, 1257, 1356, 1556, 1655, 1756, 1827, 1928, 2027, 2130, 2228.

Certain trains continue to/from Skulte, *56 km* ± 70 mins.

◧ – Jurmala's 33 km coastline has several stations; principal stations are Majori (*22 km*) and Sloka (*32 km*). There is no station called Jurmala. * – Most continue to/from Tukums 2.

TALLINN - NARVA 1870

Elron

For bus service Tallinn - St Peterburg see Table **1800**.

km		220	20 ⊖		222	224		22 ⑤⑦ ⊖	226	
0	**Tallinn** 1880 d.	0755	1114	...	1430	1726	...	1940	2155	...
77	Tapa 1880 d.	0853	1202	...	1528	1824	...	2028	2253	...
04	Rakvere d.	0911	1219	...	1547	1843	...	2045	2311	...
55	Jõhvi d.	0958	1255	...	1632	1928	...	2121	...	...
09	**Narva** EE d.	1030	1323	...	1704	1959	...	2149	...	...
	St Peterburg Glavni RU a.	...	...	...	...	...	...	...	...	...
33	Bologoye 1900 a.	...	...	...	...	...	...	...	...	...
37	Tver 1900 a.	...	...	...	...	...	...	...	...	...
54	Moskva Oktyabrskaya 1900 a.	...	...	...	...	...	...	...	...	...

	221	223		21 ⊖	225		227	23 ⑤⑦ ⊖	
Moskva Oktyabrskaya 1900 d.	...	...	...	...	...	...	...	...	...
Tver 1900 d.	...	...	...	...	...	...	...	...	...
Bologoye 1900 d.	...	...	...	...	...	...	...	...	...
St Peterburg Glavni RU d.	...	...	...	...	...	...	...	...	...
Narva EE d.	...	0717	...	1114	1430	...	1725	2027	...
Jõhvi d.	...	0748	...	1141	1501	...	1757	2054	...
Rakvere d.	0617	0833	...	1219	1547	...	1844	2134	...
Tapa 1880 d.	0636	0853	...	1236	1606	...	1905	2151	...
Tallinn 1880 a.	0733	0950	...	1323	1703	...	2002	2238	...

⊖ – Classified *Ekspress* (higher fares). EE – Estonia (UTC+2 winter, UTC+3 summer). RU – Russia (Moskva Time UTC+3).

TALLINN - TARTU - VALGA 1880

Elron

km		210	10 ⊖	12 ⊖	14 ⊖	212	16 ⊖	18 ⊖	214	60 ⊖	216	62 ⊖
0	**Tallinn** 1870 d.	0617	0812	0935	1213	1311	1411	1523	1649	1744	1917	2056
77	Tapa 1870 d.	0715	0900	1023	1301	1409	1459	1611	1748	1832	2015	2144
42	Jõgeva d.	0803	0938	1104	1339	1455	1537	1651	1837	1911	2101	2222
90	**Tartu** a.	0839	1008	1135	1410	1530	1610	1723	1917	1941	2137	2252

	211	11 ⊖	13 ⊖	15 ⊖	213	17 ⊖	19 ⊖	61 ⊖	215	63 ⊖	217
Tartu d.	0625	0734	0854	1011	1200	1412	1536	1635	1731	1854	2010
Jõgeva d.	0701	0804	0924	1041	1235	1442	1606	1708	1807	1927	2046
Tapa 1870 d.	0751	0843	1007	1120	1324	1521	1646	1748	1855	2006	2135
Tallinn 1870 a.	0848	0930	1054	1207	1421	1608	1733	1835	1952	2053	2232

km		330	332	334	336
0	**Tallinn** § d.	0812	1213	1523	1744
90	**Tartu** d.	1011	1414	1726	1944
15	Elva d.	1038	1441	1753	2011
73	**Valga** a.	1123	1526	1839	2056
73	**Valga** 1830 d.	*1504*a	*1654*c	...	...
41	**Riga** 1830 a.	*1745*a	*1945*c	...	...

	331	333	335	337
Riga 1830 d.	...	...	...	*1046*
Valga 1830 a.	...	...	...	*1341*
Valga d.	0619	0727	1257	1738
Elva d.	0705	0813	1343	1825
Tartu a.	0731	0839	1409	1851
Tallinn § a.	0930	1054	1608	2053

km		382	384 Ⓒ	386 Ⓐ	388 Ⓒ
0	**Tallinn** § d.	0812	1213	1523	1744
190	**Tartu** d.	1023	1428	1729	1930
233	Põlva d.	1109	1514	1815	2016
262	Orava d.	1133	1538	1839	2040
275	**Koidula** a.	1150	1555	1849	2050
282	**Piusa** a.	1158	1603	...	...

	381 Ⓐ	385 Ⓒ	387 Ⓐ	389 Ⓒ
Piusa d.	...	1210	1445	1704
Koidula d.	0559	1225	1500	1719
Orava d.	0609	1235	1510	1729
Põlva d.	0633	1259	1534	1753
Tartu a.	0719	1345	1620	1839
Tallinn § a.	0930	1608	1835	2053

a – Ⓐ only.
c – Ⓒ only.

⊖ – Classified *Ekspress* Tallinn - Tartu (higher fares apply).
§ – See panel above. Note different train numbers apply Tallinn - Tartu and v.v.

TALLINN - VILJANDI 1890

Elron

km										⊖	
0	**Tallinn** d.	0740	0836	1030	1142	1445	1631	1736	1909	2014	2217
54	Rapla d.	0837	0936	1131	1234	1538	1732	1829	2011	2104	2319
98	Türi d.	0911	...	1204	1308	1611	1804	1902	2043	2133	2351
51	**Viljandi** a.	0952	...	...	1349	1652	...	1943	...	2206	...

	Ⓐ	Ⓒ			⊖					
Viljandi d.	...	...	0630	...	0837	1044	...	1450	1819	...
Türi d.	0604	0620	0712	0803	0910	1126	1229	1532	1902	2055
Rapla d.	0637	0653	0745	0837	0939	1200	1302	1606	1935	2131
Tallinn a.	0728	0753	0835	0942	1028	1251	1402	1657	2027	2231

⊖ – Classified *Ekspress* (higher fares).

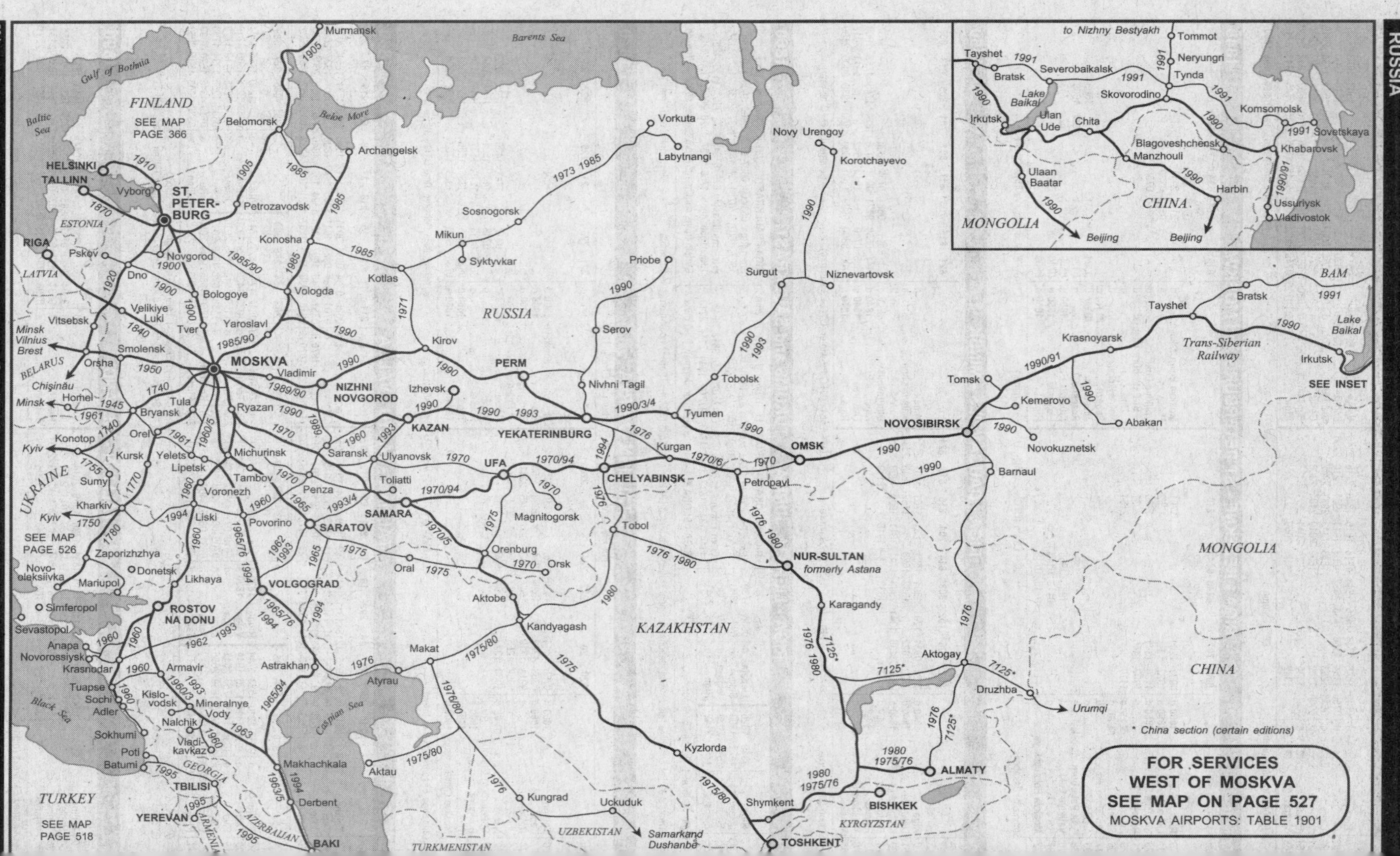

See also the map on page 527

RUSSIA and BELARUS

SEE MAPS PAGES 527 and 534

Operators : **RZhD**: Rossiskiye Zheleznye Dorogi, www.rzd.ru **BCh**: Belaruskaya Chyhunka, www.rw.by

Timings : **Valid until December 10, 2022**. All times are now shown in LOCAL time (time zone is UTC+3 all year unless otherwise shown in the notes or by a shaded column).

Tickets : Except for travel by purely local trains, prior reservation is necessary and passports and visas must be presented when purchasing tickets. Most nationalities require visas.

RAIL TRAVEL IN RUSSIA, BELARUS, UKRAINE and MOLDOVA

CARRIAGE TYPES

As trains generally operate over long distances, most accommodation is designed for overnight as well as day use. Carriage types (with their Russian names) are:

Spálny vagón SV – 2-berth sleeping compartments (9 per carriage), found only in the best trains. Sometimes referred to as 1st class. A small number of named trains also have *de luxe* carriages (also known as *VIP*) with ensuite facilities.

Kupéiny K – 4-berth compartments (9 per carriage) found in almost all long-distance trains. Sometimes referred to as 2nd class.

Platskártny – open-plan dormitory-style carriage with 54 bunks, found in all except the best trains. Sometimes referred to as 3rd class.

Óbshchi – open-plan carriages with hard seating, found in some slow trains. Sometimes referred to as 4th class and not recommended for long-distance travel.

TRAIN TYPES

The top grade of fast long-distance train is classified *Firménny* (shown as *Fir* in the tables). These are composed of higher-quality carriages dedicated to a particular service (often named) and higher fares apply. Normal long-distance express trains are classified *Skóry* (shown as *Sko* in the tables). The lowest class of long-distance train is classified *Passazhirsky* (*Pas* in the tables) which call at many stations en-route.

Trains are identified by a number, followed by a cyrillic character, or a two-letter transliteration which is shown in some tables to assist in making bookings.

High-speed train types with 1st and 2nd class seating are *Sapsan* (Peregrine Falcon) running between Moskva and St Peterburg, and the Talgo-built *Strizh* (Swift) running between Moskva and Nizhny Novgorod (also with 1st class sleeping compartments for daytime use). Fast *Lastochka* (Swallow) trains with 2nd class seats run on several routes.

INTERNATIONAL SERVICES

International services to, from and via Poland, Slovakia, Hungary and Romania convey through sleeping cars of the normal European ('RIC') types, with single and double compartments in first class, and 3- or 4-berth compartments in second class. The railways of the former Soviet Union being of broad gauge (1520mm), the bogies (trucks) of these through cars are changed at the frontier with these countries.

High-speed *Allegro* day trains are in use between St Peterburg and Helsinki, and a Talgo hotel train links Moskva with Berlin.

DAYS OF RUNNING

Many trains run on alternate days only, on even or uneven numbered dates. The examples below illustrate the system used to indicate exceptions to the pattern of even or uneven dates at the end of a month with 31 days and at the beginning of the month following:

e.g. "Uneven dates [... *29, 1* ...]" means that the train does not run on the 31st of a month with 31 days.

e.g. "Even dates [... *30, 1, 4* ...]" means that the train, **following a month with 31 days**, runs exceptionally on the 1st, but not the 2nd, of the month.

In these cases, the following symbols are used in the tables to indicate days of running:

■ – Uneven dates.	● – Even dates.
■(1) – Uneven dates [.. *29, 1* ..]	●(2) – Even dates [.. *30, 2* ..]
■(2) – Uneven dates [.. *31, 2, 3* ..]	●(3) – Even dates [.. *30, 1, 3, 8* ..]
■(3) – Uneven dates [.. *31, 3* ..]	●(4) – Even dates [.. *30, 1, 4* ..]
■(4) – Uneven dates [.. *29, 3* ..]	●(5) – Even dates [.. *30, 1, 3, 4* ..]
■(5) – Uneven dates [.. *31, 2, 5* ..]	●(6) – Even dates [.. *30, 1, 3, 6* ..]
■(6) – Uneven dates [.. *31, 2, 7* ..]	●(7) – Even dates [.. *30, 1, 6* ..]
■(7) – Uneven dates [.. *31, 2, 4, 7* ..]	●(8) – Even dates [.. *30, 1, 3, 5, 8* ..]
■(8) – Uneven dates [.. *31, 2, 4, 6, 8, 10, 11* ..]	●(9) – Even dates [.. *30, 1, 3, 5, 7, 10* ..]
■(9) – Uneven dates [.. *31, 2, 4, 6, 9* ..]	

MOSKVA - ST PETERBURG 1900

All trains suffix *AJ* except where shown otherwise. For other trains see Tables **1960**, **1989** and **1990**.

km			20*UJ*	16	82*VJ*	752	756	758	760*RJ*	762	764	766	770	748	714*JI*	726*CH*	772
			Fir	*Fir*	*Sko*	♥	♥	♥	♥	♥	♥	♥	♥	⊡	♠	❦	♥
			M	m	b				n		⑥⑦	⑥⑦		①③⑤	A		
0	**Moskva** Oktyabrskaya §	d.	0020	0041	0203**v**	0545	0650	0700	0920**k**	0940	1130	1140	1340	1340	1452**v**	1521	1530
167	Tver	d.	0212	0227	0440	|	0756	0804	1034	1047	|	|	1447	|	|	1719	|
331	Bologoye	d.	|	0440	0634	|	0853	|	|	1144	1324	|	1544	|	|	1850	1724
532	Chudovo Mos.	d.	|	|	|	|	|	1016	1233	|	1426	|	|	|	|	2106	1828
650	**St Peterburg** Glavny ‡	a.	0859	0913**d**	1035	0915	1045	1104	1320	1332	1516	1526	1744	1745	2000**d**	2220	1915

		774	776	778	780	782	784	786	18	120*VJ*	26	28	6	4	54*CH*	2
		♥	♥	♥	♥	♥	♥	♥	*Fir*	*Sko*	*Fir*	*Sko*	*Fir*	*Fir*	*Fir*	*Fir*
								②–⑤	m	b	B			⑧D	E	F
Moskva Oktyabrskaya §	d.	1540	1730	1740	1930	1940	2050	2100	2108	2136**v**	2150	2230	2250	2330	2340	2355
Tver	d.	|	|	1847	2036	2045	|	2203	2255	0044	2348	0052	|	|	|	|
Bologoye	d.	|	|	1944	2133	|	|	|	0032	0232	|	0251	|	|	|	|
Chudovo Mos.	d.	|	2030	|	|	2257	|	2357	...	|	|	|	|	|	|	|
St Peterburg Glavny ‡	a.	1925	2115	2135	2325	2344	0031	0048	...	0616**d**	0606	0640	0647	0830	0836	0755

		713*VJ*	119	751	755	757	759	761	763	765	767	769	747	771	773	725*CH*
		♠	*Sko*	♥	♥	♥	♥	♥	♥	♥	♥	♥	⊡	♥	♥	❦
		A	b						⑥⑦	⑥⑦		②–⑤	②④⑦			
St Peterburg Glavny ‡	d.	0020**d**	0012	0530	0640	0650	0900	0910	1100	1110	1300	1310	1310	1500	1510	1516
Chudovo Mos.	d.	|	|	|	0726	|	|	|	|	1157	|	1359	|	|	1559	1624
Bologoye	d.	|	0430	|	|	0848	1052	|	|	1300	1452	|	|	1652	|	1800
Tver	d.	|	0632	|	0936	0946	1149	|	|	|	1549	1608	|	1749	|	1922
Moskva Oktyabrskaya §	a.	0534**v**	0952**v**	0900	1043	1052	1258	1305	1443	1453	1700	1710	1715	1855	1905	2158

		775	777	779	781	783	81	25	27	15	19*UJ*	3	5	53*CH*	1	17
		♥	♥	♥	♥	♥	*Sko*	*Fir*	*Fir*	*Fir*		*Fir*	*Fir*	*Fir*	*Fir*	*Fir*
		n					b	B		m	M	⑧D		E	F	m
St Peterburg Glavny ‡	d.	1700	1710	1900	1910	2050	2004	2155	2231	2243**d**	2250	2330	2336	2349	2355	...
Chudovo Mos.	d.	|	|	|	1959	|	|	|	|	|	|	|	|	|	|	...
Bologoye	d.	|	1902	2052	|	|	0020	|	|	0315	|	|	|	|	|	0519
Tver	d.	1942	1959	2149	2209	|	0151	0406	0420	0455	0441	|	0507	|	|	0700
Moskva Oktyabrskaya §	a.	2057**k**	2105	2258	2313	0035	0435**v**	0604	0645	0719	0707	0830	0741	0814	0755	0850

MOSKVA - VELIKY NOVGOROD - PSKOV

km			801	79*CH*	819*VJ*	803*MJ*	10	42
				Sko	❦		*Fir*	*Sko*
				N	L			J
0	**Moskva** Oktyabrskaya §	d.	...	...	...	...	2035	2207
167	Tver	d.	...	...	...	...	2240	0036
331	Bologoye	d.	...	...	...	...	0100	0310
	St Peterburg Glavny	d.	0726	1013	...	1932	|	|
532	Chudovo Mos.	d.	0903	|	1550	2148	|	0516
	Veliky Novgorod ⊖	a.	1017	1240	1656	2308	|	0624
	Veliky Novgorod ⊖	d.	...	1325	1750	...	|	...
588	Dno	a.	...	1647	2025	...	0600	...
687	**Pskov**	a.	...	...	...	...	0805	...

		802	80*CH*	820*VJ*	804*MJ*	42*CH*	10*CH*
			Sko	❦		*Sko*	*Fir*
			N	P		K	
Pskov	d.	...	...	...	...	...	1930
Dno	d.	...	1348	1418	...	...	2120
Veliky Novgorod ⊖	a.	...	1632	1707	...	...	|
Veliky Novgorod ⊖	d.	0610	1710	1743	1806	2110	|
Chudovo Mos.	d.	0740	|	1856	1932	2256	|
St Peterburg Glavny	a.	0944	2025	...	2055	|	|
Bologoye	d.	...	...	...	...	0059	0239
Tver	d.	...	...	...	...	0314	0427
Moskva Oktyabrskaya §	a.	...	...	...	...	0515	0650

– Samara - Moskva - St. Peterburg and v.v. For days of running see Table **1989**.
– ①③④⑤⑦ until May 24; daily from May 25.
– EKSPRESS.
– GRAND EXPRESS – luxury train (🛏 1, 2 cl.).
– KRASNAYA STRELA (RED ARROW).
– ③④⑤⑥⑦ until Mar. 27; daily from Mar. 30.
– ①④⑤⑥⑦ untli Mar. 28; daily from Mar. 31.
– ①⑥⑦.
– MEGAPOLIS - operated by Tverskoy Express.
– To / from Kaliningrad. For days of running see Table **1950**.

P – ⑤⑥⑦.

b – From / to Belgorod via Tula, Orel (Table **1770**).
d – St Peterburg **Ladozhski**.
k – Moskva **Kurskaya**.
m – To / from Murmansk or Petrozavodsk (Table **1905**).
n – To / from Nizhni Novgorod (Table **1989**).
v – Moskva **Vostochny**.

♥ – *Sapsan* high-speed train, special fares. ✕ 🅁.
♠ – *Strizh* (Swift) fast Talgo day train.
❦ – *Lastochka* (Swallow) fast day train.

⊡ – NEVSKIY EKSPRESS. 1st class only. Subject to confirmation.
● – Even dates (see page 535).
■ – Uneven dates (see page 535).
§ – Also known as *Leningradski vokzal*.
‡ – Also known as *Moskovski vokzal*.
⊖ – Station is named **Novgorod na Volkhove**.

1901 MOSKVA AIRPORTS ✈

MOSKVA DOMODEDOVO AIRPORT ✈
Aeroexpress rail service Moskva Paveletskaya - Moskva Domodedovo ✈. *35 km* Journey time 45 minutes.
From **Moskva Paveletskaya**: 0530, 0600 and every 30 minutes until 2300, 2330.
From **Domodedovo** ✈: 0600, 0630 and every 30 minutes until 2300, 2330.

MOSKVA SHEREMETYEVO AIRPORT ✈
Aeroexpress rail service Moskva Belorusskaya - Moskva Sheremetyevo ✈. *35 km* Journey time 50 minutes.
From **Moskva Belorusskaya**: 0535, 0605 and every 30 minutes until 2305, 2335.
From **Sheremetyevo** ✈: 0547, 0617 and every 30 minutes until 2317, 2347.

MOSKVA VNUKOVO AIRPORT ✈
Aeroexpress rail service Moskva Kiyevskaya - Moskva Vnukovo ✈. *28 km* Journey time 35 - 40 minutes.
From **Moskva Kiyevskaya**: 0600 and hourly until 2300.
From **Vnukovo** ✈: 0600 and hourly until 2300.

1905 (MOSKVA -) ST PETERBURG - PETROZAVODSK - MURMANSK

RZhD

km		18AJ Fir	804CH ⚘	16AJ Fir	806CH ⚘	22CH Sko			
	Moskva Oktyabrskaya **1900** d.	2105	...	0041	...	...	...	...	...
0	**St Peterburg** Ladozhski d.	|	0632	1010	1800	2124	...	...	...
*114	Volkhovstroi 1 d.	0354v	0818	1204	1924	2310	...	...	...
394	**Petrozavodsk** d.	0750	1157	1710	2259	0321	...	...	...
773	Belomorsk d.	...	...	0023	...	0947	...	...	...
1161	Kandalaksha d.	...	...	0652	...	1626	...	...	...
1438	**Murmansk** a.	...	...	1145	...	2121	...	...	...

	21CH Sko	803CH ⚘	15AJ Fir	805CH ⚘	17AJ Fir			
Murmansk d.	1012	...	1935	...	...	...	...	...
Kandalaksha d.	1510	...	0057	...	...	...	...	...
Belomorsk d.	2137	...	0723	...	...	...	...	...
Petrozavodsk d.	0403	0636	1509	1800	2200	...	...	...
Volkhovstroi 1 d.	0803	1018	1950	|	0158v	...	...	...
St Peterburg Ladozhski a.	1009	1200	2149	2259	|	...	...	...
Moskva Oktyabrskaya **1900** a.	...	...	0719	...	0850	...	...	...

v – Volkhovstroi 2.
⚘ – *Lastochka* (Swallow) fast day train.
* – Moskva - Vokhovstroi: *641 km*.

1910 MOSKVA - ST PETERBURG - HELSINKI

RZhD, VR

WARNING! As of December 2021 services in this Table were only available to Finnish and Russian citizens.

km		SUMMER					WINTER				
		781 AE30 A⊡ ☆	32AJ Fir B⊡ ☆	783 AE34 A ☆	785 AE36 A ☆	787 AE38 A⊡ ☆	781 AE30 A⊡ ★	32AJ Fir B⊡ ★	783 AE34 A ★	785 AE36 A ★	787 AE38 A⊡ ★
	Moskva Okt. § d.	...	2310	...	...	...	...	2310	...	...	...
	Tver d.	...	0107	...	...	...	...	0103	...	...	...
**	**St Peterburg** Lad. ‡ d.	...	0601	...	...	...	...	0601	...	...	...
0	**St Peterburg** Fin. ‡ d.	0640	|	1130	1530	2030	0640	|	1130	1530	2030
129	Vyborg a.	0735	0754	1225	1625	2125	0735	0753	1225	1625	2125
129	Vyborg ⊞ RU d.	0745	0834	1235	1635	2135	0745	0833	1235	1635	2135
159	Vainikkala ⊞ FIN a.	0807	0914	1257	1657	2157	0707	0814	1157	1557	2057
159	Vainikkala d.	0814	1017	1304	1704	2204	0714	0914	1204	1604	2104
250	**Kouvola** 797 a.	0853	1111	1343	1743	2243	0753	1009	1243	1643	2143
312	Lahti 797 a.	0919	1157	1409	1809	2309	0819	1049	1309	1709	2209
400	Tikkurila 797 a.	0953	1252	1443	1843	2343	0853	1145	1343	1743	2243
413	Pasila 797 a.	1004	1323	1454	1854	2354	0904	1223	1354	1754	2254
416	**Helsinki** 797 a.	1010	1330	1500	1900	0001	0910	1230	1400	1800	2300

	SUMMER					WINTER				
	AE33 782 A⊡ ☆	AE35 784 A ☆	AE37 786 A ☆	31AJ Fir B⊡ ☆	AE39 788 A⊡ ☆	AE33 782 A⊡ ★	AE35 784 A ★	AE37 786 A ★	31AJ Fir B⊡ ★	AE3 78 A ★
Helsinki 797 d.	0717	1057	1557	1844	1957	0617	0957	1457	1743	185
Pasila 797 d.	0723	1103	1603	1850	2003	0623	1003	1503	1749	190
Tikkurila 797 d.	0733	1113	1613	1901	2013	0633	1013	1513	1800	191
Lahti 797 d.	0807	1147	1647	1954	2047	0707	1047	1547	1853	194
Kouvola 797 d.	0833	1213	1713	2034	2113	0733	1113	1613	1934	201
Vainikkala a.	0913	1253	1753	2130	2153	0813	1153	1653	2030	205
Vainikkala ⊞ FIN d.	0920	1300	1800	2215	2200	0820	1200	1700	2115	210
Vyborg ⊞ RU a.	0941	1321	1821	2256	2221	0941	1321	1821	2256	222
Vyborg d.	0946	1326	1826	2336	2226	0946	1326	1826	2336	222
St Peterburg Fin. ‡ a.	1047	1427	1927	|	2327	1047	1427	1927	|	232
St Peterburg Lad. ‡ a.	...	...	...	0118	...	...	...	...	0118	...
Tver a.	...	...	...	0659	...	...	...	...	0659	...
Moskva Okt. § a.	...	...	...	0919	...	...	...	...	0919	...

A – ALLEGRO – (12) ✕ R St Peterburg - Helsinki and v.v. International journeys only.
B – LEV TOLSTOI – 1 cl. (ensuite), 1, 2 cl., ✕. International journeys only.
☆ – Mar. 27 - Oct. 29 (provisional times).
★ – Oct. 31 - Mar. 26, 2022 (winter time in Finland).
§ – Moskva Oktyabrskaya, also known as Leningradski.
‡ – Lad. = Ladozhski; Fin. = Finlyandski.
⊡ – Service suspended.
** – *143 km* St Peterburg Ladozhski - Vyborg.
FIN – Finland (UTC + 2 in winter, UTC + 3 in summer).
RU – Russia (Moskva Time UTC + 3).

1920 ST PETERBURG - HOMEL and KOZYATYN

RZhD, BCh, UZ

km		55BJ Fir ◇	626BJ G	79CH Sko C	83AJ Sko	83AJ Sko ■(4) D	51BJ Fir	869BJ	657BJ E
0	**St Peterburg** Vitebski d.	...	...	...	1700	1700	1818	...	...
	St Peterburg Glavny d.	...	...	1013	|	|	|	...	...
245	Dno d.	...	...	1659	2050	2050	2143	...	...
421	Novosokolniki RU d.	...	...	2022	2359	2359	0033	...	...
568	Vitsebsk ⊖ BY d.	...	2138	2316	0230	0230	0314	...	...
670	Polatsk d.	...	0013	0114	|	|	|	0613	1743
868	Maladzechnia a.	...	0503	0348	|	|	|	0915	2117
	Moskva Bel. **1950** d.	2028	|	|	|	|	|	|	|
652	**Orsha** Tsentralnaya a.	0308	|	▽	0343	0343	0423	|	|
652	**Orsha** Tsentralnaya **1950** d.	0342	|	...	0405	0418	0447	|	|
	Minsk **1950** a.	|	0629	...	|	0631	0715	1015	2218
	Hrodna **1952** a.	|	...	...	|	1156	|	...	|
	Brest Tsent. **1950** a.	|	...	...	|	...	1156	...	0741
726	Mahilyow 1 d.	0535	...	...	0609	...	...	...	...
853	Zhlobin **1930** d.	0751	...	...	0823	...	...	...	...
	Homel **1930** a.	0912	...	...	0952	...	...	...	...
	Kyiv **1930** a.	...	...	...	...	...	...	...	...
954	Kalinkavichy BY d.	...	...	...	...	...	...	...	...
1109	Korosten ⊡ UA d.	...	...	...	...	...	...	...	...
1191	Zhytomyr d.	...	...	...	...	...	...	...	...
1267	**Kozyatyn** 1 a.	...	...	...	...	...	...	...	...
	Chisinău **1720** a.	...	...	...	...	...	...	...	...

	658BJ E	869BJ	52BJ Fir	83BJ Sko ●‡ F	83BJ Sko	625BJ H	80CH Sko C	55M Fir ◇
Chisinău **1720** d.	...	...	...	...	...	...	...	...
Kozyatyn 1 d.	...	...	...	...	...	...	...	...
Zhytomyr d.	...	...	...	...	...	...	...	...
Korosten UA d.	...	...	...	...	...	...	...	...
Kalinkavichy ⊡ BY d.	...	...	...	...	...	...	...	...
Kyiv **1930** d.	...	...	...	...	...	...	...	...
Homel **1930** d.	...	...	...	...	1716	...	...	183
Zhlobin **1930** d.	...	...	...	...	1834	...	...	194
Mahilyow 1 d.	...	...	...	...	2045	...	...	215
Brest Tsent. **1950** d.	2029	...	1412	...	|	...	...	|
Hrodna **1952** d.	|	...	|	1158	|	...	...	|
Minsk **1950** d.	0630	1723	1843	1736	|	2135	...	|
Orsha Tsentralnaya **1950** a.	|	|	2115	2041	2157	|	...	230
Orsha Tsentralnaya d.	|	|	2140	2130	2220	|	▽	232
Moskva Bel. **1950** a.	|	|	|	|	|	|	|	063
Maladzechnia d.	0756	1846	|	|	|	2321	0316	...
Polatsk d.	1025	2115	|	|	|	0458	0621	...
Vitsebsk BY d.	...	...	2302	0024	0024	0641	0822	...
Novosokolniki ⊖ RU d.	...	...	0201	0335	0335	...	1110	...
Dno d.	...	...	0426	0614	0614	...	1348	...
St Peterburg Glavny a.	...	...	|	|	|	...	2025	...
St Peterburg Vitebski a.	...	...	0755	0947	0947	...	...	...

C – For days of running see Table **1950**.
D – St Peterburg - Orsha (**3**BJ or **7**MJ) - Minsk (**687**BJ) - Hrodna.
E – Polatsk - Minsk - Brest and v.v. (Table **1950**).
F – Hrodna (**680**BJ) - Vitsebsk - St Peterburg.
G – ④⑤⑥⑦.
H – ①⑤⑥⑦.
▽ – To / from Kaliningrad via Vilnius (Table **1950**).
◇ – For Moskva - Homel via Bryansk see Table **1945**.
● – Even dates (see page 535).
■ – Uneven dates (see page 535).
‡ – Even dates [.. *28*, *2* ..].
⊖ – ⊞ : Yezyaryshcha (BY) / Zaverezhye (RU).
⊡ – ⊞ : Slovechno (BY) / Berezhest (UA).
BY – Belarus (UTC + 3)
RU – Russia (Moskva Time UTC + 3).
UA – Ukraine (UTC + 2 winter, UTC + 3 summer).

1930 MINSK - HOMEL - KYIV

BCh, UZ

km		684 ①	716	710 ⑤–⑦	748 ⑧	648	708	756 ⑤–⑦	632 F
	St P'burg Vit. **1920** d.	...	...	...	...	...	...	...	...
0	**Minsk** d.	0025	0708	1111	1457	1627	1900	1936	2357
149	Babruysk d.	0303	0837	1241	1634	1828	|	2122	0206
214	Zhlobin **1920** d.	0419	0921	1321	1717	1924	|	2218	0326
304	**Homel** **1920** a.	0551	1021	1415	1814	2041	2150	2318	0754
304	**Homel** BY d.	...	...	...	...	...	...	...	...
415	Chernihiv § UA d.	...	...	...	...	...	...	...	...
624	**Kyiv** a.	...	...	...	...	...	...	...	...
	Kharkiv **1755** a.	...	...	...	...	...	...	...	...
	Odesa **1720** a.	...	...	...	...	...	...	...	...

	755 ①⑥⑦	647	707	747 ⑤⑦	631 F	739	715	621
Odesa **1720** d.	...	...	...	...	...	...	...	...
Kharkiv **1755** d.	...	...	...	...	...	...	...	...
Kyiv d.	...	...	...	...	...	...	...	...
Chernihiv § UA d.	...	...	...	...	...	...	...	...
Homel BY a.	...	...	...	...	...	...	...	...
Homel **1920** d.	0443	0630	0700	1053	1420	1510	1908	221
Zhlobin **1920** d.	0533	0756	|	1145	1906	1602	2001	024
Babruysk d.	0617	0858	|	1228	2059	1642	2046	034
Minsk a.	0753	1057	0950	1359	2307	1808	2220	054
St P'burg Vit. **1920** a.	...	...	...	...	...	...	...	...

F – To / from Hrodna (Table **1952**).
§ – ⊞ : Teryukha (BY) / Hornostayivka (UA).
BY – Belarus (UTC + 3).
UA – Ukraine (UTC + 2 / + 3).

MOSKVA - BRYANSK - HOMEL - BREST 1945

RZhD, BCh

For trains to destinations in Ukraine see Table **1740**. For trains via Orsha see Table **1920**.

km		675BJ	302SJ	737AJ	739AJ	603BJ	107MJ	741VJ	85CH
			Pas	Sko	Sko		Sko	Sko	Sko
		⑦	A				⑤		
0	**Moskva** Belorusskaya **1740** d.	...	...	0653	1338	...	1717	1914	2241
485	**Bryansk** Orlovski **1740** d.	...	0839	1056	1741	...	2152	2322	0426
713	Zlynka RU d.	...	1255	...	...	...	...	...	...
739	Dobrush BY d.	...	...	...	...	...	...	...	...
764	**Homel** a.	...	...	...	...	...	...	...	...
764	**Homel** d.	0815	...	...	...	2010	...	...	...
892	Kalinkavichy d.	1023	...	...	...	2250	...	...	...
069	Luninets d.	1314	...	...	...	0154	...	...	...
297	**Brest** Tsentralny a.	1650	...	...	...	0557	...	...	...

	86CH	640BJ	738AJ	740AJ	108MJ	742VJ	302BJ	676BJ
	Sko		Sko	Sko	Sko	Sko	Pas	
					⑦		A	⑦
Brest Tsentralny d.	...	1940	...	...	...	...	...	1017
Luninets d.	...	0022	...	...	...	...	...	1430
Kalinkavichy d.	...	0358	...	...	...	...	...	1733
Homel a.	...	0604	...	...	...	...	...	1937
Homel d.	...	...	...	...	...	...	...	...
Dobrush BY d.	...	...	...	...	...	...	...	...
Zlynka RU d.	...	...	...	...	...	...	1650	...
Bryansk Orlovski **1740** d.	0017	...	0705	1326	1650	1906	2146	...
Moskva Belorusskaya **1740** a.	0613	...	1110	1731	2119	2311	...	...

– Adler - Minsk and v.v. For days of running see Table **1961**.
BY – Belarus (UTC+3).
RU – Russia (UTC+3).

MOSKVA - MINSK - VILNIUS, KALININGRAD and BREST 1950

RZhD, BCh

km		727BJ	737BJ	717MJ	715MJ	743CH	725BJ	731MJ	607BJ	735BJ	701BJ	360SJ	657BJ	721MJ	735MJ	79CH	29CH	55BJ	1BJ	3BJ	7MJ	51BJ	27BJ
				⇊	⇊	⇊		⇊				Pas		⇊	⇊	Sko	Fir	Fir	Fir	Sko	Sko	Fir	Sko
												B	C			⊙				● D	■(1) D		
0	**Moskva** Belorusskaya d.	...	...	0620	0715	0956	...	1159	...	...	...	...	...	1600	1917	...	1953	2028	2210	2217	2217	...	2330
243	Vyazma d.	...	...	|	0935	1217	...	1414	...	...	...	...	...	1808	2150	...	2254	2347	0125	0103	0103	...	0239
419	**Smolensk** RU a.	...	...	0956	1117	1406	...	1556	...	...	...	...	...	1941	2331	...	0034	0143	0321	0243	0243	...	0440
419	**Smolensk** RU d.	...	...	1001	...	...	...	...	...	...	...	1705	...	1946	...	...	0044	0153	0331	0253	0253	...	0450
560	Vitsebsk RU d.	...	...	|	...	...	...	...	...	...	...	|	...	|	...	...	|	|	|	|	|	...	|
662	**Polatsk** BY a.	...	...	|	...	...	...	...	...	...	...	|	...	|	...	...	|	|	|	|	|	...	|
	St Peterburg Glavny **1920** d.	...	...	|	...	...	...	...	...	...	...	|	...	|	...	1013	|	|	|	|	|	1818	|
538	Orsha Tsentralnaya BY a.	...	...	1108	...	...	...	...	...	...	...	1821	...	2052	...	|	0155	0308	0446	0401	0401	0423	0606
538	Orsha Tsentralnaya **1920** d.	...	...	1109	...	...	...	...	...	...	...	1845	...	2053	...	⊡	0223	0342	0503	0418	0418	0447	0623
750	**Minsk** **1920** a.	...	...	1310	...	...	...	...	...	...	...	2127	...	2255	...	|	0441	|	0725	0631	0631	0715	0855
750	**Minsk** d.	1035	1304	...	...	...	1559	...	1730	1826	1947	2150	2249	...	...	|	0455	△	...	0652	0652	0755	0917
827	Maladzechnia BY d.	|	|	...	...	...	|	...	|	|	|	2301	|	...	...	0402	0558	...	...	|	|	|	|
943	**Vilnius** LT a.	|	|	...	...	...	|	...	|	|	|	|	|	...	...	|	|	...	...	|	|	|	|
943	**Vilnius** LT d.	|	|	...	...	...	|	...	|	|	|	|	|	...	...	|	|	...	...	|	|	|	|
285	**Kaliningrad** Ka a.	|	|	...	...	...	|	...	|	|	|	0808	|	...	...	1317	1446	...	...	|	|	|	|
892	Baranavichy Tsentral'nyye d.	1202	1504**p**	...	...	...	|	...	1919	2008**p**	2114	...	0122**p**	...	...	...	...	...	...	0825	0825	0934	1142**p**
094	**Brest** Tsentralny a.	1359	1700	...	...	...	1859	...	2153	2202	2302	...	0741	...	...	...	...	...	...	1031	1031	1156	1437
	Warszawa Wschodnia **1050** a.	...	...	...	...	...	...	...	...	...	...	...	...	...	...	...	...	...	...	...	...	...	...

	80CH	736MJ	658BJ	722BJ	360CH	702BJ	608BJ	736BJ	716MJ	744CH	732MJ	718BJ	52BJ	728BJ	55MZ	4BJ	8BJ	738BJ	2BJ	726BJ	28BJ	30CH
	Sko	⇊		⇊	Pas				⇊	⇊	⇊	⇊	Fir		Fir	Sko	Sko		Fir		Sko	Fir
	⊕		C		B											■(1) D	● D					
Warszawa Wschodnia **1050** d.	...	...	...	...	...	...	...	...	...	...	...	...	...	...	...	...	...	...	...	...	...	...
rest Tsentralny d.	...	...	2029	...	...	0622	0628	0809	...	...	...	...	1412	1437	...	1737	1737	1746	...	2003	1823	...
aranavichy Tsentral'nyye d.	...	...	0400**p**	...	...	|	0907	1015**p**	...	...	...	...	1651	1626	...	1941	1941	2004**p**	...	2158	2204**p**	...
Kaliningrad Ka d.	1603	...	|	...	1807	|	|	|	...	...	...	...	|	|	...	|	|	|	...	|	|	1303
Vilnius LT a.	|	...	|	...	|	|	|	|	...	...	...	...	|	|	...	|	|	|	...	|	|	|
Vilnius LT d.	|	...	|	...	|	|	|	|	...	...	...	...	|	|	...	|	|	|	...	|	|	|
Maladzechna d.	0316	...	|	...	0457	|	|	|	...	...	...	...	|	|	...	|	|	|	...	|	|	2320
insk a.	|	...	0601	...	0605	0922	1056	1150	...	...	...	...	1827	1750	△	2115	2115	2141	...	2326	2354	0023
insk **1920** d.	|	...	...	0620	0633	...	...	...	...	...	...	1600	1843	...	|	2144	2144	...	2210	...	0008	0036
rsha Tsentralnaya **1920** a.	⊡	...	...	0819	0924	...	...	...	...	...	...	1758	2115	...	2303	2354	2354	...	0024	...	0230	0255
rsha Tsentralnaya BY d.	|	...	...	0820	0948	...	...	...	...	...	...	1759	2140	...	2327	0011	0011	...	0048	...	0250	0321
St Peterburg Glavny **1920** a.	2025	...	...	|	|	...	...	...	...	...	...	|	0755	...	|	|	|	...	|	...	|	|
Polatsk BY d.	...	...	...	|	|	...	...	...	...	...	...	|	...	...	|	|	|	...	|	...	|	|
Vitsebsk RU d.	...	...	...	|	|	...	...	...	...	...	...	|	...	...	|	|	|	...	|	...	|	|
molensk RU a.	...	...	...	0922	1108	...	...	...	...	...	...	1901	...	...	0042	0127	0127	...	0204	...	0405	0431
molensk RU d.	...	0752	...	0927	...	...	...	...	1602	1707	1840	1906	...	...	0052	0137	0137	...	0214	...	0415	0441
yazma d.	...	0935	...	|	...	...	...	...	1747	1857	2025	2042	...	...	0309	0344	0344	...	0434	...	0633	0624
oskva Belorusskaya a.	...	1154	...	1310	...	...	...	...	2033	2124	2246	2255	...	...	0630	0654	0654	...	0815	...	0931	0854

– Adler - Kaliningrad and v.v. For days of running see Table **1961**.
– Polatsk - Minsk - Brest and v.v. (Table **1920**).
– Conveys Moskva - Minsk (**687/688**BJ) - Hrodna and v.v. (Table **1952**).
– Baranavichy **Polesskiye**.
– To/from Homel (Table **1920**).
] – Via Novgorod na Volkhove, Vitsebsk (Tables **1900, 1920**).
– ①⑤⑦.
– ③⑤⑥.
– *Lastochka* (Swallow) fast day train.
– Even dates (see page 535).
– Uneven dates (see page 535).

BY – Belarus (UTC+3).
Ka – Kaliningrad region of Russia (UTC+2). Local time.
LT – Lithuania (UTC+2 in winter, UTC+3 in summer).
RU – Russia (Moskva Time UTC+3).

BORDER CROSSINGS:
Between Smolensk and Polatsk: Rudnya (RU) / Zavolsha (BY).
Between Smolensk and Orsha: Krasnoye (RU) / Osinovka (BY).
Between Maladzechna and Vilnius: Hudahai (BY) / Kena (LT).
Between Vilnius and Kaliningrad: Kybartai (LT) / Nesterov (Ka).

VITSEBSK - MINSK - HRODNA 1952

BCh

For Vitsebsk - Polatsk - Minsk trains see Table **1920**.

km		679BJ	687BJ	731BJ	627BJ		729BJ	631BJ	623BJ
					⑤⑦				
			EF					d	
0	**Vitsebsk** d.	0010	...	...	...	...	...	...	1807
84	Orsha Tsentralnaya a.	0135	...	...	...	...	...	...	1938
84	Orsha Tsentralnaya d.	0233	...	...	...	...	...	...	2004
296	**Minsk** a.	0555	...	...	...	...	...	...	2332
296	**Minsk** d.	0610	0708	1518	1520	...	1920	2327	2347
373	Maladzechna d.	|	0813	1614	|	...	2016	|	0058
501	Lida d.	|	1006	1745	|	...	2204	|	0307
437	Baranavichy Pol. d.	0810t	|	|	1758	...	|	0214	|
633	**Hrodna** a.	1144	1156	1910	2158	...	2333	0634	0519

	730BJ	680BJ	688BJ	632BJ		624BJ	732BJ	628BJ
								⑤⑦
		G	F	d				
Hrodna d.	0645	1158	1534	1701	...	1728	1951	2353
Baranavichy Pol. d.	|	1523t	|	2124	...	|	|	0520
Lida d.	0813	|	1724	|	...	1938	2113	|
Maladzechna d.	0947	|	1910	|	...	2140	2241	|
Minsk a.	1042	1721	2209	2341	...	2245	2337	0726
Minsk d.	...	1736	...	...	...	2302	...	...
Orsha Tsentralnaya a.	...	2041	...	...	...	0319	...	...
Orsha Tsentralnaya d.	...	2130	...	...	...	0440	...	...
Vitsebsk a.	...	2242	...	...	...	0603	...	...

– Conveys St Peterburg (**83**AJ) - Orsha (**3**BJ or **7**MJ) - Minsk - Hrodna (Table **1920**).
– Conveys Moskva (**3/4**BJ or **7**MJ/**8**BJ) - Minsk - Hrodna and v.v. (Table **1950**).
– Conveys on Even dates [.. *28, 2* ..]. Hrodna - Vitsebsk (**83**BJ) - St Peterburg (Table **1920**).

d – To/from Homel (Table **1930**).
t – Baranavichy **Tsentral'nyye**.
* – *657 km* via Baranavichy.

1960 MOSKVA - ROSTOV - SEVASTOPOL, NOVOROSSIYSK, KISLOVODSK, SOCHI and ADLER

Trains to Simferopol and Sevastopol are operated by GRAND TRAIN (www.grandtrain.ru) - these services may only be available to Russian citizens.

km	*Time zone: UTC+3*		740*ZH*	4*MJ*	28*CH*	12*MJ*	104*VJ*	815*SJ*	829*SJ*	135*AJ*	30*SJ*	102*MJ*	803*SJ*	801*SJ*	738*ZH*	20*SJ*	808*SJ*	7*AJ*	306*MJ*	146*EI*	146*EI*	92*MJ*	33*MJ*	49*AJ*	35*A*
			Fir	*Fir*	*Sko*	*Sko*	*Fir*	❈	❈	*Sko*	*Fir*	*Fir*	❈	❈	*Fir*	*Fir*	❈	*Sko*	*Sko*	*Fir*	688*SJ*	*Sko*	*Sko*	*Sko*	*Fir*
										■(5)									**A**	●	●		●(4)	**B**	
	St Peterburg Glavny	d.	...	...	...	...	...	...	...	1830	...	...	...	...	...	...	...	1720	...	...	...	...	...	1334	201
	Bologoye	d.	...	...	...	...	...	...	...	0007	...	...	...	...	...	...	...	2006	...	...	...	...	...	1727	002
	Tver	d.	...	...	...	...	...	...	...	0224	...	...	...	...	...	...	...	2127	...	...	...	...	...	1906	020
0	**Moskva** Kazanskaya	d.	0814	0822	0840	1040	1050	...	...	0532**v**	1430	1440	...	...	1652	1840	...	|	1950	2320	2320	2350	2142**p**	2249**v**	|
198	Ryazan 2	d.	1028	1048	1106	1301	1311	...	...	|	1712	1722	...	...	1906	2120	...	0209	2301	0224	0224	0245	|	|	065
412	Michurinsk Voronezhski	d.	1241	1303	1318	1514	1530	...	...	|	1928	1940	...	...	2114	2340	...	0426	0143	0446	0446	0519	|	|	094
469	Gryazi Voronezhski	d.	1326	1348	1405	1558	1613	...	...	|	2011	2025	...	...	2159	0024	...	0522	0231	0532	0532	0615	|	|	103
426	Yelets	d.	|	|	|	|	|	...	...	1414	|	|	...	...	|	|	...	|	|	|	|	|	0522	0711	|
504	Lipetsk	d.	|	|	|	|	|	...	...	1540	|	|	...	...	|	|	...	|	|	|	|	|	0634	0827	|
591	Voronezh Pridacha	d.	1439**r**	1517	1531	1726	1754	...	...	1910	2133	2147	...	...	2312**r**	0201	...	0722	0520**r**	0805**r**	0805**r**	0824	0853	1106	1255
667	Liski	d.	...	1629	1645	1842	1858	...	...	2026	2243	2257	...	...	...	0304	...	0830	0741	0951	0951	0941	1010	1223	145
786	Rossosh	d.	...	1818	1827	2026	2036	...	...	2240	0025	0035	...	...	...	0439	...	1022	0951	1156	1156	1125	1223	1447	164
1062	Likhaya	d.	...	|	|	|	|	...	...	0247	|	|	...	...	...	0817	...	|	1458	1635	1635	|	1753	1940	205
1226	**Rostov na Donu**	a.	...	2339	2349	0141	0151	...	...	0613	0539	0547	...	...	...	1035	...	1712	1747	1923	1923	1810	2141	2257	232
1226	**Rostov na Donu**	d.	...	2356	0004	0156	0206	...	...	0630	0603	0611	...	...	...	...	1719	1727	1807	1943	1943	1833	2207	2317	234
	Vladyslavivka	d.	...	|	0900	|	|	...	...	|	|	|	...	...	...	...	|	0231	|	|	|	0620	|	|	|
	Dzhankoy	d.	...	|	1045	|	|	...	...	|	|	|	...	...	...	...	|	0415	|	|	|	0805	|	|	|
	Simferopol	a.	...	|	1200	|	|	...	...	|	|	|	...	...	...	...	|	0530	|	|	|	0920	|	|	|
	Sevastopol	a.	...	|	...	|	|	...	...	|	|	|	...	...	...	...	|	0725	|	|	|	1115	|	|	|
1405	Tikhoretskaya	d.	...	0208	...	|	|	...	...	0858	|	|	...	...	...	...	|	...	|	2213	2213	...	0059	0148	|
1332	Starominskaya Tim.	d.	...	|	...	|	|	...	...	|	|	|	...	...	...	...	1836	...	1921	|	|	...	|	|	|
1510	Krasnodar 1	d.	...	|	...	|	0517	0724	0843	|	0923	|	1315	1848	...	...	2037	...	2220	|	**e**	...	|	|	0326
1645	**Novorossiysk**	a.	...	|	...	|	|	|	|	|	1230	|	|	|	...	...	|	...	|	|	...	...	|	|	|
1636	**Anapa**	a.	...	|	...	0805	|	|	|	|	...	|	|	|	...	...	|	...	|	|	...	...	|	|	|
1533	Armavir Rostovski	d.	...	0403	...	...	|	|	|	1100	...	|	|	|	...	...	|	...	|	0133	...	...	0330	0436	|
1721	Mineralnye Vody	d.	...	0643	...	...	|	|	|	1324	...	|	|	|	...	...	|	...	|	0422	...	...	0629	0817	|
1747	Pyatigorsk	d.	...	0720	...	...	|	|	|	|	...	|	|	|	...	...	|	...	|	|	...	...	|	0853	|
1785	**Kislovodsk**	a.	...	0811	...	...	|	|	|	**d**	...	|	|	|	...	...	|	...	|	**f**	...	...	**g**	0946	|
1658	Tuapse	d.	...	...	...	...	0800	0943	1102	...	...	1132	1546	2103	...	...	2325	...	0230	...	...	...	...	...	0647
1738	**Sochi**	a.	...	...	...	...	0946	1130	1246	...	...	1318	1728	2258	...	...	0109	...	0432	...	...	...	...	...	0903
1761	**Adler**	a.	...	...	...	...	1024	1203	1316	...	...	1351	1758	2327	...	...	0139	...	0511	...	...	...	...	...	0943
1800	Gagra ◐	a.	...	...	...	...	...	...	...	...	...	...	...	...	...	...	...	...	0834	...	...	...	...	...	...
1873	**Sukhumi** ◐	a.	...	...	...	...	...	...	...	...	...	...	...	...	...	...	...	...	1043	...	...	...	...	...	...

Time zone: UTC+3		306*SJ*	145*SJ*	687*SJ*	33*SJ*	808*EI*	802*SJ*	19*SJ*	92*SJ*	11*EI*	135*SJ*	804*SJ*	830*SJ*	737*ZH*	816*SJ*	49*CH*	104*ZH*	30*JI*	102*SJ*	3*SJ*	28*SJ*	739*ZH*	36*SJ*	8*SJ*
		Pas	*Fir*	145*SJ*	*Sko*	❈	❈	*Fir*	*Sko*	*Fir*	*Sko*	❈	❈	*Fir*	❈	*Sko*	*Fir*	*Fir*	*Fir*	*Fir*	*Sko*	*Fir*	*Fir*	*Sko*
		D	●(4)	●(4)	●						●					**C**								
Sukhumi ◐	d.	1423	...	...	...	...	...	...	...	...	...	...	...	...	...	...	...	...	...	...	...	...	...	...
Gagra ◐	d.	1629	...	...	...	...	...	...	...	...	...	...	...	...	...	...	...	...	...	...	...	...	...	...
Adler	d.	1948	...	...	...	0216	0519	...	...	...	...	1256	1322	...	1752	...	1857	...	2103	...	...	...	1738	...
Sochi	d.	2032	...	...	...	0246	0551	...	...	...	...	1328	1357	...	1830	...	1934	...	2135	...	...	...	1819	...
Tuapse	d.	2232	...	...	...	0436	0737	...	...	...	...	1512	1542	...	2022	...	2122	...	2324	...	...	...	2039	...
Kislovodsk	d.	|	**f**	...	**g**	|	|	...	...	...	**d**	|	|	...	|	1349	|	...	|	2040	...	...	|	...
Pyatigorsk	d.	|	|	...	|	|	|	...	...	...	|	|	|	...	|	1444	|	...	|	2136	...	...	|	...
Mineralnye Vody	d.	|	0215	...	2259	|	|	...	...	...	1131	|	|	...	|	1551	|	...	|	2215	...	...	|	...
Armavir Rostovski	d.	|	0504	...	0137	|	|	...	...	...	1352	|	|	...	|	1815	|	...	|	0034	...	...	|	...
Anapa	d.	|	|	...	|	|	|	...	...	1415	|	|	|	...	|	|	|	...	|	|	...	...	|	...
Novorossiysk	d.	|	|	...	|	|	|	...	...	|	|	|	|	...	|	|	|	2120	|	|	...	...	|	...
Krasnodar 1	d.	0151	|	**e**	|	0734	1006	...	...	|	|	1725	1802	...	2248	|	2342	2350	|	|	...	...	0003	...
Starominskaya Tim.	d.	0447	|	|	|	0937	...	...	...	|	|	...	...	...	...	|	|	|	|	|	...	...	|	...
Tikhoretskaya	d.	|	0754	0754	0345	|	...	...	...	|	1612	...	...	...	...	2030	|	|	|	0233	...	...	|	...
Sevastopol	d.	|	|	|	|	|	...	...	2055	|	|	...	...	...	...	|	|	|	|	|	...	...	|	1715
Simferopol	d.	|	|	|	|	|	...	...	2310	|	|	...	...	...	...	|	|	|	|	|	1710	...	|	1910
Dzhankoy	d.	|	|	|	|	|	...	...	0055	|	|	...	...	...	...	|	|	|	|	|	1850	...	|	2052
Vladyslavivka	d.	|	|	|	|	|	...	...	0227	|	|	...	...	...	...	|	|	|	|	|	2016	...	|	2218
Rostov na Donu	a.	0627	1012	1012	0635	1052	...	...	1504	2050	1847	...	...	...	...	2324	0248	0256	0441	0449	0457	...	0348	0709
Rostov na Donu	d.	0650	1028	1028	0704	...	...	1515	1523	2110	1905	...	...	...	...	2340	0303	0311	0456	0504	0512	...	0406	0731
Likhaya	d.	1047	1352	1352	1058	...	...	1744	|	|	2234	...	...	...	...	0244	|	|	|	|	|	...	0730	|
Rossosh	d.	1514	1745	1745	1522	...	...	2123	2133	0245	0300	...	...	...	...	0650	0829	0838	1023	1032	1041	...	1116	1427
Liski	d.	1653	1921	1921	1725	...	...	2255	2315	0426	0454	...	...	...	...	0832	1001	1020	1202	1212	1222	...	1250	1606
Voronezh Pridacha	d.	1937**r**	2128**r**	2128**r**	1851	...	...	2356	0020	0528	0612	...	...	0733**r**	...	1017	1103	1125	1302	1315	1328	1621**r**	1458**r**	1728
Lipetsk	d.	|	|	|	2131	...	...	|	|	|	0944	...	...	|	...	1258	|	|	|	|	|	|	|	|
Yelets	d.	|	|	|	2312	...	...	|	|	|	1134	...	...	|	...	1439	|	|	|	|	|	|	|	|
Gryazi Voronezhski	d.	2125	2302	2302	|	...	...	0135	0150	0658	|	...	...	0850	...	|	1246	1259	1436	1451	1506	1738	1645	1913
Michurinsk Voronezhski	d.	2230	0004	0004	|	...	...	0220	0244	0757	|	...	...	0931	...	|	1329	1344	1523	1541	1556	1819	1745	1959
Ryazan 2	d.	0119	0245	0245	|	...	...	0438	0507	1025	|	...	...	1140	...	|	1559	1607	1750	1800	1821	2032	2056	2223
Moskva Kazanskaya	a.	0430	0550	0550	0618**p**	...	...	0730	0823	1330	1915**v**	...	...	1353	...	2309**v**	1830	1840	2015	2025	2105	2246	|	|
Tver	d.	...	...	...	...	...	...	...	...	...	2340	...	...	...	...	0205	...	...	...	...	...	...	0219	0334
Bologoye	d.	...	...	...	...	...	...	...	...	...	0143	...	...	...	...	0355	...	...	...	...	...	...	0402	0455
St Peterburg Glavny	a.	...	...	...	...	...	...	...	...	...	0501	...	...	...	...	1005	...	...	...	...	...	...	0743	0800

TOMSK / BARNAUL - NOVOSIBIRSK - ROSTOV - SOCHI - ADLER

Times are local		*time zone UTC+*	115*NJ* *Sko* ⊡	140*NJ* *Sko* ⊡
Tomsk 2	d.	+7	1540	...
Tomsk 1	d.	+7	1603	...
Tayga	d.	+7	1726	...
Barnaul	d.	+7	|	1444
Novosibirsk	a.	+7	2042	2044
Novosibirsk	d.	+7	2138	2138
Omsk	a.	+6	0518	0518
Omsk	d.	+6	0553	0553
Tyumen	d.	+5	1216	1216
Yekaterinburg	a.	+5	1753	1753
Yekaterinburg	d.	+5	1825	1825
Sarapul	d.	+4	0106	0106
Kazan 2 ◧	d.	+3	0527	0527
Saransk	d.	+3	1448	1448
Penza 1	d.	+3	1805	1805
Povorino	d.	+3	0106	0106
Liski	d.	+3	0448	0448
Rossosh	d.	+3	0706	0706
Likhaya	d.	+3	1137	1137
Rostov na Donu	a.	+3	1438	1438
Rostov na Donu	d.	+3	1511	1511
Tikhoretskaya	d.	+3	1746	1746
Armavir Tuapsinkii	d.	+3	2113	2113
Tuapse	d.	+3	0254	0254
Sochi	a.	+3	0452	0452
Adler	a.	+3	0532	0532

Times are local		*time zone UTC+*	140*SJ* *Sko* ⊡	116*SJ* *Sko* ⊡
Adler	d.	+3	1344	1344
Sochi	d.	+3	1426	1426
Tuapse	d.	+3	1639	1639
Armavir Tuapsinkii	d.	+3	2234	2234
Tikhoretskaya	d.	+3	0125	0125
Rostov na Donu	a.	+3	0424	0424
Rostov na Donu	d.	+3	0440	0440
Likhaya	d.	+3	0842	0842
Rossosh	d.	+3	1317	1317
Liski	d.	+3	1548	1548
Povorino	d.	+3	1950	1950
Penza 1	d.	+3	0316	0316
Saransk	d.	+3	0631	0631
Kazan 2 ◧	d.	+3	1511	1511
Sarapaul	d.	+4	2140	2140
Yekaterinburg	a.	+5	0630	0630
Yekaterinburg	d.	+5	0705	0705
Tyumen	d.	+5	1321	1321
Omsk	a.	+6	2303	2303
Omsk	d.	+6	2343	2343
Novosibirsk	a.	+7	0834	0834
Novosibirsk	d.	+7	0947	0951
Barnaul	a.	+7	1433	|
Tayga	d.	+7	...	1329
Tomsk 1	a.	+7	...	1516
Tomsk 2	a.	+7	...	1539

A – Every 3–4 days; daily from Apr. 14.
B – ②⑤⑦ until Apr. 24; daily from Apr. 25.
C – ②④⑦ until Apr. 24; daily from Apr. 26.
D – Every 3–4 days; daily from Apr. 16.

d – To / from Vladikavkaz (a. 1815 / d. 0658) and Makhachkala (a. 2200 / d. 1937). Note that each destination is served by seperate trains.
e – To / from Stavropol (a. 0423 / d. 2330).
f – To / from Nazran (a. 0743 / d. 2100).
g – To / from Vladikavkaz (a. 1121 / d. 1743) and Nal'chik (a. 1024 / d. 1904). Note that each destination is served by seperate trains.
p – Moskva **Paveletskaya**.
r – Voronezh **1**.
v – Moskva **Vostochny**.

❈ – *Lastochka* (Swallow) fast day train.
◧ – Also known as Vosstanie Passazhirskaja.
⊡ – Subject to confirmation.
◐ – Abkhazia Autonomous Region (⊞ = Veseloe / Tsandryphsh).
● – Even dates. See page 535.
■ – Uneven dates. See page 535.

KALININGRAD - MINSK - ADLER 1961

For other trains Kaliningrad - Minsk - Smolensk see Table **1950**.

km	*UTC+3*	**360***CH*	**302***BJ*
		Pas	*Pas*
		●	■(1)
0	**Kaliningrad** .... KA d.	1807	...
342	Maladzechna .... BY d.	0457	...
535	**Minsk** .... a.	0605	...
535	**Minsk** .... d.	0633	1058
684	Babruysk .... d.	|	1306
749	Zhlobin .... d.	|	1356
839	Homel .... d.	|	1535
890	Zlynka .... d.	|	1650
747	Orsha Tsent. .... a.	0924	|
747	Orsha Tsent. .... BY d.	0948	|
866	**Smolensk** .... RU a.	1108	|
866	**Smolensk** .... d.	1143	|
1112	Bryansk O. .... a.	1600	2146
1112	Bryansk O. .... d.	1653	2236
	Kursk .... d.	2305	|
1443	Yelets .... d.	|	0531
1521	Lipetsk .... d.	|	0654
1684	Voronezh 1 .... d.	0410	0922**r**
1763	Liski .... d.	0732	1137
1882	Rossosh .... d.	1005	1550
2158	Likhaya .... d.	1443	2026
2322	**Rostov na Donu** ◧ ...... a.	1817	0044
2322	**Rostov na Donu** ◧ ...... d.	1850	0118
2428	Starominskaya Tim. ...... d.	2016	0242
2533	Krasnodar 1 .... d.	2328	0547
2753	Tuapse .... d.	0340	0932
2833	**Sochi** .... a.	0544	1221
2856	**Adler** .... a.	0622	1255

UTC+3	**302***SJ*	**360***SJ*
	Pas	*Pas*
	■(1)	■(5)
Adler .... d.	1625	2039
Sochi .... d.	1703	2118
Tuapse .... d.	1930	2347
Krasnodar 1 .... d.	2325	0431
Starominskaya Tim. ..d.	0248	0830
Rostov na Donu ◧...a.	0408	0952
Rostov na Donu ◧...d.	0423	1017
Likhaya .... d.	1121	1415
Rossosh .... d.	1736	1843
Liski .... d.	1935	2031
Voronezh 1 .... d.	2043**r**	2350
Lipetsk .... d.	2325	|
Yelets .... d.	0119	|
Kursk .... d.	|	0444
Bryansk O. .... a.	0755	1026
Bryansk O. .... d.	0839	1119
Smolensk .... a.	|	1630
Smolensk .... RU d.	|	1705
Orsha Tsent. .... BY a.	|	1821
Orsha Tsent. .... d.	|	1845
Zlynka .... d.	1314	|
Homel .... d.	1438	|
Zhlobin .... d.	1609	|
Babruysk .... d.	1711	|
Minsk .... a.	1859	2127
Minsk .... d.	...	2150
Maladzechna .... BY d.	...	2301
Kaliningrad .... KA a.	...	0808

SARATOV - ADLER 1962

km	*UTC+3*	**14***ZH*		*UTC+3*	**14***SJ*	
		A			**B**	
0	**Saratov** 1 (UTC +4) ... d.	1128	...	**Adler** .... d.	1830	...
429	Volgograd 1 .... d.	1704	...	Sochi .... d.	1910	...
964	Tikhoretskaya .... d.	0223	...	Tuapse .... d.	2110	...
1100	Krasnodar 1 .... d.	0526	...	Krasnodar 1 .... d.	0048	...
1248	Tuapse .... d.	1029	...	Tikhoretskaya .... d.	0328	...
1328	Sochi .... a.	1236	...	Volgograd 1 .... d.	1411	...
1351	**Adler** .... a.	1308	...	**Saratov** 1 (UTC +4) . a.	2116	...

ROSTOV - BAKI 1963

km	*UTC+3*			*UTC+3*		
0	**Rostov na Donu** .... d.	...	...	**Baki** .... AZ d.	...	...
307	Armavir Rost. .... d.	...	...	Derbent .... d.	...	...
495	Mineralnye Vody .... d.	...	...	Makhachkala .... d.	...	...
896	Makhachkala .... d.	...	...	Mineralnye Vody .... d.	...	...
1025	Derbent .... d.	...	...	Armavir Rost. .... d.	...	...
1286	**Baki** .... AZ a.	...	...	**Rostov na Donu** .... a.	...	...

NOTES FOR TABLES 1961, 1962 and 1963.

A – ■(3) until Mar. 19; daily from Mar. 21.
B – ●(4) until Mar. 20; daily from Mar. 22.
r – Voronezh **Pridacha**.
◧ – Rostov na Donu **Pervomajskaya**.
AZ – Azerbaijan (UTC+4). ▦ = Yalama.
KA – Kaliningrad region of Russia (UTC+2). Local time.
BY – Belarus.
RU – Russia.

MOSKVA - SARATOV, VOLGOGRAD and BAKI 1965

km	*Times are local time*	time zone UTC+	**1***IJ*	**5***GJ*		**9***GJ*	**85***VJ*		**133***MJ*	**15***JI*
			Fir	*Fir*		*Fir*	*Sko*		*Sko*	*Sko*
			C	**E**			**K**		**J**	**G**
0	**Moskva** Pavelets. .... d.	+3	1350	1820	...	1908	1927	...	1927	2010
198	Ryazan 2 .... d.	+3	|	|	...	|	0037	...	0037	|
408	Michurinsk Uralski .... d.	+3	1955**z**	0121	...	0150	0402	...	0402	0406**z**
541	Gryazi Voronezhski ...... d.	+3	2121	|	...	|	|	...	|	0528
778	Povorino .... d.	+3	0135	|	...	|	|	...	|	1010
481	Tambov 1 .... d.	+3	|	0243	...	0304	0534	...	0534	|
861	**Saratov** 1 .... a.	+4	|	0955	...	1014	1308	...	1308	|
861	**Saratov** 1 .... d.	+4	|	1043	...	...	1347	...	1347	|
1145	**Volgograd** 1 .... a.	+3	0745	|	...	...	|	...	|	1652
1595	Astrakhan 1 .... a.	+4	...	2013	...	...	0106	...	0106	...
⊡	Makhachkala .... a.	+3	...	...	...	...	1208	...	1208	...
2212	Derbent .... a.	+3	...	...	...	...	...	...	1521	...
2473	**Baki** .... AZ a.	+4	...	...	...	...	...	...	...	...

Times are local time	time zone UTC+	**9***ZH*	**1***ZH*		**5***ZH*	**15***ZH*		**85***SJ*	**133***EI*
		Fir	*Fir*		*Fir*	*Sko*		*Sko*	*Sko*
			D		**F**	**H**		**J**	**K**
Baki .... AZ d.	+4	...	...	...	...	...	...	...	...
Derbent .... d.	+3	...	...	...	...	...	...	...	1147
Makhachkala .... d.	+3	...	...	...	...	...	...	1511	1511
Astrakhan 1 .... d.	+4	...	...	...	1100	...	...	0300	0300
Volgograd 1 .... d.	+3	...	1551	...	|	1713	...	|	|
Saratov 1 .... a.	+4	...	|	...	2022	|	...	1359	1359
Saratov 1 .... d.	+4	1816	|	...	2110	|	...	1442	1442
Tambov 1 .... d.	+3	2316	|	...	0249	|	...	2049	2049
Povorino .... d.	+3	|	2210	...	|	2357	...	|	|
Gryazi Voronezhski ..... d.	+3	|	0223	...	|	0436	...	|	|
Michurinsk Uralski .... d.	+3	0056	0316**z**	...	0425	0540**z**	...	2242	2242
Ryazan 2 .... d.	+3	|	|	...	|	|	...	0204	0204
Moskva Pavelets. .... a.	+3	0722	0930	...	1110	1400	...	0700	0700

C – ■(3) until Apr. 13; daily from Apr. 15.
D – ● until Apr. 12; daily from Apr. 14.
E – ● Dec. Jan.; ■ Feb., Mar.; ● Apr.; daily from Apr. 16.
F – ■ Dec., Jan.; ● Feb., Mar.; ■ Apr.; daily from Apr. 15.
G – ●(4) until Apr. 20; daily from Apr. 22.
H – ■(3) until Apr. 19; daily from Apr. 21.
J – ● Dec., Feb., Mar., June; ■ Jan., Apr., May.
K – ■ Dec., Feb., Mar., June; ● Jan., Apr., May.
z – Michurinsk **Voronezhski**.
● – Even dates. See page 535.
■ – Uneven dates. See page 535.
⊡ – *1537 km* (*2083 km* via Volgograd).
AZ – Azerbaijan (UTC+4).

MOSKVA - SAMARA - UFA - CHELYABINSK 1970

km	*Times are local time*	time zone UTC+	**392***UJ*	**132***UJ*		**120***MJ*	**66***JI*		**138***JI*	**50***MJ*		**22***JI*	**10***JI*		**52***JI*	**14***EJ*		**14***EJ* **675***EI*	**42***JI*		**102***JI*	
			Sko	*Sko*		*Sko*	*Sko*		*Sko*	*Sko*		*Fir*	*Fir*		*Sko*	*Fir*		**K**	*Fir*		*Sko* **L**	
0	**Moskva** Kazanskaya .... d.	+3	1225	1508	...	1516	1708	...	1716	1750	...	1808	2008	...	2040	2122	...	2122	2150	...	...	...
197	Ryazan 1 .... d.	+3	1553	1833**r**	...	1814	2016	...	2038	2100	...	2110	2308	...	2342	0033	...	0033	0054	...	...	...
601	Ruzayevka .... d.	+3	2220	|	...	2332	0205	...	0255	0227	...	0239	0346	...	0512	0545	...	0545	0632	...	...	...
627	**Saransk** .... a.	+3	|	|	...	2359	|	...	|	|	...	|	|	...	|	|	...	|	0705	...	...	...
710	**Penza** 1 .... d.	+3	|	0450	...	...	|	...	|	|	...	|	|	...	0735	|	...	|	...	...	1343	...
712	Inza .... d.	+4	0133	|	...	...	0442	...	0544	0458	...	0547	|	...	...	0815	...	0815	...	...	|	...
873	**Ulyanovsk** .... d.	+4	0602	...	...	...	|	...	|	|	...	0834	|	...	...	|	...	|	...	...	|	...
908	Syzran 1 .... d.	+4	|	1026	...	...	0811	...	0912	0737	...	...	0832	...	...	1039	...	1039	...	...	1914	...
	Toliatti .... a.	+4	|	|	...	...	1056	...	|	|	...	...	|	...	...	|	...	|	...	...	|	...
1044	**Samara** .... a.	+4	|	1300	...	...	...	...	1137	0930	...	...	1011	...	...	1222	...	1222	...	...	2123	...
1044	**Samara** .... d.	+4	|	1350	...	...	...	...	1227	...	...	...	...	...	...	1310	...	1310	...	...	2210	...
1216	Buzuluk' .... d.	+5	|	1821	...	...	...	...	1634	...	...	...	...	...	...	|	...	|	...	...	|	...
1462	Orenburg .... a.	+5	|	2232	...	...	...	...	2025	...	...	...	...	...	...	|	...	|	...	...	|	...
	Orsk .... a.	+5	|	0515	...	...	...	...	...	...	...	...	...	...	...	|	...	|	...	...	|	...
1567	Ufa .... d.	+5	2107	...	...	...	...	...	...	...	...	...	...	...	...	2227	...	2227	...	...	0823	...
1933	**Magnitogorsk** .... a.	+5	|	...	...	...	...	...	...	...	...	...	...	...	...	|	...	0740	...	...	|	...
2048	**Chelyabinsk** .... a.	+5	0800	...	...	...	...	...	...	...	...	...	...	...	...	0708	...	...	...	...	1736	...

Times are local time	time zone UTC+	**391***UJ*	**49***JI*		**41***JI*	**13***UJ*		**676***UJ* **13***UJ*	**52***MJ*		**9***JI*	**21***JI*		**101***JI*	**131***UJ*		**66***EI*	**137***UJ*		**119***JI*	
		Sko	*Sko*		*Fir*	*Fir*		**K**	*Sko*		*Fir*	*Fir*		**L**	*Sko*		*Sko*	*Sko*		*Sko*	
Chelyabinsk .... d.	+5	1330	...	...	...	2320	...	...	...	...	...	...	...	1840	...	...	...	...	...	...	...
Magnitogorsk .... d.	+5	|	...	...	...	|	...	2140	...	...	...	...	...	|	...	...	...	...	...	...	...
Ufa .... d.	+5	0118	...	...	...	0852	...	0852	...	...	...	...	...	0413	...	...	...	...	...	...	...
Orsk .... d.	+5	|	...	...	...	|	...	|	...	...	...	...	...	|	2255	...	...	...	...	...	...
Orenburg .... d.	+5	|	...	...	...	|	...	|	...	...	...	...	...	|	0524	...	...	1125	...	...	...
Buzuluk' .... d.	+5	|	...	...	...	|	...	|	...	...	...	...	...	|	0952	...	...	1539	...	...	...
Samara .... a.	+4	|	...	...	...	1604	...	1604	...	...	...	...	...	1149	1159	...	...	1742	...	...	...
Samara .... d.	+4	|	1544	...	...	1657	...	1657	...	...	1955	...	...	1258	1245	...	...	1838	...	...	...
Toliatti .... d.	+4	|	|	...	...	|	...	|	...	...	|	...	...	|	|	...	1824	|	...	...	...
Syzran 1 .... d.	+4	|	1747	...	...	1917	...	1917	...	...	2140	...	...	1529	1536	...	2158	2103	...	...	...
Ulyanovsk .... d.	+4	1411	|	...	...	|	...	|	...	...	|	2042	...	|	|	...	|	|	...	...	...
Inza .... d.	+4	1748	2026	...	...	2133	...	2133	...	...	|	2359	...	|	|	...	0032	0006	...	...	...
Penza 1 .... d.	+3	|	|	...	...	|	...	|	2135	...	|	|	...	1810	1920	...	|	|	...	...	...
Saransk .... d.	+3	|	|	...	2037	|	...	|	|	...	|	|	...	...	|	...	|	|	...	0640	...
Ruzayevka .... d.	+3	1857	2108	...	2119	2211	...	2211	0005	...	0025	0040	...	...	|	...	0115	0122	...	0709	...
Ryazan 1 .... d.	+3	0155	0238	...	0256	0307	...	0307	0450	...	0500	0546	...	...	0607**r**	...	0642	0652	...	1204	...
Moskva Kazanskaya .... a.	+3	0500	0540	...	0600	0620	...	0620	0753	...	0800	0910	...	...	0952	...	1010	1025	...	1425	...

K – ■ Dec., Feb., Mar., June; ● Jan., Apr., May.
L – To / from Niznevartovsk. For days of running see Table **1993**.
r – Ryazan 2.
● – Even dates. See page 535.
■ – Uneven dates. See page 535.

1971 BELGOROD - NOVOSIBIRSK

Times are local time	time zone UTC+	124VJ Sko A	Times are local time	time zone UTC+	123NJ Sko A
Belgorod d.	+3	0910	**Novosibirsk** d.	+7	1447
Voronezh 1 d.	+3	1804	**Omsk** a.	+6	2222
Gryazi Voronezhski d.	+3	1945	**Omsk** d.	+6	2239
Michurinsk Uralski d.	+3	2117	Kurgan d.	+5	0731
Tambov 1 d.	+3	2315	**Chelyabinsk** a.	+5	1105
Penza 1 d.	+3	0610	**Chelyabinsk** d.	+5	1149
Syzran 1 d.	+4	1046	Ufa a.	+5	2112
Samara a.	+4	1310	Ufa d.	+5	2138
Samara d.	+4	1437	**Samara** a.	+4	0510
Ufa a.	+5	2351	**Samara** d.	+4	0558
Ufa d.	+5	0027	Syzran 1 d.	+4	0824
Chelyabinsk a.	+5	0925	Penza 1 d.	+3	1214
Chelyabinsk d.	+5	1020	Tambov 1 d.	+3	1855
Kurgan d.	+5	1425	Michurinsk Uralski d.	+3	2107
Omsk a.	+6	2356	Gryazi Voronezhski d.	+3	2245
Omsk d.	+6	0012	Voronezh 1 d.	+3	0200
Novosibirsk a.	+7	0934	**Belgorod** a.	+3	0925

1973 NIZHNI NOVGOROD - VORKUTA

Times are local time	time zone UTC+	90GJ Sko A	Times are local time	time zone UTC+	89GJ Sko A
Nizhni Novgorod d.	+3	1610	**Vorkuta** d.	+3	1905
Kirov d.	+3	2356	Sosnogorsk d.	+3	0855
Kotlas Yuzhny d.	+3	0903	Mikun d.	+3	1337
Mikun d.	+3	1319	Kotlas Yuzhny d.	+3	1816
Sosnogorsk d.	+3	1828	Kirov d.	+3	0316
Vorkuta a.	+3	0820	**Nizhni Novgorod** a.	+3	0925

NOTES FOR TABLES 1971 AND 1973:

A – Runs every 2–4 days.

1975 SAMARA and SARATOV - AKTOBE - TOSHKENT, BISHKEK and ALMATY

km	Times are local time	time zone UTC+	24CJ ■(1)		110KH		52KH		34TJ
0	*Moskva Kaz* **1970** d.	+3	...	...	...	...	...	...	...
1044	**Samara** d.	+4	...	...	...	...	...	...	...
•681	Ufa d.	+5	...	...	...	...	...	...	...
1462	Orenburg d.	+5	...	...	...	...	...	...	...
•894	**Saratov** 1 d.	+4	...	...	...	...	...	...	...
•459	Oral / Uralsk KA d.	+5	...	...	...	...	1510	...	...
1734	Aktobe 1 KA a.	+5	...	...	...	...	2140	...	...
1734	Aktobe 1 KA d.	+5	1400	...	1924	...	2200	...	2256
1828	Kandyagash KA d.	+5	1532	...	2110	...	|	...	0033
2924	Mangystau ⊙ KA a.	+5	|	...	1916	...	|	...	|
2767	Kyzlorda KA d.	+5	0903	...	...	...	|	...	1717
3315	**Toshkent** UZ a.	+5	|	...	...	...	◧	...	|
3738	Andizhan UZ a.	+5	|	...	...	...	|	...	|
3240	Shymkent KA d.	+6	2012	...	...	...	|	...	0425
3729	**Bishkek** 2 KY a.	+6	|	...	...	...	|	...	|
4001	**Almaty** 1 KA a.	+6	0936	...	...	...	|	...	1815
4010	**Almaty** 2 KA a.	+6	...	...	...	...	0822	...	...

Times are local time	time zone UTC+	23KH ■(3)		51KH		33CJ		109K
Almaty 2 KA d.	+6	...	...	2020	...	...	...	...
Almaty 1 KA d.	+6	1317	...	|	...	2332	...	...
Bishkek 2 KY d.	+6	|	...	|	...	|	...	...
Shymkent KA d.	+6	0322	...	|	...	1234	...	...
Andizhan UZ d.	+5	|	...	◧	...	|	...	...
Toshkent UZ d.	+5	|	...	|	...	|	...	...
Kyzlorda KA d.	+5	1221	...	|	...	2156	...	...
Mangystau ⊙ KA d.	+5	|	...	|	...	|	...	1640
Kandyagash KA d.	+5	0506	...	|	...	1432	...	1412
Aktobe 1 KA a.	+5	0625	...	0507	...	1556	...	1536
Aktobe 1 KA d.	+5	...	...	0541	...	...	...	...
Oral / Uralsk KA a.	+5	...	...	1225	...	...	...	...
Saratov 1 a.	+4	...	...	...	...	...	...	...
Orenburg d.	+5	...	...	...	...	...	...	...
Ufa a.	+5	...	...	...	...	...	...	...
Samara a.	+4	...	...	...	...	...	...	...
Moskva Kaz **1970** a.	+3	...	...	...	...	...	...	...

■ – Uneven dates. See page 535.
● – Even dates. See page 535.
⊙ – Station for Aktau (15 km).
◧ – Via Table **1980**.
• – Distance from Aktobe.
KA – Kazakhstan (Almaty = UTC+6, western zone = UTC+5).
KY – Kyrgyzstan (UTC+6).
UZ – Uzbekistan (UTC+5).

1976 SAMARA and KAZAN - NUR-SULTAN - ALMATY and TOSHKENT

See also Table 1980

km	Times are local time	time zone UTC+	106TJ		16TJ C				
0	*Moskva Kaz* **1970** d.	+3	...	...	...	...	...	...	...
1044	**Samara** d.	+4	...	...	...	...	...	...	...
2048	Chelyabinsk d.	+5	...	...	...	...	...	...	...
	Kazan **1990** d.	+3	...	...	...	...	...	...	...
	Yekaterinburg **1990** d.	+5	...	...	...	...	...	...	...
2306	Kurgan d.	+5	...	...	...	...	...	...	...
2573	Petropavl KA d.	+6	1418	...	2355	...	...	...	...
3064	**Nur-Sultan** 1 KA a.	+6	2047	...	0823	...	...	...	...
3064	**Nur-Sultan** 1 KA d.	+6	2102	...	0858	...	...	...	...
3305	Karagandy KA d.	+6	0008	...	1317	...	...	...	...
	Almaty 1 KA a.	+6	|	...	0544	...	...	...	...
4407	**Almaty** 2 KA a.	+6	1142	...	0616	...	...	...	...
4356	Bishkek 2 KY a.	+6	...	...	...	...	...	...	...
4522	Shymkent KA a.	+6	...	...	...	...	...	...	...
4755	**Toshkent** UZ a.	+5	...	...	...	...	...	...	...

Times are local time	time zone UTC+	105TJ		15TJ ●(4)				
Toshkent UZ d.	+5	...	...	...	...	...	...	...
Shymkent KA d.	+6	...	...	...	...	...	...	...
Bishkek 2 KY d.	+6	...	...	...	...	...	...	...
Almaty 2 KA d.	+6	1550	...	1532	...	...	...	...
Almaty 1 KA d.	+6	|	...	1616	...	...	...	...
Karagandy KA d.	+6	0329	...	0947	...	...	...	...
Nur-Sultan 1 KA a.	+6	0611	...	1326	...	...	...	...
Nur-Sultan 1 KA d.	+6	0626	...	1356	...	...	...	...
Petropavl KA d.	+6	1246	...	2220	...	...	...	...
Kurgan d.	+5	...	...	...	...	...	...	...
Yekaterinburg **1990** a.	+5	...	...	...	...	...	...	...
Kazan **1990** a.	+3	...	...	...	...	...	...	...
Chelyabinsk d.	+5	...	...	...	...	...	...	...
Samara a.	+4	...	...	...	...	...	...	...
Moskva Kaz **1970** a.	+3	...	...	...	...	...	...	...

MOSKVA - MAKAT - TOSHKENT and DUSHANBE

km	Times are local	zone UTC+		Times are local	zone UTC+	
0	**Moskva** Kaz. d.	+3	...	**Dushanbe** 1 TA d.	+5	...
198	Ryazan 2 d.	+3	...	Termez UZ d.	+5	...
411	Michurinsk Vor d.	+3	...	Karshi UZ d.	+5	...
1075	**Volgograd** d.	+4	...	**Toshkent** UZ d.	+5	...
1804	Atyrau KA d.	+5	...	Samarkand UZ d.	+5	...
1934	Makat KA d.	+5	...	Navoi UZ d.	+5	...
2641	Kungrad UZ d.	+5	...	Bukhara UZ d.	+5	...
3048	Urgench UZ d.	+5	...	Urgench UZ d.	+5	...
3465	Bukhara UZ a.	+5	...	Kungrad UZ d.	+5	...
3558	Navoi UZ a.	+5	...	Makat KA d.	+5	...
3714	Samarkand UZ a.	+5	...	Atyrau KA d.	+5	...
4057	**Toshkent** UZ a.	+5	...	**Volgograd** d.	+4	...
3714	Karshi UZ a.	+5	...	Michurinsk Vor d.	+3	...
4046	Termez UZ a.	+5	...	Ryazan 2 d.	+3	...
4271	**Dushanbe** 1 TA a.	+5	...	**Moskva** Kaz. a.	+3	...

NOVOSIBIRSK - ALMATY and TOSHKENT

km	Times are local	zone UTC+	1KH D	Times are local	zone UTC+	2MZ E
0	**Novosibirsk** d.	+7	...	**Toshkent** UZ d.	+7	...
228	Barnaul d.	+7	...	Shymkent KA d.	+7	1945
1121	Aktogay KA d.	+6	...	**Almaty** 2 KA d.	+6	|
	Almaty 2 KA d.	+6	1832	**Almaty** 1 KA a.	+6	|
1678	**Almaty** 1 KA a.	+6	|	**Almaty** 1 KA d.	+6	|
1678	**Almaty** 1 KA d.	+6	|	**Almaty** 2 KA a.	+6	0631
1687	**Almaty** 2 KA a.	+6	|	Aktogay KA d.	+6	...
2424	Shymkent KA d.	+6	0534	Barnaul d.	+6	...
2657	**Toshkent** UZ a.	+5	...	**Novosibirsk** a.	+5	...

C – Uneven dates [.. *31*, 5..].
D – ①③⑥. Talgo train.
E – ②④⑦. Talgo train.
KA – Kazakhstan (Almaty zone = UTC+6).
TA – Tajikistan (UTC+5).
UZ – Uzbekistan (UTC+5).

KAZAKHSTAN and UZBEKISTAN 1980

See also Tables 1975 and 1976

A UTC+6	16TJ	52KH	4CJ	712CJ	106TJ	86CJ	56CJ	21CJ	29TJ	10TJ	1KH	25TJ	87TJ
									■(3)			●	■(1)
	A ◇	B			◇				F		C		
ur-Sultan 1 d.	0858	1742	1850n	1947n	2102	2125	2220	...	...	2140n	...	...	...
aragandy d.	1317	2051	2154	2251	0008	0111	0230	...	...	0131	...	...	...
maty 1 a.	0544	|	|	|	|	|	|	0956	...	1644	...	...	...
maty 2 a.	0616	0822	1013	|	1142	|	|	|	1640	...	1832	2116	2131
ymkent a.	...	...	...	1307	...	1829	2202	2259	0246	...	0534	0938	1112
yzlorda ♡ a.	...	...	...	...	...	...	0619	0645	0902	...	...	...	...
tyrau ♡ a.	...	...	...	...	...	...	...	...	0521	...	...	...	...

KA UTC+6 (♡+5)	37KH	51KH	29TJ	57KH	47CJ	
	●(6)		■(3)	●(4)	■(3)	
		B	F			
Nur-Sultan 1 d.	1010	1103	...	2015	1944n	...
Tobol d.	2257	1954	...	1203	1203	...
Kandyagash ♡ d.	1003	|	2221	2224	2237	...
Aktobe 1 ♡ a.	|	0507	|	0031	|	...
Oral / Uralsk ♡ a.	|	1225	|	0930	|	...
Atyrau ♡ a.	|	...	0521	...	0820	...
Mangistau ⊙ ♡ a.	0759	...	...	...	...	...

A UTC+6	105TJ	712KH	56KH	3CJ	51KH	15TJ	9TJ	29KH	26TJ	2MZ	86KH	87KH	22TJ
						●(4)		■(5)	■(3)			●	
	◇				B	◇		E		G			
tyrau ♡ d.	...	...	...	...	...	...	...	0830	...	...	...	...	...
yzlorda ♡ d.	...	...	2150	...	...	...	...	0454	...	...	...	...	1350
ymkent d.	...	1435	0756	...	...	...	...	1315	1729	1945	1959	2120	2318
maty 2 d.	1550	|	|	1730	2020	1532	...	2357	0546	0631	|	1220	|
maty 1 d.	|	|	|	|	|	1616	1905	...	...	...	|	...	1312
aragandy d.	0329	0512	0429	0608	0759	0947	1052	...	...	...	1406	...	...
ur-Sultan 1 a.	0611	0752n	0830	0848	1041	1326	1405n	...	...	...	1717	...	...

KA UTC+6 (♡+5)	47TJ	58KH	37TJ	52KH	29KH	
	■(1)	●	●		■(5)	
				B	E	
Mangistau ⊙ ♡ d.	...	...	1600	...	...	...
Atyrau ♡ d.	1730	...	|	...	0830	...
Oral / Uralsk ♡ d.	|	1955	|	1510	|	...
Aktobe 1 ♡ d.	|	0524	|	2200	|	...
Kandyagash ♡ d.	0446	0734	1330	|	1627	...
Tobol d.	1825	2124	0328	0936	...	...
Nur-Sultan 1 a.	1053n	1247	1401	1721	...	...

Z UTC+5	762FJ	760FJ	10FJ	766FJ	12FJ	4CH	56CH	393FJ	72FJ	58ZJ
								①		③⑥⑦
	H	H		H					V	
oshkent d.	0728	0800	0906	1845	1852	1852	...	...	...	...
Toshkent Yuzhnyy d.	|	|	|	|	|	|	2100	2142	2215	2215
amarkand d.	0950	1016	1235	2103	2223	2239	0101	0146	0217	0217
Karshi a.	|	1121	|	|	|	0018	|	|	|	|
avoi d.	1042	...	1359	2156	0015	...	0255	0330	0443	0443
ukhara 1 a.	1119	...	1458	2234	0122	...	0357	0432	0616	0616
rgench a.	...	...	...	...	...	...	1013	1050	...	1227
hiva a.	...	...	...	...	...	...	1058	1133	...	...

UZ UTC+5	765FJ	11FJ	3FJ	761FJ	759FJ	9FJ	394FJ	58MZ	71FJ	56ZH
							②	①③⑦		
	H			H	H				W	
Khiva d.	...	...	...	...	...	...	1308	...	...	1605
Urgench d.	...	...	...	...	...	...	1441	1503	...	1800
Bukhara 1 d.	0455	0532	...	1550	...	1608	2104	2121	2121	0040
Navoi d.	0535	0648	...	1629	...	1714	2244	2302	2302	0148
Karshi d.	|	|	0710	|	1646	|	|	|	|	|
Samarkand d.	0637	0832	0849	1732	1800	1846	0058	0141	0141	0340
Toshkent Yuzhnyy a.	|	|	|	|	|	|	0505	0540	0540	0740
Toshkent a.	0847	1228	1243	1948	2010	2217	...	...	...	...

– Uneven dates [.. *31*, *5* ..].
– Oral - Nur-Sultan - Almaty and v.v.
– ①③⑥. Talgo train.
– Atyrau - Kandyagash - Shymkent (2nd day) - Almaty.
– Almaty - Shymkent (2nd day) - Kandyagash - Atyrau.
– ②④⑦. Talgo train.
– AFROSIYOB – high-speed Talgo train.

V – ①②④⑤.
W – ②③⑤⑥.
n – Nur-Sultan **Nurly Zhol**.
◇ – To / from Petropavl (Table **1976**).
⊙ – Station for Aktau (15 km).
♡ – UTC+5 (Kazakhstan western zone, local time is shown).

● – Even dates. See page 535.
■ – Uneven dates. See page 535.
KA – Kazakhstan (Almaty zone = UTC+6).
UZ – Uzbekistan (UTC+5).

MOSKVA - ARCHANGELSK, LABYTNANGI and VORKUTA 1985

km	Local time (UTC+3)	22JA	22JA	653MJ	16MJ	98JA	78JA	10JA	116SZ	42VJ
		Fir	33JA	Pas	Sko	Sko	Sko	Sko	Sko	Fir
		J	J			K	K	①⑤	L	M
0	**Moskva** Yaroslavskaya d.	1005	1005	...	1250	...	...	...	2035	2150
282	Yaroslavl d.	1513	1513	...	1702	...	...	...	0054	0203
	St Peterburg Ladozhski d.	|	|	...	|	1020	1020	1454	|	|
496	Vologda 1 d.	1908	1908	...	2125	|	|	|	0501	0552
707	Konosha 1 d.	2225	2225	...	0033	0125	0125	0506	0829	0916
134	**Archangelsk** a.	|	|	...	0902	|	|	1326	1814	|
825	Velsk d.	0051	0051	...	...	0342	0342	...	...	1126
084	**Kotlas** Yuzhny d.	0604	0604	...	...	1011	1011	...	...	1636
325	Mikun d.	0950	1021	...	...	1414	1424	...	...	2028
412	**Syktyvkar** a.	|	1232	...	...	1541	|	...	...	|
571	Sosnogorsk a.	1421	...	...	...	...	1917	...	...	0056
406	**Labytnangi** (*UTC+5*) a.	1000	...	1151	...	...	|	...	...	|
277	**Vorkuta** a.	...	...	1939	...	...	0950	...	...	1435

Local time (UTC+3)	653JA	115CH	41MJ	34CH	21NJ	77JA	98VJ	15JA	9AJ
		Sko	Fir	21NJ	Fir	Sko	Sko	Sko	Sko
		N	P	Q	J	K	K		②⑥
Vorkuta d.	0915	...	1635	...	...	2027	...	...	...
Labytnangi (*UTC+5*) d.	2105	...	|	...	1521	|	...	...	...
Sosnogorsk d.	...	...	0549	...	0703	0929	...	...	...
Syktyvkar d.	...	...	|	0852	|	|	1204	...	...
Mikun d.	...	...	1052	1147	1147	1428	1428	...	...
Kotlas Yuzhny d.	...	...	1521	1609	1609	1922	1922	...	...
Velsk d.	...	...	2029	2106	2106	0054	0054	...	...
Archangelsk d.	...	0711	|	|	|	|	|	2030	2132
Konosha 1 d.	...	1754	2225	2338	2338	0323	0323	0454	0556
Vologda 1 d.	...	2147	0154	0220	0220	|	|	0815	|
St Peterburg Ladozhski a.	...	|	|	|	|	1845	1845	|	2055
Yaroslavl d.	...	0203	0549	0620	0620	...	...	1222	...
Moskva Yaroslavskaya a.	...	0607	0927	0958	0958	...	...	1643	...

km	Local time (UTC+3)	102JA	716JA	104JA	108JA	106JA				
		Fir	❦	Fir	Sko	Fir				
					R					
0	**Moskva** Yaroslavskaya d.	0735	1510	1445	1705	1905	...	...	...	...
282	**Yaroslavl** a.	1101	1810	1824	2030	2231	...	...	...	...

Local time (UTC+3)	101JA	715JA	107JA	103JA	105JA				
	Fir	❦	Sko	Fir	Fir				
			R						
Yaroslavl d.	0701	0822	0825	1351	1939	...	...	...	...
Moskva Yaroslavskaya a.	1021	1119	1151	1711	2300	...	...	...	...

MURMANSK - ARCHANGELSK

km		143JA 371JA S		371CH 144JA S
0	**Murmansk** d.	0615	**Archangelsk** d.	1635
277	Kandalaksha d.	1146	Belomorsk d.	0445
665	Belomorsk d.	1928	Kandalaksha d.	1237
151	**Archangelsk** a.	0818	**Murmansk** a.	1800

J – ■ Dec., Feb., Mar., June; ● Jan., Apr., May.
K – Runs every 2 – 3 days.
L – ● until Apr. 26; daily from Apr. 28.
M – ■ Dec., Jan., Apr., May; ● Feb., Mar.; daily from June 1.
N – ●(4) untl Apr. 20; daily from May 1.
P – ■ Dec., Jan., Apr., May; ● Feb., Mar.; daily from June 2.
Q – ● Dec., Feb., Mar., June; ■ Jan., Apr., May.
R – ①③⑤⑦ until Mar. 28; daily from Mar. 30.

S – Runs every 2 – 4 days.
❦ – *Lastochka* (Swallow) fast day train.
● – Even dates. See page 535.
■ – Uneven dates. See page 535.

MOSKVA - NIZHNI NOVGOROD - SAMARA 1989

km	Local time (UTC+3)	701MJ	727MJ	729MJ	703MJ	705MJ	707MJ	733MJ	709MJ	775AJ
		♠	❦	❦	♠	♠	♠	❦	♠	♥
	St Peterburg Glavny d.	...	...	...	...	...	...	...	...	1700
0	**Moskva** Vostochny d.	0632	0715	0925	1035	1358	1540	1830	2015	2112k
186	Vladimir d.	0816	0900	1117	1223	1541	1723	2018	2201	2306
437	**Nizhni Novgorod** a.	1014	1100	1331	1425	1743	1932	2222	2359	0103

Local time (UTC+3)	759RJ	701NJ	729GJ	703NJ	731GJ	705NJ	733GJ	707NJ	709NJ
	♥	♠	❦	♠	❦	♠	❦	♠	♠
Nizhni Novgorod d.	0505	0745	0940	1105	1336	1538	1755	1857	2011
Vladimir d.	0704	0954	1200	1311	1549	1744	2016	2054	2216
Moskva Vostochny a.	0903k	1137	1351	1500	1739	1930	2203	2237	2359
St Peterburg Glavny a.	1320	...	...	...	...	...	...	...	...

Local time (UTC+3)	713VJ	
	♠	
	Q	
t Peterburg Ladozhski d.	0020	...
loskva Vostochny d.	0546	...
ladimir d.	0728	...
izhni Novgorod Strigino ✈ a.	0931	...
izhni Novgorod Strigino ✈ d.	0935	...
rzamas 1 d.	1116	...
aransk d.	1429	...
yzran 1 d.	1907	...
amara a.	2100	...

Local time (UTC+3)	713JI	
	♠	
	J	
Samara d.	0120	...
Syzran 1 d.	0315	...
Saransk d.	0624	...
Arzamas 1 d.	0933	...
Nizhni Novgorod Strigino ✈ a.	1048	...
Nizhni Novgorod Strigino ✈ d.	1052	...
Vladimir d.	1256	...
Moskva Vostochny a.	1440	...
St Peterburg Ladozhski a.	2000	...

J – ■ Dec., Feb., Mar., June.; ● Jan., Apr., May.
Q – ● Dec., Feb., Mar., June.; ■ Jan., Apr., May.

k – Moskva **Kurskaya**.

♥ – *Sapsan* high-speed train. ✕ Ⓡ.
♠ – *Strizh* (Swift) fast Talgo day train.
❦ – *Lastochka* (Swallow) fast day train.

● – Even dates (see page 535).
■ – Uneven dates (see page 535).

1990 MOSKVA - YEKATERINBURG - NOVOSIBIRSK - IRKUTSK - VLADIVOSTOK

km			time zone UTC +	2EI Fir	82IJ 376Y	82IJ Sko	12JA Fir	12JA 383EJ	70CH Sko	86UJ Sko	92IJ Sko	8NJ Sko	118NJ Sko	118NJ 144NJ	96NJ Sko	110EI Sko	68Y Sko	62MJ Sko	62MJ 638NJ
					A	A	B	B		B	B	A	B	B	A	A	B	C	C
0	**Moskva** Yaroslavskaya	d.	+3	0035	...	...	1335	1335	1350	...	1650	...				2150	2305	2345	2345
	Moskva Kazanskaya	d.	+3	|	1310	1310	|	|	|	1638	|	...	1920	1920	1920	|	|	|	|
282	Yaroslavl	d.	+3	0441	|	|	|	|	1801	|	|	...	|	|	|	|	0319	|	|
	Murom 1	d.	+3	|	1751	1751	|	|	|	2109	|	...	0015	0015	0015	|	|	|	|
	Kazan 1	d.	+3	|	0213	0213	|	|	|	0535	|	...	|	|	|	|	|	|	|
	Kazan 2 ◧	d.	+3	|	|	|	|	|	|	|	|	...	0755	0755	0755	|	|	|	|
	Sarapul	d.	+4	|	0855	0855	|	|	|	1159	|	...	1423	1423	1423	|	|	|	|
210	Vladimir	d.	+3	|	|	|	1650	1650	|	|	1958	...	|	|	|	0159	|	0252	0252
461	**Nizhni Novgorod**	d.	+3	|	|	|	2022	2022	|	|	2316	...	|	|	|	0502	|	0549	0549
917	Kirov	d.	+3	1837	|	|	0228	0228	0525	|	0515	...	|	|	|	1200	1500	1214	1214
1397	Perm 2	d.	+5	0540	|	|	|	|	1521	|	1513	...	|	|	|	2212	0025	2200	2200
	Perm Sortirovochnaya	d.	+5	|	|	|	1216	1216	|	|	|	...	|	|	|	|	|	|	|
	Nivhni Tagil	d.	+5	|	|	|	2126	2126	|	|	|	...	|	|	|	|	|	|	|
	Serov	d.	+5	|	|	|	|	0156	|	|	|	...	|	|	|	|	|	|	|
	Priobe	a.	+5	|	|	|	|	1335	|	|	|	...	|	|	|	|	|	|	|
1778	**Yekaterinburg**	a.	+5	1113	1746	1746	2358	...	2056	2020	2046	...	2335	2335	2335	0323	0544	0315	0315
1778	**Yekaterinburg**	d.	+5	1207	1841	1841	0034	...	2128	2057	2120	...	0010	0010	0010	0351	0616	0343	0343
2104	Tyumen	d.	+5	1733	0002	0002	0625	...	0227	0354	0219	...	0558	0558	0558	1012	1149	0842	0842
	Tobolsk	d.	+5	|	|	|	1023	...	|	0814	|	...	|	|	|	1423	|	|	|
	Surgut	d.	+5	|	|	|	1932	...	|	1752	|	...	|	|	|	2331	|	|	|
	Niznevartovsk	a.	+5	|	|	|	|	...	|	2235	|	...	|	|	|	|	|	|	|
	Korotchayevo	d.	+5	|	|	|	0832	...	|	...	|	...	|	|	|	1256	|	|	|
	Novy Urengoy	a.	+5	|	|	|	1026	...	|	...	|	...	|	|	|	1516	|	|	|
2676	Omsk	a.	+6	0215	0855	0855	...	...	1109	...	1001	...	1435	1435	1435	...	2120	1634	1634
2676	Omsk	d.	+6	0231	0920	0920	...	...	1131	...	1017	1225	1455	1455	1515	...	2136	1650	1650
3303	**Novosibirsk**	a.	+7	1147	1808	1808	...	...	2057	...	1832	2309	2349	2349	|	...	0601	0100	0100
3303	**Novosibirsk**	d.	+7	1247	1858	1858	...	...	2137	...	1910	0013	0041	0042	|	...	0651	0146	0251
	Barnaul	a.	+7	|	|	|	...	...	|	...	|	|	|	|	0830	...	|	|	|
	Novokuznetsk	a.	+7	|	|	|	...	...	|	...	|	|	0737	|	...	...	|	|	|
	Kemerovo	a.	+7	|	|	|	...	...	|	...	|	|	...	0536	...	...	|	|	|
3534	Tayga	d.	+7	1649	2229	2229	...	...	0110	...	2241	0409	...	...	...	...	1030	0507	0737
3621	**Tomsk** 2	a.	+7	|	|	|	...	...	|	...	|	|	...	...	...	...	|	|	0931
	Abakan	a.	+7	|	|	|	...	...	|	...	|	|	...	...	...	...	0535	|	...
4065	Krasnoyarsk	a.	+7	0123	0723	0723	...	...	1210	...	0743	1251	...	...	...	...	...	1325	...
4065	Krasnoyarsk	d.	+7	0203	0808	0838	...	...	1306	...	0828	1328	...	...	...	...	...	1346	...
4483	Tayshet	d.	+8	0954	1628	1658	...	...	2146	...	1638	2134	...	...	...	...	...	2118	...
	Bratsk Padunskie Porogi	d.	+8	|	2247	|	...	...	|	...	2308	|	...	...	...	...	...	|	...
	Severobaikalsk	d.	+8	|	1303	|	...	...	|	...	1402	|	...	...	...	...	...	|	...
5152	**Irkutsk**	a.	+8	2123	|	0611	...	...	0826	...	...	0816	...	...	...	...	...	0744	...
5152	**Irkutsk**	d.	+8	2203	⊡	0742	...	...	0909	...	...	0859	...	...	...	...	...	0807	...
5608	Ulan Ude	d.	+8	0625	...	1614	...	...	1756	...	...	1726	...	...	...	...	...	1530	...
6165	Chita 2	d.	+9	1819	...	...	...	...	0611	...	...	0526	...	...	...	...	...	0213	...
7274	Skovorodino	d.	+9	1658	...	...	...	...	...	...	...	0334	...	...	...	...	...	2246	...
8492	Khabarovsk	d.	+10	1645	...	...	...	...	...	...	...	0215	...	...	...	...	...	1934	...
9147	Ussuriysk	d.	+10	0407	...	...	...	...	...	...	...	1331	...	...	...	...	...	0517	...
9258	**Vladivostok**	a.	+10	0603	...	...	...	...	...	...	...	1528	...	...	...	...	...	0707	...

MOSKVA and ST PETERBURG - IZHEVSK, YEKATERINBURG, CHELYABINSK and PETROPAVL

		time zone UTC+	74EJ Sko	14NJ Fir	72EJ Fir	16KH Fir	26GJ Sko	2JI Fir	24MJ Sko
			A	B	D	A			
Moskva Kazanskaya	d.	+3	...	...	...	1638	1738	2050	2250
St Peterburg Ladozhski	d.	+3	1530	1530	1735	|	|	|	|
Vologda 1	d.	+3	0250	0250	0530	|	|	|	|
Kirov	d.	+3	1238	1238	1450	|	|	|	|
Perm 2	d.	+5	2222	2222	0015	|	|	|	|
Murom 1	d.	+3	|	|	|	2109	2240	0105	0303
Kazan 1	d.	+3	|	|	|	0535	|	0800	1048
Kazan 2 ◧	d.	+3	|	|	|	|	0530	...	...
Izhevsk	a.	+4	|	|	|	|	1139	...	...
Sarapul	d.	+4	|	|	|	1159	...	...	...
Yekaterinburg	a.	+5	0339	0339	0533	2020	...	...	...
Yekaterinburg	d.	+5	...	...	...	2105	...	...	...
Kurgan	a.	+5	...	...	...	0505	...	...	...
Chelyabinsk	a.	+5	...	...	...	1008	...	...	...
Petropavl	KA a.	+6	...	...	...	...	...	...	...

MOSKVA - ULAAN BAATAR - BEIJING

km	Trans-Mongolian route		time zone UTC+	
0	*Moskva Yar. (above)*	d.	+3	...
3303	*Novosibirsk (above)*	d.	+7	...
5152	**Irkutsk**	d.	+8	...
5608	Ulan Ude	d.	+8	...
5863	Naushki 🏛	d.	+8	...
5886	Suche Bator 🏛	MO d.	+8	...
6265	**Ulaan Baatar**	MO a.	+8	...
6265	**Ulaan Baatar**	MO d.	+8	...
6770	Dzamin Uud 🏛	MO d.	+8	...
6780	Erlan 🏛	CH a.	+8	...
7622	**Beijing**	CH a.	+8	...

MOSKVA - HARBIN - BEIJING

km	Trans-Manchurian route		time zone UTC+	602CH Pas
0	*Moskva Yar. (above)*	d.	+3	...
1778	*Yekaterinburg (above)*	d.	+5	...
3303	*Novosibirsk (above)*	d.	+7	...
5152	**Irkutsk**	d.	+8	...
6165	Chita 2	d.	+9	1939
6626	Zabaikalsk 🏛	d.	+9	0731
6638	Manzhouli 🏛	CH d.	+8	...
7573	Harbin	CH a.	+8	...
8122	Shenyang	CH a.	+8	...
8849	Tianjin	CH a.	+8	...
8986	**Beijing**	CH a.	+8	...

A – ● Dec., Feb., Mar., June; ■ Jan., Apr., May.
B – ■ Dec., Feb., Mar., June; ● Jan., Apr., May.
C – ①④⑤⑦.
D – Every 2–4 days.

⊡ – To / from Tynda and Neryungri (Table **1991**).
◧ – Also known as Vosstanie Passazhirskaja.

● – Even dates (see page 535).
■ – Uneven dates (see page 535).

CH – China (UTC+8).
MO – Mongolia (UTC+8).

VLADIVOSTOK - IRKUTSK - NOVOSIBIRSK - YEKATERINBURG - MOSKVA 1990

		69*CH* *Sko*	637*NJ* **61***MJ*	61*MJ* *Sko*	338*EJ* **11***EJ*		11*EJ* *Fir*	95*NJ* *Sko*	143*NJ* **117***NJ*	117*NJ* *Sko*		7*NJ* *Sko*	81*IJ* *Sko*	375*EI* **81***IJ*	109*MJ* *Sko*		91*IJ* *Sko*	1*EI* *Fir*	85*EJ* *Sko*	67*Y* *Sko*	
			E	**C**	**B**		**A**	**B**	**A**	**A**		**B**	**A**	**B**	**B**		**B**		**A**	**A**	
Vladivostok d.	+10	...	...	1850	...	...	...	...	...	...	...	2123	...	...	...	...	...	2318	...	...	...
Ussuriysk d.	+10	...	...	2111	...	...	...	...	...	...	...	2329	...	...	...	...	...	0150	...	...	...
Khabarovsk d.	+10	...	...	0821	...	...	...	...	...	...	...	1024	...	...	...	...	...	1425	...	...	...
Skovorodino d.	+9	...	...	0240	...	...	...	...	...	...	...	0601	...	...	...	...	...	1043	...	...	...
Chita 2 d.	+9	2100	...	2356	...	...	...	...	...	...	...	0452	...	...	...	...	...	0918	...	...	...
Ulan Ude d.	+8	0720	...	0815	...	...	...	...	...	...	...	1416	1406	...	...	...	...	1909	...	...	...
Irkutsk a.	+8	1515	...	1524	...	...	...	...	...	...	...	2207	2157	⊡	...	...	...	0314	...	...	...
Irkutsk d.	+8	1611	...	1552	...	...	...	...	...	...	...	2255	2245	│	...	...	...	0354	...	...	...
Severobaikalsk d.	+8	│	...	│	...	...	...	...	...	...	...	│	│	1515	...	...	1720	│	...	...	...
Bratsk Padunskie Porogi d.	+8	│	...	│	...	...	...	...	...	...	...	│	│	0439	...	...	0748	│	...	...	...
Tayshet d.	+8	0252	...	0233	...	...	...	...	...	...	...	1021	1031	1100	...	...	1349	1457	...	...	...
Krasnoyarsk a.	+7	0933	...	0803	...	...	...	...	...	...	...	1607	1623	1647	...	...	2001	2047	...	...	...
Krasnoyarsk d.	+7	1027	...	0824	...	...	...	...	...	...	...	1642	1742	1742	...	...	2116	2126	...	...	...
Abakan d.	+7	│	...	│	...	...	...	...	...	...	...	│	│	│	...	...	│	│	...	1800	...
Tomsk 2 d.	+7	│	1230	│	...	...	...	...	...	...	...	│	│	│	...	...	│	│	...	│	...
Tayga d.	+7	1942	1500	1628	...	...	...	...	...	...	...	0210	0244	0244	...	...	0539	0552	...	1224	...
Kemerovo d.	+7	│	│	│	...	...	...	...	0008	...	...	│	│	│	...	...	│	│	...	│	...
Novokuznetsk d.	+7	│	│	│	...	...	...	...	│	2205	...	│	│	│	...	...	│	│	...	│	...
Barnaul d.	+7	│	│	│	...	...	...	1415	│	│	...	│	│	│	...	...	│	│	...	│	...
Novosibirsk a.	+7	2327	1854	1942	...	...	...	│	0458	0507	...	0547	0610	0610	...	...	0846	0930	...	1554	...
Novosibirsk d.	+7	0026	2022	2022	...	...	...	│	0603	0603	...	0637	0701	0701	...	...	0936	1030	...	1659	...
Omsk a.	+6	0808	0238	0238	...	...	...	1335	1348	1348	...	1427	1439	1439	...	...	1648	1710	...	0029	...
Omsk d.	+6	0825	0254	0254	...	...	...	1415	1415	1415	...	...	1457	1457	...	...	1705	1726	...	0045	...
Novy Urengoy d.	+5	│	│	│	...	...	1226	│	│	│	...	...	│	│	1716	...	│	│	...	│	...
Korotchayevo d.	+5	│	│	│	...	...	1426	│	│	│	...	...	│	│	1916	...	│	│	...	│	...
Niznevartovsk d.	+5	│	│	│	...	...	│	│	│	│	...	...	│	│	│	...	│	│	0645	│	...
Surgut d.	+5	│	│	│	...	...	0520	│	│	│	...	...	│	│	0812	...	│	│	1330	│	...
Tobolsk d.	+5	│	│	│	...	...	1548	│	│	│	...	...	│	│	1825	...	│	│	2246	│	...
Tyumen d.	+5	1714	0853	0853	...	...	2046	2127	2127	2127	...	...	2136	2136	2315	...	2325	2335	0325	0701	...
Yekaterinburg a.	+5	2242	1333	1333	...	...	0223	0304	0304	0304	...	...	0239	0239	0407	...	0415	0423	0929	1244	...
Yekaterinburg d.	+5	2326	1401	1401	...	...	0325	0358	0358	0358	...	...	0348	0348	0435	...	0443	0451	1009	1345	...
Priobe d.	+5	│	│	│	1307	...	│	│	│	│	...	...	│	│	│	...	│	│	│	│	...
Serov d.	+5	│	│	│	0053	...	│	│	│	│	...	...	│	│	│	...	│	│	│	│	...
Nivhni Tagil d.	+5	│	│	│	0650	...	0650	│	│	│	...	...	│	│	│	...	│	│	│	│	...
Perm Sortirovochnaya d.	+5	│	│	│	1506	...	1506	│	│	│	...	...	│	│	│	...	│	│	│	│	...
Perm 2 d.	+5	0539	2000	2000	│	...	│	│	│	│	...	...	│	│	1128	...	1136	1144	│	1950	...
Kirov d.	+3	1131	0114	0114	2129	...	2129	│	│	│	...	...	│	│	1728	...	1738	1748	│	0104	...
Nizhni Novgorod d.	+3	│	0700	0700	0331	...	0331	│	│	│	...	...	│	│	2326	...	2337	│	│	│	...
Vladimir d.	+3	│	1110	1110	0712	...	0712	│	│	│	...	...	│	│	0228	...	0244	│	│	│	...
Sarapul d.	+4	│	│	│	│	...	│	1125	1125	1125	...	...	1113	1113	│	...	│	│	1651	│	...
Kazan 2 ◧ d.	+3	│	│	│	│	...	│	1635	1635	1635	...	...	1615	1615	│	...	│	│	│	│	...
Kazan 1 d.	+3	│	│	│	│	...	│	│	│	│	...	...	│	│	│	...	│	│	2205	│	...
Murom 1 d.	+3	│	│	│	│	...	│	0057	0057	0057	...	...	0045	0045	│	...	│	│	0450	│	...
Yaroslavl d.	+3	0054	│	│	│	...	│	│	│	│	...	...	│	│	│	...	│	0644	│	1232	...
Moskva Kazanskaya a.	+3	│	│	│	│	...	│	0520	0520	0520	...	...	0510	0510	│	...	│	│	0940	│	...
Moskva Yaroslavskaya a.	+3	0456	1358	1358	1030	..	1030	...	...	...	...	...	...	...	0522	..	0552	1113	...	1657	...

PETROPAVL, CHELYABINSK, YEKATERINBURG and IZHEVSK - ST PETERBURG and MOSKVA

	time zone UTC+	**23***GJ* *Sko*		**1***GJ* *Fir*		**71***EJ* *Fir* **D**		**25***GJ* *Sko*		**16***IJ* *Fir* **B**		**73***EJ* *Sko* **A**		**13***NJ* *Fir* **B**							
Petropavl KA d.	+6	...	...	...	...	...	...	...	...	...	...	...	...	...	...	...	...	...	...	...	...
Chelyabinsk d.	+5	...	...	...	...	...	...	...	...	2150	...	...	...	...	...	...	...	...	...	...	...
Kurgan d.	+5	...	...	...	...	...	...	...	...	0222	...	...	...	...	...	...	...	...	...	...	...
Yekaterinburg a.	+5	...	...	...	...	...	...	...	...	0816	...	...	...	...	...	...	...	...	...	...	...
Yekaterinburg d.	+5	...	...	...	...	2318	...	...	...	1009	...	2310	...	2310	...	...	...	...	...	...	...
Sarapul d.	+4	...	...	...	...	│	...	...	...	1651	...	│	...	│	...	...	...	...	...	...	...
Izhevsk d.	+4	...	...	...	...	│	...	1740	...	│	...	│	...	│	...	...	...	...	...	...	...
Kazan 2 ◧ d.	+3	...	...	...	...	│	...	2150	...	│	...	│	...	│	...	...	...	...	...	...	...
Kazan 1 d.	+3	1811	...	2000	...	│	...	│	...	2205	...	│	...	│	...	...	...	...	...	...	...
Murom 1 d.	+3	0204	...	0300	...	│	...	0502	...	0450	...	│	...	│	...	...	...	...	...	...	...
Perm 2 d.	+5	│	...	│	...	0522	...	│	...	│	...	0531	...	0531	...	...	...	...	...	...	...
Kirov d.	+3	│	...	│	...	1102	...	│	...	│	...	1121	...	1121	...	...	...	...	...	...	...
Vologda 1 d.	+3	│	...	│	...	2130	...	│	...	│	...	2214	...	2214	...	...	...	...	...	...	...
St Peterburg Ladozhski a.	+3	│	...	│	...	0840	...	│	...	│	...	1000	...	1000	...	...	...	...	...	...	...
Moskva Kazanskaya a.	+3	0630	...	0710	...	...	...	0923	...	0940	...	...	...	...	...	...	...	...	...	...	...

BEIJING - ULAAN BAATAR - MOSKVA

km	*Trans-Mongolian route*	*time zone UTC+*							
0	**Beijing** CH d.	+8	...	...	...	...	...	...	...
842	Erlan ⊞ CH d.	+8	...	...	...	...	...	...	...
852	Dzamin Uud ⊞ MO d.	+8	...	...	...	...	...	...	...
1356	**Ulaan Baatar** MO a.	+8	...	...	...	...	...	...	...
1356	**Ulaan Baatar** MO d.	+8	...	...	...	...	...	...	...
1735	Suche Bator ⊞ MO d.	+8	...	...	...	...	...	...	...
1758	Naushki ⊞ d.	+8	...	...	...	...	...	...	...
2013	Ulan Ude d.	+8	...	...	...	...	...	...	...
2469	**Irkutsk** a.	+8	...	...	...	...	...	...	...
4319	*Novosibirsk (above)* a.	+7	...	...	...	...	...	...	...
7622	*Moskva Yar. (above)* a.	+3	...	...	...	...	...	...	...

BEIJING - HARBIN - MOSKVA

km	*Trans-Manchurian route*	*time zone UTC+*		**683***CH* *Pas*		
0	**Beijing** CH d.	+8	...	...	...	...
137	Tianjin CH d.	+8	...	...	...	...
864	Shenyang CH d.	+8	...	...	...	...
1413	Harbin CH d.	+8	...	...	...	...
2348	Manzhouli ⊞ CH d.	+8	...	...	...	...
2360	Zabaikalsk ⊞ d.	+9	...	2008	...	...
2820	Chita 2 d.	+9	...	0752	...	...
3833	**Irkutsk** a.	+8	...	...	...	...
5683	*Novosibirsk (above)* a.	+7	...	...	...	...
7208	*Yekaterinburg (above)* a.	+5	...	...	...	...
8986	*Moskva Yar. (above)* a.	+3	...	...	...	...

A – ● Dec., Feb., Mar., June; ■ Jan., Apr., May.
B – ■ Dec., Feb., Mar., June; ● Jan., Apr., May.
C – ①④⑤⑦.
D – Every 2–4 days.
E – ①②④⑤.

⊡ – To/from Tynda and Neryungri (Table **1991**).
◧ – Also known as Vosstanie Passazhirskaja.

● – Even dates (see page 535).
■ – Uneven dates (see page 535).

CH – China (UTC+8).
MO – Mongolia (UTC+8).

1991 NOVOSIBIRSK - SEVEROBAIKALSK - TYNDA - NERYUNGRI - NIZHNY BESTYAKH

Baikal - Amur Magistrale (BAM) line. For other trains Moskva - Severobaikalsk see Table **1990**.

km	Times are local times		time zone UTC+	298NJ Pas	328JI Pas	71IJ Sko	376Y Pas	82IJ 376Y		
				A		A	B	A		
	Moskva Kaz. **1990**	d.	+3	...	...	...	...	1310	day 1	...
0	**Novosibirsk**	d.	+7	0511	...	...	...	1858	day 3	...
762	Krasnoyarsk	d.	+7	1721	...	...	0808	0808	day 4	...
	Irkutsk	d.	+8	|	...	2305	|	|	|	...
1180	**Tayshet**	a.	+8	0134	...	1038	1615	1615	day 4	...
1180	**Tayshet**	d.	+8	0207	...	1153	1628	1628	day 4	...
1473	Bratsk Padunskie Porogi	d.	+8	0805	...	1832	2247	2247	day 4	...
2243	**Severobaikalsk**	d.	+8	2119	...	0910	1303	1303	day 5	...
2243	**Severobaikalsk**	d.	+8	2219	...	...	1408	1408	day 5	...
3528	**Tynda**	a.	+9	0006	...	...	1614	1614	day 6	...
3528	**Tynda**	d.	+9	...	1019	...	1811	1811	day 6	...
3757	Neryungri	a.	+9	...	1516	...	2337	2337	day 6	...
3757	Neryungri	d.	+9	...	1556	...	...	...	...	...
4125	Tommot	a.	+9	...	2347	...	...	...	...	...
4125	Tommot	d.	+9	...	0002	...	...	...	...	...
4563	**Nizhny Bestyakh** ⊕	a.	+9	...	1000	...	...	...	...	...

Times are local times		time zone UTC+	375EI Pas	375EI 81IJ			297ZH Pas	327JI Pas	71Y Sko
			B	B			A		A
Nizhny Bestyakh ⊕	d.	+9	...	...	...	...	...	1700	...
Tommot	a.	+9	...	...	...	...	...	0242	...
Tommot	d.	+9	...	...	...	...	...	0257	...
Neryungri	a.	+9	...	...	...	...	...	1055	...
Neryungri	d.	+9	0606	0606	day 1	...	...	1125	...
Tynda	a.	+9	1124	1124	day 1	...	...	1601	...
Tynda	d.	+9	1312	1312	day 1	...	1312	...	...
Severobaikalsk	a.	+8	1400	1400	day 2	...	1400	...	...
Severobaikalsk	d.	+8	1515	1515	day 2	...	1515	...	1929
Bratsk Padunskie Porogi	d.	+8	0439	0439	day 3	...	0439	...	0955
Tayshet	a.	+8	1047	1047	day 3	...	1047	...	1556
Tayshet	d.	+8	1100	1100	day 3	...	1100	...	1648
Irkutsk	a.	+8	|	|	|	...	|	...	0601
Krasnoyarsk	a.	+7	1647	1647	day 3	...	1647	...	...
Novosibirsk	a.	+7	...	0610	day 4	...	0834	...	...
Moskva Kaz. **1990**	a.	+3	...	0510	day 6	...	...	...	...

km	Times are local		UTC+	364EI
0	**Tynda**	d.	+9	1642
669	Fevralsk	d.	+9	0840
951	Novy Urgal	a.	+10	1629
951	Novy Urgal	d.	+10	1704
1469	**Komsomolsk**	a.	+10	0703

Times are local		UTC+	363EI
Komsomolsk	d.	+10	1834
Novy Urgal	a.	+10	0839
Novy Urgal	d.	+10	0914
Fevralsk	d.	+9	1533
Tynda	a.	+9	0646

km	Times are local		UTC+	351EI	667EI
0	**Vladivostok** **1990**	d.	+10	1720	...
111	Ussuriysk **1990**	d.	+10	1948	...
766	**Khabarovsk** **1990**	d.	+10	0802	2105
1155	Komsomolsk	a.	+10	1738	0555
1618	**Sovetskaya Gavan**	a.	+10	0235	...

Times are local		UTC+	351JI	667ZH
Sovetskaya Gavan.	d.	+10	1724	...
Komsomolsk	d.	+10	0750	2107
Khabarovsk ... **1990**	a.	+10	1831	0603
Ussuriysk **1990**	a.	+10	0703	...
Vladivostok **1990**	a.	+10	0908	...

A – ● Dec., Feb., Mar., June; ■ Jan., Apr., May.
B – ■ Dec., Feb., Mar., June; ● Jan., Apr., May.

● – Even dates. See page 535.
■ – Uneven dates. See page 535.

⊕ – In summer a ferry (15 km from station) runs to Yakutsk. Connection by 🚌 in winter (no service in Spring or Autumn).

1993 YEKATERINBURG - KAZAN - SARATOV - VOLGOGRAD

km	Local times		time zone UTC+	445EJ Sko A	
0	**Yekaterinburg**	d.	+5	0145	...
515	Sarapul	d.	+4	1101	...
875	**Kazan 1**	d.	+3	1703	...
1121	Ulyanovsk	d.	+4	0039	...
1407	**Samara**	a.	+4	|	...
1576	**Saratov 1**	d.	+4	0906	...
2005	Volgograd 1	d.	+3	1553	...
2665	Armavir Ros.	d.	+3	0820	...
2853	Mineralnye Vody	d.	+3	1158	...
2879	Pyatigorsk	d.	+3	1234	...
2917	**Kislovodsk**	a.	+3	1328	...

Local times		time zone UTC+	445SJ Sko B	
Kislovodsk	d.	+3	2201	...
Pyatigorsk	d.	+3	2257	...
Mineralnye Vody	d.	+3	0004	...
Armavir Ros.	d.	+3	0232	...
Volgograd 1	d.	+3	1949	...
Saratov 1	d.	+4	0508	...
Samara	d.	+4	|	...
Ulyanovsk	d.	+4	1449	...
Kazan 1	d.	+3	2013	...
Sarapul	d.	+4	0318	...
Yekaterinburg	a.	+5	1222	...

km	Local times		time zone UTC+	101JI Sko A	107EJ Sko C
0	**Niznevartovsk**	d.	+5	1113	2159
216	Surgut	d.	+5	1642	0224
692	Tobolsk	d.	+5	0204	1114
921	Tyumen	d.	+5	0641	1545
1247	**Yekaterinburg**	d.	+5	1253	2232
1762	Sarapul	d.	+4	|	0558
2122	**Kazan 1**	d.	+3	◇	1217
2368	Ulyanovsk	d.	+4	|	1914
2654	**Samara**	a.	+4	1149	|
2823	**Saratov 1**	d.	+4	...	0540
3252	**Volgograd 1**	d.	+3	...	1148

Local times		time zone UTC+	107ZH Sko D	102JI Sko A
Volgograd 1	d.	+3	2310	...
Saratov 1	d.	+4	0800	...
Samara	d.	+4	|	2210
Ulyanovsk	d.	+4	1847	|
Kazan 1	d.	+3	2345	◇
Sarapul	d.	+4	0636	|
Yekaterinburg	d.	+5	1709	0018*
Tyumen	d.	+5	2311	0625
Tobolsk	a.	+5	0232	0958
Surgut	a.	+5	1135	1914
Niznevartovsk	a.	+5	1612	0105

A – ● Dec., Feb., Mar., June; ■ Jan., Apr., May.
B – ■ Dec., Feb., Mar., June; ● Jan., Apr., May.

C – Every 4 days until Mar. 14; daily from Mar. 18.
D – Every 4 days until Mar. 11; daily from Mar. 15.

◇ – To / from Penza (Table **1970**) via Ufa (Tables **1970** / **1994**).
* – More than 24 hours after previous time shown.

1994 YEKATERINBURG - SAMARA - SARATOV and KYIV - BAKI

km	Local times		time zone UTC+	101JI Sko A	
0	**Tyumen**	d.	+5	0641	...
326	**Yekaterinburg**	d.	+5	1253	...
578	Chelyabinsk	d.	+5	1840	...
1059	Ufa	d.	+5	0413	...
1582	**Samara**	d.	+4	1149	...
2019	**Saratov 1**	a.	+4	...	...
2019	**Saratov 1**	d.	+4	...	...
2695	Astrakhan 1	d.	+4	...	...
3183	**Makhachkala**	a.	+3	...	...

Local times		time zone UTC+	102JI Sko A	
Makhachkala	d.	+3	...	...
Astrakhan 1	d.	+4	...	...
Saratov 1	a.	+4	...	...
Saratov 1	d.	+4	...	...
Samara	d.	+4	2210	...
Ufa	d.	+5	0823	...
Chelyabinsk	d.	+5	1810	...
Yekaterinburg	a.	+5	2300	...
Tyumen	a.	+5	0528	...

km	Local times		time zone UTC+	
0	**Kyiv** UA	d.	◧	...
335	Poltava K UA	d.	◧	...
493	**Kharkiv** UA	d.	◧	...
861	Liski	d.	+3	...
1453	Volgograd	d.	+4	...
1903	Astrakhan 1	d.	+4	...
2391	Makhachkala	d.	+3	...
2520	Derbent	d.	+3	...
2765	**Baki** AZ	a.	+4	...

Local times		time zone UTC+	
Baki AZ	d.	+4	...
Derbent	d.	+3	...
Makhachkala	d.	+3	...
Astrakhan 1	d.	+4	...
Volgograd	d.	+4	...
Liski	d.	+3	...
Kharkiv UA	a.	◧	...
Poltava K UA	a.	◧	...
Kyiv UA	a.	◧	...

A – ● Dec., Feb., Mar., June; ■ Jan., Apr., May.
◧ – UTC+2 winter, UTC+3 summer.

AZ – Azerbaijan (UTC+4).
UA – Ukraine (UTC+2 winter, UTC+3 summer).

1995 GEORGIA

Time zone: UTC+4 Georgian Railways

km			802		804		371 ⊡			
0	**Yerevan** AR	d.	...	...	...	...	2130	...	...	...
374	**Tbilisi**	a.	...	...	...	...	0735	...	...	...
374	**Tbilisi**	d.	0820	...	1720	...	...	...	...	...
722	**Batumi**	a.	1415	...	2315	...	...	...	...	...

		803		372 ⊡		801			
Batumi	d.	0745	...	...	...	1745	...	...	...
Tbilisi	a.	1326	...	...	...	2329	...	...	...
Tbilisi	d.	...	...	2020	...	...	...	...	...
Yerevan AR	a.	...	...	0655	...	...	...	...	...

km			870		12		18		874		
0	**Baki** AZ	d.	...	...	...	...	...	...	...	...	...
551	**Tbilisi**	d.	0830	...	0850	...	0850	...	1810	...	...
772	Kutaisi	a.	|	...	|	...	1440	...	|	...	...
868	Zugdidi	a.	1450	...	|	...	...	...	|	...	...
863	Poti	a.	...	...	|	...	...	...	2357	...	...
877	**Ozurgeti**	a.	...	...	1720	...	...	...	...	...	...

		873		11		17		869		
Ozurgeti	d.	...	...	0855	...	...	...	...	...	...
Poti	d.	0720	...	|	...	...	...	...	...	...
Zugdidi	d.	|	...	|	...	...	...	1610	...	...
Kutaisi	d.	|	...	|	...	1205	...	|	...	...
Tbilisi	d.	1301	...	1746	...	1746	...	2232	...	...
Baki AZ	a.	...	...	...	...	...	...	...	...	...

⊡ – ■(3). Conveys 🛏.
■ – See page 535.

AR – Armenia (UTC+4).
AZ – Azerbaijan (UTC+4).

TBILISI - TBILISI AIRPORT (journey 40 mins.)
From Tibilisi: 0755, 1655; from Tibilisi Airport: 0835, 1740.

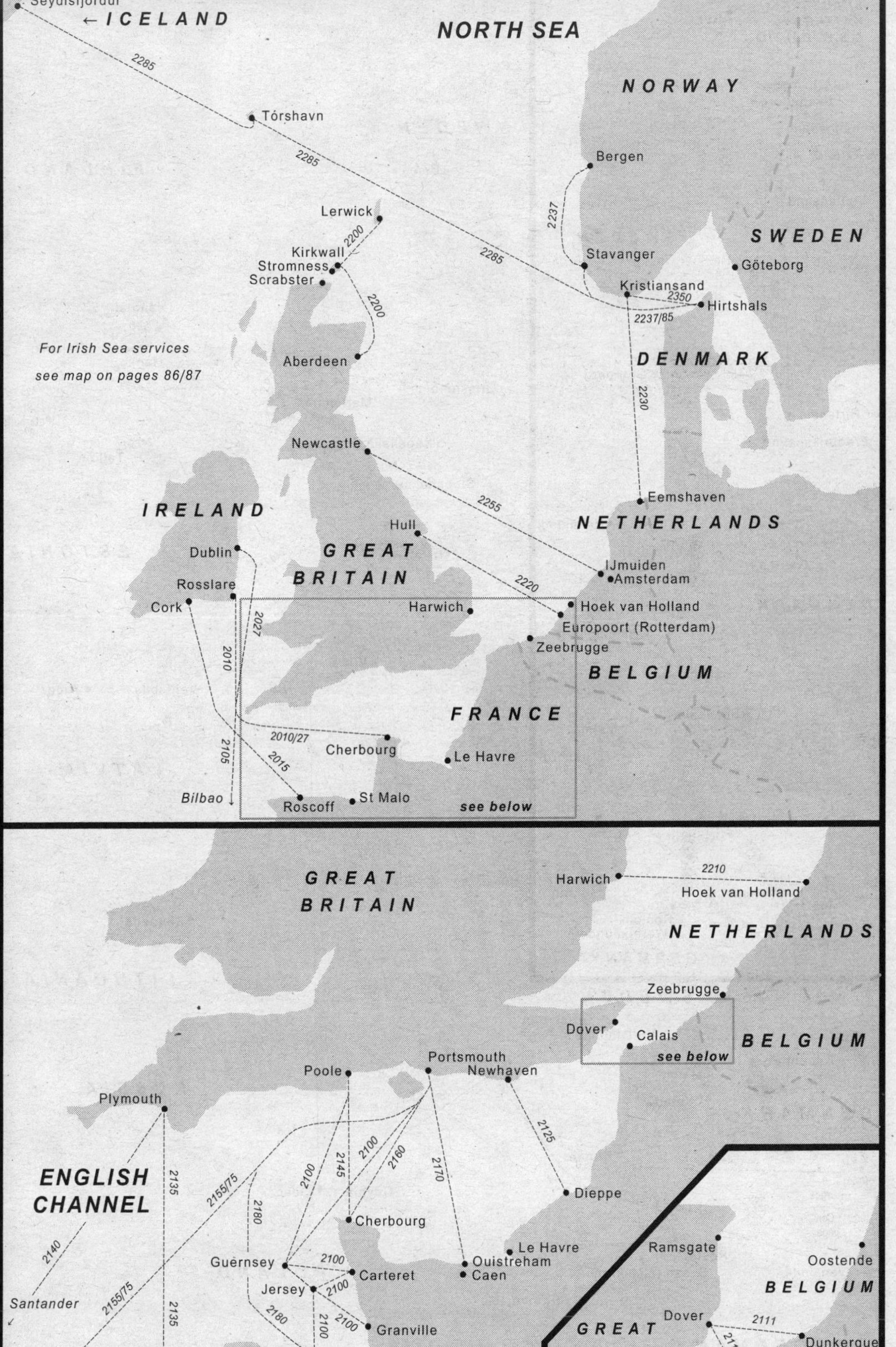
Seydisfjördur
← ICELAND
NORTH SEA
2285
Tórshavn
2285
NORWAY
Bergen
Lerwick
2200
2237
2285
SWEDEN
Kirkwall
Stromness
Scrabster
Stavanger
Göteborg
Kristiansand
2350
Hirtshals
2200
2237/85
For Irish Sea services
see map on pages 86/87
Aberdeen
DENMARK
2230
Newcastle
2255
Eemshaven
IRELAND
NETHERLANDS
Hull
Dublin
GREAT
BRITAIN
IJmuiden
Amsterdam
2220
Rosslare
Cork
Harwich
Hoek van Holland
2027
Europoort (Rotterdam)
Zeebrugge
2010
BELGIUM
FRANCE
2010/27
Cherbourg
Le Havre
2105
2015
Bilbao ↓
Roscoff
St Malo
see below
GREAT
BRITAIN
Harwich
2210
Hoek van Holland
NETHERLANDS
Zeebrugge
Dover
Calais
see below
BELGIUM
Portsmouth
Poole
Newhaven
Plymouth
2125
2100
2160
ENGLISH
CHANNEL
2135
2155/75
2180
2100
2145
2170
Dieppe
Cherbourg
2140
Le Havre
Ramsgate
Guernsey
2100
Ouistreham
Caen
Oostende
Carteret
Jersey
2100
BELGIUM
Santander
2155/75
2180
2100
2100
Granville
Dover
2111
GREAT
2110
Dunkerque
2135
BRITAIN
Calais
Roscoff
St. Malo
Boulogne
Bilbao & Santander
FRANCE
FRANCE

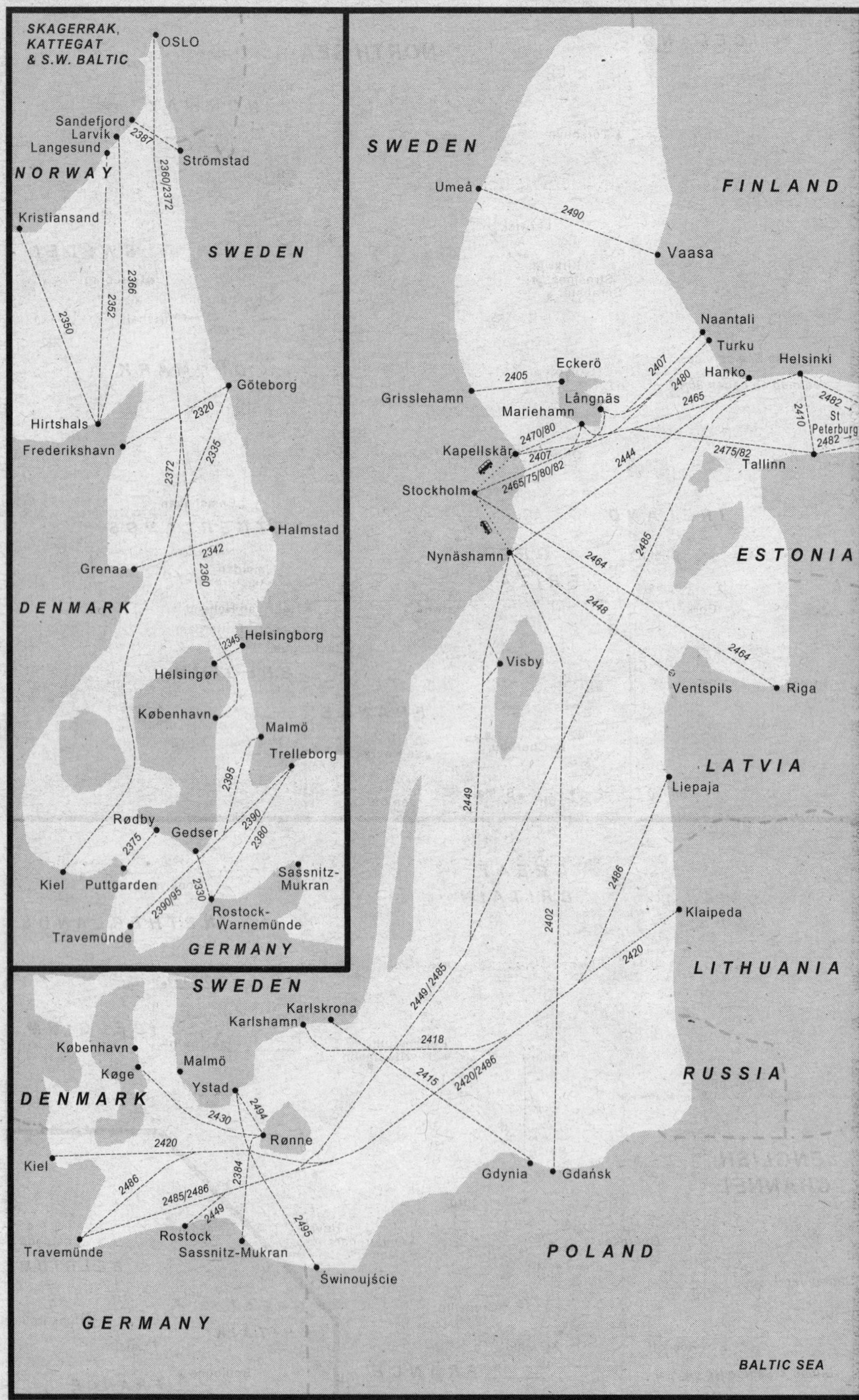

For other shipping routes see relevant country maps

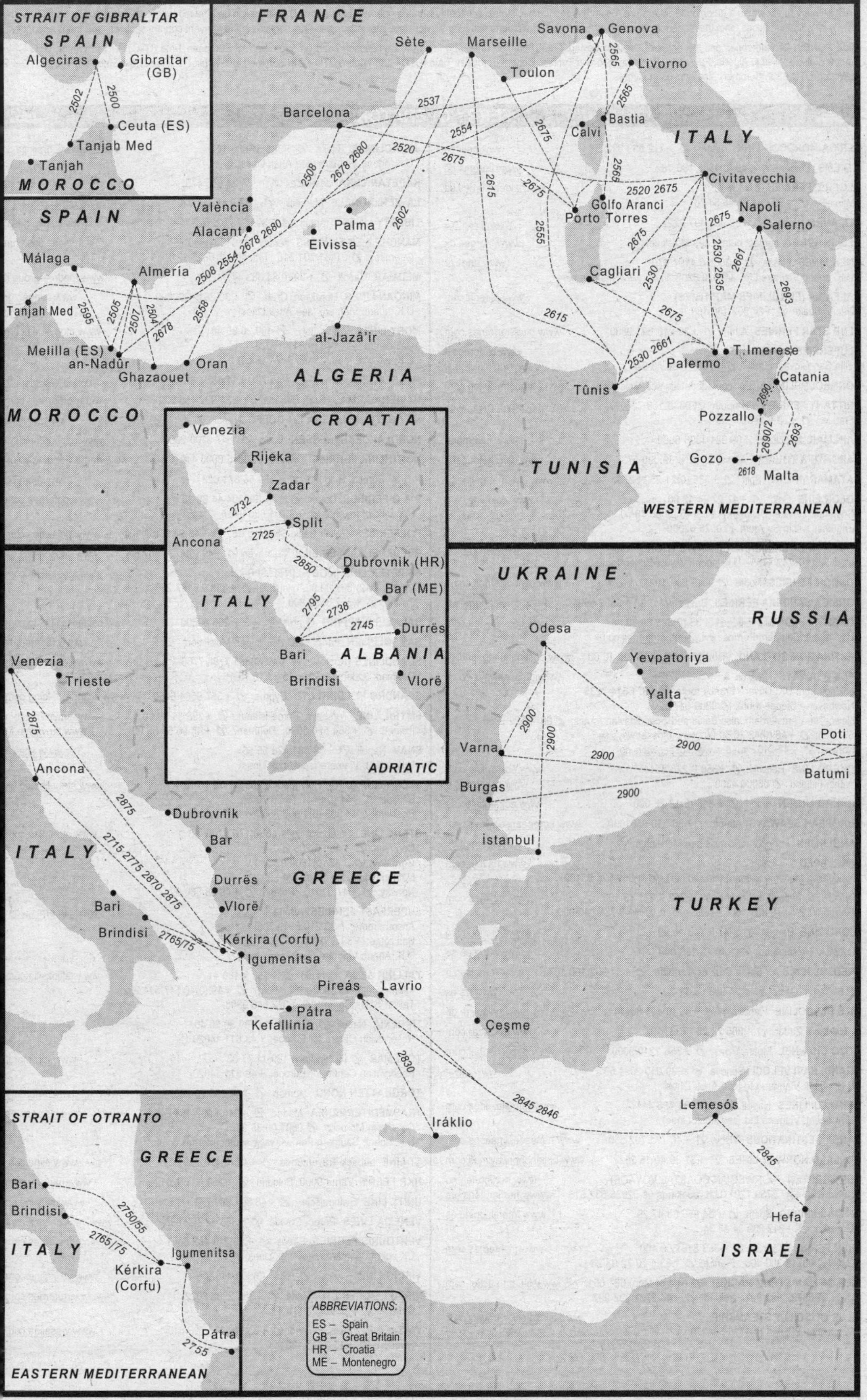
STRAIT OF GIBRALTAR
SPAIN
Algeciras
Gibraltar (GB)
2502
2500
Ceuta (ES)
Tanjab Med
Tanjah
MOROCCO
FRANCE
Sète
Marseille
Savona
Genova
Livorno
Toulon
Barcelona
2537
2554
2520
2675
Bastia
Calvi
ITALY
Civitavecchia
Golfo Aranci
Porto Torres
Napoli
Salerno
València
Alacant
Palma
Eivissa
SPAIN
Málaga
Almería
Tanjah Med
Melilla (ES)
an-Nadûr
Ghazaouet
Oran
al-Jazâ'ir
ALGERIA
Cagliari
Palermo
T.Imerese
Catania
Tûnis
Pozzallo
Gozo
Malta
TUNISIA
MOROCCO
WESTERN MEDITERRANEAN
CROATIA
Venezia
Rijeka
Zadar
Split
Ancona
Dubrovnik (HR)
Bar (ME)
Durrës
ITALY
ALBANIA
Bari
Brindisi
Vlorë
ADRIATIC
UKRAINE
RUSSIA
Odesa
Yevpatoriya
Yalta
Varna
Burgas
Poti
Batumi
istanbul
Venezia
Trieste
Ancona
Dubrovnik
Bar
ITALY
Durrës
Vlorë
GREECE
Bari
Brindisi
Kérkira (Corfu)
Igumenítsa
Pireás
Lavrio
Pátra
Kefallinia
Çeşme
TURKEY
Iráklio
Lemesós
Hefa
ISRAEL
STRAIT OF OTRANTO
GREECE
Bari
Brindisi
ITALY
Kérkira (Corfu)
Igumenitsa
Pátra
EASTERN MEDITERRANEAN
ABBREVIATIONS:
ES – Spain
GB – Great Britain
HR – Croatia
ME – Montenegro

FERRY SERVICES

Sailing times are shown as a guide and readers are recommended to check latest schedules with the operator before travel. Sailings can be affected by holidays (especially Christmas and New Year), tidal variations, ship maintenance periods, and weather. Certain domestic ferry services are shown alongside rail services in the relevent country sections (see maps and Index).

TIME ZONES: for time zones and the dates of Daylight Saving Time (Summer Time) see the Time Comparison chart on page 4. West European Time (UTC / GMT in Winter, UTC + 1 in Summer) also applies to Algeria, Faeroe Islands, Morocco and Tunisia. Central European Time (UTC + 1 in Winter, UTC + 2 in Summer) also applies in Israel. East European Time (UTC + 2 in Winter, UTC + 3 in Summer) also applies in Cyprus.

FERRY OPERATORS

AFRICA MOROCCO LINK Tanger ✆ +212 539 322253 www.aml.ma

A G EMS Emden ✆ +49 (0)1805 180 182 www.ag-ems.de

ALGERIE FERRIES (ENTMV) www.algerieferries.dz
Marseille ✆ +33 (0)4 91 90 64 70

ALILAURO Napoli ✆ +39 081 497 2222 www.alilauro.it

ALSLINJEN For contact details see Molslinjen www.faergen.dk

ANEK LINES Pireás ✆ +30 210 4197 470 www.anek.gr
U.K. agent: Viamare Ltd. ✆ 020 8206 3420 www.viamare.com

BALEÀRIA (EUROLÍNIES MARÍTIMES) www.balearia.com
Dénia, Spain ✆ +34 902 160 180

BLUE STAR FERRIES Athína ✆ +30 210 891 9800 www.bluestarferries.com

BLUFERRIES and **BLU JET** www.bluferries.it
Villa San Giovanni, Italy ✆ +39 340 98 48 540 www.blujetlines.it

BORNHOLMSLINJEN For contact details see Molslinjen www.bornholmslinjen.com

BRITTANY FERRIES Plymouth ✆ 0330 159 7000 www.brittany-ferries.co.uk
France: ✆ +33 825 828 828

CAREMAR Napoli ✆ +39 081 1896 6690 www.caremar.it

CARONTE & TOURIST Messina ✆ +39 090 5737 www.carontetourist.it

CATAMARAN LINE Split ✆ +385 (0)21 352 527 www.catamaran-line.hr

COLOR LINE Oslo ✆ +47 22 94 42 00 www.colorline.com
Customer service (Denmark): ✆ +45 99 56 19 00
Enquiries within Sweden: ✆ 0526 62000

COMPAGNIE TUNISIENNE DE NAVIGATION Tûnis www.ctn.com.tn
✆ +33 (1) 4742 1755. U.K. agent: www.southernferries.co.uk

CONDOR FERRIES Poole ✆ 0845 609 1024 www.condorferries.co.uk

CORSICA SARDINIA FERRIES Bastia ✆ +33 4 9532 9595 www.corsica-ferries.fr

CORSICA LINEA Marseille ✆ +33 (0)825 88 80 88 www.corsicalinea.com
U.K. agent: Southern Ferries www.southernferries.co.uk

DESTINATION GOTLAND Visby ✆ +46 (0)498 20 18 00 www.destinationgotland.se

DFDS SEAWAYS Harwich www.dfdsseaways.co.uk
Bookings from UK: Dover - France route: ✆ 0871 574 7235
Newhaven - Dieppe route: ✆ 0800 917 1201
Newcastle - Amsterdam, also Baltic and Scandinavian routes: ✆ 0871 522 9955
Sweden: ✆ +46 (0)42 26 60 00 www.dfdsseaways.se
Norway: ✆ +47 2162 1340 www.dfdsseaways.no

ECKERÖ LINE Helsinki: ✆ +358 9 228 8544 www.eckeroline.com
Within Finland: ✆ 06000 4300 www.eckeroline.fi

ECKERÖ LINJEN Åland ✆ +358 (0)18 28 000 www.eckerolinjen.se

EUROPEAN SEAWAYS Athína ✆ +30 210 9561630 www.europeanseaways.com

FANØLINJEN For contact details see Molslinjen www.faergen.dk

FERRYSPED www.navbul.com
Navigation Maritime Bulgare (Navibulgar) ✆ +359 526 83409

FINNLINES Finland call centre: ✆ +358 9 231 43 100 www.finnlines.com
Germany: ✆ +49 451 1507 443. Sweden ✆ +46 771 340 900

FJORD LINE Bergen ✆ +47 51 46 40 99 www.fjordline.com

FORSEA Helsingborg ✆ +46 42 186 000 www.forsea.se

FRED. OLSEN S.A. Santa Cruz de Tenerife ✆ +34 902 100 107 www.fredolsen.e

FRS Tarifa - Cádiz ✆ +34 956 68 18 30 www.frs.es

FRS HELGOLINE Flensburg ✆ +49 (0)461 86444 www.helgoline.de

G & V Line Zadar ✆ +385 23 250 733 www.gv-zadar.com

GOZO CHANNEL Mgarr, Gozo ✆ +356 2210 9000 www.gozochannel.com

GRANDI NAVI VELOCI Genova ✆ +39 010 2094 591 www.gnv.it
U.K. agent: Viamare Ltd (see Anek Lines)

GRIMALDI LINES Napoli ✆ +39 081 496 444 www.grimaldi-lines.com
U.K. agent: Viamare Ltd (see Anek Lines)

HANSA DESTINATIONS Visby ✆ +46 771 702 550 www.hansadestinations.com

HOLLAND NORWAY LINES ✆ +31 85 40 15 252 www.hollandnorwaylines.com

HURTIGRUTEN (NORWEGIAN COASTAL VOYAGE) www.hurtigruten.no
Norway ✆ +47 7759 7201. U.K. bookings ✆ 02035 532 516 www.hurtigruten.com

INTER SHIPPING Spain ✆ +34 956 68 47 29 www.intershipping.es
Morocco: ✆ +212 539 34 38 34

IRISH FERRIES Dublin ✆ +353 818 300 400 www.irishferries.com
U.K.: ✆ 08717 300 400. France: ✆ +33 1 70 72 03 26

ISLE OF MAN STEAM PACKET ✆ (Isle of Man) 661 661 www.steam-packet.com
U.K.: ✆ 08722 992 992. Ireland: ✆ +44 8722 992 992

ISLES OF SCILLY STEAMSHIP www.islesofscilly-travel.co.uk
Penzance ✆ +44 (0)1736 334220

JADROLINIJA Rijeka ✆ +385 51 666 111 www.jadrolinija.hr
U.K. agent: Viamare (see Anek Lines)

KAPETAN LUKA Jesenice ✆ +385 21 645 476 www.krilo.hr

LA MÉRIDIONALE Marseille ✆ +33 970 832 020 www.lameridionale.fr

LIBERTY LINES Trapani ✆ +39 0923 022022 www.libertylines.it

MANCHE ÎLES EXPRESS Jersey ✆ 01534 880 756 www.manche-iles.com
Guernsey: ✆ 01481 701 316. France: ✆ 0825 131 050

MEDMAR Napoli ✆ +39 (0)81 333 44 11 www.medmargroup.it

MINOAN LINES Heraklion, Crete ✆ +30 2810 399899 www.minoan.gr
U.K. agent: Viamare (see Anek Lines)

MOBY LINES Within Italy: ✆ 199 30 30 40 www.mobylines.com
Call centre: ✆ +49 (0)611 14020.
U.K. agent: Viamare (see Anek Lines)

MOLSLINJEN Aarhus ✆ +45 70 10 14 18 www.molslinjen.dk

NAVIERA ARMAS Gran Canaria ✆ +34 902 456 500 www.navieraarmas.com

NAVIGAZIONE LIBERA del GOLFO Napoli ✆ +39 081 552 07 63 www.navlib.it

NORDLANDEKSPRESSEN Bodø ✆ +47 9100 9600 www.reisnordland.no

NORTHLINK FERRIES Orkney ✆ 0845 6000 449 www.northlinkferries.co.uk

P B M Burgas, Bulgaria ✆ +359 56 871 628 www.pbm.bg

P & O FERRIES Dover ✆ +44 (0)1304 44 88 88 www.poferries.com
Republic of Ireland: ✆ +353 1 686 9467

POLFERRIES Polish Baltic Shipping Co. ✆ +48 94 35 52 102 www.polferries.com

REEDEREI CASSEN EILS Cuxhaven ✆ +49 (0)4721 667 600 www.cassen-eils.de

ST PETER LINE (MOBY LINE) St Peterburg www.stpeterline.com
✆ +7 (812) 507 89 92. Helsinki: ✆ +358 9 6187 2000
Tallinn: ✆ +372 6660 800

SALAMIS SHIPPING Cyprus ✆ +357 258 60600 www.salamisshipping.com

SAMSØLINJEN For contact details see Molslinjen www.faergen.dk

SCANDLINES Rostock: ✆ +49 (0)381 7788 7766 www.scandlines.com
Denmark (Odense): ✆ +45 33 15 15 15

SCANDRO HOLDING LTD Cyprus ✆ +357 9664 6450 www.scandroholding.com

SMYRIL LINE Tórshavn, Faroe Islands ✆ +298 34 59 00 www.smyrilline.com
Iceland: ✆ +354 570 8600. Denmark: ✆ +45 96 55 85 00 www.smyrilline.fo

SNAV Napoli ✆ +39 081 428 55 55 www.snav.it
U.K. agent: Viamare (see Anek Lines)

STENA LINE (U.K.) Holyhead ✆ 08447 70 70 70 www.stenaline.co.uk
Belfast: ✆ +44 (0)8447 70 70 70
Rosslare: ✆ +353 (0)1 907 5555

STENA LINE Göteborg ✆ +46 (0)770 57 57 00 www.stenaline.com
Denmark: ✆ +45 96 200 200
Germany: ✆ +49 (0)180 602 0100.
Netherlands: ✆ +31 (0)174 389 333
Norway: ✆ +47 02010. Poland: ✆ +48 58 660 92 00

SUPERFAST FERRIES Athína www.superfast.com
Ancona route: +30 210 8919 700
Bari route: +30 210 8919 130
U.K. Agent: Viamare (see Anek Lines).

TALLINK SILJA Helsinki ✆ +358 9 180 41 www.tallinksilja.com
International call centre (Hamburg): ✆ +49 (0)40 547 541 222
Tallinn Sales Centre: ✆ +372 640 9808

TIRRENIA Napoli ✆ (within Italy) 199 30 30 40 www.tirrenia.it
Reservation Centre for Europe: +49 611 14020

TOREMAR ✆ (within Italy) 199 11 77 33 www.toremar.it
Reservation Centre for Europe: +49 611 14020

TORGHATTEN NORD Tromsø ✆ +47 906 20 700 www.torghatten-nord.no

TRASMEDITERRANEA Madrid ✆ +34(0) 902 454 645 www.trasmediterranea.es
Calls from Morocco: ✆ 0801 00 35 36.
U.K. agent: Southern Ferries www.southernferries.co.uk

TT-LINE Lübeck-Travemünde ✆ +49 (0)4502 801 81 www.ttline.com

UKR FERRY Varna 9000, Bulgaria ✆ +359 52 602012 www.ukrferry.com

UNITY LINE Świnoujście ✆ +48 801 989 771 www.unityline.eu

VENEZIA LINES Poreč, Croatia ✆ +385 52 422 896 www.venezialines.com

VENTOURIS FERRIES Pireás ✆ +30 210 482 8001 www.ventourisferries.com
UK agent: Viamare (see Anek Lines)

VIKING LINE Finland ✆ +358 (0)600 41577 www.vikingline.com

VIRTU FERRIES LTD Malta ✆ +356 2206 9022 www.virtuferries.com
Catania: ✆ +39 095 7031211

WASALINE Vaasa, Finland: ✆ +358 (0)207 716 810 www.wasaline.com
Sweden: ✆ +46 (0)90 185 200

CONTENTS

IRISH SEA

BELFAST - CAIRNRYAN 2002

Stena Line

Belfast		Cairnryan		Cairnryan		Belfast	
0330§	→	0552	②–⑥	0345§	→	0600	②–⑥
0730	→	0952		0700	→	0945	⑦
1130	→	1352		0730	→	0945	①–⑥
1530	→	1752		1130	→	1345	
1930	→	2152		1530	→	1745	
2300§	→	0152		1930	→	2145	
				2300§	→	0145	

§ – No foot passengers conveyed. 2300 sailing departs 30 minutes later on certain days.

CAIRNRYAN - LARNE 2005

P & O Ferries Journey 2 hours

March only

Depart Cairnryan and Larne: 0400 ①–⑥, 0800, 1100 ①⑤, 1200 ②③④⑥, 1300 ⑦, 1400 ①⑤, 1600 ②③④⑥⑦, 1700 ①⑤, 2000, 2359 ⑦–⑤.

Apr. 1 - Sept. 30

Depart Cairnryan and Larne: 0400 ①–⑥, 0800 ⑦–⑤, 1000 ⑥, 1100 ⑤, 1200 ⑦–④, 1400 ⑤⑥, 1600 ⑦–④, 1700 ⑤⑥, 2000 ①–⑤, 2200 ⑦, 2359 ①–⑤.

CHERBOURG - ROSSLARE 2010

Stena Line

Cherbourg		Rosslare		Rosslare		Cherbourg	
1500	→	0900	⑦ See note **b**	1645	→	1045	⑥ See note **a**
2100	→	1230	⑤	2100	→	1600	②④
2100	→	1430	③				

a – Not Dec. 24, 31.
b – Not Jan 1.

CORK - ROSCOFF 2015

Brittany Ferries

Sailings from Cork (Ringaskiddy) and Roscoff

Cork		Roscoff	
1600③	→	0800④	Mar. 30 - Nov. 2.
1600⑥	→	0700⑦	Apr. 2 - Nov. 5.
Roscoff		**Cork**	
2215⑤	→	1000⑥	Apr. 1 - Nov. 4.
1930②	→	0930③	Mar. 29 - Nov. 1.

DOUGLAS - BELFAST 2020

Isle Of Man Steam Packet Co. Journey 2 hours 45 minutes

Infrequent sailings (2–9 sailings per month April 13 to September 4). No winter service.

DOUGLAS - DUBLIN 2025

Isle Of Man Steam Packet Co. High-speed car ferry Journey 2 hours 55 minutes

Infrequent sailings (1–4 sailings per month April 14 to September 6). No winter service.

DUBLIN - CHERBOURG 2027

Irish Ferries **March - October, 2022**

Dublin		Cherbourg	
1600	→	1100/30	②④⑥ Mar. 1 - June 11; uneven dates June 13 - July 31; even dates Aug. 2–30; uneven dates Sept. 1–17; ②④⑥ Sept. 20 - Oct. 29.
Cherbourg		**Dublin**	
1630	→	1045	③⑤⑦ Mar. 2 - June 12; even dates June 14 - July 30; uneven dates Aug. 1–31; even dates Sept. 2–18; ③⑤⑦ Sept. 21 - Oct. 30.

FISHGUARD - ROSSLARE 2030

Stena Line by ship

Fishguard		Rosslare	Rosslare		Fishguard
1300	→	1630	0730	→	1100
2345	→	0345	1815	→	2145

HEYSHAM - DOUGLAS 2035

Isle Of Man Steam Packet Co. **Jan - Dec. 2022**

Heysham		Douglas	Douglas		Heysham
0215	→	0600	0845	→	1230
1415	→	1800	1945	→	2330

Timings may vary, and departures are cancelled on certain dates

HOLYHEAD - DUBLIN 2040

Irish Ferries by ship

Sailings from Holyhead and Dublin Ferryport.

Holyhead		Dublin		Dublin		Holyhead	
0240	→	0555		0200§	→	0525	①–⑥
0815	→	1145	①–⑥	0730	→	0945	May 25 - Oct. 3 ⊕
1040	→	1255	May 25 - Oct. 3 ⊕	0805	→	1130	
1410	→	1725		1350	→	1605	May 25 - Oct. 3 ⊕
1645	→	1900	May 25 - Oct. 3 ⊕	1430	→	1800	
2015§	→	2330		2055	→	0020	

§ – Foot passengers are not normally conveyed.
⊕ – Service by *Dublin Swift* fast ferry.

Sailing times may vary owing to tidal conditions.

🚌 Dublin Ferryport - Dublin Busaras (Central Bus Station).

Stena Line by ship

Holyhead		Dublin	Dublin		Holyhead
0215	→	0530	0215§	→	0545
0900	→	1215	0815	→	1150
1445	→	1800	1445	→	1820
2030	→	2345	2030§	→	0001

§ – No foot passengers conveyed.

BIRKENHEAD (LIVERPOOL) - BELFAST 2050

Stena Line

Sailings from Birkenhead Twelve Quays Terminal and Belfast Victoria Terminal 2.

Birkenhead		Belfast		Belfast		Birkenhead	
1030	→	1830	②–⑦ a	1030	→	1830	②–⑦ a
2130	→	0630	①	2130	→	0630	①
2230	→	0630	②–⑦	2230	→	0630	②–⑦

a – Also ① July 11 - Aug. 29.

LIVERPOOL - DUBLIN 2052

P & O Ferries

Conveys passengers with vehicles only. Limited passenger facilities onboard.

Liverpool		Dublin		Dublin		Liverpool	
0300	→	1100	②–⑥ a	0900	→	1700	②–⑥ b
0930	→	1730	②–⑥ b	1500	→	2300	①–⑤ c
2100	→	0500		2130	→	0530	

a – Also ① from Apr. (not May 2, June 6, Aug. 1, 29, Oct. 31).
b – Also ① in Mar.
c – Also ⑦ from Apr. (not May 1, Aug. 28).

LIVERPOOL - DOUGLAS 2053

Isle Of Man Steam Packet Co. High-speed car ferry

Sailings from Liverpool Landing Stage and Douglas

Liverpool → Douglas: Apr. 1 - Oct. 30 a minimum of one sailing a day, two during July/Aug. Most regular timings d. 1115, a. 1400; d. 1915, a. 2200.

Douglas → Liverpool: Apr. 1 - Oct. 30 a minimum of one sailing a day, two during July/Aug. Most regular timings d. 0730, a. 1015; d. 1500, a. 1745.

Times may vary by several hours on certain dates - please check with operator.

PEMBROKE - ROSSLARE 2055

Irish Ferries

Pembroke		Rosslare	Rosslare		Pembroke
0245	→	0646	0845	→	1246
1445	→	1846	2045	→	0046

Sailing times may vary owing to tidal conditions

ENGLISH CHANNEL AND BAY OF BISCAY

CHANNEL ISLAND SERVICES 2100

Condor Ferries

POOLE - GUERNSEY by fast ferry
POOLE - JERSEY by fast ferry
PORTSMOUTH - GUERNSEY
PORTSMOUTH - JERSEY
ST MALO - GUERNSEY by fast ferry
ST MALO - JERSEY by fast ferry
GUERNSEY - JERSEY by fast ferry

Services operate all year round. Departure times vary - contact operator for details

OTHER SERVICES:

Manche îles Express operate catamaran services in summer from Jersey to Carteret, Granville, Sark and Guernsey, and from Guernsey to Alderney and Diélette.

2105 ROSSLARE - BILBAO

Brittany Ferries Nov. 2021 - Nov. 2022

Conveys passengers with vehicles only

Rosslare		Bilbao		Bilbao		Rosslare
1015③	→	1500④		1745④	→	2030⑤
2300⑤	→	0800⑦	a	1200⑦	→	1600①

a – Not Dec. 24, 31.

2110 DOVER - CALAIS

DFDS Seaways

Sailings from Dover Eastern Docks and Calais Maritime. Journey 90 minutes

Conveys passengers with vehicles only.

Depart Dover: 0015, 0220①–⑥, 0340①–⑥, 0505①–⑥, 0710, 0830, 0955①–⑥, 1155, 1315, 1440, 1640, 1805, 1930, 2130⑦–⑤, 2250.

Depart Calais: 0050⑦–⑤, 0210①–⑥, 0335①–⑥, 0540, 0610, 0700, 0825①–⑥, 1030, 1150, 1315, 1515, 1635①–⑥, 1801, 2001⑦–⑤, 2120⑦–⑤, 2245.

P & O Ferries

Sailings from Dover Eastern Docks and Calais Maritime. Journey 90 minutes

There are up to 23 sailings a day at peak times, the following is an example of July's sailings.

On night services, conveys passengers with vehicles only (foot passengers may travel 0915 - 1850 from Dover, 0950 - 1920 from Calais). Subject to variation, especially Jan. to Mar. and Christmas.

Depart Dover: 0040③, 0100⑦–④, 0140②–⑥, 0300③–⑦, 0425①②⑤⑥⑦, 0550, 0630②–⑥, 0750, 0915, 1035, 1115①②③⑤⑥⑦, 1235, 1400, 1525, 1605, 1725, 1850, 2010, 2050, 2210②④⑤⑥, 2335①③④⑤⑦.

Depart Calais: 0100②–⑥, 0130③–⑦, 0255①②⑤⑥, 0420, 0500②–⑥, 0620, 0745, 0910, 0950, 1110, 1235, 1355, 1435, 1555, 1720, 1840, 1920, 2040②–⑥, 2205 ①④⑤⑦, 2330⑥–③.

2111 DOVER - DUNKERQUE

DFDS Seaways

Sailings from Dover Eastern Docks and Dunkerque. Journey 2 hours

Conveys passengers with vehicles only. Timings vary (those shown below are based on sailings during August).

Depart Dover: 0200①–⑥, 0400①–⑥, 0600①–⑥, 0800, 1000①–⑥, 1200, 1400, 1600, 1800, 2000, 2200, 2359①–⑥.

Depart Dunkerque: 0200①–⑥, 0400①–⑥, 0600, 0800①–⑥, 1000, 1200, 1400, 1600, 1800, 2000①–⑥, 2200①–⑥, 2359⑦–⑤.

2125 NEWHAVEN - DIEPPE

DFDS Seaways

Newhaven		Dieppe	Dieppe		Newhaven
October - April					
1000	→	1500	0530	→	0830
2300	→	0400	1800	→	2100
May - September					
0900	→	1400	1230	→	1530
1730	→	2230	1800	→	2100
2300	→	0500	2359	→	0400

Newhaven ferry terminal is adjacent to Newhaven Town rail station (Table **102**).

Departure times may vary owing to tidal conditions.

2130 PENZANCE - ST. MARY'S

Isles Of Scilly Steamship Co. Mar. 21 - Nov. 6 (no winter service)

Sailings from Penzance Lighthouse Pier (South Pier) and St Mary's.

From Penzance and St Mary's: sailings on ①③⑤⑥ Mar. 21 – 26; ①–⑥ Mar. 28 - June 25; daily June 27 - Oct. 8 (not Sept. 25, Oct. 2); ①③⑤⑥ Oct. 10 - Nov 5 (also Nov. 6).

Departure times vary owing to tidal conditions (most sailings Penzance depart 0915, St Mary's depart 1630).

2135 PLYMOUTH - ROSCOFF

Brittany Ferries Mar. - Nov.

Sailings from Plymouth Millbay and Roscoff. No winter service

From Plymouth: ①②④⑤⑥⑦ Mar. 28 - Nov. 6.

From Roscoff: ①③④⑤⑥⑦ Mar. 27 - Nov. 6.

Departure times vary. Sailing time approx 6 – 9 hours.

2140 PLYMOUTH - SANTANDER

Brittany Ferries Mar. - Nov.

Sailings from Plymouth Millbay and Santander No winter service

Plymouth		Santander		Santander		Plymouth	
1545③	→	1315④	Mar. 30 - Nov. 2.	1545④	→	1045⑤	Mar. 31 - Nov. 3.
1645⑦	→	1400①	Mar. 27 - Oct. 30.	1700①	→	1400②	Mar. 28 - Oct. 31.

2145 POOLE - CHERBOURG

Brittany Ferries Mar. - Nov.

No winter service

Service from March 28

Poole		Cherbourg		Cherbourg		Poole	
0830	→	1400	See note **N**.	1815	→	2145	See note **P**.
				2145	→	0700	See note **Q**.

N – Mar 29 - Nov. 11. Departures from Poole on ② arrive Cherbourg 1430.

P – ①④⑤⑥⑦ Mar. 28 - July 4; daily July 7 - Sept 5; ①④⑤⑥⑦ Sept. 8 - Nov. 6.

Q – ②③ Mar 29 - July 6, Sept. 6 - Nov. 2.

High-speed service Cherbourg - Poole (new for 2022)

Cherbourg		Poole	
0830	→	1400	⑤⑥⑦ May 27 - June 5; ⑤⑥⑦ July 15 - Sept. 4.

*See Table **2160** for high-speed service Portsmouth to Cherbourg*

2155 PORTSMOUTH - BILBAO

Brittany Ferries Mar. - Nov.

No winter service

Portsmouth		Bilbao	
1930④	→	0800⑤	Mar. 31 - Nov. 3.
2100⑦	→	0800⑦	Mar. 27 - Nov. 6.
Bilbao		**Portsmouth**	
1400②	→	0915③	Mar. 29 - Nov. 1.
1500⑥	→	1830⑦	Apr. 2 - Nov. 5.

2160 PORTSMOUTH - CHERBOURG

Brittany Ferries by fast ferry May - Sept.

Portsmouth		Cherbourg	
0701	→	1100	⑤⑥⑦ May 27 - June 5; ⑤⑥⑦ July 15 - Sept. 4.

*See Table **2145** for high-speed service Cherbourg to Poole*

Brittany Ferries Mar. - Nov. (no winter service)

Sailings from Portsmouth Continental Ferry Port and Cherbourg.

Portsmouth		Cherbourg	
2300④	→	0800⑤	Mar. 31 - Nov. 3 (also Mar. 6, 13).
2315③	→	0800④	Mar. 23 - Nov. 2.
Cherbourg		**Portsmouth**	
1200⑤	→	1645	Apr. 1 - Oct. 28.
1200④	→	1700	Mar. 24 - Nov. 3.
1400⑦	→	1820	Nov. 6 only.
2100①	→	0600②	Mar. 7, 14 only.

Free 🚌 runs Cherbourg Port - Cherbourg town centre.

2170 PORTSMOUTH - OUISTREHAM (CAEN)

Brittany Ferries

Sailings from Portsmouth Continental Ferry Port and Ouistreham

Portsmouth		Ouistreham	
Feb. 15 - Mar. 27			
0815	→	1500	②④⑦.
1445	→	2130	①③⑥.
2200	→	0645	⑤.
2245	→	0645	②⑦.
2245	→	0730	④.
Apr. 1 - Nov. 6			
0815	→	1500	Daily.
1445	→	2130	Daily except ③.
2130	→	0645	③.
2245	→	0645	①②④⑤⑥⑦.
2245	→	0730	②.

Ouistreham		Portsmouth	
Feb. 14 - Mar. 27			
0830	→	1315	①③⑥.
1400	→	1915	⑤.
1630	→	2115	②④⑦.
2300	→	0645	①③⑥.
Mar. 28 - Nov. 6			
0830	→	1315	Daily except ③.
1400	→	1915	③.
1630	→	2115	Daily except ③.
2300	→	0645	Daily.

Local 🚌 service operated by Twisto links Caen with Ouistreham (500m from ferry terminal). Does not connect with evening ferry arrivals or departures.

2175 PORTSMOUTH - SANTANDER

Brittany Ferries

Sailings from Portsmouth Continental Ferry Port and Santander

Portsmouth		Santander	
2130⑤	→	0745⑥	Apr. 1 - Oct. 28.
2130①	→	0800②	Apr. 4 - Oct. 31 (also Mar. 28).

Other sailings: 0900 on Mar. 1, 8; 1930 on Mar. 24; 2215 on Mar. 3, 10, 17; 2300 on Mar 20.

Santander		Portsmouth	
1400③	→	2000④	Apr. 6 - Nov. 2. (also Mar. 30).
1415⑦	→	1730①	Apr. 3 - Oct. 30. (also Mar. 27).

Other sailings: 1425 on Mar. 22; 1500 on Mar. 5, 12, 19; 1730 on Mar. 2, 9, 16.

2180 PORTSMOUTH - ST MALO

Brittany Ferries Mar. 2022 - Mar. 2023

Sailings from Portsmouth Continental Ferry Port and St. Malo Terminal Ferry du Naye

From Portsmouth: in summer sails daily except ② (daily July 1 - Aug. 29). In winter (November - March) sails ①③⑤⑦. Timings vary (typical sailing Portsmouth depart 2015, St. Malo arrive 0815). Contact operator for confirmed timings.

From St. Malo: in summer sails daily except ③ (daily July - Aug. 30). In Winter (November - March sails ①②④⑥. Timings vary (typical sailing St. Malo depart 1030, Portsmouth arrive 1820). Contact operator for confirmed timings.

NORTH SEA

ABERDEEN - KIRKWALL - LERWICK 2200

NorthLink Ferries **2022/2023 service**

Aberdeen		Kirkwall		Kirkwall		Lerwick
Until March 31						
1700④⑥⑦	→	2300④⑥⑦	→	2345④⑥⑦	→	0730⑤⑦①
1900①②③⑤	→	→	→	→	→	0730②③④⑥
April 1 - October 31						
1700②④⑥⑦	→	2300②④⑥⑦	→	2345②④⑥⑦	→	0730③⑤⑦①
1900①③⑤	→	→	→	→	→	0730②④⑥

Lerwick		Kirkwall		Kirkwall		Aberdeen
November 1 - March 31 2023						
1730③⑤	→	2300③⑤	→	2345③⑤	→	0700④⑥
1900①②④⑥⑦	→	→	→	→	→	0700②③⑤⑦①
April 1 2023 - October 31 2023						
1730①③⑤	→	2300①③⑤	→	2345①③⑤	→	0700②④⑥
1900②④⑥⑦	→	→	→	→	→	0700③⑤⑦①

Subject to alteration during ship maintenance (January to March)

A 🚌 transfer service is available Kirkwall - Stromness and v.v. in conjunction with evening sailings.

HARWICH - HOEK VAN HOLLAND 2210

Stena Line

Sailings from Harwich International Port and Hoek van Holland.

Harwich		Hoek	Hoek		Harwich	
0900	→	1715	1345	→	1945	⑦
			1415	→	1945	①-⑥
2300	→	0800	2200	→	0630	

See Table **15** for connecting rail services London - Harwich and v.v.
Connection Hoek van Holland - Schiedam - Rotterdam is by RET metro line B (Table **497**).

HULL - ROTTERDAM 2220

P & O Ferries

Sailings from Hull King George Dock and Rotterdam Europoort.

Hull		Rotterdam		Rotterdam		Hull	
2030	→	0830	①②③④⑦	2030	→	0800	⑥⑦
2030	→	0900	⑤⑥	2100	→	0730	①-⑤

🚌 connections (reservation recommended):

Hull (Paragon Interchange, regular departures until 1700) - King George Dock and v.v.
Rotterdam (Centraal Station, depart 1700) - Europoort and v.v.
Amsterdam* (Prins Hedrikkade 25, depart 1700) - Europoort and v.v.

* Transfer currently suspended.

EEMSHAVEN - KRISTIANSAND 2230

Holland Norway Lines **Sailings from Apr. 7**

Eemshaven		Kristiansand	Kristiansand		Eemshaven
1500②④⑥	→	0900③⑤⑦	1500③⑤⑦	→	0900④⑥①

See Table **498** for rail services Groningen - Eemshaven and v.v.

HIRTSHALS - STAVANGER - BERGEN 2237

Fjord Line

Hirtshals		Stavanger		Bergen		Stavanger		Hirtshals
2000	→	0700	→	1230 - 1330	→	2000	→	0730§

§ – Certain sailings arrive 0800.

Stavanger ferry terminal is located at Risavik havn, approx 15 km from Stavanger: Fjord Line 🚌 service departs Stavanger bus station (stop 6) at 0550 and 1815.

HELGOLAND (Germany) services 2238

BREMERHAVEN - HELGOLAND May - Sept. Operator: Reederei Cassen Eils
BÜSUM - HELGOLAND Apr. - Oct. Operator: Adler & Eils
CUXHAVEN - HELGOLAND All year (Reederei Cassen Eils); Mar. - Oct. (FRS Helgoline)
HAMBURG - HELGOLAND Mar. - Oct. Operator: FRS Helgoline

LOFOTEN ISLANDS 2239

Map page 337

Reis Nordland fast ferry

Bodø		Svolvær		Svolvær		Bodø	
1800	→	2125	①-⑥	0600	→	0920	①-⑤
1900	→	2225	⑦	0755	→	1115	⑥
				1245	→	1600	⑦

Torghatten Nord Most sailings 3 hours 15 mins

BODØ - MOSKENES 1–2 sailings daily (up to 6 sailings daily June to August).

NORWEGIAN COASTAL SERVICES 2240

Map page 337

Hurtigruten **BERGEN - TRONDHEIM - TROMSØ - KIRKENES**

	NORTHBOUND					SOUTHBOUND			
Daily	WINTER		SUMMER ☆				ALL YEAR		
	arrive	*depart*	*arrive*	*depart*	*day*		*arrive*	*depart*	*day*
Bergen ♣	...	2030	...	2030	A	**Kirkenes**	...	1230	A
Florø	0245	0300	0245	0300	B	Vadsø	|	|	
Måløy	0515	0530	0515	0530	B	Vardø	1605	1700	A
Torvik	0820	0830	0820	0830	B	Båtsfjord	2000	2030	A
Ålesund	0945	2000	0945	1000	B	Berlevåg	2225	2235	A
Geiranger ▲	|	|	1425 s	1445 s	B	Mehamn	0120	0130	B
Ålesund	0945	2000	1900 ¶	2000	B	Kjøllefjord	0325	0335	B
Molde	2235	2305	2235	2305	B	**Honningsvåg**	0545	0600	B
Kristiansund	0245	0300	0245	0300	C	Havøysund	0800	0815	B
Trondheim	0945	1245	0945	1245	C	**Hammerfest**	1100	1245	B
Rørvik	2140	2200	2140	2200	C	Øksfjord	1550	1605	B
Brønnøysund	0135	0145	0135	0145	D	Skjervøy	1930	1945	B
Sandnessjøen	0435	0450	0435	0450	D	**Tromsø**	2345	0130	B/C
Nesna	0600	0610	0600	0610	D	Finnsnes	0420	0440	C
Ørnes	1000	1010	1000	1010	D	**Harstad**	0800	0830	C
Bodø	1305	1520	1305	1520	D	Risøyhamn	1045	1100	C
Stamsund	1915	1940	1915	1940	D	Sortland	1230	1300	C
Svolvaer	2120	2215	2120	2215	D	Stokmarknes	1415	1515	C
Stokmarknes	0130	0140	0130	0140	E	**Svolvaer**	1830	2030	C
Sortland	0255	0310	0255	0310	E	Stamsund	2215	2230	C
Risøyhamn	0435	0450	0435	0450	E	**Bodø**	0230	0330	D
Harstad	0710	0745	0710	0745	E	Ørnes	0625	0635	D
Finnsnes	1100	1130	1100	1130	E	Nesna	1025	1035	D
Tromsø	1415	1815	1415	1815	E	Sandnessjøen	1145	1215	D
Skjervøy	2210	2225	2210	2225	E	Brønnøysund	1500	1725	D
Øksfjord	0150	0200	0150	0200	F	Rørvik	2100	2130	D
Hammerfest	0505	0545	0505	0545	F	**Trondheim**	0630	0930	E
Havøysund	0830	0845	0830	0845	F	Kristiansund	1630	1730	E
Honningsvåg	1055	1430	1055	1430	F	Molde	2115	2145	E
Kjøllefjord	1640	1700	1640	1700	F	Ålesund	0030	0120	F
Mehamn	1855	1915	1855	1915	F	Geiranger	|	|	
Berlevåg	2200	2210	2200	2210	F	Ålesund	0030	0120	F
Båtsfjord	2400	0030	2400	0030	F/G	Torvik	0235	0245	F
Vardø	0330	0345	0330	0345	G	Måløy	0545	0600	F
Vadsø	0655	0710	0655	0710	G	Florø	0815	0830	F
Kirkenes	0900	...	0900	...	G	**Bergen ♣**	1445	...	F

A – 1st day .... **G** – 7th day.
s – June 2 - Sept. 1.
¶ – Via Hjørundfjorden Sept. 3 - Oct. 31 (Ålesund a. 1800).
♣ – Sailings from Bergen Nøstegaten.
☆ – June 1 - Oct. 31.
▲ – Embarkation and disembarkation take place by tender - passengers are required to be at the quay 30 minutes before departure.

Havila Voyages

Havila Voyages operate a similar tour sequence to Hurtigruten. Departing Bergen **A** 1430, arriving Kirkenes **G** 0900. Departing Kirkenes **G** 1230, arriving Bergen **12** 1430. Please refer to notes above.

NEWCASTLE - IJMUIDEN (for Amsterdam) 2255

DFDS Seaways

Sailings from Newcastle International Passenger Terminal (Royal Quays, North Shields) and IJmuiden Felison Terminal.

Newcastle		IJmuiden	IJmuiden		Newcastle
1700	→	0945	1730	→	0915

DFDS 🚌 connections:

Newcastle rail station (Bewick St, depart 1500) - Ferry Terminal, return after ship arrives.
Amsterdam (behind Centraal Station, De Ruijterkade 153) - IJmuiden and v.v. (reservation recommended, depart Amsterdam approx 1530; depart ferry terminal following arrival of ship).

STROMNESS - SCRABSTER 2280

NorthLink Ferries Journey 90 minutes

Off-peak timetable :
From Stromness at 0630 Ⓐ and 0900 Ⓒ.
From Scrabster at 0845 Ⓐ and 1200 Ⓒ.

Peak timetable May 2 - September 17, 2022 (also ⑥ Apr. 2–30, Sept. 24 - Oct. 29):
From Stromness at 0630 ①–⑥, 0900 ⑦, 1100 ①–⑥ and 1645.
From Scrabster at 0845 ①–⑥, 1200 ⑦, 1315 ①–⑥ and 1900.

ICELAND and the FAEROE ISLANDS 2285

Smyril Line **August 21, 2021 - December 31, 2022 ⊡**

Hirtshals		Tórshavn		Seydisfjördur		Tórshavn		Hirtshals
August 21, 2021 - December 25, 2021								
1600⑥‡	→	0730①/1400①	→	0900②/2000③	→	1500④/2100④	→	1130⑥‡
January 7, 2022 - June 3, 2022								
1500⑥	→	0730①/1300①	→	0900②/2000③	→	1600④/2000④	→	1100⑥
June 4, 2022 - August 19, 2022								
1130②¶	→	1730③/1800③	→	0830④/1030④	→	0300⑤/0330⑤	→	1230⑥
1530⑥	→	2230⑦	→	→	→	2330⑦	→	0930②
August 20, 2022 - December 31, 2022								
1500⑥§	→	0730①/1300①	→	0900②/2000③	→	1600④/2000④	→	1100⑥§

⊡ – No sailings Dec. 26, 2021 - Jan. 3, 2022 (ferry in dock at Hirtshals). On Jan. 4 (②) sails from Hirtshals at 1700 to Tórshavn a. 0800, d. 2100 on Jan. 6 (④), then resumes normal schedule.
‡ – On Nov. 27 Hirtshals a. 0900, d. 1900.
¶ – On June 4 Hirtshals d. 1100.
§ – On Aug. 20 Hirtshals a. 1230, d. 1630.

In poor weather conditions sailings may dock at Frederikshavn or Hanstholm (for Hirtshals) and Klaksvík or Kollafjördur (for Tórshavn). In winter season (Nov. – Mar.) sailings between Tórshavn and Seydisfjördur may be advanced, delayed or (in rare cases) cancelled at short notice due to adverse weather conditions.

For international ferry maps see pages 545–547. For ferry operator details see page 548.

SKAGERRAK, KATTEGAT & SOUTH WEST BALTIC

2301 AARHUS / EBELTOFT - SJÆLLANDS ODDE

MolsLinjen

From Aarhus / Ebeltoft and Sjællands Odde: up to 24 sailings daily. Journey 75 / 55 minutes.

2304 BØJDEN - FYNSHAV

Als-Linjen (Molslinjen) Journey 50 minutes

From Bøjden and Fynshav: approximately every two hours (additional sailings in summer).

2312 ESBJERG - FANØ

FanøLinjen (Molslinjen) Journey 12 minutes

From Esbjerg and Fanø: Frequent service (up to 3 departures hourly).

2320 FREDERIKSHAVN - GÖTEBORG

Stena Line Journey approximately 3 hours 30 minutes

From Frederikshavn (Færgehavnsvej) and Göteborg (Danmarksterminalen): 3–7 sailings daily.

2330 GEDSER - ROSTOCK

Scandlines Journey 2 hours

From Gedser and Rostock International Port: up to 10 sailings daily.

2335 GÖTEBORG - KIEL

Stena Line Journey 14½–15½ hours

Sailings from Kiel (Schwedenkai) and Göteborg (Elof Lindälvs Gata)

Göteborg		Kiel		Kiel		Göteborg
1845	→	0915		1845	→	0915

2342 GRENAA - HALMSTAD

Stena Line Journey 4½–5½ hours

From Grenaa and Halmstad: 1-2 sailings per day. Timings vary.

Grenaa port is located approximately 3 km from Grenaa railway station, which is linked with Aarhus by route L1 of the *Letbanan* light rail line, running every 30 mins (hourly on ⑦).

2345 HELSINGØR - HELSINGBORG

ForSea Journey 20 minutes

From Helsingør and Helsingborg: sailings approximately every 20 minutes (every 40 minutes at night).

2350 HIRTSHALS - KRISTIANSAND

Color Line by ship Journey 3 hours 15 minutes

From Hirtshals and Kristiansand: 2 sailings daily (normally 1215, 2045 from Hirtshals, 0800, 1630 from Kristiansand, but timings may vary particularly in January).

Fjord Line by catamaran **April. 1 - Oct. 23 (no winter service)**

Hirtshals		Kristiansand		Kristiansand		Hirtshals
April 1 - June 23 and August 7 - October 23						
1145	→	1400		0830	→	1045
1800	→	2015		1500	→	1715
June 24 - August 6						
1000	→	1215		0645	→	0900
1700	→	1915		1330	→	1545
2330	→	0145		2015	→	2230

2352 HIRTSHALS - LANGESUND

Fjord Line

Hirtshals		Langesund		Langesund		Hirtshals
0900	→	1330		1430	→	1900

2355 KALUNDBORG - SAMSØ

SamsøLinjen

From Kalundborg and Ballen (Samsø): 3–5 sailings daily in summer; 2–3 sailings daily in winter. Journey 80–90 minutes.

2360 KØBENHAVN - OSLO

DFDS Seaways

Sailings from København Dampfærgevej and Oslo Vippetangen (Akershusstranda 31).

København		Oslo		Oslo		København
1415	→	0915		1415	→	0915

Departure from Oslo on ①③ until Apr. 30 and on ⑤⑥ Oct. 24 - Dec. 15 is at 1615.

DFDS shuttle bus links København port with the city centre.

2366 LARVIK - HIRTSHALS

Color Line Journey 3 hours 45 minutes

From Larvik and Hirtshals: 1-2 sailings daily. Departure times vary.

2372 OSLO - KIEL

Color Line

Sailings from Oslo Color Line Terminalen (Filipstadveien 25) and Kiel Norwegenkai.

Oslo		Kiel		Kiel		Oslo
1400	→	1000		1400	→	1000

2375 PUTTGARDEN - RØDBY

Scandlines Journey 45 minutes

Departures every 30 minutes (at 15 and 45 minutes past each hour). Sailing times between 2215 and 0415 may vary.

2380 ROSTOCK - TRELLEBORG

Stena Line

Sailings from Rostock (Überseehafen) and Trelleborg (Kontinentplan).

Rostock		Trelleborg			Trelleborg		Rostock	
0730	→	1330	①–⑥		0730	→	1330	①–⑥
1145	→	1745	⑦		1100	→	1700	⑦
1510	→	2110	①–⑥		1500	→	2100	①–⑥
2200	→	0540	⑦		2145	→	0540	⑦
2230	→	0540	①–⑥		2255	→	0610	①–⑥

Timings may vary. An additional night sailing operates on certain dates.

TT Line Journey 6–6½ hours

Sailings from Rostock Überseehafen and Trelleborg: 1–3 sailings per day. Timings vary.

2384 SASSNITZ-MUKRAN - RØNNE

Bornholmslinjen Journey 3 hours 20 minutes

From Sassnitz : sailing at 1150 ④⑦ in winter (Nov. - Mar.), ④⑦ Apr. (also certain ①⑤⑥), ④⑤⑥⑦ May (also 1430 on certain ⑥), ①④⑤⑥⑦ June (also 1430 on certain ⑥), daily in July and Aug. (also 1430 on ⑥⑦), ①④⑤⑥⑦ Sept. and Oct. (also 1430 on certain ⑥).

From Rønne : sailing at 0800 ④⑦ in winter (Nov. - Mar.), ④⑦ Apr. (also certain ①⑤⑥), ④⑤⑥⑦ May (also 1000 on certain ⑥), ①④⑤⑥⑦ June (also 1000 on certain ⑥), daily in July and Aug. (also 1000 on ⑥⑦), ①④⑤⑥⑦ Sept. and Oct. (also 1000 on certain ⑥).

2387 STRÖMSTAD - SANDEFJORD

Color Line Journey 2½ hours

From Strømstad: 1000, 1340, 1700, 2000.
From Sandefjord: 0700, 1000, 1330, 1700.

Fjord Line Journey 2½ hours

Strømstad		Sandefjord		Sandefjord		Strømstad
1200	→	1430		0830	→	1100
1830	→	2100		1520	→	1750

2390 TRAVEMÜNDE - TRELLEBORG

TT Line

Sailings from Travemünde Skandinavienkai and Trelleborg: 3–4 sailings per day.

Local 🚌 services are available from Travemünde Skandinavienkai railway station (Table **825**) to the ferry terminal or direct 🚌 from Lübeck ZOB.

2395 TRAVEMÜNDE - MALMÖ

Finnlines

Travemünde		Malmö		Malmö		Travemünde
0100⑦	→	1030⑦		1000②–⑤	→	1900②–⑤
0230②–⑤	→	1115②–⑤		1000⑥	→	1915⑥
0300①	→	1145①		1330⑥	→	2300⑥
0300⑥	→	1200⑥		1600①–⑤	→	0045②–⑥
0900②–⑥	→	1800②–⑥		1600⑦	→	0115①
1230②–⑤	→	2130②–⑤		2100①–⑤	→	0630②–⑥
1300⑥	→	2200⑥		2230⑥	→	0830⑦
2145②–⑤	→	0715③–⑥		2200⑦	→	0730①
2200①	→	0730②		2230①–④	→	0830②–⑤
2200⑥⑦	→	0730⑦①		2330⑤	→	0915⑥

BALTIC SEA

GDAŃSK - NYNÄSHAMN 2402

Polferries — Service Mar. - Jan 2023

Gdańsk		Nynäshamn			Nynäshamn		Gdańsk	
1800	→	1200	See note A.		1800	→	1200	See note A.

A – ①–⑥ (daily June 6 - Sept. 3). Subject to alteration Dec. 23, 2022 - Jan. 2, 2023.

Suburban rail service operates every 30 minutes (60 minutes on Ⓒ) Nynäshamn - Stockholm

GRISSLEHAMN - ECKERÖ 2405

Eckerö Linjen — Valid until Aug. 14

Grisslehamn		Eckerö			Eckerö		Grisslehamn	
1000	→	1300			0830	→	0915	See note B.
1500	→	1800			1330	→	1430	
2000	→	2245	See note A.		1830	→	1930	

A – ④⑤⑥⑦ until June 15; daily from June 17.
B – ①–⑤ until June 10; daily from June 13.

🚌 connections available Stockholm and Uppsala - Grisslehamn and v.v.

NAANTALI - KAPELLSKÄR via Långnäs 2407

Finnlines — *Conveys passengers with vehicles only.* — Valid until Aug. 31

Naantali		Långnäs		Kapellskär			Kapellskär		Långnäs		Naantali	
1045	→	1545	→	1815	⑥⑦		0915	→	1410	→	1910	⑥⑦
1145	→	1645	→	1845	①–⑤		1015	→	1450	→	1940	①–⑤
2230	→	0355	→	0615	⑥⑦		2130	→	0225	→	0715	⑥⑦
2245	→	0355	→	0615	①–⑤		2145	→	0225	→	0715	①–⑤

Some services subject to cancellations in April and May.

HELSINKI - TALLINN 2410

Eckerö Line

Sailings from Helsinki Länsiterminaali 2 (West Terminal T2) and Tallinn A-terminal.

Helsinki		Tallinn			Tallinn		Helsinki	
0900	→	1115			0600	→	0815	Not ⑦
1515	→	1730			1200	→	1415	
2140	→	2350	Not ⑥		1830	→	2100	

Tram routes 7 and 6T link Helsinki railway station with the Länsiterminaali

Tallink Silja — Mar. 1 - Dec. 18

Sailings from Helsinki Länsiterminaali 1/2 and Tallinn D-terminal. Journey 2 hours.

Depart Helsinki: 0730 A, 1030, 1330, 1630, 1830, 1930, 2230 B, 2300 ② E.

Depart Tallinn: 0730 ①–⑥, 1030, 1230, 1330, 1630, 1930, 2230 C D, 2300 ② E.

A – Not ⑦ Mar. 6 - Apr. 17.
B – Ⓐ Mar. 1 - Apr. 17; ② Apr. 19 - Dec. 13.
C – Not ⑥ Mar. 5. - Apr. 16.
D – Not ② Apr. 19 - Dec. 13.
E – ② Apr. 19 - Dec. 13.

Distance between Länsiterminaali terminals approximately 700 metres

Tram routes 7 and 6T link Helsinki railway station with the Länsiterminaali

Viking Line — Journey 2½ hours

Sailings from Helsinki Katajanokka terminal and Tallinn Reisisidam:
2 sailings ⑥–④, 3 on ⑤. Departure times vary.

KARLSKRONA - GDYNIA 2415

Stena Line — Journey 10½–12 hours

From Karlskrona and Gdynia: 1–2 sailings daily. Departure times vary.

KARLSHAMN - KLAIPEDA 2418

DFDS Seaways

Sailings from Karlshamn Ferry Terminal and Klaipeda International Ferry Port.

Karlshamn		Klaipeda		Klaipeda		Karlshamn
2000	→	0900		2000	→	1000

Timings vary

KIEL - KLAIPEDA 2420

DFDS Seaways

Sailings from Kiel Ostuferhafen and Klaipeda International Ferry Port.

Kiel		Klaipeda		Klaipeda		Kiel
2100	→	1800		2200	→	1700

KØGE - RØNNE 2430

Bornholmslinjen

Køge		Rønne		Rønne		Køge
0030	→	0600		1700	→	2230

NYNÄSHAMN - HANKO 2444

Stena Line

Nynäshamn		Hanko		Hanko		Nynäshamn
1900 ⑤	→	0900 ⑥		1830	→	0630
2000 ⑥–④	→	1000 ⑦–⑤				

Note: Limited passenger accommodation available.

NYNÄSHAMN - VISBY 2445

Destination Gotland

Sailings Nynäshamn - Visby and v.v.: 1–4 sailings daily (4–6 sailings in high summer). Departure times vary. Journey 3 hrs 15 minutes to 3 hrs 30 minutes.

All sailings have 🚌 connection Stockholm City Terminal - Nynäshamn and v.v.

Suburban rail service operates every 30 minutes (60 minutes on Ⓒ) Nynäshamn - Stockholm.

NYNÄSHAMN - VENTSPILS 2448

Stena Line — Journey 8½ hours

From Nynäshamn and Ventspils: 1–2 sailings daily. Departure times vary.

Suburban rail service operates every 30 minutes (60 minutes on Ⓒ) Nynäshamn - Stockholm.

NYNÄSHAMN - ROSTOCK 2449

Hansa Destinations — Service valid until Sept. 30

Nynäshamn		Rostock		Rostock		Nynäshamn
1900 ①③⑤A	→	1300 ②④⑥		1900 ②④⑥ B	→	1330 ③⑤⑦

A – Sailing on ⑤ calls additionally at Visby (a. 2215, d. 2240).
B – Sailing on ⑥ calls additionally at Visby (a. 0930, d. 1000 on ⑦).

OSKARSHAMN - VISBY 2450

Destination Gotland

From Oskarshamn and Visby: 1–2 sailings daily (January - March runs 6 days per week). Departure times vary.

STOCKHOLM - RIGA 2464

Tallink Silja — Service suspended

Sailings from Stockholm Värtahamnen terminal and Riga passenger terminal.

Stockholm		Riga		Riga		Stockholm
1700	→	1100		1730	→	1030

Sailings on alternate days starting Apr. 6 from Riga, Apr. 7 from Stockholm.

STOCKHOLM - MARIEHAMN - HELSINKI 2465

Tallink Silja — Mar. 1 - Dec. 31

Sailings from Stockholm Värtahamnen terminal and Helsinki Olympiaterminaali.

Stockholm		Mariehamn		Helsinki		Helsinki		Mariehamn		Stockholm
1645	→	2355	→	1030 A		1700	→	0420	→	0945
1645	→	2355	→	1000 B						

A – Mar. 1 - May 31, Sept. 1 - Dec. 31. B – June 1 - Aug. 31.

Tallink Silja 🚌 transfer links Stockholm Värtahamnen with city centre.
Alternatively Stockholm Värtahamnen is 500 metres from Gärdet metro station.

Viking Line

Sailings from Stockholm Stadsgården and Helsinki Katajanokka.

Stockholm		Mariehamn		Helsinki		Helsinki		Mariehamn		Stockholm
1630	→	2345	→	1010		1715	→	0430	→	1000

The above sailings are by way of an example, please check locally with the shippiing company.

Viking Line 🚌: Stockholm Cityterminalen (near Central station) - Viking Line terminal.

(STOCKHOLM -) KAPELLSKÄR - MARIEHAMN 2470

Viking Line — Journey 2½ hours

Sailings from Kapellskär and Mariehamn: 2–3 sailings per day (timings vary).

Connecting 🚌 service: Stockholm Cityterminalen (near Central station) - Kapellskär. Overall journey time Stockholm - Mariehamn by 🚌 and ferry is 4–4½ hours.

STOCKHOLM - MARIEHAMN - TALLINN 2475

Tallink Silja — Mar. 1 - Dec. 31

Sailings from Stockholm Värtahamnen terminal and Tallinn D-terminal.

Stockholm		Mariehamn		Tallinn		Tallinn		Mariehamn		Stockholm
1730	→	0100	→	1045		1800	→	0500	→	1015

STOCKHOLM - MARIEHAMN - TURKU 2480

Tallink Silja — Service is suspended on certain dates for ship maintenance

Sailings from Stockholm Värtahamnen and Turku.

Stockholm		Mariehamn		Långnäs §		Turku
0710	→	1345	→	→	→	1915
1930	→	→	→	0255	→	0700
Turku		**Långnäs §**		**Mariehamn**		**Stockholm**
0820	→	→	→	1345	→	1815
2015	→	0045	→	→	→	0610

§ – Långnäs is 28km from Mariehamn.

Tallink Silja 🚌 transfer links Stockholm Värtahamnen with city centre.
Alternatively Stockholm Värtahamnen is 500 metres from Gärdet metro station.

Viking Line — Service is suspended on certain dates for ship maintenance

Sailings from Stockholm Stadsgården and Turku Linnansatama.

Stockholm		Mariehamn		Långnäs §		Turku
0745	→	1425	→	→	→	1950
2000	→	→	→	0320	→	0735
Turku		**Långnäs §**		**Mariehamn**		**Stockholm**
0845	→	→	→	1425	→	1855
2055	→	0110	→	→	→	0630

§ – Långnäs is 28km from Mariehamn (🚌 connection available).

Båtbussarna 🚌 links Stockholm Cityterminalen (near Central station) with ferry terminal.
In Turku 🚌 number 1 runs between city centre and the harbour.

2482 ST PETERBURG - TALLINN - STOCKHOLM

St Peter Line — **Service suspended**

Sailings operate on a two-week cycle as shown below; first sailing Aug. 1 from St Peterburg, last arrival Oct. 2 at Tallinn 1230. Two-week cycle commences Aug. 1, 15, 29, Sept. 12, 26.

St Peterburg		Helsinki		Tallinn		Stockholm		Helsinki		St Peterburg
1800⑦	→	0830①	→	1830①**a**	→	1730②**b**	→	1900③**c**	→	0900④
1900④	→	1800⑤**d**	→	→	→	→	→	→	→	0900⑥
1900⑥	→	1800⑦**d**	→	→	→	→	→	→	→	0900①
1900①	→	→	→	1830②**e**	→	1730③**b**	→	1900④**c**	→	0900⑤
1900⑤	→	1800⑥**d**	→	→	→	→	→	→	→	0900⑦

a – Arr. 1230. **b** – Arr. 0930. **c** – Arr. 1130. **d** – Arr. 0800. **e** – Arr. 0900.

2485 TRAVEMÜNDE - HELSINKI

Finnlines — **Valid until Dec. 18**

Sailings from Travemünde Skandinavienkai and Helsinki Vuosaaren satama.

Travemünde		Helsinki	Helsinki		Travemünde
0200①	→	0915②	1500⑦	→	2145①
0245②③④⑤⑦	→	0915①③④⑤⑥	1615①–⑥	→	2145②–⑦
0315⑥	→	1000⑦			

Note Vuosaari harbour (Vuosaaren satama) is located approx 18 km east of Helsinki - can be reached by metro to Vuosaari then 🚌 route 90.

2486 TRAVEMÜNDE - LIEPAJA

Stena Line Journey 21–26 hours

From Travemünde and Liepaja: 4–5 sailings per week. Departure times vary.

2490 VAASA - UMEÅ (HOLMSUND)

Wasaline Journey 4½ hours

From Vaasa and Umeå: 1–2 sailings daily. Departure times vary.

2494 YSTAD - RØNNE

Bornholmslinjen by fast ferry

2–9 sailings daily, departure times vary, journey 80 minutes.

2495 YSTAD - ŚWINOUJŚCIE

Polferries — **Valid until Jan 31, 2023.**

Ystad		Świnoujście	Świnoujście		Ystad
1340	→	1945	0115	→	0730
1630	→	2330	1230	→	1900
1915	→	0200	1900	→	0500
2245	→	0615	2230	→	0615

Services depart on various days, check with operator

Free connecting 🚌 866 operates København - Ystad ferry terminal and v.v. (1 hr 15 min).

Unity Line

Ystad		Świnoujście	Świnoujście		Ystad
0545	→	1315	1300	→	2015
2300	→	0630			

WESTERN MEDITERRANEAN

2500 ALGECIRAS - CEUTA

Baleària (Eurolínies Marítimes) Journey 1¼–1½ hours

From Algeciras and Ceuta: ①–⑥ up to10 sailings per day, ⑦ up to 8 sailings per day.

Trasmediterranea Journey 60 minutes

From Algeciras and Ceuta: Ⓐ up to 5 sailings per day, ⑥ up to 3 sailings per day, ⑦ up to 4 sailings per day.

2502 ALGECIRAS - TANJAH (TANGIERS) MED

Africa Morocco Link Journey 1½ hours

From Algeciras and Tanjah Med: 3–5 sailings daily, departure times vary.

FRS Journey 1½ hours

From Algeciras and Tanjah Med: 4–7 sailings daily, departure times vary.

Inter Shipping Journey 1½ hours

From Algeciras and Tanjah Med: 2 sailings daily, departure times vary.

2504 ALMERÍA - GHAZAOUET

Trasmediterranea — **Service valid until June 5**

Almeria		Ghazaouet
2300⑥	→	0800⑦

Ghazaouet		Almeria
2000⑦	→	0700①

2505 ALMERÍA - MELILLA

Baleària (Eurolínies Marítimes) Journey 5-6 hours

From Almería and Melilla:

Almeria		Melilla	Melilla		Almeria
0900⑤	→	1400⑤	0900①	→	0600①
1500③	→	2000③	2359③⑥	→	0600④⑦
2359⑦	→	0600①			

Trasmediterranea Journey 6-8 hours — **Valid until June 14**

Depart Almería: 2300④, 2359②⑦.
Depart Melilla: 1545⑤, 1600⑤.

Times may vary (particularly in August and early September).

2507 ALMERÍA - AN-NADÛR (NADOR)

Baleària (Eurolínies Marítimes) Journey 7 hours — **Valid until Oct. 31**

2–3 sailings a week. Timings vary.

2508 BARCELONA - TANJAH (TANGIERS) MED

Grandi Navi Veloci Departure times vary. Journey 29 - 38 hours

From Barcelona and Tanjah Med: up to 5 sailings per week

Tanjah (Tangiers) Med port is located approximately 45 km east of Tanjah. A connecting 🚌 operates between Tanjah Med and Tanjah.

Grimaldi Lines — **Service suspended**

Barcelona		Tanjah Med	Tanjah Med		Barcelona
2000⑥	→	2300⑦	1500①	→	1900②

Tanjah (Tangiers) Med port is located approximately 45 km east of Tanjah (connecting 🚌).

2510 BALEARIC ISLANDS — Map page 315

Map page 315

Baleària (Eurolínies Marítimes) — **Valid until Nov. 1**

>BARCELONA - CIUTADELLA (MENORCA) Journey 8½–9½ hours. 1–3 sailings per day (not ⑥ Apr. and May). Most sailings depart Barcelona at 2145 and Ciutadella at 1000.

BARCELONA - EIVISSA (IBIZA) Journey 9 hours. 1 sailing per day until Sept. 30 (not ⑥ Apr., May, Sept.). Most sailings depart Barcelona at 2200 and Eivissa at 1000.

BARCELONA - PALMA Journey 6½ hours. 1 sailing per day until Nov. 1 (not ⑥ Apr. and May). Most sails depart Barcelona at 2215 and Palma at 1130. Other sailings to Alcudia.

DÉNIA - EIVISSA (IBIZA) - PALMA — Additional sailings in summer

Dénia		Eivissa		Palma	Palma		Eivissa		Dénia
1700	→	1900/2000	→	2200	0800	→	1000/1100	→	1300

VALENCIA - PALMA — Additional sailings run via Eivissa
Daily: Valencia d. 2300 (Palma a. 0600); Palma d. 1130 (Valencia a. 1830).

Trasmediterranea

Departure times may vary. All routes subject to alteration on and around holidays.

BARCELONA - EIVISSA (IBIZA) Journey 8–14 hours — **Valid until Sept. 11**
Depart Barcelona: 2200①–⑤ Jan. - July; Ⓑ Aug. and until Sept. 9.
Depart Ibiza: 1100②–⑤⑦ Jan. - July; ②–⑦ Aug. and until Sept. 11.

BARCELONA - MAÓ-MAHÓN (MENORCA) Journey 8–11 hours — **Valid until Sept. 30**
Depart Barcelona: 2200①–⑥. Also operates on ⑦ July 31 - Sept. 4. **A**
Depart Maó-Mahón: 1000②–⑥, 2000⑦. Also operates on ① Aug. 1–29. **B**
A – Timings vary ⑤⑥⑦ July 29 - Sept. 4. **B** – Timings vary ①⑥⑦ July 30 - Sept 4.

BARCELONA - PALMA (MALLORCA) Journey 7½–8 hours — **Valid until Sept. 30**
Depart Barcelona: 2245Ⓑ (daily July 2 - Sept. 9). **A**
Depart Palma: 1130①–⑥ (daily July 3 - Sept. 4). **B**
A – Timings vary ⑥⑦ July 30 - Sept. 4. **B** – Timings vary ⑥⑦ July 30 - Sept 4.

PALMA (MALLORCA) - MAÓ-MAHÓN (MENORCA) Journey 5½–6 hours
Depart Palma: 0800⑦. Depart Maó-Mahón: 1715⑦. — **Valid until Sept. 25**

VALÈNCIA - MAÓ-MAHÓN (MENORCA) via Palma Journey 14–15 hours
Depart València: 2200⑥. Depart Maó-Mahón: 1715⑦. — **Valid until Sept. 25**

VALÈNCIA - PALMA (MALLORCA) Journey 8 hours — **Valid until Sept. 30**
Depart València: Daily. Departure times vary: 2200, 2230 or 2300.
Depart Palma: Daily. Departure times vary: 1030, 1100, 1130 or 2345.

2512 CANARY ISLANDS

Fred. Olsen **Inter-Island services**

Playa Blanca (Lanzarote) - Corralejo (Fuerteventura), journey 25 minutes;
Morro del Jable (Fuerteventura) - Las Palmas de Gran Canaria (Gran Canaria), journey 120 minutes;
Agaete (Gran Canaria) - Santa Cruz de Tenerife (Tenerife), journey 80 minutes;
Los Cristianos (Tenerife) - San Sebástián de la Gomera (La Gomera), journey 50 minutes;
Santa Cruz de La Palma (La Palma) - Los Cristianos (Tenerife), journey 150 minutes;
Huelva - Las Palmas de Gran Canaria (Gran Canaria), journey 36 minutes;
Santa Cruz de La Palma (La Palma) - San Sebastián de la Gomera (La Gomera), journey 230 minutes.

Naviera Armas

Huelva - Arrecife (Lanzarote) - Las Palmas (Gran Canaria) - Santa Cruz (Tenerife): weekly.
Inter-Island services link all the main islands - most services run daily.

Trasmediterranea

Cádiz		Lanzarote (Arrecife)		Gran Canaria (Las Palmas)		Tenerife (Santa Cruz)		Palma (Santa Cruz)
1600②	→	1800/1930③	→	0100④/0530④	→	0845/1500④	→	2200④

Palma (Santa Cruz)		Tenerife (Santa Cruz)		Gran Canaria (Las Palmas)		Lanzarote (Arrecife)		Cádiz
1600⑤	→	2130/0130⑥	→	0730/1200⑥	→	2200⑥/2330⑥	→	0800①

CIVITAVECCHIA - BARCELONA 2520

Grimaldi Lines

Until June 13 and Oct. 2 - Dec. 17

Civitavecchia		Barcelona	Barcelona		Civitavecchia
2200①	→	1800②	2200①②	→	1830②③
2215②	→	1930③	2300④	→	2000⑤
2300③	→	1900④	0100④	→	2100④
0100⑤	→	2100⑤	0130⑥	→	2200⑥
0130⑥	→	2200⑥	0200⑦	→	2230⑦
0200⑦	→	2230⑦			

June 12 - July 18 and Sept. 13 - Oct. 1

Civitavecchia		Barcelona	Barcelona		Civitavecchia
2200①	→	1800②*	2200①	→	1830②*
2215②③	→	1930③④*	2300②③	→	2000③④*
2359⑤⑥	→	1959⑥⑦	2359⑤⑥	→	1959⑥⑦

July 19 - Sept. 10

Civitavecchia		Barcelona	Barcelona		Civitavecchia
2230①	→	1600②	2130①	→	1600②*
2215②③④	→	1930③④⑤*	2300②③④	→	2000③④⑤*
2315⑤	→	1915⑥	2315⑤	→	1915⑥⑦

** – Arrival times may vary*

CIVITAVECCHIA - SICILY - TÛNIS 2530

Grandi Navi Veloci

Civitavecchia		Palermo		Tûnis		Palermo		Civitavecchia
1900⑤	→	0800⑥/1100⑥	→	2300⑥/2300⑥	→	1300⑥/1800⑦	→	0900①

Timings vary (sample timings shown) - please check with operator

Grimaldi Lines — **Valid until Oct. 30**

Civitavecchia		Tûnis	Tûnis		Civitavecchia
1930②③	→	1430③④	1930②③	→	1430③④

CIVITAVECCHIA - TERMINI IMERESE 2535

Grandi Navi Veloci Departure times vary. Journey 14 hours

From Civitavecchia and Termini Imerese (for Palermo): up to 5 sailings per week.

GENOVA - BARCELONA 2537

Grandi Navi Veloci Departure times vary. Journey 20–22 hours

From Genova and Barcelona: up to 3 sailings per week.

GENOVA - PALERMO 2547

Grandi Navi Veloci Departure times vary. Journey 20½ hours

From Genova and Palermo: up to 7 sailings per week.

GENOVA - TANJAH (TANGIERS) MED 2554

Grandi Navi Veloci Departure times vary. Journey 49–58 hours

From Genova and Tanjah Med: up to 3 sailings per week.

Tanjah (Tangiers) Med port is located approximately 45 km east of Tanjah.
A connecting 🚌 operates between Tanjah Med and Tanjah.
Some sailings are via Barcelona (see Table **2508**)

GENOVA - TÛNIS 2555

Grandi Navi Veloci Departure times vary. Journey 25½ hours

From Genova and Tûnis: 2–3 sailings per week.

ALACANT - ORAN 2558

Algérie Ferries (E N T M V) — **Serive until May 30**

From Alacant and Oran: 4–5 sailings per month at 1900. Journey 13 hours.

GULF OF NAPOLI 2560

Including Gulf of Salerno and Ponziane Islands

Alilauro

Napoli Beverello - Forio: up to 5 sailings daily (summer only). Sailings via Ischia in winter.
Napoli Beverello or Mergellina - Ischia: up to 14 sailings daily.
Napoli Beverello - Sorrento: 5 sailings daily.
Salerno - Capri: daily sailing.
Sorrento - Capri: up to 8 sailings daily (summer only).

Additional infrequent services to Capri operate (summer only) from Ischia, Castellammare di Stábia, Positano and Amalfi.

Caremar

Napoli - Capri: 3 sailings daily by catamaran, 3 sailings by ship (4/3 in summer).
Napoli - Ischia: 6 sailings daily by catamaran, 7 sailings by ship (6/7 in summer).
Napoli - Procida: 7 sailings daily by catamaran, 7 sailings by ship (8/7 in summer).
Pozzuoli - Procida: 1 sailing by catamaran, 3 sailings by ship (1/3 in summer).
Procida - Ischia: 6 sailings daily by catamaran, 9 sailings by ship.
Sorrento - Capri: 4 sailings daily by catamaran.

Medmar

Ischia - Pozzuoli: up to 10 sailings daily.
Additional infrequent services operate between Pozzuoli, Procida, Casamicciola, and Ischia.

Navigazione Libera del Golfo by catamaran

Napoli (Molo Beverello) - Capri: up to 10 sailings daily (more in summer). Journey 40 minutes.
Sorrento - Capri: 2 sailings daily (more in summer). Journey 25 minutes.

Additional services operate (summer only) between Castellammare di Stábia and Capri.

SNAV

NAPOLI - CAPRI By hydrofoil, journey 40 minutes

From Napoli (Beverello): 0700, 0805, 0905, 1010, 1110, 1400, 1600, 1810.
From Capri: 0805, 0910, 1010, 1210, 1450, 1710, 1810, 1910.

NAPOLI - PROCIDA By hydrofoil, journey 40 minutes

From Napoli (Beverello): 0825, 1230, 1620, 1710 ⑤⑥⑦, 1900.
From Procida: 0735, 1010, 1415, 1805, 1900 ⑤⑥⑦.

ISCHIA - PROCIDA By hydrofoil, journey 10 - 20 minutes

From Ischia (Casamicciola): 0710, 0945, 1350, 1740.
From Procida: 0910, 1215, 1315, 1705, 1945.

CORSICA 2565

MAINLAND FRANCE TO CORSICA (map page 165)

Corsica Linea — *Departure times vary*

MARSEILLE - AJACCIO Journey 12 hours. Most sailings overnight.
MARSEILLE - BASTIA Journey 11–13 hours. Most sailings overnight.
MARSEILLE - L'ÎLE ROUSSE Journey 12–13 hours. Most sailings overnight ◇.
MARSEILLE - PORTO VECCHIO Journey 14 hours. Most sailings overnight ◇.
MARSEILLE - PROPRIANO Journey 12½ hours. 3 night sailings a week operated by La Méridionale.

◇ – Most sailings ①③⑤ from Marseille, returning ②④⑥. Additional sailings in summer.

Corsica Ferries — *Departure times vary*

NICE - AJACCIO Journey 4½–9 hours. Irregular sailings. Most sailings by day.
NICE - BASTIA 3–5 sailings per week (daily July/Aug.). Most sailings by day.
NICE - L'ÎLE ROUSSE Journey 5–5½ hours. Irregular sailings. Most sailings by day.
TOULON - AJACCIO Journey 6–10 hours. 1–2 sailings daily (daily night sailing).
TOULON - BASTIA Journey 9–10 hours. 1–2 sailings daily (daily night sailing).
TOULON - L'ÎLE ROUSSE Journey 6–7 hours. Irregular sailings. Most sailings by day.

Other sailings available from Nice and Toulon to Porto Vecchio.

ITALY TO CORSICA

Corsica Ferries — *Departure times vary*

LIVORNO - BASTIA Journey 4–7½ hours. 1–3 sailings per day. Most sailings by day.
SAVONA - BASTIA Journey 6–10 hours. 1–3 sailings per day (irregular in winter).

Other sailings: Livorno and Savona to L'Île Rousse.

Moby Lines — *Departure times vary*

GENOVA - BASTIA Journey 5–10 hours. Summer only, day and night sailings.
LIVORNO - BASTIA Journey 4½ hours. Summer only, 1–2 sailings per day (not daily).

CORSICA TO SARDINIA

Corsica Ferries / Sardinia Ferries

PORTO VECCHIO - GOLFO ARANCI July - September, up to 3 sailings per week.
BONIFACIO - SANTA TERESA DI GALLURA Journey 50 minutes. 3–4 sailings daily.

Moby Lines

BONIFACIO - SANTA TERESA DI GALLURA Journey 50 minutes. 3–4 sailings daily.

ITALIAN ISLAND SERVICES 2570

Egadi, Eolie, Pantelleria, Pelagie and Ustica Islands (map page 281)

Alilauro — **Summer only**

Napoli Mergellina - Stromboli - Panarea - Salina - Vulcano - Lipari and v.v.:
Daily sailings late May to early September. Additional sailing on ⑤⑥⑦ July/August (not serving Salina and Vulcano).

Liberty Lines by hydrofoil

EGADI & EOLIAN ISLANDS and USTICA

The Sicilian ports of Messina, Milazzo, Palermo and Trapani are linked by island-hopping services serving Alicudi, Favignana, Filicudi, Levanzo, Lipari, Marettimo, Panarea, Rinella, Salina, Stromboli, Ustica and Vulcano.

Services operate to differing frequencies (additional sailings in summer).

MILAZZO - PALERMO by hydrofoil Journey 2½ hours

Milazzo		Palermo		Milazzo	
0630	→	1145/1350	→	1900	June 20 - Sept. 3

MILAZZO - VULCANO by hydrofoil Journey 50 minutes

From Milazzo and Vulcano: 10–15 departures daily.

OTHER SERVICES:

Inter-island sailings operate, also from mainland Sicily to the islands. Services operate to differing frequencies (additional sailings in summer).

2595 MÁLAGA - MELILLA

Baleària (Eurolínies Marítimes) Journey 7 hours.

From Málaga: sailing days and times vary check locally.
From Melilla: sailing days and times vary check locally.

Trasmediterranea Journey 6–8 hours. Departure times vary at Easter.

From Málaga: 1430①–⑤, 1830⑦.
From Melilla: 0200①, 2345①②④⑤.

2602 MARSEILLE - AL-JAZÂ'IR (ALGIERS)

Algérie Ferries (E N T M V) — Service until Sept. 25

Marseille		al-Jazâ'ir	al-Jazâ'ir		Marseille
1300 ⑥	→	0500 ⑦	1300 ⑦	→	0800 ①

Sailing days and times may vary check locally.
Other services operate from Marseille to Sakīkdah / Skikda.

2615 MARSEILLE - TÛNIS

Compagnie Tunisienne de Navigation / Corsica Linea

The service is currently operated by two ferry companies.
The **Corsica Linea** service runs up to 3 times a week (journey time approx. 20½ hours).
Compagnie Tunisienne de Navigation (CTN) runs up to 5 times a week (journey time approx. 24 hours).

2618 CIRKEWWA (Malta) - MGARR (Gozo)

Gozo Channel Co.

Sailings Cirkewwa (Malta) - Mgarr (Gozo) and v.v.: every 45 minutes (approx every 90 mins early morning and late evening). Journey 25 minutes.

Frequent 🚌 services serve both ferry terminals.

2625 NAPOLI - PALERMO

Grandi Navi Veloci Journey 10½ hours

From Napoli and Palermo: up to 8 sailings per week. Departure times vary.

Tirrenia

Napoli		Palermo	Palermo		Napoli
2015	→	0645	2015	→	0645

2661 SALERNO - PALERMO - TÛNIS

Grimaldi Lines — Valid until October 30

Salerno		Palermo		Tûnis
0100⑤	→	1015⑤/1230⑥	→	2230⑥
1315①	→	2330①/0230②	→	1300②
Tûnis		**Palermo**		**Salerno**
0330⑦	→	1430⑦/2000⑦	→	0700①
1930④	→	0730⑤/1030⑤	→	2000⑤

2675 SARDINIA

FRANCE TO SARDINIA

Corsica Linea

TOULON - PORTO TORRES Journey 10–16 hours. Weekly in winter; up to 4 sailings per week in summer. Winter sailings are mostly overnight.

Corsica Sardinia Ferries

Sardinia Ferries

LIVORNO / SAVONA - GOLFO ARANCI Journey 7. Overnight sailings (also by day May - Sept).

MAINLAND ITALY TO SARDINIA (map page 281)

Tirrenia

CIVITAVECCHIA - CAGLIARI Journey 10½–15½ hours. 3 sailings per week (daily in summer). All sailings are overnight.

CIVITAVECCHIA - OLBIA Journey 5½–7 hours. Night sailing every day. 1–2 additional day sailings June - August.

GENOVA - OLBIA Journey 10–12¼ hours. 3–4 sailings per week (daily July / August).

GENOVA - PORTO TORRES Journey 9½–12 hours. Daily sailings.

Grimaldi Lines

CIVITAVECCHIA - OLBIA — June 1 - Sept. 26

Civitavecchia		Olbia	Olbia		Civitavecchia
2245	→	0630	1230	→	0700

CIVITAVECCHIA - CAGLIARI — Service until Dec. 31

Civitavecchia	Cagliari	Cagliari	Civitavecchia
2000②④⑥	1100③⑤⑦	2000①③⑤	1100②④⑥

NAPOLI - CAGLIARI — Service until Dec. 31

Napoli		Cagliari	Cagliari		Napoli
1900①③⑤	→	1000②④⑥	1900②④	→	0800⑤
...		...	2359⑦	→	1430①

SAVONA - PORTO TORRES — May 16 - Dec. 12

May 16 - July 1 and Sept. 19 - Dec. 31

Savona		Porto Torres	Porto Torres		Savona
2030②③④	→	0830③④⑤	2030①③⑤	→	0830④⑥
1830⑥	→	0630⑦	...		...
July 2 - Aug. 13					
2200①–⑥	→	0830⑦–⑤	1000①–⑥	→	1830①–⑥

CIVITAVECCHIA - PORTO TORRES Journey 7¼ hours. 2 sailings per week in winter (4–5 sailings per week mid-June to mid-September).

CIVITAVECCHIA - ARBATAX Journey 9–10 hours. 2 sailings per week, (3 sailings per week Aug. 1–31).

LIVORNO - OLBIA Journey 9–10 hours. 2 sailings per day (at 1030 and 2230) in each direction (on ⑥⑦ until June 6 and Sept. 26 - Dec. 12 one sailing only at 2130).

Moby Lines

CIVITAVECCHIA - OLBIA Journey 5½–7 hours. Daily sailings.
GENOVA - OLBIA Journey 11–12 hours. 3 sailings per week (1–2 per day June - Sept.).
LIVORNO - OLBIA Journey 6½–9 hours. Daily sailings (mostly overnight).
PIOMBINO - OLBIA Journey 5–5¼ hours. 4–6 sailings per week June - Sept.

Grandi Navi Veloci

GENOVA - OLBIA Journey 12¼ hours. 3–4 sailings per week (mostly overnight).
GENOVA - PORTO TORRES Journey 11½ hours. Infrequent sailings (daily in summer).

SICILY TO SARDINIA (map page 281)

Grimaldi Lines

PALERMO - CAGLIARI Journey 13 hours. 1 weekly departure a week.

SPAIN TO SARDINIA

Grimaldi Lines

BARCELONA - PORTO TORRES Journey 12¼ hours — June 1 - 25

Barcelona to Porto Torres: ① June 13; ④ June 2, 9, 16, 23; ⑤ June 25.
Porto Torres to Barcelona: ③ June 14, 21; ④ June 8, 17; ⑥ June 24.
Timings vary check locally

Basic service June 26 - Sept. 12

Barcelona	Porto Torres	Porto Torres		Barcelona
2200①	1130②	0630②	→	1845③
2215④	1145⑤	0645⑤	→	1900⑥
2359⑥	1230⑦	0845⑥	→	2000⑦

Additional sailings operate, times may vary check locally.

2678 SÈTE - AN-NADÛR (NADOR)

Grandi Navi Veloci Departure times vary. Journey 38–44 hours

From Sète and an-Nadûr: up to 2 sailings per week.

2680 SÈTE - TANJAH (TANGIERS) MED

Grandi Navi Veloci Departure times vary. Journey ±49 hours

From Sète and Tanjah Med: up to 3 sailings per week.

Tanjah (Tangiers) Med port is located approximately 45 km east of Tanjah (connecting 🚌).

2692 VALLETTA - POZZALLO

Virtu Ferries by catamaran Journey 1 hr 45 min

From Valletta and Pozzallo: 11–16 sailings per day, departure times vary.

2695 STRETTO DI MESSINA

MESSINA - REGGIO DI CALABRIA

Blu Jet by hydrofoil Journey 30 minutes

From Messina:
①–⑤: 0555, 0700, 0730, 0830, 0900, 1025, 1130, 1305, 1350, 1430, 1525, 1600, 1640, 1740, 1900, 2020.
⑥⑦: 0800, 0930, 1100, 1340, 1530, 1700.

From Reggio di Calabria:
①–⑤: 0640, 0745, 0810, 0910, 0940, 1105, 1210, 1345, 1440, 1510, 1600, 1640, 1720, 1820, 1940, 2055.
⑥⑦: 0840, 1010, 1140, 1420, 1610, 1740.

MESSINA - VILLA SAN GIOVANNI

Caronte & Tourist Journey 20 minutes

From Messina: every 40 minutes 0520 - 2320 (also night service 0020 - 0440).
From Villa San Giovanni: every 40 minbutes 0520 - 2350 (also night service 0050 - 0410).

Bluferries Journey 30 minutes

From Messina and Villa San Giovanni: approx every 30 - 40 minutes.

Blu Jet by hydrofoil Journey 20 minutes

From Messina:
From Messina: 0540, 0640, 0740, 0830, 0930, 1150, 1300, 1440, 1640, 1730, 1830, 1930, 2035, 2135, 2230, 2330.

From Villa San Giovanni:
0610, 0715, 0805, 0900, 1000, 1215, 1410, 1605, 1705, 1800, 1900, 2010, 2110, 2200, 2305, 0010.

2699 OTHER SERVICES

Corsica Ferries

From Piombino and Portoferraio (Elba): June - Sept.: up to 6 sailings daily by fast ferry; journey time 45 minutes.
From Bastia to Portoferraio (Elba): June - Sept: ④⑤ depart 0700, return 1830. Journey time 90 minutes.
Toulon - Trapani: up to twice weekly in April - Sept.

Moby Lines / Toremar

Piombino - Portoferraio (Elba): up to 30 sailings daily in high-summer, less frequent at other times; journey time 1 hour.

Toremar

Services operate from Piombino to Cavo, Pianosa, Portoferraio and Rio Marina; from Livorno to Capraia and Gorgona; from Porto Santo Stefano to Isola del Giglio and Giannutri.

ADRIATIC / EASTERN MEDITERRANEAN

ANCONA - PÁTRA via Kérkira / Igumenítsa 2715

Anek Lines / Superfast Ferries

January 1 - June 30 and September 12 - December 31

Ancona		Igumenítsa		Pátra
1330②③④⑤	→	0800③④⑤⑥	→	1430③④⑤⑥
1630⑥⑦	→	0930⑦①	→	1500⑦①

Pátra		Igumenítsa		Ancona
1730①②③⑦	→	2359②③④①	→	1630②③④①
1730⑤⑥	→	2315⑥⑦	→	1400⑥⑦

July 1 - August 11

	Ancona		Kérkira (Corfu)		Igumenítsa		Pátra
	1330①③⑤⑦	→	→	→	0630②④⑥①	→	1200②④⑥①
	1330②	→	0530③	→	0645③		...
	1630②	→	→	→	0930③		1530③
	1500④	→	0700⑤	→	0815⑤		...
	1630④	→	→	→	0930⑤	→	1500⑤
	1330⑥	→	→	→	0630⑦		1200⑦
	1630⑥	→	→	→	0930⑦	→	1500⑦

	Pátra		Igumenítsa		Kérkira (Corfu)		Ancona
	1430①②④⑥⑦	→	2015①②④⑥⑦	→	→	→	1100②③⑤⑦①
A	1730①③⑤	→	→	→	→	→	1200②④⑥
	...		1930③⑤	→	2045③⑤	→	1045④⑥

August 12 - September 11 ●

	Ancona		Kérkira (Corfu)		Igumenítsa		Pátra
B	1330①③⑤⑦	→	→	→	0630②④⑥①	→	1200②④⑥①
	1330②	→	0530③	→	0645③	→	...
	1500④	→	0700⑤	→	0815⑤		...
	1630②④	→	→	→	→	→	1200④⑤

	Pátra		Igumenítsa		Kérkira (Corfu)		Ancona
C	1430②④⑥⑦	→	2015②④⑥⑦	→	→	→	1100③⑤⑥⑦①
	1730⑤	→	2315⑤	→	→	→	1400⑥
	...	→	1930⑤	→	→	→	1400②
	1730⑤	→	2315⑤	→	2045⑤		1045⑥

A – On July 1 departs Pátra 1430, arrives Ancona 1100 (on July 2).
B – Also Aug. 13, 20, 27, Sept. 3, 9.
C – Also Aug. 15.
● – Additional services operate in each direction on Aug. 13, 15, 17, 20, 22, 24, 27, 29, 31, Sept. 3, 5, 7, 10. Check locally for details.

🚌 connection Pátra - Pireás - Athína and v.v. operates most days in summer. For international journeys only

Grimaldi Lines / Minoan Lines — Service valid until Mar. 31

Ancona		Igumenítsa		Pátra
1730①	→	→	→	1700②
1400③	→	→	→	1330④
1400④	→	→	→	1330⑤
1600⑤	→	→	→	1530⑥
1700⑥	→	→	→	1630⑦
1630⑦	→	→	→	1600①

Pátra		Igumenítsa		Ancona
1900①	→	→	→	2030②
1830②	→	→	→	1800③
1630④	→	→	→	1400⑤
1630⑤	→	→	→	1400⑥
1700⑥	→	→	→	1430⑦
1800⑦	→	→	→	1530①

2022 service

Ancona		Igumenítsa	Igumenítsa		Ancona
1930	→	2130	2130	→	1930

ANCONA - SPLIT 2725

SNAV — April 11 to Oct. 28 (No winter service)

Ancona		Split		Split		Ancona	
1930	→	0700	①③⑤	1930	→	0700	②④⑦
2200	→	0900	⑥ July - Aug.	1030	→	2000	⑥ July - Aug.

Jadrolinija

Ancona		Split	Split		Ancona
January 2 - May 13 and October 31 - January 1, 2023					
1945②⑤	→	0700③⑥	2000⑦③	→	0700①④
May 15 - July 14 and August 29 - October 28					
1945①④⑤	→	0700②⑤⑦	2000②④⑦	→	0700③⑤①
July 15 - August 14					
1945①④	→	0700②④	2000②④	→	0700③⑤
1945⑤	→	0600⑤	1430⑥	→	0830⑦
2359⑥	→	1030⑦	2000⑦	→	1930①
August 15 – 28					
1945①③	→	0700②④	2000②④	→	0700③⑤
1945⑥	→	0600⑥	2130⑥	→	0830⑦
1030⑦	→	1930⑦	2130⑦	→	0800①

ANCONA - ZADAR 2732

Jadrolinija

Ancona		Zadar	Zadar		Ancona
June 23 - July 17					
2200④	→	0700⑤	1000⑤	→	1700⑤
July 18 - August 21					
1000①	→	1800①	2200①	→	0700②
2200④	→	0700⑤	1000⑤	→	1700⑤
August 22 – 26					
1000①	→	1700⑥⑦	2200①	→	0700②
1000①	→	1700①	2200⑤	→	0700⑥
September 1 – 9					
2200④	→	0700⑤	1000⑤	→	0700⑤
2200②	→	0700③			

BAR - BARI 2738

Jadrolinija — June 6 - Nov. 23 (no winter sailings)

Bar		Bari	Bari		Bar
2100③	→	0800④	2100②	→	0800③

BARI - DURRËS 2745

Grandi Navi Veloci / Adria Ferries

From Bari and Durrës: departs 2200 daily (timings vary in summer). Journey 9 – 11 hours. Adria Ferries also operates from Ancona and Trieste to Durrës.

Ventouris Ferries

From Bari and Durrës: 1 – 2 sailings per day, Journey 9 – 10 hours.

BARI - IGUMENÍTSA via Kérkira (Corfu) 2750

Ventouris Ferries — July 15 - Sept. 9 (no winter sailings)

Bari		Kérkira (Corfu)		Igumenítsa	
1000	→	→	→	2200	Sept. 4.
2000	→	→	→	0800	July 1, 5, 6, 8, 11, 13. Sept. 2, 5, 7, 9.
2000	→	0700 / 0730	→	0830	July 15, 18, 20*, 22, 25*, 27, 29, Aug. 1*, 3, 5, 8*, 10, 12, 15*, 17, 19, 22*, 24, 26, 29*, 31.
2359	→	→	→	1200	July 2, Sept. 10.
2359	→	1100 / 1130	→	1230	July 9, 16, 18*, 23, 25*, 30. Aug. 1*, 6, 8*, 13, 15*, 22*, 29*.

Igumenítsa		Kérkira (Corfu)		Bari	
1000	→	→	→	2000	July 2, 9, 16, 23, 28, 30, Aug. 4, 6. 11, 13, Sept. 10.
1500	→	1930/2130	→	2300	July 19* 26*, Aug. 2*, 9*, 16*, 23*, 30*.
2130	→	→	→	0730	July 3, 5, 7, 10, 12, 14.
2130	→	2230 / 2300	→	0800	July 17, 21, 24, 31, Aug. 7, 14, 18, 20, 25, 27, Sept. 1, 3, 6, 8, 11.
2359	→	0100/0130	→	1030	Aug. 21, 28, Sept. 4.

* – Also calls at Sami (Kefallinía) before and after Igumenítsa.

BARI - PÁTRA via Kérkira and Igumenítsa 2755

Anek Lines / Superfast Ferries

	Bari		Kérkira (Corfu)		Igumenítsa		Pátra
	January 1 - May 31 and October 1 - December 31						
	1330⑦	→	→	→	2300⑦	→	0700①
AD	1930①–⑥	→	→	→	0530①–⑥	→	1300②–⑦
	June 1 - June 30 and September 19 – 30						
	1330⑦	→	→	→	2300⑦	→	0700①
	1930①②③⑤⑥	→	→	→	0530①②③⑤⑥	→	1300②③④⑥⑦
	1930④	→	0430⑤	→	0600⑤	→	1300⑤
	July 1 – 21						
	1300⑦	→	→	→	2300①	→	0700①
	1930①②③	→	→	→	0530②③④	→	1300②③④
	1930④⑤⑥	→	0430⑤⑥⑦	→	0600⑤⑥⑦	→	1300⑤⑥⑦
	July 22 - August 21						
	1200⑤⑥	→	2100	→	2230⑥⑦		...
	1330⑦	→	→	→	2300①	→	0700①
	1930①②③	→	→	→	0530②③④	→	1300②③④
	1930④	→	0430⑤	→	0600⑤	→	1300⑤
	1930⑥	→	→	→	0530⑦	→	1300⑦
	August 22 - September 18						
	1330⑦	→	→	→	2300①	→	0700①
B	1930①–⑥	→	→	→	0530②–⑦	→	1300②–⑦
	1930④	→	0430⑤	→	0600⑤	→	1300⑤

	Pátra		Igumenítsa		Kérkira (Corfu)		Bari
	January 1 - May 31 and October 1 - December 31						
E	1730	→	2359	→	→	→	0900
	June 1 - June 30 and September 19 – 30						
C	1730	→	2359	→	→	→	0900
	1730③	→	2359	→	0130④	→	0930④
	July 1 - July 21						
	1730①②④⑤⑦	→	2359	→	→	→	0900②③⑤⑥①
	1730③⑥	→	2359	→	0130④⑦	→	0930④⑦
	July 22 - August 21						
	1730①②④⑦	→	2359	→	→	→	0900②③⑤①
	1730③	→	2359	→	0130④	→	0930④
	1730⑤	→	→	→	→	→	0730⑥
	...	→	2359⑤⑥	→	0130⑥⑦	→	0830⑥⑦
	August 22 - September 18						
	1730①②④⑤	→	2359	→	→	→	0900②③⑤⑥
F	1730③⑥⑦	→	2359	→	0130④⑦①	→	0930④⑦①

A – Not Dec. 25, Jan. 1.
B – On Aug. 27 sails via Kérkira a. 0430⑦, then Igumenítsa a. 0600⑦, Pátra a. 1300⑦.
C – Daily except ③.
D – On Apr. 21 sails via Kérkira a. 0430⑤, then Igumenítsa a. 0600⑤, Pátra a. 1300⑦.
E – On Apr. 25 sails via Kérkira a. 0130②, then Pátra a. 0930②.
F – On Sept. 10, 11 does not call at Kérkira, Bari a. 0900①②.

Subject to alteration during ship maintenance periods

🚌 connection Pátra - Pireás - Athína and v.v.

 For international ferry maps see pages 545 – 547. For ferry operator details see page 548.

2765 BRINDISI - IGUMENÍTSA

Grimaldi Lines

Brindisi		Igumenítsa	Igumenítsa		Brindisi
1300	→	2300	0100	→	0930

European Seaways

Sailings Brindisi - Igumenítsa 5 days per week.
Sailings also call at Kérkira (Corfu).
Check timings and days of travel with operator.

2775 BRINDISI - KÉRKIRA (CORFU)

Grimaldi Lines — July 17 - Sept. 6

Brindisi		Kérkira	Kérkira		Brindisi
1300⑥⑦	→	1900	0230①⑦	→	0830

Grimaldi Lines also operate between Ancona and Kérkira July - Sept.

2795 DUBROVNIK - BARI

Jadrolinija — No winter sailings

Dubrovnik		Bari	Bari		Dubrovnik
June 3 – 11 and September 19 - October 29					
2100①⑤	→	0800②⑥	2100④⑥	→	0800⑤⑦
June 13 - July 24 and September 1 - 18					
2100①⑤	→	0800②⑥	2100④⑥	→	0800⑤⑦
1200⑦	→	1930⑦	2200⑦	→	2200①
July 24 - August 15					
2100①	→	0800②⑥	2100④	→	0800⑤
1200⑤⑥	→	1930⑤⑥	2200⑤⑥⑦	→	0800⑥⑦①
1200⑦	→	1930⑦			
August 18 – 29					
2100⑤	→	0800 ⑥	1200①⑥⑦	→	1930②⑥⑦
2200①⑥⑦	→	0800 ②⑦①	2100④	→	0800⑤
October 31 - November 24					
2100①	→	0800②	2100④	→	0800⑤

2800 GREEK ISLANDS

Summary table of regular ferry services to the Greek Islands

Routes are operated by various ferry companies to differing schedules.
Additional inter-island routes are operated at less regular intervals.

Pireás to Égina, Póros, Ídra, Spétses, Kíthira, Andikíthira.
Pireás to Sérifos, Sífnos, Mílos, Folégandros.
Pireás to Páros, Íos, Thíra (Santorini), Iráklio.
Pireás to Náxos, Amorgós, Astipálea.
Pireás to Pátmos, Léros, Kálimnos, Kos, Nísiros, Tílos, Sími, Ródos, Kárpathos, Kásos.
Pireás to Ikaria, Sámos, Híos, Lésvos.
Pireás and **Rafína** to Síros, Dílos, Míkonos, Tínos, Ándros.
Pátra to Zákinthos (Zante), Kefallinía, Itháki, Kérkira (Corfu), Igumenítsa.
Kyllíni to Zákinthos (Zante), Kefallinía, Itháki.
Vólos, **Ágios Konstantínos** and **Kimi** to Skíathos, Skópelos, Alónissos, Skíros.
Kavála to Thásos, Samothráki, Límnos.

2830 PIREÁS - IRÁKLIO

Minoan Lines

Pireás		Iráklio		Iráklio		Pireás	
0900	→	1850	Note **A**	0900	→	1730	Note **C**
1000	→	1830	Note **B**	1000	→	1830	Note **B**
2100	→	0600		2100	→	0630	

Arrival timings may vary - sample times are given.

A – ①④⑥ May 5 - Oct. 8.
B – July 31, Aug. 5, 7, 12, 13, 21, 28 only.
C – ②⑤⑦ May 27 - Oct. 7.

Anek Lines / Blue Star Ferries

Pireás		Iráklio	Iráklio		Pireás
2100	→	0600	2100	→	0600

Additional day sailings operate on certain dates in July / August

2845 PIREÁS / LAVRIO - LEMESÓS (LIMASSOL) - HEFA

Salamis Shipping — **Passengers not currently accepted**

Pireás - Lemesós - Hefa: weekly freight sailings with limited passenger accommodation.

2846 PIREÁS - LEMESÓS (LIMASSOL)

Scandro Holding Ltd — June 19 - Sept. 16

Pireás		Lemesós	Lemesós		Pireás
0100② **A**	→	0700③	1200⑦ **C**	→	1800①
0600⑤ **B**	→	1200⑥	1300③ **D**	→	1900④

A – Not Aug. 16, Sept. 13.
B – Not Aug. 26, Sept. 2.
C – Not Aug. 14, Sept. 11.
D – Not Aug. 24, 31.

2850 SPLIT - DUBROVNIK

Jadrolinija — No winter sailings

Split		Hvar		Korčula		Dubrovnik	
1530	→	1755	→	1925	→	2125	June 3 - Sept. 25.
Dubrovnik		**Korčula**		**Hvar**		**Split**	
0700	→	0915	→	1050	→	1255	June 4 - Sept. 26.

Catamaran services Spilt → Hvar runs: 1 – 2 times daily Apr. 29 - June 2 and Oct. 3 - 22; 4 – 5 times daily June 3 - October 2

Kapetan Luka — No winter sailings

Split		Hvar		Korčula		Dubrovnik	
0740	→	0850	→	1010	→	1205	Daily Apr. 1 - Oct. 30.
Dubrovnik		**Korčula**		**Hvar**		**Split**	
1630	→	1835	→	1950	→	2055	Daily Apr. 1 - Aug. 31.
1600	→	1805	→	1920	→	2025	Daily Sept. 1 - Oct. 30.

2875 VENEZIA - PÁTRA via Ancona / Igumenítsa

Anek Lines / Superfast Ferries

Venezia		Igumenítsa		Pátra	Pátra		Igumenítsa		Venezia
January 1 - June 5 and September 25 - December 31									
1200③⑦	→	1430④①	→	2100④①	2300①	→	0630②	→	0700③
1330⑥	→	1600⑦	→	2230⑦	2359④⑤	→	0630⑤⑥	→	0700⑥⑦
June 6 - June 30 and September 12 – 24									
1200③	→	1430④	→	2100④	2359④	→	0630⑤	→	0700⑥
1330⑥	→	1600⑦	→	2230⑦	2300①	→	0630②	→	0700③
1200⑦	→	1500①c	→	2130①	2359⑤	→	0630⑥c	→	0730⑦
July 1 - September 11									
1200③	→	1430④	→	2100④	2359④	→	0630⑤	→	0700⑥
1330⑥	→	1600⑦	→	2230⑦	2300①	→	0630②	→	0730③

c – via Corfu (1345 towards Pátra, 0745 towards Venezia).

For international journeys only

2899 CROATIAN COASTAL SERVICES

Catamaran Line

Runs Pula - Mali Lošinj - Zadar, Šibenik - Kaprije - Žirje, and Split - Split (Resnik) airport.

G & V Line

Catamaran services operate from Rijeka and Zadar to the islands.

Jadrolinija

Local services operate from Rijeka, Zadar, Šibenik and Dubrovnik to the Islands.

Venezia Lines

Catamaran services run May to September linking Venezia with destinations on Croatia's Istrian Peninsula (Poreč, Pula, Rovinj and Umag), also with Piran in Slovenia. Journey time 2 hours 30 minutes to 4 hours.

2900 BLACK SEA services

Irregular services operate on the following routes (freight services; also carry passengers):

Route	Operator	
Istanbul - Odesa	**Ukrferry**	
Burgas - Batumi	**PBM**	Certain sailings call at Novorossiysk
Varna - Batumi	**Ferrysped**	
Varna - Poti	**Ferrysped**	
Varna - Odesa	**Ferrysped**	
Odesa - Batumi	**Ferrysped / Ukrferry**	Certain sailings call at Samsun
Odesa - Poti	**Ferrysped / Ukrferry**	

Odesa's ferry terminal is at Chornomorsk, 20km from Odesa.
Please confirm locally for dates and times.

TGV NORD SERVICE JULY 18 - AUGUST 28 — 250

HIGH-SPEED TRAINS. For Paris Charles de Gaulle ✈ - Lille services see Table 11. For Paris - Calais, Boulogne and Rang du Fliers services see page 166.
Journeys to / from Paris are 🅁 with supplement. For other journeys, *TGV* and ♣ trains are classified *TER-GV* and require a Grande Vitesse supplement, €3 valid all day, 🅁 not required.

PARIS - LILLE FLANDRES

km		*TGV*	*TGV*	*TGV*	*TGV*		*TGV*	*TGV*	*TGV*	*TGV*		*TGV*	*TGV*	*TGV*		*TGV*	*TGV*	*TGV*	*TGV*		*TGV*	*TGV*	*TGV*	*TGV*
		7007	**7015**	**7023**	**7025**		**7031**	**7035**	**7037**	**7043**		**7045**	**7047**	**7053**		**7057**	**7061**	**7065**	**7069**		**7073**	**7077**	**7081**	**7297**
		Ⓐ	①–⑥	⑥	Ⓑ		⑥⑦	⑥	Ⓐ	⑤⑥		†	Ⓐ	⑤⑦		Ⓐ	⑥⑦	Ⓐ			⑦	⑤	⑦	①–⑥
			d	e	f		g	e		e				h			g		A		j		j	m◧
0	**Paris** Nord d.	0746	0845	0946	1016	...	1146	1246	1315	1446	...	1516	1546	1646	...	1716	1746	1816	1846	...	1916	1946	2016	2222
227	**Lille** Flandres a.	0848	0948	1048	1118	...	1248	1348	1418	1548	...	1618	1648	1748	...	1818	1848	1918	1948	...	2018	2048	2118	2340

	TGV	*TGV*	*TGV*	*TGV*		*TGV*	*TGV*	*TGV*	*TGV*		*TGV*	*TGV*	*TGV*		*TGV*	*TGV*	*TGV*	*TGV*		*TGV*	*TGV*	*TGV*	*TGV*
	7200	**7002**	**7006**	**7014**		**7016**	**7026**	**7028**	**7030**		**7032**	**7038**	**7044**		**7046**	**7052**	**7060**	**7068**		**7072**	**7076**	**7078**	**7082**
	Ⓐ	①	①–⑥	⑥		Ⓐ		⑦	⑥		Ⓐ	⑥	Ⓐ		⑦	Ⓑ		⑤⑦		Ⓐ	⑥	⑤	
	⊡	k	n	p			A	q	e			e			j	r	g	r			e	s	B
Lille Flandres d.	0552	0642	0712	0812	...	0842	1012	1042	1112	...	1142	1312	1442	...	1512	1612	1712	1812	...	1842	1912	1942	2012
Paris Nord a.	0708	0744	0814	0914	...	0944	1114	1144	1214	...	1244	1414	1544	...	1614	1714	1814	1914	...	1944	2014	2044	2114

PARIS - LILLE EUROPE, DUNKERQUE, CALAIS, BOULOGNE and RANG DU FLIERS

km		♣	♣	*TGV*	♣	*TGV*	♣	♣	*TGV*	♣	*TGV*	*TGV*	♣	*TGV*	*TGV*	♣	*TGV*	♣	*TGV*	*TGV*	*TGV*	*TGV*	*TGV*	♣	*TGV*
				7551		**7015**			**7359**		**7363**	**7025**		**7565**	**7265**		**7365**		**7369**	**7569**	**7571**	**7571**	**7371**		**7273**
		Ⓐ	Ⓐ	Ⓐ	Ⓐ	⑦	Ⓐ	Ⓒ	⑥	Ⓐ	†	†	†	⑥	Ⓐ	⑥	⑥	Ⓐ	Ⓐ	Ⓐ	†	⑥	†	Ⓐ	⑤
			C			w		e				x		e								e			
0	**Paris** Nord d.	...	...	0652	...	0846	...	...	0852	...	0952	1016	...	1052	1052	...	1052	...	1222	1222	1352	1352	1352	...	1428
179	Arras a.	...	...	0741	...	|	...	...	0941	...	1041	|	...	1140	1141	...	1140	...	1310	1310	1440	1441	1440	...	1517
179	Arras d.	0643	0718	0745	...	|	...	...	0951	...	1051	|	...	1144	1149	...	1151	...	1314	1318	1444	1448	1451	...	1535
199	Lens a.	|	|	|	...	|	...	...	1002	...	1102	|	...	|	|	...	1203	...	1327	|	|	|	1502	...	|
218	Béthune a.	|	|	|	...	|	...	...	1016	...	1116	|	...	|	|	...	1216	...	1342	|	|	|	1516	...	|
227	**Lille** Europe a.	0704	0737	0807	...	0945	...	...	|	...	|	1116	...	1205	1208	...	|	...	|	1338	1505	1507	|	...	1601
227	**Lille** Europe d.	0721	0750	0814	0850	...	0955	1005	|	1050	|	...	1120	1215	1220	1220	|	1321	|	1345	1515	1515	|	1550	...
252	Hazebrouck a.	|	|	|	|	...	|	|	1039	|	1139	...	|	|	|	|	1239	|	1405	|	|	|	1539	|	...
292	**Dunkerque** a.	|	0820	|	0920	...	|	|	1104	1120	1204	...	1151	|	1251	1251	1304	1352	1430	|	|	|	1604	1620	...
326	**Calais** Fréthun a.	0753	...	0843	...	...	1024	1033	...	...	...	...	...	1244	...	...	...	...	...	1413	1545	1545	...	...	...
326	**Calais** Fréthun **261** d.	...	...	0853	...	...	1035	1044	...	...	...	...	...	1255	...	...	...	...	...	1424	1556	1554	...	...	...
360	**Boulogne** Ville **261** a.	...	...	0915	...	...	1055	1103	...	...	...	...	...	1317	...	...	...	...	...	1443	1617	1617	...	...	...
387	Étaples-Le Touquet **261** a.	...	...	...	...	...	...	1122	...	...	...	...	...	1336	...	...	...	...	...	1501	1636	...	...	...	...
398	**Rang du Fliers** ⊕ **261** a.	...	...	...	...	...	...	1132	...	...	...	...	...	1346	...	...	...	...	...	1512	1646	...	...	...	...

	♣	♣	*TGV*	♣	♣	*TGV*	*TGV*	♣	*TGV*	♣	*TGV*	*TGV*	♣	*TGV*	♣	*TGV*	*TGV*	♣	*TGV*	*TGV*	*TGV*	*TGV*	*TGV*	*TGV*
			7575			**7577**	**7277**		**7377**		**7581**	**7283**		**7585**		**7385**	**7289**		**7389**	**7591**	**7591**	**7391**	**7295**	**7297**
	Ⓐ	Ⓐ	⑥	Ⓐ	Ⓐ	Ⓐ	†	†	Ⓐ	Ⓐ	Ⓐ	⑥	†	†	①–⑥	Ⓑ	⑥	†	Ⓒ	Ⓐ	①–⑤	Ⓐ	†	⚒
			t												n					u	v			y
Paris Nord d.	...	...	1552	...	...	1652	1652	...	1652	...	1752	1752	...	1852	...	1852	1952	...	1952	2022	2022	2022	2152	2222
Arras a.	...	...	1640	...	...	1740	1741	...	1740	...	1840	1840	...	1940	...	1940	2042	...	2042	2111	2111	2111	2240	2311
Arras d.	...	...	1644	...	...	1744	1748	...	1751	...	1848	1848	...	1944	...	1951	2044	...	2051	2117	2117	2121	2244	2319
Lens a.	...	...	|	...	...	|	|	...	1802	...	|	|	...	|	...	2002	|	...	2102	|	|	2135	|	|
Béthune a.	...	...	|	...	...	|	|	...	1816	...	|	|	...	|	...	2016	|	...	2116	|	|	2151	|	|
Lille Europe a.	...	...	1706	...	...	1807	1807	...	|	...	1908	1907	...	2006	...	|	2107	...	|	2138	2138	|	2307	2338
Lille Europe d.	1650	1655	1718	1725	1750	1815	1820	1825	|	1850	1915	1920	1920	2015	2035	|	...	2122	|	2145	2145	|	...	...
Hazebrouck a.	|	|	|	|	|	|	|	|	1839	|	|	|	|	|	|	2039	...	|	2139	|	|	2214	...	...
Dunkerque a.	1720	|	|	|	1820	|	1851	|	1904	1920	|	1951	1951	|	|	2104	...	|	2204	|	|	2242	...	...
Calais Fréthun a.	...	1724	1746	1753	...	1842	...	1853	...	...	1943	...	...	2043	2102	...	...	2153	...	2213	2218	...	...	...
Calais Fréthun **261** d.	...	1735	1757	...	...	1854	...	1904	...	...	1954	...	...	2054	2113	...	...	2204	...	2224	|	...	...	...
Boulogne Ville **261** a.	...	1755	1818	...	...	1912	...	1925	...	...	2015	...	...	2117	2133	...	...	2225	...	2244	●	...	...	...
Étaples-Le Touquet **261** a.	...	...	1837	...	...	...	...	...	...	...	2033	...	...	2136	...	...	...	...	...	...	...	...	...	...
Rang du Fliers ⊕ **261** a.	...	...	1847	...	...	...	...	...	...	...	2043	...	...	2147	...	...	...	...	...	...	...	...	...	...

	TGV	♣	*TGV*	*TGV*	♣	*TGV*	♣	♣	♣	*TGV*	*TGV*	♣		♣	*TGV*	*TGV*	*TGV*	*TGV*	*TGV*	*TGV*	*TGV*	♣	*TGV*	*TGV*
	7304		**7208**	**7508**		**7014**				**7312**	**7212**				**7028**	**7516**	**7518**	**7218**	**7320**	**7520**	**7322**		**7522**	**7324**
	Ⓐ	Ⓐ	Ⓐ	Ⓐ	Ⓐ	⑦	Ⓐ	Ⓐ	⑥	⑥	†	Ⓐ		Ⓐ	†	①–⑥	†	†	Ⓐ	Ⓐ	⑥	⚒	⑥	†
						w			e						x	n				⊖			e	
Rang du Fliers ⊕ **261** d.	...	...	...	...	0631	...	...	...	...	...	...	...	...	...	...	...	...	...	...	...	...	...	1212	...
Étaples-Le Touquet **261** d.	...	...	...	...	0641	...	...	...	...	...	...	...	...	...	...	...	...	...	...	...	...	...	1223	...
Boulogne Ville **261** d.	...	0530	...	0632	0700	...	...	...	0731	...	...	...	...	...	...	0935	1045	...	...	1153	...	...	1241	...
Calais Fréthun **261** a.	...	0554	...	0655	0723	...	...	...	0754	...	...	...	...	...	...	0955	1104	...	...	1215	...	...	1305	...
Calais Fréthun d.	...	0605	...	0707	0734	...	...	0806	0808	...	...	...	...	...	...	1006	1115	...	...	1230	...	...	1316	...
Dunkerque d.	0556	|	0656	|	|	...	0800	|	|	0756	...	0904	...	1000	...	|	|	1125	1211	|	1256	1300	|	1356
Hazebrouck d.	0620	|	|	|	|	...	|	|	|	0820	...	|	...	|	...	|	|	|	1234	|	1320	|	|	1420
Lille Europe a.	|	0640	0729	0734	0804	...	0831	0835	0835	|	...	0935	...	1031	...	1035	1145	1157	|	1259	|	1331	1345	|
Lille Europe d.	|	...	0740	0740	...	0813	...	...	...	|	0851	...	...	...	1043	1051	1205	1205	|	1303	|	...	1351	|
Béthune d.	0643	...	|	|	...	|	...	...	...	0843	|	...	...	...	|	|	|	|	1257	|	1343	...	|	1443
Lens d.	0657	...	|	|	...	|	...	...	...	0857	|	...	...	...	|	|	|	|	1313	|	1357	...	|	1457
Arras a.	0710	...	0801	0801	...	|	...	...	...	0911	0912	...	...	...	|	1113	1225	1225	1330	1337	1409	...	1412	1511
Arras d.	0718	...	0808	0808	...	|	...	...	...	0918	0918	...	...	...	|	1118	1230	1230	1341	1341	1418	...	1418	1518
Paris Nord a.	0808	...	0859	0859	...	0914	...	...	...	1008	1008	...	...	...	1144	1208	1320	1320	1432	1432	1508	...	1508	1608

	♣	*TGV*	*TGV*	♣	*TGV*	♣	*TGV*		*TGV*	♣	*TGV*	♣	♣	*TGV*	*TGV*	♣		♣	*TGV*	*TGV*	*TGV*	♣	*TGV*	*TGV*
		7226	**7330**		**7334**		**7534**		**7434**		**7238**			**7242**	**7342**				**7344**	**7544**	**7546**		**7546**	**7546**
	Ⓐ	⑥	Ⓐ	Ⓐ	†	Ⓐ	Ⓑ		⑥	Ⓐ	Ⓐ	†	Ⓐ	⑥	†	Ⓐ		†	⑥	⑥⑦		†		†
									e				C							h	D⊖		E⊖	
Rang du Fliers ⊕ **261** d.	...	...	...	...	...	...	1611	...	...	...	...	...	...	...	...	...	...	...	...	1906	...	...	...	...
Étaples-Le Touquet **261** d.	...	...	...	...	...	...	1622	...	...	...	...	...	...	...	...	...	...	...	...	1917	...	...	...	...
Boulogne Ville **261** d.	...	...	...	...	...	...	1642	...	1641	...	...	1804	...	...	...	1844	...	...	...	1935	1955	...	1958	2040
Calais Fréthun **261** a.	...	...	...	...	...	...	1705	...	1706	...	...	1828	...	...	...	1908	...	...	...	1959	2017	...	2020	2105
Calais Fréthun d.	...	...	...	...	...	...	1715	...	1715	1806	...	1839	...	...	...	1918	...	...	...	2009	2029	...	2032	2116
Dunkerque d.	1446	...	1556	1600	1656	1700	|	...	|	|	1808	|	1834	1900	1856	|	...	1930	1956	|	|	2030	|	|
Hazebrouck d.	|	...	1620	|	1720	|	|	...	|	|	|	|	|	|	1920	|	...	|	2020	|	|	|	|	|
Lille Europe a.	1517	...	|	1631	|	1731	1744	...	1745	1835	1840	1908	1910	1931	|	1946	...	2001	|	2038	2056	2101	2100	2145
Lille Europe d.	...	1551	|	...	|	...	1751	...	1751	...	1851	...	1922	1936	|	...	...	...	|	2051	2102	...	2114	2151
Béthune d.	...	|	1643	...	1743	...	|	...	|	...	|	...	|	|	1943	...	...	...	2043	|	|	...	|	|
Lens d.	...	|	1657	...	1757	...	|	...	|	...	|	...	|	|	1957	...	...	...	2057	|	|	...	|	|
Arras a.	...	1614	1710	...	1810	...	1813	...	1813	...	1913	...	1941	1959	2010	...	...	...	2110	2113	2148	...	2148	2213
Arras d.	...	1618	1718	...	1818	...	1818	...	1818	...	1918	...	...	2018	2018	...	...	...	2118	2118	2201	...	2201	2218
Paris Nord a.	...	1708	1808	...	1908	...	1908	...	1908	...	2008	...	...	2108	2108	...	...	...	2208	2208	2250	...	2250	2308

A – ①–⑥ July 18 – 30 and Aug. 22 – 27 (also Aug. 6, 20).
B – ②③④⑦ (also Aug. 1, 8, 15).
C – 🚌12 Amiens (d. 0642 / a. 2018) - Dunkerque and v.v.
D – Ⓐ July 18 – 29; ⑤ Aug. 5 – 26 (also Aug. 22 – 25).
E – ①–④ Aug. 1 – 18 (not Aug. 15).

d – Also July 17, 24, 31; not Aug. 13, 15.
e – Not Aug. 13.
f – Not Aug. 7, 14, 15, 21, 28.
g – Not Aug. 13, 14.
h – Also Aug. 15; not Aug. 13.
j – Also Aug. 15; not Aug. 14.
k – Also July 19 – 21, 25 – 28, Aug. 16, 23 – 25; not Aug. 15.

m – July 18 – 30.
n – Not Aug. 13, 15.
p – Also July 17, 24, 31; not Aug. 13.
q – July 24, 31 only.
r – Not Aug. 14.
s – Also July 18, 25, Aug. 22.
t – Not Aug. 6, 13.
u – July 18 - Aug. 5.
v – Aug. 8 – 26 (not Aug. 12, 15).
w – Aug. 7 – 28 (also Aug. 13, 15).
x – Aug. 7 – 28.
y – Aug. 1 – 27.

◧ – To Roubaix (a. 0004) and Tourcoing (a. 0009). Via Arras (a. 2311).
⊡ – From Tourcoing (d. 0521) and Roubaix (d. 0526). Via Arras (d. 0619).
⊖ – Via Douai (see Paris - Valenciennes Table).
● – To Calais Ville (a. 2240).
⊙ – Via Lens (a. 1534).
⊕ – Full name is Rang du Fliers - Verton - Berck.
⊗ – Train **7183** on ⑥.
⊖ – Not July 24.
▲ – Runs 8 - 11 minutes later on †.
♣ – TER à Grande Vitesse (*TER-GV*) service via high-speed line.
TGV – High-speed train. 🅁. 🍸

FOR PARIS - VALENCIENNES SEE NEXT PAGE →

250 TGV NORD SERVICE JULY 18 - AUGUST 28

TGV NORD HIGH-SPEED TRAINS. For Paris Charles de Gaulle ✈ - Lille services see Table **11**.
Journeys to/from Paris are 🅁 with supplement. For other journeys, *TGV* and ♣ trains are classified *TER-GV* and require a Grande Vitesse supplement, €3 valid all day, 🅁 not required.

PARIS - VALENCIENNES

km					*TGV* 7155	*TGV* 7159		*TGV* 7163		*TGV* 7165			*TGV* 7171		*TGV* 7173			*TGV* 7177		*TGV* 7181		*TGV* 7185	*TGV* 7189	*TGV* 7195
		Ⓐ	⑥	†	Ⓐ	⑥	⑥	†	Ⓐ	Ⓐ	⑥	†	⑥	⑥	⑤ ⊙	Ⓑ ▲	⑥	†	Ⓑ ▲	⚒ ⊗	Ⓐ	Ⓐ	†	⑦ ⊖
0	**Paris** Nord d.	...	...	...	0752	0852	...	0952	...	1052	...	...	1352	...	1428	...	...	1652	...	1752	...	1852	1952	2152
179	Arras a.	...	...	...	0840	0941	...	1041	...	1141	...	...	1441	...	1517	...	...	1741	...	1840	...	1940	2041	2240
179	Arras d.	...	...	...	0844	0944	...	1044	...	1145	...	...	1444	...	1521	...	...	1744	...	1844	...	1944	2044	2248
204	Douai a.	0724	0735	0835	0858	0958	1035	1058	1124	1158	1335	1435	1458	1535	1604	1624	1735	1758	1824	1858	1924	1958	2058	2302
240	**Valenciennes** a.	0759	0808	0908	0935	1035	1108	1135	1159	1235	1408	1508	1535	1608	1631	1659	1808	1835	1859	1935	1959	2035	2135	2338

		TGV 7104				*TGV* 7112	*TGV* 7116				*TGV* 7520		*TGV* 7124		*TGV* 7130		*TGV* 7134				*TGV* 7142	*TGV* 7144	*TGV* 7546
	Ⓐ	Ⓐ	⑥	⑥	Ⓐ	Ⓒ	⚒	†	⑥	Ⓐ	Ⓐ	Ⓒ	†	Ⓐ	Ⓑ	Ⓒ	⑤	Ⓐ	Ⓐ	Ⓒ	Ⓒ	†	Ⓐ
Valenciennes d.	0601	0616	0652	0752	0801	0816	1016	1052	1152	1201	...	1252	1416	1601	1616	1652	1716	1701	1801	1852	1916	2016	...
Douai d.	0636	0651	0725	0825	0838	0851	1051	1125	1225	1236	1323	1325	1451	1636	1651	1725	1753	1736	1836	1925	1951	2051	2134
Arras a.	...	0706	...	...	...	0905	1105	...	...	...	1337	...	1505	...	1706	...	1805	...	...	...	2007	2105	2148
Arras d.	...	0718	...	...	...	0918	1118	...	...	...	1341	...	1518	...	1718	...	1818	...	...	...	2018	2118	2201
Paris Nord a.	...	0808	...	...	...	1008	1208	...	...	...	1432	...	1608	...	1808	...	1908	...	...	...	2108	2208	2250

DOUAI - VALENCIENNES TRAINS WITHOUT NUMBERS ARE TER TRAINS - 🅁/SUPPLEMENT NOT REQUIRED. FOR OTHER TGV NORD SERVICES AND FOOTNOTES SEE PAGE 559.

SALZBURG and MÜNCHEN - INNSBRUCK - FELDKIRCH - BREGENZ - LINDAU 951

AMENDED SERVICE UNTIL AUGUST 1. Subject to confirmation from July 1.

km		NJ	EN		NJ		NJ		RJ			RJX	RJ	IC	EC	NJ	RJX		NJ	RJX		EC	RJX		RJ		EC
		466	40462		464		446		666			366	668	118	81	421	368		421	660		83	160		662		85
				Ⓐ		Ⓐ		Ⓐ		Ⓒ	⚒				⊕	Ⓡ			Ⓡ				D				
		N	⊙	2	♦	2	N	2	✕	2	2	✕	✕	🍷♦	A✕	c♦	✕	2	d♦	✕	2	A✕	R✕	2	F✕	2	A✕
	Wien Hbf **950** d.	2127	2327	...	...	...	2255	...	...	...	...	...	...	...	...	...	0530	...	...	0630	...	...	0730	...	0830	...	...
	Linz Hbf **950** d.	2256	0100	...	...	...	0042	...	...	...	...	...	...	...	...	...	0646	...	...	0746	...	...	0846	...	0946	...	...
0	**Salzburg** Hbf d.	0230	0230	...	...	...	0212t	...	...	...	...	0556	0656	...	...	...	0756	...	...	0856	...	...	0956	...	1056	...	...
	München Hbf **890** ‡ d.	|	|	...	...	...	|	...	...	...	...	|	|	...	0734r	0728	|	...	0750	|	...	0934e	|	...	|	...	1134r
	München Ost **890** ‡ d.	|	|	...	...	...	|	...	...	...	...	|	|	...	0744d	|	|	...	|	|	...	0944e	|	...	|	...	1144d
⊖	Rosenheim... **890** ‡ d.	|	|	...	...	...	|	...	...	...	...	|	|	...	0813	0805	|	...	0851	|	...	1013	|	...	|	...	1213
120	Kufstein 🏛 ‡ d.	|	|	...	...	...	|	0539	...	0539	0636	0709	|	...	0836	0828	0909	...	0930	|	...	1036	1109	...	|	...	1236
134	Wörgl Hbf **960** d.	|	|	...	...	...	|	0553	...	0559	0649	0719	0817	...	0846	0839	0919	...	0941	1033	...	1046	1119	...	1233	...	1246
159	Jenbach **960** d.	|	|	...	...	...	|	0613	...	0621	0709	|	0831	...	0901	0855	|	...	0957	1049	...	1101	|	...	1249	...	1301
193	**Innsbruck** Hbf ... **960** a.	0546	0546	...	...	...	0519	0639	...	0655	0740	0744	0846	...	0918	0914	0944	...	1016	1108	...	1118	1144	...	1308	...	1318
193	**Innsbruck** Hbf d.	0552	0552	...	0453	...	0523	...	0641	0659	...	0747	▬	0854	...	...	0947	0952	...	1111	1052	...	1147	1152	1311	1252	...
239	Ötztal d.	|	|	...	|	...	0551	...	0706	0750	...	0812	...	0928	...	...	1012	1030	...	|	1127	...	1212	1230	|	1327	...
248	Imst-Pitztal d.	|	|	...	|	...	0602	...	0716	0800	...	|	...	0939	...	...	|	1041	...	1148	1139	...	|	1241	1348	1339	...
265	Landeck-Zams d.	0657	0657	...	0545	...	0622	...	0730	0815	...	0833	...	0954	...	...	1033	1056	...	1202	1154	...	1233	1256	1402	1354	...
293	St Anton am Arlberg d.	|	|	...	0616	...	0648	...	0754	...	...	0857	...	1022	...	...	1057	▬	...	|	...	...	1257	▬	|	...	...
304	Langen am Arlberg d.	|	|	...	0626	...	0659	...	0804	...	...	|	...	1032	...	...	|	...	...	1233	...	...	|	...	1433	...	...
329	Bludenz **952** d.	0751	0751	0630	0706	0730	0735	...	0831	...	...	0931	...	1102	...	...	1131	...	...	1301	...	...	1331	...	1501	...	...
350	**Feldkirch** **952** a.	0803	0803	0645	0721	0745	0749	...	0842	...	...	0942	2	1113	...	...	1142	2	...	1312	...	...	1342	2	1512	...	...
350	**Feldkirch** **952** d.	0810	0810	0647	0738	0747	0754	...	0847	...	...	0944	0947	1115	...	...	1148	1147	...	1314	...	...	1348	1347	1514	...	...
369	**Buchs** 🏛 **952** a.	0834	0834	|	0753	|	|	...	|	...	...	0959	|	|	...	...	1206	|	...	|	...	...	1406	|	|	...	...
	Zürich HB **520** a.	1020	1020	|	0920	|	|	...	|	...	...	1120	|	|	...	...	1320	|	...	|	...	...	1520	|	|	...	...
375	Dornbirn **952** d.	...	...	0709	...	0809	0821	...	0909	...	...	...	1009	1142	...	...	...	1209	...	1339	...	...	...	1409	1539	...	...
387	**Bregenz** 🏛 **952** a.	...	...	0718	...	0818	0829	...	0917	...	...	...	1018	1149	...	...	...	1218	...	1347	...	...	...	1418	1547	...	...
	Lindau Reutin 🏛 **952** a.	...	...	0728	...	0828	*0858*	...	*0929*	...	...	...	1028	1157	...	...	...	1228	...	*1359*	...	...	...	1428	*1559*	...	...
397	**Lindau**-Insel 🏛 **952** a.	...	...	0732	...	0832	*0903*	...	*0934*	...	...	...	1032	...	...	...	...	1232	...	*1403*	...	...	...	1432	*1603*	...	...

	RJX			RJX	EC	RJX	EC		RJ		RJX	ICE	EC	RJX			RJX	EC	RJX		RJX	EC		RJX	RJX		RJX
	162			860	87	564	164		1287		862	1283	89	166			864	287	168		866	289		760	868		762
	U			T					⑥			⑥		V					F								
	B✕	2▯	2	✕	A✕	F✕	✕♦	2	✕	2	F✕	✕S	A✕	✕	2	2	F✕	✕	Y✕	2	F✕	✕	2	F✕	F✕	2	F✕
Wien Hbf **950** d.	0930	...	...	0955	...	1130	...	...	...	...	1230	...	...	1330	...	...	1430	...	1530	...	1630	...	...	1730	1830	...	1930
Linz Hbf **950** d.	1046	...	...	1131	...	1246	...	...	...	...	1346	...	...	1446	...	...	1546	...	1646	...	1746	...	...	1846	1946	...	2046
Salzburg Hbf d.	1156	...	...	1256	...	1400	...	...	...	...	1456	...	...	1556	...	...	1656	...	1756	...	1856	...	...	2000	2056	...	2159
München Hbf **890** ‡ d.	|	...	...	|	1333f	|	...	...	1427a	...	|	1520h	1534f	|	...	...	|	1734v	|	...	|	1934f	...	|	|	...	|
München Ost **890** ‡ d.	|	...	...	|	1344f	|	...	...	1437	...	|	|	1544f	|	...	...	|	1744	|	...	|	1944f	...	|	|	...	|
Rosenheim **890** ‡ d.	|	...	...	|	1413	|	...	...	1507	...	|	1602	1613	|	...	...	|	1813	|	...	|	2013	...	|	|	...	|
Kufstein 🏛 ‡ d.	1309	...	...	|	1436	|	...	...	1528	...	|	1626	1636	1709	...	...	|	1836	1909	...	|	2036	2136	|	2226	...	|
Wörgl Hbf **960** d.	1319	...	...	1433	1446	1643	1502	...	1539	...	1633	1635	1646	1719	...	...	1833	1846	1919	...	2033	2046	2154	2229	2235	...	0024
Jenbach **960** d.	|	...	...	1449	1501	|	1518	...	1555	...	1649	...	1701	|	...	...	1849	1901	|	...	2049	2101	2214	|	2249	...	0038
Innsbruck Hbf **960** a.	1344	...	...	1508	1518	1714	1540	...	1615	...	1708	...	1718	1744	...	...	1908	1918	1944	...	2108	2118	2240	2254	2308	...	0053
Innsbruck Hbf d.	1347	1352	1452	1511	...	...	1547	1552	1620	1652	1711	...	...	1747	1752	1852	1911	...	1947	2052	2111	*2152*	...	2258	...	0005	...
Ötztal d.	1412	1430	1527	|	...	...	1612	1630	1652	1727	|	...	...	1812	1830	1927	|	...	2012	2128	|	*2231*	...	2323	...	0057	...
Imst-Pitztal d.	|	1441	1539	1548	...	...	|	1641	1702	1739	1748	...	...	|	1841	1939	1948	...	2022	2139	2148	*2241*	...	2337	...	0107	...
Landeck-Zams d.	1433	1456	1554	1602	...	...	1633	1656	1738b	1754	1802	...	...	1833	1856	1954	2002	...	2036	2154	2202	*2257*	...	2350	...	0122	...
St Anton am Arlberg d.	1457	▬	...	|	...	...	1657	▬	1806	...	|	...	...	1857	▬	...	|	...	2100	▬	|	...	...	0014	...	...	...
Langen am Arlberg d.	|		...	1633	...	...	|		1816	...	1833	...	...	|		...	2033	...	|		2233	...	...	0024	...	...	...
Bludenz **952** d.	1531	...	...	1701	...	...	1731	...	1854	...	1901	...	...	1931	...	...	2101	...	2134	...	2301	...	...	0051	...	...	...
Feldkirch **952** a.	1542	2	...	1712	...	...	1742	2	1905	...	1912	...	...	1942	2	...	2112	...	2145	2	2312	...	...	0103	...	...	...
Feldkirch **952** d.	1548	1547	...	1714	...	...	1744	1747	...	...	1914	...	...	1948	1947	...	2114	...	2148	2150	2314	...	...	0105	...	...	...
Buchs 🏛 **952** a.	1606	|	...	|	...	...	1759	|	...	...	|	...	...	2006	|	...	|	...	2203	|	|	...	...	|	...	...	...
Zürich HB **520** a.	1720	|	...	|	...	...	1920	|	...	...	|	...	...	2120	|	...	|	...	2327	|	|	...	...	|	...	...	...
Dornbirn **952** d.	...	1609	...	1739	...	...	...	1809	...	...	1939	...	...	...	2009	...	2139	...	...	2212	2339	...	...	0122	...	...	...
Bregenz 🏛 **952** a.	...	1618	...	1747	...	...	...	1818	...	...	1947	...	...	...	2018	...	2147	...	...	2221	2347	...	...	0130	...	...	...
Lindau Reutin 🏛 **952** a.	...	1628	...	*1759*	...	...	...	1828	...	...	*1958*	...	...	...	2028	...	...	...	...	2231	...	...	...	...	...	...	...
Lindau-Insel 🏛 **952** a.	...	1632	...	*1803*	...	...	...	1832	...	...	*2003*	...	...	...	2032	...	...	...	...	2236	...	...	...	...	...	...	...

		RJX	RJX		RJX	RJX	EC	RJX		RJX	ICE		RJX	EC	RJ		RJ			EC	RJX	EC	RJX			RJX	EC
		269	763		861	861	288	765		863	1282		161	286	865		1286			163	563	88	867			165	86
	Ⓒ				Ⓐ						⑥C		F				⑥						Z			W	
	2	✕B	F✕	2	F✕	F✕	✕	F✕		F✕	S✕	2	X✕	✕	✕	2	✕		2	✕♦	F✕	A✕	F✕	2	2	B✕	A✕
Lindau-Insel 🏛 **952** d.	...	...	...	...	...	...	...	...	...	*0621*	...	0725	...	...	...	...	...	...	0925	...	...	...	...	...	1124	...	...
Lindau Reutin 🏛 **952** d.	...	...	...	...	...	...	...	...	...	*0625*	...	0729	...	...	...	...	...	...	0929	...	...	...	...	...	1129	...	...
Bregenz 🏛 **952** d.	...	...	...	...	0407	...	...	0548	...	0639	...	0740	...	...	0804	...	...	...	0940	...	...	...	1004	...	1140	...	...
Dornbirn **952** d.	...	...	...	...	0417	...	...	0557	...	0652	...	0751	...	...	0815	...	...	...	0951	...	...	...	1015	...	1151	...	...
Zürich HB **520** d.	...	...	...	...	|	...	...	|	...	|	...	|	0640	...	|	...	...	...	|	0840	...	...	|	...	|	1040	...
Buchs 🏛 **952** d.	...	...	...	...	|	...	...	|	...	|	...	|	0754	...	|	...	...	...	|	1000	...	...	|	...	|	1154	...
Feldkirch **952** a.	...	...	...	...	0430	...	...	0611	...	0712	...	0812	0809	...	0837	...	...	...	1012	1015	...	...	1036	...	1212	1209	...
Feldkirch **952** d.	...	...	...	...	0432	...	...	0613	...	0717	...	▬	0817	...	0844	...	0850	...	▬	1017	...	...	1044	...	▬	1217	...
Bludenz **952** d.	...	...	...	...	0447	...	...	0626	...	0730	...	...	0830	...	0858	...	0905	...	...	1030	...	...	1058	...	...	1230	...
Langen am Arlberg d.	...	...	...	...	|	...	...	0652	...	0756	...	...	|	...	0927	...	0937	...	...	|	...	...	1127	...	...	|	...
St Anton am Arlberg d.	...	...	...	...	0520	...	...	0703	...	|	...	2	0903	...	|	...	0948	...	2	1103	...	...	|	...	2	1303	...
Landeck-Zams d.	0142	...	...	0430	0548	...	...	0727	...	0827	...	0901	0927	...	0957	1001	1017	...	1101	1127	...	...	1157	1201	1301	1327	...
Imst-Pitztal d.	0156	...	...	0445	0610	...	...	0740	...	0840	...	0917	|	...	1010	1020	1048g	...	1118	|	...	...	1210	1220	1318	|	...
Ötztal d.	0208	...	...	0504	0621	...	...	0751	...	|	...	0931	0948	...	|	1031	1107	...	1131	1148	...	...	|	1231	1331	1348	...
Innsbruck Hbf a.	0255	...	...	0553	0649	...	...	0814	...	0911	...	1006	1011	...	1049	1106	1136	...	1206	1211	...	...	1249	1306	1406	1411	...
Innsbruck Hbf **960** d.	0305	0510	0550	...	0654	0654	0717	0817	...	0914	...	...	1017	1040	1055	...	1146	...	...	1221	1217	1240	1255	...	...	1417	1440
Jenbach **960** d.	0339	0527	0607	...	0712	0712	0735	|	...	0931	...	...	|	1101	1112	...	1206	...	...	1244	|	1301	1312	...	...	|	1501
Wörgl Hbf **960** d.	0402	0541	0621	...	0729	0729	0749	0843	...	0945	1025	...	1043	1116	1126	...	1222	...	...	1257	1243	1316	1326	...	...	1443	1516
Kufstein 🏛 ‡ d.	0415	0551	0636	...	|	|	0759	0853	...	|	1037	...	1053	1126	|	...	1232	...	...	...	1253	1326	|	...	...	1453	1526
Rosenheim **890** ‡ a.	...	|	|	...	|	|	0818	|	...	|	1057	...	|	1145	|	...	|	...	...	...	|	1345	|	...	...	|	1545
München Ost. **890** ‡ a.	...	|	|	...	|	|	0849	|	...	|	|	...	|	1215	|	...	1322	...	...	...	|	1416	|	...	...	|	1617
München Hbf. **890** ‡ a.	...	|	|	...	|	|	0902	|	...	|	1134p	...	|	1226j	|	...	1333	...	...	...	|	1427j	|	...	...	|	1627k
Salzburg Hbf a.	...	0702	0802	...	0902	0902	...	1003	...	1102	...	...	1203	...	1302	...	...	...	...	...	1403	...	1502	...	...	1603	...
Linz Hbf **950** a.	...	0814	0914	...	1014	1014	...	1114	...	1214	...	...	1314	...	1429	...	...	...	...	...	1514	...	1614	...	...	1714	...
Wien Hbf **950** a.	...	0930	1030	...	1130	1130	...	1230	...	1330	...	...	1430	...	1605	...	...	...	...	...	1630	...	1730	...	...	1830	...

♦ – **NOTES** (LISTED BY TRAIN NUMBER)

118 – BODENSEE – [12] Innsbruck - Lindau - Stuttgart - Köln - Dortmund.

163/4 – TRANSALPIN – [12] and ✕ Zürich - Kitzbühel - Schwarzach - Graz and v.v.

421 – 🛏 1, 2 cl., ▬ 2 cl. and [2] Amsterdam / Brussels / Düsseldorf - Innsbruck; 🛏 1, 2 cl., ▬ 2 cl. and [2] (**40491**) Hamburg - Innsbruck.

464 – 🛏 1, 2 cl., ▬ 2 cl. and [2] Graz - Schwarzach - Zürich; 🛏 1, 2 cl., ▬ 2 cl. and [2] (*EN* **40414**) Zagreb - Ljubljana - Villach - Schwarzach - Zürich .

A – To Verona, Bologna or Venezia via Brennero (Table **70**).
B – From / to Budapest (Table **1250**).
C – June 18 - Oct. 15.
D – On ①–⑥ (also June 5; not June 6, Aug. 15, Nov. 1) conveys [12] (*RJ* **560**) Flughafen Wien - Wien Hbf - Innsbruck (- Feldkirch ⑤⑥ **v**).
F – From / to Flughafen Wien ✈ (Table **950**).
N – Conveys 🛏 1, 2 cl., ▬ 2 cl. and [2] .
R – From Bratislava (Table **86**).
S – To / from Schwarzach (Table **960**).
T – Conveys [12] Wien - Bregenz (*RJ* **890**) - Ulm - Stuttgart - Frankfurt (Tables **912** and **933**).
U – Conveys [12] (*RJX* **562**) Flughafen Wien - Wien Hbf - Innsbruck (- Feldkirch ⑤–⑦ **z**).
V – Conveys [12] (*RJX* **566**) Flughafen Wien - Wien Hbf - Innsbruck (- Feldkirch Ⓑ).
W – Conveys [12] (*RJX* **565**) (Feldkirch ⑥⑦ **t** -) Innsbruck - Wien Hbf - Flughafen Wien.
X – Conveys [12] (*RJX* **184**) Bolzano - Innsbruck - Wien Hbf (Tables **86**/**595**).
Y – Conveys [12] (*RJX* **185**) Wien Hbf - Innsbruck - Bolzano (Tables **86**/**595**).
Z – Conveys [12] Frankfurt - Stuttgart - Ulm - Bregenz (*RJ* **867**) - Wien (Tables **912** and **933**).

a – 1419 on June 18, 25.
b – Arrives 1715.
c – Until July 13.
d – From July 14.
e – 3–6 minutes earlier June 16 - July 12.
f – 2–10 minutes earlier June 16–29.
g – Arrives 1033.
h – 1450 until July 9.
j – 4–11 minutes later June 11–13.
k – From July 13 (arrives 1635 on July 13).
p – 1201 until July 9.
r – 17–24 minutes earlier until July 13.
t – Salzburg Süd.
v – Not June 16 - July 12.
z – Also June 6, 15; not June 5, 17.

⊕ – Train number **1281** on ⑥⑦.
⊙ – 🛏 1, 2 cl., ▬ 2 cl. and [2] Budapest (**462**) - Salzburg (**466**) - Zürich. Also conveys through cars from Praha (see Table **52**).
⊖ – Rosenheim - Kufstein is *34 km*.
‡ – See note on page 452 for other regional services Kufstein - München and v.v.

951 LINDAU - BREGENZ - FELDKIRCH - INNSBRUCK - MÜNCHEN and SALZBURG

AMENDED SERVICE UNTIL AUGUST 1. Subject to confirmation from July 1.

	RJX 869			*RJX* 167 E	*EC* 84	*RJX* 661 ⑦	*RJ* 769 ①–⑥			*RJX* 169	*EC* 82	*IC* 119	*RJX* 663		*RJX* 367	*NJ* 420 Ⓡ	*EC* 80 ⊕	*NJ* 420 Ⓡ	*RJX* 667		*RJX* 369		*NJ* 447	*NJ* 465		*EN* 40467	*NJ* 467
	F✕	2	2	R✕	A✕	v✕	w✕	2	2	✕	A✕	🍷♦	✕	2	✕	h♦	A✕	k♦	✕	2	✕	2	N	♦	2	⊙	N
Lidau-Insel 🏛 .... **952** d.	...	...	1325	...	...	...	...	...	1525	...	...	...	...	1722	...	...	...	...	*1823*	1925	...	2026	*2056*	...	2225	...	...
Lindau Reutin 🏛 **952** d.	...	...	1329	...	...	...	...	...	1529	...	...	1558	...	1729	...	...	...	...	*1827*	1929	...	2033	*2103*	...	2229	...	...
Bregenz 🏛......... **952** d.	1204	...	1340	...	...	1404	1404	...	1540	...	...	1606	...	1740	...	...	...	...	1840	1940	...	2044	2130	...	2240	...	...
Dornbirn .... **952** d.	1215	...	1351	...	...	1415	1415	...	1551	...	...	1617	...	1751	...	...	...	...	1851	1951	...	2100	2143	...	2251	...	...
Zürich HB **520**........d.	|	...	|	1240	...	|	|	...	|	1440	...	|	...	|	1640	...	...	...	|	|	1840	|	|	2040a	|	2140a	2140a
Buchs 🏛 .... **952** d.	|	...	|	1354	...	|	|	...	|	1554	...	|	...	|	1800	...	...	...	|	|	1954	|	|	2205b	|	2305b	2305b
Feldkirch .... **952** a.	1236	...	1412	1409	...	1436	1436	...	1612	1609	...	1634	...	1812	1815	...	...	...	1912	2012	2009	2130	2216	2220	2312	2321	2321
Feldkirch .... **952** d.	1244	...	▬	1417	...	1444	1444	...	▬	1617	...	1637	...	▬	1817	...	...	...	1917	▬	2017	2131	2227	2245	2314	2324	2324
Bludenz .... **952** d.	1358	...	...	1430	...	1558	1558	...	...	1630	...	1656	...	...	1830	...	...	...	1930	...	2030	2151	2242	2301	2329	2340	2340
Langen am Arlberg .... d.	1327	...	...	|	...	1527	1527	...	...	|	...	1728	...	...	|	...	...	...	1956	...	|	▬	2310	2335	...	|	|
St Anton am Arlberg .. d.	|	...	2	1503	...	|	|	...	2	1703	...	1738	...	2	1903	...	...	...	2007	...	2103	...	2320	2345	...	|	|
Landeck-Zams.........d.	1357	1401	1501	1527	...	1557	1557	1601	1701	1727	...	1805	...	1901	1927	...	...	...	2031	...	2127	...	2348	0009	...	0036	0036
Imst-Pitztal.................d.	1410	1420	1518	|	...	1610	1610	1620	1718	|	...	1821	...	1918	1940	...	...	...	2044	...	2140	...	0002	|	...	|	|
Ötztal..........................d.	|	1431	1531	1548	...	|	|	1631	1731	1748	...	1835	...	1931	1951	...	...	...	2055	...	2151	...	0013	|	...	|	|
Innsbruck Hbf..........a.	1449	1506	1606	1611	...	1649	1649	1706	1806	1811	...	1905	...	2006	2014	...	...	...	2118	2	2214	2	0039	0054	...	0120	0120
Innsbruck Hbf.... **960** d.	1455	...	...	1617	1640	1655	1655	...	...	1817	1840	...	1914	...	2017	1956	2040	2044	...	2135	2217	2235	0044	...	...	0128	0128
Jenbach............... **960** d.	1512	...	...	|	1701	1712	1712	...	...	|	1901	...	1931	...	|	2018	2101	2106	...	2209	|	2309	|	...	...	|	|
Wörgl Hbf .... **960** d.	1526	...	...	1643	1716	1726	1726	...	...	1843	1916	...	1945	...	2043	2034	2116	2123	...	2235	2243	2335	|	...	...	|	|
Kufstein 🏛.............. ‡ d.	|	...	...	1653	1726	|	|	...	...	1853	1926	...	|	...	2053	2046	2126	2135	...	2248	|	2348	|	...	...	|	|
Rosenheim.... **890** ‡ a.	|	...	...	|	1745	|	|	...	...	|	1945	...	|	...	|	2105	2145	2156	...	...	...	...	|	...	...	|	|
München Ost **890** ‡ a.	|	...	...	|	1816	|	|	...	...	|	2014z	...	|	...	|	|	2216	|	...	...	...	...	|	...	...	|	|
München Hbf **890** ‡ a.	|	...	...	|	1827j	|	|	...	...	|	2026z	...	|	...	|	2225	2227	2238	...	...	...	...	|	...	...	|	|
Salzburg Hbf............a.	1702	...	...	1802	...	1902	1902	...	...	2003	...	...	2104	...	2206	...	...	...	...	...	0130	...	0339r	...	...	0322d	0322c
Linz Hbf **950**..........a.	1814	...	...	1914	...	2014	2029	...	...	2114	...	...	2214	...	2317	...	...	...	...	...	...	...	0511	...	...	0452d	0604c
Wien Hbf **950**.........a.	1930	...	...	2030	...	2130	2205	...	...	2230	...	...	2330	...	0033	...	...	...	...	...	...	...	0734	...	...	0634d	0758c

♦ – **NOTES** (LISTED BY TRAIN NUMBER)

119 – BODENSEE – [12] Dortmund - Köln - Stuttgart - Lindau - Innsbruck.

420 – 🛏 1, 2 cl., ━ 2 cl. and [2] Innsbruck - Frankfurt - Düsseldorf - Amsterdam; 🛏 1, 2 cl., ━ 2 cl. and [2] (**40420**) Innsbruck - Hamburg.

465 – 🛏 1, 2 cl., ━ 2 cl. and [2] Zürich - Schwarzach - Graz; ━ 1, 2 cl., ━ 2 cl. and [2] (*EN* **40465**) Zürich - Schwarzach - Villach - Ljubljana - Zagreb.

A – From Verona or Venezia via Brennero (Table **70**).
E – On ①②③④⑦ conveys [12] (*RJX* **567**) (Feldkirch ⑦ **v** -) Innsbruck - Wien Hbf - Flughafen Wien.
F – To Flughafen Wien ✈ (Table **950**).
N – Conveys 🛏 1, 2 cl., ━ 2 cl. and [2].
R – To Bratislava (Table **86**).

a – Departs 1 hour earlier June 1 – 3, 7 – 9.
b – Not June 1 – 3, 7 – 9.
c – June 1 – 3, 7 – 9 arrives Salzburg 0422, Linz 0617, Wien Hbf 0818.
d – June 1 – 3, 7 – 9 arrives Salzburg 0422, Linz 0558, Wien 0745.
h – Until July 13.
j – 1837 June 11 – 13.
k – From July 14.
r – Salzburg Süd.
v – Also June 6; not June 5.
w – Also June 5; not June 6.
z – Until July 13 does not call at München Ost and arrive München Hbf 2044.
⊕ – Train number **1280** on ⑥⑦.
⊙ – 🛏 1, 2 cl., ━ 2 cl. and [2] Zürich (**467**) - Salzburg (**463**) - Budapest. Also conveys through cars to Praha (see Table **52**).
‡ – Additional local services run München - Rosenheim - Kufstein and v.v. (branded *Meridian*, operated by Bayerische Oberlandbahn). Journey time: 73 – 80 minutes.
From München at 0640, 0743, 0843 and hourly until 2043 (also Rosenheim to Kufstein at 0039, 2235 and 2335).
From Kufstein at 0600, 0702, 0801 and hourly until 1902 (also Kufstein to Rosenheim at 1959, 2058, 2158 and 2258).

970 SALZBURG - VILLACH - KLAGENFURT

AMENDED SERVICE UNTIL AUGUST 1. Subject to confirmation from July 1.

km		*NJ* 40463 R	*NJ* 40466 R	*NJ* 40294	⚒	*EN* 40465 R		⚒		*IC* 894	*IC* 898	*RJ* 111	*RJ* 596	*EC* 113	*EC* 19115	*EC* 115	Ⓐ		*RJ* 698	*EC* 19117	*EC* 117	*IC* 794 Ⓑ	*NJ* 295 R
		B	♦	2	2	♦	2	2	2	✕		✕	✕	✕		⊗♦	2	2	✕	✕	⊗♦		♦
	Wien Hbf **950**..........d.	...	2127	...	...	...	...	...	...	...	...	...	0855	...	...	...	...	...	1455	...	...	...	...
	München Hbf **890**..........d.	2220t	|	...	...	...	...	...	...	...	...	...	|	...	...	1417t	...	...	|	...	1817	...	1928t
0	**Salzburg** Hbf.......... **960 975** d.	0140	0140	...	...	...	...	...	...	0612	0812	1012	1212	1412	1612	|	...	...	1812	2012	|	2112	2202
29	Golling-Abtenau.............. **960** d.	|	|	...	...	...	...	...	...	0633	0833	1033	1233	1433	1633	|	...	...	1833	2033	|	2138	|
53	**Bischofshofen**.......... **960 975** d.	|	|	...	...	...	...	...	...	0654	0854	1054	1254	1454	1654	|	...	...	1854	2054	|	2200	|
61	St Johann im Pongau .... **960** d.	|	|	...	...	...	...	...	...	0703	0903	1103	1303	1503	1703	|	...	...	1903	2103	|	2209	|
67	**Schwarzach-St Veit**........... **960** d.	0232	0232	...	...	0425	...	...	...	0711	0911	1111	1311	1511	1709	1740	...	...	1911	2109	2154	2216	2254
86	Bad Hofgastein..........................d.	|	|	...	...	0440	...	...	...	0729	0929	1129	1329	1529	...	1758	...	...	1929	...	2212	2233	|
97	Bad Gastein.............................d.	|	|	...	...	0500	...	...	...	0742	0942	1142	1342	1542	...	1811	...	...	1942	...	2225	2245	|
113	Mallnitz-Obervellach....................d.	|	|	...	...	0515	...	0650	...	0756	0956	1156	1356	1556	...	1825	1800	...	1956	...	2239	2259	|
146	Spittal-Millstättersee............... **971** d.	|	|	...	...	0540	...	0717	0729	0820	1020	1220	1420	1620	...	1849	1827	1832	2020	...	2303	2322	|
182	**Villach** Hbf.......................... **971** a.	0357	0357	...	...	0604	...	...	0753	0843	1043	1243	1443	1643	...	1912	...	1904	2043	...	2329	2344	0019
182	**Villach** Hbf.......................... **971** d.	...	...	0417	0450	...	0620	...	0756	0847	1047	1247	1447	1648	...	1917	...	*1914*	2047	...	2332	2347	...
198	Velden am Wörthersee .... **971** d.	...	...	|	0505	...	0634	...	0806	0858	1058	1258	1458	1659	...	1928	...	*1925*	2058	...	2343	2358	...
207	Pörtschach am Wörthersee...... **971** d.	...	...	|	0513	...	0642	...	|	0904	1104	1304	1504	1705	...	1934	...	|	2104	...	2349	0004	...
220	**Klagenfurt** Hbf...................... **971** a.	...	...	0438	0529	...	0659	...	0822	0913	1113	1316	1513	1717	...	1946	...	*1937*	2116	...	0000	0013	...

	NJ 236 R	*NJ* 40236 R		*NJ* 294 R	*IC* 597 ①–⑥	⚒		*RJ* 691		*EC* 114	*EC* 19114	*EC* 112	*IC* 793		*RJ* 797	Ⓐ	Ⓐ	*RJ* 110	*IC* 895	*D* 899			*EN* 40414 R
	♦	A		♦		2		✕		⊗♦	✕	✕	🍷		✕	2	2	✕	✕	2		2	♦
Klagenfurt Hbf...................... **971** d.	...	...	...	...	0442	...	...	0645	...	0757	...	1027	1245	...	1445	1532	...	1642	1845	2045	...	2232	...
Pörtschach am Wörthersee....... **971** d.	...	...	...	...	0455	...	...	0655	...	0811	...	1040	1255	...	1455	1547	...	1655	1855	2055	...	2247	...
Velden am Wörthersee .... **971** d.	...	...	...	...	0502	...	...	0702	...	0818	...	1047	1302	...	1502	1554	...	1702	1902	2102	...	2254	...
Villach Hbf.......................... **971** a.	...	...	...	...	0513	...	...	0713	...	0831	...	1058	1313	...	1513	1609	...	1713	1913	2113	...	2309	...
Villach Hbf.......................... **971** d.	0150	0150	...	0429	0516	0529	...	0716	...	0833	...	1116	1316	...	1516	1610	...	1716	1916	2116	...	...	2326
Spittal-Millstättersee............... **971** d.	|	|	...	|	0540	0605	...	0740	...	0906	...	1140	1340	...	1540	1634	1644	1740	1940	2140	...	...	2351
Mallnitz-Obervellach....................d.	|	|	...	|	0604	0633	...	0804	...	0939	...	1204	1404	...	1604	...	1712	1804	2004	2204	...	...	0014
Bad Gastein.............................d.	|	|	...	|	0617	...	...	0817	...	0943	...	1217	1417	...	1617	...	...	1817	2017	2217	...	...	0030
Bad Hofgastein..........................d.	|	|	...	|	0630	...	...	0830	...	0956	...	1230	1430	...	1630	...	...	1830	2030	2230	...	...	0042
Schwarzach-St Veit............... **960** d.	0315	0315	...	0549	0652	...	...	0852	...	1029r	1052	1252	1452	...	1652	...	...	1852	2052	2252	...	...	0058
St Johann im Pongau .... **960** a.	|	|	...	|	0657	...	...	0857	...	|	1058	1257	1457	...	1657	...	...	1857	2057	2257	...	...	...
Bischofshofen.............. **960 975** a.	|	|	...	|	0705	...	...	0905	...	|	1107	1305	1505	...	1705	...	...	1905	2105	2305	...	...	...
Golling-Abtenau....................... **960** a.	|	|	...	|	|	...	...	0927	...	|	1128	1327	1527	...	1727	...	...	1927	2127	2327	...	...	...
Salzburg Hbf................ **960 975** a.	0404	0404	...	0649	0748	...	...	0948	...	|	1148	1348	1548	...	1748	...	...	1948	2148	2348	...	...	...
München Hbf **890**.........................a.	|	0629t	...	0920t	...	...	...	|	...	1341	...	...	...	...	|	...	...	...	...	...	...	...	...
Wien Hbf **950**..............................a.	0758	...	...	...	...	...	...	1305	...	...	...	...	...	...	2105	...	...	...	...	...	...	...	...

♦ – **NOTES** (LISTED BY TRAIN NUMBER)

114 – WÖRTHERSEE – [12] and ⊗ Klagenfurt - München - Stuttgart - Köln - Dortmund.
115 – WÖRTHERSEE – [12] and ⊗ Münster - Köln - Stuttgart - München - Klagenfurt.
117 – SALZACH – [12] and ⊗ Frankfurt - Stuttgart - München - Salzburg - Klagenfurt.
236 – 🛏 1, 2 cl., ━ 2 cl. and [2] Venezia - Tarvisio 🏛 - Villach - Salzburg - Wien.
294/5 – 🛏 1, 2 cl., ━ 2 cl. and [2] Roma - Firenze - Bologna - München and v.v.; 🛏 1, 2 cl., ━ 2 cl. and [2] (**40235/40295**) Milano - Verona - München and v.v.
40414 – 🛏 1, 2 cl., ━ 2 cl. and [2] Zagreb - Ljubljana - Villach - Schwarzach (**464**) - Innsbruck - Feldkirch - Zürich.
40465 – 🛏 1, 2 cl., ━ 2 cl. and [2] Zürich (**465**) - Feldkirch - Innsbruck - Schwarzach (**40465**) - Villach - Ljubljana - Zagreb.
40466 – 🛏 1, 2 cl., ━ 2 cl. and [2] Wien - Salzburg - Villach - Tarvisio 🏛 - Venezia.

A – 🛏 1, 2 cl., ━ 2 cl. and [2] Venezia - Villach - München. Also conveys 🛏 1, 2 cl., ━ 2 cl. and [2] (**498** – LISINSKI) Zagreb - Ljubljana - Jesenice 🏛 - Villach - München; also 🛏 1, 2 cl. and [2] (**480**) Rijeka - Ljubljana - München.
B – 🛏 1, 2 cl., ━ 2 cl. and [2] München - Villach - Venezia. Also conveys 🛏 1, 2 cl., ━ 2 cl. and [2] (**50463** – LISINSKI) München - Villach - Jesenice 🏛 - Ljubljana - Zagreb; also 🛏 1, 2 cl. and [2] (**60463**) München - Ljubljana - Rijeka.
C – ⑥⑦ June 5 - July 4; daily July 10 - Sept. 12.
R – Ⓡ for international journeys.

r – Arrives 1014.
t – Please refer to revised table **890** on page 567 for revised timings during this period.
v – Arrives 1646.

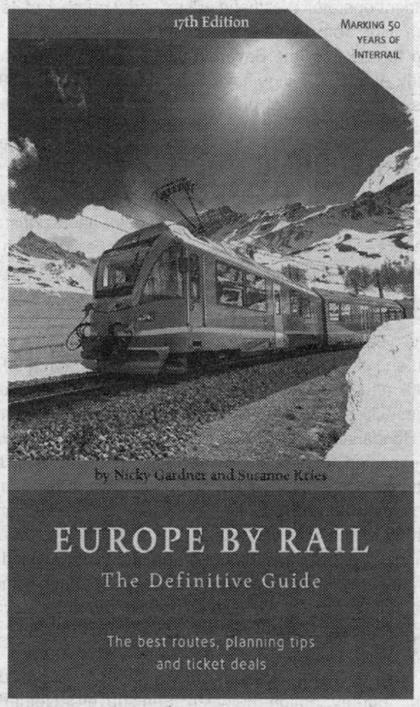

Exploring the continent by train has never been easier. Written by Nicky Gardner and Susanne Kries, two highly experienced travellers, this guidebook contains all you need for planning your journey.

★ 50 routes
★ 544 pages
★ over 44,000 km of journeys
★ over 30 countries
★ tips on fares and ticketing
★ detailed route descriptions
★ sketch maps for each route
★ index maps which show all routes
★ suggestions for overnight stays

… and a very fine read!

The 17th edition of *Europe by Rail*, published in April 2022, has improved coverage of the Alps and new routes through Germany, Italy, Slovakia and Romania. It is available directly from European Rail Timetable Ltd, all good bookshops and online retailers.

www.EuropeByRail.eu

Liège Guillemins station (photo © Erzsi Molnár / dreamstime.com)

APRIL NEWSLINES

INTERNATIONAL

Following the imposition of further sanctions against Russia, the recently reinstated *Allegro* service between Helsinki and St Peterburg has been suspended once again (Table **1910**).

FRANCE

SNCF's low-cost subsidiary *Ouigo* is now selling tickets for its new *Ouigo Classique* services which are due to start running on a daily basis from April 11. These are traditional loco-hauled trains formed of comfortable *Corail* coaches and so are considerably slower than parallel *Ouigo TGV* services. Initially, two services will run in each direction between Paris and Nantes (one via Le Mans and the other via St Pierre des Corps) with one return journey provided between Paris and Lyon (via Dijon). An additional service will be added on both routes from June. Tickets must be booked on-line with the low ticket prices (€10–30) reflecting the longer journey times. Outline timings will be found in Tables **278** (Paris – Le Mans - Nantes), **296** (Paris – St Pierre des Corps – Nantes) and **377** (Paris – Lyon) although, as timings often vary, it is important to check timings for your specific booking. Note that Nantes services generally run to and from Paris Austerlitz, although one train from Nantes to Paris is rerouted to terminate at Paris Bercy.

Italian Railways will offer a French domestic high-speed *Frecciarossa* service between Paris and Lyon from April 5 (in addition to the Paris – Lyon – Milano international services which have been running since December 18). Initially a single journey will run in each direction departing Paris Gare de Lyon at 1430 and returning from Lyon Perrache at 1711. Two additional journeys in each direction are expected to start running from June 1. Full timings will be found in Table **340**.

Journeys on the Clermont Ferrand to Aurillac route are currently subject to partial bus replacement and Table **331** has been updated with the latest available timings valid until April 24. The table will be updated further in the May digital edition.

The route from Clermont Ferrand to Le Puy and Nîmes is also affected by a period of engineering work with buses partially replacing trains until June 17. Table **333** on page 197 shows the amended service until April 18 and from May 13 to June 16. A second version of Table **333** will be found on page 562 with the service from April 19 to May 12.

SWITZERLAND

Timings of the scenic *Mont-Blanc Express* service between Chamonix and Vallorcine have been moved from Swiss Table **572** to a revamped French Table **365a** which now shows all services between St Gervais and Vallorcine, together with connecting trains between Vallorcine and Martigny. The full service between Vallorcine and Martigny (including intermediate calling points) remains in Table **572** on page 279. The extra space created on page 279 has been utilised to improve the presentation of services on the Bex – Villars – Col-de-Bretaye narrow gauge rack railway in Table **571**.

The Funicular railway between Sierre / Siders and Montana is temporarily closed until December 11 to allow essential maintenance work to be carried out. Timings of alternative bus services have been added to Table **573**.

SPAIN

Avant services between Madrid and Puertollano will be running at 93 per cent of the pre-pandemic service level from April 3 (Table **660**).

Media Distancia services between Madrid and Jaén will be restored to pre-pandemic levels from April 4 (Table **661**).

A third *AVE* service has been introduced in each direction between Madrid and Granada (Table **678a**).

A new *Avant* service between Granada and Málaga will commence on April 4, providing the first ever direct service between the two cities (Table **673**).

An additional *Media Distancia* train pair between Madrid and Vitoria / Gasteiz has been reinstated (Table **689**).

AUSTRIA

Independent operator *Westbahn* will extend a number of its services to München Hbf from April 8. Four through services will initially be provided to and from the Bavarian capital with a further two planned from early August. Timings have been added to Tables **890** and **950**. Readers should note that only *Westbahn* tickets are valid on these services.

CZECH REPUBLIC

Due to engineering work taking place until November 27, most Praha – Brno trains in Table **1152** will serve Brno dolní nádrazi instead of Brno hlavní nádrazi (see our Brno city plan on page 31 which shows the location of both stations).

SERBIA

After four years of closure for major upgrade work, the line between Beograd and Novi Sad reopened to rail traffic on March 20. Speeds of up to 200km/h are now permitted on this important route linking Serbia's two largest cities. The section of line from Novi Sad towards Subotica and the Hungarian border at Kelebia is due to receive a similar upgrade, and is expected to re-open to rail traffic in 2024. Until the work is complete passengers should make their own travel arrangements between Novi Sad and Subotica. Selected bus services are shown in Table **1360** which connect with rail services to and from Beograd. International Table **61** has also been updated with revised timings for the daily journey in each direction between Budapest and Beograd. Note that rail tickets are not valid on independent bus services.

FERRIES

A new ferry operator, Holland Norway Lines, will provide a useful overnight journey option between Eemshaven (Netherlands) and Kristiansand (Norway) from April 7, sailing three times a week in each direction. Timings will be found in Table **2230**.

BEYOND EUROPE UPDATE

On the night of March 16 an earthquake of 7.4 magnitude occurred off the coast near Fukushima in the north-east of Japan. The Tohoku Shinkansen (Tables **8015** and **8020**) was damaged leading to the suspension of services between Nasu-Shiobara (158 kilometres from Tokyo) and Morioka. On March 21 services resumed between Nasu-Shiobara and Koriyama. Services between Ichinoseki (445 kilometres from Tokyo) and Morioka resumed on March 22. The Koriyama – Sendai – Ichinoseki remains closed with services expected to resume in stages between April 2 and 20. The parallel conventional line (1067 mm gauge) had reopened on March 18 but damage to a bridge was discovered on March 21 leading to the closure of the Fukushima – Fujita section of the line. Limited Express services on the Joban Line (Table **8215**) were also suspended between Iwaki and Sendai but were expected to restart by March 24.

Thanks to members of the Vermont Rail Action Network we have received updated schedules for the Ethan Allan Express (Table **9210**), Vermonter and Valley Flyer (both Table **9220**) services, special versions of which can be found on pages 559 and 560. Of note is the introduction of a twice daily bus connection from Burlington to Albany, operated by VTransitlines, for which joint rail / bus tickets are available. The Vermont Rail Action Network write that they "expect a further update this summer when the 25 year plus project to upgrade the Vermont Rail System (VTRS) mainline from Rutland to Burlington to passenger train standards is finally completed, allowing the Ethan Allen Express to go all the way to Burlington Union Station, which will restore a service originally discontinued by the former Rutland Railroad in June of 1953 - a 59 year gap!".

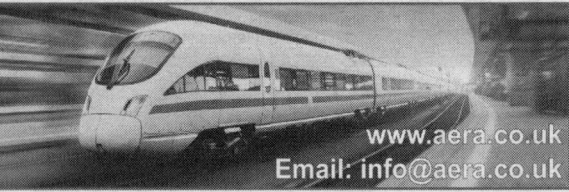

MAY NEWSLINES

We continue to see our production costs rise considerably, particularly with regards to the sourcing of paper for the printed edition. Therefore we have had to make the difficult decision to increase the price of an individual printed timetable to £22.99. We continue to offer a discount for readers wishing to pre-order four consecutive printed editions. Please note that the price of our digital products remain static as they are less affected by increased production costs. Full details of the amended prices will be found in the panel at the bottom of page 12.

INTERNATIONAL

Train **492**/**493** *Sofia Express* İstanbul – Sofia has made a welcome return, running on a daily basis since April 25 (Table **61**). The seasonal through cars İstanbul – București (**1492**/**1493** *Bosphor Express*) are expected to restart from June 2 (from İstanbul) / June 3 (from București).

Table **61** has been further updated with revised timings for the daily journey in each direction between Budapest and Beograd which, from May 1, operates via Szeged (instead of Kecskemét). A daytime journey between Wien and Beograd is now possible, but includes four trains and two buses!

SPAIN

Further services have been reinstated on the routes València – Zaragoza – Huesca (Table **670**) and Zaragoza – Caspe – Barcelona (Table **652**).

Media Distancia train **18006** has been retimed to run 20 minutes later from Palencia to Madrid Principe Pio with the return train **18007** departing Madrid Principe Pio 30 minutes earlier (Table **689**).

Schedules along the Barcelona to Latour de Carol route (Table **656**) have been recast with hourly departures (or half-hourly at certain times of the day) from Barcelona to Vic at 01 or 31 minutes past the hour, returning from Vic at 24 or 54 minutes past the hour. This new regular interval pattern runs seven days a week. Certain services extend beyond Vic to Ripoll, Ribes de Freser and Latour de Carol. Note that connections at Latour de Carol with services to and from Toulouse (Table **312**) are affected by the revised timings with southbound connections much less favourable than before.

Barcelona suburban services in Table **666** (to Mataró, Blanes and Maçanet) have also been recast with regular interval departure times operating on a daily basis.

Minor adjustments have been made to services on the Barcelona – Cerbère route (Table **657**).

All *Regional Exprés* services between Barcelona and Tortosa have now been reinstated (Table **672**).

PORTUGAL

All services on the Coimbra B – Guarda – Vilar Formoso *Linha da Beira Alta* are operated by bus until February 2023 owing to engineering work taking place along the route. Table **692** has been updated with the revised timings.

GERMANY

Table **927** has been updated with the latest FlixTrain schedules which are valid until June 9. The full service has now been reinstated following a period of running fewer trains. This includes the return of a service between Köln and München running four days a week in each direction, running as an extension of a daily service between Hamburg and Köln. Dresden has joined the FlixTrain network for the first time with the extension of a Köln – Berlin service on three days a week.

AUSTRIA

Domestic services operating via the Salzburg – Kufstein route (operating non-stop through Germany) will be affected by engineering work taking place in Germany from May 20 to August 1. This will result in amended timings for various trains. Further information will be included in the Summer (June) edition.

CZECH REPUBLIC

Many trains between Praha and Brno in Tables **1150** and **1152** are subject to extended journey times until August 31.

HUNGARY

Due to engineering work, services in Table **1280** are subject to minor alteration until June 17 with train *IC* **759** also operated by bus between Lökösháza and Békéscsaba.

The provision of rail replacement services in Table **1295** has been changed. All services via Kecskemét have been withdrawn and replaced by a pair of buses between Szeged and Kelebia which provide good connections with Budapest trains in Table **1290**. This means that the only way to travel to intermediate destinations in Table **1290** is to use scheduled bus services operated by Volánbuz (routes 653, 1115 and 5255) on which rail tickets are not valid.

BEYOND EUROPE UPDATE - JAPAN

As reported last month, some rail infrastructure was damaged by an earthquake which occurred on March 16 off the coast near Fukushima in the north-east of Japan. We are pleased to now report that services on the Tohoku Shinkansen (Tables **8015** and **8020**) and Joban Line (Table **8215**) were able to resume on April 14.

809 PADERBORN - HAMELN - HANNOVER - HANNOVER FLUGHAFEN ✈ *S-Bahn 5*

SERVICE JULY 2 - AUGUST 24

														⑤⑥
Paderborn Hbf . **805 811** d.	0534t	0634r	0734		1134	1235	1333	1434	1523	1634		2134	2231	2312
Altenbeken .... **805 811** d.	0546t	0646r	0746	and	1146	1247	1346	1446	1544	1646	and	2146	2243	2342
Bad Pyrmont .... d.	0622r	0722	0822	hourly	1222	1322	1422	1522	1622	1722	hourly	2222	2322	0022
Hameln .... a.	0636r	0736	0836	until	1236	1336	1436	1536	1636	1736	until	2236	2336	0036
Hameln .... d.	0640	0740	0840		1240	1340	1440	1540	1640	1740		2240	2340	0040
Hannover Hbf .... a.	0738	0838	0938		1338	1438	1538	1638	1738	1838		2338	0038	0138

	①–⑥	①–⑥					⑤⑥
Hannover Hbf .... d.	0448	0548	0648		2148	2248	2248
Hameln .... a.	0537	0637	0737	and	2237	2337	2337
Hameln .... d.	0544	0644	0744	hourly	2244	2344	2344
Bad Pyrmont .... d.	0600	0700	0800	until	2300	2358	0000
Altenbeken .... **805 811** d.	0633	0733	0833		2333	...	0033
Paderborn Hbf .. **805 811** a.	0646	0746	0846		2346	...	0046

SHUTTLE SERVICE HANNOVER HBF - HANNOVER FLUGHAFEN ✈ (*15 km*, journey 12 – 15 minutes)

From Hannover Hbf at 0001, 0122, 0611, 0657, 0808, 0903, 1010, 1110, 1209, 1311, 1408, 1510, 1609, 1704, 1809, 1857, 1954, 2104, 2210 and 2310.

From Hannover Flughafen at 0149, 0538, 0638, 0738, 0838, 0938, 1038, 1134, 1238, 1338, 1436, 1538, 1638, 1738, 1836, 1934, 2038, 2138, 2237 and 2341.

SERVICE AUGUST 25 - OCTOBER 25

											⑤⑥ v	
Paderborn Hbf . **805 811** d.	0534t	0634r	0734		1434	1523	1634		2234	2310	...
Altenbeken .... **805 811** d.	0546t	0646r	0746		1446	1545	1646		2246	2333	...
Bad Pyrmont .... d.	0622r	0722	0822	and	1522	1622	1722	and	2322	0022	...
Hameln .... a.	0636r	0736	0836	hourly	1536	1636	1736	hourly	2336	0036	...
Hameln .... d.	0640	0740	0840	until	1540	1640	1740	until	2340	0040	...
Hannover Hbf .... a.	0733	0833	0933		1633	1733	1833		0033	0127	...
Hannover Hbf .... d.	0735	0835	0935		1635	1735	1835		0035	0129	0129
Hannover Flughafen ✈ ... a.	0753	0853	0953		1653	1753	1853		0053	0147	0147

	⚒		⚒						⑤⑥ v	
Hannover Flughafen ✈ ... d.	0436	0436	0536	0536	0636		2136	2236	2236	2336
Hannover Hbf .... a.	0453	0453	0553	0553	0653		2153	2253	2253	2353
Hannover Hbf .... d.	0455	...	0555	...	0655	and	2155	2255	2255	2355
Hameln .... a.	0537	...	0637	...	0737	hourly	2237	2337	2337	0040
Hameln .... d.	0544	...	0644	...	0744	until	2244	2344	2344	...
Bad Pyrmont .... d.	0600	...	0700	...	0800		2300	2358	0000	...
Altenbeken .... **805 811** d.	0633	...	0733	...	0833		2333	...	0033	...
Paderborn Hbf .. **805 811** a.	0646	...	0746	...	0846		2346	...	0046	...

r – ⚒ only. t – Ⓐ only. v – Also Oct. 2.

810 (AMSTERDAM -) BAD BENTHEIM - RHEINE - HANNOVER - BERLIN

Amended Amsterdam service JUNE 25 - AUGUST 4. See page 379 and 380 for all other services during this period.

	IC 245	*IC* 141	*IC* 141	*IC* 143	*IC* 145	*IC* 147	*IC* 149	*IC* 241	*IC* 241	*IC* 243
	①–⑥	⑦	①–⑥					⑦		⑦
	🍷	🍷	🍷	🍷	🍷	🍷	🍷	🍷	🍷	🍷
Amsterdam C **22** .... d.	0502	0700	0700	0910	1100	1300	1500	1710	1710	1900
Bad Bentheim 🏛 .... **811** d.	0721	0928	0928	1128	1328	1528	1728	1928	1928	2128
Rheine .... **811** d.	0734	0942	0942	1141	1341	1541	1741	1941	1941	2141
Münster (Westf) Hbf .... a.	0810	1012	1019	1212	1412	1610	1810	2012	2012	2212
Münster (Westf) Hbf .... **800** d.	0824	1024	1023	1224	1424	1624	1824	2024	2024	2225
Hamm (Westf) .... **800** a.	|	|	1053	|	|	|	|	|	|	|
Osnabrück Hbf .... **800 811** a.	0853	1053	...	1253	1453	1653	1853	2053	2053	2253
Osnabrück Hbf .... **811** d.	0903	1103	...	1303	1503	1703	1903	2103	2103	2303
Bünde (Westf) .... **811** d.	0928	1128	...	1328	1528	1728	1928	2128	2128	2328
Bad Oeynhausen .... **811** d.	|	|	...	|	|	|	|	|	|	|
Minden (Westf) .... **811** d.	0951	1151	...	1351	1551	1751	1951	2151	2151	2351
Hannover Hbf .... **811** a.	1025	1225	...	1425	1625	1825	2025	2225	2225	0025
Hannover Hbf .... d.	1027	1227	...	1427	1627	1827	2027	2227	...	...
Wolfsburg .... **902** d.	1108	1308	...	|	1708	1908	|	2308	...	...
Stendal Hbf .... **838** d.	1141	1341	...	1531	1741	1941	|	2341	...	...
Berlin Spandau .... **838 902** a.	1225	1425	...	1625	1825	2023	2157	0021	...	...
Berlin Hbf .... **838 902** a.	1239	1439	...	1641	1852	2041	2211	0037	...	...
Berlin Ostbahnhof .... **838 902** a.	1308	1449	...	1650	1904	2108	2222	0047	...	...

	IC 242	*IC* 240	*IC* 240	*IC* 148	*IC* 146	*IC* 144	*IC* 144	*IC* 142	*IC* 140
	①–⑥	①–⑥				①–⑥	⑦		
	🍷	🍷	🍷	🍷	🍷	🍷	🍷	🍷	🍷
Berlin Ostbahnhof ..... **838 902** d.	...	0507	...	0656	0856	...	...	1256	1456
Berlin Hbf .... **838 902** d.	...	0520	...	0708	0907	...	1120	1308	1508
Berlin Spandau .... **838 902** d.	...	0534	...	0733	0930	...	1134	1331	1532
Stendal Hbf .... **838** d.	...	0611	...	0811	1011	...	1211	1411	1611
Wolfsburg .... **902** d.	...	0645	...	0845	1045	...	1245	1445	1645
Hannover Hbf .... a.	...	0719	...	0919	1119	...	1319	1519	1719
Hannover Hbf .... **811** d.	0523	0723	0723	0923	1123	...	1323	1523	1723
Minden (Westf) .... **811** d.	0608	0808	0808	1008	1208	...	1408	1608	1808
Bad Oeynhausen .... **811** d.	0618	0818	0818	1018	1218	...	1418	1618	1818
Bünde (Westf) .... **811** d.	0630	0830	0830	1030	1230	...	1430	1630	1830
Osnabrück Hbf .... **811** a.	0651	0851	0851	1051	1251	...	1451	1651	1851
Osnabrück Hbf .... **800 811** d.	0704	0904	0904	1104	1304	...	1504	1704	1904
Hamm (Westf) .... **800** d.	|	|	|	|	|	1515	|	|	|
Münster (Westf) Hbf .... **800** a.	0735	0935	0935	1135	1335	1543	1535	1735	1935
Münster (Westf) Hbf .... d.	0747	0947	0947	1147	1347	1545	1547	1747	1947
Rheine .... **811** d.	0821	1021	1021	1221	1421	1621	1621	1821	2021
Bad Bentheim 🏛 .... **811** a.	0834	1034	1034	1234	1434	1634	1634	1834	2034
Amsterdam C **22** .... a.	1100	1300	1300	1450	1650	1900	1900	2100	2300

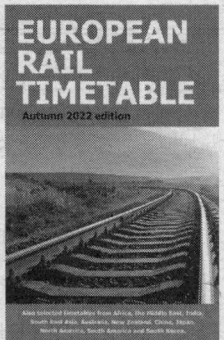

MÜNCHEN - SALZBURG 890

Bayerische Oberlandbahn; DB

JUNE 12 - AUGUST 1. See page 410 for service from August 2.

km		WB 961 ①–⑥ t⊙ 🍷	◇	RJX 265 ✕	◇	⊖	RJX 61 B✕	WB 963 ⊙ 🍷	◇	◇	RJX 63 d B✕	RJX 63 e B✕	◇	◇	RJX 65 B✕	◇	◇	RJX 67 d B✕	RJX 67 e B✕	WB 969 ⊙ 🍷	◇	EC 115 e△ 🍷♦	EC 115 c 🍷♦	◇
	Frankfurt (Main) Hbf **912** d.	...	...	...	...	...	...	...	...	...	...	...	...	...	...	...	...	...	...	...	...	...	...	...
	Stuttgart Hbf **930** d.	...	...	...	...	...	...	...	...	...	...	...	...	...	...	...	...	...	...	...	...	1158	1158	...
0	**München** Hbf **951** d.	0548	0555	0610	0655r	0703	0710e	0748	0756r	0856r	0847	0911	0955	1055	1111	1155	1255	...	1311	1348	1355	1417	|	1455
10	München Ost **951** d.	0558	0603	0622	0704	0711	0721	0758	0804	0904	|	0921	1004	1104	1121	1204	1304	1318	1322	1358	1404	1426	1430	1504
65	Rosenheim **951** d.	|	0639	0705	0735	...	0805	|	0835	0935	1005	1005	1035	1135	1205	1235	1335	1405	1405	|	1435	1456	1459	1535
82	Bad Endorf d.	|	0650	|	0746	...	|	|	0846	0946	|	|	1046	1146	|	1246	1346	|	|	|	1446	|	|	1546
90	Prien am Chiemsee d.	|	0657	|	0752	...	|	|	0852	0952	|	|	1052	1152	|	1252	1352	|	|	|	1452	|	|	1552
118	Traunstein d.	|	0720	|	0816	...	|	|	0916	1016	|	|	1116	1216	|	1316	1416	|	|	|	1516	|	|	1616
147	Freilassing **891** d.	|	0742	|	0835	...	|	|	0935	1035	|	|	1135	1235	|	1335	1435	|	|	|	1535	|	|	1635
153	**Salzburg** Hbf **891** a.	0721	0752	0802	0842	...	0902	0921	0942	1042	1102	1102	1142	1242	1302	1342	1442	1502	1502	1521	1542	|	|	1642
	Villach Hbf **970** a.	|	...	|	...	...	|	|	...	...	|	|	...	...	|	...	...	|	|	|	...	1912	1912	...
	Wien Hbf **950** a.	0950•	...	1030	...	...	1130	1150•	...	...	1330	1330	...	...	1530	...	...	1730	1730	1750•	...	...	...	...

	RJX 69 ✕	WB 971 ⊙ 🍷	◇	◇ Ⓐt	◇	RJX 261 B✕	◇ Ⓐt	◇	EC 117 e△ 🍷♦	EC 117 c 🍷♦	◇	◇	NJ 295 Ⓡ ♦§	EN 463 bⓇ 🍷♦	EN 50463 bⓇ 🍷♦	◇	◇	⊖	EN 463 kⓇ 🍷♦	EN 50463 kⓇ 🍷♦	◇	EN 463 hⓇ 🍷♦	EN 50463 hⓇ 🍷♦	◇
Frankfurt (Main) Hbf **912** d.	...	...	...	...	...	...	...	...	1420	1420	...	...	...	...	...	...	...	...	...	...	...	...	...	...
Stuttgart Hbf **930** d.	...	...	...	...	...	...	...	...	1558	1558	...	...	...	...	...	...	...	...	...	...	...	...	...	...
München Hbf **951** d.	1511e	1548	1555	1635e	1655	1708e	1722e	1755	1817	1817	1855r	1955	2004	...	...	2043	2143	2211	2218e	2218e	2243	2320	2320	2350
München Ost **951** d.	1520	1558	1604	1644	1704	1717	1735	1804	1826	|	1904	2004	2014u	2052	2052	2052	2152	2220	2231u	2231u	2252	2331u	2331u	0002
Rosenheim **951** d.	1605	|	1635	1714	1735	1805	1814	1835	1856	1914	1935	2035	2044u	|	|	2131	2231	...	2304u	2304u	2331	0003u	0003u	0038
Bad Endorf d.	|	|	1646	1726	1746	|	1826	1846	|	|	1946	2046	|	|	|	2142	2242	...	|	|	2342	|	|	0049
Prien am Chiemsee d.	|	|	1652	1732	1752	|	1832	1852	|	|	1952	2052	|	|	|	2148	2248	...	|	|	2348	|	|	0055
Traunstein d.	|	|	1716	1756	1816	|	1856	1916	|	|	2016	2116	|	|	|	2211	2311	...	|	|	0010	|	|	0118
Freilassing **891** d.	|	|	1735	...	1835	|	...	1935	|	|	2035	2135	|	|	|	2230	2330	...	|	|	...	|	|	...
Salzburg Hbf **891** a.	1702	1721	1742	...	1842	1858	...	1942	|	|	2042	2142	2152	0106	0106	2237	2336	...	0106	0106	...	0106	0106	...
Villach Hbf **970** a.	|	|	...	...	...	|	...	...	2329	2329	...	...	0019	|	0357	...	...	...	|	0357	...	|	0357	...
Wien Hbf **950** a.	1930	1950•	...	...	...	2130	...	...	...	...	...	...	...	0634	...	...	...	...	0634	...	...	0634	...	...

	◇ Ⓐt	EN 462 Ⓡ¶ 🍷♦	EN 498 Ⓡ¶ 🍷♦		◇	IC 1296 d	IC 1296 e	◇ Ⓐt	◇	NJ 294 Ⓡ ♦‡	①–⑤ t	◇	◇	◇ Ⓐt	RJX 260 ✕	⊖	◇	◇	WB 962 ⊙ 🍷	RJX 262 ✕	⊖	◇	EC 114 c 🍷♦	EC 114 e△ 🍷♦
Wien Hbf **950** d.	...	2327	...	...	...	...	...	...	...	...	...	...	...	...	0630	...	...	...	0810•	0830	...	...	...	...
Villach Hbf **970** d.	...	|	0150	...	...	...	...	...	...	0429	...	...	...	..	|	...	...	...	|	|	...	...	0833	0833
Salzburg Hbf **891** d.	...	0427	0427	...	0515	0510	0537	0600	0615	0701	0704	0715z	0815	...	0856	...	0915	1015	1039	1056	...	1115	|	|
Freilassing **891** d.	...	|	|	...	0524	0519	0545	0608	0624	|	0714	0724	0824	...	|	...	0924	1024	|	|	...	1124	|	|
Traunstein d.	0422	|	|	...	0544	0537	0608	0627	0644	|	...	0744	0844	0905	|	...	0944	1044	|	|	...	1144	|	|
Prien am Chiemsee d.	0444	|	|	...	0606	0600	0627	0650	0706	|	...	0806	0906	0927	|	...	1006	1106	|	|	...	1206	|	|
Bad Endorf d.	0451	|	|	...	0613	0607	0635	0656	0713	|	...	0813	0913	0933	|	...	1013	1113	|	|	...	1213	|	|
Rosenheim **951** d.	0504	0542s	0542s	...	0629	0625	0649	0711	0729	0836	...	0829	0929	0948	0957	...	1029	1129	|	1157	...	1229	1246	1302
München Ost **951** a.	0531	0615s	0615s	...	0656	|	0717	0738	0756	|	...	0856	0955	1016	1027	1033	1056	1155	1200	1225	1233	1256	|	1331
München Hbf **951** a.	0541	0629e	0629e	...	0706	0730	0728	0747	0806	0920	...	0906	1006	1025e	1034e	1041	1106	1206	1213	1234e	1241	1306	1341	1341
Stuttgart Hbf **930** a.	...	...	...	...	...	0959	0959	...	...	...	...	...	...	...	...	...	...	...	...	...	...	...	1559	1559
Frankfurt (Main) Hbf **912** a.	...	...	...	...	...	1140	1140	...	...	...	...	...	...	...	...	...	...	...	...	...	...	...	...	...

	◇	WB 964 ⊙ 🍷	RJX 60 B✕	⊖	◇	◇	RJX 62 B✕	⊖	◇	◇	RJX 64 e B✕	RJX 64 d B✕	◇	◇	WB 970 ⊙ 🍷	RJX 66 B✕	◇	◇	WB 972 Ⓑ ⊙	RJX 68 e B✕	RJX 68 d B✕	◇	◇	◇
Wien Hbf **950** d.	...	1010•	1030	...	...	...	1230	...	...	...	1430	1430	...	...	1610•	1630	...	...	1810•	1830	1830	...	...	...
Villach Hbf **970** d.	...	|	|	...	...	...	|	...	...	...	|	|	...	...	|	|	...	...	|	|	|	...	...	...
Salzburg Hbf **891** d.	1215	1239	1256	...	1313	1415	1456	...	1515	1615	1656	1656	1715	1815	1839	1856	1915	2015	2039	2056	2056	2115	2215	2300
Freilassing **891** d.	1224	|	|	...	1324	1424	|	...	1524	1624	|	|	1724	1824	|	|	1929	2024	|	|	|	2129	2224	2310
Traunstein d.	1244	|	|	...	1344	1444	|	...	1544	1644	|	|	1744	1844	|	|	1949	2044	|	|	|	2149	2244	2329
Prien am Chiemsee d.	1306	|	|	...	1406	1506	|	...	1606	1706	|	|	1806	1906	|	|	2011	2106	|	|	|	2211	2306	2351
Bad Endorf d.	1313	|	|	...	1413	1513	|	...	1613	1713	|	|	1813	1913	|	|	2018	2113	|	|	|	2218	2313	2357
Rosenheim **951** d.	1329	|	1357	...	1429	1529	1557	...	1629	1729	1757	1757	1829	1929	|	1957	2032	2132	|	2157	2157	2232	2332	0012
München Ost **951** a.	1355	1400	1427	1433	1456	1556	1626	1633	1656	1756	1826	|	1856	1956	2000	2025	2105	2206	2155	2223	|	2305	0008	0046
München Hbf **951** a.	1405	1413	1435e	1441	1506	1606r	1635e	1641	1706p	1806r	1837	1907	1906	2006	2013	2036	2115	2215	2207	2233	2248	2315	0017f	0058
Stuttgart Hbf **930** a.	...	...	...	...	...	...	...	...	...	...	...	...	...	...	...	...	...	...	...	...	...	...	...	...
Frankfurt (Main) Hbf **912** a.	...	...	...	...	...	...	...	...	...	...	...	...	...	...	...	...	...	...	...	...	...	...	...	...

♦ – **NOTES** (LISTED BY TRAIN NUMBER)

114 – WÖRTHERSEE – [12] and 🍷 Klagenfurt - Schwarzach - Wörgl - München - Mannheim - Bochum.
115 – WÖRTHERSEE – [12] and 🍷 Münster - Köln - Mannheim - München - Wörgl - Schwarzach - Klagenfurt.
117 – SALZACH – [12] and 🍷 Frankfurt - München - Wörgl - Schwarzach - Villach - Klagenfurt
294/5 – 🛏 1, 2 cl., ━ 2 cl. and [2] Roma - Firenze - Bologna - München and v.v.; 🛏 1, 2 cl., ━ 2 cl. and [2] Milano (**40235**/**40295**) - Verona - München and v.v.
462/3 – KÁLMÁN IMRE – 🛏 1, 2 cl., ━ 2 cl., [2] and 🍷 Budapest - München and v.v.
498 – LISINSKI – 🛏 1, 2 cl., ━ 2 cl. and [2] Zagreb - Ljubljana - Jesenice 🏛 - Villach - München; 🛏 1, 2 cl. and [2] (**480**) Rijeka - Ljubljana - München; 🛏 1, 2 cl., ━ 2 cl. and [2] (*NJ* **40236**) Venezia - Villach - München.
50463 – LISINSKI – 🛏 1, 2 cl., ━ 2 cl. and [2] München - Villach - Jesenice 🏛 - Ljubljana - Zagreb; 🛏 1, 2 cl. and [2] (**60463**) München - Ljubljana - Rijeka; 🛏 1, 2 cl., ━ 2 cl. and [2] (*NJ* **40463**) München - Villach - Venezia.

B – To / from Budapest (Table **1250**).
b – Until July 12. Departs München Ost 2113 June 11–13, 2118 on ①⑥⑦ June 18–27.
c – Until July 13. Subject to confirmation from July 1.
d – Until July 13.
e – From July 14.
f – From July 15.
h – From July 23. The departures from München on July 25, 26 do not call at Rosenheim.
k – July 13–22. Does not call at Rosenheim July 17, 19–21.
p – Not June 13–15, 17, 20–24, 27–30, July 1, 4–8, 11–13. Arrives 1709 on July 16, 17, 23, 24, 30, 31.
r – Not June 13–15, 17, 20–24, 27–30, July 1, 4–8, 11–13.
s – Calls to set down only.
t – Not June 16.
u – Calls to pick up only.
z – ⑥⑦ (also June 16).

• – Wien **Westbahnhof**.
¶ – Until July 13 does not call at Rosenheim and arrives München Ost up to 66 minutes later (please check your reservation).
§ – Until June 16 departs München Hbf 1928, München Ost 1938, Rosenheim 2028. Timings may also vary on other dates.
‡ – Timings may vary (please check your reservation).
◇ – *Meridian* regional service (operated by Bayerische Regiobahn; German holiday dates apply).
⊖ – S-Bahn service (runs from / to München Hbf underground platforms).
⊙ – Operated by *Westbahn* (special fares).
△ – Subject to confirmation.

SALZBURG - FREILASSING - BERCHTESGADEN 891

Berchtesgadener Land Bahn

SERVICE UNTIL AUGUST 1. See page 410 for service from August 2.

km		Ⓐt	Ⓒz																						
0	**Salzburg** Hbf **890** d.	0704	0715	0742	0815	0842	0915	0942	and at	1313	1342	1415	1442	1515	1542	1615	1642	1715	1742	1815	1842	1915	2042	2142	2229
6	Freilassing **890** a.	0714	0722	0754	0822	0854	0922	0954	the same	1320	1354	1422	1454	1522	1554	1622	1654	1722	1754	1822	1854	1922	2054	2154	2241
6	Freilassing d.	0718	0740	0804	0840	0859	0939	0958	minutes	1339	1358	1439	1458	1539	1558	1639	1658	1739	1758	1839	1858	1939	2100	2201	2246
21	Bad Reichenhall d.	0741	0759	0821	0901	0920	1001	1020	past each	1401	1420	1501	1520	1601	1620	1701	1720	1801	1820	1901	1920	2001	2122	2219	2306
39	**Berchtesgaden** Hbf a.	0810	0826	...	0928	...	1028	...	hour until	1428	...	1528	...	1628	...	1728	...	1828	...	1928	...	2028	2150	2247	2334

	Ⓐt	①	Ⓐt				Ⓐt																		
Berchtesgaden Hbf d.	...	0529	...	...	0621	0706	...	...	...	0932	...	and at	1532	...	1632	...	1732	...	1832	...	1932	...	2032	...	2210
Bad Reichenhall d.	0528	0559	0559	...	0654	0740	0800	0837	0937	1000	1037	the same	1600	1637	1700	1737	1800	1837	1900	1937	2000	...	2100	...	2245
Freilassing a.	0546	0616	0616	...	0712	0757	0821	0858	0957	1018	1057	minutes	1618	1657	1718	1757	1818	1857	1918	1957	2018	...	2118	...	2303
Freilassing **890** d.	0547	0618	0618	...	0722	0807	0835	0903	1007	1035	1107	past each	1635	1707	1735	1807	1835	1907	1935	2007	2035	...	2135	...	2307
Salzburg Hbf **890** a.	0558	0629	0629	...	0733	0817	0842	0913	1017	1042	1117	hour until	1642	1717	1742	1817	1842	1917	1942	2017	2042	...	2142	...	2317

t – Not June 16. **z** – Also June 16.

926 AALEN - DONAUWÖRTH

Amended service July 9 - November 13. On November 1 services run as on Ⓒ. During this period all services Harburg - Donauwörth and v.v. are operated by 🚌 (shaded timings).

km		Ⓐ🚌	Ⓒ	Ⓐ	Ⓐ		Ⓐ	Ⓐ	Ⓒ	Ⓐ	Ⓒ	Ⓐ	Ⓐ	Ⓐ	Ⓒ	Ⓐ	Ⓐ	Ⓒ	Ⓐ		Ⓐ	Ⓐ	Ⓒ		
0	**Aalen** Hbf d.	...	0531	0603	0625	0733	0833	0933	0933	1033	1135	1135	1233	1333	1333	1433	1533	1533	1635	1733	1833	1933	1933	2035	2237
39	Nördlingen a.	...	0613	0638	0706	0813	0913	1013	1013	1112	1213	1219	1313	1413	1413	1513	1613	1613	1713	1813	1913	2013	2013	2113	2314
39	Nördlingen d.	0542	0622	0639	0707	0821	0914	1015	1020	1114	1216	1221	1315	1414	1421	1514	1617	1622	1722	1826	1915	2015	2019	2116	...
50	Harburg a.	0610	0637	0654	0721	0840	0933	1034	1035	1133	1230	1240	1334	1433	1436	1533	1636	1637	1741	1845	1934	2031	2034	2135	...
50	Harburg 🚌 d.	0610	0642	0700	0726	0845	0938	1039	1040	1138	1235	1245	1339	1438	1441	1538	1641	1642	1746	1850	1939	2037	2039	2140	...
68	**Donauwörth** 🚌 a.	0635	0707	0725	0745	0910	1003	1104	1105	1203	1300	1310	1404	1503	1506	1603	1706	1707	1811	1915	2004	2102	2104	2205	...

		Ⓐ		Ⓐ	Ⓒ	Ⓐ	Ⓐ		Ⓐ	Ⓐ	Ⓒ	Ⓐ		Ⓐ		Ⓐ	Ⓐ		Ⓐ	Ⓐ		Ⓐ		Ⓐ	Ⓒ
Donauwörth 🚌 d.	....	...	...	0544	0648	0653	0752	0846	0947	1046	1048	1152	1247	1346	1446	1549	1612	1654	1718	1758	1846	2010	2048	2207	2240
Harburg 🚌 a.	...	...	...	0609	0713	0718	0817	0911	1012	1111	1113	1217	1312	1411	1511	1614	1637	1719	1743	1823	1911	2035	2113	2232	2305
Harburg d.	...	...	...	0624	0718	0723	0822	0916	1017	1116	1118	1223	1317	1416	1516	1619	1642	1724	1748	1828	1916	2040	2118	2237	2310
Nördlingen a.	...	...	...	0638	0735	0739	0839	0932	1033	1132	1134	1239	1333	1432	1532	1635	1657	1740	1804	1845	1933	2056	2134	2253	2323
Nördlingen d.	0442	0531	0641	0641	0742	0742	0842	0942	1042	1144	1144	1242	1342	1442	1542	1643	...	1742	...	1848	1942	...	2134	...	...
Aalen Hbf a.	0524	0613	0721	0720	0824	0824	0924	1024	1124	1226	1226	1324	1424	1524	1624	1726	...	1824	...	1926	2024	...	2215	...	...

942 STUTTGART - FREUDENSTADT - OFFENBURG

On June 16 services run as on ⑦

Amended service until October 8. All services are operated by 🚌 Freudenstadt - Hausach and v.v.; by train Hausach - Offenburg and v.v.

	Ⓐ	⚒		Ⓐ				Ⓐ		Ⓒ	Ⓐ				Ⓐ				Ⓐ						
Freudenstadt Hbf 🚌 d.	0510	0600	0641	0707	0741	0822	0922	0947	1022	1122	1144	1222	1322	1422	1517	1522	1622	1722	1747	1822	...	1931	2031	...	2149
Alpirsbach 🚌 d.	0541	0635	0716	|	0816	0857	0957	|	1057	1157	1217	1257	1357	1457	|	1557	1657	1757	|	1857	...	2002	2102	...	2220
Schiltach 🚌 d.	0556	0653	0734	0742	0834	0915	1015	|	1115	1215	1235	1315	1415	1515	|	1615	1715	1815	|	1915	...	2017	2117	...	2235
Wolfach 🚌 d.	0610	0709	0750	|	0850	0931	1031	|	1131	1231	1251	1331	1431	1531	|	1631	1731	1831	|	1931	...	2031	2131	...	2249
Hausach 🚌 a.	0622	0721	0802	0802	0902	0943	1043	1042	1143	1243	1303	1343	1443	1543	1612	1643	1743	1843	1842	1943	...	2043	2143	...	2301
Hausach 916 d.	0630	0727	0807	0807	0907	0948	1048	1048	1148	1248	1314	1348	1448	1548	1618	1648	1748	1848	1848	1948	...	2048	2148	...	2312
Offenburg 916 a.	0659	0755	0834	0834	0935	1014	1114	1114	1214	1314	1342	1414	1514	1614	1643	1714	1814	1914	1914	2014	...	2114	2214	...	2338

	Ⓐ	Ⓐ	⑥	Ⓐ	Ⓐ	Ⓒ		Ⓐ					Ⓐ	Ⓒ	Ⓐ				Ⓐ						
Offenburg 916 d.	0453	...	...	0558	0702	0702	0740	0759	0841	0941	1041	1141	1241	1241	1307	1341	1441	1541	1612	1641	1741	1841	1941	2041	2241
Hausach 916 a.	0520	...	...	0625	0729	0729	0808	0820	0908	1008	1108	1208	1308	1308	1340	1408	1508	1608	1640	1708	1808	1908	2008	2108	2308
Hausach 🚌 d.	0525	0555	0633	0633	0736	0734	0813	0825	0913	1013	1113	1213	1313	1313	1345	1413	1513	1613	1645	1713	1813	1913	2013	2113	2313
Wolfach 🚌 d.	0531	|	0640	0640	0743	0741	0820	|	0920	1020	1120	1220	1320	1320	|	1420	1520	1620	|	1720	1820	1920	2019	2119	2319
Schiltach 🚌 d.	0547	0613	0659	0702	0800	0800	0839	|	0939	1039	1139	1239	1337	1339	|	1439	1539	1639	|	1739	1839	1939	2037	2137	2337
Alpirsbach 🚌 d.	0604	|	0718	0718	0819	0819	0858	|	0958	1058	1158	1258	1354	1358	|	1458	1558	1658	|	1758	1858	1958	2055	2155	2355
Freudenstadt Hbf 🚌 a.	0634	0700	0752	0752	0853	0853	0932	0920	1032	1132	1232	1332	1428	1432	1440	1532	1632	1732	1740	1832	1932	2032	2125	2225	0025

945 REGENSBURG - INGOLSTADT - DONAUWÖRTH - ULM

agilis

SERVICE UNTIL AUGUST 14. See page 447 for service from August 15. On June 16 services run as on ⑦.

km		Ⓐ		Ⓐ	Ⓐ	Ⓐ	Ⓐ	Ⓐ	Ⓐ	Ⓐ	Ⓐ	Ⓐ	Ⓐ	Ⓐ	Ⓐ	Ⓐ	Ⓐ	Ⓐ	Ⓐ	Ⓐ	Ⓐ	Ⓐ	Ⓐ	Ⓐ	Ⓐ
0	**Regensburg** Hbf d.		...	0357	0452	0508	0534	0608	...	0713	0741	0846	0952	1046	1152	1246	1352	1446	1552	1614	1646	1728	1752	1846	1952
46	Neustadt (Donau) d.		...	0434	0534	0556	0626	0654	...	0803	0831	0927	1029	1128	1229	1323	1429	1528	1629	1703	1731	1811	1829	1928	2028
74	**Ingolstadt** Hbf a.		...	0454	0554	0622	0654	0720	...	0826	0851	0953	1050	1154	1250	1349	1449	1548	1650	1734	1755	1835	1852	1950	2051
74	**Ingolstadt** Hbf d.		...	0507	0607	0631	0702	...	0807	...	0908	1008	1108	1209	1307	1406	1509	1608	1709	1740	1808	1841	1908	2003	2102
95	Neuburg (Donau) d.		...	0523	0627	0648	0729	...	0828	...	0926	1028	1129	1228	1329	1428	1529	1628	1725	1802	1829	1856	1929	2026	2127
127	**Donauwörth** a.		...	0549	0653	0724	0753	...	0853	...	0951	1054	1154	1253	1353	1454	1554	1653	1753	1838	1854	1920	1953	2053	2200
			Ⓐ	Ⓐ	Ⓐ	Ⓐ	Ⓐ		Ⓐ		Ⓐ	Ⓐ	Ⓐ	Ⓐ	Ⓐ	Ⓐ	Ⓐ	Ⓐ	Ⓐ		Ⓐ	Ⓐ	|	Ⓐ	
127	**Donauwörth** d.		0452	0603	0702	0731	0803	...	0901	...	1002	1101	1202	1302	1401	1503	1601	1702	1801	...	1901	1938	2010	2101	...
153	Dillingen (Donau) d.		0513	0632	0724	0751	0823	...	0925	...	1023	1121	1223	1330	1423	1525	1623	1725	1823	...	1922	1958	2032	2124	...
176	Günzburg 930 a.		0534	0649	0741	0808	0839	...	0940	...	1039	1140	1240	1347	1439	1540	1639	1740	1839	...	1939	2022	2048	2140	...
200	**Ulm** Hbf 930 a.		0554	0710	0808	0830	0857	...	0958	...	1057	1158	1258	1410	1457	1558	1657	1758	1857	...	1957	...	2108	2209	...

	Ⓐ	Ⓐ	Ⓐ	Ⓒ	Ⓒ			Ⓒ	Ⓒ	Ⓒ	Ⓒ	Ⓒ	Ⓒ	Ⓒ	Ⓒ	Ⓒ	Ⓒ	Ⓒ	Ⓒ	Ⓒ	Ⓒ	Ⓒ	Ⓒ	Ⓒ	Ⓒ
Regensburg Hbf d.	2015	2112	2222		0024	...	...	...	0557	0649	0800	0845	1000	1045	1200	1245	1400	1445	1600	1645	1800	1845	2000	2045	2222
Neustadt (Donau) d.	2102	2204	2302		0106	...	...	...	0638	0733	0838	0933	1038	1133	1238	1333	1438	1533	1638	1733	1838	1933	2038	2133	2302
Ingolstadt Hbf a.	2123	2227	2322		0128	...	...	...	0655	0754	0855	0954	1054	1154	1254	1354	1454	1553	1654	1754	1854	1954	2054	2153	2322
Ingolstadt Hbf d.	2143	2240	2355		...	...	...	0607	0708	0808	0908	1008	1107	1208	1308	1408	1508	1608	1708	1808	1908	2008	2108	2208	2355
Neuburg (Donau) d.	2203	2257	0017		...	...	...	0627	0722	0824	0923	1024	1122	1224	1322	1424	1522	1624	1722	1824	1922	2024	2133	2228	0017
Donauwörth a.	2228	2323	0043		...	...	...	0653	0746	0853	0945	1053	1146	1253	1346	1453	1545	1653	1746	1853	1945	2053	2159	2253	0043
	Ⓐ	Ⓐ				Ⓒ	⑥	Ⓒ	|	Ⓒ	|	Ⓒ	|	Ⓒ	|	Ⓒ	|	Ⓒ	|	Ⓒ	|	Ⓒ	|	Ⓒ	
Donauwörth d.	2238	2338	...		...	0452	0607	0703	0750	0901	0950	1101	1150	1303	1350	1503	1550	1702	1750	1901	1950	2101	2201	2338	...
Dillingen (Donau) d.	2302	2358	...		...	0513	0633	0723	0807	0922	1006	1121	1206	1324	1406	1525	1606	1725	1806	1922	2007	2122	2222	2358	...
Günzburg 930 a.	2319	0014	...		...	0534	0650	0739	0824	0937	1022	1140	1222	1340	1422	1540	1622	1740	1825	1939	2024	2140	2245	0014	...
Ulm Hbf 930 a.	2337	0033	...		...	0554	0710	0758	0840	0958	1040	1158	1240	1358	1440	1558	1640	1758	1844	1957	2041	2209	2316	0033	...

	Ⓐ				Ⓐ	Ⓐ	Ⓐ	Ⓐ	Ⓐ	Ⓐ	Ⓐ	Ⓐ	Ⓐ	Ⓐ	Ⓐ	Ⓐ		Ⓐ	Ⓐ	Ⓐ	Ⓐ	Ⓐ		Ⓐ	Ⓐ
Ulm Hbf 930 d.		...	...	...	0450	0527	...	0625	...	0745	0848	0948	1048	1148	1248	1348	...	1448	1548	1648	1742	1831	...	1942	2038
Günzburg 930 d.		...	...	...	0509	0545	...	0645	0652	0804	0913	1006	1116	1206	1314	1406	...	1513	1606	1713	1803	1851	...	2003	2058
Dillingen (Donau) d.		...	...	...	0524	0608	0628	0701	0727	0828	0933	1025	1132	1223	1331	1423	...	1533	1623	1733	1826	1907	...	2019	2114
Donauwörth a.		...	...	...	0545	0629	0650	0725	0754	0849	0953	1049	1153	1246	1352	1445	...	1553	1646	1753	1847	1932	...	2042	2136
		Ⓐ	Ⓐ	Ⓐ	Ⓐ	|	Ⓐ	Ⓐ	Ⓐ	Ⓐ	Ⓐ	Ⓐ	Ⓐ	Ⓐ	Ⓐ	Ⓐ	Ⓐ	Ⓐ	Ⓐ	Ⓐ	Ⓐ	Ⓐ	Ⓐ	Ⓐ	|
Donauwörth d.		...	0456	...	0554	0631	0701	0731	0801	0859	1004	1101	1201	1302	1401	1502	...	1601	1703	1802	1901	1942	2009	2101	2138
Neuburg (Donau) d.		...	0524	...	0627	0705	0730	0804	0830	0930	1029	1128	1230	1328	1430	1530	...	1629	1735	1828	1930	2007	2038	2125	2205
Ingolstadt Hbf a.		...	0544	...	0650	0723	0747	0831	0847	0947	1046	1147	1246	1346	1448	1547	...	1647	1750	1848	1947	2023	2055	2143	2223
Ingolstadt Hbf d.		0521	0600	0628	0705	0730	0805	...	0906	1005	1105	1205	1318	1405	1505	1605	1624	1705	1805	1905	2007	2030	2108	2206	2236
Neustadt (Donau) d.		0545	0621	0655	0729	0752	0828	...	0927	1028	1127	1228	1339	1428	1527	1628	1651	1727	1829	1927	2028	2048	2133	2227	2302
Regensburg Hbf a.		0625	0706	0741	0807	0836	0911	...	1007	1111	1207	1310	1430	1510	1607	1710	1734	1807	1910	2007	2110	2129	2210	2312	2340

	Ⓐ	Ⓐ	Ⓐ	Ⓒ			Ⓒ	Ⓒ	Ⓒ	Ⓒ	Ⓒ	Ⓒ	Ⓒ	Ⓒ	Ⓒ	Ⓒ	Ⓒ	Ⓒ	Ⓒ	Ⓒ	Ⓒ	Ⓒ		Ⓒ	Ⓒ
Ulm Hbf 930 d.	2123	2219	2255		...	...	0555	0718	0745	0918	0948	1118	1148	1318	1348	1518	1550	1718	1742	1918	1942	2100	...	2148	2255
Günzburg 930 d.	2147	2245	2318		...	...	0616	0736	0804	0936	1013	1136	1213	1336	1413	1536	1613	1736	1813	1936	2003	2120	...	2210	2318
Dillingen (Donau) d.	2203	2301	2335		...	...	0631	0752	0828	0952	1032	1152	1231	1352	1431	1552	1632	1752	1831	1952	2029	2140	...	2232	2335
Donauwörth a.	2223	2323	0002		...	...	0653	0812	0849	1013	1053	1212	1252	1412	1452	1612	1652	1812	1851	2012	2051	2200	...	2253	0002
	Ⓐ	Ⓐ			Ⓒ	Ⓒ	Ⓒ	|	Ⓒ	|	Ⓒ	|	Ⓒ	|	Ⓒ	|	Ⓒ	|	Ⓒ	|	Ⓒ	|	Ⓒ	Ⓒ	
Donauwörth d.	2238	2339	...		0501	...	0701	0815	0905	1014	1101	1214	1302	1413	1502	1614	1702	1813	1901	2014	2104	2203	...	2339	...
Neuburg (Donau) d.	2308	0006	...		0526	...	0732	0838	0932	1037	1132	1237	1332	1437	1533	1637	1733	1837	1933	2037	2132	2228	...	0006	...
Ingolstadt Hbf a.	2326	0023	...		0546	...	0748	0851	0949	1051	1148	1251	1349	1451	1549	1651	1749	1852	1949	2051	2148	2244	...	0023	...
Ingolstadt Hbf d.	2359	...	...		0604	0655	0805	0905	1005	1105	1205	1305	1405	1505	1605	1705	1805	1905	2005	2105	2205	...	2359	...	...
Neustadt (Donau) d.	0019	...	...		0627	0718	0828	0922	1027	1122	1227	1322	1427	1522	1627	1722	1827	1922	2027	2122	2226	...	0019	...	...
Regensburg Hbf a.	0104	...	...		0708	0807	0911	0956	1111	1156	1311	1356	1511	1556	1711	1756	1911	1957	2111	2156	2312	...	0104	...	...

BUDAPEST - SIÓFOK - FONYÓD - KESZTHELY and NAGYKANIZSA 1220

Summer service June 18 - August 28. **WARNING!** Supplements may be payable for travel on certain trains in this table.

km			⑤–⑦	⑤–⑦	①–④	⑤–⑦		IC 860 ✕🅁	IC 200 🅁 A	IR 18500	Ex 18700 🅁Ⓒ d	IC 1842 🅁	IC 1862 ✕🅁	Ex 18802 🅁 e	IR 18502	Ex 16709 🅁Ⓒ f	Ex 18792 Ⓐ	Ex 18702 🅁Ⓒ g	IC 1852 🅁	Ex 15607 🅁 h	IC 1864 ✕🅁	Ex 1787 🅁 j	IR 18404
0	**Budapest** Déli **1225 1230** d.	0040	*0140*	0240	...	...	0505	0635	0635	0605	...	0735	0835	...	0805	...	...	...	0935	...	1035	...	1005
4	Kelenföld **1225 1230** d.	0047	*0147*	0247	...	...	0512	0642	0642	0612	0702	0742	0842	...	0812	0847	0902	0902	0942	0941	1042	1041	1012
67	**Székesfehérvár** **1225 1230** a.	0144	*0244*	0344	...	...	0550	0720	0720	0651	0742	0820	0920	...	0851	0935	0942	0942	1020	1024	1120	1125	1051
67	**Székesfehérvár** d.	0152	0252	0352	...	...	0551	0721	0721	0652	0745	0821	0921	...	0852	0937	0945	0945	1021	1025	1121	1129	1052
95	Lepsény d.	0213	0313	0413	...	...	0612	0740	0740	0719	|	|	|	...	0919	|	|	|	|	|	|	|	1119
115	**Siófok** a.	0233	0333	0433	...	...	0632	0755	0755	0744	0828	0855	0955	...	0944	1014	1028	1028	1055	1102	1155	1201	1144
115	**Siófok** d.	0236	0336	0436	...	0536	0633	0757	0757	0804	0831	0857	0957	...	1004	...	1031	1031	1057	1104	1157	1202	1204
124	Zamárdi d.	0248	0348	0448	...	0548	0644	0804	0804	0816	0842	0904	1004	...	1016	...	1042	1042	1104	1113	1204	1210	1216
130	Balatonföldvár d.	0256	0356	0456	...	0556	0653	0809	0809	0824	0855	0909	1009	...	1024	...	1055	1055	1109	1122	1209	1216	1224
139	Balatonszemes d.	0306	0406	0506	...	0606	0702	0818	0818	0834	0902	0918	1018	...	1034	...	1102	1102	1118	1140	1218	1229	1234
146	Balatonlelle d.	0313	0413	0513	...	0613	0708	0824	0824	0842	0909	0924	1024	...	1042	...	1109	1109	1124	1148	1224	1239	1242
149	Balatonboglár d.	0317	0417	0517	...	0617	0712	0830	0830	0847	0914	0930	1030	...	1047	...	1114	1114	1130	1155	1230	1243	1247
157	**Fonyód** a.	0325	0426	0525	...	0623	0718	0835	0835	0856	0923	0935	1035	...	1056	...	1123	1123	1135	1202	1235	1250	1256
157	**Fonyód** **1232** d.	0328	0426	0528	0625	0625	0723	0837	0837	...	...	0937	1037	1042	1103	...	...	...	1137	...	1237	1256	...
165	Balatonfenyves **1232** d.	0338	0435	0538	0639	0639	0730	0843	0843	...	...	0943	1043	1053	1122	...	...	...	1143	...	1243	|	...
181	Balatonszentgyörgy **1232** a.	0357	0455	0557	0657	0657	0744	0857	0857	...	...	0956	1057	1123	1142	...	...	...	1156	...	1257	1322	...
181	Balatonszentgyörgy **1232** d.	0400	0456	0601	0700	0700	0801	0900	0907	...	...	1001	1100	1124	...	...	...	...	1201	...	1300	...	...
221	**Keszthely** **1232** a.	0411	0507	|	0711	0711	|	0911	|	...	...	|	1111	1135	...	...	...	...	|	...	1311	...	...
221	**Nagykanizsa** a.	...	...	0644	...	...	0841	...	0955	...	...	1041	...	...	...	...	...	...	1241	...	...	...	...
352	*Zagreb* **1340** a.	...	...	...	...	...	...	...	1255	...	...	...	...	...	...	...	...	...	...	...	...	...	...

	Ex 16707 🅁 m	IC 1844 🅁	Ex 1677 🅁Ⓒ n	IC 1874 ✕🅁	IR 18504	IC 1854 🅁	IC 1866 ✕🅁	IR 18406	IC 204 🅁 B	IC 1876 ✕🅁	IR 18506		IC 1856 🅁	IC 868 🅁	IR 18408	IC 1204 🅁 C	IC 848 🅁	IR 18708	IC 1878 ✕🅁			④–⑥
Budapest Déli **1225 1230** d.	...	1135	...	1235	1205	1335	1435	1405	1535	1635	1605	...	1735	1835	1805	1845**k**	1935	2005	2135	2205	2240	2340
Kelenföld **1225 1230** d.	1102	1142	...	1242	1212	1342	1442	1412	1542	1642	1612	...	1742	1842	1812	1901	1942	2012	2142	2212	2247	2347
Székesfehérvár **1225 1230** a.	1142	1220	...	1320	1251	1420	1520	1451	1620	1720	1651	...	1820	1920	1851	1942	2020	2051	2220	2250	2344	0044
Székesfehérvár d.	1145	1221	1245	1321	1252	1421	1521	1452	1621	1721	1652	...	1821	1921	1852	1943	2021	2052	2221	2251	2352	0052
Lepsény d.	|	|	|	|	1319	|	|	1519	|	|	1719	...	|	|	1919	|	|	2119	|	2313	0013	0113
Siófok a.	1228	1255	1335	1355	1344	1455	1555	1544	1655	1755	1744	...	1855	1955	1944	2026	2055	2144	2255	2333	0033	0133
Siófok d.	1231	1257	...	1357	1404	1457	1557	1604	1657	1757	1804	...	1857	1957	2004	2027	2057	2150	2257	2336	0036	0136
Zamárdi d.	1242	1304	...	1404	1416	1504	1604	1616	1704	1804	1816	...	1904	2004	2016	2033	2104	2202	2304	2348	0048	0148
Balatonföldvár d.	1255	1309	...	1409	1424	1509	1609	1624	1709	1809	1824	...	1909	2009	2024	|	2109	2212	2309	2356	0056	0156
Balatonszemes d.	1302	1318	...	1418	1434	1518	1618	1634	1718	1818	1834	...	1918	2018	2034	|	2118	2222	2318	0006	0106	0206
Balatonlelle d.	1309	1324	...	1424	1442	1524	1624	1642	1724	1824	1842	...	1924	2024	2042	|	2124	2230	2324	0013	0113	0214
Balatonboglár d.	1314	1330	...	1430	1447	1530	1630	1647	1730	1830	1847	...	1930	2030	2047	|	2130	2240	2330	0017	0117	0218
Fonyód a.	1323	1335	...	1435	1456	1535	1635	1656	1735	1835	1856	...	1935	2035	2056	2059	2135	2248	2335	0025	0125	0226
Fonyód **1232** d.	...	1337	...	1437	1500	1537	1637	...	1737	1837	1900	...	1937	2037	...	2100	2137	2250	2337	...	0128	...
Balatonfenyves **1232** d.	...	1343	...	1443	1522	1543	1643	...	1743	1843	1922	...	1943	2043	...	|	2143	2300	2343	...	0138	...
Balatonszentgyörgy **1232** a.	...	1356	...	1457	1542	1556	1657	...	1756	1857	1942	...	1956	2057	...	2117	2156	2319	2357	...	0157	...
Balatonszentgyörgy **1232** d.	...	1401	...	1500	...	1601	1700	...	1801	1900	...	...	2001	2100	...	2118	2201	2320	0000	...	0200	...
Keszthely **1232** a.	...	|	...	1511	...	|	1711	...	|	1911	...	...	|	2111	...	|	|	2331	0011	...	0211	...
Nagykanizsa a.	...	1441	...	...	...	1641	...	...	1841	...	...	...	2041	...	...	2157	2241	...	...	...	...	...
Zagreb **1340** a.	...	...	...	...	...	...	...	...	2152	...	...	...	...	...	...	...	...	...	...	...	...	...

	⑤–⑦				Ⓐ	IC 1849 🅁	IC 1205 🅁 C	IC 1867 ✕🅁	IR 18509	IC 1847 🅁	IC 1877 🅁	IR 18407	IC 1857 🅁	IC 1865 ✕🅁	IR 18405	IC 1845 🅁	Ex 1674 🅁Ⓒ p	IC 1875 ✕🅁	IR 18505	IC 205 🅁 A	Ex 16706 🅁 q	IC 1863 ✕🅁
Zagreb **1340** d.	...	...	...	...	...	...	...	...	...	...	...	...	...	...	...	...	...	...	...	1005	...	...
Nagykanizsa d.	...	...	...	...	...	0517	0616	...	0530	0717	...	...	0917	...	...	1117	...	...	...	1317	...	...
Keszthely **1232** d.	...	0148	...	0428	...	|	|	0648	|	|	0848	...	|	1048	...	|	...	1248	...	|	...	1448
Balatonszentgyörgy **1232** a.	...	0159	...	0439	...	0557	0655	0659	0621	0757	0859	...	0957	1059	...	1157	...	1259	...	1357	...	1459
Balatonszentgyörgy **1232** d.	...	0202	...	0440	...	0603	0659	0702	0622	0803	0902	0820	1003	1102	...	1203	...	1302	1215	1403	...	1502
Balatonfenyves **1232** d.	...	0221	...	0458	...	0617	|	0717	0640	0817	0917	0846	1017	1117	...	1217	...	1317	1246	1417	...	1517
Fonyód **1232** a.	...	0231	...	0506	...	0622	0717	0722	0649	0822	0922	0856	1022	1122	...	1222	...	1322	1256	1422	...	1522
Fonyód d.	0133	0233	0333	0507	...	0624	0718	0724	0700	0824	0924	0902	1024	1124	1102	1224	...	1324	1302	1424	1436	1524
Balatonboglár d.	0141	0241	0341	0516	...	0630	|	0730	0712	0830	0930	0913	1030	1130	1113	1230	...	1330	1313	1430	1446	1530
Balatonlelle d.	0145	0245	0345	0520	...	0634	|	0734	0716	0834	0934	0917	1034	1134	1117	1234	...	1334	1317	1434	1450	1534
Balatonszemes d.	0153	0253	0353	0527	...	0640	|	0740	0724	0840	0940	0925	1040	1140	1125	1240	...	1340	1325	1440	1456	1540
Balatonföldvár d.	0206	0306	0406	0535	...	0649	|	0749	0732	0849	0949	0935	1049	1149	1135	1249	...	1349	1335	1449	1503	1549
Zamárdi d.	0213	0313	0413	0541	...	0654	0741	0754	0746	0854	0954	0943	1054	1154	1143	1254	...	1354	1343	1454	1513	1554
Siófok a.	0225	0325	0425	0551	...	0701	0747	0801	0756	0901	1001	0956	1101	1201	1156	1301	...	1401	1356	1501	1526	1601
Siófok d.	0228	0328	0428	0552	0622	0703	0749	0803	0815	0903	1003	1015	1103	1203	1215	1303	1355	1403	1415	1503	1530	1603
Lepsény d.	0249	0349	0449	0612	0643	0717	|	|	0840	|	|	1040	|	|	1240	|	|	|	1440	|	|	|
Székesfehérvár a.	0309	0409	0511	0635	0708	0736	0827	0836	0905	0936	1036	1105	1136	1236	1305	1336	1441	1436	1505	1536	1611	1636
Székesfehérvár **1225 1230** d.	0314	0412	0527	0636	*0712*	0737	0832	0837	0906	0937	1037	1106	1137	1237	1306	1337	...	1437	1506	1537	1614	1637
Kelenföld **1225 1230** a.	0411	0501	0611	0716	*0751*	0816	0916	0916	0946	1016	1116	1146	1216	1316	1346	1416	...	1516	1547	1616	1655	1716
Budapest Déli **1225 1230** a.	0419	0514	0619	0724	*0759*	0824	0935**k**	0924	0954	1024	1124	1154	1224	1324	1354	1424	...	1524	1554	1624	...	1724

	IR 18403	Ex 16708 🅁Ⓒ r	Ex 15606 🅁 s	IC 1843 🅁	Ex 18793 Ⓐ	Ex 18703 🅁Ⓒ t	Ex 1786 🅁 u	Ex 18803 🅁 v	IC 1873 ✕🅁	IR 18503	IC 1853 🅁		Ex 18701 🅁Ⓒ w	IC 1861 ✕🅁	IR 18401	IC 201 🅁 B	IC 1871 ✕🅁	IR 18511	④–⑥		④–⑥	
Zagreb **1340** d.	...	...	...	...	...	...	...	...	...	...	...	...	...	...	...	1635	...	...	...	...	...	...
Nagykanizsa d.	...	...	...	1517	...	...	...	...	...	...	1717	...	...	...	...	1917	...	...	...	2115	...	...
Keszthely **1232** d.	...	...	...	|	...	...	...	1626	1648	...	|	...	...	1848	...	|	2048	...	...	|	...	2348
Balatonszentgyörgy **1232** a.	...	...	...	1557	...	...	...	1637	1659	...	1757	...	...	1859	...	1957	2059	...	...	2157	...	2359
Balatonszentgyörgy **1232** d.	...	...	...	1603	...	...	1620	1638	1702	1615	1803	...	...	1902	...	2003	2102	2015	...	2202	...	0002
Balatonfenyves **1232** d.	...	...	...	1617	...	...	|	1708	1717	1646	1817	...	...	1917	...	2017	2118	2046	...	2221	...	0021
Fonyód **1232** a.	...	...	...	1622	...	...	1659	1719	1722	1656	1822	...	...	1922	...	2022	2123	2056	...	2231	...	0031
Fonyód d.	1502	...	1555	1624	1636	1636	1700	...	1724	1702	1824	...	1836	1924	1902	2024	2124	2102	2155	2233	2321	0033
Balatonboglár d.	1513	...	1603	1630	1646	1646	1703	...	1730	1713	1830	...	1846	1930	1913	2030	2130	2113	2205	2241	2341	0041
Balatonlelle d.	1517	...	1607	1634	1650	1650	1710	...	1734	1717	1834	...	1850	1934	1917	2034	2134	2117	2209	2245	2345	0045
Balatonszemes d.	1525	...	1618	1640	1656	1656	1718	...	1740	1725	1840	...	1856	1940	1925	2040	2140	2125	2221	2253	2353	0053
Balatonföldvár d.	1535	...	1634	1649	1703	1703	1728	...	1749	1735	1849	...	1903	1949	1935	2049	2149	2135	2231	2301	0006	0106
Zamárdi d.	1543	...	1644	1654	1713	1713	1734	...	1754	1743	1854	...	1913	1954	1943	2054	2154	2143	2238	2313	0013	0113
Siófok a.	1556	...	1652	1701	1726	1726	1740	...	1801	1756	1901	...	1926	2001	1956	2101	2201	2154	2250	2325	0025	0125
Siófok d.	1615	1629	1653	1703	1730	1730	1742	...	1803	1815	1903	...	1930	2003	2015	2103	2203	2155	...	2328	0028	0128
Lepsény d.	1640	|	|	|	|	|	|	...	|	1840	|	...	|	|	2040	|	|	2222	...	2349	0049	0149
Székesfehérvár a.	1705	1720	1732	1736	1811	1811	1822	...	1836	1905	1936	...	2011	2036	2105	2136	2236	2242	...	0009	0109	0209
Székesfehérvár **1225 1230** d.	1706	1722	1733	1737	1814	1814	1833	...	1837	1906	1937	...	2014	2037	2106	2137	2237	2248	...	0012	*0112*	0212
Kelenföld **1225 1230** a.	1746	1811	1816	1816	1855	1855	1916	...	1916	1946	2016	...	2055	2116	2146	2216	2316	2345	...	0101	*0201*	0301
Budapest Déli **1225 1230** a.	1754	...	...	1824	...	...	...	...	1924	1954	2024	...	...	2124	2154	2224	2324	2354	...	0109	*0209*	0309

A – GRADEC-TOPART – [2] Budapest - Zagreb and v.v.
B – AGRAM-TOPART – [2] Budapest - Zagreb and v.v.
C – ADRIA – 🛏 1, 2 cl., ▬ 2 cl., [2] Budapest - Split and v.v. From Budapest on ②⑤⑦; from Split on ①③⑥ (from Nagykanizsa on ②④⑦).
d – From Szolnok (d. 0459).
e – From Pécs (d. 0810), Szentlőrinc (d. 0830) and Kaposvár (d. 0955).
f – From Szolnok (d. 0701), Cegléd (d. 0723) and Ferihegy ✈ (d. 0805).
g – From Szob (d. 0726), Nagymaros-Visegrad (d. 0743) and Vac (d. 0759).
h – From Miskolc (d. 0700), Mezőkövesd (d. 0731), Füzesabony (d. 0740), Vámosgyörk (d. 0804) and Hatvan (d. 0819).
j – From Szeged (d. 0757), Kiskunfelegyhaza (d. 0854), Kecskemét (d. 0912), Cegléd (d. 0938) and Ferihegy ✈ (d. 1009).
k – Budapest **Keleti**.
m – From Záhony (d. 0619), Kisvárda (d. 0645), Nyíregyháza (d. 0739), Debrecen (d. 0817), Hajdúszoboszló (d. 0832), Püspökladány (d. 0838), Szolnok (d. 0944), Cegléd (d. 1006) and Ferihegy ✈ (d. 1039).

NOTES CONTINUE ON NEXT PAGE →

TABLE 1220 ADDITIONAL NOTES

n – From Nyíregyháza (d. 0857), Debrecen (d. 0931), Hajdúszoboszló (d. 0946) and Szolnok (d. 1048).
p – To Szolnok (a. 1642), Hajduszoboszlo (a. 1743), Debrecen (a. 1757) and Nyíregyháza (a. 1832).
q – To Ferihegy ✈ (a. 1718), Cegléd (a. 1754), Szolnok (a. 1815), Püspökladany (a. 1910), Hajduszoboszlo (a. 1928), Debrecen (a. 1942), Nyíregyháza (a. 2022), Kisvárda (a. 2131) and Záhony (a. 2157).
r – To Ferihegy ✈ (a. 1834), Cegléd (a. 1927), Szolnok (a. 1950).
s – To Hatvan (a. 1921), Vámosgyörk (a. 1935), Füzesabony (a. 2001),Mezökövesd (a. 2012) and Miskolc (a. 2043).
t – To Vac (a. 2002), Nagymaros-Visegrad (a. 2024) and Szob (a. 2039).
u – To Ferihegy ✈ (a. 1947), Cegléd (a. 2021), Kecskemét (a. 2046), Kiskunfelegyhaza (a. 2108) and Szeged (a. 2201).
v – To Kaposvár (a. 1809), Szentlörinc (a. 1923) and Pécs (a. 1948).
w – To Szolnok (a. 2254).

FOR OTHER NOTES SEE PREVIOUS PAGE.

1225 BUDAPEST - SZÉKESFEHÉRVÁR - BALATONFÜRED - TAPOLCA

Summer service June 18 - August 28. **WARNING!** Supplements may be payable for travel on certain trains in this table.

km												IR 19740		IC 19700	IR 19712		1972	IR 19742	IC 19702	IR 19722		16907	IR 19734	IC 19704
														R			R		R			R		R
			⑤–⑦	⑤–⑦	⑤–⑦				Ⓐ								© ◧					⊡		
0	**Budapest** Déli ..... **1220 1230** d.	...	...	...	0140	...	*0240*	...	0405	...	...	0630	...	0705	0730	...	...	0830	0905	0930	...	...	1030	1105
	Kobánya-Kispest ..... d.	...	...	...	|	...	|	...	|	...	...	|	...	|	|	...	0717	|	|	|	...	0947	|	|
4	Kelenföld ..... **1220 1230** d.	...	...	...	0147	...	*0247*	...	0412	...	...	0638	...	0712	0738	...	0802	0838	0912	0938	...	1002	1038	1112
67	**Székesfehérvár** .. **1220 1230** a.	...	...	...	0244	...	*0344*	...	0509	...	...	0716	...	0750	0816	...	0842	0916	0950	1016	...	1042	1116	1150
67	**Székesfehérvár** ..... d.	...	0046	...	0246	...	0427	...	...	0526	...	0724	...	0751	0817	...	0845	0924	0951	1017	...	1045	1124	1151
105	Balatonkenese ..... d.	...	0123	...	0322	...	0511	...	...	0619	...	0810	...	|	0852	...	0932	1010	|	1052	...	1132	1210	|
117	Balalatonalmádi ..... d.	...	0136	...	0334	...	0524	...	...	0633	...	0823	...	0837	0906	...	0945	1023	1037	1106	...	1145	1223	1237
123	Alsóörs ..... d.	...	0143	...	0340	...	0531	...	...	0640	...	0835	...	|	0922	...	0952	1035	|	1122	...	1152	1235	|
132	**Balatonfüred** ..... a.	...	0154	...	0349	...	0541	...	...	0651	...	0847	...	0851	0934	...	1003	1047	1051	1134	...	1203	1247	1251
132	**Balatonfüred** ..... d.	0015	...	0205	...	0400	...	0545	...	...	0704	...	...	0902	...	0955	1016	...	1102	...	1155	...	...	1302
157	Révfülöp ..... d.	0050	...	0241	...	0437	...	0624	...	...	0742	...	...	0943	...	1036	1049	...	1143	...	1236	...	...	1343
168	Badacsonytomaj ..... d.	0108	...	0256	...	0455	...	0639	...	...	0801	...	...	1001	...	1051	1109	...	1201	...	1251	...	...	1401
170	Badacsony ..... d.	0111	...	0259	...	0458	...	0642	...	...	0805	...	...	1005	...	1054	1113	...	1205	...	1254	...	...	1405
184	**Tapolca** ..... a.	0129	...	0317	...	0516	...	0700	...	...	0824	...	...	1024	...	1112	1129	...	1224	...	1312	...	...	1424

	IR 19714		IR 19744	IC 19794	IR 19724		IR 19736	IC 19706	IR 19716		IR 19746	IC 19796		IC 19796	IR 19726		IR 19738	IC 19708	IR 19718		IR 19748		IC 19798	
				R				R				R		R				R					R	
												⑤⑥		④⑦						⑤⑥		④⑦	⑤⑥	
Budapest Déli ..... **1220 1230** d.	1130	...	1230	1305	1330	...	1430	1505	1530	...	1630	1705	...	1705	1730	...	1830	1905	1930	...	2030	...	2105	*2205*
Kobánya-Kispest ..... d.	|	...	|	|	|	...	|	|	|	...	|	|	...	|	|	...	|	|	|	...	|	...	|	|
Kelenföld ..... **1220 1230** d.	1138	...	1238	1312	1338	...	1438	1512	1538	...	1638	1712	...	1712	1738	...	1838	1912	1938	...	2038	...	2112	*2212*
Székesfehérvár ... **1220 1230** a.	1216	...	1316	1350	1416	...	1516	1550	1616	...	1716	1750	...	1750	1816	...	1916	1950	2016	...	2116	...	2150	*2250*
Székesfehérvár ..... d.	1217	...	1324	1351	1417	...	1524	1551	1617	...	1724	1751	...	1751	1817	...	1924	1951	2017	...	2124	...	2151	2259
Balatonkenese ..... d.	1252	...	1410	|	1452	...	1610	|	1652	...	1810	|	...	|	1852	...	2010	|	2052	...	2210	...	|	2342
Balalatonalmádi ..... d.	1306	...	1423	1437	1506	...	1623	1637	1706	...	1823	1837	...	1837	1906	...	2023	2037	2106	...	2229	...	2241	2355
Alsóörs ..... d.	1322	...	1435	|	1522	...	1635	|	1722	...	1835	|	...	|	1922	...	2035	|	2122	...	2236	...	|	0002
Balatonfüred ..... a.	1334	...	1447	1451	1534	...	1647	1651	1734	...	1847	1851	...	1851	1934	...	2047	2051	2134	...	2247	...	2255	0013
Balatonfüred ..... d.	...	1355	...	1502	...	1555	...	1702	...	1755	...	1902	...	1902	...	1955	...	2102	...	2155	...	2306	2306	...
Révfülöp ..... d.	...	1436	...	1543	...	1636	...	1743	...	1836	...	1943	...	1943	...	2036	...	2145	...	2236	...	2343	2343	...
Badacsonytomaj ..... d.	...	1451	...	1601	...	1651	...	1801	...	1851	...	2001	...	2001	...	2051	...	2201	...	2251	...	0001	0001	...
Badacsony ..... d.	...	1454	...	1605	...	1654	...	1805	...	1854	...	2005	...	2005	...	2054	...	2205	...	2254	...	0005	0005	...
Tapolca ..... a.	...	1512	...	1624	...	1712	...	1824	...	1912	...	2024	...	2024	...	2112	...	2224	...	2313	...	0024	0024	...
Boba ..... **1237** d.	...	...	...	...	...	...	...	1910	...	...	...	...	...	2110	...	...	...	...	...	...	...	...	...	...
Celldömölk ..... **1237** d.	...	...	...	...	...	...	...	1919	...	...	...	...	...	2119	...	...	...	...	...	...	...	...	...	...
Szombathely ..... a.	...	...	...	...	...	...	...	1956	...	...	...	...	...	2207	...	...	...	...	...	...	...	...	...	...

								IC 19709	IR 19737		IR 19727	IC 19707	IR 19747		IR 19715	IC 19797	IR 19735		IR 19725	IC 19705	IC 19705	IR 19745	16906	
								R				R				R				R	R		R	
		⑤–⑦	⑤–⑦																	Ⓐ	©		⊖	
Szombathely ..... d.	...	...	...	...	...	...	...	...	...	...	...	...	...	...	...	0802	...	...	...	...	1002	...	...	...
Celldömölk ..... **1237** d.	...	...	...	...	...	...	...	...	...	...	...	...	...	...	...	0839	...	...	...	...	1039	...	...	...
Boba ..... **1237** d.	...	...	...	...	...	...	...	...	...	...	...	...	...	...	...	0848	...	...	...	...	1048	...	...	...
Tapolca ..... d.	0049	...	0235	...	...	0435	...	0551	...	0645	...	0738	...	0847	...	0938	...	1047	...	1138	1138	...	...	1247
Badacsony ..... d.	0105	...	0251	...	...	0452	...	0606	...	0702	...	0757	...	0906	...	0957	...	1106	...	1157	1157	...	...	1306
Badacsonytomaj ..... d.	0108	...	0254	...	...	0455	...	0609	...	0705	...	0801	...	0909	...	1001	...	1109	...	1201	1201	...	...	1309
Révfülöp ..... d.	0123	...	0309	...	...	0510	...	0621	...	0720	...	0816	...	0924	...	1016	...	1124	...	1216	1216	...	...	1324
Balatonfüred ..... a.	0156	...	0342	...	...	0544	...	0652	...	0800	...	0855	...	1008	...	1055	...	1208	...	1255	1255	...	...	1408
Balatonfüred ..... d.	...	0158	...	0350	0450	▬	0550	0708	0711	...	0823	0908	0911	...	1023	1108	1111	...	1223	1308	1308	1311	1350	...
Alsóörs ..... d.	...	0209	...	0400	0500	...	0600	|	0722	...	0843	|	0922	...	1043	|	1122	...	1243	|	|	1322	1400	...
Balalatonalmádi ..... d.	...	0216	...	0407	0507	...	0607	0721	0729	...	0851	0921	0929	...	1051	1121	1129	...	1251	1321	1321	1329	1407	...
Balatonkenese ..... d.	...	0228	...	0419	0520	Ⓐ	0619	|	0744	...	0906	|	0944	...	1106	|	1144	...	1306	|	|	1344	1427	...
Székesfehérvár ..... a.	...	0306	...	0504	0603		0703	0806	0832	...	0941	1006	1032	...	1141	1206	1232	...	1341	1406	1406	1432	1510	...
Székesfehérvár ... **1220 1230** d.	...	*0314*	...	...	...	0607	0707	0807	0840	...	0942	1007	1040	...	1142	1207	1240	...	1342	1407	1407	1440	1514	...
Kelenföld ..... **1220 1230** a.	...	*0411*	...	...	...	0651	0746	0846	0920	...	1021	1046	1120	...	1221	1246	1320	...	1421	1446	1446	1520	1555	...
Kobánya-Kispest ..... a.	...	|	...	...	...	|	|	|	|	...	|	|	|	...	|	|	|	...	|	|	|	|	1611	...
Budapest Déli ..... **1220 1230** a.	...	*0419*	...	...	...	0659	0754	0854	0929	...	1029	1054	1129	...	1229	1254	1329	...	1429	1454	1454	1529	...	...

	IR 19713	IC 19795	IR 19733		IR 19723	IC 19703	IR 19743	1973		IR 19711	IC 19793	IR 19731		IR 19721		IC 19701	IR 19741			IR 19791				
		R				R		R			R					R								
								© ●							Ⓐ	©			Ⓐ	©			①–④	⑤–⑦
Tapolca ..... d.	...	1338	...	1447	...	1538	...	1629	1647	...	1738	...	1847	...	1938	1938	...	2047	...	...	2136	2229	...	...
Badacsony ..... d.	...	1357	...	1506	...	1557	...	1644	1706	...	1757	...	1906	...	1957	1957	...	2107	...	...	2155	2246	...	...
Badacsonytomaj ..... d.	...	1401	...	1509	...	1601	...	1650	1709	...	1801	...	1909	...	2001	2001	...	2110	...	...	2201	2251	...	...
Révfülöp ..... d.	...	1416	...	1524	...	1616	...	1703	1724	...	1816	...	1924	...	2016	2016	...	2125	...	...	2216	2306	...	...
Balatonfüred ..... a.	...	1455	...	1608	...	1655	...	1736	1808	...	1855	...	2008	...	2055	2055	...	2208	...	...	2252	2345	...	...
Balatonfüred ..... d.	1423	1508	1511	...	1623	1708	1711	1750	...	1823	1908	1911	...	2023	...	2108	2111	...	2210	2210	...	...	2349	2349
Alsóörs ..... d.	1443	|	1522	...	1643	|	1722	1800	...	1843	|	1922	...	2043	...	|	2122	...	2221	2221	...	...	0002	0002
Balalatonalmádi ..... d.	1451	1521	1529	...	1651	1721	1729	1807	...	1851	1921	1929	...	2051	...	2121	2129	...	2229	2229	...	...	0009	0009
Balatonkenese ..... d.	1506	|	1544	...	1706	|	1744	1827	...	1906	|	1944	...	2106	...	|	2144	...	2241	2241	...	...	0022	0022
Székesfehérvár ..... a.	1541	1606	1632	...	1741	1806	1832	1913	...	1941	2006	2032	...	2141	...	2206	2232	...	2316	2316	...	...	0101	0101
Székesfehérvár ... **1220 1230** d.	1542	1607	1640	...	1742	1807	1840	1914	...	1942	2007	2040	...	2142	...	2207	2240	...	...	2317	...	...	...	0112
Kelenföld ..... **1220 1230** a.	1621	1646	1720	...	1821	1846	1920	1955	...	2021	2046	2120	...	2221	...	2249	2320	...	...	2356	...	...	...	0201
Kobánya-Kispest ..... a.	|	|	|	...	|	|	|	2012	...	|	|	|	...	|	...	|	|	...	...	|	...	...	...	|
Budapest Déli ..... **1220 1230** a.	1629	1654	1729	...	1829	1854	1929	...	...	2029	2054	2129	...	2229	...	2259	2329	...	...	0004	...	...	...	0209

◧ – From Szolnok (d. 0645), Cegléd (d. 0707) and Ferihegy ✈ (d. 0740).
⊡ – From Záhony (d. 0450), Kisvárda (d. 0523), Nyíregyháza (d. 0610), Debrecen (d. 0657), Hajduszoboszlo (d. 0714), Püspökladany (d. 0740), Szolnok (d. 0840), Cegléd (d. 0904) and Ferihegy ✈ (d. 0939).
⊖ – To Ferihegy ✈ (a. 1618), Cegléd (a. 1654), Szolnok (a. 1715), Püspökladany (a. 1817), Hajduszoboszlo (a. 1843), Debrecen (a. 1859), Nyíregyháza (a. 1944), Kisvárda (a. 2031) and Záhony(a. 2057).
● – To Ferihegy ✈ (a. 2019), Cegléd (a. 2054) and Szolnok (a. 2116).

TP Most trains convey 🍷 THE NORTH EAST and YORKSHIRE - MANCHESTER and LIVERPOOL 188

km	km			⑥	⑥	⑥	⑥	⑥	⑥	⑥	⑥	⑥A	⑥	⑥	⑥	⑥	⑥	⑥	⑥	⑥	⑥	⑥	⑥	⑥	⑥
0		**Edinburgh** 124 180 d.		...	...	...	...	...	...	...	...	...	...	...	0523	...	...	...	...	...	...	...	...	...	...
199		**Newcastle** 124 180 d.	⑥	...	...	...	...	...	...	...	0539	...	...	0641	0715	...	0743	...	...	0843	...	...	0947	...	...
222		Durham 124 180 d.		...	...	...	...	...	...	...	0551	...	...	0659	▬	...	0800	...	...	0859	...	...	0958	...	...
257		Darlington 124 180 d.		...	...	...	...	...	...	...	0610	...	...	0717	⑥	...	0818	...	...	0917	...	...	1016	...	...
◧	0	Redcar Central 212 d.	♠	...	...	...	...	...	...	...	|	0603	...	|	0706	...	|	0807	...	|	0907	...	|	1007	...
◧	12	**Middlesbrough** 212 d.		...	...	...	...	...	...	...	|	0621y	...	|	0720	...	|	0820	...	|	0921	...	|	1021	...
279	45	Northallerton 124 180 d.		...	...	...	...	...	...	...	0620	0650	...	0728	0750	...	0829	0850	...	0928	0950	...	1027	1050	...
292	▬	Thirsk d.		...	...	...	...	...	...	...	0630	0659	...	|	0759	...	|	0859	...	|	0959	...	|	1100	...
◧	0	**Scarborough** d.		...	...	...	...	...	...	0534	|	|	0634	|	|	0734	|	|	0834	|	|	0934	|	|	1034
◧	34	Malton d.		...	...	...	...	...	...	0601	|	|	0658	|	|	0759	|	|	0859	|	|	0959	|	|	1059
327	67	**York** 124 180 a.		...	...	...	...	...	...	0624	0647	0717	0724	0748	0817	0824	0848	0917	0924	0947	1017	1024	1046	1117	1124
		York 124 d.		0135	0252	...	0503	0550	0618	...	0649	0719	...	0750	0819	...	0850	0919	...	0949	1020	...	1048	1120	...
368		**Leeds** 124 a.		0215	0318	...	0540	0612	0642	...	0713	0742	...	0812	0842	...	0913	0943	...	1013	1042	...	1111	1142	...
		Leeds 188a d.		0220	0319	...	0545	0645	0645	...	0715	0745	...	0815	0845	...	0915	0945	...	1015	1045	...	1114	1145	...
383		Dewsbury d.		|	|	...	0557	0657	0657	...	0727	0757	...	0827	0857	...	0927	0957	...	1027	1057	...	1126	1157	...
396		Huddersfield 188a d.		0259	0355	...	0613y	0707	0707	...	|	0808	...	|	0908	...	|	1007	...	|	1107	...	|	1208	...
436		**Manchester** Victoria d.		|	|	0559	|	0724y	|	...	0824	|	...	0924y	|	...	1024v	|	...	1124v	|	...	1224v	|	...
440		**Manchester** Picc 188a a.		0332	0427	|	0645	|	0741	...	|	0839	...	|	0943	...	|	1044	...	|	1139	...	|	1244	...
456		**Manchester** Airport ✈ a.		0354	0452	|	...	|	...	...	|	...	...	|	...	...	|	...	...	|	...	...	|	...	...
487		**Liverpool** Lime Street a.		...	...	0652	...	0802	...	...	0903	...	...	1004	...	...	1102	...	...	1202	...	...	1302	...	...

	⑥	⑥	⑥	⑥	⑥	⑥	⑥	⑥	⑥	⑥	⑥	⑥	⑥	⑥	⑥	⑥	⑥	⑥	⑥	⑥	⑥	⑥	⑥	⑥	⑥
Edinburgh 124 180 d.	...	...	0933	...	...	...	...	...	...	...	...	...	...	...	...	...	...	1408	...	...	...	...	...	...	...
Newcastle 124 180 d.	1046	...	1121	1142	...	...	1244	...	...	1343	...	...	1447	...	...	1543	...	1552	1642	...	...	1743	...	...	1843
Durham 124 180 d.	1058	...	▬	1200	...	...	1259	...	...	1358	...	...	1500	...	...	1559	...	▬	1658	...	...	1759	...	...	1900
Darlington 124 180 d.	1116	...	...	1218	...	...	1317	...	...	1417	...	...	1518	...	...	1617	...	...	1716	...	...	1817	...	...	1917
Redcar Central 212 d.	|	1107	...	|	1207	...	|	1307	...	|	1407	...	|	1507	...	|	1607	...	|	1707	...	|	1807	...	|
Middlesbrough 212 d.	|	1121	...	|	1221	...	|	1321	...	|	1421	...	|	1521	...	|	1621	...	|	1721	...	|	1821	...	|
Northallerton 124 180 d.	1127	1150	...	1229	1250	...	1328	1350	...	1428	1450	...	1529	1550	...	1628	1650	...	1727	1750	...	1828	1850	...	1928
Thirsk d.	|	1159	⑥	|	1259	...	|	1359	...	|	1500	...	|	1559	...	|	1659	⑥	|	1759	...	|	1859	...	|
Scarborough d.	|	|	1134	|	|	1234	|	|	1334	|	|	1434	|	|	1534	|	|	1634	|	|	1734	|	|	1834	|
Malton d.	|	|	1159	|	|	1259	|	|	1359	|	|	1458	|	|	1559	|	|	1659	|	|	1759	|	|	1858	|
York 124 180 a.	1147	1217	1224	1248	1317	1324	1349	1417	1424	1447	1518	1524	1548	1617	1624	1647	1717	1724	1747	1817	1824	1847	1917	1923	1947
York 124 d.	1149	1220	...	1249	1320	...	1351	1420	...	1449	1520	...	1550	1620	1628	1650	1720	...	1749	1818	...	1850	1919	...	1949
Leeds 124 a.	1212	1242	...	1312	1343	...	1413	1443	...	1515	1542	...	1612	1642	1657	1713	1742	...	1812	1842	...	1912	1943	...	2012
Leeds 188a d.	1215	1245	...	1315	1345	...	1415	1445	...	1516	1545	...	1615	1645	1700	1715	1745	...	1815	1845	...	1915	1945	...	2014
Dewsbury d.	1227	1257	...	1326	1357	...	1427	1457	...	1528	1557	...	1627	1657	|	1727	1757	...	1827	1857	...	1927	1957	...	2027
Huddersfield 188a d.	|	1315v	...	|	1415v	...	|	1515v	...	|	1615v	...	|	1707	1718	|	1808	...	|	1907	...	|	2007	...	|
Manchester Victoria d.	1322v	|	...	1424v	|	...	1524v	|	...	1624v	|	...	1724v	|	...	1824y	|	...	1924v	|	...	2024v	|	...	2120v
Manchester Picc 188a a.	|	1348	...	|	1448	...	|	1548	...	|	1648	...	|	1739	...	|	1841	...	|	1939	...	|	2038	...	|
Manchester Airport ✈ a.	|	...	...	|	...	...	|	...	...	|	...	...	|	...	...	|	...	...	|	...	...	|	...	...	|
Liverpool Lime Street a.	1400	...	...	1502	...	...	1602	...	...	1702	...	...	1802	...	...	1902	...	...	2002	...	...	2103	...	...	2202

	⑥	⑥	⑥	⑥	⑥A	⑥	⑥	⑥	⑥	⑥	⑥
Edinburgh 124 180 d.	...	1734	...	...	...	1903	...	...	...	...	...
Newcastle 124 180 d.	...	1920	2006	...	...	2055	...	...	2159	...	...
Durham 124 180 d.	...	▬	2018	...	...	2112	...	...	2215	...	...
Darlington 124 180 d.	...	...	2036	...	...	2131	...	...	2233	...	...
Redcar Central 212 d.	1907	...	|	...	2022	|	2107	...	|	2204	...
Middlesbrough 212 d.	1921	...	|	...	2035	|	2121	...	|	2218	...
Northallerton 124 180 d.	1950	...	|	...	2103	2142	2150	...	2244	2248	...
Thirsk d.	1959	⑥	|	...	2111	|	2159	...	|	2256	...
Scarborough d.	|	1934	|	2034	|	|	|	2128	|	|	2242
Malton d.	|	1959	|	2058	|	|	|	2153	|	|	2306
York 124 180 a.	2017	2024	2102	2124	2131	2201	2220	2222	2306	2318	2333
York 124 d.	2020	...	2105	2128	▬	...	...	2227	...	▬	...
Leeds 124 a.	2043	...	2127	2156	⑥	...	...	2258	...	⑥	...
Leeds 188a d.	2045	...	2130	2200	2205	...	...	2300	...	2307	...
Dewsbury d.	2057	...	2142	|	2216	...	...	|	...	2318	...
Huddersfield 188a d.	2108	...	2151	2218	2225	...	...	2318	...	2331	...
Manchester Victoria d.	|	...	|	|	|	...	...	|	...	|	...
Manchester Picc 188a a.	2144	...	2236	2256	2308	...	...	2356	...	0011	...
Manchester Airport ✈ a.	...	...	|	...	...	...	...	...	...	...	...
Liverpool Lime Street a.	...	...	2333	...	...	...	...	...	...	...	...

		⑥	⑥	⑥	⑥	⑥	⑥	⑥	⑥
Liverpool Lime Street d.		...	...	...	...	...	...	...	...
Manchester Airport ✈ d.		...	0038	...	...	0419	...	...	...
Manchester Picc. 188a d.	⑥	0004	0103	0247	...	0433	...	...	...
Manchester Victoria d.		|	|	|	...	|	0500	...	...
Huddersfield 188a d.		0034	0133	0349r	...	0531y	|	...	...
Dewsbury d.		|	|	|	...	|	|	...	...
Leeds 188a a.	♠	0111	0208	0430	...	0550	0614	...	...
Leeds 124 d.		0113	0219	0432	...	0552	0616	...	...
York 124 a.		0139	0258	0457	...	0615	0638	...	...
York 124 180 d.		...	...	...	0505	0617	0640	0702	0710
Malton d.		...	...	...	|	0641	|	0727	|
Scarborough a.		...	...	...	|	0707	|	0753	|
Thirsk d.		...	...	...	0528	...	0657	▬	|
Northallerton 124 180 d.		...	...	...	0537	...	0706	...	0729
Middlesbrough 212 a.		...	...	...	0634	...	0736	...	|
Redcar Central 212 a.		...	...	...	0647	...	0749	...	|
Darlington 124 180 d.		...	...	...	0557‡	...	...	...	0742
Durham 124 180 d.		...	...	...	...	...	...	⑥	0758
Newcastle 124 180 a.		...	...	...	...	...	...	0708	0814
Edinburgh 124 180 a.		...	...	...	...	...	...	0855	...

	⑥	⑥	⑥	⑥	⑥	⑥	⑥	⑥	⑥	⑥	⑥	⑥	⑥	⑥	⑥	⑥	⑥	⑥	⑥	⑥	⑥	⑥	⑥	⑥	⑥
Liverpool Lime Street d.	...	...	0554	...	...	0653	...	...	0753	...	0854	...	...	0953	...	...	1054	...	...	1154	...	...	1254	...	...
Manchester Airport ✈ d.	0539	...	|	...	...	|	...	...	|	...	|	...	...	|	...	...	|	...	...	|	...	...	|	...	...
Manchester Picc 188a d.	0617	...	|	0714	...	|	0814	...	|	0914	|	...	1014	|	...	1114	|	...	1214	|	...	1314	|	...	1410
Manchester Victoria d.	|	...	0631	|	...	0731	|	...	0831	|	0931	...	|	1031	...	|	1131	...	|	1231	...	|	1331	...	|
Huddersfield 188a d.	0646	...	|	0746	0800	|	0846	...	|	0946	|	...	1045	|	...	1146	|	...	1246	|	...	1346	|	...	1446
Dewsbury d.	0657	...	0727	0757	|	0827	0857	...	0927	0957	1027	...	1057	1127	...	1157	1227	...	1257	1327	...	1357	1427	...	1457
Leeds 188a a.	0710	...	0740	0810	0822	0840	0910	...	0940	1010	1040	...	1110	1140	...	1210	1240	...	1310	1340	...	1410	1440	...	1510
Leeds 124 d.	0714	...	0743	0814	0827	0842	0914	...	0942	1014	1042	...	1114	1142	...	1214	1242	...	1314	1342	...	1414	1442	...	1514
York 124 a.	0736	...	0805	0836	0854	0904	0936	...	1004	1036	1105	...	1136	1205	...	1236	1305	...	1336	1404	...	1436	1504	...	1536
York 124 180 d.	0739	0803	0807	0839	0900	0906	0939	1000	1007	1039	1107	1117	1139	1207	1217	1239	1307	1317	1339	1406	1417	1439	1506	1517	1539
Malton d.	|	0828	|	|	0925	|	|	1025	|	|	|	1142	|	|	1242	|	|	1342	|	|	1442	|	|	1542	|
Scarborough a.	|	0852	|	|	0949	|	|	1052	|	|	|	1208	|	|	1308	|	|	1408	|	|	1508	|	|	1608	|
Thirsk d.	0759	...	|	0856	...	0926	0956	...	|	1057	|	...	1156	|	...	1256	|	...	1357	|	▬	1457	|	...	1557
Northallerton 124 180 d.	0808	...	0826	0906	...	0939	1007	...	1026	1107	1127	...	1207	1226	...	1305	1326	...	1405	1426	...	1505	1526	...	1605
Middlesbrough 212 a.	0838	...	|	0936	...	|	1037	...	|	1137	|	...	1237	|	...	1335	|	...	1435	|	...	1535	|	...	1635
Redcar Central 212 a.	0849	...	|	0947	...	|	1049	...	|	1149	|	...	1249	|	...	1347	|	...	1447	|	...	1546	|	...	1647
Darlington 124 180 d.	▬	...	0839	...	...	0939	...	...	1039	▬	1140	...	...	1239	...	...	1339	...	...	1439	...	...	1539	...	...
Durham 124 180 d.	⑥	...	0855	...	...	0955	...	...	1055	⑥	1156	...	...	1255	...	...	1356	...	...	1455	⑥	...	1555	...	...
Newcastle 124 180 a.	0911	...	0911	...	...	1011	...	...	1113	1206	1212	...	...	1313	...	...	1410	...	...	1513	1614	...	1613	...	...
Edinburgh 124 180 a.	1058	...	...	...	...	...	...	...	...	1356	...	...	...	...	...	...	...	...	...	...	1800	...	...	...	...

	⑥	⑥	⑥	⑥	⑥		⑥	⑥	⑥	⑥A	⑥	⑥	⑥	⑥	⑥	⑥	⑥	⑥	⑥	⑥	⑥	⑥	⑥	⑥	⑥
Liverpool Lime Street d.	1354	...	...	...	1454	...	...	1554	...	...	1654	...	...	1753	...	...	1854	...	...	...	1954	...	2054	...	...
Manchester Airport ✈ d.	|	...	...	...	|	...	...	|	...	...	|	...	...	|	...	...	|	...	...	...	|	...	|	...	...
Manchester Picc 188a d.	|	...	1510	...	|	...	1610	|	...	1715	|	...	1814	|	...	1914	|	...	2014	...	|	2121	|	2210	2245
Manchester Victoria d.	1431	...	|	...	1531	...	|	1631	...	|	1731	...	|	1831	...	|	1931	...	|	...	2031	|	2131	|	|
Huddersfield 188a d.	|	...	1546	1556	|	...	1646y	|	...	1746	|	...	1846	|	...	1946	|	...	2046	...	|	2150	|	2246y	2317
Dewsbury d.	1527	...	1557	|	1627	...	1657	1726	...	1757	1827	...	1857	1927	...	1956	2027	...	2057	...	2127	2220	2227	2257	2327
Leeds 188a a.	1540	...	1610	1621	1640	...	1710	1739	...	1810	1840	...	1910	1940	...	2009	2040	...	2110	...	2140	2213	2241	2310	2341
Leeds 124 d.	1542	...	1614	1627	1642	...	1713	1742	...	1812	1842	...	1913	1942	...	2014	2050	...	2115	...	2142	2214	2243	2311	2343
York 124 a.	1605	...	1636	1655	1705	...	1736	1805	...	1836	1906	...	1936	2005	...	2036	2129	...	2137	...	2210	2236	2305	2338	0010
York 124 180 d.	1607	1617	1639	1700	1706	...	1739	1806	1817	1839	1908	1917	1941	2007	2017	2039	2130	2117	2140	2200	...	2241	2307	...	...
Malton d.	|	1642	|	1725	|	...	|	|	1842	|	|	1942	|	|	2042	|	|	2142	|	2225	...	2305	|	...	...
Scarborough a.	|	1708	|	1751	|	...	|	|	1908	|	|	2008	|	|	2108	|	|	2208	|	2251	...	2331	|	...	...
Thirsk d.	|	...	1656	...	|	...	1756	1823	...	1856	|	▬	1958	|	...	2057	|	...	2157	...	...	...	|	...	...
Northallerton 124 180 d.	1626	...	1707	...	1726	...	1805	1831	...	1905	1927	...	2008	2026	...	2106	2202	...	2208	...	...	...	2326	...	...
Middlesbrough 212 a.	|	...	1737	...	|	...	1835	|	...	1935	|	...	2038	|	...	2136	|	...	2239	...	...	...	|	...	...
Redcar Central 212 a.	|	...	1749	...	|	...	1846	|	...	1946	|	...	2050	|	...	2147	|	...	...	...	...	...	|	...	...
Darlington 124 180 d.	1639	...	...	...	1739	...	...	1844	...	...	1940	...	...	2039	...	...	2216	...	...	...	...	...	2339	...	...
Durham 124 180 d.	1655	...	...	...	1755	...	...	1901	...	...	1957	⑥	...	2055	...	...	2233	...	...	...	...	...	2355	...	...
Newcastle 124 180 a.	1713	...	...	...	1810	...	...	1919	...	...	2011	2059	...	2113	...	...	2245	...	...	...	...	...	0012	...	...
Edinburgh 124 180 a.	...	...	...	...	...	...	...	...	...	...	...	2239	...	...	...	...	...	...	...	...	...	...	...	...	...

A – From / to Saltburn (Table **212**).
j – Arrives 2139.
r – Arrives 0315.
v – Arrives 9 – 11 minutes earlier.
y – Arrives 6 – 8 minutes earlier.
‡ – Arrival time. Departs 0607. Calls before Middlesbrough.
♠ – Service valid until July 30.

BEYOND EUROPE
AFRICA and the MIDDLE EAST

Introduction

The Beyond Europe section covers principal rail services in eight different areas around the world as follows:

- Africa and the Middle East
- India
- South East Asia, Australia and New Zealand
- China
- Japan
- North America
- South America
- South Korea.

All of the latest Beyond Europe sections will appear together, four times a year, in our printed seasonal editions: Winter (December), Spring (March), Summer (June) and Autumn (September).

Contents

General rail information can be found on the first page of each section

INDEX OF PLACES

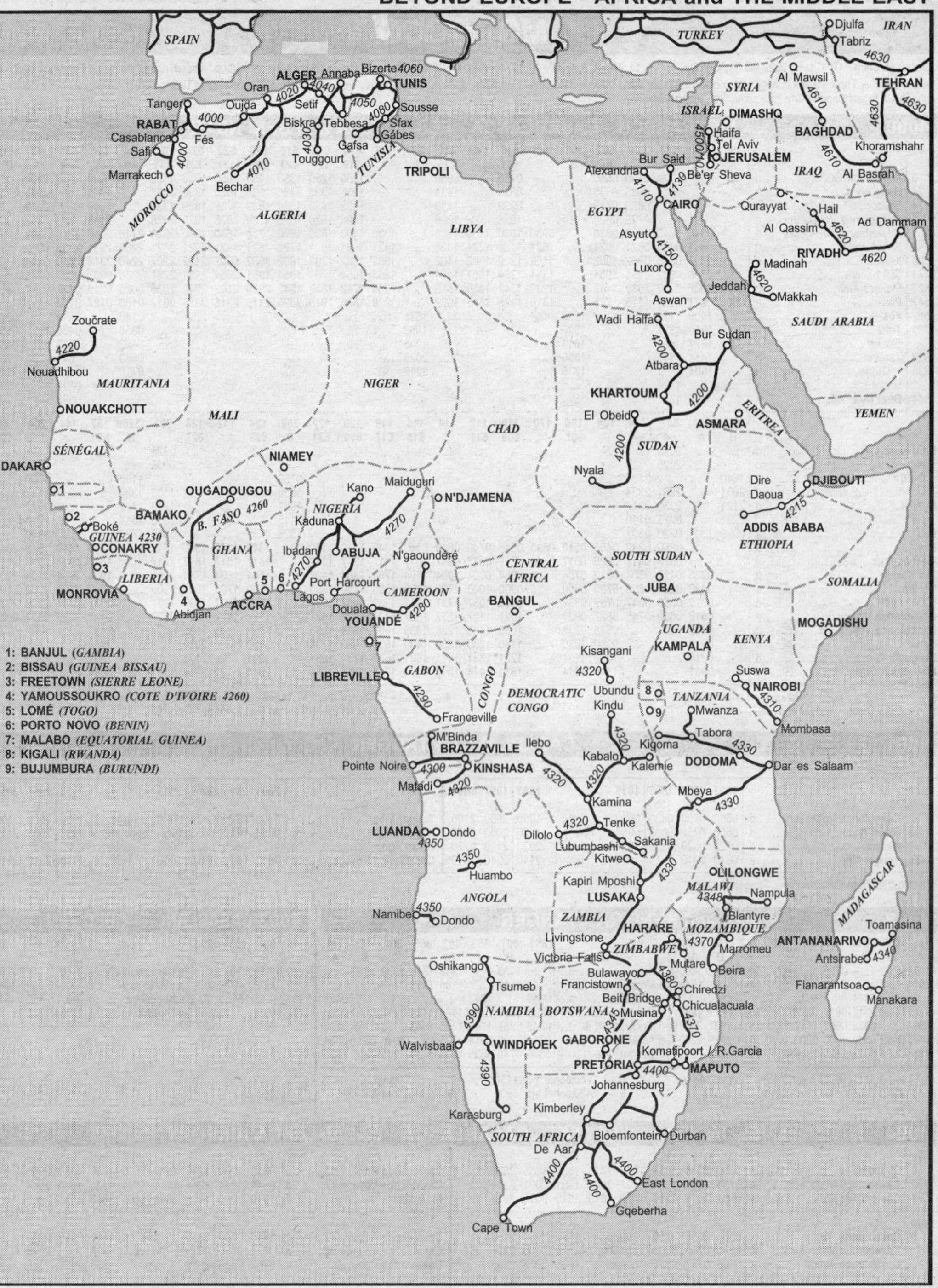

LUXURY and CRUISE TRAINS

THE BLUE TRAIN:
A luxury cruise train running between Pretoria and Cape Town with excursions along the way. The service departs on selected ①③⑤ throughout the year. Also occasional trips from Pretoria to Hoedspruit. ✆ +27 12 334 8459. Fax +27 12 334 8464. www.bluetrain.co.za. Also agents in the US: Truemarketing ✆ +1 973 832 4384, UK: Ethos Marketing ✆ +44 1403243619, Australia: Africareps ✆ +61 41 022 5580.

ROVOS RAIL:
Luxury cruise train running regularly between: Pretoria and Cape Town, Pretoria and Victoria Falls and Pretoria and Durban. Also occasional trips with excursions Pretoria and Walvis Bay (9 days) and Cape Town and Dar es Salaam (15 days). Most tours feature haulage by the company's preserved steam locomotives. ✆ +27 12 315 8242. Fax +27 12 323 0843. www.rovos.com.

SHONGOLOLO EXPRESS:
Various 12/15 day train journeys throughout Southern Africa with excursions along the way. Tours between Pretoria and Cape Town, Pretoria and Victoria Falls and Pretoria and Swakopmund. ✆ +27 12 315 8242. www.shongololo.com. Note: Now operated by Rovos Rail.

MOROCCO

Capital: **Rabat** (GMT + 1). 2022 Public Holidays: Jan. 1, 11, May 1, 3, 4, July 10, 11, 30, Aug. 14, 20, 21, Oct. 8, 9, Nov. 6, 18. Operator: Office National des Chemins de Fer (www.oncf.ma). Unless otherwise noted trains convey first and second class seated accommodation. Overnight trains may also convey sleeping cars and/or couchettes. Timings are the most recent available and are subject to alteration at any time especially during Ramadan.

4000 MARRAKECH - CASABLANCA - FÈS - OUJDA and BENI NSAR — ONCF

km		171	101	103	600	602	301	141	606	143	610	303	145	614	616	618	620	622	624	626	MA	628	139	MT	TO
		⚒			⚒	107	B		111		115	B		119	121	123	125	127	129	131	🛏	⑦	🛏	A	B
0	**Marrakech** Guéliz d.	...	...	...	0450	0550	...	...	0750	...	0950	...	...	1150	1250	1350	1450	1550	1650	1750	...	1900	...	2100	...
74	Benguerir ◧ d.	...	...	...	0535	0635	...	...	0815	...	1035	...	...	1235	1335	1435	1535	1635	1735	1835	...	1945	...	2145	...
174	Settat d.	...	...	...	0639	0739	...	...	0939	...	1139	...	...	1339	1439	1539	1639	1739	1839	1939	...	2049	...	2249	...
257	**Casablanca** Voyageurs a.	...	...	...	0728	0828	...	...	1028	...	1228	...	...	1428	1528	1628	1728	1828	1928	2028	...	2138	...	2342	...
257	**Casablanca** Voyageurs d.	...	0540	0640	0730	0830	...	0930	1030	1130	1230	...	1330	1430	1530	1630	1730	1830	1930	2030	2115	2140	2215	2348	...
346	Rabat Agdal d.	...	0631	0731	0821	0921	...	1021	1121	1221	1321	...	1421	1521	1621	1721	1821	1921	2021	2121	2208	2231	2308	0052	...
386	Kenitra d.	...	0707	0810	0902	1002	...	1102	1202	1302	1402	...	1502	1602	1702	1802	1902	2002	2102	2202	2246	2312	2346	0144	...
471	Sidi Kacem d.	...	0756	0902	0951	1054	...	1151	1254	1351	1454	...	1551	1654	1751	1854	1951	2054	2151	2251	2338	0003	0039	0246	...
526	Meknes Amir d.	0725	0835	0952	1039	1142	...	1239	1342	1439	1542	...	1639	1742	1839	1942	2029	2142	2242	2336	0025	0049	0127	...	...
582	**Fès** a.	0801	0921	1035	1115	1225	...	1315	1425	1515	1622	...	1719	1825	1915	2025	2115	2218	2315	0012	0100	0127	0157	...	...
582	**Fès** d.	...	1000	1105	...	...	1250	...	...	...	...	1635	...	...	...	...	...	...	...	...	0140	...	0218	...	0350
701	Taza d.	...	1219	1321	...	...	1520	...	...	...	...	1853	...	...	...	...	...	...	...	...	0358	...	0436	...	0558
	Guercif d.	...	1327	1425	...	...	1614	...	...	...	...	1945	...	...	...	...	...	...	...	...	0452	...	0533	...	0652
818	Taourirt d.	...	1434	1545	...	...	1656	...	...	...	...	2028	...	...	...	...	...	...	...	...	0533	...	0641	...	0750
935	**Oujda** a.	...	1604	|	...	...	1835	...	...	...	...	2212	...	...	...	...	...	...	...	...	0710	...	|	...	0940
	Nador a.	...	...	1720	...	...	...	...	...	...	...	...	...	...	...	...	...	...	...	...	...	...	0811	...	...
944	**Beni Nsar** Ville a.	...	...	1731	...	...	...	...	...	...	...	...	...	...	...	...	...	...	...	...	...	...	0823	...	...

	OT	TM	507	AM	104	106	170	110	112	114	116	118	120	122	202	124	142	128	503	15206	132	144	204	146
	B	A	🛏	🛏	⚒	607	⚒	609	611	⑦	615	617	619	621	B	623		627		B	631			⑦
Beni Nsar Ville d.	...	...	2015	...		...	...	...	...	...	...	...	...	...	...	...	...	...	0925	...	...	...	...	...
Nador d.	...	...	2026	...	...	...	...	...	...	...	...	...	...	...	...	...	...	...	0936	...	...	...	...	...
Oujda d.	1840	...	|	2135	...	...	...	...	...	...	...	...	...	...	0750	...	...	...	|	1135	...	...	1330	...
Taourirt d.	2031	...	2231	2334	...	...	...	...	...	...	...	...	...	...	0936	...	...	...	1133	1326	...	...	1517	...
Guercif d.	2121	...	2330	0017	...	...	...	...	...	...	...	...	...	...	1021	...	...	...	1219	1422	...	...	1617	...
Taza d.	2231	...	0023	0110	...	...	...	...	...	...	...	...	...	...	1115	...	...	...	1318	1517	...	...	1714	...
Fès a.	0029	...	0220	0307	...	...	...	...	...	...	...	...	...	...	1325	...	...	...	1540	1720	...	...	1910	...
Fès d.	...	...	0250	0342	0455	0540	0610	0640	0740	0840	0940	1040	1140	1240	...	1340	1440	1540	1640	...	1740	1840	1940	2040
Meknes Amir d.	...	...	0326	0417	0525	0617	0646	0717	0817	0917	1017	1117	1217	1317	...	1417	1517	1617	1717	...	1817	1917	2017	2117
Sidi Kacem d.	...	0226	0417	0504	0612	0704	...	0804	0904	1004	1104	1204	1304	1404	...	1504	1604	1704	1804	...	1904	2004	2104	2204
Kenitra d.	...	0428	0514	0608	0700	0800	...	0900	1000	1100	1200	1300	1400	1500	...	1600	1700	1800	1900	...	2000	2100	2200	2300
Rabat Agdal d.	...	0515	0555	0647	0737	0837	...	0937	1037	1137	1237	1337	1437	1537	...	1637	1737	1837	1937	...	2037	2137	2239	2337
Casablanca Voyageurs a.	...	0610	0650	0745	0827	0927	...	1027	1127	1227	1327	1427	1527	1627	...	1727	1827	1927	2027	...	2127	2227	2327	0027
Casablanca Voyageurs d.	...	0615	...	...	0835	0935	...	1035	1135	1235	1335	1435	1535	1635	...	1735	...	1935	...	...	2135	...	...	...
Settat d.	...	0712	...	...	0930	1030	...	1130	1230	1330	1430	1530	1630	1730	...	1830	...	2030	...	...	2230	...	...	...
Benguerir ◧ d.	...	0816	...	...	1030	1131	...	1231	1331	1431	1531	1631	1731	1831	...	1931	...	2131	...	...	2331	...	...	...
Marrakech Guéliz a.	...	0901	...	...	1114	1214	...	1314	1414	1514	1614	1714	1814	1914	...	2014	...	2214	...	...	0014	...	...	...

A – 🛏 1, 2 cl., [12] Marrakech - Tanger and v.v.
B – [12] Oujda - Tanger and v.v.

◧ – Safi - Benguerir and v.v. *142 km*. Journey 2 hours 5 minutes. From Safi at 0815, 1610; from Benguerir at 1155, 1955.

4001 CASABLANCA - TANGER — ONCF

Al Boraq high-speed trains

km		1001	1005	1009	1013		1053	1057	1061
		Ⓐ		⚒				†	
0	**Casablanca** Voyageurs d.	0600	0700	0800	0900	and	1900	2000	2100
	Rabat Agdal d.	0650	0750	0850	0950	hourly	1950	2050	2150
137	Kenitra d.	0720	0820	0920	1020	until	2020	2120	2220
323	**Tanger** Ville a.	0810	0910	1010	1110	⊡	2110	2210	2310

	2001	2005	2009	2013		2053	2057	2061
	Ⓐ		⚒				†	
Tanger Ville d.	0600	0700	0800	0900	and	1900	2000	2100
Kenitra d.	0653	0753	0853	0953	hourly	1953	2053	2153
Rabat Agdal d.	0725	0825	0925	1025	until	2025	2125	2225
Casablanca Voyageurs a.	0810	0910	1010	1110	⊡	2110	2210	2310

⊡ – No train from Casablanca or Tanger at 1200.

4002 FÈS and KENITRA - TANGER — ONCF

km	OT	MT	180	151	182	202	155	15206			351	301	353	303	305	307	TO	TM
	B	A				B	D	B	↓	↑	E	B		B			B	A
0	0100	...	0700	...	1115	1400	...	1800	↓	d.**Fès** d.	...	1153	...	1548	1848	2339	0310	...
56	|	...	0742	...	1157	1443	...	1843	↓	d.Meknes Amir d.	...	1110	...	1505	1813	2306	|	...
	|	0144	|	1012	|	|	1830	|	↓	d. Kenitra a.	0940	|	1242	|	|	|	|	0428
111	0234	0317	0827	1032f	1242	1532	1853f	1931	↓	d.Sidi Kacem d.	0922f	1029	1223f	1424	1724	2217	0149	0226
156	0313	0358	0906	1117	1321	1615	1937	2011	↓	d.Mechraa BK ● d.	0845	0952	1146	1345	1643	2128	0108	0149
264	0452	0544	1046	1300	1510	1814	2129	2209	↓	d.Asilah a.	0714	0820	1014	1205	1505	1946	2331	0004
312	0531	0622	1125	1349	1545	1850	2210	2245	↓	d.**Tanger** Ville a.	0635	0740	0935	1135	1430	1905	2255	2325

A – 🛏 1, 2 cl., [12] Marrakech - Tanger and v.v.
B – [12] Oujda - Tanger and v.v.
D – Additional trip: 1430.
E – Additional trip: 1630.
f – Sidi Yahia.
● – Mechraa Bel Ksir.

4003 CASABLANCA - OUED ZEM — ONCF

km	901	903	905		900	902	904
0	0810	1310	1910	d.**Casablanca** V.. a.	1018	1417	2055
58	0858	1407	2007	d.Sidi El Aidi d.	0925	1307	1946
139	1043	1542	2153	a.Khouribga d.	0735	1130	1815
177	...	...	2239	a.**Oued Zem** d.	0645	...	...

4004 EL JADIDA and SETTAT - CASABLANCA - CASABLANCA AIRPORT — ONCF

km		⚒								
0	**El Jadida** d.	0630	0835	1035	1235	1435	1635	1835	2035	...
123	**Casablanca** Voyageurs a.	0751	1001	1201	1401	1601	1801	2001	2201	...
	Casablanca Port a.	0804	1015	1215	1415	1615	1815	2015	2215	...

Casablanca Port d.	0830	1030	1230	1430	1630	1730	1830	2030	...
Casablanca Voyageurs d.	0844	1044	1244	1444	1644	1744	1844	2044	...
El Jadida a.	1010	1205	1405	1608	1805	1905	2010	2205	...

km									
0	**Casablanca** Port d.	0550	0650	0750	and	1750	1950	2150	...
	Casablanca Voyageurs d.	0605	0705	0805	hourly	1805	2005	2205	...
	Casablanca Airport a.	0635	0737	0835	until	1835	2035	2235	...

Casablanca Airport d.	0650	0750	0850	and	1850	2050	2250	...
Casablanca Voyageurs a.	0721	0825	0925	hourly	1925	2125	2325	...
Casablanca Port a.	0732	0836	0936	until	1936	2136	2336	...

km		⚒	⚒							
0	**Settat** d.	0615	0815	1015	1215	1415	1610	1815	2015	...
83	**Casablanca** Voyageurs a.	0713	0915	1113	1313	1507	1710	1915	2115	...
	Casablanca Port a.	0726	0930	1128	1328	1522	1725	1930	2130	...

	⚒	⚒							
Casablanca Port d.	0640	0840	1040	1240	1440	1640	1740	2040	...
Casablanca Voyageurs d.	0653	0853	1053	1253	1453	1653	1753	2053	...
Settat a.	0758	0958	1158	1358	1555	1758	1858	2158	..

4005 CASABLANCA - RABAT - KENITRA — *ONCF*

km		⚒		⚒		⚒																		
0	**Casablanca** Port d.	0620	0710	0735	0810	0835	0910	1010	1110	1210	1310	1410	1510	1535	1610	1635	1710	1735	1810	1835	1910	2010	2035	2125
	Ain Seeba d.	0631	0721	0746	0821	0845	0921	1021	1121	1221	1321	1421	1521	1546	1621	1646	1721	1746	1821	1846	1921	2021	2046	2136
93	**Rabat** Agdal d.	0722	0812	0833	0912	0931	1012	1112	1212	1312	1412	1512	1612	1631	1712	1731	1812	1831	1912	1933	2012	2112	2131	2218
100	Salé Ville d.	0734	0824	0845	0924	0943	1024	1124	1224	1324	1424	1524	1624	1643	1724	1743	1824	1843	1924	1945	2024	2124	2143	2230
140	**Kenitra** a.	0758	0848	0906	0948	1004	1048	1148	1248	1348	1448	1548	1648	1704	1748	1804	1848	1904	1948	2006	2048	2148	2204	2251

	⚒		⚒			⚒																	
Kenitra d.	0557	0630	0707	0730	0807	0830	0907	0930	1030	1130	1230	1330	1430	1530	1607	1630	1707	1730	1807	1830	1907	1930	2030
Salé Ville d.	0619	0652	0729	0752	0829	0852	0929	0952	1052	1152	1251	1351	1451	1552	1629	1652	1729	1752	1829	1952	1929	1952	2052
Rabat Agdal d.	0634	0707	0744	0807	0844	0907	0944	1007	1107	1207	1307	1407	1507	1607	1644	1707	1744	1807	1844	1907	1944	2007	2107
Ain Seeba d.	0725	0759	0836	0859	0932	0959	1036	1059	1159	1259	1359	1459	1559	1659	1736	1759	1836	1859	1932	1959	2036	2059	2158
Casablanca Port a.	0737	0811	0849	0910	0943	1010	1049	1110	1210	1310	1410	1510	1610	1710	1749	1810	1849	1910	1943	2010	2049	2110	2209

ALGERIA

Capital : **Alger** (GMT +1). 2022 Public Holidays : Jan. 1, 12, May 1, 3, 4, July 5, 10, 11, 30, Aug. 8, Oct. 8, Nov. 1. Operator : Société Nationale des Transports Ferroviaires (www.sntf.dz). Unless otherwise noted trains convey first and second class seated accommodation. Overnight trains may also convey sleeping cars and/or couchettes. Timings are the most recent available and are subject to alteration at any time especially during Ramadan.

SNTF — ORAN - SAIDA, GHAZAOUET and BÉCHAR — 4010

km		1112	B290	1114	1153	B264	1116	B284
		2		2	2	2	2	🛏
0	**Oran** d.	0730	1020	1250	...	1520	1600	2030
76	Sidi bel Abbès d.	0835	1119	1355	...	1625	1711	2133
210	**Saida** a.	|	|	|	...	1759	|	|
163	Tlemcen d.	0956	|	1512	1700	...	1832	|
219	Maghnia d.	1105	|	1622	1823	...	...	|
284	**Ghazaouet** a.	...	|	...	...	...	...	|
350	Naâma d.	...	1408	...	...	...	...	0116
676	**Béchar** a.	...	1711	...	...	...	...	0550

	1102	B261	B252	B208	1104	B292	1106	B242
	2	2	2	2	2		2	🛏
Béchar d.	...	...	...	...	...	0615	...	2000
Naâma d.	...	...	...	...	...	0915	...	0009
Ghazaouet d.	...	...	...	...	...	|	...	|
Maghnia d.	...	...	0600	...	...	|	1405	|
Tlemcen d.	0550	...	0724	0800	0955	|	1510	|
Saida d.	|	0700	...	|	|	|	|	|
Sidi bel Abbès d.	0706	0834	...	0922	1120	1206	1629	0430
Oran a.	0809	0942	...	1024	1222	1310	1726	0600

SNTF — ORAN - ALGER — 4020

km		1084	1002	MA	OA	1004	B16	1094	B296
		2	2			2		2	
0	**Oran** d.	...	0610	0800	1000	1230	1545	1615	1645
77	Mohammadia ◧ d.	...	0701	|	1042	1322	1627	1700	1744
126	Relizane d.	...	0734	|	1115	1356	1700	1731	1818
213	Chlef d.	0505	0829	1000	1200	1453	1740	1835	...
303	Khémis Milliana d.	0611	0939	|	|	1610	|	...	...
354	El Affroun ⊡ d.	0657	1023	|	|	1703	|	...	...
372	Blida ⊡ d.	0710	1036	|	1336	1716	1914	...	...
421	**Alger** Agha ⊡ a.	0756	1115	1200	1407	1754	1946	...	...

	1091	1093	1001	AM	B17	1003	B15	1085
	⑦–④	2	2			2		2
Alger Agha ⊡ d.	...	...	0610	0800	1035	1230	1545	1723
Blida ⊡ d.	...	...	0646	|	1110	1306	1614	1802
El Affroun ⊡ d.	...	...	0659	|	|	1319	|	1814
Khémis Milliana d.	...	...	0741	|	|	1408	|	1859
Chlef d.	...	0630	0854	1000	1300	1512	1753	2003
Relizane d.	0530	0732	0956	|	1357	1625	1839	...
Mohammadia ◧ d.	0605	0807	1029	|	1427	1658	1913	...
Oran a.	0717	0900	1125	1200	1510	1754	1946	...

◧ – Mohammadia - Mostaganem and v.v. : SERVICE SUSPENDED.

⊡ – Additional local trains available.

SNTF — TOUGGOURT — 4030

km		B7	B25
			①③⑥
		A	B
0	**Constantine** d.	...	...
49	Aïn M'Lila d.	...	...
	M'Sila d.	1642	2314
	Bârika d.	1807	0036
	Aïn Touta d.	1849	0111
117	Batna d.	1909	|
238	Biskra d.	...	0305
402	Djamâa d.	...	0432
455	**Touggourt** a.	...	0500

	B28	B5
	②④⑦	
	B	A
Touggourt d.	1730	...
Djamâa d.	1758	...
Biskra d.	1925	...
Batna d.	|	2250
Aïn Touta d.	2103	2313
Barika d.	2150	2350
M'Sila d.	2312	0115
Aïn M'Lila d.	...	..
Constantine a.	...	...

FOR FOOTNOTES SEE TABLE 4040.

SNTF — ANNABA - TEBESSA — 4035

km		251	B327
		2	2
0	**Annaba** d.	...	1645
55	Bouchegouf d.	...	1800
90	Mechrouha d.	...	1902
107	Souk Ahras ● d.	0600	1930
156	**Sidi El Hémissi** ● a.	0709	|
131	Dreá d.	...	2008
163	Oued Kéberit d.	...	2047
231	**Tebessa** a.	...	2157

	B388	252
		2
Tebessa d.	0430	...
Oued Kéberit d.	0543	...
Dreá d.	0620	...
Sidi El Hémissi ● d.	|	0719
Souk Ahras ● d.	0700	0828
Mechrouha d.	0723	...
Bouchegouf d.	0813	...
Annaba a.	0923	...

● – Also from Souk Ahras at 1335; from Sidi El Hémissi at 1602.

SNTF — ALGER - CONSTANTINE - TEBESSA and ANNABA — 4040

km		11	B7	13	19	B123	B25	B31	AT
							①③⑥	②④⑦	
		2	A		[R]	[R]	B	C	D
0	**Alger** ⊡ d.	0700	1230	1430	1530	1600	1810	1840	2045
54	Thénia ⊡ d.	0744	|	|	|	1636	1900	1927	2132
123	Bouira d.	0858	1412	1612	1717	1814	2015	2042	2243
171	Beni Mansour ⊖ d.	0939	1451	1652	1840	1855	2102	2130	2328
259	**Béjaïa** ⊖ a.	1117	|	1830	|	|	|	|	|
237	Bordj Bou Arreridj d.	...	1553	...	1859	1954	2210	2237	0035
289	**M'Sila** a.	...	1642	...	|	2041	2256	|	|
308	Setif d.	...	...	...	1948	...	...	2325	0124
464	**Constantine** d.	...	...	...	...	...	...	|	0355
521	El Harrouch d.	...	...	...	...	...	...	|	0454
	Aïn M'Lila d.	...	...	...	...	...	...	0207	|
	Aïn Beïda d.	...	...	...	...	...	...	0354	|
645	**Tebessa** a.	...	...	...	...	...	...	0607	|
620	**Jijel** a.	...	...	...	...	...	...	...	|
532	Ramdane Djamel d.	...	...	...	...	...	...	...	0502
550	**Skikda** a.	...	...	...	...	...	...	...	|
557	Azzaba d.	...	...	...	...	...	...	...	0528
631	**Annaba** a.	...	...	...	...	...	...	...	0643

	B28	B32	BA	B5	B122	18	14	16
	②④⑦	①③⑥						
	B	C	D	A	[R]	[R]		2
Annaba d.	...	...	1920	...	...	...	...	...
Azzaba d.	...	...	2016	...	...	...	...	...
Skikda d.	...	...	|	...	...	...	...	...
Ramdane Djamal d.	...	...	2041	...	...	...	...	...
Jijel d.	...	...	|	...	...	...	...	...
Tebessa d.	...	1730	|	...	...	...	...	...
Aïn Beïda d.	...	1933	|	...	...	...	...	...
Aïn M'Lila d.	...	2123	|	...	...	...	...	...
El Harrouch d.	...	|	2057	...	...	...	...	...
Constantine d.	...	|	2149	...	...	...	...	...
Setif d.	...	2339	0107	...	...	0540	...	...
M'Sila d.	2312	|	|	0115	0500	|	...	...
Bordj Bou Arreridj d.	0017	0028	0140	0204	0547	0626	...	...
Béjaïa ⊖ d.	|	|	|	|	|	|	0630	1500
Beni Mansour ⊖ d.	0142	0142	0219	0305	0647	0728	0803	1634
Bouira d.	0234	0234	0308	0344	0732	0807	0844	1718
Thénia ⊡ d.	0400	0400	0426	|	0851	|	0928	1835
Alger ⊡ a.	0500	0500	0526	0530	0935	1001	1028	1925

A – (12) Alger - M'Sila - Batna and v.v.
B – 🛏 (12) Alger - M'Sila - Touggourt and v.v.
C – 🛏 (12) Alger - Tebbesa and v.v.
D – 🛏 (12) Alger - Annaba and v.v.
⊖ – Also from Beni Mansour at 0630, 1135; from Béjaïa at 0855, 1700.
⊡ – Additional local trains available.

TUNISIA

Capital : **Tunis** (GMT +1). 2022 Public Holidays : Jan. 1, 14, Mar. 20, Apr. 9, May 1, 3–5, July 10, 11, 25, 30, Oct. 8, 15. Operator : Société Nationale des Chemins de Fer Tunisiens (www.sncft.com). Unless otherwise noted trains convey first and second class seated accommodation. Overnight trains may also convey sleeping cars and/or couchettes. Supplements may be payable in advance for the use of certain trains. Timings are the most recent available and are subject to alteration at any time especially during Ramadan. SNCFT offers the **Carte Bleue** pass. The pass allows unlimited travel on all scheduled services (except the Lézard Rouge tourist train) for a period of 7, 15, or 21 days, and is available for each of the three classes of accommodation. Prices (in Dinars) : Grand Confort Class 7 days 45.00, 15 days 90.00, 21 days 135.00. First Class 7 days 42.00, 15 days 84.00, 21 days, 126.00. Second Class 7 days 30.00, 15 days 60.00, 21 days 90.00.

SNCFT — GHARDIMAOU - TUNIS — 4050

km		2	8	12	14	20
		⚒				
0	**Annaba** d.	...	...	...	...	...
167	**Ghardimaou** d.	...	0430	1035	1245	1510
201	Jendouba d.	...	0458	1104	1313	1559
259	Béja d.	...	0600	1202	1411	1641
344	Tebourba d.	0540	0729	1324	1539	1809
353	Jedeïa d.	0552	0741	1344	1550	1828
378	**Tunis** Ville a.	0631	0821	1426	1631	1907

	7	9	13	17
Tunis Ville d.	0635	0940	1300	1715
Jedeïa d.	0715	1023	1343	1757
Tebourba d.	0730	1035	1355	1810
Béja d.	0857	1204	1527	1939
Jendouba d.	0958	1314	1631	2038
Ghardimaou a.	1025	1341	1659	2105
Annaba a.	...	...	...	...

SNCFT — BIZERTE - TUNIS — 4060

km		1/4	1/10
		⚒	†
0	**Bizerte** d.	0500	0600
34	Mateur d.	0603	0703
73	Jedeïda d.	0714	0811
98	**Tunis** Ville a.	0754	0851

	1/19	1/25
	Ⓒ	Ⓐ
Tunis Ville d.	1635	1745
Jedeïda d.	1717	1826
Mateur d.	1820	1929
Bizerte a.	1918	2027

4070 TUNIS - EL KEF and KALAÂ KASBAH SNCFT

km		6/51	6/57	6/65	6-8/89	6/79 ⚒
0	**Tunis** Ville d.	0635	0910	1415	1620	1725
63	Pont du Fahs d.	0812	1030	1549	1748	1902
120	Gaafour d.	0919	1123	1658	1852	2007
166	Le Sers d.	1017	1216	1756	1947	...
202	**El Kef** a.	|	|	|	2024	...
191	Dahmani d.	1046	1242	1824	...	...
214	Jerissa d.	|	...	...	...	...
224	**Tajerouine** a.	|	...	...	...	...
235	**Kalaâ Kasbah** a.	1148	...	...	...	...

	6/50 ⚒	8-6/54	6/60	6/68	6/76
Kalaâ Kasbah d.	...	...	...	...	1300
Tajerouine d.	...	...	...	...	|
Jerissa d.	...	...	...	...	|
Dahmani d.	...	...	0635	1320	1406
El Kef d.	...	0510	|	|	|
Le Sers d.	...	0546	0702	1346	1434
Gaafour d.	0500	0642	0803	1446	1537
Pont du Fahs d.	0603	0741	0902	1548	1638
Tunis Ville a.	0736	0907	1034	1715	1809

4080 TUNIS - SOUSSE - SFAX - TOZEUR SNCFT

km		805	5/53	5/63	5/61	5/73	815	5-79	5/87	819	5/89	821
		2	2	2	2		2	2		2	2	2
0	**Tunis** Ville ◇ d.	...	0545	0835	1105	1305	...	1450	1545	...	1720	...
23	Borj Cédria ◇ d.	0635	|	|	1140	|	1420	|	|	1715	1758	1930
59	Bir Bou Rekba d.	0708	0651	0941	1213	1408	1453	1557	1650	1748	1829	2003
64	Hammamet d.	0713	|	|	1218	|	1458	|	|	1753	|	2008
76	**Nabeul** a.	0734	|	|	1239	|	1519	|	|	1814	|	2029
142	Kalaâ Séghira d.	...	0755	|	...	1509	...	1705	|	...	1933	...
149	**Sousse** d.	...	0820	1105	...	|	...	1715	1815	...	|	...
174	Monastir d.	...	|	|	...	|	...	...	|	...	2020	...
217	**Mahdia** a.	...	|	|	...	|	...	...	|	...	2118	...
215	El Jem d.	...	0931	1217	...	1609	...	...	1925	...	...	...
278	**Sfax** d.	...	1030	1310	...	1710	...	...	2020	...	...	...
340	Ghraïba d.	...	1136	1418	...	1820	...	...	|	...	...	...
422	**Gabès** a.	...	1301	|	...	1941	...	...	2250	...	...	...
	Tataouine a.	...	...	|	...	...	...	...	...	...	...	...
482	Gafsa d.	...	...	1634	...	...	...	...	...	...	...	...
521	Metlaoui d.	...	...	1711	...	...	...	...	...	...	...	...
574	**Tozeur** a.	...	...	...	...	...	...	...	...	...	...	...

	802	12/52	5/54	5/56	5/64	5/58	5/60	812	5/72	816	5/76	5/82	820
	2	2 Ⓐ	2 Ⓒ	2	2	2		2	2	2		2	2
Tozeur d.	...	...	...	...	...	...	...	...	...	...	...	...	...
Metlaoui d.	...	...	...	...	...	...	...	...	0721	...	...	...	...
Gafsa d.	...	...	...	...	...	...	...	...	0800	...	...	...	...
Tataouine d.	...	...	...	...	...	...	...	...	|	...	...	...	...
Gàbes d.	...	...	...	...	...	...	0530	...	|	...	1105	1345	...
Ghraïba d.	...	...	...	...	...	...	|	...	1011	...	1225	1506	...
Sfax d.	...	...	...	...	...	0515	0755	...	1125	...	1335	1610	...
El Jem d.	...	...	...	...	...	0608	|	...	1216	...	1426	...	...
Mahdia d.	...	...	...	...	0540	|	|	...	|	...	|	...	...
Monastir d.	...	...	...	...	0645	|	|	...	|	...	|	...	...
Sousse d.	...	0520	0600	...	|	0730	|	...	1335	...	1550	...	...
Kalaâ Seghira d.	...	0531	0612	...	0724	0742	0954	...	|	...	|	...	...
Nabeul d.	0520	|	|	0740	|	|	|	1250	|	1610	|	...	1825
Hammamet d.	0540	|	|	0801	|	|	|	1309	|	1629	|	...	1844
Bir Bou Rekba d.	0548	0641	0722	0809	0829	0848	1045	1316	1450	1636	1701	...	1851
Borj Cédria ◇ d.	0624	0713	0757	0846	0901	|	|	1350	|	1710	|	...	1925
Tunis Ville ◇ a.	...	0747	0831	0922	0935	0955	1153	...	1557	...	1808	...	...

◇ – Regular local services operate Tunis – Borj Cédria – Erriadh and v.v.

4090 SOUSSE - MONASTIR AIRPORT - MAHDIA SNCFT

km		501	503	505	507	509	511	513	517	519	521	523	525	527	529	531	533	535	537	539	541	543	545	547	549
0	**Sousse** Bab El Jedid d.	...	0515	0545	0630	0715	0750	0835	0910	0950	1030	1110	1200	1230	1340	1355	1425	1520	1605	1650	1715	1745	1840	1925	2015
3	**Sousse** Sud d.	0505	0521	0551	0636	0724	0756	0841	0916	0956	1036	1116	1206	1236	1316	1401	1431	1526	1611	1656	1721	1751	1846	1931	2021
15	Monastir Airport ✈ d.	0519	0534	0605	0650	0735	0810	0855	0930	1010	1050	1130	1219	1250	1330	1415	1445	1540	1625	1710	1735	1805	1900	1945	2035
24	Monastir d.	0535	0544	0620	0705	0750	0830	0905	0945	1025	1105	1150	1235	1305	1345	1430	1500	1555	1645	1730	1752	1820	1915	2000	2050
47	Moknine d.	0607	...	0656	0741	0826	0911	...	1018	1056	1140	1225	1312	1336	1419	1507	1530	1631	1719	1804	1822	1854	1946	2032	2123
73	**Mahdia** a.	0650	...	0733	0820	0904	0950	...	1059	...	1215	1259	1342	...	1456	1543	...	1710	1755	1838	...	1929	2019	2105	2156

	506	508	510	514	516	518	520	522	524	528	530	532	534	536	538	540	542	544	546	548	550	552	554	556
Mahdia d.	...	0510	0555	0620	0700	0750	...	0835	0920	1010	...	1145	1230	1320	...	1425	...	1550	1640	1725	...	1810	1900	1950
Moknine d.	...	0845	0630	0700	0740	0825	...	0909	0954	1044	1135	1223	1310	1357	1416	1505	1545	1626	1716	1802	1830	1848	1937	2029
Monastir d.	0550	0625	0710	0740	0820	0905	0920	0950	1030	1125	1215	1300	1350	1435	1455	1540	1620	1705	1755	1840	1910	1925	2015	2105
Monastir Airport ✈ d.	0600	0635	0720	0750	0830	0915	0930	1000	1040	1135	1225	1310	1400	1445	1505	1550	1630	1715	1805	1849	1920	1934	2024	2114
Sousse Sud d.	0615	0650	0735	0805	0845	0930	0945	1015	1055	1150	1240	1325	1415	1500	1520	1605	1645	1730	1820	1905	1934	1950	2040	2130
Sousse Bab El Jedid a.	0620	0655	0740	08100	0850	0935	0950	1020	1100	1155	1245	1330	1420	1505	1525	1610	1650	1735	1825	1910	1939	1955	2045	2135

EGYPT

Capital: **Cairo** (GMT +2). 2022 Public Holidays: Jan. 7, 25, 27, Apr. 24, 25, 28, May 1, 3–5, June 30, July 9–13, 30, Oct. 6, 8. Operator: Egyptian National Railways (www.enr.gov.eg).
Unless otherwise noted trains convey first and second class seated accommodation. Overnight trains may also convey sleeping cars and/or couchettes. Timings are the most recent available and are subject to alteration at any time especially during Ramadan.

4100 MERSA MATRUH - CAIRO and ALEXANDRIA ENR

km						774
		2	2	2	A	AB
0	**Mersa Matruh** d.	0700	0810	1445	1715	2200
84	El Alamein d.	0936	1155	1751	1954	|
311	**Alexandria** a.	|	1455	2045	|	|
509	**Cairo** Main a.	1535	...	...	0125	0500

					773
	2	A	2	2	AB
Cairo Main d.	...	0545	0650	...	2300
Alexandria d.	0640	|	|	1340	|
El Alamein d.	0936	1100	1240	1649	|
Mersa Matruh a.	1230	1330	1525	2020	0620

A – June - Sept. only.
B – 🛏 (1, 2 class). From Mersa on ②④⑦, from Cairo on ①③⑥. Operated by Watania (www.wataniasleepingtrains.com).

ENR CAIRO - ALEXANDRIA 4110

km		119	903	905	901	1109	909	911	89	913	917	919	2001	915	923	925	921	927	931	935				
0	**Cairo** Main d.	0500	0600	0800	0810	0820	0900	1000	1115	1230	1400	1425	1500	1510	1600	1710	1800	1900	2015	2230	...	...	...	...
45	Benha d.	|	0640	|	0849	|	|	1040	|	1308	|	1505	|	1600	1640	1740	|	|	2056	|	...	...	...	...
86	Tanta d.	0755	0734	|	0929	|	|	1120	1225	1345	|	1609	|	1638	1729	1837	1907	|	2145	2337	...	...	...	...
147	Damanhūr d.	0857	0837	|	1018	1041	|	1213	|	1433	|	1712	|	1729	1830	1932	|	|	2242	|	...	...	...	...
208	**Alexandria** a.	0950	0930	1030	1115	1135	1150	1305	1355	1525	1630	1805	1730	1820	1925	2025	2035	2130	2335	0105	...	...	...	...

		1108	902	906		904	900	912	914	916		918	922	88	928	926		2008	930	934				
	Alexandria d.	0330	0600	0700	...	0800	0815	1130	1300	1400	...	1500	1530	1700	1800	1900	...	2000	2010	2215	...	...	...	...
	Damanhūr d.	0437	0659	|	...	|	0914	1229	1358	|	...	|	1633	|	|	|	...	|	2109	|	...	...	...	...
	Tanta d.	0536	0758	|	...	|	1004	1319	1455	|	...	|	1727	1833	1942	|	...	2133	2204	2343	...	...	...	...
	Benha d.	0626	0840	|	...	|	1035	1400	1540	|	...	|	1803	|	|	|	...	|	2235	|	...	...	...	...
	Cairo Main a.	0710	0925	0935	...	1030	1120	1445	1620	1630	...	1745	1850	1935	2050	2130	...	2235	2320	0050	...	...	...	...

ENR 2nd class DUMYAT 4120

km		941	965	967	568	969				
240	**Alexandria** d.	...	...	...	1815	...	...	...	...	...
205	**Cairo** Main d.	0515	0730	0915	|	1935	...	...	...	...
0	**Dumyat** a.	1015	1130	1350	2255	2359	...	...	...	...

	964	566	956	994	968				
Dumyat d.	0600	0715	1315	1615	1915	...	...	...	...
Cairo Main a.	1010	|	1815	2025	2340	...	...	...	...
Alexandria a.	...	1220	...	...	...	...	...	...	...

ENR 2nd class BÛR SA'ÎD 4130

km		945	588	185	951	955	572	961		
334	**Alexandria** d.	...	0430	...	...	...	1610	...	...	...
236	**Cairo** Main d.	0610	|	0840	1200	1440	|	1950	...	...
0	**Bûr Sa'îd** a.	1020	1110	1240	1640	1905	2225	0005	...	...

	952	570	186	956	960	590	962		
Bûr Sa'îd d.	0530	0725	0830	1300	1730	1815	1930	...	...
Cairo Main a.	0955	|	1250	1725	2145	|	2350	...	...
Alexandria a.	...	1330	...	...	...	0050	...	...	...

ENR 2nd class EL SUWEIS 4140

km		305	307	309	311					
0	**Cairo** Ain Shams d.	0630	1000	1430	1800	...	...	...	...	...
127	**El Suweis** a.	0850	1320	1750	2120	...	...	...	...	...

	304	306	308	310					
El Suweis d.	0615	1030	1400	1830	...	...	...	...	...
Cairo Ain Shams a.	0935	1355	1720	2200	...	...	...	...	...

ENR ASWÂN 4150

km		1902	980	982	986	86 ◧	988	88	996	2008
0	**Cairo** Main d.	0020	0800	1200	1300	1945	1900	2000	2200	2300
13	El Giza d.	0045	0830	1225	1325	2005	1925	2025	2230	2330
124	Béni Suef d.	|	0948	1354	1447	|	2044	2156	2348	|
247	El Menya d.	|	1115	1530	1630	|	2220	2345	0130	|
375	Asyût d.	0515	1310	1725	1840	|	0015	0150	0330	0355
467	Sohâg d.	0705	1500	1915	2015	|	0140	0320	0500	0520
609	Qena d.	0920	1800	2200	2300	|	0350	0615	0715	0735
671	Luxor d.	1020	1900	2310	2359	0555	0450	0730	0815	0840
879	**Aswân** a.	1320	2240	0225	...	0925	0750	1055	1130	1145

	981	983	2007	1903	87 ◧	997	89	989	987
Aswân d.	0530	0730	1500	1700	1715	2045	2105	2300	...
Luxor d.	0910	1055	1830	2010	2025	0005	0035	0215	0450
Qena d.	1015	1200	1925	2105	|	0100	0140	0305	0600
Sohâg d.	1255	1440	2150	2320	|	0310	0415	0510	0840
Asyût d.	1435	1630	2320	0105	|	0435	0545	0640	1015
El Menya d.	1625	1825	0105	|	|	0630	0740	0825	1220
Béni Suef d.	1754	1949	|	|	|	0800	0912	0953	1353
El Giza d.	|	2110	|	0520	0600	0855	|	1020	1515
Cairo Main a.	1935	2130	0355	0550	0625	0950	1100	1135	1535

◧ – 🛏 (1, 2 class). Operated by Watania (www.wataniasleepingtrains.com).

OTHER AFRICAN STATES

For details of capital cities and public holiday dates please see individual tables. All trains shown convey seated accommodation. Long-distance overnight trains may also convey sleeping cars and/or couchettes. The standard of accommodation varies widely with no two countries being the same so no attempt is made in the following Tables to distinguish between classes of accommodation. Timings are the latest available and may change at any time so you are advised to confirm them locally before travelling. In Muslim countries a different timetable may be operated during Ramadan.

Sudan Railways Corporation SUDAN 4200

km		222 ②	101 ④A	212 E	551 B	202 ②C	D01 ④D			
926	**Wadi Halfa** d.	1800b	...	...	...	1740b	...	...	...	...
576	Abu Hamed d.	0600c	...	...	...	⊖c	...	...	...	...
551	Dagash d.	...	...	...	...	⊖c	...	...	...	...
351	Berber d.	...	...	...	...	⊖c	...	...	...	...
810	**Bûr Sûdan** d.	...	1530d	...	...	|	...	...	...	...
	Sinkat d.	...	2000d	...	...	|	...	...	...	...
720	Gebeit d.	...	2240d	...	...	|	...	...	...	...
620	Haiya Junction d.	...	0445e	...	...	|	...	...	...	...
310	**Atbara** a.	...	1255e	...	...	⊖c	...	...	...	...
310	**Atbara** d.	...	...	2130	...	⊖c	...	...	...	...
295	Ed Dâmer d.	...	...	2300	...	⊖c	...	...	...	...
170	Shendî d.	...	...	0300	...	⊖d	...	...	...	...
0	**Khartoum** Bahri a.	...	...	0730	...	⊖d	...	...	...	...
0	**Khartoum** Bahri d.	...	...	...	...	...	2000d	...	...	...
270	Sennâr Junction d.	...	...	...	...	...	0600e	...	...	...
383	Kôsti d.	...	...	...	...	...	1030e	...	...	...
470	Tendelti d.	...	...	...	...	...	1500e	...	...	...
605	Er Rahad d.	...	...	...	⊖	...	2100e	...	...	...
629	**El Obeid** a.	...	...	...	|	...	2230e	...	...	...
983	Babanusa d.	...	...	...	⊖	...	...	...	...	...
	El Daien d.	...	...	...	⊖	...	...	...	...	...
1318	**Nyâlâ** a.	...	...	...	⊖	...	...	...	...	...

	552 B	221 ④	201 ⑥C	502 ①D	102 ①A	211 E			
Nyâlâ d.	⊖	...	...	...	...	...	...	...	...
El Daien d.	⊖	...	...	...	...	...	...	...	...
Babanusa d.	⊖	...	...	...	...	...	...	...	...
El Obeid d.	|	...	...	0700a	...	...	...	...	...
Er Rahad d.	⊖	...	...	0830a	...	...	...	...	...
Tendelti d.	...	...	...	1445a	...	...	...	...	...
Kôsti d.	...	...	...	1930a	...	...	...	...	...
Sennâr Junction d.	...	...	...	0000b	...	...	...	...	...
Khartoum Bahri a.	...	...	...	1030b	...	...	...	...	...
Khartoum Bahri d.	...	...	0900f	...	...	2130	...	...	...
Shendî d.	...	...	1545f	...	...	0200	...	...	...
Ed Dâmer d.	...	...	2200f	...	...	0600	...	...	...
Atbara a.	...	...	2300f	...	...	0730	...	...	...
Atbara d.	...	...	0100g	...	2000a	...	...	...	...
Haiya Junction d.	...	...	|	...	0415b	...	...	...	...
Gebeit d.	...	...	|	...	1015b	...	...	...	...
Sinkat d.	...	...	|	...	1120b	...	...	...	...
Bûr Sûdan a.	...	...	|	...	1545b	...	...	...	...
Berber d.	...	...	0345g	...	...	...	...	...	...
Dagash d.	...	...	1530g	...	...	...	...	...	...
Abu Hamed d.	...	1730d	⊖g	...	...	...	...	...	...
Wadi Halfa a.	...	0545e	⊖a	...	...	...	...	...	...

Capital: **Khartoum** (GMT +2). 2022 Public Holidays: Jan. 1, 7, Apr. 24, May 3–6, July 9–13, 30, Oct. 8, Dec. 25.

A – From Bûr Sûdan 1st and 3rd ④ of each month, from Atbara on following ①.
B – From El Rahad/ Nyâlâ every two weeks day and time not fixed. Conveys 🛏.
C – From Khartoum on 1st and 3rd ⑥ of each month, from Wadi Halfa on following ②. Conveys ▬.
D – From Khartoum on 2nd ④ of each month, from El Obeid on following ①. Conveys 🛏 ▬ 🍷. Not operated by SRC.
E – Conveys 🛏.

a – ①. b – ②. c – ③. d – ④. e – ⑤. f – ⑥. g – ⑦. ⊖ – No timings available.

4215 ETHIOPIA — CF Djibouti Ethiopien

km		101 ◧			102 ◧	
0	**Addis Abeba** Lebu d.	2000	...	**Djibouti** Nagad d.	...	...
	Adama d.	2235	...	Ali Sabieh ▣ d.	...	...
	Mieso d.	0335	...	Dewelé ▣ a.	...	...
	Diré Daoua a.	0700	...	**Diré Daoua** a.	...	...
	Diré Daoua d.	...	...	**Diré Daoua** d.	2100	...
	Dewelé ▣ a.	...	...	Mieso d.	0030	...
	Ali Sabieh ▣ d.	...	...	Adama d.	0530	...
	Djibouti Nagad a.	...	...	**Addis Abeba** Lebu d.	0755	...

Capital: **Addis Abeba** (GMT +3).

2022 Public Holidays: Jan. 7, 19, Mar. 2, Apr. 22, 24, May 1, 3, 5, 28, July 10, Sept. 11, 27, Oct. 8.

◧ – May not run daily.

4220 MAURITANIA — SNIM

km						
0	**Nouadhibou** d.	1450	...	**Zouèrate** d.	1215	...
652	**Zouèrate** a.	0540	...	**Nouadhibou** a.	0618	...

Capital: **Nouakchott** (GMT +0).

2022 Public Holidays: Jan. 1, May 1, 3, 25, July 10, 30, Oct. 8, Nov. 28.

Operator: Société Nationale Industrielle et Minière.

4230 GUINEA — CFG, CFB

km		①–⑤	①–⑤	①–⑤		①–⑤	①–⑤	①–⑤
0	**Conakry** Portovoya d.	...	0847	1725	**Halte Km 36** d.	0645	...	1916
	Simbaya d.	0600	0940	1829	Simbaya d.	0730	1630	1950
36	**Halte Km 36** a.	0640	...	1906	**Conakry** P'voya a.	0837	1710	...

km			①④⑦				①④⑦	
0	**Kamsar** d.	...	0930	...	**Sangaredi** d.	...	1430	...
55	Boké d.	...	1135	...	Boké d.	...	1615	...
136	**Sangaredi** a.	...	1355	...	**Kamsar** a.	...	1855	...

Capital: **Conakry** (GMT +0).

2022 Public Holidays: Jan. 1, Apr. 3, 18, 28, May 1, 13, 25, July 10, Aug. 15, Oct. 2, 8, Dec. 25.

Operators: Chemins de Fer Guinea (CFG), Chemins de Fer de Boké (CFB).

4260 BURKINA FASO and CÔTE D'IVOIRE — Sitarail

km		②④⑥	⑥ 🍷		①③⑤	④ 🍷
0	**Ouagadougou** d.	...	...	**Abidjan** Treichville d.	0900	0700
93	Koudougou d.	...	...	**Abidjan** Plateau d.	0920	|
349	Bobo Dioulasso d.	...	1400	Anyama d.	1015	0755
446	Banfora d.	...	1715	Agboville d.	1240	0918
495	Niangoloko ▣ d.	...	2030	Dimbokro d.	1615	1140
539	Ouangolodougou d.	...	2200	Bouaké d.	...	1515
576	Ferkessédougou d.	...	2310	Katiola d.	...	1730
658	Tafiré d.	...	0125	Tafiré d.	...	2020
769	Katiola d.	...	0430	Ferkessédougou d.	...	2235
820	Bouaké d.	...	0645	Ouangolodougou d.	...	2345
958	Dimbokro d.	0900	0955	Niangoloko ▣ d.	...	0215
1064	Agboville d.	1255	1219	Banfora d.	...	0345
1115	Anyama d.	1515	1344	Bobo Dioulasso d.	...	0700
1141	**Abidjan** Plateau a.	1610	|	Koudougou d.	...	...
1143	**Abidjan** Treichville a.	1625	1430	**Ouagadougou** a.	...	...

Capitals: **Ouagadougou** (Burkina Faso, GMT +0), **Yamoussoukro** (Côte d'Ivoire, GMT +0).

2022 Public Holidays: Burkina Faso: Jan. 1, 3, Mar. 8, Apr. 18, May 1–3, July 10, Aug. 5, 15 Oct. 8, Nov. 1, Dec. 11, 12, 25, 26. Côte d'Ivoire: Jan. 1, Apr. 18, 29, May 1–3, 26, July 10, Aug 7, 8, 15, Oct. 8, Nov. 1, 15, Dec. 25.

4270 NIGERIA — Nigerian Railways Corporation

km		LI1 B	LI3 Ⓑ	LI3 ⑥		IL2 B	IL4 Ⓑ	IL4 ⑥
0	**Lagos** Terminal d.	0800	1600	1800	**Kano** d.	...	...	...
14	Agege d.	0826	1626	1830	Zaria d.	...	...	...
91	Abeokuta d.	0945	1745	2007	**Kaduna** Junction d.	...	...	...
193	Ibadan d.	1048	1848	2114	Zungeru d.	...	...	...
280	Ede d.	...	...	...	Jebba d.	...	...	...
295	Oshogbo d.	...	...	...	Ilorin d.	...	...	...
391	Ilorin d.	...	...	...	Oshogbo d.	...	...	...
488	Jebba d.	...	...	...	Ede d.	...	...	...
685	Zungeru d.	...	...	...	Ibadan d.	0800	1600	1800
902	**Kaduna** Junction a.	...	...	...	Abeokuta d.	0910	1710	1913
986	Zaria d.	...	...	...	Agege d.	1027	1827	2049
1126	**Kano** a.	...	...	...	**Lagos** Terminal a.	1048	1848	2114

km						
0	**Port Harcourt** New d.	...	...	**Maiduguri** d.	...	...
63	Aba d.	...	...	Buni d.	...	...
113	Umuahia Ibeku d.	...	...	Gombe d.	...	...
243	Enugu d.	...	...	Bauchi d.	...	...
375	Oturkpo d.	...	...	**Kaduna** Junction d.	...	...
463	Makurdi d.	...	...	Kafanchan d.	...	...
565	Lafia d.	...	...	Lafia d.	...	...
737	Kafanchan d.	...	...	Makurdi d.	...	...
916	**Kaduna** Junction d.	...	...	Oturkpo d.	...	...
1333	Bauchi d.	...	...	Enugu d.	...	...
1499	Gombe d.	...	...	Umuahia Ibeku d.	...	...
1658	Buni d.	...	...	Aba d.	...	...
1801	**Maiduguri** a.	...	...	**P Harcourt** New a.	...	...

km		02	KA2	KA4	04	KA6	KA8
0	**Kaduna** Rigasa d.	...	0640	1035	...	1400	1800
	Rijana d.	...	0716	1128	...	1441	1843
	Jere d.	...	0757	1217	...	1525	1929
	Kubwa d.	...	0831	1304	...	1603	2007
	Abuja Idu a.	...	0843	1320	...	1616	2020
	Abuja Idu d.	...	...	...	...	...	...
	Itakpe d.	0830	...	...	1445	...	...
	Ajaokuta d.	0923	...	...	1538	...	...
	Itogbo d.	0951	...	...	1606	...	...
	Agenebode d.	1013	...	...	1628	...	...
	Uromi d.	1040	...	...	1655	...	...
	Ekehen d.	1107	...	...	1722	...	...
	Igbanke d.	1136	...	...	1751	...	...
	Agbor d.	1157	...	...	1812	...	...
	Abraka d.	1229	...	...	1844	...	...
	Okpara d.	1252	...	...	1907	...	...
	Warri Ujevwu a.	1319	...	...	1934	...	...

	AK1	AK3	01	AK5	AK7	03
Warri Ujevwu d.	...	...	0800	...	...	1415
Okpara d.	...	...	0829	...	...	1444
Abraka d.	...	...	0855	...	...	1510
Agbor d.	...	...	0926	...	...	1541
Igbanke d.	...	...	0949	...	...	1604
Ekehen d.	...	...	1014	...	...	1629
Uromi d.	...	...	1043	...	...	1658
Agenebode d.	...	...	1190	...	...	1724
Itogbo d.	...	...	1130	...	...	1745
Ajaokuta d.	...	...	1201	...	...	1815
Itakpe a.	...	...	1249	...	...	1904
Abuja Idu a.	...	...	...	...	...	...
Abuja Idu d.	0700	0950	...	1420	1800	...
Kubwa d.	0717	1007	...	1441	1815	...
Jere d.	0755	1043	...	1528	1846	...
Rijana d.	0835	1126	...	1617	1921	...
Kaduna Rigasa a.	0915	1201	...	1700	1958	...

Capital: **Abuja** (GMT +1). 2022 Public Holidays: Jan. 1, Apr. 15, 18, May 1, 3, 4, June 12, July 10, 11, Oct. 1, 8, Dec. 25, 26.

B – 30 minutes later on ⑥.

4280 CAMEROON — Camrail

km		185	181	191 🛏		184	192 🛏	186
0	**Douala** Bessengué d.	0630	0730	...	**N'gaoundéré** d.	...	1915	...
72	Edéa d.	0750	0952	...	Mbitom d.	...	0155	...
152	Eséka d.	0908	1415	...	Belabo d.	...	0515	...
220	Ngoumou d.	1021	1705	...	Nanga Eboko d.	...	0741	...
263	**Yaoundé** d.	1115	1825	1950	**Yaoundé** d.	0815	1107	1700
477	Nanga Eboko d.	...	...	2318	Ngoumou d.	1000	...	1749
582	Belabo d.	...	...	0152	Eséka d.	1235	...	1900
686	Mbitom d.	...	...	0554	Edéa d.	1615	...	2022
910	**N'gaoundéré** a.	...	...	1232	**Douala** B'sengué a.	1940	...	2145

km						
0	Douala Bonaberi d.	...	...	Kumba d.	...	...
	Mbanga d.	...	...	Mbanga d.	...	...
	Kumba a.	...	...	Douala Bonaberi a.	...	...

Capital: **Youandé** (GMT +1).

2022 Public Holidays: Jan. 1, Feb. 11, Apr. 15, May 1, 2, 3, 20, 26, July 10, 11, Aug. 15, Dec. 25, 26.

4290 GABON — SETRAG

km		①③⑤	②④⑦			①③⑤	②④⑦	
0	**Owendo** ◧ d.	1730	1730	...	**Franceville** d.	1700	1700	...
183	Ndjole d.	2300	2305	...	Moanda d.	1730	1730	...
340	Booué d.	0205	0203	...	Lastourville d.	1933	1930	...
485	Lastourville d.	0416	0418	...	Booué d.	2148	2146	...
625	Moanda d.	0620	0628	...	Ndjole d.	0051	0100	...
670	**Franceville** a.	0700	0710	...	**Owendo** ◧ a.	0631	0635	...

Capital: **Libreville** (GMT +1).

2022 Public Holidays: Jan. 1, Apr. 17, 18, May 1, 3, June 6, July 10, Aug. 15, 16, 17, Nov. 1, Dec. 25.

◧ – Libreville.

4300 CONGO — CF Congo Océan

km		②⑤	③⑦	⑥		②⑥ B	①④ M	⑥
0	**Brazzaville** d.	...	...	...	**Pointe Noire** d.	0800	0900	1000
137	Mindouli d.	...	...	...	M'Vouti d.	1330	|	1500
190	Loutété d.	...	0800	...	Dolisie d.	1500	1730	...
261	Nkayi d.	...	1015	...	Nkayi d.	1830	...	...
342	Dolisie d.	0330	1345	...	Loutété d.	2045	...	...
382	M'Vouti d.	|	1515	1800	Mindouli d.	...	...	...
509	**Pointe Noire** a.	1130	2045	2230	**Brazzaville** a.	...	...	...

Capital: **Brazzaville** (GMT +1).

2022 Public Holidays: Jan. 1, Apr. 18, May 1, 26, June 6, 10, Aug. 15, Nov. 1, 28, Dec. 25.

KENYA 4310

Kenya Railways

km		①–⑤	⑤–⑦	①–⑤							
0	**Mombasa** d.	...	...	0800	...	1500	2200	...	...	...	...
	Voi d.	...	...	0955	...	|	|	...	...	...	...
	Mtito Andei d.	...	...	1121	...	|	|	...	...	...	...
	Emali d.	...	...	1239	...	|	|	...	...	...	...
485	**Nairobi** Terminus ⊡ a.	...	...	1410	...	2008	0335	...	...	...	...
485	**Nairobi** Terminus ⊡ d.	0510	0850	...	1840	...	...	...	...	...	...
	Ngong d.	0552	0949	...	1922	...	...	...	...	...	...
605	**Suswa** a.	...	1110	...	...	...	...	...	...	...	...

	①–⑤			⑤–⑦	①–⑤			
Suswa d.	...	...	...	1550	...	...	...	...
Ngong d.	0620	...	...	1721	1947	...	...	...
Nairobi Terminus ⊡ a.	0704	...	...	1810	2028	...	...	...
Nairobi Terminus ⊡ d.	...	0800	1500	...	...	2200	...	...
Emali d.	...	0931	|	...	...	|	...	...
Mtito Andei d.	...	1054	|	...	...	|	...	...
Voi d.	...	1208	|	...	...	|	...	...
Mombasa a.	...	1400	2008	...	...	0335	...	...

km		⑤	
0	**Nairobi** Central d.	0900	...
	Thika d.	1114	...
160	**Nanyuki** a.	1649	...

	⑦	
Nanyuki d.	0900	...
Thika d.	1432	...
Nairobi Central a.	1646	...

km				
0	**Nairobi** d.	...	...	...
182	Nakuru d.	...	...	...
396	**Kisumu** a.	...	...	...

Kisumu d.	...	...	...
Nakuru d.	...	...	...
Nairobi a.	...	...	...

Capital: **Nairobi** (GMT +3). 2022 Public Holidays: Jan. 1, Apr. 15, 18, May 1, 2, 4, June 1, Oct. 10, 20, Dec. 12, 25, 26, 27.

⊡ – Nairobi Terminus - Nairobi Central and v.v. Journey 35 minutes:
From Nairobi Terminus at 0627, 0722, 0857, 1047, 1437, 2020; from Nairobi Central at 0635, 0800, 0935, 1200, 1730, 1820, 2010.

DEMOCRATIC CONGO 4320

Société Nationale des Chemins de Fer du Congo

km				
0	Lubumbashi d.	...	⊖	...
237	Tenke d.	...	⊖	...
757	Dilolo d.	...	|	...
600	Kamina d.	...	⊖	...
047	Kabalo d.	...	|	...
583	Kindu a.	...	|	...
320	Kalemie a.	...	|	...
913	Mwene Ditu d.	...	⊖	...
156	Kananga d.	...	⊖	...
578	Ilebo a.	...	...	...

Ilebo d.	...	⊖	...
Kananga d.	...	⊖	...
Mwene Ditu d.	...	⊖	...
Kalemie d.	...	|	...
Kindu d.	...	|	...
Kabalo d.	...	|	...
Kamina d.	...	⊖	...
Dilolo d.	...	|	...
Tenke d.	...	⊖	...
Lubumbashi a.	...	⊖	...

km			
0	**Sakania** d.	⊖	...
255	**Lubumbashi** a.	⊖	...

Lubumbashi d.	⊖	...
Sakania a.	⊖	...

km			
0	**Kinshasa** Est d.	⊖	...
366	**Matadi** a.	⊖	...

Matadi d.	⊖	...
Kinshasa Est a.	⊖	...

km			
0	**Kisangani** d.	⊖	...
125	**Ubundu** a.	⊖	...

Ubundu d.	⊖	...
Kisangani a.	⊖	...

Capital: **Kinshasa** (GMT +1). 2022 Public Holidays: Jan. 1, 4, 15, 16, 17, Apr. 30, May 1, 17, June 30, Aug. 1, Dec. 25, 31. ⊖ – No information available.

TANZANIA and ZAMBIA 4330

Tanzania Railways, TAZARA, Zambian Railways

km	*Tanzania Railways*	A	
0	**Dar es Salaam** ◧ d.	⊖	⊖
78	Ruvu d.	⊖	⊖
203	Morogoro d.	⊖	⊖
290	Kilosa d.	⊖	⊖
465	Dodoma d.	⊖	⊖
578	Manyoni d.	⊖	⊖
637	Itigi d.	⊖	⊖
840	**Tabora** a.	⊖	⊖
840	**Tabora** ⊖ d.	⊖	⊖
975	Kaliua ⊖ d.	⊖	⊖
051	**Mpanda** ⊖ a.	|	|
	Mwanza a.	|	⊖
144	Uvinza d.	⊖	...
256	**Kigoma** a.	⊖	...

	A	
Kigoma d.	⊖	...
Uvinza d.	⊖	...
Mwanza d.	|	⊖
Mpanda ⊖ d.	|	|
Kaliua ⊖ d.	⊖	⊖
Tabora ⊖ a.	⊖	⊖
Tabora d.	⊖	⊖
Itigi d.	⊖	⊖
Manyoni d.	⊖	⊖
Dodoma d.	⊖	⊖
Kilosa d.	⊖	⊖
Morogoro d.	⊖	⊖
Ruvu d.	⊖	⊖
Dar es Salaam ◧ a.	⊖	⊖

km	*Tanzania Railways*		
0	**Dar es Salaam** ◧ d.	⊖	...
78	Ruvu d.	⊖	...
	Mruazi d.	⊖	...
555	Moshi d.	⊖	...
631	**Arusha** a.	⊖	...

Arusha d.	⊖	...
Moshi d.	⊖	...
Mruazi d.	⊖	...
Ruvu d.	⊖	...
Dar es Salaam ◧ a.	⊖	...

km	*Tanzania Railways*		
0	**Dar es Salaam** ● d.	...	...
	Pugu ● d.	...	...
	Soga ● d.	...	...
	Ruvu ● d.	...	...
	Ngerengere ● d.	...	...
205	**Morogoro** ● a.	...	...

Morogoro ● d.	...	...
Ngerengere ● d.	...	...
Ruvu ● d.	...	...
Soga ● d.	...	...
Pugu ● d.	...	...
Dar es Salaam ● a.	...	...

km	*TAZARA*	② C	⑤ C
0	**Dar es Salaam** ◧ d.	1350	1550
226	Kisaki d.	1910	2013
360	Ifakara d.	2230	2258
496	Mlimba d.	0140	0152
652	Makambako d.	0803	0746
849	Mbeya d.	1440	1323
969	Tunduma d.	1853	1717
970	Nakonde 🏛 a.	1758	1622
970	Nakonde 🏛 d.	1813	1647
1226	Kasama d.	0031	2227
1412	Mpika d.	0445	0148
1652	Serenje d.	0931	0556
1761	Mkushi Boma d.	|	|
1852	**New Kapiri Mposhi** ⊡ a.	1337	0926

	⑤ C	② C
New Kapiri Mposhi ⊡ d.	1400	1600
Mkushi Boma d.	|	|
Serenje d.	1817	1947
Mpika d.	2318	0010
Kasama d.	0309	0329
Nakonde 🏛 a.	0915	0839
Nakonde 🏛 d.	0925	0909
Tunduma d.	1045	1029
Mbeya d.	1500	1428
Makambako d.	2129	2030
Mlimba d.	0351	0208
Ifakara d.	0628	0512
Kisaki d.	1035	0757
Dar es Salaam ◧ a.	1546	1210

km	*Zambia Railways*	⑤ 🛏 ✕	
0	**Kitwe** Nkana d.	1600	...
66	Ndola d.	1855	...
199	Kapiri Mposhi ⊡ d.	2357	...
262	Kabwe d.	0255	...
331	Chisamba d.	0500	...
384	**Lusaka** a.	0656	...
384	**Lusaka** d.	0736	...
432	Kafue d.	0946	...
481	Mazabuka d.	1155	...
540	Monze d.	1417	...
577	Pemba d.	1558	...
643	Choma d.	1834	...
713	Kalomo d.	2108	...
851	**Livingstone** a.	0200	...

	① 🛏 ✕	
Livingstone d.	2000	...
Kalomo d.	0100	...
Choma d.	0345	...
Pemba d.	0609	...
Monze d.	0749	...
Mazabuka d.	1015	...
Kafue d.	1244	...
Lusaka a.	1424	...
Lusaka d.	1524	...
Chisamba d.	1656	...
Kabwe d.	1946	...
Kapiri Mposhi ⊡ d.	2216	...
Ndola d.	0336	...
Kitwe Nkana a.	0600	...

km	*Zambia Railways*	③	
0	**Mulobezi** d.	1200	...
85	Ngwezi d.	⊖	...
163	**Livingstone** a.	0200	...

	②	
Livingstone d.	1400	...
Ngwezi d.	⊖	...
Mulobezi a.	0200	...

Capitals: **Dodoma** (Tanzania, GMT +3), **Lusaka** (Zambia, GMT +2).

2022 Public Holidays:
Tanzania: Jan. 1, 12, Apr. 7, 15, 18, 26, May 1, 3, July 7, 10, Aug. 8, Oct. 9, 14, Dec. 9, 25, 26.
Zambia: Jan. 1, Mar. 12, Apr. 15, 18, May 1, 25, July 4, 5, Aug. 1, Oct. 24, Dec. 25.

A – 🛏, ✕. Journey 51 hours.
C – 🛏, 🛏, ✕.
◧ – Stations are approximately 8 km from each other.
⊡ – Stations are approximately 2 km from each other.
⊖ – Service available. Timings unknown.
● – New standard gauge railway due to open in April 2022.
⊖ – No information available.

MADAGASCAR 4340

Chemins de Fer Fianarantsoa-Côte Est, Madarail

km	*Madarail*	⑤	②
0	**Toamasina** d.	...	0820
43	Tampolo d.	...	0951
86	Ambila-Lemaitso d.	0800	1125
162	Lohariandava d.	1150	1515
223	Andasibe ◇ d.	1515	1725
249	**Moramanga** a.	1740	1855

	①	④
Moramanga d.	0700	1500
Andasibe ◇ d.	0830	1600
Lohariandava d.	1050	1820
Ambila-Lemaitso d.	1340	2200
Tampolo d.	1520	...
Toamasina a.	1650	...

km	*CFFCE*	②④⑥	
0	**Fianarantsoa** d.	0700	...
39	Ranomena d.	0855	...
62	Tolongoina d.	1015	...
79	Manampatrana d.	1110	...
118	Sahasinaka d.	1330	...
163	**Manakara** a.	1600	...

	③⑤⑦	
Manakara d.	0645	...
Sahasinaka d.	0900	...
Manampatrana d.	1130	...
Tolongoina d.	1225	...
Ranomena d.	1355	...
Fianarantsoa a.	1600	...

Capital: **Antananarivo** (GMT +3). 2022 Public Holidays: Jan. 1, Mar. 8, 29, Apr. 18, May 1, 3, 26, June 6, 26, Aug. 15, Nov. 1, Dec, 25.

◇ – Special tour trains using Michelin railcars run Andasibe - Antananarivo and v.v. For dates contact operator.

BOTSWANA 4345

Botswana Railways

km			
0	**Francistown** d.	...	...
235	Mahalapye d.	...	...
435	Gaborone d.	...	...
507	**Lobatse** a.	...	...

Lobatse d.	...	...
Gaborone d.	...	...
Mahalapye d.	...	...
Francistown a.	...	...

Capital: **Gaborone** (GMT +2).
2022 Public Holidays: Jan. 1, 2, Apr. 15, 16, 18, May 1, 2, 26, July 1, 18, 19, Sept. 30, Oct. 1, Dec. 25, 26, 27.

MALAWI 4348

Nacala Logistics

km			
0	Balaka d.	...	...
16	Nkaya d.	...	...
42	Liwonde d.	...	...
114	Nayuchi a.	...	...
104	Blantyre d.	...	...
112	Limbe d.	...	...
233	Makhanga a.	...	...

Makhanga d.	...	...
Limbe d.	...	...
Blantyre d.	...	...
Nayuchi d.	...	...
Liwonde d.	...	...
Nkaya d.	...	...
Balaka d.	...	...

Capital: **Lilongwe** (GMT +2).
2022 Public Holidays: Jan. 1, 3, 15, 17, Mar. 3, Apr. 15, 16, 18, May 1–3, 14, 16, July 6, Oct. 15, 17, Dec. 25, 26, 27.

4350 ANGOLA

CF Benguela, CF Luanda, CF Moçâmedes

km	CF Luanda		①–⑤	⑥
0	Luanda Muceques	d.	0814	0819
23	Viana	d.	0851	0906
65	Catete	d.	0951	1006
135	Zenza	d.	...	...
190	Dondo (Cuanza)	a.	...	...
241	N'dalatando	d.	...	...
424	Malange	a.	...	...

		①–⑤	⑥
Malange	d.	...	...
N'dalatando	d.	...	...
Dondo (Cuanza)	d.	...	...
Zenza	d.	...	...
Catete	d.	1010	1020
Viana	d.	1115	1125
Luanda Muceques	a.	1212	1222

km	CF Moçâmedes		①⑤	
0	Namibe	d.	...	...
162	Bibala	d.	...	...
246	Lubango	d.	0900	...
424	Matala	d.	⊖	...
509	Dongo	a.	⊖	...
756	Menongue	a.	1930	...
584	Tchamutete Cidade	a.	...	...

		②⑥	
Tchamutete Cidade	d.	...	...
Menongue	d.	0700	...
Dongo	a.	⊖	...
Matala	d.	⊖	...
Lubango	d.	1730	...
Bibala	d.	...	...
Namibe	a.	...	...

km	CF Benguela		①–⑤	①	②③⑥	①–⑤	②	①	⑤	①–⑤	①–⑤
0	Lobita	d.	0620	0800	...	0835	...	...	...	1220	1520
33	Benguela	a.	0730	⊖	...	0945	...	...	...	1330	1630
355	Caála	d.	...	⊖	...		...	...	...	...	...
368	Dango	d.	...	⊖	...	...	...	...	...	...	...
383	Huambo	d.	...	⊖	...	...	...	0530	0630	...	...
413	Cambuio	d.	...	⊖	...	⑤	...	⊖	⊖	...	...
460	Katchiungo	a.	...	⊖	...		...	⊖	⊖	...	...
585	Kuito	d.	...	⊖	...	0600	0700	⊖	⊖	...	...
976	Luena	a.	...	⊖	0500	1441	1540	1810	1852	...	...
1292	Luau	a.	...	⊖	1113	...	...	...	...	...	...

		③⑥	④	⑦	③	①–⑤	①–⑤	①–⑤	①–⑤	②③
Luau	d.	...	...	...	⊖	...	...	...	...	1230
Luena	d.	0500	0500	0600	⊖	...	...	...	...	1905
Kuito	d.	⊖	1343	1602	⊖	...	...	...	...	...
Katchiungo	d.	⊖	...	...	⊖	...	...	...	...	...
Cambuio	d.	⊖	...	...	⊖	...	...	...	...	...
Huambo	d.	1901	...	...	⊖	...	...	...	...	...
Dango	d.	...	...	...	⊖	...	...	...	...	...
Caála	a.	...	...	...	⊖	...	...	...	...	...
Benguela	d.	...	...	...	⊖	0620	0835	1220	1520	...
Lobita	a.	...	...	...	0324	0730	0945	1330	1630	...

Capital: **Luanda** (GMT +1). 2022 Public Holidays: Jan. 1, Feb. 4, Mar. 1, 7, 8, 23, Apr. 4, 15, May 1, Sept. 17, Nov. 2, 11, Dec. 25. ⊖ – No information available.

4370 MOÇAMBIQUE

CD do Norte, CF Moçambique

km	CD do Norte		②⑥	④	
0	**Nampula**	d.	0400	...	...
123	Ribáuè	d.	0731	...	...
173	Iapala	d.	0851	...	...
252	Malema	d.	1142	...	...
302	Mutuáli	d.	1333	...	...
356	Cuamba	d.	1526	0600	...
464	Mitande	d.	...	⊖	...
541	**Nayuci**	a.	...	0900	...

		④⑦		
Nayuci	d.	...	1500	...
Mitande	d.	...	⊖	...
Cuamba	d.	0500	1800	...
Mutuáli	d.	0735	...	...
Malema	d.	0833	...	...
Iapala	d.	1120	...	...
Ribáuè	d.	1238	...	...
Nampula	a.	1626	...	...

km	CF Moçambique		⑥	②	①
0	**Beira**	d.	0600	1100	2100
28	Dondo 1	d.	0731	1224	2226
120	Muanza	d.	1021	1509	0154
187	Inhaminga	d.	1208	1656	0415
214	Inhamitanga	d.	1259	1742	0505
302	**Marromeu**	a.	1600	|	|
320	Dona Ana	a.	...	2125	1024
577	**Maotize**	a.	...	0526	2105

		⑦	③	③
Moatize	d.	...	0600	160
Dona Ana	d.	...	1618	001
Marromeu	d.	0800	|	|
Inhamitanga	d.	1108	2114	042
Inhaminga	d.	1159	2336	051
Muanza	d.	1346	0204	070
Dondo 1	d.	1639	0548	093
Beira	a.	1800	0718	115

km	CF Moçambique		⑥⑦	⑥	③
0	**Maputo**	d.	0730	0955	1300
208	Chókwe	d.	1216	1911	1951
534	**Chicualacuala**	a.	...	0349	0342

		④	⑦	⑥⑦
Chicualacuala	d.	1300	1000	...
Chókwe	d.	2323	2020	1420
Maputo	a.	0549	0810	1909

km	CF Moçambique		①–⑤	⑥⑦	⑧
0	**Maputo**	d.	0745	0800	1815
53	Moambe	d.	0927	0952	2032
88	**Ressano Garcia**	a.	1020	1045	2124

		①–⑥	①–⑤	⑥⑦
Ressano Garcia	d.	0346	1205	122
Moambe	d.	0506	1317	134
Maputo	a.	0645	1511	154

Capital: **Maputo** (GMT +2). 2022 Public Holidays: Jan. 1, Feb. 3, Apr. 7, May 1, 2, June 25, Sep. 7, 25, 26, Oct. 4, Dec. 25, 26. ⊖ – No information available.

4380 ZIMBABWE

National Railways of Zimbabwe

km			①④⑥	
0	**Mutare**	d.	2100	...
77	Nyazura	d.	2307	...
99	Rusape	d.	0020	...
166	Macheke	d.	0239	...
201	Marondera	d.	0345	...
273	**Harare**	a.	0605	...

		③⑤⑦	
Harare	d.	2130	...
Marondera	d.	2345	...
Macheke	d.	0100	...
Rusape	d.	0320	...
Nyazura	d.	0309	...
Mutare	a.	0600	...

km				
0	**Bulawayo**	d.	1930	...
126	Gwayi	d.	2310	...
266	Dete	d.	0300	...
339	Hwange	d.	0534	...
351	Thomson Junction	d.	0540	...
472	**Victoria Falls**	a.	0855	...

Victoria Falls	d.	1900	...
Thomson Junction	d.	2240	...
Hwange	d.	2303	...
Dete	d.	0140	...
Gwayi	d.	0456	...
Bulawayo	a.	0900	...

km			②⑤⑦	①③⑤
0	**Harare**	d.	2000	...
44	Norton	d.	2100	...
127	Chegutu	d.	2310	...
160	Kadoma	d.	0001	...
237	Kwekwe	d.	0210	...
**	Masvingo	d.	|	2000
302	Gweru	d.	0500	0345
336	Somabhula	d.	0533	...
369	Shangani	d.	0630	...
486	**Bulawayo**	a.	0840	...

		①④⑥	①③⑤
Bulawayo	d.	2050	...
Shangani	d.	2240	...
Somabhula	d.	2330	...
Gweru	d.	0130	0245
Masvingo	a.	|	0955
Kwekwe	d.	0337	...
Kadoma	d.	0520	...
Chegutu	d.	0605	...
Norton	d.	0805	...
Harare	a.	0905	...

km			③	⑦
0	**Bulawayo**	d.	1215	1730
113	Shangani	d.	1457	2016
150	Somabhula	d.	1607	2108
229	Bannockburn	d.	1848	2345
309	Ngezi	d.	2106	0205
401	Rutenga	d.	0050	0545
433	Lundi	d.	|	0934
500	**Chicualacuala** ⊙	a.	0706	|
499	Triangle	d.	...	1120
523	**Chiredzi**	a.	...	1200

		④	①
Chiredzi	d.	...	153
Triangle	d.	...	162
Chicualacuala ⊙	d.	1500	|
Lundi	d.	|	1727
Rutenga	d.	2145	2145
Ngezi	d.	0036	0036
Bannockburn	d.	0339	0339
Somabhula	d.	0700	070
Shangani	d.	0810	081
Bulawayo	a.	1100	110

km			④⑦	
0	**Bulawayo**	d.	1800	...
	Gwanda	d.	2310	...
317	**Beit Bridge**	a.	0540	...

		①⑤	
Beit Bridge	d.	2100	...
Gwanda	d.	0353	...
Bulawayo	a.	0845	...

km			802	
0	**Bulawayo**	d.	1415	...
	Plumtree 🏛	d.	1749	...
196	**Francistown**	a.	1945	...

		801	
Francistown	d.	0700	...
Plumtree 🏛	d.	0945	...
Bulawayo	a.	1230	...

Capital: **Harare** (GMT +2). 2022 Public Holidays: Jan. 1, Feb, 21, Apr. 15, 16, 18, May 1, 2, 25, Aug. 8, 10, Dec. 22, 25, 26, 27.

⊙ – 🏛 is Sango Halt.

** – Masvingo - Gweru: *199 km*.

4390 NAMIBIA

Starlin

km				
0	**Windhoek**	d.	...	...
70	Okahandja	d.	...	...
191	Karibib	d.	...	...
210	Kranzberg	d.	...	...
282	Omaruru	d.	...	...
419	**Otjiwarongo**	a.	...	...
222	Usakos	d.	...	...
373	Swakopmund	d.	...	...
411	**Walvisbaai**	a.	...	...

Walvisbaai	a.	...	...
Swakopmund	d.	...	...
Usakos	d.	...	...
Otjiwarongo	d.	...	...
Omaruru	d.	...	...
Kranzberg	d.	...	...
Karibib	d.	...	...
Okahandja	d.	...	...
Windhoek	a.	...	...

km				
0	**Windhoek**	d.	...	...
97	Rehobeth	d.	...	...
193	Kalkrand	d.	...	...
274	Mariental	d.	...	...
413	Tses	d.	...	...
495	**Keetmanshoop**	a.	...	...
495	**Keetmanshoop**	d.	...	...
670	Grünau	d.	...	...
720	**Karasburg**	a.	...	...

Karasburg	a.	...	...
Grünau	d.	...	...
Keetmanshoop	d.	...	...
Keetmanshoop	d.	...	...
Tses	d.	...	...
Mariental	d.	...	...
Kalkrand	d.	...	...
Rehobeth	d.	...	...
Windhoek	a.	...	...

km				
0	**Oshikango** ♣	d.	...	...
58	**Ondangwa** ♠	a.	...	...
58	**Ondangwa** ♠	d.	...	...
140	Omuthiya ♥	d.	...	...
213	Oshivelo	d.	...	...
305	**Tsumeb**	a.	...	...

Tsumeb	d.	...	...
Oshivelo	d.	...	...
Omuthiya ♥	d.	...	...
Ondangwa ♠	a.	...	...
Ondangwa ♠	d.	...	...
Oshikango ♣	a.	...	...

Capital: **Windhoek** (GMT +2).

2022 Public Holidays: Jan. 1, Mar. 21, Apr. 15, 18, May 2, 4, 25, 26, Aug. 26, Dec. 10, 25, 26, 27.

♣ – Full name is Oshikango Reverend Theofelus Hamutumbangela.

♠ – Full name is Ondangwa Nehale Lya Mpingana.

♥ – Full name is Omuthiya Sam Nujoma.

SOUTH AFRICA

Shosholoza Meyl — **4400**

Capital: **Pretoria** (GMT +2). 2022 Public Holidays: Jan. 1, Mar. 21, Apr. 15, 18, 27, May 1, 2, June 16, Aug. 9, Sept. 24, Dec. 16, 25, 26. Operator: Shosholoza Meyl.

Three classes of accommodation are offered: Premier Class (coaches consisting of one or two berth deluxe compartments that convert to sleeper accommodation at night and can accomodate up to 14 passengers), Tourist Class (shown as T in notes - coaches consisting of two or four berth compartments that convert to sleeper accommodation at night and can accomodate up to 28 passengers) and Economy Class (shown as 2 in notes - seated accommodation).

km					
0	**Johannesburg**	d.	...	...	...
186	Klerksdorp	d.	...	...	...
495	Kimberley	d.	...	...	...
	East London	d.	...	...	...
	Queenstown	d.	...	...	...
908	De Aar	d.	...	...	...
988	Beaufort West	d.	...	...	...
1355	Worcester	d.	...	...	...
1511	Bellville	d.	...	...	...
1530	**Cape Town**	a.	...	...	...

Cape Town	d.	...	...	...
Belleville	d.	...	...	...
Worcester	d.	...	...	...
Beaufort West	d.	...	...	...
De Aar	d.	...	...	...
Queenstown	d.	...	...	...
East London	a.	...	...	...
Kimberley	d.	...	...	...
Klerksdorp	d.	...	...	...
Johannesburg	a.	...	...	...

km			⑤ B	⑤ C	⑤ B
0	**Johannesburg**	d.	1420	1420	...
14	Germiston	d.	⊖	1452	...
75	Vereeniging	d.	⊖	1507	...
210	Kroonstad	d.	⊖	1832	...
407	**Bloemfontein**	d.	2115	2135	2145
664	Burgersdorp	d.	...	0305	|
809	Queenstown	d.	...	0610	|
1023	**East London**	a.	...	1020	|
835	Cradock	d.	...	...	⊖
1112	**Gqeberha** ◧	a.	...	...	1030

		⑦ C	⑦ B	
Gqeberha ◧	d.	...	1500	...
Cradock	d.	...	⊖	...
East London	d.	1415	|	...
Queenstown	d.	⊖	|	...
Burgersdorp	d.	⊖	|	...
Bloemfontein	d.	⊖	⊖	...
Kroonstad	d.	⊖	⊖	...
Vereeniging	d.	⊖	⊖	...
Germiston	d.	⊖	⊖	...
Johannesburg	a.	1105	1130	...

km					
0	**Johannesburg**	d.	...	...	...
14	Germiston	d.	...	...	...
70	Pretoria	d.	...	...	...
183	Witbank	d.	...	...	...
218	Middelburg	d.	...	...	...
422	Nelspruit	d.	...	...	...
461	Kaapmuiden	d.	...	...	...
530	**Komatipoort** ⊡	a.	...	...	...
292	Mokopane	d.	...	...	...
357	Polokwane	d.	...	...	...
504	Makhado	d.	...	...	...
533	**Musina** ⊖	a.	...	...	...

Musina ▶	d.	...	...	...
Makhado	d.	...	...	...
Polokwane	d.	...	...	...
Mokopane	d.	...	...	...
Komatipoort ⊡	d.	...	...	...
Kaapmuiden	d.	...	...	...
Nelspruit	d.	...	...	...
Middelburg	d.	...	...	...
Witbank	d.	...	...	...
Pretoria	d.	...	...	...
Germiston	d.	...	...	...
Johannesburg	a.	...	...	...

km					
0	**Johannesburg**	d.	...	...	...
14	Germiston	d.	...	...	...
172	Standerton	d.	...	...	...
315	Newcastle	d.	...	...	...
438	Ladysmith	d.	...	...	...
617	Pietermaritzburg	d.	...	...	...
722	**Durban**	a.	...	...	...

Durban	d.	...	...	...
Pietermaritzburg	d.	...	...	...
Ladysmith	d.	...	...	...
Newcastle	d.	...	...	...
Standerton	d.	...	...	...
Germiston	d.	...	...	...
Johannesburg	a.	...	...	...

B – ALGOA – 🛏, [T2] and ✕ Johannesburg - Port Elizabeth and v.v.
C – AMATOLA – 🛏, [T2] and ✕ Johannesburg - East London and v.v.
◧ – Formerly known as Port Elizabeth.
⊡ – Komatipoort - Ressano Garcia (Mozambique, Table **4370**): *5 km*.
⊖ – Musina - Beit Bridge (Zimbabwe, Table **4380**): *12 km*.
⊖ – Timings not available.

JOHANNESBURG - PRETORIA and v.v. *56 km*. Journey 36 mins. Operator: Gautrain.

From **Johannesburg** Park: Train call at Sandton* 8 minutes later.
①: 0529, 0539 and every 10 – 15 minutes until 1929, 1945, 2000, 2015, 2030.
⑥: 0530, 0600 and every 30 minutes until 2030.

From **Pretoria**: Trains call at Sandton* 27 minutes later.
①: 0532, 0542 and every 10 – 15 minutes until 1918, 1933, 1948, 2003, 2018, 2033, 2048.
⑥: 0533, 0603 and every 30 minutes until 2003, 2039.

* – Frequent services run throughout the day to/from Sandton and OR Tambo Airport.

ISRAEL

Capital: **Jerusalem** (GMT +2, add 1 hour in summer). 2022 Public Holidays: Apr. 16, 22, May 5, June 5, Sept. 26, 27, Oct. 10, 17. Operator: Israel Railways (www.rail.co.il).

All services convey a single class of seated accommodation. Timings are the most recent available and are subject to alteration at any time, particularly around religious holidays. Tickets and reservations may be purchased up to 7 days in advance of travel at stations or through the website.

NAHARIYYA - TEL AVIV - BEN GURION AIRPORT - MODI'IN

Israel Railways — **4500**

Overnight and weekend (⑤⑥) services are suspended due to engineering work - replacement 🚌 services are available.

km				⑦–④	⑦–④	⑦–④	⑦–④	⑦–④	⑦–④	⑦–④	⑦–④		⑦–④	⑦–④	⑦–④	⑦–④	⑦–④	⑦–④	⑦–④	⑦–④	⑦–④	⑦–④	⑦–④	
0	**Nahariyya**	d.	W	...	0448	0515	0548	0615	0648	0715	0748	and	1515	1548	1615	1648	1715	1748	1815	1848	1905	2049	2149	...
	Akko	d.	E	...	0455	0522	0555	0622	0655	0722	0755	at	1522	1555	1622	1655	1722	1755	1822	1855	1912	2056	2156	...
20	Qiryat Motzkin	d.	E	...	0505	0532	0605	0632	0705	0732	0805	the	1532	1605	1632	1705	1732	1805	1832	1905	1922	2106	2206	...
38	Haifa Hof HaKarmel	d.	K	...	0536	0603	0636	0703	0736	0803	0836	same	1603	1636	1703	1736	1803	1836	1903	1936	1953	2137	2237	...
71	Binyamina	d.	D	0528	0556	0626	0656	0726	0756	0826	0856	minutes	1626	1656	1726	1756	1826	1856	1926	1956	2016	|	|	...
123	**Tel Aviv** Savidor Center	d.	A	0601	0631	0701	0731	0801	0831	0901	0931	past	1701	1731	1801	1831	1901	1931	2001	2031	2101	2228	2328	...
	Tel Aviv HaHagana	d.	Y	0609	0639	0709	0739	0809	0839	0909	0939	each	1709	1739	1809	1839	1909	1939	2009	2039	2109	2235	2335	...
137	Ben Gurion Airport	a.	S	0619	0649	0719	0749	0819	0849	0919	0949	hour	1719	1749	1819	1849	1919	1949	2019	2050	2120	2245	2345	...
158	**Modi'in** Center	a.		0644	0714	0744	0814	0844	0914	0944	1014	until	1744	1814	1844	1914	1944	2014	2044	2114	2144	2306	...	...

Nahariyya	d.		...	...	...	...	...	...	...	...	...	...	...	S	...	...	...	...	...	...	...	...	...	...
Akko	d.	F	...	...	...	...	...	...	...	...	...	...	...	A	...	...	...	...	...	...	...	...	...	...
Qiryat Motzkin	d.	R	...	...	...	...	...	...	...	...	...	...	...	T	...	...	...	...	...	...	...	...	...	...
Haifa Hof HaKarmel	d.	I	...	...	...	...	...	...	...	...	...	...	...	U	...	...	...	...	...	...	...	...	...	...
Binyamina	d.	D	...	...	...	...	...	...	...	...	...	...	...	R	...	...	...	...	...	...	...	...	...	...
Tel Aviv Savidor Ctr	a.	A	...	...	...	...	...	...	...	...	...	...	...	D	...	...	...	...	...	...	...	...	...	...
Tel Aviv HaHagana	d.	Y	...	...	...	...	...	...	...	...	...	...	...	A	...	...	...	...	...	...	...	...	...	...
Ben Gurion Airport	a.		...	...	...	...	...	...	...	...	...	...	...	Y	...	...	...	...	...	...	...	...	...	...
Modi'in Center	a.		...	...	...	...	...	...	...	...	...	...	...		...	...	...	...	...	...	...	...	...	...

			⑦–④	⑦–④	⑦–④	⑦–④	⑦–④	⑦–④	⑦–④	⑦–④	⑦–④		⑦–④	⑦–④	⑦–④	⑦–④	⑦–④	⑦–④	⑦–④	⑦–④	⑦–④	⑦–④	
Modi'in Center	d.	W	...	...	0548	0618	0648	0718	0748	0818	0848	and	1618	1648	1718	1748	1818	1848	1918	1948	2018	2118	...
Ben Gurion Airport	d.	E	...	0538	0605	0635	0705	0735	0805	0835	0905	at	1635	1705	1735	1805	1835	1905	1935	2005	2037	2137	...
Tel Aviv HaHagana	d.	E	...	0547	0617	0646	0717	0746	0817	0846	0917	the	1646	1719	1746	1819	1846	1919	1946	2016	2049	2149	...
Tel Aviv Savidor Center	d.	K	...	0558	0628	0658	0728	0758	0828	0858	0928	same	1658	1728	1758	1828	1858	1928	1958	2028	2100	2200	...
Binyamina	d.	D	0534	0630	0700	0730	0800	0830	0900	0930	1000	minutes	1730	1800	1830	1900	1930	2000	2030	2105	2144	2244	...
Haifa Hof HaKarmel	d.	A	0555	0649	0724	0749	0824	0849	0924	0949	1024	past	1749	1824	1849	1924	1949	2024	2049	2129	2204	2304	...
Qiryat Motzkin	d.	Y	0625	0720	0755	0820	0855	0920	0955	1020	1055	each	1820	1855	1920	1955	2020	2055	2120	2200	2235	2335	...
Akko	d.	S	0635	0729	0804	0829	0904	0929	1004	1029	1104	hour	1829	1904	1929	2004	2029	2104	2129	2209	2243	2343	...
Nahariyya	a.		0646	0739	0813	0839	0913	0939	1013	1039	1113	until	1839	1913	1939	2013	2039	2113	2139	2218	2253	2353	...

Modi'in Center	d.		...	...	...	...	...	...	...	...	...	...	...	S	...	...	...	...	...	...	...	...	...	...
Ben Gurion Airport	d.	F	...	...	...	...	...	...	...	...	...	...	...	A	...	...	...	...	...	...	...	...	...	...
Tel Aviv HaHagana	a.	R	...	...	...	...	...	...	...	...	...	...	...	T	...	...	...	...	...	...	...	...	...	...
Tel Aviv Savidor Center	d.	I	...	...	...	...	...	...	...	...	...	...	...	U	...	...	...	...	...	...	...	...	...	...
Binyamina	d.	D	...	...	...	...	...	...	...	...	...	...	...	R	...	...	...	...	...	...	...	...	...	...
Haifa Hof HaKarmel	a.	A	...	...	...	...	...	...	...	...	...	...	...	D	...	...	...	...	...	...	...	...	...	...
Qiryat Motzkin	a.	Y	...	...	...	...	...	...	...	...	...	...	...	A	...	...	...	...	...	...	...	...	...	...
Akko	a.		...	...	...	...	...	...	...	...	...	...	...	Y	...	...	...	...	...	...	...	...	...	...
Nahariyya	a.		...	...	...	...	...	...	...	...	...	...	...		...	...	...	...	...	...	...	...	...	...

4510 HERTSLIYYA - TEL AVIV - JERUSALEM and BE'ER SHEVA

Israel Railways

During peak hours on ⑦–④ certain Bet Shemesh trains extend to / from Hertsliyya and certain Be'er Sheva trains extend to / from Nahariyya - timings not shown.

km			⑦–④	⑦–④		⑦–④	⑦–④	⑦–④	⑦–④	⑦–④	⑦–④		⑦–④	⑦–④	⑦–④	⑦–④	⑦–④	⑦–④	⑦–④	⑦–④	⑦–④	⑦–④	⑦–
	Hertsliyya d.	W	...	...	...	0554	...	0624	...	0654	...	and	1924	...	1954	...	2024	2054	...	2129	2203	2229	230
0	**Tel Aviv** Savidor Center d.	E	0542	0549	...	0607	0612	0637	0648	0707	0712	at the	1937	1948	2007	2012	2037	2107	2128	2144	2216	2244	231
	Tel Aviv HaHagana d.	E	0550	0556	...	0615	0620	0645	0655	0715	0720	same	1945	1955	2015	2020	2045	2115	2137	2152	2223	2252	232
12	Ben Gurion Airport d.	K	|	|	...	0626	|	0656	|	0726	|	minutes	1956	|	2026	|	2056	2126	|	2203	2233	2303	233
56	**Jerusalem** Yitzhak Navon a.	D	|	|	...	0652	|	0722	|	0752	|	past	2022	|	2052	|	2122	2152	|	2229	2259	2329	235
20	Lod d.	A	0604	0612	...	...	0634	...	0711	...	0734	each	...	2011	...	2034	...	...	|	...	...	...	...
51	**Bet Shemesh** a.	Y	|	0638	...	...	|	...	0738	...	|	hour	...	2038	...	|	...	...	|	...	...	...	...
63	Kiryat Gat d.	S	0629	...	...	...	0710	...	...	...	0811	until	...	...	...	2110	...	...	|	...	...	...	...
107	**Be'er Sheva** Center a.		0702	...	...	...	0749	...	...	...	0850	◧	...	...	...	2149	...	...	2301	...	...	...	...

		⑤	⑤	⑤	⑤	⑤		⑤	⑤	⑤	⑤	⑤	⑤	⑤			⑥	⑥	⑥	⑥	⑥	
Hertsliyya d.		0524	...	0624	0658	0724	and	1058	1124	1158	1224	1258	1324	1424	...	S	...	2120	...	2220	...	...
Tel Aviv Savidor Center d.	F	0537	0611	0637	0711	0737	at the	1111	1137	1211	1237	1311	1337	1437	...	A	2111	2132	2211	2232	2311	...
Tel Aviv HaHagana d.	R	0545	0620	0645	0720	0745	same	1120	1145	1220	1245	1320	1345	1445	...	T	2120	2141	2220	2241	2320	...
Ben Gurion Airport d.	I	0556	|	0656	|	0756	minutes	|	1156	|	1256	|	1356	1456	...	U	|	2149	|	2249	|	...
Jerusalem Yitzhak Navon a.	D	0622	|	0722	|	0822	past	|	1222	|	1322	|	1422	1522	...	R	|	2215	|	2315	|	...
Lod d.	A	...	|	...	|	...	each	|	...	|	...	|	...	...	...	D	|	...	|	...	|	...
Bet Shemesh a.	Y	...	|	...	|	...	hour	|	...	|	...	|	...	...	...	A	|	...	|	...	|	...
Kiryat Gat d.		...	|	...	|	...	until	|	...	|	...	|	...	...	...	Y	|	...	|	...	|	...
Be'er Sheva Center a.		...	0750	...	0849	...		1249	...	1349	...	1449	...	...	...		2242	...	2342	...	0042	...

		⑦–④	⑦–④	⑦–④	⑦–④	⑦–④	⑦–④	⑦–④	⑦–④		⑦–④	⑦–④	⑦–④	⑦–④	⑦–④	⑦–④		⑦–④	⑦–④	⑦–④	⑦–④	
Be'er Sheva Center d.	W	0442	...	0542	...	...	...	0642	...	and	...	...	1942	...	...	...	...	...	...	...	...	...
Kiryat Gat d.	E	0516	...	0616	...	...	...	0716	...	at the	...	...	2016	...	...	...	...	...	...	...	...	...
Bet Shemesh d.	E	|	0548	|	...	0648	...	|	...	same	1948	...	|	...	...	...	...	...	...	...	...	...
Lod d.	K	0551	0612	0651	...	0712	...	0751	...	minutes	2012	...	2051	...	...	...	...	...	...	...	...	...
Jerusalem Yitzhak Navon d.	D	|	|	|	0639	|	0709	|	0739	past	|	2009	|	2039	2109	2139	...	2202	2232	2302	2332	...
Ben Gurion Airport d.	A	|	|	|	0659	|	0729	|	0759	each	|	2029	|	2059	2129	2159	...	2222	2252	2322	2352	...
Tel Aviv HaHagana d.	Y	0605	0629	0705	0710	0729	0740	0805	0810	hour	2029	2040	2105	2110	2140	2210	...	2232	2302	2332	0002	...
Tel Aviv Savidor Centre a.	S	0615	0638	0715	0722	0738	0752	0815	0822	until	2039	2052	2115	2122	2152	2222	...	2244	2314	2344	0014	...
Hertsliyya a.		...	...	...	0734	...	0804	...	0834	◧	...	2104	...	2134	2204	2234	...	2255	2325	2355	0025	...

		⑤	⑤	⑤	⑤	⑤	⑤		⑤	⑤	⑤	⑤	⑤	⑤			⑥	⑥	⑥	⑥	⑥	
Be'er Sheva Center d.		...	0529	...	0629	...	0729	and	...	1129	...	1229	...	...	...	S	...	2129	...	2229	2329	...
Kiryat Gat d.	F	...	|	...	|	...	|	at the	...	|	...	|	...	...	...	A	...	|	...	|	|	...
Bet Shemesh d.	R	...	|	...	|	...	|	same	...	|	...	|	...	...	...	T	...	|	...	|	|	...
Lod d.	I	...	|	...	|	...	|	minutes	...	|	...	|	...	...	...	U	...	|	...	|	|	...
Jerusalem Yitzhak Navon d.	D	0539	|	0639	|	0739	|	past	1139	|	1239	|	1339	1439	...	R	2108	|	2208	|	|	...
Ben Gurion Airport d.	A	0559	|	0659	|	0759	|	each	1159	|	1259	|	1359	1459	...	D	2130	|	2230	|	|	...
Tel Aviv HaHagana d.	Y	0610	0648	0710	0748	0810	0848	hour	1210	1248	1310	1348	1410	1510	...	A	2140	2248	2240	2348	0048	...
Tel Aviv Savidor Centre a.		0622	0658	0722	0758	0822	0858	until	1222	1258	1322	1358	1422	1522	...	Y	2152	2258	2252	2358	0058	...
Hertsliyya a.		0634	0712	0734	0812	0834	0912		1234	1312	1334	1412	1434	1534	...		2203	2312	2303	0012	...	...

◧ – Also Tel Aviv Savidor Center - Be'er Sheva Center at 0642 ⑦–④, 0743 ⑦–④ and hourly until 1043 ⑦–④, 1643 ⑦–④ and hourly until 1943 ⑦–④.
Also Be'er Sheva Center - Tel Aviv Savidor Center at 0628 ⑦–④, 0728 ⑦–④, 0828 ⑦–④, 1428 ⑦–④ and hourly until 1828 ⑦–④.

4513 BEIT SHE'AN - HAIFA

Israel Railways

km		⑦–④	⑦–④	⑤	⑦–④	⑤	⑦–④	⑤		⑦–④	⑤	⑦–④	⑦–④	⑦–④	⑦–④	⑦–④	⑦–④	⑦–④	⑦–④	⑥	⑥	⑦–④	
0	**Beit She'an** d.	0531	0631	0635	0731	0735	0831	0835	and hourly	1331	1335	1431	1531	1631	1731	1831	1931	2031	2131	2135	2235	2236	...
60	**Haifa** Hof HaKarmel a.	0629	0729	0733	0829	0833	0929	0933	until	1429	1433	1529	1629	1729	1829	1929	2029	2129	2229	2233	2333	2335	...

	⑦–④	⑤		⑦–④	⑤	⑦–④	⑤		⑦–④	⑤	⑦–④	⑦–④	⑦–④	⑦–④	⑦–④	⑦–④	⑦–④	⑦–④	⑥	⑦–④	⑥	
Haifa Hof HaKarmel d.	0603	0621	...	0703	0721	0803	0821	and hourly	1303	1321	1403	1503	1603	1703	1803	1903	2003	2103	2121	2210	2221	...
Beit She'an a.	0701	0721	...	0801	0821	0901	0921	until	1401	1421	1501	1601	1701	1801	1901	2001	2101	2201	2221	2305	2321	...

4515 JERUSALEM - MODI'IN

Israel Railways

km		⑦–④	⑤	⑦–④	⑤	⑦–④	⑤	⑦–④		⑤	⑦–④	⑤	⑦–④	⑦–④	⑦–④	⑦–④	⑦–④	⑦–④	⑦–④	⑥	⑥	⑥	
0	**Jerusalem** Yitzhak Navon d.	0626	0629	0659	0729	0759	0829	0859	and hourly	1329	1359	1429	1459	1559	1659	1759	1859	1959	2059	2100	2154	2254	...
	Modi'in Center a.	0654	0652	0724	0752	0824	0852	0924	until	1352	1424	1452	1524	1624	1724	1824	1924	2024	2124	2123	2217	2317	...

	⑦–④	⑤	⑦–④	⑤	⑦–④	⑤	⑦–④		⑤	⑦–④	⑤	⑦–④	⑦–④	⑦–④	⑦–④		⑦–④	⑦–④	⑥	⑥	⑥	
Modi'in Center d.	0606	0643	0706	0743	0806	0843	0906	and hourly	1343	1406	1443	1506	1606	1706	1806	...	1906	2006	2111	2211	2311	...
Jerusalem Yitzhak Navon a.	0635	0710	0735	0810	0835	0910	0935	until	1410	1435	1510	1535	1635	1735	1835	...	1935	2035	2138	2238	2338	...

4610 IRAQ

Iraq Railways

km			21
		2 C	B
609	Umm Qasr d.	1130	...
541	**Al Basrah** Ma'qil d.	1400	2100
370	An Nasiriyah (for Ur) d.	▬	|
182	Ad Dawanyah d.	**11**	|
107	Al Hillah (for Babylon) d.	**A**	|
0	**Baghdad** Central d.	1920	0915
117	Samarra d.	2310	...
171	Tikrit d.	|	...
211	Ba'iji d.	|	...
406	**Al Mawsil** a.	0755	...

	20	12
	B	A
Al Mawsil d.	...	1900
Ba'iji d.	...	|
Tikrit d.	...	|
Samarra d.	...	0400
Baghdad Central d.	1700	0800
Al Hillah (for Babylon) d.	|	▬
Ad Dawanyah d.	|	...
An Nasiriyah (for Ur) d.	|	**2 C**
Al Basrah Ma'qil a.	0520	0800
Umm Qasr a.	...	1025

Capital: **Baghdad** (GMT +3).

2022 Public Holidays: Jan. 1, 6, Mar. 6, 21, May 1, 3, 4, 5, July 10–14, 30, Aug. 8, Oct. 3, 8 Dec. 10, 25.

Rail services in Iraq are operated by Iraq Railways. Trains convey second class seating a also sleeping cars where indicated. Information regarding rail services is still very hard to obta and the schedules shown should be treated as subject to confirmation.

A – 🛏 2 cl. Runs when required.
B – 🛏 2 cl.
C – Runs once per week. Days of operation unknown.

SAUDI ARABIA 4620

Haramain High-Speed Railway, Saudi Arabia Railways

apital: **Riyadh** (GMT +3). 2022 Public Holidays: May 3–5, July 9–12, Sept. 22.

audi Arabia Railways (SAR) (www.sar.com.sa) operates two passenger lines: **East** – between Ad Dammam and Ar Riyad, and **North** – between Qurayyat and Ar Riyad. **East** service trains convey st class (called Business which includes refreshments in the waiting rooms) and second class (Economy) seating, and have free Wi-Fi. The **North** service has day trains that convey business and conomy class and a night train that also conveys sleeper cabins which can accommodate up to four people. Reservations are available from 6 months until 1 hour before departure.

e 300km/h Haramain High-Speed Railway (www.sar.hhr.sa) links Makkah with King Abdulaziz International Airport and Madinah. Trains convey business and economy class seating.

chedules vary during Ramadan and Eid-al-Fitr.

km										
0	**Ad Dammam** d.	0442	0602	0803	1218	1449	1622	1749	1956	2214
74	Abqaiq d.	0526	0646	0847	1302	1533	1706	1833	2052	2311
139	Al Hufuf d.	0613	0722	0933	1450	1609	1753	1919	2138	2349
449	**Ar Riyad** a.	0830	...	1150	1611	...	2010	2136	2356	...

Ar Riyad d.	...	...	0702	0951	1222	1522	1648	...	1907
Al Hufuf d.	0605	0806	0932	1221	1452	1752	1918	2011	2137
Abqaiq d.	0645	0846	1012	1301	1532	1832	1958	2051	2217
Ad Dammam a.	0726	0928	1054	1343	1613	1914	2040	2133	2258

km				◧	③					
0	**Ar Riyad** d.	0930	1030	1730	2130	...	...	...	...	...
	Majma'ah d.	1058	1158	1900	2306	...	...	...	...	...
	Al Qassim d.	1209	1259	2001	0030	...	...	...	...	...
623	Hail d.	1359	...	...	0250	...	...	...	...	...
	Al Jouf d.	...	...	...	0535	...	...	...	...	...
242	**Qurayyat** a.	...	...	...	...	...	...	...	...	...

			◧	⑥					
Qurayyat d.	...	...	...	...	...	...	...	...	...
Al Jouf d.	...	...	...	2330	...	...	...	...	...
Hail d.	...	1535	...	0225	...	...	...	...	...
Al Qassim d.	1615	1745	2100	0449	...	...	...	...	...
Majma'ah d.	1726	1856	2211	0608	...	...	...	...	...
Ar Riyad a.	1850	2016	2331	0734	...	...	...	...	...

km																								
0	**Makkah** d.	...	0735	0800	...	...	0935	1135	...	1200	1335	...	...	1600	...	1635	...	1800	1835	1900	...	...	2100	2135
	KAI Airport ✈ ⊡ d.	0800	0822	|	...	0900	1022	1222	...	|	1422	1500	...	|	1700	1722	...	|	1922	|	...	2100	|	2222
78	Jeddah d.	|	...	|	...	|	...	...	...	|	...	|	...	1628	|	...	...	1828	...	1928	...	|	2128	...
182	King Abdullah Economic City d.	0835	...	0904	...	|	...	...	...	|	...	1535	...	|	|	...	...	1904	...	|	...	2135	2204	...
450	**Madinah** a.	0954	...	1025	...	1048	...	...	...	1415	...	1654	...	1820	1848	...	...	2025	...	2120	...	2254	2325	...

adinah d.	...	0800	0830	...	...	1000	...	...	1230	...	1400	...	1430	1530	...	...	1730	1800	...	...	...	2100	2130
ng Abdullah Economic City d.	...	0911	0943	...	...	|	...	...	|	...	1511	...	|	1643	...	...	|	|	...	...	...	2211	2243
ddah d.	...	|	|	...	...	|	...	...	|		|	...	1615	1721	...	...	1915	|	...	...	...	|	2321
KAI Airport ✈ ⊡ d.	0835	0954	|	...	1035	1148	1235	...	|	1535	1554	...	|	|	1735	...	|	1948	2035	...	2235	2254	|
akkah a.	0922	...	1055	...	1122	...	1322	...	1445	1622	...	...	1650	1755	1822	...	1949	...	2122	...	2322	...	2355

– Not daily. Operating days vary. ⊡ – King Abdulaziz International Airport.

IRAN 4630

apital: **Tehran** (GMT +3.5, add 1 hour in summer). 2022 Public Holidays: Jan. 6, Feb. 11, 15, Mar. 1, 19–24, Apr. 1, 2, 23, May 3, 4, 27, July 10, 18, Aug. 7, 8, Sept. 17, 25, Oct. 4, 13.

il services in Iran are provided by 11 different private companies. The ticket sales system is centralised (agents include www.raja.ir and www.iranrail.net), but every company issues its own kets. Most trains convey sleeping cars which convert to seating for daytime travel. For services to/from Turkey see Table **1575**.

km		198 ●	584 Ⓑ	318	368	354 ●	182 ●	190 ③–①	390	472	190 ②	366	320 B	396 A	346	340	348	384	474 ③–①	336 ●	474 ②	350	338 A	580
0	Tehran d.	0045	0144	0830	1505	1605	1650	1750	1820	1840	1900	1925	2005	2025	2045	2105	2125	2205	2215	2245	2315	2330	2350	2355
926	Mashhad a.	1140	1235	2050	0155	0235	0330	0430	0500	0545	0625	0550	0635	0650	0715	0735	0805	0835	0915	0930	1015	1005	1025	1050

	319	589 ●	183	191	473		581	397 ●	585	391	349		367	475	321 Ⓑ	347	355 ●		341	369	385	337	351
ashhad d.	0710	0920	1040	1335	1505	...	1545	1705	1725	1745	1805	...	1825	1945	2005	2035	2055	...	2135	2155	2215	2235	2359
hran a.	1920	2025	2150	0042	0225	...	0305	0350	0435	0420	0445	...	0500	0715	0650	0725	0740	...	0815	0840	0855	0920	1030

km		936	480	433		119 ⊖	431	731		131 ⊖	945	437		435	121	125		938	127	129				
	Djulfa d.	...	...	...	...	...	...	...	...	...	1630	...	...	...	...	...	...	...	...	...	...	...	...	...
0	Tabriz d.	...	1345	1650	...	...	1750	...	...	...	1920	2125	...	2225	...	...	...	...	...	...	...	...	...	...
	Khorramshahr d.	...	|	|	...	...	|	...	...	1450	...	|	...	|	...	...	...	...	...	...	...	...	...	...
	Ahvaz d.	...	|	|	...	1310	|	...	...	1653	...	|	...	|	...	...	...	...	...	...	...	...	...	...
	Qom d.	...	|	|	...	0230	|	0500	...	0559	...	|	...	|	0905	1445	...	...	1830	2050	...	...	...	...
736	Tehran d.	...	|	0530	...	0545	0620	0730	...	0840	...	0935	...	1050	1120	1700	...	...	2045	2305	...	...	...	...
662	Mashhad a.	1025	1300	...	...	...	...	...	...	...	...	...	...	...	...	...	...	1855	...	...	...	...	...	...
827	Sarakhs a.	1305	...	...	...	...	...	...	...	...	...	...	...	...	...	...	...	2155	...	...	...	...	...	...

km		120	124	126		130 ⊖	430	481		944	939	118 ⊖		937	128	436		730	432	434				
	Sarakhs d.	...	...	...	...	...	...	...	...	...	0605	...	...	1445	...	...	...	...	...	...	...	...	...	...
0	Mashhad d.	...	...	...	...	...	...	0635	...	...	0900	...	...	1735	...	...	...	...	...	...	...	...	...	...
926	Tehran d.	0520	1020	1500	...	1540	1650	|	...	...	...	1715	...	...	1750	2040	...	2120	2235	2335	...	...	...	...
06	Qom a.	0735	1225	1655	...	1808	|	|	...	...	...	1950	...	...	1950	|	...	2315	|	|	...	...	...	...
42	Ahvaz d.	...	...	...	...	0744	|	|	...	...	...	0835	...	...	...	|	...	...	|	|	...	...	...	...
65	Khorramshahr a.	...	...	...	...	0955	|	|	...	...	...	...	...	...	...	|	...	...	|	|	...	...	...	...
62	Tabriz a.	...	...	...	...	...	0510	0610	...	0830	...	...	...	...	...	0920	...	...	1040	1155	...	...	...	...
08	Djulfa a.	...	...	...	...	...	...	...	...	1125	...	...	...	...	...	...	...	...	...	...	...	...	...	...

km		581	585	724 ●	822	526	524	722 ●	620	
0	Tehran d.	0245	0415	1110	1515	1610	1805	2045	2145	...
94	Eşfahan d.	1020	1225	|	|	|	|	|	|	...
74	Shiraz a.	...	...	|	|	0735	0940	|	|	...
	Yazd d.	...	...	1916	2308	...	...	0501	0610	...
83	Bandar e Abbas a.	...	...	|	1020	...	...	|	...	...
	Kerman d.	...	...	0135	...	...	...	1055	...	...
58	Zahedan a.	...	...	0850	...	...	...	...	...	...

	584	527	621	723 ●	525	823	725 ●	580	
Zahedan d.	...	...	...	...	...	...	1340	...	...
Kerman d.	...	...	...	1725	...	...	2124	...	...
Bandar e Abbas d.	...	...	...	|	...	1515	|	...	...
Yazd d.	...	...	2245	2332	...	0239	0333	...	...
Shiraz d.	...	1500	|	|	1740	|	|	...	...
Eşfahan d.	1740	|	|	|	|	|	|	1545	...
Tehran a.	0204	0615	0700	0805	0905	1100	1205	2340	...

– ①③⑤⑦.
– ①②③④⑥.

● – Runs every 2nd day.
⊖ – May not call at Qom every day.

ZAHEDAN - QUETTA 4640

km		404 A	
0	**Zahedan** d.	1000	...
84	Mirjawa 🛃 a.	1220	...
84	Mirjawa 🛃 d.	1300	...
100	Kuhi Taftan a.	1550	...
100	Kuhi Taftan d.	1700	...
222	Nok Kundi d.	2156	...
389	Dalbandin d.	0535	...
578	Nushki d.	1256	...
689	Wali Khan d.	1737	...
712	Spezand d.	1930	...
737	**Quetta** a.	2025	...

	403 B	
Quetta d.	0800	...
Spezand d.	0915	...
Wali Khan d.	1014	...
Nushki d.	1500	...
Dalbandin d.	2240	...
Nok Kundi d.	0557	...
Kuhi Taftan a.	1000	...
Kuhi Taftan d.	1130	...
Mirjawa 🛃 a.	1425	...
Mirjawa 🛃 d.	1435	...
Zahedan a.	1700	...

kistan Railways and Raja Trains give different schedules for this train. This Table ows the Pakistan Railways version. The Raja version is: Quetta d. 0830 - Zahedan a. 1335 / hedan d. 0800 - Quetta a. 1515.

– (12) departs on 3rd and 17th of the month. **B** – (12) departs on 1st and 15th of the month.

QUETTA - DELHI 4650

km		23	402 ①④	14002 ①④
0	**Quetta** d.	1000	...	...
131	Sibi d.	1510	...	...
296	Jacobabad d.	1815	...	...
385	Rohri d.	2040	...	...
840	Khanewal d.	0425	...	...
1127	**Lahore** Junction a.	1015	...	...
1127	**Lahore** Junction d.	...	0800	...
	Wagah a.	...	0835	...
	Wagah d.	...	1130	...
1147	Atari 🛃 a.	...	1150	...
1147	Atari 🛃 d.	...	...	2000
1173	Amritsar Junction a.	...	...	2037
1620	**Delhi** Junction a.	...	...	0320

	14001 ③⑦	401 ①④	24
Delhi Junction d.	2310	...	...
Amritsar Junction d.	0650	...	...
Atari 🛃 a.	0715	...	...
Atari 🛃 d.	...	1100	...
Wagah a.	...	1410	...
Wagah d.	...	1610	...
Lahore Junction a.	...	1645	...
Lahore Junction d.	...	...	1700
Khanewal d.	...	...	2235
Rohri d.	...	...	0630
Jacobabad d.	...	...	0845
Sibi d.	...	...	1205
Quetta a.	...	...	1720

Timings are subject to confirmation and connections are not guaranteed.

BEYOND EUROPE
INDIA

Contents

INDEX OF PLACES

INDIA

Capital: **New Delhi** (GMT +5.5). 2022 Public Holidays: Jan. 26, Mar. 1, 18, Apr. 14, 15, May 3, 16, July 10, Aug. 8, 15, 19, Oct. 2, 5, 9, 24, Nov. 8, Dec. 25.

Rail services in India are operated by Indian Railways. Most trains convey a selection of first and second class accommodation from the several available. Trains which convey second class on are noted in either the column head or footnotes. Rajdhani and Shatabdi trains convey first class accommodation only. The exact carriage types available on each train varies.

A summary of train types and accommodation follows: **Rajdhani** (shown as *R* in column heads). Air-conditioned first class night trains. Special fares payable. Conveys First Class 2 or 4-ber sleepers (code 1A); two-tier (code 2A) and/or three-tier (code 3A) first class open plan berths; **Shatabdi** (shown as *S* in column heads). Air-conditioned first class daytime trains. Special fare payable. Conveys Chair class (code CC) and Executive Chair class seats (code EC); **Jan Shatabdi** (shown as *JS* in column heads) Conveys Chair class (code CC) and 2 berth sleepers (code 2S **Duronto** (shown in column heads as *D*). Some non-stop trains, some very limited stop trains. Conveys first class sleeping accommodation (codes 1A, 2A, 3A). Some may also convey second clas 'Sleeper Class' non air-conditioned six-berth (code SL); non air-conditioned second class seats (code 2S); **Express** (shown in column heads as *Exp*). Most services convey first class a conditioned two-tier (code 2A) or three-tier (code 3A) open plan berths; second class 'Sleeper Class' non air-conditioned six-berth (code SL); non air-conditioned second class seats (code 2S **Yuva** (shown in column heads as *Y*). Low-cost air-conditioned train. Seating accommodation only. During the day all sleepers and berths convert to seated accommodation. The codes shown a those used by Indian Railways.

Please note that on most routes only selected trains are shown, usually those that run daily or convey the best accommodation. Timings are the latest available and may change at any time. Sho notice changes are possible, especially around religious festivals and during monsoon seasons. Tickets can be purchased from stations or through authorised agents. Reservations are required f travel on all trains shown in this section. For international services to Pakistan see Table **4650**.

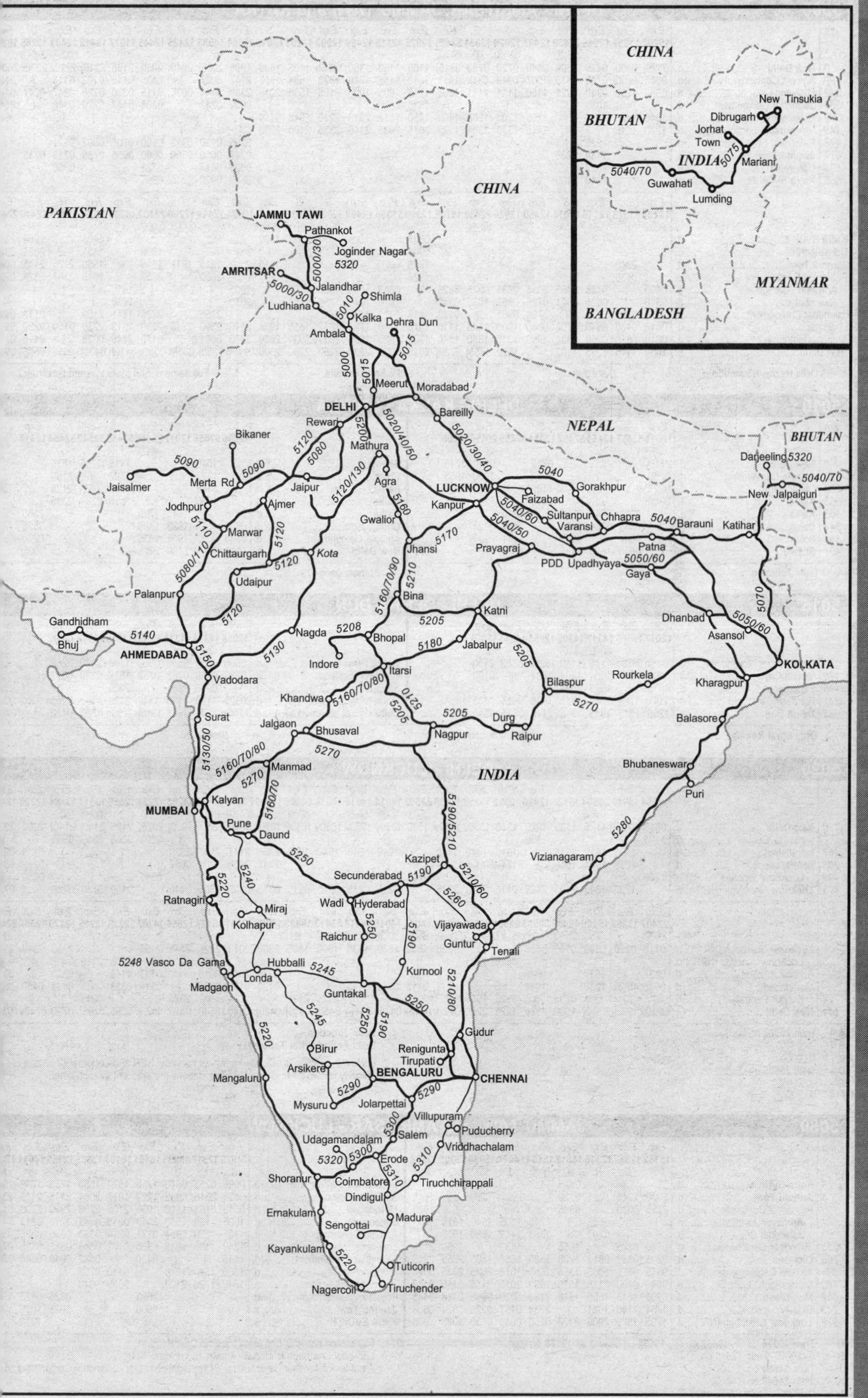
CHINA
BHUTAN
New Tinsukia
Dibrugarh
Jorhat Town
INDIA
5075
Mariani
5040/70
Guwahati
Lumding
MYANMAR
BANGLADESH
PAKISTAN
CHINA
JAMMU TAWI
Pathankot
Joginder Nagar
5320
5000/30
AMRITSAR
Jalandhar
5000/30
Shimla
Ludhiana
5010
Kalka
Dehra Dun
Ambala
5015
5000
5015
Meerut
Moradabad
DELHI
Bareilly
Rewari
5020/40/50
5020/30/40
5200
NEPAL
BHUTAN
Bikaner
5120
5080
Mathura
Darjeeling
5320
5090
5090
Agra
5040
5040/70
Jaisalmer
Merta Rd
Jaipur
5120/130
LUCKNOW
Gorakhpur
New Jalpaiguri
Jodhpur
Ajmer
Faizabad
5160
Kanpur
5040/60
Sultanpur
Chhapra
5040
Barauni
Katihar
5110
Gwalior
Varansi
Marwar
5120
5040/50
5170
Prayagraj
Patna
Chittaurgarh
5120
Kota
Jhansi
PDD Upadhyaya
5050/60
5080/110
Udaipur
Gaya
5160/70/90
5210
5070
Palanpur
Bina
Katni
5120
5205
Dhanbad
5050/60
Gandhidham
Nagda
5208
Bhopal
Asansol
5140
5180
Jabalpur
Bhuj
AHMEDABAD
5130
5205
5150
Indore
Itarsi
KOLKATA
Rourkela
Vadodara
Bilaspur
Kharagpur
Khandwa
5160/70/80
5210
5270
5205
5205
Surat
Durg
Balasore
Jalgaon
Bhusaval
Nagpur
Raipur
5270
5160/70/80
Manmad
INDIA
Bhubaneswar
5130/50
5270
Puri
Kalyan
MUMBAI
5160/70
5190/5210
Pune
Daund
5280
5250
Vizianagaram
Kazipet
5240
Secunderabad
5190
5210/60
5220
5260
Ratnagiri
Miraj
Wadi
Hyderabad
Kolhapur
5250
5190
Vijayawada
Raichur
Guntur
Tenali
5248 Vasco Da Gama
Hubballi
5245
Kurnool
Madgaon
Londa
Guntakal
5210/80
5250
5245
5250
5190
5220
Gudur
Birur
Renigunta
Tirupati
Arsikere
BENGALURU
CHENNAI
Mangaluru
5290
5290
Mysuru
Jolarpettai
5300
Villupuram
Puducherry
Udagamandalam
Salem
Vriddhachalam
5320
5300
Erode
5310
5310
Shoranur
Coimbatore
Tiruchchirappalli
Dindigul
Ernakulam
Madurai
Sengottai
Kayankulam
5220
Tuticorin
Nagercoil
Tiruchender

5000 DELHI - AMRITSAR, JAMMU TAWI and KATRA

Indian Railway

km		Exp	Exp	Exp	Exp	Exp	S	S	Exp	Exp	Exp	Exp	Exp	Exp	S	Exp	Exp	R	Exp	Exp	Exp	Exp	D	Ex
		15707	**11057**	**12919**	**22439**	**12497**	**12029**	**12031**	**22429**	**12925**	**12715**	**12459**	**12903**	**12203**	**12013**	**22461**	**14033**	**12425**	**12445**	**11077**	**12413**	**22401**	**12265**	**182**
					③–①		⑤–③	④	⑤–③					①②⑤								①③⑥	②⑤⑦	
0	**New Delhi** d.	0320j	0400	0435	0600	0640	0720	0720	0815j	1105	1140	1350	1405h	1405	1630	1905	2005j	2040	2050	2135	2210j	2220r	2220r	200
199	Ambala Cantonment d.	0655	0800	0740	0810	1007	0943	0943	1115	1440	1455	1710	1920	1654	1852	2147	0007	|	2335	0145	0102	0113	|	013
312	Ludhiana d.	0850	1255	0940	0921	1150	1111	1111	1305	1745	1805	1903	2105	1835	2019	2330	0147	0038	0115	0350	0228	0247	0247	044
365	Jalandhar Cantonment d.	|	1404	1033	|	|	|	|	|	1835	|	|	|	|	|	0022	0242	|	0208	0447	0320	0340	|	054
369	Jalandhar City d.	1040	1420	|	|	1255	1208	1208	1403	1850	1912	2013	2210	1940	2116	|	|	|	|	|	|	|	|	060
448	**Amritsar** Junction a.	1220	1615	|	|	1415	1330	1330	1520	2015	2035	2145	2335	2100	2230	|	|	|	|	|	|	|	|	073
478	Pathankot Cantonment d.	...	...	1226	|	...	...	...	...	...	...	...	...	...	...	0205	0430	0312	0500	0705	0502	0521	|	...
577	**Jammu Tawi** a.	...	...	1430	1238	...	...	...	...	...	...	...	...	...	...	0347	0650	0500	0600	0955	0735	0715	0715	...
630	Udhampur d.	...	...	1623	|	...	...	...	...	...	...	...	...	...	...	0508	0814	...	0723	...	...	0850	...	...
655	**Katra** SVDK ◧ a.	...	...	1710	1400	...	...	...	...	...	...	...	...	...	...	0610	0920	...	0805	...	...	...	...	...

	Exp	Exp	Exp	S	Exp	Exp	Exp	Exp	Exp	Exp	Exp	S	S	Exp	Exp	Exp	D	Exp	Exp	Exp	R	Exp	Ex
	12204	**11078**	**12716**	**12014**	**12460**	**12926**	**22430**	**15708**	**12920**	**11058**	**12498**	**12030**	**12032**	**22440**	**12904**	**12414**	**12266**	**22402**	**18238**	**14034**	**12425**	**12446**	**224**
	③⑥⑦						⑥–④					⑤–③	④	③–①			①③⑥	②④⑦					
Katra SVDK ◧ d.	...	...	...	...	...	...	...	...	0835	...	...	...	...	1500	...	...	...	...	...	1405	...	1955	230
Udhampur d.	...	...	...	...	...	...	...	...	0908	...	...	...	...	|	...	...	...	1800	...	1431	...	2021	232
Jammu Tawi d.	...	2340	...	...	...	...	...	...	1035	...	...	...	...	1615	...	1815	1915	1915	...	1550	2125	2143	004
Pathankot Cantonment d.	...	0138	...	...	...	...	...	...	1226	...	...	...	...	|	...	2000	|	2053	...	1815	2307	2328	022
Amritsar Junction d.	0400	|	0425	0455	0615	0735	0925	0825	|	0845	1510	1650	1650	|	1855	|	|	|	1610	|	|	|	|
Jalandhar City d.	0510	|	0535	0601	0725	0850	1035	0942	|	1010	1618	1756	1756	|	2010	|	|	|	1730	|	|	|	|
Jalandhar Cantonment d.	|	0325	|	|	0736	0901	|	0953	1418	1021	|	|	|	|	|	2155	|	2230	1741	2100	|	0113	04
Ludhiana d.	0613	0430	0640	0702	0840	1000	1148	1110	1520	1140	1725	1855	1855	1934	2110	2300	2330	2330	1913	2230	0150	0220	05
Ambala Cantonment d.	0810	0650	0950	0834	1050	1315	1350	1340	1705	1620	1925	2030	2030	2050	2300	0051	|	0110	2245	0035	|	0410	07
New Delhi a.	1050	1115	1245	1102	1415	1620	1655j	1720j	2015	2025	2230	2250	2250	2300	0345h	0350j	0355r	0355r	0410h	0430j	0555	0655	094

h – Delhi **Hazrat Nizamuddin**. j – Delhi **Junction**. r – Delhi **Sarai Rohilla**. ◧ – Full name is Shri Mata Vaishno Devi Katra.

5010 DELHI - KALKA - SHIMLA

Indian Railway

km		Exp				S		Exp	S	
		12311	**52457**	**52451**	**52453**	**12011**	**52455**	**22455**	**12005**	
								③⑦		
0	**New Delhi** d.	2110j	...	...	...	0740	...	0710	1715	...
199	Ambala Cantonment d.	0055	...	...	...	1022	...	1050	1953	...
268	Chandigarh d.	0225	...	...	...	1105	...	1132	2038	...
305	**Kalka** a.	0300	...	...	...	1140	...	1210	2115	...
305	**Kalka** ¶ d.	...	0330	0545	0620	...	1210	...	...	...
347	Barog ¶ d.	...	0555	0751	0831	...	1427	...	...	...
351	Solan ¶ d.	...	0607	|	0845	...	1441	...	...	...
401	**Shimla** ¶ a.	...	0855	1025	1135	...	1720	...	...	...

	S		S	Exp				Exp	
	12006	**52456**	**12012**	**22456**	**52458**	**52542**	**52454**	**12312**	
				④⑦					
Shimla ¶ d.	...	1040	...	...	1415	1755	1835	...	..
Solan ¶ d.	...	1323	...	...	1727	|	2109	...	..
Barog ¶ d.	...	1346	...	...	1750	2026	2125	...	..
Kalka ¶ a.	...	1610	...	...	2010	2230	2335	...	..
Kalka d.	0615	...	1745	1720	...	...	...	2355	..
Chandigarh d.	0653	...	1823	1800	...	...	...	0125	..
Ambala Cantonment d.	0738	...	1908	1855	...	...	...	0220	..
New Delhi a.	1015	...	2150	2215	...	...	...	0605j	..

j – Delhi **Junction**. ¶ – Narrow gauge railway.

5015 DELHI - DEHRA DUN

Indian Railway

km		S	Exp	Exp	Exp	JS	Exp	Exp		
		12017	**19565**	**14317**	**14309**	**12055**	**14041**	**12401**		
			⑥	①⑦	④⑤					
0	**Delhi** Hazrat Nizamuddin d.	0645n	0959a	1140	1140	1520n	2225j	2350	...	...
76	Meerut City d.	0803	1207	1304	1304	1634	|	0108	...	...
190	Saharanpur d.	1015	|	1525	1525	|	|	|	...	...
271	Haridwar Junction d.	1141	1715	1715	1715	1938	0645	0405	...	...
323	**Dehra Dun** a.	1255	1945	1945	1945	2110	0825	0540	...	...

	JS	Exp	Exp	Exp	S	Exp	Exp		
	12056	**14310**	**14318**	**19566**	**12018**	**14042**	**12402**		
		②③	⑤⑥	⑦					
Dehra Dun d.	0500	0550	0550	0550	1700	2120	2250	...	..
Haridwar Junction d.	0630	0758	0758	0758	1817	2320	0017	...	..
Saharanpur d.	|	0955	0955	|	2000	|	|	...	..
Meerut City d.	0923	1130	1130	1112	2125	|	0255	...	..
Delhi Hazrat Nizamuddin a.	1105n	1335	1335	1310n	2250n	0720j	0430	...	..

a – Delhi **Sarai Rohilla**. j – Delhi **Junction**. n – **New Delhi**.

5020 DELHI - LUCKNOW

Indian Railway

km		S	Exp	R	Exp	Exp	Exp	Exp	Exp	Exp	Exp	Exp	Exp	Exp	Exp	Exp	Exp	Exp	Exp	Exp	Exp	Exp	Exp	E
		12004	**15910**	**20504**	**15128**	**12420**	**12392**	**13258**	**12558**	**82502**	**14014**	**14016**	**14018**	**14008**	**14206**	**22418**	**22420**	**14208**	**12226**	**12556**	**13414**	**13484**	**12230**	**124**
				A						③–①	①⑥	⑤⑦	③	②④		①③⑤	B				①③⑥	C		
0	**New Delhi** d.	0610	0722j	1125	1135	1220	1310	1335v	1450v	1540	1630v	1630v	1630v	1630v	1820j	1840	1850v	1950j	2025j	2125	2140j	2140j	2200	23
	Kanpur Central d.	1125	|	|	|	1950	|	|	|	2040	|	|	|	|	|	|	|	|	0200	0305	0550	0550	|	|
167	Moradabad d.	|	1103	1410	1515	|	1610	1642	1745	|	1940	1940	1940	1940	2208	2147	2147	2320	|	|	|	|	0113	02
258	Bareilly Junction d.	|	1235	1524	1646	|	1740	|	|	|	|	|	|	|	2347	2308	2308	0057	|	|	|	|	0239	03
493	**Lucknow** Junction (NER*) a.	1250	|	|	|	|	|	|	|	2205	|	|	|	|	|	|	|	|	0345	|	|	|	0650	|
493	**Lucknow** Charbagh (NR*) a.	...	1720	1840	2105	2125	2115	2150	2245	...	0215	0215	0215	0215	0316	0305	0305	0440	...	0450	0730	0730	...	07

km		Exp	Exp	Exp	Exp	R	Exp	S	Exp	Exp	Exp	Exp	Exp	Exp	Exp	Exp	Exp	Exp	Exp	Exp	Exp	Exp	Exp	E
		22407	**13257**	**15909**	**12419**	**20503**	**82501**	**12003**	**14007**	**14013**	**14015**	**14017**	**13413**	**13483**	**14205**	**12391**	**15127**	**12556**	**14207**	**12229**	**12225**	**12429**	**12557**	**224**
		①⑤				D	③–①		④⑥	②⑦	①③	⑤	②⑤⑦	E										F
	Lucknow Charbagh (NR*) d.	0110	0220	0530	0545	0558	...	...	1828	1830	1830	1830	1905	1905	2000	2013	2025	2145	2155	...	...	2330	2340	23
0	**Lucknow** Junction (NER*) d.	|	|	|	|	|	0610	1535	|	|	|	|	|	|	|	|	|	|	|	2200	2315	|	|	|
	Bareilly Junction d.	0437	|	1037	|	0915	|	|	|	|	|	|	|	|	2336	2349	0015	|	0133	0145	|	0300	|	03
	Moradabad d.	0625	0728	1230	|	1055	|	|	0113	0113	0113	0113	|	|	0123	0135	0205	|	0318	0333	|	0435	0450	05
74	Kanpur Central d.	|	|	|	0735	|	0725	1653	|	|	|	|	2125	2125	|	|	|	2323	|	|	0045	|	|	|
511	**New Delhi** a.	0930v	1025v	1555j	1500	1338	1225	2220	0445v	0445v	0445v	0445v	0450j	0450j	0420j	0440	0540	0525	0625j	0655	0705j	0730	0740v	075

A – Train **20506** on ④⑦.
B – ②④⑥⑦.
C – ②④⑤⑦.
D – Train **20505** on ③⑦.
E – ①③④⑥.
F – ①③⑤⑦.

j – Delhi **Junction**.
v – Delhi **Anand Vihar Terminal**.
* – Lucknow Junction is officially known as Lucknow NER and Lucknow Charbagh is officially known as Lucknow NR. The stations are adjacent to each other.

5030 JAMMU TAWI and AMRITSAR - LUCKNOW

Indian Railway

km		Exp	Exp	Exp	Exp	Exp	Exp	Exp	Exp	Exp
		13152	**12332**	**12318**	**14612**	**18104**	**14674**	**15934**	**13006**	**12356**
			G	H	④	③⑤	J	⑤		③⑦
78	**Katra** SVDK ◧ d.	...	...	...	0525	...	...	...	...	...
0	**Jammu Tawi** d.	2030	2245	...	0720	...	...	...	...	1745
100	Pathankot Cantonment d.	2235	0030	...	0905	...	...	...	...	1925
**	**Amritsar** Junction d.	|	|	0555	|	1245	1305	1540	1825	|
**	Jalandhar City d.	|	|	0707	|	1358	1419	1650	1938	|
213	Jalandhar Cantonment d.	0030	0225	|	1055	|	1430	|	1950	2115
265	Ludhiana d.	0205	0330	0813	1203	1505	1555	1805	2055	2215
378	Ambala Cantonment d.	0415	0525	1005	1355	1655	1818	2025	2335	0015
460	Saharanpur d.	0545	0700	1135	1515	1820	2015	2155	0110	0140
652	Moradabad d.	0955	1013	1500	1818	2130	0020	0055	0458	0443
743	Bareilly Junction d.	1154	1140	1621	|	2254	0157	0225	0624	0608
978	**Lucknow** Charbagh (NR*) a.	1705	1520	2005	2320	0250	0610	0630	1035	1005

	Exp	Exp	Exp	Exp	Exp	Exp	Exp	Exp	E
	14673	**12317**	**15933**	**13151**	**18103**	**13005**	**12355**	**14611**	**12**
	K	L	④		②④		②⑥	⑤	M
Lucknow Charbagh (NR*) d.	0055	0253	0610	1250	1520	1550	1735	1735	19
Bareilly Junction d.	0423	0615	0932	1722	1917	2004	2115	2115	23
Moradabad d.	0613	0758	1110	1920	2100	2200	2300	2300	01
Saharanpur d.	1005	1130	1510	2340	0035	0145	0213	0213	04
Ambala Cantonment d.	1125	1250	1654	0121	0216	0320	0335	0335	05
Ludhiana d.	1350	1430	1835	0330	0403	0545	0535	0535	07
Jalandhar Cantonment d.	1445	|	|	0430	|	0647	0640	0640	08
Jalandhar City d.	1505	1540	1940	|	0510	0707	|	|	
Amritsar Junction a.	1640	1720	2100	|	0630	0840	|	|	
Pathankot Cantonment d.	...	...	...	0623	...	...	0825	0825	10
Jammu Tawi a.	...	...	...	0900	...	...	1025	1025	13
Katra SVDK ◧ a.	...	...	...	...	...	...	...	1230	.

G – Train **15098** on ②, **15652** on ③, **15654** on ⑤ and as **12588** on ⑥.
H – ①②④⑤. Train **12358** on ①④.
J – Train **14650** on ①③⑥.
K – Train **14649** on ①③⑥.
L – ①③④⑦. Train **12357** on ③⑦.
M – Train **12587** on ①, **15651** on ②, **15653** on ④ and **15097** on ⑤.

◧ – Full station name is Shri Mata Vaishno Devi Katra.
* – Lucknow Charbagh is officially known as Lucknow NR.
** – Amritsar - Jalandhar Cantonment: *84 km*. Jalandhar City - Jalandhar Cantonment: *5*

Indian Railways

DELHI - GUWAHATI 5040

km ●		Exp 15910	Exp 12506	R 20504 A	R 12424	Exp 20502 ③	Exp 14620 ①	Exp 14038 ④	Exp 22450 ③⑦	Exp 15657
0	**New Delhi** d.	0722j	0740v	1125	1620	1950v	2345	2345	2345	2340j
167	Moradabad d.	1103	|	1410	|	|	|	|	|	|
258	Bareilly Junction d.	1235	|	1524	|	|	|	|	|	|
493	Lucknow Charbagh ⊖ d.	1735	|	1850	|	|	|	|	|	|
764	Gorakhpur Junction d.	2345	|	|	|	|	|	|	|	|
981	Chhapra d.	0400	|	0212	|	|	|	|	|	|
437	Kanpur Central d.	|	1335	|	2110	0040	0540	0535	0535	0525
631	Prayagraj Junction ◧ d.	|	1615	|	2312	0452	0810	0810	0810	0800
772	PDD Upadhyaya Junction ⊡ d.	|	1853	|	0133	|	1102	1102	1102	1115
980	Patliputra d.	|	2155	|	0430	0750	1405	1405	1405	|
984	Patna Junction d.	|	|	|	|	|	|	|	|	1430
1205	Bhagalpur d.	|	|	|	|	|	|	|	|	1930
1348	New Farakka Junction d.	|	|	|	|	|	|	|	|	2242
1382	Malda Town d.	|	|	|	|	|	|	|	|	0015
1089	Barauni d.	0855	0045	|	0645	1015	1625	|	|	|
1269	Katihar d.	1240	0425	0830	0950	1340	1940	1940	1940	|
1452	New Jalpaiguri d.	1700	0745	1150	1255	1720	2300	2300	2300	0420
1703	New Bongaigaon d.	2225	1330	1542	1644	|	0357	0357	0357	0950
1854	**Kamakhya** Junction a.	|	1640	|	|	|	|	|	|	1330
1860	**Guwahati** a.	0215	...	1825	1925	2355	0805	0805	0815	...

	R 12423	Exp 20501 ②	Exp 14619 ⑤	Exp 14037 ②	Exp 22449 ③⑥	R 20503 B	Exp 15909	Exp 12505	Exp 15658
Guwahati d.	0700	0735	0600	0605	0610	0555	2200	...	...
Kamakhya Junction d.	|	|	|	|	|	|	|	1240	1435
New Bongaigaon d.	0920	|	0930	0930	0930	0820	0120	1540	1807
New Jalpaiguri d.	1325	1405	1325	1325	1325	1225	0545	1930	2305
Katihar d.	1615	1710	1635	1635	1635	1525	1000	2325	|
Barauni d.	1915	1955	2015	|	|	|	1425	0255	|
Malda Town d.	|	|	|	|	|	|	|	|	0345
New Farakka Junction d.	|	|	|	|	|	|	|	|	0419
Bhagalpur d.	|	|	|	|	|	|	|	|	0738
Patna Junction d.	|	|	|	|	|	|	|	|	1245
Patliputra d.	2150	2225	2245	2245	2245	|	|	0545	|
PDD Upadhyaya Junction ⊡ d.	0105	0135	0205	0205	0200	|	|	1005	1650
Prayagraj Junction ◧ d.	0255	|	0405	0405	0405	|	|	1230	1910
Kanpur Central d.	0505	0535	0630	0630	0630	|	|	1505	2135
Chhapra d.	|	|	|	|	|	2200	1945	|	|
Gorakhpur Junction d.	|	|	|	|	|	|	2345	|	|
Lucknow Charbagh ⊖ d.	|	|	|	|	|	0600	0530	|	|
Bareilly Junction d.	|	|	|	|	|	0915	1037	|	|
Moradabad d.	|	|	|	|	|	1055	1230	|	|
New Delhi a.	1030	1050v	1235	1235	1235	1338	1555j	2150v	0430j

A – ①②③⑤⑥.
B – ①③④⑤⑦.
j – Delhi **Junction**.
v – Delhi **Anand Vihar Terminal**.

◧ – Prayagraj (formerly Allahabad).
⊡ – Pt. Deen Dayal Upadhyaya (formerly Mughal Sarai).
⊖ – Officially known as Lucknow NR.
● – Chhapra - Barauni is *147 km*. Malda Town - New Jalpaiguri is *233 km*.

Indian Railways

DELHI - PATNA - KOLKATA 5050

km		Exp 13006	Exp 12334	Exp 12312	Exp 15484	Exp 12324 ④⑦		D 12274 ②⑥	Exp 12368	R 12314	R 12302 ⑥–④	Exp 12306 ⑤		R 12310	JS 12024	Exp 12394	Exp 12382 ①②⑤	Exp 12304 C		D 12260 D	Exp 12380 ⑦	Exp 12330 ③	Exp 20802	Exp 15657
0	**New Delhi** d.	...	...	0620j	0735j	0755j	...	1240	1315v	1630	1650	1650	...	1710	...	1730	1740	1740	...	1945	2015j	2020v	2105	2340j
440	Kanpur Central d.	...	...	1355	1510	1345	...	1740	1830	2120	2140	2140	...	2200	...	2244	2305	2305	...	0040	0115	0115	0345	0525
634	Prayagraj Junction ◧ d.	...	...	1700	1810	1630	...	|	|	|	2345	2345	...	0005	...	|	0150	0120	...	|	|	|	0625	0800
787	PDD Upadhyaya Junction ⊡ d.	...	...	2048	2138	1938	...	2212	2345	0142	0152	0152	...	0212	...	0328	0625	0355	...	0452	0623	0623	0918	1115
998	**Patna** Junction a.	2130	2255	|	0040	|	...	0100	0210	|	|	0425	...	0440	0530	0640	|	0700	...	|	|	|	1240	1420
992	Gaya d.	|	|	2335	...	2210	...	|	...	0348	0358	|	...	...	|	...	0915	|	...	|	0838	0838	...	...
1189	Dhanbad d.	|	|	0322	...	0120	...	|	...	0623	0638	|	...	...	|	...	1205	|	...	0917	1125	1125	...	...
1247	Asansol d.	0403	0423	0436	...	0230	...	0740	...	0711	0730	|	...	...	1043	...	1336	1336	...	|	1300	1300	...	...
1447	**Kolkata** Howrah a.	0730	0740	0805	...	0550	...	1035	...	1010e	0955	1215	...	...	1325	...	1700	1700	...	1315e	1635e	1635e	...	...

km		Exp 15658	Exp 12303 E	Exp 12381 ③④⑦	D 12273 ①⑤	Exp 12367		R 12309	Exp 12393	Exp 12329 ②	Exp 12379 ⑤	R 12305 ⑦		JS 12023	R 12301 ①–⑥	R 12313	D 12259 F	Exp 20801		Exp 12323 ②⑤	Exp 13005	Exp 12333	Exp 12311	Exp 15483
0	**Kolkata** Howrah d.	...	0800	0815	0835	...	...	...	...	1310e	1310e	1405	...	1405	1650	1650e	1700e	...	...	1850	1915	2000	2155	...
200	Asansol d.	...	1037	1048	1100	...	...	...	...	1607	1607	|	...	1642	1859	1920	|	...	...	2118	2156	2239	0037	...
	Dhanbad d.	...	|	1200	|	...	...	...	...	1715	1715	|	...	|	2000	2025	2035	...	...	2240	|	|	0150	...
	Gaya d.	...	|	1450	|	...	...	...	...	2005	2005	|	...	|	2237	2304	|	...	...	0152	|	|	0510	...
532	**Patna** Junction d.	1245	1605	|	1630	1705	...	1935	1945	|	|	2105	...	2220	|	|	|	1730	...	|	0340	0400	|	0320
744	PDD Upadhyaya Junction ⊡ d.	1650	1940	1800	2022	2040	...	2222	2232	2235	2235	0055	...	...	0055	0125	0135	2204	...	0435	...	...	0815	0700
896	Prayagraj Junction ◧ d.	1910	2145	2140	|	|	...	0012	|	|	|	0245	...	...	0245	|	|	0120	...	0650	...	...	1050	0935
1091	Kanpur Central d.	2135	0007	0007	0055	0110	...	0220	0230	0310	0310	0455	...	...	0455	0525	0535	0350	...	0920	...	...	1340	1300
1530	**New Delhi** a.	0430j	0600	0600	0635	0720v	...	0740	0755	0840v	0905j	1005	...	...	1005	1050	1100	1150	...	1515j	...	...	2050j	2145j

C – ③④⑥⑦.
D – ①②④⑤.
E – ①②⑤⑥.
F – ①③④⑦.

e – Kolkata **Sealdah**.
j – Delhi **Junction**.
v – Delhi **Anand Vihar Terminal**.

◧ – Prayagraj (formerly Allahabad).
⊡ – Pt. Deen Dayal Upadhyaya (formerly Mughal Sarai).

Indian Railways

LUCKNOW - PATNA - KOLKATA 5060

km ⊙		Exp 12354 ⑦	Exp 12370 G	Exp 13010	Exp 13006	Exp 12332 ①②⑤	Exp 13152	Exp 12358 ①④	Exp 12326 H	Exp 12372 ④
0	**Lucknow** Charbagh ⊖ d.	0120	0815	0845	1040	1530	1720	2015	2015	2345
77	Rae Bareli d.	0247	|	|	1205	|	|	|	|	0105
	Ayodhya d.	|	|	1132	|	|	2113	|	|	|
	Sultanpur d.	|	1023	|	|	1740	|	|	|	|
301	Varanasi Junction d.	0720	1305	1615	1705	2105	0140	0110	0110	0525
316	PDD Upadhyaya Junction ⊡ d.	0835	1425	1728	1810	2220	0255	0220	0225	0633
	Patna Junction d.	|	1730	|	2130	0120	|	|	0550	|
519	Gaya d.	1055	|	2050	|	|	0615	0435	|	0855
718	Dhanbad d.	1355	|	0108	|	|	1005	0721	|	1155
777	Asansol d.	1520	2358	0244	0403	0815	1145	0825	1128	1317
977	**Kolkata** Howrah a.	1825	0315	0700	0730	1130	1540k	1140k	1445k	1650

	Exp 12325 J	Exp 12371 ①	Exp 12353 ⑤	Exp 13151	Exp 12357 ②⑥	Exp 12369 K	Exp 13005	Exp 13009	Exp 12331 ②⑤⑥
Kolkata Howrah d.	0740k	0800	0815	1145k	1210k	1300	1915	2025	2355
Asansol d.	1037	1048	1048	1520	1452	1534	2156	0011	0235
Dhanbad d.	|	1200	1200	1655	1600	|	|	0130	|
Gaya d.	|	1450	1450	2110	1843	|	|	0500	|
Patna Junction d.	1605	|	|	|	|	2055	0350	|	0955
PDD Upadhyaya Junction ⊡ d.	1945	1755	1800	0145	2115	0035	0820	0930	1359
Varanasi Junction d.	2040	1915	1910	0250	2211	0150	0925	1030	1447
Sultanpur d.	|	|	|	|	|	0420	|	|	1648
Ayodhya d.	|	|	|	0705	|	|	|	1358	|
Rae Barali d.	|	2300	2308	|	|	|	1305	|	|
Lucknow Charbagh ⊖ a.	0243	0100	0100	1235	0243	0715	1535	1800	1935

G – Train **12328** on ④⑦.
H – ②⑤⑥. Train **12318** on ②⑤ (calls at Sultanpur d. 2213).
J – ③④⑦. Train **12317** on ③⑦ (calls at Sultanpur d. 2248).
K – Train **12327** on ②⑤.

k – **Kolkatta**.

⊡ – Pt. Deen Dayal Upadhyaya (formerly Mughal Sarai).
⊖ – Officially known as Lucknow NR.
⊙ – Lucknow - Varanasi is *324 km* via Ayodhya and *283km* via Sultanpur.
For distances PDD Upadhyaya - Patna - Asansol - Kolkata see Table **5050**.

Bangladesh Railways, Indian Railways

KOLKATA - DHAKA 5065

km		Exp 13108 ①⑥	Exp 13109 ②⑤							
0	**Kolkata** Chitpur ♠ d.	0710	0710	...	...	...	...	...	...	...
122	Gede ♠ d.	|	|	...	...	...	...	...	...	...
	Darsana 🏛 a.	|	|	...	...	...	...	...	...	...
540	**Dhaka** Cantonment a.	1605	1605	...	...	...	...	...	...	...

	Exp 13107 ⑤⑦	Exp 13110 ③⑥							
Dhaka Cantonment d.	0815	0815	...	...	...	...	...	...	...
Darsana 🏛 d.	|	|	...	...	...	...	...	...	...
Gede ♠ d.	|	|	...	...	...	...	...	...	...
Kolkata Chitpur ♠ a.	1600	1600	...	...	...	...	...	...	...

♠ – Local trains operate Kolkata - Gede and v.v.

Indian Railways

KOLKATA - NEW JALPAIGURI - GUWAHATI 5070

km		Exp 13175 ①③⑥	Exp 13173 L	Exp 15643 ⑦	Exp 13181 ①	Exp 12345	Exp 15959 M			
0	**Kolkata** Howrah d.	0635e	0635e	0730	0905k	1555	1800	...	...	...
207	Rampurhat d.	1027	1027	|	1231	1855	|	...	...	...
293	New Farakka Junction d.	1243	1243	1358	|	2040	0042	...	...	...
328	Malda Town d.	1345	1345	1510	1510	2140	0155	...	...	...
473	Kishanganj d.	1557	1557	1727	|	2337	0415	...	...	...
561	New Jalpaiguri d.	1815	1825	1910	1915	0140	0605	...	...	...
812	New Bongaigaon d.	0020	0020	0215	0040	0630	1145	...	...	...
963	**Kamakhya** Junction a.	|	|	0525	0410	|	|	...	...	...
969	**Guwahati** a.	0340	0340	...	0430	1005	1540	...	...	...

	Exp 15960 M	Exp 12346	Exp 13182 ②	Exp 13176 ①③⑤	Exp 13174 N	Exp 15644 ④			
Guwahati d.	0740	1220	1715	2250	2250	...	...	...	...
Kamakhya Junction d.	|	1239	1745	2315	2315	2345	...	...	...
New Bongaigaon d.	1140	1523	2105	0220	0220	0245	...	...	...
New Jalpaiguri d.	1625	1920	0110	0700	0700	0855	...	...	...
Kishanganj d.	1742	2027	|	0817	0817	1000	...	...	...
Malda Town d.	2210	2340	0630	1235	1235	1355	...	...	...
New Farakka Junction d.	2249	0016	|	1314	1314	1429	...	...	...
Rampurhat d.	|	0148	0830	|	1502	|	...	...	...
Kolkata Howrah a.	0600	0515	1230k	1925e	1925e	2255	...	...	...

L – ②④⑤⑦. M – ②③④⑥⑦. N – ②④⑥⑦. e – Kolkatta **Sealdah**. k – **Kolkatta**.

5075 GUWAHATI - JORHAT and DIBRUGARH
Indian Railways

km		Exp 15910	JS 12067 ①-⑥	Exp 15905 ⑦	Exp 13282 ⑦	Exp 15665	Exp 15959 A	R 20504 B	R 12424	Exp 15669
0	**Guwahati** d.	0240	0610	0910	1055	1430	1550	1850	1950	2045
87	Chaparmukh Junction d.	0410	0729	|	1222	1600	1718	|	2122	|
184	Lumding Junction d.	0605	0905	1205	1405	1810	1910	2157	2257	0010
250	Dimapur d.	0722	1017	1347	1524	1935	2040	2317	0018	0208
323	Furkating Junction d.	0932	1144	1542	1712	2117	2305	|	|	0400
376	**Jorhat Town** d.	|	1300	|	|	2238	|	|	|	0500
358	Mariani Junction d.	1012	...	1630	1755	2315	2355	0205	0235	0650
513	New Tinsukia Junction d.	1320	...	1945	2130	...	0315	|	0455	|
561	**Dibrugarh** a.	1435	...	2050	2230	...	0415	0435	0600	1015

	Exp 15666	Exp 13281 ①	JS 12068 ①-⑥	Exp 15909	Exp 15670	R 20503 B	Exp 15906 ⑥	R 12423	Exp 159 C
Dibrugarh d.	...	0520	...	1020	1400	1955	1925	2055	184
New Tinsukia Junction d.	...	0625	...	1115	|	|	2020	2155	194
Mariani Junction d.	0605	0910	...	1350	|	2215	2248	0010	232
Jorhat Town d.	0637	|	1430	|	1741	|	|	|	|
Furkating Junction d.	0810	1007	1547	1452	1950	|	2342	|	002
Dimapur d.	0926	1149	1652	1600	2110	0018	0049	0207	021
Lumding Junction d.	1120	1320	1805	1730	2320	0200	0243	0317	035
Chaparmukh Junction d.	1256	1450	1940	1845	|	|	|	0436	053
Guwahati a.	1455	1700	2120	2135	0340	0530	0625	0630	072

A – ①③④⑤⑦. B – ②③④⑥⑦. C – ①②③⑤⑥.

5080 DELHI - JAIPUR - AHMEDABAD
Indian Railway

km		S 12015	Exp 20940 ④	Exp 19408 ⑦	Exp 12215 D	Exp 12916	JS 12066 E	Exp 22950 ④	R 12958	Exp 19032
0	**Delhi** Junction d.	0610n	0630	0630	0855r	1520	1615r	1615r	1955n	2225
83	Rewari d.	0747	0805	0805	1020	1700	1737	1737	|	0010
157	Alwar d.	0845	0906	0906	1121	1807	|	|	|	0117
308	**Jaipur** d.	1045	1120	1120	1405	2035	|	|	0011	0345
444	Ajmer Junction d.	1255	1335	1335	1620	2240	2215	2300	0230	0620
581	Marwar Junction d.	...	1525	1525	|	|	...	|	|	0840
749	Abu Road d.	...	1800	1800	2025	0250	...	0320	0615	1115
801	Palanpur Junction d.	...	1855	1855	2123	0350	...	0420	0658	1208
866	Mahesana Junction d.	...	2008	2008	|	0458	...	0525	0752	1316
934	**Ahmedabad** Junction a.	...	2200	2200	0035	0640	...	0710	0930	1540

	S 12016	Exp 20939 ①	Exp 19031	R 12957	Exp 12915	Exp 12216 F	Exp 22949 ③	JS 12065 E	Exp 194 ④
Ahmedabad Junction d.	...	0800	1050	1745	1830	1855	1940	...	214
Mahesana Junction d.	...	0914	1235	1850	1937	|	2059	...	225
Palanpur Junction d.	...	1047	1410	2000	2102	2210	2305	...	001
Abu Road d.	...	1140	1505	2045	2150	2300	0005	...	010
Marwar Junction d.	...	1352	1740	|	|	|	|	...	032
Ajmer Junction d.	1545	1620	2035	0100	0215	0350	0500	0540	062
Jaipur d.	1745	1820	2250	0255	0415	0615	|	|	091
Alwar d.	1947	2016	0110	|	0631	0815	|	|	111
Rewari d.	2052	2156	0255	|	0802	0925	1000	1000	124
Delhi Junction a.	2240n	2355	0450	0730n	1000	1100r	1135r	1135r	144

D – ①②④⑥. E – ①②③⑤⑥. F – ②③⑤⑦. n – **New Delhi**. r – Delhi **Sarai Rohilla**.

5090 DELHI - JODHPUR - JAISALMER
Indian Railways

km		Exp 15014	Exp 22421	Exp 15624 ⑦	Exp 14646 G	Exp 12323 ③⑥	Exp 14810	Exp 12462	Exp 12463 ③	Exp 22482
0	**Delhi** Junction d.	0430	0705r	1005	1100	1540	...	2120	2225r	2310r
83	Rewari d.	0625	0835	1141	1335	1717	...	2313	|	0038
	Churu d.	|	1145	1520	|	2055	...	|	|	0400
	Ratangarh Junction d.	|	1245	1610	|	2155	...	|	|	0448
157	Alwar d.	0741	|	|	1455	|	...	0014	0051	|
308	Jaipur d.	1010	|	|	1745	|	...	0235	0300	|
	Ajmer Junction d.	1225	|	|	|	|	...	|	|	|
	Marwar Junction d.	1500	|	|	|	|	...	|	|	|
471	Degana Junction d.	|	1506	1825	2058	|	...	0503	0533	0716
516	Merta Road d.	|	1548	1902	2132	|	...	0544	0612	0802
620	**Jodhpur** Junction a.	1640	1800	2055	2300	0240	...	0750	0835	1005
620	**Jodhpur** Junction d.	1655	...	...	2335	...	0705	...	...	...
757	Phalodi d.	1855	...	...	0140	...	0901	...	...	...
804	Ramdevra d.	1939	...	...	0224	...	0948	...	...	...
814	Pokaran d.	|	...	...	0310	...	1015	...	...	...
921	**Jaisalmer** a.	2215	...	...	0545	...	1240	...	...	...

	Exp 15013	Exp 22422	Exp 15623 ②	Exp 22481	Exp 12464 ④	Exp 12461	Exp 12324 ③⑥	Exp 14809	Exp 1464 H
Jaisalmer d.	0255	...	...	...	...	...	...	1500	224
Pokaran d.	|	...	...	...	...	...	...	1650	002
Ramdevra d.	0442	...	...	...	...	...	...	1728	010
Phalodi d.	0531	...	...	...	...	...	...	1812	014
Jodhpur Junction a.	0800	...	...	...	...	...	...	2110	040
Jodhpur Junction d.	0815	1055	1630	1845	1940	2010	1930	...	041
Merta Road d.	|	1210	1758	2013	2055	2132	|	...	054
Degana Junction d.	|	1249	1834	2055	2153	2208	|	...	061
Marwar Junction d.	1035	|	|	|	|	|	|	...	|
Ajmer Junction d.	1305	|	|	|	|	|	|	...	|
Jaipur d.	1530	|	|	|	0045	0115	|	...	102
Alwar d.	1744	|	|	|	0231	0313	|	...	130
Ratangarh Junction d.	|	1605	2130	2340	|	|	0125	...	|
Churu d.	|	1655	2225	0035	|	|	0220	...	|
Rewari d.	1910	2025	0240	0342	|	0435	0551	...	144
Delhi Junction a.	2115	2210r	0430	0520r	0535r	0630	0730	...	165

G – ②③⑤⑦. Also runs Delhi - Jodhpur on ①④⑥ as train **14662**.
H – ①③④⑥. Also runs Jodhpur - Delhi on ①③⑥ as train **14661**.
r – Delhi **Sarai Rohilla**.

5110 BIKANER - JODHPUR - AHMEDABAD
Indian Railways

km		Exp 19224	Exp 14707	Exp 22473 ①	Exp 12489 ②⑥	Exp 16311 ②	Exp 22475 ③	Exp 22738 ⑤⑦	Exp 17624 ⑥	Exp 16588 ②⑦
0	**Bikaner** Junction d.	0025	0750	1500	1500	1815	1815	1815	1815	1905
173	Merta Road d.	0301	1012	1720	|	2057	2057	2057	2057	2145
277	**Jodhpur** Junction d.	0515	1305	1950	1940	2300	2300	2345	2345	2335
308	Luni d.	|	1335	|	|	|	2333	|	|	|
380	Marwar Junction d.	0730	1545	2140	|	0100	0100	0204	0204	0135
545	Abu Road d.	0955	1825	0010	|	0320	0320	0425	0425	0355
598	Palanpur Junction d.	1050	1923	0105	|	0420	0420	0520	0520	0455
663	Mahesana Junction d.	1147	2034	0211	0239	|	0525	0617	0617	0552
736	**Ahmedabad** Junction d.	1345	2250	0405	0435	0710	0710	0750	0755	0735

	Exp 22737 ④⑤	Exp 17623 ⑤	Exp 16312 ①	Exp 19223	Exp 16587 ①⑥	Exp 22476 ⑦	Exp 22474 ②	Exp 14708	Exp 1249 ③⑦
Ahmedabad Junction d.	0015	0055	0650	1105	2010	2135	2140	2155	231
Mahesana Junction d.	0122	0210	|	1210	2129	2257	2252	2326	001
Palanpur Junction d.	0250	0332	1027	1345	2312	0010	0010	0052	|
Abu Road d.	0335	0425	1120	1435	0055	0100	0100	0145	|
Marwar Junction d.	0608	0655	1345	1705	0245	0335	0335	0435	|
Luni d.	|	|	|	|	|	0443	|	0543	|
Jodhpur Junction d.	0800	0900	1525	1900	0435	0530	0530	0625	073
Merta Road d.	0935	1055	1715	2041	0612	0706	0706	0800	|
Bikaner Junction a.	1250	1335	2010	0055	0935	1000	1010	1130	123

5120 DELHI and JAIPUR - UDAIPUR - AHMEDABAD
Indian Railway

km		Exp 19610 ①③⑥	Exp 12992	Exp 12315 ⑤	Exp 19616 ⑥	Exp 19602 ②	Exp 22986 ⑦	Exp 19665	Exp 12963	Exp 20473
0	**Delhi** Junction d.	0030	...	...	...	1220	1615r	...	1825h	1935r
83	Rewari d.	0227	...	...	...	1510	|	...	|	2102
157	Alwar d.	0328	...	...	...	1617	1839	...	J	|
**	**Jaipur** d.	0625	1400	1610	1610	1910	2050	2225	|	|
373	Ajmer Junction d.	0855	1600	1820	1820	2135	2300	0040	|	0205
559	Chittaurgarh d.	1305	1917	|	|	|	|	0420	0455	0525
673	**Udaipur** City d.	1555	2140	0025	0025	0315	0430	0635	0720	0750
883	Himmatnagar ◧ d.	...	...	...	...	...	...	...	...	...
971	**Ahmedabad** ◧ a.	...	...	...	...	...	...	...	...	...

	Exp 12991	Exp 12316 ①	Exp 19601 ⑥	Exp 19609 ①④⑥	Exp 19615 ①	Exp 20474	Exp 12964	Exp 19666	Exp 2298 ⑥
Ahmedabad ◧ d.	...	...	...	...	...	...	...	...	...
Himmatnagar ◧ d.	...	...	...	...	...	...	...	...	...
Udaipur City d.	0600	0045	0045	1345	1600	1700	1830	2210	232
Chittaurgarh d.	0810	|	|	1610	|	1903	2103	0020	|
Ajmer Junction d.	1122	0625	0625	1935	2100	2220	|	0325	044
Jaipur d.	1335	0855	0915	2150	2255	|	K	0525	065
Alwar d.	...	...	1113	0011	...	|	|	...	091
Rewari d.	...	...	1243	0126	...	0325	|	...	|
Delhi Junction a.	...	...	1445	0310	...	0505r	0710h	...	1205

J – Via Mathura (d. 2030), Sawai Madhopur (d. 2305) and Kota (d. 0045).
K – Via Kota (d. 0020), Sawai Madhopur (d. 0125) and Mathura (d. 0440).
h – Delhi **Hazrat Nizamuddin**.
r – Delhi **Sarai Rohilla**.
◧ – Service suspended for gauge conversion.
** – Jaipur - Ajmer is *136 km*.

5130 DELHI and JAIPUR - AHMEDABAD and MUMBAI
Indian Railways

km		Exp 12904	D 12264 ①④	Exp 22934 ②	Exp 12956	Exp 12215 A	Exp 12918 ⑥	D 12240 ②④	Exp 12980 ①③⑤	Exp 12926	Exp 22950 ④	Exp 12908 ①④		Exp 12910 ③⑤⑦	Y 12248 ⑥	R 12952	R 12954	Exp 12472 B	Exp 19020	Exp 12476 ①	Exp 12474 ④	Exp 12478 ⑦	D 22210 ②⑥	Exp 2291 ④
0	**Delhi** Hazrat Nizamuddin d.	0400	0616	...	...	0855r	1325	...	...	...	1615r	1630	...	1630	1630	...	1715	...	1855	...	...	...	...	221
	New Delhi d.	|	|	...	...	|	|	...	...	1635	|	|	...	|	|	1655	|	2140	|	2140	2140	2140	2210	|
124	Mathura Junction d.	0550	|	...	...	|	1455	...	...	1915	|	|	...	1805	1805	|	1845	2325	2200	2325	2325	2325	|	000
	Jaipur d.	|	|	1300	1400	1405	|	1650	2025	|	|	|	...	|	|	|	|	|	|	|	|	|	|	|
340	Sawai Madhopur d.	0835	|	1525	1605	|	|	1855	2240	2215	|	|	...	|	|	|	2050	0135	0150	0135	0135	0135	|	023
448	Kota Junction d.	1025	1055	1635	1720	|	1815	|	0005	2345	|	2120	...	2120	2120	2140	2210	0255	0410	0255	0255	0255	0350	035
673	Nagda Junction d.	1342	|	1932	2037	|	|	|	0232	0340	|	|	...	|	|	2359	|	0555	0820	0552	0552	0552	|	|
714	Ratlam Junction d.	1425	1405	2025	2120	|	2135	2335	0315	0435	|	|	...	0018	0018	0030	0107	0640	0925	0640	0640	0640	0705	071
1075	**Ahmedabad** Junction d.	|	|	|	|	0045	0320	|	|	|	0710	|	...	|	|	|	|	|	|	1215	1215	1215	|	|
976	Vadodara Junction d.	1838	1737	0043	0110	0222	...	0318	0715	0835	0905	0405	...	0405	0405	0350	0439	1037	1435	...	...	...	1043	110
1104	Surat d.	2011	|	0237	0258	0400	...	|	0904	1035	1130	|	...	0545	0545	0518	0618	1230	1707	...	...	...	|	131
1340	Borivali d.	2255	△	0549	0600	0650	...	|	1224	1440	1414	0829	...	0829	|	0744	0912	1517	2121	...	...	...	|	160
	Mumbai Central a.	2345	...	|	0655	|	...	0820	|	|	|	|	...	|	|	0835	1005	|	|	...	...	...	1550	|
1360	**Mumbai** Bandra a.	...	...	0635	...	0735	...	...	1310	1525	1510	0915	...	0915	0915	...	...	1610	2215	...	...	...	...	165

FOR RETURN SERVICE AND FOOTNOTES SEE NEXT PAGE →

ndian Railways — MUMBAI and AHMEDABAD - JAIPUR and DELHI — 5130

km		Exp	Exp	Exp	Exp	Exp	Exp	D	R	Exp	R	Exp		Exp	Exp	Exp	Exp	Y	Exp	Exp	Exp	Exp	D	D
		19019	12471	12475	12477	12473	12917	12263	12951	22917	12953	12925		22933	12979	12907	12909	12247	12216	22949	12903	12955	22209	22239
			C	②	③	⑥	①	②⑤		③				①	②④⑥	③⑦	②④⑥	⑤	D	③			①⑤	②⑦
0	**Mumbai** Bandra d.	0005	1100	...	...	...	...	...	...	1245	...	1130	...	1705	1705	1730	1730	1730	1200	1215	...	...	...	...
	Mumbai Central d.	|	|	...	...	...	...	...	1700	|	1710	|	...	|	|	|	|	|	|	|	1845	1905	2300	2300
19	Borivali d.	0035	1126	...	...	...	...	▽	1724	1312	1735	1158	...	1740	1740	1757	1757	|	1224	1240	1922	1936	|	|
252	Surat d.	0420	1423	...	...	...	...	|	1948	1621	2015	1552	...	2040	2040	|	2052	2052	1516	1539	2202	2235	|	|
381	Vadodara Junction d.	0622	1600	...	...	...	...	1831	2113	1837	2149	1740	...	2230	2230	2225	2225	2225	1649	1711	2344	0012	0329	0329
	Ahmedabad Junction d.	|	|	1425	1425	1425	1530	|	|	|	|	|	...	|	|	|	|	|	1855	1940	|	|	|	|
642	Ratlam Junction d.	1150	1955	1955	1955	1955	2040	2200	0028	2245	0115	2145	...	0215	0215	|	0153	0153	|	|	0335	0410	0705	0705
684	Nagda Junction d.	1310	2048	2048	2048	2048	|	|	0110	|	|	2300	...	0305	0305	|	|	|	|	|	0428	0500	|	|
909	Kota Junction d.	1735	2330	2330	2330	2330	0001	0105	0320	0215	0420	0155	...	0530	0530	0445	0445	0445	|	|	0720	0755	1005	|
017	Sawai Madhopur d.	1945	0035	0035	0035	0035	|	|	|	0322	0525	0312	...	0720	0720	|	|	|	|	|	0830	0945	|	1155
148	**Jaipur** a.	|	|	|	|	|	|	|	|	|	|	|	...	0945	0945	|	|	|	0605	|	|	1150	|	1355
	Mathura Junction d.	0015	0320	0320	0320	0320	0345	|	|	0625	0800	0740	...	...	...	|	0822	0822	|	|	1150	...	|	...
	New Delhi a.	|	|	|	|	|	|	|	0832	|	|	|	...	...	...	|	|	|	|	|	|	...	1555	...
	Delhi Hazrat Nizamuddin a.	0230	0505	0505	0505	0505	0550	0645	...	0835	0943	0959	...	...	...	1015	1015	1015	1100r	1135r	1350	...	...	...

– ①②④⑥.
– ②③⑤⑥.
– ①④⑤⑦.
– ②③⑤⑦.

r – Delhi **Sarai Rohilla**.
△ – To Pune (a. 0210).
▽ – From Pune (d. 1110).

FOR RETURN SERVICE SEE PREVIOUS PAGE.

ndian Railways — BHUJ - GANDHIDHAM - AHMEDABAD — 5140

km		Exp	Exp	Exp	Exp	Exp	Exp	Exp	Exp	Exp
		16505	12473	11091	22904	12937	22952	22956	20908	20804
		②	⑥	③	①④⑥	⑥	④			⑦
58	**Bhuj** d.	...	...	1325	1605	...	...	2015	2235	...
0	**Gandhidham** d.	0900	0910	1450	1720	1810	2040	2135	2355	2305
53	Samakhiali d.	0950	1000	1549	1807	1900	2132	2232	0054	2359
170	Dhrangadhra d.	1125	|	1721	|	2024	|	0007	0230	|
236	Viramgam Junction d.	1228	1247	1835	|	|	0232	0121	0344	0232
301	**Ahmedabad** Junction a.	1400	1410	1955	2200	2255	0400	0245	0510	0400

	Exp	Exp	Exp	Exp	Exp	Exp	Exp	Exp	Exp
	20803	22955	16506	22903	11092	12938	12474	22951	20907
	⑥		①	①④⑥	②	③	⑤	⑤	
Ahmedabad Junction d.	0055	0150	0555	0640	0745	0920	1215	2235	2350
Viramgam Junction d.	0148	0243	0657	|	0838	|	1338	2328	0046
Dhrangadhra d.	|	0345	0759	|	0950	1117	|	|	0153
Samakhiali d.	0454	0542	0945	1010	1142	1309	1629	0427	0345
Gandhidham a.	0615	0650	1100	1110	1245	1425	1740	0540	0445
Bhuj a.	...	0830	...	1240	1430	...	...	...	0630

ndian Railways — AHMEDABAD - MUMBAI — 5150

km		Exp	Exp	Exp	Exp	Exp		Exp	Exp	Exp	Exp	Exp		S	Exp	Exp	Exp	Exp		Exp	Exp	Exp	Exp	
		12215	22956	12479	22952	12934		12489	20908	12932	22954	19016		12010	19218	22946	22928	14701		22904	12902	14707	12972	
		E			⑤			③⑦						①–⑥						①④⑥				
0	**Ahmedabad** Junction d.	0045	0300	0350	0415	0455	...	0455	0530	0600	0705	0715	...	1505	2000	2030	2045	2205	...	2215	2250	2305	2355	...
100	Vadodara d.	0222	0448	0530	0603	0628	...	0641	0720	0726	0840	0948	...	1635	2205	2215	2232	0008	...	2348	0030	0050	0137	...
229	Surat d.	0400	0650	0732	0756	0808	...	0830	0953	0917	1047	1242	...	1815	0025	0013	0037	0203	...	0125	0215	0244	0329	...
462	Borivali d.	0650	1042	1038	1102	1112	...	1143	1304	1206	1453	1821	...	2048	0441	0350	0430	0523	...	0406	0528	0625	0726	...
480	**Mumbai** Bandra a.	0735	1145	1130	1155	1210**c**	...	1225**d**	1350**d**	1255**c**	1524**d**	1852**d**	...	2145**c**	0545	0418**d**	0525	0616	...	0455	0615**d**	0710**d**	0815	...

	Exp	S	Exp	Exp	Exp		Exp	Exp	Exp	Exp	Exp		Exp	Exp	Exp	Exp	Exp		Exp	Exp	Exp	Exp	
	22953	12009	19015	12216	14708		12480	19217	12933	12931	22951		12490	20907	22955	12971	22927		14702	22945	12901	22903	
		①–⑥		E							⑤		③⑦									③⑤⑦	
umbai Bandra d.	0545**c**	0610**c**	0920**c**	1200	1235**d**	...	1325	1340	1405**c**	1430**c**	1440	...	1500**d**	1515**d**	1745	1910	1940	...	2100	2105**c**	2140**d**	2345	...
orivali d.	0620	0635	0954	1224	1301	...	1351	1405	1433	1455	1503	...	1525	1539	1812	1943	2014	...	2131	2154	2204	0015	...
urat d.	1003	0908	1452	1516	1704	...	1642	1740	1718	1752	1826	...	1838	1910	2142	2307	0030	...	0055	0107	0119	0310	...
adodara d.	1200	1040	1755	1649	1900	...	1823	1952	1851	1923	2013	...	2040	2125	2333	0050	0215	...	0240	0252	0258	0447	...
hmedabad Junction a.	1430	1225	2020	1840	2140	...	2030	2155	2105	2125	2220	...	2255	2335	0135	0245	0420	...	0430	0500	0555	0625	...

– ②③⑤⑦.

c – Mumbai **Central**.

d – Mumbai **Dadar**.

Indian Railways — DELHI - PUNE and MUMBAI — 5160

km		Exp	Exp	D	Exp	Exp	Exp	Exp	R	Exp
		12782	12138	12264	22686	12630	11078	12780	22222	11058
		①		①④	②⑥	③⑤				
0	**Delhi** Hazrat Nizamuddin d.	0510	0515**n**	0616	0828	0830	1130**n**	1515	1655	2053
134	Mathura Junction d.	0645	0705	|	|	|	1325	1700	|	2305
188	Agra Cantonment d.	0735	0815	|	|	|	1415	1755	1850	2335
306	Gwalior d.	0943	1009	|	|	|	1630	2032	2015	0157
403	Jhansi VGLB ⊡ d.	1130	1205	|	1425	1425	1825	2215	2136	0415
556	Bina Junction d.	1340	1430	|	|	|	2120	|	|	0710
694	Bhopal Junction d.	1530	1650	□	1830	1830	2320	0245	0040	0925
786	Itarsi Junction d.	1740	1845	|	|	|	0110	0430	|	1125
969	Khandwa d.	2005	2140	|	|	|	0450	0700	|	1425
093	Bhusaval Junction d.	2155	2335	|	0055	0055	0645	0850	|	1640
277	Manmad Junction d.	0020	0205	|	0320	0320	0930	1120	|	1920
513	Daund Chord Line d.	0450	|	|	|	|	1425	1540	|	|
589	**Pune** Junction a.	0625	|	0210	1105	1105	1555	1655	|	|
484	Kalyan Junction d.	...	0620	...	...	...	...	...	1015	2250
521	**Mumbai** CSTM ◧ a.	...	0735	...	...	...	...	...	1115	0005

	Exp	D	R	Exp	Exp	Exp	Exp	Exp	Exp
	12779	12263	22221	22685	12629	12781	11077	12137	11057
		②⑤		④⑦	③⑤	⑥			
Mumbai CSTM ◧ d.	...	...	1600	...	...	...	...	1935	2330
Kalyan Junction d.	...	...	1645	...	...	...	...	2035	0035
Pune Junction d.	0430	1110	|	0910	0910	1610	1720	|	|
Daund Chord Line d.	0610	|	|	|	|	1720	1827	|	|
Manmad Junction d.	1035	|	|	1525	1525	2155	2320	0015	0410
Bhusaval Junction d.	1300	|	|	1755	1755	0020	0155	0250	0655
Khandwa d.	1500	|	|	|	|	0225	0415	0500	0925
Itarsi Junction d.	1740	|	|	|	|	0440	0705	0800	1250
Bhopal Junction d.	1920	□	0205	0010	0010	0635	0855	0950	1535
Bina Junction d.	|	|	|	|	|	0850	1120	1205	1755
Jhansi VGLB ⊡ d.	2320	|	0511	0453	0455	1100	1400	1418	2030
Gwalior d.	0052	|	0611	|	|	1220	1526	1540	2156
Agra Cantonment d.	0315	|	0735	|	|	1445	1740	1805	2355
Mathura Junction d.	0402	|	|	|	|	1535	1833	1850	0100
Delhi Hazrat Nizamuddin a.	0625	0645	0955	1129	1140	1750	2049	2055	0319

– **New Delhi**.
□ – Via Table **5130**.

◧ – Full name is Mumbai Chhatrapati Shivaji Maharaj Terminus.
⊡ – Full name is Jhansi Virangana Lakshmibai Railway Station.

ndian Railways — LUCKNOW - PUNE and MUMBAI — 5170

km		Exp	Exp	Exp	Exp	Exp	Exp	Exp	Exp	Exp
		20104	12174	12144	15067	12104	12533	12108	22537	15029
			②④	②	③	③		②④⑦		④
0	**Lucknow** Charbagh ⊖ d.	0410**s**	0550	0655	1405	1620**j**	2130**j**	2240**s**	2335**s**	2250
72	Kanpur Central d.	0630	0755	0830	1600	1755	2310	0010	0130	0035
292	Jhansi VGLB ● d.	1103	1145	1248	2000	2140	0305	0345	0538	0425
445	Bina Junction d.	|	|	1535	|	0105	|	|	0745	0655
583	Bhopal Junction d.	1450	1615	1730	|	0305	0720	0825	1005	0900
674	Itarsi Junction d.	1630	|	|	0230	0440	0900	|	1200	1050
858	Khandwa d.	1910	|	2223	0540	0720	1200	|	1440	1400
981	Bhusaval Junction d.	2110	2235	0015	0730	0910	1355	1430	1700	1555
166	Manmad Junction d.	|	|	0232	|	1200	1620	|	1940	1845
405	Daund Chord Line d.	|	|	|	|	1700	|	|	|	|
477	**Pune** Junction a.	|	|	|	|	1845	|	|	|	0245
372	Kalyan Junction d.	|	0425	|	|	...	2125	2050	2310	...
409	**Mumbai** L Tilak Terminus a.	0435	0530	0725	1730**b**	...	2245**h**	2150	0010	...

	Exp	Exp	Exp	Exp	Exp	Exp	Exp	Exp	Exp
	22538	20103	15068	12534	12103	15030	12143	12107	12173
			⑤		②	⑥	⑦	①③⑥	②⑦
Mumbai L Tilak Terminus d.	0035	0523	0020**b**	0825**h**	...	...	1550	1625	1625
Kalyan Junction d.	0120	|	|	0915	...	...	|	1710	1710
Pune Junction d.	|	|	|	|	1045	1045	|	|	|
Daund Chord Line d.	|	|	|	|	1152	|	|	|	|
Manmad Junction d.	0505	|	|	1245	1725	1725	2030	|	|
Bhusaval Junction d.	0800	1210	1200	1510	1950	1950	2255	2325	2325
Khandwa d.	1015	1420	1440	1715	2310	2310	0110	|	|
Itarsi Junction d.	1300	1640	1705	1935	0200	0200	|	|	|
Bhopal Junction d.	1500	1825	|	2125	0345	0345	0520	0540	0540
Bina Junction d.	1720	|	|	|	0535	0535	0720	|	|
Jhansi VGLB ● d.	1915	2218	0012	0200	0755	0755	0925	0945	0945
Kanpur Central d.	0015	0340	0445	0655	1135	1150	1345	1400	1415
Lucknow Charbagh ⊖ a.	0142**s**	0600**s**	0710	0840**j**	1315**j**	1330	1530	1530**s**	1540

– Mumbai **Bandra**.
– Mumbai **Chhatrapati Shivaji Maharaj Terminus**.

j – Lucknow **Junction** (officially Lucknow NER).
s – Lucknow **Aishbagh**.

⊖ – Officially known as Lucknow NR.
● – Full name is Jhansi Virangana Lakshmibai.

5180 PATNA and VARANASI - MUMBAI

Indian Railways

km		Exp	Exp	Exp	Exp	Exp	Exp	Exp		Exp	Exp	Exp	Exp	Exp	Exp	Exp		Exp	D	Exp	Exp	Exp	Exp	Exp
		11082	**11062**	**22914**	**22972**	**13201**	**15267**	**12545**		**15547**	**12361**	**18609**	**22178**	**12321**	**12168**	**15018**		**12142**	**12294**	**12520**	**15646**	**12335**	**15648**	**1216**
		⑤		②	③		⑦	⑤		②	①	④							②⑥	⑤	①④	②⑤⑦	③	②⑤⑥
0	**Patna** Junction d.	...	...	2320	2320	2355	...	0055	...	0120**p**	0055	...	...	...	...	...	...	1055**p**	...	1320**p**	1335	1355	1355	...
212	PDD Upadhyaya Junction ⊡ d.	...	...	0304	0304	0420	...	0515	...	0510	0510	0615	...	1020	...	...	...	1500	...	1710	1750	1750	1750	...
	Varanasi Junction d.	2115	0015	|	|	|	0310	|	...	|	|	0730	1000	|	1035	1120	...	|	...	|	|	|	|	2020
356	Prayagraj Chheoki Jct. ◧ d.	0027	0320j	0517	0517	0715	0715j	0757	...	0757	0757	1030j	1305	1320	1345	1610j	...	1706	1810j	1932	2005	2002	2005	2330
448	Manikpur d.	0230	0515	|	|	0930	|	|	...	|	|	|	1510	1535	1605	1825	...	|	|	|	|	|	|	|
525	Satna d.	0335	0625	0800	0800	1150	1120	1120	...	1120	1120	1330	1630	1645	1715	1940	...	2005	2105	2200	2300	2300	2300	0220
623	Katni d.	0455	0740	0920	0920	1315	1240	1240	...	1240	1240	1445	1750	1805	1835	2100	...	|	|	2320	0025	0025	0025	0335
714	Jabalpur d.	0630	0910	1050	1050	1505	1410	1410	...	1410	1410	1605	1910	1930	2005	2220	...	2240	2350	0050	0155	0155	0155	0500
959	Itarsi Junction d.	|	1250	1410	1410	1910	|	1750	...	1750	1750	1950	2310	2350	0040	0300	...	0230	0335	0440	0520	0520	0520	0855
1143	Khandwa d.	1400	1515	|	|	2315	2030	2030	...	2030	2030	2223	0145	0230	0325	0740	...	|	|	0720	0805	0800	0800	|
1266	Bhusaval Junction d.	1555	1715	1850	1850	0115	2225	2225	...	2225	2225	0015	0340	0430	0515	0935	...	0710	0800	0910	1005	1005	1005	1325
1450	Manmad Junction d.	|	2000	|	|	0420	|	0050	...	0050	0050	0232	0615	0710	|	1220	...	0935	|	1140	1240	1240	1240	1600
1657	Kalyan Junction d.	2240	2320	|	|	0915	0450	0425	...	0450	0450	0630	1010	1140	1135	1620	...	1315	|	1515	1630	1630	1630	1950
1695	**Mumbai** L Tilak Terminus a.	2345	0025	0445**b**	0445**b**	1050	0550	0530	...	0550	0600**h**	0725	1140**h**	1330**h**	1230	1715	...	1410	1440	1615	1750	1750	1750	2050

km		Exp	Exp	Exp	Exp	Exp	Exp	Exp		Exp	Exp	Exp	Exp	Exp	Exp	Exp		Exp	Exp	D	Exp	Exp	Exp	Exp
		22177	**12165**	**15017**	**12519**	**15548**	**12336**	**15645**		**15647**	**12362**	**11061**	**13202**	**15268**	**11081**	**18610**		**12546**	**22913**	**12293**	**22971**	**12322**	**12167**	**1214**
			①④⑤		⑦	③	②④⑦	③⑥		⑤	③			①	③	⑤		⑥	⑦	①⑤	①			
0	**Mumbai** L Tilak Terminus d.	0010**h**	0600	0635	0750	0755	0805	0805	...	0805	1105**h**	1130	1455	1640	1640	1640	...	1640	1645**b**	1725	1925**b**	2215**h**	2245	2335
38	Kalyan Junction d.	0115	0640	0720	0835	0835	0840	0840	...	0840	1200	1215	1540	1720	1720	1720	...	1720	|	|	|	2315	2330	0020
245	Manmad Junction d.	0445	1005	1115	1155	1155	1225	1225	...	1225	1540	1615	1910	|	|	2200	...	2200	|	|	|	0245	|	0355
429	Bhusaval Junction d.	0725	1235	1405	1425	1425	1455	1455	...	1455	1805	1900	2210	0030	0030	0030	...	0030	0150	2305	0430	0530	0550	0625
552	Khandwa d.	0955	|	1640	1625	1625	1700	1700	...	1700	2010	2105	0030	0240	0240	0240	...	0240	|	|	|	0735	0820	|
736	Itarsi Junction d.	1225	1810	2050	1850	1850	1930	1930	...	1930	2235	2330	0355	|	|	0510	...	0510	0615	0315	0935	1000	1050	1105
981	Jabalpur d.	1600	2150	0045	2230	2230	2300	2300	...	2300	0150	0250	0745	0830	0830	0830	...	0830	0935	0610	1335	1350	1425	1440
1072	Katni d.	1710	2320	0225	2355	2355	0015	0015	...	0015	0310	0410	0910	1010	1010	1010	...	1010	1100	|	1455	1505	1555	|
1170	Satna d.	1840	0030	0350	0120	0120	0140	0140	...	0140	0440	0530	1130	1220	1220	1220	...	1220	1250	0850	1615	1630	1800	1810
1247	Manikpur d.	2050	|	0530	|	|	|	|	...	|	|	0732	1320	|	1407	|	...	|	|	|	|	1757	1922	|
1339	Prayagraj Chheoki Jct. ◧ d.	2240	0420j	0815j	0420	0420	0457	0500	...	0500	0750	1000j	1500	1630j	1542	1540j	...	1540	1610	1245j	1905	1935	2112	2120
1496	**Varanasi** Junction a.	0335	0710	1300	|	|	|	|	...	|	|	1225	|	1925	2050	1945	...	|	|	...	|	|	0125	|
	PTDD Upadhyaya Jct. ⊡ d.	...	...	...	0718	0718	0802	0802	...	0802	1037	...	1925	...	...	2115	...	1948	1948	...	2245	2255	...	0035
	Patna Junction a.	...	...	...	1015**p**	1015**p**	1230	1230	...	1230	1340	...	2355	...	...	...	...	2230	2230	...	0140	...	...	0350

b – Mumbai **Bandra**.
h – Mumbai **Chhatrapati Shivaji Maharaj Terminus**.
j – Prayagraj **Junction**.
p – **Patliputra Junction**
⊡ – Pt. Deen Dayal Upadhyaya (formerly Mughal Sarai).
◧ – Prayagraj (formerly Allahabad).

5190 DELHI - SECUNDERABAD - TIRUPATI and BENGALURU

Indian Railways

km		Exp	Exp	R	D	Exp	Exp	R	D	Exp
		12708	**12648**	**12438**	**12286**	**12724**	**22706**	**22692**	**12214**	**12722**
		③⑤⑦	③	⑦	①⑤		⑤		①	
0	**Delhi** Hazrat Nizamuddin d.	0520	0700	1535	1555	1600**n**	1703**g**	1950	2210**r**	2250
134	Mathura Junction d.	|	0835	|	|	1730	|	|	|	0050
188	Agra Cantonment d.	|	0930	|	|	1810	|	2145	|	0140
306	Gwalior d.	0958	1125	|	|	2000	|	2310	|	0322
403	Jhansi VGLB ● d.	1140	1308	2015	2050	2155	2300	0030	0355	0510
694	Bhopal Junction d.	1605	1705	2340	0018**t**	0125	0250**t**	0355	0800**t**	0950
786	Itarsi Junction d.	|	1850	|	|	|	|	0525	|	1200
1083	Nagpur d.	2225	2300	0515	0540	0715	0900	0930	|	1710
1294	Balharshah d.	0155	0230	0805	0835	1050	1250	1220	1645	2100
1528	Kazipet Junction d.	0510	0535	1105	|	1355	1600	1520	|	0030
1660	**Secunderabad** Junction a.	|	|	1335	1410	1555	1805	1710	2055	0250
1660	**Secunderabad** Junction d.	|	|	...	...	1600	1810	1725	2110	0255
	Hyderabad Deccan a.	|	|	...	...	1700	|	|	|	0350
1772	Mahabubnagar d.	1110	1030	...	...	...	|	|	|	...
1902	Kurnool City d.	1320	1245	...	...	...	|	|	|	...
1956	Dhone d.	1440	1425	...	...	...	|	|	|	...
2072	Guntakal Junction d.	|	|	...	...	...	0045	2340	0300	...
2292	Renigunta d.	2000	|	...	...	...	|	|	|	...
2302	**Tirupati** a.	2050	|	...	...	...	0625	|	|	...
2151	Dharmavaram d.	...	1715	...	...	...	...	|	|	...
2365	KSR **Bengaluru** ⊖ a.	...	2323**k**	...	...	...	...	0520	0810**v**	...

	Exp	R	D	Exp	Exp	R	D	Exp	Exp
	12721	**22691**	**12213**	**12723**	**22705**	**12437**	**12285**	**12647**	**1270**
			⑥		②	③	④⑦	⑦	①③⑤
KSR **Bengaluru** ⊖ d.	...	2000	2340**v**	...	...	...	...	2243**k**	...
Dharmavaram d.	...	|	|	...	...	...	...	0230	...
Tirupati d.	...	|	|	...	2110	...	...	|	0530
Renigunta d.	...	|	|	...	|	...	...	|	0550
Guntakal Junction d.	...	0105	0335	...	0205	...	...	|	|
Dhone d.	...	|	|	...	|	...	...	0545	1125
Kurnool City d.	...	|	|	...	|	...	...	0630	1215
Mahabubnagar d.	...	|	|	...	|	...	...	0830	1430
Hyderabad Deccan d.	2300	|	|	0600	|	...	...	|	|
Secunderabad Junction a.	2320	0705	0845	0620	0840	...	...	|	|
Secunderabad Junction d.	2325	0715	0850	0625	0850	1250	1255	|	|
Kazipet Junction d.	0115	0900	|	0825	1030	1430	|	1315	1910
Balharshah d.	0605	1225	1340	1210	1420	1750	1805	1720	2300
Nagpur d.	0925	1500	|	1525	1720	2030	2045	2100	0200
Itarsi Junction d.	1525	1918	|	|	|	|	|	0200	|
Bhopal Junction d.	1715	2100	2210**t**	2155	2310**t**	0210	0212**t**	0340	0825
Jhansi VGLB ● d.	2130	0021	0135	0125	0248	0525	0535	0743	1225
Gwalior d.	2246	0121	|	0247	|	|	|	0902	1334
Agra Cantonment d.	0040	0300	|	0432	|	|	|	1105	|
Mathura Junction d.	0120	|	|	0509	|	|	|	1151	|
Delhi Hazrat Nizamuddin a.	0340	0530	0735**r**	0725	0830**g**	1030	1050	1415	1835

g – Delhi **Safdarjang**.
k – Bengaluru **Krishnarajapuram**.
n – **New Delhi**.
r – Delhi **Sarai Rohilla**.
t – Bhopal **Rani Kamalapati**.
v – Bengaluru **Yesvantpur Junction**.
⊖ – Full name is Krantivira Sangolli Rayanna Bengaluru.
● – Full name is Jhansi Virangana Lakshmibai.

5200 DELHI - AGRA

Indian Railways

km		Exp	Exp	S	Exp	Exp	Exp	Exp	Exp	Exp	Exp	R	Exp	Exp	Exp	R	Exp	Exp	Exp	Exp	Exp	Exp	Exp	Exp
		12138	**12618**	**12002**	**12280**	**11078**	**18478**	**12716**	**12191**	**12780**	**12724**	**22222**	**12616**	**22182**	**11842**	**22692**	**20806**	**12448**	**12626**	**12156**	**12628**	**12622**	**11058**	**1272**
0	**New Delhi** d.	0515	...	0600	0655	1130	...	1245	...	...	1600	...	1610	...	1820	...	2000	...	2010	...	2020	2105	2040	...
7	**Delhi** Hazrat Nizamuddin d.	|	0540	|	0708	|	1200	|	1405	1515	|	1655	|	1745	1833	1950	|	2000	|	2040	|	|	2053	2250
141	Mathura Junction d.	0705	0745	0720	0850	1325	1355	1440	1600	1700	1730	|	1800	1910	2045	|	|	2120	2145	|	2210	|	2305	0050
195	**Agra** Cantonment a.	0810	0830	0750	0935	1410	1445	1515	1645	1750	1808	1848	1850	1948	2130	2143	2203	2210	2220	2238	2255	2328	2350	0135

	Exp	Exp	Exp	Exp	Exp	R	Exp	Exp	Exp	Exp	Exp	Exp	R	Exp	Exp	Exp	Exp	Exp	Exp	Exp	Exp	S	Exp
	12721	**22181**	**12447**	**20805**	**12615**	**22691**	**12779**	**12621**	**12723**	**12155**	**12627**	**12189**	**22221**	**12715**	**12192**	**18477**	**12617**	**12625**	**18237**	**11077**	**12137**	**12001**	**1105**
Agra Cantonment d.	0040	0130	0210	0245	0235	0300	0315	0405	0432	0525	0545	0720	0735	0805	0900	0930	1005	1015	1545	1740	1805	2120	2355
Mathura Junction d.	0120	0205	0245	|	0347	|	0402	|	0509	|	0630	0805	|	0845	0948	1025	1105	1055	1640	1833	1850	2154	0100
Delhi Hazrat Nizamuddin a.	0340	0410	0522	|	0609	0530	0625	0715	0725	0800	0831	1110	0955	1050	1220	1303	1325	1250	1945	2049	2055	|	0319
New Delhi a.	...	...	...	0540	0635	...	...	0740	0750	...	0900	...	...	1125	...	...	...	1315	...	2115	2125	2350	0345

Indian Railways — DELHI - BILASPUR — 5205

km		Exp 18238	S 12002	Exp 20808 ①④⑦	Exp 18478	Exp 12410 A	R 12442 ②⑥	Exp 12824 ②⑤⑦
0	**Delhi** Hazrat Nizamuddin d.	0425	0600	0828	1200	1505	1525n	1755
135	Mathura Junction d.	0730	0720	1001	1355	1640	|	|
189	Agra Cantonment d.	0830	0755	1050	1450	1735	|	|
307	Gwalior d.	1047	0928	1237	1652	1930	1855	|
404	Jhansi VGLB ● d.	1300	1050	1425	1905	2105	2015	2330
557	Bina Junction d.	1545	|	|	|	2302	|	|
632	Saugor d.	|	|	1805	2305	|	|	0250
819	Katni Murwara d.	|	|	2125	0220	|	|	0600
985	Anupper Junction d.	|	|	0031	0615	|	|	0908
695	Bhopal Junction d.	1805	1407	|	|	0105	2340	|
788	Itarsi Junction d.	2030	...	|	|	0305	|	|
085	Nagpur d.	0225	...	|	|	0835	0530	|
215	Gondia Junction d.	0505	...	|	|	1050	0707	|
349	Durg d.	0735	...	|	|	1255	0930	|
387	Raipur Junction d.	0835	...	|	|	1335	1010	|
***	**Bilaspur** Junction a.	1055	...	0400	0910	1530	1200	1150

	Exp 12409 B	Exp 12823 ①④⑥	R 12441 ①④	Exp 18477	Exp 20807 ②⑤⑥	Exp 18237	S 12001
Bilaspur Junction d.	0550	1500	1400	1440	1845	1415	...
Raipur Junction d.	0740	|	1535	|	|	1620	...
Durg d.	0835	|	1630	|	|	1730	...
Gondia Junction d.	1033	|	1824	|	|	1953	...
Nagpur d.	1255	|	2035	|	|	2220	...
Itarsi Junction d.	1750	|	|	|	|	0415	...
Bhopal Junction d.	1940	|	0210	|	|	0610	1530
Anupper Junction d.	|	1730	|	1715	2125	|	|
Katni Murwara d.	|	2040	|	2215	0055	|	|
Saugor d.	|	2315	|	0055	0330	|	|
Bina Junction d.	2140	|	|	|	|	0920	|
Jhansi VGLB ● d.	2338	0220	0525	0553	0743	1150	1842
Gwalior d.	0038	|	0625	0726	0902	1320	1945
Agra Cantonment d.	0220	|	|	0930	1105	1545	2120
Mathura Junction d.	0300	|	|	1025	1155	1640	2154
Delhi Hazrat Nizamuddin a.	0500	0740	1040n	1303	1404	1945	2350n

A – ①②③④⑥.
B – ①③④⑤⑥.
n – **New Delhi**.
● – Full name is Jhansi Virangana Lakshmibai.
*** – *1136 km* via Anupper, *1498 km* via Bhopal.

Indian Railways — DELHI - INDORE — 5208

km		Exp 19326 ④⑦	Exp 14318 ⑤	Exp 12920	Exp 19308 ⑤
0	**Delhi** Hazrat Nizamuddin d.	1125	1350	2030n	2300
135	Mathura Junction d.	1310	1545	2235	0100
189	Agra Cantonment d.	1400	1640	2315	0155
307	Gwalior d.	1600	1850	0127	0410
404	Jhansi VGLB ● d.	|	|	0315	|
557	Bina Junction d.	|	|	0535	|
695	Bhopal Junction d.	|	|	0750	|
534	Guna d.	1950	2305	|	0800
788	Ujjain Junction d.	|	0410	1135	1255
959	**Indore** Junction a.	0055	0610	1340	1520

	Exp 19307 ④	Exp 12919	Exp 14317 ⑥⑦	Exp 19325 ②⑤
Indore Junction d.	0530	1215	1840	1945
Ujjain Junction d.	0740	1400	2055	|
Guna d.	1335	|	0200	0200
Bhopal Junction d.	|	1730	|	|
Bina Junction d.	|	1935	|	|
Jhansi VGLB ● d.	|	2138	|	|
Gwalior d.	1810	2257	0615	0615
Agra Cantonment d.	1955	0048	0825	0820
Mathura Junction d.	2042	0125	0905	0900
Delhi Hazrat Nizamuddin a.	2305	0354	1125	1125

n – **New Delhi**.
● – Full name is Jhansi Virangana Lakshmibai.

Indian Railways — DELHI - NAGPUR - TIRUPATI and CHENNAI — 5210

km		Exp 12642 ①⑥	Exp 12652 ②④	Exp 12646 ②	Exp 12644 ⑤	R 12434 ③⑤	Exp 12612 ①	D 12270 ②⑥	Exp 16318 ②	Exp 16788 ⑤	Exp 12616	Exp 12626	Exp 12622	Exp 22404 ⑦
0	**Delhi** Hazrat Nizamuddin d.	0520	0520	0510	0510	1535	1535	1555	1413	1420	1610n	2010n	2105n	2315n
135	Mathura Junction d.	|	|	0645	0645	|	|	|	|	|	1800	2145	|	0043
189	Agra Cantonment d.	0805	|	0735	0735	1730	1730	|	1700	1710	1855	2225	2330	0125
307	Gwalior d.	|	|	0943	0943	1855	1855	1920	1952	2045	2107	0010	0115	|
404	Jhansi VGLB ● d.	1140	1140	1130	1130	2015	2015	2050	2203	2230	2310	0140	0255	0440
695	Bhopal Junction d.	1600	1600	1530	1530	2340	2340	0018t	0220	0305	0330	0525	0655	0845
788	Itarsi Junction d.	1800	|	1720	1720	|	|	|	0405	0450	0535	0720	0840	1035
1085	Nagpur d.	2225	2225	2155	2155	0510	0510	0540	0905	0955	1020	1150	1310	1500
1298	Balharshah d.	0150	0155	0125	0125	0805	0805	0835	1310	1345	1430	1520	1630	1900
1543	Warangal d.	|	|	0435	0435	1115	|	|	1610	1710	1800	1832	1950	2300
1752	Vijayawada Junction d.	0850	0850	0820	0820	1430	1430	1430	2045	2100	2140	2230	2330	0200
2046	Gudur Junction d.	1300	|	1230	1230	|	1830	|	|	|	0205	0245	|	0640
2122	Renigunta Junction d.	|	|	1345	1345	|	|	|	0245	0245	|	0420	|	|
2132	**Tirupati** a.	|	|	1410	1410	|	|	|	0315	0315	|	0440	|	|
2184	**Chennai** Central a.	1550e	1550e	...	...	2045	2050	2050	...	...	0430	...	0615	0930e

	Exp 22403 ③	Exp 12615	Exp 12621	R 12433 ⑤⑦	Exp 12611 ⑥	D 12269 ①⑤	Exp 12625	Exp 12643 ③	Exp 12645 ⑦	Exp 12641 ④⑥	Exp 12651 ②⑦	Exp 16787 ②	Exp 16317 ⑥
Chennai Central d.	1310e	1850	2200	0605	0600	0635	...	...	...	0845e	0845e	...	...
Tirupati d.	|	|	|	|	|	|	0455	0720	0720	|	|	0910	0910
Renigunta Junction d.	|	|	|	|	|	|	0520	0745	0745	|	|	0930	0930
Gudur Junction d.	1535	2045	|	|	0745	|	|	0915	0915	|	|	|	1105
Vijayawada Junction d.	2000	0100	0355	1140	1140	1210	1105	1420	1420	1555	1555	1525	1525
Warangal d.	2310	0410	0652	1414	|	|	1355	1715	1715	|	|	1815	1815
Balharshah d.	0330	0815	1040	1750	1750	1805	1820	2115	2115	2300	2300	2225	2225
Nagpur d.	0655	1135	1355	2030	2030	2045	2115	0025	0025	0200	0200	0145	0145
Itarsi Junction d.	1205	1650	1835	|	|	|	0215	0515	0505	0640	|	0730	0730
Bhopal Junction d.	1350	1845	2022	0210	0215	0212t	0355	0650	0650	0825	0825	0905	0905
Jhansi VGLB ● d.	1805	2300	0100	0525	0525	0535	0735	1100	1100	1225	1225	1340	1338
Gwalior d.	|	0005	0212	0625	0625	0635	0835	1220	1220	|	|	1450	1450
Agra Cantonment d.	2110	0235	0405	0752	0752	|	1015	1445	1445	1540	|	1700	1700
Mathura Junction d.	2220	0347	|	|	|	|	1055	1535	1535	|	|	|	|
Delhi Hazrat Nizamuddin a.	0010n	0609	0715	1030	1030	1040	1250	1750	1750	1835	1835	2016	2016

e – Chennai **Egmore**.
n – **New Delhi**.
t – Bhopal **Rani Kamalapati**.
● – Full name is Jhansi Virangana Lakshmibai.

Indian Railways — DELHI, AHMEDABAD and MUMBAI - GOA - MANGALURU - TRIVANDRUM — 5220

WARNING! A different timetable operates during the monsoon season (June - October).

km		R 12432 ②③⑦	Exp 22654 ①	Exp 22660 ①	Exp 12218 ③⑤	Exp 12484 ⑦	Exp 19578 ⑥⑦	Exp 20910 ⑤	Exp 16345	Exp 16311 ③	Exp 22475 ④	D 12284 ⑥
0	**Delhi** Hazrat Nizamuddin d.	0616	0500	1325	1323	1325	...	...	...	...	...	2140
458	Kota Junction d.	1055	1115	1815	1815	1815	...	...	...	...	...	0235
****	**Ahmedabad** Junction d.	|	|	|	|	|	0315	0315	...	0725	0725	|
986	Vadodara Junction d.	1745	1808	0130	0130	0130	0508	0508	...	0905	0905	0956
***	**Mumbai** L Tilak Terminus d.	|	|	|	|	|	|	|	1140	|	|	|
397	Panvel d.	2310	0031	0740	0740	0740	1130	1130	1250	1535	1535	1535
678	Ratnagiri d.	0310	0530	1255	1255	1255	1630	1630	1745	2025	2025	2025
917	Madgaon d.	0715	1030	1720	1720	1720	2110	2110	2240	0025	0025	0025
166	Udupi d.	1042	1402	2134	2134	2134	0112	0112	0232	0418	0418	|
234	**Mangaluru** Junction d.	1210	1610	2350	2350	2350	0310	0310	0425	0645	0645	0645
365	Kannur d.	1400	1755	0155	0155	0155	0500	0500	0635	0840	0840	|
455	Kozhikkode d.	1520	1915	0315	0315	0315	0620	0620	0810	0955	0955	0955
541	Shoranur Junction d.	1700	2120	0500	0500	0500	0800	0800	1020	1140	1125	|
574	Thrisur d.	1755	2225	0620	0620	0620	0915	0915	1115	1305	...	|
645	**Ernakulam** Junction d.	1925	0008o	0815	0815	0815	1040	1040	1245	1420o	...	1430
762	Kayamkulam Junction d.	|	0230	|	|	1025	1300	1300	1500	1735	...	...
789	Kollam d.	2210	0320	1100	1100	1100	1340	1340	1605	1815	...	...
866	**Trivandrum** Central a.	2335	0445	1230k	1225k	1230k	1435	1500k	1805	1945k	...	...
937	**Nagercoil** Town a.	...	...	...	...	...	1558	...	...	...	...	...

km		Exp 12619	Exp 20924 ①	Exp 22634 ⑤	Exp 22113 ②⑥	Exp 12201 ①⑤	D 12223 ②⑥	Exp 22629 ④	Exp 12133	Exp 16333 ④	Exp 19260 ②	Exp 16335 ⑤	Exp 16337 ①⑥
0	**Delhi** Hazrat Nizamuddin d.	...	...	2215	...	...	...	...	...	...	...	...	...
458	Kota Junction d.	...	...	0350	...	...	...	...	...	...	...	...	...
****	**Ahmedabad** Junction d.	...	0925	|	...	...	...	...	...	1540	1540	1540	1540
986	Vadodara Junction d.	...	1100	1110	...	...	...	...	...	1727	1727	1727	1727
***	**Mumbai** L Tilak Terminus d.	1520	|	|	1655	1655	2050	2040d	2202t	|	|	|	|
397	Panvel d.	1625	1700	1700	1805	1805	|	2200	2325	0005	0005	0005	0005
678	Ratnagiri d.	2105	2140	2140	2225	2225	0150	0225	0500	0425	0425	0425	0425
917	Madgaon d.	0115	0200	0200	0225	0225	0550	0715	0730	0900	0900	0900	0900
166	Udupi d.	0542	|	0612	0632	0632	|	1042	1130	1256	1256	1256	1256
234	**Mangaluru** Junction d.	0740c	0740	0740	0810	0810	1025	1210	1305	1515	1515	1515	1515
365	Kannur d.	...	|	0925	1000	1000	|	1400	...	1710	1710	1710	1710
455	Kozhikkode d.	...	1040	1040	1120	1120	1325	1520	...	1835	1835	1835	1835
541	Shoranur Junction d.	...	1230	1230	1305	1305	|	1640	...	2100	2100	2100	2100
574	Thrisur d.	...	1330	1330	1400	1400	|	...	...	2145	2145	2145	2145
645	**Ernakulam** Junction d.	...	1455	1455	1530o	1530o	1810	...	...	2305o	2305o	2305o	2355
762	Kayamkulam Junction d.	...	1720	1700	1805	1805	...	...	...	|	|	0135	...
789	Kollam d.	...	|	1755	1850	1850	...	...	...	0210	0210	0210	...
866	**Trivandrum** Central a.	...	1925	1935	2025k	2025k	...	...	...	0400	0400k	0325	...
937	**Nagercoil** Town a.	...	2105	...	...	...	...	...	...	...	...	0615g	...

FOR RETURN SERVICE AND FOOTNOTES SEE NEXT PAGE →

5220 TRIVANDRUM - MANGALURU - GOA - MUMBAI, AHMEDABAD and DELHI

Indian Railways

WARNING! A different timetable operates during the monsoon season (June - October).

		Exp	*Exp*	*Exp*	*Exp*	*Exp*	*Exp*	*Exp*	*Exp*	*Exp*	*Exp*	*Exp*	*Exp*	*Exp*	*Exp*	*D*	*Exp*	*Exp*	*Exp*	*Exp*	*Exp*	*Exp*	*R*	*D*
		22114	**22653**	**12134**	**12620**	**12202**	**12217**	**12483**	**22659**	**16346**	**20923**	**12476**	**19577**	**20909**	**22630**	**12224**	**22633**	**16338**	**16312**	**19259**	**16334**	**16336**	**12431**	**1228**
		①④	⑥			④	①⑥	③	⑤		④	⑥	①②	⑦	③	③⑦	③	③⑤	⑥	④	①	②	②④⑤	②
Nagercoil Town	d.	...	...	...	...	...	...	...	...	...	0915	...	0915	...	...	...	...	...	...	...	...	1445**g**	...	...
Trivandrum Central	d.	0035**k**	0030	...	...	0845**k**	0910**k**	0910**k**	0910**k**	0915	1055	...	1055	1110	...	...	1440	...	1545**k**	1545**k**	1545	1605	1915	...
Kollam	d.	0130	0130	...	...	0938	1008	1008	1008	1025	1240	...	1203	1203	...	...	1536	...	1645	1645	1645	1710	2023	...
Kayamkulam Junction	d.	0210	0210	...	...	1014	1044	1044	|	1110	|	...	1240	1240	...	...	1610	...	1721	1721	|	1745	|	...
Ernakulam Junction	d.	0510**o**	0510**o**	...	...	1300**o**	1300	1300	1300	1350	1420	...	1420	1420	...	2130	1835	2025	2020**o**	2020**o**	2020**o**	2030**o**	2235	232
Thrisur	d.	0620	0620	...	...	1412	1412	1412	1412	1505	1540	...	1540	1540	...	|	2004	2148	2148	2148	2148	2148	2350	|
Shoranur Junction	d.	0715	0720	...	...	1510	1510	1510	1510	1625	1705	1705	1705	1705	1705	|	2100	2250	2250	2250	2250	2250	0050	|
Kozhikkode	d.	0835	0840	...	...	1630	1630	1630	1630	1805	1825	1825	1825	1825	1825	0045	2220	0020	0015	0015	0020	0020	0200	024
Kannur	d.	1000	1005	...	...	1755	1755	1755	1755	1935	|	1950	1950	1950	1950	|	2340	0150	0140	0140	0150	0150	0315	|
Mangaluru Junction	d.	1210	1210	1400	1415**c**	2010	2010	2010	2010	2250	2200	2200	2200	2200	2200	0400	0200	0420	0420	0420	0420	0420	0525	061
Udupi	d.	1340	1340	1518	1550	2140	2140	2140	2140	0040	|	2338	2338	2338	2338	|	0344	0612	0612	0612	0612	0612	0642	|
Madgaon	d.	1720	1720	1850	2030	0125	0125	0125	0125	0445	0400	0400	0400	0400	0400	0850	0925	1135	1135	1135	1135	1135	1010	123
Ratnagiri	d.	2100	2105	2240	2335	0445	0445	0445	0445	0905	0820	0820	0820	0820	0820	1230	1345	1555	1555	1555	1555	1555	1340	171
Panvel	d.	0220	0255	0310	0505	1010	1100	1100	1100	1455	1325	1325	1325	1325	1325	|	1805	2120	2120	2120	2120	2120	1805	223
Mumbai L Tilak Terminus	a.	0345	|	0435**t**	0635	1145	|	|	|	1645	|	|	|	|	1500**d**	1815	|	|	|	|	|	|	|	|
Vadodara Junction	d.	...	0916	...	...	...	1715	1715	1715	...	1939	1928	2018	2015	...	...	0002	0435	0435	0435	0435	0435	2352	045
Ahmedabad Junction	a.	...	|	...	...	...	|	|	|	...	2120	2125	2215	2230	...	...	|	0635	0640	0640	0645	0635	|	|
Kota Junction	d.	...	1630	...	...	...	0001	0001	0001	...	...	...	...	...	...	...	0700	...	...	...	...	...	0700	115
Delhi Hazrat Nizamuddin	a.	...	2240	...	...	...	0540	0540	0550	...	...	...	...	...	...	...	1230	...	...	...	...	...	1230	172

c – Mangaluru **Central**.
d – Mumbai **Dadar**.
g – Nagercoil **Junction**.
k – Trivandrum **Kochuveli**.
o – Ernakulam **Town**.
t – Mumbai **Chhatrapati Shivaji Maharaj Terminus**.
*** – Mumbai CSMT - Panvel: *68 km*.
**** – Ahmedabad - Vadodara: *100 km*.

FOR RETURN SERVICE SEE PREVIOUS PAGE.

5230 MUMBAI - PUNE

Indian Railways

km			*Exp*	*Exp*	*Exp*		*Exp*	*Exp*	*Exp*		*Exp*	*Exp*	*Exp*		*Exp*	*Exp*	*Exp*		*Exp*	*Exp*	*Exp*		*Exp*	*Exp*	*D*
			22105	**12127**	**11007**		**11301**	**11029**	**22159**		**11019**	**17031**	**12123**		**11009**	**17411**	**16339**		**22107**	**11139**	**12701**		**12115**	**12157**	**1221**
																	A		B						③⑥
0	**Mumbai** CSMT ▶	d.	0540	0640	0700	...	0810	0840	1245	...	1400	1410	1710	...	1750	2020	2035	...	2100	2120	2150	...	2245	2255	2305
54	Kalyan Junction	d.	0635	0710	0755	...	0905	0935	1340	...	1458	1505	|	...	1850	2120	2130	...	2155	2215	2240	...	2345	2355	|
192	**Pune** Junction	a.	0905	0957	1105	...	1140	1235	1620	...	1745	1810	2025	...	2150	0010	0015	...	0030	0105	0120	...	0215	0250	020

		Exp	*Exp*	*Exp*		*Exp*	*Exp*	*Exp*		*Exp*	*Exp*	*D*		*Exp*	*Exp*	*Exp*		*Exp*	*Exp*	*Exp*		*Exp*	*Exp*	*Exp*
		12702	**11140**	**22158**		**12116**	**17412**	**22108**		**11010**	**12124**	**12220**		**22160**	**17032**	**11008**		**16340**	**11030**	**11302**		**12128**	**22106**	**1102**
								A				③⑥						A						
Pune Junction	d.	0115	0125	0200	...	0255	0335	0415	...	0605	0715	0755	...	0820	0915	1515	...	1525	1550	1605	...	1755	1835	235
Kalyan Junction	d.	0343	0400	0430	...	0520	0610	0645	...	0848	|	|	...	1050	1150	1750	...	1800	1850	1855	...	|	2052	023
Mumbai CSMT ▶	a.	0455	0510	0550	...	0635	0725	0755	...	0955	1025	1100**t**	...	1230	1305	1905	...	1915	2005	2015	...	2105	2200	040

A – ②③④⑥.
B – ①②④⑦.
t – Mumbai **Lokmanya Tilak Terminus**.
▶ – Full name is Mumbai Chhatrapati Shivaji Maharaj Terminus.

5240 MUMBAI - PUNE - KOLHAPUR and HUBBALLI

Indian Railways

km			*Exp*	*Exp*	*Exp*	*Exp*	*Exp*	*Exp*	*Exp*	*Exp*	*Exp*
			11040	**12148**	**11049**	**11029**	**17138**	**17411**	**11035**	**11021**	**11005**
				⑤	①				④	②③⑥	①⑤⑦
0	**Mumbai** Dadar	d.	...	...	...	0840**c**	2025	2035	2130	2130	2130
54	Kalyan	d.	...	...	0445	0935	|	2120	2210	2210	2210
192	**Pune** Junction	d.	0420	0640	0750	1240	2355	0015	0100	0100	0100
338	Satara	d.	0730	0930	1050	1600	|	0315	0400	0400	0400
472	Miraj Junction	d.	1045	1210	1310	1850	0550	0555	0645	0645	0645
518	**Kolhapur** CSMT ⊙	a.	1225	1330	1440	2000	|	0720	|	|	|
610	Belagavi	d.	...	...	...	...	0805	...	0905	0905	0905
661	Londa Junction	d.	...	...	...	...	0912	...	1012	1012	1012
731	Dharwad	d.	...	...	...	...	1036	...	1138	1138	1138
751	**Hubballi** Junction	a.	...	...	...	...	1135	...	1235	1235	1235

		Exp	*Exp*	*Exp*	*Exp*	*Exp*	*Exp*	*Exp*	*Exp*	*Exp*
		11030	**12147**	**11050**	**11039**	**11006**	**11022**	**11036**	**17317**	**1741**
			②	⑥		①③④	②⑤⑥	⑦		
Hubballi Junction	d.	...	...	...	...	1435	1435	1435	1530	...
Dharwad	d.	...	...	...	...	1500	1500	1500	1552	...
Londa Junction	d.	...	...	...	...	1625	1625	1625	1712	...
Belagavi	d.	...	...	...	...	1740	1740	1740	1815	...
Kolhapur CSMT ⊙	d.	0815	0910	1315	1445	|	|	|	|	2045
Miraj Junction	d.	0920	1020	1410	1550	2055	2055	2055	2115	2150
Satara	d.	1205	1240	1630	1840	2310	2310	2310	|	0015
Pune Junction	d.	1550	1555	2010	2215	0210	0210	0210	0310	0335
Kalyan	d.	1850	...	2232	...	0440	0440	0440	|	0610
Mumbai Dadar	a.	2005**t**	...	...	...	0530	0530	0530	0700	0725

c – Mumbai **Chhatrapati Shivaji Maharaj Terminus**.
t – Mumbai **Lokmanya Tilak Terminus**.
⊙ – Full name is Kolhapur Shri Chhatrapati Shahu Maharaj Terminus.

5245 HUBBALLI - BENGALURU - MYSORE

Indian Railways

km			*Exp*	*Exp*	*Exp*	*Exp*	*Exp*	*Exp*	*Exp*	*Exp*	*Exp*	*JS*	*Exp*	*Exp*	*Exp*	*Exp*	*Exp*	*Exp*	*Exp*	*Exp*	*Exp*	*Exp*	*Exp*	*Exp*	*Exp*
			17310	**12726**	**16588**	**14806**	**17325**	**16544**	**11005**	**11021**	**11035**	**12080**	**16507**	**16505**	**16209**	**17392**	**12782**	**22697**	**12650**	**17302**	**12630**	**22686**	**16542**	**16590**	**2065**
					②④	⑥		⑥	①②⑥	③④⑦	⑤		⑤⑦	③	①⑥		②	⑥	A		①④	③⑦	⑤		
0	**Hubballi** Junction	d.	0400	0600	0800	0800	0830	1120	1245	1245	1245	1340	1420	1420	1420	1800	1830	2025	2045	2145	2210	2210	2210	2230	2340
129	Harihar	d.	0630	0800	|	|	1045	1330	1437	1437	1437	1531	1625	1625	1625	2050	2110	2235	|	2352	|	|	0012	|	|
258	Birur Junction	d.	0825	1000	|	|	1247	|	1615	1615	1615	1710	1815	1815	1815	2312	2300	0027	|	0138	|	|	0152	0210	|
303	Arsikere Junction	d.	0915	1050	1215	1215	1345	1555	1710	1710	1710	1750	1915	1915	1915	0005	2355	0110	0130	0240	0240	0240	0240	0305	0345
393	Tumakuru	d.	1037	1204	1340	1340	1502	1722	1927	1927	|	1910	2022	2022	2022	0136	|	0237	0325	|	0402	0402	0402	0430	0512
469	KSR **Bengaluru** ⊖	a.	1235**v**	1405	1545**v**	1545**v**	1740	1930**v**	2120**v**	2120**v**	|	2055	2305	2305	2305	0410	|	0445**v**	0530**v**	|	0605**v**	0605**v**	0610**v**	0630	0730
614	**Mysuru** Junction	a.	...	...	...	...	2040	...	...	...	2140	...	...	...	0215	...	0330	...	...	0720	...	...	...	...	...

		JS	*Exp*	*Exp*	*Exp*	*Exp*	*Exp*	*Exp*	*Exp*	*Exp*	*Exp*	*Exp*	*Exp*	*Exp*	*Exp*	*Exp*	*Exp*	*Exp*	*Exp*	*Exp*	*Exp*	*Exp*	*Exp*	*Exp*
		12079	**11006**	**11022**	**11036**	**17326**	**16587**	**14805**	**12649**	**12725**	**12629**	**22685**	**17309**	**16541**	**12781**	**20653**	**16589**	**22698**	**16508**	**16210**	**16506**	**17301**	**16543**	**1739**
			①③④	②⑤⑥	⑦		⑤⑦	①	B		②④	③⑥		④	⑤			⑦	①③	②④	⑥		⑤	
Mysuru Junction	d.	...	...	...	0615	0550	...	...	...	...	...	...	...	...	2010	...	...	...	...	1900	...	2230	...	...
KSR **Bengaluru** ⊖	d.	0600	0630**v**	0630**v**	|	0845	1130**v**	1130**v**	1245**v**	1300	1355**v**	1355**v**	1500**v**	1815**v**	|	2100	2205	2150**v**	2245	2245	2245	|	2350	2355
Tumakuru	d.	0702	0720	0720	|	0951	1220	1220	1330	1403	1445	1445	1550	1905	|	2202	2307	2240	2347	2347	2347	|	0040	0100
Arsikere Junction	d.	0815	0915	0915	0915	1125	1315	1340	1500	1525	1612	1612	1710	2020	2305	2320	0030	0005	0105	0105	0105	0130	0205	0240
Birur Junction	d.	0850	0958	0958	0958	1210	|	|	|	1610	|	|	1750	2100	2345	|	0114	0045	0142	0142	0142	0214	|	0325
Harihar	d.	1027	1137	1137	1137	1405	|	|	|	1802	|	|	1926	2238	0150	|	0252	0222	0322	0322	0322	0357	0422	0542
Hubballi Junction	a.	1300	1425	1425	1425	1725	1940	1940	2025	2045	2140	2140	2215	0220	0425	0355	0535	0525	0610	0610	0610	0705	0800	0955

A – ①②③⑤⑦.
B – ①③⑤⑥⑦.
v – Bengaluru **Yesvantpur Junction**.
⊖ – Full name is Krantivira Sangolli Rayanna Bengaluru.

Indian Railways — HUBBALLI - MADGAON - VASCO DA GAMA — 5248

km		Exp 17322 ③	Exp 18047 C	Exp 17316 ③	Exp 17309	Exp 17021 ④
0	**Hubballi** Junction d.	0800	0900	2010	2225	2250
20	Dharwad d.	0826	0928	2036	2250	2326
90	Londa Junction d.	0942	1052	2215	0010	0052
174	Kulem d.	1205	1320	0100	0235	0215
208	**Madgaon** d.	1340	1425	0220	0330	0420
236	**Vasco Da Gama** a.	1440	1545	0325	0500	0525

	Exp 17321 ⑤	Exp 18048 D	Exp 17315 ①	Exp 17022 ⑤	Exp 17310
Vasco Da Gama d.	0515	0630	0900	0900	2225
Madgaon d.	0600	0700	0935	0935	2305
Kulem d.	0655	0750	1020	1020	2350
Londa Junction d.	0824	0945	1212	1212	0138
Dharwad d.	1001	1110	1340	1340	0300
Hubballi Junction a.	1045	1150	1420	1420	0350

– ①③④⑥. D – ②④⑤⑦.

Indian Railways — MUMBAI - SECUNDERABAD, BENGALURU and CHENNAI — 5250

km		Exp 18520	Exp 11301	Exp 22159	Exp 11017 ⑥	Exp 22179 ①	Exp 17222 ④⑦	Exp 11019	Exp 17031	Exp 12163	Exp 12701	Exp 11013	Exp 22157	D 12219 ③⑥
0	**Mumbai** CSMT ⊕ d.	0655t	0810	1245	1315t	1320t	1320t	1400	1410	1845t	2150	2235t	2255	2305t
54	Kalyan Junction d.	|	0905	1340	1405	1400	|	1458	1505	1930	2240	2320	2355	|
192	Pune Junction d.	1020	1145	1625	1640	1640	1640	1750	1815	2210	0125	0155	0255	0205
263	Daund Junction d.	|	1300	1735	|	|	|	1902	1940	|	|	|	0410	|
456	Solapur Junction d.	1415	1545	2000	2055	2055	2055	2135	2250	0200	0535	0620	0655	0600
568	Kalaburagi d.	1545	1750	2125	2255	2255	2225	2310	0035	0325	0720	0813	0850	|
605	Wadi d.	1705	1930	2240	2325	2325	2325	0035	0145	0420	0840	0925	0950	|
717	Vikarabad Junction d.	1845	|	|	|	|	|	|	0317	|	1027	|	|	|
800	**Secunderbad** Junction a.	2030	|	|	|	|	0205	0320	|	|	|	|	|	1110
790	**Hyderabad** Deccan a.	...	|	|	|	|	...	...	0530	|	1215	|	|	...
713	Raichur d.	...	2120	0015	0045	0045	...	...	...	0615	...	1105	1150	...
783	Adoni d.	...	2220	0120	|	|	...	...	...	0725	...	1210	1250	...
834	Guntakal Junction d.	...	2300	0215	0250	0250	...	...	...	0820	...	1310	1355	...
942	Dharmavaram Junction d.	...	0320	|	|	|	...	...	...	|	...	1530	|	...
147	KSR **Bengaluru** ⊖ a.	...	0750	|	|	|	...	...	...	|	...	2105	|	...
017	Cuddapah d.	...	...	0515	0545	0545	...	...	...	1115	...	...	1655	...
142	Renigunta Junction d.	...	...	0745	0810	0810	...	...	...	1335	...	...	1920	...
214	Arakkonam Junction d.	...	...	0915	0925	0925	...	...	...	1455	...	...	2030	...
283	**Chennai** Central a.	...	...	1050	1100e	1100	...	...	...	1620	...	...	2215e	...

	Exp 11020	Exp 18519	Exp 12702	Exp 22158	Exp 17221 ③⑥	D 12220 ②⑤	Exp 22160	Exp 17032	Exp 11014	Exp 22180 ②	Exp 12164	Exp 11302	Exp 11018 ①
hennai Central d.	...	...	...	0620e	...	...	1325	...	...	1550	1820	...	2210e
rakkonam Junction d.	...	...	...	|	...	...	1430	...	...	1650	1920	...	2345
enigunta Junction d.	...	...	...	0920	...	...	1610	...	...	1835	2050	...	0120
uddapah d.	...	...	...	1100	...	...	1755	...	...	2025	2245	...	0310
KSR **Bengaluru** ⊖ d.	...	...	...	|	...	...	|	...	1600	|	|	2040	|
Dharmavaram Junction d.	...	...	...	|	...	...	|	...	2025	|	|	0025	|
iuntakal Junction d.	...	...	...	1410	...	...	2100	...	2255	2330	0145	0255	0630
doni d.	...	...	...	1500	...	...	2150	...	2340	0020	0230	0340	|
aichur d.	...	...	...	1605	...	...	2250	...	0050	0120	0330	0445	0820
Hyderabad Deccan d.	...	...	1450	|	...	...	|	2055	|	|	|	|	|
Secunderabad Junction d.	1100	1255	|	|	2025	2305	|	|	|	|	|	|	|
Vikarabad Junction d.	|	1415	1602	|	|	|	|	2217	|	|	|	|	|
Vadi d.	1505	1650	1805	1855	0010	|	0115	0050	0255	0325	0535	0710	1015
alaburagi d.	1555	1730	1843	1933	0055	|	0158	0130	0340	0400	0620	0800	1055
olapur Junction d.	1805	1955	2040	2155	0305	0355	0405	0340	0545	0640	0745	1100	1225
aund Junction d.	2150	|	|	0045	|	|	0650	0735	0855	|	|	1435	|
une Junction d.	2350	0050	0115	0200	0755	0755	0820	0915	1020	1105	1150	1605	1640
alyan Junction d.	0235	|	0343	0430	|	|	1050	1150	1250	1325	1420	1855	1930
umbai CSMT ⊕ a.	0400	0415t	0455	0550	1100t	1100t	1230	1305	1345t	1425t	1540t	2015	2030t

– Chennai **Egmore**.
– Mumbai **Lokmanya Tilak Terminus**.
⊖ – Full name is Krantivira Sangolli Rayanna.
⊕ – Full name is Chhatrapati Shivaji Maharaj Terminus.

Indian Railways — HYDERABAD - SECUNDERABAD - TIRUPATI and CHENNAI — 5260

km		Exp 17406	Exp 17230	Exp 12604	Exp 12734	Exp 12764 A	Exp 12760
	Hyderabad Decan d.	...	...	1645	...	...	1800
0	**Secunderabad** Junction d.	0600	1220	1710	1810	1840	1825
281	Guntur Junction d.	|	1710	2210	2255	|	|
132	Kazipet Junction d.	0812	|	|	|	2030	2010
351	Vijayawada Junction d.	1300	|	|	|	0020	2355
382*	Tenali Junction d.	1325	1750	2250	2345	0050	0025
643	Gudur Junction d.	1915	2200	0300	0345	0435	0420
726	Renigunta Junction d.	2050	2320	|	0510	0600	|
736	**Tirupati** Junction a.	2135	2345	|	0555	0645	|
793	**Chennai** Central a.	...	...	0540	...	...	0705e

	Exp 17229	Exp 17405	Exp 12603	Exp 12763 B	Exp 12733	Exp 12759
Chennai Central d.	...	...	1645	...	...	1745e
Tirupati Junction d.	0010	0550	|	1700	1825	|
Renigunta Junction d.	0035	0610	|	1720	1840	|
Gudur Junction d.	0200	0730	1903	1855	2000	2025
Tenali Junction d.	0555	1200	2300	2235	2352	2357
Vijayawada Junction d.	|	1310	|	2330	|	0055
Kazipet Junction d.	|	1657	|	0245	|	0415
Guntur Junction d.	0635	|	2335	|	0030	|
Secunderabad Junction a.	1220	2025	0435	0545	0535	0635
Hyderabad Decan a.	...	...	0545	...	...	0750

– ①②④⑤⑦. B – ①②③⑤⑥. e – Chennai **Egmore**. * – *311 km* via Guntur.

Indian Railways — MUMBAI and PUNE - KOLKATA — 5270

km		Exp 12859	Exp 20821 ①	Exp 12869 ⑦	D 12261 C	D 12221 ①⑥	Exp 12101 D	Exp 12151 ③④	Exp 12129	Exp 12809
0	**Mumbai** CSMT◇ d.	0600	...	1105	1715	...	2035t	2035t	...	2110
*	**Pune** Junction d.	|	1040	|	|	1515	|	|	1835	|
	Daund Chord Line d.	|	|	|	|	1615	|	|	1955	|
53	Kalyan Junction d.	0655	1355	1200	|	|	2115	2115	|	2210
260	Manmad Junction d.	|	|	|	|	2020	|	|	0035	0137
420	Jalgaon Junction d.	1200	|	|	|	|	|	|	0245	0342
441	Bhusaval Junction d.	1245	1940	1805	2305	2245	0305	0310	0325	0420
584	Akola Junction d.	1450	|	2040	|	|	0505	0515	0530	0640
663	Badnera Junction d.	1615	|	2205	|	|	0635	0705	0655	0820
837	Nagpur d.	1900	0125	0140	0415	0415	0940	1020	0955	1125
967	Gondia Junction d.	2050	0313	0328	|	|	1133	1213	1155	1335
101	Durg d.	2255	0508	0535	|	|	1340	1420	1405	1545
139	Raipur Junction d.	2335	0548	0615	0824	0824	1420	1500	1445	1630
250	Bilaspur Junction d.	0135	0745	0810	1005	1005	1625	1655	1640	1835
454	Jharsuguda Junction d.	0430	1040	1105	|	|	1917	2007	1952	2155
554	Raurkela d.	0552	1208	1230	|	|	2045	2130	2115	2323
718	Tatanagar Junction d.	0825	1438	1520	1625	1625	2317	|	2345	0155
853	Kharagpur Junction d.	1028	1643	1730	|	|	0122	0430	0157	0400
969	**Kolkata** Howrah a.	1230	1835s	1930	2005	2015	0320h	0625h	0355	0600

	D 12262 E	D 12222 ④⑥	Exp 12860	Exp 12870 ⑤	Exp 20822 ⑥	Exp 12810	Exp 12102 F	Exp 12152 ⑤⑥	Exp 12130
Kolkata Howrah d.	0545	0545	1405	1435	1800s	1950	2105h	1955h	2210
Kharagpur Junction d.	|	|	1545	1613	1930	2130	2250	2140	2350
Tatanagar Junction d.	0900	0900	1748	1810	2150	2325	0040	|	0155
Raurkela d.	|	|	2020	2038	0022	0155	0308	0438	0423
Jharsuguda Junction d.	|	|	2155	2210	0150	0330	0435	0620	0552
Bilaspur Junction d.	1505	1505	0115	0130	0505	0710	0755	0935	0915
Raipur Junction d.	1637	1637	0250	0305	0640	0850	0935	1110	1055
Durg d.	|	|	0350	0405	0735	0945	1030	1215	1145
Gondia Junction d.	|	|	0542	0558	0920	1143	1223	1407	1348
Nagpur d.	2055	2055	0745	0810	1125	1400	1420	1625	1555
Badnera Junction d.	|	|	1035	1120	|	1730	1715	1920	1845
Akola Junction d.	|	|	1135	1225	|	1835	1820	2020	1945
Bhusaval Junction d.	0150	0150	1350	1430	1650	2050	2040	2235	2205
Jalgaon Junction d.	|	|	1420	|	|	2120	|	|	2240
Manmad Junction d.	|	0410	|	|	|	2325	|	|	0045
Kalyan Junction d.	|	|	2005	2145	2240	|	0250	0425	|
Daund Chord Line d.	|	0825	|	|	|	0315	|	|	0540
Pune Junction a.	|	0940	|	|	0245	|	|	|	0705
Mumbai CSMT ◇ a.	0815	...	2120	2300	...	0425	0355t	0530	...

– ②③④⑦.
– ①②⑤⑥.
– ①②③⑤.
F – ①③④⑦.
h – Kolkata **Shalimar**.
s – Kolkata **Santragachi Junction**.
t – Mumbai **Lokmanya Tilak Terminus**.
◇ – Mumbai Chhatrapati Shivaji Maharaj Terminus.
* – *314 km* from Manmad.

5280 KOLKATA - PURI, SECUNDERABAD, TIRUPATI and CHENNAI

Indian Railways

km		Exp	Exp	Exp	Exp	Exp	Exp	Exp	Exp	Exp	Exp	Exp	D	Exp	Exp	Exp	Exp	Exp	Exp	Exp	Exp	Exp	Exp	Exp
		12703	**12821**	**18045**	**22849**	**20889**	**22855**	**12841**	**12773**	**12665**	**22807**	**18409**	**22201**	**12887**	**22835**	**12895**	**12881**	**12837**	**12863**	**15644**	**12867**	**12660**	**22642**	**12839**
					③	⑥	⑦		③	①	②⑤		①③⑤	①	③	⑤	②④			⑤	⑦	③	②⑦	
0	**Kolkata** Howrah d.	0835	0915**h**	1125**h**	1220**h**	1240	1455**s**	1520**h**	1610**h**	1615	1800**s**	1905**h**	2000**d**	2045**h**	2045**h**	2045**h**	2045**h**	2240	2300	2315	2330	2350**h**	2350**h**	2355
116	Kharagpur Junction d.	1020	1055	1335	1410	1425	1630	1715	1755	1755	1930	2100	2215	2235	2230	2235	2235	0020	0045	0105	0110	0152	0152	0135
232	Balasore d.	1140	1248	1535	1540	|	1803	1837	1922	1922	2055	2257	|	0001	0001	0001	0001	0145	0212	|	0235	0323	0323	0304
409	Cuttack d.	1415	1543	1855	1810	1525	2042	2113	2150	2150	2335	0140	|	0230	0230	0230	0230	0430	0445	0505	|	0555	0555	0545
437	Bhubaneswar d.	1505	1625	1945	1850	1905	2125	2155	2230	2230	0015	0220	0300	0310	0310	0310	0310	0515	0525	0550	0550	0635	0635	0625
456	Khurda Road Junction d.	1555	1650	2025	1925	|	2155	|	2305	2305	0045	0245	|	0335	0335	0335	0335	0540	0555	0615	0630	0720	0715	0710
500	**Puri** a.	|	1800	|	|	|	|	|	|	|	|	0430	0355	0510	0510	0510	0510	0710	|	0730	|	|	|	|
819	Vizianagram Junction d.	2120	...	0228	0030	0047	0254	|	0420	|	0600	...	...	...	...	...	...	...	1115	...	1150	1300	1300	1245
879	Visakhapatanam d.	2235	...	0355	0150	0205	0415	0450	0545	0545	0725	...	...	...	...	...	...	...	1240	...	1315	1420	1420	1410
1081	Rajahmundry d.	0130	...	0730	0430	0505	0650	0720	0825	0825	1025	...	...	...	...	...	...	...	1520	...	|	1710	1710	1715
1259	Vijayawada Junction d.	0410	...	1040	|	0720	0935	1005	|	1130	1315	...	...	...	...	...	...	...	1820	...	1835	1940	1940	2000
1574	**Secunderabad** Junction a.	1010	...	1635	1410	|	|	|	1800	|	|	...	...	...	...	...	...	...	|	...	|	|	|	|
1637	Renigunta Junction d.	...	...	...	...	1310	1530	|	...	|	|	...	...	...	...	...	...	...	0020	...	0035	0125	|	|
1647	**Tirupati** a.	...	...	...	...	1355	1610	|	...	|	|	...	...	...	...	...	...	...	0035	...	0058	0155	|	|
1691	**Chennai** Central a.	...	...	...	...	...	...	1650	...	2045**e**	2030	...	...	...	...	...	...	...	...	...	...	...	0235**p**	0300

	D	Exp	Exp	Exp	Exp	Exp	Exp	Exp	Exp	Exp	Exp	Exp	Exp	Exp	Exp	Exp	Exp	Exp	Exp	Exp	Exp	Exp	Exp
	22202	**12838**	**12774**	**22850**	**12882**	**22836**	**12896**	**12888**	**15643**	**18410**	**12482**	**22808**	**12659**	**22641**	**18046**	**12704**	**20890**	**12822**	**12864**	**22840**	**22856**	**12868**	**12666**
	②④⑥		②	⑤	①③	②	④	⑦	⑥			④⑦	①	⑤⑦			⑦				①	③	⑥
Chennai Central d.	...	...	...	...	...	...	...	...	...	...	0700	0810	...	0915**p**	...	...	...	...	...	1915	...	...	1910**e**
Tirupati d.	...	...	...	...	...	...	...	...	...	...	|	|	0910	|	...	...	1610	...	1615	|	2005	1930	|
Renigunta Junction d.	...	...	...	...	...	...	...	...	...	...	|	|	0930	|	...	...	1630	...	1635	|	2024	2000	|
Secunderabad Junction d.	...	...	0355	0355	...	...	...	...	...	...	|	|	|	|	0830	1555	|	...	|	|	|	|	|
Vijayawada Junction d.	...	...	|	|	...	...	...	...	...	...	1330	1415	1515	1600	1425	2130	2200	...	2230	0130	0235	0235	0205
Rajahmundry d.	...	...	1120	1120	...	...	...	...	...	...	1550	1620	1730	1805	1635	2345	0020	...	0040	0345	0440	|	0415
Visakhapatanam d.	...	...	1530	1530	...	...	...	...	...	...	2015	2050	2150	2145	2130	0340	0440	...	0510	0825	0845	0845	0930
Vizianagram Junction d.	...	...	1630	1630	...	...	...	...	...	...	|	2150	2247	2247	2256	0445	0537	...	0610	0930	0947	0947	|
Puri d.	1920	2015	|	|	2205	2205	2205	2205	2205	2240	|	|	|	|	|	|	|	1025	|	|	|	|	|
Khurda Road Junction d.	|	2100	2140	2140	2300	2300	2300	2300	2300	2331	0150	0310	0350	0350	0440	0950	|	1115	1200	1505	1520	1520	1540
Bhubaneswar d.	2030	2135	2210	2210	2330	2330	2330	2330	2330	2358	0220	0340	0415	0415	0510	1020	1110	1150	1230	1535	1555	1555	1605
Cuttack d.	|	2205	2245	2245	0002	0002	0002	0002	0002	0030	0255	0415	0505	0505	0600	1055	1145	1225	1305	1610	1645	|	1650
Balasore d.	|	0111	0154	0154	0236	0235	0236	0236	|	0335	0633	0650	0733	0733	0912	1353	|	1508	1550	1912	1932	1928	2000
Kharagpur Junction d.	0115	0250	0340	0340	0430	0435	0440	0430	0440	0545	0825	0835	0915	0915	1145	1540	1623	1710	1740	2052	2108	2112	2145
Kolkata Howrah a.	0405**d**	0445	0605**h**	0605**h**	0650**h**	0650**h**	0650**h**	0650**h**	0705	0754	1040**h**	1025**s**	1155**h**	1155**h**	1440**h**	1740	1830	1915	1955	2300	2310**s**	2325	2355

d – Kolkata **Sealdah**.
e – Chennai **Egmore**.
h – Kolkata **Shalimar**.
p – Chennai **Perambur**.
s – Kolkata **Santragachi Junction**.

5290 CHENNAI - BENGALURU - MYSURU

Indian Railways

km		S	Exp	Exp	Exp	Exp	Exp	S	Exp	Exp
		12007	**22625**	**12639**	**12296**	**12609**	**12607**	**12027**	**16021**	**12657**
		④–②						③–①		
0	**Chennai** Central d.	0600	0725	0740	0945**p**	1335	1530	1730	2115	2250
68	Arakkonam Junction d.	|	0825	0840	1040	1440	1635	|	2220	2350
130	Katpadi Junction d.	0740	0915	0940	1150	1545	1735	1910	2330	0035
214	Jolarpettai d.	|	1030	1100	1320	1715	1855	|	0050	0155
361	KSR **Bengaluru** ⊖ a.	1045	1315	1340	1625	1945	2135	2225	0345	0430
506	**Mysuru** Junction a.	1300	...	...	...	2250	...	...	0640	...

	S	Exp	Exp	Exp	Exp	Exp	S	Exp	Exp
	12028	**12608**	**12609**	**12295**	**22626**	**12640**	**12008**	**12658**	**1602**
	③–①						④–②		
Mysuru Junction d.	...	...	0500	...	...	...	1415	...	2100
KSR **Bengaluru** ⊖ d.	0600	0620	0800	0910	1430	1450	1615	2240	2350
Jolarpettai d.	|	0840	1030	1125	1650	1710	|	0050	0240
Katpadi Junction d.	0900	0955	1150	1255	1810	1830	1920	0200	0350
Arakkonam Junction d.	|	1050	1300	1345	1900	1930	|	0250	0510
Chennai Central a.	1100	1215	1430	1435**p**	2025	2055	2130	0415	0645

p – Chennai **Perambur**.
⊖ – Full name is Krantivira Sangolli Rayanna Bengaluru.

5300 CHENNAI and BENGALURU - TRIVANDRUM

Indian Railways

km		Exp	Exp	Exp	Exp	Exp		Exp	Exp	Exp	Exp	Exp		Exp	Exp	Exp	Exp	Exp		Exp	Exp	Exp	Exp	Exp
		12660	**22642**	**16318**	**12508**	**12626**		**22677**	**12777**	**12697**	**12644**	**12695**		**16315**	**16320**	**12623**	**16526**	**12257**		**12671**	**12511**	**22645**	**22647**	**1723**
		⑤	②④	④	⑦			④	③	⑦	⑥				⑤⑦			②④⑦			①⑤⑥	②	④⑦	
0	**Chennai** Central d.	...	0240**p**	...	0315**p**	...	...	...	...	1510	...	1520	...	...	...	1945	...	...	...	2105	2315	2315	2315	...
	Tirupati d.	0200	|	0320	|	0445	...	...	...	|	1415	|	...	...	...	|	...	...	...	|	|	|	|	2350
130	Katpadi Junction d.	0420	0435	0520	0535	0650	...	...	...	1705	1640	1715	...	...	...	2130	...	...	...	2300	0110	0110	0110	0155
214	Jolarpettai d.	0540	0610	0635	0655	0810	...	...	...	1820	|	1830	...	...	...	|	...	...	...	|	0225	0225	0225	0310
	KSR **Bengaluru** ⊖ d.	|	|	|	|	|	...	1520**v**	1545**b**	|	|	|	...	1650	1900**b**	|	2010	2045**v**	...	|	|	|	|	|
	Bangarapet d.	|	|	|	|	|	...	|	1648	|	|	|	...	1807	2009	|	2125	|	...	|	|	|	|	|
335	Salem Junction d.	0710	0740	0810	0830	0945	...	1950	1950	1950	1925	2010	...	2120	2240	0015	0025	0112	...	0150	0355	0355	0355	0455
394	Erode Junction d.	0820	0845	0920	0940	1055	...	2050	2050	2050	2030	2110	...	2230	2340	0115	0130	0215	...	0300	0500	0500	0500	0615
494	Coimbatore Junction d.	1020	1030	1120	1135	1230	...	2240	|	|	2215	2315	...	0015	0105	0240	0300	0400	...	0520	0650	0650	0650	0805
530	**Mettupalaiyam** a.	|	|	|	|	|	...	|	|	|	|	|	...	|	|	|	|	|	...	0615	|	|	|	|
548	Palakkad Junction d.	1140	1140	1230	1250	1355	...	2345	2320	2320	2345	0030	...	0135	0215	0355	0420	0510	...	...	0800	0800	0800	0920
626	Thrisur d.	1330	1343	1400	1420	1535	...	0105	0020	0020	0105	0135	...	0250	0315	0505	0545	0630	...	...	0923	0923	0923	1135
697	Ernakulam Town d.	1505	|	1530	1550	1700	...	0215	0150	|	|	0250	...	|	0430	0640	0725	0820	...	...	1044	1044	1050	1300
	Ernakulam Junction d.	|	1520	|	|	|	...	|	|	0215	0255	|	...	0415	|	|	|	|	...	...	1100	|	|	|
814	Kayankulam Junction d.	|	1715	|	1825	1930	...	|	|	|	0440	0515	...	0630	|	0910	1030	1100	...	...	1310	1310	1310	1545
842	Kollam Junction d.	1815	1805	1850	1935	2035	...	0520	0500	0500	0520	0600	...	0720	0803	0955	1120	1140	...	...	1405	1405	1405	1650
919	**Trivandrum** Central a.	1925	1955	2020	2045	2155	...	0605**k**	0635**k**	0640	0705	0750	...	0915**k**	0925**k**	1130	1235	1310**k**	...	...	1550**k**	1550**k**	1550**k**	1830
991	**Nagercoil** Junction a.	2140	...	2215	...	...	...	...	...	...	...	...	...	...	...	...	1510	...	...	...	...	...	...	...

km		Exp	Exp	Exp	Exp	Exp		Exp	Exp	Exp	Exp	Exp		Exp	Exp	Exp	Exp	Exp		Exp	Exp	Exp	Exp	Exp
		22648	**12612**	**22646**	**17229**	**12625**		**12778**	**22678**	**12672**	**16525**	**12643**		**12624**	**16317**	**12659**	**16316**	**12507**		**22641**	**12258**	**12696**	**16319**	**1269**
		①④	②③⑦	⑥				④	⑤			②			⑤	⑦		②		④⑥	①③⑤		④⑥	⑥
	Nagercoil Junction d.	...	...	...	...	...	...	...	...	...	1030	...	...	...	1445	1445	...	...	...	...	...	...	...	...
0	**Trivandrum** Central d.	0615**k**	0635**k**	0635**k**	0700	1220	...	1250**k**	1250**k**	...	1240	1415	...	1500	1605	1605	1645**k**	1655	...	1655	1700**k**	1715	1805**k**	1915
77	Kollam Junction d.	0708	0735	0735	0803	1323	...	1343	1343	...	1400	1513	...	1603	1710	1710	1740	1753	...	1753	1753	1818	1910	2013
105	Kayankulam Junction d.	0745	0820	0820	0848	1400	...	|	|	...	1455	1546	...	1638	1745	1745	1818	1835	...	1835	1835	1856	|	|
	Ernakulam Junction d.	|	1045	1045	|	|	...	|	|	...	|	1815	...	|	|	|	2035	|	...	2115	|	|	|	2225
222	Ernakulam Town d.	1045	|	|	1120	1625	...	1700	1700	...	1755	|	...	1920	2045	2045	|	2115	...	|	2115	2145	2215	|
293	Thrisur d.	1218	1218	1218	1240	1740	...	1813	1813	...	1940	2015	...	2043	2220	2220	2210	2240	...	2240	2240	2300	2340	2350
371	Palakkad Junction d.	1350	1350	1350	1510	1915	...	1935	1935	...	2120	2140	...	2220	2350	2350	2325	0010	...	0010	0010	0040	0100	0120
	Mettupalaiyam d.	|	|	|	|	|	...	|	|	2120	|	|	...	|	|	|	|	|	...	|	|	|	|	|
425	Coimbatore Junction d.	1525	1525	1525	1635	2055	...	|	2110	2225	2300	2320	...	2340	0120	0120	0055	0135	...	0135	0135	0205	0230	|
525	Erode Junction d.	1705	1705	1705	1815	2235	...	2225	2245	0005	0030	0055	...	0120	0305	0255	0235	0315	...	0315	0315	0345	0430	0405
584	Salem Junction d.	1805	1805	1805	1915	2335	...	2325	2345	0100	0130	0150	...	0215	0405	0355	0335	0415	...	0415	0415	0440	0525	0500
	Bangarapet d.	|	|	|	|	|	...	0235	|	|	0410	|	...	|	|	|	0634	|	...	|	|	|	0832	|
853	KSR **Bengaluru** ⊖ a.	|	|	|	|	|	...	0343**b**	0430**v**	|	0640	|	...	|	|	|	0830	|	...	|	0930**v**	|	1030**b**	|
705	Jolarpettai d.	1945	1945	1945	2100	0135	...	...	...	|	...	|	...	|	0600	0600	...	0600	...	0600	...	0630	...	0700
789	Katpadi Junction d.	2055	2055	2055	2215	0300	...	...	...	0405	...	0530	...	0500	0730	0730	...	0725	...	0725	...	0740	...	0805
912	**Tirupati** a.	|	|	|	0005	0453	...	...	...	|	...	0715	...	|	0905	0905	...	|	...	|	...	|	...	|
919	**Chennai** Central a.	2310	2310	2310	...	...	...	...	...	0620	...	...	...	0745	...	...	...	0910**p**	...	0910**p**	...	1000	...	1025

b – Bengaluru **Banaswadi**.
k – Trivandrum **Kochuveli**.
p – Chennai **Perambur**.
v – Bengaluru **Yesvantpur Junction**.
⊖ – Full name is Krantivira Sangolli Rayanna Bengaluru.

Indian Railways CHENNAI - PUDUCHERRY, SENGOTTAI, TUTICORIN, TIRUCHENDER and NAGERCOIL 5310

km		Exp 12898 ③	Exp 16127	Exp 22404 ②	Exp 16105	Exp 12642 ②⑦	Exp 16101	Exp 12633	Exp 16115	Exp 12667 ④	Exp 22657 ①③⑦	Exp 12693	Exp 16723	Exp 16181 ③⑤⑥	Exp 12661	Exp 12665 ②	Exp 16191
0	**Chennai** Egmore d.	0830	0900	0945	1605	1615	1700	1720	1810	1855	1930t	1930	2010	2025	2040	2110	2300t
56	Chengalpattu d.	0920	1000	|	1705	1715	1800	1820	1915	2000	2000	2030	2110	2125	2140	2210	2330
159	Villupuram Junction d.	1055	1130	1220	1850	1855	1925	2000	2120	2135	2135	2215	2250	2300	2315	2352	0055
197	**Puducherry** a.	1200	|	1315	|	|	|	|	2215	|	|	|	|	|	|	|	|
214	Vriddhachalam Junction d.	...	1212	...	|	1937	2007	2042	...	2217	2217	2257	2332	2342	2357	0035	|
340	Tiruchchirappalli Junction d.	...	1405	...	0010	2130	2155	2230	...	0030	0030	0055	0135	0210	0155	0230	0615
433	Dindigul Junction d.	...	1520	...	0115	2235	2305	2358	...	0135	0135	0215	0255	|	0310	0345	0740
495*	Madurai Junction d.	...	1630	...	0215	2350	0015	0105	...	0235	0235	0315	0355	|	0425	0450	0900
538	Virudunagar Junction d.	...	1710	...	0255	0025	0130	0145	...	0315	0315	0355	0435	0600	0515	0525	0955
662	Tenkasi d.	...	|	...	|	|	0335	|	...	|	|	|	|	0820	0735	|	|
670	**Sengottai** a.	...	|	...	|	|	0345	|	...	|	|	|	|	0855	0815	|	|
	Kollam Junction a.	...	|	...	|	|	0730	|	...	|	|	|	|	...	...	|	|
623	Vanchi Maniyachchi d.	...	1840	...	|	|	...	|	...	|	|	0525	|	...	...	|	|
656	**Tuticorin** a.	...	|	...	|	|	...	|	...	|	|	0635	|	...	...	|	|
652	Tirunelveli Junction d.	...	1940	...	0600	0225	...	0350	...	0525	0525	...	0700	...	...	0750	1235
714	**Tiruchendur** a.	...	|	...	0800	|	...	|	...	|	|	...	|	...	...	|	|
726	**Nagercoil** Junction a.	...	2110	...	...	0330	...	0500	...	0725	0725	...	0905	...	...	0925	1420

	Exp 16102	Exp 16182 ③⑥⑦	Exp 16192	Exp 12668 ⑤	Exp 22658 ①②④	Exp 12662	Exp 12634	Exp 12694	Exp 16724	Exp 12641 ③⑤	Exp 16116	Exp 16106	Exp 22403 ③	Exp 12666 ⑥	Exp 16128	Exp 12897 ③
Nagercoil Junction d.	...	...	1545	1615	1615	...	1725	...	1755	1925	...	...	...	0600	0730	...
Tiruchendur d.	...	...	|	|	|	...	|	...	|	|	...	1910	...	|	|	...
Tirunelveli Junction d.	...	...	1705	1750	1750	...	1920	...	2005	2130	...	2115	...	0800	0930	...
Tuticorin d.	...	...	|	|	|	...	|	2015	|	|	...	|	...	|	|	...
Vanchi Maniyachchi d.	...	...	|	|	|	...	|	2045	|	|	...	|	...	|	1000	...
Kollam Junction d.	1200	...	|	|	|	...	|	|	|	|	...	|	...	|	|	...
Sengottai d.	1505	1650	|	|	|	1820	|	|	|	|	...	|	...	|	|	...
Tenkasi d.	1517	1705	|	|	|	1835	|	|	|	|	...	|	...	|	|	...
Virudunagar Junction d.	1745	1910	1840	1950	1955	2040	2110	2205	2220	2315	...	2300	...	0945	1120	...
Madurai Junction d.	1900	|	1950	2105	2105	2150	2205	2305	2320	0055	...	0015	...	1100	1230	...
Dindigul Junction d.	2005	|	2110	2205	2205	2250	2320	0015	0035	0200	...	0130	...	1205	1330	...
Tiruchchirappalli Junction d.	2120	2355	2230	2320	2320	0015	0035	0135	0155	0310	...	0245	...	1345	1500	...
Vriddhachalam Junction d.	2250	0125	|	0050	0050	0145	0205	0310	0325	0440	...	|	...	1520	1640	...
Puducherry d.	|	|	|	|	|	|	|	|	|	|	0535	|	0950	|	|	1845
Villupuram Junction d.	0010	0235	0320	0155	0155	0300	0307	0415	0435	0545	0625	0730	1032	1615	1740	1930
Chengalpattu d.	0200	0355	0450	0315	0315	0420	0435	0555	0625	0710	0805	0910	|	1740	1905	2045
Chennai Egmore a.	0305	0525	0550t	0435	0410t	0550	0610	0730	0755	0830	0930	1030	1250	1850	2035	2155

t – Chennai **Tambaram**.

* – *596 km* via Salem.

Indian Railways HILL and MOUNTAIN RAILWAYS 5320

DARJEELING HIMALAYAN RAILWAY

km		52546 ⑥⑦	52541	52556 🚂
0	**New Jalpaiguri** Junction d.	...	1000	...
8	Siliguri Junction d.	...	⊖	1330
18	Sukna d.	...	⊖	1425
26	Rangtong d.	...	⊖	1500
32	Chunbhati d.	...	|	...
38	Tindharia d.	...	⊖	...
50	Mahanadi d.	...	⊖	...
57	Kurseong d.	1315	⊖	...
65	Tung d.	1346	⊖	...
73	Sonada d.	1431	⊖	...
82	Ghum d.	1527	⊖	...
88	**Darjeeling** a.	1605	1720	...

	52540	52545 ⑥⑦	52556 🚂
Darjeeling d.	0900	0830	...
Ghum d.	⊖	0905	...
Sonada d.	⊖	0946	...
Tung d.	⊖	1030	...
Kurseong d.	⊖	1100	...
Mahanadi d.	⊖	...	...
Tindharia d.	⊖	...	...
Chunbhati d.	|	...	...
Rangtong d.	⊖	...	1520
Sukna d.	⊖	...	1600
Siliguri Junction d.	⊖	...	1635
New Jalpaiguri Junction a.	1615	...	...

KANGRA VALLEY RAILWAY

km		52464	52466	52472	52474	52466	52470
0	**Joginder Nagar** d.	...	...	0705	1155	...	...
23	Baijnath Paprola d.	0400	0710	0915	1410	1625	1755
37	Palampur Himachal d.	0432	0750	0955	1450	1653	1835
66	Kangra Mandir d.	0549	0918	1132	1624	|	1953
164	**Pathankot** Junction ◧ a.	1105	1430	1705	2100	2140	2355

	52471	52465	52475	52473	52467	52469
Pathankot Junction ◧ d.	0205	0600	0845	1010	1250	1520
Kangra Mandir d.	0626	1029	|	1519	1816	2045
Palampur Himachal d.	0755	1146	1308	1645	2018	2158
Baijnath Paprola d.	0930	1240	1355	1827	2110	2245
Joginder Nagar a.	1100	...	...	1955	...	...

MATHERAN HILL RAILWAY

km		52111	52101	52103	52105	52109
0	**Neral** Junction ⊡ d.	0640	0750	0910	1040	1705
21	**Matheran** ⊡ a.	0840	0950	1120	1235	1900

	52102	52104	52106	52108	52112
Matheran ⊡ d.	0720	0955	1250	1515	1630
Neral Junction ⊡ a.	0855	1140	1425	1655	1810

NILGIRI MOUNTAIN RAILWAY

km		56141	56136	56143	56138
0	**Mettupalaiyam** ● d.	...	0710	...	...
28	Coonor d.	0745	1040	1235	1600
56	**Udagamandalam** (Ooty) a.	0905	1155	1350	1715

	56139	56142	56137	56140
Udagamandalam (Ooty) d.	0915	1215	1400	1730
Coonor d.	1025	1320	1515	1840
Mettupalaiyam ● a.	...	...	1730	...

⊖ – No information currently available.
◧ – For connections to / from Delhi see Table **5000**.
● – For connecting trains to Chennai see Table **5300**.

⊡ – Services are normally suspended during Monsoon season. Connections Mumbai - Kalyan - Neral and v.v. are available by local train.

Indian Railways, Nepal Railway Company DELHI and KOLKATA - JAYNAGAR - KURTHA 5325

km		Exp 12562
0	**New Delhi** d.	2115
440	Kanpur Central d.	0240
634	Prayagraj Junction d.	0535
758	Varanasi Junction d.	0815
964	Chhapra d.	1255
1166	Darbhanga Junction d.	1750
1234	**Jaynagar** a.	1923

	Exp 12561
Jaynagar d.	1720
Darbhanga Junction d.	1900
Chhapra d.	0045
Varanasi Junction d.	0450
Prayagraj Junction d.	0725
Kanpur Central d.	0940
New Delhi a.	1540

◇ – Subject to confirmation.

km		Exp 13185
0	**Kolkata** Sealdah d.	1745
220	Asansol Junction d.	2214
467	Barauni Junction d.	0350
556	Darbhanga Junction d.	0620
624	**Jaynagar** a.	0845

	Exp 13186
Jaynagar d.	1610
Darbhanga Junction d.	1730
Barauni Junction d.	2045
Asansol Junction d.	0148
Kolkata Sealdah a.	0700

km		2◇	2◇
0	**Jaynagar** ▦ d.	0830	1500
28	Janakpurdham d.	0955	1630
33	**Kurtha** a.	1030	1700

	2◇	2◇
Kurtha d.	1100	1730
Janakpurdham d.	1120	1750
Jaynagar ▦ a.	1245	1915

BEYOND EUROPE
SOUTH EAST ASIA, AUSTRALIA and NEW ZEALAND

Contents

INDEX OF PLACES

by table number

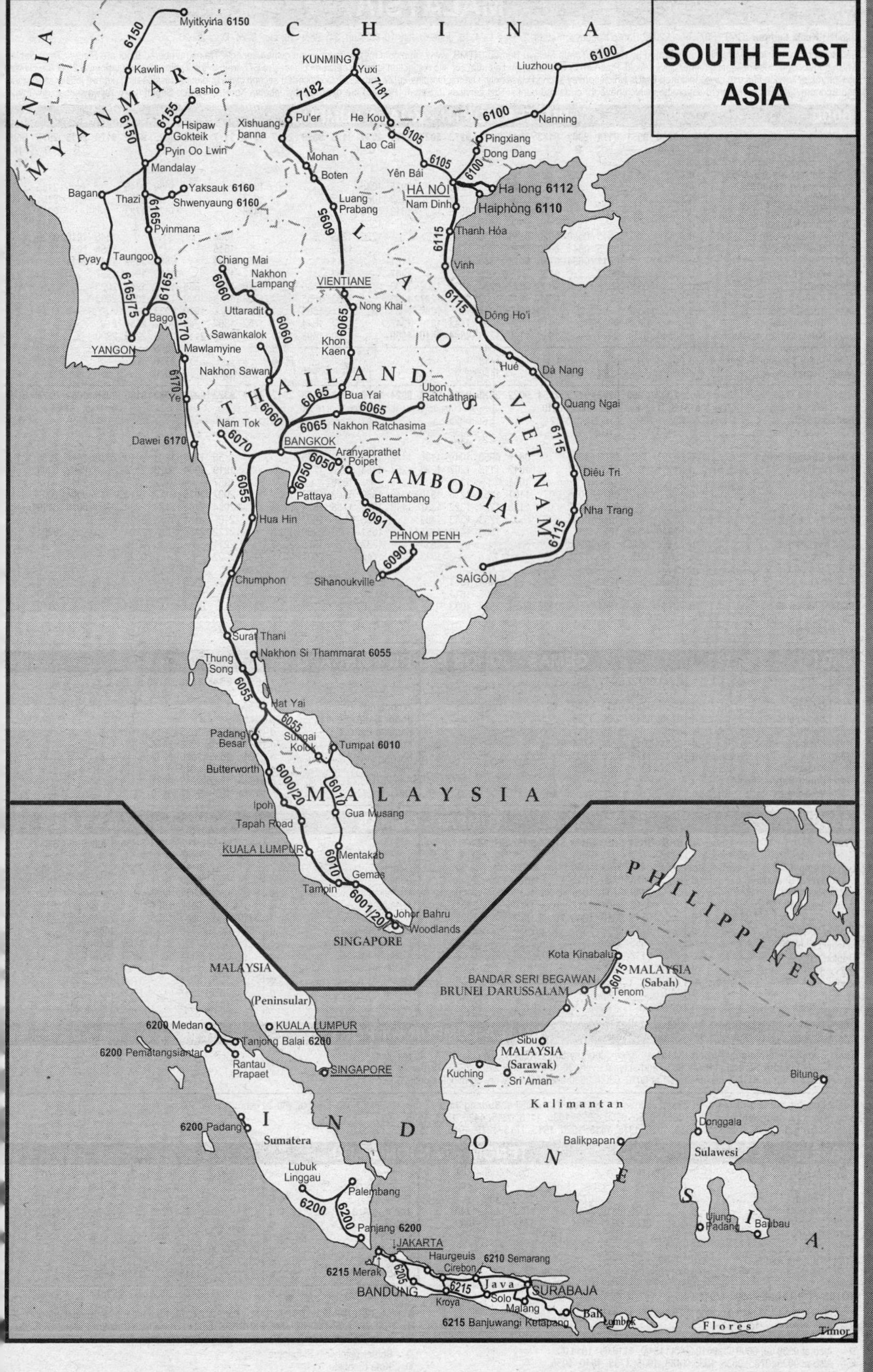
SOUTH EAST ASIA
CHINA
INDIA
MYANMAR
LAOS
THAILAND
VIETNAM
CAMBODIA
MALAYSIA
PHILIPPINES
INDONESIA
Myitkyina 6150
Kawlin
Lashio
Hsipaw
Gokteik
Pyin Oo Lwin
Mandalay
Bagan
Thazi
Yaksauk 6160
Shwenyaung 6160
Pyinmana
Pyay
Taungoo
Bago
YANGON
Mawlamyine
Ye
Dawei 6170
KUNMING
Yuxi
Pu'er
Xishuangbanna
He Kou
Lao Cai
Mohan
Boten
Luang Prabang
Yên Bái
HÁ NÔI
Nam Dinh
Ha long 6112
Haiphòng 6110
Thanh Hóa
Vinh
Dông Ho'i
Huê
Dà Nang
Quang Ngai
Diêu Tri
Nha Trang
SAIGÔN
Liuzhou
Nanning
Pingxiang
Dong Dang
Chiang Mai
Nakhon Lampang
Uttaradit
Sawankalok
Nakhon Sawan
VIENTIANE
Nong Khai
Khon Kaen
Bua Yai
Ubon Ratchathani
Nakhon Ratchasima
Nam Tok
BANGKOK
Aranyaprathet
Poipet
Pattaya
Battambang
PHNOM PENH
Sihanoukville
Hua Hin
Chumphon
Surat Thani
Nakhon Si Thammarat 6055
Thung Song
Hat Yai
Padang Besar
Sungai Kolok
Tumpat 6010
Butterworth
Ipoh
Tapah Road
Gua Musang
KUALA LUMPUR
Mentakab
Gemas
Tampin
Johor Bahru
Woodlands
SINGAPORE
6000/20
6001/20
6010
6050
6055
6060
6065
6070
6090
6091
6100
6105
6115
6150
6155
6165
6165/75
6170
7181
7182
MALAYSIA (Peninsular)
KUALA LUMPUR
SINGAPORE
6200 Medan
Tanjong Balai 6200
6200 Pematangsiantar
Rantau Prapaet
6200 Padang
Sumatera
Lubuk Linggau
Palembang
Panjang 6200
JAKARTA
6215 Merak
BANDUNG
Haurgeulis
Cirebon
6210 Semarang
Kroya
Java
Solo
SURABAJA
Malang
6215 Banjuwangi Ketapang
Bali
Lombok
Flores
Timor
6205
6215
Kota Kinabalu
BANDAR SERI BEGAWAN
BRUNEI DARUSSALAM
MALAYSIA (Sabah)
Tenom
6015
Sibu
MALAYSIA (Sarawak)
Kuching
Sri Aman
Kalimantan
Balikpapan
Bitung
Donggala
Sulawesi
Ujung Padang
Baubau

MALAYSIA

Capital: **Kuala Lumpur** (GMT +8). 2022 Public Holidays: Feb. 1, 2, May 1–4, 15, June 6, July 10, 30, Aug. 31, Sept. 16, Oct. 9, 24, Dec. 25, 26.

Rail services in mainland Malaysia are operated by Keretapi Tanah Melayu Berhad (KTMB, www.ktmb.com.my), a government owned agency. Trains numbered **9xxx** are *Electric Train Service* which convey one class of seating (either Silver, Gold, Platinum or Business) and a buffet car. No distinction is made between classes of *ETS* train in the Tables. Trains numbered **29xx** are classed as Commuter service and use air-conditioned EMUs which convey second class only. Overnight trains **26/27** convey air-conditioned second class and third class seating (known locally as Superior and Economy) and air-conditioned couchettes which have 40 curtained bunks. Rail services in Sabah (Borneo) are operated by Jabatan Keretapi Negeri Sabah (www.railway.sabah.gov.my).

6000 BUTTERWORTH - KUALA LUMPUR

For footnotes see below Table 6015 KTMB

km		5003	9051	9171	2901	9173	2941	9321	9273	9027	9275	2951	9175	9029	2057	9277	9177	9035	9425	9279	9179	2913	2975	*EOE*
		Ⓐ A			B		C					C			Ⓐ A							B	C	H
	Bangkok **6055** d.	...	...	...	...	...	...	...	...	...	...	...	...	...	...	...	...	...	...	...	...	...	...	◧
0	**Hat Yai** Junction **6055** d.	...	...	...	...	...	...	...	...	...	...	...	...	...	...	...	...	...	...	...	...	...	...	|
45	**Padang Besar** ▦ d.	...	...	...	...	...	0520	...	0730	...	0935	1035	...	...	...	1340	...	...	1550	1645	...	...	2135	|
76	Arau d.	...	...	...	...	...	0539	...	0747	...	0952	1054	...	...	...	1357	...	...	1607	1702	...	...	2154	|
114	Alor Setar d.	...	...	...	...	...	0603	...	0808	...	1013	1118	...	...	...	1418	...	...	1629	1723	...	...	2218	|
205	Bukit Mertajam d.	...	...	...	...	...	0700	...	|	...	|	1203	...	...	...	|	...	...	|	|	...	...	2315	|
216	**Butterworth** d.	...	...	0515	0530	0620	0711	0750	|	...	|	1226	1245	...	...	|	1605	...	|	|	1845	1910	2326	|
227	Bukit Mertajam d.	...	...	0525	0541	0630	▬	0800	|	...	|	...	1255	...	...	|	1615	...	|	|	1855	1921	...	|
312	Taiping d.	...	...	0611	0634	0716	**9025**	0848	0946	...	1151	...	1341	...	...	1556	1701	...	1808	1859	1941	2014	...	|
344	Kuala Kangsar d.	...	...	0627	...	0732		0905	1002	...	1207	...	1357	...	...	1612	1717	...	1825	1915	1957	...	...	|
398	**Ipoh** d.	...	0510	0655	...	0800	0822	0934	1030	1202	1235	...	1425	1530	...	1640	1745	1835	1855	1943	2025	...	...	|
434	Kampar d.	...	0536	0723	...	0828	0847	1002	1058	1227	1303	...	1453	1555	...	1708	1813	1900	1923	2011	2053	...	...	|
450	Tapah Road d.	...	0546	|	...	|	0857	1012	|	1237	|	...	|	1605	...	|	|	1910	1933	|	|	...	...	|
517	Tanjong Malim d.	...	0625	0807	...	0912	0936	1051	1142	1316	1347	...	1537	1644	...	1752	1857	1949	2012	2055	2137	...	...	|
604	**Kuala Lumpur** Sentral d.	0540	0751	0929	...	1034	1100	1214	1304	1440	1509	...	1700	1808	1840	1914	2020	2113	2135	2223	2300	...	...	|
677	Seremban d.	0716	...	...	...	...	...	1344	...	...	...	...	...	...	2016	...	...	...	2305	...	...	...	...	|
726	Pulau Sebang/Tampin d.	0756	...	...	...	...	...	1418	...	...	...	...	...	...	2056	...	...	...	2338	...	...	...	...	|
779	**Gemas** d.	...	...	...	...	...	...	1452	...	...	...	...	...	...	...	...	...	...	0010	...	...	...	...	◧

	2002	2900	9272	9172	2954	9022	9274	9420	9174	9024	9176	9028	9178	2912	2974	9322	9276	9032	9180	2058	9052	9278	*EOE*
	Ⓐ D	F			E									F	E					Ⓐ D			H
Gemas d.	...	...	...	...	...	...	...	0805	...	...	...	...	...	...	...	1520	...	...	...	...	...	...	◧
Pulau Sebang/Tampin d.	0445	...	...	...	...	...	...	0836	...	...	...	...	...	...	...	1553	...	...	...	1820	...	...	|
Seremban d.	0526	...	...	...	...	...	...	0909	...	...	...	...	...	...	...	1627	...	...	...	1901	...	...	|
Kuala Lumpur Sentral d.	0703	...	0708	0803	...	0847	0950	1040	1108	1132	1337	1500	1555	...	...	1755	1831	1903	2010	2036	2140	2250	|
Tanjong Malim d.	▬	...	0831	0921	...	1012	1113	1207	1226	1257	1455	1620	1713	...	...	1919	1954	2023	2128	...	2302	0008	|
Tapah Road d.	...	...	|	|	...	1051	|	1245	|	1336	|	1659	|	...	...	1957	|	2102	|	...	2341	|	|
Kampar d.	...	...	0915	1005	...	1101	1157	1255	1310	1346	1539	1709	1757	...	...	2007	2038	2112	2212	...	0004	0052	|
Ipoh d.	...	...	0942	1032	...	1128	1224	1322	1337	1413	1606	1736	1824	...	...	2034	2105	2139	2239	...	0018	0119	|
Kuala Kangsar d.	...	...	1011	1101	...	...	1253	1353	1409	...	1635	...	1853	...	...	2105	2134	...	2308	...	...	0148	|
Taiping d.	**2940**	0532	1027	1117	...	...	1309	1410	1425	...	1651	...	1909	1927	...	2122	2150	...	2324	...	...	0204	|
Bukit Mertajam d.	**E**	0625	|	1203	...	...	|	|	1511	...	1737	...	1955	2020	...	2211	|	...	0010	...	...	|	|
Butterworth d.	0520	0636	|	1215	1235	...	|	|	1523	...	1749	...	2007	2031	2135	2222	|	...	0022	...	...	|	|
Bukit Mertajam d.	0531	...	|	...	1246	...	|	|	...	...	...	...	...	...	2146	...	|	...	...	...	...	|	|
Alor Setar d.	0628	...	1202	...	1343	...	1444	1551	...	...	...	...	...	...	2243	...	2325	...	...	...	...	0339	|
Arau d.	0652	...	1223	...	1407	...	1505	1614	...	...	...	...	...	...	2307	...	2346	...	...	...	...	0400	|
Padang Besar ▦ d.	0711	...	1241	...	1426	...	1523	1633	...	...	...	...	...	...	2326	...	0004	...	...	...	...	0418	|
Hat Yai Junction **6055** a.	...	...	...	...	...	...	...	...	...	...	...	...	...	...	...	...	...	...	...	...	...	...	|
Bangkok **6055** a.	...	...	...	...	...	...	...	...	...	...	...	...	...	...	...	...	...	...	...	...	...	...	◧

6001 GEMAS - JOHOR BAHRU - SINGAPORE

For footnotes see below Table 6015 KTMB

km		ES41	ERT27	ES43	ES45	*EOE*				
			[R] G			H				
0	**Gemas** d.	0200	0744	0930	1520	◧	...	...	...	...
26	Segamat d.	0236	0849	1006	1556	|	...	...	...	...
85	Paloh d.	0357	|	1145	1717	|	...	...	...	...
112	Kluang d.	0434	1013	1222	1754	|	...	...	...	...
163	Kulai d.	0542	1136	1330	1902	|	...	...	...	...
	Kempas Baru a.	0607	1208	1355	1927	|	...	...	...	...
195	**Johor Bahru** Sentral a.	...	...	...	...	|	...	...	...	...
199	**Woodlands** ◇ a.	...	...	...	...	◧	...	...	...	...

	ES42	ES44	ES46	ERT26	*EOE*				
				[R] G	H				
Woodlands ◇ d.	...	...	...	...	◧	...	...	...	...
Johor Bahru Sentral d.	...	...	...	...	|	...	...	...	...
Kempas Baru d.	0850	1500	1825	2044	|	...	...	...	...
Kulai d.	0918	1528	1908	2114	|	...	...	...	...
Kluang d.	1044	1636	2016	2237	|	...	...	...	...
Paloh d.	1114	1706	2047	|	|	...	...	...	...
Segamat d.	1240	1832	2213	0031	|	...	...	...	...
Gemas a.	1314	1906	2247	0118	◧	...	...	...	...

6010 TUMPAT - GEMAS

For footnotes see below Table 6015 KTMB

km		SH35	SH51	SH53	SH55	SH37	SH57	SH59	ERT27	•
		•							[R] ◆	
0	**Tumpat** d.	...	0410	0705	1000	...	1605	...	2030	...
14	Wakaf Bharu d.	...	0425	0720	1031	...	1621	...	2045	...
25	Pasir Mas d.	...	0440	0734	1045	...	1636	...	2100	...
53	Tanah Merah d.	...	0512	0804	1117	...	1710	...	2131	...
85	Kuala Krai d.	...	0549	0910	1206	...	1819	...	2208	...
135	Dabong d.	...	0717	1033	1335	...	2030	...	2331	...
206	Gua Masang d.	...	0955	1229	...	...	2233	2240	0123	...
300	Kuala Lipis d.	1020	1142	...	...	1610	...	0022	0309	...
353	Jerantut d.	1120	...	...	...	1710	...	...	0402	...
406	Mentakab d.	1219	...	...	...	1827	...	...	0456	...
492	Bahau d.	1407	...	...	...	2015	...	...	0638	...
528	**Gemas** a.	1502	...	...	...	2110	...	...	0744	...

	SH50	SH52	ERT26	SH34	SH56	SH58	SH60	SH36	
			[R] ◆						
Gemas d.	...	...	0118	0925		...	...	1535	...
Bahau d.	...	...	0213	1021	...	...	...	1631	...
Mentakab d.	...	...	0354	1228	...	...	...	1820	...
Jerantut d.	...	...	0507	1327	...	...	...	1919	...
Kuala Lipis d.	0320	...	0611	1425	...	...	1635	2017	...
Gua Masang d.	0500	0505	0748	...	...	1450	1818	...	...
Dabong d.	...	0730	0937	...	1455	1646	2019	...	...
Kuala Krai d.	...	0858	1114	...	1623	1808	2220	...	...
Tanah Merah d.	...	0936	1151	...	1717	1845	2256	...	...
Pasir Mas d.	...	1010	1222	...	1750	1915	2327	...	...
Wakaf Bharu d.	...	1025	1237	...	1805	1929	2341	...	...
Tumpat a.	...	1042	1254	...	1822	1946	2357	...	...

6012 KUALA LUMPUR AIRPORTS

For footnotes see below Table 6015 KTMB

Kuala Lumpur International Airport (KLIA) ✈. *57 km.* Journey times: KLIA 37 minutes, KLIA2 40 minutes.
From **Kuala Lumpur Sentral** at 0500, 0530 and at least every 30 minutes until 2200, 2230, 2310.
From **KLIA2** ✈ (from **KLIA** 5 minutes later) at 0010, 0500, 0530 and at least every 30 minutes until 2300, 2330.

Kuala Lumpur Subang Skypark ✈. *26 km.* Journey 37 minutes. Trains call at **Subang Jaya** 18 minutes after Kuala Lumpur and 20 minutes after Subang Airport.
From **Kuala Lumpur Sentral** at 0555, 0655, 0750, 0850, 0925, 1035, 1125, 1315, 1425, 1525, 1625, 1825.
From **Subang Skypark** ✈ at 0750, 1035, 1220, 1315, 1415, 1520, 1615, 1715, 1815, 1915, 2015, 2125, 2245.

6015 TENOM - TANJONG ARU

JKNS

km			①–⑥	⑦			⑦	①–⑥	①–⑥	
0	**Tenom** d.	...	...	...	0730	...	1230	1300	...	...
	Halogilat d.	...	0600	0810	0854	...	1353	1444	1740	...
49	Beaufort a.	...	0658	0911	0951	...	1455	1545	1839	...
49	Beaufort d.	0500	...	...	...	1101	...	...	...	...
101	Papar d.	0611	...	...	...	1216	...	...	...	...
134	**Tanjong Aru** ◐ d.	0658	...	...	...	1310	...	...	...	...
	Sembulan ◐ a.	0710	...	...	...	1323	...	...	...	...

	①–⑥	⑦			⑦	①–⑥	①–⑥	⑦	①–⑥
Sembulan ◐ d.	...	...	...	...	...	...	...	1700	1730
Tanjong Aru ◐ d.	...	...	...	0745	...	...	...	1706	1736
Papar d.	...	...	...	0829	...	...	...	1750	1823
Beaufort a.	...	...	...	0940	...	...	...	1900	1934
Beaufort d.	0500	0700	0750	...	1300	1330	1630	...	...
Halogilat d.	0559	0758	0853	...	1353	1444	1730	...	...
Tenom a.	...	...	1013	...	1510	1555	...	...	...

NOTES FOR TABLES 6000 - 6015:

A – Also at 0851 Ⓒ, 1443 Ⓐ, 1500 Ⓒ, 1653 Ⓐ, 1743 Ⓐ, 1806 Ⓒ, 1905 Ⓒ.
B – Also at 0700, 1210, 1740.
C – Also at 0620, 0735, 0835, 1235, 1435, 1635, 1735, 1835, 1935.
D – Also at 0538 Ⓒ, 0600 Ⓒ, 0610 Ⓐ, 1115 Ⓐ, 1116 Ⓒ, 1811 Ⓒ.
E – Also at 0625, 0735, 0835, 1035, 1435, 1635, 1735, 1840, 1935.
F – Also at 0712, 1347, 1742.

G – EKSPRES RAKYAT TIMURAN – 🛏 2 cl., (23) Kempas Baru - Tumpat and v.v.
H – EASTERN AND ORIENTAL EXPRESS. Luxury cruise train Bangkok - Woodlands and v.v. (www.belmond.com/trains/asia/eastern-and-oriental-express).

◇ – Border point with Singapore.
◐ – Kota Kinabalu.
◧ – Contact operator for timings.

THAILAND

Capital: **Bangkok** (GMT +7). 2022 Public Holidays: Jan. 1, 3, Feb. 16, Apr. 6, 13 – 15, May 1, 2, 4, 13 – 16, June 3, July 12, 14, 28, Aug. 12, Oct. 13, 23, 24, Dec. 5, 10, 12, 31.

Rail services are operated by State Railway of Thailand (SRT www.railway.co.th). Trains may convey any combination of first, second or third class seating as shown in either columns or footnotes. Overnight trains may also convey sleeping cars or couchettes. Sleeping cars have lockable two berth compartments which convert into seats during the day. Couchettes are arranged 'open plan' along the coach and during the day the bottom bunks are used as seats. Dining cars are operated on all important trains. The Thailand Rail Pass offers twenty days unlimted travel in seated accommodation. Two passes are available. Pass A costs 1550 Baht and does not include supplements for express trains or sleeping cars. Pass B costs 3000 Baht and includes all supplements.

BANGKOK - BAN PLU TA LUANG and ARANYAPRATHET — 6050

3rd class only

km		275	997	283	283	281	279	277	371	383
			⑥⑦		①–⑤					
0	**Bangkok** Hua Lamphong. ◧ d.	0555	0645	0655	0655	0800	1305	1525	1740	1825
5	Makkasan ◧ d.	0620	0659	0716	0716	0816	1317	1545	1802	1843
31	Hua Takhe ‡ ◧ d.	0703	0733	0814	0814	0857	1348	1618	1842	1924
61	Chachoengsao Junction ◧ d.	0740	0802	0856	0859	0932	1421	1644	1924	2000
131	Si Racha Junction d.	|	0855	...	1013	|	|	|	|	...
155	Pattaya d.	|	0914	...	1035	|	|	|	|	...
184	**Ban Plu Ta Luang** a.	|	0950	...	1120	|	|	|	|	...
122	Prachin Buri d.	0846	...	...	...	1046	1514	1741	2032	...
161	Kabin Buri d.	0933	...	...	...	1135	1550	1820	...	...
255	**Aranyaprathet** a.	1110	...	...	...	...	1720	...	...	...
260	Ban Klong Luk 🚌 a.	1117	...	...	...	...	1727	...	...	...

	372	278	280	368	282	284	284	998	276
							①–⑤	⑥⑦	
Ban Klong Luk 🚌 d.	...	...	0658	...	...	...	...	...	1353
Aranyaprathet d.	...	...	0705	...	...	...	...	...	1400
Kabin Buri d.	...	0630	0839	...	1325	...	...	...	1549
Prachin Buri d.	0500	0719	0919	...	1416	...	...	...	1640
Ban Plu Ta Luang d.	|	|	|	...	|	...	1335	1550	|
Pattaya d.	|	|	|	...	|	...	1421	1626	|
Si Racha Junction d.	|	|	|	...	|	...	1452	1645	|
Chachoengsao Junction ◧ d.	0619	0831	1022	1235	1534	1620	1620	1737	1800
Hua Takhe ‡ ◧ d.	0701	0911	1107	1316	1609	1706	1706	1806	1842
Makkasan ◧ d.	0751	0958	1148	1354	1655	1801	1801	1838	1925
Bangkok Hua Lamphong ◧ a.	0815	1015	1205	1410	1715	1815	1815	1855	1940

◧ – Additional trains are available Bangkok - Chachoengsao and v.v.

‡ – For Suvarnabhumi International Airport ✈.

BANGKOK - HAT YAI - SUNGAI KOLOK — 6055

km		453	43		261	171		31	37		463	451		83	447		167	85		39	455		445	
		3	2		3						3	3			3					2	3		3	
						A		B	C					D			A	D						
0	**Bangkok** Hua Lamphong d.	...	0750	...	0920	1230	...	1430	1510	...	...	...	...	1700	...	...	1830	1930	...	2205	...	...	...	...
64	Nakhon Pathom d.	...	0908	...	1057	1411	...	1553	1646	...	...	...	...	1834	...	...	2009	2109	...	2320	...	...	...	...
117	Rachaburi d.	...	1013	...	1209	1512	...	1649	1747	...	...	...	...	1934	...	...	2113	2218	...	0004	...	...	...	...
229	Hua Hin d.	...	1209	...	1415	1743	...	1915	2015	...	...	...	...	2209	...	...	2339	0053	...	0218	...	...	...	...
377	Bang Saphan Yai d.	...	1504	...	...	2100	...	|	2334	...	...	...	...	0121	...	...	0318	0426	...	0542	...	...	...	...
485	Chumphon d.	...	1636	...	...	2243	...	0005	0122	...	...	...	...	0305	...	...	0506	0602	...	0712	...	...	0615	...
651	Surat Thani ⊡ d.	...	1850	...	...	0138	...	0243	0349	...	...	...	...	0538	0620	...	0757	0842	...	0925	...	...	0959	...
773	Thung Song Junction d.	...	...	...	...	0344	...	0437	0545	...	...	...	...	0741	0848	...	1019	1058	...	...	...	...	1246	...
832	**Nakhon Si Thammarat** d.	...	...	...	...	|	...	|	|	...	...	0600	...	|	|	...	|	1205	...	...	0950	...	|	...
845	Trang a.	...	...	...	...	|	...	|	|	...	...	|	...	0850	|	...	1142	...	...	...	|	...	|	...
866	**Kantang** a.	...	...	...	...	|	...	|	|	...	...	|	...	...	|	...	1205	...	...	...	|	...	|	...
862	Phatthalung d.	...	...	...	...	0520	...	0607	0723	...	0625	0841	...	...	1039	...	...	...	...	...	1243	...	1458	...
943	Hat Yai Junction d.	...	...	...	...	0705	...	0725	0906	...	0816	1028	...	...	1246	...	...	...	...	...	1433	...	1700	...
1009	Pattani d.	...	...	...	...	0818	...	...	1017	...	0939	1159	...	...	1448	...	...	...	...	...	1553	...	...	...
1055	Yala d.	0630	...	...	...	0906	...	...	1055	...	1018	1236	...	...	1525	...	...	...	...	...	1630	...	...	...
1159	**Sungai Kolok** a.	0840	...	...	...	1050	...	...	1230	...	1255	1445	...	...	1735	...	...	...	...	...	...	...	...	...

	262	40		446	456		168	448		86	452		44	84		172	464		32	38		454	
	3	2		2	3			3			3		2				3					2	
							A			D				D		A			B	C			
Sungai Kolok d.	...	...	...	...	...	...	...	0630	...	...	0900	...	...	...	...	1200	1255	...	...	1420	...	1525	...
Yala d.	...	...	...	...	0635	...	...	0835	...	...	1117	...	...	...	...	1353	1453	...	...	1611	...	1740	...
Pattani d.	...	...	...	...	0717	...	...	0916	...	...	1158	...	...	...	...	1416	1528	...	...	1642	...	...	...
Hat Yai Junction d.	...	...	...	0635	0854	...	...	1115	...	...	1400	...	...	...	...	1550	1705	...	1745	1815	...	...	...
Phatthalung d.	...	...	...	0829	1046	...	...	1316	...	...	1531	...	...	...	...	1700	1850	...	1859	1934	...	...	...
Kantang d.	...	...	...	|	|	...	1240	|	...	...	|	...	...	...	...	|	...	...	|	|	...	...	...
Trang d.	...	...	...	|	|	...	1329	|	...	...	|	...	...	1700	...	|	...	...	|	|	...	...	...
Nakhon Si Thammarat d.	...	...	...	|	1340	...	|	|	...	1520	1805	...	...	|	...	|	...	...	|	|	...	...	...
Thung Song Junction d.	...	...	...	1045	...	...	1517	1531	...	1635	...	...	...	1820	...	1853	...	...	2040	2118	...	...	...
Surat Thani ⊡ d.	...	1025	...	1331	...	...	1738	1755	...	1852	...	...	2105	2014	...	2116	...	...	2227	2314	...	...	...
Chumphon d.	...	1236	...	1705	...	...	2031	...	...	2125	...	...	2323	2251	...	0008	...	...	0100	0142	...	...	...
Bang Saphan Yai d.	...	1352	...	...	...	...	2216	...	...	2256	...	...	0122	0037	...	0200	...	...	|	0343	...	...	...
Hua Hin d.	1430	1623	...	...	...	...	0116	...	...	0240	...	...	0430	0413	...	0529	...	...	0555	0709	...	...	...
Rachaburi d.	1717	1813	...	...	...	...	0306	...	...	0512	...	...	0632	0655	...	0758	...	...	0817	0934	...	...	...
Nakhon Pathom d.	1829	1922	...	...	...	...	0405	...	...	0636	...	...	0735	0816	...	0920	...	...	0939	1053	...	...	...
Bangkok Hua Lamphong a.	2020	2110	...	...	...	...	0535	...	...	0825	...	...	0910	1005	...	1115	...	...	1130	1245	...	...	...

A – RAPID – 🛏 2 cl., [23].
B – SPECIAL EXPRESS – 🛏 1, 2 cl. [12].
C – SPECIAL EXPRESS – 🛏 1, 2 cl. [23].
D – EXPRESS - 🛏 1, 2 cl. [23].
⊡ – Station is at Phun Phin, *13 km* away.

BANGKOK - CHIANG MAI — 6060

km		403	407	401		303	111	7		201	209	211		109	207	301		317	9	313		13	107	51
		3	3	3		3	23	2		23	3	23			3	3		3		3				
														A					B			B	A	E
0	**Bangkok** H Lamphong **6065** d.	...	...	...	...	0420	0700	0830	...	0925	1120	1255	...	1345	1405	1630	...	1725	1810	1820	...	1935	2010	2200
58	Bang Pa In d.	...	...	...	...	0536	0825	|	...	1114	1251	1419	...	|	1543	1816	...	1900	|	2000	...	|	|	|
71	Ayutthaya **6065** d.	...	...	...	...	0550	0838	0948	...	1128	1305	1432	...	1519	1558	1833	...	1914	1945	2013	...	2107	2144	2236
133	Lop Buri d.	...	...	0600	...	0705	0944	1029	...	1241	1423	1538	...	1623	1727	1945	...	2020	2042	...	...	2200	2239	0031
246	Nakhon Sawan d.	...	0500	0811	...	...	1124	1140	...	1511	...	1753	...	1827	1935	...	...	...	2217	...	...	2331	0006	0224
319	Taphan Hin d.	...	0616	0936	...	...	1242	1226	...	1640	...	1915	...	1937	...	...	...	...	|	...	...	|	0130	0337
389	Phitsanulok d.	0555	0728	1055	...	...	1345	1322	...	1755	...	...	...	2037	...	...	...	...	0018	...	...	0149	0238	0440
485	Uttaradit d.	0737	0904	...	...	...	1524	1427	...	...	...	...	...	2223	...	...	...	...	|	...	...	0308	0405	0606
488	Sila At d.	0740	0909	...	...	...	1529	1433	...	...	...	...	...	2237	...	...	...	...	0154	...	...	0321	0418	0620
534	Den Chai d.	...	1012	...	...	...	1630	1524	...	...	...	...	...	2342	...	...	...	...	0251	...	...	0419	0515	0720
642	Nakhon Lampang d.	...	1233	...	...	...	...	1733	...	...	...	...	...	0204	...	...	...	...	0501	...	...	0633	...	1001
683	Khun Tan d.	...	1330	...	...	...	...	1823	...	...	...	...	...	0258	...	...	...	...	0606	...	...	0737	...	1105
729	Lamphun d.	...	1415	...	...	...	...	1915	...	...	...	...	...	0344	...	...	...	...	0651	...	...	0821	...	1150
751	**Chiang Mai** a.	...	1435	...	...	...	...	1930	...	...	...	...	...	0405	...	...	...	...	0715	...	...	0840	...	1210

	318	208	304		212	202	112		210	102	8		402	408	410		108	52	14		10	314	302
	3	3	3		3	23	23		3	23	2		3	3	3							3	3
																	A	E	B		B		
Chiang Mai d.	...	...	...	...	...	...	...	...	...	0630	0850	...	...	0930	...	...	...	1530	1700	...	1800	...	...
Lamphun d.	...	...	...	...	...	...	...	...	...	0652	0905	...	...	1000	...	...	...	1548	1720	...	1820	...	...
Khun Tan d.	...	...	...	...	...	...	...	...	...	0736	0947	...	...	1103	...	...	...	1650	1824	...	1921	...	...
Nakhon Lampang d.	...	...	...	...	...	...	...	...	...	0837	1041	...	...	1202	...	...	...	1804	1927	...	2017	...	...
Den Chai d.	...	...	...	...	...	...	0730	...	...	1046	1239	...	...	1419	...	...	1905	2026	2141	...	2236	...	...
Sila At d.	...	...	...	...	...	...	0827	...	...	1147	1326	...	...	1533	1630	...	2012	2130	2236	...	2333	...	...
Uttaradit d.	...	...	...	...	...	...	0833	...	...	1153	1332	...	...	1538	1633	...	2019	2137	2242	...	|	...	...
Phitsanulok d.	...	...	...	...	...	0605	1003	...	...	1318	1444	...	1345	1724	1810	...	2209	2301	0001	...	0050	...	...
Taphan Hin d.	...	...	...	...	0530	0718	1112	...	...	1428	1532	...	1458	1842	...	...	2320	0007	|	...	|	...	...
Nakhon Sawan d.	...	0500	...	...	0701	0835	1242	...	...	1556	1622	...	1630	1955	...	...	0048	0114	0159	...	0241	...	...
Lop Buri d.	0600	0706	0800	...	0918	1056	1439	...	1732	1806	1728	...	1845	...	...	...	0228	0245	0324	...	0405	...	0430
Ayutthaya **6065** d.	0711	0826	0901	...	1027	1248	1559	...	1848	1916	1806	...	...	...	...	...	0321	0339	0424	...	0459	0507	0558
Bang Pa In d.	0722	0840	0912	...	1039	1229	1616	...	1903	|	|	...	...	...	...	...	|	|	|	...	|	0820	0613
Bangkok Hua Lamphong **6065** a.	0905	1020	1035	...	1210	1405	1800	...	2035	2110	1925	...	...	...	...	...	0510	0525	0615	...	0650	0655	0745

A – RAPID – 🛏 2 cl., [23].
B – SPECIAL EXPRESS – 🛏 1, 2 cl. [12].
E – EXPRESS – 🛏 2 cl., [23].

6065 BANGKOK - UBON RATCHATHANI and NONG KHAI

km		421	21	419	135	71	427	139	23	141
		3	2	3	23	23	3	A	B	23
0	**Bangkok** H Lamphong . **6060** d.	...	0545	...	0640	1005	...	1855	2030	2245
71	Ayutthaya .... **6060** d.	...	0659	...	0826	1125	...	2026	2153	0017
113	Saraburi ....d.	...	0734	...	0910	1204	...	2110	2236	0059
125	Kaeng Khoi Junction ....d.	...	0745	...	0923	1216	...	2124	2237	0115
180	Pak Chong ....d.	...	0853	...	1056	1327	...	2249	0010	0259
264	Nakhon Ratchasima ....d.	0610	1011	1115	1224	1443	1420	0023	0146	0429
376	Buri Ram ....d.	0810	1137	1317	1422	1617	1635	0226	0334	0634
420	Surin ....d.	0910	1211	1403	1510	1711	1723	0317	0414	0729
515	Si Sa Ket ....d.	1107	1320	1550	1703	1843	1906	0509	0539	0908
575	**Ubon Ratchathani** ....a.	1215	1400	1645	1800	1950	2015	0615	0635	1020

	72	428	136	426	22		142	24	140
	23	3	23	3	2		23	B	A
Ubon Ratchathani ....d.	0540	0620	0700	1235	1450	...	1735	1900	2030
Si Sa Ket ....d.	0624	0716	0804	1344	1531	...	1841	1956	2124
Surin ....d.	0749	0905	0939	1528	1641	...	2022	2123	2256
Buri Ram ....d.	0835	0953	1027	1615	1715	...	2117	2204	2344
Nakhon Ratchasima ....d.	1018	1145	1233	1825	1847	...	2325	2359	0142
Pak Chong ....d.	1127	...	1400	...	1948	...	0103	0131	0303
Kaeng Khoi Junction ....d.	1228	...	1530	...	2053	...	0216	|	0425
Saraburi ....d.	1241	...	1545	...	2105	...	0232	|	0441
Ayutthaya .... **6060** d.	1317	...	1637	...	2142	...	0313	0342	0531
Bangkok H Lamphong .... **6060** a.	1455	...	1840	...	2255	...	0500	0515	0720

km		415	431	75	25	133				
		3	3	23	B	3				
0	**Bangkok** H Lamphong . **6060** d.	...	...	0820	2000	2045	...	...	...	...
71	Ayutthaya .... **6060** d.	...	...	0942	2141	2218	...	...	...	...
113	Saraburi ....d.	...	...	1018	2223	2302	...	...	...	...
125	Kaeng Khoi Junction ....d.	...	0500	1030	2235	2315	...	...	...	...
180	Pak Chong ....d.	...	0618	|	|	|	...	...	...	...
264	Nakhon Ratchasima ....d.	0620	0829	|	|	|	...	...	...	...
346	Bua Yai Junction ....d.	0758	1009	1414	0250	0357	...	...	...	...
450	Khon Kaen ....d.	0935	1226	1532	0412	0522	...	...	...	...
569	Udon Thani ....d.	1121	...	1658	0544	0707	...	...	...	...
621	**Nong Khai** ....a.	1205	...	1730	0625	0755	...	...	...	...
627	**Tha Na Laeng** (Laos) ....a.	...	...	...	...	...	...	...	...	...

	76	432	418	134	26				
	23	3	3	3	B				
Tha Na Laeng (Laos) ....d.	...	...	...	...	...	...	...	...	...
Nong Khai ....d.	0745	...	1255	1850	1940	...	...	...	...
Udon Thani ....d.	0816	...	1340	1938	2020	...	...	...	...
Khon Kaen ....d.	0932	1430	1533	2112	2149	...	...	...	...
Bua Yai Junction ....d.	1045	1601	1705	2246	2317	...	...	...	...
Nakhon Ratchasima ....d.	|	1740	1835	|	|	...	...	...	...
Pak Chong ....d.	|	1914	...	|	|	...	...	...	...
Kaeng Khoi Junction ....d.	1444	2030	...	0237	0308	...	...	...	...
Saraburi ....d.	1455	...	...	0252	0321	...	...	...	...
Ayutthaya .... **6060** d.	1535	...	...	0348	0404	...	...	...	...
Bangkok H Lamphong .... **6060** a.	1710	...	...	0545	0600	...	...	...	...

A – 2 cl., 23.

B – 1, 2 cl., 12.

6070 BANGKOK - NAM TOK

km		909	257
		©C	3D
0	**Bangkok** Thon Buri .... d.	...	0745
	Bangkok H Lamphong . d.	0630	|
64	Nakhon Pathom .... d.	0820	0852
82	Nong Pla Duk Jct .... d.	0836	0921
133	Kanchanaburi .... d.	0927	1035
210	**Nam Tok** .... a.	...	1235

	258	910
	3D	©C
Nam Tok ....d.	1255	...
Kanchanaburi ....d.	1448	1653
Nong Pla Duk Jct ....d.	1608	1755
Nakhon Pathom ....d.	1630	1809
Bangkok H L'hong ....a.	|	1925
Bangkok Thon Buri ....a.	1740	

C – Tourist train to River Khwae Bridge (a. 0935) and allied war cemetery at Kanchanaburi. Conveys 23. R. Fare 740 Baht. SERVICE SUSPENDED.

D – Also from Bangkok at 1355; also from Nam Tok at 0520.

6075 SUVARNABHUMI AIRPORT ✈

Phaya Thai - Makksan - Suvarnabhumi International Airport ✈ (journey 26 minutes):

From Phaya Thai (from Makksan 4 minutes later) at 0529 and every 10 – 15 minutes until 2400.

From Suvarnabhumi International Airport ✈ at 0529 and every 10 – 15 minutes until 0002.

CAMBODIA

Capital: **Phnom Penh** (GMT +7). 2022 Public Holidays: Jan. 1, 7, Mar. 8, Apr. 14 – 16, May 1, 14, 15, 19, Sept. 24 – 26, Oct. 15, 29, Nov. 7 – 9.

Rail services are operated by Royal Railway (www.royal-railway.com). Trains convey one class of accommodation and also car and motorcycle carriers.

6090 PHNOM PENH - SIHANOUKVILLE

km		7	
0	**Phnom Penh** .... d.	0700	...
75	Takeo .... d.	0840	...
	Kep .... d.	1015	...
166	Kampot .... d.	1040	...
263	**Sihanoukville** .... a.	1250	...

	8	
Sihanoukville ....d.	1400	...
Kampot ....d.	1600	...
Kep ....d.	1620	...
Takeo ....d.	1800	...
Phnom Penh ....a.	1940	...

6091 PHNOM PENH - POIPET

km		3	
0	**Phnom Penh** .... d.	0640	...
166	Pursat .... d.	1100	...
273	Battambang .... d.	1330	...
384	**Poipet** .... a.	...	...

	4	
Poipet ....d.	...	...
Battambang ....d.	1500	...
Pursat ....d.	1800	...
Phnom Penh ....a.	2230	...

LAOS

6095 VIENTIANE - BOTEN

km		C82	K12	C84
0	**Vientiane** ....d.	0750	0900	1605
	Vang Vieng ....d.	0849	1026	1702
238	Luang Prabang ....d.	0948	1149	1800
422	**Boten** ....a.	1125	1420	...

	C81	K11	C83
Boten ....d.	1155	1640	...
Luang Prabang ....d.	1334	1901	1825
Vang Vieng ....d.	1430	2025	1924
Vientiane ....a.	1530	2155	2025

Capital: **Vientiane** (GMT +7). 2022 Public Holidays: Jan. 1, Mar. 8, May 1, Dec. 2.

Rail services to China are operated by China Railway Kunming Group. Services to Thailand are operated by the State Railway of Thailand (see Table **6065**). Rail services will eventually operate between Vientiane and Kunming in China. Timings from Kunming to the Chinese border (Mohan) can be found on Table **7182**.

VIÊT NAM

Capital: **Há Nôi** (GMT +7). 2022 Public Holidays: Jan. 1, 3, 31, Feb. 1 – 5, Apr. 10, 30, May 1 – 3, Sept. 2.

Rail services are operated by Duớng Sát Viêt Nam (DSVN www.vr.com.vn). Unless stated trains convey first and second class accommodation. First class has four berth compartments, whilst second class has six. Dining facilities (meals brought to your seats) are provided on some trains. Services may alter during Lunar New Year.

6100 HÁ NOI - BEIJING

km		T8702	Z6	Z286
0	**Há Nôi** Gia Lam .... d.	...	...	...
162	Dong Dang .... a.	...	...	...
162	Dong Dang .... d.	...	...	...
207	Pingxiang .... a.	...	...	...
207	Pingxiang .... d.	0631	...	...
430	Nanning .... a.	1010	...	...
430	Nanning .... d.	...	1052	1725
861	Guilin bei .... d.	...	1437	2130
1409	Changsha .... d.	...	1940	0251
1771	Wuhan Wuchang .. d.	...	2306	0618
2307	Zhengzhou .... d.	...	0352	1110
2996	**Beijing** xi .... a.	...	0948	1703

	Z5	T8701	Z285
Beijing xi ....d.	1609	...	2105
Zhengzhou ....d.	2212	...	0311
Wuhan Wuchang .....d.	0258	...	0757
Changsha ....d.	0619	...	1124
Guilin bei ....d.	1139	...	1622
Nanning ....a.	1535	...	2101
Nanning ....d.	...	1805	...
Pingxiang ....a.	...	2201	...
Pingxiang ....d.	...	...	...
Dong Dang ....a.	...	...	...
Dong Dang ....d.	...	...	...
Há Nôi Gia Lam .....a.	...	...	...

6105 HÁ NOI - LÂO CAÍ

km		SP3		
		⑤E		
0	**Há Nôi** .... d.	2200	...	...
6	**Há Nôi** Gia Lâm .... d.	2218	...	...
155	Yên Bái .... d.	0220	...	...
262	Phõ Lu .... d.	0506	...	...
296	**Lâo Caí** .... a.	0605	...	...

	SP4		
	⑦E		
Lâo Caí ....d.	2140	...	...
Phõ Lu ....d.	2236	...	...
Yên Bái ....d.	0128	...	...
Há Nôi Gia Lâm .....a.	0512	...	...
Há Nôi ....a.	0530	...	...

NOTES FOR TABLES 6100 - 6112:

E – 1, 2 cl., 12 Há Nôi - Lâo Caí and v.v.

F – Also from Há Nôi at 0600; also from Hai Phòng at 0610.

6110 HÁ NOI - HAI PHÒNG

km		LP3	LP5	LP7
		F		
0	**Há Nôi** .... d.	0917	1520	1815
6	**Há Nôi** Gia Lâm .... d.	0948	1545	1846
57	Hai Duong .... d.	1053	1652	1949
76	Phú Thái .... d.	1121	1721	2017
102	**Hai Phòng** .... a.	1200	1800	2055

	LP6	LP8	HP2
	F		
Hai Phòng ....d.	0905	1500	1840
Phú Thái ....d.	0941	1537	1916
Hai Duong ....d.	1008	1605	1946
Há Nôi Gia Lâm .....a.	1121	1719	2051
Há Nôi ....a.	1140	1738	2106

6112 HÁ NOI - HA LONG

km				
0	**Há Nôi** Yen Vien ... d.	...	...	...
58	Kép .... d.	...	...	...
116	Mao Khê .... d.	...	...	...
164	**Ha Long** .... a.	...	...	...

Ha Long ....d.	...	...	...
Mao Khê ....d.	...	...	...
Kép ....d.	...	...	...
Há Nôi Yen Vien .....a.	...	...	...

HÁ NÔI - SAÍ GÔN 6115

km		SE7 A	SPT1	SQN1 ④⑥⑦	SE21 A	SE5 A	SE3 A	QB1	SE1 A
0	**Há Nôi** d.	0600	...	...	...	1545	1925	1955	2215
87	Nam Dinh d.	0743	...	...	...	1728	2108	2133	2353
116	Ninh Binh d.	0819	...	...	...	1804	2144	|	0027
175	Thanh Hóa d.	0933	...	...	...	1918	2253	2313	0128
319	Vinh d.	1206	...	...	...	2151	0141	0208	0349
522	Dông Ho'i d.	1640	...	...	...	0252	0600	0622	0811
688	Hué d.	2029	...	...	...	0602	0902	...	1108
791	**Dà Nang** d.	2325	...	...	0800	0917	1202	...	1408
928	Quang Ngai d.	0200	...	...	1128	1224	1502	...	1631
1095	Diêu Tri d.	0514	...	1340	1449	1540	1816	...	1922
1315	Nha Trang d.	0938	...	1810	1906	1945	2211	...	2311
	Phan Thiet d.	|	1350	|	|	|	|	...	|
1551	Binh Thuan d.	1331	1419	|	0033	0113	0217	...	0305
1649	Long Khánh d.	1522	|	|	0224	0259	0402	...	|
1726	**Saí Gôn** (Ho Chi Minh) a.	1710	1820	0320	0410	0445	0547	...	0632

	SE8 A	SPT2	SE22 A	SE6 A	QB2	SE4 A	SQN2 ③–⑥	SE2 A
Saí Gôn (Ho Chi Minh) d.	0600	0645	1025	1600	...	1900	1830	2110
Long Khánh d.	0749	|	1214	1754	...	2049	|	|
Binh Thuan d.	0940	1026	1416	1945	...	2235	2200	0030
Phan Thiet a.	|	1037	|	|	...	|	|	|
Nha Trang d.	1349	...	1814	0017	...	0223	0350	0415
Diêu Tri d.	1833	...	0002	0429	...	0627	0848	0813
Quang Ngai d.	2147	...	0316	0732	...	0925	...	1058
Dà Nang d.	0057	...	0555	1051	...	1228	...	1342
Hué d.	0334	...	...	1351	...	1515	...	1616
Dông Ho'i d.	0725	...	...	1722	1650	1830	...	1921
Vinh d.	1243	...	...	2147	2112	2252	...	2338
Thanh Hóa d.	1515	...	...	0032	0051	0131	...	0220
Ninh Binh d.	1630	...	...	0158	|	0241	...	0326
Nam Dinh d.	1705	...	...	0233	0251	0316	...	0359
Há Nôi a.	1912	...	...	0417	0435	0500	...	0540

A – 1, 2 cl., [1] ✕.

☛ Additional trains are available Há Nôi - Vinh and Nha Trang - Saí Gôn.

MYANMAR

Capital: **Yangon** (GMT +6½). 2022 Public Holidays: Jan. 1, 4, Feb. 12, Mar. 2, 16, 27, Apr. 13–16, May 1, July 10, 13, 19, Oct. 9–11, Nov. 8, 9, 18, Dec. 25, 31.

Rail service in Myanmar is provided by Myanmar Railways Corporation (MRC). Unless noted all trains convey first and second class seating (known locallly as upper and ordinary). All seating is allocated on purchase of tickets. Sleeping cars are operated on overnight trains and bedding is supplied. Sleepers have 6 compartments comprising 4 x 4-berth and 2 x 2-berth.

MYITKYINA - MANDALAY 6150

km		42	56 B	54	38	58
0	**Myitkyina** d.	0640	0815	...	1200	1600
299	Kawlin d.	2320	2000	2215	2015	0435
446	Shwebo d.	0520	0030	0200	0026	0921
539	**Mandalay** a.	0540	0345	0445	0800	1320

	57	37	53	55 B	41 B
Mandalay d.	0900	1130	1530	1600	1745
Shwebo d.	1155	1426	1803	1839	2145
Kawlin d.	1650	1852	2150	2323	0540
Myitkyina a.	0540	0630	...	1115	2025

B – sleeper, [12].

LASHIO - MANDALAY 6155

km		132
0	**Lashio** d.	0500
74	Hsipaw d.	0930
105	Kyaukme d.	1110
148	Gokteik d.	1315
213	Pyin Oo Lwin a.	1555
213	Pyin Oo Lwin d.	1640
280	**Mandalay** a.	2115

	131
Mandalay d.	0400
Pyin Oo Lwin a.	0752
Pyin Oo Lwin d.	0822
Gokteik d.	1108
Kyaukme d.	1322
Hsipaw d.	1448
Lashio a.	1905

THAZI - YAKSAUK 6160

km		141 z	147
0	**Thazi** d.	0800	0500
197	Kalaw d.	1450	1140
208	Aungban d.	⊖	⊖
236	Heho d.	1657	1354
255	Shwenyaung a.	1820	1500
255	Shwenyaung d.	...	1600
315	**Yaksauk** a.	...	1900

	142 z	148
Yaksauk d.	...	0700
Shwenyaung a.	...	1000
Shwenyaung d.	0700	1100
Heho d.	0810	1210
Aungban d.	⊖	⊖
Kalaw d.	1025	1435
Thazi a.	1720	2145

z – From / to Naypyitaw (Table **6165**). ⊖ – Information unavailable at press date.

MANDALAY - BAGAN - YANGON 6165

km		8 ⑤	6	4 A	120	62 B	10/144	32	12	118
0	**Mandalay** d.	...	1500	1700	2100	...	y	...	0600	0720
136	Thazi d.	...	1749	1949	|	...	2200	...	0854	|
	Naypyitaw d.	2000	2036	2251	|	...	0209	0800	1154	|
***	**Bagan** a.	|	|	|	0500	...	|	|	|	1845
***	**Bagan** d.	|	|	|	...	1600	|	|	|	...
335	Taungoo d.	2235	2318	0127	...	|	0536	1059	1451	...
548	Bago d.	0258	0316	0549	...	|	1211	1523	1859	...
622	**Yangon** a.	0435	0500	0745	...	1040	1440	1700	2100	...

	11	31	9/143	5	61 B	3 A	7 ⑦	119	117
Yangon d.	0600	0800	1100	1500	1600	1700	2030	...	...
Bago d.	0748	0943	1313	1644	|	1848	2213	...	...
Taungoo d.	1231	1410	1937	2059	|	2325	0223	...	...
Bagan a.	|	|	|	|	1045	|	|	...	...
Bagan d.	|	|	|	|	...	|	|	2100	0400
Naypyitaw d.	1522	1700	2255	2332	...	0157	0500	|	|
Thazi d.	1815	...	0330	0211	...	0458	...	|	|
Mandalay a.	2100	...	z	0500	...	0745	...	0525	1555

A – sleeper and [12] Yangon - Mandalay and v.v.
B – sleeper and [12] Runs via Pyay line.
y – From Shwenyaung (Table **6160**).
z – To Shwenyaung (Table **6160**).
*** – Yangon - Bagan: *644 km*. Mandalay - Bagan: *179 km*.

YANGON - MAWLAMYINE - DAWEI 6170

km		89	175	35
0	**Yangon** d.	0715	1825	2000
78	Bago d.	0904	2019	2250
	Kyaikto d.	1157	2320	0130
281	**Mawlamyine** a.	1650	0400	0600
281	**Mawlamyine** d.	...	0430	
425	Ye d.	...	1025	
589	**Dawei Port** a.	...	1900	

	90	36	176
Dawei Port d.	...	...	0540
Ye d.	...	...	1438
Mawlamyine a.	...	...	2025
Mawlamyine d.	0800	1930	2055
Kyaikto d.	1233	2355	0130
Bago d.	1524	0245	0413
Yangon a.	1730	0420	0620

⊖ – Information unavailable at press date.

YANGON - PYAY 6175

km		63 *	75 *	71
0	**Yangon** d.	0700	1100	1300
257	**Pyay** a.	1800	2215	2130

	76 *	64 *	72
Pyay d.	0200	0615	2330
Yangoon a.	1340	1730	0750

* – Trains **63, 64, 75, 76** use Rangoon Kyemyindine station.

INDONESIA

Capital: **Jakarta** (GMT +7). 2022 Public Holidays: Jan. 1, Feb. 1, 28, Mar. 3, Apr. 15, May 1–3, 16, 26, June 1, July 9, 30, Aug. 17, Oct. 8, Dec. 25.

Rail services in Indonesia are operated by PT Kereta Api (Indonesian Railways, www.kai.id). Trains may convey any of three classes of seated accommodation which are known locally as Eksekutif, Bisnis and Ekonomi, shown in the tables as 1, 2 and 3.

SUMATRA 6200

Medan - Pematangsiantar: *127 km* Journey 3½ hours

Medan depart: 1340◐.
Pematangsiantar depart: 0730◐.

Medan - Rantau Prapat: *266 km* Journey 5½ - 6 hours

Medan depart: 0750, 1500, 2220.
Rantau Prapat depart: 0745, 1445, 2200.

Medan - Tanjung Balai: *173 km* Journey 4½ hours

Medan depart: 0655◐, 1210◐, 1925◐.
Tanjung Balai depart: 0655◐, 1215◐, 1710◐.

◐ – Conveys 3rd class only.

Padang - Pariaman: *54 km* Journey 2 - 2 ½hours.

Padang depart: 0545◐, 0925◐, 1345◐, 1705◐.
Pariaman Naras depart: 0535◐, 0940◐, 1400◐, 1630◐.

Palembang - Lubuk Linggau: *305 km* Journey 7 - 8½ hours

Palembang Kertapati depart: 0930, 2015.
Lubuk Linggau depart: 0930, 1945.

Palembang - Panjang ♠: *401 km* Journey 8 - 8½ hours

Palembang Kertapati depart: 0830◐, 2100.
Panjang depart: 0830◐, 2100.

♠ – Panjang is also known as Tanjungkarang Telukbetang.

6205 JAKARTA - BANDUNG

km		44	38	40	42	50	68A	40	46	42	50	52
			13	13	13	13	13	13	13	13	13	13
0	**Jakarta** Gambia d.	0455	0640	0855	1045	1230	1425	1530	1810	1800	2205	2255
12	**Jakarta** Jatinegara d.	|	|	|	|	|	|	|	|	|	|	|
173	**Bandung** a.	0742	0920	1213	1409	1532	1751	1819	2105	2040	0127	0205

	37	43	39	45	39	41	43	41	51	53	51
	13	13	13	13	13	13	13	13	1	13	13
Bandung d.	0500	0610	0645	0850	1110	1135	1350	1510	1815	1900	2205
Jakarta Jatinegara a.	|	|	0954	1137	1356	1442	1658	1748	2101	2114	0105
Jakarta Gambia a.	0745	0850	1012	1155	1414	1500	1716	1750	2119	2151	0123

6210 JAKARTA - SEMARANG - SURABAJA

km		183	268	204	14	2	130	282	206	256	128	80	74	12	106	26	151	264	252	78	4	124	310	210
		13	3	13	1	1	13	3	13	3	12	1	1	1	13	13	12	3	3	1	1	12	3	
	Bandung d.	...	...	...	...	...	...	...	...	...	...	...	...	...	...	...	1720	...	...	...	...	2020	...	...
	Jakarta Gambir d.	...	...	...	0705	0820	...	...	...	...	...	1520	1540	1625	...	1720	|	...	...	1900	2035	|	...	...
	Jakarta Pasar Senen d.	...	...	...	|	|	0855	1020	...	1410	1550	|	|	|	1645	|	|	1925	2010	|	|	|	2335	...
0	**Jakarta** Jatinegara d.	...	...	...	|	|	|	|	...	|	|	|	|	|	|	|	|	|	|	|	|	|	|	...
	Haurgeulis d.	...	...	...	|	|	|	|	...	1614	|	|	|	|	|	|	|	|	2215	|	|	|	0144	...
212	Cirebon d.	...	...	0900p	0959	1048	1220p	1355p	...	1734p	1852	1818	1833	1915	1949	2013	2137	2234p	2330p	2152	2303	0037	0309p	...
288	Tegal d.	0707	...	1019	1054	|	1305	1513	1700	1843	1953	1919	1932	2011	2056	2120	2306	2336	0033	2249	|	0141	0437	0505
348	Pekalongan d.	0804	...	1113	1138	1212	1409	1607	1754	1935	2110	2013	2018	2055	2152	...	0003	0058	0124	2333	0027	0231	0538	0600
443	**Semarang** Tawang d.	0931	1245	1228n	1246	1318	1535	1737	1915n	2104n	2231	2143	2132	2202	2321n	...	0130	0220	0252	0044	0133	0358	0700n	0721n
644	Madiun d.	...	|	...	...	|	|	2149	...	|	|	0126	0111	...	|	...	...	...	0643	|	|	|	...	...
737	Kediri d.	...	|	...	...	|	|	2334	...	|	|	|	0236	...	|	...	...	...	0813	|	|	|	...	...
573	Cepu d.	...	1413	...	...	|	1731	|	...	2317	0038	♣	|	...	0133	...	...	...	|	0237	|	0601	...	...
610	Bojonegoro d.	...	1446	...	...	1516	1805	|	...	2350	0110	|	|	...	0205	...	...	...	|	0307	0331	0634	...	...
713	**Surabaja** Pasar Turi a.	...	1618	...	...	1630	1935	|	...	0125	0245	0357b	|	...	0339	...	...	...	|	0430	0445	0805	...	...
881	**Malang** a.	...	...	...	...	...	...	0224	...	...	...	...	0500	...	0628	...	...	...	1050	...	...	...	...	...

	15	203	11	267	185	27	1	25	309	205	13	281	105	149	127	79	123	77	73	3	255	251	129
	13	13	1	3	13	13	1	13	3	13	1	3	13	12	12	1	12	1	1	1	13	3	13
Malang d.	...	...	...	...	...	...	...	...	...	...	...	0925	1150	...	...	...	...	...	1600	...	...	1830	...
Surabaja Pasar Turi d.	...	...	...	0600	...	...	0900	...	...	...	...	|	1420	...	1555	1600b	1740	1855	|	2105	2120	|	2235
Bojonegoro d.	...	...	...	0736	...	...	1017	...	...	...	...	|	1556	...	1731	|	1914	2019	|	2219	2254	|	0011
Cepu d.	...	...	...	0813	...	...	|	...	...	...	...	|	1632	...	1807	♥	1949	2051	|	|	2332	|	0047
Kediri d.	...	...	...	|	...	...	|	...	...	...	...	1230	|	...	|	|	|	|	1825	|	|	2105	|
Madiun d.	...	...	...	|	...	...	|	...	...	...	...	1416	|	...	|	1833	|	|	1952	|	|	2240	|
Semarang Tawang d.	...	0500	0600	1038	1111	...	1245	...	1325	1350n	1600	1811	1853n	1930	2012	2224	2150	2243	2313	0015	0145n	0225	0300
Pekalongan d.	...	0623	0708	...	1226	...	1334	...	1450	1506	1708	1933	2011	2100	2131	2346	2305	2352	0025	0109	0310	0343	0421
Tegal d.	...	0721	0754	...	1317	1300	|	1445	1554	1600	1754	2028	2111	2159	2233	0047	2359	0038	0113	|	0403	0438	0516
Cirebon d.	0600	0832p	0852	...	...	1415	1515	1605	1716p	...	1852	2140p	2212	2302	2339	0155	0104	0137	0214	0245	0515p	0547p	0625
Haurgeulis d.	0709	...	|	...	...	|	|	1712	1829	...	|	|	|	0009	|	|	|	|	0449	|	0628	|	|
Jakarta Jatinegara a.	0566	...	1122	...	...	1706	|	1859	|	...	2128	0103	0112	|	|	0437	|	0410	|	|	|	0836	0912
Jakarta Pasar Senen a.	|	...	|	...	...	|	|	|	2034	...	|	0114	0125	|	0238	|	|	|	|	|	0825	0847	0925
Jakarta Gambir a.	0914	...	1140	...	...	1724	1745	1915	...	...	2144	...	...	|	...	0453	|	0427	0506	0515	...	...	...
Bandung a.	...	...	...	...	...	...	...	...	...	...	...	...	...	0308	...	...	0452	...	...	...	...	...	...

b – Surabaya Gubeng. n – Semerang Poncol. p – Cirebon Prujakan. ♣ – Via Jombang (d. 0255). ♥ – Via Jombang (d. 1704).

6215 JAKARTA - YOGYAKARTA - SURABAJA

km		112	134	154A	140A	10	176	7012	116	104	122A	180	110	76	254	72A	102	156A	8A	136	84A	86A	7026	7006	248
		12	13	13	13	1	12	1	13	13	13	13	13	1	3	1	13	13	1	12	1	1	1	1	23
	Jakarta Kota d.	...	...	...	...	...	...	...	...	...	...	...	...	...	...	...	...	...	...	...	...	...	...	...	...
	Jakarta Gambir d.	...	...	...	...	0850	...	1030	...	...	...	...	...	1700	1710	1840	...	...	2045	...	2125	2200	2305	2330	...
	Jakarta Pasar Senen d.	...	0555	0715	0805	|	...	|	...	1100	1145	...	1330	|	|	|	1730	1845	|	2105	|	|	|	|	...
0	**Jakarta** Jatinegara d.	...	|	|	|	|	...	|	...	|	|	...	|	|	|	|	|	|	|	|	|	|	|	|	...
212	Cirebon d.	0615	0900	1022	1101	1123	...	1332	...	1425p	1500p	...	1648p	1956	2016	2122	2046	2139	2253	0018	2357	0108	0205	0228	...
343	Purwokerto d.	0837	1113	1241	1315	1341	...	1540	...	1649	1711	...	|	2205	2246	2330	2305	2359	0105	0240	0152	0333	0412	0430	0530
370	Kroya d.	0904	1139	1308	1342	|	...	1608	1557	1716	1737	...	◄	2232	2313	2355	2331	0022	|	0309	0215	0358	0440	|	0559
445	Kutoarjo d.	1020	1246	1431	1505	|	...	1713	1725	1832	1851	...	|	2336	0031	0052	0119	0145	|	0420	0308	...	0548	0621	0737
508	**Yogyakarta** d.	1115	1338	—	1605	1504	1710	1804	1820	1938l	1947	2005	|	0029	0144l	0139	0219l	—	0259	0514	0350	...	0636	0729	0845
568	Solo Balapan d.	1210	1429	...	...	1554	1759	...	1911	|	2045	2106	2238j	0115	0237	0220	|	...	0349	0611	...	...	...	0823	|
663	Madiun d.	1337	—	...	...	...	1911	...	2036	2203	2214	2234	0012	0227	0413	0325	0449	...	...	...	...	...	...	0941	1122
756	Kediri d.	|	**313**	...	...	...	|	...	|	|	|	|	0150	|	|	0441	0623	...	...	...	...	...	...	1114	|
826	Blitar d.	|	3	...	...	...	|	...	|	|	|	|	0244	|	|	0536	0720	...	...	...	...	...	...	1206	|
900	**Malang** a.	|	1630	**288**	...	...	|	...	|	|	|	|	...	|	|	0709	...	**317**	...	...	...	...	...	1342	|
750	Jombang d.	1458	|	3	...	...	2017	...	2151	2328	2339	2354	...	0340	0537	...	...	3	...	...	...	...	...	...	1251
831	**Surabaja** Gubeng a.	1557	|	1340	...	...	2115	...	2250	0040	...	0053	...	0436	0637	...	...	0530	...	...	...	...	...	...	1400
	Jember d.	2008	2050	1649	...	...	...	...	0318	...	...	0500	...	...	...	...	...	1000	...	...	...	...	...	...	1840
1140	**Banyuwangi Ketapang** a.	...	2345	2005	...	...	...	...	0545	...	...	0730	...	...	...	...	...	1230	...	...	...	...	...	...	...

	175	111	250	103	109	141	155A	314	133A	253A	71	83A	287	101	75A	115	7005	179	153A	81A	7A	121A	135A	7025	318
	13	12	23	13	13	13	13	3	13	3	1	1	3	13	1	13	1	13	13	1	1	13	12	1	13
Banyuwangi Ketapang d.	...	...	...	...	...	...	...	0515	...	...	...	...	0700	...	...	1130	...	1730	...	...	...	...	...	...	1445
Jember d.	...	0510	0600	...	...	...	...	0801	...	...	...	...	0924	...	...	1357	...	2010	...	...	...	...	...	...	1718
Surabaja Gubeng d.	0900	0922	1036	1200	...	...	...	|	...	1430	...	...	1311	...	1710	1812	...	0010	...	...	...	...	...	...	2136
Jombang d.	0955	1021	1146	1311	...	...	...	|	...	1530	...	...	...	...	1806	1919	...	0122	...	...	...	0510	...	...	—
Malang d.	|	|	|	|	...	...	...	1250	...	|	1425	...	...	...	|	|	1745	|	...	...	...	|	...	...	...
Blitar d.	|	|	|	|	1215	...	...	...	...	|	1557	...	—	1635	|	|	1920	|	...	...	...	|	...	...	...
Kediri d.	|	|	|	|	1327	...	...	—	...	|	1652	...	**9A**	1732	|	|	2016	|	...	...	...	|	...	...	...
Madiun d.	1104	1143	1346	1442	1513	...	...	**141A**	...	1653	1817	...	1	1907	1923	2038	2145	0311	...	...	...	0640	...	...	...
Solo Balapan d.	1215	1310	|	|	1657j	...	...	13	1800	1830	1928	...	1955	|	2034	2219	2302	0441	...	...	0830	0812	0850	...	...
Yogyakarta d.	1304	1410	1623l	1705l	|	1750	...	1845	1853	1926l	2014	2105	2047	2153l	2121	2313	2355	0535	...	0850	0922	0907	0947	1035	**85**
Kutoarjo d.	...	1510	1730	1810	►	1845	1900	1943	1958	2021	2108	2156	|	2257	2215	0009	0053	...	0700	0941	|	1017	1040	1129	1
Kroya d.	...	1623	1905	1925	|	2000	2029	2103	2118	2131	2212	2302	|	0017	2323	0124	0205	...	0828	1054	|	1148	1205	1236	1530
Purwokerto d.	...	1722	1931	1957	|	2030	2100	2136	2155	2206	2231	2330	2258	0050	2353	...	0240	...	0903	1115	1118	1220	1236	1313	1602
Cirebon d.	...	1933	...	2217p	2237p	2251	2317	2348	2331	0004	0022	0057	0036	0311	0157	...	0438	...	1122	1237	1300	1425p	1454	1542	1802
Jakarta Jatinegara a.	...	...	...	0119	0132	0144	0206	0237	0217	|	0247	0313	0338	0609	0434	...	0721	...	1410	1452	1610	|	1758	1827	2045
Jakarta Pasar Senen a.	...	...	...	0132	0145	0155	0219	0250	0230	0325	|	|	|	0623	|	...	|	...	1423	|	|	1722	1808	|	|
Jakarta Gambir a.	...	...	...	...	...	...	...	...	...	...	0303	0330	0310	...	0450	...	0740	...	...	1510	1535	...	...	1844	2103
Jakarta Kota a.	...	...	...	...	...	...	...	...	...	...	...	...	...	...	...	...	...	...	...	...	...	...	...	...	...

6220 JAKARTA - BANDUNG - SURABAYA

km		160	6	7006	286	170	80	158	120	132	172
		12	1	13	3	13	1	12	123	13	13
	Jakarta Gambir d.	...	...	0530	...	...	...	...	...	...	
0	**Bandung** d.	0705	0815	0915	1010k	...	1820	1910	1700	2030	...
124	Tasikmalaya d.	0952	1054	1230	1300	...	2100	2154	2004	2316	...
156	Banjar d.	1043	1136	1323	1412	...	2146	2245	2055	0014	...
249	Kroya d.	1207	1242	...	1545	1848	2300	0016	2221	0148	...
324	Kutoarjo d.	1319	1335	...	1708	1956	0007	0139	2342	0317	...
387	**Yogyakarta** d.	1435	1421	...	1828l	2050	0100	0238	0036	0411	0740
447	Solo Balapan d.	1525	1504	...	|	2141	0147	0328	0122	0502	0841
542	Madiun d.	...	1609	...	2126	2303	0301	...	0243	0622	1025
629	Jombang d.	...	1712	...	2259	|	0412	...	|	0741	|
710	**Surabaya** Gubeng a.	...	1810	...	0006	|	0509	...	|	0845	|
635	Kediri d.	...	...	...	...	0035	...	...	0409	...	1147
705	Blitar d.	...	...	...	...	0130	...	...	0503	...	1332
779	**Malang** a.	...	...	...	...	0306	...	...	0638	...	1541

	159	175	285	5	169	157	79	119	131	173
	12	13	3	1	13	12	1	123	13	13
Malang d.	...	...	...	...	0820	...	...	1710	...	2005
Blitar d.	...	...	...	...	1002	...	...	1848	...	2158
Kediri d.	...	...	...	...	1057	...	...	1945	...	2302
Surabaya Gubeng d.	...	...	0550	0730	|	...	1845	|	1945	|
Jombang d.	...	...	0708	0824	|	...	1941	|	2046	|
Madiun d.	...	...	0840	0927	1237	...	2052	2117	2208	0051
Solo Balapan d.	0720	...	|	1031	1356	1840	2202	2237	2324	0220
Yogyakarta d.	0815	...	1131l	1114	1448	1935	2251	2328	0014	0314
Kutoarjo d.	0913	...	1238	1200	1543	2035	2343	0023	0110	...
Kroya d.	1036	...	1354	1253	1649	2152	0050	0144	0235	...
Banjar d.	1228	1410	1529	1359	...	2354	0206	0318	0408	...
Tasikmalaya d.	1323	1505	1623	1447	...	0053	0257	0413	0503	...
Bandung a.	1610	1817	1943k	1725	...	0339	0534	0656	0800	...
Jakarta Gambir a.	...	2225	...	...	...	...	...	...	...	...

Notes for Tables **6215**, **6220**.
a – **Jakarta** Pasar Senen.
j – Solo Jebres.
k – Bandung Kiaracondong.
l – Yogyakarta Lempuyangan.
p – Cirebon Prujakan.
t – **Surabaja** Pasar Turi.
► – Via Semarang Tawang (d. 1919) and Tegal (d. 2128).
◄ – Via Tegal (d. 1756) and Semarang Twang (d. 2008
Note: Connections between Jakarta and Merak are available using suburban and local trains via Rangkasbitung.

AUSTRALIA

Capital: **Canberra** (GMT +10). 2022 Public Holidays: Jan. 1, 26, Mar. 7 (WA), 14 (ACT, SA, TAS, VIC), Apr. 15, 17, 18, 25, June 6 (WA), 13 (not Qld, WA), Dec. 25, 26.

Long-distance interstate trains are operated by Great Southern Rail (GSR) (www.gsr.com.au). Intrastate services are operated by Government owned agencies NSW Train Link (New South Wales www.transportnsw.info), Queensland Rail (QR) (Queensland www.qr.com.au), V/Line (Victoria www.vline.com.au) and Transwa (Western Australia, www.transwa.wa.gov.au). Unless indicated all trains convey first and second class seated accommodation. On GSR and some overnight trains the first class accommodation is usually a private compartment which converts to sleeping berths for night time travel. The exact offering varies by operator and by train. Most longer distance trains also convey a refreshment facility. Due to the low frequency of trains reservations are recommended, even if they are not always compulsory. NSW Train Link offer the Discovery Pass which gives either 14 day, 1 month, 3 months or 6 months unlimited travel on their rail and coach network and are available for travel in either economy or premium. Prices range from AU$ 232 for a 14 day economy pass to AU$ 550 for a 6 month premium pass. QR have the Explorer Pass which offers either 1 month (AU$ 299) or 2 months (AU$ 389) unlimited travel on their services. They also offer the Costal Pass for unlimited travel in one direction between Brisbane and Cairns or vice versa. Prices 1 month AU$ 209, 2 months AU$ 289. Reservations are required for all journeys and supplements may also be payable. See www.acprail.com

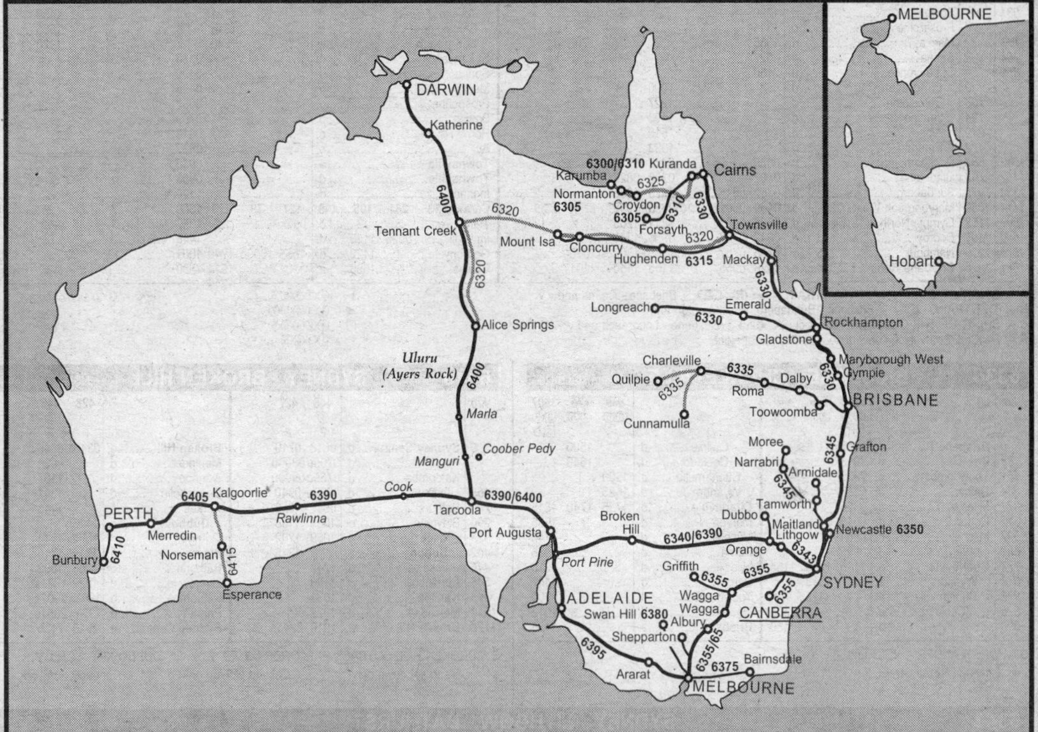

Queensland Rail	CAIRNS - KURANDA					6300
km		3K30 2d	3K32 2d		3C61 2d	3C65 2d
0	**Cairns** d.	0830	0930	**Kuranda** d.	1400	1530
	Freshwater d.	0855	0955	Freshwater d.	1532	1702
33	**Kuranda** a.	1025	1125	**Cairns** a.	1555	1725

d – Not June 17, 18, Oct. 14, 15, Dec. 25.

Queensland Rail	NORMANTON - CROYDON					6305
km		③ A			④ A	
0	**Normanton** d.	0830	...	**Croydon** d.	0830	...
90	Blackbull a.	1115	...	Blackbull a.	1015	...
152	**Croydon** a.	1330	...	**Normanton** a.	1330	...

A – GULFLANDER – (2).

CKST	CAIRNS - FORSAYTH					6310
km		4 ③B	4 ④B		5 ⑤B	5 ⑥B
0	**Cairns** d.	0630	...	**Forsayth** d.	0830	...
33	Kuranda d.	0810	...	Einasleigh d.	1215	...
74	Mareeba d.	0930	...	Mount Suprise a.	1415	...
194	Almaden a.	1315	...	Mount Suprise d.	...	0815
194	Almaden d.	...	0800	Almaden a.	...	1145
302	Mount Suprise a.	...	1130	Almaden d.	...	1215
302	Mount Suprise d.	...	1215	Mareeba d.	...	|
357	Einasleigh d.	...	1445	Kuranda a.	...	1650
423	**Forsayth** a.	...	1730	**Cairns** a.	...	1830

B – SAVANNAHLANDER – (2). The Savannahlander operates from March to the last week in November. Operator: Cairns Kuranda Steam Ltd Tel. +61 7 4053 6848.

Queensland Rail	TOWNSVILLE - MOUNT ISA					6315
km		3M34 ③⑥C			3231 ④⑦C	
0	**Townsville** d.	1240	...	**Mount Isa** d.	1330	...
138	Charters Towers d.	1540	...	Duchess d.	1515	...
388	Hughenden d.	2020	...	Cl oncurry d.	1745	...
502	Richmond d.	2245	...	Julia Creek d.	2100	...
648	Julia Creek d.	0210	...	Richmond d.	0005	...
780	Cloncurry d.	0520	...	Hughenden d.	0240	...
890	Duchess d.	0745	...	Charters Towers d.	0705	...
977	**Mount Isa** a.	0935	...	**Townsville** a.	1010	...

C – INLANDER – (2) and (glass) Townsville - Mount Isa and v.v. [R].

Greyhound	TOWNSVILLE - TENNANT CREEK					6320
km		489 (bus) ①	882 (bus) D		880 (bus) E	849 (bus) ②
0	**Townsville** d.	0600	...	**Alice Springs** d.	1730	...
135	Charters Towers d.	0745	...	Barrow Creek d.	2115	...
378	Hughenden d.	1030	...	**Tennant Creek** d.	0005	0300
490	Richmond d.	1235	...	Barkly Homestead d.	...	0530
634	Julia Creek d.	1405	...	Camooweal d.	...	0835
768	Cloncurry d.	1545	...	**Mount Isa** a.	...	1040
886	**Mount Isa** a.	1715	...	**Mount Isa** d.	...	1130
886	**Mount Isa** d.	1800	...	Cloncurry d.	...	1245
1074	Camooweal d.	2000	...	Julia Creek d.	...	1415
1353	Barkly Homestead d.	2245	...	Richmond d.	...	1600
1547	**Tennant Creek** a.	0100	0130	Hughenden d.	...	1805
1771	Barrow Creek d.	...	0350	Charters Towers d.	...	2030
2072	**Alice Springs** a.	...	0735	**Townsville** a.	...	2205

D – From Darwin dep. 0955. E – To Darwin arr. 1535.
Operator: Greyhound Australia Tel. 07 3258 1600.

Trans North Bus	CAIRNS - KARUMBA					6325
km		(bus) ①③⑤			(bus) ②④⑥	
0	**Cairns** Central ◇ d.	0630	...	**Karumba** d.	0630	...
33	Kuranda ◇ d.	0705	...	Normanton d.	0725	...
75	Mareeba d.	0735	...	Croydon d.	0925	...
109	Atherton d.	0820	...	Georgetown d.	1055	...
140	Herberton d.	0835	...	Mount Surprise d.	1240	...
160	Ravenshoe d.	0955	...	Undara d.	1305	...
211	Mount Garnet d.	1025	...	Mount Garnet d.	1355	...
287	Undara d.	1110	...	Ravenshoe d.	1450	...
321	Mount Surprise d.	1135	...	Herberton d.	1520	...
422	Georgetown d.	1335	...	Atherton d.	1540	...
579	Croydon d.	1525	...	Mareeba d.	1615	...
744	Normanton d.	1705	...	Kuranda ◇ d.	1640	...
820	**Karumba** a.	1800	...	**Cairns** Central ◇ a.	1730	...

◇ – Additional service available Cairns – Kuranda and v.v.
Operator: Trans North Bus and Coach Tel. 07 4095 8644.

6330 CAIRNS, TOWNSVILLE and LONGREACH - BRISBANE

Queensland Rail

km	km			V9Q4	Q904		A960	Q902			
				◀	⊡		①④				
				A	B		C	B			
0		**Cairns**	d.	0835	...	...	...	...	...	...	...
23		Gordonvale	d.	0901	...	...	...	...	...	...	...
87		Innisfail	d.	1018	...	...	...	...	...	...	...
135		Tully	d.	1125	...	...	...	...	...	...	...
178		Cardwell	d.	1209	...	...	...	...	...	...	...
232		Ingham	d.	1301	...	...	...	...	...	...	...
340		**Townsville**	a.	1439	...	...	...	...	...	...	...
340		**Townsville**	d.	1454	...	...	...	...	...	...	...
421		Ayr	d.	1557	...	...	...	...	...	...	...
432		Home Hill	d.	1614	...	...	...	...	...	...	...
531		Bowen	d.	1720	...	...	...	...	...	...	...
596		Proserpine	d.	1811	...	...	...	...	...	...	...
717		Mackay	d.	1956	...	...	...	...	...	...	...
754		Sarina	d.	2027	...	...	...	...	...	...	...
869		St Lawrence	d.	2150	...	...	...	...	...	...	...
	0	**Longreach**	d.	|	...	...	1000	...	...	...	...
	108	Barcaldine	d.	|	...	...	1227	...	...	...	...
	194	Jericho	d.	|	...	...	1403	...	...	...	...
	249	Alpha	d.	|	...	...	1518	...	...	...	...
	422	Emerald	d.	|	...	...	1933	...	...	...	...
1042	687	Rockhampton	d.	0039	...	...	0017	0710	...	...	...
1152	797	Gladstone	d.	0202	...	...	0308	0826	...	...	...
1330	975	Bundaberg	d.	0352	0515	...	0526	1005	...	...	...
1414	1059	Maryborough West	d.	0450	0601	...	0635	1058	...	...	...
1507	1152	Gympie North	d.	0608	0701	...	0811	1205	...	...	...
1550	1195	Cooroy	d.	0642	0737	...	0856	1240	...	...	...
1575	1220	Nambour	d.	0705	0757	...	0925	1302	...	...	...
1681	1326	**Brisbane** Roma St	a.	0920	0955	...	1155	1450	...	...	...

		Q301		AW57	VCQ5			Q303	AW57	
		◇		⑥	▶	②⑦		☆	②	
		B		C	A	B		B	C	
Brisbane Roma St	d.	1100	...	1355	1545	1655	...	1655	1810	...
Nambour	d.	1235	...	1619	1731	1838	...	1838	2023	...
Cooroy	d.	1258	...	1649	1754	1858	...	1858	2049	...
Gympie North	d.	1337	...	1745	1828	1929	...	1929	2145	...
Maryborough West	d.	1440	...	1905	1929	2028	...	2028	2305	...
Bundaberg	d.	1531	...	2036	2022	2125	...	2125	0013	...
Gladstone	d.	1712	...	2309	2223	2317	...	...	0246	...
Rockhampton	d.	1845	...	0103	0011	0030	...	...	0440	...
Emerald	d.	...	...	0602	|	...	...	...	0940	...
Alpha	d.	...	...	1012	|	...	...	...	1350	...
Jericho	d.	...	...	1121	|	...	...	...	1459	...
Barcaldine	d.	...	...	1316	|	...	...	...	1655	...
Longreach	a.	...	...	1540	|	...	...	...	1920	...
St Lawrence	d.	...	...	...	0230	...	...	...	...	...
Sarina	d.	...	...	...	0400	...	...	...	...	...
Mackay	d.	...	...	...	0454	...	...	...	...	...
Prosperine	d.	...	...	...	0632	...	...	...	...	...
Bowen	d.	...	...	...	0709	...	...	...	...	...
Home Hill	d.	...	...	...	0818	...	...	...	...	...
Ayr	d.	...	...	...	0832	...	...	...	...	...
Townsville	a.	...	...	...	0938	...	...	...	...	...
Townsville	d.	...	...	...	0953	...	...	...	...	...
Ingham	d.	...	...	...	1126	...	...	...	...	...
Cardwell	d.	...	...	...	1300	...	...	...	...	...
Tully	d.	...	...	...	1357	...	...	...	...	...
Innisfail	d.	...	...	...	1446	...	...	...	...	...
Gordonvale	d.	...	...	...	1601	...	...	...	...	...
Cairns	a.	...	...	...	1630	...	...	...	...	...

A – SPIRIT OF QUEENSLAND TILT TRAIN – 🛏 (R), (2) 🍸 Brisbane - Cairns and v.v.
B – TILT TRAIN – (12) 🍸 Brisbane - Bundaberg, Rockhampton and v.v.
C – SPIRIT OF THE OUTBACK – 🛏 1 cl., ✕, (2) 🍸 Brisbane - Longreach and v.v.
R – RailBed. Seat which converts to a lie-flat bed at night.

▶ – ①②③⑤⑥.
◀ – ①③④⑤⑦.
⊡ – ①②④⑤⑥.
☆ – ①③④⑤.
◇ – ①②④⑤⑥⑦.

6335 BRISBANE - CHARLEVILLE

Queensland Rail

km			9386	🚌	🚌
			②④	③⑤	③⑤
			R D		
0	**Brisbane** ‡	d.	1915	...	...
38	Ipswich	d.	2013	...	...
161	Toowoomba	d.	2325	...	...
244	Dalby	d.	0117	...	...
371	Miles	d.	0325	...	...
512	Roma	d.	0615	...	...
597	Mitchell	d.	0805	...	...
687	Morven	d.	0955	...	...
777	**Charleville**	a.	1145	1155	1155
875	Wyandra	a.	...	1315	|
972	Cunnamulla	a.	...	1425	|
876	Cooladdi	a.	...	...	1305
998	Quilpie	a.	...	...	1430

		🚌	🚌	3907
		③⑤	③⑤	③⑤
				R D
Quilpie	d.	...	1500	...
Cooladdi	d.	...	1640	...
Cunnamulla	d.	1500	|	...
Wyandra	d.	1625	|	...
Charleville	d.	1735	1740	1815
Morven	d.	...	...	1955
Mitchell	d.	...	...	2145
Roma	d.	...	...	2335
Miles	d.	...	...	0210
Dalby	d.	...	...	0447
Toowoomba	d.	...	...	0700
Ipswich	d.	...	...	1012
Brisbane ‡	a.	...	...	1125

D – WESTLANDER – (2) and 🍸.
‡ – Brisbane **Roma Street**.

6340 SYDNEY - BROKEN HILL

NSW Train Link

km			445	427	
			①		
			E	F	
0	**Sydney** Central	d.	0618	0719	...
	Penrith	d.	0705u	0805u	...
	Katoomba	d.	0759u	0900u	...
155	Lithgow	d.	0839u	0940	...
240	Bathurst	d.	0947	1052	...
290	Blayney	d.	1035	1138	...
323	Orange	d.	1059	1202	...
462	**Dubbo**	a.	|	1345	...
446	Parkes	d.	1248	|	...
546	Condobolin	d.	1400	|	...
816	Ivanhoe	d.	1631	|	...
1017	Menindee	d.	1822	|	...
1125	**Broken Hill**	a.	1910	*2245**	...

		428	446
			②
		F	E
Broken Hill	d.	*0345**	0745
Menindee	d.	|	0924
Ivanhoe	d.	|	1107
Condobolin	d.	|	1341
Parkes	d.	|	1443
Dubbo	d.	1415	|
Orange	d.	1552	1644
Blayney	d.	1619	1716
Bathurst	d.	1705	1802
Lithgow	d.	1820	1921s
Katoomba	d.	1902s	2002s
Penrith	d.	1954s	2054s
Sydney Central	a.	2048	2138

E – BROKEN HILL OUTBACK EXPLORER – (2) 🍸. F – DUBBO XPT – (12) 🍸.
s – Calls to set down only. u – Calls to pick up only. * – Connection by 🚌.

6343 SYDNEY - LITHGOW - BATHURST

Sydney Trains, NSW Train Link

km		505	517		509	529	525	527	4507	503	533	4501
		Ⓐ	Ⓐ		Ⓐ	Ⓒ	Ⓐ	†		†	Ⓐ	
				A					f			
0	**Sydney** Central d.	0422	0848	1018	1218	1224	1418	1424	1505	1624	1717	1747
55	Penrith u d.	0511	0936	1106	1305	1314	1505	1513	1555	1713	1806	1843
110	Katoomba d.	0622	1032	1217	1416	1425	1616	1624	1652	1824	1910	1938
127	Mount Victoria d.	0642	1050	1237	1436	1445	1636	1644	1708	1844	1932	1958
155	**Lithgow** a.	0710	1117	1305	1505	1515	1705	1715	1734	1915	2004	2024
240	**Bathurst** a.	*0815**	*1227**	...	*1625**	*1625**	*1820**	*1825**	1847	*2020**	...	2133

		4502	4502	4508	502	506	508	534	538		
	Ⓐ	Ⓐ	Ⓒ		⚒	⚒	Ⓐ	Ⓑ	Ⓑ	Ⓐ	Ⓒ
	B				g			h	h		
Bathurst d.	...	0546	0607	0735	...	*1005**	...	*1410**	*1815**	*1925*b	*1925*
Lithgow d.	0300	0655	0716	0842	0924	1124g	1318	1530	1930	2130	2219
Mount Victoria d.	0331	0723	0743	0910	0954	1154g	1346	1601	2001s	2201	2248
Katoomba d.	0350	0740	0759	0924	1013	1213g	1403	1620	2020s	2220	2308
Penrith d.	0500	0838s	0856s	1028	1123	1323g	1459	1730	2130s	2330	0022
Sydney Central a.	0551	0927	0944	1119c	1215	1415g	1548	1820	2221	0022	0112

A – Additional services: Ⓐ 0018, 0623, 0818, 1518, 1617, 1833, 2018, 2218; Ⓒ 0024, 0424, 0624, 0824, 1024, 1424, 1624, 1824, 2024, 2224.
B – Additional services: Ⓐ 0415, 0508, 0538, 0608, 0724, 1330, 1730, 1930; Ⓒ 0349, 0549, 0648, 0748, 0948, 1148, 1348, 1548, 1748, 1948.
Note: Additional services operate from Sydney to Katoomba and Mount Victoria.

b – Not ③.
c – Arrives 1146 on ③.
f – Runs 50 minutes later on ③.
g – Runs 26 mintues later on ⑥.
h – Runs 18–21 minutes later on ⑦.
s – Calls to set down only.
u – Calls to pick up only.
* – Connection by 🚌.

6345 BRISBANE, ARMIDALE and MOREE - SYDNEY

NSW Train Link

km	km			036	244	224	032		034	2138	
				R	R	R	R		R	Ⓐ	
				H	J	K	L		M		
0		**Brisbane** Roma Street	d.	...	...	...	0555	...	*1430**	...	...
182		Casino	d.	...	...	...	0820	...	1930	...	...
291		Grafton City	d.	0515	...	...	0953	...	2058	...	...
379		Coffs Harbour	d.	0626	...	...	1105	...	2210	...	...
		Nambucca Heads	d.	0708	...	...	1147	...	2251r	...	...
		Macksville	d.	0721	...	...	1200	...	2305r	...	...
483		Kempsey	d.	0805	...	...	1243	...	2347	...	...
532		Wauchope	d.	0844	...	...	1322	...	0024	...	...
608		Taree	d.	0952	...	...	1441	...	0131	...	...
	0	**Armidale**	d.	|	...	0840	|	...	|	...	...
	124	Tamworth	d.	|	...	1027	|	...	|	...	...
	◐	**Moree**	d.	|	0805	|	|	...	|	...	...
	◐	Narrabri	d.	|	0910	|	|	...	|	...	...
	◐	Gunnedah	d.	|	1014	|	|	...	|	...	...
	168	Werris Creek	d.	|	1107	1107	|	...	|	...	...
	264	Scone	d.	|	1228	1228	|	...	|	...	...
	290	Muswellbrook	d.	|	1248	1248	|	...	|	...	...
794	387	Maitland	d.	1253	1355	1355	1730	...	0406	...	...
824	416	Broadmeadow	d.	1319	1418	1418	1752	...	0428	0930	...
897	499	Gosford	d.	1420s	1520s	1520s	1857s	...	0529s	1037s	...
953	545	Hornsby	d.	1504s	1603s	1603s	1938s	...	0612s	1122s	...
987	579	**Sydney** Central	a.	1544	1639a	1639a	2012	...	0650	1159	...

		033	243	223	035	031		2157		
		R	R	R	R	R				
		M	J	K	H	L		Ⓐ		
Sydney Central	d.	0708	0930	0930	1141	1441	...	1515	...	...
Hornsby	d.	0747u	1003u	1003u	1216u	1517u	...	1551u	...	...
Gosford	d.	0829u	1044u	1044u	1258u	1600u	...	1634u	...	...
Broadmeadow	d.	0933	1145	1145	1404	1704	...	1741	...	...
Maitland	d.	0959	1210	1210	1430	1727	...	...	...	...
Muswellbrook	d.	|	1316	1316	|	|	...	...	...	...
Scone	d.	|	1337	1337	|	|	...	...	...	...
Werris Creek	d.	|	1507	1457	|	|	...	...	...	...
Gunnedah	d.	|	1545	|	|	|	...	...	...	...
Narrabri	a.	|	1652	|	|	|	...	...	...	...
Moree	a.	|	1800	|	|	|	...	...	...	...
Tamworth	a.	|	...	1537	|	|	...	...	...	...
Armidale	a.	|	...	1735	|	|	...	...	...	...
Taree	d.	1240	...	...	1725	2008	...	...	...	...
Wauchope	d.	1347	...	...	1831	2113	...	...	...	...
Kempsey	d.	1425	...	...	1910	2152	...	...	...	...
Macksville	d.	1506	...	...	1955	2234	...	...	...	...
Nambucca Heads	a.	1518	...	...	2009	*2305**	...	...	...	...
Coffs Harbour	d.	1557	...	...	2050	2335	...	...	...	...
Grafton City	d.	1711	...	...	2215	0049	...	...	...	...
Casino	a.	1840	...	...	...	0219	...	...	...	...
Brisbane Roma Street	a.	*2234**	...	...	...	0453	...	...	...	...

H – GRAFTON XPT – (12).
J – MOREE EXPLORER – (12) 🍸.
K – ARMIDALE XPLORER – (12) 🍸.
L – BRISBANE XPT – (12) Brisbane - Sydney; 🛏 1 cl., (2) Sydney - Brisbane.
M – CASINO XPT – 🛏 1 cl., (2) Casino - Sydney; (12) Sydney - Casino.

a – Arrives 1645 on Ⓒ.
r – Calls on request.
s – Calls to set down only.
u – Calls to pick up only.
* – Connection by 🚌.

☛ Note: During NSW Daylight Savings services will arrive and depart QLD locations 1 hour earlier than shown.
◐ – Moree - Narrabri: *97 km*. Moree - Gunnedah: *190 km*. Moree - Werris Creek: *255 km*.

Sydney Trains — NEWCASTLE - SYDNEY — 6350

km			Ⓐ	Ⓐ	Ⓐ	Ⓐ	Ⓐ	Ⓐ	Ⓐ	Ⓐ	Ⓐ	Ⓐ	Ⓐ		Ⓐ	Ⓐ	Ⓐ	Ⓐ	Ⓐ	Ⓐ	Ⓐ	Ⓐ	Ⓐ	Ⓐ	Ⓐ
0	**Newcastle** Interchange . d.	Ⓐ	0230	0423	0502	0520	0548	0620	0642	0725	0735	0824	0835	and at the same	1324	1334	1420	1434	1512	1534	1624	1634	1724	1824	1834
	Hamilton .... d.		0232	0427	0504	0523	0550	0623	0645	0728	0738	0827	0838	minutes	1327	1337	1422	1438	1515	1537	1627	1638	1727	1827	1838
88	Gosford...................... d.		0358	0539	0609	0634	0704	0734	0807	0838	0902	0937	1002	past each	1437	1501	1533	1602	1638	1701	1738	1802	1838	1937	2005
168	**Sydney** Central......... a.		0528	0657	0726	0757	0827	0857	0929	0959	1029	1059	1129	hour until	1557	1629	1659	1729	1759	1829	1859	1929	1959	2059	2129

	Ⓐ	Ⓐ	Ⓐ	Ⓐ		Ⓒ	Ⓒ	Ⓒ	Ⓒ	Ⓒ	Ⓒ	Ⓒ	Ⓒ	Ⓒ	Ⓒ	Ⓒ	Ⓒ	Ⓒ	Ⓒ	⑥	⑦	Ⓒ	Ⓒ	Ⓒ	Ⓒ	Ⓒ
Newcastle Interchange d.	1924	1945	2046	2146	Ⓒ	0246	0348	0453	0543	0653	0743	0853	0943	1053	1143	1253	1343	1453	1543	1653	1656	1755	1853	1929	2029	2156
Hamilton .... d.	1927	1948	2048	2148		0248	0350	0455	0545	0655	0745	0855	0945	1055	1145	1255	1345	1455	1545	1655	1658	1757	1855	1931	2031	2158
Gosford .... d.	2038	2114	2213	2313		0414	0512	0607	0706	0807	0906	1006	1106	1206	1306	1406	1506	1606	1706	1806	1807	1918	2014	2057	2157	2324
Sydney Central .... a.	2159	2239	2339	0039		0544	0644	0729	0829	0929	1029	1129	1229	1329	1429	1529	1629	1729	1829	1929	1929	2035	2129	2229	2329	0101

		Ⓐ	Ⓐ	Ⓐ	Ⓐ	Ⓐ	Ⓐ	Ⓐ	Ⓐ		Ⓐ	Ⓐ	Ⓐ	Ⓐ	Ⓐ	Ⓐ	Ⓐ	Ⓐ	Ⓐ	Ⓐ	Ⓐ	Ⓐ	Ⓐ	Ⓐ
Sydney Central ....d.	Ⓐ	0147	0345	0445	0515	0545	0615	0645	0715	and at the same	1345	1415	1515	1550	1620	1635	1650	1704	1720	1734	1750	1820	1915	2015
Gosford ....d.		0311	0512	0612	0635	0713	0736	0813	0840	minutes	1514	1537	1636	1707	1741	1800	1811	1824	1839	1857	1910	1941	2036	2136
Hamilton ....a.		0436	0636	0736	0746	0837	0859	0937	0955	past each	1642	1704	1746	1808	1850	1926	1930	1946	1951	2019	2025	2053	2158	2258
Newcastle Interchange..a.		0440	0640	0740	0750	0841	0903	0941	0959	hour until	1645	1708	1749	1817	1855	1930	1934	1949	1955	2023	2029	2057	2201	2302

	Ⓐ	Ⓐ	Ⓐ	Ⓐ		Ⓒ	Ⓒ	Ⓒ	Ⓒ	Ⓒ	Ⓒ	Ⓒ	Ⓒ	Ⓒ	Ⓒ	Ⓒ	Ⓒ	Ⓒ	Ⓒ	Ⓒ	Ⓒ	Ⓒ	Ⓒ	Ⓒ	Ⓒ
Sydney Central ....d.	2115	2148	2248	2348	Ⓒ	0147	0448	0548	0715	0818	0918	1018	1118	1218	1318	1418	1518	1618	1716	1818	1918	2018	2148	2248	2348
Gosford ....d.	2236	2316	0019	0117		0311	0618	0713	0839	0939	1039	1139	1239	1339	1439	1539	1639	1739	1839	1939	2039	2144	2316	0016	0116
Hamilton ....a.	2358	0042	0146	0244		0436	0743	0844	0950	1100	1150	1300	1350	1500	1550	1700	1750	1900	1950	2100	2155	2310	0040	0140	0240
Newcastle Interchange..a.	0001	0046	0150	0248		0440	0747	0848	0954	1104	1154	1304	1354	1504	1554	1704	1754	1904	1954	2104	2159	2314	0044	0144	0244

Operator: Sydney Trains ✆ 02 4907 7500.

NSW Train Link/Vline — SYDNEY - CANBERRA, GRIFFITH and MELBOURNE — 6355

km		631	641	631	Vline	NSW	623	633	641	633	635	635	621
		⑥⑦	⑥	Ⓐ	🚌	🚌		Ⓐ	③	⑥⑦	⑥⑦	Ⓐ	
		A	B	A		781	C	A	B	A	A	A	D
0	**Sydney** Central.... d.	0705	0705	0712	...	...	0740	1201	1201	1206	1736	1742	2042
143	Moss Vale............ d.	0847	0847	0854	...	...	0925	1343	1343	1348	1918	1940	2225
222	Goulburn.............. d.	0939	0939	0944	...	...	1013	1432	1432	1437	2007	2029	2314
318	Queanbeyan ..... d.	1101	|	1104	...	0908	|	1553	|	1558	2128	2150	|
326	**Canberra** .... a.	1115	|	1120	0800t	0937t	|	1609	|	1613	2144	2205	|
320	Yass Junction ...... d,	...	1103	...	0845u	1045	1124	...	1549	...	...	...	0022r
383	Harden................ d.	...	1153r	...	|	1153	1213r	...	1639	...	...	...	0112r
427	Cootamundra .... d.	...	1226	...	|	1222	1247	...	1712	...	...	...	0147
483	Junee.................. d.	...	1307	...	|	...	1326	...	1753	...	...	...	0225
580	Narrandera .... d.	...	1421	...	g	▬	|	...	1929	...	...	...	|
658	**Griffith** .... a.	...	1525	...	|	...	|	...	2033	...	...	...	|
518	Wagga Wagga ..... a.	...	...	...	|	...	1354	...	...	...	...	...	0252
547	The Rock............. d.	...	...	...	|	Vline	1414r	...	...	...	...	...	0310r
594	Culcairn .... d.	...	...	...	|		1441r	...	...	...	...	...	0334r
643	**Albury** ....6365 a.	...	...	...	1235v	1254v	1510	...	...	...	...	...	0408
727	Wangaratta ..6365 d.	...	...	...	...	1339	1553	...	...	...	...	...	0450
765	Benalla ....6365 d.	...	...	...	...	1404	1619	...	...	...	...	...	0514
961	**Melbourne** S C ... a.	...	...	...	...	1640	1831	...	...	...	...	...	0730

	632	642	634	Vline	Vline	624	NSW	636		622
		④⑦			🚌		🚌			
	A	B	A			C	782	A		D
Melbourne SC .. d.	...	...	...	0705	...	0830	...	...	...	1950
Benalla..... 6365 d.	...	...	...	0930	...	1041	...	...	...	2154
Wangaratta6365 d.	...	...	...	0955	...	1106	...	...	...	2220
Albury ..... 6365 d.	...	...	...	1037v	1100v	1149	...	...	...	2305
Culcairn............ d.	...	...	...	...	|	1221r	...	...	...	2334r
The Rock .... d.	...	...	...	...	|	1249r	...	...	...	0002r
Wagga Wagga .. d.	...	...	...	...	|	1307	...	...	...	0022
Griffith .... d.	...	0725	...	...	|	|	...	...	...	|
Narrandera..... d.	...	0827	...	...	g	|	...	...	...	|
Junee .... d.	...	0940	...	...	|	1351	...	...	...	0048
Cootamundra..... d.	...	1032	...	...	|	1438	1450	...	...	0135
Harden .... d.	...	1108r	...	...	|	1514r	1521	...	...	0215r
Yass Junction.... d.	...	1200	...	...	1450s	1605	1620	...	...	0306r
Canberra....... d.	0655	|	1155b	...	1535t	|	1722t	1708	...	|
Queanbeyan .. d.	0704	|	1159b	...	...	|	1755	1717	...	|
Goulburn .... d.	0822	1320	1317b	...	...	1714	...	1835	...	0413
Moss Vale......... d.	0914	1414	1414	...	...	1802	...	1927	...	0501
Sydney Central . a.	1104	1603	1603	...	...	1950	...	2116	...	0652

A – CANBERRA XPLORER – (12) and 🍸.
B – GRIFFITH XPLORER – (12) and 🍸.
C – MELBOURNE XPT – (12) and 🍸.
D – MELBOURNE XPT – 🛏 1 cl., (12) and ✕.
b – 5 minutes earlier on ④⑦.
g – Via Gundagai.
r – Calls on request.
t – Canberra Civic Centre.
v – Timings at Wodonga.

V/Line — MELBOURNE - SHEPPARTON — 6360

km		①–⑤	①–⑤	⑥⑦	①–⑤	①–⑤	⑥⑦	①–⑤	①–⑤	⑥⑦	①–⑤
			2					2A			
0	**Melbourne** S Cross....d.	0555	0705	0916	0926	1236	1236	1436	1607	1836	1907
99	Seymour ☛ ....a.	0729	0833	1050	1102	1402	1408	1603	1747	2002	2035
99	Seymour......................d.	0735	0843*	1055	1107	1408	1413	1613*	1752	2007	2040
147	Murchison East...........d.	0809	|	1129	1141	1442	1447	|	1826	2041	2114
	Murchison....................d.	|	|	|	|	|	|	1706*	|	|	|
182	**Shepparton** ....a.	0841	0958*	1200	1212	1514	1519	1738*	1857	2113	2145

	①–⑤	①–⑤	⑥⑦	①–⑤	①–⑤	⑥⑦	①–⑤	⑥⑦	①–⑤	⑤
	2			2B						2
Shepparton.............d.	0512	0624	0702	0831*	0944	1242	1258	1602	1605	1813*
Murchison ....d.	|	|	|	0901*	|	|	|	|	|	1845*
Murchison East ....d.	0540	0652	0730	|	1012	1310	1326	1630	1633	|
Seymour ....a.	0616	0728	0806	1001*	1052	1346	1402	1706	1709	1938*
Seymour ☛ ....d.	0618	0730	0808	1016	1054	1348	1404	1708	1711	1953
Melbourne S Cross .a.	0802	0910	0937	1139	1221	1517	1539	1837	1848	2119

A – Additional trips: ①–⑤ 1036, 1733. ⑥⑦ 1636.
B – Additional trips: ①–⑤ 0736, 1040, 1636. ⑥⑦ 0757, 1417.
* – By 🚌.
☛ Additional trains are available Melbourne - Seymour and v.v.

V/Line — MELBOURNE - ALBURY — 6365

km				①–⑤		①–⑤					
			C			2		D			
0	**Melbourne** S Cross....d.	0705	0830	0926	1205	1436	1802	1950	...	...	...
99	Seymour ☛ ....a.	0824	|	1102	1319	1603	1930	|	...	...	...
99	Seymour......................d.	0826	0948u	1112*	1321	1613*	1932	2059u	...	...	...
196	Benalla ....d.	0930	1041	1225*	1425	1728*	2036	2154	...	...	...
234	Wangaratta..................d.	0955	1106	1302*	1450	1803*	2101	2220	...	...	...
301	Wodonga......................d.	1039	|	1342*	1534	1848*	2145	|	...	...	...
318	**Albury**.........................a.	1100	1149	1352*	1555	1858*	2205	2305	...	...	...

		①–⑤		①–⑤						
	D					C				
Albury......................d.	0408	0521*	0635	0901*	1245	1510	1720	...	...	...
Wodonga ....d.	|	0531*	0644	0911*	1254	|	1729	...	...	...
Wangaratta ....d.	0450	0601*	0729	1001*	1339	1552	1814	...	...	...
Benalla ....d.	0514	0636*	0754	1036*	1404	1617	1839	...	...	...
Seymour ....a.	|	0801*	0857	1201*	1507	|	1942	...	...	...
Seymour ☛ ....d.	0105s	0816	0859	1216	1509	1711s	1944	...	...	...
Melbourne S Cross .a.	0730	0947	1035	1339	1640	1830	2145	...	...	...

C – MELBOURNE XPT – (12) and 🍸 Sydney Central - Melbourne Southern Cross and v.v.
D – MELBOURNE XPT – 🛏 1 cl., (12) and ✕ Sydney Central - Melbourne Southern Cross and v.v.
* – By 🚌.
☛ Additional trains are available Melbourne - Seymour and v.v.

V/Line — MELBOURNE - WARRNAMBOOL — 6370

km		⑥⑦	①–⑤		⑥⑦	①–⑤		①–⑤	①–⑤	⑥⑦	①–⑤
								2			
0	**Melbourne** S Cross....d.	0655	0746	...	1300	1309	...	1530	1707	1900	1913
73	Geelong ☛ ....a.	0808	0845	...	1409	1408	...	1631	1806	1958	2012
73	Geelong.......................d.	0813	0850	...	1414	1410	...	1641*	1811	2003	2017
133	Colac............................d.	0924	0959	...	1519	1525	...	1808*	1926	2107	2129
267	**Warrnambool** ....a.	1045	1125	...	1636	1648	...	...	2053	2227	2249

	①–⑤	①–⑤	⑥	⑦	①–⑤	⑥⑦	①–⑤		⑥⑦	①–⑤
	2									
Warrnambool..........d.	...	0609	0737	0737	0933	1150	1215	...	1732	1739
Colac ....d.	0600*	0730	0855	0855	1105	1308	1332	...	1850	1856
Geelong ....a.	0730*	0832	1013	1013	1211	1413	1435	...	1957	2014
Geelong ☛ ....d.	0736	0834	1015	1015	1213	1415	1437	...	1959	2016
Melbourne S Cross .a.	0837	0935	1114	1127	1315	1528	1541	...	2109	2117

☛ Additional trains are available Melbourne - Geelong and v.v.
* – By 🚌.

V/Line — MELBOURNE - TRARALGON - BAIRNSDALE — 6375

km		①–⑤	⑥⑦	①–⑤	⑦	⑥	①–⑤	⑥⑦	①–⑤	⑥⑦	①–⑤
		🅁	🅁	2C	2	🅁	🅁	2	2	🅁	🅁
0	**Melbourne** S Cross....d.	0716	0754	0826	1024	1224	1324	1424	1524	1824	1833
32	Dandenong..................d.	0804u	0832u	0910u	1110u	1310u	1410u	1510u	1608u	1910u	1919u
101	Warragul......................d.	0859	0925	1004	1203	1403	1503	1603	1702	2001	2013
131	Moe..............................d.	0916	0946	1025	1224	1424	1524	1624	1720	2020	2032
145	Morwell........................d.	0934	0956	1039	1239	1439	1539	1639	1733	2031	2043
159	**Traralgon** ☛ ....d.	0946	1010	1058*	1250	1450	1551	1658*	1754*	2046	2058
207	Sale..............................d.	1021	1045	1143*	1400*	1525	1626	1748*	1834*	2123	2134
276	**Bairnsdale**..................a.	1115	1139	1243*	1500*	1619	1720	...	...	2217	2229

	①–⑤	①–⑥	①–⑤	⑦	①–⑥	⑦	①–⑤	⑥	⑥⑦	①–⑤
	2	🅁	2B	🅁	🅁	2	2	2	🅁	🅁
Bairnsdale ....d.	0427*	0614	...	0734	1254	1254*	1515*	...	1653	1806
Sale ....d.	0527*	0708	0817*	0828	1348	1409	1615*	1522*	1747	1900
Traralgon ☛ ....d.	0632	0746	0922	0906	1427	1447	1720	1725	1825	1938
Morwell ....d.	0640	0756	0930	0916	1435	1455	1728	1733	1833	1946
Moe ....d.	0649	0807	0939	0927	1445	1505	1741	1743	1843	2001
Warragul......................d.	0704	0826	1004	0946	1504	1524	1802	1803	1903	2021
Dandenong ....d.	0755s	0920s	1059s	1040s	1559s	1619s	1900s	1859s	1959s	2120s
Melbourne S Cross .a.	0847	1006a	1144	1126	1644	1704	1948	1944	2044	2205

B – Additional trip: ①–⑤ 0922.
C – Additional trip: ①–⑤ 1657.
a – Arrives 1000 on ⑥.
* – By 🚌.
☛ Additional trains are available Melbourne - Traralgon and v.v.
NOTE: Trains will depart Bairnsdale 4 minutes earlier until Jan. 16.

s – Calls to set down only. u – Calls to pick up only.

6380 MELBOURNE - BENDIGO - SWAN HILL and ECHUCA — V/Line

km		①-⑤		⑥⑦	①-⑤					①③⑤	②④	①-⑤	⑥⑦	⑥⑦	①-⑤	⑥⑦	①-⑤	⑤	①-⑤	⑥⑦	①-⑤	⑥	①-⑤	⑥⑦	①-⑤	⑥
		2	Ⓡ🍷	2	2	2	2	2	2	🚌	🚌	2	2	2	Ⓡ🍷	Ⓡ🍷	2	🚌	2	2	2	2	2	2	2	2
0	**Melbourne** S Cross .. d.	0625	0739	0905	0905	1006	1106	1206	1306	...	...	1506	1506	1806	1808	1843	1908	...	2025	2037	2107	2137	2157	2237	2357	2355
38	Sunbury ..... d.	0655	|	0935	0935	1035	1135	1235	1335	...	...	1537	1535	1835	|	|	1940	...	2054	2107	2136	2207	2226	2307	0026	0025
78	Woodend ..... d.	0726	0849	1004	1005	1105	1205	1305	1405	...	...	1606	1605	1905	1919	1950	2009	...	2124	2136	2206	2236	2256	2323	0056	0054
92	Kyneton ..... d.	0736	0859	1012	1013	1113	1212	1312	1412	...	...	1614	1612	1912	1929	2000	2017	...	2131	2144	2214	2244	2303	2336	0103	0102
125	Castlemaine ..... d.	0754	0926	1031	1033	1133	1231	1332	1432	...	...	1632	1632	1932	1952	2023	2035	...	2151	2203	2233	2303	2323	2344	0123	0121
162	**Bendigo** ☛ ..... a.	0820	0955	1057	1058	1158	1257	1357	1457	1507	1509	1656	1657	1959	2021	2052	2100	2110	2216	2229	2258	2329	2341	0029	0148	0147
289	Kerang ..... a.	|	1135	|	...	1353*	...	|	...	|	1729	|	...	|	2201	2231	...	2320	...	...	...	...	...	...	...	...
345	**Swan Hill** ..... a.	|	1222	|	...	1435*	...	|	...	1817	1814	|	...	|	2248	2319	...	0004	...	...	...	...	...	...	...	...
222	Rochester ..... a.	0925*	...	1155	...	...	...	1515*	...	...	...	1755	...	2052	...	...	...	...	...	...	...	...	...	...	...	...
248	**Echuca** ..... a.	0948*	...	1226	...	...	...	1538*	...	...	...	1826	...	2123	...	...	...	...	...	...	...	...	...	...	...	...

	⑥	①-⑤	⑦	⑥	①-⑤	⑥⑦	①-⑤	⑦	⑥	①-⑤	①③⑤	②④	⑥	2	①-⑤	⑦	①-⑤	⑥⑦	⑥	①-⑤	⑥⑦	①-⑤	⑦	⑦	⑥	①-⑤
	2	2	2	2	2	Ⓡ🍷	Ⓡ🍷	2	2	2	🚌	🚌	🚌		2Ⓡ	2	2	2	Ⓡ🍷	Ⓡ🍷	2	2Ⓡ	Ⓡ🍷	2	2	2
Echuca ..... d.	...	...	...	0715	0716	...	...	0854	0855*	0855*	...	...	...	...	...	1245*	1250*	...	...	...	1554	...	...	...	...	...
Rochester ..... d.	...	...	...	0738	0739	...	...	0917	0925*	0925*	...	...	...	...	...	1310*	1315*	...	...	...	1617	...	...	...	...	...
Swan Hill ..... d.	...	...	...	|	|	0656	0656	|	|	|	0856	0856	0940	...	1055*	|	|	1250**b**	1337	1337	|	1550**a**	1638	...	...	...
Kerang ..... d.	...	...	...	|	|	0740	0740	|	|	|	|	0946	1026	...	1141*	|	|	1336**b**	1421	1421	|	1630**a**	1722	...	...	...
Bendigo ☛ ..... d.	0728	0749	0750	0847	0848	0920	0920	1026	1026	1030	1211	1211	1157	1226	1326	1426	1426	1526	1601	1601	1726	1901	1902	2100	2140	2300
Castlemaine ..... d.	0749	0812	0811	0905	0909	0948	0948	1049	1049	1053	...	...	...	1249	1349	1449	1449	1549	1628	1628	1749	1926	1929	2123	2201	2321
Kyneton ..... d.	0811	0832	0833	0928	0928	1012	1012	1109	1109	1113	...	...	...	1309	1409	1509	1509	1609	1655	1655	1809	1953	1956	2143	2221	2341
Woodend ..... d.	0820	0840	0842	0938	0938	1022	1022	1118	1118	1123	...	...	...	1318	1418	1518	1518	1618	|	|	1818	2002	2006	2152	2231	2351
Sunbury ..... d.	0850	0911	0912	1011	1011	|	|	1152	1152	1156	...	...	...	1352	1452	1552	1552	1652	|	|	1852	2035	|	2226	2304	0024
Melbourne S Cross ... a.	0922	0946	0954	1043	1044	1130	1128	1224	1224	1228	...	...	...	1425	1525	1624	1624	1724	1809	1811	1924	2109	2112	2259	2338	0056

☛ Additional trains are available Melbourne - Bendigo and v.v. a – Connection by 🚌 on ⑤ only. b – Connection by 🚌 on ⑦ only. * – By 🚌.

6385 MELBOURNE -BALLARAT - MARYBOROUGH and ARARAT — V/Line

km		①-⑤	⑥⑦	①-⑤	①-⑤	⑥⑦	⑥ 🚌	⑥⑦	①-⑤	⑥⑦	①-⑤	①-⑤	①②④ 🚌	①-⑤		①-⑤	①-⑤	①-⑤	⑤ 🚌	①-⑤	⑥⑦	⑥⑦	①-⑤	⑦	①-⑤	E 🚌	①-⑤
0	**Melbourne** SC d.	0753	0814	0836	0916	0914	...	1014	1116	1214	1236	1316	...	1436	1514	1617	...	1658	...	1738	1814	...	1818	1914	2048	2110	2352
41	Melton ..... d.	0830	0851	0913	0953	0951	...	1051	1153	1251	1313	1353	...	1513	1551	|	...	|	...	|	1851	...	1848	1951	2125	|	0029
53	Bacchus Marsh d.	0838	0858	0921	1001	0958	...	1058	1201	1258	1321	1401	...	1521	1558	1655	...	1736	...	1816	1858	...	1855	1958	2133	|	0037
82	Ballan ..... d.	0857	0916	0940	1020	1016	...	1116	1220	1316	1340	1420	...	1540	1616	1713	...	1751	...	1834	1916	...	1913	2016	2151	|	0055
122	**Ballarat** ☛ .... a.	0921	0943	1001	1041	1043	1053**d**	1143	1241	1343	1401	1441	1451**d**	1601	1643	1733	1801**d**	1814	1824	1854	1943	1948**d**	1934	2037	2211	2240	0115
180	**Maryborough** a.	|	|	|	*1143*	...	1159	|	|	|	|	...	1603	|	|	...	1857	|	1931	|	|	2044	|	|	...	2358	...
210	**Ararat** ..... a.	1022	1042	*1137**	...	...	...	*1308**	1342	1442	*1521**	...	...	1702	1821*	...	...	1915	...	*2020**	2042	...	2035	2202*	...	...	...

	⑦-⑤ 🚌	①-⑤	①-⑤	①-⑤	①-⑤	⑥	⑥	D 🚌	⑦	⑥⑦	①-⑤	⑥ 🚌	⑥	⑥	①-⑤	⑥⑦	①-⑤	①-⑤	①-⑤	⑥⑦	①-⑤	①-⑤	⑦	⑥⑦	①-⑤
Ararat ..... d.	...	...	0617	0714	...	0713	...		0813	...	*0730**	...	*0838**	*0942**	*1031**	1114	1148	1428	...	1614	1717	*1719**	*1750**	...	...
Maryborough ..... d.	0407	...	|	|	0709	|	0709	0741	|	0809**b**	|	0856	|	|	|	|	|	|	1457	|	|	|	|	...	...
Ballarat ☛ ..... d.	0503**a**	0524	0724	0807**a**	0819	0808	0820	0850**a**	0908**a**	0920	0924	1005	1020	1120	1204	1220	1244	1524	1604	1720	1814	1854	1920	2128	2334
Ballan ..... d.	|	0542	0742	...	0837	...	0838	...	...	0938	0942	...	1038	1138	1222	1238	1302	1542	1623	1738	1835	1915	1938	2149	2352
Bacchus Marsh ..... d.	|	0559	0800	...	0900	...	0855	...	...	0956	0959	...	1056	1156	1239	1256	1319	1559	1640	1756	1858	1931	1956	2206	0014
Melton ..... d.	|	0608	|	...	0909	...	0909	...	...	1009	1010	...	1109	1209	1250	1309	1330	1610	1650	1809	1907	1942	2009	2215	0022
Melbourne S Cross ..... a.	0705	0640	0846	...	0951	...	0948	...	...	1048	1051	...	1148	1248	1331	1348	1411	1651	1722	1848	1947	2023	2048	2256	0103

☛ Additional trains are available Melbourne - Ballarat and v.v. D – ①②④⑤. E – ①②③④⑤⑦. a – Arrive. b – ⑦ only. d – Depart. * – By 🚌.

6390 SYDNEY - PERTH — Journey Beyond Rail

km		WE1 Ⓡ③A			WE2 Ⓡ⑦A	
0	**Sydney** Central ..... d.	1500a	③	East **Perth** ..... d.	1000	⑦
1125	Broken Hill ◇ ..... a.	◇	④	Kalgoorlie ◇ ..... a.	2050	:
1688	**Adelaide** Parklands ◇ .... a.	1515	④	Nullarbor ..... d.	◇	①
1688	**Adelaide** Parklands ◇ .... d.	2140	④	**Adelaide** Parklands ◇ .. a.	0720	②
	Cook ..... a.	◇	⑤	**Adelaide** Parklands ..... d.	1015	:
	Nullarbor ..... d.	◇	⑤	Broken Hill ..... d.	◇	:
4343	East **Perth** ..... a.	1500	⑥	**Sydney** Central ..... a.	1245b	③

A – INDIAN PACIFIC – 🛏 P 1 cl., and ✕ Sydney - Adelaide - Perth and v.v.
a – Departs Sydney 1325 Feb., Mar. 2022, Sept. 2022 – Mar. 2023.
b – Blue Mountain Excursion available arrive in Sydney at 1515.
◇ – Off train excursion **Note**:Train **WE2** has a additional off train excursion at Cook on ①.
NOTE: Services are due to re-start Feb. 9, 2022.

6395 MELBOURNE - ADELAIDE — Journey Beyond Rail

km		8701 ⓇB ①	8701 ⓇB ⑤		8702 ⓇB ⑦	8702 ⓇB ④
0	**Melbourne** S Cross ..... d.	0805	0805	**Adelaide** Parklands ..... d.	0745	0655
74	Geelong North Shore ..... d.	0935	0915	Murray Bridge ..... d.	0935	0910
265	Ararat ..... d.	1135	1115	Nhill ..... d.	1301	1236
381	Horsham ..... d.	1251	1300	Dimboola ..... d.	1334	1330
416	Dimboola ..... d.	1320	1328	Horsham ..... d.	1401	1337
454	Nhill ..... d.	1347	1355	Ararat ..... d.	1519	1455
734	Murray Bridge ..... d.	1610	1618	Geelong North Shore .... d.	1723	1740
828	**Adelaide** Parklands ..... a.	1800	1805	**Melbourne** S Cross ..... a.	1850	1850

B – THE OVERLAND – 12 and 🍷 Melbourne - Adelaide and v.v.

6400 DARWIN - ADELAIDE — Journey Beyond Rail

km		8506 Ⓡ③D			8505 Ⓡ⑦C	
0	**Darwin** △ ..... d.	1000	③	**Adelaide** Parklands ..... d.	1215	⑦
310	Katherine ◇ ..... d.	◇	:	Snowtown ..... d.	|	:
	Newcastle Waters ..... d.	|	:	Crystal Brook ..... d.	|	:
947	Tennant Creek ..... a.	|	:	Maria ◇ ..... d.	◇	①
947	Tennant Creek ..... d.	|	:	Port Augusta ..... a.	|	:
1414	**Alice Springs** ..... a.	0910	④	Port Augusta ..... d.	|	:
1414	**Alice Springs** ..... d.	1245	④	**Alice Springs** ..... a.	1345	①
2661	Port Augusta ..... a.	|	:	**Alice Springs** ..... d.	1815	①
2661	Port Augusta ..... d.	|	:	Tennant Creek ..... a.	|	:
2751	Manguri ◇ ..... d.	◇	④	Tennant Creek ..... d.	|	:
2775	Crystal Brook ..... d.	|	:	Newcastle Waters ..... d.	|	:
2827	Snowtown ..... d.	|	:	Katherine ◇ ..... d.	◇	②
2973	**Adelaide** Parklands ..... a.	1300	⑤	**Darwin** △ ..... a.	1730	②

C – THE GHAN – 🛏 P, 1 cl., ✕ and 🍷 Adelaide - Darwin. From Adelaide on ⑦ Feb. - Nov. 2022; service will also stop at Maria and Katherine for an off train excursion. Also from Adelaide on ③ Apr. - Aug. 2022 departing 1210, arriving Darwin 1950 on ⑤.
D – THE GHAN – 🛏 P, 1 cl., ✕ and 🍷 Darwin - Adelaide. From Darwin on ③ Feb. and Nov. 2022 only. On ③ from Apr. to Oct. 2022 will operate as THE GHAN EXPEDITION arriving Adelaide 1050 on ⑥. An additional GHAN EXPEDITION will operate on ⑥ Apr. - Aug. 2022 departing Darwin 0900 arriving Adelaide 1135 on ②. Off train excursions are included.
☛ The Ghan will not operate Jan 2022 or Dec. 2022. Instead a service called GREAT SOUTHERN will operate between Adelaide and Brisbane. Adelaide d. 0900 on ⑤, Brisbane a. 1710 on ⑦. Brisbane d. 1115 on ①, Adelaide a. 0930 on ④.
△ – Darwin station is in the suburb of Berrimah. 🚌 connections to and from Darwin city centre are provided by the operator.
◇ – Off train Excursion.

6405 KALGOORLIE - PERTH — All trains 2 cl. 🍷 and Ⓡ — TransWA

km		AVO2 ①-⑤	PL02 ①③⑤	PA02 ②④⑥	MO2 ⑤	MO2 ①	MO2 ③		PA56 ⑦	PA52 ①	PA54 ⑤
0	**Kalgoorlie** ..... d.	...	0705	0705	...	...	...	...	1405	1500	1500
250	Southern Cross ..... d.	...	0912	0912	...	...	...	...	1612	1707	1715
371	Merredin ..... d.	...	1023	1023	1305	1310	1310	...	1723	1818	1829
427	Kellerberrin ..... d.	...	1102**s**	1102	1336	1341	1341	...	1802	1857	1908
531	Northam ..... d.	0630	1209	1209	1441	1446	1454	...	1907	2002	2013
641	Midland ..... d.	0750	1323	1323	1555	1600	1610	...	2020	2115	2125
653	East **Perth** ..... a.	...	1345	1345	1620	1620	1630	...	2040	2135	2145

	PL01 ①③⑤	PA01 ②④⑥		M01 ①③⑤		PA55 ⑦	PA51 ①		PA53 ⑤	AVO1 ①-⑤
East **Perth** ..... d.	0710	0710	...	0850	...	1410	1515	...	1515	...
Midland ..... d.	0727	0727	...	0912	...	1427	1533	...	1532	1750
Northam ..... d.	0850**u**	0850	...	1027	...	1547	1645	...	1655	1910
Kellerberrin ..... d.	0956**u**	0956	...	1138	...	1653	1750	...	1800	...
Merredin ..... d.	1027	1027	...	1210	...	1728	1821	...	1831	...
Southern Cross ..... d.	1144	1144	...	...	...	1845	1938	...	1948	...
Kalgoorlie ..... a.	1400	1400	...	...	...	2100	2150	...	2205	...

s – Set down only. u – Pick up only. NOTE: Trains will only call at intermediate stations if bookings are made in advance.

6410 PERTH - BUNBURY — All trains 2 cl TransWA

km		B03 Ⓡ	B55 Ⓡ			B02 Ⓡ	B56 Ⓡ	
0	**Perth** City ..... d.	0930	1755	...	**Bunbury** ..... d.	0600	1445	...
30	Armadale ..... d.	0956	1825	...	Brunswick Junction d.	0617	1502	...
85	Pinjarra ..... d.	1042	1911	...	Harvey ..... d.	0632	1517	...
111	Waroona ..... d.	1100	1929	...	Waroona ..... d.	0656	1538	...
136	Harvey ..... d.	1121	1950	...	Pinjarra ..... d.	0712	1555	...
157	Brunswick Junction d.	1136	2005	...	Armadale ..... d.	0755	1639	...
183	**Bunbury** ..... a.	1155	2025	...	**Perth** City ..... a.	0830	1715	...

NOTE: Trains will only call at intermediate stations if bookings are made in advance.

6415 KALGOORLIE - ESPERANCE — TransWA

km		671 🚌 ①③	651 🚌 ⑤			700 🚌 ⑦	690 🚌 ③⑤	
0	**Kalgoorlie** ..... d.	1430	1430	...	**Esperance** ..... d.	0800	0835	...
208	Norseman ..... d.	1715	1730	...	Norseman ..... d.	1045	1120	...
409	**Esperance** ..... a.	1930	1945	...	**Kalgoorlie** ..... a.	1315	1335	...

NEW ZEALAND

Capital: **Wellington** (GMT +12, add one hour in Summer). 2022 public holidays: Jan. 1–4, Feb. 6, 7, Apr. 15, 18, 25, June 6, 24, Oct. 24, Dec. 25, 26, 27.

Long distance rail services are operated by Kiwi Rail (www.greatjourneysofnz.co.nz). Two classes of accommodation are offered, Scenic Plus Class and Scenic Class (shown in tables as 1 and 2). Scenic Plus Class includes refreshments. Carriages have both panoramic windows and skylights or have open sides. All services require reservation. There are two Rail Passes; the Fixed Pass offers unlimited travel on the TranzScenic network (not the Capital Connection) and also allows one journey on the Interislander ferry service (adult: 7 days NZ$599, 14 days NZ$699, 21 days NZ $799). The Freedom Pass allows flexible travel from 3 to 10 days (adult: 3 days NZ$ 417 to 10 days NZ$ 1290). **Rail Passes are currently unavailable.**

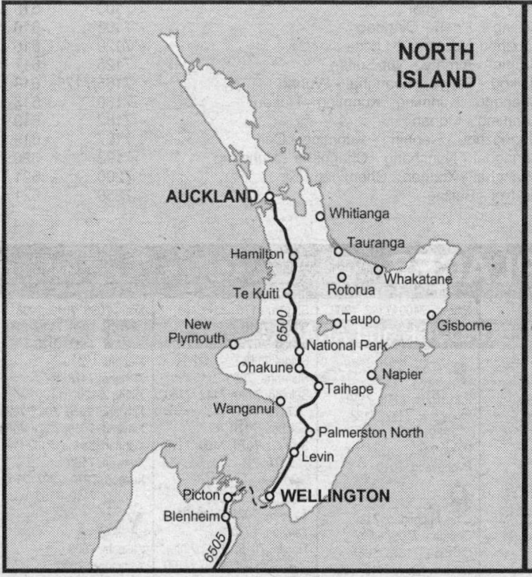

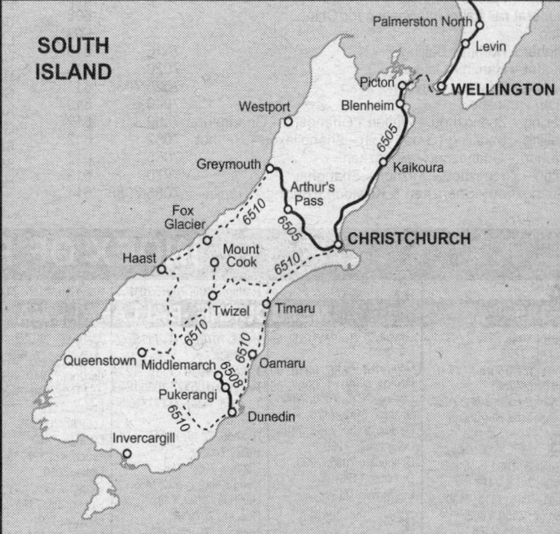

KiwiRail Scenic — AUCKLAND - WELLINGTON — 6500

km		1203	0201
		①-⑤	①④⑥
		R B	R A
0	**Auckland** Strand .... d.	...	0745
34	Papakura .... d.	...	0840
139	Hamilton .... d.	...	1015
183	Otorohanga .... d.	...	1105
334	National Park .... d.	...	1315
364	Ohakune .... d.	...	1345
544	**Palmerston North** .... d.	0615	1625
590	Levin .... d.	0653	|
632	Paraparaumu .... d.	0732	1725
681	**Wellington** .... ⊡ a.	0820	1825

	0200	1205
	③⑤⑦	①-⑤
	R A	R B
Wellington .... ⊡ d.	0755	1715
Paraparaumu .... d.	0845	1803
Levin .... d.	|	1842
Palmerston North .... d.	1000	1920
Ohakune .... d.	1245	...
National Park .... d.	1315	...
Otorohanga .... d.	1545	...
Hamilton .... d.	1625	...
Papakura .... d.	1755	...
Auckland Strand .... a.	1850	...

NOTES FOR TABLES 6500 and 6505.

☛ Trains are permitted to depart earlier if all booked passengers have boarded.

A – NORTHERN EXPLORER – [2]. From Sept. 25.
B – CAPITAL CONNECTION – [2]. Not public holidays.
C – COASTAL PACIFIC – [12]. ④-⑦ from Sept. 29.
D – THE TRANZALPINE – [12]. ⑤-① until Dec. 24; daily from Dec. 26.
s – Calls to set down only.
u – Calls to pick up only.
⊡ – Wellington - Picton ferry service ('Interislander'). Journey 3 - 3½ hours.
Operator: Interislander (www.greatjourneysofnz.co.nz/interislander).
From **Wellington** at 0845, 1600. From **Picton** at 1100, 1415.
Days and times of sailings may vary - please contact the operator for confirmed timings.

KiwiRail Scenic — PICTON - CHRISTCHURCH — 6505

km		0803	0701
		R D	R C
0	**Picton** .... ⊡ d.	...	1340
28	Blenheim .... d.	...	1409
157	Kaikoura .... d.	...	1605
318	Rangiora .... d.	...	1852
348	**Christchurch** .... a.	...	1920
348	**Christchurch** .... d.	0815	...
417	Springfield .... d.	0920	...
484	Arthur's Pass .... d.	1052	...
498	Otira .... d.	1126	...
	Moana .... d.	1206	...
579	**Greymouth** .... a.	1305	...

	0700	0804
	R C	R D
Greymouth .... d.	...	1405
Moana .... d.	...	1503
Otira .... d.	...	1551
Arthur's Pass .... d.	...	1628
Springfield .... d.	...	1739
Christchurch .... a.	...	1831
Christchurch .... d.	0700	...
Rangiora .... d.	0730	...
Kaikoura .... d.	0958	...
Blenheim .... d.	1214	...
Picton .... ⊡ a.	1240	...

TAIERI GORGE — 6508

km		E	
0	**Dunedin** .... d.	E	...
58	Pukerangi .... d.	E	...
77	**Middlemarch** .... a.	E	...

	E	
Middlemarch .... d.	E	...
Pukerangi .... d.	E	...
Dunedin .... a.	E	...

E – Various excursions operate from Dunedin - contact operator for Details.

The Taieri Gorge Railway runs through some of New Zealand's most spectacular scenery. The train travels along the Taieri branch across the Taieri Plains and climbs into the Taieri Gorge, travelling through ten tunnels and over countless bridges and viaducts on its 58km journey.

Operator: Dunedin Railways (www.dunedinrailways.co.nz).

SELECTED SOUTH ISLAND BUS SERVICES — 6510

km	Operator	IC	IC	AS	AS	IC	AS			
		①③⑦		F	⑦	G	⑤			
0	**Christchurch** Interchange ... d.	0830	0800	0915	1315	1425	1615	...	...	...
82	Ashburton .... d.	0945e	0930	1100	1500	1550	1800	...	...	...
160	Timaru .... d.	|	1050	1245	1645	1730	1945	...	...	...
240	Oamaru .... d.	|	1230	1400	1800	1845	2100	...	...	...
366	**Dunedin** Moray Place .... a.	|	1415	1530	1930	2020	2230	...	...	...
516	Gore .... a.	|	1720	...	...	...	...	...	...	...
580	**Invercargill** .... a.	|	1830	...	...	...	...	...	...	...
144	Geraldine .... d.	1045	...	...	...	...	...	...	...	...
191	Fairlie .... d.	1125	...	...	...	...	...	...	...	...
341	**Mount Cook** .... a.	|	...	...	...	...	...	...	...	...
281	Twizel .... d.	1330	...	...	...	...	...	...	...	...
435	Cromwell .... d.	1530	...	...	...	...	...	...	...	...
496	**Queenstown** .... a.	1640	...	...	...	...	...	...	...	...

Operator	IC	AS	IC	IC	AS	AS			
	G	F	①③⑦		⑦	⑤			
Queenstown .... d.	...	...	0805	...	...	...	...	...	...
Cromwell .... d.	...	...	0910	...	...	...	...	...	...
Twizel .... d.	...	...	1115	...	...	...	...	...	...
Mount Cook .... d.	...	...	|	...	...	...	...	...	...
Fairlie .... d.	...	...	1315	...	...	...	...	...	...
Geraldine .... d.	...	...	1410	...	...	...	...	...	...
Invercargill .... d.	...	...	|	0810	...	...	...	...	...
Gore .... d.	...	...	|	0925	...	...	...	...	...
Dunedin Moray Place .... d.	0730	0915	|	1235	1315	1615	...	...	...
Oamaru .... d.	0925	1100	|	1500	1500	1800	...	...	...
Timaru .... d.	1120	1245	|	1610	1645	1945	...	...	...
Ashburton .... d.	1225	1350	1455e	1730	1750	2050	...	...	...
Christchurch Interchange .... a.	1350	1517	1615	1905	1933	2217	...	...	...

km	Operator	IC	AS	AS						
			⑦	⑤						
0	**Greymouth** .... d.	...	...	...	...	...	...	...	...	...
41	Hokitika .... d.	...	...	...	...	...	...	...	...	...
189	Franz Josef .... d.	...	...	...	...	...	...	...	...	...
213	**Fox Glacier** .... d.	...	...	...	...	...	...	...	...	...
	Paringa .... d.	...	...	...	...	...	...	...	...	...
331	Haast .... d.	...	...	...	...	...	...	...	...	...
476	Wanaka .... d.	...	...	...	...	...	...	...	...	...
593	**Queenstown** .... d.	0800	1600	2100	...	...	...	...	...	...
654	Cromwell .... d.	0856	1640	2155	...	...	...	...	...	...
685	Alexandra .... d.	0926	1725	2225	...	...	...	...	...	...
727	Roxburgh .... d.	1015	1800	2300	...	...	...	...	...	...
817	Milton .... d.	1126e	1915	2350	...	...	...	...	...	...
873	**Dunedin** Moray Place .... a.	1225	2040	0045	...	...	...	...	...	...

Operator	AS	IC	AS						
	⑦		⑤						
Dunedin Moray Place .... d.	1100	1430	1520	...	...	...	...	...	...
Milton .... d.	1145	1525e	1615	...	...	...	...	...	...
Roxburgh .... d.	1300	1650	1820	...	...	...	...	...	...
Alexandra .... d.	1345	1720	1900	...	...	...	...	...	...
Cromwell .... d.	1405	1800	1920	...	...	...	...	...	...
Queenstown .... d.	1500	1855	2010	...	...	...	...	...	...
Wanaka .... d.	...	...	...	...	...	...	...	...	...
Haast .... d.	...	...	...	...	...	...	...	...	...
Paringa .... d.	...	...	...	...	...	...	...	...	...
Fox Glacier .... d.	...	...	...	...	...	...	...	...	...
Franz Josef .... d.	...	...	...	...	...	...	...	...	...
Hokitika .... d.	...	...	...	...	...	...	...	...	...
Greymouth .... a.	...	...	...	...	...	...	...	...	...

F – ①②④⑥.
G – ①④⑤⑦.

e – Will only call to pick up pre-booked passengers.

AS – Atomic Travel (www.atomictravel.co.nz).
IC – Intercity Coachlines (www.intercity.co.nz).

BEYOND EUROPE
CHINA

Contents

INDEX OF PLACES

CHINA

Capital: Beijing (GMT + 8). 2022 Public Holidays: Jan. 1, 31, Feb. 1 – 6, Mar. 8, Apr. 5, May 1, 4, June 3, Sept. 10, Oct. 1 – 7.

Rail services in the People's Republic are generally operated by Chinese Railways. High-speed services are operated by China Rail High Speed. All times shown are Beijing time unless otherwise stated. Schedules in this section are as per the latest information available and are liable to change at any time.

Trains are numbered using a combination of letters and numbers, with the letter indicating the type of train. The fastest trains carry prefixes **C** and **G**. These use the new high- speed railways and run at speeds up to 350 km/h on routes Beijing to Tianjin and Beijing to Shanghai and up to 300 km/h on routes such as Wuhan to Guangzhou. Other high-speed trains running at speeds of up to 200 km/h are prefixed with the letter **D** and **Z**. These trains use both dedicated high-speed railways and normal lines. Ordinary long distance trains are prefixed **T** or **K**. **T** trains make fewer stops and thus are considerably quicker than **K** trains. Most **K** trains in this section are only shown to highlight additional connections between major points and may not be shown in their entirety. Also shown are a few trains without prefix letters.

Train classes are shown in the chart below. It should be noted that not all classes will be available on every train and that the exact train compositions are **not** shown in the tables. Hard seats are cheapest class available and are often very busy as Standing ticket holders can stand in the aisles. Soft seats are larger and generally can be reclined. Second class seats have five seats per row. First class has four seats per row. Business and VIP seats have three seats per row. Hard sleepers consist of open cabins of six berths (upper, middle and lower), with three beds on either side. Soft sleepers have four berths and a sliding door. Deluxe Soft cabins have two berths and an en-suite bathroom.

High-Speed	Business Class	VIP Class	1st Class	2nd Class	Soft Sleepers	Deluxe Sleeper	Regular	Hard Seats	Soft Seats	Hard Sleepers	Soft Sleepers	Deluxe Sleeper
G	Yes	Yes	Yes	Yes	No	Yes	Z	No	No	No	Yes	Yes
D	No	No	Yes	Yes	Certain trains	No	T	Yes	Yes	Yes	Yes	No
C	No	No	Yes	Yes	No	No	K	Yes	Yes	Yes	Yes	No

All travel should be reserved in advance either at stations or through an agent. At many stations you may find it possible to only book for trains calling there, however in major cities such as Beijing, Shanghai and Guangzhou you may be able to purchase all tickets. Some major stations may have English speakers available at ticket desks. Reservations for **Z** and **D** usually open 10 – 21 days in advance. Other classes of train are only usually available 7 – 10 days before departure. In peak seasons such as Spring Festival holidays reservations may only open 5 days before departure. Identity documents, such as passports for most foreigners or ID cards for Chinese citizens, are required to buy tickets for and to board **C, D** and **G** trains.

Because of space we are only able to show selected services in many tables. Additional services and other information can be found in the footnotes. More comprehensive train schedules are available from Chinese Railways official website: www.12306.cn/en/index/. Other websites such as www.chinahighlights.com, www.trains.ctrip.com and www.travelchinaguide.com have more detailed class information with photographs, timetable search facilities in English and can arrange tickets.

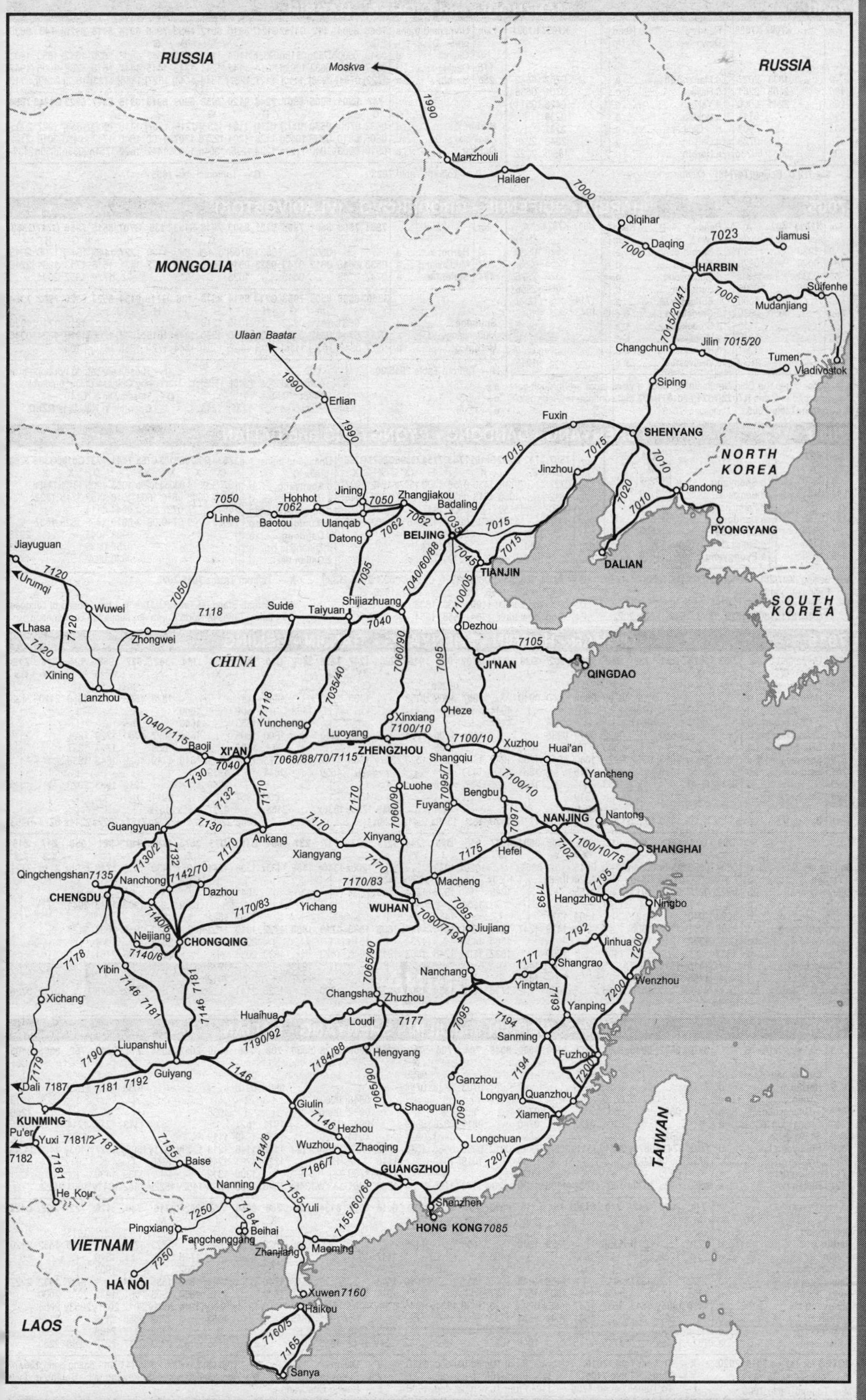
RUSSIA
Moskva
1990
Manzhouli
Hailaer
7000
Qiqihar
Daqing
7000
7023
Jiamusi
HARBIN
7005
Sifenhe
Mudanjiang
7015/20/47
Changchun
Jilin 7015/20
Tumen
Vladivostok
Siping
MONGOLIA
Ulaan Baatar
1990
Erlian
1990
Fuxin
SHENYANG
7015
7015
7010
NORTH KOREA
Jinzhou
Dandong
7020
7010
PYONGYANG
DALIAN
Jining
7050
Hohhot
7062
7050
Zhangjiakou
Badaling
Linhe
Baotou
Ulanqab
Datong
7062
7062
7035
BEIJING
7015
7015
7045
TIANJIN
Jiayuguan
Urumqi
7120
7050
7035
7040/60/88
7100/05
SOUTH KOREA
Wuwei
7118
Suide
Taiyuan
Shijiazhuang
7040
Lhasa
7120
7120
Zhongwei
Dezhou
7105
CHINA
7060/90
7095
JI'NAN
QINGDAO
Xining
Lanzhou
7035/40
7118
Heze
Xinxiang
Yuncheng
7040/7115
Luoyang
7100/10
7100/10
Baoji
XI'AN
ZHENGZHOU
Shangqiu
Xuzhou
Huai'an
7040
7068/88/70/7115
7130
7132
7170
7170
Luohe
7100/10
Yancheng
Fuyang
7095/7
Bengbu
7060/90
7097
NANJING
Nantong
Guangyuan
7130
Ankang
7170
Xinyang
7102
SHANGHAI
7130/2
7132
7170
Xiangyang
7170
7175
Hefei
7100/10/75
Qingchengshan 7135
Nanchong
7142/70
Dazhou
7170/83
Macheng
7195
CHENGDU
7170/83
Yichang
WUHAN
7095
7193
Hangzhou
Ningbo
7140/6
Neijiang
CHONGQING
7090/7194
Jiujiang
7192
Jinhua
7200
7178
7140/6
7065/90
Shangrao
Yibin
7181
Nanchang
7177
Wenzhou
7146
7181
7200
Yingtan
Xichang
7146
Changsha
Zhuzhou
7193
Huaihua
Loudi
7177
7095
7194
Yanping
7190/92
Sanming
Liupanshui
Hengyang
Fuzhou
7179
7190
7184/88
7194
7200
7181
7192
Guiyang
7146
Ganzhou
Dali 7187
7065/90
Longyan
Quanzhou
KUNMING
Giulin
Shaoguan
7095
Xiamen
TAIWAN
7146
Hezhou
Pu'er
Yuxi 7181/2
7187
7155
Longchuan
7182
7181
Wuzhou
Zhaoqing
7201
Baise
7184/8
7186/7
GUANGZHOU
Nanning
7155
7155/60/68
He Kou
Yuli
Shenzhen
7184
7250
HONG KONG 7085
Pingxiang
Beihai
Fangchenggang
VIETNAM
Zhanjiang
Maoming
7250
HÀ NỘI
Xuwen 7160
Haikou
LAOS
7160/5
7165
Sanya

7000 MANZHOULI and QIQHAR - HARBIN

Chinese Railways, China Rail High Speed

km		K7092	K7058	Read Down / Read Up		K7057	K7091
0	...	1833	2027	↓ d.**Manzhouli** a. ↑	...	0752	0842
186	...	2103	2251	↓ d.Hailaer d. ↑	...	0701	0636
268	...	2211	0000	↓ d.Yakeshi d. ↑	...	0425	0511
396	...	|	0147	↓ d.Boketu d. ↑	...	0239	|
693	...	|	0608	↓ d. Qiqihar a. ↑	...	2231	|
776	...	|	0728	↓ d.Daqing d. ↑	...	2043	2238
935	...	0633	0923d	↓ a.**Harbin** d. ↑	...	1850x	2022

km	Unmarked trains prefix 'D'	7946 G	6904	112	G1262	G1247	6910	6912	7953 D	7956 G	6914	6918	6920	T48 C	9830
0	Qiqihar d.	0549	0600	0759n	0918n	0935n	1104	1151	1259	1342	1403	1520	1642	1853	1903
116	Daqing xi d.	0627	0650	0832	1003d	1014	1142	1241	1343	1415	1447	1610	1738	2005	1942
286	**Harbin** xi a.	0722j	0751j	0938j	1110j	1127	1237j	1348	1444j	1527j	1548j	1723j	1833j	2149j	2110

	T47 C	6901	6905	6907	7944 D	9129	7958 G	6909	6913	6915	6917	6923	G1248	7954
Harbin xi d.	0633	0700j	0830	1001j	1031j	1101	1136j	1216j	1257j	1418	1608j	1853j	1927	2005j
Daqing xi d.	0805	0815	0958	1046d	1128	1204	1227d	1307	1700	1540	1717	1948d	2019	2102
Qiqihar a.	0910	0903	1040	1128n	1222	1235n	1304n	1343	1442	1622	1754n	2033n	2050n	2139n

C – 🛏 1, 2 cl. Beijing(**T47/48**) - Qiqihar and v.v.

D – To/from Table **7023**.

G – To/from Table **7005**.

7005 HARBIN - SUIFENHE - GRODEKOVO - (VLADIVOSTOK)

Chinese Railways

km	K7023	402 2	A ③⑥	Read Down ⊡ Read Up	401 2	K7024	A ①④
0	1930	...	1930	d.**Harbin** dong a.	...	0620	0620
161	0026	...	0026	↓ d.Yimianpo d. ↑	...	0255	0255e
355	0331	...	0331a	d.Mudanjiang d.	...	2325	2325
548	0505	...	0505	↓ a.**Suifenhe** d. ↑	...	2056	2056
548	...	1000	1000	d.**Suifenhe** 🏛 a.	1714	...	1714c
569	...	0630	0630	↓ a.**Grodekovo** ◐ d. ↑	1043	...	1043
569	...	...	1115	d.**Grodekovo** ◐ a.	...	...	0415
766	...	...	1245	↓ a.Ussruiysk ◐ d. ↑	...	...	0240c
766	...	...	2241	d.Ussruiysk ◐ a.	...	...	1410
878	...	...	0100f	↓ a.**Vladivostok** ◐ d. ↑	...	...	1215

km		7961	7963	8501 k	7965	9127	8503	7946 G	9133	135	G707 H	8515	7956 G	G717 H	G3601
0	**Harbin** xi d.	..	...	0602	...	0623	0708j	0742j	1040	1130	1227	1445j	1547j	1706	2048
307	Mudanjiang a.	0638	0640	0812	0743	0823	0916	2046	1239	1322	1431	1615	1743	1904	2246
444	**Suifenhe** a.	0747	0743	...	0845	...	1025	...	...	...	...	1724	1852	2004	...

	G3602	8506	8508 m	7958 G	G714 H	8514	8518	136	G716 H	9154	8522	8526	7962	7964
Suifenhe d.	...	0631	...	0822	...	1046	1216	...	...	...	...	1810	1719	1920
Mudanjiang a.	0737	0744	0842	0936	1002	1200	1330	1345	1516	1643	1706	1919	1824	0946
Harbin xi a.	0927	0948j	1010j	1116j	1213	1352j	1504j	1544	1720	1855	1840j	2105	...	...

A – According to the Chinese timetable, twice a week there are through cars attached to trains **K7023/7024** and **401/402** that continue to Vladivostok.

G – To/from Table **7000**.

H – To/from Table **7015/20**.

a – ④⑦.

c – ②⑤.

e – ③⑥.

f – ①⑤.

k – Additional trips: 1348j, 1506j, 1838j, 1900j.

m – Additional trips: 1135j, 1244.

⊡ – These services do not appear on any Chinese online timetables.

◐ – Moscow time (GMT +3). Operator in Russia is **RZhD**.

7010 SHENYANG - DANDONG - PYONGYANG and DALIAN

China Rail High Speed, Chinese Railways

km	K27 A			K28 A	
0	0340	...	↓ d.**Shenyang** a. ↑	2207	...
84	0453	...	↓ d.Benxi d. ↑	2100	...
217	|	...	↓ d.Fengcheng d. ↑	|	...
277	0735	...	↓ a.**Dandong** d. ↑	1818	...
277	0935	...	↓ d.**Dandong** a. ↑	1623	...
282	1346	...	↓ d.Sinuiji 🏛 ⊗ a. ↑	|	...
506	1930	...	↓ a.**Pyongyang** ⊗ d. ↑	1010	...

km	7607 B	7742 E	G782	G8105 X	7743	7754 F	G395 X	G3677 X	G786 X	Unmarked trains prefix 'D'	7634 C	G3678 X	G8103 X	G788 X	7741	7737 D	G8106 X	G396 X	7753
0	0727	...	1021b	1430	0755	1300	1507n	1642	1907	↓ d.**Shenyang** a. ↑	0753	0844	0905b	1039b	1058	1225	1812b	1746n	...
76	0812	...	1058	1513	0828	1339	1531	1708	1946	↓ d.Benxi d. ↑	0720	0808	0816	1003	1018	1152	1715	1722	...
178	0850	...	1130	|	0906	1417	|	1746	2019	↓ d.Fengcheng dong d. ↑	0641	0727	0737	0930	0944	1114	|	|	...
223	0907	...	1147	1603	0929	1435	1514	1803	2036	↓ a.**Dandong** d. ↑	0623	0709	0719	0912	0920	1058	1625	1637	...
223	...	0758	...	...	0941	1447	...	...	...	↓ d.**Dandong** a. ↑	...	...	...	...	0908	1043	...	...	2035
371	...	0914	...	...	1047	1603	...	...	...	↓ d.Zhuanghe bei d. ↑	...	...	...	...	0752	0935	...	...	1933
517	...	1040	...	...	1210	1735	...	...	...	↓ a.**Dalian** bei d. ↑	...	...	...	...	0630	0832	...	...	1758

A – Beijing (**K27/28**) - Dandong ①③④⑥ (**6/5**) - Pyongyang and v.v.

B – Additional trips: 0531, 0755, 0836, 0917, 1137, 1154, 1211, 1300, 1522, 1558, 1617, 1722, 2022.

C – Additional trips: 0800, 0920, 0935**b**, 1023, 1055, 1329, 1401, 1425, 1456, 1724, 1828, 1842, 1926, 2002.

D – Additional trips: 1100, 1230, 1633.

F – Additional trips: 1154, 1558, 1654.

X – To/from Tables **7015/7020**.

⊗ – Korean Standard Time (GMT +9, 1 hour ahead of Chinese time). Times in North Korea are subject to confirmation.

7015 QIQHAR - HARBIN - SHENYANG - TIANJIN - BEIJING

China Rail High Speed, Chinese Railways

km	Unmarked trains prefix 'G'	952	3678 X	D24	238	912	1207 Y	902	D26 J	D74	D102	928	916	220	1247 Y	1238 J	3602	D30	D22	396 X	384	382	922	938	924	Z16 🛏	Z18 🛏
293	Qiqihar d.	...	...	...	...	...	...	...	...	...	...	0826n	...	...	0937	...	...	1258n	...	...	...	...	...	...	...	...	...
0	**Harbin** xi d.	...	...	...	...	0709	0806	0840	0910	...	0957	1008	1058	...	1133	1210	...	1448	ra	...	...	1526	1558	...	1656	2120	2133
**	Jilin d.	...	...	...	0758	|	|	|	|	1044	|	|	|	...	|	|	1453	|	1509	...	1600	|	|	...	|	|	|
**	Changchun d.	...	...	...	0841	|	|	|	|	1127	|	|	|	...	|	|	1536	|	1553	...	1643	|	|	...	|	|	|
240	Changchun xi d.	...	...	0650	|	0822	0919	0938	|	|	1128	1106	1204	...	1238	1316	|	1600	1605	...	1655	1627	1700	1729	1808	|	|
358	Siping dong d.	...	...	|	|	0850	|	|	1058	|	|	1135	|	...	|	|	|	|	1636	...	|	1655	|	1757	1837	|	|
538	**Shenyang** bei ♥ d.	0830	0852y	0853	0957	0937	1040	1046	1200	1242	1308	1229	1320	1327y	1353	1432	1650	1725	1731	1806n	1810	1749	1829	1843	1930	|	|
761	Jinzhou nan d.	|	|	1019	|	|	1218	|	1331	|	1433	|	|	|	|	1550	|	1844	|	1939	|	|	|	|	|	|	|
695	Fuxin d.	0917	0940	|	|	1033	|	|	1436	|	|	1318	|	|	|	|	|	|	|	2050	|	|	1919	1933	2020	|	|
926	Shanhaiguan d.	|	|	1131	|	|	1310	|	|	|	|	|	|	|	1603	|	|	2006	1957	|	|	2011	|	|	|	|	|
	Tianjin a.	|	|	|	|	|	1451x	|	|	|	|	|	|	1649	1730x	1836x	|	2158x	|	2217	2155x	2151x	|	|	|	|	|
1241	**Beijing** ♥ a.	1145z	1213z	1410	1359n	1312z	...	1332z	1715	1629	1830	1549z	1641z	1728n	...	...	1936z	...	2248	2252n	2241n	2229n	2151z	2222z	2244z	0724	0753

	D29	D21	383	381	913	395 X	1208 Y	3601	1237 J	915	D25 J	1248 Y	1275	933	917	237	901	D101	D73	3677 X	D23	919	921	955	Z17 🛏	Z15 🛏
Beijing ♠ d.	0634	0639	0648n	0754n	0916z	0945	...	0959z	...	1020z	1039	...	...	1206z	1345z	1430	1434z	1338	1241	1305z	1430	1626	1710	1806z	2115	2121
Tianjin d.	|	|	0726x	0845	|	1026	1038x	|	1050x	|	|	1229x	1408	|	|	|	|	|	|	|	|	|	|	|	|	|
Shanhaiguan d.	0922	0929	0913	1013	|	1158	|	|	1240	|	1328	1414	1545	|	|	|	|	1641	1525	|	|	|	|	|	|	|
Fuxin d.	|	|	|	|	1144		|	|		1254		|		|	|	|	|	|	|	1539	|	1909	1943	2041	|	|
Jinzhou nan d.	1023	1040	|	1121	|	1304	1321	|	|	|	1437	|	|	|	|	|	|	1752	1621	|	1808	|	|	|	|	|
Shenyang bei ♠ d.	1158	1211	1146	1300	1240	1445n	1439	1247	1511	1344	1610	1640	1503	1530	1716	1830	1722	1910	1752	1626y	1940	1958	2036	2127	|	|
Siping dong d.	|	1337	1240	1353	|	...	|	|	1604	1437	|	1734	|	1619	|	|	|	2003	1851	...	2041	|	|	...	|	|
Changchun xi d.	1333	|	|	1423	1400	...	1600	|	1632	1505	1745	1803	1913	1645	1823	|	1830	2036	|	...	2112	2106	2151	...	|	|
Changchun a.	|	1415	1314	|	|	...	|	1401	|	|	|	|	|	...	|	1943	|	|	1928	...	...	|	|	...	|	|
Jilin a.	|	1458	1354	|	|	...	|	1441	|	|	|	|	|	...	|	2027	|	|	2012	...	...	|	|	...	|	|
Harbin xi a.	1439	r	...	1533	1456	...	1656	...	1736	1616	1854	1909	2024	...	1920	...	1926	2141	...	...	...	2203	2248	...	0712	0725
Qiqihar a.	1630n	...	...	...	...	...	...	...	...	...	...	2050n	...	...	...	...	...	...	...	...	...	...	...	...	...	...

7020 QIQIHAR - HARBIN and JILIN - SHENYANG - DALIAN

China Rail High Speed

km	All trains prefix 'G'	8070	8002	8046	8004	702	9148	8006	8048	704	706	782 X	8248	8008	8128 ta	8050	708	766	8010	8052	8054	710	8012	768	8056	8105 X
	Qiqihar nan d.	...	...	...	...	...	...	...	...	...	...	0558	...	...	...	...	...	0713	...	...	...	...	...	1002	...	...
0	**Harbin** xi d.	...	...	...	...	0616	...	...	...	0703	0728	0754	...	...	...	...	0904	0916	...	...	...	1038	...	1133h	...	...
**	**Jilin** d.	...	...	...	0610	|	...	...	...	|	|	|	...	0848	0903	...	|	|	...	...	...	|	...	|	...	1213
**	Changchun d.	...	0602	...	0653	|	...	0728	...	|	|	|	...	0932	0946	...	|	|	1036	...	...	|	...	|	...	1256
240	Changchun xi d.	...	|	...	0704	0722	...	0740	...	0815	0828	0859	...	0945	1001	...	1011	1021	|	...	...	1143	1211	1214	...	|
358	Siping dong d.	...	0637	...	0737	|	...	0809	...	|	0903	0927	...	1014	1029	...	1039	1049	1119	...	...	|	|	1312	...	|
538	**Shenyang** bei d.	0635	0742y	0821y	0824y	0841y	0858y	0906y	0912	0930	0950	1018	1046	1107y	1126y	1122	1132	1146	1213	1239y	1311y	1305y	1327	1403y	1422	1430y
638	Anshan xi d.	0724	0814	0900	0906	|	0932	0938	|	1019	1040	...	1116	|	1159	|	1216	1231	1249	|	1355	|	|	|	|	...
715	Yinkou dong d.	|	0836	|	|	|	|	1001	|	|	|	...	1140	1209	|	|	|	1300	1312	|	|	1359	1430	|	|	...
921	**Dalian** bei a.	0850	0935	1020v	1031	1034	1108	1100	1120v	1143	1155	...	1233	1301	1333v	1346v	1346	1400	1424v	1452v	1522v	1452	1541v	1601	1622v	...

All trains prefix 'G'	714 M	8022	752 J	770	8130	764	718 J	8016	754 J	8058	720	8018	8020	8184	724	786 X	8066	772 J	8024	716 M	730	8126 t	722	728	D122 J
Qiqihar nan d.	...	...	...	...	...	...	...	...	...	...	...	...	...	...	...	1505	...	...	...	...	...	...	1613	...	...
Harbin xi d.	1219	...	1231h	1308	...	1329	1340	...	1406	...	1425	...	...	...	1540	1629	...	1649	...	1723	1749	...	1815	1832	2120
Jilin d.	|	1238	|	|	1336	|	|	1406	|	...	|	1447	1545	...	|	|	...	|	1718	|	|	1816	|	|	|
Changchun d.	|	1321	|	|	1419	|	|	1452	|	...	|	1530	1628	...	|	|	...	|	1802	|	|	1903	|	|	|
Changchun xi d.	1323	|	1357	1412	|	1439	1445	|	1511	...	1530	1548	|	...	1647	1740	...	1748	1815	1835	1854	|	1927	1932	2227
Siping dong d.	1351	|	|	1446	1454	1507	1521	1527	|	...	|	1616	1704	...	|	1809	...	1816	1850	1903	|	1939	2002	2000	...
Shenyang bei d.	1438	1455y	1513	1537	1547	1605y	1612y	1620	1630	1634y	1645	1714y	1803	1749y	1810y	1907y	1926y	1921y	1944	2001y	2012	2037y	2053y	2054	...
Anshan xi d.	|	1527	...	|	1631	1644	1651	1702	...	1713	1729	|	|	1821	1855	...	|	1953	|	2039	2055	2116	|	2138	...
Yinkou dong d.	|	1550	...	|	1652	...	|	1723	...	|	|	1815	1849	|	|	...	|	|	|	2108	2117	2138	|	2200	...
Dalian bei a.	1629	1655v	...	1715	1745	...	1806	1823	...	1835	1852	1934v	1942	1935	2010	...	2140v	2115	2133	2202	2217	2232	2248	2253	...

NOTES for Tables **7015**, **7020**.

J – To/from Table **7023**.

M – To/from Table **7005**.

X – To/from Table **7010.**

Y – To/from Table **7105.**

r – To Tumen bei arr 1706.

ra – From Tumen bei dep. 1300.

ta – From Tumen bei. dep. 0700.

t – From Tumen bei dep. 1606.

v – Dalian.

y – Shenyang.

z – Beijing Chaoyang.

** – Changhcun *0 km* - Jilin 111 km - Siping dong *130 km.*

♥ – Additional services **Shenyang** bei – **Beijing** and v.v.

b – bei. d – dong. n – nan. x – xi. j – Harbin.

DALIAN - SHENYANG - JILIN and HARBIN — 7020

China Rail High Speed

All trains prefix 'G'	8041	701	8001	703	771 J	8103 X	8003	705	8125 t	707 M	47	788 X	8045	8005	709	8007	711	8009	8049	713	8011	3721	8013	8051
alian bei ... d.	0538	0549	0624	0644	0650	...	0700	0728	0733	0748	0830	...	0833v	0836	0919	0916v	0947	1023	1040v	1100	1108v	1114	1146v	1151v
inkou dong ... d.	|	0644	0731	0740	0751	...	0800	|	0844	|	|	...	0941	0931	|	|	|	|	|	|	|	1209	1255	1307
nshan xi ... d.	|	0706	0753	0802	0813	...	0829	|	|	0913	|	...	1003	|	|	|	|	|	1204	|	|	|	1318	1329
henyang bei ... d.	0758y	0753y	0826y	0852	0856	0908	0918	0931	0940y	0946y	1006	1038y	1051	1030	1112y	1131	1132y	1215y	1235	1251y	1311y	1304y	1356	1359
iping dong ... d.	...	|	0930	0938	0944	1001	1010	|	|	1049	|	1135	...	|	1208	|	1230	|	...	1348	1408	▬	1456	▬
hangchun xi ... d.	...	0911	|	1007	1013	|	|	1045	|	1116	1112	1204	...	|	1237	|	1259	|	...	1417	|	D121 J	|	D131 J
Changchun ... a.	...	|	1001	|	|	1032	1046	|	1113	|	|	|	...	1150	|	1258	|	1340	...	|	1441	1447	1537	1925↓
Jilin ... a.	...	|	...	|	|	1116	1126	|	1153	|	|	|	...	...	|	1338	|	1420	...	|	1522	|	1617	1840
arbin xi ... a.	...	1015	...	1110	1131	...	...	1142	t	1222	1206	1317	...	...	1341	...	1356	...	...	1513	...	1601	...	2034
iqihar nan ... a.	...	...	...	...	...	...	...		...	...	...	1445	...	...	...	...	1554	...	...	...	...	...	...	...

All trains prefix 'G'	717 M	719	8015	753 J	8053	733 J	8127 ta	8017	8055	725	765	8057	8106 X	8019	767	8059	9147	729	8067	769	8023	731	8069	8043
alian bei ... d.	1210	1240	1335	...	1353v	1412	1416v	1444v	1514v	1535	1547	1545v	...	1602v	1643	1646v	1712	1750	1805v	1841	1844	1903	1925	2051
inkou dong ... d.	|	1342	1430	...	|	1521	1531	|	1631	|	|	1654	...	|	1745	1754	1827	1859	|	|	1939	|	|	|
nshan xi ... d.	1334	|	|	...	1523	|	1553	|	|	1659	|	|	...	1731	1807	1816	1849	1921	1942	1910	|	|	2035	2208
henyang bei ... d.	1424	1445y	1523	1539	1553y	1622y	1628y	1651	1721	1742	1743y	1746y	1815	1817y	1901	1853y	1934y	2000y	2023	1949y	2051	2104	2122	2242
iping dong ... d.	1517	|	1609	1632	...	1713	1725	1744	...	1828	1833	...	1902	1913	1954	...	...	2050	...	|	|	2150	...	...
hangchun xi ... d.	1545	1617	1638	1700	...	1741	1754	1813	...	1856	1908	...	|	|	2022	...	...	2119	...	2100	2205	2218	...	...
Changchun ... a.	|	|	1654	|	...	|	1805	1826	...	|	|	...	1936	1948	|	...	...	|	...	|	2215	|	...	...
Jilin ... a.	|	|	1734	|	...	|	1848	1906	...	|	|	...	2017	2028	|	...	...	|	...	|	...	|	...	...
arbin xi ... a.	1650	1728	...	1816h	...	1838	ta	...	...	2000	2029x	...	...	...	2119	...	...	2216	...	2157	...	2315	...	...
iqihar nan ... a.	...	...	...	...	...	...	...	...	...	...	2154	...	...	...	...	...	...	...	...	...	...	...	...	...

– To/from Table **7023**. **M** – To/from Table **7005**. **X** – To/from Table **7010**. **t** – To Tumen bei a. 1404. **ta** – To Tumen bei a. 2050. **v** – Dalian. **y** – Shenyang.

HARBIN - JIAMUSI — 7023

China Rail High Speed

km	All trains prefix 'D'	9121	7803	7805	7807	7809	7813	9123	G771 K		7817	7819	7953 F		121 K	G1237 K	G753 K	G733 K	25 K	7829	131 K			
0	**Harbin** xi ... d.	0532	0702	0725	0805h	0909h	1047h	1132h	1135	...	1310h	1400h	1504h	...	1605	1740	1819h	1842	1858	1920h	2040	...	...	...
350	**Jiamusi** ... a.	0755	0942	1000	1039	1107	1303	1342	1357	...	1532	1558	1726	...	1827	2009	2042	2104	2121	2130	2244	...	...	...

All trains prefix 'D'	7802	7804		26 K	7944 F	9122	G1238 K	G752 K	7812	G718 K	G754 K		7816	9124	G772 K	7820	7954 F	7822		122 K			7828
Jiamusi ... d.	0518	0616	...	0639	0743	0852	0930	1006	1028	1102	1133	...	1323	1436	1423	1613	1705	1807	...	1854	...	...	2029
Harbin xi ... a.	0746h	0838h	...	0901	1011h	1108h	1152h	1228h	1250h	1327	1400	...	1522	1707	1646	1841h	1945	2005h	...	2116	...	...	2226h

– To/from Table **7000**. **K** – To/from Tables **7015/20**. **h** – Harbin.

BEIJING - TAIYUAN - YUNCHENG — 7025

China Rail High Speed

km		G601		G627	G91	G603	G605	G607	G609		G683		D2003	G613		G615	D2005	G681	G791	G621	G623	G629	G625	
0	**Beijing** xi ... d.	0722	...	0805	0840	1010	1028	1114	1133	...	1219	...	1316	1410	...	1503	1529	1658	1802	1807	1841	1923	2005	...
281	Shijiazhuang ... d.	0853	...	0934	|	1134	1156	1245	1254	...	1416	...	1514	1538	...	1636	1722	1820	1924	1940	2020	2105	2115	...
384	Yangquan bei ... d.	|	...	1030	|	|	1238	|	1339	...	|	...	1555	1620	...	1718	1810	|	2007	2022	2103	|	|	...
513	**Taiyuan** nan ... d.	1015	...	1124	1107	1256	1347	1407	1425	...	1538	...	1650	1706	...	1804	1902	1942	2053	2110	2153	2228	2237	...
746	Linfen xi ... d.	...	...	1252	...	...	1522	...	...	...	...	...	1824	...	...	...	2044	...	...	...	...	...	...	...
869	**Yuncheng** bei ... d.	...	...	1337	...	...	1615	...	...	...	...	...	1917	...	...	...	...	...	...	...	...	...	...	...

	G602	G604	G792	G630	G92	G682	D2002	G610	D2004	G612		G684	G616	G618	G620	G622		G628	G624		G626		
uncheng bei ... d.	...	...	...	...	...	...	...	...	0810	...	...	...	1153	...	...	...	...	1417	...	...	...	...	...
infen xi ... d.	...	...	...	...	...	...	0740	...	0904	...	...	...	1240	...	...	...	...	1511	...	...	...	...	...
aiyuan nan ... d.	0642	0700	0802	0824	0833	0841	0927	1100	1109	1136	...	1332	1429	1458	1524	1649	...	1707	1807	...	1928	...	...
angquan bei ... d.	|	|	0852	|	|	|	1021	|	1158	1231	...	1423	1518	1546	1614	1737	...	1758	|	...	2018	...	...
hijiazhuang ... d.	0815	0827	0934	0959	|	1009	1102	1229	1251	1314	...	1505	1605	1629	1658	1822	...	1843	1934	...	2105	...	...
eijing xi ... a.	0935	0956	1053	1122	1100	1141	1252	1403	1501	1436	...	1633	1727	1741	1817	1943	...	2025	2057	...	2232	...	...

DATONG - TAIYUAN - XI'AN — 7035

Chinese Railways

km	All trains prefix 'D'	2501 A	1901	2567 D	2561	2583	2563	2581	1903	2565	2525	2527 E
	Datong nan ... d.	...	...	...	...	0743	...	1050	...	...	...	...
0	**Taiyuan** nan ... d.	0700	0720	0750	0935	1025	1215	1316	1433	1501	1627	1720
233	Linfen xi ... d.	0819	0840	|	1055	1215	|	|	|	1636	|	|
356	Yuncheng bei ... d.	0906	0930	|	1142	|	|	1539	1656	1715	|	1933
579	**Xi'an** bei ... a.	1032	1042	1132	1308	1413	1548	1658	1815	1828	1945	2059

All trains prefix 'D'	2504	2582	2566 C	2518 B	2904	2524	2562	2584	2568 F	2564	1906
Xi'an bei ... d.	0808	0915	1155	1257	1215	1450	1622	1650	1811	1821	1935
Yuncheng bei ... d.	0826	|	1311	|	|	|	1751	|	1934	1951	2055
Linfen xi ... d.	|	1131	1405	|	1433	1641	1838	|	|	|	2141
Taiyuan nan ... a.	1148	1305	1531	1647	1559	1808	1956	2025	2148	2155	2251
Datong nan ... a.	...	1644	...	...	...	...	...	2248	...	...	...

– Additional trips: 0825, 1208, 1237, 1620, 1753. **C** – Additional trips: 0741, 1107, 1206, 1315, 1327. **E** – Additional trips: 0628, 0814, 0928, 1025, 1745, 1845.
– Additional trips: 0720, 0845, 1004, 1129, 1520. **D** – Additional trips: 0800, 1131, 1521, 1553, 1909. **F** – Additional trips: 1045, 1415, 1526, 1709, 1724, 1750, 1907.

XI'AN - LANZHOU — 7040

China Rail High Speed

km	All trains prefix 'D'	2671 Z	2701 Z	2685 Z	311 V	2737 Z	2567 Y	G437 X	2657	2561 Y	G1970 V	2673 Z	G671 X	1874 V	3180 V	2695 Z	2563 Y	G96 W	G1713 X	G429 X	G852 W	2697 Z	3164 V	2565 Y	3184 V	G2095 X	G844 W
0	**Xi'an** bei ♥ ... d.	0735	0800	0900	0943	1026	1136	1106	1206	1315	1323	1340	1402	1423	1501	1551	1556	1635	1624	1629	1645	1710	1814	1834	1910	1924	2120
167	**Baoji** nan ♥ ... a.	0836	0811	|	1034	1123	1233	|	1303	1410	1420	1443	1459	1516	1601	1648	1657	↓	1730	1733	1738	1807	1911	1931	2007	2032	|
568	**Lanzhou** xi ♥. a.	1102	1057	1141	1247	1335	1446	1338	1509	...	1641	1654	...	1734	1812	1907	...	1916	1940	1954	2002	2021	2125	2147	2220	2242	2354

All trains prefix 'D'	G672 X	G834 W	3166 V	2566 Y	3186 V	G430 X	2688 Z	G2096 X	G846 W	G1972 V	3182 V	G854 W	G1876 V	2682 Z	2562 Y	2672 Z	G438 X	G674 X	2722 Z	2738 Z	2568 Y	2564 Y	2666	D27086 Z	312 V	2674 Z
anzhou xi ♥ ... d.	...	0813	0830	0847	0900	0954	1003	1018	1036	1049	1108	1105	1159	1230	...	1316	1429	...	1545	1625	1458	...	1528	2016	1709	1738
aoji nan ♥ ... d.	0830	1034	1043	1054	1115	1214	1224	1239	1252	1302	1321	1315	1416	1450	1516	1543	|	1621	1808	1818	1712	1722	1743	2223	1929	2000
i'an bei ♥ ... a.	0930	1129	1140	1149	1208	1315	1320	1335	1347	1403	1420	1410	1520	1546	1617	1638	1657	1720	1903	1913	1807	1817	1838	2313	2023	2101

– To/from Table **7070**. **W** – To/from Table **7068**. **X** – To/from Table **7088**. **Y** – To/from Table **7035**. **Z** – To/from Table **7120**. ♥ – Additional services available.

HARBIN - TIANJIN and BEIJING — 7047

Chinese Railways

km	Z188 ♦	K28 ♦	T122 ♦	Z238 ♦	T48 ♦	Read Down ↓ / Read Up ↑	K27 ♦	T47 ♦	Z237 ♦	T121 ♦	Z187 ♦
0	...	...	...	2139	2204x	d.**Harbin** ... a.	...	0618	0648x	...	...
242	...	...	2128	|	|	d.Changchun ... a.	...	|	|	0649	...
546	...	...	0012	0159	0257	a.**Shenyang** bei .. d.	...	0129	0233	0400	...
546	1725	2224y	0019	0205	0303	d.**Shenyang** bei .. a.	0320y	0121	0225	0327	0530
934	2309	0304	0406	|	|	d.Shanhaiguan ... d.	2242	|	|	2301	2327
235	0300	0649	0801	0750	|	a. **Tianjin** ... d.	1909	|	2039	1934	2013
249	...	0840	...	...	0944	a.**Beijing** ... d.	1727	1855	...	...	...

BEIJING - HOHHOT - LANZHOU — 7050

Chinese Railways

km	K55	Z311	K41	Z179 ♦	K888	Read Down ↓ / Read Up ↑	Z180 ♦	K887	K42	Z312	K56
665	0248	...	2045	2104x	2343	d.**Beijing** ... a.	0955x	1125	1945	...	0422
485	0610	...	0010	0030	0306	d.Zhangjiakou ... d.	0628	0748	1606	...	0103
307	0909	...	0303	0322	0602	d.Datong ... d.	0355	0504	1326	...	2227
180	1052	...	0517	0507	0743	d.Jining nan ... d.	0155	0237	1133	...	2036
0	1236	1728h	0700	0622	0929	d.**Hohhot** dong ... d.	0040	0103	0939	1332h	1904
165	1505	1940	0908	0819	1219	d.Baotou ... d.	2246	2259	0730	1153	1644
383	...	2204	1124	1034	1454	d.Linhe ... d.	2014	2034	0439	0929	...
838	...	0512	1824	1648	2226	d.Zhongwei ... d.	1421	1439	2153	0205	...
1095	...	|	2213	2012	|	a. **Wuwei** ... d.	1034	|	1800	|	...
1562	...	|	0330	0047	|	a. Jiayuguan ... d.	0544	|	1214	|	...
970	...	0723	...	...	|	d.Jingtai ... d.	...	1217	...	2323	...
1057	...	0852	...	...	|	d.Beiyin xi ... d.	...	1040	...	2129	...
1144	...	1052	...	...	0522	a.**Lanzhou** xi ... d.	...	0827	...	1945	...

27/28 – Beijing (**K27/28**) - Dandong ①③④⑥ (**6/5**) - Pyongyang and v.v.
47/48 – 1, 2 cl.Qiqihar (**T48/47**) - Beijing.
121/122 – Changchun (**T122/21**) - Tianjin (**T123/24**) - Guangzhou and v.v.

Z179/180 – Beijing (**Z178/180**) - Urümqi and v.v.
Z187/188 – Shenyang bei (**Z188/87**) - Tianjin (**Z185/86**) - Shenzhen and v.v.
Z237/238 – Harbin (**Z238/37**) - Tianjin (**Z235/36**) - Guangzhou and v.v.

h – Hohhot.
y – Shenyang.

7060 BEIJING - ZHENGZHOU - WUHAN - CHANGSHA- GUANGZHOU - SHENZHEN

China Rail High Speed

km	All trains prefix 'G'		93	551	541	423	485	403	73	71	531	529	279	83	81	421	79	405	65	545	305	553	549	2055	401	533	67
						D						D				D											
0	**Beijing** xi	d.	...	...	...	...	0703	0800	...	0726	...	0834	...	0855	0900	0905	1000	1005	1033	...	1057t	...	...	...	1143	1302	1405
281	Shijiazhuang	d.	...	...	...	0753	0831	0909	...	0858	0914	0947	...	1005	1010	1034	1109	1125	1159	...	1232	...	...	1226	1309	1411	1514
496	Anyang dong	d.	...	...	...	|	|	|	0945	|	|	|	...	|	|	1135	|	1233	1303	...	|	...	...	1331	|	|	|
595	Xinxiang dong	d.	...	...	...	0932	|	|	|	|	|	|	...	|	|	|	|	|	|	...	|	...	...	1406	1437	|	|
663	**Zhengzhou** dong	d.	0757	...	0825	0959	1026	1033	1043	1056	1106	1114	1123	1129	1134	1221	1234	1320	1351	1405	1411	...	1417	1432	1509	1535	1640
799	Luohe xi	d.	|	0756	0901	1036	|	|	1125	|	|	|	1213	|	|	1305	|	|	1426	1456	|	...	1502	1515	|	|	|
960	Xinyang dong	d.	|	0850	0948	1123	1145	|	|	|	1310	|	|	|	|	1352	|	1430	1507	|	|	1522	1600	1558	1625	|	|
1136	**Wuhan**	a.	0958	0945	1039	1207	1229	1220	1256	1314	1413	1303	1346	1316	1321	1436	1420	1518	1605	1631	1600	1621	1648	1643	1717	1723	1828
1345	Yueyang dong	d.	|	|	|	1320	1331	|	|	|	1511	|	1448	|	|	1535	|	|	1704	1730	1652	1719	1746	|	|	|	|
1483	**Changsha** nan	d.	1120	1125	1208	1353	1406	1344	1419	1439	1550	1424	1525	1437	1447	1609	1545	1640	1740	1808	1730	1757	1824	1813	1853	1845	1950
1523	Zhuzhou xi	d.	|	|	|	...	...	...	|	|	|	...	|	...	...	...	|	...	1758	1825	|	1814	|	1830	...	...	|
1632	Hengyang dong	d.	1159	1214	1247	...	...	...	|	|	1629	...	|	...	...	...	|	...	|	1854	1809	1843	1904	1859	...	...	|
1894	Shaoguan	d.	|	1322	1359	...	...	...	|	1621	|	...	1706	...	...	...	|	...	|	|	|	1952	2012	2007	...	...	|
2104	**Guangzhou** nan	a.	1350	1426	1456	...	...	...	1704	1717	1834	...	1818	...	...	...	1805	...	2024	2053	2959	2048	2107	2103	...	...	2212
2206	**Shenzhen** bei	a.	...	1500	...	...	...	...	1745	1805f	1915	...	1859	...	...	...	...	...	...	...	...	...	2139	...	...	...	...

All trains prefix 'G'		69	547	503	505	D901	D903	D909	D921	D927	D923
						A	A	A	C	A	A
Beijing xi	d.	1307	...	1441	1540	2010	2015	2020	2030	2025	2035
Shijiazhuang	d.	1448	...	1606	1703	2134	2140	2145	2201	2156	2206
Anyang dong	d.	|	...	1659	|	2236	|	|	|	|	|
Xinxiang dong	d.	|	...	|	|	|	|	|	|	|	|
Zhengzhou dong	d.	1620	1651	1744	1857	|	|	|	|	|	|
Luohe xi	d.	|	|	1826	|	|	2332	2337	2347	2342	2352
Xinyang dong	d.	|	1815	|	|	|	|	|	|	|	|
Wuhan	a.	1821	1910	1949	2059	|	|	|	|	|	|
Yueyang dong	d.	1917	2006	|	2158	|	|	|	|	|	|
Changsha nan	d.	2002	2049	2114	2232	|	|	|	|	|	|
Zhuzhou xi	d.	|	2106	...	...	|	|	|	|	|	|
Hengyang dong	d.	2041	2135	...	...	|	|	|	|	|	|
Shaoguan	d.	2146	2243	...	...	|	|	|	|	|	|
Guangzhou nan	a.	2242	2339	...	...	0628	0633	0638	0653	0659	0643
Shenzhen bei	a.	...	...	...	...	0706	0711	0716	...	0740	...

All trains prefix 'G'		534	502	84	276	94	72	2056	280	82	80	74
Shenzhen bei	d.	...	...	...	...	...	0701f	...	0926	...	0826	0841
Guangzhou nan	d.	...	...	...	0648	0737	0747	0805	0815	...	0900	0922
Shaoguan	d.	...	...	...	|	0830	0840	0858	0908	...	|	|
Hengyang dong	d.	...	...	...	0837	|	0951	|	|	...	|	1123
Zhuzhou xi	d.	...	...	...	0906	|	|	|	1036	...	|	|
Changsha nan	d.	0710	0736	0900	0929	1019	1037	1044	1102	1138	1120	1207
Yueyang dong	d.	0745	|		1005	|	1118	|	|	|	|	1253
Wuhan	d.	0838	0911	1020	1110	1152	1217	1209	1230	1258	1241	1349
Xinyang dong	d.	0930	|	|	1158	|	1302	|	|	|	|	1434
Luohe xi	d.	|	|	|	|	|	|	1334	|	|	|	1521
Zhengzhou dong	d.	1047	1103	1208	1312	1343	1458	1411	1416	1447	1429	1602
Xinxiang dong	d.	1110	1132	|	...	...	|	...	...	|	|	...
Anyang dong	d.	1137	|	|	...	...	|	...	...	|	|	...
Shijiazhuang	d.	1246	1258	1332	...	...	1703	...	...	1614	1554	...
Beijing xi	a.	1419	1424	1441	...	...	1822	...	...	1721	1701	...

All trains prefix 'G'		552	66	542	404	532	306	68	422	486	402	424	506	70	554	544	530	406	546	76	548	D922	D924	D902	D904	D910	D928
									D			D					D					C	A	A	A	A	A
Shenzhen bei	d.	...	...	...	...	0945	...	...	...	...	...	...	...	...	1326	...	...	...	...	1546	...	...	...	1934	1945	1950	1955
Guangzhou nan	d.	0932	1000	0943	...	1025	1050	1117	...	...	...	...	...	1250	1408	1356	...	...	1413	1626	1621	2005	2010	2015	2020	2025	2030
Shaoguan	d.	|	|	|	...	1119	|	1210	...	...	...	...	...	1343	|	|	...	...	|	1726	|	|	|	|	|	|	|
Hengyang dong	d.	1133	|	|	...	|	1237	|	...	...	...	1414	...	1500	1602	1557	...	...	1617	|	1824	|	|	|	|	|	|
Zhuzhou xi	d.	1206	|	|	...	|	|	1340	...	...	...	|	...	|	|	|	...	...	1649	|	|	|	|	|	|	|	|
Changsha nan	d.	1230	1220	1235	1302	1307	1322	1402	1422	1427	1446	1501	1507	1538	1652	1647	1657	1703	1713	1915	1920	|	|	|	|	|	|
Yueyang dong	d.	|	|	|	|	|	1357	1437	|	|	|	1536	1541	|	1731	1722	|	1742	1748	|	2006	|	2303	|	2313	2318	2323
Wuhan	d.	1352	1341	1358	1425	1455	1450	1534	1601	1611	1621	1639	1644	1707	1944	1841	1822	1836	1846	2041	2105	|	|	|	|	|	|
Xinyang dong	d.	1447	|	1443	|	1540	|	1619	1647	1656	1707	1724	1729	1752	2037	1927	|	|	1938	2126	2150	|	|	|	|	|	|
Luohe xi	d.	...	|	1530	|	|	|	1706	1719	1737	1755	1804	1809	|	2130	|	|	|	2019	2206	|	|	|	|	|	|	|
Zhengzhou dong	d.	...	1528	1617	1612	1653	1639	1753	1806	1814	1834	1841	1848	1914	...	2041	2013	2030	2100	2247	2304	|	|	|	|	|	|
Xinxiang dong	d.	...	|	...	|	|	|	|	|	|	1856	1908	|	|	...	...	|	|	...	...	...	|	|	|	|	|	|
Anyang dong	d.	...	|	...	|	|	1735	1847	|	1857	1924	1951	1935	1957	...	...	|	|	...	...	...	|	|	|	|	|	|
Shijiazhuang	d.	...	1653	...	1735	1843	1816	1950	1938	2000	2040	2051	2045	2100	..	...	2139	2206	...	...	...	0518	0523	0528	0533	0544	0550
Beijing xi	a.	...	1800	...	1846	...	1948t	2110	2053	2126	2159	...	2204	2227	...	...	2247	2318	...	...	...	0640	0651	0656	0701	0713	0718

A – Conveys 🛏 1cl, 🚃2 Runs ①⑤⑥⑦ only.
C – ①⑤⑥⑦ 🛏 1cl, 🚃2 Beijing - Zhanjiang and v.v.
D – To/from Table **7184**.
f – Shenzhen Futian.
t – Time at Tianjin xi NOT Beijing.

7061 BEIJING - ZHENGZHOU - WUHAN

China Rail High Speed

km	All trains prefix 'G'		507	309	801	511	487	517	491	587	557	555	805	587	521	573	585	561	525	563	527	565	509	567	807	4867
0	**Beijing** xi ♣	d.	0636	0818	0915	0927	1052	1158	1233	1448	1107	1256	1330	1448	1523	1618	1623	1653	1714	1719	1814	1828	1900	1916	2000	2219
281	Shijiazhuang	d.	0816	0956	|	1049	1206	1348	1355	1611	1222	1406	|	1611	1652	1747	1758	1815	1837	1848	1936	1953	2009	2038	|	2353
496	Anyang dong	d.	0917	1112	|	1204	|	|	|	1718	|	|	|	1718	1753	|	1905	1925	1937	1955	|	2115	|	|	|	|
595	Xinxiang dong	d.	|	|	|	1232	|	|	1543	1753	1359	|	|	1753	|	1903	1933	1953	|	2023	|	2143	|	|	|	|
663	**Zhengzhou** dong ♣	d.	1010	1157	1203	1256	1337	1540	1613	1817	1431	1530	1555	1817	1847	1929	2000	2014	2029	2037	2107	2204	2134	2232	2225	0130
799	Luohe xi	d.	|	|	...	1337	|	|	|	1911	1507	|	...	1911	1936	|	2044	...	2111	...	|	...	|	...	...	|
960	Xinyang dong	d.	1129	|	...	|	|	|	1721	1951	1645	|	...	1851	2030	2044	2126	...	2158	...	|	...	|	...	...	|
1136	**Wuhan**	a.	1220k	1349k	...	1500k	1528	1737	1810	2101k	1753	1725h	...	2101k	2121	2128	2211	...	2250	...	2255	...	2324k	...	...	0340

All trains prefix 'G'		802	520	562	508	564	510	588	512	586	556	572	514	556	806	518	488	516	524	310	486	808	492	528	406
Wuhan	d.	...	0700k	...	0716	...	0810	0830	0921k	1042	1045k	1031	0953	1040k	...	1245	1246	1330	1520	1610k	1611	...	1726	1759	1836
Xinyang dong	d.	...	|	...	0801	...	0855	|	1014	|	1137	1116	|	1134	...	1341	|	|	1614	|	1656	...	1812	1844	|
Luohe xi	d.	...	|	...	0848	...	0953	|	|	|	1225	1203	1148	|	...	|	|	|	1655	|	1737	...	|	|	|
Zhengzhou dong ♣	d.	0800	0854	0919	0932	0948	1034	1017	1132	1231	1310	1240	1248	1312	1400	1453	1434	1518	1734	1824	1814	1908	1924	2006	2036
Xinxiang dong	d.	|	|	|	|	|	1057	|	|	|	1333	|	|	1334	|	|	|	|	|	|	|	|	1947	|	|
Anyang dong	d.	|	|	|	|	1034	|	|	1222	|	1409	1331	1339	1409	|	|	|	|	1824	1915	1857	|	|	|	|
Shijiazhuang	d.	|	1018	1110	1116	1140	1219	|	1324	1401	1522	1426	1448	1522	|	1634	1559	1642	1919	2017	2000	|	2117	2156	2206
Beijing xi ♣	a.	1025	1126	1232	1228	1314	1339	1242	1456	1521	1646	1554	1609	1646	1626	1746	1706	1750	2043	2146	2126	2135	2242	2322	2318

k – Wuhan Hankou.
♣ – Additional services operate Beijing – Zhengzhou and v.v.

7062 BEIJING - BADALING - ZHANGJIAKOU - HOHHOT - BAOTOU

China Rail High Speed

km	All unmarked trains prefix 'G'		7871	2403	2503	2481	2505	8883	2483	2409	2507	2411	8885	2415	2419	8813	2485	2425	8815	2515	2487	2435	2437	2521	2443	2523
							A					C														
0	**Beijing** bei ⊖	d.	...	0715	0810	0818	...	0851	...	0909	...	...	...	1051	1118	1135	...	1322	...	...	1539	1720	1750	1840	1945	1938
11	Qinghe	d.	0610	0730	|	0833	0855	0906	0918	0924	0945	1009	1100	1105	1133	1150	1248	1337	1443	1510	1554	|	|	|	2000	1954
56	Badaling Changcheng ◇ ⊖	d.	|	|	|	|	|	0927	|	|	|	|	1129	|	|	1209	1308	|	1502	|		|	|	|	|	|
172	Zhangjiakou	d.	0657	0828	|	0930	0951	0901	1014	1028	1048	1113	▬	1208	1231	...	1350	1435	...	1612	1651	|	|	|	2104	205
338	Datong nan	d.	...	|	0956	|	1101	...	|	|	1151	|	**D6759**	|	|	...	|	|	...	1723	|	|	|	2026	|	2159
333	Ulanqab	d.	...	0924	...	|	...	...	|	|	...	1207	▶	|	1327	...	|	1525	...	...	|	|	|	...	2154	...
459	**Hohhot** dong	a.	...	1001	...	1102h	...	...	1149h	1155	...	1244	1312	1344	1404	...	1521h	1602	...	...	1827h	1933	2007	...	2231	...
632	Baotou	a.	...	...	...	1220	...	...	1254	...	...	...	1430	...	...	...	1627	...	...	...	1940	...	2111	...	...	...

		D6770	2502	2404	2504	2408	2482	8884	8812	2484	2508	2412	2516	2418	8886	2486	2424	8888	2434	2432	8818	2518	2488	2490	2520	244
		▶	B	D																						
Baotou	d.	0622	...	...	...	...	0729	...	...	0820	...	...	...	...	...	1310	...	...	...	...	...	...	1403	1742	...	...
Hohhot dong	d.	0732	...	0717	...	0800	0833	...	...	0931h	...	1021	...	1222	...	1421h	1406	...	1625	1620	...	...	1515h	1900h	...	2033
Ulamqab	d.	▬	...	0758	...	|	|	...	...	|	...	1100	...	|	...	|	1445	...	|	|	...	...	1558	|	...	211
Datong nan	d.	**7872**	0706	|	0820	|	|	...	...	|	1018	|	1531	|	...	|	|	...	|	|	...	1715	|	|	1801	|
Zhangjiakou	d.	0720	0809	0846	|	|	|	...	...	110	1129	1151	1642	1357	...	1547	1542	...	1807	|	...	|	1649	2033	1904	220
Badaling Changcheng ◇ ⊖	d.	|	|	|	|	|	|	1003	1034	|	|	|	|	|	1547	|	1622	1734	1847	|	1958	|	|	|	|	|
Qinghe	d.	0816	0910	0946	|	|	|	1029	1056	1202	1229	1247	1738	1454	1607	1651	1644	1756	1909	|	2018	|	1749	2129	2010	225
Beijing bei ⊖	a.	0830	...	...	1005	1012	1049	...	1109	...	...	1301	1752	1508	...	1704	1658	1809	1923	1832	...	1900	...	2143	2024	231

A – Additional trips: 1032, 1300, 1400, 1610.
B – Additional trips: 1121, 1228, 1334, 1900.
C – Additional trips: 0800, 1027, 1232, 1346, 1625, 1656, 1735, 1818.
D – Additional trips: 1055, 1320, 1354, 1439, 1709, 1939, 1948, 2003.
h – Hohhot.

▶ – Regular high-speed services run throughout the day.
⊖ – Suburban services (Line S2) operate between Beijing Huangtudian and Badaling. Journey time: 1hr 30 min
From Beijing Huangtudian at 0655, 1033, 1403, 1430 ⑤–① and 1729.
From Badaling at 0830, 1042 ⑤–①, 1206, 1535 and 1859.
◇ – Badaling Changcheng station is right under the Great Wall.

China Rail High Speed — WUHAN - CHANGSHA - GUANGZHOU - SHENZHEN — 7065

km	All trains prefix 'G'	6011	6101	6013	6015	6029	1001	1003	1005	1107	77	6041	1013	1009	6031		1035	85	1113	813	1031	1117	1168	1148
																		A						
	Yichang dong d.	...	...	...	...	...	...	...	...	...	...	...	...	...	...	...	0735	...	...	...	0837	...	0916	0937
0	**Wuhan** ♥ 7060 d.	...	...	...	...	...	0722	0755	0812	0826	0900	...	0930	1007	...	...	1022	...	1027	1059	1126	1145	1201	1148
209	Yueyang dong d.	...	...	...	...	0724	│	│	0910	0937	│	...	1028	│	...	...	1134	...	1119	1200	1235	1243	│	1323
347	**Changsha** nan ♥ d.	0700	0716	0728	0755	0809	0854	0930	0947	1016	1022	1010	1107	1131	1155	...	1221	1227	1203	1237	1314	1320	1346	1402
387	Zhuzhou xi d.	│	0733	│	0812	0826	│	│	│	1036	│	│	1124	│	│	...	│	│	│	1254	│	│	1403	│
496	Hengyang dong d.	│	│	0807	0841	0902	0933	│	│	1105	│	1059	1153	│	│	...	│	│	│	│	1353	1410	1432	1444
758	Shaoguan d.	0840	│	0915	│	1003	│	│	│	│	│	│	│	│	1338	...	1412	│	1343	│	│	│	│	1549
968	**Guangzhou** nan ♥ a.	0949	1006	1011	1049	1106	1131	1201	1224	1310	1246	1305	1407	1402	1436	...	1509	1451	1441	1526	1602	1625	1637	1647
070	**Shenzhen** bei ♥ a.	1035	...	1051	1133	1138	1214	1247	1308	...	1321	1347	1445	1435	1520	...	1557	...	...	1608	1643	...	...	...

ll trains prefix 'G'	1013	6001	1015	6003	1017	1301	275	1311	1127.	1309	6117	1183	695	1021	1025	99	1315	1151	6027	1133	6025	1305	1747
						A										A						A	
ichang dong d.	...	...	...	...	...	...	...	...	...	...	...	...	...	...	...	...	1430	...	...	...	...	...	...
Vuhan ♥ 7060 d.	1206	...	1340	...	1439	...	1504	1512	1529	1546	...	1626	...	1658	1713	...	1728	1745	...	1757	...	...	1905
ueyang dong d.	1258	...	│	...	1530	...	1603	│	1620	1647	...	1724	...	1756	1820	...	1826	1836	1847	│	...	...	1957
hangsha nan ♥ d.	1336	1500	1510	1555	1607	1612	1639	1644	1701	1725	1747	1802	1829	1840	1900	1900	1905	1915	1925	1931	2039	2045	2051
huzhou xi d.	1353	│	│	│	│	│	1656	1701	│	│	1804	1819	│	│	│	│	│	1932	│	1948	2056	2106	│
engyang dong d.	1422	│	1553	1634	1646	1651	│	│	│	1804	1833	1848	1909	1919	1939	│	1944	│	2011	2017	2125	2135	2130
haoguan d.	│	│	1701	│	1754	1759	1820	│	│	1925	1942	2000	2017	2027	2047	2037	2056	│	│	│	│	2243	2238
uangzhou nan ♥ a.	1620	1724	1755	1844	1851	1856	1922	1935	1940	2029	2037	2058	2113	2123	2143	2132	2153	2158	2219	2224	2325	2340	23335
henzhen bei ♥ a	1702	1800	1828	1920	1931	...	...	2020	...	2114	...	...	...	2158	2222	...	...	...	2252	...	2358	...	...

l trains prefix 'G'	1408	696	1316	1744	1022	6058	86	1312	1184	1004	6182	6004	6030	1006	1110	1040	6028	6016	1010	100	1026	6186	6018
							A													A			
henzhen bei ♥ d.	...	...	...	...	0658	0708	...	0724	...	0820	0845	0913	0919	0930	...	1027	...	1054	1124	...	1130	...	1152
uangzhou nan ♥ d.	0608	0613	0637	0658	0732	0754	0800	0810	0836	0905	0927	0954	1005	1010	1031	1100	1112	1142	1159	1205	1205	1210	1233
haoguan d.	│	│	0730	│	0825	0852	│	0903	0929	│	1020	1053	1059	1104	│	│	1205	│	│	1258	1258	1303	│
engyang dong d.	0802	0818	0842	0859	│	│	│	│	1044	1106	1128	1155	1200	│	│	1254	1306	1343	│	│	│	│	│
huzhou xi d.	0838	0859	0911	│	│	│	│	│	│	│	│	│	│	│	│	1323	│	1416	│	│	1421	│	1459
hangsha nan ♥ d.	0901	0923	0934	0950	1013	1036	1023	1050	1126	1148	1233	1237	1246	1252	1312	1347	1347	1435	1438	1434	1443	1445	1520
ueyang dong d.	...	0958	1010	1042	1048	...	...	1125	1201	│	...	...	1319	│	│	1422	...	...	│	...	1522	...	...
Vuhan ♥ a.	...	1059	1109	1143	1138	...	...	1216	1251	1320	...	...	...	1417	1432	1523	...	...	1559	...	1624	...	...
chang dong a.	...	...	1333	...	...	...	...	...	...	...	...	...	...	...	...	...	...	...	...	...	...	...	...

ll trains prefix 'G'	6034	1304	1032	78	6020	6146	6022	1146	1128	6062	1306	1028	1036		1014	6050	6160	1020	1134	1136	1002	6042	6032
		A									A												
henzhen bei ♥ d.	1157	...	1238	1342	1403	1409	1414	...	...	1445	...	1505	1515	...	1520	1604	1609	1625	...	...	1703	1725	2005
uangzhou nan ♥ d.	1238	1347	1319	1434	1445	1450	1455	1500	1500	1533	1538	1543	1549	...	1601	1643	1653	1705	1720	1730	1745	1800	2055
haoguan d.	1338	1428	│	1527	1538	1543	1552	│	│	│	│	1636	1642	...	1654	│	│	1758	1813	1823	1838	│	2148
engyang dong d.	│	1536	│	│	1646	1651	1702	1657	1656	│	│	1744	1750	...	1802	1849	1901	1906	1921	1931	1946	2001	│
huzhou xi d.	1509	│	│	│	│	1728	│	│	│	│	1754	│	1819	...	1831	│	│	│	│	2000	2015	2030	2318
hangsha nan ♥ d.	1532	1617	1611	1708	1727	1707	1749	1743	1742	1755	1812	1831	1842	...	1853	1931	1942	1950	2006	2023	2042	2048	2337
ueyang dong d.	1605	...	1648	│	...	...	1822	1818	1817	...	...	1913	│	...	1928	...	...	2026	2041	2058	2125	...	...
Vuhan ♥ a.	...	...	1749	1827	...	...	...	1910	1925	...	...	2003	2015	...	2021	...	...	2117	2131	2149	2215	...	...
ichang dong a.	...	...	2020	...	...	...	...	2143	...	...	...	2235	2245	...	...	...	...	...	...	...	...	...	...

– To/from Table **7192**. **N** – To/from Table **7146**. **P** – To/from Table **7186**. ♥ – Additional services operate Wuhan/Changsha – Guangzhou/Shenzhen and v.v.

China Rail High Speed — XI'AN - ZHENGZHOU - WUHAN - CHANGSHA- GUANGZHOU — 7068

km	All trains prefix 'G'	850	98	820	824	834	838	828	876	846	854
						H				H	H
0	**Xi'an** bei d.	...	1001	0948	1117	1140	1243	1303	1324	1352	1415
121	Huashan bei d.	...	│	│	│	│	1313	1333	1400	│	1446
257	Sanmenxia nan d.	...	│	1050	│	1231	│	│	│	│	1514
380	Luoyang Longmen d.	0741	│	1123	1236	1304	1408	1427	1454	1524	1548
520	**Zhengzhou** d.	0838	1150	1202	1315	1350	1447	1510	1536	1617	1636
713	Luohe xi d.	0959	│	1255	1401	1444	│	│	│	1704	1732
895	Xinyang dong d.	1046	│	1339	1452	│	1613	│	1703	1752	1834
050	**Wuhan** d.	1134	1351	1427	1540	1616	1704	1740	1750	1844	1925
259	Yueyang dong d.	1225	│	1518	1632	1714	1802	1831	│	1938	...
397	**Changsha** nan d.	1303	1515	1600	1711	1752	1845	1910	1915	2023	...
437	Zhuzhou xi d.	│	│	│	│	1809	│	│	│	│	...
546	Hengyang dong d.	1343	│	1639	1750	1838	1924	1941	2006	2105	...
808	Shaoguan d.	1451	│	│	1858	1947	2032	│	│	2213	...
'018	**Guangzhou** nan a.	1547	1736	1839	1955	2043	2128	2148	2208	2309	...
'120	**Shenzhen** bei a.	...	...	1925	2044	...	...	2238	...	...	...

All trains prefix 'G'	852	832	96	878	818	822	836	844	868	826
	H		H					H		
Shenzhen bei d.	...	...	...	...	0930	0955	...	...	...	1248
Guangzhou nan d.	...	0703	0855	0842	1015	1036	1127	1223	...	1330
Shaogun d.	...	│	│	│	1109	│	1220	1316	...	1423
Hengyang dong d.	...	0911	│	1051	│	1243	1322	│	...	1531
Zhuzhou xi d.	...	│	│	│	│	│	1351	1453	...	│
Changsha nan **7065** d.	...	0956	1115	1132	1257	1327	1412	1517	...	1616
Yueyang dong d.	...	1032	│	1216	│	1402	1447	1553	...	│
Wuhan d.	1147	1128	1236	1323	1435	1500	1545	1651	1701	1748
Xinyang dong d.	│	1213	│	│	1520	1552	1630	1737	1758	1834
Luohe xi d.	1317	│	│	1445	│	│	1718	│	│	1928
Zhengzhou d.	1408	1351	1439	1543	1654	1718	1803	1914	1930	2027
Louyang Longmen d.	1456	1437	│	1634	1733	1809	1851	1953	2016	2106
Sanmenxia nan d.	1529	1510	│	│	│	│	│	│	│	2145
Huashan bei d.	1604	│	│	1728	│	│	│	2048	2118	│
Xi'an bei **7070** a.	1632	1601	1626	1802	1903	1932	2014	2116	2153	2235

– To/from Lanzhou (Table **7040**).

China Rail High Speed — XI'AN - ZHENGZHOU - XUZHOU - NANJING - SHANGHAI and HANGZHOU — 7070

km	Prefix 'G' unless noted	1914	362	1918	1922	1972	1938	1976	1942	D308	D312
				F		H		G			H
										🛏	🛏
0	**Xi'an** Bei d.	0628	0851	0938	1037	1405	1510	1515	1553	1935	2023
121	Huashan bei d.	│	│	1008	│	1436	1540	1545	│	2024	│
257	Sanmenxia nan d.	0728	│	│	│				1651	2109	│
380	Luoyang Longmen d.	0801	│	1102	1204	1531	1634	1639	│	2148	2202
523	**Zhengzhou** dong d.	0843	1042	1147	1250	1622	1715	1720	1805	2245	2253
713	Shangqiu d.	│	│	1246	1348	1721	│	1818	1914	│	│
883	**Xuzhou** dong d.	1033	1220	1346	1446	1828	1853	1920	2016	0038**p**	0046**p**
039	Bengbu nan d.	│	│	1425	│	1913	│	2013	│	│	│
214	**Nanjing** nan d.	1201	1337	1509	1609	1956	2011	2057	2157	0338**f**	0344**f**
344	Changzhou bei d.	1239	│	│	1643	2037	│	│	2230	0442**c**	0448**c**
428	Suzhou bei d.	1310	│	1615	1715	│	2123	2202	│	0528**g**	0534**g**
509	**Shanghai** Hongqiao a.	1341	1445	1645	1739	2126	2146	2225	2323	0620**h**	0626**h**

Prefix 'G' unless noted	1970	1975	361	1920	1928	1932	1937	1940	D311	D306
	H	G		E					H	
									🛏	🛏
Shanghai Hongqiao d.	0610	0717	0836	0924	1255	1344	1612	1706	2244**h**	2250**h**
Suzhou bei d.	0635	0743	│	│	│	1420	1637	│	2331**g**	2337**g**
Changzhou bei d.	0659	0814	│	1014	│	1444	1705	│	0019**c**	0025**c**
Nanjing nan d.	0739	0849	0946	1051	1431	1532	1741	1821	0149**f**	0155**f**
Bengbu nan d.	0823	0941	│	1145	│	│	│	│	│	│
Xuzhou dong d.	0907	1025	1106	1225	1616	1700	1901	1943	0522**d**	0528**d**
Shangqiu d.	│	1129	│	│	│	│	│	2029	│	│
Zhengzhou dong d.	1110	1222	1240	1414	1808	1834	2052	2137	0716	0722
Luoyang Longmen d.	1148	1300	│	│	1847	│	2132	│	│	0807
Sanmenxia nan d.	│	│	│	1525	│	1937	2205	2242	│	0846
Huashan bei d.	1249	1355	│	1554	│	2008	│	│	0902	0920
Xi'an Bei a.	1318	1442	1429	1622	2004	2036	2255	2332	0943	1003

km	1896	3166	3186	3188	3182	1876	1880		All trains prefix 'G		1878	1874	3180	1882	3164	3184	1894
		H	H	B	H	H						H	H		H	H	D
0	0845	1143	1210	1235	1420	1525	1629	↓	d.**Xi'an** Bei a.	↑	1301	1423	1501	1540	1814	1910	1856
21	0919	1213	1240	1307	1451	1555	1659		d.Huashan bei d.		│	1350	1425	│	1735	1829	1824
257	│	│	│	│	│	│	1727	↓	d.Sanmenxia nan d.	↑	1209	│	1356	1448	│	│	│
380	1013	1314	1343	1402	1451	1649	│		d.Luoyang Longmen d.		1136	│	1323	1415	│	1734	│
523	1059	1356	1425	1452	1638	1737	1844	↓	d.**Zhengzhou** dong d.	↑	1058	1217	1245	1337	1553	1651	1657
713	1158	1447	1528	1547	1731	1839	1946		d.Shangqiu d.		1001	1113	1136	1230	1442	1547	1603
393	1254	1551	1632	1651	1835	1934	2051	↓	a.Fuyang xi d.	↑	0850	1012	1032	1137	1340	1444	1506
029	1329	1640	1715	1733	1917	2009	2133		d.Huainan nan d.		0806	│	0941	1058	1246	1400	1429
133	1412	1712**h**	1755	1815	1949**h**	2103	2211	↓	a.**Hefei** nan d.	↑	0725	0854	0912	1017	1317**h**	1319	1348
290	│	1808	...	│	2012	│	...		a.Nanjing nan d.		...	│	0807	│	1120	...	│
420	│	1908**c**	...	│	│	│	...	↓	d.Changzhou bei d.	↑	...	│	0731	│	1043	...	│
504	│	1942**g**	...	│	2219	│	...		d.Suzhou bei d.		...	│	0707	│	1009	...	│
585	│	2015	...	│	2243	│	...	↓	a.**Shanghai** Hongqiao a.	↑	...	│	0642	│	0944	...	│
303	1458	...	...	1854	...	2149	...		d. Wuhu d/		...	0804	...	0933	...	...	1301
573	1637	...	...	2030	...	2317	...	↓	a. **Hangzhou** dong d.	↑	...	0628	...	0742	...	...	1119

km	3298	3172	3294		All trains prefix 'G		3171	3293	3297
	A								
0	0912	1047	1248	↓	d.**Xi'an** Bei a.	↑	1832	1927	2200
121	0950	│	1318		d.Huashan bei d.		│	1859	│
257	1018	│	│	↓	d.Sanmenxia nan d.	↑	│	│	│
380	1052	1209	1412		d.Luoyang Longmen d.		1645	1757	2030
523	1137	1257	1502	↓	d.**Zhengzhou** dong d.	↑	1606	1719	1950
713	1237	1406	│		d.Shangqiu d.		1502	1625	1848
883	1340	1518	1634	↓	a.**Xuzhou** dong d.	↑	1414	1532	1756
1087	1445	1623	1739		d.Huai'an dong d.		1305	1417	1646
1196	1528	1659	│	↓	d.Yancheng d.	↑	1230	│	1612
	│	│	1827		d. Jiangdu d.		│	1326	│
1397	1623	1754	1951	↓	d.Natong xi d.	↑	│	1155	│
1561	1739	1915	2116		a.**Shanghai** Honggiao d.		1017	1036	1358

– Additional trip: 1450. **D** – Additional trip: 0943. **F** – Additional trip: 1230. **G** – To/from Table **7132.** **c** – Changzhou. **g** – Suzhou. **p** – Xuzhou.
– Additional trip: 1342. **E** – Additional trip: 1134. **H** – To/from Lanzhou Table **7040**. **f** – Nanjing. **h** – Shanghai.

7085 BEIJING, SHANGHAI and GUANGZHOU - SHENZHEN and HONG KONG

GUANGZHOU DONG - SHENZHEN via Dongguan — China Rail High Spee

High-speed '**C**' trains (**C70xx** and **C71xx**). *139 km.* Journey 70 minutes. Trains call at **Dongguan** 34–37 minutes after Guangzhou dong and 28–32 minutes after Shenzhen. *Also calls at Guangzh

Guangzhou dong depart: 0600, 0608, 0618*, 0627, 0636*, 0648, 0657*, 0705, 0715, 0734*, 0748, 0800, 0822, 0833, 0844*, 0853, 0906, 0913*, 0936, 0944, 0952, 1009, 1017, 1033, 1041, 104 1055, 1102, 1110, 1120, 1137, 1145, 1201, 1209, 1225, 1232, 1200, 1310*, 1318, 1334, 1345, 1353, 1402*, 1410, 1418, 1429, 1430, 1456, 1504, 1513, 1520, 1530*, 1536, 1546, 1612, 1619, 164 1655, 1705, 1715, 1723, 1735, 1743, 1752*, 1810, 1819, 1828*, 1837, 1853, 1900, 1909*, 1917, 1925, 1933*, 1941, 2006, 2014, 2030, 2038*, 2050, 2101*, 2116, 2126, 2152, 2205, 2234*.

Shenzhen depart: 0612, 0640*, 0647, 0702, 0710*, 0720, 0730, 0742, 0800*, 0809, 0821, 0830, 0840*, 0854, 0903, 0915, 0924, 0933, 0955, 1007, 1014, 1023, 1039, 1058, 1106, 1113, 1125, 11 1152, 1202, 1211, 1218, 1229, 1237*, 1245, 1255, 1308, 1316, 1333*, 1341, 1355, 1408, 1418, 1430, 1439*, 1447, 1507, 1515, 1523, 1531, 1540*, 1552, 1602, 1620*, 1626, 1638, 1644, 1656, 170 1717, 1726, 1740*, 1749, 1802, 1818*, 1827, 1837, 1846*, 1858, 1906, 1918, 1925, 1940*, 1950, 1958, 2010, 2023, 2032*, 2041, 2054, 2103, 2116, 2142, 2154, 2203, 2219, 2227, 2237.

GUANGZHOU NAN - SHENZHEN BEI — China Rail High Spee

High-speed '**G**' trains (**G60xx, 61xx, 62xx, G63xx, G89XX**)*102 km.* Journey 29 - 44 minutes.

Guangzhou nan depart: 0704, 0711, 0729, 0735, 0745, 0750, 0800, 0813, 0859, 0905, 0915, 0928, 1011, 1046, 1052, 1102, 1119, 1130, 1140, 1150, 1201. 1231, 1232, 1240, 1252, 1304, 13 1339, 1344, 1354, 1359, 1440, 1450, 1455, 1510, 1541, 1551, 1546, 1646, 1705, 1803, 1813, 1818, 1905, 1949, 1954, 2016, 2031, 2036, 2049, 2058, 2121, 2230.

Shenzhen bei depart: 0715, 0816, 0821, 0837, 0847, 0858, 0902, 0914, 0925, 0950, 1031, 1043, 1053, 1103, 1108, 1145, 1150, 1155. 1200, 1233, 1322, 1347, 1404, 1409, 1414, 1429, 1434, 14 1552, 1620, 1632, 1652, 1729, 1805, 1820, 1829, 1836, 1842, 1847, 1857, 1902, 1914, 1919, 1929, 2012, 2026, 2041, 2046, 2056, 2107, 2129, 2212, 2225, 2250, 2300.

GUANGZHOU NAN - SHENZHEN BEI - WEST KOWLOON (HONG KONG) — China Rail High Speed, MTR Corporatio

High-speed '**G**' trains (**G65xx**)*142 km.* Journey 55 – 75 minutes. ** Non-stop Journey 47 minutes. Trains call at **Shenzhen** 39 – 52 minutes after Guangzhou and 19–24 minutes after West Kowlo

Guangzhou nan depart: 0648, 0723, 0808, 0819, 0831, 0836, 0949, 1000**, 1027, 1041, 1114, 1124, 1155, 1215, 1226, 1314, 1349, 1410, 1500, 1525, 1633, 1652, 1735**, 1742, 1831, 2132

West Kowloon depart: 0825, 0910, 0938, 1005**, 1036, 1052, 1115, 1153, 1226, 1251, 1325, 1354, 1509, 1514, 1613, 1618, 1657, 1709, 1735**, 1839, 1900, 1930, 2002, 2054, 2220, 225

For long distance services beyond Shenzhen bei see Table 7065.

GUANGZHOU - KOWLOON — MTR Corporation

km			Z801	Z811	Z815	Z807	Z803	Z817	Z809	Z805	Z819
0	**Guangzhou** dong........... d.	...	0819	0930	1037	1203	1404	1538	1733	1933	2040
82	Dongguan (Changping).... d.	...	0903	1014	1121	|	1448	1622	1817	2018	2124
174	**Kowloon** Hung Hom ...... a.	...	1017	1128	1233	1356	1602	1734	1931	2133	2236

		Z814	Z806	Z802	Z812	Z816	Z808	Z804	Z818	Z810
Kowloon Hung Hom .... d.	...	0800	0924	1052	1223	1311	1432	1635	1805	2001
Dongguan (Changping) .... d.	...	0910	1036	1204	|	1421	1544	1747	1915	2113
Guangzhou dong........................ a.	...	0957	1123	1251	1417	1508	1631	1834	2002	2200

BEIJING & SHANGHAI - KOWLOON — Chinese Railway

	Z97	Z99
	A	B
Beijing xi .... d.	1240	...
Shanghai.............. d.	|	1745
Kowloon Hung Hom . a.	1301	1301

	Z100	Z9
	A	B
Kowloon Hung Hom d.	1515	15
Shanghai........... a.	1037	|
Beijing xi............... a.	...	15

Note: Trains make no intermediate passenger stops.

A – Odd dates in (2020): Feb., Apr., May, Aug., Nov., Dec. Even dates in (2020): Jan., Mar., June, July, Sept., Oct.

B – Odd dates in (2020): Jan., Mar., June, July, Sept., Oct. Even dates in (2020): Feb., Apr., May, Aug., Nov., Dec.

7086 BEIJING - TIANJIN

China Rail High Spee

As well as the long distance high-speed **G** services {shown on Tables **7097**, **7100**, **7102**} frequent high-speed intercity trains (numbered **C2xxx**) operate the *120 km* journey between Beijing a Tianjin in 30 – 37 minutes. Services operate at least every 15 minutes from approximately 0600 to 2300.

7088 BEIJING - ZHENGZHOU - XI'AN

China Rail High Spee

km	437	89	671	571	307	1713	87	429	2095	1293	679	25		All trains prefix 'G'
	K	H	K	H	H	K		K	K				↓	
0	0626	0653	0749	0922	0938	0935t	1400	1045	...	1519t	1731	1855		d.**Beijing** xi ♣........a.
281	0741	0802	0930	1044	1054	1141	|	1211	1519	1658	1853	2004		d.Shijiazhuang........d.
496	|	|	|	1157	1212	1257	|	1313	|	|	|	|	↓	d.Anyang dong.......d.
595	|	|	|	1225	1240	1336	|	1341	1649	|	|	|		d.Xinxiang dong .....d.
663	0914	0932	1127	1254	1311	1409	1631	1408	1714	1852	2059	2132	↓	d.**Zhengzhou** dong d.
788	|	|	1212	|	1349	1447	|	1447	1752	1932	2137	|		d.Luoyang Longmen d.
947	|	|	1245	1339	|	|	|	|	|	|	|	|	↓	d.Sanmenxia nan ... d.
1047	|	|	1325	1435	|	1542	|	1549	1848	|	|	|		d.Huashan bei........d.
1168	1105	1124	1402	1503	1543	1624	1819	1626	1924	2050	2300	2320	↓	a.**Xi'an** Bei ♣ ....d.

All trains prefix 'G'		26	672	2096	658	430	88	574	1294	308	438	674	9
	↑		K	K		K		H		H	K	K	H
d.**Beijing** xi ♣........a.		1350	1511	...	1826	1853	1755	1954	1726t	2038	2142	2309	22
d.Shijiazhuang........d.		1241	1345	1735	1708	1726	1648	1827	1540	1905	2030	2149	21
d.Anyang dong.......d.	↑	|	|	|	1606	|	|	1718	1438	1803	|	|	|
d.Xinxiang dong .....d.		|	1201	1607	1525	1602	|	|	|	1735	|	|	|
d.**Zhengzhou** dong d.	↑	1111	1139	1545	1503	1540	1523	1627	1345	1713	1854	1946	20
d.Luoyang Longmen d.		|	1057	1504	1417	1447	|	1543	1259	1629	|	1903	|
d.Sanmenxia nan ... d.	↑	|	|	|	|	|	|	|	|	|	|	1830	|
d.Huashan bei........d.		|	|	1407	1323	1349	|	1441	1158	1532	|	1802	|
a.**Xi'an** Bei ♣ ....d.	↑	0920	0933	1337	1253	1319	1332	1410	1128	1455	1703	1724	18

H – To/from Table **7132**. K – To/from Table **7040**. t – Time at Tianjin xi not Beijing. ♣ – Additional services operate Beijing – Xi'an and v.v.

7090 BEIJING and TIANJIN - WUHAN - NANCHANG and GUANGZHOU

Chinese Railway

km	Z235	T123	Z49	Z161	Z3	Z201	Z1	Z95	Z167	Z285	Z137	T289		
	♦	♦	C	♦	C	♦		C	♦	♦	♦	♦	↓	
0	...	...	1128	1155	1748	1754	1800	1806	...	2108	...	2200		d.**Beijing** xi...........a.
	0758	0824	|	|	|	|	|	|	...	|	...	|	↓	d. **Tianjin**............a.
281	1147	1236	1405	1426	2019	2025	2031	2037	...	2340	...	0055		d.Shijiazhuang........d.
689	1558	1704	1736	1810	|	2356	0002	0008	0151	0309	0447	0457	↓	d.Zhengzhou..........d.
1225	2058	2323	2200h	2313	0411h	0441	0447	0432h	0701	0757	0953	1054		d.**Wuhan** Wuchang d.
1587	0022	0256	...	0259	...	0810	0810	...	1040	1117	1323	1414	↓	d.Changsha............d.
1772	0222	0455	...	...	...	|	...	...	1237	...	1525	...		d.Hengyang............d.
2297	0830d	1048	...	...	...	1542	...	...	1851d	...	2117	...	↓	a.**Guangzhou** ....d.

		Z138	Z202	Z162	Z2	Z50	Z4	Z96	Z286	T290	T124	Z236	Z1
	↑	♦	♦	♦		C	C	C	♦	♦	♦	♦	♦
d.**Beijing** xi...........a.		...	0646	0652	0816	1003	1011	1051	1703	1810	...	...	...
d. **Tianjin**............a.	↑	...	|	|	|	|	|	|	|	|	1925	2021	..
d.Shijiazhuang........d.		...	0414	0420	0545	0726	0731	0803	1433	1517	1542	1658	..
d.Zhengzhou..........d.	↑	0128	0047	0053	0158	0358	|	0411	1110	1122	1128	1254	164
d.**Wuhan** Wuchang d.		2026	2000	2006	2112	2327h	2332h	2340h	0618	0548	0518	0732	11
d.Changsha............d.	↑	1634	1622	1628	1734	...	...	...	0247	0153	0108	0354	07
d.Hengyang............d.		1411	|	...	...	...	...	...	...	...	2248	0144	044
a.**Guangzhou** ....d.	↑	0818	0840	...	...	...	...	...	...	...	1705	1949d	225

♦ – **NOTES** (by train number):

T123/124 – Changchun (**T122/121**) – Tianjin (**T123/124**) – Guangzhou and v.v.
Z137/38 – Urumqi (**Z136/35**) – Zhengzhou (**Z137/38**) – Guangzhou and v.v.
Z168/70 – Guangzhou dong (**Z168/67**) – Jinan (**Z169/70**) – Qingdao and v.v.
Z161/62 – Beijing (**Z161/62**) – Kunming and v.v. **Z201/02** – Beijing(**Z201/02**) – Sanya and v.v.
Z237/238 – Harbin (**Z238/37**) – Tianjin (**Z235/36**) – Guangzhou and v.v.
Z285/286 – Beijing (**Z285/286**) – Nanning and v.v.
T289/290 – Beijing(**T289/290**) – Nanning and v.v.

C – Beijing – Chongqing bei and v.v. **b** – Beijing. **h** – Hankou.

7095 BEIJING - NANCHANG - SHENZHEN

China Rail High Speed, Chinese Railway

km		D739	D733	D737	D727		K105	Z185	K1619	T127
		🛏	🛏	🛏	🛏			♦		♦
0	**Beijing** xi..............................d.	1822	1835	1947	1959	...	2318	...	...	...
	Tianjin ....d.	|	|	|	|	...	|	0312	2220	...
426	Liaocheng ....d.	2203	2211	|	2335	...	0422	0742	0335	...
582	Heze......................................d.	2314	2324	|	|	...	0555	0853	0508	...
687	Shangqiu nan ....d.	|	|	|	|	...	0720	1000	0627	...
855	Fuyang ....d.	0131	|	|	0302	...	0926	1154	0849	...
	Wuhan Wuchang..........d.	|	|	|	|	...	|	|	|	1536
1091	Macheng.................................d.	|	|	|	|	...	1208	1408	|	|
1314	Jiujiang ....d.	0522	0535	0627	|	...	1429	1613	|	|
1449	**Nanchang** ....d.	0638	0638	0734	0754x	...	1616	1735	1720	1941
1675	Ji'an.......................................d.	...	...	...	0959	...	|	1952	2011	|
1861	Ganzhou..................................d.	...	...	...	1149	...	2045	2139	2213	|
2102	Longchuan...............................d.	...	...	...	|	...	0018	|	0207	0251
2310	Dongguan dong ....d.	...	...	...	|	...	0315	0330	0450	0524
2372	**Shenzhen** ....a.	...	...	...	1724	...	0420	0430	0536d	...

		D738	D746	T128	K1620	D728	K106	D740	Z1
		🛏	🛏	♦		🛏		🛏	♦
Shenzhen ....d.	...	...	...	...	0826d	1417	1050	...	19
Dongguan dong ....d.	...	...	...	1140	0914	|	1157	...	20
Longchuan ....d.	...	...	...	1425	1155	|	1436	...	|
Ganzhou ....d.	...	...	...	1712	1523	2007	1739	...	02
Ji'an ....d.	...	...	...	1910	1746	|	|	...	04
Nanchang..............................d.	...	1951	2313	2156	2037x	0020	2222	1738	061
Jiujiang....................................d.	...	2052	|	|	2207	|	|	1845	07
Macheng ....d.	...	|	|	|	0058	|	|	2043	09
Wuhan Wuchang ....a.	...	|	|	0135	|	|	|	|	|
Fuyang.....................................d.	...	|	0408	...	0435	05150	0630	2249	11
Shangqiu nan ....d.	...	|	|	...	0655	|	0834	|	13
Heze ....d.	...	|	0623	...	0804	0730	0949	0108	14
Liaocheng.................................d.	...	|	0733	...	1009	0840	1131	0218	15
Tianjin..................................a.	...	|	|	...	1533	|	|	|	20
Beijing xi ....a.	...	0742	1113	...	...	1219	1627	0602	..

♦ – **NOTES** (by train number):

Z185/86 – Shenyang bei (**Z188/87**) – Tianjin (**Z185/86**) – Shenzhen and v.v.
T127/28 – Chengdu (**T126/25**) – Wuhan Wuchang (**T127/28**) – Dongguan dong and v.v.

7096 NANCHANG - GANZHOU

China Rail High Spee

km		5033	5035	5041	9801	5043	5045	5047	9803	5021	1461	1385
0	**Nanchang** xi .. d.	0817	0819c	1018	1241	1342	1427	1610c	1835	1905	1920	2123
226	Ji'an xi............d.	0914	0941	|	1338	|	1545	1718	1932	2016	2026	2220
418	Ganzhou xi.....d.	1002	1042	1231	1426	1554	1640	1829	2020	2110	2127	2308

	1386	5034	1462	5038	5022	9804	5044	5046	9802	5050	50
Ganzhou xi .....d.	0627	0809	0953	1108	1120	1327	1618	1802	1840	1919	21
Ji'an xi ....d.	0715	0857	1055	1156	1222	1415	1713	1904	1928	2021	22
Nanchang xi.. a.	0837	0958	1209	1312	1331	1510	1829	2023c	2023	2129	23

c – Nanchang.

China Rail High Speed — BEIJING - BENGBU - HEFEI — 7097

km	All trains prefix 'G'	1741	7421	345	2551	45	2553	2555	321	244	329	323	301	325	303	41	2557	2559	43	245	2563	2565		454
	↓			C		C			C	CD	C	C	C	C	C					D				D
0	**Beijing** nan ... d.	...	...	...	0634	0654	0721	0834	0847	...	...	1009	1026	1204	1153	1255	1404	1437	1556	...	1709	1853	...	...
122	Tianjin nan ... d.	...	...	...	0710	0727	|	|	0930	...	1030	|	|	1240	|	1328	|	|	|	...	|	|	...	...
406	Ji'nan xi ... d.	...	...	0648	0844	0829	0904	1032	1047	1104j	1152	1158	1210	1353	1348	1428	1546	|	1710	1613j	1851	2052	...	2138j
692	Xuzhou dong ... ◀ d.	0633	0703	0816	0956	0928	1030	1147	1155	1234	1304	1310	1335	1529	|	|	1659	1735	|	1752	2011	2212	...	2310
848	**Bengbu** nan ... d.	0712	0749	0901	1035	1004	|	|	1234	1320	1350	1405	1414	1608	1554	|	1737	1821	|	1845	2049	|	...	...
891	Huainan dong ... d.	0730	0807	|	1056	|	1127	|	1252	1338	|	|	1432	1626	|	|	|	1839	|	1903	2107	|	...	...
980	**Hefei** nan ... ◀ a.	0757	0856	0958	1124	1055	1213	1309	1331	1417	1447	1455	1459	1705	1653	1638	1827	1919	1931	1949	2146	2334	...	...

km	All trains prefix 'G'	453	246	2552	2554	2556	302	7428	2558	42	2560	2562	242	2564	322	330	324	7780	2566	304	326	46	348	44
	↓	D	D				C						CD		C	C	C			C	C	C	C	
	Hefei nan ... ◀ d.	...	0640	0704	0903	0942	1121	1130	1136	1141	1201	1254	1320	1331	1339	1412	1513	1606	1616	1639	1709	1855	1923	1958
	Huainan dong ... d.	...	0720	0744	0933	|	|	1227	|	|	1241	1334	|	|	|	|	1554	1634	1656	|	|	|	|	|
	Bengbu nan ... d.	...	0740	0803	|	1045	1214	1246	|	1233	1300	1356	1415	1423	1431	1504	1618	1653	1718	1739	1806	1947	2020	|
	Xuzhou dong ... ◀ d.	0635	0826	0848	1040	1127	1253	1324	1311	|	|	1443	1500	|	1522	1554	1707	1744	|	1818	1851	|	2116	|
	Ji'nan xi ... d.	0808j	0949j	0955	1154	1244	1420	...	1425	1400	1458	1558	1627j	1621	1637	1718	1827	...	1903	1932	2022	2114	2241	2211
	Tianjin nan ... d.	...	...	|	1310	|	1526	...	1531	|	|	|	...	|	|	1829x	1941	...	|	|	|	|	...	|
	Beijing nan ... a.	...	...	1144	1354	1435	1600	...	1605	1526	1648	1808	...	1754	1817	...	2016	...	2054	2114	2205	2240	...	2335

C – To/from Table **7193**. D – To/from Table **7105**. h – Hefei. j – Jinan. ◀ – Additional services Xuzhou – Hefei and v.v.

China Rail High Speed — BEIJING - TIANJIN - XUZHOU - NANJING - SHANGHAI and HANGZHOU — 7100

km	All unmarked trains 'G'	D2281	7349	1377	D3135	7291	101	103	1	105	109	3	111	113	5	263	115	117	119	7	121	232	267	123	123
		A	A	B	A																	Q			
0	**Beijing** nan ... d	...	...	...	...	...	0611	0620	0700	0717	0745	0800	0814	0839	0900	...	0910	0920	0945	1000	1005	...	...	1020	1046
122	**Tianjin** nan ... d.	...	...	...	...	...	0646	|	0733	|	|	|	|	|	|	0927x	|	0958	1001	|	|	...	1041x	|	1139
314	Dezhou dong ... d.	...	...	...	...	...	0732	|	|	|	0917	|	0932	1011	|	|	|	|	1047	|	|	...	1137	1146	1226
406	Ji'nan xi ... d.	...	...	...	...	...	0758	0801	|	0900	0944	0926	0959	1043	1025	1052	1056	1104	1115	1126	1148	1227j	1206	1214	1254
692	**Xuzhou** dong ... d.	...	...	...	...	0752	0920	0907	|	1025	1055	|	1121	1151	|	1206	|	1230	1239	|	|	|	1331	1340	|
848	Bengbu nan ... d.	...	...	...	...	0830	|	0956	|	|	|	|	|	|	|	|	|	|	|	|	|	|	|	|	|
1023	**Nanjing** nan ... d.	0632	0730	0739	0810	0929	1047	1040	1026	1147	1213	1125	1243	1314	1226	1337	1333	1346	1402	1326	1416	1500	1448	1505	1526
1153	Changzhou bei ... d.	0729c	0810	0819	0916c	1009	|	|	|	1221	|	|	1324	1354	|	|	|	1439	1436	|	|	|	1522	1539	1603
1237	Suzhou bei ... d.	0803g	0842	0852	1002g	1034	1145	|	|	|	1318	|	1348	1433	1312	1429	1425	|	1501	|	1507	|	|	|	|
1318	**Shanghai** Hongqiao ... a.	0845	0907	0922	1037	1109h	1209	1158	1129h	1303	1348	1231h	1411	1456	1337	1456h	1448	1502	1532	1435	1542	1609	1616	1626	1650
1477	Hangzhou dong ... a.	1006	1001	...	1210	...	...	...	...	...	...	...	...	...	...	...	1548	...	...	...	...	...	...	...	...

km	All unmarked trains 'G'	127	9	11	1227	137	13	141	15	143	269	228	147	17	G1202	19	21	161	23	25	27	D717	D703	D709	D705
												Q													
	Beijing nan ... d.	1105	1100	1200	...	1245	1300	1334	1400	1408	...	...	1427	1500	...	1600	1700	1733	1800	1804	1900	1918	1936	1946	2121
	Tianjin nan ... d.	1143	|	1233	1251x	|	1333	|	|	|	1446x	...	|	|	1540x	|	|	1809	1831	1837	|	|	2050	|	|
	Dezhou dong ... d.	1231	|	|	|	1412	|	1450	|	|	1540	...	1546	|	|	|	|	1855	|	|	|	2221	|	|	|
	Ji'nan xi ... d.	1258	1224	1335	1419	1438	1432	1518	1525	1551	1607	1631j	1616	1627	1702	1724	|	1923	1932	1938	|	|	|	|	|
	Xuzhou dong ... d.	|	1323	|	1456	1550	|	|	|	1703	1731	1758	1739	|	1829	|	|	2045	|	2036	|	|	|	|	|
	Bengbu nan ... d.	|	|	|	|	|	|	1719	|	|	|	1838	1825	|	1908	|	|	2124	|	|	|	|	|	|	|
	Nanjing nan ... d.	1540	1434	1535	1703	1708	1632	1802	1724	1832	1905	1931	1911	1826	1959	1926	2016	2147	2135	|	2213	0452f	0458f	0516f	0651f
	Changzhou bei ... d.	1615	|	|	1739	1802	|	1836	|	1906	1958	2011	1954	1857	2051	|	|	2244	|	|	|	|	|	|	|
	Suzhou bei ... d.	1640	|	|	1825	1833	|	|	1810	1943	2022	2043	2018	|	|	|	|	|	|	2226	|	|	0637g	|	|
	Shanghai Hongqiao ... a.	1712	1537	1638	1848	1856	1735h	1924	1833	2007	2053	2111h	2043	1934	2140	2028	2118	2332	2243	2249	2329h	|	0712n	0744h	0921h
	Hangzhou dong ... a.	...	...	...	1943	...	...	...	...	...	...	...	...	...	...	...	...	...	...	...	...	0854k	...	...	...

km	All unmarked trains 'G'	102	2	222	104	106	1232	6	112	8	262	1236	1204	118	10	122	12	1252	14	132	136	16	138	140	18
				Q																					
	Hangzhou dong ... d.	...	...	...	...	...	...	...	...	...	...	...	...	...	...	...	...	...	...	...	...	...	...	...	...
	Shanghai Hongqiao ... d.	0639	0700h	0705	0713	0722	0747	0800	0805	0900	0833	0904	0933	0943	1000	1034	1100	1110	1153	1221	1247	1255	1329	1334	1400
	Suzhou bei ... d.	|	|	0735	0739	0748	0827	|	0831	|	0859	0929	0958	1008	|	|	|	1135	|	1246	1312	1322	|	|	|
	Changzhou bei ... d.	|	0742	|	0803	0812	0851	|	0855	|	|	0953	1022	1043	|	1116	|	|	1239	|	1342	|	1411	|	|
	Nanjing nan ... d.	0804	0813	0828	0837	0850	0928	0902	0934	1001	1014	1034	1106	1125	1101	1156	1202	1238	1310	1350	1426	1408	1453	1512	1502
	Bengbu nan ... d.	0856	|	|	|	|	1021	|	|	|	|	|	|	1210	|	1250	|	|	|	1436	1517	|	1545	1555	|
	Xuzhou dong ... d.	0934	|	0943	1007	|	1115	|	1107	|	1140	1207	1244	1248	|	1330	|	1416	|	1528	1558	|	1631	|	1613
	Ji'nan xi ... d.	1042	1012	1054j	1122	1134	1228	1101	1220	1202	1307	1322	1353	1411	1300	1438	1402	1531	1510	1642	1704	1610	1743	1747	1711
	Dezhou dong ... d.	|	|	...	1149	1204	|	|	|	|	1333	|	1426	|	|	|	|	1557	|	1710	1733	|	|	|	|
	Tianjin nan ... d.	1156	|	...	1238	1248	1345x	|	|	|	1426x	1433x	1519x	|	|	1553	|	1657x	|	|	|	|	1857	1908	|
	Beijing nan ... a.	1239	1136	...	1312	1322	...	1224	1407	1327	...	...	...	1547	1426	1629	1531	...	1638	1831	1849	1736	1931	1942	1835

km	All unmarked trains 'G'	142	144	20	264	146	148	22	152	234	24	154	158	26	7292	28	D3136	7792	D718	1378	28	D702	D706	D710	D2282
										Q							A	A		B					A
	Hangzhou dong ... d.	...	...	...	...	...	...	...	...	...	...	...	1613	...	...	...	1640	1706	1725k	1828	...	...	...	...	2001
	Shanghai Hongqiao ... d.	1416	1443	1500	1507	1521	1542	1600	1619	1632	1700	1711	1721	1755	1743h	1900	1746	1829	|	1923	1900	1908h	2114h	2123h	2125
	Suzhou bei ... d.	1447	|	|	1532	|	1609	|	|	|	1723	|	1746	|	1819	|	1822g	1901	|	1948	|	|	|	2210g	2155g
	Changzhou bei ... d.	|	|	|	1556	1603	|	|	|	1714	|	|	1813	|	1850	|	1921c	1935	|	2019	|	|	|	|	2232c
	Nanjing nan ... d.	1537	1619	1601	1630	1636	1717	1701	1735	1749	1810	1827	1846	1906	1925	2002	2019	2019	2138f	2103	2002	2146f	2357f	0002f	2321
	Bengbu nan ... d.	|	1703	|	1714	1722	|	|	1819	|	|	|	|	|	|	|	...	2110	|	...	|	|	|	|	...
	Xuzhou dong ... d.	1655	1742	|	|	1801	1841	1812	1859	1915	|	1944	2021	|	2052	|	...	2154	|	...	|	|	|	|	...
	Ji'nan xi ... d.	1823	1854	1802	1859	1919	1955	1911	2036	2024j	2009	2058	2135	2110	...	|	...	...	|	...	|	|	|	|	...
	Dezhou dong ... d.	|	|	|	|	1945	2003	|	2104	...	|	2136	|	|	...	|	...	...	|	...	|	|	|	|	...
	Tianjin nan ... d.	|	2009	1903	2024x	2031	|	|	|	...	|	|	2241	|	...	|	...	...	0553x	...	|	|	0810x	|	...
	Beijing nan ... a.	2029	2045	1936	...	2105	2143	2037	2220	...	2133	2249	2314	2235	...	2318	...	...	0707	...	2318	0712	0924	0922	...

– To/from Table **7200**. Q – To/from Qingdao (Table **7105**). g – Suzhou. j – Jinan. **Note**: Additional services operate between Beijing/Tianjin/Nanjing and Shanghai/Hangzhou.
– To/from Table **7192**. c – Changzhou. f – Nanjing. h – Shanghai. k – Hangzhou.

China Rail High Speed — BEIJING -TIANJIN - NANJING - HANGZHOU - NINGBO — 7102

km	All trains prefix 'G'	1379	1503	1665	7609	171	1481	173	284	31	197	1675	1495	169	35	37	445	181	1223	183	187	1861	185	D2224	193	256	39
		B	B	B	A		B		Q		A	C	B							A				D		Q	
0	**Beijing** nan... d.	...	...	...	...	0630	...	0704	...	0756	0810	...	...	0938	0956	1056	...	1042	...	1249	1338	...	1320	...	1607	...	1904
122	Tianjin nan... d.	...	...	...	...	0706	...	|	...	|	|	...	...	1014	|	|	1055x	|	1201x	|	|	...	|	...	|	...	|
314	Dezhou dong .. d.	...	...	...	...	|	...	0829	...	|	0928	...	...	|	|	|	1150	|	1303	|	1454	1603	1446	...	1729	...	|
406	Ji'nan xi... d.	...	...	...	...	0818	...	0855	0928j	0922	0954	...	...	1134	1121	1220	1229	1239	1343	1443	1529	1713	1513	...	1755	1900j	|
692	Xuzhou dong... d.	...	...	0720	...	0943	...	|	1050	|	1106	...	...	1243	|	1319	1348	1358	1455	1555	1651	1836	1629	...	1916	2029	|
1023	**Nanjing** nan ... d.	0735	0827	0900	0851	1112	1136	1140	1207	1123	1240	1339	1405	1409	1322	1433	1515	1535	1617	1712	1812	2005	1800	1941	2049	2157	2219
1152	Yixing... d.	0835	0909	0950	0933	|	1218	1223	1250	|	1317	1414	1449	1459	|	|	1605	1625	1700	|	1848	2041	1843	2051	2125	2233	|
1208	Huzhou... d.	0855	0931	1018	0958	|	1247	1242	|	1211	|	1439	1507	1517	|	|	|	|	1718	1814	1906	2109	|	2121	2143	2252	|
1279	**Hangzhou** dong a.	0928	0952	1039	1024	1221	1308	1303	1342	1234	1350	1516	1528	1538	1426	1543	1638	1705	1739	1835	1927	2130	1916	2151	2204	2313	2322
1439	Ningbo... a.	...	...	...	1127	...	...	1405	...	...	1454	...	...	...	1513	...	...	...	1836	1929	2034	...	2029	...	...	...	...

km	All trains prefix 'G'	172	1862	32	254	D2223	1221	174	176	178	170	184	1496	198	34	282	1676	442	194	196	1484	1666	36	7682	40	1380	1504
					Q	D						A	B	A		Q	C				B	B		A		B	B
	Ningbo... d.	...	...	...	...	...	0718	0745	...	...	...	1036	...	1155	...	...	...	1345	...	1437	...	...	1605	1708	...	...	...
	Hangzhou dong ... d.	0654	0708	0748	0844	0815	0830	0849	0857	0949	1134	1139	1203	1246	1300	1403	1414	1446	1517	1543	1618	1648	1654	1810	1900	1906	2039
	Huzhou... d.	0724	0731	0811	|	0839	0855	0912	0930	|	|	|	1226	1309	1323	1432	1437	|	1543	1606	1641	1714	|	1833	|	|	2105
	Yixing... d.	0743	0757	|	0927	0859	0915	0932	|	1024	1215	1221	1245	|	|	|	1503	1528	|	|	1701	1732	|	1859	|	1946	2129
	Nanjing nan... d.	0833	0841	0858	1021	0943	1008	1010	1026	1112	1302	1315	1335	1439	1412	1547	1549	1614	1645	1705	1737	1819	1806	1943	2006	2019	2210
	Xuzhou dong... d.	|	1016	|	1154	...	1131	1135	1150	1234	1433	1449	...	|	|	1716	...	1738	1822	1837	...	1933	|	...	|	...	...
	Ji'nan xi... d.	1117	1129	1057	1321j	...	1248	1252	1312	1342	1546	1602	...	1726	1614	1840j	...	1850	1936	1949	...	...	2005	...	|	...	...
	Dezhou dong... d.	1144	1222	|	...	...	1326	1322	1338	|	1612	1645	...	|	|	...	...	|	2004	|	...	...	|	...	|	...	...
	Tianjin nan... d.	1232	...	|	...	...	1422x	|	|	1501	|	1738	...	1838	|	...	...	2008x	|	2104	...	...	|	...	|	...	...
	Beijing nan... a.	1308	...	1220	...	...	...	1440	1451	1543	1749	1812	...	1912	1740	...	...	...	2124	2138	...	...	2128	...	2323	...	...

– To/from Table **7200**. C – To/from Table **7193**. Q – To/from Qingdao (Table **7105**). j – Jinan. **Note**: Additional services operate between Beijing/Nanjing and Hangzhou.
– To/from Table **7192**. D – To/from Table **7183**. k – Hangzhou.

Please see black bar at foot of page for standard notes **b**, **d**, **n** and **x**.

7105 BEIJING - JI'NAN - QINGDAO

Chinese Railways, China Rail High Speed

km	All unmarked trains prefix 'D'	Z169 A	G6905	G209	G453 D	G6909	G177	G6953	G246 D	8181	8183	G222 S	G6991	G179	G6915	G171	G181	1631	G254 S	G183	G185	G187	G5555	G189	G191	G251	G242 D
426	**Beijing** nan ..... d.	...	...	0655	...	...	0729	...	...	...	...	...	...	0935	...	...	1039	...	...	1147	1225	1240	...	1315	1420	1445	...
304	**Tianjin** nan . d.	...	...	|	...	...	0805	...	...	...	...	...	...	|	...	1053x	1117	...	...	|	|	1318	...	|	|	|	...
122	Dezhou dong .. d.	...	...	|	...	...	0901	...	...	...	...	...	...	1050	...	1157	1214	1153	...	1312	|	1404	...	1433	1535	|	...
0	**Ji'nan** ♥ .... d.	0140	0652d	|	0808	0835x	0937d	0920	0952	1001	1021	1057	1124	1135	1156d	1235d	1259	1315	1326	1400	1427d	1440d	1530	1524	1623	1627d	1629
130	Zibo .... d.	0247	0719b	|	0859	0931b	1009b	1016	1036	1045	1105	1142	1208	1220	1227b	1259b	1343	1359	1410	1447	1452b	1506b	1614	1608	1707	|	1714
230	Weifang .... d.	0346	0748b	0913b	|	1015b	1045b	1053	1113	1128	|	1219	|	1304	1304b	1335b	1421	1436	1447	1530	1521b	1536b	|	1645	1749	|	|
413*	**Qingdao** ♥ .... a.	0502	0910	1001b	1107	1132	1131b	1235	1227	1248	1303	1324b	1353	1418	1424	1501	1536	1533b	1602	1645	1631	1622b	1632	1825	1929	1751b	1917

	G1207 E	1639	G193	G1267	G195	G282 S	G197	G199	G205	G1247 E	G235 S	335
Beijing nan ......d.	...	...	1520	...	1610	...	1650	1721	1755	...	...	2242
Tianjin nan ...d.	1458x	...	|	1600x	|	...	1730	1755	|	1825	...	|
Dezhou dong ....d.	|	...	|	1709	1733	...	1816	1845	|	|	...	|
Ji'nan ♥ ....d.	1639	1723d	1727	1800	1817	1845	1908	1941	|	2001	2029	|
Zibo ....d.	1726	1756b	1811	1845	1904	1934	1954	|	|	|	2113	0410
Weifang ....d.	1809	1828b	|	1935	|	|	2033	2104	|	2116	2150	0516
Qingdao ♥ ......a.	1913b	1924b	2001	2037b	2100	2131	2153	2224	2053b	2212	2310	0639b

	G1268	G1208 E	G6949	G284 S	6004	1636	G178	G210	G182	G1248 E	G244 D	G180
Qingdao ♥ ..d.	0600b	0610b	0650b	0626	0700	0727	0752	0753b	0758	0811b	0815	0823b
Weifang ....d.	0657	0713	|	0751	0811	0806	0858b	0840b	0930	0919	0932	|
Zibo ....d.	0740	0750	0825b	0835	0848	0929	0927b	|	1008	0958	1015	0939b
Ji'nan ♥ ......d.	0829	0839	0902d	0922	0935	1016	0953d	|	1058	1048	1102	1011
Dezhou dong d.	0917	0929	...	...	...	...	1037	|	|	1132	...	1048
Tianjin nan..a.	1012	1032x	...	...	...	...	1123	|	1227	1225	...	|
Beijing nan ..a.	...	...	...	...	...	...	1158	1058	1302	...	...	1203

	G188	G232 S	G184	G5537	G186	G190	8184	G192	G252	G6906	Z170 A	G245 D	6008	G228 S	G6910	G194	G6976	G6912	G196	1632	G174	G256 S	G198	G6954	G454 D	G206	336
Qingdao ♥ ......d.	0850	0933	0924	1016b	1020	1208	1216	1253b	1314b	1313	1430	1320	1333	1354b	1408	1436	1446b	1526	1554	1558	1610	1620	1705	1831	1831	1920	2123b
Weifang ....d.	1010	1053	1047	1212	1138	|	|	1347b	|	1457b	1602	1438	|	1456	1521b	1549	1540b	1638b	1711	1655	1722b	1733	1828	1924	2003	|	2235
Zibo ....d.	1051	1137	1130	1251	1221	|	1419	1434b	|	1533b	1647	1521	1528	1542	1550b	|	|	1714b	1753	1733	1806b	1811	1908	2031	2040	|	2333
Ji'nan ♥ ....d.	1140	1224	1219	1339	1310	1450	1506	1510d	1440d	1622x	1800	1608	1615	1629	1645x	1709	1639d	1753d	1843	1830	1847d	1858	1958	2125	2135	|	|
Dezhou dong ....d.	1232	...	|	...	|	1540	...	1550	|	...	...	...	...	...	...	|	...	...	|	1939	1931	...	|	...	...	|	|
Tianjin nan......a.	|	...	|	...	|	1626	...	1640	|	...	...	...	...	...	...	|	...	...	2006	...	2039x	...	|	...	...	|	0441
Beijing nan ......a.	1354	...	1418	...	1503	1700	...	1714	1622	...	...	...	...	...	...	1913	...	...	2040	...	...	...	2156	...	...	2218	0603

A – Guangzhou dong (**Z168/67**) – Jinan (**Z169/70**) – Qingdao and v.v.
D – To/from Table **7097**.
E – To/from Table **7015**.
S – To/from Table **7100/7102**.
* – 344 kms via high-speed line.
♥ – Additional trips Jinan – Qingdao.

7110 SHANGHAI - NANJING - ZHENGZHOU

Chinese Railways

km			K290 ♦	T112 ♦	Z167 ♦	T116 ♦	Z252 ♦	K152	Z40 ♦	Z164 ♦	K282 ♦
0	**Shanghai** ....d.	...	...	A	...	1531	1552	1631	1617	2007	2013
84	Suzhou ....d.	...	1013	1312	...	1635	1643	1739	1713	2058	2125
165	Changzhou ....d.	...	1116	1408	...	1730	1736	1844	1804	|	2226
301	**Nanjing** ....d.	...	1259	1540	...	1855	1903	2042	1919	2301	0049
485	Bengbu ....d.	...	1514	1731	...	2047	2054	0016	2100	0039	0253
***	**Ji'nan** ....d.	...	|	|	1808	|	|	|	|	|	|
649	Xuzhou ....d.	...	1728	1926	2214	2224	2230	|	2254	0212	0453
795	Shangqiu ....d.	...	1910	|	2340	2356	2350	0441	|	|	0653
998	**Zhengzhou** ....a.	...	2126	2254	0136	0145	0137	0726	0203	0507	0904

	Z163 ♦	Z39 ♦	Z254 ♦	T115 ♦	T111 ♦	Z168 ♦	K289 ♦	K154	K284 ♦	
Zhengzhou ....d.	0258	0306	0347	0313	0608	1643	1750	1802	1916	...
Shangqiu ....d.	|	|	0525	0505	|	1838	2006	2050	...	...
Xuzhou ....d.	0556	0602	0650	0640	0922	2014	2157	|	2340	...
Ji'nan ....a.	|	|	|	|	|	0128	|	|	|	...
Bengbu ....d.	0720	0726	0820	0832	1105	...	2345	|	0127	...
Nanjing ....d.	0901	0907	1000	1025	1311	...	0151	0250	0400	...
Changzhou ....d.	|	1013	1108	|	1437	...	0317	0417	|	...
Suzhou ....d.	1057	1104	1159	1230	1540	...	0424	0545	|	...
Shanghai ....a.	1151	1159	1250	1330	B	...	...	0648	0710	...

For ♦ footnotes see Table **7120**.
A – From Hangzhou d. 1023.
B – To Hangzhou a. 1854.

7115 ZHENGZHOU - XI'AN - LANZHOU

Chinese Railways

km	G2025	G2021	Z135 ♦	T117 ♦	Z252 ♦	Z165 ♦	Z41 ♦	T197 ♦	Z151 ♦	T113 ♦	Z323 ♦	Z223 ♦	↓ Read Down		Read Up ↑	Z254 ♦	T118 ♦	Z42 ♦	Z166 ♦	Z136 ♦		T114 ♦	T198 ♦	Z152 ♦	Z324 ♦	Z224 ♦	
0	0653	0850	0135	0202	0144	0514	0211	2054	...	2302	...	...	d.	**Zhengzhou**	a.	0338	0303	0257	0250	0439	...	0601	0705	...	...	...	...
124	0736	|	0308	0336	0314	|	0345	2236	...	0035	...	...	d.	Luoyang	d.	|	|	0133	|	0315	...	0431	0532	0636	...	...	...
512	0910	1101	0750	0822	0754	1122	0843	0339	0359	0519	...	...	d.	**Xi'an**	d.	2135	2017	2050	2044	2234	...	2327	0040	0140	...	...	...
685	1007n	1204n	0929	1017	...	|	1025	0558	0536	0725	0240g	0240g	d.	Baoji	d.	...	1833	1912	|	2049	...	2128	2252	|	0123g	0123g	...
840	1055n	1253n	1106	1200	...	|	1209	0737	0713	0907	|	|	d.	Tianshui	d.	...	1546	1620	|	1804	...	1825	2006	2129	|	|	...
1188	1217x	1417x	1503	1616	...	1816	1548	1139	1128	1251	0910	0910	a.	**Lanzhou**	d.	...	1114	1210	1224	1335	...	1356	1540	1658	1948	1948	...

For ♦ footnotes see Table **7120**.
g – Arrival time at Guangyuan.

7118 BEIJING - LANZHOU and XI'AN

Chinese Railways

km		Z69 ♦	T175 ♦	T41	Z55	Z129	Z151 ♦	T7 ♦	Z21 ♦	Z19
0	**Beijing** xi ....d.	1000	1305	1422	1458	1557	1603	1640	2000	2040
291	Shijiazhuang bei.....................d.	1312	1601	1728	1757	1827	1833	2003	2236	|
395	Yangquan bei ....d.	1412	|	|	1904	|	|	|	|	|
516	**Taiyuan** ....d.	1509	1829	1954	2005	|	|	2222n	0026	|
701	Lvliang ....d.	1650	2030	2205	|	|	|	2358	|	|
790	Suide ....d.	1744	2131	2345	|	|	|	|	|	|
1283	**Xi'an** ....a.	|	|	0530	|	0353	0351	0621	|	0829
1267	Zhongwei ....d.	2243	0225	...	0245	|	|	...	0716	...
1524	**Wuwei** ....a.	0212	|	...	|	|	|	...	|	...
1573	**Lanzhou** ....a.	...	0731	...	0748	1042	1128	...	1214	...

	Z20	Z22 ♦	T42	T176 ♦	T8 ♦	Z152 ♦	Z130	Z56	Z70 ♦
Lanzhou ....d.	...	1629	...	1501	...	1658	1718	2111	...
Wuwei ....d.	...	|	...	|	...	|	|	|	0458
Zhongwei ....d.	...	2132	...	2027	...	|	|	0223	0837
Xi'an ....d.	1854	|	1939	|	2252	0140	0147	|	|
Suide ....d.	|	|	0139	0153	|	|	|	|	1252
Lvliang ....d.	|	|	0239	0253	|	|	|	|	1352
Taiyuan ....d.	|	0400	0427	0447	0727	|	|	0906n	1536
Yangquan bei ....d.	|	|	|	|	0832	|	|	|	1641
Shijiazhuang bei ....d.	|	0555	0626	0645	0941	1148	1154	1104	1744
Beijing xi ....a.	0658	0828	0931	0937	1236	1426	1432	1338	2022

7120 LANZHOU - ÜRÜMQI and LHASA

Chinese Railways, China Rail High Speed

km		D55	D2703	D2701 X	D2711	D2695 X	T197 ♦	Z135 ♦	Z179 ♦	T295	Z41 ♦	Z69 ♦
	Zhongwei .....d.	...	...	...	...	...	...	...	1652	...	...	2243
0	**Lanzhou** ....d.	0852x	0930x	1103x	1204x	1913	1156	1518	|	1745	1603	|
188	Xining ....d.	1007	1052	1218	1321	2044	|	|	|	|	|	|
303	Wuwei ....d.	|	|	|	|	...	1506	1825	2027	2100	1915	0218
770	Jiayuguan ....d.	1334n	1416n	1518n	1659n	...	1951	2251	0102	0140	2336	0650
1067	Liuyuan..............d.	1527n	|	1703n	1850n	...	2315	0149	0352	|	|	0949
1339	Hami ....d.	1703	1737	1835	2022	...	0350	0438	0643	0726	0511	1244
1749	Turpan bei ....d.	1850	1924	2015	2217	...	0652	0721	0926	1100	0805	1527
1892	**Ürümqi** nan......a.	1945	2019	2110	2312	...	0826	0849a	1051	1352	0930a	1652

	D2688 X	D56	D2708 X	D2706	D2712	Z70 ♦	T296	Z180 ♦	Z42 ♦	T198 ♦	Z136 ♦
Ürümqi nan ...d.	...	0818	0955	1100	1146	1410	1517	1942	1840	1850a	1952
Turpan bei .....d.	...	0913	1053	1155	1241	1540	1616	2104	2023	2039	2114
Hami ....d.	...	1057	1239	1359	1432	1835	2049	2355	2306	0018	0004
Liuyuan ....d.	...	1228n	1410n	1532n	1603n	2123	|	0243	|	0340	0251
Jiayuguan ......d.	...	1427n	1601n	1723n	1801n	0025	0234	0545	0437	0659	0557
Wuwei ....d.	...	|	|	|	|	0458	0713	1047	0855	1210	1019
Xining ....d.	0840	1759	1901	2110	2127	|	|	|	|	|	|
Lanzhou ....a.	0956	1908	2010x	2219x	2236x	|	1025	|	1151	1515	1318
Zhongwei ..a.	...	...	...	...	...	0821	...	1406	...	...	...

km		D2741 E	T175 ♦	Z323 Z223 ♦	D2671 X	Z151 ♦	D2685 X	Z21 ♦	D2737 X	D2673 X	Z165 ♦	D2697 X
0	**Zhongwei** ....d.	...	0225		...	...	...	0716	...	...	...	...
306	**Lanzhou** ....d.	0704x	0739	0926	1108	1149	1149x	1231	1334x	1700	1837	2025x
534	Xining ....d.	0824	1034	1225	1231	1427	1258	1521	1507	1815	2127	2143
	Jiayuguan nan .a.	1144	...	|	1556	...	...	|	1834	2147	|	...
1352	Golmud..............d.	...	...	1942	...	...	...	2235	...	...	0430	...
2172	Naqu ....d.	...	...	0611	...	...	...	0839	...	...	1411	...
2449	**Lhasa**................a.	...	...	0956	...	...	...	1240	...	...	1936	...

	Z166 ♦	D2682 X	D2672 X	T176 ♦	D2746 F	D2722 X	D2738 X	Z22 ♦	Z152 ♦	D2674 X	Z324 Z224
Lhasa ....d.	1130	...	...	...	...	...	...	1550	...	...	1840
Naqu ....d.	1521	...	...	...	...	...	...	1936	...	...	2205
Golmud ....d.	0226	...	...	...	...	...	...	0641	...	...	0910
Jiayuguan nan.a.	|	...	0813	...	1004	...	1124	|	...	1257	|
Xining ....d.	0930	1112	1156	1210	1339	1421	1441	1345	1410	1615	1650
Lanzhou.........a.	1208	1223x	1307x	1442	1449x	1538	1559x	1614	1642	1732x	1933
Zhongwei.......a.	...	...	...	2020	...	...	...	2126	...	...	...

♦ – **NOTES** for Tables **7110**, **7115 7118** and **7120** (by train number):

T7/8 – Beijing xi (**T7/8**) – Chengdu and v.v.
Z21/22 – Beijing xi (**Z21/22**) – Lhasa and v.v.
Z39/41 – Urumqi (**Z42/41**) – Zhengzhou (**Z39/40**) – Shanghai and v.v.
Z69/70 – Beijing xi (**Z69/70**) – Urumqi and v.v.
T111/114 – Lanzhou (**T114/13**) – Zhengzhou (**T111/12**) – Hangzhou and v.v.
T115/118 – Lanzhou (**T118/17**) – Zhengzhou (**T115/16**) – Shanghai and v.v.
Z135/36 – Urumqi (**Z136/35**) – Zhengzhou (**Z137/38**) – Guangzhou and v.v.
Z151/152 – Beijing xi (**Z151/152**) – Xining and v.v.
Z163/166 – Lhasa (**Z166/165**) – Zhengzhou (**Z163/164**) – Shanghai and v.v.
Z168/70 – Guangzhou dong (**Z168/67**) – Jinan (**Z169/70**) – Qingdao and v.v.
T175/76 – Beijing xi (**T175/76**) – Xining xi and v.v.
Z179/180 – Beijing (**Z179/80**) – Hohhot – Urumqi and v.v.
T193/194 – Zhengzhou (**T193/194**) – Urumqi and v.v.
T197/198 – Zhengzhou (**T197/198**) – Urumqi and v.v.
Z223/224 – Lhasa (**T224/223**) – Chongqing and v.v. Runs alternate days only.
Z252/54 – Xian (**Z254/252**) – Zhengzhou – Shanghai and v.v.
K282/284 – Shanghai (**K282/284**) – Zhengzhou (**K283/281**) – Chengdu and v.v.
K289/290 – Suzhou (**K290/289**) – Zhengzhou (**K291/292**) – Chengdu and v.v.
Z323/24 – Chengdu (**Z322/21**) – Lanzhou (**Z323/24**) – Lhasa and v.v. Runs alternate days only.

E – Additional trips: 0736, 0801, 1509, 1720.
F – Additional trips: 1207, 1238, 1700
X – To/from Table **7040**.

a – Ürümqi.

* * * – Jinan *0 km* - Xuzhou *319 km*.

ÜRÜMQI - ALMATY - NUR-SULTAN 7125

km		5801	13 *CJ* ①	13/53 ①
0	**Ürümqi** d.	2242	2333	2333
144	Shihezi d.	0129	|	|
241	Kuitun d.	0259	|	|
486	Bortala a.	0708	|	|
477	Alashankou a.	...	0800	0800
477	Alashankou 🏛 d.	...	1100	1100
493	Druzhba 🏛 a.	...	0920	0920
493	Druzhba d.	...	1240	1240
654	Beskol' d.	...	1621	1621
797	**Aktogay** a.	...	1828	1828
797	**Aktogay** d.	...	1858	1935
1051	Ush Tobe d.	...	2311	|
1283	Kapchagay d.	...	0345	|
1354	**Almaty** 1 a.	...	0454	|
1363	**Almaty** 2 a.	...	0545	|
1657	Karagandy a.	...	...	0809
1898	**Nur-Sultan** a.		...	1301

	5802	54/14 ⑥	13 *KH* ⑦
Nur-Sultan d.	...	1658	...
Karagandy d.	...	2119	...
Almaty 2 d.	...	|	0022
Almaty 1 d.	...	|	0113
Kapchagay d.	...	|	0225
Ush Tobe d.	...	|	0654
Aktogay a.	...	1030	1053
Aktogay d.	...	1123	1123
Beskol' d.	...	1346	1346
Druzhba a.	...	1635	1635
Druzhba 🏛 d.	...	1950	1950
Alashankou 🏛 a.	...	2210	2210
Alashankou d.	...	2350	2350
Bortala d.	0800	|	|
Kuitun d.	1224	|	|
Shihezi d.	1341	|	|
Ürümqi a.	1630	0854	0854

Operators: Chinese Railways and Kazakstan Temir Zholy.

Chinese Railways XI'AN - CHENGDU 7130

km		K291 C	K245	T7 A		Z324 B	Z224 E	K282 C		K545
	Zhengzhou d.	2150	2320	...	...	...	...	0927	...	...
0	**Xi'an** d.	|	0653	0638	...	...	...	|	...	0623
173	Baoji d.	b	0926	0832	...	...	...	b	...	0901
523	Guangyuan d.	1345	1811	1546	...	0158	0205	0342	...	1712
727	Mianyang d.	1711	2133	1908	...	|	C	0707	...	2027
842	**Chengdu** a.	1858	2315	2036	...	0626	...	0835	...	2155

	T8 A	K546		K284 C	K292 C	Z223 E	Z323 B	K246	
Chengdu d.	0840	0737	...	1903	1750	...	2137	2126	...
Mianyang d.	1017	0917	...	2037	1928	e	|	|	...
Guangyuan d.	1353	1306	...	0022	2328	0240	0240	0250	...
Baoji d.	2055	2116	...	b	b	...	...	1032	...
Xi'an a.	2232	2348	...	|	0826n	...	...	1227	...
Zhengzhou a.	...	...	...	1856	1728	...	...	1934	...

A – Bejing xi (**T7/8**) – Chengdu and v.v.
B – Chengdu (**X323/21**) – Lanzhou (**Z323/24**) – Lhasa and v.v. Runs alternate days only.
C – Suzhou - Zhengzhou – Chengdu and v.v.
E – Lhasa (**Z224/23**) – Chongqing. Runs alternate days only.

b – Via Table **7170**. e – From Chongqing xí dep. 2225.
c – To Chongqing arr. 0640.

China Rail High Speed XI'AN - CHENGDU - CHONGQING 7132

km		D1911 B	D1913 A	D1701	G2201	G89 Z	G2213	D1979 F	G1976 Z	G571 Z	G307 Z
0	**Xi'an** bei d.	0711	0750	0815	0929	1128	1154	1205	1442	1512	1523
	Guangyuan d.	0922	1003	1031	1141	|	1405	1422	1642	1710	1729
	Mianyang d.	1034	|	|	1235	|	|	|	1742	1819	1830
658	**Chengdu** dong a.	1118	1147	|	1319	1438	1537	|	1832	1900	1914
	Nanchong bei d.	...	...	|	...	...	...	1558	|	|	...
977	**Chongqing** bei a.	...	..	1325x	...	...	..	1706	2019x	2034x	..

	D1914 D	G2204	D1918 E	G1282	G574 Z	G308 Z	G90 Z	G2210	D1965 G	D1969	G1975 Z
Chongqing bei d.	...	...	...	...	0840x	...	...	...	0833	0905	0915
Nanchong bei d.	...	...	...	...	|	...	...	...	0959	|	|
Chengdu dong d.	0736	0802	0900	0908	1021	1051	1502	1522	|	|	1056
Mianyang d.	0823	0857	|	0955	1102	1136	|	|	|	|	1141
Guangyuan d.	0936	1001	1025	1052	1200	1240	|	1711	1144	|	1246
Xi'an bei a.	1144	1211	1220	1301	1405	1450	1816	1916	1345	1354	1515

A – Additional trips: 0826, 0900, 1133, 1233.
B – Additional trips: 0924, 0936, 1003, 1036, 1054, 1143, 1205, 1315, 1410, 1430, 1517, 1620, 1805, 1823, 1829, 1853, 1905.
D – Additional trips: 0706, 0752, 0809, 0917, 1029, 1138, 1240, 1300, 1351, 1517, 1639, 1758, 1903.
E – Additional trips: 1208, 1402, 1430, 1507, 1527, 1659, 1807.
F – Additional trips: 1250, 1457, 1612, 1747.
G – Additional trips: 1235, 1418, 1805, 1832.
Z – To/from Table **7070** and **7088**.

China Rail High Speed CHENGDU - QINGCHENGSHAN 7135

High-speed '**C**' trains (numbers **C61xx**). *65km 50km from Xipu.* Journey 45 - 50 minutes. Journey 25 - 35 minutes from Xipu. * – To/from Xipu.
Regular services operate through out the day from about 0630 until about 2200.

China Rail High Speed CHENGDU - CHONGQING 7140

km	All unmarked trains prefix 'D'	C6007	G8601 ●	2244 C	5104	1781	638 C	G8701	954 C	354 C	2208 C	2256 C	616 C	2264 C	2374 C	6196	2260 C	368 C	634	G8619	G8625	6198	5102	G8633 C	G8639	G8641
0	**Chengdu** dong ● d.	0609	0622	0618	0705	0710	0710	0725	0747	0757	0807	0813	0903	0909	0924	0919x	1022	1052	1327	1305	1554	1604x	1729	1820	1931	2153
146	Suining d.	|	|	0732	|	|	0810	|	|	|	|	0924	|	|	1022	|	|	|	|	|	|	1731	1840	|	|	|
198	Tongnan d.	|	|	|	0822	|	|	|	|	|	0928	0953	|	|	|	1114	1138	1211	1444	|	|	|	1911	|	|	|
247	Hechuan d.	|	|	0829	0850	|	0903	|	|	0943	|	1020	|	1047	1114	|	|	1237	1510	|	|	|	|	|	|	|
313	**Chongqing** bei ● 7183 a.	0754x	0732y	0854	0915	0900x	0928	0922	0943	1000	1018	1045	1059	1112	1139	1157	1222	1302	1535	1423y	1656y	1840	1955	1938	2104x	2310x

All unmarked trains prefix 'D'	G8588 ●	5101	6197	G8620	633 C	G8626	367 C	1782	6195	619 C	2373 C	5103	2259 C	G8632	353 C	2255 C	953 C	C6006	2237	361 C	2207 C	2242 C	G8640	2263 C	G8642
Chongqing bei ● 7183 d.	0635x	0740	1047	1258y	1357	1442y	1450	1543	1615	1634	1656	1707	1725	1748y	1810	1825	1900	1918x	1855	1914	1927	2001	2030y	2052	2159y
Hechuan d.	|	0807	|	|	1424	|	1518	|	|	1701	1723	1736	|	|	|	|	|	|	|	1941	1955	2029	|	2119	|
Tongnan d.	|	0832	|	|	1450	|	|	|	1702	1730	1749	|	1811	|	1859	1913	|	|	|	2007	2022	2058	|	2145	|
Suining d.	|	0902	1202	|	1525	|	|	|	1733	|	1821	|	1842	|	1933	|	|	|	|	2039	|	|	|	2215	|
Chengdu dong ● a.	0801	1010	1335x	1418	1623	1552	1707	1727	1908x	1848	1919	1926	1939	1906	2030	2036	2058	2102	2052	2150	2144	2215	2132	2315	2310

C – To/from Table **7183**. y – To/from Shapingba. ● – Regular additional high-speed services operate Chengdu – Chongqing bei / Chongqing Shapingba and v.v. Note: Trains numbered **G8XXX** go via Neijiang.

China Rail High Speed CHENGDU - DAZHOU 7142

km	All trains prefix 'D'	C5742	5182	C5744	C5750 A	5184	5186	C5754	5188	C5742	C5758
0	**Chengdu** dong d.	0840	0752	0823	1102	1230	1342	1500	1645	1606	1900
146	Suining d.	0749	|	|	|	|	1441	1618	|	1721	2009
213	Nanchong d.	0826	|	|	1242	1358	|	1656	1815	1758	2046
372	**Dazhou** a.	0954	1028	1110	1358	1512	1627	1835	1927	1943	2214

All trains prefix 'D'	C5741 B	5181	C5743	5183	C5745	C5747	5185	5187	5189	C5755
Dazhou d.	0710	0916	1020	1048	1130	1349	1535	1733	1950	2010
Nanchong d.	0835	1028	|	|	1247	1506	1648	|	|	|
Suining d.	0912	|	|	|	1324	|	|	|	|	2202
Chengdu dong a.	1020	1153	1340	1319	1432	1712	1814	1959	2222	2309

A – Additional trips: 0720, 1027, 1038, 1352. B – Additional trips: 1410, 1422, 1441, 1857. Note: Additional services operate Chengdu dong – Nanchong and v.v.

China Rail High Speed, MTR CHENGDU - CHONGQING - GUIYANG - GUILIN - GUANGZHOU 7146

km	All trains prefix 'D'	211	G2929	1861	G2938 Y	G2924 Y	G319	1841	1751	1865	G410 Y	1812	1801	1859	G6579	G2963	1820	1755	1761	1821	G2934 Y	1875	1825	G2928 Y	1851	1877	1833
519	**Chengdu** dong ♠ d.	...	...	...	...	...	...	0655	0712	...	...	0741	0805	0828	...	0943	1012	1135	1141	1149	...	...	1326	...	1316	...	1353
	Suining d.	...	...	...	...	...	...	|	|	...	...	0842	|	|	...	|	|	|	|	|	...	...	|	...	N	...	N
345	**Chongqing** xi ♠ d.	...	...	0719	...	...	0820	X	X	0854	...	1010	X	X	...	X	1223	X	X	X	...	1442	X	...	1529	1609	1623
	Zunyi d.	...	...	0845	...	...	0940	|	|	|	...	|	|	|	...	|	|	|	|	|	...	|	|	...	1701	1735	1750
0	**Guiyang** bei ♠ d.	0800	0844	0946d	0950	1013	1032d	1107d	1038d	1115d	1126	1229d	1153d	1206d	...	1309d	1432d	1507d	1527d	1538d	1650	1709d	1720d	1735	1754d	1829d	1843d
408	**Guilin** xi ♠ d.	|	1106	1200	1205	|	1238	1327	1249	1347	1336	1501	1407	1436	...	1517	1642	1735	1749	1800	|	1924	1955	|	2021	2051	2102
593	Hezhou d.	|	1214	1316	|	|	|	|	|	1445	|	|	|	1542	...	|	1748	1841	1901	1912	|	2041	|	|	|	2157	2207
778	Zhaoqing dong d.	|	1313	1419	|	|	1420	1531	|	1546	|	|	1556	|	...	1703	1857	1939	2004	2013	|	|	2144	|	|	2254	2304
854	**Guangzhou** n ♠ a.	1210	1354	1453	1424	1429	1459	1606	1508	1624	1555	1800	1632	1721	0910	1738	1939	2016	2045	2049	2111	2215	2221	2158	2253	2330	2340
956	**Shenzhen** bei a.	...	1429	...	...	1504	1541	...	...	...	1604	...	...	...	0946	1822	...	...	...	...	...	...	...	2233	...	...	...
996	**West Kowloon** a.	...	...	...	...	...	1610	...	...	...	1657	...	...	...	1014	...	...	...	...	...	...	...	...	...	...	...	...

All trains prefix 'D'	1862	1849	G2932 Y	1864	1806	1842	G2926 Y	1810	1762	1818	1756	1822	G2964	1826	1857	G408 Y	1834	212	G2936 Y	1874	G2930	1752	G320	1878	G2922 Y	G6580
West Kowloon d.	...	...	...	...	...	...	...	...	...	...	...	...	...	...	...	1205	...	...	...	...	...	...	1453	...	...	2021
Shenzhen bei d.	...	...	...	...	...	...	0800	...	...	...	...	...	1032	...	...	1227	...	...	...	...	1452	...	1510	...	1526	2051
Guangzhou nan ♠ d.	0657	0723	0750	0746	0821	0847	0835	0917	0927	1031	1043	1101	1112	1230	1232	1307	1318	1355	1448	1508	1526	1528	1543	1612	1607	2132
Zhaoqing dong d.	0734	0801	|	|	0903	|	|	0959	1009	1109	1126	|	1149	1313	1325	|	|	|	|	1545	|	|	1620	|	|	2220
Hezhou d.	0830	0917	|	|	1003	1033	|	1059	1109	1212	1222	1234	|	1414	1423	|	1450	|	|	|	|	|	|	1745	|	...
Guilin xi ♠ d.	0937	1025	|	1005	1125	1143	|	1213	1233	1324	1329	1353	1338	1520	1545	1530	1557	|	1707	1750	1752	1745	1805	1859	|	...
Guiyang bei ♠ a.	1145d	1239d	1213	1216d	1340d	1403d	1256	1431d	1454d	1602d	1555d	1608d	1537d	1741d	1759d	1738	1839d	1814	1925	2029d	2023d	1953d	2006d	2113d	2025	...
Zunyi d.	1246	1341	...	1307	|	|	...	|	|	1659	|	1705	|	|	|	...	1940	...	...	2124	|	|	2101	2208	...	...
Chongqing xi ♠ d.	1417	1517	...	1445	X	X	...	X	X	1836	X	1841	X	X	X	...	2105	...	...	2243	2231	X	2219	2334	...	...
Suining d.	...	N	...	...	|	|	...	|	|	|	|	N	|	|	|	...	2235	...	...	...	...	|	...	...	...	...
Chengdu dong ♠ a.	...	1707	...	...	1722	1744	...	1827	1849	2047	1932	2050	1856	2131	2142	...	2333	...	...	...	...	2310	...	...	...	...

N – Via Neijiang. Y – To/from Table **7187**. ♠ – Additional services available: Guangzhou – Guilin / Guiyang and Guangzhou – Chongqing / Chengdu.
X – Via Yibin xi / Bijie.

7155 NANNING - GUANGZHOU — Chinese Railways

km		K366	K1206	K232		K231	K365	K1205
	Kunming d.	0750	0816	1651	**Guangzhou** d.	0529	0948	1641
	Baise d.	1649	1808	0421	Fuoshan d.	0558	1019	1710
0	**Nanning** d.	2024	2156	0700	Zhaoqing d.	0729	1147	1834
263	Yulin d.	2348	0125	1037	Maoming d.	1150	1514	2222
438	Maoming d.	0256	|	1354	Yulin d.	1534	1821	0154
700	Zhaoqing d.	0629	0926	1733	**Nanning** a.	1934	2208	0614
787	Fuoshan d.	0802	1043	1907	Baise d.	|	0027	0914
809	**Guangzhou** a.	0828	1120	1953	**Kunming** a.	0916	1100	2051

7160 GUANGZHOU - SANYA — Chinese Railways

km		K385	K511	Z201	Z111		K386	Z112	K512	Z202
			C	B					C	B
0	**Guangzhou** d.	0457	1731	1602	2124	**Sanya** d.	0802	...	...	1722
22	Fuoshan d.	|	1801	|	2154	Haikou d.	1150	1746	1915	2045
109	Zhaoqing d.	0630	1922	1735	2306	Xunwen d.	|	2124	2237	|
361	Maoming d.	0938	2301	2054	0213	Zhanjiang xi d.	1646	2314	0027	0147
488	Zhanjiang xi d.	1030	0003	2148	0309	Maoming d.	1740	0008	0137	0243
601	Xunwen d.	|	|	|	0520	Zhaoqing d.	2046	0416	0536	0551
794	Haikou a.	1600	0620	0440	0910	Fuoshan d.	2152	0600	0704	0737
1157	**Sanya** a.	2000	...	0812	...	**Guangzhou** a.	2222	0711	0751	0820

B – Beijing (**Z201/02**) – Sanya and v.v. C – Shanghai (**K511/12**) – Haikou and v.v.

7165 HAIKOU - SANYA — China Rail High Speed

High-speed '**C**' trains (numbers **C73xx**). *Eastern Ring 308 km from Haikou, 284km from Haikou dong*. Journey 2 - 2¼ hours. *Western Ring 345 km from Haikou. Journey: 3 hours.*
Frequent services operate throughout the day from about 0650 until about 2200.
Note: Services on the Eastern Ring operate between Haikou and Sanya whereas services that operate on the Western Ring are generally round trip services from Sanya to Sanya.

7168 GUANGZHOU - ZHANJIANG — China Rail High Speed

km	All unmarked trains prefix 'C'	921	9451	7493	7461	G9761	7471	7479	7495	7485	7487
		A									
0	**Guangzhou** nan ♥ d.	0704	0714	0836	1023	1113	1300	1445	1609	1745	2003
	Yangjiang d.	0836	0856	0959	1200	1243	1450	1618	1748	1946	2131
	Maoming d.	0924	0951	|	1242	1332	1539	1706	1837	2035	2214
421	**Zhanjiang** xi ♥ d.	0955	1033	1108	1318	1407	1616	1739	1917	2117	2248

	7454	7460	7470	7476	G6128	922	7484	7192	7492	7496
						A				
Zhanjiang xi ♥ d.	0817	0942	1308	1445	1620	1715	1740	1840	1910	2031
Maoming d.	|	1022	1348	1519	1654	1749	1814	1922	1946	2105
Yangjiang d.	0927	1110	|	|	1747	1831	1902	2010	2040	|
Guangzhou nan ♥ d.	1047	1301	1608	1715	1922	2000	2042	2144	2215	2301

A – ①⑤⑥⑦ 1cl, (2) Beijing (**D921/22**) – Zhanjiang and v.v. ♥ – Additional services operate.

7170 ZHENGZHOU and WUHAN - CHENGDU and CHONGQING — Chinese Railways

km	Z3	K354	K290	K205	Z49	K283	T247	K15	T125	Z95	K357	↓ ↑	Z50	Z4	K358	T248	K292	K206	K284	K353	T126	Z96	K16
	D		B		D	B			C	D			D	D	D		B		B		C	D	
	...	...	2150	0614	1736	0927	...	1628	...	0008	...	d. **Zhengzhou** a.	0352	...	...	...	1728	1842	1856	...	...	0405	0618
0	0434h	0829	|	|	2220h	|	1952	|	0140	0452h	2236	d. **Wuhan** Wuchang a.	2258h	2308	1616	0500	|	|	|	1910	1530	2314h	|
165	|	1102	|	|	|	|	2147	|	|	|	|	d. Suizhou d.	|	|	|	|	|	|	|	1608	1317	|	|
334	|	1241f	|	1336	|	1714	2320f	2345	0444f	|	0223	d. Xiangyang d.	|	|	1242	0148f	|	1147	1135	1400f	1158f	|	2337
	0701	|	|	|	0037	|	|	|	|	0709	0511	d. Yichang dong d.	1941	2053	0936	|	|	|	|	|	|	2104	|
500	|	1454	|	1548	|	1919	0116	0145	0639	|	|	d. Shiyan d.	|	|	|	2338	|	0858	0906	|	0940	|	2102
	|	1806	0800	1828	|	2207	0342	0408	0903	|	|	d. Ankang d.	|	|	|	2029	0533	0539	0559	0753	0632	|	1803
702	|	|	|	|	|	|	0718	0805	1254	|	1245	d. Dazhou d.	|	|	0206	1728	|	|	|	|	0330	|	1503
978	|	0045	1346	0019	|	0342	|	|	|	|	|	d. Guangyuan d.	|	|	|	|	2328	2306	0022	0208	|	|	|
1137	|	|	|	|	|	|	0859	|	1457	|	|	d. Nanchong d.	|	|	|	1505	|	|	|	|	0128	|	|
1204	|	|	|	|	0735	|	0950	|	|	|	|	d. Suining d.	1255	|	|	1416	|	|	|	|	0034	|	|
1375	|	0555	1858	0520	0856	0853	1134d	|	1723	|	|	a. **Chengdu** d.	1137	|	|	1245	1750	1710	1903	2100	2250	|	|
1233	1212	...	...	...	0606↑	...	...	1058x	...	1649	1543	a. **Chongqing** bei d.	1437↑	1521	2316	...	...	...	...	...	...	1133	1208

B – Shanghai – Zhengzhou – Chengdu and v.v.
C – Chengdu (**T126/25**) – Wuhan Wuchang (**T127/28**) – Dongguan dong and v.v.
D – Beijing – Chongqing bei and v.v.
f – Xiangzhou.
h – Wuhan Hankou.
y – Via Yichang dong.

7175 SHANGHAI - NANJING - WUHAN — China Rail High Speed

km	All trains prefix 'D'	3077	353	637	G1772	2207	3073	3057	2213	G598	3090	G577	953	G677	2217	3022	3064	3069	G1724	G1716	3027	3007	3033	3015	G1728	3043	3047
		A	A	A		A	A		A				A		A												
0	**Shanghai** ♣ d.	...	0613	0632	0647	0601	0702	0719	0742	0755	0823	0824	0830	0830	0737	0916	0921	1008	1140	1150	1327	1353	1516	1606	1655	1647	1753
84	Suzhou d.	...	0649	0711	0712b	|	0739	0755	0822	|	|	0850b	|	0859b	|	0946	|	1044	1206b	1227b	1354	1432	1552	1643	|	1737	1832
165	Changzhou d.	...	0729	0744	0736b	|	0812	0834	0906	|	f	|	|	0935b	|	1024	f	1118	|	1251b	1440	1507	|	1718	|	1812	1907
311	**Nanjing** nan d.	0802	0835	0850	0831	|	0918	0944	1019	0858	|	1002	1014	1026	|	1177	|	1230	1300	1338	1538	1605	1725	1823	1758	1910	2009
468	Hefei nan d.	0854	0927	0955	0923	1017	1022	1038	1122	0948	1309	1104	1108	1131	1207	1240	1409	1322	1353	1459	1637	1703	1823	1923	1849	2012	2102
555	Lu'an d.	0924	0957	1025	|	1047	1052	|	|	|	1339	1139	|	1201	1233	1310	|	1351	|	1535	1707	1733	1855	1957	|	2044	2132
827	**Wuhan** Hankou a.	1105	1119	1156	1108	1210	1236	1225	1316	1134	1510	1325	1254	1336	1420	1520g	1615	1530	1543	1708	1852	1920	2036	2133	2025	2223	2301
1119	Yichang dong **7182** a.	1306	1324	1351	a	1417	1448	1427	1531	...	...	a	1443	...	1625	...	...	...	...	...	2058	2134	...	...	...	...	...

All trains prefix 'D'	3028	3016	G1722	G1738	3034	3008	G1770	3044	G1730	3048	3074	G678	2214	3066	G600	G1774	2218	954	3092	3024	G1726	G578	638	354	3078	2208
											A		A				A	A					A	A	A	A
Yichang dong **7182** d.	...	...	...	...	0633	0655	...	...	...	...	1055	...	1131	...	...	a	1300	1406	...	...	...	a	1414	1446	1515	1455
Wuhan Hankou d.	0740	0800	0800	0825	0900	0906	1019	1006	1047h	1200g	1305	1335	1342	1426	1500	1510	1514	1553	1536	1604	1615	1632	1631	1700	1731	1714
Lu'an d.	0923	|	|	0954	1023	1117	|	1152	1216	|	1439	1455	1530	1605	|	1632	1647	|	1657	1746	|	|	1825	1834	1859	1844
Hefei nan d.	0958	1008	0939	1030	1059	1152	1209	1225	1252	1434	1513	1528	1604	1638	1643	1705	1720	1741	1730	1821	1801	1814	1902	1907	1932	1917
Nanjing nan d.	1048	1104	1029	1120	1202	1246	1259	1323	1411	1525	1616	1623	1702	|	1733	1759	|	1833	|	1920	1852	1909	1956	2001	2020	|
Changzhou d.	1151	1209	|	|	1302	1352	1419b	1434	1452b	1616	1712	1714b	1809	f	|	|	|	1923	f	2028	|	1950b	2102	2113	...	|
Suzhou d.	1227	1244	|	1253b	1420	1436	1443b	1524	|	1700	1747	1738b	1843	|	|	1858b	|	1952	|	2103	|	2015b	2137	2147	...	|
Shanghai Hongqiao a.	1302	1318	1130	1317	1446	1515	1507	1600	1556	1730	1825	1808	1920	2101	1835	1923	2133	2021	2159	2151	1954	2045	2213	2221	...	2316

A – To/from Table **7183**. a – To/from Changsha Nan. f – Via Nantong xi. g – Wuhan Wuchang. h – Wuhan. ♣ – **Shanghai** Hongqiao.

7177 SHANGHAI - ZHUZHOU - GUANGZHOU — Chinese Railways

km		T77	T81	K79	K511	K739		K80	K512	K740	T82	T78
		B	A	D	C	E		D	C	E	A	B
0	**Shanghai** nan d.	1125	1605	1826	1921	1936	**Guangzhou** d.	...	0811	...	...	...
188	Hangzhou dong d.	1334	1811	2058	2142	2154	Shaogun dong d.	...	1131	...	...	...
312	Yiwu d.	|	|	|	|	2304	Hengyang d.	...	1518	...	2255	1937
446	Quzhou d.	|	2056	0012	0137	0145	**Zhuzhou** d.		1704	...	|	|
557	Shangrao d.	|	2244	0131	0304	|	Pingxiang d.	1728	1841	...	|	|
673	Yingtan d.	1807	0004	0306	0418	0427	Yingtan d.	2130	2237	...	0625	|
1044	Pingxiang d.	|	|	0654	0866	0821	Shangrao d.	2240	2347	0527	0728	|
1125	**Zhuzhou** d.	|	|	0828	0925	0926	Quzhou d.	0022	|	0819	0843	0515
1259	Hengyang d.	0048	0752	...	1055	...	Yiwu d.	0205	0352	1033	1014	0643
1559	Shaoguan dong d.	...	...	...	1428	...	Hangzhou nan d.	0255	0509	1142	1128	0742
1780	**Guangzhou** a.	...	...	...	1710	...	**Shanghai** nan a.	0535	0832	1436	1327	1018

7178 CHENGDU - PANZHIHUA

km		T8869	T8871	T8867		T8871	T8870	T886
0	**Chengdu** d.	0639n	0805	0900n	Panzhihua nan d.	0722	0818	090
557	Xichang d.	1742	1856	1826	Xichang d.	1036	1152	122
749	Panzhihua nan d.	2112	2159	2149	**Chengdu** d.	2157	2155n	2225

7179 PANZHIHUA - KUNMING — BCh

km		D785	D789	D791		D790	D786	D79
		j	j				j	j
0	Panzhihua nan d.	0700	1412	1710	**Kunming** d.	1058	1419	193
163	Guangtong bei d.	|	|	1847	Guangtong bei d.	|	|	|
351	**Kunming** a.	0919	1636	1941	Panzhihua nan a.	1322	1639	221

A – Shanghai nan (**T81/82**) – Nanning and v.v.
B – Shanghai nan (**T77/78**) – Nanning and v.v.
C – Shanghai (**K511/12**) – Haikou and v.v.
D – Shanghai nan (**K79/80**) – Kunming and v.v.
E – Shanghai nan (**K739/40**) – Kunming and v.v.
j – To/from Yuxi (Table **7181**).

7181 CHENGDU - KUNMING - HEKOU — China Rail High Speed, Chinese Railways

km	All 'G' trains	2837	2803	2883	2801	2885	2845	2887	2829	2821	2827	2825
		a					aa					
0	**Chengdu** dong d.	0735	0800	0850	0913	0945	1345	1504	1550	1609	1705	1725
153	Neijiang bei d.	|	|	|	|	1034	|	|	|	|	|	|
276	Yibin xi d.	0915	|	|	1057	|	|	|	1739	1751	1850	1910
302	Chongqing xi d.	|	|	1017	|	1129	|	1648	|	|	|	|
650	Guiyang bei d.	1107	1136	1222	1312	1342	1653	1912	1973	2012	2047	2114
1113	**Kunming** nan a.	1323	1343	1429	1520	1611	1906	2156	2206	2246	2312	2321

	2886	2822	2830	2846	2828	2890	2884	2870	2802	2838	2882
		G		b						bb	
Kunming nan d.	0805	0811	0859	0938k	1025	1322	1435	1451	1547	1631k	1633
Guiyang bei d.	1035	1015	1137	1215	1304	1545	1714	1707	1818	1910	1858
Chongqing xi d.	1300	|	|	|	|	1806	1949	1926	|	|	2112
Yibin xi d.	|	|	1345	1417	1459	|	|	|	2041	2120	|
Neijiang bei d.	|	|	|	|	|	1903	2103	2026	|	|	2157
Chengdu dong a.	1439	1319	1320	1548	1640	1951	2151	2115	2217	2257	2238

km		C558	D785	C561	C568	K9603	C572	D789	C597	
0	**Kunming** nan d.	0815	0925k	1114	1415	1458	1623	1644k	1727	...
106	Yuxi a.	0900	1033	0159	1456	1613	1704	1752	1808	...
369	**Hekou** bei a.	1215	...	1500	1809	2203	2025	...	2116	...

	C596		D786	K9604		C570	C552	D794	C55
Hekou bei d.	0820	...	...	0859	...	1256	1707	...	181
Yuxi d.	1158	...	1307	1429	...	1630	|	1835	211
Kunming nan a.	1236	...	1413k	1556k	...	1708	2104	1938k	215

G – Additional trips: 1050, 1411. a – To Dali a. 1531. aa – To Dali a. 2130. b – From Dali d. 0725. bb – From Dali d. 1431. k – Kunming.

KUNMING - XISHUANGBANNA - MOHAN 7182

hina Rail High Speed

km		C379	C381	C341	C281	C293	C309	C385	C315	C323	C327
0	**Kunming** nan ♠ d.	...	0829	0918	1016	1135	1411	1419	1543	1743	1844
06	Yuxi d.	...	0910	0959	|	1216	|	1500	|	|	1925
	Pu'er d.	...	1119	1224	|	1417	|	1717	1825	|	2142
	Xishuangbanna ♠ d.	0740	1215	1306	1316	1459	1711	1805	1907	2043	2224
	Mengia d.	0840	1311	...	...	...	...	1901	...	...	...
13	**Mohan** 🛃 d.	0855	...	...	...	...	...	...	...	...	...

	C262	C270	C378	C346	C278	C286	C386	C316	C320	C380
Mohan 🛃 d.	...	...	0920	...	...	...	...	...	...	...
Mengia d.	...	...	0938	...	...	...	1419	...	...	1958
Xishuangbanna ♠ d.	0800	0932	1034	1207	1327	1350	1526	1905	1950	2058
Pu'er d.	|	1016	...	1251	|	1434	1622	|	2034	2148
Yuxi d.	|	1228	...	1510	|	1645	1849	|	|	...
Kunming nan ♠ a.	1104	1306	...	1548	1628	1723	1927	2206	2259	...

– Additional services operate Kunming nan - Xishuangbanna and v.v.
te: Eventually services will operate between Kunming and Vientiane in Laos. Timings from Vientiane to the Laos border (Boten) can be found on Table **6095**.

WUHAN - YICHANG - CHONGQING 7183

hina Rail High Speed

km	All unmarked trains prefix 'D'	633	629	367	619	2373	2259	3077	353	2255	637	2236	2207	361	3073	2223	2213	953	2242	2263	2217	2269	2271	2226	G318	2377
		D		D	D	D	D		D	D		B	D	D		A		D	BD	D				B		B
	Shanghai **7175** d.	...	...	...	...	...	...	...	0613	...	0632	...	0601	...	0702	...	0742	0830	...	...	0737	0801	...	...	...	...
	Nanjing nan **7175** d.	...	...	...	...	0720	...	0802	0836	0840	0850	...	|	...	0918	0948	1019	1014	...	...	|	|	1157	...	...	...
	Nanchang **7194** d.	...	...	...	...	|	...	|	|	|	|	0842	|	...	|	|	|	|	1033x	...	|	|	|	1238x	...	1310x
0	**Wuhan** Hankou ♣ d.	0649	0725	0759	0923	1026	1041	1107	1128	1133	1200	1205	1215	1210	1243	1248	1328	1259	1304	1404	1432	1437	1509	1544	1611	1605
04	Jingzhou d.	0807	0846	0927	1050	|	1203	1232	1250	|	1316	1326	1336	|	1413	1422	1457	|	1441	|	1549	1559	1648	|	1726	1736
92	**Yichang** dong ♣ d.	0851	0932	1007	1136	1226	1243	1312	1329	1349	1400	1406	1417	1425	1452	1506	1536	1447	1521	1616	1630	1640	1731	1803	1800	1816
67	Lichuan d.	1134	1206	1239	1423	1450	1520	1544	1601	1622	1633	1644	1717	1654	|	1747	1814	|	1805	1851	1914	1924	2023	2030	...	2043
45	**Chongqing** bei **7140** a.	1345	1405	1437	1626	1648	1718	1735	1800	1819	1836	1847	1920	1904	1915	1938	2010	1853	1957	2048	2113	2121	2212	2228	...	2241
58	**Chengdu** dong **7140** a.	1623	...	1707	1848	1919	1939	1944	2030	2036	2042	2052	2144	2150	...	2156	...	2058	2215	2315	...	...	...	...	...	...

unmarked trains efix 'D'	2378	3074	G316	2214	2234	2272	2218	2228	620	954	354	2244	638	2224	2208	3078	2256	616	2264	2238	2374	368	2260	630	634
	B				B			B		D	D	BD	D	A	D		D	D	D	B	D	D	D		D
engdu dong **7140** d.	...	...	...	...	...	...	...	...	0700	0747	0757	0618	0710	0735	0807	0818	0813	0903	0909	0918	0924	1052	1022	...	1327
ongqing bei **7140** d.	0550	0632	...	0713	0738	0821	0837	0849	0908	0953	1017	0900	0936	0947	1026	1037	1100	1105	1117	1126	1148	1308	1227	1431	1541
chuan d.	|	0825	...	0905	|	1020	1029	|	|	|	1216	1101	|	1153	|	|	|	1319	|	|	|	|	|	1622	|
chang dong ♣ d.	1013	1105	1107	1131	1231	1250	1300	1317	1327	1406	1446	1343	1414	1422	1455	1515	1529	1622	1545	1547	1617	1738	1653	1859	2003
gzhou d.	1049	1138	1143	1208	1322	1330	1336	1354	1405	|	1522	1426	1451	1503	1532	1552	1611	1704	1627	1636	1653	1814	1730	1938	2041
uhan Hankou ♣ a.	1207	1256	1302	1329	1455	1501	1507	1519	1525	1549	1645	1555	1617	1634	1702	1716	1749	1835	1759	1805	1825	1945	1859	2050	2157
Nanchang **7194** a.	1500x	|	...	|	1736x	|	|	1816x	...	|	|	1852x	|	|	|	|	|	...	...	2110	|	...	...	...	...
Nanjing nan **7175** a.	...	1612	...	1654	...	1757	|	...	...	1830	1955	...	1950	1936	|	2019	2056	...	...	...	2149	...	...	...	...
Shanghai Hongqiao **7175** a.	...	1825	...	1920	...	...	2133	...	...	2021	...	...	2213	...	2316	...	...	...	...	...	...	...	...	...	...

– Wuchang. **x** – Nanchang xi. **A** – To/from Table **7102**. **D** – To/from Table **7140**. ♣ – Additional frequent services operate Wuhan – Yichang and v.v.
– Wuhan. **B** – To/from Table **7194**.

CHANGSHA - GUILIN - NANNING - BEIHAI and FANGCHENGGANG 7184

hina Rail High Speed

km	D8262	431	D8266	423	2065	1503	529	2339	D8271	421	435		All unmarked trains prefix 'G'		2066	422	2344	424	1502	530	D8268	1504	D8272	432	D8280
				Ak		B	Ah			A						A		At	B	Aj		B			
362	...	0706	...	1214	1449	...	1303	...	...	1444	1329	↓	d.Wuhan a.	↑	1442	1554	...	1633	...	1822	...	...	...	2244	...
0	...	0848	...	1356	1624	1444	1424	1655	...	1617	1504	↓	d.**Changsha** nan a.	↑	1313	1419	1441	1458	1524	1657	...	1600	...	2120	...
177	...	0927	...	1436	1711	1523	|	1746	...	1704	|	↓	d.Hengyang dong d.	↑	1230	1331	1348	1414	1434	|	...	1512	...	2021	...
*	0808	|	1356	|		|	|	|	1754	|	|		d. Hezhou a.		|	|	|	|	|	|	1338	|	1727	|	2227
519	0931	1225	1511	1716b	1949b	1801b	1702b	2015	1916	1941b	1823	↓	d.**Guilin** d.	↑	1005	1055b	1116	1137	1152	1413b	1221	1236b	1551	1743	2058
675	1101	1334	1641	1832	2106	1924	1818	2139	2047	2059	1941	↓	d.Liuzhou d.	↑	0841	0937	0951	1018	1027	1256	1050	1111	1428	1612	1934
887	1218	1444	1758	1943	2223	2024	1948h	2224	2152	2210	2052	↓	a.**Nanning** dong d.	↑	0726	0823	0836	0904	0913	1148	0929	1008	1307	1504	1819

km	8401	8451	3949	3561	3563	1793	8493	8205	1779	1797	3571		All trains prefix 'D'		8202	3572	1780	8408	1798	3494	8214	3570	8454	8218	9690
	G		E								C				F	D		H							
	...	...	...	...	0702	0749	...	...	0947	1136	...		d.**Chongqing** xi a.				1818		2129	...		...			
	...	...	...	0718	0929d	1013	...	...	1200d	1348	1447		d.**Guiyang** bei a.		...	1340	1549	...	1903	...	...	2218	...	...	...
0	0753	0704	0843	1002	1201	1250	1313	1405	1445	1659	1740	↓	d.**Guilin** a.	↑	1011	1039	1257	1616	1626	1709	2140	1929	2219	2312	...
156	0906	0835	0954	1124	1327	1401	1433	1529	1603	1817	1857	↓	d.Liuzhou d.	↑	0857	0929	1149	1508	1518	1555	2041	1839	2111	2207	2240
368	1017	0946	1105	1235	1429	1518	1550	1640	1710	1932	2008	↓	a.**Nanning** dong d.	↑	0738	0803	1041	1347	1350a	1435	1915	1641a	1950	2052	2124
368	1038	1006	...	1256	1501	1541	1610	...	1733	1954	...	↓	d.**Nanning** dong a.	↑	...	...	1035	1344	1331a	1432	...	1622a	1947	...	2117
496	1122	|	...	1340	1545	1625	|	...	1817	2038	...	↓	d.Qinzhou dong d.	↑	...	...	0904	1217	1241	1303	...	1532	|	...	|
587	1205	|	...	1423	1621	1708	|	...	1900	2121	...	↓	a.Beihai d.	↑	...	...	0827	1134	1158	1226	...	1449	|	...	|
539	...	1106	...	...	...	...	1710	...	...	...	...	↓	a.Fangchenggang bei d.	↑	...	...	...	...	...	...	...	...	1802	...	1930

– To/from Table **7060**. **E** – Additional trips: 0857, 1040, 1609, 1846, 1943, 2040. **a** – Nanning. **t** – From Beihai d. 0704.
– To/from Table **7192**. **F** – Additional trips: 0843. 0855, 1723, 2001. **h** – To Beihai a. 2058. ***** – *185* km from Guilin.
– Additional trips: 1003, 1147. **G** – Additional trips: 0812, 0932, 1139, 1716. **j** – From Beihai d. 0950.
– Additional trips: 0924, 1337. **H** – Additional trips: 0836, 1318, 1753, 1833. **k** – To Beihai a. 2120.

FANGCHENGGANG and BEIHAI - NANNING - GUANGZHOU 7186

hina Rail High Speed

km	All unmarked trains prefix 'D'	3603	3613	G2911	201	3708	3704	8344	3712	G417	G2913	203	8456	3745	8350	205	3720	3724	G2917	3728	8354	3732	3736	207	3740	8356
		A								K																
71	Fangchenggang bei d.	...	...	...	...	...	...	0955	...	...	...	...	1137	1143	1302	...	...	...	...	...	1618	...	...	...	...	2150
97	**Beihai** ▶ d.	...	...	...	...	0810	0855	|	0922	...	...	...	|	|	|	...	1402	1441	1812	1534	|	1550	1659	...	1744	|
06	Qinzhou dong d.	...	...	...	...	0853	0940	|	0959	...	...	...	|	|	|	...	1445	1524	|	1611	|	1627	1742	...	1829	|
0	**Nanning** dong ▶ d.	0721	0821	0833	0900	0955	1045	1055	1102	1114	1153	1213	1327	1304	1402	1520	1548	1627	1949	1715	1718	1732	1845	1829	1937	2250
40	Guigang d.	|	|	|	|	1039	1129	...	1146	|	1235	|	...	1354	...	|	|	1711	2033	|	...	|	1935	|	|	...
18	Wuzhou nan d.	0912	0959	1005	|	1146	1230	...	1251	1245	1332	|	...	1501	...	|	1733	1819	2129	1907	...	1922	2035	|	2122	...
87	Zhaoqing dong d.	1009	|	|	|	1243	1326	...	|	|	1436	|	...	1559	...	|	1831	1916	2217	2004	...	|	2132	|	2222	...
63	**Guangzhou** nan ▶ a.	1058	1152	1129	1146	1320	1411	...	1419	1412	1517	1503	...	1640	...	1807	1914	2000	2258	2046	...	2104	2215	2116	2305	...
65	Shenzhen bei a.	...	...	1202	...	...	...	...	...	1450	1551	...	...	...	...	...	...	...	2332	...	...	...	...	...	...	...

unmarked trains efix 'D'	8341	8455	G2912	3602	8345	3706	3710	202	3719	3714	8347	3722	3726	204	3730	G2918	8351	3734	3738	206	3742	3747	G418	G2916	208
				B																			N		
Shenzhen bei d.	...	...	0702	...	...	...	...	...	...	...	...	...	...	...	...	1221	...	...	...	...	...	...	1556	1613	...
uangzhou nan ▶ d.	...	...	0736	0736	...	0832	0909	0904	0956	1006	...	1141	1153	1210	1225	1302	...	1430	1438	1522	1602	1630	1636	1647	1830
aoqing dong a.	...	...	0815	0820	...	0922	0947	|	1044	1049	...	1218	1237	|	1303	|	...	1514	1522	|	|	1719	|	1725	|
uzhou nan d.	...	...	0907	0913	...	1015	1042	|	1148	1142	...	1310	1340	|	1414	1432	...	1614	1626	|	1738	1826	1803	1817	|
uigang d.	...	...	1000	1018	...	|	1147	|	1259	1247	...	1409	1440	|	1530	1525	...	1713	1743	|	1856	1927	|	|	|
anning dong ▶ a.	0813	0929	1043	1101	1119	1205	1249	1141	1342	1330	1446	1452	1523	1457	1619	1608	1741	1802	1832	1809	1939	2010	1932	1947	2117
nzhou dong d.	|	|	...	...	|	1307	1333	...	1452	1435	|	1600	|	...	|	|	|	1911	1937	...	2047	|	...	...	...
eihai ▶ a.	|	|	...	...	|	1343	1409	...	1528	1511	|	1636	1719	...	1801	1745	|	1947	2020	...	2130	|	...	...	...
Fangchenggang bei a.	0913	1029	...	...	1219	...	...	...	...	...	1546	...	...	...	...	...	1841	...	...	...	...	2130	...	...	...

– To West Kowloon a. 1513. **N** – From West Kowloon d. 1453. **a** – Nanning. ▶ – Frequent additional services operate Beihai – Nanning / Nanning – Guangzhou and v.v.

GUANGZHOU - NANNING - KUNMING - DALI 7187

hina Rail High Speed

km		3802	G2932	3810	G2926	3818	3830	3838	G408	G2936	3862	G2922
							D		H			
	Shenzhen bei d.	...	...	...	0800	...	...	...	1227	...	...	1526
0	**Guangzhou** nan d.	0652	0750	0742	0835	0847	1036	1105	1307	1448	1550	1607
76	Zhaoqing dong d.	0736	|	0826	|	0930	|	1150	|	|	1635	|
46	Wuzhou nan d.	0834	|	0918	|	1032	1212	1242	|	|	1726	|
23	Guigang d.	0934	G	1024	G	1137	1311	|	G	G	1825	G
63	**Nanning** dong d.	1027	|	1113	|	1222	1402	1424	|	|	1912	|
97	Baise d.	1220	|	1314	|	1400	1549	1616	|	|	2051	|
33	**Kunming** nan ♥ a.	1457	1417	1605	1503	1635	1820	1902	1948	2154	2305	2240
39	Dali ♥ a.	1728	...	1841	...	1911	...	...	...	...	...	...

All trains prefix 'D'	G2938	G2924	3816	G410	3820	3824	3844	3852	G2934	G2928	3856
				J	C						
Dali ♥ d.	...	...	...	...	...	...	1010	1133	...	...	1153
Kunming nan ♥ d.	0730	0753	0919	0921	1004	1038	1308	1409	1445	1523	1435
Baise d.	|	|	1204	|	1249	1306	1545	1640	|	|	1714
Nanning dong d.	|	|	1355	|	1432	1451	1743	1818	|	|	1855
Guigang d.	G	G	|	G	1516	1541	1827	1912	G	G	1945
Wuzhou nan d.	|	|	1546	|	1622	1651	1934	2019	|	|	2051
Zhaoqing dong d.	|	|	1649	|	1719	|	2033	2117	|	|	2143
Guangzhou nan a.	1424	1429	1736	1557	1812	1831	2127	2200	2105	2158	2226
Shenzhen bei a.	...	1504	...	1604	...	...	...	...	...	2233	...

– Additional trips: 0736, 0752, 0848, 1059, 1118, 1209, 1333. **G** – Via Guiyang bei (Table **7146**). **J** – To West Kowloon a. 1657.
– Additional trips: 0827, 0946, 0954, 1127, 1146, 1232, 1244, 1411. **H** – From West Kowloon d 1205. ♥ – Frequent additional services operate Kunming – Dali and v.v.

7188 CHANGSHA/ZHUZHOU - NANNING Chinese Railways

km	T81 A	T77 B	T289 C	Z285 D				T78 B	T290 C	T82 A	Z286 D
	...	...	...	...	↓	d. **Nanchang** d.		...	...	...	...
	...	...	...	...		d. Pingxiang a.	↑	...	...	...	...
* *	...	...	1424	1125	↓	d. **Changsha 7090** a.		...	0145	...	0241
0	...	...	|	|		d. **Zhuzhou** a.	↑	...	|	...	|
134	0752	0054	1625	1323		d. Hengyang d.		1931	2349	0255	0041
490	|	0422	|	1624	↓	d. Guilin bei d.		1559	|	|	2128
672	|	0608	|	1814		d. Liuzhou d.	↑	1316	|	|	1941
807	1908	|	|	|		d. Litang d.		|	|	1149	|
927	2058	0840	0505	2101	↓	a. **Nanning** a.	↑	0958	1208	1018	1725

A – Shanghai nan (**T81/82**) - Nanning and v.v.
B – Shanghai nan (**T77/78**) - Guilin and v.v.
C – Beijing (**T289/90**) - Nanning and v.v.
D – Beijing (**Z285/6**) - Nanning and v.v.
* * – Changsha *0 km* - Zhuzhou *52 km*.

7190 CHANGSHA/ZHUZHOU - KUNMING Chinese Railway

km	Z161 G		K79 H	K739 E				K80 H	Z162 G		K74 E
* *	0303	...	...	...	↓	d. **Changsha** a.		...	1607	...	...
0	|	...	0836	0931		d. **Zhuzhou** a.	↑	...	|	...	...
145	|	...	1020	1119	↓	d. Loudi d.		1416	1351	...	203
440	0921	...	1416	1615		d. Huaihua d.	↑	0948	0928	...	155
709	1321	...	|	|	↓	d. Kaili d.		|	|	...	|
917	1604	...	2207	2335		d. **Guiyang** d.		0303	0257	...	082
1146	1933	...	0154	0322	↓	d. Liupanshui d.	↑	2337	2344	...	042
1378	2147	...	0444	0638		d. Qujing d.		2050	2116	...	011
1525	2303	...	0618	0818	↓	a. **Kunming** a.	↑	1903	1956	...	233

E – Shanghai nan (**K739/40**) - Kunming and v.v.
G – Beijing (**Z161/62**) - Kunming and v.v.
H – Shanghai nan (**K79/80**) - Kunming and v.v.
* * – Changsha *0 km* - Loudi *177 km*

7192 SHANGHAI - HANGZHOU - NANCHANG - CHANGSHA – GUIYANG – KUNMING China Rail High Speed

km	All trains prefix 'G'	1321	1421	1383 G	1371	2189	85 C	1379 A	1337	1373	1503 AB	1377 A	1347	1665 A	1301 C	2193	1375	1333	1481 A	1387	1369	1329	99 C	1495 A	1357	1305 C	13 H
0	**Shanghai** ♥ d.	0610	...	0644	0721	0727	0800	...	0822	0853	...	0926	0951	...	1018	1048	1112	1137	...	1220	1240	1340	1409	...	1508	1525	17
84	Jiaxing nan d.	|	0642	0713	0750	0803	|	...	0853	|	...	1003	|	...	1053	1117	1142	1215	...	1249	|	1409	|	...	|	|	18
159	**Hangzhou** ♣ d.	0700	0731	0747	0825	0834	0847	0930	0926	0946	0959	1029	1052	1042	1128	1143	1210	1240	1311	1323	1342	1441	1500	1531	1556	1613	18
320	Jinhua d.	0752	0830	0840	0918	0930	|	1037	1025	1032	1058	1127	1144	1149	1227	1242	1309	1342	1358	|	|	1535	1548	1628	|	|	19
398	Quzhou d.	0832	|	0904	0946	0953	|	|	1052	|	1122	|	|	|	1250	|	1332	|	1421	1436	|	|	|	1657	|	|	|
500	Shangrao d.	|	0923	0936	1015	1025	|	1129	1124	|	|	1217	|	1241	|	|	1411	1429	|	1505	1519	1623	1635	1735	|	1748	20
604	Yingtan bei d.	|	0951	1004	1041	1053	|	1157	1152	1141	1220	1246	|	|	1347	1352	|	1457	1520	1533	1547	1651	|	1802	|	|	20
744	**Nanchang** xi a.	1015	1026	1046	1116	1126	1100	1232	1227	1216	1306	1321	1334	1338	1422	1435	1521	1539	1602	1615	1622	1726	1735	1846	1810	1855	21
1086	**Changsha** nan a.	1200	1206	...	1249	1311	1223	1416	1411	1349	1436	1500	1517	...	1606	1613	1713	1723	1747	...	1814	1914	1854	...	1933	2034	23
1211	Loudi nan d.	|	1250	...	1339	1354	...	1458	|	1431	...	1609	...	...	...	1708	1757	1805	1841	...	1905	1956	...	...	...	...	..
1418	Huaihua nan d.	1347	1400	...	1431	1449	...	1601	1550	1528	...	1712	...	...	...	1805	1900	1908	1943	...	2018	2058	...	...	...	...	..
1586	**Guiyang** bei a.	1540	1545	...	1626	1634	...	1750	1724d	1713	...	1850	...	...	...	1946	2047	2049	2131	...	...	2236	...	...	...	...	..
2252	**Kunming** nan a.	...	1837	...	1914	Pa	...	2016	Ja	1934	...	2125	...	...	...	Ta	2301	Ka	...	...	...	...	...	...	...	...	..

All trains prefix 'G'		1384 E	1346 F	1496 A	1348	86 C	1370	1484 A	1666 A	1322	2194	1380 A	1378 A	100 C	1372	1334	1502 B	1328	1504 AB	1304 C	1374	2190	1376	1338	1306 C	14
Kunming nan d.	...	...	...	...	...	...	...	...	...	...	Tb	0724	0736	...	0821	Kb	...	...	...	...	0957	Pb	1037	Jb	...	11
Guiyang bei d.	...	...	...	...	...	...	...	0758	...	0906	0942	0956	1008	...	1047	1122	...	1154	...	...	1235	1316	1320	1401	...	14
Huaihua nan d.	...	...	...	...	...	...	0917	0945	...	1057	1143	1156	1204	...	1243	1329	...	1351	...	...	1436	1505	1521	1547	...	16
Loudi nan d.	...	...	...	...	...	...	1017	1047	...	1157	1236	1257	1304	...	1336	1423	...	1455	...	...	1536	1609	1621	|	...	
Changsha nan d.	...	...	0802	...	0919	1026	1102	1128	...	1251	1337	1353	1348	1441	1435	1509	1527	1543	1609	1621	1636	1653	1702	1735	1815	18
Nanchang xi d.	...	0823	0943	0903	1040	1147	1238	1324	1401	1428	1525	1558	1537	1604	1623	1649	1707	1718	1746	1802	1809	1826	1833	1917	1936	20
Yingtan bei d.	...	0859	1020	|	|	|	1321	1400	1437	1505	1601	|	1614	|	1700	1726	1743	1801	1822	1838	1846	|	1918	1954	2013	
Shangrao d.	...	0937	|	1007	|	|	1349	1428	1505	1533	1629	1714	|	1702	|	1801	1811	1829	1844	1906	1914	1931	1947	2022	|	21
Quzhou d.	...	|	1110	1037	|	|	1419	1458	|	1603	|	1749	1719	|	|	1832	|	1907	|	|	|	2007	2047	|	2103	|
Jinhua d.	...	1030	|	|	|	|	1442	1522	1551	1627	1722	1812	|	1749	1805	1855	1904	1935	1945	1952	2000	2030	2111	2115	2126	22
Hangzhou dong d.	...	1123	1219	1203	1256	1402	1534	1613	1643	1716	1822	1906	1828	1839	1859	1956	2010	2034	2039	2055	2058	2123	2209	2214	2219	22
Jiaxing nan d.	...	1148	|	...	|	|	1609	...	...	|	1901	...	1853	|	|	|	2035	2111	...	2121	2123	2148	|	|	|	23
Shanghai Hongqiao a.	...	1216	1317	...	1342	1448	1636	...	...	1822	1928	...	1920	1925	1944	2055	2113	2139	...	2151	2153	2219	2259	2300	2304	..

A – To/from Table **7100/2**.
B – To/from Table **7184**.
C – To/from Table **7065**.
E – Additional trips: 0721, 0857, 0958, 1339, 1546, 1810.
F – Additional trips: 0658, 0929, 1032, 1142, 1327, 1712.
G – Additional trips: 1307, 1632, 1659, 1828.
H – Additional trips: 0710, 1003, 1324, 1537, 1637, 1709.
Ja – To Chongqing xi a. 1955.
Jb – From Chongqing d. 1142.
Ka – To Chongqing xi a. 2305.
Kb – From Chongqing d. 0848
Pa – To Chengdu dong a. 2033.
Pb – From Chengde dong d. 0928.
Ta – To Chengdu dong a. 2321.
Tb – From Chengdu dong d. 0610.
♥ – Shangha Hongqiao
♣ – Hangzho dong.

7193 BEIJING - HEFEI and SHANGHAI - HANGZHOU - FUZHOU - XIAMEN China Rail High Speed

km	All trains prefix 'G'	1651	1631	1661	1601	345 A	45 A	1905	1659	7375	329 A	321 A	1675 C	244 A	1635	323 A	301 A	325 A	303 A	1639	1689	7381	7491	73
	Beijing nan d.	...	...	...	...	...	0654	...	...	...	...	0847	...	...	...	1019	1026	1204	1153	...	...	...	...	..
	Xuzhou dong d.	...	...	...	...	0816	0928	...	...	...	1304	1155	...	1234	...	1310	1335	1529	|	...	...	...	...	..
	Hefei nan d.	...	...	...	0925	1004	1058	1014	...	1003	1451	1344	...	1422	...	1500	1532	1720	1653	...	...	...	...	..
0	**Shanghai** Hongqiao ⊙ d.	0654	0754	...	|	|	|	|	1255	1244	|	|	...	|	1435	|	|	|	|	1722	1840	1909	1931	21
84	Jiaxing nan d.	|	|	...	|	|	|	|	1324	1320	|	|	...	|	1506	|	|	|	|	|	1924	1940	|	21
159	**Hangzhou** dong d.	0802	0853	0953	|	|	|	|	1352	1347	|	|	1516	|	1538	|	|	|	|	1832	1953	2018	2036	22
352	Jinhua d.	0902	0948	1048	|	|	|	|	|	|	|	|	1614	|	1623	|	|	|	|	|	2039	2117	2135	23
438	Quzhou ⊙ d.	|	|	1111	|	|	|	|	|	1505	|	|	1639	|	1646	|	|	|	|	1934	2102	2145	2203	23
549	Shangrao d.	0954	1055	1149	1216	1247	1259	1308	|	...	1734	1605	1714	1704	1721	1743	1814	2001	1919	2016	2132	...	...	..
768	Yanping d.	|	1156	1258	323	|	1359	1415	|	...	1843	|	1816	1804	1829	|	1914	|	2026	2138	...	...	...	..
889	**Fuzhou** d.	S	1238	1357	1411	1427	1437	1540	1653	...	1920	1802	1905	1859	1906	S	1951	2143	2103	2218	...	...	...	..
1063	Quanzhou d.	|	...	1523	1529	...	...	...	|	...	2054	1927	|	|	...	|	...	2308	...	...	...	...	...	..
1134	**Xiamen** bei a.	1339	...	1550	1554	...	...	...	1849	...	2120	1958	2048	2102	...	2142	...	2333	...	...	...	...	...	..

All trains prefix 'G'	7372	7382	7764	1690	302 A	1632	1634	322 A	242 A	330 A	46 A	7390	2380	1676 C	324 A	304 A	7376	1636	326 A	1638	1654	1638	348 A	19
Xiamen bei d.	...	...	...	...	...	...	...	0654	0656	0745	...	...	0601	...	0852	...	...	...	...	...	1311	...	...	.
Quanzhou d.	...	...	...	...	...	...	...	|	0747	0818	...	...	|	...	0929	...	...	...	...	...	|	...	...	.
Fuzhou d.	...	...	...	...	0730	0759	0855	S	0920	0945	1515	...	S	1022	1105	1215	...	1226	1252	1258	S	1257	1451	15
Yanping d.	...	...	...	...	0806	0842	0942	|	0956	1021	1551	...	|	1112	|	|	...	1309	|	1335	|	1337	1527	16
Shangrao d.	...	...	...	0820	0913	0953	1042	1050	1056	1128	1651	...	0937	1220	1235	1359	...	1409	1428	1436	1725	1438	1627	17
Quzhou ⊙ d.	0642	0716	0747	|	|	1026	|	|	|	|	|	1216	|	|	|	|	1424	1441	|	|	1808	|	|	
Jinhua d.	0715	0746	0817	0919	|	1049	1150	|	|	|	|	1240	|	1320	|	|	1447	1505	|	|	1832	|	|	
Hangzhou dong d.	0807	0853	0928	1011	|	1140	1242	|	|	|	|	1334	1214	1411	|	|	1540	1553	|	1617	1932	1620	|	
Jiaxing nan d.	0845	|	1000	1044	|	1207	|	|	|	|	|	|	...	...	|	|	|	1619	|	1650	|	|	|	
Shanghai Hongqiao ⊙ a.	0923	0953	1035	1113	|	1234	1339	|	|	|	|	1430	...	...	|	|	1633	1654	|	1722	2025	1652	|	
Hefei nan a.	1226	...	|	...	1118	...	...	1328	1316	1406	1851	...	...	...	1507	1633	1924	...	1655	...	...	1722	1923	19
Xuzhou dong d.	...	...	1352	...	1253	...	...	1522	1452	1542	|	...	...	...	1707	1818	...	...	1851	...	...	...	2116	..
Beijing nan a.	...	...	...	...	1600	....	...	1817	...	...	2240	...	...	...	2016	2114	...	...	2205	...	...	...	...	

A – Via Table **7097**.
B – To/from Table **7102**.
S – Via Sanming and Longyan.
z – Xiamen.
⊙ – Additional services available.

7194 WUHAN - NANCHANG - FUZHOU and XIAMEN China Rail High Speed

km	All trains prefix 'D'	3303	2361	6501	G5314	6523	6525	G1692	6505	3262	3277	6529	6507	G2048	3287	G647	2378 B	G1686	3273	G2295	G1647	6531	2234 B	2228 B	2244 B	22 B
0	**Wuhan** ⊕ d.	...	...	...	...	...	...	...	...	0835	0855	...	...	1034	1050	1125	1247	...	1307	1205	1427	...	1524	1557	1641	18
118	Huangshi bei d.	...	...	...	...	...	...	...	...	0918	0937	...	...	1113	1134	1210	1319	...	1345	1244	1505	...	1601	|	|	19
368	**Nanchang** xi ⊕ d.	0706	0719	0747h	0808h	0852	0907h	1015	1030h	1111	1131	1241h	1349h	1313	1332	1421	1507	1506	1544	1453	|	1730h	1742	1822	1858	21
732	Sanming bei d.	0933	0944	1022	G	1117	1145	G	1313	1335	1354	1527	1620	G	1552	1649	1730	G	1810	L	G	2017	2006	2045	2107	.
927	**Fuzhou** a.	1043	|	1142	1104	|	|	1324	1423	1446	|	|	1728	1636	|	1817	|	1828	|	|	2038	|	|	2209	2216	.
1068	**Xiamen** bei a.	...	1202	...	...	1343z	1358	1508	...	...	1611	1740	...	1825	1758	...	2029	2026	2023	1909	...	2240z	2216	...	...	.

All trains prefix 'D'	2236 B	2242 B	G1648	G2046	2227 B	2377 B	6522	3274	G2296	G648	9620	3288	6504		6508	6526	3264	3278	G1694	6528	6510	G5312	3304	746	65
Xiamen bei d.	...	...	...	0707	...	0814z	0818z	0812	0919	...	0941	1028	...	...	...	1401	...	1447	1553	1612	...	...	...	1748	18
Fuzhou d.	...	0702	0819	0853	0847	|	|	|	|	1045	|	|	1311	...	1440	|	1536	|	1743	|	1748	1830	1919	|	
Sanming bei d.	...	0819	G	G	1005	1052	1104	1035	L	1203	1211	1247	1428	...	1601	1627	1652	1707	G	1823	1905	G	2037	2027	21
Nanchang xi ⊕ d.	0841h	1033	|	1147	1238	1308	1334h	1318	1355	1431	1452	1525	1701h	...	1823	1850h	1918	1929	2045	2036	2145h	2125h	2258	2305h	23
Huangshi bei d.	1047	|	1350	1423	1434	1455	...	1530	1619	|	...	1724	...	...	...	...	2103	2133	...	...	...	...	...	...	
Wuhan ⊕ a.	1156	1256	1407	1503	1539	1558	...	1612	1658	1728	...	1755	...	...	...	...	2141	2204	...	...	...	...	...	...	

B – Via Table **7183**.
G – Via Shangrao.
L – Via Longyan.
h – Nanchang.
z – Xiamen.
⊕ – Additional services available.

d – dong. Shaded services are not currently operating.

China Rail High Speed — SHANGHAI - HANGZHOU - FUZHOU - XIAMEN - SHENZHEN and LONGYAN — 7200

km	All trains prefix **D**	3111	3145	3131	377	2281	2289	3107	3125	3135	2283
				S		Z				NZ	
	Nanjing nan d.	...	...	...	...	0632	...	...	...	0810	...
0	**Shanghai** Hongqiao d.	...	0638	0732	0747	0848	0900	0939	1027	1042	1118
84	Jiaxing nan d.	...	0708	0809	0841	0932	0944	1027	1058	1132	1150
159	**Hangzhou** dong d.	0732	0741	0839	0909	1013	1019	1123	1134	1215	1228
314	Ningbo d.	0849	0908	0952	1017	1115	1131	1224	1235	1325	1339
466	Taizhou d.	0951	1010	|	1113	1211	1233	1326	1337	1427	1435
589	Wenzhou nan d.	1042	1100	1150	1209	1307	1329	1424	1442	1519	1531
883	**Fuzhou** nan d.	1253	1315	1355	1413	1529	1535	1622	1639	1729	1746
038	Quanzhou d.	1354	1418	1455	1512	|	1634	1727	1739	|	1839
109	**Xiamen** bei d.	1428	1449	1528	1546	1658	1704	1756	1809	1913	1908
151	Zhangzhou d.	1450	|	1549	1605	|	|	1817	1829	1937	1928
	Longyan a.	|	1557	1637	|	|	|	|	|	2023	|
318	Chaoshan d.	1602	...	...	1715	1823	1828	1920	1933	...	2035
567	Huizhou nan d.	1740	...	...	|	1944	1949	|	2054	...	2156
623	**Shenzhen** bei a.	1810	...	...	1914	2017	2023	2109	2126	...	2224

All trains prefix **D**	3136	378	3132	2290	2282	3146	2284	3108	2288	3112
	GZ		H		Z					
Shenzhen bei d.	...	0832	...	0913	0950	...	1031	1132	1050	1115
Huizhou nan d.	...	|	...	|	|	...	1055	1202	1118	|
Chaoshan d,	...	|	...	1102	1144	...	1223	1328	1255	1336
Longyan d.	0824	|	1052	|	|	1256	|	|	|	|
Zhangzhou d.	0912	|	1148	1226	1246	|	1332	|	|	1451
Xiamen bei d.	0934	1159	1210	1248	1307	1400	1354	1439	1437	1516
Quanzhou d.	1007	1226	|	1321	1335	|	1427	1507	1504	1544
Fuzhou nan d.	1123	1337	1352	1423	1441	1533	1549	1618	1618	1649
Wenzhou nan d.	1321	1551	1600	1624	1650	1740	1750	1826	1826	1901
Taizhou d.	1418	1637	1658	1720	1741	1830	|	|	|	|
Ningbo d.	1521	1746	1757	1829	1846	1938	1950	2016	2024	2052
Hangzhou dong d.	1640	1903	1917	1938	2001	2049	2102	2139	2142	2206
Jiaxing nan d.	1712	1929	2004	2013	|	2132	2128	2203	|	...
Shanghai Hongqiao a.	1742	1958	2034	2042	2119	2201	2159	2234	2237	...
Nanjing nan a.	2019	...	...	...	2321	...	...	...	...	...

km	All unmarked trains prefix 'D'	6207	3239	G7331	G7501	3111	G7549	G1653	3201	3295	G7349	3205	G7461	G7609		G1673	2293	G7539	G197	3213	G7575	3101	31035	G7571	G183	G7661
		♣		♣	♣						Z			Y					Y						Y	
	Nanjing nan d.	...	0614	...	...	...	...	...	...	0751	0730	...	...	0851	...	...	1057	...	1240	...	1213	...	...	1403	1712	1726
0	**Shanghai** Hongqiao d.	...	|	0615	0649	...	0809	0814	0818	|	0909	0935	0957	|	...	1152	|	1331	|	...	1419	1501	1557	1611	|	|
84	Jiaxing nan d.	...	|	|	0721	...	0849	|	0901	|	0936	1011	|	|	...	1223	|	1413	|	...	1456	|	|	1641	|	|
159	**Hangzhou** dong d.	...	0725	0716	0757	0732	0921	0904	0931	0939	1008	1040	1057	1024	...	1310	1248	1446	1405	...	1521	1629	1700	1717	1837	1900
314	Ningbo d.	...	0838	j	0854	0849	1023	|	1047	1058	j	1200	1202	1131	...	1426	1358	1601	1457	1551	1629	1751	1814	1827	1933	2007
466	Taizhou xi d.	...	0934	|	|	0951	1125	|	|	1206	|	1302	|	1233	...	1528	1500	1704	1559	1647	1742	1859	1916	1929	2047	2103
589	**Wenzhou** nan d.	...	1030	0940	1044	1039	1217	|	1234	1256	1223	1358	1406	1333		1618	1550	1753	1649	1738	1831	1944	2008	2018	2141	2152
883	**Fuzhou** nan d.	0728	1241	...	...	1253	...	1158f	1450	1502	...	1602	...	...	...	1834	1758	...	1942	2000	...	2151f	2241	...	...	...
038	Quanzhou d.	0839	|	...	...	1354	...	|	1608	1614	...	|	...	...	...	1938	|	...	...	2124	...	...	...	...	...	...
109	**Xiamen** bei a.	0907	1639	...	...	1426	...	1331	1634	1639	...	1721	...	...	...	2008	1917	...	...	2223	...	...	...	...	...	...

All unmarked trains prefix 'D	G7504	G7572	G7506	G7332	G154	G7540	3102	G198	G7662	3234	6204	G7546	G7516	3214	G1674	G7792	G7682	2294	G7550	3206	3202	3146	G7462	G7536	3212
	♣			♣	Y			Y			♣					Z	Y								
Xiamen bei d.	...	...	...	...	...	...	...	...	...	0713	0827	...	...	0939	1007	...	...	1137	...	1254	1328	1359	...	...	1714
Quanzhou d.	...	...	...	...	...	...	...	...	...	0741	0908	...	...	1012	|	..	...	1215	...	1327	1355	|	...	...	1741
Fuzhou nan d.	...	...	...	...	...	...	0740f	0720	...	0849	0959	...	...	1116	1145	...	...	1317	...	1434	1502	1532	...	...	1843
Wenzhou nan d.	0630	0641	0723	0828	0829	0900	0952	1002	1011	1058	...	1121	1216	1314	1355	1401	1517	1530	1540	1637	1711	1740	1949	1926	2048
Taizhou xi d.	0720	0744	|	|	0925	|	1037	1052	1107	|	...	1223	1306	1410	1446	|	1608	|	|	|	|	1830	|	2028	|
Ningbo d.	0824	0854	0905	j	1036	1106	1149	1155	1218	1246	...	1326	1416	1512	1547	1553	1708	1713	1741	1835	1906	1938	j	2127	|
Hangzhou dong d.	0919	0943	0953	1050	1139	1204	1300	1242	1315	1343	...	1430	1518	...	1645	1706	1810	1818	1843	1950	2019	2049	2221	2230	2254
Jiaxing nan d.	0944	|	|	1122	|	|	1326	|	|	...	...	|	|	...	1721	|	|	|	1922	2016	2106	2132	|	|	...
Shanghai Hongqiao a.	1017	1104	1038	1149	|	1256	1413	|	|	...	...	1532	1610	...	1804	1816	|	|	1949	2051	2145	2201	2306	2314	...
Nanjing nan a.	...	1320	...	...	1312	...	...	1420	1449	...	...	...	...	...	...	2007	1938	1958	...	...	...	...	...	...	..

– Regular additional trips throughout the day.
G – Additional trip: 0701.
H – Additional trip: 0850.
N – Additional trip: 1119.
S – Additional trip: 1214.
Y – To/from Beijing, Table **7102**.
Z – To/from Table **7100**.
f – Fuzhou.
j – Via Jinhua.

China Rail High Speed — FUZHOU - XIAMEN - SHENZHEN and LONGYAN — 7201

km	All trains prefix 'D'	G6383	2315	G3001	689	2311	6409	G1609	6567	685	G3003	6407	6591	2325	2331	3111	G3007	6381	G1601	3295	G3005	G4309	3125	2353	2293	3291	6419
		F			♣	E	P			♣																	
•	Fuzhou d.	...	...	0825	...	...	0735	0805	...	...	...	0922	...	1022	1227	...	...	...	1412	...	...	...	...	1649	...	...	1955
0	**Fuzhou** nan d.	...	...	|	...	0800	|	0824	0847	...	...	0940	0946	|	|	1253	...	1335	1430	1504	...	1546	1639	1712	1758	1842	2013
155	Quanzhou d.	...	0713	0936	...	0839	0904	0930	0950	...	...	|	1051	1141	1348	1354	...	|	1529	1614	...	|	1739	1812	|	1944	|
226	**Xiamen** bei d.	...	0743	1006	0831	0929	0941	1011	1019	1047x	1015	1106	1126	1217	1423	1428	1453	1510	1559	1646	1709	1715	1809	1841	1925	2017	|
268	Zhangzhou d.	...	0804	|	0852	0951	1002	|	1041	1122	1050	1128	1156	1238	1445	1450	1527	1532	1620	|	1750	1738	1834	1908	1945	2039	2213
382	**Longyan** a.	...	|	|	|	|	1051	|	1132	|	|	1217	1250	|	|	|	|	1628	|	1750	|	|	|	|	|	2128	2256
435	Chaoshan d.	0847	0907	1121	0959	1100	...	1127	...	1227	1155	...	...	1346	1548	1605	1634	...	1725	...	1857	1845	1944	2026	2046	...	...
582	Huizhou nan d.	|	1039	|	1137	|	...	|	...	1408	1328	...	...	1524	1726	1740	1816	...	|	...	2030	2017	2122	2204	2207	...	...
740	**Shenzhen** bei a.	1110	1112	1333	1205	1258	...	1330	...	1435	1419	...	...	1555	1758	1810	1905	...	1920	...	2120	2055	2153	2235	2235	...	...
	West Kowloon a.	1128	...	1353	...	...	...	a	...	...	1438	...	...	...	...	...	1924	...	...	...	2139	c	...	...	...	...	...

All trains prefix 'D'	6383	3297	2350	6577	G6382	2308	G1602	G3006	G4310	6437	6441	6593	688	6569	3336	G3002	2304	6445	G3004	G1610	2326	2330	G5065	690	2332	G3008
			♣		K								♣								D					
West Kowloon d.	...	...	...	...	0726	...	...	0845	cc	...	...	...	...	...	...	1433	...	...	1525	aa	...	...	...	...	...	1949
Shenzhen bei d.	...	...	0741	...	0808	0838	0854	0926	0948	...	...	...	1222	...	1425	1451	1453	...	1602	1547	1620	1706	...	1828	1834	2031
Huizhou nan d.	...	...	0815	...	0836	|	0928	0954	1022	...	...	...	1256	...	1453	|	|	...	1630	|	1654	1734	...	|	|	2059
Chaoshan d.	...	...	0952	...	1009	|	1113	1136	1205	...	...	...	1432	...	1640	1659	1659	...	1814	1757	1842	1917	...	2038	2044	|
Longyan d.	0708	0830	|	1014	...	|	|	|	|	1302	1457	1522	|	1606	|	|	|	1854	|	|	|	|	2057	|	|	|
Zhangzhou d.	0752	0927	1100	1111	...	1200	1214	1242	1312	1352	1556	1613	|	1651	1755	|	|	1952	1918	1901	1957	2026	|	|	2206	|
Xiamen bei d.	0822	0950	1132	1135	...	1224	1240	1315x	1336	1417	1622	1638	1616x	1720	1821	1823	1847	2016	1955x	1926	2021	2050	2207	2202	2227	2352x
Quanzhou d.	0855	1018	...	|	...	|	1307	...	1403	1444	1656	1706	...	1746	1911	1852	1922	2043	...	1953	|	2123	|	...	...	...
Fuzhou nan a.	1004	1127	...	1300	...	1400	1411	...	1505	1553	1759	1809	...	1848	2014	|	|	|	...	|	2158	2226	|	...	...	...
Fuzhou a.	...	...	...	1316	...	...	1429	...	...	1608	1818	...	...	...	...	2003	2037	2158	...	2106	...	2246	2331	...	...	...

– Regular additional trips throughout the day.
– Additional trips: 0719, 0828, 1206, 1557, 1645, 1655.
– Additional trips: 0817, 0915, 0956, 1019, 1407, 1457.
F – Additional trips: 1042, 1243, 1825, 1951.
K – Additional trips: 0922, 1148, 1414, 1640.
P – Additional trips: 0728, 1424.
a – To Guangzhou nan a.1419.
aa – From Guangzhou nan d.1454.
c – To Guangzhou nan (a. 2158).
cc – From Guangzhou nan (d. 0914).
x – Xiamen.

China Rail High Speed — SHANGHAI - HANGZHOU - NINGBO — 7202

km	All trains prefix 'G'	7331	7333	7317	7349	7351	7301	7303	7305	7555	7355
		♣									♣
0	**Shanghai** Hongqiao d.	0615	0627	0836	0909	1133	1328	1621	1726	2105	2130
84	Jiaxing nan d.	|	|	0911	0938	1209	|	1657	1802	2146	2159
169	**Hangzhou** d.	0707**d**	0722**d**	0936**d**	1001	1250	1427	1731**d**	1832**d**	2218**d**	2228

All trains 'G'	7558	7552	7554	7330	7304	7308	7560	7318	7336	7314
	♣									♣
Hangzhou d.	0700**d**	0715d	0755	0905**d**	1107	1447	1529**d**	1549**d**	1651**d**	1927
Jiaxing nan d.	|	0754	0826	0923	1152	|	1556	1615	1717	1955
Shanghai Hongqiao d.	0813	0821	0856	1014	1219	1547	1624	1650	1751	2030

km	All trains prefix 'G'	7503	7505	7507	7509	7511	7515	7517	7519	7525	7527
		♣									♣
0	**Shanghai** Hongqiao d.	0803	0857	1014	1054	1206	1356	1456	1552	1808	2020
84	Jiaxing nan d.	0833	0928	1043	1123	|	1426	|	|	1835	|
159	**Hangzhou** dong d.	0859	0956	1106	1153	1256	1505	1551	1653	1905	2119
314	**Ningbo** a.	0953	1058	1208	1253	1347	1554	1651	1755	2018	2221

	7502	7504	7572	7508	7510	7512	7514	7518	7520	7522
	♣									♣
Ningbo d.	0708	0823	0854	1027	1124	1228	1314	1527	1614	1724
Hangzhou dong d.	0815	0919	0955	1132	1226	1323	1419	1626	1725	1833
Jiaxing nan d.	0853	0944	|	1158	1259	|	1450	1658	1758	1908
Shanghai Hongqiao a.	0929	1017	1104	1226	1327	1437	1520	1725	1832	1953

– Regular additional trips throughout the day.

Chinese Railways, Duóng Sát Viêt Nam — HÁ NOI - BEIJING — 7250

km		MR1	K9332	Z6	Z286	DD5
		BC	BC	C		
0	**Há Nôi** Gia Lam d.	2140	...	...	...	0705
162	Dong Dang a.	0155	...	...	...	1140
162	Dong Dang 🛃 d.	0250	...	...	...	...
207	Pingxiang 🛃 a.	0431	...	...	...	...
207	Pingxiang d.	▬	0605	...	...	...
430	Nanning a.	**G422**	1006	...	...	...
430	Nanning d.	0823**d**	...	1052	1725	...
861	Guilin bei d.	1055	...	1438	2128	...
409	Changsha d.	1422**n**	...	1939	0247	...
771	Wuhan Wuchang d.	1601**a**	...	2306	0618	...
307	Zhengzhou d.	1806	...	0352	1105	...
996	**Beijing** xi a.	2053	...	0951	1703	...

	G421	Z5	K9331	MR2	Z285
		D	BD	BD	
Beijing xi d.	0905	1609	...	...	2108
Zhengzhou d.	1221**d**	2215	...	...	0311
Wuhan Wuchang d.	1444**a**	0301	...	...	0757
Changsha d.	1617**n**	0624	...	...	1125
Guilin bei d.	1941	1135	...	...	1622
Nanning a.	2210**d**	1534	...	...	2101
Nanning d.	...	...	1805	...	...
Pingxiang a.	...	...	2218	...	▬
Pingxiang 🛃 d.	...	...	...	2241	**DD6**
Dong Dang 🛃 a.	...	...	...	2322	
Dong Dang d.	...	...	...	0022	1530
Há Nôi Gia Lam a.	...	...	...	0520	1946

B – Conveys 🛏 1 cl. Nanning (**T8701/2**) – Pingxiang (**MR2/1**) – Há Nôi and v.v.
C – Runs daily. On ②⑤ (from Há Nôi) conveys 🛏 1 cl. Há Nôi – Beijing (2 nights).
D – Runs daily. On ④⑦ (from Beijing) conveys 🛏 1 cl. Beijing – Há Nôi (2 nights).

a – Wuhan.

BEYOND EUROPE
JAPAN

Contents

INDEX OF PLACES

by table number

JAPAN

Capital: Tokyo (GMT + 9). 2022 Public Holidays: Jan. 1, 10, Feb. 11, 23, Mar. 21, Apr. 29, May 3 – 5, July 18, Aug. 11, Sept. 19, 23, Oct. 10, Nov. 3, 23.

Most rail services in Japan are operated by the six private regional railway companies which are marketed as a whole as Japan Railways (JR); there are also a number of private railways, som quite large, which are not shown in this section. The six regional operators are JR Central (jr-central.co.jp), JR East (www.jreast.co.jp), JR Hokkaido (www.jrhokkaido.co.jp), JR Kyushu (www.jrkyushu.co.jp), JR Shikoku (www.jr-shikoku.co.jp) and JR West (www.westjr.co.jp).

Except where noted, all trains convey first and second class seated accommodation (known locally as "Green" and "Standard" respectively). Seat reservation is obligatory in first class and supplement must be paid. Passengers travelling on Shinkansen services shown on Tables 8000 and 8005 who are traveling with oversized baggage (total dimensions between 160cm and 250cr will be required to purchase a seat with oversized baggage area ticket, which includes use of the oversized baggage area. see https://www.westjr.co.jp/global/en/howto/baggage/. No train conve restaurant cars, but some main-line services have some kind of refreshment service available, often in form of box-meals or in vending machines. The few remaining overnight trains have one ber in first class and 1 or 2 berths in second. Trains are very punctual and delays are rare.

The latest available timings are shown. The availability of english language timetable information varies by operator. An english language booklet of timetables for high-speed and principal lo distance trains is available on application from the Japan National Tourism Organization in London (✆ 020 7398 5678 or www.seejapan.co.uk), however it does not list all stations. More detaile information can be obtained using the Hyperdia website, which is available in english (www.hyperdia.com/en). A holiday service operates Dec. 30 - Jan. 3.

Tickets can be purchased from windows or machines at stations. A basic one-class fare structure applies according to the distance travelled. Rural lines have a slightly higher fare. Supplemer are payable for travel on high-speed and express services, for the use of first class, and in some cases where a JR group train uses the line of a private operator.

The Japanese Railways Group offers the Japan Rail Pass (www.japanrailpass.net). To qualify for a pass you must enter the country under the status of 'temporary visitor' and your passport mu be endorsed with this stamp. When you purchase your pass from a JR designated sales office or overseas agent you will receive an Exchange Order which must be exchanged, within 3 months, f an actual pass. This is done at any of 62 JR stations (most of which do not open until 1000) and Chubu Central Japan International Airport, (see www.japanrailpass.net/en/exchange.html). Tl actual pass can now be purchased in Japan at the same 62 JR stations and Chubu Central Japan International Airport or online via the website (see https://www.japanrailpass-reservation.net) purchased via the website you can also reserve seats upto one month in advance. The JR Pass is not valid on Nozomi and Mizuho trains and a supplement is payable for any sleeping bertl but it is valid for all other JR Group Railways, some JR buses and the JR ferry from Miyajima to Miyajimaguchi. You can travel in a higher class by paying the relevant supplements. The pass valid from the date it is first used. Ages for the child pass are from 6 to 11. Prices: Adult first (Green) class 7 Day ¥44810/14 Day ¥ 72310/21 Day ¥91570, Adult second (Ordinary) class 7 D ¥33610/14 Day ¥52960/21 Day ¥66200, Child first (Green) class 7 Day ¥22400/14 Day ¥36150/21 Day ¥45830, Child second (Ordinary) class 7 Day ¥16800/14 Day ¥26480/21 Day ¥331C A variety of more region specific passes are also available.

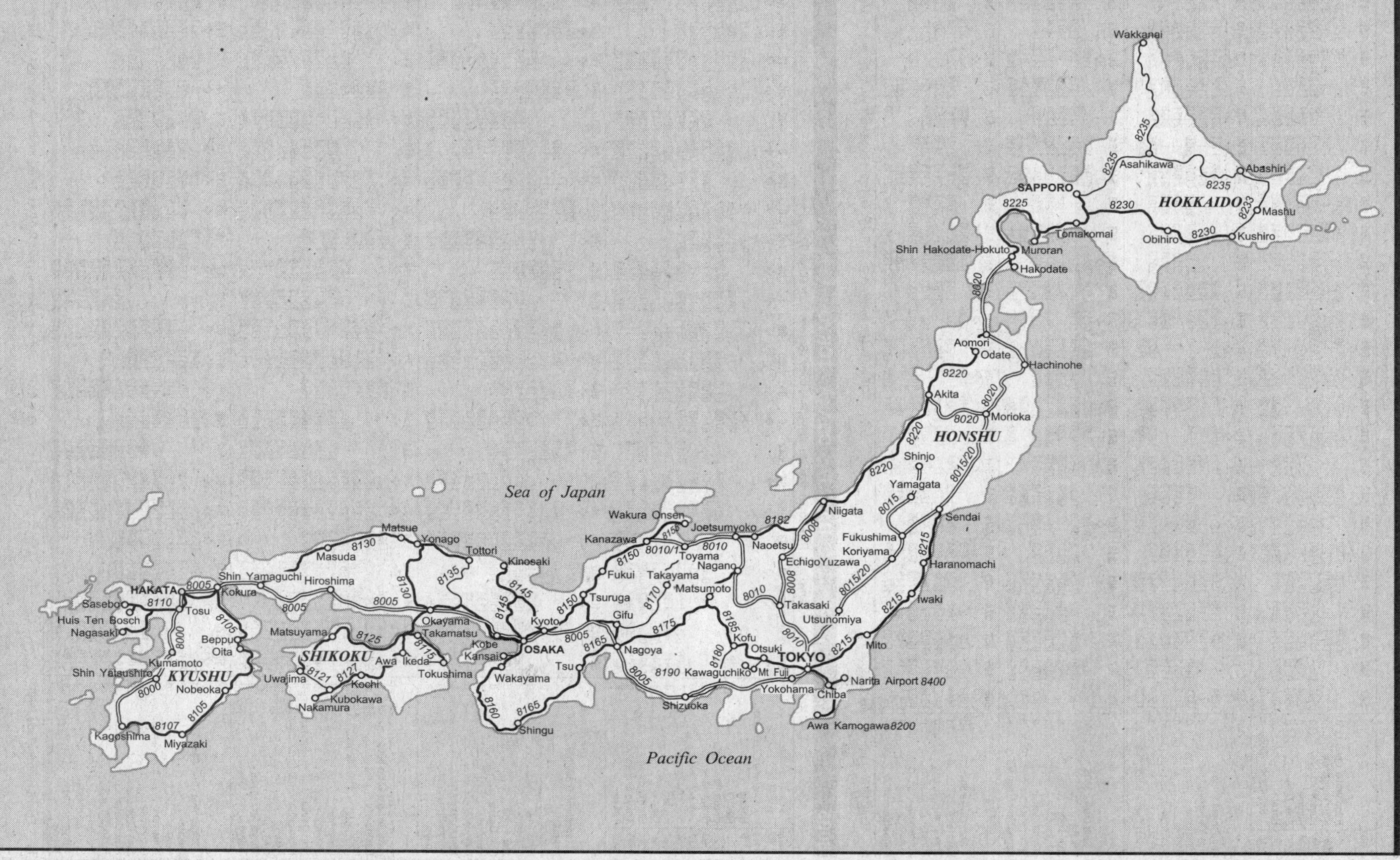

HOKKAIDO
HONSHU
SHIKOKU
KYUSHU
Sea of Japan
Pacific Ocean
Wakkanai
Asahikawa
Abashiri
SAPPORO
Mashu
Tomakomai
Obihiro
Kushiro
Shin Hakodate-Hokuto
Muroran
Hakodate
Aomori
Odate
Hachinohe
Akita
Morioka
Shinjo
Yamagata
Niigata
Sendai
Fukushima
Koriyama
Haranomachi
Wakura Onsen
Joetsumyoko
Kanazawa
Naoetsu
Toyama
Nagano
EchigoYuzawa
Takayama
Fukui
Tsuruga
Matsumoto
Takasaki
Iwaki
Utsunomiya
Gifu
Kyoto
Kofu
Otsuki
Mito
TOKYO
Nagoya
OSAKA
Kobe
Kansai
Tsu
Wakayama
Shingu
Kawaguchiko
Mt Fuji
Yokohama
Chiba
Narita Airport 8400
Awa Kamogawa 8200
Shizuoka
Matsue
Yonago
Tottori
Kinosaki
Masuda
Shin Yamaguchi
Hiroshima
Kokura
HAKATA
Sasebo
Tosu
Huis Ten Bosch
Nagasaki
Beppu
Oita
Matsuyama
Okayama
Takamatsu
Awa Ikeda
Tokushima
Uwajima
Kochi
Kubokawa
Nakamura
Kumamoto
Shin Yatsushiro
Nobeoka
Kagoshima
Miyazaki
8235
8225
8230
8233
8020
8220
8015/20
8015
8182
8008
8215
8158
8150
8010/1
8010
8170
8175
8185
8145
8135
8130
8005
8165
8180
8190
8160
8110
8105
8000
8107
8125
8115
8121
8127

8000 KAGOSHIMA - HAKATA

JR Kyushu

Kyushu Shinkansen high-speed line.

km		540	300	400	302	304	600 ❖	306	542	308	310	602 ❖	544	604 ❖	546	548	312	550	606	314	552	554	316	402	556	318
0	**Kagoshima** Chuo ..... d.	...	...	0608	...	0625	0700	...	0703	...	0732	0748	0802	0850	0902	0935	...	1003	1049	...	1106	1134	...	1200	1235	1242
126	Shin Yatsushiro .... d.	...	...	0653	...	0710	|	...	0748	...	0818	|	0847	|	0947	|	...	1049	|	...	1151	|	...	1245	|	1328
158	Kumamoto .... d.	0601	0637	0705	0709	0722	0746	0734	0800	0810	0837	0834	0859	0933	0959	1021	1040	1101	1132	1140	1203	1221	1238	1257	1322	1340
224	Kurume .... d.	0633	0709	0726	0741	0753	|	0811	0824	0842	0908	|	0923	0954	1024	1042	1112	1123	1154	1211	1224	1242	1310	1319	1343	1411
230	Shin Tosu .... d.	0638	0713	0731	0745	0759	|	0816	0829	0847	0913	|	0928	|	1028	1047	1117	1128	|	1216	1228	1247	1315	1324	1348	1416
256	**Hakata** .... a.	0650	0727	0744	0758	0811	0819	0828	0842	0900	0925	0908	0941	1008	1041	1100	1131	1141	1208	1228	1241	1300	1329	1337	1400	1430
810	*Shin Osaka* **8005** ... a.	0938	...	...	...	...	1049	...	1128	...	...	1138	1228	1238	1328	1338	...	1428	1438	...	1528	1538	...	...	1638	...

	558	320	560	562	564	404	608 ❖	324	566	610 ❖	568	328	612 ❖	570	572	330	408	332	334	614 ❖	408 a	336	338	410	340
Kagoshima Chuo .... d.	1334	...	1405	1435	1505	1525	1551	...	1605	1646	1718	1732	1804	1807	1828	...	1906	...	1933	1951	2013	2056	2136	2219	2300
Shin Yatsushiro .... d.	|	...	1450	|	1550	1612	|	...	1650	|	|	1818	|	1852	1913	...	1952	...	2019	|	2058	2142	2222	2306	2345
Kumamoto .... d.	1421	1440	1502	1521	1602	1624	1635	1640	1702	1734	1804	1830	1849	1904	1925	1930	2004	2012	2038	2035	2110	2153	2234	2317	2356
Kurume .... d.	1442	1513	1524	1542	1623	1645	|	1711	1723	|	1825	1902	|	1925	1946	2001	2025	2044	2109	|	2131	2225	2305	2338	...
Shin Tosu .... d.	1447	1518	1528	1547	1628	1650	|	1716	1728	|	1830	1907	|	1930	1951	2006	2030	2049	2114	|	2136	2230	2310	2342	...
Hakata .... a.	1500	1531	1541	1600	1641	1703	1708	1728	1741	1809	1843	1920	1923	1942	2004	2018	2043	2101	2127	2107	2148	2243	2323	2355	...
Shin Osaka **8005** .... a.	1738	...	1828	1838	1928	...	1938	...	2032	2039	2128	...	2147	2221	2249	...	...	...	...	2337	...	...	...	...	...

	305	307	309	311	401 a	313	601 ❖	403	315	541	543	317	545	603 ❖	547	605 ❖	405	319	549	551	321	407	607 ❖	323	553
Shin Osaka **8005** .... d.	...	...	...	...	...	...	0600	...	...	0625	0650	...	0715	0751	0804	0855	...	...	0918	1006	...	...	1106	...	1118
Hakata .... d.	...	0610	0645	0722	0758	0808	0830	0839	0852	0906	0929	0941	0954	1016	1040	1125	1139	1150	1204	1244	1250	1313	1336	1350	1404
Shin Tosu .... d.	...	0624	0658	0736	0811	0821	|	0852	0905	0920	0942	0954	1008	|	1055	|	1152	1205	1217	1257	1303	1326	|	1403	1418
Kurume .... d.	...	0629	0703	0740	0816	0827	|	0857	0910	0925	0947	0959	1013	|	1059	|	1157	1210	1222	1303	1308	1331	1352	1408	1423
Kumamoto .... d.	0636	0701	0735	0812	0837	0858	0903	0918	0941	0946	1008	1029	1034	1049	1120	1158	1218	1241	1245	1324	1339	1352	1412	1439	1444
Shin Yatsushiro .... d.	0647	0713	0747	0824	0849	...	|	0930	...	|	1020	...	|	|	1132	|	1230	...	1256	|	...	1404	|	...	1455
Kagoshima Chuo .... a.	0732	0758	0833	0909	0933	...	0946	1015	...	1033	1104	...	1120	1132	1216	1241	1315	...	1341	1410	...	1449	1455	...	1541

	555	325	557	324	409	559	329	411	561	331	563	609 ❖	565	611 ❖	335	567	613 ❖	337	569	339	571	341	615 ❖	573	343
Shin Osaka **8005** .... d.	1206	...	1306	...	...	1406	...	...	1506	...	1518	1606	1618	1706	...	1718	1806	...	1818	...	1906	...	1955	2018	...
Hakata .... d.	1444	1513	1544	1605	1624	1644	1704	1722	1744	1749	1804	1836	1904	1936	1944	1957	2036	2044	2057	2122	2143	2203	2224	2254	2310
Shin Tosu .... d.	1457	1526	1557	1618	1637	1657	1718	1735	1757	1802	1818	|	1917	|	1957	2010	|	2057	2110	2136	2157	2216	|	2307	2324
Kurume .... d.	1502	1531	1602	1623	1642	1702	1723	1740	1803	1807	1823	|	1922	1951	2002	2015	|	2102	2115	2141	2202	2221	|	2312	2328
Kumamoto .... d.	1523	1603	1623	1654	1703	1723	1755	1801	1824	1838	1843	1909	1946	2012	2033	2040	2110	2134	2140	2212	2223	2300	2256	2343	2359
Shin Yatsushiro .... d.	|	1615	|	...	1715	|	...	1813	|	...	1855	|	1959	|	...	2052	|	...	2152	...	|	2313	...	...	...
Kagoshima Chuo .... a.	1610	1701	1710	...	1759	1809	...	1858	1911	...	1941	1955	2044	2054	...	2137	2157	...	2236	...	2309	2357	...	...	...

a – To/from Hiroshima see Table **8005**.

❖ – NOT available to holders of Japan Rail Pass. To use these trains you must pay the full fare

8005 HAKATA - OSAKA - TOKYO

JR Central, JR West

Sanyo and *Tokaido Shinkansen* high-speed lines. Service from March 12.

km		200 ❖	634	80 ❖	84 ❖	638	88 ❖	92 ❖	642	2 ❖	94 ❖	500	96 ❖	4 ❖	98 ❖	540 k	6 ❖	102 ❖	8 ❖	502	10 ❖	12 ❖	600 ❖	14 ❖
	Kagoshima Chuo **8000** ...... d.	...	...	...	...	...	...	...	...	...	...	...	...	...	...	...	...	...	...	...	...	...	0700	...
0	**Hakata** .... d.	...	...	...	...	...	...	...	...	0600	...	...	...	0639	...	0656	0715	...	0739	...	0754	0815	0821	0839
56	Kokura .... d.	...	...	...	...	...	...	...	...	0618	...	...	...	0656	...	0715	0731	...	0755	...	0810	0831	0837	0855
248	Hiroshima .... d.	...	...	...	...	...	0600	0644	...	0708	0718	0614	0730	0746	0757	0811	0822	...	0842	...	0901	0922	0927	0942
393	Okayama .... d.	...	...	...	0601	...	0642	0725	...	0744	0758	0729	0807	0822	0837	0853	0858	0906	0923	0825	0937	0958	1004	1023
521	Shin Kobe .... d.	...	...	...	0637	...	0716	0801	...	0816	0831	0834	0843	0855	0910	0925	0930	0943	0955	0934	1010	1030	1037	1055
554	Shin **Osaka** .... d.	0600	0612	0624	0651	0718	0730	0815	0818	0830	0845	0848	0857	0909	0924	0938	0945	0957	1009	0948	1024	1045	1049	1109
593	Kyoto .... d.	0614	0626	0638	0706	0733	0745	0830	0833	0845	0901	0908	0913	0924	0939	...	1001	1013	1024	1008	1039	1101	...	1124
727	Nagoya .... d.	0649	0716	0713	0741	0831	0820	0906	0931	0920	0936	0943	0949	0959	1014	...	1036	1049	1059	1043	1114	1136	...	1159
1044	Shin Yokohama .... a.	0805	0850	0832	0859	0954	0937	1026	1053	1037	1057	1124	1106	1116	1134	...	1156	1206	1216	1224	1234	1257	...	1316
1063	**Tokyo** Shinagawa .... a.	0816	0902	0843	0911	1005	0949	1038	1105	1049	1108	1135	1117	1128	1146	...	1208	1217	1228	1235	1246	1308	...	1328
1069	**Tokyo** .... a.	0823	0909	0851	0918	1012	0957	1045	1112	1057	1115	1142	1124	1136	1154	...	1215	1224	1236	1242	1254	1315	...	1336

	504	542	104 ❖	602 ❖	16 ❖	18 ❖	506	544	106 ❖	604 ❖	20 ❖	22 ❖	508	546	108 ❖	548	24 ❖	26 ❖	510	550	110 ❖	606 ❖	28 ❖
Kagoshima C **8000** .... d.	...	0703	...	0748	...	...	...	0802	...	0850	...	...	...	0902	...	0935	...	...	...	1003	...	1048	...
Hakata .... d.	...	0844	...	0910	0915	0939	...	0943	...	1010	1015	1039	...	1043	...	1102	1115	1139	...	1143	...	1210	1215
Kokura .... d.	...	0900	...	0926	0931	0955	...	1000	...	1026	1031	1055	...	1100	...	1119	1131	1155	...	1200	...	1226	123
Hiroshima .... d.	...	0950	0957	1012	1022	1042	...	1050	1057	1112	1122	1142	...	1150	1157	1211	1222	1242	...	1250	1257	1312	132
Okayama .... d.	0927	1037	1033	1053	1058	1123	1029	1137	1133	1153	1158	1223	1129	1237	1233	1253	1258	1323	1229	1337	1333	1353	1358
Shin Kobe .... d.	1034	1115	1110	1125	1130	1155	1134	1215	1210	1225	1230	1255	1234	1315	1310	1325	1330	1355	1334	1415	1410	1425	1430
Shin **Osaka** .... d.	1048	1128	1124	1138	1145	1209	1148	1228	1224	1238	1245	1309	1248	1328	1324	1338	1345	1409	1348	1428	1424	1438	1445
Kyoto .... d.	1108	...	1139	...	1201	1224	1208	...	1239	...	1301	1324	1308	...	1339	...	1401	1424	1408	...	1439	...	150
Nagoya .... d.	1143	...	1214	...	1236	1259	1243	...	1314	...	1336	1359	1343	...	1414	...	1436	1459	1443	...	1514	...	153
Shin Yokohama .... a.	1324	...	1334	...	1356	1416	1424	...	1434	...	1457	1516	1524	...	1534	...	1556	1616	1624	...	1634	...	165
Tokyo Shinagawa .... a.	1335	...	1346	...	1408	1428	1435	...	1446	...	1508	1528	1535	...	1546	...	1608	1628	1635	...	1646	...	170
Tokyo .... a.	1342	...	1354	...	1415	1436	1442	...	1454	...	1515	1536	1542	...	1554	...	1615	1636	1642	...	1654	...	171

	30 ❖	512	552	112 ❖	554	32 ❖	34 ❖	514	114 ❖	556	36 ❖	38 ❖	516	116 ❖	558	42 ❖	44 ❖	518	46 ❖	560	118 ❖	48 ❖	562
Kagoshima Chuo **8000** .... d.	...	...	1106	...	1134	...	...	...	...	1235	...	...	...	...	1334	...	...	...	...	1405	...	...	143
Hakata .... d.	1239	...	1243	...	1302	1315	1339	...	...	1402	1415	1439	...	...	1502	1515	1539	...	1554	1543	...	1615	160
Kokura .... d.	1255	...	1300	...	1319	1331	1355	...	...	1418	1431	1455	...	...	1518	1531	1555	...	1610	1559	...	1631	161
Hiroshima .... d.	1342	...	1350	1357	1411	1422	1442	...	1457	1511	1522	1542	...	1606	1611	1622	1642	...	1701	1649	1706	1722	171
Okayama .... d.	1423	1329	1437	1433	1453	1458	1523	1429	1533	1553	1558	1623	1529	1642	1653	1658	1723	1626	1737	1730	1742	1758	175
Shin Kobe .... d.	1455	1434	1515	1510	1525	1530	1555	1534	1610	1625	1630	1655	1634	1719	1725	1730	1755	1734	1810	1815	1819	1830	182
Shin **Osaka** .... d.	1509	1448	1528	1524	1538	1545	1609	1548	1624	1638	1645	1709	1648	1733	1738	1745	1809	1748	1824	1828	1833	1845	183
Kyoto .... d.	1524	1508	...	1539	...	1601	1624	1608	1639	...	1701	1724	1708	1748	...	1801	1824	1808	1839	...	1848	1901	...
Nagoya .... d.	1559	1543	...	1614	...	1636	1659	1643	1714	...	1736	1759	1743	1823	...	1836	1859	1843	1914	...	1923	1936	...
Shin Yokohama .... a.	1716	1724	...	1734	...	1756	1816	1824	1834	...	1857	1916	1924	1945	...	1956	2016	2024	2034	...	2041	2057	...
Tokyo Shinagawa .... a.	1728	1735	...	1746	...	1808	1828	1835	1846	...	1908	1928	1935	1956	...	2008	2028	2035	2046	...	2052	2108	...
Tokyo .... a.	1736	1742	...	1754	...	1815	1836	1842	1854	...	1915	1936	1942	2003	...	2015	2036	2042	2054	...	2100	2115	...

	50 ❖	520	52 ❖	564	608 ❖	54 ❖	56 ❖	522	566	58 ❖	610 ❖	60 ❖	668	62 ❖	568	64 ❖	612 ❖	76 ❖	570	78 ❖	572•	614 ❖	410
Kagoshima Chuo **8000** .... d.	...	...	...	1505	1551	...	...	...	1605	...	1646	...	...	...	1718	...	1804	...	1807	...	1828	1951	201
Hakata .... d.	1639	...	1654	1643	1710	1715	1739	...	1743	1803	1811	1818	...	1836	1845	1859	1925	1930	1944	2001	2006	2109	215
Kokura .... d.	1655	...	1710	1659	1726	1731	1755	...	1800	1819	1827	1834	...	1853	1901	1915	1941	1946	2001	2017	2023	2125	220
Hiroshima .... d.	1742	...	1757	1750	1812	1822	1842	...	1854	1910	1917	1925	...	1939	1951	2001	2027	2037	2052	2103	2119	2212	225
Okayama .... d.	1823	1726	1833	1838	1853	1858	1923	1829	1942	1946	1954	2001	...	2015	2032	2036	2103	2113	2132	2144	2200	2248	...
Shin Kobe .... d.	1855	1834	1910	1915	1925	1930	1955	1934	2019	2019	2026	2034	...	2052	2115	2108	2134	2145	2209	2216	2237	2325	...
Shin **Osaka** .... d.	1909	1848	1924	1928	1938	1945	2009	1948	2032	2033	2039	2048	2045	2106	2128	2124	2147	2200	2221	2230	2249	2337	...
Kyoto .... d.	1924	1908	1939	...	...	2001	2024	2008	...	2047	...	2102	2059	2121	...	2138	...	2215	...	2246	...	...	...
Nagoya .... d.	1959	1943	2014	...	...	2036	2059	2043	...	2122	...	2137	2139	2156	...	2212	...	2249	...	2320	...	...	...
Shin Yokohama .... a.	2116	2124	2132	...	...	2156	2216	2224	...	2238	...	2253	2311	2314	...	2327	...	...	...	...	...	...	...
Tokyo Shinagawa .... a.	2128	2135	2143	...	...	2208	2228	2235	...	2250	...	2305	2322	2325	...	2338	...	...	...	...	...	...	...
Tokyo .... a.	2136	2142	2151	...	...	2215	2236	2242	...	2257	...	2312	2329	2332	...	2345	...	...	...	...	...	...	...

k – From Kumamoto (Table **8000**).

❖ – NOT available to holders of Japan Rail Pass. To use these trains you must pay the full far

For return service see next page ▷ ▷ ▷

JR Central, JR West

HAKATA - OSAKA - TOKYO 8005

Sanyo and *Tokaido Shinkansen* high-speed lines. Service from March 12.

	401	601	541	543	75	545	603	77	547	79	1	3	605	5	549	7	501	9	11	551	81	13	503
		❖			❖		❖	❖		❖	❖	❖	❖	❖		❖		❖	❖		❖	❖	
okyo d.	...	...	...	...	...	...	...	...	...	...	0600	0615	...	0633	...	0651	0703	0709	0730	...	0742	0751	0803
okyo Shinagawa d.	...	...	...	...	...	...	...	...	...	0600	0607	0622	...	0640	...	0658	0710	0717	0737	...	0749	0759	0810
hin Yokohama d.	...	...	...	...	...	...	...	...	...	0611	0618	0633	...	0651	...	0709	7021	0729	0748	...	0800	0810	0821
agoya d.	...	...	...	...	0620	...	...	0706	...	0728	0735	0751	...	0812	...	0827	0903	0847	0910	...	0923	0932	1003
yoto d.	...	...	...	...	0655	...	...	0741	...	0803	0809	0826	...	0847	...	0902	0943	0922	0946	...	0959	1007	1043
hin **Osaka** d.	...	0600	0625	0650	0711	0715	0751	0756	0804	0818	0824	0841	0855	0902	0918	0917	0957	0938	1002	1006	1014	1023	1059
hin Kobe d.	...	0613	0638	0703	0724	0728	0804	0809	0817	0831	0837	0854	0908	0915	0931	0930	0959	0951	1015	1019	1027	1036	1112
kayama d.	...	0651	0715	0741	0756	0805	0836	0842	0854	0903	0910	0926	0941	0947	1008	1007	1116	1023	1048	1052	1103	1109	1216
iroshima d.	0643	0726	0756	0822	0837	0846	0913	0918	0934	0939	0950	1002	1017	1028	1055	1043	...	1104	1124	1133	1139	1145	...
okura d.	0741	0812	0848	0911	0924	0937	0959	1008	1021	1030	1037	1053	1107	1115	1147	1130	...	1151	1214	1224	...	1236	...
akata a.	0756	0828	0904	0927	0939	0952	1014	1024	1038	1046	1052	1109	1123	1130	1202	1145	...	1206	1230	1242	...	1251	...
Kagoshima Chuo **8000** a.	0933	0946	1033	1110	...	1120	1132	...	1216	...	...	...	1241	...	1341	...	...	...	...	1410	...	...	...

	15	17	607	553	83	505	19	21	555	85	507	23	25	557	87	509	27	29	559	89	511	31	33
	❖	❖	❖		❖		❖	❖		❖		❖	❖		❖		❖	❖		❖		❖	❖
okyo d.	0809	0830	...	...	0851	0903	0909	0930	...	0951	1003	1009	1030	...	1051	1103	1109	1130	...	1151	1203	1209	1230
okyo Shinagawa d.	0817	0837	...	...	0859	0910	0917	0937	...	0959	1010	1017	1037	...	1059	1110	1117	1137	...	1159	1210	1217	1237
hin Yokohama d.	0829	0848	...	...	0910	0921	0929	0948	...	1010	1021	1029	1048	...	1110	1121	1129	1148	...	1210	1221	1229	1248
agoya d.	0947	1010	...	...	1032	1103	1047	1110	...	1132	1203	1147	1210	...	1232	1303	1247	1310	...	1332	1403	1347	1410
yoto d.	1022	1046	...	...	1107	1143	1123	1146	...	1207	1243	1222	1246	...	1307	1343	1322	1346	...	1407	1443	1422	1446
hin **Osaka** d.	1038	1102	1106	1118	11213	1159	1138	1202	1206	1223	1259	1238	1302	1306	1323	1359	1338	1402	1406	1423	1459	1438	1502
hin Kobe d.	1051	1115	1119	1131	1136	1212	1151	1215	1219	1236	1312	1251	1315	1319	1336	1412	1351	1415	1419	1436	1512	1451	1515
kayama d.	1123	1148	1152	1208	1212	1316	1223	1248	1252	1312	1416	1323	1348	1352	1412	1516	1423	1448	1452	1512	1616	1523	1548
iroshima d.	1204	1224	1233	1255	1248	...	1304	1324	1333	1348	...	1404	1424	1433	1448	...	1504	1524	1533	1548	...	1604	1624
okura d.	1251	1314	1319	1347	...	...	1351	1414	1424	...	...	1451	1514	1524	...	...	1551	1615	1624	...	...	1651	1714
akata a.	1306	1330	1334	1402	...	...	1406	1430	1442	...	...	1506	1530	1542	...	...	1606	1630	1642	...	...	1706	1730
Kagoshima Chuo **8000** a.	...	...	1455	1541	...	...	...	...	1610	...	...	...	...	1710	...	...	...	...	1809	...	...	...	...

	561	563	91	513	35	37	609	565	93	515	39	41	611	567	95	517	43	45	613	97	519	47	49
			❖		❖	❖	❖		❖		❖	❖	❖		❖		❖	❖	❖	❖		❖	❖
okyo d.	...	...	1251	1303	1309	1330	...	...	1351	1403	1409	1430	...	...	1451	1503	1509	1530	...	1551	1603	1609	1630
okyo Shinagawa d.	...	...	1259	1310	1317	1337	...	...	1359	1410	1417	1437	...	...	1459	1510	1517	1537	...	1559	1610	1617	1637
hin Yokohama d.	...	...	1310	1321	1329	1348	...	...	1410	1421	1429	1448	...	...	1510	1521	1529	1548	...	1610	1621	1629	1648
agoya d.	...	...	1432	1503	1447	1510	...	...	1532	1603	1547	1610	...	...	1632	1703	1647	1710	...	1732	1803	1747	1810
yoto d.	...	...	1507	1543	1522	1546	...	...	1607	1643	1622	1646	...	...	1707	1743	1722	1746	...	1807	1843	1822	1846
hin **Osaka** d.	1506	1518	1523	1559	1538	1602	1606	1618	1623	1659	1638	1702	1706	1718	1723	1759	1738	1802	1806	1823	1859	1838	1902
hin Kobe d.	1519	1531	1536	1612	1551	1615	1619	1631	1636	1712	1651	1715	1719	1731	1736	1812	1751	1815	1819	1836	1912	1851	1915
kayama d.	1552	1608	1612	1716	1623	1648	1652	1708	1712	1816	1723	1748	1755	1808	1812	1916	1823	1848	1852	1912	2016	1923	1948
iroshima d.	1633	1655	1648	...	1704	1724	1732	1755	1748	...	1804	1824	1833	1848	1852	...	1859	1924	1933	1952	...	1959	2024
okura d.	1724	1746	...	...	1751	1814	1819	1846	...	...	1851	1914	1919	1939	...	...	1951	2014	2019	...	...	2050	2115
akata a.	1742	1802	...	...	1806	1830	1834	1902	...	...	1906	1930	1934	1955	...	...	2006	2030	2034	...	...	2106	2130
Kagoshima Chuo **8000** a.	1911	1941	...	...	...	...	1955	2044	...	...	...	...	2054	2137	...	...	...	...	2157	...	...	...	...

	-571	51	521	53	615	55	573	99	655	57	101	59	659	103	105	107	109	663	111	113	115	263	265
		❖		❖	❖	❖	k	❖		❖	❖	❖		❖	❖	❖	❖		❖	❖	❖	❖	❖
okyo d.	...	1651	1703	1709	...	1730	...	1751	1803	1809	1830	1851	1903	1909	1921	1939	2000	2012	2021	2033	2054	2112	2124
okyo Shinagawa d.	...	1659	1710	1717	...	1737	...	1759	1810	1817	1837	1859	1910	1917	1928	1946	2007	2019	2028	2040	2101	2119	2131
hin Yokohama d.	...	1710	1721	1729	...	1748	...	1810	1821	1829	1848	1910	1921	1929	1939	1958	2018	2031	2039	2051	2113	2131	2142
agoya d.	...	1832	1903	1847	...	1910	...	1932	2002	1947	2010	2033	2102	2047	2058	2117	2139	2207	2157	2211	2232	2249	2258
yoto d.	...	1907	1943	1922	...	1946	...	2007	2056	2022	2046	2107	2150	2122	2133	2153	2214	2259	2232	2246	2307	2323	2332
hin **Osaka** d.	1906	1923	1959	1938	1955	2002	2018	2023	2109	2038	2102	2123	2203	2138	2148	2208	2229	2312	2247	2302	2323	2336	2345
hin Kobe d.	1919	1936	2012	1951	2008	2015	2031	2036	...	2051	2115	2136	...	2151	2203	2221	2242	...	2300	2315	2336	...	...
kayama d.	1955	2012	2108	2023	2043	2048	2105	2112	...	2123	2151	2209	...	2227	2238	2257	2314	...	2335	2350	...	...	...
iroshima d.	2038	2049	...	2104	2120	2124	2145	2152	...	2159	2231	2245	...	2307	...	2332	2354	...	...	...	...	...	...
okura d.	2125	2136	...	2151	2207	2214	2236	...	...	2251	...	2336	...	...	...	...	...	...	...	...	...	...	...
akata a.	2141	2151	...	2206	2222	2230	2252	...	...	2306	...	2351	...	...	...	...	...	...	...	...	...	...	...
Kagoshima Chuo **8000** a.	2320	...	...	...	2340	...	...	...	...	...	...	...	...	...	...	...	...	...	...	...	...	...	...

– To Kumamoto (Table **8000**).

❖ – NOT available to holders of Japan Rail Pass. To use these trains you must pay the full fare.

JR East

TOKYO - ECHIGO YUZAWA - NIIGATA 8008

Joetsu Shinkansen high-speed line.

km		481	301	401	303	471		305	403	307	309	311		313	315	317	319	321		323	325	327	329	331
						⚒																		
0	**Tokyo** **8010/15/20** d.	...	0608	0636	0704	0736	...	0748	0804	0824	0852	0912	...	0928	1016	1040	1140	1240	...	1340	1440	1516	1540	1616
4	**Tokyo** Ueno **8010/15/20** d.	...	0614	0642	0710	0742	...	0754	0810	0830	0858	|	...	0934	1022	1046	1146	1246	...	1346	1446	1522	1546	1622
31	Omiya **8010/15/20** d.	...	0633	0701	0729	0801	...	0813	0829	0849	0917	0934	...	0953	1041	1105	1205	1305	...	1405	1505	1541	1605	1641
109	Takasaki d.	...	0658	0736	|	0832	...	0838	0905	0918	0949	|	...	1025	1105	1133	1230	1330	...	1430	1529	|	1630	1711
183	**Echigo Yuzawa** d.	0700	0724	0805	0814	...	...	0908	0934	0944	1022	|	...	1050	1135	|	1300	1401	...	1500	1559	|	1700	|
245	Nagaoka d.	0726	0749	...	0839	...	...	0932	...	1004	1047	|	...	1111	1200	1216	1325	1426	...	1525	1624	1644	1725	1753
269	Tsubame Sanjo d.	0736	0759	...	0849	...	...	0941	...	1014	1057	|	...	1121	1210	1226	1335	1436	...	1536	1634	|	1735	1803
301	**Niigata** a.	0749	0812	...	0901	...	...	0955	...	1027	1110	1048	...	1133	1224	1239	1347	1448	...	1547	1646	1703	1748	1816

	333	335	405	337		407	339	409	411		341	413	343	415		345	347	349	475	351		417	477
okyo **8010/15/20** d.	1640	1708	1712	1740	...	1752	1812	1816	1832	...	1852	1912	1936	1948	...	2004	2024	2052	2108	2140	...	2228	2300
okyo Ueno **8010/15/20** d.	1646	1714	1718	1746	...	1758	1818	1822	1838	...	1858	1918	1942	1954	...	2010	2030	2058	2114	2146	...	2234	2306
miya **8010/15/20** d.	1705	1733	1737	1805	...	1817	1837	1841	1857	...	1917	1937	2001	2013	...	2029	2049	2117	2133	2205	...	2253	2325
akasaki d.	1730	1800	1809	1831	...	1854	1903	1916	1929	...	1949	2011	2030	2056	...	|	2121	2146	2205	2238	...	2325	2357
chigo Yuzawa d.	1800	|	1839	1856	...	1923	1930	1945	1959	...	2015	2041	2056	2125	...	|	2147	2216	...	2308	...	2354	...
agaoka d.	1824	1843	...	1921	...	...	1950	...	...	...	2040	...	2116	...	...	2133	2212	2237	...	2332	...	...	...
subame Sanjo d.	1834	|	...	1931	...	...	2000	...	...	...	2050	...	2127	...	...	2143	2322	|	...	2342	...	...	...
iigata a.	1847	1902	...	1943	...	...	2012	...	...	...	2103	...	2140	...	...	2155	2235	2256	...	2355	...	...	...

	470	472	400	474	300		476	402	302	304	404		306	308	310	312	406		314	408	316	410	318
							Ⓐ																
iigata d.	...	...	...	...	0609	...	...	...	0634	0658	...	...	0719	0750	0826	0905	...	...	0924	...	1018	...	1120
subame Sanjo d.	...	...	...	...	0621	...	...	...	0646	0711	...	...	0732	0803	0838	|	...	...	0936	...	1030	...	1132
agaoka d.	...	...	...	...	0632	...	...	...	0657	0721	...	...	0743	0814	0849	|	...	...	0947	...	1041	...	1143
chigo Yuzawa d.	...	...	0608	...	|	...	...	0709	0722	|	0749	...	0809	0841	0909	|	0929	...	1013	1031	1107	1130	1209
akasaki d.	0616	0631	0638	0653	0714	...	0723	0739	0749	0803	0818	...	0839	0912	0935	|	1003	...	1038	1103	1136	1203	1239
miya **8010/15/20** d.	0648	0700	0710	0728	0747	...	0755	0816	0824	0836	0852	...	0916	0940	1004	1021	1036	...	1104	1136	1204	1236	1304
okyo Ueno **8010/15/20** d.	0707	0719	0731	0747	0807	...	0815	0835	0843	0855	0911	...	0935	0959	1023	|	1055	...	1123	1155	1223	1255	1323
okyo **8010/15/20** a.	0712	0724	0736	0752	0812	...	0820	0840	0848	0900	0916	...	0940	1004	1028	1043	1100	...	1128	1200	1228	1300	1328

	320	322	324	326		328	412	330	332	334		336	338	340	342		414	344	346	348		416	350
iigata d.	1220	1320	1414	1420	...	1510	...	1537	1610	1624	...	1657	1721	1744	1812	...	...	1854	1937	2021	...	...	2136
subame Sanjo d.	1232	1332	|	1432	...	1522	...	|	1623	1637	...	|	1733	1757	1825	...	...	1906	1949	2033	...	...	2148
agaoka d.	1243	1343	1433	1443	...	1533	...	1556	1634	1648	...	1717	1744	1808	1835	...	...	1917	2000	2044	...	...	2159
chigo Yuzawa d.	1309	1409	|	1509	...	|	1601	1622	|	1714	...	1738	1810	1829	1902	...	1914	1938	2026	2110	...	2141	2225
akasaki d.	1339	1439	|	1539	...	|	1631	1648	|	1742	...	1804	1839	1859	|	...	1943	2007	2055	2139	...	2211	2251
miya **8010/15/20** d.	1404	1504	1536	1604	...	1636	1704	1716	1735	1815	...	1835	1912	1928	1948	...	2016	2032	2128	2204	...	2243	2315
okyo Ueno **8010/15/20** d.	1423	1523	1555	1623	...	1656	1723	1735	1755	1835	...	1855	1931	1947	2007	...	2035	2051	2147	2223	...	2303	2335
okyo **8010/15/20** a.	1428	1528	1600	1628	...	1700	1728	1740	1800	1840	...	1900	1936	1952	2012	...	2040	2056	2152	2228	...	2308	2340

8010 TOKYO - NAGANO - TOYAMA - KANAZAWA

JR East, JR Wes

Hokuriku Shinkansen high-speed line.

km		591	501	551	601	503	603	553		505	555	605	507	557	607	509		559	609	561	611	563	613	56
			R			R				R			R			R								
0	**Tokyo** 8008/15/20 d.	...	0616	0628	0652	0720	0724	0752	...	0836	0844	0904	0920	0932	0944	1024	...	1032	1104	1124	1204	1224	1304	132
4	**Tokyo** Ueno 8008/15/20 d.	...	0622	0634	0658	0726	0730	0758	...	0842	0850	0910	0926	0938	0950	|	...	1038	1110	1130	1210	1230	1310	133
31	Omiya 8008/15/20 d.	...	0641	0653	0717	0745	0749	0817	...	0902	0909	0928	0945	0957	1009	1047	...	1057	1129	1149	1229	1249	1329	134
109	Takasaki d.	...	|	0718	0745	|	0822	0843	...	|	0933	0952	|	|	1043	|	...	1122	1201	1215	1301	1315	1401	141
151	Karuizawa d.	...	|	0734	0807	|	0843	0859	...	|	0949	1008	|	1034	1104	|	...	1139	1217	|	1322	|	1417	|
194	Ueda d.	...	|	0753	0826	|	0901	0918	...	|	1008	1027	|	1053	1123	|	...	1154	1236	|	1340	|	1436	|
226	**Nagano** d.	0611	0739	0807	0837	0844	0913	0932	...	1001	1021	1038	1047	1106	1134	1145	...	1208	1247	1253	1352	1357	1447	145
285	Joetsumyoko d.	0635	|	0830	...	|	...	0957	...	|	1045	...	|	1125	...	|	...	1234	...	1316	...	1416	...	151
392	**Toyama** d.	0716	0826	0911	...	0931	...	1038	...	1047	1126	...	1134	1206	...	1232	...	1316	...	1357	...	1457	...	155
412	Shin Takaoka d.	0725	|	0920	...	|	...	1047	...	|	1134	...	|	1215	...	|	...	1324	...	1406	...	1506	...	160
454	**Kanazawa** 8150 a.	0738	0845	0934	...	0950	...	1101	...	1106	1148	...	1153	1228	...	1251	...	1338	...	1419	...	1519	...	161

	615	567	617	569	619	511	571		621	513	623	573	515	625	575		517	627	577	629	519	631	63
						R				R			R				R				R		
Tokyo 8008/15/20 d.	1404	1424	1504	1524	1552	1624	1632	...	1652	1724	1732	1804	1824	1840	1904	...	1924	1932	2012	2036	2104	2128	220
Tokyo Ueno 8008/15/20 d.	1410	1430	1510	1530	1558	1630	1638	...	1658	1730	1738	1810	1830	1846	1910	...	1930	1938	2018	2042	2110	2134	221
Omiya 8008/15/20 d.	1429	1449	1529	1549	1678	1649	1657	...	1717	1749	1757	1829	1849	1905	1929	...	1949	1957	2037	2101	2129	2153	223
Takasaki d.	1501	1515	1601	1613	1649	|	1722	...	1749	|	1826	|	|	1933	1955	...	|	2022	2103	2126	|	2221	230
Karuizawa d.	1522	|	1617	1629	1710	|	1738	...	1808	|	1847	1910	|	1954	2012	...	|	2043	2120	2147	|	2241	232
Ueda d.	1540	|	1636	|	1729	|	1757	...	1827	|	1907	1930	|	2013	2031	...	|	2102	2139	2205	|	2301	234
Nagano d.	1552	1557	1648	1654	1741	1747	1811	...	1839	1850	1918	1951	1947	2025	2051	...	2047	2113	2153	2217	2227	2312	235
Joetsumyoko d.	...	1616	...	1717	...	|	1834	...	...	|	...	2014	|	...	2114	...	|	...	2216	...	|	...	...
Toyama d.	...	1657	...	1759	...	1834	1915	...	...	1937	...	2055	2034	...	2155	...	2134	...	2257	...	2315	...	...
Shin Takaoka d.	...	1706	...	1808	...	|	1924	...	...	|	...	2104	|	...	2204	...	|	...	2306	...	|	...	...
Kanazawa 8150 a.	...	1719	...	1822	...	1853	1937	...	...	1956	...	2118	2054	...	2218	...	2153	...	2320	...	2334	...	...

	600	602	604	500	606	608	552		502	610	504	554	612	506	556		508	558	614	560	616	562	61
				R					R		R			R			R						
Kanazawa 8150 d.	...	...	...	0601	...	...	0614	...	0701	...	0749	0724	...	0849	0824	...	0947	0922	...	1057	...	1157	...
Shin Takaoka d.	...	...	...	|	...	...	0628	...	|	...	|	0738	...	|	0838	...	|	0937	...	1111	...	1211	...
Toyama d.	...	...	...	0620	...	...	0638	...	0720	...	0808	0748	...	0908	0848	...	1006	0946	...	1120	...	1220	...
Joetsumyoko d.	...	...	...	|	...	...	0718	...	|	...	|	0828	...	|	0928	...	|	1026	...	1200	...	1300	...
Nagano d.	0602	0618	0643	0708	0712	0722	0743	...	0808	0825	0856	0900	0926	0956	1000	...	1054	1100	1127	1225	1228	1321	132
Ueda d.	0614	|	0655	|	0724	0734	0756	...	|	0837	|	0912	0939	|	1012	...	|	1112	1139	|	1240	|	133
Karuizawa d.	0634	0643	0715	|	0742	0755	0815	...	|	0857	|	0931	1000	|	1033	...	|	1132	1159	|	1300	|	135
Takasaki d.	0650	0703	0735	|	0759	0815	0831	...	|	0916	|	0947	1020	|	|	...	|	1147	1219	1302	1315	1402	141
Omiya 8008/15/20 d.	0715	0736	0800	0808	0828	0844	0856	...	0908	0948	0956	1012	1048	1056	1112	...	1156	1212	1248	1328	1348	1428	144
Tokyo Ueno 8008/15/20 d.	0735	0755	0819	0827	0847	0903	0915	...	0927	1007	1015	1031	1107	1115	1132	...	1215	1231	1307	1347	1407	1447	150
Tokyo 8008/15/20 a.	0740	0800	0824	0832	0852	0908	0920	...	0932	1012	1020	1036	1112	1120	1136	...	1220	1236	1312	1352	1412	1452	151

	564	620	566	622	624	568	626		510	628	570	512	572	514	630		574	576	516	632	578	518	59
									R			R		R					R			R	
Kanazawa 8150 d.	1257	...	1357	...	...	1447	...	...	1556	...	1610	1648	1651	1756	...	...	1810	1903	1919	...	2018	2101	213
Shin Takaoka d.	1311	...	1411	...	...	1501	...	...	|	...	1624	|	1705	|	...	...	1824	1917	|	...	2032	|	214
Toyama d.	1320	...	1420	...	...	1510	...	...	1616	...	1634	1707	1715	1816	...	...	1833	1926	1938	...	2042	2121	215
Joetsumyoko d.	1400	...	1500	...	...	1554	...	...	|	...	1714	|	1758	|	...	...	1914	2010	|	...	2122	|	223
Nagano d.	1425	1428	1521	1524	1541	1619	1624	...	1704	1709	1735	1756	1822	1904	1908	...	1939	2035	2027	2116	2147	2209	230
Ueda d.	|	1440	|	1536	1553	1631	1637	...	|	1722	1747	|	1835	|	1920	...	1951	2047	|	2128	2159	|	...
Karuizawa d.	|	1500	|	1555	1612	1647	1656	...	|	1741	1807	|	1855	|	1940	...	2010	2106	|	2148	2219	|	...
Takasaki d.	1502	1515	1602	1615	1628	1703	1715	...	|	1801	1823	|	1911	|	1959	...	2026	2122	|	2208	2234	|	...
Omiya 8008/15/20 d.	1528	1548	1628	1648	1656	1728	1748	...	1804	1828	1848	1855	1936	2001	2027	...	2051	2148	2132	2236	2300	2306	...
Tokyo Ueno 8008/15/20 d.	1547	1607	1647	1707	1715	1747	1807	...	1823	1847	1907	1915	1955	|	2047	...	2111	2207	2151	2255	2319	2327	...
Tokyo 8008/15/20 a.	1552	1612	1652	1712	1720	1752	1812	...	1828	1852	1912	1920	2000	2023	2052	...	2116	2212	2156	2300	2324	2332	...

ADDITIONAL SERVICES TOYAMA - KANAZAWA AND V.V.

km		701	703	705		707	709	711		713	715	717		719	721	723		725	727	729		731	733	73
						Ⓐ																		
0	**Toyama** d.	0612	0642	0734	...	0751	0831	1022	...	1113	1246	1343	...	1417	1517	1618	...	1711	1820	1941	...	2016	2142	233
19	Shin Takaoka d.	0621	0652	0743	...	0800	0840	1031	...	1122	1255	1352	...	1426	1526	1627	...	1720	1829	1951	...	2025	2151	234
59	**Kanazawa** a.	0635	0706	0756	...	0814	0853	1045	...	1136	1309	1406	...	1439	1540	1640	...	1734	1843	2004	...	2038	2204	235

	700	702	704		706	708	710		712	714	716		718	720	722		724	726	728		730	732	73
Kanazawa d.	0651	0758	0949	...	1034	1128	1231	...	1328	1431	1505	...	1540	1735	1838	...	1924	2025	2104	...	2220	2306	233
Shin Takaoka d.	0706	0812	1003	...	1048	1142	1245	...	1342	1446	1519	...	1555	1750	1852	...	1938	2039	2118	...	2234	2320	235
Toyama d.	0714	0821	1012	...	1057	1151	1254	...	1351	1454	1528	...	1603	1758	1901	...	1946	2048	2127	...	2242	2329	235

8015 TOKYO - SHINJO and MORIOKA

JR Eas

Yamagata and *Tohoku Shinkansen* high-speed line.

km		51	121	201	203	123	123	125	205	127	127	53	129	131	131	55	133	133	207	57	135	135	59	137	137	6
			R			R			A	R			R	R			R				R			R		
0	**Tokyo** 8010/20 d.	0604	0612	0620	0640	0712	0712	0740	0744	0808	0808	0848	0856	0924	0924	0940	1000	1000	1012	1036	1100	1100	1136	1200	1200	123
4	**Tokyo** Ueno 8010/20 d.	0610	0618	0626	0646	0718	0718	0746	0750	0814	0814	0854	0902	|	|	0946	1006	1006	1018	1042	1106	1106	1142	1206	1206	124
31	Omiya 8010/20 d.	0629	0637	0645	0705	0737	0733	0806	0809	0833	0833	0913	0921	0947	0947	1005	1025	1025	1037	1101	1125	1125	1201	1225	1225	130
109	Utsunomiya d.	0653	0701	0718	0736	0803	0803	0829	0843	0904	0904	0939	0945	|	|	1031	1051	1051	1107	1130	1149	1149	1230	1249	1249	133
214	Koriyama d.	0724	0730	0756	0823	0831	0831	0857	0925	0931	0932	1007	1016	|	|	1059	1119	1119	1151	1158	1218	1218	1258	1318	1318	135
255	Fukushima d.	0738	0748	0814	0837	0848	0852	0915	0939	0949	0950	1024	1033	1048	1050	1113	1135	1137	1205	1217	1235	1237	1317	1336	1337	14
295	Yonezawa d.	|	0820	|	|	0926	|	|	|	1025	|	|	1105	1121	|	|	1210	|	|	|	1307	|	|	1409	|	|
342	Yamagata d.	|	0859	|	|	1008	|	|	|	1104	|	|	1137	1152	|	|	1246	|	|	|	1344	|	|	1444	|	|
369	Murayama d.	|	0927	|	|	1031	|	|	|	...	|	|	...	1212	|	|	1308	|	|	|	...	|	|	1507	|	|
404	**Shinjo** a.	|	0955	|	|	1054	|	|	|	...	|	|	...	1235	|	|	1331	|	|	|	...	|	|	1530	|	|
325	Sendai (Honshu) d.	0800	...	0844	0858	...	0918	0938	1005	...	1011	1049	...	...	1113	1136	...	1204	1226	1239	...	1304	1339	...	1404	143
497	**Morioka** a.	0917	...	...	...	...	...	...	...	...	...	1206	...	...	...	1254	...	...	...	1354	...	...	1454	...	...	155

	139	139	63	141	141	65	143	143	67	145	145	147	149	149	151	153	153	157	157	219	69	159	159	221	22
	R			R			R			R			R			R		R				R			
Tokyo 8010 8020 d.	1300	1300	1336	1400	1400	1436	1500	1500	1536	1600	1600	1636	1700	1700	1728	1800	1800	1916	1916	1928	2020	2044	2044	2056	214
Tokyo Ueno 8010 8020 d.	1306	1306	1342	1406	1406	1442	1506	1506	1542	1606	1606	1642	1706	1706	1734	1806	1806	1922	1922	1934	2026	2050	2050	2102	215
Omiya 8010 8020 d.	1325	1325	1401	1425	1425	1501	1525	1525	1601	1625	1625	1701	1725	1725	1753	1825	1825	1941	1941	1953	2045	2109	2109	2121	220
Utsunomiya d.	1349	1349	1430	1449	1449	1530	1549	1549	1630	1649	1649	1730	1749	1749	1817	1849	1849	2008	2008	2025	2110	2133	2133	2149	223
Koriyama d.	1418	1418	1458	1518	1518	1558	1618	1618	1658	1718	1718	1802	1818	1818	1854	1918	1918	2038	2038	2101	2141	2202	2202	2227	230
Fukushima d.	1435	1437	1517	1535	1537	1617	1635	1637	1717	1735	1737	1817	1836	1837	1917	1937	1938	2056	2057	2117	2155	2219	2220	2241	232
Yonezawa d.	1512	|	|	1611	|	|	1707	|	|	1808	|	|	1909	|	|	2012	|	2128	|	|	|	2251	|	|	|
Yamagata d.	1550	|	|	1650	|	|	1746	|	|	1844	|	|	1945	|	|	2047	|	2159	|	|	|	2326	|	|	|
Murayama d.	...	|	|	1714	|	|	...	|	|	1906	|	|	...	|	|	...	|	2221	|	|	|	...	|	|	|
Shinjo a.	...	|	|	1741	|	|	...	|	|	1929	|	|	...	|	|	...	|	2245	|	|	|	...	|	|	|
Sendai (Honshu) d.	...	1504	1539	...	1605	1639	...	1705	1739	...	1806	1839	...	1903	1937	...	1959	...	2123	2142	2220	...	2246	2302	234
Morioka a.	...	...	1654	...	...	1754	...	...	1854	...	...	...	...	...	...	...	...	...	...	...	2331	...	...	...	...

A – Additional trips: 0856, 1212, 1412, 1612, 1736, 1828, 1836.

For return service see next page ▷ ▷ ▷

JR East — TOKYO - SHINJO and MORIOKA — 8015

Yamagata and *Tohoku Shinkansen* high-speed line.

	202	204	206	122	122	124	124	126	50	128	128	210	130	132	132	134	136	136	52	138	138	212	54	140	140	56
			C	[R]		[R]				[R]				[R]			[R]			[R]				[R]		
orioka ... d.	...	...	...	...	...	...	*0631*	...	0701	...	...	...	...	...	...	...	...	...	1008	...	...	...	1108	...	...	1208
endai (Honshu) ... d.	0607	0625	0651	...	0711	...	0745	0806	0821	...	0840	0900	0925	...	0941	1016	...	1041	1125	...	1144	1200	1225	...	1244	1325
Shinjo ... d.	|	|	|	0540	|	...	|	|	|	0716	|	|	|	...	|	|	0916	|	|	...	|	|	|	1117	|	|
Murayama ... d.	|	|	|	0603	|	...	|	|	|	0740	|	|	|	...	|	|	0940	|	|	...	|	|	|	1140	|	|
Yamagata ... d.	|	|	|	0625	|	0708	|	|	|	0802	|	|	|	0903	|	|	1002	|	|	1057	|	|	|	1208	|	|
Yonezawa ... d.	|	|	|	0702	|	0738	|	|	|	0840	|	|	|	0937	|	|	1037	|	|	1138	|	|	|	1238	|	|
ukushima ... d.	0633	0647	0717	0739	0739	0815	0815	0835	0843	0916	0916	0923	0950	1014	1014	1041	1116	1116	1151	1216	1216	1223	1251	1316	1316	1351
oriyama ... d.	0647	0705	0731	0754	0754	|	|	0850	0857	0930	0930	0937	1004	1028	1028	1100	1130	1130	1206	1230	1230	1237	1306	1330	1330	1406
tsunomiya ... d.	0723	0743	0811	0823	0823	|	|	0919	0935	0958	0958	1021	1034	1058	1058	1135	1158	1158	1235	1258	1258	1321	1335	1358	1358	1435
miya ... **8010/20** d.	0751	0812	0840	0848	0848	0914	0914	0944	1000	1024	1024	1052	1100	1124	1124	1200	1224	1224	1300	1324	1324	1352	1400	1424	1424	1500
okyo Ueno . **8010/20** d.	0811	0831	0859	0907	0907	|	|	1003	1019	1043	1043	1111	1119	1143	1143	1219	1243	1243	1319	1343	1343	1411	1419	1443	1443	1519
okyo ... **8010/20** a.	0816	0836	0904	0912	0912	0935	0935	1006	1024	1048	1048	1116	1124	1148	1148	1224	1248	1248	1324	1348	1348	1416	1424	1448	1448	1524

	142	142	214	58	144	144	60	146	146	216	62	148	148	150	150	154	154	156	156	64	66	158	158	68	160	70
	[R]				[R]			[R]				[R]		[R]		[R]		[R]				[R]			[R]	
orioka ... d.	...	...	...	1308	...	...	1408	...	...	...	1508	...	...	...	...	...	...	...	...	1754	1841	...	...	1940	...	2029
endai (Honshu) ... d.	...	1344	1400	1425	...	1444	1525	...	1544	1600	1625	...	1634	...	1644	...	1743	...	1844	1911	2001	...	2017	2055	...	2148
Shinjo ... d.	...	|	|	|	1318	|	|	...	|	|	|	...	|	1517	|	...	|	1712	|	|	|	1843	|	|	1957	|
Murayama ... d.	...	|	|	|	1342	|	|	...	|	|	|	...	|	1542	|	...	|	1737	|	|	|	1906	|	|	2021	|
Yamagata ... d.	1304	|	|	|	1404	|	|	1503	|	|	|	1546	|	1607	|	1705	|	1804	|	|	|	1931	|	|	2043	|
Yonezawa ... d.	1340	|	|	|	1438	|	|	1540	|	|	|	1623	|	1638	|	1741	|	1838	|	|	|	2013	|	|	2117	|
ukushima ... d.	1416	1416	1423	1451	1516	1516	1551	1616	1616	1623	1651	1702	1702	1716	1716	1816	1816	1916	1916	1932	2023	2049	2049	2125	2156	2210
oriyama ... d.	1430	1430	1437	1506	1530	1530	1606	1630	1630	1640	1706	1716	1716	1730	1730	1830	1830	1930	1930	1949	2042	2105	2105	2139	2210	2225
tsunomiya ... d.	1458	1458	1521	1535	1558	1558	1635	1658	1658	1721	1735	1747	1747	1758	1758	1858	1858	1958	1958	2023	2110	2135	2135	2207	2238	2254
miya ... **8010/20** d.	1524	1524	1552	1600	1624	1624	1700	1724	1724	1733	1800	1812	1812	1824	1824	1924	1924	2024	2024	2048	2135	2200	2200	2232	2304	2319
okyo Ueno ... **8010/20** d.	1543	1543	1611	1619	1643	1643	1719	1743	1743	1811	1819	1831	1831	1843	1843	1943	1943	2043	2043	2107	2155	2219	2219	2251	2323	2339
okyo ... **8010/20** a.	1548	1548	1616	1624	1648	1648	1724	1748	1748	1816	1824	1836	1836	1848	1848	1948	1948	2048	2048	2112	2200	2224	2224	2256	2328	2344

– Additional trips: 0734, 1725, 1743, 1812, 1919, 2038.

or return service see previous page.

JR East, JR Hokkaido — TOKYO - AKITA and AOMORI - HAKODATE — 8020

Akita, Tohoku and Hokkaido Shinkansen high-speed lines.

km		91	93	95	95	1	1	101	5	5	103	7	11	11	13	15	17	17	19	21	21	23	23	25
		[R]	[R]	[R]	[R]	[R]	[R]	[R]	[R]	[R]	[R]	[R]	[R]	[R]	[R]	[R]	[R]	[R]	[R]	[R]	[R]	[R]	[R]	[R]
0	**Tokyo** ... **8010 8015** d.	...	...	...	...	0632	0632	0716	0732	0732	0756	0820	0908	0908	0936	1004	1020	1020	1044	1120	1120	1220	1220	1320
4	**Tokyo** Ueno ... **8010 8015** d.	...	...	...	...	0638	0638	0722	0738	0738	0802	|	0914	0914	|	1010	1026	1026	1050	1126	1126	1226	1226	1326
31	Omiya ... **8010 8015** d.	...	...	...	...	0657	0657	0741	0757	0757	0821	0843	0932	0932	0959	1029	1045	1045	1109	1145	1145	1245	1245	1345
325	Sendai (Honshu) ... d.	...	...	0640	0640	0806	0805	0850	0905	0905	0937	0951	1041	1041	1107	1139	1153	1153	1217	1253	1253	1353	1353	1453
497	Morioka ... d.	...	0654	0758	0759	0850	0848	1002	0946	0948	1048	1031	1123	1125	1147	...	1235	1237	1305	1335	1337	1435	1437	1535
537	Tazawako ... d.	...	|	0832	|	|	0922	...	1026	|	...	|	1202	|	|	...	1311	|	|	1407	|	1511	|	1607
555	Kakunodate ... d.	...	|	0846	|	|	0935	...	1040	|	...	|	1218	|	|	...	1325	|	|	1421	|	1525	|	1621
572	Omagari ... d.	...	|	0901	|	|	0948	...	1052	|	...	|	1231	|	|	...	1337	|	|	1433	|	1537	|	1633
624	**Akita** ... a.	...	|	0932	|	|	1024	...	1125	|	...	|	1302	|	|	...	1408	|	|	1504	|	1608	|	1708
593	Hachinohe ... d.	...	0726	...	0835	0922	...	...	...	|	...	|	...	1202	|	...	...	1305	1334	...	1414	...	1505	...
675	Shin **Aomori** ... d.	0632	0756	...	0904	0951	...	...	...	1052	...	1120	...	1229	1236	...	...	1329	1359	...	1443	...	1531	...
824	S **Hakodate Hokuto 8225** ♥ a.	0734	0858	...	1001	1053	...	...	...	...	...	1217	...	...	1333	...	...	...	1501	...	...	...	1630	...
842	*Hakodate* **8225** ... ♥ a.	*0807*	*0934*	...	*1030*	*1124*	...	...	...	...	...	*1251*	...	...	*1402*	...	...	...	*1529*	...	...	...	*1705*	...

	25	27	27	29	31	31	33	35	35	105	39		39	107	41	41	109	43	43	111	45	45	47
	[R]	[R]	[R]	[R]	[R]	[R]	[R]	[R]	[R]	[R]	[R]		[R]	[R]	[R]	[R]	[R]	[R]	[R]	[R]	[R]	[R]	[R]
okyo ... **8010 8015** d.	1320	1420	1420	1428	1520	1520	1528	1620	1620	1656	1720	...	1720	1756	1820	1820	1856	1920	1920	1940	2016	2016	2136
okyo Ueno ... **8010 8015** d.	1326	1426	1426	1434	1526	1526	1534	1626	1626	1702	1726	...	1726	1802	1826	1826	1902	1926	1926	1946	2022	2022	|
miya ... **8010 8015** d.	1345	1445	1445	1453	1545	1545	1553	1645	1645	1721	1745	...	1745	1821	1845	1845	1921	1945	1945	2005	2041	2041	2159
endai (Honshu) ... d.	1453	1553	1553	1603	1653	1653	1702	1753	1753	1830	1854	...	1854	1930	1953	1953	2030	2054	2054	2114	2148	2148	2307
orioka ... d.	1537	1635	1637	1653	1735	1737	1753	1835	1837	1944	1935	...	1937	2044	2035	2037	2143	2136	2138	2222	2230	2231	...
Tazawako ... d.	|	1712	|	|	1809	|	|	1912	|	...	2007	...	|	...	2111	|	...	2206	|	...	|	|	...
Kakunodate ... d.	|	1728	|	|	1823	|	|	1927	|	...	2021	...	|	...	2124	|	...	2219	|	...	|	|	...
Omagari ... d.	|	1741	|	|	1835	|	|	1941	|	...	2033	...	|	...	2136	|	...	2232	|	...	2323	|	...
Akita ... a.	|	1812	|	|	1906	|	|	2012	|	...	2104	...	|	...	2207	|	...	2302	|	...	2353	|	...
achinohe ... d.	1614	...	1705	|	...	1812	|	...	1909	...	...	...	2013	...	...	2109	...	...	2206	...	...	2308	...
in **Aomori** ... d.	1645	...	1729	1743	...	1839	1845	...	1937	...	...	...	2042	...	...	2137	...	...	2232**a**	...	...	2336	...
in **Hakodate Hokuto 8225** ... ♥ a.	1747	...	...	1840	...	...	1947	...	...	...	...	...	2144	...	...	...	...	...	2329**a**	...	...	...	...
Hakodate **8225** ... ♥ a.	*1820*	...	...	*1905*	...	...	*2015*	...	...	...	...	...	*2214*	...	...	...	...	...	*2359*	...	...	...	...

	2	102	4	104	6	6	8	106	10	10	108	14	14	16	16	18	18	20	22	22	24	24	28
	[R]	[R]	[R]	[R]	[R]	[R]	[R]	[R]	[R]	[R]	[R]	[R]	[R]	[R]	[R]	[R]	[R]	[R]	[R]	[R]	[R]	[R]	[R]
Hakodate **8225** ... ♥ d.	...	...	...	...	...	...	...	...	...	*0607*	...	...	*0659*	...	...	...	*0848*	...	...	*1021*	...	...	...
in **Hakodate Hokuto 8225** ... ♥ d.	...	...	...	...	...	...	...	...	...	0639	...	...	0738	...	...	...	0935	...	...	1053	...	...	...
in **Aomori** ... d.	...	...	0618	...	...	...	0649	...	...	0743	...	...	0837	...	0952	...	1039	1122	...	1152	...	1239	...
achinohe ... d.	...	...	0642	...	...	...	0717	...	...	0811	...	...	0905	...	1017	...	1107	|	...	1216	...	1307	...
Akita ... d.	...	...	|	...	0608	...	|	...	0716	|	...	0811	|	0912	|	1007	|	|	1107	|	1213	|	1306
Omagari ... d.	...	...	|	...	0641	...	|	...	0748	|	...	0843	|	0950	|	1039	|	|	1141	|	1246	|	1339
Kakunodate ... d.	...	...	|	...	|	...	|	...	0758	|	...	0856	|	1000	|	1054	|	|	1156	|	1257	|	1350
Tazawako ... d.	...	...	|	...	|	...	|	...	0812	|	...	0909	|	1014	|	1108	|	|	1212	|	1311	|	1408
orioka ... d.	...	0610	0711	0728	0737	0737	0802	0811	0850	0850	0906	0950	0950	1050	1050	1150	1150	1217	1250	1250	1350	1350	1450
endai (Honshu) ... d.	0637	0721	0753	0845	0817	0817	0857	0922	0931	0931	1022	1031	1031	1131	1131	1231	1231	1257	1331	1331	1431	1431	1531
miya ... **8010 8015** d.	0744	0832	0900	0952	0925	0926	1008	1032	1040	1040	1132	1140	1140	1240	1240	1340	1340	1407	1440	1440	1540	1540	1640
okyo Ueno ... **8010 8015** d.	|	0851	|	1011	|	|	1027	1052	1059	1059	1151	1159	1159	1259	1259	1359	1359	1427	1459	1459	1559	1559	1659
okyo ... **8010 8015** a.	0807	0856	0923	1016	0947	0947	1032	1056	1104	1104	1156	1204	1204	1304	1304	1404	1404	1432	1504	1504	1604	1604	1704

	28	30	32	32	110	34	34	112	36	38	38		40	42	42	44	46	46	48	48	96	96	98
	[R]	[R]	[R]	[R]	[R]	[R]	[R]	[R]	[R]	[R]	[R]		[R]	[R]	[R]	[R]	[R]	[R]	[R]	[R]	[R]	[R]	[R]
Hakodate **8225** ... ♥ d.	*1202*	...	...	*1302*	...	...	*1419*	...	...	...	...	...	*1545*	...	...	*1655*	...	...	...	*1808*	...	*1906*	*2006*
in **Hakodate Hokuto 8225** ... ♥ d.	1248	...	...	1339	...	...	1448	...	...	...	...	...	1620	...	...	1726	...	...	...	1840	...	1941	2043
in **Aomori** ... d.	1352	...	...	1438	...	...	1552	...	1617	...	1638	...	1722	...	1744	1825	...	1838	...	1944	...	2040	2147
achinohe ... d.	1416	...	...	1506	...	...	1616	...	1641	...	1706	...	|	...	1812	|	...	1906	...	2012	...	2108	2215
Akita ... d.	|	...	1414	|	...	1506	|	...	|	1612	|	...	|	1710	|	|	1816	|	1910	|	2014	|	|
Omagari ... d.	|	...	1447	|	...	1539	|	...	|	1647	|	...	|	1743	|	|	1848	|	1943	|	2047	|	|
Kakunodate ... d.	|	...	1458	|	...	1551	|	...	|	1658	|	...	|	1754	|	|	1858	|	1953	|	2057	|	|
Tazawako ... d.	|	...	1512	|	...	1608	|	...	|	1712	|	...	|	1810	|	|	1912	|	2009	|	2111	|	|
orioka ... d.	1450	...	1550	1550	1608	1650	1650	1707	1716	1750	1750	...	1817	1850	1850	1914	1950	1950	2050	2050	2151	2151	2248
endai (Honshu) ... d.	1531	1557	1631	1631	1722	1731	1731	1822	1757	1831	1831	...	1857	1931	1931	1954	2031	2031	2131	2131	2301	2301	...
miya ... **8010 8015** d.	1640	1708	1740	1740	1832	1840	1840	1931	1908	1940	1940	...	2008	2040	2040	2101	2140	2140	2240	2240	...	...	...
kyo Ueno ... **8010 8015** d.	1659	1727	1759	1759	1851	1859	1859	1951	1927	1959	1959	...	2027	2059	2059	|	2159	2159	2259	2259	...	...	...
kyo ... **8010 8015** a.	1704	1732	1804	1804	1856	1904	1904	1956	1932	2004	2004	...	2032	2104	2104	2123	2204	2204	2304	2304	...	...	...

– Suspended on ⑦ until July 24.

– [R] not required for Hakodate - Shin Hakodate Hokuto connecting trains. For other trains see Table **8225**.

NOTE: Some trains run on a different schedule on ©.

8105 HAKATA - OITA - MIYAZAKI

JR Kyush

km																								
0	**Hakata** d.	...	...	...	...	...	...	0622	0700	0730	0802	0822	...	0921	...	...	1019	...	...	1119	...	...	1219	12
67	Kokura d.	...	...	...	...	...	0639	0714	0800	0834	0857	0917	...	1009	...	...	1109	...	...	1209	...	...	1309	13
186	Beppu d.	...	...	...	...	0739	0804	0833	0922	0952	1014	1034	...	1128	...	...	1225	...	...	1327	...	...	1428	14
198	Oita d.	...	...	...	0700	0749	0816	0844	0932	1007	1024	1044	...	1138	...	1207	1236	...	...	1336	...	1406	1437	15
322	Nobeoka d.	0512	0710	0804	0912	...	1032	...	...	1208	...	...	1312	...	...	1409	...	...	1514	...	...	1612	...	
405	**Miyazaki** d.	0620	0836	0916	1020	...	1139	...	...	1310	...	...	1415	...	...	1523	...	...	1625	...	...	1729	...	
412	**Miyazaki** Airport a.	0630	0847	0929	1032	...	1149	...	...	1319	...	...	1426	...	...	1533	...	...	1637	...	...	1740	...	

Hakata d.	...	1319	1357	...	1419	1457	...	1519	1557	...	1619	1657	1719	1757	...	1819	1857	1919	1959	2020	2104	2205	22
Kokura d.	...	1409	1439	...	1509	1541	...	1608	1641	...	1709	1741	1808	1841	...	1911	1941	2012	2047	2110	2153	2302	23
Beppu d.	...	1525	1550	...	1627	1650	...	1726	1752	...	1827	1852	1925	1953	...	2035	2052	2136	2205	2228	2315	0026	...
Oita d.	...	1535	1600	1605	1636	1700	1706	1736	1802	1805	1837	1904	1935	2003	2018	2041	2102	2145	2216	2238	2325	0035	...
Nobeoka d.	1731	...	...	1819	...	...	1913	...	...	2018	...	...	...	...	2231	...	...	...	...	...	...	...	...
Miyazaki d.	1843	...	...	1931	...	...	2018	...	...	2133	...	...	...	...	2344	...	...	...	...	...	...	...	...
Miyazaki Airport a.	1853	...	...	1940	...	...	2030	...	...	...	...	...	...	...	...	...	...	...	...	...	...	...	

	Ⓒ	Ⓐ	Ⓒ	Ⓐ	Ⓒ	Ⓐ				Ⓐ	Ⓒ												
Miyazaki Airport d.	...	...	...	...	...	...	...	...	...	...	...	...	...	...	0642	...	...	...	...	...	...	1013	...
Miyazaki d.	...	...	...	...	...	...	...	...	...	...	...	0554	...	...	0658	...	...	0810	...	...	...	1029	...
Nobeoka d.	...	...	...	...	...	...	...	...	...	...	...	0706	...	...	0806	...	...	0913	...	...	...	1141	...
Oita d.	0518	0518	0556	0556	0640	0640	0714	0746	0810	0842	0842	0909	0911	0939	1007	1011	1045	1108	1110	1210	1312	1340	14
Beppu d.	0527	0527	0604	0604	0648	0648	0722	0755	0819	0851	0851	...	0919	0947	...	1020	1053	...	1119	1218	1320	...	14
Kokura d.	0650	0650	0732	0732	0810	0810	0844	0919	0939	1005	1005	...	1041	1105	...	1141	1205	...	1241	1341	1441	...	15
Hakata a.	0746	0748	0820	0834	0753	0857	0940	1003	1023	1047	1049	...	1128	1148	...	1228	1248	...	1328	1428	1528	...	16

Miyazaki Airport d.	1119	...	1209	...	1309	...	...	1419	...	...	1519	...	...	1618	...	1717	...	1819	1918	2019	2118	...	...
Miyazaki d.	1135	...	1225	...	1330	...	...	1436	...	...	1536	...	...	1637	...	1731	...	1833	1935	2034	2134	...	22
Nobeoka d.	1242	...	1339	...	1438	...	...	1543	...	...	1641	...	...	1744	...	1847	...	1950	2045	2139	2241	...	23
Oita d.	...	1511	1543	1610	...	1645	1710	1741	1744	1811	...	1843	1911	1942	2012	2055	2143	...	...	...	...	2255	
Beppu d.	...	1520	...	1618	...	1653	1718	...	1753	1820	...	1852	1919	1951	2020	2104	2151	...	...	...	...	2305	
Kokura d.	...	1639	...	1739	...	1805	1839	...	1905	1943	...	2009	2041	2114	2139	2229	2311	...	...	...	...	...	
Hakata a.	...	1728	...	1828	...	1849	1930	...	1948	2030	...	2057	2128	2203	2226	...	2359	...	...	...	...	...	

8107 MIYAZAKI - KAGOSHIMA

JR Kyush

km											
0	**Miyazaki** d.	0551	0714	0921	1017	1226	1419	1622	1735	1900	...
79	Kirishima-Jingu d.	0715	0836	1039	1138	1342	1538	1741	1857	2026	...
95	Hayato d.	0733	0853	1057	1156	1400	1555	1758	1914	2043	...
126	Kagoshima **Chuo** a.	0809	0927	1128	1227	1428	1625	1831	1944	2116	...

Kagoshima Chuo d.	0551	0737	0849	0959	1150	1419	1618	1828	2020	...
Hayato d.	0624	0819	0922	1032	1224	1448	1651	1906	2057	...
Kirishima-Jingu d.	0641	0836	0939	1050	1241	1505	1708	1923	2115	...
Miyazaki a.	0809	1001	1057	1210	1402	1621	1828	2044	2236	...

8110 HAKATA - SASEBO and NAGASAKI

JR Kyush

km																								
								A			A						A				A		A	
0	**Hakata** d.	0555	0633	0717	0729	0753	0814	0836	0852	0916	0931	0955	...	1032	1055	...	1131	1155	1231	1255	1331	1355	1431	...
29	Tosu d.	0617	0654	0740	0757	0816	0838	0859	0914	0939	0956	1016	...	1058	1116	...	1159	1215	1258	1315	1358	1416	1457	...
31	Shin Tosu d.	0621	0658	0745	0802	0820	0842	0903	0918	0943	1000	1020	...	1102	1120	...	1203	1220	1302	1320	1402	1420	1503	...
54	Saga d.	0635	0712	0801	0815	0833	0856	0916	0932	0956	1017	1034	...	1118	1133	...	1217	1233	1317	1333	1416	1433	1517	...
108	Haiki d.	|	|	|	0916	|	...	1015	|	|	1115	|	...	1224	|	...	1317	|	1417	|	1523	|	1618	...
117	**Sasebo** a.	|	|	|	0927	|	...	1026	|	|	1126	|	...	1234	|	...	1327	|	1427	|	1533	|	1628	...
154	**Nagasaki** a.	0801	0835	0927	...	0952	...	...	1054	1123	...	1156	...	...	1252	...	...	1351	...	1450	...	1554	...	...

Hakata d.	1455	...	1531	1555	1615	1631	1655	1715	1731	1755	1815	1831	...	1915	1933	1955	2033	2100	2133	...	2210	2234	2334
Tosu d.	1517	...	1558	1616	1639	1658	1715	1738	1758	1816	1838	1858	...	1942	1957	2017	2058	2121	2159	...	2230	2256	2357
Shin Tosu d.	1521	...	1603	1620	1643	1703	1720	1742	1802	1820	1842	1902	...	1946	2001	2022	2102	2125	2204	...	2235	2300	0001
Saga d.	1534	...	1617	1633	1657	1718	1734	1757	1816	1834	1858	1916	...	2000	2017	2037	2118	2138	2220	...	2248	2313	0015
Haiki d.	|	...	1717	|	|	1817	|	|	1915	|	|	2015	...	|	2124	|	2218	|	2319	...	|	0008	...
Sasebo a.	|	...	1726	|	|	1827	|	|	1925	|	|	2026	...	|	2134	|	2227	|	2328	...	|	0018	...
Nagasaki a.	1655	...	...	1755	1826	...	1854	1925	...	1954	2026	...	...	2122	...	2159	...	2258	...	...	2359	...	...

		Ⓒ	Ⓐ	Ⓒ	Ⓐ	Ⓒ	Ⓐ	Ⓐ	Ⓒ	Ⓐ			Ⓒ				Ⓐ	Ⓒ						A
Nagasaki d.	...	...	...	0558	0558	...	...	...	0625	0625	...	0726	...	...	...	0827	...	...	0847	0920	...	0948	1020	
Sasebo d.	...	...	...	|	|	0621	0621	...	|	|	0708	|	...	0806	...	|	0847	0847	|	|	0942	|	|	10
Haiki d.	...	...	...	|	|	0636	0636	...	|	|	0723	|	...	0821	...	|	0902	0902	|	|	0958	|	|	10
Saga d.	0625	0705	0705	0717	0717	0729	0729	0737	0755	0755	0819	0846	0859	0912	0926	0947	0955	0955	1013	1036	1053	1114	1136	11
Shin Tosu d.	0640	0718	0718	0730	0730	0743	0743	0753	0809	0809	0834	0859	0914	0925	0939	0959	1007	1007	1026	1049	1107	1128	1149	12
Tosu d.	0644	0722	0722	0734	0734	0747	0747	0803	0813	0813	0839	0903	0918	0932	0943	1003	1012	1012	1030	1053	1111	1131	1153	12
Hakata a.	0707	0741	0744	0754	0759	0809	0815	0825	0831	0835	0906	0923	0938	0953	1006	1024	1034	1035	1052	1113	1134	1153	1213	12

		A						A		A		A												
Nagasaki d.	1117	...	1216	...	1319	...	1419	...	1519	...	1617	...	1646	1718	...	1818	...	1851	1918	...	1955	2051	...	21
Sasebo d.	|	1141	|	1242	|	1341	|	1437	|	1545	|	1641	|	|	1742	|	1845	|	|	1945	|	|	2046	
Haiki d.	|	1201	|	1259	|	1359	|	1456	|	1602	|	1659	|	|	1759	|	1900	|	|	2000	|	|	2101	
Saga d.	1238	1254	1336	1353	1435	1454	1536	1552	1637	1655	1737	1755	1815	1838	1856	1937	1956	2017	2039	2057	2117	2212	2151	23
Shin Tosu d.	1250	1307	1349	1406	1447	1507	1549	1608	1649	1707	1749	1808	1828	1851	1908	1950	2009	2030	2052	2110	2130	2225	2204	23
Tosu d.	1254	1311	1353	1411	1452	1511	1553	1611	1653	1712	1753	1812	1832	1855	1912	1954	2014	2034	2056	2114	2134	2229	2207	23
Hakata a.	1315	1334	1415	1434	1514	1534	1614	1633	1713	1734	1814	1835	1852	1917	1934	2014	2038	2055	2116	2136	2157	2251	2229	23

km												
	Hakata ⊙ d.	*0729*	0836	0931	1131	*1231*	1331	1431	*1531*	*1631*	*1731*	*1933*
0	Haiki d.	0933	1016	1116	1316	1425	1518	1619	1738	1906	2013	2148
14	Huis Ten Bosch a.	0938	1022	1123	1323	1430	1524	1625	1743	1911	2018	2153

Huis Ten Bosch d.	0910	1043	1145	1233	1336	...	1441	1546	1645	1733	1840	1949	20
Haiki a.	0916	1057	1159	1238	1342	...	1456	1602	1659	1738	1846	1954	20
Hakata ⊙ a.	*1134*	1234	1334	*1434*	*1534*	...	1636	1734	1835	*1934*	*2038*	*2136*	22

A – Conveys [12] Hakata - Haiki - Huis Ten Bosch and v.v. See sub-table for timings.

⊙ – See main table for intermediate timings Hakata - Haiki and v.v.

8115 TAKAMATSU - TOKUSHIMA

JR Shiko

km																							
									a											a			
0	**Takamatsu** d.	0612	0705	0824	0911	1010	...	1105	1206	1310	...	1412	1510	1612	...	1715	1813	...	1917	2004	2121	...	2222
10	Yashima d.	0622	0714	0833	0921	1022	...	1115	|	1323	...	1423	1522	1622	...	1725	1822	...	1927	2015	2131	...	2232
64	Ikenotani d.	|	0804	0924	1009	1116	...	1206	|	1407	...	|	1612	|	...	1814	|	...	2017	2108	2225	...	|
75	**Tokushima** a.	0730	0814	0936	1018	1125	...	1215	1304	1415	...	1520	1620	1715	...	1823	1923	...	2027	2116	2234	...	2334

				b											b							
Tokushima d.	0541	0659	...	0823	0923	...	1026	1132	1224	...	1324	1427	...	1528	1646	1728	...	1830	1932	2035	...	2202
Ikenotani d.	0552	0711	...	0834	0932	...	|	1141	1233	...	|	1436	...	1537	|	1737	...	1838	|	|	...	2212
Yashima d.	0645	0804	...	0921	1022	...	|	|	1322	...	1423	1522	...	1622	|	1822	...	1927	2029	2131	...	2310
Takamatsu a.	0654	0813	...	0931	1031	...	1136	1234	1331	...	1433	1531	...	1632	1744	1832	...	1936	2040	2140	...	2320

a – From Okayama (depart 1 hour earlier).

b – To Okayama (arrive 1 hour later).

8118 TOKUSHIMA - AWA IKEDA

JR Shiko

km		LEX	LEX	A	LEX				LEX	LEX		LEX	
0	**Tokushima** d.	0646	0900	1138	1200	1443	1545	1638	1800	1900	1915	2015	2106
74	**Awa Ikeda** a.	0810	1014	1347	1317	1642	1745	1851	1917	2021	2128	2134	2255

	LEX	B	LEX		LEX		LEX				LEX	
Awa Ikeda d.	0646	0652	0832	0912	1130	1259	1430	1609	1713	1809	1949	2
Tokushima a.	0802	0850	0946	1128	1243	1525	1544	1827	1928	2014	2104	2

A – Additional trips: 0608, 0720.

B – Additional trips: 0547, 0622, 0753, 1905.

UWAJIMA - KUBOKAWA 8121

JR Shikoku For footnotes see Table 8140

km																					
0	**Uwajima** ‡ d.	0604	0933	1215	1730	...	...	...	...	...	**Kubokawa** ‡ d.	0622	1043	1321	1740	...	...	...	...	...
82	**Kubokawa** ‡ a.	0809	1206	1423	1940	...	...	...	...	...	**Uwajima** ‡ d.	0837	1329	1557	2015	...	...	...	...	...

OKAYAMA / TAKAMATSU - MATSUYAMA / UWAJIMA 8125

JR Shikoku For footnotes see Table 8140

km																									
72	**Okayama** ▶ d.	...	...	...	...	...	...	0722	...	...	0832	...	...	0925	...	...	1035	...	...	1135	...	...	1235	...	...
0	**Takamatsu** ▶ d.	...	...	0517	...	0600	...	|	0737	...	|	0845	...	|	0942	...	|	1047	...	|	1150	...	|	1250	...
46	Utazu d.	...	...	|	...	0618	...	0801	0801	...	0913	0913	...	1006	1006	...	1113	1113	...	1213	1213	...	1314	1314	...
164	Imabari d.	...	...	0711	...	0756	...	0930	0930	...	1041	1041	...	1136	1136	...	1241	1241	...	1339	1339	...	1443	1443	...
214	**Matsuyama** a.	0548	0647	0758	0810	0836	0907	1006	1006	1018	1115	1115	1127	1210	1210	1224	1315	1315	1324	1413	1413	1428	1517	1517	1527
311	**Uwajima** a.	0710	0813	...	0930	...	1030	...	...	1140	...	...	1247	...	...	1350	...	...	1447	...	...	1551	...	...	1649

kayama ▶ d.	1335	...	...	1435	...	...	1535	...	...	1635	...	...	1735	...	...	1835	...	...	1935	...	2039	...	2200	...
Takamatsu ▶ d.	|	1350	...	|	1450	...	|	1550	...	|	1650	...	|	1753	...	|	1859	...	|	1952	|	2059	|	2220
azu d.	1414	1414	...	1515	1515	...	1615	1615	...	1715	1715	...	1809	1813	...	1910	1917	...	2009	2012	2115	2118	2236	2236
nabari d.	1541	1541	...	1644	1644	...	1745	1745	...	1847	1847	...	1948	1948	...	2053	2053	...	2158	2158	2256	2257	...	...
atsuyama a.	1616	1616	1630	1723	1723	1728	1826	1826	1843	1923	1923	1936	2028	2028	2045	2132	2132	2200	2238	2238	2333	2333	...	...
wajima a.	...	...	1750	...	...	1855	...	...	2010	...	...	2057	...	...	2205	...	...	2219	...	...	...	...	...	...

wajima d.	...	...	...	...	...	0526	...	...	0635	...	...	0738	...	...	0840	...	...	0955	...	...	1045	...	...	1150
atsuyama d.	0505	0505	...	0613	0613	0654	0720	0720	0802	0810	0810	0905	0915	0915	1010	1021	1021	1120	1123	1123	1214	1221	1221	1316
nabari d.	0541	0541	...	0650	0650	...	0756	0756	...	0847	0847	...	0957	0957	...	1059	1059	...	1202	1202	...	1259	1259	...
azu d.	0715	0714	0753	0827	0826	...	0926	0925	...	1020	1019	...	1134	1133	...	1234	1233	...	1335	1334	...	1435	1434	...
Takamatsu ▶ a.	|	0736	0811	|	0845	...	|	0946	...	|	1039	...	|	1154	...	|	1254	...	|	1355	...	|	1455	...
kayama ▶ a.	0751	...	...	0900	...	...	1000	...	...	1058	...	...	1210	...	...	1310	...	...	1410	...	...	1511	...	...

wajima d.	...	...	1255	...	...	1359	...	...	1456	...	...	1602	...	...	...	1708	...	...	1808	...	1908	...	2017	2116
atsuyama d.	1326	1326	1416	1423	1423	1520	1528	1528	1619	1627	1627	1725	...	1737	1737	1835	1839	1839	1928	1932	2032	2036	2137	2243
nabari d.	1405	1405	...	1501	1501	...	1606	1606	...	1704	1704	...	...	1813	1813	...	1919	1919	...	2008	...	2113	...	...
azu d.	1535	1534	...	1635	1634	...	1736	1735	...	1837	1836	...	...	1939	1938	...	2053	2052	...	|	...	|	...	...
Takamatsu ▶ a.	|	1555	...	|	1654	...	|	1757	...	|	1854	...	...	|	1956	...	|	2111	...	2155	...	2256	...	...
kayama ▶ a.	1611	...	...	1711	...	...	1811	...	...	1911	...	...	...	2012	...	...	2129	...	...	...	...	...	...	...

OKAYAMA and TAKAMATSU - KOCHI - NAKAMURA 8127

JR Shikoku For footnotes see Table 8140

km																										
0	**Okayama** d.	...	...	0708	...	...	0852	...	1005	1105	...	1205	1305	...	1405	1505	1605	...	1705	...	...	1805	...	1905	2005	2139
	Takamatsu d.	0604	0723	|	...	0825	|	...	|	|	...	|	|	...	|	|	|	...	|	...	1827	|	...	|	|	|
97	Awa Ikeda d.	0706	0829	0829	...	0924	1020	...	1122	1234	...	1332	1425	...	1523	1631	1735	...	1834	...	1935	1935	...	2029	2138	2259
179	**Kochi** a.	0818	0939	0939	0953	1037	1130	1140	1229	1341	1349	1442	1539	1543	1639	1741	1848	1855	1943	1953	2050	2050	2123	2146	2251	0006
251	Kubokawa ‡ d.	0927	...	...	1057	...	...	1249	...	...	1454	...	...	1651	*1806*	...	...	2010	...	2104	...	...	2233	...	...	...
294	**Nakamura** ‡ a.	1004	...	...	1132	...	...	1324	...	...	1531	...	...	1727	*1846*	...	...	2049	...	2139	...	...	2308	...	...	...

km																										
	Nakamura ‡ d.	...	...	...	...	*0608*	0700	...	...	0924	...	...	1111	...	...	1324	...	...	1510	...	1648	...	1745	...	...	...
	Kubokawa ‡ d.	...	...	...	...	*0648*	0741	...	...	1004	...	...	1156	...	...	1402	...	...	1551	...	1729	...	1824	...	...	...
0	**Kochi** d.	0451	0600	0700	0700	0801	0904	0913	1013	1106	1113	1213	1302	1313	1413	1504	1513	1613	1700	1713	1834	1836	1928	1931	1931	2034
82	Awa Ikeda d.	0600	0709	0813	0813	0907	...	1020	1122	...	1223	1322	...	1424	1523	...	1621	1720	...	1824	...	1946	...	2040	2040	2148
158	**Takamatsu** a.	0702	|	0921	|	|	...	|	|	...	|	|	...	|	|	...	|	|	...	|	...	|	...	2142	|	2246
	Okayama a.	...	0838	...	0938	1033	...	1140	1240	...	1340	1441	...	1541	1641	...	1741	1847	...	1941	...	2111	...	...	2157	...

TOTTORI and OKAYAMA - YAMAGUCHI 8130

JR West For footnotes see Table 8140

km																											
															⑤Ⓒ			⑤Ⓒ									⑤Ⓒ
	Tottori d.	...	0704	...	...	0823	...	0929	...	...	1140	...	...	1306	...	...	1509	...	...	1742	...	1842	...	...	2049	...	...
	Kurayoshi d.	...	0733	...	...	0858	...	1001	...	...	1209	...	...	1339	...	...	1540	...	...	1811	...	1913	...	...	2122	...	...
0	**Okayama** d.	...	|	...	0705	|	0805	|	0905	1005	|	1105	1205	|	1305	1405	|	1505	1605	|	1705	|	1804	1905	|	2005	2120
80	Niimi d.	...	|	...	0810	|	0908	|	1012	1108	|	1208	1312	|	1414	1509	|	1610	1708	|	1808	|	1908	2010	|	2110	2225
159	**Yonago** d.	0601	0811	...	0917	0930	1016	1038	1119	1219	1241	1318	1419	1411	1521	1622	1615	1723	1824	1849	1922	1947	2029	2124	2156	2221	2334
188	Matsue d.	0623	0835	...	0942	...	1039	1100	1142	1241	1303	1341	1444	1436	1544	1647	1638	1748	1848	1916	1946	...	2051	2147	...	2244	2357
220	**Izumoshi** d.	0649	0905	...	1010	...	1104	1124	1209	1307	1329	1412	1512	1504	1609	1717	1709	1815	1920	1942	2019	...	2115	2211	...	2308	0021
	Odashi d.	0715	0929	...	...	...	...	1148	...	...	1358	...	...	1543	...	...	1738	...	...	2009	...	...	...	...	...	...	...
	Hamada d.	0800	1016	...	...	...	...	1231	...	...	1444	▬	...	1617	...	...	1827	...	...	2052	...	...	...	...	...	...	...
	Masuda d.	0858	1051	1123	...	...	...	1306	...	...	1516	1615	...	1655	...	...	1904	...	...	2124	...	...	...	...	...	...	...
	Tsuwano d.	0931	...	1205	...	...	...	1338	...	...	...	1659	...	1727	...	...	...	...	...	...	...	...	...	...	...	...	...
	Yamaguchi a.	1023	...	1324	...	...	...	1426	...	...	...	1806	...	1819	...	...	...	...	...	...	...	...	...	...	...	...	...
	Shin **Yamaguchi** a.	1039	...	*1403*	...	...	...	1441	...	...	...	1851	...	1835	...	...	...	...	...	...	...	...	...	...	...	...	...

km																											
										⑤Ⓒ			⑤Ⓒ										⑤Ⓒ				
0	Shin **Yamaguchi** d.	...	...	...	...	...	...	...	...	...	...	...	...	0852	...	*0913*	...	...	...	1301	...	*1337*	...	...	...	1712	...
13	Yamaguchi d.	...	...	...	...	...	...	...	...	...	...	...	...	0908	...	0939	...	...	...	1315	...	1402	...	...	...	1727	...
63	Tsuwano d.	...	...	...	...	...	...	...	...	...	...	...	...	0958	...	1105	...	...	...	1403	...	1518	...	...	...	1815	...
94	Masuda d.	...	...	...	...	...	0536	...	0655	...	...	...	...	1031	...	1149	1217	...	...	1438	...	1558	...	1603	...	1851	...
135	Hamada d.	...	...	...	...	...	0611	...	0730	...	...	...	...	1104	...	▬	1257	...	...	1515	...	...	...	1642	...	1925	...
191	Odashi d.	...	...	...	...	...	0653	...	0830	...	...	...	...	1147	...	...	1338	...	...	1558	...	...	...	1726	...	2008	...
224	**Izumoshi** d.	0442	0527	...	0624	0721	0728	0831	0854	0934	1031	...	1134	1212	1234	1331	1403	1433	1530	1622	1630	...	1718	1750	1827	2036	...
256	Matsue d.	0507	0552	...	0658	0749	0758	0857	0924	1002	1059	...	1201	1235	1301	1359	1426	1501	1559	1647	1701	...	1744	1818	1855	2104	...
285	Yonago d.	0532	0621	0658	0723	0819	0825	0922	0950	1026	1125	1217	1226	1303	1326	1428	1452	1527	1626	1711	1726	...	1816	1841	1924	2127	2040
	Niimi d.	0640	0729	|	0834	0934	|	1037	|	1136	1236	|	1337	...	1439	1538	|	1638	1738	|	1838	...	1926	|	2031	...	|
	Okayama a.	0741	0834	|	0939	1035	|	1139	|	1239	1339	|	1439	...	1540	1639	|	1739	1839	|	1939	...	2025	|	2136	...	|
338	Kurayoshi d.	...	...	0733	...	...	0858	...	1025	...	...	1255	...	...	...	...	1523	...	...	1743	...	...	...	1913	...	...	2112
378	**Tottori** a.	...	...	0803	...	...	0927	...	1058	...	...	1324	...	...	...	...	1553	...	...	1816	...	...	...	1942	...	...	2140

KYOTO - KURAYOSHI 8135

JR West For footnotes see Table 8140

km		1	3	5	7	9	11	13				2	4	6	8	10	12	14		
0	**Kyoto** d.	0706	0850	1054	1252	1454	1656	1935	...	...	**Kurayoshi** d.	0608	0812	1013	1219	1423	1622	*1743*	...	...
39	Shin Osaka d.	0730	0915	1118	1316	1518	1719	2000	...	...	Tottori d.	0639	0852	1046	1254	1454	1654	1840	...	...
43	Osaka d.	0737	0925	1125	1324	1524	1726	2006	...	...	Chizu ‡ d.	0708	0921	1115	1323	1523	1724	1908	...	...
131	Himeji d.	0836	1022	1220	1421	1620	1822	2108	...	...	Kamigori ‡ d.	0751	1003	1202	1401	1601	1804	1947	...	...
166	Kamigori ‡ d.	0902	1048	1244	1444	1644	1845	2131	...	...	Himeji d.	0814	1025	1225	1424	1624	1828	2009	...	...
222	Chizu ‡ d.	0944	1130	1323	1524	1724	1931	2214	...	...	Osaka d.	0924	1120	1321	1521	1719	1936	2107	...	...
254	Tottori d.	1013	1159	1353	1554	1752	2002	2243	...	...	Shin Osaka d.	0929	1124	1326	1526	1724	1942	2113	...	...
294	**Kurayoshi** a.	1043	1230	1421	1621	...	2033	...	...	...	**Kyoto** a.	0953	1147	1348	1548	1748	2006	2137	...	...

OKAYAMA - TOTTORI 8140

JR West

km																				
0	**Okayama** d.	0647	0913	1105	1343	1724	1946	...	...	...	**Tottori** d.	0705	1002	1400	1620	1857	2035	...	...	...
54	Kamigori ‡ d.	0725	0950	1142	1419	1803	2022	...	...	...	Chizu ‡ d.	0734	1033	1427	1652	1932	2103	...	...	...
110	Chizu ‡ d.	0811	1035	1226	1501	1845	2104	...	...	...	Kamigori ‡ d.	0820	1115	1511	1733	2014	2148	...	...	...
142	**Tottori** a.	0838	1104	1253	1532	1917	2131	...	...	...	**Okayama** a.	0857	1148	1545	1811	2048	2222	...	...	...

NOTES FOR TABLES 8121 - 8140:

‡ - Japan Rail Pass holders must pay a supplement to travel between these stations.

▶ – Frequent local services operate throughout the day.

8145 KYOTO and OSAKA - KINOSAKI

Ⓡ on all trains — JR West

km	Station																							
				⑤Ⓒ						⑤Ⓒ				⑤Ⓒ					⑤Ⓒ			⑤Ⓒ		
0	**Kyoto** d.	0732	0838	0924	...	1025	1125	1225	...	1325	1425	1525	...	1625	1728	1828	...	1928	...	2037	...	2137	...	...
76	Ayabe d.	0839	0946	1031	...	1136	1231	1339	...	1431	1535	1631	...	1735	1843	1948	...	2047	...	2150	...	2246	...	...
89	Fukuchiyama d.	0849	0954	1040	...	1145	1244	1348	...	1446	1544	1648	...	1743	1852	2001	...	2055	2001	2159	...	2255	...	...
148	Toyooka d.	0943	...	...	...	...	1340	...	...	1540	...	1751	...	...	...	2058	...	...	2058	...	...	...	...	...
158	**Kinosaki** Onsen a.	0952	...	...	...	...	1349	...	...	1549	...	1800	...	...	...	...	...	...	...	...	...	...	...	...

Station																							
			⑤Ⓒ			⑤Ⓒ				⑤Ⓒ				⑤Ⓒ							⑤Ⓒ		
Kinosaki Onsen d.	...	...	...	...	...	...	...	...	...	1039	...	...	1231	...	1435	...	...	1631	...	...	...	...	...
Toyooka d.	...	...	...	...	...	0742	...	...	...	1049	...	...	1242	...	1445	...	...	1641	...	...	...	...	...
Fukuchiyama d.	0602	0656	0743	...	0838	0838	0945	...	1044	1146	1243	...	1346	1442	1543	...	1644	1749	1854	...	2005	...	...
Ayabe d.	0612	0712	0753	...	0855	0855	0955	...	1100	1156	1300	...	1356	1459	1556	...	1659	1759	1910	...	2014	...	...
Kyoto a.	0718	0821	0903	...	1007	1007	1107	...	1207	1307	1407	...	1507	1607	1707	...	1808	1909	2021	...	2119	...	...

km	Station																							
						⑤Ⓒ					⑤Ⓒ						⑤Ⓒ			⑤Ⓒ				
0	Shin **Osaka** d.	0808	0904	...	1005	1105	...	1205	1305	...	1405	1505	...	1705	1801	...	1906	2006	...	2106	2204	...	...	...
4	**Osaka** d.	0814	0910	...	1012	1111	...	1211	1311	...	1411	1511	...	1711	1811	...	1912	2012	...	2112	2210	...	...	...
118	Fukuchiyama d.	0955	1046	...	1147	1243	...	1350	1442	...	1546	1646	...	1900	1958	...	2058	2157	...	2301	2351	...	...	...
178	Toyooka d.	1050	1143	...	1242	...	...	1445	...	...	1641	...	...	1957	...	...	...	...	...	...	...	...	...	...
188	**Kinosaki** Onsen a.	1058	1152	...	1251	...	...	1454	...	...	1650	...	...	...	...	...	...	...	...	...	...	...	...	...

Station																							
				⑤Ⓒ			⑤Ⓒ				⑤Ⓒ								⑤Ⓒ				
Kinosaki Onsen d.	...	...	...	...	...	...	...	0933	...	1133	...	...	1329	...	...	1530	...	...	1742	1853	...	...	...
Toyooka d.	...	...	...	...	...	...	...	0943	...	1143	...	...	1339	...	...	1541	...	...	1752	1903	...	...	...
Fukuchiyama d.	0549	0652	...	0745	0840	...	0950	1046	...	1246	1344	...	1443	1545	...	1647	1800	...	1900	2000	...	...	...
Osaka a.	0735	0839	...	0926	1021	...	1123	1223	...	1424	1523	...	1623	1722	...	1822	1937	...	2037	2136	...	...	...
Shin **Osaka** a.	0741	0846	...	0932	1027	...	1129	1229	...	1429	1529	...	1628	1727	...	1828	1944	...	2044	2144	...	...	...

8150 OSAKA and NAGOYA - KANAZAWA

JR West

km	Station																							
			Ⓐ							a								⑤Ⓒ	b					⑤Ⓒ
0	**Osaka** d.	...	...	...	0630	0700	...	0740	...	0758	0810	0840	...	...	0912	0942	...	1012	1042	...	1142	...	1212	1242
4	Shin **Osaka** d.	...	...	...	0634	0704	...	0744	...	0803	0814	0844	...	...	0917	0946	...	1016	1046	...	1146	...	1216	1246
43	Kyoto d.	...	...	...	0659	0729	...	0810	...	0831	0841	0909	...	...	0942	1009	...	1040	1110	...	1210	...	1240	1310
	Nagoya 8175 d.	...	...	...	|	|	...	|	0750	|	|	|	...	0850	|	|	0948	|	|	...	|	1148	|	|
	Gifu 8170 d.	...	...	...	|	|	...	|	0810	0956	|	|	...	0911	|	|	1012	|	|	...	|	1212	|	|
	Maibara d.	...	...	...	|	|	0810	|	0857	0922↑	|	|	...	0956	|	|	1056	|	|	1156	|	1256	|	|
137	Tsuruga d.	...	0643	...	0758	0822	0841	0903	0926	...	0938	|	...	1026	1035	1103	1125	1133	1202	1225	1303	1327	|	1403
191	Fukui d.	0650	0719	0742	0831	0855	0915	0938	1001	...	1012	1032	...	1101	1110	1136	1200	1208	1235	1300	1338	1402	1407	1437
268	**Kanazawa** 8010 a.	0737	0809	0833	0913	0938	1005	1025	1048	...	1102	1114	...	1148	1158	1220	1248	1256	1320	1348	1423	1449	1455	1526

km	Station																							
							⑤Ⓒ			⑤Ⓒ								⑤Ⓒ						
	Osaka d.	...	1342	...	1442	...	1512	1542	...	1642	...	1712	1742	...	1812	1842	...	1912	1927	...	2007	2054	...	...
	Shin **Osaka** d.	...	1346	...	1446	...	1516	1546	...	1646	...	1716	1746	...	1816	1846	...	1916	1931	...	2012	2058	...	...
	Kyoto d.	...	1410	...	1510	...	1540	1610	...	1709	...	1740	1809	...	1840	1910	...	1940	1954	...	2038	2121	...	...
0	**Nagoya** 8175 d.	...	|	1348	|	...	|	|	1548	|	...	|	|	1748	|	|	...	|	|	1948	|	|	...	...
30	Gifu 8170 d.	...	|	1412	|	...	|	|	1611	|	...	|	|	1811	|	|	...	|	|	2012	|	|	...	...
80	Maibara d.	1355	|	1456	|	1556	|	|	1656	|	1756	|	|	1856	|	|	1956	|	|	2056	|	|	2156	2248
126	Tsuruga d.	1426	1502	1525	1603	1627	1632	1703	1725	1801	1825	1833	|	1927	1933	2007	2025	|	2049	2125	2133	2215	2225	2317
180	Fukui d.	1500	1540	1601	1637	1702	1708	1740	1800	1833	1900	1908	1930	2002	2008	2039	2100	2107	2125	2201	2208	2248	2301	2352
257	**Kanazawa** 8010 a.	1548	1630	1650	1726	1751	1755	1827	1847	1916	1949	1955	2013	2050	2056	2123	2148	2153	2209	2250	2256	2329	2348	0040

Station																							
				⑤Ⓒ					⑤Ⓒ			Ⓐ	Ⓒ					b	⑤Ⓒ				
Kanazawa 8010 d.	0510	0535	0548	0607	0645	0648	0715	0748	0805	0815	0848	0902	0902	0948	0954	1048	1056	1124	1148	1214	1248	1320	1348
Fukui d.	0600	0620	0639	0701	0729	0739	0803	0838	0848	0905	0936	0945	0945	1036	1042	1136	1143	1208	1236	1306	1336	1408	1436
Tsuruga d.	0633	0653	0712	0737	0801	0812	0838	0912	|	0939	1010	1016	1016	1110	1116	1210	1216	1241	1310	1342	1410	1441	1510
Maibara d.	0708	|	0752	|	|	0844	|	0950	|	|	1045	|	|	1152	|	1245	|	|	1351	|	1445	|	1550
Gifu 8170 d.	...	|	0829	|	|	...	|	1026	|	|	...	|	|	1227	|	...	|	|	1427	|	...	|	1620
Nagoya 8175 a.	...	|	0851	|	|	...	|	1049	|	|	...	|	|	1248	|	...	|	|	1448	|	...	|	1649
Kyoto a.	...	0751	...	0837	0855	...	0934	...	1011	1037	...	1109	1109	...	1209	...	1309	1337	...	1437	...	1536	...
Shin **Osaka** a.	...	0817	...	0901	0918	...	0958	...	1035	1102	...	1132	1132	...	1232	...	1332	1400	...	1500	...	1559	...
Osaka a.	...	0822	...	0906	0922	...	1003	...	1039	1106	...	1137	1139	...	1237	...	1337	1405	...	1505	...	1604	...

Station																							
				⑤Ⓒ							a						⑤Ⓒ					Ⓐ	
Kanazawa 8010 d.	1354	1420	1448	1457	1519	1548	1600	1629	1648	1655	...	1731	1748	1754	1842	1853	1908	1947	2006	2047	2108	2140	221
Fukui d.	1442	1508	1536	1543	1608	1636	1644	1722	1736	1744	...	1815	1837	1841	1928	1942	1952	2034	2055	2132	2156	2231	230
Tsuruga d.	1516	1542	1610	|	1642	1710	1715	1756	1810	1816	...	|	1910	1916	2000	2016	|	2108	2129	2204	...	2307	...
Maibara d.	|	|	1650	|	|	1744	|	|	1850	|	1823↓	|	1944	|	|	2055	|	|	2201	|	...	...	...
Gifu 8170 d.	|	|	1726	|	|	...	|	|	1925	|	1743	|	...	|	|	2129	|	|	...	|	...	...	...
Nagoya 8175 a.	|	|	1749	|	|	...	|	|	1946	|	|	|	...	|	|	2154	|	|	...	|	...	...	...
Kyoto a.	1609	1637	...	1707	1739	...	1809	1853	...	1909	1918	1938	...	2009	2054	...	2119	2202	...	2259	...	...	...
Shin **Osaka** a.	1632	1701	...	1731	1803	...	1833	1916	...	1933	1944	2003	...	2034	2119	...	2144	2226	...	2323	...	...	...
Osaka a.	1637	1706	...	1736	1809	...	1839	1921	...	1938	1950	2009	...	2038	2123	...	2149	2231	...	2328	...	...	...

a – To/from Takayama (see Table **8170**).

b – To/from Wakura Onsen (see Table **8155**).

8155 KANAZAWA - WAKURA ONSEN

JR West

km	Station			c						
0	**Kanazawa** 8150 d.	0856	1123	1327	1500	1835	2010	...	...	...
66	Nanao d.	0949	1216	1424	1554	1932	2107	...	...	...
71	**Wakura Onsen** a.	0954	1222	1430	1559	1938	2112	...	...	...

Station			c						
Wakura Onsen d.	0700	0902	1014	1256	1519	1730	...	...	...
Nanao d.	0706	0908	1020	1303	1527	1737	...	...	...
Kanazawa 8150 a.	0805	1005	1118	1404	1630	1831	...	...	...

c – To/from Osaka (see Table **8150**).

8160 OSAKA - SHINGU

Ⓡ on all trains — JR West

km	Station	1	3	5	7		9	11	13	15		17	19	21	23		25	27	29	31		33	35	
				⑤Ⓒ						⑤Ⓒ										⑤Ⓒ				
39	Kyoto d.	*0703*	*0829*	*0900*	*0945*	...	*1045*	*1145*	*1245*	*1345*	...	*1445*	*1545*	*1644*	1747	...	...	*1844*	*1944*	*2044*	...	*2114*	*2209*	...
0	Shin **Osaka** d.	0733	0903	0930	1015	...	1115	1215	1315	1415	...	1515	1615	1715	1815	...	1845	1915	2015	2115	...	2146	2250	...
14	**Osaka** Tennoji d.	0759	0921	0949	1033	...	1132	1232	1332	1432	...	1532	1632	1735	1835	...	1905	1935	2036	2136	...	2206	2311	...
75	Wakayama d.	0848	1006	1035	1117	...	1218	1318	1418	1516	...	1618	1718	1825	1926	...	1953	2025	2125	2223	...	2255	2358	...
181	Shirahama d.	1012	1137	1200	1246	...	1347	1443	1547	1640	...	1743	1845	1956	2055	...	...	2155	2253	...	...	...	...	...
234	Kushimoto d.	1107	...	1255	...	...	...	1540	...	...	...	1838	...	2050	...	...	...	2256	...	...	...	...	...	...
261	**Kii Katsuura** d.	1140	...	1333	...	...	...	1617	...	...	...	1911	...	2123	...	...	...	2333	...	...	...	...	...	...
276	**Shingu** a.	1158	...	1352	...	...	...	1639	...	...	...	1928	...	2141	...	...	...	2350	...	...	...	...	...	...

Station	2	4	6	8		10	12	14	16		18	20	22	24		26	28	30	32		34	36	
											⑤Ⓒ							⑤Ⓒ			⑤Ⓒ		
Shingu d.	...	...	...	...	...	...	0630	...	0832	...	...	...	1127	...	...	1329	...	1504	...	...	...	1746	...
Kii Katsuura d.	...	...	...	...	...	...	0646	...	0849	...	...	...	1148	...	...	1346	...	1524	...	...	...	1804	...
Kushimoto d.	...	...	...	...	...	...	0720	...	0923	...	...	...	1221	...	...	1420	...	1557	...	...	...	1838	...
Shirahama d.	...	...	...	0640	...	0712	0820	0920	1026	...	1120	1220	1326	1420	...	1526	1620	1656	1720	...	1820	1937	...
Wakayama d.	0514	0603	0626	0810	...	0841	0950	1050	1150	...	1249	1350	1450	1550	...	1650	1750	1820	1850	...	1949	2102	...
Osaka Tennoji d.	0602	0701	0725	0901	...	0931	1034	1135	1235	...	1335	1435	1535	1635	...	1734	1834	1904	1934	...	2034	2151	...
Shin **Osaka** a.	0621	0721	0750	0922	...	0950	1050	1150	1250	...	1350	1450	1550	1649	...	1750	1850	1920	1950	...	2050	2206	...
Kyoto a.	*0701*	*0805*	*0835*	*0953*	...	*1029*	1117	*1229*	*1329*	...	*1429*	*1529*	*1629*	*1729*	...	*1829*	*1929*	*1953*	*2029*	...	*2137*	*2249*	...

NAGOYA - SHINGU 8165

JR Central

km		1	3	5	7						
0	**Nagoya** d.	0805	1001	1258	1947	...	...	...	...	...	...
37	Yokkaichi ‡ d.	0837	1037	1337	2019	...	...	...	...	...	...
48	Suzuka ‡ d.	0846	1046	1345	2027	...	...	...	...	...	...
66	Tsu ‡ d.	0901	1101	1400	2042	...	...	...	...	...	...
86	Matsusaka d.	0916	1116	1416	2057	...	...	...	...	...	...
93	Taki d.	0924	1129	1424	2105	...	...	...	...	...	...
206	Kumano Shi d.	1114	1318	1605	2254	...	...	...	...	...	...
228	**Shingu** a.	1134	1337	1624	2314	...	...	...	...	...	...
244	**Kii Katsuura** a.	1156	1358	1643	...	...	...	...	...	...	...

	2	4	6	8						
Kii Katsuura d.	...	0855	1223	1711	...	...	...	...	...	...
Shingu d.	0620	0913	1245	1731	...	...	...	...	...	...
Kumano Shi d.	0640	0933	1305	1750	...	...	...	...	...	...
Taki d.	0819	1118	1449	1931	...	...	...	...	...	...
Matsusaka d.	0826	1126	1456	1938	...	...	...	...	...	...
Tsu ‡ d.	0841	1142	1512	1954	...	...	...	...	...	...
Suzuka ‡ d.	0854	1154	1525	2006	...	...	...	...	...	...
Yokkaichi ‡ d.	0904	1205	1534	2015	...	...	...	...	...	...
Nagoya a.	0941	1241	1610	2049	...	...	...	...	...	...

– Japan Rail Pass holders must pay a supplement to travel between these stations.

NAGOYA - TOYAMA 8170

JR Central, JR West

km				a							
0	**Nagoya** d.	0745	0843	0939	1048	1143	1248	1448	1603	1813	2017
30	Gifu **8150** d.	0805	0903	1011	1108	1206	1308	1508	1623	1839	2042
58	Mino Ota d.	0827	0923	1032	1129	1225	1328	1530	1653	1900	2102
119	Gero d.	0927	1015	1133	1227	1330	1425	1631	1758	2003	2203
167	Takayama d.	1016	1101	1223	1315	1418	1512	1719	1843	2049	2249
182	Hida Furukawa d.	...	1116	1242	1330	...	1526	1732	...	...	...
256	**Toyama** a.	...	1230	...	1447	...	1639	1852	...	...	...

								b		
Toyama d.	...	...	0758	0959	...	...	1302	...	...	1714
Hida Furukawa d.	...	...	0913	1107	...	1311	1419	...	...	1826
Takayama d.	0646	0800	0938	1132	1233	1329	1440	1538	1636	1847
Gero d.	0732	0846	1027	1220	1319	1414	1527	1624	1721	1929
Mino Ota d.	0827	0948	1119	1315	1418	1519	1620	1717	1819	2022
Gifu **8150** d.	0851	1012	1141	1341	1441	1541	1641	1741	1840	2043
Nagoya a.	0912	1034	1204	1404	1504	1608	1704	1806	1906	2103

– [12] Nagoya – Hida Furukawa; [2] Osaka (Table **8150**) – Takayama.

b – [12] Takayama – Nagoya; [2] Takayama – Osaka (Table **8150**).

NAGOYA - NAGANO 8175

JR Central

km		A										
0	**Nagoya** **8150** d.	0700	0800	1000	1100	1200	1300	1500	1600	1740	1840	1940
80	Nakatsugawa d.	0749	0850	1049	1149	1249	1350	1549	1649	1830	1930	2032
133	Kiso Fukushima d.	0829	0925	1125	1225	1325	1425	1625	1725	1907	2007	2110
175	Shiojiri d.	0859	0957	1155	1255	1354	1456	1655	1755	1937	2035	2139
188	Matsumoto d.	0909	1007	1206	1306	1404	1506	1705	1805	1947	2046	2149
251	**Nagano** a.	1003	1059	1254	1353	1456	1559	1800	1858	2039	2134	2239

	B										
Nagano d.	0609	0745	0901	1001	1200	1403	1500	1600	1700	1811	1940
Matsumoto d.	0704	0838	0952	1051	1253	1453	1553	1653	1752	1907	2031
Shiojiri d.	0714	0849	1003	1103	1303	1503	1603	1703	1803	1919	2041
Kiso Fukushima d.	0743	0916	1030	1130	1330	1531	1631	1731	1830	1948	2108
Nakatsugawa d.	0822	0953	1106	1206	1406	1610	1710	1810	1910	2026	2144
Nagoya **8150** a.	0917	1053	1201	1301	1501	1706	1805	1905	2005	2121	2234

– Additional trips: 0900, 1400.

B – Additional trips: 1100, 1300.

SHIZUOKA - KOFU 8180

JR Central

km											
0	**Shizuoka** d.	0817	0945	1145	1345	1545	1745	1945	...	...	...
34	Fuji d.	0844	1015	1215	1415	1615	1815	2015	...	...	...
131	**Kofu** a.	1031	1205	1403	1603	1803	2001	2206	...	...	...

Kofu d.	0620	0845	1044	1237	1435	1635	1836	...	...	...
Fuji d.	0814	1037	1234	1429	1629	1828	2031	...	...	...
Shizuoka a.	0842	1102	1302	1456	1656	1855	2058	...	...	...

NIIGATA - NAOETSU - JOETSUMYOKO 8182

JR East

km		*LEX*	*LEX*	*LEX*		*LEX*					
0	**Niigata** d.	0738	1021	1306	1701	2002	...	...	...	...	...
63	Nagaoka d.	0829	1118	1358	1803	2054	2141	...	...	...	...
136	Naoetsu d.	0925	1212	1451	1918	2148	2243	...	...	...	...
146	**Joetsumyoko** ‡ a.	0939	1225	1506	1934	2201	...	...	...	...	...

		LEX	*LEX*	*LEX*	*LEX*					
Joetsumyoko ‡d.	...	0725	1033	1307	1724	*1824*	...	...	...	...
Naoetsu d.	0613	0741	1048	1323	1738	1843	...	...	...	...
Nagaoka d.	0714	0835	1140	1415	1830	1955	...	...	...	...
Niigata a.	...	0928	1230	1506	1925	2055	...	...	...	...

– Japan Rail Pass holders must pay a supplement to travel between these stations.

TOKYO - KOFU - MATSUMOTO 8185

JR East R on all trains

km			C	B																				
0	**Tokyo** Shinjuku d.	0700	0730	0800	0830	...	0900	1000	1100	1130	...	1200	1300	1400	1500	...	1600	1700	1730	1800	...	1900	2000	2100
37	Hachioji d.	0729	0802	0833	0907	...	0936	1031	1129	1202	...	1231	1331	1431	1531	...	1631	1732	1809	1835	...	1936	2034	2134
77	Otsuki d.	0756	0833	|	0938	...	|	|	|	1229	...	|	|	|	|	...	|	|	1833	|	...	|	|	2201
124	Kofu d.	0828	0909	0929	1014	...	1036	1129	1224	1304	...	1328	1427	1526	1627	...	1728	1829	1908	1932	...	2033	2130	2233
185	Chino d.	0908	0952	1007	...	...	1112	1206	1300	...	...	1403	1507	1607	1707	...	1804	1906	...	2011	...	2115	2208	2318
192	Kami Suwa d.	0913	0957	1012	...	...	1117	1212	|	...	...	1410	1512	1614	1713	...	1809	1912	...	2017	...	2120	2213	2323
212	Shiojiri d.	0928	1014	1028	...	...	|	1227	|	...	...	|	1528	1629	1728	...	|	1927	...	2031	...	2136	2229	2339
225	**Matsumoto** a.	0938	1023	1037	...	...	1139	1236	1325	...	...	1432	1537	1639	1737	...	1834	1937	...	2041	...	2146	2238	2349

																A						
latsumoto d.	0630	0710	0810	...	...	0910	1010	1110	1210	...	1310	1345	1450	1510	...	1550	1630	1720	1840	...	...	...	2010
hiojiri d.	0638	0718	0819	...	...	0918	|	1118	1218	...	1318	1355	|	1520	...	1558	1638	1729	|	...	...	...	2018
ami Suwa d.	0654	0733	0835	...	...	0934	|	1133	1233	...	1333	1410	1512	1536	...	1606	1653	1746	1901	...	...	...	2033
hino d.	0700	0739	0843	...	...	0940	1035	1139	1239	...	1339	1416	1518	1542	...	1620	1659	1752	1906	...	...	...	2039
ofu d.	0740	0817	0926	0943	...	1020	1111	1217	1316	...	1416	1454	1554	1631	...	1702	1736	1835	1942	...	2004	2036	2116
tsuki d.	|	|	|	1016	...	1054	|	|	|	...	|	|	|	|	...	1745	|	1905	|	...	2038	2109	|
achioji d.	0834	0913	1020	1044	...	1120	1205	1311	1410	...	1510	1549	1650	1730	...	1811	1831	1933	2036	...	2105	2136	2213
okyo Shinjuku a.	0913	0946	1054	1116	...	1153	1233	1342	1441	...	1541	1624	1723	1804	...	1843	1906	2010	2106	...	2137	2207	2245

km												
0	**Tokyo** Shinjuku d.	0930	1030	1230	1330	1430	1530	1630	1830	1930	2200	2300
37	Hachioji d.	1009	1102	1302	1401	1502	1602	1703	1906	2008	2235	2335
77	Otsuki d.	1038	1129	1328	1428	1529	1630	1730	1932	2034	2301	0001
124	**Kofu** a.	1114	1205	1403	1503	1604	1705	1806	2012	2111	2337	0037

Kofu d.	0703	0818	0924	1132	1232	1332	1430	1515	1611	1748	1902
Otsuki d.	0736	0852	0957	1206	1306	1406	1506	1557	1647	1830	2036
Hachioji d.	0803	0919	1025	1233	1333	1433	1533	1624	1714	1857	2003
Tokyo Shinjuku a.	0842	0956	1059	1304	1404	1504	1603	1658	1751	1927	2037

ote: Some trains run to a slightly different schedule on ©. A – From Minami Otari (d. 1501). B – To Minami Otari (a. 1159). C – From Chiba (d. 0638). D – To Chiba (a. 2052).

TOKYO - MOUNT FUJI - KAWAGUCHIKO 8190

JR East, Fujikyu Railway

km		R A	R	D R	R	F C	R ©	E	D R	F	E Ⓐ
0	**Tokyo** Shinjuku d.	0730	0830	...	0930	...	1113	...	...	...	...
37	Hachioji d.	0802	0909	...	1009	...	1146	...	...	...	...
77	Otsuki ‡ ◧ d.	0837	0942	0954	1042	1151	1217	1249	1349	1455	1552
101	Mt Fuji ⊖ d.	0917	1019	1050	1120	1234	1303	1333	1445	1541	1638
104	**Kawaguchiko** ‡ ◧ a.	0923	1025	1056	1125	1240	1309	1339	1451	1549	1644

	D R	F	E	D R	F	E	R	R ©	R	R
Kawaguchiko ‡ ◧ d.	0824	0940	1109	1209	1311	1403	1503	1557	1651	1736
Mt Fuji ⊖ d.	0833	0949	1117	1217	1319	1412	1512	1606	1659	1745
Otsuki ‡ ◧ d.	0926	1021	1159	1310	1400	1453	1557	1651	1745	1830
Hachioji d.	...	...	...	...	...	...	1624	1725	1811	1855
Tokyo Shinjuku a.	...	...	...	...	...	...	1658	1759	1843	1927

– From Chiba d. 0638.
– Runs 4 minutes earlier on ©.
D – Fuji Tozan Densha. Japan Rail Pass not valid.
E – Fujisan Express. Japan Rail Pass not valid.
F – Fujisan View Express. Japan Rail Pass not valid.
◧ – Frequent additional local services available.
‡ – Japan Rail Pass not valid between Otsuki and Kawaguchiko.
⊖ – Altitude is 809 m. Bus service to Fuji-Subaru Line 5th Station (Altitude 2305m) is available.

TOKYO - IZUKYU SHIMODA and SHUZENJI 8195

JR East R on all trains

km				C	©	F			©	
0	**Tokyo** d.	0900	0900	1000	1030	1100	1200	1200	1225j	1300
29	Yokohama d.	0924	0924	1024	1054	1124	1224	1224	1258	1324
84	Odawara d.	1002	1002	1102	1132	|	1301	1301	|	|
105	Atami d.	1023	1025	1121	1156	1218	1323	1325	1352	1422
122	Ito ‡ d.	1046	|	1145	|	1238	1346	|	1422	1444
168	**Izukyu Shimoda** ‡ a.	1150	|	1241	|	1329	1447	|	1530	1543
121	Mishima ‡ d.	...	1040	...	1211	...	...	1340	...	...
141	**Shuzenji** ‡ a.	...	1108	...	1239	...	...	1406	...	...

	©	A						B	G
Shuzenji ‡ d.	...	...	...	1235	...	...	...	1539	...
Mishima ‡ d.	...	...	...	1305	...	...	...	1606	...
Izukyu Shimoda ‡ d.	...	0952	1204	|	1301	1412	1507	|	1634
Ito ‡ d.	1004	1047	1305	|	1405	1509	1602	|	1735
Atami d.	1030	1113	1333	1333	1430	1531	1629	1629	1800
Odawara d.	1047	1130	1350	1350	1448	|	1648	1648	|
Yokohama d.	1127	1208	1427	1427	1526	1628	1725	1725	1857
Tokyo a.	1150	1232	1449	1449	1549	1649	1748	1748	1920

– Additional trips on © at 1134, 1344.
– Additional trip on © at 1418.
– Additional trip on © at 1030.
F – Additional trip on ①④⑤© at 1230.
G – ①④⑤⑥⑦.
j – Tokyo **Shinjuku**.
‡ – Japan Rail Pass holders must pay a supplement to travel between these stations.

8200 TOKYO - AWA KAMOGAWA

JR Eas

km									A			
0	**Tokyo**	d.	0715	0901	1000	1100	1300	1500	1702	1800	1900	2100	2201
43	Soga	d.	0753	0935	1033	1134	1334	1534	1734	1834	1935	2134	2233
62	Oami	d.	0805	0947	1047	1146	1346	1546	1746	1848	1949	2148	2247
74	Mobara	d.	0813	0955	1055	1155	1354	1554	1754	1856	1957	2156	2254
82	Kazusa Ichinomiya	d.	0820	1002	1106	1202	1401	1601	1801	1903	2008	2203	2301
110	Katsuura	a.	0845	1028	1130	1228	1426	1626	1826	...	2035	2228	2326
133	**Awa Kamogawa**	a.	...	1053	1159	1252	1452	...	...	...	...	...	...

Awa Kamogawa	d.	...	0739	0840	...	1141	1406	1535	1639	...	...	...
Katsuura	d.	0726	0808	0908	1036	1207	1436	1600	1704	1814	...	200
Kazusa Ichinomiya	d.	0754	0833	0933	1101	1234	1503	1631	1738	1840	1928	204
Mobara	d.	0800	0839	0939	1108	1241	1509	1638	1744	1846	1936	204
Oami	d.	0810	0847	0947	1117	1249	1518	1646	1752	1854	1948	205
Soga	d.	0824	0902	1002	1130	1302	1531	1700	1805	1908	2001	210
Tokyo	a.	0901	0934	1036	1205	1335	1603	1734	1840	1940	2034	214

A – Additional trip: Ⓐ 2000. Note: Some trains run on a slightly different schedule on Ⓒ.

8205 TOKYO - NAGANOHARA KUSATSUGUCHI and MAEBASHI

JR Eas

km			Ⓒ			Ⓐ[R]	Ⓐ[R]	a	Ⓐ[R]	a
0	**Tokyo** Ueno	d.	0900	1000	1210	1800	1830	1900	1930	2000
27	Omiya	d.	0926	1026	1235	1828	1856	1925	1955	2026
62	Kumagaya	d.	0952	1051	1302	1900	1925	1953	2025	2055
102	**Takasaki**	d.	1020	1119	1333	*1942*h	*2011*h	2028	*2115*h	2124
164	**Naganohara Kusatsuguchi**	a.	1124	1218	1434	|	|	|	|	|
112	**Maebashi**	a.	...	...	...	*1956*k	*2026*k	*2053*	*2130*k	*2143*b

		Ⓐ[R]	Ⓐ[R]	Ⓐ[R]	Ⓐ[R]	Ⓒ	Ⓒ	Ⓒ		
Maebashi	d.	...	*0551*	*0717*	*0749*	*0749*	*0824*	...	...	...
Naganohara Kusatsuguchi	d.	...	|	|	|	|	|	1205	1307	154
Takasaki	d.	...	0552	0740	0811	0810	0850	1306	1405	164
Kumagaya	d.	0606	0628	0810	0842	0842	0920	1333	1434	171
Omiya	d.	0640	0709	0839	0912	0912	0950	1401	1500	174
Tokyo Ueno	a.	0705	0737	0907j	0939	0939	1013	1424	1526	180

a – [R] required on Ⓐ. b – Arrives 2156 on Ⓒ. h – Change trains at Honjo. j – Tokyo **Shinjuku**. k – Change trains at Takasaki.

8210 TOKYO - NIKKO

JR Eas

km			[R]	[R]	[R]	[R]						
0	**Tokyo** Shinjuku	d.	0731	1031	1300	1732	...	...	...	...	...	...
27	Omiya	d.	0802	1102	1330	1802	...	...	...	...	...	...
135	Tobu **Nikko**	‡ d.	0928	|	|	|	...	...	...	...	...	...
140	**Kinugawa** Onsen	‡ a.	...	1243	1505	1942	...	...	...	...	...	...

		[R]	[R]	[R]	[R]						
Kinugawa Onsen	‡ d.	0810	1039	1506	...	...	...	...	...	...	...
Tobu **Nikko**	‡ d.	|	|	|	1639	...	...	...	...	...	...
Omiya	d.	0949	1217	1646	1804	...	...	...	...	...	...
Tokyo Shinjuku	a.	1018	1247	1719	1836	...	...	...	...	...	...

‡ – Japan Rail Pass holders must pay a supplement to travel to/from this station. Tobu Railway (www.tobu.co.jp) operate regular services Tokyo Skytree - Tobi Nikko/Kinugawa Onsen.

8215 TOKYO - IWAKI - SENDAI

[R] on all trains JR Eas

km							Ⓐ	Ⓒ																			
	Tokyo Shinagawa	d.	0645	0715	0743	...	...	0845	0915	0945	1015	1045	1115	1145	1215	1245	1315	1345	1415	1445	1515	1545	1615	1645	1715	1745	181
0	**Tokyo** Ueno	d.	0700	0730	0800	0830	0900	0900	0930	1000	1030	1100	1130	1200	1230	1300	1330	1400	1430	1500	1530	1600	1630	1700	1730	1800	183
67	Tsuchiura	d.	0742	0816	0850	0917	|	|	1016	|	1115	|	1215	|	1313	|	1413	|	1513	|	1614	|	1711	|	1816	*1907*	191
118	Mito	d.	0811	0850	0919	0950	1016	1016	1048	1106	1148	1207	1248	1307	1345	1407	1445	1507	1546	1607	1647	1706	1744	1808	1848	1909	194
124	Katsuta	d.	0817	0855	0925	0955	1021	1021	1053	1111	1153	1212	1252	1312	1350	1412	1450	1512	1551	1612	1652	1712	1749	1813	1853	1914	195
150	Hitachi	d.	0834	0915	0941	...	1040	1040	...	1126	...	1232	...	1327	...	1430	1511	1527	...	1630	...	1730	...	1831	...	1932	201
212	**Iwaki**	a.	0918	...	1025	...	1124	1124	...	1207	...	1315	...	1409	...	1515	...	1609	...	1714	...	1814	...	1915	...	2015	...
290	Haranomachi	d.	...	...	1132	...	...	...	...	...	...	...	...	...	...	1621	...	...	...	...	...	1924	...	...	...	...	...
361	**Sendai** (Honshu)	a.	...	...	1229	...	...	...	...	...	...	...	...	...	...	1726	...	...	...	...	...	2028	...	...	...	...	...

Tokyo Shinagawa	d.	1845	1915	1945	2045	2115	2145	2215	2245	...	...
Tokyo Ueno	d.	1900	1930	2000	2100	2130	2200	2230	2300	...	...
Tsuchiura	d.	*2010*	2018	|	2142	2221	2242	2319	2351	...	...
Mito	d.	2008	2052	2108	2211	2255	2314	2353	0024	...	...
Katsuta	d.	2014	2057	2113	2217	2300	2319	2358	0029	...	...
Hitachi	d.	2032	...	2131	2235	...	2338	...	...	...	...
Iwaki	a.	2116	...	2214	2319	...	...	...	...	...	...
Haranomachi	d.	...	...	...	...	...	...	...	...	...	...
Sendai (Honshu)	a.	...	...	...	...	...	...	...	...	...	...

Sendai (Honshu)	d.	...	...	...	...	...	...	...	...	...	...
Haranomachi	d.	...	...	...	...	...	...	...	...	...	...
Iwaki	d.	...	...	...	0614	...	0703	...	0818	...	092
Hitachi	d.	...	...	0556	0701	0719	0745	0821	0901	...	100
Katsuta	d.	...	0539	0616	0720	0739	0804	0841	0921	0947	102
Mito	d.	...	0545	0622	0726	0745	0810	0848	0927	0953	102
Tsuchiura	d.	0605	0620	0656	0758	0819	0839	0920	|	1025	|
Tokyo Ueno	a.	0706	0723	0759	0858	0915	0933	1006	1037	1108	113
Tokyo Shinagawa	a.	0721	...	0813	0913	0931	0950	1021	1051	1122	115

Sendai (Honshu)	d.	...	...	...	...	...	1013	...	...	...	...	...	...	...	...	...	...	...	...	...	1611	...	...	...	1802	...
Haranomachi	d.	...	...	...	...	...	1107	...	...	...	...	...	...	...	...	...	...	...	...	...	1706	...	...	...	1906	...
Iwaki	d.	...	1017	...	1120	...	1218	...	...	1323	...	1418	...	1518	...	1618	...	1721	...	...	1817	...	1918	...	2016	...
Hitachi	d.	1027	1102	...	1202	...	1302	...	...	1405	...	1502	...	1602	1626	1702	...	1803	...	...	1900	...	2000	...	2100	...
Katsuta	d.	1047	1121	1147	1221	1247	1321	1347	...	1421	1447	1521	1547	1621	1647	1721	1747	1821	...	1847	1921	1947	2021	2047	2121	214
Mito	d.	1053	1127	1153	1227	1253	1327	1353	...	1427	1453	1527	1553	1627	1653	1727	1753	1827	...	1853	1927	1953	2027	2053	2127	215
Tsuchiura	d.	1125	|	1225	|	1325	|	1425	...	|	1525	|	1625	|	1725	|	1824	|	...	1924	|	2024	|	2124	2156	222
Tokyo Ueno	a.	1208	1237	1308	1337	1408	1437	1509	...	1537	1609	1639	1708	1738	1808	1839	1908	1938	...	2010	2037	2109	2139	2208	2238	230
Tokyo Shinagawa	a.	1222	1251	1322	1351	1422	1451	1522	...	1551	1623	1653	1723	1752	1823	1852	1922	1952	...	2023	2052	2123	2154	2223	2253	232

Note: Some trains run on a slightly different schedule on Ⓒ.

8220 NIIGATA - AOMORI

Limited Express trains JR Eas

km													
0	**Niigata**	d.	...	0822	...	1056	...	1232	1457	...	1715	1854	2111
168	Sakata	◧ d.	*0634*	1037	...	1303	...	1441	1712	...	1922	2106	2318
273	Akita	◧ d.	0839	1203	1240	...	1552	...	1841	1923	...	...	...
377	Odate	d.	1006	...	1409	...	1723	...	...	2103	...	...	...
421	Hirosaki	d.	1044	...	1447	...	1802	...	...	2140	...	...	...
455	Shin Aomori	d.	1113	...	1516	...	1831	...	...	2212	...	...	...
459	**Aomori**	a.	1119	...	1521	...	1837	...	...	2218	...	...	...

Aomori	d.	...	...	...	...	0904	...	...	1241	...	1556	...
Shin Aomori	d.	...	...	...	...	0911	...	...	1248	...	1603	...
Hirosaki	d.	...	...	...	...	0940	...	...	1320	...	1632	...
Odate	d.	...	...	...	...	1017	...	...	1357	...	1710	...
Akita	◧ d.	...	...	...	1035	1144	...	...	1527	1635	1841	204
Sakata	◧ d.	0529	0645	0904	1201	...	1431	1556	...	1805	...	223
Niigata	a.	0732	0849	1109	1405	...	1637	1801	...	2010	...	...

◧ – Additional local trains available.

8225 HAKODATE and MURORAN - SAPPORO

JR Hokkaid

km			**1001**	**1003**	**1**	**1005**	**3**	**5**	**7**	**9**	**1007**	**11**	**13**	**1009**	**15**	**1011**	**17**	**19**	**21**					
0	**Hakodate**	d.	...	...	0602	...	0737	0900	1005	1045	...	1215	1331	...	1501	...	1640	1752	1848	1912	2011	2116	2222	231
18	Shin **Hakodate Hokuto**	d.	...	...	0620	...	0757	0919	1023	1105	...	1234	1350	...	1520	...	1658	1811	1906	1931	2033	2138	2248	233
50	Mori	d.	...	...	0648	...	0824	0947	1051	1133	...	1302	1423	...	1548	...	1726	1838	1933	...	...	...	...	...
112	Oshamambe	d.	...	...	0730	...	0906	1029	1133	1214	...	1344	1505	...	1628	...	1808	1919	2015	...	...	...	...	...
154	Toya	d.	...	...	0757	...	0931	1054	1158	1239	...	1409	1530	...	1653	...	1834	1944	2040	...	...	...	...	...
	Muroran	d.	0525	0654	|	...	|	|	|	|	1338	|	|	1630	|	1812	|	|	|	...	...	...	...	...
190	Higashi-Muroran	d.	0540	0708	0825	0922	0959	1122	1225	1309	1351	1437	1558	1643	1722	1825	1905	2011	2108	...	...	...	...	...
207	Noboribetsu	d.	0554	0722	0837	0936	1011	1134	1237	1322	1407	1449	1610	1658	1734	1840	1918	2023	2121	...	...	...	...	...
248	Tomakomai	d.	0619	0748	0903	1001	1037	1159	1303	1348	1435	1514	1636	1725	1800	1907	1945	2049	2148	...	...	...	...	...
275	Minami Chitose	d.	0638	0805	0919	1019	1054	1216	1318	1406	1453	1530	1653	1743	1816	1927	2003	2105	2206	...	...	...	...	...
319	**Sapporo**	a.	0713	0838	0950	1053	1128	1249	1352	1438	1528	1604	1730	1816	1847	2002	2035	2136	2237	...	...	...	...	...

km						**2**	**4**	**1002**		**6**	**8**	**10**	**1004**	**12**		**1006**	**16**	**18**	**1008**	**20**	**22**	**1010**	**12**	
0	**Sapporo**	d.	...	...	...	0600	0652	0730	...	0843	0938	1057	1132	1209	...	1356	1438	1534	1603	1651	1847	1914	2200	...
44	Minami Chitose	d.	...	...	...	0628	0723	0801	...	0916	1012	1127	1202	1241	...	1428	1512	1605	1638	1726	1918	1948	2234	...
71	Tomakomai	d.	...	...	...	0644	0740	0819	...	0932	1030	1144	1221	1259	...	1446	1529	1622	1656	1743	1935	2007	2252	...
112	Noboribetsu	d.	...	...	...	|	0803	0845	...	0958	1056	1210	1246	1326	...	1511	1555	1647	1721	1808	2000	2036	2317	...
129	Higashi-Muroran	d.	...	...	...	0718	0816	0858	...	1011	1111	1224	1301	1339	...	1454	1608	1701	1736	1821	2013	2052	2322	...
136	**Muroran**	a.	...	...	...	|	|	...	...	|	|	|	1313	|	...	1538	|	|	1747	|	|	2106	2344	...
	Toya	d.	...	...	...	|	0844	...	...	1039	1139	1251	...	1408	...	...	1634	1727	...	1848	2039	...	...	...
	Oshamambe	d.	...	...	...	0809	0911	...	...	1106	1205	1317	...	1437	...	...	1701	1757	...	1915	2105	...	...	...
	Mori	d.	...	...	...	0850	0954	...	...	1149	1248	1359	...	1520	...	...	1743	1839	...	1957	2148	...	...	...
	Shin **Hakodate Hokuto**	a.	0641	0719	0832	0917	1023	...	1110	1219	1319	1426	...	1552	1718	...	1811	1906	...	2023	2214	...	...	233
	Hakodate	a.	0706	0747	0859	0933	1038	...	1136	1234	1335	1441	...	1608	1743	...	1826	1924	...	2059	2251	...	...	235

SAPPORO - KUSHIRO 8230

JR Hokkaido

km												
0	**Sapporo** d.	0648	0758	0851	1033	1150	1415	1552	1729	1840	1939	2110
44	Minami Chitose d.	0720	0827	0926	1105	1225	1448	1626	1807	1914	2012	2142
143	Tomamu d.	0827	0934	1046	1215	1326	1605	1735	1920	2020	2125	2254
220	Obihiro d.	0921	1041	1139	1312	1418	1704	1836	2017	2120	2219	2348
349	**Kushiro** a.	1058	...	1320	...	1551	1839	...	2159	...	2355	...

Kushiro d.	...	0625	...	0821	...	1124	...	1342	1612	...	1859
Obihiro d.	0645	0801	0842	0953	1108	1257	1335	1525	1748	1924	2033
Tomamu d.	0741	0905	0946	1046	1215	1402	1438	1618	1841	2030	2125
Minami Chitose d.	0902	1014	1102	1151	1328	1503	1551	1729	1954	2140	2228
Sapporo a.	0934	1047	1136	1223	1404	1538	1624	1803	2028	2215	2258

KUSHIRO - ABASHIRI 8233

JR Hokkaido

km											
0	**Kushiro** d.	...	...	0638	0857	1414	1632	1741	1852	2209	...
44	Mashu d.	...	...	0800	1011	1530	1759	1921	2010	2323	...
132	Shiretoko-Shari d.	0645	0728	0906	1112	1633	1859	...	2119	...	...
143	**Abashiri** a.	0731	0817	0951	1153	1717	1947	...	2200	...	...

Abashiri d.	...	...	0641	1024	1510	1617	1854	2014	2209	...
Shiretoko-Shari d.	...	...	0726	1111	1557	1715	1945	2100	2250	...
Mashu d.	0520	0630	0825	1217	1710	1832	2115	...	...	...
Kushiro a.	0637	0747	1000	1334	1845	1955	2208	...	...	...

SAPPORO - WAKKANAI and ABASHIRI 8235

JR Hokkaido

km												
0	**Sapporo** d.	0656	0730	1100	...	1200	...	1530	...	1730	1830	...
83	Takikawa d.	0755	0824	1152	...	1252	...	1622	...	1829	1922	...
137	**Asahikawa .. 8240** a.	0832	0858	1225	...	1325	...	1655	...	1905	1955	...
137	**Asahikawa .. 8240** d.	0835	0900	...	1241	...	1335	...	1705	1908	...	2006
213	Nayoro d.	|	0956	...	|	...	1431	...	|	|	...	2103
396	**Wakkanai** a.	|	1240	...	|	...	1723	...	|	|	...	2347
185	Kamikawa d.	0916	...	...	1327	...	...	...	1745	1949	...	...
375	**Abashiri** a.	1217	...	...	1635	...	...	...	2049	2300	...	...

Abashiri d.	0556	...	...	0806	...	1235	...	...	...	1725	...
Kamikawa d.	0901	...	...	1111	...	1540	...	...	...	2036	...
Wakkanai d.	|	0636	...	|	...	|	...	1301	...	|	1744
Nayoro d.	|	0925	...	|	...	|	...	1548	...	|	2032
Asahikawa... 8240 a.	0944	1019	...	1150	...	1619	...	1648	...	2114	2126
Asahikawa... 8240 d.	0947	...	1030	...	1200	...	1630	...	1700	2117	2130
Takikawa d.	1022	...	1102	...	1232	...	1702	...	1733	2152	2204
Sapporo a.	1119	...	1155	...	1325	...	1755	...	1825	2253	2257

SAPPORO - ASAHIKAWA 8240

JR Hokkaido

km																								
0	**Sapporo** d.	0635	0749	0830	0900	1000	1100	...	1200	1300	1400	1430	1500	1530	1600	1700	1800	...	1830	1900	2000	2100	2200	2305
83	Takikawa d.	0727	0841	0922	0952	1052	1152	...	1252	1352	1452	1522	1552	1622	1652	1752	1852	...	1922	1952	2052	2152	2252	2357
137	**Asahikawa** 8235 a.	0800	0914	0955	1025	1125	1225	...	1325	1425	1525	1555	1625	1655	1725	1825	1925	...	1955	2025	2125	2225	2325	0030

sahikawa 8235 d.	0518	0600	0645	0718	0755	0830	...	0900	1000	1030	1100	1200	1300	1400	1500	1600	...	1630	1700	1800	1900	2000	2200
'akikawa d.	0550	0632	0717	0750	0827	0902	...	0932	1032	1102	1132	1232	1332	1432	1532	1632	...	1702	1732	1832	1932	2032	2232
apporo a.	0643	0733	0826	0846	0920	0955	...	1025	1125	1155	1225	1325	1425	1525	1625	1725	...	1755	1825	1925	2025	2125	2325

SUMMARY OF OVERNIGHT TRAINS 8300

km		C [R]	B [R]	A [R]
0	**Tokyo** d.	...	2150	2150
29	Yokohama d.	...	2215	2215
181	Shiuoka a.	...	0020	0020
543	Kyoto d.	2115	|	|
557	Osaka d.	2228	|	|
733	**Okayama** d.	|	0631	0634
814	Niimi d.	|	|	0744
892	Yonago d.	0756	|	0905
921	Matsue d.	0857	|	0931
954	**Izumoshi** a.	0931	|	0958
761	Kojima d.	...	0653	...
805	**Takamatsu** a.	...	0727	...

	C [R]	A [R]	B [R]
Takamatsu d.	...	...	2126
Kojima d.	...	...	2201
Izumoshi d.	1600	1851	|
Matsue d.	1705	1927	|
Yonago d.	1748	1956	|
Niimi d.	|	2120	|
Okayama d.	|	2234	2234
Osaka d.	0612	0033	0033
Kyoto a.	0643	|	|
Shizuoka d.	...	0440	0440
Yokohama d.	...	0645	0645
Tokyo a.	...	0708	0708

A – SUNRISE IZUMO 1, 2 cl., Izumoshi - Tokyo and v.v. (see note ⊙).
B – SUNRISE SETO 1, 2 cl., Takamatsu - Tokyo and v.v. (see note ⊙).
C – WEST EXPRESS GINGA 2 cl., . Only available to tour passengers. From Kyoto on ①⑤ May 6 - Sept. 19 (not June 6, July 1–8, Aug. 8–19, Sept. 5); from Izumoshi on ③⑥ May 7 - Sept. 21 (not June 8, July 2–9, Aug. 10–20, Sept. 7).

⊙ – Trains convey Deluxe, single and twin berth compartments. They also convey *Nobinobi* - open-plan sleeping areas categorised as seats.

AIRPORT RAIL LINKS 8400

HUBU CENTRAL JAPAN INTERNATIONAL AIRPORT – ***NOTE: Around 50% of 'SKY' services have been cancelled, slower trains are not affected.***

'SKY' Limited Express service ([R]) Meitetsu Nagoya - Central Japan International Airport and v.v. *44 km*. Journey 30 minutes. (Additional slower trains are available, not [R]). Operator: Meitetsu.

rom Meitetsu Nagoya on Ⓐ at 0600, 0628, 0648, 0720, 0751, 0823, 0850 and every 30 minutes until 1650, 1719, 1749, 1819, 1849, 1919, 1949, 2019, 2049, 2119; on Ⓒ at 0602, 0630, 0653, 720, 0750 and every 30 minutes until 2050, 2120.

rom Central Japan International Airport on Ⓐ at 0703, 0726, 0800, 0834, 0907 and every 30 minutes until 1637, 1706, 1736, 1806, 1836, 1906, 1936, 2007, 2037, 2107, 2137, 2207; on Ⓒ at 0713, 729, 0759, 0829, 0907 and every 30 minutes until 2137, 2207.

ANSAI AIRPORT

IARUKA' Limited Express service Kyoto - Shin Osaka ■ - Kansai Airport and v.v. *100 km*. Journey 80 - 90 minutes. Operator: JR West.

rom Kyoto at 0545, 0621, 0644, 0745 Ⓐ, 0749 Ⓒ, 0820 Ⓒ, 0821 Ⓐ, 0845, 0930, 1730, 1830, 1930, 2030.

rom Kansai Airport at 0630 Ⓐ, 0640 Ⓒ, 0727 Ⓐ, 0741 Ⓒ, 0755 Ⓐ, 0808 Ⓒ, 0843 Ⓒ, 0845 Ⓐ, 0946, 1714 Ⓒ, 1716 Ⓐ, 1816, 1916, 2016, 2125, 2216.

■ – Trains call at Shin Osaka 28 - 33 minutes after Kyoto and 45 - 50 minutes after Kansai Airport.

OKYO HANEDA AIRPORT

imited Express service Tokyo Shinagawa - Haneda Airport Terminal 3 (△) and v.v. *14 km*. Journey 20 minutes. Operator: Keikyu Railway.

rom Tokyo Shinagawa at 0552 and every 10 - 15 minutes until 2300. From Haneda Airport Terminal 3 at 0530 and every 10 - 15 minutes until 2330.

△ – Most trains continue to/from Haneda Aiport Terminal 1, journey 3 minutes.

lonorail service Tokyo Hamamatsucho – Haneda Airport Terminal 3 (□) and v.v. (JR pass valid) *14 km*. Journey 13 - 24 minutes. Operator: Tokyo Monorail Co Ltd.

rom Tokyo Hamamatsucho at 0459 and every 3 - 10 minutes until 0001. From Haneda Airport Terminal 3 at 0518 and every 3 - 10 minutes until 0010.

□ – All trains continue to/from Haneda Aiport Terminal 1, journey 3 - 5 minutes and Terminal 2, journey 5 - 7 minutes.

OKYO NARITA AIRPORT – ***NOTE: Around 30% of 'NARITA EXPRESS' services have been cancelled, slower trains are not affected.***

IARITA EXPRESS' Limited Express service ([R]) Tokyo - Narita Airport Terminal 1 (▽) and v.v. *79 km*. Journey 55 minutes. Operator: JR East.

rom Tokyo at 0618, 0700, 0715, 0731, 0755, 0830, 0900, 1003, 1033, 1103, 1133, 1203, 1233, 1303, 1333, 1403, 1433, 1503, 1533, 1603, 1633, 1703, 1733, 1803, 1833, 1903, 2003.

rom Narita T1 at 0743, 0813, 0850, 0915, 0945, 1015, 1045, 1114, 1145, 1220, 1245, 1314, 1345, 1420, 1446, 1514, 1544, 1620, 1645, 1717, 1746, 1815, 1848, 1912, 1948, 2044, 2144.

▽ – Trains also call at Narita Aiport Terminal two, 2/3 minutes before/after Terminal one. Additional slower trains(not [R]) are available about hourly each direction.

KYLINER' Limited Express service ([R]) Tokyo Ueno Keisei - Narita Airport Terminal 1 (▷) and v.v. *69 km*. Journey 45 minutes. Operator: Keisei Electric Railway.

rom Tokyo Ueno Keisei at 0540, 0600, 0620, 0640, 0700, 0720, 0740, 0800, 0817, 0840 and at the same minutes past each hour until, 1600, 1617, 1640, 1700, 1717 Ⓒ, 1720 Ⓐ, 1740, 1820, 900, 1940, 2020.

rom Narita Airport Terminal 1 at 0723 Ⓐ, 0730 Ⓒ, 0812 Ⓐ, 0830 Ⓒ, 0906 Ⓐ, 0919 Ⓒ, 0936 Ⓐ, 0939 Ⓒ, 0959, 1019, 1039, 1059 and at the same minutes past each hour until 1719, 1739, 1759, 818, 1839, 1859, 1920, 1939, 2000, 2030, 2100, 2130, 2200, 2230, 2300.

– Trains also call at Narita Airport Terminal 2, 3 minutes before / 5 minutes after Terminal 1. Additional slower trains are available.

APPORO SHIN CHITOSE AIRPORT

apporo - Shin Chitose Airport and v.v. *47 km* Journey 38 - 48 minutes. Operator: JR Hokkaido.

rom Sapporo at 0550, 0602*, 0616, 0629, 0642, 0656, 0722, 0735, 0748, 0802, 0808, 0821, 0836, then at 00, 12, 23, 35 and 47 minutes past the hour (●) until 2004, 2010, 2024, 2047, 2053, 100, 2113, 2137, 2151.

rom Shin Chitose Airport at 0639, 0656, 0702, 0722, 0733, 0751, 0819, 0830, 0840, 0852, 0906, 0918, 0930, then at 06, 18, 30, 42 and 54 minutes past the hour (●) until 2006, 2019, 2032, 2046, 052, 2120, 2131, 2144, 2155, 2205, 2216, 2235, 2253.

– Timings may vary by up to 3 minutes. All trains call at Minami-Chitose 3 minutes before / 4 minutes after Shin Chitose Airport.

BEYOND EUROPE
NORTH AMERICA

INDEX OF PLACES

by table number

CANADA

Capital: **Ottawa** (GMT - 5; add one hour in summer, except Saskatchewan).
2022 public holidays: Jan. 1, Apr. 15, 18 (NT, NU, QC), May 23 (not NB, NS, PE, QC), July 1, Sept. 5, Oct. 10 (not NB, NS, PE), Nov. 11 (not MB, NS, ON, QC), Dec. 25, 26 (NL, NT, NU, ON).
The principal operator in Canada is Via Rail (Via Rail ✆ 1 888 842 7245. www.viarail.ca). Timings shown are the most recently available and are subject to alteration at any time, but especially around public holidays. Details of other operators can be found in relevant tables. Unless otherwise noted all trains carry first and second class seated accomodation. In Canada first class is called 'Business' and second class is called 'Economy'. Most very long distance trains convey sleeping cars called 'Sleeper Plus' which has two berths per compartment, some of which are en-suite, The *Canadian* also offers 'Prestige Class' and one to four berth 'Sleeper Plus' compartments some of which are en-suite. Most trains also convey some form of catering, but again the actual service offered varies considerably. Tickets are available from staffed stations, websites and through authorised ticketing agents. A reservation is neccessary for travel on very long distance Via Rail trains, and also strongly recommended for corridor services.

Via Rail has several passes giving flexible and affordable travel across their network. The **Canada Pass** allows travel on the entire network and you can choose from 6, 12 or unlimited one-way trip tickets for either 15, 30, or 60 days. 6 trips cost $649 for 15 days, $779 for 30 days and $974 for 60 days. 12 trips cost $714 for 15 days, $1090 for 30 days and $1266 for 60 days. Unlimited trips cost $821 for 15 days, $1308 for 30 days and $1519 for 60 days. The **Leisure Pass** operates along the Québec - Windsor corridor and is for 6 one-way trip tickets, valid for 6 months. The corridor is split into 5 zones: Zone 1, Toronto - Windsor (including Niagara Falls) $299, Zone 2, Kingston - Toronto $359, Zone 3 Montréal - Ottawa - Kingston $359, Zone 4, Québec City - Montréal - Ottawa $319 and Zone 5 Québec City - Windsor $449. Service and fares are based on Escape fare. The **Multi Pass** also operates along the Québec - Windsor corridor and uses the same zones but are for 10, 20, 50 or 100 one-way trip tickets which are transferable and the service and fares are based on Economy or Business class. Costs range from $799 for 10 Economy tickets for Zone 1 to $19,656 for 100 Business class tickets in Zone 5. Discounts and upgrades are available with these passes. Passes aimed at students, youths and commuters are also available. For conditions and more information see www.viarail.ca.

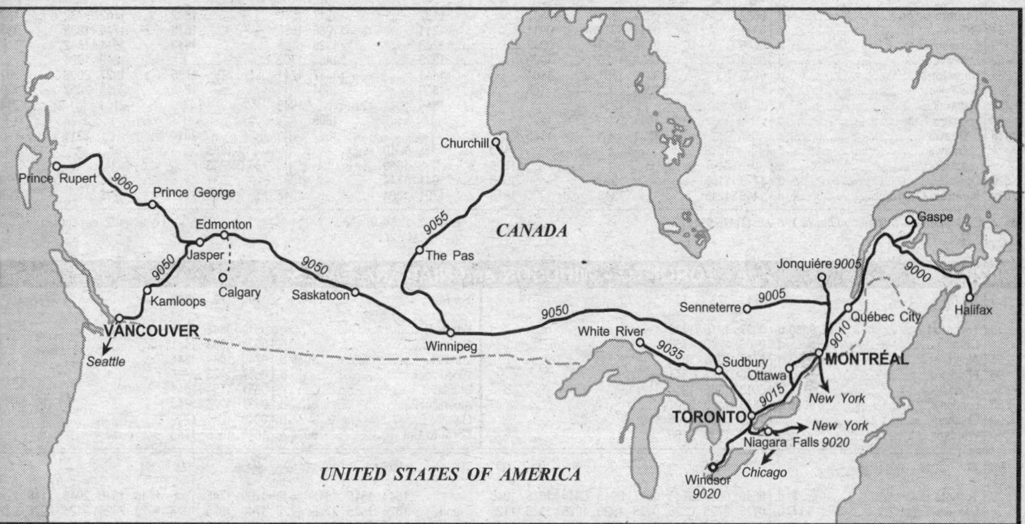

Via Rail — MONTRÉAL - HALIFAX — 9000

km		708 ③⑤⑦ 🚌 🅁	14 ③⑤⑦ A 🅁		15 ③⑤⑦ A 🅁	703 ①④⑥ 🚌 🅁
	Québec City Palais.... d.	2100	...	**Halifax** d.	1300	...
0	**Montréal** Central .. **9010** d.	|	1900	Truro d.	1431	...
251	**Sainte Foy** .... **9010** d.	2130	2249	Amherst d.	1608	...
448	Rivière-du-Loup d.	...	0113	**Moncton** a.	1717	...
552	Rimouski d.	...	0301	**Moncton** d.	1732	...
581	Mont-Joli d.	...	0339	Miramichi d.	1937	...
731	Matapédia d.	...	0610	Bathurst d.	2128	...
874	Bonaventure d.	...	|	Campbellton d.	2318	...
993	Percé d.	...	|	**Gaspé** d.	|	...
1056	**Gaspé** a.	...	|	Percé d.	|	...
750	Campbellton d.	...	0748	Bonaventure d.	|	...
851	Bathurst d.	...	0937	Matapédia d.	2252	...
922	Miramichi d.	...	1123	Mont-Joli d.	0126	...
1051	**Moncton** a.	...	1323	Rimouski d.	0201	...
1051	**Moncton** d.	...	1338	Rivière-du-Loup d.	0353	...
1128	Amherst d.	...	1442	**Sainte Foy** .... **9010** a.	0613	0640
1252	Truro d.	...	1622	**Montréal** Central **9010** a.	1003	|
1355	**Halifax** a.	...	1751	**Québec City** Palais .a.	...	0710

– OCEAN – 🛏 (2) ✕ Montréal - Halifax and v.v.

Via Rail — JONQUIÈRE and SENNETERRE — 9005

km		606 2 🅁 ⑦	602 2 🅁 ⑦		601 2 🅁 ⑤	603 2 🅁 ⑤
717	**Senneterre** d.	0845	...	**Montréal** Central d.	0815	0815
561	Clova d.	1050	...	Shawinigan d.	1043	1043
495	Parent d.	1150	...	**Hervey** a.	1130	1130
431	Weymont d.	1301	...	**Hervey** d.	1140	1200
297	La Tuque d.	1453	...	Rivière à Pierre d.	1234	|
510	**Jonquière** d.	|	1110	Lac-Édouard d.	1408	|
444	Chambord d.	|	1211	Chambord d.	1605	|
341	Lac-Édouard d.	|	1405	**Jonquière** a.	1710	|
251	Rivière à Pierre d.	|	1540	La Tuque d.	...	1318
217	**Hervey** a.	1625	1640	Weymont d.	...	1504
217	**Hervey** d.	1700	1700	Parent d.	...	1625
170	Shawinigan d.	1748	1748	Clova d.	...	1721
0	**Montréal** Central a.	2015	2015	**Senneterre** a.	...	1940

Via Rail — QUÉBEC CITY - MONTRÉAL — 9010

km		15 ①④⑥ A	35 B	37 B	39 B					
0	**Québec City** Palais △ d.	...	0800	1236	1500	...	...	...	...	...
21	Ste. Foy △ d.	0628	0826	1302	1526	...	...	...	...	...
26	Charny △ d.	|	0834	|	|	...	...	...	...	...
172	Drummondville d.	0836	1005	1445	1654	...	...	...	...	...
219	St. Hyacinthe d.	0915	1038	1516	|	...	...	...	...	...
265	St. Lambert △ d.	0950	1114	1543	1800	...	...	...	...	...
272	**Montréal** Central △ a.	1003	1125	1554	1811	...	...	...	...	...

	24 B	26 B	28 B	14 ③⑤⑦ A					
Montréal Central △ d.	1245	1640	1825	1900	...	...	...	...	...
St. Lambert △ d.	1308	1702	1848	1925	...	...	...	...	...
St. Hyacinthe d.	1335	1729	1916	1958	...	...	...	...	...
Drummondville d.	1403	1815	1945	2047	...	...	...	...	...
Charny △ d.	1558	1954	2124	|	...	...	...	...	...
Ste. Foy △ d.	1606	2003	2132	2234	...	...	...	...	...
Québec City Palais △ a.	1628	2026	2156	...	...	...	...	...	...

– OCEAN – 🛏 (2) ✕ Montréal Central - Halifax and v.v. (Table **9000**).
– (12) Québec - Montréal - Ottawa and v.v. (Table **9015**).

△ – Local traffic not carried.

9015 MONTRÉAL - OTTAWA - TORONTO

Via Ra

km		41	61		51	643		63	65		53	47	35	67	645		69	37		59	669		39
		①–④	①–⑥		①–⑤	⑥⑦						⑤⑦									⑤⑦		
													A					A					A
0	**Montréal** Central △ d.	...	0651	...	0611	...	...	0850	1100	...	...	...	1154	1323	...	...	1656	1630	...	...	1822	...	185
19	Dorval △ d.	...	0718	...	0635	...	...	0915	1126	...	...	...	1229	1347	...	...	1720	1704	...	...	1847	...	192
100	Alexandria d.	...	|	...	0719	...	...	|	|	...	...	...	1317	|	...	...	|	1751	...	...	|	...	201
187	**Ottawa** a.	...	|	...	0811	...	...	|	|	...	...	...	1405	|	...	...	|	1835	...	...	|	...	210
187	**Ottawa** d.	0530	|	...	0826	0835	...	|	|	...	1145	1231	...	|	1432	...	|	...	...	1749	|	...	...
253	Smiths Falls d.	0622	|	...	0915	0924	...	|	|	...	1235	|	...	|	|	...	|	...	...	1850	|	...	...
	Cornwall d.	|	0809	...	|	|	...	1005	1217	...	|	|	...	1436	|	...	1811	...	...	|	1940	...	...
298	Brockville d.	0651	|	...	0944	0953	...	1051	|	...	1310	1359	...	|	|	...	1854	...	...	1919	|	...	...
378	**Kingston** d.	0734	0938	...	1027	1036	...	1138	1345	...	1401	1448	...	1602	1637	...	1937	...	...	2002	2107	...	...
451	Belleville d.	0816	1016	...	1103	1120	...	1221	1427	...	1443	1531	...	1642	1718	...	|	...	...	2042	|	...	...
520	Cobourg d.	0851	|	...	1137	1158	...	1302	1504	...	1521	|	...	1721	|	...	|	...	...	2120	|	...	...
581	Oshawa d.	0927	1125	...	1214	1238	...	1340	1539	...	1556	1641	...	1756	1825	...	2121	...	...	2154	2256	...	...
633	**Toronto** Union a.	1002	1203	...	1248	1318	...	1418	1618	...	1633	1718	...	1833	1903	...	2203	...	...	2233	2333	...	...

km		60	24		50	62		52	26		64	28		42	66		38	46		68	54		668
																		①–⑥					⑤
		B	A						A			A											
0	**Toronto** Union d.	0632	...	...	0632	0832	...	0832	...	...	1132	...	...	1217	1517	...	...	1532	...	1702	1732	...	180
51	Oshawa d.	0711	...	...	0711	0911	...	0911	...	...	1211	...	...	1255	1556	...	...	1610	...	1740	1808	...	183
113	Cobourg d.	0746	...	...	0746	0943	...	0943	...	...	1248	...	...	1329	|	...	...	1643	...	1811	1842	...	|
182	Belleville d.	0821	...	...	0821	1020	...	1020	...	...	1329	...	...	1407	1702	...	...	|	...	1849	1924	...	|
254	**Kingston** d.	0903	...	...	0903	1101	...	1101	...	...	1411	...	...	1447	1741	...	...	1755	...	1927	2006	...	202
335	Brockville d.	|	...	...	1000	|	...	1156	...	...	1500	...	...	1534	|	...	...	1840	...	2013	2052	...	|
428	Cornwall d.	1040	...	...	|	1234	...	|	...	...	1549	...	...	|	1908	...	...	|	...	2104	|	...	214
380	Smiths Falls d.	|	...	...	1031	|	...	1225	...	...	|	...	...	1608	|	...	...	|	...	|	2126	...	|
446	**Ottawa** a.	|	...	...	1121	|	...	1325	...	...	|	...	...	1657	|	...	...	2014	...	|	2211	...	|
	Ottawa d.	|	1015	...	...	|	...	...	1420	...	|	1610	...	...	|	...	1855	...	...	|	...	...	|
	Alexandria d.	|	1107	...	...	|	...	...	1508	...	|	1659	...	...	|	...	1946	...	...	|	...	...	|
520	Dorval △ d.	1129	1155	...	...	1323	...	...	1555	...	1641	1744	...	...	1957	...	2037	...	...	2153	...	...	223
539	**Montréal** Central △ a.	1149	1215	...	...	1343	...	...	1615	...	1701	1804	...	...	2018	...	2057	...	...	2213	...	...	225

A – [12] Québec - Montréal - Ottawa and v.v. (Table **9010**).
B – ①②③④⑥.
△ – Local traffic not carried.

9020 TORONTO - WINDSOR and NIAGARA FALLS

GO Transit, Via Ra

km	*Via Rail*	71	73	75					
0	**Toronto** Union 9030 d.	0637	1215	1730	...	...	...	...	...
34	Oakville d.	0702	1240	1756	...	...	...	...	...
56	Aldershot d.	0718	1258	1812	...	...	...	...	...
96	Brantford d.	0746	1327	1844	...	...	...	...	...
139	Woodstock d.	0818	1355	1914	...	...	...	...	...
185	London 9030 d.	0853	1430	2001	...	...	...	...	...
290	Chatham d.	1006	1539	2106	...	...	...	...	...
360	**Windsor** a.	1055	1630	2158	...	...	...	...	...

Via Rail	70	72	76					
Windsor d.	0540	0848	1346	...	...	...	...	...
Chatham d.	0628	0933	1431	...	...	...	...	...
London 9030 d.	0740	1044	1544	...	...	...	...	...
Woodstock d.	0817	1123	|	...	...	...	...	...
Brantford d.	0851	1154	1641	...	...	...	...	...
Aldershot d.	0931	1226	1714	...	...	...	...	...
Oakville d.	0946	1241	1729	...	...	...	...	...
Toronto Union 9030 a.	1010	1305	1753	...	...	...	...	...

km	*GO Transit*	Ⓒ	Ⓐ			Ⓐ	Ⓒ	Ⓐ	Ⓒ		Ⓐ	Ⓒ	Ⓒ	Ⓐ	Ⓐ		Ⓐ	Ⓒ				
0	**Toronto** Union ◧ d.	0645	0645	0745	0845	0945	0945	1045	1045		1545	1545	1645	1645	1700	1745	1845	1845	1945	2045	2145	224
34	Oakville ◧ d.	0725	0725	0825	0925	1025	1025	1125	1125	and	1625	1625	1725	1725	1740	1825	1925	1925	2025	2125	2225	232
51	Burlington ◧ d.	0743	0743	0843	0943	1043	1043	1143	1143	hourly	1643	1643	1743	1743	1758	1843	1943	1943	2043	2143	2243	234
56	Aldershot ◧ d.	0750	0750	0850	0950	1050	1050	1150	1150	until	1650	1650	1750	1750	1805	1850	1950	1950	2050	2150	2250	235
114	St. Catharines d.	0845*	0848*	0948*	1048*	1148*	1158*	1248*	1258*	⊡	1755*	1758*	1853*	1855*	1908	1948*	2045*	2048*	2145*	2245*	2345*	004
133	**Niagara Falls** (Canada) a.	0918*	0923*	1023*	1123*	1223*	1233*	1323*	1333*		1831*	1833*	1928*	1931*	1933	2023*	2118*	2123*	2218*	2318*	0018*	011

GO Transit	Ⓒ	Ⓐ	Ⓐ	Ⓒ	Ⓐ	Ⓒ	Ⓐ	Ⓒ	Ⓐ	Ⓒ		Ⓐ	Ⓒ	Ⓒ	Ⓐ	Ⓒ	Ⓐ	Ⓒ	Ⓐ	Ⓒ	Ⓐ
Niagara Falls (Canada) d.	0549*	0557	0613*	0649*	0704*	0744*	0804*	0839*	0904*	0939*		1709*	1728*	1834*	1839*	1939*	1944*	2039*	2044*	2139*	214
St. Catharines d.	0619*	0620	0643*	0719*	0739*	0814*	0839*	0914*	0939*	1014*	and	1744*	1808*	1909*	1914*	2009*	2019*	2109*	2119*	2209*	221
Aldershot ◧ d.	0725	0725	0755	0825	0855	0925	0955	1025	1055	1125	hourly	1855	1925	2025	2025	2125	2125	2225	2225	2325	232
Burlington ◧ d.	0731	0731	0801	0831	0901	0931	1001	1031	1101	1131	until	1901	1931	2031	2031	2131	2131	2231	2231	2331	233
Oakville ◧ d.	0748	0748	0818	0848	0918	0948	1018	1048	1118	1148	⊡	1918	1948	2048	2048	2148	2148	2248	2248	2348	234
Toronto Union ◧ a.	0830	0830	0900	0930	1000	1030	1100	1130	1200	1230		2000	2030	2130	2130	2230	2230	2330	2330	0030	003

⊡ – Timings may vary by up to 11 minutes; earlier departures and later arrivals are possible.
◧ – Full service Toronto - Aldershot and v.v.: from Toronto at 0645 and every 30 minutes until 2345; from Aldershot at 0525 and every 30 minutes until 2325.
* – Connection by 🚌 to / from **Burlington**. Buses call at St. Catharines Fairview Mall a Nlagara Falls Bus Terminal, **not** at the railway stations.

9025 TORONTO - COCHRANE

Ontario Northland

km		🚌	🚌	🚌		🚌	🚌	422 [R] C
0	**Toronto** Yorkdale d.	0930	...	...	**Moosonee** d.	...	...	1700
143	Washago d.	1145	...	...	Moose River d.	...	...	1815r
164	Gravenhurst d.	1205	...	...	Fraserdale d.	...	...	2000r
219	Huntsville d.	1315	...	...	**Cochrane** d.	0850	...	2145
351	**North Bay** d.	1450	1615	...	Timmins d.	|	0900	━
513	Cobalt d.	━	1805	...	Matheson d.	1000	1005	...
529	New Liskeard d.	...	1830	...	Engleheart d.	...	1155	...
571	Engleheart d.	...	1910	...	New Liskeard d.	...	1235	🚌
677	Matheson d.	**421**	2115	2120	Cobalt d.	...	1305	
	Timmins a.	[R] C	2205	|	**North Bay** d.	...	1505	1600
754	**Cochrane** d.	0900	...	2225	Huntsville d.	...	...	1740
	Fraserdale d.	1035r	...	...	Gravenhurst d.	...	...	1850
	Moose River d.	1230r	...	...	Washago d.	...	...	1910
1053	**Moosonee** a.	1350	...	...	**Toronto** Yorkdale a.	...	...	2140

C – POLAR BEAR EXPRESS – ①②④⑤. [2] Cochrane - Moosonee and v.v. Timings at request stops (**r**) are approximate and will vary.

9030 TORONTO - SARNIA

GO Transit, Via Ra

km		GO Ⓐ	87		GO Ⓐ	84
0	**Toronto** Union 9020 d.	1634	1740	**Sarnia** d.	...	084
34	Brampton d.	1716	1814	London 9020 d.	0533	095
47	Georgetown d.	1734	1826	Stratford d.	0657	111
79	Guelph d.	1801	1851	Kitchener d.	0745	120
101	Kitchener d.	1822	1918	Guelph d.	0802	122
143	Stratford d.	1913	1955	Georgetown d.	0830	124
195	London 9020 d.	2037	2114	Brampton d.	0853	130
290	**Sarnia** a.	...	2220	**Toronto** Union 9020 a.	0928	133

9035 WHITE RIVER - SUDBURY

Via Ra

km		186 2 ⑦			185 2 ⑥	
0	**White River** d.	0700	...	**Sudbury** § d.	0900	...
79	Franz d.	0820	...	Biscotasing d.	1120	..
209	Chapleau d.	1045	...	Chapleau d.	1335	..
341	Biscotasing d.	1245	...	Franz d.	1550	...
484	**Sudbury** § a.	1550	...	**White River** a.	1705	..

§ – Sudbury is *10 km* from Sudbury Junction (Table **9050**).

9040 SAULT STE MARIE

km		🚌 Ⓑ D	E		E	Ⓑ D
	Sudbury d.	1740	...	**Agawa Canyon** d.	1400	...
	Sault Ste. Marie a.	2201	...	**Sault Ste. Marie** a.	1800	...
0	**Sault Ste. Marie** d.	...	0800	**Sault Ste. Marie** d.	...	1030
183	**Agawa Canyon** a.	...	1200	**Sudbury** a.	...	1517

D – Operated by Ontario Northland.
E – Agawa Canyon Train. Aug. 1 - Oct. 10, 2022. www.agawatrain.com

9045 THE PAS - PUKATAWAGAN

Keewatin Railwa

km		291 ①④ F			290 ②⑤ F	
0	**The Pas** d.	1115	...	**Pukatawagan** d.	1000	..
88	Cranberry Portage d.	1355	...	Cranberry Portage d.	1515	...
158	**Pukatawagan** a.	1845	...	**The Pas** a.	1730	..

F – Operated by Keewatin Railway Company. To book ✆ 204 623 5255.

Via Rail TORONTO - VANCOUVER 9050

km		1 ℝA			2 ℝA	
0	**Toronto** Union d.	0945	③⑦	**Vancouver** Pacific a.	1500	①⑤
143	Washago ⊗ d.	1225	:	Agassiz ⊗ d.	1703	:
241	Parry Sound ⊗ d.	1427	:	**Kamloops** North a.	0017	②⑥
422	Sudbury Junction § d.	1657	:	**Kamloops** North d.	0052	:
444	**Capreol** a.	1722	:	Valemount ⊗ d.	0701	:
444	**Capreol** d.	1752	:	**Jasper** a.	1100	:
683	Foleyet ⊗ d.	2244	:	**Jasper** d.	1230	:
859	Oba ⊗ d.	0138	①④	Hinton ⊗ d.	1345	:
921	Hornepayne d.	0309	:	Edson ⊗ d.	1519	:
1084	Longlac ⊗ d.	0534	:	**Edmonton** a.	1850	:
1537	Sioux Lookout d.	1155	:	**Edmonton** d.	1950	:
1652	Red Lake Road ⊗ d.	1341	:	Wainwright ⊗ d.	0014	③⑦
1943	**Winnipeg** a.	1930	:	Biggar d.	0331	:
1943	**Winnipeg** d.	2130	:	**Saskatoon** a.	0557	:
2032	Portage la Prairie ⊗ d.	2304	:	**Saskatoon** d.	0657	:
2173	Rivers ⊗ d.	0131	②⑤	Melville d.	1257	:
2394	Melville d.	0504	:	Rivers d.	1722	:
2702	**Saskatoon** a.	0950	:	Portage la Prairie ⊗ d.	1915	:
2702	**Saskatoon** d.	1050	:	**Winnipeg** a.	2200	:
2792	Biggar d.	1239	:	**Winnipeg** d.	2330	:
3017	Wainwright ⊗ d.	1633	:	Red Lake Road ⊗ d.	0351	①④
3221	**Edmonton** a.	2050	:	Sioux Lookout d.	0651	:
3221	**Edmonton** d.	0001	③⑥	Longlac ⊗ d.	1411	:
3430	Edson ⊗ d.	0252	:	Hornepayne d.	1839	:
3518	Hinton ⊗ d.	0358	:	Oba ⊗ d.	1930	:
3600	**Jasper** a.	0630	:	Foleyet ⊗ d.	2227	:
3600	**Jasper** d.	0930	:	**Capreol** a.	0347	②⑤
3721	Valemount ⊗ d.	1050	:	**Capreol** d.	0427	:
4052	**Kamloops** North a.	1828	:	Sudbury Junction § d.	0449	:
4052	**Kamloops** North d.	1903	:	Parry Sound ⊗ d.	0842	:
4360	Hope ⊗ d.	0201	④⑦	Washago ⊗ d.	1059	:
4466	**Vancouver** Pacific a.	0800	:	**Toronto** Union a.	1429	:

A – THE CANADIAN – 🛏 [2] ✕ Toronto - Edmonton - Vancouver and v.v.
⊗ – Request stop, advanced booking required.
§ – Sudbury Junction is *10 km* from Sudbury (Table **9035**).

Via Rail WINNIPEG - CHURCHILL 9055

km		691/3 ℝB			690/2 ℝB	
0	**Winnipeg** d.	1205	②⑦	**Churchill** d.	1930	②④⑥
88	Portage la Prairie ⊗ d.	1315	:	Herchmer d.	0003	③⑤⑦
283	Dauphin ⊗ d.	1706	:	Gillam (Nelson River) d.	0530	:
484	Canora d.	1946	:	**Thompson** a.	1130	:
549	Endeavour ⊗ d.	2054	:	**Thompson** d.	1400	:
635	Hudson Bay ⊗ d.	2232	:	Thicket Potage d.	1622	:
777	**The Pas** a.	0145	①③	Wabowden d.	1811	:
777	**The Pas** d.	0230	①③⑤	Cormorant d.	2147	:
843	Cormorant d.	0412	:	**The Pas** a.	2330	③⑤⑦
996	Wabowden d.	0748	:	**The Pas** d.	0315	⑤⑦
1073	Thicket Potage d.	0937	:	Hudson Bay ⊗ d.	0427	:
1149	**Thompson** a.	1200	①③⑤	Endeavour ⊗ d.	0555	:
1149	**Thompson** d.	1700	:	Canora d.	0718	:
1401	Gillam (Nelson River) d.	2330	:	Dauphin ⊗ d.	1206	:
1540	Herchmer d.	0426	②④⑥	Portage la Prairie ⊗ d.	1537	:
1697	**Churchill** a.	0900	:	**Winnipeg** a.	1645	:

B – 🛏 [2] ✕ Churchill - Winnipeg and v.v.
⊗ – Request stop, advanced booking required.

Via Rail PRINCE RUPERT - JASPER 9060

km		5 ℝ			6 ℝ	
0	**Jasper** d.	1245	⑦	**Prince Rupert** d.	0800	③
174	McBride d.	1444	:	Terrace (Kitimat) d.	1025	:
409	**Prince George** ⊖ a.	1908	:	New Hazelton ⊗ d.	1230	:
409	**Prince George** ⊖ d.	0800	①	Smithers d.	1424	:
560	Fort Fraser ⊗ d.	1032	:	Fort Fraser ⊗ d.	1757	:
795	Smithers d.	1420	:	**Prince George** ⊖ a.	2029	:
869	New Hazelton ⊗ d.	1537	:	**Prince George** ⊖ d.	0815	④
1007	Terrace (Kitimat) d.	1805	:	McBride d.	1218	:
1160	**Prince Rupert** a.	2025	:	**Jasper** a.	1700	:

⊖ – Passengers must arrange their own overnight accommodation in Prince George.
⊗ – Request stop, advanced booking required.

ROCKY MOUNTAINEER 9065

km		C	D		D	C
0	**Vancouver** Cottrell St. d.	0730	0730	**Banff** d.	...	0740
	Kamloops ◧ a.	1730	1730	Lake Louise d.	...	0900
	Kamloops ◧ d.	0625	0745	**Jasper** d.	0810	|
	Jasper a.	|	1800	Kamloops ◧ a.	1700	1815
	Lake Louise a.	1830	...	Kamloops ◧ d.	0735	0735
	Banff a.	1930	...	**Vancouver** Cottrell St. a.	1730	1730

km		E			E	
0	**North Vancouver** d.	0740	...	**Jasper** d.	0655	...
	Whistler ◧ a.	1130	...	Quesnel ◧ a.	1930	...
	Whistler ◧ d.	0710	...	Quesnel ◧ d.	0710	...
	Quesnel ◧ a.	1930	...	Whistler ◧ a.	1930	...
	Quesnel ◧ d.	0710	...	Whistler ◧ d.	1510	...
	Jasper a.	2030	...	**North Vancouver** a.	1900	...

C – FIRST PASSAGE TO THE WEST – for 2022 dates contact operator.
D – JOURNEY THROUGH THE CLOUDS – for 2022 dates contact operator.
E – RAINFOREST TO GOLD RUSH – for 2022 dates contact operator.
◧ – Compulsory overnight stop - hotels included in travel packages. Arrival times are flexible.
Operator: Rocky Mountaineer Railtours (www.rockymountaineer.com)

VANCOUVER - MISSION CITY 9070

km		Ⓐ		Ⓐ		Ⓐ		Ⓐ	
0	**Vancouver** Waterfront d.	1550	...	1650	...	1730	...	1820	...
26	Coquitlam Central d.	1619	...	1719	...	1759	...	1849	...
68	**Mission City** a.	1705	...	1805	...	1845	...	1935	...
		Ⓐ		Ⓐ		Ⓐ		Ⓐ	
	Mission City d.	0525	...	0625	...	0655	...	0725	...
	Coquitlam Central d.	0610	...	0710	...	0740	...	0810	...
	Vancouver Waterfront a.	0640	...	0740	...	0810	...	0840	...

Operator: West Coast Express (www.translink.ca).

🚌 CALGARY - EDMONTON 🚌 9090

km		RA ①–⑥	EB	RA †	RA		EB	RA	RA ⑤†
0	**Calgary** d.	0800	0845	1000	1200	...	1545	1630	1830
	Red Deer Quality Inn d.	0955	1115	1155	1410	...	1815	|	2015
303	**Edmonton** a.	1140	1315	1340	1555	...	2020	1950	2200
		RA ①–⑥	EB	RA †	RA		EB	RA	RA ⑤†
	Edmonton d.	0800	0815	1000	1200	...	1515	1630	1830
	Red Deer Quality Inn d.	0955	1100	1155	1355	...	1800	|	2015
	Calgary a.	1155	1320	1355	1555	...	2040	1950	2200

Times for Calgary and Edmonton are the operator's Downtown ticket offices.
EB – Ebus (www.myebus.ca). *RA* – Red Arrow (www.redarrow.ca).

UNITED STATES OF AMERICA

apital: **Washington DC** (GMT -5; add one hour in summer). 2022 public holidays: Jan. 1, 17, Feb. 21, May 30, June 19, 20, July 4, Sept. 5, Oct. 10, 11, Nov. 11, 24, Dec. 25, 26.

ne principal operator in the USA is Amtrak (✆ 1 800 872 7245. www.amtrak.com). Details of other operators can be found in relevant tables. Unless otherwise noted all trains carry two classes of eated accomodation known as 'Business' and 'Coach' shown as 1 and 2 in the tables. All Acela Express trains running between Boston, New York and Washington convey business class and an nhanced seated accommodation called 'First Class'. Most very long distance trains convey sleeping cars, and where this is the case it is detailed in the footnotes. Almost all sleeping car ccommodation in North America has two berths per compartment, some of which are en-suite, although the exact product offering varies by operator and route. Most trains also convey some form catering, but again the actual service offered varies considerably and often the full dining is available for sleeping car passengers. Timings shown are the latest available and are subject to teration around public holidays and it is recommended that you confirm all timings locally as short notice changes are possible. Tickets are available from staffed stations, websites and through uthorised ticketing agents. Amtrak requires reservations on practically all of its services, and also requires that you have identity documents available for inspection.

mtrak offers the 'USA Rail Pass' It is available to both US citizens and foreign nationals: The pass is for 10 segments of travel over a 30 day period. The adult price is $499, a 50% reduction for nildren aged 2 - 12. The pass is valid in coach class on the entire Amtrak system. Be warned though: this program is now revenue/capacity managed and may not be available on all trains all the ne. The pass is not valid on the Autotrain, Acela Express trains, Thruway buses numbered 7000 – 7999 and the Canadian portion of trains operated jointly by Amtrak and VIA Rail Canada. The ass alone is not valid for travel; tickets and, where neccessary, reservations must be obtained for each segment of travel. Upgrades to higher levels of accommodation may be possible subject to apacity and the payment of relevant supplements. Travel is limited to no more than four one-way journeys over any given route segment. A segment is any time you get on and then get off a train bus, regardless of the length of that journey. A 7 day California Rail Pass is also available. The pass costs $159 for adults, $79.50 for children. The pass cannot be booked on line. For full details both passes see the Amtrak website (www.amtrak.com).

White Pass and Yukon Railroad SKAGWAY - WHITEHORSE 9100

km		1 ℝF	🚌 ℝF		🚌 ℝF	2 ℝF
0	**Skagway** Shops d.	0745	1430	**Whitehorse** d.	0745	...
22	White Pass 🏛 d.	|	|	Carcross a.	0900	...
41	Fraser a.	0900	1530	Carcross d.	0915	1300
41	Fraser d.	0900	1535	Bennett a.	|	1430
65	Bennett a.	1015	|	Bennett d.	|	1500
65	Bennett d.	1100	|	Fraser a.	1015	1600
108	Carcross a.	1230	1630	Fraser d.	1025	1600
108	Carcross d.	...	1635	White Pass 🏛 d.	|	|
177	**Whitehorse** a.	...	1800	**Skagway** Shops a.	1130	1745

Additional round-trip excursions, including some hauled by steam locomotives, operate from Skagway to White Pass, Fraser and Bennett. For services crossing the US / Canadian border passengers must provide proof of citizenship. All times shown are Alaska time.

F – May 31 - Sept. 24. ②③④ (also certain ⑥⑦ - check with operator).

Operator: White Pass & Yukon Railroad (www.wpyr.com).

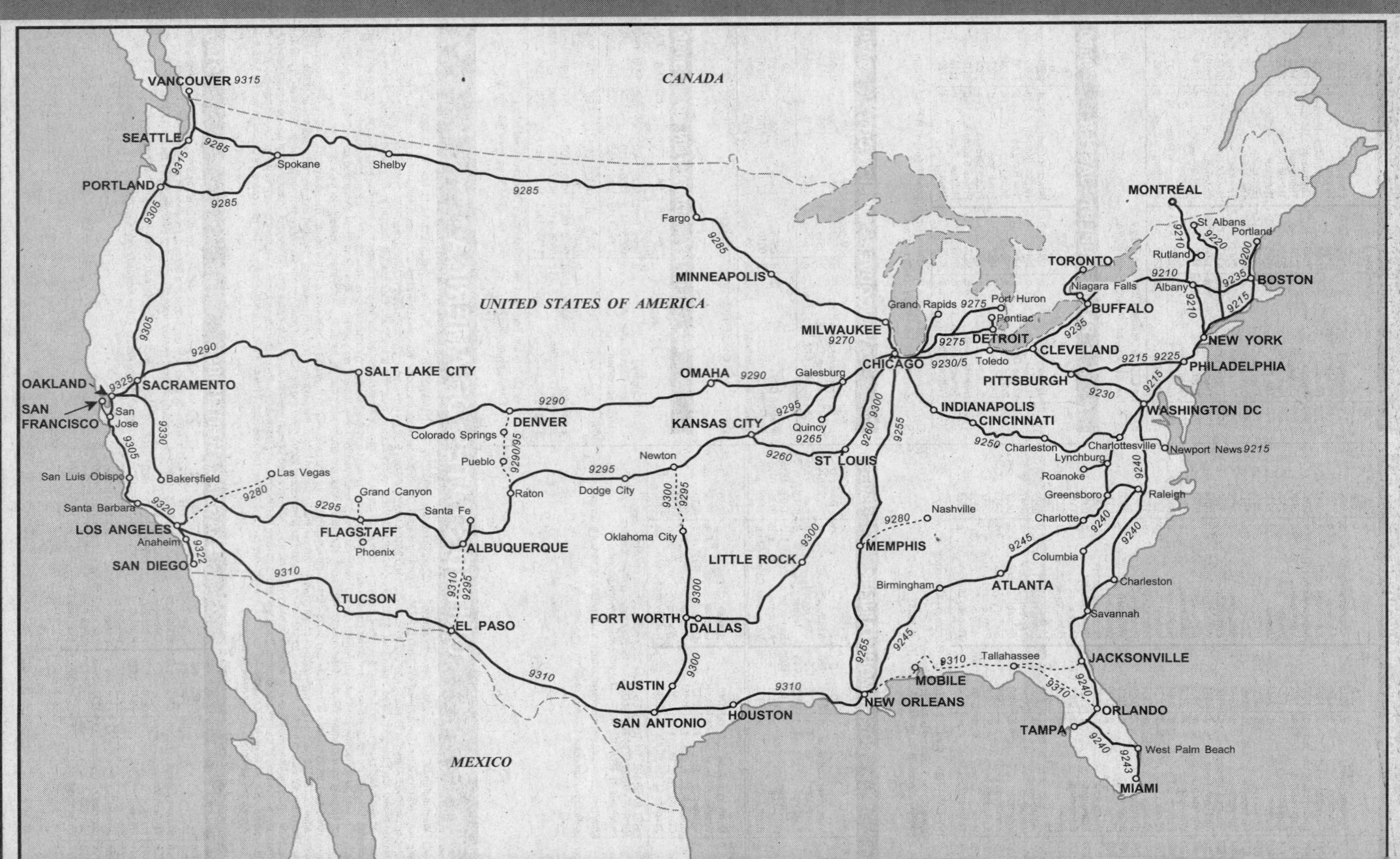
CANADA
UNITED STATES OF AMERICA
MEXICO
VANCOUVER 9315
SEATTLE
9285
Spokane
Shelby
9315
PORTLAND
9285
9285
9305
Fargo
9285
MINNEAPOLIS
9305
9290
OAKLAND
9325
SACRAMENTO
SAN FRANCISCO
San Jose
9330
9305
SALT LAKE CITY
9290
DENVER
Colorado Springs
Pueblo
9290/95
Raton
OMAHA
9290
Galesburg
KANSAS CITY
9295
Quincy
9265
MILWAUKEE
9270
CHICAGO
Grand Rapids 9275
Port Huron
Pontiac
9275
DETROIT
9230/5
Toledo
TORONTO
Niagara Falls
BUFFALO
9235
CLEVELAND
PITTSBURGH
9230
9215
9225
PHILADELPHIA
NEW YORK
MONTRÉAL
9210
St Albans
9220
Rutland
Portland
9200
9210
Albany
9210
9235
BOSTON
9215
9215
WASHINGTON DC
INDIANAPOLIS
CINCINNATI
9250
Charleston
Charlottesville
Newport News 9215
Lynchburg
Roanoke
Greensboro
Raleigh
9240
Charlotte
9240
9240
Columbia
Charleston
Savannah
9245
ATLANTA
Birmingham
9245
JACKSONVILLE
9240
ORLANDO
TAMPA
9240
West Palm Beach
9243
MIAMI
9310
Tallahassee
9310
MOBILE
NEW ORLEANS
9265
9255
9260
9300
ST LOUIS
9260
9280
Nashville
MEMPHIS
9300
LITTLE ROCK
Newton
9295
Dodge City
9300
9295
Oklahoma City
9300
FORT WORTH
DALLAS
9300
AUSTIN
SAN ANTONIO
HOUSTON
9310
9310
EL PASO
9310
9295
ALBUQUERQUE
Santa Fe
Grand Canyon
9295
FLAGSTAFF
Phoenix
Las Vegas
9280
San Luis Obispo
Bakersfield
Santa Barbara
9320
LOS ANGELES
Anaheim
9322
SAN DIEGO
9310
TUCSON

ALASKA — 9105

Alaska Railroad 2nd class only

km		✕A	🍸B	C	✕D	✕E ⑦	F ④–①
0	**Fairbanks** d.	...	...	...	0820	0830	...
195	Denali d.	...	...	...	1230	1230	...
305	Hurricane d.	...	...	1445	1455	1445	1630
392	Talkeetna d.	...	...	1645	1710	1645	1915
498	Wasilla d.	...	...	1825	1825	1825	...
572	**Anchorage** d.	0645	0945	2000	2000	2000	...
636	Girdwood d.	0805	1100	...	...	...	...
652	Portage a.	|	1135	...	...	...	...
**	Whittier d.	|	1245	...	...	...	...
652	Portage d.	|	1325	...	...	...	...
666	Spencer d.	|	1355	...	...	...	...
683	Grandview a.	|	1520	...	...	...	...
750	**Seward** a.	1115	...	...	...	...	...

	✕D ⑥	✕E	C	F ④–①	🍸B	✕A
Seward d.	...	...	...	...	...	1800
Grandview d.	...	...	...	...	1530	|
Spencer d.	...	...	...	...	1640	|
Portage a.	...	...	...	...	1725	|
Whittier d.	...	...	...	...	1845	|
Portage d.	...	...	...	...	1920	|
Girdwood d.	...	...	...	...	1945	2055
Anchorage d.	0820	0830	0830	...	2115	2215
Wasilla d.	0955	0950	0950	...	...	...
Talkeetna d.	1120	1125	1125	1300	...	...
Hurricane a.	1320	1320	1320	1530	...	...
Denali d.	1610	1555	...	...	...	...
Fairbanks a.	2000	2000	...	...	...	...

A – COASTAL CLASSIC – May 7 - Sept. 18.
B – GLACIER DISCOVERY – June 4 - Sept. 11.
C – HURRICANE TURN (WINTER) – First ④ of the month Oct. - Feb, Apr. May.
D – DENALI STAR – From Anchorage May 11 - Sept. 17; from Fairbanks May 12 - Sept. 18.
E – AURORA – Sept. 18, 2021 - May 8, 2022.
F – HURRICANE TURN (SUMMER) – May 12 - Sept 18.

** – Whittier is *20 km* from Portage.

Operator : Alaska Railroad (www.alaskarailroad.com).

BRUNSWICK - PORTLAND - BOSTON — 9200

Amtrak

WARNING! Train **689/699** will run 55 minutes later when there are major events at TD Garden and Fenway Park - check with operator for dates.

km	*Weekday train number* / *Weekend train number*	680 / 690	682 / 692	684 / 694	686 / 696	688 / 698
0	**Brunswick** d.	0430	0710	1100	1255	1745
14	Freeport ◧ d.	0443	0723	1113	1308	1758
47	**Portland** d.	0518	0758	1148	1343	1833
72	Saco d.	0540	0820	1210	1405	1855
98	Wells d.	0559	0839	1229	1424	1914
124	Dover d.	0617	0857	1247	1442	1932
133	Durham d.	0625	0905	1255	1450	1940
151	Exeter d.	0639	0919	1309	1504	1954
178	Haverhill d.	0700	0940	1330	1525	2015
232	**Boston** North a.	0750	1030	1420	1615	2105

Weekday train number / *Weekend train number*	681 / 691	683 / 693	685 / 695	687 / 697	689 / 699
Boston North d.	0850	1150	1545	1720	2230
Haverhill d.	0938	1238	1633	1808	2318
Exeter d.	0959	1259	1654	1829	2339
Durham d.	1012	1312	1707	1842	2352
Dover d.	1020	1320	1715	1850	2359
Wells d.	1038	1338	1733	1908	0018
Saco d.	1055	1355	1750	1925	0035
Portland a.	1125	1425	1820	1955	0100
Freeport ◧ d.	1155	1455	1850	2025	0130
Brunswick a.	1210	1510	1905	2040	0145

◧ – Trains call on request.

NEW YORK - ALBANY - RUTLAND, MONTREÁL and NIAGARA FALLS — 9210

Amtrak

Frequent local trains New York - Poughkeepsie and v.v. are operated by Metro North Railroad. Trains may depart early if all booked passengers have boarded.

km		63 G	81	6281 🚌	233	283	291 J	49 K	237 ①–⑤	253 ⑥⑦	6337 🚌	239 ①–⑤	241	243 ①–⑤	259 ⑥⑦	261 ⑦
0	**New York** Penn d.	0715	1020	...	1120	1320	1420	1540	1640	1715	...	1747	1915	2055	2115	2335
24	Yonkers △ d.	0744	|	...	1144	1344	1444	|	|	1739	...	|	1939	2119	2139	|
54	Croton Harmon △ d.	0803	1101	...	1203	1403	1503	1626	1724	1758	...	1832	1958	2138	2158	0016
118	Poughkeepsie △ d.	0845	1143	...	1245	1445	1545	1710	1805	1840	...	1922	2040	2220	2240	0058
142	Rhinecliff Kingston d.	0900	1200	...	1300	1500	1604	1727	1817	1856	...	1938	2055	2236	2255	0113
184	Hudson d.	0921	1233	...	1328	1529	1620	|	1838	1917	...	1959	2116	2256	2316	0134
229	**Albany** Rensselaer a.	0950	1255	...	1350	1550	1650	1820	1905	1945	...	2028	2145	2325	2345	0205
229	**Albany** Rensselaer 9235 d.	1000	1310	1300	...	1600	1705	1905	...	...	1955	...	...	...	...	...
258	Schenectady 9235 d.	1024	1333	|	...	1623	1728	1933	...	...	|	...	...	...	...	...
288	Saratoga Springs d.	|	|	|	...	|	1754	|	...	...	|	...	...	...	...	...
391	**Rutland** a.	|	|	1528*	...	|	1952	|	...	...	2233*	...	...	...	...	...
	Burlington Transit Center d.	|	|	1747	...	|	...	|	...	...	0042	...	...	...	...	...
436	Westport d.	|	|	...	...	|	...	|	...	...	...	...	...	...	...	...
500	Plattsburgh d.	|	|	...	...	|	...	|	...	...	...	...	...	...	...	...
617	**Montréal** Central a.	|	|	...	...	|	...	|	...	...	...	...	...	...	...	...
382	Utica 9235 d.	1141	1450	...	...	1740	...	2050	...	...	...	...	...	...	...	...
459	Syracuse 9235 d.	1243	1555	...	...	1844	...	2205	...	...	...	...	...	...	...	...
597	Rochester 9235 d.	1357	1719	...	...	1958	...	2329	...	...	...	...	...	...	...	...
706	Buffalo Exchange St. a.	1514	1844	...	...	2123	...	0029**d**	...	...	...	...	...	...	...	...
745	**Niagara Falls** USA a.	1626	1926	...	...	2211	...	...	...	...	...	...	...	...	...	...
	Toronto Union a.	...	...	...	...	...	...	...	...	...	...	...	...	...	...	...

	232 ①–⑤	250 ⑥⑦	234 ①–⑤	260 ⑥⑦	236 ①–⑤	6280 🚌	280	238	284	256 ⑦	290 J	48 K	244	6064 🚌	64 G
Toronto Union d.	...	...	...	...	...	...	...	...	...	...	...	...	...	...	...
Niagara Falls USA d.	...	...	...	...	...	...	0352	...	0647	...	...	...	...	...	1217
Buffalo Exchange St d.	...	...	...	...	...	...	0431	...	0725	...	...	0905**d**	...	...	1255
Rochester 9235 d.	...	...	...	...	...	...	0542	...	0836	...	...	1006	...	...	1403
Syracuse 9235 d.	...	...	...	...	...	...	0706	...	0956	...	...	1142	...	...	1518
Utica 9235 d.	...	...	...	...	...	...	0801	...	1051	...	...	1242	...	...	1619
Montréal Central d.	...	...	...	...	...	...	|	...	|	...	...	|	...	...	|
Plattsburgh d.	...	...	...	...	...	...	|	...	|	...	...	|	...	...	|
Westport d.	...	...	...	...	...	...	|	...	|	...	...	|	...	...	|
Burlington Transit Center d.	...	...	...	...	...	0458	|	...	|	...	...	|	...	1318	|
Rutland d.	...	...	...	...	...	0707*	|	...	|	...	1220	|	...	1537*	|
Saratoga Springs d.	...	...	...	...	...	|	|	...	|	...	1355	|	...	|	|
Schenectady 9235 d.	...	...	...	...	...	|	0923	...	1216	...	1433	1421	...	|	1805
Albany Rensselaer 9235 a.	...	...	...	...	...	0945	0944	...	1237	...	1455	1453	...	1805	1832
Albany Rensselaer d.	0555	0615	0700	0810	0825	...	1005	1205	1257	1410	1510	1610	1648	...	1915
Hudson d.	0617	0637	0722	0832	0847	...	1028	1227	1320	1432	1531	|	1710	...	1937
Rhinecliff Kingston d.	0639	0659	0744	0854	0909	...	1051	1249	1351	1454	1553	1655	1734	...	1959
Poughkeepsie ▽ d.	0655	0710	0759	0910	0920	...	1110	1310	1410	1510	1610	1713	1747	...	2015
Croton Harmon ▽ d.	0734	0750	0841	0950	0959	...	1150	1350	1450	1550	1650	1753	1827	...	2056
Yonkers ▽ d.	|	0811	|	1011	1021	...	|	1411	1511	1611	1711	|	|	...	2116
New York Penn a.	0818	0845	0925	1040	1050	...	1245	1445	1545	1645	1745	1842	1915	...	2155

G – THE MAPLE LEAF – 🚃12 🍸 Niagara Falls - New York and v.v.
J – ETHAN ALLEN EXPRESS – 🚃12 🍸 New York - Rutland and v.v.
K – LAKE SHORE LIMITED – 🛏 1, 2 cl., 🚃2 ✕ Boston - Albany - Chicago and v.v.
d – Buffalo **Depew**.

△ – Trains call to pick up only.
▽ – Trains call to set down only.
* – 🚌 call at Marble Valley Regional Transit Center.

9215 BOSTON - NEW YORK - WASHINGTON - NEWPORT NEWS

Most trains 🍸 Amtrak

km			2103	89	51	183		79	79	2203	153		185	2151	2205	155		141	143	2249	95		2155	195	91
			Ⓐ		③⑤⑦	Ⓐ		Ⓒ	Ⓐ	⑥	Ⓒ		Ⓐ	Ⓐ	†	⑥		Ⓐ	†	⑥	Ⓐ		Ⓐ	Ⓒ	
			☆	A	B			C	C	☆				☆	☆					☆			☆		D
0	**Boston** South	d.	...	...	...	...	...	...	...	...	...	...	...	0505	...	...	...	...	...	0605	0610	...	0715	0635	...
69	Providence	d.	...	...	...	...	...	...	...	...	...	...	...	0540	...	...	...	...	...	0641	0650	...	0750	0715	...
169	New London	d.	...	...	...	...	...	...	...	...	...	...	...	|	...	...	...	...	...	|	0745	...	|	0812	...
	Springfield MA (below)	d.	...	...	...	...	...	...	...	...	...	...	...	|	...	...	...	0550	...	|	|	...	|	|	...
251	New Haven	d.	...	...	...	...	...	...	...	...	...	...	...	0706	...	...	...	0737	...	0810	0843	...	0914	0906	...
301	Stamford	d.	...	...	...	...	...	...	...	...	...	...	...	0752	...	...	...	0827	...	0855	0930	...	0959	0955	...
373	**New York** Penn	a.	...	...	...	...	...	...	...	...	...	...	...	0847	...	...	...	0921	...	0952	1022	...	1047	1051	...
373	**New York** Penn	d.	0600	0602	0645	0705	...	0717	0725	0800	0805	...	0810	0900	0900	0905	...	0935	0947	1003	1035	...	1100	1105	1102
389	Newark NJ	d.	0615	0619u	0705u	0722	...	0739	0744	0814	0822	...	0827	0915	0914	0922	...	0952	1004	1017	1053	...	1115	1123	1122
519	**Philadelphia** 30th St.	d.	0716	0740	0815	0829	...	0854	0853	0910	0933	...	0936	1008	1013	1030	...	1102	1118	1117	1200	...	1211	1230	1233
670	Baltimore Penn	d.	0829	0853	0939	0949	...	1007	1008	1023	1054	...	1057	1121	1126	1152	...	1220	1242	1228	1325	...	1323	1345	1355
687	BWI Airport	d.	|	0906	|	1003	...	|	|	1036	1107	...	1110	1134	1139	1205	...	1233	1255	1241	1338	...	|	1358	|
735	**Washington** Union	a.	0900	0934	1018	1036	...	1046	1045	1100	1138	...	1140	1157	1200	1237	...	1305	1328	1306	1407	...	1356	1427	1435
735	**Washington** Union	d.	...	0959	1059	...	...	1108	1108	...	...	...	...	...	...	...	...	...	...	...	1435	...	...	1450	1504
822	Fredricksburg	d.	...	|	|	...	...	1219	1219	...	...	...	...	...	...	...	...	...	...	...	1551	...	...	1601	|
911	Richmond Staples Mill Road	d.	...	1211	|	...	...	1327	1327	...	...	...	...	...	...	...	...	...	...	...	1701	...	...	1658	1713
1042	**Newport News**	a.	...	...	|	...	...	...	...	...	...	...	...	...	...	...	...	...	...	...	|	...	...	...	...
1092	Norfolk	a.	...	...	|	...	...	...	...	...	...	...	...	...	...	...	...	...	...	...	1916	...	...	...	...
	Virgina Beach	a.	...	...	|	...	...	...	...	...	...	...	...	...	...	...	...	...	...	...	*2000**	...	...	...	...
915	Charlottesville	a.	...	...	1343	...	...	...	...	...	...	...	...	...	...	...	...	...	...	...	...	...	...	...	...
1012	**Lynchburg**	a.	...	...	...	...	...	...	...	...	...	...	...	...	...	...	...	...	...	...	...	...	...	...	...

		125	2251	2213	157		147	171	145	2159		99	93	161	19		2163	2253	87	85		173	189	163
		Ⓐ	⑥	†	†		⑥	Ⓐ	†	Ⓐ		Ⓒ	Ⓐ	Ⓒ	④–①		Ⓐ	Ⓒ	Ⓒ	Ⓐ		Ⓐ	†	⑥
			☆				◧	◧	◧	☆					E		☆	☆						
Boston South	d.	...	0805	...	...	...	...	0815	...	0910	...	0840	0920	0940	...	...	1105	1105	...	...	...	1110	...	1140
Providence	d.	...	0840	...	...	...	...	0855	...	0946	...	0919	1001	1020	...	...	1141	1140	...	...	...	1151	...	1220
New London	d.	...	|	...	...	...	...	0948	...	|	...	1017	1102	1115	...	...	|	|	...	...	...	1243	...	1320
Springfield MA (below)	d.	...	|	...	0758	...	0835	|	...	|	...	|	|	|	...	...	|	|	...	...	...	|	...	|
New Haven	d.	...	1008	...	0934	...	1018	1040	...	1116	...	1105	1158	1206	...	...	1315	1310	...	...	...	1335	...	1406
Stamford	d.	...	1055	...	1025	...	1111	1129	...	1201	...	1155	1255	1255	...	...	1401	1355	...	...	...	1429	...	1455
New York Penn	a.	...	1148	...	1124	...	1213	1222	...	1250	...	1253	1347	1351	...	...	1449	1447	...	...	...	1522	...	1551
New York Penn	d.	1135	1200	1200	1205	...	1250	1235	1255	1300	...	1317	1402	1405	1415	...	1500	1500	1504	1505	...	1535	1605	1605
Newark NJ	d.	1152	1214	1214	1222	...	1307	1252	1312	1315	...	1335	1419	1422	1437	...	1515	1514	1521	1522	...	1553	1622	1622
Philadelphia 30th St.	d.	1300	1313	1313	1333	...	1418	1413	1417	1410	...	1446	1525	1533	1554	...	1611	1613	1632	1629	...	1703	1733	1735
Baltimore Penn	d.	1424	1426	1423	1453	...	1532	1540	1536	1524	...	1558	1640	1656	1717	...	1723	1727	1753	1755	...	1827	1850	1855
BWI Airport	d.	1438	1439	1436	1506	...	1545	1555	1549	1537	...	1611	1653	1709	|	...	1737	1740	1805	1809	...	1841	1903	1909
Washington Union	a.	1510	1503	1500	1538	...	1612	1625	1621	1600	...	1636	1723	1738	1805	...	1800	1804	1835	1838	...	1911	1941	1941
Washington Union	d.	1550	...	...	1600	...	1635	1649	1649	...	...	1700	1745	...	1830	...	...	...	1900	1910	...	...	...	...
Fredricksburg	d.	1707	...	...	1710	...	|	|	|	...	...	1808	1902	...	|	...	...	...	2012	2022	...	...	...	...
Richmond Staples Mill Road	d.	1826	...	...	1822	...	|	|	|	...	...	1913	2017	...	|	...	...	...	2122	2121	...	...	...	...
Newport News	a.	2020	...	...	|	...	|	|	|	...	...	2106	|	...	|	...	...	...	|	...	...	...	...	...
Norfolk	a.	*2110**	...	...	2036	...	|	|	|	...	...	*2150**	2231	...	|	...	...	...	2336	...	...	...	...	...
Virgina Beach	a.	*2150**	...	...	*2130**	...	|	|	|	...	...	*2230**	*2315**	...	|	...	...	...	*0020**	...	...	...	...	...
Charlottesville	a.	...	...	...	...	...	1901	1923	1916	...	...	...	...	...	2052	...	...	...	...	...	...	...	...	...
Lynchburg	a.	...	...	...	...	...	2017	2039	2032	...	...	...	...	...	2200	...	...	...	...	...	...	...	...	...

		2167	2255	149	193		2169	135	137	2257		55	57	175	2259		165	2173	123	167		139	177	169
		Ⓐ	†	†	Ⓐ		Ⓐ	Ⓒ	Ⓐ	†		Ⓐ	Ⓒ	Ⓐ	†		†	Ⓐ	†	⑥		†	Ⓐ	Ⓒ
		☆	☆				☆			☆		F	F		☆			☆						
Boston South	d.	1305	1310	1215	...	...	1400	1340	1350	1500	...	...	...	1520	1605	...	1510	1615	...	1625	...	1740	1735	1840
Providence	d.	1341	1344	1257	...	...	1436	1419	1437	1537	...	...	...	1601	1640	...	1550	1650	...	1708	...	1820	1815	1920
New London	d.	|	|	1354	...	...	|	1513	1538	|	...	...	...	1657	|	...	1648	|	...	1809	...	1915	1921	2016
Springfield MA (below)	d.	|	|	|	...	...	|	|	|	|	...	1450	1450	|	|	...	|	|	...	|	...	|	|	|
New Haven	d.	1516	1510	1443	...	...	1606	1604	1631	1709	...	1639	1634	1745	1810	...	1735	1820	...	1906	...	2006	2023	2106
Stamford	d.	1601	1555	1531	...	...	1654	1655	1719	1755	...	1727	1723	1833	1855	...	1825	1905	...	1955	...	2055	2113	2155
New York Penn	a.	1650	1648	1633	...	...	1748	1751	1810	1848	...	1825	1825	1928	1948	...	1932	2000	...	2050	...	2152	2206	2252
New York Penn	d.	1700	1700	1705	1727	...	1800	1805	1825	1900	...	1845	1901	1940	2000	...	2001	2013	2106	...	...	2205	...	...
Newark NJ	d.	1715	1714	1722	1744	...	1815	1822	1842	1914	...	1902	1917	1958	2014	...	2018	2028	2122	...	...	2222	...	...
Philadelphia 30th St.	d.	1810	1813	1834	1848	...	1909	1933	1953	2013	...	2009	2026	2110	2113	...	2138	2126	2236	...	...	2333	...	...
Baltimore Penn	d.	1923	1926	1955	2011	...	2022	2100	2112	2126	...	2128	2139	2235	2226	...	2256	2242	2353	...	...	0050	...	...
BWI Airport	d.	1936	1939	2009	2024	...	2035	2113	2125	2139	...	2144	2153	2249	2239	...	2310	|	0006	...	...	0103	...	...
Washington Union	a.	2000	2004	2045	2053	...	2100	2143	2203	2204	...	2214	2228	2322	2304	...	2343	2313	0040	...	...	0136	...	...
Washington Union	d.	...	...	...	...	...	...	...	...	...	...	...	...	...	...	...	...	...	...	...	...	...	...	...
Fredricksburg	d.	...	...	...	...	...	...	...	...	...	...	...	...	...	...	...	...	...	...	...	...	...	...	...
Richmond Staples Mill Road	d.	...	...	...	...	...	...	...	...	...	...	...	...	...	...	...	...	...	...	...	...	...	...	...
Newport News	a.	...	...	...	...	...	...	...	...	...	...	...	...	...	...	...	...	...	...	...	...	...	...	...
Norfolk	a.	...	...	...	...	...	...	...	...	...	...	...	...	...	...	...	...	...	...	...	...	...	...	...
Virgina Beach	a.	...	...	...	...	...	...	...	...	...	...	...	...	...	...	...	...	...	...	...	...	...	...	...
Charlottesville	a.	...	...	...	...	...	...	...	...	...	...	...	...	...	...	...	...	...	...	...	...	...	...	...
Lynchburg	a.	...	...	...	...	...	...	...	...	...	...	...	...	...	...	...	...	...	...	...	...	...	...	...

km	*2nd class unless noted*		4451	141	495	405	4405		157	147	471	461	473		463	409	55	57	475		467	417	479	497	499
			Ⓐ	Ⓐ	Ⓐ	⑥	†		†	⑥	Ⓐ	Ⓒ	Ⓐ		⑥	†	Ⓐ	Ⓒ	Ⓐ		⑥	Ⓐ	Ⓐ	†	Ⓒ
			🚌		G		🚌		H	J	G	G					F	F							G
0	**Greenfield** **9220**	d.	...	...	0545	...	...	...	...	...	0735	0915	...	...	...	...	1336	1336	...	...	...	...	...	...	201
34	Northampton **9220**	d.	...	...	0610	...	...	...	...	...	0800	0940	...	...	...	...	1401	1401	...	...	...	...	...	...	2035
71	**Springfield** MA **9220**	a.	...	...	0653	...	...	...	...	...	0843	1023	...	...	...	...	1435	1435	...	...	...	...	...	...	211
71	**Springfield** MA	d.	0510	0550	0705	0725	0725	...	0758	0835	0855	1034	1205	...	1230	1305	1450	1450	1530	...	1730	1745	1925	1930	...
112	Hartford	d.	|	0631	0736	0759	|	...	0833	0910	0926	1105	1239	...	1305	1339	1524	1524	1604	...	1805	1820	1959	2007	...
172	**New Haven** Union	a.	0630	0722	0827	0847	0847	...	0920	1002	1018	1156	1328	...	1352	1427	1615	1614	1653	...	1852	1908	2048	2054	...
	New York Penn	a.	*0847*	0921	*1022*	*1051*	*1051*	...	1124	1213	*1222*	*1351*	*1522*	...	*1551*	*1648*	1825	1825	*1928*	...	*2050*	*2206*	...	2252	...
	Washington Union	a.	*1157*	1305	*1407*	*1427*	*1427*	...	1538	1612	*1625*	*1738*	*1911*	...	*1941*	*2004*	2214	2228	*2322*	...	...	...	...	...	...

km	*2nd class unless noted*		601	605	611	661	661	641	663	643	43	645	615		609	665	647	649	667	651	653	669	671	657	619
			Ⓐ	Ⓐ	Ⓒ	⑥	†	Ⓐ	Ⓒ	Ⓐ		Ⓐ	†		Ⓐ	Ⓒ	Ⓐ	Ⓐ	Ⓒ	Ⓐ	Ⓐ	Ⓒ	Ⓒ	Ⓐ	Ⓐ
											K														
0	**New York** Penn	d.	...	...	...	0700	...	0717	0909	0930	1052	1205	...	...	1254	1305	1411	1444	1513	1603	1710	1717	1953	2030	...
16	Newark NJ	d.	...	...	...	0717	...	0734	0927	0946	1109	1222	...	...	1310	1323	1428	1459	1532	1620	1727	1734	2009	2047	...
146	**Philadelphia** 30th St	a.	...	...	...	0820	...	0846	1035	1050	1215	1325	...	...	1419	1426	1533	1612	1638	1723	1832	1836	2115	2155	...
146	**Philadelphia** 30th St	d.	0520	0620	0725	0830	0830	0856	1050	1100	1242	1335	1355	...	1445	1445	1545	1645	1655	1735	1842	1855	2135	2205	225
178	Paoli	d.	0546	0646	0750	0855	0855	0919	1115	1123	1312	1359	1420	...	1510	1510	1610	1711	1721	1802	1907	1921	2200	2230	232
255	Lancaster	d.	0632	0735	0837	0942	0942	1006	1203	1211	1352	1446	1506	...	1558	1558	1655	1802	1808	1851	1956	2008	2250	2318	001
300	Elizabethtown	d.	0649	0752	0853	0958	0958	1023	1220	1228	1406	1503	1523	...	1615	1614	1709	1818	1824	1907	2012	2024	2306	2335	002
315	**Harrisburg**	a.	0710	0815	0915	1020	1020	1046	1245	1250	1426	1525	1542	...	1640	1635	1730	1840	1845	1930	2035	2045	2330	2356	005

A – PALMETTO – 🍽12 🍸 New York - Savannah and v.v.
B – CARDINAL – 🛏 1, 2 cl., 2 🍸 Chicago - New York and v.v.
C – CAROLINIAN – 12 🍸 New York - Charlotte and v.v.
D – SILVER STAR – 🛏 1, 2 cl., 2 ✕ New York - Miami and v.v.
E – CRESCENT – 🛏 1, 2 cl., 2 ✕ New York - New Orleans and v.v.
F – VERMONTER – 12 🍸 Washington - St Albans and v.v. (Table **9220**).
G – VALLEY FLYER.
H – NORTHEAST REGIONAL – 12 🍸 Springfield - Norfolk.
J – NORTHEAST REGIONAL – 12 🍸 Springfield - Roanoke.
K – PENNSYLVANIAN – 12 🍸 Pittsburgh - New York and v.v. (Table **9225**).

n – Connection by 🚌 to Norfolk.
s – Calls to set down only.
u – Calls to pick up only.
◧ – To Roanoke (a. 2133 ⑥ / 2148 † / 2155 Ⓐ).
⊡ – From Roanoke (d. 0620 Ⓐ / 0855 Ⓒ).
* – Connection by 🚌.
☆ – *Acela* service - higher fares payable.

FOR RETURN SERVICE SEE NEXT PAGE →

Amtrak Most trains 🍸 NEWPORT NEWS - WASHINGTON - NEW YORK - BOSTON 9215

	2190 Ⓐ ☆	190 Ⓐ	150 Ⓒ	2152 Ⓐ ☆	160 †		162 ⑥	162 †	130 Ⓐ	2154 Ⓐ ☆	172 Ⓐ		54 Ⓒ F	2248 ⑥ ☆	56 Ⓐ F	152 Ⓒ	2250 † ☆		2158 Ⓐ ☆	86 Ⓐ	164 Ⓒ	174 Ⓐ	154 †
Lynchburg d.	...	...	...	...	...	...	...	...	...	...	...	...	...	...	...	...	...	...	...	...	...	...	...
Charlottesville d.	...	...	...	...	...	...	...	...	...	...	...	...	...	...	...	...	...	...	...	...	...	...	...
Virginia Beach d.	...	...	...	...	...	...	...	...	...	...	...	...	...	...	...	...	...	...	...	...	...	...	...
Norfolk d.	...	...	...	...	...	...	...	...	...	...	...	...	...	...	...	...	...	...	...	...	...	...	...
Newport News d.	...	...	...	...	...	...	...	...	...	...	...	...	...	...	...	...	...	...	...	...	...	0520	...
Richmond Staples Mill Road d.	...	...	...	...	...	...	...	...	...	...	...	...	...	...	...	...	...	...	...	0605	0625	0710	...
Fredericksburg d.	...	...	...	...	...	...	...	...	...	...	...	...	...	...	...	...	...	...	...	0702	0722	0810	...
Washington Union a.	...	...	...	...	...	...	...	...	...	...	...	...	...	...	...	...	...	...	...	0822	0850	0942	...
Washington Union d.	...	...	...	0550	...	...	...	0610	0620	0650	0705	...	0720	0750	0800	0812	0845	...	0850	0852	0915	1010	1010
BWI Airport d.	...	...	...	|	...	...	...	0638	0647	0711	0733	...	0745	0811	0823	0840	0906	...	0911	0919	0943	1037	1037
Baltimore Penn d.	...	...	...	0619	...	...	...	0653	0706	0724	0748	...	0800	0824	0838	0856	0919	...	0924	0935	0958	1053	1054
Philadelphia 30th Street d.	...	...	...	0732	...	...	...	0817	0827	0836	0909	...	0919	0939	0958	1024	1031	...	1036	1052	1112	1211	1218
Newark NJ d.	...	...	...	0828	...	...	...	0926	0935	0929	1026	...	1025	1040	1101	1138	1132	...	1134	1146	1229	1319	1326
New York Penn a.	...	...	...	0849	...	...	...	0945	1000	0952	1044	...	1045	1058	1121	1159	1148	...	1152	1215	1247	1339	1346
New York Penn d.	0615	0650	0700	0900	0900	...	1000	1000	...	1003	1100	...	1130	1110	1133	...	1205	...	1203	1230	1300	1400	...
Stamford d.	0701	0745	0749	0947	0948	...	1048	1048	...	1048	1148	...	1219	1155	1216	...	1249	...	1248	1318	1348	1448	...
New Haven d.	0800	0841	0844	1040	1047	...	1147	1147	...	1142	1246	...	1315	1255	1311	...	1343	...	1344	1410	1446	1544	...
Springfield MA (below) a.	|	|	|	|	|	...	|	|	...	|	|	...	1455	|	1455	...	|	...	|	|	|	|	...
New London d.	|	0931	0933	|	1132	...	1234	1234	...	|	1335	...	...	|	...	...	|	...	|	1452	1534	1635	...
Providence d.	0922	1027	1029	1205	1228	...	1331	1331	...	1300	1426	...	...	1418	...	...	1503	...	1506	1545	1632	1730	...
Boston South a.	1003	1110	1116	1245	1318	...	1422	1422	...	1345	1518	...	...	1502	...	...	1549	...	1550	1638	1722	1830	...

	82 ⑥	2252 Ⓒ ☆	84 Ⓐ	88 Ⓒ		2164 Ⓐ ☆	176 Ⓐ ⊡	140 Ⓒ	2254 Ⓒ ☆		194 ⑥	96 †	184 Ⓐ	2168 Ⓐ ☆		94 Ⓐ	20 ⑥⑦ E	20 ①②⑤ E	156 Ⓒ ⊡		2256 †	2218 ⑥ ☆	148 Ⓐ
Lynchburg d.	...	...	...	...	...	...	0739	...	...	...	...	...	...	...	...	...	0941	0941	1014	...	...	...	...
Charlottesville d.	...	...	...	...	...	...	0853	...	...	...	...	...	...	...	...	...	1054	1054	1128	...	...	...	...
Virginia Beach d.	...	...	*0515**	*0515**	...	...	|	...	...	...	*0640**	*0640**	...	...	...	*0800**	|	|	|	...	...	...	...
Norfolk d.	0530	...	0615	0615	...	...	|	...	...	...	*0725**	*0725**	...	...	...	0900	|	|	|	...	...	...	...
Newport News d.	|	...	|	*0515*n	...	...	|	...	...	...	0830	0830	...	...	...	*0800*n	|	|	|	...	...	...	...
Richmond Staples Mill Road d.	0738	...	0825	0825	...	...	|	...	...	...	1019	1019	...	...	...	1108	|	|	|	...	...	...	...
Fredericksburg d.	0836	...	0925	0925	...	...	|	...	...	...	1117	1117	...	...	...	1209	|	|	|	...	...	...	...
Washington Union a.	0954	...	1046	1056	...	...	1122	...	...	...	1235	1235	...	...	...	1328	1345s	1345s	1402	...	...	...	...
Washington Union d.	1020	1050	1110	1120	...	1150	1155	1215	1250	...	1300	1315	1315	1350	...	1355	1410s	1415s	1430	...	1450	1450	1455
BWI Airport d.	1047	1111	1138	1148	...	|	1222	1242	1311	...	1327	1342	1342	|	...	1423	1436s	1441s	1457	...	1511	1511	1522
Baltimore Penn d.	1102	1124	1154	1203	...	1220	1237	1258	1324	...	1342	1357	1357	1420	...	1438	1454s	1458s	1513	...	1524	1524	1537
Philadelphia 30th Street d.	1220	1238	1314	1319	...	1332	1357	1417	1437	...	1505	1521	1522	1531	...	1558	1614s	1621s	1634	...	1638	1641	1700
Newark NJ d.	1328	1336	1418	1428	...	1430	1502	1528	1536	...	1615	1630	1634	1630	...	1705	1734s	1745s	1741	...	1736	1739	1802
New York Penn a.	1346	1353	1438	1446	...	1449	1520	1551	1553	...	1636	1648	1655	1649	...	1722	1756	1808	1801	...	1752	1759	1830
New York Penn d.	1400	1410	...	1500	...	1500	1530	1630	1603	...	1700	1725	...	1700	...	1738	...	...	...	...	1803	...	1849
Stamford d.	1450	1456	...	1548	...	1545	1618	1718	1648	...	1749	1812	...	1750	...	1830	...	...	...	...	1848	...	1941
New Haven d.	1552	1550	...	1647	...	1638	1715	1826	1740	...	1846	1905	...	1840	...	1927	...	...	...	...	1937	...	2052
Springfield MA (below) a.	|	|	...	|	...	|	|	1954	|	...	|	|	...	|	...	|	...	...	...	...	|	...	2231
New London d.	1644	|	...	1736	...	|	1806	...	|	...	1938	1955	...	|	...	2014	...	...	...	...	|	...	...
Providence d.	1739	1717	...	1830	...	1754	1902	...	1907	...	2031	2047	...	2002	...	2108	...	...	...	...	2058	...	...
Boston South a.	1828	1803	...	1923	...	1843	2002	...	1950	...	2118	2136	...	2049	...	2202	...	...	...	...	2145	...	...

	132 †	168 ⑥	134 ⑤	2172 Ⓐ ☆		92 D	178 Ⓐ	126 †	2122 Ⓐ ☆		2222 † ☆	196 Ⓐ	80 C	166 †		192 ⑥	2224 † ☆	138 Ⓐ	158 Ⓒ		2126 Ⓐ ☆	50 ③⑤⑦ B	90 A
Lynchburg d.	...	...	...	...	...	...	...	...	...	...	...	...	...	...	...	...	...	...	...	...	...	...	...
Charlottesville d.	...	...	...	...	...	...	...	...	...	...	...	...	...	...	...	...	...	...	...	...	...	1544	...
Virginia Beach d.	...	...	...	...	...	...	...	...	...	...	...	...	...	...	...	...	...	...	...	...	...	|	...
Norfolk d.	...	...	...	...	...	...	...	...	...	...	...	...	...	...	...	...	...	...	...	...	...	|	...
Newport News d.	...	...	...	...	...	...	...	...	...	...	...	...	...	...	...	...	...	...	...	...	...	|	...
Richmond Staples Mill Road d.	...	...	...	...	...	1239	...	...	...	...	...	...	1411	...	...	...	...	...	...	...	...	|	1641
Fredericksburg d.	...	...	...	...	...	|	...	...	...	...	...	...	1507	...	...	...	...	...	...	...	...	|	|
Washington Union a.	...	...	...	...	...	1504s	...	...	...	...	...	...	1631s	...	...	...	...	...	...	...	...	1844s	1910
Washington Union d.	1505	1515	1525	1550	...	1536s	1552	1615	1650	...	1650	1655	1715s	1710	...	1710	1750	1755	1800	...	1850	1909s	1957
BWI Airport d.	1532	1542	1549	1611	...	|	1619	1641	|	...	1711	1722	|	1737	...	1736	1811	1823	1827	...	1911	|	2024
Baltimore Penn d.	1547	1557	1604	1623	...	1621s	1636	1657	1720	...	1724	1737	1750s	1754	...	1753	1824	1838	1844	...	1924	1941s	2042
Philadelphia 30th Street d.	1709	1718	1735	1734	...	1735s	1758	1818	1832	...	1838	1900	1904s	1918	...	1919	1938	2000	2005	...	2039	2056s	2155
Newark NJ d.	1828	1828	1837	1829	...	1845s	1904	1923	1930	...	1935	2009	2012s	2027	...	2027	2036	2118	2125	...	2139	2203s	2303
New York Penn a.	1846	1846	1856	1848	...	1910	1924	1945	1950	...	1955	2030	2035	2045	...	2045	2055	2136	2145	...	2157	2223	2323
New York Penn d.	1930	1900	...	1900	...	...	1950	...	...	...	...	...	...	2100	...	...	...	...	...	...	...	...	...
Stamford d.	2017	1948	...	1950	...	...	2045	...	...	...	...	...	...	2148	...	...	...	...	...	...	...	...	...
New Haven d.	2116	2044	...	2043	...	...	2142	...	...	...	...	...	...	2246	...	...	...	...	...	...	...	...	...
Springfield MA (below) a.	|	|	...	|	...	...	|	...	...	...	...	...	...	|	...	...	...	...	...	...	...	...	...
New London d.	2209	2135	...	|	...	...	2232	...	...	...	...	...	...	2336	...	...	...	...	...	...	...	...	...
Providence d.	2305	2235	...	2204	...	...	2329	...	...	...	...	...	...	0025	...	...	...	...	...	...	...	...	...
Boston South a.	2357	2326	...	2250	...	...	0015	...	...	...	...	...	...	0115	...	...	...	...	...	...	...	...	...

2nd class unless noted	400 Ⓒ G	490 Ⓐ	460 ⑥		470 Ⓐ	460 †	54 Ⓒ F		56 Ⓐ F	464 Ⓒ	474 Ⓐ		488 Ⓒ G	476 Ⓐ	140 Ⓒ		494 Ⓐ G	4416 † 🚌	148 Ⓐ		432 †	478 Ⓐ G	4412 Ⓐ 🚌
Washington Union d.	...	...	...	...	*0550*	...	0720	...	0800	*0915*	*1010*	...	*1120*	*1155*	1215	...	*1355*	*1450*	1455	...	*1505*	*1552*	...
New York Penn d.	...	*0650*	...	...	*0900*	*0900*	1130	...	1133	*1300*	*1400*	...	*1500*	*1530*	1630	...	*1738*	*1803*	1849	...	*1930*	*1950*	...
New Haven Union d.	...	0900	1045	...	1050	1100	1330	...	1330	1500	1600	...	1700	1725	1826	...	1935	1950	2052	...	2130	2155	2259
Hartford d.	...	0945	1131	...	1134	1146	1408	...	1408	1547	1646	...	1743	1809	1912	...	2017	|	2145	...	2215	2238	|
Springfield MA a.	...	1024	1208	...	1213	1223	1455	...	1455	1624	1725	...	1824	1848	1954	...	2059	2113	2231	...	2253	2318	0030
Springfield MA **9220** d.	0750	...	...	...	...	...	1515	...	1515	...	...	...	1845	...	...	...	2115	...	...	...	...	2330	...
Northampton **9220** d.	0832	...	...	...	...	...	1557	...	1557	...	...	...	1927	...	...	...	2157	...	...	...	...	0012	...
Greenfield **9220** a.	0858	...	...	...	...	...	1622	...	1622	...	...	...	1953	...	...	...	2223	...	...	...	...	0038	...

2nd class unless noted	640 Ⓐ	642 Ⓐ	600 Ⓐ	660 Ⓒ	644 Ⓐ	662 ⑥	662	664 Ⓒ	648 Ⓐ	666 Ⓒ	650 Ⓐ	42 K	670 Ⓒ	652 Ⓐ	654 Ⓐ	672 Ⓒ	656 Ⓐ	618 ①–④	658 ⑤	610 Ⓒ	620 Ⓐ	612 †	622 Ⓐ
Harrisburg d.	0500	0555	0640	0720	0755	0830	0830	0930	1005	1120	1205	1300	1405	1515	1630	1705	1735	1840	1840	1905	2000	2020	2115
Elizabethtown d.	0517	0612	0657	0737	0811	0847	0847	0947	1021	1137	1222	1318	1422	1532	1647	1722	1752	1857	1857	1922	2017	2037	2132
Lancaster d.	0535	0630	0716	0755	0827	0905	0905	1005	1037	1155	1241	1340	1440	1552	1705	1740	1810	1912	1912	1940	2032	2055	2148
Paoli d.	0619	0723	0804	0841	0905	0951	0951	1049	1116	1241	1322	1424	1528	1636	1750	1825	1855	1955	1955	2025	2114	2140	2230
Philadelphia 30th St a.	0645	0750	0833	0905	0930	1015	1015	1115	1141	1305	1352	1459	1555	1705	1826	1850	1923	2020	2020	2050	2140	2210	2256
Philadelphia 30th St d.	0700	0805	0846	0923	0945	1030	...	1125	1155	1330	1405	1525	1610	1718	1850	1910	1940	...	2036	...	...	...	...
Newark NJ d.	0811	0906	0947	1031	1047	1144	...	1231	1256	1440	1508	1632	1713	1832	1954	2014	2044	...	2141	...	...	...	...
New York Penn a.	0830	0926	1011	1049	1105	1202	...	1249	1315	1457	1526	1650	1732	1854	2012	2034	2103	...	2200	...	...	...	...

FOR RETURN SERVICE AND FOOTNOTES SEE PREVIOUS PAGE.

9220 ST ALBANS - SPRINGFIELD — Amtrak

km		55 ⒶA	57 ⒸA		54 ⒸA	56 ⒶA
0	**St. Albans** d.	0915	0915	*Washington U* **9215** d.	0720	0800
38	Burlington Essex Jct. d.	0944	0944	*New York Penn* **9215** d.	1130	1133
70	Waterbury d.	1010	1010	**Springfield** MA **9215** d.	1515	1515
90	Montpelier d.	1025	1025	Northampton **9215** d.	1557	1557
133	Randolph d.	1059	1059	Greenfield **9215** d.	1622	1622
189	White River Junction d.	1137	1137	Brattleboro d.	1656	1656
205	Windsor VT d.	1156	1156	Bellows Falls d.	1726	1726
225	Claremont d.	1206	1206	Claremont d.	1747	1747
252	Bellows Falls d.	1230	1230	Windsor VT d.	1756	1756
291	Brattleboro d.	1259	1302	White River Junction d.	1815	1815
326	Greenfield **9215** d.	1336	1336	Randolph d.	1856	1856
360	Northampton **9215** d.	1401	1401	Montpelier d.	1934	1934
397	**Springfield** MA **9215** a.	1435	1435	Waterbury d.	1950	1950
609	*New York Penn* **9215** a.	1825	1825	Burlington Essex Jct. d.	2018	2018
974	*Washington U* **9215** a.	2214	2228	**St. Albans** a.	2050	2050

A – VERMONTER – (12) Y Washington - St Albans and v.v.

9225 HARRISBURG - PITTSBURGH — Amtrak

km		43 B			42 B	
	New York Penn **9215** d.	1052	...	**Pittsburgh** d.	0730	...
0	**Harrisburg** d.	1436	...	Greensburg d.	0810	...
95	Lewistown d.	1546	...	Latrobe d.	0820r	...
154	Huntingdon d.	1623	...	Johnstown d.	0903	...
186	Tyrone d.	1649r	...	Altoona d.	1001	...
213	Altoona d.	1713	...	Tyrone d.	1018r	...
275	Johnstown d.	1810	...	Huntingdon d.	1045	...
334	Latrobe d.	1851r	...	Lewistown d.	1124	...
346	Greensburg d.	1902	...	**Harrisburg** a.	1250	...
401	**Pittsburgh** a.	1959	...	*New York Penn* **9215** a.	1650	...

B – PENNSYLVANIAN – (12) Y New York - Pittsburgh and v.v.
r – Calls on request.

9230 WASHINGTON - CLEVELAND - CHICAGO — Amtrak

km		29 C			30 C	
0	**Washington** Union d.	1605	...	**Chicago** Union d.	1840	...
88	Harper's Ferry d.	1716	...	South Bend d.	2109	...
118	Martinsburg d.	1745	...	Elkhart d.	2129	...
234	Cumberland d.	1924	...	Waterloo d.	2223	...
478	Pittsburgh d.	2359	...	Toledo d.	2349	...
613	Alliance d.	0139	...	Sandusky d.	0040	...
702	**Cleveland** d.	0259	...	**Cleveland** d.	0154	...
798	Sandusky d.	0402	...	Alliance d.	0305	...
873	Toledo d.	0522	...	Pittsburgh d.	0520	...
998	Waterloo d.	0636	...	Cumberland d.	0932	...
1086	Elkhart d.	0729	...	Martinsburg d.	1101	...
1113	South Bend d.	0751	...	Harper's Ferry d.	1131	...
1248	**Chicago** Union a.	0845	...	**Washington** Union a.	1305	...

C – CAPITOL LIMITED – 🛏 1, 2 cl., (2) ✕ Washington - Chicago and v.v.

9235 BOSTON - ALBANY - CHICAGO — Amtrak

km		449 D	49 D		448 D	48 D
0	**Boston** South d.	1250	...	**Chicago** Union d.	2130	2130
70	Worcester d.	1406	...	South Bend d.	2359	2359
157	Springfield MA d.	1526	...	Elkhart d.	0027	0027
242	Pittsfield d.	1642	...	Waterloo d.	0120	0120
	New York Penn **9205** d.	|	1540	Toledo d.	0315	0315
320	**Albany** Rensselaer a.	1810	1820	Sandusky d.	0407	0407
320	**Albany** Rensselaer ◧ d.	1905	1905	**Cleveland** d.	0550	0550
349	Schenectady ◧ d.	1933	1933	Erie d.	0724	0724
473	Utica ◧ d.	2050	2050	Buffalo Depew ◧ d.	0905	0905
558	Syracuse ◧ d.	2205	2205	Rochester ◧ d.	1006	1006
686	Rochester ◧ d.	2329	2329	Syracuse ◧ d.	1142	1142
784	Buffalo Depew ◧ d.	0039	0039	Utica ◧ d.	1242	1242
931	Erie d.	0216	0216	Schenectady ◧ d.	1421	1421
1083	**Cleveland** d.	0403	0403	**Albany** Rensselaer ◧ a.	1453	1453
1179	Sandusky d.	0513	0513	**Albany** Rensselaer d.	1527	1610
1254	Toledo d.	0633	0633	*New York Penn* **9205** a.	|	1842
1379	Waterloo d.	0751	0751	Pittsfield d.	1630	...
1467	Elkhart d.	0843	0843	Springfield MA d.	1804	...
1494	South Bend d.	0907	0907	Worcester d.	1932	...
1629	**Chicago** Union a.	1012	1012	**Boston** South a.	2032	...

D – LAKE SHORE LIMITED – 🛏 1, 2 cl., (2) Y Boston(**449/448**) - Albany(**48/49**) - Chicago and v.v; 🛏 1, 2 cl., (2) ✕ New York(**49/48**) - Albany - Chicago and v.v.
◧ – See also Table **9210**.

9240 WASHINGTON - MIAMI — Amtrak

km		89 E	91 F		92 F	90 E
	New York Penn **9215** d.	0602	1102	**Miami** Amtrak d.	1140	...
0	**Washington** U **9245** d.	0959u	1504u	Hollywood FL ⊡ d.	1204u	...
174	Richmond **9245** d.	1219	1723	Fort Lauderdale ⊙ d.	1218u	...
219	Petersburg **9245** d.	1254	1759	West Palm Beach ⊙ d.	1310u	...
376	Rocky Mount **9245** d.	1432	1929	Sebring d.	1445	...
490	**Raleigh** **9245** d.	|	2110	Winter Haven d.	1531	...
520	Fayetteville d.	1616	|	**Tampa** a.	1706	...
653	Florence d.	1757	|	**Tampa** d.	1720	...
805	Charleston SC d.	1937	|	Kissimmee d.	1841	...
814	Columbia d.	|	0149	**Orlando** a.	1909	...
966	Savannah d.	2125	0437	**Orlando** d.	1925	...
1203	**Jacksonville** a.	...	0706	Winter Park d.	1942	...
1203	**Jacksonville** d.	...	0726	**Jacksonville** a.	2244	...
1430	Winter Park d.	...	1010	**Jacksonville** d.	2304	...
1438	**Orlando** a.	...	1033	Savannah d.	0130	0735
1438	**Orlando** d.	...	1047	Columbia d.	0409	|
1467	Kissimmee d.	...	1111	Charleston SC d.	|	0915
1597	**Tampa** a.	...	1255	Florence d.	|	1054
1597	**Tampa** d.	...	1309	Fayetteville d.	|	1222
	Winter Haven d.	...	1407	**Raleigh** **9245** d.	0904	|
1593	Sebring d.	...	1448	Rocky Mount **9245** d.	1023	1413
1758	West Palm Beach ⊙ a.	...	1657s	Petersburg **9245** d.	1151	1544
1827	Fort Lauderdale ⊙ a.	...	1757s	Richmond **9245** d.	1239	1641
	Hollywood FL ⊡ a.	...	1812s	**Washington** U **9245** a.	1504s	1910s
1862	**Miami** Amtrak a.	...	1835	*New York Penn* **9215** a.	1910	2323

E – PALMETTO – (12) Y New York - Savannah and v.v.
F – SILVER STAR – 🛏 1, 2 cl., (2) ✕ New York - Miami and v.v.
s – Calls to set down only.
u – Calls to pick up only.
⊙ – Amtrak / Tri-Rail station (for distance to / from Brightline station see Table **9248**).
⊡ – Frequent Tri-Rail services available to / from Miami International Airport.

9243 MIAMI - WEST PALM BEACH — Brightline

WARNING! Schedules are subject to alteration, especially on ⑤⑥⑦ - please check locally

km		①–⑤	①–⑤	①–⑥		①–⑥				
0	**Miami** Central d.	0648	0748	0848	0948	1048	1148	1348	1448	1548
35	Fort Lauderdale ● d.	0720	0820	0920	1020	1120	1220	1420	1520	1620
104	**West Palm Beach** ⊕ a.	0800	0900	1000	1100	1200	1300	1500	1600	1700
			①–⑤						⑥⑦	
	Miami Central d.	1648	1718	1748	1848	1948	2048	2148	2248	2348
	Fort Lauderdale ● d.	1720	1750	1820	1920	2020	2120	2220	2320	0020
	West Palm Beach ⊕ a.	1800	1830	1900	2000	2100	2200	2300	0000	0100
		①–⑤	①–⑥	①–⑤		①–⑥		①–⑥		
	West Palm Beach ⊕ d.	0610	0648	0710	0748	0848	0948	1048	1148	1348
	Fort Lauderdale ● d.	0647	0725	0747	0825	0925	1025	1125	1225	1325
	Miami Central a.	0722	0800	0822	0900	1000	1100	1200	1300	1500
								⑥⑦		⑥
	West Palm Beach ⊕ d.	1448	1548	1648	1748	1848	1948	2048	2148	2248
	Fort Lauderdale ● d.	1525	1625	1725	1825	1925	2025	2125	2225	2325
	Miami Central a.	1600	1700	1800	1900	2000	2100	2200	2300	0000

● – Approximately 3 km by 🚌 from the Amtrak / Tri-Rail station (Table **9240**).
⊕ – Approximately 800 metres from the Amtrak / Tri-Rail station (Table **9240**).

9245 WASHINGTON - CHARLOTTE - ATLANTA - NEW ORLEANS — Amtrak

km		73 H	75 H	77 H	79 Ⓒ J	79 Ⓐ J	19 ④–① K
	New York Penn **9215** d.	...	...	...	0717	0725	1415
0	**Washington** Union **9240** d.	...	...	...	1108	1108	1830
174	Richmond **9240** d.	...	...	...	1336	1336	|
219	Petersburg **9240** d.	...	...	...	1413	1413	|
376	Rocky Mount **9240** d.	...	...	...	1546	1546	|
490	**Raleigh** **9240** d.	0630	1000	1500	1730	1730	|
619	Greensboro d.	0803	1133	1633	1916	1916	0032
645	High Point d.	0819	1149	1649	1932	1932	0049
699	Salisbury d.	0853	1223	1723	2006	2006	0127
766	**Charlotte** a.	0940	1310	1810	2056	2056	0230
766	**Charlotte** d.	...	...	...	...	...	0255
890	Spartanburg d.	...	...	...	...	...	0424
940	Greenville d.	...	...	...	...	...	0531
1102	Gainesville d.	...	...	...	...	...	0728
1179	**Atlanta** d.	...	...	...	...	...	0908
1344	Anniston d.	...	...	...	...	...	1030
1447	Birmingham d.	...	...	...	...	...	1303
1536	Tuscaloosa d.	...	...	...	...	...	1402
1692	Meridian d.	...	...	...	...	...	1619
1829	Hattiesburg d.	...	...	...	...	...	1753
2018	**New Orleans** a.	...	...	...	...	...	2102

	20 ⑤⑥ K	20 ①④⑦ K	80 J	74 H	76 H	78 H
New Orleans d.	0915	0915	...	...	...	...
Hattiesburg d.	1145	1145	...	...	...	...
Meridian d.	1337	1337	...	...	...	...
Tuscaloosa d.	1514	1514	...	...	...	...
Birmingham d.	1724	1724	...	...	...	...
Anniston d.	1859	1859	...	...	...	...
Atlanta d.	2329	2329	...	...	...	...
Gainesville d.	0024	0024	...	...	...	...
Greenville d.	0223	0223	...	...	...	...
Spartanburg d.	0304	0304	...	...	...	...
Charlotte a.	0506	0506	...	...	...	...
Charlotte d.	0531	0531	0645	1030	1515	1900
Salisbury d.	0617	0617	0728	1111	1556	1941
High Point d.	0701	0701	0802	1144	1629	2014
Greensboro d.	0729	0729	0824	1203	1648	2033
Raleigh **9240** d.	|	|	1013	1341	1826	2211
Rocky Mount **9240** d.	|	|	1140	...	...	...
Petersburg **9240** d.	|	|	1311	...	...	...
Richmond **9240** d.	|	|	1411	...	...	...
Washington Union **9240** a.	1345	1345	1631	...	...	...
New York Penn **9215** a.	1756	1808	2035	...	...	...

H – PIEDMONT – (2) Y Raleigh - Charlotte and v.v.
J – CAROLINIAN – (12) Y New York - Charlotte and v.v.
K – CRESCENT – 🛏 1, 2 cl., (2) ✕ New York - New Orleans and v.v.

WASHINGTON - CHICAGO 9250

Amtrak

km		51 ③⑤⑦ A	
	New York Penn **9215** d.	0645	...
0	**Washington** Union d.	1059	...
109	Culpeper d.	1225	...
181	Charlottesville d.	1352	...
338	Clifton Forge d.	1613	...
393	White Sulpher Springs d.	1705	...
528	Charleston WV d.	2029	...
606	Huntington d.	2151	...
678	South Shore ◧ d.	2257	...
872	Cincinnati d.	0141	...
1069	**Indianapolis** a.	0515	...
1069	**Indianapolis** d.	0600	...
1144	Crawfordsville d.	0658	...
1187	Lafayette d.	0736	...
1383	**Chicago** Union a.	1000	...

	50 ②④⑥ A	
Chicago Union d.	1755	...
Lafayette d.	2156	...
Crawfordsville d.	2230	...
Indianapolis a.	2349	...
Indianapolis d.	0015	...
Cincinnati d.	0337	...
South Shore ◧ d.	0555	...
Huntington d.	0726	...
Charleston WV d.	0831	...
White Sulpher Spings d.	1201	...
Clifton Forge d.	1309	...
Charlottesville d.	1544	...
Culpepper d.	1700	...
Washington Union a.	1844	...
New York Penn **9215** a.	2223	...

– CARDINAL – 🛏 1, 2 cl., [2] 🍷 Chicago - New York and v.v.
– For Portsmouth KY.

CHICAGO - NEW ORLEANS 9255

Amtrak

km		393 C	59 ①–⑤ D
0	**Chicago** Union d.	1605	2005
92	Kankakee d.	1712	2123r
208	Champaign Urbana d.	1815	2234
323	Effingham d.	1919	2337r
408	Centralia d.	2006	0025r
498	Carbondale d.	2135	0126
725	Newbern d.	...	0356r
850	**Memphis** d.	...	0640
1051	Greenwood d.	...	0900
1136	Yazoo City d.	...	0951r
1207	Jackson d.	...	1120
1334	McComb d.	...	1240r
1419	Hammond d.	...	1328
1503	**New Orleans** a.	...	1547

	58 ①–⑤ D	390 C
New Orleans d.	1345	...
Hammond d.	1445	...
McComb d.	1532r	...
Jackson d.	1744	...
Yazoo City d.	1842r	...
Greenwood d.	1937	...
Memphis d.	2240	...
Newbern d.	0022r	...
Carbondale d.	0316	0730
Centralia d.	0410r	0823
Effingham d.	0457r	0907
Champaign Urbana d.	0610	1014
Kankakee d.	0713r	1115
Chicago Union a.	0915	1300

C – ILLINI / SALUKI – [12] 🍷 Chicago - Carbondale and v.v.
D – CITY OF NEW ORLEANS – 🛏 1, 2 cl., [2] ✕ Chicago - New Orleans and v.v.
r – Calls on request.

CHICAGO - ST. LOUIS - KANSAS CITY 9260

Amtrak

km		301 F	303 F	313 E	21 G	3 ③–⑦ H	305 F	307 F		
0	**Chicago** Union **9295** d.	0715	0930	...	1345	1450	1720	1910	...	...
60	Joliet Union d.	0812	1020	...	1440u	|	1810	2000	...	...
148	Pontiac IL d.	|	1107	...	1526	|	1900	2048	...	...
204	Bloomington d.	0926	1143	...	1601	|	1932	2123	...	...
252	Lincoln d.	|	1212	...	1630	|	2004	2153	...	...
298	Springfield IL d.	1023	1244	...	1706	|	2036	2223	...	...
360	Carlinville d.	|	1325	...	1738r	|	2118	|	...	...
414	Alton d.	1129	1354	...	1809	|	2147	2333	...	...
457	**St. Louis** d.	1221	1450	1600	1913	|	2236	0023	...	...
480	Kirkwood d.	...	...	1629	...	|	...	...	...	...
536	Washington MO d.	...	...	1706	...	|	...	...	...	...
658	Jefferson City d.	...	...	1827	...	|	...	...	...	...
760	Sedalia d.	...	...	1937	...	|	...	...	...	...
866	Lee's Summit d.	...	...	2054	...	|	...	...	...	...
891	Independence d.	...	...	2110	...	|	...	...	...	...
912	**Kansas City** **9295** a.	...	...	2140	...	2200	...	...	...	...

	300 F	302 F	22 G	4 ⑤–② H	314 E	304 F	306 F		
Kansas City **9295** d.	...	...	...	0728	0815	...	...	...	...
Independence d.	...	...	...	|	0834	...	...	...	...
Lee's Summit d.	...	...	...	|	0851	...	...	...	...
Sedalia d.	...	...	...	|	1004	...	...	...	...
Jefferson City d.	...	...	...	|	1125	...	...	...	...
Washington MO d.	...	...	...	|	1238	...	...	...	...
Kirkwood d.	...	...	...	|	1322	...	...	...	...
St. Louis d.	0430	0640	0755	|	1355	1500	1740	...	...
Alton d.	0514	0725	0843	|	...	1543	1824	...	...
Carlinville d.	|	0752	0909r	|	...	1611	1848	...	...
Springfield IL d.	0615	0832	0951	|	...	1651	1930	...	...
Lincoln d.	0642	0856	1020	|	...	1718	1954	...	...
Bloomington d.	0713	0930	1102	|	...	1750	2027	...	...
Pontiac IL d.	0740	0959	1134	|	...	1816	2058	...	...
Joliet Union d.	0838	1104	1248s	|	...	1911	2157	...	...
Chicago Union **9295** a.	0939	1205	1344	1450	...	2025	2305	...	...

– RIVER RUNNER – [12] 🍷 St Louis - Kansas City and v.v.
– LINCOLN SERVICE – [12] 🍷 Chicago - St. Louis and v.v.
G – TEXAS EAGLE - see Table **9300**.
H – SOUTHWEST CHIEF - see Table **9295**.
r – Calls on request.
s – Calls to set down only.
u – Calls to pick up only.

CHICAGO - QUINCY 9265

Amtrak

km		381 J	5 ②–⑥ K	3 ③–⑦ H	383 M					
0	**Chicago** Union **9295** d.	0740	1400	1450	1755	...	...	...	...	...
166	Princeton d.	0926	1544	1634	1941	...	...	...	...	...
259	Galesburg **9295** d.	1023	1638	1723	2038	...	...	...	...	...
413	Quincy IL a.	1202	...	...	2217	...	...	...	...	...

	380 M	4 ⑤–② H	6 ④–① K	382 J					
Quincy IL d.	0612	...	...	1730	...	...	...	...	...
Galesburg **9295** d.	0737	1148	1141s	1855	...	...	...	...	...
Princeton d.	0830	1238	1233s	1948	...	...	...	...	...
Chicago Union **9295** a.	1033	1450	1450	2151	...	...	...	...	...

– SOUTHWEST CHIEF – see Table **9295**.
– CARL SANDBURG – [12] 🍷 Chicago Union - Quincy and v.v.
K – CALIFONIA ZEPHYR – see Table **9290**.
M – ILLINOIS ZEPHYR – [12] 🍷 Chicago Union - Quincy and v.v.
s – Calls to set down only.

CHICAGO - MILWAUKEE 9270

Amtrak 2nd class

HIAWATHA SERVICE

km		329 ①–⑤	331	333	335	337	339	341	8307 🚌	343 ⑤
0	**Chicago** Union d.	0610	0825	1105	1305	1515	1708	2005	2105	2325
100	Sturtevant d.	0710	0925	1205	1405	1615	1814	2105	|	0025
125	**Milwaukee** Airport a.	0724	0939	1219	1419	1629	1828	2119	|	0039
138	**Milwaukee** a.	0739	0954	1234	1434	1644	1845	2134	2340	0054

	330 ①–⑥	332		334	336	338		340	342
Milwaukee d.	0615	0805	...	1100	1305	1500	...	1745	1935
Milwaukee Airport d.	0626	0815	...	1110	1315	1510	...	1755	1945
Sturtevant d.	0643	0828	...	1123	1328	1523	...	1808	1958
Chicago Union a.	0757	0934	...	1229	1434	1629	...	1914	2104

CHICAGO - GRAND RAPIDS, PORT HURON, DETROIT and PONTIAC 9275

Amtrak

km		350 N	352 N	364 P	354 N	370 Q				
0	**Chicago** Union CT d.	0645	1415	1600	1750	1830	...	...	...	...
140	Benton Harbour ET d.	|	|	|	|	2114	...	...	...	...
282	**Grand Rapids** ET a.	|	|	|	|	2334	...	...	...	...
34	Michigan City CT d.	|	|	|	|	...	...	...	...	...
141	Niles ET d.	0929	1652	1832	2024	...	...	...	...	...
221	Kalamazoo a.	1014	1726	1911	2058	...	...	...	...	...
258	Battle Creek a.	1056	1803	1938	2135	...	...	...	...	...
335	East Lansing d.	|	|	2100	|	...	...	...	...	...
382	Durand d.	|	|	2137	|	...	...	...	...	...
409	Flint d.	|	|	2208	|	...	...	...	...	...
513	**Port Huron** a.	|	|	2331	|	...	...	...	...	...
331	Jackson d.	1153	1857	...	2230	...	...	...	...	...
390	Ann Arbor d.	1230	1937	...	2310	...	...	...	...	...
439	Dearborn ⊡ d.	1314	2028	...	2354	...	...	...	...	...
450	**Detroit** ⊡ d.	1342	2057	...	0027	...	...	...	...	...
494	**Pontiac** MI a.	1428	2146	...	0118	...	...	...	...	...

	371 Q	351 N	365 P	353 N	355 N				
Pontiac MI d.	...	0543	...	0850	1728	...	...	...	...
Detroit d.	...	0626	...	0935	1811	...	...	...	...
Dearborn d.	...	0644	...	0953	1829	...	...	...	...
Ann Arbor d.	...	0714	...	1023	1900	...	...	...	...
Jackson d.	...	0751	...	1058	1937	...	...	...	...
Port Huron d.	...	|	0620	|	|	...	...	...	...
Flint d.	...	|	0735	|	|	...	...	...	...
Durand d.	...	|	0808	|	|	...	...	...	...
East Lansing d.	...	|	0854	|	|	...	...	...	...
Battle Creek d.	...	0850	1000	1203	2035	...	...	...	...
Kalamazoo d.	...	0918	1026	1230	2102	...	...	...	...
Niles ET d.	...	|	1104	1303	2144	...	...	...	...
Michigan City CT d.	...	|	|	|	|	...	...	...	...
Grand Rapids ET d.	0600	|	|	|	|	...	...	...	...
Benton Harbour ET d.	0810	|	|	|	|	...	...	...	...
Chicago Union CT a.	0908	1049	1200	1419	2257	...	...	...	...

– WOLVERINE – [12] 🍷 Chicago - Pontiac and v.v.
– BLUE WATER – [12] 🍷 Chicago - Port Huron and v.v.
Q – PERE MARQUETTE – [2] Chicago - Grand Rapids and v.v.
⊡ – Trains may depart early if all booked passengers have boarded.
CT – Central Time.
ET – Eastern Time.

SELECTED BUS ROUTES 9280

Greyhound

km	*Greyhound* 🚌 *service*	1541	1535	1511						
0	**Nashville** d.	0400	0650	2230	...	...	...	...	...	...
337	**Memphis** a.	0800	1050	0215	...	...	...	...	...	...

Greyhound 🚌 *service*	1502	1510	1520						
Memphis d.	0500	1315	1735	...	...	...	...	...	...
Nashville a.	0850	1720	2125	...	...	...	...	...	...

km	*Greyhound* 🚌 *service*	1683	6027	6011	6025					
0	**Las Vegas** NV d.	0305	1155	1610	2345	...	...	...	...	...
501	**Los Angeles** a.	0915	1735	2205	0440	...	...	...	...	...

Greyhound 🚌 *service*	6048	6002	6024	1684					
Los Angeles d.	0030	0650	0830	1825	...	...	...	...	...
Las Vegas NV a.	0545	1415	1410	0035	...	...	...	...	...

9285 CHICAGO - SEATTLE / PORTLAND Amtrak

km		7	27		28	8
		⑥–③	⑥–③		⑥–③	⑥–③
		A	A		A	A
0	**Chicago** Union d.	1415	1415	**Portland** d.	1645	...
137	Milwaukee d.	1552u	1552u	Vancouver WA d.	1707	...
241	Columbus d.	1702	1702	Pasco d.	2057	...
285	Portage WI d.	1731	1731	**Seattle** King St. ◧ d.	|	1640
314	Wisconsin Dells d.	1749	1749	Everett d.	|	1739
386	Tomah d.	1827	1827	Wenatchee d.	0013	2042
452	La Crosse d.	1911	1911	**Spokane** a.	0040	0040
673	**Minneapolis / St Paul** d.	2220	2220	**Spokane** d.	0125	0125
773	St. Cloud d.	0024	0024	Sandpoint d.	0230	0230
1058	Fargo d.	0324	0324	Whitefish d.	0741	0741
1194	Grand Forks d.	0441	0441	Shelby d.	1133	1133
1332	Devils Lake d.	0602	0602	Havre d.	1322	1322
1522	Minot d.	0906	0906	Malta d.	1442	1442
1958	Glasgow d.	1226	1226	Glasgow d.	1537	1537
2072	Malta d.	1325	1325	Minot d.	2147	2147
2212	Havre d.	1504	1504	Devils Lake d.	2337	2337
2381	Shelby d.	1722	1722	Grand Forks d.	0102	0102
2624	Whitefish d.	2116	2116	Fargo d.	0218	0218
2924	Sandpoint d.	2349	2349	St. Cloud d.	0519	0519
3030	**Spokane** a.	0140	0140	**Minneapolis / St Paul** d.	0800	0800
3030	**Spokane** d.	0215	0245	La Crosse d.	1047	1047
3306	Wenatchee d.	0535	|	Tomah d.	1126	1126
3501	Everett d.	0838	|	Wisconsin Dells d.	1208	1208
3554	**Seattle** King St. ◧ a.	1025	|	Portage WI d.	1227	1227
3265	Pasco d.	...	0535	Columbus d.	1257	1257
3621	Vancouver WA d.	...	0918	Milwaukee d.	1407s	1407s
3638	**Portland** a.	...	1010	**Chicago** Union a.	1555	1555

FOR NOTES SEE FOOT OF PAGE.

9290 CHICAGO - SAN FRANCISCO Amtrak

km		5			6	
		②–⑥			②–⑥	
		B			B	
0	**Chicago** Union 9265 d.	1400	...	**Emeryville** ⊡ d.	0910	...
166	Princeton 9265 d.	1544	...	Martinez d.	0954	...
261	Galesburg 9265 d.	1638	...	Sacramento d.	1109	...
330	Burlington d.	1725	...	Truckee d.	1438	...
450	Ottumwa d.	1853	...	Reno d.	1606	...
806	**Omaha** a.	2255	...	Winnemucca d.	1908	...
806	**Omaha** d.	2305	...	Elko d.	2131	...
892	Lincoln d.	0014	...	**Salt Lake City** a.	0305	...
1049	Hastings d.	0147	...	**Salt Lake City** d.	0330	...
1261	McCook d.	0343	...	Provo d.	0435	...
1668	**Denver** Union ◇ a.	0715	...	Green River d.	0759	...
1668	**Denver** Union ◇ d.	0805	...	Grand Junction d.	1023	...
1770	Fraser-Winter Park d.	1007	...	Glenwood Springs d.	1210	...
1791	Granby d.	1037	...	Granby d.	1512	...
1966	Glenwood Springs d.	1353	...	Fraser-Winter Park d.	1550	...
2109	Grand Junction d.	1610	...	**Denver** Union ◇ a.	1838	...
2279	Green River d.	1758	...	**Denver** Union ◇ d.	1910	...
2516	Provo d.	2126	...	McCook d.	2349	...
2587	**Salt Lake City** a.	2305	...	Hastings d.	0142	...
2587	**Salt Lake City** d.	2330	...	Lincoln d.	0326	...
3010	Elko d.	0303	...	**Omaha** a.	0459	...
3232	Winnemucca d.	0540	...	**Omaha** d.	0514	...
3514	Reno d.	0836	...	Ottumwa d.	0909	...
3569	Truckee d.	0937	...	Burlington d.	1036	...
3785	Sacramento d.	1425s	...	Galesburg 9265 d.	1141s	...
3879	Martinez d.	1532s	...	Princeton 9265 d.	1233s	...
3922	**Emeryville** ⊡ a.	1610	...	**Chicago** Union 9265 a.	1450	...

FOR NOTES SEE FOOT OF PAGE.

9295 CHICAGO - LOS ANGELES Amtrak

km		3			4	
		③–⑦			③–⑦	
		C			C	
0	**Chicago** Union 9265 d.	1450	...	**Los Angeles** Union d.	1755	...
166	Princeton 9265 d.	1634	...	San Bernardino d.	1939	...
261	Galesburg 9265 d.	1726	...	Victorville d.	2050	...
329	Fort Madison d.	1830	...	Barstow d.	2146	...
677	**Kansas City** a.	2200	...	Needles d.	0013	...
677	**Kansas City** d.	2242	...	Kingman * d.	0125	...
783	Topeka d.	0029	...	**Flagstaff** * ⊙ d.	0420	...
1001	Newton ⊕ d.	0245	...	Winslow * d.	0520	...
1247	Dodge City d.	0519	...	Gallup d.	0806	...
1488	Lamar d.	0638	...	**Albuquerque** ‡ a.	1120	...
1572	La Junta d.	0804	...	**Albuquerque** ‡ d.	1148	...
1704	Trinidad d.	0924	...	Lamy d.	1302	...
1741	Raton ◇ d.	1030	...	Las Vegas NM d.	1451	...
1918	Las Vegas NM d.	1212	...	Raton ◇ d.	1642	...
2022	Lamy d.	1358	...	Trinidad d.	1741	...
2132	**Albuquerque** ‡ a.	1529	...	La Junta d.	1929	...
2132	**Albuquerque** ‡ d.	1619	...	Lamar d.	2023	...
2391	Gallup d.	1846	...	Dodge City d.	2347	...
2595	Winslow * d.	1928	...	Newton ⊕ d.	0219	...
2690	**Flagstaff** * ⊙ d.	2038	...	Topeka d.	0440	...
2967	Kingman * d.	2328	...	**Kansas City** a.	0653	...
3067	Needles d.	0031	...	**Kansas City** d.	0728	...
3337	Barstow d.	0345	...	Fort Madison d.	1049	...
3398	Victorville d.	0424	...	Galesburg 9265 d.	1148	...
3472	San Bernardino d.	0542	...	Princeton 9265 d.	1238	...
3588	**Los Angeles** Union a.	0800	...	**Chicago** Union 9265 a.	1450	...

FOR NOTES SEE FOOT OF PAGE.

9300 CHICAGO - SAN ANTONIO Amtrak

km		21			22	
		D			D	
0	**Chicago** Union 9260 d.	1345	...	**San Antonio** d.	0700	...
148	Pontiac IL 9260 d.	1526	...	San Marcos d.	0832	...
298	Springfield IL 9260 d.	1706	...	Austin d.	0931	...
457	**St. Louis** 9260 a.	1913	...	Taylor d.	1022	...
457	**St. Louis** d.	1955	...	Temple d.	1125	...
717	Poplar Bluff d.	2342	...	**Fort Worth** a.	1358	...
813	Walnut Ridge d.	0037	...	**Fort Worth** d.	1420	...
1007	Little Rock d.	0310	...	**Dallas** a.	1520	...
1127	Arkadelphia d.	0420	...	**Dallas** d.	1540	...
1240	Texarkana d.	0558	...	Longview d.	1815	...
1384	Longview d.	0828	...	Texarkana d.	2043	...
1588	**Dallas** a.	1130	...	Arkadelphia d.	2202	...
1588	**Dallas** d.	1150	...	Little Rock d.	2339	...
1638	**Fort Worth** a.	1325	...	Walnut Ridge d.	0141	...
1638	**Fort Worth** d.	1410	...	Poplar Bluff d.	0244	...
1844	Temple d.	1643	...	**St. Louis** a.	0724	...
1906	Taylor d.	1736	...	**St. Louis** 9260 d.	0755	...
1962	Austin d.	1830	...	Springfield IL 9260 d.	0951	...
2011	San Marcos d.	1912	...	Pontiac IL 9260 d.	1134	...
2060	**San Antonio** a.	2155	...	**Chicago** Union 9260 a.	1344	...
km		821			822	
		E			E	
0	**Oklahoma City** ⊕ d.	0825	...	**Fort Worth** d.	1725	...
164	Ardmore d.	1017	...	Gainesville d.	1828	...
227	Gainesville d.	1103	...	Ardmore d.	1911	...
336	**Fort Worth** a.	1227	...	**Oklahoma City** ⊕ a.	2127	...

FOR NOTES SEE FOOT OF PAGE.

9305 SEATTLE - LOS ANGELES Amtrak

km		11			14	
		F			F	
0	**Seattle** King St. ◧ 9315 d.	0950	...	**Los Angeles** Union d.	0951	...
64	Tacoma 9315 d.	1038	...	Santa Barbara d.	1227	...
105	Olympia 9315 d.	1119	...	San Luis Obispo d.	1511	...
142	Centralia 9315 d.	1143	...	Paso Robles d.	1621	...
210	Kelso Longview 9315 d.	1227	...	Salinas d.	1819	...
273	Vancouver WA 9315 d.	1310	...	San Jose d.	2004	...
289	**Portland** 9315 a.	1350	...	**Oakland** a.	2112	...
289	**Portland** 9315 d.	1422	...	**Oakland** 9330 d.	2127	...
373	Salem 9315 d.	1539	...	Emeryville ⊡ 9330 a.	2137	...
487	Eugene 9315 d.	1715	...	Emeryville ⊡ 9330 d.	2147	...
682	Chemult d.	2013	...	Martinez 9330 d.	2226	...
799	Klamath Falls d.	2208	...	**Sacramento** d.	2349	...
967	Dunsmuir d.	0045	...	Chico d.	0137	...
1058	Redding d.	0231	...	Redding d.	0305	...
1177	Chico d.	0412	...	Dunsmuir d.	0458	...
1311	**Sacramento** d.	0648	...	Klamath Falls d.	0743	...
1388	Martinez 9330 d.	0754	...	Chemult d.	0859	...
1432	Emeryville ⊡ 9330 a.	0829	...	Eugene 9315 d.	1237	...
1432	Emeryville ⊡ 9330 d.	0839	...	Salem 9315 d.	1404	...
1440	**Oakland** 9330 a.	0854	...	**Portland** 9315 a.	1540	...
1440	**Oakland** d.	0909	...	**Portland** 9315 d.	1556	...
1564	San Jose d.	1026	...	Vancouver WA 9315 d.	1616	...
1615	Salinas d.	1206	...	Kelso Longview 9315 d.	1651	...
1771	Paso Robles d.	1357	...	Centralia 9315 d.	1736	...
1826	San Luis Obispo d.	1537	...	Olympia 9315 d.	1801	...
2036	Santa Barbara d.	1819	...	Tacoma 9315 d.	1843	...
2181	**Los Angeles** Union a.	2111	...	**Seattle** King St. ◧ 9315 a.	1951	...

9310 NEW ORLEANS - LOS ANGELES Amtrak

km		1	421		2	422
		①③⑥	②④⑦		③⑤⑦	③⑤
		G	D		G	D
0	**Orlando** d.	...	...	**Los Angeles** Union d.	2200	2200
235	Jacksonville d.	...	...	Pomona d.	2241	2241
509	Tallahasse d.	...	...	Palm Springs d.	0036	0036
998	Mobile d.	...	...	Yuma * d.	0247	0247
1230	**New Orleans** a.	...	...	Maricopa * d.	0540	0540
1230	**New Orleans** d.	0900	...	Tucson * d.	0815	0815
1434	New Iberia d.	1156	...	Benson * d.	0915	0915
1462	Lafeyette d.	1224	...	Lordsburg d.	1215	1215
1581	Lake Charles d.	1355	...	**El Paso** ⊖ a.	1510	1510
1678	Beaumont d.	1548	...	**El Paso** ⊖ d.	1535	1535
1810	**Houston** a.	1818	...	Alpine d.	2045	2045
1810	**Houston** d.	1855	...	Del Rio d.	0102	0102
2146	**San Antonio** a.	0005	...	**San Antonio** a.	0450	0450
2146	**San Antonio** d.	0245	0245	**San Antonio** d.	0625	
2418	Del Rio d.	0549	0549	**Houston** a.	1110	
2765	Alpine d.	1038	1038	**Houston** d.	1210	
3114	**El Paso** ⊖ a.	1322	1322	Beaumont d.	1405	
3114	**El Paso** ⊖ d.	1347	1347	Lake Charles d.	1529	
3350	Lordsburg d.	1613	1613	Lafeyette d.	1715	
3539	Benson* d.	1718	1718	New Iberia d.	1741	
3619	Tucson* d.	1935	1935	**New Orleans** a.	2140	
3757	Maricopa* d.	2102	2102	**New Orleans** d.	...	
4021	Yuma* d.	2349	2349	Mobile a.	...	
4253	Palm Springs d.	0202	0202	Tallahasse a.	...	
4371	Pomona d.	0404s	0404s	Jacksonville a.	...	
4422	**Los Angeles** Union a.	0535	0535	**Orlando** a.	...	

NOTES FOR TABLES 9285 - 9310

A – EMPIRE BUILDER – 🛏 1, 2 cl., 🚃 ✕ Chicago - Spokane - Seattle and v.v.; 🛏 1, 2 cl., 🚃 🍸 Chicago (7/8) - Spokane (27/28) - Portland and v.v.
B – CALIFORNIA ZEPHYR – 🛏 1, 2 cl., 🚃 ✕ Chicago - Emeryville and v.v.
C – SOUTHWEST CHIEF – 🛏 1, 2 cl., 🚃 ✕ Chicago - Los Angeles and v.v.
D – TEXAS EAGLE – 🛏 1, 2 cl., 🚃 ✕ Chicago - San Antonio (421/422) - Los Angeles and v.v. For running days and times San Antonio - Los Angeles and v.v., see Table 9310.
E – HEARTLAND FLYER – 🚃 🍸 Oklahoma City - Fort Worth and v.v.
F – COAST STARLIGHT – 🛏 1, 2 cl., 🚃 ✕ Seattle - Los Angeles and v.v.
G – SUNSET LIMITED – 🛏 1, 2 cl., 🚃 ✕ New Orleans - Los Angeles and v.v.
s – Calls to set down only.
u – Calls to pick up only.

◧ – See Table 9315 for Thruway 🚌 service Seattle - Vancouver BC.
⊡ – See Table 9325 for Thruway 🚌 service Emeryville - San Francisco.
◇ – Thruway 🚌 available Denver - Colorado Springs - Pueblo - Raton.
⊕ – Thruway 🚌 available Newton - Wichita - Oklahoma City.
⊙ – Thruway 🚌 available Flagstaff - Grand Canyon and Flagstaff - Phoenix.
⊖ – Thruway 🚌 available El Paso - Albuquerque.
‡ – Thruway 🚌 available Albuquerque - El Paso. Local rail service available Albuquerque - Santa Fe (New Mexico Rail Runner www.nmrailrunner.com).
* – Does not observe DST. Times will be one hour later from Nov. 6, 2022.

VANCOUVER - SEATTLE - PORTLAND - EUGENE 9315

Amtrak

km		5541	503	5605	11	5547	505	5677	507	5507
		🚌	A	🚌	B		A	🚌	A	🚌
0	**Vancouver** (Canada) ◧ d.	...	...	...	...	...	...	...	...	...
93	Bellingham d.	...	...	1045	...	...	...	1500	...	...
135	Mount Vernon d.	...	...	1120	...	...	...	1535	...	...
198	Everett d.	...	...	1205	...	...	...	1620	...	...
251	**Seattle** King Street ◧ a.	...	...	1325	...	...	...	1740	...	...
251	**Seattle** King Street d.	...	0722	—	0950	...	1412	...	1810	...
269	Tukwila (SeaTac ✈) d.	...	0736	...	|	...	1426	...	1824	...
315	Tacoma d.	...	0808	...	1038	...	1458	...	1856	...
356	Olympia d.	...	0840	...	1119	...	1530	...	1928	...
393	Centralia d.	...	0900	...	1143	...	1550	...	1948	...
461	Kelso Longview d.	...	0940	...	1227	...	1630	...	2028	...
524	Vancouver WA d.	...	1021	**5545**	1310	...	1711	...	2109	...
540	**Portland** a.	...	1047	🚌	1350	...	1737	...	2135	...
540	**Portland** d.	0700	1110	1200	1422	1700	1805	...	...	2155
624	Salem d.	0805	1222	1320	1539	1825	1917	...	...	2305
669	Albany OR d.	0840	1253	1355	1614	1900	1948	...	...	2335
738	**Eugene** a.	0935	1350	1450	1708	1950	2040	...	...	0030

	500	5622	5504	504	5518	14	5528	508	5548
	A	🚌	🚌	A	🚌	B	🚌	A	🚌
Eugene d.	0530	...	0815	...	1145	1237	1310	1630	1800
Albany OR d.	0611	...	0910	...	1240	1323	1405	1711	1845
Salem d.	0641	...	0950	...	1320	1404	1445	1741	1925
Portland a.	0805	...	1105	...	1435	1540	1610	1905	2040
Portland d.	0820	...	...	1200	—	1556	...	1925	...
Vancouver WA d.	0838	...	...	1218	...	1616	...	1943	...
Kelso Longview d.	0911	...	...	1251	...	1651	...	2016	...
Centralia d.	0952	...	...	1332	...	1736	...	2057	...
Olympia d.	1013	...	...	1353	...	1801	...	2118	...
Tacoma d.	1054	...	...	1434	...	1843	...	2201	...
Tukwila (SeaTac ✈) d.	1124	...	...	1503	**5604**	|	...	2227	...
Seattle King Street a.	1145	...	...	1532	🚌	1951	...	2250	...
Seattle King Street ◧ d.	...	1215	...	...	1600	...	...	...	...
Everett d.	...	1300	...	...	1645	...	...	...	...
Mount Vernon d.	...	1345	...	...	1730	...	...	...	...
Bellingham d.	...	1415	...	...	1800	...	...	...	...
Vancouver (Canada) ◧ a.	...	...	...	...	...	...	...	...	...

A – CASCADES – (12) 🍸 Ⓡ.
B – COAST STARLIGHT – see Table **9305**.

◧ – Thruway 🚌 service Seattle - Vancouver and v.v. Journey 3½ hours. Operator: Cantrail (www.cantrail.com). From Seattle King Street at 1045, 1345, 1645, 2100; from Vancouver Pacific Central station at 0530, 0900, 1130, 1600.

SAN LUIS OBISPO - LOS ANGELES 9320

Amtrak, Metrolink

Trains with numbers are *Pacific Surfliners* operated by Amtrak. Trains without numbers are operated by Metrolink.
Metrolink ticket holders may use trains noted ⊖ between Oxnard and Los Angeles.

km											🚌	770			774			🚌	784				🚌	794
		Ⓐ	Ⓐ	Ⓐ		Ⓐ	Ⓐ	Ⓐ		Ⓐ		⊖		⑥		Ⓐ			⊖	Ⓐ		Ⓐ		
0	**San Luis Obispo** d.	...	...	...	...	...	...	...	...	...	0400	...	...	...	0611	...	...	1045	...	...	...	...	...	1622
40	Santa Maria ⊡ d.	...	...	...	...	...	...	...	...	...	0440	...	...	...	0647	...	...	1125	...	...	...	...	...	1658
190	Santa Barbara d.	...	...	...	...	...	...	...	...	...	0630	0653	...	...	0849	...	...	1325	1345	...	...	...	1450	1904
248	Oxnard d.	...	0534	0612	...	...	0712	...	...	...	...	0757	...	0830	0955	...	...	...	1453	...	...	...	1610	2005
280	Moorpark d.	0502	0556	0634	...	...	0734	0755	...	...	...	0824	...	0853	1023	1417	...	...	1523	...	...	1646	|	2034
310	Chatsworth d.	0527	0621	0700	...	...	0759	0822	...	...	...	0853	...	0918	1052	1444	...	...	1552	...	...	1712	|	2108
325	Van Nuys d.	0541	0634	0714	...	0800	0814	0834	...	0859	...	0909	...	0931	1107	1457	...	...	1613	1700	...	1726	|	2119
334	Burbank Airport South ✈ d.	0549	0641	0721	...	0807	0821	0842	...	0906	...	0917	...	0938	1115	1505	...	...	1621	1707	...	1733	|	2127
340	Downtown Burbank d.	0554	0646	0726	...	0812	0826	0846	...	0911	...	0922	...	0943	|	1510	...	...	1626	1712	...	1738	|	|
355	**Los Angeles** Union a.	0615	0710	0749	...	0834	0849	0907	...	0933	...	0946	...	1005	1143	1533	...	...	1648	1734	...	1759	1840	2156
	Oceanside **9322** a.	...	...	...	...	...	...	...	...	...	...	1208	...	...	1405	...	...	...	1905	...	...	...	*2105*	*0015*
	San Diego SF ● **9322** a.	...	...	...	...	...	...	...	...	...	...	1307	...	...	1504	...	...	...	2004	...	...	...	*2204*	*0114*

	761	765	🚌								777										785	🚌	🚌
	⊖				Ⓐ	Ⓐ	Ⓐ		Ⓐ	Ⓐ	⊖		Ⓐ	Ⓐ	⑥		Ⓐ	Ⓐ	Ⓐ				
San Diego SF ● **9322** d.	0401	0601	...	...	...	...	...	...	...	...	1201	...	...	...	...	...	...	...	...	...	1601	...	*1901*
Oceanside **9322** d.	0457	0657	...	...	...	...	...	...	...	...	1257	...	...	...	...	...	...	...	...	...	1657	...	*1957*
Los Angeles Union d.	0713	0913	...	...	0611	0652	0805	...	1243	1449	1513	...	1603	1628	1628	...	1710	1754	1826	...	1913	...	2210
Downtown Burbank d.	0733	|	...	...	0630	0711	0824	...	1301	1507	1533	...	1622	1646	1646	...	1728	1812	1844	...	|	...	|
Burbank Airport South ✈ d.	0739	0936	...	...	0636	0717	0830	...	1307	1512	1539	...	1628	1651	1652	...	1733	1817	1850	...	1936	...	2250
Van Nuys d.	0747	0944	...	...	0644	0727	0840	...	1315	1519	1547	...	1638	1658	1700	...	1740	1824	1857	...	1944	...	2310
Chatsworth d.	0802	0959	...	...	0658	...	...	...	1329	1532	1601	...	...	1712	1714	...	1754	1838	1910	...	1959	...	2330
Moorpark d.	0827	1024	...	...	0727	...	...	...	1357	1602	1626	...	...	1736	1739	...	1818	1905	1936	...	2025	...	2355
Oxnard d.	0856	1051	...	...	...	...	...	...	...	...	1651	...	...	1758	1801	...	1839	...	1956	...	2059	...	0020
Santa Barbara a.	0955	1150	1155	...	...	...	...	...	...	...	1746	...	...	...	...	...	...	...	...	...	2159	2205	0115
Santa Maria ⊡ a.	1154	...	1325	...	...	...	...	...	...	...	1956	...	...	...	...	...	...	...	...	...	...	2335	...
San Luis Obispo a.	1239	...	1410	...	...	...	...	...	...	...	2046	...	...	...	...	...	...	...	...	...	...	0025	...

⊡ – 🚌 call at the IHOP Restaurant, 205 South Nicholson Avenue. Trains call at Guadalupe Santa Maria station. These locations are approximately 16 km from each other.

● – San Diego Santa Fe, also known as Downtown.

LOS ANGELES - SAN DIEGO 9322

Amtrak, Metrolink

Trains with numbers are *Pacific Surfliner* service operated by Amtrak. Trains without numbers are operated by Metrolink. For Coaster trains Oceanside - San Diego see Table **9366**.
Coaster Day and Monthly Pass holders may use Amtrak services between Oceanside and San Diego.

km		562		564			770		572	774			580						784		586		588	594
			Ⓐ		Ⓐ	Ⓒ		Ⓒ			Ⓒ	Ⓐ		Ⓐ	Ⓐ	Ⓐ	Ⓒ	Ⓐ		Ⓐ		Ⓐ		
	San Luis Obispo **9320** d.	...	...	...	...	...	*0400**	...	...	0611	...	...	...	...	...	...	...	...	*1045**	...	...	...	...	1622
	Santa Barbara **9320** d.	...	...	...	...	...	0653	...	...	0849	...	...	...	...	...	...	...	...	1345	...	...	...	*1450**	*1904*
	Oxnard **9320** d.	...	...	...	...	...	0757	...	...	0955	...	...	...	...	...	...	...	...	1453	...	...	...	*1610**	*2005*
0	**Los Angeles** Union d.	0610	0629	0710	0758	0840	1010	1050	1110	1210	1400	1411	1510	1523	1547	1630	1640	1647	1710	1740	1810	1831	1910	2220
42	Fullerton d.	0641	0705	0741	0834	0916	1041	1127	1141	1241	1437	1448	1541	1602	1627	1709	1717	1724	1741	1819	1841	1908	1941	2251
51	Anaheim d.	0649	0712	0749	0841	0924	1049	1135	1149	1249	1445	1455	1549	1611	1635	1716	1725	1731	1749	1826	1849	1915	1949	2259
	Orange d.	|	0716	|	0845	0929	|	1140	|	|	1450	1500	|	1616	1640	1721	1730	1736	|	1831	|	1920	|	|
58	Santa Ana d.	0701	0722	0801	0851	0935	1101	1145	1201	1301	1455	1505	1601	1621	1645	1726	1735	1741	1801	1836	1901	1925	2001	2311
74	Irvine d.	0712	0736	0812	0904	0949	1112	1159	1212	1312	1509	1519	1612	1636	1703	1740	1749	1755	1812	1850	1912	1939	2012	2322
93	San Juan Capistrano d.	0726	...	0826	0920	1006	1125	1215	1225	1326	1525	...	1626	1651	...	1756	1805	...	1826	1906	1926	1955	2026	2336
106	San Clemente d.	|	...	|	0930	1016	|	1225	|	|	1538	...	|	1704	...	1805	1818	...	|	1915	|	2004	|	|
140	Oceanside **9366** d.	0805	...	0905	1001	1048	1208	1255	1308	1405	1608	...	1705	1731	...	1834	1848	...	1905	1944	2005	2033	2105	0015
167	Solana Beach **9366** d.	0820	...	0920	...	...	1223	...	1323	1420	...	...	1720	...	...	...	...	...	1920	...	2020	...	2120	0030
	San Diego Old Town **9366** a.	0850	...	0950	...	...	1253	...	1353	1450	...	...	1750	...	...	...	...	...	1950	...	2050	...	2150	0100
208	**San Diego** SF ● **9366** a.	0904	...	1004	...	...	1307	...	1407	1504	...	...	1804	...	...	...	...	...	2004	...	2104	...	2204	0114

		761					765		567			573		777		581		583		785		591	595
	Ⓐ		Ⓐ	Ⓐ	Ⓐ	Ⓐ		Ⓐ		Ⓐ	Ⓒ		Ⓒ		Ⓒ		Ⓐ		Ⓐ		Ⓒ		
San Diego SF ● **9366** d.	...	0401	...	...	...	...	0601	...	0701	...	...	1001	...	1201	...	1401	...	1501	...	1601	...	1901	2101
San Diego Old Town **9366** d.	...	0410	...	...	...	...	0610	...	0710	...	...	1010	...	1210	...	1410	...	1510	...	1610	...	1910	2110
Solana Beach **9366** d.	...	0440	...	...	...	...	0640	...	0740	...	...	1040	...	1240	...	1440	...	1540	...	1640	...	1940	2140
Oceanside **9366** d.	0435	0457	0516	0550	...	0634	0657	...	0757	*0739*	0830	1057	1124	1257	1328	1457	1526	1557	...	1657	1736	1957	2157
San Clemente d.	0459	|	0540	0614	...	0659	|	...	|	*0803*	0856	|	1155	|	1355	|	1550	|	...	|	1803	|	|
San Juan Capistrano d.	0508	0534	0549	0626	...	0708	0734	...	0834	*0813*	0908	1134	1205	1334	1405	1534	1600	1637	...	1737	1816	2034	2234
Irvine d.	0524	0549	0605	0642	0710	0724	0749	0814	0849	0904	0924	1149	1222	1349	1423	1549	1616	1652	1717	1752	1834	2049	2249
Santa Ana d.	0538	0601	0618	0655	0724	0737	0801	0828	0901	0916	0938	1201	1235	1401	1437	1601	1629	1704	1730	1804	1848	2101	2301
Orange d.	0543	|	0624	0700	0729	0743	|	0833	|	0921	0943	|	1241	|	1443	|	1634	|	1736	|	1854	|	|
Anaheim d.	0548	0610	0628	0705	0734	0748	0810	0838	0910	0926	0948	1210	1246	1410	1448	1610	1639	1713	1741	1813	1859	2110	2310
Fullerton d.	0556	0618	0636	0712	0742	0756	0818	0846	0918	0935	0956	1218	1253	1418	1456	1618	1646	1721	1748	1821	1907	2118	2318
Los Angeles Union a.	0636	0657	0720	0756	0822	0839	0857	0931	0957	1014	1037	1257	1334	1457	1539	1657	1727	1800	1829	1857	1951	2157	2357
Oxnard **9320** a.	...	0856	...	...	...	...	1051	...	...	...	...	...	...	1651	...	...	...	...	...	2059	...	0020*	...
Santa Barbara **9320** a.	...	0955	...	...	...	...	1150	...	...	...	...	...	...	1746	...	...	...	...	...	2159	...	0115*	...
San Luis Obispo **9320** a.	...	1239	...	...	...	...	*1410**	...	...	...	...	...	...	2046	...	...	...	...	...	*0025**	...	...	...

● – San Diego Santa Fe, also known as Downtown.

* – Connection by 🚌.

9325 SAN JOSE - SACRAMENTO

2nd class · Most trains 🍸 · Amtrak

CAPITOL CORRIDOR

km		522	720	524	724	528		728	532	534	732	536		736	538	540	542	742		546	744	746	548	748
		Ⓐ	Ⓒ	Ⓐ	Ⓒ	Ⓐ		Ⓒ	Ⓐ	Ⓐ	Ⓒ	Ⓐ		Ⓒ	Ⓐ	Ⓐ	Ⓐ	Ⓒ		Ⓐ	Ⓒ	Ⓒ	Ⓐ	Ⓒ
0	**San Jose** d.	...	...	0618	0805	0848	...	1005	1105	...	1305	...	...	1505	1505	...	1605	1705	...	1805	1805	...	...	2005
75	**Oakland** Jack London Sq. d.	0612	0712	0724	0912	0957	...	1112	1217	1412	1412	1512	...	1611	1612	1642	1712	1810	...	1912	1912	2012	2012	2112
83	Emeryville d.	0621	0721	0735	0921	1006	...	1121	1226	1421	1421	1521	...	1620	1621	1651	1721	1819	...	1921	1921	2021	2021	2121
128	Martinez d.	0658	0758	0813	0959	1045	...	1158	1304	1458	1458	1600	...	1657	1659	1728	1758	1857	...	1958	1959	2058	2059	2159
219	**Sacramento** a.	0810	0910	0922	1110	1157	...	1314	1416	1610	1615	1716	...	1802	1806	1841	1910	2009	...	2110	2115	2210	2218	2315

	521	523	723	525	527		727	729	531	737	541		741	543	743	545	745		547	549	747	551	751
	Ⓐ	Ⓐ	Ⓒ	Ⓐ	Ⓐ		Ⓒ	Ⓒ	Ⓐ	Ⓒ	Ⓐ		Ⓒ	Ⓐ	Ⓒ	Ⓐ	Ⓒ		Ⓐ	Ⓐ	Ⓒ	Ⓐ	Ⓒ
Sacramento d.	0410	0510	0555	0610	0643	...	0655	0855	0855	1055	1155	...	1255	1355	1455	1555	1655	...	1703	1755	1855	1955	2055
Martinez d.	0510	0610	0655	0710	0743	...	0755	0955	0955	1155	1255	...	1355	1455	1555	1655	1755	...	1803	1855	1955	2055	2155
Emeryville d.	0549	0649	0734	0749	0823	...	0834	1034	1034	1234	1334	...	1434	1536	1634	1736	1835	...	1842	1935	2034	2136	2134
Oakland Jack London Square a.	0600	0659	0744	0804	0838	...	0844	1044	1044	1244	1344	...	1443	1552	1644	1752	1852	...	1852	1949	2042	2152	2252
San Jose a.	0715	0814	0901	...	0953	...	1002	1203	1211	1401	1505	...	1559	...	1703	...	...	...	2016	...	2201	...	...

THRUWAY 🚌 CONNECTIONS SAN FRANCISCO - EMERYVILLE*

	Ⓐ	Ⓒ	Ⓐ		②–⑥	Ⓒ		Ⓐ	Ⓐ	Ⓒ		Ⓐ		Ⓐ	Ⓒ	Ⓐ		Ⓐ	Ⓒ	Ⓐ	Ⓐ	Ⓒ	Ⓒ
San Francisco Mission Street ⊡ d.	0540	0640	0655	0700	0800	0840	...	0900	0925	1035	1100	1145	1250	1335	1340	1435	...	1535	1540	1610	1640	1650	1730
Emeryville a.	0610	0710	0725	0730	0830	0910	...	0930	0955	1105	1130	1215	1320	1405	1410	1505	...	1605	1610	1640	1715	1730	1805

	Ⓐ	Ⓒ		Ⓐ	Ⓒ		Ⓒ	
San Francisco Mission Street ⊡ d.	1830	1840	...	1930	1940	...	2040	2050
Emeryville a.	1905	1910	...	2005	2010	...	2110	2125

	Ⓐ	Ⓐ		Ⓒ	Ⓐ		Ⓐ	Ⓒ
Emeryville d.	0550	0650	...	0735	0750	...	0825	0835
San Francisco Mission Street ⊡ a.	0620	0730	...	0805	0830	...	0900	0905

				Ⓒ	Ⓐ			Ⓒ	Ⓐ	④–①	Ⓒ	Ⓐ			Ⓒ	Ⓐ	Ⓐ			Ⓒ	Ⓐ		Ⓒ
Emeryville d.	0850	1015	1035	1235	1335	1420	...	1435	1540	1625	1635	1740	...	1825	1835	1845	1940	...	2020	2035	2140	2220	2235
San Francisco Mission Street ⊡ a.	0920	1045	1105	1305	1405	1450	...	1505	1610	1700	1705	1810	...	1855	1905	1915	2010	...	2050	2105	2205	2245	2305

⊡ – San Francisco Chase Bank, 555 Mission Street / SF Salesforce Plaza.

* – Most Thruway 🚌 services can only be booked with a train ticket.

9330 OAKLAND - BAKERSFIELD

2nd class · Most trains 🍸 · Amtrak

SAN JOAQUINS

km		702	710	712	714	716	718			
0	**Oakland** Jack London Sq. d.	...	0736	0936	1136	1336	1736	...	...	...
8	Emeryville ‡ d.	...	0746	0946	1146	1346	1746	...	...	...
53	Martinez d.	...	0825	1025	1225	1425	1825	...	...	...
90	**Sacramento** d.	0626	|	|	|	|	|	...	...	...
148	Lodi d.	0704	|	|	|	|	|	...	...	...
167	Stockton San Joaquins St. d.	0722**d**	0923	1123	1323	1523	1923	...	...	...
215	Modesto d.	0756	0956	1156	1356	1556	1956	...	...	...
271	Merced d.	0845	1045	1245	1445	1645	2045	...	...	...
329	Madera d.	0919	1119	1319	1519	1719	2119	...	...	...
364	Fresno d.	0949	1149	1349	1549	1749	2149	...	...	...
412	Hanford d.	1024	1224	1424	1624	1824	2224	...	...	...
542	**Bakersfield** a.	1157	1357	1557	1757	1957	2357	...	...	...
704	**Los Angeles** a.	*1435**	*1635**	*1835**	*2035**	*2235**	*0215**	...	...	...

	711	713	715	717	719	703			
						①–⑥			
Los Angeles d.	*0100**	*0500**	*0900**	*1050**	*1250**	*1455**	...	...	...
Bakersfield d.	0412	0812	1212	1412	1612	1812	...	...	...
Hanford d.	0534	0934	1339	1539	1739	1939	...	...	...
Fresno d.	0612	1016	1416	1616	1816	2016	...	...	...
Madera d.	0638	1042	1442	1642	1842	2042	...	...	...
Merced d.	0723	1123	1523	1723	1923	2119	...	...	...
Modesto d.	0803	1203	1603	1803	2003	2157	...	...	...
Stockton San Joaquins St. d.	0840	1240	1640	1840	2040	2229**d**	...	...	...
Lodi d.	|	|	|	|	|	2244	...	...	...
Sacramento a.	|	|	|	|	|	2335	...	...	...
Martinez d.	0931	1331	1732	1932	2131	...	...	...	...
Emeryville ‡ d.	1010	1415	1815	2016	2218	...	...	...	...
Oakland Jack London Sq. a.	1028	1428	1828	2031	2230	...	...	...	...

THRUWAY 🚌 CONNECTIONS SACRAMENTO - STOCKTON

km		🚌	🚌	🚌	🚌	🚌				
0	**Sacramento** d.	0715	0950	1205	1355	1805	...	...	...	...
	Lodi d.	|	1030	|	1435	|	...	...	...	...
	Stockton Cabral / ACE (**d**) a.	0805	1055	1300	1500	1900	...	...	...	...
	Stockton San Joaquins St. a.	0815	1105	1310	1510	1910	...	...	...	...

	🚌	🚌	🚌	🚌	🚌				
Stockton San Joaquins St. d.	0845	1245	1645	1845	2045	...	...	...	...
Stockton Cabral / ACE (**d**) d.	|	1255	1655	1955	2055	...	...	...	...
Lodi d.	0910	1320	1720	1920	|	...	...	...	...
Sacramento a.	0950	1400	1800	2005	2210	...	...	...	...

d – Stockton **Cabral**. Also known as ACE or Downtown station.

* – Connection by 🚌.

‡ – For 🚌 connections to / from San Francisco see Table **9325**.

9350 SAN FRANCISCO - SAN JOSE

Caltrain

km			Ⓐ	Ⓐ	Ⓐ	Ⓐ	Ⓐ	Ⓐ	Ⓐ	Ⓐ	Ⓐ	Ⓐ	Ⓐ	Ⓐ		Ⓐ	Ⓐ	Ⓐ	Ⓐ	Ⓐ	Ⓐ	Ⓐ	Ⓐ
0	**San Francisco** 4th / King St. d.	Ⓐ	0005	0606	0612	0639	0706	0712	0739	0806	0812	0839	0914	0938	and	1414	1438	1511	1539	1606	1612	1639	1706
22	Millbrae Transit Center ◧ d.		0030	0625	0633	0704	0725	0733	0804	0825	0833	0904	0934	1004	at the	1434	1504	1532	1604	1624	1633	1704	1724
44	Redwood City d.		0056	0641	0654	0730	0741	0754	0830	0841	0854	0932	0951	1032	same	1451	1532	1553	1630	1641	1654	1730	1741
47	Menlo Park d.		0102	|	|	0736	|	|	0836	|	|	0938	0957	1038	minutes	1457	1538	|	1636	|	|	1736	|
55	Palo Alto d.		0106	0649	0701	0740	0749	0801	0840	0849	0901	0941	1000	1041	past	1500	1541	1600	1640	1649	1701	1740	1749
58	Mountain View d.		0118	0657	0709	0752	0757	0814	0852	0857	0914	0954	1008	1054	each	1508	1554	1608	1652	1657	1709	1752	1757
71	Santa Clara d.		0133	|	0722	0811	|	0822	0911	|	0922	1010	1020	1110	hour	1520	1610	1621	1711	|	1722	1811	|
75	**San Jose** Diridon a.		0141	0712	0729	0823	0812	0829	0919	0911	0929	1018	1028	1118	until	1528	1619	1630	1718	1711	1728	1821	1811

	Ⓐ	Ⓐ	Ⓐ	Ⓐ	Ⓐ	Ⓐ	Ⓐ	Ⓐ	Ⓐ	Ⓐ	Ⓐ	Ⓐ	Ⓐ	Ⓐ			Ⓒ	Ⓒ	Ⓒ		Ⓒ	Ⓒ
San Francisco 4th / King St. d.	1712	1739	1806	1812	1843	1914	1938	2014	2032	2102	2130	2200	2230	2300	...	Ⓒ	0005	0828	0958	and	2158	2258
Millbrae Transit Center ◧ d.	1733	1804	1824	1833	1908	1934	2003	2034	2057	2128	2155	2226	2256	2326	...		0031	0853	1024	at the	2224	2324
Redwood City d.	1754	1830	1841	1854	1935	1951	2031	2051	2126	2156	2224	2254	2323	2353	...		0059	0921	1052	same	2252	2352
Menlo Park d.	|	1836	|	|	1940	1957	2038	2057	2133	2203	2231	2301	2329	2359	...		0105	0928	1058	minutes	2258	2358
Palo Alto d.	1801	1840	1849	1901	1944	2000	2042	2100	2137	2207	2235	2305	2332	0003	...		0109	0932	1102	past	2302	0002
Mountain View d.	1809	1852	1857	1909	1956	2008	2055	2108	2150	2221	2248	2319	2345	0017	...		0121	0945	1116	each	2316	0015
Santa Clara d.	1822	1911	|	1922	2012	2020	2110	2120	2205	2236	2303	2334	0001	0032	...		0137	1001	1132	hour	2332	0031
San Jose Diridon a.	1829	1919	1911	1928	2019	2028	2119	2128	2214	2244	2313	2342	0011	0040	...		0144	1010	1140	until	2338	0039

		Ⓐ	Ⓐ	Ⓐ	Ⓐ	Ⓐ	Ⓐ	Ⓐ	Ⓐ	Ⓐ	Ⓐ	Ⓐ	Ⓐ		Ⓐ	Ⓐ	Ⓐ	Ⓐ	Ⓐ	Ⓐ	Ⓐ	Ⓐ
San Jose Diridon d.	Ⓐ	0559	0623	0644	0659	0723	0742	0759	0823	0844	0856	0943	0954	and	1443	1454	1522	1544	1559	1624	1644	1659
Santa Clara d.		|	|	0650	|	|	0750	|	|	0850	0902	0949	1000	at the	1449	1500	|	1550	|	|	1650	|
Mountain View d.		0613	0642	0703	0713	0742	0803	0813	0842	0903	0917	1001	1015	same	1501	1515	1543	1603	1613	1643	1703	1713
Palo Alto d.		0621	0654	0711	0721	0754	0811	0821	0854	0911	0929	1009	1028	minutes	1509	1628	1555	1611	1621	1655	1711	1721
Menlo Park d.		|	0658	|	|	0758	|	|	0858	|	0933	1012	1032	past	1512	1632	1558	|	|	1658	|	|
Redwood City d.		0628	0703	0717	0728	0803	0817	0828	0903	0917	0938	1018	1037	each	1518	1637	1604	1617	1628	1704	1717	1728
Millbrae Transit Center ◧ d.		0646	0721	0738	0746	0821	0838	0846	0921	0939	1006	1038	1105	hour	1538	1605	1622	1638	1646	1721	1738	1746
San Francisco 4th / King St. a.		0705	0738	0800	0805	0838	0900	0905	0938	1001	1032	1057	1133	until	1557	1633	1639	1700	1705	1738	1800	1805

	Ⓐ	Ⓐ	Ⓐ	Ⓐ	Ⓐ	Ⓐ	Ⓐ	Ⓐ	Ⓐ	Ⓐ	Ⓐ	Ⓐ	Ⓐ	Ⓐ			Ⓒ	Ⓒ		Ⓒ	Ⓒ	Ⓒ
San Jose Diridon d.	1723	1744	1759	1823	1844	1856	1943	1954	2024	2049	2119	2149	2219	2312	...	Ⓒ	0719	0912	and	2112	2219	2312
Santa Clara d.	|	1750	|	|	1850	1902	1949	2000	2030	2055	2125	2155	2225	2318	...		0725	0918	at the	2118	2225	2318
Mountain View d.	1742	1803	1813	1842	1903	1917	2002	2015	2045	2110	2140	2210	2240	2333	...		0740	0934	same	2134	2235	2334
Palo Alto d.	1754	1811	1821	1858	1911	1929	2009	2027	2057	2123	2152	2223	2252	2346	...		0752	0946	minutes	2146	2353	2346
Menlo Park d.	1758	|	|	1858	|	1932	2012	2030	2100	2126	2156	2226	2256	2350	...		0755	0950	past	2150	2356	2350
Redwood City d.	1803	1817	1828	1903	1917	1938	2018	2036	2106	2133	2202	2233	2302	2356	...		0801	0956	each	2156	2302	2356
Millbrae Transit Center ◧ d.	1821	1838	1846	1922	1938	2008	2037	2106	2136	2201	2231	2301	2331	0025	...		0829	1026	hour	2226	2332	0026
San Francisco 4th / King St. a.	1838	1900	1906	1939	2000	2035	2057	2133	2203	2230	2300	2329	0000	0053	...		0856	1052	until	2252	2359	0052

◧ – SamTrans 🚌 route **SFO** connects Millbrae Transit Center with San Francisco International Airport.

SAN JOSE - STOCKTON — 9352

Altamont Corridor Express

km		Ⓐ	Ⓐ	Ⓐ	Ⓐ				
0	**San Jose** Diridon d.	1535	1635	1735	1838	...	...	...	...
	Santa Clara d.	1540	1640	1740	1843	...	...	...	...
	Great America d.	1549	1649	1749	1852	...	...	...	...
	Fremont d.	1605	1705	1805	1908	...	...	...	...
	Pleasanton d.	1628	1728	1828	1931	...	...	...	...
	Livermore d.	1637	1737	1837	1940	...	...	...	...
	Tracy ⊕ d.	1711	1811	1911	2014	...	...	...	...
125	**Stockton** Cabral ◧ a.	1747	1847	1947	2050	...	...	...	...

	Ⓐ	Ⓐ	Ⓐ	Ⓐ					
Stockton Cabral ◧ d.	0410	0535	0640	0732	...	...	...	...	...
Tracy d.	0441	0606	0711	0803	...	...	...	...	...
Livermore d.	0515	0640	0745	0837	...	...	...	...	...
Pleasanton d.	0523	0648	0753	0845	...	...	...	...	...
Fremont d.	0545	0710	0815	0907	...	...	...	...	...
Great America ⊕ d.	0603	0728	0833	0925	...	...	...	...	...
Santa Clara ⊕ d.	0610	0735	0840	0932	...	...	...	...	...
San Jose Diridon a.	0622	0747	0852	0944	...	...	...	...	...

⊕ – Trains may leave early if all passengers have exited.

◧ – Also known as ACE or Downtown station.

LANCASTER - LOS ANGELES — 9356

Metrolink Antelope Valley Line

km		Ⓐ	Ⓐ	Ⓐ		Ⓐ	Ⓒ	Ⓐ		Ⓐ	Ⓒ	Ⓐ		Ⓒ	Ⓐ		Ⓒ	Ⓐ	Ⓒ		Ⓐ	Ⓐ	Ⓒ	
0	**Lancaster** d.	0341	0441	0511	...	0611	0622	0711	...	...	0904	0911	...	1115	1205	...	1240	1411	1423	...	...	1811	1823	...
	Via Princessa d.	0440	0540	0615	...	0715	0722	0815	...	0915	1003	1015	...	1214	1309	...	1339	1515	1523	...	1615	1915	1924	...
82	Santa Clarita d.	0447	0547	0621	...	0721	0728	0821	...	0921	1009	1021	...	1220	1315	...	1345	1521	1529	...	1621	1921	1930	...
	Burbank Airport North ✈ d.	0521	0621	0655	...	0755	0800	0855	...	0955	1042	1055	...	1253	1349	...	1417	1555	1602	...	1655	1955	2003	...
106	Downtown Burbank d.	0527	0627	0701	...	0801	0805	0901	...	1001	1046	1101	...	1258	1355	...	1422	1601	1607	...	1701	2001	2007	...
121	**Los Angeles** Union a.	0546	0646	0720	...	0820	0825	0920	...	1020	1110	1120	...	1320	1414	...	1443	1620	1628	...	1720	2020	2029	...

	Ⓐ	Ⓐ	Ⓒ		Ⓐ	Ⓒ	Ⓐ		Ⓒ	Ⓐ	Ⓐ		Ⓒ	Ⓐ		Ⓒ	Ⓐ	Ⓐ		Ⓐ	Ⓒ	Ⓐ	
Los Angeles Union d.	0639	0739	0840	...	0939	1137	1139	...	1358	1439	1539	...	1551	1639	...	1725	1739	1839	...	1939	2053	2139	...
Downtown Burbank d.	0658	0758	0858	...	0958	1155	1158	...	1416	1458	1558	...	1609	1658	...	1743	1758	1858	...	1958	2111	2158	...
Burbank Airport North ✈ d.	0703	0803	0904	...	1003	1201	1203	...	1422	1503	1603	...	1615	1703	...	1748	1803	1903	...	2003	2116	2203	...
Santa Clarita d.	0740	0840	0938	...	1040	1235	1240	...	1458	1540	1640	...	1649	1740	...	1822	1840	1940	...	2040	2150	2240	...
Via Princessa d.	0747	0847	0944	...	1047	1241	1247	...	1505	1547	1647	...	1655	1747	...	1828	1847	1947	...	2047	2156	2247	...
Lancaster a.	0852	...	1052	...	1152	1348	1352	...	1612	...	1752	...	1759	1852	...	1930	1952	2052	...	2152	2300	2352	...

LOS ANGELES - SAN BERNARDINO — 9358

Metrolink San Bernardino Line

km		Ⓐ	Ⓐ		Ⓐ	Ⓒ	Ⓐ	Ⓐ	Ⓒ			Ⓐ	Ⓒ	Ⓐ	Ⓐ	Ⓐ	Ⓐ	Ⓐ	Ⓐ	Ⓒ	Ⓐ	Ⓐ	Ⓒ	Ⓐ
0	**Los Angeles** Union d.	0537	0734	0838	0938	1038	1138	1238	1338	1438	1538	1557	1638	1638	1655	1726	1737	1757	1838	1938	1938	2038	2138	2138
25	El Monte d.	0609	0802	0859	1010	1059	1200	1300	1359	1459	1559	1618	1659	1700	1719	|	1759	1821	1900	1959	2000	2100	2159	2200
30	Covina d.	0616	0820	0917	1017	1117	1217	1317	1417	1517	1617	1635	1717	1718	1736	1803	1817	1838	1917	2017	2017	2117	2217	2217
70	Pomona North d.	0630	0833	0930	1030	1130	1230	1330	1430	1530	1630	1652	1730	1731	1751	|	1830	1852	1930	2030	2030	2130	2230	2230
95	**San Bernardino** Depot a.	0721	0921	1016	1116	1216	1316	1416	1516	1616	1716	1735	1816	1820	1836	1846	1921	1935	2016	2116	2116	2216	2316	2316

	Ⓐ	Ⓐ	Ⓐ	Ⓐ	Ⓒ	Ⓐ	Ⓐ	Ⓒ	Ⓐ	Ⓐ	Ⓒ	Ⓐ	Ⓒ	Ⓒ	Ⓐ	Ⓒ	Ⓐ	Ⓐ	Ⓐ	Ⓒ	Ⓐ	Ⓐ	Ⓒ
San Bernardino Depot d.	0516	0546	0615	0626	0641	0646	0746	0841	0843	0943	1141	1143	1241	1341	1343	1441	1443	1543	1643	1741	1744	1848	1941
Pomona North d.	0558	0629	|	0710	0726	0730	0828	0926	0925	1025	1226	1225	1326	1426	1425	1526	1525	1625	1730	1826	1829	1931	2026
Covina d.	0609	0640	0654	0721	0737	0742	0842	0937	0940	1040	1237	1240	1337	1437	1440	1537	1540	1640	1741	1837	1840	1942	2037
El Monte d.	0627	0655	|	0738	0755	0759	0859	0955	0956	1056	1255	1256	1355	1455	1456	1555	1600	1658	1759	1855	1858	2000	2055
Los Angeles Union a.	0649	0717	0729	0802	0822	0821	0922	1022	1021	1121	1322	1321	1422	1522	1521	1622	1626	1728	1827	1922	1921	2020	2122

LOS ANGELES - RIVERSIDE - PERRIS — 9360

Metrolink Riverside / Perris Valley Lines

km		Ⓐ	Ⓐ	Ⓐ	Ⓐ	Ⓐ				
0	**Los Angeles** Union d.	1320	1610	1650	1720	1800	...	...	...	...
	Industry d.	1355	1645	1725	1755	1835	...	...	...	...
70	Pomona Downtown d.	1404	1654	1734	1804	1844	...	...	...	...
101	**Riverside** Downtown a.	1448	1737	1817	1848	1928	...	...	...	...

	Ⓐ	Ⓐ	Ⓐ	Ⓐ	Ⓐ	Ⓐ			
Riverside Downtown d.	0435	0526	0606	0650	0810	1510	...	...	...
Pomona Downtown d.	0511	0602	0642	0726	0846	1546	...	...	...
Industry d.	0520	0611	0651	0735	0855	1555	...	...	...
Los Angeles Union a.	0603	0654	0734	0818	0938	1638	...	...	...

km		Ⓐ	Ⓐ	Ⓒ	Ⓐ	Ⓐ	Ⓐ	Ⓐ	Ⓐ	Ⓒ
0	**Los Angeles** Union d.	0545	0730	1525	1539	1621	1657	1731	1852	1920
	Fullerton d.	0620	0807	1602	1614	1656	1733	1807	1928	1957
	Corona West d.	0644	0830	1626	1638	1720	1757	1831	1952	2021
99	**Riverside** Downtown a.	0714	0857	1652	1706	1747	1827	1858	2022	2047
	Perris Downtown a.	...	0940	1737	1750	1831	1911	1941	...	2139

	Ⓐ	Ⓐ		Ⓐ	Ⓐ	Ⓒ		Ⓒ	Ⓐ
Perris Downtown d.	0442	0521	...	0606	0642	0711	...	0814	1501
Riverside Downtown d.	0516	0556	...	0640	0716	0748	...	0851	1536
Corona West d.	0542	0622	...	0706	0742	0814	...	0916	1608
Fullerton d.	0606	0646	...	0730	0806	0838	...	0940	1631
Los Angeles Union a.	0647	0728	...	0811	0847	0919	...	1021	1714

SAN BERNARDINO - RIVERSIDE - OCEANSIDE — 9362

Metrolink Inland Empire Line

km		Ⓐ	Ⓐ	Ⓐ	Ⓐ	Ⓒ	Ⓐ	Ⓒ	Ⓐ	Ⓐ
0	**San Bernardino** Downtown d.	0429	0518	0554	...	0700	...	0856	1259	...
	Riverside Downtown d.	0450	0539	0615	0650	0722	0728	0917	1319	1448
25	Corona West d.	0515	0604	0640	0716	0756	0753	0951	1344	1513
	Anaheim Canyon d.	0535	0623	0700	0736	0816	0812	1011	1404	1532
	Orange 9320 d.	0541	0630	0706	0734	0823	0819	1018	1410	1541
78	Santa Ana 9320 d.	0547	0636	0712	0748	0828	0824	1023	1416	1547
94	Irvine 9320 d.	0601	0653	0726	0802	0843	0838	1037	1429	1602
113	San Juan Capistrano 9320 d.	0617	...	...	...	0859	...	1054	1445	...
126	San Clemente 9320 d.	0626	...	...	...	0909	...	1104	1455	...
160	**Oceanside** 9320 a.	0656	...	...	...	0941	...	1136	1523	...

	Ⓐ	Ⓐ	Ⓒ	Ⓐ	Ⓐ	Ⓐ	Ⓐ	Ⓒ	Ⓐ
Oceanside 9320 d.	0739	...	1435	...	...	...	1625	1628	...
San Clemente 9320 d.	0803	...	1502	...	...	...	1652	1655	...
San Juan Capistrano 9320 d.	0813	...	1512	...	...	...	1701	1705	...
Irvine 9320 d.	0829	0922	1528	1538	1606	1702	1727	1726	1845
Santa Ana 9320 d.	0842	0936	1541	1551	1619	1715	1741	1739	1858
Orange 9320 d.	0847	0941	1547	1556	1624	1720	1746	1744	1904
Anaheim Canyon d.	0954	0948	1554	1603	1631	1727	1753	1752	1911
Corona West d.	0914	1008	1614	1623	1651	1747	1813	1812	1930
Riverside Downtown a.	0943	1033	1639	1652	1716	1812	1838	1837	2000
San Bernardino Downtown a.	...	1058	1705	...	1741	1837	1903	1903	...

OCEANSIDE - SAN DIEGO — 9366

Coaster

Coaster Day Pass and Monthly Pass holders may use Amtrak services south of Oceanside. See Table **9320** for schedules.

km		Ⓐ	Ⓐ	Ⓐ	Ⓐ			Ⓒ	Ⓐ	Ⓒ	Ⓐ	Ⓒ			Ⓐ	Ⓒ	Ⓐ	Ⓐ			Ⓐ			⑤Ⓒ
0	**Oceanside** 9320 d.	0516	0556	0636	0716	0736	...	0916	0936	1036	1136	1216	...	1336	1436	1516	1536	1616	...	1636	1716	1816	1936	2116
	Carlsbad Village d.	0523	0603	0643	0723	0743	...	0923	0943	1043	1143	1223	...	1343	1443	1523	1543	1623	...	1643	1723	1823	1943	2123
	Encinitas d.	0535	0615	0655	0735	0755	...	0935	0955	1055	1155	1235	...	1355	1455	1535	1555	1635	...	1655	1735	1835	1955	2135
27	Solana Beach 9320 d.	0541	0621	0701	0741	0801	...	0941	1001	1101	1201	1241	...	1401	1501	1541	1601	1641	...	1701	1741	1841	2001	2141
	Sorrento Valley d.	0550	0630	0710	0750	0810	...	0950	1010	1110	1210	1250	...	1410	1510	1550	1610	1650	...	1710	1750	1850	2010	2150
	San Diego Old Town 9320 a.	0611	0651	0731	0811	0831	...	1011	1031	1131	1231	1311	...	1431	1531	1611	1631	1711	...	1731	1811	1911	2031	2211
68	**San Diego** Santa Fe ● 9320 a.	0617	0657	0737	0817	0837	...	1017	1037	1137	1237	1317	...	1437	1537	1617	1637	1717	...	1737	1817	1917	2037	2217

	Ⓐ	Ⓐ	Ⓐ	Ⓐ		Ⓒ	Ⓐ		Ⓒ	Ⓐ	Ⓒ	Ⓒ	Ⓐ	Ⓐ	Ⓒ		Ⓐ	Ⓐ		Ⓐ			⑤Ⓒ
San Diego Santa Fe ● 9320 d.	0640	0740	0820	0840	0920	1040	1120	...	1220	1320	1340	1520	1540	1620	1640	...	1720	1740	1820	1840	1940	2120	2340
San Diego Old Town 9320 d.	0647	0747	0827	0847	0927	1047	1127	...	1227	1327	1347	1527	1547	1627	1647	...	1727	1747	1827	1847	1947	2127	2347
Sorrento Valley d.	0709	0809	0849	0909	0949	1109	1149	...	1249	1349	1409	1549	1609	1649	1709	...	1749	1809	1849	1909	2009	2149	0009
Solana Beach 9320 d.	0719	0819	0859	0919	0959	1119	1159	...	1259	1359	1419	1559	1619	1659	1719	...	1759	1819	1859	1919	2019	2159	0019
Encinitas d.	0725	0825	0905	0925	1005	1125	1205	...	1305	1405	1425	1605	1625	1705	1725	...	1805	1825	1905	1925	2025	2205	0025
Carlsbad Village d.	0737	0837	0917	0937	1017	1137	1217	...	1317	1417	1437	1617	1637	1717	1737	...	1817	1837	1917	1937	2037	2217	0037
Oceanside 9320 a.	0742	0842	0922	0942	1022	1142	1222	...	1322	1422	1442	1622	1642	1722	1742	...	1822	1842	1922	1942	2042	2222	0042

● – Also known as San Diego Downtown.

OCEANSIDE - ESCONDIDO — 9368

Sprinter

km									
0	**Oceanside** d.	0533	0633	0733	0833	and	1833	1933	2033
	Vista Transit Center d.	0556	0656	0756	0856	hourly	1856	1956	2056
	San Marcos Civic Ctr d.	0613	0713	0813	0913	until	1913	2013	2113
34	**Escondido** a.	0626	0726	0826	0926	⊙	1926	2026	2126

Escondido d.	0533	0633	0733	0833	and	1833	1933	2033
S. Marcos Civic Ctr d.	0544	0644	0744	0844	hourly	1844	1944	2044
Vista Transit Center d.	0557	0657	0757	0857	until	1857	1957	2057
Oceanside a.	0626	0726	0826	0926	⊙	1926	2026	2126

⊙ – Additional services: from **Oceanside** at 0403 Ⓐ and hourly until 1003 Ⓐ, 1103 and hourly until 1803, 1903 Ⓐ, 2003 Ⓐ; from **Escondido** at 0403 Ⓐ and hourly until 0903 Ⓐ, 1003 and hourly until 1703, 1803 Ⓐ, 1903 Ⓐ, 2003 Ⓐ. Additional later evening services are available on ⑤⑥.

9900 MEXICO — Ferromex

km		⑥	②⑦ Aa	③⑥ B		⑥	①⑤ Ab	④⑦ B
0	**Chihuahua** d.	...	...	0600	**Los Mochis** d.	...	0800	0600
132	Cuauhtémoc d.	...	...	0825	El Fuerte d.	...	1020	0819
295	Creel d.	0800	0800	1147	Témoris d.	...	|	1124
355	Divisadero d.	0955	0955	1342	Bahuichivo d.	...	1425	1224
358	Posada Barrancas d.	...	|	1352	San Rafael d.	...	|	1315
370	San Rafael d.	...	|	1416	Posada Barrancas d.	...	|	1346
400	Bahuichivo d.	...	1115	1512	Divisadero d.	1600	1615	1425
440	Témoris d.	...	|	1612	Creel d.	1740	1740	1539
570	El Fuerte d.	...	1535	1919	Cuauhtémoc d.	...	...	1907
655	**Los Mochis** a.	...	1740	2130	**Chihuahua** a.	...	...	2134

km		⑥ D	⑥ 🚌		⑥ D	⑥ 🚌
0	**Guadalajara** d.	0900	0930	**Tequila** d.	1800	1830
72	**Tequila** a.	1100	1030	**Guadalajara** a.	2000	2000

A – EL CHEPE EXPRESS – [12] and Tourist Class ✕.
B – EL CHEPE REGIONAL – [2] and ✕. **Note: Currently available for locals only.**
D – JOSÉ CUERYO EXPRESS – [12]. Outward by train, return by 🚌 or v.v.
a – Also runs on ④ Dec. 16 - Jan. 6, Apr.14, 21 and ④ July 7 - Aug. 11.
b – Also runs on ③ Dec. 15 - Jan. 5, Apr.13, 20 and ③ July 6 - Aug. 10.

9905 HONDURAS — FC de Honduras

km		①-⑤	①-⑤		①-⑤	①-⑤		①-⑤	①-⑤	
0	**S Pedro Sula** Est d.	1240	1335	...	1430	1530	...	1630	1730	
3	**S Pedro Sula** Central a.	1300	1355	...	1450	1550	...	1650	1750	
		①-⑤	①-⑤		①-⑤	①-⑤		①-⑤	①-⑤	
	S Pedro Sula Central d.	1305	1400	...	1500	1600	...	1700	1755	...
	S Pedro Sula Est a.	1325	1420	...	1520	1620	...	1720	1815	...

All services subject to confirmation.

9910 PANAMA — Panama Canal Rly

km		①-⑤			①-⑤	
0	**Ciudad Panama** d.	0715	...	**Colon** d.	1715	...
77	**Colon** a.	0815	...	**Ciudad Panama** a.	1815	...

9915 COSTA RICA — INCOFER

km		①-⑤	①-⑤	①-⑤		①-⑤	①-⑤	①-⑤	①-⑤	①-⑤		①-⑤	①-⑤	①-⑤
0	**San José** Pacifico d.	0515	0632	0705	...	0716	1500	1510	1520	1620	...	1643	1703	1832
3	Pavas Metropolis III d.	0545	0702	0735	...	0746	1530	1540	1550	1650	...	1713	1733	1902
10	**S Antonio de Belén** a.	0555	0712	...	...	0756	1540	...	1600	...	...	1723	1743	1912
		①-⑤	①-⑤	①-⑤		①-⑤	①-⑤	①-⑤	①-⑤	①-⑤		①-⑤	①-⑤	①-⑤
	S Antonio de Belén d.	0610	0720	...	...	0804	1548	...	1608	...	...	1723	1751	1920
	Pavas Metropolis III d.	0620	0730	0739	...	0814	1558	1544	1618	1654	...	1733	1801	1930
	San José Pacifico a.	0655	0805	0814	...	0849	1633	1619	1653	1729	...	1808	1836	2005

km		①-⑤				
0	**Freses de Curidabat** d.	0605	...	...	...	...
4	Universidad Costa Rica d.	0613	...	...	...	...
15	**San José** Pacifico a.	0632	...	...	...	...
		①-⑤	①-⑤			
	San José Pacifico d.	1619	1729	...	...	...
	Universidad Costa Rica d.	1644	1754	...	...	...
	Freses de Curidabat a.	1652	1802	...	...	...

km		①-⑤	①-⑤	⑥	①-⑤	⑥a	⑥	⑥	⑥	①-⑤	①-⑤
0	**San José** Atlantico ▲d.	0445	0645	0630	0800	0730	0830	0930	1030	1530	1730
10	**Heredia** ▲a.	0512	0712	0657	0827	0757	0857	0957	1057	1557	1757
22	Alajuela a.	0535	0735	0720	0850	0820	0920	1020	1120	1620	1820

	①-⑤	⑥⑤	⑥	①-⑤	⑥	⑥c	⑥	⑥	①-⑤	①-⑤
Alajuela d.	0545	0630	0730	0745	0830	0930	1030	1130	1630	1830
Heredia ▲d.	0609	0654	0754	0809	0854	0954	1054	1154	1654	1854
San José Atlantico ▲a.	0635	0720	0820	0835	0920	1020	1120	1220	1720	1920

a – Also at: ⑥ 1130, 1230.   c – Also at: ⑥ 1230, 1330.   ▲ – Additional services operate **San José** Atlantico - **Heredia** and v.v.

9920 CUBA — Unión de los Ferrocarriles Cubanos

km			101 2	1 12🍷	7 12🍷	50 12🍷	5 12🍷	3 12🍷	103 2		73
0	**Habana** La Coubre d.	...	...	1530	1720	...	1835	2050	2220	...	0715a
90	Matanzas d.	...	...	1729	2009	...	2039	2249	0045	...	|
	Varadero d.	...	...	|	|	...	|	|	|	0815	|
286	Santa Clara d.	...	1226	2022	2309	...	2239	0142	0625	|	|
	Cienfuegos d.	...	|	|	|	...	|	|	|	1325	1745
	Trinidad d.	...	|	|	|	...	|	|	|	1500	▬
382	Sancti Spiritus d.	...	|	|	|	...	|	|	0945	...	...
436	Ciego de Avila d.	...	1835	2303	0211	...	0248	0426	...	...	...
538	Camagüey d.	...	2128	0125	0440	...	0517	0651	...	...	...
714	Bayamo d.	...	|	|	0945	1000	|	|	...	...	...
770	**Manzanillo** a.	...	|	|	...	1200	|	|	...	...	...
652	Las Tunas d.	...	|	0337	...	...	0729	0903	...	...	...
729	Cacocúm d.	...	0255	|	...	...	0900	1032	...	...	
747	Holguim d.	...	|	|	...	...	0945	|	...	...	
	Baracoa d.	...	|	|	...	...	...	|	...	...	1330
884	**Guantanamo** a.	...	|	|	...	...	...	1434	...	...	1640
854	**Santiago de Cuba** a.	...	0600	0720	...	...	...	...	...	...	1820

	⊡ 2 ◧	104 1 ⊠		2 12🍷 ⊖	51 12 ⊠	8 2 ⊠	6 🍷12 ⊠	4 12 ◧	102 2 ⊠	⊡ ◧
Santiago de Cuba d.	0735	...	...	1640	...	...	...	...	0715	...
Guantanamo d.	0930	...	...	|	...	...	...	1150	|	...
Baracoa a.	1235	...	...	|	...	...	...	|	|	...
Holguim d.	▬	...	...	|	...	...	2135	|	|	...
Cacocúm d.	...	...	...	|	...	...	2220	1603	|	...
Las Tunas d.	...	...	...	2040	...	...	2356	1732	1035	...
Manzanillo d.	...	...	...	|	1755	...	|	|	|	...
Bayamo d.	...	...	...	|	1940	2030	|	|	|	...
Camagüey d.	...	...	...	2305	...	0028	0233	1957	1602	...
Ciego de Avila d.	⊡ **74**	...	...	0117	...	0238	0513	2209	1819	...
Sancti Spiritus d.	⊠	1505	...	|	...	|	|	|	|	...
Trinidad a.		|	...	|	...	|	|	|	|	1500
Cienfuegos d.	0700	|	...	|	...	|	|	|	|	1640
Santa Clara d.	|	1825	...	0349	...	0516	0745	0053	2325	|
Valadero a.	|	|	...	|	...	|	|	|	...	2145
Matanzas d.	|	0046	...	0641	...	0803	1042	343	...	...
Habana La Coubre a.	1730a	0315	...	0905	...	1150	1235	0535	...	...

a – Havana Tulipan.   Note: trains are believed to run once every 4 days - all services are subject to confirmation, please check locally.

9925 VENEZUELA — IFE

km		①-⑤	①-⑤	①-⑤		①-⑤		⑥⑦		⑥⑦		
0	**Caracas** d.	0514	0534	0554		2224		0456		2222	...	...
24	Charallave Norte d.	0531	0551	0611	and every	2241	...	0513	and every	2239	...	...
32	Charallave Sur d.	0536	0556	0616	20 minutes	2246	...	0518	30 minutes	2244	...	...
41	**Cúa** a.	0545	0605	0625	until	2255	...	0527	until	2353	...	...
		①-⑤	①-⑤	①-⑤		①-⑥		⑥⑦		⑥⑦		
	Cúa d.	0430	0450	0510	and every	2144	...	0500		2141	...	...
	Charallave Sur d.	0439	0459	0519	20 minutes	2153	..	0509	and every	2149	...	...
	Charallave Norte d.	0444	0504	0524	until	2158	...	0514	30 minutes	2154	...	...
	Caracas a.	0501	0521	0541		2215	....	1051	until	2211	...	...

km		Ⓐ	Ⓒ	Ⓐ	Ⓐ	Ⓐ	Ⓒ	Ⓐ
0	**Puerto Cabello** d.	...	...	...	...	...	...	...
140	Yaritagua d.	0610	0755	0900	0948	1500	1605	1700
168	San Jacinto d.	0652	0835	0930	1030	1530	1635	1730
174	**Barquisimeto** a.	0705	0845	0940	1045	1540	1645	1740
		Ⓐ	Ⓐ	Ⓒ	Ⓐ	Ⓐ	Ⓒ	Ⓐ
	Barquisimeto d.	0640	0710	0850	1250	1540	1650	1800
	San Jacinto d.	0652	0732	0900	1300	1550	1700	1820
	Yaritagua d.	0722	0812	0938	1330	1620	1738	1858
	Puerto Cabello a.	...	...	...	...	...	...	...

9930 COLOMBIA

BARRANCABERMEJA — Coopsercol Ltda

km										
0	**Puerto Parra** d.	...	...	0510	...	...	...	...	...	1655
65	Barrancabermeja d.	0600	...	0725	...	1130	...	1430	1700	1910
95	**García Cardena** a.	0700	...	...	...	1230	...	1530	1800	...

García Cardena d.	...	0700	...	...	...	1230	...	1530	...	1800
Barrancabermeja d.	0515	0800	...	1300	...	1330	...	1630	...	1900
Puerto Parra a.	0730	...	...	1515	...	...	...	...	...	...

All services subject to confirmation, please check locally.

BOGOTÁ - ZAPAQUIRÁ — Turistren

km		Ⓐ	Ⓒ	Ⓐ			Ⓐ	Ⓒ	Ⓒ	Ⓐ
0	**Bogotá Sabana** d.	0525	0815	1715	...	**Zapaquirá** d.	...	1235	...	...
15	Usaquen d.	0547	0915	1743	...	Cajicá d.	0700	1305	1515	1850
34	La Caro d.	0632	1015	1822	...	La Caro d.	0719	...	1540	1908
40	Cajicá d.	0648	|	1838	...	Usaquen d.	0803	...	1640	1953
53	**Zapaquirá** a.	...	1105	...	...	**Bogotá** Sabana a.	0824	...	1730	2014

9935 ECUADOR — FC del Ecuador

km	All trains Ⓡ		②		All trains Ⓡ			③
0	**Quito** d.	...	0800	...	**Latacunga** d.	...	...	...
45	Machachi d.	...	1010	...	Lasso d.	...	...	...
62	Cotopaxi d.	...	1100	...	Cotopaxi d.	...	...	1500
80	Lasso d.	...	...	...	Machachi d.	...	...	1550
110	**Latacunga** a.	...	...	...	**Quito** a.	...	...	1756

km	All trains Ⓡ	40 ④-⑦	31 ⑤-⑦		All trains Ⓡ	32 ⑤-⑦	🚌 ⑤-⑦	43 ④-⑦
0	**Otavalo** a.	...	0800	...	**Salinas** d.	1510	...	1445
30	**Ibarra** d.	1030	1122	...	**Ibarra** a.	1705	1705	1615
61	**Salinas** a.	1200	1315	...	**Otavalo** d.	...	1755	...

km	All trains Ⓡ	A ②-⑦	★ ②-⑤	②-⑦
0	**Riobamba** d.	...	0630	...
41	Colta d.	...	0730	...
98	Alausi d.	0800	1040	1100
111	Sibambe d.	0900	...	1200
154	**Bucay** a.	...	...	...
		④-⑦		
87	**Bucay** d.	1440	...	...
21	Yaguachi d.	1645	...	...
0	**Duran** a.	1800	...	...

All trains Ⓡ	④-⑦		★
Duran d.	0800	...	...
Yaguachi d.	0910	...	...
Bucay a.	1135	...	...
	②-⑦	B ②-⑦	②-⑤
Bucay d.	...	...	...
Sibambe d.	1000	1300	...
Alausi d.	1030	1330	1245
Colta d.	...	...	1645
Riobamba a.	...	...	1745

A – Additional trip 1400.   B – Additional trip 1600.   ★ – Suspended.

PERU 9940

POROY - MACHU PICCHU — Inca Rail / Perurail

km		71	41	301	61	83	601	33	33	501	31	31	203	203	11	11	43	43	91		73	303	603	45	75		51
		B	G	A	F	AB	A	AB⊗	AB⊕	A	AB⊗	AB⊕	A⊗	AB⊕	C⊗	C⊕	EG	F	B	F	AB	A	A	G	AB	G	B
13	**Cusco** San Pedro .... d.	...	0410f	...	0500g	...	...	...	0550j	...	0640	0630j	0730	0750j	...	0720j	0828g	0850f	...	0955f	...	...	...	...	...	1615f	...
0	**Poroy** .... d.	...	|	...	0555g	...	U	0640	|	...	0735	|	0825	|	0905	0940e	0928g	|	...	|	...	...	...	...	...	|	...
48	Ollantaytambo .... d.	0505	0640	0705	0722	0745	0800	0829	0829	0853	0915	0915	1032	1032	|	|	1115	1130	1152	1236	1255	1327	1537	1636	1904	1927	2100
86	**Machu Picchu** .... a.	0635	0801	0827	0848	0915	0924	0954	0954	1029	1052	1052	1211	1211	1224	1224	1241	1306	1334	1400	1425	1450	1702	1809	2045	2109	2245

	50	72	42		302	204	44	74	34	34	304	64	504	32	32	604	604	12	12	606	84	46	92		86		76
	B	B	G	F	A	A	G	AB	AB⊗	AB⊕	A	G	AB	AB⊗	A⊕	AB⊗	A⊕	C⊗	C⊕	A	AB	EG	S	G	B	G	AB
Machu Picchu .... d.	0535	0853	0830	1032	1055	1337	1430	1455	1520	1520	1548	1612	1622	1643	1643	1723	1723	1750	1750	1810	1820	1900	1930	2020	2050	2130	2150
Ollantaytambo............. a.	0744	1052	1010	1212	1232	1504	1556	1631	1708	1708	1729	1750	1810	1831	1831	1902	1902	|	|	1951	2005	2041	|	2159	2220	2254	2335
Poroy .... a.	...	...	...	|	...	...	|	...	1905	|	U	1939g	...	2023	|	2052	|	2116	2050e	...	...	2235g	Ua	...	...	|	...
Cusco San Pedro......... a.	...	...	...	1432f	...	...	1830f	...	...	1930j	...	2035g	...	2123	2055j	2152	2130	...	2210j	...	...	2335g	...	...	...	0115f	...

PERURAIL www.perurail.com

A – VISTADOME – [1] and 🍸. B – EXPEDITION – [2] and 🍸.
C – HIRAM BINGHAM – [1] and ✕. Does not operate on the last ⑦ each month.
S – SACRED VALLEY – [1] and ✕. Does not operate on the first ⑦ each month.
U – To/from Urubamba dep. 0650, arr. 1843.
Ua – To/from Urubamba dep. 1030, arr. 2237.
⊗ – Not Jan. to April. ⊕ – Jan. to April only.
j – Connection by 🚌 from Cusco Wanchaq.
e – Belmond Hotel Rio Sagrado.

INCA RAIL www.incarail.com

E – [1] and ✕. F – THE 360 [1] and 🍸. G – VOYAGER [2] and 🍸.

f – Connection by 🚌 from Av. El Sol 843.
g – Not Jan. to April.

CUSCO - PUNO

TITICACA TRAIN. *385 km. Journey 10½ hours.*
From Cusco (Wanchaq) at 0710③, 0750 ⑤⑦.
From Puno at 0730. ①④⑥
Trains convey [1] and ✕. Operator: Perurail.
The BELMOND ANDEAN EXPLORER operates between CUSCO and PUNO/AREQUIPA. Perurail

LIMA - HUANCAYO

TREN DE LA SIERRA. *332 km. Journey 12 hours.*
From Lima at 0700 on dates in note **E** but may vary.
From Huancayo at 0700 on dates in note **F** but may vary.
Trains convey [12] and ✕. Operator: FC Central Andino.
E – Currently Suspended.
F – Currently Suspended.

TACNA - ARICA

62 km. Journey 1¼ hours. 2nd class.
From Tacna. 0600, 1630
From Arica. 0800, 1815
Operator: FC Tacna Arica.

HUANCAYO - HUANCAVELICA

EL TREN MACHO
127 km. Journey 5¼ hours.
From Huancayo. ①③⑤ 0630.
From Huancavelica. ②④⑥ 0630
Operator: FC HH.

BOLIVIA 9945

Ferroviária Andina / Ferroviária Oriental

PUERTO QUIJARRO - SANTA CRUZ DA LA SIERRA — FO

km			13✕	7🍸
			②④⑦	①③⑤
0	**Puerto Quijarro** .... d.	...	1300	1800
125	Rivero Torrez.......... d.	...	1537	2010
240	Roboré .... d.	...	1854	2245
374	San José Chiquitos d.	...	2304	0150
640	**SC da la Sierra**..... a.	...	0540	0700

		14✕	8🍸
		①③⑤	②④⑦
SC da la Sierra .. d.	...	1320	1800
San José Chiquitos d.	...	1930	2308
Roboré .... d.	...	2342	0212
Rivero Torrez...... d.	...	0309	0448
Puerto Quijarro . a.	...	0602	0700

SANTA CRUZ DE LA SIERRA - YACUIBA — FO

km		64		
		④		
0	**SC de la Sierra**..... a.	1530	...	...
115	Cabezas .... d.	1945	...	...
239	Charaguá .... d.	2322	...	...
360	Boyuibe .... d.	0229	...	...
434	Villa Montes.......... d.	0513	...	...
533	**Yacuiba** .... a.	0805	...	...

	63		
	⑤		
Yacuiba............. d.	1700	...	...
Villa Montes......... d.	1948	...	...
Boyuibe .... d.	2235	...	...
Charaguá............ d.	0135	...	...
Cabezas .... d.	0535	...	...
SC de la Sierra .. a.	0955	...	...

OURO - VILLAZÓN — FCA

km		2	16	68
		②⑤	③⑦	①④
0	**Oruro**............... d.	1530	1900	...
313	Uyuni.................. d.	2240	0250	0800
391	**Avaroa** .... a.	|	|	1430
404	Atocha .... d.	0055	0520	...
501	Tupiza .... d.	0410	0905	...
602	**Villazón** .... a.	0705	1205	...

	1	15	67
	③⑥	①④	①④
Villazón.............. d.	1530	1530	...
Tupiza .... d.	1825	1900	...
Atocha .... d.	2145	2300	...
Avaroa............... d.	|	|	1630
Uyuni .... d.	0005	0145	2359
Oruro .... a.	0700	0910	...

⊡ – Train services currently suspended bus connections are available at different timings.

OTHER SERVICES IN BOLIVIA — FA

km	②④⑥			③⑤⑦
	❦		❦	
0	0800	↓	d.**Cochabamba** .... d.	1645
216	1645	↓	a.**Aiquille** .... a. ↑	0800

km	①④			②⑤
0	0830		d.**Viacha**............. d.	1510
208	1450	↓	a.**Charaña** .... a. ↑	0900

km	❦			❦
0	...		d.**Potosí** .... d.	...
171	...	↓	a.**Sucre** El Tejar ...... a. ↑	...

km	A			A
0	0800		d.**El Alto**.............. d.	1850
77	1250	↓	a.**Guaqui**............ a. ↑	1530

❦ – Service suspended.

A – 2nd Sunday of every month.

BRAZIL 9950

Estrada de Ferro do Carajás / Estrada de Ferro Vitória a Minas

SÃO LUIS - PARAUAPEBAS — EFC

km		①④⑥ 12✕				②⑤⑦ 12✕	
0	...	0800		d.**São Luis** .... a.		2200	...
126	...	1016	↓	d.Arari .... d.	↑	1941	...
145	...	1040		d.Vitória do Mearim .. d.		1913	...
213	...	1156	↓	d.Santa Inês............. d.	↑	1804	...
264	...	1256		d.Alto Alegre .... d.		1659	...
299	...	1340	↓	d.Auzilândia.............. d.	↑	1613	...
315	...	1402		d.Altamira.................. d.		1551	...
334	...	1430	↓	d.Presa de Porco ..... d.	↑	1525	...
384	...	1526		d.Nova Vida .... d.		1429	...
513	...	1741	↓	d.Acailandia.............. d.	↑	1219	...
650	...	1957		d.São Pedro .... d.		0956	...
738	...	2131	↓	d.Marabá................... d.	↑	0829	...
785	...	2222		d.Itainopolis .... d.		0731	...
861	...	2350	↓	a.**Parauapebas** .... d.	↑	0600	...

BELO HORIZONTE - VITÓRIA — EFVM

km		12				12	
0	...	0730		d.**Belo Horizonte**.....a.		2010	...
71	...	0903	↓	d.Dois Irmãos...........d.	↑	1830	...
97	...	1002		d.Rio Piracicaba.......d.		1732	...
149	...	1048	↓	d.Drumond...............d.	↑	1639	...
173	...	1116		d.Antonio Dias..........d.		1605	...
286	...	1315	↓	d.Periquito...............d.	↑	1405	...
339	...	1420		d.G Valadares..........d.		1314	...
415	...	1547	↓	d.Conselheiro Pena..d.	↑	1125	...
484	...	1704		d.Aimorés.................d.		1026	...
532	...	1804	↓	d.Colatina.................d.	↑	0927	...
588	...	1859		d.Piraqueacú.............d.		0829	...
612	...	1926	↓	d.Fundão ....d.	↑	0802	...
657	...	2012		d.Flexal....................d.		0715	...
664	...	2030	↓	a.**Vitória** ....d.	↑	0700	...

DRUMOND - ITABIRA — EFVM

km		2				2	
0	...	1645		d.**Drumond** .... a.		1026	...
35	...	1741	↓	a.**Itabira** .... d.	↑	0930	...

PORTO SANTANA - SERRA DO NÁVIO

km		②④⑦ 2		Temporarily suspended.		①③⑥ 2	...
0	...	1000	↓	d.**Porto Santana** .... a.	↑	1205	...
	...	1320		d.Porto Grande .... d.		0847	...
130	...	1403	↓	d.Dona Maria............ d.	↑	0807	...
150	...	1445		d.Cupixi...................... d.		0725	...
162	...	1505	↓	d.Munquba .... d.	↑	0705	...
179	...	1540		d.Pedra Branca do Amapari d.		0630	...
194	...	1610	↓	a.**Serra do Návio** ..... d.	↑	0600	...

URUGUAY 9955

Ferrocarriles del Estado

km		①-⑤	①-⑤	⑥	①-⑤	⑥	①-⑤	①-⑤
0	**Montevideo** ◧ ...... d.	0655	1545	1550	1750	1810	1845	1950
8	Sayago.................. d.	0709	1600	1604	1804	1824	1900	2004
19	Las Piedras .... d.	0730	1627	1629	1827	1845	1923	2025
26	Progreso .... d.	0743	1641	1643	1841	1858	1937	2038
42	Canalones .... d.	...	...	1707	1904	1916	2000	...
63	**25 de Augosto** ..... a.	...	...	1737	1934	1940	2029	...

	①-⑤	⑥	①-⑤	①-⑤	⑥	①-⑤	①-⑤
25 de Augosto .....d.	0435	0530	0530	...	0635	...	...
Canalones...............d.	0504	0600	0559	...	0705	...	...
Progreso ....d.	0529	0623	0623	0715	0728	1555	1700
Las Piedras.............d.	0544	0638	0638	0731	0743	1607	1714
Sayago ....d.	0607	0701	0702	0754	0806	1628	1738
Montevideo ◧ ......a.	0622	0716	0717	0809	0821	1642	1753

km	①-④	①⑤				①⑤	2
0	...	...	↓	d.**Paso de los Toros** a.		...	...
172	0630	0700		d.**Tacuarembó** ....d.	↑	1324	1810
221	0727	0757	↓	d.Laureles ....d.		1228	1714
246	0754	0824		d.Paso Tranqueras ...d.	↑	1200	1646
264	0810	...		d.Paso Ataques ....d.		...	1630
290	0840	...	↓	a.Rivera ....d.	↑	...	1600

◧ – Montevideo Nueva Terminal.

ARGENTINA 9960

BUENOS AIRES - MAR DEL PLATA — SOFSE

km		301	319	303	303	303	305			
				⑥	Ⓐ	†	⑤			
0	**B. Aires** P. Constitución ......d.	0622	0622	0930	0935	0942	1710	...	...	...
114	Chascomús......................d.	|	|	1122	1122	1129	|	...	...	...
152	Lezama.............................d.	|	|	1147	1147	1154	|	...	...	...
	Dolores ....d.	0923	0923	1246	1246	1249	|	...	...	...
245	General Guido ....d.	1003	1030	1327	1327	1330	|	...	...	...
	Santo Domingo..................d.	|	1105	|	|	|	|	...	...	...
	General Juan Madariaga ..d.	|	1215	|	|	|	|	...	...	...
	Divisadero de Pinamar ...a.	|	1255	|	|	|	|	...	...	...
271	Maipú ....d.	|	...	1355	1355	1358	|	...	...	...
399	**Mar del Plata** ....a.	1210	...	1545	1545	1548	2246	...	...	...

	306	302	302	302	320	304			
	①	Ⓐ	⑥	†					
Mar del Plata........................ d.	0122	1106	1107	1108	...	1412	...	...	...
Maipú .... d.	|	1255	1256	1259		|	...	...	...
Divisadero de Pinamar..... d.	|	|	|	|	1315	|	...	...	...
General Juan Madariaga .... d.	|	|	|	|	1355	|	...	...	...
Santo Domingo .... d.	|	|	|	|	1505	|	...	...	...
General Guido .... d.	|	1321	1323	1325	1615	1615	...	...	...
Dolores.................................. d.	|	1414	1415	1418	1655	1655	...	...	...
Lezama .... d.	|	1511	1512	1515	|	|	...	...	...
Chascomús .... d.	|	1536	1537	1540	|	|	...	...	...
B. Aires P. Constitución........ a.	0702	1726	1727	1730	2005	2005	...	...	...

‡ – Buenos Aires Plaza Constitución.

9960 ARGENTINA

BUENOS AIRES - BAHÍA BLANCA

km		1333 ②⑤			1334 ③⑦	
0	**B. Aires** P. Constitución .. a.	1306	...	**Bahía Blanca** d.	2152	...
107	Monte d.	1518	...	Tornquist d.	0010	...
179	Las Flores d.	1704	...	Saavedra d.	0111	...
	Cacharí d.	1924	...	Pigüé d.	0143	...
289	Azul d.	2048	...	Coronel Suárez d.	0255	...
332	Olavarria d.	2249	...	General La Madrid d.	0441	...
	General La Madrid d.	0109	...	Olavarria d.	0708	...
488	Coronel Suárez d.	0255	...	Azul d.	0901	...
538	Pigüé d.	0407	...	Cacharí d.	1024	...
	Saavedra d.	0438	...	Las Flores d.	1245	...
	Tornquist d.	0540	...	Monte d.	1431	...
680	**Bahía Blanca** a.	0755	...	**B. Aires** P. Constitución a.	1635	...

BUENOS AIRES - JUNIN — SOFSE

km		563	567 ⑤		564 A	568 ⑦
0	**Buenos Aires** Retiro d.	1800	2010	**Rufino** d.	...	2310
	José C. Paz d.	1900	2117	Iriarte d.	...	0133
	Pilar d.	1920	2138	Alberdi d.	...	0151
111	Mercedes d.	2030	2246	Vedia d.	...	0233
	Franklin d.	2106	2312	Alem d.	...	0251
	Rivas d.	2120	2339	**Junin** a.	...	0350
	Castilla d.	2135	2354	**Junin** d.	0050	0355
	Rawson d.	2154	0012	O'Higgins d.	0120	0425
209	Chacabuco d.	2236	0053	Chacabuco d.	0146	0451
	O'Higgins d.	2304	0122	Rawson d.	0223	0528
255	**Junin** a.	2330	0155	Castilla d.	0242	0547
255	**Junin** d.	...	2000	Rivas d.	0256	0601
	Alem d.	...	0251	Franklin d.	0308	0613
	Vedia d.	...	0306	Mercedes d.	0346	0651
336	Alberdi d.	...	0347	Pilar d.	0520	0815
	Iriarte d.	...	0406	José C. Paz d.	0537	0832
421	**Rufino** a.	...	0640	**Buenos Aires** Retiro a.	0625	0925

A – Runs 65–70 minutes later on ⑥.

VIEDMA - BARILOCHE — SEFEPA

km		363 ⑤			364 ⑦	
0	**Viedma** d.	1800	...	**Bariloche** d.	1700	...
189	San Antonio Oeste d.	2220	...	Pilcaniyeu d.	1829	...
	Valcheta d.	0035	...	Comallo d.	1937	...
	Ramos Mexia d.	0245	...	Clemente Onelli d.	2036	...
	Sierra Colorada d.	0350	...	Ing Jacobacci d.	2204	...
	Los Menucos d.	0443	...	Maquinchao d.	2314	...
	Maquinchao d.	0617	...	Los Menucos d.	0048	...
625	Ing Jacobacci d.	0730	...	Sierra Colorada d.	0141	...
	Clemente Onelli d.	0750	...	Ramos Mexia d.	0239	...
	Comallo d.	0947	...	Valcheta d.	0456	...
	Pilcaniyeu d.	1055	...	San Antonio Oeste d.	0744	...
819	**Bariloche** a.	1228	...	**Viedma** a.	1134	...

BUENOS AIRES - BRAGADO — SOFSE

km		151 ①⑤			156 ①	152 ③
0	**Buenos Aires** Once d.	1835	...	**Bragado** d.	0230	0520
	Lujan d.	2016	...	Mechita d.	0245	0535
98	Mercedes d.	2113	...	Vaccarezza d.	0305	0555
	Suipacha d.	2144	...	Chivilcoy Sud d.	0341	0631
158	Chivilcoy Sud d.	2233	...	Suipacha d.	0423	0714
	Vaccarezza d.	2310	...	Mercedes d.	0456	0748
	Mechita d.	2330	...	Lujan d.	0600	0852
209	**Bragado** a.	2356	...	**Buenos Aires** Once a.	0742	1030

BUENOS AIRES - ROSARIO - CÓRDOBA / TUCUMÁN — SOFSE

km		267 ②⑤	265 ③⑦		268 ③⑦	266 ②⑤
0	**B. Aires** Retiro ⊖ d.	1130	2130	**Tucumán** d.	...	2130
	Campana ⊖ d.	1330	2335	La Banda d.	...	0230
92	Zárate ⊖ d.	1350	2355	Colonia Dora d.	...	0655
	Baradero ⊖ d.	1455	0100	Pinto d.	...	0900
	San Pedro ⊖ d.	1530	0135	Ceres d.	...	1145
	San Nicolás ⊖ d.	1703	0308	Sunchales d.	...	1440
294	Rosario Sur ⊖ d.	1835	0440	Rafaela d.	...	1545
314	Rosario Norte ⊖ d.	1915	0520	Gálvez d.	...	1810
384	Cañada de Gómez d.	2200	|	Serodino d.	...	1950
	Marcos Juárez d.	2350	|	**Córdoba** Mitre ● d.	2120	|
	Leones d.	0023	|	Villa Maria ● d.	0235	|
	Bell Ville d.	0135	|	Bell Ville d.	0445	|
566	Villa Maria ● d.	0355	|	Leones d.	0555	|
708	**Córdoba** Mitre ● a.	0855	|	Marcos Juárez d.	0630	|
	Serodino d.	...	0655	Cañada de Gómez d.	0825	|
	Gálvez d.	...	0835	Rosario Norte d.	1035	2110
523	Rafaela d.	...	1055	Rosario Sur d.	1125	2220
	Sunchales d.	...	1155	San Nicolás d.	1255	2350
684	Ceres d.	...	1515	San Pedro d.	1425	0120
791	Pinto d.	...	1800	Baradero d.	1500	0155
858	Colonia Dora d.	...	2020	Zárate d.	1615	0310
1020	La Banda d.	...	0050	Campana d.	1635	0330
1170	**Tucumán** ⊡ a.	...	0530	**B. Aires** Retiro a.	1835	0530

⊡ – Currently services start and finish at **Cevil Pozo**, not Tucumán.
⊖ – Also from Buenos Aires at 1515; from Rosario Norte at 0030.
● – Also Córdoba - Villa Maria at 1800 ⑤⑦; Villa Maria - Córdoba at 0500 ①, 0700 ⑥.

SALTA — SOFSE

km		①–⑤	①–⑤		①–⑤	①–⑤
0	**Campo Quijano** d.	0600	1107	**Salta** d.	0744	1250
41	**Salta** a.	0720	1230	**Campo Quijano** a.	0907	1410

km		①–⑥	①–⑤		①–⑥	①–⑤
0	**Salta** d.	1230	1930	**Güemes** d.	0615	1500
46	**Güemes** a.	1359	2059	**Salta** a.	0744	1629

CÓRDOBA - VALLE HERMOSO — SOFSE

km		2300	2352 ①–⑤	2002 ⑥⑦	2202 ①–⑤	2102 ①–⑤	2302 ⑥⑦	2204 ①–⑤	2302 ①–⑤	2354 ①–⑤	2004 ⑥⑦	2006 ⑥⑦	2104 ①–⑤	2206 ①–⑤
	Córdoba Mitre d.	...	...	...	0645	0808	...	0939	...	...	...	...	1450	1601
0	**Alta Córdoba** d.	...	0525	0626	|	|	...	|	...	1218	1126	1430	|	|
	La Calera d.	...	0621	0723	0754	0923	...	1048	...	1314	1223	1531	1605	1710
55	Cosquín d.	0600	...	0901	...	1054	1100	...	1245	...	1401	1710	1736	...
72	**Valle Hermoso** a.	0645	...	0946	...	1139	1145	...	1330	...	1446	1755	1821	...

	2300 ①–⑤	2203 ①–⑤	2101 ①–⑤	2001 ⑥⑦	2301 ⑥⑦	2353 ①–⑤	2301 ①–⑤	2205 ①–⑤	2003 ⑥⑦	2103 ①–⑤	2355 ①–⑤	2005 ⑥⑦	2303 ⑥⑦	2303 ①–⑤
Valle Hermoso d.	...	...	0700	0700	1005	...	1150	...	1200	1342	...	1509	1810	1835
Cosquín d.	...	...	0745	0746	1050	...	1235	...	1246	1427	...	1555	1855	1920
La Calera d.	0633	0812	0923	0925	...	1100	...	1325	1425	1605	1725	1733	...	...
Alta Córdoba a.	|	|	|	1021	...	1158	...	|	1527	|	1821	1829	...	...
Córdoba Mitre a.	0738	0918	1033	...	...	...	...	1431	...	1715	...	...	...	...

EL TREN DEL FIN DEL MUNDO

km		a	b	c			a	b	c	
0	**Fin Del Mundo** d.	0930	1000	1200	1500	**Parque Nacional** d.	1040	1115	1310	1610
8	**Parque Nacional** a.	1030	1050	1300	1600	**Fin Del Mundo** a.	1140	1155	1410	1710

a – Oct. 1 - Dec. 31. **b** – May 1 - Sept. 30. **c** – Departs 30 minutes later May 1 - Sept. 30.

9965 CHILE

Empresa de los Ferrocarriles del Estado

km			Ⓐ	Ⓒ	Ⓑ		⑤
0	**Santiago** Estación Central ◧ d.	...	0800	0930	...	1630	1730
85	Rancagua ◧ d.	...	0901	1028	...	1729	1831
138	San Fernando d.	...	0942	1107	...	1810	1916
191	Curicó d.	...	1019	1142	...	1845	1951
258	Talca d.	0745	1104	1230	1610	1930	2036
	Gonzalez Bastias d.	0912	|	|	1737	|	|
347	**Constitución** a.	1057	|	|	1922	|	|
308	Linares d.	...	1141	1307	...	2008	2113
348	Parral d.	...	1211	1337	...	2038	2143
382	San Carlos d.	...	1236	1402	...	2103	2208
400	**Chillán** a.	...	1253	1419	...	2120	2225

	Ⓐ	⚒	⑥			†
Chillán d.	0710	...	1000	1530	...	1730
San Carlos d.	0728	...	1018	1548	...	1748
Parral d.	0753	...	1043	1613	...	1815
Linares d.	0823	...	1114	1643	...	1845
Constitución d.	|	0720	|	|	1547	|
Gonzalez Bastias d.	|	0910	|	|	1735	|
Talca d.	0901	1032	1155	1722	1857	1927
Curicó d.	0944	...	1241	1808	...	2010
San Fernando d.	1020	...	1315	1844	...	2044
Rancagua ◧ d.	1101	...	1355	1924	...	2124
Santiago Estación Central ◧ a.	1159	...	1453	2022	...	2222

km		Ⓐ	Ⓐ				Ⓐ			Ⓐ
0	**Victoria** d.	0635	0800	1140	1840	**Temuco** d.	0935	1655	2010	2045
44	Lautaro d.	0727	0852	1232	1932	Lautaro d.	1007	1727	2042	2117
73	**Temuco** a.	0800	0925	1305	2005	**Victoria** a.	1100	1820	2135	2210

◧ – Local service **Santiago - Rancagua** and v.v. Journey 70 minutes:

From **Santiago** Estación Central at 0610 Ⓐ, 0720 Ⓐ, 0735 Ⓐ, 0800 ⑥, 0820 Ⓐ, 0840 Ⓐ, 0900, 0930 Ⓐ, 1000, 1030 Ⓐ, 1100, 1130 ⑥, 1200, 1300, 1400, 1500, 1530 Ⓐ, 1600, 1700, 1730 †, 1740 Ⓐ, 1800, 1815 Ⓐ, 1830 ⚒, 1845 Ⓐ, 1900, 1940 Ⓐ, 1930 †, 2000, 2030 Ⓑ, 2130 †. Trains call at San Bernardo 13 minutes later.

From **Rancagua** at 0540 Ⓐ, 0600 Ⓐ, 0615 Ⓐ, 0631 Ⓐ, 0645 Ⓐ, 0701 Ⓐ, 0730 ⚒, 0745Ⓐ, 0800 ⚒, 0830 ⑥, 0845 Ⓐ, 0900, 0930 Ⓒ, 0940 Ⓐ, 1000Ⓐ, 1030, 1130, 1200 Ⓐ, 1230, 1300 Ⓐ, 1320 Ⓒ, 1400 Ⓐ, 1430 Ⓒ, 1500 Ⓐ, 1530 Ⓒ, 1600 Ⓐ, 1630 Ⓒ, 1700 ⚒, 1730, 1800 †, 1830, 1900 Ⓑ, 1940 ⚒, 2000 †. Trains call at San Bernardo 56 minutes later.

SOUTH KOREA

Rail services in South Korea are operated by Korea National Railways under the brand names 'Korail', 'Supreme Railways' and 'AREX'. All services convey at least Economy class seating (shown in the tables as '2nd class') with many trains (and all KTX and SRT high-speed services) also conveying 1st class accommodation. Timings shown are the latest available.

Korail offer the *KORAIL PASS* which allows foreign visitors to take almost all trains operated by *Korail*. It cannot be used on SRT services, metro and temporary tourist trains. Adult prices: 138,000KRW for a 3 consecutive day pass; 210,000KRW for a 5 consecutive day pass; 121,000 KRW for a 2 day select pass; 193,000 KRW for a 4 day select pass. Select passes can be used over a 10 day period. Discounts for youths (13 - 27), children (6 - 12) and groups of 2 to 5 persons are available for all passes. www.letskorail.com

Korail — SEOUL - BUSAN — 9970

km	*KTX/SRT high-speed*		1	3	303	5	7	309	11	313	15	121	17	101	323	123	23	327	25	27	29	31	337	33	83 183	35	341
	Seoul Suseo	d.	...	...	0600	...	...	0705	...	0800	...	...	...	...	1000	...	...	1050	...	...	...	...	1330	...	...	...	1430
0	**Seoul** Main	d.	0515	0530	|	0600	0635	|	0730	|	0800	0814	0900	0945	|	1014	1030	|	1100	1200	1227	1300	|	1320	1352	1400	|
*96***	Cheonan Asan	d.	|	0609	0635	0639	|	0745	|	|	|	|	|	1025	1029	|	1109	1119	1139	1239	1306	1339	1405	1359	|	1435	1504
160	Daejeon	d.	0614	0634	0700	0704	0734	0816	0834	0854	0900	0957	0952	1050	1059	1159	1139	1149	1205	1305	1332	1409	1435	1429	1451	1505	1529
293	Dongdaegu	d.	0657	0723	0743	0747	0823	0859	0923	0937	0948	1040	1035	1133	1142	1242	1227	1232	1248	1348	1416	1501	1518	1512	1539	1548	1612
372	Ulsan	d.	0728	0754	|	0812	0854	0923	|	1001	1020	|	|	|	1206	1313	1252	1303	1319	1419	1441	|	1542	1536	|	|	1637
*418**	**Busan**	a.	0749	0815	0823	0833	0915	0945	1003	1023	1041	1120	1115	1245	1228	1334	1313	1325	1341	1441	1503	1547	1604	1558	1625	1635	1658

KTX/SRT high-speed		41	43	347	125	49	353	51	355	53	57	361	59	91 ©	367	61	93 ©	63	955 ©	371	67	69	375	71	73	97 ©	117
Seoul Suseo	d.	...	...	1555	...	...	1700	...	1730	...	...	1837	...	...	1930	...	...	...	...	2028	...	...	2130	...	...	...	...
Seoul Main	d.	1500	1540	|	1604	1700	|	1725	|	1810	1830		1900	1922	|	1937	1956	2000	2015	|	2100	2130	|	2200	2230	2251	2300
Cheonan Asan	d.	1539	|	|	|	|	|	1805	|	1834	1905	1917	1939	|	|	|	2035	2039	2055	2108	2139	|	|	2239	2309	|	2339
Daejeon	d.	1609	1644	1650	1751	1805	1800	1830	1819	1900	1934	1942	2009	2019	2029	2034	2058	2109	2118	2139	2204	2235	2229	2304	2334	2348	0009
Dongdaegu	d.	1653	1727	1733	1834	1854	1843	1913	1902	1949	2017	2031	2052	2103	2112	2123	2141	2151	2201	2227	2253	2318	2312	2347	0017	0031	0056
Ulsan	d.	1718	1752	1758	1859	1919	|	1944	1927	2014	2048	|	2117	2128	|	2148	|	2216	|	|	2318	2349	2337	0012	0042	|	...
Busan	a.	1739	1813	1819	1920	1940	1929	2005	1948	2035	2110	2117	2138	2149	2158	2209	2228	2237	2241	2314	2339	0010	2358	0033	0103	0111	...

KTX/SRT high-speed		302	2	4	6	8	308	10	12	312	14	122	104	16	318	20	22	24	324	26	162 ©	28	330	32	34	124	338
Busan	d.	0500	0510	0520	0540	0610	0655	0700	0730	0740	0810	0820	0815	0840	0900	0906	0936	1003	1015	1020	1006	1100	1210	1230	1310	1325	1345
Ulsan	d.	0523	0533	|	0603	0633	|	0723	0753	|	0833	0843	|	0903	|	0929	|	|	|	1043	|	1123	1234	1253	1333	|	|
Dongdaegu	d.	0548	0558	0607	0628	0703	0742	0748	0823	0829	0858	0908	0928	0933	0949	0954	1017	1044	1102	1113	1122	1148	1305	1323	1358	1406	1427
Daejeon	d.	0630	0645	0649	0710	0751	0829	0835	0906	0911	0946	0851	1010	1016	1031	1036	1058	1126	1145	1155	1210	1237	1353	1406	1440	1448	1509
Cheonan Asan	d.	0654	0709	|	0740	0821	|	|	0931	0941	1010	|	|	|	|	1106	|	1150	|	|	|	|	1417	|	1510	|	|
Seoul Main	a.	|	0751	0755	0822	0903	|	0941	1012	|	1046	1132	1117	1127	|	1147	1151	1231	|	1302	1309	1343	|	1512	1546	1629	|
Seoul Suseo	a.	0734	...	...	...	...	0929	...	...	1016	...	...	...	...	1124	...	...	...	1244	...	...	...	1452	...	...	...	1608

KTX/SRT high-speed		36	38	40	42	346	44	352	446	48	52	356	54	360	56	58	364	100 ©	128	62	370	112	68	376	72	74	80 ©
Busan	d.	1400	1420	1430	1510	1530	1545	1600	1623	1650	1720	1730	1800	1810	1835	1905	1935	1945	1955	2005	2030	2045	2129	2150	2200	2210	2250
Ulsan	d.	1423	|	1453	|	1553	1608	1623	|	1713	1743	1753	1823	1834	1858	1928	1958	|	|	2028	2053	|	2152	2213	2223	|	2313
Dongdaegu	d.	1448	1507	1524	1551	1618	1633	1653	1710	1744	1813	1818	1849	1859	1929	1953	2023	2032	2036	2058	2123	2159	2222	2238	2248	2257	2338
Daejeon	d.	1536	1549	1612	1632	1700	1715	1735	1757	1826	1855	1905	1938	1947	2016	2035	2105	2114	2119	2140	2205	2242	2310	2320	2330	2339	0020
Cheonan Asan	d.	1607	|	|	|	|	1739	1806	|	1850	1919	|	2009	|	|	|	2129	2138	|	2204	|	|	|	|	|	0003	0044
Seoul Main	a.	1648	1650	1723	1725	|	1820		1903	1931	2006	|	2050	|	2122	2150	|	2224	2300	2246	|	2348	0009	|	0025	0038	0120
Seoul Suseo	a.	...	...	...	...	1754	...	1841	...	...	...	1957	...	2047	...	...	2210	...	...	...	2311	...	...	0020	...	...	...

☛ Note: Frequent additional services run to/from Seoul Main operated by KTX and Seoul Suseo operated by SRT they have various stopping patterns but all services call at Daejeon and Dongdaegu.

Some KTX services operate via Miryang.
* – *409km* via Miryang. ** – *82 km* from Seoul Suseo.

Korail — SEOUL - MASAN - JINJU — 9971

km	*KTX high-speed*		201 E	203 D	207	209	211	213	215	219	221	223
0	**Seoul** Main	**9970** d.	0505	0540	0906	1005	1250	1340	1620	1805	2040	2210
96	Cheonan Asan	**9970** d.	|	0619	0945	1044	|	1414	|	1845	2119	|
160	Daejeon	**9970** d.	0604	0649	1010	1109	1355	1439	1724	1910	2149	2309
293	Dongdaegu	**9970** d.	0650	0735	1059	1159	1438	1522	1810	1953	2235	2357
348	Miryang	d.	0723	0813	1132	1231	|	1555	1843	2026	|	0030
387	Changwon Jungang	d.	0753	0839	|	1257	1537	1621	1914	2052	2335	|
397	Changwon	d.	0802	|	1207	|	1546	|	|	|	2344	0102
401	**Masan**	a.	0809	0849	1212	1309	1551	1632	1924	2102	2350	0107
450	Jinju	a.	0833	0915	...	1333	...	1657	...	...	0015	...

KTX high-speed		202	204	206	208	212	414 B	216	218	222 C	224
Jinju	d.	...	0616	0858	1006	1252	1434	...	1745	...	...
Masan	d.	0500	0641	0924	1032	1318	1500	1650	1811	2108	2143
Changwon	d.	0506	0647	|	1038	1324	|	1656	|	|	2149
Changwon Jungang	d.	0514	|	0936	1046	1332	1512	1704	1823	2120	|
Miryang	**9970** d.	0542	0720	1004	1111	|	1536	|	1847	|	2219
Dongdaegu	**9970** d.	0618	0759	1040	1145	1430	1610	1802	1921	2217	2252
Daejeon	**9970** d.	0700	0844	1122	1228	1517	1652	1849	2003	2259	2334
Cheonan Asan	**9970** d.	|	|	|	1253	|	|	1913	|	2323	|
Seoul Main	**9970** a.	0759	0950	1228	1334	1635	1751	1955	2102	0009	0034

B – Additional trips: 1124⑤©, 1525⑤©, 2005⑤©. C – Additional trips: 1240, 1821⑤©, 2000. D – Additional trips: 0605⑤©, 0825, 0930⑤©, 1511. E – Additional trips: 1430⑤©, 1735.

Korail SRT — SEOUL - GWANGJU - MOKPO — 9972

km	*KTX/SRT high-speed*		651 G	401	403	405	653	407	411 E	409	605 H	475	413	415	417	419	421	423	661	427	481	529	615	433	435	667	439
	Seoul Suseo	d.	0508	...	...	...	0640	...	...	...	0833	...	...	...	...	...	...	...	1611	...	...	...	1805	...	...	2108	...
0	**Seoul** Yongsan	**9973** d.	|	0510	0550	0631	|	0749	0922	0822	|	0936	1041	1220	1247	1332	1449	1536	|	1645	1712	1745	|	1943	2035	|	2225
93	Cheonan Asan	**9973** d.	|	|	0628	|	0719	|	|	0855	|	1014	1114	1258	|	1410	1527	|	|	1723	|	|	1840	|	2113	2144	2303
121	Osong	d.	0544	0555	0640	0716	0731	|	|	0907	0919	1027	1126	|	1327	|	1539	1621	|	|	|	1825	|	2028	2126	|	2316
240	Iksan	**9973** d.	0612	0623	0708	0751	0759	0904	1030	0935	0954	1145	1154	1340	1355	1445	1614	1649	1724	1805	1910	1853	1922	2102	2154	2226	2344
287	Jeongeup	d.	0628	0639	0724	0807	0815	0920	|	0951	1010	1213	1210	|	1411	1501	1630	|	|	1821	1937	|	1938	2118	2210	|	2359
337	**Gwangju** Songjeong	d.	0647	0658	0743	0825	0834	0939	1057	1011	1027	1245	1229	1409	1430	1521	1649	1718	1753	1840	2010	1922	1956	2137	2229	2255	0019
405	**Mokpo**	a.	0723	0729	0821	0901	0910	1014	...	1043	...	1323	1304	1444	1501	1556	1720	1753	1828	1915	2048	1957	...	2212	2304	2331	0054

KTX/SRT high-speed		602 J	402	404	472	652 K	406	408	410	412	414 F	416	418	658	420	422	424	662	426	482	430	432	434	666	438	440	1668
Mokpo	d.	...	...	0525	0537	0630	0707	0820	0915	1003	...	1105	1255	1310	1353	1433	1600	1645	1703	1651	1802	1852	1952	2025	2055	2157	2230
Gwangju Songjeong	d.	0515	0541	0602	0614	0704	0744	0857	0952	1037	1125	1142	1332	1347	1430	1507	1637	1722	1740	1728	1839	1929	2029	2102	2128	2234	2307
Jeongeup	d.	0533	0559	0621	0647	|	0803	0916	|	|	1143	|	1351	1406	1449	1525	1656	1741	1759	1801	1858	1948	2048	2121	2147	|	2326
Iksan	**9973** d.	0550	0616	0640	0716	0736	0820	0935	1024	1106	1200	1214	1408	1423	1506	1545	1713	1758	1818	1830	1915	2005	2108	2138	2206	2303	2343
Osong	d.	0619	0645	0717	|	|	0856	1004	|	|	|	1243	1436	1451	1542	|	|	1826	|	1948	1951	|	2144	2214	2235	|	|
Cheonan Asan	**9973** d.	0633	0659	|	0840	0812	|	1018	|	|	1244	1257	|	1505	|	|	1756	|	1854	2001	2005	|	|	|	2249	|	0019
Seoul Yongsan	**9973** a.	|	0739	0807	0922	|	0944	1103	1134	1221	1323	1337	1525	|	1630	1709	1840	|	1934	2041	2045	2115	2234	|	2333	0013	
Seoul Suseo	a.	0708	...	...	...	0853	...	...	...	...	...	...	...	1540	...	...	...	1910	...	...	...	...	...	2251	...	...	0054

E – Additional trips: 1610, 1835, 2123.
F – Additional trips: 1823, 2100.
G – Additional trips: 0940, 1100, 1310, 1710, 1910.
H – Additional trips: 0540, 0740, 1020, 1220, 1410, 1520, 1940, 2220, 2300.
J – Additional trips: 0620, 0755, 1020, 1115, 1300, 1625, 1830, 2025, 2155.
K – Additional trips: 0800, 1010, 1405, 1905.

☛ Note: Additional services running to/from Seoul Suseo operated by SRT and have different stopping patterns (but all services call at Iksan and Gwangju Songjeong).

Korail — SEOUL - YEOSU — 9973

km	*KTX high-speed*		501 B	503	505	509	513	583	515	519	521	523
0	**Seoul** Yongsan	**9972** d.	0510	0712	0840	1055	1411	1440	1645	1850	2005	2150
93	Cheonan Asan	**9972** d.	|	0750	|	1133	|	1518	1723	1928	2043	|
	Osong	d.	0555	0802	0925	1146	1457	|	|	|	|	|
240	Iksan	**9972** d.	0626	0837	0959	1220	1531	1643	1810	2010	2119	2257
266	Jeonju	d.	0642	0854	1016	1237	1548	1659	1827	2026	2135	2314
326	Namwon	d.	0709	0921	1043	1304	1615	1726	1854	2053	2202	2341
394	Suncheon	d.	0741	0955	1121	1339	1647	1800	1931	2128	2236	0012
434	**Yeosu** Expo	a.	0803	1017	1143	1401	1709	1822	1953	2150	2258	0034

KTX high-speed		502	504	506	508 A	510	514	518	584	522	524
Yeosu Expo	d.	0500	0709	0842	1036	1200	1402	1635	1857	2022	2155
Suncheon	d.	0521	0731	0904	1058	1222	1424	1657	1919	2045	2216
Namwon	d.	0555	0805	0937	1128	1256	1458	1731	1953	2118	2247
Jeonju	d.	0620	0830	1003	1154	1322	1524	1757	2019	2145	2313
Iksan	**9972** d.	0640	0847	1024	1214	1338	1545	1818	2036	2206	2329
Osong	d.	0717	0923	|	1243	|	|	|	|	2235	2358
Cheonan Asan	**9972** d.	|	0937	|	1257	1422	|	1854	2200	2249	|
Seoul Yongsan	**9972** a.	0807	1019	1134	1337	1457	1709	1934	2240	2333	0040

A – Additional trips: 1209, 1305, 1458, 1805. B – Additional trips: 0745, 0955, 1215, 1220, 1745.

9974 SEOUL - POHANG — Korail

km	KTX high-speed	231 A	233	235	239	243	241	245	247	249	253
0	**Seoul** Main .... **9971** d.	0540	0645	0810	1045	1241	1300	1435	1620	1735	2220
96	Cheonan Asan ... **9971** d.	0619	0725	0851	1124	|	1339	1514	|	|	|
160	Daejeon .... **9971** d.	0649	0750	0950	1154	1339	1409	1539	1724	1839	2324
293	Dongdaegu .... **9971** d.	0732	0833	1004	1237	1422	1457	1628	1807	1928	0008
374	**Pohang** .... a.	0807	0908	1039	1312	1457	1533	1703	1843	2003	0043

KTX high-speed	232	234	236	238 B	240	244	248	250	252	254
Pohang .... d.	0537	0715	0959	1015	1104	1404	1623	1800	1922	2135
Dongdaegu ..... **9971** d.	0618	0757	1040	1052	1145	1445	1704	1837	2003	2217
Daejeon .... **9971** d.	0700	0841	1122	1134	1228	1527	1751	1919	2045	2259
Cheonan Asan **9971** d.	|	|	|	1204	1253	1558	|	1949	2115	2323
Seoul Main ..... **9971** a.	0759	0950	1228	1246	1334	1639	1857	2031	2154	0009

A – Additional trips: 0505 ©, 0925 ④–②, 1511 ④–②, 2040. **B** – Additional trips: 1041 ⑤©, 1237 ④–②, 1537, 1856 ⑤©, 1900 ①②④.

9975 SEOUL - GANGNEUNG — Korail

km	KTX high-speed	801 A	805	807	809	811	813	815	817	819	825	827
8	**Seoul** Main .... d.	0511	0801	0901	1001	1301	1331	1401	1601	1801	2131	2211
0	**Seoul C** .... d.	0532	0822	0922	1022	1322	1352	1422	1625	1822	2152	2232
107	Manjong .... d.	0623	0911	|	1111	1411	1441	|	1714	1911	2241	2318
166	Pyeongchang .... d.	0645	0940	|	1137	1436	|	1534	1738	1939	2311	|
223	**Gangneung** ..... a.	0708	1001	1057	1158	1502	1523	1556	1804	2004	2333	2359

KTX high-speed	802	804	808	810	812	814	816	818	820	826	828
Gangneung ... d.	0530	0630	0830	1030	1132	1225	1530	1640	1725	2128	2230
Pyeongchang . d.	|	0659	0859	|	|	1254	1554	|	1754	|	2254
Manjong .... d.	0614	0724	0924	|	|	1319	1618	|	1815	2220	2314
Seoul C .... d.	0703	0815	1015	1209	1304	1408	1707	1819	1908	2308	0003
Seoul Main ...... a.	0723	0838	1035	1229	1324	1427	1727	1839	1928	2328	0023

A – Additional trips: 0601, 1901, 2001. **B** – Additional trips: 0730, 1840, 2030. **C** – **Seoul** Cheongnyangni.

9976 SEOUL - ANDONG and DAEGU - BUSAN — Koraill 2nd class

km	**7xx** services KTX high-speed	701	703	705	707	1709	711	713	1601 B	1603 B
0	**Seoul** Cheongnyangni .... d.	0600	0900	1100	1400	1600	1900	2200	0650	1450
105	Wonju .... d.	0649	0947	1152	1447	1650	1948	2250	0800	1558
155	Jecheon .... d.	0706	1004	1209	1505	1707	2005	2307	0830	1626
219	Yeongju .... d.	0742	1043	1242	1544	1742	2044	2340	0918	1715
248	**Andong** .... d.	0802	1103	1302	1604	1804	2104	2359	0935	1732

7xx services KTX high-speed	702	704	706	708	710	712	714	1602 B	1604 B
Andong .... d.	0600	0830	1130	1335	1630	1900	2125	1104	1818
Yeongju .... d.	0620	0851	1150	1355	1650	1921	2145	1129	1846
Jecheon .... d.	0657	0930	1227	1432	1727	2001	2219	1210	1927
Wonju .... d.	0714	0947	1244	1448	1744	2019	2235	1234	1952
Seoul Cheongnyangni .... a.	0803	1036	1333	1537	1830	2105	2324	1352	2055

km		1773 C	1775	1779	1781	1601 B	1783	1603 B	1791	1681 A	1795
241	**Andong** .... **9978** d.	...	...	...	...	0937	...	1733		1918	...
185	**Dongdaegu** .... **9978** d.	0740	0825	1045	1135	|	1300	|	1920	|	2135
	Gyeongju .... d.	0847	0937	1154	1246	1131	1405	1929	2029	2108	2242
	Taehwagang (Ulsan) ... d.	0926	1017	1233	1328	1210	1446	2011	2109	2146	2319
	ShinHaeundu .... d.	1014	1106	1322	1417	1259	1539	2100	2158	2236	0008
0	**Busan** Bujeon .... a.	1030	1124	1340	1433	1317	1555	2118	2216	2254	0026

	1774 D	1602 B	1776	1682 A	1780	1784	1604 B	1788	1790	1794
Busan Bujeon .... d.	0620	0715	0800	0850	1138	1412	1435	1605	1707	2018
ShinHaeundu .... d.	0638	0733	0818	0908	1156	1430	1453	1623	1723	2036
Taehwagang (Ulsan) d.	0730	0824	0908	0957	1248	1518	1543	1714	1810	2127
Gyeongju .... d.	0809	0902	0955	1032	1326	1555	1621	1750	1850	2205
Dongdaegu 9978 a.	0921	|	1105	|	1433	1706	|	1900	2000	2315
Andong .... **9978** a.	...	1100	...	1218	...	...	1847	...	...	...

A – To/from Donghae (Table **9978**). **B** – **Seoul** Cheongnyangni – Andong – Bujeon and v.v. **C** – Additional trips: 0935, 1645, 2035. **D** – Additional trips: 1243, 1830, 2134.

9977 SEOUL - DONGHAE - GANGNEUNG — Koraill 2nd class

km		1631	1633	1635	1641	1637	1639		
0	**Seoul** Cheongnyangni .... **9976** d.	0735	0955	1230	...	1700	1910	...	...
105	Wonju .... **9976** d.	0907	1101	1339	...	1814	2035	...	...
155	Jecheon .... **9976** d.	0933	1127	1404	1516	1840	2100	...	...
	Yemi .... d.	1023	1220	1457	1608	1931	2151	...	...
	Mindungsan .... d.	1045	1241	1518	1630	1954	2213	...	...
	Dogye .... d.	1143	1340	1617	1728	2052	2311	...	...
315	**Donghae** .... a.	1226	1418	1657	1808	2132	2349	...	...
	Jeongdongjin .... a.	...	...	...	...	...	...	...	...
360	**Gangneung** .... a.	...	...	...	...	...	...	...	...

		1632	1634	1642	1636	1638	1640	
Gangneung .... d.	...	...	...	...	...	...	...	...
Jeongdongjin .... d.	...	...	...	...	...	...	...	...
Donghae .... d.	...	0555	0723	0921	1203	1517	1813	...
Dogye .... d.	...	0634	0804	1002	1242	1600	1854	...
Mindungsan .... d.	...	0733	0904	1102	1345	1702	1955	...
Yemi .... d.	...	0754	0925	1122	1406	1723	2016	...
Jecheon .... **9976** d.	...	0849	1023	1214	1503	1816	2110	...
Wonju .... **9976** d.	...	0913	1048	...	1527	1841	2134	...
Seoul Cheongnyangni .... **9976** a.	...	1026	1154	...	1633	2005	2240	...

9978 DAEGU - DONGHAE — Korail 2nd class

km		1672	1682 A	1674	
0	**Dongdaegu 9976** d.	0625	...	1800	...
127	Andong .... **9976** d.	0803	1220	1947	...
164	Yeongju .... **9976** d.	0830	1245	2012	...
	Cheoram .... d.	1014	1425	2155	...
	Dogye .... d.	1043	1453	2222	...
348	**Donghae** .... a.	1125	1533	2300	...
393	Gangneung .... a.	...	...	...	...

	1671	1681 A		1673
Gangneung .... d.	...	...	...	...
Donghae .... d.	1102	1558	...	1723
Dogye .... d.	1144	1639	...	1804
Cheoram .... d.	1211	1706	...	1830
Yeongju ... **9976** d.	1404	1856	...	2018
Andong .... **9976** d.	1422	1916	...	2036
Dongdaegu 9976 a.	1606	...	...	2213

A – To/from Busan Bujeon (Table **9976**).

9979 DAEGU - POHANG — Korail 2nd class

km		1751	1753	1755	1757
0	**Dongdaegu** .... d.	0542	0900	1500	1833
	Yeongcheon .... d.	0610	0928	1528	1902
103	**Pohang** .... a.	0732	1051	1651	2028

	1752	1754	1756	1758
Pohang .... d.	0630	1130	1425	1925
Yeongcheon ..... d.	0739	1251	1546	2026
Dongdaegu ...... a.	0808	1321	1616	2055

9980 DAEGU - MASAN — Korail 2nd class

km		1901	1903	1031	1905	1907	1909	1231	1911	1033
	Seoul .... d.	...	...	0853	...	...	...	1543	...	1927
0	**Dongdaegu** .... d.	0640	0922	1219	1345	1735	1825	1938	2150	2256
57	Miryang .... d.	0729	1009	1253	1429	1819	1912	2019	2234	2328
	Changwon Jungang .... d.	0802	1040	1321	1503	1856	1949	2057	2308	2359
101	Changwon .... d.	0812	1049	1330	1512	1905	1958	2106	2317	0008
105	**Masan** .... a.	0816	1053	1336	1516	1910	2002	2112	2321	0014
171	Jinju .... a.	...	...	1406	...	1952	...	2153	...	0045

	1902	1232	1904	1032	1906	1908	1034	1910	1912
Jinju .... d.	...	0647	...	0908	...	...	1547	...	2015
Masan .... d.	0545	0730	0840	0939	1200	1505	1618	1840	2059
Changwon .... d.	0551	0736	0846	0945	1205	1611	1614	1846	2105
Changwon Jungang .... d.	0600	0745	0855	0955	1215	1520	1634	1854	2115
Miryang .... d.	0636	0812	0929	1022	1249	1554	1700	1929	2150
Dongdaegu .... a.	0727	0854	1017	1058	1337	1645	1733	2017	2239
Seoul .... a.	...	1252	...	1429	...	...	2058	...	...

9981 MOKPO - BUSAN — Korail 2nd class

km		1944	1972		1952	1954	1441		1942	1974
0	**Mokpo** .... d.	...	...	...	...	0928	...	...	...	...
	Gwangju Songjeong .... d.	...	0607	...	...	1030	...	...	...	1912
85	Seogwangju .... d.	...	0616	...	...	1040	1321	...	...	1922
	Boseong .... d.	...	0726	...	...	1150	1430	...	...	2030
206	**Suncheon** .... d.	0630	0825	...	0915	1248	1527	...	1739	2125
284	Jinju .... d.	0731	...	...	1016	1350	...	...	1836	...
350	Masan .... d.	0814	...	...	1059	1434	...	...	1919	...
354	Changwon .... d.	0821	...	...	1105	1440	...	...	1925	...
	Changwon Jungang .... d.	0829	...	...	1114	1449	...	...	1934	...
385	Samnangjin .... d.	0856	...	...	1140	1517	...	...	1957	...
433	**Busan** Bujeon .... a.	0943	...	...	1226	1604	...	...	2043	...

	1971	1442	1951	1941	1953	1973	1943		
Busan Bujeon .... d.	...	...	0601	1020	1340	...	1849	...	...
Samnangjin .... d.	...	...	0652	1107	1428	...	1936	...	...
Changwon Jungang .... d.	...	...	0719	1134	1455	...	2006	...	...
Changwon .... d.	...	...	0728	1143	1504	...	2015	...	...
Masan .... d.	...	...	0734	1149	1511	...	2022	...	...
Jinju .... d.	...	...	0817	1232	1554	...	2105	...	...
Suncheon .... d.	0604	0651	0918	1332	1654	1800	2205	...	...
Boseong .... d.	0703	0750	1017	...	...	1859	...	...	...
Seogwangju .... d.	0816	0901	1132	...	...	2011	...	...	...
Gwangju Songjeong .... a.	0824	...	1141	...	...	2019	...	...	...
Mokpo .... a.	...	...	1239	...	...	...	...	...	...

9983 SEOUL - CHUNCHEON — 2nd class Korail

Seoul Yongsan - **Namchuncheon** and v.v. *93 km*. Journey 69 – 78 minutes.

From **Seoul** Yongsan. Most trains call at **Gapyeong** 56 – 64 mins later: ①–⑤ 0600, 0656, 0752, 0852, 0955, 1058, 1200, 1253, 1400, 1510, 1600, 1700, 1759, 1856, 1958, 2032, 2120, 2248; ⑥⑦ at 0615, 0655 0755, 0820, 0845, 0919, 0950, 1020, 1100, 1130, 1157, 1300, 1415, 1447, 1514, 1547, 1628, 1656, 1730, 1800, 1826, 1900, 1930, 2008. 2035, 2120, 2205 ⑥, 1230, 1330, 2145.

From **Namchuncheon**. Most trains call at **Gapyeong** 15 – 19 minutes later: ①–⑤ 0612, 0706, 0739, 0814, 0925, 1027, 1118, 1213, 1318, 1410, 1531, 1618, 1709, 1817, 1858, 1942, 2113, 2218; ⑥⑦ at 0613 0711, 0808, 0851, 0931, 0956, 1021, 1125, 1231, 1313, 1342, 1406, 1456, 1511, 1556, 1619, 1659, 1730, 1802, 1831, 1904, 1938, 2004, 2037, 2113, 2152, 2217. ⑥, 0742, 1057, 1202

9984 INCHEON AIRPORT ✈ - SEOUL — AREX

Incheon Airport ✈ - **Seoul** Main and v.v. *61 km*. 2nd class only. Journey 51 minutes from Terminal two. Trains also calll at Terminal one 8 minutes before/after Terminal two.

From **Incheon Airport** ✈ Terminal 2 at 0515, 0550, 0630, 0720, 0800, 0840, 0920, 1000, 1040, 1120, 1200, 1240, 1320, 1400, 1440, 1520, 1600, 1640, 1720, 1800, 1840, 1920, 2000, 2050, 2140, 2240. Frequent additional slower services (calling at Gimpo Airport ✈) run 5 – 6 times per hour 0523 – 2342 (journey 55 – 60 minutes Incheon - Seoul).

From **Seoul** Main at 0610, 0650, 0730, 0810, 0850, 0930, 1010, 1050, 1130, 1210, 1250, 1330, 1410, 1450, 1530, 1610, 1650, 1730, 1810, 1850, 1930, 2010, 2050, 2130, 2210, 2250. Frequent additional slower services (calling at Gimpo Airport ✈) run 5 – 6 times per hour 0520 – 2338 (journey 55 – 60 minutes Seoul - Incheon).

RAIL *EXTRA* is an additional feature published in our Winter, Spring, Summer and Autumn editions, giving the editorial team an opportunity to include further information on rail travel throughout Europe to supplement the timetables in our regular editions. In particular we have selected a number of tourist and heritage lines from the many hundreds on offer, with timetable details where possible (though it's always best to check before travel in case of late changes, especially owing to the ongoing coronavirus pandemic). We would also encourage readers to seek out the many museum and hertitage lines which we cannot show for space reasons, many of which include steam operation.

AUSTRIA

RAIL TRAVEL

See Tables **950 - 999**. Most trains are operated by Österreichische Bundesbahnen (ÖBB) www.oebb.at. For train types see page 449. Scenic highlights include the Semmeringbahn (Table **980**), the Arlberg route (**951**) and the Salzburg to Villach Tauern line. Many minor routes are also scenic.

Opening of the Wien to St Pölten high-speed line in 2012, along with upgrading elsewhere, has led to significant journey time improvements on the key east to west 'Westbahn' route linking Wien with Linz and Salzburg. ÖBB's latest high-quality *Railjet* trains take advantage of this, running at up to 230 km/h. Private operator *Westbahn* competes with ÖBB on the route. ÖBB also operate the *Nightjet* brand for overnight trains, with a network of both international and domestic routes.

Services around Wien (Vienna) were revolutionised following the opening of the new Hauptbahnhof (central station) in December 2015. The station allows through services on a site (the old Südbahnhof) where all trains previously had to terminate. A notable feature of the station is the diamond shaped roof employing 25,000 square metres of translucent glass and steel. Westbahnhof is now only used by *Westbahn* and ÖBB regional services.

Several local lines are run by private operators, and a small selection of tourist and heritage lines is shown below.

MARIAZELLERBAHN

Niederösterreichische Verkehrsorganisationsgesellschaft (NÖVOG) run several local lines including the 84 km narrow gauge Mariazellerbahn from St Pölten Hbf to Mariazell. Full details are shown in Table **994**.

The electrified Mariazellerbahn is widely recognised as one of the most attractive railway journeys in the Alps and an excursion is highly recommended. There are 21 tunnels and 75 bridges or viaducts along the route and the highest point (892m) is actually situated in the 2368m Gösing Tunnel. Between Kirchberg and Laubenbachmühle the line passes through the spectacular gorge of the River Pielach and at Winterbach there are some particularly fine views. On between May and October a heritage electric train runs one trip each way, whilst a steam hauled journey runs on several dates.

STEYRTAL-MUSEUMSBAHN

A 10 minute walk from Steyr station (Table **976**) takes you to the Lokalbahn station from where the 17 km line operated by ÖGEG www.oegeg.at takes you to Grünburg. Opened in 1889, the Steyrtalbahn is the oldest narrow gauge (760mm) line in Austria. Passing through the scenic Steyr valley, it has been operating as a heritage line since 1986 using steam traction.

Operates on ⑦ in June and July; on ⑥⑦ in Aug. and Sept. (also on Oct. 26). Two or three services operate in each direction. Journey time is 60 minutes each way.

NIEDERÖSTERREICHISCHE SCHNEEBERGBAHN

This 9.8 km narrow gauge rack railway runs from Puchberg am Schneeberg to Hochschneeberg. Timings, which include a steam service on Sundays and public holidays in high summer, can be found in Table **984**.

Construction was completed in 1897. The journey to the summit provides wonderful views of the Schneeberg mountain range, with Hochschneeberg station being the highest in Austria at 1795m above sea-level.

WALDVIERTLER SCHMALSPURBAHNEN

A narrow gauge (760mm) network based on Gmünd NÖ close to the Czech border, running through enchanting, densely wooded landscapes. The line runs for 68 km Groß Gerungs - Gmünd - Alt Nagelberg - Litschau. Operated by NÖVOG www.noevog.at

Gmünd to Groß Gerungs runs May 1 - Nov. 1 as follows. Operated by railcars except on ③⑥ when trains are hauled by heritage diesel (steam on 1st / 3rd ⑥ of the month).

	③A	†	C	†	B		D	C	†	B	
Gmünd NÖ . d.	0900	0900	1300	1330	1400	G. Gerungs d.	1115	1615	1615	1645	...
Weitra......... d.	0928	0928	1331	1358	1428	Weitra........ d.	1213	1715	1713	1743	...
G. Gerungs . a.	1030	1030	1450	1500	1530	Gmünd NÖ a.	1240	1755	1740	1810	...

Gmünd to Litschau runs May 1 - Nov. 1 as follows. Operated by railcars except on ③⑥ when trains are hauled by heritage diesel (steam on 1st / 3rd ⑦ of the month).

	B	③A		③A	⑥E	⑥E	†	†
Gmünd NÖ .... d.	1000	1000	...	1430	1000	1430	1000	1430
Alt Nagelberg............... ▷ d.	1030	1030	...	1500	1030	1500	1030	1500
Litschau........................... a.	1055	1055	...	1455.	1055	1525	1055	1525
	B	**③A**		**③A**	**⑥G**	**⑥G**	**†**	**†**
Litschau........................... d.	1245	1130	...	1600	1300	1600	1300	1600
Alt Nagelberg............... ▷ d.	1315	1200	...	1630	1330	1630	1330	1630
Gmünd NÖ .... a.	1335	1220	...	1650	1350	1650	1350	1650

A – ③ May 4 - Sept. 28.
B – ①②④⑤ July 4 - Sept. 2.
C – ③⑥ May 4 - Sept. 28; ⑥ Oct. 1 – 29.
D – ③† May 1 - Sept. 28; † Oct. 2 - Nov. 1.
E – ⑥ May 7 - Oct. 29.
G – ⑥ May 7 - Oct. 29.
▷ – Heritage trains also run Alt Nagelberg - Heidenreichstein on ③Ⓒ July 13 - Aug. 31. From Alt Nagelberg 1035, 1505 ,1700; from Heidenreichstein 0945, 1245Ⓒ, 1345③, 1545 . Journey 40 minutes. www.wackelsteinexpress.at

ACHENSEEBAHN

This short (6.8 km) narrow gauge steam-operated rack railway runs from Jenbach, adjacent to the ÖBB station, to Seespitz-Bahnstation. The timetable is shown in Table **956**. The line climbs from Jenbach (532m) to the southern tip of the Achensee (931m), the departure point for Achensee boat excursions.

RAILWAY MUSEUMS

One of Austria's principal railway museums is the Eisenbahnmuseum Strasshof, also known as *Das Heizhaus*, situated adjacent to Silberwald station on the Wien to Břeclav line and served by local trains. Open ②–⑦ Apr. 1 - Oct. 26 (also winter weekends, except Dec. 24 - Jan. 31). Steam is in operation within the large site on several dates (in 2022 on June 12, 26, July 8, Sept. 18, Oct. 1, 2, 26.

Another large railway museum is the Lokpark Ampflwang, operated by ÖGEG. Steam / diesel trips run on most ⑦ July - Sept. on the 11 km line which links the museum with Timelkam, which is served by local trains from Linz.

Austrian Railways *CityJet* suburban service, Wien

BELGIUM

RAIL TRAVEL

See Tables **400 - 449**. Operated by NMBS (in Dutch) / SNCB (in French) www.b-rail.be. With over 3,500 km of lines, Belgium is well served by frequent rail services, mostly running to regular-interval timetables at the same minutes past each hour (with some peak hour extras). Note, however, that timetables and the route network can vary on Saturdays and Sundays, as shown in our tables. The most scenic lines are those in the Ardennes region, for example Liège to Gouvy and on to Luxembourg.

The two principal stations in Brussels, Midi/Zuid (south) and Nord, were long ago linked by a cross-city line, including the uninspiring Central station with its underground platforms, and most trains run through Brussels by way of this line, many also serving Brussels Airport. However, a further line serves Luxembourg and Schuman stations in the European quarter of Brussels, and this too has a link to the airport via a recently opened tunnel.

Journeys between Brussels and Liège (Table **400**), as well as international journeys to Germany, were considerably speeded up by the opening of the high-speed line in 2002, and from Liège to Aachen in 2009. Other high-speed lines are used by *Eurostar* trains to London and by trains to the Netherlands.

Belgium's coastal resorts are linked with each other not by the national rail system but by a frequent coastal tramway (the *Kusttram*) operated by De Lijn. For details see Table **406**.

Heritage lines include Stoomtrein Dendermonde-Puurs www.stoomtrein.be, Stoomcentrum Maldegem, which links Eeklo (Table **413**) with Maldegem www.stoomtreinmaldegem.be, and the historic Tramway Vicinal des Grottes de Han. However, the most significant heritage operation is the 'Three Valleys' CFV3V, detailed below.

Brussels also has a recently opened railway museum close to Schaerbeek station. See www.trainworld.be for further details. Closed on Mondays.

CHEMIN DE FER À VAPEUR DES TROIS VALLÉES (CFV3V)

This 14 km line runs from Mariembourg (800m from the SNCB/NMBS station in Table **421**) to Treignes, where there is a railway museum on the site of the old international station building. See www.cfv3v.eu for details.

Trains run ⑥† April 2 - Nov. 6 (also ②④ July 7 - Aug. 30). There are three return services departing Mariembourg 1130, 1420 and 1730 (1700 certain dates) returning from Treignes 1310, 1620 and 1810. Many dates include steam-hauled journeys but check the website for details. Journey time is 30 minutes each way by diesel railcar or by steam train. A special steam festival takes place on September 24, 25 and special timetables run on a handful of other dates.

BULGARIA

RAIL TRAVEL

See Tables **1500 - 1560**. Bulgarian State Railways (BDZ) www.bdz.bg run on a network of a little over 4,000 km, the principal lines of which link the capital Sofia with the Black Sea resorts of Burgas and Varna. Trains are often crowded and reservations are recommended for long-distance travel (and are obligatory for certain express trains). Signs at stations are in Cyrillic, although the website does have an English version.

BDZ has one narrow gauge line, running 125 km from Septemvri to Dobrinishte, serving en route the winter resort town of Bansko. Timings for this (very slow) line are in Table **1510**.

The Museum of Transport is in a former railway station in the outskirts of Ruse (see link foot of http://fan.bdz.bg). There is little else in the form of heritage lines, although there are occasional steam specials, and Plovdiv has a 600mm gauge Children's Railway (formerly Pioneer Railway).

CROATIA

RAIL TRAVEL

See Tables **1300 - 1358**. National railway company is Hrvatske Željeznice (HŽ) www.hzpp.hr. The network is centered on the capital Zagreb, but services are generally infrequent, even on the main lines to Rijeka and Split. The Zagreb to Split line (Table **1330**) is particularly scenic; the day trains on this line are operated by modern diesel units, with compulsory reservation. Sadly, connections from Knin to Zadar are no longer by train but provided by bus, although the route is still considered part of the rail network for ticketing purposes. Buses along the coast from Split to Ploče and Dubrovnik are, however, privately operated - brief details are given in Table **1325**.

The Croatian Railway Museum consists of an outdoor collection of exhibits in Zagreb, accessed from Ulica grada Vukovara 47, with limited opening hours (see http://muzej.hzinfra.hr). It remains closed for reconstruction.

CZECH REPUBLIC

RAIL TRAVEL

See Tables **1100 - 1169**. National rail company is České Dráhy (ČD) (www.cd.cz), whilst the railway infrastructure is administered by Správa Železnic (www.spravazeleznic.cz). An extensive network of over 9,000 km is operated, with many branch lines serving towns and villages away from the main lines, making it possible to visit almost anywhere by rail. If you like to explore on slow, winding, country branch lines, this is definitely a country to visit. With a rail pass or day ticket you can hop on and off trains at will, since the only trains requiring advance reservation are the handful of *SC* (*SuperCity*) Pendolino trains, which run mainly on the Praha - Ostrava route (reservation fee varies up to a maximum of CZK 250).

Other high-quality trains are classified *IC*, *EC* or *Ex*, whilst *Railjet* trains also run on the Praha - Wien axis (whilst *Railjet* is an Austrian train type, there are also some in the colours of Czech Railways). Regular fast trains are classified *R* (for rychlík) or *Rx* and are shown in our tables with just the train number. Seats can be reserved on all of these train types (recommended at busy times), and many convey buffet cars. Semi-fast trains are *Sp* or spešný. Local trains, which can be very slow, are *Os* or osobný.

Other operators compete with ČD on several major routes, principally Regiojet from Praha to Ostrava, Bratislava, Košice and Wien, and Leo Express to Ostrava and Košice. Tickets are not interchangeable with those of ČD. Some lines are now franchised to private companies.

In Praha, most services are concentrated on Praha hlavní nádraži (which means main station) though some services of a more local nature leave from the nearby Masarykovo station (10 minute walk). Holešovice station is of less importance with a line enabling all through trains to serve hlavní nádraži.

Chomutov depository: Czech loco 498.106 built by Škoda in 1955

As with many countries in this listing, it is possible to book tickets online (with an account) and to print tickets at home. Although Praha airport is not rail connected, the Airport Express (AE) bus between the airport and Praha hlavní is included in ČD's ticket system so it is possible to print your own ticket from the airport to rail stations in the Czech Republic - very handy for a quick getaway and avoiding ticket office queues!

HERITAGE LINES

Heritage operations mainly consist of special trains on parts of the Czech rail system, and these are shown in ČD's online timetable (some in a special section listed on their website as ZVL). Many of these trains are run by KŽC (www.kzc.cz) with heritage diesel railcars or locos, mainly on summer weekends.

Recommended is a short 30 minute trip from Praha hlavní nad. over the scenic so-called *Prague Semmering* line to Praha-Zličín. Operated by KŽC and known as *Pražský motoráček*, it is included in the Prague public transport tariff. Departures are on © at 0842, 1034, 1234 and 1434, returning at 1025, 1225, 1425, 1625 (or by tram from adjacent terminus).

Another popular journey is the scenic *Posázavsky motoráček* line from Praha to Týnec nad Sázavou via Vrané nad Vltavou. As well as ČD local trains, KŽC runs heritage journeys in summer (Apr. to Oct.) from Praha to Týnec nad Sázavou at 0739 ⑥, 1455 ⑦, returning at 1029 ⑥, 1928 ⑦.

ČD's only narrow gauge line is also worth a mention, running to the village of Osoblaha close to the Polish border - see Table **1169** for brief details.

The principal railway museum is at Lužna u Rakovnika, 64 km from Praha (Table **1105**), open daily May / September; (not ① during September). Steam trips operate on certain summer weekends to and from Lužna (for example from Praha or Chomutov). The museum's website is www.cdmuzeum.cz - click on the ČD Nostalgie link for a document listing the many heritage events and trips or www.cdnostalgie.cz.

The National Technical Museum also has a large railway depository in Chomutov, open ⑤–⑦ June 1 - Oct. 30 (also ②–④ June 28 - Sept. 4). www.muzeum-chomutov.cz. Approx 1.4 km on foot from Chomutov station via Globus car park.

JHMD - JINDŘICHOHRADECKÉ MÍSTNÍ DRÁHY

This privately operated narrow gauge railway runs from Jindřichův Hradec (Table **1135**) for 33 km to the small town of Nová Bystřice, close to the Austrian border. A steam hauled train with buffet runs in summer. For timings see Table **1169**. www.jhmd.cz

JHMD also operates a second narrow gauge line from Jindřichův Hradec, which runs for 46 km in a northerly direction to Obrataň (which is also served by a local ČD line from Tábor to Horní Cerekev). Trains run approximately every two hours, taking around 90 minutes for the journey. Aimed mostly at local travellers, it provides plenty of atmosphere for those who relish slow local lines. For the tourists, a steam train with buffet runs 21 km from Jindřichův Hradec to Kamenice nad Lipou on ②④ July 1 - Aug. 31, leaving at 0909 and returning at 1150.

DENMARK

RAIL TRAVEL

See Tables **700 - 728**. Operator is Danske Statsbaner (DSB) www.dsb.dk. There are also some independent lines, and certain former DSB services in Jutland are now operated by private company ArrivaTog www.arriva.dk. See page 338 for further information.

Principal trains linking København with the rest of Denmark are classified InterCity (*IC*) and InterCityLyn (*Lyn*), travelling at up to 200 km/h.. Reservations are recommended but not compulsory, and can be made by telephone ✆ 70 13 14 15 as well as online and on the DSB app.

Travel from Sjælland (the island on which København sits) to the rest of the country (Fyn and Jylland) is by way of the impressive 18 km Great Belt Fixed Link (Storebælt), consisting of a bridge and a tunnel, with an island inbetween. Prior to 1997 trains were conveyed on board ferries to make the crossing. On the other side of København, the equally impressive 16 km Øresund Bridge, opened in 2000, links the city with Malmø in Sweden, with a frequent rail service which also serves København's Kastrup Airport en route. The airport is also linked to the city by metro.

There are also plans for a Fehmarn Belt fixed link between Denmark and Germany (an undersea tunnel between Rødby and Puttgarden), although it's several years away. The process of loading trains to Germany on ferries has now ceased with trains to Hamburg now routed via Padborg.

Denmark's railway museum is situated in Odense, adjacent to the railway station and open daily all year. www.jernbanemuseet.dk

MUSEUMSBANEN MARIBO-BANDHOLM

Starting at Maribo on the privately operated Nykøbing to Nakskov line (see footnote in Table **720**), this short museum line in the south of Denmark heads 8 km north to Bandholm. After pausing for 20 minutes at Bandholm station, where the railway is based, the train continues for a further 400 metres to a platform adjacent to the harbour. www.museumsbanen.dk

Trains run ⑦ June 27 - Aug. 22 (also ③ June 30 - Aug. 4, ④ July 8 - Aug. 12 and Oct. 20, 21). Trains are steam hauled on certain dates.

Maribo	d.	1000	1300	1500	Bandholm havn	d.	1048	1348	1548
Bandholm	a.	1027	1327	1527	Bandholm	d.	1051	1351	1551
Bandholm havn	a.	1033	1333	1533	Maribo	a.	1147	1447	1647

ESTONIA

RAIL TRAVEL

See Tables **1870 - 1890**. Local services are run by the state owned railway company under the name Elron www.elron.ee using modern diesel multiple units on broad gauge tracks. The most important route links Tallinn with the country's second largest city, Tartu (Table **1880**).

The only international service is that to St Peterburg and Moskva (Table **1870**), which is operated by GoRail (www.gorail.ee). There are good bus links to Latvia's capital Riga (Table **1800**), and to St Peterburg (Table **1870**), whilst those determined to reach Riga by rail (taking much longer) can do so at certain times by changing at Valga (Tables **1880 / 1830**). Note that Tallinn's bus station is 3 km from the railway station, linked by tram. A new standard gauge rail project known as *Rail Baltica* will eventually link Tallinn with the other Baltic States and Poland, possibly by 2026.

Tallinn's proximity to Helsinki means that many tourists combine a trip to both cities. The various ferry routes linking the two cities are shown in our Ferry section (Table **2410**).

There is a railway museum in the impressive former station at Haapsalu, which can no longer be reached by rail (1h 45m by bus). Open ③–⑦ 1100 - 1700 see the Raudtee ja Sidemuuseum link on www.salm.ee. There is also a narrow gauge railway museum at Lavassaare, 17 km from Pärnu. www.museumrailway.ee

FINLAND

RAIL TRAVEL

See Tables **790 - 799**. Trains are run by national rail company VR www.vr.fi. Long distance day trains are generally high-speed tilting Pendolinos (up to 220 km/h) or modern double-deck trains. Trains are spacious, helped by the wider 'Russian' track gauge of 1524mm. Fares depend on train type - for further information on train types and ticketing see the introduction to the Finland section on page 360.

Focal point of the rail system is Helsinki's iconic 19-platform central rail station, designed by Eliel Saarinen in *Art Nouveau* style and incorporating four giant granite figures on the frontage. No fewer than 10 tracks head north for 3 km to Pasila, where lines start to divide.

Helsinki's Vantaa airport was added to the rail network in 2015 and can be reached either way around a loop, the anti-clockwise service (lettered 'I') being slightly quicker than the clockwise service ('P').

JOKIOINEN MUSEUM RAILWAY

Finland's only 750mm gauge railway (www.jokioistenmuseorautatie.fi) starts from Humppila on the Turku to Tampere line (Table **795**) and runs for 14 km to Jokioinen. The line also features a collection of preserved Finnish narrow gauge engines and rolling stock at Minkiö station, where the museum is open June – August.

⑦ June 5 - July 31 and ⑥ Aug. 6 – 27. A special timetable applies during the Minkiö Steam Festival on July 3.

	⑦**b**	⑦**b**	⑦**c**		⑦**b**	⑦**b**	⑦**b**	⑦**c**
Humppila ....d.	1025	1310	1600	Jokioinen..........d.	...	1145	1440	1700
Minkiö ....a.	1049	1334	1624	Minkiö ....a.	...	1203	1458	1717
Minkiö ....d.	1115	1410	1635	Minkiö ....d.	0945	1225	1520	...
Jokioinen ....a.	1134	1429	1652	Humppila..........a.	1011	1250	1545	...

	⑥**d**	⑥**d**	⑥**d**		⑥**d**	⑥**d**	⑥**d**	
Humppila ....d.	1040	1310	1605	Jokioinen..........d.	...	1150	1445	...
Minkiö ....a.	1104	1334	1629	Minkiö ....a.	...	1208	1503	...
Minkiö ....d.	1120	1410	...	Minkiö ....d.	1000	1225	1525	...
Jokioinen ....a.	1139	1429	...	Humppila..........a.	1025	1250	1530	...

b – ⑦ June 5 - July 31. **c** – ⑦ July 3 – 31. **d** – ⑥ Aug. 6 – 27.

FINNISH RAILWAY MUSEUM

Rail enthusiasts will find the 59 km trip from Helsinki to Hyvinkää worthwhile, served by half-hourly regional trains (Table **790**). A short walk from the station is the excellent Finnish Railway Museum, open most days (but not Mondays Sept. to May). The museum is closed on Bank Holidays, including the Midsummer holiday June 24 – 26. www.rautatiemuseo.fi

Finnish Railway Museum

FRANCE

RAIL TRAVEL

See Tables **250 - 399**. The national operator is SNCF - Société Nationale des Chemins de fer Français. www.sncf.com

Within France, the premium rate customer service line is ✆ 36 35.

France has an excellent network of dedicated high-speed lines, fanning out in all directions from Paris. The longest is that to Marseille, with the 750 km being covered in around 3h 20m. The most recent extensions, opened in 2017, are from Tours to Bordeaux and from Le Mans to Rennes. The line to the north is of international significance, with Thalys trains to Brussels, Amsterdam and Köln, together with *Eurostar* trains through the Channel Tunnel to London. Other high-speed lines include services to Germany, Switzerland and Spain. Speeds of up to 320 km/h (200 mph) are attained, with many trains continuing on conventional track to serve most parts of France. The high-speed *TGV* trains (*TGV* stands for Train à Grande Vitesse) are branded *TGV inOui*, whilst *Ouigo* is a name used for a network of special low-cost high-speed services, which is set to further expand in the future.

TGV trains require compulsory reservation, but there are exceptions for journeys between Lille and the coast (Calais, Boulogne, Dunkerque; see Table **250** for details). Although reservations can be made at the last minute (space permitting), it does make it difficult to make last-minute travel decisions. It also increases the cost for rail pass holders, who need to take into account the cost of reservation fees (for normal tickets the reservation fee is included in the ticket price). Light refreshments are available on *TGV* trains, except on short routes such as Paris to Lille.

Other long-distance (non-TGV) services are branded *Intercités*, some of which also require compulsory reservation (as indicated in our tables). Some low-cost traditional loco-hauled services have recently been introduced on the Paris - Nantes and Paris - Lyon routes which are branded *Ouigo Classique*.

On other lines, most local and regional trains (outside Paris) are branded *TER* (Transport Express Régional), organised in conjunction with regional authorities. Off-peak services are often infrequent. Some departures may be provided by bus - if the bus uses the *TER* branding and is running on a route normally provided by train then rail tickets and passes are valid.

With France being western Europe's largest country, with much long-distance travel, there are huge peaks in travel demand, notably on Friday afternoons and Sunday evenings. Fares are higher at these times, known as white periods, as well as during the normal Monday to Friday peaks. When summer holiday and winter sports peaks are also taken into account, this leads to many complications in the timetables. Most public holidays are on fixed dates which also leads to timetable variations (with extra demand either side of holidays too). Note that when engineering work affects schedules, it is not uncommon for trains to leave earlier than normal, so a last-minute check of timings is recommended.

Until recently domestic overnight services were in decline with only a handful of socially necessary services remaining. However, the French government is implementing a stategy to revive overnight rail travel, which started with the reintroduction of a daily service between Paris and Nice. Several other new routes are planned over the next few years.

Terminal stations in Paris are scattered around the periphery of the city centre (see page 33), linked by metro lines, or in some cases by *RER* services which are cross-city outer suburban routes. Beware of pickpockets operating on these lines, which can be very crowded.

CHEMIN DE FER TOURISTIQUE DU VERMANDOIS

On Sundays in July and August a heritage train runs from the SNCF station at St Quentin (Tables **255/7/8**) to Origny-Ste Benoîte (22 km). www.cftv.fr. **Services suspended due to a structural fault on a bridge.**

A luxurious dining car experience can also be had on the *Restaurant Art-Deco Express* which normally operates during May, June, July, Aug. and Oct. with an authentic restaurant car built in 1928.

Contact www.cftv.fr direct for timings and dates.

CHEMIN DE FER DE LA BAIE DE SOMME

As the name suggests, the line runs around the Somme Bay, an area north of Abbeville on the Picardy coast noted for its varied flora and fauna. Operated by historic narrow gauge steam trains, the line runs for 27 km on the route Le Crotoy - Noyelles - St.Valery - Cayeux. At Noyelles-sur-Mer connections can be made with SNCF trains (Table **261**). www.cfbs.eu

Services operate daily Apr. 9 - Sept. 25, then ②③④⑥⑦ Sept. 27 - Nov. 5 (also Oct. 31, Nov. 11, 12) with a mixture of steam and diesel traction. Two to four services run in each direction between Le Crotoy and St. Valery with a journey time of 60 minutes. A connecting diesel service from St. Valery to Cayeux on the south side of the bay operates in the summer.

TRAIN THUR DOLLER ALSACE

Situated west of Mulhouse, this 14 km standard-gauge line runs from Cernay St André to Sentheim. The station at Cernay is approximately 2 km from the SNCF station, which is served by trains on the Mulhouse - Thann line. Certain journeys are steam hauled. www.train-doller.org

Splendid scenery and varied wildlife are features of the trip along this line. Some of the railway's rolling stock dates back to 1892 and includes traditional wooden-bodied coaches. The French National Railway Museum (Cité du Train, see below) is situated nearby in Mulhouse.

Services operate from June 6: On ⑦ June to September trains depart Cernay at 1030 and 1500 (journey 90 mins) returning from Sentheim at 1330 and 1730 (journey 60 mins). On ③ in July and August trains depart Cernay at 1000 and 1430 (journey 80 mins) returning from Sentheim at 1300 and 1645 (journey 50 mins).

CHEMIN DE FER DE LA VENDÉE

Situated in the Pays de la Loire region, Mortagne-sur-Sèvre is 10 km from Cholet (Table **299**). This tourist line, normally steam hauled, runs for 22 km on the route Mortagne-sur-Sèvre - Les Épesses - Les Herbiers, noted for its three spectacular viaducts. Les Herbiers station features a 1930s period style bar.

The train runs ③⑤⑦ July 3 - Aug. 31 and ⑦ June 5 – 26, Sept. 4 – 25, departing Mortagne at 1530 for the one hour journey to Les Herbiers. Arrival back at Mortagne is at 1800. www.vendeetrain.fr

Special *Grands Express* restaurant car services also operate most ④–⑦ April 7 to October 31, departing Mortagne at 1200 for a three-hour dining experience. Bookings can be made online.

LE PETIT TRAIN DE LA RHUNE

This vintage rack railway with panoramic views takes passengers to the summit of La Rhune, a mountain in the Basque country close to the Spanish border. The electrified metre-gauge line is 4.2 km long and climbs to a height of 905 metres. www.rhune.com

The start point is Col de St Ignace (11 km from St Jean de Luz, Table **305**) which can be reached by bus. Trains run daily Apr. 14 to Sept. 4. Low Season departures from Col de St Ignace are at 0930 and every 40 minutes until 1610. High Season departures (July 11 - Sept. 4) are at 0820, 0850 then every 40 minutes until 1730.

Opened in 1924, the line uses traditional wooden-bodied coaches. The journey to the summit takes 35 minutes at a leisurely speed of 8 km/h. The wonderful scenery of the western Pyrenees can be enjoyed during the journey and the views at the summit are spectacular. A return journey takes approx two hours. There are a number of scenic walking routes from the summit station including a signed route back to Col de St Ignace.

LIGNE DE CERDAGNE (SNCF)

Also known as *Le Petit Train Jaune* (the little yellow train), this narrow gauge line is part of the SNCF (French Railways) system and runs for 63 km from Latour de Carol to Villefranche. Timings are shown in Table **354**.

Construction of this steeply graded line was completed as late as 1929 and it provides some fine views of the Pyrenees. The bright yellow trains are electrically powered using a third rail system and during the summer most trains include open sightseeing carriages. Rail or bus connections are available at both ends of the line - at Latour de Carol for Toulouse (Table **312**) and at Villefranche for Perpignan (Table **354**).

TRAIN À VAPEUR DES CÉVENNES

Based at Anduze in the foothills of the Cévennes mountains in southern France, this standard gauge line runs for 14 km to St Jean du Gard. The nearest SNCF station is Alès (Table **333**), about 15 km from Anduze.

The 40 minute journey includes some fine panoramas as the line crosses a number of spectacular viaducts. A notable nearby attraction is the *Bambouseraie* botanical gardens, originally created in 1855.

The high-season timetable runs from July 12 to Aug. 25 with departures from Anduze at 0930, 1130, 1430 and 1630, returning from St Jean du Gard at 1030, 1330, 1530 and 1730. Trains are steam hauled except for the 0930 from Anduze and 1730 from St Jean du Gard.

There is also a low-season service on most days June 2 - July 11 and Aug. 26 - Oct. 31 (but note that the line is closed on certain days in June, Sept. and Oct.). Departures from Anduze are at 1130, 1500 and 1700, returning at 1030, 1400, 1600 (with the last journey in each direction being diesel hauled). www.trainavapeur.com

CITÉ DU TRAIN - MULHOUSE RAILWAY MUSEUM

One of the largest railway museums in the world, Cité du Train (the French National Railway Museum) is situated in Mulhouse in eastern France. It is open every day except Christmas day and is served by the *Musées* stop on tram line 3 from Mulhouse railway station. www.citedutrain.com

Thalys TGV trains at Paris Nord

GERMANY

RAIL TRAVEL

See Tables **800 - 949**. National operator is Deutsche Bahn (DB) www.bahn.de. Telephone enquiries: ✆ 030 2970 (24 hrs).

The vast rail network of over 33,000 km covers all parts of Germany, with dedicated high-speed lines in various parts of the country helping to speed up long distance journeys, whether they be north to south or east to west. The sleek white *ICE* trains (InterCity Express) provide the fastest service, and whilst they have higher fares, reservation is not compulsory, and therefore there is no extra charge for pass holders. Several other train categories are in use, and these are explained at the start of the German section on page 366. Independent operator FlixTrain offers an expanding network of domestic German routes using refurbished rolling stock.

In addition to DB, there are a large number of private operators running local lines. Also, services are increasingly being franchised out to other operators, including certain *S-Bahn* networks, which are suburban services in large cities. Most urban areas have integrated ticketing, with day and period tickets being valid on all modes of public transport.

A common abbreviation in timetables is Hbf. which refers to the main station (Hauptbahnhof), whilst a mere station is simply Bf. In most cities, principal rail services are concentrated on a single main station. Since 2006 this has included Berlin, with its impressive Hauptbahnhof, with east to west and north to south lines on two different levels.

Several major airports are rail connected, that at Frankfurt having long-distance trains to various parts of the country, as well as local services.

Readers interested in the many museum and heritage lines in Germany may find the following website useful: www.vdmt.de.

DB has its own museum in Nürnberg (closed Mondays), 750m west of the main station: www.dbmuseum.de.

HARZER SCHMALSPURBAHNEN

With a total length of 140 km this system of narrow gauge lines is one of the most extensive in Europe with scheduled steam and diesel services running throughout the year. It has the added advantage of being easily accessible with no less than three interchanges with the DB network. The journey to the 1125m summit at Brocken, the highest point in northern Germany, is particularly impressive (weather permitting) passing through the scenic Hochharz National Park. Three and five day tickets are available for unlimited travel over the whole network. www.hsb-wr.de

Timings are shown in Table **867**. Connections with DB services are made at Nordhausen (Tables **865/9**), Wernigerode (Table **860**) and Quedlinburg (Table **862**).

SÄCHSISCH-OBERLAUSITZER EISENBAHNGESELLSCHAFT

A narrow gauge steam operated line situated close to the Polish and Czech border with services running throughout the year. The line, which is 16 km in total, runs from Zittau to a junction at Bertsdorf, from where trains continue to Kurort Oybin or Kurort Jonsdorf. The timetable features simultaneous steam departures from Bertsdorf to Oybin and Jonsdorf which create an impressive sight! www.zittauer-schmalspurbahn.de

Timings are shown in Table **853**, and Zittau can be reached by means of Tables **854**, **855** and **1117**.

LÖSSNITZGRUNDBAHN

Operated by Sächsische Dampfeisenbahngesellschaft mbH, this steam-operated narrow gauge line starts in the unlikely setting of the Dresden suburbs at Radebeul Ost, running for 16.6 km via Moritzburg to Radeburg. Radebeul Ost can be reached by train (Tables **842** and **857**) and the narrow gauge service runs daily throughout the year (see Table **853** for timings). The main tourist attraction in the area is the impressive Moritzburg Castle. www.loessnitzgrundbahn.de

DAMPFBAHN FRÄNKISCHE SCHWEIZ

From Forchheim in the area known as Upper Franconia (Oberfranken) in northern Bavaria, an hourly train service (VGN route R22) brings you 20 minutes later to Ebermannstadt. From there the steam railway (sometimes diesel) runs 16 km to Behringersmühle.

Trains run on ⑦ and public holidays from May to October.
Departures from Ebermannstadt are at 1005, 1405, 1605, returning from Behringersmühle at 1105, 1505, 1705. The first two journeys are generally steam operated, otherwise journeys are behind a diesel locomotive. Journey time is 45 minutes each way. There are also Christmas specials in December. Steam trains convey a buffet car.
www.dfs.ebermannstadt.de

BROHLTAL EISENBAHN

The Brohltalbahn (also known as the 'Vulkan-Express') is a charming narrow gauge railway located a few kilometres nort-west of Andernach. Services run on many dates from April to October (daily except Mondays from June to September). Steam locomotives haul trains on selected dates. The 17½ km route between Brohl and Engeln is located in the ancient volcanic region of Laacher See. The journey takes 85 minutes, climbing 400 metres from the Rhein river to the summit through attractive Eifel countryside. Brohl can be reached using hourly Mittelrheinbahn stopping services between Köln and Koblenz. www.vulkan-express.de

RÜGENSCHE BÄDERBAHN

This well-known 26.7 km narrow gauge (750 mm) line nicknamed *Rasender Roland* runs on the route Lauterbach (Mole) - Putbus - Binz - Göhren on the island of Rügen in north-eastern Germany. Timings are shown in Table **844a**. Connections with DB trains are made at Putbus where there is a service from Bergen auf Rügen (also in Table **844a**). The Lokalbahn station in Binz, however, is over 2 km from DB's Ostseebad Binz station. www.ruegensche-baederbahn.de

Services operate throughout the year with steam traction. However, the Putbus to Lauterbach narrow gauge section is seasonal.

ÖCHSLE MUSEUMS-SCHMALSPURBAHN

A 19 km narrow gauge steam railway running from Warthausen to Ochsenhausen. Warthausen is located 34 km south of Ulm and 3 km north of Biberach (Table **933**) and is served by the adjacent Warthausen station. Note, however, that most trains in Table **933** do not call at Warthausen (suggested DB connections are shown below). www.oechsle-bahn.de. Trains run on ⑦ May 1 - Oct. 9 and first ⑥ of the month June 4 - Sept. 6; also on ④ July 14 - Sept. 8.

Ulm Hbf (DB)	d.	*0947*	*1347*	Ochsenhausen	d.	1200	1615
Biberach (DB)	d.	*1009*	*1409*	Warthausen	a.	1310	1725
Warthausen	d.	1030	1445	*Biberach* (DB)	a.	*1321*	*1748*
Ochsenhausen	a.	1140	1555	*Ulm Hbf* (DB)	a.	*1347*	*1811*

Completed in 1899, the Öchsle Museums-Schmalspurbahn was one of five narrow gauge railways built by the old *Königlich Württembergischen Staats-Eisenbahnen*. Passenger traffic ceased in 1964, although freight traffic continued to use the line for a further 19 years. Tourist trains have been running since 1985.

BUCKOWER KLEINBAHN

This short standard gauge electric railway is situated in the picturesque *Märkische Schweiz* region, approximately 50 km east of Berlin. The railway's museum at Buckow station has a number of exhibits charting the region's railway heritage. The line runs 5 km from its base at Buckow to Müncheberg. Connecting trains from Berlin Ostkreuz or Lichtenberg to Müncheberg run hourly, as shown in Table **832**. The 2022 season commences on April 16.

The Kleinbahn runs on © Apr. 16 - Oct. 3 with departures from Buckow at 0955, 1055, 1155, 1425, 1525, 1625 and 1725; from Müncheberg 1020, 1120, 1220, 1450, 1550, 1650 and 1750. Journey time is 12 – 13 minutes each way. www.buckower-kleinbahn.de

GREAT BRITAIN

RAIL TRAVEL

See Tables **100 - 229**. Rail services in Great Britain are franchised out to a number of different train operating companies - a list is provided in the introduction to the Great Britain section on page 88, and codes are used in our tables to show the operator. Collectively the railway companies work together as National Rail (www.nationalrail.co.uk) which means that timetable enquiries are available irrespective of operator, as are full price tickets, which are available between any two stations. A 24-hour national telephone enquiry line is available ✆ 03457 48 49 50.

The railway infrastructure is in the hands of publicly owned Network Rail (www.networkrail.co.uk), which also runs major stations.

Best value advance purchase tickets are usually only valid on a specified train, and some other tickets may be restricted to a particular operator. Many ticket types have complex time restrictions, and there can be vast differences in the price of tickets (travelling to or from London in the rush hour can be particularly expensive).

The network of over 15,000 km of lines covers most parts of Britain, although closures in the 1960s and 1970s has left some gaps in coverage. Services are particularly dense in the south-east, where outer suburban lines from London stretch right to the coast. Kent has also benefitted from high-speed services on the line (known as HS1) to the Channel Tunnel. A dense network also operates around the northern conurbations, notably Manchester and Liverpool. Key long distance routes are the East Coast Main Line from London King's Cross to Leeds, Newcastle and Edinburgh, and the West Coast Main Line from London Euston to Birmingham, Manchester, Liverpool and Glasgow. A new high-speed line (HS2) from London to Birmingham is under construction.

All major airports have good rail links (see Table **100** for London airports). London's stations are mostly terminals linked by London Underground lines, but there are also north-south through services known as Thameslink (Tables **103/185**). Crossrail is a major project to build an east-west line in tunnel through the centre of London for cross-city suburban trains, also serving Heathrow Airport. The line will be known as the Elizabeth Line and, after numerous delays, is finally expected to open during 2022.

When major engineering work takes place it is usually at weekends and at times when commuting is at its lowest (for example Christmas and Easter), and buses may replace trains.

HERITAGE AND TOURIST RAILWAYS

There are numerous heritage railway operations up and down Great Britain, many with steam locomotives, and only a small number can be described below. In addition, contact details for the following will be found in our Great Britain section: Isle of Wight Steam Railway, Table **107**; Dartmouth Steam Railway, Table **111**; Dean Forest Railway, Table **117**; Talyllyn Railway, Table **148**, Ravenglass and Eskdale Railway, Table **159**; Ecclesbourne Valley and Peak Rail, Table **172**; North Norfolk Railway and Bure Valley Railway, Table **203**. A useful independent website is www.heritage-railways.com.

Several organisations run occasional heritage trains on the main line network - see www.railadvent.co.uk for further details.

The National Railway Museum at York is a major tourist attraction and is free of charge (www.railwaymuseum.org.uk). There is also an offshoot at Shildon (Table **212**), known as *Locomotion* (www.locomotion.org.uk). Many of the heritage railways also have their own small museums.

WEST SOMERSET RAILWAY

Based in Minehead, the West Somerset Railway runs for 32 km to Bishops Lydeard, with no fewer than eight intermediate stations. This former Great Western Railway country branch line is now one of the largest tourist attractions in south-west England. From Minehead the line runs close to the coastline through Dunster, Blue Anchor and Watchet before turning inland at Williton. The railway continues alongside the Quantock Hills before arriving at Bishops Lydeard. Most services are steam-hauled and a buffet car is conveyed on most trains. www.west-somerset-railway.co.uk

The heritage railway runs daily August. (also most dates May to Oct. and specials in December), with between three and five journeys each way. The journey takes approximately 80 minutes. Bishops Lydeard can be reached in around 30 minutes by First Bus route 28 from Taunton bus station, also calling at Taunton railway station (Tables **110**, **115**, **116**).

SEVERN VALLEY RAILWAY

Connected to the National Rail network at Kidderminster (Table **128**), the long-established Severn Valley Railway is within easy reach of Birmingham and the West Midlands. The line runs for 25 km to the attractive Shropshire town of Bridgnorth, serving four beautifully restored intermediate stations en route, which are ideal starting points for walks around the surrounding area. The railway is based at the first of these stations, Bewdley. Refreshments are available at most stations and on most trains, and a full dining car service operates most weekends, for which advance booking is required. www.svr.co.uk

Trains run regularly from Apr. 2 to Oct. 30 (but generally not ①②; please check locally) with at least six journeys each way (eight on peak dates). Trains are hauled by a steam loco or heritage diesel, the journey taking 70 - 80 minutes each way. As with most heritage lines, there are also 'Santa Specials' in December.

BLUEBELL RAILWAY

Making a connection with National Rail services at the West Sussex town of East Grinstead (48 km south of London, Table **102**) the well known Bluebell Railway runs for 17.7 km via Horsted Keynes to Sheffield Park, where the railway has its main base. Stations have been restored to show how they would have been at various points in history, that at Sheffield Park having a Victorian ambience. The line has featured in many films and TV programmes including Downton Abbey. Most trains are steam hauled.

The timetable features between three and seven journeys each way depending on the date. During the summer peak period in August, trains leave Sheffield Park at 1030, 1145, 1300, 1415, 1530, returning one hour later from East Grinstead. The journey takes 40 - 50 minutes each way. www.bluebell-railway.com

KEIGHLEY & WORTH VALLEY RAILWAY

Starting at Keighley, where it shares the station with the famously scenic Leeds - Settle - Carlisle rail line (Tables **173/4**), this attractive heritage railway runs to Haworth and Oxenhope in 'Brontë Country'. Along the way is the *Rail Story* museum at Ingrow. Trains operate Mar. 5 - Nov. 20 (daily in August, most days in June and July). Special events take place on selected dates. Timetables vary according to the date, with between four and nine return trips. Trains are steam or diesel hauled. www.kwvr.co.uk

Another popular line is the Great Central Railway, a double track main line heritage railway from Loughborough to Leicester. A *Standard 5* built at Doncaster in 1956 .

NORTH YORKSHIRE MOORS RAILWAY

Running through the North Yorkshire Moors National Park, this 29 km standard gauge line runs from Pickering to Grosmont, passing through the villages of Levisham and Goathland along the way. Grosmont is a station on the National Rail line between Middlesbrough and Whitby (Table **211**). Indeed some of the heritage line's steam trains continue on this line to the popular resort of Whitby, with the through journey taking up to two hours.

Most trains are steam hauled and convey refreshment facilities. Trains run daily from April to October, with a limited winter timetable on certain dates outside this period. www.nymr.co.uk

Details of the summer timings can be found in Table **211**. Pickering can be reached by *Yorkshire Coastliner* bus from Leeds and York.

FFESTINIOG RAILWAY

The Ffestiniog Railway, a former industrial narrow gauge line, starts on the Cambrian coast at Porthmadog, before heading inland for 22 km through the magnificent scenery of the Snowdonia National Park. The 75 minute journey ends at Blaenau Ffestiniog by which time the line has climbed over 200m. The huge slate mines clearly visible at Blaenau Ffestiniog provide a reminder of this line's original purpose when built back in 1832. Indeed, the railway can claim to be the oldest railway company in the world still operating trains. Most trains are steam-hauled, with some locomotives being over 150 years old. www.festrail.co.uk

Trains run from Mar. 26 to Nov. 3. Porthmadog station is a short walk from the town's station on the Welsh Coast line to Pwllheli (Table **148**), and interchange is also possible at Minffordd. At Blaenau Ffestiniog there are connections with the National Rail service to Llandudno (Table **160**).

WELSH HIGHLAND RAILWAY

Also running from Porthmadog (Table **148**), and operated by the same company as the Ffestiniog Railway, the recently reopened Welsh Highland Railway is the UK's longest heritage line, running for 39 km across stunning landscape to Caernarfon. The journey across Snowdonia takes a little over two hours. At Porthmadog the railway shares a newly rebuilt station with the Ffestiniog Railway, whilst Caernarfon can be reached by bus from Bangor (Table **160**) on the Chester - Holyhead line.

Trains run Mar. 29 to Oct. 29 (daily July & Aug.). Timings can be found in Table **160**. www.festrail.co.uk

SNOWDON MOUNTAIN RAILWAY

Yet another line in Wales, this narrow gauge (800mm) railway to the summit of Snowdon dates back to the 1890s and is Britain's only public rack and pinion railway. Starting from Llanberis, Summit station is reached after an arduous 7.5 km climb with the steepest gradient being 1 in 5.5. A return trip takes two and a half hours, which includes approximately 30 minutes at the summit (single tickets are also available for those who wish to walk down). www.snowdonrailway.co.uk

Trains, which may be steam or diesel operated, run from April to October at regular intervals, subject to demand. **The summit station is currently closed; the unsheltered Clogwyn station is the destination station during 2022**. Advance reservation is recommended during the summer months and during school holiday periods.

The nearest railhead is Bangor on the Chester to Holyhead line (Table **160**). Bus number 85 operated by Gwynfor Coaches runs every two hours or so from Bangor to Llanberis taking 55 minutes.

VALE OF RHEIDOL RAILWAY

The final Welsh line in our listing is the 19 km narrow gauge steam line from Aberystwyth (adjacent to the mainline station in Table **147**) to Devil's Bridge. Opened in 1902, it has operated continuously since then, and unusually remained part of the nationalised British Rail network until being privatised in 1989.

The journey through the spectacular Rheidol Valley to Devil's Bridge takes 60 minutes. From there it is possible to walk to the Mynach Falls, Jacob's Ladder, and Devil's Punch Bowl. www.rheidolrailway.co.uk

Trains run daily Mar. 26 - Nov. 3 with departures from Aberystwyth at 1030 and 1400, taking one hour to Devil's Bridge and returning at 1230 and 1615 (1605 on certain days). Additional journeys run on certain dates, mostly midweek at 1210 and 1545 and returning at 1415 and 1745.

STRATHSPEY RAILWAY

Representing Scotland in our listing, the Strathspey Railway runs from Aviemore, where connections can be made with trains on the Edinburgh to Inverness line (Table **223**), to Broomhill via Boat of Garten. The 14 km standard gauge line is mainly steam operated.

Trains run ②–⑦ in July and Aug., ④–⑦ in May, June, Sept. and Oct. (also on various dates in winter). A round trip takes 1h 40m, with trains leaving Aviemore at 1030, 1245, 1500. Light lunches are served on the 1245 departure. However, the dining car service on ⑦ and evening dining trips on ⑤ are currently suspended. www.strathspeyrailway.co.uk

ISLE OF MAN RAILWAYS

Situated in the Irish Sea some two or three hours by ferry from Heysham or Liverpool, the Isle of Man is a self-governing British dependency which is synonymous with heritage transport, and a mecca for enthusiasts and tourists alike. The main transport attractions consist of:

Isle of Man Steam Railway: Douglas - Port Erin (25 km)

Manx Electric Railway: Douglas - Laxey - Ramsey (29 km)

Snaefell Mountain Railway: Laxey - Snaefell Summit (8 km)

In Douglas, the famous horse drawn trams (dating from 1876) run along the promenade linking the town centre Sea Terminal with the Electric Railway station.

The Manx Electric Railway serves Laxey station en route where there is interchange with the Snaefell Mountain Railway. The original electric trains, dating back to 1895, are used for the journey to Snaefell Summit from where it is possible to see England, Wales, Scotland and Ireland on a clear day.

Go Explorer travelcards give unlimited travel on all scheduled rail and bus services for 1/3/5/7 days. **Go Explorer Heritage** additional provides admission to Heritage sites. Further details: see Table **229**. www.iom-ssp.unicard-uk.com.

The Electric Railway has a small museum in Douglas open on Sundays, whilst the Steam Railway has a museum in Port Erin. Further attractions on the island (not included on the Go Explore ticket) are the steam operated Groudle Glen Railway (www.ggr.org.uk) and the miniscule Great Laxey Mine Railway (www.laxeyminerailway.im). The annual heritage transport festival takes place July 27 – 31.

NORTHERN IRELAND

In Northern Ireland, trains are operated by Northern Ireland Railways (NIR), part of Translink, and are not administered by National Rail.

Apart from the line across the border to Dublin, the principal line runs from Belfast to Londonderry, with a branch to Portrush (Table **231**). Local lines run from Belfast to Bangor and Larne.

✆ +44 (0)28 90 66 66 30 www.translink.co.uk

Tourist railways in Northern Ireland include the 914mm gauge (3 foot) Giant's Causeway and Bushmills Railway, which is a great way to visit the famous Giant's Causeway on the County Antrim coast, with its thousands of interlocking basalt columns, a major tourist attraction. Running at weekends Easter to October, the 3.2 km line starts from Bushmills, which can be reached by bus from Portrush. Trains leave Giant's Causeway at 1100, 1300, 1500, and from Bushmills 30 minutes later. www.freewebs.com/giantscausewayrailway

Located adjacent to Cultra Halt on the Belfast - Bangor line (Table **233**), the Ulster Folk and Transport Museum houses one of Europe's largest transport collections. Closed Mondays. www.nmni.com

Snaefell Mountain Railway, Isle of Man. This car was built in 1895.

GREECE

RAIL TRAVEL

See Tables **1400 - 1460**. Trains in Greece are operated by TrainOSE S.A., which was state owned until 2017 but has now been privatised and is a subsidiary of Italian Railways. www.trainose.gr Call centre for reservations and information (0630-2200 daily, english spoken): ✆ 14 511.

The network of a little over 2,200 km is centered on the 500 km main line between Athína (Athens) and Thessaloníki (Table **1400**). Daytime services on the route are operated by modern InterCity trains, on which reservation is compulsory and a supplement is payable. The line has recently been electrified and upgraded with daytime trains now taking around 4 hours 20 mins, and there is also a night train taking 5½ hours.

International services consist of the summer *Hellas* Beograd - Skopje - Thessaloniki (Table **1380**), and a daytime train Sofia - Thessaloniki (Table **1560**). However, many travellers arrive by sea from one of several ports in Italy, arriving at Pátra (Patras) in the northern Peloponnese; for schedules see our ferry section. Patras, Greece's third largest city, is a destination in itself, but for those continuing to Athens there is a frequent bus service. Alternatively there are OSE buses to Kiáto (Table **1450**), connecting with trains to Athens (Table **1440**). Athens airport is also rail connected.

Tickets can be purchased at major stations (principally Athens, Thessaloniki, Larissa and Volos), and also online.

DIAKOFTÓ - KALÁVRITA RAILWAY (OSE)

Also known as the Odontotos Rack Railway, this historic 750mm gauge rack line runs for 22 km through spectacular Peloponnese scenery. Starting at Diakoftó, its climb to Kalávrita involves numerous bridges and tunnels and a height difference of 700m. Shortly after departure the line turns inland and enters the dramatic canyon of the Vouraikos river.

Operated by OSE (Greek Railways), the line runs daily throughout the year. Timings are shown in Table **1455**. www.odontotos.com

Diakoftó can be reached by OSE bus from Patra or Kiáto as shown in Table **1450**; rail services operate between Athína and Kiáto (Table **1440**).

THE PELION RAILWAY *Services advertised until Mar. 27 only*

The 16 km narrow gauge (600 mm) mountainous line from Ano Lehonia to Milies closed in 1971 but was resurrected as a museum line in 1996, operated by OSE. The scenic route, with two tunnels and nine bridges, affords spectacular views over Pagasitikos Bay. The nearest OSE station is Vólos (Table **1415**). www.trainose.gr

Trains run on ⑥⑦ leaving Ano Lehonia at 1000 for the 90 minute journey. Return from Milies is at 1500. A 15 minute stop is made at Ano Gatzea in both directions. On ⑥⑦ there is also 1200 from Milies, 1330 from Ano Lehonia (this service is currently suspended).

Services are operated using a diesel locomotive disguised to look somewhat like a steam loco, with historic wooden carriages.

HUNGARY

RAIL TRAVEL

See Tables **1200 - 1299**. A comprehensive network of over 7,000 km is operated by Hungarian State Railways (MÁV) www.mav.hu. Principal cities are connected by *IC* trains, with compulsory reservation (see the introduction to the Hungary section on page 496 for further information about reservations and supplements).

The main holiday area is around Lake Balaton, and services in the area have different schedules from mid June to late August. Northern Hungary around Eger and Miskolc is another popular area for tourism, and some of the forest railways that we have selected below are situated in this region.

The three main stations in Budapest are named after points of the compass: Keleti (East), Nyugati (West) and Déli (South). However, don't take this as an indication of the direction of travel; trains from Nyugati can go north and east, and as some international trains serve Keleti your train from the 'East' station might well be heading west! Note, however, that the day trains to Bratislava, Praha and beyond have switched from Keleti to Nyugati giving a shorter route.

A curiosity is that hourly *IC* trains leave Budapest Keleti, circumnativate Eastern Hungary via Miskolc and Debrecen, ending up back in Budapest at Nyugati station (Tables **1260** and **1270**). Main stations are connected by metro as shown on the city plan, page 31.

Apart from the metro and MÁV lines, suburban rail services in Budapest include several unconnected lines known as the HÉV, which have only recently become the responsibility of MÁV, through a subsidiary company. Day tickets for Budapest are, however, valid on almost all transport, including some MÁV lines.

BUDAPEST CHILDREN'S RAILWAY (GYERMEKVASÚT) *2021 times*

Running through the Buda hills on the outskirts of Budapest, this charming and popular diesel operated narrow gauge line, formerly known as the Pioneer Railway, runs for 12 km from Hüvösvölgy to Széchenyihegy. Apart from the engine drivers, it is operated mainly by children, who stand and salute as the train leaves the station.

The intermediate station of Jánoshegy is close to the highest point of Budapest where there is a look-out tower, and is only a short walk from the chair lift (Libegö) which offers excellent views of Budapest on the way down to Zugliget (connected by bus 291 to/from Nyugati station).

The Hüvösvölgy end of the line can be reached by taking metro line M2 to Széll Kálmán tér, then tram 61 to Hüvösvölgy terminus.

To reach the southern end of the line at Széchenyihegy take tram 59 or 61 two stops from Széll Kálmán tér to Városmajor, then the rack railway (route 60) which terminates 250m from the Children's Railway.

Trains run throughout the year (except winter Mondays), hourly 0910 to 1610 from Hüvösvölgy, and 1003 to 1703 from Széchenyihegy, increasing to every 45 minutes in summer. Journey time is 40 – 50 minutes each way. Diesel trains are the norm, but there are steam hauled journeys on certain weekends. Full timings are available from www.gyermekvasut.hu

NAGYCENK MUSEUM RAILWAY

Nagycenki Széchenyi Múzeumvasút is a 3.6 km narrow gauge tourist railway situated in the north-western corner of Hungary on the GySEV operated Sopron to Györ line (Table **1251**). The museum line starts from Fertöboz which is 11 km from Sopron (certain Sopron trains call there).

The route is Fertöboz - Barátság - Kastély (Nagycenk), so named because Kastély (Castle) station is located close to Nagycenk village and is about 25 minutes walk from Nagycenk station on the Sopron - Szombathely line (12 km from Sopron, most trains in Table **1233** call there). The Kastély terminus of this 760mm gauge light railway is adjacent to the Schloss Széchenyi, a major tourist attraction in this area. The station also features an outdoor display of plinthed narrow gauge steam locomotives.

The museum line is operated by GySEV. As the line is currently being reconstructed, trains may only be running between Kastély and Barátság and details should be verified from the GySEV website www.gysev.hu

ÁLLAMI ERDEI VASUTAK *HUNGARIAN FOREST RAILWAYS*

There are a number of narrow gauge forest railways in Hungary, mostly operated by ÁEV using diminutive diesel locomotives. Timings are available on www.kisvasut.hu. For this feature we have selected the following lines in the scenic Matra mountains area in north-eastern Hungary, which are of particular interest to tourists:

ÁEV SZILVÁSVÁRAD *Forest Railway - see above*

Route: Szalajka Fatelep - Szalajka Fátyolvizesés (5 km). Szalajka-Fatelep is situated 2 km from Szilvásvárad-Szalajkavölgy station, on the Eger - Szilvásvárad line (one stop from Szilvásvárad, Table **1299**).

Apr. 1 - Oct. 31: from Szalajka-Fatelep 0930, 1030, 1130, 1300, 1400, 1500 (also 1600 May - Sept.; 1700 June - Aug.). Trains return from Szalajka-Fátyolvizesés 1015. 1115, 1215, 1345, 1445, 1545 (also 1645 May - Sept.; 1745 June - Aug.). Journey 16 minutes. Limited winter service. Check timings locally www.szilvasvarad.hu.

ÁEV MÁTRAVASÚT *Forest Railway - see above*

Route: Gyöngyös -Szalajkaház (13 km). Connections with MÁV are made at Gyöngyös (Table **1258**); from the station approach road turn right, then about 400 metres to the ÁEV station. Journey time is 22 minutes.

Depart Gyöngyös: 0940 **E**, 1210 **E**, 1510 **F**.
Depart Szalajkaház: 1050 **E**, 1320 **E**, 1620 **F**.
E – © Mar. 12 - Apr. 30; daily May 1 - Sept. 30.
F – © Mar. 12 - Apr. 30; daily May 1 - Aug. 28; ⑥⑦ Sept. 3 – 25.
ÁEV route Gyöngyös and Mátrafüred (7 km) currently suspended.

ÁEV LILLAFÜRED *Forest Railway - see above*

Route: Miskolc (Dorottya utca) - Papírgyár - Lillafüred - Garadna (13 km). From Miskolc station (Tables **1260/1**) take tram number 1 towards Felsö-Majláth and alight at Dorottya utca (approx. 8 km).

The 13 km journey takes approximately one hour. Timings can be found on www.kisvasut.hu (click oh Menetrendek then Lillafüred Menetrend).

HUNGARIAN RAILWAY MUSEUM

Based at a 34-track roundhouse built in 1911, this extensive railway museum opened in the year 2000. www.vasuttortenetipark.hu

Located at Tatai út 95 in the northern suburbs of Budapest, it is open May. 2 to Nov. 1 daily except Mondays. During opening times, certain trains on the Budapest - Esztergom line make a special stop at *Vasútmúzeum* - see Table **1299** for timings. Otherwise, access is by bus or tram to the Rokolya utca stop. The urban transport museum at Szentendre also has some railway exhibits (21 km from Budapest by HÉV train).

Budapest's impressive Keleti (East) station

IRELAND

RAIL TRAVEL

See Tables **230 - 245**. Rail services are operated by Iarnród Éireann (IÉ) www.irishrail.ie. Telephone enquiries can be made 0800-1800 daily on ✆ +353 (0)1 8366 222.

Running on a network of nearly 2,000 km based on Dublin, many services are operated by modern diesel multiple units, with loco-hauled trains on the Dublin - Cork and Dublin - Belfast routes. The trains to Belfast, branded *Enterprise*, are operated jointly with Northern Ireland Railways (for NIR see separate section under Great Britain). The local IÉ north-south electric line in Dublin is called DART (Dublin Area Rapid Transit). Tracks in Ireland are built to the 'Irish gauge' of 1600mm (5ft 3in), not found elsewhere in Europe.

A scenic highlight of the Irish rail system is the Dublin to Wexford line, particularly the section between Dun Loaghaire (pronounced Dun Leery) and Greystones where the line hugs the coast.

The two railway stations in Dublin are named Connolly and Heuston. Both gained their current names in 1966 on the 50th anniversary of the Easter Rising and are named after James Connolly and Sean Heuston, both of whom were executed following the Rising. The two stations are linked by the frequent red line service of Dublin's LUAS tram system.

WATERFORD & SUIR VALLEY RAILWAY

Part of the abandoned Waterford to Dungarvan track bed was used to build this 8.5 km narrow gauge heritage railway, which runs mostly along the picturesque banks of the River Suir. A restored Simplex locomotive pulls two partially open carriages travelling at 15 km/h on a 40 - 50 minute round trip. www.wsvrailway.ie

Situated 12 km from Waterford, and sadly not accessible by public transport, trains run daily Apr. to Sept. leaving Kilmeaden hourly 1100 - 1500. On ⑦ these times are one hour later (also 1700 July and Aug.).

Other short heritage lines in Ireland include the Fintown Railway, the Cavan & Leitrim Railway, and the West Clare Railway.

ITALY

RAIL TRAVEL

See Tables **580 - 648**. The national operator is Trenitalia, a division of Ferrovie dello Stato (FS) www.trenitalia.com. A 24-hour telephone line is available for information and reservation changes: ✆ 89 20 21 (calls from abroad can be made 0700-2359 daily on ✆ +39 06 6847 5475). The network exceeds 16,000 km, most of which is electrified.

Dedicated high-speed lines have been a major feature of the Italian rail network since the Roma - Firenze *Direttissima* was opened in 1977. Backbone of the system is the high-speed line stretching for nearly a thousand kilometres from Torino in the north via Milano, Bologna, Firenze, Roma and Napoli to Salerno in the south (Table **600**). Headline journey time for the Milano - Roma journey is just 2h 55m. High-speed trains are branded *Frecciarossa* (Red Arrow), whilst those which divert off the line to other desinations are *Frecciargento* (Silver Arrow). Best trains on the traditional network are another colour of arrow, this time white, being branded *Frecciabianca*. Reservation is required on all high-speed trains. For other train categories see the start of the Italian section on page 282.

Whilst several countries these days have competing operators on their main lines (thanks to EU rules which favour liberalisation), Italy is unique in having an 'open access' competitor running high-speed trains. In fact, NTV (Nuovo Trasporto Viaggiatori) runs over the entire length of the core high-speed line; timings can be found on the first page of Table **600**. Private operators are also found on a multitude of local lines across the country, whilst local services in Lombardy (the Milano region) are handled by *Trenord*, jointly owned by Trenitalia and FNM (Ferrovie Nord Milano).

Italy's vast coastline, along with its Appennine mountain range stretching for over 1,000 km along the spine of the country, means that there is no shortage of scenic railway lines. For example, much of the line from the French border at Ventimiglia to La Spezia follows the coast, although a newly opened route has taken part of the line inland. Bear in mind that the most scenic routes across the mountains are by the slower conventional routes, as the high-speed line is constantly in and out of tunnels.

There are often long queues at stations, but tickets and reservations can also be made at travel agencies displaying the FS symbol.

TRENINO VERDE DELLA SARDEGNA

As well as the Trenitalia services in Table **629**, Sardinia is blessed with a network of scenic narrow gauge tourist railways (the 'green' trains) running on five different routes during the summer. Services have been cut back over the years and now run on just a few days per week on the following routes: Tempio to Palau (59 km), Mandas to Laconi (37 km), Mandas to Sadali (58 km), Arbatax to Gairo (62 km) and Sindai to Bosa (33 km). Services are diesel hauled or use diesel railcars. Details can be found on www.treninoverde.com.

PIETRARSA RAILWAY MUSEUM

Italy's principal railway museum is located in the suburbs of Naples in the old works adjacent to Pietrarsa station. Recently reopened following redevelopment work, the museum is open Friday to Sunday (also 1400-2000 on Thursdays). www.fondazionefs.it

LATVIA

RAIL TRAVEL

See Tables **1800** and **1830 - 1860**. Trains in Latvia are operated by LDZ (www.ldz.lv) using the 'Russian' track gauge of 1520mm. Hub of the network is Riga's centrally located station. Services to other Latvian cities, such as Daugavpils, are not very frequent. However, good local services run from Riga to the nearby coastal resorts.

Riga has a nightly train to Moskva and St Peterburg, a train every four days to Kyiv via Vilnius and Minsk, and a further service to Minsk via Daugavpils. There is also a weekend service from Daugavpils to Vilnius. Until the *Rail Baltica* scheme is complete (see under Estonia), there are no trains to Tallinn, apart from occasional connections at Valga. However, express bus services (Table **1800**) are available from Riga's busy coach station a few hundred metres from the railway station.

Riga has an interesting railway museum open on Tuesdays to Saturdays, a short tram ride from the city centre on the other side of the river (alight at Nacionala biblioteka). www.railwaymuseum.lv

GULBENE - ALUKSNE

Catering for both locals and tourists this 33 km narrow gauge (750 mm) line is situated in the north east of the country. Gulbene is no longer linked to the rest of the rail network (except by special trains) but there is a bus service from Riga. Trains leave Gulbene once a day at 1300 and 1800 for the 1h 25m journey to Aluksne, returning at 1525 and 1955. Steam hauled services have been temporarily withdrawn. www.banitis.lv

LITHUANIA

RAIL TRAVEL

See Tables **1800 - 1820**, **1950**. Services are operated by Lithuanian Railways (www.litrail.lt) using the 'Russian' track gauge of 1520mm. ✆ +370 700 55111. A frequent service is run from Vilnius to Kaunas, Lithuania's second city - fans of old funicular railways will enjoy a visit there. Vilnius Airport is rail connected.

Vilnius sits astride the main line linking Russia with its detached federal outpost, Kaliningrad (Table **1950**), and Vilnius also has reasonably good services to Minsk, capital of Belarus, served by the same line.

The *Rail Baltica* project to link Lithuania (and ultimately the other Baltic States) to Poland with a standard-gauge line has been slow off the ground, but a limited service runs across the border between Bialystok and Kaunas (Tables **93** and **1042**). There are plans to eventually reach Tallinn, and possibly even Helsinki. In the meantime, travel between Lithuania and its northern neighbours is mostly by bus (Table **1800**).

A small indoor railway museum is located within the station building at Vilnius, and some outdoor exhibits are stabled in an adjacent siding.

A train from Vilnius having arrived at Kaunas

LUXEMBOURG

RAIL TRAVEL

See Tables **445/6/9** (also **384**, **390**, **915**). Operator is Société Nationale des Chemins de fer Luxembourgeois (CFL) www.cfl.lu. Telephone enquiry line: ✆ +352 2489 2489.

This small country has a rail network of only 275 km, but services are fairly frequent, and there are good international links, including *TGV* services to Paris and hourly trains to Brussels and Koblenz.

The country is heavily forested, with some attractive scenery, particularly on the main line to the north. One of the attractions of exploring the country by rail is that 2nd class travel has been free since March 2020. Most rail stations are small with few facilities.

AMTF TRAIN 1900

Luxembourg's only preserved steam railway is situated close to the French and Belgian borders, operated by Assoc. des Musée et Tourisme Ferroviaires (AMTF). The line runs from Pétange to Bois-de-Rodange, pausing at Fond-de-Gras where the railway is based. www.train1900.lu

Pétange can be reached by regular CFL local train (Table **449**) whilst Rodange CFL station is approximately 2 km from Bois-de-Rodange.

Trains run on ⑦ and holidays May to September. Services marked 🚂 are known as *Le Train 1900* and are hauled by an historic steam locomotive. Other services are operated by a diesel railcar.

		🚂		🚂		🚂		
Pétange-TRAIN 1900...... d.	1315	1415	1515	1615	1715	1820	1858	...
Fond-de-Gras .... a.	1344	1442	1527	1642	1737	1855	1916	...
Fond-de-Gras .... d.	1420	1520	1620	1720	1810	...	...	...
Bois-de-Rodange .... a.	1425	1525	1625	1725	1815	...	...	...
		🚂		🚂		🚂		
Bois-de-Rodange .... d.	...	...	1430	1530	1730	1730	1820	...
Fond-de-Gras .... a.	...	...	1435	1535	1736	1736	1824	...
Fond-de-Gras .... d.	1245	1320	1445	1540	...	1740	1830	...
Pétange-TRAIN 1900...... a.	1309	1345	1506	1603	...	1803	1853	...

NETHERLANDS

RAIL TRAVEL

See Tables **450 - 499**. National rail company is Nederlandse Spoorwegen (NS) www.ns.nl ✆ +31 30 751 5155.

A comprehensive network of over 3,000 km provides frequent regular-interval services linking most towns and cities. Most services are provided by NS, although other operators, notably Arriva, are contracted to run local train services in some parts of the north and east.

Fast domestic trains, calling only at principal stations, are classified *Intercity*, whilst local stopping trains are known as *Sprinter* services. A further category is *Intercity direct* for which a supplement is payable - these use the *HSL-Zuid* high-speed line which opened in 2009 linking Amsterdam and Schiphol Airport with Antwerpen via Rotterdam. Through services to Paris via Brussels are operated by *Thalys*, and *Eurostar* run direct services between Amsterdam and London. Schiphol airport is well served by rail, not only to Amsterdam but to other parts of the country.

Through tickets can be purchased between all stations in the Netherlands, regardless of operator. A national stored-value smartcard scheme operates throughout the country known as OV-chipkaart, used for all public transport (for further information see the introduction to the Netherlands section on page 242). Cycle hire and cycle and baggage storage are usually available at larger stations. Smaller stations are usually unstaffed, but all stations have ticket vending machines. Seat reservations are not available for domestic journeys.

A recent development (2019) is the conversion of the Hoek van Holland to Rotterdam line, once traversed by many long distance trains connecting with ferries, into a metro line, now part of Rotterdam's metro system.

MUSEUMSPOORLIJN S.T.A.R.

Located in the north-eastern corner of the Netherlands, this former NS line runs from Veendam to Stadskanaal, where the railway is based. Veendam can be reached by local train from Groningen (Table **498**). Trains can be steam or diesel hauled. www.stadskanaalrail.nl

The timetable below operates on ③⑦ July 11 - Aug. 28. Trains also run on numerous other dates between June and Dec.

Stadskanaal .... d.	1045	1400	...	Veendam .... d.	1200	1510	...
Veendam .... a.	1125	1440	...	Stadskanaal .... a.	1240	1550	...

VELUWSCHE STOOMTREIN MAATSCHAPPIJ (VSM)

Running on the route Apeldoorn - Eerbeek - Dieren (22 km), this line connects with NS services at both ends: Apeldoorn (Table **498**) and Dieren (Table **475**). It runs through the Veluwe nature area and, on certain dates, a ride on the train can be combined with a boat trip along the River IJssel between Dieren and Zutphen (boats are scheduled to connect with the trains). The journey back to Apeldoorn can be completed by train from Zutphen (Table **498**). Special tickets are available for this interesting day trip known as *De Veluwe-IJssel-Boemel*. www.stoomtrein.org.

Steam services operate ⑦ June 5 - July 3 (also June 6) between Apeldoorn and Eerbeek. Between July 10 - Aug. 28 steam services operate ⑦–⑤ between Apeldoorn to Dieren, via Eerbeek.

During both operating periods services call at the museum and allow a 45 minutes to visit the Steam Depot.

MUSEUMSTOOMTRAM HOORN - MEDEMBLIK

This long-established standard gauge line runs for 20 km between Hoorn and Medemblik and is easily accessible from Amsterdam (Table **461**/**470**). All trains are operated by steam traction. A popular triangular journey (known locally as *De Historische Driehoek*) uses the boat between Medemblik and Enkhuizen (see below), returning to Hoorn or Amsterdam by rail. A day ticket valid on steam tram and boat services is available. The station at Hoorn includes a steam tram museum. www.stoomtram.nl

(tram)		A	B	(boat)		A	B
Hoorn .... d.	...	1040	1140	Enkhuizen .... d.	...	1040	1040
Medemblik .... a.	...	1200	1310	Medemblik .... a.	...	1155	1155
(boat)		A	B	(tram)		A	B
Medemblik .... d.	...	1320	1320	Medemblik .... d.	...	1320	1420
Enkhuizen .... a.	...	1450	1450	Hoorn .... a.	...	1440	1540

A ②–⑦ June 1 – 26 (also June 6); daily June 28 - Sept. 4; ②–⑦ Sept. 6 - Oct. 2 (also Oct. 8, 9); daily Oct. 15 – 23; ⑥⑦ Oct. 29 - Nov. 12.

B June 5, 6, July 16 - Aug. 31, Oct. 15 – 23.

NARROW GAUGE

Fans of narrow gauge trains will enjoy the Stoomtrein Katwijk Leiden along the shore of Lake Valkenburg, along with the associated museum. Open weekends June to Sept. (also ②④ July 12 - Aug. 18). Reach by bus from Den Haag or Leiden. www.stoomtreinkatwijkleiden.nl

A further narrow gauge line and museum is the RTM Ouddorp situated in Zeeland and reached by bus from Roterdam's Spikenisse metro station to Port Zelande, which is part way along this short line.

Operates ③⑥ June, Sept. and Oct. (not Sept. 24), ③④⑥ July & Aug. www.rtm-ouddorp.nl

MUSEUM STOOMTREIN GOES - BORSELE

Evoking railways of the 1930's, this standard gauge line runs for 16 km across the beautiful landscape of the province of Zeeland. Starting from Goes (a short walk from the NS station, Table **450**) steam trains run for 40 minutes to the scenic village of Hoedekenskerke calling at Kwadendamme. Departures from Goes ⑦ Apr. 3 - Oct. 23 at 1045 and 1415, returning at 1240 and 1610. Main operating days are ⑦–④ July 3 - Aug. 28 (also ②③⑦ Oct. 18 – 26). An additional diesel service runs the full length of the line to Baarland on ②③ July 10 – Aug. 31. www.destoomtrein.nl

UTRECHT RAILWAY MUSEUM

The National Railway Museum is located in the former Maliebaan railway station in Utrecht, open ②–⑦ (also ① in school holidays). The museum has a dedicated hourly railway service from Utrecht Centraal (or 1.6 km on foot). www.spoorwegmuseum.nl

A London to Amsterdam *Eurostar* train at Rotterdam

NORWAY

RAIL TRAVEL

See Tables **770 - 787**. Many trains are operated by the Vy Group (using the name Vy), owned by the Norwegian government. www.vy.no. Services between Oslo and Stavanger are now operated by GoAhead Nordic while services Oslo – Trondheim / Åndalsnes, Hamar – Røros – Trondheim and Trondheim – Steinkjer - Bodø are mostly operated by SJ Nord.

As you might expect, a high proportion of the country's 4,000 km rail network can be regarded as scenic. For those touring the country by rail, a circular route can often be arranged by including buses or boats in the itinerary. Trips to the far north can also be extended by catching the bus from Bodø to Narvik (Table **787**) and returning through Sweden. Since Norway also has a border with Russia, our Lapland bus table (**799**) even includes a service to Murmansk.

Trains convey 2nd-class seating, whilst most medium- and long-distance trains also convey *Komfort* accommodation, a dedicated area with complimentary tea/coffee and newspapers (supplement payable). Sleeping cars have one- and two-berth compartments; a sleeper supplement is payable per compartment (for two people travelling together, or sole use for single travellers). Long-distance trains convey a bistro car serving hot and cold meals, drinks and snacks. Reservation is possible (and recommended) on all long-distance trains. Reserved seats may not be marked, but your confirmation specifies carriage and seat/berth numbers.

FLÅMSBANA

Branching off the Olso to Bergen line (Table **781**), this is undoubtedly one of Europe's most spectacular railway journeys. Trains descend from an altitude of 865m at Myrdal to sea-level at Flåm in just 20 km. In between the 20 tunnels there is some breathtaking scenery and, to reassure passengers, the trains have no less than five sets of brakes, each of which can stop the train on the extremely steep inclines! Timings are shown in Table **781**. This journey can be included as part of various circular excursions, such as the *Norway in a Nutshell* tour (see Table **781a** for boat and bus connections). For further details see www.visitflam.com

KRØDERBANEN

This former NSB line closed to passengers in 1958 but was resurrected as a museum line in the 1980s. Operated by the Norwegian Railway Club, it is Norway's longest museum railway at 26 km and makes an ideal day trip from Oslo. It runs from the railway's base at Krøderen to Vikersund; which is situated between Drammen and Hønefoss (Table **780**). It's 150th anniversary is celebrated this year on August 13, when trains run for invited guests only.

Trains run every ⑦ from June 26 to Aug. 28 (also on Aug. 6, 20). For timings see www.njk.no.

GAMLE VOSSEBANEN

Also operated by the Norsk Jernbaneklubb, the 18 km 'Old Voss Steam Railway' during 2021 runs from Garnes to Haukeland, crossing the Bergen to Voss line (Table **781**) at Arna, where the station is 300m from the old station on the steam railway. Both ends of the line can also be reached by bus from Bergen bus station.

Services are hauled by one of the original steam locomotives built for the Bergen Railway in 1913 and the restored teak coaches are from the same period. Until 1964 the line was actually part of the main Oslo - Bergen railway. www.njk.no. Trains run on ⑦ June 12 - Sept. 11 as follows:

Garnes .... d.	1130	1430	...	Haukeland .... d.	1215	1515	...
Arna (old station) ...... d.	1140	1440	...	Arna (old station) .. d.	1235	1535	...
Haukeland .... a.	1200	1515	...	Garnes.................. a.	1245	1545	...

NORWEGIAN RAILWAY MUSEUM

The museum is located 3 km from the centre of Hamar, on the Oslo - Lillehammer - Trondheim line (Table **785**), and is open daily except Mondays (daily June / August). Bus number 1 runs from the railway station. www.jernbanemuseet.no.

POLAND

RAIL TRAVEL

See Tables **1000 - 1099**. Long-distance trains are operated by PKP Intercity (www.intercity.pl). The best trains on the principal routes are classified *EIP* (Express InterCity Premium), which are operated with the latest sleek *Pendolino* type trains. Other fast trains are *EIC* or *IC* (along with international *EC* trains), plus the cheaper *TLK* trains which make more stops. Reservation is compulsory on all trains operated by PKP Intercity, whose trains are shown in red on PKP timetables and station departure sheets. See page 465 for further details of train classifications.

Trains on the Warszawa - Berlin route are operated jointly with German Railways and are branded *Berlin-Warszawa Express*, whilst Russian Railways operate several trains to or through Warszawa (including the Berlin - Moscow *Talgo* train).

Things get more complicated when it comes to local trains. Przewozy Regionalne is the main operator, using the name PolRegio (polregio.pl), with train categories *RE* or *R* (local trains are shown without numbers in our tables). However, several local authorities have set up their own railway organisations, such as Koleje Wielkopolskie and Koleje Ślaskie. Outer suburban services in the Warsaw area come under Koleje Mazowieckie, whilst local electric services in the Tricity area (Gdansk, Sopot, Gdynia) have long been the preserve of PKP subsidiary SKM Trojmiasto. Ticket inter-availability between operators is complex.

Poland is a large country with many scenic rail routes, notably in the more hilly areas in the south of the country. In addition to the standard gauge network, the country used to be covered with hundreds of kilometres of narrow gauge lines, and some of these survived in PKP ownership as late as 2001. Since closure, many sections have resurfaced as museum lines, some with regular summer operation, others with only occasional trains. Although timings are not up to date, further information can be found on www.narrowrail.net, and two of the lines are included below.

WOLSZTYN

Wolsztyn (Table **1099**) is located some 80 km south-west of Poznań and is famous for its steam depot running the last regularly timetabled steam hauled passenger services on a main line in Europe. Although these ceased in 2014, a service was resurrected in May 2017 running between Wolsztyn and Poznań on Saturdays, and on Monday to Fridays between Wolsztyn and Leszno. This year services run between Wolsztn and Leszno only until June 10 as detailed below.

	Ⓐ		Ⓐ			Ⓐ		Ⓐ	
Wolsztyn......... d.	0603	...	1148	...	Poznań .... d.	...	...	...	...
Leszno .... a.	0721	...	1300	...	Leszno......... d.	0743	...	1343	...
Poznań .... a.	...	...	...	...	Wolsztyn .... a.	0907	...	1506	...

For latest timings see www.parowozowniawolsztyn.pl; steam services may be suspended at certain times. The atmospheric steam depot at Wolsztyn is a short walk from the station and can be visited for a small fee.

WARSAW RAILWAY MUSEUM

Warsaw's railway museum is located in the former Warszawa Glówna terminus in the city centre, between Centralna and Zachodnia stations in ul.Towarowa. There is an extensive outdoor display of rolling stock as well as indoor exhibits. Open daily. www.stacjamuzeum.pl

SOCHACZEW MUSEUM RAILWAY

A short walk from Sochaczew station (local trains approximately hourly from Warszawa Wschodnia) is the narrow gauge station which has been made into a museum with a large collection of narrow gauge rolling stock, open daily. See www.stacjamuzeum.pl (link top right).

The season operates Apr. 30 - Sept. 24 mainly on ⑥⑦. On ⑤⑥⑦ July 1 - Aug. 28 a steam hauled 'Retro' train leaves the museum at 1030 for a trip to Wilcze Tułowskie in the Kampinos Forest. The itinerary includes a guided forest walk, and arrival back at Sochaczew is at 1520.

ZNINSKA KOLEJ WASKOTOROWA

The 12 km Znin - Gasawa railway is the last remaining section of a much larger narrow gauge (600mm) network in this area which, by 1913, had reached 79 km in length. Regular passenger services were withdrawn in 1962 but since 1976 tourist trains have been running regularly between Znin and Gasawa. Znin can be reached by bus from Bydgoszcz.

A varied collection of narrow gauge rolling stock is situated adjacent to Wenecja Muzeum station, where trains arrive 10 - 15 minutes before the time shown. www.muzeumznin.pl

Trains run May 1 - Aug. 28, also during the Archeological Festival during September. Please confirm timings locally.

				R	S				S	R	R
Znin......... d.	0900	1030	1205	1350	1440	Gasawa ... d.	1030	1205	1345	1400	1530
Wenecja § d.	0940	1110	1250	1435	1525	Wenecja § d.	1110	1250	1435	1520	1620
Gasawa ... a.	1015	1150	1330	1515	1610	Znin......... a.	1140	1320	1505	1550	1745

Other services: from Zinin 1535 ⑥⑦ July / Aug.
from Gasawa 1625 **R**, 1705 ⑥⑦ July / Aug.

R – ①–⑤ May / June, ⑥⑦ July / Aug. **S** – ⑥⑦ May / June, ①–⑤ July / Aug.
§ – Wenecja Muzeum.

CHABÓWKA AND JAWORZYNA ŚLĄSKA

The 'Skansen' at Chabówka is an extensive open air railway museum, located on the scenic Kraków - Zakopane line (Table **1066**). Steam trips normally run on several summer dates June - August from the Skansen to Kasina Wielka. www.parowozy.pl

Another railway museum is located at Jaworzyna Śląska on the Wroclaw - Jelenia Góra line (Table **1084**), open April - Sept. (closed ① Oct. - Apr.). www.muzeumtechniki.pl

Polish EIP (Express InterCity Premium) *Pendolino* train

Photos in this Rail Extra feature are by
Brendan Fox - pages 653 - 655, 657, 658, 660 - 662
Graham Benbow - pages 656, 659, 663, 664

PORTUGAL

RAIL TRAVEL

See Tables **690 - 699**. Operator is Comboios de Portugal (CP) www.cp.pt Telephone enquiries (24 hours): ✆ 808 109 110.

The network is approximately 2,500 km, and as with Spain, trains run on tracks of 'Iberian' gauge, 1668 mm. Backbone of the network is the 337 km line between Lisboa and Porto, with the longest distance trains running all the way from Faro in the south to Porto in the north. The best trains are the modern *AP* (Alfa Pendular) trains, which along with *IC* and international trains require advance reservation. Lines in the north of the country are particularly scenic, especially the Duoro Valley line to Régua and Pocinho (see Table **694** and the tourist train below).

Lisboa's traditional terminus at Santa Apolónia was joined by an impressive through station in 1998 called Oriente, located 6 km north of the centre. Noted for its metal and glass roof, it is part of a major transport hub including metro and bus links. Trains to Cascais, however, leave from Cais do Sodre station, whilst Rossio is the city centre terminus for trains to Sintra (see city plan on page 32).

Another impressive feature of Lisbon's transport network is the *25 de Abril* bridge across the Tagus, to which railway tracks were added under the road in 1999, and which is sometimes compared to San Francisco's Golden Gate Bridge. As well as CP trains to the south, it carries local trains of private operator *Fertagus*.

The national railway museum is located at Entroncamento, open on ②–⑦ 10.00 to 18.00. www.fmnf.pt Access is from Rua Ferreira de Mesquita on the north side of the tracks across the footbridge. There are also several small regional railway museums.

COMBOIO HISTÓRICO

This steam hauled tourist train runs in summer on the scenic Douro line between Régua and Tua. Details of dates and timings can be found in Table **694**. The train is operated by CP at special fares.

ROMANIA

RAIL TRAVEL

See Tables **1600 - 1680**. State railway Căile Ferate Române (CFR) operates an extensive network of over 10,000 km, and trains of its passenger subsidiary CFR Călători link all major towns. www.cfrcalatori.ro Telephone information is available on ✆ 021 9521 for domestic traffic or ✆ 021 314 5528 for international services.

Most main lines are electrified and quite fast, but branch line services are very slow. Trains are fairly punctual and very cheap. Except for local trains, reserve and pay a speed supplement in advance (tickets issued abroad include the supplement). Cheapest are *regio* (very slow), then *Interregio*, and finally *IC* trains, whose prices approach Western levels. Food and drink is normally available only on *IC* and some *IR* trains. Couchette (*cuşeta*) or sleeper (*vagon de dormit*) accommodation is inexpensive. An increasing number of services are now operated by private operators, such as Regio Călători, Transferoviar Grup SA, and Softrans S.R.L., as indicated in relevant tables.

VIŞEU DE SUS / MURAMUREŞ FOREST RAILWAY

Situated in the north of Romania, the Vaser Valley forest railway has been transporting wood to a processing plant in Vişeu de Sus since its opening in 1932, and claims to be the last European forestry railway. The 22 km narrow gauge railway also started running steam hauled tourist trains in the year 2000. Visitors can enjoy the remote mountain scenery during the very leisurely two hour journey from Vişeu de Sus along the winding valley to Paltin, where there is a break before the return journey.

Vişeu de Sus is situated 7 km from the CFR station at Vişeu de Jos (Table **1660**) and it can also be reached by bus from Baia Mare or Sighetu Marmatiei. The train runs on ④–⑦ Mar. 3 - Dec. 18, (daily May - Oct.) leaving Vişeu de Sus at 0900, arriving back at approximately 1500. www.mocanita-maramures.com

RUSSIA

RAIL TRAVEL – Consult latest official government travel advice

Operator of this vast system is RZhD www.rzd.ru. Flagship trains are those running between Moskva and St Peterburg (Table **1900**), which consist of high-speed *Sapsan* trains by day, taking under four hours, and a variety of night trains to suit every budget, from low-cost double deck trains to expresses offering the height of luxury. Modern high-speed trains are also found on the St Peterburg - Helsinki route, branded *Allegro*. Russian trains are spacious and run on broad gauge tracks (1520mm).

Our tables also include the famous Trans-Siberian Railway (Table **1990**), with the *Rossiya* running over 9,000 km between Moskva and Vladivostok, as well as trains to Beijing, either via Mongolia or the Trans-Manchurian route. The more northerly 'BAM' route is shown in Table **1991**.

Details of the various types of accommodation to be found on Russian trains will be found on page 535. Many trains in Russia run on alternate days, and this page also explains our system for what happens to trains running on even or uneven dates at the end of months with 31 days.

All times in Russia are now shown in local time. Russia and Belarus do not observe daylight saving time, so complications arise when countries to the west change their clocks on the last Sundays in March and October; this is handled in our tables with footnotes or duplicate columns.

The Museum of Russian Railways is located in St Petersburg. Museum tours include visiting a collection of rare and legendary steam trains, diesels, electric locomotives, railcars and other rolling stock. Open daily expect ②. www.rzd-museum.ru

SERBIA

RAIL TRAVEL

See Tables **1360 - 1380**. The 3,300 km network is operated by Srbija Voz www.srbvoz.rs which is the passenger arm of the state railway company.

Both daytime and nighttime international services link Beograd with Ljubljana, Zagreb and Budapest, whilst Sofia has one daytime train. There is also a night train on the lengthy run to Thessaloniki via Skopje, whilst travel to Timisoara in Romania involves trains of a more local nature, changing at Vršac.

Scenic highlight, however, is the line from Beograd to neighbouring Montenegro, passing through its capital Podgorica before continuing to the coast at Bar. Opened as late as 1976, this winding 524 km line (Table **1370**) involves no fewer than 435 bridges and 254 tunnels!

There is an indoor railway museum in Beograd at 6 Nemanjina Street, open on Mondays to Fridays 0900-1500 hrs., and a narrow gauge section near Pozega station. For details see the *Museum* link: www.zeleznicesrbije.com

ŠARGANSKA OSMICA (ŠARGAN EIGHT)

Threading its way through the scenic Mokra Gora mountain region, close to the border with Bosnia, this line was originally part of a narrow gauge route between Beograd and Sarajevo which was closed in 1974. Between 1999 and 2003 the line was rebuilt as a tourist railway using diesel or steam traction. www.zeleznicesrbije.com

The 15.4 km narrow gauge (760 mm) line runs from Mokra Gora to Šargan Vitasi, passing through 22 tunnels and over five bridges. The nearest mainline ŽS station is Užice on the Beograd - Bar main line (Table **1370**). The 40 km journey from Užice to Mokra Gora can be made by bus or taxi.Trains run daily Apr. 15 - Oct. 31, departing Mokra Gora at 1030 and 1330. Total journey time for a return trip is approximately 2½ hours.

SLOVAKIA

RAIL TRAVEL

See Tables **1170 - 1197**. The national rail operator is Železničná spoločnosť (ŽSSK) www.slovakrail.sk. Track and infrastructure is managed by ŽSR www.zsr.sk. Call centre (24h) is ✆ 18 188, or from abroad ✆ +421 24 48 58 188.

An efficient network of 3,600 km is operated, with the fastest trains being the handful of *IC* trains on the principal route between Bratislava and Košice (Table **1180**). On the international Praha (Prague) to Košice route, the state railways compete for passengers with two other companies, Regiojet and Leo Express.

Trains are cheap, but often crowded. In fact most resident children, seniors and students qualify for free travel (except on *IC* trains or cross-border services) in a recently introduced scheme. Qualifying EU citizens may also be entitled to register for the scheme (especially children under 15 and seniors of 62 or over).

Apart from the small number of *EC* and *IC* trains, for which higher fares apply, the fastest trains are *expresný* (*Ex*) and *Rýchlik* (*R*, usually those with three-digit train numbers). Cheaper are *zrýchlený* (semi-fast) and *osobný* (very slow). Sleeping cars and couchettes are provided on most overnight trains (reserve at all main stations, well in advance in summer). Seat reservations may be made at station counters marked R, and are recommended for express trains.

The most scenic areas are close to the Tatra mountains, particularly the High Tatras (Vysoké Tatry) where a network of electrified narrow gauge lines is run by ŽSR subsidiary TEŽ (Table **1182**). Most lines in the centre of the country, radiating from Banská Bystrica, are also scenic, particularly the line following the River Hron (Table **1188**).

ČIERNOHRONSKÁ ŽELEZNICA

After closure in 1982, enthusiasts eventually managed to save this narrow gauge (760 mm) forestry railway and transform it into a tourist railway. It is the last remaining section of a once extensive system in central Slovakia.

The line starts at Chvatimech, which is served by all trains between Banská Bystrica and Brezno (Table **1188**, eight minutes before Brezno). The first 7 km to Šánske is, however, currently being rebuilt. 5 km further on is Čierny Balog, the railway's headquarters, where the line continues 4 km to Dobroč, and there is also a 4 km branch to Vydrovo. www.chz.sk

Chvatimech - Šánske - currently no service.

Čierny Balog - Šánske: ⑥ Apr. 3 - June 30, Sept. 9 - Oct. 29; daily July 1 - Sept. 4. From Čierny Balog: 1000, 1200, 1500. From Šánske: 1030, 1230, 1530. Journey time 20 minutes; steam hauled in high-season.

Čierny Balog - Vydrovo Konečná: daily July 1 - Sept. 4. From Čierny Balog: 0930, 1030, 1130, 1300, 1400, 1500, 1600. From Vydrovo Konečná 0950, 1050, 1150, 1320, 1420, 1520, 1620. Journey time 20 - 25 minutes.

Čierny Balog - Dobroč: ⑥ Apr. 3 - June 30, Sept. 9 - Oct. 29; daily July 1 - Sept. 1. From Čierny Balog: 1100, 1400. From Dobroč: 1125, 1425. Journey time 20 minutes; steam hauled in high season.

DETSKÁ ŽELEZNICA KOŠICE

This short railway in Košice was completed in 1956 as one of the Pioneer Railways in the former Czechoslovakia. The line was built to allow children to learn how railways operate, so most of the railway's functions were performed by children. Some of the railway's rolling stock dates from as far back as 1884. www.detskazeleznica.sk

The 4.2 km narrow gauge line runs from Čermel' to Alpinka. Čermel' can be reached from the main station by tram 2 to Havlíčkova then bus 14.

Trains run on © Apr. to Oct. (daily in July and August) with between four and six journeys each way.

A long-distance train at Bratislava Hlavná Stanica (main station)

NATIONAL RAILWAY MUSEUM

This is located at Bratislava Vychod depot and is open daily Apr. 15 to Oct. 15 (1000-1700). Nearest station is Bratislava Rača, served by local trains on the line to Trnava, and 1.6 km from the museum. The website (www.mdc.sk) also has a list of special heritage trains running on the Slovak network on various dates throughout the year. A special annual *Rendez* event takes place at the museum in June.

There is also an indoor transport museum near Bratislava hlavná station at Šancová 1/A, closed on Mondays. www.muzeumdopravy.com.

SLOVENIA

RAIL TRAVEL

See Tables **1300 - 1320**. Slovenia's relatively small network of 1,200 km is operated by Slovenske Železnice (SŽ) www.slo-zeleznice.si. Telephone information is available from within Slovenia on ✆ 080 81 11.

Hub of the network is the capital Ljubljana. The best trains are the *IC* trains on the Maribor route, and the *EC* trains which continue beyond Maribor into Austria. Other international links include those to München, Budapest and Beograd, all with a choice of daytime or overnight timings, except that the night train to Budapest runs only in high summer.

LJUBLJANA RAILWAY MUSEUM

Ljubljana has a railway museum in a former roundhouse at Parmova 35, open daily except Mondays from 1000 to 1800.

Steam-hauled heritage trains run between Jesenice and Nova Gorica on the scenic Bohinj line, which can also be booked as part of a guided tour. Operating two to four times per month from May to October, the train leaves Jesenice at 0903, returning at 1953. **No dates currently advertised for 2022**. Details: www.slo-zeleznice.si

SPAIN

RAIL TRAVEL

See Tables **650 - 689**. National rail company is Red Nacional de los Ferrocarriles Españoles (RENFE) www.renfe.es. ✆ 912 320 320.

The opening of the Madrid - Sevilla high-speed line in 1992 was just the start of what is now Europe's longest high-speed network. Particularly important is the 620 km Madrid - Barcelona line, which also continues northwards into France, and which has taken a large market share away from the airlines. Another principal route runs from Madrid to Valencia and Alicante, and in fact travel to just about any area of Spain can benefit from a high-speed train for at least part of the way. Trains which run purely on these lines are classified *AVE* (Alta Velocidad Española). For other train categories see the introduction to the Spanish section on page 316.

The traditional network is built to the 'Iberian' track gauge of 1668 mm, whereas the new high-speed network is standard gauge (1435 mm). Trains which switch between the two networks, such as the *Altaria* and *Alvia* trains, therefore have to have gauge changing equipment.

Spain also has around 1,200 km of narrow gauge lines, built to metre gauge, and in the main these are in the hands of a separate division of RENFE known as FEVE. These are largely in coastal areas, and particularly interesting is the long and scenic narrow gauge line along the north coast of Spain (Table **687**), along with the associated Bilbao to León line (Table **683**). Several narrow gauge lines are run by other operators, such as Euskotren, FGC, and FGV.

Reservation is compulsory on all services for which a train category (*AVE*, *IC* etc) is shown in the timing columns of this timetable. RENFE attaches a high degree of importance to punctuality and has a comprehensive scheme of refunds if trains run late.

VALL DE NÚRIA

A 12.5 km rack railway operated by Ferrocarrils de la Generalitat de Catalunya (FGC) runs from Ribes Enllaç to Núria. The train climbs from 905m at Ribes to 1967m at Nuria and passes through some fine scenery. At one point the train is travelling above the narrow gorge of the River Nuria. Table **658** has the timings. www.valldenuria.cat

Ribes Enllaç station is adjacent to RENFE's Ribes de Freser station on the Barcelona to Latour de Carol line (Table **656**).

CERCEDILLA - COTOS MOUNTAIN RAILWAY

Apart from the FEVE network, RENFE has a narrow gauge line of its own. It runs from Cercedilla to Cotos and is actually part of Madrid's suburban network, allocated route number **C9**. The 18 km journey through the scenic *Sierra de Guadarrama* region takes around 45 minutes (25 minutes Cercedilla to Puerto de Navacerrada). This is excellent walking country and a number of marked routes are available at stations en-route.

Regular services (at least hourly) operate between central Madrid and Cercedilla (line **C8** - journey 80 minutes from Atocha or 70 mins from Chamartín). Special *C9* return fares are available between any station on the Cercanías network and any station on the narrow gauge line. See www.renfe.com under the heading 'Cercanias' (suburban) then 'Madrid'.

Trains generally run from Cercedilla at 0935, 1135, 1335, 1535, 1735, returning from Cotos at 1043, 1243, 1443, 1643, 1843.

C9 route is currently suspended.

FERROCARRIL DE SÓLLER

Opened in 1912, the line from Mallorca's capital Palma to the northern town of Sóller is operated by historic electric traction and runs through the scenic *Sierra de Tramuntana* region. The 28 km line is built to the unusual gauge of 914mm (one yard).

From Sóller a narrow gauge tramway runs for 5 km to Port de Sóller. Further details of both lines are in Table **674**. www.trendesoller.com

A modern RENFE suburban train at Bilbao Abando station, previously known as Estación del Norte

SWEDEN

RAIL TRAVEL

See Tables **730 - 768**. National rail company is SJ AB www.sj.se. The company was formed when Statens Järnvägar (SJ) was split into different companies. Telephone enquiries: ✆ +46 771 75 75 75 (daily 0600-2200, but ticket purchase only available Mon-Fri 0800-1700).

The best services are operated by high-speed trains (*Snabbtåg*, shown as *Sn* in our tables) running at up to 200 km/h and using either X2000 trains or the newer SJ 3000 units. Supplements are required on *Snabbtåg*. Some local lines are run by regional authorities or private companies such as Norrtåg www.norrtag.se; see page 345 for other operators.

Sleeping-cars have one or two berths in 2nd class, couchettes have six berths; female-only compartments are available. 1st-class sleeping-cars with en-suite shower and WC run on many overnight services; 2nd-class compartments have washbasins, while a shower and WC are at the end of the carriage. Long-distance trains have a refreshment service. Many trains have a family coach with a playroom, and facilities for the disabled. Seat reservations are compulsory on *Sn*, *IC* and overnight trains, also on services operated by independent operators *Snälltåget*, *MTR Express* and *FlixTrain*. *Sn* services also operate between Sweden and Copenhagen via the Öresund bridge and tunnel but it is better to use the frequent local trains for short journeys.

'C' (for Central) in timetables etc. means the town's main station. *Biljetter* indicates the station ticket office, often with limited opening hours, but ticket machines are also widely in use.

Journeys north from Stockhom along the coast to Umeå and beyond have been revolutionised by the *Botniabanan* which opened in 2010. An interesting alternative route to the far north of Sweden, albeit much slower, is the privately operated *Inlandsbanan*, with a single train each way in summer taking all day for the 746 km journey between Östersund and Gälllivare (Table **766**).

UPPSALA - LENNA JERNVÄG

Starting at Uppsala (Tables **760 / 761**), head for tracks 9/10 at the Central station from where this narrow gauge heritage line runs for 33 km east to Faringe. The focal point of the railway is Marielund station, where trains often pass and steam trains refill their water tanks. A popular station café is also located there. The railway's collection of rollling stock is based at the Faringe engine sheds. Track gauge is 891mm (Swedish 'three foot'), unique to Sweden.

Trains run on ⑥ June 2 - Sept. 10, ⑦ June 26 - Sept. 11, ③④ June 29 - Aug. 10 (also June 6). There are seven departures from Uppsala depending on the date, with some journeys hauled by steam. A round trip takes three to four hours. For timings see www.lennakatten.se

ÖSTRA SÖDERMANSLAND JÄRNVÄG

Mariefred - Läggesta - Taxinge is the route of this 11 km narrow gauge (600mm) museum line. Läggesta nedre station is a 500m walk from the SJ station in Table **732**, located west of Stockholm on the line to Eskilstuna. The narrow gauge line offers some great views of Lake Mälaren. Starting on the north side of the lake at Mariefred, trains reverse at Läggesta nedre with several services continuing along the south shore to Taxinge.

On summer weekends it is possible to cross the lake by steamer between Mariefred and Taxinge (round trip fares are available), giving an ideal day out from Stockholm.

Trains run ⑥⑦ July and August (with additional midweek services) with several trains each day. Timings, including boat schedules and connections from Stockholm, can be found at www.oslj.nu

SWITZERLAND

RAIL TRAVEL

See Tables **501 - 578**. The principal rail carrier is Swiss Federal Railways (SBB / CFF / FFS) www.sbb.ch. A 24 hour premium rate helpline is available on ✆ 0848 44 66 88 (German, French, Italian, English spoken).

As might be expected, there are a large number of scenic routes and mountain lines, with endless possibilities for exciting days out. Rail travel can often be combined with other modes such as lake steamers, buses, funicular railways and even cable cars to complete a round trip. Several examples are given on the official tourism site www.myswitzerland.com.

The Swiss rail system is characterised by the large number of rail operators other than SBB. Many of these are narrow gauge, notably the Rhätische Bahn (RhB), which has a large network in the south-east, and the Matterhorn-Gotthard-Bahn (MGB) in the south-west. Together these two railways provide the famous *Glacier Express* running for 290 km from St Moritz to Zermatt (Table **575**). This requires a supplement and advance reservation, but of course the exact same lines can also be traversed with a series of local trains (Tables **576** and **545**).

Other services very popular with tourists include the *Bernina Express* from Chur to Tirano, just across the border in Italy (Table **545**), MOB's *Golden Pass* trains from Montreux to Zweizimmen, some of which have panorama cars (Table **566**), and Zentralbahn's Luzern to Interlaken route with its many lakeside views (Table **561**). Some other highlights are mentioned below, but there are many more. The Swiss rail network is, of course, synonymous with punctuality and spotlessly clean trains.

CHEMIN DE FER - MUSÉE BLONAY - CHAMBY (BC)

Situated in the south-west corner of Switzerland close to Lake Geneva, this narrow gauge railway museum has an extensive collection of rolling stock. Trains run from Blonay to Chamby (3 km) before changing direction to reach the nearby Chaulin museum. Trains leaving the museum return to Blonay. Both steam and electric trains are operated. Passengers are treated to fine views over Lake Geneva during the short journey. Rail connections are available at both Blonay (regular trains from Vevey) and Chamby (Table **566**). www.blonay-chamby.ch

Trains run on ⑥⑦ May 7 - Oct. 30 (also June 6).

		b	a		🚂		🚂		a	🚂
Blonay ....d.	1010	1110	1120	1210	1410	1445	1525	1610	1655	1710
Chamby ....d.	1026	1126	|	1226	1428	1500	1545	1626	|	1726
Chaulin-Musée.......a.	1030	1130	1135	1230	1432	1507	1549	1630	1710	1730
	b		🚂		🚂	a		🚂		a
Chaulin-Musée.......d.	1040	1140	1340	1425	1500	1510	1540	1640	...	1750
Blonay ....a.	1055	1155	1355	1440	1515	1525	1555	1655	...	1805

a – Last Sunday of the month. **b** – 🚂 on ⑦. 🚂 – Steam train.

BRIENZ ROTHORN BAHN (BRB)

Within easy reach of Interlaken by rail (Table **561**) or boat (Table **508**), this narrow gauge (800mm) mountain rack railway from Brienz can claim the unusual fact that its lowest and highest stations have the greatest height difference of any railway in Switzerland. With stunning views, the distance to the summit at Rothorn (2244m) is 7.6 km, and the journey takes about one hour. Built in 1892, an added attraction is that most trips are steam operated, since it is one of the very few non-electrified routes in Switzerland. Trains run between May and October - timings are shown in Table **553**. www.brienz-rothorn-bahn.ch

DAMPFBAHN FURKA-BERGSTRECKE (DFB)

This tortuous narrow gauge mountain route is the original main line over the Furkapass which was closed in 1982 following the opening of the Furka base tunnel. Since 1992 the line has reopened in stages as a spectacular tourist route, the final section between Gletsch and Oberwald being completed in 2010. Steam-hauled journeys over the full 18 km route from Realp to Oberwald via Furka take over two hours (reservation is compulsory), whilst shorter diesel hauled journeys are available between Oberwald and Gletsch taking 25 minutes. Itineraries are also available using both steam and diesel services with a break of journey at Gletsch, near to the Rhone Glacier.

Trains run ④–⑦ June 23 - Sept. 25. For timings and reservations see www.dfb.ch. Both ends of the route can be reached by means of the hourly MGB trains between Brig and Andermatt in Table **576**. In Realp the DFB station is a 10 minute walk from the MGB station.

RIGI-BAHNEN (RB)

There are two electrified rack railways to the Rigi-Kulm summit (1750m), an 8.5 km line from Arth Goldau on the Gotthard main line, and a 7 km line from Vitznau by the lake. Opening in 1871, the latter was Europe's first rack railway, and is the more scenic of the two routes. The lines are also notable for being the highest standard gauge railway in Europe. At the summit, one of the finest Swiss panoramas, overlooking the *Vierwaldstättersee*, awaits the visitor. www.rigi.ch

Trains run hourly all year on both routes, but evening services run only in summer; timings are shown in Table **553**. Arth-Goldau, where the RB station is adjacent to the main line station, can be reached by means of rail services in Tables **525** and **550**. In Vitznau the station is by the quayside (lake steamer services: Table **507**).

PILATUS BAHN (PB)

The world's steepest rack railway runs from Alpnachstad, south-west of Lake Luzern, to the mountain's summit at Pilatus Kulm, a distance of 4.6 km, reaching a height of 2070m. The 800mm gauge line was first opened in 1889 and uses an unusual rack system with teeth on either side of a horizontal rail. The line has been electrified since the 1930s.

Alpnachstad is 13 km from Luzern on the line to Interlaken (Table **561**). A popular excursion from Luzern is to take the train or boat to Alpnachstad, rack railway to Pilatus Kulm, cable-car and gondolas down to Kriens, then trolleybus route **1** back to central Luzern.

The Pilatus Bahn runs early-May to mid-November; there is no winter service - see Table **553** for timings. www.pilatus.ch

JUNGFRAUBAHNEN (JB)

Reached from Interlaken by two different routes (Table **564**), Kleine Scheidegg is the start point for the Jungfraubahn, which burrows through the Mönch and the Eiger to reach Europe's highest station at Jungfraujoch (3454m). The 9.3 km electrified narrow gauge rack railway is mostly in tunnel but stops twice on the way up at Eigerwand and Eismeer from where there are spectacular views through windows incorporated into the mountain side. On a clear day the views from the summit are breathtaking. Visitors are strongly advised to check weather conditions at the summit before travelling. The Eiger Express was launched in December 2020 enabling a 47 minute quicker trip to the summit. www.jungfrau.ch

The line runs all year, every 30 minutes, but may sometimes be affected by snowfall in winter. The journey takes 35 minutes. See Table **564** for timings.

GORNERGRAT BAHN (GGB)

Starting from Zermatt, western terminus of the famous *Glacier Express* (Table **575**, also local services in Table **576**), the Gornergratbahn runs for 9.4 km to the summit at 3089m. Gornergrat is the highest open-air station in Europe, since the higher Jungfraujoch station described above is actually situated inside the mountain! www.gornergratbahn.ch

The journey on this electrified narrow gauge rack railway takes 33 minutes (44 downhill) and initially provides a birds-eye view of Zermatt followed by fine views of the Matterhorn. From Zermatt sit on the right-hand side for the best views. The GGB station at Zermatt is close to the MGB station, at right angles to it. The service runs all year; see Table **578** for timings.

SWISS MUSEUM OF TRANSPORT

Known as the Verkehrshaus, the museum is located eight minutes by local train from Luzern station (route S3 to the Verkehrshaus stop), and can also be reached by bus or boat. It is open daily. www.verkehrshaus.ch

TURKEY

RAIL TRAVEL

See Tables **1570 - 1590** (also **1550 / 60** for European Turkey). Operator is TCDD (Turkish State Railways) www.tcddtasimacilik.gov.tr. The principal Istanbul - Ankara route has been revolutionised in recent years by the opening of a new high-speed line via Eskişehir, with another high-speed section linking these cities with Konya. Further lines are under construction to Karaman, and Ankara to Sivas / Izmir. Traditional routes are tortuous and slow, but the coaching stock is generally comfortable.

The Marmaray Tunnel under the Bosphorus opened in 2013, joining the Asian and European parts of Istanbul by local rail service for the first time. Following a period when the high-speed trains from Istanbul to Ankara were starting from Pendik in the suburbs, these trains now use the more centrally located Söğütlüçeşme station, with certain trains starting from Halkali on the European side and using the tunnel (Table **1570**). The neoclassical pseudo-castle Haydarpasa station building on the Asian side of the Bosphorus is sadly out of use but is being restored.

UKRAINE

RAIL TRAVEL – Consult latest official government travel advice

See Tables **1700 - 1790**, which also include neighbouring Moldova. Ukrainian Railways goes under the initials UZ. www.uz.gov.ua

This vast 1520mm gauge railway network links all major towns and many small ones, and the introduction of modern diesel multiple units in recent years has seen a new *InterCity* category of train, giving fast links on key routes. The most scenic routes are in the south west of the country.

Determined railfans may find the remaining narrow gauge lines of interest, although services are sparse, time consuming to access, and information scarce. One of the lines, that between Rudnytsia and Holovanivs'k, is actually Europe's longest 750mm gauge line at 130 km, but its future is far from certain.

There are no through trains to the Crimea, and the continuing conflict in the Donbass region means there are no trains to Donetsk or Luhansk.

Robert Foster's Column

Robert Foster is a long-standing customer and supporter of the European Rail Timetable who played a key role in its rebirth in 2014. In an occasional column Robert shares some of his personal thoughts based on his recent travel experiences.

THE VENICE SIMPLON ORIENT EXPRESS (VSOE)

I have a particular personal interest in this train which began operation in 1982. Travelling in student days in September 1982 from Zürich Flughafen to Bern, by chance I shared a compartment with two gentleman from whose conversation I realised that they were operating the VSOE. Gingerly I interjected into their conversation that I considered that their train left the Channel Port too early, and passed through Switzerland in the early hours, moreover on the least exciting route namely the Simplon Tunnel which was Europe's longest until the advent of the Channel Tunnel in 1994. I suggested that their train should go to Zürich and cross the Alps from there. When I said that I was alighting at Bern - to reinforce my credibility I had dropped into the conversation that I was to spend a week with Samuel Stähli the architect of the Swiss *Taktfahrplan* which was also introduced in May of that year – one of the gentlemen Mr Colin Bather took down my name and address. Some months later a brochure arrived at home containing on its cover words to the effect of 'new improved route'. Since then the VSOE has operated via Zürich, beyond there traversing either the Gotthard summit line via Chiasso with its wonderful loops and spirals or the Arlberg and Brenner passes via Innsbruck to Verona. So three of the four names in the train's title do not in fact apply!

We had booked a party of six of us in May 2020 from Venice over the Brenner/Arlberg route. That was cancelled owing to lockdown, and rescheduled for May 2021, which was again cancelled and finally took place in May 2022. Our booking was through Railbookers, as advised by Mark Smith of that indomitable website Seat61, by far the most comprehensive and informative railway website that exists and which gives far more information about the train than the website of Belmond, now the operator of the VSOE. Our 'package' included three nights in a hotel in Venice and a private water taxi to take us from our hotel to Venezia Santa Lucia station for our return journey on the VSOE. Outbound we had intended, and indeed booked all trains, to go overland via Lausanne. However in the event, at our third time lucky, feeling unable to rely on the trains, we flew from LHR to VCE where we took an Allaguna Vaporetta waterbus to Fundamente Nova stop, near to where our hotel was situated on a canal in a quiet backwater of Venice.

Mark Smith asks himself in which direction one should travel on the VSOE and concludes by a narrow margin that southbound is the better. As for rail travel itself that is correct, but I think that northbound is the better option for the simple reason that while in Venice one has the journey on the VSOE, the highlight of the short holiday, ahead rather than having accomplished the highlight in the first 30 hours.

So what was it like? Here again Mark Smith's Seat61 website has all the information one needs, including the history of the 'Orient Express', a combination of various trains over more than a century and going via different routes, and the history of many of the vehicles in the train. It comprised ten wagon-lits, five situated either side of three restaurant cars and a bar car, plus an FS couchette car at the rear for staff accommodation. Our wagon-lits car was built in 1929 by Metro-Cammell in Saltley, although how it reached France over the restricted British loading gauge I don't know. Some of the wagon-lits coaches were bought in 1972 by the late James Sherwood at auction in Monaco and it was he who assembled the remainder and arranged their unparalleled restoration to exactly their condition when introduced in the 1920s: he died in 2021. Mark Smith gives a detailed description of the bar car (formerly operated between Paris and Cherbourg) and the three restaurant cars and suggests that you try each one in turn over the three meals (two more light meals are served in the compartment), although being a group of six we asked for and were given the restaurant car of the Cote d'Azur which had a longitudinal table and we occupied this for all main meals.

A VSOE representative met us at our hotel, who labelled and transferred our luggage onto the water taxi which took us via the Rialto Bridge and the Grand Canal to Santa Lucia station, where our luggage was transferred to the platform and, when the empty stock (a rather poor description) arrived at 1100, into our respective compartments of the train prior to departure at 1131. Our Steward, named Marios from Romania and speaking perfect English, greeted us on the platform and was to give the most attentive service I have experienced on a train. One surprise was that on the departure board at Santa Lucia, the train was simply shown as a normal train '1131 Brennero': I should have preferred 'Parigi, Calais, Londra'.

In addition to the service given by Marios, the service in our restaurant car was truly outstanding and the meals were exceptional. We chose the earlier lunch and dinner sittings at 1200 and 1900 respectively, the later sittings being at 1400 and 2130. Choices of main dish were limited understandably to two, but if neither pleased you then a third would be offered. While at dinner, Marios converted our compartment from daytime to night-time mode, a process reversed in the morning.

The train did not quite run according to plan. There was a long wait at Verona where a second locomotive was added, followed by single-line working on both sides of the Brenner Pass with the result that Innsbruck was left two hours late which had the slightly unfortunate result that by the time we traversed the Arlberg pass darkness had fallen. The train operated non-stop to Buchs, passing the Lindau/Bregenz-Wien Nightjet as it was adding its car carriers at Feldkirch. To my surprise, we were held by the Swiss 15 minutes outside Buchs to allow the 2140 Zürich-Wien/Budapest/Praha to clear the station. Here the train reversed, the two OBB locomotives, one from Brennero and one from Innsbruck being replaced at the other end by two veteran SBB Re420 Bo-Bo locomotives, still performing front-line service after 50 years. Of historical interest for many years the 2140 from Zürich and its equivalent westbound working was titled the *Wiener Waltzer*, although after World War 2 the Swiss referred to it colloquially as the Dienstmädchen Express, as it brought many young girls from war-torn Austria to work in service or as nannies in Switzerland.

The VSOE than ran via Zürich Altstetten, so avoiding Zürich HB which would in any event have involved reversal and another change of traction, to Basel SBB where power was changed to an SNCF locomotive. The route was then via Strasbourg and Nancy, the classic route now supplanted by the LGV Est, to Paris Gare de l'Est recouping an hour of lost time in the process. Here the train was watered, and the restaurant cars serviced before reversing out. However a long process of changing the loco which drew the train out to the front end saw time lost. The train manager Austrian Wolfgang Eipeldauer, whose acquaintance I was fortunate to make soon after departure from Venezia, had the unenviable decision as to whether to continue to Calais, or to implement Plan B. Let me explain. Owing to Brexit issues and P&O ferries being unavailable between Calais and Dover, the scheduled crossing by coach from Calais Ville to Folkestone West followed by the British Pullman to London Victoria was replaced by a series of minibuses (in fact Mercedes 6-seater taxis) to Lille Europe to take the 1635 Eurostar to St Pancras. To compensate for the absence of the British Pullman, passengers were offered a reduction or alternatively an out and back journey in the next three years on the British Pullman from London, the option which we had no hesitation in choosing. In the event, Wolfgang implemented Plan B which was to terminate the train at Lens, 25 km from Lille, the minibuses having been summoned from Calais to transport us. We then went from Lille to St Pancras during which we were given the perfectly acceptable Eurostar Business Premier meal, although very different from the meals which we had enjoyed in the previous 24 hours, but with as much champagne (gratis) as we wished. The Eurostar was 40 minutes late but we still had plenty time for our booked 1830 from Euston to Lancaster and then train back to our local North Yorkshire station at Gargrave near Skipton.

Was the cost of the journey worth it? Mark Smith says definitely 'Yes'. Provided you are not breaking your bank, I would certainly agree. It was a wonderful experience. Also, from my point of view it brought back childhood memories of seeing those beautiful dark blue Wagon-lits coaches and restaurant cars with their gold lettering in Paris, Zürich and elsewhere on trains where we as a family were travelling in couchettes. [My first continental rail journey, in December 1967 by the Arlberg Express to Innsbruck, left Calais Maritime behind a steam engine.]

Would I change anything? Yes, although not the train itself which is impossible to better. I would improve substantially the Belmond website. I might also change the travel mode between London and Calais. That worked well when ferries were sailing between Folkestone Harbour and Boulogne Maritime but transfer to a coach or minibus to join a Eurotunnel vehicle shuttle is potentially a disappointment and can detract from what is otherwise an absolutely outstanding railway journey. My suggestion would be to use Eurostar in each direction between London and Calais Frethun, where customs examination and cross-platform is theoretically possible.

EUROPEAN RAIL PASSES

Rail passes represent excellent value for train travellers who are touring around Europe (or parts of it) or making a number of journeys within a short period. They can offer substantial savings over point-to-point tickets, as well as greater flexibility.

The principal pass schemes for Europe are **Interrail** for residents of Europe, and **Eurail** for those resident outside Europe. Both schemes have a choice of **Global** passes covering 33 countries, or **One Country Passes** for individual countries. Note, however, that you cannot use the pass in your country of residence. Passes are available in either a mobile (for use on your smart phone) or the more traditional Paper format.

Passes either cover a specified number of consecutive days, or are of the *flexi* type where you get so many 'travel days' within a specified period (you record your travel dates on each type of pass). Free travel requires the use of a travel day, whereas discounted travel does not.

Passes generally cover the ordinary services of the national rail companies, but supplements often have to be paid for travel on high-speed services, night trains, and 'global price' trains. Independent rail operators may not accept passes but may give discounts to passholders.

Interrail and Eurail

Europe-wide or single-country passes   website: www.interrail.eu   www.eurail.com

Anyone of any age can buy a pass, either for pretty much the whole of Europe, or for an individual country. **Global** passes cover 33 countries of Europe and can either be *Continuous* passes for a set number of consecutive days or months, or *Flexi* passes for a certain number of travel days within a period of one or two months (you choose the travel days as you go along, writing the date on the pass). **One Country Passes** are all flexi passes for a certain number of days within one month (sometimes there is more than one country, as with the Benelux pass).

The two pass schemes (Interrail and Eurail) are now very similar, but Interrail passes are for **residents of Europe**, whilst Eurail passes are for those resident **outside Europe**. Turkey, Russia and the CIS countries count as Europe for this purpose. You may need proof of residence.

Passes can be purchased up to eleven months before travel begins. It's best to buy the pass online or in your own country before travelling, although most passes can also be purchased at major stations in Europe. Note, however, that the 4 day Global pass cannot be purchased from stations. Recommended retail prices are now the same for both Interrail and Eurail and are in Euros as shown below, but prices may vary between different outlets. At certain times of year special offer prices may be available. All passes are either for second class or first class travel (of course first class passes can also be used to travel in second class).

Passes come with a travel diary which has to be filled in with each journey. You cannot use the pass in your own country of residence. However, with an Interrail Global Pass you can make one outbound and one inbound journey in your country of residence (see next page).

INTERRAIL / EURAIL GLOBAL PASS - valid in 33 countries:

Austria, Belgium, Bosnia-Herzegovina, Bulgaria, Croatia, Czech Republic, Denmark, Estonia, Finland, France, Germany, Great Britain, Greece, Hungary, Ireland (including Northern Ireland), Italy, Latvia, Lithuania, Luxembourg, Montenegro, Netherlands, North Macedonia, Norway, Poland, Portugal, Romania, Serbia, Slovakia, Slovenia, Spain, Sweden, Switzerland and Turkey.

NOT VALID in the passholder's country of residence.

PRICES - INTERRAIL / EURAIL GLOBAL PASS - FIRST CLASS

Current prices	Adult (28-59) 1st cl.	Senior (60+) 1st cl.	Youth (12-27) 1st cl.	Child * (under 12) 1st cl.
FLEXI PASSES:				
4 days within 1 month	€328	€295	€246	€0
5 days within 1 month	€376	€338	€282	€0
7 days within 1 month	€446	€401	€335	€0
10 days within 2 months	€534	€481	€401	€0
15 days within 2 months	€657	€591	€493	€0
CONTINUOUS DAYS:				
15 days	€590	€531	€443	€0
22 days	€690	€621	€518	€0
1 month	€893	€804	€670	€0
2 months	€975	€878	€731	€0
3 months	€1202	€1082	€902	€0

PRICES - INTERRAIL / EURAIL GLOBAL PASS - SECOND CLASS

Current prices	Adult (28-59) 2nd cl.	Senior (60+) 2nd cl.	Youth (12-27) 2nd cl.	Child * (under 12) 2nd cl.
FLEXI PASSES:				
4 days within 1 month	€246	€221	€185	€0
5 days within 1 month	€282	€254	€212	€0
7 days within 1 month	€335	€302	€251	€0
10 days within 2 months	€401	€361	€301	€0
15 days within 2 months	€493	€444	€370	€0
CONTINUOUS DAYS:				
15 days	€443	€399	€332	€0
22 days	€518	€466	€389	€0
1 month	€670	€603	€503	€0
2 months	€731	€658	€548	€0
3 months	€902	€812	€677	€0

* Child: two children per fare paying Adult (not Senior) travel free.

INTERRAIL / EURAIL ONE COUNTRY PASS (OCP)

Covers any one of the participating countries below. **NOT** available for the passholder's country of residence. Note that Benelux passes (also the Eurail Scandinavia pass) actually cover more than one country. As with the Global pass, two children per fare paying Adult travel free.

Bosnia-Herzegovina and Montenegro do not have One Country Passes. There are some variations between Eurail and Interrail as shown below, for example Germany, Great Britain and Switzerland participate in the Interrail OCP scheme but not the Eurail OCP scheme as they have their own passes for overseas visitors (for Great Britain see under Britrail). The Scandinavia Pass only applies to Eurail, not Interrail.

Interrail: Germany* or Great Britain. **Eurail: Germany* or Scandinavia** (Norway, Sweden, Denmark, Finland combined)

**Senior passes not available.*

	Adult 1st cl.	Senior 1st cl.	Youth 1st cl.	Adult 2nd cl.	Senior 2nd cl.	Youth 2nd cl.
3 days within 1 month	€256	€230	€205	€192	€173	€166
4 days within 1 month	€291	€262	€233	€218	€196	€183
5 days within 1 month	€321	€289	€257	€241	€217	€209
6 days within 1 month	€349	€314	€279	€262	€236	€227
8 days within 1 month	€396	€356	€317	€297	€267	€257

Norway, Spain or Sweden *Norway only available for 2nd class*

	Adult 1st cl.	Senior 1st cl.	Youth 1st cl.	Adult 2nd cl.	Senior 2nd cl.	Youth 2nd cl.
3 days within 1 month	€227	€204	€182	€170	€153	€148
4 days within 1 month	€263	€237	€210	€197	€177	€171
5 days within 1 month	€294	€265	€235	€221	€199	€191
6 days within 1 month	€323	€291	€258	€242	€218	€210
8 days within 1 month	€374	€337	€299	€281	€253	€243

Interrail: Austria, France or Switzerland
Eurail: Austria or France

Eurail France Pass: 1, 2 and 7 day passes also for sale outside Europe

	Adult 1st cl.	Senior 1st cl.	Youth 1st cl.	Adult 2nd cl.	Senior 2nd cl.	Youth 2nd cl.
3 days within 1 month	€195	€176	€156	€146	€131	€127
4 days within 1 month	€230	€207	€184	€173	€156	€150
5 days within 1 month	€262	€236	€210	€197	€177	€170
6 days within 1 month	€291	€262	€233	€218	€196	€189
8 days within 1 month	€344	€310	€275	€258	€232	€224

Benelux, Denmark, Finland, Ireland or Italy*

Benelux is Belgium, Netherlands and Luxembourg combined
Ireland includes Northern Ireland
** Prices for Passes are 5% higher than shown*

	Adult 1st cl.	Senior 1st cl.	Youth 1st cl.	Adult 2nd cl.	Senior 2nd cl.	Youth 2nd cl.
3 days within 1 month	€161	€145	€129	€121	€109	€105
4 days within 1 month	€194	€175	€155	€146	€131	€126
5 days within 1 month	€225	€203	€180	€169	€152	€146
6 days within 1 month	€253	€228	€202	€190	€171	€164
8 days within 1 month	€305	€275	€244	€229	€206	€198

Czech Republic, Estonia, Greece, Hungary, Portugal or Romania

	Adult 1st cl.	Senior 1st cl.	Youth 1st cl.	Adult 2nd cl.	Senior 2nd cl.	Youth 2nd cl.
3 days within 1 month	€123	€111	€98	€92	€83	€80
4 days within 1 month	€152	€137	€122	€114	€103	€99
5 days within 1 month	€179	€161	€143	€134	€121	€116
6 days within 1 month	€205	€185	€164	€154	€139	€133
8 days within 1 month	€253	€228	€202	€190	€171	€164

Bulgaria, Croatia, Latvia, Lithuania, North Macedonia, Poland, Serbia, Slovakia, Slovenia or Turkey

	Adult 1st cl.	Senior 1st cl.	Youth 1st cl.	Adult 2nd cl.	Senior 2nd cl.	Youth 2nd cl.
3 days within 1 month	€78	€70	€62	€59	€53	€51
4 days within 1 month	€99	€89	€79	€74	€67	€64
5 days within 1 month	€119	€107	€95	€89	€80	€77
6 days within 1 month	€139	€125	€111	€104	€94	€90
8 days within 1 month	€176	€158	€141	€132	€119	€114

Interrail and Eurail - continued

GREEK ISLANDS PASS

This is a special ferry pass available in both the Interrail and Eurail schemes. It is valid on ferries operated by the Attica Group, which includes Superfast Ferries, Blue Star Ferries and Hellenic Seaways. The 4 day pass is valid for five domestic trips on ferries within Greece. The 6 day pass is valid for two international trips between Italy and Greece plus four domestic trips in Greece. The 6 day pass includes accommodation in either 1st or 2nd class, also rail/bus transfers between Patras and Piraeus. Both passes give 30% discount on additional ferry trips.

	Adult 1st cl.	Senior 1st cl.	Youth 1st cl.	Adult 2nd cl.	Senior 2nd cl.	Youth 2nd cl.
4 days within 1 month	N/A	N/A	N/A	€90	€81	€68
6 days within 1 month	€208	€187	€182	€176	€159	€155

OVERNIGHT TRAVEL

Passes do not include supplements for travel in sleeping car or couchette accommodation and these have to be purchased separately. Many overnight trains have a *global* price where the ticket price includes the sleeping accommodation - in these cases pass holders pay a specified supplement or passholder fare (see below for further details).

Holders of flexi passes travelling overnight and leaving before midnight need to record the date of departure in the travel diary, and of course the pass can be used for the whole of that day. Pass holders will not need to activate a second day on their pass for the day of arrival unless they board a second train (but the day of arrival does need to be within the overall validity of the pass). The rule can also be used for late evening trains arriving after midnight. If you need to use a connecting train having arrived overnight it may be worth buying a regular ticket to avoid having to use a travel day.

Note that this replaced the previous 7pm rule whereby pass holders had to write the day of arrival on their passes, rather than the day of departure, for night trains departing after 7pm.

FREE TRAVEL TO THE BORDER, AIRPORT OR SEAPORT

Although it is not possible to purchase an Interrail pass for the holder's own country of residence, a Global pass entitles the holder to two free journeys (one outbound, one inbound) between any station in their country of residence and its border, an airport or seaport. Each journey must be completed in one day (no overnight stops allowed), at any time within the overall validity of the pass, or include a travel day if using a flexi pass. Details must be entered in the travel diary.

SUPPLEMENTS AND RESERVATION FEES

Required for certain types of high-speed or 'global price' train.

International day train examples, 2nd class (subject to change): France - Italy *TGV* €31; *Berlin - Warszawa Express* €4; *Switzerland - Italy EC* €11; *Eurostar* €30 - 35 (€38 - 43 in standard premier with 1st class pass); *TGV/ICE* France - Germany from €13; *TGV Lyria* (France - Switzerland) from €21; *SJ Snabbtåg* Stockholm - København €6.60; *IC bus* Klagenfurt - Venezia €9. Higher fares apply if pass not valid in both countries.

Domestic examples (approximate; subject to alteration): **Croatia** *IC/ICN* €3.60. **Czech Republic** *SC* up to €8. **Finland** *Pendolino* €5 - 10. **France** *TGV* €10 limited allocation (otherwise €20), *Intercités* wit compulsory reservation €10. **Hungary** *IC* €3.50. **Italy** *FA, FB* and *F* €10, *IC* €3. **Norway** long-distance trains €6. **Poland** *EIP* €0 - 3.5C *EIC/TLK* €0 - 3.50. **Portugal** *AP/IC* €5. **Romania** *IC/IR* €1 - 3.6C **Slovakia** *IC* €3 - 9. **Slovenia** *ICS* €2 - 4. **Spain** *AVE* €10, most othe long-distance trains €6.50, *MD/Avant* €4. **Sweden** *Snabbtåg* €7.

Night trains: sleeping accommodation is typically €15 to €75 for couchette, and €35 to €144 for a berth in a sleeping car. Some train also include reclining seats. Many night trains are globally priced an fares for passholders vary widely.

As some of the supplements/passholder fares can be rather high, it' worth checking whether a regular advance purchase ticket might be better option, particularly if booked a month or two ahead. Supplement can often be avoided altogether by taking slower regional trains.

VALIDITY ON PRIVATE RAILWAYS

Passes are valid on the national railway companies in each country, plu many privately run railways (some give discounts). For details se www.interrail.eu, www.eurail.com, or the Traveller's Guide that come with your pass.

Selected details are as follows (subject to change): **Austria**: free trave on WESTbahn, GYSEV, RegioJet and ROeEE. **Czech Republic**: vali on Leo Express and RegioJet. **Denmark**: free travel on Arriva, DSB Øresund/S-Tog, and Nordjyske Jernbaner. **France**: SNCF bus service included. **Germany**: free on most regional services and many privat companies. **Hungary**: GySEV services are included. **Italy**: free travel o Trenord and Leonardo Express (1st class only). **Netherlands**: private run regional lines are included. **Norway**: Flåmsbana (Myrdal - Flåm gives 30% discount. **Poland**: valid on Koleje Dolnośląskie, Przewoz Regionaine. **Spain**: FEVE is included. **Sweden**: most private operator are included. **Switzerland**: free travel on AB, ASM, AVA, BDWM, BLS BLT, CJ, FART, FW, LEB, MBC, MGB, MOB/MVR, NStCM, RA, RhE SOB, SSIF, THURBO, TMR, TPC, TPF, TRAVYS, TRN, WB, WSB an ZB. Others offer 25 - 50% discount, including BET, BGF, BLM, BOB, HE LSMS-Isms, JB, PB, RB, SMF-Ism, SthB, WAB. Discounted fare o William Tell Express (rail and boat tour).

VALIDITY ON FERRY AND BUS SERVICES

Global passes includes free deck passage between Italy and Greece o SuperFast Ferries (you pay port taxes and possibly a fuel surcharge) free air-type seats for 1st class pass holders; 30% discount if pass onl valid in Italy or Greece. Many other ferry companies offer discounts (nc usually on cabins), for example: Balearia 20%, Finnlines 50%, Fjord Lin 30%, Grimaldi 20%, Irish Ferries 30%, Minoan Ferries 20%, Stena Lin 30%, Tallink Silja 20% (high-season), up to 50% (low-season), Vikin Line up to 50%.

Most Swiss lakes give 50% The following bus services in Scandinavi between Sweden and Finland are included; Luleå - Haparand (Länstrafiken Norrbotten), Haparanda - Tornio - Kemi (Net-matkat).

Other benefits are often available, such as hotel discounts, bike hir discounts, free entry to railway museums, and access to railway statio lounges.

Where to Buy your Pass

Sources of rail passes (and point to point tickets) include the following:

ACP Rail - see www.acprail.com

All Aboard - see www.allaboard.eu

Deutsche Bahn UK (German Railways)
UK Booking Centre ✆ 08718 80 80 66 www.bahn.com

Eurail – buy on www.eurail.com or see www.eurailgroup.org for a list of sales partners. All participating European railway companies sell passes.

Ffestiniog Travel
Former St Mary's Church, Tremadog, Porthmadog, Gwynedd LL49 9RA
✆ 01766 512400 www.ffestiniogtravel.com

French Railways – see www.sncf.com

International Rail
PO Box 153, Alresford, Hampshire SO24 4AQ
✆ 0871 231 0790 www.internationalrail.com

Interrail – see www.interrail.eu. All participating railway companies sell passes.

Interrail by National Rail – see www.myinterrail.co.uk

Loco2 - now Rail Europe

Rail Canterbury
PO Box 1178, Canterbury, Kent CT1 9QJ
Email rail@rail-canterbury.co.uk www.rail-canterbury.co.uk

Rail Europe (formerly Loco2) – see www.raileurope.co.uk
Also raileurope.de, raileurope.it, raileurope.es

RailTourGuide
Suite 42, 7 - 15 Pink Lane, Newcastle upon Tyne, NE1 5DW
✆ 0191 246 0708 www.railtourguide.com

Real Russia - Temporarily Closed
122 Minories, London EC3N 1NT (also office in Moscow)
✆ 0207 100 4981 www.realrussia.co.uk

Switzerland Travel Centre
30 - 33 Minories, London, EC3N 1DD
✆ 0207 420 4900 www.stc.co.uk

Trainseurope
4th Floor, Silverstream House, 45 Fitzroy Street, Fitzrovia, London, W1T 6EB. **Visits by appointment only.**

✆ 01354 660222 www.trainseurope.co.uk email sales@trainseurope.co.uk.

Other useful websites:

www.seat61.com
www.ricksteves.com

BritRail

3ritRail is a pass for overseas visitors to Great Britain, allowing unlimited ravel on the national rail network in England, Scotland and Wales. It is not available to residents of Great Britain, Northern Ireland, the Isle of Man or the Channel Islands. Passes must be purchased before arriving in 3ritain. Youth prices apply to ages 16 to 25, senior applies to 60+. All passes are available for First or Standard class. For further details see www.britrail.com or www.acprail.com.

3RITRAIL CONSECUTIVE PASS

USD prices)	Adult 1st cl.	Youth 1st cl.	Senior 1st cl.	Adult Std cl.	Youth Std cl.	Senior Std cl.
2 days	214	129	181	141	86	121
3 days	319	192	272	211	127	180
days	397	238	338	262	157	223
3 days	566	340	481	380	206	323
15 days	836	502	711	566	340	481
22 days	1062	637	903	708	425	602
month	1258	755	1069	836	502	711

3RITRAIL FLEXIPASS

USD prices)	Adult 1st cl.	Youth 1st cl.	Senior 1st cl.	Adult Std cl.	Youth Std cl.	Senior Std cl.
days within 1 month	266	160	226	180	109	154
days within 1 month	397	238	338	269	161	229
days within 1 month	488	293	415	336	202	286
3 days within 1 month	718	431	610	481	289	409
15 days within 2 months	1072	643	911	724	435	616

3RITRAIL ENGLAND PASSES

The Britrail England Pass excludes Wales and Scotland, giving a saving of approximately 20%. Britrail South West and North of England Rover passes are also available. All three are available in consecutive and flexi versions (no 2-day passes).

BRITRAIL LONDON PLUS PASS

This 'flexi' pass allows unlimited rail travel in London and the surrounding area. You can visit such places as Canterbury, Salisbury, Bristol, Bath, Oxford, Cambridge, Stratford-Upon-Avon, Worcester, Ely, Kings Lynn, and anywhere on the coast between Harwich to Weymouth.

(USD prices)	Adult 1st cl.	Youth 1st cl.	Senior 1st cl.	Adult Std cl.	Youth Std cl.	Senior Std cl.
3 days within 1 month	231	150	196	165	107	140
4 days within 1 month	267	174	227	201	131	171
8 days within 1 month	378	246	321	279	181	237

BRITRAIL SCOTLAND PASSES

Three different passes are available, all standard class adult passes: Spirit of Scotland covers the whole country; available as 4 days within 8 days, or 8 days within 15 days. The other areas are Central Scotland (3 days consecutive), and Highlands (4 days within 8 days).

M-PASS

All Britrail Passes are available as a mobile ticket on your mobile phone (saving shipping cost) - see www.acprail.com.

DISCOUNTS

Saver Discount: groups of 3 to 9 people receive a discount of up to 20%. Passes must be of the same type (BritRail, BritRail England and BritRail SouthWest passes only) and duration and the party must travel together at all times. Cannot be combined with the family discount.

Family Discount: if any adult or senior pass is purchased, one accompanying child (aged 5-15) may receive a free pass of the same type and duration. Any further children travelling receive a 50% discount. All children under 5 travel free..

Other International Passes

3ALKAN FLEXIPASS

Jnlimited travel in Bosnia & Herzegovina, Bulgaria, Greece, Montenegro, North Macedonia, Serbia and Turkey (also trains operated by Regio Călători in Romania). Valid for any 3/5/7/10/15 days in two months: 1st class €169/240/324/418/503; 2nd class €122/179/244/310/373. 40% discount for under 28s, 20% for 60+, 50% for children (4-12), 33% discount for residents of the above countries. Supplements for *IC* trains.

Free travel on Attica Group ferries (Superfast Ferries/Blue Star/ANEK) Patras-Corfu/Ancona/Bari (port taxes and high season supplements apply); 30% discount on Attica Group (Superfast/Blue Star) routes within Greece. Note that if purchased from one of the above countries the pass allows only a return journey from place of issue to the border of a neighbouring participating country before unlimited travel is possible.

BODENSEE TICKET

Jnlimited travel by rail, bus and ferry in border region Austria/Germany/Switzerland surrounding the Bodensee (Lake Constance). One day 48 CHF/€37, 3 days 74 CHF/€58. Discounts for children and families. Not valid on ICE/IC/EC trains In Germany or on Friedrichshafen - Konstanz catamarans. Zonal versions also available for smaller areas.

EUREGIO TICKET MAAS-RHEIN

One days unlimited travel in border region Belgium/Netherlands/Germany by rail and bus (covers Liège, Hasselt, Maastricht, Roermond, Aachen, Düren). In Germany and Belgium covers only local trains and buses. Price €19. At weekends/public holidays valid as a family ticket (2 adults plus 3 children under 12).

EUROPEAN EAST PASS (Currently unavailable)

Offers unlimited rail travel throughout Austria, Czech Republic, Hungary and Slovakia for any 5 to 10 days within a month. Valid also on direct services through Germany between Kufstein and Salzburg (the passholder cannot leave the train). Available to European residents (except those from countries where the ticket is valid) as well as non-European residents. 1st class €271 (5 days) to €411 (10 days); 2nd class €186 (5 days) to €316 (10 days). Children aged 4-11 half price. Discounts available on river cruises, Children's Railway etc.

ÖRESUND RUNDT

Two days unlimited travel on trains and buses in the København, Malmö and Helsingborg area (includes the metro in København). The Öresund can only be crossed by rail in one direction; the Helsingborg - Helsingør ferry (included) must be used in the other direction. Available in Denmark from København Tourist Office (price 249 DKK) and in Sweden from Skånetrafiken (price 299 SEK); children 7-15 half price.

PASS ALSACE-RHEIN-NECKAR

A day ticket valid on Saturdays, Sundays and French public holidays covering local trains (2nd class), buses and trams in the Rhein-Neckar area (VRN) centered on Mannheim and Heidelberg, the Karlsruhe area (KVV), plus local trains in the Bas Rhin area of France centered on Strasbourg. Price €19 for one person or €31.50 for a group of 2-5 people.

PASSBASK

One day's travel in the area between Bayonne in France and San Sebastian in Spain on SNCF trains (includes *TGV* but not night trains) and EuskoTren services. A barrier pass for EuskoTren should be obtained at Hendaye station. Price €12, child aged 4-12 €8.

SAAR-LOR-LUX TICKET

One day's unlimited 2nd class travel on Saturday or Sunday throughout Saarland (i.e. Saarbrücken area of Germany, local trains only), Lorraine (i.e. Metz, Nancy, Épinal area of France) and all CFL trains in Luxembourg. Price €26 (€28 over the counter in Germany); for groups of 2-5 people add €10 per extra person. Not valid on *TGV* or *ICE* trains.

OTHER PASSES

A range of day tickets is available covering areas of the Czech Republic and adjoining countries:
Euro-Neisse Ticket (Liberec, Jelenia Góra, Zittau, Görlitz area; www.zvon.de). **EgroNet-Ticket** (Cheb, Karlovy Vary, Plauen, Zwickau, Hof, Bayreuth; www.egronet.de).
Bayern-Böhmen Ticket (border areas of Bavaria/Bohemia).
Sachsen-Böhmen Ticket (Liberec, Děčín, Dresden area).
Elbe-Labe Ticket (Chomutov, Ústí nad Labem, Dresden area).

Railplus

Railplus cards are valid for one year and offer a discount of 15% on cross-border rail travel (excluding supplements) between the participating countries, which are Austria, Bosnia and Herzegovina, Bulgaria, Czech Republic, Denmark, Finland, Germany, Greece, Hungary, Italy, Latvia, Lithuania, Luxembourg, Montenegro, Netherlands, North Macedonia, Poland, Romania, Serbia, Slovakia, Slovenia and Switzerland.

There are no discounts on Eurostar, Thalys or TGV services. Cards are not available for sale in all participating countries, and you may be required to hold a national railcard for the country where you buy the pass, in addition to the Railplus card. In the Netherlands it is only available to annual season ticket holders.

This extended Rail Passes feature appears in the printed seasonal editions of the European Rail Timetable (published in June and December). Other monthly editions include details of Interrail and Eurail passes as well as Britrail and other international passes.

Passes for Domestic Travel

Most cities offer day tickets valid on public transport (some include local trains). Larger cities often have Visitor Cards (some are shown below) which include tourist attractions as well as public transport; these are available from airports and tourist information offices, often also from hotels and online.

AUSTRIA

See separate sections for Interrail / Eurail Global and One Country passes, European East Pass, Bodensee Ticket.

KlimaTicket Ö: a single ticket providing 365 days of travel on all public transport throughout Austria (not valid on tourist railways).

KlimaTicket Ö Youth - 25 and under, €821
KlimaTicket Ö Classic - 26 to 64 €1095
KlimaTicket Ö Senior - 65 and over €821
KlimaTicket Ö Special - travellers with disabilities €821

Up to 4 children between 6 and 15 (children 5 and under travel free) can be added for an additional €110 to each category of ticket.

Regional versions are available except for Upper Austria, which is expected to be released later this year. 1st class upgrades available.

Einfach-Raus-Ticket: one day's 2nd class travel (until 0300 hrs the following day) on regional and local trains in Austria (except Vorarlberg) for groups of 2 to 5 people, €35 - 47. On Mon to Fri not valid before 0900 hrs. Add €9 to include bicycles.

Vorteilscard annual discount card gives 50% discount; the *Classic* version (€99), online version (€66) are available to all but there are cheaper cards for families, seniors and those under 26.

ÖBB Österreichcard gives unlimited travel on Austrian Railways and many private railways for one year, €1,944 (1st class €2,998). Cheaper cards for families, seniors and those under 26.

Wien all public transport (not airport): day ticket €5.80; 24 / 48 / 72 hours €8 / 14.10 / 17.10; weekly ticket (starts Monday, photo required) €17.10; any 8 days (not necessarily consecutive, transferable) €40.80.

Vienna City Card: unlimited travel on local transport (excludes airport) plus discounted museum entry, 24 / 48 / 72 hours €17 / 25 / 29. Similar **Easy City Pass Vienna** also available.

Other visitor cards giving local travel plus museum / sights discounts for 24 / 48 / 72 hours: **Salzburg Card** €30 / 39 / 45 (reduced by €3 - 5 low season Nov. to Apr.); **Innsbruck Card** €53 / 63 / 73. Children half price.

BELGIUM

See separate sections for Interrail / Eurail Global and Benelux passes, Euregio Ticket Maas-Rhein.

Netabonnement / Abonnement Réseau: unlimited travel on rail network; 1 month €336 / 517 (2nd / 1st class), 3 months €940 / 1447, 1 year €3357 / 5169. Add-ons for city transport also available.

Tickets available on NMBS/SNCB rail network include: **Rail Pass** (age 26+) allows 10 single journeys within Belgium for €87 2nd class, €132 1st class, valid 1 year. **Go Pass 10** is under 26 version, €55 2nd class. **Weekend Ticket**: gives 50% discount, from Friday 1900 hrs. **Senior Ticket** (65+), flat fare of €7.20 2nd class, €15.30 1st class, from 0900 Mon-Fri.

Brussels: **Brupass** (formerlly Jump ticket) covers all transport in greater Brussels (De Lijn, NMBS/SNCB, MIVB/STIB and TEC) Day pass €7.80. Personal Mobib or Mobib Basic card required (€5). STIB also has a contactless day ticket for €7.50, no Mobib card required.

De Lijn has 1 or 3-day system passes (€7.50 / 15) for its trams and buses; includes coastal tram. Buy in advance. A 24h smartphone ticket is also available costs €7.50.

BULGARIA

See separate sections for Interrail / Eurail Global and One Country passes, Balkan Flexipass.

Sofia: metro, tram and bus: 1 day 4 BGN, 3 days 10 BGN (the 3 day card requires an electronic card, cost 2 BGN). A 10-trip card costs 12 BGN.

Sofia PASS: metro, tram and bus, also discount at tourist and commercial sites, valid for 3 consecutive days, costs 20 BGN.

CROATIA

See separate section for Interrail / Eurail Global and One Country passes.

Zagreb: day ticket (dnevna karta) all ZET tram / bus (zone 1): 30 HRK, available as paper ticket. Also multi-day tickets (višednevne karte): 3 / 7 / 15 / 30 days, 70 / 150 / 200 / 400 HRK, requires stored value card 10 HRK.

Zagreb Card adds museums, discounts, 24 hrs 98 HRK, 72 hrs 135 HRK.

CZECH REPUBLIC

See separate sections for Interrail / Eurail Global and One Country passes, European East Pass.

See also under *Other International Passes* for a range of passes covering border areas.

Day ticket (Celodenní Jízdenka): 2nd class travel on whole rail network 599 CZK (reservation payable on *SC* trains, up to 250 CZK). 10 regional areas also available, 159 - 249 CZK. Certain regions also have day tickets including border areas of Germany or Poland, 259 - 319 CZK. Other day tickets cover specific cross-border areas: EgroNet (200 CZK), Labe-Elbe (300 CZK), Euro-Nisa (160 CZK); most have discounts for groups of two or more. Day tickets (also Interrail / Eurail passes) are not valid on services operated by GW Train Regio.

Group Weekend ticket (Skupinová víkendová jízdenka): 2nd class travel on whole network on Sat. or Sun. for 2 adults and up to 3 children, 699 CZK (849 CZK including local transport in Praha). Reservation fee payable on *SC* trains. Valid cross-border to first station on local trains (except Austria). Regional areas also available, 229 - 389 CZK. Versions for Czech Republic plus border areas of Germany or Poland, including regional areas, are also available.

Summer Ticket (Jízdenka na leto): unlimited rail travel for 7 or 14 days during July and August only, 7 days 890 CZK, 14 days 1290 CZK.

Praha: all public transport: 24 hrs 120 CZK, 3 days (72 hrs) 330 CZK, 30 days 550 CZK. Wider areas available. **COOLPASS**: (formerly Prague Card) 2 / 3 / 4 day admission card, includes public transport, €76 - 94 (child/student €55 - 69). Most cities have day tickets for city transport.

DENMARK

See separate sections for Interrail / Eurail Global and One Country passes, Eurail Scandinavia pass, Öresund Rundt.

Fares based on national zonal system; 30-day **Pendlerkort** is available (photocard required) including all-zones version. **Rejsekortet** is a pre-pay travel card aimed at Danish residents, but a **Rejsekort Anonymt** may be purchased by anyone (card costs 80 DKK, plus an initial amount for travel purposes).

København: **City Pass Small** zones 1 - 4 (includes airport) on bus, metro and train 24 - 120 hrs 80 - 300 DKK (child half price); **City Pass Large** at double the price, zones 1 - 99 includes Helsingør, Roskilde etc.

Copenhagen Card: public transport (whole region), free entry to over 80 attractions, 24 / 48 / 72 / 96 / 120 hrs €60 / 88 / 108 / 125 / 142 (two children 0-11 free).

ESTONIA

Estonian Railways: a zonal system operates; there is no network pass.

Tallinn: tram / bus / trolley-bus **Ühiskaart** pre-pay travel card (deposit €2) available for 1 / 3 / 5 / 30 days: €4.50 / 7.50 / 9 / 30.

Tallinn Card: public transport plus over 50 museums and attractions, 24 hrs €35, 48 hrs €52, 72 hrs €62, under 18s €21 / 27 / 33. **Tallinn Card PLUS** adds free bus tour of city, €49 / 66 / 78 (tour currently suspended).

FINLAND

See separate sections for Interrail / Eurail Global and One Country passes, also Eurail Scandinavia pass.

Helsinki: single-charge electronic cards for all public transport including local trains: 1 / 2 / 3 days €8 / 12 / 16; 7 days €32 (1 - 7 days available).

Helsinki Card: public transport plus free entry to 25+ attractions and bus tour, 24 / 48 / 72 hrs €51 / 63 / 74, child 7-16 half price; Region version includes airport for €4 - 8 extra.

FRANCE

See separate sections for Interrail / Eurail Global and One Country passes, Pass Alsace - Rhein-Neckar, Passbask, Saar-Lor-Lux Ticket.

Annual discount cards: **Carte Avantage Jeune** (ages 12 - 27), **Carte Avantage Senior** (over 60), **Avantage Weekend** (ages 27 - 59) and **Avantage Famille** (ages 27 - 59) all cost €49 and give 30% discount off normal rail fares for one year including certain international journeys. They also give discounts on Prem's and last minute tickets, and 60% discount for up to three accompanying children.

Regional Tickets: several regions offer day tickets on TER (local) trains at weekends and holidays. Conditions vary and some only valid in summer. Details generally available on TER website www.ter.sncf.com.

Alsa Plus 24h: a zonal day pass (24 hours) for the Alsace region, which includes Strasbourg, Colmar and Mulhouse. Valid on train (not TGV), bus and tram. €37.40 for the whole region; group ticket (2-5 people) available at weekends for €39.10. Smaller areas are also available.

Paris Visite: public transport within Paris including metro, RER, SNCF suburban trains, bus and tram. Available for two areas: zones 1 - 3 (central Paris) or zones 1 - 5 which includes airports and trains to Versailles and Disneyland. Prices for zone 1 - 3 are €13.20 / 21.50 / 29.40 for 1 / 2 / 3 days, €42.20 for 5 days. Prices for zones 1 - 5 are €27.80 / 42.20 / 59.20 for 1 / 2 / 3 days, €72.40 for 5 days. Child 4 - 11 half price.

Passes for Domestic Travel

Mobilis: Paris one-day public transport ticket (excludes airport services), €7.50 (zones 1 - 2) to €17.80 (zones 1 - 5).

Navigo weekly and monthly passes also available; all zones 7 day (Mon to Sun) ticket costs €22.80; monthly €75.20; photocard required at extra cost. Also available is the Navigo Easy pass for smart phones.

Lille City Pass: local public transport (metro, tram, bus) plus museums and attractions, 24 / 48 / 72 hrs, €25.00 / 35.00 / 45.00. The 72-hour pass includes TER trains in regional area for 24 hours (includes Dunkerque) and additional attractions in the wider area.

Most cities have day tickets for urban bus and tram services, e.g. **Lyon**: 24 / 48 / 72 hrs €6 / 12 / 16.50; **Lille** 1 to 5 days, €5.10 to €16.10.

GERMANY

See separate sections for Interrail / Eurail Global pass, Interrail One Country pass, Bodensee Ticket, Euregio Ticket Mass-Rhein, Sar-Lor-Lux Ticket. Note that Eurail/Interrail effectively issue German Railways (DB) passes as shown below.

German Rail Pass is available only to non-European residents and gives unlimited travel on DB trains in Germany, also to certain destinations in Switzerland, Austria and Italy. Includes IC Bus. Available in flexi and consecutive versions as shown below. No supplements on *ICE*, *EC*. Youth passes apply to those aged 12 to 27. All versions are also available for 4 days within 1 month and 4 consecutive days. A **Twin Pass** offers a discount of approx 50% for a second adult. Accompanied children aged 6 - 11 get a free pass (two with an adult pass, four with a twin pass).

	Adult 1st cl.	Adult 2nd cl.	Youth 1st cl.	Youth 2nd cl.
FLEXI PASSES:				
3 days within 1 month	€256	€192	€205	€154
5 days within 1 month	€321	€241	€257	€193
7 days within 1 month	€375	€280	€300	€224
10 days within 1 month	€479	€349	€383	€279
15 days within 1 month	€659	€479	€527	€383
CONSECUTIVE DAYS:				
3 days	€243	€182	€195	€146
5 days	€305	€229	€244	€183
7 days	€356	€266	€285	€213
10 days	€431	€314	€345	€251
15 days	€593	€431	€474	€345

Quer-durchs-Land-Ticket: one day's unlimited travel (not before 0900 Mon. - Fri., but valid until 0300 following day) on local trains (IRE/RE/RB/ S-Bahn), 2nd class. Valid for up to 5 people. €42 for one person (€70 for a group of five).

9 Euro Ticket: for €9 travel throughout Germany on local / regional trains and buses for a whole month in June, July or August 2022.

Regional tickets (Länder-Tickets): one day's unlimited 2nd class travel for up to 5 people on DB local trains (not before 0900 on Mon.-Fri., valid to 0300 the following day). Buy on the day. First class versions also available for some regions. Some tickets include other public transport. Regions available:
Baden-Württemberg: 1 person €24 (add €6 per additional person).
Bayern: 1 person €25 (add €8 for each additional person).
Brandenburg-Berlin: €33 (up to 5 passengers).
Hessen: €36 (up to 5 passengers).
Mecklenburg-Vorpommern: 1 person €23 (add €3.50 per person).
Niedersachsen: 1 person €23 (add €5 for each additional person).
Nordrhein-Westfalen (SchönerTag Ticket NRW): 1 person €31, 2 - 5 people €46.
Rheinland-Pfalz: 1 person €24 (add €5 for each additional person).
Saarland: 1 person €24 (add €5 for each additional person).
Sachsen: 1 person €24.50 (add €7.50 for each additional person).
Sachsen-Anhalt: 1 person €24.50 (add €7.50 for each additional person).
Schleswig-Holstein: 1 person €28 (add €3 for each additional person). Includes public transport in Hamburg.
Thüringen: 1 person €24.50 (add €7.50 for each additional person).

Annual Railcards: **Bahncard 25 / 50**: gives discounts of 25% or 50% on all national DB trains for €56.90 / 234 in 2nd class (1st class €115 / 474). A Youth Bahncard 25 is available for those aged 6 to 18, price €9.50 (valid for 1st and 2nd class). **Bahncard 100** gives unlimited travel for one year, €4,144 in 2nd class, €7,010 in 1st class, passport photo required. All adult Bahncards entitle the holder to discounts on flexible fares between Germany and up to 26 European countries. 3 month trail cards available.

Harz: HSB narrow gauge railway, 3 / 5 days €99 / 149; children aged 6 - 14 pay €59.50 / 89.50.

Tageskarte (day ticket): most urban areas offer 24 / 48 / 72 hour tickets valid on most public transport; generally a zonal system operates.

Welcome Tickets: most public transport in selected cities, also includes free or reduced entry to many museums and visitor attractions. Buy from Tourist Information, main stations, some airports and hotels. Examples:

Berlin Welcome Card: one adult and up to 3 children aged 3 - 14; all public transport plus up to 50% off at 200 attractions: 48 hrs €29, 72 hrs €39, 4 days €46, 5 days €50, 6 days €53. Covers zones A, B, C (includes Potsdam and Schönefeld Airport); subtract €3 - 5 for zones A, B only. Also available 72 hrs + Museum Island (free entry) €55.

Dresden City Card: 1 day €13.50, 7 day €22.90 ; A i day family card also available for 2 adults and up to 4 children under 15 €22.50.

Frankfurt Card: 1 day €11.50, 2 days €17; group ticket (up to 5 people) €24 / €34. Includes travel from / to the airport.

Hamburg Card: Day Ticket €10.90, also 2 - 5 days €19.70 - 43.90; group version (up to 5 people) €18.90 one day, €33.80 - 77.90 for 2 - 5 days. **Hannover Card**: 1 day €10, 2 days €16, 3 days €19, group ticket (up to 5 people) €21 / 28 / 36. **Köln Card**: 24 / 48 hrs €9 / 18, group ticket (up to 5 people) €19 / 38. **Leipzig Card**: 1 day €12.90, 3 days €25.90, 3 day group ticket (2 adults and up to 3 children under 14) €47.90. **Nürnberg Card**: 2 days €33 (children aged 6 - 11 €11).

GREAT BRITAIN

See separate sections for Interrail / Eurail Global pass, Interrail One Country pass, Britrail.

Railcards: annual cards giving 34% discount on most rail fares; 16 - 25 Railcard, 26 - 30 Railcard, Two Together Railcard, Family & Friends Railcard, Senior Railcard (60 +), Veterans: all £30; HM Forces Railcard £21, Disabled Persons, £20. Some have 3-year versions (£54 - £70 online). Network Railcard gives off-peak discount in South East England, £30. There is also a 16 - 17 Saver card giving 50% (£30).

All-Line Rail Rover: covers whole National Rail network. 1st / standard class £818 / 540 (7 days), £1250 / 818 (14 days), children 5 - 15 half price. 34% discount for holders of Senior / Disabled / Two Together railcard, and (standard class only) 16 - 25, 26 - 30 and Family & Friends railcards. Some restrictions before 1000 Mon. - Fri. Not valid on Eurostar, Heathrow Express, London Underground. Valid on Ffestiniog Railway and Welsh Highland Railway but not other private railways.

Spirit of Scotland Travelpass: all rail services in Scotland (includes Carlisle and Berwick) plus Caledonian MacBrayne ferry services and some buses. Standard class only. Valid 4 out of 8 days £149, or 8 out of 15 days £189; not before 0915 Mon. to Fri. (except on Glasgow - Oban / Mallaig / Stranraer services and north of Inverness). 34% discount with most annual railcards. 50% discount for children (5 - 15). 20% discount on Northlink Ferries to Orkney and Shetland. Smaller areas also available: **Highland Rover**, 4 out of 8 days £95; **Central Scotland Rover** 3 days (consecutive) £55.

Explore Wales Pass: standard class rail travel on any 4 days out of 8 (not valid before 0930 Mon. - Fri.), plus most buses on all 8 days, price £99, children half price, railcard discounts apply. Tickets available from staffed stations and on the train. Other areas available: **South Wales** £69, **North and Mid Wales** £69.

A range of **Rover** tickets is available covering various areas, typically for 7 days, 3 in 7 days, 4 in 8 days, or 8 in 15 days. Most not valid until after the morning peak on Mon. to Fri. Examples: Anglia Plus, Coast and Peaks, East Midlands, Freedom of Devon & Cornwall, Freedom of North East, Freedom of Severn & Solent, Freedom of North West, Freedom of South West, Heart of England, Kent, North Country, North Wales, Thames Rover. Details: www.nationalrail.co.uk or www.railrover.org.

Ranger day tickets also available: e.g. Cheshire, Cotswolds, Cumbria, Cumbian Coast, Devon, East Midlands, Isle of Wight, Lakes, Lancashire, Lincolnshire, North Downs, Oxfordshire, South Pennines, Thames Branches, Tyne & Tees, West Midlands, West Yorkshire, Yorkshire Coast. Details: www.nationalrail.co.uk or www.railrover.org.

London: Day Travelcards cover almost all transport (Underground, bus and rail) in the London area; peak version from £14.40 (central London, zones 1 - 4) to £20.30 (zones 1 - 6), off-peak version (not before 0930 Mon. - Fri.) £14.40 (zones 1 - 6). 7-day tickets from £38.40 (zones 1 - 2) to £70.30 (zones 1 - 6), no off-peak version. Wider zones also available. For single journeys contactless debit and credit cards, or stored-value Oyster cards offer the best value as prices are capped. Visitor Oyster cards are available preloaded from £10 to £50 (plus £5 fee, non-refundable). Children under 11 travel free on buses and trams (also on Tube, DLR and some rail services) when accompanied by a fare paying adult.

All-day tickets (some off-peak) covering local rail and most buses are available in Derbyshire, Glasgow, Greater Manchester, Merseyside, South Yorkshire, West Yorkshire, Tyneside and West Midlands.

Isle of Man: Go Explore card: all buses and trains, Douglas horse trams (excludes Groudle Glen Railway, Great Laxey Mine Railway), 1 / 3 / 5 / 7 days, £19 / 36 / 43 / 52, children aged 5 - 15 half price. Family card (two adults and up to three children): £43.50 / 82 / 102 / 122. Prices include card fee.

GREECE

See separate sections for Interrail / Eurail Global, One Country and Greek Islands passes, Balkan Flexipass.

ATH.ENA ticket: 24-hour ticket valid on metro, tram and bus (excludes airport) €4.10, 5 days €8.20 (airport is €9 single). 3-day tourist ticket including metro or bus to / from airport (one journey each way) €20.

Passes for Domestic Travel

HUNGARY

See separate sections for Interrail / Eurail Global and One Country passes, European East Pass.

2nd class travel by rail and local transport is free for over-65s with an EU passport or ID card; rail tickets need to be obtained but are zero cost.

START Klub Card: gives 50% discount on 2nd class travel. Valid for either 6 months or one year: HUF 19900 / 34900 (HUF 14900 / 24900 under 26 years). Requires passport style photograph. On Saturdays cardholders may obtain 50% discount for a second person.

Budapest: tram / metro / bus / rail, 24 hr travelcard HUF 1,650, 72 hrs HUF 4,150, 7 days HUF 4,950. Also 24 hr group (1 - 5 people), HUF 3,300.

Budapest Card also includes museums, walking tour and discounts: 24 hrs HUF 8,597, 48 hrs HUF 12,895, 72 hrs HUF 16,803. Also for 96 / 120 hrs (HUF 20,711 / 24,419); 72 hr has Junior version for 12,895.

Balaton 24 / Balaton 72: Includes tourist attractions and entertainment venues along the coastal settlements. 2nd class only with the option to upgrade to 1st class. Tickets available from railway stations. Only available for purchase April 15 - Nov. 1.
Balaton 24 (24hrs from first validation): HUF 1090; under 26 HUF 750.
Balaton 72 (72hrs from first validation): HUF 2740; under 26 HUF 1850.

IRELAND

See separate sections for Interrail / Eurail Global and One Country passes. Interrail and Eurail passes valid in the Republic of Ireland are also valid in Northern Ireland.

REPUBLIC OF IRELAND ONLY:

Irish Explorer: any 5 days in 15 on IÉ rail services, €160 (child €80), standard class. **Trekker** gives 4 consecutive days on Irish Rail for €110.

Dublin area: **Leap Visitor Card**: smartcard 24 hrs €10, 72 hrs €19.50, 7 days (168 hrs) €40. Includes rail in Short Hop zone, Luas tram and bus (also Airlink); purchase at airport or tourist offices (not railway stations). Can top up with additional periods. Luas **Flexi** ticket (tram only): 1 day €5.80, zonal tickets available for 7 days. **Leap** cards are also available for the bus network in Cork and most other cities.

NORTHERN IRELAND ONLY:

iLink Travel Card: unlimited bus and rail travel on Translink services (Northern Ireland Railways, Ulsterbus and Belfast Citybus). Zone 4 covers the whole of Northern Ireland: 1 day £16.50, 7 days £60, 1 month £205. Zone 1 covers Belfast city (£5 / 19 / 67). Children half price. North West zone: £13.50 / 51 / 180. Initial £1 fee for card (waived online).

Belfast Visitor Pass: local public transport (includes rail to Cultra; not bus to Belfast International Airport) plus visitor discounts: 1 / 2 / 3 days, adult £6 / 11 / 14.50, child £3.50 / 6 / 7.75.

ITALY

See separate sections for Interrail / Eurail Global and One Country passes. Prices quoted are indicative, please check locally.

Mobilcard Südtirol: regional trains, buses, funiculars and cable cars in Bolzano, Malles, Brennero area: 1 / 3 / 7 days; €15 / 23 / 28 (child under 14 €7.50 / 11.50 / 14).

Roma: Roma Tourist Ticket covers rail / metro / bus in urban area (excludes Fiumicino Airport), 24 / 48 / 72 hrs, €7 / 12.50 / 18; 7-day ticket (CIS) €24.

Roma Pass: 48 hr / 72 hr transport pass (€32 / 52) with museum discounts.

Milano: zonal system, includes rail services: 24 hour ticket €7 (zones Mi1 to Mi3) to €15.50 (all zones); 3-day pass €12 - 26.50.

Napoli: 'Campania > artecard' is a 3-day transport + museum visitors card, allowing free entry or disounts. Two areas available, Napoli (€21 adult, €12 for ages 18 - 25) and wider Campania area (€32 / 25).

Venezia: Travel cards for ACTV buses and boats: 1 / 2 / 3 / 7 days €20 / 30 / 40 / 60. Each card is also available with airport transfer add-on (€8 single or €15 return).

LATVIA

Latvian Railways: tickets are available for 1 / 3 / 4 / 5 days for unlimited travel between specified stations, but there are no network passes.

Riga: trams and buses 24 hrs €5, 3 / 5 days €10 / 15. **Riga Pass**: public transport, bus tour, plus free / discounted museum entry, €25 / 30 / 35 for 24 / 48 / 72 hours. Prices quoted are indicative, please check locally.

LITHUANIA

See separate section for Interrail / Eurail Global and One Country passes.

Vilnius: 1 / 3 / 10 day tickets available on local VVT buses / trolleybuses; €5 / 8 / 15. **Vilnius Pass** includes public transport, free entry to museums and various discounts, 72 hrs, €62.00.

LUXEMBOURG

See separate sections for Interrail / Eurail Global and Benelux passes, Sar-Lor-Lux Ticket.

All public transport is free of charge throughout the country (on the railways this applies only in 2nd class).

Dagesbilljee / Billet longue durée: unlimited 1st class travel on all public transport throughout the country for one day (until 0400 hrs following morning), not valid to border points €6 (not for sale on the train).

Monatsabo: 1st class network season ticket, valid one month, €75; from CFL offices.

Luxembourg Card: unlimited 2nd class travel on trains and buses throughout the country, plus free entry to 90 attractions. 1 day €13, 2 days €20, 3 days €28. Group pass for 3 - 5 people (max 2 adults) for 1 / 2 / 3 days: €28 / 48 / 68.

MONTENEGRO

See separate sections for Interrail / Eurail Global pass, Balkan Flexipass.

NETHERLANDS

See separate sections for Interrail / Eurail Global and Benelux passes, Euregio Ticket Maas-Rhein.

A national stored-value OV-chipkaart is used for public transport, initial cost €7.50, which can be loaded with day tickets. A single-use chipcard or e-ticket may be used by less frequent travellers. A 24 hour-ticket is also available. Suppllements payable on IC Direct trains. **Railrunner**: Children aged 4 - 11 travel for a flat rate of €2.50 each, valid all day.

Day ticket: unlimited rail travel (NS and other carriers) for one day; 1st class €93.18, 2nd class €55.80.

Holland Travel Ticket: valid one day on all public transport (not Thalys), includes 2nd class on all NS and private operators' trains, tram, bus and metro, €64 all day, or Off-Peak version (not 0630 - 0900 Mon-Fri) €44.

Amsterdam: GVB tram / bus / metro 24 / 48 / 72 hrs €8.50 / 14.50 / 20. Also available for 4 / 5 / 6 / 7 days (€25.50 to €37.00).

Amsterdam Travel Ticket: adds local NS trains (includes Schiphol airport): 1 / 2 / 3 days €17 / 22.50 / 28, valid to 0400 next day.

Amsterdam Region Travel Ticket: covers wider area (e.g. Haarlem, Almere, Hilversum) and regional buses, 1 / 2 / 3 days €19.50 / 28 / 36.50.

I amsterdam Card: GVB tram / bus / metro, canal tour, plus discounted or free entry to 70+ attractions; 24 / 48 / 72 / 96 hrs, €65 / 90 / 110 / 125.

South Holland: **Tourist Day Ticket** gives tram / bus / metro / waterbus throughout Rotterdam and Den Haag area, €14.50. Excludes NS trains.

NORTH MACEDONIA

See separate sections for Interrail / Eurail Global and One Country passes, Balkan Flexipass.

NORWAY

See separate section for Interrail / Eurail Global and One Country passes Eurail Scandinavia pass.

Oslo: 24 hour ticket for all 'Ruter' public transport in zone 1, 117 NOK, 7 days 323 NOK; all zones (includes airport) 267 NOK, 7 days 782 NOK Children, youth (18 - 19) and seniors (67 +) half price.

Oslo Pass: all public transport including Vy local trains (zones 1 - 2, excludes airport), free entry to 30 attractions, discounts on sightseeing buses / boats: 24 / 48 / 72 hours 445 / 655 / 820 NOK (child approx 50%).

Bergen Card: local bus and tram travel plus free or discounted entry to various attractions; 24 / 48 / 72 hrs, 300 / 380 / 460 NOK (child 3 - 15 pay 35%).

POLAND

See separate section for Interrail / Eurail Global and One Country passes

PKP Intercity have withdrawn their **Bilet Weekendowy** (weekend ticket), **Weekendowy MAX** and **Bilety Sieciowe** (network tickets) and recommended passengers use Interrail and Eurail tickets.

Colour Intercity Card: available in both 1st and 2nd class. Tickets entitle unlimited domestic trips on PKP Intercity and other carriers, (cards are named or bearer). Monthly named 1st 2250PLN, 2nd 1650PLN, bearer 3150/2250PLN. Discounts for Seniors and children of up to 50%. Applications are made in writing at PKP customer service centres.

Polregio operates REGIO and IR trains: **Bilety Sieciowe** (network tickets) are weekly or monthly tickets. **REGIOpass**: valid for any 3 days out of 2 months, 75 PLN (Polregio plus most other regional operators) or 65 PLN for a **miniREGIOpass** valid on Polregio REGIO trains only; validate ticket before travel.

Bilet Turystyczny (tourist ticket): valid 1800 Friday to 0600 Monday, 48 PLN (Polregio plus most other regional operators); or 39 PLN for

Mini version (Polregio REGIO trains only). Holders of these tickets can travel on selected lines in the Czech Republic and Germany.

Koleje Mazowieckie (KM) trains: wide area around Warsaw, 24 hr and 3 day passes are available (Sieciowy Imienny KM).

Warsaw ZTM tram / bus / metro / rail, Zone 1 (includes Chopin airport): 1 day 15 PLN, 3 days 36 PLN. Zones 1+2, 1 day 26 PLN, 3 days 57 PLN, weekend ticket valid 1900 Fri. - 0800 Mon. 24 PLN, group weekend ticket for up to 5 people, 40 PLN.

PORTUGAL

See separate section for Interrail / Eurail Global and One Country passes.

Intra-Rail: for ages 12-30, rail travel with free nights at youth hostels; *XCape* version valid 3 days €58 (€64 without youth card). *XPlore* version valid 7 days €127 (€146 without youth card). Not valid on *AP* trains. Buy at main stations. Show Card and ID to obtain free travel ticket.

Lisboa: Carris tram / bus / metro - one-day ticket (bilhete diário 24 h) €6.45; with Transtejo (Cacilhas) included €9.60. Carris, metro and local CP trains €10.70. Includes the funiculars and lift.

Lisboa Card: public transport plus free / discounted attractions: 24 / 48 / 72 hrs, €21 / 35 / 44 (children aged 4-15: €13.50 / 19.50 / 23).

Porto: *Andante Tour Card* gives metro + STCP bus + local rail, all zones, 24 hrs €7, 72 hrs €15. **Porto Card** also includes free / discounted entry to museums etc, 1 day €13, 2 days €20, 3 days €25, 4 days €33.

Coimbra: day ticket on SMTUC local buses €3.50.

ROMANIA

See separate section for Interrail / Eurail Global and One Country passes.

Bucureşti: STB tram, bus, trolleybus and metro network (not express buses): 1 / 3 / 7 days, 14/35/50 RON, fares are loaded onto an 'Activ' smartcard. The metro also has a day ticket. A free 3-day **Bucharest City Card** is available giving tourist discounts.

RUSSIA

This section has not been updated

Moskva: smartcards for unlimited number of metro journeys, 1 day 240 RUB, 3 days 455 RUB. Troika smart card valid on all public transport 50 RUB deposit, top up to maximum 3000 RUB. A City Pass is available which includes attractions and 15 transport rides.

St Peterburg: passes for 10 / 20 / 40 metro journeys available. All modes one month pass (70 trips) 3255 RUB. **St Petersburg City Pass** has been withdrawn, replaced with a City Pass which does not include public transport.

SERBIA

See separate sections for Interrail / Eurail Global and One Country passes, Balkan Flexipass (currently unavailable).

SLOVAKIA

See separate sections for Interrail / Eurail Global and One Country passes, European East Pass.

Zero fare rail tickets for most trains can be obtained by EU citizens under 16 and over 62. Supplements on *EC* and *SC*.

Bratislava: urban trams, buses and local trains, 24 hrs €3.50, 3 days €8, 7 days €11.40. **Bratislava Card** includes many discounts, 24 hrs €20, 48 hrs €25, 72 hrs €28, available online or from tourist offices.

SLOVENIA

See separate section for Interrail / Eurail Global and One Country passes.

Ljubljana Card: city buses, castle funicular, tourist boat and museums, valid for 24, 48 or 72 hours, €31.00 / 39.00 / 45.00, child 6-14 years €18.00 / 23.00 / 27.00 (online purchases receive 10% discount).

SPAIN

See separate sections for Interrail / Eurail Global and One Country passes, Passbask.

RENFE Spain Pass: for people resident outside Spain giving 4, 6, 8 or 10 individual journeys. Tickets must be obtained in advance using the pass; reservations are compulsory but free. Valid 1 month from first journey. Can be purchased and printed online (www.renfe.com).

Madrid: **Abono Turístico** (Tourist Ticket) gives all public transport in zone A, 1 / 2 / 3 days €8.40 / 14.20 / 18.40, also 5 / 7 days €26.80 / 35.40, children under 11 years 50%. Available for wider area (zone T) at double the price. Various museum passes are available but these exclude public transport.

Barcelona T-Dia ticket: valid 1 day on metro / TMB bus / tram / local rail, €10.50 (zone 1, includes airport), wider areas available.

Hola Barcelona zone 1 travelcard available for 2 / 3 / 4 / 5 days, approx €16.40 / 23.80 / 31.00 / 38.20.

Barcelona Card: adds free or discounted museums, 3 to 5 days approx €46 / 56 / 61 (children 4-12 years €22 / 28 / 33).

SWEDEN

See separate sections for Interrail / Eurail Global and One Country passes, Eurail Scandinavia pass, Öresund Rundt.

Stockholm: Travelcards give all SL public transport in Greater Stockholm, 24 / 72 hours 165 / 330 SEK, 7 days 430 SEK; SL Access smartcard required (20 SEK). Discount for under 20s / 65+. **Go Stockholm Pass** gives bus / boat tour plus free museums, 1 / 2 / 3 / 5 days (549 - 1399 SEK); add Travelcard (above) to include public transport.

SWITZERLAND

See separate sections for Interrail / Eurail Global pass, Interrail One Country pass, Bodensee Ticket.

Swiss Travel Pass: available to all non-Swiss residents. Consecutive days on Swiss Railways, boats and most alpine postbuses and city buses. Valid for 3, 4, 8 or 15 days; 1st class 369 / 447 / 617 / 675 CHF, 2nd class 232 / 281 / 389 / 429 CHF. Youth Pass (16-25 years) gives approximately 15% reduction. All versions give up to 50% reduction on most funicular and mountain railways. Includes free admission to over 500 tourist sites. Children aged 6-15 travel free with a Family Card if accompanied by a parent (not other relatives), otherwise half fare.

Swiss Travel Pass Flex: as above but for 3 / 4 / 8 / 15 days within 1 month. Prices 1st / 2nd class: 424 / 267 CHF (3 days), 514 / 323 CHF (4 days), 649 / 409 CHF (8 days), 706 / 449 CHF (15 days). Youth version (16-25 years) gives approximately 15% reduction.

Swiss Half Fare Card: discount card offering up to 50% off most public transport, valid for 1 month, 120 CHF. For non-Swiss residents.

Holders of the Swiss Half Fare Card can purchase a **1-day Travelpass** for 75 CHF 2nd class or 127 CHF 1st class, valid on most trains and public transport. A **Saver Day Pass** is also available but is more restrictive, from 29 CHF (or from 52 CHF without a Half Fare Card); prices vary according to when it is purchased, passes may sell out.

Bernese Oberland Regional Pass: valid April to October. Available for 3, 4, 6, 8 or 10 days unlimited travel in the area; 230 - 399 CHF 2nd class, 276 - 479 CHF 1st class. Flat fare of 30 CHF for children under 16.

Regional Passes: other areas available include Lake Geneva - Alps and Tell-Pass (Central Switzerland).

Jungfrau Travel Pass: valid 15 April to 23 October for 3 / 4 / 5 / 6 days travel, 190 / 215 / 250 / 270 CHF (7 / 8 days 290 / 310 CHF). Covers most routes in area; connecting ticket for Jungfraujoch €63 (or €75 June to August). 5 to 8 day passes include boats on Lakes Brienz and Thun. Reduced fare for holders of Travel Pass or Half Fare Card.

Bern: day ticket for city area (2 zone) 9.20 CHF. **Bern Ticket** is issued to overnight guests offering free LIBERO bus and tram travel within city zones 100/101. Also includes Gurten and Marzilibahn funiculars.

Genève: Day ticket (Carte 24 Heures) includes buses, trams, trains and boats: 10 CHF. **Carte 9 h** is valid from 0900 hrs, 8 CHF. Day ticket for wider regional area 18.50 CHF (13.20 CHF after 0900). The **Geneva Transport Card** is given to those staying at a hotel or youth hostel in the city and allows unrestricted travel on all public transport for the duration of the stay.

Zürich: ZVV Tageskarte gives 24 hours on all transport including SBB trains, 14.60 / 8.80 CHF 1st / 2nd class (zones 1-2 only); all zones in Canton 56.80 / 34.40 CHF. Off-peak version is 9-UhrPass, all zones, not before 0900 Mon. - Fri., 42.80 / 26 CHF. **Zürich Card** includes most museums and other discounts: 24 hours 27 CHF, 72 hours 53 CHF (children 19 / 37 CHF), includes airport.

Ticino: **Ticino Ticket** is given to those staying at a hotel, hostel or campsite in the Canton and allows free public transport and discounts on tourist attractions including mountain railways and boat trips.

TURKEY

See separate sections for Interrail / Eurail Global and One Country passes, Balkan Flexipass.

Gezgin Paketi: this 30 day network pass covering travel in standard class and couchettes was originally proposed in 2016 but has not yet been launched. **Gezgin Plus Paketi** is the proposed version for business class travel. All prices to be advised when launched.

UKRAINE

This section has not been updated

Kyïv: With either an e-ticket, Kyïv Smart Card, Kyïv Card or QR-code paper ticket travel on all modes of public transport, the more trips the cheaper the fare. **Kyïv Pass** gives metro trips and various museums, 24 / 48 / 72 hours, €15 / 25 / 35.

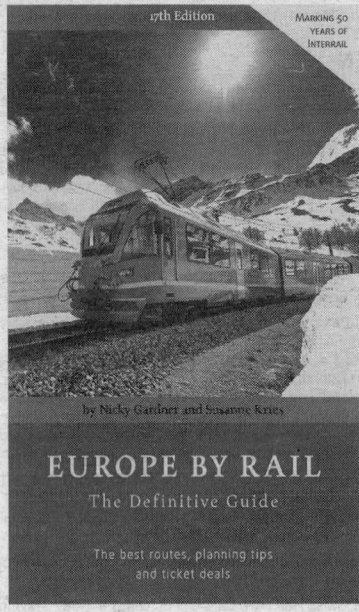